C000071652

THE EDITOR'S PAGE

LAST YEAR a management consultancy, Wheeler Associates, carried out the first independent survey of legal directories. It showed that among the largest companies nearly three-quarters (73%) said they would refer to a directory when identifying suitable law firms. And whatever the size of the company, far more of them used Chambers than used any other directory.

As Wheeler Associates put it: "The Chambers UK Directory is the best-known and the most widely used."

The directories were assessed by market awareness, by use, and by various other criteria. On all of them, Chambers was ahead. It's the best researched, says Wheeler. It's considered the most authoritative. It's used by more clients to identify lawyers. And the margin by which we lead the field increases the larger the client.

Such overwhelming recognition is a tribute to the research effort we put into the directory. We're proud of our research team. We're confident in our methodology. Every year, we ask BMRB (the British Market Research Bureau) to audit our methods and our findings. This year, again, we have their approval. Our objectivity was commented on: "Among participants in the research," they said, "the process is seen to be . . objective, in that it requests the opinions of clients and those in the profession rather than being clouded by sales or marketing hype."

There is a high degree of consensus, said BMRB, that "the research interviewers display both objectivity and professionalism."

Michael Chambers

CONTENTS

INTRODUCTION

The Chambers Survey of the best business lawyer

Fees and profits of the UK's top 100 law firms

Reviews of the largest firms in the regions, showing partner and assistant numbers

THE LAW FIRMS

SOLICITORS: SPECIALIST AREAS

Chambers & Partners Legal Recruitment:
(020) 7 606 8844

Published by **Chambers & Partners Publishing**
(a division of Orbach & Chambers Ltd)
Saville House, 23 Long Lane, London EC1A 9HL
Tel: (020) 7 606 1300 **Fax:** (020) 7 600 3191

ISBN: 0-85514-110 7

Editor: Michael Chambers
Deputy Editor: James Fairweather

Assistant Editor: Catherine Willberg
Consultant Editor: Reena SenGupta
Editorial Assistant: Jo Morgans
Profiles Manager: Mark Lomelí
Profiles Assistants: Emily Kerry, Al Baker, Richard Pettet
Project Co-ordination: Fiona Boxall, Kate Hinze
Database Manager: Derek Wright
Production Manager: John Buck
Business Development Manager: Brad Sirott

Orders to: Chambers & Partners Publishing
Also available on CD-Rom

Copyright © 2000 **Michael Chambers** and **Orbach & Chambers Ltd**

Printed in England by Polestar Wheatons Limited

SOLICITORS: A- Z OF LAW FIRMS

IN-HOUSE LAWYERS & COMPANY SECRETARIES

SUPPORT SERVICES

THE BAR

THE BAR: SPECIALIST AREAS

A-Z OF BARRISTERS' CHAMBERS

LEADERS AT THE BAR

INDEXES

INDEX OF PRACTISING BARRISTERS

THE CHAMBERS 3000

INTRODUCTION

CHAMBERS RESEARCH TEAM

Chambers researchers work full-time for six months researching the legal profession. They conduct thousands of telephone interviews discussing the strengths of leading specialists and their rankings. This research is audited by the British Market Research Bureau and provides an objective survey of the profession's leading practitioners.

- **Greg Lascelles**

Read Law and French at King's College, London and the Sorbonne, Paris. Masters in International Economics and Management at Università Bocconi, Milan. Trilingual. In-house at three international merchant banks before becoming a strategy consultant.

- **Sheena Lee**

Solicitor. Read Chemistry at University of York. Trained with leading niche City practice specialising in environmental law and personal injury. Qualified in 1997 and practised personal injury at legal aid firm.

- **Paula Wasley**

Read English at Princeton University and took Diploma in French at the Sorbonne. Subsequently a bi-lingual assistant at a top Paris Hotel and a research assistant to a correspondent at the Paris office of a major news agency.

- **Rieta Ghosh**

Read Ancient History at University of Durham. Former Client Information Manager with European market research agency. Previously worked as a recruitment consultant at a leading business advisory company.

- **William Salomone**

Read Economics/International Relations at the London School of Economics. Bilingual. Has worked as a researcher for a current affairs publication and for a leading NGO aimed at the promotion of Arab-British understanding.

- **Ross Cogan**

Read Philosophy at Nottingham University. M.Phil at St. John's College, Cambridge. PhD in Logic from Bristol in 1998. Has taught at several universities and previously worked in underwriting.

- **Ian McLachlan**

Read Classics at Brasenose College, Oxford. Worked in Italy for three years, first as an English teacher, then as a writer and translator for a computer software company. Has recently written a novel. Fluent in Italian.

- **Alexis Roitman**

Solicitor. Read Law and Commerce at the University of Queensland before taking her Masters in Law at Queen Mary & Westfield College, London. Worked as a securities lawyer in a leading Australian firm, and then for a leading international firm.

- **Neil Ford**

Read History and Geography at Sunderland and Aalborg Universities. Masters in African History and a Doctorate on the History of Tanzania at Edinburgh University. Worked as a Danish-English translator, mostly for the European Union.

- **Daniel Stott**

Read Philosophy at Kings College, London graduating with first class honours. Has worked as a researcher at the Institute of Psychiatry, University of London and recently as a news summariser at a media evaluation company.

- **Matthew Usher**

MA in English Literature from University of Edinburgh. After graduating, worked as a trainee at the Racecourse Holdings Trust and as a Research Associate for the Corporate Strategy Board.

- **Anna Williams**

Solicitor (1991.) Read Human Sciences at St Anne's College, Oxford. Practised commercial property and social housing at a top West End firm for eight years.

- **Lloyd Pearson**

Read Politics at University of Leeds. Worked as a political researcher for a government minister. Subsequently took up graduate scheme in publishing and worked as researcher for a travel organisation.

- **Jonathan Kingham**

Read History at Edinburgh. Took CPE at City University and completed LPC at Guildford College of Law. Will commence training contract at a leading City charities firm in September 2000.

- **Robert Wainwright**

Solicitor. Read Law and English at University of Queensland, Australia. Practised mainly litigation in Queensland and wrote for a national legal journal.

- **Baron Armah-Kwantreng**

Read History at University College, London. Project manager on aid-funded projects in former Soviet Union, India and Nigeria for procurement consultancy.

- **Joshua Butler**

Read law at University of London. Studied law, business management and theology in South Africa, Israel and USA. Has worked as public relations director for a major charity and as a rabbi in London and South Africa. Involved in listed internet site as a writer.

- **Angela Woodruff**

Solicitor. Read Psychology/Criminology at Melbourne University followed by Law at Monash University. Trained in Melbourne in general commercial law before joining the banking and finance practice of a leading Australian law firm.

- **Caroline Murphy**

Graduated from Brasenose College, Oxford, with a First in Classics. Previously freelanced for The Independent newspaper.

- **David Nicholls**

Read Theology at Keble College, Oxford, before working as a Political Researcher for an MP and the campaign Business for Sterling.

- **James Baxter**

Read Law at the London School of Economics. Worked as litigation fee-earner in a leading East Midlands law firm before moving into a business development position for a national newspaper.

BMRB APPROVAL

RESEARCH AUDIT

As independent auditors of the Chambers and Partners' research process, BMRB conducted a review of their research methodology in July 2000. The audit covered all elements of the process from researcher training, questionnaire and data gathering through to analysis and reporting. As part of the audit, BMRB re-contacted a number of participants in the Chambers and Partners' research programme to verify their contribution, to qualify their appropriateness to be interviewed, and to obtain their perspective on the research process.

RESEARCH METHODS

The focus of Chambers – a guide to the legal profession – is to provide an objective list of recommended legal practitioners (law firms, sets of chambers and individual practitioners). This is based on a research programme conducted by a full-time research team in the first half of 2000. This research covered 61 areas of law (Property, Corporate Finance, Environment, Advertising and Marketing and so on).

Chambers concentrates on corporate law, rather than high street practice, and this is reflected in the type of firms included in the universe for this study, coverage being of firms with 5+ practitioners, or established individual practitioners in the commercial sector.

In total 6083 interviews were conducted during the first half of 2000, of which 1077 were with major purchasers of legal services. The practitioner interviews were conducted with senior personnel, usually heads of relevant departments and other key personnel in each area of law. Interviews with clients were usually conducted with the senior personnel in charge of selecting suppliers of legal services. Interviews, lasting 30 minutes on average, were conducted by telephone. This form of data collection has the advantage of eliminating regional bias and avoids respondent self-selection, thereby enhancing objectivity of findings.

Within each area of law, the number of interviews varied according to the universe, but in all cases sample sizes were sufficient for the purpose. In some areas, particularly where there are relatively few practitioners, a full census was attempted. In other areas the interviews were conducted with a representative sample. The sample of client lists interviewed was derived largely from a combination of independent sources and practitioner client lists. In sampling for the research programme, Chambers and Partners have continued to act on previous recommendations by BMRB to ensure that client perceptions are included and representation of the universe is maximised as far as possible. These efforts are reflected in an increase in the number of interviews conducted in 2000, both among practitioners and clients.

THE RESEARCH TEAM

Chambers' research programme utilises a team of full-time researchers, each dedicated to specific areas of law. Prior to commencement of the programme, all researchers undertake a comprehensive induction and spend time thoroughly investigating the background and current trends in the areas of specialism for which they are responsible.

For each area of law, a team member (or number of team members) has the responsibility for all data gathering, analysis, validation and reporting.

THE RESEARCH AUDIT
By Warren Linsdell, Project Director at BMRB

RESEARCH AUDIT

As independent auditors of the Chambers and Partners' research process, BMRB conducted a review of their research methodology in July 2000. The audit covered all elements of the process from researcher training, questionnaire and data gathering through to analysis and reporting. As part of the audit, BMRB re-contacted a number of participants in the Chambers and Partners' research programme to verify their contribution, to qualify their appropriateness to be interviewed, and to obtain their perspective on the research process.

RESEARCH METHODS

The focus of Chambers – a guide to the legal profession – is to provide an objective list of recommended legal practitioners (law firms, sets of chambers and individual practitioners). This is based on a research programme conducted by a full-time research team in the first half of 2000. This research covered 61 areas of law (Property, Corporate Finance, Environment, Advertising and Marketing and so on).

Chambers concentrates on corporate law, rather than high street practice, and this is reflected in the type of firms included in the universe for this study, coverage being of firms with 5+ practitioners, or established individual practitioners in the commercial sector.

In total 6083 interviews were conducted during the first half of 2000, of which 1077 were with major purchasers of legal services. The practitioner interviews were conducted with senior personnel, usually heads of relevant departments and other key personnel in each area of law. Interviews with clients were usually conducted with the senior personnel in charge of selecting suppliers of legal services. Interviews, lasting 30 minutes on average, were conducted by telephone. This form of data collection has the advantage of eliminating regional bias and avoids respondent self-selection, thereby enhancing objectivity of findings.

Within each area of law, the number of interviews varied according to the universe, but in all cases sample sizes were sufficient for the purpose. In some areas, particularly where there are relatively few practitioners, a full census was attempted. In other areas the interviews were conducted with a representative sample. The sample of client lists interviewed was derived largely from a combination of independent sources and practitioner client lists. In sampling for the research programme, Chambers and Partners have continued to act on previous recommendations by BMRB to ensure that client perceptions are included and representation of the universe is maximised as far as possible. These efforts are reflected in an increase in the number of interviews conducted in 2000, both among practitioners and clients.

THE RESEARCH TEAM

Chambers' research programme utilises a team of full-time researchers, each dedicated to specific areas of law. Prior to commencement of the programme, all researchers undertake a comprehensive induction and spend time thoroughly investigating the background and current trends in the areas of specialism for which they are responsible.

For each area of law, a team member (or number of team members) has the responsibility for all data gathering, analysis, validation and reporting.

VALIDATION OF FINDINGS

A number of checks are implemented to validate the findings and ensure that they are not biased by individual responses. Quality is ensured via:

- Weight of numbers, i.e. that there were sufficient respondents to form a representative sample.
- Comparison of client views with those of practitioners to check for consistency.
- Checks against former years to identify trends and variations over time.
- Investigation of dramatic changes or anomalies or contradictions within the findings through further interviews.
- The interactive nature of the research process provides several opportunities to identify errors.

The research methods employed and quality control measures implemented serve to ensure that the findings can be reported with confidence.

Warren Linsdell, Project Director at BMRB

BMRB's Business Solutions division which specialises in customer and business relationship research, carried out this research audit of the Chambers and Partners Guide to the Legal Profession. BMRB International is the longest-established UK market research company, and one of the five largest in the UK.

THE LEGAL PROFESSION 10 YEARS ON

You're at a party. A young graduate comes up to you and asks your advice: "I'm thinking of becoming a lawyer?" he says, hopefully. He seems bright. He seems confident. He has the talent, no doubt, to do almost anything. "I've also been thinking of banking," he says, "but the law appeals most." What would you say? If he asked us here at Chambers, we would say: "Yes, but . . ." Yes, we'd say, join one of the firms recommended in our Guide. But avoid the High Street practice. Join one of the mega-firms with their international reach; or a niche firm with a profitable specialism. You will work hard, but you'll have an interesting career and you'll make a good living.

TEN YEARS OF CHANGE

If he wanted an explanation, we would go back ten years – to 1990, the year this book was first published. The legal profession was on the brink of the worst recession it ever experienced. From there we would take him through the successes of the past decade. It's an encouraging story.

US law firms

Looking through the first edition of Chambers, no American firms were included. This was not because the US firms had no presence in London in 1990. They did. But their London offices were small and were staffed by US lawyers who merely coordinated European transactions and liaised with London law firms. This role changed in the mid-1990s. The London offices began hiring English lawyers to practise English law. At the same time, the biggest English firms hired US lawyers. "Dual capability" became the watchword: law firms capable of handling both English and New York law. The change was driven by capital markets work spanning both sides of the Atlantic. It was also driven by increasing competition for project finance work around the world – especially in Europe and the Far East (where the work was done under both English and US law).

So, for the first time, the large City firms faced serious competition on their doorstep – serious and well-funded. The London-New York axis at the centre of global finance has generated a new-style London-New York law firm. Clifford Chance took the lead: others will follow. A select group of global firms will emerge to dominate international finance-related business. Their strength will create a base on which to build other areas of practice.

City law firms have responded by strengthening their position in Europe. They are well on the way to dominating the European legal scene, creating crisis and division among local law firms in one jurisdiction after another. In doing so, the English firms are retaining their true partnership 'one-firm' structure. They are holding onto the principle of partnership equality, with equity partners throughout Europe (and indeed the world) on the 'lock-step' basis of profit-sharing. They are forging powerful, cohesive organisations. An elite among the world's lawyers. And to staff these growing mega-firms, they are siphoning off the cream of the local professions – not only in Europe but in every jurisdiction where they practise. They are also targeting the recruitment markets in Australia, New Zealand, and other common-law jurisdictions.

The growth of the global law firm is the most significant development in today's legal profession, and it has many years to run. London appears to be the global centre, sharing this distinction with New York. So the 'threat', so-called, of the US law firms is in fact a blessing – another sign of the legal role that London plays in the world's financial economy. Lawyers should only worry about this 'threat' if US firms start to move their offices from London to Frankfurt or Paris or Berlin. For the moment, the London-New York axis seems supreme.

The first edition

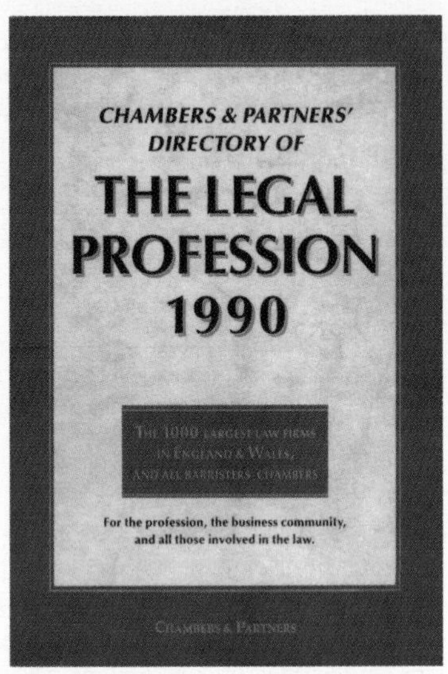

CHAMBERS & PARTNERS'
DIRECTORY OF
THE LEGAL
PROFESSION
1990
For the profession, the business community, and all those involved in the law.

The accountants

The mid-1990s also saw a 'threat' to the legal profession in the form of accountants' law firms. The Big Six, led by Arthur Andersen, decided to move into legal work, envious at the profits which law firms were making. At the time, many commentators saw the accountants as a greater threat than the US lawyers. Andersens said they would soon have the world's largest law firm. They had the clients, they said. They had the global presence, they had the management skills, and they had the sharp business minds of the accountant. What chance the lawyers?

This hype reached its peak in 1996-97. It was finally punctured by Andersen's failure to acquire Simmons & Simmons in the autumn of 1997 and by its embarrassing merger breakdown with Wilde Sapte in the spring of 1998. Since then, the accountants' practices have faded from the limelight. True, they continue to exist, and indeed around the world they are steadily developing. There is a place, it seems, for the accountants' lawyers. They service the middle-market – the clients which are too small to have an in-house legal department and which value the simplicity of having their legal and accountancy advisers under one roof (despite the possible conflicts of interest).

The national firm

The third threat – this time a threat to the London firms – was the emergence in the early 1990s of the 'national firm'. As the recession swept the country, regional firms saw their opportunity to acquire offices in London and to merge with firms in other regional centres. Thus, firms like Hammond Suddards, Dibb Lupton and Eversheds mounted their assault on the 'soft underbelly' – as they put it – of the London market. Offices in London became available at low rents. Top quality solicitors, partners as well as assistants, were becoming redundant. They could be hired to staff the new national firms and compete with London firms by charging lower fees. Clients, too, were feeling the pinch, and the low fees offered by these new groupings appealed to them. In the worst years of the recession, 1991-92, the new national firms were able to adopt an aggressive stance. They made the most of it. They seized the opportunity and carved a presence in London. Now, of course, that particular window of opportunity has closed.

The great divide

But just as the threat from the 'national' firms receded, the second and third tier firms in London came under threat from the mega-firms above them. For twenty years and more, there has been a huge gulf between the company and commercial practices on the one hand and the High Street practices on the other. The two sides of the profession have nothing in common. But within the company/commercial practices themselves another wide gulf has emerged – a gulf between the mega-firms and the rest. We saw this happening in our first 1990 edition ('A review of the profession'):

The mega-firms, we wrote, "are being lifted out of the English legal community and finding a place on the world stage . . . They could well become the dominant force among the world's lawyers. Only the US firms can challenge them."

These top City firms are in a league of their own. Their quality is unsurpassed. They attract the best lawyers and the largest clients. They have an international presence which other firms cannot challenge. Two different worlds, and an unbridgeable gap between them. Now we see the effect of this on salaries. The global firms are beginning to pay salaries at global levels, which makes it even harder for the firms below them to recruit and retain the best young lawyers.

At the moment, however, no-one's complaining. Since the recession, we have seen unprecedented prosperity for the firms listed in this book. High Street firms may not have recovered from the loss of the conveyancing monopoly, but all the commercial practices have flourished. Plateau partners in the City's 'magic circle' firms are now earning profits of around £1million a year (joining the dozen or so top QCs who earn at this level). And down through the second and third tier firms the story is the same – record profitability.

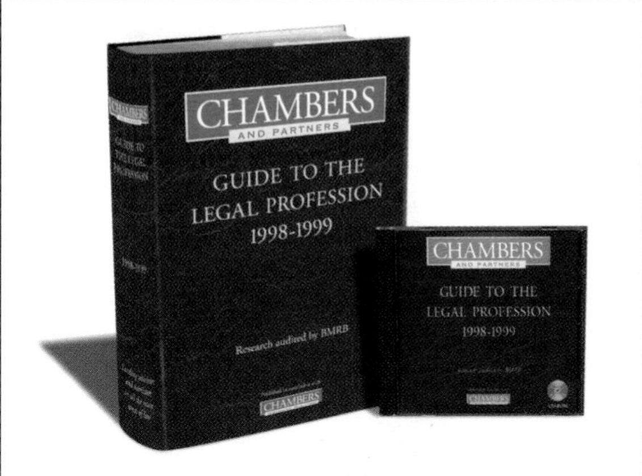

Chambers Directory also produced on CD.

THE FUTURE

Not all commentators are entirely fond of the legal profession. Many tend to foresee disaster. Once they talked about the threat of the accountants. Now they talk about the threat of the computer. Law will be available online, they say, and lawyers will be replaced by 'legal technicians'. As legal software advances, clients will become 'do-it-yourself' lawyers.

This is the armchair wisdom of academic lawyers with little experience of practice. They see lawyers as learned scholars – like themselves – with a profound knowledge of the law. They think, therefore, that once computers become 'knowledgeable' and adept at applying the entire corpus of laws and regulations to all eventualities, they will replace the lawyer.

This view, surely, is misconceived. Practising lawyers are not learned professors who know all the rules, the cases, the statutes, and every legal article ever published. Certainly, they know the law, but that is just the beginning of their expertise, the starting point. What they then do, which is beyond the academic purview, is to grapple with the facts of the case – the letters, the faxes, the conversations, the contracts and related documents – the bulging files which the client dumps on their desk. They have to understand enough about business and how their clients operate to pick their way through to the crucial issues.

Practising law is not a matter of 'knowing' the law and applying it, like a judge, to some agreed unequivocal facts. It's deciding what facts are relevant, assessing the merits, judging the relative positions of the parties, and seeing a way forward. In other words, being a practical adviser; being a negotiator and advocate; being, above all, a shrewd problem-solver.

Computers will be able to tell us, for instance, whether VAT applies to businesses with a certain turnover. This is the application of rules to standard facts. But it's not the practice of law, even when it's done by lawyers.

Like the other threats to the legal profession that we've discussed earlier, the threat of the computer is not something lawyers need worry about.

A law-governed world

So, if the young graduate is still with us after this detour into the past, we should encourage him. There will always be plenty of work for good lawyers. The organisations they work in – the law firms – will change in size and structure and in the kind of law they practise. Some will 'focus'; some will broaden out. Some will go international; others will stay at home. Some will stand alone and some will link up with other professions. But whatever form their organisation takes, the lawyers themselves will flourish.

The world is increasingly rule-bound. Relationships of all kinds – public and private, commercial and personal – are being enmeshed within a growing network of laws. As we wrote in the first edition of this book: "Lawyers will have an increasingly central role in society, and their status and remuneration will reflect it."

The Editor

BEST BUSINESS LAWYER 2000

A turbulent year for the legal profession, but some things at least remain constant – Nigel Boardman of Slaughter and May has completed a hat-trick of victories in the annual Chambers survey to determine the leading business lawyer. Although not unpredictable, the award is clearly merited. A technical master of his craft, he is also commended for his "practical and commercial mind. He just gets the deal done." More succinctly, one leading in-house lawyer observed: "He's one of our heroes."

In joint second place are two more corporate heavyweights. Boardman's colleague William Underhill has built himself a first-class reputation. Involved in the recent defence of Blue Circle, he is described as a "proactive and imaginative" practitioner. Underhill is joined by Will Lawes of Freshfields Bruckhaus Deringer. A rising star of Chambers' recent corporate finance tables, Lawes is said to "take the pain out of transactions," and is one of the brightest jewels in the firm's glittering corporate crown.

Rounding out the top six are three practitioners from very different firms. Michael Pescod is yet another thoroughbred from the Slaughter and May stable. Possessing "a wealth of experience and an astute mind," he is regarded as a superb developer of client relationships. At Clifford Chance, Adam Signy has stood out all year. "Insightful, pragmatic and commercial," he provides the firm with a real corporate heavy hitter. Paul Maher of Rowe & Maw may be a surprise package to some, but clients are in no doubt about his "aggression, tenacity and energy."

Once again, the vast majority of nominated practitioners are corporate finance experts. Obviously, big-ticket mergers carry the highest profile and provide lawyers with the greatest exposure. Nevertheless, quality will out. Equity buy-out king Charles Geffen at Ashurst Morris Crisp and jack-of-all-trades Matthew Middleditch at Linklaters prove that it is not essential to be a pure M&A transactional wizard to poll well.

Among law firms, Slaughter and May stand unchallenged this year, with more than double the recommendations of their nearest rivals, Linklaters. Interestingly, the results of this survey closely mirror the Chambers corporate finance table, with Freshfields Bruckhaus Deringer, Herbert Smith, Allen & Overy and Clifford Chance all being well represented this year. Clifford Chance have shown a notable advance on last year's figures, and now stand joint sixth in the table.

Will Lawes, Freshfields Bruckhaus Deringer

Nigel Boardman, Slaughter and May

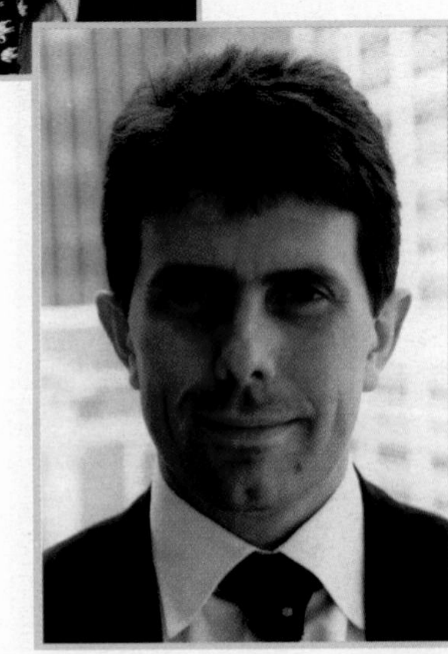

William Underhill, Slaughter and May

Paul Maher, Rowe & Maw

Michael Pescod, Slaughter and May

Adam Signy, Clifford Chance

LAW FIRMS WITH BEST BUSINESS LAWYERS

Showing number of individual recommendations.

Slaughter and May	29
Linklaters	14
Freshfields Bruckhaus Deringer	13
Herbert Smith	10
Allen & Overy	9
Clifford Chance	7
Lovells	7
Macfarlanes	6
DLA	5
Ashurst Morris Crisp	4
Baker & McKenzie	4
CMS Cameron McKenna	4
Eversheds	4
Denton Wilde Sapte	3
Nabarro Nathanson	3
Pinsent Curtis	3
Rowe & Maw	3

BEST BUSINESS LAWYERS

Nigel Boardman *Slaughter and May*

Will Lawes *Freshfields Bruckhaus Deringer*
William Underhill *Slaughter and May*

Paul Maher *Rowe & Maw*
Michael Pescod *Slaughter and May*
Adam Signy *Clifford Chance*

Guy Beringer *Allen & Overy*
Charles Geffen *Ashurst Morris Crisp*
Glen James *Slaughter and May*
Jonathan Macfarlane *Macfarlanes*
Matthew Middleditch *Linklaters*
James Palmer *Herbert Smith*
Anthony Salz *Freshfields Bruckhaus Deringer*
Robert Stern *Slaughter and May*
Nilufer von Bismarck *Slaughter and May*
Stephen Wilkinson *Herbert Smith*

SOLICITORS CHARGES

THIS IS A REPRESENTATIVE sample of headline rates. These figures are only a general guide as firms invariably consider a number of factors when setting fees. Indeed, a number of firms interviewed confessed that they had dispensed with hourly rates altogether and instead used a charge tailored to the specific requirements of the case. Factors other than the number of hours include the complexity of the matter, its urgency, and the level of resources and expertise required. Major clients are in a strong position to negotiate special rates based on the volume of business they bring. Fixed fees and capped rates are also more common nowadays. Nevertheless, these figures should offer a helpful guide as to the differences between the levels of firm and how fees vary between major business centres. For London there are three categories. The 'magic circle' (Allen & Overy, Clifford Chance, Freshfields Bruckhaus Deringer, Linklaters, Slaughter and May); second tier (those just outside the magic circle and usually having over two hundred lawyers); and third tier (major City firms with over fifty lawyers.) For other centres we focus on large (with more than fifty lawyers) and medium sized firms (with less than fifty lawyers). The low and high figures are the absolute lowest and absolute highest. The average is the medium figure within each area of practice.

PARTNERS

Area of Practice	Corporate			Commercial Litigation			Commercial Property		
	Low	Average	High	Low	Average	High	Low	Average	High
London–Magic Circle	380	450	550	375	430	525	380	430	500
London–2nd Tier	290	340	400	250	310	375	240	320	375
London–3rd Tier	220	315	400	210	290	400	220	285	385
Bristol–large	130	175	200	125	165	200	140	170	200
Bristol–medium	130	150	195	125	140	160	130	145	160
Birmingham–large	220	260	325	220	260	325	220	260	325
Birmingham–medium	195	210	220	195	210	220	195	210	220
Manchester–large	160	235	300	145	200	300	145	215	300
Manchester–medium	140	165	190	140	165	190	140	165	190
Leeds–large	150	180	210	150	180	210	150	180	210
Leeds–medium	125	150	165	125	150	165	125	150	165
Edinburgh–large	150	175	200	150	165	200	150	170	200
Edinburgh–medium	140	155	180	125	140	160	140	155	175
Glasgow–large	150	175	200	150	165	200	150	170	200
Glasgow–medium	130	155	200	150	160	200	150	165	200

ASSISTANT SOLICITORS									
Area of Practice	**Corporate**			**Commercial Litigation**			**Commercial Property**		
	Low	**Average**	**High**	**Low**	**Average**	**High**	**Low**	**Average**	**High**
London–Magic Circle	185	280	375	175	265	350	175	270	325
London–2nd Tier	215	245	280	150	230	275	185	225	275
London–3rd Tier	130	220	300	130	200	265	130	200	275
Bristol-large	100	140	175	100	135	175	100	140	170
Bristol–medium	75	110	150	75	100	120	75	105	140
Birmingham–large	160	200	250	160	200	250	160	200	250
Birmingham–medium	160	170	180	160	170	180	160	170	180
Manchester–large	110	160	240	110	150	240	110	155	240
Manchester–medium	100	120	140	100	120	140	100	120	140
Leeds–large	120	140	160	120	140	160	120	140	160
Leeds–medium	85	105	120	85	105	120	85	105	120
Edinburgh–large	120	145	165	120	135	150	120	140	155
Edinburgh–medium	100	110	120	100	110	120	100	110	120
Glasgow–large	120	145	165	120	135	150	120	140	155
Glasgow–medium	100	120	150	100	120	150	100	125	150

SOLICITORS REMUNERATION

FOR THE FIRST TIME this year, we include a table indicating the range of annual salaries for both newly-qualified solicitors and assistants at the five-year mark. It is clear that the presence of the highest salaries at the City-based US firms has led the push this year to increased starting salaries in the most prominent London firms. However, although the magic circle and larger firms have increased starting salaries this year, they have yet to reach the heady levels offered by the American firms. Naturally, regional firms and primarily non-commercial practices will always struggle to follow suit. The table below shows the broad range of salaries for 2000, varying across the regions, and within each region, varying depending on practice. The threefold distinction between the London firms is the same as that in the table above on solicitor hourly rates.

REMUNERATION		
	Newly Qualified	**5 Years PQE**
London - magic circle	£42,000	£70-95,000
London - 2nd tier	£38-42,000	£65-75,000
London - 3rd tier	£33-35,000	£50-70,000
South	£18-35,000	£28-45,000
Midlands	£19-30,000	£25-50,000
North	£18-30,000	£25-55,000
Scotland	£18-28,000	£25-50,000
US firms (London offices)	£55-80,000	£100-130,000

THE TOP 100 UK LAW FIRMS - BY PROFITABILITY

These figures are taken from the August 2000 issue of *Commercial Lawyer* magazine. Most were supplied by the firms themselves, either officially or unofficially. A few, however, were estimated on the basis of journalists' research.

FIRM	FEES	EQUITY PTNRS	FEE EARNERS	LEVERAGE	FEES/ FEE EARNERS	PROFITS PER EQUITY PARTNER	PROFIT RANK
Addleshaw Booth & Co	£61,800,000	80	516	1 : 5.45	£119,767	£218,000	57
Allen & Overy	£320,000,000	244	1653	1 : 5.77	£193,587	£752,500	2
Ashurst Morris Crisp	£130,000,000	105	440	1 : 3.19	£295,455	£545,000	12
Baker & McKenzie	£62,000,000	45	233	1 : 4.18	£266,094	£350,000	22
Barlow Lyde & Gilbert	£50,500,000	69	209	1 : 1.03	£241,627	£210,100	59
Beachcroft Wansbroughs	£65,700,000	76	433	1 : 4.7	£151,732	£180,700	72
Berrymans Lace Mawer	£39,600,000	33	208	1 : 5.3	£190,385	£257,500	44
Berwin Leighton	£55,300,000	43	222	1 : 4.16	£249,099	£326,000	24
Bevan Ashford	£26,763,000	39	206	1 : 4.28	£129,917	£150,500	85
Biddle	£13,100,000	20	65	1 : 2.25	£201,538	£270,000	40
Bird & Bird	£34,895,000	28	211	1 : 6.54	£165,379	£400,000	19
Blake Lapthorn	£16,300,000	32	135	1 : 3.22	£120,741	£112,500	98
Bond Pearce	£22,700,000	32	152	1 : 3.75	£149,342	£157,300	81
Bristows	£14,000,000	20	67	1 : 2.35	£208,955	£207,500	62
Browne Jacobson	£16,845,000	23	123	1 : 4.35	£136,951	£152,200	84
Burges Salmon	£24,000,000	45	150	1 : 2.33	£160,000	£250,000	48
Charles Russell	£30,000,000	42	162	1 : 2.86	£185,185	£182,600	71
Clarke Wilmott & Clarke	£13,600,000	23	119	1 : 4.17	£114,286	£103,000	100
Clifford Chance	£586,500,000	336	2680	1 : 6.98	£218,843	£560,000	9
Clyde & Co	£62,000,000	60	240	1 : 3	£258,333	£276,600	37
CMS Cameron McKenna	£136,000,000	154	592	1 : 2.84	£229,730	£287,500	32
Cobbetts	£13,650,000	21	110	1 : 4.24	£124,091	£178,600	74
Cripps Harries Hall	£13,500,000	22	75	1 : 2.41	£180,000	£136,400	89
D J Freeman	£28,500,000	23	123	1 : 4.35	£231,707	£187,000	68
Davies Arnold Cooper	£31,000,000	19	134	1 : 6.05	£231,343	£113,500	97
Davies Wallis Foyster	£15,200,000	21	98	1 : 3.67	£155,102	£178,200	75
Dechert	£33,200,000	38	180	1 : 3.74	£184,444	£280,000	35
Denton Hall	£86,700,000	80	462	1 : 4.78	£187,662	£296,000	30
Dickinson Dees	£21,000,000	28	170	1 : 5.07	£123,529	£185,000	69
Dickson Minto WS	£17,000,000	11	63	1 : 4.73	£269,841	£600,000	5
DLA	£139,840,000	102	670	1 : 5.57	£208,716	£305,000	26
Dundas & Wilson CS	£30,000,000	53	207	1 : 2.91	£144,928	£166,650	76

FIRM	FEES	EQUITY PTNRS	FEE EARNERS	LEVERAGE	FEES/ FEE EARNERS	PROFITS PER EQUITY PARTNER	PROFIT RANK
Edge Ellison*	£37,000,000	38	193	1 : 4.08	£191,710	£152,600	82
Eversheds	£212,400,000	201	1652	1 : 7.22	£128,571	£260,200	43
Farrer & Co	£18,700,000	19	59	1 : 2.11	£316,949	£208,500	61
Field Fisher Waterhouse	£32,000,000	39	154	1 : 2.95	£207,792	£250,000	49
Finers Stephens Innocent	£14,000,000	17	87	1 : 4.12	£160,920	£165,000	77
Fladgate Fielder	£14,100,000	17	68	1 : 3	£207,353	£269,000	41
Freethcartwright	£15,000,000	25	100	1 : 3	£150,000	£104,800	99
Freshfields Bruckhaus Deringer	£380,000,000	275	1213	1 : 3.41	£313,273	£675,000	4
Garretts	£33,000,000	48	165	1 : 2.44	£200,000	£200,000	64
Gouldens	£33,500,000	25	108	1 : 3.32	£310,185	£569,000	8
Halliwell Landau	£21,800,800	19	188	1 : 8.89	£115,962	£300,000	28
Hammond Suddards*	£84,200,000	59	621	1 : 9.53	£135,588	£291,500	31
Herbert Smith	£170,000,000	102	709	1 : 5.95	£239,774	£500,000	13
Hewitson Becke + Shaw	£15,400,000	32	110	1 : 2.44	£140,000	£148,500	87
Hill Dickinson	£22,000,000	39	138	1 : 2.54	£159,420	£198,000	65
Holman Fenwick & Willan	£43,000,000	45	165	1 : 2.67	£260,606	£267,000	42
Howard Kennedy	£14,800,000	21	82	1 : 2.9	£180,488	£114,000	96
Hugh James Ford Simey	£16,000,000	38	112	1 : 1.95	£142,857	£131,000	92
Ince & Co	£34,100,000	37	135	1 : 2.65	£252,593	£248,000	50
Irwin Mitchell	£48,700,000	42	233	1 : 4.55	£209,013	£255,000	46
Kennedys	£21,000,000	23	128	1 : 4.57	£164,063	£162,000	79
Lawrence Graham	£41,600,000	44	175	1 : 2.98	£237,714	£280,000	36
Linklaters	£400,000,000	227	1026	1 : 3.52	£389,864	£725,000	3
Lovells	£200,000,000	160	892	1 : 4.58	£224,215	£400,000	20
Macfarlanes	£49,000,000	53	167	1 : 2.15	£293,413	£500,000	14
Maclay Murray & Spens	£22,000,000	46	230	1 : 4	£95,652	£150,000	86
MacRoberts	£15,600,000	20	105	1 : 4.25	£148,571	£226,000	51
Manches	£21,330,000	27	112	1 : 3.15	£190,446	£165,000	78
Martineau Johnson	£14,700,000	16	90	1 : 4.63	£163,333	£190,000	67
Masons	£60,930,000	42	390	1 : 8.29	£156,231	£285,700	33
McGrigor Donald	£27,250,000	43	175	1 : 3.07	£155,714	£196,500	66
Mills & Reeve	£24,615,021	36	194	1 : 4.39	£126,882	£136,500	88
Mishcon de Reya	£15,750,000	21	102	1 : 3.86	£154,412	£252,500	47
Morgan Cole	£37,000,000	97	248	1 : 1.56	£149,194	£125,000	93

*Edge Ellison and Hammond Suddards merged in August 2000

UK TOP 100 LAW FIRMS

FIRM	FEES	EQUITY PTNRS	FEE EARNERS	LEVERAGE	FEES/ FEE EARNERS	PROFITS PER EQUITY PARTNER	PROFIT RANK
Nabarro Nathanson	£77,250,000	92	386	1 : 3.2	£200,130	£300,000	29
Nelsons	£31,200,000	39	213	1 : 4.46	£146,479	£160,000	80
Nicholson Graham & Jones	£24,894,000	24	98	1 : 3.08	£254,020	£284,500	34
Norton Rose	£140,000,000	119	532	1 : 3.47	£263,158	£453,700	15
Olswang	£35,069,000	33	170	1 : 4.15	£206,288	£587,500	7
Osborne Clarke OWA	£35,000,000	39	270	1 : 5.92	£129,630	£310,000	25
Paisner & Co	£24,000,000	48	115	1 : 1.4	£208,696	£202,000	63
Pannone & Partners	£13,800,000	26	165	1 : 5.35	£83,636	£115,000	95
Penningtons	£14,700,000	20	104	1 : 4.2	£141,346	£124,000	94
Pinsent Curtis	£56,700,000	60	334	1 : 4.57	£169,760	£225,000	53
Reynolds Porter Chamberlain	£25,363,566	47	151	1 : 2.21	£167,971	£179,000	73
Richards Butler	£68,700,000	56	308	1 : 4.5	£223,052	£400,000	21
Rowe & Maw	£46,000,000	43	203	1 : 3.72	£226,601	£302,000	27
Shearman & Sterling	£30,625,000	15	82	1 : 4.47	£373,476	£600,000	6
Shepherd & Wedderburn WS	£15,600,000	17	103	1 : 5.06	£151,456	£226,000	52
Shoosmiths	£42,300,000	25	186	1 : 6.44	£227,419	£152,500	83
Simmons & Simmons	£117,300,000	126	480	1 : 2.81	£244,375	£270,491	38
Sinclair Roche & Temperley	£17,600,000	22	86	1 : 2.91	£204,651	£135,000	90
SJ Berwin & Co	£72,500,000	46	257	1 : 4.59	£282,101	£554,000	10
Slaughter and May	£309,000,000	103	440	1 : 3.27	£702,273	£900,000	1
Speechly Bircham	£17,540,000	23	95	1 : 3.13	£184,632	£221,700	55
Stephenson Harwood	£50,300,000	49	291	1 : 4.94	£172,852	£219,700	56
Taylor Joynson Garrett	£48,104,000	50	204	1 : 3.08	£235,804	£402,000	18
Theodore Goddard	£39,000,000	31	186	1 : 5	£209,677	£403,000	17
Thomas Eggar Church Adams	£16,800,000	30	80	1 : 1.67	£210,000	£133,000	91
Travers Smith Braithwaite	£36,000,000	47	136	1 : 1.89	£264,706	£420,000	16
Trowers & Hamlins	£27,530,000	25	133	1 : 4.32	£206,992	£215,000	58
Walker Morris	£22,000,000	25	124	1 : 3.96	£177,419	£340,000	23
Watson, Farley & Williams	£42,500,000	50	190	1 : 2.8	£223,684	£210,000	60
Weightmans	£21,000,000	28	160	1 : 4.71	£131,250	£184,500	70
Weil, Gotshal & Manges	£26,500,000	11	82	1 : 6.45	£323,171	£550,000	11
Wilde Sapte	£50,200,000	45	288	1 : 5.4	£174,306	£224,000	54
Withers	£23,800,000	27	65	1 : 1.41	£366,154	£270,370	39
Wragge & Co	£54,500,000	82	339	1 : 3.13	£160,767	£257,000	45

REGIONAL REVIEWS

NATIONWIDE FIRMS

Eversheds The firm raised its total number of solicitors by over 3 percent in the last 12 months. A total lawyer count now in excess of 1000 sees almost half of them located in the three core offices of London, Leeds and Birmingham. The remainder are strung out over 10 offices, ensuring blanket nationwide coverage. Nationally, the firm attains a *Chambers* ranking in 45 different practice areas. A whopping 147 solicitors achieve *Chambers* recognition. The firm is felt to be under-achieving slightly in London corporate finance, where, despite its international links and enviable national resources, it is not quite making the expected headway. Education and franchising are the highest-achieving areas, although employment, fraud, litigation and IP all record a steady showing.

The firm's profile still lags behind Wragge & Co as King of Birmingham, but a year of progress puts it firmly into a challenging spot. The commercial property department is felt to have assumed a position of national influence. The smaller East Midlands branches have also made strides: Nottingham increasingly as a serious commercial player, while the Derby pensions litigation practice still rules the roost nationally. The policy decision of the Leeds office to shelve all non-corporate and commercial practice areas saw trusts and agriculture get the chop. However, the office retains its eminence in most of the core commercial disciplines. The office continues to be a shining national beacon for its local authority, PFI and environmental practices. In the North East, the 40-partner Newcastle office performed admirably, outstripping expectations, and overtaking or closing down rivals in many key commercial areas. It painlessly absorbed local insurance practice Linsley and Mortimer in May 2000. The healthcare practice still stands out as a centre of excellence, and is boosted by personnel arrivals. Wales' second largest firm, the Cardiff office took a prominent

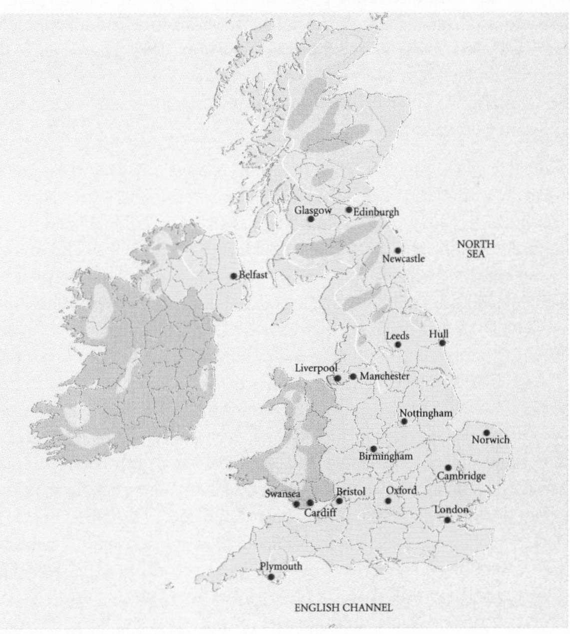

lead on the Bloody Sunday inquiry. The public sector flavoured aspect of the office remains a key feature, as does the thriving commercial property department.

The Manchester office performed above par. Upper-tier standings in the vital commercial triumvirate are underpinned by star corporate finance

NATIONWIDE: the 50 Largest Firms

		Ptnrs	Assts	Other Fee Earners	Total Sols
1	Eversheds	346	660	536	**1006**
2	Clifford Chance	197	727	242	**924**
3	Freshfields Bruckhaus Deringer	148	633	163	**781**
4	Linklaters	181	515	211	**696**
5	Allen & Overy	159	532	202	**691**
6	DLA	250	435	368	**685**
7	Hammond Suddards Edge	180	348	262	**528**
8	Slaughter and May	93	420	0	**513**
9	CMS Cameron McKenna	154	344	138	**498**
10	Lovells	127	346	200	**473**
11	Herbert Smith	128	342	196	**470**
12	Denton Wilde Sapte	163	303	162	**466**
13	Beachcroft Wansbroughs	130	301	199	**431**
14	Norton Rose	120	304	165	**424**
15	Simmons & Simmons	107	271	153	**378**
16	Ashurst Morris Crisp	83	274	151	**357**
17	Wragge & Co	94	254	199	**348**
18	Pinsent Curtis	129	199	105	**328**
19	Addleshaw Booth & Co	110	208	171	**318**
20	Nabarro Nathanson	105	208	136	**313**
21	SJ Berwin & Co	80	184	56	**264**
22	Masons	80	171	72	**251**
23	Morgan Cole	98	142	110	**240**
24	Baker & McKenzie	70	164	70	**234**
25	Berrymans Lace Mawer	83	140	129	**223**
26	Barlow Lyde & Gilbert	76	143	65	**219**
27	Osborne Clarke OWA	69	148	60	**217**
28	Berwin Leighton	66	147	51	**213**
29	Irwin Mitchell	77	134	633	**211**
30	Bird & Bird	60	150	35	**210**
31	Rowe & Maw	80	125	70	**205**
32	Taylor Joynson Garrett	87	116	62	**203**
33	Bevan Ashford	71	127	101	**198**
34	Dundas & Wilson CS	53	144	49	**197**
35	Clyde & Co	78	112	79	**190**
36	Mills & Reeve	59	130	83	**189**
37	Shoosmiths	78	107	328	**185**
38	Theodore Goddard	59	120	36	**179**
39	Garretts	48	125	52	**173**
40	Lawrence Graham	79	92	67	**171**
41	Thompsons	68	103	147	**171**
42	Burges Salmon	44	124	42	**168**
43	Stephenson Harwood	65	101	54	**166**
44	Macfarlanes	52	114	61	**166**
45	Richards Butler	72	88	61	**160**
46	Bond Pearce	51	108	79	**159**
47	Field Fisher Waterhouse	65	91	61	**156**
48	Charles Russell	76	79	51	**155**
49	McGrigor Donald	57	98	44	**155**
50	Olswang	45	96	40	**141**

The rankings in this table are determined by the number of solicitors working in the region. They are based on partner and assistant solicitor figures only: all other fee-earners are excluded.

partner Edward Pysden, some weighty property deals and a top-notch litigation department. This has become a vital link in the national chain. The buoyant East Anglian offices feed most profitably on the brand name of national repute. In corporate finance deals and on large pieces of litigation, these small satellites have exploited national resources to raise the profile of their own offices. The Norwich and Ipswich offices are increasingly involved with national or international mega-sums deals. The merger with Dutch firm Boekel De Nerée offers supporting evidence of the firm's overseas ambitions. Nationally, the firm can lay claim to the accolade of best integrated organisation.

DLA Have added almost 100 solicitors to its national total. Many originate from the former Bird Semple in Scotland, where the firm is the first English outfit to gain a major foothold. Overall, 78 individual lawyers are ranked in 30 different practice areas. Making a big push in the London corporate market where the firm's national strengths are increasingly felt to swing bigger deals in its favour. Its long-standing northern private equity credentials are beginning to reap rewards in the capital, where they make headway on the back of the technology boom. The combined Liverpool and Manchester offices represent the North West's largest firm. They have yet to rival Addleshaw's corporate pre-eminence but are sailing along nicely in property and litigation. In Yorkshire, the overall performance in some key sections (corporate finance and property) was slightly below par, but offset by a residually powerful litigation capability. Top tier status in insolvency, IP and pensions bear testimony to the abilities of the offices in Leeds and Sheffield. Less mature in the Midlands market place, and still fighting for recognition and respect, adequate progress in some practice areas (litigation, property, banking) is counterbalanced by lost ground in others (IP, IT, construction.) Still a leading choice for PFI work. The prospect of an English firm successfully cracking the insular Scottish market looked to be on the cards with the Bird Semple merger. A highly rated defamation practice and acknowledged expertise in corporate finance, insolvency, litigation and property are now additional Scottish strings to the firm's British bow.

Hammond Suddards Edge An exciting year for a firm who, after merging with Edge Ellison, catapulted themselves into the national top 10 largest firms. With a combined force of 528 solicitors, they snap at the heels of DLA and can now concentrate on presenting a sustained challenge to other national competitors. 64 individuals nationally were ranked in 29 different practice areas. Now the firm's second biggest office, Edge Ellison's former Birmingham home undeniably had a harrowing time competing on the commercial front line. It fared better in areas such as debt recovery, partnership, sport and media law. The closure of the Leicester office was a visible casualty of the firm's shake-up. However, there is clearly a reservoir of underlying strength at the firm (rankings in 25 areas and for 23 individuals) and such a sizeable entity *"will not suddenly disappear."* Solidity in London is the most tangible benefit of the union; the new combined force of 69 partners (180 solicitors) sits in good company in London's top 25 firms. It can count a raised corporate reputation as a plus point. Richard Burns oversees a high quality team attracting bigger ticket work. The former Edge office adds an advertising and marketing dimension to the new unit. Litigator Stephen York stands as another highly recommended name. Leeds continues to be a national hub for contentious matters, and is home to a team of highly tuned and astute litigators. The property department waned slightly, but this is offset by consistent delivery in a clutch of key financial and commercial areas, including general corporate, banking, IP and tax. A variable year in Manchester saw pluses in employment, property, construction, and insolvency, but slight dips elsewhere. A *"brazenly commercial and slick approach"* keeps the firm in the commercial top flight, if rarely at the summit itself.

Beachcroft Wansbroughs Solicitor numbers at the firm have risen to 431, an increase of almost 10 percent on last year's total. It may come as a surprise that across the firm as a whole the various offices register in over 18 distinct practice areas, an impressive statistic for a firm built on a core bedrock of health and insurance. 24 leading individuals left their mark on *Chambers* tables. Healthcare supremo Diane Hallatt keeps her top spot. Not quite so shiny was the loss of Barry Francis' PFI team to Buchanan Ingersoll. This resulted in loss of ranking in London and the North. Julian Gizzi has conducted a number of high profile public law cases, touching on education and health matters. Corporate finance, traditionally an area of low visibility for the firm, upped the ante, delivering a sterling effort characterised by an *"organised and collective attitude."* Advice to Hellenic Bottling Company SA on its £4.2 billion merger with Coca-Cola Beverages was an unusually large deal stemming from the firm's private client base. Bristol, the second largest office, has virtually *"sewn up the market"* for defendant personal injury work, another area of core expertise nationwide. Unsurprisingly, it sits comfortably at the top or thereabouts in professional negligence, clinical negligence and insurance. The teams embody a *"progressive and cutting-edge approach"* to litigation. Audaciously acquired the Crawford Owen property team to breathe new life into a previously uninspired area. A renaissance in commercial litigation hints at a firm attempting to push out its traditional boundaries, although the Manchester office paid for a lack of profile on general litigation matters. Health care, clinical negligence and PI are the hallmarks of the small but high quality Winchester office, which only features in 3 sections, but is top in 2 of them. The wider implications of the firm's public sector standing were acknowledged this year. The firm attained a new public law ranking in London and improved their Sheffield position.

Pinsent Curtis Recorded an impressive growth statistic by acquiring 71 more solicitors than this time last year. A total of 328 represents an increase in excess of 25 percent. The practice is recommended in 29 different practice areas nationally. 51 ranked individuals, a substantial increase on last year, were identified in this year's *Chambers*. A remarkable 43 of that number were listed as either band 1 or 2 performers. The London office increasingly benefits from its regional connections, and has built on its existing private equity reputation. Associated with the technology and new economy markets, the corporate finance practice has made substantial inroads into this lucrative sector. Gareth Edwards and the e-commerce team are members of the inaugural *Chambers* tables in this area of practice. Elsewhere in the 23-partner London office, the employment and professional negligence practices continue to win plaudits. In Birmingham, the perceived *"high quality of lawyer and client,"* have shown up strongly this year. In banking and corporate tax, the practices are nationally rated. Star partner Andrew Paton keeps the litigation flag flying high. Not yet challenging for corporate finance and property gold medals, the firm is nevertheless perceived to retain a high-quality brand. The pattern of improvement is repeated in the firm's Yorkshire backyard, which has had a productive year. The commercial litigation and IP practices both emerge as front runners, while the firm is still top-ranked in employment, tax and projects. Employment star John McMullen remains *"in a class of his own."*

Dundas & Wilson/Garretts The influence of the Andersen's overlords has been more acutely felt this year, certainly in Scotland. Garretts, however, delivered a report card of mixed grades, and still struggles to keep pace with their rivals. The banking practice in its two northern offices, Leeds and Manchester, continues to slide. In Yorkshire, it failed to attain a ranking at all, while Sue Molloy's defection to Halliwells in Manchester results in a reduced rating. The unfortunate northern tale also involves loss of ranking in education and employee share schemes. The situation is a little healthier in the tiny Cambridge office, where Gerard Fitzsimons and assistants have a good reputation for *"getting deals done."* Their particular niche in venture capital and technology was acknowledged by the market. Cross-border transactions and a steady flow of juicy work are recurrent features of the Birmingham, Leeds and Manchester corporate finance practices. The firm is felt to need to draw in further work from beyond the Andersen network in order to sustain a regional challenge. Individually, corporate finance players Timothy Hamilton in Manchester and Leeds-based *"class act"* Nick Painter have survived colleagues' departures, and keep the embers burning. The Reading office outshone its colleagues in several areas this year. The IT practice retains some *"impressive international clients"* and has a forte in e-commerce. A retained IP ranking and improvement in commercial litigation, are indicative of a year of consolidation. Garretts Birmingham attained a construction ranking after last year's blip, and they also remain a player in the local pension market.

Andersen Legal's Scottish arm Dundas and Wilson, fares much better. It features in over 30 separate Chamber's practice areas, showing a consistently high-level of performance. Of the 31 named individuals, only 10 sit outside the top two tiers of their respective sections. Star lawyers include top banking man Michael Stoneham, reliable litigator Colin MacLeod and David Hardie in the corporate finance department. Planning doyen Ann Faulds and leading property solicitor David Steel help to complete a glowing picture. Ousted only by Dickson Minto in corporate finance, it outperforms rivals in the majority of commercial and financial areas.

LONDON PRELIMS 1-10

Courtesy of British Airways Millenium Wheel

The London Eye and the River Thames

Clifford Chance The world-wide brand of the world's largest firm carries a heavyweight punch. comfortably ensconced in its mergers with Puender in Germany and Rogers and Wells in the US, the organisation continues to thrive in the UK. Still one of the world's banking powerhouses, the firm's relationship with Merrill Lynch has pulled in a slew of high-profile transactions. Financing advice on such transactions as the France Telecom takeover of Orange is work of an order beyond most of the firm's competitors. Although the firm has 101 ranked individuals this year, it still has to suffer criticisms of patchiness amongst its lawyers. With such a huge stable, it is inevitable that not all will excel, but in spite of possessing numerous ranked players, only five are awarded a star rating. They are head of competition Chris Bright, shipping giant Tony Vlasto, ADR legend Tony Willis, admin and public law expert Michael Smyth and James Johnson, a new acquisition from the former Wilde Sapte, who takes the palm for his debt buy-out excellence. Overall, the firm is ranked top in fifteen areas of practice, with derivatives and international arbitration showing an improvement on last year's performance. In spite of the departure of Teddy Bourne, the commercial property department continues to prosper. It is snapping at the heels of market leaders Linklaters. The litigation practice, where versatile Jeremy Sandelson is the firm's leading performer, is felt to promise much with the added muscle of Rogers & Wells. In corporate finance, though, accession to the ranks of market leaders seems as far away as ever. Not felt to have the depth of the leading trio, the firm's profile this year has been carried by the "insightful, pragmatic and effective" Adam Signy.

Freshfields Bruckhaus Deringer Even in a year of continued accomplishment, the firm's merger with German heavyweights Bruckhaus Westrick Heller Löber overshadowed all else. This event, together with aggressive expansion in Holland and successful offices throughout Europe and South-East Asia, underlines that Freshfields is clearly a force of world stature. The picture continues to be rosy in London. Ranked in 28 areas of practice, the firm carries off top honours in seven, and has 75 lawyers ranked by Chambers. Once again, corporate finance and its related areas of law provide richest pickings. An immovable fixture among the leading triumvirate for corporate finance, the team also maintains top slot for corporate tax and competition/anti-trust. A top-drawer clientele enabled the firm to act on both corporate and tax aspects of the EMI/Time Warner merger, and the competition aspects of the GEC Marconi/British Aerospace link. Elsewhere, the firm is ranked in the top band for environment, where Paul Bowden, ranked in three areas of practice, achieves tier one status. Other sectors similarly recognised are asset finance, rail transport and pensions. In the latter category, Kenneth Dierden is elevated to a star ranking, in recognition of his "charismatic leadership." PFI guru Nick Bliss gains the same accolade this year. The commercial litigation team maintains its pursuit of Herbert Smith, while the property group has become known as "the firm of choice for Canary Wharf tenants."

Linklaters Another year of huge success for the firm, whose European Alliance continues to benefit from the flourishing London office. Considered to be the firm which comes closest to harnessing a successful corporate practice with an equally proficient banking team, Linklaters has seldom been far from the headlines this year. Top billing again goes to the corporate finance machine, where, among a host of blue-chip practitioners, David Cheyne is acknowledged as one of the world's premier players. The huge Vodafone/Mannesmann merger and the defence of NatWest from two hostile bids are just two notches on his resumé. Mention should also be made of the "calmly authoritative" Matthew Middleditch, who is promoted in both corporate finance and non-contentious insurance, as well as retaining top tier status for investment funds. In all, the firm is ranked in 33 areas of practice and boasts 84 ranked practitioners. The team's "Rolls-Royce" property team still leads the field, while the litigation team has performed admirably in a radically overhauled list to lie in band three. "No-nonsense" head of litigation, Christopher Style receives a star rating. Under the guidance of Vanessa Havard-Williams, the environment group has shown noticeable improvement, while in international debt and equity, employee share schemes, financial services, civil fraud, investment funds and pensions, the firm retains top slot. The banking team is now recognised by many as the leading challenger to the long-term hegemony of Allen & Overy and Clifford Chance, acting for such leading financial institutions as Chase Manhattan.

Allen & Overy A year of progress, with the acquisition of a leading Dutch office. This was followed by the election of a new Senior Partner, Guy Beringer. He can look at a London office which is in rude health, ranked in 32 sectors, and containing eighty practitioners of unusual merit. As is traditional, everything revolves around the financial areas of practice. The banking team is considered to have a "quality edge" domestically, an edge underpinned by ten ranked lawyers, including the City's star performer David Morley. Among other high-profile successes, the firm advised an 11-bank syndicate financing a 30 billion Euro loan for Vodafone's hostile bid for Mannesmann, at the time thought to be the largest ever syndicated loan. In other areas, the projects/PFI team is felt to be pulling away from its nearest rivals under the aegis of top players Graham Vinter and Anne

Baldock. The capital markets group is the envy of most of London, although in securitisation and repackaging, it ranks second to Clifford Chance this year. The firm is also considered a leading force in civil fraud, insolvency, debt buy-outs and partnership law. The environment group gains promotion to the top band, and is now considered to be "operating at the highest level." Less positively, the commercial property practice takes a further fall, while the litigation team still does not threaten the market leaders.

Slaughter and May A glance at the firm's achievements this year confirms that to consider it merely a giant corporate finance machine is an over-simplification. While certain areas, notably commercial litigation, investment funds and financial services have seen a fall from grace, the team is still ranked in 25 areas of practice, scoring maximum marks in corporate tax and competition/anti-trust, as well as corporate finance. Both the derivatives team and environment department rise in the tables. As *Chambers* was constantly told this year, you go to Slaughter and May if you seek individual quality. A comment on the asset finance practice serves to illustrate the firm as a whole: "If what matters is how well rather than how much, they're at the top." Naturally, the corporate finance team remains the jewel in the crown. "Kingpin" Nigel Boardman heads a group which retains a matchless appetite for the big-ticket transaction. Glaxo Wellcome/SmithKline Beecham is only one of the firm's recent successes. Steve Edge has a Boardmanesque reputation for tax. Clients are said to seek him out "for his blessing," and he is constantly in demand. He is one of 57 lawyers at the firm to be ranked this year. With the aid of a decent Brussels office, the competition team also maintains its position at the top of the pile, advising on such mergers as British Steel/Hoogovens and Rothmans/BAT. The issue of the firm's international strategy has been exhaustively debated. Suffice to say that the absence of a conventional international network still shows no sign of harming the firm's global prestige and influence.

Lovells A mixed year for the firm. The generally well-received merger with Boesebeck Droste has given the organisation European muscle, but at home, certain events have conspired to put the firm on the back foot. Peter Voisey's departure to Clifford Chance has seriously compromised the ranking of the securitisation and repackaging team, Dan Mace's retirement to consultant status leaves the corporate team without a top tier big-hitter, and the tragic death of John Penson left the firm bereft of its star banking and debt buy-out practitioner. Under the circumstances, the firm has performed creditably in a number of areas. The firm still has an impressive range of ranked specialisms (35), of which civil fraud, non-contentious insurance, parliamentary/public affairs and pensions litigation boast band one ratings. Led by top-rated Robert Kidby, the commercial property team continues to flourish, while the "extraordinarily wise" Neil Fagan is the stand-out practitioner of a widely-admired commercial litigation group, which inter alia dealt with the Young vs Robson Rhodes case. In all, 57 practitioners are ranked this year, of whom non-contentious insurance expert John Young and VAT tax wizard Greg Sinfield achieve star billing.

CMS Cameron McKenna Ranked in 29 areas of practice, the firm has undergone a year of quiet consolidation rather than stellar achievement. The key areas of practice present a mixed picture. Although not a team of stars, the commercial litigation group is highly respected, keeping in the public eye through cases such as Spice Girls Ltd vs Aprilia World Service BV. The commercial property group is also esteemed for its "ability to integrate" the practice with other departments to provide a comprehensive service. However, the corporate finance team is considered to have "failed to capitalise on the firm's presence in the European market," and moves down a band. Construction remains a particular forte, with the firm leading the pursuit of Masons, and ranking top for construction-related professional negligence. Other areas where the firm holds a band one rating are health and safety, business immigration and product liability. In the latter section, the firm has three tier one practitioners, including long-time guru, Ian Dodds-Smith. 51 lawyers are ranked this year, including electricity star Fiona Woolf and Tony Kitson, "one of London's planning greats."

Herbert Smith In spite of numerous rumours of possible European liaisons, it is a comparative lack of international stature which is most commonly cited as a factor differentiating the firm from the so-called 'Magic Circle.' This has, though, been another fine year for the London office. Rated in 34 areas of practice, the firm's performance in the key commercial areas continues to stand out. Just below the top for corporate finance, the department nevertheless has eight ranked practitioners, including new Senior Partner Richard Bond, and has acted on such notable transactions as Publicis' £4 billion acquisition of Saatchi & Saatchi. The commercial litigation team continues to stand alone. Now "much more user-friendly," the department, which includes star players Ted Greeno and David Gold, represented the Law Society on its high-profile case against Kamlesh Bahl. The commercial property team still merits great respect, fortified by institutional clients such as Greycoat and Standard Life. After two years of knocking on the door, the firm now has a band one competition team, one of a total of six departments with such a ranking. The energy team remains at the top, further bolstered by the acquisition of Paul Griffin from Cadwalader, Wickersham & Taft. In total, 58 practitioners are ranked in Chambers this year.

Denton Wilde Sapte Six months on from the union, the merger is widely regarded to be a success. In spite of the loss of some star names, the melding of Wilde Sapte's banking know-how with Denton Hall's more corporate-based expertise has produced an office with increased scope. The firm is ranked in 31 areas of practice and is ranked top in five. The media and entertainment field is particularly fruitful. Michael Ridley heads the top-rated broadcasting team, while the publishing group is now felt to be pulling away from the rest of the field. However, it is the energy practice which shows the best of the firm. Internationally renowned, the group has advised on a host of big-ticket transactions, including acting for Petronas on its investment in Premier Oil. Other areas in which the firm takes a band one rating are aviation (regulatory) and sports law. In the latter sector, Adrian Barr-Smith, considered "right at the top of the tree," is a star practitioner. A total of 44 individuals are rated in Chambers this year. Although the corporate finance team is not felt to be one of the "mainstream leaders," the commercial litigation outfit is said to have "interesting possibilities," while the property team has also had a respectable year.

Norton Rose Ranked in 27 sectors this year, the firm has enjoyed a consistent year, continuing to win plaudits for strength in asset finance in general and shipping finance in particular. Reports of talks with German firm Gaedertz emphasise the firm's abiding ambition to bring its international strength more in line with that of its leading competitors. Peter Thorne is the leading player at an asset finance practice which has acted on such deals as the formation and financing of a joint venture between SAS and GECAS. The shipping finance team remains top-rated, and a growing strength in shipping litigation has also been apparent this year. Although it is also top-rated for civil fraud, the firm's corporate finance team has perhaps been the stand-out performer this year. Said to be "in the ascendancy" following its advice on a number of high-profile transactions, the team has shown particular expertise in big-ticket telecoms matters, acting for Mannesmann on its £19.5 billion bid for Orange and its defence of the £86.6 billion hostile bid from Vodafone Airtouch. The commercial litigation team has been noted as "a player on serious mainstream work," while the commercial property team maintains a fine reputation among its developer client base. In neither of these two sectors, however, does the firm yet approach the market leaders. 48 individuals are ranked by Chambers this year, including Brian Greenwood, a star of the planning firmament.

LONDON PRELIMS 11-25

Simmons & Simmons A slightly depressed year with "internal rumblings" continuing to distract from the overall firepower of the firm. Consequently the firm has dropped in a number of the *Chambers* rankings. However, the firm has retained its key stars, with Kevin Mooney and Janet Gaymer maintaining the integrity of the IP and Employment practices respectively. They receive *Chambers* highest recommendation and overall this firm has 35 leaders in their field. The firm also features highly for its well established 'pure' environmental practice. Internationally the reputation of the firm has brought much cross-border activity and Simmons is still a favourite with US corporates, not least retail mammoth Wal-Mart. In corporate finance the firm has made a play for the technology market, and is still one of the top ten practices in the City.

Ashurst Morris Crisp There can be no doubt that the firm is ambitious, but its ultimately unsuccessful merger talks firstly with Clifford Chance and more recently US powerhouse Latham & Watkins have been seen to have had an unsettling effect. A highly commercial firm, ranked in 25 *Chambers* sections, it leads the field in private equity financing where the "sparkling personality" of Charlie Geffen shines. The planning team continue to show prowess, where Michael Cunliffe is said to "rule the roost." 38 individuals are ranked in the *Chambers* lists. Having broken its three year alliance with Italian firm Negri-Clementi the firm has gone it alone, adding Milan to its well established Frankfurt and Paris offices. In emulating the expansionist policy of the largest firms, it hopes to bolster its corporate offering in the face of stiff competition. But what of the US connection? With *Chambers* rankings showing an overall downward drift (a particularly poor showing in Energy & Utilities) this firm needs to cement relationships with major international investment banks and the larger corporates to give bite to the ambitions of its partners.

SJ Berwin & Co A broad-based young firm said to have "the brightest personality in the city" and a "seamless" multi-disciplinary approach to all practice areas. Thought to be driven by a strong property department which has crossed the traditional strengths of the firm and led to deals such as acting for mainstay client British Land on its £1.17 billion acquisition of Meadow Hall Shopping Centre. The well regarded planning team also played a part in this huge transaction with "whirlwind" Patricia Thomas earning our star rating. Ranked in 19 *Chambers* sections, four of which are rated as top of the class, Commercial Litigation (Under 40 Solicitors), Parliamentary: Public Affairs, Media & Entertainment: Film Financing and Travel: Hotels and Leisure. 25 individuals receive *Chambers* rankings this year including the star rated Stephen Kon, a competition heavy hitter. The

LONDON: the 150 Largest Firms (continued overleaf)

		Ptnrs	Asst Solrs	Total No of Solicitors '00	'99	'98	'97
1	**Clifford Chance**	197	727	**924**	932	863	773
2	**Freshfields Bruckhaus Deringer**	148	633	**781**	577	516	449
3	**Linklaters**	181	515	**696**	721	597	573
4	**Allen & Overy**	159	532	**691**	614	573	537
5	**Slaughter and May**	93	420	**513**	400	361	356
6	**Lovells**	127	346	**473**	473	450	403
7	**CMS Cameron McKenna**	147	324	**471**	432	394	399
8	**Herbert Smith**	128	342	**470**	456	409	369
9	**Denton Wilde Sapte**	158	290	**448**	-	-	-
10	**Norton Rose**	120	304	**424**	380	344	321
11	**Simmons & Simmons**	107	271	**378**	404	400	353
12	**Ashurst Morris Crisp**	83	274	**357**	356	310	280
13	**SJ Berwin & Co**	80	184	**264**	198	193	113
14	**Baker & McKenzie**	70	164	**234**	177	165	145
15	**Nabarro Nathanson**	83	144	**227**	255	255	237
16	**Barlow Lyde & Gilbert**	76	143	**219**	190	184	189
17	**Berwin Leighton**	66	147	**213**	191	196	169
18	**DLA**	86	124	**210**	194	203	146
19	**Bird & Bird**	60	150	**210**	125	98	86
20	**Rowe & Maw**	80	125	**205**	203	183	159
21	**Taylor Joynson Garrett**	87	116	**203**	186	166	162
22	**Eversheds**	76	120	**196**	184	187	135
23	**Beachcroft Wansbroughs**	64	131	**195**	187	-	-
24	**Hammond Suddards Edge**	69	111	**180**	-	-	-
25	**Theodore Goddard**	59	120	**179**	147	147	133
26	**Lawrence Graham**	79	92	**171**	168	154	133
27	**Stephenson Harwood**	65	101	**166**	161	155	167
28	**Macfarlanes**	52	114	**166**	145	139	126
29	**Richards Butler**	72	88	**160**	149	146	132
30	**Field Fisher Waterhouse**	65	91	**156**	134	129	98
31	**Masons**	52	98	**150**	132	131	155
32	**Olswang**	45	96	**141**	109	85	69
33	**Gouldens**	36	102	**138**	114	101	97
34	**Dechert**	46	90	**136**	127	123	103
35	**Clyde & Co**	57	73	**130**	128	133	109
36	**Travers Smith Braithwaite**	43	85	**128**	125	120	113
37	**Ince & Co**	53	70	**123**	90	112	102
38	**Reynolds Porter Chamberlain**	50	68	**118**	117	110	95
39	**D J Freeman**	58	56	**114**	114	104	100
40	**Holman Fenwick & Willan**	52	62	**114**	100	91	90
41	**Davies Arnold Cooper**	35	78	**113**	150	141	120
42	**Charles Russell**	56	56	**112**	109	107	86
43	**Paisner & Co**	53	58	**111**	116	91	87
44	**Withers**	47	58	**105**	101	91	89
45	**Shearman & Sterling**	19	84	**103**	68	-	-
46	**Nicholson Graham & Jones**	56	46	**102**	101	87	81
47	**Weil, Gotshal & Manges**	21	79	**100**	97	61	42
48	**Watson, Farley & Williams**	30	68	**98**	91	89	78
49	**Trowers & Hamlins**	45	51	**96**	96	92	78
50	**Farrer & Co**	41	50	**91**	88	81	76
51	**Kennedys**	40	49	**89**	86	76	62
52	**Berrymans Lace Mawer**	31	52	**83**	135	81	77
53	**Speechly Bircham**	37	44	**81**	71	67	73
54	**Manches**	33	46	**79**	79	73	72
55	**Finers Stephens Innocent**	41	36	**77**	-	-	-
56	**Osborne Clarke OWA**	24	52	**76**	45	45	36
57	**Bristows**	26	49	**75**	60	56	60
58	**Howard Kennedy**	40	32	**72**	64	48	38
59	**Bircham & Co.**	32	38	**70**	49	37	44
60	**White & Case**	23	47	**70**	42	30	28
61	**Harbottle & Lewis**	18	50	**68**	68	65	57
62	**Sinclair Roche & Temperley**	28	36	**64**	64	62	68
63	**Garretts**	23	41	**64**	58	57	47
64	**Mishcon de Reya**	31	31	**62**	58	82	73
65	**Vizards, Staples & Bannisters**	30	32	**62**	70	-	-
66	**Radcliffes**	32	28	**60**	59	58	62
67	**Pinsent Curtis**	23	37	**60**	60	54	37
68	**Lewis Silkin**	29	30	**59**	58	57	63
69	**Kingsley Napley**	33	25	**58**	56	47	42
70	**Biddle**	32	26	**58**	68	70	69
71	**Fladgate Fielder**	28	30	**58**	54	44	44
72	**Russell Jones & Walker**	23	35	**58**	48	46	59
73	**Singhania & Co**	8	50	**58**	58	-	-
74	**Wedlake Bell**	29	28	**57**	51	53	51
75	**Capsticks**	23	34	**57**	55	45	45
76	**Morgan Cole**	26	30	**56**	25	-	-
77	**Landwell**	11	45	**56**	-	-	-

The rankings in this table are determined by the number of solicitors working in the region. They are based on partner and assistant solicitor figures only: all other fee-earners are excluded.

commercial litigation team is praised to the hilt with a strong international reputation and a "no nonsense" approach. Clearly at the forefront of a number of legal developments, including the payment of US-style salaries to newly qualified solicitors, this has been an excellent year for the firm.

Baker & McKenzie The "ultimate in international franchises" highly rated for its global network. Has developed a successful following for having a man in every port with a particularly good showing in the Eastern European markets. Often on major cross-border transactions, the London team has had only a reasonable performance in a year which has seen a massive commercial consolidation overseas. Ranked in 19 areas of the *Chambers* Guide, with first rate achievements in IT and Commercial Litigation. In the latter the team has scored highly with the Grupo Torras case. Its traditional base of Telecoms has fallen slightly this year as the team struggles to find a figurehead. This may be true of the practice overall which is not thought to be as personality-driven as its major competitors. 18 solicitors make the *Chambers* ranking this year with the excellent Robert West bolstering the Pensions team. Other areas of strength include employment, where the team is starting to recover from the loss of its leading practitioner Fraser Younson.

Nabarro Nathanson Associated primarily with its public sector bias and solid foundations in the property arena, this firm has had a good year. "Elder statesman" Geoffrey Lander remains at the forefront of the property group's assault which has successfully spread work into the corporate team. An admirable reputation with local authorities has seen the firm shine in a number of practice areas including planning and PFI. In both areas the teams are thought to benefit from a buoyant property market. The firm is ranked in 21 *Chambers* sections with first rate showings in property litigation, pensions litigation and local government. Although it maintains its prominence for property financing, in corporate work the firm has joined the dot.com bandwagon and scored well with clients such as private equity group, Alchemy Partners. This "slick" commercial firm has 36 ranked individuals.

Barlow Lyde & Gilbert An outstanding performance from a firm which dominates the fields of general claims insurance, reinsurance and professional negligence. The focus of the firm has really paid off with lead rankings in these areas and an appearance in 10 *Chambers* sections. Admired by clients, solicitors and barristers for its technical excellence and a client list that includes heavy weights such as AXA Reinsurance and Lloyd's. Graham Dickinson is in the premier league for personal injury, while Ian Awford leads the aviation charge. 18 individuals make it into the *Chambers* ranking this year. With plans to open an office in Shanghai to complement its existing Hong Kong offering, there can be no doubt that this firm has its sights set high, with the Asian insurance market just one of the targets.

Berwin Leighton "A classic property firm" at its core and across the board it has shone this year. Ranked in 14 sections of *Chambers* with strong showings in planning, local government and naturally enough, property litigation and commercial property. Ian Trehearne and Timothy Pugh continue to lead the planning team with a "commercial approach." Old hand Laurie Heller may no longer be running the commercial property show but he is still thought of as a rainmaker and major influence on the firm's profitability. These two areas of strength have also encouraged "quality practitioners" in the local government field. While the loss of its main private equity partners to Olswang has meant the firm drops out of *Chambers* buyout section, the corporate work of the firm has been strong with both bricks (property) and clicks (internet) type clients. 18 leading individuals make the *Chambers* ranking with 6 ranked in the top band.

DLA Well established national outfit who have successfully refocused and consolidated in London after a major round of recruitment. The firm is ranked in 29 *Chambers* sections with strong showings in transport (road and rail) and debt financed buyouts. Has made huge strides in the parliamentary: public affairs market with a highly proactive team led by Liberal peer Tim Clement-Jones. In corporate finance Peter Wayte maintains the firm's reputation for "first rate service," particularly excelling in the private equity field. It has also ridden the dot.com wave to secure some major clients. With companies like Easyjet on board, its client base has an entrepreneurial flavour. On the fringes of our rankings in commercial property and litigation, the firm is said to be "efficient" and "coming up fast."

Bird & Bird An outstanding performance from a firm which takes its centralised excellence in IT/IP related issues and feeds the success through to other practice areas. Ranked in 8 *Chambers* sections the firm is leading the pack in telecoms, IP (patent and general), IT and e-commerce. Across the board the firm is praised for its "quality" and focus on these areas. Trevor Cook is a "smooth operator" who retains his stellar reputation in the IP field. Shining alongside him in our rankings are fellow practitioner David Harriss and IT guru Hamish Sandison. 13 individuals receive mention in the *Chambers* lists with 8 ranked as top of the class. Said to be "an IBM choice" in telecoms, with BT plc putting its faith in this "clever" firm. The specialist approach has paid dividends in the financial sphere, with a fine reputation for developing government-backed PFI schemes and convergence-based corporate work. If there is a down side it may rest with the decision not to push forward the planned merger with San Francisco based Orrick Herrington & Sutcliffe. The firm is felt to lose out on corporate work because of a lack of US capability.

Rowe & Maw "A no nonsense" firm that has had a good, balanced year. Ranked in 20 *Chambers* sections the firm is thought of as leaders in pensions, professional negligence, timeshare, partnerships and mid tier corporate finance work. In local government, the presence of Anna Forge (ex Berwin Leighton) has added breadth to Tony Child's strong team. The firm has 25 highly rated individuals in *Chambers* this year. Continuing to steam ahead, the pensions practice has a considerable reputation for its client base packed with trustees of very large occupational schemes. As always, Richard Linsell's partnership practice provides "imaginative" solutions to its commercial clients. The firm has fared well in construction this year, thanks to partners who are always "good news." In corporate finance, the firm also scored well. With cross border M&A deals for clients such as Cable & Wireless and ICI, this is a commercial firm which has successfully raised its profile this year.

Taylor Joynson Garrett Holding its own this year, the firm is ranked in 11 areas of the *Chambers* Guide. IP is still seen as the main driver for this firm, praised as leaders for both general and patent advice. Mark Hodgson is the team's star practitioner with a varied base of clients and an emphasis on contentious work. This reputation feeds into the firm's solid niche in media and publishing where Paul Mitchell has gained a vast experience acting for estates. A good jump in its IT ratings with a "cracking" team leading the way and clients of the calibre of Sony Computer Entertainment. In insolvency the firm has a steady profile advising banks on reconstruction and recovery. The corporate team is "on the up," acting on international M&A work and boasting an array of US clients. The firm has been seen to successfully leverage its IP reputation to capture the growing e-commerce based flotation work. 13 individuals make it into *Chambers* ranks this year.

Eversheds A balanced year for this heavily commercial office of the national power-house. A strong showing in education (some say they are the preeminent firm), as the noted constitutional expert John Hall retains his stellar reputation. "The grandfather of franchising" Martin Mendelsohn leads this acclaimed practice area, thought to be the experts on multi-jurisdictional deals. The office also performs well in employment, investment funds and holds steady in fraud, litigation, IP and immigration. Ranked in 17 *Chambers* sections this year. In areas such as commercial property and corporate finance the firm is seen to trade off the national franchise giving it a natural, competitive advantage. Fears are occasionally raised about the level of commitment to the London office, with corporate deals often felt to rely on the national network. 15 individuals are ranked as leaders in their field this year.

LONDON: the 150 Largest Firms continued

		Ptnrs	Asst Solrs	Total No of Solicitors '00	'99	'98	'97
78	**McDermott, Will & Emery**	12	43	**55**	-	-	-
79	**Davenport Lyons**	23	28	**51**	41	30	28
80	**Forsters**	17	33	**50**	47	-	-
81	**LeBoeuf, Lamb, Greene & MacRae**	9	41	**50**	44	32	28
82	**Russell-Cooke, Potter & Chapman**	21	26	**47**	40	41	42
83	**Boodle Hatfield**	27	19	**46**	43	35	35
84	**Sidley & Austin**	16	30	**46**	51	30	30
85	**KLegal**	11	35	**46**	-	-	-
86	**Jeffrey Green Russell**	23	21	**44**	45	51	43
87	**Hodge Jones & Allen**	21	23	**44**	42	35	30
88	**Rakisons**	16	28	**44**	37	27	22
89	**Tarlo Lyons**	26	17	**43**	40	30	24
90	**Hill Taylor Dickinson**	19	24	**43**	23	54	48
91	**Le Brasseur J Tickle**	17	26	**43**	44	44	35
92	**Skadden, Arps, Slate, Meagher & Flom LLP**	9	34	**43**	32	25	25
93	**Beaumont and Son**	19	23	**42**	37	37	29
94	**Salans Hertzfeld & Heilbronn HRK**	17	25	**42**	43	40	-
95	**Penningtons**	16	25	**41**	36	38	37
96	**Fox Williams**	14	27	**41**	37	33	26
97	**Latham & Watkins**	9	32	**41**	22	16	8
98	**Pritchard Englefield**	26	14	**40**	39	34	34
99	**Winckworth Sherwood**	19	21	**40**	43	33	42
100	**Cleary, Gottlieb, Steen & Hamilton**	9	31	**40**	38	26	28
101	**Brecher & Co**	25	13	**38**	38	-	-
102	**Fisher Meredith**	11	27	**38**	36	34	32
103	**Brobeck Hale and Dorr**	7	31	**38**	-	-	-
104	**Devonshires**	18	19	**37**	19	26	24
105	**Rosling King**	11	26	**37**	50	39	39
106	**David Levene & Co**	9	28	**37**	34	23	18
107	**Kingsford Stacey Blackwell**	22	14	**36**	35	35	22
108	**Hextall Erskine**	21	15	**36**	35	31	29
109	**Jones, Day, Reavis & Pogue**	7	29	**36**	-	-	-
110	**Lee & Pembertons**	20	15	**35**	33	39	34
111	**Constant & Constant**	22	12	**34**	29	33	34
112	**Dawson & Co**	22	12	**34**	31	26	25
113	**Warner Cranston**	18	16	**34**	34	42	35
114	**Teacher Stern Selby**	16	18	**34**	30	26	26
115	**T.V. Edwards**	9	25	**34**	34	30	30
116	**Sacker & Partners**	17	16	**33**	31	30	23
117	**Hobson Audley**	13	20	**33**	37	35	36
118	**Davis Polk & Wardwell**	9	24	**33**	33	-	-
119	**Sullivan & Cromwell**	7	26	**33**	33	-	-
120	**Edwin Coe**	22	10	**32**	33	30	27
121	**Bates, Wells & Braithwaite**	21	11	**32**	42	25	22
122	**Collyer-Bristow**	20	12	**32**	28	27	27
123	**Hempsons**	17	15	**32**	29	28	43
124	**Campbell Hooper**	15	17	**32**	35	37	32
125	**Tuckers**	1	31	**32**	-	-	-
126	**Prince Evans**	7	24	**31**	31	27	30
127	**Vizard Oldham**	22	8	**30**	-	-	-
128	**Park Nelson**	19	11	**30**	32	27	22
129	**Amhurst Brown Colombotti**	17	13	**30**	24	25	25
130	**Bindman & Partners**	15	15	**30**	26	25	21
131	**Coudert Brothers**	14	16	**30**	31	29	23
132	**Fishburn Morgan Cole**	12	18	**30**	30	-	-
133	**Goodman Derrick**	20	9	**29**	25	27	24
134	**Payne Hicks Beach**	19	10	**29**	20	28	25
135	**William Sturges & Co**	17	12	**29**	25	22	22
136	**Mayer, Brown & Platt**	10	19	**29**	31	20	20
137	**Milbank, Tweed, Hadley & McCloy**	7	22	**29**	20	16	-
138	**Middleton Potts**	19	9	**28**	30	29	30
139	**Dewey Ballantine**	10	18	**28**	-	-	-
140	**Crockers Oswald Hickson**	9	19	**28**	27	27	22
141	**Bolt Burdon**	8	20	**28**	31	37	31
142	**Hamlins**	18	9	**27**	30	27	26
143	**Clintons**	17	10	**27**	22	19	19
144	**Rooks Rider**	12	15	**27**	32	29	26
145	**Thomas Cooper & Stibbard**	16	10	**26**	25	23	26
146	**Memery Crystal**	12	14	**26**	25	25	23
147	**McGrigor Donald**	10	16	**26**	26	21	19
148	**The Simkins Partnership**	20	5	**25**	27	32	41
149	**Seddons**	15	10	**25**	23	20	18
150	**Stringer Saul**	14	11	**25**	24	24	23

The rankings in this table are determined by the number of solicitors working in the region. They are based on partner and assistant solicitor figures only: all other fee-earners are excluded.

Beachcroft Wansbroughs Generally acknowledged to be a year of consolidation for the recently merged firm, with the strongest showing in the traditional heart of the firm: healthcare. There have been setbacks, however. The departure of Barry Francis and his PFI team to Buchanan Ingersoll has meant those remaining are forced to bow out of our Projects/PFI section. In personal injury, on the other hand, the firm is said to be "expanding and expanding." Overall, nine players make it onto the *Chambers* rankings. Julian Gizzi maintains his leading profile as the mainstay of the education team. The firm is most respected for its following among public sector local authorities. The corporate team attained its highest profile deal to date when the Hellenic Bottling Co showed loyalty to the firm over its £4 billion merger with Coca Cola Beverages.

Hammond Suddards Edge A match made in heaven? The jury is still out on that question but in merging, these major regional players are said to have London on their mind. The firm is ranked in 10 sections of *Chambers*, and is thought to lead the pack in the smaller corporate finance teams (under 30 solicitors). Richard Burns continues to tower over this team and is praised for cementing relationships with the private equity houses. Deals are starting to fall in the £100 – £200 million range, showing an increase in capability for the larger transactions. Edge Ellison brings a "reinforced" profile in advertising and marketing to the table, with work for its major client WPP. Has 9 individuals ranked in *Chambers*, with "inventive and idiosyncratic" Stephen York making a good showing in commercial litigation and ADR.

Theodore Goddard Distracted by high profile partner departures to US firms bolstering their London bases, this solid firm has played well on its strengths, notably in the entertainment world. Ranked in 18 practice areas this year, the firm is doing particularly well in media, advertising and defamation. Although the advertising team has seen the loss of Rafi Azim-Khan (to McDermott, Will & Emery) it continues to be noted for its regulatory work. Jonathan Berger is the driving force of the film financing team, seen to be acting for bigger ticket production clients this year. Paddy Grafton-Green continues to be enormously well liked and is the mainstay of an excellent media/music practice. The corporate team is also "packed with bright people" but has suffered from the defection of its head to Jones Day Reavis & Pogue. 15 individuals are recommended to the *Chambers* ranks this year. Corporates such as Signet Group and Diageo are among the most notable members of the client base.

LONDON PRELIMS 26-40

Lawrence Graham Ranked in 14 sections, Lawrence Graham maintains its position as a well regarded full-service firm. In an improvement on last year, 14 partners are now rated in their respective fields of expertise. Their strongest asset is the "prominent team" responsible for corporate finance. This is guaranteed a high-profile by the presence of band-one rated Michael Storar (an "impressive force"). It is respected in property, where it is popular with existing clients such as J. Sainsbury Developments, and is seen to have won new clients. Commercial litigation is another successful department and has risen to band three in the rankings of firms in its size-group (10-39 litigators).

Macfarlanes The firm shows strength in 15 areas of practice, and fields 19 noteworthy individuals. It demonstrates top-tier prowess in advertising & marketing, agriculture & bloodstock, and trusts & personal tax. The jewel in its crown is the "professional" corporate finance team, ranked in the highest tier in its group (30-60 lawyers). Robert Sutton is the star player, and is seen as personally responsible for the team's involvement in big-ticket deals, such as the £4 billion acquisition of Saatchi & Saatchi by Publicis. However, the firm is comparatively weak in commercial litigation and property.

Stephenson Harwood Ranked in 14 areas of practice, and sporting 18 notable individual practitioners, Stephenson Harwood has had a mixed year. The shipping operation that was the firm's backbone last year draws mixed comment. Nonetheless, it remains solid in the rankings and Paolo Ghiradani earns praise for his asset tracing work. In corporate finance the firm has slipped by two ranks, largely because of the loss of the team leader to a US firm. Despite this, the team has a reputation for being "lovely to work for," and acted on seven public bids last year. A robust commercial litigation department is boosted by the elevation of "natural leader and great motivator," John Fordham, to the top tier of practitioners.

Richards Butler A sturdy showing from this firm sees it listed in 18 sections, with 20 partners singled out for mention. Richards Butler are band-one rated for licensing & leisure, media & entertainment (film finance) and for physical commodities. The physical commodities team is a powerhouse that boasts four rated individuals, with the luminary David Pullen deemed so far ahead of his peers that he earns a star rating. An active corporate finance team with "fine international clients" secures a band two rating, while the commercial litigation team is solid despite dropping a band. Commercial property has provided a black spot of the year, exiting the *Chambers* rankings.

Field Fisher Waterhouse With 17 noteworthy individuals spread over 20 areas of practice, Field Fisher Waterhouse has put in a sterling performance. It shows its customary excellence in the areas of travel (tourism & package holidays), franchising and licensing & leisure. All are band-one rated for the fourth year running. A poor year for commercial litigation and commercial property sees the firm drops out of the running in both categories. The firm's corporate finance team, however, is in the ascendent, and is perceived to have capitalised on the firm's overall success in the telecoms, e-commerce and leisure sectors. Michael Chissick has a particularly good name in the convergence areas of law.

Masons Masons fields 12 notable individuals across seven legal disciplines. The firm has devoted itself to carving a niche in one area of practice. Described as "construction juggernauts," the firm continues to pull away from the competition in this sphere. The team features five rated individuals, amongst whom the first-class John Bishop and Anthony Bunch stand out. The team is substantial enough for the departure of a sixth key player to have caused hardly a ripple to its smooth operation. It counts amongst its clients Alstom, Mowlem, and Wembley National Stadium Ltd.

Olswang In a distinct improvement on last year's figures, Olswang now boasts no fewer than 19 noteworthy individuals distributed across 15 legal disciplines. The firm's commercial property team is one success story. It has moved back into the rankings, and is thought to have created a "considerable splash" by leading the purchase of the £400 million P&O property portfolio by the Whitehall Green Partnership. Star-rated, "top-class" practitioner, Geraldine Proudler, is the leading-light of a formidable defamation team, that represents, among others, Dame Julie Andrews. The corporate finance team maintains its central position, demonstrating a new, specialist "understanding of its core market" in media, telecoms and technology. The opening of its new corporate finance house, Longacre Associates, has been seen as an innovative and bold move. The firm's internet/e-commerce team is a premier league outfit, as is its media & entertainment practice (band-one for both broadcasting and film/TV production).

Gouldens Last year's stable results are reproduced, with seven practitioners of merit being spread across eight areas of practice. This year Gouldens consolidate their genuine strength in the key commercial areas. Their "driven" corporate practice still runs with the best of the mid-tier firms and is making significant inroads into the international market. It boasts three named individuals. The firm's "quality" commercial property team acted for Pillar Property plc in a limited partnership joint venture with Equitable Life Assurance for 12 UK retail parks valued at £245 million. The firm also move up two tiers in commercial litigation (under 40 litigators.)

Dechert The firm is ranked for 12 areas of practice and reckoned to have ten notable players. It looks poised to exploit its international capabilities more fully following the formalisation of its merger, while the feed through of US work already appears substantial. The "user friendly" corporate finance team puts in a solid showing. It is held to provide the "perfect balance between commercial and legal advice." The commercial property team, led by band-one rated Steven Fogel, is likewise respected, and counts Nike amongst its clients. In the key areas, commercial litigation is this year's star turn, rising two ranks and reportedly "getting better and catching up with certain other strong firms." Elsewhere, the firm's customs and excise team is rated first-class for the fourth consecutive year.

Clyde & Co The firm has ten high-profile individuals rated in 10 areas of practice. It performs with customary excellence in the shipping practices for which it is famed, and again achieves a band-one rating for the general claims side of its insurance & reinsurance practice. Although slipping a band in both transport and aviation, in both areas it remains well-regarded. The team maintains its position, attained for the first time last year, in the commercial litigation rankings.

Travers Smith Braithwaite The firm is now ranked in 13 practice areas with fifteen recommended partners. The corporate finance team remains the firm's greatest asset, ranked at two and boasting three "quality" individuals. The team's success can be put down to its "highly commercial" outlook and its user-friendly style. Although they drop out of the tables for commercial property, their commercial litigation team remains robust. Ranked at three in their group (10-39 litigators), they are responsible for some "top-class work." The pensions team rises a band, while Paul Stannard is awarded star-ranking in recognition of his ability to breeze through "seemingly intractable problems."

Ince & Co After considerable expansion, Ince & Co are now firmly ensconced among the forty largest firms in London. The shipping practice vies with that of Holman Fenwick & Willan for pole position and is seen to secure both "volume and quality" work. There is an enviable depth of talent here. Of the six partners ranked, two merit star status, while a further three are band-one rated. The firm is ranked in 6 areas of practice, and fields 13 notable individuals. Although no longer ranked as band one players, the firm's insurance and reinsurance practices remain well respected.

Reynolds Porter Chamberlain The firm moves up a band in the financial side of professional negligence, and thus consolidates its position as a leading professional negligence practice. Second only to the far larger Barlow Lyde & Gilbert in this sphere, Reynolds Porter Chamberlain is "hugely respected," while key player Paul Nicholas is adjudged first class for the fourth time. The firm's defamation practice also flourishes, rising by two ranks. It is led by Elizabeth Hartley, now recognised as one of the foremost practitioners in the field. The commercial litigation team is also on the up, tipped as "interesting to watch" by pundits. Overall, the firm is ranked in seven practice areas, and has six listed individuals.

Holman Fenwick & Willan Holman Fenwick & Willan have grown in size. In this they resemble Ince & Co, their principal rivals in the shipping market. A "supremely confident" shipping team with an enviable record for salvage work, their global expansion has earned them an upgrade for their dry work. They are now band-one rated in both areas of practice, and have links with German, Far Eastern, and Greek owner-markets. The shipping team boasts seven ranked practitioners, one of whom, Archie Bishop, earns his fourth consecutive star. On the negative side, the firm drops out of the rankings for commercial litigation. It now is rated in six practice areas and features eleven noteworthy individuals.

DJ Freeman A great year for the firm's defamation department saw it act for Mohammed al-Fayed in his high profile, successful action against Neil Hamilton. It moves upwards in this practice area, while its leading defamation lawyer, the "extra-competent" Susan Aslan, rises to join the highest echelon of practitioners in that field. A sturdy performance from the commercial litigation team sees that practice ranked in the second tier for its size (10-39 litigators.) In the contentious spheres, the firm sinks down for fraud and reinsurance but remains solid in property litigation and media. The corporate finance team has grown and continues to flourish. The team advised Shell on the sale of ShellMex House. Figuring in 12 sections, the firm has nine individual practitioners mentioned in *Chambers*.

THE SOUTH

Portsmouth harbour and the River Solent

Blake Lapthorn Another year at the top and the firm still manages to improve on excellence. It leads the tables in the core areas of corporate, litigation and property. Ten individuals from the firm appear in the *Chambers* lists, whilst the firm itself is ranked in seventeen sectors. Blue chip clients are serviced by a strong corporate engine with a large spread of work. Real strength is found in complementary areas, such as banking, employment, environment, insolvency and tax. This year sees the firm move to the top in commercial litigation. Additionally has good marks for charities, licensing, clinical negligence and commercial fraud work. From its Southampton and Portsmouth homes it is handling more London-sourced work in areas such as property, banking and licensing. Still gaining new clients, another great year for the firm.

DMH Top in Brighton, but much more should be said of the firm. More than a mainstream commercial firm, it is the full-service firm of the South, an effective and professional practice with a multitude of specialisms. Litigation is the major strength, both commercial and property, with managing partner Tim Aspinall a leading name. However, the year has seen the firm move down the tables in corporate finance. Derek Sparrow's departure will be a major test to the corporate team. But it seems able to embrace the future having already gained a top reputation for IT work. Individuals at the firm seem to have more than a regional influence, with four individuals recommended in the tables this year. As last year, the firm has most *Chambers* rankings in the South, appearing in eighteen sectors.

Lester Aldridge Noted this year for its ambition, vigour and energy, Bournemouth's number one has been attracting major work. Property and corporate remain the firm's key areas, with banking and finance giv-

THE SOUTH: the 20 Largest Firms

	Firm	Ptnrs	Assts	Total Sols
1	**Blake Lapthorn** *Fareham, Portsmouth (2), Southampton*	41	79	**120**
2	**Argles Stoneham Burstows** *Aylesford, Brighton, Chatham, Crawley, Horsham,*	30	52	**82**
3	**Thomas Eggar Church Adams** *Chichester, Horsham, Reigate, Worthing*	43	32	**75**
4	**Cripps Harries Hall** *Crowborough, Tunbridge Wells*	31	40	**71**
5	**Bond Pearce** *Southampton (3)*	20	39	**59**
6	**Clyde & Co** *Guildford*	20	38	**58**
7	**Thomson Snell & Passmore** *Tonbridge, Tunbridge Wells*	34	21	**55**
8	**Lester Aldridge** *Bournemouth*	31	24	**55**
9	**Penningtons** *Basingstoke, Godalming, Newbury*	21	34	**55**
10	**DMH** *Brighton, Crawley, Worthing*	28	24	**52**
11	**Hart Brown** *Cobham, Cranleigh, Farnham, Godalming, Guildford (2), Woking*	17	34	**51**
12	**Stevens & Bolton** *Farnham, Guildford*	19	27	**46**
13	**Shoosmiths** *Basingstoke, Solent*	16	30	**46**
14	**Moore & Blatch** *Lymington, Milford-on-Sea, Southampton*	15	27	**42**
15	**Coffin Mew & Clover** *Cosham, Fareham, Gosport, Havant, Portsmouth, Southampton*	23	18	**41**
16	**Wynne Baxter Godfree** *Eastbourne, Kemp Town, Lewes (2), Lingfield, Seaford, Uckfield*	19	21	**40**
17	**Brachers** *Maidstone*	17	22	**39**
18	**Paris Smith & Randall** *Southampton*	12	24	**36**
19	**Warner Goodman & Streat** *Fareham, Parkgate, Portsmouth, Southampton, Waterlooville*	14	20	**34**
20	**Barlows** *Chertsey (2), Godalming*	12	22	**34**

The rankings in this table are determined by the number of solicitors working in the region. They are based on partner and assistant solicitor figures only: all other fee-earners are excluded.

ing it a competitive edge. A coming force in litigation, the firm enters the Chamber's ranking in commercial litigation for the first time. Has premier reputations in niche areas such as asset and consumer finance as well as licensing. Includes a number of national big hitters, such as Pip Giddins in asset finance, Colin Patrick in licensing, Stephen Foster in family and Andrew Hignett in planning. These 'stars' are ably supported by large, well-respected teams. Offers a diverse range of services, from health and safety to IT via private client tax. Noticed for its marketing and head-hunting efforts, the momentum is definitely forward. The firm is ranked in seventeen areas, with seven individuals in the rankings.

Cripps Harries Hall In corporate matters the firm has a top presence in 'new' industries, such as technology, fund management and healthcare. Litigation and property are sturdy. Whilst keeping a keen eye on the three main areas it is continuing to develop other areas, such as agriculture. Trusts and personal tax are a major strength. Thus, from its former private client focus, the firm has successfully expanded to offer a broad range of competencies. Mentioned in fourteen areas, four individuals are ranked in *Chambers*.

Thomas Eggar Church Adams Considered to have the culture, the organisation and the clients to keep it amongst the cream of the South. Moves down in the *Chambers* rankings for corporate work this year, but remains strong in property and litigation. Has a real reputation in the private client field, with Chichester as the firm's private client centre. Other less mainstream commercial areas such as agriculture, education, charity and church see the firm make a strong showing. Its investment management arm is doing well. Ranked in nine areas, with three individuals in the tables.

Brachers The busy Maidstone firm has had a good year. Its outstanding agriculture practice continues to forge ahead. As a whole, the firm's reputation seems to rest on a few high quality partners with national influence, such as Stuart Butler Gallie in corporate, Douglas Horner in agriculture and environment and Henry Abraham in planning. However, this does not prevent the firm from having a team image in areas such as debt recovery, litigation and property. Ranked in thirteen areas, with four recommended individuals.

Bond Pearce The merger with Hepherd Winstanley & Pugh was the initial push, and the firm continues to make strides. Its current successful expansion into Bristol is the main focus of market attention. But from its Southampton and Portsmouth offices it has kept up its high profile in the South. Some say that it has really got motoring this year, and indeed the year's achievements are impressive. Noted for its exceptional range of skills, the firm's corporate, property and planning teams have been seen getting the type of work normally associated with City firms. Has support from strong teams in competition, insolvency and banking. Property is first class and planning, environment and personal injury capacities are well regarded. The firm enters the litigation rankings for the first time this year. In the South, it ranks in nine areas covered by *Chambers*, with an impressive eight individuals recommended in the region.

Thomson Snell & Passmore This year the firm moves down in the rankings for corporate finance, but maintains its profile in litigation and property. An esoteric range of skills sees the firm also ranked in *Chambers* in areas such as charities, clinical negligence, personal tax and family. Mentioned in ten practice areas, four individuals are recommended this year.

Paris Smith & Randall Well-rounded and efficient are the words summing up this firm. However, there is a perception that the firm may be losing some of its winning ways in areas such as property and corporate. For the moment, strong showings by individual partners keep the firm well placed. Litigation remains a real strength with Clive Thomson at the helm. The firm is ranked in seven areas, with four individuals recommended in *Chambers*.

Argles Stoneham Burstows After the late 1999 merger, the firm is still settling in. Market comments were received on the firm's noticeable commitment to its clients. Now a large corporate practice which is well set for the future, currently leaders in insolvency and licensing. In *Chambers* the firm is ranked in five areas, with two recommended individuals.

Coffin Mew & Clover Property litigation and property in general are the fortes of the firm, stemming from its premier regional reputation in social housing. In social housing Jennifer Bennett is the region's number one. Housing associations are the firm's main clients. In *Chambers*, the "sensible" firm is recommended in 4 areas.

Rawlison & Butler Departures have weakened the firm, yet it seems to have held itself up well. The challenge for the next year is to regain forward momentum. If the development of the venture capital client base is anything to go by, it should be able to do this. Areas where the firm scores well are the core ones of corporate, property and litigation. In *Chambers* this year, the firm is ranked in four areas, with two recommended individuals.

THAMES VALLEY

Oxford

Morgan Cole This firm is ranked in no fewer than 15 practice areas and features six leading individuals making it the outstanding practice in the region by a wide margin. With offices in Oxford and Reading it is the largest in the region. The litigation practice retains its first tier rank but it is felt to be overly insurance driven. In property, the practice is seen to have taken a major step forwards and is now perceived as a serious leading presence. Martin Billings joins the tables as a new entry going straight into the top band. The corporate finance team has suffered a number of defections and has drawn on the Welsh practice for support. The firm is top ranked (band one) in 7 practice areas which include construction, employment and agriculture.

Clarks Fifth largest in the region with 49 solicitors. The firm has grown steadily by recruitment, concentrating on younger practitioners. Alongside the growth in numbers has been increased investment in support services and management tools. Based in Reading, the firm is featured in nine sections this year with three leading individuals. The firm is moving upwards in the tables in most of these nine practice areas. The litigation practice continues to rise in the rankings and this year reaches the top rank. The property practice maintains its fine reputation as does the corporate finance department under leading individual Richard Lee. Also top ranked

THAMES VALLEY: the 20 Largest Firms

	Firm	Ptnrs	Asst Solrs	Total Solrs
1	**Morgan Cole** *Croydon, Oxford (2), Reading*	33	46	**79**
2	**Pictons** *Bedford, Central Milton Keynes, Hemel Hempstead, Luton, St. Albans, Stevenage, Watford*	34	35	**69**
3	**Bower & Bailey** *Banbury, Oxford, Witney*	20	36	**56**
4	**Taylor Walton** *Harpenden, Hemel Hempstead, Luton, St Albans*	20	34	**54**
5	**Clarks** *Reading*	16	33	**49**
6	**Iliffes Booth Bennett** *Chesham, Slough, Uxbridge (3)*	19	28	**47**
7	**Blaser Mills Winter Taylors** *Aylesbury, Chesham, Harrow, High Wycombe (2), Marlow, Princes Risborough, Rickmansworth*	10	36	**46**
8	**Shoosmiths** *Banbury, Milton Keynes, Reading*	19	25	**44**
9	**Henmans** *Oxford, Woodstock*	15	27	**42**
10	**Winter-Taylors** *Aylesbury, Hazlemere, High Wycombe, Marlow, Princes Risborough*	10	31	**41**
11	**Pitmans** *Reading*	14	25	**39**
12	**Linnells** *Bicester, Oxford*	19	15	**34**
13	**Boyes Turner & Burrows** *Reading*	16	16	**32**
14	**Matthew Arnold & Baldwin** *Watford*	16	16	**32**
15	**Manches** *Oxford*	16	15	**31**
16	**B P Collins** *Beaconsfield, Chalfont St. Peter, Gerrards Cross*	16	14	**30**
17	**Darbys Mallam Lewis** *Oxford*	15	15	**30**
18	**Marshall & Galpin** *Abingdon, Cowley, Oxford, Summertown, Thame*	9	19	**28**
19	**Harris & Cartwright** *Burnham, Langley, Slough (2)*	8	19	**27**
20	**Garretts** *Reading*	7	20	**27**

The rankings in this table are determined by the number of solicitors working in the region. They are based on partner and assistant solicitor figures only: all other fee-earners are excluded.

for construction. The firm's solid client base continues to grow. Owner-managed businesses are a new area of special focus.

Henmans Operating out of Oxford and featured in eight sections albeit with only one named individual. The firm is eighth largest in the region with fourty-two lawyers. It has enjoyed a year of expansion and has invested heavily in IT and client services. The market seems to have recognised this with the firm receiving a higher profile than in the past, although it has yet to break into the tables on property, litigation and corporate finance. The strongest improvement is in Agriculture, an area where the firm is diversifying its areas of expertise as farmers struggle to meet the needs of a changing market. The team now regularly advises on land – use changes and environmental law. Other areas where the firm has risen are trusts & personal tax and employment law. New areas featured this year are charities, personal injury and professional negligence, and they are one of the few regional firms on the Solicitors Indemnity Fund panel.

Manches Oxford based Manches is the fifteenth largest in the region with 31 lawyers. Despite its relatively small size, it is ranked in eight practice areas and fields four named individuals. In three practice areas the firm moves up this year: family/matrimonial, media & entertainment and corporate finance under highly rated Peter Angel. In keeping with the nature of business in the region, the firm focuses heavily on IT, e–commerce and biotechnology and around 80% of their corporate clients are from those sectors. On the property side, it is the firm's Housing Association practice that stands out. As for litigation, the firm is not currently ranked in this field but is active in litigation in IP and related litigation for high–tech clients.

Boyes Turner & Burrows Based in Reading, this firm has 32 lawyers. A reasonably strong showing with; seven practice areas ranked and three individuals named. It moves up in debt recovery and personal injury. New entries for commercial litigation, where directors disqualification is seen to be a speciality, and trusts & personal tax. Clinical negligence, insolvency and IT are other practice areas where the firm is ranked and all maintain their positions in the tables. Leaders in two areas – clinical negligence and insolvency. At present it is not ranked in property or corporate finance.

Linnells Twelfth largest practice with 34 solicitors. Oxford based Linnells is represented in six practice areas and hosts four named players. Both construction & civil engineering and partnership show strong upward movement in the tables. Jonathan Lloyd Jones retains his position as a leader in ADR, a part of the practice which has been increasingly busy. The commercial property side has been slightly affected by the restructuring of the firm which is moving away from bulk legal aided work and concentrating on corporate and commercial property work. Two branches of Linnells, in Newport Pagnell and Milton Keynes, have linked up with a Bedfordshire firm to become Borneo Linnells. Although not currently ranked in the corporate section, it will be interesting to see how the firm's new focus affects this in the next edition.

SOUTH WEST

Bevan Ashford Another good year, with commentators noting that "the Bristol office has taken on an awful lot of people recently." Twenty practitioners are ranked in 22 areas of practice and, where a change has occurred, it's usually an improvement. Strong in defendant clinical negligence work ("a huge player,") healthcare ("a class outfit,") and administration and public law ("they've achieved great depth in NHS work.") Very sound in commercial litigation and commercial property too. The Bristol office initially lost some important players to Osborne Clarke OWA, but seems to have regrouped well since then. Not always the strongest, but always a player due to its extensive resources.

Burges Salmon Ranked in 28 areas of practice, and top tier in 16 of those, with 37 individuals mentioned, Burges Salmon's name is synonymous with quality. They're "head and shoulders above the rest" in agriculture; they "stand out amongst Bristol firms" for commercial litigation; and they're pre-eminent in agricultural property litigation. Their advice on pensions is "pragmatic and generally timely," and they "have the market sewn up for old money" in trusts and personal tax. "Together with Osborne Clarke they tower above the rest" in corporate finance. Similarly, "they divide the market with Osborne Clarke" in banking. Overall, they continue to compare favourably with Osborne Clarke, but are generally considered more conservative and locally focused.

Osborne Clarke OWA "A very good firm, extremely well focused and very successful in developing relationships with IT companies." 24 Bristol practitioners are ranked in 25 areas of practice, an improvement in both areas on last year. They "have pulled ahead" of Burges Salmon in corporate finance; they are "hungry for business and focused on building" their pen-

Clifton Suspension bridge

sions practice; and they are "pulling in the higher grade work" in banking. In 4 areas of practice, employment, environmental law, IT and commercial property, they have pulled their departments up into the premier *Chambers* category since last year. The fundamental question is whether Osborne Clarke OWA is now a regional firm with a London office, or a London firm with regional offices. Commentators have already noted that "there's not enough work for them in Bristol" and that "they're slowly moving the balance of their work to their London office."

Bond Pearce Pre-eminent in Plymouth, they've recently doubled their office space in Bristol, and there's some evidence of a transferral of resources to Bristol. Also showing signs of expansion; they've just taken their first step into the Northern market by opening an office in Leeds. For the moment, the Plymouth office remains the strongest, with 14 individuals being ranked in 24 areas of practice. Top tier in 7 areas of practice in the region, they're "one of the leading regional practices" for professional negligence, and possess a "very pleasant" insolvency team with "good back-up people." The Plymouth and Exeter offices provide "very sound" advice on corporate finance, though, again, commentators note that "the focus of their practice is shifting to Bristol." The Bristol office itself has acquired a reputation for insolvency and professional negligence work.

Clarke Willmott & Clarke Now marketing themselves as a litigation and commercial property firm, rather than a corporate finance firm. They are "strong in the Somerset area," and "very strong in Taunton," where their major office is located. A little less so in Bristol, where they are seen to have "lost a bit of direction." Good environmental and commercial property teams, but perhaps rather dependent on a first-rate planning department for their reputation. Ranked in 13 areas of practice overall, with 10 practitioners mentioned in *Chambers*, they're redefining themselves to suit their strengths.

TLT Solicitors "I'd put TLT third (in Bristol), subject to how the merger goes." Though its rivals have claimed that the two merged firms (Lawrence Tucketts and Trumps) are "not natural soul-mates," general market reaction to the merger seems to be fairly positive. Ranked in 12 areas of practice, with five individuals mentioned, TLT has increased its strength in corporate finance and maintained its dominant position in family/matrimonial and partnership. Strong also on debt recovery and commercial litigation. All five of its *Chambers*-listed individuals are either top or second tier.

Beachcroft Wansbroughs Have largely maintained their position in the market, though perhaps a little less strong than last year. This year's *Chambers* sees them ranked in 11 areas of practice, with seven individuals making our tables. Strong in healthcare, their defendant personal injury team "nearly has the market sewn up," while a very strong professional negligence team is "maintaining its market share." The clinical negligence team is reputedly "sensible" and "on the ball." Recently gave the lie to their conservative image by doubling the size of their commercial property department and grabbing a place on Railtrack's litigation panel. Gradually acquiring the confidence to spread their focus beyond traditional areas of strength.

Foot Anstey Sargent The recent merger between Anstey Sargent & Probert and Foot & Bowden has generally been considered "a good, sensible move," that has created a "more dynamic, younger partnership," and made the firm "more formidable." In insolvency, they're "the leader in Exeter." They're strong, too, in family/matrimonial and defamation. And the corporate finance, commercial litigation and commercial property departments have all apparently benefited from the merger. Ranked overall in 11 areas of practice, with eight individuals appearing in our tables, they're a powerful new force in Devon.

Stephens & Scown "Have good individuals" in both their Devon and Cornwall offices, six of whom have been ranked by *Chambers* this year. The Exeter office comes particularly highly recommended, with eleven areas of practice recognised by *Chambers*. Of these, the family/matrimonial department is respected for its general family practice, while the Exeter office's

SOUTH WEST: the 20 Largest Firms

	Firm	Ptnrs	Asst Solrs	Total No of Solicitors '00	'99	'98	'97
1	**Bevan Ashford** *Bristol, Exeter, Plymouth, Taunton, Tiverton*	65	110	**175**	160	146	133
2	**Burges Salmon** *Bristol*	44	124	**168**	148	146	122
3	**Osborne Clarke OWA** *Bristol*	39	84	**123**	137	117	95
4	**Bond Pearce** *Bristol, Exeter, Plymouth*	31	69	**100**	94	89	82
5	**Clarke Willmott & Clarke** *Bristol, Taunton (2), Yeovil*	40	51	**91**	93	96	73
6	**TLT Solicitors** *Bristol (2)*	29	49	**78**	-	-	-
7	**Foot Anstey Sargent** *Budleigh Salterton, Exeter (3), Plymouth*	35	35	**70**	-	-	-
8	**Beachcroft Wansbroughs** *Bristol*	20	50	**70**	63	-	-
9	**Stephens & Scown** *Exeter, Liskeard, Plymouth, St Austell, Truro*	35	26	**61**	64	59	59
10	**Veale Wasbrough** *Bristol*	20	35	**55**	49	59	56
11	**Lyons Davidson** *Bristol, Plymouth*	15	39	**54**	47	50	40
12	**Wolferstans** *Bristol, Plymouth, Plympton, Plymstock, Taunton*	29	19	**48**	42	42	37
13	**Davies and partners** *Bristol, Gloucester*	15	24	**39**	42	39	40
14	**Hugh James Ford Simey** *Bristol, Exeter, Exmouth, Sidmouth, Southernhay Gdns*	21	15	**36**	29	-	-
15	**Wilsons** *Salisbury*	18	18	**36**	29	26	26
16	**Woollcombe Beer Watts** *Bovey Tracey, Chagford, Exeter, Newton Abbot, Torquay*	21	14	**35**	36	35	31
17	**Stones** *Exeter (2), Okehampton, Torrington*	18	17	**35**	32	25	-
18	**Cartwrights** *Bristol*	14	20	**34**	46	43	42
19	**Michelmores** *Exeter*	16	17	**33**	23	18	18
20	**Rickerby Watterson** *Cheltenham*	17	15	**32**	34	30	32

The rankings in this table are determined by the number of solicitors working in the region. They are based on partner and assistant solicitor figures only: all other fee-earners are excluded.

expert criminal practice has now been supplemented by a year-old Plymouth 'LawDirect' office. Ranked by *Chambers* for the first time in commercial property and trusts and personal tax.

Veale Wasbrough "Picking up" after a rough few years and now generally considered to be a "sensible" firm with "a super client list." This year, 9 individuals have been ranked in 16 areas of practice. Possesses a top-tier reputation in education (where they're still "pre-eminent"), partnership, and claimant personal injury work. Also strong in commercial litigation and energy. The successful poaching of a major property lawyer from Burges Salmon clearly signals that they're on the road to recovery.

Cartwrights Traditionally strong in licensing and transport, they're top tier in the one and nationally ranked in the other once again this year. Their food practice has also earned a mention in *Chambers*. They show a good hand, too, in personal injury. However, a number of departments have fallen out of our tables, and overall, they are down, with six partners now ranked in ten areas of practice. One commentator observed that they're "a good niche firm, but they never seem to acquire any critical mass." And with several partners now expected to divide their time between Bristol and the newly-opened Cardiff office, the firm runs the risk of "spreading itself a little thin."

WALES

Courtesy of Cardiff County Council

Cardiff Civic Centre

Morgan Cole With 105 solicitors, this is the largest firm in Wales by a wide margin. Ranked in 24 areas, the firm fields 21 leading individuals. Leaders in eight areas including corporate finance which maintains its position despite having to divert resources to Reading, and litigation which is gaining a national reputation. The commercial property practice is also showing strongly, with the Swansea office drawing particular praise and is currently in the second band. The EU competition practice rejoins the tables this year as a leading player. Among a number of recommended practitioners, Philip Howell-Richardson remains a regional star for ADR, while the versatile Alun Cole is considered one of the Principality's leaders for Admin and Public Law.

Eversheds Snapping on the heels of Morgan Cole, Eversheds is ranked in 27 areas, with 17 leading individuals. The second largest firm in Wales, with 85 solicitors, it is in the leading band in no fewer than 13 areas. The litigation practice is ranked in the first band and has been involved in managing the Bloody Sunday inquiry as well as acting for the more usual clients, and this area in particular has seen constant and heavy investment by the firm in IT and support systems. For commercial property, the firm is the leader in Wales and has won some substantial national tenders. Corporate finance has had a period of rebuilding following some departures, but is seen to be "picking up the pace." The public sector is still seen as the backbone of the firm, with Eric Evans a number one ranked practitioner in three sectors.

Hugh James Ford Simey Third in size with 78 solicitors. Increase their presence to 15 sectors with 12 named individuals. Leaders in 6 areas including commercial litigation, which is still seen as an insurance-driven engine. The corporate finance and property practices still have a way to go though, to reach the profile of the market leaders. On the property side the firm is felt to excel as a housing association entity, but is building a reputation in wider commercial work. The corporate finance practice is perceived as being less mainstream, focusing on private client and e–business. Michael Jefferies is the firm's litigation guru, claiming a band one ranking.

Edwards Geldard Now feature in 19 fields and have 8 leaders. Fourth largest in Wales, with 56 lawyers. Leaders in litigation, where the firm has moved up the tables 2 years running. For corporate finance and commercial property the firm is highly ranked in the second band. Environment and IT are areas which have seen notable improvement during the past 12 months, with individuals such as Ceri Delemore and Paul Hopkins now established as practitioners to be reckoned with.

Palser Grossman Seventh largest in Wales with 33 lawyers. This practice is ranked in four areas and has two named individuals and is the only one outside of the "big four" to be ranked. Practice areas ranked include commercial litigation, where the firm is felt to be on the upgrade, a sentiment which applies equally to the commercial property team. Also ranked for employment and personal injury (mainly defendant), the firm rates as a top player in the latter sector. Property star Alison Ivin is the firm's standout practitioner.

WALES: the 10 Largest Firms

	Firm	Ptnrs	Asst Solrs	Total No of Solicitors '00	'99	'98	'97
1	**Morgan Cole** *Cardiff, Swansea*	39	66	**105**	112	-	-
2	**Eversheds** *Cardiff*	32	53	**85**	86	51	83
3	**Hugh James Ford Simey** *Bargoed, Blackwood, Cardiff, Merthyr Tydfil, Pontlottyn, Talbot Green, Treharris*	38	40	**78**	66	-	-
4	**Edwards Geldard** *Cardiff*	21	35	**56**	66	57	51
5	**Leo Abse & Cohen** *Cardiff*	11	40	**51**	51	48	43
6	**John Collins & Partners** *Swansea (2)*	9	31	**40**	-	-	-
7	**Palser Grossman** *Cardiff Bay, Swansea*	15	18	**33**	27	25	28
8	**Dolmans** *Cardiff (2)*	12	20	**32**	26	26	27
9	**Gamlins** *Colwyn Bay, Conwy, Flintshire, Llandudno, Rhos-on-Sea, Rhyl*	11	16	**27**	27	27	27
10	**Douglas-Jones Mercer** *Swansea*	12	13	**25**	23	21	22

The rankings in this table are determined by the number of solicitors working in the region. They are based on partner and assistant solicitor figures only: all other fee-earners are excluded.

MIDLANDS

Birmingham Town Hall

Wragge & Co One corporate lawyer's description of Wragge's as the "firm everyone tries to emulate" just about encapsulates the position of this Midlands runaway success story. The firm has not merely consolidated but increased its lead in the region. It is very large, very profitable and very good. Having announced a record 30 percent increase in turnover in May, it is now ranked in 29 of *Chamber's* practice areas, and top in 17, with an impressive 46 leading individuals. The firm's strength is genuinely across the board, and recent strategic mergers with Midlands niche construction team Neil F. Jones and London IP practice Needham and Grant highlight its intention to advance across all sectors. The last year has seen it at the top in the key commercial disciplines of corporate finance, commercial property and commercial litigation. It has benefited from the increasing trend of corporates going outside London. Recent examples include high profile work for FTSE clients of the calibre of Marconi and British Airways. It remains to be seen whether this work will lead to the highest echelon of corporate instructions. In other sectors, the firm has moved up the rankings in banking, employee share schemes, financial services and local government. Their one-office policy is "clearly paying huge dividends for them" (with the new London base confined to IP) while their Brussels office assists a growing international presence.

Eversheds Though still a good way behind its rival Wragges in terms of size, big deals (and publicity), Eversheds (Midlands) remains a thriving hub within the national operation. The last year has recorded steady progress, and the firm runs a clear second in the region. Now ranked in 23 of *Chamber's* specialist areas, it has reached the top flight in 7, including employment and insolvency and also in commercial property, which is seen as a local and national powerhouse. Birmingham's environmental and IT practices are now regional leaders. Derby's pensions litigation practice is considered top-ranking in the whole country. In other core fields of corporate finance, commercial litigation and banking, the practice maintains highly rated teams, which some feel are held back from the juiciest work by their competition within the national network. Nevertheless, appointment to advise on the last minute Project Phoenix purchase of the Rover Group only serves to highlight the capabilities of the practice. The East Midlands has also made strides over the last year, with the Nottingham office increasingly gaining plaudits as a robust commercial outfit.

Pinsent Curtis "Quality people" and "blue chip clients" seem to be the watchwords for the Pinsent Curtis practice over the last year, two epithets which cropped up persistently while researching their teams. A recent announcement that the firm is to focus on eight principal markets and high-spend clients may boost this reputation further. Top of the tree in eight *Chambers* specialist areas, and ranked in a further 21 (an increase of five from last year), the practice may not match Wragge's in size or overall

MIDLANDS: the 30 Largest Firms

	Firm	Ptnrs	Asst Solrs	Total No of Solicitors '00	'99	'98	'97
1	**Wragge & Co** *Birmingham*	91	249	**340**	275	224	213
2	**Eversheds** *Birmingham, Derby, Nottingham*	63	182	**245**	167	160	183
3	**Pinsent Curtis** *Birmingham*	57	89	**146**	105	108	90
4	**Hammond Suddards Edge** *Birmingham*	46	81	**127**	-	-	-
5	**Browne Jacobson** *Birmingham, Nottingham*	38	64	**102**	95	88	80
6	**Freethcartwright** *Derby, Leicester, Nottingham (2)*	47	53	**100**	104	104	109
7	**Shoosmiths** *Northampton (2), Nottingham*	43	52	**95**	108	101	92
8	**Martineau Johnson** *Birmingham*	34	60	**94**	64	79	71
9	**DLA** *Birmingham*	28	53	**81**	75	71	53
10	**Nelsons** *Derby (2), Grantham, Leicester, Nottingham*	36	36	**72**	72	61	56
11	**Harvey Ingram Owston** *Leicester, Oadby, Wigston*	26	26	**52**	54	50	44
12	**Lee Crowder** *Birmingham*	22	29	**51**	38	38	25
13	**Shakespeares** *Birmingham*	24	26	**50**	52	49	44
14	**Gateley Wareing** *Birmingham, Leicester*	14	35	**49**	36	40	34
15	**Berryman Shacklock** *Mansfield, Nottingham (2)*	23	24	**47**	-	-	-
16	**Irwin Mitchell** *Birmingham (2)*	13	33	**46**	35	35	15
17	**Mills & Reeve** *Birmingham*	7	39	**46**	38	-	-
18	**Challinors Lyon Clark** *Birmingham, Edgbaston, Smethwick, West Bromwich*	20	25	**45**	44	43	42
19	**The Smith Partnership** *Burton-on-Trent, Derby (2), Leicester, Longton, Swadlincote*	20	25	**45**	39	39	36
20	**Anthony Collins Solicitors** *Birmingham*	15	30	**45**	41	11	-
21	**Morton Fisher** *Bewdley, Bromsgrove, Kidderminster, Stourport-on-Severn, Worcester*	19	24	**43**	43	43	39
22	**The Wilkes Partnership** *Birmingham (2)*	17	25	**42**	41	38	37
23	**Thompsons** *Birmingham, Nottingham, Stoke-on Trent*	12	30	**42**	41	41	33
24	**Higgs & Sons** *Brierley Hill, Dudley, Kingswinford, Stourbridge*	25	15	**40**	36	35	34
25	**Toller Hales & Collcutt** *Corby, Kettering, Northampton, Wellingborough*	21	16	**37**	35	33	31
26	**Weightmans** *Birmingham, Dudley, Leicester*	17	17	**34**	34	6	-
27	**Wright Hassall** *Leamington Spa*	18	14	**32**	30	29	25
28	**Hewitson Becke + Shaw** *Northampton*	17	15	**32**	33	34	33
29	**Tinsdills** *Leek, Newcastle-under-Lyme, Northampton, Tunstall*	16	15	**31**	32	30	27
30	**Garretts** *Birmingham*	7	24	**31**	27	27	17

The rankings in this table are determined by the number of solicitors working in the region. They are based on partner and assistant solicitor figures only: all other fee-earners are excluded.

capability, but it comes close in a number of commercial areas. This is particularly the case in the fields of banking and corporate tax, where its teams are nationally rated. Across other sectors the firm is newly recognised in partnership and trusts and personal tax. It remains top ranked in commercial litigation, with team head Andrew Paton keeping his starred ranking in ADR. In the core fields of corporate finance and commercial property, the firm lacks the size and depth of the market leaders, but it is recognised in both as one of the best of the rest. As for the individuals, there are now 26 ranked.

Hammond Suddards Edge The recent rushed merger of Hammonds Suddards and Edge Ellison shocked most in the legal market, but it had been clear for some time that Edge Ellison's 'Way Forward' plan had not succeeded in re-igniting the practice or even halting the drift. One immediate result of the merger is the closure of the Leicester office. Initial impressions are that the City of London is to be the focus of the new firm, which may lead to a de-emphasis in the Birmingham operation, or even staff cuts in an attempt to sharpen up the operation. Away from speculation, this year's Chamber's figures for Edge Ellison paint a picture of a firm "trying to hang on to its role as one of the big boys," but finding it heavy weather. Though ranked in 25 areas, it only made the top grade in debt recovery, partnership, sport and media law. The practice has even relinquished its long-standing top spot in pensions. While maintaining quality teams in commercial property, employment and financial services, the corporate finance and commercial litigation departments were not felt to challenge the leading Birmingham players. However, there have been some glints of light through the mist. There are an enviable 23 individuals at the firm deemed to be leaders of their field, and they practice in a wide range of disciplines. In the words of one corporate lawyer, "firms as good as this one was don't disappear into the abyss overnight."

Browne Jacobson Another good year for this leading Nottingham practice which seems to increase its profile every year. While its market recognition remains largely confined to Nottingham city limits, the recent opening of a Birmingham office to add to its established London outpost shows that its aspirations do not stop at the Trent. Now ranked in 18 areas, it has crashed into an impressive six new fields: commercial property, banking, clinical negligence, construction, trusts and healthcare. Ten individuals are now considered to be leaders in their field. The firm maintains its litigation strength. Top rated in defendant personal injury and professional negligence, it moves up the rankings in the national insurance tables and is highly regarded in commercial litigation. In addition, the practice is now seen to stand "head and shoulders above" other East Midlands firms in non-contentious work. The corporate team maintains its ability to "churn out a phenomenal amount of work" (with an increasing high value and some international M&A activity), while the property team has now gained enough market recognition to enter the tables. When we also consider its noted public sector, health and social housing expertise, it is difficult to foresee anything but sustained, focused progress.

Freethcartwright A shortened name and the departure of their crime department signal a shift of emphasis within this large East Midlands firm. Known primarily as a litigation practice, there is now a clear attempt underway to emphasise the commercial arm of the operation. Judging by the *Chambers* rankings this year, the early signs are good. The practice has made significant progress in the core non-contentious areas. Market recognition of expanding teams and clients pushes it up the rankings in corporate finance and property. Its increased capability was highlighted in a recent £54 million transaction where a 13 partner corporate team acted for leading book suppliers, Cypher Group Ltd, in the purchase of Bertram Books Ltd. It may be that this re-emphasis has led to a downgrading of other fields, and this year the firm has dropped out of the admin and public law and insolvency tables. It has also moved down a rung in property litigation and family. However, the wider picture remains the same. The jewel in the crown remains claimant clinical negligence, where the firm is ranked top, and claimant personal injury and product liability are also strong. Well known "crusader" Paul Balen is ranked as a leader in all three. The firm has 7 individuals ranked in total. Also as in previous years, it is the Nottingham office which maintains the lion's share of market profile, and Derby and Leicester only warrant one mention apiece.

Shoosmiths With Northampton as its centre of gravity, there are some signs of renaissance in the wider regional market. Most obviously, the arrival of rising star Iain Gilbey from Ashurst Morris Crisp has boosted the profile of the Northampton planning team, which rises in the *Chambers* rankings this year. The commercial property team also moves up the tables, in recognition of its serious retail and development clients. Progress was also seen in increased market recognition of the firm's employment, construction and banking departments, which are newly ranked this year. In food law, the practice remains pre-eminent. However, the firm is only ranked in 10 areas, with 3 listed individuals, slim pickings for such a large and well-known firm. The firm does not come close to the regional leaders in corporate finance or commercial litigation. It is still seen as a solid practice, strong in its catchment areas and proficient in profitable high volume work.

Martineau Johnson A steady year all round for this Birmingham institution. It is now ranked in 16 of *Chambers'* specialist areas, and top in an impressive five. The engine room of the firm remains the nationally rated education practice. The firm acts for substantial higher education institutions across all disciplines, from which originates its reputation in additional fields such as employment and administrative and public law. One downside of this success has been the demotion of the commercial property practice this year. Market opinion has been critical of over-emphasis on the education sector, which is seen to hold them back from A grade commercial work. The firm also maintains its long-established position in the world of private client. Its agriculture practice has moved up the rankings, and its trusts and personal tax, charities and church law teams remain regional leaders. However, while strong in these niche fields, commercial expertise is far from lacking here. This year's research has confirmed a respected corporate finance operation, a busy and sophisticated energy practice and a commercial litigation team seen as a "a match for any of the big guns." Its insolvency and banking teams are similarly well-known and the firm is newly ranked in pensions this year, as "one to watch". As if to emphasise this pervading quality, 14 practitioners are now ranked as leading individuals.

DLA Overall, the comment of a rival commercial litigator sums up another mixed year for DLA, Birmingham, still seen by many as a new kid on the block. "Despite good people and good clients, they haven't cracked the local market as successfully as they have elsewhere in the UK." But it's not quite as simple as that, and this year's *Chambers* rankings paint an interesting picture. On the face of it, there has been little change. The firm is now ranked in 13 areas as opposed to 14 last year, and has 13 individuals listed as compared with 12. But looking at shifts within the specialist areas, we see an interesting two-way split. In certain areas, such as commercial litigation, property, tax and banking, the practice has moved up the tables and is "beginning to make an impact", though still adrift of the real heavyweights. Its corporate finance outfit is "getting there", its commercial litigation team "tough but professional," and its property team "a rising entity." Elsewhere though, the firm has lost ground – out in IP and IT, down in construction, employment, local government and planning. While still top in PFI, the firm now shares the plinth with two other firms. It remains to be seen whether there has been a conscious shift in focus by the firm, or whether our rankings merely highlight the vagaries of the market. Still a middle tier firm, then, in a crammed and competitive marketplace.

Lee Crowder Though still an outfit "characterised by old school charm," the last year has seen stirrings of a potential commercial predator lurking within. On the face of it, the figures are modest. The firm is now ranked in 7 of *Chambers* practice areas, with only four individuals listed. Its reputation in private client work continues to flourish, with a new ranking in charities to add to its mantelpiece. However the real story here has been the consolidation of the property department. Market recognition of its impressive client wins has kept the team high in the commercial property rankings, and substantial lateral hires have boosted the social housing and construction operations. The arrival of Andy Ballard and his team from Irwin Mitchell has pushed the firm up the social housing tables. That leading construction lawyer Jeffrey Brown chose to move here rather than join Wragges on its merger with Neil F. Jones highlights further the potential of this operation. In the other two core areas, corporate and litigation, the firm has hung on to past advances. Its corporate team, though still heavily associated with 3i, retains a respectable position in the market. Its commercial litigation department is seen to punch above its weight, and benefits from an in-house advocacy unit. Definitely one to watch.

EAST ANGLIA

Cambridge

Mills & Reeve The firm has for some time now been expanding westward from their East Anglian base. The November 1998 merger with the Lewington Partnership was a major step, giving them a presence in Birmingham and Cardiff, but progress has been equally relentless this year. And their success is well reflected in our tables. 33 leading lawyers ranked in 27 practice areas is a superb performance, an increase over 1999's already excellent show. And where they're ranked they're usually leaders – an astonishing 18 out of the 27 tables – including all three of the key areas. The property market in Cambridge is buoyant, and Mills & Reeve have been well placed to take advantage of it. Expanding rapidly into the high technology/biotech sectors they haven't lost track of their traditional client base – a strategy which has also seen them take "the lion's share" of regional commercial litigation. As other firms lose or down-grade their private client departments, Mills & Reeve remains "one of the leading three or four firms in the country" for agriculture with a similar reputation for matrimonial, trusts and personal tax. Meanwhile, in their key areas of healthcare and education, they have established a truly national practice with, for example, 150 NHS clients across the country. At a smaller level, the success this year of their local government department in winning the contract to provide legal services to Leicester City Council deserves a mention. Apart from seeing them bound up this year's table, it confirms the practice's national ambitions and its westward spread.

Eversheds Small regional solicitors often seem to welcome an Eversheds in their town. While they are not seen as competitors for the day-to-day work, they undeniably raise the profile of the area and help to put it on the legal map. This is particularly true in Ipswich and Norwich where the Eversheds offices have a reputation for doing work, much of it from outside the area, of a national or international importance. In corporate finance, for instance, where they are considered by some the top firm in the region, their "national profile" means they can do "the sort of deal that needs a lot of people and resources thrown at it." A good example is the recent establishment of 24Seven, the joint venture vehicle set up by TXU Europe Group plc and London Electricity to operate and maintain their entire network distribution systems. Not merely an enormous undertaking, this was also the first such deal of its type in the industry. The situation is even more marked in their fantastically strong commercial litigation department, recently kept busy with a multi-million pound, multi-partner, multi-jurisdictional breach of contract case for international freight forwarders. Ranked in 23 practice areas and a leading player in 10, they have 19 leading solicitors, a jump of three from last year. The region's leading practice in banking and insolvency, a recent drop in the profile of their agriculture and trusts departments suggests that they are stepping away from traditional private client work. Certainly the firm nationally is placing greater emphasis on commercial work, as recent profit figures prove. And with their merger with Dutch firm Boekel De Neree pointing the way to a brave future in Europe, you can bet that the East Anglian branches will be at the forefront of that too.

Hewitson Becke + Shaw There's quite a drop in size between Eversheds and Hewitson Becke + Shaw, which makes the success of this Cambridge firm all the more impressive. The pathfinders through silicon fen country, they're leaders in the high-tech, fast-moving fields that Cambridge brings to mind. The intellectual property department remains the region's strongest and is now targeting clients in the US. A superb reputation for contentious work has involved the firm in high-profile biotech litigation and ground-breaking trademark disputes, while on the IT side they retain

EAST ANGLIA: the 10 Largest Firms

	Firm	Ptnrs	Asst Solrs	Total No of Solicitors '00	'99	'98	'97
1	Mills & Reeve *Cambridge, Norwich*	50	89	**139**	129	127	133
2	Eversheds *Cambridge, Ipswich, Norwich*	45	78	**123**	99	89	95
3	Hewitson Becke + Shaw *Cambridge, Saffron Walden*	34	25	**59**	50	49	46
4	Taylor Vinters *Cambridge*	23	32	**55**	47	43	38
5	Ashton Graham *Bury St Edmunds, Felixstowe, Ipswich, Stowmarket*	19	18	**37**	43	37	-
6	Prettys *Ipswich*	16	20	**36**	34	31	26
7	Greenwoods *Peterborough*	15	16	**31**	33	31	33
8	Birketts *Ipswich*	20	9	**29**	29	29	39
9	Merricks *Chelmsford, Ipswich*	11	18	**29**	-	-	-
10	Steele & Co *Diss, Norwich, Thetford*	11	16	**27**	30	22	18

The rankings in this table are determined by the number of solicitors working in the region. They are based on partner and assistant solicitor figures only: all other fee-earners are excluded.

expertise in all aspects of new media. If IP/IT is the figure head, then the engine room is the key trio of corporate finance, commercial property and commercial litigation. Their corporate finance department showed international credentials again this year with the £30 million, cross jurisdictional sale of Chadwyck-Healey, including US, UK and Spanish companies, to US firm Bell & Howell, while the expanding commercial property team scored a coup by picking up Cambridge University's Estates Management and Building Service against stiff competition. And with 12 ranked individuals in 14 sections, their success is well reflected in this year's tables.

Taylor Vinters With 12 ranked individuals in 11 sectors, Taylor Vinters is, at first sight, a match for local rival Hewitson Becke + Shaw. A closer look, however, reveals a more complicated picture which mirrors their mixed fortunes this year. The success of their "absolutely excellent" corporate finance department is one of the year's highlights, while the agricultural practice is busy establishing the basis of a national reputation. Their technology and engineering based commercial litigation practice also scored some notable goals this year, not least by successfully acting for Benfica against former manager Graeme Souness. Against this, however, the commercial property department wasn't able to hold onto its position and loss of profile sees the firm slip down in trusts and out of construction. The intellectual property department, whose collapse last year was so spectacular, has started exhibiting the green shoots of recovery, but not enough to warrant promotion. Overall, though, this is probably just the temporary instability of a firm that has gone through some recent upheavals and, with their energy and ambition, we can confidently expect a more consistent performance next year.

Prettys The firm surprised a lot of people this year by winning an NFU panel contract against stiff opposition. This was a fitting reward for a smaller firm renowned for its commitment to teamwork and client service, and a particular strength in commercial litigation. Skilful and adept litigators, currently growing their ADR and IT work, their ability to turn their hands to anything is demonstrated by their appearance in 11 tables, as many as Taylor Vinters and almost as many as Hewitson Becke + Shaw. Yet they manage only three ranked individuals, a reflection perhaps of a less personality based approach, or possibly of a lower overall profile. The highly respected corporate finance department, also seeing a growth in IT related work, has particular strength in agribusiness and transport, while its insolvency practice is regarded as the strongest in Ipswich. In commercial property, however, they have had a mixed year. Widely regarded as suffering from the competition in the relatively slow Ipswich property market, they have been at the forefront of developing innovative business methods, even to the extent of gaining expertise in French commercial property. And it is this confident and forward-thinking approach that can be relied upon to keep them near the head of the tables for years to come.

NORTH WEST

© Marketing Manchester

Gmex and Bridgewater Hall, Manchester

DLA A foreshortened name for this national giant, which is also the region's largest firm. A new acronym, a new image? Maybe, although their 'red meat' litigation style of old appears to have done them no harm. The former rottweiler edges into the top bracket of *Chambers* commercial litigation tables this year, while three individual litigators were ranked. Andrew Harris in particular grows in stature this year. In all, 27 individuals achieved a ranking in 19 different practice areas spread across Manchester and Liverpool. The corporate finance department is still going strong in band two, although has yet to catch up with the Addleshaws' juggernaut in pole position. Acted for the vendors and the owners (Legal & General/Target Express) in a secondary buyout, the largest regional deal of the year valued at £210 million. Michael Prince at the Liverpool office remains one of Merseyside's biggest corporate names. The firm still sits pretty in commercial property, where the Manchester and Liverpool teams continue to occupy top spot. Head of team, Roy Beckett scored another band one rating. Likewise, in banking, employment and pensions, the firm enjoys band one status. In pensions, Liverpool-based leader David Wright runs a unit with an "unassailable position in the region."

Addleshaw Booth & Co Top drawer positions in a remarkable nine sections are indications of a powerful regional champion. An incredible 31 individual solicitors were ranked. Corporate finance rivals are still felt to be labouring in the firm's wake. Acting for North West based Airtours, the team won kudos for its handling of the attempted hostile take-over by German tour operator C & N group. Leading light Keith Johnston was one of several ranked personnel. The low-key commercial litigation team naturally profits from this ever-flowing stream of corporate gold. A clutch of lawyers in the commercial property department are also threatening to establish themselves as *the* leading practice in Manchester. Market doyen Egan Brooks also continues his domination of the local insolvency market.

Halliwell Landau Ranked in 17 of *Chambers* different practice areas, the firm has lost headway in one individual practice area: licensing. The banking department, spearheaded by "brightest lawyer in town" John Whatnall, and bolstered by the arrival of ex-Garretts Sue Molloy, made real progress by climbing into the top bracket for the first time. In corporate finance, Halliwells are not yet felt to be competing with Manchester's meatier practices. Paul Rose's commercial litigation team sit just a shade adrift of the top band, but continue to win business through a "slick and uncompromising approach." The future continues to look bright for charismatic Stephen Goodman's property team who sit in the top band. The group's ability to pull in developer clients looks to have paid dividends. The North West's planning advocate *extraordinaire*, Roger Lancaster, stands out again as the regions top inquiry supremo. Geoffrey Shindler is still felt to be the regions pre-eminent name for trusts, holding sway over Manchester's leading practice. The only firm with two IP lawyers ranked in the top band, *Chambers* continues to recognise the team's "acknowledged presence" in the sector.

Berrymans Lace Mawer A slightly indifferent year for a firm who, between the two North West offices, only managed to attain a ranking in 4 different practice areas. This may not be entirely surprising given their undoubted focus on, and pre-eminence in, insurance litigation and defendant PI, by far the largest slices of the firm's activity. The Liverpool centred insurance practice, much of it company/commercial related, continues to be held in the highest esteem nationally. The largest defendant personal injury practice in the North West stays rooted to the number one spot, its high volumes of work for the larger composite insurers consistently acknowledged.

NORTH WEST: the 12 Largest Firms

	Firm	Ptnrs	Asst Solrs	Total No of Solicitors '00	'99	'98	'97
1	**DLA** *Liverpool, Manchester*	57	113	**170**	145	144	104
2	**Addleshaw Booth & Co** *Manchester*	53	95	**148**	122	122	112
3	**Halliwell Landau** *Manchester*	48	78	**126**	132	103	84
4	**Berrymans Lace Mawer** *Liverpool, Manchester*	40	74	**114**	101	101	81
5	**Hill Dickinson** *Chester, Liverpool, Manchester, Stockport*	61	49	**110**	110	109	109
6	**Hammond Suddards Edge** *Manchester*	26	68	**94**	-	-	-
7	**Pannone & Partners** *Manchester*	57	36	**93**	82	78	62
8	**Weightmans** *Liverpool, Manchester*	40	53	**93**	93	93	84
9	**Davies Wallis Foyster** *Liverpool, Manchester*	43	48	**91**	119	110	110
10	**Cobbetts** *Manchester*	41	46	**87**	87	69	64
11	**Eversheds** *Manchester*	33	44	**77**	114	74	68
12	**Mace & Jones** *Huyton, Knutsford, Liverpool, Manchester*	27	42	**69**	60	42	50

The rankings in this table are determined by the number of solicitors working in the region. They are based on partner and assistant solicitor figures only: all other fee-earners are excluded.

More worrying is the dip in fortunes of the corporate finance and trusts practices, which both failed to attain a ranking this year. The latter suffered a blow when former partner David Bishop left to set up on his own. The commercial property team keeps putting on a good show in the hotly contested North West development market. Its characteristic strengths in retail and urban regeneration work were especially commended this year. The commercial litigation department also manages to sustain its position.

Hill Dickinson A year of remarkable consistency for a firm whose overall positions have changed little from this time last year. As ever, the pulse of its legal heart continues to beat loudest in its Liverpool heartland, where the office scores a decent ranking in thirteen different areas of practice. Still at the zenith of the shipping table, where they have a "top tier" reputation for both wet and dry work. 3 leading shipping lawyers are profiled in the top 2 bands of the individual rankings. Similarly, in transport, the firm's London, Liverpool and Manchester offices combine to keep the practice flying high. No fewer than 3 individual experts are ranked in the top 7 nationwide. The firm's star shines a little brighter in partnership, defendant personal injury and professional negligence where they edge up slightly. The large and experienced defendant clinical negligence department has done a fine job of carving up the local NHS trust market. Research suggests that Tony Gibbons and Allan Mowat are due the lion's share of the credit. Phillip Wood's "IP oasis" in Stockport adds a further niche string to the regional bow and maintains its position well. In the key commercial litigation arena, there is a slight dropping off. The commercial property department is known for its high volume housebuilding work, but has not managed to achieve quite the higher profile that some expected.

Hammond Suddards Edge Headline writers had a field day when the merger with Edge Ellison was announced in June 2000. The welcome reality for Hammond Suddards is a long-sought Midlands presence, and the 28-partner London jewel in the crown. In its northern heartland, it's been a slightly different sort of roller-coaster ride, performing well in some notable areas while slipping in others. Overall, rankings in 13 areas represents a slight drop on last year's total. Sue Nickson still stands out regionally as a key component of the top-ranked employment practice. In commercial litigation, there isn't a huge gulf between the pack of top firms, although HSE may lack the weightier team of the very top players. Ian Meredith continues to epitomise the Hammonds "commercial and businesslike spirit," albeit a restrained mediation-driven version of the old warrior-like litigation approach. The firm is struggling to keep pace with Manchester's leading corporate finance practices, although William Downs, well rated this year, is keeping the fires burning. "Hard-working bright spark" property lawyer Liam Buckley has been the catalyst for a year of raised profile. The "ultra-commercial" team have acted on the property aspects of some large transactions, and accordingly, rise a tier. Still "*moving in the right direction*" Nigel Proctor, David Moss and Chris Wilcock continue to be the principal challengers to Mason's construction pre-eminence. The insolvency practice stays a well-nominated unit, top ranked Mark Simpson continues to keep the Manchester tax practice at a high level and Mike Shepherd for health, safety and environmental matters features again in our lists. The firm can also count a slightly improved pensions practice amongst its achievements in the *Chambers* guide.

Pannone & Partners Scoring 11 individual rankings in a total of 16 Chambers sections, the firm reported a 23 percent rise in turnover for the financial year to May (total £13.8 million) with profits also growing by 29 percent. Two new areas of practice make an appearance this year. The trusts department scored a number of recommendations, as did the customs and exercise practice for its work on fraud and business crime. Still resolutely classified as the North West's premier PI claimant practice. Consistent recognition of the combined strengths of Carol Jackson, Pauline Chandler and Catharine Leech are again reflected in pre-eminent status. Even more impressive was the rise of the claimant clinical negligence team to assume sole leading firm status. *Chambers* recognises the individual qualities of its two leading practitioners, John Kitchingman and Stephen Jones, and the backing of a "solid, thorough team." The family practice made great strides this year, leaping into the very highest tier. Catherine Jones and Beth Wilkins have overseen a remarkable success story, the team widely endorsed as market leaders for its size, client care and identifiable service style. The growth of the defamation claimant practice, and the impact of fraud lawyers Paul Taylor and Paul Barnfeather are reflected in higher rankings for both areas of practice. In the core commercial arena, Pannone's star doesn't shine quite so brightly. True, the profile of the commercial property practice is felt to have expanded with some notable client wins, but in the cut and thrust of corporate finance and commercial litigation, the firm continues to lack the heavy hitting powers of its City rivals. Tough litigator Vincent O'Farrell picks up points for his contentious work, much of it property related, but is one of few commercially focused solicitors recommended.

Cobbetts No change in the number of recommended practice areas for this well established and permanent feature on the Manchester landscape. 13 sections carry Cobbetts' name, the only vanishing point being the planning practice, although this was offset by an entrance into the family/matrimonial list. Perform highly in some notable and important sections. Most of the property based practice areas saw Cobbetts occupy top spot. With one of the largest commercial property practices in the area, the property litigation team comfortably holds onto an unassailable lead. Enlarged by Alan Walker's arrival from Addleshaws, Peter Stone (also rated highly for libel and defamation) and colleagues were well recommended for high value work, a chunk of it for brewery clients. Likewise, the "magnificent" licensing team, with Hamish Lawson and Simon Jones at the helm, strengthens its leading position. In corporate finance, the firm has not managed to increase its profile, but "outstanding litigator" Robert Roper keeps the flag flying for the litigation team.

Davies Wallis Foyster The Liverpool office continues to outgun its M62 rival to the east, scoring recommendations in nine practice areas to Manchester's four. The Merseyside bedrock provides the home for moderately ranked commercial property, trusts and debt recovery practices. The latter, a large stand-alone department, climbs this year. The banking and finance team is actively raising its profile in both major North West centres and has "more than its fair share of work." Andrew Gregory and the insolvency team are also felt to be emerging as more visible contenders in the local market. The employment practice can also consider the year a good one as its position rises slightly. Not quite such a good year for the commercial litigation team, which in some quarters is felt to be past its prime. Kit Sorrell's move to Manchester based Wacks Caller did not go unnoticed. Licensing, where Nick Dickinson's move to Pannone's was a severe blow, has suffered similarly this year.

Eversheds Chambers research this year identified 21 leading solicitors in 18 different practice areas. In the crucial triumvirate of corporate finance, commercial property and litigation, the firm score highly. With property deals amounting to £1.75 billion and Stephen Sorrell nudging into the leading band of individuals, it has been a good year. There's no stopping corporate finance supremo Edward Pysden ruling the roost as Manchester's star partner. This year more than ever, the practice is considered the one most likely to threaten Addleshaws' domination. A trio of well-known litigators also continue to prop up the fine commercial contentious practice. The employment practice caught up with its competitors, jumping from the third to the top band. Peter Norbury is still highly rated. Nigel Dale's banking and acquisition finance practice, and involvement in substantial recent deals, keeps them well in contention at the top of the pile.

YORKSHIRE

York Minster

DLA The firm's offices in Bradford, Leeds and Sheffield have combined to ensure that it is ranked in the very top band in five specialisms for the region this year. It stepped up from band 2 into the top band for licensing & leisure, and maintained its ranking in the top band for commercial litigation, insolvency, intellectual property and pensions. It is ranked in 18 specialisms in total, up from 17 last year, with 23 recommended individuals, up from 21 last year. The key areas of corporate finance and commercial property have suffered relegations this year, with the firm unable to match the profile of the market leaders. The firm's litigation departments have maintained their historical strength, with property litigation stable in band two, and its top ranked commercial litigation department receiving more overall recommendations for the best Leeds litigation practice than any other. The office's head of litigation, ex-Clifford Chance practitioner Paul Stone, was singled out by the London Bar as being "top drawer in his own particular way – he's an all round thinker who makes time to cover everything." Overall, DLA has turned in a performance this year which is substantially similar to that of the previous year. Clearly major players in Yorkshire, the firm still has a little way to go to regain its former pre-eminence.

YORKSHIRE: the 30 Largest Firms

	Firm	Ptnrs	Asst Solrs	Total Solrs
1	**DLA** *Bradford, Leeds, Sheffield*	64	124	**188**
2	**Addleshaw Booth & Co** *Leeds (2)*	53	106	**159**
3	**Irwin Mitchell** *Leeds, Sheffield*	56	85	**141**
4	**Eversheds** *Leeds*	44	95	**139**
5	**Hammond Suddards Edge** *Bradford, Leeds*	39	88	**127**
6	**Pinsent Curtis** *Leeds*	49	73	**122**
7	**Walker Morris** *Leeds*	35	86	**121**
8	**Beachcroft Wansbroughs** *Leeds, Sheffield*	21	56	**77**
9	**Nabarro Nathanson** *Sheffield*	15	47	**62**
10	**Andrew M. Jackson & Co** *Hull*	22	31	**53**
11	**Lupton Fawcett** *Leeds*	20	30	**50**
12	**Gordons Cranswick Solicitors** *Bradford, Keighley, Leeds*	31	18	**49**
13	**Rollit Farrell & Bladon** *Beverley, Helmsley, Hull, York*	33	14	**47**
14	**Ford & Warren** *Leeds*	14	33	**47**
15	**Gosschalks** *Hull*	26	20	**46**
16	**Keeble Hawson** *Leeds (2), Sheffield*	24	22	**46**
17	**Hempsons** *Harrogate*	3	34	**37**
18	**Ison Harrison & Co** *Chapeltown, Crossgates, Garforth, Goldthorpe, Leeds, York*	13	21	**34**
19	**Hamers** *Doncaster, Hull, Leeds, Sheffield*	6	28	**34**
20	**Attey Dibb and Clegg** *Barnsley, Doncaster(2), Goldthorpe, Mexborough, Rotherham, Thorne, Wath*	23	9	**32**
21	**Harrowell Shaftoe** *Haxby, York (2)*	16	13	**29**
22	**Lee & Priestley** *Bradford, Leeds (3)*	14	15	**29**
23	**Howells** *Sheffield (3)*	12	15	**27**
24	**Brooke North** *Leeds*	17	9	**26**
25	**Read Hind Stewart** *Leeds*	15	11	**26**
26	**Wrigleys** *Leeds, Sheffield*	10	15	**25**
27	**Denison Till** *Leeds, York*	14	10	**24**
28	**Taylor & Emmet** *Sheffield (2)*	13	10	**23**
29	**Last Cawthra Feather Solicitors** *Bradford, Ilkley, Shipley*	12	11	**23**
30	**Nelson & Co** *Leeds*	11	12	**23**

The rankings in this table are determined by the number of solicitors working in the region. They are based on partner and assistant solicitor figures only: all other fee-earners are excluded.

Addleshaw Booth & Co This firm has made yet another strong showing in Yorkshire this year. It is ranked in 25 specialisms, with 30 recommended individuals. Most impressively, it is ranked in the very top band for 13 of these specialisms, including the key areas of general corporate finance, commercial property and both commercial and property litigation. In terms of general corporate finance, the department is still the one to catch, or at least emulate, with its strength "across the board," particularly in relation to private equity. The department's relationship with venture capital houses, particularly 3i, continues to bring in a substantial volume of corporate finance work. It is seen to have the edge over its competitors for its depth and especially its ability to attract and retain quality individuals, in particular Sean Lippell, who has consolidated his position as a leading individual after arriving from Garretts last year. While he is better known as a rainmaker than a technician, he is nevertheless seen by his peers to be "top class." The firm's commercial property department has also continued its dream run. It still leads the field in Yorkshire with its depth of expertise, the quality of its client base, the high standards of work and its clear ability to handle most aspects of property work, including matters which would be expected to go to leading City firms. The department is regarded as being "just that bit ahead of the crowd", with John Pike remaining "a premier property lawyer in the region." Solid showings in a number of other areas have given the firm a lead in the region which it shows no signs of relinquishing.

Irwin Mitchell The Yorkshire offices of this firm are ranked in 21 areas this year. The offices also have 8 recommended individuals, and retained their rankings in the top band for three areas, namely product liability, claimant clinical negligence and claimant personal injury. The firm retains its reputation as "the leading claimant practice in the North", and is best known for acting on behalf of private clients with severe injuries. However, it also has experience in multi-party claims, including the Vibration White Finger and Respiratory Disease cases against British Coal. The practice also contains a motor division, which, in combination with the Birmingham motor practice, provides the only serious competition to Shoosmiths on a national basis. The head of the practice, John Pickering, is a recognised expert in catastrophic injury claims, while Andrew Tucker is "one of the best technical lawyers around", and led the claims against British Coal. A drop in corporate finance this year has been offset by the firm's entry into the rankings for admin & public law (at band 4), construction and civil engineering (at band 6), customs & excise (at band 5) and travel, tourism & package holidays (at band 3). A steady showing in commercial property and promotion to band 2 in the commercial litigation tables round out a successful year, in which the firm underlined that in its niche areas, it is a match for the best.

Eversheds The Leeds office of this national giant is ranked in 19 specialisms, with 27 recommended individuals. It is ranked in the very top band for 6 specialisms. The firm has dropped from band 1 into band 2 for property litigation, where the loss of "mainstay" Penny Belcher and a number of major clients to Irwin Mitchell was clearly a severe blow. Its most notable slip was in the field of construction & civil engineering, which plummeted out of the top band into band 4 this year. The primary reason for this drop is that the Yorkshire and North East offices of Eversheds have had a "real shake-up" in this department in the past 12 months. Key players and assistants in the department have moved between offices nationally and regionally and some have left for other firms. In local government, the Leeds office is regarded as the nation's leading practice. Its practitioners "dominate local government work nationally – everything funnels out of the Leeds office." The environmental law department is also seen to be "opening up a clear lead", with an extensive industrial, chemical and manufacturing client base, and the "immensely charismatic" Paul Smith attains a star rating for his work in the department this year. At the end of last year, the Leeds office made a policy decision to concentrate purely on corporate and commercial work. As a result of this decision, it off-loaded its private client practice to Leeds firm Wrigleys, and consequently no longer features in the specialisms of agriculture & bloodstock or trusts & personal tax. However, the leading regional telecoms practice, a corporate practice which remains hard on the heels of Addleshaw Booth & Co, and a solid commercial property outfit all reinforce the firm's unchallenged right to be ranked among the leading players in Yorkshire.

Hammond Suddards Edge The Yorkshire offices of this firm are ranked in 15 different specialisms this year, with 19 recommended individuals. This is slightly down on last year's rankings, where the offices were ranked in 18 different specialisms with the same number of individuals. However, the more significant statistic is that the offices are ranked in the very top band for three separate specialisms this year, which is up from just one last year, namely commercial litigation. Pensions and debt recovery are the two new pre-eminent specialisms. The Leeds office is seen as the national hub of the firm's commercial litigation engine. The department is seen to offer a collectively strong team of litigators who are "well-trained and sharp, if sometimes slightly aggressive." The "effective and no-nonsense" Peter Crossley has a particularly strong name. It seems unlikely that the firm's merger with Edge Ellison will have a material difference in the North. A solid showing by the commercial property team and corporate finance teams underpin a solid year of achievement.

Walker Morris The firm is ranked in 18 areas in the region, which is up from 17 last year, with 17 recommended individuals. A year of consolidation, on the face of it. However, the firm has fallen in a number of specialisms, including banking, construction and corporate finance, which, although "solid and reliable" departments per se, have suffered by comparison with the Leeds market leaders. No longer ranked in the top band for any specialism, consistency is now the name of the game. Band 2 rankings exist for, inter alia, commercial property, insolvency, sports law and commercial and property litigation. In addition, the firm has improved slightly in debt recovery and pensions, and secures new entries for employee share schemes and local government. Commercial property is one specialism where the firm is seen to have broken away from the pack, and is now chasing Addleshaw Booth & Co in the region. The strength here is the high quality of the team, rather than just a few big names. However, Richard Innes is regarded as an "important player" in the region and is building a good reputation on the retail side in particular. The firm's one-office approach shows no sign of alteration, and competitors have queried how long this can be sustained if there is to be a genuine challenge to Yorkshire's legal aristocracy.

Pinsent Curtis This year saw another impressive performance from the firm's Leeds office. The firm has 24 recommended individuals, up from 18 last year, and is ranked in 22 areas in total. Furthermore, it is ranked in the top band for seven of these areas, up from five last year. The specialisms for which it remains in the top band are projects/PFI, corporate tax, employment law, employee share schemes and property litigation. The office's two new entries into band 1 are crucial – commercial litigation and intellectual property. In the former, the market has noted the firm's "sheer volume of work" and the team is "now well and truly back as a contender." At the forefront of the practice is "active coal-face litigator" and "real mover and shaker" Stuart Chapman. In IP, the practice is developing an increasing focus on emerging technologies. The firm's employment team is regarded as one of the country's finest, with John McMullen leading a group with a stranglehold on further education clients. Although not yet threatening the very summit, both corporate finance and commercial departments are renowned for their "professionalism," and remain respected players.

Beachcroft Wansbroughs The effects of the 1998 merger have become more evident this year, and the firm as a whole has performed slightly less well than it did last year. It is ranked in eight areas, down from nine last year, and only has four recommended individuals, down from six last year. Having said that, however, the firm remains in the top band for both healthcare and professional negligence, and is top ranked for personal injury. Healthcare remains the firm's most prominent department in both the Leeds and Sheffield offices. The highly regarded Diane Hallatt leads the team, and also remains the firm's leading practitioner in its superb clinical negligence practice. This practice represents approximately 70 NHS trusts, and is recognised by its competitors as "a major player" in the region. In the key commercial areas, the firm holds station for commercial litigation, but still has no profile for commercial property or corporate finance.

Nabarro Nathanson The Sheffield office of this firm is ranked in 11 areas, up from 10 last year, with 9 individuals making the tables yet again. It remains ranked in the very top band for environmental law, and is top-rated for energy. In addition, it has entered the rankings at band five for projects/PFI. These areas of practice have built on the firm's expertise in the coal industry. The firm recently won the 1999 tender to act for the Coal Authority for a further five years, and also advises private companies in England and Wales such as Celtic Energy and RJB Mining. The firm is regarded as having particular expertise in contentious issues, most notably on waste-related matters, where it acts for major industrial clients. Michael Renger is regarded a "leading northern figure," although he still spends some time in London. Martin Grabiner continues to lead a "valuable component" of the firm's national commercial property strength, and despite no real show in litigation or corporate finance rankings, the firm's northern office is considered to be "making substantial progress."

Andrew M. Jackson & Co This firm is ranked in ten different areas of law in the region this year, with six recommended individuals. It is particularly strong in food law and shipping and maritime law, in both of which it is ranked in the second category. However, although consistently mentioned as one of the market leaders in Hull, the firm has been unable to make an impression on the Leeds giants. In the three key commercial sectors, the firm maintains a highly respectable ranking, but geography continues to conspire against a wider appreciation of the organisation's talents.

NORTH EAST

Photo: Colin Cuthbert/© Arup

The Angel of the North, Gateshead

Dickinson Dees "Undoubtedly the leading firm in the North East." This quote could have come from almost any section of this book, but appropriately it comes from agriculture where they are in a league of their own. Amongst the best firms in the country for traditional private client work like agriculture and trusts, on corporate and commercial matters they are less visible than the top Leeds outfits but still tower over the smaller Newcastle market. (With 29 leading individuals, up seven on last year, they are ranked in 24 categories, and in the leading band of no fewer than ten, which makes them comfortably the region's leading performer). Merely observing that they are a regional giant, however, does not do them justice. They increasingly attract work from across the country, and as more and more companies realise that they can get technical excellence and constructive service, this trend looks set to continue. Their national profile has been raised this year by representing Thames Trains in the public inquiry into the Ladbroke Grove rail crash, but on a smaller level the success of their licensing department deserves mention. Up from nothing into the second band, their rapid growth holds out the real possibility of establishing a national licensing practice. And, with the prospect of a new office in the Tees valley, there is every likelihood that their domination of the North East will continue.

Eversheds Like the European Union, Eversheds is creeping ever closer to full integration. Unlike the EU, however, they are capable of acting in unison while remaining fully committed to the principle of subsidiarity. Individual practices work together as required to win deals on the international, national, regional or local stage, and do so with an impressive efficiency. Within this set-up, the Newcastle office holds an important place. Admittedly they're not as big as their neighbours in Leeds and Manchester, but when you examine the statistics they're performing with an ability which belies their size. This year they were ranked in 19 sectors and were leaders in six, with 15 ranked individuals, an increase of two over last year. In the key area of commercial litigation they overtook Dickinson Dees after a fantastic spell that saw them absorb the Newcastle insurance firm of Linsley & Mortimer. In the other central areas of commercial property and corporate finance their progress has been less spectacular, but the excellent corporate finance team has closed the gap on their rival, while the enviable public sector expertise of the property department made it one of the region's strongest performers. Extremely strong in construction and employment, in a part of the country where the public sector is the major employer competitors cannot afford to overlook the strength of their public sector practice. Healthcare especially, their "centre of excellence," was recently strengthened by the recruitment of Richard Slack from Crutes, and won 7 out of 9 recent competitive tenders. With strength across the board, this practice remains one of the stars on the Eversheds flag.

NORTH EAST: the 10 Largest Firms

	Firm	Ptnrs	Asst Solrs	Total Solrs
1	**Dickinson Dees** *Newcastle upon Tyne*	50	70	**120**
2	**Eversheds** *Middlesbrough, Newcastle upon Tyne*	43	67	**110**
3	**Ward Hadaway** *Newcastle upon Tyne, South Shields*	38	39	**77**
4	**Tilly Bailey & Irvine** *Barnard Castle, Darlington, Hartlepool, Stockton on Tees*	14	28	**42**
5	**Watson Burton** *Newcastle upon Tyne*	19	22	**41**
6	**Crutes** *Middlesbrough, Newcastle-upon-Tyne, Sunderland*	16	22	**38**
7	**Robert Muckle** *Newcastle-upon-Tyne*	11	22	**33**
8	**Hay & Kilner** *Gosforth, Newcastle-upon-Tyne, Wallsend*	23	9	**32**
9	**Jacksons** *Gateshead, Stockton-on-Tees*	19	11	**30**
10	**Browell Smith & Co** *Ashington, Cramlington, Forest Hall, Newcastle-upon-Tyne (2)*	4	14	**18**

The rankings in this table are determined by the number of solicitors working in the region. They are based on partner and assistant solicitor figures only: all other fee-earners are excluded.

Ward Hadaway Nothing if not ambitious, Ward Hadaway have unveiled a business plan aimed at doubling fee income and increasing staffing levels by 60 percent. Merger was felt to be a good strategy and at the start of the year they were looking around for possible partners, entering into abortive talks with Watson Burton and eventually choosing three-partner Gateshead firm Keenlyside & Forster. The absorption of this niche practice has strengthened their commercial property department, and in the key area of commercial litigation they have overtaken Dickinson Dees and stepped into the leading band, thanks largely to the high profile of their leading practitioners. On a smaller level, their insolvency practice leaps up the rankings this year after a push in creditor-led work increased their reputation outside the region. Quality people and a commercial, friendly approach has seen them maintain and augment an impressive client base and achieve rankings in 11 sectors, but there have been setbacks. The agriculture and trusts departments slide down the rankings, perhaps suffering from competition with Dickinson Dees, while they drop out of the construction tables totally. Still, these are minor considerations, and with fees hitting the £10 million mark for the first year ever there is every possibility of their great expectations being realised.

Watson Burton If we had to chose a word to describe this medium sized, Tyneside firm, it would be 'focused.' There's nothing spare, nothing unnecessary, each department reinforces the rest so that the whole is greater than the sum of the parts. It only achieves five rankings, but three of those are in the key 3 sections of commercial property, commercial litigation and corporate finance. In corporate finance, for example, its small team has the skill and ambition to work on £100 million transactions, while its commercial property arm is large enough to compete for the major deals but nimble enough to complete a tax-driven office block sale in just 3 working days. The real jewel, though, is commercial litigation which rests on the contentious skill of their construction department, and particularly "*out and out litigator*" Robert Langley. Blunt in style but at the forefront of alternative dispute resolution, his department has been active in Holland and Belgium and recently wrested a major European client from a large London firm. A return to the rankings in insolvency caps a year of solid progress for them and growth across all areas.

SCOTLAND

Edinburgh from Calton Hill

Dundas & Wilson CS The firm still holds pole position in Scotland. It is ranked in an impressive 30 areas of practice. It boasts the highest number of individual practitioners identified as leaders in their field (14 of whom are ranked in first position.) While the firm maintains its top-tier profile in litigation and property, in corporate finance it has been ousted from first rank by specialist financial outfit, Dickson Minto. This upset, after three secure years at the top, reflects a decline in the corporate finance team's visibility, the result, some say, of the link-up with the Andersen Network. In some areas, such as in property, the market sees the Andersen link as clearly advantageous, but in others, it views it as more of a hindrance. Nevertheless, this is an organisation which, in both its Edinburgh and its Glasgow office, has unquestionably succeeded in marrying talent to considerable size. Consequently it appears to have no difficulty in retaining partners and its impressive client base. Its legion of choice clients includes the Royal Bank of Scotland.

McGrigor Donald Once again, this firm demonstrates remarkable prowess in all areas of practice. It is ranked in no fewer than 26 of these areas, and numbers 22 rated individual practitioners. A worthy rival to the Dundas & Wilson throne, it now occupies the same rankings as that firm in the three key commercial areas of property, litigation and corporate finance. The emergence of solicitor advocate Craig Connal has greatly fortified the commercial litigation practice, while his increased profile in planning has also boosted the firm's ranking in that sector. Praised for taking 'the independence route' to success (in pointed contrast to their rival's association with Andersens) the organisation remains strong in most areas and continues to marshal an impressive array of clients. These include Deutsche Bank and Lloyds TSB.

MacRoberts The firm continues its rampant growth and is now reckoned to be Scotland's third largest firm, although it is still more visible in Glasgow than in Edinburgh. It now has 16 important individual practitioners in 18 Chambers sections and includes a number of key players who excel across legal disciplines. Ian Dickson is among the best for both energy and utilities and general corporate finance, while David Flint is master of four disciplines. The firm is strong in construction and pre-eminent in projects/PFI. In employment it is the only leading commercial player to offer a challenge to Mackay Simon. However, the organisation, although steady is still unable to muster a threat to the leaders in the key commercial areas. This will have to be addressed before MacRoberts can be mentioned in the same breath as the very best of Scottish law.

Maclay Murray & Spens The sterling performance of the past year sees the firm achieve a solid band two rating in corporate finance and commercial litigation. The latter practice area is boosted by "stellar" Magnus Swanson's elevation to the top tier of practitioners. After last year's brief upgrade in commercial property, the firm drops back to the second tier. The banking department, however, finally moves into the uppermost echelon. The firm is consistently outstanding in the cutting-edge areas of information technology and intellectual property: "brilliant" Fiona Nicholson is band-one rated in both disciplines for the fourth year running. Overall, the firm is ranked in 24 sections, and boasts 26 eminent individuals. Amongst its clients are heavyweights such as Microsoft and Scottish Widows.

Shepherd & Wedderburn WS The firm has turned in a sturdy performance which guarantees their place in the premier league. It is ranked in 23 practice areas, and fields 20 noteworthy individuals. It shows solidity in the fundamental practice areas, although the commercial property department has lapsed to band two after a strong showing last year. The firm includes a number of multi-talented practitioners. Ian MacLeod, one of the foremost exponents of commercial litigation, is also ranked in employment law and in administrative and public law. Hugh Donald is back after a spell as Chief Executive. Not only is he top flight for clinical negligence and aviation, two of the firm's most powerful areas of practice, but is newly acknowledged for prowess as a commercial litigator. The outfit as a whole

SCOTLAND: the 30 Largest Firms

	Firm	Ptnrs	Asst Solrs	Total No of Solicitors '00	'99	'98	'97
1	**Dundas & Wilson CS** *Edinburgh, Glasgow*	52	141	**193**	168	165	163
2	**McGrigor Donald** *Edinburgh, Glasgow*	47	82	**129**	129	112	109
3	**MacRoberts** *Edinburgh, Glasgow*	31	71	**102**	87	72	58
4	**Shepherd & Wedderburn WS** *Edinburgh, Glasgow*	32	65	**97**	90	90	83
5	**Maclay Murray & Spens** *Edinburgh, Glasgow*	37	57	**94**	95	103	87
6	**Tods Murray WS** *Edinburgh, Glasgow*	36	46	**82**	69	69	52
7	**Brodies WS** *Edinburgh*	30	52	**82**	73	72	73
8	**Paull & Williamsons** *Aberdeen (2), Edinburgh*	31	46	**77**	70	59	51
9	**Burness** *Edinburgh, Glasgow*	30	35	**65**	67	57	59
10	**Morison Bishop** *Cumbernauld, Edinburgh (2), Glasgow, West Lothian*	30	35	**65**	65	-	-
11	**Ledingham Chalmers** *Aberdeen, Edinburgh, Inverness*	27	35	**62**	51	57	60
12	**Henderson Boyd Jackson WS** *Edinburgh, Glasgow*	21	40	**61**	61	49	39
13	**Biggart Baillie** *Edinburgh, Glasgow*	24	36	**60**	53	52	53
14	**McClure Naismith** *Edinburgh, Glasgow*	20	34	**54**	52	58	58
15	**Anderson Strathern WS** *Edinburgh, Haddington*	25	27	**52**	53	53	53
16	**Morton Fraser, Solicitors** *Edinburgh*	20	28	**48**	49	49	49
17	**Semple Fraser WS** *Edinburgh, Glasgow*	14	31	**45**	32	27	24
18	**Thorntons WS** *Arbroath, Dundee, Forfar, Perth*	23	19	**42**	41	40	41
19	**Simpson & Marwick WS** *Aberdeen, Dundee, Edinburgh, Glasgow*	14	27	**41**	39	38	35
20	**Stronachs** *Aberdeen (4), Inverness, Inverurie*	20	17	**37**	34	38	28
21	**DLA** *Edinburgh, Glasgow*	15	21	**36**	-	-	-
22	**Turcan Connell WS** *Edinburgh*	13	22	**35**	37	-	-
23	**Drummond Miller WS** *Bathgate, Dalkeith, Dunfermline, Edinburgh, Glasgow, Kirkcaldy, Livingston, Musselburgh*	20	14	**34**	34	36	36
24	**Fyfe Ireland WS** *Edinburgh*	15	19	**34**	35	42	33
25	**Steedman Ramage WS** *Edinburgh, Glasgow*	16	17	**33**	27	28	26
26	**Brechin Tindal Oatts** *Edinburgh, Glasgow*	13	20	**33**	31	29	28
27	**Balfour & Manson** *Edinburgh*	18	14	**32**	32	36	29
28	**Harper Macleod** *Glasgow*	15	15	**30**	29	24	21
29	**Ross Harper & Murphy WS** *Bellshill, East Kilbride, Glasgow, Glasgow Shawlands, Hamilton*	12	17	**29**	43	47	47
30	**Miller Hendry** *Crieff, Dundee (2), Perth*	19	9	**28**	24	23	23

The rankings in this table are determined by the number of solicitors working in the region. They are based on partner and assistant solicitor figures only: all other fee-earners are excluded.

is still seen as firmly Edinburgh based, and its Glasgow office is recognised in only four legal disciplines.

Brodies WS The firm is Scotland's young pretender. It features in 17 areas of practice, with 14 individuals ranked. The statistics reveal a subtle upwards trend in the majority of legal disciplines. The most dynamic performance comes from the commercial litigation team. This leap-frogs two bands and boasts three ranked individuals. David Williamson, also highly-rated in professional negligence, is the only Scottish lawyer in any discipline to be star rated: he is an undisputed colossus of commercial litigation. Another distinguished arena is environmental law, largely because of the continued presence of the esteemed Charles Smith. The firm is sound for property, but has slipped in corporate finance, a rare blot in an otherwise cloudless sky.

Paull & Williamsons Although predominant in the Aberdeen marketplace, the firm suffers from being less visible to the market leaders in Glasgow or Edinburgh. It is ranked in eight categories and is deemed to be at the cutting-edge of oil and gas energy work. In that area, at least, being based in Aberdeen appears to pay. Five individuals earn a place in the rankings, but the firm is hit by the departure of James Tierney to become a sheriff. His place is filled comfortably enough in employment by Sean Saluja. The firm continues to hold down a comfortable niche in the leading commercial sections, but wider recognition still appears elusive.

Tods Murray WS Ranked in 15 areas of practice and sporting 11 notable legal practitioners, the firm puts in a respectable showing. It displays its full potential in the investment fund sphere, where, with "talented and trustworthy" Christopher Athanas at the helm, it runs with the very best financial firms. However the firm performs patchily in the three key areas: although thought to be "on the up" in property, it slumps slightly in corporate finance, whilst in commercial litigation it drops out of the lists altogether.

Burness As detected last year, the firm's strategy of focusing on the core commercial areas of law is paying off. A robust display in corporate finance (consolidated by having three ranked players in this area) is matched by the "new breed" commercial litigation department. This is capped by the firm's showing in property, where the team is showing "concerted improvement," and teeters on the edge of band one status. As in corporate, the Royal Bank of Scotland is a key client. Marsali Murray leads one of Scotland's best defendant product liability practices which reckons a number of multi-national companies amongst its clients. The "meticulous and client driven," Andrew Sleigh, excellent in corporate finance, insolvency and sports law, likewise deserves mention. In a marked improvement on last year, the firm is rated in 22 practice areas, and is deemed to have 15 cutting-edge lawyers.

Simpson & Marwick WS Although significantly smaller than the firms listed above, Simpson & Marwick WS is an operation of great quality. In all eight areas of practice in which they are ranked, they appear in bands 1 and 2. Furthermore, all 3 rated individual practitioners fall into band 1. One of them, Peter Anderson ("so skilled a litigator" that "he's an expert in everything he does,") is first class in no fewer than four different disciplines: aviation, personal injury, professional negligence and commercial litigation. His pre-eminence in commercial litigation accounts for the immense success of this department, which now ranks alongside those of Scotland's legal elite.

FIRMS AT A GLANCE – THE LIST OF LISTS

These lists show the key strengths of an individual firm. Please note: they only list the areas of practice for which a firm is ranked in bands 1-3 of the tables. Bold type indicates the areas of law in which the firm is ranked in 'band one'.

A

ADAMS & REMERS
Trusts & Personal Tax

ADAMS WHYTE
Crime

ADDLESHAW BOOTH & CO
Agriculture, Asset Finance & Leasing: Consumer Finance, **Banking**, Charities, **Competition/Anti-trust**, **Construction**, **Corporate Finance**, Education: Institutions, Employee Share Schemes, **Employment**, Environment, **Family/Matrimonial**, **Financial Services**, Health & Safety, Information Technology, **Insolvency/Corporate Recovery**, **Intellectual Property**, **Litigation (Commercial)**, **Litigation (Property)**, **Pensions**, Planning, **Projects/PFI**, **Property (Commercial)**, Social Housing: Advising Lenders, Sport, **Tax (Corporate)**, Trusts & Personal Tax

AE SMITH & SON
Education: Individuals

AE WYETH & CO
Personal Injury: Mainly Defendant

AGNEW, ANDRESS, HIGGINS
Personal Injury: Mainly Claimant

ALEXANDER HARRIS
Clinical Negligence: Mainly Claimant, Product Liability, Product Liability: Mainly Claimant

ALISTAIR MELDRUM & CO
Crime

ALLAN JANES
Licensing

ALLEN & FRASER
Licensing

ALLEN & OVERY
Administrative & Public Law: Commercial, Arbitration (International), Asset Finance & Leasing, **Banking**, **Capital Markets: Derivatives**, **Capital Markets: International Debt & Equity**, Capital Markets: Securitisation & Repackaging, Charities, Competition/Anti-trust, Corporate Finance: 60+ Solicitors in Corporate Team, **Corporate Finance: Debt**, Corporate Finance: Equity, Energy & Natural Resources, **Environment**, Financial Services, **Fraud: Civil**, Information Technology, **Insolvency/Corporate Recovery**, **Partnership**, **Partnership: Large International Mergers**, Pensions, **Projects/PFI**, Shipping: Finance, Social Housing: Advising Lenders, Tax (Corporate), Telecommunications, Trusts & Personal Tax

ALLINGTON HUGHES
Church: Other Denominations

AMERY-PARKES
Personal Injury: Mainly Claimant

ANDERSON STRATHERN WS
Agriculture, **Charities**, **Clinical Negligence: Mainly Claimant**, Education: Institutions, Litigation (Commercial), Media & Entertainment, Personal Injury: Mainly Claimant, **Sport**, Trusts & Personal Tax

ANDREA & CO
Travel

ANDREW KEENAN & CO
Crime

ANDREW M. JACKSON & CO
Agriculture, Family/Matrimonial, Food, Shipping, **Shipping: Wet**, Trusts & Personal Tax

ANNE HALL DICK & CO.
Family/Matrimonial

ANTHONY COLLINS SOLICITORS
Charities, **Church: Other Denominations**, Clinical Negligence: Mainly Claimant, Licensing, Local Government, **Social Housing**

ARCHIBALD CAMPBELL & HARLEY WS
Litigation (Property), Planning

ARGLES STONEHAM BURSTOWS
Corporate Finance, Employment, **Insolvency/Corporate Recovery**, Licensing, Litigation (Commercial)

ARNOLD THOMSON
Agriculture

ARTHUR COX
Banking

ASHTON GRAHAM
Corporate Finance, Debt Recovery

ASHURST MORRIS CRISP
Competition/Anti-trust, Corporate Finance: Debt, **Corporate Finance: Equity**, Environment, **Litigation (Commercial): Fewer than 40 Litigators**, Litigation (Property), Local Government, Media & Entertainment: Broadcasting, Planning, Product Liability: Mainly Defendant

A S LAW
Human Rights (Civil Liberties), Immigration

B

BABINGTON & CROASDAILE
Crime, **Family/Matrimonial**

BACKHOUSE JONES
Transport: Road - Regulatory

BAKER & MCKENZIE
Corporate Finance: 30-60 Solicitors in Corporate Team, Customs & Excise, E-commerce, Employment: Mainly Respondent, **Information Technology**, Intellectual Property: General, **Litigation (Commercial): Fewer than 40 Litigators**, Pensions, Telecommunications

BALFOUR & MANSON
Charities, **Clinical Negligence: Mainly Claimant**, **Family/Matrimonial**, Personal Injury: Mainly Claimant, Professional Negligence, Trusts & Personal Tax

BANNATYNE, KIRKWOOD, FRANCE & CO
Defamation, Media & Entertainment

BANNERS JONES MIDDLETON
Crime

BARCAN WOODWARD
Clinical Negligence: Mainly Claimant

BARKER GOTELEE
Agriculture

BARLOW LYDE & GILBERT
Aviation: Insurance & Litigation, **Insurance: General Claims**, **Insurance: Reinsurance**, **Personal Injury: Mainly Defendant**, **Professional Negligence: Financial**, **Professional Negligence: Insurance**, **Professional Negligence: Legal**, Travel

BARLOWS
Charities

BARRATT GOFF & TOMLINSON
Personal Injury: Mainly Claimant

BARRIE WARD & JULIAN GRIFFITHS
Crime

BARTRAM & CO
Immigration: Personal

BATES, WELLS & BRAITHWAITE
Administrative & Public Law: Traditional, **Charities**, Family/Matrimonial, Immigration: Business, Partnership: Medical

BEACHCROFT WANSBROUGHS
Administrative & Public Law (Sheffield), Church (London), Clinical Negligence (Birmingham, Bristol, London), **Clinical Negligence: Mainly Defendant (Sheffield, Winchester)**, Education (London), **Healthcare (Leeds, Sheffield)**, Healthcare (Birmingham, Bristol, London, Winchester), Information Technology (Bristol), **Insurance (Birmingham, Bristol, Leeds, Manchester)**, Intellectual Property (Bristol), Litigation (Commercial) (Bristol), Personal Injury (Manchester), **Personal Injury: Mainly Defendant (Birmingham, Bristol, Leeds, London, Winchester)**, **Professional Negligence (Bristol, Leeds)**, Professional Negligence (Birmingham, London), Property (Commercial) (Bristol, Manchester)

BEALE AND COMPANY
Professional Negligence: Construction

BEAUMONT AND SON
Aviation: Insurance & Litigation, Aviation: Regulatory

BEECHAM PEACOCK
Personal Injury: Mainly Claimant

BELL & BUXTON
Church: Church of England

BELMORES
Crime, Licensing

BELTRAMI & CO
Crime

BERMANS
Debt Recovery

BERRY SMITH
Property (Commercial)

BERRYMAN SHACKLOCK
Licensing

BERRYMANS LACE MAWER
Insurance, **Personal Injury: Mainly Defendant**, Professional Negligence: Construction, Transport: Road - Carriage/Commercial

BERWIN LEIGHTON
Corporate Finance: 30-60 Solicitors in Corporate Team, Litigation (Property), Local Government, **Planning**, Property (Commercial): 100+ Fee-Earners

BETESH FOX & CO
Crime, Fraud: Criminal

BEVAN ASHFORD
Administrative & Public Law: General, **Clinical Negligence: Mainly Defendant**, Construction, Corporate Finance, Defamation, **Employment**, Environment, Food, Health & Safety, **Healthcare**, Intellectual Property, Licensing, Litigation (Commercial), **Local Government**, Personal Injury: Mainly Defendant, Planning, **Projects/PFI**, Property (Commercial), Social Housing, Trusts & Personal Tax

BHATT MURPHY
Human Rights (Civil Liberties)

BIDDLE
Corporate Finance: Fewer than 30 Solicitors in Corporate Team, Defamation, Licensing, Pensions Litigation

BIGGART BAILLIE
Charities, Competition/Anti-trust, **Energy: Electricity**, Insurance, Personal Injury: Mainly Defendant

BIGGER & STRAHAN
Debt Recovery

BINDMAN & PARTNERS
Administrative & Public Law: Traditional, Clinical Negligence: Mainly Claimant, **Crime**, Education: Individuals, Employment: Mainly Applicant, **Human Rights (Civil Liberties)**, **Immigration: Personal**

BIRCH CULLIMORE
Agriculture, **Charities**, Church: Church of England, Trusts & Personal Tax

BIRCHAM & CO.
Parliamentary Agency, **Parliamentary: Public Affairs**

BIRD & BIRD
Corporate Finance: Fewer than 30 Solicitors in Corporate Team, **E-commerce**, **Information Technology**, **Intellectual Property: General**, **Intellectual Property: Patent**, Sport, **Telecommunications**

BIRKETTS
Agriculture, Corporate Finance, Debt Recovery, Property (Commercial)

BIRNBERG PEIRCE & PARTNERS
Crime, Human Rights (Civil Liberties), **Immigration: Personal**

BLACKLOCK THORLEY
Debt Recovery

BLAIR & BRYDEN
Crime

BLAIR ALLISON & CO
Family/Matrimonial

BLAKE LAPTHORN
Charities, **Clinical Negligence: Mainly Claimant**, Construction, **Corporate Finance**, Debt Recovery, Employment, **Environment**, Fraud: Criminal, **Insolvency/Corporate Recovery**, **Licensing**, **Litigation (Commercial)**, Personal Injury: Mainly Claimant, **Professional Negligence**, **Property (Commercial)**, Tax (Corporate), Trusts & Personal Tax

BLANDY & BLANDY
Family/Matrimonial, Licensing, Trusts & Personal Tax

BOBBETTS MACKAN
Crime, **Fraud: Criminal**, **Immigration**, Personal Injury: Mainly Claimant

BOGUE AND MCNULTY
Crime

BONAR MACKENZIE WS
Debt Recovery

BOND PEARCE
Banking, Charities, Competition/Anti-trust, **Corporate Finance**, **Debt Recovery**, **Education: Institutions**, **Employment**, **Energy & Natural Resources**, **Environment**, **Family/Matrimonial**, Health & Safety, Insolvency/Corporate Recovery, Insurance, Litigation (Commercial), Local Government, Partnership, **Personal Injury: Mainly Claimant**, **Personal Injury: Mainly Defendant**, **Planning**, **Professional Negligence**, Property (Commercial), Trusts & Personal Tax

BOODLE HATFIELD
Property (Commercial): Fewer than 100 Fee-Earners, **Trusts & Personal Tax**

BOYES TURNER & BURROWS
Clinical Negligence: Mainly Claimant, Debt Recovery, **Insolvency/Corporate Recovery**, Litigation (Commercial), Personal Injury: Mainly Claimant

BRABNER HOLDEN BANKS WILSON
Charities, Defamation, **Social Housing**, **Trusts & Personal Tax**

BRABY & WALLER
Debt Recovery

BRACHERS
Agriculture, Clinical Negligence: Mainly Defendant, **Debt Recovery**, Employment, **Environment**, Family/Matrimonial, Litigation (Commercial), Litigation (Property), Planning

BRECHIN TINDAL OATTS
Insurance, Social Housing

BRENDAN KEARNEY KELLY & CO
Crime

BRETHERTONS
Crime

BRIAN KOFFMAN & CO
Crime

BRISTOWS
Intellectual Property: General, **Intellectual Property: Patent**, Partnership

BRODIES WS
Administrative & Public Law: General, **Agriculture**, Debt Recovery, Employment, **Environment**, Family/Matrimonial, Franchising, **Litigation (Commercial)**,

These lists show the key strengths of an individual firm. Please note: they only list the areas of practice for which a firm is ranked in bands 1-3 of the tables. Bold type indicates the areas of law in which the firm is ranked in 'band one'.

Litigation (Property), Local Government, Planning, Property (Commercial), Tax (Corporate), Trusts & Personal Tax

BROOKSTREET DES ROCHES
Charities, Partnership: Medical, Property (Commercial)

BROWELL SMITH & CO
Personal Injury: Mainly Claimant

BROWNE JACOBSON
Administrative & Public Law: General, Clinical Negligence: Mainly Defendant, Debt Recovery, Healthcare, Insurance, Litigation (Commercial), **Personal Injury: Mainly Defendant**, **Professional Negligence**, Social Housing, Trusts & Personal Tax

BRUNTON MILLER
Licensing

BRUTTON & CO
Church: Church of England

BUCKLE MELLOWS
Family/Matrimonial

BULLER JEFFRIES
Personal Injury: Mainly Defendant

BULLIVANT JONES
Property (Commercial)

BURGES SALMON
Agriculture, **Banking**, Charities, **Competition/Anti-trust**, Corporate Finance, **Debt Recovery**, **Employment**, **Environment**, **Family/Matrimonial**, **Financial Services**, Information Technology, Intellectual Property, **Investment Funds**, **Litigation (Commercial)**, **Litigation (Property)**, **Partnership**, **Pensions**, Planning, Professional Negligence, Projects/PFI, **Property (Commercial)**, Social Housing, **Tax (Corporate)**, **Trusts & Personal Tax**

BURNESS
Administrative & Public Law: General, Banking, Charities, **Competition/Anti-trust**, Energy: Electricity, Insolvency/Corporate Recovery, Litigation (Commercial), Litigation (Property), Local Government, Partnership, Pensions, **Product Liability**, Property (Commercial), Sport, Tax (Corporate)

BURNETT & REID
Agriculture, Family/Matrimonial

BURNSIDE KEMP FRASER
Employment, Personal Injury: Mainly Claimant

BURTON COPELAND
Crime, **Fraud: Criminal**

C

C & H JEFFERSON
Litigation (Commercial), **Personal Injury: Mainly Defendant**

C & J BLACK
Trusts & Personal Tax

CAMPBELL HOOPER
Media & Entertainment: Theatre

CAPSTICKS
Clinical Negligence: Mainly Defendant, **Healthcare**

CARNSON MORROW GRAHAM
Family/Matrimonial

CARRICK READ INSOLVENCY
Debt Recovery

CARSON & MCDOWELL
Construction, Corporate Finance, **Litigation (Commercial)**, Property (Commercial)

CARTER LEMON CAMERONS
Church: Other Denominations

CARTMELL SHEPHERD
Agriculture

CARTWRIGHT KING
Fraud: Criminal

CARTWRIGHTS
Employment, Food, **Licensing**, Litigation (Commercial), Personal Injury: Mainly Defendant

CARTWRIGHTS ADAMS & BLACK
Licensing

CHAFFE STREET
Asset Finance & Leasing, Banking

CHALLINORS LYON CLARK
Clinical Negligence: Mainly Claimant, **Family/Matrimonial**

CHAPMAN EVERATT
Personal Injury: Mainly Defendant

CHARLES RUSSELL
Charities, Clinical Negligence: Mainly Claimant, Family/Matrimonial, Trusts & Personal Tax

CHRISTIAN FISHER
Crime, Human Rights (Civil Liberties)

CLAIRMONTS
Travel

CLARK HOLT
Information Technology

CLARKE WILLMOTT & CLARKE
Administrative & Public Law: General, Agriculture, **Debt Recovery**, Environment, Family/Matrimonial, Licensing, **Planning**, Property (Commercial), **Sport**, Trusts & Personal Tax

CLARKS
Construction, Corporate Finance, Debt Recovery, Employment, **Litigation (Commercial)**, **Pensions**, **Planning**, Property (Commercial)

CLARKSON WRIGHT & JAKES
Employment, Partnership: Medical

CLAUDE HORNBY & COX
Crime

CLAYTONS
Church: Church of England

CLEARY, GOTTLIEB, STEEN & HAMILTON
Corporate Finance: US firms acting from London

CLEAVER FULTON RANKIN
Administrative & Public Law: General, Construction, Debt Recovery, Employment, **Environment**, Litigation (Commercial), Property (Commercial), **Trusts & Personal Tax**

CLIFFORD CHANCE
Administrative & Public Law: Commercial, **Arbitration (International)**, Asset Finance & Leasing, **Banking**, **Capital Markets: Derivatives**, Capital Markets: International Debt & Equity, **Capital Markets: Securitisation & Repackaging**, **Commodities: Futures**, Competition/Anti-trust, Corporate Finance: 60+ Solicitors in Corporate Team, **Corporate Finance: Debt**, **Corporate Finance: Equity**, E-commerce, Employee Share Schemes, Energy & Natural Resources, **Financial Services**, **Fraud: Civil**, **Information Technology**, Insolvency/Corporate Recovery, Insurance: Non-contentious, Insurance: Reinsurance, Intellectual Property: General, **Investment Funds**, Litigation (Property), Media & Entertainment: Broadcasting, **Parliamentary: Public Affairs**, Pensions, Projects/PFI, Property (Commercial): 100+ Fee-Earners, **Social Housing: Advising Lenders**, Tax (Corporate), **Telecommunications**, Transport: Rail, **Travel: Hotels & Leisure**

CLINTONS
Media & Entertainment: Music, Media & Entertainment: Theatre

CLYDE & CO
Aviation: Insurance & Litigation, Information Technology, Insurance: General Claims, Insurance: Reinsurance, Litigation (Commercial): Fewer than 40 Litigators, Property (Commercial), Shipping, Shipping: Wet, Transport: Road - Carriage/Commercial

CMS CAMERON MCKENNA
Aviation: Insurance & Litigation, Banking, Construction, Energy & Natural Resources, **Energy: Oil and Gas**, Environment, Fraud: Civil, **Health & Safety**, **Immigration: Business**, Insolvency/Corporate Recovery, Insurance: General Claims, Insurance: Reinsurance, Litigation (Property), Pensions, Pensions Litigation, Planning, **Product Liability: Mainly Defendant**, Professional Negligence, **Professional Negligence: Construction**, Professional Negligence: Financial, Professional Negligence: Insurance

COBBETTS
Defamation, Employment, Family/Matrimonial, **Licensing**, Litigation (Commercial), **Litigation (Property)**, **Property (Commercial)**, **Social Housing**, Trusts & Personal Tax

COFFIN MEW & CLOVER
Family/Matrimonial, Litigation (Property), **Social Housing**

COKER VIS PARTNERSHIP
Immigration: Personal

COMERTON & HILL
Debt Recovery

CONDIES
Crime

CONINGSBYS
Education: Individuals

COPLEYS
Crime

COVINGTON & BURLING
Food

COZENS-HARDY & JEWSON
Charities, Trusts & Personal Tax

CRIPPS HARRIES HALL
Agriculture, Charities, Construction, Corporate Finance, Employment, Family/Matrimonial, Insolvency/Corporate Recovery, **Litigation (Commercial)**, Litigation (Property), **Professional Negligence**, Property (Commercial), **Trusts & Personal Tax**

CROCKERS OSWALD HICKSON
Defamation

CROFTONS
Social Housing

CROSSE & CROSSE
Crime, Licensing

CRUTES
Church: Church of England, Clinical Negligence: Mainly Defendant, Healthcare, Personal Injury: Mainly Defendant, **Professional Negligence**

CUFF ROBERTS
Family/Matrimonial, **Partnership**, Trusts & Personal Tax

CUNNINGHAM JOHN
Clinical Negligence: Mainly Claimant, **Personal Injury: Mainly Claimant**

CUNNINGHAMS
Crime

CURREY & CO
Trusts & Personal Tax

D

DALE & CO SOLICITORS
Shipping

DARBYS MALLAM LEWIS
Family/Matrimonial, **Immigration**, Insolvency/Corporate Recovery

DARLINGTON & PARKINSON
Crime

DAVENPORT LYONS
Defamation, Licensing, Media & Entertainment: Film & TV Production, Media & Entertainment: Film Finance

DAVID CHARNLEY & CO
Crime

DAVID GIST & CO
Personal Injury: Mainly Claimant

DAVID GRAY & COMPANY
Crime, Human Rights (Civil Liberties), **Immigration**

DAVID LEVENE & CO
Administrative & Public Law: Traditional, Education: Individuals

DAVID PRICE & CO
Defamation

DAVIES AND PARTNERS
Planning, Property (Commercial)

DAVIES ARNOLD COOPER
Insurance: General Claims, Personal Injury: Mainly Defendant, Product Liability: Mainly Defendant, Professional Negligence: Construction

DAVIES LAVERY
Personal Injury: Mainly Defendant, Transport: Road - Carriage/Commercial

DAVIES WALLIS FOYSTER
Asset Finance & Leasing, Debt Recovery, Property (Commercial), Trusts & Personal Tax

DAVIES, JOHNSON & CO
Shipping

DAVIS BLANK FURNISS
Immigration

DAWSON & CO
Agriculture

DEAS MALLEN
Personal Injury: Mainly Defendant

DEBORAH MILLS ASSOCIATES
Energy & Natural Resources

DECHERT
Customs & Excise, Fraud: Criminal, Litigation (Commercial): Fewer than 40 Litigators, Litigation (Property)

DEIGHTON GUEDALLA
Human Rights (Civil Liberties), **Immigration: Personal**

DENISON TILL
Church: Church of England

DENTON WILDE SAPTE
Asset Finance & Leasing, **Aviation: Regulatory**, Commodities: Futures, Competition/Anti-trust, Corporate Finance: Debt, Debt Recovery, E-commerce, **Energy & Natural Resources**, Environment, Insolvency/Corporate Recovery, Litigation (Property), **Media & Entertainment: Broadcasting**, Media & Entertainment: Film Finance, **Media & Entertainment: Publishing**, Planning, **Property (Commercial)**, Social Housing: Advising Lenders, **Sport**, Telecommunications, Transport: Rail, Travel: Hotels & Leisure

DEVONSHIRES
Social Housing

DICKINSON DEES
Agriculture, **Banking**, Charities, Competition/Anti-trust, Construction, **Corporate Finance**, **Employment**, Energy & Natural Resources, Environment, **Family/Matrimonial**, **Financial Services**, **Insolvency/Corporate Recovery**, Licensing, Litigation (Commercial), Litigation (Property), Pensions, **Planning**, Projects/PFI, **Property (Commercial)**, **Social Housing**, **Trusts & Personal Tax**

DICKSON MINTO WS
Banking, **Corporate Finance**, Corporate Finance: Debt, Corporate Finance: Equity, Financial Services, Investment Funds

DIGBY BROWN
Personal Injury: Mainly Claimant

DIXON, COLES & GILL
Church: Church of England

D J FREEMAN
Defamation, Litigation (Commercial): Fewer than 40 Litigators, Litigation (Property)

DLA
Aviation (London), **Banking (Liverpool, Manchester)**, Construction (Birmingham, Leeds, Liverpool, Manchester, Sheffield), Corporate Finance (Birmingham, Leeds, Liverpool, London, Manchester, Sheffield), Debt Recovery (Bradford), Defamation (Glasgow), Education (Leeds, Liverpool, Sheffield), **Employment (Liverpool, Manchester)**, Employment (Birmingham, Leeds, Sheffield), **Environment (Manchester)**, Environment (Sheffield), **Food (Birmingham)**, Fraud (London, Manchester), **Insolvency/Corporate Recovery (Leeds, Sheffield)**, Insolvency/Corporate Recovery (Glasgow, Liverpool, Manchester), **Intellectual Property (Leeds, Sheffield)**, Intellectual Property (Liverpool, Manchester), **Licensing (Sheffield)**, **Litigation (Commercial) (Leeds, Liverpool, Manchester)**, Litigation (Commercial) (Birmingham), Litigation

FIRMS AT A GLANCE

These lists show the key strengths of an individual firm. Please note: they only list the areas of practice for which a firm is ranked in bands 1-3 of the tables. Bold type indicates the areas of law in which the firm is ranked in 'band one'.

(Property) (Leeds, Liverpool, Manchester), Local Government (Birmingham), Media & Entertainment (Leeds), **Parliamentary: Public Affairs (London), Pensions (Leeds, Liverpool, Manchester, Sheffield),** Personal Injury (Leeds, Sheffield), Planning (Manchester), **Projects/PFI (Birmingham)**, **Property (Commercial) (Liverpool, Manchester)**, Property (Commercial) (Birmingham, Leeds, Sheffield), Shipping (Liverpool, Manchester), Tax (Corporate) (Birmingham), Transport (Liverpool, London, Manchester)

DMH
Church: Other Denominations, Corporate Finance, **Employment**, **Environment**, Family/Matrimonial, Fraud: Criminal, **Information Technology**, Intellectual Property, Licensing, Litigation (Commercial), **Litigation (Property)**, Planning, Property (Commercial), **Shipping**

DOLMANS
Personal Injury: Mainly Defendant

DONNELLY & WALL
Crime

DOUGLAS & PARTNERS
Crime

DRUMMOND MILLER WS
Clinical Negligence: Mainly Claimant, Family/Matrimonial, Personal Injury: Mainly Claimant

DUNDAS & WILSON CS
Administrative & Public Law: General, **Banking**, Competition/Anti-trust, Construction, Corporate Finance, **Education: Institutions**, **Employee Share Schemes**, Employment, **Energy: Electricity**, Environment, **Financial Services**, Information Technology, **Insolvency/Corporate Recovery**, Insurance, Intellectual Property, **Investment Funds**, Licensing, **Litigation (Commercial)**, **Litigation (Property)**, **Local Government**, Media & Entertainment, **Partnership**, Personal Injury: Mainly Defendant, **Planning**, Professional Negligence, **Projects/PFI**, **Property (Commercial)**, Sport

DUNDONS
Crime

DUTHIE HART & DUTHIE
Crime

E

E. & L. KENNEDY
Licensing

EAMONN MCEVOY & CO
Personal Injury: Mainly Claimant

EDDOWES WALDRON
Crime

EDWARD FAIL BRADSHAW & WATERSON
Crime

EDWARD HARRIS & SON
Agriculture

EDWARDS & CO
Personal Injury: Mainly Claimant

EDWARDS GELDARD
Administrative & Public Law: General, Banking, Church: Church of England, Clinical Negligence: Mainly Claimant, **Competition/Anti-trust**, Corporate Finance, Debt Recovery, Employment, Energy & Natural Resources, **Environment**, **Information Technology**, Insolvency/Corporate Recovery, **Intellectual Property**, **Litigation (Commercial)**, Litigation (Property), Local Government, **Planning**, Property (Commercial), Social Housing, **Trusts & Personal Tax**

E. EDWARDS SON & NOICE
Personal Injury: Mainly Claimant, Personal Injury: Mainly Defendant

ELAINE MAXWELL & CO
Education: Individuals

ELLIOT MATHER
Crime

ELLIOTT DUFFY GARRETT
Construction, **Defamation**, Employment, Insolvency/Corporate Recovery, **Litigation (Commercial)**, Partnership, **Product Liability**, Property (Commercial)

ELLIOTTS
Food, Licensing, Professional Negligence

ELLIS WOOD
Church: Other Denominations

ENSOR BYFIELD
Personal Injury: Mainly Defendant

ERIC ROBINSON & CO
Immigration

ERSKINE MACASKILL & CO
Administrative & Public Law: General, Family/Matrimonial

EVERATT & COMPANY
Personal Injury: Mainly Defendant

EVERSHEDS
Administrative & Public Law (Cambridge, Norwich), **Administrative & Public Law: General (Cardiff, Leeds, Manchester)**, Agriculture (Norwich), Asset Finance & Leasing (Cardiff, Leeds), **Banking (Cambridge, Cardiff, Ipswich, Manchester, Norwich)**, Banking (Birmingham, Leeds, Newcastle upon Tyne, Nottingham), Charities (Cambridge, Norwich), **Clinical Negligence: Mainly Defendant (Newcastle upon Tyne)**, **Competition/Anti-trust (Cardiff, Leeds, Manchester, Middlesbrough, Newcastle upon Tyne)**, Competition/Anti-trust (Birmingham), **Construction (Newcastle upon Tyne)**, Construction (Cardiff, Ipswich, Norwich), **Corporate Finance (Ipswich, Norwich)**, Corporate Finance (Birmingham, Cardiff, Leeds, Manchester, Middlesbrough, Newcastle upon Tyne), **Debt Recovery (Cardiff, Norwich)**, Debt Recovery (Birmingham, Leeds, Nottingham), Education (Cardiff, Ipswich, Leeds, Manchester, Middlesbrough, Newcastle upon Tyne, Norwich, Nottingham), **Education: Institutions (London)**, Employee Share Schemes (Birmingham), **Employment (Birmingham, Cardiff, Ipswich, Manchester, Newcastle upon Tyne, Norwich)**, Employment (Bristol, London), Energy & Natural Resources (Birmingham, Leeds), **Environment (Birmingham, Cardiff, Leeds, Manchester)**, Environment (Norwich), Family (Cambridge, Norwich), **Food (Birmingham, Norwich)**, **Franchising (London, Newcastle upon Tyne)**, Fraud (London), **Health & Safety (Cardiff, Leeds),** Healthcare (Newcastle upon Tyne), **Immigration (Cardiff)**, Immigration (London), **Information Technology (Birmingham, Nottingham)**, Information Technology (Cardiff, Leeds), **Insolvency/Corporate Recovery (Birmingham, Cambridge, Cardiff, Ipswich, Norwich)**, Insolvency/Corporate Recovery (Newcastle upon Tyne), **Intellectual Property (Leeds)**, Intellectual Property (Cambridge, Cardiff, Ipswich, London, Norwich), Investment Funds (London), **Licensing (Bristol, Cardiff)**, Licensing (Ipswich, Norwich), **Litigation (Commercial) (Cardiff, Ipswich, Leeds, Manchester, Newcastle upon Tyne, Norwich)**, Litigation (Commercial) (Birmingham, Bristol, London, Nottingham), **Litigation (Property) (Cardiff, Ipswich, Norwich)**, Litigation (Property) (Birmingham, Derby, Leeds, Manchester, Nottingham), **Local Government (Cardiff, Leeds)**, Local Government (Nottingham), Media & Entertainment (Leeds, Manchester), **Pensions (Cardiff, Leeds)**, Pensions (Birmingham, Derby, Manchester, Norwich), **Pensions Litigation (Derby)**, Personal Injury (Cardiff), **Personal Injury: Mainly Defendant (Newcastle upon Tyne, Norwich)**, **Planning (Cardiff)**, Planning (Birmingham, Leeds, Manchester), **Projects/PFI (Nottingham)**, Projects/PFI (Cardiff, Manchester), **Property (Commercial) (Birmingham, Cambridge, Cardiff, Ipswich, Manchester, Norwich, Nottingham)**, Property (Commercial) (Leeds, Newcastle upon Tyne), **Shipping (Ipswich)**, Shipping (Newcastle upon Tyne), **Social Housing (Cardiff)**, Social Housing (Manchester), Tax (Corporate) (Leeds, Manchester, Norwich, Nottingham), **Telecommunications (Leeds)**, Transport (Birmingham, Leeds, London), Travel (Middlesbrough, Newcastle upon Tyne), Trusts & Personal Tax (Cardiff, Norwich)

EVILL AND COLEMAN
Clinical Negligence: Mainly Claimant, Personal Injury: Mainly Claimant

F

FARLEYS
Family/Matrimonial

FARRER & CO
Agriculture, Charities, **Defamation**, Family/Matrimonial, Sport, Trusts & Personal Tax

FENNEMORES
Debt Recovery, Personal Injury: Mainly Claimant

FENWICK ELLIOTT
Construction

FIELD CUNNINGHAM & CO
Property (Commercial)

FIELD FISHER WATERHOUSE
Advertising & Marketing, Clinical Negligence: Mainly Claimant, Corporate Finance: Fewer than 30 Solicitors in Corporate Team, E-commerce, **Franchising**, **Licensing**, Partnership, Product Liability: Mainly Claimant, **Travel**, Travel: Hotels & Leisure

FIELD SEYMOUR PARKES
Licensing

FIELDINGS PORTER
Church: Other Denominations

FINERS STEPHENS INNOCENT
Property (Commercial): Fewer than 100 Fee-Earners

FISHBURN MORGAN COLE
Professional Negligence: Construction

FISHER MEREDITH
Crime, Education: Individuals

FLADGATE FIELDER
Property (Commercial): Fewer than 100 Fee-Earners

FLETCHERS
Crime

FLYNN & MCGETTRICK
Crime, **Family/Matrimonial**

FOLLETT STOCK
Church: Church of England

FOOT ANSTEY SARGENT
Defamation, **Family/Matrimonial**, Information Technology, Insolvency/Corporate Recovery, Licensing, Litigation (Commercial), **Shipping**, Trusts & Personal Tax

FORBES
Crime

FORD & WARREN
Transport: Road - Regulatory

FORSTERS
Agriculture, **Property (Commercial): Fewer than 100 Fee-Earners**

FOSTERS
Crime, Family/Matrimonial

FOX WILLIAMS
Employment: Mainly Respondent, **Partnership**

FRANCIS HANNA & CO
Personal Injury: Mainly Claimant

FREEMANS
Licensing

FREETHCARTWRIGHT
Clinical Negligence: Mainly Claimant, Debt Recovery, Family/Matrimonial, Partnership, Personal Injury: Mainly Claimant, Product Liability, Social Housing, Trusts & Personal Tax

FRESHFIELDS BRUCKHAUS DERINGER
Arbitration (International), **Asset Finance & Leasing**, Banking, Capital Markets: Derivatives, Capital Markets: International Debt & Equity, Capital Markets: Securitisation & Repackaging, **Competition/Anti-trust**, **Corporate Finance: 60+ Solicitors in Corporate Team**, Employee Share Schemes, **Environment**, Financial Services, Insolvency/Corporate Recovery, Insurance: Non-contentious, Litigation (Commercial): 40+ Litigators, **Pensions**, Projects/PFI, **Tax (Corporate)**, Telecommunications, **Transport: Rail**

FYFE IRELAND WS
Clinical Negligence: Mainly Claimant

FYNN & PARTNERS
Environment, **Licensing**, Planning

G

GABB & CO
Agriculture

GADSBY WICKS
Clinical Negligence: Mainly Claimant

GALLEN & CO
Crime

GAMLINS
Crime, Fraud: Criminal

GAMON ARDEN & CO
Church: Church of England

GARRETTS
Corporate Finance (Cambridge), Information Technology (Reading), Intellectual Property (Reading), Litigation (Commercial) (Reading)

GARSTANGS
Crime, Fraud: Criminal

GATELEY WAREING
Banking, Charities, **Church: Other Denominations**, Construction

GEORGE DAVIES
Clinical Negligence: Mainly Defendant, Sport

GEORGE IDE, PHILLIPS
Personal Injury: Mainly Claimant

GEORGE MATHERS & CO
Crime

GEORGE, JONAS & CO
Crime, Fraud: Criminal

GEPP & SONS
Crime

GHERSON & CO
Immigration: Business

GILFEDDER & MCINNES
Crime

GILL & CO
Immigration: Personal

GILL AKASTER
Family/Matrimonial

GILLESPIE MACANDREW WS
Agriculture

GILLS
Education: Individuals

GIRLINGS
Licensing

GLAISYERS
Crime, Fraud: Criminal

GLAZER DELMAR
Immigration: Personal

GOLDS
Debt Recovery

GOODMAN DERRICK
Media & Entertainment: Broadcasting

GORDON & SMYTH
Crime

GORDON DADDS
Family/Matrimonial

GORDONS CRANSWICK SOLICITORS
Church: Church of England, Family/Matrimonial, Litigation (Commercial)

GORNA & CO
Litigation (Property), Sport

GOSSCHALKS
Licensing

FIRMS AT A GLANCE

These lists show the key strengths of an individual firm. Please note: they only list the areas of practice for which a firm is ranked in bands 1-3 of the tables. Bold type indicates the areas of law in which the firm is ranked in 'band one'.

GOTELEE & GOLDSMITH
Crime, Debt Recovery

GOULDENS
Corporate Finance: 30-60 Solicitors in Corporate Team, Litigation (Commercial): Fewer than 40 Litigators

GRAHAM EVANS & PARTNERS
Crime

GRAHAME STOWE, BATESON
Crime, Family/Matrimonial

GRANT & HORTON MARINE SOLICITORS
Shipping

GRANVILLE-WEST
Family/Matrimonial

GRAYS
Agriculture, Charities, **Church: Other Denominations**

GREEN & CO
Family/Matrimonial

GREENE & GREENE
Corporate Finance

GREENWOODS
Charities, Construction, Corporate Finance, Debt Recovery, **Family/Matrimonial**, Licensing, Litigation (Commercial), Personal Injury: Mainly Defendant

GREGG GALBRAITH QUINN
Food, Licensing

GRIFFITH SMITH
Charities

GROSS & CO
Immigration

H

HADENS
Family/Matrimonial

HALL & HAUGHEY
Crime

HALLINAN, BLACKBURN, GITTINGS & NOTT
Crime

HALLIWELL LANDAU
Banking, Charities, Corporate Finance, Health & Safety, Information Technology, Insolvency/Corporate Recovery, **Intellectual Property**, Litigation (Commercial), Personal Injury: Mainly Defendant, **Planning**, Professional Negligence, **Property (Commercial)**, **Trusts & Personal Tax**

HAMMOND SUDDARDS EDGE
Advertising & Marketing (London), Asset Finance & Leasing (Birmingham), Banking (Leeds), Construction (Birmingham, Leeds, Manchester), Corporate Finance (Leeds, Manchester), **Corporate Finance: Fewer than 30 Solicitors in Corporate Team (London)** , **Debt Recovery (Birmingham, Bradford)** , Debt Recovery (London), **Employment (Manchester)** , Employment (Birmingham, Leeds), Energy & Natural Resources (Birmingham), Environment (Birmingham, Manchester), Franchising (Manchester), Fraud (Birmingham), **Health & Safety (Birmingham, Manchester)** , Insolvency/Corporate Recovery (Leeds, Manchester), Intellectual Property (Birmingham, Leeds, Manchester), Licensing (Birmingham), **Litigation (Commercial) (Leeds)** , Litigation (Commercial) (Birmingham, Manchester), Litigation (Property) (Birmingham, Leeds, Manchester), **Media & Entertainment (Birmingham)** , **Partnership (Birmingham)** , **Pensions (Leeds)** , Pensions (Birmingham, Manchester), Personal Injury (Birmingham), Planning (Leeds), Product Liability (Birmingham), Professional Negligence (Leeds), Property (Commercial) (Birmingham, Leeds, Manchester), **Sport (Birmingham)** , Tax (Corporate) (Leeds, Manchester)

HARBOTTLE & LEWIS
Aviation: Regulatory, Corporate Finance: Fewer than 30 Solicitors in Corporate Team, Media & Entertainment: Film & TV Production, Media & Entertainment: Publishing

HARDING EVANS
Family/Matrimonial

HARPER MACLEOD
Employment, Energy: Electricity, Licensing, **Social Housing**, **Sport**

HARRIS & HARRIS
Church: Church of England

HARRISON BUNDEY & CO.
Human Rights (Civil Liberties), Immigration

HARRISON CURTIS
Media & Entertainment: Theatre

HARRISON, LEITCH & LOGAN
Personal Injury: Mainly Defendant

HARVEY INGRAM OWSTON
Church: Church of England, Social Housing

HASTIES
Licensing

HATCH BRENNER
Crime

HAWLEY & RODGERS
Crime

HAY & KILNER
Clinical Negligence: Mainly Claimant, Family/Matrimonial, Litigation (Commercial), Personal Injury: Mainly Claimant, Personal Injury: Mainly Defendant, Professional Negligence

HBM SAYERS
Crime, Insurance, Personal Injury: Mainly Defendant

HEGARTY & CO
Crime

HEMPSONS
Clinical Negligence: Mainly Defendant, **Healthcare**, **Partnership: Medical**

HENDERSON BOYD JACKSON WS
Debt Recovery, **Shipping**, Social Housing, Sport

HENMANS
Agriculture, Charities, Employment, Family/Matrimonial, Personal Injury: Mainly Claimant, Personal Injury: Mainly Defendant, **Professional Negligence**, Trusts & Personal Tax

HENRY HYAMS & CO
Crime

HENRY MILNER & CO
Crime

HEPTONSTALLS
Clinical Negligence: Mainly Claimant

HERBERT SMITH
Administrative & Public Law: Commercial, Arbitration (International), **Competition/Anti-trust**, Construction, Corporate Finance: 60+ Solicitors in Corporate Team, Employee Share Schemes, **Energy & Natural Resources**, **Fraud: Civil**, Insurance: Non-contentious, Intellectual Property: General, Intellectual Property: Patent, Investment Funds, **Litigation (Commercial): 40+ Litigators**, Litigation (Property), Partnership, **Partnership: Large International Mergers**, Planning, Professional Negligence: Financial, Professional Negligence: Legal, Property (Commercial): 100+ Fee-Earners

HEWITSON BECKE + SHAW
Agriculture, Charities, Construction, **Corporate Finance**, **Debt Recovery**, **Employment**, Environment, Information Technology, **Intellectual Property**, Litigation (Commercial), **Pensions**, Planning, Property (Commercial), **Trusts & Personal Tax**

HEXTALL ERSKINE
Personal Injury: Mainly Defendant, Professional Negligence: Construction

HICKMAN & ROSE
Crime

HIGGS & SONS
Employment, Trusts & Personal Tax

HILL DICKINSON
Church: Other Denominations, Clinical Negligence: Mainly Defendant, Health & Safety, Healthcare, Intellectual Property, Partnership, Personal Injury: Mainly Defendant, Professional Negligence, **Shipping**, **Shipping: Wet**, **Transport: Road - Carriage/Commercial**

HILL TAYLOR DICKINSON
Commodities: Physicals, Shipping, Shipping: Wet

HODGE JONES & ALLEN
Crime, Product Liability: Mainly Claimant

HOLLINGWORTH BISSELL
Transport: Rail

HOLMAN FENWICK & WILLAN
Insurance: Reinsurance, **Shipping**, **Shipping: Wet**

HOLMES HARDINGHAM
Transport: Road - Carriage/Commercial

HOOPER & WOLLEN
Family/Matrimonial

HOWARTH GOODMAN
Social Housing

HOWELLS
Crime, **Human Rights (Civil Liberties)**, **Immigration**

HOWES PERCIVAL
Licensing, Trusts & Personal Tax

HUGH JAMES FORD SIMEY
Church: Other Denominations, Clinical Negligence: Mainly Claimant, Construction, **Family/Matrimonial**, Health & Safety, Insolvency/Corporate Recovery, **Litigation (Commercial)**, **Litigation (Property)**, **Personal Injury: Mainly Claimant**, **Personal Injury: Mainly Defendant**, **Social Housing**, Trusts & Personal Tax

HUMPHREYS & CO
Intellectual Property

HUNT & COOMBS
Crime, **Family/Matrimonial**

HUTTONS
Clinical Negligence: Mainly Claimant, **Crime**, Fraud: Criminal

I

IAIN SMITH & COMPANY
Family/Matrimonial, Insolvency/Corporate Recovery

IAN DOWNING FAMILY LAW PRACTICE
Family/Matrimonial

ILIFFES BOOTH BENNETT
Charities, Family/Matrimonial, Property (Commercial), Trusts & Personal Tax

INCE & CO
Insurance: General Claims, Insurance: Reinsurance, **Shipping**, **Shipping: Wet**

IRWIN MITCHELL
Administrative & Public Law: General, Charities, **Clinical Negligence: Mainly Claimant**, Crime, Family/Matrimonial, Fraud: Criminal, Human Rights (Civil Liberties), Litigation (Commercial), **Personal Injury: Mainly Claimant**, Personal Injury: Mainly Defendant, **Product Liability**, Professional Negligence, Social Housing, Travel

J

JACKSON & CANTER
Immigration

JACKSONS
Personal Injury: Mainly Defendant

JAMES & CO
Immigration

JAMES CHAPMAN & CO
Personal Injury: Mainly Defendant, **Professional Negligence**, **Sport**

JAMESON & HILL
Planning

J.B. WHEATLEY & CO
Crime

JEFFREY GREEN RUSSELL
Debt Recovery, **Licensing**

JENKINS & HAND
Social Housing

J.J. RICE
Crime

JOELSON WILSON & CO
Licensing

JOHN BOYLE AND CO
Crime

JOHN COLLINS & PARTNERS
Clinical Negligence: Mainly Claimant, Debt Recovery

JOHN FORD MORRISON
Education: Individuals

JOHN GAUNT & PARTNERS
Licensing

JOHN HODGE & CO
Clinical Negligence: Mainly Claimant

JOHN MCKEE & SON
Debt Recovery, Insolvency/Corporate Recovery

JOHN PICKERING & PARTNERS
Personal Injury: Mainly Claimant

JOHN WESTON & CO
Shipping, Transport: Road - Carriage/Commercial

JOHNS ELLIOT
Construction, Litigation (Commercial), Property (Commercial), Trusts & Personal Tax

JOHNSONS
Defamation, Litigation (Commercial)

JONES & CASSIDY
Employment

JONES MAIDMENT WILSON
Clinical Negligence: Mainly Claimant, Crime, Family/Matrimonial

JONES MYERS GORDON
Family/Matrimonial

JOY MERRIAM & CO
Crime

K

KENNEDYS
Construction, Insurance: General Claims, Personal Injury: Mainly Defendant, **Professional Negligence: Construction**

KENNETH BUSH
Licensing

KENNETH CURTIS & CO
Licensing

KENT JONES AND DONE
Energy & Natural Resources, Environment, Media & Entertainment

KEOGHS
Insurance, **Personal Injury: Mainly Defendant**, Professional Negligence

KERSHAW ABBOTT
Partnership

KIDSTONS & CO
Employment

KIERAN & CO
Crime

KIMBELL & CO
Corporate Finance

KINGSFORD STACEY BLACKWELL
Licensing

KINGSLEY NAPLEY
Clinical Negligence: Mainly Claimant, **Crime**, Fraud: Civil, **Fraud: Criminal**, **Immigration: Business**, **Partnership**

KIRK JACKSON
Construction

KNIGHT & SONS
Agriculture, Energy & Natural Resources

KNIGHTS
Administrative & Public Law: General

L

LAMPORT BASSITT
Licensing, Personal Injury: Mainly Claimant

LANE & PARTNERS
Aviation: Regulatory, Travel

FIRMS AT A GLANCE

These lists show the key strengths of an individual firm. Please note: they only list the areas of practice for which a firm is ranked in bands 1-3 of the tables. Bold type indicates the areas of law in which the firm is ranked in 'band one'.

LANYON BOWDLER
Family/Matrimonial

LARBY WILLIAMS
Family/Matrimonial

LARCOMES
Church: Other Denominations

LATIMER HINKS
Agriculture

LAWFORD KIDD
Clinical Negligence: Mainly Claimant, Personal Injury: Mainly Claimant

LAWFORDS
Education: Institutions

LAWRENCE GRAHAM
Corporate Finance: Fewer than 30 Solicitors in Corporate Team, Environment, Litigation (Commercial): Fewer than 40 Litigators, Litigation (Property), Local Government, Trusts & Personal Tax

LAYTONS
Construction, Family/Matrimonial, Information Technology, Insolvency/Corporate Recovery, Intellectual Property, Litigation (Commercial)

LE BRASSEUR J TICKLE
Clinical Negligence: Mainly Defendant, Healthcare

LEA & COMPANY
Media & Entertainment

LEATHES PRIOR
Charities, **Immigration**, Personal Injury: Mainly Claimant

LEDINGHAM CHALMERS
Energy: Oil and Gas, Trusts & Personal Tax

LEE & PEMBERTONS
Agriculture

LEE & PRIESTLEY
Family/Matrimonial

LEE & THOMPSON
Media & Entertainment: Film & TV Production, Media & Entertainment: Music

LEE BOLTON & LEE
Church: Church of England, Education: Institutions

LEE CROWDER
Charities, Property (Commercial), Social Housing, Trusts & Personal Tax

LEES LLOYD WHITLEY
Debt Recovery

LEIGH, DAY & CO
Administrative & Public Law: Traditional, **Clinical Negligence: Mainly Claimant**, **Environment**, Personal Injury: Mainly Claimant, **Product Liability: Mainly Claimant**

LEO ABSE & COHEN
Family/Matrimonial, **Personal Injury: Mainly Claimant**

LEONARD GRAY
Family/Matrimonial

LÉONIE COWEN & ASSOCIATES
Local Government

LESTER ALDRIDGE
Asset Finance & Leasing, **Asset Finance & Leasing: Consumer Finance**, Charities, Debt Recovery, **Family/Matrimonial**, Health & Safety, Information Technology, Insolvency/Corporate Recovery, Intellectual Property, Licensing, **Partnership**, Planning, Property (Commercial)

L'ESTRANGE & BRETT
Banking, **Construction**, **Corporate Finance**, Employment, **Litigation (Commercial)**, **Partnership**, **Property (Commercial)**, **Trusts & Personal Tax**

LEVI & CO
Crime

LEVISON MELTZER PIGOTT
Family/Matrimonial

LEVY & MCRAE
Crime, **Defamation**, Media & Entertainment, Personal Injury: Mainly Claimant

LEWIS SILKIN
Advertising & Marketing, Social Housing

LG WILLIAMS & PRICHARD
Church: Other Denominations

LINDER MYERS
Clinical Negligence: Mainly Claimant

LINDSAYS WS
Administrative & Public Law: General, Agriculture, Charities, Licensing

LINKLATERS
Aviation: Regulatory, Banking, Capital Markets: Derivatives, **Capital Markets: International Debt & Equity**, Capital Markets: Securitisation & Repackaging, Commodities: Futures, **Competition/Anti-trust**, **Corporate Finance: 60+ Solicitors in Corporate Team**, **Employee Share Schemes**, Energy & Natural Resources, Environment, **Financial Services**, **Fraud: Civil**, Insolvency/Corporate Recovery, Insurance: Non-contentious, Intellectual Property: General, Intellectual Property: Patent, **Investment Funds**, Litigation (Commercial): 40+ Litigators, Litigation (Property), Partnership: Large International Mergers, **Pensions**, Pensions Litigation, Projects/PFI, **Property (Commercial): 100+ Fee-Earners**, Tax (Corporate), Telecommunications, Transport: Rail, Travel: Hotels & Leisure

LINNELLS
Charities, **Construction**, Family/Matrimonial, **Immigration**, **Partnership**

LIVINGSTONE BROWNE
Crime

LOCHNERS TECHNOLOGY SOLICITORS
Intellectual Property

LODDERS
Trusts & Personal Tax

LOOSEMORES
Personal Injury: Mainly Claimant

LOUDONS WS
Family/Matrimonial

LOVELLS
Administrative & Public Law: Commercial, Banking, Competition/Anti-trust, Corporate Finance: Debt, Corporate Finance: Equity, Employment: Mainly Respondent, **Fraud: Civil**, Information Technology, Insolvency/Corporate Recovery, **Insurance: Non-contentious**, Intellectual Property: General, Intellectual Property: Patent, Litigation (Commercial): 40+ Litigators, Litigation (Property), Media & Entertainment: Publishing, **Parliamentary: Public Affairs**, Pensions, **Pensions Litigation**, Product Liability: Mainly Defendant, Professional Negligence: Financial, Professional Negligence: Legal, Property (Commercial): 100+ Fee-Earners, Travel: Hotels & Leisure

LOXLEYS
Licensing

LUCAS & WYLLYS
Crime

LUPTON FAWCETT
Debt Recovery, Intellectual Property, Licensing, Litigation (Commercial)

LUQMANI THOMPSON
Immigration: Personal

LYONS DAVIDSON
Environment, Health & Safety, **Personal Injury: Mainly Claimant**

M

MACDONALDS
Debt Recovery

MACE & JONES
Employment, Partnership, Partnership: Medical

MACFARLANES
Advertising & Marketing, **Agriculture**, **Corporate Finance: 30-60 Solicitors in Corporate Team**, Investment Funds, **Trusts & Personal Tax**

MACKAY SIMON
Employment

MACKINNONS
Shipping

MACKINTOSH DUNCAN
Administrative & Public Law: Traditional

MACLAY MURRAY & SPENS
Aviation, **Banking**, **Competition/Anti-trust**, Corporate Finance, Education: Institutions, Financial Services, **Information Technology**, Insolvency/Corporate Recovery, **Intellectual Property**, Investment Funds, Litigation (Commercial), **Litigation (Property)**, Partnership, Pensions, Projects/PFI, Property (Commercial), **Shipping**, Tax (Corporate), Trusts & Personal Tax

MACROBERTS
Charities, **Competition/Anti-trust**, **Construction**, **Employee Share Schemes**, **Employment**, **Energy: Electricity**, Information Technology, Insolvency/Corporate Recovery, Intellectual Property, Litigation (Commercial), **Projects/PFI**, Tax (Corporate), Trusts & Personal Tax

MADDEN & FINUCANE
Administrative & Public Law: General, **Crime**

MADGE LLOYD & GIBSON
Church: Church of England

MAGRATH & CO
Crime, Immigration: Business

MAIDMENTS
Crime

MANBY & STEWARD
Church: Church of England

MANCHES
Charities, Corporate Finance, **Family/Matrimonial**, Information Technology, Media & Entertainment, Property (Commercial): Fewer than 100 Fee-Earners

MARGETTS & RITCHIE
Food

MARGRAVES
Agriculture, Trusts & Personal Tax

MARRONS
Personal Injury: Mainly Claimant, **Planning**

MARTINEAU JOHNSON
Administrative & Public Law: General, Agriculture, Banking, **Charities**, Church: Church of England, **Education: Institutions**, Employment, **Energy & Natural Resources**, Insolvency/Corporate Recovery, Intellectual Property, Litigation (Commercial), **Trusts & Personal Tax**

MARTYN PROWEL SOLICITORS
Crime, **Family/Matrimonial**, **Fraud: Criminal**

MASON & MOORE DUTTON
Agriculture

MASON BOND
Travel

MASONS
Construction, Environment, Health & Safety, **Information Technology**, Local Government, **Projects/PFI**

MATTHEW ARNOLD & BALDWIN
Debt Recovery

MAX BARFORD & CO
Family/Matrimonial

MAX BITEL, GREENE
Sport

MAXWELL BATLEY
Property (Commercial): Fewer than 100 Fee-Earners

MAY, MAY & MERRIMANS
Agriculture

MCCANN & GREYSTON
Licensing

MCCLENAHAN CROSSEY & CO
Crime

MCCLURE NAISMITH
Asset Finance & Leasing, Asset Finance & Leasing: Consumer Finance, **Debt Recovery**, Employment, Projects/PFI

MCCORMACKS
Crime

MCCORMICKS
Fraud: Criminal, **Media & Entertainment**, **Sport**

MCCOURTS
Crime

M C DARLINGTON
Church: Church of England

MCGRATH & CO
Human Rights (Civil Liberties), Immigration

MCGRIGOR DONALD
Administrative & Public Law: General, Banking, Construction, Corporate Finance, Employment, Energy: Electricity, Financial Services, Information Technology, **Intellectual Property**, Investment Funds, Licensing, **Litigation (Commercial)**, Litigation (Property), **Local Government**, Media & Entertainment, Partnership, Pensions, Planning, **Product Liability**, Projects/PFI, **Property (Commercial)**, **Tax (Corporate)**

MCKAY & NORWELL WS
Crime

MCKENZIE BELL
Licensing

MCKINTY & WRIGHT
Construction, Debt Recovery, **Defamation**, Litigation (Commercial), **Personal Injury: Mainly Defendant**, **Product Liability**, Property (Commercial)

MCMANUS & KEARNEY
Insolvency/Corporate Recovery

MEMERY CRYSTAL
Corporate Finance: Fewer than 30 Solicitors in Corporate Team

MERRICKS
Personal Injury: Mainly Defendant, Professional Negligence

MICHELMORES
Church: Church of England, Education: Institutions, Property (Commercial)

MIDDLETON POTTS
Commodities: Physicals

MILES PRESTON & CO
Family/Matrimonial

MILLAR SHEARER & BLACK
Crime

MILLER HENDRY
Agriculture

MILLER SANDS
Family/Matrimonial

MILLS & CO
Shipping

MILLS & REEVE
Administrative & Public Law: General, **Agriculture**, Banking, **Charities**, Church: Church of England, **Clinical Negligence: Mainly Defendant**, **Construction**, **Corporate Finance**, **Education: Institutions**, **Employment**, **Environment**, **Family/Matrimonial**, **Healthcare**, Insolvency/Corporate Recovery, Intellectual Property, Licensing, **Litigation (Commercial)**, **Litigation (Property)**, **Local Government**, **Personal Injury: Mainly Defendant**, **Planning**, **Professional Negligence**, Projects/PFI, **Property (Commercial)**, Tax (Corporate), **Trusts & Personal Tax**

MILLS SELIG
Corporate Finance, **Defamation**, Litigation (Commercial), **Product Liability**, Property (Commercial)

MINCOFFS
Family/Matrimonial, Licensing

MOORE & BLATCH
Trusts & Personal Tax

MORE & CO
Crime

MORGAN COLE
Administrative & Public Law: General, **Agriculture**, Banking, **Competition/Anti-trust**, **Construction**, **Corporate Finance**, Debt Recovery, Education: Institutions, **Employment**, **Environment**,

These lists show the key strengths of an individual firm. Please note: they only list the areas of practice for which a firm is ranked in bands 1-3 of the tables. Bold type indicates the areas of law in which the firm is ranked in 'band one'.

Family/Matrimonial, Healthcare, Information Technology, Insolvency/Corporate Recovery, Intellectual Property, **Licensing**, **Litigation (Commercial)**, Litigation (Property), Local Government, **Media & Entertainment**, **Personal Injury: Mainly Defendant**, Planning, **Professional Negligence**, Projects/PFI, **Property (Commercial)**, Social Housing

MORGAN JONES & PETT
Clinical Negligence: Mainly Claimant, Personal Injury: Mainly Claimant

MORISON BISHOP
Debt Recovery, Environment, Litigation (Commercial), **Pensions**, Professional Negligence, Sport

MORTON FISHER
Agriculture, Family/Matrimonial

MORTON FRASER, SOLICITORS
Asset Finance & Leasing, Charities, Debt Recovery, Environment, Family/Matrimonial, Trusts & Personal Tax

MOWAT DEAN & CO WS
Family/Matrimonial

MUNDAYS
Corporate Finance, Franchising, **Partnership**

MURRAY BEITH MURRAY W.S.
Trusts & Personal Tax

MYER WOLFF & MANLEY
Crime

N

NABARRO NATHANSON
Administrative & Public Law: Traditional, Charities, Corporate Finance, Corporate Finance: 30-60 Solicitors in Corporate Team, **Energy & Natural Resources**, **Environment**, **Health & Safety**, **Information Technology**, Intellectual Property, Litigation (Commercial), Litigation (Commercial): Fewer than 40 Litigators, **Litigation (Property)**, **Local Government**, Pensions, **Pensions Litigation**, Personal Injury: Mainly Defendant, Planning, Property (Commercial): 100+ Fee-Earners

NAPIER & SONS
Insolvency/Corporate Recovery

NAPTHEN HOUGHTON CRAVEN
Agriculture

NEEDHAM & JAMES
Social Housing

NELSONS
Crime, **Family/Matrimonial**, **Fraud: Criminal**, Immigration, Personal Injury: Mainly Claimant

NESS GALLAGHER
Crime

NICHOLSON GRAHAM & JONES
Corporate Finance: Fewer than 30 Solicitors in Corporate Team, Litigation (Commercial): Fewer than 40 Litigators, Sport, Travel

NICOL, DENVIR & PURNELL
Family/Matrimonial

NOLAN MACLEOD
Debt Recovery

NORTON ROSE
Asset Finance & Leasing, **Aviation: Regulatory**, Banking, Capital Markets: Derivatives, Corporate Finance: 60+ Solicitors in Corporate Team, Corporate Finance: Debt, Energy & Natural Resources, Financial Services, **Fraud: Civil**, Investment Funds, Projects/PFI, **Shipping: Finance**, Travel, Travel: Hotels & Leisure

O

OFFENBACH & CO
Crime

OGLETHORPE STURTON & GILLIBRAND
Agriculture

OLSWANG
Corporate Finance: 30-60 Solicitors in Corporate Team, **Defamation**, **E-commerce**, Information Technology, **Media & Entertainment: Broadcasting**, **Media & Entertainment: Film & TV Production**, Media & Entertainment: Film Finance, Telecommunications

O'REILLY STEWART
Licensing, Personal Injury: Mainly Defendant, **Product Liability**

OSBORNE CLARKE OWA
Advertising & Marketing, **Banking**, Charities, **Corporate Finance**, **Corporate Finance: Fewer than 30 Solicitors in Corporate Team**, **Debt Recovery**, Employee Share Schemes, **Employment**, **Environment**, **Health & Safety**, **Information Technology**, **Insolvency/Corporate Recovery**, **Intellectual Property**, **Litigation (Commercial)**, Litigation (Property), Partnership, **Pensions**, Planning, **Property (Commercial)**, **Sport**, **Tax (Corporate)**, **Trusts & Personal Tax**

OSBORNE MORRIS & MORGAN
Clinical Negligence: Mainly Claimant, **Personal Injury: Mainly Claimant**

OSWALD GOODIER & CO
Charities, Church: Other Denominations

OVER TAYLOR BIGGS
Clinical Negligence: Mainly Claimant

OVERBURY STEWARD EATON & WOOLSEY
Crime

OWEN WHITE
Franchising, **Social Housing**

P

PAISNER & CO
Asset Finance & Leasing: Consumer Finance, Charities, **Corporate Finance: Fewer than 30 Solicitors in Corporate Team**, **Food**, **Licensing**, Travel: Hotels & Leisure

PALSER GROSSMAN
Litigation (Commercial), **Personal Injury: Mainly Defendant**, Property (Commercial)

PANNONE & PARTNERS
Charities, **Clinical Negligence: Mainly Claimant**, **Family/Matrimonial**, Fraud: Criminal, Litigation (Property), **Personal Injury: Mainly Claimant**, Trusts & Personal Tax

PARIS SMITH & RANDALL
Corporate Finance, Employment, Family/Matrimonial, Insolvency/Corporate Recovery, Property (Commercial), Trusts & Personal Tax

PARKER & GREGO
Crime

PARLETT KENT
Clinical Negligence: Mainly Claimant

PATTINSON & BREWER
Employment, **Employment: Mainly Applicant**, Personal Injury: Mainly Claimant

PAULL & WILLIAMSONS
Employment, **Energy: Oil and Gas**, Personal Injury: Mainly Defendant

PAYNE HICKS BEACH
Agriculture

PAYNE MARSH STILLWELL
Partnership: Medical

PEDEN & REID
Family/Matrimonial

PENNINGTONS
Clinical Negligence: Mainly Claimant

PETER CARTER-RUCK AND PARTNERS
Defamation

PETER MAUGHAN & CO
Clinical Negligence: Mainly Claimant

PETERS & PETERS
Fraud: Civil, **Fraud: Criminal**

PINSENT CURTIS
Administrative & Public Law (Leeds), **Administrative & Public Law: General (Birmingham)**, **Banking (Birmingham)**, **Competition/Anti-trust (Birmingham)**, Competition/Anti-trust (Leeds), Corporate Finance (Birmingham, London), Education (Leeds), **Employee Share Schemes (Birmingham, Leeds)**, **Employment (Leeds)**, Employment (Birmingham), Energy & Natural Resources (Birmingham, Leeds), **Environment (Birmingham)**, **Financial Services (Birmingham)**, Franchising (Birmingham), Information Technology (Birmingham), Insolvency/Corporate Recovery (Leeds), **Intellectual Property (Leeds)**, Intellectual Property (Birmingham), **Litigation (Commercial) (Birmingham, Leeds)**, **Litigation (Property) (Leeds)**, Litigation (Property) (Birmingham), Local Government (Birmingham, Leeds), **Partnership (Birmingham)**, Pensions (Birmingham, Leeds), Planning (Birmingham), Professional Negligence (Birmingham, London), **Projects/PFI (Birmingham, Leeds)**, Property (Commercial) (Birmingham, Leeds), **Tax (Corporate) (Birmingham, Leeds)**, Trusts & Personal Tax (Birmingham, Leeds)

PITMANS
Corporate Finance, Insolvency/Corporate Recovery, **Planning**, **Property (Commercial)**

POPPLESTON ALLEN
Licensing

POTHECARY & BARRATT
Church: Other Denominations

POWELL & CO
Immigration: Personal

POWELL SPENCER & PARTNERS
Crime

PRAXIS PARTNERS
Personal Injury: Mainly Defendant

PRESTON GOLDBURN
Clinical Negligence: Mainly Claimant

PRETTYS
Clinical Negligence: Mainly Claimant, Corporate Finance, Debt Recovery, Insolvency/Corporate Recovery, Litigation (Commercial), Personal Injury: Mainly Defendant

PRYCE COLLARD CHAMBERLAIN
Agriculture

PULLIG & CO
Licensing

PURCELL PARKER
Crime

R

R. & J.M. HILL BROWN & CO
Licensing

RAEBURN CHRISTIE & CO
Employment

RAMSBOTTOM & CO
Media & Entertainment

RAWLISON & BUTLER
Corporate Finance, **Partnership**

RAYFIELD MILLS
Shipping, **Shipping: Wet**

REES & FRERES
Parliamentary Agency

REES PAGE
Crime

REYNOLDS PORTER CHAMBERLAIN
Defamation, Insurance: General Claims, Litigation (Commercial): Fewer than 40 Litigators, Partnership, Professional Negligence: Construction, **Professional Negligence: Financial**, Professional Negligence: Insurance, **Professional Negligence: Legal**

RICHARD BUXTON
Administrative & Public Law: General, **Environment**

RICHARD MONTEITH
Crime

RICHARDS BUTLER
Commodities: Futures, **Commodities: Physicals**, Corporate Finance: Fewer than 30 Solicitors in Corporate Team, Fraud: Civil, **Licensing**, Media & Entertainment: Broadcasting, Media & Entertainment: Film Finance, Shipping, Travel: Hotels & Leisure

RICKERBY WATTERSON
Education: Institutions

RIDLEY & HALL
Education: Individuals

R.M. BROUDIE & CO
Crime

ROBERT LIZAR
Human Rights (Civil Liberties)

ROBERT MUCKLE
Banking, Construction, Insolvency/Corporate Recovery, Litigation (Commercial), Property (Commercial)

ROBERTSONS
Crime, Family/Matrimonial

ROBSON MCLEAN WS
Partnership

RODGERS HORSLEY WHITEMANS
Church: Other Denominations, **Partnership**

ROEBUCKS
Church: Church of England

ROLLIT FARRELL & BLADON
Agriculture, Litigation (Commercial), **Social Housing**

ROSS HARPER & MURPHY WS
Crime

ROTHERA DOWSON
Church: Church of England

ROWE & MAW
Administrative & Public Law: Traditional, Construction, **Corporate Finance: 30-60 Solicitors in Corporate Team**, Employment: Mainly Respondent, Local Government, **Partnership**, **Partnership: Large International Mergers**, **Pensions**, Pensions Litigation, **Professional Negligence: Construction**, Professional Negligence: Financial, **Travel: Timeshare**

ROWLEY ASHWORTH
Employment: Mainly Applicant, **Personal Injury: Mainly Claimant**

ROYTHORNE & CO
Agriculture

RUPERT BEAR MURRAY DAVIES
Family/Matrimonial

RUSSELL & RUSSELL
Crime

RUSSELL JONES & WALKER
Clinical Negligence: Mainly Claimant, Crime, Employment: Mainly Applicant, Fraud: Criminal, **Personal Injury: Mainly Claimant**

RUSSELL-COOKE, POTTER & CHAPMAN
Crime

RUSSELLS
Media & Entertainment: Music

RUSSELLS GIBSON MCCAFFREY
Family/Matrimonial

S

SACKER & PARTNERS
Pensions, **Pensions Litigation**

SALANS HERTZFELD & HEILBRONN HRK
Asset Finance & Leasing: Consumer Finance, Debt Recovery

SAMUEL PHILLIPS & CO
Clinical Negligence: Mainly Defendant, Family/Matrimonial, Immigration

SAUNDERS & CO
Crime

SCHILLING & LOM AND PARTNERS
Defamation

SCRIVENGER SEABROOK
Clinical Negligence: Mainly Defendant

SEARS TOOTH
Family/Matrimonial

SEMPLE FRASER WS
Litigation (Property), Property (Commercial)

SHADBOLT & CO
Construction, Corporate Finance

SHAKESPEARES
Charities, Debt Recovery, Education: Institutions, Trusts & Personal Tax

FIRMS AT A GLANCE

These lists show the key strengths of an individual firm. Please note: they only list the areas of practice for which a firm is ranked in bands 1-3 of the tables. Bold type indicates the areas of law in which the firm is ranked in 'band one'.

SHARPE PRITCHARD
Administrative & Public Law: Traditional, Local Government, Parliamentary Agency

SHEAN DICKSON MERRICK
Licensing

SHEARMAN & STERLING
Corporate Finance: US firms acting from London

SHEPHERD & WEDDERBURN WS
Administrative & Public Law: General, **Aviation**, Banking, Charities, **Clinical Negligence: Mainly Defendant**, **Competition/Anti-trust**, Corporate Finance, Employment, **Energy: Electricity**, Financial Services, Information Technology, Insolvency/Corporate Recovery, Intellectual Property, Investment Funds, Litigation (Commercial), Litigation (Property), **Local Government**, **Pensions**, Projects/PFI, Property (Commercial), Social Housing

SHERWIN OLIVER SOLICITORS
Insolvency/Corporate Recovery, Property (Commercial)

SHOOSMITHS
Corporate Finance, **Debt Recovery**, **Food**, Litigation (Commercial), **Personal Injury: Mainly Claimant**, Planning

SHORT RICHARDSON & FORTH
Employment

SILKS
Crime

SILVER FITZGERALD
Family/Matrimonial

SIMMONS & SIMMONS
Administrative & Public Law: Commercial, Commodities: Futures, **Employment: Mainly Respondent**, **Environment**, Financial Services, Food, Fraud: Civil, Health & Safety, Intellectual Property: General, Intellectual Property: Patent, Investment Funds, Telecommunications, Transport: Rail

SIMONS MUIRHEAD & BURTON
Crime, Fraud: Criminal

SIMPSON & MARWICK WS
Administrative & Public Law: General, Aviation, **Insurance**, Litigation (Commercial), Local Government, **Personal Injury: Mainly Defendant**, **Product Liability**, **Professional Negligence**

SINCLAIR ROCHE & TEMPERLEY
Corporate Finance: Fewer than 30 Solicitors in Corporate Team

SINCLAIR TAYLOR & MARTIN
Charities

SINTON & CO
Family/Matrimonial, Personal Injury: Mainly Defendant

SJ BERWIN & CO
Competition/Anti-trust, Corporate Finance: 30-60 Solicitors in Corporate Team, Financial Services, **Litigation (Commercial): Fewer than 40 Litigators**, Media & Entertainment: Film & TV Production, **Media & Entertainment: Film Finance**, **Parliamentary: Public Affairs**, Planning, Sport, **Travel: Hotels & Leisure**

SJ CORNISH
Professional Negligence

SJ DIAMOND & SON
Debt Recovery, Personal Injury: Mainly Claimant

SKADDEN, ARPS, SLATE, MEAGHER & FLOM LLP
Corporate Finance: US firms acting from London

SKENE EDWARDS WS
Social Housing

SLAUGHTER AND MAY
Asset Finance & Leasing, Banking, **Competition/Anti-trust**, **Corporate Finance: 60+ Solicitors in Corporate Team**, Employee Share Schemes, Fraud: Civil, Insurance: Non-contentious, Partnership: Large International Mergers, Pensions, **Tax (Corporate)**

SMITH LLEWELYN PARTNERSHIP
Clinical Negligence: Mainly Claimant, Personal Injury: Mainly Claimant

SPEECHLY BIRCHAM
Property (Commercial): Fewer than 100 Fee-Earners

SPIRO GRECH & CO
Crime

STAMP JACKSON AND PROCTER
Agriculture, Clinical Negligence: Mainly Claimant

STANLEY TEE & COMPANY
Agriculture

STEEDMAN RAMAGE WS
Litigation (Property), Property (Commercial)

STEELE & CO
Employment, Licensing, **Local Government**

STEPHENS & SCOWN
Administrative & Public Law: General, Agriculture, Crime, Environment, Family/Matrimonial, Licensing, Planning

STEPHENSON HARWOOD
Fraud: Civil, **Litigation (Commercial): Fewer than 40 Litigators**, Shipping: Finance

STEPHENSONS
Family/Matrimonial

STEPIEN LAKE GILBERT & PALING
Property (Commercial): Fewer than 100 Fee-Earners

STEVENS & BOLTON
Corporate Finance, Employment, **Environment**, Property (Commercial), Trusts & Personal Tax

STONE KING
Charities, **Church: Other Denominations**, Education: Institutions

STONES
Crime, Licensing, Sport, Travel, Travel: Timeshare

STURTIVANT & CO
Immigration: Business

SUGARÉ & CO
Crime

T

TARLO LYONS
Media & Entertainment: Theatre

TAYLOR JOYNSON GARRETT
Food, Information Technology, Intellectual Property: General, Intellectual Property: Patent, Media & Entertainment: Publishing

TAYLOR NICHOL
Crime

TAYLOR VINTERS
Agriculture, **Charities**, **Corporate Finance**, Employment, Insolvency/Corporate Recovery, Litigation (Commercial), Personal Injury: Mainly Claimant, Planning, Property (Commercial), Trusts & Personal Tax

TC YOUNG & SON
Charities, Social Housing

TEACHER STERN SELBY
Administrative & Public Law: Traditional, **Education: Individuals**

THANKI NOVY TAUBE
Crime

THE BERKSON GLOBE PARTNERSHIP
Crime

THE JOHNSON PARTNERSHIP
Crime

THE LAW OFFICES OF MARCUS J. O'LEARY
Information Technology, **Intellectual Property**

THE MAX GOLD PARTNERSHIP
Crime

THE SIMKINS PARTNERSHIP
Advertising & Marketing, Media & Entertainment: Film & TV Production, Media & Entertainment: Theatre

THE SMITH PARTNERSHIP
Crime

THEODORE GODDARD
Defamation, Media & Entertainment: Film & TV Production, Product Liability: Mainly Defendant

THOMAS A. HIGGINS & CO
Debt Recovery

THOMAS EGGAR CHURCH ADAMS
Agriculture, **Charities**, **Church: Church of England**, Litigation (Commercial), Property (Commercial), **Trusts & Personal Tax**

THOMPSONS
Employment, Employment: Mainly Applicant, **Family/Matrimonial**, **Personal Injury: Mainly Claimant**

THOMSON SNELL & PASSMORE
Charities, **Clinical Negligence: Mainly Claimant**, Corporate Finance, Family/Matrimonial, Litigation (Property), Personal Injury: Mainly Claimant, **Professional Negligence**, Property (Commercial), Trusts & Personal Tax

THOMSON WEBB CORFIELD
Crime

THORNHILL INCE
Immigration

THORNTONS WS
Agriculture

TLT SOLICITORS
Corporate Finance, Debt Recovery, **Family/Matrimonial**, Litigation (Commercial), **Partnership**, Partnership: Medical, Planning, Property (Commercial), Trusts & Personal Tax

TODS MURRAY WS
Administrative & Public Law: General, Agriculture, Banking, Charities, Financial Services, **Investment Funds**, Local Government, **Media & Entertainment**, Pensions, Property (Commercial), **Travel: Timeshare**, Trusts & Personal Tax

TOWNLEYS
Sport

TOZERS
Charities, **Church: Other Denominations**, Clinical Negligence: Mainly Claimant, **Family/Matrimonial**

TRAVERS SMITH BRAITHWAITE
Corporate Finance: 30-60 Solicitors in Corporate Team, Litigation (Commercial): Fewer than 40 Litigators, Pensions

TRETHOWANS
Immigration, **Licensing**

TREVOR SMYTH & CO
Crime

TROWERS & HAMLINS
Local Government, Property (Commercial): Fewer than 100 Fee-Earners, **Social Housing**, Social Housing: Advising Lenders

TUCKERS
Crime

TUGHAN & CO
Construction, Corporate Finance, Litigation (Commercial), Personal Injury: Mainly Defendant, Property (Commercial)

TUNNARD CROSFIELD
Church: Church of England

TURBERVILLES WITH NELSON CUFF
Licensing

TURCAN CONNELL WS
Agriculture, **Charities**, **Trusts & Personal Tax**

TURNBULL, SIMSON & STURROCK WS
Agriculture

TV EDWARDS
Crime

TWITCHEN MUSTERS & KELLY
Crime

TYNDALLWOODS
Administrative & Public Law: General, Crime, **Family/Matrimonial**, **Human Rights (Civil Liberties)**, **Immigration**

U

UNDERWOODS
Employment

V

VARLEY HADLEY SIDDALL
Fraud: Criminal

VEALE WASBROUGH
Charities, **Education: Institutions**, Employment, Energy & Natural Resources, Environment, Health & Safety, Litigation (Commercial), **Partnership**, Partnership: Medical, **Personal Injury: Mainly Claimant**, Professional Negligence, Property (Commercial)

VEITCH PENNY
Personal Injury: Mainly Defendant

VENTERS REYNOLDS
Crime

VICTOR LISSACK & ROSCOE
Crime

VIZARDS, STAPLES & BANNISTERS
Personal Injury: Mainly Defendant

VOLKS HEDLEY
Travel: Timeshare

W

WACE MORGAN
Family/Matrimonial

WAKE DYNE LAWTON
Energy & Natural Resources, **Environment**, Planning, Transport: Road - Regulatory

WALKER CHARLESWORTH & FOSTER
Social Housing

WALKER LAIRD
Family/Matrimonial

WALKER MORRIS
Debt Recovery, Employee Share Schemes, Insolvency/Corporate Recovery, Intellectual Property, Litigation (Commercial), Litigation (Property), Pensions, Planning, Property (Commercial), Sport

WALKER SMITH & WAY
Agriculture

WALTONS & MORSE
Transport: Road - Carriage/Commercial

WARD GETHIN
Family/Matrimonial

WARD HADAWAY
Agriculture, Banking, Clinical Negligence: Mainly Defendant, Corporate Finance, Employment, Insolvency/Corporate Recovery, **Litigation (Commercial)**, Planning, Property (Commercial)

WARNER CRANSTON
Corporate Finance: Fewer than 30 Solicitors in Corporate Team, Debt Recovery, Immigration: Business

WARNER GOODMAN & STREAT
Personal Injury: Mainly Claimant

WATMORES
Personal Injury: Mainly Defendant

WATSON BURTON
Construction, Litigation (Commercial), Property (Commercial)

WATSON, FARLEY & WILLIAMS
Corporate Finance: Fewer than 30 Solicitors in Corporate Team, Shipping: Finance

WEDLAKE SAINT
Transport: Road - Regulatory

WEIGHTMANS
Health & Safety, Insurance, Licensing, **Personal Injury: Mainly Defendant**, **Professional Negligence**

WEIL, GOTSHAL & MANGES
Corporate Finance: US firms acting from London

WELLMAN & BROWN
Church: Church of England

WENDY HOPKINS & CO
Family/Matrimonial

These lists show the key strengths of an individual firm. Please note: they only list the areas of practice for which a firm is ranked in bands 1-3 of the tables. Bold type indicates the areas of law in which the firm is ranked in 'band one'.

WESLEY GRYK
Immigration: Personal

WHITE & BOWKER
Agriculture, Church: Church of England

WHITELOCK & STORR
Crime

WHITTLES
Employment, Personal Injury: Mainly Claimant

WIGGIN & CO
Defamation, **Media & Entertainment**, Media & Entertainment: Broadcasting, Tax (Corporate), **Trusts & Personal Tax**

WILBRAHAM & CO
Planning

WILDE & PARTNERS
Debt Recovery

WILLOUGHBY & PARTNERS
Information Technology, **Intellectual Property**, Intellectual Property: General

WILSON NESBITT
Family/Matrimonial

WILSONS
Agriculture, Charities, **Trusts & Personal Tax**

WINCKWORTH SHERWOOD
Charities, **Church: Church of England**, Education: Institutions, **Parliamentary Agency**, Social Housing

WINSTANLEY-BURGESS
Immigration: Personal

WITHERS
Agriculture, Charities, **Family/Matrimonial**, Trusts & Personal Tax

WITHY KING
Clinical Negligence: Mainly Claimant

WOLFERSTANS
Clinical Negligence: Mainly Claimant, Crime, **Family/Matrimonial**, Fraud: Criminal, Personal Injury: Mainly Claimant

WOLLASTONS
Immigration

WOODFORD-ROBINSON
Crime

WOOLLCOMBE BEER WATTS
Clinical Negligence: Mainly Claimant, Crime

WRAGGE & CO
Banking, **Charities**, **Competition/Anti-trust**, **Construction**, **Corporate Finance**, **Debt Recovery**, Education: Institutions, Employee Share Schemes, **Employment**, **Energy & Natural Resources**, **Environment**, Financial Services, Franchising, **Information Technology**, Insolvency/Corporate Recovery, **Intellectual Property**, Intellectual Property: Patent, **Litigation (Commercial)**, **Litigation (Property)**, **Local Government**, **Pensions**, Planning, Professional Negligence, Projects/PFI, **Property (Commercial)**, **Tax (Corporate)**, Trusts & Personal Tax

WRIGHT HASSALL
Agriculture, Social Housing

WRIGHT, JOHNSTON & MACKENZIE
Media & Entertainment

WRIGLEYS
Agriculture, **Charities**, Employee Share Schemes, Energy & Natural Resources, Pensions, **Trusts & Personal Tax**

Y

YOUNG & LEE
Education: Individuals, Family/Matrimonial

YOUNG & PEARCE
Licensing

YUILL & KYLE
Debt Recovery

Z

ZERMANSKY & PARTNERS
Family/Matrimonial

THE LAW FIRMS

ADMINISTRATIVE & PUBLIC LAW

London 51; The South: 54; South West: 54; Wales: 55; Midlands: 55; East Anglia: 56; The North: 56; Scotland: 57; Northern Ireland: 57; *Profiles*: 58

OVERVIEW: Administrative and public law covers advice to public bodies and challenges to the decisions of public bodies by means of judicial review (JR) or statutory appeals. It is a process rather than a subject.

The major development of 2000 is expected to be the incorporation of the European Convention on Human Rights into English law (The Human Rights Act) in October 2000. This is set to lead to a large increase in the amount of public law challenges and judicial reviews that are brought and will affect firms acting for regulatory and commercial clients as well as traditional civil liberties applicant practices. Already, solicitors are attempting to develop strategies and bring their organisations up to date on the implications of the changes in anticipation of a boom in related work.

In London, we continue with the broad distinction between traditional public law firms and the commercial regulatory/judicial review section (renamed slightly to reflect a general upturn in the level of regulatory challenges.) The former embraces public law practices in firms active in a variety of sectors including local authority, health, education, immigration, community care and housing. The commercial section attempts to profile the leading firms acting for prominent regulatory as well as commercial clients. The distinction is not made in the regions where inevitably there will be a degree of overlap.

RESEARCH APPROVED BY BMRB: *For this edition,* Chambers' *researchers conducted 6083 interviews – 4408 with law firms, 598 with barristers and 1077 with clients.*

The validity of the research was scrutinised by BMRB International, who audited both the methodology and the results at our offices in July 2000. They interviewed Chambers' *researchers and cross-checked sample interviews. Details of the audit appear on page 7.*

LONDON

TRADITIONAL PUBLIC LAW FIRMS

ADMINISTRATIVE & PUBLIC LAW: TRADITIONAL • London	Ptnrs	Assts
❶ Bindman & Partners	6	4
❷ Bates, Wells & Braithwaite	2	3
Leigh, Day & Co	1	2
Nabarro Nathanson	2	2
Rowe & Maw	2	8
❸ David Levene & Co	1	2
Mackintosh Duncan	2	1
Sharpe Pritchard	4	4
Teacher Stern Selby	1	2
❹ Anthony Gold, Lerman & Muirhead	1	6
Beachcroft Wansbroughs	3	2
Winckworth Sherwood	5	–
Winstanley-Burgess	3	2

LEADING INDIVIDUALS	
❶ **CHILD Tony** Rowe & Maw	**GROSZ Stephen** Bindman & Partners
RABINOWICZ Jack Teacher Stern Selby	**RUEBAIN David** David Levene & Co
STEIN Richard Leigh, Day & Co	
❷ **AMBROSE Ray** Nabarro Nathanson	**BINDMAN Geoffrey** Bindman & Partners
BURGESS David Winstanley-Burgess	**DAY Martyn** Leigh, Day & Co
MACKINTOSH Nicola Mackintosh Duncan	
TROTTER John Bates, Wells & Braithwaite	
❸ **GRIFFITHS Trevor** Sharpe Pritchard	**ILEY Malcolm** Nabarro Nathanson
UP AND COMING	
SCHWEHR Belinda Rowe & Maw	**SILAS Douglas** David Levene & Co

Within each band, firms are listed alphabetically. *See* ***Profiles*** *on page 58*

Bindman & Partners This human rights-driven practice retains the lead position in our rankings again *("definitely right at the top")* after a successful year in which the high profile Pinochet case dominated the judicial review landscape. Despite advancing years, **Geoffrey Bindman** has *"retained a radical edge"* and is still considered the *"numero uno – the doyen of his field."* He fronted the Pinochet case, acting for Amnesty International while hands-on partner **Stephen Grosz** *("strong on the interplay between human rights and public law,")* continues to build his reputation as heir apparent. Praised for an *"innovative approach"* and *"strength across a range of departments,"* the firm continues to take on a mixture of judicial reviews. Strong on individually driven applicant challenges, these are fused with pure public law, touching on education, family, immigration and crime. Recently acted for two noise-affected Soho residents challenging the night-club licensing policies of Westminster City Council. **Clients:** Amnesty International; The Law Society.

Bates, Wells & Braithwaite With strengths in a number of key applicant areas, public and judicial review work at the firm feeds off established niches in immigration and charities. It has also branched out to include regulatory work and other public interest organisations. Litigation partner, the *"honest and efficient"* **John Trotter** is *"easy-going and good to work with"* and has amassed a healthy reputation in the public law field. Act for a variety of environmental and wildlife organisations. **Clients:** ICTIS; Environmental organisations.

Leigh Day & Co The department has earned promotion after a prominent year. Considered a *"crusading"* but highly respected and committed applicant firm, it is associated with work across several public law fields – including clinical negligence, environmental and community care. Involved in one of the biggest JR's of recent times – namely acting for Human Rights Watch and the Belgian government on separate issues relating to the Pinochet extradition and the release of his medical records. **Richard Stein** *("very punchy and pushes for his clients")* took the lead on this case and is considered to be an *"intuitive practitioner with a real feel for public law."* Other noted partner **Martyn Day** keeps a lower profile than his colleague, but has not escaped market attention himself. He has been involved in a number of major cases – most significantly on behalf of the plaintiffs in the tobacco litigation wars. **Clients:** Individual applicants; human rights organisations.

Nabarro Nathanson Praised by contemporaries as *"an exciting firm,"* it draws on related expertise in local government and planning, acting primarily for local authorities and public bodies in an advisory role. This often involves protecting their clients from potential JR challenges. **Ray Ambrose** *("a fine lawyer")* is recognised for his *"specialism in advising on local authority powers"* as well as judicial review. Able ex-local authority and public sector lawyer, **Malcom Iley** is regarded as *"more of a generalist,"* but focuses on PFI and housing. Recently completed a major audit case on behalf of a local authority defending allegations of an overpaid pension to an ex-council worker. **Clients:** Lewisham Council; Hackney Council; Islington Council; Denbighshire Council.

Rowe & Maw As head of the firm's dedicated public law group, former Audit Commissioner **Tony Child** continues to enjoy a high reputation for local authority audit work and a large client base. The firm's public law expertise has, however, witnessed a diversification in recent years from local authority audit and finance work. His approach and individual style is regarded as *"conservative"* but his *"knowledge and persistence"* are praised by commentators, as is his ability to *"tune in to the courts."* **Belinda Schwehr** enters the up and coming lists this year; she *"has arrived in community care and health work."* The firm continues to act for the auditor in the well-publicised Westminster Council 'homes for votes' case as it moves to the House of Lords appeal stage. Acting on behalf of Thorn UK Ltd in challenging the Finance Act 1997 which imposes higher rate insurance premium tax. Acted for the Zurich insurance company in a dispute with the Inland Revenue over whether anniversary gifts to staff would incur National Insurance payments. **Clients:** Local authority and NHS trust auditors; Northern Ireland local government auditors; Public and private community care and health service providers.

David Levene & Co Small high-street niche practice with a major public law dimension across the disability, education and community care spheres. Ex-local government man, **David Ruebain** is *"a tough cookie who won't suffer fools gladly."* Highly thought of by contemporaries, he is considered one of the *"top education and community care lawyers"* and *"has a sympathetic understanding of applicant needs."* Colleague **Douglas Silas** *("felt to be independently building up his own profile and reputation")* enters the up and coming rankings this year. He is especially noted for his track record in a number of education and care driven JRs. Acted for the British Deaf Association in a challenge to the Lord Chancellor concerning a refusal to allow deaf people to sit on juries. Also advised on R v Kent County Council ex p S – a child disability case which tested the extent to which local educational authorities could challenge the nature of provisions to disabled people. **Clients:** Public Concern At Work; Independent Panel for Special Educational Advice; Network 81.

Mackintosh Duncan Mentioned last year as one to watch, the firm has enjoyed a good year and some very visible cases, and enters the lists proper only 18 months after starting to trade. This small traditional public practice has particular expertise in health and community care issues and has conducted some high profile JRs, led by the *"energetic"* **Nicola Mackintosh**. Her own reputation has been enhanced through acting against the Legal Aid Board in a judicial review challenging the policy of allocation of new legal aid contracts. Within her fields of expertise – health and community care – she is *"undoubtedly an expert."* The team successfully challenged The North and East Devon Health Authority in the ex p Coughlan case over the responsibilities of the NHS to provide long-term non-acute care. **Clients:** Individual applicants.

Sharpe Pritchard Continues to be ranked on account of their prodigious work-rate and vast local authority client list. Considered to place heavy emphasis on a high volume of work at attractive rates, the *"effective"* **Trevor Griffiths** is *"extremely efficient, good at pinpointing the legal issues and serves his clients well."* Local authority work has included a range of injunction and planning cases as well as seeking to prevent a number of Millennium Parties. **Clients:** Several local authorities including West Dorset District Council.

Teacher Stern Selby Leading education applicant firm which continues to be well placed on account of its vast experience of statutory appeals and judicial proceedings. Regarded as one of the best special education needs lawyers around, **Jack Rabinowicz** is credited with developing the whole educational/public law sphere and bringing out issues such as bullying and stress. In praising his knowledge and commitment, one observer suggested that *"what he doesn't know isn't worth knowing!"* Beyond the niche educational backbone, other public law work has included reviewing a number of health authority decisions, and proceeding with both community care and social security judicial reviews. Recently acted for the families of a number of children involved in school exclusion disputes. **Clients:** Individual applicants.

Anthony Gold, Lerman & Muirhead Still active in bringing a number of challenges across the public field, usually with a housing, community care or social welfare dimension. The impact of the loss of previously ranked housing/public law department head Robin Levett in April 2000 has yet to be assessed, as new acquisitions have offset his departure. Recently brought a number of housing applications on behalf of the homeless, as well as cases involving asylum seekers' claims for welfare benefits. Advised on R v London Borough of Lambeth ex p Khan, a community care case which challenged the level of services a local authority is obliged to provide under community care legislation. **Clients:** Individual applicants.

Beachcroft Wansbroughs *"First rate!"* commented a London barrister on the *"huge amounts"* of administrative health authority and clinical negligence work carried out here. In the regulatory field, have achieved prominence with some major challenges and judicial reviews for large institutional clients in the public and health sector. Acted for the National Institute for Clinical Excellence (NICE) in Glaxo Wellcome's appeal against NICE's appraisal of the anti-flu drug, Relenza. Also acted for the Human Fertilisation & Embryology Authority in connection with the licensing of IVF treatment using frozen eggs. **Clients:** HM Land Registry; General Medical Council; Further Education Funding Council; Qualifications & Curriculum Authority.

Winckworth Sherwood Moved into the traditional public law section this year as a reflection of their strengths in a broad range of non-commercial public law areas. Well-rated by solicitors and barristers for housing, church and schools work. One barrister who worked with them on a City of London Corporation case felt they offered a *"good, professional service."* **Clients:** Local authorities.

Winstanley-Burgess Strong legal aid-driven immigration firm who enter the public law domain as a result of consistent judicial review turnover, much of it stemming from asylum applications. However, the firm is not felt to have sufficient breadth to be considered a definitive public law practice. Nevertheless, strength in depth amongst the immigration practitioners gives the firm a high quality reputation. Experienced partner **David Burgess** has taken on *"some testing and innovative cases,"* and is highly thought of as a *"long-standing immigration name."* Straddling public law, human rights and crime, he has carved out a niche offering expertise on national security cases. Recently involved in a major action against the Metropolitan Police, acting for eight different demonstrators challenging the robust conduct and tactics of the police during the recent visit of Chinese President Jiang Zemin. **Clients:** Individual applicants; asylum seekers.

COMMERCIAL REGULATORY / JUDICIAL REVIEW

ADMINISTRATIVE & PUBLIC LAW: COMMERCIAL • London	Ptnrs	Assts
❶ Herbert Smith	6	7
❷ Allen & Overy	3	4
Clifford Chance	4	9
❸ Lovells	12	7
Simmons & Simmons	6	8
❹ Denton Wilde Sapte	18	35
Freshfields Bruckhaus Deringer	6	10
Slaughter and May	3	-
Travers Smith Braithwaite	2	4
❺ CMS Cameron McKenna	6	9
Theodore Goddard	3	3
❻ Olswang	2	6

LEADING INDIVIDUALS
✪ LIDBETTER Andrew Herbert Smith
SMYTH Michael Clifford Chance
❶ MCDERMOTT Jennifer Lovells
WATSON Peter Allen & Overy
❷ BOWDEN Paul Freshfields Bruckhaus Deringer
GRANDISON Richard Slaughter and May
❸ HULL John Denton Wilde Sapte
KRAMER Martin Theodore Goddard
LESLIE Jonathan Travers Smith Braithwaite

Within each band, firms are listed alphabetically. See **Profiles** on page 58

Herbert Smith Edged slightly ahead of the pack this year after a plethora of favourable comments; their top tier status reflects a slick and refined practice driven by the *"tough and practical"* **Andrew Lidbetter** *("lots of creativity and knowledge of complicated issues")* who has channelled his mainstream civil litigation abilities into a formidable commercial JR specialism. Lidbetter has been published widely on the forthcoming implications of the Human Rights Act on commercial regulatory law, and is one of only a small number of City solicitors credited with spearheading these cutting-edge developments. Acting both on respondent and applicant side, the firm has been praised for the *"excellent breadth and sheer volume of work"* and the way they effectively *"exploit their litigation strength in the regulated industries."* Acted for Lord Mayhew in a challenge to the House of Lords Bill before the Committees for Privileges. Acting for Severn Trent Water in proceedings establishing that sewerage undertakers have statutory power to discharge into British Waterways Board's canals. **Clients:** London Electricity; Anglian Water; Horserace Betting Levy Board; The Law Society.

Allen & Overy Still considered to be a consistently high-performing and thorough public law team. The loss of the core repeat client ITC on conflict grounds over a year ago is still felt. However, the firm have a diversified and substantial body of work, both for public bodies and increasingly, blue-chip commercial applicants seeking to bring judicial review proceedings. Market opinion is that *"they have a good hold on a number of the bodies that are subject to JR."* Partner **Peter Watson** *"runs a good JR practice,"* operating from the litigation and dispute resolution department and is *"well liked,"* a *"thorough proceduralist"* and an *"effective commercial litigator."* The last year's highlights include acting on behalf of the Radio Authority in resisting an application for judicial review of its decision not to award a radio licence to AIO FM. Advised the Hong Kong Airport Authority in connection with the judicial inquiry into the initial operating problems experienced at the airport. Advising clients in connection with the Bloody Sunday inquiry, and also representing a number of witnesses to the BSE inquiry. **Clients:** The Radio Authority; Securities and Futures Authority; Council of the Inns of Court; Building Societies Ombudsman Company Ltd.

Clifford Chance Another leading performer, one of very few firms with a dedicated public law group, which is headed by the *"dry and witty"* **Michael Smyth** who *"has a good grasp of the law"* and *"fills the role well."* He is a leading commercial public lawyer who is felt to have kept a step ahead of the commercial implications of the impending Human Rights Act. Strong on a range of public law issues, when a big case or judicial review comes along, market opinion is that the firm *"will be there."* The firm is acting for Source Infomatics in its judicial review of the Department of Health. Acting for British investors petitioning the Human Rights Court in Strasbourg about French handling of an investment development on Lake Geneva. **Clients:** Public Health Laboratory Service; London Electricity; Cambridge University; Association of Train Operating Companies.

Lovells Climbs this year after a successful period in which the firm made waves acting on high profile tobacco advertising litigation cases. The firm has advised the four principal UK tobacco manufacturers seeking to prevent the banning of advertising in judicial review proceedings both at national and European level. Judicial review department head, the *"calm and sensible"* **Jennifer McDermott** is regarded as a leading light *("strong on the interplay between human rights, judicial review and commercial work,")* and has been favourably described as *"extremely capable, very committed and providing a devoted service."* Other notable judicial review successes include a victory against the Dept of Health on the prohibition on the commercial use of anonymous patient data (ex p Source Infomatics Ltd.) Mirroring the increasing City trend to act for both applicant and government/regulatory organisations, the team is acting for the Banking Code Standards Board in ensuring that its disciplinary and regulatory procedures are compliant with the requirements of the ECHR. **Clients:** Tobacco Manufacturers' Association; British American Tobacco; Rothmans; The Law Society.

Simmons & Simmons Retains a leading firm ranking this year on account of a continually strong commercial and regulatory practice with clients in several key industry sectors *("a very active and consistent operation.")* The team acts for key regulatory authorities, while bringing a number of claimant challenges. The ITC (regulators of all non-BBC television) has been the regulatory jewel in the client crown and has kept the firm on track with a string of repeat work. Appear to lack any individual big hitters, but the solidity of the practice keeps the firm well in the hunt. In the telecommunications industry, acted for One2One in a series of disputes with OFTEL, relating to the right of the regulators to make changes to existing licence agreements. Represented a number of international oil and gas companies in a dispute with Greenpeace over the issuing of exploration licences in the Atlantic Frontier. **Clients:** Three Valleys Water plc; ITC; Railtrack; OFGEM.

Denton Wilde Sapte Newly merged firm combines the strengths of both of last year's ranked constituent parts. The ex-Denton Hall team brings public and administrative law strength stemming from expertise in the key planning and local government areas. This is bolstered by clients in the major regulated energy and utilities sectors. Ex-Wilde Sapte **John Hull** *("a bright bloke who knows his stuff")* adds a broader dimension to the new practice by bringing his well-known university client work. Advised the Irish electricity regulator (OFGEM) on electricity trading, licensing and other regulatory matters. Also represented the Civil Aviation Authority on a new regulatory regime for privatised National Air Transport Services, including air traffic control. **Clients:** MoD; OFGEM; University College London; ATOC.

Freshfields Bruckhaus Deringer Major player, the *"firm and commercial"* **Paul Bowden** continues to receive impressive reviews from the market for his quality reputation in environmental and energy judicial review work. The other core areas of public law expertise are product liability, pharmaceuticals and sports. Recently defended a European pharmaceutical company who were obtaining permits to market a new drug product across Europe from a variety of different judicial review challenges. Advising Milk Marque Ltd in a JR of the Monopolies and Mergers Commission and the Secretary of State for Trade and Industry following the commission's report on the supply of cow's milk. **Clients:** Football Association; Olympic Committee; English Welsh and Scottish Railways; One2One.

Slaughter and May Strong team which operates out of the litigation and arbitration department. Acts for both commercial clients and industry regulators. Public law and commercial JR work is led by the *"effective, absolute gentleman"* **Richard Grandison** who is *"a pleasure to deal with."* He is well supported by a team of multi-specialist commercial litigation partners who have received praise and are felt to be future stars. Acting on behalf of an electricity company challenging OFFER on a price review. Have advised a number of clients in relation to the decisions of the Inland Revenue, in particular a decision on the tax treatment of limited liability. **Clients:** Post Office; Central Railway Transport Group; Commonwealth Development Corporation.

Travers Smith Braithwaite Strength across a wide spectrum of the commercial judicial review arena, although acting on behalf of applicants is the firm's forte. The experienced **Jonathan Leslie** *("a thoughtful and careful operator")* retains his individual profile as a result of his direct and forthright approach. In addition to work in the financial services, media and health fields, the team was active for Ulster Bank Ltd in a major challenge against the Inland Revenue and their entitlement to request customer documents from banks. Currently challenging a new statutory regulatory body, the General Osteopathic Council, in the way it goes about its hiring and qualification procedural duties. **Clients:** Ulster Bank Ltd; Shepherd Neame Ltd; Lawrie Plantation Services Ltd; Channel 5 Broadcasting Ltd.

CMS Cameron McKenna As a leading firm for both pharmaceuticals and planning work, it is no surprise that the judicial review team feeds off these specialisms. In addition, commercial regulatory activity in the energy sector is increasingly prominent. The firm is viewed as a progressive and cutting edge firm *("their work is a springboard for classic new style JR.")* Utilising a cross-departmental team across the breadth of public law work, a number of the product liability/pharmaceutical partners have been praised for *"steering the pharmaceutical industry through the regulatory minefield."* The team acted for the National Grid in challenging the regulators on its charging system. Also acting for an organisation challenging the Broadcasting Complaints Commission. **Clients:** National Grid; pharmaceutical companies.

Theodore Goddard Acts for a number of industry regulatory bodies and commercial applicants across a range of fields including sports, education and the media. The *"dapper"* **Martin Kramer**, *("an old fashioned gentleman")* leads the team and has a healthy number of admirers. The major client on the books is the Advertising Standards Authority, a profitable source of repeat work. Recently defended them against allegations by regional department store chain Charles Robertson Developments Ltd in relation to the 'Triplehound' column in regional newspapers. Acted for Airport Co-Ordination in a successful defence of a JR application brought by the States of Guernsey Transport Board challenging the slots allocation decisions at Heathrow Airport. **Clients:** Airport Co-Ordination Ltd; Advertising Standards Authority; Times Newspapers Ltd; News International plc.

Olswang Not a major public law practice, but effectively exploit industry knowledge in media and entertainment *("certainly a leader in this industry sector.")* Operating from the commercial litigation department, the team have engaged in a clutch of judicial reviews in both the media and telecoms fields. Recently acted for One2One in a judicial review of licensed conditions for the new generation of mobile telephone licences. Also acted for Classic FM in a JR of the decision of the director general of telecommunications. The dispute centred around the issue of payments relating to the ownership of transmission masts. **Clients:** Classic FM, Jupiter; Tattersalls Ltd; One2One.

THE SOUTH

ADMINISTRATIVE & PUBLIC LAW • The South	Ptnrs	Assts
❶ **Knights** Tunbridge Wells	2	1

LEADING INDIVIDUALS
❶ **KNIGHT Matthew** Knights

Within each band, firms are listed alphabetically. *See **Profiles** on page 58*

Knights **Matthew Knight**'s reputation for his niche involvement in countryside, sports and rural issues has extended to London, with observers commenting on the *"interesting"* nature of his individual specialism. This small practice offers advice to a range of countryside and country sports individuals and organisations affected by administrative decisions, including hunts, farming estates and pro-country sports campaigning organisations. Acted on a recent judicial review claim (Smart & Others v East Hampshire District Council.) **Clients:** National Farmers Union; National Smallbore Rifle Association; Countryside Alliance.

SOUTH WEST

ADMINISTRATIVE & PUBLIC LAW • South West	Ptnrs	Assts
❶ **Bevan Ashford** Bristol	2	2
❷ **Clarke Willmott & Clarke** Taunton	3	2
Stephens & Scown Exeter	2	-

LEADING INDIVIDUALS
❶ **JARMAN Chris** Bevan Ashford
PARKER Mike Clarke Willmott & Clarke

Within each band, firms are listed alphabetically. *See **Profiles** on page 58*

Bevan Ashford The firm have received a swathe of positive comments both at regional and London level. The core of the public law work revolves around advice and representation for a number of local health authorities and NHS trusts. Market consensus is that *"they've achieved great depth in NHS work, with many specialists in that area."* This has expanded to include education and some commercial work, although the firm retains a policy of never acting for applicants against the NHS. Among a series of offices in the region, *"Bristol is the driving force,"* with a public law cross-sectional team drawn from several different departments, including planning and local government. PFI and local authority specialist **Chris Jarman** is newly recommended this year. Involved in the high profile ex p Coughlan case defending North and East Devon Health Authority over the closure of a small unit for the young disabled. Also acted for Gwent Health Authority in the Russell Hall case concerning after-care for a discharged patient. **Clients:** Somerset Health Authority; NHS trusts.

Clarke Willmott & Clarke Strong across the region in a number of public law fields including local authority (particularly registered care homes,) planning and farming. A small cross-departmental team acts together on advisory and judicial review work. This includes Yeovil-based new entrant **Mike Parker**, recommended for his *"thoroughness and rigour"* in local authority judicial review. Acted for Gloucestershire County Council in a judicial review being mounted by parent groups protesting against school closures. Acted for another local authority in a case concerning a footpath alongside the River Severn that was washed away by a tidal wave. The dispute revolved around a challenge from ramblers groups over where it should be rebuilt. **Clients:** Individual farmers; local authorities.

Stephens & Scown Operating in a number of locations across the South West, the head office in Exeter is respected and retains a position in our tables this year. Known for particular expertise in farming issues, the firm acts for a number of farmers bringing judicial review proceedings. Have advised over 100 farmers in Cornwall and acted for two NFU members on potential JR matters during 1999. **Clients:** Individual farmers; NFU; local authorities.

WALES

ADMINISTRATIVE & PUBLIC LAW • Wales	Ptnrs	Assts
❶ **Eversheds** Cardiff	7	3
❷ **Edwards Geldard** Cardiff	1	2
Morgan Cole Cardiff	8	12

LEADING INDIVIDUALS
❶ **COLE Alun** Morgan Cole
EVANS Eric Eversheds
WILLIAMS Huw Edwards Geldard

Within each band, firms are listed alphabetically. *See* ***Profiles*** *on page 58*

Eversheds Enters in pole position in the newly constituted Welsh list. Observers were quick to point out that this *"tremendous Welsh practice generates a great deal of work."* In addition to a healthy client roster of local authorities, a recent coup was a successful beauty parade in which the firm was appointed to act as external advisors to the National Assembly of Wales. The vastly experienced local government lawyer **Eric Evans** heads a team who turn their hand to the gamut of public law, including planning, land acquisitions, vires issues and substantial PFI work. Were instructed to assist in the wind up of the Cardiff Bay development, ensuring all the assets were invested in other public bodies. Advised Ceredigion County Council on the first Welsh private finance school, including advice on capital finance regulations, vires issues and local management of schools. **Clients:** Local authorities; NHS trusts; Development agencies.

Edwards Geldard **Huw Williams** continues to be recognised for his abilities across the public law domain, embracing planning and local government strengths in addition to pure public law. Well known in the market and considered *"a safe pair of hands"* for local authority work, he has a good reputation for acting for public bodies on the respondent side. Retained by both the Welsh Development Agency and Cardiff County Council to advise on transfers of assets from Cardiff Bay Development Corporation. Acted in the judicial review of a local authority's process of tendering subsidised bus service contracts (R v Bridgend CBC ex parte Alison Jones.) **Clients:** Cardiff Bay Development Corporation; Welsh Development Agency; Wales Millennium Centre.

Morgan Cole Another prominent Welsh practice with key strengths across the range of administrative and local government work. Ex-Home Office and Welsh Office **Alun Cole** is *"a likeable fellow"* with a *"strong public sector background"* who leads a small admin and public law team. Acting for both public and private sector clients, the advisory case-load includes public authority powers and duties, PFI, PPP, European funding issues and the impact of new Human Rights legislation. Acted for Cardiff Bay Development Corporation on the £120 million Bute Avenue Road and Urban Regeneration Scheme. **Clients:** University of Wales; local authorities; health authorities; NHS trusts.

MIDLANDS

ADMINISTRATIVE & PUBLIC LAW • Midlands	Ptnrs	Assts
❶ **Pinsent Curtis** Birmingham	9	8
Tyndallwoods Birmingham	5	7
❷ **Martineau Johnson** Birmingham	3	6
❸ **Browne Jacobson** Nottingham	4	15

LEADING INDIVIDUALS
❶ **GOULD Jean** Tyndallwoods
SHINER Philip Public Interest Lawyers
WALLACE Alastair Tyndallwoods
WHITE Martin Pinsent Curtis

Within each band, firms are listed alphabetically. *See* ***Profiles*** *on page 58*

Pinsent Curtis Still regarded as *"the major player in Birmingham"* by one interviewee, the firm draw on related expertise in local government, planning and PFI to co-head the Midlands list. Regarded as *"a nice team to deal with,"* its star name is **Martin White** *("co-operative, not old-fashioned, and very reasonable,")* who brings individual competence in PFI-related planning work for large organisational clients. Acted for Barnsley MBC on the transfer of all its leisure facilities to a non-profit making organisation. On behalf of Optident Ltd/Utradent Products Inc, acted against the Secretary of State for Trade and Industry and Secretary of State for Health on a breach of EC directive on the free movement of goods. **Clients:** Local authorities; Commission for the New Towns; police authorities.

Tyndallwoods *"A fine public interest law firm"* still felt to belong at the top of the pile. The loss of ranked *"driving force"* Phil Shiner to his own individual niche environmental practice was undoubtedly a blow, although the firm collectively appear not to have suffered excessively. *"Although they've lost on the one hand they've gained on the other,"* as new partners begin to develop their own client base. Shiner's departure precipitated the establishment of a dedicated public law department, whose head, the *"highly rated"* **Alistair Wallace** enters our rankings for his planning and local authority abilities. Considered to have specific expertise on individually driven applicant challenges, the firm has strengths in planning and education, in addition to legal aid-generated work such as immigration, housing and welfare benefits. **Jean Gould**, formerly of Winstanley Burgess and the Public Law Project, appears to *"have found her feet,"* and brings a civil liberties bias with specialisms in education, discrimination, community care cases and actions against the police. The firm was recently involved in a number of actions on behalf of residents living in close proximity to football stadiums. **Clients:** Individual applicants in cases such as R v Oldham MBC ex p Foster (environmental assessment) and R v Birmingham City Council ex p Killigan (community care.)

Martineau Johnson Established firmly as the Midlands education firm, public law and judicial review capacity spin off from this *("they're pretty* *lively in this field")* as they act predominantly on the respondent side for a series of educational institutions. In addition, health authority work is perceived to be on the increase. Recently acted for Nottingham Trent University in a judicial review proceeding brought by a foreign student concerning the issue of fees. Advised the General Osteopathic Council on its statutory powers regarding the recognition of qualifications. **Clients:** University of Birmingham; Leicester University; Warwick University; Gallifords plc.

Browne Jacobson Dedicated public authority group which oversees extensive client roster of local authorities and other public bodies with emphasis on planning, urban renewal and environmental cases. Acting for a large Midlands district council, in which judicial review proceedings have been brought arising from a disputed planning permission for a property development plc. Advising English Nature on a wildlife and environmental case brought against a large utilities plc. **Clients:** Countryside Council for Wales; Nottingham City Council; Bassetlaw District Council, Mansfield District Council.

Other Notable Practitioners Ex Tyndallwoods **Phil Shiner** took several environmental and organisational clients with him when he established this new niche practice in late 1999. With a human rights and public law dimension to the firm, it is anticipated that his considerable individual experience and expertise will allow the firm to attain a full ranking as they become established.

EAST ANGLIA

ADMINISTRATIVE & PUBLIC LAW • East Anglia	Ptnrs	Assts
❶ **Richard Buxton** Cambridge	1	1
❷ **Eversheds** Cambridge, Norwich	5	6
Mills & Reeve Cambridge, Norwich	6	3

LEADING INDIVIDUALS
❶ **BUXTON Richard** Richard Buxton

Within each band, firms are listed alphabetically. *See **Profiles** on page 58*

Richard Buxton *"An effective niche practice."* Rarely straying beyond his specialisms in environmental, planning and public law *("he's made it his forte,")* **Richard Buxton**, a *"skilful lawyer"* and *"confident operator"* is highly respected for his *"pioneering work"* on High Court challenges to the new environmental assessment rules. Acting almost exclusively for applicants and third parties, the firm is regarded as a dedicated campaigning unit, frequently bringing challenges on behalf of residents and action groups. Recently acted on behalf of a local resident in the Plymouth City Airport case where the client was financially disadvantaged by the noise from a newly built helicopter pad. **Clients:** CPRE; wildlife trusts; individual applicants.

Eversheds With established track records in planning and local government, Eversheds' East Anglian offices enter the public law lists after several recommendations. Considered *"a strong planning group,"* both offices are felt to work closely together on public and judicial review work. On the public sector front, acted for Norwich City Council in connection with the externalisation of its Direct Labour Organisation, known as 'City Works'. **Clients:** Local authorities; police authorities; airports.

Mills & Reeve Another fresh entrant into the dedicated East Anglian public law list and the beneficiary of a clutch of positive comments, the firm has been involved in judicial review work – most of it deriving from core strengths in planning and local government. The team has advised on a number of high-profile judicial reviews on behalf of Hanson in connection with the extension of Whately Quarry. Have also managed to quash two of the Secretary of State's decisions relating to airfields. **Clients:** NHS trusts; local authorities; universities.

THE NORTH

ADMINISTRATIVE & PUBLIC LAW • The North	Ptnrs	Assts
❶ **Eversheds** Leeds, Manchester	5	13
❷ **Beachcroft Wansbroughs** Sheffield	1	2
Irwin Mitchell Sheffield	1	4
Pinsent Curtis Leeds	-	5

LEADING INDIVIDUALS
❶ **CIRELL Stephen** Eversheds

Within each band, firms are listed alphabetically. *See **Profiles** on page 58*

Eversheds *"Certainly ahead in the regions,"* commented a London barrister on the strength and quality of Eversheds' northern offices, and *"in terms of public law and local government, one of the pre-eminent firms."* Felt to have benefited from *"a general upturn in public authority work,"* ex-Leeds City Council stalwart **Stephen Cirell** is a local government supremo and regarded as an expert on *"best value"* techniques. Notable highlights included a strategic waste disposal procurement under PFI terms for East Sussex County Council and Brighton and Hove Council. **Clients:** Local authorities; regional development agencies.

Beachcroft Wansbroughs *"Couldn't endorse them too highly."* Felt to be a productive unit doing *"huge amounts of admin work,"* public law continues to stem from key strengths in health and clinical negligence defence litigation. Recent cases have included R v Leicestershire General Hospital / NHS ex parte Wieclawski regarding an injunction to prevent the discharge of a patient who was fully fit. Also acted on R v Rotherham General Hospital ex parte Mandell concerning the right to pursue a disciplinary route through the GMC. **Clients:** Worcestershire Health Authority; Leeds Health Authority.

Irwin Mitchell *"Absolutely excellent in public law"* commented a London barrister, and the firm's work covers a wide spectrum including education, community care and regulatory activities. Felt to have *"established themselves in these fields,"* they have moved to the forefront of developments in creating a dedicated human rights department as a means of exploiting opportunities thrown up by the incorporation of the new European Human Rights Act. Acted in the Wilkinson case, challenging the legal aid board over the issue of funding of mediation. Acted for Josephine Hayes in her successful challenge to the Attorney General on selection procedures for the appointment of Treasury Counsel. **Clients:** Regulatory authorities.

Pinsent Curtis Already well regarded for local government work, this was bolstered last year with the hire of an experienced in-house solicitor from Doncaster Council. Considered to be *"very productive"* and felt by the market to be *"pushing quite hard on public law,"* they are another key player in Leeds with a mix of both public authority and commercial clients. Another partner brings individual expertise to JR work. Continue to act for the DfEE on commercial contracting issues in relation to training and education. Selected by the DETR in late 1999 to advise on PFI and PPP. Act for MAFF on property issues across the South of England. **Clients:** Government bodies; local authorities; NHS trusts; universities.

SCOTLAND

ADMINISTRATIVE & PUBLIC LAW • Scotland	Ptnrs	Assts
❶ **Brodies WS** Edinburgh	1	1
Erskine MacAskill & Co Edinburgh	1	1
McGrigor Donald Glasgow	1	3
Simpson & Marwick WS Edinburgh	1	2
❷ **Burness** Edinburgh	7	5
Dundas & Wilson CS Edinburgh	12	25
Lindsays WS Edinburgh	1	1
Shepherd & Wedderburn WS Edinburgh	2	3
Tods Murray WS Edinburgh	3	4

LEADING INDIVIDUALS
❶ **SHAW Catherine** Simpson & Marwick WS
❷ **HOLLIGAN William** Brodies WS
MACLEOD Ian Shepherd & Wedderburn WS

Within each band, firms are listed alphabetically. *See **Profiles** on page 58*

Brodies WS **William Holligan** remains a respected figurehead *("I have a lot of regard for him")* as a widely published creator and head of The Administrative Law and Judicial Review Group. The firm still provides substantial advisory services to public authorities and statutory bodies *("they're still big players")* in relation to the exercise of powers and judicial review avoidance. Given the Scottish lead on incorporation of the European convention on human rights, the firm have sought to offer advice to industry clients affected by European administrative law. **Clients:** Local authorities; statutory authorities.

Erskine MacAskill & Co Heavily legal-aid flavoured practice *("they have a social conscience!")* acting for petitioners in judicial review proceedings brought against housing, community care, immigration and social security authorities. One Scottish solicitor felt *"they do more JR than anyone else in Scotland."* Undoubtedly, the team is prolific in bringing large numbers of social security and homeless JRs – one of very few Scottish firms active in this field. Acted for the petitioner in KM v Sec State for Social Security, an army HIV case in which there was a dispute over the award of an army pension. **Clients:** Individual applicants; asylum seekers.

McGrigor Donald Rises into our leading category this year. Contains a dedicated administrative and public law unit headed by a director with extensive experience of public law as an in-house lawyer. A small litigation team with collective strength in planning, local government and judicial review *("their size and client list is good.")* Advises local authorities and development authorities on planning issues, and public and corporate clients on challenges related to the Human Rights Act. Acting in the Trinity Holdings case – a dispute concerning a major supermarket chain dissatisfied with a planning decision. **Clients:** Local authorities; Caledonian McBrayne; Lanarkshire Development Agency; Scottish Metropolitan Property.

Simpson & Marwick WS Another leading respondent practice *("no question about their top status")* with extensive experience of acting for local authorities in judicial review disputes. The *"sensible"* **Catherine Shaw** *"always knows the issues," "cuts to the chase"* and can draw upon extensive connections and insights into local authority clients. Her *"top reputation"* rests on her abilities to defend a long client list of local authorities from challenges to their decisions. **Clients:** Several local authorities including East Ayrshire and West Lothian.

Burness Public law work emerges from the public sector group where the firm acts for a number of local authorities in sector specific areas such as health, education and urban regeneration. Acting for City of Edinburgh Council in the £350 million Waterfront Edinburgh urban regeneration project. Also acting for Glasgow Alliance in the development of a framework for all of the Social Inclusion partnerships within Glasgow. **Clients:** Department of Social Security; East of Scotland Water; Millennium Commission; North Ayrshire Council.

Dundas & Wilson CS A new name in this year's list. Not considered to be a mainstream public law player but still recommended for general public sector work in health, education and local authority. One commentator believed that *"sheer scale has stood them in good stead in winning work,"* while another pointed to *"quality work on externalising power and the use of charitable trusts"* for public sector clients. On the local governemnt side, have developed partnership arrangements with Stirling Council. Appointed to act for City of Edinburgh Council on its £90 million schools project. **Clients:** Local authorities; East of Scotland Water; University of Edinburgh; Stoke Mandeville Hospital Trust.

Lindsays WS This traditional litigation firm has acted on immigration and asylum hearings and JR challenges. One solicitor praised them for persevering with immigration JR against a wider trend of *"dodging the legal aid work."* Not a main player in the public law field, but the ranking reflects the firm's productivity in this important area. **Clients:** Individual applicants; asylum seekers.

Shepherd & Wedderburn WS Quiet on the JR front, but strong for general local authority advisory work, largely derived form local government and planning applications and appeals. The *"senior and well-established"* **Ian MacLeod** is *"good to work with," "has a serious grasp of the law"* and is *"effective on vires issues."* His reputation for quality public authority advice also rests on substantial PFI and PPP work. Recently assisted East Dumbartonshire council on a flood prevention scheme and acted on housing-related judicial reviews. **Clients:** The Accounts Commission; Aberdeenshire Council; Fife Council.

Tods Murray WS Has a particular area of specialisation in environmental actions and planning work, to which public law acts as an adjunct. A broad cross-departmental team offers expertise in authority powers, housing, litigation and JR. Acted for the RSPB in challenging a public sector planning authority over the issue of geese on the island of Islay. Won a PFI contract to establish an Economic Development Company for Dundee City Council. **Clients:** WWF; Forestry Commission; Local Government Property Commission; local authorities.

NORTHERN IRELAND

ADMINISTRATIVE & PUBLIC LAW • Northern Ireland	Ptnrs	Assts
❶ **Cleaver Fulton Rankin** Belfast	2	–
Madden & Finucane Belfast	2	1

LEADING INDIVIDUALS
❶ **FARIS Neil** Cleaver Fulton Rankin
RITCHIE Angela Madden & Finucane

Within each band, firms are listed alphabetically. *See **Profiles** on page 58*

Cleaver Fulton Rankin **Neil Faris** heads the firm's public law unit, which offers a wide breadth of public law expertise. Has been actively advising the Sentence Review Commission (an independent body supervising the post-Good Friday Agreement prisoner release programme) against the Home Secretary in a dispute over the length of sentence of a convicted terrorist bomber. Also handles a number of planning and environmental JR for applicants – in particular a local authority challenging a major retail chain's plans for a regional shopping centre. **Clients:** NIGEN; BT; Sports Council; local authorities.

Madden & Finucane Human rights-driven public law and judicial review firm noted for acting for individual applicants in challenges against the Northern Ireland Office, the police and prison service. The *"straightforward and sensible"* **Angela Ritchie** campaigns and acts for prisoners and those affected by miscarriages of justice. **Clients:** Individual applicants.

LEADERS IN ADMINISTRATIVE & PUBLIC LAW

AMBROSE, Ray
Nabarro Nathanson, London (020) 7518 3177
Specialisation: Local government and administrative law (powers and duties, statutory interpretation, capital controls, companies). Formerly at GLC and London Residuary Body. Recently advised on 'best value' housing management contract; PFI for civic accommodation, new-build social housing scheme; regeneration schemes (SRB and others) and partnership structures, Redbridge audit inquiry and establishment of Regional Development Agency.
Prof. Memberships: Law Society.
Career: Qualified 1975; Head of Administrative Law and Parliamentary Branch GLC 1985-86; Deputy Director of Legal Services, London Residuary Body 1986-90. Joined *Nabarro Nathanson* 1991.

BINDMAN, Geoffrey
Bindman & Partners, London (020) 7833 4433
See under Human Rights, p.433

BOWDEN, Paul
Freshfields Bruckhaus Deringer, London (020) 7936 4000
See under Litigation (Commercial), p.558

BURGESS, David C.W.
Winstanley-Burgess, London (020) 7278 7911
See under Immigration, p.441

BUXTON, Richard
Richard Buxton, Cambridge (01223) 328933
law@richardbuxton.co.uk
See under Environment, p.373

CHILD, Tony
Rowe & Maw, London (020) 7248 4282
Specialisation: Practice covers the full range of public and administrative law. Specialist in local government and NHS law. Acts for public bodies and those who deal with them. Adviser to local government and NHS external auditors. Renowned expertise and experience in acting for both applicants and respondents in judicial review and public law proceedings. This includes the first successful challenge in any commonwealth jurisdiction to the adequacy of a government consultation exercise; bringing down the Rate Support Grant (RSG) and ratecapping regime in 1985; overcoming retrospective legislation on RSG; having interest rate swaps declared by the House of Lords to be ultra vires local authorities; 'Bookbinder v Tebbit (No. 2)' (1992); 'Allsop v North Tyneside MBC' (1992); 'Burgoine and Cooke v Waltham Forest LBC' (1996) and many more successes. Currently advising the Westminster City Council Auditor in the "homes for votes" case. Previous experience includes 19 years in local government, adviser to both the Association of Metropolitan Authorities and the Association of London Authorities and 8 years as Solicitor to the Audit Commission. Author of many articles and a regular speaker at conferences and seminars. User friendly.
Career: Articled Redbridge London Borough Council; qualified 1971. Assistant Solicitor 1971-74. Senior Solicitor 1974-76. Chief Solicitor Greenwich LBC 1976-79. Assistant Chief Executive and Solicitor 1979-83; Deputy Chief Executive 1983-87; Solicitor to Audit Commission 1987-95; partner *Rowe & Maw* 1995. Education: Ilford County High School; University College, London (LLB First Class Hons). Solicitor (Hons).
Personal: Born 1947. Resides Chelmsford. Interests include football (player/manager Braintree and Bocking United FC), cricket (wicket-keeper, batsman, Redbridge Parks CC), sports generally, crosswords.

CIRELL, Stephen
Eversheds, Leeds (0113) 243 0391
stephencirell@eversheds.com
See under Local Government, p.586

COLE, Alun
Morgan Cole, Cardiff (029) 2038 5385
alun.cole@morgan-cole.com
Partner in Public Law and Commercial Unit.
Specialisation: Principal area of practice is public law and commercial work for public bodies. Advises a wide range of public bodies on the scope of their powers and on the effective use of those powers. Undertakes major commercial work on their behalf (including PFI transactions, privatisations, contracting out and joint ventures) and advises on the implications/opportunities presented by EU law. Undertakes corresponding transactional work for the private sector. Also deals with mainstream commercial work, with an emphasis on transactions with an international element. Clients in the public sector include health authorities, NHS Trusts, universities and FEC's, development agencies, executive agencies of government departments, local authorities, housing associations and a number of "quangos". Regular speaker at conferences and seminars.
Prof. Memberships: Law Society, Welsh Centre for International Affairs, Wales Public Law and Human Rights Association.
Career: Qualified in 1977. Senior Principal Legal Assistant at the Home Office 1977-85, then at the Welsh Office 1985-88. Joined *Morgan Cole* in 1988.
Personal: Born 9th June 1951. Educated at the London School of Economics 1969-73 (LL.B and LL.M). Spare time activities include voluntary work, outdoor pursuits, sport and politics. Lives in Pontsticill, Glamorgan.

DAY, Martyn
Leigh, Day & Co, London (020) 7650 1200
See under Product Liability, p.674

EVANS, Eric
Eversheds, Cardiff (02920) 471147
See under Property (Commercial), p.726

FARIS, Neil C.
Cleaver Fulton Rankin, Belfast (028) 9024 3141
n.faris@cfrlawonline.com
Specialisation: Commercial Property with special emphasis on Environmental Law. Practice also covers issues of Administrative and Public Law and European Union/Competition Law with special reference to Northern Ireland.
Prof. Memberships: Member: UKELA, IAEL, Competition Working Party.
Career: Qualified in 1977 and Managing Partner and Head Consultancy Department.
Personal: Born 1950, educated in Belfast and at Trinity College Dublin and University of Cambridge.

GOULD, Jean
Tyndallwoods, Birmingham (0121) 624 1111
jean_gould@tyndallwoods.co.uk
Specialisation: Particularly interested in social welfare and human rights applications of public law and in public interest litigation. Cases include R v Sefton MBC ex parte Help the Aged and others, R v DPP ex parte Bull (for Amnesty International) and R v North Lancashire Health Authority ex parte A, D & G.
Career: Formerly project solicitor at the public law project and now a partner and joint head of public law at *Tyndallwoods* and trainer in community care law for Carers National Association. Member of the Legal Services Commission Public Interest Advisory Panel.
Publications: Contributes articles to 'Legal Action' and other journals.
Personal: BA Hons. Taught in Inner London before qualifying in 1990.

GRANDISON, Richard
Slaughter and May, London (020) 7600 1200
Head of Commercial Litigation and Arbitration department.
Specialisation: Extensive experience in commercial litigation, arbitration and commercial judicial review for a wide range of corporate clients in commercial disputes in England and overseas – including international trade and commodity disputes, sovereign immunity issues, oil and gas and financial services.
Prof. Memberships: The Law Society and City of London Solicitors Society.
Career: Qualified in 1978 with *Slaughter and May*. Partner since 1987. Educated at Fettes College, Edinburgh and Pembroke College, Cambridge.

GRIFFITHS, Trevor
Sharpe Pritchard, London (020) 7405 4600
Specialisation: Partner specialising in judicial review, statutory and planning appeals, including appellate courts. In addition deals with assessment of costs and environmental and planning injunction work.
Career: Joined *Sharpe Pritchard* in 1982, qualified in 1984 and became a Partner in 1987.
Personal: Born 6th December 1957. Educated at Bishop Wordsworth School 1969-76 and U.W.I.S.T 1976-79. Recreations include golf and cricket. Lives in London.

GROSZ, Stephen
Bindman & Partners, London (020) 7833 4433
See under Human Rights, p.433

HOLLIGAN, William
Brodies WS, Edinburgh (0131) 228 3777
wholligan@brodies.co.uk
Specialisation: Partner in *Brodies'* litigation department dealing mainly with commercial and administrative law matters. Wide experience through involvement in judicial review matters involving councils and central government, and also European administrative law. Contributor to Scots Law Times on litigation matters. Part time lecturer at Edinburgh University on civil court practice. Solicitor-Advocate. Qualified to practice in South Australia.
Prof. Memberships: Writer to the 'Signet', Law Society of Scotland.
Career: Education: University of Edinburgh (LLB); Adelaide (LLM). Qualified 1981; Assistant Solicitor *Brodies* 1981-85; Assistant Solicitor and Partner *Finlaysons*, Adelaide, Australia 1985-91; Partner *Brodies* since 1992.
Personal: Married, lives in Edinburgh.

HULL, John
Denton Wilde Sapte, London (020) 7242 1212
jkh@dentonwildesapte.com
Partner in Media and Technology.
Specialisation: Handles contentious and non-contentious intellectual property, with an emphasis on copyright, trade mark and passing off issues. Also IT law including hardware and software supply disputes. Special interest in breach of confidence, trade secrets, privacy and data protection. Also IP/IT related to banking and finance and industry/university collaboration. Other main area of practice is judicial review, particularly in relation to commercial matters and the higher educational sphere. Important cases handled include G.D. Searle v. Celltech [1982] (employees/breach of confidence/biotechnology), Swedac Ltd v. Magnet and Southerns PLC [1989] (Anton Piller/copyright infringement/interference with trade), P.A. v. Manchester City [1986] (photocopying/copyright infringement), CIS v. Forward Trust [1987] (computer programs/"look and feel"), Cantor Fitzgerald v. Tradition [1997] (computer software; copyright; substantiality); Dalgety Spillers Foods Ltd v. Food Brokers [1994] (passing off/get up/survey evidence), R v. Joint Committee on Higher Surgical Training ex p. Milner [1994] (judicial review/consultant's training) and R v. Cardiff City Council ex p. Gooding [1995] (judicial review/EPA 1990/local authority tendering). R v. University College London, ex parte Idriss (Entrance Qualifications); R v. University College London ex parte Christofi (falsified scientific data, inquiry). Author of "Commercial Secrecy: Law and Practice" (Sweet & Maxwell 1998) and over fifty articles on intellectual property, commercial litigation and company law. Frequent conference speaker on intellectual property and commercial legal subjects.
Prof. Memberships: Society for Computers and the Law, Chartered Institute of Patent Agents (Associate Member), Intellectual Property Lawyers Organisation, Licensing Executives Society.
Career: Qualified in 1979. Lecturer in Law at Exeter University 1978-81. At *Coward Chance* 1981-89. Joined *Wilde Sapte* in 1989 and became a Partner in 1990.
Personal: Born 22nd June 1951. Educated at Southmoor School, Sunderland 1962-69, Monkwearmouth College, Sunderland 1969-70, Warwick University 1970-73 (LL.B Hons) and the London School of Economics 1973-74 (LL.M). Leisure interests include writing, squash and wine. Lives in London.

ILEY, Malcolm
Nabarro Nathanson, London (020) 7524 6000
Partner specialising in public sector and local government. Head of *Nabarro Nathanson*'s Public Sector Team.
Specialisation: Main practice area is public law relating to local government, government departments and public sector powers generally. Experience in local authority outsourcings, asset transfer, regeneration, compulsory purchase, planning, education, competition and PFI, including the consideration of wider European involvement. Currently advising on one of the first "best value" partnership joint ventures. Clients have included London boroughs, district and county councils, government departments, local authority related companies, higher and further education, LAWDAC, and urban development corporations. Currently involved in research concerning the proposed regional development agencies. Media advisor and broadcaster on public sector legal issues. Regular contributor to local government and regional press.
Career: Qualified in 1976. Began career in the private sector, transferred to local government and later became a senior lawyer with Leeds City Council. Appointed City Solicitor and Deputy Chief Executive for Plymouth City Council. Held other senior posts in Lancashire, Sussex and Norfolk. Joined *Nabarro Nathanson* in 1997 as a partner.
Personal: Born 12 April 1950. College Governor. F.E. Governor, company director, director of environmental trust and Business in the Community.

JARMAN, Christopher
Bevan Ashford, Bristol (0117) 975 1621
c.jarman@bevanashford.co.uk
Specialisation: Project work. Member of the PFI and Projects Group. Deals with local authorities, NHS Trusts and M.O.D. work for the private sector. Recently: pathfinder local authorities PFI; closed largest NHS PFI in Wales; advising on largest (£9bn) PFI scheme to date.
Prof. Memberships: Law society.
Career: Sidcot School; University College, London (BA History). Articled, qualified 1987 and partner 1989 at *Sharpe Pritchard*; joined *Bevan Ashford* 1997 as associate partner, became partner, *Bevan Ashford*, 1998.
Publications: Editor and contibutor to 'Public Private Partnerships', Sweet & Maxwell. Contributor to 'TUPE and the Acquired Rights Directive', edited by Sharland and Isaacs Q.C.
Personal: Reading, walking, playing with my children, and Axbridge Saxons Football Club.

KNIGHT, Matthew
Knights, Tunbridge Wells (01892) 537311
knights@atlas.co.uk
Senior partner.
Specialisation: Main area of practice is judicial review. Also handles defamation, crime, trespass, compulsory purchase compensation, commercial litigation and advising on and drafting legislation. Acted in Sawrij & Swalesmoor Mink Farm Ltd v Lynx & Others; in R v Somerset County Council ex parte Fewings, Leyland & Down and in British Field Sports Society ats Commissioners of HM Customs & Excise. Author of various articles.
Prof. Memberships: Law Society.
Career: Qualified in 1982 after joining *Farrer & Co* in 1980. Worked at *Sinclair Roche & Temperley* 1982-84, then at *Cripps Harries Hall* 1984-94, from 1986 as a partner. Established *Knights* in 1994.
Personal: Born 2nd April 1957. Attended Eltham College 1970-76, Newcastle University 1976-79 and College of Law 1979-80. Leisure interests include hunting and shooting.

KRAMER, Martin
Theodore Goddard, London (020) 7606 8855
Specialisation: Acts for both applicants and respondents. Has acted for newspaper publishers, pharmaceutical, biotechnology and television companies, pressure groups and foreign governments challenging decisions of local authorities, Secretaries of State, the Controller of the Patent Office, the Independent Television Commission and the Inland Revenue. Regulatory clients include advertising, sporting and educational bodies.
Prof. Memberships: Law Society.
Career: Main areas of practice are administrative and public law and media-related litigation. Qualified 1969. Partner 1978.

LESLIE, Jonathan
Travers Smith Braithwaite, London (020) 7295 3000
Jonathan.Leslie@TraversSmith.com
Specialisation: Practice includes most areas of commercial litigation and arbitration, particularly for financial institutions, corporations and professional advisers; and judicial review in commercial cases.
Prof. Memberships: Fellow Chartered Institue of Arbitrators, The City of London Solicitors' Company.
Career: Qualified 1978. Partner, *Travers Smith Braithwaite*, 1984.
Personal: Educated Highgate School; Magdalen College, Oxford.

LIDBETTER, Andrew
Herbert Smith, London (020) 7374 8000
andrew.lidbetter@herbertsmith.com
Specialisation: Commercial litigation partner specialising in public and administrative law and other contentious regulatory matters, particularly judicial review, statutory appeals, ECHR issues, DTI investigations, other inquiries, disciplinary proceedings, local government and environmental cases. Clients include both applicants and regulators. Member of the advisory board of 'JR' (Judicial Review) and frequently writes on public law. Author of 'Company Investigations and Public Law – A Practical Guide to Government Investigations' (Hart Publishing, 1999), and contributor of Judicial Review chapter to Blackstone's 'Civil Practice' (2000).
Prof. Memberships: Administrative Law Bar Association.
Career: Qualified 1990. Partner 1998.
Personal: Educated at Worcester College, Oxford (First class law degree and BCL).

MACKINTOSH, Nicola
Mackintosh Duncan, London (020) 7357 6464
admin@mackdunc.co.uk
Specialisation: Partner in specialist firm with expertise in Judicial Review proceedings relating to all aspects of Community Care, Health, Mental Health and Human Rights Law. Major test cases include ex parte Coughlan (NHS responsibilities for long term care, substantive legitimate expectation, ECHR), ex parte Mackintosh Duncan (challenge to the LCD's

exclusive contracting regime for legal aid) ex parte Cobham (charging for psychiatric after care services) and numerous other cases involving hospital/day centre/care home closures and obligations of public bodies in health and social care field. Member of Law Society Mental Health and Disability Committee, editorial board of Community Care Law Reports, Co-ordinator of Community Care Practitioners' Group, co-author of 'Community Care Assessments', and Fellow of Society of Advanced Legal Studies.

MACLEOD, Ian
Shepherd & Wedderburn WS, Edinburgh
(0131) 228 9900
ian.macleod@shepwedd.co.uk
Partner in litigation department.
Specialisation: Main areas of practice are general commercial litigation and employment law. Accredited as Employment Law Specialist by Law Society of Scotland. Solicitor in Scotland to Department for Education and Employment. Also solicitor in Scotland to HM Customs & Excise and to Health and Safety Executive. Member of Court of Session Rules Council.
Prof. Memberships: Law Society of Scotland, WS Society, Scottish Law Agents Society, Edinburgh Bar Association.
Career: Qualified in 1960. Joined *Shepherd & Wedderburn WS* in 1957, becoming a partner in 1964.
Personal: Born 19th April 1937. Attended Aberdeen and Edinburgh Universities 1954-59 (MA, LLB). Governor of Rannoch School; Lt. Cdr. RNR (Rtd.)

MCDERMOTT, Jennifer
Lovells, London (020) 7296 2000
jennifer.mcdermott@lovells.com
Specialisation: Commercial litigation with specialisation in administrative law and media litigation, particularly including defamation, privacy, confidentiality and broadcasting regulatory matters. Extensive expertise in commercial judicial review having been involved in a number of high profile applications against and in conjunction with a wide variety of regulatory authorities. On the editorial board of Communications Law; contributes to publications such as the Press Gazette and PLC and speaks at conferences on both judicial review and media law.
Prof. Memberships: Member of the Media Society, the Royal Television Society, council of JUSTICE; Law Society, Amnesty International.
Career: Qualified 1981 with *Lovells; partner 1989.*

PARKER, Mike
Clarke Willmott & Clarke, Yeovil (01278) 458 622
mparker@cw-c.co.uk
Specialisation: Associate commercial litigation department. Practice covers all aspects of contentious work with particular experience in the fields of contract and property litigation and professional negligence. Specialises in administrative and public law particularly judicial review, acting for individuals against local authorities and government departments. Member of the firm's Agricultural and Food Services team. Has acted in a wide range of agricultural disputes and has particular expertise in subsidy claims against MAFF. Acted in R v MAFF ex parte Janes which forced a change in the Sheep Annual Premium Regulation.
Prof. Memberships: Law Society.
Career: Articled *Withers*, qualified 1994. *Lamport Bassitt* 1994-1997. Joined *Clarke Willmott & Clarke* in 1997 and became an associate in 1999.
Personal: Educated at Loughborough Grammar School and New College, Oxford (MA). Leisure interests include cycle racing and gardening.

RABINOWICZ, Jack
Teacher Stern Selby, London (020) 7242 3191
See under Education, p.310

RITCHIE, Angela
Madden & Finucane, Belfast (028) 9023 8007
Specialisation: Barristers' application for Judicial Review of the Chancellor and Lord Chief Justice regarding the requirement that they make a declaration to the queen as a condition of their appointment as QC's. Law graduates challenge limited numbers admitted to solicitors' professional training course. Application by a political representative of the refusal to grant him legal aid due to his membership of a political party. Application for review by a mother of the decision of the MOD army Board, retainig in the army two soilders convicted of the murder of her son. Solicitors' application for review of the refusal by Legal Aid to give reasons for reductions made when costs assessed.
Career: Partner at *Madden & Finucane.*

RUEBAIN, David
David Levene & Co, London (020) 8881 7777
info@davidlevene.co.uk
Head of Education and Disability Law Department.
Specialisation: The Department specialises in all aspects of education law, health law, community care law and disability discrimination. The work of the department has an expanding human rights dimension. He has published and taught extensively on education and disability law and is author of the Code of Practice on Admission, Exclusion and Reinstatement Appeals for Maintained Schools in England and Wales; co-author of the 1995 and 1997 Disabled Persons' (Civil Rights) Bills; consultant editor to Disability Discrimination: Advising on the Law and Practice; author of Notes on the Disability Discrimination Act; co-author of Taking Action, a guide for parents of children with Special Educational Needs an editorial board member of Disability and Society; and co-author of the Legal Action Group's Education and the Law.
Prof. Memberships: Trustee of the Disability Discrimination Act Representation and Advice Project, a trustee of the Disability Law Service, Vice Chair of the Rights Now Campaign, a member of the Law Society's Mental Health and Disability Committee, Vice Chair of Disability Equality in Education and a member of the Advisory Board of the Disablement Policy and Law Research Unit.

SCHWEHR, Belinda
Rowe & Maw, London (020) 7248 4282
bschwehr@roweandmawe.co.uk
Specialisation: Conducts judicial review proceedings for applicants and respondents and advises on the interaction between public and private law principles for a wide range of clients. Practice ranges from adults' social services law to PFI. Recent work has involved the implementation of statutory functions in the context of scarce resources and the risk of tortious claims for breach of statutory duty given the implications of the Human Rights Act, for the principles in X v Bedfordshire; the scope for public law challenge in actions for the recovery of debts arising from statutory charges; hospital discharge disputes; the extent of statutory powers of guardianship in respect of the mentally incapacitated given the possibility of an action for trespass and false imprisonment after Bournewood; limitations on the powers of local authorities to contract; the Local Government (Contracts) Act 1997; and preparation for the implications of the Human Rights Act for the private and public sector, including collaboration with the LGA in the preparation of its booklet on the Act, for all local authorities. Advises both local authority and NHS auditors; currently acting for the proprietor of a clinic regarding his dealings with the Human Fertility and Embryology Authority. A solicitor-advocate. Offers annual advice packages to local authorities (in particular social services departments), involving preventative public law advice for departmental lawyers and Members, and training of care managers.
Prof. Memberships: Administrative Law Bar Association.
Career: Barrister 1985, private practice until 1990 in civil common law chambers; LLM in public law, UCL 1990; university lecturer in public law and a consultant 1990-97; legal consultant to author of Community Care Practice and the Law (Jessica Kingsley Ltd 1994); joined *Rowe & Maw* 1997; re-qualified as solicitor 1998; author of many articles on public law issues, regular speaker at national conferences, seminars and training sessions.
Personal: Born 1962; Visiting Fellow of the University of Westminister.

SHAW, Catherine
Simpson & Marwick WS, Edinburgh
(0131) 557 1545
Specialisation: Acts for a number of Scottish local authorities and other government departments in EL and PL claims and administrative law. Expertise in judicial review actions, Inner House appeals and licensing appeals. Has a particularly detailed knowledge of the unique pressures and difficulties faced by clients in the public sector, both economic and political.
Prof. Memberships: Law Society of Scotland
Career: Qualified 1978, partner in litigation department since 1982.

SHINER, Philip
Public Interest Lawyers, Birmingham
(0121) 777 5187
phil_shiner@publicinterestlawyers.co.uk
See under Environment, p.378

SILAS, Douglas
David Levene & Co, London (020) 8881 7777
info@davidlevene.co.uk
Specialisation: Education and disability law. In particular, special educational needs and disability discrimination cases. Developing human rights practice. Mainly applicant work for individuals and charities. Formerly a registered trainee British Sign Language Interpreter. Recently represented Jeff McWhinney, the first deaf Chief Executive of the British Deaf Association, in a test case challenge against the refusal to allow deaf people to serve as jurors.
Prof. Memberships: Trustee of the Disability Law Service. Member of Law Society, Education Law Association, Disability Discrimination Act Advisors Group, Deaf Legal Access Group, and British Deaf Association Advisory panel.
Career: Joined *David Levene & Co* in 1995 as trainee solicitor. Admitted 1997.

Personal: Born on 28 September 1966. Educated: John Lyons, Harrow; South Bank University (LL.B (Hons)); College of Law (LPC).

SMYTH, Michael
Clifford Chance, London (020) 7600 1000
michael.smyth@cliffordchance.com
Specialisation: Partner with extensive experience in all kinds of commercial disputes, including media litigation and public law cases. Clients include public authorities, newspapers, book publishers and news agencies. Heads pre-publication unit providing advice on 24-hour basis. Also ranked in the annual International Commercial Litigation survey. Author of 'Business and the Human Rights Act'. Runs firm's pro bono practice.
Prof. Memberships: Law Society, City of London Solicitors' Company, Administrative Law Bar Association. Member of the Law Society's Human Rights Act Task Force and of the Liason Group to the Home Office's Human Rights act Task Force. Member of the Law Society's Defamation Pre-action Protocol Committee.
Career: Royal Belfast Academical Institution; Clare College, Cambridge (MA Law). Qualified 1982; partner *Clifford Chance* 1990; also admitted in Hong Kong and Northern Ireland.

STEIN, Richard
Leigh, Day & Co, London (020) 7650 1200
Specialisation: Practice covers administrative and public law including environmental town planning and community care matters. Acts principally for campaigning and community groups and individuals in judicial reviews of local authorities and public authorities. Co-author of 'Planning and Environmental Law' by Longmans. Acted in R v HFEA exp Diane Blood, forced caesarian re S and Save Our Railways anti-privatisation case.
Prof. Memberships: United Kingdom Environmental Law Association and Environmental Law Foundation.
Career: Called to the Bar 1982. Admitted solicitor 1994. Joined *Leigh Day & Co* 1993.
Personal: Born 15th December 1954.

TROTTER, John M.
Bates, Wells & Braithwaite, London
(020) 7551 7777
Partner and head of litigation department since 1976.
Specialisation: Administrative Law and Judicial Review for both Applicants and Respondents. Advises in particular regulatory bodies in various fields including telecommunications and accountancy.
Personal: Born 1948.

WALLACE, Alastair
Tyndallwoods, Birmingham (0121) 624 1111
Partner
Specialisation: Joint head of Public Law Department. Practice specialises in the administrative and public law on behalf of applicants in a range of, mainly, local government related issues, in particular education, community care, planning and health law. Considerable experience in judicial review on behalf of individuals and campaigning groups in public interest – type cases. Has particular expertise in asylum seekers rights, village green law, quarries and football stadia. Has contributed articles to Legal Action and Mineral Planning. Experience in advocacy at planning enquiries, village green registration hearings and in education matters.
Career: Joined *Tyndallwoods* in 1991
Personal: Film, music and cycling.

WATSON, Peter M.
Allen & Overy, London (020) 7330 3000
Specialisation: Acts for both applicants and respondents in judicial review and administrative law matters. Advises a number of public bodies including The Radio Authority, Radiocomments Agency and The Arts Council of England. Member of the Civil Procedure Rules Committee.
Career: Assistant solicitor *Allen & Overy* 1981-86, seconded to *Allen & Overy* Dubai office 1984-86; partner *Allen & Overy* 1987.
Personal: BA Oxford University 1978. Born 1956.

WHITE, Martin
Pinsent Curtis, Birmingham (0121) 200 1050
martin.white@pinsents.com
Partner in property department. Head of planning and environment. Member of major projects unit.
Specialisation: Handles planning and related areas including environmental issues, with emphasis on planning appeal work, development plans, issues of planning gain, Section 106 agreements and waste matters. Has acted in appeals relating to major inward investment, airports and business parks, for local Planning Authorities and private sector clients. Also handles local government and public law generally. Involved generally in advice given to local authorities. Involved with substantial PFI projects. Author of articles, speaker at conferences and seminars on planning gain and environmental issues.
Prof. Memberships: Law Society (Member of Planning Panel), Legal Associate of Royal Town Planning Institute.
Career: Qualified in 1979. Articled at Solihull Council 1977-79. Joined *Pinsent & Co.* in 1981. Partner in 1987.
Personal: Born 1953. Attended Cambridge University 1972-76; Newcastle Polytechnic 1976-77. Interests include drama and music.

WILLIAMS, Huw
Edwards Geldard, Cardiff (029) 2023 8239
huw.williams@geldards.co.uk
Partner, Public Law.
Specialisation: Principal area of practice encompasses public, planning and environmental law. Has worked extensively since 1987 on major urban renewal projects for the Welsh Development Agency, Cardiff Bay Development Corporation and local authorities, including numerous compulsory purchase orders, Parliamentary procedures relating to the Cardiff Bay Barrage project and joint ventures. Advice to both public and private interests on planning law and related matters including highways and utilities. Environmental experience includes cases relating to water pollution and contaminated land. Retained on a number of Millennium projects including Wales Millennium Centre and National Botanic Garden of Wales. Other public bodies advised include Cardiff University, National Library of Wales and the Arts Council of Wales. Currently preparing advice for clients on the implications of the establishment of the National Assembly for Wales.
Prof. Memberships: Law Society.
Career: Qualified 1978. Assistant Solicitor, Mid Glamorgan County Council 1978-80, Senior Assistant Solicitor 1980-84 and Principal Assistant Solicitor (Environmental Services) 1984-87. Joined *Edwards Geldard* in 1987 and became Partner in charge of Public Law in 1988.
Personal: Born 4th January 1954. Attended Llanelli Grammar School 1965-72, then Jesus College, Oxford 1972-75 (MA). Member of Council and Chairman, South East Wales branch, The Oxford Society; Member, Steering Committee, Welsh Public Law and Human Rights Association. Member of the Advisory Committee, Centre for Professional Legal Studies, Cardiff University; Member of the Regional Committee of Fairbridge. Leisure pursuits include sailing, skiing, scuba diving, art history and architecture.

ADVERTISING & MARKETING

London: 62; *Profiles*: 64

RESEARCH APPROVED BY BMRB: *For this edition,* Chambers' *researchers conducted 6083 interviews – 4408 with law firms, 598 with barristers and 1077 with clients.*

The validity of the research was scrutinised by BMRB International, who audited both the methodology and the results at our offices in July 2000. They interviewed Chambers' *researchers and cross-checked sample interviews. Details of the audit appear on page 7.*

LONDON

Lewis Silkin *"Still a serious advertising and marketing practice"* which retains its high profile in the sector, with across the board capability and a strong client list of leading 'above' and 'below the line' agencies, blue chip advertisers and new media agencies. The team was praised by clients as *"knowledgeable about the industry"* and *"good on the technical level."* The *"brilliant"* **Roger Alexander** remains well-known for his relationships with agencies and is highly rated in corporate and employment work, while the young head of department **Brinsley Dresden** *"is working hard"* and continues to build his reputation in pure copy clearance and contract work. The team's experience in the sector is best exemplified by its recent commission to produce a model industry contract for sales promotion, direct marketing and marketing communications. Recent trends of practice include pan-European campaigns in the traditional media and internet campaigns. Acted for Havas Advertising SA in their successful 'white knight' bid for the fully listed marketing services group Lopex plc. **Clients:** Abbott Mead Vickers Group Ltd; Havas Advertising SA; Modem Media Poppe Tyson Inc.

Macfarlanes Remains a top class outfit, its strong relationships with Omnicom and leading brand owners highlighting the significance of its *"impressive corporate capability"* in an increasingly acquisitive marketplace. It remains to be seen whether the retirement of William King will affect the team's strong reputation on the operational side, but in the *"bright and creative"* **Jeremy Courtenay-Stamp** the group has an individual to fill the gap. He is respected by clients for turning around work *"with the minimum of fuss and bluster."* The team acts for top advertising agencies, PR agencies, below the line agencies, advertisers and brand owners. Recent growth areas include e-commerce marketing and sponsorship deals (such as negotiating the multi-million pound sponsorship deals for the Jaguar Formula One team with HSBC, Becks and DHL.) Acted in the US$185 million acquisition by Cordiant Communication Group of Healthworld Corporation. **Clients:** Bates UK; Omnicom Europe; Saatchi & Saatchi plc.

Osborne Clarke OWA Rises in the rankings to reflect the team's growing reputation in the field, with expertise in the corporate and internet sectors complementing the established profile of the *"innovative"* and *"commercial"* **Stephen Groom.** He is seen by many as *"the best"* on the operational side *("the man to go to with a cutting edge, contentious campaign.")* Corporate lawyer **Timothy Birt** is also *"steeped in the industry"* and was particularly praised by clients for his *"sound, robust, analytical mind."* Clients include major existing and start-up agencies and brand owners. The team is also notable for its strong presence in the interactive sector and advises internet portal organisations, including Yahoo!, on marketing issues such as website joint ventures, traffic in-sites and website supply and design contracts. Acted for Rainey Kelly Campbell Roalfe in their merger with Young and Rubicam's UK advertising agency. **Clients:** Partners BDDH; New PHD; Colleagues Direct Marketing Limited.

LEADING IN-HOUSE LAWYERS

Giles CROWN, Head of Legal & Business Affairs, *TBWA*

Kate FULTON, Chief UK Counsel, *Young & Rubicam*

Larisa JOY, Director of Strategic Development, *Ogilvy*

Giles Crown is highly regarded for his work in advertising law and industry regulation. Since arriving from the bar, he now *"has a very good grip of the industry"* and shows *"an impressive commercial attitude."* He also plays a management role, liaising between staff and management. More focused on strategy than the law is **Larisa Joy** who is known for her management work. There is *"no one better in the business of advertising."* Also recommended is **Kate Fulton** who is praised for her commercial understanding of the industry, which covers communications, marketing and PR, as well as advertising.

In-House lawyers profiles: page 1177

ADVERTISING & MARKETING • London	Ptnrs	Assts
❶ Lewis Silkin	12	12
Macfarlanes	6	8
Osborne Clarke OWA	6	10
❷ The Simkins Partnership	2	1
❸ Field Fisher Waterhouse	2	6
Hammond Suddards Edge	6	6
❹ CMS Cameron McKenna	5	5
Theodore Goddard	3	4
❺ Lawrence Graham	4	3
Rowe & Maw	2	2
Taylor Joynson Garrett	2	6
❻ Baker & McKenzie	2	3
Beachcroft Wansbroughs	1	5
Clifford Chance	1	2
Lovells	Fu	Fu
Olswang	5	5
Townleys	1	4

LEADING INDIVIDUALS
❶ **ALEXANDER Roger** Lewis Silkin
GROOM Stephen Osborne Clarke OWA
HALL-SMITH Vanessa The Simkins Partnership
SWAN Charles The Simkins Partnership
❷ **BIRT Timothy** Osborne Clarke OWA
COURTENAY-STAMP Jeremy Macfarlanes
STALLARD Hayley Field Fisher Waterhouse
❸ **AZIM-KHAN Rafi** McDermott, Will & Emery
BRAFMAN Guilherme CMS Cameron McKenna
BYRT Sarah Rowe & Maw
THOMAS Richard Clifford Chance
UP AND COMING
DRESDEN Brinsley Lewis Silkin

Within each band, firms are listed alphabetically. *See **Profiles** on page 64*

Fu *Figures unavailable at time of going to press.*

The Simkins Partnership Unanimous praise for the team's 'pure' advertising expertise raises the practice to the major leagues this year, but its perceived lack of serious corporate capacity hinders progress to the very top. Undertakes all aspects of copy clearance, disputes and contract work for a large client base including four of the top ten 'above the line' ad agencies. Direct marketing agencies, broadcasters and internet clients also feature on the roster. The team has particular expertise in media and entertainment-related issues such as negotiating talent contracts. **Charles Swan** is seen as *"well balanced, knowledgeable and approachable,"* while **Vanessa Hall-Smith** joins him in the top band this year after strong market recommendation. Some corporate work is also handled, and the practice is currently acting for the London managers of Fallon McElligott Ltd in relation to the sale of the Fallon McElligott Group to Publicis. **Clients:** Lowe Lintas; J. Walter Thompson; Fallon McElligott.

Field Fisher Waterhouse Known for its presence in the brand-owning and sponsorship sectors, the practice rises this year, following repeated recommendations as *"the firm to watch."* Content specialist **Hayley Stallard** is now recognised as a *"serious player."* Particularly strong on the IP side, with an in-house trademark agency providing assistance on branding issues, the practice is also noted for its expertise on internet advertising and has recently launched a website to provide legal information to the advertising and marketing industry. International work is another area of growth, with particular regard to campaign clearance across several jurisdictions. Advised First Quench Retailing Limited on its merchandising agreement with Rugby World Cup 1999. **Clients:** The Incorporated Society of British Advertisers; Whitbread; Black Cat.

Hammond Suddards Edge Rises in the rankings to reflect its *"reinforced London profile."* Particularly known for the corporate work it undertakes for major client the WPP group, the team handles a full range of services, including specialist copy clearance and contract work. Its client base includes leading advertising agencies, advertisers and marketing agencies. Increasingly active in the media buying, sports marketing and internet sectors. Advised OgilvyOne on its provision of advertising and marketing services in respect of the collection of the BBC television licence fee. **Clients:** Ogilvy & Mather; J.Walter Thompson; Woolworths.

CMS Cameron McKenna Although **Guilherme Brafman** *("a good client man")* has received wide-ranging market plaudits, the team itself is still felt to be a low-profile unit. Better-known for corporate matters than its content advice, the group also includes a trademarks litigator. Possessing a strong niche in pharmaceutical advertising, the team acts for a clientele which includes advertising agencies and financial institutions. Advised on contract issues for a worldwide advertising campaign for BP Amoco. **Clients:** Grey Advertising; Camelot; Mediacom.

Theodore Goddard Retains a solid reputation in the sector, though it remains to be seen how the departure of Rafi Azim-Khan to McDermott, Will & Emery will affect the activity and profile of the department. Notable for its regulatory work for the Advertising Standards Agency, the practice has a client portfolio of agencies and advertisers. Typically handles copy clearance, direct marketing, sales promotion, sponsorship and internet work. Acted for ASA in its successful defence of an application for judicial review of the decision of the ASA in R v Advertising Standards Authority ex parte Charles Robertson (Developments) Limited. **Clients:** Arks Advertising; Signet Group; VarTec Telecom.

Lawrence Graham Particularly active in the fields of home shopping, direct marketing and related e-commerce advertising issues. The team is noted in the market for its expertise in competition implications, and is experienced in pan-European campaigns and UK and EC inquiries on marketing practices. Acts for agencies, branded goods producers and several leading 'below the line' agencies. Has recently advised a new internet advertising company on all the marketing aspects of its start-up, including referral structures, advertising contracts, membership agreements and data protection issues. **Clients:** Sony Computer Entertainment; Direct Selling Association; Financial Times.

Rowe & Maw Seen to be *"having a push"* in this area, the team rises in the rankings this year. **Sarah Byrt** remains rated by the market, and provides an impressive agency client base with advice on copy clearance, contracts, sales promotions and disputes with artists. In addition, the firm has assisted with agency mergers and sales, employment and property advice. Advised a number of US based companies on extending their internet-based promotions. **Clients:** McCann Ericsson; Collett Dickenson Pearce; St Luke's.

Taylor Joynson Garrett Though known in the market for its IP and litigation expertise, the practice is also active on the corporate side, and acts for Omnicom Group Inc in negotiating and documenting its international TBWA network acquisitions outside North America. Members of the IP department act for large advertisers and several agency clients, with expertise in copy clearance, disputes, agency agreements, internet advertising and regulatory work. Advised TBWA, Hong Kong in its acquisition of three agencies in New Zealand. **Clients:** TBWA International Network; Design & Artists Copyright Society.

Baker & McKenzie Based within the IP group, the practice's recognised expertise in comparative advertising issues, notably in telecoms, and online promotion work, lead it into the rankings this year. The firm's international network allows the practice to advise multi-national advertisers on multi-jurisdictional campaigns and UK compliance. Advised Sony in connection with an ASA investigation into advertisements which were the subject of competitor complaints. **Clients:** Orange; Leo Burnett; Network Associates/McAfee.

Beachcroft Wansbroughs Known particularly for its close relationship with D'Arcy, the team remains respected for its *"genuine advertising practice."* Work handled includes clearance issues, negotiation of agency/client contracts, sales promotions, disputes and corporate advice. Growth areas include sponsorship and internet advertising, often with a pan-European dimension. Advised Walsh Trott Chick Smith on its series of confrontational press campaigns for Channel 5. **Clients:** D'Arcy; Osprey; IMP Ltd.

Clifford Chance Part time team with a strong reputation for acting for advertisers. In addition to copy clearance and commercial regulatory advice, the team has particular expertise in pursuing and defending complaints through complaints authorities. E-commerce activity, direct marketing strategic and operation advice and cross-border transactions are other areas of expertise. Group co-ordinator **Richard Thomas** is primarily a public policy lawyer, but is seen as a *"guru on regulation generally"* and has recognised expertise in the advertising field. Retained by the Radio Authority to update and re-draft its Advertising and Sponsorship Code. **Clients:** HSBC; Radio Authority; Morgan Stanley Dean Witter.

Lovells Although not felt to be specialists, the team is commended for its *"cracking work"* on brand support matters. Although best-known for a high-powered corporate client base, the team does advise a well-known acquisitive agency. Do not currently possess a recognised individual big-hitter. **Clients:** Well-known corporates; agencies.

Olswang Respected media firm which provides the full range of advertising law advice to a range of agencies, advertisers, production companies and brand consultants. Highly rated in the market for its presence in the sponsorship and new media fields, with particular ability in conditions and data protection issues. Corporate advice is another area of strength, which draws on the firm's experience in the media sector. Acted for Music Industry Chart Services Ltd in its agreement with Worldpop for the latter's sponsorship of the Official UK Top 40 singles and Artists' album charts. **Clients:** M&C Saatchi; Carphone Warehouse; Granada Media Group Limited.

Townleys Included in the rankings for its leading profile in sports sponsorship. The team acts for both rights holders and sponsors in all contractual and brand exploitation matters. Recent trends include sponsorship of music events and internet advertising issues. Acted for the Nationwide Building Society in its football sponsorship package which covered the Nationwide Football League, the Nationwide Conference and the English, Scottish and Welsh national teams. **Clients:** Nationwide Building Society.

Other Notable Practitioners **Rafi Azim-Khan** at McDermott, Will & Emery remains recommended for his advertising knowledge, though it is too early for his new firm to have made an impression on the market. His practice will concentrate on sponsorship and promotions work.

LEADERS IN ADVERTISING & MARKETING

ALEXANDER, Roger
Lewis Silkin, London (020) 7227 8001
Partner in Corporate Department.
Specialisation: Advising companies in the Marketing Services Industry in relation to corporate finance, mergers, acquisitions, flotations and high level employment issues including share incentivisation schemes and corporate governance. Acts for a raft of companies in the sector, both public and private, including some of the largest agency groups; also advises industry bodies. Lectures in the UK and overseas on issues and trends in the industry.
Prof. Memberships: Law Society, Solicitors European Group, Society of Share Scheme Practitioners.
Career: Qualified 1965. Partner at *Lewis Silkin* 1965. Head of Marketing Services Law Group. Lead Partner 1989-1998. Senior Partner 1999.

AZIM-KHAN, Rafi
McDermott, Will & Emery, London
(020) 7577 6900
europe@mwe.com
Head of *McDermott, Will & Emery's* Marketing and E-Commerce Groups.
Specialisation: Specialises in advertising/marketing, entertainment, intellectual property, internet/e-commerce and commercial law. Has considerable experience of advising both advertisers and agencies on "clearance" of materials and IP, consumer, media and marketing law and regulation both above and below the line. Has advised on a wide range of sales promotions and sports related deals (e.g. France '98 World Cup), prize competitions, lotteries, newspaper and television promotions (e.g. UK's first £1 million prize promotions on TFI Friday and Virgin Radio), formats, terms and conditions. Net-shopping, gaming, portals, exchanges, auctions, B2B and B2C sites. Also has particular experience of drafting a wide range of e-commerce, internet, marketing, media, music, sports sponsorship, player/performer, agent, merchandising, licensing and various other commercial agreements. Lectures and writes regularly on e-commerce, sports, intellectual property, marketing and various other related topics. Is the firm's representative to the Advertising Law Group.
Career: Qualified 1993. Previously at *Lewis Silkin* 1993-1995, *Cameron McKenna* 1995-1997, *Theodore Goddard* 1997-2000.
Personal: Educated at Cranbrook College and at Queen Mary College, University of London 1987 to 1990 (LLB Hons. Studied IP at IP Law Unit). Keen sportsman and enjoys travel, music and motor racing. Resides London.

BIRT, Timothy D.
Osborne Clarke OWA, London (020) 7809 1022
tim.birt@osborneclarke.com
Partner in Corporate Department and member of Brandlegal Group.
Specialisation: Corporate, with a bias towards advising clients in marketing services, media, retail and new economies sectors. Has been particularly active in the new issues market over the last few years, handling flotations of leading technology clients including Stepstone and Redstone. Although responsible for managing a team of specialist solicitors, remains very actively involved in transactions. Co-edits Butterworths company law service, contributing to the section on structuring joint ventures and owner-managed business.
Career: Qualified in 1985. With *D.J. Freeman* 1983-87. Joined *Osborne Clarke* in 1987 and became a Partner in 1988.

BRAFMAN, Guilherme
CMS Cameron McKenna, London
(020) 7367 2754
gb@cmck.com
Specialisation: Corporate, M&A, Advertising & Marketing, IT, e-commerce, media, copyright, Financial Services and sitting as arbitrator. All aspects of advertising, client contracts, artists' agreements, campain clearance, and especially the buying and selling of agencies, P.R. companies and financial services businesses. Advertising disputes and high-level hiring and firing.
Prof. Memberships: M.C.I. Arb; City of London Solicitors Company; The Law Society.
Career: Qualified 1979 with *Slaughter and May.* 1983 founded *Brafmans* which (as *Brafman Morris*) merged in 1989 with *Cameron Markby Hewitt* (now *CMS Cameron McKenna*).
Publications: Various articles and chapter in an encyclopaedia of International Joint Ventures.
Personal: Educated at Downing College, Cambridge. Lives in London and Norfolk. Married, 2 sons. Interests: Family, tennis, swimming, food, etc. Fluent in Portuguese and French.

BYRT, Sarah
Rowe & Maw, London (020) 7248 4282
Specialisation: Intellectual property with a particular emphasis on advertising, publishing and media matters. Acts for several agencies including McCann-Erickson, CDP, Camp Chipperfield Hill Murray and Maher Bird Associates. UK contributor to a major French advertising law textbook.
Career: LLB (Law with French) Birmingham and Limoges Universities. Joined *Rowe & Maw* as trainee in 1986. Has specialised in IP since qualifying in 1988. Made partner in 1995.
Personal: Food, travel, friends.

COURTENAY-STAMP, D. Jeremy
Macfarlanes, London (020) 7831 9222
Partner in Company, Commercial and Banking Department.
Specialisation: Specialises in advertising and marketing. Acting for 5 of the top 20 advertising agencies, as well as a number of other above, below and through the line agencies. Has written articles and lectured extensively on this subject. Also advises on all aspects of commercial and intellectual property.
Prof. Memberships: City of London Law Society. Member of Commercial Law sub-committee.
Career: Qualified in 1986 while with *Macfarlanes.* Became a Partner in 1992.

DRESDEN, Brinsley
Lewis Silkin, London (020) 7227 8000
Specialisation: Head of Advertising Law and Partner in the Intellectual Property Unit specialising in non-contentious IP law. Advises a wide range of advertising agencies and advertisers, as well as clients seeking other IP advice. Frequently advises on clearance issues such as parodies of feature films, unauthorised references to living individuals, incorporation of third party IP rights; negotiating on contracts between advertisers and agencies, and for talent appearing in advertising campaigns; also advises on making and defending complaints to the ITC, the BACC and the ASA. Participated in negotiating and drafting standard form client/agency agreements for both the advertising and Direct Marketing and Sales Promotion industry. Increasingly involved with new media advertising, including clearances for internet advertising and sales promotion and drafting web site design and hosting contracts. Regularly lectures on a wide range of legal issues concerning advertising and marketing.
Prof. Memberships: European Advertising Lawyers Association; Global Advertising Lawyers Alliance.
Career: Born 25.2.66; Educated King's College School, Wimbledon; University of Bristol (LLB Hons 1987); College of Law, Guildford; King's College London (LLM 1999). Trained *Nabarro Nathanson* and qualified 1991. *BT Group Legal Services* 1993-1996; *Lewis Silkin* 1996; Partner 1999.
Personal: Interests include sailing, swimming and the arts.

GROOM, Stephen
Osborne Clarke OWA, London (020) 7809 1260
stephen.groom@osborneclarke.com
Head of Br@ndlegal Group.
Specialisation: Specialises in advertising, marketing, media and intellectual property law. Extensive contentious and non-contentious experience having advised 17 out of today's top 30 advertising agencies on compliance, disputes and contracts with suppliers and clients. Principal author of 'The Contract', the leading industry-approved template agreement for the provision of advertising services. Co-author of Kluwer's 'Advertising Law in Europe and North America'.
Prof. Memberships: European Advertising Lawyers' Association, Global Advertising Lawyers'

Alliance, Advertising Law Group, Promotional Marketing Association.
Career: With *Oswald Hickson Collier* 1975-82, *Macfarlanes* 1982-85, *Lewis Silkin* 1985-99. Joined *Osborne Clarke* as a partner in 1999.

HALL-SMITH, Vanessa
The Simkins Partnership, London (020) 7907 3000
Partner in Advertising and Marketing Department.
Specialisation: Principal area of practice is advertising and marketing. Work includes clearance advice on TV, print and direct marketing campaigns, agency/client contracts, talent contracts, TV production issues, sales promotion, data protection, sponsorship, e-commerce and new media. Clients include advertising agencies, advertisers, sales promotion and direct marketing agencies, photo libraries and photographers. Also handles employment-related immigration, with focus on entertainment and leisure industries. Speaks frequently on advertising and marketing at conferences and seminars and is a regular contributor to legal and trade publications.
Career: In practice at the Bar 1987-91. Qualified as a Solicitor in 1993. Partner with *The Simkins Partnership* since 1996.
Personal: Educated at Exeter University, Johannes Gutenberg Universitat, Mainz, Germany and the Universite d'Aix/ Marseille, France. Lives in London.

STALLARD, Hayley
Field Fisher Waterhouse, London (020) 7861 4000
Specialisation: Main area of practice is intellectual property with almost exclusive emphasis on advertising, marketing, sponsorship, merchandising, endorsement and lotteries. Clients include major advertisers such as Whitbread PLC, Evian/Volvic, Pizza Hut and Avon, and leading promotional agencies and trade organisations such as ISBA and the Lotteries Council. Regular speaker at conferences.
Prof. Memberships: Member of the European Sponsorship Consultants Association (ESCA); the British Association of Sport and Law (BASL); the Institute of Sports Sponsorship (ISS); the Advertising Law Group; and the Executive Committee/V-P Intellectual Property Commission of the Association Internationale des Jeunes Avocats (AIJA).
Career: Qualified at *Winckworth Sherwood*, 1990, becoming a partner in January 1995. Joined *Field Fisher Waterhouse* October 1996, Partner October 1999.
Publications: Legal consultant editor to 'Essential Facts: Sales and Marketing' and author of second edition of 'Sponsorship, Merchandising and Endorsement' (published by Sweet and Maxwell).

SWAN, Charles
The Simkins Partnership, London (020) 7907 3060
charles.swan@simkins.com
Partner in advertising and marketing department.
Specialisation: Main area of practice is advertising law, covering copy clearance, contracts, disputes, new media issues, intellectual property and general advice to advertisers, their agencies and trade associations. Also advises generally on intellectual property law, especially in relation to photographers, photo libraries and on-line publishers. Co-author of Butterworth's 'Encyclopaedia of Forms and Precedents' (Advertising title), co-author of 'The ABC of UK Photographic Copyright', author of the Advertising Industry section in 'Copinger and Skone James on Copyright', 14th edition, Editorial Board member for 'Intellectual Property Lawyer' and author of numerous articles in legal and trade journals. Frequent speaker at advertising, publishing and photographic trade seminars.
Career: Qualified 1983. Articled at *Woodham Smith* 1981-83 before moving to the *Speechly Bircham* litigation department. Joined *The Simkins Partnership* in 1985 and became a partner in 1990. General Secretary of Advertising Law International.
Personal: Born 1956. Attended Cambridge University 1975-78. Leisure interests include hill walking.

THOMAS, Richard
Clifford Chance, London (020) 7600 1000
richard.thomas@cliffordchance.com
Specialisation: Joined *Clifford Chance* in 1992 after six years as Director of Consumer Affairs at the Office of Fair Trading where (amongst other statutory functions) he implemented the Misleading Advertisements Regulations. Has an extensive network of contacts within governmental and regulatory bodies, self-regulatory organisations and trade associations. Holds the following positions:- Member, Independent Television Commission Advertising Committee: Member, Direct Marketing Authority; Vice-President, Institute of Trading Standards; Member, Board of Financial Ombudsman Services. Richard Thomas is the author of 'Plain English for Lawyers'
Prof. Memberships: Law Society; Royal Society of Arts.
Career: *Freshfields* (1971 - 1974); CAB Legal Service (1974 - 1979); National Consumer Council (1979 - 1986); Office of Fair Trading (1986 - 1992); *Clifford Chance* (1992 - present).

AGRICULTURE

OVERVIEW: The current recession in agriculture has highlighted the vulnerability of the industry and, with EU and UK policy moving towards lower subsidies and higher regulation, the trend towards larger farms and more intensive farming is set to continue.

A similar trend is occurring within the agricultural law sector. Squeezed from above by the market leaders and from below by land agents keen to do more of the routine legal work, many smaller firms are finding agricultural law unremunerative. For those with a range of expertise, however, the current situation provides opportunities. Farmers and estate owners alike are focusing more keenly on alternative sources of income, share or contract farming and minimising tax liability. Increasing MAFF and EU regulation and concern about the government's environmental programme are providing work for those firms with the requisite skills. In the regions in particular the work is being concentrated into a smaller number of hands, of which Burges Salmon, *"the national agricultural practice,"* still stands out. The market has been further shaken up by the decision of the NFU to reduce its panel to nine names. The effectiveness of this move is still in doubt, but it has seen the entry into the sector of several high profile practices better known for commercial litigation.

RESEARCH APPROVED BY BMRB: *For this edition,* Chambers' *researchers conducted 6083 interviews – 4408 with law firms, 598 with barristers and 1077 with clients.*

The validity of the research was scrutinised by BMRB International, who audited both the methodology and the results at our offices in July 2000. They interviewed Chambers' *researchers and cross-checked sample interviews. Details of the audit appear on page 7.*

LONDON

AGRICULTURE • London	Ptnrs	Assts
❶ Farrer & Co	4	5
Macfarlanes	2	5
Withers	3	3
❷ Dawson & Co	*	*
Lee & Pembertons	2	1
Payne Hicks Beach	3	-
❸ Forsters	*	*
May, May & Merrimans	4	1
❹ Boodle Hatfield	3	3
Currey & Co	*	*

LEADING INDIVIDUALS
❶ JESSEL Christopher Farrer & Co
LANE Andrew Withers
❷ MOORE John Macfarlanes
❸ FURBER James Farrer & Co
HORNBY John Macfarlanes
PRING Simon Farrer & Co
UP AND COMING
KEDDIE Joanne Dawson & Co

Within each band, firms are listed alphabetically. *See* ***Profiles*** *on page 73*

** See editorial entries for explanations of team sizes.*

Farrer & Co Three hundred years old next year, this *"outstandingly good"* practice continues to grow. They have had *"a spectacular year"* acting for the Duchy of Cornwall in the purchase of the 28,000 acre Prudential land portfolio, and the core of their work remains acquisitions and sales for large landed estates. Also highly rated for heritage work, they have niche expertise on such diverse matters as treasure, commons rights and the law of the manor. *"Outstanding"* **Christopher Jessel** combines work for the firm with lecturing and writing, currently on overage. He is supported by the *"intelligent and well organised"* **Simon Pring**, especially on tenancies and tax. The *"first class, efficient"* **James Furber**, solicitor to the Duchy of Cornwall, is ranked for the first time this year. **Clients:** Duchy of Cornwall; Duchy of Lancaster.

Macfarlanes *"Thoroughbred"* firm with *"a marvellous selection of private clients."* It represents pension funds alongside landed estates and wealthy foreign owners. Considered to be more commercial than the other two leading London firms, the team is developing a particular expertise advising on EU regulations and environmental law. **John Moore** is *"exceptionally good on large transactions"* while **John Hornby** was also widely commended. Acted last year in the acquisition of 1,800 acres of the Wilton Castle Estate, including a golf club, nursery, aerial sites, agricultural tenancies and the greater part of a village.

Withers Acting for over 130 landed estates, this strong practice claims a large share of the market in farm and estate conveyancing. The core of the business remains transactional work but the team is also particularly strong on agricultural holdings issues. **Andrew Lane** is in the front rank of agricultural lawyers, and he and his team *"always know precisely what they're on about."* Last year dealt with green field development sites worth over £75 million and a £5 million sale of an estate to sitting tenants.

Dawson & Co (6 ptnrs & 2 assts 45%) Strong contentious practice with expertise in landlord and tenant disputes, milk quota disputes and claims against MAFF and the EU. **Joanne Keddie** is a *"national expert on EC quotas"* and *"an outstanding litigator."* The team also has some *"substantial private clients"* for whom it provides a comprehensive tax planning and property service.

Lee & Pembertons According to market perception, this firm has been *"upgrading its agricultural practice"* recently. Praised for being *"constructive"* and *"good to deal with,"* the practice acts for estate owners and farmers throughout the country and, alongside agricultural tenancy, conveyancing and estate management work, have niche expertise in sporting leases. Acted in the purchase and break-up of the Hackwood Park estate.

Payne Hicks Beach With an established private client base, this practice is perceived as one of the busiest London based firms in this sector outside the top three. Acting mainly for large estates, the team provides a full service including agricultural land transactions and tenancy work, with an emphasis on tax structuring.

Forsters (2 ptnrs & 1 asst 25%) Represent landed estates across the country, advising on acquisitions, partnership issues, tenancies and business reorganisation. Acted last year in the acquisition of two farms, each of several thousand acres.

May, May & Merrimans Long established private client firm acting for landed estates across the country. Core work includes agricultural conveyancing and estate planning and the team is developing a niche expertise in the disposal of land for development. Also negotiate certain town and country planning agreements with local authorities.

Boodle Hatfield Praised for the intelligence of its team and the clarity of its submissions, this practice represents large rural estates and the rural holdings of urban estates and institutions. Along with acquisitions, sales and advising on farm reorganisations, the team has a particular strength in the area of agricultural property taxation.

Currey & Co (7 ptnrs spend some time on agriculture) Newly ranked firm regarded as *"one of the best landed estate firms in London."* The practice boasts an impressive list of clients, are *"super conveyancers"* and excel in all aspects of agricultural land transfers.

THE SOUTH

AGRICULTURE • South	Ptnrs	Assts
❶ **Brachers** Maidstone	6	4
❷ **White & Bowker** Winchester	3	2
❸ **Cripps Harries Hall** Tunbridge Wells, Kent	1	1
Thomas Eggar Church Adams Chichester	1	2
❹ **Knights** Tunbridge Wells	3	1
Penningtons Godalming	2	2

LEADING INDIVIDUALS
❶ **HORNER Douglas** Brachers
❷ **KNIGHT Matthew** Knights
KYRKE Richard Venables Thomas Eggar Church Adams
MULCARE John Cripps Harries Hall
STEEL John White & Bowker

Within each band, firms are listed alphabetically. See *Profiles* on page 73

Brachers *"A force to be reckoned with,"* market opinion suggests that, having won an NFU panel contract, Brachers has edged ahead of the local competition. Much of the practice's success is due to the excellent all-round reputation of **Douglas Horner**, a *"charming man with an excellent knowledge of his subject."* Dealing with agricultural clients ranging from smallholders to large estates, the team has experience in all areas of agricultural law from multi-million pound property transactions, complex tenancies and milk quota disputes to planning and environmental work. Successfully defended a farmer in the Court of Appeal against a claim of polluting private water supplies by historic agricultural operations. **Clients:** NFU.

White & Bowker Broad practice striking a balance between contentious and non-contentious work. **John Steel**, an *"intelligent man with a good presence,"* heads a *"young and vigorous"* team. Acted last year in the acquisition of an estate with over £500,000 of milk quotas. The group has particular expertise on rights of way issues and has advised a number of clients on the Countryside Bill.

Cripps Harries Hall This firm has *"moved ahead in the last few years"* under the guidance of *"smashing mediator"* **John Mulcare**. Experienced in all areas of agricultural and countryside law from conveyancing and tenancies to planning and animal welfare proceedings, the practice is seen as having particular expertise in milk quota advice. Also specialises in equine law and advised last year on establishing a point-to-point. **Clients:** Union Railways Property.

Thomas Eggar Church Adams Perceived as more involved on the contentious side of agriculture, this firm has a lower profile among peers this year. Its private client side remains strong, however, and the team is increasingly involved in transactional and diversification work. *"High quality"* **Richard Kyrke** stands out.

Knights *"Aggressive, efficient litigator"* **Matthew Knight** heads this respected contentious practice specialising in judicial review, rights of way and sporting disputes. Represent sporting estates, countryside organisations and breed societies. Typical work includes defending farmers from criminal prosecutions over alleged blocked rights of way and animal welfare, and disputes over sporting rights. **Clients:** Countryside Alliance.

Penningtons Working for large estates and corporate clients, this practice specialises in secured lending work to the agricultural community and is also strong on tax planning, business restructuring, partnership disputes and environmental work. Highly regarded but hitherto perceived as *"very much a Surrey-focused operation,"* the firm's Newbury office is beginning to give them more of a profile further north. **Clients:** Agricultural Mortgage Corporation; Clydesdale Bank.

THAMES VALLEY

AGRICULTURE • Thames Valley	Ptnrs	Assts
❶ **Morgan Cole** Oxford	1	1
❷ **Henmans** Oxford	2	1
❸ **Pryce Collard Chamberlain** Abingdon	1	1
Stanley Tee & Company Bishop's Stortford	3	1

LEADING INDIVIDUALS
❶ **FINDLEY Christopher** Morgan Cole

Within each band, firms are listed alphabetically. See *Profiles* on page 73

Morgan Cole The *"stimulating"* **Christopher Findley** heads a practice renowned for its knowledge of the Agricultural Holdings Act. Also active on agricultural property and business matters, quotas, development and planning issues.

Henmans Acting for agricultural charities, offshore companies and landed estates across the country, this highly rated firm has particular expertise in development work, succession planning and partnership restructuring. Involved last year in the purchase of a large mixed agricultural estate with a let farm, fishing rights and development potential. **Clients:** West Wycombe Estate; Royal Agricultural Benevolent Institution.

Pryce Collard Chamberlain Strengthened by its November 1999 merger, this firm now works for around forty farms of up to 2,000 acres. Work includes acquisitions and disposals, and tenancy disputes, and the practice has particular expertise in quota advice and development work. Last year involved in the complex partitions of two farming partnerships.

Stanley Tee & Co Representing insurers, large estates and owner occupiers, this practice combines a strong private client side with expertise in agricultural, environmental and commercial litigation. **Clients:** Royal & Sun Alliance; Grupama.

SOUTH WEST

AGRICULTURE • South West	Ptnrs	Assts
❶ **Burges Salmon** Bristol	13	21
❷ **Wilsons** Salisbury	6	7
❸ **Clarke Willmott & Clarke** Taunton	4	3
Stephens & Scown Exeter	3	1
❹ **Bevan Ashford** Bristol	3	-
Bond Pearce Plymouth	1	3
Things & Long Bath	4	1
❺ **Battens (with Poole & Co)** Yeovil	1	-
Pardoes Bridgwater	2	6
❻ **Beviss & Beckingsale** Chard	2	1
Every & Phillips Honiton	*	*
Humphries Kirk Wareham	*	*
Osborne Clarke Bristol	3	6
Porter Dodson Yeovil	2	-

LEADING INDIVIDUALS
❶ **BUXTON James** Burges Salmon
DENSHAM Andrew Burges Salmon
NEVILLE William Burges Salmon
WILLIAMS Peter Rhys Burges Salmon
❷ **EVANS Della** Burges Salmon
FITZGERALD Peter Wilsons
MORRISON Alastair Burges Salmon
SWIFT Robert Wilsons
❸ **BATSTONE William** Burges Salmon
CHEAL Jonathan Thrings & Long
FARREN Miles Burges Salmon
RUSS Timothy Clarke Willmott & Clarke

Within each band, firms are listed alphabetically. *See **Profiles** on page 73*

* *See editorial entries for explanations of team sizes.*

Burges Salmon Still the *"pre-eminent firm in the whole country,"* they stand *"head and shoulders above the rest." "Superstar"* **Andrew Densham** is perhaps first among equals in a department that includes *"excellent"* **William Batstone**, *"leading advocate"* **James Buxton**, *"technically superb"* **Della Evans** and the *"tenacious and energetic"* **Peter Williams. William Neville** *"a tough litigator,"* is *"hugely knowledgeable,"* especially on European issues, while **Alastair Morrison** is *"fine and sensible"* on the non-contentious side. **Miles Farren** joins them from Roythorne & Co. Over the year they acted in £60 million worth of agricultural sales and have been developing their presence in the food sector acting for important food businesses as well as large estates and institutional clients. Particular strengths include agricultural insolvency, farming partnerships, EU and agri-business.

Wilsons Peter Fitzgerald and **Robert Swift** are the leading lights in what is uniformly agreed to be an excellent practice on the non-contentious side, with a superb client base including around seventy estates. *"Major specialists in land transactions,"* they are strong on tax planning and have developed a national expertise on heritage law.

Clarke Willmott & Clarke Praised for *"demonstrating a commitment to agriculture,"* this respected firm has particular expertise in planning and environment law, European law, judicial review and quota litigation. Newly rated **Tim Russ** is *"one of the best litigation solicitors in agriculture."* Involved this year in several widely publicised cases including R v MAFF ex parte Eastside Cheese Co RA Duckett & Co intervening (Court of Appeal).

Stephens & Scown A *"major player in Devon and Cornwall"* with a strong client base, the practice acts for estates, working farmers and corporate clients. Farm conveyancing continues to be a major area of work, with one transaction valued at £1.75 million. They are also active in tenancy, partnerships, share farming, pollution and planning advice, and have particular expertise in milk quota issues. **Clients:** Aggregate Industries UK Ltd; AMC; ECC International Ltd.

Bevan Ashford Large regional firm with an impressive client base and experience in partnership structuring and contentious work including quota disputes, European Court litigation and arbitrations. Successful this year in Floyer-Acland v Osmond (Court of Appeal).

Bond Pearce *"Efficient"* practice with a commercial litigation focus. The team recently won an NFU panel contract and also works for major lenders and large estates. Active in most contentious fields: product liability, boundary actions, partnership disputes and, increasingly, environmental and employment issues. Involved in the landmark decision of Swift v Dairywise. **Clients:** NFU; AMC.

Thrings & Long Successful NFU panel firm headed by the highly regarded **Jonathan Cheal**. Increasingly involved in agricultural litigation, the team also handles substantial conveyancing work and has niche expertise in public and private rights of way and non-contentious work in relation to quotas and subsidies. **Clients:** NFU.

Battens (with Poole & Co) Strong regional presence acting for a number of estates and farmers, both freeholders and tenants. Work includes the full range of agricultural law with particular expertise in diversification, share farming and cooperation agreements. Recently involved in Ward v Brunt, on partners' duty to fellow partners following dissolution.

Pardoes Acting for five large estates and numerous smaller farmers, this respected firm is experienced in agricultural conveyancing and tenancy work, and particularly strong on succession and 'nursing home fee' planning.

Beviss & Beckingsale Mainly acting for Blackdown Hill farms up to 2,000 acres, this well established local firm has a good reputation for agricultural work. Active in the full range of agricultural law with a particular specialism in water extraction, discharge consents and pollution in connection with private water supplies. **Clients:** Cricket St Thomas Estate.

Every & Phillips (4 ptnrs & 1 asst 25-50%) Established local firm mainly acting for smaller owner occupiers. Along with conveyancing and partnership work, have been involved in diversification and tax planning.

Humphries Kirk (3 ptnrs 20-30%) Working for farmers, farmers' co-operatives and landowners, this firm has been active in tenancy, pollution and milk quota cases. Have specialist farming and engineering expertise and also work for German banks on agricultural lending.

Osborne Clarke OWA Continue to be recognised largely in the non-contentious spheres, acting principally on estates work for a diverse regional client base.

Porter Dodson Still seen to be local players, albeit on a relatively small scale, the team acts for a number of individual farming clients and undertakes some estates work.

WALES

AGRICULTURE • Wales	Ptnrs	Assts
❶ **Margraves** Llandrindod Wells	1	-
❷ **Edward Harris & Son** Swansea	*	*
❸ **Gabb & Co** Abergavenny	1	-
Morgan Cole Cardiff	*	*

LEADING INDIVIDUALS
❶ **HARRIS Edward** Edward Harris & Son
MARGRAVE-JONES Clive Margraves
STEPHENS Jonathan Jonathan Stephens & Co

Within each band, firms are listed alphabetically. See **Profiles** on page 73

* *See editorial entries for explanations of team sizes.*

Margraves Leading firm with a strong practice, especially in mid-Wales, they represent estates, large companies and working farmers. *"Bright"* **Clive Margrave-Jones** is highly rated, especially on trusts, and also advises on tenancies and environmentally sensitive areas. **Clients:** Hyder Plc.

Edward Harris & Son (1 ptnr & 3 assts 25-33%) *"An expert on common land,"* **Edward Harris** gives this practice a high profile in that area and the firm is currently appealing to the House of Lords on rights of common. Work for commoners' associations across South Wales, and also do tenancy work and conveyancing.

Gabb & Co Respected local firm whose agricultural experience includes conveyancing, easements, overage, planning and quota work.

Morgan Cole (3 ptnrs & 3 assts spend some time on agriculture) NFU panel firm for South Wales and Herefordshire, it offers a broad range of expertise to the agricultural client. Typical work includes partnership and commercial disputes, environmental planning and quota advice.

Other Notable Practitioners Sole practitioner **Jonathan Stephens** has a solid and long-standing reputation for his advice on non-contentious agricultural matters.

MIDLANDS

AGRICULTURE • Midlands	Ptnrs	Assts
❶ **Roythorne & Co** Nottingham	1	-
❷ **Arnold Thomson** Towcester	1	4
Wright Hassall Leamington Spa	1	2
❸ **Hewitson Becke + Shaw** Northampton	2	2
Knight & Sons Newcastle-under-Lyme	*	*
Martineau Johnson Birmingham	2	1
Morton Fisher Worcester	6	-
❹ **Gabb & Co** Hereford	*	*
Lanyon Bowdler Shrewsbury	-	1
Lodders Stratford-upon-Avon	1	2
Manby & Steward Wolverhampton	1	1
Gwynnes Wellington	2	1

LEADING INDIVIDUALS
❶ **DAVIS Nigel** Roythorne & Co
OGG Robin Wright Hassall
THOMSON Michael Arnold Thomson
❷ **BARNETT Ian** Hewitson Becke + Shaw
QUINN James Stephen Christopher Morton Fisher
❸ **LODDER David** Lodders

Within each band, firms are listed alphabetically. See **Profiles** on page 73

* *See editorial entries for explanations of team sizes.*

Roythorne & Co Accepted as the leading Midlands firm because of its *"expertise in depth."* Represent traditional landlords and working farmers from across the entire region on the spectrum of agricultural work from large transactions to partnership restructuring and tax planning. Chair of the Agricultural Law Association, **Nigel Davis** is praised for his *"enthusiastic approach"* and ability to *"spot the salient points."*

Arnold Thomson *"Straight and hardworking"* **Michael Thomson** stands out at this niche agricultural practice. Acting mainly for working farmers, the firm takes a lot of tenancy work on referral and is highly regarded for its knowledge of IACS and other subsidies.

Wright Hassall & Co With a solid core of owner occupiers, this firm also acts for a number of agricultural and charitable institutions. **Robin Ogg** has an established reputation for offering *"practical, straightforward advice."* Strong on transactional work and tax planning, the team has expert knowledge of the Agricultural Holdings Act and negotiating development agreements. Involved this year in the sale of 23 acres of development land as a single transaction. **Clients:** Royal Agricultural Society; Rural Housing Trust; Rare Breeds Survival Trust; National Playing Fields Association.

Hewitson Becke + Shaw Historically acting for large estates, for whom it provides property and taxation advice, the firm has broadened its client base amongst smaller farmers. Experienced in quota advice and EU regulations the practice recently acted in the reorganisation and resettling of a large estate. **Ian Barnett** *"knows his law and is good at applying it."*

Knight & Sons (6 ptnrs & 2 assts 40-50%) *"Technically very good,"* this *"impressive set-up"* won a place on the NFU legal panel and also acts for a number of large companies and landed estates. Provides a range of services including quota, taxation and tenancy advice and last year acted in a £6.3 million estate acquisition involving tenancies, IACS, woodland grants and shooting rights. **Clients:** ARC Ltd; Hepworth Minerals & Chemicals Ltd; Josiah Wedgwood & Sons Ltd; NFU.

Martineau Johnson Possessing a strong base amongst landowners, the firm's expertise also attracts developers, major lenders, local authorities and land-owning institutions. Involved last year in major tax planning exercises encompassing development agreements and property work.

Morton Fisher The *"excellent"* **James Quinn** with his *"in depth knowledge of agricultural legislation"* is the leading light in this practice. With a strong litigation slant and expertise on partnership disputes and arbitrations, the team also acts for a number of large land-owners doing the range of non-contentious work.

Gabb & Co (2 ptnrs & 1 asst spend some time on agriculture) Regional firm providing a full range of services to the rural community. Niche expertise in organo-phosphate claims.

Lanyon Bowdler Mainly working for the smaller owner-occupier, the team handles a range of work including conveyancing, partnership disputes, farm business tenancies, boundary work and taxation advice.

Lodders Highly rated for his advice on behalf of estates clients, **David Lodder** is praised for his *"common sense."* Work includes the full range of agricultural law, but the practice is especially noted for its expertise in resolving partnership disputes.

Manby & Steward With experience in conveyancing, tenancies and succession planning, this firm's work is divided between smaller farmers and large estates. Expertise in claw-backs for future development value, and the team also does some equestrian work.

Gwynnes Small firm which retains a good share of the Herefordshire area and *"know what they are doing."*

EAST ANGLIA

AGRICULTURE • East Anglia	Ptnrs	Assts
❶ **Mills & Reeve** Norwich	8	8
Roythorne & Co Spalding	6	3
❷ **Barker Gotelee** Ipswich	2	5
Taylor Vinters Cambridge	5	2
❸ **Birketts** Ipswich	3	2
Eversheds Norwich	2	-
Hewitson Becke + Shaw Cambridge	3	1
❹ **Ashton Graham** Ipswich, Bury St Edmunds	2	-
Howes Percival Norwich	2	1
Prettys Ipswich	3	3
❺ **Chattertons** Horncastle	1	2
Greene & Greene Bury St. Edmunds	1	-
Rustons & Lloyd Newmarket	*	*
Wilkin Chapman Louth, Lincoln	2	-

LEADING INDIVIDUALS
❶ **BARR William** Mills & Reeve
SMITH Graham Roythorne & Co
❷ **ARROWSMITH-BROWN Matthew** Mills & Reeve
BARKER Richard Barker Gotelee
HEAL Jeremy Howes Percival
HORWOOD-SMART Adrian Taylor Vinters
SYDENHAM Angela Birketts
PLUMMER Alan Roythorne & Co
❸ **AUBREY Michael** Mills & Reeve
DENNIS Jeanette Taylor Vinters
WHITTAKER Geoff Barker Gotelee
WYBAR David Kenneth Ashton Graham

Within each band, firms are listed alphabetically. *See **Profiles** on page 73*
** See editorial entries for explanations of team sizes.*

Mills & Reeve *"Bright"* and *"effective"* **William Barr**, *"East Anglia's answer to Andrew Densham,"* heads what is regarded as *"one of the leading three or four firms in the country."* He is ably supported by **Michael Aubrey** and **Matthew Arrowsmith-Brown**, singled out from a strong team as knowledgeable and *"good to deal with."* Traditionally providing a comprehensive service to landowners and large farmers, the firm is expanding into the food industry and has been active in establishing commercial structures to assist farmers in fulfilling supply contracts.

Roythorne & Co Particularly active in Lincolnshire and the west of the region, this large firm has clients ranging from 500 to 5,000 acres. Highly rated for transactional work, the practice is increasingly involved in setting up machinery co-operatives and contract farming arrangements, and has particular expertise in business structuring and restructuring and agricultural tax advice. **Graham Smith**, rated for his *"encyclopaedic knowledge"* and *"great enthusiasm,"* is supported by *"technically able"* **Alan Plummer**.

Barker Gotelee Recognised agricultural and transport practice with *"high profile"* **Richard Barker** doing *"cutting-edge, coal-face work,"* supported by the *"switched on"* **Geoff Whittaker**. Best known for a close working relationship with the European Commission, the team is moving into the agri-food business, advising major companies on quality assurance and trademarks.

Taylor Vinters Working for large estates, farms, food businesses and other institutions, this practice is beginning to establish a national reputation. Core areas include conveyancing, tenancy advice, planning and environmental issues. Active in setting up 'innovative farming arrangements' such as combined farming companies. **Jeanette Dennis** and **Adrian Horwood-Smart** are the main practitioners of a team which also has a sizeable bloodstock practice. **Clients:** University of Cambridge; Jockey Club Estates.

Birketts *"Excellent"* and *"academically sound"* **Angela Sydenham** does much to raise the profile of this highly regarded practice. The group has a national reputation for rights of way issues, but also acts for landowners and councils on issues ranging from acquisitions, tenancy and planning to commons, navigation and milk quota advice.

Eversheds *"Traditionally strong"* primarily non-contentious practice, with strength in conveyancing, tenancies, partnership structuring and negotiating development agreements. Mainly act for working farmers and landowners, but increasingly involved with agri-business and non-landowning clients diversifying into agriculture.

Hewitson Becke + Shaw Highly regarded in the agricultural sphere, this practice represents some large landowning charities alongside farmers and large estates.

Ashton Graham *"High profile"* **David Wybar** is the leading practitioner at this respected regional firm. Provide a full range of agricultural services to estates and large commercial farms and recently completed a complex conditional contract for a large area of development land.

Howes Percival Private client practice acting for over forty landowning families with assets over £1 million. They have expertise in estate planning, farm conveyancing, town and country planning work, tenancy work and negotiating development land agreements. *"Practical"* **Jeremy Heal** stands out for his *"sharp advice,"* particularly on taxation. **Clients:** Her Majesty's Sandringham Estate; RICS Arbitration Service; Harwich Haven Authority; International League for the Protection of Horses.

Prettys Having won an NFU panel contract, the firm is *"promoting their agricultural department"* and is considered to be building up its expertise. Tend to act for the smaller owner-occupier on commercial disputes, diversification and partnership advice, but also represent some large estates and food companies.

Chattertons Acting for medium to large owner-occupiers, many with holdings over 1,000 acres, this rural firm acts in partnership structuring and restructuring, share farming arrangements and tenancy arrangements. The firm is currently involved in a number of high-value acquisitions and disposals and has particular expertise in agricultural cooperative work.

Greene and Greene *"Well-organised"* firm with a sound client base, which is active on the non-contentious side, establishing farm business tenancies and partnership agreements. Currently involved in a number of large farm transactions.

Rustons & Lloyd (4 ptnrs 25-33%) Better known for a nationally regarded bloodstock practice, this firm also represents large estates and farms. Expert in heritage work, the team was involved last year in the sale of an estate worth over £2 million.

Wilkin Chapman Concentrated in the North Lincolnshire area, although acting for clients across the country, this firm works mainly for farms ranging from 100 to 5,000 acres. Equally experienced in contentious and non-contentious matters, they were involved last year in several land transactions exceeding £2 million.

NORTH WEST

AGRICULTURE • North West	Ptnrs	Assts
❶ **Cartmell Shepherd** Carlisle	1	3
❷ **Oglethorpe Sturton & Gillibrand** Lancaster	1	1
Walker Smith & Way Chester	3	-
❸ **Birch Cullimore** Chester	2	1
Mason & Moore Dutton Chester	2	-
Napthen Houghton Craven Preston	3	2

LEADING INDIVIDUALS
❶ **CARTMELL Timothy** Cartmell Shepherd
GILLIBRAND Martin Oglethorpe Sturton & Gillibrand
❷ **COLLINS Peter** Walker Smith & Way

Within each band, firms are listed alphabetically. *See **Profiles** on page 73*

Cartmell Shepherd Beyond dispute the premier firm in the North West, with an enviable national reputation. The *"brilliant"* **Timothy Cartmell** stands out for the quality of his advice. Typical work includes conveyancing, quota and subsidy advice, tenancies and tax planning, with a recent increase in insolvency work, partnership and boundary disputes. **Clients:** English Nature; North West Water.

Oglethorpe Sturton & Gillibrand **Martin Gillibrand** is a renowned litigator with *"a good knowledge of quotas,"* but it is his expertise on sporting and commonland issues which sets this practice apart. Involved last year in the sale of a large grouse moor.

Walker Smith & Way The leading firm in Cheshire, it acts for landowners and tenants advising on dairy farming matters, tenancies, diversification and, increasingly, business reorganisations. **Peter Collins** is the stand-out practitioner here.

Birch Cullimore Long established *"efficient"* firm with a strong landlord connection. The group represents a number of large regional estates on work such as tenancy disputes, milk quota issues, tax planning, diversification and conveyancing.

Mason & Moore Dutton The firm acts primarily for working farmers, particularly in the dairy sector. Typical work includes tax planning, milk quota advice, conveyancing, and tenancy and succession work.

Napthen Houghton Craven Having won an NFU panel contract, this practice are doing much more agricultural work than previously, particularly on the contentious side. Their clients tend to be working farmers, often in dairying, and they have particular expertise in retirement planning, partnership restructuring and negotiating development options. **Clients:** NFU.

YORKSHIRE

AGRICULTURE • Yorkshire	Ptnrs	Assts
❶ **Rollit Farrell & Bladon** Hull	2	1
❷ **Addleshaw Booth & Co** Leeds	4	7
Grays York	2	-
Wrigleys Leeds	2	-
❸ **Andrew M. Jackson & Co** Hull	1	1
Stamp Jackson and Procter Hull	*	*

LEADING INDIVIDUALS
❶ **STONE James** Addleshaw Booth & Co

Within each band, firms are listed alphabetically. *See **Profiles** on page 73*
** See editorial entries for explanations of team sizes.*

Rollit Farrell & Bladon Strong contentious practice in the forefront of EU litigation, particularly over IACS. The practice also acts for a number of large estates on non-contentious matters. Recently acting in over £4 million worth of farm transactions, the team has also just been appointed to act for one of the largest estates in the north following a beauty parade.

Addleshaw Booth & Co Strong local presence especially highly rated for conveyancing, the firm acts primarily for private clients and large estate owners, and also has expertise in landlord and tenant work, quota issues and tax planning. **James Stone** has a specific name for agricultural property work.

Grays *"Excellent firm"* with a strong following amongst Yorkshire's landowners. Provide an all round service, primarily on the non-contentious side, from conveyancing and tenancy work to quota advice. Recently involved in a rolling programme of farm building conversions resulting in over twenty commercial lettings.

Wrigleys Formed from the private client departments of a number of firms, to which Eversheds (Leeds) was added last year, the firm concentrates on acquisitions, tax and heritage advice and do no contentious work. Clients include large estates and trusts, and the team has particular expertise in rural regeneration projects.

Andrew M. Jackson & Co Primarily non-contentious practice working for smaller farmers and large landowners in the Yorkshire and North Lincolnshire area. Typical work includes purchase and disposal of land, tax and succession planning and tenancy work. Recently involved in a number of successful farm partitions.

Stamp Jackson and Proctor (5 ptnrs & 2 assets spend between 20 & 40% of time on agriculture) New entry this year, providing a full range of services to the agricultural client including acquisitions, disposals and business restructuring.

NORTH EAST

AGRICULTURE • North East	Ptnrs	Assts
❶ **Dickinson Dees** Newcastle upon Tyne	4	4
❷ **Ward Hadaway** Newcastle upon Tyne	4	5
❸ **Latimer Hinks** Darlington	3	-
❹ **Jacksons** Stockton-on-Tees	*	*

LEADING INDIVIDUALS
❶ **HARGREAVE Hume** Dickinson Dees
HEWITT Christopher Ward Hadaway
❷ **KIRKUP Simon** Dickinson Dees

Within each band, firms are listed alphabetically. *See **Profiles** on page 73*

** See editorial entries for explanations of team sizes.*

Dickinson Dees *"Undoubtedly the leading firm in the North East,"* it boasts a wide-ranging client base. **Hume Hargreave** is *"one of the doyens of the agricultural world"* while *"professional but approachable"* **Simon Kirkup** and a strong team lend support. As well as land transfers and partnership structuring, the team has particular strengths in planning, quota and European issues and is highly rated for tax advice. Recently involved in transfers of agricultural and sporting estates of around 20,000 acres.

Ward Hadaway **Christopher Hewitt** stands out in this well established practice for his *"first rate agricultural advice."* A strong client base includes landed estates, farmers, public bodies and agri-business, for whom the practice provides the full range of agricultural services. Their planning department is considered particularly strong and niche expertise exists on rights of way.

Latimer Hinks Sound, well-regarded local firm with an expanding agricultural practice. Primarily advising tenant farmers on a range of agricultural issues, the team has also been involved in diversification and restructuring work.

Jacksons (5 ptnrs & 8 assts spend some time on agriculture) There was some surprise when the practice won the NFU contract, but this is regarded as a practice giving *"robust advice"* and making strenuous efforts in the sector. Mainly act for smaller farmers on conveyancing, landlord and tenant and commercial disputes.

SCOTLAND

AGRICULTURE • Scotland	Ptnrs	Assts
❶ **Anderson Strathern WS** Edinburgh	7	5
Brodies WS Edinburgh	7	13
Turcan Connell WS Edinburgh	5	12
❷ **Thorntons WS** Dundee	5	1
❸ **Burnett & Reid** Aberdeen	2	1
Gillespie MacAndrew WS Edinburgh	3	2
Lindsays WS Edinburgh	1	1
Miller Hendry Perth	2	1
Tods Murray WS Edinburgh	3	4
Turnbull, Simson & Sturrock WS Jedburgh	2	-
❹ **Grigor & Young** Elgin	1	-
McLean & Stewart Dunblane	3	-
Murray Beith Murray WS Edinburgh	1	2
Paull & Williamsons Aberdeen	1	1

LEADING INDIVIDUALS
❶ **FOX Alasdair** Anderson Strathern WS
RENNIE Donald Donald Rennie WS
STRANG STEEL Malcolm Turcan Connell WS
❷ **DALRYMPLE Hew** Brodies WS
ROBERTSON Jonathan Turcan Connell WS
SHEARER Roy Lindsays WS
STURROCK David Turnbull, Simson & Sturrock WS
TURCAN Robert Turcan Connell WS
❸ **BLAIR Michael** Thorntons WS
HOULDSWORTH David Brodies WS
KIRKPATRICK Denbeigh Turnbull, Simson & Sturrock WS

Within each band, firms are listed alphabetically. *See **Profiles** on page 73*

Anderson Strathern WS *"Practical"* and *"knowledgeable"* **Alasdair Fox** heads this large team which has a *"profile throughout Scotland."* Particularly experienced in transactional work, the practice is also highly regarded for its skill in tax planning and landlord and tenant work. Acted this year in numerous large acquisitions and sales. **Clients:** The Crown Estate; National Trust for Scotland; Douglas and Angus Estates; The Buccleuch Estates Ltd.

Brodies WS Represent offshore, mineral and forestry companies, expatriate and foreign clients and farmers and landowners with interests across Scotland. Land conveyancing forms the mainstay of the caseload, with other work coming from in-house surveying, estate agency and accountancy. **Hew Dalrymple** has a *"strong client following,"* while **David Houldsworth** is also rated a practitioner of unusual merit.

Turcan Connell WS *"First class firm"* acting for landowners and an increasing number of non-agricultural clients diversifying into agriculture. **Malcolm Strang Steel** *"does an excellent job for his clients,"* while paterfamilias **Robert Turcan** is particularly rated in trusts and tax planning, and **Jonathan Robertson** is an *"omniscient"* performer. Acted in the purchase of Schiehallion and Ben Nevis for the John Muir trust.

Thorntons WS Highly regarded firm with a strong client base focused on the Angus area. Act for estates, working farmers and several forestry companies, doing the full range of agricultural law, including, last year, the sale of a large stretch of salmon fishings. **Mike Blair** has gained a substantial client following this year.

Burnett & Reid *"Competent and experienced"* firm acting for working farmers and over a dozen large estates. Main areas of work include acquisitions and sales, quota work and setting up partnerships.

Gillespie MacAndrew The team represents a range of agricultural clients, from large estates and farming plcs, down to smallholders. Specific expertise in tenancy disputes, sporting estates and crofting law, with an augmented agri-environmental practice. **Clients:** Moray Estates Development Co; Alcan Highland Estates; J & JD Anderson, Lands Improvement Holdings plc; Hopetoun Estates Development Co.

Lindsays WS Historically acting for landed estates around Scotland, the team does the full range of estate work, including tax planning, conveyancing, sporting rights and mineral extraction. **Roy Shearer** is *"pleasant and upright"* and has the best knowledge of crofting law outside the Highlands.

Miller Hendry Strong local practice with a *"knowledge and expertise"* which they apply *"in a non-aggressive but confident way."* Clients include major highland estates of up to 70,000 acres, and numerous forestry companies, with forestry transactions forming a considerable area of expertise. Acted last year in the sale of Glenfintaig lodge and the surrounding land. **Clients:** Strathconan Estate; Glenfeshie Estate; Fountain Forestry.

Tods Murray WS Act for an impressive list of around 200 private and institutional landowners, and have particular experience of the forestry sector. Also provide a dedicated service to overseas individuals and companies wishing to invest in Scottish rural property. **Clients:** RSPB; The Forestry Commission; The Woodland Trust.

Turnbull, Simson & Sturrock WS Strong local firm dealing with conveyancing, diversification advice, quotas and landlord and tenant work for the spectrum of agricultural clients. *"Technically expert"* **David Sturrock** combines *"genuine knowledge of the law with sound organisational skills"* while **Denbeigh Kirkpatrick** is also highly rated.

Grigor & Young Smaller regional firm working for some large estates, companies, and ordinary working farmers on a wide range of agricultural work. Also undertake referral work from other solicitors.

McLean & Stewart Highly regarded regional firm with a high proportion of accredited practitioners and a strong agricultural base amongst working farmers. Work includes all aspects of agricultural law, with notable expertise in land conveyancing and tenancy work.

Murray Beith Murray WS Niche private client firm acting for over 100 landowners throughout Scotland. Work focus is non-contentious and the team is particularly highly regarded for tax and investment expertise. Also skilled in transactions involving agricultural/commercial mixed estates and sporting estates, acting in a number of these last year.

Paull & Williamsons Strong Aberdeen operation acting for landed families and, increasingly, non-agricultural clients diversifying into agriculture. Contract farming is another growth area, and the practice has conducted a number of recent transactions with a corporate emphasis.

Other Notable Practitioners **Donald Rennie** maintains his place as the highest profile sole practitioner specialising exclusively in agricultural and farming matters.

LEADERS IN AGRICULTURE

ARROWSMITH-BROWN, Matthew R.
Mills & Reeve, Norwich (01603) 693 215
matthew.arrowsmith-brown@mills-reeve.com
Specialisation: Advising farming businesses and families. Examples of particular issues covered last year are: advising member of farming family on a separation of his interests from those of the rest of the family; advising on various forms of cooperative arrangement; advising on irrigation schemes.
Prof. Memberships: Law Society; Agricultural Law Association; Royal Agricultural Society of England; Royal Norfolk Agricultural Association; Farmers' Club.
Career: Clifton College; University of York; articles and 2.5 years post qualification with *Slaughter and May* 1974-79; *Mills and Reeve* 1979 to date; partner since 1981.
Personal: Brought up on Dartmoor farm; married; two daughters (19 and 21); Driving fast cars.

AUBREY, Michael J.
Mills & Reeve, Cambridge (01223) 222 397
michael.aubrey@mills-reeve.com
Partner in Agriculture Department.
Specialisation: Practice covers all areas of agricultural property work and in particular corporate and institutional agriculture. Main areas of work include acquisition and disposal of agricultural and development land and estates, the imposition of reserving future development value, agricultural tenancies, minerals, share farming, contract farming and partnerships.
Prof. Memberships: Royal Forestry Society; Law Society; Agricultural Law Association.
Career: BSc (Hons) in Agricultural Economics from University of Newcastle Upon Tyne. Joined *Mills & Reeve* in 1989 and became a partner in 1997.
Personal: Leisure interests include rugby, cricket and golf.

BARKER, Richard
Barker Gotelee, Ipswich (01473) 611211
Specialisation: Acting for landowners and farmers throughout the UK. Head of Agricultural team dealing with all aspects of agricultural law both UK and EC Community legislation. His particular expertise is EC legislation and lobbying the EC Institutions on matters including state aids, competition, food quality standards and food health issues. Has recently opened an office in Brussels. Council member Suffolk Agricultural Association. Chairman Suffolk Professional European Committee. CLA branch member. Member of the EU Team Europe Panel of specialist speakers. Speaks nationally at seminars on agricultural and EU matters and writes regularly for specialist publications and newspapers and broadcasts on agricultural and EU matters.
Prof. Memberships: Qualified 1969. Now Senior Partner of *Barker Gotelee, Solicitors*, and Managing Director of Stanyer Consulting Limited dealing with the non-legal aspects of lobbying and EU and UK policy.

BARNETT, Ian G.
Hewitson Becke + Shaw, Northampton (01604) 233233

BARR, William D.W.
Mills & Reeve, Cambridge (01223) 222 480
william.barr@mills-reeve.com
Partner in Agriculture Department.
Specialisation: Work covers farm tenancies and partnerships, share farming, quotas and farm taxation. Most recently he has been involved in food chain issues and reviewing the structures of farm businesses and co-operatives. Co-author of 'Farm Tenancies'. Lectures frequently and contributes the share farming section to 'Agricultural Law Tax & Finance' and agricultural articles to Solicitors' Journal.
Prof. Memberships: Law Society, Agricultural Law Association, USA Agricultural Law Association.

BATSTONE, William
Burges Salmon, Bristol (0117) 902 2716
william.batstone@burges-salmon.com
Specialisation: Acting for landowners and farmers he practises mainly in contentious agricultural holdings work. He undertakes advisory work and regularly appears as advocate before the Courts, Agricultural Land Tribunals, in particular presenting and responding to applications for succession, and Arbitrators, in particular dealing with rent review and notice to quit arbitrations. He also heads up the firm's growing bloodstock practice. He is a regular contributor to the Lawyer's Remembrancer and is a consultant to the RICS/CAAV joint 2000 Guidance Notes on Rent Review under the Agricultural Holdings Act 1986. He regularly addresses RICS and local Law Society meetings on agricultural topics.
Prof. Memberships: Law Society, Solicitors Association of Higher Court Advocates, Agricultural Law Association.
Career: University of York 1976-79, Philosophy. Called to the Bar in 1982, joined *Burges Salmon* and re-qualified as a solicitor in 1994, granted rights of audience in the Higher Courts in 1994 and became a Partner in 1996.

BLAIR, J. Michael G.
Thorntons WS, Forfar (01241) 872683

BUXTON, James
Burges Salmon, Bristol (0117) 902 2758
james.buxton@burges-salmon.com
Specialisation: His practice covers all aspects of the law relating to agricultural holdings including disputes relating to security of tenure, succession cases, rent reviews and end of tenancy compensation claims together with all aspects of milk and other commodity quotas.
Prof. Memberships: Agricultural Law Association, Law Society, Solicitors' Association of Higher Court Advocates.
Career: Called to the Bar in 1971, joined *Burges Salmon* in 1982 and became a partner in 1984. Granted rights of audience in the Higher Courts in 1994. Contributor to Halsbury's Laws of England Agriculture volume and Butterworth's Encyclopaedia of Forms and Precedents.
Personal: Born 1948, studied at Trinity College, Cambridge.

CARTMELL, Timothy H.
Cartmell Shepherd, Carlisle (01228) 514077
cartmell.rosehill@dial.pipex.com
Partner in Agriculture Department
Specialisation: Work covers agricultural quotas, Landlord & Tenant matters, Agricultural Land Tribunal work, arbitrations and litigation in the courts. Also farming legal generally, partnerships and private client work.
Personal: Glenalmond College 1961-66, Christ's College, Cambridge 1966-69. Articled with *Walker Martineau* in London 1970-72.

CHEAL, Jonathan
Thrings & Long, Bath (01225) 340000
Partner in Agriculture Department.
Specialisation: Main areas of practice are agricultural law and real property law. Work includes farm sales and purchases, landlord and tenant, partnerships, succession and wills, tax, quotas, town and country planning and farm buildings, rights of way, easements and housing of farm workers and has wide experience of public speaking, lectures and seminars.
Prof. Memberships: Previously Legal Adviser at Country Landowners Association Head Office in London, 1983-87. Currently a professional member of CLA, NFU and TFA. Sits on CLA Somerset Committee; approved panel AMC solicitors, Agricultural Law Association.
Career: Qualified in 1976. Articled in London and Sussex. Worked in Hong Kong 1976-82; CLA 1983-87. Joined *Thrings & Long* in 1987, becoming a Partner in 1989.
Personal: Born 30th June 1950.

COLLINS, Peter
Walker Smith & Way, Chester (01244) 357 400

DALRYMPLE, Hew D.K.
Brodies WS, Edinburgh (0131) 228 3777
Specialisation: He specialises in all aspects of Rural Property Law, Country Estate work and Private Client practice. He has a special interest in farming, asset protection, and capital taxation and minerals and acts for a number of prominent landowners and their families and other high net worth individuals and commercial concerns with rural interests.
Prof. Memberships: Society of Her Majesty's Writers to the Signet.
Career: Edinburgh Academy; Edinburgh University; *Brodies WS* from 1975 to date.
Personal: Married to Sheriff Deirdre MacNeill, QC, one son. Leisure interests include shooting, fishing, painting and sketching and travel.

DAVIS, Nigel R.
Roythorne & Co, Nottingham (0115) 948 4555

DENNIS, Jeanette A.
Taylor Vinters, Cambridge (01223) 423444
jad@taylorvinters.com
Partner in agriculture department.
Specialisation: Principal area of practice is agriculture. Work includes sales and purchases of farms and land, tenancies (including Agricultural Holdings Act 1986, Agricultural Tenancies Act 1995 and short term business leases), crop loss claims and financial arrangements for farmers.
Prof. Memberships: Cambridge Young Solicitors, Cambridge Law Society. Agricultural Law Association, Committee member of the Game Conservancy Trust.
Career: Joined *Taylor Vinters* in 1988 and qualified in 1990. Has specialised in agricultural law since qualification. National AgriLaw Lecturer and BBC Radio contributor.
Personal: Graduated from Hull University in 1987(LL.B).

DENSHAM CBE, Andrew
Burges Salmon, Bristol (0117) 939 2000
andrew.densham@burges-salmon.com
Specialisation: An established expert in his practice area he has been involved in a substantial proportion of the leading agricultural holdings cases. Clients range from large landowners to substantial farming clients. A regular speaker all over the country for the CAAV, RICS and others.
Prof. Memberships: Law Society, Agricultural Law Association, honorary member of the CAAV.
Career: Articled with *Stanley Wasbrough* in Bristol 1962-65, joined *Burges Salmon* in 1969 and became a Partner in 1970, Senior Partner 1992-98. Crown Court Assistant Recorder 1982-90.
Publications: Joint author of Scammell & Densham's 'Law of Agricultural Holdings' 8th edition (current) plus 6th & 7th editions. Contributor to Halsbury's Encyclopaedia of Forms and Precedents (title 'Agriculture') and principal contributor to the 5th (current) edition 1968 and1993 re-issue. Contributory editor to 'Agricultural Holdings' Halsbury's Laws of England – 4th edition.
Personal: University of Bristol 1958-62. Freeman of the City of Bristol, Past President Antient Society of St Stephen's Ringers, member of the Society of Merchant Venturers. Leisure pursuits include skiing, golf and walking.

EVANS, Della
Burges Salmon, Bristol (0117) 902 2781
della.evans@burges-salmon.com
Specialisation: Agriculture, primarily agricultural business advice; farming partnerships – advice and disputes; agricultural landlord and tenant – advice and disputes.
Prof. Memberships: Law Society, Agricultural Law Association.
Career: . Qualified at *Burges Salmon* in 1991 and became a Partner in 1995. Author of Sweet & Maxwell's Legislation Handbook on the Agricultural Tenancies Act 1995 and a contributor to Butterworths Encyclopaedia of Forms and Precedents on Agriculture. Also co-author of Scammell & Densham's Law of Agricultural Holdings.
Personal: University of West of England and LLM at University of Bristol.

FARREN, Miles
Burges Salmon, Bristol (0117) 939 2000

FINDLEY, Christopher D.
Morgan Cole, Oxford (01865) 262600
christopher.findley@morgan-cole.com
Specialisation: All aspects of law including Agricultural Holdings and Arbitrations and Farm Business Tenancy legislation, advising Agricultural Estates on land and tax issues. Town & Country planning, experience includes Options and Sales of farm land and buildings for development, representation at Planning Appeals, Local Plan Inquiries and Judicial Review proceedings. Milk Quota and subsidy law CAP Reform. Extensive experience in creation and dissolution of Farming Partnerships and Companies. Advising on Mineral Extraction and Waste Disposal sites.
Prof. Memberships: Country Landowners Association (Oxfordshire Committee) and Legal & Parliamentary Sub-Committee member, Agricultural Law Association (Committee), National Farmers Union, Tenant Farmers Association.
Career: Qualified in 1979 Head of Agricultural Law Department at *Thomas Mallam* Oxford 1983-93. Joined *Cole & Cole* as Partner and Head of Agricultural Law Department 1994.

FITZGERALD, Peter R.
Wilsons, Salisbury (01722) 412412
See under Trusts & Personal Tax, p.820

FOX, Alasdair
Anderson Strathern WS, Edinburgh (0131) 220 2345
Specialisation: Head of Rural Department and Land Ventures Unit with 30 years experience of all aspects of rural property law. Particular expertise in the area of agricultural landlord and tenant law and agricultural arbitrations (acting principally for arbiters but also for parties). Practice also covers advice to major estate proprietors, purchase and sale of rural properties and land ventures including Diversification Agreements, opencast mining options and licences.
Prof. Memberships: Society of Writers to H.M. Signet; Law Society of Scotland's Rural Affairs Committee, Agricultural Law Association. Member of Scottish Office Consultative Panel on Land Reform (Landlord and tenant).
Career: Qualified in 1969. Partner at *Anderson Strathern WS* since 1972. Accredited by the Law Society of Scotland as a specialist in agricultural law 1993. Renewed 1998.
Personal: Educated at Lime House School, Carlisle 1954-59, Fettes College, Edinburgh 1959-64 and at the University of Edinburgh 1964-67. Leisure pursuits include sailing, ski-ing, shooting and fishing. Born 1st January 1946. Lives in Edinburgh.

FURBER, W. James
Farrer & Co, London (020) 7242 2022
Specialisation: Agricultural estates, property and institutional investment and most other aspects of property law. Solicitor to the Duchy of Cornwall. Partner in and Head of Estates and Private Property Team.
Prof. Memberships: Law Society, Holborn Law Society (President 1996-7).
Career: Joined *Farrer & Co* in 1976. Qualified in 1979. Became an Associate in 1981 and a Partner in 1985.
Publications: 'Encyclopaedia of Forms & Precedents, Volume 36, Sale of Land - Trusts for Sale and Requisitions on Title.' Contributor to Television Education Network 1991-1996.
Personal: Born 1 September 1954. Attended Westminster School and Gonville & Caius College, Cambridge. Married with 3 children. Lives in Blackheath. Leisure interests include golf.

GILLIBRAND, R. Martin
Oglethorpe Sturton & Gillibrand, Lancaster (01524) 67171
Partner in Agriculture Department.
Specialisation: Has over 25 years experience in general agricultural work, including agricultural tax planning and conveyancing, quotas, and law relating to common land. Also handles tax, probate and

industrial conveyancing. Clerk to the General Tax Commissioners. Has handled a number of Commons Enquiries and general upland negotiations. Has addressed numerous Moorland seminars.
Prof. Memberships: Agriculture Law Association, Secretary of Moorland Association.
Career: Qualified in 1972. Joined *Oglethorpe Sturton & Gillibrand* in 1972, becoming a Partner in 1973.
Personal: Born 9th October 1946. Attended Shrewsbury School 1960-65 and Pembroke College, Cambridge 1965-68. Leisure interests include gardening and shooting. Lives in Tatham, near Lancaster.

HARGREAVE, R.Hume M.
Dickinson Dees, Newcastle upon Tyne (0191) 279 9234
Partner and Head of Agriculture Group.
Specialisation: Main area of practice agriculture, encompassing all aspects of land ownership and management, partnerships, agricultural tenancies and European Law. Speaks frequently at RICS/ CAAV conferences and seminars; writes regularly for the press.
Prof. Memberships: Agricultural Law Association.
Career: Qualified in 1971. Partner in *Dickinson Dees* since 1974.
Personal: Born 24th September 1940. Shrewsbury School 1954-59, Merton College, Oxford 1959-63.

HARRIS, Edward
Edward Harris & Son, Swansea (01792) 652007
Specialisation: Senior Partner specialising in the Law of Commons, the Manorial System and Lordship of Manors and appurtenant rights and interests, also agricultural law and tenancies. Other areas of law include rights of way, footpaths and other easements, copyholds, mineral rights, together with countryside law, town and country planning and other areas of agricultural law. Acted in the reported cases of 'Lewis and Others v. Mid Glamorgan County Council' (1995) (House of Lords) 1ALL ER 760 and 'Re:Merthyr Mawr Common' (1989) 3 ALL ER 451 and 'Hancock v. Brecon Water' etc. plus Commons Commissioners hearings etc. Acts for various Commoners Associations and Lords of the Manors. Appointed by the Countryside Commission to be Welsh Representative on the Common Land Forum. Co-author of Common Land Forum Report 1985. On Department of Environment list of Consultees in respect of Common Land legislation.
Prof. Memberships: Law Society, Agricultural Law Association, Country Land-Owners Association (Legal & Parliamentary Sub-Committee).
Career: Qualified in 1964 (Hons.). Partner at *Edward Harris & Son* since 1965. Senior Partner since 1988.
Personal: Born 2nd April, 1941. Educated at St. Edwards, Oxford 1954-59. Lives in Swansea.

HEAL, Jeremy P W
Howes Percival, Norwich (01603) 762103
jpwh@howes-percival.co.uk
Partner, Head of Estates Division
Specialisation: Acts for landowners and others in all areas of agricultural law, tax and land transactions, including agricultural tenancies and contracting agreements, minerals, farming partnerships, acquisition and disposal of farms and estates, town and country planning, landowners' consortia and joint ventures. Specialises in capital tax planning for landowners, and lectures regularly on inheritance tax and trusts, valuation and other tax-related topics. Work also includes charity law; and is a trustee of a substantial grant-making charity. Author of various articles in 'Farmers Weekly,' 'Taxation,' 'Personal Tax Planning Review' and other periodicals.
Prof. Memberships: Agricultural Law Association; Chartered Institute of Arbitrators; Society of Trust & Estate Practitioners; Law Society; Country Landowners Association; Royal Norfolk Agricultural Association.
Personal: Born 1942. Educated Marlborough College and Queen's College, Cambridge. MA, LLM (Cantab), ACIArb, TEP.

HEWITT, Christopher
Ward Hadaway, Newcastle upon Tyne (0191) 204 4000
Partner in Property Department.
Specialisation: Agricultural holdings, quotas, partnerships, business and property law, land use, minerals and planning. Wide ranging cases for farmers, landowners and rural institutions. Spoken at CLA, RICS, CAAV and many other conferences on agricultural law. Regular contributor to local press.
Prof. Memberships: Law Society, Country Landowners Association, Agricultural Law Association.
Career: Qualified in 1971, Partner in 1987 upon joining *Ward Hadaway.*
Personal: Born 16th September 1947. Attended Sedbergh School and the University of Newcastle upon Tyne.

HORNBY, John H.
Macfarlanes, London (020) 7831 9222
Partner in Property Department.
Specialisation: Commercial work covering the leisure industry, agricultural law, housing and residential work. Acts for investors, private estate landlords and working farmers. Has acted on a significant number of transactions involving hotels, golf courses, caravan sites and other rural business ventures. Recent and current work includes the Millennium Commission funded £80 million development – The Renaissance of Portsmouth Harbour, a substantial flow of sales and purchases of prime landed estates and farms and advising a national firm of land agents on agricultural and housing landlord and tenant matters. Author of 'Leasehold Enfranchisement- The New Proposals Put in Context' (1993).
Prof. Memberships: Law Society.
Career: Qualified in 1980 while with *Macfarlanes.* Became a Partner in 1987.

HORNER, Douglas G.
Brachers, Maidstone (01622) 690691
Specialises in Agricultural Law, Environmental Law and Town Planning.
Specialisation: Agricultural Law: agricultural holdings and arbitrations, CAP regimes and legislation, health and safety, UKASTA, NASPM and other contracts and issues. Environmental Law: waste regulation, statutory nuisance, cases involving leachate, methane, water pollution, airbourne pollution and noise. Town planning: advocacy in Public Inquiries, handling High Court appeals and Judicial Review, applications, appeals and cases ranging from industrial development, offices, residential, major and minor farm development to port facilities and aviation. Lectures have included RICS-CPD, Rural Arbrix, CBI, NFU and others.
Prof. Memberships: Law Society's Planning Panel, Legal Associate RTPI, UK Environmental Law Association, Agricultural Law Association, NFU, CLA, Kent Valuers Club, Canterbury Farmers Club.
Career: Qualified 1969, Partner *Brachers* 1972; Legal Adviser to Kent County NFU 1975 to date; Legal Adviser to East Sussex NFU; past member Law Society's Civil Litigation Committee and Senate of the Bar Committee on Law Reporting; elected member CBI South East Region Council; Member and past Chairman Kent Economic Forum.
Personal: Born 1945. Sutton Valence School. St John's College Cambridge. Enjoys sailing and lives in Sevenoaks.

HORWOOD-SMART, Adrian
Taylor Vinters, Cambridge (01223) 423444
ahs@taylorvinters.com
Partner in agriculture department.
Specialisation: Principal area of practice is agriculture. Work includes landlord and tenant, contracting and management agreements, other joint farming operations, partnership arrangements, quota and set-aside transactions and the land law aspects of landed estates and farms. Regularly lectures at seminars and conferences.
Prof. Memberships: Law Society, Agricultural Law Association, Notaries Society.
Career: Qualified in 1977. At *Waltons & Morse* 1977-79 before joining *Taylor Vinters.* Became a partner in 1983.

HOULDSWORTH, David H.
Brodies WS, Edinburgh (0131) 228 3777
dhouldsworth@brodies.co.uk
Private Client Department Partner
Specialisation: Private Client Department Partner specialising in agricultural and related matters, including landlord/tenant issues, farming contracts and all other matters relating to rural businesses; he acts for a number of large estates and advises on every aspect of their business affairs; David has overall responsibility for the clients' tax and succession planning.
Prof. Memberships: Director: North Atlantic Salmon Fund (UK) Limited; Member of the Cairngorm Recreation Trust and past Director of Cairngorm Chair Lift Company Limited.
Personal: Received an LLB (Hons) from the University of Edinburgh in 1974 and qualified in 1977. He has been a Partner with *Brodies* since 1981. He is married with one daughter and his interests include family farming and forestry businesses and the future of the countryside. When time allows he plays golf at Muirfield and Nairn, he fishes and shoots throughout Scotland; he is an avid gardener and enjoys contemporary art.

JESSEL, Christopher.R.
Farrer & Co, London (020) 7242 2022
Partner in Estates and Private Property Team.
Specialisation: Main area of practice covers rural estates, agriculture and manors. Acts on farms, common land and rural estate work generally including development sales with trust and personal advice. Also covers charity and constitutional work, establishing and advising charities on parliamentary and administrative law. Author of 'The Law of the Manor 1998,' 'Farms and Estates – A conveyancing handbook 1999' and numerous articles in professional and investment magazines. Lectures extensively in London and elsewhere.
Prof. Memberships: Law Society.

Career: Joined *Farrer & Co* in 1967. Qualified in 1970. Became a Partner in 1979.
Personal: Born 16th March 1945. Attended Bryanston School 1958-63, Balliol College, Oxford 1964-67. Leisure interests include archaeology. Lives in Guildford.

KEDDIE, Joanne
Dawson & Co, London (020) 7421 4800

KIRKPATRICK, Denbeigh
Turnbull, Simson & Sturrock WS, Jedburgh (01835) 862391
Partner specialising in agricultural law.
Specialisation: Handles the purchase, sale and leasing of agricultural holdings and associated matters. Also deals with commercial work including purchase of ground for development for housing, arrangement of all necessary servitude rights etc, and subsequent selling. Clients include substantial private landowners and farmers. Convener of the Law Society of Scotland's Agricultural Law Accreditation Panel and member of its Rural Affairs Committee.
Prof. Memberships: Law Society of Scotland; Society of Writers to Her Majesty's Signet; The Scottish Agricultural Arbiters' Association; The South of Scotland and Border Valuers' Association.
Career: Qualified in 1965. Partner at *Turnbull Simson & Sturrock* since 1967. Member of Council, Law Society of Scotland 1982-88.
Personal: Born 15th December 1940. Educated at Jedburgh Grammar School 1945-51, The Edinburgh Academy 1951-58 and Edinburgh University 1958-64. Leisure pursuits include reading, golf and fishing. Lives in Wark, Cornhill-on-Tweed.

KIRKUP, Simon
Dickinson Dees, Newcastle upon Tyne (0191) 279 9374
Specialisation: Handles all aspects of agricultural law. Particular expertise in landlord and tenant issues, quotas and livestock premiums, Agricultural Land Tribunal matters, arbitrations, farming partnerships and farm sales and purchases. Regularly lectures at seminars and conferences.
Prof. Memberships: Agricultural Law Association.
Career: Attended Sedbergh School 1979-84 and Exeter University 1985-88. Joined *Dickinson Dees* in 1990 and qualified in 1992. Is a Partner in the firm's Agricultural Law Group.
Personal: Born 31 August 1966. Leisure interests including fishing, shooting and golf.

KNIGHT, Matthew
Knights, Tunbridge Wells (01892) 537311
knights@atlas.co.uk
See under Administrative & Public Law, p.59

KYRKE, Richard Venables
Thomas Eggar Church Adams, Horsham (01403) 214 503
richard.kyrke@teca.co.uk
Partner & head of agricultural law unit.
Specialisation: Handles all aspects of agricultural law, particularly landlord and tenant issues, and advises on commercial property matters, including sales and purchases.
Prof. Memberships: Agricultural Law Association, CLA, NFU.
Career: Born 1951. Educated Marlborough College. Qualified 1976. Partner in *Thomas Eggar Church Adams* since 1979.

LANE, Andrew
Withers, London (020) 7936 1000
Partner in Property Department.
Specialisation: Practice covers all types of agricultural property work including agricultural holdings law, estate management and sales and acquisitions of farms and estates. Also advises on tax implications of property transactions; particularly Capital Gains Tax and VAT. Clients range from private individuals through family trusts and institutions to major plcs.
Prof. Memberships: Agricultural Law Association, Royal Agricultural Society of England.
Career: Was a full-time farmer between 1978 and 1987. Joined *Withers* in 1987 qualifying in 1992 and becoming a partner in 1994.
Personal: Born 22nd January 1957. Educated Malvern College 1970-74 Christ's College Cambridge 1975-78. Lives near Salisbury, Wiltshire.

LODDER, David
Lodders, Stratford-upon-Avon (01789) 293259
david.lodder@lodders.co.uk
Specialisation: Agricultural Law in respect of: Agricultural Holdings Act Farm Successions; Re-arranging the family farming partnership; Diversification schemes. Major cases include succession case in Agricultural Land Tribunal, Acquisition of farming estate, settling number of complicated partnership disputes.
Prof. Memberships: Country Landowners Association. Legal Parliamentary Committee Member. National Farmers Union. Agricultural Law Association.
Career: Educated at Uppingham School/Sheffield University. Articled in Sheffield. Joined family firm (then *G F Lodder & Sons*) 1974, became Partner in 1978. Head of large Commercial Department.
Personal: Farms 120 acre family farm – formerly sheep & cattle, now diversified into number of enterprises. Enjoys shooting, fishing and fell running.

MARGRAVE-JONES, Clive
Margraves, Llandrindod Wells (01597) 825565

MOORE, John E.
Macfarlanes, London (020) 7831 9222
Partner in Property Development.
Specialisation: Has acted since qualification for Institutional Investors, including Insurance Companies and Pension Funds, in connection with the investment and development of land, and agricultural law. Represents tenants as well as landlords in relation to their agricultural holdings and Public Bodies (including NHS Trusts) in relation to agricultural tenancy rights on surplus land when considering developments and PFI proposals. Lectures on agricultural law.
Career: Joined *Macfarlanes* in 1970. Qualified 1973. Partner in 1979.

MORRISON, Alastair
Burges Salmon, Bristol (0117) 939 2258
alastair.morrison@burges-salmon.com
Specialisation: Is in the complexities of sale and purchase of farms and estates, and commercial farm investment and development. Also advises on agricultural tenancies and agricultural mortgages.
Prof. Memberships: Law Society; main Committee member and chairman of the Parliamentary sub-committee of the Agricultural Law Association, member of Legal and Parliamentary sub-committee of the Country Landowners Association.
Career: Trained and practised for five years with *Macfarlanes* before moving to practise in the North East for five years. Joined *Burges Salmon* as a partner in 1997.

MULCARE, John
Cripps Harries Hall, Tunbridge Wells, Kent (01892) 515121
Partner and Head of Agriculture department.
Specialisation: Experience includes most aspects of farming work including ancillary matters e.g. town and country planning, commercial litigation, criminal and civil litigation and sitting as a legal adviser in agricultural arbitrations.
Prof. Memberships: Member of the Agricultural Law Association; Member of the Chartered Institute of Arbitrators; an accredited mediator with the Centre for Dispute Resolution and a Director of Disputes Resolved.
Career: Educated at Hurstpierpont College; articled at firms in West Sussex and London; qualified in 1962; partner at *A L Mulcare & Co* 1965; founded *John Mulcare & Co* 1988; partner, *Cripps Harries Hall* 1996.
Personal: Sailing, hill walking, farming.

NEVILLE, William
Burges Salmon, Bristol (0117) 939 2202
william.neville@burges-salmon.com
Specialisation: Food, agriculture and agribusiness where his industry knowledge and advice is not just for farmers but also for large and small food production companies. As a specialist litigator he works also on milk quotas, arable area payments, sheep and beef quotas and premium and EC legislation relating to agriculture. Frequent speaker at conferences on CAP and Agenda 2000.
Prof. Memberships: Law Society. Member of ALA, Law Society Food Group, BIAC, RABDF, NIAB, Countryside Alliance and ARAGS.
Career: Joined *Burges Salmon* after 8 years at the Bar, re-qualified as a solicitor in 1987 and became a partner in 1989. Author of 'A Guide to the Reformed Common Agricultural Policy', and contributing author to Halsbury's Laws of England Agriculture volume.
Personal: Leisure interests include fly fishing and mountain biking.

OGG, Robin
Wright Hassall, Leamington Spa (01926) 886688

PLUMMER, Alan J.
Roythorne & Co, Spalding (01775) 724141
Partner in Litigation Department.
Specialisation: Main areas of practice are Landlord and Tenant litigation, particularly relating to Agricultural holdings, contentious trust matters, employment law, professional indemnity litigation. Speaker at seminars and other professional conferences.
Prof. Memberships: ALA
Career: Qualified in 1979. Joined *Roythorne & Co* in 1976.

PRING, Simon J.
Farrer & Co, London (020) 7242 2022
Partner in the Estates and Private Property Team.
Specialisation: All aspects of property law with an emphasis on agricultural estates, charity land holding and VAT. Assistant Solicitor to the Duchy of Lancaster.
Prof. Memberships: Holborn Law Society.

Career: Blundell's School, Devon, Robinson College, Cambridge. Joined *Farrer & Co* 1986, Partner 1995.
Personal: Born 24 March 1964. Married. Lives in London. Leisure: country pursuits and golf.

QUINN, James Stephen Christopher
Morton Fisher, Worcester (01905) 610410
Partner in Business Division.
Specialisation: Principal field of activity relates to Agricultural matters, including landlord and tenant issues, agreements and disputes, tribunal and arbitration work, general estate advice and quota work. Also advises on commercial property matters, including sales and purchases and commercial and agricultural estate development. Acted in Williamson v Thompson [1980] AC 854 and McCarthy v Bence [1990] 1 EGLR 1. Acts for landed estates and the farming community in Hereford and Worcester and Shropshire. Has spoken extensively at conferences and seminars.
Prof. Memberships: Member Law Society; Agricultural Law Association; LawNet Agriculture Unit.
Career: Qualified in 1964. Joined *Morton Fisher* and became a Partner in 1964.
Personal: Born 11th July 1939. LL.B Birmingham University 1960. Leisure interests include golf, computing, caravanning and family. Is a Board Member of the Princes Youth Business Trust (Hereford & Worcester Region). Lives in Malvern.

RENNIE O.B.E., Donald G.
Donald Rennie WS, Edinburgh (0131) 476 7007
Sole Practitioner.
Specialisation: Specialist agricultural practice. Handles landlord and tenant, quotas, professional negligence claims, and partnerships. Author of articles on the valuation of agricultural leases and succession to agricultural tenancies. Has lectured extensively at seminars organised by the Law Society of Scotland, RICS and Agricultural Law Association. Editor, Connell on the Agricultural Holdings (Scotland) Acts.
Prof. Memberships: Agricultural Law Association, Scottish Lawyers' European Group, Society of Trust and Estate Practitioners.
Career: Qualified in 1972. Joined *Connell & Connell WS* in 1976, becoming a Partner in 1977-96. Secretary of the Scottish Agricultural Arbiters' Association 1989-1999; Member of the Panel of Arbiters
Personal: Born 25th April 1947. Attended Aberdeen University (MA 1968, LLB 1970). Lives in Edinburgh.

ROBERTSON, Jonathan
Turcan Connell WS, Edinburgh (0131) 228 8111
jmr@turcanconnell.com
Specialisation: Partner. Specialist in Agricultural Law including all aspects of farm sales and purchases, agricultural tenancy matters, agricultural arbitrations and quotas. Other main areas of work include rural conveyancing, mining and development work, rural planning and environmental law, forestry, sporting and aquaculture.
Prof. Memberships: Member Agricultural Law Association. Accredited as a specialist in agricultural law by the Law Society of Scotland. Writer to the Signet. Notary Public.
Career: Attended University of Aberdeen (LLB, DipLP). Articled *Dundas & Wilson CS* 1984-1986; qualified 1986; assistant solicitor 1986-1990; associate 1990; Partner 1990-97. Partner *Turcan Connell* 1997.
Personal: Born 1960. Resides East Lothian. Leisure interests include walking.

RUSS, Timothy
Clarke Willmott & Clarke, Taunton
(01823) 442 266
truss@cw-c.co.uk
Partner and Head of the Agriculture and Food team
Specialisation: Tim's practice includes Landlord and Tenant work for both landowners and tennants, partnership disputes, agricultural land tribunal succession work, professional negligence and EU quotas. He regularly deals with judicial review and related administrative work. Often, particularly on partnership and tenancy cases, Timm works with the client's othe advisors including accountants and land agents. He is a qualified mediator with both CEDR and ADR Group and has successfully mediated 20 cases to settlemant, the greater part of which were related to agricultural issues. He is experianced in arbitration law and regularly acts as advocate or advisor in agricultural arbitrations. He has dealt with several high profile judicial reviews including those related to the IACS and Milk/Sheep quota schemes and represented the cheese producer in R v Minister of Health ex parte Eastside cheese company, the first case interpreting the powers of the state under ss 9 and 13 Food Safety Act. He is currently involved in several cases linked to the Swift v Dairywise litigation as to the nature of milk quota.
Prof. Memberships: Agricultural Law Association, Country Landowners Association, Fellow of the Chartered Institute of Arbitrators, The Food Law Group.
Career: Articled with *McFarlane Guy*; joined *CW&C* in October 1987, qualified November 1988 and made partner in 1994.
Personal: Attended Bristol Polytechnic (LLB); leisure intrests include golf and rugby.

SHEARER, Roy G.
Lindsays WS, Edinburgh (0131) 229 1212

SMITH, Graham C.H.
Roythorne & Co, Spalding (01775) 724141
Partner in Private Client/Agriculture department.
Specialisation: Partner in Private Client/Agriculture department. Main area of practice, agriculture and private client work.
Career: Qualified in 1974 having joined *Roythorne & Co* in 1972. Notary Public 1990. Author of practice text 'Agricultural Law'and editor of CGT newsletter on 'Agricultural Law.' Speaker at seminars, various accountants' and surveyors' conferences and for Central Law Training on 'Agricultural Law.'
Personal: Born 19th May 1949.

STEEL, John R.
White & Bowker, Winchester (01962) 844440
Partner in Environmental Law Group.
Specialisation: Main areas of practice are environmental and agricultural, including agricultural tenancy successions, farm partnership disputes, public rights of way, mineral abstraction and landfill, and water pollution cases. Also handles charity and education work, including formation of charities, advice to school governors and work for Higher and Further Education Colleges. Has written on pollution for the Agricultural Law Association Journal and the Royal Institution of Chartered Surveyors Technical Bulletin. Lectures on farm pollution, rights of way, independent schools. Holds Masters degree in Environmental Law from De Montfort University.
Prof. Memberships: Country Landowners Association, Agricultural Law Association.
Career: Qualified 1975, having joined *White & Bowker* in 1973. Became a Partner in 1977. Member of the Country Landowners Association Legal and Parliamentary Committee 1988-92 and of its Hampshire Branch Committee 1981-86 and 1987-92. Agricultural Law Association Treasurer 1990-94.
Personal: Born 9th May 1949. School Governor. Leisure interests include woodland management. Lives in Winchester.

STEPHENS, Jonathan
Jonathan Stephens & Co, Usk (01291) 673344

STONE, James F.
Addleshaw Booth & Co, Leeds (0113) 209 2000
jfs@addleshaw-booth.co.uk
Partner in Commercial Property Group.
Specialisation: Main areas of practice are agriculture, commercial property and property tax. Work includes property investment, tenancy issues (including termination, compensation and succession rights), quotas, property finance, capital taxation and VAT.
Prof. Memberships: Law Society, Agricultural Law Association.
Career: Qualified in 1981. Joined the firm in 1981, becoming a Partner in 1988.
Personal: Attended Bristol Grammar School 1964-75 and Exeter University 1975-78. Leisure interests include mountaineering, photography and travel. Lives in Harrogate.

STRANG STEEL, Malcolm
Turcan Connell WS, Edinburgh (0131) 228 8111
mgss@turcanconnell.com
Specialisation: Handles mainly rural property matters, including landlord and tenant, acting for proprietors of a number of landed estates with let farms and fishing interests; and purchase and sale of landed estates. Handles related taxation issues, and timeshare matters including fishings. Has lectured on numerous occasions to the Law Society of Scotland and other seminars on agricultural law and sporting law.
Prof. Memberships: Convener of Law Society of Scotland's Rural Affairs Committee; Convener of Law and Parliamantary Committee of Scottish Landowners' Federation; Secretary of Scottish Agricultural Arbiters Association; Member, Agricultural Law Association; Member, Securities Institute.
Career: Partner *W & J Burness* 1973-97; partner *Turcan Connell* 1997-date.
Personal: Eton College; Trinity College, Cambridge; Edinburgh University.

STURROCK, David P.
Turnbull, Simson & Sturrock WS, Jedburgh
(01835) 862391
dps@tssjed.co.uk
Managing partner.
Specialisation: Main area of practice is agricultural law. Handles all aspects of land ownership, Agricultural Holdings (Scotland) Acts, quotas and arbitrations. Also handles wills, succession and inheritance tax planning. Has addressed a variety of Conferences and Seminars.
Prof. Memberships: Law Society of Scotland; Accredited by Law Society of Scotland as a Specialist in Agricultural Law; Writer to the Signet; Notary Public.

Career: Qualified in 1966. Joined *Turnbull, Simson & Sturrock* in 1966, becoming a partner in 1968 and managing partner in 1990.
Personal: Born 16th March 1943. Attended Rugby School 1956-61 and Edinburgh University 1961-65. Lives in Jedburgh.

SWIFT, Robert D.
Wilsons, Salisbury (01722) 412412
Specialisation: Head of Farms and Estates department. Advises farmers and landowners on Agricultural Law, business restructuring, farm tenancies (including successions) and in connection with the sale and purchase of farms and estates.
Prof. Memberships: Agricultural Law Association, Country Landowners Association and the Farmers Club.
Career: Spent a number of years in industry before qualifying as a solicitor. Qualified in 1989. Partner since 1994. Head of Farms and Estates Department since 1998. A member of the Agrilaw Committee and a regular speaker at agricultural conferences.
Personal: Born 1959. Lives in Broadchalke near Salisbury. Interests include walking, cricket and speaking Spanish badly !

SYDENHAM, Angela
Birketts, Ipswich (01473) 232300

THOMSON, Michael
Arnold Thomson, Towcester (01327) 350266
miket@arnoldthomson.com
Partner specialising in agriculture.
Specialisation: Main area of work covers agricultural property, development work, tenancies, quotas and livestock premia. Regularly addresses farming and professional audiences.
Prof. Memberships: Agricultural Law Association, Country Landowners Association, National Farmers Union.
Career: Qualified 1981. Co-founder of *Arnold Thomson* in 1990.
Personal: Born July 1954. Attended Wrekin College 1967-71, then University College, London 1972-76. Leisure pursuits include shooting, golf and cricket. Lives in Blakesley, Northants.

TURCAN, Robert
Turcan Connell WS, Edinburgh (0131) 228 8111
rct@turcanconnell.com
Specialisation: Joint Senior Partner specialising in land law, trusts and tax planning, adviser to a substantial number of Landowners and farmers.
Prof. Memberships: The Law Society of Scotland, Society of Writers to HM Signet.
Career: Trinity College, Oxford (MA) and University of Edinburgh (LLB). Articled *Shepherd & Wedderburn WS*; qualified 1972; Partner at *Dundas & Wilson CS* 1973-1997. Chairman of Law and Parliamentary Committee, Scottish Landowners Federation; director of the Abercairny Estates Limited and others.
Personal: Born 1947. Resides Fife. Married with four children. Leisure interests include fox hunting, gardening, shooting and fishing.

WHITTAKER, Geoff
Barker Gotelee, Ipswich (01473) 611211
Specialisation: Specialist in land and estate sales, sales and purchases, agricultural holdings, farm business tenancies, IACS, milk and livestock quotas, specialist-crop contracting arrangements and land exploitation. Director of Stanyer Consulting Ltd. dealing with non-legal affairs, especially EU and national grant funding.
Prof. Memberships: Law Society, Agricultural Law Association (Committee Member 1997-).
Career: Qualified in 1980. Trained in native Liverpool before moving to Midlands, practised for 16 years.
Personal: Amatuer musician (choral and small-group *a capella* singing) and computers. Confirmed cricket nut!

WILLIAMS, Peter Rhys
Burges Salmon, Bristol (0117) 939 2223
peter.williams@burges-salmon.com
Specialisation: All forms of dispute concerning agricultural property, primarily agricultural banking, the dissolution of farming partnerships, and quota disputes.
Prof. Memberships: British Institute of Agricultural Consultants. A Fellow of the Chartered Institute of Arbitrators, Agricultural Law Association and non-Administration Receivers Association.
Career: Joined *Burges Salmon* in 1980, qualified in 1982 and became a partner in 1987. Joint author of the Encyclopaedia of Forms and Precedents on Agriculture; Halsbury's Laws on Agriculture and Longman's Agricultural Law, Tax and Finance and the RICS publication Farm Receiverships. He is a contributor to Scammell & Densham's Law of Agricultural Holdings. Was a Blundell Memorial lecturer in 1992. Author of CAAV Publication 'Dispute Resolution'.

WYBAR, David Kenneth
Ashton Graham, Ipswich 01473 232425
david.wybar@ashtongraham.co.uk
Specialisation: Acts for farmers, landowners and farming businesses and related throughout East Anglia.
Prof. Memberships: Agricultural Law Association. Council Member of Suffolk Agricultural Association. Suffolk Farming and Wildlife Advisory Group, Country Landowners Association. Suffolk Professionals European Committee.
Career: Winchester College and St. Andrews University. Trained with *Macfarlanes* in London and worked for *Mills & Reeve* in Norwich immediately before joining *Bankes Ashton* in Bury St Edmunds in 1991. *Bankes Ashton* merged with *Graham & Oldham* in October 1998 to become *Ashton Graham*.
Personal: Married with three children. Member of Bury St. Edmunds Farmers' Club, Ipswich and Suffolk Club, Royal and Ancient Golf Club of St. Andrews, Aldeburgh Golf Club, Golf House Club, Elie, Gentlemen of Suffolk Cricket Club and Newmarket and Suffolk Real Tennis Club. Chairman of Earl Soham Parish Council.

ALTERNATIVE DISPUTE RESOLUTION

London: 79; The Regions: 80; *Profiles*: 81

OVERVIEW: The Centre for Dispute Resolution (CEDR) figures suggest that in the year following the introduction of the new rules, the number of cases brought to mediation has approximately doubled. Most neutral mediators have also reported a dramatic increase in their mediation case load since the Woolf reforms. The consensus is that the market will continue to expand, both due to the increasing reluctance of judges to consider cases without seeing evidence of previous mediation attempts, and due to the growing awareness and acceptance of mediation among litigators.

The Lord Chancellor's report on ADR, which is currently undergoing its consultative phase, is expected to further consolidate and promote the role of mediation. It is unlikely that parties will be universally compelled to seek mediated settlements, although it has been suggested that mediation under the new code will be assumed unless an 'opt out' is sought. The market may also be made subject to new regulatory powers.

The ADR section focuses primarily on neutral mediators, rather than lawyers who have gained a reputation for advocacy in the mediation process. Lawyers who practise other species of dispute resolution, which include expert determination and early neutral evaluation, are also included. Arbitration is dealt with under a separate heading.

RESEARCH APPROVED BY BMRB: *For this edition,* Chambers' *researchers conducted 6083 interviews – 4408 with law firms, 598 with barristers and 1077 with clients.*

The validity of the research was scrutinised by BMRB International, who audited both the methodology and the results at our offices in July 2000. They interviewed Chambers' *researchers and cross-checked sample interviews. Details of the audit appear on page 7.*

LONDON

INDIVIDUALS • London
✪ **WILLIS Tony** Clifford Chance
❶ **BROWN Henry** Penningtons
MILES David Glovers
PRYOR Nicholas Sole Practitioner
SHAPIRO David SJ Berwin & Co
❷ **ANDREWARTHA Jane** Clyde & Co
BISHOP John Masons
CARROLL Eileen CEDR
CORNES David Winward Fearon
MARSH William CEDR
SIBLEY Edward Berwin Leighton
YORK Stephen Hammond Suddards Edge
❸ **DODSON Charles** CEDR
FINCHAM Anthony CMS Cameron McKenna
NEWMARK Chris Baker & McKenzie
TESTER Stephen CMS Cameron McKenna
❹ **HOLLOWAY Julian** Greenwoods
LUX Jonathan Ince & Co

*See **Profiles** on page 81*

Tony Willis, Clifford Chance *"Quite simply the best mediator in the country."* An expert proponent of the 'facilitative' CEDR style. He is *"hard on the issues but soft on the people,"* an approach which makes him the favourite of law firm clients. His *"commercial and innovative"* skills and *"dogged intimate knowledge of the process"* have proved extremely effective in arranging settlements. Has notched up an impressive 50 mediations in the past year. Universally commended for the range of his expertise, from professional negligence and insurance to insolvency, commercial contracts and banking.

Henry Brown, Penningtons An *"acknowledged leader"* and a *"guru"* to his peers. This *"calm, persistent and intuitive"* mediator is not as busy as some of his peers in the commercial sphere but his authority and knowledge of the process are undoubted. Although experienced in all types of commercial dispute, his main focus is in family and matrimonial mediations, particularly those involving breakdown in working and familial relationships.

David Miles, Glovers One of the *"founding fathers,"* he is an active promoter of mediation. *"Technically excellent,"* he secures people's confidence quickly, with his *"sensible and tolerant"* approach. The majority of his mediations involve construction disputes. Active within CEDR and PI.

Nicholas Pryor, Sole Practitioner The *"impressive and smooth"* Nicholas Pryor has gained a solid reputation. Clients praise his *"commercial common sense"* and *"swift grasp"* of key points. Formerly on the CEDR board and now one of the PIM 'gang of seven,' Pryor mediates in any dispute with a commercial bent. Recent cases have involved insurance/reinsurance, financial, and professional indemnity issues. He has been a neutral mediator in several multi-party disputes.

David Shapiro, SJ Berwin The *"robust"* and *"proactive"* Shapiro is recommended for the depth and variety of his experience and for his undoubted ability in securing settlements. He adopts a *"forceful, interventionist and idiosyncratic"* approach. Favoured by commercial clients more than law firms, he can be *"supremely effective and constructive."* His track record in mediating high-value, complex multi-party disputes is outstanding and he is amongst the most distinguished, high-profile and commercially acute mediators in the country.

Jane Andrewartha, Clyde & Co *"Articulate and intelligent"* Andrewartha's reputation is in the ascendant. The last year has seen her gain experience, expertise and glowing praise. The bulk of her mediation work involves insurance and reinsurance disputes but she also mediates in other commercial areas, having recently settled contentious professional indemnity and mortgage fraud cases.

John Bishop, Masons A *"natural mediator"* with brains and personality, Bishop has mediated eight cases in the past year. He has also acted as a facilitator in several executive inter-boardroom disputes. His particular expertise is in settling high-value and complex construction disputes, but he has also undertaken mediations involving professional negligence matters.

Eileen Carroll, CEDR Deputy chief executive at CEDR, she is ranked for the first time this year, after several positive recommendations.

David Cornes, Winward Fearon This *"impressive"* and *"quietly persuasive"* mediator is popular for his *"prescient, sparing and effective"* style. He has an impressive body of mediation experience, with 13 cases in the past year. He has gained a reputation for his expertise in mediating construction disputes. Recently settled a property dispute in the Far East and a contentious intellectual property matter for an electronics company.

William Marsh, CEDR Director of Mediation at CEDR. He has a breadth of general mediation experience. Recent cases have involved breach of contract disputes, medical negligence cases and chancery actions.

Edward Sibley, Berwin Leighton A *"strident and confident"* mediator and a founder member of CEDR, Sibley has long been a mainstay on the mediation circuit. Niche areas of expertise include solicitors' negligence and international commercial claims. He can, however, draw on a wealth of experience in most types of general commercial dispute.

Stephen York, Hammond Suddards Edge An *"inventive and idiosyncratic mediator"* York takes an interventionist and evaluative 'muscular' approach, of the Shapiro school. Particularly experienced in construction disputes, he has recently mediated in a large case involving two clearing banks. Also an experienced mediation advocate and robust promoter of ADR.

Charles Dodson, CEDR A full-time mediator and consultant to CEDR, Dodson has acquired a reputation as a solid and steady performer who is *"a good listener, informal and easy to talk to."* Considered a safe pair of hands, he is well equipped to mediate in most types of commercial case, including high-value professional negligence, breach of contract and partnership disputes.

Anthony Fincham, CMS Cameron McKenna A *"thoughtful and effective"* mediator whose star is rising although he has yet to acquire the breadth of experience demanded by many clients. His most significant recent case as a neutral mediator involved a £7m dispute over property rights. He has set up a London-based ADR group to promote the use of mediation within the capital's law firms.

Chris Newmark, Baker & McKenzie This *"keen up and coming"* mediator is gaining experience and reputation. He is active on the ICC ADR group and as a member of the CPR Institute for Dispute Resolution. He has recently settled a £300m telecoms dispute after four days of mediation.

Stephen Tester, CMS Cameron McKenna Praised for his *"active and incisive"* style, he is still building his reputation as a mediator. He is better known to some for his advocacy work and instrumental role in setting up the MAC initiative, which has engineered a commitment to ADR among insurance companies involved in the professional indemnity market. His mediation work is mainly in construction and insurance/reinsurance disputes.

Julian Holloway, Greenwoods A *"good mediator of the old school,"* very much in the CEDR mould. Mainly handles construction and civil engineering cases.

Jonathon Lux, Ince & Co *"He has mediator written all over his forehead."* An established and experienced player on the mediation circuit, the bulk of his work involves shipping, commodities and insurance/reinsurance disputes. He has recently worked on promoting the use of mediation among marine brokers.

THE REGIONS

INDIVIDUALS • The Regions
✪ **HOWELL-RICHARDSON Phillip** Morgan Cole
PATON Andrew Pinsent Curtis
❶ **LLOYD-JONES Jonathan** Linnells
❷ **ALLEN Anthony** Bunkers
BRADBEER Ronald Eversheds
DAVIES Michael Veale Wasbrough
GATENBY John Addleshaw Booth & Co
GLAISTER Anthony Denison Till
GOYDER William Jacksons
WINKWORTH-SMITH John Sole Practitioner
❸ **BLOOM Robin** Dickinson Dees
HOUGHTON Paul Lupton Fawcett
KENDALL John Sole Practitioner
LANGLEY Robert Watson Burton
SMITH Quentin Addleshaw Booth & Co
TEMPLE Euan Toller Hales & Collcutt

*See **Profiles** on page 81*

Phillip Howell-Richardson, Morgan Cole *"Quite brilliant"* and universally highly regarded. Recognised as an expert in the CEDR facilitative mediation tradition. He is said to be increasingly busy this year. Has successfully mediated a high-value dispute over a property joint venture. Richardson is now involved in PIM and he is also a director of ADR Net, part of ADR Group.

Andrew Paton, Pinsent Curtis A vastly experienced mediator, Paton continues to command universal respect from mediators and advocates alike. *"Tenacious and accomplished,"* he is consistently successful in securing settlements despite the increasing complexity of his caseload. Recently appointed to the panel of mediators used by the Court of Appeal Mediation Scheme.

Jonathan Lloyd-Jones, Linnells This *"highly intelligent, thoughtful and effective"* mediator just misses out on a top ranking – not because of doubts regarding his ability but because he lacks the depth of experience of the leaders. Commended for his expertise in professional negligence disputes.

Anthony Allen, Bunkers Takes a *"humorous and affable"* approach. Has developed a niche in mediating personal injury disputes, an area which has been slow to embrace ADR as a means of settlement. Has also handled clinical negligence and professional negligence cases. CEDR accredited.

Ronald Bradbeer, Eversheds A sound CEDR mediator, who is an experienced advocate as well as mediator. Much of his mediation work has involved construction disputes, but he also has a solid reputation for settling clinical negligence cases. A member of CEDR's training faculty, he was one of the co-founders of Northern Dispute Resolution.

Michael Davies, Veale Wasbrough An *"effective"* mediator who is praised by peers for his success in settling employment, professional negligence and construction disputes. Most of his work comes through referrals from ADR Net.

John Gatenby, Addleshaw Booth & Co A high profile individual on the mediation scene with *"just the right personality"* for the job. A non-executive director of CEDR and a member of ADR Group and the Association of Northern Mediators. Mediates in all types of commercial dispute, particularly those involving contractual issues.

Anthony Glaister, Denison Till A sound, if *"enigmatic"* mediator. Chairman of the Association of Northern Mediators, and an active mediator on the local circuit. Handles general commercial and contractual disputes.

William Goyder, Jacksons A man of *"experience and avuncular charm,"* he has a strong reputation. Has mediated in five cases in the past year. Acted as neutral mediator in a six party insolvency case referred to him by the receiver.

John Winkworth-Smith, Sole Practitioner *"Able and impressive."* Particularly recommended for his expertise in grasping the details of unwieldy technical disputes in engineering and construction cases. All of his work comes through CEDR referrals, where he has been a board member for ten years.

Robin Bloom, Dickinson Dees Less active since his recent move from Jacksons, Bloom's style is *"calm but firm."* Mediates all types of commercial dispute, especially contentious construction matters.

Paul Houghton, Lupton Fawcett One of CEDR's regional representatives in the North. Has acquired a solid reputation for his work mediating commercial contract and clinical negligence diputes. Recently mediated in a high value dispute over alleged loss of profits caused by the supply of defective parts to a manufacturer.

John Kendall, Sole Practitioner *"Quiet and capable."* A dedicated ADR practitioner, Kendell is to be found more in the role of expert determinator than mediator, although he does have some experience of the latter. He literally wrote the book on expert determination.

Robert Langley, Watson Burton Takes a strong, if not *"pugnacious"* approach which is not universally popular. Strong reputation for resolving construction and professional negligence disputes. Seen as yet to acquire a real breadth of mediation experience despite the fact that he was instrumental in founding NDR.

Quentin Smith, Addleshaw Booth & Co Following his CEDR accreditation in 1998 has already made a good impression on the mediation circuit. He has mediated a range of disputes in the personal injury, professional negligence and property sectors. Also recommended for his neutral work in the UK's first two defamation cases settled by mediation.

Euan Temple, Toller Hales & Collcutt Specialises in disputes arising out of non-contentious issues, including patent disputes, shareholder disputes, and some professional negligence disputes.

LEADERS IN ALTERNATIVE DISPUTE RESOLUTION

ALLEN, Anthony P.C.
Bunkers, Hove (01273) 329797

ANDREWARTHA, Jane
Clyde & Co, London (020) 7623 1244
Partner in Insurance and Reinsurance Department.
Specialisation: Practice is rooted in major insurance and reinsurance litigation, claims and liability work. Is an accredited and experienced CEDR mediator. Was responsible, jointly with another Partner, for the first major London Market Insurance (tri-partite) mediation settlement of a matter proceeding before the Commercial Court. Clients include most major London market insurance and reinsurance companies and many Lloyd's syndicates. Is a regular conference speaker and contributor to insurance industry publications. Currently involved in London marine insurance market initiative on mediation.
Prof. Memberships: Law Society, CEDR Accredited Mediator, Update Author of the international publication Journal of Maritime Law & Commerce, Association of Average Adjusters (Associate Member), Lloyds (Associate Member), member of Lir Law Group of Royal Aeronautical Society.
Career: Qualified in 1976, having joined *Clyde & Co* in 1974. Became a Partner in 1980. London Head of the firm's Latin American offices from 1989-1997 and Finance Partner from 1993.
Personal: Born 20th December 1952. Attended Exeter University 1970-73 (LLB Hons). Leisure activities include skiing, powerboat racing and swimming. Lives in London.

BISHOP, John
Masons, London (020) 7490 4000
john.bishop@masons.com
Senior Partner. Chairman of the Board and of Construction and Engineering Group.
Specialisation: Specialised in UK and International Construction and Engineering matters since qualifying, more recently also in Professional Negligence disputes. Major matters include LTRS, MTR, SSDS and Second Harbour Crossing in Hong Kong, Falklands Airfield, Tiffany Oil Platform, Channel Tunnel, Eurostar, Cairo Plaza, Jubilee Line, Keadby Power Station, LNG facilities (Brunei), Lloyds Building, M25, A27, several arbitrations from Indonesian Geothermic programme; conducted disputes at all levels of the English Courts, domestic arbitrations and international arbitrations under ICC, UNCITRAL and Stockholm Chamber rules as well as ADR processes. Expereince as Arbitrator and ADR practitioner.
Prof. Memberships: Dean of the Faculty of Mediation & ADR, Chairman of the Joint Consultative Committee of the London Court of International Arbitration, Vice Chairman of the Academy of Experts, President of the Technology and Construction Solicitors Association (TeCSA), Chairman of TeCSA IT Committee. Past Chairman of TeCSA, Past Member of TCC (Technology and Construction Court) Users Committee, TCC's Rules Committee, IT Committee, ADR Committee, Law Society Civil Litigation Committee, ICE Committees on Expert Evidence and Woolf Reforms, Founder Member of CEDR, Chartered Institute of Arbitrators' Committees on new forms of arbitration and ADR, British Academy of Experts Sub Committee on Expert Evidence. Editorial board of Construction Law Journal. Lectures include Blundell Memorial lecture, Bar Conference, Judicial Studies Board, National Contractors Group annual lecture, Chartered Institute of Arbitrators, Kings College (Univ. of London).
Career: Qualified 1971, Partner 1972, Admitted Hong Kong 1983, Managing Partner 1986 1990,Senior Partner 1990 to date. Qualified Adjudicator (TeCSA), Mediator (CEDR);
Personal: Sherborne School. LLB Hons Queen Mary College, University of London. Leisure interests include golf, fishing, cooking and tomatoes.

BLOOM, J. Robin
Dickinson Dees, Newcastle upon Tyne (0191) 279 9000
Specialisation: Employment law and commercial litigation (including use of alternative dispute resolution).
Prof. Memberships: Law Society. Founder Member Newcastle Industrial Tribunal User Group.
Career: Educated: Rugby School, Durham University and Chester College of Law. Career: Articled *Cohen Jackson* and *Addleshaw Sons and Latham*. Admitted: October 1982, worked for and subsequently partner in *Cohen Jackson*, now *Jacksons*. Trained as Mediator by ADR Net Ltd.
Personal: Married with two children. Main leisure interests are sport (mainly watching but still play the occasional game of cricket); foreign travel; gardening.

BRADBEER, Ronald
Eversheds, Newcastle upon Tyne (0191) 261 1661
bradeer@eversheds.com
Senior partner and senior litigation partner.
Specialisation: Principal area of practice is medical negligence. Principal legal advisor to area health authorities and trusts for many years. Specialised in medical negligence for over 25 years. Also handles commercial disputes specialising in commercial contracts, industrial tribunal cases and construction matters.
Prof. Memberships: Accredited Mediator with Centre for Dispute Resolution (1993), a member of the CEDR Training Faculty, Law Society.
Career: Joined *Wilkinson Maughan* in 1960. Qualified in 1963. Partner in 1967, managing partner in 1993 and senior partner in 1996.

BROWN, Henry
Penningtons, London (020) 7457 3000
brownj@compuserve.com
Consultant in commercial and family departments.
Specialisation: Principal areas of practice are ADR (mediation), intellectual property, partnerships and family business/matrimonial. Author of Law Society's ADR Report (1991), co-author of 'ADR Principles and Practice' (1993/1999). Commercial and family mediation trainer.
Prof. Memberships: Law Society, SFLA, FMA, UK College of Family Mediators, CEDR, Mediation UK, Academy of Family Mediators (US), Society of Professionals in Dispute Resolution.
Career: Qualified South Africa, 1962 and England & Wales 1975. Established *Simanowitz & Brown* 1975. Partner *Birkbeck Montagu's* 1980-91, *Penningtons* 1991-94. Consultant from 1994.
Personal: Born 29th May 1939. Educated at University of Cape Town and University of South Africa. Certificate in Fundamentals of Psychotherapy and Counselling (Regents College, 1994).

CARROLL, Eileen
CEDR, London (020) 7600 0500

CORNES, David L.
Winward Fearon, London (020) 7420 2800
See under Construction, p.198

DAVIES, Michael
Veale Wasbrough, Bristol (0117) 925 2020
mdavies@vwl.co.uk
Founder member of ADR Group. Involved in ADR since 1991.
Specialisation: Background in all aspects of litigation with particular mediation experience in employment issues, contract disputes, professional negligence claims, and financial services litigation. Currently specialising in employment related litigation.
Career: M.A., Ph.D. Partner *Veale Wasbrough*, since 1981. Head of Employment Law Department. Two cases successfully taken to the Court of Appeal in 1999.

DODSON, Charles
CEDR, London (020) 7600 0500
inbrncpd@aol.com
Specialisation: Mediator, primarily of broad range of UK and international commercial disputes. Became involved in ADR when resident partner in *Lovell White & King's* New York office in mid 80's. Subsequently involved in setting up CEDR (The Centre for Dispute Resolution), now one of the leading ADR bodies internationally. One of CEDR's original directors, five month secondment 1995, accredited mediator 1996, consultant from 1998, and a member of mediator and lawyer training faculties.
Career: Partner *Lovell White & King/Lovell White Durrant* 1981-98; Managing Partner 1991-1995. Insead AMP 1991.

FINCHAM, Anthony
CMS Cameron McKenna, London
(020) 7367 3000
Specialisation: Employment and Commercial Litigation.
Career: Degree in Modern History (Oriel College, Oxford). Qualified 1980. Partner *Cameron McKenna* from 1984.
Personal: Married with three children.

GATENBY, John
Addleshaw Booth & Co, Manchester
(0161) 934 6000
See under Litigation (Commercial), p.561

GLAISTER, Anthony
Denison Till, Leeds (0113) 246 7161
Specialisation: Using the widest spectrum of alternatives to resolve commercial disputes to match all means. Experience includes mediation by executive tribunal and combined with arbitration. Visiting lecturer on mediation studies at Leeds Metropolitan University. Charges £125 per hour or agreed fee.
Prof. Memberships: ORSA Adjudicator, CEDR Mediator, Administrator Association of Northern Mediators, and Chartered Institute of Arbitrators.
Career: Qualified in 1980. Partner in *Fox & Gibbons*, London from 1985 to 1989 and *Denison Till* since.
Personal: Born April 1953. Very active leisure pursuits where family and farming activities allow. Regional Deputy Chairman PYBT.

GOYDER, William A.
Jacksons, Stockton-on-Tees (01642) 643643

HOLLOWAY, Julian
Greenwoods, London (020) 7323 4632
jpwh@greenwoods-law.co.uk
Partner.
Specialisation: Construction and commercial litigation/arbitration and alternative dispute resolution. Director of Centre for Dispute Resolution Limited ("CEDR"). Vice Chairman of CEDR's Construction Industry Working Party. Member of Drafting Committee of CEDR's Model Rules for Adjudication. Case Notes Editor of Construction Law Journal. CEDR accredited mediator (1993). Acts as mediator and for parties engaged in the mediation process. On CEDR's panel of adjudicators and is actively engaged in numerous adjudications.
Prof. Memberships: Law Society. Technology and Construction Court Solicitors Association.
Career: Articles with *Denton Hall & Burgin* 1979-1981. Qualified solicitor since 1981. Assistant solicitor *Brecher & Co* 1981-1983. Assistant solicitor with *McKenna & Co* 1984-1988. Partner *McKenna & Co* 1988-1992. Partner *Greenwoods* 1993 to date.
Personal: Born 1954.

HOUGHTON, Paul
Lupton Fawcett, Leeds (0113) 280 2000

HOWELL-RICHARDSON, Phillip
Morgan Cole, Cardiff (029) 2038 5385
phillip.howell-richardson@morgan-cole.com
Partner in Commercial Litigation department.
Specialisation: Heavyweight High Court Litigation arbitration and dispute resolution. Has extensive experience in advising institutions, companies, banks, government bodies and individuals on a wide range of corporate, financial and statutory issues. Has conducted or led actions ranging from substantial corporate fraud to money and asset recovery to defamation. Has developed an expertise in construction litigation and has a long standing involvement in mediation in the UK. A highly experienced mediator who has taken part in pilot mediation programmes as well as conducting mediations in a wide range of disputes throughout the country. Cases have included an international shareholders dispute and an arbitration involving a public company claim in excess of £10 million which settled successfully after the first phase of the hearing. Addresses conferences on the development of ADR.
Prof. Memberships: Law Society, Chairman of ADR Net, TECSA, Association of European Lawyers, Wales Medico-Legal Society, Wales Public Law Association. A member of the panel of Court of Appeal Mediators and a founder member of the Panel of Independent Mediation.
Career: Qualified in 1975. *Stanley Wasbrough* from 1975-76, then *Osborne Clarke* 1976-81. Joined *Morgan Cole* in 1981, becoming a Partner in 1982.
Personal: Born 21st June 1950. Clifton College, Bristol 1963-69, University of Kent 1969-72. Leisure interests include sailing, tennis and restoration of classic cars. Lives in Cardiff.

KENDALL, John
John Kendall, Presteigne (01544) 260019
jkendall@btinternet.com
Specialisation: Mediator, arbitrator, lecturer and trainer. CEDR consultant in expert determination, chairman, *ArtResolve*. Author of 'Expert Determination', the only textbook on the subject, now in its second edition (FT Law & Tax 1996); co-author, 'Russell on Arbitration' (21st edition 1997). Registered mediator, CEDR; accredited adjudicator, TeCSA; Fellow, Chartered Institute of Arbitrators and chartered arbitrator.
Prof. Memberships: Member the Law Society, the Society of Construction Law, the Technology and Construction Solicitors Association.
Career: Articled *Stephenson Harwood*, qualified 1976, partner *Allen & Overy* 1985-1998; now freelance.
Personal: Oxford University (1972 BA, 1976 MA). Born 1950.

LANGLEY, Robert L.
Watson Burton, Newcastle upon Tyne
(0191) 244 4444
See under Construction, p.203

LLOYD-JONES, Jonathan
Linnells, Oxford (01865) 248607
jlj@linnells.co.uk
Senior partner–head of commercial dispute resolution.
Specialisation: Construction and professional negligence litigation. Company, especially publishing, and general commercial disputes. Mediation.
Prof. Memberships: Law Society. Director of ADR Group Ltd.
Career: Qualified 1979. *Stephenson Harwood* 1977-1980. *Claude Hornby & Cox* 1980-1988 (Partner 1982-1988). *Linnells* 1988 to date (partner 1990). Trained Mediator 1991.
Personal: Born 23rd November 1954. Educated at Sevenoaks School and Southampton University. Interests: Fly fishing, British water colours, family life. Lives in Oxford.

LUX, Jonathan
Ince & Co, London (020) 7623 2011
See under Shipping, p.748

MARSH, William L.
Ince & Co, London (020) 7623 2011

MILES, David
Glovers, London (020) 7629 5121
Partner in Construction Department.
Specialisation: Has specialised in construction since 1978. Deals with contract negotiations, joint venture agreements, claims involving both arbitration and litigation acting both for employers and contractors in the UK and overseas. Acted in the cases Rees Hough, Viking Grain and St Martins. Contributing Author 'Construction Conflict Management and Resolution.' Co-Author 'Commercial Dispute Resolution–an ADR Practice Guide'. Director of CEDR and TECSA training faculty and lecturer on ADR. Mediator (CEDR/AE). Adjudicator TECSA and CEDR.
Prof. Memberships: F.C.I.Arb, Committee Member Technology and Construction Court Solicitors Association, Society of Construction Law.
Career: Commission Regular Army (1966-1971). Joined *Alan Wilson & Co* in 1978, Partner 1979. Merged with *Glovers* in 1986.
Personal: Born 22nd June 1946. Haileybury 1960-64. Chairman of Moreton Cricket Club. Leisure interests: tennis, cricket, shooting, opera. Lives in North Moreton, Oxon.

NEWMARK, Chris
Baker & McKenzie, London (020) 7919 1000
Partner.
Specialisation: Practices commercial international arbitration and litigation as well as alternative dispute resolution techniques (including mediation and expert determination). Has advised clients in mediation in both England and the United States and practices as mediator for commercial disputes. Has

particular experience as both mediator and counsel in disputes related to the telecoms industry.
Prof. Memberships: The Law Society.
Career: Qualified 1990. At *Baker & McKenzie* since 1988. Elected Partner in 1997. Spent 1993-94 working in the firm's Chicago office. Trained as mediator with CPR, New York in 1994. Accredited CEDR mediator in 1995. Trained community mediator with LAMP (Lewisham Action for Mediation Project). Member of the ICC Commission on International Arbitration and CPR International Panel of Distinguished Neutrals.
Personal: Born 16 January 1964. Educated at Abingdon School, Birmingham University and the University of Limoges, France. Interests include golf and photography. Lives in Greenwich

PATON, Andrew J.

Pinsent Curtis, Birmingham (0121) 200 1050
andrew.j.paton@pinsents.com
Partner and head of litigation in Birmingham.
Specialisation: Defending claims against professionals on instructions of their insurers. Uses mediation extensively to resolve claims. Acts as mediator in wide range of cases.
Prof. Memberships: Training faculty of CEDR. Director of ADR Net Limited. Member of the Panel of Independent Mediators. Chairman of the Association of Midlands Mediators. Member of Council of Birmingham Law Society–Chairman of the Civil Litigation Committee; member of the Policy Committee.
Career: Articled *Cripps Harries Hall & Co*, Tunbridge Wells. Qualified 1981. Joined *Pinsent & Co* (now *Pinsent Curtis*) September 1981. Partner 1985.
Personal: Born 1957. Educated at Bishop Vesey's Grammar School, Sutton Coldfield and Exeter University (LLB). Interests include yacht and dinghy racing, cycling and tennis.

PRYOR, Nicholas

Nicholas Pryor–Sole Practitioner, London
(020) 7359 2819
nicholaspryor@Sotheby-Road.co.uk
Specialisation: ADR and mediation. Have been mediating since 1986. Now acting full time as an independent mediator, and in representing parties at mediation and/or advising on the use of mediation. Specialises in large scale, multi-party mediations, particularly insurance, reinsurance and professional indemnity matters.
Prof. Memberships: Founder member, Panel of Independent Mediators; Registered Mediator, CEDR; Accredited Mediator, ADR Group; Member, CPR Institute for Dispute Resolution (New York); Member, mediation panel, London Court of International Arbitration; Member, British Association of Lawyer Mediators.
Career: Called to Bar (Middle Temple) 1970. Admitted Solicitor 1980. Assistant, *Rowe & Maw* (1980-82), Assistant, *Coward Chance / Clifford Chance* (1982-89), Partner, *Manches* (1990-95), Company Solicitor, KWELM Management Services Ltd (1995-96).
Personal: Born 1946. Lives Highbury, London.

SHAPIRO, David

SJ Berwin & Co, London (020) 7533 2421
d.shapiro@sjberwin.com
Specialisation: Alternative Dispute Resolution: accredited as a mediator by CEDR (Britain's Centre for Dispute Resolution), is on numerous mediation panels, was Director and Chief Mediator of JAMS Endispute Europe, and is currently Visiting Professor of Law, Nottingham Law School and Visiting Fellow, Department of Law, London School of Economics and Political Science, where he teaches mediation and mediation advocacy. He was organiser of and lead-off speaker on 'Introduction to ADR', part of the Judicial Studies Board's Stage 1 seminars for UK judges, and is a lecturer and writer on mediation issues. Since arriving in the UK in 1996, he has successfully mediated more than fifty major disputes in this country and Europe. He is a Consultant to S J Berwin & Co where he serves as Director of that firm's ADR Services Unit.
Prof. Memberships: Centre for Dispute Resolution; CPR Institute for Dispute Resolution (Panel of Distinguished Mediators); British Assn. of Lawyer Mediators; City Disputes Panel; Int. Bar Assn.; American Bar Assn.; The Chartered Inst. of Arbitrators; Soc. of Professionals in Dispute Resolution (SPIDR); International Academy of Mediators (IAM).
Career: Formerly senior founding partner and Head of Litigation, *Dickstein, Shapiro & Morin*, New York and Washington DC. In 1995 he was principal engineer of the national class-action settlement of claims arising out of silicone breast implants, affecting more than 800,000 potential plaintiffs world-wide. In 1990, he was the court-appointed Settlement Master in New York for hundreds of claims for injuries from asbestos. In 1988 was the court-appointed Examiner (Special Master) in the bankruptcy proceedings for Eastern Airlines. In 1986 he served as Chairman of the American Bar Association's National Institute on 'New Techniques for Resolving Complex Litigation.' In 1985 he was the court-appointed Settlement Master in the 'Agent Orange' litigation brought by Vietnam veterans for their exposure to dioxin. In 1981, after having litigated antitrust cases against American Telephone & Telegraph, leading to the Modified Final Judgement that broke the U.S. telephone monopoly, Mr. Shapiro was retained by AT&T to resolve a myriad of antitrust actions spawned in part by his earlier representation of plaintiffs. For the next eleven years he served as settlement counsel for AT&T and its offspring, the Regional Bell Operating Companies, as well as numerous other major corporations. Lead trial counsel in landmark U.S. cases from 1950 to the early 1980s.
Publications: Publications include: 'Consumer Participation in Antitrust Class Actions', 41 ABA Antitrust L.J. 257 (1972); 'Management of Consumer Class Actions after Eissen', 26 Mercer L.Rev. 851 (1975) (with James vanR. Springer); 'Trained Neutrals', New Law Journal (March 1997); 'Expert Mediators Not Experts as Mediators', 16 CEDR Resolutions (Spring 1997); 'ADR in the Commercial Court–One Year Later', 17 CEDR Resolutions (Summer 1997); 'ADR Under the New Civil Procedure Rules', Durham Univ. L. Rev. (Summer 1999); 'Publishing the Envelope–Selective Techniques in Tough Mediations, Solicitors' Journal (September 1999).

SIBLEY, Edward, LL.B., F.C.I. Arb.

Sibley & Co, London (020) 7395 9790
Senior partner.
Specialisation: Principal area of practice is international and domestic civil litigation, arbitration and mediation, including insurance and re-insurance disputes, professional negligence, product liability and civil fraud. Has acted as a mediator and advocate in over 90 commercial mediations. Publications include 'The European Community 1992 and Beyond'. He has addressed conferences worldwide on issues relating to the conflict of laws and comparative law.
Prof. Memberships: Member of Litigation Sub-Committee City of London Law Society; Union Internationale des Avocats; American Bar Association; International Bar Association; The Law Society and the New York State Bar.
Career: Qualified in 1965. Articled with *Clifford Turner* 1961-64 and joined *Berwin & Co.* upon qualification. Became a partner in 1968. Thereafter became a founder partner *Berwin Leighton* in 1970 and managing partner 1984-86. Also admitted New York State Bar 1985 and founder member and director of the Centre for Dispute Resolution (CEDR) 1989; CEDR appointed mediator 1992; Solicitor Advocate Higher Courts (Civil) 1995; Fellow of the Chartered Institute of Arbitrators 1999.
Personal: Born 21st July 1935. Educated at Rhymney Grammar School and University of Wales, Aberystwyth 1958-61 (First Class Honours and Sir Samuel Evans Prize for the best student of the year). Member of Reform Club and MCC.

SMITH, Quentin P.G.

Addleshaw Booth & Co, Manchester
(0161) 934 6000
qps@addleshaw-booth.co.uk
Specialisation: Professional negligence; personal injury (employers liability; motors; public liability); health and safety; insurance (mediated two out of three defamation cases).
Career: Articled clerk, solicitor and partner at *James Chapman & Co* 1986-96; partner *Addleshaw Sons and Latham* 1996-97; partner *Addleshaw Booth & Co* 1997 to date. Articles for various publications.
Personal: Arts; sports; travel.

TEMPLE, Euan M.F.

Toller Hales & Collcutt, Northampton
(01604) 258558
info@tollers.co.uk
Specialisation: European Law, M&A work, competition law, MBOs, joint ventures, e-commerce, partnerships, intellectual property licensing, R&D contracts, mediation.
Prof. Memberships: Director–ADR Net Ltd.
Career: Graduated Cambridge. Qualified 1970. Accredited mediator 1990. Has lectured on mediation in the UK and abroad, and contributed articles on the subject. A regular speaker at conferences on e-commerce, commercial and competition law.
Personal: Western and central European history. Hockey (player and umpire).

TESTER, Stephen

CMS Cameron McKenna, London
(020) 7367 2894
skt@cmck.com
Specialisation: Practises in construction and surveyors' PI, D & O and Contractor All Risk Insurance (both litigation and policy interpretation and drafting). Clients include insurance companies, Lloyds syndicates, insurance brokers and construction companies. Has extensive experience in alternative forms of dispute resolution both as a mediator and as an adviser to individual parties.
Prof. Memberships: Society of Construction Law. CEDR Accredited Mediator.
Career: KCS Wimbledon and St. John's College Cambridge. Qualified 1981. Partner since 1988.
Personal: Interests include family and friends, golf and squash.

WILLIS, Tony
Clifford Chance, London (020) 7600 1000
tony.willis@cliffordchance.com
Specialisation: Consultant to *Clifford Chance* after more than 25 years as a partner and now a full time independent mediator. Mediates for CEDR and other ADR institutions and also when instructed direct. Advises on ADR and dispute process design. Founder member, Panel of Independent Mediators. Member International Academy of Mediators. International Panellist, CPR Institute for Dispute Resolution in New York and Advanced Panel, LEADR in Australia and New Zealand. More than 50 mediations conducted in 1999.
Career: Fellow of Chartered Institute of Arbitrators 1990; CEDR Accredited Mediator 1993. Qualified 1966 (LL.B New Zealand); solicitor England & Wales 1971; partner at *Clifford Chance* 1973; joint Managing partner 1987-1988 and litigation managing partner 1989 to 1996. Consultant since end of 1998.
Personal: Born 1941. Married with six children. Lives in London.

WINKWORTH-SMITH, John
John Winkworth-Smith, Bakewell (01629) 640269
Specialisation: Solicitor and former regional managing partner of *Dibb Lupton Alsop*. Founder director of CEDR and a board member until 1999. Until retirement from DLA in 1999 was a practising litigation lawyer with experience in the following fields: mechanical engineering, steel production, electrical engineering, civil engineering and construction, plastics production, glass production, waste disposal systems, plumbing and piping systems in clay and plastics, industrial design, packaging, road vehicles, intellectual property, charities, residential care homes, shareholder disputes, professional negligence, employment and farming.
Prof. Memberships: Accredited mediator to CEDR and Academy of Experts.
Career: Former chairman and director of a number of companies. Much experience of foreign disputes, particularly in Italy, Japan and USA.

YORK, Stephen D.
Hammond Suddards Edge, London
(020) 7655 1000
stephen.york@hammondsuddardsedge.com
See under Litigation (Commercial), p.569

ARBITRATION (INTERNATIONAL)

London: 85; *Profiles*: 87

OVERVIEW: This year we have slightly adjusted the criteria for rankings. These are based on the international arbitration capacity of the team, taking into account its work handled in the London office only. This has the immediate effect of dropping Freshfields from the top band. Paris and the rest of the world are covered in Chambers Global.

This year's list is considerably shorter than in previous years. There are undoubtedly many more firms who do some international commercial arbitrations. We simply identify the best. The US firms seem to recognise the importance of London as an arbitral venue and at least three firms are putting some significant effort into their London arbitration practices. All are listed, despite the small size of their teams.

The Arbitration Act 1996 has made arbitration in many cases the desirable alternative to litigation, particularly in the 'wait and see' climate following Woolf. However, there is a growing trend to challenge the decisions of arbitrators, thereby increasing time and costs, which is of concern to many practitioners. It will be interesting to see how the area develops over the next 12 months.

RESEARCH APPROVED BY BMRB: *For this edition,* Chambers' *researchers conducted 6083 interviews – 4408 with law firms, 598 with barristers and 1077 with clients.*

The validity of the research was scrutinised by BMRB International, who audited both the methodology and the results at our offices in July 2000. They interviewed Chambers' *researchers and cross-checked sample interviews. Details of the audit appear on page 7.*

LONDON

Clifford Chance The clear leaders in London, seen to be handling *"top level"* work. The excellent team fields *"trustworthy and pragmatic opponents"* from its *"army"* of people. Headed by the *"savvy"* **John Beechey**, a *"truly dedicated"* international practitioner. Other members of the team, said not to *"miss a trick,"* include *"shrewd"* and *"thorough"* **Audley Sheppard** and **Robert Lambert**. **Highlights/Work:** This year has seen a dispute between a multi-national, multi-party entity and a major energy firm over a power station in Europe. The case will be heard in Geneva under UNCITRAL rules. Also instructed to act for a joint Japanese-British venture in a claim brought by a subcontractor in relation to the construction of an LNG plant in the middle-east. Again under UNCITRAL rules, this time in Paris.

Freshfields Bruckhaus Deringer A close second place. The firm's first class international arbitration practice is led from its strong Paris office, strengthened by the sheer quality of Freshfields offices world-wide. London still has a way to go to match the 'superstar' reputation of Paris. The team is led by the *"excellent"* **Nigel Rawding** who is said to be doing a *"good job."* He is assisted by **Philip Croall** and **Nigel Blackaby**, a *"smart guy."* **Highlights/Work:** Dominated by oil but this is certainly not all Freshfields do! In the past year the firm has been acting for a consortium of more than 10 international oil companies in respect of disputes arising under a production sharing agreement with a Caspian Sea state-owned oil company. Also case involving an American oil company in disputes with three other international oil companies over exploration projects in South America.

Herbert Smith Out of a firm traditionally viewed as the UK's litigation giant, a significant international arbitration force is emerging. Of over 70 new instructions in the last year over half come from outside the UK. The *"lightning rod"* for the practice is the *"learned"* **Dr Julian Lew**. However, **David Brynmor Thomas** is now considered by some to be of equal stature. Others give similar recognition to **Larry Shore**, a new entry to the table, said to be *"as good as the best."* **Highlights/Work:** Representing a US petroleum services company in an ICC arbitration in Singapore concerning indemnities in a service contract. Also advising claimants against the ruler of a Middle-Eastern state in an ICC arbitration over the expropriation of businesses worth many millions of dollars.

Allen & Overy Snapping at the heels of Herbert Smith, this firm is seen more by the International Court of Commerce than any other in our tables. The consensus is that the London team is increasing its profile in

ARBITRATION (INTERNATIONAL) • London	Ptnrs	Assts
❶ Clifford Chance	4	12
❷ Freshfields Bruckhaus Deringer	4	11
Herbert Smith	4	8
❸ Allen & Overy	5	13
❹ Linklaters	5	10
Lovells	15	19
Masons	15	15
Norton Rose	5	16
Wilmer, Cutler & Pickering	3	11
❺ Baker & McKenzie	3	6
Clyde & Co	4	10
CMS Cameron McKenna	6	14
Debevoise & Plimpton	1	3
Holman Fenwick & Willan	40*	50*
Ince & Co	43*	50*
Richards Butler	27	29
Shearman & Sterling	-	4
Simmons & Simmons	7	12

LEADING INDIVIDUALS	
❶ **BEECHEY John** Clifford Chance	**LEW Julian** Herbert Smith
MARRIOTT Arthur Debevoise & Plimpton	
❷ **BORN Gary** Wilmer, Cutler & Pickering	**CAPPER Phillip** Lovells
GILL Judith Allen & Overy	
RAWDING Nigel Freshfields Bruckhaus Deringer	**SUTTON David** Allen & Overy
❸ **BLACKABY Nigel** Freshfields Bruckhaus Deringer	
BRYNMOR THOMAS David Herbert Smith	**COLBRIDGE Christopher** Shearman & Sterling
CROALL Philip Freshfields Bruckhaus Deringer	**KNUTSON Robert** Masons
LAMBERT Robert Clifford Chance	**MITCHARD Paul** Wilmer, Cutler & Pickering
NAIRN Karyl Simmons & Simmons	**SHEPPARD Audley** Clifford Chance
STYLE Christopher Linklaters	
UP AND COMING	
FRASER David Baker & McKenzie	**MORGAN Simon** Simmons & Simmons
O'CONOR John Allen & Overy	**SHACKLETON Stewart** Simmons & Simmons
SHORE Larry Herbert Smith	**WINTER Jeremy** Baker & McKenzie

Within each band, firms are listed alphabetically. *See **Profiles** on page 87*

** These figures include arbitration practitioners also concentrating on high volume shipping and commodities areas.*

arbitration. *"Elder statesman"* **David Sutton** still commutes from Paris to head up the practice. The *"wonderful"* **Judith Gill** may not be a keen self-promoter but is nonetheless universally well spoken of. **John O'Conor** remains in the up and coming list – well-respected but *"not quite in the thick of things yet."* **Highlights/Work:** Acting in claims totalling $3.6 billion against a central Asian state and entities arising out of oil and gas ventures. Arbitrations under ICC rules in the USA and Europe. Instructed by a major pharmaceutical company in their $190 million claim against insurers. The dispute turns on proper interpretation of the policy governed by New York law.

Linklaters Those in the know see the firm acting in many arbitrations at the *"highest level"* such as the longest running ICC arbitration over the cancellation of a major weapons system. *"Smart operator"* **Christopher Style** heads the team which is both *"active"* and *"effective."* The derivatives arbitration practice is increasingly busy and the Alliance partners add a global capability not easily matched. **Highlights/Work:** Acting in a widely reported dispute for an independent power producer against the Pakistan Water and Power Development Authority over terms of the tariff for electricity generated by it. The ICC arbitration clause is subject to injunction proceedings in the Supreme court of Pakistan and has drawn criticism by the IMF and the World Bank. Also conducted two arbitrations for Bankers Trust against defaulting companies in swap transactions in Indonesia under LCIA rules and related litigation.

Lovells Seen to suffer slightly from a lack of big names, although *"tough"* ex-Masons man **Phillip Capper**'s contacts with the international arbitration bodies and his construction arbitration credentials should help in this regard. The firm is said to be doing some *"big ones"* and *"getting respect."* **Highlights/Work:** Acting for a major international oil company in an arbitration under UNCITRAL rules in London. Dispute is with a West African joint venture co-licensee and subject to the law of a West African state. Also acting as principal counsel in a dispute over the design and manufacture of complex electrical and mechanical engineering equipment. One aspect is before arbitration in Spain, while related issues are referable to two other distinct European jurisdictions.

Masons The construction firm and *"fantastic"* at it. Lesser known for international commercial arbitration but now *"making strides."* Doing battle all over the world and with many of our interviewees on a surprising range of issues this firm seems equally at home with silicon as with bricks. *"Formidably clever"* **Robert Knutson** takes over from Philip Capper as top man here. **Highlights/Work:** Represented an Asian state utility in three UNCITRAL arbitrations involving complex claims worth over $3 billion, arising from the construction and operation of a thermal power plant. The firm regularly acts for governments and major international companies on engineering, energy, technology and other issues.

Norton Rose Having advised clients in arbitrations conducted under virtually every set of rules available this firm has an *"impressive"* reputation. Known for particular expertise in commodities, shipping, insurance and construction the firm is reportedly involved in a *"huge"* number of arbitrations. **Highlights/Work:** Acted for an Indian publishing company in an LCIA arbitration against a European corporation and for an American company in an ICC arbitration against a major European corporation concerning supply of equipment and technology.

Wilmer, Cutler & Pickering Currently the highest ranking of the US firms, impressive considering the size of the team compared to the company it keeps. This is in no small measure due to the *"innovative"* **Gary Born** who is so *"energetic"* he caused at least one interviewee to ask *"does he ever sleep?"* Add the *"immensely impressive"* **Paul Mitchard** who is said to be *"overwhelmed with work"* and the firm's ranking is assured. **Highlights/Work:** Represented a European telecommunications provider in a multi-billion dollar arbitration under ICC rules. Acted in a large LCIA arbitration in London arising from disputes in the financial services sector worth nearly $1 billion.

Baker & McKenzie Two new names in our lists are getting recognition for the *"substantial"* cases handled by the firm. *"Awfully good"* **Jeremy Winter** is joined in the tables by **David Fraser** who is doing a *"huge number"* of important arbitrations. The practice's international credentials are augmented by its offices in over 35 jurisdictions Has acted in arbitrations arising out of manufacturing, construction, engineering projects and telecommunications disputes among others. **Highlights/Work:** Acting for six industrial enterprises in Kazakhstan in four LCIA and two UNCITRAL arbitrations arising out of management disputes worth over $200 million. Acting for an Italian equipment manufacturer in defending an arbitration claim by an Asian purchaser over alleged deficiencies in equipment supplied.

Clyde & Co Does an *"enormous"* amount of international arbitrations. Primarily known as one of the leading shipping firms, the practice however has a much broader base of client. It has been involved in some 300 arbitrations over the past year, many non-shipping related. Has acted for oil companies, insurers, trading houses and government departments. **Highlights/Work:** Acted in a $200 million claim under a non-marine reinsurance treaty in an LCIA arbitration. Also involved in substantial claims arising out of losses incurred on Russian pipe-lines against former states of the USSR.

CMS Cameron McKenna The International Arbitration Group is focusing on central and eastern Europe and is said to be doing some *"good stuff."* The transnational legal services organisation, CMS, adds a European dimension to the firm's dispute resolution services. **Highlights/Work:** Acting for US reinsurers in a series of London arbitrations with claims exceeding £280 million. The firm is also acting for a European party in two ICC arbitrations in relation to the construction of manufacturing plants in the middle-east with claims exceeding $200 million.

Debevoise & Plimpton An *"excellent operation"* under the *"terrific"* and *"ingenious"* **Arthur Marriott QC** who is an *"eminence grise"* on the international arbitration scene. Initial excitement over his acquisition has slightly abated, however, as he is not felt to enjoy sufficient support of his own quality. Nevertheless, the practice continues to pull in work and receives many referrals from the New York office. **Highlights/Work:** An ICC arbitration for a Japanese client arising out of a joint venture in a developing country. Also acted for a leading Asian vehicle manufacturer in an ad-hoc arbitration against a European vehicle manufacturer.

Holman, Fenwick & Willan Another leading shipping and commodities practice with a lesser known yet substantial international commercial arbitration practice. **Highlights/Work:** Acted in an ICC arbitration involving a US commodities house in dispute with a PRC oil company over an LNG development. Heard in London with the substantive law of both England and the PRC involved. Acted in dispute between a major international consulting and systems integration services company and a transport logistics PLC concerning design and development of a Y2K compliant software system.

Ince & Co This *"first-rate"* shipping firm has substantial practices in insurance/reinsurance, commodities and energy. Unlike many others in our list, this firm takes the view that specialists in those areas need be proficient themselves in arbitration, rather than maintain a specialist arbitration section. **Highlights/Work:** Represented the owners of the Aegean Sea in an arbitration arising out of the loss of the vessel and cargo of crude oil and related environmental claims. Acted for a contractor in connection with a dispute arising from the construction of two FPSO's for the oil and gas industry, in multi-million dollar arbitrations in London.

Richards Butler The firm is a market leader in physical commodities work and shipping. It is seen mainly on arbitrations in these sectors. Known to have a long portfolio of cases, and currently active in some 200 arbitrations, Richards Butler are generally held to be worthy players. **Highlights/Work:** A substantial supply contract dispute worth at least $100 million and two linked countertrade disputes valued at around $140 million. Also acting in a $300m LCIA arbitration arising out of a shipbuilding contract dispute.

Shearman & Sterling The only practice in our tables with no partners in the team – yet. This *"classy"* firm seems to be building up its London practice nicely under the *"charming"* **Chris Colbridge** who is *"very good indeed."* Aided by a strong Paris team. **Highlights/Work:** Acting in a $500 million arbitration in Singapore for an Asian Television company. The practice is also advising an EU institution on designing, implementing and running its dispute resolution systems.

Simmons & Simmons **Karyl Nairn** heads this team which is felt to be *"pushing hard."* The *"academic"* **Stewart Shackleton** is considered to be an asset to the practice, as is former Hong Kong Attorney General **Simon Morgan** who adds to the Asian expertise of the practice. **Highlights/Work:** Acted for Esso against the UK subsidiaries of three international petroleum companies in a multi-party dispute over a participation agreement for the construction and operation of an oil pipeline. The firm brought one of the first successful challenges to an award in the English courts under the Arbitration Act 1996.

LEADERS IN ARBITRATION (INTERNATIONAL)

BEECHEY, John
Clifford Chance, London (020) 7600 1000
john.beechey@cliffordchance.com
Specialisation: Partner and head of international commercial arbitration group dealing with all arbitration, ADR, contentious construction and commercial litigation.
Prof. Memberships: Fellow of the Chartered Institute of Arbitrators; Member of the Board of the American Arbitration Association; *Clifford Chance* representative on the Corporate Counsel Committee of the AAA since 1987; appointed to the AAA Arbitrators' Panel in 1991; Member of the Board of the London Court of International Arbitration; Member of the ICC UK Arbitration Panel since March 1992 and a British representative on the ICC Commission. Member of the Council of the ICC Institute; appointed to the Arbitrator panel of the Regional Centre for International Arbitration in Cairo and of Korea Commercial Arbitration Board in 1995.
Career: MA (Oxon) French and German. Partner *Clifford Chance* 1983.

BLACKABY, Nigel A.
Freshfields Bruckhaus Deringer, London
(020) 7936 4000
nblackaby@freshfields.com
Specialisation: International Arbitration Group. International commercial arbitration, including acting as counsel in ad hoc arbitrations and arbitrations under the rules of the AAA, LCIA, ICC, UNCITRAL and ICSID with a particular focus on Latin American disputes and disputes under investment treaties. Also advises on the drafting of arbitration clauses in international contracts. Author and a frequent speaker on arbitration topics including 'International Arbitration in Latin America' and 'Dispute Resolution in Mercosur'.
Prof. Memberships: Law Society, IBA, LCIA, British Brazilian and Portuguese Law Association, Canning House.
Career: Articled *Freshfields* 1991 to 1993. Qualified March 1993. Editor Arbitration International (1995-), founder and co-chair LCIA Young International Arbitration Group (1996-). Secretary to LCIA Latin American Users' Group.
Personal: Born 20 April 1967. Attended University of Exeter, Université d'Aix en Provence and College of Law, Chester. Speaks French, Spanish and Portuguese.

BORN, Gary B.
Wilmer, Cutler & Pickering, London
(020) 7872 1000
gborn@wilmer.com
Managing Partner in International Arbitration/Litigation Department.
Specialisation: Principal area of practice is international arbitration. Represents European, US, Asian and other corporate clients in international commercial arbitration under all major institutional rules (ICC, LCIA, AAA, Stockholm, IACAC) and ad hoc (UNCITRAL) in all leading fora. Other main area of practice is international litigation (US) including advice on issues of jurisdiction, foreign sovereign immunity, international judicial assistance, conflict of laws. Particular expertise in joint ventures, telecommunications, M&A, construction, sales and agency disputes.
Prof. Memberships: American Law Institute, International Bar Association, American Bar Association, British Institute of International and Comparative Law, American Society of International Law.
Career: Joined *Wilmer, Cutler & Pickering* in 1984. Became a Partner in 1988 and Managing Partner in London office in 1991.
Publications: Author of 'International Commercial Arbitration: International and US Aspects' (2nd edition, Kluwer 2000), 'International Civil Litigation in United States Courts' (3rd edition, Kluwer 1996) and 'International Arbitration and Foreign Selection Agreements' (Kluwer 1999). Has undertaken numerous speaking engagements. Editor, *International Litigation Newsletter*.
Personal: Educated at Haverford College, Haverford, Pennsylvania 1973-78 (BA, summa cum laude) and University of Pennsylvania Law School 1978-81 (J.D., summa cum laude); law clerk to Chief Justice William H. Rehnquist and Judge Henry J. Friendly. Proficient in German.

BRYNMOR THOMAS, David
Herbert Smith, London (020) 7374 8000
Specialisation: International arbitration and litigation, particularly in relation to civil, chemical and process engineering and large scale infrastructure projects (especially energy and rail). Has acted in ad hoc arbitrations and arbitrations under the rules of the ICC, LCIA, SIAC and UNCITRAL involving parties and transactions from the UK, the US, Africa, India, the Gulf States and South-East Asia. Also has experience in project related expert determinations. Drafts and advises on dispute resolution provisions for projects, including IPPs, United Kingdom PPP projects, the Channel Tunnel Rail Link and the liberalisation of utility industries.
Prof. Memberships: The Law Society, London Court of International Arbitration.
Career: Articled at *Herbert Smith*, 1991 to 1993. Member of the *Herbert Smith* construction and engineering department since qualification in September 1993. Became a partner in 2000.
Personal: Born 1964. Originally qualified in and practised Medicine. Educated at the University of Edinburgh (MB, ChB 1987).

CAPPER, Phillip
Lovells, London (020) 7296 2000
phillip.capper@lovells.com
See under Construction, p.198

COLBRIDGE, Christopher
Shearman & Sterling, London (020) 7655 5000
CColbridge@shearman.com
Represents *Shearman & Sterling's* International Commercial Arbitration Group in London.
Specialisation: Has acted as Counsel in international arbitrations, both institutional (ICC, LCIA, ICSID and other rules) and ad hoc around the world. Has represented multi-national corporations and governments in disputes involving international contracts, particularly investments, infrastructure and energy projects. Also specialises in law and practice of international litigation, conflict of laws and jurisdiction.
Prof. Memberships: London Court of International Arbitration. International Arbitration Institute. IBA.
Career: Qualified England & Wales, 1992. Admitted to Paris bar, 1999. *Clifford Chance* 1990-99.
Personal: Born 1967. Educated at Kings College, University of London (LLB Hons), 1987. University of Paris I Panthéon-Sorbonne (Licence and Maîtrise in French private law), 1989.

CROALL, Philip M.
Freshfields Bruckhaus Deringer, London
(020) 7936 4000
Partner specialising in arbitration, ADR and commercial litigation.
Specialisation: Handles all aspects of international commercial arbitration work. Has appeared on Counsel in arbitrations under rules of the major arbitration institutions including the ICC, the LCIA as well as in ad hoc arbitration under the UNCITRAL Rules. Speaks regularly at seminars and writes articles on arbitration and international dispute resolution techniques. Also involved in all kinds of commercial litigation including cases relating to banking and financial services regulation.
Prof. Memberships: Associate of the Chartered Institute of Arbitrators.
Career: Qualified at *Freshfields* in 1985. Partner at *Freshfields* 1992.
Personal: Born 22 August 1959.

FRASER, David
Baker & McKenzie, London (020) 7919 1000
david.fraser@bakernet.com
Specialisation: Business disputes with experience in the areas of insurance and reinsurance, trade finance, sovereign immunity, professional liability, and carriage by sea, telecommunications, corporate joint ventures, minority shareholders right and contentious insolvency. Has acted as counsel in and

managed several major commercial arbitrations in England and elsewhere and has brought a number of cases to trial in the Commercial Court and the Court of Appeal in London. Has recently represented the owners of the Kazakhstan metals industry in complex arbitration proceedings against former joint venture partners. Led the team acting for Geest in the banana wars with Fyffes. Acts for a number of professional consultancy firms including Tillinghast and LEK. Acts in contentious issues for Camelot. Adviser on crisis management and senior management responsibilities. Member of City Disputes Panel Users Committee and LCIA.
Prof. Memberships: The Law Society and New York Bar.
Career: Qualified in 1973. Joined *Baker & McKenzie* in 1975, becoming a partner in 1982.
Publications: Arbitration of International Commercial Disputes Under English Law – The American Review of International Arbitration 1997/vol.8. no.1.
Personal: Born 1948. University of Birmingham. Lives in London.

GILL, Judith A.E.
Allen & Overy, London (020) 7330 3000
Partner in Litigation Department.
Specialisation: Principal areas of practice are arbitration and commercial litigation. Extensive experience in all forms of arbitration proceedings, both domestic and international, particularly arbitration under LCIA and ICC rules. Also handles general commercial litigation - acts for a number of large quoted public limited companies on a range of matters including warranty claims, pensions litigation and insurance disputes.
Prof. Memberships: Law Society, City of London Solicitors' Company, Fellow of the Chartered Institute of Arbitrators. Committee member of the International Arbitration Club. Fellow of the Institute of Advanced Legal Studies.
Career: Qualified in 1985. Joined *Allen & Overy* in 1983 and became a Partner in 1992. Director of the London Court of International Arbitration. Co-Author of the 21st Edition of 'Russell on Arbitration'.
Personal: Born 30th September 1959. Educated at Worcester College, Oxford University 1979-1982. Awarded an MA (Jurisprudence) from Oxford University 1988. Diploma in International Commercial Arbitration from University of London 1990. Lives in Surrey.

KNUTSON, Robert
Masons, London (020) 7490 4000
robert.knutson@Masons.com
Specialisation: International Commercial Arbitration and Sale of Goods; International Construction Contracts and disputes; Comparative law and conflicts of law; practising arbitrator.
Prof. Memberships: Canadian member, ICC Court of Arbitration and ICC Commission on International Arbitration; member, Canadian ICC Arbitration Committee (member qualifications sub-committee); Fellow, Chartered Institute of Arbitrators (England); CIA registered Construction Industry Adjudicator; member, IBA Committees on International Sale of Goods and sub-committee Chairman International Construction Projects (Newsletter Editor for committee and Publications sub-committee chairman); ABA Associate member, member, Society of Construction Law; co-founder, and Treasurer, International Arbitration Club; member European Panel of Distinguished Neutrals of the (US) CPR Institute, LCIA Panelist and Fellow of the Indian Council of Arbitration.
Career: LLB University of British Columbia, 1982; Barrister and Solicitor, Canada, 1983; LLM, LSE, 1984; Solicitor, England and Wales, 1988; MSc Construction Law and Arbitration, 1991; partner, *Masons* 1996; MPhil University of London 1997; practised in Canadian, American and English law firms, numerous publications; visiting lecturer on arbitration, Kings College, London; regular speaker on international construction and arbitration. Recently nominated as an arbitrator in International Sale of Goods, construction and telecommunications disputes.
Personal: Born 22/10/56; lives in Dulwich, married, two children.

LAMBERT, Robert
Clifford Chance, London (020) 7600 1000
robert.lambert@cliffordchance.com
Specialisation: Partner specialising in the law and practice of international arbitration, conflict of laws and jurisdiction. Particular experience in disputes involving international engineering, construction and infrastructure projects. Represents clients as counsel (advocate) before domestic and international arbitral tribunals. Regularly advises on the drafting of dispute resolution provisions for projects and other commercial contracts.
Career: Oxford University (St Edmund Hall), BA (Hons) Law (1st class). Trained *Clifford Chance*; qualified 1989.

LEW, Julian
Herbert Smith, London (020) 7374 8000
Head of international commercial arbitration practice group. Partner in litigation and arbitration division. 1970 (Bar) 1981 (Solicitor) 1985 (Attorney-at-Law, New York).
Specialisation: Main area of practice is international commercial arbitration, acting as an adviser and representing clients in different forms of arbitrations: concerning all kinds of international contracts, particularly engineering and infrastructure projects, investments, distribution, intellectual property licenses and joint ventures. Has also been appointed as an arbitrator in ICC, LCIA, AAA, Ad hoc and other arbitrations. Author of numerous publications including: 'Applicable Law in International Commercial Arbitration' (1978). Editor, 'Contemporary Problems in International Commercial Arbitration' (1985), 'The Immunity of Arbitrators' (1990) and 'Enforcement of Foreign Judgements' (1994). Head of the School of International Arbitration, Centre for Commercial Law Studies, Queen Mary & Westfield College, University of London; Chairman of the Chartered Institute of Arbitrators' Committee on Arbitral Practice, and Chairman of the ICC Working Party on Intellectual Property Disputes in Arbitration.
Prof. Memberships: British Institute of International and Comparative Law, London Court of International Arbitration, Chartered Institute of Arbitrators, American Society of International Law, American Bar Association, Swiss Arbitration Association, French Arbitration Committee, Hong Kong International Arbitration Centre, International Bar Association, Arbitral Centre of the Federal Economic Chamber, Vienna.
Personal: Born 3rd February 1948. LLB (Hons) London, 1969; Academy of International Law 1970-71; and Doctorat special en droit international, Université Catholique de Louvain, Belgium, 1977.

MARRIOTT Q.C., Arthur
Debevoise & Plimpton, London (020) 7786 9000
amarriott@debevoise.com
Partner, *Debevoise & Plimpton* London.
Specialisation: International commercial arbitration, mediation, oil and gas law and practice, joint venture agreements and civil engineering construction law and practice. Co-author with Henry Brown of 'ADR Principles and Practice' (Sweet & Maxwell 1993), Co-editor of 'Handbook of Arbitration Law and Practice' (Sweet & Maxwell 1999) and author of numerous articles.
Prof. Memberships: Chairman of the Private Group engaged in the preparation of a new English arbitration statute; Member of Mediation Sub-committee of Civil Justice Council; Member of the Steering Committee, Central London County Court Pilot Mediation Scheme; Member of the Steering Committee, Court of Appeal Pilot Mediation Scheme; Member of Council of International Council for Commercial Arbitration (ICCA); Member of Board of Hong Kong International Arbitration Centre (HKIAC) and of London Court of International Arbitration (LCIA); Fellow of Chartered Institute of Arbitrators.
Career: Solicitor of the Supreme Court of England and Wales since 1966; Solicitor of the Supreme Court of Hong Kong since 1976; Partner *Debevoise & Plimpton*; Recorder (part-time criminal judge) 1998; Queen's Counsel 1997; Deputy High Court Judge 1997.
Personal: Born 1943. Languages: English, German and some French.

MITCHARD, Paul
Wilmer, Cutler & Pickering, London (020) 7872 1000
Partner.
Specialisation: Main areas of practice are international arbitration and commercial litigation, covering the conduct of ICC, LCIA, RSA, Lloyd's arbitrations, commercial, financial and administrative and public law disputes. Also handles dispute resolution and mediation. Accredited CEDR mediator, member of CPR's panel of distinguished neutrals and a Fellow of the Chartered Institute of Arbitrators. Has represented domestic and international companies and State organisations in many major disputes. Has given seminars in London, the USA and the Middle East on international arbitration.
Prof. Memberships: Law Society, American Bar Association, International Bar Association, City of London Solicitors' Company.
Career: Qualified in 1977. Worked at *Slaughter and May* 1977-84 in London and Hong Kong. Joined *Simmons & Simmons* in 1984, becoming a Partner in 1985 and was Head of Litigation 1994-98 before joining the London office of *Wilmer, Cutler & Pickering* in January 1999.
Personal: Born 2nd January 1952. Attended Taunton School 1960-70 and Lincoln College, Oxford 1971-74. Leisure interests include travel, reading and walking. Lives in Chalfont St. Giles, Bucks.

MORGAN, Simon
Simmons & Simmons, London (020) 7628 2020
Specialisation: International Commercial Arbitration.
Prof. Memberships: International Bar Association;

Chartered Institute of Arbitrators; London Court of International Arbitration; Institute for Transnational Arbitration, Inter Pacific Bar Association; International Chamber of Commerce (Commission Member); CEDR; CPR, European Advisory Committee; The Law Society.
Career: Joined *Simmons & Simmons* in 1981, from 1986 to 1988 and 1996 to 2000, Partner in the firm's Litigation Department in London, from 2000, Litigation Department Managing Partner, from 1988 to 1995 Head of Commercial Litigation and Arbitration in the firm's Hong Kong office. Admitted as a solicitor in England and Wales (1980) and Hong Kong (1985).
Personal: Married with three children.

NAIRN, Karyl
Simmons & Simmons, London (020) 7628 2020
Specialisation: Practises in general international commercial arbitration and litigation. Major cases in 1999-2000 include institutional and ad hoc arbitrations for various European technology companies, a multi-national pharmaceutical company, an international financial organisation, a worlwide banking consortium, a US property partnership and US and European fashion companies. Counsel to a working group advising the European Telecommunications Platform on dispute resolution issues.
Prof. Memberships: The Law Society of England and Wales, The Law Council of Australia, The Law Society of Western Australia, American Bar Association, International Bar Association, The International Arbitration Club, London Court of International Arbitration, Fellow of the Society for Advanced Legal Studies, Fellow of the Chartered Institute of Arbitrators, Member for Australia (alternate) on the Internation Court of Arbitration of the ICC.
Career: Qualified as a barrister and solicitor of the Supreme Court of Western Australia and the Federal and High Courts of Australia in 1988, admitted as a solicitor in England and Wales in 1991. 1985-90 worked at *Michell Sillar McPhee Meyer*, Australia; 1990 Tutor at Law School of University of Western Australia; joined *Simmons & Simmons* in 1991, became a Partner in 1996. Head of *Simmons & Simmons'* International Arbitration Group.
Personal: Educated at University of Western Australia (B.Juris(Hons), L.L.B.(Hons)) and London School of Economics, University of London (L.L.M.).

O'CONOR, John
Allen & Overy, London (020) 7330 3000
Specialisation: Partner specialising in commercial litigation, international arbitration and ADR. Member of the firm's Arbitration and Banking & Finance Litigation Groups based in London. Special emphasis on banking and financial disputes and development of dispute resolution systems for the financial markets. Particular interest in and practical court experience of jurisdictional and conflict issues. Extensive experience of international commercial arbitration in financial and reinsurance fields, as well as general commercial matters. Has conducted arbitrations in several international centres under various arbitral systems and governing laws.
Career: Qualified in 1990; assistant solicitor *Allen & Overy* 1990-1997; Partner since 1997.
Personal: Born 1964. Educated at Randley College and Gonville & Caius College, Cambridge (1982-86). Lives in Islington, London.

RAWDING, Nigel K.
Freshfields Bruckhaus Deringer, London (020) 7936 4000
Partner in litigation department and London head of *Freshfields'* London/Paris International Arbitration Group.
Specialisation: International dispute resolution specialist representing clients in major commercial disputes involving litigation, international arbitration and ADR procedures. International arbitration experience includes ICC, LCIA, UNCITRAL and ad hoc cases. Litigation experience comprises a wide variety of High Court commercial cases. Co-author of The *Freshfields* Guide to Arbitration and ADR (Second revised edition Kluwer, 1999). Member of ICC Commission on International Arbitration and director of the LCIA. Regular contributor to arbitration journals and conference speaker on subjects relating to the resolution of international disputes.

SHACKLETON, Stewart
Simmons & Simmons, London (020) 7628 2020
Paris +33 1 53 053 131 International Arbitration Group.
Specialisation: Has acted in over 70 international commercial and construction arbitrations. Counsel and arbitrator in public international law disputes, including arbitration involving States, State entities and public international organisations. Advises on jurisdiction and conflicts of law disputes. Practice also includes advising on challenges to arbitral awards in France and England; acting in multi-jurisdictional banking and commercial litigation; advocacy before courts in France and before international arbitral tribunals in French and English; acting in CEDR administered international mediation proceedings. Sitting as party - appointed arbitrator. chairman and sole arbitrator in ICC proceedings.
Prof. Memberships: Member for Canada, ICC Commission on International Commercial Arbitration; London Court of International Arbitration; Fellow, Chartered Institute of Arbitrators; Swiss Arbitration Association; French Arbitration Association; French Arbitration Committee; Indian Council of Arbitration; British Institute of International and Comparative Law; British Columbia International Commercial Arbitration Centre; Vice-President of the European Lawyer's Association; Member for Canada of the International Arbitration Committee, International Law Association.
Career: Has practised in Canada, Hong Kong, Paris and London. Avocat au Barreau de Paris (1994) (conseil juridique stagiaire 1991-94); Solicitor of the Supreme Court of England and Wales (1994); Solicitor of the Supreme Court of Hong Kong (1995); Barrister and Solicitor, Ontario (1993).
Personal: MSC in Construction Law and Arbitration (University of London); DEA in Public International Law (University of Paris I); DSU in Private International Law (University of Paris II); MaÓtrise en Droit Civil - mention droit des affaires (University of Paris II); DEA in African Law (University of Paris I); DiplÙme in Comparative Law (University of Paris II); LLB (University of Western Ontario). Working languages: French, English and Scandinavian languages, knowledge of German and Spanish.

SHEPPARD, Audley W.
Clifford Chance, London (020) 7600 1000
audley.sheppard@cliffordchance.com
Specialisation: Partner specialising in the resolution of disputes, in particular arising out of infrastructure projects (including investment, engineering and construction disputes).
Career: Lindisfarne College, Hastings, NZ; Victoria University of Wellington, NZ (LLB Hons 1983) (BCA 1984); Cambridge University, UK; (LLM 1986). Articled *Bell Gully Buddle Weir*, NZ; qualified New Zealand 1985, England 1990, made partner *Clifford Chance* 1995.
Personal: Sports, theatre. Born 1960; resides London.

SHORE, Larry
Herbert Smith, London (020) 7374 8000
laurence.shore@herbertsmith.com
Specialisation: Counsel, acting in international commercial arbitrations.
Prof. Memberships: London Court of International Arbitration; Research Advisory Committee of the Global Center for Dispute Resolution Research.
Career: Joined *Herbert Smith* in 1995. Became a partner in 1999. 1989-1995: associate, *Williams & Connolly* (Washington DC). 1995: Attorney Adviser International, Office of the Legal Adviser, US State Department.
Publications: The Advantages of Arbitration for Banking Institutions, 'Journal of International Banking Law' (Nov. 1999); 'Making Applicants Take Evidence Properly: Challenges to Letters of Request,' 'International Commercial Litigation' (July/August 1998); 'Southern Capitalists' (U. of N. Carolina Press 1986).
Personal: Born 3 December 1954. J.D. with distinction, Emory Univ. School of Law; PhD (History) The Johns Hopkins University; MA (History) The Johns Hopkins University; BA with highest honours, The University of North Carolina at Chapel Hill.

STYLE, Christopher J.D.
Linklaters (A member firm of Linklaters & Alliance), London (020) 7456 4286
christopher.style@linklaters.com
See under Litigation (Commercial), p.89

SUTTON, David St. John
Allen & Overy, London (020) 7330 3000
Specialisation: Head of the firm's arbitration practice. He specialises in dispute resolution, particularly international arbitration and contentious construction. He sits as an arbitrator as well as advises and appears as an advocate in others. He is a CEDR accredited mediator.
Prof. Memberships: Member of the London Court of Arbitration; the International Chamber of Commerce (Member Court of Arbitration); Member of the Hong Kong International Arbitration Centre and Fellow of the Chartered Institute of Arbitrators; former member of the Advisory Committee, International School of Arbitration, Queen Mary College and the University of London; visiting lecturer to the Faculty of Law, University of Hong Kong; former joint chairman of committee 'D'; International Bar Association (Settlement of Disputes).
Career: Articled *Robins, Hay, Long & Gardiner*, qualified 1967; Assistant Solicitor 1967-68; Assistant Solicitor *Allen & Overy* 1968-70; Partner 1970.

Admitted as English and Hong Kong Solicitor; Advocate of Paris bar.
Personal: Born 1941. Educated at Highgate School, Open University (BA).

WINTER, Jeremy
Baker & McKenzie, London (020) 7919 1000
jeremy.winter@bakernet.com
Partner and Head of Construction & Projects Department, Solicitor Advocate.
Specialisation: Resolution of construction and projects disputes by arbitration, litigation and ADR. Particular expertise in civil engineering matters. 18 years' experience in a total of 30 countries around the world (particularly Europe, Africa and the Middle East). Conducts own advocacy in arbitration and in High Court. Frequent speaker and writer on construction and arbitration topics.
Prof. Memberships: Hon Fellow of Institution of Civil Engineering Surveyors, Society of Construction Law, Technology and Construction Solicitors Association (Member of IT Sub-committee). Member of Association for Project Management, Member of the Geological Society. Member of LCIA.
Career: Qualified 1979. Joined *Baker & McKenzie* London 1980. Worked in *Baker & McKenzie* Sydney Office 1982-84. Partner 1987.
Personal: Born 26 December 1953. Warwick University (LLB Hons 1975). Lives in Toys Hill, Kent.

ASSET FINANCE & LEASING

London: 91; The Regions: 94; Consumer Finance – National: 95; *Profiles*: 96

OVERVIEW: The tightening of international and domestic tax regimes is demanding an increasingly sophisticated service from asset finance departments with expertise expected in tax, banking and capital markets. Increased work is expected in rail, where licences are up for renewal in the next few years. With aircraft being the most commonly financed asset, all the leaders have excellent aircraft finance capabilities. A separate section deals with ship finance.

In general this is an area where in-house specialists have a major role, particularly in the regions. Of the regional players Pip Giddins and Bruce Wood are the truly national figures, having *"written the book"* on their respective sides of the border.

A notable evolution at the small ticket end of asset finance work is that the traditional dominance of the 'big four' finance houses owned by the clearing banks has gone. A number of captive houses and big players such GE Capital and First National are now at the forefront of the market.

Consumer finance often overlaps with asset finance, though some finance companies do not do consumer lending. In consumer finance, work is of three natures, transactional, product development and litigation. In-house specialists are a significant factor in consumer finance, with the minority of leading players being in private practice. The spread of expertise is large and in addition to those in the rankings, individuals were mentioned in City firms such as Allen & Overy and Clifford Chance, as well as regional firms such as Shoosmiths.

LEADING IN-HOUSE LAWYERS

Tony BOCHENSKI, Head of the Compliance Group, *Bank of Scotland*

Simon ELLIOTT, Company Solicitor, *Barclays Mercantile*

Stephen GARRATT-FROST, Head of Legal Services, *HSBC Holdings*

Janet GREGORY, Legal Director, *GE Capital Equipment Finance Ltd*

Tom PRICE, Head of Legal Services, *Lombard Asset Finance*

Ian WOODCOCK, Director of Legal Services, *RoyScot Trust*

"Switched on" **Tony Bochenski** is a *"very competent and experienced practitioner"* who is well-established in the industry. He is praised for being *"strong on the legal-technical side"* and is *"one of the best"* on the big-ticket deals. *"Bright spark"* **Simon Elliott** is well-recommended for being *"very capable and very experienced."* Also *"well-experienced"* is **Stephen Garratt-Frost**. **Janet Gregory** is widely praised and *"inspires confidence."* **Tom Price** has *"lots of experience"* and is *"highly regarded." "Super chap"* **Ian Woodcock** is *"very clever and good to work with."*

In-House lawyers profiles: page 1177

RESEARCH APPROVED BY BMRB: *For this edition,* Chambers' *researchers conducted 6083 interviews – 4408 with law firms, 598 with barristers and 1077 with clients.*

The validity of the research was scrutinised by BMRB International, who audited both the methodology and the results at our offices in July 2000. They interviewed Chambers' *researchers and cross-checked sample interviews. Details of the audit appear on page 7.*

LONDON

Freshfields Bruckhaus Deringer *"The hot name at the moment, the buzz-word."* When asked where they would go with their own money for asset finance expertise, almost every major competitor of the firm said Freshfields. It has major strength at the top level and has noted strength in depth, with a *"solid spread of work"* both in the UK and internationally. Premier tax, securitisation and regulatory practices also make the firm's asset finance team stand out. Perhaps as proof of the quality of its product, clients are seeing them *"on every transaction"* and *"they seem to be turning up all over the place."* Joined this year by the *"personable and commercially-minded"* **Bob Charlton** from Clifford Chance, this *"successful and aggressive"* practice moves into a band of its own. Charlton was a rail finance specialist with his former firm, working on the provision of new equipment to TOCs such as Virgin West Coast, and is regarded as *"a fantastic craftsman."*

Recognised for its broad variety of work, the team is active on ships, rail, high-value equipment and planes, with the emphasis this year on aviation. In aircraft, where the firm has *"always been the obvious first choice,"* the practice's leading lights are **Tim Lintott** and **Simon Hall**, both *"protégés"* of the evergreen **Mark Freeman**. Freeman is an *"extremely impressive"* practitioner of the elder-statesman mould, and used to be head of the asset finance group. Lintott is now the head of the department, and is noted for his international work, mainly on aircraft, with a bias towards airline clients such as Iberia. The *"excellent"* Hall is head of the finance practice in its entirety, and he mixes this role with aviation and rail work. Although his work rate is perceived to have decreased with his managerial responsibilities, he is *"first class when he does it."* The *"incredibly diligent and thorough"* **Andrew Littlejohns**' work is evenly spread between rail and aviation, working for manufacturers and lenders. Major rail work this year includes advising Angel Trains on a $780 million securitisation to finance the acquisition of 53 high speed tilting trains to be leased to Virgin Rail, and acting for CIBC Wood Gundy on a €1 billion financing through a securitisation and loans from EIB/EIF for new freight rolling stock for AAE Cargo AG. In aviation, the practice advised Iberia on enhanced secured aircraft notes (Essans) for the financing of Airbus A320 family aircraft, a first in the Eurobond markets. **Clients:** Air One; Airbus Industries; Angel Train Contracts; Bank of America; Boeing; Crédit Agricole Indosuez; GE Capital Aviation Services; Iberia; Rolls Royce.

Clifford Chance Following the retirement of Anne Williamson and the departure to Freshfields of Bob Charlton, the practice is perceived to be less of a dominant force by some commentators. The departure of Charlton may have dented the rail practice, but competitors observed that the size of the team meant that its effect *"should not be overestimated."* The return from Hong Kong of the *"impressive"* **Clive Carpenter** will no doubt strengthen the London base. *"Technically brilliant"* **Geoffrey White** is the global head of asset finance and is regarded as *"abrasive but excellent."* The highly-respected **Tom Budgett** is the other big name in the department. The practice is seen as international rather than UK-oriented and is now a global player for aircraft financings. Along with its aviation reputation, the

ASSET FINANCE & LEASING • London	Ptnrs	Assts
❶ Freshfields Bruckhaus Deringer	10	30
❷ Clifford Chance	8	34
Norton Rose	11	34
Slaughter and May	4	12
❸ Allen & Overy	*	*
Denton Wilde Sapte	13	17
❹ Linklaters	7	28
Watson, Farley & Williams	*	*
❺ CMS Cameron McKenna	4	5
Herbert Smith	10	10
Lovells	9	7
Simmons & Simmons	5	6
Theodore Goddard	7	7
Weil, Gotshal & Manges	1	7
❻ Beaumont and Son	2	3
Harbottle & Lewis	2	4

LEADING INDIVIDUALS

❶ **BUDGETT Tom** Clifford Chance
CHARLTON Bob Freshfields Bruckhaus Deringer
HALL Simon Freshfields Bruckhaus Deringer
JOLLIFFE Peter Slaughter and May
KINNERSLEY Tom Slaughter and May
LINTOTT Tim Freshfields Bruckhaus Deringer
THORNE Peter Norton Rose
WHITE Geoffrey Clifford Chance

❷ **CARPENTER Clive** Clifford Chance
COLLINS Andrew Denton Wilde Sapte
GIBBS Ronald Linklaters
HALLAM Robin Lovells
KAHN Gregory Denton Wilde Sapte
LITTLEJOHNS Andrew Freshfields Bruckhaus Deringer
MILES Adrian Denton Wilde Sapte
SALT Julia Allen & Overy
WATTERS James Watson, Farley & Williams

❸ **CRANE David** Norton Rose
CROOKES Alan Norton Rose
FREEMAN Mark Freshfields Bruckhaus Deringer
HALL Gordon Norton Rose
JACOVIDES Mario Allen & Overy
JOYCE Andrew Allen & Overy
SMITH David Allen & Overy
TOTT Nicholas Herbert Smith

❹ **BRAND Giles** Norton Rose
EDWARDS Jeremy Norton Rose
GIBB Jeremy Norton Rose
HOMAN Hugh Berwin Leighton
OSBORNE David Watson, Farley & Williams
VALLANCE Philip Norton Rose
WALKLING Kim Simmons & Simmons
WILLIAMS Geoffrey Watson, Farley & Williams

UP AND COMING
MARKS Lisa Denton Wilde Sapte
SMITH Graham Allen & Overy
WITTMANN David Slaughter and May

Within each band, firms are listed alphabetically. *See **Profiles** on page 96*
** See editorial entries for explanations of team sizes.*

firm is also considered to have a *"depth of experience"* in rail. Most of the firm's asset finance work is in the transport sector, and around half of the firm's transport work is in aircraft. Work this year includes acting for the financiers on Sabena's 34 Airbus order and advising the lead manager on an Iberia Enhanced Equipment Trust Certificate (EETC) securitisation. Additionally, the practice advised on O-FSC Financings for KLM, Qantas, Cathay Pacific and Cargolux, and on Airbus aircraft financings for Lan-Chile and Air Canada. **Clients:** Citibank; Barclays Capital; Deutsche Bank; HSBCIB.

Norton Rose The asset finance practice operates from two core groups within the firm. One concentrates on ships, an area where the firm is regarded as a leader, the other on rail, aircraft and equipment. Of the many recommended names, **Peter Thorne** is the practice's stand out practitioner. An asset finance all-rounder, he would be part of *"anybody's dream team."* **David Crane** is primarily involved with projects work, yet has dealt with rail, plant and machinery asset finance work. **Gordon Hall** is another projects hand who is noted for his shipping and rail skills. **Alan Crookes** is a PFI specialist with a bias on assets such as aircraft and dockyards. The department was joined this year by the *"sensible and able"* **Giles Brand** from Denton Wilde Sapte. Other esteemed asset finance specialists from the team include **Philip Vallance** and **Jeremy Gibb**. The *"user-friendly"* **Jeremy Edwards** *("a pleasure to deal with")* led the team advising Amsterdam-based concern debis Airfinance BV, on the acquisition of 15 aircraft from Airbus.

Outside the UK, the firm has five specialist practitioners at partner level in Paris, Singapore, Piraeus, Bahrain and Moscow. Although the market commented that the firm could beef up its international capability, the international nature of the team's business has meant that the practice has kept a high level of activity in spite of a relative slowdown in the UK tax-leasing market. Deals this year include advising all three ROSCOs in both the arrangements to replace the pooling system for scarce spares and the introduction of train protection and warning system equipment. The firm acted for SAS in relation to the formation and financing of a joint venture between SAS and GECAS. **Clients:** Credit Lyonnais; SAS; Lloyds TSB Leasing Limited; Abbey National; HSBC Rail; CCF; Den Norske Bank; debis Airfinance BV; Singapore Aircraft Leasing Enterprise; Forward Trust Ltd.

Slaughter and May *"If it matters how well rather than how much, they're at the top."* Though this practice is smaller and has less transactional volume than the other major players, *"for sheer class and technical ability they're as good as, if not better than, the top firms."* The team is seen as an exception to the strong aviation orientation of the other major asset finance and leasing practices. In a practice where *"there is not one bad practitioner,"* the calibre of **Tom Kinnersley** and **Peter Jolliffe** ensures that the firm keeps its place at the top. *"For sheer unadulterated brain power, go to them, they do a first class job."* Kinnersley is *"a gent to deal with,"* and the sort of lawyer whom *"chairmen of major companies pay attention to."* Enjoying a similar reputation is Jolliffe, a *"high-class and bright operator."* New to the lists is **David Wittmann**, whose main expertise is in corporate work, but who also turns his hand to asset finance, and is *"accomplished at it."* UK tax-leasing is the practice's bread and butter, working on all types of assets, from ships to car plants and equipment.

Clients enthused about the firm's strong tax capability, citing the firm's *"tax-aggressive attitude."* Clients include international banks, UK lessors, lessees and equipment manufacturers. Work this year includes advising SK shipping of Korea on the UK tax lease financing of three LNG carriers, and advising RBS on the securitisation of lease receivables derived from rolling stock leased by Angel Trains to West Coast Trains. **Clients:** British Airways; Royal Bank of Scotland; Abbey National.

Allen & Overy (37 partners, 100 assistants worldwide) An increasingly strong, *"diverse and busy"* practice, with global operations and strength in depth. *"They are chasing the leaders hard, and have class and clout behind them."* The practice is well-rounded, advising on aircraft, shipping, rolling stock, telecoms and infrastructure financing for financiers, manufacturers, lessees, operating lessors, export credit agencies and governmental and international organisations. The bulk of the London team's work is of a cross-border nature, with teams in Frankfurt and Amsterdam particularly busy this year. The *"charming"* **Julia Salt** *("pragmatic," "easy to get on with")* and **Graham Smith** lead the expanding team. Salt is an all-rounder whose intelligence enables her to *"see it all before others can."* Smith is a *"terribly bright and sensible operator,"* with a bias towards non-aircraft work. **Mario Jacovides** is making a name for himself, particularly in the aviation market, with commentators seriously impressed by his work. **Andrew Joyce** and **David Smith** have leading reputations in rail and aircraft financing. The team is supported by first-rate tax, capital markets and securitisation departments. Work this year includes advising the lenders on financing ultra-luxury apartments at sea ($262 million) and advising on the first German leveraged lease into New Zealand. Other international work includes advising LOT Polish Airlines on the delivery of two Embraer EMB 145 aircraft under the first Polish leveraged lease. **Clients:** CIBC World Markets; DB Export Leasing GmbH; City of Dusseldorf; Citibank; GE Capital; Société Générale.

Denton Wilde Sapte Although the former Wilde Sapte's asset finance team had suffered a number of departures, the market considers sufficient depth to remain, an appraisal reinforced by the merger with Denton Hall. The latter brings strong regulatory and corporate skills to the table, particularly in rail matters. Whilst waiting for the combined firm to bed down, the combination of experience, depth, international networks and an *"extremely loyal client base"* is held to bode well for the firm's future.

The *"hugely experienced technician"* **Adrian Miles** is the main figure in the team, working mainly on non-aviation asset finance. Aviation expert Colin Thaine is now based in Paris, though his team operates on a cross-Channel basis – one satisfied London client commented, *"I'd still use them if they were in Timbuktu."* Peers find **Gregory Kahn** a *"star when on form."* With *"a brain the size of a planet,"* it is no wonder that **Andrew Collins** is considered to know the leasing market *"inside out."* Following strong market recommendation, **Lisa Marks** enters the rankings this year.

This year has seen the practice relatively more active for financiers than manufacturers and operators. Aviation work this year includes acting for Sabena on the export credit agency supported financing of a fleet of 34 Airbus A320 family and two AVRO RJ100 aircraft and for Airtours on the warehouse financing and subsequent German leveraged lease financing of two Airbus A330 aircraft. In rail, the practice acted on leasing arrangements for various companies in the Lombard Group, including Lombard Business Leasing Ltd on steel coil wagons and Lombard Asset Finance on arrangements for a track renewal machine and sleeper wagons. **Clients:** Halifax; Sabena; Airbus; Airtours; Credit Lyonnais; Deutsche Bank; Olympic; easyJet; Rolls Royce; Barclays Mercantile; ABN AMRO; GE Capital; NatWest.

Linklaters The practice is known for its mix of UK and US expertise, with some major European transactions advised out of New York as well as London. The assets team is perceived as a support to the highly rated projects group, yet this year will see the asset finance team forming a distinct department. A broad practice, advising on aircraft, rail, ship, and general equipment (telephony, cables, printing presses etc.) On trains, the firm acts for the Shadow Strategic Rail Authority. With a strong capital markets team, the practice is well placed for the more hybrid structures which are coming into the market. **Ronald Gibbs** maintains his reputation in a team which, through a *"painstaking approach, always produces quality."*

Deals advised from London include acting for Centrica on the sale and leaseback of two offshore gas production platforms with Bankers Trust and a further platform with CIBC. The team also acted for National Power on a £350 million sale and leaseback of power generation equipment and for Cofiri SpA on the procurement, financing and leasing of a satellite to EUTELSAT. Aircraft work includes advising Flightlease AG on the ECA-supported financing of six Airbus A320 aircraft (and subsequent Japanese Operating lease financing for five of those) for Air Europe SpA. The US capability has provided the team with success on the continent, and from New York, the practice has advised on deals for BAA, SNCF and Metropolitano de Lisboa. **Clients:** Orange; British Airways; AT&T; Flightlease AG; British Aerospace.

Watson, Farley & Williams (26 partners, 51 assistants worldwide) The firm's ship finance practice is regarded as so strong that market observers are tempted to believe that ships are the only asset financed by the team. Ship finance does take up around 65-70 percent of the London practice's time, but the team is visible in other areas, particularly in the Paris and New York offices. An example was acting as French and US counsel to the US lessors in the US leveraged lease of French high speed railcars.
In London, **Geoffrey Williams**' profile is not as strong as previously, but his reputation and his continued availability means that he maintains his status as a leading individual. **James Watters** is *"definitely a player,"* and is known throughout the UK for his general leasing work. **David Osborne** maintains his reputation as a leader, particularly for his international work. The firm's tax practice is seen to add greatly to the asset finance practice, again particularly for shipping. Work includes acting for the UK lessor on a series of tax-structured lease financings for offshore drilling platforms. **Clients:** Barclays Capital; Citibank; Daiwa Europe; Dresdner Kleinwort Benson; Robert Fleming; The CIT Group.

CMS Cameron McKenna Without the asset finance numbers of the leading firms, the team is attempting to develop a rail and aircraft finance practice. Aside from transport, the firm has been involved in general equipment asset financing, such as equipment for a crisp factory. In aviation, work includes advising US lessors on the leasing of Airbus, Embraer and Boeing aircraft, and advising the financiers on funding purchases of aircraft for subsequent lease. The international arena has seen the firm acting as local lawyers in places such as Uzbekistan on aircraft transactions. The firm has been active in rail, advising on rail financing transactions both for passenger and freight carrying rolling stock, acting for a ROSCO and TOCs. Film finance is a growing area. Amongst other rail deals, the group advised on the financing, acquisition and leasing of numerous diesel multiple unit trains for Angel Train Contracts Limited and Chiltern Rail. **Clients:** National Australia Bank; BP Amoco; Angel Train Contracts; Lloyds TSB; Westdeutsche Landesbank; GATX Capital Corporation; Flightlease AG; US Eximbank.

Herbert Smith Recognised as a player in the market, the firm's highly regarded projects/PFI practice is seen to overshadow its pure asset finance capabilities. Perhaps as a reflection of this, lawyers in the asset finance group are generalists in that they also turn their hand to projects and PFI work. **Nick Tott** is one such generalist, although he is regarded as *"the one here"* for asset finance expertise. This year, the firm advised on the provision of heavy equipment transporters for the MoD on a PFI basis, acting for the Fasttrax consortium. Aviation and rail work accounts for around 80 percent of the practice's work, with the rest taken up on work in areas such as water and PFI-related asset financing. In rail, the firm works mainly for the rolling stock leasing companies, such as Porterbrook and HSBC Rail. In aviation, where the firm works for financiers, manufacturers and operators, work this year includes acting for the EIB on its funding for two new Airbus A340s and acting for CNAC-Zhejiang Airlines on the acquisition of three Airbus A320 aircraft using ECA-backed financing. **Clients:** Eurotunnel; London and Continental Railways; South West Trains; Stagecoach; Bombardier.

Lovells Peers have a high regard for asset finance expert **Robin Hallam**, who was unanimously referred to as *"great to deal with."* His practice is mainly in aviation, with rail forming the remainder. Two other partners also work on asset finance matters, with expertise in niches such as engine leasing. Aviation is regarded as the practice's strong point, with around 70 percent of its caseload in that area. Other financing matters include water treatment plants and cold storage plants. More than half the practice's clients come from financial institutions.

On aviation matters, the team advised Bank of Nova Scotia on a limited recourse secured debt financing of a Boeing 737-400 aircraft and Virgin Atlantic on the sale and leaseback of three Boeing 747-2000. In other matters, the department has continued to advise Alsthom on rolling stock transactions and has maintained its expertise in the tax-based financing of North Sea Oil equipment. **Clients:** Ford Motor Company; Barclays Bank; Trinity Mirror plc; Vickers; ING Lease; United Bank of Kuwait plc; British Regional Airlines; Granada; Texaco.

Simmons & Simmons A newly-ranked aviation-biased practice, where aircraft deals take up to 75 percent of the practice's time. The rest is spent on rolling stock and general equipment financing. **Kim Walkling** is a recognised name in the field and accordingly moves into the tables this year. The London office benefits from a strong international practice, with respected teams in Paris and Hong Kong. With a highly rated capital markets practice, the asset finance team is set to gain business working on hybrid structures. Advisory work this year has seen the team analysing Iberia's lease portfolio (around 120 aircraft leases) prior to its IPO. It has also been involved in considering UK and international regulatory regimes and potential finance structures for one of the largest aviation finance deals ever, the MoD's Future Strategic Tanker Aircraft Project (around £9 billion.) The practice has additionally acted for the EIB on a number of aircraft deals, and in rolling stock, the firm is known for its work for Railtrack. **Clients:** Ministry of Defence; Barclays Capital; Iberia/SEPI; Dragonair.

Theodore Goddard A *"reasonably broad"* practice covering transportation, general equipment, media finance and PFI work. This year has seen the firm primarily active in rolling stock, media and property-based financings. Active in leasing deals for large groups such as Freightliner and Anglia. Advised on the financing and delivery of the second of two cruise ships for the Walt Disney Company in the US. **Clients:** Freightliner; Anglia Railways; Lan Chile; Lloyds TSB Leasing; NatWest; Abbey National.

Weil, Gotshal & Manges New to our lists this year, the firm has *"hired aggressively"* in the sector. Although the firm has suffered departures, the practice is considered *"to have the capacity, particularly in aircraft."* Indeed, around 80 percent of the practice's work is in aircraft, where the team is primarily known for its strong relationship with GECAS. Work this year includes acting for GECAS on the securitisation of 33 aircraft on operating leases in 16 jurisdictions. Also acted for Dresdner in respect of its acquisition of a Japanese lease portfolio from Tokai and on a purchase, sale and leaseback of an A320 aircraft for Airtours. **Clients:** GECAS; Airtours; Dresdner Kleinwort Benson; Hamburgische Landesbank.

Beaumont and Son Having been pre-eminent in aviation insurance work since the Second World War, the firm has capacity on the finance side. It is well thought of for finance work in the small-to-medium ticket bracket. The practice acts for over 30 banks and leasing companies. Predominantly the lessor's lawyers, the team acts for an increasing number of foreign airlines and aircraft operators in connection with operating leases and funding. Acted for a Middle Eastern airline on the acquisition of a new fleet. **Clients:** Airline manufacturers, operators and financiers.

Harbottle & Lewis Considered a niche firm, the practice is primarily known for its strong relationship with Virgin Atlantic, and acts exclusively for airlines in this sphere. For tax-driven work, the practice acts alongside the main accountants. The team has handled transactions from TNT's A300 acquisition programme, worked on re-financings for Virgin Atlantic Airways and British Midland, and advised BWA on a major expansion programme including the acquisition of ATP's and B737s. **Clients:** British Midland Airways; TNT; British World Airlines; Caribjet; Virgin Atlantic Airways.

Other Notable Practitioners Now in a consultant role at Berwin Leighton, the well regarded **Hugh Homan** has set up his own practice with the firm's blessing. He advises leasing companies on non-transactional matters such as documentation, strategy and training.

THE REGIONS

ASSET FINANCE & LEASING • The Regions	Ptnrs	Assts
❶ **Lester Aldridge** Bournemouth	4	10
Morton Fraser, Solicitors Edinburgh	3	4
❷ **Hammond Suddards Edge** Birmingham	2	5
❸ **Chaffe Street** Manchester	[illegible]	[illegible]
Davies Wallis Foyster Manchester	1	3
McClure Naismith Glasgow	3	4
❹ **Burges Salmon** Bristol	1	3
Osborne Clarke OWA Bristol	4	4

LEADING INDIVIDUALS	
❶ **GIDDINS Pip** Lester Aldridge	**WOOD Bruce** Morton Fraser, Solicitors
❷ **CAMPBELL Morag** McClure Naismith	**DAVIS Angela** Hammond Suddards Edge
LUMSDEN Christopher Chaffe Street	**MASKILL Andrew** Davies Wallis Foyster

Within each band, firms are listed alphabetically. *See **Profiles** on page 96*
** See editorial entries for explanations of team sizes.*

Lester Aldridge An asset finance practice which is well known nationwide. A broad practice, covering transactional and litigation work. Clients consider the large team to have the *"knowledge and the skills"* for complex work. Acting on small-to-medium transactions, the practice covers transport and general equipment asset financing and leasing, principally advising finance houses rather than companies. The practice's leading light is **Pip Giddins**, an *"established presence,"* whose remit with clients goes *"beyond the purely legal role."* Formerly with Lloyds Bowmaker and then head of legal at British Credit Trust, he founded the team which has subsequently grown into the largest regional practice. The department's day to day workload covers hire purchase for motor cars and equipment leasing for plant and machinery. The firm has recently been advising a specialist in car schemes and on financial products for the healthcare sector. **Clients:** Finance houses; leasing institutions; commercial and consumer lending institutions.

Morton Fraser, Solicitors Having *"written the book"* in Scotland, **Bruce Wood** is a well known figure throughout the Isles. The practice's remit goes beyond Scotland, with around 90 percent of the workload for Scottish companies operating outside Scotland. Otherwise, the practice works on Scottish deals and transactions with a Scottish element for a variety of clients. The practice advises on some ship and aircraft work, but its meat and drink is in trucks and motor-cars, as well as industrial machinery. Recent work includes a £36 million financing for a major bus company though Dublin's IFSC. **Clients:** British Linen Finance Ltd; Royal Bank Leasing Ltd; Five Arrows Finance Ltd; GE Capital Pallas; Mercedes Benz Finance.

Hammond Suddards Edge A practice primarily known for its contentious expertise. The transactional side will be reinforced with the arrival of two banking lawyers from London. **Angela Davis** is perceived as the strength of the team, and accordingly maintains her reputation as a leader in the field. The majority of work is in the small to medium ticket sector, mainly on domestic issues such as fleets, trucks, presses and capital equipment. The team's premier league litigation reputation was reinforced this year when the team successfully acted on the defence of a claim against a lessor for over £1 million, under a computer equipment lease (decision in Anglo Group plc v Winther Browne.) Non-contentious work includes working on documentation for a transport fleet for a plc and on sale and leaseback documentation for a car fleet. **Clients:** GE Capital Group; RoyScot Trust; Barclays Mercantile; Capital Bank.

Chaffe Street Predominantly working on aircraft issues this year, the firm has continued to act for Jersey European Airways in aircraft loan financing. Acts for a mix of financiers and end-users. Typical deal size ranges from £15-20 million. On motor vehicle financing matters, the practice tends to act for manufacturers. **Christopher Lumsden** has continued to receive market commendation this year. **Clients:** Jersey European Airways.

Davies Wallis Foyster Works on all aspects of middle and big-ticket leasing, including receivables funding, tax-based structures and equipment leasing. The practice acts mainly for finance houses, including foreign banks, on a mixture of work including such equipment as cranes and computer software. **Andrew Maskill** is a recognised full-time specialist in the area. Advised a finance company in a £70 million pan-European receivables transaction. **Clients:** Bank of Scotland (including Capital Bank plc); Cattles plc; Lex Vehicle Leasing; Sovereign Finance plc.

McClure Naismith **Morag Campbell** is a well known name nationwide for her documentation skills. She acts for a wide range of finance houses on leasing and hire-purchase agreements. The team's workload has encompassed reviewing documentation for invoice discounting and factoring schemes and reviewing documentation for middle and small-ticket leasing. **Clients:** Capital Bank plc; General Guarantee; Singer & Friedlander Commercial Finance; RoyScot Trust; Barclays Mercantile.

Burges Salmon Known for its transport skills, the firm has experience in the bus and rail sectors, where it acts for four of the train-operating companies. Advised First North Western, a subsidiary of FirstGroup, on its procurement, depot and leasing arrangements for 70 new fully-maintained vehicles. Other work includes advising various FirstGroup subsidiaries on a hire purchase facility of £21 million put into place with Barclays Mercantile and First Great Eastern in relation to its finance lease arrangements with each of the ROSCOs. The practice has additionally advised on the leasing of Airbus freighter aircraft and general equipment and machinery financing. **Clients:** First Great Western; FirstGroup plc; WAGN Rail; Standard Chartered Bank.

Osborne Clarke OWA The firm acts for two of the world's largest asset financiers, who have their UK bases in the area. The asset finance practice is led by the banking team, and incorporates players from the corporate, tax and litigation practices. Most of the practice's work this year has involved computer-based and general equipment machinery. Advised Newcourt Credit Ltd on a stock financing agreement and various corporate clients on transactions involving equipment finance and lease finance. **Clients:** Newcourt Credit Limited; GE Capital Equipment Finance Limited; John Deere Credit Limited; 3i Group.

CONSUMER FINANCE - NATIONAL

CONSUMER FINANCE • National	Ptnrs	Assts
❶ **Lester Aldridge** Bournemouth	4	6
❷ **Paisner & Co**	3	2
❸ **Addleshaw Booth & Co** Leeds	⚐	⚐
Hammond Suddards Edge Birmingham	2	5
Eversheds Cardiff, Leeds	2	-
McClure Naismith Glasgow	4	5
Salans Hertzfeld & Heilbronn HRK	3	6

LEADING INDIVIDUALS
❶ **GIDDINS Pip** Lester Aldridge
JOHNSTONE Frank McClure Naismith
ROSENTHAL Dennis Paisner & Co
❷ **DAVIS Angela** Hammond Suddards Edge
FINCH Stephen Salans Hertzfeld & Heilbronn HRK
GAINES Alison Salans Hertzfeld & Heilbronn HRK
GUEST Jonathan Eversheds

Within each band, firms are listed alphabetically. *See **Profiles** on page 96*

⚐ *Figures unavailable at time of going to press.*

Lester Aldridge *"A big team and a big player in consumer finance."* **Pip Giddins** is the stand-out name in the practice, though there is a *"raft of players behind him."* In September/October 2000 he is moving into a professorial role at the Centre for Instalment Credit Law, but will continue to work in the field. Although considered to be oriented towards non-contentious work, the firm's litigation team also continues to pick up work. Acts for finance houses more than companies and has been involved in training sessions for staff at such houses. Advised on the implications of Dimond v Lovell, the court case of the year for consumer credit. **Clients:** Captive finance houses; banks; specialist financial institutions.

Paisner & Co **Dennis Rosenthal** (*"well known and recognised in the area"*) cut his teeth working with one of the sector's principal gurus, Professor Roy Goode. Considered to have a *"loyal client following,"* his practice includes retail banking, asset and consumer finance, and financial services law. The team's bread and butter is in advising financial institutions and trade associations on new products, standard form documentation, equipment and vehicle financing, retail credit schemes, sales and purchases of receivables and joint ventures. The firm has been involved in creating flexible mortgage products for various lending institutions. E-commerce work is increasing for the firm, and the consumer finance has recently been involved in advising a newly-created website concentrating on providing on-line mortgage and ISA advice. **Clients:** Bradford & Bingley; Northern Rock; CCTA; the Great Universal Stores plc; FTYourMoney.com.

Addleshaw Booth & Co The bulk of the national firm's work in this area is performed from the Leeds office. However, London also has some capacity, particularly on data protection. In Leeds, a full-time partner works mainly with financial institutions, most actively in motor finance and credit card work. Advised on online banking and affinity card-related joint ventures between retailers and banks. **Clients:** Britannia Building Society; National Australia Group.

Hammond Suddards Edge Although highly regarded for contentious matters, where it is *"probably the pre-eminent practice,"* the firm has considerable experience on non-contentious CCA-related work. Two partners have solid profiles in the area, with **Angela Davis** particularly well-regarded by the market for her contentious skills. The firm has been active in vehicle financing, and its client base includes clearing banks, sales aid companies, factors, brokers, non-UK lenders, second tier European banks, receivables financiers and US banks. Advised a regeneration funder on documentation and consumer credit compliance. **Clients:** GE Capital; Barclays Mercantile; RoyScot Trust; Capital Bank Cashflow Finance Ltd.

Eversheds **Jonathan Guest**, based in the Midlands, is considered a stand-out practitioner. He started in the area via a retail finance group when initial consumer credit legislation was passed, and has specialised ever since. This year has seen the practice active on corporate manoeuvres in the sector. Work for some of the major US credit card players on product development. The Cardiff office has a retail finance specialism, and is particularly strong in mortgage-related finance. **Clients:** Capital Bank.

McClure Naismith Known throughout the industry as the man who *"puts the kilt on"* consumer finance issues, **Frank Johnstone** is the high profile lawyer of this team. He is well known for his litigation skills and is a popular figure who is *"excellent and up to date."* The firm has a dedicated department, working on contentious issues and on documentation. Acts almost exclusively for finance houses (including start-ups) and also advises industry groups such as the CCTA on Scottish legal matters. Works on asset recovery, motor vehicle and general equipment litigation, and on document drafting, with an increased activity in data protection issues. Advised a credit card company on its rights and liabilities following the liquidation of one of its merchants. Also advised on actions for payment of sums due under a variety of personal loan and credit card agreements. **Clients:** Capital Bank plc; First National Wagon Finance; General Guarantee Corporation Ltd; RoyScot Trust; Marks and Spencers Financial Service Ltd; Mercedes-Benz Finance Ltd; Ford Motor Credit Company Ltd; Barclays Mercantile Business Finance Ltd.

Salans Hertzfeld & Heilbronn HRK A large and respected team dealing with contentious and non-contentious matters relating to consumer credit legislation. A feature of the team is that most of its practitioners have extensive in-house experience in finance houses or motor finance specialist arms. While many individuals are well regarded, **Alison Gaines** stood out in our research for the number of recommendations she received from the market. All-rounder **Stephen Finch** also received market plaudits. The practice generally works on matters related to motor finance, credit cards, secured loans and mortgages, in addition to offering general credit advice in areas including advertising, marketing and data protection. **Clients:** FCE Bank; Nissan Finance (GB) Limited; Bank of Ireland; Barclays; Daewoo; Guinness Mahon; Saab Group; Jaguar Financial Services; Volkswagen Financial Services.

LEADERS IN ASSET FINANCE & LEASING

BRAND, Giles
Norton Rose, London (020) 7283 6000

BUDGETT, Tom
Clifford Chance, London (020) 7600 1000
tom.budgett@cliffordchance.com
Specialisation: Partner specialising in aircraft finance, ship finance, general asset finance and leasing, export credit finance and structured trade finance.
Career: Educated Pembroke College Cambridge (1966-69). Qualified 1972; Hong Kong 1975; Dubai 1978; Tokyo 1980; made partner 1981; Paris 1991; London 1996.
Personal: Born 1948.

CAMPBELL, Morag
McClure Naismith, Glasgow (0141) 204 2700
mcampbell@mcclurenaismith.com
Specialisation: Asset Finance: sale and leaseback; securing property and assets generally including heritable (real) property, vehicles, receivables, income streams; block and invoice discounting; tailoring English financial products for effective use in Scotland; advising on differences between English and Scots law in specialist area.
Prof. Memberships: Admitted as a solicitor in Scotland: 1981
Career: Hillhead High School, Glasgow; University of Glasgow: LL.B (Hons) 1979; *Anderson & Gardiner*: Apprentice 1979-1981; Assistant Solicitor 1981-1983: Partner 1983-1984; *McClure Naismith*: Partner 1984-date.
Personal: Singing (choral); Music; Theatre.

CARPENTER, Clive
Clifford Chance, London (020) 7600 1000
Partner. Asset finance and banking group.
Specialisation: Principal areas of work involve acting for financiers on all aspects of asset finance, leasing and banking in relation to heavy transportation assets (aircraft, ships, rolling stock), satellites and plant and machinery, the securitisation of transportation assets and tax driven structures employed in such financings.
Career: Qualified 1983, partner 1994.
Personal: B.C.L., M.A. (Oxon) in Jurisprudence.

CHARLTON, Bob
Freshfields Bruckhaus Deringer, London (020) 7936 4000
Specialisation: Partner specialising in asset finance and leasing (in particular, aircraft and rolling stock), cross-border financings, structured finance, export credit finance and project finance.
Career: Educated Trinity Hall, Cambridge (1975-1978). Qualified England 1981; Hong Kong 1986; Brunei 1987; partner with *Freshfields* since November 1999; partner in another leading international law firm since 1987.
Personal: Born 1957.

COLLINS, Andrew
Denton Wilde Sapte, London (020) 7242 1212

CRANE, David
Norton Rose, London (020) 7283 6000
See under Projects/PFI, p.96

CROOKES, Alan
Norton Rose, London (020) 7283 6000
crookesam@nortonrose.com
Specialisation: Partner whose practice ranges from asset finance (particularly equipment leasing) to corporate acquisitions and disposals (including private equity transactions). He has acted on two major acquistions of rail rolling stock companies: Angel Train Contracts (for Royal Bank of Scotland); and Eversholt Leasing (for Forward Trust). He acted for AES on its acquisition of Drax Power Station and also for the Finalrealm Consortium on its bid for United Biscuits.
Prof. Memberships: City of London Solicitors' Company.
Career: Qualified in 1981 while at *Norton Rose*. Became a partner in 1988.
Personal: Born 27th May 1957. Educated at Durham University 1975-78. Enjoys music (particularly opera). Lives in Shenfield.

DAVIS, Angela C.
Hammond Suddards Edge, Birmingham (0121) 200 2001
angela.davis@hammondsuddardsedge.com
Head of Asset Finance Group.
Specialisation: Principal area of practice, all legal aspects of Asset Finance, Leasing and Consumer Credit with particular expertise on the contentious side and with experience of mediation in the finance sector. Responsible for two leading Court of Appeal decisions; RoyScot Trust plc v Rogerson and RoyScot Trust plc v Ismail on damages and indemnities respectively. This year has acted successfully for the claimant in the case of Anglo Group Plc v Winther Browne on the financiers role in computer equipment leases. Has also advised on regulatory issues.
Prof. Memberships: Law Society, Birmingham Law Society and Associate of the Chartered Institute of Arbitrators.
Career: Qualified in 1982. Joined *Edge Ellison*, becoming a Partner in 1990.
Personal: Born 4 March 1958. Attended West Kirby Grammar School for Girls, Wirral 1969-1976. Durham University 1976-79. Leisure interests include antique maps, reading and Everton FC.

EDWARDS, Jeremy
Norton Rose, London (020) 7283 6000
edwardsjp@nortonrose.com
Partner in banking department. Head of international aviation business group.
Specialisation: Specialises in structured and asset finance, particularly of aircraft and rolling stock. Expertise includes all aspects of operating and finance leases, sales and purchases of aircraft and rolling stock, cross-border leases and export credit financing. Recent transactions have included advising various airlines on a number of Japanese Operating Leases, some export credit backed, advising an airline on its US$250 million multi-option aircraft financing facility, advising the Lessor in connection with the Brazilian export credit backed financing and Leasing of five Embraer RJ 145 aircraft, advising the financing subsidiary of a European flag carrier on the asset backed securitisation of six Boeing 747 aircraft using a European based conduit vehicle and advising one of the UK's three rolling stock companies on its purchase and leasing of new and used rolling stock.
Career: Joined *Norton Rose* as a trainee in 1987. Qualified 1989. Spent three years in the firm's Paris office. Elected to partnership May 1997. Speaks fluent French.

FINCH, Stephen
Salans Hertzfeld & Heilbronn HRK, London (020) 7509 6000
SFinch@salans.com
Partner in charge of Banking and Finance Department.
Specialisation: Since 1978 has advised lending institutions on all legal aspects of their activities, both consumer and commercial lending. Served on the Legislation Committee of the Finance Houses Association whilst Company Solicitor at Citibank. Current work includes providing advice on asset finance and leasing arrangements including offshore and tax based leasing and securitisations, factoring agreements, syndicated loans, finance house management and service contracts and providing advice on the Consumer Credit Act 1974. Wide lecturing experience with particular emphasis on Consumer Credit Act.

FREEMAN, Mark
Freshfields Bruckhaus Deringer, London (020) 7936 4000
mfreeman@freshfields.com
Specialisation: Finance, in particular Asset Finance, Leasing and Structured Finance. Main specialisation is aircraft financing.
Prof. Memberships: Law Society; admitted in UK and Hong Kong.
Career: Qualified 1969. Partner 1974.

Personal: Educated at Emmanuel College Cambridge. Leisure interests include motor racing, skiing, scuba.

GAINES, Alison
Salans Hertzfeld & Heilbronn HRK, London (020) 7509 6000
Specialisation: Banking, asset finance, consumer finance and non-contentious insolvency.
Prof. Memberships: Law Society, IBA
Career: Articled *Fremont & Co* London. Qualified 1980. In-house counsel, leading financial company, London 1980-1984. Community Law Centre, New York City 1984-1986. Partner *Hill Bailey* London 1986-1989. Partner *Salans Hertzfeld & Heilbronn HRK* 1989.
Publications: Various articles.
Personal: Education: Birmingham University 1977 (LLB Hons). Married with two children, Joe & Lauren. Leisure interests include hill walking, climbing and football.

GIBB, Jeremy S.P.
Norton Rose, London (020) 7283 6000
See under Shipping, p.746

GIBBS, Ronald
Linklaters (A member firm of Linklaters & Alliance), London (020) 7456 5984
ron.gibbs@linklaters.com
Partner. Project and Asset Finance Department.
Specialisation: Principal area of practice has been in the field of asset finance with emphasis on aviation, including finance, commercial and regulatory aspects of airlines, airports and air traffic control systems.
Career: *Linklaters*, partner 1989.

GIDDINS, Pip
Lester Aldridge, Bournemouth (01202) 786161
Pip.Giddins@lester-aldridge.co.uk
Specialisation: (for Asset Finance & Leasing) Small and middle ticket asset finance. Advises finance houses and captive leasing companies throughout UK. Typical work is with operating leases, employee car schemes, and sales aid rental agreements; and the funding of them. From long and wide experience, advises on strategy and the commercial aspects and opportunities as well as technical law.
Specialisation: (for Asset Finance & Leasing: Consumer Finance) Small and middle ticket asset finance and consumer credit. Advises finance houses, banks and building societies throughout UK, particularly for motor finance, personal loans and credit cards, and application of the Consumer Credit 1974. Advises on product development, documentation, procedures, advertising and marketing, and portfolio acquisitions. Recent work has included advice on application of CCA 1974 in unsuspected situations eg. Dimond v Lovell, insurance premium finance or refinancings. Developed and leads the Finance & Leasing Association's training courses on consumer credit and advertising and marketing of credit, and in-house training for clients. Speaks at public conferences and contributes articles. Undertakes work for other law firms on a consultancy basis.
Prof. Memberships: Director of the Centre for Instalment Credit Law - University of Wales. Chief Examiner for the Chartered Institute of Bankers Elements of Finance and Leasing course. Member of Finance and Leasing Association's Examination Board.
Career: Qualified 1976. Lecturer at College of Law Guildford. In-house solicitor with *Lloyds Bowmaker*; Head of Legal Services for British Credit Trust; joined *Lester Aldridge* as a partner in 1988 and developed a specialist department of non-contentious and litigation solicitors to serve providers of asset finance and consumer credit. Now concentrating on his work for the Centre for Instalment Credit Law and independent finance law consultancies.

GUEST, Jonathan
Eversheds, Leeds (0113) 243 0391
jonathanguest@eversheds.com
Specialisation: Consumer credit–acting for banks, building societies, finance houses and retailers in the provision of credit card products, fixed term loan documentation and compliance and advertising issues. Experience includes selling credit card receivable and debt transfer arrangements, data protection compliance, data warehousing arrangements and joint ventures in the retail credit sector. Lectures and provides seminars on the consumer credit legislation and provides input on proposals to deregulate the legislation.
Prof. Memberships: Consumer credit–trade association and data protection forum.
Career: Qualified 1982, partner 1986.
Personal: Interests include walking, trying to keep classic cars on the road and skiing.

HALL, Gordon
Norton Rose, London (020) 7283 6000
hallgcc@nortonrose.com
Specialisation: Partner specialising in asset finance: ships; aircraft; rolling stock. Emphasis on structured financing involving tax and operating leases.
Prof. Memberships: City of London Solicitor's Company; International Bar Association; Baltic Exchange.
Career: Admitted 1980. Partner at *Norton Rose* 1988. 1985-1988 resident in Singapore office. 1988-1989 resident in Bahrain office.

HALL, Simon A.D.
Freshfields Bruckhaus Deringer, London (020) 7936 4000
Head of Finance Department.
Specialisation: Main areas of practice are asset and aircraft finance, and banking and structured finance. Co-author of 'Aircraft Financing' (Euromoney 3rd edition, 1998); co-author of 'Leasing Finance' (Euromoney 3rd edition, 1997).
Prof. Memberships: Law Society, City of London Solicitors Company, American Bar Association.
Career: Qualified 1979 after joining *Freshfields* in 1977. Became a Partner in 1985.
Personal: Born 6th February 1955. Leisure interests include shooting and fishing.

HALLAM, Robin
Lovells, London (020) 7296 2000
robin.hallam@lovells.com
Specialisation: Aviation, rail and asset finance; secured lending, leveraged and operating leasing, tax based and defeased leases, securitisation, export credit and vendor sales finance, engine and equipment leasing principally in aviation but also in ships, containers, rolling stock and other forms of large assets. Substantial experience in aircraft securitisations and other aircraft finance transactions involving capital markets.
Prof. Memberships: City of London Law Society, Aviation Club–Associate Member, American Bar Association.
Career: Qualified 1980. Hong Kong 1981-82; Singapore 1982-83; partner *Lovells* 1995; various articles on aircraft finance.

HOMAN, Hugh
Berwin Leighton, London (020) 7760 1000
hugh.homan@berwinleighton.com
Partner in corporate department.
Specialisation: Principal area of practice is asset finance, equipment leasing and securitisation. Also handles general corporate finance work.
Prof. Memberships: Law Society, City of London Solicitors Company.
Career: Qualified in 1970. Partner at *Berwin Leighton* from 1975 to 1990. Now a consultant in the firm.
Personal: Born 26th June 1945. Educated at Worcester College, Oxford 1964-67. Lives in London.

JACOVIDES, Mario
Allen & Overy, London (020) 7330 3000
Specialisation: Asset Finance and Leasing. Partner in Asset Finance Group of the Finance Department. Specialising in asset finance and leasing including structured and large scale tax based and cross border lease financings, export credit supported transactions and US leases for aircraft, ships, satellites and other assets. Acted recently for LOT Polish Airlines S.A. in the first Polish leveraged lease financing of two Embraer aircraft using an innovative structure (awarded Deal of the Year 1999/2000–New Tax Jurisdiction by Asset Finance International)
Career: Qualified in 1989, Associate, *Wilde Sapte*, Partner *Wilde Sapte* 1996, Partner *Allen & Overy* 1998.
Personal: Interests include golf, squash and ornithology.

JOHNSTONE, Frank R.
McClure Naismith, Glasgow (0141) 204 2700
fjohnstone@McClureNaismith.com
Partner specialising in consumer credit law, asset recovery and data protection.
Specialisation: Consumer credit law. Represents a number of finance houses, leasing companies, banks and creditcard companies, with particular emphasis on litigation/debt recovery, sale and supply of goods and data protection. Convener of the Consumer Law Committee of the Law Society of Scotland, convener of the Privacy Committee of the Law Society of Scotland, member of the Legal Advisory Group of the Scottish Consumer Council, member of the Consumer Law Committee of the International Bar Association, chairman of Money Advice Liaison Group (Scotland) and a frequent lecturer on consumer/credit law, data protection and debt recovery.
Career: Qualified 1982, joined present firm in 1985. Became a partner in 1988.
Personal: Born 12th October, 1957. Graduated M.A., LL.B., Glasgow University, British Universities Lightweight Boxing Champion 1979–Runner up 1980.

JOLLIFFE, Peter
Slaughter and May, London (020) 7600 1200
Specialisation: Aircraft and Asset Financing.
Prof. Memberships: The Law Society.
Career: Qualified in 1981 after joining *Slaughter and May* in 1979. Became a Partner in 1989.
Personal: Born 6 June 1957. Educated Downing College, Cambridge. Lives in London.

JOYCE, Andrew L.
Allen & Overy, London (020) 7330 3000
Specialisation: Partner specialising in asset financing and leasing, including aircraft, shipping and rolling stock finance. His recent experience includes advising on BCI's $900 million acquisition of Sanwa's European aircraft finance portfolio, advising on Singapore Airlines' share acquisition in Virgin Airlines, and EIB's financing of aircraft for TAP.
Prof. Memberships: City of London Solicitors.
Career: Oxford University, Keble College. Graduated in 1985 (BA Jurisprudence). Admitted as solicitor in England and Wales, 1988. Admitted as solicitor, Hong Kong 1981.
Personal: Welsh rugby, skiing. Married with three sons.

KAHN, Gregory
Denton Wilde Sapte, London (020) 7242 1212

KINNERSLEY, Tom
Slaughter and May, London (020) 7600 1200
Specialisation: General banking, in particular structured finance and asset finance.
Career: Qualified 1972. Partner 1980.
Prof. Memberships: The Law Society.
Personal: Born 28 May 1947. Educated Hertford College, Oxford. Lives in London.

LINTOTT, Tim
Freshfields Bruckhaus Deringer, London (020) 7936 4000
Specialisation: Asset and project finance, including power stations and transmission, aviation, airports.
Prof. Memberships: Admitted in UK, Hong Kong.
Career: 1976-94 *Freshfields*, London and New York; 1984-92 *Baker & McKenzie*, Hong Kong; 1992 to date *Freshfields*, London.
Personal: Married, three daughters.

LITTLEJOHNS, Andrew
Freshfields Bruckhaus Deringer, London (020) 7936 4000
Specialisation: Specialises in international banking, international finance, aviation finance, aircraft leasing, railway leasing and finance, and other equipment leasing. Involvement in aircraft financing includes a wide experience of cross-border tax leases, syndicated multi-option facilities, securitisations, asset value underwriting, joint ventures and operating leases.
Career: Education: Lincoln College, Oxford. Became partner in 1987.

LUMSDEN, Christopher
Chaffe Street, Manchester (0161) 236 5800
See under Banking, p.119

MARKS, Lisa
Denton Wilde Sapte, London (020) 7242 1212

MASKILL, Andrew
Davies Wallis Foyster, Manchester (0161) 228 3702
asm@dwf-law.com
Specialisation: Middle and big ticket asset finance including receivables funding, tax based structures and equipment leasing.
Prof. Memberships: Law Society.
Career: Articled *Wilde Sapte*; qualified 1990; *Eversheds*; *Alsop Wilkinson*; partner *Davies Wallis Foyster* 1998.
Publications: 'Leasing Life'; 'Manchester Evening News'; 'Industry Northwest'.
Personal: Leeds Grammar School; Manchester University (LL B Hons Law); guitar (blues and rock); golf; running; languages–French and German; resides Manchester

MILES, Adrian
Denton Wilde Sapte, London (020) 7242 1212

OSBORNE, David
Watson, Farley & Williams, London (020) 7814 8000

ROSENTHAL, Dennis
Paisner & Co, London (020) 7353 0299
Partner in company and commercial department
Specialisation: Advises banks, finance and leasing companies, building societies and trade associations on all aspects of their commercial activities; deals with transactions; drafts agreements including standard form agreements; structures and advises on equipment and vehicle financing arrangements, retail credit schemes, sales and purchases of receivables, joint ventures and innovative products, including in relation to credit cards, personal loans, point of sale agreements, mortgages and bank savings products. Advises on commercial law, banking law, consumer credit law, advertising and marketing law, financial services law, insurance, fraud prevention, money laundering and data protection. Assistant editor of 'Goode: Consumer Credit Law and Practice' and 'Goode: Consumer Credit Reports'; author of 'Guide to Consumer Credit Law & Practice' (Butterworths) and 'Financial Advertising and Marketing Law' (Sweet & Maxwell); contributor to 'Consumer Credit' in Halsbury's Laws of England and to various legal journals.
Prof. Memberships: Member of The Law Society, IBA, British South Africa Law Association.

SALT, Julia
Allen & Overy, London (020) 7330 3000
Specialisation: Partner specialising in asset based finance. Has extensive experience in aircraft and other asset financing including finance and operating leasing, cross-border transactions, securitisations and structured loans. Experience also includes project financing, telecommunications financing and securitisation.
Career: Articled *Allen & Overy*, qualified 1980, partner 1985.
Personal: Oxford University (1977 MA French and German). Born 1955. Enjoys sailing, golf, opera, literature.

SMITH, David
Allen & Overy, London (020) 7330 3000
Partner Asset Finance and Leasing, Shipping and Maritime Law.
Specialisation: Partner specialising in banking and asset finance, primarily relating to ships, aircraft and railways representing financiers, operators and manufacturers in domestic and cross-border structured transactions, both leasing and debt-based. Transaction structures have included export credit backed government-guaranteed debt facilities, tax-based lease structures (including UK tax leases, Japanese leveraged leases and US leases), off-balance sheet structures and non tax-based leases including operating leases both with and without residual value support. A significant part of his experience has involved combining these structures. Also regularly involved in sale and purchase, construction and registration matters relating to ships and aircraft.
Career: BA Jurisprudence, Brasenose College, Oxford, 1981; Admitted as a Solicitor, 1984; Solicitor *Richards Butler*, 1984; Partner *Richards Butler*, 1989; Partner *Wilde Sapte*, 1991; Partner *Allen & Overy*, 1999.
Personal: Born 1960, married with two children, enjoys family, motor cars, golf, cricket, eating out and theatre.

SMITH, Graham
Allen & Overy, London (020) 7330 3000
Specialisation: Asset Financing & Leasing. Partner specialising in banking and finance work with a particular emphasis on leasing for over 15 years; has been involved in the financing of all types of assets, including those in the transport, energy and telecoms sectors; has extensive experience at all levels of the asset finanace industry from high-value, complex cross-border financings to advising on retail finance documentation, including setting up vendor programmes as well as sale and purchase of leasing companies and portfolios.
Career: Royal Grammar School Guilford; Nottingham University (1979 BA Hons Law); Guildford College of Law (1980). Trained *Wilde Sapte*; qualified 1982; assistant solicitor 1982, partner asset finance group 1987, head of leasing 1993; partner *Allen & Overy* asset finance group,1999.
Personal: Born 1958; resides London. Enjoys modern art, golf, classic cars, food and wine.

THORNE, Peter
Norton Rose, London (020) 7283 6000
thornepg@nortonrose.com
Partner in banking department.
Specialisation: Asset finance. Clients include airlines, manufacturers, banks, leasing companies and arrangers. Major transactions in 99/00 included advising lessors on operating lease financing of regional jet aircraft for UK regional operators, advising lessors on structured lease financing of ten A319 aircraft and advising various institutions on purchases and sales (subject to leases) of various Airbus and Boeing aircraft. Author of 'Aircraft Mortgages' chapter in 'Interests in Goods' (Second edition, Lloyds of London Press 1998).
Prof. Memberships: International Bar Association, Royal Aeronautical Society.
Career: Qualified 1971. Joined *Norton Rose* that year. Partner since 1977.
Personal: Born 2nd June 1948. Attended Clifton College 1962-65.

TOTT, Nicholas P.
Herbert Smith, London (020) 7374 8000
nicholas.tott@herbertsmith.com
Specialisation: Principal areas of work include all forms of financing and banking work with particular emphasis on asset finance, leasing, project financing and Private Finance Initiative (PFI) Projects. Seconded to the Private Finance Panel Executive for fifteen months with responsibility for PFI Projects in Scotland, Northern Ireland and the Ministry of Defence. Publications include a chapter 'Public Finance in the U.K.' in Leasing Finance (Euromoney 1997, 3rd Edition.) Co-author of 'The PFI Handbook' (Jordans, March 1999).
Prof. Memberships: Law Society; City of London Solicitors' Company.
Career: Qualified Scotland (1985), England and Wales (1991). Partner 1992.

Personal: Born 8th May 1960. Educated at Edinburgh University. Leisure pursuits include Golf and skiing.

VALLANCE, Philip
Norton Rose, London (020) 7283 6000
Specialisation: Principal area of work is structured asset finance transactions. Assets involved have been predominantly aircraft, but include offshore oil production vessels, locomotives, telecommunications and printing presses. Extensive experience in Japanese leveraged and operating leases, UK tax leases, export credit finance, operating leases, debt finance and residual value insurance.
Prof. Memberships: Law Society, City of London Solicitors Company.
Career: Qualified in N.S.W, Australia in 1982, after completing degrees in law and financial studies. Joined *Norton Rose* 1986. Spent two years with Japanese firm of *Nishimura + Partners* in Tokyo 1989-1991. Partner at *Norton Rose* 1993.

WALKLING, Kim
Simmons & Simmons, London (020) 7628 2020
kim.walkling@simmons-simmons.com
Specialisation: Big ticket asset finance and leasing, predominantly aviation. 1999/2000 Acts for MOD on FSTA project; for SEPI on Iberia IPO; for European Investment Bank on multi aircraft financing.
Prof. Memberships: European Air Law Association.
Career: Qualified 1982.
Publications: Various contributions to magazines.
Personal: LLB (Hons) London (UCL). Married, two children.

WATTERS, James
Watson, Farley & Williams, London
(020) 7814 8000

WHITE, Geoffrey
Clifford Chance, London (020) 7600 1000
geoffrey.white@cliffordchance.com
Specialisation: Partner specialising in asset financing, banking and leasing and head of firm's international asset finance group.
Career: The Hutchins School, Hobart, Tasmania; University of Melbourne (LLB Hons and B Comm) 1966-71; Southern Methodist University, Dallas, Texas (LLM 1972-73). Articled *Freehill Hollingdale and Page*, Melbourne, Australia; qualified 1972 Melbourne Victoria, 1977 England, 1987 Japan; *Nakagawa Godo* Law Office, Tokyo 1977-80, 1986-87; partner *Clifford Chance* Tokyo office in 1987.
Personal: Born 1947.

WILLIAMS, Geoffrey
Watson, Farley & Williams, London
(020) 7814 8000

WITTMANN, David
Slaughter and May, London
(020) 7600 1200
Specialisation: Corporate, acquisitions and asset financing.
Prof. Memberships: The Law Society.
Career: Qualified in 1990 after joining *Slaughter and May* in 1988. Became a partner in 1997.
Personal: Born 9 August 1964. Educated Girton College, Cambridge. Lives in London.

WOOD, R. Bruce
Morton Fraser, Solicitors, Edinburgh
(0131) 247 1000
rbw@morton-fraser.com
Partner and Head of Corporate Division.
Specialisation: Main areas of practice are asset and project finance and leasing, banking and debt factoring. Acts for Scottish finance companies throughout the UK and for English-based (and foreign-based) finance companies in Scotland: large, medium and small ticket work. Also handles general corporate work. Author of 'Location: Leasing and Hire of Moveables' in the Laws of Scotland, Scottish section of Salinger; 'Factoring Law and Practice', section on Moveables in 'Green's Practice Styles', 'Die Floating Charge Als Kreditsicherheit Im Schottischen Recht'. Has lectured widely at legal seminars on, inter alia, leasing of moveables, joint ventures, Consumer Credit Act, banking practices in Scotland, corporate law in Scotland, the globalisation of law firms and of the practice of law.
Prof. Memberships: Law Society of Scotland, WS Society, Association of Pension Lawyers, Finance and Leasing Association.
Career: Qualified 1976. Joined *Morton Fraser Milligan WS* in 1974, becoming a Partner in 1977 and Head of Corporate Division in 1991. Lecturer in Conveyancing at Edinburgh University 1979-89; Convenor of Conveyancing Teachers of the Scottish Universities in the Diploma in Legal Practice 1986-89. World Chairman of Interlaw 1988-91. Member of the former Law Society working party on security over moveables. Member of the CBI Companies Committee.
Personal: Born 2nd October 1951. Holds an LLB (1st class Hons, Edinburgh 1973) and an LLM (UC Berkeley, 1974). Leisure interests include medieval history and golf. Lives near Penicuik.

AVIATION

OVERVIEW: Individual expertise is vital in the aviation sector, so work tends to follow the leading names rather than firms. The one exception is Beaumont and Son – *"the aviation firm."* The larger airports and airlines have their own in-house teams, though outside talent is employed as and when required. Regulatory work is all done in London, and although some insurance underwriting work is carried out in the regions, genuine aviation specialists are few and far between outside London.

Although much aviation regulation is governed by the EU, London firms without a Brussels office are not at a major disadvantage. Lane & Partners continue to demonstrate breadth and depth, while Beaumonts' profile is increasing. Competition issues have largely been settled by market liberalisation within the EU, but because of international requirements on national control and ownership of airlines, the market is unlikely to shrink much further. New legislation on consumer rights and slot regulation issues are expected soon.

RESEARCH APPROVED BY BMRB: *For this edition,* Chambers' *researchers conducted 6083 interviews – 4408 with law firms, 598 with barristers and 1077 with clients.*

The validity of the research was scrutinised by BMRB International, who audited both the methodology and the results at our offices in July 2000. They interviewed Chambers' *researchers and cross-checked sample interviews. Details of the audit appear on page 7.*

LEADING IN-HOUSE LAWYERS

Regulatory

Rupert BRITTON, Secretary & Legal Adviser, *Civil Aviation Authority*

Tim BYE, Legal Director & Company Secretary, *British Midland*

Richard CHURCHILL-COLEMAN, Group General Counsel, *Thomsons Travel Group plc*

Richard EVERITT, Group Strategy & Compliance Director, *BAA*

Robert HERGA, Head of Legal Services, *BAA*

Owen HIGHLEY, Commercial Lawyer, *British Airways*

Robert WEBB, QC, General Counsel, *British Airways*

"Very experienced" **Rupert Britton** *"knows his stuff"* and *"commands respect for his detailed knowledge."* He is the *"epitome of discretion"* and is praised for being *"helpful on the regulatory side."* **Tim Bye** is recommended for being *"very commercial."* He has a *"very wide experience of the industry."* Facing a wide range of work is the *"efficient"* **Richard Churchill-Coleman**, while *"held in high regard"* is **Richard Everitt** who *"understands the business aspects of aviation."* His great experience *"lends weight to his opinions."* Also at BAA, is **Robert Herga** who is *"very very commercial."* **Owen Highley** has built up *"lots of experience"* at BA and is a *"safe pair of hands"* especially on regulatory matters. But *"leading in this field"* is the *"doyen of aviation law"* **Robert Webb QC**. This *"top echelon lawyer"* is *"very commercially minded"* and appears *"head and shoulders above everyone else."*

Insurance

Maria CETTA, Director of Claims & Legal Affairs, *Amlin Aviation*

Ken WALDER, Director of Operations, *BAIG*

On the insurance side, **Maria Cetta** has had a *"significant effect"* at Amlin and *"she can make a difference."* **Ken Walder** was also recommended.

In-House lawyers profiles: page 1177

LONDON

REGULATORY

AVIATION REGULATORY • London	Ptnrs	Assts
❶ Denton Wilde Sapte	1	3
Lane & Partners	1	1
Norton Rose	3	15
❷ Beaumont and Son	2	2
Harbottle & Lewis	2	4
❸ Linklaters	1	4
❹ Barlow Lyde & Gilbert	2	6
❺ Clark Ricketts	2	2

LEADING INDIVIDUALS	
❶ **BALFOUR John** Beaumont and Son	**O'DONOVAN Hugh** Denton Wilde Sapte
SOAMES Trevor Norton Rose	**VENABLES Richard** Lane & Partners
❷ **FARRELL Patrick** Norton Rose	**GIMBLETT Richard** Barlow Lyde & Gilbert
HOWES Colin Harbottle & Lewis	
❸ **ALLAN Bill** Linklaters	
SCULLY Dermot Harbottle & Lewis	

Within each band, firms are listed alphabetically. See *Profiles* on page 102

Denton Wilde Sapte Highly rated by their clients, the firm constitutes one-third of the ruling aviation regulatory triumvirate. It is currently advising on the CAA privatisation. **Hugh O'Donovan** has *"a good grasp of the issues"* and is noted for the breadth of his practice. A former barrister, he is a noted advocate, and *"employs a hand of steel in a velvet glove."* Widely respected for competition expertise in the sector, the team acted for easyJet on its continuing High Court action against BA. This concerned the latter's initiation of its low fare airline subsidiary Go. **Clients:** easyJet; United Airlines; Airtours.

Lane & Partners *"One of the main players,"* the firm has a huge domestic clientele. The only caveat expressed by competitors was whether market liberalisation may erode the advantage of a firm which lacks the resources of some of its leading rivals. **Richard Venables** is perceived as *"an old-world gentleman who is still a tough cookie,"* and has vast experience in this area. His team advises on all facets of regulatory work, including CAA hearings and competition issues. Highlights of the past year include work on a Competition Commission inquiry on helicopters flying in the North Sea. **Clients:** KLM (UK); Bristow Helicopters; Continental Airlines.

Norton Rose *"Definitely a top three firm."* **Trevor Soames** is *"one the best of the bunch,"* a competition lawyer with niche aviation expertise who is stationed in Brussels, but who handles work for the London office. He is considered *"idiosyncratic and bullish,"* and advises all seven airlines making up the Star Alliance. **Patrick Farrell** has more of a domestic reputation, working on regulation, litigation and travel. He is known for combining in-depth knowledge with a relaxed attitude. He acts for banks as an aircraft repossession litigator. The firm is representing the consortium of airlines bidding to be allowed to run the privatised air traffic control system. **Clients:** United Airlines; Olympic Airways; British Midland.

Beaumont and Son Insurance kings, the firm has a growing reputation for its regulatory practice *("they're first-class on European regulatory work.")* The *"quiet and thoughtful"* **John Balfour** is *"academically the most knowledgeable of the leading players."* The firm represented BA, Lufthansa and Virgin in suing ABTA and acted for IATA in challenging European regulations. **Clients:** Lufthansa; Virgin.

Harbottle & Lewis Generally perceived to have had an average year, the firm has not been seen on the major aviation work this year. The team still does a lot of work with ATOLLS, continues to work with the Virgin in-house team and advise on slot transfers. *"Understated"* **Colin Howes** is said to develop *"excellent client relationships,"* while a bright future is predicted for **Dermot Scully**. The team advised on the establishment of a medium-haul airline. **Clients:** Virgin Express; Color Air; TNT.

Linklaters Widely perceived as a competition practice which works with the British Airways in-house team, the firm also works on deal structures. The link with BA makes it difficult to attract other clients and the practice is known for the quality rather than the quantity of its work. **Bill Allan** is considered *"a great chap and a great lawyer,"* but he is perceived to be a competition rather than an aviation specialist. **Clients:** British Airways.

Barlow Lyde & Gilbert The firm's aviation insurance expertise has enabled them to become players in the regulatory market. The team consists of *"impressive performers,"* headed by **Richard Gimblett**, although he is equally reputed for insurance and litigation work. The team undertakes safety liability work for the CAA, and advises airlines on competition issues. **Clients:** IATA; CAA; UPS.

Clark Ricketts A niche aviation firm, it *"knows the industry inside out."* It specialises in start-ups, such as that of Excel Aviation, and has handled litigation for Ghana Airways. Also worked on a dispute between a helicopter distributor and a police force. Possessing a *"loyal"* client base, the team is perceived to give *"excellent value for money."* **Clients:** Excel Aviation; a UK helicopter distributor.

INSURANCE AND LITIGATION

AVIATION INSURANCE & LITIGATION • London	Ptnrs	Assts
❶ Beaumont and Son	8	8
❷ Barlow Lyde & Gilbert	5	6
❸ Clyde & Co	12	5
CMS Cameron McKenna	3	7
DLA	4	4

LEADING INDIVIDUALS
❶ **AWFORD Ian** Barlow Lyde & Gilbert
GATES Sean Beaumont and Son
❷ **BRYMER Tim** CMS Cameron McKenna
FRANKLIN Mark DLA
❸ **ANDREWARTHA Jane** Clyde & Co
CLARK David Beaumont and Son
FARRELL Patrick Norton Rose
GIMBLETT Richard Barlow Lyde & Gilbert
HUGHES Nicholas Barlow Lyde & Gilbert
McGILCHRIST Neil Beaumont and Son
SCORER Tim DLA
WILLCOX David Beaumont and Son
UP AND COMING
KAVANAGH Giles Barlow Lyde & Gilbert

Within each band, firms are listed alphabetically. *See **Profiles** on page 102*

Beaumont and Son *"Everyone knows they're the best."* Possessors of an enormous client base, the team has been described as *"the IBM of the aviation world."* Particular strength on airline liability work was highlighted by advice to Kenya Airways on the recent crash off Abidjan. Despite personnel changes, the firm continues to boast an impressive line-up. Exuding *"great kudos and personality,"* **Sean Gates** is *"the chief,"* and is said to perform like *"a quiet assassin."* **Neil McGilchrist** has returned to the fold and is widely commended for his work. *"Thinking lawyer,"* **David Willcox** *"always works in his clients' best interests"* and can now be said to have arrived. **David Clark** is another noted member of the team. **Clients:** Korean Airlines; Kenya Airways.

Barlow Lyde & Gilbert There are some indications that the *"gap with Beaumonts may be narrowing"* and many consider the team to be *"man for man as good as the best."* Acted for Messieur Dowty on the failure of landing gear on a Sabena plane and represented the insurers of Air Malta over the Lockerbie air crash. With *"some good middle ranking talent coming through"* the firm is felt to be *"buoyant"* and is especially noted for its product liability clientele. Father figure **Ian Awford** is *"dogged in his defence of his clients"* and *"good fun to have a fight with." "Impressive"* **Richard Gimblett** is a player here as in the regulatory sector, while **Nicholas Hughes** is noted for his product liability work. New acquisition **Giles Kavanagh** appears to be the man to watch. He is considered by many to be Ian Awford's *"heir apparent"* and has *"star quality."* **Clients:** Rolls Royce; British Aerospace; Air 2000.

Clyde & Co Noted for insurance and re-insurance work, the firm's clients include major insurers in the London market. Involved in the inquiry over Hong Kong airport and a helicopter hijacking in Papua New Guinea. The team also advised on a case arising from the destruction of the entire Air Botswana fleet by a pilot who deliberately flew his plane into two other planes on the ground. **Jane Andrewartha** is the leading light here. **Clients:** ACE; Polygon; Lloyds.

CMS Cameron McKenna The firm maintains its position, working on liability claims for airlines and product manufacturers. Handles Airbus' insurance work, although this does present conflict problems where major airlines are concerned. During the past year, the firm worked on a helicopter disaster in Cape Town and acted for the UN on several notable losses. **Tim Brymer** remains *"an effective performer."* **Clients:** Eurocopter; Airbus; Lucas; Association of American Underwriters.

DLA Principally advising on post-accident work, the team deals with UK work for major US airlines. The firm is perceived to be *"a shade over-aggressive"* but its *"go-getting style"* is felt by some to pose the greatest long-term challenge to the Beaumonts – Barlows duopoly. Highly-rated **Mark Franklin** is complemented by *"dedicated and hard working"* **Tim Scorer**. The team recently worked on two crashes which occurred within four days of each other – one in Guatemala, the other in Venezuela. **Clients:** Westminster Aviation Insurance Group; Virgin Express; Colonian Baltica.

Other Notable Practitioners **Patrick Farrell** at Norton Rose is respected here as well as for regulatory matters, and is considered to be *"good at heavyweight documentation."*

SCOTLAND

AVIATION • Scotland	Ptnrs	Assts
❶ Maclay Murray & Spens Glasgow	⚐	⚐
Shepherd & Wedderburn WS Edinburgh	1	1
❷ Simpson & Marwick WS Edinburgh	1	2

LEADING INDIVIDUALS
❶ ANDERSON Peter Simpson & Marwick WS
CLARK Richard Maclay Murray & Spens
DONALD Hugh Shepherd & Wedderburn WS

Within each band, firms are listed alphabetically. *See **Profiles** on page 102*

⚐ *Figures unavailable at time of going to press.*

Maclay Murray & Spens Highly respected team considered to be *"particularly good litigators."* **Richard Clark** is noted as a claims man and is held to be *"technically accurate."* Advises claimants, both insurers and individuals, on a variety of post-accident matters, and acted for the insurers of BIH, following the ditching in the North Sea of a Sikorsky helicopter. **Clients:** CAA; Jetstream.

Shepherd & Wedderburn WS Felt to perform *"much of the aviation insurance work north of the border."* During the past year, the firm appeared at the inquiry for Bristow Helicopters and its insurers over the death of a winchman during a search and rescue operation. Also instructed by the insurers in connection with the Glasgow Air Accident. **Hugh Donald** has a national reputation. **Clients:** Bristow Helicopters; air carriers; insurers.

Simpson & Marwick WS Insurance and litigation specialists, the firm acted for Airtours in the recent Glasgow crash. **Peter Anderson** is considered by the market to be *"a genuine specialist."* **Clients:** Boeing; BAA; BA; Air UK.

LEADERS IN AVIATION

ALLAN, Bill

Linklaters (A member firm of Linklaters & Alliance), London (020) 7456 3574
bill.allan@linklaters.com
See under Competition/Anti-trust, p.179

ANDERSON, Peter

Simpson & Marwick WS, Edinburgh (0131) 557 1545
Partner in commercial litigation department. Solicitor Advocate 1993.
Specialisation: Work includes professional negligence, personal injury, commercial litigation and aviation litigation. Acted in the Lockerbie inquiry (for Pan-Am) and all related claims, advocacy for C.A.A. in litigation and inquiries including Cormorant Alpha, Brent Spar, for BTA in EL and passenger cases, commercial aviation contract cases.
Prof. Memberships: Law Society of Scotland, International Association Defence Counsel, I.B.A., senior lecturer Edinburgh University.
Career: Qualified 1977, partner since 1980. Solicitor advocate 1993.

ANDREWARTHA, Jane

Clyde & Co, London (020) 7623 1244
Partner in Insurance and Reinsurance Department.
Specialisation: Practice is rooted in major insurance and reinsurance litigation, claims and liability work. Acted in the Swazi Airline hijack, involved in personal injury aspect of Piper Alpha claims settlement and reinsurance aspects of the Eastern European Newbuildings. Aviation practice consists of representing insurers and aviation interests in defence and policy matters and most recent major case involved TAM crash 1996. Also involved in general aviation – light aircraft and helicopters. Clients include most major London and foreign market insurance and reinsurance companies and many Lloyd's syndicates. Is a regular conference speaker and contributor to insurance industry publications.
Prof. Memberships: Law Society, CEDR Accredited Mediator, Update Author of the international publication Journal of Maritime Law & Commerce, Association of Average Adjusters (Associate Member), Lloyds (Associate Member). Member of Air Law Group of the Royal Aeronautical Society.
Career: Qualified in 1976, having joined *Clyde & Co* in 1974. Became a Partner in 1980. London Head of the firm's Latin American offices from 1989-1997. Now Head of Aviation and has sat on the Board of Management as Finance Partner from 1993.
Personal: Born 20th December 1952. Attended Exeter University 1970-73 (LLB Hons). Leisure activities include skiing, powerboat racing and swimming. Lives in London.

AWFORD, Ian

Barlow Lyde & Gilbert, London (020) 7247 2277
iawford@blg.co.uk
Senior Partner in Aviation Department.
Specialisation: Main area of practice is aviation law and the law relating to commercial uses of outer space. Also handles insurance law, litigation, arbitration and mediation. Has acted in many major air disaster cases. Author of various publications on legal issues concerning carriage by air, product liability and the law relating to outer space.
Prof. Memberships: International Institute of Space Law of the International Astronautics Federation; International Society of Air Safety I nvestigators; European Society of Air Safety Investigators; Federation of Insurance and Corporate Counsel; International Associate of the American Bar Association; Air Law Group of the Royal Aeronautical Society; European Centre for Space Law; Air Law Working Party of the International Chamber of Commerce; Product Liability Advisory Council; International Association of Defense Counsel. European Air Law Association; Aviation Insurance Association; The Guild of Air Traffic Control Officers; International Court of Aviation and Space Arbitration.
Career: Qualified in 1967, in Hong Kong in 1988 and in Tasmania 1998. Joined *Barlow Lyde & Gilbert* in 1969, becoming a Partner in 1973. Chairman of the Outer Space Committee of the International Bar Association: Section of Business Law 1987-90; Aerospace Law Committee, Inter Pacific Bar Association 1990-1993; Elected fellow of the Royal Aeronautical Society 1988. Fellow of the Institute of Advanced Legal Studies 1998, CEDR Accredited Mediator 1998.
Personal: Born 15th April 1941. Attended Wellingborough School, Northants, then Sheffield University LLB (Hons). Leisure interests include skiing, theatre, music and painting. Married with five sons and one daughter. Lives in London.

BALFOUR, John

Beaumont and Son, London (020) 7481 3100
jbalfour@beaumont.co.uk
Partner in aviation department.
Specialisation: Practice includes regulation, EC, and CAA work; accidents, liability and insurance; sale, purchase and leasing and other commercial arrangements; and international issues. Author of 'European Community Air Law' and of many articles on aviation in the professional press. Lectures extremely widely; recent engagements include conferences and courses organised by the Royal Aeronautical Society, IFURTA Aix-en-Provence, ENAC Toulouse, Cranfield University, European Aviation Club and European Air Law Association.
Prof. Memberships: Royal Aeronautical Society (past chairman, Air Law Group), European Air Law Association (secretary) and European Aviation Club (board member).
Career: Qualified 1979, having joined *Frere Cholmeley Bischoff* in 1977. Became a partner in 1986 and head of the aviation group in 1993. Joined *Beaumont and Son* as a partner in 1997.

BRYMER, Tim

CMS Cameron McKenna, London (020) 7367 3000
Specialisation: Partner – aviation group specialising in aviation and aerospace law and claims. Represents aviation insurers, airlines and manufacturers worldwide. Responsible for pioneering use of common law injunction in restraining forum shopping following aviation disasters.
Prof. Memberships: Founder member of Lawyers' Flying Association. Member of Guild of Pilots and Air Navigators. Elected member of Royal Aeronautical Society Air Law Discussion Group and Insurance Institute of London Aviation Committee. Holder of current pilot's licence.
Career: Dulwich College, College of Air Training, Hamble. College of Law, Lancaster Gate. Qualified 1977.
Personal: Art, music, tennis, cycling and flying.

CLARK, David
Beaumont and Son, London (020) 7481 3100
dclark@beaumont.co.uk
Partner in aviation department.
Specialisation: Main areas of practice are all aspects of aviation liablility work; also handles personal injury work for defendants. Deals extensively with matters relating to countries where French or Spanish are spoken.
Prof. Memberships: Law Society.
Career: Qualified 1980.
Personal: Born 8th March 1952. Attended University of Southampton, and College of Law.

CLARK, Richard
Maclay Murray & Spens, Glasgow
(0141) 248 5011
rafc@maclaymurrayspens.co.uk
Specialisation: Senior litigation partner specialising in aviation, fraud and financial services and shipping litigation. Recent cases include Silkair crash in Indonesia. Landcatch v. The Braer Corporation and IOPCF. Co-author of the Scottish section of Butterworths 'Aircraft Finance'.
Career: Edinburgh University (LL.B 1973).
Personal: Born 1949.

DONALD OBE, Hugh R.
Shepherd & Wedderburn WS, Edinburgh
(0131) 228 9900
hugh.donald@shepwedd.co.uk
See under Clinical Negligence, p.162

FARRELL, Patrick
Norton Rose, London (020) 7283 6000
Specialisation: (for Aviation: Insurance & Litigation) Advises airlines, brokers, banks, financiers and underwriters on aviation insurance matters including liability claims world-wide, coverage disputes, advice on wordings and insurance claims generally. Acts for underwriters in political risk matters arising out of aircraft finance transactions.
Specialisation: (on Aviation: Regulatory) Advises airlines, tour operators and travel agents on the domestic and European regulatory regime. In conjunction with *Norton Rose's* Brussels office, advises start up airlines and their financiers on their relationship with regulators, competitors, airport authorities and contracting parties.
Prof. Memberships: MRAeS, Chairman of the Royal Aeronautical Society Air Law Group, Chairman of the UK ICC Commission on Air Transport, Member of Institute of Travel and Tourism, IBA, LSLA, CLLS (Chairman of the CLLS Aeronautical Law Sub-Committee).

FRANKLIN, Mark B.
DLA, London (020) 7796 6522
mark.franklin@dla.com
Head of aviation group
Specialisation: Aviation: predominantly the handling of post accident legal liabilities, but also undertakes commercial and regulatory work. Notable projects include acting as Outside Counsel to IATA on the Inter-Carrier Agreement; representing EL AL re claims arising from B747 disaster in Amsterdam.
Prof. Memberships: MRAeS
Career: LL.B (Hons) Southampton University: qualified 1984; Partner at *Frere Cholmeley Bischoff* 1993-97; Honorary Solicitor to Aircraft Owners and Pilots Association (AOPA); Contributor to IATA 'Liability Reporter 2000'; Contributor to 'Encyclopaedia of Forms and Precedents' (Butterworths) on 'Carriage by Air' and 'Civil Aviation'; lecturer on international air law issues on courses organised by the College of Aeronautics at Cranfield University; Member of Board of Editors 'Air and Space Law' (Kluwer).
Personal: Sailing: member of Royal Southern Yacht Club, and Junior Offshore Group.

GATES, Sean
Beaumont and Son, London (020) 7481 3100
sgates@beaumont.co.uk
Joint senior partner and head of aviation claims department.
Specialisation: Main area of practice is aviation insurance and liability. Represents insurers and airlines in respect of claims made against them, and insurers in respect of policy decisions with airlines and reinsurers. Also handles libel and slander work, representing both plaintiffs and defendants in defamation actions. Author of articles in numerous journals, frequent speaker on aviation issues. Legal adviser International Union of Aviation Insurers. Former Chairman Air Law Committee, Royal Aeronautical Society.
Career: Qualified in 1972. Joined *Beaumont and Son* in 1973, becoming a partner in 1978 and head of aviation claims department in 1991. Senior partner 1st November 1997. Arbitrator with Cour Internationale d'Arbitrage Aerien et Special.
Personal: Born 4th February 1949. Leisure pursuits include collecting 19th Century illustrated books. Lives in London.

GIMBLETT, Richard
Barlow Lyde & Gilbert, London (020) 7247 2277
Specialisation: Aviation and Travel Law; Commercial Litigation.
Prof. Memberships: Member of the IATA International Law Faculty; Member of the European Centre for Space Law.
Career: B.A. Hons (Oxon) (1981) Called to Bar 1982. Legal Adviser, UK Civil Aviation Authority 1985-1988. Admitted as a Solicitor in 1990.
Personal: Director of F.T.O Trust Fund Ltd, Private Pilot.

HOWES, Colin M.
Harbottle & Lewis, London (020) 7667 5000
Partner.
Specialisation: Handles regulatory, commercial, e-business and corporate work for a variety of clients, most of whom are in the entertainment, leisure and travel industries. Author of 'Slot Allocation at Heathrow Airport: The Legal Framework'.
Prof. Memberships: Law Society, European Air Law Association.
Career: Qualified in 1981. Joined *Harbottle & Lewis* in 1979, became a Partner in 1984.
Personal: Born 3rd March 1956. Attended Ipswich School 1967-74, then Oriel College, Oxford 1975-78. Lives in London.

HUGHES, Nicholas M.L.
Barlow Lyde & Gilbert, London (020) 7247 2277
Partner in Aerospace Department.
Specialisation: Main area of practice is aviation law, covering aviation insurance and reinsurance, liability law, carriage of goods and aviation regulatory law. General Editor of 'Contracts for the Carriage of Goods by Land, Sea and Air' (LLP); Editorial Consultant of 'Transport Law and Policy'.
Prof. Memberships: Royal Aeronautical Society, United Kingdom Environmental Law Association, Law Society, International Bar Association, American Bar Association.
Career: Qualified in 1981. Joined *Barlow, Lyde & Gilbert* in 1979, becoming a Partner in 1984. Director of Association of Insurance and Risk Managers (AIRMIC).
Personal: Born 10th October 1955. Attended Sheffield University, BA Law (Hons). Lives in London.

KAVANAGH, Giles
Barlow Lyde & Gilbert, London (020) 7247 2277
gkavanagh@blg.co.uk
Specialisation: Partner specialising in all aspects of aviation law. His practice includes insurance disputes (claims and coverage), product liability, regulatory and transactonal advice. Also advises on the sale and leasing of aircraft and has appeared for lessors and lessees in disputes arising out of aircraft leases. Cases in the past twelve months have included: acting for insurers of landing gear manufacturer in very substantial multi- jusrisdictional product liability dispute (ongoing); representing successful appelants in Western Digital v BA (CA) on whether an owner of goods who is neither consignor nor consignee has title to sue under the Amended Warsaw and Guadalajara Conventions; advising Kuoni on EU regulatory issues arising out its proposed merger with First Choice Holidays; and advising airline on sale of B-737s to special purpose off-shore company.
Prof. Memberships: Royal Aeronautical Society.
Career: Before joining BLG in 1999, He was recommended as a leading aviation barrister in the Chambers and Partners Directory: he appeared for the regulator in the reported cases of Philcox v CAA (CA) and in Perrett v Popular Flying Association (CA) and for Insurers in mass diaster litigatin, including the Kegworth crash. As a barrister he also appeared in a number of arbitrations.
Publications: Regular contributor to aviation / legal publications.
Personal: Education: St John's College, Cambridge; MA., LL.M. President of Cambridge Union Society, Michaelmas 1981. Recreation: Swimming, golf, tennis, deep sleep. Family details: Lives Kensington Hill with wife, Anna and two children, Tierney and Conall.

MCGILCHRIST, Neil R.
Beaumont and Son, London (020) 7481 3100
nmcgilchrist@beaumont.co.uk
Joint senior partner.
Specialisation: Work includes re-insurance, aerospace and insurance litigation.
Prof. Memberships: Law Society.
Career: Qualified in 1969 as a barrister of the Middle Temple, becoming a partner in *Beaumont and Son* in 1981.
Personal: Born 8th December 1946. Attended Wadham College, Oxford, then Inns of Court School of Law. President of University of Oxford Law Society, 1966.

O'DONOVAN, Hugh
Denton Wilde Sapte, London (020) 7424 1212
hod@dentonwildesapte.com
Partner in Company Commercial Department and Aviation Industry Group.
Specialisation: Main area of practice is aviation, covering international aviation regulation,

commercial agreements in aviation, EC and competition law, airline and airport operations, aircraft leasing and airport financing. Also covers travel agents and tour operators. Regular speaker at various conferences and seminars on aviation-related topics.
Prof. Memberships: Law Society, International Bar Association, Royal Aeronautical Society, Aviation Committee of the UK International Chambers of Commerce, member of Council of the Airport Operators' Association.
Career: Called to the Bar in 1975. Practised as a barrister before joining *Knapp Fishers* in 1985. Left for *Richards Butler* in 1987 (Partner 1989). Joined *Wilde Sapte* as a Partner in 1991.
Personal: Born 19th August 1952. Attended Royal Grammar School, Guildford 1963-69 then Balliol College, Oxford 1970-73. Leisure pursuits include golf, skiing, flying and rugby refereeing. Lives in Witley, Surrey.

SCORER, T.R.

DLA, London (08700) 111 111
tim.scorer@dla.com
Partner in Aviation Department.
Specialisation: Practice deals principally with aviation claims and aviation insurance disputes, litigation and arbitration. Handles a wide range of aviation interests including airlines, aircraft operators, airports and aerodromes, helicopters, gliders and parachuting and contractual documents relative to those interests. Author and lecturer on a wide range of legal issues affecting the aviation industry such as airworthiness, airport operations, carriage by air and aviation legal liabilities generally.
Prof. Memberships: Member of the Royal Aeronautical Society, Lawyers Flying Association (Chairman), Lawyer Pilots Bar Association (International Vice-President), City of London Law Society, Guild of Air Pilots and Air Navigators (Liveryman).
Career: Qualified in 1966. 10 years with provincial firm as litigation partner followed by 2 years in the Public Relations Department of the Law Society. Partner in *Barlow Lyde & Gilbert* 1980-1992. Aviation Partner in *Jarvis & Barrister* 1992-97.
Personal: Born 25 June 1941. Attended Repton School, Derbyshire, followed by College of Law. Leisure interests include flying as a Private Pilot, photography and wine growing. Lives in Essex.

SCULLY, Dermot

Harbottle & Lewis, London (020) 7667 5170
dscully@harbottle.co.uk
Specialisation: Dermot Scully is head of the Aviation Group at *Harbottle & Lewis. Harbottle & Lewis* acts for airlines and other aviation businesses advising on all legal aspects of their operations, particularly aircraft acquisition and regulatory issues. Clients include Virgin Atlantic, TNT, British World Airlines and British Midland. Dermot holds an air law qualification from University College, London and is a member of the Air Law Committee of the Royal Aeronautical Society. He has written articles for many industry publications and is a speaker at industry conferences.

SOAMES, Trevor

Norton Rose, Brussels (00) 32 2 237 6111
soamest@nortonrose.com
Partner in competition and EC department.
Specialisation: Main area of practice is all aspects of EC and UK competition; trade and regulatory law in many economic sectors. Well known for his transportation expertise and aviation, in particular. In 1999, he was identified by Euromoney as one of the World's 20 Leading Aviation Lawyers. In the field of aviation, clients have included a wide range of Governments, regulatory agencies and multinational corporations from around the world. He has represented airlines, airports, Governments and national regulatory bodies. Most recent cases include representing: United Airlines in its proposed merger with US Airways as well as the European Commission's continuing Article 85 investigation of the alliance between United Airlines with its European partners, Lufthansa and SAS, as well as the concurrent investigation under Article 84 by the German FCO; United Airlines in opposing the hostile bid by Onex/AirCo for Air Canada and its subsequent arrangements with Air Canada; British Midland, Lufthansa and SAS jointly in the notification of their alliance; British Midland (on a variety of major cases including the Aer Lingus Article 82 interlining case, the Brussels Airport Article 86 case, the Aer Lingus and Air France state aid cases, the BA PRS and override case); Iberia in the Commission's investigation of the Spanish ground handling monopoly under Articles 82 and 86; Olympic Airways and the Greek Government in the Greek Article 82 and 86 ground handling case, successfully closed by a Commission Decision in 1997 dismissing the complaints, as well as in the Olympic airways and Spata Airport state aid cases; Ryanair in the Aer Lingus Article 82 predatory pricing and state aid cases including Ryanair v Commission case before the European Court. Advises a number of leading scheduled and charter airlines and financial institutions on other key aviation regulatory issues including ownership and licencing requirements and represents clients before the UK CCA and EC Commission. He also has specific expertise in the field of UK aviation licensing and scarce capacity procedures, appearing as an advocate before the CAA and other authorities in a number of cases including Warsaw, Moscow I, Moscow II and Prague. Has advised various Central and Eastern European Governments on air transport liberalisation related matters including those of the Czech Republic, Slovenia, Poland and Russia. In 1998, Trevor advised the rapporteur to the European Parliament's Transport Committee on important legislative proposals put forward by the Commission, the amendments suggested were subsequently adopted by the Parliament and the Commission.
Career: A graduate of Cambridge University. Called to the Bar of England and Wales in 1984. Worked at the UK Department of Trade and Industry before entering private practice. Author of many articles on competition and regulatory law as well as being editor of, or contributor to a number of books including: 'Corporate Mergers and Acquisitions', 'Air Transport and the European Community: Recent Developments', 'Airline Mergers and Co-operation', 'State Aids to Airlines', 'European Air Law Association' Volume 12 and Volume 13. Trevor is also an Associate Editor of Butterworths 'Competition Law Encyclopaedia'. Recent aviation-related articles include: 'Predatory Pricing and Air Transport' and 'State Aid and Air Transport, European Competition Law Review; All Bark and No Bite', Airline Business; 'Ground Handling Liberalisation', Journal of Air Transport Management; Royal Aeronautical Society; 'Essential Facilities and Air Transport', European Air Law Association 1998; 'The Application of the EU Competition Rules to Aviation and Alliances' European Aviation Club 1999 and many others.
Personal: Born 17 September 1959. Leisure interests are many and varied but unfortunately He has less time to pursue them than he would wish.

VENABLES, Richard

Lane & Partners, London (020) 7242 2626
venables@lane.co.uk
Head of aviation and travel department.
Specialisation: Principal area of work is aviation law advising British and foreign airlines on regulatory matters including UK and European licensing regulations, competition law and all other matters affecting airlines' commercial operations. Other main area of work is advising UK-based tour operators, particularly on air travel organisers' licensing, UK and European legal developments and contractual matters. Recently involved in slots issues and matters concerning ownership and control of airlines. Regular attender before CAA. Contributes articles to trade publications and lectures on air law topics.
Prof. Memberships: Institute of Logistics and Transport, Royal Aeronautical Society, European Air Law Association.
Career: Qualified in 1971 while with *Gregory, Rowcliffe & Co.*, then joined *Norton Rose* in 1973. Moved to *Booth & Co.* in Leeds 1975-76, then returned to *Norton Rose* 1976-82. Joined *Lane & Partners* in 1982 and became a partner in 1983.
Personal: Born 6th December 1946. Attended Uppingham School 1960-65, then Keble College, Oxford 1965-68. Leisure pursuits include golf, walking, tennis and family activities. Lives in Hampton, Middlesex.

WILLCOX, David J.

Beaumont and Son, London (020) 7481 3100
dwillcox@beaumont.co.uk
Partner in aviation department.
Specialisation: Main areas of practice are aerospace, commercial litigation and insurance litigation. His practice in aviation law covers handling of passenger and hull claims in respect of major accidents involving fixed and rotary wing operations including a large number of accidents in Africa, passenger cargo and baggage liability claims, advising on rights and liabilities of aviation engineering and maintenance organisations, and commercial litigation.
Prof. Memberships: Law Society.
Career: Qualified in 1981. Became a partner in 1987.
Personal: Born 25th March 1957. Attended Sheffield University.

BANKING

OVERVIEW: The connection between banking and capital markets is becoming increasingly important as financings mixing debt and equity become commonplace. Some have commented that there is an increasing trend for clients to look for lawyers with integrated and more generalist skills.

Allen & Overy and Clifford Chance are *"comfortably out ahead,"* both being *"comprehensive and all-embracing."* Investment grade work, including 'jumbo' loans, tends to be dominated by these two, with fierce battles raging in the more aggressive LBO secured lending market. Both Allen & Overy and Clifford Chance have the capacity to churn out commoditised work while advising on more sophisticated transactions. 20 out of 38 ranked practitioners in the sector hail from these firms. Below the two leaders, Linklaters and Freshfields have pulled away, as the international magic circle firms put *"clear blue water"* between themselves and the rest.

RESEARCH APPROVED BY BMRB: *For this edition,* Chambers' *researchers conducted 6083 interviews – 4408 with law firms, 598 with barristers and 1077 with clients.*

The validity of the research was scrutinised by BMRB International, who audited both the methodology and the results at our offices in July 2000. They interviewed Chambers' *researchers and cross-checked sample interviews. Details of the audit appear on page 7.*

LEADING IN-HOUSE LAWYERS

Laurie ADAMS, Regional General Counsel, *Citibank*

Mitchell CALLER, Senior Vice-President & Associate General Counsel, *The Chase Manhattan Bank*

Alex CAMERON, Legal Director for London & Europe, *Barclays Capital*

Paul CHELSOM, Director of Legal & Compliance, *Credit Suisse First Boston International*

Simon DODDS, General Counsel, *Deutsche Bank AG Ltd*

Martin HAYMAN, Group Secretary and Group Head of Legal Services, *Standard Chartered*

Therese MILLER, Managing Director & General Counsel, *Goldman Sachs International* - US qualified only

Kevin STUDD, Managing Director & General Counsel for Europe, *Credit Suisse First Boston International*

Howard TRUST, General Counsel, Barclays Group, and Company Secretary, *Barclays plc*

"Energetic" **Laurie Adams** is known as an *"effective manager"* and *"very good value." "First-class"* **Mitch Caller** is *"truly commercial"* and has developed his role on the American model. He is a *"good technical lawyer"* with a *"good sense of humour."* Praised for his understanding of the pressures faced by private practice is **Alex Cameron** but he also *"understands the industry, the law and the product." "Helpful and proactive"* **Paul Chelsom** is well-recommended for his work. **Simon Dodds** is a *"star"* who is a *"good manager."* He was widely commended for his *"good judgement and good humour." "Effective"* **Martin Hayman** *"understands the legal risk and difficulties."* He is recognised for his *"good commercial acumen"* and his work in dispute resolution. *"Robust"* **Therese Miller** *"doesn't suffer fools gladly"* and she is *"professional and able."* **Kevin Studd** has a good reputation, focusing on emerging markets, and *"cerebral"* **Howard Trust** is known to be *"able and effective."* He *"manages a diversified team well."*

In-House lawyers profiles: page 1177

LONDON

Allen & Overy Perceived to have retained the *"quality edge"* over Clifford Chance on the domestic scene, this *"first class"* firm's banking output is described as *"top products produced by focused and tough negotiating players"* who *"never make mistakes."* Although non-transactional, *"senior guru"* **Philip Wood**, currently involved on internal knowledge-management programmes, continues to generate enormous influence amongst peers as the *"wise old man of banking."* The banking department's managing partner is the *"young yet vastly experienced"* **David Morley**. Regarded as *"urbane, easy to deal with and well organised,"* Morley is *"the one to turn to if you need to raise money in a hurry."* Lawyers admire him for being *"comfortable with billions"* and most observers see in him *"the quintessential banking lawyer."* He accordingly moves to the top band in our lists. Other highly rated practitioners include the *"solid and practical project manager"* **Michael Duncan** and **Peter Schulz**. The *"influential"* veteran **Jonathan Horsfall Turner** and the *"tenacious"* **Tony Humphrey** are active in both banking and projects. The bulk of the firm's work is for lenders, with around 20 percent of the client base consisting of large borrowers such as GEC and British Aerospace. One of the stand-out features of the banking practice is the *"great lengths the firm goes to to teach the juniors what is in the documents."* Split into five groups, the *"balanced and constructive"* London banking team has around 150 lawyers whose total billings increased by over 20 percent in 1999, advising 800-plus banking and borrower clients. London is still the centre of gravity for financial transactions in Europe, although its continental offices (particularly Amsterdam, Paris and Frankfurt) continue to gain in strength and prestige. Already, over 40 percent of the firm's banking partners are based outside the UK, a number that is set to increase. This translated into acting on more than 40 cross-border deals worth over $1 billion in the past year. These deals include advising an 11-bank syndicate financing a €30 billion loan for Vodafone's hostile bid for Mannesmann (at the time thought to be the largest ever syndicated loan,) and advising KPN on its $13 billion loan to purchase E-Plus Mobilfunk GmbH. Other large deals include Repsol's acquisition of YPF ($16 billion) and Air Liquide's joint bid for the BOC Group ($8 billion). In pure acquisition finance, leading lights include the *"dogged and tough"* **Tony Keal**, who is *"irascible, but one of the best; not a lot goes by him."* Lawyers acting opposite the *"pleasant"* **Stephen Gillespie** regard him as *"so client-wise that you're scared he'll steal yours."* Rising practitioners, the *"progressive and solid"* **Trevor Borthwick**, and *"Tony Keal protégé"* **Euan Gorrie** continue to receive recommendations. In other banking areas the firm worked with Clifford Chance and the LMA on efforts to standardise primary documentation for syndicated loans. It has additionally launched 'newchange,' an internet-based deal-room allowing the firm to manage complex transactions on the web, considerably reducing delay in documenting, amending and concluding transactions. **Clients:** Goldman Sachs; Barclays; Citibank; Bank of America; Crédit Agricole.

Clifford Chance *"They are still the firm with the broadest spread of offices and as a result have the geographical edge on A&O."* A practice which has grown dramatically and continues to do so, enables the firm to have a base of spe-

BANKING • London	Ptnrs	Assts
❶ Allen & Overy	43	128
Clifford Chance	35	170
❷ Freshfields Bruckhaus Deringer	13	35
Linklaters	17	93
❸ Lovells	12	40
Norton Rose	27	90
Slaughter and May	32	-
❹ Ashurst Morris Crisp	16	20
Denton Wilde Sapte	28	72
Herbert Smith	12	35
Shearman & Sterling	5	17
❺ CMS Cameron McKenna	3	5
Macfarlanes	4	5
Simmons & Simmons	5	30
Taylor Joynson Garrett	6	7
Travers Smith Braithwaite	4	7
Weil, Gotshal & Manges	4	17
❻ Baker & McKenzie	4	15
Berwin Leighton	6	12
DLA	7	16
Gouldens	6	7
Stephenson Harwood	4	12
Theodore Goddard	7	14
Watson, Farley & Williams	13	-

LEADING INDIVIDUALS	
✪ **MORLEY David** Allen & Overy	
❶ **BRAY Michael** Clifford Chance	**EREIRA David** Freshfields Bruckhaus Deringer
POPHAM Stuart Clifford Chance	**PULESTON JONES Haydn** Linklaters
WOOD Philip Allen & Overy	
❷ **ALLEN Maurice** White & Case	**BALFOUR Andrew** Slaughter and May
HUMPHREY Anthony Allen & Overy	**JOHNSON James** Clifford Chance
KEAL Anthony Allen & Overy	**SLATER Richard** Slaughter and May
STEWART Mark Clifford Chance	**SWEETING Malcolm** Clifford Chance
❸ **CAMPBELL Mark** Clifford Chance	**DUNCAN Michael** Allen & Overy
EVANS Edward Freshfields Bruckhaus Deringer	
GILLESPIE Stephen Allen & Overy	**HORSFALL TURNER Jonathan** Allen & Overy
MOSTYN-WILLIAMS Stephen Shearman & Sterling	
PIERCE Sean Freshfields Bruckhaus Deringer	
❹ **COTTIS Matthew** Lovells	**CULLINANE Lee** Clifford Chance
ELLIOTT Robert Linklaters	**FOX Ruth** Slaughter and May
FURMAN Mark Macfarlanes	**INGLIS Alan** Clifford Chance
POLGLASE Timothy Norton Rose	**SCHULZ Peter** Allen & Overy
SPENDLOVE Justin Ashurst Morris Crisp	
TUCKER John C. Linklaters	**VICKERS Mark** Ashurst Morris Crisp
UP AND COMING	
BORTHWICK Trevor Allen & Overy	**GORRIE Euan** Allen & Overy
ONE TO WATCH	
KILNER Peter Clifford Chance	

Within each band, firms are listed alphabetically. *See* ***Profiles*** *on page 116*

cialists, a depth of practice and a range which keeps them at the top of the pile. This has been further developed with the addition of strong US and German banking capabilities. The firm's recent mergers have added expertise in other financial areas – Rogers & Wells includes a leading finance litigation practice whilst Pünder has an active securities practice. Finance as a whole (including asset finance and capital markets) now takes up 35 percent of the firm's workload (of which banking is half.) Additionally, there has been a 30 percent increase in the turnover of the banking team in 1999. The market perceives the upper echelons of CC's banking practice to be peopled with *"charmers."* These include **Michael Bray**, who although not fee-earning is vastly influential, the *"sensible, constructive and fantastic"* **Stuart Popham** and the *"classic CC men"* – **Mark Campbell** *("relaxed, sensible and good on the commercial argument")* and **Malcolm Sweeting** *("easy-going, commercial, quick and effective.")* In acquisition finance, where **Mark Stewart** has a name, the firm has been joined by **James Johnson** from Wilde Sapte, widely regarded as an important capture. Some market reservations have been expressed over the consistency of quality at junior level. Nevertheless, it was widely accepted that *"when they dedicate themselves to a task and resource it properly"* they *"get it right and don't mess around."* The majority of deals are of a cross-border nature, and include financing France Telecom's takeover of Orange. Other major transactions include the bond issue in Olivetti, handled by the *"bright"* **Alan Inglis**, and acting for Deutsche Bank in financing Mannesmann purchases from Olivetti. The main relationship partner for Chase Manhattan, **Lee Cullinane**, is another warmly recommended practitioner. The majority of the firm's clients are financials, with Chase Manhattan, Citibank, Merrill Lynch and Morgan Stanley among the firm's largest sources of fees. The firm advised on the financing on such deals as the British Steel/Hoogevens link-up, RMC's acquisition of Rugby Group plc, Cable & Wireless' investment in the One2One network and the attempted Air Products/BOC link-up. Buy-out activity saw the firm active on Akzo Nobel, the Money Store, Findus European frozen fish and Thomson Directories buy-outs. The firm is becoming more active in new areas such as telebanking, e-commerce and intra-day trading, and has introduced an on-line deal room. **Clients:** Chase Manhattan; Citigroup; JP Morgan; Halifax; Morgan Stanley; Fuji Bank; Goldman Sachs; UBS; Nomura; CSFB; KKR; CVC; WestLB; NatWest; Barclays; Deutsche; UBS; ABN Amro; HSBC; Candover Partners; Apax Partners; Electra Fleming; PPM Ventures; Schroder Venture Advisers.

Freshfields Bruckhaus Deringer Known for its borrower client base, the firm is widely respected for its work on large cross-border lending work, including Repsol's acquisition of YPF, Air Liquide's joint bid for BOC, Thomson-CSF's bid for Racal and Generali's bid for INA. **David Ereira** is a *"class act"* whose *"vast experience," "keen mind"* and *"commercial ability"* see him move into a top band this year. Other notable individuals include the *"affable"* **Edward Evans** and **Sean Pierce**. The latter also moves up a band this year, with observers praising his *"original thinking"* and *"pragmatic approach."* Two factors contribute to the Freshfields reputation as a banking team concentrated on borrowers – the immense reputation of the corporate teams and the firm's historic relationship with the Bank of England. This was a relationship which once seemed to preclude the firm from developing close relationships with private lenders. However, although heavily involved in acquisitions generated from the corporate side, the banking practice now also advises lending clients such as Citibank and Chase Manhattan, and borrower clients such as One2One, who have no relationship with the corporate team. Although not regarded as a *"volume outfit,"* the firm is considered to do an *"excellent job"* on complex transactions, including tax-driven work. **Clients:** Citibank; Chase Manhattan; Cinven; HSBC; WestLB; Morgan Stanley; Zurich Financial Services; Rolls Royce.

Linklaters Making inroads into lender work, this *"supremely competent"* banking team is seen to have *"come on apace"* to such an extent that many see them as *"slightly ahead of the rest,"* although still below the two London banking giants. The group has hired extensively during the year and is perceived to be *"a good crowd to deal with."* Moving into the top tier of individuals is *"number one man"* **Haydn Puleston Jones**. *"Relentless in his pursuit of perfection,"* he is a *"grinding, wonderful technician"* who some regard as the *"best draftsman in the City."* Other rated individuals include the *"serious"* **Robert Elliott**, who is also an insolvency player, and **John Tucker** *("has a great intellect,")* the global head of banking. As a whole, work for the lenders takes up around 60 percent of the practice's workload, yet owing to the firm's famed corporate capacity, borrowers tend to dominate in M&A-related financings (the firm advised Vodafone on corporate and financing issues for its Airtouch and Mannesmann bids.) In 1999, the team acted on 54 M&A related financings totalling $93.8 billion. The firm utilises the reach of its Alliance network to advise on cross-border financings, advising US and continental-based banks and venture capital houses. Deals this year for the lenders include advising HSBC on facilities provided to John Mansfield Group and Barclays Capital for the £1.05 billion takeover financing of Trinity plc prior to its merger with Mirror Group. On the borrower side, as well as the Vodafone financings, the team advised Jazz Telecom, a Spanish start-up telecoms provider, on a €300 million secured syndicated loan facility. **Clients:** Barclays Capital; Chase Manhattan; NatWest; ABN Amro; HSBC; Halifax; Dresdner Bank; Morgan Stanley; Credit Lyonnais; Lehman Brothers; Commerzbank; Anglo-American; Billiton; BP Amoco; British Telecom; Coca-Cola; Vodafone AirTouch.

Lovells The firm was dealt a body-blow this year with the untimely death of the popular head of UK-based banking, John Penson. *"Considered and pensive"* **Matthew Cottis** moves up a tier this year, his *"easy going, intelligent and understated approach"* being widely appreciated. The practice is seen to be *"excellent"* on MBOs and general acquisition finance and has an active retail banking and bank regulatory practice. High-profile deals this year include advising Merrill Lynch as bridge finance provider and Schroders and Merrill Lynch as financial advisers on the £1,160 million bid by Hicks Muse for United Biscuits plc. The team also represented Deutsche Bank on the £230 million financing of Pipetronix by Pipeline Integrity International. Other work includes advising new client, CIBC World Markets, on the £220m buyout of Thomson Directories by Apax Partners, acting for the Bank of Scotland on the £215 million buyout of PHS by Charterhouse and advising Dresdner Kleinwort Benson on the £114 million take-private of Sanderson Group plc by Alchemy Partners. **Clients:** Dresdner Kleinwort Benson; Bank of Scotland; Barclays; KBC Bank; EBRD; Prudential Bank; CSFB; Standard Bank; Barclays Capital Group.

Norton Rose The firm takes a 'precision bombing approach' to banking, concentrating resources on specific financial areas. Although the banking team is perceived to be a large one, it does not have the resources for 'commodity' (ie high volume) lending work. New to our rankings is the *"clever and able"* **Tim Polglase**, highly regarded for his *"technical and careful approach."* Concentrating on acquisition finance, he has the highest profile of a team which is a *"pleasure to work with."* Main areas of work include acquisition finance, bid financing and telecoms financing, with additional competence in trade finance, export credit work, sovereign and regulatory work. Perceived to be *"pulling the international side together,"* the finance team has a total of 40 banking partners around the world. Correspondingly, the proportion of international work is increasing. Complementary finance areas, such as asset finance and capital markets are flourishing, thereby boosting the banking practice. Transactions this year include advising banks on a £1.5 billion financing of TeleWest Communications Networks Ltd to finance ongoing expenses, a £585 million financing for Iliad 6 in relation to the acquisition of Zeneca and financing the acquisition of Hillsdown Holdings. The team additionally advised AXA on its recommended offer for GRE and acted on the £1.6 billion refinancing

Top Ten Syndicated Loans to UK Borrowers (July 1999 to June 2000)

#	Borrower	Mandated Arrangers	Loan Type	Purpose of Loan	Value US$million	Lawyers to the Borrowers	Lawyers to the Arrangers
1	Vodafone AirTouch plc	Bank of America, Barclays, Citibank NA, Goldman Sachs International Ltd, National Australia Bank Ltd, Royal Bank of Scotland plc, Toronto-Dominion Bank, UBS Warburg, WestLB	Revolving Credit	Merger with Mannesmann (Germany)	30,238.889	Linklaters	Allen & Overy
2	British Telecommunications plc	Barclays, Royal Bank of Scotland, Deutsche Bank AG, HSBC, Citibank NA, Lloyds TSB Capital Markets, Bank of Tokyo-Mitsubishi Ltd.	Revolving Credit	Various, including acquisition of UK 3G Licence 'C'	24,191.109	Linklaters	Clifford Chance
3	Unilever plc	ABN-AMRO Bank NV, Deutsche Bank AG, Goldman Sachs International, UBS Warburg	Revolving Credit	Merger with Best Foods (USA)	22,000.000	Slaughter and May	Allen & Overy
4	Granada Group	ABN-AMRO Bank NV, Bank of America, Barclays, Citibank NA, HSBC, Royal Bank of Scotland plc	Revolving Credit	Merger with Compass Group	7,594.168	Lovells	Clifford Chance
5	TIW UMTS UK Ltd. Guarantor: Hutchison Whampoa Ltd.	Chase Manhattan plc, HSBC	Revolving Credit	Acquisition of 3G Licence 'A'	7,000.000	Borrower: Cleary Gottlieb Steen & Hamilton Guarantor: Freshfields Bruckhaus Deringer	Linklaters
6	Orange plc	Chase Manhattan plc, CIBC World Markets, Dresdner Kleinwort Benson, HSBC	Revolving Credit	Acquisition of UK 3G Licence 'E'	5,521.376	Slaughter and May	Allen & Overy
7	Vodafone AirTouch plc	Barclays, Citibank NA, ABN-AMRO Bank NV, Bank of America, BNP Paribas, Deutsche Bank AG, Goldman Sachs International Ltd, HSBC, ING Barings, Lehman Brothers.	Revolving Credit	Merger with Airtouch (USA)	5,000.000	Linklaters	Allen & Overy
8	Scottish & Newcastle plc	Barclays, Royal Bank of Scotland plc, UBS Warburg	L/C Facility	Merger with Greenhalls	4,958.174	Linklaters	Allen & Overy
9	HSBC Holdings	HSBC	Revolving Credit	Merger with Credit Commercial (France)	4,000.000	Norton Rose	Allen & Overy
10	Powergen plc	Deutsche Bank AG, Dresdner Kleinwort Benson, HSBC, JP Morgan Securities Ltd, Warburg Dillon Read.	Revolving Credit	Acquisition of LG&E Energy (USA)	4,000.000	Freshfields Bruckhaus Deringer	Allen & Overy

Source: Syndicated Loans – Capital Data Loanware; Law Firms – Chambers & Partners

of Mercury Personal Communications. **Clients:** Chase Manhattan; HSBC; CIBC Wood Gundy; ANZ; Société Générale; ABN Amro; UBS; Deutsche; Lloyds TSB; RBS.

Slaughter and May The firm's specialist financiers **Richard Slater** and **Andrew Balfour** both continue to attract regular market plaudits. Balfour is regarded as a *"clever, knowledgeable and commercial lawyer,"* whilst Slater is simply *"excellent."* Whilst the corporate firm tag sticks to Slaughter's, the firm is also doing *"high quality"* and *"effective"* banking work. It is a testament to this ability that, although not perceived by peers to have the volume of the more banking-centric City firms, the team has nevertheless acted on some of the largest financings of the year, including acting for Telecom Italia's banks on the defence to Olivetti's takeover. Acting at the top end of acquisition finance work, the practice has also been involved on legal developments in the bank lending area, as part of the LMA's working group on loan agreements. The strength of the firm's domestic and international client base means that it has experience dealing at the highest end of acquisition finance deals. Large deals where the firm advised the banks include a €13 billion facility for KPN (for the E-Plus acquisition) and a €2.6 billion facility for companies within the Royal Numico Group. Major lending clients include JP Morgan, CSFB and ABN Amro. On the borrower side, the firm worked on raising £1 billion for Punch Taverns' bid for Allied Domecq's retailing business, and the firm has advised borrowers including British Steel, Huntsman and Mannesmann on financing activities. The firm also acts for the corporate treasury function of major corporates, including Diageo and Bunzl. Particularly strong on cross-discipline transactions, the team is regularly seen on tax-driven transactions. The firm is also noted for banking regulatory work, where the *"able and versatile"* **Ruth Fox** is well-known to the market. **Clients:** Dresdner Kleinwort Benson; Abbey National; Norwich Union; Tomkins.

Ashurst Morris Crisp The *"high-quality"* finance team is perceived to have *"clawed back some ground,"* and is now consolidating after recent departures. **Justin Spendlove** *"knows what he's doing,"* and was recommended as a *"broad-shouldered"* banking man. *"Top notch intellectual"* **Mark Vickers** impresses clients through his *"rolled-up sleeves approach"* and organisational skills. Although the team's quality is beyond dispute (particularly in European high-yield transactions,) it is not felt to have the broad international punch of some of its rivals. Felt to have a comparatively narrow banking focus, the firm is seen most frequently on the corporate side, acting for the predators on MBO transactions where the practice is deemed to be *"ultra-active."* Transactions include advising on National Express Group plc acquisitions and related financings of £750 million and acting for Imetal SA on its £750 million public bid for English China Clays plc. The team also advised Lehman Brothers as underwriter of the £745 million facilities in respect of the Candover-backed bid for Hillsdown Holdings. **Clients:** Merrill Lynch; Lehman Brothers; Paribas; Deutsche Bank; Alfred McAlpine plc; Bank of Scotland; RBS; SG; WestLB.

Denton Wilde Sapte The *"sensible"* and *"complementary"* merger between Denton Hall and Wilde Sapte has created one of the largest banking practices in the country. Although market perception is that the departure of big names (such as James Johnson) from the former Wilde Sapte is a setback, it is acknowledged that the merger provides a welcome boost in areas such as bank regulatory work and trade finance. Overall, observers predict that with a *"challenging year ahead of them,"* this *"strong team will respond."* The former Denton Hall's powerful international network (especially in Eastern Europe,) now gives the new firm one of the largest international networks of any operation. Although still felt to rely heavily on major client NatWest, the team has expanded its lender client base, and has offered advice on financing in areas such as telecoms, energy and the media. Transactions this year include acting for NatWest Acquisition Finance in relation to a refinancing facility for Bioglan Pharma plc, incorporating two loans totalling £40 million. The team also acted for the Bank of Scotland in relation to a £60 million loan facility for acquiring shares in Really Useful Holdings Ltd. On the borrower side, the department advised Ardagh plc on financing the acquisition of the glassware business of Rockware. **Clients:** CSFB; Citibank; Lloyds TSB; RBS; ABN Amro; J Sainsbury; National Westminster Bank; Morgan Stanley; SocGen; HSBC.

Herbert Smith On the strength of the deals it completed in 1999, this *"cruising"* banking practice is *"one to watch,"* as it gains a *"volume of work comparable to the traditional banking firms."* Internationally, the practice's profile is increasing, following its advice on financing aspects of the Olivetti/Telecom Italia and BoS/NatWest take-over bids and the BSKH and Time Warner/EMI link-ups. The banking practice has increased its turnover fourfold in as many years, and although more recognised for its borrower profile, has developed its lending client base. With all-round debt financiers in the banking practice, the team has advised groups such as Chase Manhattan and Barclays on a range of banking, property and projects financial work. Private equity groups also make up some of the practice's client base and the firm has worked on a number of public-to-privates in the last year. On the borrower side, the firm has advised BSkyB on a number of financing matters. Only the absence of a recognised big-hitter mars an otherwise rosy picture. **Clients:** Bank of Tokyo Mitsubishi; Bank of Scotland; Chase Manhattan; Barclays.

Shearman & Sterling With a UK:US lawyer ratio of 2:1, the firm has a leading reputation as an arranger of mixed US/UK law financings. The firm's leading US high yield capital markets expertise can also be found in London, which it has combined with UK bank debt proficiency to create what is arguably London's leading leveraged financing practice. The strength of this *"big buy out"* capability sees the team move up a band this year. *"Smooth client man"* **Stephen Mostyn-Williams** is known as *"an effective, high-impact lawyer."* His team is felt to have *"the potential to make the big time,"* having *"built one of the best launch pads."* However, the team's relatively narrow focus means that it is less active on standard transactions, where it has not yet threatened the dominance of the traditional City firms. The practice has acted on a number of multi-jurisdictional financings, straight private equity group acquisitions and public-to-private deals. The London office worked on a number of the largest European LBOs of 1999. **Clients:** DLJ; Goldman Sachs; Morgan Stanley; Merrill Lynch; WDR.

CMS Cameron McKenna A *"busy"* firm known for its PFI strengths, its banking team is regarded as a *"jack of all trades."* Whilst some commentators stress the Lloyds TSB connection which has given the firm a *"high street tag,"* others are adamant that the firm does *"much more than high street work."* The practice has been active in acquisition finance, advising venture capital houses and large lenders such as RBS. Although the firm as a whole has concentrated on international expansion, the banking practice has predominantly been active on UK-based transactions. General market consensus is that the firm's strengthening focus on leasing and projects has led to a diminution of the firm's pure banking profile. The practice has been active in the sale and purchase of loan portfolios, and in finance as a whole has been increasing its consumer finance, capital markets and e-banking profiles. Other work has seen the firm advise on new loan and security documentation for the merged Lloyds TSB Bank. **Clients:** RBS; National Australia Bank; First Union Bank; Lloyds TSB.

Macfarlanes A broad banking practice which has a reputation for *"quality people,"* including the well regarded **Mark Furman**. The firm has property finance, trade finance and acquisition finance capabilities. Generally acting for borrowers, the team has a large lending client base in property and trade finance. The firm has also been active for venture capital houses in areas such as advertising, PR and the hotel industry. Transactions this year include advising Saint-Gobain in its £1.1 billion financing for the take-over of Meyer International plc, and acting on the €800 million MBO of Groupe Danone's Glasspack division for CVC Capital Partners. Other work has seen the practice advising on general lending for RBS, and for borrowers such as JD Wetherspoon and members of the Virgin Group. **Clients:** Westdeutsche Landesbank, Rheinhyp, Barclays, 3i Group plc, ING.

Simmons & Simmons Using its international and capital markets strengths the firm has continued to be seen on high yield work and has consequently been active in cross-border leveraged loans. Seen to advise on a *"nice blend"* of bank debt and capital markets work. Historically known for doing a *"good job for the borrower,"* the year has seen a stronger focus on lending clients (with regular work for around 15 banks) which has consequently seen the growth of banking as a practice area within the firm. Internationally, the firm has been involved in bank restructuring work for the Bank of Latvia. The group has been seen more frequently on *"problem loans than mainstream transactions."* However, the capital markets ability has been combined with banking in the European high-yield market where the practice often works on transactions in conjunction with Fried, Frank, Harris, Shriver & Jacobson of the US. Nevertheless the market is generally upbeat about a banking practice which is seen to have *"a platform for the future."* **Clients:** Barclays Bank; Railtrack; Bank of Latvia; CSFB; Bank of China; NatWest.

Taylor Joynson Garrett A *"sound finance practice,"* with *"sensible ambitions,"* the team is seen to be going places in banking, to the point where some market observers see them *"moving up within a couple of years."* They are *"very good at what they do."* This encompasses a mixture of projects, advisory property finance and more mainstream corporate financings. The property finance side and MBO practice (on the management side) were particularly noted by the market. Financing in the context of telecoms, IP and e-commerce are growing areas. **Clients:** BHF-Bank AG; MeesPierson; Barclays; Citibank; Halifax; Lloyds TSB; Anglo-Irish Bank.

Travers Smith Braithwaite Perceived to be dependent on the firm's corporate reputation, the banking team has been more active on the borrower side. A versatile team which *"man-for-man can match the best,"* but operates on a much less exalted scale than the market leaders. High-profile deals are to be found in acquisition finance, such as the financing for NTL's £3 billion acquisition of the consumer division of Cable & Wireless, and in specialised areas such as securitisation. The practice is also known for its property finance capabilities, an area in which *"they know what they're doing."* **Clients:** RBS; Helaba; Bank of Scotland; Barclays; Charterhouse Bank; HypoVereinsbank; Candover; 3i Group.

Weil Gotshal & Manges The US firm has an established reputation in capital markets, which it has combined with its banking practice to good effect in high-yield and senior debt financings. The firm is recognised as *"increasingly influential,"* and is seen as *"aggressive and hungry."* However, the departure of Maurice Allen to White & Case, on top of last year's loss of Sean Pierce could undermine the firm's efforts to challenge the London leaders. The practice is seen to be making ground on acquisition finance work, particularly in telecoms, although it is felt to lack the corporate and tax back-up of its leading competitors. The team advised Hicks Muse Tate & Furst on the £1.26 billion offer for United Biscuits, then one of the largest ever public-to-private buy-outs. **Clients:** Chase Manhattan; Hicks Muse Tate & Furst; Bank of America; Deutsche Bank.

Baker & McKenzie In its niche of multi-jurisdictional financings, it is difficult to match this team, whose London bread and butter is multi-jurisdictional acquisition financings. Large deals, such as Japan Tobacco's acquisition of RJR Nabisco's tobacco business, are run out of the London office which has now become the largest office in the firm. The practice works for borrowers more than lenders, including venture capital houses such as Apax, for whom it has worked on continental deals. Seen on tax-based financings, telecoms and trade-related financings. Deals include advising on financing the acquisition of BTR Paper by Xerium SA. **Clients:** Credit Suisse; Apax Partners; Standard Bank; Telecom Italia; Nortel.

Berwin Leighton On the financial side, the firm is known for its property finance expertise, an area where the market rates them especially highly. Other areas of activity are media and film finance and general acquisition finance, working for an even mix of borrowers and lenders. Major transactions include advising Nationsbank on the English law aspects of financing Wal-Mart's $10 billion take-over of Asda. **Clients:** Barclays; Bank of Nova Scotia; Banca Nazionale del Lavoro; ABSA Bank; Helaba Landesbank.

DLA Seen on acquisition finance transactions, the firm's practice is perceived to *"punch below its weight"* due to the loss of leading players to other City firms. However, the firm has a strong presence in private equity, and the London team is known for its good relationships with the UK venture capital community. The team *"has handled deals well under testing circumstances."* Deals include acting for the syndicate led by Chase Manhattan in the restructuring of £300 million of facilities to the Derby Cycle Corporation. MBOs/MBIs continue to be a strength, with the firm advising the debt providers on MBOs such as those of the Denby Group, Warner Howard plc, the Wyko Group, Apollo Metals plc, The Aspen Group, Bertram Books and Salehurst plc. **Clients:** Chase Manhattan; Barclays Bank plc; Newcourt Financial; RBS; HSBC Private Equity; AIB; Paribas.

Gouldens Accounting for around ten percent of the firm's total turnover, the banking practice of the *"highly profitable, fantastic mid-tier firm"* is gaining a higher profile in conjunction with the firm's M&A practice. The firm does a mix of borrower and lending work and acts in the mainstream banking markets. The practice is viewed by the market as being *"corporate-led,"* in addition to having a rated property finance team. Transactions include advising Bankers Trust in relation to the US$2.1 billion financing of Huntsman Corporation's acquisition of some of ICI's chemical interests. Also acted on a £120 million facility prior to Delancey Estates' bid for Milner Estates plc. **Clients:** Delancey Estates; London Forfaiting Company; ABN Amro; Chase Manhattan.

Stephenson Harwood Working primarily for lenders, the team consists of a broad range of banking specialists. The team also works on trade, projects and recovery and insolvency matters. Main clients are the London branches of Continental and South African banks. While the team has suffered some departures, it still has strength in acquisition finance and recovery/insolvency work. Seen less on mainstream banking than previously, trade finance and e-commerce are now growth areas for the firm. The firm acted for Dresdner Kleinwort Benson on a £90 million financing for Cobham plc. **Clients:** BSCH; BNP; Deutsche Hypo; HSBC; RBS; Fortis; ANZ; EBRD; Bank of Scotland.

Theodore Goddard A team which has gained a reputation for its *"user friendly, practical"* attitude and its *"get on with it"* approach. The majority of the team's work is for lenders, though the team also works for large corporate borrowers such as Halifax, Flagship and Vosper Thorneycroft. The finance reputation is stronger for PFI, construction and property financing than for more mainstream banking. The practice advises NatWest on structured and specialised financing, often acting on university financings. With strong continental banking clients, the practice has seen an increase in international work. **Clients:** Abbey National; Commerzbank; Credit Lyonnais; Anglo-Irish; Bayerische; Bank of Nova Scotia; Orix; Dai-Ichi Kangyo Bank; Paribas.

Watson, Farley & Williams Although its primary reputation lies in ship, trade and asset finance, the banking practice is said to be *"spreading and growing"* away from this focus to cover a broader range. Trade finance has been busy, and the practice has been involved on a large number of cross-border financings in this area. The practice has advised US and French banks and borrowers on trade finance and MTN programmes. **Clients:** Chase Manhattan; Citibank; RBS; Vivendi; AES; P&O Nedlloyd.

Other Notable Practitioners

"Super, classic banking man" **Maurice Allen**, formerly with Weil Gotshal & Manges, has moved with some of his banking team to international firm White & Case. He has a particular reputation for acquisition finance expertise.

THE SOUTH & SOUTH WEST

BANKING • South & South West	Ptnrs	Assts
❶ **Burges Salmon** Bristol	2	5
Osborne Clarke OWA Bristol, Reading	7	9
❷ **Bond Pearce** Plymouth, Bristol, Southampton	3	5
❸ **CMS Cameron McKenna** Bristol	3	6
❹ **Blake Lapthorn** Southampton, Fareham	4	–
Lester Aldridge Bournemouth	5	4

LEADING INDIVIDUALS	
❶ **FORBES Sandra** Burges Salmon	**JEFFRIES Graham** Bond Pearce
KINSEY Julian Bond Pearce	**WILTSHIRE Peter** CMS Cameron McKenna
UP AND COMING	
LEEMING Richard Burges Salmon	

Within each band, firms are listed alphabetically. See **Profiles** on page 116

Burges Salmon *"They divide the market with Osborne Clarke."* **Sandra Forbes** maintains her reputation as a top flight banking lawyer, with **Richard Leeming** also recommended for his *"technical ability"* and for *"getting the deal done."* The banking practice is considered to be a team which *"can deliver."* Up to half of the practice's work is sourced from London, and it is growing its lenders' client base. Core work is acquisition finance where the firm works for an even mix of borrowers and lenders. The team is also active in asset finance, trade finance, treasury work and property finance. Work this year includes acting for FirstGroup plc on a £850 million multi-option syndicated facility arranged by Warburg Dillon Read, advising AIB Capital Markets on a £13.6 million MBI, and advising lenders and borrowers on funding activities. **Clients:** Nationwide; Standard Chartered; FirstGroup; Bank of Scotland; Citibank NA; Lloyds TSB.

Osborne Clarke OWA The retirement of Margaret Childs has brought new blood into the Bristol office, and recent recruitment has seen a strengthening of the Reading office. Acquisition finance is the practice's bread and butter, working for senior lenders as well as management and venture capital companies (the firm has a strong corporate practice.) Involved in property, corporate restructuring and insolvency. Appreciated for its *"proactive attitude,"* the team is seen to be *"pulling in the higher grade work"* with the help of the London office. **Clients:** Bank of Scotland; NatWest; Lloyds TSB; Barclays Bank; 3i Group; Hypo Vereinsbank; Close Brothers.

Bond Pearce *"Very much a regional firm, top in the wider South West,"* with a solid presence in Bristol, Southampton and Plymouth. The Bristol office is focused on lenders, whereas Southampton, with its strong corporate practice, has a more even borrower-lender client base. The *"sensible"* **Graham Jeffries** is regarded as *"Southampton's banking lawyer."* **Julian Kinsey** in Bristol spends half his time on acquisition finance, and also works on general lending, development finance and restructuring. MBO work includes acting for the funders on a £9 million acquisition of Hammer Distribution Ltd and a £30 million acquisition of a nationwide motor dealership. **Clients:** Bank of Scotland; Fortis; Lloyds TSB; Nationwide; PSA Wholesale Ltd.

CMS Cameron McKenna Traditionally big in insolvency, the practice has been *"generally boosting its corporate profile"* which has brought an increased role in banking. **Peter Wiltshire** is a *"recognised name,"* straddling the line between insolvency and banking. Lloyds TSB is still perceived as the firm's number one client. **Clients:** Lloyds TSB.

Blake Lapthorn Developing a lending client base, the practice is enlarging its Southampton presence, where it is already well regarded, and from where it is active on local and London-sourced transactions. The year has seen an increase in business for the banking team in both corporate lending and property finance. Work this year includes a £60 million refinancing for a borrower. **Clients:** Bank of Scotland; RBS; HSBC; NatWest; Lloyds TSB; 3i.

Lester Aldridge The firm has a respected profile in the region, working on mainstream lending, corporate recovery work and general banking. It continues to provide advice to local, national and overseas banks on lending and other financial transactions. This has included the setting up of a community bank in Portsmouth. **Clients:** Lloyds Bank Commercial Services; Coutts & Co; Bank of Ireland.

WALES

BANKING • Wales	Ptnrs	Assts
❶ **Eversheds** Cardiff	8	10
❷ **Edwards Geldard** Cardiff	5	-
Morgan Cole Cardiff	6	8

LEADING INDIVIDUALS
❶ **VAUGHAN Philip** Eversheds
❷ **MORGAN Meryl** Morgan Cole

Within each band, firms are listed alphabetically. See **Profiles** on page 116

Eversheds With the lion's share of local work, Eversheds' banking practice stands out in Cardiff. A significant amount of the practice's work is non-local, mainly London-sourced. **Philip Vaughan** maintains his quality reputation. The team embraces a broad practice including general banking, MBO and standard documentation work. Work this year includes acting for Investec on a £21 million acquisition finance facility, acting for a major national insurance company on a £350 million financing transaction and advising Bank of Wales on the MBO of Atlantic Technology. **Clients:** Abbey National; Bank of Scotland; Lloyds TSB; Legal & General; Bank of Wales; Barclays; Deutsche Hypo Bank; Investec Bank.

Edwards Geldard The banking practice is active in acquisition and project finance, working for the region's main clearing banks. Transactions this year include financing a £6 million manufacturing MBO and a £7.5 million acquisition in the brewing sector. **Clients:** Main local clearing banks and corporates.

Morgan Cole A general practice, working on mainstream secured lending work, property finance and acquisition finance, with deals in the range of £10-15 million. Work for an even mix of lenders and borrowers. **Meryl Morgan** is well regarded locally and nationally. Work includes acting for RBS on a fund set aside to develop health care centres, and working on MBOs and MBIs in industries including hi-tech and automobiles. **Clients:** HSBC; RBS; Lloyds TSB; Barclays Bank; Bank of Wales; Bank of Ireland.

MIDLANDS

BANKING • Midlands	Ptnrs	Assts
❶ **Pinsent Curtis** Birmingham	7	7
Wragge & Co Birmingham	4	18
❷ **Eversheds** Birmingham, Nottingham	5	20
❸ **Gateley Wareing** Birmingham	3	9
Martineau Johnson Birmingham	2	2
❹ **DLA** Birmingham	2	3
Hammond Suddards Edge Birmingham	1	2
❺ **Browne Jacobson** Nottingham	4	8
Shoosmiths Northampton	6	1

LEADING INDIVIDUALS	
❶ **BAKER Ian** Martineau Johnson	**COOKE David** Pinsent Curtis
JOHNSTONE Pat Eversheds	**MADDEN Andrew** Gateley Wareing
PALLETT Julian Wragge & Co	**TWIST Patrick** Pinsent Curtis
❷ **ALTON Philip** Garretts	**BRIERLEY Chris** Wragge & Co
MILES Stephen Pinsent Curtis	**WOOLCOCK Brian** DLA
UP AND COMING	
BROADFIELD Alice Eversheds	

Within each band, firms are listed alphabetically. *See **Profiles** on page 116*

Pinsent Curtis Excellent reputation in banking is ascribed to the *"size and quality of the team."* The *"intellectual"* **David Cooke** works in acquisition finance, general lending and restructuring. *"Gentlemanly"* **Patrick Twist** is *"focused and technically able,"* and peers have the highest respect for his team, which also handles PFI work. Younger partner **Stephen Miles** is new to our lists this year following strong market recommendation for his *"commercial and committed"* MBO work. Public-to-privates this year include Pemberstone plc and Epwin Group. The practice works mainly for large regional lenders, but also advises borrowers in conjunction with a strong corporate team. Over half the team's work has a London element, such as an £85 million financing for BSS Group by HSBC and a £183.5 million bond issue and senior debt refinancing. The firm also works on legal opinions for US-based and other foreign clients. **Clients:** HSBC; Barclays; NatWest.

Wragge & Co The banking team is highly rated for its *"hands-on, co-operative"* approach. The firm works on City-generated, national and international deals from its Birmingham base, for a mixed base of borrowers and lenders. Corporate lending (including acquisition finance) takes up a third of the practice's time, with restructuring and insolvency taking a third and property and projects the remainder. Within pure banking, the bulk of work is in acquisition finance, where **Chris Brierley** has a solid reputation. Seen more by the market on the insolvency side, **Julian Pallett** also maintains his high reputation in banking, bringing *"practical solutions to the table."* The team acted for the Nationwide Building Society on the £66 million refinancing of the public-to private buy-out of Pemberstone. **Clients:** HSBC; Lloyds TSB; RBS; Caterpillar; DaimlerChrysler Capital Services; NatWest; Nationwide.

Eversheds The team has taken on new assistants this year, and is viewed as having *"done well,"* becoming *"more prominent"* this year. Works for an even mix of borrowers and lenders, mainly on acquisition finance, including buy-outs and public-to-privates (such as the £128 million take-private of Wyko Group.) **Pat Johnstone** is the *"leading figure"* in the banking team, which also includes the *"effective"* **Alice Broadfield**, an associate who moves into our lists this year, following sustained market support. Property and IT-related finance are growing areas of transactional strength. Deals this year include working on the provision of £50 million of facilities to AEA Technology and for the banks on a £90 million facility for Aggregate Industries. **Clients:** Bank of Scotland; NatWest; HSBC; RBS.

Gateley Wareing Having built up a banking practice around private equity and SMEs, the firm is seen to be doing *"some fine work."* In the last year the practice has typically been involved on £40-50 million deals in acquisition and property finance. **Andrew Madden** was singled out for praise as a *"superb, proactive and genuine deal-maker."* His *"all-round skills"* and *"sensible"* approach are appreciated by lawyers and clients alike. **Clients:** Major UK clearing banks; Allied Irish Bank; Clydesdale Bank.

Martineau Johnson The practice's work is split 70 percent for lenders and 30 percent for borrowers. The *"cerebral"* **Ian Baker** is seen to be *"confident and technically able."* Main spheres of activity are property finance, which takes up around a third of the practice's time, and acquisition finance, which takes up around two-thirds. Involved on high value deals this year, transactions include buy-outs close to £20 million for major banks, as well as restructuring facilities and revolving credit facilities around the £40-50 million mark. **Clients:** Bank of Scotland; RBS; NatWest; HSBC; Lloyds TSB.

DLA The firm has been involved on a wide range of transactions this year, including public-to-privates, development lending, general lending and invoice discounting. Although the national (particularly London) and international offices have aided the Birmingham practice's workload, the team is *"still to make serious inroads into the local market." "Details man"* **Brian Woolcock** leads the banking team, and is known for his property financing expertise. Advised the banks on debt raising for the Wyko and Symonds public-to-privates. **Clients:** Bank of Scotland; RBS; Bank of New York; Barclays.

Hammond Suddards Edge Perceived to be *"less visible"* this year, the firm's London lawyers have been seen more than their Birmingham counterparts on local transactions. The firm has brought a full time partner and assistant from London to bolster its team here. A strong corporate buy-out team has meant that the banking side has been active on buy-out financing for borrowers, and has also been active in senior debt on the lender side, as well as in consumer finance. Large deals this year include a £120 million syndicated loan for T&S Stores for its acquisition of One Stop, and a €51 million facility to ACM Wood Chemicals plc. **Clients:** Barclays Bank; Lloyds TSB; RBS; Bank of Scotland.

Browne Jacobson Viewed as *"a player in the East Midlands,"* following some high profile hiring, the firm has made *"great progress"* and accordingly enters our rankings this year. Works principally in acquisition finance and general corporate lending, including property finance. A dedicated banking team singles the practice out in Nottingham, and the firm works for local and London-based banks, including branches of overseas banks. **Clients:** Regional banks.

Shoosmiths Seen occasionally by their Birmingham counterparts, the firm's centre in Northampton operates across the spectrum of banking transactions, in which they have a reputation for competence. Working largely for lenders, the firm also acts for borrowers on acquisition finance deals. **Clients:** Nationwide.

Other Notable Practitioners **Philip Alton** of Garretts received market recommendation for his general finance work, and clearly stands out at his department.

EAST ANGLIA

BANKING • East Anglia	Ptnrs	Assts
❶ **Eversheds** Cambridge, Norwich, Ipswich	3	10
❷ **Mills & Reeve** Cambridge, Norwich	5	7

LEADING INDIVIDUALS
❶ **CROOME Andrew** Eversheds

Within each band, firms are listed alphabetically. *See **Profiles** on page 116*

Eversheds With dedicated resources and the ability to shuffle these between Norwich, Ipswich and Cambridge, the firm has the region's leading banking practice. **Andrew Croome** maintains his high-profile reputation. Noted for its property finance capabilities, the team acted for NHP plc on a fixed-rate asset-backed bond issue in November 1999. **Clients:** Bank of Scotland; Barclays; Norwich and Peterborough Building Society.

Mills & Reeve Members of the firm work on banking transactions from their corporate and property bases. Active across a range of financial transactions, including acquisition finance and refinancings. **Clients:** Lloyds TSB; Barclays; NatWest.

NORTH WEST

BANKING • North West	Ptnrs	Assts
❶ **DLA** Manchester, Liverpool	2	11
Eversheds Manchester	1	3
Halliwell Landau Manchester	3	2
❷ **Addleshaw Booth & Co** Manchester	*	*
❸ **Chaffe Street** Manchester	3	2
❹ **Cobbetts** Manchester	2	8
Davies Wallis Foyster Liverpool, Manchester	2	2
Garretts Manchester	6	10
Hammond Suddards Edge Manchester	1	1
❺ **Kuit Steinart Levy** Manchester	3	3

LEADING INDIVIDUALS	
❶ **DALE Nigel** Eversheds	**WHATNALL John** Halliwell Landau
WOOLLEY Simon DLA	
❷ **LUMSDEN Christopher** Chaffe Street	**MOLLOY Susan** Halliwell Landau
REARDEN Shaun Chaffe Street	

Within each band, firms are listed alphabetically. *See **Profiles** on page 116*

* *See editorial entries for explanations of team sizes.*

DLA Seen to be the *"most active"* in the market, *"you can't avoid"* the firm's broad Manchester-Liverpool coverage. Acting almost exclusively for banks, the firm has cornered most of the largest deals in the market this year. These transactions include a £173 million debt deal for RBS, one of the largest of the year to date. The firm has made a steady push in acquisition finance, where **Simon Woolley**'s team is admired for producing a *"quality product."* Woolley's *"diplomatic"* approach means that he *"invariably gets good results."* Deals this year include a £68 million IBO, a £180 million acquisition financing in sports retail, a £47 million acquisition facility for purchase of Everest double glazing and various restructurings and refinancings. **Clients:** Bank of Scotland; Barclays Bank; HSBC; NatWest; RBS; Co-operative Bank.

Eversheds In acquisition finance, the firm is considered to be *"neck and neck"* with DLA. The team works mainly for lenders, but also has a substantial borrower practice. The *"excellent"* **Nigel Dale** maintains his reputation and is seen to have an *"aggressive"* approach. He is *"great at fighting his corner."* Deals include advising Barclays on a £56 million financing to Genus plc, acting for FKI plc on a £350 million syndication and for Bank of Scotland on the MBO of Pennine Computers. The practice covers a broad range of finance, including acquisition finance, large value syndications and property finance. **Clients:** Barclays; Bank of Scotland; BBA Group plc; HSBC; Co-operative Bank plc.

Halliwell Landau Bolstered by the arrival of **Sue Molloy** from Garretts, the team is perceived to have *"moved ahead,"* and rises in the rankings this year. They have *"caught up in their ability to do the deals,"* but the market warns that this is *"the year they consolidate their place."* The *"likeable"* **John Whatnall**, the *"third musketeer"* of Manchester acquisition finance, is regarded by some as *"probably the brightest lawyer in town."* The team is, however, occasionally seen as a little top-heavy. A large part of the firm's practice is in acquisition finance, for an even mix of lenders and borrowers, and it also works on property finance and capital markets transactions. Highlight deals include acting for NatWest on a £70 million acquisition and restructuring, and advising on the restructuring of Birse Group's bond facilities from Zurich Insurance Company. **Clients:** NatWest; Bank of Scotland; Co-operative Bank plc; RBS; Anglo Irish Bank; Lloyds TSB.

Addleshaw Booth & Co (13 partners, 19 assistants across Manchester and Leeds) Although perceived to have lost some momentum recently, the firm has spent time on reinforcing the Manchester banking practice, which, it is felt, will *"bring the practice back into the fray."* Perceived as *"deal-doers,"* the market outside Manchester still views the practice as a leading one *("they have an unparalleled and institutional reputation,")* respected for mainstream banking work. It is felt though, to lack an outstanding individual. The practice has been active in treasury, housing association, restructurings and building society work as well as in pure banking. Transactional highlights include an £18 million IBI acting for the banks and a £75 million acquisition financing, acting for the buyer. **Clients:** 3i plc; Barclays Bank; Clydesdale Bank; HSBC; Co-operative Bank plc.

Chaffe Street Perceived as a niche practice, with a leading reputation in asset finance and insolvency, the practice is not seen so often on mainstream banking deals, being involved on large and more esoteric transactions. It is however seen as a banking team which has *"made strides,"* and is *"becoming a force."* **Chris Lumsden** maintains his reputation, though his fame lies more in asset finance. *"Bright lad"* **Shaun Rearden** is also a recommended practitioner. The practice is involved in property and acquisition finance, large MBOs and disposals, working mainly for banks, both inside and outside the region. Transactions include advising Bank of Scotland on the funding of the MBO of Caledonia Motor Group. **Clients:** NM Rothschild; NatWest; Adam & Co; Bank of Scotland; RBS.

Cobbetts One of the four units of the firm's finance team (the other units being corporate recovery, litigation and mortgages,) the banking team concentrates on corporate lending and security work, and is also involved in acquisition finance and regulatory work. Tend to work more for lenders than borrowers. The firm is considered strong in property finance, an area where it has been active in housing association and development finance fields, and it has picked up building society work during the year. **Clients:** Lloyds TSB; Bank of Scotland; RBS; Britannia Building Society; AIB.

Davies Wallis Foyster The team covers acquisition finance, core banking and property finance. With a solid presence in Liverpool, where the practice has *"more than its fair share of work,"* the firm is now increasing its profile in Manchester. The firm works less on straightforward transactional work than on restructurings and refinancings, asset finance and more esoteric deals. **Clients:** Lloyds TSB; Bank of Scotland (including Capital Bank;) RBS; NatWest; Rothschilds.

Garretts Perceived by some in the market to have suffered due to recent departures, particularly that of Sue Molloy. However, the firm still has a local reputation for acquisition finance, property finance and structured finance instruments. The team has provided advice on secured facilities for a number of leading financial institutions. **Clients:** Manchester Building Society; NatWest.

Hammond Suddards Edge A pan-Pennine banking practice, the Leeds component is considered to overshadow the Manchester practice. The Manchester team is developing, following a recent recruitment drive, and is becoming more prominent. Working for an even mix of borrowers and lenders, the practice is principally active in acquisition finance. Amongst other transactions, the team worked for the lenders on a £76 million facilities for the MBO of Amtrak Ltd and, later in the year, £61.25 million in facilities to Amtrak for an acquisition. **Clients:** RBS; Bank of Scotland; Barclays; Lloyds TSB; NatWest; NM Rothschild.

Kuit Steinart Levy Small banking practice which enters our lists this year. They are not viewed as banking specialists, yet are generally seen as *"excellent"* and are best known for their long-term relationship with Lloyds TSB. Focus on the SME market, with a typical deal range between £1-2 million and £15 million. The banking side is now picking larger work for lenders and is also active in the property finance market. **Clients:** RBS; AIB; Anglo-Irish; MCFC.

YORKSHIRE

BANKING • Yorkshire	Ptnrs	Assts
❶ **Addleshaw Booth & Co** Leeds	*	*
❷ **Hammond Suddards Edge** Leeds	1	3
❸ **Eversheds** Leeds	5	6
❹ **DLA** Leeds	3	5
Pinsent Curtis Leeds	3	5
Walker Morris Leeds	7	14

LEADING INDIVIDUALS	
❶ **CHIDLEY Mark** Addleshaw Booth & Co	
MITCHELL Patrick Hammond Suddards Edge	
❷ **DAY Sarah** DLA	**GOSNAY Andrew** Pinsent Curtis
HOPKINS Stephen Eversheds	**PAPWORTH Richard** Addleshaw Booth & Co
❸ **AKITT Ian** Walker Morris	**CLELAND John** Pinsent Curtis
SMITH Mark DLA	**TAYLOR Michael** Walker Morris
UP AND COMING	
OWEN Simon Eversheds	

Within each band, firms are listed alphabetically. *See **Profiles** on page 116*

** See editorial entries for explanations of team sizes.*

Addleshaw Booth & Co (13 partners, 19 assistants across Leeds and Manchester) *"The best all-round team."* With trans-Pennine strength and an office in London, the firm is now more of a national player. Relationships with such clients as Yorkshire Bank and 3i Group ensure that the firm is still seen as dominant in the Leeds market for *"general"* banking work. However, market perception is that local rivals Hammond Suddards Edge have caught up in acquisition finance. With 3i less dominant in acquisition finance in Leeds, the firm has been doing more recent work on the lending side. Other major banking areas include property finance, Housing Association finance, building society and treasury and capital markets work, where the firm works principally for issuers. *"Delight of a bloke"* **Mark Chidley** is back permanently in the Leeds office after a brief spell in London. Although perceived to be more managerial (he is the national head of the banking and finance group,) he is *"outstanding,"* having *"experience and technical competence,"* and is viewed as someone who *"will deliver the deal." "Hyper-intelligent"* **Richard Papworth** is a banking all-rounder who maintains his reputation as a *"details man."* Significant deals include a £76 million public-to-private, acting on the lending side, a €625 million eurobond issue for Kelda Group plc and a £250 million social housing portfolio acquisition. **Clients:** Yorkshire Bank; NatWest; NM Rothschild; Barclays; Bank of Scotland; RBS; 3i Group plc; Bradford & Bingley.

Hammond Suddards Edge Regarded as *"top in acquisition finance."* The firm's premier reputation in acquisition finance is seen to rest squarely on the shoulders of the *"exceptional"* **Patrick Mitchell** – *"he's the mover and shaker." "Respected, if not feared,"* clients are *"glad to have him on board"* and he is regarded by peers as the *"strongest competition."* The firm is involved in housing association, reconstruction and property finance work, working for banks, building societies and corporates. Among a number of transactions, major public-to-privates include those of S.Lyles and of the Adscene Group plc (the last for £75.4 million.) **Clients:** RBS; Bank of Scotland; Barclays; Lloyds TSB; Co-operative Bank; NatWest.

Eversheds A team with a broad spread of banking expertise, the practice's work ranges from corporate treasury matters to Muslim banking products. In finance the firm is known more for its PFI work, but the banking side is seen as a *"cracking general practice which knows what it's doing."* Areas of activity have included property and telecoms financing, and e-commerce business. The *"charismatic"* **Stephen Hopkins** has a corporate background and his *"technical skills"* are appreciated, especially on the equity side of deals. Younger partner **Simon Owen** is regarded as a *"steady operator"* and moves into our lists as an up and coming individual. Work this year includes advising on the funding of the £320 million take-private of Evans of Leeds and acting for Peterhouse Group in its acquisitions. **Clients:** NatWest; Peterhouse Group plc; Fortis Bank; HSBC; Lloyds TSB.

DLA The *"wonderful"* **Sarah Day** moves up our lists following strong market recommendation, while *"easy going"* **Mark Smith** maintains his reputation, and is especially visible on property finance work. Typical acquisition finance transactions range between £40-100 million. The firm is also active in other areas such as property finance, structured finance and securitisation. A regular stream of work also comes from Barclays and Bank of Scotland. Work this year includes acting on debt financing for the banks and acting for Paramount Hotels in a £110 million refinancing. **Clients:** Halifax; Norwich Union; Barclays; Lloyds TSB; Deutsche; Bank of Scotland.

Pinsent Curtis The Leeds banking practice is seen less in general banking and acquisition finance work than in esoteric, higher value deals, working on large derivatives transactions and tax-driven financings. On acquisition finance, the firm tends to work more for the banks than the borrowers, acting for a number of leading national lenders. Joining the *"able"* **Andrew Gosnay** in our lists is *"good operator"* **John Cleland**. Last year, the team advised on over 100 transactions, with a total value of £6 billion, the deals including the £20 million Brown Shipley acquisition. **Clients:** Bradford & Bingley; Skipton Building Society; HSBC; NatWest; Barclays; HSBC; BoS; RBS; BPT plc.

Walker Morris *"Watch this space."* Seen on *"less straightforward"* structures, the firm has been involved in a wide range of transactions this year. The highly rated **Michael Taylor** splits his time between banking and insolvency work, with new partner **Ian Akitt** (previously head of banking at Garretts) being active on acquisition finance deals. Deals have included a £125 million eurobond transaction for Cattles plc, distressed debt work and legal documentation for a northern building society setting up an e-banking site. More traditional work has seen the practice involved on around twenty MBO/MBI transactions, on senior debt financings and on property financings. While tending to work more for the lender, supporting the firm's active corporate group has also meant a busy year advising the borrower. **Clients:** RBS; Bank of Scotland; Lloyds TSB; Barclays; Halifax; Yorkshire Bank.

NORTH EAST

BANKING • North East	Ptnrs	Assts
❶ **Dickinson Dees** Newcastle upon Tyne	4	5
❷ **Eversheds** Newcastle upon Tyne	5	6
Ward Hadaway Newcastle upon Tyne	1	1
❸ **Robert Muckle** Newcastle-upon-Tyne	2	-

LEADING INDIVIDUALS	
❶ **HARKER Chris** Dickinson Dees	
❷ **HARRISON Julie** Ward Hadaway	
❸ **KIRTLEY Deborah** Dickinson Dees	**ON Nicholas** Eversheds

Within each band, firms are listed alphabetically. *See **Profiles** on page 116*

Dickinson Dees *"Broad, strong and dominant."* Full time banking lawyer **Deborah Kirtley** enters our lists this year following market recommendation. *"Amiable and approachable"* **Chris Harker** is seen as more of an all-rounder, but is widely regarded as *"probably the most experienced"* in Newcastle. The practice deals for a majority of lending clients, although a strong corporate capacity brings in the borrower work which has enabled the practice to gain solid acquisition finance experience. Have acted on a broad and substantial range of transactions this year, including the £51 million securitisation for the re-development of St James' Park, following earlier participation in a £50 million facility for the same purposes. **Clients:** Barclays; Bank of Scotland; Northern Rock; 3i Group; Newcastle Building Society.

Eversheds **Nick On**, who enters the tables this year, is the full-time banking lawyer in this team. An acquisition finance specialist, he *"stands out for his commercial and pragmatic approach."* Property finance work, however, provides the bulk of the team's caseload. The firm is considered to act on a large part of the enterprise zone market. A brand name nationally, 50 percent of the Newcastle practice's work is sourced from outside the region. Work this year includes advising Lloyds TSB in the senior debt funding of Brian Reed Print & Design's acquisition of Kelly Packaging. Also represented Bank of Scotland on the funding of the IBO of Aviation Services Group. **Clients:** Bank of Scotland; Lloyds TSB.

Ward Hadaway Three partners work on banking transactions, with responsibilities split between property finance, insolvency and acquisition finance. The highly regarded **Julie Harrison**, who concentrates on acquisition finance and mainstream lending, enters our lists this year. She is considered to put Ward Hadaway *"on the banking map."* The practice generally acts on behalf of lenders. **Clients:** Northern Rock.

Robert Muckle The banking practice is organised into three units – transactional banking, mainstream banking and business recovery work. Work is for an even mix of borrowers and lenders in sectors including property finance and enterprise zone development work. Transactions include several facilities for Co-op Bank. **Clients:** Bank of Scotland; Newcastle Building Society; HSBC; Lloyds TSB.

SCOTLAND

BANKING • Scotland	Ptnrs	Assts
❶ **Dickson Minto WS** Edinburgh	1	6
Dundas & Wilson CS Glasgow	5	27
Maclay Murray & Spens Glasgow, Edinburgh	8	10
❷ **McGrigor Donald** Glasgow, Edinburgh	3	-
❸ **Burness** Edinburgh	7	6
Shepherd & Wedderburn WS Edinburgh	2	1
Tods Murray WS Edinburgh	5	4
❹ **MacRoberts** Glasgow	3	7
❺ **Brodies WS** Edinburgh	3	3
McClure Naismith Glasgow	5	5

LEADING INDIVIDUALS	
❶ **McHALE Colin** Dickson Minto WS	**STONEHAM Michael** Dundas & Wilson CS
❷ **KELLY Susan** Maclay Murray & Spens	**McKAY Colin** McGrigor Donald
❸ **BURNSIDE Graham** Tods Murray WS	**LAING Robert** Maclay Murray & Spens
MACFARLANE John McGrigor Donald	**MEIKLEJOHN Iain** Shepherd & Wedderburn
MORTON David Dundas & Wilson	**PATRICK Hamish** Tods Murray WS
PHILLIPS Stephen Dundas & Wilson	**SANDERS Shona** Shepherd & Wedderburn WS
SCOTT Christopher Burness	

Within each band, firms are listed alphabetically. *See **Profiles** on page 116*

Dickson Minto WS Viewed as a *"niche banking practice,"* the banking department essentially concentrates on acquisition/structured finance and corporate banking. There is *"no one better on the other side"* than *"key figure"* **Colin McHale**, a *"technically able, commercial and hands-on"* lawyer. *"He has made and held on to his reputation"* as the leader in acquisition finance in Scotland. The practice itself is mainly known for this specialism (*"they are not interested in anything else,"*) and it is this niche corporate and private equity work focus which has brought them prestige. The year saw the firm act on three separate public-to-private transactions (Clyde Blowers, Wainhomes and CALA,) the £85 million IBO of Motherwell Information Systems and on the funding of various other large acquisitions. **Clients:** Bank of Scotland, RBS, Allied Irish Banks, Christian Salvesen.

Dundas & Wilson CS The banking team is still regarded among Scotland's best as a result of its great breadth of expertise. One of the firm's 12 industry groups, the large banking practice is split into four groups – acquisition finance for corporates, property finance, retail finance (financial services oriented – including the internet) and a 7-man project finance team. In Edinburgh, **Michael Stoneham** is the firm's leading light. One of the first banking specialists in Scotland, his focus has moved more towards projects and the management side, yet his ability to *"come in and add value"* to transactions means he maintains his leading reputation. The firm is rated as a balanced firm geographically, and **David Morton** in Glasgow is also well regarded. The banking practice also has capital markets know-how, an area amongst others where *"impressive operator"* **Stephen Phillips** has an enviable reputation. The practice acts on big-ticket work and profits from the advantages that the English and international links of the Andersen network bring. Strengths include asset finance, securitisation, property finance and PFI, but the firm is not seen as dominant in acquisition finance and straight lending, a perception which may result from the practice's significant element of non-Scottish work. Typical deals in property finance range from £25-100 million. Acted for Bank of Scotland on a £54 million syndicated term loan facility to Next Generation Clubs Ltd. **Clients:** RBS; Bank of Scotland; Barclays; Clydesdale Bank; Halifax; NatWest; HSBC; Lloyds TSB.

Maclay Murray & Spens A large and *"strong general banking practice,"* highly regarded for acquisition finance. Working between Glasgow (where the firm has a two lawyer banking team) and Edinburgh, the *"visible and able"* **Susan Kelly** is particularly active, while *"generalist"* **Robert Laing** is also well-regarded. Prominent across the gamut of acquisition financings, the firm has recent experience of publics-to-privates, including Clyde Blowers, Wainhomes, Crown Leisure and the £550 million private acquisition of Highland Distillers plc. The finance department also deals with shipping and project finance. More than half of the practice's transactions are of an international nature. Significant deals of the year include a £150 million loan for the Bank of Scotland. **Clients:** Lloyds TSB; Deutsche Bank; Bank of Ireland; Den Norske Bank; Hypobank.

McGrigor Donald Created in Spring 1999, the banking practice, which covers acquisition finance, retail banking, corporate rescue, property and projects, is considered to be *"a general banking leader."* Prominent in the banking practice is *"key figure"* **Colin McKay**, who is regarded as having *"a positive influence on transactions,"* and is notably active on acquisition financings. The team has been active in retail banking, (especially internet-based,) working on on-line banking for groups such as Halifax. New to our rankings is the highly rated **John McFarlane** who is perceived as a corporate-style banking lawyer. Active in Scotland's two major cities, the practice is seen by some as the *"best in Glasgow."* The acquisition finance team works mainly on the side of lenders, other areas including capital markets and a strong property finance team. With a large influx of new business, the firm was not perceived to have the same junior resources as the larger firms, but is continuing to recruit actively. Over the 1999 year, the unit advised lenders on transactions of a combined value of over £1.5 billion. This included advising Bank of Scotland on the funding of a £600 million offer for Highland Distillers. **Clients:** Bank of Scotland; HSBC; RBS; NatWest; Halifax; MBNA Bank.

Burness The firm has been *"gaining momentum"* in banking over the past year, and is now viewed to be a *"well-established"* stand-alone practice. Acting for lenders has increased from a traditional borrower base. A two city practice with across-the-board banking capability, including consumer finance and motor finance. *"Sensible"* **Chris Scott** is well regarded, and a newcomer to the ratings. **Clients:** Chase Manhattan; Bank of Scotland; Royal Bank of Scotland; Tesco Personal Finance; Royal Bank of Canada.

Shepherd & Wedderburn WS Having not previously had a specialist banking practitioner, the recruitment of new banking head **Shona Sanders**, formerly with Dundas & Wilson and European General Counsel of the National Australia Bank, is viewed by the market as a *"good move."* The team was restructured in September to service a broad banking umbrella, and is primarily known for its trade finance, securitisation and PFI work, supplemented by a strong core banking practice involved in loans and acquisition financings. **Iain Meiklejohn** is perceived by the banking fraternity as *"more of a corporate man,"* and is involved on the equity side of acquisition financings. The firm is viewed as having its principal strength in Glasgow. **Clients:** HSBC; Bank of Scotland.

Tods Murray WS Covering a broad range of finance, the firm has separate banking and capital markets departments. In banking the firm is known for its property finance and acquisition finance, where *"able and bright"* **Hamish Patrick** is well regarded. **Graham Burnside** is known for his securitisation work, an area where the firm is *"probably more active than anyone north of the border."* Indeed it was involved on more than 20 securitisation transactions last year, including the securitisation of pub receivables of the Pubmaster Group, involving the issues of £305 million in various debt instruments. Known for its large and growing referrals practice from City firms, an area where they are *"number one."* Acting predominantly on the lender side, the firm also works for equity houses. Transactions this year include the buy-outs of Saltire plc and The Medwyn Partnership Ltd. **Clients:** Bank of Scotland; Barclays; Chase Manhattan; Citibank; Clydesdale Bank; NatWest; RBS; Deutsche Bank.

MacRoberts Perceived by the market to have *"built up their banking practice."* Having recognised expertise in construction which they have transferred to PFI transactions, the banking practice now consists of acquisition finance and project finance capabilities. Known primarily for their role on the equity side, the practice's work is in fact split 70 percent lender, 30 percent borrower. Property is an area of strength, and the practice is seen as *"one to watch in Glasgow."* **Clients:** 3i Group; Bank of Scotland; RBS; Clydesdale.

Brodies WS The majority of the practice's time is taken up with mainstream bank lending, local authority banking work, refinancing, securitisation and film finance. The firm works mainly for the lenders, with RBS being the firm's main domestic client. UK and foreign banks based in London provide a good flow of work, with a substantial amount of the practice's time spent on work sourced from outside the jurisdiction. The banking team has members within the corporate and commercial property departments, with property being a recognised area of strength. **Clients:** Main UK clearing banks, including RBS and HSBC.

McClure Naismith More active on smaller-scale transactions than the larger Scottish practices, the firm is present in acquisition and property-related financings. Clients include major US banks clients. The firm has recently appointed a former Director of Legal Operations at Bank of Scotland as the partner in charge of the UK Banking Unit. **Clients:** Bank of Scotland; Lloyds TSB; RoyScot Trust plc; Chase Manhattan.

NORTHERN IRELAND

BANKING • Northern Ireland	Ptnrs	Assts
❶ **Arthur Cox** Belfast	1	1
L'Estrange & Brett Belfast	4	4

LEADING INDIVIDUALS
❶ **CREED Angus** Arthur Cox
❷ **HENDERSON Brian** L'Estrange & Brett

Within each band, firms are listed alphabetically. *See **Profiles** on page 116*

Arthur Cox The practice advises the main commercial banks in the locality, working on general corporate lending, acquisition and property finance. **Angus Creed** maintains his high reputation. Deals include a refinancing for Yorkgate (acquisition of a shopping centre) and an industrial centre acquisition, both deals between £10-14 million. **Clients:** Bank of Ireland; Irish Intercontinental; Anglo-Irish; Ulster Bank; Northern Bank.

L'Estrange & Brett A similar practice to Arthur Cox, the two compete in mainstream banking. **Brian Henderson** is highly regarded. The banking group straddles the corporate and property departments, generally working on deals in the £5-15 million range. The firm also works on securitisations and has an active practice working on referrals from City-based firms. Through its alliance with McCann Fitzgerald in the Republic, the firm has pan-Irish capabilities. **Clients:** Ulster Bank.

LEADERS IN BANKING

AKITT, Ian
Walker Morris, Leeds (0113) 283 2500
iaa@walkermorris.co.uk
Specialisation: Acquisition finance, MBO/MBI Finance, Project Finance and Property Development Funding. Highlights include: £25 million multicurrency acquisition finance facility with UK and overseas banks. £100m facilities for a recent PFI project. Launch of an internet savings account.
Career: Qualified 1988 – *Norton Rose*; *Pinsent Curtis* (Leeds) 1989-1994; *Garretts* (Leeds) 1994-1999; *Walker Morris* 1999.
Personal: Educated Wettleby High School and University of Sheffield. Leisure interests include golf, tennis, skiing. Married with four children. Resides Bardsey.

ALLEN, Maurice
White & Case, London (020) 7600 7300
mallen@whitecase.com
Specialisation: Leading international finance lawyer with particular expertise in banking and acquisition finance.
Prof. Memberships: Law Society of England & Wales.
Career: Head of banking, *White & Case*, London. Former head of *Weil, Gotshal & Manges'* London office. Former *Clifford Chance* banking partner.

ALTON, Philip
Garretts, Birmingham (0121) 698 9000
philip.alton@glegal.com
Specialisation: Bankings, asset financing, acquisition finance, building societies, consumer credit. Recent highlights include acting for a client on a £235m syndicated facility, acting for a finance house on a joint venture with a UK bank and numerous e-commerce initiatives.
Prof. Memberships: Law Society.
Career: Upon qualification joined Forwart Trust Group Ltd as legal advisor. Joined *Edge Ellison* in 1987 before becoming associate in 1989. Moved to *Hammond Suddards* in 1994 before joining *Garrets* in 1997.
Personal: Born 1959. Interests include classical music (member of the Warwickshire Symphony Orchestra), classic cars, motor racing and photography.

BAKER, Ian P.
Martineau Johnson, Birmingham (0121) 678 1575
ian.baker@martjohn.com
Specialisation: Advises on banking and debt finance of all kinds including acquisition and project finance, restructurings and security issues and all aspects of non-contentious insolvency.
Prof. Memberships: SPI. Association of Business Recovery Professional.
Career: Bablake School, Coventry. Oriel College Oxford. Qualified 1983; Partner 1987.
Personal: Arts, cricket, rugby, soccer. Church – missionary and development work in Europe and Africa. Married, two children.

BALFOUR, Andrew
Slaughter and May, London (020) 7600 1200
Specialisation: Works mainly on banking and capital markets transactions. Particular experience in syndicated loans, structured finance, project finance, acquisition finance, international equity issues, bonds, commercial paper and medium term notes. Also advises banks and corporate clients on general banking and treasury matters.
Prof. Memberships: The Law Society.
Career: Qualified 1981 and became a partner of *Slaughter and May* in 1988. Resident partner in New York office 1991-1993.
Personal: Educated at Nailsea School (1968-75) and Manchester University (1975-78).

BORTHWICK, Trevor
Allen & Overy, London (020) 7330 3000
Specialisation: Partner in the banking department specialising in domestic and international structured finance with particular emphasis on syndicated loans, acquisition finance and securitisation, project finance, structured trade finance and workouts and reschedulings.
Career: Tonbridge School; Magdalene College, Cambridge. Trained *Allen & Overy*, qualified 1989; partner 1997.
Personal: Born 1962, resides Wimbledon, enjoys golf and rugby.

BRAY, Michael
Clifford Chance, London (020) 7600 1000
michael.bray@cliffordchance.com
Specialisation: Banking, project finance and debt restructuring.
Career: Liverpool University. Partner *Clifford Chance* 1976.

BRIERLEY, Chris
Wragge & Co, Birmingham (0121) 214 1067
chris_brierly@wragge.com
Specialisation: Debt finance (for borrowers and institutions), principally acquisition finance (buyouts and other corporate acquisitions including coded offers and public to privates), property finance, project finance and PFI and refinancing and restructuring; key transactions include acting for borrower and equity provider on the MBO of Adams Childrenswear Ltd, for Nationwide Building Society on the provision of £44m syndicated property finance facilities to a Jersey borrower and for MEPC as sponsor and contractor on the financing aspect of Bute Avenue, Cardiff Bay PFI Project.
Prof. Memberships: Member of the Law Society and the UK Committee on Banking Technique and Practice of the International Chamber of Commerce.
Career: Qualified and joined *Wragge &Co* 1988, partner 1997.
Publications: Edited Chapter on Debt Finance in 'Dywer's MBA Book', published by Butterworth's.
Personal: Born 1962. Educated Clifton College, Bristol. Birmingham University and Limoges University, France. Interests include painting, walking and music.

BROADFIELD, Alice
Eversheds, Birmingham (0121) 232 1000
alicebroadfield@eversheds.com
Specialisation: Corporate banking, acquisition finance, lending and security arrangements. Also acts for corporate borrowers.
Career: Trained at *Watson, Farley and Williams.* Qualified and joined *Eversheds* in 1997.
Personal: Born 1973. Educated Bablake School, Coventry; Selwyn College, Cambridge (MA Law). Interests include horse riding, theatre and reading. lives in Lemington Spa, Warwickshire.

BURNSIDE, Graham M.
Tods Murray WS, Edinburgh (0131) 226 4771
graham.burnside@todsmurray.co.uk
Partner in banking department.
Specialisation: Asset and corporate finance, including securitisation, banking and refinancing. Developed, with partner Hamish Patrick, structures used in securitisation of Scottish assets. Has presented papers on securitisation of Scottish assets.
Prof. Memberships: Writer to the Signet.
Career: Qualified in 1978 *Dundas & Wilson CS*. Coal Industry Pension Fund 1979. Joined *Tods Murray WS* in 1983. Partner in 1984.
Personal: Born 1954. Educated at George Heriot's School, Edinburgh University (LLB Hons 1976). Governor of St. Columba's Hospice. Leisure: music, hill-walking.

CAMPBELL, Mark
Clifford Chance, London (020) 7600 1000
mark.campbell@cliffordchance.com
Specialisation: Partner dealing with all types of banking work including syndicated loans, public bid finance, leveraged transactions, insolvency, structured finance and corporate reconstruction.
Prof. Memberships: City of London Law Society Banking Law Sub-Committee.
Career: Oriel College, Oxford (BA 1981). Articled *Coward Chance*; qualified 1984; partner *Clifford Chance* since 1991; managing partner of finance practice 1998.

CHIDLEY, Mark A.
Addleshaw Booth & Co, Leeds (0113) 209 2049
mac@addleshaw-booth.co.uk
Head of banking and finance group.
Specialisation: Work covers acquisitions, buy-out/buy-in finance, general banking law and private equity transactions. Also reconstructions of banking facilities and workouts.
Prof. Memberships: IBA.
Career: Qualified in 1979. Joined the firm in 1982, becoming a Partner in 1984.
Personal: Attended Ardingly College, Haywards Heath, Sussex 1968-73; then Southampton University 1973-76. Leisure interests include fishing, gardening and 60s/70s sports cars.

CLELAND, John
Pinsent Curtis, Leeds (0113) 244 5000
john.cleland@pinsents.com
Specialisation: Partner and Head of Banking, Leeds, with a particular expertise in Project Finance and PFI. Acted for RBS in £46 million facility for Bradford & Northern HA. Secured and unsecured funding, asset financing and mortgage book acquisitions and disposals.
Career: Qualified 1990. Solicitor *Simmons & Simmons* 1990-96; Partner *Simmons & Simmons* 1996-97; Partner *Pinsent Curtis* 1997 to date.
Publications: Various articles on legal implications of EMU.
Personal: Belmont Academy, Ayr; Cambridge University 1983-87; London University 1989-91. Principal interest – family; other interests reading and football.

COOKE, David J.
Pinsent Curtis, Birmingham (0121) 200 1050
david.j.cooke@pinsents.com
Head of banking and insolvency department, Birmingham. Licensed insolvency practitioner.
Specialisation: Main area of practice is non contentious banking and corporate insolvency. Work includes lending, security, restructurings, work outs, receiverships and administration. Also handles corporate finance, including mergers and acquisitions and professional indemnity and other litigation involving corporate, banking, security or insolvency issues.
Prof. Memberships: Law Society, Birmingham Law Society, Insolvency Lawyers Association.
Career: Qualified 1981. Joined *Pinsent & Co* in 1979, becoming a partner in 1983.
Personal: Born 1956. Educated at Cambridge University 1975-78. Leisure interests include golf and sailing.

COTTIS, Matthew J.
Lovells, London (020) 7296 2000
matthew.cottis@lovells.com
See under Corporate Finance, p.246

CREED, Angus
Arthur Cox – Northern Ireland, Belfast (028) 9023 0007
Partner and Head of Banking Group
Specialisation: Banking security and advisory work.
Prof. Memberships: Law Society of Northern Ireland.
Career: Qualified 1976. In-house lawyer with Bank of Ireland from 1976 to 1987. Joined *Norman Wilson & Co.* 1987. Became partner in *Arthur Cox* – Northern Ireland in May 1996.
Personal: Born: 10th June 1951. Educated at Campbell College, Belfast and Pembroke College, Cambridge.

CROOME, Andrew
Eversheds, Norwich (01603) 272727
Specialisation: Non contentious company and banking work, handling a wide variety of matters for lenders and borrowers.
Career: Qualified in 1978 with *Allen & Overy*. Joined *Eversheds* in 1979 becoming a partner in 1982.
Personal: Born in Essex in 1954. Educated in Essex, Suffolk and at Trinity Hall, Cambridge. Lives in North Norfolk.

CULLINANE, Lee
Clifford Chance, London (020) 7600 1000
lee.cullinane@cliffordchance.com
Specialisation: General banking with emphasis on acquisition, telecoms and project finance.
Career: London University (LLB 1985, SFC 1986). Qualified 1988; partner *Clifford Chance* 1995.
Personal: Born 1964; resides Winchester.

DALE, Nigel A.
Eversheds, Manchester (0161) 832 6666
nigeldale@eversheds.com
Partner and head of banking department, *Eversheds*, Manchester.
Specialisation: Advises on all aspects of banking related matters, acting for banks and other financial institutions as well as borrowers. Main areas of practice include acquisition finance transactions, the full range of bilateral and syndicated facilities of all types, property finance, and advising on security. Regularly acts for a large number of banks and other financial institutions including Bank of Scotland, The Royal Bank of Scotland plc, Barclays Bank PLC, HSBC Bank PLC, The Co-operative Bank PLC, NM Rothschild & Sons Limited and Intermediate Capital Group PLC. Significant practice in advising large corporates on major banking transactions including advising BBA Group PLC on a £550m syndicated facility, FKI on a £350m bridging facility and Reynold PLC on a £62m syndicated acquisition finance facility, as well as other significant funding for other corporates. During 1999 the team advised on a further 17 major acquisition finance transactions. During 1999 significant property finance work was also undertaken acting both for banks and developers.
Career: Qualified in 1986 whilst at *Eversheds Hepworth & Chadwick*. Joined *Hammond Suddards* 1990 and became partner at *Hammond Suddards* in 1993. Became partner at *Eversheds* in 1996.
Personal: Born 1962. Leisure pursuits include motor sports and cars generally, gardening and walking.

DAY, Sarah Jane
DLA, Leeds (08700) 111 111
sarah.day@dla.com
Specialisation: Specialises in acquisition and corporate finance work, including management and institutional buyout transactions, bilateral and syndicated facilities. Also invoice and asset financing, public/private partnership financing work and corporate restructuring and refinancing. Previous transactions include: acting for three European banks in the provision of acquisition funding, including taking securities in six jurisdictions, acting for Newcastle United in the first UK football club securitisation based on ticket sales (total funding £55m) and acting for senior lenders on MBO transactions totalling hundreds of £m.
Career: May 1998 *Dibb Lupton Alsop*. Partner, banking Group. September 1990 – June 1996 *Hammond Suddards*. Trainee then banking unit, Leeds and Manchester. Qualified September 1992.
Personal: Good food eaten in or out as long as I am not the cook. Walking, reading from Trollope to trash.

DUNCAN, Michael G.
Allen & Overy, London (020) 7330 3000
Specialisation: Partner dealing in areas of practice comprising all types of banking and corporate finance, including in particular syndicated loans (acting for a variety of banks and borrowers), acquisition finance, asset financing, property finance, work-outs/reschedulings.
Career: Articled *Allen & Overy*. Qualified 1981, Partner 1987.
Personal: Cambridge University (1978 BA). Born 1957.

ELLIOTT, Robert
Linklaters (A member firm of Linklaters & Alliance), London (020) 7456 4478
robert.elliott@linklaters.com
See under Insolvency/Corporate Recovery, p.476

EREIRA, David P.
Freshfields Bruckhaus Deringer, London (020) 7936 4000
Partner in finance department.
Specialisation: Responsible for co-ordination of banking and property finance practices. Acts for banks, international institutions and borrowers on banking and finance related work. Acts for banks, property developers and investors on property related investments.
Prof. Memberships: Law Society, City of London Solicitors Company sub-committee on Banking Law; International Bar Association, sub-committees B and E; Justice Working Group of the Financial Law Panel.
Career: Qualified in 1981. Worked at *Wilde Sapte* 1981-90, from 1984 as a partner. Joined *Freshfields* in 1990, becoming a partner in 1991. Postgraduate student with the Open University studying for an MSc in mathematics. Lives in London.

EVANS, Edward T.H.
Freshfields Bruckhaus Deringer, London (020) 7936 4000
Partner in Finance Department.
Specialisation: Main areas of practice are banking and project and asset finance. Also handles energy law work. Has addressed numerous conferences and seminars on these subjects.
Career: Qualified 1980, having joined *Freshfields* in 1978. Became a Partner in 1986.
Personal: Born 12th December 1954. Attended RGS High Wycombe 1964-72, then Trinity College Cambridge 1973-77. Leisure interests include rugby, fishing and racing. Lives in London.

FORBES, Sandra
Burges Salmon, Bristol (0117) 902 2707
sandra.forbes@burges-salmon.com
Specialisation: Head of the Finance Group specialising in Corporate Banking (including Acquisition Finance) and Asset Finance. Important transactions in the last 12 months have included: acting for First-Group plc on the £690 million syndicated facility financing the acquisition of Ryder Public Transportation Services, Inc; re-drafting standard loan and security documentation for Nationwide Building Society; and advising Great Western Holdings on the financing of 27 new trains for First North Western having a contract value of £80 million.
Prof. Memberships: Law Society.
Career: Trained with *Frere Chomeley*, qualified in 1989, joined *Burges Salmon* in 1991, becoming a Partner in 1996.
Personal: Manchester University 1983-86. First Class Honours in Law Society Finals.

FOX, Ruth
Slaughter and May, London (020) 7600 1200
Specialisation: Practice covers a wide range of commercial work, with an emphasis on banking and capital markets, now focusing on financial regulation. Has acted extensively for banks and also for building societies, including in relation to conversions, and for corporate trustees.
Prof. Memberships: The Law Society.
Career: Qualified in 1979 with *Slaughter and May*. Became a partner in 1986.
Personal: Born 3 October 1954. Educated at St Helena School, Chesterfield and University College, London. Married with three sons. Lives in London and Hertfordshire.

FURMAN, Mark
Macfarlanes, London (020) 7831 9222
Specialisation: Specialises in acquisition finance and property finance and generally acting for lenders and borrowers in all aspects of debt finance.
Career: Dulwich College; St. John's College, Oxford (MA, 1980). Qualified as solicitor 1983.
Personal: Married with two children. Interests: guitar, wine, reading.

GILLESPIE, Stephen
Allen & Overy, London (020) 7330 3000
Specialisation: Partner at *Allen & Overy* in 1995. Has extensive experience in all types of international financing, including acquisition financing, structured financing, project financing, and a number of multi-source financings. Has led/is leading the teams advising the underwriters/arrangers/lenders on the leveraged acquisitions of Bosch Telecom, Giraudy, IPC Magazines, Panta Electronics and Newmond Holdings. Also advised the arrangers/underwriters on the api Energia IGCC financing (and refinancing) in Italy, the £1.5 billion Bouygues Telecom third mobile telecommunications financing in France and the Euro595 million financing for KPN Orange Belgium N.V., the third Belgian mobile telecommunications operator. Is currently leading the team advising the arrangers/underwriters of the Euro2.43 billion financing for WIND Telecommunicazioni, the third Italian mobile operator. Has recently led the team advising Chase, Deutsche and IBJ as lead arrangers of the £1.725 billion financing for the acquisition of the Drax Power Station by AES from National Power. In the rail sector, he led the team advising Virgin Rail Group in connection with the financing of its rolling stock procurement programme for the UK's West Coast and Cross-Country Passenger rail franchises (the largest single rolling stock procurement ever undertaken in the UK). Also has extensive expertise in PFI transactions: he advised the sponsors/project company in connection with the Law Hospital PFI financing and is currently leading the teams advising the sponsors/project company in connection with the King's College hospital, St George's Hospital and Dumfries and Galloway Hospital PFI financings. Is also leading the team advising the financiers on the Scottish/Northern Irish electricity interconnector project.
Prof. Memberships: Law Society. City of London Solicitors Company.
Career: Articled *Stephenson Harwood* 1985-87, Solicitor *Freshfields* 1987-91, Solicitor *Allen & Overy* 1991-95, Partner 1995.
Personal: Born 1962. Educated at Foyle and Londonderry College and Trinity College, Oxford (MA (Hons) Jurisprudence 1984). Interests include family, reading, outdoor pursuits and music. Lives in St. Albans.

GORRIE, Euan
Allen & Overy, London (020) 7330 3000
See under Corporate Finance, p.251

GOSNAY, Andrew W.
Pinsent Curtis, Leeds (0113) 244 5000
andrew.gosney@pinsents.com
Partner and head of banking.
Specialisation: Mainstream banking, asset finance, leasing, property project finance and debt issues. Acted for FKI Plc in US$205m, US$120m US private placings by US subsidiary. Acted in £42m PFI project financing for the Royal Armouries Museum. Handled £123m banking facilities for Lurpak and dairy giant, MD Foods' International Division.
Career: Qualified 1985. *Cameron Markby Hewitt* 1983-86. Joined *Simpson Curtis* in 1986, becoming a partner in 1990.
Personal: Born 1961. Uppingham School 1974-79; Newcastle University 1979-82 and College of Law 1982-83. Interests include walking, skiing, travel and theatre.

HARKER, Chris
Dickinson Dees, Newcastle upon Tyne
(0191) 279 9254
chris.harker@Dickinson-Dees.com
Partner in company and commercial department.
Specialisation: Main areas of practice are banking and commercial lending and venture capital. Works for banks and building societies as well as quoted and unquoted companies as borrowers. Major transactions in the last year have been for Newcastle Building Society (eight facilities aggregating over £85m), Bank of Scotland, Barclays and Co-operative Bank.

HARRISON, Julie
Ward Hadaway, Newcastle upon Tyne
(0191) 204 4000
Specialisation: Head of Banking Unit. Acts for clearing banks, financial institutions and borrowers in relation to secured and unsecured loans, acquisition finance, property development and project finance, refinancing and security issues, debt restructuring and invoice discount.
Prof. Memberships: Law Society.
Career: Qualified January 1984, articled at *Norton Rose*, joined *Ward Hadaway* in 1997 as a partner having worked for *Middleton Potts* and *Robert Muckle*.

HENDERSON, Brian L.
L'Estrange & Brett, Belfast (028) 9023 0426
Partner and head of Banking Unit.
Specialisation: All types of banking and finance work.
Prof. Memberships: The Law Society of Northern Ireland. Member of Non-Contentious Business Committee; Solicitors European Group (NI)
Career: Qualified 1976. Administrative Trainee European Commission; Partner in *L'Estrange & Brett* since 1979.
Personal: Born 1951. Education: Trinity College Dublin, BA (Mod) LLB.

HOPKINS, Stephen Martyn
Eversheds, Leeds (0113) 243 0391
stephenhopkins@eversheds.com
See under Corporate Finance, p.253

HORSFALL TURNER, Jonathan
Allen & Overy, London (020) 7330 3000
Specialisation: Partner dealing with syndications, securitisations, project finance, capital markets, privatisations, debt restructurings, bank and financial institution acquisitions and disposals and general banking.
Career: Articled *Allen & Overy*, qualified 1970, Partner 1973.
Personal: Cambridge University (1968 MA). Born 1945.

HUMPHREY, Anthony R.
Allen & Overy, London (020) 7330 3000
anthony.humphrey@allenovery.com
Specialisation: Partner specialising in structured finance with substantial experience in a wide range of corporate and financing transactions. Has extensive experience in all aspects of financing, particularly tiered or structured debt/equity financings including international project financings, acquisition financings and other complex multi-sourced financings. Has advised on transactions worldwide including the North Sea, North America, the Gulf, the Far East and Australia. Has given numerous public lectures on various aspects of financing, including project financing and has delivered papers on 'The Bankability of Project Agreements', 'Project Finance – The Security Package', 'Sponsor Support' and 'Comparative Off-take Arrangements'.
Prof. Memberships: Member, Section on Energy and Natural Resources Law of the International Bar Association.
Career: Articled *Allen & Overy*, qualified 1975, Partner 1981.
Personal: Durham University (1972 BA). Born 1951.

INGLIS, Alan
Clifford Chance, London (020) 7600 1000
alan.inglis@cliffordchance.com
Specialisation: Partner specialising in banking, corporate finance, insolvency and corporate reconstruction.
Career: Exeter School; Birmingham University (LLB). Articled *Clifford Turner/Clifford Chance*; qualified 1985; partner *Clifford Chance* since 1992.

JEFFRIES, Graham
Bond Pearce, Southampton (023) 8033 2001
gdj@bondpearce.com
Partner in the specialist Banking and Insolvency Group and head of Southampton banking team.
Specialisation: Specialises in banking and insolvency work. Advises clearing and secondary banks, finance houses, invoice discounter and other financial institutions specialising in structured and acquisition finance, regulatory matters, engineering of new products, restructuring, workouts, recovery and bank related insolvency matters.
Prof. Memberships: Member of R3 and the Society of Computers and Law.
Career: Articled with *McKenna & Co*, qualified 1989. Joined *Lester Aldridge* 1992. Partner banking and finance department 1994. Joined *Bond Pearce* 1999 as partner in Banking & Insolvency Group.

JOHNSON, James
Clifford Chance, London (020) 7600 1000
Partner, general banking group, banking department.
Specialisation: Advises on all forms of corporate banking but in particular is a leading specialist in acquisition finance, workouts, structured finance and housing assocation finance.
Career: Articled at *Wilde Sapte* and qualified in 1987. Partner at *Wilde Sapte* in 1991.
Personal: Born 1963. Educated: Roundhill College, Thurmaston, Leicester 1974-77, Wreake Valley College, Syston, Leicester 1977-81, Collingwood College, Durham University.

JOHNSTONE, Pat
Eversheds, Birmingham (0121) 232 1000
Specialisation: Corporate banking, lending and security arrangements.
Career: Qualified 1986. Joined *Evershed & Tomkinson* in 1984.
Personal: Born 1955. Educated Dumfries Academy, Glasgow University (MA), Grenoble University. Interests include ballet and horse riding. Lives near Stratford upon Avon.

KEAL, Anthony C.
Allen & Overy, London (020) 7330 3000
Specialisation: Partner at *Allen & Overy* in 1982. Specialises in domestic and cross-border acquisition finance and other structured finance products. Recent transactions include financing (for Barclays)

the successful public bid for Westminster Healthcare plc and its subsiquent acquisition of the Priory Group; (for Deutche Bank) the LBO of TA Health GmbH and a series of subsequent acquisitions by that company (creating the Domus Healthcare Group); (for Credit Suisse First Boston) the LBO of Reed Regional Newspapers Ltd and Westminster press by KKR and affiliates (creating the Newsquest Group) and refinancings, the LBO of Frida Alimentaria SA and the public takeover of Triplex-Lloyd plc by Doncaster plc; (for Goldman Sachs) the LBO of Cartiere del Garda SpA and its subsiquent acquisition of Smurfit Condat S.A., the original Pacificorp bid for The Energy Group plc and the LBO of Swebus AB; (for Rabobank International) the LBO of BOCM Pauls Ltd and the leveraged acquition of The Tetley Group by Tata Tea; (for WestLB) the leveraged joint venture of the Thornand Granada consumer rentals business. Also acts frequently for investors on the debt side of LBOs for example, for Maoran Grenfell Private Equity in a number of LBOs over a long period; for Investcorp in the LBOs of Welcome Break and Helly-Hansen, the public bid for Watmoughs plc and private acquisition of BPC (creating the Polestar Group); and for KKR, the public bid for Wassall plc.
Prof. Memberships: Law Society and City of London Solicitors Company.
Career: Articled *Allen & Overy,* qualified 1976; legal adviser/CoSec, Libra Bank plc 1976-78; Assistant Solicitor *Allen & Overy* 1979-81; Partner 1981.
Personal: Born 1951. Educated Stowe School and New College, Oxford (1973).

KELLY, Susan M.
Maclay Murray & Spens, Edinburgh
(0131) 226 5196
smk@maclaymurrayspens.co.uk
Specialisation: Banking. Acting for the Edrington Group Ltd in connection with loan facilities aggregating £550m to finance the acquisition of Highlord Distillers plc; Wainhomes public to private (acting for bidco); Sears refinancing acting for Bank of Scotland; Ferograph MBO acting for Royal Bank of Scotland. Acting for the Bank of Scotland in connection with a PFI project to find a new police HQ in Derby.
Career: Strathclyde University (1987-1991); Trainee, *Maclay Murray & Spens* (1991-1993); Assistant solicitor *Maclay Murray & Spens* (1993-1996); Bank of Scotland secondment (1994); Associate, *Maclay Murray & Spens* (1996-1998); Partner, *Maclay Murray & Spens* (1998 to date).
Personal: Theatre, opera, antiques, travelling.

KINSEY, Julian
Bond Pearce, Bristol (0117) 929 9197
xcjk@bondpearce.com
Specialisation: Partner in the specialist Banking and Insolvency Group. Specialises in banking and asset finance work for banks, building societies and other financial institutions. Deals with all aspects of lending, refinancing and security issues particularly in connection with acquisition finance for clients based in Bristol, London and the South. Particular experience of issues relating to the financing of the motor sector.
Career: Qualified in 1984, joined *Bond Pearce* in 1988 having worked for City firm *Linklaters and Paines*, becoming partner in 1993.
Publications: Regular contributor to 'Corporate Briefing' published by Monitor Press.

KIRTLEY, Deborah
Dickinson Dees, Newcastle upon Tyne
(0191) 279 9000
Specialisation: Specialises in mainstream banking, corporate and acquisition finance work and in particular management buyout transactions. Acted for Barclays Bank plc in the £40m redevelopment facility of Newcastle United Stadium, St. James Park and the £55 million securitisation. Other transactions include acting for MBO team on £38 million buy out, acting for bank in £35 million sterling and US dollar acquisition facility and acting for bank in interest and foreign exchange transactions.
Career: Partner, banking group April 1999. Qualified 1991.
Personal: Travel and Sunderland AFC.

LAING, Robert J.
Maclay Murray & Spens, Edinburgh
(0131) 226 5196
rjl@maclaymurrayspens.co.uk
Partner and head of banking unit.
Specialisation: Acts for major clearing banks and other financial institutions as well as for borrowers in the provision of debt finance, including term loans, secured and unsecured lending and MBO/MBI finance. Also general corporate law.
Career: Qualified in 1977 (England) and 1985 (Scotland). University of Cambridge (MA 1974). At *Slaughter and May* 1975-83.
Personal: Born 1953.

LEEMING, Richard
Burges Salmon, Bristol (0117) 939 2216
richard.leeming@burges-salmon.com
Specialisation: Corporate Banking Partner – carrying out a range of corporate banking work in particular structured finance (including both acquisition finance and property finance). Special work includes advising Nationwide Business Finance on syndicated property finance transactions and preparing for them, new standard form loan and security documents, advising Bayerische Landesbank on various banking matters and advising Lloyds TSB, NatWest, Royal Bank of Scotland and Bank of Scotland on acquisition finance and property finance transactions.
Prof. Memberships: Law Society.
Career: Trained at *Ashurst Morris Crisp* 1991-93, secondment to Bankers' Trust 1994. Joined *Burges Salmon* later that year . Partner from 1.5.2000
Personal: University of Southampton 1985-88.

LUMSDEN, Christopher
Chaffe Street, Manchester (0161) 236 5800
Partner in Banking Department.
Specialisation: Main area of practice is banking, including debt/equity swaps, documentary credits, management buy-ins and buy-outs, invoice discounting, reconstructions, refinancings and ship and aircraft financing. Also experienced in corporate acquisitions and disposals. Contributed 'Financial Assistance Problems in Management Buy-Outs' to Journal of Business Law.
Prof. Memberships: Law Society.
Career: Qualified 1977. With *Freshfields* in London 1975-82, then *Freshfields* Singapore 1982-84. Moved to *Alsop Wilkinson*, Manchester 1984-90. Practised in Hong Kong 1988. Joined *Chaffe Street* as Partner 1990.
Personal: Born 4th April 1953. Attended Rossall School 1966-70, then University of Newcastle-upon-Tyne 1971-74. Leisure pursuits include tennis, skiing and reading.

MACFARLANE, John
McGrigor Donald, Edinburgh (0131) 226 7777
Partner in Banking Unit.
Specialisation: Principal area of practice is corporate insolvency. Also handles corporate banking. Recently acted in the receivership of Pierre Victoire Ltd and obtained a definitive VAT ruling in Sheraton Caltrust liquidation. Other cases include Heat & Control Limited, Lees Group (Scotland) Ltd, Allan Timber Products Group, Charles Gray (Builders) Ltd. Major clients include KPMG, Ernst & Young, PricewaterhouseCoopers, Grant Thorton and Bank of Scotland. Contributor to legal journals on insolvency and related topics (e.g.'Impecunias'). Formerly tutor in Diploma of Legal Practice, Strathclyde and Edinburgh Universities. Speaker at various conferences e.g. 'Insolvency and the Construction Industry'.
Prof. Memberships: Law Society of Scotland; Joint Insolvency Specialists Group.
Career: Qualified 1971. Partner at *Bird Semple, Fyfe Ireland* 1976-90. Joint Convenor, Joint Insolvency Specialists Group (Law Society of Scotland/ Institute of C.A. Scotland) 1995-1998.
Personal: Born 18th September 1949. Educated at Glasgow University 1967-71 (LL.B Hons). Interests include horse riding and point to point (not riding). Lives in East Lothian.

MADDEN, Andrew
Gateley Wareing, Birmingham (0121) 234 0000
amadden@gateleywareing.co.uk
Specialisation: Partner, Corporate Services Department, specialising in management buy-outs, venture capital and acquisition finance.
Prof. Memberships: The Law Society.
Career: 1981-84, University of Birmingham (LLB); 1984-85, College of Law, Chester; 1985-87 articles *Duggan Lea & Co* 1987-1996 *Edge & Ellison*; 1996 Partner *Gateley Wareing.*
Personal: Born 1962. Leisure interests include good beer and food, and looking after his son Scott. Birmingham City FC supporter.

MCHALE, Colin J.
Dickson Minto WS, Edinburgh (0131) 225 4455
colin.mchale@dmws.com
Partner 1997.
Specialisation: Banking

MCKAY, Colin
McGrigor Donald, Edinburgh (0131) 226 7777
Head of Banking Unit.
Specialisation: Banking and debt finance generally; more particularly acquistion finance and property finance.
Prof. Memberships: Law Society of Scotland. The Law Society (England and Wales)
Career: *Biggart Baillie & Gifford* 1986-1988; *Freshfields*(London & Tokyo) 1988-1993; *Biggart Baillie & Gifford* (Glasgow) 1993 – March 1999; *McGrigor Donald* April 1999 to date.

MEIKLEJOHN, Iain M.C.
Shepherd & Wedderburn WS, Edinburgh
(0131) 228 9900

MILES, Stephen
Pinsent Curtis, Birmingham (0121) 200 1050
stephen.miles@pinsents.com
Specialisation: Non-contentious banking and finance work. Acts for both financial institutions and corporates – including, in particular, the national acquisition finance teams of the major clearing banks. Acted on the £170.5 million Mettis Group institutional purchase and the £183.5 million DONCASTERS plc bond issue and senior debt refinancing.
Prof. Memberships: Law Society and Birmingham Law Society; ICC United Kingdom.
Career: Joined *Pinsent Curtis* (then *Pinsent & Co*) 1989; Qualified 1991; Partner 1997.

MITCHELL, J. Patrick
Hammond Suddards Edge, Leeds (0113) 284 7000
Partner responsible for acquisition finance in the corporate finance and banking department.
Specialisation: Acquisition Finance, primarily for structured finance departments of Banks, and related funding issues in the context of buy out/institutional purchase transactions. Also handles bank lending, venture capital and corporate finance generally.
Career: Qualified 1981 with *Cameron Markby*. Worked for Robert Holmes a Court's company Bell Group before joining *Hammond Suddards* in 1987. Became a partner in 1989.
Personal: Born 24th February 1957. Attended Ardingly College, Haywards Heath, and Magdalen College, Oxford. Leisure interests include running, riding, football and sport generally. Lives in Harrogate.

MOLLOY, Susan
Halliwell Landau, Manchester (0161) 835 3003
Specialisation: Practice covers loan and other credit/facilities letters/agreements, single bank, sydicated, single/multi-borrower, multi-option facilities, tender panel agreements and working capital facilities, acting for senior mezzanine lenders and borrowers. Dealing with property development and investment finance, leasing and hire purchase facilities, guarantees, loan notes, standstills, intercreditors, providing a full range of banking services. Acts for clearing banks, specialised finance banks, merchant and foreign banks as well as borrowers.
Career: Qualifed in 1981 at *Addleshaw Sons & Latham*. Partner at *Alsop Wilkinson* 1989-95. Joined *Garretts* as a partner in June 1995. Joined *Halliwell Landau* January 2000.
Personal: Interests include theatre, walking, reading, cinema and wine.

MORGAN, Meryl
Morgan Cole, Cardiff (029) 2038 5385
meryl.morgan@morgan-cole.com
Specialisation: All aspects of bank and debt finance including working capital, multicurrency syndicated loan facilities, loan stock, invoice discounting, asset finance, and Consumer Credit Act. Experienced in a range of finance, particularly acquisition, buy-out, buy-in, debt restructuring and project finance, including PFI funding. Advises all aspects of security documents including ship and aircraft mortgages. Acts on behalf of range of lenders (generally clearing and non-clearing banks and building societies) and borrowers (including housing associations, finance companies, plcs and private companies).
Prof. Memberships: Associate of the Chartered Institute of Bankers.
Career: Qualified banker with ten years experience of banking. Articled with *Morgan Cole*. Qualified as a solicitor in 1992.
Personal: Attended University College Cardiff, (LLB 2.1). Playing bridge, theatre, walking, eating out, and spending time with family.

MORLEY, David H.
Allen & Overy, London (020) 7330 3000
Specialisation: Banking and Corporate Finance: Debt. Partner acting for banks and financial institutions, as well as borrowers, on all types of debt and structured finance transactions with particular emphasis on syndicated loans, project finance, telecommunications finance, public bid and other acquisition finance, property and asset finance.
Career: Articled *Allen & Overy*, qualified 1982, trainee solicitor Brussels 1981, assistant solicitor 1982-88. One year on secondment at Chase Investment Bank Limited 1985, partner 1988. Managing Partner, Banking Department 1998.
Personal: St John's College, Cambridge (1979 MA). Born 1956, enjoys cycling, sailing, skiing, family.

MORTON, David E
Dundas & Wilson CS, Glasgow (0141) 222 2200

MOSTYN-WILLIAMS, Stephen R.P.
Shearman & Sterling, London (020) 7655 5000
SMostyn-Williams@shearman.com
Partner and Head of European Acquisition Finance.
Specialisation: Structured finance, concentrating on cross-border leverage finance. Principally works in transactions involving both the bank and bond markets, advising institutions such as Morgan Stanley, Goldman Sachs, Merrill Lynch, Warburg Dillon Read and Deutche Bank. The Acquisition Finance Group, with over thirty US/UK legal staff, is unique in having market leadership in both bank and bond products, working under both US and English law.

ON, Nicholas
Eversheds, Newcastle upon Tyne (0191) 261 1661
nicholason@eversheds.com
Partner
Specialisation: All aspects of non-contentious banking and finance work including transactional lending and finance, regulatory work and restructuring. Regularly acts for a large number of banks and other financial institutions as well as large corporate borrowers. Particular expertise in property development finance on a national basis and acquisition finance.
Career: Qualified 1991 at *Robert Muckle*. Secondment with Bank of Scotland Legal Services in Edinburgh in 1993. Partner at *Robert Muckle* 1995. Joined *Eversheds* as partner August 1999.
Personal: Born 1963. Educated Cheltenham Grammar School, St. Catherine's College, Oxford (BA) and University of Northumbria. Married with two children. Plays the piano, golf and football.

OWEN, Simon
Eversheds, Leeds (0113) 243 0391
simonowen@eversheds.com
Specialisation: Banking and commercial lending, handling all forms of acquisition and structured finance, general corporate banking and treasury, trade finance and derivatives documentation. Acting for the funders on the £320m take private of Evans of Leeds plc, advising Peterhouse Group Plc on its successful bid for Eve Group Plc, acting for Malayan Banking Berhard in connection with a Malayan /UK trade financing, advising a leading defence contractor on various treasury activities and advising Fortis Bank on refinancing a NASDAQ quoted borrower.
Prof. Memberships: Law society.
Career: Articled: 1990 *Simmons & Simmons*. Qualified: 1992 *Simmons & Simmons*. Joined *Eversheds*: 1996. Partner: 1999.
Personal: Education: Maidenstone Grammar School. Newcastle University, Chester Law School. Interests: Most sports but particularly rugby, music and films. Resides: Harrogate. Family: Married to Caroline, two children William and Oliver.

PALLETT, Julian C.
Wragge & Co, Birmingham (0121) 214 1060
julian_pallett@wragge.com
Specialisation: Banking: Lending and security arrangements, intercreditor arrangements, project and acquisition finance, transaction funding. Insolvency: Receivership, liquidations, administration, troubled companies, refinancing, restructuring.
Career: Articled *Wragge & Co*. Qualified 1983. Partner at *Wragge & Co* from 1990.
Personal: Born 1958.

PAPWORTH, Richard
Addleshaw Booth & Co, Leeds (0113) 209 2030
rnp@addleshaw-booth.co.uk
Partner in banking and financial services group.
Specialisation: Corporate banking, acquisition finance, property finance, housing association finance, project finance, education sector finance, building society treasury work, capital markets and derivatives.
Career: Qualified 1989. Joined the firm 1991. Appointed Partner 1995.
Personal: Educated at Christ Church, Oxford. Interests include golf and football. Lives in Harrogate.

PATRICK, Hamish A.
Tods Murray WS, Edinburgh (0131) 226 4771
hamish.patrick@todsmurray.co.uk
Partner in banking department.
Specialisation: Debt finance and recovery, including conventional banking, asset finance, PFI/project finance, innovative funding structures and funding reorganisation. Developed, with partner Graham Burnside, structures for securitisation of Scottish assets. Author, speaker and university examiner in field. Member of Scottish Law Commission Contract Advisory Group.
Career: Qualified 1989. Partner 1992.
Personal: Born 1962. Attended Dollar Academy, Edinburgh University (LLB 1st Class Hons 1984; DipLP 1985; PhD 1994: Cross-border securities and insolvency). Leisure: family, music, sports.

PHILLIPS, Stephen J.
Dundas & Wilson CS, Edinburgh (0131) 228 8000

PIERCE, Sean
Freshfields Bruckhaus Deringer, London (020) 7936 4000
spiece@freshfields.com
Specialisation: Partner in the London office. Practice encompasses all aspects of banking work. Sean specialises in representing lenders but his clients also include corporates and other borrowers. In terms of products, has recently focused on cross-border leveraged buyouts and 'jumbo' acquisition financings. Has practised in New York and Hong Kong as well as London.

POLGLASE, Timothy
Norton Rose, London (020) 7283 6000
polglaset@nortonrose.com
Specialisation: Principal area of practice is structured finance, including the financing of leveraged buy-outs and public bids, telecoms finance and project finance.
Career: Articled *Norton Rose*; qualified 1986; seconded to *Milbank, Tweed, Hadley & McCloy* (New York) 1988-1989; seconded to Banking Supervision Division, Bank of England 1990-1991; partner *Norton Rose* 1994.
Personal: Born 1962. Educated at St. John's College, Oxford.

POPHAM, Stuart
Clifford Chance, London (020) 7600 1000
stuart.popham@cliffordchance.com
Specialisation: Partner. Banking and finance, head of global finance practice. Principal area of work relates to finance for corporates including acquisition financing, work-outs, syndicated and capital market financing, structured and tax driven financing, acting for lenders and borrowers.
Career: Southampton University (LLB 1975). Qualified 1978; made partner 1984.

PULESTON JONES, Haydn
Linklaters (A member firm of Linklaters & Alliance), London (020) 7456 4454
haydn.pulestonjones@linklaters.com
Partner in International Finance Department, Banking Group. Head of *Linklaters & Alliance's* Banking Management team
Specialisation: Principal area of practice is in the field of banking. Areas of specialisation include syndicated, secured and structured financings and corporate rescues and recoveries. Has had extensive experience of advising banks, syndicates, steering committees and distressed companies on UK and international defaults and reschedulings.
Prof. Memberships: Member of The Law Society and (from 1994 to 1998) Chairman of Banking Law Sub-Committee of the City of London Law Society.
Career: Qualified 1973 becoming a Partner with *Linklaters* in 1979.

REARDEN, Shaun
Chaffe Street, Manchester (0161) 236 5800
Partner in Banking & Financial Services Group.
Specialisation: Banking with emphasis on facility (including syndicated facilities) and security documentation, acquisition finance, restructuring, project finance and asset finance. Other area of work is regulatory, covering consumer credit, financial services and data protection. Regular presenter at seminars.
Career: Qualified in 1979, while at *Rutherfords* in Liverpool. Was in-house solicitor at Littlewoods 1980-82, then Manager of Legal Department at North West Securities plc to 1986. In-house legal advisor at The Co-operative Bank plc in Manchester 1986-89 before joining *Davies Wallis Foyster* as a Partner. Joined the firm in 1990.
Personal: Born 10th April 1954. Attended West Park Grammar School 1965-72, then King's College, London 1972-75. Leisure pursuits include rugby and sunshine. Lives in Wilmslow.

SANDERS, Shona
Shepherd & Wedderburn WS, Edinburgh (0131) 228 9900
shona.sanders@shepwedd.co.uk
Specialisation: Acquisition and project finance.
Prof. Memberships: Law Society of Scotland. Law Society (England and Wales).
Career: 1987 -1991 *Dundas & Wilson*; trainee (1987-1989); assistant in banking group (1989-1991). 1992 Sabbatical; including time at *Allen, Allen & Hemsley*, Sydney. 1993-1998 *Dundas & Wilson*; Assistant to partner in banking group. 1998-1999 *Mallesons Stephen Jaques*, Sydney; senior associate in project finance team. 1999 to date *Sheperd and Wedderburn*; partner in and head of banking group.
Personal: Born 1966. University of Edinburgh: LLB (1986), DIP LP (1987). Qualified in English Law 1998.

SCHULZ, Peter F.
Allen & Overy, London (020) 7330 3000
Specialisation: Has has a broad practice in banking and international finance, which includes both UK and international syndicated and structured lending, exports credits and multi-sourced project financings, acting for numerous arranging banks as well as borrowers and export credit agencies. Recent transactions he has led include telecoms projects in Poland, sovereign loans and reshedulings, warehousing facilities and several jumbo multi-jurisdictional corporate credits involving borrowers across Western Europe. Also frequently leads team advising on corporate workouts and resturcturings.
Career: Articled *Allen & Overy*, qualified 1983, partner 1989.
Personal: Educated at Haberdashers' Aske's School, Elstree; Downing College, Cambridge (MA Law). Currently trying (unsuccessfully) to restore a listed London Georgian house.

SCOTT, Christopher
Burness, Edinburgh (0131) 473 6000
cs@burness.co.uk
Specialisation: Banking and corporate finance, including senior/mezzanine/equity funding packages in the context of acquisitions, development projects and joint ventures, reviewing and advising on the Scottish aspects of international financings involving Scottish borrowers, debt reorganisations/capitalisations. Also experience of private equity investment and listed/AIM corporate finance work. Recent deal: acting for Bank of Scotland in relation to £90m of senior/subordinated development facilities to Ocean Terminal Limited (leisure/retail development).
Prof. Memberships: Member of the Securities Institute; Writer to the Signet.
Career: Trainee at *W & J Burness WS* (now *Burness*); qualified 1985; assistant solicitor 1985-87; assistant solicitor *Travers Smith Braithwaite* 1987-88; assistant solicitor *Burness* 1988-89; partner 1989.
Personal: Edinburgh University (1982 LLB Hons 1st; 1983 Diploma in Legal Practice). Leisure: fly fishing, hill walking and motor cycling.

SLATER, Richard
Slaughter and May, London (020) 7600 1200
Partner in Financial/Commercial Department. Head of Banking Stream.
Specialisation: Principal area of practice is debt financing of all types, including syndicated loan facilities, structured financings, project financings and bond and note issues. Has also acted on international equity offerings, flotations, privatisations and corporate and commercial work of a general nature.
Prof. Memberships: The Law Society.
Career: With *Slaughter and May* throughout. Articles 1970, qualified 1972, Partner 1979. Hong Kong office 1981-1986.
Personal: Born 18 August 1948. Educated at University College School, Hampstead (1956-1965), Lycée Michelet, Paris (1965-1966) and Pembroke College, Cambridge 1966-1969. Lives in London.

SMITH, Mark
DLA, Leeds (08700) 111111
mark.smith@dla.com
Specialisation: The whole range of banking and finance matters, both domestic and cross-border. Since arriving in Leeds in 1991, founded a non-contentious banking and finance practice, has built up a thriving practice of three partners and ten other fee-earners, acting for northern-based clearing banks and building societies and London-based merchant banks and overseas financial institutions. Specialisations include aquisition finance, structured property finance, housing association finance, syndicated loans, mortgage-book acquisitions, PFI and restructuring and work-outs.
Career: Matthew Humberstone Foundations School, Cleethorpes 1969-75. St. Edmund Hall, Oxford University 1975-78. Qualified 1984. Partner *Dibb Lupton Broomhead* 1991.
Personal: Rugby, cricket, walking and theatre. Lives in Leeds.

SPENDLOVE, Justin
Ashurst Morris Crisp, London (020) 7638 1111
Banking Department.
Specialisation: Partner in the banking department specialising in structured leveraged acquisition finance.
Career: Articled at *Wilde Sapte* where he became a partner in 1989. Joined *Ashurst Morris Crisp* as a partner in 1996.

STEWART, Mark
Clifford Chance, London (020) 7600 1000
mark.stewart@cliffordchance.com
See under Corporate Finance, p.265

STONEHAM, Michael P.
Dundas & Wilson CS, Edinburgh (020) 7200 7310

SWEETING, Malcolm
Clifford Chance, London (020) 7600 1000
malcolm.sweeting@cliffordchance.com
Specialisation: Partner in finance practice.
Career: BA Business Law 1978; Law Finals 1979. Partner 1990.

TAYLOR, Michael F.
Walker Morris, Leeds (0113) 283 2500
Specialisation: Work includes acquisition finance, MBO/MBI finance and general banking, lending and security advice, restructuring and work outs.
Career: Qualified 1986; Partner *Walker Morris* 1991.
Personal: Attended King Edward VI School, Lichfield and University of Bristol 1980-83. Leisure interests include hockey and fly-fishing. Lives in Leeds.

TUCKER, John C.
Linklaters (A member firm of Linklaters & Alliance), London (020) 7456 4496
john.tucker@linklaters.com
Head of Banking.
Specialisation: Areas of specialisation include syndicated lending, secured and structured financings, acquisition and project finance and reorganisation work. Represents banks, bank syndicates and other creditors as well as borrowers in both UK and international financing transactions.
Career: Qualifications LL B (Hons), BA Accountancy. Admitted as a Barrister and Solicitor in South Australia 1980. Partner of *Finlaysons*, Adelaide 1984-89. Qualified, England & Wales, 1988. Became a *Linklaters* Partner in 1990.

TWIST, G. Patrick A.S.
Pinsent Curtis, Birmingham (0121) 200 1050
patrick.twist@pinsents.com
See under Projects/PFI, p.701

VAUGHAN, Philip D.
Eversheds, Cardiff (02920) 471147
Partner.
Specialisation: Practice covers a wide-range of non-contentious banking and finance work and includes transactional work (including project and acquisition finance), regulatory advice and drafting of standard documentation for banks, building societies and finance companies. Has a particular expertise in consumer credit work. Also involved in a wide range of non-contentious insolvency work acting for receivers, administrators and liquidators and advising lenders on enforcement of security and restructuring/refinancings.
Career: Qualified 1984. Formerly with *Clifford Chance* and *National Westminster Bank* Legal Department. Joined current firm in 1987 and became Partner in 1988.
Personal: Born 14th December 1958. Educated at Haverfordwest Grammar School, St. Edmund Hall, Oxford (M.A.) and Emmanuel College, Cambridge (LL.M.).

VICKERS, Mark H.
Ashurst Morris Crisp, London (020) 7638 1111
mark.vickers@ashursts.com
Partner banking and capital markets group.
Specialisation: Corporate banking and international finance: specialising in UK and cross-border acquisition finance and leveraged acquisitions, particularly management buy-outs/buy-ins and institutional purchases; structured finance; and global syndicated lending. Is one of the market's leading experts on the debt funding of public to private takeovers.
Career: Joined *Ashurst Morris Crisp* in 1999 having been Head of european acquisition finance at a top 10 UK law firm (1980-1999).
Publications: Author: 'Senior Debt Market for Management Buy-outs' and 'Public to Private Takeovers: The New Paradigms'.
Personal: Helicopter pilot.

WHATNALL, John
Halliwell Landau, Manchester (0161) 835 3003
Partner in corporate department.
Specialisation: Main areas of practice are banking and corporate finance. Acted for NatWest Acquisition Finance on Pets at Home's acquisition of PETsMART and for Barclays Acquisition Finance on BIMBO of Ferranti Technologies.
Prof. Memberships: Law Society, Securities Institute.
Career: Qualified in 1981. Worked at *Herbert Oppenheimer Nathan & Vandyk* 1981-6. Joined *Halliwell Landau* in 1986, becoming a partner in 1987.
Personal: Born 22nd June 1957. Attended The Queen's College, Oxford 1975-78. Leisure interests include opera. Lives in Wilmslow.

WILTSHIRE, Peter
CMS Cameron McKenna, Bristol (0117) 930 0200
Specialisation: Non-contentious banking, including rescue and work-outs.
Career: Articled *Cameron Markby/Cameron Markby Hewitt* 1988-1990. Qualified *Cameron Markby Hewitt*, London, 1990. Bristol *Cameron Markby Hewitt* to date (now *CMS Cameron McKenna*). Partner 1999.
Personal: Regular provider of seminars for SPI (3R's). Church. Armchair sports critic. Singing. Married, five children.

WOOD, Philip
Allen & Overy, London (020) 7330 3000
Specialisation: Partner, head of banking department, and head of the firm's knowledge management and education. Specialises in all aspects of international banking, including syndicated loans, project finance, title finance, trade finance, secured finance, payment and clearing systems, shipping and aircraft, insolvency and business reconstructions, bank regulation, and legal systems, expert in comparative financial law.
Prof. Memberships: Member of City of London Law Society Banking Law Sub-Committee; Board of the Institute of Advanced Legal Studies; Visiting Professor, Faculty of Law, Queen Mary and Westfield College. Editorial Board of Butterworth's Journal of International Banking and Financial Law, Practical Law for Companies, European Financial Services Law. Advisory Board of Asia Business, Law Review and Business Law International. Unidroit correspondent.
Career: Articled *Allen & Overy*, qualified 1970, Partner 1974. Author of ten books on aspects of the law of international finance.
Personal: Born 1942 Livingstone, Zambia. University of Cape Town (BA), Oxford University (MA). Interests include landscaping, piano, walking, history, science and econimics.

WOOLCOCK, Brian
DLA, Birmingham (08700) 111111
brian.woolcock@dla.com
Specialisation: All types of transactions and debt finance, including factoring, invoice discounting and development finance.
Career: Qualified 1982. Assistant/associate/partner – *Glaisyers* to 1990; assistant/associate – *Edge Ellison* to 1998; partner – *DLA* 1998 to date.
Personal: Interests revolve around James and Edward and their mother Julia. Also enjoys bridge, cars, computers and sport.

WOOLLEY, R.S.
DLA, Manchester (08700) 111111
simon.woolley@dla.com
Specialisation: £68m institutional buy-out of Maccers Group; £52m expansion finance for NES Group; £62m public to private buy-out of Joseph Holt plc.
Prof. Memberships: Law Society.
Career: Trained at *Travers Smith Braithwaite.* UK Legal Advisor to Istituto Bancario San Paolo di Torino SPA. Joined *Alsop Wilkinson* in September 1993.
Personal: Golf, skiing, motorsport, family. Married with two daughters.

CAPITAL MARKETS

OVERVIEW: Another area where the *"gang of four"* international Magic Circle firms dominate. Many consider that there has been a further consolidation of the market in their favour, which is *"perhaps unhealthy, but that's what the clients want."* Strong foreign offices are deemed helpful by clients, with Clifford Chance's merger having been generally well-received by the market.

A dual US-UK capability is considered vital by clients, and the top firms have that. Perhaps unsurprisingly, US firms are making an impact in equity capital markets. US and European investment banks report using US firms with highly satisfactory results. Of those not mentioned in the editorial, Skadden Arps Slate Meagher & Flom's London office is a leading investment banking client's *"secret weapon"* and Cleary Gottlieb Steen & Hamilton are considered *"brave in their advice."*

The debt and equity section will appear to readers to be skewed towards debt. This is a reflection of the fact that many equity issues are dealt with by the corporate departments of firms. Thus further information on equity issuance appears in the corporate finance section. Clients for all three areas covered in this section (debt and equity, securitisation and repackaging, derivatives) are mentioned under the debt and equity editorial.

LEADING IN-HOUSE LAWYERS

International Debt & Equity Issues

Tracy KINGSLEY-DANIELLS, Director of Transaction Management, *Credit Suisse First Boston International*

Carol MOIR, Executive Director of Transactions Legal, *UBS Warburg*

Roger MUNGER, Head of Transaction Management, *ABN Amro Bank NV*

Roger SCOTTS, Executive Director, *Goldman Sachs International*

Kevin SOWERBUTTS, Head of Legal, *BNP Paribas*

Jennifer TAYLOR, Director of Law & Compliance, *Merrill Lynch International*

Tracy Kingsley-Daniells works on the structured bonds side. She has a *"strong team"* and *"understands the markets well."* **Carol Moir** does a *"very good job"* and is perceived as *"a star of the future"* for her work in the debt capital markets. *"Experienced"* **Roger Munger** *"manages a professional team"* and *"keeps an eye on the big picture." "First-class"* **Roger Scotts** has a *"very good understanding of the business."* He is described as *"brilliant, pragmatic, knowledgeable, efficient."* Also *"highly thought of"* is **Kevin Sowerbutts** who is *"very commercial."* The *"excellent"* **Jennifer Taylor** *"is able to harness the different aspects of the business with her understanding,"* particularly on the debt capital markets.

In-house lawyers profiles: page 1177

RESEARCH APPROVED BY BMRB: *For this edition,* Chambers' *researchers conducted 6083 interviews – 4408 with law firms, 598 with barristers and 1077 with clients.*

The validity of the research was scrutinised by BMRB International, who audited both the methodology and the results at our offices in July 2000. They interviewed Chambers' *researchers and cross-checked sample interviews. Details of the audit appear on page 7.*

LONDON

INTERNATIONAL DEBT & EQUITY

Allen & Overy Clients' perceptions of the practice are summarised by the comment of one investment banker: *"We use them particularly on anything nasty; they offer a consistently high standard and the associates are well trained."* An expanding international practice, with expertise recognised in key continental and far eastern jurisdictions. Also has a *"serious and quality"* US capability in capital markets and complementary areas including tax.

Although perceived as a loss to the team, the retirement of Richard Sykes has not significantly dented the firm's abilities in the area. While lacking the numbers of high profile individuals available to Linklaters, the team is still felt to have the *"quality and the experience"* to remain at the top. The team's principal focus is on debt work, but most lawyers in the group have expertise outside straight debt work. Often referred to as *"the MTN firm,"* the team has a *"successful"* and prolific volume debt practice, and a strong profile in high-yield work.

Practice manager **Boyan Wells** is a *"first rate lawyer"* who has been *"immersed in it for years."* Most lawyers find him a *"good guy to have on the other side,"* and clients appreciate his *"technical excellence and sense of humour"* and use him for strategic matters. New to the rankings is client favourite **Stephen Miller**, a capital markets all-rounder known for his debt and structured work. He is regarded as someone who *"gets the deal done without confrontation, doesn't mess around and is clever and personable."*

With the convergence of many aspects of domestic and international floats, a separate equity capital markets group was launched at the beginning of the year. Members of the team advised on around 30 equity offerings in 1999, often acting for the underwriters. Although it is not perceived to have as high a profile as its immediate competitors in equity transactions, the practice is still viewed as *"active and quality,"* both domestically and internationally.

Other practitioners to enter the rankings this year are **Roger Wedderburn-Day** *("reliable and technically excellent")* and **Daniel Shurman**, who is especially respected for his emerging markets work.

Matters handled this year include advising the banks on Halifax's issue of £245 million and €415 million of preferred securities, and Bank Austria Creditanstalt on a $100 million multi-currency commercial paper issue for Pliva (the Croatian pharmaceutical company). MTN work includes advising the dealers on the establishment of a new EMTN Programme for EDP and advising Alpha Credit Bank on the establishment of its EMTN Programme (Greece's first non-sovereign programme). Last year saw the firm advise on 19 convertible and exchangeable bond issues, including advising Deutsche Bank as lead manager of a €1.2 billion exchangeables into shares of Total Fina SA. On the equity side, work includes advising KPNQwest NV in relation to its US$1.05 billion flotation and advising the sponsor and financial adviser to The eXchange Holdings plc on the company's £200 million flotation. **Clients:** ABN Amro, BSCH, Bear Stearns, CIBC, CSFB, Goldman Sachs, ING Barings, Lehman Brothers, HSBC, JP Morgan, Merrill Lynch, Morgan Stanley DW, Paribas, WDR, West Merchant Bank, Deutsche Bank, Salomon Smith Barney, Nomura International, Citibank, Barclays Capital, British Aerospace and Government of Singapore.

CAPITAL MARKETS: INTERNATIONAL DEBT & EQUITY • London	Ptnrs	Assts
❶ Allen & Overy	37*	143*
Linklaters	21	111
❷ Clifford Chance	20	115
❸ Freshfields Bruckhaus Deringer	30*	30*
❹ Slaughter and May	12*	15*
❺ Ashurst Morris Crisp	3	7
Baker & McKenzie	7	14
Herbert Smith	16	45
Lovells	6*	16*
Norton Rose	5	12
Simmons & Simmons	13*	28*
Weil, Gotshal & Manges	6	18

LEADING INDIVIDUALS	
❶ **BURN Lachlan** Linklaters	**CANBY Michael** Linklaters
EASTWELL Nicholas Linklaters	**WELLS Boyan** Allen & Overy
❷ **DUNNIGAN David** Clifford Chance	**EDLMANN Stephen** Linklaters
FRANK David Slaughter and May	
❸ **BROWN Jane** Linklaters	**MILLER Stephen** Allen & Overy
PITKIN Jeremy Freshfields Bruckhaus Deringer	**THOMSON Keith** Linklaters
❹ **BICKERTON David** Clifford Chance	**CLARK Charles** Linklaters
DUNLOP Stewart Clifford Chance	**SHURMAN Daniel** Allen & Overy
THIEFFRY Gilles Norton Rose	**WEDDERBURN-DAY Roger** Allen & Overy
ONES TO WATCH	
EATOUGH David Clifford Chance	**OVENDEN Simon** Linklaters
PRIDMORE Nigel Linklaters	

Within each band, firms are listed alphabetically. *See **Profiles** on page 129*
** Figures denote total capital markets team sizes.*

Linklaters *"They have a superb capital markets practice and have had for a long time."* Particular strengths are in free-standing bond issues and emerging market debt and equity. The team advised lead managers on 193 stand alone bond issues in 1999. With its traditionally strong M&A side, the firm has strength in equity issues (including internet issues) and is recognised as the most balanced of the volume capital markets players. The team's international network is expanding and it has a recognised US capacity, with a leading position on 144A transactions. Most clients appreciate the partner involvement on deals, the strength at associate level and note the *"effort the firm puts into us."*

The team's lawyers all do a mix of debt and equity work, with domestic equity issues usually dealt with by the corporate finance team. The popular **Lachlan Burn** is considered *"the senior honcho on the technical points"* – a *"judgement call man."* He is a combination of *"law and lore,"* and clients appreciate his *"knowledge of the history and of what's going on now."* Market consensus is that he is *"second to none on regulatory matters."* **Nick Eastwell** *("a good person to have on your side")* is primarily known for his equity work in emerging markets, but can turn his hand to many things. Clients find in him *"an investment banker, regulator and accountant as well as a lawyer,"* while others praise his *"business acumen, technical ability and charm."* Also *"excellent with a client"* is the *"outstanding"* **Michael Canby.** He is *"astute and able to see the point quickly"* and is appreciated for his *"commitment and sleeves rolled up approach."* Practice leader **Stephen Edlmann** *("you can tell he's got bags of experience")* divides his time between management and transactional work. **Charles Clark** remains respected for his technical ability and for his *"basic courtesy – he sticks by his word."* Joining the rankings this year are the *"technical and thorough"* **Jane Brown,** who *"doesn't miss a point"* and the *"excellent"* all-rounder **Keith Thomson** *("reliable and not over-ambitious.")* Both are respected for their debt work. Equity issues this year include advising the banks on the listing of South African Breweries plc, of Freeserve, of Thus and of e-bookers.com, the last being a London-driven global offering including a listing on Nasdaq and the Neuer Markt. The team advised on Adecco's convertible notes and share offering to raise approximately US$700 million. It also advised on the first ever issue by a UK bank of tax-deductible Tier 1 capital, advising Halifax on a £500 million issue of guaranteed, non-voting, non-cumulative preferred securities. Work on the debt side includes a $235 million high yield bond issue by Jazztel plc. **Clients:** CSFB, JP Morgan, Robert Fleming & Co Ltd, Barclays Capital. Goldman Sachs, Lehman Brothers, Merrill Lynch, Nomura, Paribas, Salomons/Citibank, WDR.

Clifford Chance A mainstream capital markets practice with strengths on free-standing bond work, MTN programmes and non-UK equity, particularly emerging markets work. Members of the team are *"helpful and responsive,"* with *"a high degree of commerciality."* Concerns were raised about the perceived high turnover of the group and the consistency of quality in some of the firm's continental offices (although offices in Southern Europe and Germany are considered *"excellent."*) Post-mergers, the distinguishing feature of the firm continues to be its international orientation. *"Hands-on client man"* **David Dunnigan** is *"a great networker who, if he doesn't know, knows someone who does."* New to our lists are the *"accommodating"* **David Bickerton** and the *"personable"* **Stewart Dunlop.** Bickerton is *"diligent and technically extremely good,"* and is known for his expertise on warrants and project bonds. Client favourite Dunlop is *"in the David Dunnigan mould"* – he *"gets the deal done."*

Traditionally thought of as a debt capital markets practice, the merger with Pünder, which has a significant IPO practice, helps balance the team on a European level. Deals this year include the Olivetti take-over financing and British Aerospace plc's £596 million exchangeable to shares of Orange. High-yield bond deals include those of TDL Infomedia Group plc and ONO/Cableuropa SA. The team also worked on the largest ever non-gilt sterling offering with a guarantee by the UK Government, the London & Continental Railways Eurobond offer. **Clients:** LIFFE, British Bankers Association, The Bond Market Association, The Futures and Options Association.

Freshfields Bruckhaus Deringer The head of the capital markets practice, **Jeremy Pitkin,** is *"a joy to have on a deal."* The practice is *"not at the top for the range of debt work,"* principally because it is not perceived to have gone for the debt commodity business as most of its immediate competitors have. In debt however, the firm has advised on a number of MTN programmes this year, for arrangers and for issuers such as AXA, Kingfisher and the Republic of Lebanon. *"Good on free standing bonds,"* stand-alone issues include offerings by Repsol, Compass, China Telecom and Pearson, for a mix of issuers and arrangers.

The general feeling is that the practice is *"much stronger on equity,"* where it is rated *"at the top,"* both for UK and non-UK company work. Internationally, particular developments this year have been a strengthening of teams in European offices, particularly France and Germany, and continued recognition for strength in Southern Europe. Also has recognised US capacity. Cross-border work includes the first ever listing of a UK plc on the Neuer Markt and the Easdaq, the IPO by Dialog Semiconductor plc and advising on an Alpha Credit Bank issuance, listed in Athens, with GDRs in London and a US 144A component. The firm has been active this year, advising on the IPOs of service providers, companies providing technologies for access to the web over wireless networks and other internet businesses. Issues include those of Thus, lastminute.com and The eXchange Holdings. Other work includes a €336 million listing for MG plc and equity and bond issuances for groups such as Fortis and Stagecoach. **Clients:** CIBC, Deutsche Bank/Bankers Trust, DKB, Financial Security Assurance, Goldman Sachs, JP Morgan, RBS, Salomon Smith Barney, Nomura, WDR, Paribas, AIG Financial Products, AMP.

Slaughter and May The firm is not considered to have the emphasis on capital markets of its immediate rivals – *"they are client-led, not product-led, so they only go in when their clients tap the market."* It is testament to the firm's ability that competitors can regard the firm as having de-emphasised capital markets, yet still concede that the firm is a leader for UK and non-UK equity work (notably Scandinavian equity). Regarded as *"superb company people"* with *"some of the best lawyers,"* the firm tends to appear principally on the side of the underwriters. While most of the principal M&A and banking partners were mentioned as leaders for equity issuance, the capital markets stand-out name is the structured debt-oriented **David Frank**. *"Long-standing and well-known,"* his work includes banking, and he is considered *"hard-working and diligent."*

Work this year includes advising the Enron Corporation on its debut Eurobond issue of €400 million, Abbey National on a new US$15 billion MTN programme and debt issues for domestics such as Diageo, Unilever, Cadbury Schweppes and Bradford and Bingley. The group has also represented foreign companies such as United Utilities and Oesterreichische Kontrollbank.

Equity work has involved a €775 million global offering for Fortis, a £700 million placing for Colt Telecom, the ebookers flotation, the Old Mutual demutualisation and global offer, and advising the banks on a British Aerospace issue to GEC shareholders. Other work includes the £438 million Millennium & Copthorne and £162.5 million Eurotunnel rights issues. International work has encompassed advice on convertible bonds for Société Foncière Lyonnaise, advising on issues such as Finmatica for the underwriters and Parques Reunidos for the global co-ordinators **Clients:** Fortis, Abbey National Treasury Services, Enron Corporation, Unilever, Deutsche Bank, Moody's, RBS, Warburgs.

Ashurst Morris Crisp A well respected group which is not seen as a *"bread and butter outfit."* However, it is particularly noted for its equity and European high-yield debt work. High-yield work this year includes advising on Clubhaus plc's £50 million issue and a subsequent £10 million tranche, and on an issue for Atlantic Telecom Group plc. Other debt work involved advising on Imperial Tobacco's €2 billion debt issuance programme and its €650 million first drawing, and advising on $530 million's worth of exchangeable notes for Swiss Re. Project bonds are also an area of expertise. Equity tends to be dealt with by the corporate department, and here, the firm advised the issuers on a £100 million placing for Kingston Communications (HULL) plc and a $665 million rights issue for Henlys Group plc, following its acquisition of Blue Bird Corporation. **Clients:** Abbey National Financial Products/Treasury Services, Swiss Re, ING Barings, Daiwa SBCM Europe, Sumitomo, Invesco, West LB.

Baker & McKenzie Focused on international transactions, the team is particularly known for its work on equity offerings for emerging European companies. This year has seen a string of deals out of Central and Eastern Europe and Egypt. These include advising Al Ezz Steel Rebars SAE on offering and listing of shares in Cairo, Alexandria and London and advising the lead underwriter CSFB, in a MATAV share offering. Strength in telecoms work has seen the practice advise on telecoms offerings in Eygpt, Lithuania, Hungary, Poland and Croatia. The firm also advised on the $175 million US/German dual listing of PrimaCom AG and on a high yield issue for Pannon GSM Tavkozlesi Rt. On the structured side, the firm was international and Italian counsel to WestLB as arranger of the €118 million securitisation of Italian lease receivables by Landes Srl. **Clients:** CSFB, Schroders, CAIB, DLJ, Chase Securities, PrimaCom AG, Pannon GSM Tavkozlesi Rt, Al Ezz Steel Rebars S.A.E.

Herbert Smith Although involved on some of the most important internet IPOs of the year, the undoubted ability of the capital markets practice has not translated into a high market profile in this area. Two significant internet IPOs were the Freeserve and QXL.com IPOs, with London and New York listings. Other equity work saw the team advise Stagecoach on the first open offer using book building techniques. On the debt side, the practice advised on a £1.2 billion bond issue by Edison First Power Limited and advised LCR on the issue of £2.65 billion worth of Government guaranteed bonds to finance the construction of section 1 of the Channel Tunnel Rail Link. Other work includes advising Olivetti in connection with their refinancing of borrowings following the hostile take-over of Telecom Italia. The firm has also been active on a range of securitisation and derivatives work. **Clients:** BSkyB, Credit Lyonnais, Lazards, CSFB, Merrill Lynch, Eurotunnel, Colonial Financial Services.

Lovells A balanced practice working for an even mix of issuers and lead managers, domestically and internationally. Active this year on high-yield issues, in emerging markets and in the hi-tech sector. Has an expanding US capability. Debt work this year has seem the firm active on Kappa Beheer BV's €370 million high yield bond issue and Barclays Bank's £4 billion debt issuance programme. Equity work includes advising on the South African Breweries IPO for £3.5 billion, the Finmatica €67.5 million combined Italian public offer and international institutional offer, and the £305 million IPO of Morse Holdings. **Clients:** Bank of Scotland, Barclays Bank, CA Indosuez, DLJ, Dresdner Kleinwort Benson, Henderson Investors, ING Barings, Société Générale, Alstom, Slough Estates, Xerox Corporation, Granada, BNP Paribas, JP Morgan, Rothschilds.

Norton Rose A comparatively small team with recognised strengths in debt and securitisation. The year has seen a vast increase in the firm's derivatives capacity and the first full year for the US securities team. A balanced team whose steady growth and increased profile has seen it break into the market for US investment bank work this year. This is London's up and coming capital markets practice.

Debt practice leader **Gilles Thieffry** is a debt all-rounder, working on straight debt and convertible issues, and has expertise in the insurance world. The team advised the EBRD on 24 bond issues of various denominations (totalling approximately €4 billion) under its EMTN programme. The practice advised Lehman Brothers on a €110 million upper tier II issue by Cofinoga and a $100 million issue for French reinsurance company SCOR. Work for BNP Paribas included four issues of embedded option bonds of $50 million each and four issues of $55 million each and floating rate notes.

Equity work is handled out of the corporate finance department and the firm has a strong emerging markets capacity. The team acted on a $3 billion share offering by HSBC and advised the lead managers on the $100 million share and global depository receipt issue by Al Ezz Steel Rebars of Egypt. **Clients:** BNP Paribas, Lehman Brothers International, Bank of Ireland, HSBC, EBRD, BMW, Kingdoms of Sweden and Belgium, AXA, Ashanti, Lukoil, Fox Kids.

Simmons & Simmons Work on debt and equity for a variety of lead managers and issuers, and praised for its perceived strength in the high-yield arena. Debt work this year saw the group act for the banks on Jazztel's high yield debt issue and on £400 million of exchangeables for Railtrack. On the equity side, the firm advised on the HK$4.8 billion international offering of New World China Land Ltd. Other work includes a secondary listing on the LSE for Esprit and for AlliedSignal after its merger with Honeywell. The team also advised the Indian Government on the GDR issue of the Gas Authority of India. The non-exclusive link-up with Fried Frank of the US gives the firm a strong US securities capacity as well as strength on structured matters. Corporate Treasury and Corporate Trustee work are also active areas. **Clients:** Deutsche Bank, NatWest, BAT, Railtrack, Dresdner Kleinwort Benson, Fuji International, Barclays Capital.

Weil, Gotshal & Manges A mix of US and English partners in a firm particularly known for its securitisation and structured work. The practice nevertheless provides a broad range of debt and equity advice. *"Clearly trying to compete with the Magic Circle,"* the departure of high-profile names on the banking side has *"hurt their firepower,"* but clients still believe that the firm has *"retained strong people just below partner level."* The firm advised the MediaOne Group on its US$1.129 billion offering of mandatory exchangeable notes into ADRs of Vodafone Airtouch and acted for Hicks Muse in a US$299 million offering and £75 million high yield notes in connection with the buyout of Hillsdown Holdings plc. Also acted on

Matsushita's €1.5 billion SEC-registered IPO of EPCOS AG, a former Siemens/Matsushita joint venture. The firm's Warsaw and London offices combined on the largest international offering in Eastern Europe in 1999, representing Nafta Polska on the sale of 30% of the Polish Oil Corp. (PKN), with a subsequent listing in London and Warsaw. **Clients:** JP Morgan Securities Ltd, Morgan Stanley, Deutsche Bank AG, Telewest Communications plc, Hicks Muse, CSFB, Chase, Merrill Lynch, NatWest, Nikko Europe.

SECURITISATION & REPACKAGING

CAPITAL MARKETS: SECURITISATION & REPACKAGING • London	Ptnrs	Assts
❶ Clifford Chance	8	40
❷ Allen & Overy	37*	143*
Freshfields Bruckhaus Deringer	30*	30*
❸ Linklaters	10	28
❹ Sidley & Austin	13	21
❺ Ashurst Morris Crisp	3	5
Lovells	6*	16*
Norton Rose	4	8
Simmons & Simmons	13*	28*
Slaughter and May	12*	15*
Weil, Gotshal & Manges	3	12

LEADING INDIVIDUALS	
❶ **FALCONER Ian** Freshfields Bruckhaus Deringer	
KRISCHER David Allen & Overy	
❷ **BEDFORD Paul** Allen & Overy	**FULLER Geoff** Allen & Overy
INGRAM Kevin Clifford Chance	**KELLY Jacky** Weil, Gotshal & Manges
RAINES Marke Shearman & Sterling	**TROTT David** Freshfields Bruckhaus Deringer
❸ **FORRYAN Andrew** Clifford Chance	**HUGHES Richard** Linklaters
MACKENZIE Marcus Freshfields Bruckhaus Deringer	
OAKLEY Chris Clifford Chance	**PENN Graham** Sidley & Austin
RUSSELL John Brown & Wood	**SMITH Michael** Ashurst Morris Crisp
VOISEY Peter Clifford Chance	**VOISIN Michael** Linklaters
WALSH Jonathan Norton Rose	**WOODHALL John** Clifford Chance
❹ **BEAUMONT Rupert** Slaughter and May	**BRESSLAW James** Simmons & Simmons
HANDLING Erica Weil, Gotshal & Manges	**HUDD David** Lovells
RICE James Linklaters	**SMITH Christopher** Slaughter and May
SMITH Sarah Sidley & Austin	**TUCKER Julian** Allen & Overy

Within each band, firms are listed alphabetically. *See **Profiles** on page 129*
** Figures denote total capital markets team sizes.*

Clifford Chance The depth of the team, international reach, volume of deals and breadth of practice make the firm's securitisation practice stand out. Lateral hires, internal promotions, partners returning from overseas offices and departmental moves have doubled the size of the practice's partnership in the last year.

Head of the London practice is the *"charming and well-connected"* **Chris Oakley**, who is appreciated for his *"painstaking and meticulous"* approach. The popular **Kevin Ingram** is considered *"an awesome mind who is not a cheap point scorer. The only problem is getting hold of him."* He is regarded by some as the *"best concepts guy"* – *"you get him to think and his partners to draft and you have a dream combination."* The *"user-friendly"* **John Woodhall** enters our rankings this year, following his return from Hong Kong. **Andrew Forryan** also enters our lists this year. *"Urbane, sensible, polite and professional,"* he is regarded as a *"bright guy,"* particularly on property-related work. Further boosting the team's capability was the arrival of the highly-regarded **Peter Voisey** from Lovells.

Main areas of work are UK and European public bond issues, private placement conduit work and property securitisations. A *"strong franchise"* spread through Europe, Asia and the Americas, significant deals this year have involved multi-office co-ordinations, including the Formula One, Amstel and INPS transactions, as well as the $1 billion Gracechurch Card Funding (No. 1) plc. The practice advised BNP on the first synthetic CLO transaction to be realised by a bank incorporated in the European Union using credit default swap technology. Also advised the banks on the Iberbond 1999 plc securitisation of lease receivables and, closer to home, acted on the St James's Park Finance plc securitisation.

Allen & Overy Considered to have a smaller practice than Clifford Chance, the team is still perceived to be a balanced unit which has had *"a really good year considering the size of their team."*

While not denting the team's capacity, the departure of Marke Raines (to Shearman & Sterling) and a high profile associate, is seen to have affected the forward momentum of the practice. A top name in securitisation is *"motivator"* **David Krischer**, regarded as *"light years ahead in terms of technical excellence."* He is a dual qualified US/UK lawyer. He is *"going from strength to strength"* and is *"the main guy for a client to go to."* With his *"non-confrontational"* approach, the *"charming and delightful"* **Paul Bedford** is *"the one to front a deal."* A *"details man,"* highly regarded for his brain power, he comes from a corporate trustee background. **Julian Tucker** enters our rankings this year following strong market recommendation for his *"commercial approach,"* with clients appreciating his *"flamboyant nature, refreshing in an area where the hours are enough to drive you potty."* An all-rounder, he has experience in property-related work.

Large deals this year include advising on the landmark £1.54 billion securitisation of the Broadgate Estate in the City of London, and the Madame Tussauds securitisation, the first backed by leisure assets. The team was also involved on the Unique Pubs Group securitisation and the £610 million securitisation of rental income within the Trafford Centre in Manchester. In addition, the group was involved on the world's first ever securitisation of airport revenues without an external guarantee (London City Airport.) In the more discreet world of repackaging, **Geoff Fuller** is one of London's top names. In 1999, the practice advised on approximately 160 repackaging issues, dealing with a wide range of financial instruments. Advised Deutsche Bank on the establishment of a secured repackaging programme for Repackaged Offshore Collateralised Kredit (ROCK,) the first repackaging programme with an issuer incorporated in Gibraltar. The practice also represented Nomura International plc in connection with the Y32.4 billion repackaging of a variety of Japanese corporate credits.

Freshfields Bruckhaus Deringer A *"high-quality"* team *"involved on the more interesting deals."* While the practice is considered to have international breadth, notably in Germany following the historic merger with Bruckhaus, it is not yet considered to have the critical mass of its immediate competitors. **Ian Falconer**'s reputation precedes him. He has *"all the attributes one would look for,"* and is a *"great draftsman who gets deals done without aggro."* Such is his reputation, that some have said that he is *"overworked."* Competitors have *"excellent dealings"* with **David Trott** and **Marcus Mackenzie**. Trott is *"technically extremely good, and he knows it."* Mackenzie, new to the rankings, is well regarded and has *"a nice way about him."*

The team works on complex matters across Europe and has been involved this year on securitisation transactions involving mortgages, pub businesses, rolling stock, ferry businesses, autoloans, student loans and care homes businesses. Advised JP Morgan as lead manager of Abbey National's benchmark £1 billion residential mortgage securitisation through Holmes Funding No 1. Also represented on the first transaction in the Eurobond markets involving the issue of enhanced secured aircraft notes.

Linklaters *"Aggressive on price,"* the securitisation team is *"chasing hard."* The firm has made a push in the area with recruitment of the well regarded **Richard Hughes** *("he will make a good practice out of it.")* He is new to our rankings, as is securitisation all-rounder **Jim Rice**. The firm's dominant figure for repackaging work, Andrew Carmichael, resides in the Hong Kong office. **Michael Voisin** is an all-rounder, well regarded for his structured work in repackaging and credit-linked notes. Clients described him as *"technical"* and a *"thinker."*

Strengths are found in the non-conforming ('sub-prime') mortgage sector and in the credit card market. Acted for the banks on the £600 million residential mortgage securitisation for Northern Rock plc, and on the $1 billion Gracechurch Card Funding (No.1) plc, at the time the largest UK credit card securitisation.

Sidley & Austin Well-known in the securitisation field, with a large team and a perceived focus on asset-backed conduit work. With complementary practices in areas such as tax and regulatory work, the firm is considered to have *"brought in the armoury,"* and many view the firm as *"the leader of the US practices."* Practice leader is the *"technically excellent"* **Graham Penn**, while newly-ranked **Sarah Smith** is a *"sensible and clever lawyer."*

Known for its work for rating agencies such as Duff & Phelps (recently merged with Fitch IBCA), the firm has a broad range of clients including originators, issuers of securities and liquidity providers. Work this year includes the £360m European Loan Conduit No.2 BV acting for Morgan Stanley. This was the first European commercial mortgage securitisation in which the notes were offered for sale in the US under 144A. The practice acted for a Dutch bank sponsor, and for Morgan Stanley in the securitisation of a portfolio of pubs by Alehouse Finance plc.

In the murky waters between securitisation and derivatives, the firm advised credit derivatives leader BCI in its capacity as originator of a synthetic CLO transaction involving the use of a credit default swap (€280 million.)

Ashurst Morris Crisp The *"busy"* **Michael Smith**, who *"does a bit of everything,"* is particularly well regarded for his structured work. In this area the firm is considered to be *"one of the more experienced London outfits"* for CDO work. Work this year includes acting for Immediate Capital Group plc on the Eurocredit CDO 1, BV issue of €416,000,500 asset backed notes, the first euro-denominated high yield CDO transaction closed in the Euro Markets. The team also advises on a broad range of derivatives issues.

Lovells This is an area of strength for the firm but the recent departure of Peter Voisey to Clifford Chance is perceived by the market to have affected the team's capacity. However, *"figurehead"* **David Hudd** remains well regarded for his structured work. The firm is regarded as having a *"niche in repackaging"* where it has acted this year on repackagings of financial instruments for clients such as BNP Paribas, DLJ and CA Indosuez. A highlight of the year was acting on the First Active Financial plc securitisation of flexible mortgages, a first for the UK. The team advised on credit card receivables securitisations such as the Citibank Credit Card Master Trust 1's €1 billion credit card participation certificates. The team has also acted on car loan and personal loan receivables securitisations.

Norton Rose *"Nice guy"* **Jonathan Walsh** has a *"great reputation"* in securitisation. He heads a team which acted on a $5 billion conduit (Loch Ness) for Royal Bank of Scotland, a £116 million securitisation of a Boeing 747-400 by KLM and a £120 million commercial property securitisation for Workspace Group plc. The team also acted for SG in relation to a credit card receivable securitisation for a company providing credit card services to major UK retailers.

Simmons & Simmons The firm is known for its focus on structured finance and structured securities (repackaging) work, an area where securitisation expert **James Bresslaw** continues to be respected. The departure of John Russell and a fellow partner to Brown & Wood is perceived to have weakened the team, although it is still regarded as *"good for the lead managers on securitisation."*

The firm advised on the securitisation of revenues generated by London City Airport and advised British Land in the £1.54 billion Broadgate Development securitisation. The team acted on approximately 350 repackaging trades last year. Major clients continue to be Warburg Dillon Reed, Merrill Lynch, CSFB and Deutsche Bank, the last of which was advised on more than 280 structured securities offerings during the year. The structured practice is closely connected to the derivatives side, where as well as credit derivatives, the practice has strengths in metals and energy-related transactions.

Slaughter and May **Rupert Beaumont** is *"a legendary figure,"* who *"built up the market in the early days."* He is still active in the area, mainly on energy deals. **Christopher Smith** is also a respected name. Owing to the nature of the firm, which tends to spawn generalists, securitisation is not an area where the firm is felt to have genuine specialists. Thus, although the quality and complexity of the work is unquestioned, the individuals do not have the profile of the market leaders.

The practice advises underwriters and lead managers, rating agencies and bank originators. Advised on the issue of asset-backed notes by West Coast Train Finance plc, and Eastern Electricity (part of TXU Group) on a £550 million electricity receivables programme. Along with German 'best friend' Hengeler Mueller, the firm advised on a €4 billion asset-backed global commercial paper programme for BILLS Securitisation Ltd.

Weil, Gotshal & Manges Both **Jacky Kelly** and **Erica Handling** received praise from the market for building up a strong and busy practice. Client favourite Handling is new to the rankings, and is an all-rounder particularly rated for collateralised debt/loan/bond obligation work. The practice is mainly known for its work on the synthetic securitisation side as opposed to traditional securitisation, and are *"particularly strong on the CBO, CLO and structured side."* Worked on the First Flexible transaction, which JP Morgan arranged for First Active, the first securitisation in the UK of flexible mortgages. Other work includes an asset-backed conduit for Greenwich, while the team was involved in almost 50% of the residential mortgage-backed deals completed in the UK and Ireland in 1999. The practice also advised Morgan Stanley as the arranger on the first ever CDO with a wholly Euro-denominated European asset portfolio.

Other Notable Practitioners A major move this year was the arrival at Shearman & Sterling of **Marke Raines** *("a real thinker")* from Allen & Overy. With the firm making a push in providing a comprehensive range of UK finance advice, his arrival will *"change its profile"* in securitisation. The capital markets all-rounder **John Russell** at Brown & Wood has a high profile in the repackaging world. Recently arrived with another colleague from Simmons & Simmons, his reputation fortifies the UK practice of the *"pre-eminent asset-backed practice in the US."*

DERIVATIVES

CAPITAL MARKETS: DERIVATIVES • London	Ptnrs	Assts
❶ Allen & Overy	37*	143*
Clifford Chance	9	32
❷ Freshfields Bruckhaus Deringer	30*	30*
Linklaters	10	21
❸ Norton Rose	2	7
❹ Baker & McKenzie	1	2
Slaughter and May	12*	15*

LEADING INDIVIDUALS	
❶ **GOLDEN Jeffrey** Allen & Overy	**HENDERSON Schuyler** Norton Rose
MOTANI Habib Clifford Chance	
❷ **BENTON David** Allen & Overy	**BROWN Claude** Clifford Chance
FIRTH Simon Linklaters	
❸ **HADDOCK Simon** Allen & Overy	**LEVINE Iona** Baker & McKenzie
RUDIN Simeon Freshfields Bruckhaus Deringer	
WARNA-KULA-SURIYA Sanjev Slaughter and May	

Within each band, firms are listed alphabetically.
See **Profiles** on page 129
* *Figures denote total capital markets team sizes.*

Allen & Overy Popular US lawyer **Jeffrey Golden** maintains a high profile as the *"big picture man"* of the practice, and is primarily recognised for his ISDA work. Among an *"active and able"* team, **David Benton** and *"moderniser"* **Simon Haddock** stand out. The team is regarded as especially proficient in OTC derivative advice, although it is recognised for its general breadth and depth – *"they can bring a range of guns to bear against you."* Although involved in structured work, the practice's high profile stems more from its involvement on plain vanilla transactions and for acting as European and South East Asian counsel to ISDA. The team's strong relationship with ISDA continues, helping it to advise both central banks and governments. This year, the practice advised the Hungarian Forex Association on the development of standard form documentation for the Hungarian domestic market. Transactional work has seen the firm involved in the credit derivatives market and, increasingly, in energy and commodity derivatives.

Clifford Chance The *"pleasant"* and *"drop-dead smart"* **Habib Motani** leads the derivatives group. **Claude Brown** enters the rankings this year following market recommendation. Respected for his credit derivatives expertise, he *"knows the business side of things and presents the facts well."* This is seen as a global practice which is increasing its volume of business. Considered to have *"depth on exchange traded"* derivatives in addition to its recognised OTC capabilities. In conjunction with other departments, the group advised BNP on the first synthetic CLO transaction to be realised by a bank incorporated in the European Union using credit default swap technology. The practice also acted for the Bond Market Association on a Cross Product Master Netting Agreement, and has represented ISDA on European regulatory matters.

Freshfields Bruckhaus Deringer Part of the structured finance practice, the derivatives practice is primarily known for its advice on structured work rather than on straight derivatives matters. On structured matters, **Simeon Rudin** is considered *"the main man,"* with a particularly strong grasp of tax issues. The practice does cover the breadth of derivatives work, from standard schedules to ISDA Master Agreements and synthetic securitisations, the latter being a niche strength. The team advises trade organisations, financial institutions and end-users, and has recently been active in insurance derivatives.

LEADING IN-HOUSE LAWYERS

Derivatives

Richard Atkinson, Director of Law & Compliance and Senior Counsel, *Merrill Lynch International*

David Bloom, Senior Legal Adviser, *HSBC Holdings plc*

Edmond Curtin, Director of Legal and Compliance, *Credit Suisse First Boston International*

David Geen, Executive Director and Senior Counsel, *Goldman Sachs International*

David Lewis, Vice-President and Assistant General Counsel, *JPMorgan Securities Ltd*

John Ormond, Legal Adviser, *Deutsche Bank AG Ltd*

Charles Ross-Stewart, Executive Director, *UBS Warburg*

"Articulate" **Richard Atkinson** is recommended for *"dealing with the issues commercially rather than with the minutiae of the law."* *"Approachable"* **David Bloom** is seen as *"sensible and co-operative"* and he *"always finds a solution."* The *"world-class"* **Edmond Curtin** is recognised for his *"good work"* and his *"technical understanding."* Well-recommended is **David Geen** who is a *"no-nonsense guy"* who *"gets on with the job."* The *"proactive and professional"* **David Lewis** has a *"very broad range of experience"* and is widely recommended. Although fairly junior, the *"well-renowned"* **John Ormond** is widely perceived as *"very smart"* and *"at the cutting edge."* **Charles Ross-Stewart** *"manages the business process well"* and has a *"strong mind"* but is *"not overly lawyerish"*.

In-house lawyers profiles: page 1177

Linklaters The popular **Simon Firth** *("terrific as a pure derivatives lawyer and good on structured deals")* leads the derivatives practice. Less high profile than CC's or A&O's, the team has a broad practice and is known for its regulatory work. As well as straight derivatives work, the practice has been heavily involved in credit derivatives and has handled a number of synthetic CLOs. The team has also been advising on structures which enable insurance companies to tap the derivatives market.

Norton Rose The arrival of **Schuyler Henderson** from Baker & McKenzie has propelled the firm to the ranks of serious players in derivatives. The *"eminent senior guy in the field,"* some call him simply the *"grandfather of derivatives."* A broad practice with a name in ISDA-related work, it is seen to have *"made a particular effort in credit derivatives."* Work includes advising on hedging transactions in relation to the EBRD's EMTN programme.

Baker & McKenzie The departure of Schuyler Henderson and another partner was initially seen to have crippled the derivatives practice. However, the recruitment of the former head of HSBC's Global Treasury & Capital Markets legal team, **Iona Levine**, from Hammond Suddards Edge, has breathed new life into the derivatives team. She is considered to have a *"focus on derivatives, notably on OTC work where she has considerable experience."*

Slaughter and May **Sanjev Warna-Kula-Suriya** is a structured finance all-rounder, working on capital markets, securitisation and derivatives. Clients say that he *"can sometimes be professorial,"* but emphasise that this is compensated by his commercial experience gained from his time working in the derivatives field for Credit Suisse Financial Products. He is considered to be *"overworked, but if you can isolate him, we would go for him any day."* The firm itself is held to be a *"class act"* which works on a range of derivatives matters. The group advised on an online website for Enron, making contracts available on a bilateral basis, and acted on Yosemite 2, the securitisation of energy-linked financial contracts for an international energy company. Additionally, the firm has advised on product creation for Morgan Stanley, Fortis, Zurich Capital Markets and the Emerging Markets Clearing Corporation.

LEADERS IN CAPITAL MARKETS

BEAUMONT, Rupert
Slaughter and May, London (020) 7600 1200
Specialisation: Structured finance and securitisation; project finance.
Prof. Memberships: Association of Corporate Treasurers (Honorary Fellow).

BEDFORD, Paul
Allen & Overy, London (020) 7330 3000
Specialisation: Member of securitisation group.
Career: Qualified 1982. At *Allen & Overy* since 1980. Partner from 1988.
Personal: Born 26th October 1956. Educated at Brighton College and Warwick University. Lives in Islington.

BENTON, David
Allen & Overy, London (020) 7330 3000
Partner in the derivatives practice
Specialisation: Derivatives.
Career: Articled 1988. Qualified 1990. Partner 1997. Educated: Corpus Christi College, Cambridge.
Personal: Born 1966.

BICKERTON, David
Clifford Chance, London (020) 7600 1000
David.Bickerton@cliffordchance.com
Specialisation: Structured finance including: project bonds, acquisition finance and PFI/PPP. Recent highlights include: MoD Main Building Refurbishment, Owengate Keele Bonds, Kings Hospital Bonds, A13 Road Bonds, Bond Refinancings.
Career: *Clifford Chance* 1987 to date. Seconded to Citibank (1992) and Bankers Trust (1993). Partner 1997.
Personal: Education: Downing College, Cambridge – MA. Family Details: three daughters.

BRESSLAW, James
Simmons & Simmons, London (020) 7628 2020
Specialisation: Securitisation and structured finance.
Prof. Memberships: Law Society.
Career: *Simmons & Simmons* 1984 to date.

BROWN, Claude
Clifford Chance, London (020) 7600 1000

BROWN, Jane A.
Linklaters (A member firm of Linklaters & Alliance), London (020) 7456 4642
jane.brown@linklaters.com
Specialisation: Partner dealing with global securities, advises underwriters and issuers in connection with issues of debt, equity, derivative & structured products.
Career: Qualified 1986. Foreign lawyer programme, *Sullivan & Cromwell* 1986-1987.
Assistant solicitor – *Linklaters* 1987-88 (New York).
Assistant solicitor – *Linklaters* 1988-92 (London).
Partner *Linklaters* 1992-to date.

BURN, Lachlan
Linklaters (A member firm of Linklaters & Alliance), London (020) 7456 4614
lachlan.burn@linklaters.com
Partner, International Finance Department.
Specialisation: Specialises in banking and capital markets issues, with over 24 years' experience in the field. Typical matters handled include GDRs, convertible bonds and derivatives of all types. Is Adviser to the International Primary Market Association. Articled at *Linklaters* and qualified in 1976, becoming a Partner in 1982. Seconded to the Paris office from 1982-87.

CANBY, Michael
Linklaters (A member firm of Linklaters & Alliance), London (020) 7456 4624
michael.canby@linklaters.com
Partner, International Finance Department. Head of Global Securities Group
Specialisation: Specialist in capital markets work advising on debt and equity financings, derivative products and documentation (having been involved for over 9 years in the drafting of the various stages of industry standard documentation), and structured financings.
Career: Qualified 1980, seconded to New York 1982-84, Partner from 1986. Seconded to Paris 1988-95 (and Managing Partner of the Paris office 1992-95) Partner in charge of the Securities Group, 1995 to present.

CLARK, Charles
Linklaters (A member firm of Linklaters & Alliance), London (020) 7456 4630
charles.clark@linklaters.com
Partner – Global Securities Group, International Finance Department.
Specialisation: Extensive experience of international securities issues and derivatives transactions.
Career: Articled at *Linklaters*, made Partner 1989.

DUNLOP, Stewart
Clifford Chance, London (020) 7600 1000
Stewart.Dunlop@cliffordchance.com
Specialisation: Advising arrangers/borrowers in connection with EMTN Programmes and bond issues by developed and emerging market borrowers; regulatory capital issues; structured notes and equity related issues.
Career: Articled, *Allen & Overy*. Qualified 1991. Partner, *Clifford Chance* May 2000.

DUNNIGAN, David
Clifford Chance, London (020) 7600 1000
david.dunnigan@cliffordchance.com
Specialisation: Partner in international capital markets group specialising in Debt and Equity Capital Markets transactions.
Career: Nottingham University (LLB 2.1) 1980-1983. Articled *Turner Kenneth Brown*; qualified 1986; *Coward Chance/ Clifford Chance*; partner *Clifford Chance* since 1992.
Personal: Born 1961; resides Highgate.

EASTWELL, Nick
Linklaters (A member firm of Linklaters & Alliance), London (020) 7456 4660
nick.eastwell@linklaters.com
Managing Partner of Central and Eastern Europe; Partner in International Finance Department, Global Securities Group.
Specialisation: Specialises in capital markets transactions, including issues of debt, equity related debt, equity and depositary receipts in international markets, with a particular emphasis on emerging markets (in 1999/2000 in particular in South Africa, Egypt, Croatia, Romania, and Turkey). Areas of practice include repackagings of bonds, funds and other financial assets, debt issuance programmes and derivatives.

EDLMANN, Stephen
Linklaters (A member firm of Linklaters & Alliance), London (020) 7456 4512
stephen.edlmann@linklaters.com
Partner. International Finance Department.
Specialisation: Has over 15 years' experience in debt and equity capital markets, banking and related matters. Main areas of practice include debt, equity and equity-related issues, for foreign and international companies. Member of International Bar Association. Has contributed to legal text books on capital markets products, including 'The Law & Practice of International Banking', Sweet & Maxwell, 1987. Joined *Linklaters* in their New York Office in 1981, became Partner in 1985.

FALCONER, Ian
Freshfields Bruckhaus Deringer, London (020) 7936 4000
Partner in finance department.
Specialisation: Main area of practice is complex structured capital markets transactions, in particular securitisations and credit derivatives. Has been at the centre of developments in the securitisation market since its inception. Among significant transactions he advised the Annington consortium on the £1.66 billion acquisition of the Ministry of Defence Married Quarters Estate, including a £904 million securitisation of lease rentals and subsequent £3.14 billion property securitisation, Citibank on its groundbreaking £893 million credit default swap on a UK mortgage portfolio originated by Prudential and Glencore on its innovative US$1.2 billion CP and MTN funded trade receivables securitisation.
Career: *Freshfields* Assistant 1984. Partner 1990.

FIRTH, Simon
Linklaters (A member firm of Linklaters & Alliance), London (020) 7456 3764
simon.firth@linklaters.com
Partner. Financial Markets Group, Corporate Department.
Specialisation: Specialises in the structuring and documentation of derivitives products, the structuring of financial services businesses and the regulatory capital treatment of financial products. He was part of the team which developed Blue FlagR Confirms, the system which enables ISDA-based derivatives confirmations to be generated electronically.
Career: Articled at *Linklaters* in 1987, made Partner in 1996.

FORRYAN, Andrew
Clifford Chance, London (020) 7600 1000
Andrew.Forryan@cliffordchance.com
Specialisation: Securitisation of: real estate; mortgages; whole businesses; sports rights; consumer finance assets and Italian law governed assets. Partner responsible for the Royal Bank of Scotland plc securitisation of its credit card recievables in the Arran1 transaction.
Career: Associate with: *Slaughter and May; Sidley & Austin.* Joined *Clifford Chance* as a partner in 1997.

FRANK, David
Slaughter and May, London (020) 7600 1200
Specialisation: Extensive eurobond and international equity experience with issuers in the UK and around the world. Also handles corporate and banking work with a number of listed plc clients and is active in the venture capital and project financing areas.
Prof. Memberships: The Law Society. International Bar Association.
Career: Qualified 1979. Assistant Solicitor, *Slaughter and May*, 1979-1986. Partner *Slaughter and May*, 1986. Head of Capital Markets, 1993.
Personal: Born 29 April 1954. Educated Shrewsbury School 1967-1972. University of Bristol 1973-1976. Interests include cars and lawn tennis. Lives in Surrey.

FULLER, Geoff
Allen & Overy, London (020) 7330 3000
Specialisation: Partner specialising in international and domestic capital markets matters, with particular experience in repackagings and other structured finance transactions, debenture stocks and advising corporate trustees. Head of *Allen & Overy's* repackaging group.
Prof. Memberships: Fellow, Society for Advanced Legal Studies.
Career: Articled *Allen & Overy*. Qualified 1986, partner 1994.
Personal: Educated Borden Grammar School and Mansfield College, Oxford (1983 MA). Born 1961. Resides Islington. Author 'Corporate Borrowing, Law and Practice', (1st edition 1995, 2nd edition 1999). Contributor to 'Gore Browne on Companies.'

GOLDEN, Jeffrey
Allen & Overy, London (020) 7330 3000
Specialisation: Partner responsible for US law practice; areas of practice include a wide range of international capital markets matters, including swaps and derivatives, international equity and debt offerings and US private placements and listings; advises the International Swaps and Derivatives Association and a broad range of commercial and investment banks, borrowers, arrangers, underwriters and issuers.
Prof. Memberships: American Bar Association (Chairman US Lawyers Practising Abroad Committee (1990-96); Council, Section of International Law and Practice (1996-)). New Jersey State Bar Association, New York State Bar Association, American Society of International Law, International Bar Association, The Law Society.
Career: Admitted New York Bar 1979, New Jersey 1978, and the Supreme Court of the United States 1983. *Cravath, Swaine & Moore*, New York 1978-83; *Cravath, Swaine & Moore*, London 1983-94; Partner *Allen & Overy* since 1994.
Personal: Education Duke University, USA; The London School of Economics and Political Science; Columbia University School of Law, USA. Born 1950.

HADDOCK, Simon A.
Allen & Overy, London (020) 7330 3000
Specialisation: Partner specialising in all areas of derivatives and structured finance.
Prof. Memberships: Law Society.
Career: Articled *Allen & Overy*, qualified England and Wales 1986, Hong Kong 1992, assistant solicitor 1986-92, Partner 1992, Hong Kong office 1993. London Office 1997.
Personal: Leeds University (1982 LL.B). Born 1960. Resides in the U.K

HANDLING, Erica
Weil, Gotshal & Manges, London (020) 7903 1000
erica.handling@weil.com
Specialisation: International finance partner with experience of a wide range of international financing transactions from syndicated loans to the raising of capital in the international debt and equity markets. She has particular experience of cross-border leveraged acquisitions and structured finance transactions. She has been involved in advising in connection with a variety of structured notes issues and programs, collateralised bond and debt obligations and derivative instruments.

HENDERSON, Schuyler K.
Norton Rose, London (020) 7283 6000
hendersonsk@nortonrose.com
Specialisation: Practice covers the full range of lending, credit enhancement and securities transactions. Since moving to London in 1977, he has worked closely with many international financial institutions in creating, developing and documenting swaps and related derivatives and structured finance products and advising with respect to enforcement, regulatory, tax and capacity issues.
Personal: Obtained his undergraduate degree (B.A.) from Princeton University in 1967 and his law degree (J.D.) and business degree (M.B.A.) from the University of Chicago in 1971 and is a member of the New York and Illinois bars.

HUDD, David G.T.
Lovells, London (020) 7296 2000
david.hudd@lovells.com
Specialisation: Head of Lovells' capital markets and securitisation practice. Extensive experience of securitisations and repackagings, debt issues (including high yield bonds), international equity and equity-linked offerings and derivatives.
Prof. Memberships: The City of London Solicitors' Company, The Law Society.
Career: Christ Church, Oxford University 1977-80 (MA Jurisprudence). Qualified 1983. *Linklaters* 1981-85; Paribas 1985-90; Sanwa International 1990-93; Indosuez 1993-94; joined *Lovells* as a partner in 1994.

HUGHES, Richard
Linklaters (A member firm of Linklaters & Alliance), London (020) 7456 4508
richard.hughes@linklaters.com
Specialisation: Partner, securitisation, asset finance, syndicated loans & property finance.
Career: Partner *Linklaters* – 1998-to date. Partner *Herbert Smith* 1995-98. Qualified 1987.
Publications: United Nations: 'The Privatisation of African Airlines'.

INGRAM, Kevin
Clifford Chance, London (020) 7600 1000
Kevin.Ingram@cliffordchance.com

KELLY, Jacky
Weil, Gotshal & Manges, London (020) 7903 1000
Specialisation: Heads up the firm's securitisation practice in London. She has been closely involved in the UK securitisation market since its inception in the mid-eighties. Her securitisation experience spans a number of asset types, including residential and commercial mortgages, commercial property, trade receivables, chargecards, computer leases, autoloans, corporate loans, aerospace assets and intellectual property assets in a number of jurisdictions including the UK, Ireland, France, Spain, Italy, Belgium, Germany, Scandinavia, Hong Kong and Japan.

KRISCHER, David S.
Allen & Overy, London (020) 7330 3000
Partner and head of the Securitisation Group.
Specialisation: All forms of securitisation and asset backed transactions in the UK and a variety of European jurisdictions.
Career: Qualified in the US 1982, practised Chicago, U.S.A. 1982-1985. Joined *Allen & Overy* 1986, qualified in UK 1992, Partner 1992.
Personal: Born 1956. BA Oberlin College 1978; JD Northwestern University, 1982; BCL Oxford University, 1986.

LEVINE, Iona
Baker & McKenzie, London (020) 7919 1000
Head of the Derivatives Practice.
Specialisation: Undertakes a wide range of derivatives and treasury related work. Advises on new products and structured transactions, exchange traded and OTC matters. Advises on the newer areas of Global energy trading and e.trading. Advises on the standard key issues which are of concern to the derivatives markets, e.g. Netting, Collateral and Legal Risk Management e.trading. Acts for banks, securities houses, brokers, fund managers, energy companies, corporates and e-commerce entrepreneurs. Recent experience includes: undertaking a high level consultancy assignment with a major international bank in which she acted as the senior in-house derivatives counsel providing derivatives expertise and management experience and helped the bank to restructure its derivatives legal and documentation teams. Providing legal advice and support to enable a US Securities house to establish its global equities broking business. Enabling various institutions to develop and revise their netting policies. Involved in the purchase of and undertook the English due diligence in relation to the purchase of a prime brokerage business. Providing advice on a variety of structured transactions and notes. Undertaking derivatives litigation. Other experience includes: Responsibility for setting global policy and for providing treasury and capital markets legal advice throughout the Hong Kong Banking Group. Helping to establish the world's first clearing house for the multilateral netting of foreign exchange transactions ('Echo'). Chairing the London part of the British Bankers Association/New York Foreign Exchange Legal Committee which was responsible for drafting and developing the first version of International Foreign Exchange Master Agreement (IFEMA).
Career: Pre-1984, Qualified as a Barrister. 1984-86 Citibank Legal Counsel advising on a wide range of international commercial banking matters. 1986-95, Hong Kong and Shanghai Banking Corporation/Midland specialised in Treasury, Capital Markets, Banking, Emerging Markets and Payment Systems – ultimately head of the Global Treasury and Capital Markets Legal Department. 1996 to 2000, Head of the Derivatives Practice at *Hammond Suddards*.
Personal: Educated at London School of Economics and The Inns of Court School of Law. Member of Lincoln Inn called February 1982. General Editor of

'Derivatives and Related Markets: Law and Documentation' to be published by Sweet & Maxwell Autumn 2000.

MACKENZIE, Marcus
Freshfields Bruckhaus Deringer, London (020) 7936 4000
mmackenzie@freshfields.com
Specialisation: Partner in finance department specialising in whole business and other asset securitisations and other capital markets/derivatives and banking transactions acting for investment banks, originators and issuers. Recent transactions include acting for: Citibank on the £1.484 billion Punch Funding transaction; Deutsche Bank on the £305 million Pubmaster transaction; Angel Trains on the £480 million West Coast Train lease receivables transaction; and HFC on various consumer loan and credit card recievables transactions.
Prof. Memberships: Law Society
Career: 1988: Joined *Freshfields.* 1993: Worked in *Freshfields* New York office. 1994: Seconded to *Salomon Brothers International* in London. 1998: Joined partnership.
Personal: Educated at Bristol University and Guildford Law School. Speaks French, German and Spanish.

MILLER, Stephen M.
Allen & Overy, London (020) 7330 3000
Specialisation: Debt capital markets.
Prof. Memberships: Law Society.
Career: Qualified 1992. Partner 1998.

MOTANI, Habib
Clifford Chance, London (020) 7600 1000
habib.motani@cliffordchance.com
Specialisation: Partner specialising in derivatives, capital markets and financial markets.
Career: Partner *Clifford Chance* 1986.

OAKLEY, Chris
Clifford Chance, London (020) 7600 1000
chris.oakley@cliffordchance.com
Specialisation: Partner specialising in international asset securitisation, structured repackagings and all types of structured finance transactions.
Career: Redborne School, Ampthill, Beds; Worcester College, Oxford (BA Hons Jurisprudence). Articled *Coward Chance*; qualified 1983; partner *Clifford Chance* since 1990.
Personal: Theatre, opera, travel. Born 1956; resides London.

PENN, Graham
Sidley & Austin, London (020) 7360 3600
gpenn@sidley.com
Specialisation: Securitisation, structured finance, banking and bank regulation.
Career: Partner *Cameron Markley Hewitt* 1988-1994. Partner *Sidley & Austin* since 1994.

PITKIN, Jeremy
Freshfields Bruckhaus Deringer, London (020) 7936 4000
Partner specialising in Debt and Equity Capital Markets.

RAINES, Marke
Shearman & Sterling, London (020) 7655 5000
MRaines@shearman.com
Partner in Securitisation Group
Specialisation: Securitisation and structured finance. Acts for investment banks and corporates in developing a wide range of UK and international securitisation structures and top rated structured investment vehicles.
Prof. Memberships: ABA; IBA; City of London Solicitors' Company; Fellow of the Society for Advanced Legal Studies.
Career: Called to the Bar in Ontario (1982) and New York (1990). Admitted as a solicitor in England and Wales (1990). Practised with *Stikeman, Elliott* (1982-89) and *Clifford Chance* (1991-94). Joined *Allen & Overy* in 1994 (Partner from 1996). Joined *Shearman & Sterling* as partner in 2000. Senior Visiting Fellow at Queen Mary and Westfield College, University of London (2000).
Personal: Born 17th June, 1953. Educated at Simon Fraser University (BA), University of British Columbia (LL.B) and Trinity Hall, University of Cambridge (LL.M). Interests include flying and skiing.

RICE, Jim
Linklaters (A member firm of Linklaters & Alliance), London (020) 7456 4525
jim.rice@linklaters.com
Partner in the International Finance Department, Securities Group.
Specialisation: Experience in all aspects of capital markets work including equity and equity-related, straight debt and MTNs. Now specialises in structured finance and securitisations.
Career: Qualified 1982 at *Linklaters*, becoming a Partner in 1989.

RUDIN, Simeon
Freshfields Bruckhaus Deringer, London (020) 7936 4000
Specialisation: Partner in the finance department advising on all aspects of capital markets work, including private and public debt, including equity, credit and commodity linked debt issues, tax structured financings, securitisations, CLOs, CBOs, CDOs, repackagings and all aspects of derivatives transactions (both exchange trade and over the counter), including repo and stocklending. Advises on alternative risk transfer and structured insurance products and transactions. Advises extensively on product development. Head of *Freshfields* Derivatives Unit.
Prof. Memberships: Law Society; City of London Solicitors Company.
Career: Joined *Freshfields* in 1983, qualifying in the Tax Department in 1985; joined the Finance Department in 1993; became a partner in 1995.
Personal: Born 1961. Attended St. Catharines College, Cambridge.

RUSSELL, John
Brown & Wood, a Multinational Partnership, London (020) 7778 1800
jrussell@brownwoodlaw.com
Specialisation: International capital markets work, with particular emphasis on international equity offerings, derivative issues and structured finance. Emerging markets experience, particularly in India. Transactions include a large number of GDR issues and structured securities programmes and trades.
Prof. Memberships: Member of the Securities Institute and Member of Capital Markets Forum.
Career: Qualified in 1977 and in Hong Kong in 1981. Associate Director *Merrill Lynch* 1985-1988. Partner *Simmons & Simmons* 1988-1999. Partner *Brown & Wood* since 1999.
Personal: Ski mountaineer.

SHURMAN, Daniel J.
Allen & Overy, London (020) 7330 3000
daniel.shurman@allenovery.com
Specialisation: Specialises in international capital markets transactions and has extensive experience of private and public offerings of equity and debt securities.
Career: Assistant solicitor, *Theodore Goddard* 1990 - 1996. Seconded to *Dewey Ballantine*, New York 1994 - 1995. Associate, *Allen & Overy* 1996 - 1999. Partner, *Allen & Overy* 1999.
Personal: Born 1965, Highgate School, Nottingham University. Leisure interests include sailing. Resides in London.

SMITH, Christopher
Slaughter and May, London (020) 7600 1200
Specialisation: Main areas of practice include securitisations, structured financings and the full range of capital markets and banking transactions.
Career: Qualified 1980; Partner 1987.

SMITH, Michael
Ashurst Morris Crisp, London (020) 7638 1111
Specialisation: Securitisation, structured finance, repackagings and derivatives.
Prof. Memberships: Law Society.
Career: Partner *Ashurst Morris Crisp* 1997.

SMITH, Sarah
Sidley & Austin, London (020) 7360 3600
sarah.smith@sidley.com
Specialisation: Securitisation; structured finance; banking and financial services regulation.
Career: Qualified 1990; Partner 1995.

THIEFFRY, Gilles
Norton Rose, London (020) 7283 6000
thieffrygjy@nortonrose.com
Specialisation: International securities transactions. Leading expert on the implications of EMU on financial markets and on cross border capital raising. Leading expert on settlement and clearing issues.
Prof. Memberships: Member of the Paris Bar (Avocat). Member of the New York Bar. Solicitor of the Supreme Court of England and Wales.
Career: Head of Legal Department at BNP Capital Markets Ltd. (1992-94). Director of Legal Services UBS Phillips & Drew (1988-92).

THOMSON, Keith
Linklaters (A member firm of Linklaters & Alliance), London (020) 7456 4584
keith.thomson@linklaters.com
Specialisation: Capital market transactions, advising lead managers in respect of issues of debt, equity-related debt, equity & depositary receipts in the international capital market.
Career: Partner-1986 to date. Solicitor (International Finance department) 1983-1986. Solicitor (Hong Kong) 1981-1983. Solicitor – Corporate department, 1979-81.

TROTT, David
Freshfields Bruckhaus Deringer, London (020) 7936 4000
dtrott@freshfields.com
Specialisation: He has worked extensively in the banking and capital markets field acting for lenders, borrowers and arrangers on secured and unsecured transactions. He has particular experience of, and expertise in, asset-backed and structured transactions. He has been involved in securitisations since

1988, working on a number of the early mortgage backed deals to take place in the UK. He advised on the first residential and commercial mortgage securitisations by UK building societies. In addition, he has acted for a number of arrangers of commercial paper conduits as well as originators selling assets into such conduits and has worked on a wide range of different asset classes that have been securitised through them. More recently, he advised on the first whole business securitisation in the UK (Craegmoor) and, since then, on the Welcome Break, Punch Taverns and Wightlink transactions. He also advised BT.Alex Brown on the structuring and arranging of the Euro Freight railcar securitisation, involving lease receivables derived from freight rolling stock operating in some 17 different European jurisdictions.

TUCKER, Julian A.
Allen & Overy, London (020) 7330 3000
Specialisation: Partner in the securitisation Group. Noteworthy deals include Canary Wharf I + II, Unique Pubs and Northern Rock's Granite Programme.
Prof. Memberships: Law Society.
Career: *Lovells* 1987-1992. *Cameron Markby Hewett* Jan 1993-July 1994, *Allen & Overy* July 1994-present.
Personal: University College London LLB 1985. London University LLM 1986. Food, wine, cooking, horse riding, music + travel. Married, two daughters.

VOISEY, Peter G.
Clifford Chance, London (020) 7600 1000
PeterG.Voisey@cliffordchance.com
Specialisation: Partner specialising in capital markets, securitisation and structured finance. Extensive experience of securitisations and repackagings, international securities issues (bonds and equities) and derivatives.
Prof. Memberships: City of London Solicitors' Company. Law Society.
Career: Joined *Lovell White Durrant* in 1985. Qualified in 1987. Made partner in 1994.
Personal: Sir Anthony Browne's School, Brentwood. Trinity Hall, Cambridge University 1978-82 (MA Hons Modern and Medieval Languages).

VOISIN, Michael
Linklaters (A member firm of Linklaters & Alliance), London (020) 7456 4606
michael.voisin@linklaters.com
Specialisation: Partner international finance department, global securities group specialising in capital markets securities work with particular emphasis on sophisticated financial products, note programmes and regulatory capital raising for financial institutions; responsible for the development of *Linklaters'* medium-term note programme practice and one of core partners in *Linklaters'* derivatives practice.
Career: Qualified 1991, partner since 1996.

WALSH, Jonathan
Norton Rose, London (020) 7283 6000
walshjgf@nortonrose.com
Specialisation: Securitisation/repackaging. Acts for investment banks, corporates, arrangers and sponsors on a variety of UK and international securitisation and repackaging transactions, including synthetic structures, asset backed securities issues and asset-backed commercial paper conduits.
Prof. Memberships: Law Society. The Oriental Club.
Career: Kings College London, LLB, called to the bar 1984, requalified as a solicitor 1988. Partner *Norton Rose* International Securities Group 1997.
Personal: Obscure rock music (pop trivia bore), cooking and mixing cocktails, swimming, skiing and surfing (very badly).

WARNA-KULA-SURIYA, Sanjev
Slaughter and May, London (020) 7600 1200
Specialisation: Partner specialising in capital markets, derivatives, securitisation and structured finance.
Career: Articled *Slaughter and May*; qualified 1990; partner 1997.
Personal: Born 1964. Educated at Kings College, London University (1986 LLB First Class Hons). Resides London. Leisure: Cricket, theatre.

WEDDERBURN-DAY, Roger
Allen & Overy, London (020) 7330 3000
Specialisation: Partner, areas of practice include advising managers and issuers an all aspects of both debt and equity international capital markets work; particular specialisations include emerging markets issues and privatisation. Spoken at conferences around the world.
Prof. Memberships: Law Society
Career: Articled *Allen & Overy*. Qualified 1987, partner 1995.
Personal: Bishop Wordsworth's school. University college London 1985. Born 1962. Resides Sevenoaks.

WELLS, Boyan S.
Allen & Overy, London (020) 7330 3000
Specialisation: Partner, areas of practice include advising managers and issuers on all aspects of international capital markets work, high yield issues and derivative transactions; particular specialisations include medium term note programmes, listed and unlisted warrant issues and programmes and building societies. Spoken at conferences on derivatives and on the Euromarkets.
Prof. Memberships: Law Society.
Career: Articled *Allen & Overy*, qualified 1981, partner 1987.
Personal: Educated Colston's School and Wadham College, Oxford (1978 MA). Born 1956. Resides Dulwich.

WOODHALL, John
Clifford Chance, London (020) 7600 1000
john.woodhall@cliffordchance.com
Head of International Securitisation Practice.
Career: 1980-date *Clifford Chance.* Partner 1988. Educated at Leicester University – LL.B.

CHARITIES

OVERVIEW: The nature of charities and charitable giving continues to shift, and with it the demands on charities lawyers. Charities are facing increasing commercial pressures, with arts and millennium-funded charities competing in the commercial entertainment arena, and a burgeoning fund-raising sector also to be considered. It is hoped that tax breaks announced in the Budget will go some way to redressing the balance, in addition to simplifying the process of trading for smaller charities, but many charities are now choosing the merger option. All charities are now facing stiffer regulation, most notably the SORP accounting regulations and an increased willingness of the Charity Commission to investigate any perceived mismanagement of trustees. More and more charities are choosing to incorporate as a result. When acting for large charitable organisations, then, corporate/commercial issues such as joint ventures, mergers and branding are becoming as important as traditional trust and constitutional questions. While the largest charities continue to shop around for their legal services, across the board strength and a commercial approach are becoming increasingly important traits of the charity specialist.

RESEARCH APPROVED BY BMRB: *For this edition,* Chambers' *researchers conducted 6083 interviews – 4408 with law firms, 598 with barristers and 1077 with clients.*

The validity of the research was scrutinised by BMRB International, who audited both the methodology and the results at our offices in July 2000. They interviewed Chambers' *researchers and cross-checked sample interviews. Details of the audit appear on page 7.*

LONDON

Bates, Wells & Braithwate Remains the leading firm, and *"its profile is still growing."* Known particularly for its large number of voluntary sector clients who appreciate the team's *"approachability"* and understanding of the sector. Charity work is one of the firm's core businesses, with **Stephen Lloyd** *"strong on the commercial side,"* and constitutional/governance expert **Fiona Middleton** (who rises a band this year) *"a force to be reckoned with."* Work ranges from constitutional and restructuring issues through to intellectual property and employment. **Andrew Phillips** retains his *"deservedly high profile"* and his activities in the House of Lords keeps the practice in touch with policy making. Recent work included a major constitutional overhaul for the Civil Servants' Benevolent Fund. **Clients:** Charities Aid Foundation, Tate Gallery, British Red Cross Society.

Farrer & Co Renowned in the market for its royal connections and heritage and endowed clients, the firm's charity unit is led by the *"bright and able"* **Judith Hill**. Areas of expertise include incorporating charities, setting up trading companies and tax issues. Clients also include museums, literary companies, independent schools and quasi-governmental bodies. One recent highlight was the transfer of the Commonwealth Institute from FCO control to a fully independent charity. **Clients:** The Prince's Trust, National Heritage Memorial Fund, The National Endowment for Science, Technology and the Arts.

Paisner & Co This *"high profile"* practice is traditionally known for its Jewish, Islamic and Christian charities and heritage work, but clients also extend to new government appointed education agencies, active charities and not for profit organisations such as Credit Unions and Friendly Societies. Specialisms include mergers, re-organisations and complex Charity Commission investigations. The *"dedicated"* **Anne-Marie Piper** is seen by many as the focus of the practice, and *"gives as good as she gets"* in her dealings with the Charity Commission, with **Martin Paisner** remaining *"a name in the field."* **Clients:** National Family and Parenting Institute, and the University For Industry.

Withers The practice's *"integrated"* approach takes it up a band this year. Its traditional skills in legacy and NHS charity work remain recognised and it has been expanding and picking up clients over the last year. Combining traditional constitutional and tax advice with other services, including a specialist charity litigation team, the firm is also well-versed in issues relating to government "hive off" organisations. **Alison Paines,** whose *"very cultured approach"* and competence were noted by many, also goes up a rung. **Clients:** Macmillan Cancer Relief, Salvation Army, RSPCA.

Allen and Overy Still seen as the leading City firm charities practice, with *"a dedicated team."* Its large and wide-ranging client base benefits from the firm's formidable corporate/commercial capability, while recent lateral hires have bolstered the practice's renowned pure charity and Royal Charter expertise. The well known **Peter Mimpriss** is *"still a name people know,"* and the practice is active in after-care client service, producing a quarterly Charity bulletin and running a series of workshops on chartered bodies (Charter 2000.) Acting for the Trustees of the Esmee Fairbairn Charitable Trust in their sale of their third share in M&G to Prudential was a major piece of work last year. **Clients** British Library, Royal Shakespeare Company, Wellcome Trust.

Charles Russell The charities group in the firm has been seen as *"working very hard in this area."* This includes running a survey and conference on charity sector mergers and re-organisations. The firm has built on its strong private client base and offers commercial advice on a range of charity issues. One recent highlight was the restructuring of the Insolvency Practitioners Association. **Clients:** Eton College, RAF Benevolent Fund, Royal College of Nursing, Bailey Thomas Trusts.

Nabarro Nathanson Large cross-departmental charity group which acts for many significant charities and has won widespread respect from its peers as a *"top level"* outfit. The firm's practice is based in Reading, but draws resources from its London branch and competes strongly with the London market, so it is included here and leaps by two bands. Headed by the Reading-based *"all-rounder"* **Jonathan Burchfield**, the practice is particularly active in public sector work such as regeneration and fundraising website contracts which draw on the firm's industry sector strengths. On the pure charity side it has recently been involved in advising several high-profile charities on controversial membership relationship issues. **Clients:** National Trusts, English Partnerships, RSPCA.

Sinclair, Taylor and Martin *"Well-known in the voluntary sector,"* with several lawyers coming to the firm from a charity background, this small specialist firm acts particularly for service delivery charities and Learned Societies. Work includes mergers, management re-structuring, service contracts with local authorities and volunteer employment issues. **James Sinclair Taylor** *("all he does is charities and all he does is first-class")* and

CHARITIES • London	Ptnrs	Assts
❶ Bates, Wells & Braithwaite	7	4
❷ Farrer & Co	1	5
Paisner & Co	5	5
Withers	4	7
❸ Allen & Overy	1	3
Charles Russell	3	5
Nabarro Nathanson	2	1
Sinclair Taylor & Martin	5	4
❹ Bircham & Co.	8	10
Claricoat Phillips	2	-
Harbottle & Lewis	1	2
Speechly Bircham	2	3
Trowers & Hamlins	1	3
❺ Lawrence Graham	2	3
Lee Bolton & Lee	2	1
Macfarlanes	7	15
Radcliffes	2	1
Winckworth Sherwood	2	-
❻ Field Fisher Waterhouse	1	1
Herbert Smith	5	6
Lee & Pembertons	2	3
Linklaters	1	1
SJ Berwin & Co	1	1
Vizard Oldham	2	1

LEADING INDIVIDUALS	
❶ **HILL Judith** Farrer & Co	**LLOYD Stephen** Bates, Wells & Braithwaite
MIDDLETON Fiona Bates, Wells & Braithwaite	
PAINES Alison Withers	**PIPER Anne-Marie** Paisner & Co
❷ **BURCHFIELD Jonathan** Nabarro Nathanson	
CLARICOAT John Claricoat Phillips	**DOLLIMORE Jean** Trowers & Hamlins
DRISCOLL Lindsay Sinclair Taylor & Martin	
MIMPRISS Peter Allen & Overy	**PHILLIPS Hilary** Claricoat Phillips
PHILLIPS Andrew Bates, Wells & Braithwaite	
SINCLAIR TAYLOR James Sinclair Taylor & Martin	
❸ **MEAKIN Robert** Stone King	**PAISNER Martin** Paisner & Co
PHILLIPS Ann Stephenson Harwood	
PORTRAIT Judith Portrait Solicitors	
WEIL Simon Bircham & Co.	
UP AND COMING	
HARWOOD Ros Speechly Bircham	**PROTANI Moira** SJ Berwin & Co

Within each band, firms are listed alphabetically. *See **Profiles** on page 141*

the *"extremely competent and able"* **Lindsay Driscoll** head the team which has received widespread praise from the market, and rises in the rankings. **Clients:** St Christopher's Fellowship; BBC Children in Need; Unicef.

Bircham & Co **Simon Weil** leads this practice which continues to *"attract a big team,"* with two recent lateral hires, and remains a strong player. The firm offers niche specialisms in trusts and taxation along with pure charity law expertise and effective liaising with the Charity Commission. An office in Brussels makes it well-placed to monitor the effect of EC law on UK charity law and to lobby for the sector. Notable recent work includes the formation of the Coalfields Regeneration Trust. **Clients:** Blue Cross, Mothers Union, Coalfields Regeneration Trust.

Claricoat Phillips A well respected *"boutique"* firm, which is known by lawyers and clients alike for its in-depth knowledge of charity law and the workings of the Charity Commission. Receive many referrals on specifically charity matters. Partners **John Claricoat** *("he's so very knowlegable")* and **Hilary Phillips** *("an extremely good charity lawyer")* were both at the Commission and co-wrote 'Charity Law A-Z.'

Harbottle & Lewis Known in the market for a number of significant and high profile clients and niche expertise in cause-related marketing, the practice is seen as *"getting serious about the sector"* and rises in the rankings this year. Combines formation and regulatory work with brand protection, fundraising compliance and media management skills. Well-versed in acting for large scale fundraising events, the team organised the formation of NetAid (UK) Ltd. **Clients:** The Diana, Princess of Wales Memorial Fund, Comic Relief, 1 Twenty.

Speechly Bircham Seen by the market as *"a force for the future,"* the firm's charities unit focuses on the commercial side of charity work, with particular knowledge in mergers formations and VAT issues. **Ros Harwood**, secretary of the Charity Law Association, and up and coming this year, *"has an interesting slant on things,"* and leads the unit, whose clients range from family charitable trusts to national fundraising organisations, schools and religious bodies. **Clients:** Mental After Care Association, Scope, John Groom Association for the Disabled.

Trowers and Hamlins *"Pre-eminent"* in the field of housing association charities, and known for other niche specialities such as Industrial and Provident Societies, the firm also acts for a number of national charities. The *"practical"* **Jean Dollimore** looks after the pure charity side, which takes in formation, mergers, widening of objects and constitutional issues, while employment and other questions are dealt with by a cross-departmental group. **Clients:** St Dunstans, National Childbirth Trust, Leonard Cheshire Foundation.

Lawrence Graham A cross-departmental group within the firm offers employment, property and contracts advice for charities in addition to specifically charitable issues. General market feeling is that the quality of the practice's clients and work entitles it to promotion this year. The firm is strong in the local and public authority sector, acting for charitable trusts on leisure facilities and housing, as well as related sector clients. It is also active in the education field and counts several significant private schools amongst its clients. **Clients:** Motability, Action against Hunger, Laura Ashley Foundation.

Lee, Bolton & Lee *"Well-connected"* practice which maintains an important, if traditional presence in the sector. Acts for *"a lot of major clients,"* particularly educational and ecclesiastical charities. **Clients:** Educational charities.

Macfarlanes The charity practice has grown from its private client department, and the firm has been seen by the market as *"devoting more resources to the area."* As a result the team rises in the rankings this year. The team continues to act for significant charitable and grant-making trusts, but has broadened out to both corporate and operational charity work. Practice specialisms include setting up trading subsidiaries and constitutional issues. A sophisticated application to the Court to make an old foundation fully charitable and rewriting an entire Royal Charter in modern English are recent examples of the team's work. **Clients:** Royal Academy, National Missing Persons Helpline, Trusthouse Forte Foundation.

Radcliffes Established Westminster firm which acts for 170 charity clients, many of whom are based in the animal welfare, education and medicine sectors. The practice is increasingly focusing on mental health and welfare charities to link with its mental health practice. In addition to constitutional and charity law advice from restructuring to mergers, it also provides employment, property and commercial advice. Recent work includes acting for the Children's Society in fundraising project work for Children's

Promise. **Clients:** Children's Society, Animal Health Trust, Worshipful Company of Brewers.

Winckworth Sherwood Large and *"professional"* team which is particularly prominent in the religious and education fields. An all-round service is provided, with employment work a recent growth area. **Clients:** Marshall's Charity, Greycoat Foundation, National Energy Action.

Field Fisher Waterhouse The practice acts for many well known medical and cultural charities and institutions, and is also involved in advising charities active in the commercial world. Charitable issues arising from public procurement and major projects are a particular speciality, with pure charity law advice and cross-departmental services for charitable clients also offered. Recent work has included advising on the implications of race discrimination legislation on the Architectural Foundation's proposed setting up of the Stephen Lawrence scholarship for young black architects. **Clients:** Royal College of Physicians, Great Ormond Street Hospital, Royal Academy of Dancing.

Herbert Smith A separate trusts and charity group acts mainly for substantial asset-based and commercial charities and advises on commercial transactions involving charities. VAT issues, brand and asset protection, Housing Association work and Common Investment Funds are specialisms, with notable recent work including a complex re-organisation for the Order of St John. **Clients:** Wellcome Foundation, Weston Trust, Weinstock Trust.

Lee & Pembertons Long-established charities practice whose clients include independent schools, grant-making charities and service providers. Charity expertise includes compliance with the charities SORP, registration of new charities, Charity Commission compliance and schemes dealing with trustee disputes. **Clients:** Harrow School, Order of St John, Corporation of Sons of the Clergy.

Linklaters The firm does have an impressive and growing client base, particularly amongst large institutional and grant-making charities, but also a number of active and arts-based charities. Based in the trusts department, the main focus of the practice is on providing specialist charitable advice to other departments acting for charities on property, IP and banking issues. However, constitutional and start-ups are also dealt with. **Clients:** Royal Opera House, Tate Gallery, CAFOD.

SJ Berwin Small but growing charity practice within a large commercial firm, whose clients range from grant-making to cause-related marketing charities. Up and coming **Moira Protani** *"has put the practice on the map,"* and provides charity law advice from Charity Commission investigations to trustee advice. Recently acted for the Clore Foundation in its distribution of a number large grants, including to the Royal Opera House. **Clients:** Friends of Hebrew University of Jerusalem, Clore Foundation, Beaverbrook Fund.

Vizard Oldham Has a specialism in public sector work, acting for a number of NHS Trusts, National Health Litigation Authorities and Housing Associations. The team also acts for grant-makers, training charities and old established charities. Royal Charter work is an area of particular expertise, but the practice covers all charity areas from membership disciplinary problems to commercial, property, employment and IP (such as brand protection of the poppy as a British Legion symbol.) **Clients:** Dunhill Medical Trust, Royal British Legion, Training for Life.

Other Notable Practitioners **Ann Phillips** from Stephenson Harwood and **Judith Portrait** of Portrait Solicitors/Denton Wilde Sapte are recommended as individuals for the strength of their personal practices. The former is known for her longstanding expertise in mergers and arts/heritage charities, the latter for her strong clients, particularly the Sainsbury Trust. The *"academic"* ex-Charity Commission lawyer **Robert Meakin** has left Simmons & Simmons and taken its charities practice to the London office of highly rated Bath practice Stone King. It remains to be seen whether his new firm will be able to establish a substantial presence in the London market.

THAMES VALLEY

CHARITIES • Thames Valley	Ptnrs	Assts
❶ **Manches** Oxford	1	1
Winckworth Sherwood Oxford	1	1
❷ **BrookStreet Des Roches** Witney	1	-
❸ **Henmans** Oxford	1	-
Iliffes Booth Bennett Uxbridge	1	-
Linnells Oxford	1	1

LEADING INDIVIDUALS
❶ **BROOKS Kenneth** BrookStreet Des Roches
POULTER Alan Manches
REES John Winckworth Sherwood
❷ **SAUNDERS Joss** Linnells

Within each band, firms are listed alphabetically. See **Profiles** on page 141

Manches Well known for its Oxford University and college clients, the practice advises grant-making, educational, medical and several national charities on constitutional matters and wider employment, IP and property issues. Overhauling complex charity constitutions to widen objects is a particular area of expertise. **Alan Poulter** is a *"a well-respected Oxford lawyer."* **Clients:** Islamic Trust, National Trust, over half of the Oxford Colleges.

Winckworth Sherwood Known particularly for its ecclesiastical clients, the firm has a strong emphasis on the not-for-profit sector and acts for a variety of charity clients and housing associations. All aspects of constitutional work is dealt with in addition to property and employment law, and a particular recent emphasis has been on the the charitable aspects of PFI/projects work. **John Rees** is known as a *"good all-rounder."* **Clients:** Ecclesiastical charities.

Brook Street Des Roches *"Extremely efficient operator"* **Kenneth Brooks** is the lead figure at this recommended practice, which has noted expertise in constitutional advice and commercial property work. **Clients:** Educational charities.

Henmans Entering the tables for the first time this year, the practice has a growing reputation in legacy work, and acts for several national charities in this field. Constitutional work includes mergers, restructuring, formations and trading subsidiaries, while a full range of employment and property services are provided from across the firm. Rewriting the Royal Charter of a major benevolent society to increase the scope of its beneficiaries was a recent highlight. **Clients:** RSPCA, RNIB, Oxfam.

Iliffes Booth Bennett Acts for several well-known religious, musical and educational charities. Provides general charitable advice in addition to litigation and employment matters. **Clients:** Institute of Our Lady of Mercy, Musicians Benevolent Fund, Rugby School.

Linnells The practice acts for significant national, educational and medical research charities. Advice ranges from trading, fundraising and constitutional issues to property matters and local authority contracts with charities. **Joss Saunders,** who has written a book on the latter subject, and spends much of his time in his role as in-house legal secretary to Oxfam, is new to the leaders' table this year. Recent work includes involvement in the setting up of Oxfam's free internet service. **Clients:** Oxfam, Wateraid, several Oxford colleges.

THE SOUTH

CHARITIES • The South	Ptnrs	Assts
❶ **Blake Lapthorn** Portsmouth	-	1
Thomas Eggar Church Adams Chichester	1	1
Thomson Snell & Passmore Tunbridge Wells	2	2
❷ **Barlows** Guildford	*	*
Cripps Harries Hall Tunbridge Wells	4	12
Griffith Smith Brighton	1	-
Lester Aldridge Bournemouth	1	-

LEADING INDIVIDUALS
❶ **CAIRNS Elizabeth** Elizabeth Cairns
❷ **DAVIS Elizabeth** Blake Lapthorn
SMITH Tim Griffith Smith

Within each band, firms are listed alphabetically. *See **Profiles** on page 141*

** See editorial entry.*

Blake Lapthorn The *"well-known"* **Elizabeth Davis** is the firm's charities specialist and acts for a range of carer, arts, fund-raising, environmental and disabled charities. Has particular expertise in acting for local authorities, charities and voluntary organisations. Recently carried out a major constitutional reconstruction for a housing association charity. **Clients:** Cottage Homes, Hampshire Wildlife, Mary Rose Trust.

Thomas Eggar Church Adams Alongside its large number of ecclesiastical charities, the firm's private client department offers a full range of legal and financial services to charities ranging from almshouses and colleges to grant-making and local arts charities. The firm's financial services arm is able to provide tax and accounts advice and several partners at the firm act as trustees to local and national charities. **Clients:** Diocese of Chichester, Dean and Chapter of Chichester Cathedral.

Thomson Snell & Passmore Respected private client team which acts for local arts charities, charitable trusts and an increasing number of educational charities. Typical work includes formations, incorporations and drafting and reorganising charity constitutions. **Clients:** Arts charities, educational charities.

Barlows Although there is no dedicated team, the firm undertakes a variety of commercial work for several substantial charity clients, including contracts, property and employment. Legacy and constitutional work is handled from the firm's private client department. Recently incorporated a major UK charity. **Clients:** World Wild Life Fund for Nature, CHASE.

Cripps Harries Hall A well-respected private client firm which has a specialist charity unit to handle charity law and investment management advice for private and public charitable trusts. Pure charity work includes setting up charities and reviewing/updating constitutions. **Clients:** Great Britain Sasakawa Foundation, Royal Historical Society, Japan Festival Fund.

Griffith Smith Ex-voluntary sector manager **Tim Smith** specialises in acting for community organisations such as youth employment, learning disability and community development charities. Handles registration, development of management structures and processes, constitutional changes and Charity Commission investigations. **Clients:** Community organisations, charitable trusts, public schools.

Lester Aldridge Acts for a variety of local and regional charities, with particular experience in formations, taxation and funding issues. Several partners act as trustees to local charities and the department is company secretary to several charitable companies. **Clients:** Bournemouth Orchestras, Army Air Corps Fund, Western Association of Ballet Schools.

Other Notable Practitioners Sole practitioner **Elizabeth Cairns** is *"clearly a specialist in the field"* and retains her reputation as a *"charities guru."*

SOUTH WEST & WALES

CHARITIES • South West & Wales	Ptnrs	Assts
❶ **Stone King** Bath	1	1
❷ **Bond Pearce** Exeter	2	1
Burges Salmon Bristol	1	1
Osborne Clarke OWA, Bristol	2	4
❸ **Tozers** Exeter	2	1
Veale Wasbrough Bristol	2	3
Wilsons Salisbury	2	2
❹ **Michelmores** Exeter	1	1
Parker Bullen Salisbury	2	2
Thrings & Long Bath	2	3
❺ **Clarke Willmott & Clarke** Taunton	1	-
Edwards Geldard Cardiff	-	1
Eversheds Bristol	1	1
Rickerby Watterson Cheltenham	2	3

LEADING INDIVIDUALS
❶ **KING Michael** Stone King
❷ **WOODWARD Mark** Osborne Clarke OWA
❸ **KING Richard** Tozers
WYLD Charles Burges Salmon

Within each band, firms are listed alphabetically. *See **Profiles** on page 141*

Stone King Remains *"way ahead"* in the region. The firm is renowned for its Roman Catholic charity clients and acts for a growing number of service provider and educational charities. **Michael King**, the current Chairman of the Charity Law Association, is *"obviously a leading figure"* both on the national and regional charity scenes, and in 1999 was the first ever solicitor to be appointed as the Receiver and Manager of a charity. Particular work specialisms include constitutional issues, mergers, joint ventures, Charity Commission investigations and quasi-governmental charities. One notable highlight is ongoing advice to the three national charities who are combining to promote the Petroleum Geology Conference 2003. **Clients:** Westminster Diocese, LSU College Trustees, Royal Photographic Society.

Bond Pearce Cross-departmental charities group acts for a range of charities, particularly in the heritage property and further education sectors. Pure charity law work such as formations and constitutions is dealt with in addition to IP, employment and other issues. **Clients:** Theatre Royal, Plymouth; Vincent Wildlife Trust; University of Southampton.

Burges Salmon Large commercial firm which offers charity law advice on matters such Charity Commission investigations, mergers and dissolutions to clients ranging from grant-making trusts to heritage charities. The firm has a strong involvement in advising on lottery-funded and other large-scale charity projects, and is known in the market for its tax expertise and ability to take on *"difficult"* work. The *"excellent"* **Charles Wyld** is the charities specialist of the team. **Clients:** @Bristol, Bath Spa Trust, National Trust.

Osborne Clarke OWA Acts for charitable trusts, local and national charities and is able to offer them a full range service across their corporate/commercial, employment and IP capabilities. The practice has also been involved in advising corporate clients on the charitable aspects of millennium projects. The *"down to earth"* **Mark Woodward** rises a band this year in recognition of his increasing presence in the sector. **Clients:** Sue Ryder Foundation, Macmillan Cancer Relief, Shaw Trust.

Tozers Known in the market for its preponderance of religious charities, the practice is expanding to encompass educational and community start-up clients. **Richard King** heads the practice, whose charity specialisms include advice on constitutional aspects, mergers, liaising with the Charity Commission, and setting up trading subsidiaries and VAT schemes. **Clients:** Plymouth Roman Catholic Diocese, Prior Park College, Forward Living.

Veale Wasbrough Advising a significant number of educational institutions on charity law issues on the back of its education practice. Weight of recommendation sees the firm rise in the tables this year. The practice is also involved in public sector work, such as millennium projects, particularly in managing the relationship between public and charitable funding. **Clients:** Arts (South West), Harry Crook Foundation.

Wilsons Solicitors A *"solid team"* which has developed a separate charity practice to include conveyancing, employment and corporate/commercial specialists. Specific charity work includes formation, trading activities, and constitutional issues. Clients range from traditional charitable trusts to ecclesiastical and educational charities. **Clients:** Stanley Picker Trust, National Rifle Association, Salisbury Diocesan Board of Finance.

Michelmores Acts for a range of local endowed, ecclesiastical and educational charities. Work includes pure charity law and related employment, contracts and property advice. **Clients:** University of Exeter, Diocese of Exeter, Exeter Hospice.

Parker Bullen Charity practice operates out of the private client department and deals with formation, administration and general advice for local and educational charities. A full range of related employment, litigation and other legal services are also offered to charity clients. Recent work includes setting up will schemes for members of several national charities and forming a charity to offer engineering scholarships in the UK for Japanese students. **Clients:** South Wiltshire Mencap, Civil Service Benevolent Fund.

Thrings & Long Based in the commercial department, the firm offers full charity law and other legal services to local and national grant-making charities, almshouses, arts, religious, educational and medical charities. Land charity work, issues related to lottery-funded projects and development projects have been highlights of recent work. **Clients:** St John's Hospital, Mr Willats' Charity, RJ Harris Trust.

Clarke Wilmott & Clarke Provides a range of services including formations, incorporations and commercial advice for a variety of charities. Recent matters have included educational governance work for private education institutions and involvement in quasi-government agency work. **Clients:** Countryside Agency, Community Forest Partnerships.

Edwards Geldard New to the tables this year, this expanding practice operates out of the trusts team, and acts for a range of charities, particularly in the cultural sector. Endowed charitable trusts, youth fundraising and educational charities are other clients. Work specialisms include formation, structural re-organisation, trustee issues and investment. **Clients:** National Botanical Garden for Wales, Wales Millennium Centre, Arts Council of Wales.

Eversheds The firm's charity practice is ancillary to its education and housing association practices, with charitable and tax advice being provided to its clients in those areas. Other clients include heritage charities and local voluntary organisations, and services include establishment and registration of charitable companies. **Clients:** Welsh National Opera, National Museum of Wales, Jane Hodge Foundation.

Rickerby Watterson Known for its work for educational institutions, the firm provides tax planning and general charity advice ranging from incorporation of charitable companies and setting up trading subsidiaries through to constitutional changes and liaising with the Privy Council. **Clients:** National Meningitis Trust, Cheltenham Ladies College, Cheltenham and Gloucester College of Higher Education.

MIDLANDS

CHARITIES • Midlands	Ptnrs	Assts
❶ **Anthony Collins Solicitors** Birmingham	1	1
Martineau Johnson Birmingham	3	3
Shakespeares Birmingham	-	1
Wragge & Co Birmingham	2	2
❷ **Gateley Wareing** Birmingham	1	1
Hewitson Becke + Shaw Northampton	2	2
Lee Crowder Birmingham	2	2

LEADING INDIVIDUALS	
❶ **DE'ATH Gary** Wragge & Co	**FEA Michael** Martineau Johnson
THOMPSON Romaine Anthony Collins Solicitors	**WOODHEAD Louise** Wragge & Co
❷ **GATELEY Stephen** Gateley Wareing	

Within each band, firms are listed alphabetically. *See **Profiles** on page 141*

Anthony Collins Solicitors Respected particularly for their housing association charities, in which they are *"acknowledged leaders in the community,"* the firm has a portfolio of active local and national charity clients, with strength in the religious and regeneration fields. Recent work has included constitutional issues and strategic/structuring advice, while employment and IP are also catered for. **Romaine Thompson** works exclusively in the areas and is seen as *"very much a charities person."* **Clients:** Shaftesbury, Spring Harvest, Parkinson's Disease Society.

Martineau Johnson Commercial firm which *"has made quite a name for itself in this area."* Its long-standing relationship with a large number of significant charitable trusts stems from its private client reputation, and it is also known for the service it provides to the charitable wings of its traditional education and religious client base. The firm has been increasingly involved in lottery-funded charity work for churches and joint venture work for charitable companies. Team leader **Michael Fea** is noted as a leader in the field with *"a broad range of experience."* **Clients:** Foundation of Conductive Education, Christian Vision, The Sequel Trust.

Shakespeares Seen as a voluntary sector practice with a grassroots community bias, the firm also acts for some grant-making, religious and education charities and traditional charitable trusts. The main focus of the practice is on start-up health, environmental and training charities, often with a multi-cultural element. It remains to be seen how the defection of Gary De'ath to Wragge & Co will affect the team's reputation. Charity specialisms include incorporation, constitution amendments and commercial and strategic advice, while employment, IP and property issues are dealt with by a cross-departmental team. **Clients:** Muscular Dystrophy Group, Association of Child Psychologists and Psychiatrists, Newtown Cutural Project (The Drum.)

Wragge & Co *"A commercial stall"* which is recognised throughout the market to be seriously developing its charity practice, as can be seen in the recent recruitment of *"dedicated charities practitioner"* **Gary De'ath** from Shakespeares. The *"effective"* **Louise Woodhead** comes from a corporate background and heads up a team which acts for a mixture of grant-making and active charities.The firm involves itself beyond legal advice to providing trustees and fundraising for its clients. Local authority outsourcing and millennium-funded projects have provided much recent work. **Clients:** Discovery Centre, Sutton Coldfield Municipal Charity, Edward Cadbury Charitable Trust.

Gateley Wareing Known for its traditional presence in the religious charity field, the practice acts for the Roman Catholic Diocese of Birmingham and related charities. Also handles ongoing constitutional advice, employment, property and corporate work for smaller service provider charities. **Stephen Gateley** remains active in the local charity sector. **Clients:** RC Archdiocese of Birmingham, Oscott College, Fr. Hudsons Society.

Hewitson, Becke + Shaw Acts for a range of clients, including grant-making and large service providing charities, and several Oxford and Cambridge colleges. Advice extends beyond pure charity law to construction, property, employment and IP issues. **Clients:** St Andrew's Hospice, Harpur Trust, RSPB.

Lee Crowder Entering the tables this year on the recommendation of their peers. Charities work is co-ordinated from a newly-established unit which gives across the board advice to charitable trusts and educational, religious, grant-making and animal welfare charities. The merger between the Selly Oak colleges of Birmingham University was a highlight of last year's practice . **Clients:** King Edward's School Foundation, United Reform West Midlands Province, National Townswomen's Guild.

EAST ANGLIA

CHARITIES • East Anglia	Ptnrs	Assts
❶ Cozens-Hardy & Jewson Norwich	2	1
Mills & Reeve Norwich	1	1
Taylor Vinters Cambridge	2	1
❷ Eversheds Norwich	1	-
Greenwoods Peterborough	1	1
Hewitson Becke + Shaw Cambridge	2	-
Leathes Prior Norwich	-	1

LEADING INDIVIDUALS	
❶ HERRING John Mills & Reeve	MARTIN Matthew Cozens-Hardy & Jewson
WARREN Jennifer Taylor Vinters	
❷ NORTON Philip Eversheds	PEROWNE John Eversheds
WOMACK Michael Taylor Vinters	

Within each band, firms are listed alphabetically. *See **Profiles** on page 141*

Cozens-Hardy & Jewson Stand-alone charity practice, which is known for acting for major local established charities. Guidance to trustees, administration and establishment of trustees are the main aspects of work covered. Respected consultant **Matthew Martin** *"entirely deserves to remain at the top,"* and acts as clerk to a number of local charities. **Clients:** Norwich Consolidated Charities, Norwich Town Close Estate Charity, Anguish's Educational Foundation.

Mills & Reeve Practice is respected for its *"serious lawyers"* and its strength in ecclesiastical and educational charity work and private charitable trusts. **John Herring** is particularly known for his church work, and the team has experience in advising as to the terms of charitable trusts and all aspects of administration in addition to property and other matters. On the back of its well regarded education practice, the firm acts for several large charitable educational institutions. **Clients:** Major landowning charities and ecclesiastical bodies.

Taylor Vinters Known for its work for Cambridge University colleges, the team has particular expertise in pension funds and the acquisition, development and leasing of properties for charitable trusts. **Jennifer Warren** is recommended for her experience in charity property work, while **Michael Womack** concentrates on constitutional, tax and investment work. Advised on the reorganisation of an educational charity after changes in the charity accounting rules. **Clients:** University of Cambridge and colleges.

Eversheds, The Norwich office heads the firm's charities practice, whose main focus lies in servicing the charitable activities of its significant corporate clients. Much of the work is referred from other regions. Other clients include private foundations, medical trusts and some local charities. As well as advising on constitutional issues such as trustee relationships, a cross-departmental team is able to offer property, corporate, litigation and employment services. **Philip Norton** concentrates on the business side, while **John Perowne** is the team's trusts expert, and looks after some Cambridge College work. **Clients:** Sue Ryder Foundation, Anglo-Spanish Society, RICS.

Greenwoods Acts for a range of charitable companies and professional institutes, particularly in the environmental, arts and educational fields. Based within the company and commercial department, the team specialises in corporate/commercial work for charities, including mergers, reorganisations, relationships with subsidiary trading companies and investment issues. **Clients:** Institute of Credit Management, Wyggeston & Queen Elizabeth I College, Peterborough Environment City Trust.

Hewitson Becke + Shaw Respected practice which counts large service-providers, research institutes, Cambridge colleges and art charities as clients. In addition to general charity law advice and administration, a cross-departmental team provides employment, environmental, construction and tax work. Advised on the merger and incorporation of a substantial property-owning and service-providing charity. **Clients:** Fund for Addenbrookes.

Leathes Prior Small firm which acts for several local charities and local branches of national charities. Work runs from administration and changing schemes to related areas such as employment and property. **Clients:** The Great Hospital, Norfolk RSPCA.

NORTH WEST

CHARITIES • North West	Ptnrs	Assts
❶ Birch Cullimore Chester	1	-
Brabner Holden Banks Wilson Liverpool	1	1
❷ Oswald Goodier & Co Preston	1	-
❸ Halliwell Landau Manchester	⚐	⚐
Pannone and Partners Manchester	1	-

LEADING Individuals • North West
❶ HOLDEN Lawrence Brabner Holden Banks Wilson
❷ BELDERBOS Mark Oswald Goodier & Co

Within each band, firms are listed alphabetically. *See **Profiles** on page 141*
⚐ *Figures unavailable at time of going to press.*

Birch Cullimore Well-respected charities practice which administers and advises religious and educational charities, almshouses and service providers. Work handled includes formation, incorporation and additional employment and company services.

Brabner Holden Banks Wilson Known in the market for their housing association and arts charities work, the practice has recently become particularly involved in the regeneration and enterprise creation field. Constitutional, governance and general advice is available in addition to cross-departmental IP, employment and litigation work. **Lawrence Holden** remains highly respected, and has recently written a guide for charity trustees 'A Sense of Purpose.' **Clients:** Merseyside Youth Association, Furniture Resource Centre, Huyton Community Partnership.

Oswald Goodier & Co Long established private client firm known in the charity field for its Roman Catholic diocese and religious order clients, with other charity clients including educational and general welfare charitable trusts. **Mark Belderbos** leads the team, which offers property, general trust and constitutional advice, the latter including alteration of trusts, establishing new charities, and dealing with the Charity Commission. **Clients:** RC Diocese of Lancaster, Montfort Missionary Society, Congregation of the Daughters of Wisdom.

Halliwell Landau The practice is based in the trusts and estates department and acts mainly for new, "cutting edge" charities in the education, health and media sections as well as a smattering of Jewish charities. Work includes formation, general administration, accountancy and Charity Commission regulation. Its will administration work for the Barclays Bank Trust Company also throws up many charitable issues. **Clients:** North West Media Charitable Trust, several university and medical bodies.

Pannone and Partners Members of the firm's private client and corporate department provide charity law services such as formation and revising schemes to a range of charities including educational institutions, sports and outdoor trusts and almshouses. **Clients:** Community Foundation for Greater Manchester, Sustainability North West.

NORTH EAST

CHARITIES • North East	Ptnrs	Assts
❶ **Wrigleys** Leeds	2	3
❷ **Grays** York	1	-
❸ **Addleshaw Booth & Co** Leeds	1	1
Dickinson Dees Newcastle upon Tyne	3	4
Irwin Mitchell Sheffield	2	1
❹ **Eversheds** Newcastle upon Tyne	2	3
Keeble Hawson Sheffield	4	2
McCormicks Leeds	3	3
Pinsent Curtis Leeds	1	1

LEADING INDIVIDUALS	
❶ **LAWTON Tony** Grays	**LYNCH Malcolm** Wrigleys
WRIGLEY Matthew Wrigleys	

Within each band, firms are listed alphabetically. *See **Profiles** on page 141*

Wrigleys With the recent addition of Eversheds' Leeds private client practice bolstering its strength further, this exclusively private client/charities practice firm rises to the top band this year. This was confirmed by the firm's August 2000 merger with rival top firm, Malcolm Lynch. From the latter firm, **Malcolm Lynch** is viewed as a *"true specialist"* in the area. He has specific knowledge of charity employment issues, mergers and establishing trading subsidiaries. Known in the market for its portfolio of *"all sorts of interesting clients"* Wrigleys has a large number of significant heritage, religious, educational charities and private family charitable trusts under its belt. The *"able and well respected"* **Matthew Wrigley** leads the expanded team which advises on the full range of charity and tax issues. Recent *"cutting edge"* work includes lottery-funded and conservation projects. The former Malcolm Lynch has been involved with large regeneration charities such as the Ulster Investment Foundation. **Clients:** Major heritage, educational and religious charities.

Grays Long-established practice which is known in the market for its religious and educational clients, with **Tony Lawton** recommended for his *"specialist ecclesiastical knowledge."* The team also acts for landed charities, housing associations, arts charities and charitable trading companies. Has particular experience in charitable land transactions, Charity Commission schemes, fundraising and cy-pres matters. **Clients:** Roman Catholic Diocese of Middlesbrough, Dean and Chapter of York, Lady Elizabeth Hastings Charity.

Addleshaw Booth & Co This large commercial firm's growing charities practice is headed from the private client department. On top of educational, local charities and private trusts, the firm is able to call on a cross-departmental team to take on larger-scale work such as government "hive-off" charities and advising and setting up charitable wings of existing corporate clients. The team is also experienced in advising commercial clients on the specific issues relating to projects involving charities. **Clients:** Charitable subsidiary of a major plc, £50m government funded charity.

Dickinson Dees Well-regarded charities practice which builds on the firm's leading private client and corporate/commercial strength. Niche expertise includes contracting out of council leisure services, funding issues and charities' accounts. Recently appointed as one of the five firms to handle grant/property work for the Millennium Commission on a national basis. **Clients:** The Freemen of Newcastle, St Mary Magdalene and Holy Jesus Trust, Northern Arts.

Irwin Mitchell On top of major local educational and arts charities, the practice is focusing on public sector "hive offs" and charities which links in to its substantial personal injury practice (such as head injury charities.) A full range of charity law services are provided, with a particular specialism in Charity Commission regulatory matters. Significant recent work includes acting for the local authority in its arrangements for the operation of Sheffield New Millennium Gallery. **Clients:** Sheffield City Trust, Sheffield Galleries and Museums Trust, The Royal Armouries.

Eversheds Moving beyond its traditional base in Community Foundations, the practice is focusing on the commercial element to charity work and fields a split commercial/private client team. Clients include large medical, educational and local fundraising charities, with lottery-funded public sector projects and advice to commercial clients on their charitable activities seen as important growth areas. Acting for Scottish Newcastle Breweries in their sponsorship of Marie Curie Cancer was a recent highlight. **Clients:** Great North East Air Ambulance, International Centre for Life Trust, Stockton Arts Centre.

Keeble Hawson Based within the private client department, the practice is rated in the market for its work for religious and education charities. Carries out constitutional work, administration and some litigation.

McCormicks Seen by the market as a *"very specialist"* firm, with a strong client base amongst sporting and outdoor charities, the practice is expanding to encompass constitutional, tax, estate advice, commercial property and other services for a variety of charity clients ranging from religious orders to local and national fundraising charities. **Clients:** The Duke of Edinburgh's Award, The Order of the Holy Paraclete, The Harrogate Women's Centre.

Pinsent Curtis Much of the firm's charities work lies in the field of local government "hive-offs," deriving from its local authority practice. Other clients include private charitable trusts and commercially aware charities, and the team have allied experience in advising corporate clients on their charitable activities. Pure charity constitutional and administration advice is offered in addition to a full range of employment, property, commercial and other services. Recent work includes advising Barnsley Metropolitan Borough Council on the proposed outsourcing of heritage services to a new charity. **Clients:** British Epilepsy Association, York Archaeological Trust.

SCOTLAND

CHARITIES • Scotland	Ptnrs	Assts
❶ Anderson Strathern WS Edinburgh	2	1
Turcan Connell WS Edinburgh	-	1
❷ Biggart Baillie Glasgow	1	-
Tods Murray WS Edinburgh	2	-
❸ Balfour & Manson Edinburgh	5	2
Burness Glasgow	2	1
Lindsays WS Edinburgh	2	1
MacRoberts Glasgow	1	1
Morton Fraser, Solicitors Edinburgh	4	3
Shepherd & Wedderburn WS Edinburgh	-	1
TC Young & Son Glasgow	2	-
❹ Brechin Tindal Oatts Glasgow	1	-
Gillespie Macandrew WS Edinburgh	2	2

LEADING INDIVIDUALS	
❶ CONNELL Douglas Turcan Connell WS	MACKINTOSH Simon Turcan Connell WS
REITH David Lindsays WS	RENNIE Brenda Balfour & Manson
RUSSELL George Anderson Strathern WS	WYLLIE Gordon Biggart Baillie

Within each band, firms are listed alphabetically. *See **Profiles** on page 141*

Anderson Strathern WS A wide range of major educational, heritage, religious, grant-making and private charitable trusts are serviced by this commercial firm. **George Russell** heads up the practice which advises on all constitutional and pure charity issues. A cross-departmental approach enables clients to also receive full accountancy, taxation and investment advice in addition to employment, property and other legal services. Setting up satellite organisations of a new cancer care centre was a recent highlight of the team's work. **Clients:** National Trust of Scotland, Iona Cathedral Trust, Fettes College.

Turcan Connell WS Niche private client firm with a strong reputation in heritage charity work and a substantial client list of private and public charities. Several partners within the private client department are experienced in constitutional and administration matters, including *"strong performer"* **Douglas Connell** and **Simon Mackintosh**, who has recently been appointed to the Scottish Executive's Commission on the future of charity law in Scotland. One recent trend has been the establishment of large privately endowed charitable trusts by entrepreneurial clients. **Clients:** National Galleries of Scotland, Lloyds TSB Foundation for Scotland, Scottish Hospital Endowments Research Trust.

Biggart Baillie Rises in the rankings to reflect its increasing profile in the market. The team gives constitutional and cross-departmental advice to charities ranging from private to corporate charitable trusts, heritage and service provider charities. The firm is particularly known for its close association with the Glasgow Trades. Recent work includes assisting Glasgow Tradeshall in its receiving Stage 1 approval for a lottery grant. **Gordon Wyllie** is new to the rankings this year after repeated recommendation. **Clients:** Deacon Convenor of the Trades of Glasgow, East Park, Lennoxlove Trust.

Tods Murray WS Remains a highly rated practice, with a large and wide-ranging client base which includes national and community organisations. The team is split across the private client and commercial departments. Has particular experience in acting for grant-giving bodies, arts-related charities and gay community charities. Charity law advice includes formations, incorporations and alteration of charitable objects, while other services include IP protection, commercial contracts, tax and employment work. **Clients:** RSPB, The Moredun Foundation, Royal Lyceum Theatre Company Limited.

Balfour & Manson The practice has a specialism in medical and welfare charities and **Brenda Rennie** has lectured extensively on developments in the law in relation to managing finances for the elderly and disabled. The practice is based in the private client department, with members of other departments able to provide a full back up service. Recent work includes setting up and acquiring charitable status for Edinburgh Mosque. **Clients:** Age Concern Scotland, the High Blood Pressure Foundation, Penumbra.

Burness Despite the loss of the private client department to Turcan Connell this commercial firm continues to service and win a large number of major charity clients. Work derives from a cross-departmental charities group which also includes two full time charity administrators. The main focus of work comes from the not for profit sector, with significant arts and medical charities, voluntary organisations and community projects amongst its clients. Involvement in the formation of new child abuse charity, the Moira Anderson Foundation, was one highlight of a busy year. **Clients:** Scottish Arts Council, The Big Issue in Scotland, Scottish Council for Voluntary Organisations.

Lindsays WS Niche expertise in building preservation trusts is complemented by substantial educational and national service provider clients. Recently advised in the establishment of the Scottish Seabird Centre. **David Reith** remains rated in the market. **Clients:** Scottish Historic Buildings Trust, Scottish Association of Citizens Advice Bureaux, Scottish Seabird Centre.

MacRoberts Advises a range of national and local charities on constitutional and governance issues. Particularly experienced in the administration of charitable foundations. **Clients:** KIND, SENSE.

Morton Fraser Solicitors Well-respected charity practice which is known for acting for the Edinburgh trades and significant educational and grant-giving charities. Also active in the environmental and government "hive off" fields. A progressive and cross-departmental approach is taken, with a charities brochure produced to assist clients. Several members of the firm act as trustees and directors of other charities. An increasing number of mergers and reorganisations characterised last year's work. **Clients:** George Watsons College, Scottish Agriculture College, Scottish Wildlife Trust.

Shepherd & Wedderburn WS Retains its reputation in the sector, with clients ranging from environmental and armed forces charities to well-known voluntary organisations. Has particular expertise in establishing and servicing charitable companies for its corporate clients. Recently set up a charity for Scottish Power to further research into renewable energy sources. **Clients:** Dunblane Help Fund, Barnardo's, Scottish Power Green Energy Tariff Trust.

T.C. Young & Son Highly rated team which acts largely for service provider charities and private charitable trusts. Work ranges from constitutional issues, governance and registration to corporate restructuring and employment matters. Recently advised on the demerger of Turning Point Scotland. **Clients:** Erskine Hospital, Princess Royal Trust for Carers, Turning Point Scotland.

Brechin Tindal Oatts Specialists in acting for medical and housing sector charities, the team has specific expertise in constitutional and employment issues. **Clients:** The Children's Hospice Association, Scotland; Quarriers; Glasgow & West of Scotland Society for the Blind.

Gillespie Macandrew WS Strong private client firm whose charity practice offers constitutional and investment advice to charities in addition to related employment, property and commercial issues. Clients include several major military, environmental, regeneration and heritage charities. Recent work includes rewriting the constitution of the Royal British Legion (Scotland.) **Clients:** SSPCA, Earl Haig Fund, Scottish Spina Bifida Association.

LEADERS IN CHARITIES

BELDERBOS, Mark J.
Oswald Goodier & Co, Preston (01772) 253841
Specialisation: All aspects of Charity Law, acting for many charitable organisations, both religious and secular. Ecclesiastical and Education. Commercial Property, particularly on behalf of charitable organisations. Substantial amounts of General Trust work.
Career: Qualified 1967. Partner 1968.
Personal: Born 09.11.1942. Educated at Stonyhurst College and University of Liverpool (LLB).

BROOKS, Kenneth Williams
BrookStreet Des Roches, Witney (01993) 771616
Company and Commercial Partner
Specialisation: All types of commercial property transaction including, in particular, work for national retail chains, site acquisitions and disposals, development work, joint ventures, general estate work, stautory agreements, retail parks, building schemes, security work, funding, planning, taxation and environmental matters. Also specialises in charity work including the establishment and administration of charities and their property work. Clients include a number of publicly quoted companies and banks, charities such as Oxfam and Merton College, Oxford; Co-operative Societies like Oxford, Swindon and Gloucester Co-operative Society Limited and substantial UK and international retailers like Blockbuster Entertainment Ltd, Electronics Boutique plc and Historical Collections Group plc.
Prof. Memberships: Law Society, Association of Charity Lawyers, European Law Group, Thames Valley Commercial Lawyers Association, Berks Bucks and Oxon Law Society, Oxford & District Solicitors Association.
Career: Qualified in 1982. With *Linnells* from 1980 to 1994; as a partner from 1985. Co-founder of *BrookStreet des Roches* in April 1994.
Personal: Born 23 January 1956. Educated at King Edward VI Guildford. Leisure interests include things historical and archaeological; reading music and walking; dining out and good company. Lives in South Leigh outside Witney.

BURCHFIELD, Jonathan R.
Nabarro Nathanson, Reading (0118) 925 4606
j.burchfield@nabarro.com
Partner and Head of Charity Group.
Specialisation: Work includes constitutions of charities, the impact of charity law on all areas of charities' activities; and private client work, including trust and tax planning for individuals. Contributed to 'Charity Appeals: the Complete Guide to Success'.
Prof. Memberships: Deputy Chairman of the Charity Law Association, Chartered Institute of Taxation, Society of Trust and Estate Practitioners.
Career: Qualified in 1978, having joined *Turner Kenneth Brown* in 1976. Became a Partner in 1983.
Personal: Born 22nd February 1954. Trustee of HSBC Charitable Common Investment Funds. Leisure interests include family and cricket. Lives in Guildford.

CAIRNS, Elizabeth
Elizabeth Cairns, Maidstone (01622) 858191
Specialisation: Specialist Charity law practice established since 1990. Areas of particular interest include charitable status, constitutional issues, incorporation of charities and dispute resolution. She aims to give a high quality and sophisticated service to a wide range of charities and voluntary organisations.
Career: Charity Commission 1972-79; *Jaques & Lewis* 1979-90 (Partner 1984). Publications: 'Charities: Law & Practice' (Sweet & Maxwell) 3rd edn 1996; 'Fundraising for Charity' (Tolley) 1996.

CLARICOAT, John
Claricoat Phillips, London (020) 7226 7000
philcoat@aol.com
Specialisation: Specialist in charity law. Fellow of the Society for Advanced Legal Studies. Consultant to several large national charities and city solicitors. Joint author with Hilary Phillips of 'Charity Law A-Z Key Questions Answered' published by Jordans.
Career: In private practice before joining the Government Service. Joined the charity commission in 1966. Served for 28 years reaching grade 5.

CONNELL, Douglas A.
Turcan Connell WS, Edinburgh (0131) 228 8111
dac@turcanconnell.com
Specialisation: Joint Senior Partner. Specialist in trusts, tax planning, asset protection, charities and heritage property; acts as principal adviser to many chairmen and chief executives regarding their personal business and to the trustees of a number of major national charities, as well as private charitable foundations.
Prof. Memberships: President Scottish Young Lawyers Association 1975-76; member of Revenue Committee the Law Society of Scotland 1979-92; chairman Edinburgh Book Festival 1991-95; member Scottish Arts Council and chairman Lottery Committee, Scottish Arts Council 1994-97.
Career: Attended University of Edinburgh (LLB). Articled *Dundas & Wilson CS*; qualified 1976; Partner 1979-97.
Personal: Born 1954. Resides Edinburgh. Leisure interests include books, travel and good food.

DAVIS, Elizabeth
Blake Lapthorn, Portsmouth (023) 9222 1122
ejdavis@blakelapthorn.co.uk
Specialisation: Charities law and Company Commercial law.
Prof. Memberships: Member of the Executive Committee of the Charity Law Association.
Career: Qualified in 1982. Has practised in UK and Hong Kong. First joined *Blake Lapthorn* in 1986, and now practises as the charities adviser to the firm's Charity Business Unit. Expertise includes charity start ups, major restructuring, mergers and incorporations, trading and fundraising. The Unit provides specialist charity law advice coupled with general, commercial, property, employment and tax issues to charities and voluntary organisations.
Personal: Born 11th January 1956. Governor, University College Chichester. Lives near Chichester.

DE'ATH, Gary R.
Wragge & Co, Birmingham (0121) 629 1827
gary_de'ath@wragge.com
Associate, Human Resources Group.
Specialisation: Main areas of practice are charities formation and constitutional issues, (including consortia and joint working arrangements), strategic development, operational matters including interpretation and recovery of legacies, fund raising agreements and advice, conflicts of interest, employment matters, property law and general commercial contractual issues.
Prof. Memberships: West Midlands Charitable Trusts Group, West Midlands Charity Trustees Forum, The Institute of Charity Fund-Raising Managers, West Midlands Advisory Panel of NCVO. The Charity Law Association, The Society of Trust and Estate Practitioners. Member of the Society for Advanced Legal Studies.
Career: Qualified in 1976. Joined *Shakespeares* in 1986 and became a partner in 1989, *Wragge & Co* 2000.
Personal: Born 21st December 1951. Educated at Gilberd School, Colchester 1963-70 and Kings College, University of London 1970-73, West Midlands Honorary Consul Elect to Cote d'Ivoire.

DOLLIMORE, Jean
Trowers & Hamlins, London (020) 7423 8000
jdollimore@trowers.com
Partner, private client. Head of charities services.
Specialisation: All aspects of charity law with an emphasis on constitutional structures, the establishment of subsidiaries and trading companies, and the powers and duties of trustees. Also experienced in wills and trusts, estate planning, and the administration of estates. Experienced speaker and contributor to charity publications.
Prof. Memberships: Law Society; City of London Solicitors Company; Member of the Executive Committee of the Charity Law Association; Charities Correspondent for Private Client Business.
Personal: Educated Hitchin Girls Grammar School and Lady Margaret Hall, Oxford.

DRISCOLL, Lindsay
Sinclair Taylor & Martin, London 0208 969 3667
ld@sinclairtaylor.co.uk
Specialisation: All aspects of charity law advising on a wide range of matters including constitutional reviews, establishment of charities, legal aspects of fund raising, trading companies, Charity Commission schemes, trustee issues. Experienced speaker and author of many articles in charity press and co-author of NCVOs Guide to Charities Acts.
Prof. Memberships: Law Society. Charity Law Association. Executive Committee member.
Career: Qualified 1971. At *Biddle & Co.* 1969-73. Assistant Public Trustee Kenya 1974-78, Lecturer Kenya School of Law 1973-78, Charity Law Consultant 1981-87. Assistant Legal Adviser then Legal Adviser of NCVO 1987-95.
Personal: Born 17th April 1947. Educated St Hugh's College Oxford (MA). Trustee of several charities. As director of International Centre for Not for Profit Law participates in conferences on law and regulation of NGOs all over the world.

FEA, Michael
Martineau Johnson, Birmingham (0121) 678 1480
michael.fea@martjohn.com
Specialisation: 30 years specialisation in Estate Planning, all aspects of charity law, wills, trusts, succession and probate. Trustee/Clerk to a number of charities.
Prof. Memberships: Society of Trust and Estate Practitioners; Charity Law Association; Law Society.
Career: Partner 1971. Notary Public. Member West

Midlands Mental Health Tribunal. Deputy Registrar Birmingham Diocese.
Personal: Born 1939. Attended Winchester College (1954-1958). Recreations include: tennis, shooting, concerts, opera and gardening. Lives in Worcestershire.

GATELEY, Stephen
Gateley Wareing, Birmingham (0121) 234 0000

HARWOOD, Ros J.
Speechly Bircham, London (020) 7427 6400
ros.harwood@speechlys.co.uk
Specialisation: Charity law exclusively. Acting for a wide range of charities on all aspects of charity law. Has written numerous articles for national newspapers and charity sector periodicals. Also frequent speaker at seminars.
Prof. Memberships: Secretary of the Charity Law Association. Law Society. ACEVO – Association of Chief Executives for Voluntary organisations.
Career: Head charity group at *Speechly Bircham*. Partner since joined in 1998.
Personal: Born 20th May 1965. Educated at Bath High School for Girls, GDST and Churchers College, Petersfield; Birmingham University LLB. Enjoys hockey, cycling, walking, gardening. Lives in Wimbledon.

HERRING, John
Mills & Reeve, Norwich (01603) 693 209
john.herring@mills-reeve.com
Specialisation: All aspects of charity law with particular emphasis on ecclesiastical charities and charity property. Also Registrar of Diocese of Norwich and legal secretary to the Bishop of Norwich.
Prof. Memberships: Law Society, Ecclesiastical Law Association (Executive Committee Member), Ecclesiastical Law Society.

HILL, Judith L.
Farrer & Co, London (020) 7242 2022
Partner in charge of the charity team and member of the Management Board.
Specialisation: Main area of practice is charity law, including the establishment of charities, constitutional issues and trading companies. Also experienced in art and heritage law, general private client work, covering trusts, wills, capital taxation. Contributor to Trust Law International, The Charity Law and Practice Review, NGO Finance and Assistant Editor of Art, Antiquity & Law, on Advisory Editorial Board of The Charity Law & Practice Review and the Editorial Board of Trust Law International. Regularly addresses conferences on charity law topics.
Prof. Memberships: Law Society, Holborn Law Society, International Bar Association (Co-Chairman Committee 20), Charity Law Association (Chairman.)
Career: Joined *Farrer & Co* in 1973, qualifying in 1975. Moved to *Shoosmiths & Harrison* in Northampton in 1979, until 1981. Re-joined *Farrer & Co* in 1985. Partner 1986.
Personal: Born 8th October 1949. Attended Brighton & Hove High School 1956-69, Newnham College, Cambridge 1969-72. Appointed Lieutenant of the Victorian Order in 1995. Leisure pursuits include gardening and reading. Lives in London.

HOLDEN, Lawrence
Brabner Holden Banks Wilson, Liverpool
(0151) 236 5821
lawrence.holden@bhbw.co.uk
See under Social Housing, p.760

KING, Michael
Stone King, Bath (020) 7796 1007
michaelking@stoneking.co.uk
Partner in charity and education unit.
Specialisation: Charity and Education Law, originally amongst religious and educational charities but growing involvement with service-providing charities in other parts of the sector.
Prof. Memberships: Law Society, Charity Law Association, Education Law Association.
Career: Articled: *Stone King & Wardle*, and *Charles Russell & Co.* 1969-74 Qualified 1974; Partner *Stone King* 1975 (Chairman: 1996); Opened London Office 1990. Chairman, Catholic Charity Conference since 1991. Chairman, Charity Law Association 1997 to 2000.
Publications: 'The Charities Acts Explained' (stationery office 2000) ISBN 0 11 702384 1.
Personal: Born 9th February 1949. Trustee of several charities. Leisure interests include tennis, sailing, shooting and watching rugby. Married with three children; lives in Bath.

KING, Richard
Tozers, Exeter (01392) 207020

LAWTON, F. A. (Tony)
Grays, York (01904) 634771
Partner in 1967.
Specialisation: Main area of practice is charity law, especially conveyancing in relation to charity property, formation of charities and negotiating with Charity Commissioners. Also experienced in work relating to education (especially statutory interpretation of the Education Acts and representations to the Education Assets Board), unincorporated associations, non-Companies Act companies and housing associations.
Prof. Memberships: Law Society, Yorkshire Law Society, Education Law Association.
Career: Qualified 1966. Joined *Grays* in 1967. Partner 1967. Home Office Correspondent of Approved School 1967-73. Board Member Trustee Savings Bank of Yorkshire & Lincoln 1976-89. Committee Member Conference of Solicitors for Catholic Charities 1967-present. (Chairman 1998-)
Personal: Born 9th July 1940. Attended Bordeaux University 1958-59, then Corpus Christi College, Cambridge 1959-62. Leisure pursuits include history, gardening and foreign travel. Lives in York.

LLOYD, Stephen T.
Bates, Wells & Braithwaite, London
(020) 7551 7777
Partner in charity and company commercial department.
Specialisation: Acts for a large number of leading charitable organisations on a wide range of matters, including constitutional, contract, intellectual property and charity law. Also provides advice to small and medium sized businesses. Author of 'Barclays Guide to the Law for the Small Business' and 'Charities, Trading and the Law' and of numerous articles. Co-author with Fiona Middleton of 'The Charities Acts Handbook'. Contributor to 'The Charities Administration Handbook' and 'The Fundraisers Guide to the Law'. Gave at least 20 lectures in 1999.
Prof. Memberships: Charity Law Association, Law Society.
Career: With *Freshfields* 1975-78. Qualified in 1977. Joined *Bates, Wells & Braithwaite* in 1980 and became a partner in 1984.
Personal: Educated at Bristol University 1969-72 (History) and Cambridge University 1973 (Law). Trustee of three charities and of executive committee of Charity Law Association. Recreations include reading, cycling, theatre and music.

LORD PHILLIPS OF SUDBURY OBE, Andrew Wyndham
Bates, Wells & Braithwaite, London
(020) 7551 7777
Founding partner.
Specialisation: Main area of practice is charities, and secondarily business law and defamation. Author of 'Charitable Status: A practical handbook', now in its fourth edition; 'Charity Investment: Law and Practice'; and 'The Living Law', a guide to the law for young people. Occasional freelance journalist, regular broadcaster, particularly as Legal Eagle on BBC 2's Jimmy Young Show.
Prof. Memberships: Law Society.
Career: Qualified 1964. Founded *Bates Well & Braithwaite, London* in 1970. Co-founder in 1971 and first Chairman of the Legal Action Group. Founder and first Chairman of the Citizenship Foundation in 1989 (continuing). Initiated the Lawyers in the Community scheme and Solicitors Pro Bono Group (of which first President, continuing). Founder in 1971 of PARLEX Group of European Lawyers. Lib Dem Life Peer 1998.
Personal: Born 15th March 1939. Attended Uppingham school, then Trinity Hall, Cambridge. Trustee of Guardian/Observer newspapers and various charities. Non-Executive Director of four commercial companies. Leisure pursuits include politics, golf, cricket, history and the arts. Born, bred and lives in Sudbury, Suffolk.

LYNCH, Malcolm
Malcolm Lynch, Leeds (0113) 242 9600
law@malcolmlynch.com
Specialisation: A solicitor who specialises in charity law and financial services, particularly relating to socially responsible investment. Advises on commercial contracts, the establishment and mergers of charities, including overseas charities, and the establishment and regulation of trading subsidaries of charities and social economy companies generally. A specialist in industrial and provident societies and adviser to registered social landlords. Has been involved in several studies for the European Commission on banking and financing of micro-firms and for the DTI on the financing of renewable energy. Earlier work has encompassed employee share schemes and business succession through employee ownership.
Prof. Memberships: Member of Charity Law Association, Co-operative Law Association.
Career: Qualified in 1983 while with *Booth & Co* in Leeds. Joined *Titmuss Sainer & Webb* in 1983, then economic development solicitor to Kirklees Metropolitan Council, West Yorkshire, 1984-1987. Became solicitor to Industrial Common Ownership Movement Limited, 1987-1989 and then principal of *Malcolm Lynch* in1989.
Personal: Born 29.4.55. Attended Colchester Royal Grammar School 1996-1973. University of Birming-

ham 1974-1977. Postgraduate School of Yugoslav Studies, University of Bradford and Skopje University, Yugoslavia 1977-1979. Fellow of RSA. Director of Ecology Building Society. Lives in Leeds.

MACKINTOSH, Simon A.
Turcan Connell WS, Edinburgh (0131) 228 8111
sam@turcanconnell.com
Specialisation: Main areas of practice are tax, trusts and charities. Work includes tax planning, heritage property, charity law and practice; and trust establishment, variation and practice. Lead partner for a number of the firm's major charity clients. Joint head of the firm's Charity Unit. Co-author of 'Revenue Law in Scotland', 1987. Convener of the Law Society of Scotland Tax Law Committee.
Prof. Memberships: Society of Trust and Estate Practitioners, International Academy of Estate and Trust Law.
Career: Partner *Turcan Connell* 1997; Partner *W & J Burness WS* 1985-1997; Non-executive Director of Macphie of Glenbervie Ltd and Director of the Edinburgh Book Festival. Member of the Scottish Executive Commission on reform of charity law.

MARTIN, Matthew T.
Cozens-Hardy & Jewson, Norwich
(01603) 625231
Consultant in private client department.
Specialisation: Main areas of practice are charity law and administration. Solicitor and clerk to Trustees of a number of charities, including Norwich Consolidated Charities, Norwich Town Close Estate Charity, Anguish's Educational Foundation, The Memorial Trust of the 2nd Air Division USAAF and Laura Elizabeth Stuart Memorial Trust.
Prof. Memberships: Law Society, Charity Law Association.
Career: Joined *Cozens-Hardy & Jewson* in 1962. Qualified in 1967. Became partner in 1969. Consultant in 1996.
Personal: Born 28th June 1943. Attended Bradfield College, Berkshire 1957-61. Under Sheriff of City of Norwich 1987-94. Leisure pursuits include golf and gardening.

MEAKIN, Robert
Stone King, London (020) 7628 2020 ext: 4432
Specialisation: Practice covers the full range of Charity Law advice including Charitable Status and applications for registration as a charity, applications for Schemes and Orders from the Charity Commissioners and representing charity trustees subject to investigation by the Charity Commissioners. In addition specialises in Charity tax, VAT, trading and fundraising, Commercial Sponsorship, lottery, PFI and partnership funding. Regularly writes articles on charity law and gives seminars to charity officers and trustees. Regularly sits on Charity Law Association Working Party Committees dealing with specialist areas of Charity Law. To coincide with the 50th anniversary of the Foundation of the NHS, has written a book entitled 'Charity in the NHS: Policy and Practice' (Jordans 1998).
Prof. Memberships: Charity Law Association, Charities' Tax Reform Group, Advisory Board Member of The European Association for Planned Giving.
Career: Legal Adviser to the Charity Commissioners 1988-1993. *Lovell White Durrant* Charity Group 1993-1995. *Speechly Bircham* 1995-1997; *Simmons & Simmons* 1997-2000
Personal: Born 29/11/63. Married with three children.

MIDDLETON, Fiona
Bates, Wells & Braithwaite, London
(020) 7551 7777
f.middleton@bateswells.co.uk
Charity Commision 1979 to 1988. Partner in charity department 1990.
Specialisation: Deals with all aspects of law relating to charities and other voluntary organisations. Operates the Charirty Law Advisory Service for Solicitors. Co-author of 'Charity Investment, Law & Practice', 'The Charities Acts Handbook' and Jordans Charities Administration Service. Member of the NCVO/ Charity Commission working party on trustee training which produced the report 'On Trust: Increasing the Effectiveness of Charity Trustees and Management Committees'.
Prof. Memberships: Charity Law Association. Law Society.
Career: Lecturer in Law, Kings College, London University 1972-79. Legal Adviser to the Charity Commission 1979-87. Joined *Bates, Wells & Braithwaite* in 1988 and became a partner in 1990.
Personal: Born 18th January 1948. Trustee of Barnardos. Recreations include gardening, bee keeping and opera.

MIMPRISS, Peter
Allen & Overy, London (020) 7330 3000
Partner in Private Client Department.
Specialisation: Main areas of practice are private client and major national charities including universities, professional institutions, national museums and art centres.
Prof. Memberships: Law Society. Charity Law Association.
Career: Qualified 1967. Joined *Allen & Overy* in 1968, and became a Partner in 1972. Chairman of the Charity Law Association in 1992-97. Chairman of the Chariguard Group of Common Investment Funds in 1994-2000.
Personal: Born 22nd August 1943. Trustee or director of The Prince's Trust, Leeds Castle Foundation, The Edward Heath Charitable Trust, Michael Bishop Foundation, the Edwina Mountbatten Trust SolCare and The Institute of Philanthropy. Appointed University Solicitor, University of London in 1994. Interests include the development of charity law, maritime history, book collecting, contemporary art and driving vintage sports cars.

NORTON, Philip
Eversheds, Norwich (01603) 272727
philipnorton@eversheds.com
Specialisation: Creation and administration of charities; constitutional & governance issues. Honorary Solicitor for Age Concern Norwich, Norfolk and Norwich Benelovent Medical Society, Friends of Kelling Hospital and the Norfolk & Norwich Healthcare NHS Trust Hospital Arts Project. Also acts as solicitor for and trustee of a number of hospital based charities e.g. Norfolk Renal Fund, Norwich and Norfolk Diabetes Trust and NANIME Charitable Trust and private foundations. Advises commercial clients on charity issues. Lectures to charities, hospital management and retirement groups on charity law and personal affairs.
Prof. Memberships: Law Society, Charity Law Association, Norfolk & Norwich Medico-Legal Society, Society of Trust and Estate Practitioners.
Career: Qualified 1984 while with *Hill & Perks*, now *Eversheds*, and became a Partner in 1990.
Personal: Born 17th September 1959. Attended Queen Elizabeth's School, Barnet 1972-78, then Sheffield University 1978-81. Leisure includes mountain walking, travel, food and wine. Lives near Wymondham, Norfolk.

PAINES, Alison J.S.
Withers, London (020) 7936 1000
Partner in Private Client Department, Head of Charities Practice.
Specialisation: Charity law and related tax and trust advice for not-for-profit organisations and their donors. Advises on structure, status, operations (including trading issues) and funding. Particular expertise in charitable issues relating to the NHS and government related charities. On editorial board and contributor to Kluwer's 'International Charitable Giving: Law and Taxation' and contributor to Tolley's 'Charities Manual' and FT Law and Tax's 'Practical Trust Precedents'.
Prof. Memberships: Charity Law Association (Executive Committee member); Society of Trusts and Estates Practitioners.
Career: Qualified 1981. Solicitor with *Crossman, Block & Keith* 1981-87; joined *Withers* 1988 and became a partner in 1991.
Personal: Educated Notting Hill and Ealing High School GPDST 1966-73; Girton College Cambridge 1974-78 (classics and law); trustee of two grant-making foundations.

PAISNER, Martin D.
Paisner & Co, London (020) 7353 0299
Specialisation: Practice embraces tax and estate planning advice with particular emphasis on the high net worth entrepreneur, including trust structures both for the UK based (whether domiciled or not) and an international clientele. In addition, he advises widely on all aspects of charity law involving both grant-making and functional charities and serves as trustee of, and solicitor to numerous charitable bodies.
Prof. Memberships: Law Society, Society of Trust and Estate Practitioners, Charity Law Association.
Career: Born 1 September 1943. Attended St Paul's School, London 1956 – 1961, Sorbonnne University , Paris 1961 – 1962, Worcester College, Oxford 1962 – 1965 and Ann Arbor, Michigan 1966- 1967. Honorary Fellow of Queen Mary and Westfield College, University of London. Qualified 1970. Partner at *Paisner & Co* in 1972.
Personal: Leisure pursuits include antiquarian book-collecting (18th and 19th Century English and American literature), inter-war travel posters, music, reading, communal interests and learning from his children all the things he never knew! Currently Chairman of The Jerusalem Foundation (UK). Member of The Reform Club.

PEROWNE, John
Eversheds, Norwich (01603) 272 875
johnperowne@eversheds.com
and Cambridge (01223) 355933
Specialisation: Probate, Trust, Charity, Personal Tax and Wills.
Prof. Memberships: STEP
Career: Partner *Eversheds* (previously *Daynes Hill & Perks* previously *Daynes Chittock*) since 1978.

PHILLIPS, Ann
Stephenson Harwood, London (020) 7809 2064
ann.phillips@shlegal.com
Senior Associate, Tax Department and Head of the Charity Group.
Specialisation: All aspects of charity law and related tax issues. Work ranges from charity formation and advice to charities on constitutional, taxation and governance issues, to variation, mergers and dissolution. Also advises commercial institutions and local authorities on charity issues and dealings with charities. Articles in NGO Finance, Charities Management, Trusts and Estates Law Journal and others.
Prof. Memberships: Law Society, Charity Law Association, Society of Trust and Estate Practitioners.
Career: Qualified in 1979. Joined *Stephenson Harwood* in 1977 and became a Senior Associate in 1984.
Personal: Born 23 December 1954. Educated at St Hugh's College, Oxford (MA). Married with two children. Vice-chairman of the Research Ethics Committee of Great Ormond Street Hospital/Institute of Child Health.

PHILLIPS, Hilary
Claricoat Phillips, London (020) 7226 7000
Specialisation: Specialist in charity law. Fellow of the Society of Advanced Legal Studies. Consultant to several large national charities and city solicitors. Joint author with John Claricoat of numerous articles on charity law topics.
Career: In private practice before joining DES in 1970. Joined the Charity Commission in 1973. Served for 21 years reaching Grade 6.

PIPER, Anne-Marie
Paisner & Co, London (020) 7353 0299
ampiper@paisner.co.uk
Head of firm's charities group.
Specialisation: Practice encompasses charity law ranging from the formation and registration of new charities; advice to "charity trustees" on various matters including permissible activities, trading and commercial activities and tax-efficient fundraising through to the restructuring, variation and dissolution of charities. Acts for sponsors of new charities; directors, trustees and organisers of existing charities; and companies making charitable gifts or having dealings with charities. Frequent contributor of articles to professional publications on charity law subjects.
Prof. Memberships: Founder Charity Law Association.
Career: Called to the Bar in 1980. Noble Lowndes Personal Financial Services 1980-83. Joined private client department at *Richards Butler* in 1983. Admitted as a solicitor in 1988 and became a partner in 1989. Joined *Paisner & Co.* as a partner in 1994.
Personal: Born 27th January 1958. Attended North Walsham Secondary School 1969-74, then Norfolk College of Arts & Technology 1974-76. Went on to University College, London, 1976-79 and the Council of Legal Education 1979-80. Charity trustee. Leisure pursuits include family life and reading. Lives in London.

PORTRAIT, Judith
Portrait Solicitors in Association with Denton Wilde Sapte, London (020) 7320 3888
Specialisation: All aspects of charity law, advising both grant-making and service-providing charities. Also advising on private trusts, estate and tax planning for individuals and trustees.
Career: Appointed Treasurer of Henry Smith's Charities on 1 January 1999; Trustee and Legal Adviser to the Sainsbury Family Charitable Trusts.
Personal: Educated St Paul's Girls' School and St Hugh's College Oxford. Married; resides in Cambridge.

POULTER, Alan
Manches, Oxford (01865) 722106
alan.poulter@manches.co.uk
Specialisation: Principal areas of practice include work for charitable and educational institutions, including universities and the colleges of Oxford University, private trusts, tax-planning and related work for private clients.
Prof. Memberships: Charity Law Association; Society of Trust and Estate Practitioners.
Career: Qualified 1971 while at *Biddle & Co.* Joined *Morrell Peel & Gamlen* 1974 and became a partner in 1975. Became partner in *Manches* on the merger of *Morrell Peel and Gamlen* in 1997.
Personal: Born 4th November 1945. School Governor and Trustee of various charities.

PROTANI, Moira
SJ Berwin & Co, London (020) 7533 2712
moira.protani@sjberwin.com
Specialisation: Head of the Charities Group. Advises on all aspects of the law as it affects charities, donors and businesses which deal with charities. Encompasses a whole range of matters including establishment of charities, trustee powers and duties, taxation, grant-making, fundraising, mergers, constitutional and good governance issues. Acted for the Charity Commission, was appointed receiver and manager and acted for two charities involved in litigation and alternative dispute resolution. Also acted in a large scale charity merger and the incorporation of an unincorporated association. Frequently lectures on charity law issues.
Prof. Memberships: Charity Law Association, the Law Society and the Royal Society of Arts.
Career: Trained at and employed by *SJ Berwin & Co.* Qualified in 1990. Became a partner of *SJ Berwin & Co.* in 1998.
Publications: Has written numerous articles on charity law. Most recently 'A Culture of Giving' PLC May1999; 'The Risk of Good Intentions – Should Charities Insure their Trustees?', NGO Finance September1999; 'Incorporation – a Safer Bet?', Association Manager March 2000; 'Dealing with Founder Syndrome', NGO Finance April 2000.
Personal: Born 1 October 1957; interests include international travel; food and wine. Sits on the board of two charities in her spare time.

REES, John
Winckworth Sherwood, Oxford (01865) 297 200
jrees@winckworths.co.uk
See under Church, p.150

REITH, David S.
Lindsays WS, Edinburgh (0131) 477 8708
Partner in commercial department.
Specialisation: Main area of practice is commercial property, but specialises in charities, including building preservation and other conservation work. Acted for Lothian Building Preservation Trust in successful campaign to save Mavisbank House, near Edinburgh, from demolition. Legal adviser to the Scottish Seabird Centre millennium founded project and the Scottish Association of Citizens Advice Bureaux. Has spoken at various seminars on charity law.
Prof. Memberships: Law Society of Scotland, WS Society.
Career: Qualified in 1974, having joined *Lindsays WS* in 1972. Became a Partner in 1976. Director of Scottish Historic Buildings Trust, Cockburn Conservation Trust, Scottish Sculpture Trust, Boilerhouse Theatre Company and other charitable companies. Secretary of Scottish Seabird Centre and Queensberry House Trust. Treasurer of the Cockburn Association and Fet-Lor Youth Club.
Personal: Born 15th April 1951. Educated at Fettes College 1965-69 and Aberdeen University 1969-72. Leisure interests include winemaking, gardening and architectural heritage. Lives in East Lothian.

RENNIE, Brenda L.
Balfour & Manson, Edinburgh (0131) 2001275
blr@balfour-manson.co.uk
Head of Private Client Department.
Specialisation: As part of a general private client practice, has developed a particular interest in charities and in the elderly and disabled. Has considerable experience in setting up charities and giving ongoing advice. The administration of private charitable trusts is a specialty. Is the Solicitor to Age Concern Scotland.
Prof. Memberships: W.S.; Member of the W.S. Society Legal Education Committee; Member of Society of Trust and Estate Practitioners; Member of Board of EDINVAR Housing Association; Trustee and chairman – High Blood Pressure Foundation.
Career: Qualified in 1971, having joined *Balfour & Manson* in 1969. Became a Partner in 1976.
Personal: Born 21st December 1947. Educated in Aberdeen and graduated University of Aberdeen LLB Hons 1969. Enjoys reading, walking and looking at buildings when time permits. Lives in Edinburgh.

RUSSELL, George R.
Anderson Strathern WS, Edinburgh (0131) 220 2345
Specialisation: Main areas of practice are charities, trusts and tax planning and financial services. Charity work includes setting up charities and ongoing advice for a number of charitable trusts and large charities; clients include Napier University.
Career: Edinburgh University, qualified 1973, partner 1976; Chairman Scottish Solicitors' Staff Pension Fund; member Executive of Queen's Nurses Institute of Scotland; member Scottish Council for National Parks; Council Member National Trust for Scotland 1991-96; awarded MBE in 1995.
Personal: Born 1946; resides Linlithgow, West Lothian. Enjoys hill walking, skiing, music and golf.

SAUNDERS, Joss
Linnells, Oxford (01865) 248607
jss@linnells.co.uk
Specialisation: Partner and head of charity unit. Company Secretary at Oxfam. Acts for educational, medical, development, childrens' and church charities, and grant-making trusts. Also active in e-business, intellectual property and publishing.
Prof. Memberships: Charity Law Association, Society for Computers and Law, Oxford Publishing Society.
Career: Qualified 1988. *Theodore Goddard* 1986-1992. Eastern Europe 1992-1995. Ran Polish branch of Prince of Wales Business Leaders' Forum. Lecturer, Warsaw University. Joined *Linnells* 1995.
Publications: NCVO's Guide to Contracts with Public Bodies (1998); Business Law and Practice

(Cambridge Board of Continuing Education); Contributor to Higher Education and the Law (Open University).
Personal: Born 1962. Educated Trinity College, Oxford. LLM London. Family, church, e-business. Trustee of charities working in education, in Africa, and grant-making Trust. Advisory Council Oxford University Law Foundation. Advisory Board of Hugh Pilkington Charitable Trust.

SINCLAIR TAYLOR, James
Sinclair Taylor & Martin, London 0208 969 3667
jst@sinclairtaylor.co.uk
Partner specialising in charity law.
Specialisation: Main area of practice is charity law. Work includes charity formation and mergers, company law, property transactions, internal structure and employment law, trading VAT and contracts with funders. Also deals with not for profit organisations, housing associations, schools and local authorities, advising on property, employment, corporate and charity law. Has substantial involvement in the urban regeneration development trust movement, learned societies, pressure groups, third world charities and housing and care. Author of numerous articles and of the 'Voluntary Sector Legal Handbook' and of the 'Company Handbook and Registers for Voluntary Organizations'. Involved in training for charities and Housing Associations with A.C.E.V.O. Directory for Social Change, Charity Finance Directors Group and other organisations.
Prof. Memberships: Charity Law Association.
Career: Qualified in 1975. Founded *Sinclair Taylor & Martin* in 1981.
Personal: Charity trustee of a wide variety of organisations.

SMITH, Tim
Griffith Smith, Brighton (01273) 324041
Specialisation: Specialises in all aspects of charity law (registration, constitutional issues, charity property, fundraising etc.) and provides an initial free 'legal audit' service as a way of identifying potential problems. He also draws on his experience of working full-time in charity management throughout the 1980s which gives him particular understanding of the practical issues facing charity managers and trustees.
Prof. Memberships: Charity Law Association.
Career: Qualified as Solicitor in 1979. Worked full time in charity management 1981-1990. With Griffith Smith since 1990 (Partner 1991).
Personal: Married with two children. Interested in wide range of social and community issues – and jazz and hill-walking when time allows.

THOMPSON, Romaine
Anthony Collins Solicitors, Birmingham (0121) 200 3242
Specialisation: Provides specialist legal services to numerous charities and churches throughout the UK. The department advises charities on all legal aspects of their activities such as formation and registration, compliance with the Charity Commission requirements, restructuring, fund-raising, trustee training, advice on employment law, copyright and property management issues. The department publishes a free newsletter to clients updating them on legal issues and also offers a fixed fee legal audit.
Prof. Memberships: Romaine is a member of the Charity Law Association, the Ecclesiastical Law Society.
Career: Educated at Trinity Hall, Cambridge. Qualified 1988. Romaine joined *Anthony Collins* Solicitors in 1989 and became a Partner in 1993. She has written articles for professional journals and lectures on charity law issues.

WARREN, Jennifer
Taylor Vinters, Cambridge (01223) 423444

WEIL, Simon
Bircham & Co., London (020) 7222 8044
simonweil@bircham.co.uk
Specialisation: Specialist areas comprise charities, tax planning, commercial property for institutional investment clients (frequently with charitable status) and the resolution of potentially contentious issues for charities and others, arising out of wills, trusts and co-ownership of property. Important cases have included advising a substantial corporate charity with a turnover running into ten figures on governance and trustee duties; converting an educational trust from an unincorporated charity to a company limited by guarantee; arranging the reorganisation of a livery company's charitable trust with a view to protecting individual members of the company who had previously been personally liable to third parties; the disposal by legally binding tender to companies invited to bid, of a major commercial site in High Holborn; the establishment of a comprehensive divestment programme for a group of charities with a common trustee, involving the setting up of real property and securities investment pooling schemes; creating a corporate vehicle for the service provider aspects of a group of almshouse charities.
Prof. Memberships: CLA. EAPG. ACTAPS. Law Society.
Career: Served on the Firm's Premises and General Purposes Committee and Staff Committee, becoming the partner responsible for the firm's practice development in 1988. Continued in the latter role until 1992 and was head of the Private Client Department between 1991 and 1995. Financial Services Act Compliance Officer between 1991 and 1997 and took a leading role in establishing Bircham Investment Management. Head of the Charities Group since 1996.
Personal: Opera, singing and music generally; drawing; wine; reading history and novels (normally pre-1900); member of Chatham House (RIIA) with a particular focus on central Europe; tennis; swimming; riding; member of Oxford and Cambridge Club. Also active within St. Mary's Church Islington.

WOMACK, Michael
Taylor Vinters, Cambridge (01223) 423444
Specialisation: Mainly educational and fundraising charities, universities, colleges, schools and grant awarding bodies. The major tasks of this year have been to assist charities to use their assets as flexibly as possible by the use of constitutional changes approved by the Charity Commission or by schemes that the Charity Commission approves.
Prof. Memberships: Law Society; Anglo-German Lawyers; Law Society European Group; Licensing Executive's Society; Educational Law Association. Charity Law Association.
Career: Trinity Hall, Cambridge; LLM University College, London. Articled in City firm and joined *Taylors* as it then was in 1975.
Personal: Ornithology, hill-walking, photography, foreign languages and travel.

WOODHEAD, Louise S.
Wragge & Co, Birmingham (0121) 214 1002
louise_woodhead@wragge.com
Specialisation: Extensive experience in charity law, including formation of charities, advice to trustees, mergers and re-organisations of charities and general administration.
Prof. Memberships: Charity Law Association, STEP, Law Society.
Career: Qualified in 1983. Became a partner in 1994. Head of private client team.

WOODWARD, Mark
Osborne Clarke OWA, Bristol (0117) 917 3000
mark.woodward@osborneclarke.com
Head of Charity Unit.
Specialisation: Acts for several national as well as local charities, advising on all aspects of charity law. Is particularly interested in establishing new charities and acting for charities in legacy disputes. Also handles Charity Commission investigations. Member of the Charity Law Association.
Career: Qualified in 1985. Legal Officer for the Charity Commission, London, 1987-88, before joining *Wansbroughs Willey Hargrave* in 1988. Joined *Osborne Clark* as a partner in 1999.

WRIGLEY, W.Matthew
Wrigleys, Leeds (0113) 244 6100
See under Trusts & Personal Tax, p.826

WYLD, Charles
Burges Salmon, Bristol (0117) 902 2773
charles-wyld@burges-salmon.com
See under Trusts & Personal Tax, p.826

WYLLIE, Gordon M.
Biggart Baillie, Glasgow (0141) 228 8000
gwyllie@biggartbaillie.co.uk
Specialisation: Advises a range of public charitable bodies, including the Trades House of Glasgow and its related trusts, the Edinburgh Dog and Cat Home and several heritage bodies such as the Trades Hall Trust, The Clyde Maritime Trust and the Pollokshields Burgh Hall Trust. Founding Member of the Scottish Grant Making Trust Administrators' Forum and Clerk to the Commissioners of Income Tax for both Glasgow North and Glasgow South divisions. Also advises on succession matters and particularly enjoys problems with unusual or foreign elements.
Prof. Memberships: International Bar Association, Law Society of Scotland, Society of Trust and Estate Practitioners, Society of Writers of the Signet and Scottish Grant Making Trust Administrators' Forum.
Career: Head of Executry Department *Strathearn and Blair WS*, Edinburgh 1975-77. Head of Private Client Services and Charities at *Biggart Baille* (Partner since 1980).
Publications: The Scottish contribution to the 'International Dictionary of Succession Terms'.
Personal: History, music and the arts, architecture and design, language (Italian, French, Spanish and Greek), country dancing, country walks and gardening.

CHURCH LAW

OVERVIEW: This section is divided into two parts. The first is Church of England, whose rules have the status of law. The second covers other denominations where work for clients includes property, trusts, education, charity and other law as it relates to the church. These will usually be clients in the Roman Catholic community, but also include Free Church or Orthodox bodies and other institutions. Most firms act for clients of one denomination, although there are exceptions such as Winckworth Sherwood which acts for the Church of England and Roman Catholic bodies. The Church of England has a Registrar for each Diocese who will normally undertake most of the work for that Diocese, whereas other churches are more autonomous and will often turn to a variety of sources for advice.

RESEARCH APPROVED BY BMRB: *For this edition,* Chambers' *researchers conducted 6083 interviews – 4408 with law firms, 598 with barristers and 1077 with clients.*

The validity of the research was scrutinised by BMRB International, who audited both the methodology and the results at our offices in July 2000. They interviewed Chambers' *researchers and cross-checked sample interviews. Details of the audit appear on page 7.*

LONDON

CHURCH OF ENGLAND

CHURCH LAW (CHURCH OF ENGLAND) • London	
❶ Lee Bolton & Lee	
Winckworth Sherwood	
LEADING INDIVIDUALS	
❶ BEESLEY Peter Lee Bolton & Lee	MORRIS Paul Winckworth Sherwood
❷ RICHENS Nicholas Lee Bolton & Lee	THATCHER Michael Winckworth Sherwood

Within each band, firms are listed alphabetically. *See **Profiles** on page 149*

Lee Bolton & Lee The firm is one of the two clear leaders in London. The *"extremely professional"* **Peter Beesley** is the senior partner specialising in ecclesiastical law. He is praised for his *"incredible depth and breadth of experience."* Partner **Nick Richens** is *"very knowledgeable"* on education and heritage issues among others. The firm advises three diocesan Bishops as Registrars and focuses on the Church of England.

Winckworth Sherwood The other leading firm in London. One of the few firms advising Roman Catholic bodies and other denominations as well as Church of England clients. The Ecclesiastical and Education Law Department is headed by **Paul Morris**, who is highly regarded and has acted on a number of controversial cases. **Michael Thatcher** has a particular expertise in Church education and school law and is *"well respected."* The firm advises the Archbishop of Canterbury in addition to working as Registrars.

OTHER DENOMINATIONS

Simon Howell at **Ellis Wood** has a *"loyal clientele."* He has great experience acting for Roman Catholic clients and continues to attract praise. **Carter Lemon Camerons** is very active in this field. The team acts for Baptist clients and has recently been enlarged. **Pothecary & Barrett** have a longstanding reputation for acting on behalf of the Methodist church as well as Baptists and others. **Beachcroft Wansboroughs** undertake some work for Catholic clients.

CHURCH LAW (OTHER DENOMINATIONS) • London
❶ Ellis Wood
❷ Beachcroft Wansbroughs
Carter Lemon Camerons
Pothecary & Barratt
LEADING INDIVIDUALS
❶ HOWELL Simon Ellis Wood

Within each band, firms are listed alphabetically. *See **Profiles** on page 149*

THE SOUTH & SOUTH WEST

CHURCH OF ENGLAND

Follett Stock The firm acts for the Diocese of Truro and a number of other churches. **Martin Follett** heads the team.

Harris & Harris **Timothy Berry** is Registrar to the Dioceses of Bath & Wells and Bristol and is recommended.

Michelmores **Richard Wheeler** enjoys a strong reputation and acts as Registrar for the Diocese of Exeter. The firm is currently concentrating on commercial redevelopment of property.

Thomas Eggar Church Adams The firm's ecclesiastical practice includes the Diocese of Chichester and the Dean and Chapter of Westminster.

Brutton & Co **Hilary Tyler** has a good reputation and acts for the Diocese of Portsmouth.

CHURCH LAW (CHURCH OF ENGLAND) • The South & South West	
❶ Follett Stock Truro	
Harris & Harris Wells	
Michelmores Exeter	
Thomas Eggar Church Adams Chichester	
❷ Brutton & Co Fareham	
Madge Lloyd & Gibson Gloucester	
White & Bowker Winchester	
LEADING INDIVIDUALS	
❶ BERRY Timothy Harris & Harris	FOLLETT Martin Follett Stock
WHEELER Richard Michelmores	WHITE Peter White & Bowker
❷ PEAK Chris Madge Lloyd & Gibson	TYLER Hilary Brutton & Co

Within each band, firms are listed alphabetically. *See **Profiles** on page 149*

Madge Lloyd & Gibson This firm is a new entry following recommendations for **Chris Peak**, the Registrar for Gloucester Diocese.

White & Bowker **Peter White** remains a consultant at this practice which commands a *"considerable amount of respect."* Clients include the Diocese of Winchester and some Mormon and Baptist churches.

OTHER DENOMINATIONS

CHURCH LAW (OTHER DENOMINATIONS) • The South & South West
❶ **DMH** Brighton
Larcomes Portsmouth
Rodgers Horsley Whitemans Guildford
Stone King Bath
Tozers Exeter

LEADING INDIVIDUALS	
❶ **KING Michael** Stone King	**KING Richard** Tozers
❷ **TISDALL Miles** Larcomes	

Within each band, firms are listed alphabetically. *See **Profiles** on page 149*

DMH Have long advised religious bodies and acts for two Roman Catholic dioceses, various free churches and orders. They also represent individual members of the clergy. At present they are very involved in property work as well as education and employment issues.

Larcomes The *"dynamic"* **Miles Tisdall** is well regarded. The firm acts for the Diocese of Portsmouth.

Rodgers Horsley Whitemans Maintains its reputation.

Stone King Is regarded as one of the leading firms in this area. **Michael King** is highly recommended. The firm acts for the Roman Catholic Dioceses of Clifton and Westminster and has undertaken an increased amount of work in this field.

Tozers This leading firm has 150 years of involvement with the Roman Catholic Church and currently acts for one Catholic Diocese (Plymouth) and several religious orders. **Richard King** is warmly recommended.

WALES

OTHER DENOMINATIONS

CHURCH LAW (OTHER DENOMINATIONS) • Wales
❶ **Allington Hughes** Wrexham
LG Williams & Prichard Cardiff
❷ **Hugh James Ford Simey** Cardiff

Within each band, firms are listed alphabetically.

Allington Hughes Acts for Roman Catholic clients and retains a good reputation.

LG Williams & Prichard Acts for the Diocese of Cardiff and maintains its reputation.

Hugh James Ford Simey Advises the Presbyterian Church of Wales as well as Methodist and Baptist clients.

MIDLANDS & EAST ANGLIA

CHURCH OF ENGLAND

CHURCH LAW (CHURCH OF ENGLAND) • Midlands & East Anglia
❶ **Winckworth Sherwood** Chelmsford
❷ **Edwards Geldard** Derby
Manby & Steward Wolverhampton
Martineau Johnson Birmingham
Wellman & Brown Lincoln
❸ **Claytons** Luton
Harvey Ingram Owston Leicester
Mills & Reeve Norwich
Rothera Dowson Nottingham
❹ **Leeds Day** Sandy

LEADING INDIVIDUALS • Midlands & East Anglia	
❶ **CHEETHAM David** Claytons	**REES John** Winckworth Sherwood
ROBSON Frank Winckworth Sherwood	
❷ **BATTIE James** Edwards Geldard	**BLOOR Richard** Harvey Ingram Owston
CARSLAKE Hugh Martineau Johnson	**HODSON Christopher** Rothera Dowson
HOOD Brian Winckworth Sherwood	**THORNEYCROFT John** Manby & Steward
WELLMAN Derek Wellman & Co	

Within each band, firms are listed alphabetically. *See **Profiles** on page 149*

Winckworth Sherwood Is the outstanding firm here, with offices in Oxford and Chelmsford. The *"persuasive"* **John Rees** is now the provincial Registrar for Canterbury as well as solicitor to the Anglican Consultative Council and has a *"keen brain."* The respected **Frank Robson** remains a consultant. **Brian Hood** is also well regarded and is Registrar for Chelmsford.

Edwards Geldard Looks after the Diocese of Derby and also does individual work for the Bishop. **James Battie** is said to be *"conscientious and well respected."*

Manby & Steward The group, under **John Thorneycroft**, does substantial amounts of conveyancing and property work in the Diocese of Lichfield.

Martineau Johnson Is viewed as well above average. **Hugh Carslake** heads the department which acts as legal secretary to the Bishop of Birmingham in addition to faculty and registrars work.

Wellman & Brown **Derek Wellman** is Registrar for Lincoln and has cemented his reputation.

Claytons **David Cheetham** is frequently recommended and has *"loads of experience."*

Harvey Ingram Owston Advises the Diocese of Leicester. **Richard Bloor** continues to be a popular market choice.

Mills & Reeve Are increasing their profile in this sector and act as the Registrar for Norwich.

Rothera Dowson The *"go ahead"* **Christopher Hodson**, Registrar for the Diocese of Southwell, is increasingly recommended.

Leeds Day Advises the Diocese of Ely.

OTHER DENOMINATIONS

CHURCH LAW (OTHER DENOMINATIONS) • Midlands & East Anglia
❶ **Anthony Collins Solicitors** Birmingham
Gateley Wareing Birmingham

Within each band, firms are listed alphabetically.

Anthony Collins Solicitors A well regarded team which acts for a number of independent and community churches around the country as well as certain individual Anglican churches.

Gateley Wareing Acts for the Roman Catholic Archdiocese of Birmingham and is a key player on behalf of the Roman Catholic church.

THE NORTH

CHURCH OF ENGLAND

CHURCH LAW (CHURCH OF ENGLAND) • The North
❶ **Denison Till** Leeds
❷ **Birch Cullimore** Chester
Dixon, Coles & Gill Wakefield
Gamon Arden & Co Liverpool
Gordons Cranswick Solicitors Leeds
❸ **Bell & Buxton** Sheffield
Crutes Newcastle-upon-Tyne
M C Darlington Manchester
Roebucks Blackburn
Tunnard Crosfield Ripon

LEADING INDIVIDUALS	
❶ **ARDEN Roger** Gamon Arden & Co	**BOX Linda** Dixon, Coles & Gill
DARLINGTON Michael M C Darlington	**LENNOX Lionel** Denison Till
McALLESTER Alan Birch Cullimore	
MACKRELL Jeremy Gordons Cranswick Solicitors	
❷ **HOYLE Thomas** Roebucks	**LOWDON Jane** Crutes
MYERS Miranda Bell & Buxton	**TUNNARD Chris** Tunnard Crosfield

Within each band, firms are listed alphabetically. See **Profiles** on page 149

Denison Till Widely regarded as the pre-eminent practice in the North. **Lionel Lennox** is Provincial Registrar for the Archdiocese of York and is recommended as *"extremely conscientious," "careful"* and having a *"very detailed mind."*

Birch Cullimore The *"able"* **Alan McAllester** heads the practice and is registrar for the Chester Diocese.

Dixon, Coles & Gill The firm has acted for the Diocese of Wakefield since 1888 and now also advises some Methodist and United Reformed Church clients in addition to their Church of England work. **Linda Box** is praised for her advocacy skills.

Gamon Arden & Co The *"broad sweep"* of *"academically gifted"* **Roger Arden**'s mind keeps him placed at the top of the table.

Gordons Cranswick Gordons Wright & Wright has now merged with Cranswick Watson. The highly respected **Jeremy Mackrell** has retired as a partner from the firm and is now a sole practitioner. He maintains a connection to the firm which handles primarily the conveyencing work.

Bell & Buxton A new entry to this list following the move of **Miranda Myers** from Keeble Hawson Moorhouse and is said to be *"gaining experience rapidly."* She is Registrar to the Diocese of Sheffield.

Crutes **Jane Lowdon** has received increased commendation and heads the ecclesiastical practice.

MC Darlington The *"creative"* **Michael Darlington** is seen as a *"safe pair of hands."* He is solicitor to the Manchester Diocesan Board of Finance and Board of Education; other clients include parish church councils and Church of England schools.

Roebucks **Tom Hoyle**, described as a *"natural litigator,"* is the recommended practitioner at this firm.

Tunnard Crosfield **Chris Tunnard** is a new addition following recommendations by fellow practitioners and is joint Registrar for Ripon and Leeds.

OTHER DENOMINATIONS

CHURCH LAW (OTHER DENOMINATIONS) • The North
❶ **Grays** York
❷ **Hill Dickinson** Liverpool
Oswald Goodier & Co Preston
❸ **Fieldings Porter** Bolton

LEADING INDIVIDUALS	
❶ **LAWTON Tony** Grays	
❷ **BELDERBOS Mark** Oswald Goodier & Co	**NALLY Edward** Fieldings Porter

Within each band, firms are listed alphabetically. See **Profiles** on page 149

Grays Regarded as the premier practice in the North. **Tony Lawton** is strongly recommended for his *"wide experience"* in charity and church law. Although Grays is primarily associated with Roman Catholic clients, the firm has also acted for the Dean and Chapter of York for 300 years and advises in relation to Church of England schools.

Hill Dickinson Advises the Archdiocese of Liverpool and has particular experience in church insurance matters.

Oswald Goodier & Co Act for the Diocese of Lancaster and a number of religious congregations. The *"utterly ethical"* **Mark Belderbos** *"deserves his high reputation."*

Fieldings Porter Act for Roman Catholic clients. The *"respected"* **Edward Nally** is recommended particularly for his knowledge of charitable property matters.

LEADERS IN CHURCH LAW

ARDEN, Roger Hollins
Gamon Arden & Co, Liverpool (0151) 709 2222

BATTIE, James S.
Edwards Geldard, Derby (01332) 31631
Specialisation: Solicitor to Derby Diocesan Board of Finance since 1972. Diocesan Registrar and Legal Secretary to the Bishop of Derby since 1986.
Prof. Memberships: Law Society. Ecclesiastical Law Association. Ecclesiastical Law Society.
Career: Ashby Boys Grammar School and Keble College Oxford. Partner *Hollis Briggs & Co* and *Edwards Geldard* 1966-96 (now consultant).
Personal: Gardening. Hill walking. Follows most sports (especially cricket). Trips overseas to sites of historic interest. Church of England lay reader.

BEESLEY, Peter
Lee Bolton & Lee, London (020) 7222 5381
Senior partner in ecclesiastical education and charity department.
Specialisation: Particular expertise in Church of England work. Chapter Clerk of St Alban's Cathedral; Joint registrar of the Diocese of Ely; registrar of the Diocese of Guildford; joint registrar of the Diocese of Hereford; registrar of the Faculty Office of the Archbishop of Canterbury; a member of the Legal Advisory Commission of the General Synod of the Church of England. Also handles education and charity work. Solicitor to the National Society and to the Board of Education of the General Synod; registrar of the Woodard Corporation. Joint contributor to Volume 13 (2) 'Encyclopaedia of Forms and Precedents-Ecclesiastical Law'. Speaker at and promoter of several conferences and seminars on ecclesiastical charity and education matters.
Prof. Memberships: Law Society, City of Westminster Law Society (ex-President), Ecclesiastical Law Association (Vice-Chairman), Ecclesiastical Law Society (Secretary), Charity Law Association (member of Executive Committee).
Career: Qualified 1967. Joined *Lee Bolton & Lee* in 1968, becoming a partner in 1969.
Personal: Born 30th April 1943. Attended Kings School Worcester, then Exeter University 1961-64 and College of Law 1964-65. Lives in London.

BELDERBOS, Mark J.
Oswald Goodier & Co, Preston (01772) 253841
See under Charities, p.141

BERRY, Timothy F.
Harris & Harris, Wells (01749) 674747
Specialisation: Ecclesiastical and charity law. Registrar, Diocese of Bath and Wells and Diocese of Bristol. Has expertise in trust and inheritance tax law.
Prof. Memberships: Ecclesiastical Law Association, Ecclesiastical Law Society, member of STEP.
Career: Qualified in 1970. Joined *Harris & Harris* as a partner in 1970. Now senior partner.
Personal: Born 5th January 1945. Holds an LLB (Liverpool 1966). Leisure interests include gardening, walking and music. Lives at West Cranmore near Shepton Mallet, Somerset.

BLOOR, R.H.
Harvey Ingram Owston, Leicester (0116) 254 5454

BOX, Linda
Dixon, Coles & Gill, Wakefield (01924) 373467
Specialisation: Ecclesastical law, charity law.
Prof. Memberships: Law Society. Ecclesiastical Law Association; Ecclesiastical Law Society.
Career: LLB 1970; Qualified solicitor December 1973; Deputy Diocesan Registrar 1979–1993; Diocesan Registrar 1994 to date.
Personal: Married with two sons. Interests include walking in the Lake District, theatre and the opera.

CARSLAKE, Hugh
Martineau Johnson, Birmingham (0121) 678 1486
hugh.carslake@martjohn.com
Partner in Private Client Department.
Specialisation: Main area of practice covers tax planning, trusts and estate planning and ecclesiastical law. Acts for the owners of landed estates and private individuals in their personal and trustee capacities. Registrar for and legal adviser to the Diocese of Birmingham.
Prof. Memberships: Law Society, STEP. Ecclesiastical Law Association (ELA).
Career: Qualified in 1973, having joined *Martineau Johnson* in 1972. Became a Partner in 1974, Notary Public in 1981, Head of Private Client Department in 1991 and Diocesan Registrar in 1992.
Personal: Born 15th November 1946. Attended Rugby School, 1960-65, then Trinity College, Dublin, 1966-70. Chairman of the Barber Institute of Fine Arts (University of Birmingham); Member of the Council of the University of Birmingham; Trustee of the Worcester Cathedral Appeal Trust. Council Member of the Notaries Society. Leisure interests include family, music and gardening. Lives in Warwickshire.

CHEETHAM, David N.
Claytons, St. Albans (01727) 865765

DARLINGTON, Michael C.
M C Darlington, Manchester (0161) 834 7545

FOLLETT, Martin
Follett Stock, Truro (01872) 241700
martin@follettstock.co.uk
Specialisation: Full range of ecclesiastical work including property, charity, education and contentious faculty work.
Career: Sidney Sussex College, Cambridge. Qualified 1977. Deputy Registrar 1983. Registrar of the Diocese of Truro 1987.

HODSON, Christopher Charles
Rothera Dowson, Nottingham (0115) 9100 600
Specialisation: As Diocesan Registrar for the Diocese of Southwell involved in all aspects of Ecclesiastical law including advice to bishops, archdeacons, clergy, parochial church councils and any persons requiring ecclesiastical legal advice. The extent of the work includes property matters, clergy discipline matters, advice as to qualifications and rights of marriage, ecclesiastical planning law, i.e. faculty jurisdiction and even extends to having advised other dioceses in connection with ecclesiastical matters. In addition works for the Southwell Diocesan Board of Finance and in this context is required to give advice in all areas of work affecting Church of England including commercial matters, property matters and employment matters.
Prof. Memberships: Member of the Ecclesiastical Lawyers Association, the Ecclesiastical Law Society and the Notaries Society.

HOOD, Brian J.
Winckworth Sherwood, Chelmsford
(01245) 262212
bjhood@winckworths.co.uk
Partner in Ecclesiastical Department (Chelmsford).
Specialisation: Specialises in ecclesiastical law. Deputy Registrar to Bishop of Chelmsford 1976-89. Registrar and Bishop's Legal Secretary since 1989. Also handles property and charities law, private and commercial matters.
Prof. Memberships: Ecclesiastical Law Association, Ecclesiastical Law Society.
Career: Qualified as a solicitor in New Zealand in 1966. Qualified in the UK in 1976. Joined *Winckworth Sherwood* as a partner in 1977.
Personal: Born 8th February 1943. Educated at Marlborough College, New Zealand 1956-62 and the University of Canterbury, New Zealand 1963-67 (LLM Hons). Leisure interests include golf, tennis, music and theatre. Lives in Terling, Essex.

HOWELL, Simon P.J.
Ellis Wood, London (020) 7242 1194

HOYLE, Thomas
Roebucks, Blackburn (01254) 668855

KING, Michael
Stone King, Bath (020) 7796 1007
michaelking@stoneking.co.uk
See under Charities, p.142

KING, Richard
Tozers, Exeter (01392) 207020

LAWTON, F. A. (Tony)
Grays, York (01904) 634771
See under Charities, p.142

LENNOX, Lionel
Denison Till, York York (01904) 611411
Partner.
Specialisation: Main area of practice is ecclesiastical law. Registrar of the Province and Diocese of York; Registrar of the Convocation of York; Legal Secretary to the Archbishop of York; Member of the Legal Advisory Commission of the General Synod. Expanding areas of practice are town and country planning and charity law. Advanced Professional Diploma in Planning and Environmental Law from Leeds Metropolitan University 1994. Legal advisor to various charities. Notary Public 1992.
Prof. Memberships: Yorkshire Law Society, Ecclesiastical Law Society.
Career: Qualified in 1973. Worked at *Denison Suddards* as a partner 1976-80; assistant legal advisor to the General Synod of the Church of England 1981-7. Joined *Denison Till* as a partner in 1987.
Personal: Attended St John's School Leatherhead 1962-67 and University of Birmingham 1967-70. Notary Public 1992. Lives in York. Trustee: St. Leonard's Hospice, York and Yorkshire Historic Churches Trust.

LOWDON, B. Jane
Crutes, Newcastle-upon-Tyne (0191) 281 5811

MACKRELL, Jeremy George Holroyde
Gordons Cranswick Solicitors, Bradford (01274) 202 132 jeremy.mackrell@gordonscranswick.co.uk
Specialisation: Ecclesiastical Law. Registrar of Diocese of Bradford and Legal Secretary to Bishop of Bradford. Legal Adviser to the Dean and to the Chapter, Bradford. Notary Public.
Prof. Memberships: Chairman of the Ecclesiastical Law Association. Member of the Ecclesiastical Law Society. Law Society
Career: Joined *Wright & Wright* on qualifying in 1963. Partner in 1964. Senior Partner in 1990. On merger in 1993 Joint Senior Partner of *Gordons Wright & Wright* until retirement in 1997
Personal: Born 24 April, 1937. Trinity College Glenalmond. Lieutenant RNR. Leeds University. Honorary Lay Canon Bradford Cathedral. Interests include all country sports

MCALLESTER, Alan K.
Birch Cullimore, Chester (01244) 321066

MORRIS, Paul C.E.
Winckworth Sherwood, London (020) 7593 5000 pcemorris@winckworths.co.uk
Partner and head of ecclesiastical and education law department.
Specialisation: Head of department since 1987; previously Joint head of institutional property department 1984-87, with expertise in commercial property law. Has acted in controversial cases involving clergy discipline, re-ordering of church buildings and re-development of redundant churches and church land.
Prof. Memberships: Law Society, City of Westminster Law Society, Ecclesiastical Law Society, Ecclesiastical Law Association.
Career: Qualified in 1978. Joined *Winckworth & Pemberton* in 1978, becoming a Partner in 1981. Registrar and Bishop's Legal Secretary, Diocese of London. Registrar and Bishop's Legal Secretary, Diocese of Southwark. Joint Registrar, Diocese of Leicester. Solicitor to Southwark Diocesan Board of Finance. Solicitor to the London Diocesan Fund. Chapter Clerk of Southwark Cathedral.
Personal: Born 21st September 1950. Attended Westminster Abbey Choir School 1960-64, Westminster School 1964-68 and UCNW Bangor 1968-72. Leisure interests include music and the family. Lives in West London and Charlbury, Oxfordshire.

MYERS, Miranda
Bell & Buxton, Sheffield (0114) 249 5969 m.myers@bellbuxton.co.uk
Specialisation: Ecclesiastical law and private client work.
Prof. Memberships: Ecclesiastical Law Association, Ecclesiastical Law Society, STEP.

NALLY, Edward
Fieldings Porter, Bolton (01204) 387742
Specialisation: Acts as diocesan solicitor for Salford Roman Catholic Diocese and has also represented various religious and educational charities.
Prof. Memberships: Council member of the Law Society for Central Lancashire and Northern Greater Manchester.
Career: De La Salle College, Salford and Nottingham University.
Personal: Married with two children

PEAK, Chris
Madge Lloyd & Gibson, Gloucester (01452) 520 224

REES, John
Winckworth Sherwood, Oxford (01865) 297 200 jrees@winckworths.co.uk
Partner in ecclesiastical, education and charities department.
Specialisation: Main area of practice is ecclesiastical law. Joint Registrar, Diocese of Oxford: Deputy Registrar, Province of Canterbury: Legal Adviser to the Anglican Consultative Council (the international liaison body for the Anglican Communion worldwide). Extensive experience in contested faculty cases, including Court of Arches Judgment in Re St. Luke, Maidstone: wide acquaintance with education law issues on behalf of governors and trustees.
Prof. Memberships: Ecclesiastical Law Association, Ecclesiastical Law Society (Treasurer).
Career: Qualified 1975. Joined *Winckworth Sherwood* 1986. Partner 1988.
Personal: Born 21 April 1951. Holds LLB (Southampton 1972), MA (Oxon 1984) and MPhil (Leeds 1984). Leisure interests include photography and cycling. Lives in Oxford.

RICHENS, Nicholas J.
Lee Bolton & Lee, London (020) 7222 5381
Specialisation: Education law and charity law, particularly with reference to church schools and school sites. Advised the General Synod Board of Education on the School Standards and Framework Bill. Joint contributor to Volume 13(2) 'Encyclopaedia of Forms and Precedents–Ecclesiastical Law'. Joint author of 'Charity Land and Premises' (Jordans 1996). Deputy registrar, Diocese of Guilford.
Prof. Memberships: Ecclesiastical Law Society (Deputy Secretary); Ecclesiastical Law Association (Secretary); Charity Law Association.
Career: Admitted 1985. Joined *Lee Bolton & Lee* in 1991.
Personal: Born 1960; Educated Marple Hall High School, Stockport and Downing College Cambridge. Lives in East London.

ROBSON, Frank E.
Winckworth Sherwood, Oxford (01865) 297 200 ferobson@winckworths.co.uk
Consultant in ecclesiastical department.
Specialisation: Main area of practice is ecclesiastical law. Registrar to Diocese of Oxford since 1970; Registrar to Province of Canterbury and legal adviser to the Archbishop 1982-2000; Vice-Chairman of Legal Advisory Commission of the General Synod.
Prof. Memberships: Ecclesiastical Law Association (Chairman 1984-86), Ecclesiastical Law Society (Chairman 1996-).
Career: Qualified 1954. Joined *Winckworth Sherwood* in 1958, becoming a partner in 1960 and senior partner in 1990.
Personal: Born 14th December 1931. Attended Selwyn College, Cambridge 1954-57. Leisure interests include supporting Oxford United, walking and travel. Lives in Stanton St. John, Oxford.

THATCHER, Michael C.
Winckworth Sherwood, London (020) 7593 5000 mcthatcher@winckworths.co.uk
See under Education, p.310

THORNEYCROFT, John
Manby & Steward, Bridgnorth (01746) 761436 manbys.bridgenorth@dial.pipex.com
Specialisation: Main area of practice cover ecclesiastical law, charity law, trusts and asset prorection. As Registrar of Lichfield Diocese has experience in all areas of ecclesiastical law and his firm has particular experience in conduct matters and contested faculty matters.
Prof. Memberships: STEP Ecclesiastical Law Association and Ecclesiastical Law Society.
Career: Admitted 1966. With *Manby & Steward* since 1966.
Personal: Born 1939. Eduacated Pembroke College Cambridge. Lives near Shifnal in Shropshire. Married with four children.

TISDALL, Miles
Larcomes, Portsmouth (023) 92661531
Specialisation: Charity law. Acts for Roman Catholic Diocese of Portsmouth.
Prof. Memberships: Law Society.

TUNNARD, Chris
Tunnard Crosfield, Ripon (01765) 600 421

TYLER, Hilary A.G.
Brutton & Co, Fareham (01329) 236171

WELLMAN, Derek
Wellman & Brown, Lincoln (01522) 525463

WHEELER, Richard K.
Michelmores, Exeter (01392) 436244

WHITE, Peter M.
White & Bowker, Winchester (01962) 844440 peter.white@wandb.co.uk
Consultant in ecclesiastical and residential property department.
Specialisation: Principal area of practice covers all aspects of ecclesiastical law. Appointed Diocesan Registrar for the Diocese of Winchester and Bishop's Legal Secretary 1981. Other main area of work is residential property.
Prof. Memberships: Current Secretary of Hampshire Law Society, member of Ecclesiastical Law Association, Ecclesiastical Law Society, Notaries Society, Law Society.
Career: Qualified in 1970 while at *White & Bowker* and became a partner in 1974.
Personal: Born 28th August 1945. Attended Winchester College 1958-63, then New College, Oxford 1964-67. Leisure pursuits include golf, cricket and fives. Lives in Romsey.

CLINICAL NEGLIGENCE

OVERVIEW: Due to the institution of various regulatory panels, the number of firms with the capacity to take on complex or high value clinical negligence cases is constantly shrinking. As a result, all specialist firms report a tremendous increase in new case applications within the past twelve months. On the claimant side, only firms with solicitors on either of the two referral panels, Law Society and Action for Victims of Medical Accidents are eligible for legal aid. On the defendant side, membership in the select NHSLA panel determines which firms can undertake significant defence work. However, new regulations promoting the use of conditional fee agreements may in time open the market to other practices who do not qualify for either of the claimant or defendant panels.

RESEARCH APPROVED BY BMRB: *For this edition,* Chambers' *researchers conducted 6083 interviews – 4408 with law firms, 598 with barristers and 1077 with clients.*

The validity of the research was scrutinised by BMRB International, who audited both the methodology and the results at our offices in July 2000. They interviewed Chambers' *researchers and cross-checked sample interviews. Details of the audit appear on page 7.*

LONDON

MAINLY CLAIMANT

CLINICAL NEGLIGENCE: MAINLY CLAIMANT • London	Ptnrs	Assts
❶ Leigh, Day & Co	6	5
❷ Bindman & Partners	2	3
Kingsley Napley	3	8
Parlett Kent	4	2
❸ Alexander Harris	1	1
Charles Russell	1	4
Evill and Coleman	3	3
Field Fisher Waterhouse	1	3

LEADING INDIVIDUALS
❶ **FAZAN Claire** Bindman & Partners
LEIGH Sarah Leigh, Day & Co
LEVY Russell Leigh, Day & Co
VALLANCE Richard Charles Russell
WINYARD Anne Leigh, Day & Co
❷ **BARTON Grainne** Alexander Harris
CAHILL Julia Kingsley Napley
LEE Terry Evill and Coleman
McNEIL Paul Field Fisher Waterhouse
❸ **BATTEN Elizabeth** Parlett Kent
JENKINS Caroline Helen Clare Parlett Kent
MARSH Christine Kingsley Napley
MARTINEZ Liz Evill and Coleman
ROHDE Kate Kingsley Napley

Within each band, firms are listed alphabetically. *See **Profiles** on page 160*

Leigh Day & Co Continues as the *"first port of call for claimant clinical negligence"* with its members *"at the spearhead of driving initiatives."* While perceived to spend an increasing amount of time in management and public forum roles, **Sarah Leigh** is still considered to have *"a leading profile in the field."* *"Innovative"* **Russell Levy** and *"thoughtful"* **Anne Winyard** maintain a *"heavyweight"* caseload in undiagnosed cancer claims, infectious disease work, and cerebral palsy cases. Involved in RAGE claims, securing an award of £465,000 for damages resulting from excessive radiotherapy following a lumpectomy. This specialist practice also includes two qualified nurses and a forensic accountant handling quantum calculations.

Bindman & Partners Climbs the tables this year largely due to the *"exceptional talent"* of **Claire Fazan** who heads a team of *"straightforward"* clinical negligence claimant lawyers. Reputed for dealing with severe and permanently disabling injuries arising from birth, cancer misdiagnosis, anaesthetic accidents, plastic surgery and wrongful birth claims. Secured an admission of liability with damages awarded for psychiatric injuries and financial loss to two Latin American dancers in Parkin v Bromley Health Authority, involving failure to respond to cardiac arrest during childbirth.

Kingsley Napley A *"professional and experienced team,"* includes the highly regarded **Julia Cahill**, **Christine Marsh** and **Kate Rohde**. Member of the LawAssist clinical negligence panel. Involved in substantial obstetric negligence, neurosurgical, and delayed diagnosis of breast cancer claims. Currently handling a large number of compartment syndrome cases resulting in muscular atrophy and major surgery or amputation of the leg. Obtained admission of liability on six major brain injury birth claims. Team includes a nurse/solicitor and a CEDR accredited mediator.

Parlett Kent Remain well regarded for claimant clinical negligence work with a large proportion of solicitors on either the AVMA or law society clinical negligence panels. **Caroline Jenkins** and **Elizabeth Batten** have respected expertise in obstetric, neurosurgery and maximum severity claims, as well as a particular niche in psychiatric negligence. Recently settled significant cerebral palsy claims with damages of £4.5 and £2.5 million. Team includes a qualified nurse and it maintains a strong link with the firm's Exeter branch. Offers an express clinical justice plan through Litigation Protection Limited.

Alexander Harris Although a relatively new office, the fledgling practice is establishing its hold on the London market. The *"excellent"* **Grainne Barton** received enormous praise as a *"caring and careful solicitor."* Barton leads the firm's multi-party action department involved in MMR vaccine and LSD litigation.

Charles Russell A *"small niche practice," "committed to medical negligence work."* Team led by *"detailed"* **Richard Vallance**, recommended as *"a star"* who *"has been at it for years and years and knows all the right experts."* Practice's expertise in clinical negligence has been strengthened by the arrival of a qualified doctor. Acted in Das v Ganju, a maximum severity case expanding the scope of the McFarlane ruling on the recovery of costs for future care.

Evill & Coleman A *"sensible crew"* includes **Terry Lee** and **Liz Martinez,** recommended as *"good negotiators"* who *"don't take their eyes off the ball."* Handles complex cases of catastrophic injury, anaesthetic disaster, and paediatric cerebral palsy. Obtained substantial damages for a rugby player with catastrophic spinal injuries in a case against a referee in Smolden v. Nolan.

Martinez is a qualified mediator, and an in-house financial expert assists the group with quantum settlements.

Field Fisher Waterhouse Although *"efficient and businesslike"* **Paul McNeil** leads an *"able team"* that *"obviously knows what they're doing,"* the group is not felt to be as prominent as in previous years. A comprehensive health care group handles inquests and cases in areas ranging from obstetrics/gynaecology to orthopaedics and ophthalmology. Represented a six month autistic boy blinded during cataract surgery in Baby J v The Bolton Health Authority, recovering damages of £720,000. The practice also handles a substantial number of conditional fee agreements.

MAINLY DEFENDANT

CLINICAL NEGLIGENCE: MAINLY DEFENDANT • London	Ptnrs	Assts
❶ Capsticks	14	21
❷ Beachcroft Wansbroughs	2	18
Hempsons	8	8
Le Brasseur J Tickle	11	19

LEADING INDIVIDUALS
❶ **HOLMES John** Beachcroft Wansbroughs
LEIGH Bertie Hempsons
MASON David Capsticks
❷ **SMITH Janice** Capsticks
SUMERLING Robert Le Brasseur J Tickle
WILDER Gay Browne Jacobson
YEAMAN Anthony George Beachcroft Wansbroughs
❸ **BARBER Janice** Hempsons
HAY Katie Capsticks

Within each band, firms are listed alphabetically. *See **Profiles** on page 160*

Capsticks Described as *"leaders in the field,"* outstanding recommendations keep this *"well organised team"* offering *"high quality service across the board"* at the top of the defendant tables. Team includes a number of *"top-notch"* performers, particularly the *"eccentric" "top flight defence lawyer"* **David Mason**, who has a wealth of experience in obstetric, neurosurgery and anaesthetic cases. Partners **Katie Hay** and **Janice Smith** *"do a good job for clients"* and are perceived as substantial assets to the group's profile. Draws upon the expertise of three in-house doctors and operates a twenty-four hour emergency hotline service. Acted successfully in Alayan v Nothwick Park NHS Trust, recovering £100,000 for the NHS in a cerebral palsy quantum trial in which the claimant failed to beat the payment into court. **Clients:** Range of Acute, Community, and Mental Health NHS Trusts.

Beachcroft Wansboroughs A *"formidable firm"* with an *"established reputation"* for defending a wide range of health authorities against clinical negligence claims. Both **John Holmes** *("a class apart")* and the *"enthusiastic"* **Anthony Yeaman** were widely recommended for their *"reasonable"* approach. Handle a high proportion of obstetric claims and act for numerous teaching hospitals. Involved in Lakey v Merton Sutton & Wandsworth Health Authority, arguing whether a judge should be required to give reasons for preferring one medical expert to another. **Clients:** Royal London, University Hospital, Chelsea & Westminster Healthcare NHS Trust.

Hempsons A niche firm well known for covering all aspects of health care litigation. Big hitters include **Bertie Leigh**, said to offer *"good value for money"* for defendant clinical negligence work, and the *"authoritative"* **Janice Barber** who has a particular specialism in clinical disciplinary cases. Acting frequently for the MDU, the practice is highly regarded for its defence of private doctor GPs as well as individual NHS organisations. Also maintains a high profile in mental health inquiries. Successfully defended a cerebral palsy case based on a breach of duty, with potential damages of £3 million in Ebony Wilson v Brighton Health Care NHS Trust. **Clients:** NHSLA; MDU; Lambeth, Southwark & Lewisham Health Authority.

Le Brasseur J Tickle Perceived as somewhat *"old-fashioned"* in approach, this large, *"straightforward"* team receive a large volume of instructions from both health authorities and private GPs. *"Impressive"* **Robert Sumerling** was highly rated for his *"professional"* style. Covers the spectrum of clinical negligence defence work, including mental health claims. Acts frequently for the Medical Protection Society. Commands extensive experience in class actions, acting in Myedol, RAGE, and infected blood litigations. Team also includes mental health specialists. **Clients:** NHSLA.

Other Notable Practitioners **Gay Wilder** at Browne Jacobson was once again recommended although the firm itself is not seen to be making an impact on the London market.

THE SOUTH

MAINLY CLAIMANT

CLINICAL NEGLIGENCE: MAINLY CLAIMANT • The South	Ptnrs	Assts
❶ Blake Lapthorn Portsmouth	2	2
Thomson Snell & Passmore Tunbridge Wells	2	4
❷ Penningtons Godalming	1	4

LEADING INDIVIDUALS
❶ **MATHER Christopher** Penningtons
McCLURE Alison Blake Lapthorn
WATSON Andrew Thomson Snell & Passmore

Within each band, firms are listed alphabetically. *See **Profiles** on page 160*

Blake Lapthorn Covers a wide range of clinical negligence work with particular specialisms in misdiagnosis of breast cancer, obstetric, and orthopaedic negligence. Acclaimed for her *"enormous experience"* and *"ability to get things sorted,"* **Alison McClure** is a new entrant to our tables this year. Obtained a £1.84 million settlement in the Johnson v Portsmouth and South East Hampshire Health Authority cerebral palsy claim, related to delayed treatment of jaundice.

Thomson Snell & Passmore A well regarded practice with a *"co-operative"* and *"realistic"* approach to clinical negligence litigation. The team is led by *"constructive"* **Andrew Watson** who was particularly noted for his expertise in quantum work. Experienced in gynaecology, orthopaedic, and oncology claims. Successfully acted in case relating to nerve damage due to complications of varicose vein surgery (Czornenskys v Camden & Islington Health Authority.)

Penningtons Highly regarded practice, sharing work between the Godalming and Basingstoke offices. Team includes two practitioners, formerly at Beachcroft Wansbroughs, with extensive clinical negligence experience on the defendant side. Senior consultant **Chris Mather**, an *"experienced, tactical litigator,"* enters the tables this year. Covers the range of clinical negligence issues, with particular interest in cerebral palsy, obstetric, and neurosurgery cases. Handles an increasing number of CFA cases, including Sheppard v Moore, obtaining a settlement of £1.56 million for a claimant against a private GP for failure to diagnose a heart attack.

MAINLY DEFENDANT

CLINICAL NEGLIGENCE: MAINLY DEFENDANT • The South	Ptnrs	Assts
❶ **Beachcroft Wansboroughs** Winchester	2	13
❷ **Brachers** Maidstone	2	4

LEADING INDIVIDUALS
❶ **McGRATH Matthew Beachcroft Wansbroughs**
SHEATH John Brachers

Within each band, firms are listed alphabetically. See **Profiles** on page 160

Beachcroft Wansboroughs A *"large and reputable"* team with acknowledged expertise in high value claims. **Matthew McGrath** was newly recommended. Group advises on risk management, issues of consent, confidentiality and access to records. Successfully opposed an application for judicial review in Glass v Portsmouth Hospitals NHS Trust. **Clients:** NHSLA.

Brachers Respected for defence of area health authorities, primary care trusts, and private GPs against clinical negligence claims. Active in a series of cervical smear cases, including Penny Palmer & Cannon v Kent & Canterbury Hospital. Increasingly involved in medical risk management and policy matters. *"Sensible"* **John Sheath** was once again recommended. **Clients:** Medway Health Authority; East Kent Hospitals NHS Trusts; Dartford & Gravesham NHS Trust.

THAMES VALLEY

MAINLY CLAIMANT

CLINICAL NEGLIGENCE: MAINLY CLAIMANT • Thames Valley	Ptnrs	Assts
❶ **Boyes Turner & Burrows** Reading	2	2
❷ **Osborne Morris & Morgan** Leighton Buzzard	2	2

LEADING INDIVIDUALS
✪ **DESMOND Adrian** Boyes Turner & Burrows
❶ **OSBORNE Thomas** Osborne Morris & Morgan

Within each band, firms are listed alphabetically. See **Profiles** on page 160

Boyes Turner & Burrows A small, *"sensible"* team led by *"personable"* **Adrian Desmond** has built up a *"strong reputation for serious claims."* Particular strength in catastrophic injury cases. Taking on a substantial amount of conditional fee work. Operate a brain injury support group for families of brain injured clients. Acted for nine year old Edward Parry against the North West Surrey Health Authority, securing damages of £3.30 million for a claim of athetoid quadriplegic cerebral palsy resulting from midwives' negligence.

Osborne Morris & Morgan An *"established"* medical negligence practice of recognised *"strength and depth."* Self styled *"neurolawyer"* with a *"tigerish"* reputation, **Thomas Osborne** specialises in brain injury/cerebral palsy cases. Also increasingly involved in medical accident inquests.

SOUTH WEST

MAINLY CLAIMANT

CLINICAL NEGLIGENCE: MAINLY CLAIMANT • South West	Ptnrs	Assts
❶ **Barcan Woodward** Bristol	1	1
Over Taylor Biggs Exeter	1	1
Preston Goldburn Falmouth	1	-
❷ **John Hodge & Co** Weston-super-Mare	2	1
Russell Jones & Walker Bristol	1	2
Withy King Bath	2	-
Wolferstans Plymouth	1	2
❸ **Tozers** Exeter	2	3
Woollcombe Beer Watts Newton Abbot	2	2

LEADING INDIVIDUALS	
✪ **BARCAN Richard** Barcan Woodward	
❶ **ENGLAND Richard** John Hodge & Co	**FERGUSON Gerry** Withy King
GOLDBURN Tim Preston Goldburn	**YOUNG Magi** Parlett Kent
❷ **OVER Christopher** Over Taylor Biggs	**PARFORD Simon** Wolferstans
REED Derek Woollcombe Beer Watts	**SOLLY Gillian** Russell Jones & Walker
VICK Laurence Michelmores	

Within each band, firms are listed alphabetically. See **Profiles** on page 160

Barcan Woodward (An additional partner devotes 50% of his time to clinical negligence.) A strong team with a reputation for *"fantastic client care,"* headed by *"pre-eminent"* **Richard Barcan**. Act in a wide range of clinical negligence cases, including cerebral palsy and other brain damage cases. Representing the widow of a man who suffered a myocardial infraction and died 18 months after being placed on an 'urgent' waiting list for a coronary artery bypass graft.

Over Taylor Biggs *"Realistic"* **Christopher Over** maintains a solid reputation for claimant clinical negligence work as a complement to his transport and construction practice. This small team handles cases from all over the country and is particularly experienced in birth defects, spinal and catastrophic injury. Continues co-ordination of numerous claims of failure to diagnose breast cancer against the East Devon Breast Screening Services. Recently settled a spinal injury case at £675,000 on a shared liability basis.

Preston Goldburn *"Imaginative"* **Tim Goldburn** was once again recommended for his *"pro-active approach"* and *"empathy with clients."* Team includes an in-house nurse/legal executive. Handles a large number of gynaecology and urology cases and maintains a strong interest in clinical negligence mediation. Obtained an order in a case of an accidental sterilisation in which the hospital agreed to underwrite the costs of future treatment and assisted reproduction techniques.

John Hodge & Co A *"solid"* practice recently strengthened by the arrival of a new partner from Veale Wasbrough. Team leader **Richard England** *"has been doing it for a long time and has the necessary knowledge."* Experienced in the full range of clinical negligence matters, with particular expertise in dental, paediatric, and obstetric claims. Involved in the Bristol heart baby cases and an on-going group action regarding damage incurred by contraceptive pill use.

Russell Jones & Walker A growing practice better known on a national rather than local level. Department head **Gillian Solly** continues to be recommended. Receives a considerable amount of trade union work. Experienced in group actions in breast cancer treatment and dental care claims. Recently secured settlements of £1.7 million and £2.38 million in maximum severity cerebral palsy cases.

Withy King Continues to be well rated despite the resignation of an experienced partner. **Gerry Ferguson** was recommended for his *"phenomenal attention to detail."* Areas of expertise include birth injury cases, laparoscopic surgery, and hepatitis claims. Settled a case of failure to diagnose a phaeochromocytoma resulting in quadriplegia at £2.6 million.

Wolferstans Practice recognised as a *"presence"* throughout the Southwest, with three franchised offices in the area. *"Experienced"* **Simon Parford** *"fights hard for his clients."* Areas of expertise include hip dislocation cases, misdiagnosis of cancer, spinal injury, and infant brain damage claims. Obtained £350,000 in damages for a client who became deaf as a result of a failure to diagnose meningitis.

Tozers The defection of highly regarded Laurence Vick to Michelmores was widely perceived as a serious setback to Tozers' clinical negligence practice. Remaining team members cover the range of obstetric, gynaecological, dental, orthopaedic, and ophthalmic cases. Group has a particular specialism in Erb's palsy claims.

Woollcombe Beer Watts Recognised for substantial clinical negligence experience, but not seen as a specialist practice. Involved in Exeter breast screening cases and Bristol heart baby claims. Experienced in spinal injury, laparoscopic, and obstetric claims. Also handles a number of psychiatric negligence claims. **Derek Reed** continues to be recommended.

Other Notable Practitioners Exeter-based **Magi Young** of Parlett Kent & Co commands an impressive reputation for claimant clinical negligence work, but remains much more visible on the London circuit than locally. **Laurence Vick** was once again recommended for his work in the Bristol Royal Infirmary inquiries, although it still remains to be seen how his move to Michelmores will affect his profile in clinical negligence.

MAINLY DEFENDANT

CLINICAL NEGLIGENCE: MAINLY DEFENDANT • South West	Ptnrs	Assts
❶ **Bevan Ashford** Bristol	12	49
❷ **Beachcroft Wansbroughs** Bristol	1	5

LEADING INDIVIDUALS	
❶ **ANNANDALE Richard** Bevan Ashford	**BARBER Paul** Bevan Ashford
BROADHEAD Jill Bevan Ashford	
❷ **MONTGOMERY Nigel** Beachcroft Wansbroughs	
WHITEFIELD Andrew Bevan Ashford	

Within each band, firms are listed alphabetically. *See **Profiles** on page 160*

Bevan Ashford A large *"formidable"* team well known throughout the UK as a *"huge player"* for defendant clinical negligence work. The practice is divided into teams covering all the regions. **Richard Annandale**, **Paul Barber**, **Jill Broadhead** and **Andrew Whitefield** were all commended for their *"up to date knowledge of the law"* and *"aggressive"* approach to litigation. Team includes a number of former doctors, nurses, and one barrister. Specialise in high value mental health and brain damage baby cases. Also involved in Consent and Treatment litigation, including a judicial review case of R v Collins Pathfinder St Georges ex parte S, reaffirming the rights of a child over a mother required by an emergency order to undergo a caesarean section operation. Advised the Avon Health Authority in relation to the Bristol Royal Infirmary Inquiry. **Clients:** NHSLA; Royal United Hospital Bath NHS Trust; Birmingham Children's Hospital NHS Trust.

Beachcroft Wansboroughs A *"sensible," "on the ball"* team seen to be encroaching on Bevan Ashford's traditional lead. Acts for a large number of hospital trusts in the Bristol area. Particular expertise in obstetric cerebral palsy claims and renal cases. Advised UBHT in relation to the Bristol Royal Infirmary Public Inquiry. The practice is considerably strengthened by the addition of **Nigel Montgomery** and a team of people from Lyons Davidson. **Clients:** NHSLA; United Bristol Healthcare Trust, North Bristol NHS Trust.

WALES

MAINLY CLAIMANT

CLINICAL NEGLIGENCE: MAINLY CLAIMANT • Wales	Ptnrs	Assts
❶ **Huttons** Cardiff	1	2
❷ **Edwards Geldard** Cardiff	2	3
Hugh James Ford Simey Cardiff	3	6
John Collins & Partners Swansea	2	1
Smith Llewelyn Partnership Swansea	2	3

LEADING INDIVIDUALS	
❶ **MUSGRAVE Tim** Huttons	
❷ **DAVIES Andrew** Hugh James Ford Simey	**THOMAS Keith** John Collins & Partners

Within each band, firms are listed alphabetically *See **Profiles** on page 160*

Huttons A *"growing practice"* with a *"long established reputation."* **Tim Musgrave** and his team remain *"head and shoulders above everybody else."* Recently recruited an associate partner from Leo Abse. Practice covers the full range of clinical negligence claims from orthopaedic and general surgery suits to obstetric and spinal injury cases. The group includes an in-house nurse.

Edwards Geldard Practice has recently appointed two newly qualified solicitors and a registered nurse to take on a growing volume of clinical negligence claims. Expertise in maximum severity cases, including birth-related brain damage, spinal injury, and fatal accident claims. Undertake a substantial amount of legal expenses work. Acted in a lithium toxicity case in which damages exceeded £1 million.

Hugh James Ford Simey A large and well respected team supported by three qualified nurse executives, a medical records officer, and a social worker with branch offices throughout Wales. Department is led by Bargoed-based **Andrew Davies** *("a claimant lawyer through and through.")* Strong in orthopaedic, oncology, and obstetric claims, the practice is being instructed on a class action concerning negligent cervical smears performed at Prince Charles Hospital. Notably, also obtained rare admission of liability in a GP negligence case involving the coicosteroid Prednisolne.

John Collins & Partners A new entrant to Chambers' tables this year, this *"experienced"* group receive a large volume of clinical negligence claimant work in the area. **Keith Thomas** was recommended as a *"fair and open litigator."* Team includes a doctor of medicine who plays a crucial role in reviewing medical records for legal aid screenings. The department is particularly developing its cerebral palsy practice, having already acted in a number of high value cp claims.

Smith Llewelyn Partnership Team combines a high level of medical and legal expertise, including an in-house doctor, nurse, midwife, and two medically and scientifically qualified partners. Act in a number of cases involving obstetric, anaesthetic awareness, and GP negligence claims. The firm was felt to have *"kept the department and service going"* after the departure of Peter Llewelyn to the judiciary. Recently settled both a high value cerebral palsy case and a claim relating to the removal of the wrong breast during surgery.

MAINLY DEFENDANT

CLINICAL NEGLIGENCE: MAINLY DEFENDANT • Wales	Ptnrs	Assts
❶ **Bevan Ashford** Cardiff	2	5

LEADING INDIVIDUALS	
❶ **LANG Jane** Bevan Ashford	**MAYERS Chris** Bevan Ashford
SHELLENS Tessa Morgan Cole	

Within each band, firms are listed alphabetically. *See **Profiles** on page 160*

Bevan Ashford *"A good firm with tentacles everywhere,"* it remains the only private firm handling a substantial amount of clinical negligence defence work in Wales. **Jane Lang** and **Chris Mayers**, were rated for their *"enormous experience,"* although Tessa Shellens has moved to Morgan Cole. Involved in clinical governance, medical inquests, and the formulation of policies relating to telemedicine, the team devotes a notable amount of time to advising health service bodies on a range of medico-legal issues. **Clients:** NHSLA; North Glamorgan NHS Trust; Pembrokeshire & Derwin NHS Trust; Powys Health Care NHS Trust.

Other Notable Practitioners **Tessa Shellens** is a well-known name in the area who has moved from Bevan Ashford to Morgan Cole. It remains to be seen whether she can build a substantial practice there.

MIDLANDS

MAINLY CLAIMANT

CLINICAL NEGLIGENCE: MAINLY CLAIMANT • Midlands	Ptnrs	Assts
❶ **Freethcartwright** Nottingham, Derby	3	5
❷ **Irwin Mitchell** Birmingham	3	4
❸ **Anthony Collins Solicitors** Birmingham	1	4
Challinors Lyon Clark Birmingham	1	4

LEADING INDIVIDUALS	
❶ **BALEN Paul** Freethcartwright	**FOLLIS Richard** Irwin Mitchell
❷ **HALL Antony** Anthony Collins Solicitors	
❸ **BANNISTER Richard** Challinors Lyon Clark	**JORDAN Lisa** Irwin Mitchell

Within each band, firms are listed alphabetically *See **Profiles** on page 160*

Freethcartwright Clinical negligence practice spread over three franchised offices. Group includes a barrister, allowing the team to do their own advocacy. Continues to act in high profile cases, including MMR children's vaccine cases, and pursued a claim on behalf of a patient who contracted malaria in a hospital. *"Determined"* **Paul Balen** was highly esteemed as a *"resourceful"* individual with a *"big reputation."*

Irwin Mitchell The addition of a number of people from Challinors Lyon Clark, including the *"high profile"* **Richard Follis** and *"first rate"* **Lisa Jordan** has brought the practice up significantly in public opinion, establishing it as a *"national presence."* The team was praised for its involvement in *"forward thinking initiatives"* and *"superb client care."* Strengths in obstetrics/gynaecology, oncology, and failure to diagnose. After split trials on liability and quantum, achieved an award of £1.3 million for the wrongful birth of a handicapped child.

Anthony Collins Solicitors A well regarded practice *"firmly rooted in the region."* **Tony Hall** continues to be recognised for his *"commitment to clients"* and for a *"number of notable successes"* in high profile cases. Has notable expertise in meningitis cases. The team recently settled Milloshas v Staffordshire Health authority for £4.5 million as compensation for significant brain damage to a six month old child, after failure to diagnose meningitis. The practice has also developed an interest in clinical negligence mediation.

Challinors Lyon Clark Although the practice has been weakened by the *en masse* departure of a number of its clinical negligence specialists, the *"committed"* **Richard Bannister** has received kudos for his *"admirable"* work in rebuilding a team and re-establishing the practice's position in the field. The practice is admittedly in a state of flux, but retains its legal aid clinical negligence franchise and is seen to be *"still holding on"* to a substantial amount of work. Covers all aspects of clinical negligence including inquests and assistance in NHS complaints.

MAINLY DEFENDANT

CLINICAL NEGLIGENCE: MAINLY DEFENDANT • Midlands	Ptnrs	Assts
❶ **Mills & Reeve** Birmingham	3	29
❷ **Beachcroft Wansbroughs** Birmingham	1	2
❸ **Browne Jacobson** Nottingham, Birmingham	3	7

LEADING INDIVIDUALS
❶ **KING Stephen** Mills & Reeve
KNOWLES Stuart Mills & Reeve
UP AND COMING
SWANTON Vicki Browne Jacobson

Within each band, firms are listed alphabetically. *See **Profiles** on page 160*

Mills & Reeve A very large and ever-expanding team, sometimes described as *"patchy,"* but retaining a recognised stronghold on clinical negligence defendant work in the area. **Stephen King** was voted *"one of the best senior clinical negligence solicitors"* but questions were raised as to the volume of his casework, in view of his largely managerial role in the practice. **Stuart Knowles** *"knows his stuff"* and is a new entrant to the clinical negligence tables. The team employs a number of dual qualified medical specialists on the team. Co-ordinated a structured settlement to resolve a multi-million pound claim for a brain damaged child, and successfully defended a major limitation case relating to constructive knowledge. The bulk of the work is NHS-derived, although the team also receives a small proportion of instructions from the insurance market. **Clients:** NHSLA

Beachcroft Wansboroughs A fairly young team, too recently established in Birmingham to have made more of a mark on the Midlands market. Although no particular leaders were identified, the team generally was recommended as a group of *"provocative, bold litigators."* **Clients:** NHSLA.

Browne Jacobson Firm recently joined the NHSLA list, and enters the tables as *"a firm to watch for the future."* In the Birmingham office, **Vicki Swanton**, lately of Mills & Reeve, was noted as an up and coming practitioner for her *"sensible approach"* and growing profile. Team includes registered medical practitioners and advises trusts on management of high profile risk management catastrophes. Acting in on-going smear cases and a number of birth asphyxia claims. **Clients:** NHSLA; Nottingham City Hospital; Royal Wolverhampton Hospitals; Redbridge and Waltham Forest Health Authority.

EAST ANGLIA

MAINLY CLAIMANT

CLINICAL NEGLIGENCE: MAINLY CLAIMANT • East Anglia	Ptnrs	Assts
❶ **Cunningham John** Thetford	4	7
❷ **Gadsby Wicks** Chelmsford	3	4
Morgan Jones & Pett Great Yarmouth	2	2
❸ **Prettys** Ipswich	1	2

LEADING INDIVIDUALS	
❶ **JOHN Simon** Cunningham John	
❷ **JONES David** Morgan Jones & Pett	**WICKS Roger** Gadsby Wicks
❸ **GADSBY Gillian** Gadsby Wicks	

Within each band, firms are listed alphabetically. *See **Profiles** on page 160*

Cunningham, John & Co A large team of *"niche specialists"* whose reputation as *"big players"* transcends East Anglia. *"Outstanding"* **Simon John** demonstrates a *"terrific commitment to clinical negligence."* The team is a participant in the express clinical negligence scheme. Handles a large number of paediatric brain damage cases and colostomy claims with damages exceeding £100,000. Appointed to act for a group of 100+ clients in claims against obstetrician/gynaecologist Richard Neil, including badly performed laparoscopy, hysterectomy, failed sterilisation, and undiagnosed ovarian cancer.

Gadsby Wicks Team recognised as *"doing a lot of work"* throughout East Anglia and the South East. Supported by an in-house registered nurse, active in risk assessment and case screening, particularly for cases funded on a conditional fee basis. Takes on group actions for claimants in relation to pharmaceutical and medical product liability claims. Recovered £20 million in compensation in 1999. **Roger Wicks** and **Gillian Gadsby** were rated as *"capable litigators."*

Morgan Jones & Pett A *"specialised"* practice recommended as being *"very good at what they do." "Down to earth"* **David Jones** was reported to be *"frank and open"* and remains a leader in the field. Offices in Great Yarmouth and Norwich cover a general range of clinical negligence claims. Recent settlements include a £1.95 million cerebral palsy claim and a £950,000 embolism case.

Prettys Although seen to be somewhat *"lacking in flair,"* nevertheless remains a *"solid"* practice ably coping with a wide range of clinical negligence work. Handles a number of cases involving complications following birth, including a recent cerebral palsy claim settled at £850,000.

MAINLY DEFENDANT

CLINICAL NEGLIGENCE: MAINLY DEFENDANT • East Anglia	Ptnrs	Assts
❶ **Mills & Reeve** Cambridge, Norwich	3	6
Scrivenger Seabrook St. Neots	5	1

LEADING INDIVIDUALS
❶ **CHAPMAN John** Mills & Reeve
DYBALL John Scrivenger Seabrook
SCRIVENGER Mark Scrivenger Seabrook
SEABROOK Vicki Scrivenger Seabrook

Within each band, firms are listed alphabetically. *See **Profiles** on page 160*

Mills & Reeve A practice with *"a long track record"* in the area which is sometimes perceived as excessively *"systematic"* in approach. Acts for large number of acute units and health and community trusts in East Anglia. Operates a 24 hour NHS helpline for emergency actions. Team includes dual qualified nursing and medical specialists and covers a range of cerebral palsy cases valued between £3 and £5 million. Involved in a court of appeal case relating to an order of costs against the legal aid board, who had reinstated a legal aid certificate in a no-hope case. **John Chapman** was commended for a *"realistic, pragmatic attitude to settling claims."* **Clients:** NHSLA.

Scrivenger Seabrook Praised for their *"creative and proactive approach"* **John Dyball, Mark Scrivenger** and **Vicki Seabrook** are *"innovative dealmakers"* with an acknowledged expertise in complex and high value clinical negligence cases. The practice is almost entirely partner led and acts for a number of NHS Trusts over a broad geographic area. Dyball has particular experience of structured settlements. Negotiated a quantum damages figure of £2.5 million where the original claim was £3.4 million, in a claim of utmost severity sustained at birth (Abbot v. Barking & Havering Health Authority). **Clients:** Forrest Healthcare NHS Trust; Havering Hospitals NHS Trust; Hinchingbrooke Healthcare NHS Trust.

NORTH WEST

MAINLY CLAIMANT

CLINICAL NEGLIGENCE: MAINLY CLAIMANT • North West	Ptnrs	Assts
❶ **Pannone & Partners** Manchester	5	3
❷ **Alexander Harris** Altrincham	3	6
Jones Maidment Wilson, Manchester	2	1
Linder Myers Manchester	2	5
❸ **Leigh, Day & Co** Manchester	2	4

LEADING INDIVIDUALS
❶ **JONES Stephen** Pannone & Partners
KITCHINGMAN John Michael Pannone & Partners
❷ **ALEXANDER Ann** Alexander Harris
SCATES Olivia Jones Maidment Wilson
❸ **CASTLE Nicola** Alexander Harris
JONES Eddie Jones Maidment Wilson
POTTER Hugh Hugh Potter & Company
WARD Trevor Linder Myers

Within each band, firms are listed alphabetically. *See **Profiles** on page 160*

Pannone & Partners A *"fair and sensible"* group who *"drives a claim hard for the client."* The firm moves up the tables largely due to the quality of two leading partners. **John Kitchingman** *("fights his corner well")* and **Stephen Jones** *("won't miss an angle")* are backed by a *"solid, thorough team."* Involved in several high profile inquiries, particularly the Alder Hey inquiry into a Liverpool hospital's retention of body parts of dead children. Recent highlights include high value cerebral palsy settlements of £3.25 million and £1.75 million, and the representation of a 16 year old anorexic girl in proceedings brought by a local trust to obtain an order enabling her to be fed without her consent. Practice draws upon the experience of four in-house nurses and maintains a multiparty franchise for group actions.

Alexander Harris A large team *"committed to the work,"* with an impressive *"deployment of resources,"* although sometimes criticised for inconsistent quality among its junior lawyers. Despite an increasingly managerial role, **Ann Alexander** retains *"an excellent profile for the firm"* and is heavily involved in mounting a class action suit against Dr. Harold Shipman. *"Professional"* **Nicola Castle** was also recommended as *"relatively junior but very able."* Emphasis on high value maximum severity cases, receiving a large number of instructions on birth injury, cerebral palsy, and anaesthetic awareness claims.

Jones Maidment Wilson A smaller but *"able"* and *"consistent"* group with both partners **Olivia Scates** and the newly ranked **Eddie Jones** recommended as clinical negligence specialists who *"look after their clients' interests".* Handles the full range of work, with a notably high proportion of cancer and orthopaedic cases. Achieved a number of recent successes in cerebral palsy claims, including an admission of 75% liability in a claim valued at £2.33 million in Jameson v. Wigan & Bolton Health Authority.

Linder Myers An *"old fashioned firm"* that has *"been doing the work a long time."* Team includes two qualified nurses and a barrister active in quantum research and the preparation of in-house pleading. *"Hardworking"* **Trevor Ward** *"knows what he's doing"* and enters the tables for the first time this year. Covers a variety of clinical negligence cases, including psychiatric claims. Acted in Clough v Tameside & Glossop Health Authority on the disclosure of experts' reports.

Leigh Day & Co Manchester branch of the specialist London firm, *"not regarded as a big market player"* despite its strong links with the high profile London office. Strengths in spinal surgery, misdiagnosis of cancer, and head injury. The firm's legal aid application for clinical negligence remains pending.

Other Notable Practitioners *"Effective"* **Hugh Potter** operates his own franchised firm, Hugh Potter & Co, and was recommended as having *"carved his own niche,"* particularly in respect to head injury claims.

MAINLY DEFENDANT

CLINICAL NEGLIGENCE: MAINLY DEFENDANT • North West	Ptnrs	Assts
❶ **Hempsons** Manchester	7	26
❷ **Hill Dickinson** Liverpool	6	15
❸ **George Davies** Manchester	5	5

LEADING INDIVIDUALS
❶ **GIBBONS Anthony** Hill Dickinson
HARRISON Frances Hempsons
❷ **BATCHELOR Claire** George Davies
BRIGGS Christopher Hempsons
MOWAT Allan Hill Dickinson

Within each band, firms are listed alphabetically. *See **Profiles** on page 160*

Hempsons A large *"well managed practice"* maintains its position as the leading *"specialist defendant firm"* in the area. **Frances Harrison** takes a *"constructive, co-operative attitude"* to litigation while the *"careful"* **Christopher Briggs** was newly recommended for his *"sensible judgement."* Covers the full range of medical negligence work, including mental health and dental negligence, regularly settling cases with damages over the £1 million mark. Frequently called upon by the MDU to represent general medical and dental practitioners in private practice, the practice is heavily involved in ethical and disciplinary matters and received much publicity for its defence of Dr. Harold Shipman. **Clients:** NHSLA; Royal College of Pediatrics & Child Health; Central Manchester Health Authority.

Hill Dickinson *"A large specialised department of very experienced people"* reputed to take an *"aggressive stance"* in litigation. **Tony Gibbons** and **Allan Mowat** are rated for their success at building up the firm's clinical negligence practice. Act for all NHS Trusts in the Merseyside region in a variety of medical negligence issues, including mental health and nursing negligence. Co-ordinated class Benzodiazopine actions in the Northwest. **Clients:** NHSLA.

George Davies & Co Seen as a *"responsible"* practice with *"a substantial number of clients,"* although sometimes described as *"unnecessarily aggressive"* in approach. Leader **Claire Batchelor** however, stands out as *"sensible and co-operative"* and remains highly rated in our tables. Group acts for a number of teaching hospitals and have a particular strength in neurosurgical and brain damage baby cases. **Clients:** NHSLA; South Manchester University Hospital NHS Trust; Salford Royal Hospital NHS Trust.

YORKSHIRE

MAINLY CLAIMANT

CLINICAL NEGLIGENCE: MAINLY CLAIMANT • Yorkshire	Ptnrs	Assts
❶ **Irwin Mitchell** Sheffield	2	6
❷ **Heptonstalls** Goole	2	1
Stamp Jackson and Procter Hull	3	4
LEADING INDIVIDUALS		
❶ **BODY David** Irwin Mitchell		

Within each band, firms are listed alphabetically See **Profiles** on page 160

Irwin Mitchell A *"well set-up, dedicated department"* known for *"getting results for claimants."* The team is led by *"razor sharp"* **David Body** who was widely acclaimed as a *"national leader in trailblazing cases."* Handles all mainstream clinical negligence cases, but maintains a high profile in birth trauma, medical products, and multi-party cases. Achieved total settlements of £4.5 million for 78 families in a group action concerning the human growth hormone CJD. Also currently representing the nvCJD family at the BSE Inquiry.

Heptonstalls A highly regarded practice with a rising case-load in head injury, cerebral palsy, and cancer cases. Small team received plaudits for experience and tenacity. Recently secured an admission of liability in a £2 million cerebral palsy case.

Stamp Jackson & Procter A combined clinical negligence/PI practice thought to do *"a good bit of work"* in the area. Dealt with two recent cerebral palsy cases involving seven figure sums.

MAINLY DEFENDANT

CLINICAL NEGLIGENCE: MAINLY DEFENDANT • Yorkshire	Ptnrs	Assts
❶ **Beachcroft Wansbroughs** Sheffield	6	20
Hempsons Harrogate	2	25
Le Brasseur J Tickle Leeds	4	7
LEADING INDIVIDUALS		
❶ **HALLATT Diane** Beachcroft Wansbroughs		
❷ **LOVEL John** Hempsons		

Within each band, firms are listed alphabetically See **Profiles** on page 160

Beachcroft Wansbroughs A *"well-respected"* practice acting for a number of trusts in Trent. *"Sharp"* **Diane Hallatt** maintains a *"national reputation"* for defence work. Handled emergency applications for urgent treatment of children of Jehovah's Witness parents and successfully defended cervical screening case following Penney & Ors v East Kent Health Authority. **Clients:** range of teaching hospitals, health authorities, and NHS Trusts.

Hempsons A *"sound"* team regarded as *"pre-eminent in the region"* for its work on behalf of NHS trusts and health authorities in Yorkshire and N. Lincolnshire. The department is led by **John Lovel**, who retains his reputation for long-standing experience in clinical negligence defence work, particularly in regards to oncology and high value cerebral palsy cases. Also active in risk management, advising NHS bodies. Successfully defended, on the basis of causation, a claim with potential damages of £2 million brought by a stroke victim in Rosenom-Lanng v Scunthorpe & Goole Hospitals NHS Trust. **Clients:** NHSLA; Leeds Health Authority; Bradford Hospitals NHS Trust.

Le Brasseur J Tickle Widely recommended as a team of *"good technicians"* with a *"dogged"* approach to clinical negligence litigation. The only firm in Leeds on the NHSLA panel. Specific specialisms include brain damage baby cases, neurosurgical, paediatric, and cancer claims. Known particularly for its work for the Medical Protection Society in representing general practitioners. **Clients:** MDU; MPS; MDDU; Harrogate Healthcare; Salford Mental Health Trust; Medical Protection Society.

NORTH EAST

MAINLY CLAIMANT

CLINICAL NEGLIGENCE: MAINLY CLAIMANT • North East	Ptnrs	Assts
❶ **Peter Maughan & Co** Gateshead	2	1
❷ **Hay & Kilner** Newcastle-upon-Tyne	3	2
LEADING INDIVIDUALS		
❶ **MAUGHAN Peter** Peter Maughan & Co		
❷ **BLEWITT Tom** Mincoffs		
CURRAN Angela Watson Burton		

Within each band, firms are listed alphabetically. See **Profiles** on page 160

Peter Maughan & Co A respected, small, specialist practice whose *"reputation transcends the Northeast." "A larger than life character,"* **Peter Maughan** receives high ratings for his *"realistic"* approach and impressive client manner. The team's excellent reputation brings in a high volume of clinical negligence work from a wide geographic area. Building up a reputation for gynaecological claims and offers a free clinic once a week for women with medico-legal problems. Acting on behalf of a young footballer whose leg was incorrectly set after a fracture sustained during his first professional match.

Hay & Kilner Although historically a defendant firm, Hay and Kilner has managed to establish a well respected claimant practice, appointed to both the Legal Aid clinical negligence and multi-party panels. Team draws upon the expertise of a dual-qualified obstetrician in a fair number of cerebral palsy, meningitis, and general birth accident claims. Also involved in a several cases with the General Medical Council.

Other Notable Practitioners **Tom Blewitt** of Mincoffs received tremendous recommendations for *"doing a lot of substantial cases in a practical fashion."* **Anglela Curran** from Watson Burton was once again rated as *"efficient"* and a *"dedicated"* leader in her practice.

MAINLY DEFENDANT

CLINICAL NEGLIGENCE: MAINLY DEFENDANT • North East	Ptnrs	Assts
❶ **Eversheds** Newcastle upon Tyne	4	8
❷ **Crutes** Newcastle-upon-Tyne	2	3
❸ **Samuel Phillips & Co** Newcastle upon Tyne	1	3
Ward Hadaway Newcastle upon Tyne	2	2

LEADING INDIVIDUALS
❶ **BRADBEER Ronald** Eversheds
SLACK Richard Eversheds
❷ **SPEKER Barry** Samuel Phillips & Co

Within each band, firms are listed alphabetically. *See **Profiles** on page 160*

Eversheds Practice looks to be on an upswing as interviewees predict that the recent addition of the highly rated **Richard Slack**, formerly of Crutes, will considerably raise the team's comparatively low profile reputation. **Ronald Bradbeer** remains *"an established presence"* although is *"far less visible"* in the marketplace due to his increased involvement in the mediation pilot scheme and training on mediation involvement. Practice acted in over 100 clinical negligence cases with damages in the region of £1 million. Represented the NHSLA, Tees Health Authority, and the North Tees NHS Trust in the Court of Appeal case of Beverley Palmer. **Clients:** Bradford Hospitals NHS Trust; Scarbrough Acute Hospitals NHS Trust; Hartlepool & East Durham NHS Trust.

Crutes A respected firm with a good track record, but perceived as badly hit by the loss of Richard Slack. A young team remains with the *"tenacity"* to *"fight tooth and nail,"* but no leaders of Slack's stature have emerged to fill the gap. In addition to the standard range of clinical negligence litigation and inquests, the practice places enormous emphasis on mediation and ADR, embracing the Northern/Yorkshire mediation pilot scheme. Involved in one of the first mediated clinical negligence claims, reaching a settlement in excess of £1 million in connection with a CNST scheme for trusts. **Clients:** NHSLA.

Samuel Phillips & Co Only firm to undertake both claimant and defendant work, although still heavily weighted towards the defence side. Not an NHSLA panel member, but receives a large volume of instructions from private hospitals and GPs, in addition to NHSLA work below the £100,000 mark. Interviewees predict a rough transition for the firm as they look to develop their claimant practice, but the team has obtained a legal aid franchise in clinical negligence and still retains the *"meticulous"* and *"direct"* **Barry Speker**, who was highly rated for his years of experience in the field.

Ward Hadaway Although not a member of the NHSLA panel, the firm is permitted to carry out work for a large number of NHS trusts, who were secured as clients before the panel was established. This client case ensures that the team remains in the bandings as a highly regarded clinical negligence practice. Acts for acute trusts in orthopaedics, obstetrics, and oncology. Represented family in child M case of a teenager who refused a heart transplant. **Clients:** South Tyneside Healthcare NHS Trust; County Durham Health Authority; Newcastle Upon Tyne Hospitals NHS Trust.

SCOTLAND

MAINLY PURSUER

CLINICAL NEGLIGENCE: MAINLY PURSUER • Scotland	Ptnrs	Assts
❶ **Anderson Strathern WS** Edinburgh	3	9
Balfour & Manson Edinburgh	5	5
Drummond Miller WS Edinburgh	2	2
Fyfe Ireland WS Edinburgh	-	3
Lawford Kidd Edinburgh	1	1

LEADING INDIVIDUALS
❶ **CARR Robert** Anderson Strathern WS
TYLER Alfred Balfour & Manson

Within each band, firms are listed alphabetically. *See **Profiles** on page 160*

Anderson Strathern WS A new entrant to Chambers' tables, both *"conscientious"* **Robert Carr** and his team received glowing recommendations for both pursuer and defender clinical negligence work. Well known for acting for the Royal College of Nursing. Represented the family of Darren Denholm at a Fatal Accident Inquiry involving the death of a child during a dental extraction.

Balfour & Manson A quality clinical negligence/PI team with an *"understanding of how to pursue claims."* **Fred Tyler** *"deals with a considerable number of high profile cases"* including four or five high value cerebral palsy cases and the ground-breaking McFarlane v Tayside Health Board wrongful conception case.

Drummond Miller WS This expanding team includes two law society accredited medical negligence specialists. Undertakes a number of obstetric, general surgery and dental claims. Recently appeared before the sheriff in two Fatal Accident Inquiries, one involving a young boy who was detained by police after sustaining severe head injuries.

Fyfe Ireland WS Covers the full range of clinical negligence pursuer work and involved in an increasing number of high profile Fatal Accident Inquiries. Active in Anderson v Forth Valley Health Board case concerning the right to compensation for the additional costs of upbringing a disabled child in instances of wrongful birth. The loss to the team of Kathrine Mackie, however, following her appointment as a Sheriff, leaves a hole which may prove difficult to fill.

Lawford Kidd Acting principally on behalf of the unions, the firm continues to be ranked for its clinical negligence work as a spin-off from its personal injury practice.

MAINLY DEFENDER

CLINICAL NEGLIGENCE: MAINLY DEFENDER • Scotland	Ptnrs	Assts
❶ **Shepherd & Wedderburn WS** Edinburgh	2	2

LEADING INDIVIDUALS
❶ **DONALD Hugh** Shepherd & Wedderburn WS
GRIFFITHS John Shepherd & Wedderburn WS

Within each band, firms are listed alphabetically. *See **Profiles** on page 160*

Shepherd & Wedderburn WS Practice emerges as the leader for Scottish defender work as **John Griffiths** of Simpson & Marwick joined **Hugh Donald** on May 1st, 2000. Represents doctors in fatal accident inquiries, and has recently been involved in advising dental practitioners involved in dental anaesthetic death in Scotland. **Clients:** Medical Protection Society; Royal College of Surgeons; Scottish Ambulance Service; Medical and Dental Defence Union of Scotland.

LEADERS IN CLINICAL NEGLIGENCE

ALEXANDER, Ann
Alexander Harris, Altrincham (0161) 925 5555
ann@alexharris.co.uk
Managing partner and partner in charge of clinical negligence department.
Specialisation: All areas of clinical negligence and concomitant issues of public and legal policy. The treatment of children has become a centre of excellence, with a long history of cerebral palsy and anaesthetics cases. To this expertise has been added work with criminal law aspects (representing families of Beverly Allitt's victims), and wider issues including the conduct of inquests (for example, into the death of Robert Benton) and inquiries (for example, into the death of Nicholas Geldard). More recently involved in representing over 100 relatives of 55 victims of the serial killer Dr Harold Shipman. The practice represents families of victims of BSE/CJD, and is involved in a number of high profile multiparty actions including the MMR/MR vaccination. It also acts for patients suffering harmful consequences following their treatment with LSD. Ann contributes regularly to television news and current affairs programmes, is an expert frequently consulted by radio reporters and producers, and has been extensively quoted in the press. Lectures on medical negligence issues to legal and medical audiences, and is a visiting Fellow at the Department of Journalism Studies, University of Sheffield.
Prof. Memberships: Law Society, AVMA, ATLA (Member of Executive Committee Birth Trauma Litigation Group), assessor to Law Society Specialist Medical Negligence Panel. Member of Editorial Board of Health Care Risk Report.
Career: Qualified in 1978 and then became co-founder of *Alexander Harris* in May 1989. First practice in this country specialising exclusively in clinical negligence and pharmaceutical product liability. The practice also has a specialist personal injury department.
Personal: Born 5th November 1954. Attended University College, London (LL.B 1974), Nottingham Law School 1997 (MBA). Lives in Altrincham, Cheshire.

ANNANDALE, Richard H
Bevan Ashford, Bristol (0117) 923 0111
Specialisation: Partner in the health and social care group specialising in clinical litigation, medical law and risk management, particularly for hospitals with acute services. He handled a large number of compensation claims arising from a serious and widely publicised radiotherapy incident and succeeded in reaching over 100 settlements without a single writ being issued by using a novel method of mediation. He is now involved in a high profile series of claims arising from the breast screening programme and with nationally sensitive issues relating to the retention of childrens' organs.
Career: Qualified 1977. Partner since 1993. Director of QRM Healthcare Limited (*Bevan Ashford's* healthcare risk management company) since 1993.
Personal: Educated at Manchester University (LL.B) 1968-71.

BALEN, Paul
Freethcartwright, Nottingham (0115) 9369 369
paul.balen@freethcartwright.co.uk
Offices also at Derby and Leicester Partner in Civil Litigation Department.
Specialisation: Main areas of practice are medical negligence and product liability. Acts in claims for compensation arising from accidents of all types, co-ordination of group actions and medical negligence claims. Acted in Benzodiazepine litigation and the Allitt victims parents cases and is co-ordinating the MMR, 3M hip and breast implant claims. Editorial board member of Health Care Risk Bulletin. Lecturer on medico-legal matters to doctors and lawyers. Is a Radio Nottingham phone-in 'Legal Eagle'. Co-author of Multi-Party Actions (LAG 1995).
Prof. Memberships: Law Society (Personal Injury Specialist Panel and Medical Negligence Specialist Panel assessor) National Secretary of APIL 1998-2000; Referral Solicitor for AVMA. Member of ATLA, APILA.
Career: Joined *Freeth Cartwright* in 1975. Qualified in 1977. Partner 1980.
Personal: Born 25 February 1952. Attended Nottingham High School 1960-71, then Cambridge University 1971-74.

BANNISTER, Richard
Challinors Lyon Clark, Birmingham (0121) 212 9393

BARBER, Janice C.
Hempsons, London (020) 7836 0011
jcb@hempsons.co.uk
See under Healthcare, p.

BARBER, Paul H
Bevan Ashford, Bristol (0117) 923 0111
See under Healthcare, p.

BARCAN, Richard
Barcan Woodward, Bristol (0117) 925 8080

BARTON, Grainne
Alexander Harris, London (020) 7430 5555
grainnebarton@alexharris.co.uk
Partner and head of medical negligence department, London.
Specialisation: Handles exclusively claimant medical negligence matters and is renowned for her commitment, energy and enthusiasm in this area of the law. Main areas of practice are cerebral palsy, anaesthetic awareness, cancer, keyhole surgery and dental matters. Acted in Tredget v. Bexley Health Authority (nervous shock) in 1994 and Smyth v. Riverside Health Authority (malaria case) in 1993.
Prof. Memberships: APIL, AVMA, Law Society, Medical Negligence Panel.
Career: With *Boyes Turner & Burrows* 1987-90. Qualified in 1989. Joined *Pritchard Englefield* in 1990 and became a partner in 1993. Joined *Alexander Harris* as partner April 1999.
Personal: Born 8th October 1963. Educated at Brunel University 1982-86. Past Honorary Secretary of TSG. Lives in Epsom, Surrey.

BATCHELOR, Claire
George Davies, Manchester (0161) 236 8992
Partner and head of healthcare/clinical negligence department.
Specialisation: Specialises in defendant healthcare related law advising Health Authorities and NHS Trusts. Principal area of work is in the field of clinical negligence handling a wide spectrum of claims including complex high value obstetric and neurosurgical claims. Work also involves all areas of NHS advisory work including administrative law, representation at inquests and advice on risk management strategies.
Prof. Memberships: Law Society and Manchester Medico-Legal Society.
Career: Joined *George Davies* in 1985. Qualified in 1987 and became a Partner in 1991. Deputy District Judge.
Personal: Educated at Manchester High School for Girls. Bristol University 1980-83 LLB. Trinity Hall Cambridge 1983-84 LLM. Leisure interests include the arts, walking and yoga. Lives in Altrincham, Cheshire.

BATTEN, Elizabeth
Parlett Kent, London (020) 7430 0712
Specialisation: Clinical negligence specialist since 1991. Particular interest in oncology, brain injury, accident and emergency cases and in psychiatric negligence, also negligence and abuse of people with learning disabilities. Reported case of 'Mahmood v. Siggins'. Has lectured to lawyers and health professionals on clinical negligence and related topics.
Prof. Memberships: Law Society. Law Society Medical Negligence panel. AVMA referral panel member. APIL member.
Career: Admitted 1977. Partner in *Parlett Kent* from 1993. BA (Cantab) in Economics.

BLEWITT, Tom
Mincoffs, Newcastle-upon-Tyne (0191) 281 6151
Specialisation: Clinical negligence, high value personal injury–Swales v. Newcastle Health Authority–failed sterilisation–probably the last such case before the House of Lords decision in McFarlane v. Tayside Health. Mrs Swales recovered £80,250–not appealed.
Prof. Memberships: Law Society, API:, AVMA, Law Society Personal Injury Panel and Clinical Negligence Panel. Member of Headway Personal Injury Panel.
Career: Qualified 1982. Assistant solicitor with *Mincoffs*, equity partner 1984. Part-time chairman of the Social security Appeals Service.
Publications: Various articles over the years.
Personal: Boys grammar school Gateshead, Newcastle-upon-Tyne Polytechnic. Interests include contemporary guitar music, red wine.

BODY, David
Irwin Mitchell, Sheffield (0114) 276 7777
Bodyd@irwinmitchel.co.uk
Partner in Personal Injury Department. Head of Clinical Negligence Team.
Specialisation: Main area of practice is medical negligence on behalf of plaintiffs. Acted in Maynard v West Midlands RHA; Davis v City and Hackney Health Authority; Aboul-Hosn v Governors of National Hospital for Nervous Diseases, Bolitho v City and Hackney Health Authority, Hopkins v McKenzie, Fisher v North Derbyshire Health Authority and the Creutzfeldt-Jacob Disease Litigation. Represented all the variant CJD victims' families at the BSE Inquiry 1998-2000. Author of chapter on

'The Conduct of Proceedings' in Powers & Harris 'Medical Negligence' (all editions). Lectures regularly to both doctors and lawyers. Chair of Medical Negligence Special Interest Group of APIL (1992-95).
Prof. Memberships: APIL, AVMA, ATLA (on ATLA Birth Trauma Litigation Group).
Career: Qualified in 1981. Worked at *Halls* 1981-91, from 1984 as a Partner. Joined *Irwin Mitchell* in 1991 as a Partner.
Personal: Born 1st August 1955. Attended Hereford High School and Corpus Christi College, Oxford (BA Hons, 1976). Leisure interests include taking blurred photographs and revelling in the revival of the Welsh rugby team. Lives in Sheffield.

BRADBEER, Ronald
Eversheds, Newcastle upon Tyne (0191) 261 1661
bradeer@eversheds.com
See under Alternative Dispute Resolution, p.81

BRIGGS, Christopher
Hempsons, Manchester (0161) 228 0011
cjb@hempsons.co.uk
Specialisation: Defence of healthcare professionals on behalf of the Medical Defence Union,Trusts and Health Authorities. Clinical negligence, defence of serious crime (manslaughter, indecent assault, fraud). Advice on consent issues. Advice and representation at various tribunals, including GMC, GDC, Inquest, Misuse of Drugs Tribunal. Particular interest in Judicial Review of resource-based decisions in the NHS. Represented four Health Authorities in the successful defence of the recombinant Factor 8 case.
Prof. Memberships: Law Society. Member of the Board of Clinical Practice of the Institute of Medicine Law and Bioethics at the University of Manchester.
Career: Articles Herbert and Gowers, Oxford. Qualified 1987. Joined Hempsons 1987. Partner 1995.
Publications: Chapter in 'Medicolegal Reporting in Orthopaedic Trauma' (co-author).
Personal: Educated Bishops Stortford College 1971–1981 Manchester University (1981-1984) LLB.Hons. Chairman St Anselm Hall Association, University of Manchester. Interests: Sport (hockey, cricket).

BROADHEAD, Jill F.H.
Bevan Ashford, Bristol (0117) 923 0111
See under Healthcare, p.429

CAHILL, Julia
Kingsley Napley, London (020) 7814 1200
Specialisation: Partner and specialist in medical negligence and professional negligence litigation. Cases mainly involve serious disability or death. Advises on inquests into death during medical care. Particular expertise in obstetric negligence claims on behalf of mother and child. Special interest in delayed diagnosis of meningitis in children and delayed diagnosis in adults of cervical cancer, bowel cancer and breast cancer. Practice also covers legal negligence involving the pursuit of claims against legal advisers in medical negligence cases. Interesting recent cases include 'McAllister v. Lewisham and North Southwark Health Authority' [1994] MEDLR. 'Davis v. Jacobs, Camden & Islington Health Authority & Novartis Pharmaceuticals (UK) Ltd' [1999] Lloyds Law Reports 72.
Prof. Memberships: Law Society Panel of Specialist Medical Negligence Solicitors; AVMA Lawyers Referral Panel; Member APIL, APLA, ATLA. Secretary to the APIL Medical Negligence Special Interest Group 1998/99. CEDR Accredited Mediator.
Career: DIP Physiotherapy 1976. Qualified LL.B 1980. Assistant Director, Action for Victims of Medical Accidents 1984-1988. Partner *Parlett Kent & Co* 1992-1994. Joined *Kingsley Napley* as Partner in September 1994.
Personal: Two children. Lives in Islington, London.

CARR, Robert
Anderson Strathern WS, Edinburgh
(0131) 220 2345
Partner in litigation department. Accredited by the Law Society of Scotland as a medical negligence specialist and admitted as a solicitor/advocate with extended rights of audience in the higher Scottish civil courts.
Specialisation: Almost 20 years of practice in civil litigation, covering all areas of court and tribunal work. One of a team involved in advising insurers, particularly in personal injuries and related actions, and in advising the Royal College of Nursing as their appointed Scottish agents. The RCN instructions cover the full spectrum of criminal and civil court work and employment law matters, including frequent advice on medical negligence issues and regular appearance at fatal accident enquiries. Also speaks and lectures to insurers, nurses and doctors on many aspects of civil law and court procedure and practice. Head of the fim's parliamentary and public affairs unit and assisted the Royal College of Nursing in its evidence before the Scottish parliament on the Adults with an Incapacity Bill. Represented the Denholm family at the recent much publicised fatal accident inquiry in relation to the death of Darren Denholm who died while undergoing dental surgery under general anaesthetic resulting in a finding that dental surgery under general anaesthetic should no longer be conducted outwith a hospital setting. *Anderson Strathern* dealt with the case of Richard Adamson, one of the first medical negligence actions in Scotland to proceed before a jury for almost 50 years resulting in an award for pain and suffering of £100,000 for a young man whose only testicle was negligently removed by doctors at a hospital in West Lothian. Has also been pioneering in Scotland damages for children who have suffered disability as a consequence of their mothers undergoing anticonvulsant therapy whilst pregnant.

CASTLE, Nicola
Alexander Harris, Altrincham (0161) 925 5555
nickycastle@alexharris.co.uk
Specialisation: Principal area of practice is clinical negligence on behalf of Claimants. Specialises in substantial claims involving injury from birth trauma, cerebral palsy and serious head injury. Acted in 'Mansell v. Pembrokeshire Health Authority'; 'Murphy v. Wirral Health Authority', 'Wiszniewski v. Central Manchester Health Authority' and 'Stephens v. Doncaster Health Authority'. Responsible for the first structured settlement involving a medical protection society.
Prof. Memberships: The Law Society and member of the Medical Negligence Panel.
Career: Joined *Alexander Harris* in 1991 and qualified in 1993. Made partner in 1998.
Personal: Born 15th October 1968. Attended Manchester Metropolitan University (LLB 2:1). Nottingham Law School 1999 (LL.M. Distinction)

CHAPMAN, John
Mills & Reeve, Norwich (01603) 693 380
john.chapman@mills-reeve.com
Specialisation: Partner specialising in medical negligence defence.
Career: Articled *Daynes Chittock & Back*; qualified 1976; partner *Eversheds Daynes Hill & Perks* 1979; member of *Eversheds*' board of management; Head of Litigation Department 1996; joined *Mills & Reeve* April 1999 as partner in medical negligence team.
Personal: Amateur dramatics, vintage farm machinery, gardening, classic cars.

CURRAN, Angela
Watson Burton, Newcastle upon Tyne
(0191) 244 4444
Specialisation: Acts for claimants in all types of medical negligence cases. Special interest in obstetric cases. Accredited and experienced mediator; involved in the NHSLA clinical negligence mediation pilot scheme.
Prof. Memberships: Member of the Law Society Personal Injury and Medical Negligence Panels. AVMA, APIL and ADR Net.
Career: Joined *Watson Burton* 1992 as articled clerk. Associate 1998. Head of Medical Negligence Unit.
Personal: Educated at Newcastle University (BSC 1983) and College of Law, York. Native of Newcastle. Leisure time devoted to family, gardening and wine.

DAVIES, Andrew K.
Hugh James Ford Simey, Bargoed (01443) 822022
andrew.davies@hjfs.co.uk
Partner and Head of Clinical Negligence Group.
Specialisation: His experience in medical negligence work includes obsteric negligence involving injuries of the utmost severity such as brain damage. His work has a broad spectrum however and involves a substantial number of orthapaedic medical negligence cases.
Career: Qualified 1988. Partner 1994.
Prof. Memberships: One of only a handful of solicitors in Wales on the Law Society's Medical Negligence Panel, and is also a member of the Law Society's Personal Injury Panel and the AVMA Solicitors Referral Panel.

DESMOND, Adrian
Boyes Turner & Burrows, Reading
(0118) 959 7711
adesmond@b-t-b.co.uk
Head of clinical negligence and personal injury.
Specialisation: Acts for claimants in all types of clinical accident and personal injury cases with special interest in cases of maximum severity, brain, spinal, obstetric and paediatric injury. Has acted in many high profile and reported cases. AVMA referral solicitor since 1984. Assessor to and member of Law Society specialist medical negligence panel since formed in 1995. Secretary then co-ordinator of medical negligence special interest group of the Association of Personal Injury Lawyers. Founding member of Richard Grand Society. Author of legal and medical articles on issues related to medical negligence. Deputy Taxing Master Supreme Court Taxing Office 1994-98. Spinal Injuries Association and Headway Panel Solicitor.
Prof. Memberships: AVMA, APIL, SIA, Headway, ATLA, European Brain Injury Society, Richard Grand Society.
Career: Qualified and joined *Boyes Turner & Burrows* in 1980.

DONALD OBE, Hugh R.
Shepherd & Wedderburn WS, Edinburgh
(0131) 228 9900
hugh.donald@shepwedd.co.uk
Partner.
Specialisation: Specialist in medical negligence, representing doctors and dentists in civil claims, inquiries and disciplinary proceedings. Lecturer at a number of conferences on medico-legal subjects. Also aviation representing airline and helicopter operators in both civil claims and accident inquiries.
Career: Qualified in 1975, having joined *Shepherd & Wedderburn WS* in 1973. Became a partner in 1977. Administrative head of litigation department 1990-94. Appointed managing partner in April 1994, and chief executive from April 1995–April 1999.
Personal: Born 5th November 1951. Educated at Edinburgh University. Family Mediator. Chairman, Family Mediation Scotland. Leisure interests include gardening, walking and church. Lives in Edinburgh. Awarded OBE for services to family mediation in Scotland.

DYBALL, John
Scrivenger Seabrook, St. Neots (01480) 214900
Specialisation: Defendant medical negligence with particular interest in respect of quantum and/or structural settlements.
Prof. Memberships: Law Society, Fellow of Institute of Legal Executives.
Career: Legal Executive Trent regional Health Authority 1987-1989. Assistant solicitor *Oxley and Coward* Sheffield 1989-1995. Associate solicitor *Wansborough Willey Hargrave* 1995-1996. Partner *Scrivenger Seabrook* January 1997 to date. Member of NHSLA Clinical Negligence Panel.
Publications: Dyball/Simons-model for fast track medical negligence litigation. 'The Litigator' 1996. Assisted Lord Woolf working party in response of medical negligence.
Personal: Born July 1956. Lives Cambs.

ENGLAND, Richard P.B.
John Hodge & Co, Bristol (0117) 929 2281

FAZAN, Claire
Bindman & Partners, London (020) 7833 4433
Partner in charge of personal injury and clinical negligence department.
Specialisation: Clinical negligence litigation on behalf of claimants. Experienced in claims involving all types of injury. Extensive experience of claims on behalf of adults and children who have suffered brain and spinal cord injury and other permanent and severe disabilities including those arising from obstetric and anaesthetic care and failure to diagnose, for example, subarachnoid haemorrhage and cancer. Has regularly recovered awards in excess of £1 million. Major cases since 01.01.00 include Parkin & Parkin v. Bromley Hospitals NHS Trust and Miles v. Redbridge & Waltham Forest Health Authority. Advises in relation to inquests into deaths during medical care. Experience in respect of provision and refusal of treatment. Advises under the Legal Aid Scheme. Co-author of 'Medical Negligence Litigation: A Practitioners Guide', by Irwin, Fazan & Allfrey [published by LAG] and contributor to 'The Medical Accidents Handbook'. Frequently writes and lectures on clinical negligence litigation and associated topics. She is a CEDR accredited mediator.
Prof. Memberships: Law Society Medical Negligence Panel. Association of Personal Injury Lawyers, AVMA. Lawyers Referral Panel.
Career: Qualified in 1985. Joined *Bindman & Partners* in 1987 and became a partner in 1989.

FERGUSON, Gerry M.
Withy King, Bath (01225) 425731
gerry.ferguson@withyking.co.uk
Specialisation: Partner specialising in medical negligence and product liability claims for plaintiffs, including benzodiazepine/breast implant multi party litigation. Experience of high value claims, cerebral palsy, paraplegia, and psychiatric negligence cases.
Prof. Memberships: Law Society (Personal Injury Specialist Panel /Clinical Negligence Specialist Panel), APIL, ATLA, APLA and AVMA (panel member). Legal Services Commission Funding Review Committee. Bath and North East Somerset Racial Equality Council, Clinical Society of Bath, MIND Legal Network.
Career: Involved in medical negligence litigation since 1981. Joined *Withy King* in 1989. Legal Services Commission Franchise Coordinator–Bath area.
Personal: Born 23.7.53. Education: Epsom College; Birmingham University. Married with two sons. Lives in Bath. Leisure interests: Motor sport photography.

FOLLIS, Richard T.
Irwin Mitchell, Birmingham (0121) 212 1828
follisr@irwinmitchell.co.uk
Partner heading claimant clinical negligence team in Birmingham.
Specialisation: Handles claimant only medical negligence litigation with a substantial proportion of legally aided work. Involved in medical negligence claims since 1979. Now heads a group of 6 solicitors and 3 SRNs and support staff dealing with all types of clinical negligence claims, including obstetric, orthopaedic, psychiatric, oncological, gynaecological, ophthalmological, general surgical and GP liability. Provides representation at inquests. Member of Medico-Legal Training Services Panel. Lectures regularly to both Doctors and Lawyers on medico-legal matters.
Prof. Memberships: Law Society, Council Birmingham Law Society, Council Birmingham Medico-Legal Society, AVMA Lawyers Support Group. Chairman AVMA Midlands LSG. Hon. Part-time tutor department of Bio-medical ethics, University of Birmingham. Member of Law Society and AVMA referral clinical negligence panels. Legal Services commission funding Review Committee.
Career: Qualified in 1981. Became a Partner, Irwin Mitchell 1999.
Personal: Educated Halesowen Grammar School 1968-74. University College, Cardiff 1976-79. Lives in Worcestershire.

GADSBY, Gillian
Gadsby Wicks, Chelmsford (01245) 494929
Partner dealing with medical negligence and medical product liability.
Specialisation: Principal area of practice is medical negligence. Acts exclusively for plaintiffs and has specialised in medical negligence since qualification. Particular specialisation in women's health issues. Other main area of practice is medical product liability. Has handled a number of cases involving products affecting women, including the oral contraceptive pill, copper 7 IUD and tampon induced toxic shock syndrome, both here and in the USA. Article 'Special issues facing women in medical negligence' published in *AVMA Journal* in 1992. Extensive radio and broadcasting experience on national and local TV and radio, including Radio 1 and GMTV.
Prof. Memberships: Association of Personal Injury Lawyers (APIL), Association of Trial Lawyers of America.
Career: Qualified in 1989. Established *Gadsby Wicks* in 1993.
Personal: Born 15th November 1965. Educated at the University of East Anglia 1983-86 (LL.B Hons). Leisure activities include skiing and following Luton Town F.C. Lives in Chelmsford.

GIBBONS, Anthony
Hill Dickinson, Liverpool (0151) 236 5400
Partner in Health Department.
Specialisation: Principal areas of practice are medical negligence, employment law and NHS advisory work. Handles a large volume of medical negligence cases, particularly brain damage cases of high value. Another significant element of work involves NHS property transactions acting on behalf of major NHS clients in the disposal of surplus property and in particular redundant hospitals. Important cases handled include Booth v Warrington Health Authority (disclosure of witness statements referred to in experts reports), Ashcroft v Mersey Regional Health Authority (standard of care of consultants in medical negligence cases) and O'Toole v Liverpool Health Authority (first self-funded structural settlement case in the medical negligence field). Major clients include North West Regional Health Authority and all NHS trusts in Cheshire and Merseyside. Has given lectures to various NHS clients. Participated as a presenter in Liverpool Law Society course on medical negligence.
Prof. Memberships: Law Society.
Career: Qualified in 1972. Former in-house Legal Adviser with Mersey RHA 1980-90. Joined *Hill Dickinson* as a Partner in 1990. Presently a Partner *Hill Dickinson.*
Personal: Born 10th October 1947. Educated at Xaverian College, Manchester 1959-66 and Nottingham University 1966-69 (Nottingham Co-operative Society Prize 1968, Hill Prize 1969). Leisure pursuits include food, wine and watching sport. Lives in Chester.

GOLDBURN, Tim
Preston Goldburn, Falmouth (01326) 318900
Tim.Goldburn@btinternet.com
Specialisation: Claimant's clinical negligence claims with particular emphasis on gynaecological and urological injuries. Based in the Falmouth Business Park, in an office with diabled access, facilities and equipment, and have a fully qualified nurse on the team.
Prof. Memberships: APIL, The Law Society Clinical Negligence panel, and also the Co-ordinator for the AVMA South west Lawyers Support Group.
Career: Admitted in 1977, articled at *Ince & Co*, post qualification experience at *Richards Butler* before joining *Stephens & Scown* in St Austell in 1979–leaving to set up in partnership in *Preston Goldburn* specialising in personal injury and clinical negligence claims in 1982.
Personal: Enjoys SCUBA diving and sailing.

GRIFFITHS, John
Shepherd & Wedderburn WS, Edinburgh
(0131) 228 9900
john.griffiths@shepwedd.co.uk
Partner.
Specialisation: Main area of practice is medical negligence: previously Solicitor at the Central Legal

Office for the Scottish Hospital Service, advising and acting for the fifteen Scottish Health Boards. With present firm, acts for a leading Medical Defence organisation. Chairman of Law Society Panel to certify solicitors with specialist experience in medical negligence work. Has been responsible for the conduct of litigation in the Scottish Supreme Court, the Court of Session, House of Lords and Sheriff Courts all over Scotland. Has specialist interest in representing parties at Fatal Accident Inquires and advising generally on all aspects of work relating to medical negligence and the National Health Service. Is engaged at any one time in an average of 300 claims, litigations or contentious matters relating to medical or dental negligence. Also advises on administrative and management structure of the NHS and on employment law with a particular emphasis on disciplinary cases against doctors and dentists with regular appearances before the GMC anbd GDC. Accredited specialist by the Law Society of Scotland. Has spoken and chaired conferences on medical negligence frequently. Author of a number of chapters in a textbook edited by Sir Michael Drury 'Clinical Negligence in General Practice' Radcliff Medical Press Ltd.
Prof. Memberships: Law Society of Scotland.
Career: Qualified in 1971. Trainee at *Shepherd & Wedderburn WS* and *MacAndrew Wright and Murray WS* 1969-71. Joined Central Legal Office for National Health Service in Scotland in 1972, becoming Chief Assistant Solicitor in 1984 and Acting Legal Adviser 1988-89. Joined *Simpson & Marwick WS* as Partner in 1989. *Shepherd & Wedderburn* May 2000.
Personal: Born 16th September 1944. Attended Edinburgh Academy; Wadham College, Oxford 1962-65 and Edinburgh University 1967-69. Lives in Edinburgh.

HALL, Antony
Anthony Collins Solicitors, Birmingham (0121) 200 3242
Specialisation: Acts for both legally aided and privately funded claimants or under conditional fee agreements in all aspects of medical and personal injury litigation, but especially obstetric, GP, cancer misdiagnosis, orthopaedic and brain damage claims. Expertise in medical ethics claims including those involving refusal of consent to treatment.
Prof. Memberships: Law Society Medical Negligence Panel, Referral panel solicitor for Action for Victims of Medical Accidents (AVMA), Law Society Personal Injury Panel, member of Medical Negligence Special Interest Group of Association of Personal Injury Lawyers, Clinical Negligence Specialist Member of Legal Aid Board Committee, member of Birmingham Medico-Legal Society.
Career: Qualified 1986. Assistant solicitor with *Anthony Collins* 1986-89. Associate with a Worcestershire law firm 1989-90. West Midlands Regional Health Authority 1990-92. *Anthony Collins* 1992 onwards (Partner since 1994).

HALLATT, Diane
Beachcroft Wansbroughs, Sheffield (0114) 209 5000 dhallatt@bwlaw.co.uk

HARRISON, Frances A.
Hempsons, Manchester (0161) 228 0011 fah@hempsons.co.uk
Partner in Medical & Healthcare Department and Senior Partner in the firm's Manchester office.
Specialisation: Principal area of practice is the law relating to hospitals and general practice. Work includes medico-legal advice to and representation of Health Authorities, NHS Trusts and individual practitioners in medical negligence actions. Advises on ethics in relation to healthcare and also concerning the conduct of and representation at enquiries. Other main areas of practice are defamation and the law relating to children. Major cases include Whitehouse v. Jordan (HL) [1981], McKay v. Essex Area Health Authority (CA) [1982], Wilsher v. Essex Area Health Authority (HL) [1988] and Naylor v. Preston Area Health Authority (CA) [1987]. Lectures and writes widely. Is a member of ethics and risk management committees within the NHS.
Prof. Memberships: Law Society.
Career: Qualified in 1978 and joined *Hempsons*. Became a Partner in 1982. Moved to Manchester in 1990 to lead the firm's Manchester office.

HAY, Katie
Capsticks, London (020) 8780 2211
Partner in clinical law department.
Specialisation: Handles all types of medical negligence litigation for NHS clients. Has a particular interest in larger cases, especially birth injury baby cases. She is an authority on structured settlements having helped to pioneer structures in the health service. She has advised on the drafting of the NHS Executives Guidance on the subject and has had articles published on this and other medico-legal issues. She manages a team of lawyers and is responsible for business process systems in the department.
Prof. Memberships: Law Society, Association of Women Solicitors.
Career: Qualified in 1988 following articles at *Howard Kennedy*. With *Cole & Cole*, Oxford 1988-90. Joined *CAPSTICKS* in 1990. Became a partner in November 1992 and a consultant in July 1996.
Personal: Born 24th January 1964. Educated at Reading Abbey School 1976-82, Oxford Polytechnic (BA Hons in Law with History) 1982-85. Interests include running, reading and cinema. Lives in London.

HOLMES, John
Beachcroft Wansbroughs, London (020) 7242 1011 jholmes@bwlaw.co.uk
Partner in health law group.
Specialisation: Principal area of practice is medical negligence acting for health service bodies in defence claims. Also gives general advice in clinical issues (including risk management), mental health and staff claims. Reported claims include Burton v. Islington Health Authority, Sion v. Hampstead Health Authority, Clunis v. Camden & Islington Health Authority and R v. Bournewood NHS Trust. Acts for Health Service bodies throughout Southern England, mainly in the Thames region, including many major teaching hospitals. The Firm is on the panel for the NHS Litigation Authority (NHSLA).
Prof. Memberships: Law Society.
Career: Qualified in 1984. Joined *Beachcroft Stanleys* in 1986 and became a Partner in 1992.
Personal: Educated at Bristol University 1978-81.

JENKINS, Caroline Helen Clare
Parlett Kent, London (020) 7430 0712
Senior Partner in Personal Injury/Clinical Negligence Department.
Specialisation: Principal area of practice is clinical negligence (claimant PI). Particular interest in gynaecological, oncological, obstetrics and professional negligence cases. Important cases handled include Gascoine v. Sheridan & Co & Latham (MLR Dec 1994), Kirk v S.E. London Health Authority, and Leech v Gloucester Health. Member of Law Society's Medical Negligence Panel from 1995. Author of chapter on Quantum in AVMA Medical Accidents Handbook.
Prof. Memberships: AVMA, APIL, Law Society, ATLA.
Career: Qualified in 1980. Joined *Parlett Kent & Co* in 1982. Became a Partner in 1983. Now Senior Partner.
Personal: King's College, London University (BA, 1975).

JOHN, Simon G.
Cunningham John, Thetford (01842) 752401
Specialisation: Main area of practice is catastrophic injuries. Leads a team of nineteen PI/Clinical Negligence (CN) lawyers and paralegals. Has particular expertise in head, spinal injuries and CN. Notable and landmark cases: Farrant v Thanet D.C. (Diving/tidal pool); Webb (a child) v Darbon (1st Judgement for identifying 30mph too fast); Edwards v Ogg (largest CN award for child £3.9m); Mullings v Breckland DC (1st Judgement for Councils failure to grit); First NHS Mediation; First Structured Settlement in East Anglia; First Order for evidence by Satelite link; largest award for amputee; Many awards in excess of £1m. Responses to a recent client survey included: "I've never had that kind of service from anyone–let alone a solicitor". Considerable experience in litigation in Canada and many US States. Recent awards: $3.5m CN & $2,040m Head Injury. Editor of BPILS Chapter 'PI Litigation in the USA'. Author of 'Plaintiff's Offer to Settle'–resulting in CPR change; Split Trial. Lectures widely.
Prof. Memberships: AVMA, Headway and SIA Solicitor Panels; Law Society CN and PI Panels, Sustaining Member of ATLA, Richard Grand Society, Secretary APIL CLinical Negligence SIG, UKABIF (Treasurer). Fellow of Society for Advanced Legal Studies. European Brain Injury Society.
Career: Qualified 1969, partner 1971, formed *Cunningham John* 1973.

JONES, David
Morgan Jones & Pett, Great Yarmouth (01493) 334700
Specialisation: Clinical Negligence since 1981. Member of Law Society Clinical Negligence Panel since 1995. Special interest in cerebal palsy cases, most recent settlement £1.85 million. Founder member of Norfolk & Norwich Medico-Legal Society.
Prof. Memberships: APIL, AVMA, Headway, SIA, Law Society Clinical Negligence and Personal Injury Panels.
Career: Qualified in 1981, became Partner in 1984.

JONES, Eddie
Jones Maidment Wilson incorporating Hatton Scates Horton, Manchester (0161) 832 8087 eddiej@jmw.co.uk

JONES, Stephen L.
Pannone & Partners, Manchester (0161) 909 3000
Partner in Clinical Negligence Department.
Specialisation: Specialised in Medical Negligence work since qualification. Also covers mental health and has a specific interest in psychiatric negligence, represented patients at Ashworth Hospital in the Fallon Inquiry which reported in January 1999. In

Febuary 2000 appointed solicitor to the Royal Liverpool Childrens inquiry into the retention of organs following postmortems at Alderhey Hospital. Previously a member of Birmingham Royal Orthopaedic Hospital Cancer Cases Co-ordinating Committee.
Prof. Memberships: Member of Law Society Medical Negligence Panel, AVMA Solicitors Referral Panel, MIND Legal Network.
Career: Joined *Pannone & Partners* in 1984, qualified in 1986 and became a Partner in 1992.
Personal: Educated at Manchester Grammar School and Queens College, Cambridge. Leisure interests include football.

JORDAN, Lisa
Irwin Mitchell, Birmingham (0121) 200 3343
Specialisation: Partner in clinical negligence team in Birmingham. Handles claimant only clinical negligence litigation with particular expertise in birth trauma cases. As well as legally aided clients, Also does pro-bono work. Significant experience in representing clients at inquests. Regular lecturer on the medico-legal circuit.
Prof. Memberships: From a political family and is the secretary of the West Midlands Labour Lawyers. Law Society clinical negligence panellist. Member of AVMA and APIL.
Career: Trained at *Robin Thompson & Partners* working for trade union clients. Became partner in previous firm in 1993 and moved to *Irwin Mitchell* as a partner in 1999.
Personal: Educated Shenley Court Comprehensive School, Lancaster University. Lives in Birmingham with her husband and three children.

KING, Stephen
Mills & Reeve, Norwich (0121) 454 4000
stephen.king@mills-reeve.com
Partner in health care team.
Specialisation: Specialises in professional negligence, including medical negligence. Acts for specialist Lloyds underwriters and also acts for NHS Trusts and Health Authorities, including the NHS Litigation Authority, advising on claims made against them for damages. Also covers mental health law, coroners' inquests, drug trials, and acts as client partner for health care clients. Has acted in many self-funded structured settlements financing the payment of substantial damages in brain damage cases. Regular lecturer to hospitals on health care law, negligence, risk management and awareness and claims management. Editorial Board Member of Health Care Risk Report (Eclipse Publications), Personal Injury Journal (John Wiley Publications).

KITCHINGMAN, John Michael
Pannone & Partners, Manchester (0161) 909 3000
Partner in Clinical Negligence Department.
Specialisation: Head of department, dealing with all aspects of plaintiff medical litigation for victims of medical accidents with emphasis on cases of maximum severity.
Prof. Memberships: Law Society Medical Negligence panel, AVMA referral panel, APIL Medical Negligence Special Interest Group, ATLA.
Career: Qualified in 1975, became partner in *Pannone & Partners* 1978.
Personal: Fellow of RSA. Leisure pursuits include walking, birdwatching, and travel. Lives in Altrincham.

KNOWLES, Stuart
Mills & Reeve, Birmingham (0121) 456 8204
stuart.knowles@mills-reeve.com
Specialisation: Medical Negligence, especially claims of utmost severity and neurological injuries. Successfully defended Parker v North Staffordshire Health Authority, Sherlock v Birmingham Health Authority to the Court of Appeal. Defending group action against Birmingham Health Authority following bone tumour misdiagnosis. Also expert on Patient Confidentiality and Consent to Treatment, Medical Ethics, Inquests and Personal Injury.
Prof. Memberships: The Law Society. Birmingham Medico – Legal Society.
Career: Oxford graduate who qualified in 1986. Joined West Midlands RHA in 1988 to specialise in clinical negligence. Partner in *The Lewington Partnership* 1995. Partner with *Mills & Reeve* following the merger with *The Lewington Partnership* in November 1998. Regular contributor to medical journals and lectures to health care professionals.
Personal: Hobbies: Travel, motorcycling, radio and diving.

LANG, Jane
Bevan Ashford, Cardiff (029) 2046 2562
j.lang@bevanashford.c.uk
Specialisation: Main areas of practice are clinical negligence, personal injury and general advisory work for the NHS in Wales. Broad range of clinical negligence cases. Lectures frequently to managers and clinicians on medical negligence, the Woolf reforms and NHS matter. Also provides advice to NHS staff on child protection issues.
Prof. Memberships: Wales Medico-Legal Society. Swansea Medico-Legal Society. Welsh Personal Injury Lawyers Association.
Career: Qualified 1991. Joined *Bevan Ashford* in 1996. Associate since 1997.
Publications: Medico-legal issues in telemedicine –'Medical Law'.
Personal: University of Exeter (LL.B Hons 1988).

LEE, Terry
Evill and Coleman, London (020) 8789 9221
evill@globalnet.co.uk
Partner of personal injury department.
Specialisation: Main areas of practice are catastrophic injuries, clinical negligence, particularly brain damage at birth, head injuries, multiple injuries, fatal accident claims and Court of Protection work. Has been involved in a number of significant actions including Brown v. Merton & Sutton Health Authority, Head v. East Anglia Health Authority, Hall v. Pirie and Lambert v. Devon County Council. A further important case, Joyce v. Wandsworth Health Authority, provided clarification of the judicial approach to causation in a clinical neglignce case. Recently was involved in the well known sporting injury case which was the first of its kind brought against a rugby referee and which was successful. This was the case of Smoldon v. Whitworth & Nolan. Further, the case of Dudley v. East Dorset Health Authority is an important case relating to the removal of a litigation friend in an application that was contested. Some of the actions conducted include cases where damages well in excess of £2,500,000 have been awarded. Has also been instrumental in dealing with a number of cases which involve the formation of a structured settlement. Is an assessor to the Personal Injury Panel as well as a member of the Personal Injury Panel of Solicitors. Is also a member of the Medical Negligence Specialist Panel of Solicitors. Author of articles for legal magazines and a book on dealing with cases involving catastrophic injuries. Lectures extensively at conferences and seminars. Is also a referral solicitor to various organisations including AVMA, Spinal Injuries Association, Headway etc.
Prof. Memberships: Member of the Association of Personal Injury Lawyers, British Academy of Forensic Science and the Environmental Law Foundation.
Career: Qualified and joined *Evill & Coleman* in 1972. Became a partner in 1976.
Personal: Born 14th August 1945. Educated at Wimbledon College. Recreations include golf and tennis. Lives in Esher, Surrey.

LEIGH, Bertie
Hempsons, London (020) 7836 0011
mamsl@hempsons.co.uk
See under Healthcare, p.430

LEIGH, Sarah
Leigh, Day & Co, London (020) 7650 1200
Partner in medical negligence department.
Specialisation: Handles primarily major medical negligence cases involving severe disability and death and cases involving mental handicap problems (e.g. Re F in 1989–a leading case on consent in mental handicap). Has spoken at many conferences and seminars and written several articles.
Prof. Memberships: AVMA, Justice, APIL.
Career: Qualified in 1971. Founder partner (1974) of *Bindman & Partner*. Left to set up own firm in 1985 (renamed *Leigh Day & Co* in 1988).
Personal: Born 29th July 1942. Trustee of Immigrants Aid Trust. Campaigner for changes in medical negligence litigation system..

LEVY, Russell
Leigh, Day & Co, London (020) 7650 1200
Partner in medical negligence department.
Specialisation: Principal area of practice is plaintiff medical negligence and medical devices (product liability) litigation. Has written numerous articles for various specialist publications and is a regular speaker on medical negligence topics.
Prof. Memberships: AVMA. Secretary and then Co-ordinator of APIL Medical Negligence Special Interest Group 1992-1996. Member of APIL Executive Committee 1996-99. Member Lord Chancellor's Department Medical Negligence Working Party, Council member of Campaign for Freedom of Information, member Steering Group UK Collaborative Network of Cerebral Palsy Registers. ATLA.
Career: Qualified 1984. Joined *Leigh Day & Co* as a partner in 1991.
Personal: Born 15th March 1956.

LOVEL, John
Hempsons, Harrogate (01423) 522331
wjml@hempsons.co.uk
Specialisation: Medical Negligence. National Health Service Law. Project Leader (Northern and Yorkshire) Department of Health, Clinical Negligence Mediation Pilot.
Prof. Memberships: Law Society.
Career: Shrewsbury School; University College London–LLB Hons 1971; CEDR accredited mediator 1996; Trained at *Sintons* – qualified 1974; Partner at *Maughan & Hall* 1975; Solicitor with Yorkshire Regional Health Authority 1976; Legal Adviser to

Yorkshire Regional Health Authority 1989; Head of Yorkshire Health Legal Services 1990; Partner *Hempsons* 1996.
Personal: Squash, cycling, skiing.

MARSH, Christine
Kingsley Napley, London (020) 7814 1200
Consultant to clinical negligence and personal injury department.
Specialisation: Handles claimant medical negligence. Undertakes Legal Aid work. Emphasis on maximum severity injuries. Has acted in several cases reported in national newspapers. Co-author of 'Fatal Accident Litigation' (Tolley's, 1993). Has lectured and presented seminars. Panel Solicitor on Law Society's Medical Negligence and Personal Injury Panels. AVMA Referral Panel.
Prof. Memberships: APIL, AVMA, Headway, Spinal Injuries Association, Medico-legal Society.
Career: Qualified 1986. Partner at *Bolt Burdon* 1989-92. Joined *Kingsley Napley* as a partner in December 1992, became consultant to *Kingsley Napley* in December 1999.
Personal: Two children. Lives in Oxfordshire. Educated at Royal Latin School, Buckingham 1974-80 and Leicester University 1980-83. Leisure interests include tennis, ski-ing, music and gardening.

MARTINEZ, Liz
Evill and Coleman, London (020) 8789 9221
evill@globalnet.co.uk
Partner.
Specialisation: Specialist in medical negligence. Mediator. Interests include anaesthetic brain damage, cerebral palsy and birth trauma, obstetrics, gynaecology, cardiology, general surgery and fatal cases. Lectures extensively at conferences and seminars.
Prof. Memberships: APIL, Law Society Personal Injury Panel. CEDR Accredited Mediator.
Career: Qualified 1990. *Osborne Morris Morgan* 1988-1993 (Partner from 1991). Yorkshire Health Legal Services 1993-1994. *Evill and Coleman* 1994 (Partner from 1995).

MASON, David
Capsticks, London (020) 8780 2211
Partner in clinical law department.
Specialisation: Principal area of practice is medical negligence with specialisation in obstetrics and neurosurgery cases. Also deals with mental health law. Acted for health authorities in successful defence of a number of reported cases including Moore v Worthing Health Authority, Saad v Mid Surrey Health Authority, Joyce v Merton Sutton and Wandsworth Health Authority, de Martell v Merton Sutton and Wandsworth Health Authority, Muzio v North West Herts Health Authority, Waters v West Sussex HA, Corley v North West Hertfordshire Health Authority, Knight v West Kent HA, Buckingham Smart v NHS Litigation Authority and Thomas and Alayan v Northwick Park NHS Trust. Handles many of the cases in *CAPSTICKS* where court orders are required relating to future medical care, including Re R (adult): Medical Treatment–one of the leading cases on when care can be withheld. Co-author of 'Litigation–A Risk Management Guide for Midwives', published by the Royal College of Midwives, and articles on medical law for specialist publications. Regular lecturer on medical law and risk management topics, especially obstetrics-related. Honorary legal adviser to College of Health. Defence solicitor representative and executive Committee Member of the Clinical Disputes Forum. Co-author of the Pre Action Protocol for the Resolution of Clinical Disputes, and the CDF 'Guidelines on Experts' Discussions in the Context of Clinical Disputes'.
Career: Called to Bar 1984. Employed Barrister with *Thomas Watts & Co* 1986-1988. Joined *CAPSTICKS* in 1988 as employed Barrister. Requalified as Solicitor and became a Partner in 1990. Elected Fellow of the Society for Advanced Legal Studies 1998. Associate member of ATLA since 1998.
Personal: Born 16th October 1955. Attended Winchester College 1969-73, then Oriel College, Oxford 1974-77 (MA in Experimental Psychology). Dip L (City University) 1983. Lives in Wimbledon.

MATHER, Christopher
Penningtons, Basingstoke (01256) 406300
Specialisation: Personal injury and clinical negligence handling claims of utmost severity, including where appropriate structured settlements. Member of Steering committees for the Clapham, Severn Tunnel, Southall and Ladbroke Grove rail crashes. Higher Courts (All Proceedings) Qualification, April 1994. Panel Solicitor Spinal Injuries Association. CEDR accredited mediator.
Prof. Memberships: AVMA, Committee Member of Solicitors Association Higher Courts Advocates. Member of the Law Society Personal Injury Panel.
Career: Qualified in 1973. Joined *Penningtons* in 1994. Assistant Recorder 1991. Recorder 1996. Part time Special Ajudicator (Immigration and Asylum)
Personal: Born 20th June 1947. Attended Ellesmere College and College of Law. Leisure interests include a small holding. Lives in Romsey, Hants.

MAUGHAN, Peter J.
Peter Maughan & Co, Gateshead (0191) 477 9779
Specialisation: Claimant medical negligence and personal injury claims. Visiting lecturer in nursing law to the University of Northumbria at Newcastle.
Prof. Memberships: FCIArb, FSALS, ADR Group, ATLA, APIL, APLA, AVMA.
Career: Principal and Senior Partner of *Peter Maughan & Co* since 1981.
Personal: Liberal Democrat Councillor and Parliamentary and Euro-Parliamentary Candidate. Rotarian. RSPCA Chairman Newcastle. Married, 3 sons. Highlands of Scotland–history and language.

MAYERS, Chris
Bevan Ashford, Cardiff (029) 20462562
c.mayers@bevanashford.co.uk
Specialisation: Principal areas of practice are clinical negligence and NHS advisory matters, with a particular interest in psychiatric claims and mental health issues. In clinical negligence matters he has acted for nearly every NHS Trust in Wales at some stage during his career.
Career: Qualified as a solicitor in 1983. Spent the first five years of his career acting for plaintiffs, most notably the majority of claimants in respect of the outbreak of legionnaires disease in Stafford District Hospital 1985. Deputy Managing Solicitor of Welsh Health Legal Services, in effect, the in-house legal team for the NHS in Wales. In this position he conducted a substantial caseload of medical negligence, personal injury and employment claims involving Welsh NHS Trusts and Health Authorities. Joined *Bevan Ashford* as a partner in the NHS Litigation Department in November 1998. He is an experienced litigator and a regular advocate in Coroners Inquests and frequently lectures NHS staff on a variety of issues.
Personal: Chris was educated at Merchant Taylors' School Crosby and Cardiff University.

MCCLURE, Alison
Blake Lapthorn, Portsmouth (023) 8063 1823
ajmcclure@blakelapthorn.co.uk
Partner in Personal & Medical Injuries Litigation Department.
Specialisation: Specialist in clinical negligence and personal injury litigation. Member of the Law Society Personal Injury Panel and Clinical Negligence Panels. Panel Solicitors for Action for Victims of Medical Accidents. Particular experience in clinical negligence claims of maximum severity, particularly in the areas of obstetric negligence and oncology.
Prof. Memberships: Member of AVMA, APIL, SIA, Headway, member of the Royal Defence Medical College Clinical Research Committee. Lectures on clinical negligence issues, recent publications: 'Clinical Risk'.
Career: Qualified in 1986, having joined *Blake Lapthorn* in 1984. Became a Partner in 1990.
Personal: Educated at Shelley High School, Huddersfield 1974-80 and Southampton University 1980-83.

MCGRATH, Matthew
Beachcroft Wansbroughs, Winchester (01962) 705500
mmcgrath@bwlaw.co.uk
Specialisation: Partner specialising in all aspects of clinical negligence and health service law. Regularly advises clients on issues of consent, confidentiality and access to records. Lectures on risk management issues to clinicians as well as advising on clinical governance. Deals with high-value obstetric claims for a number of trusts and health authorities and is member of the firm's quality control group. Previous extensive experience of insurance and personal injury litigation, both in England and Australia.

MCNEIL, Paul
Field Fisher Waterhouse, London (020) 7861 4000
Specialisation: Partner in the Medical Litigation Department of *Field Fisher Waterhouse* specialising in Clinical Negligence, Personal Injury and Product Liability, acting mainly for Plaintiffs. Has particular experience in cases involving head and other serious injuries. Publications include "International Product Liability" (1993) co-author and "The Medical Accidents Handbook" (1998) co-editor and contributor. Also lectures on various aspects of medical law.
Prof. Memberships: Law Society Medical Negligence Panel; Association of Personal Injury Lawyers; AVMA; Fellow Society for Advanced Legal Studies.
Career: Qualified 1983. *Field Fisher Waterhouse* 1992. Partner since 1994.
Personal: Educated at All Saints' Comprehensive, Huddersfield 1975-1977 and Sheffield University 1977-1980. Leisure pursuits include tennis, running and skiing. Born 26th July 1958. Lives in Putney, London.

MONTGOMERY, Nigel
Beachcroft Wansbroughs, Bristol (0117) 918 2000
Partner and head of clinical negligence litigation in Bristol.
Specialisation: Widely experienced in all areas of clinical litigation and related advisory work. Principal area of case practice is the defence of obstetric and neurology/neuro-surgery claims. Recent advisory work, includes advice on consent issues, responsibility for the funding of care, and product liability advice

in relation to the maintenance of equipment. In addititon acts in the defence of claims for insurers principally in the field of alleged toxic poisoning. Regular contributor to health and insurance publications and frequent speaker at conferences and seminars on medico-legal issues.
Career: Qualified 1985; partner, *Lyons Davidson* 1990-1999, joined *Beachcroft Wansboroughs*May 1999.

MOWAT, Allan R.
Hill Dickinson, Liverpool (0151) 236 5400
Specialisation: Head of Health Department at *Hill Dickinson*, specialising in Health Care Law, particularly medical negligence, nursing home registration and advisory work for NHS bodies. Clients include NHS Trusts and Health Authorities, the NHSLA and healthcare related insurance companies. Successfully defended the NHS in Benzodiazepine class action.
Prof. Memberships: Law Society, Liverpool Law Society.
Career: Qualified in 1980; in house legal advisor to Mersey Regional Health Authority 1982-90; Partner *Hill Dickinson Davis Campbell* 1990; Appointed Head of Health Department at *Hill Dickinson* 1994.

MUSGRAVE, Tim
Huttons, Cardiff (029) 2037 8621
Partner.
Specialisation: Clinical negligence and personal injury, acting for plaintiffs.
Prof. Memberships: AVMA, APIL, Member of Law Society Clinical Negligence and Personal Injury Panels and AVMA Panel.
Career: Qualified in 1987, with *Thomson Snell & Passmore*, Tunbridge Wells, then *Edwards Geldard* in Cardiff 1988-93. Joined *Huttons* in September 1993.
Personal: Born 1st September 1963. Bristol University 1981-84. Lives in Cardiff.

OSBORNE, Thomas R.
Osborne Morris & Morgan, Leighton Buzzard (01525) 378177

OVER, Christopher
Over Taylor Biggs, Exeter (01392) 823811

PARFORD, Simon W.
Wolferstans, Plymouth (01752) 663295
medneg@wolferstans.com
Partner in charge of Clinical Negligence & Head Injury Unit.
Specialisation: Specialising in clinical negligence and head/brain injury claims, particularly those involving injuries at birth.
Prof. Memberships: Law Society Clinical Negligence Panel Assessor. Law Society Clinical Negligence Panel. AVMA Referral Panel. Law Society Personal Injury Panel. APIL.
Career: Qualified with *Wolferstans* in 1983 and became a partner in 1988.
Personal: Born 12 November 1958. Educated Plymouth College and Birmingham Polytechnic. Leisure pursuits include rugby, wine and photography.

POTTER, Hugh
Hugh Potter & Company, Serious Injury Solicitors, Manchester (0161) 237 5888

REED, Derek S.
Woollcombe Beer Watts, Newton Abbot
(01626) 202404
derekreed@wbw.co.uk
Senior partner since 1997.
Specialisation: Principal area of practice involves substantial clinical negligence work including supervising Clinical Negligence Franchise in offices at Torquay and Exeter. Has recently specialised in birth injury and cerebral palsy cases. Also considerable experience in cases involving delayed diagnoses of cancer including Exeter Breast Cancer cases. Has dealt with a substantial number of cases involving obstetrics and gynaecology. Very experienced advocate. Handled numerous substantial cases.
Prof. Memberships: Law Society Clinical Negligence Panel Assessor. Law Society Clinical Negligence Panel member of AVMA Clinical Negligence panel. Regularly sits as Chariman of Legal Services Commission funding review committees.
Career: Qualified in 1971 with *Woollcombe Beer Watts* and became a partner in 1972. Senior partner since 1997.
Personal: Born 8th September 1946. Attended Liverpool University (LLB 1968). School Governor. Leisure pursuits include golf, sport, walking and gardening. Lives in Ipplepen.

ROHDE, Kate
Kingsley Napley, London (020) 7814 1200
Specialisation: Majority of practice is medical negligence and clinical negligence lititgation on behalf of Plaintiffs. Experienced in claims involving all types of injury. Particular interest in obstetric claims and claims on behalf of children. Also handles education litigation.
Prof. Memberships: AVMA, APIL.
Career: Qualified in 1989. With *Compton Carr* 1987 to December 1995, as a partner from 1993. Joined *Teacher Stern Selby* as partner in 1996. Moved to *Kingsley Napley* as a partner in March 1997.
Personal: Born 3rd November 1963, educated at University College London, lives in London.

SCATES, Olivia
Jones Maidment Wilson incorporating Hatton Scates Horton, Manchester (0161) 832 8087
olivias@jmw.co.uk

SCRIVENGER, Mark John
Scrivenger Seabrook, St. Neots (01480) 214900
Founding partner specialising in medical negligence.
Specialisation: Firm was founded to act in clinical negligence and personal injury cases. Individual specialism is defendant clinical negligence. Acted in Royal College of Nursing v. DHSS [1981] AC 800 (House of Lords–instructing solicitor for the RCN). Acts for numerous NHS Trusts and Health Authorities and is a member of the NHSLA clinical negligence panel. Has lectured for many years on law and nursing and NHS topics, and for the Law Society on practice management.
Career: LLB Qualified, Melb (1967), Supreme Court of Victoria 1968 and High Court of Australia 1976. Qualified in England & Wales 1977. Principal solicitor, Royal College of Nursing 1977-87. Founded *Scrivenger Seabrook* in 1988.

SEABROOK, Vicki
Scrivenger Seabrook, St. Neots (01480) 214900
Founding partner in litigation firm.
Specialisation: Has specialised in personal injury since qualification. Later expanded into defendant medical negligence, now acts on behalf of both claimants in personal injury and NHS defendants. Acted in Davis v. Barking Havering and Brentwood Health Authority. Clients include NHS healthcare and community Trusts and Health Authorities. Member of Personal Injury and NHSLA Clinical Negligence Panel.
Career: Qualified in 1979. At the Royal College of Nursing 1979-85, *Merriman & White* 1985-86, *Beachcroft Stanley* 1986-88 and *Le Brasseurs* 1988-89 before establishing *Scrivenger Seabrook*.
Personal: Educated at Barnet College 1970-72 and Central London Polytechnic 1973-76 (LL.B Hons).

SHEATH, John Christopher
Brachers, Maidstone (01622) 690691
Specialisation: Deals principally with clinical negligence and Health Service law. Has had the conduct of successful defence in many high profile decisions including 'Dobbie v. Medway Health Authority', PVS and mental health consent cases.
Prof. Memberships: Kent Medico Legal Society. Member Maidstone Local Research Ethics Committee, Chair West Kent GP Performance Review Panel.
Career: Educated at Sir Joseph Williamson's Mathematical School, Rochester. 1963-69. Southampton University 1970-73. *Norton, Rose, Botterell & Roche* 1974-81. Joined *Brachers* in 1981. Partner 1983. Formed medical negligence department which has expanded since Crown indemnity in January 1990 and appointed to NHSLA panel April 1998. Head of Commercial Litigation Department. Regularly lectures on selected health topics and tutor in Advanced Litigation Practice Diploma.

SHELLENS, Tessa
Morgan Cole, Cardiff (029) 2038 5385
tessa.shellens@morgan-cole.com
Specialisation: Main areas of practice are medical negligence and general NHS advisory work. Has 20 years experience of practice in these areas, with extensive knowledge of advising Health Authorities and Trusts in medical negligence claims, as well as general NHS advisory issues. Also deals with public law, giving general advice to other public bodies in Wales on matters of statutory interpretation and judicial review. Lectures extensively on medical and nursing law throughout England and Wales.
Career: Qualified in 1974. *Bevan Ashford* 1991-2000. Joined *Morgan Cole* May 2000.
Personal: Born 9th May 1949. Attended Southampton University (BA Hons, History 1970).

SLACK, Richard
Eversheds, Newcastle upon Tyne (0191) 261 1661
Specialisation: Medical Negligence; Employment Law; Registration of Nursing Homes.
Prof. Memberships: Law Society.
Career: Upper Second Class Honours Law Degree; Law Society Finals.
Personal: Water sports.

SMITH, Janice
Capsticks, London (020) 8780 2211
Partner in clinical law department.
Specialisation: Principal area of practice is medical negligence with particular interest in cases involving obstetrics, orthopaedics, A&E and cardiology. Coordinates *Capsticks'* clinical governance programme including running training for Trust Boards. Advises Trusts on their risk management arrangements, par-

ticulary helping to identify high risk specialities and develop incident reporting schemes. Regular lecturer on the Open University Diploma in Risk Management and also lectures on various aspects of medical law.
Prof. Memberships: Law Society and its committees concerning issues of medical negligence.
Career: Qualified in 1985. Assistant Solicitor with *Herbert Smith* 1985-86. Assistant solicitor at *Beckman & Beckman* 1987-90. Joined *Capsticks* in 1990 and became a partner in 1991.
Personal: Born 24th March 1960. Attended Tunbridge Wells Grammar School for Girls 1971-78, then Leeds University 1978-81 before taking a year out to work for the Boys Brigade. Vice President of London District Boys' Brigade and Director of Oasis Trust. Lives in Bicester.

SOLLY, Gillian
Russell Jones & Walker, Bristol (0117) 927 3098
g.c.solly@rjw.co.uk
Specialisation: Clinical negligence mainly, although some serious personal injury including Heil v Rankin Court of Appeal: general damages. Otherwise a varied caseload of clinical negligence matters including a £1.7 million CP settlement and several awards over £100,000.
Prof. Memberships: Bristol Law Society, Bristol Medico Legal Society, APIL.
Career: Managing partner Bristol office since 1994. Specialising in clinical negligence and personal injury since 1983. Founder member of APIL and first Treasurer.
Personal: Educated at Beverley High School for Girls followed by Warwick University for Law Degree. Married with two children.

SPEKER, Barry N.
Samuel Phillips & Co, Newcastle upon Tyne (0191) 232 8451
Senior partner and head of litigation department.
Specialisation: Medical negligence, personal injury, family (including child care and adoption) and employment law. Legal adviser for Newcastle Health Authority and various NHS trusts, NSPCC and Barnardo's North East. Regular lecturer on child care law, medical negligence and employment law. Affiliate of Institute of Risk Management.
Prof. Memberships: Law Society (Medical Negligence and Children Panels). President Newcastle Law Society 2000.
Career: Qualified 1971 while with *Leigh Gold & Co*, then joined *Samuel Phillips & Co*. Partner 1973, senior partner 1987. Part time Employment Tribunal Chairman.
Personal: Born 28th June 1947. Heaton Grammar School, London University. Member of Mensa. Leisure pursuits include golf, debating and the Times Crossword.

SUMERLING, Robert W.
Le Brasseur J Tickle, London (020) 7836 0099
rsumerli@lbjt.co.uk
Specialisation: Main area of practice is within the National Health Service with major and varied experience in all fields of health related law. Major experience in clinical negligence defence in NHS cases and previously in individual practioner cases. Wide experience in public enquiry work including the Cleveland Child Abuse Enquiry in 1987 and in professional conduct work including the Bristol Child Heart Surgery GMC Enquiry. Negotiated first NHS bottom up structure in 1996. Particular interests in obstetric casework and mental health law. Frequent lecturer to NHS management and clinical staff. Member of Court of Appeal mediation scheme.
Prof. Memberships: The Law Society. Society for Computers and Law.
Career: Admitted in 1969. Partner in 1975.

SWANTON, Vicki
Browne Jacobson, Nottingham (0115) 976 6000
Specialisation: Associate in medical negligence department. Defends claims on behalf of Health Authorities and Trusts throughout the Midlands. Also has an advisory/training role on clinical risk issues, consent to treat, child protection and the procedure of the Coroner's Court.
Career: Qualified in 1994 and has specialised in medical negligence since that date. Joined *Browne Jacobson* in 1999.

THOMAS, Keith
John Collins & Partners, Swansea (01792) 773773
k.thomas@johncollins.co.uk
Specialisation: Cerebal Palsey
Prof. Memberships: Law Society Clinical Negligence Panel; Law Society Personal Injury Panel; Association of Personal Injury Lawyers; Welsh Personal Injury Lawyers Association.
Career: Qualified 1982. Partner and head of Personal Injury and Clinical Negligemce at *John Collins & Partners* since 1986.
Personal: Education: LLB (Wales). Interests: Sport and all things Welsh.

TYLER, Alfred J.
Balfour & Manson, Edinburgh (0131) 200 1210
ajt@balfour-manson.co.uk
See under Personal Injury, p.647

VALLANCE, Richard A.
Charles Russell, London (020) 7203 5000
richardv@cr-law.co.uk
Partner in Litigation Department.
Specialisation: Began medical negligence work in 1978 with cases concerning children suffering deafness as a result of treatment for burns. Dealt with numerous maternity cases in the early 1980's and was in the forefront of the development of medical negligence litigation from then on. Acted for plaintiffs in the leading cases of Naylor v. Preston Area Health Authority, 1987 2 All ER 353 and Thomas v Brighton HA 1998 3 All ER 481. Has lectured on medical negligence to lawyers, doctors and nurses since about 1984 including LAG/ AVMA seminars and conferences and the Law Society Litigation Conference in Birmingham. Contributed a chapter to Powers and Harris's book 'Medical Negligence' (Butterworths) and has written numerous articles. Has appeared on Legal Network TV.
Prof. Memberships: The Law Society and its Committees concerning issues of medical negligence, AVMA & AVMA Lawyers Support Group, Chairman of APIL Medical Negligence Special Interest Group, Medico-Legal Society.
Career: Qualified in 1970. Partner in *Compton Carr* 1972 and, following merger, in *Charles Russell* 1996 where now Head of Litigation. Assessor of the Law Society Medical Negligence Panel from July 1994. Member of AVMA Specialist Panel. Appointed mediator in Court of Appeal in 1997.
Personal: Born 26th January 1947. Secondary School Governor. Recreations include squash, tennis, reading, opera and theatre. Lives near Saffron Walden.

VICK, Laurence N.
Michelmores, Exeter (01392) 436244

WARD, Trevor
Linder Myers, Manchester (0161) 832 6972
Specialisation: Obstetrics; oncology; general surgery: Jones v Central Manchester HA: CP–2.15M (190 PSL2A). Involved in Group action cases re. failure to diagnose and treat.
Prof. Memberships: AVMA, APIL, Law Society, ATLA, Greystoke.
Career: 1984–*Linder Myers*, Manchester. Predominantly claimant clinical negligence and personal injury.
Publications: Book chapter–'Funding of Claimant Injury Claims'–due for publication in July 2000.
Personal: Manchester Metropolitan University 1981 (Maxwell Law Prize) Qualified October 1986. Married with two daughters. Interests include shooting. Lives in Glossop.

WATSON, Andrew S.
Thomson Snell & Passmore, Tunbridge Wells (01892) 510000
awatson@ts-p.co.uk
Partner and head of personal injury & clinical negligence department.
Specialisation: Deals exclusively with medical negligence and personal injury claims. Special areas of expertise are head and spinal injuries. Acted in Dobbie v. Medway Health Authority, Bova v. Spring, Harris v. Bromley Health Authority and Taylor v. West Kent Health Authority.
Prof. Memberships: A.P.I.L.
Career: Qualified in 1975, having joined *Thomson Snell & Passmore* in 1973. Became a partner in 1981. Legal Aid Area Committee member. Panel solicitor for AVMA. Member of Law Society's Personal Injury Panel. Member of the Law Society's Medical Negligence Panel.
Personal: Born 29 March 1950. Educated at Oxford (MA 1st Class Honours) 1968-71. Recreations include literature, music, running and cuisine. Lives in Tunbridge Wells.

WHITEFIELD, Andrew T.E.
Bevan Ashford, Bristol (0117) 923 0111
Partner in the claims department.
Specialisation: Adviser to Trusts and Health Authorities on legal and ethical issues and clinical risk management. Handles major medical negligence claims, inquests, internal and independent inquiries. Speaker on health law topics, including: the Litigation Culture at the NHS Litigation Authority's conference in Bristol; organised events by the Royal College of Midwives, the Royal College of Nursing and the Royal Society of Medicine. International conferences include Biotechnology, Ethics and Law in 1995; Consent Issues in Philadelphia in 1997; The Mediator's Legal Privilege, Delhi 1999. Lectures regularly to Trusts on Health Law issues and Risk Management.
Prof. Memberships: Law Society. Past President of the Tort Law Commission of the U.I.A. International Association of Lawyers.
Career: Admitted 1968. Joined *Bevan Ashford* 1970; Partner 1972. Fellow of Chartered Institute of Arbitrators. CEDR Accredited Mediator. ADR Group Accredited Mediator.

WICKS, Roger
Gadsby Wicks, Chelmsford (01245) 494929
Specialisation: Specialises in clinical negligence and pharmaceutical and medical products liability claims on behalf of claimants. He is co-ordinating measles vaccine damage cases and was a lead solicitor in connection with the Myodil and Benzodiazepine litigation. Has also litigated claims in relation to Bjork-Shiley heart valves, depo-provera, depomedrone, diethystilbestrol, dymer-x, septrin, copper 7 IUDs, human growth hormone, breast implants, steroids and orthopaedic implants. Chief Assessor to The Law Society's Medical Negligence Specialisation Panel.
Career: Founding partner of *Gadsby Wicks* in 1993.
Prof. Memberships: Law Society, Association of Personal Injury Lawyers; Association of Trial Lawyers of American and the Environmental Law Foundation. Fellow of the Royal Society of Medicine.

WILDER, Gay E.
Browne Jacobson, London (020) 7404 1546
Partner in Medical Negligence Department and Health Law Group.
Specialisation: Principal area of practice is defending medical negligence claims for health service bodies. Also advises on all aspects of care including clinical risk management. Regular contributor of articles to health publications and Editorial Board Member of the 'Medical Law Review'. Frequent speaker at conferences and seminars on medico-legal issues. The Firm is on the panel for the NHS Litigation Authority (NHSLA).
Prof. Memberships: Law Society.
Career: Qualified in 1982. With *Hempsons* 1980-88 (Partner from 1985). Joined *Beachcroft Stanleys* in 1988 and became a Partner in 1989. Joined *Browne Jacobson* 1st July 1999.
Personal: Educated at Reading University 1976-79 (LL.B).

WINYARD, Anne H.
Leigh, Day & Co, London (020) 7650 1200
Specialisation: Partner and specialist in medical negligence. Acts for plaintiffs. Cases mainly involve serious disablities or death, including both adults and children who have suffered brain damage as a result of medical treatment. Publications include chapters in both 'Medical Negligence' (Powers & Harris) and 'Safe Practice in Obstetrics and Gynaecology' (Clements). Regular speaker at medico-legal conferences and seminars.
Prof. Memberships: AVMA, APIL, ATLA.
Career: Qualified 1977. Partner, *Fisher Meredith* 1983-92. Joined *Leigh Day & Co* as partner in 1992.
Personal: Born 1948.

YEAMAN, Anthony George
Beachcroft Wansbroughs, London (020) 7242 1011
tyeaman@bwlaw.co.uk
Partner in health law group.
Specialisation: Principal area of practice is high value and complex medical negligence, handling claims for Health Service bodies and advising on all aspects of Health Service law, particularly issues concerning patient care consent and complaints. Has dealt with multi-party litigation, structured settlements and internal NHS inquiries. Acts for Health Service bodies throughout Southern England, mainly in the Thames region and including many major teaching hospitals. Frequent speaker at conferences and seminars on medico-legal and related issues. The Firm is on the panel for the NHS Litigation Authority (NHSLA).
Career: Qualified in 1988. Assistant Regional Solicitor to former Wessex Regional Health Authority 1988-94. Joined *Beachcroft Stanleys* in 1994.
Personal: Born 11th November 1961. Educated at Middlesex University 1983-85, The College of Law, Guildford 1985-86 and Bournemouth University 1991-99 MBA.

YOUNG, Magi
Parlett Kent, Exeter (01392) 494 455
London (020) 7430 0713
myoung@exeter.parlett.co.uk
Specialisation: Clinical Negligence Specialist with particular expertise in cases of maximum severity (e.g. recent awards in excess of £2 million). Specialises in acting for children injured at or around birth (eg cerebral palsy and Erbs Palsy), for people injured as a result of psychiatric negligence, handles brain injury and spinal injury cases and has particular expertise in obstetric and gynaecology cases and cancer cases. Acts for many people with learning difficulties and has an interest in education and community care provision. Has particular specialism in cases of sexual abuse of patients by health care workers. Also handles personal injury claims including claims against local authorities. Interested in issues of accountability and regularly trains nurses, social workers, doctors and clinical risk managers and lawyers. Also interested in psychological effects of litigation. Undertook research on 'Why patients sue doctors' (Lancet 1994) and has trained solicitors on dealing with distressed clients. Acts for clients nationwide particularly in the South East and South West of England and heads *Parlett Kent*'s Exeter office which opened in March 1997.
Prof. Memberships: AVMA referral solicitor, member of and assessor for Law Society Medical Negligence Panel and Personal Injury Panel. ATLA.
Career: Qualified in 1987 with *Pannone Napier* and *Pannone Blackburn* from 1987 to 1992. Partner from 1991. Joined *Parlett Kent* in 1992 and became a partner in 1993.
Personal: Born 08.12.60. Bristol University (B.Soc. Sci. 1982).

COMMODITIES

London – Physicals: 169; Futures: 170; *Profiles*: 170

RESEARCH APPROVED BY BMRB: *For this edition,* Chambers' *researchers conducted 6083 interviews – 4408 with law firms, 598 with barristers and 1077 with clients.*

The validity of the research was scrutinised by BMRB International, who audited both the methodology and the results at our offices in July 2000. They interviewed Chambers' *researchers and cross-checked sample interviews. Details of the audit appear on page 7.*

LONDON

PHYSICALS

COMMODITIES: PHYSICALS • London	Ptnrs	Assts
❶ Richards Butler	4	6
❷ Middleton Potts	4	4
❸ Hill Taylor Dickinson	2	1
❹ Clifford Chance	2	8
Clyde & Co	7	12
Holman Fenwick & Willan	2	3
❺ Ince & Co	4	5
Lovells	2	4
RD Black & Co	1	3
Sinclair Roche & Temperley	4	4
❻ Holmes Hardingham	1	3

LEADING INDIVIDUALS	
✪ **PULLEN David** Richards Butler	
❶ **LUCAS David** Middleton Potts	**POTTS Christopher** Middleton Potts
SWINBURN Richard Richards Butler	
❷ **BLACK Richard** RD Black & Co.	**GALLOWAY Diane** Richards Butler
ISAACS Jeffrey Hill Taylor Dickinson	**MARTIN Patricia** Holman Fenwick & Willan
PARSON Robert Middleton Potts	**PATTON Edwin** Clifford Chance
❸ **BEST David** Clyde & Co	**EMMOTT John** Richards Butler
HICKEY Denys Ince & Co	**LEACH Ben** Sinclair Roche & Temperley
QUENBY Philip Lovells	
❹ **SHEPHERD Stuart** Ince & Co	**TURNER Paul** Clyde & Co
WALSER Nicholas Holmes Hardingham	
ONE TO WATCH	
EVAGORA Kyriacos Richards Butler	

Within each band, firms are listed alphabetically. *See **Profiles** on page 170*

Richards Butler Pre-eminent commodities team, which continues to have a slight edge over its rivals. Perceived by the market to have a highly commercial ethos *("they don't waste their clients' time with pointless actions")* the firm's rated individuals are considered to be *"real stars."* Elder statesman **David Pullen** *("he pops up everywhere in international trade")* is universally accepted as London's premier soft commodities lawyer. Viewed as *"personable and competent yet aggressive when required,"* his long experience in the field is virtually unmatched. **Richard Swinburn** garners praise from all sections of the market. Characterised by one observer as *"the best young lawyer I have seen in years,"* his practice is predominantly grain and sugar based. Grain specialist **Diane Galloway** is closely linked with Glencore and is considered *"sound and commercial"* while **John Emmott** is also rated a *"player"* for the scope of his international practice. The team regularly acts as legal advisor to a range of trade associations and represented the International Petroleum Exchange (IPE) on the only three actions in the IPE to go to arbitration in 1999. **Clients:** Tradigrain SA; Louis Dreyfus.

Middleton Potts Seen as the main competition to Richards Butler *("it's a straight fight between the two")* the team is admired for its *"sheer effectiveness."* Clients were impressed by the partner-led approach *("you get a name, you're never passed down the line")* and the firm's ultra-commercial attitude. Adept at handling all physical commodities advice (it acts for four of the big five soft commodity houses,) the team is increasingly involved in trade finance matters on behalf of financial institutions. Senior partner **Chris Potts**, although not quite as prominent this year, is considered a *"commodities doyen"* and continues to head the international trade practice. **David Lucas** is *"undoubtedly a star"* and is admired by arbitrators for his *"clear and lucid"* style. Metals specialist **Robert Parson**, meanwhile, is considered *"good to do business with."* **Clients:** Major international trading houses; financial institutions.

Hill Taylor Dickinson Felt to be growing steadily stronger, the team is seen as the nearest competition to the 'big two'. **Jeff Isaacs** *("convivial and knows the business")* has an excellent market profile and is known to have particularly strong GAFTA connections. He led the team advising arbitrators (and drafting awards) at the Refined Sugar Association, Grain and Feed Trade Association and the Sugar Association of London. **Clients:** International commodity houses.

Clifford Chance The firm for the bigger-ticket disputes *("if they do something they do it well,")* with a particularly strong position in trade finance work. Front man **Ed Patton** *("intellectually top-notch")* is associated predominantly with oil trading work, and led the team representing a German oil company in an ongoing US$12 million ICC arbitration with a Yemeni state company. The team retains a substantial presence in the sugar market, advising the Refined Sugar Association and the Sugar Association of London on a number of arbitrations this year. **Clients:** LIFFE; London Clearing House; J. Aron; BP Amoco.

Clyde & Co Perceived as *"steady and sound"* although there are *"no fireworks here."* The recent merger with Turner & Co is likely to give the team a boost to its sugar practice, with **Paul Turner** bringing solid GAFTA connections with him. The team has particular experience of working in foreign jurisdictions in Africa and South America. A major client here is Glencore, for whom the team acted on the Metro case in a high-profile piece of litigation involving major oil companies. **David Best** *("won't let you down")* is another recommended practitioner here. **Clients:** Glencore; Bank Nationale de Paris; Masefield Ltd.

Holman Fenwick & Willan A world famous shipping practice with a small yet respected commodities presence. High-profile partner **Patricia Martin** has strong GAFTA connections and is considered *"sharp and intelligent."* She led the team acting for a major grain house in a series of high value arbitrations arising from defaults by Asian purchasers of edible commodity cargoes. Some said, that she would benefit from greater support. **Clients:** Vitol; Continental Grain Co; Russian sugar trading houses.

Ince & Co Premier league shipping firm spinning off a medium-sized commodities practice. Known to be particularly strong on oil and gas contracts, the team represented Romanian exporters of lost fuel oil consignments, a case which resulted in high value ICC arbitration. The team also acts across the board on commodity disputes, particularly those relating to coffee, grain and sugar. **Denys Hickey** *("commercial and doesn't posture unnecessarily")* is known for the quality of his oil practice while **Stuart Shepherd** is perceived as *"a perfectly sound lawyer."* **Clients:** Vitol SA; major international commodity houses.

Lovells Known predominantly for the quality of its IPE and LME-based practice, the team has also established a good reputation for trade financing work. The team acted for Standard Chartered Bank on a number of London Metal Exchange arbitration proceedings against its Mocatta metals trading division by Metallgesellschaft Limited. Growth areas include advising on internet exchange proposals. **Philip Quenby** is rated for the scope of his international practice. **Clients:** Standard Chartered Bank.

R D Black & Co The *"enigmatic"* **Richard Black** is the face of this expanding practice, which is known for its unyielding litigation style and polarises market opinion. Involved in soft and hard commodities work, the team has growing connections with the French market. Disputes involving Far Eastern and Indian trading houses are a growth area. **Clients:** International trading houses.

Sinclair Roche & Temperley The team are *"undoubtedly knowledgeable"* about both soft and hard commodities, but is *"clearly not the force of old."* Long-established **Ben Leach** has *"star quality"* but has only been seen infrequently during the past twelve months. The practice is considered to have a *"hard-nosed, commercial ethos,"* retains strong GAFTA ties and handled a substantial case involving wrongful delivery of cargoes in Asia. **Clients:** International commodity trading houses.

Holmes Hardingham Agricultural commodities are the emphasis of this respected shipping firm. Known in the market as legal advisers to FOSFA, the team also acts for a small number of international oil traders. In the Commercial Court appeal of Soules CAF v Transap Indonesia (1999) the team successfully acted for French buyers who argued that bills of lading tendered by sellers did not comply with the CIF sale contract. The move of name partner Tony Holmes to consultant status is considered a loss to the team, although **Nicholas Walser** retains a sound reputation. **Clients:** International grain houses; FOSFA; foreign oil traders.

FUTURES

COMMODITIES: FUTURES • London	Ptnrs	Assts
❶ Clifford Chance	3	8
❷ Denton Wilde Sapte	3	4
Linklaters	1	1
Simmons & Simmons	2	5
❸ Richards Butler	4	4

LEADING INDIVIDUALS	
❶ **FINNEY Robert** Denton Wilde Sapte	**MELROSE Jonathan** Simmons & Simmons
PLEWS Tim Clifford Chance	
❷ **BLACK Edward** Denton Wilde Sapte	**FIRTH Simon** Linklaters
JOHANSEN Lynn Clifford Chance	**MAYHEW David** Clifford Chance
❸ **CORNISH Martin** Landwell	**CULLEN Iain** Simmons & Simmons

Within each band, firms are listed alphabetically. *See **Profiles** on page 170*

Clifford Chance The undisputed kings of futures advice *("nobody understands the market better than them")* specialise in acting for exchanges and a number of leading investment banks. Leader **Tim Plews** is known for his strong LIFFE connections, the experienced **Lynn Johansen** is highly rated for her clearing and financial product knowledge, while **David Mayhew** is considered a *"subtle"* litigator who represents the exchanges in disciplinary matters. E-commerce advice is a major growth area. **Clients:** International trading houses.

Denton Wilde Sapte A broad futures and other commodity derivatives practice, capitalising on the firm's energy and e-commerce strength. **Robert Finney** is considered *"rock solid"* for energy trading work and is a leader in the field. He led the team acting for Ofgem (the combined electricity and gas regulator) on the development and implementation of the new UK electricity trading arrangements (NETA) scheduled for October 2000. The arrival of futures specialist **Ed Black** from Mayer Brown & Platt has boosted the team's profile substantially. Black and Finney are considered to be *"a formidable pairing."* The firm's Middle Eastern expansion has provided some notable Islamic finance work. **Clients:** Ofgem; ED&F Man; BG Transco.

Linklaters Admired by the market for the quality of its core clients, the firm is considered *"first-rate"* for institutional and regulatory advice. Known for its long standing representation of the London Metal Exchange, the team advised on the LME's new SWORD system. Acted for a major investment bank in relation to an OTC metal financing arrangement, which involved putting OTC trades through the LME. Group head **Simon Firth** is a derivatives expert whose name is also highly respected in the commodities futures market. **Clients:** LME; international investment banks; commodity traders.

Simmons & Simmons Perceived as the pre-eminent LME practice, the team acts mainly for market participants and a number of exchanges including the Swiss Exchange and Eurex Zurich. **Jonathan Melrose** has a good market profile and is known to have vast experience in the metals sector. **Iain Cullen**, while considered *"absolutely charming to deal with"* has been more involved in hedge fund work this year. The team acted for Derivatives Net (Blackbird), an ECN for swaps trading, on the establishment of its UK and European operations. **Clients:** AIG International Trading Group; Sempra Energy Trading Corp; Ofgem.

Richards Butler Felt to be *"gearing up a bit,"* the team is still better known for its contentious caseload, acting for trading companies, banks and trade associations. Has hired laterally in an attempt to beef up this practice, but it still lacks the profile of the firm's physicals team. Acted on a $25 million LME arbitration for the successful party. **Clients:** Trading companies; trade associations.

Other Notable Practitioner **Martin Cornish** of Landwell has long-standing experience in futures work and retains a sizeable reputation. He is known to represent small to medium-sized market participants.

LEADERS IN COMMODITIES

BEST, David
Clyde & Co, London (020) 7623 1244
Specialisation: Litigation disputes concerning oil and gas, metal, sugar and other international commodity contracts, both in arbitration and court, and related charterparty and bill of lading disputes. Client base is world wide with current disputes in the London High Court and arbitration and in foreign courts e.g. Dubai, Paris and Hong Kong, working with *Clyde & Co*'s regional offices. Acts principally for commodity traders and charterers. Part of the team acting for Glencore following the collapse of Metro Trading International Inc.

BLACK, Edward
Denton Wilde Sapte, London (020) 7242 1212

BLACK, Richard
RD Black & Co., London (020) 7600 8282
Partner specialising in shipping and commodities litigation and arbitration.

Specialisation: Wide experience since 1978 of maritime and commodity arbitrations (both physical and futures) and Commercial Court hearings relating to shipping, trading, insurance and commercial litigation disputes and regulatory work with a particular emphasis on charterparty and cargo claims and commodity disputes including GAFTA, FOSFA, crude oil and petroleum and LME. Clients include international trading houses, commodity and derivatives traders, oil majors and traders, ship owners, charterers and marine insurers. Major cases include Deutsche Schachtbau v Raknoc & Shell International; Kloeckner v Gatoil; the M.V. 'P', The 'Taria', Comdel v Siporex.
Prof. Memberships: Law Society, GAFTA and FOSFA, supporting member LMAA.
Career: Qualified in 1977. Joined *Middleton Potts* from *Coward Chance* in 1984, becoming a partner in 1985. In December 1996, resigned from Middleton Potts to set up *R.D. Black & Co.*
Personal: Born 22nd March 1951. Holds an LLB from Manchester, 1969-72. Leisure interests include golf, tennis, chess and reading. Lives in Oxshott.

CORNISH, Martin
Landwell, London (020) 7212 1616
Partner. Head of financial services.
Specialisation: Advises banks, broker/dealers, investment managers and insurance companies on the full range of financial services regulation and exchange traded and OTC documentation and related issues. Author of numerous articles in the professional press. Regular speaker at conferences and seminars.
Prof. Memberships: Law Society.
Career: Qualified in 1980. Assistant solicitor and then partner with *Simmons & Simmons* 1980-88. European Legal Director at *Lehman Brothers* 1988-92. Established *MW Cornish & Co* in 1992 and in July 1997 the firm's financial services practice joined *Arnheim & Co*, now *Landwell*, the UK correspondent law firm of PricewaterhouseCoopers.
Personal: Born 28th February 1955. Attended Millfield School 1970-74, then Downing College, Cambridge 1974-76. Leisure pursuits include tennis and golf. Lives in Billericay, Essex.

CULLEN, Iain
Simmons & Simmons, London (020) 7628 2020
Partner in Corporate Department.
Specialisation: Handles all types of work relating to commodities, futures and options, unit trusts, offshore funds and investment management. Author of numerous articles in the professional press. Regular speaker at conferences and seminars.
Prof. Memberships: Law Society, International Bar Association, American Bar Association, Alternative Investment Management Association, Board of Editors of Futures and Derivatives Law Report, Advisory Board of World Securities Law Report.
Career: Qualified in 1980, having joined *Simmons & Simmons* in 1977. Became a Partner in 1986.
Personal: Born 13th May 1953. Took a BA in Law in 1975. Lives in London.

EMMOTT, John F.
Richards Butler, London (020) 7247 6555
Partner in shipping unit.
Specialisation: Specialises in international trade and commodities.
Career: Qualified in 1978 (Australia), 1985 (UK). Partner at *Richards Butler* since 1986.
Personal: Born 1953. Educated at the University of Sydney (BA, LL.B).

FINNEY, Robert
Denton Wilde Sapte, London (020) 7320 6389

FIRTH, Simon
Linklaters (A member firm of Linklaters & Alliance), London (020) 7456 3764
simon.firth@linklaters.com

GALLOWAY, Diane
Richards Butler, London (020) 7247 6555
Specialisation: Principal areas of practice are commodities arbitrations and litigation, including in Grain and Feed Trade Association, Liverpool Cotton Association, Refined Sugar Association and FOSFA. Recent experience also includes Chinese Trade Arbitration (CIETAC). Has lectured for GAFTA and Sugar Association of London. Also specialises in sanctions related litigation.
Career: LL.B Trinity College, Cambridge, then Masters in International Law, Harvard Law School, USA. Joined *Richards Butler* in 1984 after internship with New York firm.

HICKEY, Denys
Ince & Co, London (020) 7623 2011
Partner.
Specialisation: A major part of his practice involves oil and gas trading disputes. Has acted in disputes involving many of the Majors and independant oil traders in connection with contracts for the sale of crude, products and gas. Also involved in metals trading including LME disputes, tolling contracts, offtake agreements and other aspects of metals trading with particular reference to the FSU. Involved in disputes relating to time and voyage charters, long term contracts of affreightment, storage contracts, and shortage and contamination claims. Has advised on short and long term contracts and problems arising out of letters of credit and trade finance and the application of EU and UK competition law. Has spoken at numerous conferences on the legal aspects of transport, trading, letters of credit and EC competition law, and is a regular speaker at the Centre for Petroleum and Mineral Law at the University of Dundee, and the College of Petroleum Studies in Oxford.
Career: Post-graduate studies in Public International and EC Law, then qualified as a barrister. Joined *Ince & Co.*, requalified as a solicitor and became a Partner in 1986.
Personal: Born 1952. Lives Saffron Walden. Leisure interests include golf, cycling and skiing.

ISAACS, Jeffrey
Hill Taylor Dickinson, London (020) 7283 9033
jeff.isaacs@htd-london.com
Partner.
Specialisation: Practice covers the full range of maritime and Sale of Goods law, but with a specialisation in 'dry' shipping and Commodities disputes including both High Court litigation and arbitration at the various Trade Associations, including GAFTA, FOSFA, The Refined Sugar Association, The Sugar Association of London, LME and IGPA. Regularly sits as legal assessor to arbitration panels at the Sugar Associations and GAFTA. Author of articles on Shipping and Commodities matters. Speaks at seminars and on the GAFTA Trade Education Course. Shipping Editor of 'Law and Transport Policy'.
Prof. Memberships: Law Society, and through *Hill Taylor Dickinson* GAFTA, FOSFA and Refined Sugar Association.
Career: Qualified in 1983 having joined *Hill Taylor Dickinson* in 1981. Associate in 1987. Partner in 1989.
Personal: Born 11th April 1959. Attended Dulwich College then Christ's College, Cambridge (BA 1980). Leisure interests include tennis, badminton, horse riding, wine making and tasting and skiing. Lives in Putney.

JOHANSEN, Lynn
Clifford Chance, London (020) 7600 1000
lynn.johansen@cliffordchance.com
Specialisation: Principal area of work is advising on derivatives and financial regulation with a particular focus on exchange-traded derivatives issues for exchanges and clearing houses, banks and securities houses and other investment firms and commodity derivatives with a focus on energy products. Also specialises in establishing exchanges.
Career: MA (CANTAB) in History. Qualified 1985; partner 1995.

LEACH, Ben
Sinclair Roche & Temperley, London
(020) 7452 4000
Partner.
Specialisation: Main area of specialisation is commodity trades, from litigation and arbitration to drafting and advising on commodity sales, contracts and associated documentation. Conducted over 100 arbitrations before GAFTA, FOSFA, Refined Sugar Association, London Metal Exchange, London Rice Brokers' Association and various other hard and soft commodity trade associations in London and abroad. Contributed to the Law Commission Working Group on title to goods forming part of a bulk. Also a specialist in shipping and oil trade litigation (see separate listing under Shipping & Maritime Law).
Prof. Memberships: Law Society
Career: Articled to *Richards Butler* in 1969, qualified as a solicitor in 1971, joined *Sinclair Roche & Temperley* in 1975 and became a partner in 1978.
Personal: Born 24th October 1945. Attended Leeds University 1965-68. Accredited CEDR mediator.

LUCAS, David
Middleton Potts, London (020) 7600 2333
Partner in commercial litigation department.
Specialisation: Main area of practice is commodities and shipping. Extensive experience of arbitration and litigation, acting for commodity trading houses (including the majors), oil companies and traders, shipowners, leading trade finance banks, insurers and P&I Clubs. Also acts extensively as legal adviser to Trade Association arbitrators. Major cases handled include Bremer v Vanden-Avenne, The Montone, The Caspian Sea, The Pegase, The Afovos, The Golden Bear, The Future Express and Czarnikow-Rionda v Standard Bank.
Prof. Memberships: Law Society.
Career: Qualified in 1972. Associate, *Crawley & de Reya* 1974-76. Founding partner at *Middleton Potts* in 1976.
Personal: Born 15th December 1947. Attended St Paul's School 1960-65, then Bristol University 1966-69.

MARTIN (FORMERLY FRANCIES), Patricia
Holman Fenwick & Willan, London
(020) 7488 2300
patricia.martin@hfw.co.uk
Partner in commercial litigation department.
Specialisation: Litigation, soft and hard commodities, oil and gas trading disputes, international sale of goods including acting for Fiat's railway division in the Channel Tunnel disputes, the Santa Clara House of Lords Case for Vitol SA, acts for Cargill SA, Continental Grain, Minermet SA and many others.
Prof. Memberships: Supporting member of LMAA, GAFTA, FOSFA, member of Law Society.
Career: LL.B Auckland 1978, LL.M London 1979, called to New Zealand Bar 1980, admitted as solicitor in England/Wales 1988. P&I Club 1979-1987. Claims Manager *Tindall Riley & Co.* (Director of the Management Co. 1983-1987). *Middleton Potts* 1988-1990. *Holman Fenwick and Willan* 1990-present. Partner 1993.

MAYHEW, David
Clifford Chance, London (020) 7600 1000
david.mayhew@cliffordchance.com
See under Fraud, p.419

MELROSE, Jonathan
Simmons & Simmons, London (020) 7628 2020
Partner in Corporate Department.
Specialisation: Handles all types of work relating to commodities/derivatives, securities, collective investment vehicles and asset management. Regular speaker at conferences and seminars.
Prof. Memberships: Union Internationale des Avocats, Law Society, The Securities Institute, Member of Commodities Committee of the Futures and Options Association.
Career: Qualified 1985, having joined *Simmons & Simmons* in 1983. Became a Partner in 1991.
Personal: Born 21st April 1959. Holds an MA (Hons) Oxon, 1981.

PARSON, Robert Michael
Middleton Potts, London (020) 7600 2333
Partner in international trade and commodities department.
Specialisation: Specialised since 1987 in international sale of goods and commodity trade finance. Advises trade finance banks and other financial institutions, trading houses and insurers. Strong practice in GAFTA, FOSFA, IGPA, LME and other trade arbitrations. Speaks and publishes on trade, finance and e-commerce issues. UK editor of 'L/C Monitor', the trade finance monthly journal.
Prof. Memberships: Law Society.
Career: Qualified 1986. Joined *Middleton Potts* from *Richards Butler* in 1992. Partner in 1995.
Personal: Born 7th February 1961. Sheffield University LLB 1979-1982.

PATTON, Edwin
Clifford Chance, London (020) 7600 1000
edwin.patton@cliffordchance.com
Specialisation: Partner specialising in maritime and international trading of commodities, energy, oil, gas, natural resources, and shipping litigation.
Career: Sullivan Upper School, Holywood, N Ireland 1953-1959; Queen's University, Belfast (LLB 1963) 1959-1963. Lectured in law at University of Bristol 1964-1967; articled *Coward Chance* 1968-1970; assistant solicitor 1970-1974; partner *Coward Chance/ Clifford Chance* since 1974.
Personal: Theatre, golf, bridge. Born 1942; resides London.

PLEWS, Tim
Clifford Chance, London (020) 7600 1000
tim.plews@cliffordchance.com
Specialisation: Specialises in law and regulation of international financial markets including technology and e-commerce developments.
Career: Trinity College, Cambridge (MA 1984). Articled *Coward Chance*; qualified 1988; partner 1994.
Personal: Born 1962; resides Surrey.

POTTS, Christopher Reginald
Middleton Potts, London (020) 7600 2333
Senior partner at *Middleton Potts.*
Specialisation: Over 30 years experience of law and practice relating to commodities, carriage of goods, insurance (marine and non-marine) and international trade. Many major cases handled are leading authorities. Clientele includes major trading houses, carriers, insurers and banks. Regularly lectures to trade audiences.
Prof. Memberships: Law Society
Career: Qualified in 1965. Partner at *Crawley & de Reya* 1967-76. Founding partner of *Middleton Potts* in 1976, and is currently senior partner.
Personal: Born 1st July 1939. Attended University of London 1958-61. Lives in London.

PULLEN, David
Richards Butler, London (020) 7247 6555
Partner in International Trade and Commodities.
Specialisation: Main area of practice is commodity trading disputes, including arbitration and advice work in grain (GAFTA), vegetable oil (FOSFA), sugar (RSA and SAOL), metals and oil trading (ICC). Also handles documentary credits advice work, and advises on litigation disputes in customs and EC matters. Cases have included the 1973 US Prohibition cases, Naxos, Panchaud Freres and Toepfer v Continental Grain. Instructor at the University of Pennsylvania Law School 1963-64. Regular speaker at trade related conferences.
Prof. Memberships: Supporting Member of London Maritime Arbitration Association; Associate Member Chartered Institute of Arbitrators.
Career: Qualified 1967 At *Richards Butler* since 1964.
Personal: Born 1941. Taunton School 1954-59, then University College Oxford 1960-63.

QUENBY, N. Philip
Lovells, London (020) 7296 2000
philip.quenby@lovells.com
Specialisation: Commodity trading and financing (physicals and futures), covering crude and refined petroleum products, LNG, LPG, agriproducts, metals and other bulk commodities. Includes IPE and LME transactions and all aspects of transactional shipping work.
Prof. Memberships: Law Society, London Maritime Arbitrators' Association.
Career: Articled *Lovells* qualified 1986, partner 1992.

SHEPHERD, Stuart
Ince & Co, London (020) 7623 2011
Specialisation: Main areas of practice are commodities and shipping. Is involved in advising those trading in various commodities, in particular oil, oil products and commodities traded on GAFTA terms, and handles all aspects of dry shipping work, with particular emphasis on carriage of goods by sea and charterparty disputes with particular emphasis on litigation. Leading reported cases have included ' 'Mathraki' (1989), 'Lefthero' (1992), 'Boucraa' (1993) and 'Kriti Rex' (1996). Chairman of International Bar Association Committee on Commodities and author of articles on a number of commodity matters. Speaks at Lloyds of London shipping seminars and on the GAFTA's CPDP programme.
Prof. Memberships: Member of IBA, LMAA, and through *Ince & Co.*, GAFTA, FOSFA and Refined Sugar Association.
Career: Qualified in 1984, having joined *Ince & Co.* in 1982. Became a Partner in 1990.
Personal: Born 17th October 1959. Attended Bexhill Grammar 1971-78, then University College, Cardiff 1978-81. Leisure interests include golf and skiing. Lives in Mayfield, East Sussex.

SWINBURN, Richard
Richards Butler, London (020) 7247 6555
Specialisation: Advises trading companies, trade associations, banks and governments on all aspects of the buying, selling, financing and transporting of commodities.
Career: Qualified in 1988. Partner at *Richards Butler* 1994.
Personal: Born 1963. Educated at Sedbergh School, Cumbria and Robinson College, Cambridge.

TURNER, Paul
Clyde & Co, London (020) 7623 1244
Partner handling Commodities.
Specialisation: Work includes trade arbitrations before the Sugar Associations, GAFTA, FOSFA, Cocoa Association, Coffee Trade Federation and Rice Association. Also handles oil disputes, bills of lading and charter party disputes, largely before commercial courts or the London Maritime Arbitrators Association.
Prof. Memberships: Law Society, Associate Member of the Sugar Association of London.
Career: Qualified 1973. Partner with *Thomas Cooper & Stibbard* from 1977-85. Founder Partner of *Turner & Co.* in 1985. Turner & Co merged with *Clyde & Co* in January 2000.
Personal: Born 16th September 1948. Attended Skegness Grammar School 1960-67, then University College, London, 1967-70. Leisure interests include walking, travelling and eating. Lives in Esher, Surrey.

WALSER, Nicholas
Holmes Hardingham, London (020) 7283 0222
Nicholas.Walser@HHL.co.uk
Partner specialising in 'dry' shipping law.
Specialisation: 'Dry' shipping law, including commodity trade disputes. Work covers charterparty disputes, cargo loss/ damage claims, and international sale contracts including agricultural commodities (GAFTA and FOSFA contracts) and oil trading. Major cases include the 'TFL Prosperity' (1984) and Soules v.Intertradex (1991) and Soules v. P.T. Transap (1998). Associate member of French Maritime Law Association. Fluent French. Working knowledge of German.
Career: Qualified in 1977. Partner in *Ingledew Brown Bennison & Garrett* 1979-89. A founding partner of *Holmes Hardingham* in 1989.
Personal: Born 31st December 1952. Attended Cambridge University (MA 1975). Lives in London.

COMPETITION / ANTI-TRUST

OVERVIEW: The introduction of the UK Competition Act is predicted to bring competition law closer to home for UK law firms. This year, practitioners who are seen to be based mainly in Brussels have been removed from the UK guide. These names include Rachel Brandenburger and John Davies of Freshfields, John Boyce and William Sibree of Slaughter and May, Alec Burnside of Linklaters, Michael Reynolds of Allen & Overy, Stephen Kinsella of Herbert Smith, Philip Collins of Lovells and Mark Clough QC of Ashurst Morris Crisp. Although most firms operate single-unit Brussels-London operations, their competition in Brussels is wider than can be reflected in a UK guide.

Competition law is a mixture of anti-trust and trade work, and most practitioners can turn their hand to both. Pure competition work is considered to include both merger control and behavioural issues. In the London section we have attempted to separate pure competition work from work such as public procurement, state aid and the free movement of goods.

More work is expected as business is seen to be more willing to resort to competition law as a competitive tool.

Economics has gradually become more important over the last ten years, and there are more economists and more lawyers with economics backgrounds now playing key roles in the sector. Telecoms and media firms are beginning to make more of an impact as their specialities generate work in the regulatory field.

RESEARCH APPROVED BY BMRB: *For this edition,* Chambers' *researchers conducted 6083 interviews – 4408 with law firms, 598 with barristers and 1077 with clients.*

The validity of the research was scrutinised by BMRB International, who audited both the methodology and the results at our offices in July 2000. They interviewed Chambers' *researchers and cross-checked sample interviews. Details of the audit appear on page 7.*

LONDON

Freshfields Bruckhaus Deringer Clearly an anti-trust powerhouse with *"corporate professionalism an overriding feature of the firm." "Imaginative and tough,"* **Nick Spearing** and **Deidre Trapp** are *"major players"* who *"cut to the quick."* Spearing is *"good on the deal side,"* working on a broad range of competition matters, whilst Trapp *("proactive, responsive, first rate")* is perceived to be more oriented to behavioural work. The firm's Brussels-based partners all still command immense market respect. Economists find the London team *"particularly easy to deal with; they get you involved early and don't tell you your job."* While some perceive the work to be *"skewed towards M&A,"* the team is nevertheless considered to have many other strengths.

Merger expertise has been highlighted by such work as the GEC Marconi/British Aerospace, RBS/NatWest and Telewest/Flextech link-ups. Non-merger work includes Competition Commission inquiries into grocery retailing and milk, and work in the financial services, brewing, media, telecoms and railway sectors. Litigation is another expanding area. Truly pan-European, particularly in the wake of the stunning merger with German powerhouse Bruckhaus Westrick Heller Löber, the practice is officially known as the European Competition and Trade Group, with clients and economists confirming the cross-office capability and mode of functioning. The practice has also worked on most major European cartel cases in sectors such as banking, cement, gas, graphite electrodes, media, newsprint, steel beams and pipes. Other international work includes the Formula One EU Investigation, PepsiCo's response to Coke's proposed acquisition of part of Cadbury Schweppes, and advising the Mexican government in their negotiation of an FTA with the EU. **Clients:** Telewest; Tesco; Milk Marque; GEC/BAe; Kingfisher; Scottish Telecom; RBS; BNFL; Sotheby's; PepsiCo; Mars.

Herbert Smith After knocking on the door for two years, this *"extremely strong"* practice moves into the top tier this year. A broad and balanced team, the partners all do a range of work. Working on media and telecoms matters of late, **Dorothy Livingston** *"has been enormously impressive in steering through BSkyB."* She *"reduces things to a sensible level"* and *"intellectually has most people licked."* On the utilities side, **Elizabeth McKnight** is regarded as *"fantastic to work with"* by economists, who appreciate her persuasiveness with regulatory bodies. Clients find her *"hugely impressive"* as she is *"switched on and gets to grips quickly with issues."* The *"pretty bullish"* **Jonathan Scott** *"sticks his neck out for you and he gets it right."* A competition all-rounder, he is known for his litigation skills, and is regarded as *"user-friendly, personable, practical and effective."*

Now involved in the firm's management, **Richard Fleck** also adds weight to the team, and remains the relationship partner for clients such as Time Warner and Stagecoach. The firm additionally has partners respected for newspaper regulation and transport work. The year has also seen the hiring of Lord Brittan, the ex-EC trade commissioner, as a consultant.

A wide range of competition and regulatory work is dealt with, including mergers and take-over battles such as those of First Choice with Kuoni and Airtours and NatWest with Bank of Scotland and RBS. In the newspaper industry, the firm advised Trinity Plc on the competition aspects of its proposed acquisition of the Mirror Group. In utilities, the firm advised water and electricity companies on their price control reviews and gas shippers on issues arising from new gas trading arrangements. Other work includes defending BSkyB's exclusive contract to televise live Premier League football, advising the FIA on the Formula One investigation and advising the Indian and Armenian governments on trade issues. **Clients:** London Electricity plc; Viridian Group; North West Water; First Choice; Pilkington; BSkyB; Federation Internationale de L'Automobile; BAT; Stagecoach; Chiquita.

Linklaters Whilst many in the market observed that David Hall's retirement, added to Chris Bright's departure last year left *"two pretty big holes,"* clients still commented on the *"strength in depth"* of the team. Partners and young associates alike are *"all impressive,"* and while *"there are few superstars, that is part of their attraction."* Linklaters & Alliance operates an integrated European practice group, and the market also noted the strength of some of the firm's Brussels players. *"Quiet and full of common sense,"* the *"superlative"* **Bill Allan** *"doesn't make a drama out of a crisis."* Among the younger partners, **Gavin Robert** is *"tremendous,"* and clients like *"bright"* **Michael Cutting.** Well known for its merger work, the practice advised on the link-ups of BAT/Rothmans, Vodafone/Airtouch, Vodafone/Mannesmann, Lafarge/Blue Circle, Scottish & Newcastle/Kronenbourg, BP Amoco/Cas-

COMPETITION/ANTI-TRUST • London	Ptnrs	Assts
❶ Freshfields Bruckhaus Deringer	6	65
Herbert Smith	7	15
Linklaters	6	17
Slaughter and May	5	23
❷ Lovells	10	23
❸ Allen & Overy	4	21
Ashurst Morris Crisp	6	15
Clifford Chance	6	20
Denton Wilde Sapte	5	9
SJ Berwin & Co	7	11
❹ Norton Rose	4	17
Simmons & Simmons	6	11
❺ Baker & McKenzie	5	8
Theodore Goddard	3	6
❻ Bristows	6	6
CMS Cameron McKenna	4	6
Eversheds	3	7
Richards Butler	2	5

LEADING INDIVIDUALS

✪ **AITMAN David** Denton Wilde Sapte
BRIGHT Chris Clifford Chance
KON Stephen SJ Berwin & Co
NICHOLSON Malcolm Slaughter and May
WHISH Richard Sole Practitioner

❶ **ALLAN Bill** Linklaters
CARSTENSEN Laura Slaughter and May
LIVINGSTON Dorothy Herbert Smith
McKNIGHT Elizabeth Herbert Smith
POLITO Simon Lovells
SPEARING Nicholas Freshfields Bruckhaus Deringer
TRAPP Deirdre Freshfields Bruckhaus Deringer

❷ **FREEMAN Peter** Simmons & Simmons
FRIEND Mark Allen & Overy
PARR Nigel Ashurst Morris Crisp
PHEASANT John Lovells
SCOTT Jonathan Herbert Smith

❸ **CHAPPATTE Philippe** Slaughter and May
FINBOW Roger Ashurst Morris Crisp
HUTCHINGS Michael Michael Hutchings
LEIGH Guy Theodore Goddard
MAITLAND-WALKER Julian Maitland Walker
MARTIN ALEGI Lynda Baker & McKenzie
SMITH Martin Simmons & Simmons
SOAMES Trevor Norton Rose

❹ **AINSWORTH Lesley** Lovells
COHEN Ralph SJ Berwin & Co
COOK John Norton Rose
FLECK Richard Herbert Smith
HOLMES Katherine Richards Butler
OSBORNE John Clifford Chance
ROBERT Gavin Linklaters
ROSE Stephen Eversheds
ROWE Michael Slaughter and May
SINGLETON Susan Singletons
WHEATON Jim Clifford Chance
WOTTON John Allen & Overy

UP AND COMING
CUTTING Michael Linklaters
FARQUHARSON Melanie Simmons & Simmons
HOLMES Simon SJ Berwin & Co
LOUVEAUX Bertrand Slaughter and May
WEITZMAN Polly Denton Wilde Sapte

Within each band, firms are listed alphabetically. *See **Profiles** on page 178*

trol, BAe/GEC Marconi, NatWest/RBS and other multi-jurisdictional mergers. With its Alliance partners, the firm has acted on more than 10% of EU merger notifications in the past year. Other work includes regulatory (particularly utilities) and advisory work. The team advised British Airways in connection with travel agents' commissions and the launch of Go, and has also been involved in the milk and car Competition Commission investigations. Cartel work, and trade law work are also an important feature of the practice, with a recent arrival boosting the WTO practice. **Clients:** Vodafone, British Airways, Allied Domecq plc, BG, Centrica plc.

Slaughter and May This year, the firm provoked a wide range of sharply differing opinion. The practice is *"not everyone's cup of tea,"* with some finding the team *"tricky to deal with,"* principally due to a perceived *"confrontational"* approach. However, all agree that the practice is *"extremely good at representing a client"* – it *"instils trust"* and is *"tough and often right." "The lawyer to go to in London if there's a problem,"* **Malcolm Nicholson** *"goes down very well with clients"* for his *"imaginative, aggressive and tough"* approach. Equally appreciated is all-rounder **Laura Carstensen,** who *"gets it right from the company's perspective," "understands the authorities"* and whose *"intelligence and eye for detail"* make her drafts *"so good."* **Philippe Chappatte** *("doesn't give an inch")* is best known for his telecoms and media work. Of the younger generation, **Michael Rowe** continues to win plaudits and the *"excellent"* **Bertrand Louveaux** enters the ratings this year. The latter *"is down to earth and relates well to the client."*

Like all firms with top M&A practices, the competition team is sometimes seen to be a merger shop. However, the practice is also considered to be *"top on behavioural work,"* advising on Article 81 and 82 cases, and restructurings in the broadcasting, electricity and building products industries. Merger work this year encompassed the uncompleted Telia/Telenor merger (the first attempted merger of two incumbent telcos) and on the attempted Airtours/FirstChoice merger. Rothmans/BAT, Kingfisher/Asda, British Steel/Hoogovens and Reckitt & Colman/Benckiser were also headline transactions in which the firm featured strongly. The group also offered advice at inquiries into the ice cream, supermarkets, public medical insurance and hospital services industries. **Clients:** Telenor; Airtours; Unilever; ASDA; BUPA; NATS; First Hydro; Home Office.

Lovells *"Class act"* **John Pheasant,** who has become the firm's international partner, now splits his time between management issues and competition issues, where he has been involved in shipping and cartel matters. **Simon Polito** is now considered the *"main name"* – a *"top operator"* who is *"suited to slightly political and difficult cases."* Whilst some in the market commented that Polito *"has to do a lot on his own,"* clients also observed that he *"works well as part of a team."* His colleague **Lesley Ainsworth** is *"sensible, practical and down to earth."* London operates as one group with the Brussels office, where the practice remains a key player. Lauded for its *"highly commercial"* character, the team maintains a leading reputation for its non-merger control competition expertise. Trade law and a *"pre-eminent marine competition practice,"* are of particular note. However, the practice is perceived to be less involved than its foremost competitors on the higher profile merger and utilities work.

Advised on the attempted Telia/Telenor merger, and on a joint venture between Alstom and ABB. Other work includes advising on the clearance for the pooling and rating agreements of the International Group of P&I Clubs, who insure the third party risks of 90% of the world's ocean-going tonnage. Inquiry work includes advising Mars in the ice cream 'wars,' and working on appeals subsequent to the 'steel tubes' and 'steel beams' investigations. **Clients:** Aegon; Albright and Wilson; AMP; British Energy; Granada; Johnson & Johnson; Schroders; Vickers; Port of Singapore.

Allen & Overy A *"solid"* team, whose stand-out practitioner in London is **Mark Friend.** He is particularly rated for his work on matters which straddle the line between competition and regulation. **John Wotton,** *("thoroughly likeable")* is respected for his experience in broadcasting and media matters. Although felt to lack nothing in quality, the team is felt to need *"more weight at the top."*

The high-tech area is one where the team is a recognised leader, drawing on a large Silicon Valley client base. Anti-cartel advice is another specific area of expertise. Acted for Cable & Wireless on the sale of One2One, on the clearance of the Global One alliance, and for the General Electric Company in connection with its acquisition of the heavy-duty gas turbine business of Alstom. The practice advised Singapore Airlines on the competition and regulatory aspects of its proposed acquisition of a 49% interest in Virgin Atlantic and represented Thomas Cook in Phase II of the attempted Airtours/First Choice merger. Contentious cases have included acting for Coca-Cola before the Court of First Instance on the appeal against the Commission's decision on the Coke/Cadburys link-up. **Clients:** Bass; Cable & Wireless; Coca-Cola & Schweppes Beverages; General Electric Company; Global One; Nissan; Northern Electric; Sprint; Time Warner; 20th Century Fox.

Ashurst Morris Crisp A *"responsive"* team whose main name is **Nigel Parr**; someone who *"moves transactions forward"* with a *"balanced and practical"* approach. He is regarded as one of the *"top names for stand-alone competition work."* The *"sound"* **Roger Finbow** works primarily on competition issues in broadcasting and sport. The team includes in-house economists and its legal-economic expertise is felt to be *"second to none."* As a consequence, *"you don't see the economic howlers in their documents that you do in others."*

On commercial transaction work, the team acted on the link-ups of United News and Media/Carlton Communications, Imetal SA/English China Clays Plc, Lufthansa/British Midland and Express Dairies/Avonmore Waterford. Stand-alone competition work has involved working on the cars and milk inquiries and on major litigation, while WTO trade law advice is also a feature of the department. **Clients:** Allied Domecq plc; BT; Centrica plc; Cinven; Coca-Cola Enterprises plc; IBM; Motorola; Royal & Sun Alliance; Ford Motor Company.

Clifford Chance **Chris Bright** is certainly perceived to have given the practice *"more credibility"* since he arrived from Linklaters, as well as some new clients. Clients like him for his *"exceedingly good grasp of commercial realities."* He is considered a *"great team leader,"* a heavyweight who *"knows the right people and knows how to handle them."* A competition generalist, he advises principally on anti-trust and regulation (utilities). Perceptions of the practice as a *"one man band"* have been allayed by the presence of **Jim Wheaton** and **John Osborne**, both praised as *"easy to get on with."*

The US and German mergers have given an added dimension to the team, now capable of serving both the Washington and Brussels anti-trust hubs on contentious and non-contentious, merger and non-merger work. Represented clients on a quarter of Phase II investigations last year. The year has seen the firm heavily involved in merger work, working on the BP Amoco/ARCO, Aerospatiale/DASA, Carrefour/Promodes, Edison Mission/Powergen, Wessex Water/Enron, and Futjitsu/Siemens link-ups. Other work has seen the practice advise NTL on the Competition Commission's inquiry into its acquisition of Cable & Wireless' UK businesses. The team has additionally been acting for two clients in each of the cars and supermarkets inquiries. State aids cases have been a growth area in the past year. The firm's litigation capacity has been consolidated through the formation of a litigation division dubbed *EUCLID*. **Clients:** Coca-Cola; British Energy; CVC Capital Partners; General Electric Company (USA); Kimberly-Clark; Pfizer; Philip Morris; Suez-Lyonnaise; Schroder Ventures; Air Products; Edison Mission; Reuters.

Denton Wilde Sapte *"Smooth operator"* **David Aitman** *("thoughtful and skilled")* is the firm's outstanding practitioner. He has a *"particular niche in broadcasting and media"* yet is considered to be *"excellent in every respect"* – a *"bloody good anti-trust and regulatory man with a bit of flair."* He heads a *"well rounded practice"* with *"good sensible people,"* where **Polly Weitzman** has made a name for herself, leading on a conclusive victory against the OFT in the Premier League case (successfully defending the collective selling of football rights to television). As well as advising on sports-related matters, she has also been active in gas regulatory and merger issues. The newly-merged firm has added strength in finance and aviation, and the team acted for easyJet Airline Company Ltd in its claim in the high court against British Airways plc for abuse of a dominant position. Media-related work continues, with the team successfully defending the joint venture between Paramount, Universal and MGM before the EU Commission, and acting for the FA in opposing the BSkyB bid for Manchester United. The firm also advised on the clearing of EDF's acquisition of London Electricity and (indirectly) of SWEB. **Clients:** Premier League; UIP; J Sainsbury; EDF; Energis; RFU; Mastercard/Europay; Bertelsmann; Rentokil.

SJ Berwin & Co *"Mighty oak"* **Stephen Kon** continues to cast a long shadow here. Clients and lawyers comment that he is *"getting even better"*, and admire him for *"spotting and exploiting a case."* He is *"incredibly dynamic and intellectually sound"* and impresses with his ability to guide a client. However, the perception that this is a one-man band is fading, as other members of the team make their mark. *"Healthy billers"* **Ralph Cohen** and **Simon Holmes** also received recommendations this year. The former has *"good instincts"* and *"gives sensible trade law advice."* Holmes, a *"steady"* all-rounder, is *"as bright as a button"* and *"highly commercial."*

Around half of the practice's work last year was merger-related, including opposing the Rhone Poulenc/Hoechst healthcare deal. Work this year includes advising on Diageo's disposal of Cruzcampo to Heineken, British Land's acquisition of Meadowhall, the purchase of Shell's polystyrene business and a number of private equity and venture capital transactions. Inquiry work saw the team advising on the Formula One investigation and in the supermarkets case. The team also acted for Rado/Tissot and Omega (Swatch Group) on a contested distribution agreement and is highly rated for its advice on contentious matters. **Clients:** Ladbroke Group; Universal Music Group; Qantas; Merck Generics; Coca-Cola Enterprises; Diageo; Aerolineas Argentinas; NM Rothschild.

Norton Rose A substantial merger control practice with a significant contentious element. Utilities, transport, IT/IP and mergers form the backbone of the department's caseload. Perceived to have kept a lower profile this year, the team was at least able to celebrate the return of prodigal son **John Cook** from Macfarlanes. He acted for Thomson in opposing the proposed Airtours take-over of First Choice. Popular all-rounder **Trevor Soames** continues to have an immense reputation for aviation/airport work, and divides his time evenly between London and Brussels. Telecoms has been a strong area this year, with clients such as France Telecom, Siemens and Mannesmann. Financial and insurance work saw the firm advise on the AXA/GRE link-up, and advise Switch Card and Halifax on competition matters. In energy and utilities, the team advised the AES Corporation on the acquisition of the Drax power station and on regulatory issues. The firm also advised car manufacturers during the Competition Commission's inquiry. **Clients:** Cinven; Carlsberg-Tetley; William Grant & Sons; United Airlines; TXU Europe (Eastern Electricity); Kelda plc (ex-Yorkshire Water); Hydrogas UK.

Simmons & Simmons A strong core practice in mergers and cartel work, with a highly respected regulatory practice in utilities, transport and media. The *"able and experienced"* **Peter Freeman** is a *"clever lawyer,"* who is *"good with the authorities."* The head of the group, he is an all-rounder, working on mergers and active on railway and broadcasting work. The *"absolutely straightforward"* **Martin Smith** *("he knows what he's doing and is easy to collaborate with")* has recent experience in the brewing, utilities and telecoms sectors, doing substantial merger control work. **Melanie Farquharson** is a younger name said to be *"coming through."*

Merger control work includes acting on the Bass/Punch Taverns and Vivendi/BSkyB deals. Investigation work has seen the firm active in seamless steel tubes, newsprint, vitamins, cement and airlines. The firm continues to provide regulatory advice in transport (Railtrack), telecoms, utilities and broadcasting (ITC). **Clients:** Interbrew SA; EFPIA (pharmaceuticals); Elkem ASA; UK MoD; Cadbury Schweppes; GKN plc; Aventis Pharma Ltd; Gallaher Group plc; BA; One2One.

Baker & McKenzie Head of the practice is the *"outstanding"* **Lynda Martin Alegi**. She is *"pragmatic and down to earth"* and is regarded as being *"so client-friendly that she gets the respect of the most obnoxious and difficult clients."* Global work includes multi-jurisdictional filings, cartel and trade work. A highlight of the year was the firm's advice to an intervening party on the attempted FirstChoice/Airtours link-up. Inquiry work includes cement, pharmaceuticals and the Competition Commission's car investigation. The firm continues to have niche strength in telecoms and electricity work. **Clients:** Shell International; Levi Strauss; Cisco; Archer Daniels Midland; Mercedes Benz; Nortel; McLaren; Kellogg; BG plc; Apple; Kuoni Reisen Holdings plc; Tetra Pak.

Theodore Goddard The practice's leading light is the *"down to earth and coherent"* **Guy Leigh**, the Chairman of the UK Competition Law Association. His principal areas of activity this year have been in IT, pharmaceuticals, healthcare and manufacturing, where he *"knows what he's talking about and doesn't panic."* The team is mainly known for its new economy work, in leisure, media, IT and telecoms. Less than half the practice's workload is M&A-related. The remainder involves advisory and strategic work such as pricing issues advice and resisting or forwarding complaints. The department also has a substantial trade group. Work this year includes acting for the governing body of a major sport in persuading the OFT to reject a complaint made against it. Abroad, the group advised a Latin American steel producer/exporter of steel and iron products in relation to anti-dumping investigations in the EU and Turkey, and an overseas pharmaceutical company on the regulatory issues resulting from approvals granted by the European Medicines Evaluation Agency. **Clients:** OFTEL; Oracle Corporation; VarTec; CR Bard; Nortel Networks; GE Capital; National Westminster; Freightliner.

Bristows Considered *"brilliant"* in IP/IT competition-related work, the firm has been active in other innovative industries, including the pharmaceutical, biotechnology, engineering and medical sciences sectors. Known for its contentious abilities, this year just under half the practice's caseload has been litigation-oriented. Other work has included merger control and general issues such as licensing matters. The practice continued to work on the BiB joint venture (Panasonic/Matsushita) which was launched in October 1999. Have advised UDV and Du Pont on general competition issues. **Clients:** BBC; Du Pont; Eastman Kodak; Gillette; ICI; Monsanto; MTV Europe; Lighting Industry Federation; Philips NV; Panasonic; Tetley; United Distillers & Vintners.

CMS Cameron McKenna Not a large scale merger house, the practice is perhaps best known for its utilities work. Inquiry work this year includes advising Nestlé in relation to the ice-cream and supermarkets matters. The team advised the Camelot Group plc on all the EC and UK competition law considerations relating to the investment to be made by the Post Office in Camelot if it is awarded the next national lottery licence. Also advised the Metronet Consortium which is bidding for the PPP service contract on London Underground, covering a range of EC and UK regulatory law issues. The team has been involved on post-Competition Act work and has been particularly active in the rail and infrastructure, financial services, air transport and energy sectors. **Clients:** Post Office; Nestlé; Metronet; DETR; LOT; NETA; Camelot Group plc.

Eversheds A young team and the only one comprehensively to cover the whole country through its well regarded offices in and outside London. *"Constructive to deal with,"* competition generalist **Stephen Rose** has been active this year on merger control matters. Other partners are experienced in the water industry, electricity and the automobile industry, where the practice was active in the Competition Commission's car inquiry. Other work has involved putting forward amendments to the Competition Act on behalf of the Electricity Association and advising on the acquisition by Alanod Aluminium-Veredelung GmbH of Metalloxyd-Ano Coil Ltd. The team wrote the CBI guide to the Competition Act. **Clients:** Volkswagen Group UK; Electricity Association; Ty Inc (Beanie babies); Envirologic.

Richards Butler **Katherine Holmes** is the practice's stand-out name following her work for the BBC, for whom she acted in the successful Premier League case. An all-rounder, she is also known for general media and transport work. The practice has been active in the supermarket inquiry, and other work has seen the firm advising RTE (Radio Telefis Eireann) in connection with a claim that its licence fee funding constitutes state aid. Niche strengths are found in leisure, media, transport and retailing. **Clients:** BBC; Galileo International; Rank Group plc; De Luxe; McBride plc.

Other Notable Practitioners The *"guru we all respect,"* **Richard Whish**, is still in demand, despite his reduced level of 'coal-face' activity. He is *"a rare example of an individual who can carry a substantial practice,"* and has a reputation as *"an academic with practical experience."* Some believe that *"in terms of legal knowledge he has no equal in the country."* Clients, lawyers and economists particularly appreciate his ability to give fresh views – *"you go to him for strategy and deep thought,"* and he is felt to be *"an ideas and knowledge man rather than a proceduralist."*

Ex-Lovells **Michael Hutchings** has a broad client base for whom he does advisory work. He *"knows what he's doing,"* and is *"particularly good at walking the corridors of power."* **Julian Maitland-Walker** has made a name for himself in litigation, recently in petrol station and brewing sector work. Half his practice remains advisory, and he acts as consultant to several other law firms. Ex-Bristows **Susan Singleton** is a specialist in IP and competition, working on litigation and advisory work. Recent work has seen her busy on drafting compliance programmes for UK plcs.

THE SOUTH & SOUTH WEST

COMPETITION/ANTI-TRUST • The South & South West	Ptnrs	Assts
❶ **Burges Salmon** Bristol	2	6
❷ **Bond Pearce** Plymouth	1	3

LEADING INDIVIDUALS	
❶ **CLAYDON Laura** Burges Salmon	**COPPEN Simon** Burges Salmon
MURRAY Rob Bond Pearce	

Within each band, firms are listed alphabetically. *See **Profiles** on page 178*

Burges Salmon The *"worthy"* **Laura Claydon** and *"solid all-rounder"* **Simon Coppen** are the practice's main players. Claydon has an extensive merger-related practice, which includes regulatory and commercial agreement work. Coppen works more on the commercial side, on joint ventures, licensing, distribution and dawn raid/compliance issues. Adding to an impressive transport work portfolio (particularly in the bus and rail sectors) the practice advised on clearing the CHC Helicopter Corporation/HSG link-up. Inquiry and review work includes successfully reducing undertakings for FirstGroup/SB Holdings. Other sectors of activity include building, soft drinks, hi-tech, sports and media rights. **Clients:** FirstGroup plc; Great Western Trains; CHC Helicopter Corporation/Scotia Helicopters; Honda; Racecourse Association Ltd.

Bond Pearce Among what one client described as the firm's *"exceptionally diverse range of esoteric legal skills,"* lies the EU and competition team. This is led by the *"personable and technically excellent"* **Rob Murray**. He spent his formative years with Clifford Chance, including five years in Brussels, and is considered to offer *"specific experience and a high level of capability,"* as well as the client's dream, *"competitive rates."* As a consequence of his experience, the practice has a remit extending beyond its Southampton base. Most of the work is of a behavioural nature, though merger control work does exist here. Notable expertise is in retail, transport (maritime and aviation), pharmaceuticals, chemicals and defence. The firm was instructed in relation to intended High Court proceedings against Birdseye Walls Ltd, alleging breaches of EC Competition law and claiming compensation under the Commercial Agents' Regulations. **Clients:** Superdrug plc; B&Q plc.

WALES

COMPETITION/ANTI-TRUST • Wales	Ptnrs	Assts
❶ **Edwards Geldard** Cardiff	1	3
Eversheds Cardiff	2	1
Morgan Cole Cardiff	6	3

Within each band, firms are listed alphabetically.

Edwards Geldard Boasting an ex-Slaughter and May competition partner, the practice is involved on a wide range of issues, from merger notification to behavioural work. The practice is supported by utilities experts, and has been involved on public procurement matters. Commercial agreements, including distribution and licensing matters, are also dealt with. As with most practices in the principality, compliance work is a busy area. **Clients:** Public bodies and private corporates.

Eversheds The Cardiff office is essentially known for its state aid and public procurement work. The practice therefore advises many public sector bodies on all aspects of competition work, including on PFI work. **Clients:** Welsh Development Agency; National Museum of Wales.

Morgan Cole A generalist competition group active in mergers, regulation, state aid and public procurement. The practice acted in the world-wide outsourcing of BP Amoco's telecoms service to MCI Worldcom, a deal worth £650m. Also advised on the merger of Addis Group Ltd with a leading German company. **Clients:** Clarins; Carlton International Distributors; TBI; Shimano; Mitel Corporation.

MIDLANDS

COMPETITION/ANTI-TRUST • Midlands	Ptnrs	Assts
❶ **Pinsent Curtis** Birmingham	2	2
Wragge & Co Birmingham	2	2
❷ **Eversheds** Birmingham	1	3

LEADING INDIVIDUALS	
❶ **LOUGHER Guy** Wragge & Co	**REES Kate** Pinsent Curtis
❷ **PROWSE Richard** Eversheds	

Within each band, firms are listed alphabetically. *See **Profiles** on page 178*

Pinsent Curtis The Birmingham office works alongside the London and Leeds offices in what is a national competition team with a *"fine reputation."* **Kate Rees** is a star player in Birmingham. She is a competition all-rounder with strong experience in airport/aircraft and utilities (gas) regulatory work. Around a third of the practice's work is on mergers and this year the team advised Arriva plc on transactions in the bus and rail sectors. The rest of the team's work is oriented to the behavioural side, with a substantial amount of procurement work (eg. for the procurement arm of the NHS) and post-Competition Act advisory work. **Clients:** Arriva plc, BG Transco plc, Argos, Connex Rail, Telecom Eireann, Booker plc.

Wragge & Co **Guy Lougher** has established a national reputation, with firms in other regions citing him as their first port of call on conflict matters. *"Technically top,"* he has a *"grasp of the issues"* and is a *"good case manager who gives sound advice."* He is seen to lead an *"ambitious practice,"* which has gone against a perceived trend (where Brussels is leaving more work to the individual member states) by recently opening a Brussels office. The strength of the corporate client base gives the competition team a steady flow of merger work and this year the team acted for HJ Heinz Europe on its acquisition of United Biscuits Frozen & Chilled Foods Ltd. Other areas of activity have been the energy, automobile and aviation industries. The team has also advised on public procurement, regulatory, anti-dumping and complaint work. **Clients:** HJ Heinz Europe, British Airways, AT&T, PowerGen, NatWest Equity Partners.

Eversheds **Richard Prowse** maintains his reputation as a leading regional player. The benefits of a national practice were exemplified by the Birmingham office's ability to advise clients on the Competition Commission's car inquiry as a direct result of the involvement of the London group. Regular corporate support work includes mergers (Partco/Unipart) and commercial contract (distribution agreements) work. The team has been particularly active in the motor manufacturing and airport sectors this year. **Clients:** Britax International; Partco Group; Hampson Industries.

THE NORTH

COMPETITION/ANTI-TRUST • The North	Ptnrs	Assts
❶ **Addleshaw Booth & Co** Leeds, Manchester	3	10
Eversheds Leeds, Manchester, Middlesbrough, Newcastle	2	5
❷ **Dickinson Dees** Newcastle upon Tyne	2	3
Pinsent Curtis Leeds	1	1

LEADING INDIVIDUALS	
❶ **COLLINSON Adam** Eversheds	**DAVEY Jonathan** Addleshaw Booth & Co
JURKIW Andrij Pinsent Curtis	**LINDRUP Garth** Addleshaw Booth & Co
❷ **McDONNELL Phil** Garretts	
❸ **HARRISON Geoff** Eversheds	**SCHOLES Jeremy** Walker Morris
WARWICK Neil Dickinson Dees	

Within each band, firms are listed alphabetically *See **Profiles** on page 178*

Addleshaw Booth & Co **Garth Lindrup** and **Jonathan Davey** are held in high regard by the northern legal community. Based in Manchester and covering the north west and north east, they are *"technically expert."* Lindrup *"directs from a high level,"* and is known for his general competition, regulatory (especially utilities) and public procurement work. The *"intelligent"* Davey is a respected all-rounder. The competition team is part of the wider trade and regulatory group. The firm's blue chip client base means that it has been involved on merger control issues, commercial agreements, investigations and compliance work following the Competition Act. The bulk of the practice's workload involves public procurement and state aid matters. The team was appointed by Kelda to advise on periodic price reviews and general regulatory matters. **Clients:** Asda; Airtours plc; Guardian Media Group plc; International Paper; Kelda Group plc; Kettle Foods; Servisair plc; Yorkshire Group plc.

Eversheds *"Direct and smooth,"* **Adam Collinson** (of the Leeds office) is considered to be the *"star"* of the firm's Northern practice. **Geoff Harrison** in Newcastle has been involved on some investigations work this year, but he has a lower market profile in competition due to his national role as part of the firm's integration board. The practice works on mergers, commercial arrangements, investigatory, compliance and contentious work. The utility sector has been an area of particular activity. As well as advising clients on their multi-jurisdictional mergers, the firm advises third parties to transactions. An example was the firm's advice to American Securities LP, a US merger arbitrage firm, in connection with the hostile bid by Vodafone Airtouch for Mannesmann. **Clients:** Yorkshire Electricity; Asda; Invensys Power Systems; British Gypsum.

Dickinson Dees **Neil Warwick** heads the competition team in a practice known for its strong base of active corporate clients. Merger work has seen the firm act on merger clearances at the EU and OFT level for Go-Ahead, and on disposals and acquisitions for other clients. Transport, particularly trains and buses, is a notable area of expertise. **Clients:** The Go-Ahead Group; Arriva plc; Nike UK Ltd.

Pinsent Curtis **Andrij Jurkiw** has a good reputation for his *"personable and bright"* approach. A practice which has traditionally been very active in merger control work advised Polypipe plc on the merger implications of a £337million bid by IMI plc (involving merger clearances in five jurisdictions). Coal, steel and transport have been particular areas of activity. The firm was involved in the Competition Commission inquiry into the supply of groceries from multiple stores, and advised on Early Guidance applications to the OFT. **Clients:** Smith & Nephew plc; SIG plc; Pace Micro Technology plc; MD Foods plc; Schneider Electric Ltd; Polypipe plc.

Other Notable Practitioners **Jeremy Scholes** of Walker Morris in Leeds is perceived to be an *"academic"* practitioner who *"knows his stuff and is enthusiastic."* Although he still does some lecturing, he has been involved in merger control and litigation cases. The head of Garretts' national competition unit is **Phil McDonnell**, who is based in Manchester. He has a general competition practice, working on mergers and behavioural work in areas such as transport and pharmaceuticals.

SCOTLAND

COMPETITION/ANTI-TRUST • Scotland	Ptnrs	Assts
❶ **Burness** Edinburgh	3	3
Maclay Murray & Spens Edinburgh, Glasgow	1	4
MacRoberts Glasgow	3	3
Shepherd & Wedderburn WS Edinburgh	1	2
❷ **Biggart Baillie** Glasgow	1	1
Dundas & Wilson CS Edinburgh	1	4

LEADING INDIVIDUALS	
❶ **DEAN Michael** Maclay Murray & Spens	**McLEAN James** Burness
❷ **DOWNIE Gordon** Shepherd & Wedderburn WS	
FLINT David MacRoberts	
UP AND COMING	
MILLER Colin Biggart Baillie	

Within each band, firms are listed alphabetically. *See **Profiles** on page 178*

Burness The department leader is **Jim McLean**, a lawyer with a *"technical and philosophical approach"* who has *"seen it all."* Behavioural work, ranging from cartels and price-fixing cases to commercial agreements, is the practice's mainstay. **Clients:** Harris Tweed; sports bodies; finance houses.

Maclay Murray & Spens Practice head is the *"commercial"* **Michael Dean**, a *"non-technical"* lawyer who enjoys *"a good rapport with clients."* This is an all-round anti-trust practice, advising on multi-jurisdictional merger filings, state aid and regulatory work, as well as merger control matters. The practice has recent experience in the transport, electricity, pharmaceutical and insurance sectors. The team advised on a joint venture between two non-UK corporations. **Clients:** OFGEM; Grampian Holdings plc; Marsh Mercer; Weir Group plc; Scottish Enterprises.

MacRoberts **David Flint** *("turns his hand to most things")* is the firm's main competition expert. Known for his IP/IT work, he advises primarily on general competition work and procurement issues in those areas. The team has advised on Scottish Nuclear contracts and competition work for British Energy plc. **Clients:** Coca-Cola Schweppes; Johnston Press plc; First Group plc.

Shepherd & Wedderburn WS **Gordon Downie**'s profile has been rising lately at a firm which advises on mergers, regulatory, procurement, state aid and compliance work. The water, electricity, media/telecoms and travel sectors have been especially profitable this year. Advised Scottish Power plc on competition and utility regulation clearances for work in Northern Ireland, and GEC on the acquisition of Govan shipyard premises from Kvaerner. **Clients:** Scottish Power plc; Thus plc; Stagecoach Holdings plc; SRU; GEC; John Wood Group; Sir Robert McAlpine Ltd; Manweb plc.

Biggart Baillie A generalist mergers and commercial agreement-oriented practice, which makes its debut in the ratings. It is led by the young **Colin Miller**, a *"true specialist"* who *"knows his onions."* As well as private corporates such as Scottish Power and Scottish Telecom, the practice advises trade associations. Advised The Drambuie Liqueur Company Ltd on the implications for its EU distribution network of new national and EU legislation. **Clients:** BSW Timber plc; ScotRail Railways Ltd.

Dundas & Wilson CS With a leading corporate practice it is no surprise that the competition team has been busy this year. Particular sectors of activity have been media and broadcasting, banking and insurance. The firm has advised clients such as RBS and Scottish Media Group on competition aspects of their acquisitions. It has also worked on commercial contracts and on compliance manuals pursuant to the Competition Act. The firm also advises public and semi-public bodies on state aid and public procurement matters. **Clients:** Tullis Russell Group Ltd; Sidlaw Group plc; Independent Television Network Ltd; Bank of Scotland; West of Scotland Water Authority; University of Edinburgh.

LEADERS IN COMPETITION / ANTI-TRUST

AINSWORTH, Lesley M.

Lovells, London (020) 7296 2000
lesley.ainsworth@lovells.com
Specialisation: Specialist work includes UK and EC competition law (advisory work, investigations by the Office of Fair Trading, the Competition Commission and the EC Commission and proceedings before the European Court of Justice and national courts; state aids; free movement of goods and services; public procurement; EC agricultural regimes; advice on proposed EC legislation and the implementation of EC legislation in Member States.
Prof. Memberships: Examiner, Qualified Lawyers Transfer Test Board; Member, Solicitors' European Group.
Career: Articled *Lovells*; qualified 1981; London 1979-1983; Brussels office 1983-1985; secondment to *LeBoeuf, Lamb, Leiby & McRae* 1985-1986; London since 1986; partner 1988.

AITMAN, David

Denton Wilde Sapte, London (020) 7320 6332
dca@dentonwildesapte.com
Partner, Head of Competition and EC Department.
Specialisation: Advising on all areas of EC and domestic competition law, particularly in the energy, transport, manufacturing, retail, communications and media sectors; and on regulation, in connection with privatised utilities. Practice covers notifications and complaints to the European Commission, the Office of Fair Trading, the Monopolies and Mergers Commission, Oftel, the Restrictive Practices Court and the DTI.
Prof. Memberships: Competition Law Association, International Bar Association.
Career: Qualified in 1982 after articles at *Denton Hall*. Became a Partner of the firm in 1988.
Publications: Editor of section on intellectual property licensing in Butterworth's 'Encyclopedia of Competition Law', of the sections on competition law in 'Practical Intellectual Property' and in the 'Yearbook of Media Law' and author of telecoms chapter in 'Bellamy & Child'.
Personal: Born 1956. Educated at Clifton College, Bristol, then Sheffield University 1975-78 (English Literature) and the Royal Academy of Music (1978). Leisure interests include music, theatre, reading, wind-surfing and skiing.

ALLAN, Bill
Linklaters (A member firm of Linklaters & Alliance), London (020) 7456 3574
bill.allan@linklaters.com
Partner 1982. Corporate Department.
Specialisation: Specialises in EC and UK anti-trust law, mergers and acquisitions, and other competition and trade-related areas of the law. He has extensive experience in the UK and EC context, representing clients from diverse industries including utilities, food, transport, brewing, leisure, chemicals, construction materials and computers. Publications include 'Competition Laws of the United Kingdom and Republic of Ireland', which he co-authored. Qualified 1976.

BRIGHT, Chris
Clifford Chance, London (020) 7600 1000
chris.bright@cliffordchance.com
Specialisation: Competition and regulatory law in the EU and the UK, including strategic anti-trust advice, merger control, including global filings, cartels, abuse of dominance, economic regulation of utilites–particularly water, energy, rail and telecoms; state aid; public procurement; the Brussels process.
Prof. Memberships: Solicitor, England and Wales; IBA, ABA.
Career: Head of *Clifford Chance* competition and regulatory practice 1999; trainee 1983-89; assistant solicitor and partner *Linklaters & Paines*; seconded to competition policy division; DTI 1989-91; Lecturer, Jesus College Oxford 1984-86.

CARSTENSEN, Laura
Slaughter and May, London (020) 710 4265
Partner, EU/Competition Department.
Specialisation: Practice in UK and EU Competition law, predominantly in relation to strategic corporate events (M&A; key changes in business policy and practice) and contentious situations (cartel/abuse of dominance inquiries). Extensive experience before the European Commission, Office of Fair Trading and Competition Commission.
Prof. Memberships: The Law Society.
Career: Qualified 1987 with *Slaughter and May* and became a partner in 1994.
Personal: Born 11 November 1960. Educated Withington Girls School, Manchester then St.Hilda's College, Oxford (English Lang. & Lit.). Lives in Hampstead, London.

CHAPPATTE, Philippe P.
Slaughter and May, London (020) 7600 1200
Specialisation: Competition law specialist. Provides a wide range of UK and EU Competition law advice (including on state aid) in connection with transactions, litigation and regulatory investigations and has been responsible for a large number of notifications to the EC Commission under the EC Merger Regulation and Article 85. Major cases have included the Alcazar project (the proposed merger of SAS/KLM/Austrian Airlines/Swissair in 1993), the Montedison/Shell JV in polypropylene and polyethylene and the SAS/Lufthansa Alliance. Recent deals include Canal+/ Nethold (pay-TV), Williams/Chubb (security and fire protection), Shell/BASF polyethylene JV (Elenac) and Telia/Telenor. He has also been involved in a number of European Court cases. Experience of UK Competition law has included Competition Commission investigations both in monopoly and in merger cases. Cases include acting for 'Punch' in its contested acquisition of the Allied pub estate and the Carlton/United/Granada and Anglo/Tarmac mergers.
Prof. Memberships: Co-founder of European Competition Lawyers Forum. Contributor to Bellamy & Child 'Common Market Law of Competition'.
Career: Bryanston School. Oxford University (BA Law, First Class). Université Libre de Bruxelles (Lic.Sp.Dr.Eur., Highest Distinction). Qualified *Slaughter and May* 1982. Partner 1989. Responsible for running and development of Brussels office between April 1991 and August 1996.
Personal: Three children.

CLAYDON, Laura
Burges Salmon, Bristol (0117) 939 2273
laura.claydon@burges-salmon.com
Specialisation: Main area of practice is competition and regulatory law; has conducted many merger cases and competition investigations before the OFT acting particularly for clients in the transport, food, sports and media and oil and gas industries. Recent cases include: the MMC inquiry into the acquisition by FirstBus plc (now FirstGroup plc) of SB Holdings Limited and subsequent review by the DTI/OFT which reduced divestment to behavioural undertakings; the Competition Commission inquiry into the acquisition by CHC Helicopter Corporation of Helicopter Services Group (referred September 1999); many cases involving allegations of price-fixing, market sharing, predatory behaviour, predatory pricing and refusal to supply. Advises on competition audits and compliance procedures in view of the new Competition Act 1998.
Prof. Memberships: Solicitors European Group, Law Society
Career: On qualification in 1988 joined *Burges Salmon*–Partner 1996.
Personal: Hull University 1982-85. Interests: racing and the great outdoors.

COHEN, Ralph J.
SJ Berwin & Co, London (020) 7533 2701
ralph.cohen@sjberwin.com
Specialisation: Partner specialising in EC and UK Competition Law and EC Trade and Customs Law. Has extensive experience representing clients before the OFT, MMC and European Commission across a wide range of industries. Practice areas include EC and UK merger clearances and coordinating multi jurisdictional filings, advising on compatibility of commercial agreements with competition law compliance, anti-dumping investigations, WTO and general customs related issues.
Prof. Memberships: Solicitors European Group.
Career: Qualified 1983. Partner at *S J Berwin & Co* 1991.
Personal: Born 10th May 1959. Attended Clifton College, and University of Southampton. Married with three sons.

COLLINSON, Adam G.
Eversheds, Leeds (0113) 243 0391
adamcollinson@eversheds.com
Partner in commercial department and head of EU/competition practice for Leeds/Manchester.
Specialisation: EU and UK competition and related commercial law. Significant exposure to automotive and chemical industries. Particular experience in advising on competition law compliance, merger control and pricing and distribution strategies. Advised Asda in its campaigns to end resale price maintenance for books and OTC medicines. Co-authored CBI Business Guide to Competition Law (July 1999).
Prof. Memberships: Solicitors European Group (Committee member–Yorkshire Branch).
Career: Qualified in 1990 (*McKenna & Co*). Joined *Eversheds* in 1994. Became a partner in 1998. Educated at Oundle School and Durham University (Hatfield College).
Personal: Married with two daughters. Lives in Wetherby. Trustee of Constance Green Foundation.

COOK, C. John
Norton Rose, London (020) 7444 3096
cookcj@nortonrose.com
Partner, competition and EC department.
Specialisation: Competition law, EC law, (including international trade, public procurement and state aids) and transport and utilities regulation. A regular conference speaker and writer, he is the author, with C.S. Kerse, of 'EC Merger Control', the leading text book on EC merger control–published by Sweet & Maxwell–third ed. December 1999.
Career: Called to the Bar of Grays Inn in 1975. Lectureship, Magdalen College, Oxford 1976-81. UK government legal service 1976-88. *Norton Rose* 1988-1997 (headed Competition and EC Department). Rejoined *Norton Rose* in February 2000 after two years at *Macfarlanes*.

COPPEN, Simon
Burges Salmon, Bristol (0117) 939 2291
simon.coppen@burges-salmon.com
See under Transport, p.799

CUTTING, Michael
Linklaters (A member firm of Linklaters & Alliance), London (020) 7456 3514
michael.cutting@linklaters.com
Specialisation: Partner, competition & regulatory law group, specialist in EU & UK competition, utility law & practice, competition law.
Career: Partner–1995–to date. Assistant solicitor, *Linklaters* 1988-95. Qualified–1988.

DAVEY, Jonathan
Addleshaw Booth & Co, Manchester (0161) 934 6349
jwd@addleshaw-booth.co.uk
Partner in Trade & Regulatory Department, Commercial Group.
Specialisation: Main areas of work in this field are UK and EC competition law (including the law relating to restrictive practices, mergers and anti-competitive behaviour), public procurement law and state aids. Has been involved in the recent past in a number of significant notifications and complaints to the EC Commission and has considerable experience of UK Merger Control and of advising on UK competition law generally.
Prof. Memberships: Association Internationale des Jeunes Avocats, CBI National Consumer Law Advisory Panel, North West Solicitors European Group.
Career: Joined the firm in 1986 and qualified in 1988. Became an Associate in 1992 and a Partner in 1994.
Personal: Educated at Manchester University 1982-85 (LL.B Hons) and the College of Law, Chester 1985-86 (1st Class Hons in Law Society Final Examination). Enjoys hill walking, travel and good food.

DEAN, Michael
Maclay Murray & Spens, Glasgow (0141) 248 5011
Brussels +32 2 282 8415
Specialisation: Partner in the corporate department specialising in EU and UK competition matters. Prac-

tice covers agency, distribution, EC, UK and Multi-state merger clearances, cartels, Competition Commission proceedings, procurement issues, procedures and notices. Recent cases have involved the successful mediation of a $15m claim against a US client by a European agent; advising on competition issues in the financial services sector; provision of Eurodefence in Scottish courts in licensing litigation; advising public sector bodies on European state aid obligations; retained by several multinationals for competition investigations; advised on a range of Bosman issues; has advised Law Society of Scotland and is on a panel of advisors to the UK electricity and gas regulator. Frequently gives presentations to businesses on export issues and to lawyers on European law.
Prof. Memberships: Law Society of Scotland; Scottish Lawyers European Group. Chairman German-British Chamber of Commerce in Scotland; Chair, Glasgow Export Club.
Career: Qualified 1986. Assistant solicitor, *McKenna & Co.*, London 1986-1988. Assistant solicitor, *Lovell White Durrant*, London 1988-1990. Assistant solicitor and partner *McGrigor Donald* 1991-1997. Recruited by *Maclay Murray & Spens* as partner. Former external examiner, Europa Institute, Edinburgh.
Personal: Educated at St. Aloysius' College, Glasgow 1968-1978, University of Glasgow (LL.B Hons and Diploma in Legal Practice) 1978-1983, and at the College of Europe, Bruges, (Diploma in Advanced European Studies) 1983-1984. Interests include local politics. Born 15th January 1960. Lives in Glasgow.

DOWNIE, Gordon
Shepherd & Wedderburn WS, Edinburgh (0131) 228 9900
gordon.downie@shepwedd.co.uk
Specialisation: Head of the firm's competition and regulation group, which deals with the full range of UK and EC competition law work, ranging from merger and anti-trust clearances, to contentious proceedings and complaints to the OFT and European Commission. Experienced in assisting clients in setting up and maintaining compliance programmes to minimise their exposure to the legal consequences of breach of competition laws. Also advises clients across a variety of regulated sectors in their dealings with sectoral regulators, such as OFGEM, OFWAT, and OFTEL, and on compliance with their regulatory obligations.
Prof. Memberships: Law Society of Scotland, WS Society, Scottish Lawyers European Group, member of LSS Competition Law Sub-Committee.
Career: Qualified 1992 with *Shepherd & Wedderburn WS*. Assumed as partner in 1998.
Personal: Born 7 May 1966. University of Edinburgh, graduated LLB (Hons) 1988. European University Institute, graduated LLM 1990. Lives in Edinburgh.

FARQUHARSON, Melanie A.
Simmons & Simmons, London (020) 7628 2020
Specialisation: EC and competition law and regulation, with particular focus on utilities, transport (air and rail) pharmaceuticals and food and drink.
Prof. Memberships: International Bar Association. Solicitors' European Group. Competition Law Association.
Career: Qualified 1988. Partner 1994.
Publications: 'Parallel Trade in Europe' (Sweet & Maxwell, 1998), Editor of the Rail Transport Section of Butterworth's 'Competition Law' (5-volume loose-leaf Practitioner's textbook)
Personal: Graduate from St. Catharines College, Cambridge.

FINBOW, Roger J.
Ashurst Morris Crisp, London (020) 7638 1111
Specialisation: Partner in company department. Member of competition group. Head of sports law group. Handles all aspects of corporate and commercial law for principally public company clients; and competition law, especially mergers regulation. Recent matters include: Competition Commission inquiries into the acquisition by National Express of Scotrail and Central Trains; the merger of United News & Media and Carlton Communications; the acquisition by Air Canada of Canadian Airways, and other inquiries; the regulatory aspects of Imperial Tobacco Group's acquisition of Douwe Egberts Van Nelle and of the merger between NFC and Ocean Group; joint author of 'UK Merger Control: Law and Practice'.
Career: Qualified in 1977. Joined *Ashurst Morris Crisp* in 1975, becoming a Partner in 1984.
Personal: Born 13th May 1952. Attended Woodbridge School 1963-70 and Mansfield College Oxford 1971-74 (MA 1977). Leisure interests include classic cars, collecting model cars, motor biking, keeping fit, ballet and gardening. Director of Ipswich Town Football Club Co. Limited; governor of The Seckford Foundation. Lives in the Suffolk/Essex borders.

FLECK, Richard J.H.
Herbert Smith, London (020) 7374 8000
richard.fleck@herbertsmith.com
Practice Development Partner
Specialisation: Handles EC and competition law, commercial disputes and accounting law. Has extensive experience of references of proposed merger and monopoly situations and on other competitive and regulatory matters such as investigations under the Competition Act. Also of European competition authorities, the Department of Trade and the Bank of England. Other areas of expertise include major commercial disputes and advising major accounting firms and the Institute of Chartered Accountants on technical and accounting matters. He is the only lawyer on the Auditing Practices Board.
Career: Qualified in 1973. Partner at *Herbert Smith* since 1979.
Personal: Educated at Southampton University.

FLINT, David
MacRoberts, Glasgow (0141) 332 9988
df@macroberts.co.uk
See under Information Technology, p.

FREEMAN, Peter J.
Simmons & Simmons, London (020) 7628 2020
Head of EC and Competition Law.
Specialisation: Main area of practice is EC and UK competition and regulatory law, including mergers. Sector specialisations include broadcasting, energy and railways. Joint General Editor (with Richard Whish) of 'Butterworths Competition Law'. Author (with Richard Whish) of 'A Guide to the Competition Act 1998'. (Butterworths, 1999). Chairman of the Regulatory Policy Institute, Oxford.
Prof. Memberships: IBA, UIA, Law Society, Competition Law Association.
Career: Qualified 1972. Joined *Simmons & Simmons* in 1973.
Personal: Born 2nd October 1948. Attended Kingswood School, Bath, 1961-66, Goethe Institut, Berlin, 1967, Trinity College, Cambridge 1967-71, and Université Libre de Bruxelles 1972-73. Leisure interests include naval history and music.

FRIEND, Mark
Allen & Overy, London (020) 7330 3000
Specialisation: Partner specialising in UK and EC competition law and utilities regulation. Has wide experience of dealing with the OFT, competition commission, sectoral regulators and the EC Commission. Author of numerous articles in leading academic and professional journals.
Prof. Memberships: Member of City of London Law Society Competition Law Sub-Committee, Solicitors European Group, IBA.
Career: Qualified 1982, Partner 1990.
Personal: Cambridge University (1979 BA Law) Université Libre de Bruxelles (Lic Spec en Droit Eur 1983). Born 1957.

HARRISON, Geoff
Eversheds, London
Specialisation: Practises in EU and UK competition law. Experience of other national systems. Advises major UK, European and US clients on merger control, pricing, supply policy and regulatory investigations.
Prof. Memberships: Law society.
Career: University of Leicester 1971. Admitted 1974.

HOLMES, Katherine
Richards Butler, London (020) 7247 6555
kmh@richardsbutler.com
Specialisation: Partner in Corporate and Commercial Department; specialises in EC and UK competition law and EC law generally. Advises clients from a wide variety of industries, including transportation, leisure, food and drink, construction, media and entertainment, pharmaceuticals and computer software.
Prof. Memberships: Chairman of Joint Working Party of the UK Bars and Law Societies on Competition Law; Solicitors European Group; former Chairman and Vice-President of the Bar Association for Commerce, Finance and Industry (BACFI).
Career: Qualified as a barrister (1973). Joined *CBI* in 1976 becoming Head of Commercial Law; from 1981 Senior Legal Adviser to two major public companies; in 1989, joined *Richards Butler* and after admission as Solicitor became Partner in 1991.
Personal: Born 10th May 1952. Leisure pursuits include sailing, skiing, swimming, theatre and entertaining. Lives in London.

HOLMES, Simon
SJ Berwin & Co, London (020) 7533 2222
simon.holmes@sjberwin.com
Specialisation: A wide range of work including: extensive range of merger work acting for the parties, complainants or third parties; advising on dominance issues (pricing/discounts/parallel imports etc); and a wide range of commercial arrangements both on and off-line.
Prof. Memberships: Recent Chairman, Solicitors' European Group.
Career: 1st Class Honours, Law and Economics from Cambridge. Grande Distinction, Licence Speciale en Droit Européen, Brussels University.
Personal: Married, 2 daughters. Walking, cycling, tennis, film.

HUTCHINGS, Michael B.
Michael Hutchings, Warminster (07768) 105777
mbh@dircon.co.uk
Fax: (01373) 832785
Specialisation: Advice on all aspects of EU law,

especially internal market, competition and regulation; UK implementation of EU law; UK competition law.
Prof. Memberships: British Institute of International and Comparative Law (Chairman of Executive Committee). Solicitors European Group (Former Chairman). European Competition Law Review (Editorial Board).
Career: Qualified 1973; articled with *McKenna & Co*; partner *Lovell White Durrant* 1981-96; established independent sole practice 1996.
Personal: Born 8 November 1948.

JURKIW, Andrij
Pinsent Curtis, Leeds (0113) 244 5000
andrij.jurkiw@pinsents.com
Head of competition, Leeds.
Specialisation: Specialises in Merger Clearances, OFT & Competition Commission investigations; notifications and complaints to EC Commission; Competition Law litigation; Competition Law compliance programmes; parallel imports and public procurement. Important cases: merger clearance advice for Polypipe plc in the Polypipe/IMI Merger (5 jurisdictions); acting for MD Foods plc in landmark RTPA case of MD Foods v. Baines; acting for companies who participated in ceiling tiles cartel; acting for MD Foods plc in relation to MMC inquiry into raw milk; acting in one of the few concluded Early Guidance Applications under the Competition Act 1998.
Prof. Memberships: Law Society. Solicitors' European Group.
Career: Articled *Slater Heelis* 1987-89; *Hammond Suddards* EC Unit 1989-91; *Eversheds* (Manchester) 1991-94, setting up EC Practice. *Pinsent Curtis* 1994 to date. Partner 1999. Law Degree–Leeds Metropolitan University.
Personal: Travel, choral singing, fine wines, classic cars, photography.

KON, Stephen D.
SJ Berwin & Co, London (020) 7533 2337
stephen.kon@sjberwin.com
Specialisation: Partner specialising in EU and competition law. Stephen heads the department. He acts in a wide variety of EU and competition matters, including UK and EU merger clearances. He regularly appears before the European Commission, the Monopolies and Merger Commission, the Office of Fair Trading, The Court of First Instance and the European Court; he also has an active EU/competition litigation practice before the UK domestic courts. Significant merger clearance work has included acting for Guinness on the second phase EU clearance of the merger with Grand Metropolitan (reportedly Europe's largest merger), for which the department won last year's Legal Business Award for 'Competition Team of the Year'; and a large number of EU and UK merger clearances including, most recently, the EU clearance of the joint venture between Fyffes and Capespan. He has also acted in a number of leading competition and state aid cases before the European Courts and has been instructed to act for the European Commission in a number of competition cases before the CFI and ECJ. Leading cases in which he acted last year before the European Court include the Laserdisken case before the ECJ, in which he successfully represented Warner Home Video, and the Generics case, a successful judicial review decided by the European Court; previous leading cases in which he successfully represented clients before the ECJ include a number of competition and state aids cases for the Ladbroke group before the ECJ and CFI, the Banks case for the European Commission, a leading authority on the availability of damages for breaches of EU competition law, and the Commerzbank and Allen & Hanburys cases before the ECJ. Publications include: 'Competition and Business Regulation in the Single Market' as well as articles in the 'European Competition Law review' and the 'European Law Review', amongst others.
Prof. Memberships: International Bar Association; Law Society's Solicitors' European Group (former Chairman).
Career: Law lecturer at Reading University and Sussex University. Qualified in 1980. Partner at *S J Berwin & Co* 1982.
Personal: Educated at Sussex University (BA Hons). Born 26th September 1949. Lives in London.

LEIGH, Guy I.F.
Theodore Goddard, London (020) 7606 8855
Specialisation: Guy Leigh heads the firm's competition and regulation group, based in both London and Brussels. His practice focuses on EC and UK competition and regulatory work. He has extensive experience of joint venture, technology transfer, state aids and competition, regulatory and compliance issues, and has advised in relation to such issues particularly in the IT, media and communications, sports, pharmaceutical and healthcare, telecommunications, and transport sectors. Experience includes representing the Intellectual Property Owners Inc. of the US before the European Court of Justice in the Magill TV Listings case and advising a leading software manufacturer, with regard to a wide range of EC competition law issues. Guy also dealt successfully with the merger control aspects of the acquisition by MAID plc, now The Dialog Corporation plc, of Knight-Ridder Information Inc and Knight-Ridder AG. Guy's past experience includes having been involved with the TSB vesting and flotation, the acquisition by British Airways of British Caledonian, a major Monopolies and Mergers Commission reference concerning the bus industry and a number of newspaper merger references. Guy is Chairman of the English Competition Law Association, a Vice President and past Reporter General and International Reporter of the International League for Competition Law. He is also a member of the Brussels-based European Competition Lawyers Forum and of the Law Society Bar Joint Working Party on Competition. Guy is co-author with Diana Guy of 'The EEC and Intellectual Property', the author of various articles on EC law and a frequent speaker at the competition law conferences.

LINDRUP, Garth
Addleshaw Booth & Co, Manchester (0161) 934 6000
Partner in trade & regulatory department, commercial group.
Specialisation: Work includes UK and EU competition law, especially merger control, articles 81 and 82, public procurement, joint ventures, distribution, agency and franchising, state aid. Editor, 'Butterworths Competition Law Handbook' and various other publications; Chairman, Law Society's European Group 1994/95.
Prof. Memberships: IBA, LIDC, CBI Competition Panel, ICC Competition Committee.
Career: Qualified 1975. Joined firm in 1979 and became Partner in 1984.
Personal: Holds BA, LLM (Cantab).

LIVINGSTON, Dorothy K.
Herbert Smith, London (020) 7374 8000
dorothy.livingston@herbertsmith.com
Partner, deputy head of european and competition law department and head of public sector and utilities procurement unit.
Specialisation: Her areas of expertise cover the full range of EU and UK competition law, including restrictive agreements, monopolies, anti-competitive practices, abuse of dominant position, mergers, public procurement, state aids and utility regulation. Also contributes to the work of the firm's international finance and banking department with particular reference to EMU and state guarantees. She is the joint author of 'Competition Law Sources' and author of 'Competition Law and Practice' (Sweet & Maxwell) and has contributed three chapters on competition and EC law to 'Finance Leasing' (Euromoney, 3rd ed.), as well as being author of The Competition Act 1998 (Sweet & Maxwell, in preparation). Sits on the advisory board of the Centre for European Law at King's College, London.
Prof. Memberships: City of London Law Society (Chairman of Banking Law and Member of EC and Competition Law Sub-Committees), Financial Law Panel Working Party on State Aids.
Career: Qualified in 1972. With *Herbert Smith* since articles. Became a partner in 1980.
Personal: Educated at St Hugh's College, Oxford, Central Newcastle High School GDST.

LOUGHER, Guy
Wragge & Co, Birmingham (0121) 265 2202
guy_lougher@wragge.com
Head of EU/Competition Group.
Specialisation: EU and competition law, particularly its application to merger control, trading and IP Licensing Agreements and public procurement.
Prof. Memberships: Committee Member of Law Society's Europe Group, Competition Law Association, Competition Law Committee of the ICC United Kingdom (International Chamber Of Commerce).
Career: Qualified 1989. Joined *Wragge & Co* 1994, made Partner 1996.
Personal: Born 1964.

LOUVEAUX, Bertrand
Slaughter and May, London (020) 7600 1200
Specialisation: Provides a broad range of UK and EC Competition Law. Has wide experience before the European Commission, the Office of Fair Trading and the Competition Commission (including both merger and monopoly enquiries). Recent merger cases have included Shell/Exxon (EC), British Steel/Hoogovens (EC), BAT/Rothmans (EC), Kodak/Imation (EC), Victoria Wine/Threshers (UK) and Carlton/United/Granada (UK). On the contentious front, recently acted for Nomura/GPC in obtaining the landmark Article 81 'pubco' decision.
Career: Qualified 1994 with *Slaughter and May*.
Personal: Born 28 April 1967. Educated Rugby School and London School of Economics (Msc Economics). Married with two children.

MAITLAND-WALKER, Julian
Maitland Walker, Minehead (01643) 707777
Specialisation: Main area of practice is European trade and competition law including UK restrictive trade practices, monopolies and merger control, state aids, public procurements and anti-dumping issues. Has acted in several references to the MMC, including beer supply, motor vehicle distribution and the phar-

maceutical industry. Other areas of practice include intellectual property, registration and licensing, agency distribution, franchising, joint ventures and R & D agreements. Editor of the 'European Competition Law Review' and author of several texts including 'Competition Laws of Europe' (Butterworths), 'A Guide to European Company Laws' (Sweet & Maxwell), 'EC Insurance Directives' and 'EC Banking Directives' (Lloyds of London Press).

MARTIN ALEGI, Lynda
Baker & McKenzie, London (020) 7919 1000
Partner in EC, Competition and Trade Department.
Specialisation: Main area of practice is competition law. Also distribution, franchising, computers and I.T. Author of competition chapter in Sweet & Maxwell's 'Encyclopaedia of Information Technology Law'.
Prof. Memberships: Law Society, Competition Law Society. International Bar Association.
Career: Qualified in 1977, having joined *Baker & McKenzie* in 1975. Became a Partner in 1981. Member of the CBI Competition Panel. Member of the International Chamber of Commerce UK Competition Law Committee.
Personal: Born 7th March 1952. Educated at Cambridge University (MA in Law, 1973) and the Institute of European Studies, Brussels (1975). Lives in London.

MCDONNELL, Phil
Garretts, Manchester (0161) 228 0707
phil.mcdonnell@glegal.com
Specialisation: Advises on EC and UK competition law and merger control including all aspects of business practices, pricing, distribution and sales strategies, corporate acquisitions, joint ventures and alliances; deals with complaints, investigations and compliances matters. Also advises on public procurement (particularly relating to the utility sector) and data protection matters.
Prof. Memberships: Law Society, Solicitors European Group.
Career: Articled *Lovell White Durrant* (London and Hong Kong), 1988–1993 *Lovell White Durrant* London, New York and Brussels; 1994-1995 commercial manager North West Water International Ltd; 1995 *Garretts* (partner 1999) head of competition and trade.
Personal: Educated St Ambrose College Hale Barns; Wadham College Oxford.

MCKNIGHT, Elizabeth S.
Herbert Smith, London (020) 7374 8000
elizabeth.mcknight@herbertsmith.com
Specialisation: Principal area of work covers UK and EC Competition law, including cases relating to the exploitation of intellectual property rights and cases relating to regulated industries (electricity, water, gas, telecommunications, media).
Prof. Memberships: Law Society, International Bar Association.
Career: Qualified in 1988 and became a partner in 1994.
Personal: Born 3rd May 1961. Attended Jesus College, Oxford 1979-1983, then took an LLM at London School of Economics, 1989.

MCLEAN, James
Burness, Edinburgh (0131) 473 6000
Specialisation: Jim McLean graduated in English and Scots Law at Cambridge and Edinburgh Universities. His competition practice covers national and European competition laws and their impact on the contracts and conduct of business undertakings and public authorities. His wider European Union practice involves other aspects of law affecting undertakings and authorities, as well as the interaction among the UK Parliament and executive, the Scottish Parliament and Executive and the United Kingdom's European Community, European Union and European Human Rights Convention obligations.

MILLER, Colin B.
Biggart Baillie, Glasgow (0141) 228 8000
cmiller@biggertbaillie.co.uk
Specialisation: All areas of UK and EU competition law including applying for merger clearances from OFT and EU Commission; EU public procurement issues; monopoly investigations by Competition Commission; investigations by EU Commission; notifying agreements for exemption and complaints to both OFT and EU Commission; compliance with block exemptions and in particular the Technology Transfer block exemption. Previous experience includes advising in connection with the MMC investigation into car prices in the UK and on restructuring and privatisation of the electricity industry. Acted for *Miller & Bryce* in the first ever successful action for interim interdict in the Court of Session based on EU competition rules. The case was against the Keeper of the Registers of Scotland and was based on the rules relating to abuse of a dominant position arising from the Keeper's refusal to give access to its databases to independent searching companies. Highlights of the last year include advising Drambuie on implications of abolition of duty free and the new EU block exemption for vertical agreements; advising numerous clients on implications of Competition Act 1998 including BSW Timber plc, Global Video plc, and ScotRail; advising on competition implications of restructuring within the Scottish energy market; advising the Highland Council on EU public procurement implications of the Highland Council IS/IT Public/Private Partnership.
Prof. Memberships: Qualified as a solicitor in both Scotland and England. Member of society for Computers and the Law, Scottish Software Federation and sits on the Intellectual Property Committee of the Law Society of Scotland.
Career: Assistant at two London City firms, *Linklaters* and *Eversheds*, before returning to Scotland in 1996. Partner at *Biggart Baillie* in July 1997.
Publications: Numerous articles in Journal of the Law Society of Scotland; New Law Journal; Gazette; CA Magazine; European Competition Law Review; Business Finance; Scotland on Sunday and others. Interviewed for Radio 4 and BBC TV on EU legal developments.
Personal: Educated at the Universities of Glasgow and Ludwig Maximilians University, Munich. Currently studying for LLM at University of Bristol. Leisure interests include classical music, choral singing and hill walking. Married with two young children.

MURRAY, Rob P.
Bond Pearce, Southampton (023) 8082 8866
rpm@bondpearce.com
Partner and head of the firm's EU\Competition Law Group.
Specialisation: Specialises in EU and UK competition law, both contentious and non contentious, commercial agreements and European law, particularly internal market and international trade issues. Frequent speaker at national and international conferences on competition law issues.
Prof. Memberships: Member of the Solicitors European Group, Treasurer (Central Southern Region).
Career: Law degrees from the Universities of Oxford and Brussels. Articled with *Clifford Chance* (London and Brussels); qualified 1989. Joined *Hepherd Winstanley & Pugh* 1996 and *Bond Pearce* in 1998 on its merger with *HWP* as a partner in the Commercial Group.

NICHOLSON, Malcolm
Slaughter and May, London (020) 7600 1200
Specialisation: EU, competition and regulatory law. Head of *Slaughter and May's* EU Competition Group. His practice covers the full range of UK and EU antitrust work for a number of blue chip clients (including RECs and other utilities), governments and regulatory authorities. On the UK competition front, he has extensive experience before the Competition Commission, including both merger and monopoly enquiries and deals regularly with the OFT. On the European front, he has been engaged in a number of competition cases before the Commission and the Court of Justice and in obtaining regulatory clearances from the Merger Task Force. He was heavily involved in the regulatory and competition aspects of the major UK privatisations and currently advises a number of electricity and water utilities with regard to price controls and other regulatory matters.
Career: Qualified in 1974 with *Slaughter and May*, and became a partner in 1982.
Personal: Born March 1949. Educated Haileybury, Cambridge University, Brussels University. Married with six children.

OSBORNE, John
Clifford Chance, London (020) 7600 1000
John.Osborne@cliffordchance.com
Partner in European Competition and Regulation Group.
Specialisation: Full range of EC and UK competition law from merger control, strategic alliances, joint ventures and commercial agreements to monopoly and cartel investigations. Extensive experience in conducting cases and investigations before the EC Commission, the OFT, the MMC and the CFI, ECJ for parties and complaints, and co-ordinating clearances in cross-border transactions. Acts for clients across a wide-range of business sectors including banking, financial services and broadcasting. Also advises on the EC law generally and utility regulation. Original contributing editor and author of "Butterworths Competition Law" division on permitted horizontal agreements.
Prof. Memberships: IBA, Solicitors European Group, Competition Law Association.
Career: Qualified 1973. Partner 1980.
Personal: Born 23 October 1947. LLB Bristol (1968); LLM London School of Economics (1969). Leisure interests include military history, cricket and horseracing. Lives in Richmond.

PARR, Nigel
Ashurst Morris Crisp, London (020) 7638 1111
Specialisation: Advises in relation to all aspects of UK and EC competition law and utilities regulation, particularly merger control. Has acted in relation to

28 UK Competition Commission inquiries including monopoly investigations, mergers and anti-competitive practices for clients including Alcatel, Allied Domecq, Smith & Nephew, United News and Media, Pioneer, Express Dairies, Northern Foods, Ford, Volvo, The Dairy Industry Federation, Johnston Press and Regional Independent Media. He has acted in relation to a number of bids in the utility sector, and recently acted for Imetal in its bid for English China Clays under the EC Merger Regulation. He regularly acts for clients in relation to notifications and investigations by the EC Commission, and has drafted many competition law compliance programmes.
Career: LLB, LLM, PhD, partner in the Company Department and Head of the Competition Group, co-author (with Roger Finbow) of 'UK Merger Control Law & Practice' (Sweet & Maxwell, 1995), and author of the competition section of PLC's Asset and Share Purchases Manuals, as well as numerous articles on EC law and competition-related matters. Committee member of the Solicitors European Group; tutor in EC law and intellectual property law at Exeter University 1984-86.

PHEASANT, John E.
Lovells, London Brussels (00) 32 2 647 0660
john.pheasant@lovells.com
Specialisation: EC and UK competition law in all its aspects, but particularly contentious proceedings and competition policy/regulation. Significant experience as an advocate before the Commission in administrative proceedings, and before the Court of First Instance and European Court of Justice on appeals (including interim measures). Co-author 'Competition Law' (Butterworths) and Editor of division on prohibited horizontal agreements.
Prof. Memberships: Member of the Advisory Board of the Regulatory Policy Institute, Oxford.
Career: Articled *Lovells*. Qualified 1979; partner since 1985. Brussels office: 1980-1983 and 1986–present.

POLITO, Simon W.
Lovells, London (020) 7296 2000
simon.polito@lovells.com
Specialisation: Principally EC and UK competition law. Expertise acquired since late 1970s in numerous Commission cases under Articles 85 and 86 and the Merger Regulation as well as UK merger and monopoly inquiries. Advises mainly UK, European and US multinationals on competition issues affecting manufacturing and service industries. Also advises on regulatory aspects of privatised industries, utilities and broadcasting.
Prof. Memberships: Member Joint Working Party on Competition Law of UK and Irish Bars and Law Societies; also of UK Committee of ICC on Competition Law and European Lawyers Forum.
Career: Called to Bar (Middle Temple) 1972. Qualified as solicitor with *Lovells* in 1976, partner 1982. Worked in Brussels 1977-81 (including 1990 "stage" with the Commission) and as a resident Brussels partner from 1988. Now based primarily in London.

PROWSE, Richard
Eversheds, Birmingham (0121) 232 1000
Partner and head of EU and competition practice in Birmingham.
Specialisation: EU and UK competition law including merger clearances, joint ventures and strategic alliances, agency and distribution and restrictive trade practices. Advises widely on compliance programmes. Particular knowledge of automotive and airport sectors.
Prof. Memberships: Law Society, Solicitors European Group, Member of the Advisory Committee of the Institute of European Law (University of Birmingham).
Career: University of Birmingham 1982-85. Qualified with *Eversheds* 1988. Partner 1998.
Personal: Born 1964. Interests include family and golf.

REES, Kate
Pinsent Curtis, Birmingham (0121) 200 1050
kate.rees@pinsents.com
Specialisation: EU and UK Competition Law including UK and EU merger clearances and OFT, Competition Commission and European Commission enquiries. Very extensive public procurement practice.
Career: LLB Hons 1st class. Qualified in 1988. Partner in *Pinsent Curtis*.

ROBERT, Gavin
Linklaters (A member firm of Linklaters & Alliance), London (020) 7456 3364
gavin.robert@linklaters.com
Specialisation: Partner in EU competition and regulatory department, with experience in all aspects of EU and competition law, public procurement and state aid. Particular focus on multimedia, healthcare, food and drink and energy. Recent major cases include state aid aspects of Channel Tunnel Rail Link and advising SB on its proposed mergers with AHP and Glaxo.
Career: Articled *Linklaters*; qualified 1992; stagiare in European Commission Legal Service; *Linklaters* Brussels office 1994-99; partner London office since May 1999.

ROSE, Stephen
Eversheds, London (020) 7919 4500
roses@eversheds.com
Specialisation: All aspects of EU and UK competition law with a focus on the Competition Act 1998 and mergers, acquisitions and joint ventures.
Prof. Memberships: Solicitors European Group. Competition Law Association.
Career: Qualified 1991. Articled with *Slaughter and May*. Partner at *Eversheds* 1997.
Personal: Born 27.5.65. Educated at St Edmund Hall, Oxford (1984-87). Lives in Great Chesterford Essex.

ROWE, Michael
Slaughter and May, London (020) 7600 1200
Specialisation: Practises all aspects of EU and UK competition law with particular expertise in M&A related competition issues. Recent matters include on-going proceedings before the European Commission, the Irish Courts and the European Courts in relation to impulse ice cream freezer cabinet exclusivity; notifications to the EU Commission and other authorities, including notifications in connection with the formation of the Symbian joint venture by Psion, Nokia, Ericsson and Motorola and in relation to the acquisition of Sedgwick by Marsh & McLennan. Gained experience of US M&A antitrust practices and procedures whilst on secondment to *Cravath Swaine & Moore* in New York in 1999, including in relation to the merger of British Aerospace with Marconi Electronic Systems.
Prof. Memberships: The Law Society, Solicitors' European Group.
Career: Qualified with *Slaughter and May* in 1994. Has practised in the firm's EU/ Competition group since that date.
Personal: Born 1968. Educated at Wesley College, Dublin, Trinity College, Dublin (LLB) and Christ Church, Oxford (BCL).

SCHOLES, Jeremy
Walker Morris, Leeds (0113) 283 2500
jas@walkermorris.co.uk
Specialisation: 20 years' experience of applying competition and EU law (the main areas of his practice) in a wide range of commercial contexts (transactions, litigation, dealing with regulatory authorities, compliance/advisory work). Highlights in the past year have included R v. The Law Society, ex p Dalton (the 'test case' litigation against the Solicitors' Indemnity Fund monopoly) and representing one of the large grocery supermarket chains in the Competition Commission enquiry.
Prof. Memberships: Law Society's European Group (former chairman of the East Midlands branch); Competition Law Association (led the CLA's working group on the Competition Bill); LIDC (International Competition Law Association) (a national reporter for 1997/98).
Career: Law degrees from Cambridge and the CollĚge d'Europe, Brugge, Belgium. Qualified 1981. *Freshfields*; *Waltons & Morse*; *Wells & Hind/Eversheds* Nottingham (partner till 1993; set up and led the *Eversheds* competition law practice group nationally); then several years a sole practitioner; now head of *Walker Morris*'s competition and EU law practice. Also a law lecturer at Sheffield University and a visiting lecturer at the Université de Nancy II in eastern France.
Publications: Various, including the commercial agency chapter in the PLC Commercial Contracts manual.
Personal: Works in French; also speaks good German and Dutch.

SCOTT, Jonathan W.
Herbert Smith, London (020) 7374 8000
jonathan.scott@herbertsmith.com
Head of EC/Competition department.
Specialisation: Work includes mergers, joint ventures, anti-trust investigations and European Court of Justice work. Acted in major investigations involving the television industry, electricity industry, the food and drink industry; and most recently the travel, dairy and domestic appliance industries and EC merger investigations in the insurance, financial services, glass, spirits, titanium, petro-chemical and travel industries. Editor of EC Merger Reporter. Editor merger chapters of Longman's 'Competition Law and Practice'.
Prof. Memberships: IBA.
Career: Qualified in 1981. Worked at the Council of Europe Human Rights Directorate 1979. Joined *Herbert Smith* in 1979, becoming a Partner in 1988.
Personal: Born 4th May 1956. Attended Shrewsbury School 1969-74, then St Catherine's College, Cambridge 1975-78. Lives in Cambridge.

SINGLETON, E. Susan
Singletons, London (020) 8866 1934
susan@singlelaw.com
See under Information Technology, p.459

SMITH, Martin
Simmons & Simmons, London (020) 7628 2020
Partner.
Specialisation: Main area of practice is European Community Law with particular emphasis on competition and regulatory work (both EC and UK). Has experience of dealing with all the main EC and UK competition law authorities. He advises on EC and UK merger control and regularly coordinates multiple merger filings. His experience extends to a number of regulated industries, notably water, broadcasting and radio. Also undertakes more general commercial work, usually with a significant competition law or regulatory element. Author of two major divisions of the three-volume 'Butterworths Competition Law'. Has also written a number of articles. Frequently speaks at conferences and seminars.
Prof. Memberships: Law Society, City of London Solicitors' Company Competition Law Sub-Committee, CBI Competition Panel, Solicitors European Group, International Bar Association, American Bar Association.
Career: Qualified in 1981. Joined *Simmons & Simmons* in 1977, becoming a Partner in 1986, having worked at *Dechert Price & Rhoads* (Philadelphia) 1978 and *Linklaters & Paines* 1983-5.
Personal: Born 27th August 1955. Attended St Catharine's College, Cambridge 1974-77 (MA) and University of Pennsylvania (LLM) 1978-9. Leisure interests include sport, music and walking. Lives in London.

SOAMES, Trevor
Norton Rose, Brussels (00) 32 2 237 6111
soamest@nortonrose.com
Specialisation: Main area of practice is all aspects of EC and UK competition, trade and regulatory law. Trevor has substantial experience in handling major merger and joint venture cases under the EC Merger Regulation (most recently representing United Airlines in its merger with US Airways, opposing the hostile takeover of Air Canada by Onex/AirCo and the merger of Sea-Land with Maersk) as well as under Article 81. Has handled a number of important recent multi-national cartel cases (such as Cement where, together with John Cook, the Norton Rose team was successful in quashing the fine imposed on Castle Cement and reducing the fines imposed on other clients). His many cases include major recent decisions of the European Commission under Articles 81, 82, and 86 in a number of economic sectors. In addition, Trevor has handled a number of high-profile state aid cases before the European Commission and the European Court on behalf of complainants as well as for donor Governments and recipients. Trevor represents and advises a substantial number of major U.S. and EU corporations in a wide variety of economic sectors on all matters relating to competition law, including Article 81 and 82 investigations as well as the implementation of compliance programmes. Recent clients include: Honeywell, Monsato, British Midland, United Airlines, the Greek Goverment, Stena AB, Stena Line AB, Olympic Airways, Sea-Land, CSX, P&OStena Line, Bombardier and Castle Cement. Trevor is an experienced litigator and proficient advocate, representing clients before the European Commission and European Court, as well as before the UK competition authorities.
Career: A graduate of Cambridge University. Called to the Bar of England and Wales in 1984. Worked UK Department of Trade and Industry befor entering private practice.
Publications: Author of many articles on competition and regulatory law as well as being editor of, or contributor to a number of books including: 'Corporate Mergers and Acquisitions', 'Air Transport and the European Community: Recent Developments', 'Airline Mergers and Co-operation and State Aids to Airlines'. Trevor is also an Associate Editor of 'Butterworths Competition Law Encyclopaedia'.
Personal: Born 17 September 1959. Member of the IBA, ABA, EALA, EMLO and others. Leisure interests are many but unfortunately with insufficient time to pursue them, particularly cricket which goes on forever.

SPEARING, D. Nicholas
Freshfields Bruckhaus Deringer, London (020) 7936 4000
Head of Competition Trade Group.
Specialisation: Main area of practice is EC/Competition law. Extensive experience in monopolies, mergers and restrictive practices cases at both UK and EC levels. Acted for leading companies in MMC inquiries into car prices, perfumes, ice-cream, electrical goods and underwriting fees. Merger control work for a range of clients including ICI, Nestlé, PepsiCo, Kingfisher, Royal Bank of Scotland and PowerGen. Co-Author of 'Mergers' section of Butterworth's Competition law. Numerous contributions to legal journals.
Prof. Memberships: Law Society, City of London Solicitors Company, Former Chairman Solicitors' European Group.
Career: Joined *Gordon, Dadds & Co.* in 1976, qualifying in 1978. Left to join *Freshfields* in 1978. Partner 1984. Head of Competition Trade Group.
Personal: Born 4th May 1954. Attended Caterham School 1965-72, then Hertford College, Oxford 1972-75. Leisure pursuits include family, travel and golf. Lives in Haslemere, Surrey.

TRAPP, Deirdre
Freshfields Bruckhaus Deringer, London (020) 7936 4000
Specialisation: Main area of practice is competition and regulatory law. Has conducted monopolies, mergers and restrictive practices cases under both EU and UK jurisdictions. Extensive experience in utility, transport and media regulation.
Prof. Memberships: Law Society, City of London Solicitors Company, Solicitors European Group.
Career: Joined *Freshfields* in 1987. Partner 1995.
Personal: Born 1961. Attended St. Hilda's College Oxford 1980-1983 reading Philosophy, Politics and Economics.

WARWICK, Neil
Dickinson Dees, Newcastle upon Tyne (0191) 279 9375
neil.warwick@dickinson-dees.com
Specialisation: Competition law (both UK and EU) and EU law including european funding, anti-dumping and state aid. Major cases include Cowie/British MMC Inquiry, Merger Task Force reference (case IV/M.901), Polish Metals anti-dumping case. Highlights of the last 12 months include full compliance programmes for a number of clients (in particular Arriva and Go-Ahead), work with Nike, Stagecoach and Coca Cola. Successful ERDF regional funding application for the North East Investment Fund and a number of contentious cases (including defending cartels cases).
Prof. Memberships: Law Society.
Career: Joined *Dickinson Dees* as a trainee in 1991, qualified in 1993, associate in 1997, senior associate April 2000.
Publications: 'Croner Risk Management'.
Personal: Dame Allan's School, Newcastle University. Hobbies–football (five-a-side, eleven-a-side and Newcastle United), hockey, gym and running. Leisure–cooking, reading, DIY. Married with a young family.

WEITZMAN, Polly
Denton Wilde Sapte, London (020) 7242 1212
fmaw@dentonwildesapte.com
Specialisation: EU and UK competition law specialist advising on non-contentious (mergers, joint ventures, restrictive agreements) and contentious (cartel, restrictive practices, abuse of market power) issues with particular experience in the media and energy sectors. Extensive experience before the European Commission, Office of Fair Trading, Competition Commission and Restrictive Practices Court. Most recent major case is the successful defence of the collective and exclusive selling arrangements for the television rights to the Premier League Championship before the Restrictive Practices Court. Editor of section on gas in Butterworths 'Encyclopaedia of Competition Law'.
Prof. Memberships: Competition Law Society; The Law Society.
Career: Qualified in 1988 with *Denton Hall*. Became a partner in 1995.
Personal: Born 1961. Educated Godolphin & Latymer School, London; then Edinburgh University (Modern History).

WHEATON, Jim
Clifford Chance, London (020) 7600 1000
jim.wheaton@cliffordchance.com
Specialisation: Partner specialising in EU and competition law.
Career: Birmingham (LLB). Qualified 1973; partner *Clifford Chance* 1978.

WHISH, Richard P.
Richard Whish–Sole Practitioner, London (020) 7848 2237

WOTTON, John P.
Allen & Overy, London (020) 7330 3000
Specialisation: Partner specialising in UK, EC and international competition and trade law and in broadcasting and communications law; member of the European Anti-Trust Group and the Communications, Media and Technology Group at Allen & Overy; has represented clients in numerous UK merger and monopoly investigations, EC proceedings and international anti-trust cases; also distribution and licensing, public procurement and state aids; has acted for clients from a wide range of industrial and service sectors in these matters, including newspapers and publishing, chemicals, pharmaceuticals, food, financial services, sports, media, telecommunications and the motor industry; acted for many years for broadcasting regulators in the UK; advises on competition and regulatory issues in the utilities sector, particularly water and rail.
Career: Articled *Allen & Overy*; qualified 1978; partner 1984.
Personal: Born 7th May 1954. Graduate of Jesus College, Cambridge 1972-75. Treasurer, Law Society's European Group.

CONSTRUCTION

London: 185; South: 189; Thames Valley: 189; South West: 189; Wales: 190; Midlands: 190; E. Anglia: 191; North West: 192; Yorkshire: 193; North East: 194; Scotland: 194; N. Ireland: 195; *Profiles*: 196

OVERVIEW: Construction litigators have had to change from marathon runners into sprinters. The days of the many-years-long case with rooms full of evidence are numbered. Now, by dint of statute and a mild variant of industrial revolution, clients want to mediate, adjudicate and arbitrate. There's a recognition that swift and (albeit sometimes) approximate justice can be more beneficial than deeply dug battle trenches. Surely the work of the construction litigators is drying up? Not so. Clients know that early resolution will cost less and allow a contractor/employer relationship to continue into the future. They visit the lawyers earlier and more often. The extent to which claims consultants have muscled in on the solicitors' territory cannot go without mention. On the non-contentious side, PFI and projects provide all the work that the profession can handle. Initiatives, such as partnering, extend their influence.

RESEARCH APPROVED BY BMRB: *For this edition,* Chambers' *researchers conducted 6083 interviews – 4408 with law firms, 598 with barristers and 1077 with clients.*

The validity of the research was scrutinised by BMRB International, who audited both the methodology and the results at our offices in July 2000. They interviewed Chambers' *researchers and cross-checked sample interviews. Details of the audit appear on page 7.*

LEADING IN-HOUSE LAWYERS

Michael BLACKER, Head of Legal Services, AMEC CAPITAL PROJECTS
Peter BRINLEY-CODD, Legal Services Manager, SIR ROBERT MACALPINE LTD
John FENWICK, Head of Group Legal Services, AMEC PLC
Dirk FITZHUGH, Company Secretary and Head of Legal Services, *Carillion plc*
Graham GIBSON, Head of Group Legal Services, *John Laing plc*
Martin LENIHAN, barrister, John Laing plc
Frank MCCORMACK, Head of Legal Services, Balfour Beatty plc
Hilary WILSON, Legal Adviser, Kvaerner Construction Group Ltd

Michael Blacker and his team work on the UK and the Asia-Pacific sectors. He is seen as a *"mover and shaker"* and a *"leader amongst lawyers."* At the same firm, **John Fenwick** is known for being *"commercially-minded."* The *"very bright"* **Peter Brinley-Codd** is well-recommended for his good *"technical understanding"* of the industry. Also praised is **Dirk FitzHugh** who is *"good on the law."* Both **Martin Lenihan** and the *"competent and commercial"* **Graham Gibson** were singled out for acknowledgement. The *"canny and equitable"* **Frank McCormack** is known for his *"commercial view and technical understanding."* **Hilary Wilson** is an *"outstanding lawyer"* who *"understands the business"* and *"seeks to add value."*

In-House lawyers profiles: page 1177

LONDON

Masons *"Construction juggernauts"* and the *"brickies'"* firm, Masons is still streets ahead of the competition. The firm's army of clients are those with core activities in construction and engineering, the team is at the epicentre of construction disputes in the UK, and is spreading its sphere of influence overseas. It represented the joint venture company in arbitration proceedings against the Government of Hong Kong arising from its Strategic Sewage Disposal Scheme. Opponents confirm that *"you are put on your mettle"* by the firm. *"Vast expertise"* and *"absolute excellence"* are shown at partner level, although one or two of our interviewees indicated that the lawyers are *"not all black belts. They are not old and ugly enough."*

"Cool customer" **John Bishop** is dubbed *"Mr Strategy."* For some, **Anthony Bunch** *"is the real player there"* and he rises into our top band of leaders. The *"rakish and charming"* **Martin Harman**'s particular focus is on international infrastructure projects. *"Good guy"* **Mark Roe** achieves a high profile in many aspects of his varied caseload and *"gets on well with clients."* **Mark Lane**, who heads the firm's Water Sector Group and **Martin Roberts** are also well endorsed. Although Philip Capper has surprised many by leaving the firm for Lovells, the sheer strength of the Masons team means that such a high-profile departure is perceived as unfortunate rather than disastrous. Advised Arrow Light Rail Ltd as project sponsor on the £270 million Nottingham Light Rail PFI. **Clients:** ALSTOM; Mowlem; Wembley National Stadium Ltd.

CMS Cameron McKenna The three separate units within the group are perceived to adhere to strict divisions but it is now recognised that for the first time in a number of years the group is achieving a good balance between dispute resolution and non-contentious work. Its reputation is enhanced by the firm's strength in PFI, property and health and safety. **Ann Minogue** has gained an almost regal reputation for her *"wonderful drafting skills"* and comes with an impressive heavyweight CV. She is primarily responsible for the firm's reputation as the *"voice of the employer."* It is *"a pleasure to work with"* **Trevor Butcher** on major projects, an aspect of the firm's work for which it has a fine reputation. On the non-contentious side, **Peter Long** is rated for his substantial experience. Heading the dispute work are two partners who feature in the list of leaders. **Henry Sherman** has a reputation for reliability, while new entrant **Caroline Cummins** has been particularly recognised by the bar and is now considered the major force in a contentious team which acts for the contractor as much as it does for the employer. Acted for Panatown in Alfred McAlpine Construction Ltd v Panatown which went to the House of Lords in October 1999. **Clients:** AMEC plc; Balfour Beatty Ltd; Tishman Speyer Properties.

Rowe & Maw Truly overwhelming endorsement for this group, with whom *"you can identify the real issues."* Partners and assistants display ambidextrous qualities in that they handle both contentious and non-contentious matters for both employers and contractors. There is a distinct impression that the department retains its own character within a firm that is becoming increasingly 'City' in its focus. *"They are reflective litigators – thinking practitioners who do more than operate the machinery."* **John Rushton** joins the elite in our top band of leading lawyers. *"He's the person of choice for reliability and intellect"* and handles matters with *"a lovely touch."* Also recognised is **Michael Regan**. *"You know where you stand with him. He's good news."* **Gillian Birkby** is *"hard working, accurate and conscientious."* She is the choice of The Maitreya Buddha Project. The firm represented VHE in VHE Construction plc v RBSTB Trust Co. Ltd, a case concerning the effect of an adjudicator's decision on set-offs. **Clients:** Laing; Haden Young; Southern Water.

Fenwick Elliott Acting for some big name contractors and employer clients, it is seen to perform well on contentious work, including international arbitration of construction disputes. This small and niche practice is headed by the almost legendary and larger than life **Robert Fenwick Elliott**, *"a remarkable and energetic practitioner"* who *"you can't ignore."*

CONSTRUCTION • London	Ptnrs	Assts
❶ Masons	19	51
❷ CMS Cameron McKenna	7	21
Rowe & Maw	5	11
❸ Fenwick Elliott	6	7
Herbert Smith	3	11
Shadbolt & Co	4	3
❹ Berwin Leighton	5	12
Hammond Suddards Edge	5	14
Linklaters	6	26
Lovells	7	18
Nicholson Graham & Jones	5	6
Norton Rose	4	13
Winward Fearon	5	5
❺ Ashurst Morris Crisp	3	14
Clifford Chance	9	30
Freshfields Bruckhaus Deringer	10	18
Taylor Joynson Garrett	5	5
❻ Allen & Overy	3	8
Baker & McKenzie	2	6
Barlow Lyde & Gilbert	3	6
Beale and Company	8	4
Berrymans Lace Mawer	5	6
Corbett & Co	1	3
Davies Arnold Cooper	3	6
Denton Wilde Sapte	6	9
Glovers	1	2
Simmons & Simmons	2	8
SJ Berwin & Co	2	8
Trowers & Hamlins	6	7
Warner Cranston	2	3
Wedlake Bell	1	2

Within each band, firms are listed alphabetically.

Julian Critchlow is strengthening the non-contentious aspect of the firm's reputation, although this is still the smaller part of the caseload. He earns *"great respect"* for his *"proven abilities"* and rises in our ranking of individuals. Roughly a third of the team's turnover relates to international disputes, and the team also acts on a number of large developments. **Clients:** Contractors; insurers; financial institutions.

Herbert Smith The firm's construction and engineering team has pulled together several strands into a single cord. On the contentious side, domestic and international disputes are of equal value to the practice and head of department **Michael Davis** has been singled out for his expertise in international arbitration. He is acting for a state-owned oil company in the Middle East on arbitrations concerning a port which services the country's natural gas resources. However, the contentious work is only one half of the story. The majority of the positive feedback was for the firm's projects/PFI related work. It is presently advising GCHQ in the PFI project for the development of its new facility. *"Gearing up"* and *"really up there"* reported the market, acknowledging a leading *"stand-alone practice in addition to the cross-departmental work."* The strength of Herbert Smith's corporate, property and PFI groups has provided a stream of top-quality work including advising Standard Life on its development of Finsbury Square in London. **Clients:** General Electric; Halliburton; Daewoo Motors.

Shadbolt & Co In spite of the fact that the power house of this practice is located in Reigate, we also rank it in London through its newer, smaller office in the capital. The firm is regarded in the market as a competitor of the top London practices. Most agree that the firm has *"done wonders"* and that it is so busy and successful purely on the strength of the individuals involved. A key figure in the industry called it *"the most interesting firm out there for my money."* At the centre of everything is *"the eternal strategist"* **Dick Shadbolt**, an experienced operator described as *"sheer class." "He'll give you grey hairs,"* confirm opponents. Also making a name for himself is *"John Bull character"* **Dominic Helps**. The *"knowledgeable"* **Victoria Russell** has recently arrived from Berrymans Lace Mawer, and is Chair of the Society of Construction Lawyers. Acted for parties involved in three of the leading reported decisions relating to enforcement of adjudication awards – Outwing v Randell, A&D Maintenance v Pagehurst and Sherwood Casson v McKenzie. **Clients:** SAE International; Taylor Woodrow plc; WS Atkins plc.

Berwin Leighton Viewed as a *"comprehensive and serious construction practice,"* contentious and non-contentious work is covered by two separate groups. Litigation is the smaller part of the workload but there appears to have been an upturn in the number of instructions from contractors. It is the domestic development and PFI/projects work for which the firm is best known and others typically encounter the team acting for developers and banks. Head of department **Terry Fleet** is *"innovative and a reliable operator."* **Mike Gibson** has a breadth of experience in non-contentious and PFI/projects. *"He concentrates on the important details and gets down to business with no point-scoring."* Continues to advise the House of Commons on the construction aspects of the new £300 million Parliamentary Building and act for Arcadia Group plc (Burton) on their new £90 million flagship HQ in Oxford Street. **Clients:** Ove Arup & Partners; CGU Insurance; The Highways Agency.

Hammond Suddards Edge The recent merger has combined two London practices of undoubted quality. The former Hammond Suddards was seen as a *"hungry"* group known for domestic dispute work, particularly for London Transport. **David Jones** is the stand-out name here. The team enjoyed a marked increase in non-contentious instructions at a time when the group aligned itself with new directions in public procurement of construction services. Appointed as external legal advisor to the government's steering committee on Prime Contracting. Continues to advise London Underground on general project matters, conciliations, mediations and High Court litigation. The erstwhile Edge Ellison team had already enjoyed a stellar year, primarily appreciated for its technical expertise on behalf of a client base including a number from the M&E/process engineering sector. **Jonathan Hosie**, a *"smart lad,"* continues to impress his peers. **Clients:** Dahl Jenson; Environment Agency; Kier Construction Ltd.

Linklaters The construction and engineering group sits within the commercial property department and it is this that defines the practice. Domestic property developments account for nearly a third of the work, with a marked increase in instructions on large-scale corporate HQs. PFI/projects colleagues feed through even more work for the team. *"They fight over the points worth fighting for"* say the opposition, impressed by the non-contentious expertise on offer. Headed by *"highly competent"* and *"capable draftsman"* **Marshall Levine** and supported ably by New Zealander **Simon Burch**, the construction group is building up its non-contentious profile. On litigation there are *"bright people but they seem a bit rudderless – they don't always coalesce on a case."* Advised the sponsors, Health Management Group, on the £330 million UCLH hospital PFI project. **Clients:** Goldman Sachs; Enron/Construction; Lend Lease.

Lovells *"A formidable team"* described as *"one to watch."* The international arbitration side of the dispute work has been given a real boost by **Philip Capper**, described as a *"novel and special"* lawyer and unanimously thought to bring an enormous amount of focus to the department. His arrival from Masons is a major coup for head of department **Nick Gould**, *"an eminent expert in the contentious field"* and variously described as *"a classic"* and *"outstanding."* On PFI/projects (both domestic and international), the team has established itself as a key player. It has acted for Kings Healthcare NHS Trust on the hospital PFI and a number of other major

LEADING INDIVIDUALS • London	
❶ **BISHOP John** Masons	**BLACKLER Anthony** Macfarlanes
BUNCH Anthony Masons	**CAPPER Phillip** Lovells
FENWICK ELLIOTT Robert Fenwick Elliott	**MINOGUE Ann** CMS Cameron McKenna
RUSHTON John Rowe & Maw	**SHADBOLT Richard** Shadbolt & Co
❷ **BUTCHER Trevor** CMS Cameron McKenna	**CORBETT Edward** Corbett & Co
CORNES David Winward Fearon	**CRITCHLOW Julian** Fenwick Elliott
DAVIS Michael Herbert Smith	**GOULD Nicholas** Lovells
GOWAN Daniel Davies Arnold Cooper	**HARMAN Martin** Masons
HOSIE Jonathan Hammond Suddards Edge	**HUDSON James** Nicholson Graham & Jones
JONES David Hammond Suddards Edge	**LEVINE Marshall** Linklaters
REGAN Michael Rowe & Maw	**ROE Mark** Masons
ROE Sally Freshfields Bruckhaus Deringer	
❸ **BIRKBY Gillian** Rowe & Maw	**BRIDGEWATER Martin** Norton Rose
BURCH Simon Linklaters	**FLEET Terry** Berwin Leighton
LANE Mark Masons	**LONG Peter** CMS Cameron McKenna
MOSEY David Trowers & Hamlins	**REES Peter** Norton Rose
ROBERTS Martin Masons	**RUSSELL Victoria** Berrymans Lace Mawer
SHAW Peter Taylor Joynson Garrett	**SHERMAN Henry** CMS Cameron McKenna
STEADMAN Tim Clifford Chance	**WINTER Jeremy** Baker & McKenzie
❹ **BOURGEOIS Christopher** Taylor Joynson Garrett	
CUMMINS Caroline CMS Cameron McKenna	
GARTHWAITE Helen Lewis Silkin	**GIBSON Michael** Berwin Leighton
HELPS Dominic Shadbolt & Co	**RACE David** Nicholson Graham & Jones
REEVES Suzanne Wedlake Bell	**SMITH Ian** Lovells
UP AND COMING	
CANHAM Stephanie Trowers & Hamlins	**JENKINS Jane** Freshfields Bruckhaus Deringer
POPE Caroline Barlow Lyde & Gilbert	**SPEED Nick** Warner Cranston

*See **Profiles** on page 196*

projects. **Ian Smith**, although now a consultant spending only a part of his time on fee earning work, is still lauded as a fine practitioner and someone who is *"pragmatic – he knows when to push points."* High-profile dispute instructions included those from the defendant in the British Airways v ALSTOM Automation Ltd case. **Clients:** ALSTOM; Kings Healthcare NHS.

Nicholson Graham & Jones *"A proper construction group"* which includes five acknowledged names at partner level, most notable of which are litigator **James Hudson** and large projects man **David Race**. The team as a whole is favoured because it is *"pragmatic and commercial and they don't pursue needlessly esoteric points."* There are five accredited adjudicators on the team, which deals with slightly more dispute-related work than it does non-contentious matters. International work includes a number of large engineering projects in the Middle East and Africa. Also seen to serve institutional investors well on non-contentious domestic developments and, by contrast, have a specialism in M&E work. Representing Pirelli Cables in relation to disputes on the Jubilee Line upgrade and extension. **Clients:** Regalian Properties; Haden Young Ltd; Blue Circle Industries.

Norton Rose A visible practice, now *"stealing a march"* on many of its competitors. Seen to have *"a solid engineering base and lots of turnkey projects."* This year's success is primarily attributed to the team's *"high quality individuals,"* including **Martin Bridgewater** on the projects side and the *"bright, commercial"* litigator **Peter Rees**. The latter leads a *"decent, no funny business"* team who *"play it straight."* Internationally there have been a number of instructions from Europe, Asia, the Middle East and North America and the contentious side of the practice has particularly benefited from these. Altogether this group is now regarded as *"a class act."* Acted for funders RBS, Bank of America, Toronto Dominion Bank and Bayerische Landesbank in relation to the £350 million replacement and refurbishment of London Underground's telecommunications system. **Clients:** Siemens AG; Capital Shopping Centres plc; Taylor Woodrow plc.

Winward Fearon *"Quiet giants"* with a name for quality dispute resolution work, both domestic and international. A former engineer, **David Cornes** has now thrown himself into the dual role of mediator and construction specialist. Particularly noted for international contentious work, the team advised on a high-profile project in South America and for a foreign contractor on an International Chamber of Commerce arbitration concerning a residential project. The team has also advised on a number of non-contentious matters, including a £40 million office development in the City of London. **Clients:** AIG; Powergen International; Coventry City FC.

Ashurst Morris Crisp A heavily PFI-oriented caseload in which the firm is almost always seen acting for the client or the sponsor rather than for the contractor. The perception is that the construction department does well off its corporate, property, finance and PFI groups but is not so noted for contentious work. This judgement is perhaps a little harsh, given that it achieved the settlement of a number of large-scale disputes in 1999. The team's client base here leans towards infrastructure and engineering, including coal. The approach is *"sensible and commercial with no posturing."* An increased PFI caseload has included instructions concerning new accommodation projects for GCHQ and the London Transport Police. **Clients:** Amey; BT plc; British Gas Trading Ltd.

Clifford Chance On projects and international arbitration, the firm is seen to be *"going from strength to strength,"* hardly surprising given its supremacy in London-based international arbitration. **Tim Steadman** is praised for his ability to *"grasp difficult issues and structures"* and brings the qualities of a *"fine technical construction lawyer"* to the firm, generally perceived as a lenders' operation *("they always do a quality job for us.")* The team acted for Petrobras, the Brazilian state owned oil and gas company, on the procurement of US$660 million of new offshore gas recovery and transportation facilities. **Clients:** Bovis Lendlease; Petrobras.

Freshfields Bruckhaus Deringer *"A serious outfit"* known to be strong on non-contentious issues for large clients such as London Transport and the procurers on PFI/PPP schemes within the UK. Utility companies, governments, institutional investors and major industrial concerns all use the team's services along with major contractors (often as project sponsors). The Freshfields brand is often cited by clients as the firm's principal draw, a brand which has clearly been strengthened overseas by the firm's high-profile merger with Bruckhaus Westrick Heller Löber. **Sally Roe** is *"fresh and excellent"* and the main name at the team. She is joined in the tables by rising star **Jane Jenkins**. Continues to work for HSBC Holdings plc on construction issues in connection with its new HQ at Canary Wharf. **Clients:** BNFL; Scottish Widows; Credit Suisse First Boston.

Taylor Joynson Garrett A blend of many types of work for this department. Disputes have the edge over non-contentious instructions and emanate from projects around the world, but international projects work is also increasing in significance. **Peter Shaw** and **Christopher Bourgeois** are both respected practitioners. Acting for M W Kellogg and joint venture partners on disputes concerning the Bonny Island liquefied natural gas project in Nigeria. **Clients:** ABB; Canada Life; Lidl UK GmbH.

Allen & Overy Visible for funders on PFI but also acting for sponsors. Around a third of the team's work concerns large-scale international projects, sometimes acting for overseas governments. Power and water provide particularly rich pickings. Such a strong emphasis on international work, however, has led to a relatively low profile in the domestic market. The partners have contributed to and edited Sweet & Maxwell's new publication on the contractual side of major construction projects. The team has advised Nigeria LNG Ltd on the £1 billion+ contract relating to a third LNG train at Bonny Island, Nigeria. **Clients:** Edison Capital; The National Grid Company; Hong Kong Airport Authority.

Baker & McKenzie A department sometimes referred to by the market as the **Jeremy Winter** show. Such is the established nature of his international practice that he is felt to have *"been around the block"* on this type of work. Internationally, the firm's profile on large projects, especially infrastructure and energy, is high, but does not translate to a comparable influence in the domestic market. Presently advising on a number of pan-European and national telecommunications projects involving cable laying and network build-outs. **Clients:** Derech Eretz; Autostrada Wielkopolska S.A.; Pangea Management Services.

Barlow Lyde & Gilbert **Caroline Pope**, a new entry to our leaders' table this year, and her colleagues have *"done very well in the market place and built a good, underrated practice."* Clients praise them for *"working the way we want; they're cost effective and client friendly."* From a mainstay of employer clients, including two water companies and a power company, the firm has turned to face the contractor market and now acts for a number of big names. The non-contentious work has blossomed in the last couple of years, but disputes still dominate. Acting for Kelda Group plc in respect of a multi-million pound delay and disruption claim over a treatment plant. **Clients:** Southern Water; Balfour Beatty; Scottish Power.

Beale and Company From a practice firmly rooted in insurance litigation, the firm's construction lawyers are now advising many of their professional clients on non-contentious as well as dispute-related matters. Much of the work comes from the ACE scheme, and it is felt that team members are *"thorough and know what they are doing."* Acted for Thames Water in Skandia Properties v Thames Water Utilities Ltd. **Clients:** CGU; The Wren Insurance Association; Ove Arup Partnership.

Berrymans Lace Mawer The loss of three partners from the construction department including Victoria Russell, must have a serious effect on the practice. However, instructions come from insurance companies, professionals and M&E subcontractors. The team has a specific profile in litigation and adjudication matters. Acting for mechanical engineers in attempts to mediate disputes over the Royal Brompton Hospital. **Clients:** Leading insurance companies; Henry Boot; Hochtief Ltd.

Corbett & Co A big reputation for a tiny team. **Edward Corbett** *("an interesting man with a sense of humour")* and a small band of assistants operate at the highest level, ensuring that others in the market *"don't hear a bad thing about them."* The firm has plenty of high quality international engineering work and Corbett himself is closely associated with the drafting and analysis of the standard forms of FIDIC contracts. Working for a consortium of Swedish, Norwegian and Dutch companies involved in the aborted project to recover the sunken ferry Estonia. **Clients:** Van Oord ACZ bv; Gibraltar Homes Ltd; SIETCO .

Davies Arnold Cooper A compact team of pure construction lawyers is led by *"nice guy"* **Danny Gowan**. Gowan *"understands litigation and he understands clients' needs,"* but, as the firm's relatively recently appointed senior partner, will shoulder a heavy workload. An industry-focused construction group. It is developing its international work, particularly in the petrochemicals industry. The team last year concluded a substantial arbitration on behalf of the Petroleum Company of Trinidad and Tobago. **Clients:** Alfred McAlpine Construction Ltd; Independent Insurance Co Ltd; Victorian Channels Authority of Australia.

Denton Wilde Sapte Some believe that the firm can compete with any in the UK on non-contentious work. Plenty of engineering instructions here come from clients in the energy sector, where the firm already has a powerful reputation. All that is missing is an acknowledged big-hitter. PFI and overseas projects feature in the group's caseload, as does international arbitration of construction and engineering disputes. Much of the domestic work is carried out in the firm's Milton Keynes office, which for the purposes of this section is treated as one with London. Acted for Essex County Council on the £104 million A130 DBFO road project, the first local authority highway project to be brought to a close under the PFI. **Clients:** Highways Agency; EDF; Carillion plc.

Glovers A small but well-qualified team with a reputation for high quality litigation, traditionally for contractors but increasingly for insurers. Acted for Cardiff County Council and the Cardiff Bay Development Co. in relation to £8 million of claims concerning the Cardiff Bay Barrage. **Clients:** Laserbore Ltd; Sir Robert MacAlpine Ltd.

Simmons & Simmons So closely is the firm associated with construction work for Railtrack that much of its other work receives little recognition by the market. However, PFI work goes beyond railways to defence, while in the private sector, domestic development involves some substantial instructions, many of which relate to the City of London. International disputes have included an arbitration arising from a dispute concerning a sugar refining plant in Swaziland. Last year's highlight project was the South Tees Hospital PFI in which the team acted for Crown House Engineering and Carillion plc. **Clients:** BP Amoco plc; Nationwide BS; MoD.

S J Berwin & Co A depleted team following losses at partner and assistant level, but it still retains a decent reputation amongst property and developer clients *("they're doing pretty well with what they have left.")* While not quite a 'bolt on', the construction team is certainly a support to more clearly identified focus areas, notably property and PFI. Acting for specialist cabling and mechanical subcontractors on disputes arising from the Jubilee Line Extension. **Clients:** British Land Company plc; AXA Sun Life; Bouygues.

Trowers & Hamlins The team is generally commended for its *"effort"* and *"thoroughness."* **David Mosey** is *"committed to getting on with things"* while new up and coming name **Stephanie Canham** is *"sensible and go-getting."* The firm already has a profile in the public and housing sectors and is established as an employer's firm, but it is now seeing an increase in contractor work, especially on the contentious side. It has acted for London Borough of Hackney on its programme for strategic procurement of all of its housing repair/maintenance works and related capital works. **Clients:** Berkeley Group plc; Amphion Consortium (LB Hackney and 18 RSLs); Sir Robert MacAlpine Ltd.

Warner Cranston Primarily dispute related work for employers, contractors and their insurers. A good proportion of the cases are professional indemnity matters. **Nick Speed** is the stand-out name, in spite of his relative youth. The team handles a volume of work for The Wren Insurance Association Ltd. **Clients:** R J Wallace Syndicate; AMEC Construction Ltd; Hastings & Rother NHS Trust.

Wedlake Bell **Suzanne Reeves** has a good name and keeps that of Wedlake Bell alive for construction law. Many of the clients are consulting engineers and specialist subcontractors but instructions also come from developers and funders. Operates a helpline for members of the National Specialist Contractors Council. On the non-contentious side, the team acted for Hilton Hotels on the Great Western Hotel, Paddington. **Clients:** Scott Wilson Kirkpatrick; Stent Foundations Ltd; National Specialist Contractors Council.

Other Notable Practitioners **Anthony Blackler** retains his position as one of the most respected of the UK's construction lawyers, following his move to Macfarlanes in 1998. However, he has so far been unable to convince the market of the firm's overall construction prowess. **Helen Garthwaite**, the recognised force at Lewis Silkin, has been described as *"refreshing"* and *"dynamic."*

THE SOUTH

CONSTRUCTION • The South	Ptnrs	Assts
❶ **Shadbolt & Co** Reigate	11	12
❷ **Cripps Harries Hall** Tunbridge Wells, Kent	2	2
❸ **Blake Lapthorn** Portsmouth	3	2

Within each band, firms are listed alphabetically.

Shadbolt & Co See London editorial.

Cripps Harries Hall *"A fair and reasonable"* opponent, which last summer acquired a partner from the in-house legal team at Wates. Primarily a housebuilding client base for whom work is evenly split between contentious and non-contentious. **Clients:** Persimmon Homes (South East) Ltd; Berkeley Homes (Eastern) Ltd; Wates Group plc.

Blake Lapthorn Construction dispute resolution services for the firm's commercial clients are provided from the heart of the commercial litigation department, and a further partner offers non-contentious advice. Advises leisure client David Lloyd Leisure/Design Collective on design and build management. Also handled an ICC arbitration concerning the installation of a telecommunications system. **Clients:** Pirelli; Alcatel; local authorities.

THAMES VALLEY

CONSTRUCTION • Thames Valley	Ptnrs	Assts
❶ **Clarks** Reading	1	2
Linnells Oxford	⚐	⚐
Morgan Cole Oxford	1	1

Within each band, firms are listed alphabetically.

⚐ *Figures unavailable at time of going to press*

Clarks The construction law unit sits within the commercial litigation department and in addition to the team size shown, lawyers from the property department handle non-contentious work. Historically acts for employer clients but has seen recent growth in its subcontractor client base. Defended a client in and satisfactorily concluded a £1 million arbitration brought by a leading contractor. **Clients:** BOC Ltd; Blue Circle Developments plc; NHS trusts.

Linnells Housebuilders and professionals are amongst the clients of this regionally respected firm. There is no dedicated unit, but lawyers of various disciplines from within the commercial group handle construction work. Represented Oxford University in a claim against their architects over the construction of a new departmental building. **Clients:** Berkeley Homes (Oxford) Ltd; J B Leadbitter & Co Ltd; professionals.

Morgan Cole A heavily employer/developer-led client base, which is developing an energy orientation in addition to a noted public sector client portfolio. An even split exists between contentious and non-contentious work. Acted for BP in adjudication proceedings brought by Mott MacDonald for extra costs on a design contract relating to a central control building in an oil refinery. **Clients:** Amey; Oxford Brookes University; Bickerton plc.

SOUTH WEST

CONSTRUCTION • South West	Ptnrs	Assts
❶ **Masons** Bristol	4	9
❷ **Bevan Ashford** Bristol, Exeter	3	6
❸ **Laytons** Bristol	2	2
❹ **Beachcroft Wansbroughs** Bristol	1	3
Veale Wasbrough Bristol	1	3
❺ **Bond Pearce** Plymouth	1	5
Burges Salmon Bristol	1	3
Osborne Clarke OWA Bristol	3	3

LEADING INDIVIDUALS	
✪ **REDMOND John** Osborne Clarke OWA	
❶ **COLLINGWOOD Mark** Masons	**HARRIS Adam** Masons
VASEY John Beachcroft Wansbroughs	
❷ **FOLEY Richard** Masons	**GUPPY Nicholas** Laytons
HARLING Marcus Burges Salmon	**HOWE Martin** Bevan Ashford
HOYLE Roger Veale Wasbrough	
❸ **BIRCH John** Bevan Ashford	**BUECHEL Peter** Alexander Paul
DAVIES Lawrence Masons	**GARD William** Bevan Ashford
UP AND COMING	
HANLEY Christine Bond Pearce	

Within each band, firms are listed alphabetically. See **Profiles** on page 196

Masons *"Sensible people who know their stuff"* acting for national contractors and employers as well as locally-based clients. A massive volume of high quality work and the sheer size and focus of the team makes the firm *"by far the leader in Bristol."* Seen to operate in the Masons way – *"doing a Rolls Royce job on every case."* Clients think particularly highly of joint heads of department **Mark Collingwood** and **Adam Harris**. *"Technically accurate"* **Richard Foley** receives a number of commendations, as does **Lawrence Davies**. Last year, highlights included acting on a multi-million pound dispute for part of the AMEC group, and defending a government department on a £95 million claim concerning valuation issues. **Clients:** Carillion Construction Ltd; TBV Power; NHBC.

Bevan Ashford Has impressed lawyers and clients around the country as a *"good team who have been trying for a few years and now have things going their way."* **Martin Howe**, who has recently arrived from Veale Wasbrough, is *"a thinking person who likes to do a proper job."* He was recruited by head of the non-contentious department, **Will Gard**. The quieter Exeter office is headed by **John Birch**, newly arrived from Townsends in Swindon. Acted on numerous hospital PFI projects including Bro Morgannwg (£60 million) and Cornwall NHS Trust (£20 million.) **Clients:** Approx. 30 NHS Trusts; Lorne Stewart plc; Border Biofuels Ltd.

Laytons This is a time of great change for Laytons following the departure of key man John Redmond to Osborne Clarke in May. Although some believe that *"until now* **Nick Guppy** *has had a low-profile role,"* others counter that *"he knows the work and has the client loyalty."* However, these are early days, and the firm, partly due to Guppy, has a long-held reputation amongst contractor clients. The team has recently advised London Transport in connection with disputes over contractors' final accounts for work carried out on the Jubilee Line Extension. **Clients:** University of Wales College Newport; Cowlin Construction; Staveley Industries plc.

Beachcroft Wansbroughs Around half the construction group's work is professional indemnity insurance litigation for architects and other professionals. The team also carries out non-contentious development advice for clients of the firm's large property department. Healthcare clients, including half a dozen major trusts provide dispute resolution instructions and the Bristol office is beginning to see some PFI work, hitherto the domain of the firm's London office. *"Hands on"* **John Vasey** is a *"straightforward man who comes across well and gives clear messages."* **Clients:** NHS trusts; architects.

Veale Wasbrough Much of the work is the defence of professional indemnity claims for consulting engineers, who remain the bedrock of this practice. Major national employers add to an impressive client roster. **Roger Hoyle** *("he's got drive")* has *"professional standards."* Advised Bath & North East Somerset Council in connection with the Bath Spa Millennium Project. **Clients:** CGU Insurance (ACE Scheme); Jordan Engineering Ltd; PB Kennedy & Donkin Ltd.

Bond Pearce A rising profile for this Plymouth team as a result of the increased experience of newly ranked **Christine Hanley**, a *"strong personality"* who *"has been plugging away for a long time."* The team has also recruited a new lawyer from Masons' Bristol office. The firm has a regional client base, typically acting for employers and developers. This year it has been appointed to advise English Heritage on non-contentious matters. The team advised Plymouth and South West Co-operative Society Ltd on a number of retail developments. **Clients:** Plymouth & South West Co-Operative Society Limited; Arjo Wiggins; Hogjaard & Schultz Ltd.

Burges Salmon A practice which focuses almost exclusively on employer clients, including developers, colleges, the public sector, and the National Trust. Non-contentious work is supplemented by a small amount of litigation, usually insurance-related and arising from professional contracts. **Marcus Harling** is generally regarded as *"an extremely capable chap."* Acting for National Trust on its proposals to convert Ickworth House in Suffolk into a 40 bed hotel. **Clients:** First Group/Bristol International Airport; London Fire Brigade; MoD.

Osborne Clarke OWA *"Rainmaker"* **John Redmond** has caused a flurry of excitement in Bristol. The big question is whether or not he can persuade key clients to accompany him from Laytons. Whilst Redmond himself is *"very much a leading light,"* Osborne Clarke have hitherto shown no real promise as a construction firm. The team is acting in Birse Construction Ltd v St David Ltd, which results from a partnering project in Cardiff. **Clients:** Birse Construction Ltd; Nishimatsu Construction Co Ltd; Unipol Assicurazioni.

Other Notable Practitioner Renowned for his technical reliability, **Peter Buechel** has left Stones and set up in practice on his own.

WALES

CONSTRUCTION • Wales	Ptnrs	Assts
❶ **Morgan Cole** Cardiff	1	5
❷ **Eversheds** Cardiff	2	2
Hugh James Ford Simey Cardiff	2	2

LEADING INDIVIDUALS	
❶ **HERBERT Mary** Eversheds	
❷ **JEFFERIES Michael** Hugh James Ford Simey	**JONES Peter** Eversheds
NEWMAN Paul Hugh James Ford Simey	**WILLIAMS Jeremy** Morgan Cole

Within each band, firms are listed alphabetically. *See **Profiles** on page 196*

Morgan Cole In addition to the team size shown, lawyers from other departments litigate construction-related cases. **Jeremy Williams** remains the dominant figure in the team. Instructed by employer/developer clients in both public and private sectors, the team is said to *"dig in and show good sense,"* and now leads the construction field in Wales. Engineering, energy clients and PFI work are all developing areas. Advised TBI plc on negotiations with Tarmac for the construction of the Cardiff Hilton Hotel. **Clients:** Macob Civil Engineering; BP; Associated British Ports/Cardiff Bay Development Corporation.

Eversheds The past year has been a time of upheaval in the firm's Cardiff office. A senior assistant left to the Midlands and a partner sadly died. However, transferring from the firm's Newcastle office, **Mary Herbert** is well known and is felt to be the name to restore equilibrium. The highly respected **Peter Jones** has not been so prominent on construction issues recently. The team acted for Carillion plc on the defence of a multi-million pound claim by Eurostar in relation to the Waterloo International Terminal. **Clients:** Carillion plc; Hanson Construction; Sir Robert MacAlpine Construction Ltd.

Hugh James Ford Simey HJFS have a pure construction lawyer in **Paul Newman.** He is a non-practising barrister and some feel he displays a *"very academic approach."* **Michael Jefferies** is a forceful general litigator who does a decent number of construction cases. Particularly noted for adjudication work, the team handled the construction-related work on the Millennium Stadium. **Clients:** Welsh Rugby Union; local authorities; contractors.

MIDLANDS

Wragge & Co The merger of specialist construction practice Neil F. Jones into Wragge & Co is the fusion of two very different types of practice, the former being primarily a contractor's firm with a litigation bent, and the latter serving mainly developer and utility clients. The result is a rounded national client base with a slight tilt towards contractors. In terms of personnel, all but two of the partner heavy NFJ outfit have moved to beef up the partner-light Wragges team. The top names at the new department are those of **Kevin Barrett**, a *"practical"* lawyer, and **Simon Baylis**, who is seen as more academic. **Ashley Pigott** remains as head of department, overseeing the fusion of the two cultures. **Ian Yule** *("a good all-round contentious lawyer")* rises up the table this year. The team acts for Harmon CFEM Facades (UK) in its £14 million claim against the House of Commons arising from breaches of the procurement regulations. **Clients:** AMEC; Carillion plc; Taylor Woodrow; Birse Construction; New Sadlers Wells; Miller Construction.

Hammond Suddards Edge A preponderance of non-contentious instructions from developer clients in a relatively hot market has allowed the firm to build further on a strong reputation. There is also a niche in M&E/process engineering litigation. Clients rate **David Lloyd Jones**, who *"scores well on the non-contentious side."* The team acted for Prologis Developments Ltd on the redevelopment of the old Coventry Cathedral site. **Clients:** Wilson Bowden Developments Ltd; Alfred McAlpine Special Projects; Galliford (UK) Ltd.

DLA The team supports the client base of the property department and backs up the PFI/projects team. Other sources of instruction are focus

CONSTRUCTION • Midlands	Ptnrs	Assts
❶ **Wragge & Co** Birmingham	8	22
❷ **Hammond Suddards Edge** Birmingham	4	4
❸ **DLA** Birmingham	2	4
Gateley Wareing Birmingham	2	4
❹ **Pinsent Curtis** Birmingham	-	4
❺ **Eversheds** Derby/Nottingham/ Birmingham	3	9
Freethcartwright Nottingham	3	4
Lee Crowder Birmingham	3	3
Merricks Birmingham	1	2
❻ **Browne Jacobson** Nottingham	2	2
Garretts Birmingham	1	6
Shoosmiths Northampton	1	3

LEADING INDIVIDUALS	
❶ **BARRETT Kevin** Wragge & Co	**BAYLIS Simon** Wragge & Co
LLOYD JONES David Hammond Suddards Edge	
❷ **BRADLEY Graeme** DLA	**DAVIES Peter** Gateley Wareing
PIGOTT Ashley Wragge & Co	
❸ **BROWN Jeffrey** Lee Crowder	**YULE Ian** Wragge & Co

Within each band, firms are listed alphabetically. *See **Profiles** on page 196*

energy and engineering clients. National head of construction, **Graeme Bradley**, has a good reputation and *"comes with a good track record."* Acted for Selfridges on the £40 million development of a site in Birmingham City Centre. **Clients:** Bryant Construction Ltd; Royal Bank of Scotland; Thermal Engineering International Ltd.

Gateley Wareing A strong house-building orientation flavours the work on behalf of a contractor client base, mostly on contentious matters. **Peter Davies** is recommended. Last year, the team settled a multi-million pound claim against an international contractor being sued by an M&E subcontractor over a substantial project in Southampton, and pursued a claim against the public body for whom the building was constructed. **Clients:** George Wimpey; Christiani & Nielson Ltd; Alfred McAlpine Construction Ltd.

Pinsent Curtis A new face from Eversheds Cardiff has been *"parachuted in"* to head the team and give extra strength. Market perception is that the team has need of a real figurehead. Sound commercial back-up makes the firm a viable client choice and it has a niche ability in engineering matters. Acted for Swindon and Marlborough NHS Trust in connection with the development of a new £90 million hospital. **Clients:** ALSTOM UK Ltd; Castlemore Securities; Property Advisers to the Civil Estate.

Eversheds Although the firm acts for an impressive client base, it has yet to shake off the market impression that, in its quest to provide a full-service construction practice, it has lost a degree of specialist expertise. However, the team is noted for its work on engineering contracts, and on contentious matters, advised on a claim concerning groundwork engineering on a development site in the south of England. Acting for Nottinghamshire County Council in the run-up to work starting on Nottingham's Express Transit tram project. **Clients:** Amec; Birmingham Mailbox; Severn Trent Property.

Freethcartwright Predominantly developer clients involved with both house building and commercial developments from office blocks to pubs. Principal non-contentious work has come on behalf of the Millennium Commission. Also acts on a range of contentious issues. Acted for the developer Sowden Group Ltd on the construction of a new 60,000 sq ft premises for Barclays Bank in Leicester. **Clients:** Brydon Developments; Mansell Construction Services; Monk Estates Ltd.

Lee Crowder Now on the map following the arrival of **Jeffrey Brown** from Neil F. Jones. The firm is now a different force from the end of 1999 and is predicted by the market to develop further. Also benefits from a high-class property department, providing a number of overlapping clients. **Clients:** Developers; contractors.

Merricks The team acts primarily on insurance-based litigation pertaining to construction disputes, generally for a clientele of insurance companies and some contractors. **Clients:** Employers; contractors.

Browne Jacobson A contentious workload with a PI angle but not a huge volume of development. This firm enters our tables this year for a *"sensible"* approach, which has impressed the major players. **Clients:** Employers; insurance companies.

Garretts Has scooped up another established lawyer from the former Edge Ellison but is still considered a small force in the region. The team has been drafting the construction contracts for the Merseyside PTE light rail project. **Clients:** Balfour Beatty; W S Atkins; Finning (UK) Ltd.

Shoosmiths The firm is considered to have made progress in this area, and has been able to call on the services of rated planning and property departments. Acts for a number of developers and home-builders. **Clients:** Persimmon Homes plc.

EAST ANGLIA

CONSTRUCTION • East Anglia	Ptnrs	Assts
❶ **Mills & Reeve** Cambridge	3	3
❷ **Hewitson Becke + Shaw** Cambridge	2	2
❸ **Eversheds** Norwich/Ipswich	2	5
Greenwoods Peterborough	1	2

LEADING INDIVIDUALS	
❶ **PICKUP Raith** Mills & Reeve	**PLASCOW Ronald** Mills & Reeve
❷ **WOOD Martin** Greenwoods	
❸ **OATS Simon** Eversheds	
RICHARDS Timothy Hewitson Becke + Shaw	

Within each band, firms are listed alphabetically. *See **Profiles** on page 196*

Mills & Reeve Comfortably at the top of the regional rankings, the firm has a mixed client base and a broad spread of work. **Raith Pickup** excels on non-contentious matters, particularly PFI-related work. His profile in the education and healthcare PFI sectors is substantial. **Ron Plascow** is *"business-like and no-nonsense."* He has a *"deep knowledge of the industry"* but is deemed to be *"quieter and not so forthright"* as Pickup. Benefiting from a buoyant property market, there is a steady stream of drafting instructions from employer clients. Contractors also feature. Acting for the Environment Agency in several sets of proceedings including the reported CA decision of Harbour and General Works Ltd v Environment Agency. **Clients:** SCA Packaging New Hythe; LB Barking & Dagenham; Norplan A.S.

Hewitson Becke + Shaw Ex-City lawyer **Tim Richards** heads a moderate-sized team whose work concentrates on developments and a property client base. It forms part of the firm's 'Development division,' which includes planning and commercial property lawyers. Plenty of science-based employer clients, reflecting the firm's reputation in the hi-tech/biotech sectors. Acting for the University of Cambridge Estates Management office on the new development of university buildings in the west of the city. **Clients:** Travis Perkins; Velux Industries; Medical Research Council.

Eversheds **Simon Oats** is widely felt to be a substantial gain for the firm, which will secure its position as a respected player. Its *"reach and client base really helps,"* although some saw the firm acting primarily for employers *"as an adjunct to property work."* The team handles both contentious and non-contentious matters, acting on construction contacts and advising Harland & Wolff on a major arbitration. **Clients:** Eastern Contracting.

Greenwoods The sudden death of star name John Hardwick in December 1999 was a grievous blow to the team. Another key player in the team has gone to Hammond Suddards Edge in Leeds leaving **Martin Wood** as lone partner. He is known to be *"a fighter on contentious matters"* and to show *"persistence."* Currently advising RG Carter in its bid to undertake construction of accommodation for student midwives for the University of East Anglia on the Norfolk and Norwich 2000 Hospital site. **Clients:** R G Carter Holdings; Willmott Dixon; RMC Group Services Ltd.

NORTH WEST

CONSTRUCTION • North West	Ptnrs	Assts
❶ **Masons** Manchester	6	16
❷ **Hammond Suddards Edge** Manchester	4	13
❸ **Addleshaw Booth & Co** Manchester	1	7
DLA Manchester, Liverpool	2	4
Kirk Jackson Manchester	2	*
❹ **Halliwell Landau** Manchester	3	3
Pannone & Partners Manchester	3	*
❺ **Elliotts** Manchester	3	6
Hill Dickinson Liverpool	1	2

LEADING INDIVIDUALS	
❶ **DAVIES Edward** Masons	
❷ **BAKER Huw** Masons	**MOSS David** Hammond Suddards Edge
WOOD Peter Masons	
❸ **PINSENT Jim** DLA	**PROCTOR Nigel** Hammond Suddards Edge
SALMON Kenneth Kirk Jackson	**WILCOCK Christopher** Hammond Suddards Edge
WILLCOCK Andrew Towers & Hamlins	

Within each band, firms are listed alphabetically. *See **Profiles** on page 196*
** See editorial entries for explanations of team sizes.*

Masons The firm is *"top dog"* for domestic contentious work and many contractor clients prefer this office above all others. The *"tough"* Masons house style is on offer (although this is occasionally described as *"off the wall aggressive"*). *"Experienced"* player, **Edward Davies**, has the lead role in the office. He takes no prisoners with his *"inimitable"* style. **Huw Baker** displays an *"enthusiastic"* approach and *"launches himself at the work."* **Peter Wood** spends only a minority of his time on fee-earning in Manchester; much is spent away from the coal-face looking after the Masons national and international reputation. The team undertakes a range of work, including international projects, cross-border disputes and contract drafting. Acted for Wembley National Stadium Ltd on the Wembley Stadium project, and for a contractor on a £20 million claim relating to the construction of a government central science laboratory. **Clients:** Carillion Group; ABB Power Construction Ltd; John Laing plc.

Hammond Suddards Edge Seen to be *"moving in the right direction"* and to have come a considerable distance since the inception of the department eight years ago. Last year's recruit **Nigel Proctor** has made a difference to the strength of a team which is rated highly across the country. He is *"good at his craft,"* working on mainly on non-contentious matters, including PFI but also ably handling contentious issues. **David Moss** was already renowned both for his charm and skills. **Chris Wilcock** is commended for his engineering and litigation capability. A number of the firm's clients are nationally based specialist subcontractors in power, process engineering and heavy engineering. Work for these clients extends into international arbitration of disputes. On the employer side, the client list includes regional concerns, utilities and local authorities. Act for Manchester Airport in relation to the £65 million ground transport interchange. **Clients:** Shaw Group Inc; Birse Process Engineering; Norwest Holst Engineering.

Addleshaw Booth & Co Although clearly among the leaders in the region, there has been a degree of market disquiet about a certain inflexibility here. One company reported that *"they don't like to argue – just impose."* Acted for the Royal Exchange Theatre throughout its multi-million pound redevelopment following bomb damage. Has provided construction advice for public sector, sponsors and banks on various PFI projects. **Clients:** Central Manchester/Manchester Childrens' NHS Trust; AMEC Developments Ltd; Green Property Ltd.

DLA An improving profile in both north-western offices, each led by a recognised expert, particularly **Jim Pinsent** in Liverpool. He received recommendations nationwide. The two offices operate closely, sharing the workload and their resources. PFI and development work dominate with occasional big disputes ringing the changes. **Clients:** English Partnerships; John Mowlem plc; AMEC.

Kirk Jackson A Quantity Surveyor works with the two partners. The client base is primarily comprised of specialist subcontractors; M&E, heating and ventilation etc. A niche is developing in the enforcement of awards. An increasing trend is for clients to approach the firm for pre-contract advice, thus increasing the profile outside the contentious field. **Ken Salmon** is well known, and has recently carried out three ICE adjudications. **Clients:** Civil engineering; employers and contractors.

Halliwell Landau Known especially for its work for bondsmen and for its rather unconventional, *"entrepreneurial"* style. That style is seen to lean to the commercial rather than the details and to be somewhat forceful in delivery. Has been acting in a complex multi-party action BICC v Parkman and Ors. for a firm of consulting engineers. **Clients:** Banks; contractors; developers.

Pannone & Partners Known to act for public sector clients and has a position in the PI insurance market. Has carried out work pertaining to power plants and receives instructions for both domestic and international matters. Currently defending a public body in a £54 million claim. **Clients:** Public sector clients.

Elliotts Professional indemnity and insurance-oriented construction work, generally on the contentious side, are the fortes here. **Clients:** Insurers; contractors.

Hill Dickinson Heavily involved in disputes and contractual advice to a spread of clients ranging from public bodies through to subcontractors. Presently advising the Iliad Group on a large development in Liverpool city centre **Clients:** Metropolitan Borough of Wirral; Denbighshire County Council; BDL Contracts & Design plc.

Other Notable Practitioner **Andrew Willcock** is the name mentioned at Trowers & Hamlins, although the firm has not yet managed to establish itself in the regional market.

YORKSHIRE

CONSTRUCTION • Yorkshire	Ptnrs	Assts
❶ **Addleshaw Booth & Co** Leeds	2	5
❷ **Hammond Suddards Edge** Leeds	3	10
❸ **DLA** Sheffield, Leeds	2	3
Masons Leeds	2	8
❹ **Eversheds** Leeds	3	7
Walker Morris Leeds	3	3
❺ **Pinsent Curtis** Leeds	2	3
❻ **Denison Till** York	2	1
Irwin Mitchell Sheffield	2	3
Nabarro Nathanson Sheffield	1	2

LEADING INDIVIDUALS	
❶ **BENTLEY Bruce** DLA	**COCKRAM Richard** Addleshaw Booth & Co
❷ **HARTLEY Keith** Masons	**PALMER Simon** Hammond Suddards Edge
ROBSON Nigel Eversheds	
❸ **GLAISTER Anthony** Denison Till	**HILTON Mark** Hammond Suddards Edge
RICHARDS Mark Masons	**SCOTT Martin** Walker Morris
STANIFORTH Alison Eversheds	
UP AND COMING	
STUBBS Jane Addleshaw Booth & Co	

Within each band, firms are listed alphabetically. *See **Profiles** on page 196*

Addleshaw Booth & Co Acknowledged to be *"the Yorkshire leaders,"* the firm is commended for *"putting resources into building a team of good people."* The property, PFI/projects and banking capabilities of the firm together provide a major construction capacity. A modest amount of international work, both projects and dispute-related mixes into the primarily domestic caseload. Major developments, PFI, civil and process engineering are key elements of the practice. **Richard Cockram** is singled out as *"the best non-contentious construction lawyer in Leeds."* New up and coming name **Jane Stubbs** *"has developed enormously; she's really sound."* Acting for Leeds Mental Health NHS Trust in the £45 million PFI project to re-provision mental health facilities in Leeds. **Clients:** Halifax plc; Kelda Group plc; Stadium Group.

Hammond Suddards Edge Just a shade behind the leader, the firm has embarked on successful raids on other firms, enticing among others, the well-known **Simon Palmer**, who it is felt *"will soften the Rottweiler approach."* Head of department, **Mark Hilton** is the name behind the growth of the department over the last couple of years. Engineering and process engineering are particular strengths, and while the client base is dominated by contractors, there are also a substantial number of employer clients. Advising Whites Property Company Ltd in relation to disputes concerning the Priory Meadow Shopping Centre in Hastings. **Clients:** Boots Properties Ltd; Morrison Construction Ltd; NG Bailey.

DLA Operates from within the property group and has a non-contentious focus, although has seen a growth in litigation in the last 18 months. Now has a partner in the Leeds office. In Sheffield, **Bruce Bentley** is *"well respected, charming and level headed."* He is warmly endorsed by practitioners all over the country and is one of the top non-contentious construction lawyers outside London. Acted for Chirex (Annan) Ltd in its successful opposition of the enforcement of an adjudicators award in Homer Burgess Ltd v Chirex (Annan) Ltd. **Clients:** Henry Boot plc; Alfred McAlpine Construction Ltd; Amco Engineering Ltd.

Masons Deemed to have *"impressive knowledge and ability."* **Keith Hartley** is *"a tough cookie,"* while **Mark Richards** has been involved in a number of PFI and large projects and has a track record in nuclear establishments, such as the Shelter Implementation Plan for the destroyed Unit 4 at Chernobyl. Regionally, it has a strong position, acting on a number of Leeds projects, including South Leeds Stadium, the pedestrianisation of Leeds city centre and the re-roofing of Leeds Railway Station. **Clients:** John Mowlem plc; Leeds City Council; AMEC Process and Energy Ltd.

Eversheds The Yorkshire and North East offices of Eversheds have had a real shake up in the last year. Key players and assistants have moved between offices nationally and regionally and some have left for other firms. What has resulted is *"a more focused practice."* Non-contentious and particularly PFI-related work is of key importance. **Nigel Robson** has moved from the Newcastle office, where he was managing partner. He is now a fee earning partner in the Leeds office, with a second role as mastermind of the Eversheds regional construction strategy. **Alison Staniforth** is a *"dominant character"* and a *"tenacious litigator."* Simon Palmer has moved on to Hammond Suddards Edge. The team has acted on two arbitrations for a large mechanical and electrical sub-contractor, with a total value in dispute of £8 million. **Clients:** The NG Bailey Organisation Ltd; ASDA; NTL.

Walker Morris A well rounded practice advising employer and contractor clients on a variety of developments. **Martin Scott** is viewed as *"sensible, commercial and practical."* Has advised property developer Priority Sites Ltd on a variety of development documents for the delivery of one million sq ft over the next three years. **Clients:** Ballast Wiltshire plc; Bradford & Northern Housing Association; Jarvis plc.

Pinsent Curtis Unashamedly employer-oriented, the firm has pushed itself forward into the spotlight on PFI and development work. Also handles a substantial volume of disputes, acting for contractors. From a standing start little more than two years ago, it is now known for the quality of its lawyers. Has *"out and out terrific"* litigation capability and is *"very positive"* at assistant level, with a crew who *"know their onions."* Acts for Sunderland Association FC in connection with its Stadium of Light. **Clients:** Leeds Bradford International Airport Ltd; Barrett Steel Ltd; Carillion plc.

Denison Till Dispute based work for contractors and sub-contractors with ad hoc non-contentious advice to institutional property companies. Well known **Anthony Glaister** is particularly noted for his mediation work. Acted on an injunction for MEM BV against Kvaerner Energy Systems to stop a call on a bond for US$1.6 million on a power station in China. **Clients:** Allens plc; National Federation of Roofing Contractors; P S Turner (Constructions) Ltd.

Irwin Mitchell New in our rankings this year. Has traditionally had a stronghold in industry and manufacturing and the construction practice has taken advantage of this client base. Leans more to the non-contentious acting for employers but also advise a number of contractors. **Clients:** Employers; contractors.

Nabarro Nathanson Has recently lost a key member of the team to Osborne Clarke OWA in Bristol. The last year has seen a variety of contentious and non-contentious matters. PFI has been of importance, including a number of schools schemes. Internationally, it acted for Saudi sub-contractor Al Yusr Townsend & Bottum Co. Ltd on a claim against the main contractor in respect of piping installation works in Jubail, Saudi Arabia. **Clients:** HSBC; RJB Mining; Bonus Energy A/S.

NORTH EAST

CONSTRUCTION • North East	Ptnrs	Assts
❶ **Eversheds** Newcastle upon Tyne	3	4
❷ **Dickinson Dees** Newcastle upon Tyne	2	5
Watson Burton Newcastle upon Tyne	4	5
❸ **Robert Muckle** Newcastle upon Tyne	1	2

LEADING INDIVIDUALS	
❶ **LANGLEY Robert** Watson Burton	**LEWIS Simon** Dickinson Dees
WRIGHTON Ralph Eversheds	
❷ **GORDON Roderick** Robert Muckle	
UP AND COMING	
ROWLAND Simon Watson Burton	

Within each band, firms are listed alphabetically. *See **Profiles** on page 196*

Eversheds The Eversheds restructuring still leaves the Newcastle office as the strongest in the North East. It has been viewed as *"a proactive construction team"* and has strong links with the firm's engineering client base. **Ralph Wrighton** is the hitherto unsung hero of this year. He has caught the attention of clients and other practitioners around the country as an *"unassuming"* but *"down to earth litigator who gets into the nitty gritty."* Mary Herbert has moved to the firm's Cardiff office. The team acted for the University of Northumbria at Newcastle on the construction of its Coach Lane Campus, valued at £42 million. **Clients:** Rolls Royce plc; University of Northumbria at Newcastle.

Dickinson Dees **Simon Lewis** has developed an enviable client base for the firm, which is seen as *"affable and reasonable to deal with."* A non-contentious bias is illustrated by the fact that the team is currently working on 16 PFI schemes in addition to regular development work. Has a foothold in energy, utilities and offshore infrastructure. Handled the £100 million Tyne and Wear Metro extension to Sunderland for Nexus. **Clients:** City Hospitals Sunderland NHS Trust; Enron; Crown House Construction.

Watson Burton **Rob Langley** is *"an out and out litigator"* and it is said of him that *"initially he comes across as fairly aggressive."* This is felt to be indicative of the firm's *"own style – blunt!"* **Simon Rowland** is the up and coming name. Some feel that the construction group are *"treading water"* but this impression may be the result of the fact that a team of four lawyers has been running a large piece of litigation for the last two years – a £25 million North Sea oil construction dispute in the TCC concerning a floating production and storage facility. **Clients:** Bellway plc; Bowey Group; Carillion plc.

Robert Muckle A *"tough"* operating style characterises a firm where **Roddy Gordon** is the stand-out name. Acts for a range of local developers, including successfully pursuing an arbitration claim against a local architect's practice. **Clients:** John S Dorrin Ltd; Svenska Palmer Construction Ltd; City and Northern Projects Ltd.

SCOTLAND

CONSTRUCTION • Scotland	Ptnrs	Assts
❶ **MacRoberts** Edinburgh, Glasgow	6	14
Masons Glasgow	3	6
❷ **McGrigor Donald** Edinburgh, Glasgow	3	13
❸ **Dundas & Wilson CS** Edinburgh, Glasgow	2	10
❹ **DLA** Edinburgh	3	6
❺ **Burness** Edinburgh	1	5
Ledingham Chalmers Aberdeen	1	1
Maclay Murray & Spens Glasgow	1	6
Morison Bishop Glasgow	2	3
Shepherd & Wedderburn WS Edinburgh	3	3

LEADING INDIVIDUALS	
❶ **MORRISON Alastair** Masons	**NOLAN Brandon** McGrigor Donald
PATTERSON Lindy MacRoberts	
❷ **CONNOR Vincent** Masons	**McLEAN Alistair** Dundas & Wilson CS
WELSH John Morison Bishop	
❸ **KELLY Neil** MacRoberts	**MASON Fenella** DLA
UP AND COMING	
CASSELS Sandra DLA	**TURNBULL Craig** MacRoberts

Within each band, firms are listed alphabetically. *See **Profiles** on page 196*

MacRoberts Until challenged by Masons, MacRoberts was the contentious construction practice north of the border. It has now deepened its profile in PFI (for which Scotland accounts for some 60 percent of the UK's total spend) and carries out plenty of adjudication work, which is stealing a march on arbitration. It is widely acknowledged that construction law is one of the firm's strongest suits. The team is headed by the un-missable, *"in your face"* **Lindy Patterson**, who is one of the best-recognised and best-respected Scottish construction practitioners. She and **Neil Kelly** (*"gets on with it"* with a *"no frills"* style) act primarily for main contractors and employers. Up and coming *"ankle-snapper"* **Craig Turnbull** continues to reinforce his growing reputation, particularly on contentious work for subcontractors. James Arnott now acts as a consultant and is Chair of the Scottish Building Contractor's Committee. In the last year the firm was involved in three major reported cases on adjudicators' decisions and published the first dedicated book on Scottish Building Contracts. **Clients:** AMEC Construction; Railtrack plc; Miller Construction.

Masons Masons Glasgow office has risen up into our top band this year but its Edinburgh operation has come into being so recently as to have precluded any sensible analysis of its strengths. The two big guns here are **Alastair Morrison** and **Vincent Connor**. The level of loyalty inspired in clients by these two lawyers is unmistakable. Morrison is felt to always *"look to the end result – he's not aggressive"* and clients recognise that they get *"good advice from affable"* Connor. The client focus is on leading contractors and in the engineering sector. The volume of contentious work is not quite matched by the non-contentious, with the latter dominated by PFI, including projects in water, education and courts. Last year the firm advised Bovis Lendlease Ltd in relation to issues arising from construction of the £250 million Braehead Shopping Centre. **Clients:** National Museums of Scotland; HBG Ltd; Laing Ltd.

McGrigor Donald A *"keen rival"* of the top two firms, McGrigor Donald has put emphasis on disputes, resolved either through arbitration or litigation run by its team of advocates. While **Brandon Nolan** is the only name in our tables this year, *"it is not quite a cult of one."* Teamwork is said to be the order of the day and this is one of the largest dedicated teams in Scotland. Five lawyers are based in Edinburgh with the remainder located in Glasgow. Five of the lawyers are dual qualified in England and Scotland. Edward MacKechnie's secondment to the Lockerbie trial team has impacted significantly on his presence in the mainstream of construction cases. On the non-contentious side, the firm advised on the documentation for the new national HQ of Scottish Enterprise in Glasgow. **Clients:** Sir Robert MacAlpine Ltd; Morrison Developments Ltd; Kvaerner Construction Group Ltd.

Dundas & Wilson CS A *"pragmatic, sensible and down to earth"* construction group felt to be more of a supporting pillar to the practice as a whole than a construction industry-facing department. Its core of clients are banks, public bodies and developers. Now part of the Arthur Andersen empire, it gets a fair bite of the plump Scottish PFI market, acting mainly for the funders and local authorities. **Alistair McLean** is acknowledged to be *"doing a good job of holding things together,"* and presides over a team servicing *"a great client base."* Advised the developer on all construction issues for the Buchanan Galleries retail development in Glasgow city centre. **Clients:** The Miller Group Ltd; Standard Life Assurance Company; West of Scotland Water Authority.

DLA Known as Bird Semple until its recent tie-up with the English firm. Overall the concept of the merger has been received favourably by other practitioners. **Fenella Mason** is felt to have *"glued things together"* in the department, and her reputation is that of being *"straight forward, down the line and easy."* The other dedicated construction partner is up and coming name, **Sandra Cassels**. **Clients:** Employers; sub-contractors; developers.

Burness A small team said to have *"done well in PFI,"* including instructions for Bank of Scotland, which funded two major educational projects that closed last year – James Watt College and West Lothian College. The non-contentious work dominates with clients ranging from public and quasi-public bodies through to contractors. The firm acted for the Royal Bank of Scotland on the procurement and construction of its HQ at St James House, Edinburgh. **Clients:** BBC; Ballast Wiltshier plc; Jarvis plc.

Ledingham Chalmers The Aberdeen office of this firm has been recommended as a new entrant into our Scottish table this year. Favourable feedback was received for the volume and quality of the work being done for clients in the North East of the country. One of the partners acts as Arbiter's Clerk to two of the North-East's most active Arbiters. The firm has been advising Rigblast Energy Services Ltd in its negotiations with Railtrack over various matters concerning the refurbishment of the Forth Rail Bridge. **Clients:** Highland and Islands Enterprise; Medical Centres (Scotland) Ltd; Harty Holdings Ltd.

Maclay Murray & Spens A large but young team, led by one partner and primarily acting for employer clients. The practice is primarily a non-contentious one with a number of PFI instructions and large-scale development projects. The link with the firm's strong property practice is evident. Clients range widely from the engineering sector, particularly offshore, to retail and leisure. Advised on a £50 million leisure development for Bondway Properties Ltd in Edinburgh. **Clients:** Kilmartin Developments Ltd; Kvaerner Oil & Gas Ltd; Bank of Scotland.

Morison Bishop A merger between Bishop & Robertson Chalmers and Alex Morison & Co is not seen to change the nature of this insurance litigation-led construction practice. *"Absolutely excellent"* **John Welsh** *("he's been doing it for donkeys years!")* is an experienced and admired specialist whose name is well known, especially amongst construction related professional indemnity lawyers across the UK. Has undertaken a number of actions for insurers in connection with professional negligence claims against engineers, architects and surveyors. **Clients:** Insurers and their professional clients; contractors and subcontractors.

Shepherd & Wedderburn WS This is still a relatively new construction group in relation to many of the other players in Scotland but it is acknowledged to have recently had *"more exposure because of PFI and has done really well out of it."* The team services clients in a myriad of sectors, including government, house building, financial, property, utilities and retail. Worked on the procurement package for Mercury Asset Management, and Parlison Properties in relation to the office development and computerised robotic carpark at Edinburgh One. **Clients:** Scottish Power plc; J C Decaux (UK) Ltd; Teesland/New Tollcross.

NORTHERN IRELAND

CONSTRUCTION • Northern Ireland	Ptnrs	Assts
❶ **Carson & McDowell** Belfast	1	2
Elliott Duffy Garrett Belfast	4	4
Johns Elliot Belfast	1	1
L'Estrange & Brett Belfast	*	*
❷ **Cleaver Fulton Rankin** Belfast	1	3
Kennedys Belfast	2	-
McKinty & Wright Belfast	4	2
Tughan & Co Belfast	2	1

LEADING INDIVIDUALS	
❶ **BECKETT Samuel** L'Estrange & Brett	**BUTLER Maurice** Johns Elliot
❷ **CRAIG Seán** Kennedys	**DAVISON Peter** Carson & McDowell

Within each band, firms are listed alphabetically. *See **Profiles** on page 196*

** See editorial entries for explanations of team sizes.*

Carson & McDowell A full service practice, the team benefits from the corporate, commercial and litigation strengths of the firm. The team, which includes the *"fine"* **Peter Davison**, acts for employers and contractors. Has been active in PFI which is on the increase in Northern Ireland, and advises on construction of agreements and warranties. Advising University of Ulster in respect of preliminary agreements for proposed new development at Springvale, West Belfast. **Clients:** Department of the Environment; University of Ulster.

Elliott Duffy Garrett Primarily contentious practice acting mainly for contractors. The team are seen to be *"involved"* and are *"my choice if I were conflicted out."* Also handle planning appeals and applications for judicial review. **Clients:** Contractors.

Johns Elliot Team includes **Maurice Butler**, a *"thorough operator of the old school."* This *"respected"* firm continues to act for the Northern Ireland Housing Executive. The defence of claims brought by contractors is a speciality and contentious work reportedly makes up the bulk of the practice. **Clients:** Northern Ireland Housing Executive.

L'Estrange & Brett (1 partner 50%, 1 partner 30%) The *"cool and collected"* **Samuel Beckett** leads this team which is an often mentioned choice. Primarily a non-contentious practice, the team advises PFI consortia, as well as on professional appointments and collateral warranties. On the contentious side, the team acts primarily for main contractors in contractual disputes. Also acts in Professional Indemnity cases, usually for the insurers. Advised on the Halifax's new UK-wide call centre at the old Belfast Gasworks site. **Clients:** Gilbert Ash (NI) Ltd; Braidwater Ltd; Morrison Developments Ltd.

Cleaver Fulton Rankin Acts for property development companies, building contractors, local councils and housing associations. Areas of expertise include claims for loss and expense and defending claims for defective work. The team is also active in arbitrations. Acted in Stothers v Mardown, a case concerning a development in Dublin. **Clients:** Lisburn BC; H&J Martin Ltd; James R Knowles Ltd.

Kennedys A team seen *"regularly"* on construction matters. **Seán Craig** is *"thorough and forward-thinking."* The practice focuses on professional indemnity cases acting often for insurers. Also advises on professional appointments. **Clients:** McNicholas; Independent; Chartwell.

McKinty & Wright This practice acts primarily on contentious construction matters, usually on the defence side for insurers of builders, engineers and others. The tragic loss of Owen Catchpole earlier this year is felt to have been a hard blow to the firm. Continues to advise the Royal Society of Ulster Architects on avoidance of PI claims. **Clients:** Royal Society of Ulster Architects.

Tughan & Co These *"recognised players"* act primarily in contentious work, mainly defending claims by contractors and others. Has a strong PFI practice and so handles non-contentious matters as well. **Clients:** Developers.

LEADERS IN CONSTRUCTION

BAKER, Huw
Masons, Manchester (0161) 234 8234
Partner in charge of PFI and major project work.
Specialisation: Work covers all aspects of PFI and major project work including project agreements, finance, building contracts and FM contracts.
Prof. Memberships: Society of Construction Lawyers. Member of TECSA. TECSA accredited Adjudicator.
Career: Qualified in 1987 while with *McKenna & Co*, then joined *Booth & Co* in Leeds in 1990. Joined *Addleshaw Sons & Latham* (now *Addleshaw Booth & Co*) in 1993 as Partner in charge of the Construction Team in Manchester. In September 1998 moved from *Addleshaw Booth & Co* to head up PFI and Major Project Work in *Masons'* Manchester office.
Personal: Born 22nd September 1962. Graduated from Cambridge University in 1984 with First Class Honours in Law. Leisure pursuits include gardening, walking and reading. Lives in Hebden Bridge, West Yorkshire.

BARRETT, Kevin John
Wragge & Co, Birmingham (0121) 629 1841
kevin_barrett@wragge.com
Qualified 1985; Partner 1989.
Specialisation: Construction litigation, arbitration and alternative dispute resolution as well as non-contentious work relating to the drafting of contracts, bonds, warranties and guarantees and general advisory work in relation to construction. Lectures on the law relating to construction. Edits Construction Law Digest and has contributed to other publications.
Prof. Memberships: Law Society, Fellow of the Chartered Institute of Arbitrators.
Career: Joined Neil F. Jones & Co. 1987. Partner 1989. Partner *Wragge& Co* 1999.
Personal: Born 1957. Attended Sheffield University, graduating in Law.

BAYLIS, Simon E.
Wragge & Co, Birmingham (0121) 629 1841
simon_baylis@wragge.com
Specialisation: Building and civil engineering work, both contentious and non contentious. Particular interest in adjudication and arbitration, and has acted as arbitrator. Non contentious work includes drafting sub contracts for use with major government sponsored contracts. Lectures extensively on construction contracts and related issues; co-author with Neil Jones of third edition of 'The JCT Intermediate Form.'
Prof. Memberships: Fellow of the Chartered Institute of Arbitrators; Associate of the Royal Institution of Chartered Surveyors; Law Society; TeCSA.
Career: Formerly practised in construction industry as Chartered Quantity Surveyor; called to Bar 1985; joined *Neil F. Jones & Co.* in 1989. Partner *Wragge & Co* – 1999.
Personal: Born 1954. Educated Bristol Grammar School and University of Sheffield.

BECKETT, Samuel R.
L'Estrange & Brett, Belfast (028) 9023 0426
sam.beckett@lestrangeandbrett.com
See under Litigation (Commercial), p.558

BENTLEY, Bruce
DLA, Sheffield (0114) 283 3457
bruce.bentley@dla.com
Fax: (0114) 272 4941 Partner in Real Estate Group and Construction and Engineering Group.
Specialisation: Construction and Engineering project work. Involves contracts for the implementation of building and engineering development projects and the negotiation and drafting of development agreements, construction and engineering contractors and related documents relating to office and industrial developments, disputes and arbitrations between public and private employers and contractors. Delivered a paper at first International Construction Management Conference, UMIST, 1992. Lectured on building contract terms, collateral warranties, JCT insurance clauses and JCT insolvency provisions. Contributor to Construction Management and Resolution.
Prof. Memberships: Society of Construction Law.
Career: Qualified with *Oxley & Coward*, Rotherham, 1971. Partner 1972. Left to join *Dibb Lupton Broomhead* as Partner in 1986.

BIRCH, John P.
Bevan Ashford, Exeter (01392) 663388
j.birch@bevan-ashford.co.uk
Specialisation: Specialist construction lawyer having extensive experience of dispute resolution in the construction industry. Acts for and advises international and national contractors in mediations, adjudications, arbitrations and litigation. Recent reported cases – Midland Veneers Ltd v Unilock, Hescorp Italia Spa v Morrison. Heads up the *Bevan Ashford* construction law team based in Exeter. Recently spoke at conferences on adjudication, non-concluded contracts and current construction issues. Former quantity surveyor having wide and varied experience of construction industry.
Prof. Memberships: Society of Construction Law, Law Society
Career: Quantity surveyor for 17 years prior to entering legal profession. Chief Quantity Surveyor for international contractor in Middle East. Qualified 1986, *Townsends* 1984 – 1999. Joined *Bevan Ashford* as partner 1999.
Personal: Resides South Hams, Devon. Leisure interests include, walking and reading.

BIRKBY, Gillian
Rowe & Maw, London (020) 7248 4282
gbirkby@roweandmaw.com
Specialisation: Construction and Engineering Law, both contentious and non-contentious. Involved in innovative forms of contracting leading to reduced confrontation. Expert in the application of the CDM Regulations (Health and Safety).
Prof. Memberships: ACIArb. Honorary Member of the Association of Planning Supervisors. Chairman of the Construction Industry Council's Task Force on Health and Safety.
Career: Joined the construction and engineering group of *Rowe & Maw[IT+-] in 1982. Became a partner in 1988.*
Personal: Walking, archaeology.

BISHOP, John
Masons, London (020) 7490 4000
john.bishop@masons.com
Senior Partner. Chairman of the Board and of Construction and Engineering Group.
Specialisation: Specialised in UK and International Construction and Engineering matters since qualifying, more recently also in Professional Negligence disputes. Major matters include LTRS, MTR, SSDS and Second Harbour Crossing in Hong Kong, Falklands Airfield, Tiffany Oil Platform, Channel Tunnel, Eurostar, Cairo Plaza, Jubilee Line, Keadby Power Station, LNG facilities (Brunei), Lloyds Building, M25, A27, several arbitrations from Indonesian Geothermic programme; conducted disputes at all levels of the English Courts, domestic arbitrations and international arbitrations under ICC, UNCITRAL and Stockholm Chamber rules as well as ADR processes. Expereince as Arbitrator and ADR practitioner.
Prof. Memberships: Dean of the Faculty of Mediation & ADR, Chairman of the Joint Consultative Committee of the London Court of International Arbitration, Vice Chairman of the Academy of Experts, President of the Technology and Construction Solicitors Association (TeCSA), Chairman of TeCSA IT Committee. Past Chairman of TeCSA, Past Member of TCC (Technology and Construction Court) Users Committee, TCC's Rules Committee, IT Committee, ADR Committee, Law Society Civil Litigation Committee, ICE Committees on Expert Evidence and Woolf Reforms, Founder Member of CEDR, Chartered Institute of Arbitrators' Committees on new forms of arbitration and ADR, British Academy of Experts Sub Committee on Expert Evidence. Editorial board of Construction Law Journal. Lectures include Blundell Memorial lecture, Bar Conference, Judicial Studies Board, National Contractors Group annual lecture, Chartered Institute of Arbitrators, Kings College (Univ. of London).
Career: Qualified 1971, Partner 1972, Admitted Hong Kong 1983, Managing Partner 1986 1990,Senior Partner 1990 to date. Qualified Adjudicator (TeCSA), Mediator (CEDR);
Personal: Sherborne School. LLB Hons Queen Mary College, University of London. Leisure interests include golf, fishing, cooking and tomatoes.

BLACKLER, Anthony
Macfarlanes, London (020) 7831 9222
Partner, Property Department.
Specialisation: Tony Blackler graduated from Downing College, Cambridge, as a Harris Scholar in law, and qualified as a solicitor in 1967. He has since specialised in construction law, initially on the contentious side, where he has been involved over the years in major disputes before the courts and in arbitration. More recently he has become involved in front-end work, negotiating contract documentation and advising on procurement generally. Until recently Tony chaired a sub-committee of the International Bar Association's Committee T (International Construction Projects). He is a lecturer, and currently writes a column for Building magazine. He was the principal author of a book published by Sweet & Maxwell on the JCT Management Contract. Tony is a trained and accredited mediator, and undertakes mediations when he is available to do so. He has advised a number of industry bodies about the legislation affecting construction contracts which is now embodied in the Housing Grants, Construction & Regeneration Act 1996, and more recently upon the likely effect of the Contracts (Rights of Third Parties) Bill upon the construction industry.

BOURGEOIS, Christopher
Taylor Joynson Garrett, London (020) 7300 7000
cbourgeois@tjg.co.uk
Partner in Construction and Engineering Department.
Specialisation: Principal area of practice is construction and engineering, and on and off-shore contract law. Advises employers, main contractors, specialist subcontractors, professionals and insurers on all forms of contract, standard form and 'bespoke', and all points of practice and procedure, ADR and mediation. Clients include national and international construction and engineering companies (including process engineering), UK and foreign companies engaged in the manufacture of electrical and other technical components, UK and foreign government agencies, water companies, professional indemnity insurers, health trusts and developers. Lectures to local authorities, architects, engineers, quantity surveyors and management on building and engineering contracts, contentious and non-contentious matters, company reorganisations.
Prof. Memberships: Society of Construction Law, Worshipful Company of Arbitrators. Fellow of the Chartered Institute of Arbitrators.
Career: Qualified in 1975. Joined *Freedmans*in 1977 and became a Partner in 1979. Admitted Hong Kong 1983. Joined *Taylor Joynson Garrett* as a Partner in 1996.
Personal: Born 17th May 1946. Leisure interests include shooting, vintage/classic car restoration and driving, property restoration and theatre. Lives in Bookham, Surrey.

BRADLEY, Graeme
DLA, Birmingham (08700) 111111
graeme.bradley@dla.com
Specialisation: Contentious and Non-Contentious Construction matters. International Arbitration (Construction). ADR.
Prof. Memberships: Law Society/Arbitration Club/Society Construction Law.
Career: *Masons* 1985-1989 (London). *Masons* 1989-1993 (Hong Kong) Hong Kong Solicitor. *Archibald Andersen* 1993-1995 (Paris) (French Avocat). *Eversheds* 1995- 1997, Head of Construction group. 1997 to date Partner Construction Group DLA. May 2000 – Head of DLA National Construction & Engineering group.
Personal: Main interests: Information technology.

BRIDGEWATER, Martin
Norton Rose, London (020) 7283 6000
bridgewaterm@nortonrose.com
Partner in Construction and Engineering Group.
Specialisation: Main area of practice covers non-contentious construction and engineering contracts, both UK and international (including associated export credit arrangements) and PFI/PPP projects. Generally advises developers or contractors on major UK building projects and banks or sponsors on infrastructure, process plant and independent power projects.
Prof. Memberships: International Bar Association, Society of Construction Lawyers.
Career: Qualified in England and Wales in 1976, and in Hong Kong in 1978. Joined *Nabarro Nathanson* in 1980, became a Partner in 1984 and headed their Construction Department from 1986-1997. Joined *Norton Rose* in 1997.

BROWN, Jeffrey C.
Lee Crowder, Birmingham (0121) 236 4477
Specialisation: Contentious and non-contentious work on behalf of developers, main contractors, subcontractors and their insurers.
Prof. Memberships: Technology and Construction Solicitors Association, Chartered Institute of Arbitrators, Chartered Insurance Institute.
Career: *Pinsent & Co* 1981-1982 Assistant Solicitor (now *Pinsent Curtis*), *Johnson & Co* 1982-1984 Assistant solicitor (now *Martineau Johnson*), *Neil F Jones* 1984-1999 Partner 1986, Senior Partner (1993-1999), *Lee Crowder* 1999- Partner and Head of Construction and Engineering Department (with effect from April 2000)
Publications: Co-Author 'Professional Negligence in the Construction Industry' – Published in 1998 by LLP.
Personal: Resident – Nant-Y-Deri, Gwent. Married with one son. Interests – sailing, windsurfing, swimming.

BUECHEL, Peter
Alexander Paul, Tiverton (01884) 252361
peterbuechel@alexanderpaul.com
Specialisation: Construction, drawn from a wide ranging experience. Represents employers, contractors, sub-contractors and professionals both in the context of contentious issues and project documentation at all levels.
Prof. Memberships: Fellow Chartered Institute of Arbitrators – Committee Member and Public Relations Officer Western Counties Branch Chartered Institute of Arbitrators, Member Society of Construction Law.
Career: Qualified 1986, *Herbert Oppenheimer, Nathan & Vandyk* 1986-1988, *Speechly Bircham* 1988-1993, *Stones* 1993, Partner 1996, Consultant 2000. Founded Alexander Paul June 2000.
Personal: Born 8 April 1962. Educated at Poole Grammar School and Oxford University (Honours School of Jurisprudence) BA 1983, MA 1989. King's College London (School of Physical Sciences and Engineering) MSc 1992. Interests; valuing work in progress!!

BUNCH, Anthony
Masons, London (020) 7490 6216
Worldwide Managing Partner, Partner in Construction and Engineering Group, Head of Energy Sector.
Specialisation: Has experience in all aspects of contentious and non-contentious matters relating to construction law. Has drafted a full range of contracts for major projects (including BOT schemes) in the UK and the Far East on behalf of employers, major contractors and international consultants. Has conducted proceedings to all levels, including the House of Lords, and in other countries including Hong Kong, Singapore and China. His primary experience concerns all forms of arbitration proceedings and in particular proceedings which concern the Energy sector. The majority of his dispute resolution work during recent years relates to major disputes concerning the oil and gas industry. Acted in the Channel Tunnel House of Lords case. Author of numerous articles on dispute resolution and in particular ADR. Joint author on the chapter on Hong Kong in the International Handbook on Commercial Arbitration and the specialist chapter on construction in the Handbook of Arbitration Practice. Speaks widely on construction issues.
Prof. Memberships: Member of the Chartered Institute of Arbitrators, Council Member of Chartered Institute of Arbitrators, Member of TECSA, Member of the Departmental Advisory Committee responsible for the Arbitration Act 1996, Member of the International Advisory Board to the Arbitration Institute of the Stockholm Chamber of Commerce.
Career: Qualified in 1978, having joined *Masons* in 1976. Became a Salaried Partner in 1980 and Equity Partner in 1982. Admitted as a Solicitor in Hong Kong in 1985; Senior resident Partner in Hong Kong office 1985-90. Became Managing Partner in 1991.
Personal: Born 8th February 1953. Holds a BA (Hons) from Nottingham. Leisure interests include cycling, music and theatre. Lives in Radlett, Herts.

BURCH, Simon
Linklaters (A member firm of Linklaters & Alliance), London (020) 7456 3582
simon.burch@linklaters.com
Partner, Construction & Engineering Group, Commercial Property Department.
Specialisation: Specialist in construction and engineering law and contracts providing primarily non-contentious advice in connection with major construction projects in the UK and overseas. Particular specialisation in drafting construction contracts and ancillary documents in connection with project financing with emphasis on power, energy and infrastructure projects. Also experience in concession agreements, operation and maintenance agreements, fuel supply agreements and facilities management agreements. Project experience includes major buildings, civil engineering works, power stations, petrochemical plants, industrial plants and offshore projects.
Prof. Memberships: ACI Arb; Society for Construction Law.
Career: Qualified 1974 (New Zealand), 1991 (UK).

BUTCHER, Trevor
CMS Cameron McKenna, London (020) 7367 3000
Partner in Projects Group.
Specialisation: Main areas of practice are construction and major projects, particularly private finance

work in the UK and internationally including central and eastern Europe. Particular specialisation in infrastructure projects especially roads, rail, water and power. Acted on numerous DBFO road projects leading teams on the M40, A55 and A130 deals and acting on similar projects overseas including road and rail projects in Poland. During 1994 based in Hong Kong advising the Hong Kong Government on projects related to the new airport. Author of various articles and speaker at a number of conferences on subjects including project management, partnering and DBFO roads. Drafted the Association for Project Management standard form appointment.
Career: Qualified in 1986, having joined *McKenna & Co.* in 1984. Became a Partner in 1992.
Personal: Born 10th February 1960. Graduated from Leicester University in 1983.

BUTLER, Maurice R.
Johns Elliot, Belfast (028) 9032 6881
See under Corporate Finance, p.

CANHAM, Stephanie
Trowers & Hamlins, London (020) 7423 8000
scanham@trowers.com
Specialisation: Partner, Projects and Construction Group. Has specialised in construction law for the past 13 years and is well known and respected, particularly among developers, as a commercial construction specialist. Has considerable experience in construction related matters, having advised in negotiations on major projects across the private and public sectors with substantial involvement in PFI, joint ventures, partnering, Egan compliant procurement and major commercial developments.
Prof. Memberships: Member of Chartered Institute of Arbitrators.
Career: Member of the Construction Clients Forum/JCT Working Party and a regular contributor of articles to journals. Lectures widely on construction and development issues and is a well known IBC/SBIM speaker by invitation for developers.
Publications: Has contributed to several construction-based publications and co-authored a guide to JCT 81.
Personal: Two children and a house husband (previously a lawyer).

CAPPER, Phillip
Lovells, London (020) 7296 2000
phillip.capper@lovells.com
Partner, specialising in International Arbitration, Engineering and Construction.
Specialisation: Recognised authority on engineering and construction risks and contracts. Substantial experience of international arbitration; as adviser, advocate and arbitrator. Worked on projects for highways, rail, power, defence, and process plant, building and construction in many countries worldwide. Lead counsel for TML, the Channel Tunnel contract consortium, under English and French law – keynote speaker on this at US AAA DART conference. Advised foreign state electricity generator/distributors, national gas distributors, high-speed rail authorities and suppliers, metro and light rail projects and privately financed infrastructure projects. Has sat as Arbitrator in ICC and LCIA arbitrations. Drafted the disputes clauses in standard forms NEC 2nd edition and ICE 7th. Engaged as expert by French Association of International Contractors (SEFI) to evaluate FIDIC's EPC Silver Book.
Prof. Memberships: UK member of the ICC Commission on International Arbitration in Paris; and of European Advisory Committee of the CPR Institute for Dispute Resolution, New York. Directs the International Diploma of the Chartered Institute of Arbitrators.
Career: Formerly partner in construction and engineering and Head of International Arbitration at *Masons.* He is a visiting Professor in Construction Law and Arbitration at King's College London, and before moving to London in 1988 he was Chairman of the Faculty of Law at the University of Oxford. He has been a Fellow of Keble College Oxford for 23 years.
Publications: For CIRIA's 'Client's Guide to Risk in Construction' wrote legal risk management. Founding Editor of 'Construction Industry Law Letter' from 1983 to 1990. Recent publications include Construction Industry Arbitrations in Sweet & Maxwell's 'Handbook of Arbitration Practice 3rd ed, and former General Editor of 'Emden's Construction Law'.
Personal: Born 1952. French language.

CASSELS, Sandra
DLA, Edinburgh (0131) 242 5533
sandra.cassels@dla.com
Specialisation: Partner with extensive experience in construction and engineering law, arbitration, adjudication and mediation; particular experience in advising the construction industry on all contentious matters and on health and safety.
Prof. Memberships: Fellow of the Chartered Institute of Arbitrators (FCIArb) and Vice Chairman of the Scottish Branch Committee; Registered Adjudicator with CEDR Panel of Adjudicator and Chartered Institute of Arbitrators Panel. Accredited CEDR Mediator.
Career: Assistant then associate *MacRoberts*, Glasgow; Head of Construction Unit *Shepherd & Wedderburn*, Edinburgh; partner *DLA Edinburgh* 1997. University of Edinburgh (1985 LLB Hons) Dip LP; FCI Arb.

COCKRAM, Richard
Addleshaw Booth & Co, Leeds (0113) 209 2000
rac@addleshaw-booth.co.uk
Partner, Head of Construction Unit.
Specialisation: Construction drafting, litigation, arbitration and PFI projects. Visiting lecturer in Construction Law at Leeds Metropolitan University.
Prof. Memberships: Fellow, Chartered Institute of Arbitrators. Member, Society of Construction Lawyers.
Career: Qualified 1973. Partner, *McKenna & Co.*, 1986-89. Joined the firm in 1989.
Publications: 'Manual of Construction Agreements' (Jordans, 1998).
Personal: Educated: Cambridge University 1967-70: MA in law. Interests include books and walking.

COLLINGWOOD, Mark
Masons, Bristol (0117) 924 5678
Partner in Construction and Engineering Group.
Specialisation: Heads *Masons'* thirty lawyer Bristol office and the firm's Construction and Engineering group in Bristol office. Specialist construction lawyer since qualification. Particular specialisms include litigation, arbitration, adjudication and dispute resolution generally, contract and project documentation negotiation and drafting. Has acted in many 'heavyweight' construction cases — civil engineering and building in the UK and abroad. Drafted project documentation for £350m Devonport dockyard redevelopment scheme. Lectures frequently on the law relating to the construction industry.
Prof. Memberships: Law Society, Faculty of Building.
Career: Qualified in 1980. Articled at *Crossman Block and Keith* 1978-80, before joining *Masons.* Became a Partner in 1985.
Personal: Born 19th December 1954. Attended Durham University, taking a BA in law and politics. Leisure interests include tennis. Has four young children.

CONNOR, Vincent
Masons, Glasgow
(0141) 248 4858/(0131) 718 6006
vincent.connor@masons.com
Specialisation: Partner specialising in contentious construction law, including tactical and strategic advice and the pursuit and defence of claims in litigation, arbitration and ADR.
Prof. Memberships: Law Society of Scotland.
Career: Educated at Glasgow University 1982-87 (LLB 1st class honours. 1986, DipLP 1987). Assistant Solicitor *Hughes Dowdall* 1987-90. Qualified as Notary Public in 1989. Joined *McGrigor Donald* in 1990, became an Associate in 1993 and assumed as a Partner in 1995. Accredited as a Solicitor Mediator in 1994. Jointly established *Masons Scotland* in 1998.
Personal: Born 1964. Leisure interests include music, cinema and running. Married. Resides in Glasgow.

CORBETT, Edward
Corbett & Co, Teddington (020) 8943 9885
ecorbett@corbett.co.uk
Specialisation: Active in the UK and all over the world advising contractors, clients, consultants and others on building and civil engineering procurement, contract preparation and negotiation, on dispute avoidance, management and resolution including mediation, adjudication and, if unavoidable, arbitration. Author of 'FIDIC 4th – A Practical Legal Guide'. Regular seminar speaker.
Prof. Memberships: FCIArb, SCL, IBA Committee T – Chair, FIDIC Sub-committee, TeCSA, Affiliate Member of FIDIC, FIDIC Mediator and Adjudicator, AAA Panellist. Former partner at *Masons.*
Personal: Born 10th September 1957. MSc in Construction Law and Arbitration, King's College. MA Jurisprudence, Oxford; Accredited Adjudicator and Mediator. Keen sailor and windsurfer.

CORNES, David L.
Winward Fearon, London (020) 7420 2800
Founding Partner.
Specialisation: Gives advice to those involved in building, civil engineering and the construction professions (architects, engineers and quantity surveyors) and their insurers. Handles High Court and arbitration work, including abroad. Involved in major non-contentious projects including private finance. Author of 'Design Liability in the Construction Industry', contributor to 'Construction Contract Policy'. Joint author of 'Collateral Warranties'. CEDR accredited Mediator (42 mediations completed). Arbitrator. Regular speaker at conferences in the UK and occasionally abroad.
Prof. Memberships: Fellow of the Institution of Civil Engineers, Fellow of the Chartered Institute of Arbitrators, Law Society, Society of Construction Law, Official Referees Solicitors Association, International Bar Association.

Career: Qualified in 1979. Worked with contractors and consulting engineers before joining *Masons* in 1976. Partner *Fenwick Elliott & Co.*, 1982-85, before founding *Winward Fearon* in 1986.
Personal: Born 31st August 1944. Attended King's College, University of London. Member of Electoral Reform Society and Charter 88. Leisure interests include walking, travelling, opera. Lives Berkhamsted, Herts.

CRAIG, Seàn T.
Kennedys, Belfast (028) 90240067
s.craig@kennedys-law.com
Specialisation: Construction related litigation. Disputes against professionals: Architects, Engineers, Surveyors, Geophysicists etc. Also claims against brokers and financial advisers. Acted for Lewis and Tucker on the BBL case. Acting for the Engineer on DED v Kennedys & Co, Loughrey Agnew etc.
Prof. Memberships: Qualified: English Bar, 1985; Law Society (England), 1988; Law Society (Northern Ireland), 1994; Law Society (Republic of Ireland), 1998.
Career: Joined *Kennedys'* City office in June 1987, becoming a Partner in January 1993. Helped establish *Kennedys'* Belfast office which opened in March 1996.

CRITCHLOW, Julian
Fenwick Elliott, London (020) 7956 9354
jcritchlow@fenickelliott.co.uk
Specialisation: Partner specialising in both non-contentious and contentious construction matters and arbitration. Author of Making Partnering Work in the Construction Industry (Chandos 1998), joint author of Arbitration Forms and Precedents (LLP 2000), Arbitration Editor of Amicus Curiae, Construction Law Editor of the Journal of ADR, Mediation and Negotiation.
Prof. Memberships: Fellow of the Chartered Institute of Arbitrators; CEDR accredited mediator; TeCSA registered adjudicator; Associate Fellow of the Society for Advanced Legal Studies; member of TeCSA; member of the Arbitration Club, member of the American Judicature Society; member of King's College Construction Law Association. Commissioner of the Foundation for International Commercial Arbitration.
Career: Qualified 1984. University College London (LL.B. 1981). King's College London (M.Sc. 1993). King's College London (Ph.D. commenced 1994). Articled *Field Fisher and Martineau.*
Personal: Born 1958. Married, two children. Leisure interests include riding, shooting, English poetry.

CUMMINS, Caroline
CMS Cameron McKenna, London
(020) 7367 2914
cxc.cmck.com
Specialisation: Concentrates on disputes resolution work for the construction industry. Clients are generally main contractors and employers. Cases have involved a wide range of issues and projects. Best known current case is McAlpine v Panatown in which she acts for Panatown. Has also advised on non-contentious matters including PFI projects. CEDR accredited mediator and TeCSA accredited adjudicator.
Prof. Memberships: Law Society; Society of Construction Law; TeCSA (committee member).
Personal: Attended St George's School, Ascot 1972-78 then Jesus College Oxford 1979-82. Qualified in 1989 after spending some years working for *United Biscuits plc.* Joined *CMS Cameron McKenna* in 1992 and became a partner in the construction group in 1996.

DAVIES, Edward
Masons, Manchester (0161) 234 8234
Heads *Masons*construction and engineering, energy and infrastructure groups in Manchester office.
Specialisation: Construction and engineering work, together with technology expertise. Litigation, arbitration and ADR (trained as mediator by American Arbitration Association in San Francisco). Contract drafting and procurement advice for major projects – especially transport and infrastructure – and construction aspects of the PFI. Joint editor – 'Dispute Resolution and Conflict Management in Construction (An International Review).'
Prof. Memberships: Law Society, Manchester Law Society, Society of Construction Law, American Arbitration Association. Joint co-ordinator of CIB International Research Group on conflict management. Visiting research fellow UMIST (University of Manchester Institute of Science and Technology).
Career: Qualified 1982. Joined *Masons* 1986 in London. Became partner and established Manchester office in 1989.
Personal: Born 1958. Manchester University (LLB); College of Law Guildford then Kings College London MSc. Lives in Manchester.

DAVIES, Lawrence
Masons, Bristol (0117) 924 5678
Partner in Construction & Engineering Group.
Specialisation: Specialises in contentious and non-contentious work related to the construction and engineering industries for contractors, sub-contractors, employers and consultants. Represented Tarmac in the case of Tarmac v Esso (1996).
Prof. Memberships: Law Society. Member of Society of Computers & Law. Secretary of Bristol Construction Law Forum. ORSA adjudicator.
Career: Articled at *Lovell White & King*. Qualified in 1984. Assistant solicitor *Lovell White & King* (then *Lovell White Durrant*) 1984-1990. Joined *Masons* in 1990. Became a Partner 1992.
Personal: Born 1959. Lives in North Somerset. Leisure interests include squash, golf, gardening and DIY.

DAVIES, Peter G.
Gateley Wareing, Birmingham (0121) 234 0000
pdavies@gateleywareing.co.uk
Specialisation: Construction – mainly contentious but some non-contentious. Head of Construction Unit.
Career: Trained at *Needham & James*, Birmingham (now *Dibb Lupton Alsop*) and spent many years there, becoming an equity partner. Moved to *Gateley Wareing* in 1992.
Prof. Memberships: Law Society, Chartered Institute of Arbitrators, The Arbitration Club, Official Referees' Solicitors' Association.

DAVIS, Michael E.
Herbert Smith, London (020) 7374 8000
Head of construction and engineering department.
Specialisation: Has specialised in major national and international construction and civil engineering projects since qualification, advising UK and overseas clients and conducting construction and civil engineering disputes both within the English jurisdiction and in international arbitrations, both ad hoc and subject to ICC, LCIA and UNCITRAL rules worldwide. He is also responsible for the preparation and negotiation of contracts for all aspects of process, construction and civil engineering projects acting on behalf of all sectors of the industry, project companies and banks and has advised in numerous projects both nationally and internationally including a number of major infrastructure projects.
Prof. Memberships: Law Society, City Solicitors Company, International Bar Association, LCIA, Society of Construction Law, United Kingdom Energy Lawyers Group, British Academy of Experts, Founder Member of the Centre for Dispute Resolution (Alternative Dispute Resolution), Founder Member of the City Disputes Panel.
Career: Qualified in 1977, became a partner in 1986, head of construction and civil engineering law 1986. Lectured widely in respect of construction, civil engineering and arbitration, including the International Bar Association, ICC, LCIA and the Law Society Commerce and Industry Group Center for International Legal Studies and most recently published a paper in the Sweet Lectures 'Comparative Studies in Construction Law' entitled 'Choice of Law Rules in International Construction Contracts'.
Personal: Born 14th August 1951, educated BA (London).

DAVISON, Peter William
Carson & McDowell, Belfast (028) 9024 4951
peter.davison@carson-mcdowell.com
Specialisation: Over 20 years of practical experience in general Commercial Litigation, with particular reference to construction matters, working for both Private and Public Sector under ICE/JCT/GC and other forms of contract. Established links with leading Construction Counsel in Belfast and London and experienced expert witnesses if required.
Prof. Memberships: Law Society of Northern Ireland. Society of Construction Law.
Career: 1974 MA Trinity College, Dublin (Legal Science), joined *Carson & McDowell* and admitted solicitor 1977. Partner 1979.

FENWICK ELLIOTT, Robert J.
Fenwick Elliott, London (020) 7956 9354
rjfe@fenwickelliott.co.uk
Senior Partner.
Specialisation: Senior Partner of firm, which specialises in construction law. Emphasis on resolution of disputes in the area of building and civil engineering contracts. Also advises on the drafting of building contracts. Has handled many large cases in adjudication, litigation, arbitration and mediation. Author of 'Building Contract Litigation' and 'Building Contract Disputes: Practice and Precedents.' Accredited TeCSA, CIC, CIOB Adjudicator. Qualified CEDR mediator.
Prof. Memberships: Chairman of TeCSA. Chairman of ICLA. Society of Construction Law Member.
Career: Qualified 1977. Worked at *Masons* from 1976 to 1980 before founding *Fenwick Elliott* in 1980.
Personal: Born 17th March 1952. Attended Eastbourne College 1965-69, then the University of Kent 1969-72. Leisure interests include music and motorbikes. Lives in London.

FLEET, Terry
Berwin Leighton, London (020) 7760 1000
terry.fleet@berwinleighton.com
Partner and Head of Construction Department.
Specialisation: Principal area of practice is construction law advising on building and civil

engineering projects in the UK and internationally, including procurement strategy, contract drafting and negotiation, bonds, warranties, insurance, contract advice and dispute resolution. Has advised in connection with major projects in the UK, the Caribbean, Europe (including Eastern Europe), Africa, the Middle East and the Far East. Currently involved in major office, retail, road, power, leisure and PFI projects in the UK, and overseas most recently in Bahrain, the Congo, Hungary, Norway, Poland, and Russia. Clients include institutions, government departments, funders, developers, major construction and engineering companies and professional architectural and civil engineering consultants. Has written articles in *Construction Law, Building, Property Week, Estates Gazette* and *Chartered Surveyor Weekly*. Co-Author of Tolleys Guide to Construction Contracts. Speaks at conferences on construction law matters.
Prof. Memberships: The Law Society, International Bar Association and Society of Construction Law.
Career: Qualified in 1980. Articled at *Heald & Nickinson* 1977-79 and moved to *Speechly Bircham* 1979-80. Legal Advisor to Costain Group 1980-82, Babcock International 1982-84 and Cementation International, (Trafalgar House) 1984-87. Joined *Berwin Leighton* in 1987 before becoming a Partner in 1988.
Personal: Born 1954. Attended Southampton University (graduated 1976 LLB Hons.). Leisure interests include flying, travel and family. Lives in Twickenham.

FOLEY, Richard
Masons, Bristol (0117) 970 5205
richard.foley@masons.com
Specialisation: A specialist construction lawyer undertaking contentious and non-contentious work principally for contractors and employers and increasingly in the energy sector. Recently advised on suite of contracts for multimillion pound processing facility and acted in major arbitrations regarding combined cycle power stations. Also has an extensive adjudications practice including reported decisions.
Career: Qualified in 1987. Joined *Masons* in 1990. Partner 1997.
Personal: Born 6th November 1962. Educated at Colston's School, Bristol and Liverpool University (LLB). Interests include golf, cricket, rugby and squash.

GARD, William
Bevan Ashford, Bristol (0117) 923 0111
w.gard@bevanashford.co.uk
Partner in Construction Department
Specialisation: Principally advising public and private sector employers in construction and engineering projects procurement and dispute resolution (particularly PFI/PPP). Particular focus: energy, infrastructure, waste and engineering. Also heavily involved with health, education and leisure sectors. Practising arbitrator and adjudicator – handled multiparty and multinational disputes including building and engineering defects, PFI, contract construction and professional negligence. Advising NHS Estates on Member of ICE Advisory Panel for Legal Affairs.
Prof. Memberships: Chartered Engineer; Institution of Civil Engineers; Fellow of the Chartered Institute of Arbitrators; Faculty of Building; Society of Construction Law; Law Society.
Career: BSc (Eng) London University 1985. Chartered Engineer 1991. Law Society Finals (1st) 1993. Qualified 1995. Partner 1998.
Personal: Born 1963. Resides Bristol. Educated Marlborough College, Wiltshire. Leisure: Golf (St Mellion, Bristol and Clifton); Tennis.

GARTHWAITE, Helen
Lewis Silkin, London (020) 7227 8000
Specialisation: All aspects of construction contract drafting, negotiation and advice, drafting and advising in connection with project finance and security taking; advising on day to day contract administration issues and on their solution including arbitration and dispute resolution. Has acted for a wide range of corporations and institutions owning, occupying and investing in commercial property and involved in development projects in the office, retail, industrial and leisure sectors and engaged in civil engineering projects. Writes and lectures regularly. Joint Editor of Construction, Law and the Environment.
Prof. Memberships: Secretary and Council Member, Society of Construction Law; Associate, Chartered Institute of Arbitrators.
Career: Qualified 1990. Solicitor, *Nabarro Nathason* 1990-1996. Partner and Head of Construction and Engineering Unit, *Lewis Silkin* 1996.
Personal: M.Sc. Construction Law and Arbitration (1992). Interests include yachting. Resides in Westminster.

GIBSON, Michael R.
Berwin Leighton, London (020) 7760 1000
mike.gibson@berwinleighton.com
Partner.
Specialisation: All aspects of law and practice relating to construction and engineering procurement in the UK and internationally, advising authorities, developers, funds, Government agencies, Health Trusts, contractors and designers on contracts for design, construction, financing and facilities management of major building and engineering projects and resolution of disputes arising from them. Principally involved with projects assembled under the Government's Private Finance Initiative.
Prof. Memberships: Society of Construction Law.
Career: Admitted in 1977. Legal department of Costain Group 1975-78. Head of Legal Department, Construction Division, Trafalgar House plc, 1981-87. Joined *Berwin Leighton* in 1987 and co-founder of its Construction Group. Head of Construction Group until 1998.
Personal: Born 1952. Educated at St. Edward's School, Oxford 1965-70 and Southampton University 1970-74. Lives in Oxshott, Surrey.

GLAISTER, Anthony
Denison Till, Leeds (0113) 246 7161
Specialisation: All areas of construction law to include arbitration and alternative dispute resolution. Solicitor for NFB and FMB regional members. Charges £185 per hour.
Prof. Memberships: ORSA adjudicator, CEDR mediator, administrator Association of Northern Mediators, and Chartered Institute of Arbitrators. Visiting lecturer on adjudication and mediation at Leeds Metropolitan University.
Career: Qualified in 1980. Partner in *Fox & Gibbons*, London from 1985 to 1989 and *Denison Till* since.
Personal: Born April 1953. Very active leisure pursuits where family and farming activities allow. Regional Deputy Chairman PYBT.

GORDON, Roderick C.P.R.
Robert Muckle, Newcastle-upon-Tyne
(0191) 232 4402
Partner and Head of Construction Unit. Main area of practice covers construction and engineering disputes, including High Court, arbitration and Alternative Dispute Resolution work as well as non-contentious work.
Career: Qualified 1988. Moved from *Masons* to *Robert Muckle* as a Partner in 1993. Member of Chartered Institute of Arbitrators; adjudicator approved by the Technology & Construction Court Solicitors Association TeCSA, CEDR accredited mediator.

GOULD, R. Nicholas H.
Lovells, London (020) 7296 2000
nicholas.gould@lovells.com
Specialisation: Principal area of practice is construction, with particular emphasis on engineering and international projects and energy. Has drafted, advised on, and helped resolve disputes on a wide range of construction, project, engineering and energy contracts over 30 years in the UK and many overseas countries. Has experience of project finance and of all forms of dispute resolution. Co-authored the book "International Commercial Arbitration" (LLP 1996).
Prof. Memberships: Law Society, International Bar Association, (Member of the Council of the Section on Business Law and past Co-Chairman of the International Contruction Projects Committee), Fellow of the Chartered Institute of Arbitrators and Associate of the Chartered Institute of Patent Agents.
Career: Qualified in 1967 with *Lovells*, became a partner in 1971. Established construction and engineering practice in the late 1960s.

GOWAN, Daniel
Davies Arnold Cooper, London (020) 7936 2222
Partner in Construction Department.
Specialisation: Handles all aspects of contentious and non-contentious construction work, contract drafting and reviewing, joint ventures, arbitration and litigation. Experienced in mechanical and civil engineering and building. Also handles construction insurance, including professional indemnity, contractors all risks and public liability claims. Acted for Petrotrin (Trinidad) in dispute with SNC Lavalin; PI insurers in Heathrow Tunnel collapse and Eurotunnel disputes; Project Insurer on Hong Kong Airport; Victorian Channels Authority in dredging dispute with Van Oord. Has spoken on many publicly-paid-for seminars for Hawkesmere, and for a number of in-house seminars and presentations to the construction industry.
Prof. Memberships: Fellow, Chartered Institute of Arbitrators;
Career: Qualified in New Zealand in 1976, and in England in 1983. Worked at *Meredith Connell & Co.*, New Zealand, 1975-78, then *Freedman & Co.*, London, 1980-83. Joined *Davies Arnold Cooper* in 1983, becoming a Partner in 1987.
Personal: Born 2nd October 1951. Leisure interests include cricket, tennis, golf, theatre, opera, music and reading. Lives in Rotherwick, Hampshire.

GUPPY, W. Nicholas
Laytons, Bristol (0117) 929 1626
bristol@laytons.com
Head of Construction Law and Editor of quarterly publication, 'Laytons Building'. Qualified in 1976 and worked in London until 1990 with ever increasing

specialisation in construction law. Acts for a wide range of employers, contractors and sub-contractors on both contentious matters (now mainly adjudication, but litigation and arbitration not dead yet!) and non-contentious. Regularly speaks at seminars.
Prof. Memberships: Law Society.
Career: Qualified in 1976. Joined *Laytons* in 1990 and became a Partner in 1992.
Personal: Born in 1951. Leisure interests include family life, squash and golf. Lives in London.

HANLEY, Christine
Bond Pearce, Plymouth (01752) 266633
xcmh@bondpearce.com
Partner & Head of the Construction Group.
Specialisation: Specialises in Construction Dispute Avoidance and resolution including adjudication, TCC litigation and arbitration. Contract drafting and project work.
Prof. Memberships: Fellow of the Chartered Institute of Arbitrators and member of the Society of Construction Lawyers. Committee member of the South West Construction Network.
Career: Qualified 1989. Associate 1997. Partner 1998.
Publications: Regularly invited to lecture on construction law. Paper presented at Kings College University of London likely to be published by Kings College Centre of Construction Law in a book on the Housing Grants Construction and Regeneration Act 1996 part II in October.

HARLING, Marcus
Burges Salmon, Bristol (0117) 939 2206
marcus.harling@burges-salmon.com
Specialisation: Head of Construction Unit advising on all aspects of construction and engineering projects, insurance and risk and related liability and claim issues. Specialises in project structures procurement and implementation. Current projects include a series of waste to energy projects, chp projects, a £40m process plant, 6 education ppp projects, a hotel project for The National Trust, £300m of lottery funded projects including @-Bristol which opened this year, and advising on a range of PFI projects in the defence and transport sectors.
Prof. Memberships: Society of Construction Law, Committee of the Technology and Construction Solicitors' Association (TeCSA). Specialist practice consultant to RIBA.
Career: Qualified in 1985, joined *Burges Salmon* in 1986 and became a Partner in 1992.
Publications: Author, TeCSA Protocol on Expert Evidence, Contributing Editor to Tolley's 'Knights Best Value and Public Procurement', RICS training video; Copyright in the Construction Industry.

HARMAN, Martin
Masons, London (020) 7490 4000
martin.harman@masons.com
Partner and Head of Infrastructure Group worldwide.
Specialisation: Main area of practice major infrastructure projects covering both contentious and transactional work. Advising various international entities, both governmental and private, upon the procurement of major infrastructure projects in collaboration with the private sector, and in that capacity, advising upon contract procurement strategy and drafting of project documentation. Substantial experiance of Light Rail Transit Systems and Airport Projects Worldwide. Has undertaken international arbitrations in Hong Kong, Lebanon, Singapore, Egypt, Kuwait, Yemen, Pakistan and India. Lectures widely for various international conference organisers.
Prof. Memberships: Faculty of Building, International Bar Association, Law Society of Hong Kong. Member of editorial team of the International Arbitration Law Review; member of Chartered Institute of Logistics and Transport; Chairman British Consultants Bureau's East Asia and Pacific Group, committee member of British Trade International's Asia Pacific Advisory Group.
Career: Qualified in 1971. Joined *Masons* in 1975, becoming a Partner in 1976. Admitted in Hong Kong 1983; first resident Partner at *Masons* in Hong Kong 1983. Worldwide Head of Infrastructure Group of *Masons.*
Personal: Born 24th December 1946. Attended Brighton College, Brighton 1960-65, then Bristol University 1966-69. Leisure interests include wooden toy making, walking, reading and music. Lives in London.

HARRIS, Adam
Masons, Bristol (0117) 924 5678
adam.harris@masons.com
Partner in Construction and Engineering Group.
Specialisation: Contentious and non-contentious work with a particular interest in PFI. A specialist in the building, civil engineering, process plant and electricity industries. Acts for both contractors and employers.
Career: Qualified 1981. *Lovell White Durrant* 1982-1988 (Hong Kong 1983-1987). Admitted Hong Kong 1984. Partner at *Masons* 1990.
Personal: Born 3rd January 1956. Educated Wellington School and Birmingham University (LLB). Interests include cricket and gardening.

HARTLEY, Keith
Masons, Leeds (0113) 233 8905
Partner in Construction & Engineering group
Specialisation: Leads 15-lawyer Construction & Engineering team in Leeds. Dispute resolution including High Court, arbitration and ADR and major project work, including many PFI and BOT schemes. Particular interests are transport systems and infrastructure and off shore process installations. Worked in UK and several Asian countries.
Prof. Memberships: Law Society, Chartered Institute of Arbitrators, Pacific Lawyers Association.
Career: Joined *Masons* in1980. Admitted as solicitor in England (1982) and in Hong Kong (1984) and became a partner in 1986. Resident in Hong Kong for 10 years before becoming Managing Partner of Leeds office in 1995.
Personal: Born 11 October 1957. Educated at King's College, London. Lives at Adel near Leeds.

HELPS, Dominic
Shadbolt & Co, Reigate (01737) 226277
Dominic_Helps@shadboltlaw.co.uk
Specialisation: Specialises in the handling of building and civil engineering project disputes, both domestic and international, including the Tsing Ma Bridge, Heathrow Tunnel Collapse, the Broadgate development and MEPAS tunnel dispute. Also acted for a major German contractor on a number of substantial ICC Arbitrations. Non-contentious experience includes drafting documentation for a major project finance project and acting for funds, developers, contractors and consultants on a wide variety of drafting work. Regular contributor to the construction and legal press and speaker on construction law. Accredited adjudicator (TeCSA).
Prof. Memberships: Technology and construction Solicitors Association (secretary); Society of Construction Law; Law Society; Arbitration Club. Chairman, Law Courts Branch.
Career: Articled and qualified with Linklaters & Paines 1983. Joined Lovell White & King (later Lovell White Durrant) in Hong Kong in 1985, returning to London office in 1986. Became a Partner with Shadbolt & Co in 1996.
Personal: Born 8th July 1956. Attended Radley College, Oxon, then Cambridge University 1975-1978 and 1979-1980. In between was staff writer for Management Today. Leisure interests include playing cricket, Arsenal FC, scuba-diving, reading novels/history and cinema. Lives in Reigate.

HERBERT, Mary
Eversheds, Cardiff (02920) 471147
maryherbert@eversheds.com
Specialisation: Defects claims, particularly claims against professionals, loss and expense claims. Considerable experience of health sector, energy, offshore and process plant as well as general building and engineering. Also very experienced in PFI, contract drafting, amending and professional appointments and warranties.
Prof. Memberships: Law society.
Career: Qualified in 1988 and joined Eversheds, becoming a Partner in 1993.
Personal: Theatre, art and gardening. Lives in Cardiff.

HILTON, Mark W.
Hammond Suddards Edge, Leeds (0113) 284 7000
mark.hilton@hammondsuddardsedge.com
Partner in Construction and Engineering Unit
Specialisation: Main area of practice is construction law. Acts on behalf of contractors, sub-contractors and employers in relation to non-contentious and contentious matters and contractual and other disputes in all areas of construction, in arbitration and litigation. Also handles commercial litigation work. Acted in Duquemin v. Slater, Preston v. Torfaen, Yorkshire RHA v. Fairclough and Percy Thomas, Strachan and Henshaw v. Stein Industrie.
Prof. Memberships: Law Society, ORSA, Fellow of the Chartered Institute of Arbitrators.
Career: Qualified in 1982. Worked at *Last Suddards* in Bradford 1980-82, *Barlow Lyde & Gilbert* 1982-84 and rejoined *Last Suddards* (later Hammond Suddards) in 1984, becoming a Partner in 1985.
Personal: Born 15th July 1958. Attended Wrekin College 1972-76 and University of Leeds 1976-79. Leisure interests include swimming, scuba diving, skiing and tennis. Lives in Harrogate.

HOSIE, Jonathan
Hammond Suddards Edge, London
(020) 7655 1000
jonathan.hosie@hammondsuddardsedge.com
Specialisation: Partner in the Construction and Engineering Unit practice of *Hammond Suddards Edge* in London. Handling drafting of documentation for construction and major projects and the resolution of complex construction disputes. Has published over 50 papers and articles and regularly addresses conferences and seminars on the legal aspects of construction and arbitration.
Prof. Memberships: Society of Construction Law

(Council member); Technology & Construction Court Solicitors Association (TECSA accredited adjudicator); Chartered Institute of Arbitrators; Arbitration Club, King's College Branch (Chairman); Chairman of Working Group 3 of the Design Build Foundation. Tutor at the Centre for Construction Law, Kings College.
Career: Qualified 1984. Associate with *Baker & McKenzie*'s Construction and Engineering Law Department 1989-95 before joining *Edge Ellison*.
Personal: Educated at the University of Wales (LL.B Hons) and at King's College, London (MSc Construction Law and Arbitration) 1989-91. Winner of the Alfred Hudson Prize awarded by Society of Construction Law 1993. Interests include family and Manchester United FC. Born 5th December 1958. Lives in London.

HOWE, Martin
Bevan Ashford, Bristol (0117) 923 0111
m.howe@bevanashford.co.uk
Partner.
Specialisation: Construction law, both contentious and non-contentious.
Prof. Memberships: Regional co-ordinator for the Society of Construction Law in Bristol. Member of the Reading Construction Forum. Fellow Member of the Faculty of Building.
Career: Qualified 1983. Joined *Bevan Ashford* as a partner in May 2000. Previously partner and Head of Construction at *Veale Wasbrough*.
Personal: Born 1958. Educated King's College, London.

HOYLE, Roger V.
Veale Wasbrough, Bristol (0117) 925 2020
rhoyle@vwl.co.uk
Head of Construction Department.
Specialisation: Construction law. Has extensive experience of dispute resolution in the construction industry, involving claims concerning defective design and construction, the liability of professionals and their insurers, and the interpretation and enforcement of contracts, including claims for loss and expense.
Prof. Memberships: Committee Member of the Technology and Construction Solicitors Association, Law Society (London and Bristol).
Career: Qualified 1971. Became a partner of *Veale Wasbrough* in 1973.
Personal: Born 1947. Educated at Sedbergh School.

HUDSON, James J.S.
Nicholson Graham & Jones, London
(020) 7648 9000
Partner in Construction and Engineering Department.
Specialisation: Principal area of practice is construction and civil engineering law. Has extensive experience of litigation, arbitration and other forms of ADR including mediation and adjudication (both as solicitor and adjudicator) Important cases have included 'Minter v. WHTSO' and 'ICI v. Bovis' and others. Speaker at construction seminars.
Prof. Memberships: Past Chairman (now Vice President) of Technology and Construction Solicitors Association, TeSCA accredited adjudicator, Member of TCC Users Committee. Society of Construction Law, International Bar Association and was a member of the Official Referees Working Group to the Woolf Enquiry.
Career: Called to the Bar in 1972. Qualified as a Solicitor in 1977. Joined *Bristows Cooke & Carpmael* in 1979 and became a Partner in 1984. Joined *Nicholson Graham & Jones* as a Partner in 1998.
Personal: Born 13th May 1949. Educated at Winchester College 1962-66 and King's College, London (LL.B Hons, 1971). Leisure activities include golf, tennis and cricket.

JEFFERIES, Michael
Hugh James Ford Simey, Cardiff (029) 2022 4871
Partner in Construction and Civil Engineering Department.
Specialisation: Has specialised in construction law for over 20 years, engaged in major litigation and arbitration for all sectors of the industry, as well as advising on non-contentious matters. Particular emphasis on professional indemnity matters, acting on behalf of a variety of professionals including architects, engineers, surveyors and their insurers (including contractor's design liability insurers). Important cases handled include Mid Glamorgan C.C. v. Devonald Williams; H.H.C v. W.H.T.S.O and Mid Glamorgan C.C. v. Land Authority for Wales. Member of Salford University Working Party on Intelligent Authoring of Building Contracts. Lead Partner for the Welsh Rugby Union redevelopment of the National Stadium.
Prof. Memberships: Institute of Arbitrators.
Career: Joined *Hugh James* in 1970. Qualified and became a Partner in 1972.
Personal: Born 21st November 1947. Educated at University College, London. Lives in Cardiff.

JENKINS, Jane
Freshfields Bruckhaus Deringer, London
(020) 7936 4000
jjenkins@freshfields.com
Specialisation: Has broad experience of dispute resolution on and the drafting and negotiation of major construction and engineering projects. Contentious work covers ADR, arbitration and litigation in construction and energy sectors including public procurement bid challenge advice. Non-contentious work covers PFI (including road, rail and prisons projects,) process plant and power projects and institutional development.
Prof. Memberships: City of London Solicitors Company; CEDR accredited mediator.
Career: Qualified 1988, partner with *Freshfields* 1996.
Publications: Contributor to Sweet & Maxwell's 'Construction Law: Themes and Practice' and LLP's 'Privity of Contracts: Impact of the Contract: (Rights of Third Parties) Act 1999.'
Personal: Born 20 March 1963, educated at Lincoln College, Oxford (1981-1985). Married with two children.

JONES, David M.
Hammond Suddards Edge, London
(020) 7655 1000
david.jones@hammondsuddardsedge.com
Specialisation: Large scale construction and civil engineering disputes both national and international. Experienced in ADR and has successfully concluded a number of Mediation/Conciliations for clients as well as more traditional forms of Dispute Resolution, Arbitration, Litigation (including a year long trial in the Caribbean). He is also an expert in Environmental Law, Construction Insurance and Health & Safety. He has been involved in non-contentious work and more recently with Tunnelling & Railway contracts and some PFI work. Also involved in the development of prime contracting for the MoD.
Prof. Memberships: Official Referees Solicitors Association; Court Member of the Company of Water Conservators.
Career: Qualified 1976; Articles at *Lovell White Durrant*; *Masons* (Equity Partner 1982-94) 1980-94; *Hammond Suddards* (Equity Partner) 1995.
Personal: Married with two teenage daughters. Interests: football and golf.

JONES, Peter
Eversheds, Cardiff (02920) 471147
peterjones@eversheds.com
See under Litigation (Commercial), p.563

KELLY, Neil J.
MacRoberts, Edinburgh (0131) 226 2552
njk@macroberts.co.uk
Specialisation: Practice covers full range of advice to commercial clients in connection with dispute avoidance and resolution (Arbitration, Court, ADR) with particular reference to the construction and civil engineering industries acting for related professions, contractors, sub-contractors and suppliers.
Prof. Memberships: Notary Public, Associate of the Chartered Institute of Arbitrators, Commissioner of the Scottish Council for International Arbitration.
Career: Born 28th June 1961. Aberdeen University (LLB with Distinction and Dip. L.P.). Interests include opera and classical music. Lives in Edinburgh.

LANE, Mark
Masons, London (020) 7490 6214
mark.lane@masons.com
Partner in infrastructure group. Head of water sector.
Specialisation: Principally contract drafting and dispute resolution. Includes ICC arbitrations, domestic litigation and contract drafting for international and UK infrastructure projects. Also handles EU public procurement advising contracting authorities (including government departments, agencies and utilities) on tendering procedures and structuring tendering procedures under PFI schemes. Acted for Eric Cumine Associates on Harbour City litigation in Hong Kong. Member of the firm's team on Channel Tunnel and Canary Wharf projects and on a number of PFI projects including hospitals (procurement issues) and water and waste water treatment works (project agreements and construction issues). Contract drafting on other water related projects in the recent past includes projects in India, the Philippines, Australasia, and Scotland. Editor-in-chief of Mason's 'Water Yearbook'. Has extensive African experience (much of it FIDIC related) including matters in Nigeria, Gambia, Ghana, Mozambique, Kenya and Mali. Has recently worked on projects in Maldives (airport) and Belgium. In March of 1998, led Masons' team acting for the Government of Ukraine in negotiations to establish the Project Management Unit to manage the project to render the Chernobyl Nuclear Reactor No4 safe. (The project is ongoing.) Experienced conference speaker nationally and internationally.
Prof. Memberships: Society of Construction Law; IBA (Committee T) Chairman of sub-committee on International Procurement in Construction Projects; European Construction Institute (Member of Executive Committee) (Chairman of European Legislation Task Force).
Career: Qualified in 1975. Partner at *Masons* since 1988.

Personal: Born 18th March 1950. Educated at Cranleigh School 1962-67 and Trinity College, Cambridge 1968-72. Lives in London.

LANGLEY, Robert L.
Watson Burton, Newcastle upon Tyne
(0191) 244 4444
Partner in Commercial Litigation Department. Head of Construction Unit (5 Partners, 5 Solicitors, 4 Paralegals).Practising Mediator and Adjudicator.
Specialisation: Specialises in construction law and professional indemnity. Head of Commercial Litigation. Handles contractual disputes in construction, engineering and fabrication. Also undertakes professional indemnity and professional negligence work, both tortious and contractual. Has acted in a wide range of disputes including those in the construction process, injunctive work and particularly in the context of off-shore fabrication and engineering and a number of major arbitrations. Clients include fundholders, developers, further education institutions, design consultants, estate surveyors and valuers, foreign lawyers and Underwriters. Regular speaker at conferences and seminars including degree courses and CPD.
Prof. Memberships: Law Society, Chartered Institute of Arbitrators, ADR Net, NDR, Technology and Construction Solicitors Association, Fellow of the Society of Advanced Legal Studies.
Career: Called to the Bar in 1975. Re-qualified as a Solicitor in 1979. Partner in 1981 at *Watson Burton*, Newcastle upon Tyne.
Personal: Educated at Oxford University (BA Jurisprudence 1974). Leisure interests include yachting, skiing, the hills and history. Lives in Newcastle upon Tyne.

LEVINE, Marshall
Linklaters (A member firm of Linklaters & Alliance), London (020) 7456 3580
marshall.levine@linklaters.com
Specialisation: Partner and Head of the Construction and Engineering Group. Involved in a wide range of construction and engineering matters, including advice in relation to many construction and engineering projects and major real estate joint ventures, property developments and construction financing. Highly experienced in drafting construction contracts, and in advising on dispute resolution over a wide variety of projects including process plants, civil engineering, substantial headquarter office redevelopment, relocations and refurbishments as well as PFI transactions in the health, property, transportation and waste water sectors. Was involved in the BR privatisaton. Publications include 'Construction Insurance' (Lloyds); 'Commercial Development Property Precedents' (Longman); Construction and Engineering Precedents and and Consultant Editor on Butterworth's PFI Manual.

LEWIS, Simon
Dickinson Dees, Newcastle upon Tyne
(0191) 279 9552
simon.lewis@dickinson-dees.com
Specialisation: Covers full range of Construction Law, including offshore and minerals industries. In particular deals with dispute resolution, including litigation, arbitration, ADR and Adjudication. Also extensively involved in PFI work. Acts for all sectors of the Construction industry. Writes and lectures extensively on construction law and PFI issues. Has a regular column in Building magazine. General Editor of and contributor to 'Tolley's Guide to Construction Contracts.'
Prof. Memberships: Member of the Chartered Institute of Arbitrators, member of TECSA (accredited adjudicator) and ARCOM.
Career: Qualified 1986. Joined *Lovell White Durrant* 1988. Joined *Dickinson Dees* 1992 (Partner from 1995).
Personal: Born 20 November 1960. Bristol University 1979-83 : LL.B, LL.M. Interests include: cinema, hillwalking and American Football. Lives in Newcastle upon Tyne.

LLOYD JONES, David
Hammond Suddards Edge, Birmingham
(0121) 200 2001
david.lloydjones@hammondsuddardsedge.com
Specialisation: Extensive experience in contentious and non-contentious construction. Principal areas of work involve drafting and negotiation of construction and engineering contracts and development agreements covering all aspects of property development, rail, road and engineering projects whether acting for developers, owners, funders, contractors or consultants.
Prof. Memberships: Fellow, Chartered Institute of Arbitrators, Technology and Construction Solicitors Association (Committee Member), CEDR accredited mediator, Society of Construction Law.
Career: Joined Edge Ellison in 1989 (Partner from 1991).

LONG, Peter
CMS Cameron McKenna, London
(020) 7367 2507
pjl@cmck.com
Partner in Construction Group.
Specialisation: Specialist in construction law with over 20 years experience advising contractors, consultants and employers in the construction industry. Includes advice on construction aspects of major projects and PFI schemes, procurement advice, drafting and negotiation of construction contracts, consultancy agreements, collateral warranties, concession agreements and operating and maintenance agreements. Also advising on contractual claims against and by contractors and consultants, dispute resolution procedures and conduct of litigation, arbitration and ADR procedures. Experienced in all kinds of construction projects including large-scale commercial buildings, civil engineering projects and process plant and heavy engineering. Contributor of articles to the construction press. Speaker at construction law seminars. Accredited mediator with CEDR (Centre for Dispute Resolution).
Prof. Memberships: Law Society, Society of Construction Law, Technology and Construction Solicitors Association.
Career: Qualified in 1978, having joined *McKenna & Co.* in 1975. Became a Partner in 1984. Worked in Hong Kong office 1981-1985, having qualified as a solicitor in Hong Kong in 1981. Partner in *Cameron McKenna* 1997.
Personal: Born 18th October 1950. Attended Balliol College, Oxford 1969-1973 (1st Class Honours in Classics).

MASON, Fenella Mary
DLA, Edinburgh (0131) 242 5534
fenella.mason@dla.com
Specialisation: Partner in and Head of DLA's Scottish Construction and Engineering team. Advises on contentious and non-contentious construction matters from procurement advice through to dispute resolution by mediation, litigation, arbitration and adjudication. Acts for contractors, sub-contractors and employers in wide range of major public and private sector projects and disputes.
Prof. Memberships: Council Member of the Society of Construction Law. Regular contributor to Construction journals and speaker at Construction Seminars.
Career: Qualified 1989. Partner in *Bird Semple* 1995-2000, *DLA*.

MCLEAN, Alistair
Dundas & Wilson CS, Edinburgh (0131) 228 8000

MINOGUE, Ann
CMS Cameron McKenna, London
(020) 7367 2505
eam@cmck.com
Partner in Construction Group.
Specialisation: Principal area of work is procurement advice and drafting building and construction-related contracts for major developments and projects. Other main area of work is construction disputes. Drafted standard forms for ACA and BPF. Handled construction work on Broadgate, Canary Wharf, Minster Court, Royal Opera House, Tate Modern and other projects.
Prof. Memberships: University of Reading, Construction Management Forum, and Design-Build Foundation, BPF Construction Committee, 'Justice' Committee (legal remedies for home-owners), Latham Working Group 10, JCT Drafting Sub-Committee.
Career: Joined the firm in 1978 as an articled clerk. Qualified in 1980 and became a Partner in 1985.
Publications: Contributes two monthly columns to 'Building' magazine.
Personal: Born 17th October 1955. Attended Aylesbury Girls' High School 1966-73, then Clare College, Cambridge 1974-77. Speaks Russian. Leisure pursuits include films and tennis. Lives in Buckinghamshire.

MORRISON, Alastair
Masons, Glasgow (0141) 248 4858/Edinburgh (0131)718 6006
alastair.morrison@masons.com
Specialisation: Partner providing legal and strategic advice on all aspects of construction and engineering projects, drafting of bespoke contracts and construction arbitration and litigation.
Prof. Memberships: International Bar Association Construction Division.
Career: Attended University of Cape Town, University of Glasgow (LLB Hons, Dip LP). Assistant solicitor *Digby Brown* 1986 – 1989; assistant solicitor *McGrigor Donald* 1989 – 1993; associate partner *Dundas & Wilson CS* 1993 – 1994; Partner and Head of Construction and Engineering Group 1994-1998; Jointly established *Masons Scotland* in 1998.
Personal: Born 1962. Resides Glasgow. Leisure interests include running and rugby.

MOSEY, David
Trowers & Hamlins, London (020) 7423 8000
dmosey@trowers.com
Partner, Commercial. Head of Projects and Construction Group.
Specialisation: Has advised for more than 20 years on UK and international construction law, including major projects in the commercial, industrial, housing,

urban regeneration, health and education sectors. Substantial involvement in PFI and leading adviser on partnering and Egan-compliant procurement. Particular expertise in procurement strategies, risk analysis, standard and bespoke contracts and professional appointments. Author of 'PPC2000' (the first standard form of Project Partnering Contract) and of 'Design and Build in Action' (Chandos 1998).
Prof. Memberships: A core member of the Housing forum and a member of the Society of Construction Law, also a highly experienced conference/seminar speaker.

MOSS, David J.
Hammond Suddards Edge, Manchester (0161) 830 5000
david.moss@hammondsuddardsedge.com
Partner in Construction and Engineering Unit. Head of Manchester Unit.
Specialisation: Principal area of practice is contentious construction and engineering industry claims. Wide experience of the standard form of building and engineering contract (including JCT, ICE, RMR '80, MF/I, IMechEE, FIDIC).
Prof. Memberships: O.R.S.A., ACIAArb, Society of Construction Law, O.R.S.A. Accredited Adjudicator.
Career: Qualified in 1986. Joined *Hammond Suddards* in 1990.
Personal: Born November 1961. Educated at Edge End High School, Nelson. University of Sheffield 1980-83. The College of Law Guildford. Leisure activities include family, necessary gardening, cricket, football and golf. Lives in Stirton.

NEWMAN, Paul
Hugh James Ford Simey, Cardiff (029) 2039 1171
paul.newman@hjfs.co.uk
Senior Associate (Barrister) in Construction and Civil Engineering Department
Specialisation: Contentious and non-contentious construction law. Regularly appears as advocate in Arbitration hearings and sits as an adjudicator. Has provided seminars on construction law to many organisations, including the College of Law and professional bodies. Author and/or co-author of 10 books as well as papers on construction law. Books include 'Tactics in Construction Litigation' 1996, 'ADR' 1999 and 'Securing Payment and Other Obligations Under Construction Contracts' 1999.
Prof. Memberships: Called to the Bar by Gray's Inn November 1982, Fellow of the Chartered Institute of Arbitrators, accredited Adjudicator for the Royal Institute of British Architects and the Construction Industry Council.
Career: Called to the Bar in November 1982 and joined *Edwards Geldard* as a non-practising barrister in 1990. Joined *Hugh James Ford Simey* in 1999.
Personal: Born 5 March 1958. Educated at Clare College, Cambridge (1976-1980), City University, London (1980-81) and the Inns of Court School of Law (1981-82).

NOLAN, Brandon
McGrigor Donald, Glasgow (0141) 248 6677
Head of Construction Unit.
Specialisation: All aspects of construction law including contract drafting, appointment documentation, contract advice and disputes work. Currently involved in procurement and dispute work in England and Northern Ireland as well as in Scotland. Has conducted the advocacy in a number of substantial arbitrations. A frequent speaker at commercially organised seminars.
Prof. Memberships: Member of the Chartered Institute of Arbitrators; Society of Construction Law; International Bar Association; Technology and Construction Solicitors Association.
Career: Qualified 1980 with *McGrigor Donald & Co* (as it was then). Became a partner in 1987. Head of the Construction and Engineering Unit at *McGrigor Donald.*
Personal: Born 4th November 1955. Educated at Glasgow University 1974-1978. Leisure interests include visiting a gym and films.

OATS, Simon D.
Eversheds, Ipswich (01473) 284428
Specialisation: Construction and engineering related law encompassing contractual advice and disputes resolution. Acts for a number of substantial construction clients including employers, developers, contractors and professionals. Particular experience in engineering contracts, official referees business, arbitration and adjudication.
Prof. Memberships: Law society, Society of Construction Law, Interact.

PALMER, Simon
Hammond Suddards Edge, Leeds (0113) 284 7000
simon.palmer@hammondsuddardsedge.com
Specialisation: Construction and engineering. Adjudication; technology and construction court litigation; arbitration; forms of Alternative Dispute Resolution; advising on construction and engineering contracts, consultants' appointments and collateral warranties. Visiting lecturer: arbitration and construction law on MSc at Leeds Metropolitan University. Speaker on a wide range of construction issues to other forums.
Prof. Memberships: Member of the Chartered Institute of Arbitrators; Honorary Secretary of the North East Branch of the CIArb; member and regional Coordinator of the Society of Construction Law; member of the Yorkshire Construction Association; visiting lecturer.
Career: Qualified 1987. Partner *Eversheds*, 1994-1999. Partner *Hammond Suddards.*
Personal: Born May 1963. BA in law at Durham University. Interests include: music, rugby, walking, socialising. Lives in York.

PATTERSON, Lindy A.
MacRoberts, Edinburgh (0141) 332 9988
lindyp@macroberts.co.uk
Specialisation: Specialises in contentious building and civil engineering matters. Lindy is widely regarded as one of Scotland's leading construction and civil engineering law experts. She acts for a number of the UK's leading construction and engineering companies, regularly handling disputes in arbitration and litigation covering all aspects of building and civil engineering disputes. She represents clients in the Commercial Court and the Court of Session, as one of Scotland's first Solicitor-Advocates and the first female Solicitor Advocate. She speaks regularly at industry seminars and contributes to building and civil engineering publications.
Prof. Memberships: Member of Law Society Accreditation Panel for Construction Law; Member of Commercial Court Working Party set up to establish the need for and rules of such a Court; Member of the Consultative Committee on the Commercial Court to monitor its progress; Member of Working Party set up by Scottish Office to advise on Scheme for Construction Contracts required by Housing Grants Construction and Regeneration Act 1996. Liaison Committee of the Department of Building & Surveying, Napier University.
Career: Trainee Solicitor *W & J Burness* 1980-1982. Solicitor *Biggart Billie & Gifford* and *Menzies Dougal* 1982-1985. Joined *Bird Semple* 1985, became partner 1988; solicitor-Advocate 1993. Head of Construction Group MacRoberts.
Personal: Graduated LLB (Hons) Edinburgh University 1980. Skiing, hillwalking and watersports.

PICKUP, Raith
Mills & Reeve, Cambridge (01223) 222 283
raith.pickup@mills-reeve.com
Specialisation: Has extremely wide experience of drafting and negotiating the documentation for many substantial projects. These include business parks, retail developments, university campuses, hospitals and large infrastructure projects such as power stations. He heads the *Mills & Reeve* Private Finance Initiative (PFI) team and has advised on more than 30 PFI projects in the health, education, defence and local authority sectors.
Prof. Memberships: Lectures regularly on the legal aspects of the building and engineering industries as well as PFI and is a member of the Society of Construction Law.

PIGOTT, Ashley R.
Wragge & Co, Birmingham (0121) 214 1092
ashley_pigott@wragg.com
Specialisation: Acts for a number of national and international contractors and developers. All aspects of construction and engineering law.
Prof. Memberships: Former committee member Chartered Institute of Arbitrators, West Midlands Region, member Technology and Construction Solicitors Association, Accredited Adjudicator. Career: Articled *MacFarlanes*. Qualified 1986. Partner at *Wragge & Co* from 1995.
Personal: Born 1962.

PINSENT, C.Jim
DLA, Liverpool (08700) 111111
jim.pinsent@dla.com
Specialisation: Specialises in all aspects of contentious and non contentious construction work acting for parties across the industry. Contentious work includes litigation, arbitration and adjudication. Non contentious work involves advising on and drafting building and engineering contracts, appointments, development agreements and PFI contracts.
Career: Qualified 1977, partner with *DLA* since 1989.
Personal: Born 1953. Liverpool University LLB. Interests family, cricket & horse racing.

PLASCOW, Ronald H.
Mills & Reeve, Cambridge (01223) 222 261
Ron.plascow@mills-reeve.com
Partner in Construction and Civil Engineering Department.
Specialisation: Has practised exclusively in construction and civil engineering since 1982 beginning in industry at Trafalgar House plc and subsequently at *Lovell White Durrant* in London . Regularly advises on the JCT, ICE and most other forms of standard contracts used in the UK and on FIDIC Contracts used abroad. Prepares and drafts construction contracts, consultants' appointments and bonds and warranties. Represents employers and contractors

involved in litigation in the Courts, or in arbitration. A trained mediator familiar with the use of other ADR techniques to resolve disputes and has represented clients in mediations and conciliations. Editor of Arbitration Practice and Procedure, Interlocutory and Hearing Problems (Lloyd's of London Press Ltd) first edition, contributing author to Tolleys Guide to Construction Contracts, regular speaker at conferences arranged by the RICS, RIBA, ICE and CIArb. Past Secretary to the East Anglia Branch of the CIArb.

POPE, Caroline
Barlow Lyde & Gilbert, London (020) 7247 2277
cpope@blg.co.uk
Specialisation: Partner specialising in contentious and non-contentious construction and civil engineering. Represents clients from all sides of the construction and engineering industry in both non-contentious drafting and project advice and a wide range of dispute resolution. Has particular experience of large tunnelling projects and defects claims in prestigious office buildings and shopping centres. Has been involved in expert determinations under the IChemE form of contract.
Prof. Memberships: Society of Construction Law; The Law Society of England and Wales; the British Tunnelling Society and the Technology and Construction Solicitors' Association.
Career: Articled *Stilgoes*; qualified 1985; solicitor *Rowe & Maw* 1985-93; solicitor *Barlow Lyde & Gilbert* 1993, partner 1997.
Personal: Born 1958; Sherborne School for Girls; London School of Economics (BSc Economics). Resides in Berkshire.

PROCTOR, Nigel
Hammond Suddards Edge, Manchester (0161) 830 5000
nigel.proctor@hammondsuddardsedge.com
Partner in Construction & Engineering Unit.
Specialisation: Chartered Civil Engineer and Solicitor handles all aspects of contentious and non-contentious construction and engineering work. Contentious work includes major domestic and international disputes. Non-contentious work includes advising on property development schemes, various forms of management contract and PFI. Recent experience includes: Acting on social housing PFI's for Manchester City Council; advising Manchester Airport plc on construction documentation for major infrastructure projects. Acting for North West Water on large arbitration in connection with a water treatment plant in Manchester.
Prof. Memberships: Member Institution of Civil Engineers. Chartered Engineer. Society of Construction Law. Official Referees Solicitors Association.
Career: Civil Engineer 1977 – 1984. Joined *McKenna & Co* 1984. Qualified 1990. Joined *Davies Arnold Cooper* 1995. Partner 1997.
Personal: Born 20 May 1956. Leisure interests: include golf, football and family. Lives in Wilmslow, Cheshire.

RACE, David W.
Nicholson Graham & Jones, London (020) 7648 9000

REDMOND, John V.
Osborne Clarke OWA, Bristol (0117) 917 3458
john.redmond@osborneclarke.com
Head of Construction Department.
Specialisation: Main area of practice is construction law, primarily arbitration and litigation, with contract preparation and other non-contentious work undertaken. Particular experience with regard to extensions of time/loss and expense claims. Regular speaker at seminars and conferences in the UK and other European countries.
Prof. Memberships: Fellow of the Chartered Institute of Arbitration, Chartered Arbitrator, members of several panels of adjudicators Society of Construction Law (Council Member and former National Chairman).
Career: Qualified in 1976. Worked for *Cobbetts* in Manchester 1973-4. Moved to *Clyde & Co.* (Guildford and London) in 1974. Left for *Laytons* in 1978. Partner 1983. Head of Construction Law 1992. Joined *Osborne Clarke*2000.
Personal: Attended University of Kent at Canterbury 1970-73.

REES, Peter
Norton Rose, London (020) 7283 6000
reespj@nortonrose.com
Head of *Norton Rose* Litigation Department and Senior Partner in the Construction and Engineering Law Group.
Specialisation: All aspects of contentious and non-contentious construction and engineering law. Particular expertise in international arbitration (especially ICC) and in BOT and PFI projects. Has advised government departments, multilateral agencies, international organisations and international contractors. Sits as an arbitrator.
Prof. Memberships: Chairman International Construction Projects Committee of IBA; past Secretary Technology and Construction Solicitors Assocation; solicitor representative on Technology and Construction Court User's Committee; Fellow Chartered Institute of Arbitrators; accredited TECSA adjudicator; Board of Advisers, Centre for International Legal Studies, Member Institute of Petroleum.
Career: Qualified 1981 with *Norton Rose.* Partner 1987.
Personal: Born 21st April 1957. MA from Downing College, Cambridge University. MBA from Nottingham Trent University. Leisure interests include football (still crazy enough to be playing), golf and scuba diving.

REEVES, Suzanne
Wedlake Bell, London (020) 7395 3000
Partner and head of the construction team.
Specialisation: Construction and Engineering. Acts for all sectors of the industry. Non-contentious work focuses on developers, financial institutions and consultants. Contributor to industry publications. Speaks at industry seminars and conferences. Has close association with major subcontractor organisations. Places emphasis on finding cost-effective solutions in both contentious and non-contentious matters.
Prof. Memberships: Accredited adjudicator, Law Society, Technology and Construction Solicitors Association.
Career: Qualified in 1979. Joined *Wedlake Bell* the same year, becoming a Partner in 1986. Head of Construction Team.
Personal: Born 13th August 1955. LLB (Exon) 1976. Lives in London.

REGAN, Michael
Rowe & Maw, London (020) 7248 4282
Partner in and Head of Construction and Engineering Department.
Specialisation: Advises contractors, employers and professionals, and also insurers, particularly in relation to professional indemnity matters.
Prof. Memberships: Law Society, Chartered Institute of Arbitrators, Society of Construction Law.
Career: Qualified in 1980, having joined *Rowe & Maw* in 1978. Became a Partner in 1985.
Personal: Born 4th October 1955. Attended Westcliff High School 1969-74, then Pembroke College, Oxford 1974-77. Leisure interests include watching cricket, talking about football and playing tennis. Lives in London and Gloucestershire.

RICHARDS, Mark
Masons, Leeds (0113) 233 8905
Specialisation: Specialises in construction and engineering both contentious and non-contentious work. Has recently been involved in the drafting and negotiation of the project management and consultant contracts for the making safe of the destroyed Unit 4 of the Chernobyl Nuclear Power Plant in Ukraine. Led the team which advised the project company on the Humberside Magistrates Court PFI project. Is leading teams advising on three further courts PFI projects. Is involved in running a number of multi-million pound engineering and construction disputes for contractors.
Prof. Memberships: Law Society. Society of Construction Law. International Bar Association. International Nuclear Law Association. Lighthouse Club.
Career: Qualified 1987. Joined *Masons* 1988. Became a partner in1993. LLB(Hons) Birmingham University 1982. Msc in Construction Law and Arbitration – King's College London.
Personal: Born May 1961 – 2 children. Leisure interests: cricket, golf, squash.

RICHARDS, Timothy J.
Hewitson Becke + Shaw, Cambridge (01223) 461155

ROBERTS, Martin
Masons, London (020) 7490 4000
martin.roberts@masons.com
Partner and Manager of Construction & Engineering Group.
Specialisation: Specialises in dispute resolution and non-contentious advice on construction and engineering matters. Leads team of lawyers advising contractors, employers, professionals and insurers on wide range of issues and projects. Recently involved in advising on Croydon Tramlink, Peterborough and Corby CCGT Power Stations, Navotas Power Station where advised successful Plaintiff in Hopewell Project Management Ltd v Ewbank Preece Ltd 1998 1 LLR, major refurbishment of holiday centres for UK leisure group, CHP Plant in UK and major road project in South East. Currently advising on various issues relating to HGCR Act, Arbitration Act and on several adjudications and mediations. Accredited CEDR Mediator and Adjudicator.
Prof. Memberships: Law Society, elected committee member of City of London Law Society, member of Litigation Sub-Committee of City of London Law Society, Society of Construction Law, ORSA, CEDR.
Career: Qualified 1979, partner with *Masons* 1983, member of *Masons'* Partnership Strategy Board 1992 to 1997.
Personal: Born 11th April 1955. Attended City of London Freeman's School, Kingston University (BA Hons) Law. Leisure interests include theatre, cinema,

pop music, tennis, swimming and two children. Lives in Sussex.

ROBSON, Nigel R.

Eversheds, Leeds (0113) 243 0391
nigelrobson@eversheds.com
Partner in Construction and Engineering Unit.
Specialisation: Principal area of practice involves handling contractual disputes arising from construction or engineering projects on JCT, ICE, GC Works and FIDIC forms of contract or bespoke contracts with particular emphasis on loss and expense claims and defects claims. Has considerable experience in relation to hospitals, process engineering, power stations, off-shore, waste incinerators, major civil engineering and defence related projects. Other main area of work involves drafting and amending commercial agreements for construction and engineering projects.
Prof. Memberships: Law Society; Fellow, Chartered Institute of Arbitrators.
Career: Qualified in 1977 and went on to join *Eversheds*, becoming a Partner in 1980. Managing Partner of *Eversheds* North East since 1992-2000. Head of Construction South 2000.
Personal: Born 23rd May 1951.

ROE, Mark

Masons, London (020) 7490 4000
mark.roe@masons.com
Partner specialising in major projects and dispute resolution in the Construction Industry.
Specialisation: Expert in advising on major projects in the engineering construction and related industries. Has advised and acted extensively in the resolution of disputes by mediation and mini-trial/structured settlement procedures, adjudication arbitration (both UK and international), expert determination and litigation. Has also sat as a mediator. Also advises on transactional matters, partnering and PFI. Has advised on two major PFI deals in the last twelve months. Currently advising on a major partnering initiative. Lectures on ADR, partnering, project management and construction law matters. Described last year in Chambers as a "flamboyant streetfighter with a good grasp of the issues" – a description which his clients apparently recognised.
Prof. Memberships: TECSA Committee Member, Former Director of CEDR 1989-1999, Accredited Mediator.
Career: Qualified in 1981. Joined *Masons* in 1981. Partner of *Masons* since 1985.
Personal: Born 30th May 1955. Attended the John Fisher School 1965-73, educated at Balliol College, Oxford 1974-77. Leisure interests include rugby, tennis, cycling, skiing, theatre and the arts and crafts movement. Lives in Central London.

ROE, Sally

Freshfields Bruckhaus Deringer, London (020) 7936 4000
Partner in Litigation Department. Authorised to exercise rights of audience in the Higher Courts (Civil Proceedings), July '95.
Specialisation: Head of Construction and Engineering Group. Extensive experience of litigation and arbitration in these fields, acting for employers and contractors. Also handles non-contentious projects including property developments and infrastructure projects. Other areas of practice include advising on the application of the EC Procurement Regime.
Prof. Memberships: City of London Solicitors Company.
Career: Qualified in 1981. Joined *Freshfields* in 1988, becoming a Partner in 1990.
Personal: Born 4th September 1956. Attended Wakefield Girls' High School 1965-74 and St Hilda's College, Oxford 1974-77.

ROWLAND, Simon J.

Watson Burton, Newcastle upon Tyne (0191) 244 4444
Specialisation: Non-Contentious work. Acts for clients from all disciplines of the construction industry including developers, funders, main and sub-contractors and designers. Particular emphasis on development work but also experienced in heavy civil engineering, process engineering and off-shore work. This year has acted for Newcastle International Airport on its main ternminal extension, the City of Durham on its Millennium Project and Bellway Plc on a series of developments in London Docklands. Regularly speaks on such topics as building contracts, appointments, warranties and development.
Prof. Memberships: Law Society.
Career: Educated at University of Newcastle Upon Tune (LLB Hons). Articled at Watson Burton. Qualified Sept. 1992. Partner Jan 1999.
Personal: Born 5th December 1967. Enjoys playing football and golf, listneing to music and socialising.

RUSHTON, John Michael

Rowe & Maw, London (020) 7248 4282

RUSSELL, Victoria E.

Fenwick Elliott, London (020) 7956 9354
v.russell@fenwickelliott.co.uk
Partner in Construction Department.
Specialisation: Handles contentious and non contentious construction and engineering matters with a special emphasis on litigation, adjudication, arbitration and ADR. Advises employers, main contractors, specialist subcontractors and members of the professional team on a variety of points of law, practice and procedure. Has dealt with a number of complex construction disputes, some arising from the various JCT and ICE standard forms of contract and others from bespoke contractual arrangements. German speaker. Experienced arbitrator, CEDR accredited mediator and TECSA adjudicator.
Prof. Memberships: TECSA, IBA (Business Section), LCIA, Society of Construction Law (Council Member since 1990, Chairman 2000-), Chartered Institute of Arbitrators (Fellow (1991.)) Member of the Diploma in Arbitration Advisory Board of the College of Estate Management in Reading (1991-97). Member of the Court of Assistants and Senior Warden-elect of the Worshipful Company of Arbitrators and Chairman of its Charitable Trust.
Career: Qualified and joined *Freedmans* in 1981. Became a Partner in 1985. Joined *Berrymans* in 1996.
Personal: Born 12th October 1956. Educated at Benenden School, Kent 1968-73 and Exeter University 1974-77 (LL.B Hons). Member of Benenden School Trust and Alumni Board of Exeter University. Lives in West London. Sons aged seven and nine.

SALMON, Kenneth T.

Kirk Jackson, Manchester (0161) 794 0431
law@kirk_jackson.com
Partner Construction Law Department.
Specialisation: Main area of work is building and civil engineering disputes, in court adjudication and arbitration, and advising on contract documentation. Conducts in-house seminars for clients.
Prof. Memberships: Law Society, JECSA, Northern Arbitration Association, Manchester Law Society, A.C.I. Arb.
Career: Qualified 1973 while at *Kirk Jackson* and became a Partner in 1975.
Personal: Born 16th April 1946. Leisure pursuits include cycling, five-a-side soccer, hill-walking, music and reading. Lives in Warrington.

SCOTT, Martin L.

Walker Morris, Leeds (0113) 283 2500
mls@walkermorris.co.uk
Partner and Head of Construction Group.
Specialisation: Practice covers the full rage of construction and engineering law, both contentious and non-contentious. Particularly active in the field of disputes where defects whether by design or in construction are the central issue. Acts mainly for Employers/Developers and specialist sub-contractors but also undertakes work for main contractors within the region.
Career: Qualified 1985. At *Scott Turnbull & Kendall*, now *Walker Morris*, since 1984. Became a Partner in 1992.
Personal: Born 13th August 1959. Educated at Ashville College, Harrogate and Leicester Polytechnic BA Law. Interests include flying, farming and family. Lives in Harrogate.

SHADBOLT, Richard A.

Shadbolt & Co, London (020) 7332 5750
Dick_Shadbolt@shadboltlaw.co.uk
Senior Partner.
Specialisation: Main area of practice is construction law, including work on engineering and major projects, with experience in UK and internationally since 1967. Particular experience of structuring and drafting of contracts for major projects and construction. Litigation and arbitration work covered as well as environmental, trade and other commercial matters. Involved with the drafting of the widely praised Association of Consultant Architects standard contract form. Author of articles in professional and other periodicals and occasional lecturer on International Construction Contracts. Regular speaker at professional conventions and international conferences on construction contract and other legal topics.
Prof. Memberships: Law Society, Law Society of Hong Kong, American Bar Association (Associate Member), International Bar Association, Inter-Pacific Bar Association, British Consultants Bureau.
Career: Joined *E T Ray & Co.* in Bletchley in 1965. Qualified 1968. Joined *McKenna & Co.* in London in 1967. Partner, *McKenna & Co.* in London, Brussels, Bahrain, Hong Kong, Singapore, Tokyo and Jakarta, from 1971 until 1991. Established *Shadbolt & Co.* as Senior Partner in 1991.
Personal: Born 18th December 1942. Attended Okehampton Grammar School 1954-60; King's College, London 1961-64 then College of Law, Guildford 1967. Leisure pursuits include family life.

SHAW, Peter R.

Taylor Joynson Garrett, London (020) 7300 7000
pshaw@tjg.co.uk
Partner specialising in construction and engineering law.
Specialisation: Handles both contentious and non-contentious matters. Non-contentious work includes

contract procurement, commercial drafting, collateral warranties, bonds, funding agreements, professional service agreements, project insurance, legal audits, contract adminstration procedures and BOT and PFI projects. Also provides representation in all forms of arbitration tribunal, adjudication and ADR, statements of case drafting, opinions and advices. Examples of contentious work include advising clients in an arbitration dispute with a main contractor regarding design and construction work during the building of a railway in Jordan for the transport of phosphates (FIDIC contract); acting for clients as defendants in arbitration concerning the construction of a military airbase in the Middle East (amended FIDIC contract); representing plaintiffs in disputes with quarry owners concerning the construction of a £25 million mineral processing and crushing plant in the UK (I Chem E contract), and joint action in court by services engineering companies against oil rig jacket constructors in one of the English North Sea fields involving the joining of the Oil Companies Consortium as third parties (amended ICE contract). Clients include national and international construction companies, government agencies, health trusts and professional indemnity insurers in construction design disciplines. Contributor to legal section in trade/ professional publications that circulate in the construction industry. Also presents seminars and lectures to various bodies and institutions involved in the construction industry.
Prof. Memberships: Reading Construction Forum, IBA Business Section, Technology and Construction Court Solicitors Association and Fellow Chartered Institute of Arbitrators.
Career: Qualified in 1980. With *Freedmans/ Freedman Church* since 1973. Became a partner in 1980 and senior partner in 1991.
Personal: Born 10th January 1946. Educated at Huddersfield Grammar School and the University of Lancaster (BA Hons in History). Interests include golf, sailing, skiing, gardening, walking and good food and wine. Lives in London.

SHERMAN, Henry C.
CMS Cameron McKenna, London
(020) 7367 2526
hcs@cmck.com
Partner in Construction Group.
Specialisation: Main practice area is domestic and international construction advice. Acts for all sectors of the construction industry in relation to major construction projects and disputes in the United Kingdom, Central and Eastern Europe and the Middle and Far East. Specialises in international arbitration and litigation as well as disputes resolution by mediation, adjudication and other informal routes. Regularly addresses seminars and workshops and writes on legal subjects in the construction and legal press.
Prof. Memberships: Society of Construction Law. Board member, Design and Build Foundation.
Career: Qualified in 1977. Worked at *Frere Cholmeley* 1975-83. Joined *McKenna & Co* in 1983, becoming a Partner in 1986. 1985-87 Hong Kong with *McKenna & Co* and from 1997 with *CMS Cameron McKenna* in Hong Kong and London.
Personal: Born 16th February 1952. University of Oxford 1970-73 (BA) and University of Aix-Marseilles 1973-4. Leisure interests include idling whenever possible with his family on the Isle of Wight.

SMITH, Ian D.
Lovells, London (020) 7296 2000
ian.smith@lovells.com
Specialisation: Principal work area is advising on contracts for national and international construction and energy projects. Recent work includes the construction contracts for the new Hong Kong airport, construction and operation contracts for cogeneration facilities, a range of EPC, alliance, target price, leasing and operating contracts for North Sea oil and gas developments, DBFO road and rail contracts and hospital projects as part of the Private Finance Initiative and build/operate contracts for distribution centres. Works closely with the firm's property team on the construction documentation for all types of development.
Prof. Memberships: Law Society, Society of Construction Law.
Career: Articled *Lovells*. Qualified 1976 and became a Partner in 1981. Resident Partner in Hong Kong 1984 to 1989. Consultant 1998-date.

SPEED, Nick P.
Warner Cranston, London (020) 7403 2900
Specialisation: Advises all sides of the construction industry on both contentious and non-contentious construction work. Also specialises in professional indemnity insurance disputes (particularly for architects and engineers), adjudication, ADR, domestic and international arbitration, technical disputes (including IT) and insurance and reinsurance. Speaker at conferences, seminars and presentations.
Prof. Memberships: Society of Construction Law, Technical and Construction Solicitors Association.
Career: *Kennedys* 1981-84, *Denton Hall* 1985-86. Joined *Warner Cranston* in 1986 before becoming a partner in 1987.
Personal: Born 1955. Leisure interests include skiing, football, The Arsenal, walking, good food and wine and laughing.

STANIFORTH, Alison J.
Eversheds, Leeds (0113) 243 0391
alisonstaniforth@eversheds.com
Partner in Litigation Department (Head of Construction and Engineering).
Specialisation: Principal area of practice is construction/engineering including litigation, arbitration and ADR (both domestic and international). Also non-contentious including drafting and negotiating amendments to standard and bespoke contracts, warranties, performance bonds, parent company guarantees and professional appointments. Important matters handled include facilities management agreements; power generation projects; PFI projects; projects in China and Poland; science laboratories; railway track and maintenance. Other clients include Yorkshire Electricity, British Waterways Board, Weir Pumps Ltd, Morrison Construction. Visiting Lecturer at Leeds Metropolitan University (MSc in Arbitration and Construction Law). Conference speaker for e.g. RICS, CIOB, the Institute of Structural Engineers and IRR.
Prof. Memberships: CIArb, TeCSA, Common Purpose Graduate, OPP 2K, Network.
Career: Qualified in 1985. With *Herbert Smith* 1983-86. Joined *Hepworth & Chadwick* in 1986 and became a Partner at *Eversheds Hepworth & Chadwick* in 1991.
Personal: Born 13th December 1957. Leeds University 1976-79 (LL.B) and Trinity Hall, Cambridge 1980-83 (MLitt). Interests include golf, malt whiskey and gardening.

STEADMAN, Tim
Clifford Chance, London (020) 7600 1000
tim.steadman@cliffordchance.com
Specialisation: Partner and Head of Construction Group, specialising in the drafting of construction contracts and related documents. Particular experience in connection with privately financed projects, such as those arising from the UK Public Private Partnerships programme and PPP schemes elsewhere, and with the construction aspects of private sector project financings
Prof. Memberships: European Construction Institute; IBA committee "T".
Career: Hertford College; Oxford University. Trainee and assistant *Lovell White & King* 1976-1982; associate *Baker & McKenzie* 1982-1985; partner *Baker & McKenzie* 1985-1997; partner *Clifford Chance* since March 1997.
Personal: Born 1955; resides London.

STUBBS, Jane
Addleshaw Booth & Co, Leeds
jlts@addleshaw-booth.co.uk
Specialisation: Non-contentious construction and PFI work. Acts for a variety of clients including developers, funding institutions, the public sector, consultants and contractors. Extensive experience in drafting of development and funding agreements, partnering contracts, construction contracts, consultancy agreements and warranties.
Career: Articles with *Lovells*, qualifying in 1993. Joined *Booth & Co* on qualification and became a partner of *Addleshaw Booth and Co* in February 2000.
Personal: Born 1967. Educated at Nottingham University. Leisure interests include golf, travel and cinema. Lives in Leeds.

TURNBULL, Craig
MacRoberts, Glasgow (0141) 332 9988
craigt@macroberts.co.uk
Specialisation: Partner in Construction Group representing employers, contractors, sub-contractors and consultants in litigation adjudication and arbitration; in addition represents construction clients in health and safety and environmental prosecutions. Acted in the first Scottish case seeking enforcement of an adjudicators award. Co-author of 'MacRoberts on Scottish Building Contracts'
Prof. Memberships: Law Society of Scotland, Society of Construciton Law, Associate of the Chartered Institute of Arbitrators.
Personal: Born 1966. Lives Glasgow. Married, one son. Leisure interests include golf and football.

VASEY, John R.
Beachcroft Wansbroughs, Bristol (0117) 918 2000
jvasey@bwlaw.co.uk
Specialisation: Specialises in construction-related claims for insurers. He has detailed knowledge and experience of the insurance provisions of construction and development contracts. Typically he handles the contract aspects of major property damage and contractors' 'all risks' claims. He also deals with professional indemnity claims on behalf of architects and engineers and is involved in defending construction-related health and safety precautions. In addition to his work for insurers John acts for major contractors, public authorities and developers. He is a keen exponent of cheaper and quicker methods of resolving disputes. He has in particular spoken and written on the adjudication procedure under the Construction Act. Recent work includes: advising on the new

research and manufacturing facility at Dyson's Appliances, a vacuum cleaner factory in Malmesbury; advising on professional appointments for Greenwich Millennium Dome; and advising on the construction aspects of a major hospital redevelopment in Bath.
Career: Qualified in 1980. *McKenna & Co* 1984-87. Joined *Wansbroughs Willey Hargrave* in 1988. 1999 – Partner in *Beachcroft Wansbroughs.*

WELSH, John

Morison Bishop, Glasgow (0141) 248 4672
Chairman of Morison Bishop and Partner in the Litigation Division.
Specialisation: Main area of practice is construction law, including professional negligence claims against engineers, architects and surveyors, arbitrations, drafting and advising on construction law contracts, appointments and warranties. Speaks frequently at conferences and seminars on construction law and related topics including mediation.
Prof. Memberships: Law Society of Scotland, Royal Faculty of Procurators in Glasgow.
Career: Qualified in 1968. Assistant Solicitor and Partner at *Robertson Chalmers & Auld* 1969-86. Partner with *Bishop and Robertson Chalmers* (now known as *Morison Bishop* from 1986. Accredited by the Law Society of Scotland as a Specialist in Construction Law in 1993 and as a Solicitor-Mediator in 1994.
Personal: Born 12th September 1945. Educated at Glasgow University 1963-66. Enjoys golf and fishing. Lives in Bearsden.

WILCOCK, Christopher

Hammond Suddards Edge, Manchester (0161) 830 5190
chris.wilcock@hammondsuddards.co.uk
Specialisation: Main practice areas are construction and engineering. Contentious and non-contentious work. Lectured on adjudication/arbitration. Acting for major utility. Acted as adjudicator. Acts for diverse clients involved in the construction/engineering sectors.
Prof. Memberships: Associate: Chartered Institute of Arbitrators. Member: Pipeline Industries Guild.
Career: Qualified 1987. Specialised in construction/engineering since then.
Personal: Leisure interests – Manchester United FC, walking, golf.

WILLCOCK, Andrew

Trowers & Hamlins, Manchester (0161) 211 0000
awillcock@trowers.com
Partner in Construction Department.
Specialisation: Main areas of practice are construction, civil engineering and Private Finance Initiative construction. Includes both contentious and non-contentious matters involving building, civil engineering and mechanical engineering work.
Prof. Memberships: Technology and Construction Solicitors Association, Society for Computers and Law.
Career: Qualified in 1972. Joined *Trowers & Hamlins* in 1998 as a Partner.
Personal: Born 13 September 1945. Leisure pursuits include hill walking. Lives in Manchester.

WILLIAMS, Jeremy

Morgan Cole, Cardiff (029) 2038 5385

WINTER, Jeremy

Baker & McKenzie, London (020) 7919 1000
jeremy.winter@bakernet.com
Partner and Head of Construction & Projects Department, Solicitor Advocate.
Specialisation: Resolution of construction and projects disputes by arbitration, litigation and ADR. Particular expertise in civil engineering matters. 18 years' experience of construction law in a total of 30 countries around the world (particularly Europe, Africa and the Middle East). Conducts own advocacy in arbitration and in High Court. Frequent speaker and writer on construction and arbitration topics. Chairman of Society of Construction Law Working Group on delay analysis.
Prof. Memberships: Hon Fellow of Institution of Civil Engineering Surveyors, Society of Construction Law, Technology and Construction Solicitors Association (Member of IT Sub-committee). Member of Association for Project Management, Member of the Geological Society, Member of LCIA.
Career: Qualified 1979. Joined *Baker & McKenzie* London 1980. Worked in *Baker &McKenzie* Sydney Office 1982-84. Partner 1987.
Personal: Born 26 December 1953. Warwick University (LLB Hons 1975). Lives in Toys Hill, Kent.

WOOD, Martin

Greenwoods, Peterborough (01733) 887700

WOOD, Peter

Masons, Manchester (0161) 877 3777
Called to Bar 1979 (Solicitor 1985) Partner in Construction & Engineering Group.
Specialisation: Handles all aspects of contentious and non-contentious construction and engineering law. Also deals with all aspects of energy law. Has handled numerous reported cases including Lorne Stewart v. William Sindall, Walter Lawrence v. Commercial Union Props, Emson v. Protea, AMEC v. Crown House and Davy v. Tate & Lyle. Former editor of *Construction Law Journal*; currently editorial board member. Lectures extensively on construction and engineering law.
Prof. Memberships: Law Society, Northern Arbitration Association, Energy Industries Council.
Career: Qualified for the Bar in 1979 and as a solicitor in 1985. Joined *Masons* in 1982, becoming a Partner in 1985, Senior Partner in Manchester office in 1989 and UK Managing Partner in 1997. Editor of *Construction Law Journal* in 1988 and editorial board member in 1991. Council Member Northern Arbitration Association in 1992.
Personal: Born 17th August 1956. Attended Altrincham Grammar School to 1975, and King's College London to 1978. Leisure interests include gardening and family. Lives in Prestbury, Cheshire.

WRIGHTON, Ralph

Eversheds, Newcastle upon Tyne (0191) 261 1661
ralphwrighton@eversheds.com
Specialisation: Partner. Head of Construction & Engineering Group in North East. Specialising exclusively in construction law since 1979 in connection with civil engineering, power generation, offshore engineering, environmental and process engineering and building projects in the public and private sectors both in the UK and overseas. Over 10 years' involvement in international arbitration conducted in the main European arbitration centres. Regularly advising on major infrastructure contracts including education, health and local government projects and major dispute management and resolution.
Prof. Memberships: Law Society. The Society of Construction Law. Northern Dispute Resolutions.
Career: Articled *Berwin Leighton.* 1976 Qualified. 1979 *Trafalgar House Plc.* 1986 *Herbert Oppenheimer.* 1987 *Church and Church.* 1990 *Eversheds.*
Personal: Born 1951. Educated at University College London. Interests include music, theatre and history.

YULE, Ian R.

Wragge & Co, Birmingham (0121) 629 1843
ian_yule@wragge.com
Specialisation: Handles contentious and non-contentious construction and engineering matters. Emphasis is on arbitration, litigation and mediation. Also advises on forms of contract, bonds, warranties. Lectures on I.Chem.E Forms and New Engineering Contract. Advises a number of local authorities. Acts for insurers of construction professionals and has contributed book chapters on architect's liability to "Professional Liability: Law and Insurance" (ed. Hodgin 2nd Edition, 1999) and "Professional Negligence in the Construction Industry" (Neil F Jones) both published by Lloyds of London Press. Has also written and lectured widely on construction and professional indemnity matters. Tutor for the Chartered Institute of Arbitrators.
Prof. Memberships: F.C.I. Arb, TeCSA Society of Construction Law.
Career: Qualified in 1984, joined *Neil F Jones & Co* in 1990 becoming a partner in 1992. Partner an *Wragge & Co* upon merger with *Neil F Jones* (1999)
Personal: Born 1958. Educated Worcester College, Oxford. Leisure interests include squash, tennis and West Ham FC.

CORPORATE FINANCE

London: 210; The South: 225; Thames Valley: 226; South West: 227; Wales: 229; Midlands: 230; East Anglia: 232; North West: 233; Yorkshire: 235; North East: 237; Scotland: 237; Northern Ireland: 239; *Profiles*: 240

OVERVIEW: Globalisation has been the watchword of the corporate finance world with immense consolidation across all industry sectors and a staggering growth in the realm of new media, internet and e-commerce based activity. The scent of change is in the air as firms with international offices, mergers and alliances appear to be in the ascendant. Not all would agree; a defiant band crossing all practice sizes are following the Slaughter's *Best Friends* policy, praised for its efficiency, caution and a safeguard of cultural independence. Indeed a marked number of regional firms are targeting regional firms abroad, focusing on second level centres for a more receptive audience than the City. However with a steady flow of mergers between UK and continental European firms, are these firms destined to be always the bridesmaid and never the bride?

In this edition of Chambers we offer a ranking of the US law firms undertaking corporate work from their London offices. In a market dominated by US investment banks there is a natural relationship waiting to be exploited and enviable resources to draw upon from the States. That is not to say a sea change is complete – the US firms themselves are well aware of the difficulty in generating repeat transactions from discerning banks who in turn keenly understand what it takes to run these deals. Lateral hires have added credibility to these teams which are also bolstered by rotating US partners. With banks and private equity institutions such as Warburg Dillon Read and Hicks Muse attracted by the US/UK mix, perhaps it is time to pay more attention to these increasingly familiar faces.

So what of our big three leaders? While the weight of both corporate and financial transactions (volume and more significantly value) is in their favour, their dominance of the market is felt to rest on the simplest of levels: that clients adore the excellence and depth of partners. Though jostling to be at the top of the international tree may continue, it is the development of junior partners which affects a firm's transactional status and where our leaders succeed.

This year has seen a hugely expanded market with growth in IT related corporate work, and the mid-tier players have shown their commercial colours by focusing teams onto these growth areas. While the corporate bubble looks nowhere near bursting, the market feels that those firms which can translate their experience into acting for the increasingly powerful equity houses are those that will command the future.

TOP CORPORATE FINANCE FIRMS IN LONDON

TOP TWELVE (ranked by users and non-users)

FIRMS	OVERALL SCORE	NO. OF 1st RANKS	1999 POSITION
1) Linklaters	533	21	3rd
2) Slaughter and May	521	23	2nd
3) Freshfields Bruckhaus Deringer	455	13	1st
4) Clifford Chance	445	10	5th
5) Allen & Overy	400	6	4th
6) Herbert Smith	284	8	6th
7) Ashurst Morris Crisp	276	9	7th
8) Norton Rose	223	0	9th
9) Simmons & Simmons	161	4	10th
10) Macfarlanes	145	5	12th
11) Lovells	135	0	8th
12) Travers Smith Braithwaite	120	0	11th

TOP TWELVE (ranked by users only)

FIRMS	OVERALL SCORE	NO. OF 1st RANKS	1999 POSITION
1) Linklaters	307	19	1st
2) Slaughter and May	239	14	3rd
3) Clifford Chance	236	7	6th
4) Freshfields Bruckhaus Deringer	197	9	2nd
5) Allen & Overy	192	3	4th
6) Herbert Smith	157	7	5th
7) Ashurst Morris Crisp	131	6	8th
8) Simmons & Simmons	94	3	9th
9) Norton Rose	92	0	7th
10) Macfarlanes	60	3	12th
11) Lovells	58	0	10th
12) Travers Smith Braithwaite	55	0	11th

THE SURVEY

Each year, we conduct a client-only survey among the FTSE All Share companies. All respondents are key buyers of legal services. We ask them which corporate finance teams they rate in the Top Ten, The results published here are based on the first 100 replies and should be used in conjunction with our main tables.

RESEARCH APPROVED BY BMRB: *For this edition,* Chambers' *researchers conducted 6083 interviews – 4408 with law firms, 598 with barristers and 1077 with clients.*

The validity of the research was scrutinised by BMRB International, who audited both the methodology and the results at our offices in July 2000. They interviewed Chambers' *researchers and cross-checked sample interviews. Details of the audit appear on page 7.*

LONDON

60+ SOLICITORS IN CORPORATE FINANCE TEAM

CORPORATE FINANCE: 60+ SOLICITORS IN CORPORATE TEAM • London	Ptnrs	Assts
❶ Freshfields Bruckhaus Deringer	50	170
Linklaters	47	160
Slaughter and May	*	*
❷ Allen & Overy	32	75
Clifford Chance	35	125
Herbert Smith	40	110
❸ Norton Rose	33	75
❹ Ashurst Morris Crisp	43	140
Lovells	22	50
❺ Simmons & Simmons	26	54
❻ CMS Cameron McKenna	28	35
Denton Wilde Sapte	30	50

Within each band, firms are listed alphabetically.
** See editorial entries for explanations of team sizes.*

Freshfields Bruckhaus Deringer European M&A opportunities are said to be behind the merger with Bruckhaus Westrick Heller Lober and this has strengthened the firm's expansionist policy, setting out its stall to be the pre-eminent European firm. This fits well with market perception of it *"leading the global domination charge."* A *"centrally-led, tight management structure"* has led to *"rigorous quality"* at partner level and a collegiate atmosphere which encourages its younger partners to gain invaluable experience on big ticket deals.

Head of Corporate Finance and Investment Banking, **Barry O'Brien** prospers under his reputation as *"the institutions' favourite"* with clients such as Merrill Lynch (on its agreed £3.1 billion cash bid for Mercury Asset Management) and BZW (on proposed sale of its equity and corporate advisory business to CSFB.) He is a *"top-drawer operator"* who *"infuses deals with his common sense"* and receives praise for his successful rapport with clients, managing the team and running day to day transactions with enthusiasm. **Anthony Salz** now faces increased managerial responsibilities with his role as senior partner of the merged firm and is perceived by the market to be the firm's trouble-shooter. Used as a *"check on the most complex matters, particularly when a wall is hit,"* he has *"the most astute brain in the City"* and *"sees the most important parts of the deal,"* although he is now regarded as less of a transactional force.

Will Lawes is admired by the banks as *"the brightest lawyer in the City,"* he is *"approachable, sharp and innovative"* and often seen on the most complex hostile work. His media work received particular praise and includes acting for Scottish Media Group on its merger with Grampian and for Pearson on the UK aspects of its acquisition of Simon & Schuster. *"Delightful"* **Mark Rawlinson** is recommended for big ticket M&A work. He is *"the first port of call for complex hostile deals,"* and has *"excellent legal knowledge and a fantastic bedside manner."* Seen to strike a good balance between acting for corporates and financials, recent transactions include advising EMI on the merger between its music businesses and Time Warner, and advising P&O on its proposed demerger. He also continues his role as the Morgan Stanley relationship partner. Insurance specialist **Philip Richards** *"never utters a dud word,"* and received universal praise for his work which includes advising AMP on its world wide demutualisation and listing. *"Charming"* **Charles ap Simon** has been indisposed for part of the year but retains his reputation, particularly for his work with GEC.

Tim Emmerson *("incredibly bright and intelligent")* is perceived to be an aggressive force for his clients with a substantial reputation for his IPO work, and has also acted for Bass on the sale of its brewing business. A familiar face due to her committee profile (as Chairman of the City of London Law Society: Company Law,) **Vanessa Knapp** is recommended as *"an intellectual lawyer."* **James Davis** is a *"charming client man"* whose work for Cinven is *"excellent."* Respected for his private equity work, **Edward Braham** has a wide client base which includes Kingfisher (he acted on its bid for Asda.) Recognised as the rising star of the firm, **Julian Long** is *"hard-working, sensible, calm and not adversarial,"* and is a familiar name on big-ticket deals including advising AstraZeneca on the demerger of its agricultural chemicals business, subsequently merged with Novatis. **Clients: Corporates:** Alcan; Avis; AstraZeneca; BNFL; BT; Bass; Caradon; Compass; EMI; Enron; Ford; Hays plc; Hewlett Packard; ICI; Kingfisher; Marconi; Pearson Group; P&O; Powergen; Prudential; Tesco. **Financials:** CSFB; Deutsche Bank; Goldman Sachs; Société Générale; Warburg Dillon Read; Morgan Stanley; Dresdner Kleinwort Benson; Schroders; Salomon Smith Barney; Lazard Brothers; Merrill Lynch; NM Rothschild & Sons; Lehman Brothers; Allied Zurich; Warburg Pincus.

Linklaters Currently facing a massive management challenge as it spreads its *"philosophy of control and seduction"* throughout the Alliance partners, yet perceived by the market to have already *"achieved amazing inroads, acting on a global scale."* The firm has a culture of commerciality with *"lawyers bred to think about the client first."* However, it is occasionally felt to have too heavily pursued a cult of the personality which overshadows its junior partners.

"Charming" **David Cheyne** is *"an impressive presence," " thoroughly nice but very tough"* and *"likes hostile transactions or anything he can get his teeth into."* He is praised for inspiring loyalty in his clients and securing the biggest deals, which include acting for Vodafone on its hostile bid for Mannesmann, as well as its merger with Airtouch, and the defence of NatWest from a hostile bids from RBS (£21billion) and the Bank of Scotland (£25 billion.) **Anthony Cann** has *"a brilliant mind"* and is said to be a pleasure to work with. He has *"nothing to prove and no need to score points."* As Global Head of Corporate, he does have other responsibilities, but appears to have no intention of taking a back seat. This year he has advised Scottish & Newcastle on its acquisition of the pubs and restaurant business from Greenalls. **Richard Godden**, perceived as *"the brainbox,"* is praised by his clients as *"a creative thinker"* but is said to have *"an intense, parsonical manner."* Seen to handle large cross-border transactions including advising Dixon Group on its bid for Elkjop Group, he is said to have the *"delicate touch"* needed to run a smooth deal. *"Outstanding"* **Matthew Middleditch** has produced *"calm authoritative work"* this year, and is praised by clients for *"achieving complex commercial objectives."* Seen to inspire loyalty in the investment banks, he has a growing portfolio of corporate clients. Acted for Unigate on its merger with Dairy Crest and for AXA Sun Life on its acquisition of Provincial. Slightly removed from transactional work as senior partner, **Charles Allen-Jones** is seen as a key client man. He continues his role as relationship partner for Goldman Sachs. *"Valuable asset"* **Andrew Peck** is said to be *"a complete terrier"* with *"a fantastic control over huge deals,"* particularly in hostile takeover situations, although he has also received praise for his building society demutualisation work. Acted for M&G on its sale to Prudential for £1.9 billion. **Tim Clarke** is respected for his large-scale privatisation work, and is responsible for the firm's International Privatisation practice. He was heavily involved with the South African government in the role of lead counsel on the privatisation of South African Airways (SAA.) Recognised for his strong tax background and his work in the telecoms field, **John Ellard** has also advised Coca-Cola beverages on its £4 billion merger with Hellenic Bottling Company. **Michael Sullivan** has had a lower profile this

LEADING INDIVIDUALS: 60+ SOLICITORS IN CORPORATE TEAM • LONDON	
✪ **BOARDMAN Nigel** Slaughter and May	**CHEYNE David** Linklaters
❶ **CANN Anthony** Linklaters	**GODDEN Richard** Linklaters
LAWES William Freshfields Bruckhaus	**MACAULAY Anthony** Herbert Smith
O'BRIEN Barry Freshfields Bruckhaus	**PAUL Alan** Allen & Overy
PESCOD Michael Slaughter and May	**RAWLINSON Mark** Freshfields Bruckhaus
SALZ Anthony Freshfields Bruckhaus	**UNDERHILL William** Slaughter and May
❷ **ASHWORTH Chris** Ashurst Morris Crisp	**BOND Richard** Herbert Smith
BROWNLOW Jeremy Clifford Chance	**COOKE Stephen** Slaughter and May
EMMERSON Tim Freshfields Bruckhaus	**FRANCIES Michael** Weil, Gotshal & Manges
HATTRELL Martin Slaughter and May	**LEWIS David** Norton Rose
MIDDLEDITCH Matthew Linklaters	**PALMER James** Herbert Smith
RICHARDS Philip Freshfields Bruckhaus	**SIGNY Adam** Clifford Chance
❸ **ALLEN-JONES Charles** Linklaters	**AP SIMON Charles** Freshfields Bruckhaus
BRAHAM Edward Freshfields Bruckhaus	**CHILDS David** Clifford Chance
CLARK Adrian Ashurst Morris Crisp	**CLARK Tim** Slaughter and May
CLARKE Tim Linklaters	**CRANFIELD Richard** Allen & Overy
EVANS Stuart Simmons & Simmons	**HATCHARD Michael** Skadden, Arps
HENDERSON Giles Slaughter and May	**JAMES Glen** Slaughter and May
KNIGHT Adrian Shearman & Sterling	**KNIGHT William** Simmons & Simmons
LONG Julian Freshfields Bruckhaus	**PARSONS Christopher** Herbert Smith
PEARSON Chris Norton Rose	**PECK Andrew** Linklaters
RANDELL Charles Slaughter and May	**SACKMAN Simon** Norton Rose
WIPPELL David Allen & Overy	**WOOTTON David** Allen & Overy
❹ **BARNARD Stephen** Herbert Smith	**BERINGER Guy** Allen & Overy
BIRD Alistair Simmons & Simmons	**CHARNLEY William** McDermott, Will & Emery
DAVIDSON John Lovells	**DAVIS James** Freshfields Bruckhaus
ELLARD John Linklaters	**GODFREY Keith** Allen & Overy
GOODALL Caroline Herbert Smith	**HOLLAND Peter** Allen & Overy
HYMAN Neil Slaughter and May	**JONES Arfon** CMS Cameron McKenna
KING Peter Linklaters	**KNAPP Vanessa** Freshfields Bruckhaus
MACFARLANE David Ashurst Morris Crisp	**MURPHY Frances** Slaughter and May
NEWHOUSE Anthony Slaughter and May	**PEARSON David** Clifford Chance
PELL Marian Herbert Smith	**READ Nigel** Lovells
STEPHENSON Barbara Norton Rose	**STERN Robert** Slaughter and May
SULLIVAN Michael Linklaters	**WATSON Sean** CMS Cameron McKenna
UP AND COMING	
BELLIS Tim Herbert Smith	**COPPIN Jonathan** Norton Rose
NORMAN Guy Clifford Chance	**RYDE Andy** Slaughter and May
TWENTYMAN Jeff Slaughter and May	**VON BISMARCK Nilufer** Slaughter and May
ONE TO WATCH	
HUNTER Ian Freshfields Bruckhaus	**MARCHANT Simon** Freshfields Bruckhaus

See ***Profiles*** *on page 240*

year but is recommended for his international M&A energy deals which includes the National Power demerger into two listed companies, and the sell-off of power stations. *"Phenomenally bright"* **Peter King** is universally respected for his privatisations and high level securities work where he is said to be *"impressive, clear headed and easy to work with."* The team also has partners focusing on specialist industry groups such as healthcare, telecoms and IT, utilities and transport. **Clients: Corporates:** BP Amoco; BT; Scottish & Newcastle; SmithKline Beecham; Vodafone Airtouch; Unigate plc; Cable & Wireless Communications; Benckiser NV; AstraZeneca; ICI; Dixons; Gucci Group IV; National Westminster Bank. **Financials:** Morgan Stanley; CSFB, Goldman Sachs; ABN Amro; Paribas; Dresdner Kleinwort Benson; Warburg Dillon Read.

Slaughter and May (60 partners undertake a mixture of corporate work, includes 35 devoted to M&A.) *"Traditionally the best franchise of the three"* with an enviable dominance of the global plc market. The question most posed by the market is the credibility of its *Best Friends* policy. This international strategy has divided opinion with the firm seen as *"conservative," "uniquely British, holding a dominant position"* and *"certainly no fool"* in its relationships with highly regarded firms such as Hengeler Mueller Weitzel Wirtz (Germany) and Uria y Menendez (Spain.) However, the huge consolidation in the European corporate market has led concerned competitors to opine that a strong marriage will be more effective than friendships in the long run.

Regarded as having *"excellence through and through,"* the team is praised for encouraging a *"rich tier of senior assistants." "Charming, with a striking intellect,"* **Nigel Boardman** maintains his reputation as *"the king-pin of the practice," "a fantastic force for the City."* He is *"highly commercial, a great tactician"* who, like Cheyne, is seen to relish the most complex transactions and always puts up *"a spirited battle."* Like all good operators in the hostile market he can be *"belligerent"*, but there is no dispute that he has succeeded in satisfying an enviable client base of major global corporates and powerful financial institutions. Acted for Orange on its sale to France Telecom (includes the assumption of £1.8 billion of debt,) for Hyder on bids from St David's Capital and the unilateral cash offer from WPD. **Michael Pescod** is *"an excellent old school M&A man"* whom clients say *"combines a wealth of experience with an astute business mind." "Charming with his own inimitable, playful style"* he is praised for developing clients relationships for the practice as well as transactional work which includes acting for Unilever on its proposed acquisition of Bestfoods and for Glaxo Wellcome on its merger with SmithKline Beecham (combined market capitalisation of £114 billion.)

"The well known aggressor of the firm" **William Underhill** is *"bright and rumbustious"* and underpins his work with *"the strength of a superb generalist."* He is praised as *"an original thinker"* but is perceived as *"more inflexible than most."* Recent big-ticket deals include acting for Blue Circle Industries in its successful defence of a takeover bid by Lafarge and Prudential Corporation on its flotation of Egg, its internet banking subsidiary. *"A leading light for major public companies,"* **Stephen Cooke** is said to be *"pragmatic"* and *"technically minded."* Acted for Scottish Media Group on its acquisition of Ginger Media Group. *"Impressive"* **Martin Hattrell** is *"technically excellent"* and a *"super bloke to deal with who only ever delivers the best."* He is well regarded for his work acting for Whitbread on the sale of its brewing business to Interbrew of Belgium and the disposal of the pubs and restaurants acquired as part of the Swallow Group acquisition.

Senior partner **Giles Henderson** is more removed from day to day transactions, but continues to be regarded as a *"powerful force"* in terms of client development. **Tim Clark** is seen to undertake huge transactions with *"the minimum of fuss,"* and is *"thoroughly capable, not overly aggressive and certainly not vain."* He is well regarded for advising BOC on its £7.15 billion break up and Carlton Communications on its £7.8 billion merger with United News & Media. **Glen James** has *"an outstanding legal brain"* and is an *"inventive"* practitioner with particular expertise in insurance work. He acted for Norwich Union on its merger with CGU (to form CGNU, a merger effected through a scheme of arrangement,) and advised (with Hattrell) Schroders on the disposal of its investment banking business to Salomon Smith Barney. With the benefit of his *"excellent international experience"* (he ran the defunct Frankfurt office) **Charles Randell** is said to be *"demanding and uncompromising"* in his desire for excellence and *"has the makings of a future senior partner."* Advised Bertelsmann on the merger of CLT-UFA and Pearson's Televison business to form Audiofina, and in conjunction with Hengeler acted for QXL.com plc on its merger with ricardo.de (uniting two of Europe's largest online auction companies.)

Frances Murphy has the reputation as the firm's technician. She is *"tenacious and commercial"* but can be *"a bit of a stickler."* Has acted for Marconi on its disposal of the Avery Berkel Group and tends to be a favourite with similar industrial clients. **Anthony Newhouse** is said to be the man to turn to with *"crisis work."* He advised troubled United Assurance Group on the agreed £1.6 billion bid by Royal London (largest takeover of a listed company by a mutual in the UK.) The *"accomplished"* **Robert Stern** is a *"helpful and personable"* practitioner and received praise for his recent big-ticket deals, including acting for C&N Touristic, the German travel group, on its £1.3 billion bid for Thomson. **Neil Hyman** is admired by his peers for being *"succinct and easy to deal with."* His recent big ticket transactions include acting for Panmure West LB on the Unigate disposal and for Punch Taverns on its battle with Whitbread for the Allied Domecq chain of pubs where *"his achievements were remarkable."* Such deals have led to a perception that he is *"racier than the usual Slaughters mould."*

Andy Ryde joins our up and coming ranking for his increased prominence on major deals, including acting for Regus on its delayed £250 million IPO. He has the *"right attitude"* for producing a smooth deal, and is a *"skilled negotiator."* **Nilufer von Bismarck** is *"one of the unsung heroes,"* and received recognition for her *"commerciality and pragmatic business solutions."* She has acted for Sun Life & Provincial on its sale of Guardian Royal Exchanges to Aegon UK (£759 million.) Developing an enviable client base, **Jeff Twentyman** has *"excellent legal knowledge"* and has achieved particular prominence with his work for Blue Circle and in the telecoms sector. **Clients: Corporates:** Old Mutual; E-Bookers; Mannesmann AG; British Steel (merger with Hoogovens); Reckitt & Colman (merger with Benckiser); Inchcape; Lex Holdings; Sun Life & Provincial; BAT (merger with Rothmans); Shire Pharmaceuticals; Carlton Communications; Ladbrokes; Asda; Kwik-Fit; Blue Circle Industries; FirstGroup; Hanson; Whitbread. **Financials:** Norwich Union; GRE; Standard Chartered; Schroders; JP Morgan; Robert Fleming; Cazenove & Co; Dresdner Kleinwort Benson; GE Capital; 3i Group.

Allen & Overy A firm which had *"made a fortune with its remarkable banking and securities practice"* is perceived to be moving out of that shadow with heavy investment in the corporate team. That said, the team is still perceived to *"lack clout with the corporates"* and is more often seen acting as counsel for the financials in the largest M&A transactions, such as the finance arrangers for Vodafone's bid for Mannesmann. The international network, particularly strong in Germany, France, Italy and Spain, has led to extensive *"impressive, deal-generating capabilities"* both in cross border transactions and those requiring multi-jurisdictional advice.

In his new role as Head of Corporate, **Richard Cranfield** has received less exposure to the transactional market, although he did advise Cable & Wireless on the sale of One2One to Deutsche Telekom (value £8.4 billion.) He is thought to be well-suited to his role as *"a great cheerleader"* for the corporate team, and it is seen as a *"major boost for the firm to have such a high profile political animal in its corner."* **Alan Paul** is seen to be the *"driving force"* transactionally. He is *"thorough, straight as an arrow"* and *"impressive to watch."* He inspires loyalty in his clients, who agree *"he puts commerciality first"* and *"can turn his hand to anything."* This has also led to suggestions that he is in danger of spreading himself too thinly. Paul is also the focus for the firm's strong reputation in private equity financing. Acted for Heineken on the acquisition of Cruzcampo (Spain's largest brewer, value $1 billion) and for CSFB and Morgan Stanley on Bank of Scotland's £22 billion bid for NatWest. Senior partner **Guy Beringer** is well regarded as the firm's *"rainmaker,"* and although not thought to be a key transactional figure, *"is there when it matters most to the client."* *"General corporate heavy weight"* **David Wootton** is a senior M&A figure, advised Whitbread plc on its £578 million recommended cash offer for Swallow Group plc and acted for Singapore Airlines on its £600 million investment in Virgin Atlantic. *"Charming"* **Keith Godfrey** is seen as an *"old guard"* corporate presence and is respected for his cross-border experience. **Peter Holland** *"plays a sensible hand"* and is thought of as *"reliable not pushy, an excellent corporate lawyer"* who *"knows the building society market like the back of his hand."* **Mark Wippell** has *"great takeover code experience"* and *"a highly commercial approach."* Acted for global consumer packaging group Rexam on its recommended cash offer for American National Can Group (£1.3 billion.)

Sector strengths include telecoms and energy, where the international

UK M&A Top Ten Deals (Jan 1st to Jun 19th 2000)*

Target	Lawyers to Target	Acquirer	Lawyers to Acquirer	Value of Deal ($m)
SmithKline Beecham	Linklaters	Glaxo Wellcome (UK)	Slaughter and May	**78,384.5**
Orange (Mannesmann)	Slaughter and May	France Telecom (France)	Norton Rose	**45,967.1**
Allied Zurich	Herbert Smith	Zurich Allied (Switzerland)	Freshfields Bruckhaus Deringer	**19,399.1**
Norwich Union	Slaughter and May	CGU (UK)	Clifford Chance	**11,858.3**
Compass Group	Freshfields Bruckhaus Deringer	Granada Group (UK)	Lovells	**8,089.7**
Robert Fleming Holdings	Allen & Overy Cleary, Gottlieb, Steen & Hamilton	Chase Manhattan Corp, NY (US)	Clifford Chance	**7,697.6**
MEPC	Linklaters	Leconport Estates (Multi-National)	Allen & Overy	**5,233.2**
Burmah Castrol	Allen & Overy	BP Amoco (UK)	Linklaters	**5,104.4**
Pearson Television	Freshfields Bruckhaus Deringer	CLT-UFA (Cie Luxembourgeoise) (Lux)	Linklaters	**4,249.1**
Flextech	Weil, Gotshal & Manges	Telewest Communications (UK)	Freshfields Bruckhaus Deringer	**3,750.5**

Source: M&A Deals – Thomson Financial Securities Data/FT; Law Firms – Chambers and Partners

* Based on table published in FT Survey June 30 2000 "International Mergers and Acquisitions" (p.9)
(Publication approved by Jill Plimmer for FT on the telephone 7/7/00 and Justin Brocklebank for Acquisitions Monthly on telephone 13/7/00)

network and repeat business from financials is seen to generate a high profile. A recent example of this work was advising Thomas Cook on its joint venture with Carlson and Preussag which covered 40 jurisdictions. **Clients: Corporates:** Cable & Wireless; ICI; BAe; Singapore Airlines; United News & Media; United Biscuits; Wellcome Break; Thomson Travel Group; Smiths Industries; WPP Group; Ericsson; Siemens; SWEB. **Financials:** Morgan Grenfell; ABN Amro; Barclays Bank; Commerzbank; GE Capital; HSBC Investment Bank; Merrill Lynch; Warburg Dillon Read; Goldman Sachs; DLJ Phoenix; Deutsche Bank; Schroders.

Clifford Chance *"Proud of what they have done for the London profession,"* is a universally reflected view of the firm's international strategy. Its multi-jurisdictional capabilities and, in particular, the merger with Rogers & Wells and Pünder, Volhard, Weber & Axster has strengthened the M&A resource in North America, Asia and across Europe, also providing an essential securitisation facility. The firm is now able to boast 200 partners world-wide. A prime example of this transatlantic approach appeared in the integrated US and UK advice given to Lend Lease Corporation on the acquisition of Bovis from P&O. However, overall perception is of increased volume rather than value, and the team is said to need a boost in the number of big ticket practitioners as *"it lacks the level of 30-40 year old deal makers necessary to generate the flow."*

Adam Signy is thought to be the main face for transactional work. He is *"insightful, pragmatic and effective"* and has advised both CGU on its merger with Norwich Union and Morgan Stanley on the formation of Allied Zurich into a single holding company valued at £24 billion. **Jeremy Brownlow** is a senior M&A figure highly praised for his work on hostile public company takeovers. He has particular client responsibilities which lessen his transactional profile (such as for Volvo) and is said to be *"similar to Salz in his big ticket work."* Global Head of Corporate **David Childs** is seen to benefit from a strong banking background in forging strong client relationships with financial institutions, and is *"an impressive deal-maker."* He acted for Energis on its unsuccessful bid for Racal's telecoms arm and advised Chase Manhattan on its successful bid for Flemings. **David Pearson** also has a strong following with institutional investment banks. He is said to be *"a rising star," "with a good feel for his clients' needs."* He advised Nomura's Principal Finance Group and Unique Pubs Co on its securitisation, and Tudor Street Acquisitions on its purchase of Inn Partnership from Greenalls. **Guy Norman**, who joins our up and coming ranks, is praised for *"his fantastic energy"* and is said to have *"a real taste for the complex hostile side"* and *"gravitas beyond his years."* He is establishing a *"fine client base"* since a two year secondment on the Takeover Panel.

The firm overall is said to lack *"that necessary base of anchor clients"* to dominate pan-European transactional work. Nevertheless, its global performance is increasing in profile with deals such as advising Carrefour on its merger with Promodes. The firm also continues to hold firm with the major financials: acted for Merrill Lynch and Goldman Sachs on RBS's hostile bid for NatWest, advised Goldman Sachs and Warburg Dillon Read on Vodafone's bid for Mannesmann and acted for Morgan Stanley on NTL's acquisition of C&W's cable television division. **Clients: Corporates:** CGU; Coca-Cola; HJ Heinz; Kimberley-Clark; Intel; Siemens; Volvo; British Energy; Air Products; Reuters; Philip Morris; Lend Lease; Carrefour; Lagardere. **Financials:** CSFB; GE Capital; Goldman Sachs; Merrill Lynch (includes the €37.7 billion merger of Banco Bilbao Vizcaya and Argentaria;) Morgan Stanley; Schroders; UBS Warburg; KKR.

Herbert Smith *"Refocused well and made great strides."* The firm is praised across the board for promoting *"hard working, fine individuals"* into the driving seat of its major deals, thereby producing a *"bright, intelligent"* team who are *"fired up."* This is reflected in the number of high profile partners recommended to our lists. Big-ticket deals have been abundant this year, particularly *"out of the ordinary cross border transactions"* in the IT sector, and the team is felt to be a clear beneficiary from others' conflicts. However, the lack of a clearly-defined international strategy is considered by many to be a drawback for the firm's future prospects, and it is felt that *"it will be difficult for them to sustain growth in a primarily international field."*

"Bloody good" **Anthony Macaulay** is a senior figure with *"a keen mind and bags of experience"* and is recommended for his work with investment banks. He has advised Publicis on its £4 billion acquisition of Saatchi & Saatchi. His *"demanding style"* has meant he is not to everyone's taste, and he is considered at his best in hostile, complex transactions. **James Palmer** is *"a good communicator"* and can be *"a tough negotiator."* Clients respond to his *"commercial acumen"* which helps him *"take advantage of the law."* He is rapidly becoming one of the firm's most high-profile transactional lawyers as a result of acting for Time Warner on the European and EU aspects of its merger with AOL and on its acquisition of EMI's music business. Senior partner **Richard Bond** has a strong reputation, is *"admired by clients and lawyers alike"* and is seen to be a strong force for developing client relationships. Transactional work includes advising Amerada Hess on its strategic alliance with Petronas. *"Quick-witted"* **Chris Parsons** has increased his profile hugely with his work on Olivetti's successful hostile bid for Telecom Italia (€26 billion.) He also advised Dorling Kindersley on the recommended offer from Pearson. **Stephen Barnard** has a low profile but is well regarded for corporate restructurings and reorganisation, has advised the London Stock Exchange on its demutualisation and continues to provide advice to PricewaterhouseCoopers on the reorganisation of its global network. As the recently appointed Head of Corporate Finance, **Caroline Goodall** is anticipated to be less visible on transactions, but is recommended for her work for Koninglijke Hoogovens on its proposed merger with British Steel, where Herbert Smith advised on English and US securities law. Her *"energetic and robust"* personality must fill the void left by Edward Walker-Arnott, who has retired but will retain a role as consultant. Insurance specialist **Marian Pell** is *"pragmatic"* and respected for work which includes acting for AXA on the restructuring of the inherited estate of AXA Equity and Law and advising Standard Chartered Bank on the Bancassurance joint venture with CGU plc in the Far East. Younger partner **Tim Bellis** is gaining stature as a *"proactive"* practitioner and has acted for Loot on its sale to Scoot. He was also involved in the British American Tobacco plc / Rothmans merger (with Palmer,) and on the subsequent restructuring of BAT following the BAT/Zurich deal.

The firm's outstanding reputation for attracting technology clients has seen a growth in e-commerce IPOs, building on *"a superb track record"* in acting for major global arrangers. Advised CSFB on the QXL.com's listing and IPO. **Clients: Corporates:** Time Warner; Olivetti; Automobile Association; Securicor plc; Pearson plc; Stagecoach Holdings plc; First Choice Holidays; BAA; Hillsdown Holdings; BAT; BSkyB; Sears (on demerger of Selfridges;) De La Rue; Hillsdown Holdings; Tottenham Hotspur. **Financials:** CSFB; Cazenove & Co; Goldman Sachs; Lazard Capital Markets; Warburg Dillon Read; Deutsche Bank; ABN Amro; Hoare Govett; Kleinwort Benson Securities; Henderson Investors; Invesco Enterprise Trust.

Norton Rose *"In the ascendancy,"* owing to its presence on major headline deals, this firm is currently *"punching above its weight."* With strong connections overseas, particularly in Asia, the firm is said to be *"undertaking complex transactions that the 'big five' would envy."* Senior partner **David Lewis** is an established presence in the M&A market and *" a good chap to have in your corner"* with his *"professional attitude and bright intellect."* He has acted for the AA committee members on the £1.1 billion sale to GB Gas Holdings. **Simon Sackman** has also benefited from *"big-ticket experience"* but his drive for technical accuracy has left some to consider him *"sticky."* He is one of NR's high-profile deal-doers and has acted for Finalrealm (and its backers, Paribas, Cinven and Deutsche Bank) on its £1.25 billion bid for United Biscuits and advised Prudential on the sale of its UK equity business to Deutsche Asset Management for £12 billion.

Managing partner of the Corporate Finance team, **Barbara Stephen-**

son is strongly recommended for her relationship with investment banks, which has *"pushed NR into a healthy run of placings."* Her style is said to be *"feisty,"* which may have overshadowed her *"undoubted ability,"* particularly with public company takeovers and placings. She advised Citigroup and Salomon Smith Barney (jointly with Skaddens) on the acquisition of Schroders Investment Banking Division. *"Bright"* **Jonathan Coppin** *"has the right attitude"* and is recommended to our up and coming lists primarily for his work advising P&O on the disposal of Bovis (£315 million) and for advising utilities group Kelda on its plans to turn Yorkshire Water into a mutual company. *"A real star,"* **Chris Pearson** runs a *"first rate deal"* and *"always pulls in the best clients."* He has a strong reputation for his telecoms experience, which includes acting for Mannesmann on its £19.5 billion bid for Orange and its defence of the £86.6 billion hostile bid from Vodafone Airtouch. This specialist experience may be forced to the forefront now that the firm has lost its corporate head of Media & Telecoms to Clifford Chance. The firm had advised France Telecom on its initial investment in NTL and their joint bid for the third generation mobile phone licences. Concentrating on the domestic and European corporate markets has raised the firm's profile over the last year, yet the perception is that the firm needs to *"avoid being marginalised on the international scene."* **Clients: Corporates:** Mannesmann; Norsk Hydro; Kelda (formerly Yorkshire Water); P&O; Taylor Woodrow; Trinity Mirror; Automobile Association; Robert Bosch; Siemens; Harvey Nichols Group; Mansfield Brewery; Blacks Leisure Group. **Financials:** HSBC; Credit Lyonnais; Deutsche Bank; Schroders; Cinven; Dresdner Kleinwort Benson; Baxi; Warburg Dillon Read; Hawkpoint Partners; Investec Henderson Crosthwaite; Merrill Lynch; Mercury Asset Management.

Ashurst Morris Crisp The failed mergers talks with Latham & Watkins (and previously Clifford Chance) has raised market concerns that *"this is not a happy ship."* While universal perception is of an *"overall unsettling effect"* the corporate team is perceived to have *"an excellent client base and a sound business."*

David Macfarlane is a *"strong plus"* for the team with his *"excellent deal knowledge"* and strong client relationships, particularly with the banks. He *"keeps his eye on the ball"* during transactions such as advising ING Barings on the disposal of Cambridge Water to Spanish utility Union Fenosa ACEX. **Chris Ashworth** is *"more punchy"* but retains that *"laid-back Ashursts style."* He is the name seen on big-ticket deals such as advising BTP on its takeover of Clariant AG and its listing on the Swiss and Frankfurt Stock Exchanges, and acted for Henlys Group on its £420 million takeover of Blue Bird Corp. **Adrian Clark** is said to be a *"favourite of the UK investment banks"* and advised Goldman Sachs International on Preussag's recommended cash offer (£1.8 billion) for Thomson Travel Group.

The firm is still a force on big-ticket deals and acted for Nabisco Holdings Corp on its joint bid (with Hicks Muse) for United Biscuits. The M&A practice is somewhat overshadowed by the strength and popularity of its buy-outs team, which forms the basis of a well respected dominance of the private equity market.

"A strong cultural identity" with telecoms and energy specialisms has led to interesting deals such as acting for Virgin on its joint venture with One2One to create Virgin Mobile Communications Ltd, acting for Kingston Communications on its £800 million floatation and for NRG Energy on its acquisition of the Killingholme Power Station for £410 million. Clients admire the firm's *"pragmatic, commercial approach,"* and it is seen to be building a reputation for *"solid"* work with investment banks. **Clients: Corporates:** Deutsche Telekom; Nabisco Holdings Corp; Celcius AB; Virgin Group; Kingston Communications plc; PowerGen; National Power; Henlys Group; United News & Media; Skansa; The Carlyle Group; Express Dairies plc; Dunlop Slazenger; McBride plc; Bovis Ltd. **Financials:** Barclays Capital; Deutsche Bank; Bank of Scotland; Chase Manhattan; Chase Capital Partners; Salomon Smith Barney; West LB Panmure.

Lovells The firm has recently been noted operating on mid-sized transactions and is felt to lack the global clout of the market leaders with corporates. Considered to have pursued a *"sensible strategy"* internationally, the firm's merger with German firm Boesebeck Droste has been generally approved by the market. However, investment bank relationships remain an area in which the firm is said to be *"playing catch up."*

The team itself is said to *"lack a face"* now that highly regarded Dan Mace has retired (he retains a consultancy role for client relationships.) **Nigel Read** has a well-established reputation with the investment banks as a former Lazards man. He is *"pleasant to work with"* but is said to lack a continuous *"high impact"* deal profile. He is leading the charge in bolstering the team's investment bank work, acting for JP Morgan on the £4 billion TRW bid for Lucas Varity, and is advising Preussag on its recommended £1.8 billion bid for Thomson Travel. *"Pragmatic"* **John Davidson** is said to be a *"sensible"* practitioner who runs a *"smooth"* deal. He ran a major international equity offering this year, acting for South African Breweries on its IPO and listing on the LSE (£3.5 billion) and Aegon on its offer for Guardian Royal Exchange. The team *"has a fine spread"* of clients and focuses on the particular growth areas of telecoms, e-commerce, retail and manufacturing. It acted on Racal Electronic's sale of its telecoms business to Global Crossing (£1 billion) and acted for Baltimore Technologies plc on its Nasdaq float. Like Ashursts the firm is seen as strong on the private equity front and has demonstrated its international securities capabilities. Cross-border activity benefits from a strong Paris office which proved important on the IPO of Laurent Perrier where the firm acted as French counsel to the joint global co-ordinators JP Morgan Securities and Banque National de Paris. **Clients: Corporates:** Racal; South African Breweries,; Microsoft; Mirror Group; Ford; Vickers; Interpublic; Granada. **Financials:** JP Morgan; Schroders; Lazards; Merrill Lynch; Lehman Brothers.

Simmons & Simmons A firm with a *"spirited attitude"* that has inspired loyalty in its core clients. However, a rather turbulent year has seen the loss of the firm's capital markets association with Fried Frank Shriver & Jacobson which had bolstered the team's reputation with US investment banks, an area it must now fight to retain.

"Terrific" **Stuart Evans** may be *"an eccentric character"* but there can be no doubting his big-ticket appeal. He has successfully traded on the respect garnered by acting for Wal-Mart on its £6.8 billion bid for Asda. He is said to be *"fun to work with"* and has impressed peers and clients alike. Evans advised Interbrew (of Belgium) on its £400 million acquisition of the Whitbread beer company business. The firm is said to have the ability to mobilise large teams at short notice and run deals concurrently. *"Superb lawyer"* **William Knight** is less transactional as senior partner, but retains his reputation as an intelligent practitioner *"with a great deal-doer's mind." "Adored"* by clients, he is now the firm's leading developer of new relationships. **Alistair Bird** is recommended for his *"easy manner"* and his *"attention to detail."* He is felt to benefit from his international experience (previously managing partner in the New York office) and is developing a strong telecoms reputation. **Clients: Corporates:** Bass Brewers Ltd; Cadbury Schweppes plc; Invensys plc; Internet Technology Group plc; Booker plc; Railtrack plc; Shell International Ltd; Sea-Land Service Inc; Wal-Mart Stores. **Financials:** Deutsche Bank AG; Charterhouse Bank; Hawkpoint; Lloyds TSB Group plc; ABN Amro; CDC Group plc; DLJ Phoenix Private Equity.

CMS Cameron McKenna Well known in the market as an international operator, with particular strength in Central and Eastern Europe through the firm's CMS network. The firm has a low profile for its domestic M&A work and, although prominent for Eastern European mid-tier deals, is said to have *"failed domestically to have capitalised on its international presence."* Packed with *"personable lawyers"* producing *"quality work"* the main complaint appears to be a lack of *"consistent deal flow."*

Sean Watson maintains his high profile, particularly as a *"sound and able presence"* in the energy market. He advised the National Grid both on its £2 billion acquisition of the New England Electric System (US) and on the sale of its 25% stake in Energis. *"Excellent"* **Arfon Jones** *("bright and clever")* is seen as a mainstay of the firm, part of the older generation, and has a profile due in part to his membership of the CLSC committee. The firm advised Erste Bank on the proposed acquisition of Cefka sporitelna (The Czech Savings Bank.) Cross-border activity is an important part of the corporate fabric with 32 offices in 19 jurisdictions undertaking transactional work resulting in a number of new clients. The team advised Swets and Zeitlinger on the acquisition of BH Blackwell and US subsidiaries to form an $11 billion subscription agency in London and Utrecht. The practice has a traditionally *"impressive"* profile in the pharmaceutical and biotech market acting for Warner Lambert and the Wellcome Trust. It has also made inroads into the internet technology market and has a strong reputation for flotation work. Nevertheless, the firm is still felt to lack a significant presence with major financial institutions. **Clients: Corporates:** Fortnum Oil & Gas; Energis plc; National Grid Group plc; NSB Retail Systems; Post Office; Roland Berger GmbH; Swets and Zeitlinger BV; Warner Brothers; Blockbuster Entertainment; Camelot; Warner Lambert; George Wimpey plc; Black & Decker; Vivendi. **Financials:** NatWest Equity Partners; Lloyds TSB plc; HSBC; Banque Nationale de Paris; Hawkpoint Partners.

Denton Wilde Sapte The merger between Denton Hall and Wilde Sapte has created *"a fascinating firm"* but one not considered by the market as a *"mainstream corporate finance"* player. Despite the loss of key players in the WS banking team, the firm has capitalised on the strength of its debt financing team. The firm acted for a bidder of the Swedish Telia Cable TV Network (value £1 billion) with assistance from the Denton International Swedish office and has the capacity to advise on a mix of debt and equity financing.

The firm is active in a number of industry sectors, including energy, media, insurance and aviation. However, it lacks a big-hitter for corporate work and is felt to *"face an uphill struggle"* to climb the domestic pecking order. The firm's excellent energy regulatory practice is a prime generator of big-ticket deals. Acted for Energis on its £352 million acquisition of EnerTel and for Petronas on its subscription with Amerada Hess for £136 million worth of new shares in Premier Oil. Media and entertainment is another productive source. The team acts for Bertelsmann and also competes with Freshfields and Herbert Smith for Pearson's corporate work. E-Commerce IPOs have also increased, with the firm acting for Tadpole Technologies, an internet incubator.

Said to have *"lots of bodies"* to throw at major deals, the firm is starting to build a profile with the financials, and has acted for Greenwich NatWest on its sale of two leasing subsidiaries, NatWest Asset Leasing Ltd and Corporate Leasing Facilities Ltd (aggregate value £500 million.) **Clients: Corporates:** Shell; J Sainsbury; Allied Leisure; London Electricity; Brambles, Energis; Tibbett & Britten Group plc; Dixons; Tadpole Technology; Bertelsmann; Pearson; Rentokil International; Microsoft. **Financials:** Greenwich Lloyds Underwriters; Greenwich NatWest; GE Capital.

LONDON OFFICES OF MAJOR US CORPORATE FIRMS

CORPORATE FINANCE: US FIRMS ACTING FROM LONDON	Ptnrs	Assts
❶ Shearman & Sterling	3	16
Weil, Gotshal & Manges	6	18
❷ Skadden, Arps, Slate, Meagher & Flom LLP	⚐	⚐
❸ Cleary, Gottlieb, Steen & Hamilton	*	*

Within each band, firms are listed alphabetically. *See Profiles on page 240*
⚐ *Figures unavailable at time of going to press.*
* *See editorial entries for explanations of team sizes.*

Shearman & Sterling Regarded as one of the few established US firms in the market making a determined effort to build a London presence. *"Impressive cross-border"* activity is the key for a team in which the *"intelligent"* **Adrian Knight** *"makes his mark"* on the deal process. The team's transactional work is 80% pure M&A, aiming to provide a one-stop shop for its major US and European corporate client base. Provided advice on both US and UK law to BT plc on its white knight bid for Esat Telecom Group plc. The team has an enviable showing amongst private equity houses. The London office advised Soros Private Equity Partners on two UK (includes acquisition of Storm Telecommunications,) and two US focused transactions. Although unable to rely on organic growth, the firm has undertaken a European recruitment strategy mirroring that of the magic circle, and has benefited from the break-up of Schilling Zutt & Anschutz in Germany. Acted for British Steel plc on the international aspects of its merger with Koninglijke Hoogovens NV to form Corus Group plc (market capitalisation £3 billion.) **Clients: Corporates:** British Steel plc; BG plc; BT plc; Concentric Network Corp; Danone SA. **Financials:** Soros Private Equity Partners; Morgan Stanley; Deutsche Bank AG.

Weil, Gotshal & Manges Seen to have risen above the mid-tier market with big ticket transactions, the firm's stability in London has been rocked by recent departures. However, *"class act"* **Mike Francies** is *"a real fighter"* whom clients are said to follow loyally. Thought to have leveraged the firm's traditional relationships with international investment banks, it has also developed strengths in the hi-tech arena, including telecoms, media and biotech. Although the firm continues to bolster its full-service offering, it was able to provide support structures when advising MediaOne on the £8.4 billion sale of its 50% sale of stake in One2One to Deutsche Telekom. The team additionally acted for US private equity fund Hicks Muse on its successful bid for UK public company Hillsdown Holdings plc (includes the use of high yield bonds to fund the acquisition.) Currently advising Flextech on its proposed merger with Telewest (aggregate value £12 billion.) **Clients: Corporates:** MediaOne; Flextech; Pirelli (on its $2.15 billion sale to Cisco Systems;) SUN Brewing; Simply Internet; Burford Group; Sara Lee (on hostile bid for Courtaulds Textile plc.) **Financials:** GE Capital; Hicks, Muse, Tate & Furst; Nomura International.

Skadden, Arps, Slate, Meagher & Flom LLP **Michael Hatchard** maintains his outstanding reputation. *"Incredibly bright,"* he is said to *"have the presence of a leader."* UK based clients find the team offers *"impressive advice,"* noting the firm's experience in dual US and European listings as a major attraction. The success of the corporate team has split views; said to be *"an after thought"* servicing the Wall Street giant's international strategy or *"most active of the bunch,"* capturing instructions concerning dual-listed companies with increasing regularity. Also recommended for its growing portfolio of Nasdaq listings. Highlights of the year include advising Cendant Corporation on the disposal of Green Flag Holdings to Direct Line (value £220 million.) **Clients:** Cendant Corporation.

Cleary, Gottlieb, Steen & Hamilton (Three English qualified, seven New York qualified, German, Russian, French and Italian partners act out of London.) Seen to be well established in the European market, the firm has notable strength in Brussels and Eastern Europe. The corporate team lacks a figurehead, seen to rely on rotating a number of US partners as transactions dictate. US capacity is intrinsic to the nature of practice, such as acting as US adviser to Goldman Sachs over Prudential's offering of shares in Egg. Highlights of the year include advising Robert Fleming & Co on its £4.8 billion takeover by Chase Manhatten and acting for HSBC Holdings plc on its acquisition of Crédit Commercial de France (value £6.6 billion.) **Clients: Corporates:** Abbey National; Cable & Wireless; Deutsche Telekom. **Financials:** Goldman Sachs; Dresdner Kleinwort Benson; Morgan Stanley; HSBC.

Other Notable Practitioners **William Charnley** of McDermott, Will & Emery *("work sticks to him")* is well regarded for his market presence and is said to bring a *"larger than life personality"* to the deal process. Hi-tech venture capital investment is a prominent area for him.

30-60 SOLICITORS IN CORPORATE FINANCE TEAM

CORPORATE FINANCE: 30-60 SOLICITORS IN CORPORATE TEAM • London	Ptnrs	Assts
❶ Macfarlanes	12	33
Rowe & Maw	17	34
❷ SJ Berwin & Co	17	40
Travers Smith Braithwaite	17	35
❸ Baker & McKenzie	17	29
Berwin Leighton	12	36
Gouldens	16	28
Nabarro Nathanson	*	*
Olswang	14	44
❹ DLA	14	30
Taylor Joynson Garrett	19	23
Theodore Goddard	16	18
❺ Dechert	13	17
D J Freeman	15	20
Eversheds	12	22
Stephenson Harwood	6	32

LEADING INDIVIDUALS	
❶ **BELL Christopher** Travers Smith Braithwaite	**SUTTON Robert** Macfarlanes
❷ **SUMMERFIELD Spencer** Travers Smith Braithwaite	
❸ **BARNES Oliver** Travers Smith Braithwaite	**BENNETT John** Berwin Leighton
BOTT Adrian Olswang	**BURROW Robert** SJ Berwin & Co
GREAVES Adam Gouldens	**LETH Mary** Macfarlanes
MAHER Paul Rowe & Maw	**STEINFELD Michael** Dechert
❹ **BURGESS Patrick** Gouldens	**CHESTER Martin** Theodore Goddard
DILLON Martin Taylor Joynson Garrett	**GEE Tim** Baker & McKenzie
LEVY Graeme Olswang	**THORNEYCROFT Max** Gouldens
WAYTE Peter DLA	
UP AND COMING	
CARPANINI Fabrizio Olswang	**MACKIE Chris** Olswang
NEWMAN Iain Nabarro Nathanson	
ONE TO WATCH	
WALKER Mark Rowe & Maw	

Within each band, firms are listed alphabetically. *See **Profiles** on page 240*
** See editorial entries for explanations of team sizes.*

Macfarlanes A *"professional team"* which is particularly respected for private equity transactions (including a high profile buy-out team) and an international client base, despite its domestic focus and lack of overseas offices. The firm caters for FTSE 250 clients and the second tier of FTSE 100 transactional work, such as advising Whitbread on its acquisition of Racquets and Healthtrack Group for £78.3 million.

"Energetic" **Robert Sutton** is seen as the *"aggressive networker"* of the firm, with an excellent reputation as a deal-doer. Although some may find him *"abrasive,"* he is said to have *"a great political touch."* He advised Compagnie de Saint-Gobain on its recommended offer of £1.4 billion for Meyer International and advised Saatchi & Saatchi on its £4 billion acquisition by Publicis. **Mary Leth** is seen as the technician of the firm and has acted for the brokers Intercapital on its merger with Garban. Despite her profile, the firm is said to be in danger of becoming a one man band, and lacks the rising stars to assume Sutton's mantle. The team has advised, however, on a number of recent big-ticket deals, acting for Virgin on its sale of a 49% stake in Virgin Atlantic (for £551 million) and for Vivendi on its acquisition of a 24% interest in BSkyB for £2.5 billion. **Clients: Corporates:** PPG Industries; Whitbread; Virgin Group; Intercapital plc; HAVAS SA; Carlton Communications; Kingspan Group plc; Retail Decisions plc; Vivendi. **Financials:** Hawkpoint Partners; Greenhill & Co; ING Barings; Cinven; 3i plc; Candover; Royal Bank of Scotland; Barclays Bank.

Rowe & Maw The market admires the firm's *"clear focus,"* which has led to instructions from major clients such as ICI, Cable & Wireless and EMI. *"Effective operator"* **Paul Maher**, Head of Corporate is *"energetic and commercial,"* and clients like his *"tenacity and commitment."* The firm's corporate focus is on its core competencies of telecoms, chemical markets, media and, increasingly, IT/convergence-related deals. Highlights of the year include acting for Reuters Group in the formation of a joint venture with Dow Jones & Co to form Factiva (combined revenue exceeding $225 million.) The team also acts for Reuters Greenhouse Fund, through which the company takes minority stakes in internet-related companies. A fine example of the firm's cross-border activity is its work for ICI plc, advising on its disposal of its Fluoropolymers business to Asahi Glass Company Ltd, Japan for $136 million. At home, the team acted for Hodder Headline on the £185 million recommended cash offer from WH Smith Group. **Clients: Corporates:** EMI Group; Cable & Wireless plc; ICI plc; GEC; HMV Media Group plc; Global Telesystems Europe; DHL International (UK) Ltd; AstraZeneca Group; Hodder Headline plc; Monsanto plc; NBC.

SJ Berwin A firm which has *"risen to the dotcom challenge"* and has expanded its client base despite a number of losses at partner level. Retains its traditional profile in corporate property financings. The firm is said to be *"exceptionally strong"* in private equity and is the *"brightest, bounciest"* firm in the mid-level market, although this has been interpreted as *"aggressive."* Clients respond well to its *"trustworthy, rapport-building"* skills which are mixed with a *"sound technical knowledge."*

The practice is seen to benefit hugely from the presence of **Robert Burrow**. Peers admire his intellect and *"incisive command of the law."* He is seen acting on the firm's major deals, particularly those with an international element. Recent work includes acting for NM Rothschild as financial adviser to Finalrealm Ltd on its recommended bid for United Biscuits. E-commerce is a focus for the firm and has brought in some big-ticket cross-border work. Acting for Future Network on its acquisitions (including Imagine Media Inc) has involved Italy, Germany and the UK markets. After the company's IPO (valued at £575 million) the firm has also advised on a secondary share offering. Retaining its anchor clients such as British Land, the team has acted on its acquisition of a 29.7% stake in South African-based Liberty International (value £514 million.) **Clients: Corporates:** British Land (on acquisition of Meadowhall;) Hilton Group; Future Network; OneSwoop.com; Nova Chemicals Corporation (acquisition of Shell's polystyrene business.) **Financials:** Philip Drew Ventures; NM Rothschild; Electra Partners Europe.

Travers Smith Braithwaite *"A highly commercial"* firm which has a base of *"quality"* partners but is considered to lack depth. Has a broad base of clients and handles transactions across continental Europe, with a particular focus on private equity financings. The team is also praised for its growing base of FTSE and AIM listed clients.

Senior Partner, the *"delightful"* **Christopher Bell**, has taken on the role left vacant by Alan Keat's retirement (who continues as a consultant) and has been seen less transactionally. As *"an old school advisor"* and client man, he continues to be the main force of the corporate team. Head of Corporate **Oliver Barnes** is recommended for his *"excellent market knowledge"* and his feel for private equity clients. He represented Workplace Technologies on a recommended cash offer of £81 million from NTL. Younger partner **Spencer Summerfield** has impressed his peers with a *"strikingly good attitude and impressive legal acumen."* He has a *"great sense of humour"* and *"knows how to make the process smooth."* He is the focal point for the firm's relationship with NTL (nine major transactions in 1999) and has acted on its purchase of the cable business from

Cable & Wireless Communications for £9.8 billion. An *"efficient and effective"* team is able to handle the larger deals, such as acting for the Greenalls Group plc on its disposal of Stretton Leisure Ltd and on the sale of its pubs and restaurant business to Scottish Newcastle plc for £1.35 billion. **Clients: Corporates:** NTL Inc; The Greenalls Group; London Bridge Software; Carpetright, Beazer Group; Crestco, Devere; Channel 5; Shepherd Neame Ltd. **Financials:** Hawkpoint; HSBC.

Baker & McKenzie A low profile on the domestic front belies the impact that this firm has on the international M&A market, in which clients see it as a *"successfully integrated corporate practice."* It is seen to be acting in a *"completely different market,"* which is reflected in a lack of profiled players. Steeped in cross-border work, the firm can count Fortune 500 corporates among its client base. It also has strengths in chemicals/pharmaceuticals and telecoms, all of which has naturally led to convergence work. Clients like the *"global service"* and the London team is seen to *"assume a harmonising role"* co-ordinating big-ticket deals with full UK and US service (including capital markets) and local law expertise in the principal European jurisdictions.

Tim Gee offers *"trustworthy sound advice"* and is a high-profile figure in the international market. He is seen to handle the biggest deals, which include acting for global speciality chemicals company Clariant AG on its $2.8 billion recommended public offer for BTP plc. The firm also advised Japan Tobacco on its $8 billion acquisition of RJ Reynolds International. In the telecoms sector, the team has acted for WorldxChange on its acquisition of ACC Telecom from AT&T in England, Germany, France and Italy. **Clients: Corporates:** Clariant AG; Kuoni, Japan Tobacco; BAT plc; Apple Computers Inc; Cisco; Solutia Inc; Telecom Italia; Toyota; United News & Media; McLaren International; Mitsubishi Electric; Kellogg; DaimlerChrysler UK Ltd **Financials:** Apax Funds; Crédit Agricole Indosuez; Schroders; JP Morgan; Salomon Smith Barney; CSFB, DLJ.

Berwin Leighton *"Not a firm that grabs the headlines,"* yet clients like the *"commercial, pragmatic attitude"* of this younger team. Approaching corporate finance from a strong property angle, this *"bright"* team has also scored well on the new media front. Its traditional client base has remained loyal despite significant losses (two private equity partners to Olswang,) while the team has been boosted by gains from the defunct Edward Lewis.

Head of Corporate **John Bennett** is the mainstay of the practice with clients praising his *"special grasp of corporate needs,"* and the energy and attention he gives to deals. He has a strong reputation with financial investors such as Durlacher. With the low profile of the remaining team members, however, the practice has been seen as *"a one-man band."*

The firm has gained a fine reputation for advising financial investors in the property market, for example acting for Norwich Union Investment Management in its joint venture with Milner Estates for five town centre shopping schemes, and for Mercury Asset Management on a £150m fund to acquire and manage high-yielding industrial and commercial property. Although the firm is not known for its international work, its activity in the IPO market has led the firm to act for Del Monte Pacific Ltd on its flotation on the Singapore Stock Exchange (an IPO of 25% of the company's share capital raised $180 million.) The team also acted for the largest shareholder (Tim Jackson) on the flotation of QXL.com (issue price £263 million) and acted for Hollinger Digital Inc on the flotation of Interactive Investor International (value £245 million.) **Clients: Corporates:** Lex Services; Tesco; Transamerica Corp; Royal Del Monte Foods International; QXL.com plc; Interactive Investor International; Bell group plc; LA Fitness; Legal & General. **Financials:** Deutsche Bank; Mercury Asset Management; Durlacher; ABN Hoare Govett; Friends Ivory & Syme; Dresdner Kleinwort Benson.

Gouldens *"A driven team"* packed with *"strong characters,"* this firm is finding its way onto larger, international deals, although its brand name remains in acting for the mid-market corporates and financial intermediaries with a focus on property and IT. A recent highlight saw the team acting for Bankers Trust (now Deutsche Bank) on the $2.1 billion financing of Huntsman Corporation's acquisition of chemical businesses from ICI.

Head of Corporate, *"personable"* **Max Thorneycroft** is seen as an important presence, particularly on the larger deals where his deal-management skills are praised. Alongside a banking partner, he led the financing of Huntsman and also acted for the shareholders on the sale of Integralis Ltd in exchange for shares in Articon Information Systems AG, the reverse of a UK business into a Neuer Markt company. Although seen as less transactional, senior partner **Patrick Burgess** maintains his reputation as the team's heavyweight hitter and has acted for Liberty Life Group on its participation in a £1.5 billion scheme of arrangement with London listed Liberty International Holdings plc. **Adam Greaves** is a visible player in the market, praised for his rapport with clients and his *"efficient expertise"* on transactions. A strong profile with the investment banks sees him acting for ABN Amro, Crédit Lyonnais and Gresham Trust. As well as an increase in cross-border activity, the firm has continued to build on its private equity practice with a bias towards the technology sector. Advised Fexco (Irish international financial services company) on the MBO of Global Refund Group, backed by Apax Partners (Euro 150 million.) Active in the IPO market despite a general lull, the firm advised Peel Hunt on the £31 million AIM floatation of Gameplay.com and maintained its property reputation by acting for Delancey Estates on both its hostile bid for Greycoats plc (unsuccessful) and its successful offer for Milner Estates. **Clients: Corporates:** UGC; Delancey Estates; Intergralis Ltd; Hanson; Energizer UK; Ted Baker plc; Liberty Life Group. **Financials:** Peel Hunt; West LB Panmure Ltd; ABN Amro Causeway; NatWest Ventures; Gresham Trust; Invested Henderson Crosthwaite; Fexco.

Nabarro Nathanson (Up to 26 partners undertake a mixture of corporate work supported by 20 senior associates and upto a further 40 assistants.) Primarily known as a dominant player in property financing, although the market perceives a danger of the firm becoming *"a little one-dimensional."* The firm's focuses are on new media, IT and telecoms.

A familiar name on the largest property deals, the group has acted for Land Securities on the £800 million Birmingham Bull Ring and Martineau development, involving its participation in three limited partnerships established with Hammersons plc and Pearl Assurance. A cross-border element is not unusual in these types of deals and has led to US company BAA MacArthur Glen's joint venture agreements with BP Pension fund, Norwich Union, NPI and CIS to fund designer outlets in Wiltshire and Wales.

In private equity, Alchemy Partners has proved to be an active source of instructions with three public to private transactions in 1999 with a total value of £332 million (Warle Storeys plc, Sanderson Group and CrestaCare plc.) The team itself has a growing reputation for its private equity practice, undertaking M&A transactions and floats for venture capitalists and investment funds such as Klesch & Co. This reputation is also assisting the growth of IT-based work, where the team's *"excellent knowledge of AIM and listed company law"* has proved essential. **Iain Newman** joins our lists due to his *"broad commercial knowledge"* and his strong technology focus. Acted for New Media Spark plc on its £47 million flotation on AIM and subsequent fund-raisings. **Clients: Corporates:** BAA-McArthur Glen; Land Securities; Great Portland Estates; Westminster Healthcare; Holmes Place; OSC Group; Dana (UK and ex-UK); Granada; First Technologies; New Media Spark plc. **Financials:** Alchemy Partners; Investec; HSBC Ventures; Klesch & Co.

Olswang A *"bright and friendly team"* seen to have a *"clear understanding of its core market,"* which is media, telecoms and technology. A successful move away from a more generalist commercial reputation has been helped by lateral hires. The highly respected, *"trustworthy"* figures of **Fabrizio Carpanini** and **Chris Mackie** (formerly Berwin Leighton) are *"a* *major boost"* to the private equity offering of this firm, and add *"a certain gravitas."* Their presence also strengthens the start-up and pre-float funding of the firm's technology clients.

Department head **Adrian Bott** is seen as *"the mover and shaker"* of the firm and is a *"client magnet."* Well regarded for his AIM experience, he has acted on the floats of VirtualInternet, Gameplay.com and RTS Network Group. **Graeme Levy** is seen as the perfect foil to Bott. Less high-profile in the corporate field, he is *"extremely bright and reliable"* and *"can do any work you throw at him."* He is admired for his reputation with venture capitalist investors and mainstream banks. The telecoms sector has seen the team acting for Thus plc (Scottish Telecom) on its £2.2 billion flotation and Carphone Warehouse on its acquisition of Intertan UK (Tandy) and its subsequent float. Also acted for Talk Radio (agreed bid for Independent Radio Group plc) and Granada (£22 million minority investment stake in Liverpool FC.) The market awaits the effect of the launch of Long Acre Partners, an independent corporate finance house in which JP Morgan Corsair II Capital Partners has taken a 15% stake. **Clients: Corporates:** Carphone Warehouse; BBC Worldwide Ltd; Granada; Motorola Inc; Talk Radio Inc; Warner Bros/Warner Music; Body Shop International; gameplay.com; VirtualInternet; RTS Network Group plc; Freeserve plc; Belgo Group plc. **Financials:** Mainly VC and investment funds such as Jupiter Dividend & Growth Trust plc.

DLA A regular face on the London scene although the firm overall is said to be *"more regionally focused."* It is the national strengths that are beginning to play an important role in resourcing the larger deals. Primarily known as a private equity player, the firm is also building its reputation in mainstream M&A with help from the internet boom.

Peter Wayte maintains his status as this growing team's biggest hitter. He offers a *"first-rate service"* but peers detect a lack of consolidation in the London team. Has acted for Havant International on its world wide technology business (Xyratex Technology division) to Netherlands based Teleplan. The firm receives instructions from a wide range of sectors including telecoms, media, publishing and property with a mid-range deal size of £50-100 million and the national capacity to do higher-value deals. It has advised Easynet Group plc on its introduction to the Official List and acted for Flightbookers plc on the disposal of its internet booking business to e-bookers.com, in connection with the latter's flotation on Nasdaq. **Clients: Corporates:** JJB Sports; Singer & Friedlander; Easynet Group; Jazz FM plc; Granada Group plc; UK Estates plc; MEPC plc; Flightbookers; Genus plc (OFEX listing); Concurrent Technologies plc; Tempus Group plc. **Financials:** CCF Charterhouse.

Taylor Joynson Garrett A team *"on the up,"* channelling its *"good collective energy"* into M&A work, often on an international scale. The firm has offices in Brussels and Bucharest and is admired for capturing major US clients such as SunMicrosystems. Major sectors of practice include technology and life sciences and the firm successfully leverages its IP reputation to boost cross-over e-commerce corporate work.

"Reliable deal-doer" **Martin Dillon** is the most prominent transactional partner but this is generally a low-profile team, commended for its innovative attitude. On the technology front, the firm has advised 365 Corporation on the acquisition of C-Sports Communications SA and Electron Libre SARL. This prominence also leads to venture capital work such as advising Newbury Ventures on seed and early stage financing in IT and healthcare companies. A highlight of the year was advice to Geron Corporation on its acquisition of Roslin BioMed (who cloned Dolly the sheep) by way of an exchange of 2.1 million shares of stock. **Clients: Corporates:** 365 Corporation plc; Landis NV; Eidos plc; Ericsson Business Networks AB; Crane Co; Macmillan Publishers Ltd; PETsMART; Diageo; Barbican Healthcare plc; Ferrero. TDK Corporation. **Financials:** Bank of America NT & SA; Liontrust Asset Management; Mees Pierson NV; Nomura International plc; Investec Henderson Crosthwaite.

Theodore Goddard The loss of its head of corporate to US firm Jones Day Reavis & Pogue has been seen to distract but not hamper this team, well regarded for its involvement in complex cross border activity. It is *"packed with bright people,"* mainly seen acting for a range of financial institutions such as Warburg Dillon Read and Peel Hunt.

Martin Chester has *"transactional credibility,"* but is not seen as a rainmaker. He advised Signet Group on its acquisition of US jewellery chain Marks & Morgan for £105 million (Weil Gotshal & Manges advised on US aspects) and advised Blagden on the sale of its chemical manufacturing business to a US company, Borden Chemical Inc (value £45 million.) The team has also advised Diageo plc on its disposal of an 88% shareholding in Grupo Cruzcampo, the Spanish brewery to Heineken on a debt free basis (value £570 million.) **Clients: Corporates:** Diageo; Signet Group; Blagden plc; United Distillers & Vinters; Cleveland Trust; Text 100 Group; Universal Music Leisure Ltd; The Dialog Corporation; Watts Blake Bearne. **Financials:** Peel Hunt; BT Alex Brown; Hoare Govett; Warburg Dillon Read; Beeson Gregory.

Dechert After a six year engagement, Titmuss Sainer Dechert has tied a transatlantic knot with US firm Dechert Price & Rhoads, creating a base of 580 lawyers in ten offices across Europe and the US. The team is admired for its international relationships with US investors in Europe, yet is said to lack the *"prominent anchor clients"* to raise its mainstream corporate profile. US and UK teams advised jointly on the Travelex MBO and the flotation of Globalnet Financial.com. Noted also for its US lawyers based in the London office.

Clients appreciate **Michael Steinfeld**'s *"commercial decisions"* and his good understanding of the equity markets. The *"user-friendly"* team itself offers a *"perfect balance between commercial and legal advice"* and is seen as most active on IPOs and advice to owner-managed entrepreneurial businesses. Achieving prominence in the retail sector by advising Sears on its transactions following its takeover by Philip Green, including the disposal of Freemans to Otto Versand, the sale of its womenswear businesses to Arcadia Group (£151 million) and on the MBO of Adams Childrenswear (£87 million.) Retains traditional expertise in property and insurance, advising BRIT Insurance Holdings on its agreed offer for Wren plc for £300 million and acting for Chesterfield Properties plc on a portfolio sale to GE Capital and a subsequent successful bid for the company by Quintain Estates. **Clients: Corporates:** Granvelle plc, Fairview New Home; Bloomsbury; Travelex; Marylebone Warwick Balfour Group plc; Elonex plc; Betterware plc; Ocwen UK Ltd; Hambro Insurance Services Group; Benfield Grieg Group. **Financials:** Mellon Bank Corporation; Beeson Gregory Ltd.

DJ Freeman A corporate finance practice which follows three distinct industry lines: insurance, property and media/communications. While this allows for a broad base of clients and partners with highly developed sector knowledge, it also falls prey to the criticism of merely delivering a service to existing clients. Corporate deals tend to fall within the £20-£100 million range.

Of the three industry sectors, the property deals have the highest profile. The team advised Shell on the sale of ShellMex House and acted for Regus Business Ventures on its joint venture with Arlington Securities to provide services office accommodation. It also has a growing reputation for AIM flotations and the support of internet start-ups seed capital fund raising. It acted for eXchange Holdings plc on a conditional contract to acquire share capital of Homepages. **Clients:** Chartwell; Exchange Holdings; Leisureplant International; Sedgewick Oakwood; SEA Multimedia plc; Cox Insurance plc; Goshawk Insurance plc; Syndicate Capital Trusts plc.

Eversheds Well established in the London market (formerly the office of Jakes & Lewis,) this national firm has an international capability. Offices across Europe have encouraged cross-border deals; forming approximately 40% of the team's activity. Average deal size is in the £50-£75 million range. Despite being at *"the top of the tree"* in the regions, peers question the degree of firepower offered by the London office alone.

The team does have major clients, such as advising Du Pont on joint ventures with Sabanci of Turkey ($1 billion) and with Teijin of Japan

($1.4 billion,) and has undertaken major restructuring work for Alldays, including acquisitions aggregating £158 million (includes assumed debt.) A traditional reputation in buy-outs saw the team advising the management on its buy-out of Admiral Insurance Services and creation of Admiral Group. **Clients: Corporates:** DuPont (UK) Ltd; Alldays plc; Thomson CSF; Frangi Investments (on £22.6 million cash bid for Tie Rack plc;) Page Group; Bechtel Enterprises; Streamline International Ltd. **Financials:** Mainly VC; Royal Bank Development Capital; HSBC Investment Bank.

Stephenson Harwood Loss of the head of Corporate Finance to US firm Gibson Dunn & Crutcher has further weakened a team perceived to be *"treading water."* The group has proved itself capable of handling transactions with an international dimension, acting for the Government of Uganda on a series of privatisations including Uganda Airlines and Uganda Telecom.

"A lovely firm to work with," despite the upheavals, the team is praised for attempts to refocus on the IT field including launches and increased investment by financial services groups. Advised Virgin Unlimited on the proposed establishment of Virgin's internet shopping mall, and Bass on its stake in lastminute.com. The team has acted on seven public bids (including three hostile) last year. Advised Wace Group plc on a hostile bid from Photobition Group plc and a subsequent auction between two US based white knights. **Clients: Corporates:** Racal Electronics; Wang Holdings Ltd; Christies International; Chubb Security; Bertram Holdings; The Tussauds Group Ltd; Accor SA; Wace Group; Minit Group plc; Pathe; Virgin Unlimited. **Financials:** Royal Bank of Scotland plc; HSBC Investment Bank; Collins Stewart Ltd; Hoare Govett Ltd.

FEWER THAN 30 SOLICITORS IN CORPORATE FINANCE TEAM

Hammond Suddards Edge *"Becoming more visible"* in traditional M&A transactions and continues to bolster the team with lateral hires, including a senior corporate partner from SJ Berwin. This has yet to smooth over the perception of a team still finding its feet in the London market and overshadowed by regional successes. The team is *"making a huge push"* and has broadened its mid-tier corporate client base.

National Head of Corporate **Richard Burns** is *"a sensible lawyer"* who maintains influential relationships with the mid-sized equity houses. Deals tend to fall within the £100-£200 million range and include acting for Pubmaster Group Ltd on the acquisition of 662 tenanted pubs from Swallow Group plc (value £127.5 million.) Opportunities in the London market are said to be the main driver for Hammond Suddards' merger with Edge Ellison and the market awaits the effect on the corporate team, although a continued push is expected, with regional support. **Clients: Corporates:** Pubmaster; Illinois Tool Works Inc; Eyecare Products plc; Baltic plc; Aspinall's Club plc; Trafiagura Beheer BV; Cork Industries. **Financials:** Société Générale; Legal & General Ventures; Apax Partners; Mees Pierson.

Osborne Clarke OWA Once seen purely as a first-rate Bristol operation, the *"balance of power is shifting"* and the firm is now held to possess *"real City punch."* Peers consider this to be *"the best cross-fertilised practice around." "Likeable"* **Tim Birt** is perceived to be the mainstay of the firm and is praised for his intelligence and ability to close a deal efficiently. He recently acted for Stepstone ASA on the English law aspects of its float on the UK and Norwegian Stock Exchanges (value £500 million.) The team has continued to develop its IT/Telecoms and media focus with a solid deal flow from NatWest IT Fund and other technologically-minded venture capitalists. Advised XKO Group plc, a systems integration software company, on its triple reverse takeover and transfer from AIM to the Official List. Also acted for 3i plc and the management team on the IBO for Isotrak (the vehicle tracking software division of NFC) for £29 million. **Clients: Corporates:** XKO Group plc; Radio Partnership; ZodiaSignCorp plc; Vestey Group; Chesterton Group; Isotrak. **Financials:** 3i Group; ABN Amro Causeway; Beeson Gregory; Lloyds TSB Development Capital; NatWest Equity Partners; NatWest IT Fund; SG Securities.

Paisner & Co *"Entrepreneurial"* and *"confident,"* this firm has a good focus on corporate work with the market noting strengths in new media, retail and leisure. An impressive client list includes second-tier work for FTSE 100 companies such as GUS and Diageo and a solid base of private owner-managed businesses. *"Bright and enthusiastic"* **Keith Stella** *"has a real drive"* about him, and clients respond well to his *"complete dedication and excellent advice."* He advised First Leisure on its £210 million sale of its bar division and scheme of arrangement and acted for Alpha Airport on the $155 million disposal of its US ground handling operations. The team has seen a marked transactional increase of inward investment from US corporations to the UK. **Stephen Rosefield** brings a *"sensible attitude"* to the deal process and has been a driving force behind the firm's progress in the e-commerce field. The team acted for Apax Partners on its investment in qlx.com and has also undertaken the financing and flotation of internet companies such as netvest.com plc (AIM listed.) **Clients: Corporates:** Chorion plc; Esporta plc; Medisys plc; Cellcom Ltd; Courts plc; Diageo plc; Burberry Ltd; Tie Rack Ltd; First Leisure Corporation; Great Universal Stores plc; The AON Group. **Financials:** Apax Partners; Durlacher Ltd

Bird & Bird A *"full service firm,"* with a great reputation in telecoms, media and technology and an enviable set of blue-chip clients. The drive towards convergence has broadened the team's client base as it fully exploits the growth in e-commerce based corporate work.

With a clear focus the team is said to act as *"a good collective force,"* but on deals can be *"hard negotiators and a touch arrogant."* **Charles Crosthwaite** joins our ranks this year, recommended for his *"excellent telecoms knowledge."* He advised CSF Group on its placing and open offer to raise £10 million. In the telecoms sector the team advised Viatel Inc on its acquisition of AT&T Communications (UK) Ltd for £125 million. Perceived to attract the most innovative clients, the team has also advised Video Networks in connection with is £20 million equity fund raising to provide video on demand in conjunction with BT and Kingston Communications. **Clients: Corporates:** BT plc; Orchestream Ltd; Philips Electronics UK; Sony Music International; Racal Telecoms Ltd (now Global Crossing,) Philips Electronics UK; Carlton Communications; EMAP plc; Viatel Inc; British Information Systems UK Ltd; Compaq Computer Corporation; The Football Association; Storehouse plc. **Financials:** GE Capital Ltd; CSFB.

Field Fisher Waterhouse Respected practitioners seen to have *"capitalised on a traditional profile in new media markets."* The team is said to be *"pushing aggressively"* with success in telecoms, e-commerce and the leisure industry. Despite producing *"quality"* work, the team has yet to raise the profile of its individuals and is said to *"need a figurehead"* with a purely transactional background.

In telecoms it has continued to advise US-based RSL Communications Ltd on its European acquisition programme, including the purchase of Advanced Telecom plc which has bolstered its reputation for convergence work. Other cross-border activity includes advising Sopra SA, a French quoted company, on its acquisition of UK-based Mentor Computer Service Ltd. **Clients: Corporates:** RSL Communications Ltd; GMG Endemol Entertainment plc; BBC Worldwide Ltd; ComputerLand (UK) plc; Level 3 Communications LLC; Whitbread plc. **Financials:** Mitsubishi Corporation Finance plc.

Lawrence Graham A *"prominent team"* with a *"good spread of fine individuals,"* primarily known for AIM flotation work and its strong ties to the private equity houses and investment funds. Has a well regarded reputa-

CORPORATE FINANCE: FEWER THAN 30 SOLICITORS IN CORPORATE TEAM • London	Ptnrs	Assts
❶ Hammond Suddards Edge	7	12
Osborne Clarke OWA	9	18
Paisner & Co	9	8
❷ Bird & Bird	7	14
Field Fisher Waterhouse	8	14
Lawrence Graham	9	18
Pinsent Curtis	12	14
Richards Butler	8	16
Warner Cranston	6	7
❸ Biddle	8	7
Harbottle & Lewis	5	3
Memery Crystal	5	11
Nicholson Graham & Jones	12	12
Sinclair Roche & Temperley	3	10
Watson, Farley & Williams	7	18
❹ Howard Kennedy	5	4
Lewis Silkin	9	8
❺ Beachcroft Wansbroughs	8	10
Charles Russell	4	12
Coudert Brothers	Fu	Fu
Fox Williams	5	3
Hobson Audley	7	8
Laytons	5	4
Marriott Harrison	3	3
Wedlake Bell	5	4
❻ Manches	5	4
Middleton Potts	4	4
Radcliffes	8	10
Rakisons	4	6

LEADING INDIVIDUALS	
❶ **BIRT Timothy** Osborne Clarke OWA	**STELLA Keith** Paisner & Co
STORAR Michael Lawrence Graham	
❷ **AUDLEY Max** Hobson Audley	**BEHARRELL Steven** Coudert Brothers
BURNS Richard Hammond Suddards Edge	**FAGELSON Ian** Warner Cranston
GRAYSTON Clare Lewis Silkin	**GREGORY Lesley** Memery Crystal
JOHNS Michael Nicholson Graham & Jones	**ROSEFIELD Stephen** Paisner & Co
WEBSTER Martin Biddle	**WINTER Martin** Biddle
❸ **BAKER Andrew** Wedlake Bell	**SWEET Jon** Marriott Harrison
WILLIAMS Christine Fox Williams	
UP AND COMING	
CROSTHWAITE Charles Bird & Bird	**DEAN Kevin** Sinclair Roche & Temperley

Within each band, firms are listed alphabetically. *See **Profiles** on page 240*
Fu Figures unavailable at time of going to press.

tion in the leisure, retail, media and technology sectors with a good smattering of high profile corporates on its client list.

Michael Storar is the team's *"front-line man"* and perceived to be *"an impressive force on the AIM market."* The team has struck a balance between acting for companies and the nominated advisors/brokers and is also active in joint admissions to AIM and the Developing Companies Market (DCM) in Dublin. Acted for JellyWorks plc on its admission to AIM (market capitalisation £175 million,) and advised London & Regional Properties Ltd on the acquisition of the property-owning subsidiaries of TBI plc for £190 million. **Clients: Corporates:** Coffee Republic plc; Regents Inn plc; London & Regional Properties Ltd; Lasmo plc; JellyWorks plc; Inter-Alliance plc; Pure Entertainment Games plc (£11 million AIM listing,) BSS Group. **Financials:** Greig Middleton & Co; Investec Henderson Crosthwaite; Teather & Greenwood Ltd; Peel Hunt; Beeson Gregory.

Pinsent Curtis *"A practical, commercial team with good support systems."* Recognised for its national base and benefiting from resources in both Leeds and Birmingham, the team attracts an entrepreneurial client base. The private equity practice is firmly established on the London market, encouraging a growth in associations with mid-tier financial houses. While clients appreciate the firm's *"proactive tailored solutions,"* some in the market suggest that the office may be *"under-resourced for its ambitions."* Advised Royal Bank Development Capital on its investment in the £510 million MBO of Ocwen Ltd from its US parent, and advised shareholders and the management on the 3i-backed MBO of Tempo/KF Group electrical retailers (value £130 million.) The team has developed its experience in the dotcom markets with particular emphasis on AIM listings. Advised Just2Clicks.com plc on its £130 million flotation. **Clients: Corporates:** Just2Clicks plc; Blakes Clothing plc; Ocwen Ltd; AM Paper Group Tempo/KF Group Ltd; MediaKey plc; Acquisitor plc; Lionheart plc; Sutherlands Ltd; GiroVend Cashless Systems plc. **Financials:** ACP Investments; Royal Bank Development Capital Ltd; HSBC.

Richards Butler The firm's wide base of small and mid-sized corporates covers media, leisure, IT and transport. *"Fine international clients"* distinguish this practice which has advised on cross-border activities for MTV and US-based Lennox International. Approximately 60% of the team's work contains a cross-border element or comes from overseas clients with a strong presence in Asia, US, and Australia. Advising on two telecoms privatisation projects in Eastern Europe. Clients appreciate a *"commercial and flexible approach,"* which has led to high profile work, acting for Direct Line Group Ltd on its acquisition of Green Flag Holdings from US Cedant Corporation (value £220 million.) **Clients:** The Rank Group; Direct Line Ltd; Provalis plc; MTV; Hellenic Telecoms Organisation; Sea Containers/GNER; First Pacific Davies; Allied Signal Inc; Lennox International Inc.

Warner Cranston *"A good efficient team,"* well regarded for advising foreign corporations, particularly French and US investors in Europe. **Ian Fagelson** has a reputation for *"technical knowledge and deal control," "follows a strong line"* and is *"highly commercial."* He acted for Israeli GEO Interactive Media on its raising of £240 million by way of private placement in the UK, US and the continent. A respectable name for high profile deals has seen the team acting for InterTan (UK) Ltd on the sale of 350 retail outlets to Carphone Warehouse and undertaking corporate transactions for Courtaulds Textiles and Akzo Nobel. **Clients:** Courtaulds Textiles plc; Swiss Re New Markets; Akzo Nobel; Family Assurance Friendly Society Ltd; GEO Interactive Media; Touchstone Securities Ltd.

Biddle A respected corporate team that has strong relationships with institutional private equity clients and is said to act with *"full service strength across the board."* Seen in the main on public to private transactions the team is seen to benefit from a high level of partner involvement on transactions. Senior partner **Martin Winter** displays *"an impressive depth of knowledge"* and is recommended for pushing the private equity focus of the team, establishing a strong client base. He acted for the Press Association on its sale of its sponsored news business to United News & Media Group (£17 million.) **Martin Webster** maintains his reputation as a *"natural, technically-minded lawyer."* He advised media client Lopex on its successful defence of a hostile bid from Incepta plc and its subsequent recommended takeover of Havas Advertising (value £67 million.) Comfortable handling deals up to £200 million, the average deal size is £50-£75 million. Benefiting from the increase of US investment into the UK, the team has acted for CarrAmerica Realty Coporation on the UK aspects of the $1 billion merger between affiliate HQ Global Workplaces and Frontline Capital Group. **Clients: Corporates:** Lopex plc; Cedar Group plc; Press Association; Dawson Holdings plc; CarrAmerica Realty Corporation; MetaDesign UK. **Financials:** ABN Amro Mezzanine; 3i; Bank of Scotland; Albert E Sharp Securities; NatWest Equity Partners.

Harbottle & Lewis A *"bright, media savvy"* team seen to offer a full service covering corporate and commercial work. The fields of internet, entertainment and media are driving this team with clients ranging from individual entrepreneurs to multi-national corporates. The team has capitalised on its *"fantastic"* reputation in the entertainment sector with high profile and active corporate clients such as Virgin and Ginger Media Group and institutional investors such as the Dawnay Day Lander Incubator Fund. Advised Chris Evans on the sale of Ginger Media Group Ltd to Scottish Media Group (value £225 million) and advised the MBO team on its successful acquisition of Primesight International Ltd from Scottish Media Group. **Clients:** Chrysalis Group plc; Primesight International Ltd; Chris Evans (Ginger Media Group,) Sci Entertainment Group plc; Talkcast Corporation; Wagadon (Nick Logan); Virgin Group/Richard Branson; Lothian Investments Ltd.

Memery Crystal **Lesley Gregory** is the mainstay of this respected corporate team. She has a *"strong institutional following"* and *"excellent deal management skills."* Most active on the AIM market, the team has a growing base of internet-based clients. Advised Printpotato.com on its £3 million AIM listing and crossing over into institutional work, and advised Seymour Pierce, the nominated advisor and broker, on the AIM listing of Pure Entertainment Games (£20 million.) The firm is also praised for its involvement in the MBO market and corporate reconstruction where it has advised Gieves & Hawkes plc on the demerger of Chivers Press. **Clients:** Gieves & Hawkes; Gladstone plc; Pure Entertainment Games plc; Oxygen plc; Radio First; Fulcrum Pharma plc.

Nicholson Graham & Jones Although less transactional due to his role, the firm's managing partner, **Michael Johns**, maintains his reputation as the rainmaker for the corporate team. His *"all-round legal skills"* and *"rapport with clients"* have boosted the team's profile. The team is advising Henderson Investors on the creation of The Birmingham Alliance, a JV between the former, Land Securities and Hammerson plc to develop Birmingham's city centre (total investment approximately £800 million.) With a strong reputation in media and leisure, it has acted on high profile joint ventures including acting for Leeds Sporting plc, the listed company that owns Leeds United FC, on the share subscription by and strategic alliance with BSkyB plc. **Clients: Corporates:** GWR Group; Arena Leisure plc; Eurodis Electron plc; Granada Group plc; Merchant Retail Group; 4Front Group plc; Union plc. **Financials:** Henderson Investors; Singer & Friedlander Group plc; Peel Hunt.

Sinclair Roche & Temperley A small team praised for its hard-working assistants and quality cross-border deals. Perceived to have grown on the skill and reputation of Head of Corporate, **Kevin Dean**. He has a *"good instinct for what matters in a deal"* and is slowly moving the team away from its well-regarded reputation for shipping work. Seen to have *"an ideal base"* for international deals, with a particular focus on transport and leisure. Acted on the reconstruction of Daewoo Group and advised Active Value Funds on its investments in UK-listed companies such as John Mansfield and Greycoat. **Clients:** Daewoo Corporation; Carnival Corporation; Cunard; Harland & Wolff.

Watson, Farley & Williams Regarded by the market as a *"good strong team,"* towed along by the firm's outstanding shipping reputation. This has led to a high cross-border element to its transactions with support from a highly visible presence in Paris, New York and Singapore. The team acted for Vivendi SA on its $1.2 billion investment in a joint venture with Elektrim SA, the Polish electrical engineering and telecoms company, involving partners from Paris and London. The team also has a strength in domestic flotations where a strong association with Charles Stanley has seen it acting as nominated advisors/brokers on AIM listings (for example General Industries plc and XS Leisure plc.) **Clients:** Vivendi SA; Trefick Ltd; ICB Shipping AB; KBC Advanced Technologies plc; Middlesex Holdings; Eurosov Energy plc; Charles Stanley & Co; Citadel Holdings plc; Voss Net plc; Anglo St James plc.

Howard Kennedy Has *"developed a good little profile"* for AIM and OFEX deals. Rated for its friendly approach, this team is said to be a *"pleasure to work with,"* and has a *"sound understanding"* of the commercial needs of its clients. Renowned for its strength in insurance, the team also has a significant presence in leisure and financial services. Acted for Friendly Hotels on the acquisition of seven hotels from Lyric Hotels (value £23 million) and advised Goodvibes on its recommended offer for Shani Group (value £7 million.) **Clients:** Friendly Hotels; Allied Irish Bank (GB); Invex Capital Ltd; Beeson Gregory; Updata Software plc; Nabarro Wells & Co Ltd; Downing Corporate Finance Ltd.

Lewis Silkin *"Energetic and competent"* team which has been seen as *"aggressive"* for its clients. Good sector knowledge covering IT/telecoms and advertising agencies with a number of blue chip names. *"Bright"* **Clare Grayston** is *"a star beyond doubt"* and is recommended for her *"clarity of focus."* Acted for the French-listed Havas Advertising on its successful cash bid for Lopex plc (a white knight move valuing the latter at £67 million.) Cross-border work saw the team acting on the sale of Added Value Group to Tempus Group plc for £35 million, covering the former's operations in France, Germany, Australia, South Africa and Singapore. Handling deals of up to £500 million with a median range of £20-£80 million, including a strong presence in AIM flotations (particularly e-commerce related) and MBOs. Acted for Charriol plc on its AIM float and subsequent acquisition of VirtualInternet.net plc (market capitalisation £20 million.) **Clients:** Abbott Mead Vickers Group Ltd; Havas Advertising SA; The Millennium Commission; Toyzone; Internetaction.com plc; House of Fraser plc; PizzaExpress plc.

Beachcroft Wansbroughs The market acknowledges that this has generally been a good year of consolidation for a team with a more visible profile. The team itself is said to be *"well-organised,"* approaching deals with a *"cool calm and collected attitude."* Insurance, a traditional sector for the firm, has continued to be a source of instruction, including advising Cornhill Insurance plc on its purchase of DBI Insurance Ltd (value £10 million.) Advised the Hellenic Bottling Company SA on its £4.2 billion merger with Coca-Cola Beverages. **Clients:** AssiDoman AB Group; Topjobs.net plc; Free Dot Net plc; Leda Media Products; Cambridge Water plc; Hellenic Bottling Company.

Charles Russell Seen by the market to be bolstered by a strong private client base, this *"highly commercial"* firm is well regarded for corporate work. Performing well in the telecoms, insurance and recruitment sectors. In its highest profile deal to date, the team has demonstrated its capacity to undertake big-ticket, cross-border work such as advising Select Appointments (Holdings) plc on the recommended offer by Vedio NV (£1.1 billion.) A telecoms reputation has encouraged prominence in digital media, acted for Scoot.com on the acquisition of Diva Solutions Ltd. **Clients:** Select Appointments; Morgan Sindall plc; Scoot.com plc; Reichold Inc; Methven's plc; Ivy Medical Chemicals plc; KLM Royal Dutch Airlines; Apax Partners; Beeson Gregory; William Baird plc; Britannia Group plc; Langbourn Properties Ltd.

Coudert Brothers A global firm with a *"big US engine,"* which is seen to be acting from the heart of Europe, advising on English, US and French law from this office. This year merged with Frankfurt-based Schurmann & Partners. **Steven Beharrell** is praised as a *"great lawyer"* who is *"commercially-minded"* and is seen on the biggest deals, notably in energy. Advised Norwegian company Telenor AS on its $720 million acquisition of a stake in Thai United Communications Industry. **Clients:** TelenorAS.

Fox Williams Seen to benefit from the *"energetic"* presence of **Tina Williams**, who gives the firm a *"clear corporate focus"* despite often fighting against the shadow cast by the firm's employment and partnership reputation. Undertaking both public and private M&A transactions, the firm has an entrepreneurial client base and has acted on deals up to £250 million. Williams advised the Morris family on the MBI of Earls Court and Olympia for £183 million. E-commerce and entertainment have an increased prominence, including the EU Smart on its £20 million fund raising. A reputation for company reconstruction work saw the team acting for the partners of Moores Rowland on the firm's demerger and subsequent union with BDO Stoy Hayward. **Clients:** Earls Court & Olympia Ltd; Paragon Publishing Holdings; EU Smart; Epoch Software Holdings; Ultramind Group plc.

Hobson Audley Corporate finance is the main engine of this small firm, which has suffered some disruptive partner defections recently. The firm's stand-out practitioner, **Max Audley**, retains his *"impressive"* reputation, however. He has *"real insight into the root of a deal"* and is well liked by clients. The *"efficient"* team benefits from the firm's relationship with Minneapolis-based Faegre & Benson, not only in encouraging the flow of US corporations as clients but also for the support offered by a multinational network. Main industry sectors for the firm are technology and telecoms, with the team concentrating on AIM, OFEX and secondary issues on the Official List. Advised Equator Group plc (film production) on its AIM placing and advised Investec Henderson Crosthwaite on the placing of Coffee Republic. **Clients:** Paladin Resources plc; Amway Corporation; Metron Technology; Viacom/Simon & Schuster; UK Land plc; Investec Henderson Crosthwaite; Seymour Pierce Ltd.

Laytons A national practice with active offices in Bristol, Manchester and Surrey. Perceived to be a *"good but not mainstream"* corporate practice with a particular focus on emerging businesses. A broadening client base includes e-commerce start-ups and a significant cross-border element. The team has acted for a listed UK company on its acquisition of a number of Eastern European companies to form a distribution network. Average deal size ranges from £5-£50 million and a varied client base includes smaller listed corporates and private equity investors. The team acted for Close Investment Partners on the sale of Oxford Aviation Holdings to BBA Group for £55 million (on a debt free cash basis.) **Clients:** United Kitchens plc; AMEC plc; Biofocus; Compel Group plc; Goodhead Group plc; Infobank plc; Oxford Instruments plc.

Marriott Harrison The firm is especially recommended for developing strong relationships with private equity houses, and is universally well regarded for its corporate work in the media sector. **Jon Sweet** is an all-rounder who *"gets straight to the point"* and has the *"perfect attitude for closing a deal."* He is seen as broadening the client base of the corporate team, acting for Durlacher on the start-up nothing-ventured.com. Despite the volume of growth in acting for venture capitalists and internet related start-ups, it is the firm's traditional field of entertainment that has brought the largest transactions. The team acted for long standing client Formula One on a number of deals, including the £1.2 billion acquisition of a 50% interest by EM.TV (the latter acquiring the stake from Deutsche Morgan Grenfell and Hellmann & Friedman.) **Clients:** Chrysalis Group plc; Shepperton Studios; Formula One; Durlacher Ltd; EagleRock Entertainmnet plc; Foreign & Colonial Ventures; Global Asset Management.

Wedlake Bell *"An old-fashioned firm with a deep well of clients."* Main industry sectors for the firm are healthcare, food and leisure with an average deal size of £5-£30 million and a number of deals over £100 million. Advised The Global Group on its £22 million recommended takeover of Sims Food Group. **Andrew Baker** is seen as a *"dependable figure to have in your corner."* A varied client base includes entrepreneurs, smaller listed companies, brokers and a set of international corporates. **Clients:** Lambert Smith Hampton plc; Global Group plc; Nestor Healthcare Group plc; Hartest Holdings plc; William Nash plc.

Manches A solid team currently *"making a lot of noise"* with headline deals. It advised Blackwell Ltd on the merger of its subscription agency business with Swets Blackwell International to form the largest global subscriptions agency (turnover $1 billion.) Media is an important area for the firm, alongside a specialism in water and a growing reputation in biotech and internet technology-related start-ups. *"An ambitious team,"* it acted for Conexant Systems (Nasdaq listed) on the acquisition of shares and options in Bristol-based Microcosm Communications Ltd (overall consideration $120 million.) **Clients:** Blackwell Ltd; Bouyges/Saur Group; Villiers; Conexant Systems; Music Unsigned.

Middleton Potts Market reputation rests on its *"considerable proportion of international clients."* Indeed, 75% of the team's transactions involve foreign-based or controlled companies. Offers an *"effective"* mix of company and commercial work, and it is seen to have strengths in the insurance sector. The team acted for Italian insurance giant Assicurazioni Generali (and Spanish subsidiary Generali Espana) on the disposal of Northern Star Insurance to Fortis UK. Energy-related corporate work and ship financing are also noted areas for the corporate team. **Clients:** Assicurazioni Generali.

Radcliffes A strong private client firm seen to be doing smaller corporate work with *"quiet efficiency."* Notable areas here are inward investment to the UK from North America and South Africa. Capitalising on the growth of its e-commerce base, the firm has established a Growing Business Group offering commercial and corporate advice. Acted for HLM Design Inc on the cross-border acquisition of GA Design International Ltd in the UK. **Clients:** Cap Gemini; FI Group plc; Netcom Internet Ltd; HML Design Inc; GA Design International; Software Centre Ltd; Radio Italia.

Rakisons Not seen as a mainstream corporate practice but offering a *"solid, commercial approach."* Has capitalised on a firm reputation in media and telecoms, acting on deals in the £10-£50 million range. The team has seen an increase in deals involving US investment into Europe. Internet-related floats (particularly AIM listings) have seen the team acting on the financing of start-ups such as Funmail Ltd, e-Marketing and Safeonline. A highlight of the year was the firm's work for Dutch WorldPort on its $600 million disposal to Energis plc. **Clients:** Vitrex plc; Nu-Swift Ltd; Healthworld Corporation; Stanley Leisure plc; Causeway Technologies Inc; Playboy Enterprises; Funmail Ltd; Chiltern Group plc.

BUYOUTS: EQUITY & DEBT

Ashurst Morris Crisp **Equity:** *"The private equity firm of choice,"* benefiting from the momentum of *"a host of excellent players."* Head of Private Equity **Charles Geffen** has won a huge following with his *"commercial constructive advice"* and *"sparkling personality." "Never flustered,"* he is *"the man most wanted"* for the largest private equity deals. Although widely perceived to have a managerial, client relationship role, there can be no doubting **Geoffrey Green**'s position as the firm's *"rainmaker,"* offering a *"huge boost"* to the team's visibility and gravitas. Clients appreciate **Bruce Hanton** for his *"intelligence and organisational skills,"* and **Simon Beddow** is widely respected as a *"get on and do it man."* **Jeremy Sheldon** joins our lists, recommended as a *"capable, trustworthy"* lawyer. Although European offices, in particular Paris and Frankfurt, are adding a credible capability to the London offering, critics fear the team will find it difficult to sell *"the complete package"* without further international refocusing. Currently advising Nabisco on its joint £1.2 billion bid with Hicks Muse for United Biscuits. **Debt:** Clients feel the presence of *"the outstanding"* **Mark Vickers** adds credibility to a debt team that lacks the punch of its equity partners. He has a *"strong hold on the middle market banks,"* and clients trust him to *"run a smooth deal."* **Justin Spendlove** is *"at the forefront"* of the market and is often seen on *"complex"* deals which *"he takes in his stride."* **Clients: Equity:** Advent International; Apax; Candover; Cinven; Legal & General Ventures; PPM Ventures; Berkshire Partners. **Debt:** Deutsche Morgan Grenfell among others.

Clifford Chance **Equity:** *"An excellent client base"* and an *"integrated product offering"* has encouraged this *"great"* team. Cross-border activity and

CORPORATE FINANCE: EQUITY • London	Ptnrs
❶ Ashurst Morris Crisp	7
Clifford Chance	6
❷ Allen & Overy	3
❸ Dickson Minto WS	*
Lovells	6
❹ Macfarlanes	6
Travers Smith Braithwaite	6
❺ CMS Cameron McKenna	6
DLA	⚐
SJ Berwin & Co	4
❻ Freshfields Bruckhaus Deringer	4
Hammond Suddards Edge	3
Nabarro Nathanson	4

LEADING INDIVIDUALS	
✪ GEFFEN Charles Ashurst Morris Crisp	
❶ BAIRD James Clifford Chance	DICKSON Alastair Dickson Minto WS
LAYTON Matthew Clifford Chance	
❷ BARTER Charles Travers Smith Braithwaite	CLARKE Julia Clifford Chance
COMPAGNONI Marco Lovells	GREEN Geoffrey Ashurst Morris Crisp
HALE Chris Travers Smith Braithwaite	HANTON Bruce Ashurst Morris Crisp
PAUL Alan Allen & Overy	TUFFNELL Kevin Macfarlanes
❸ BEDDOW Simon Ashurst Morris Crisp	BOWN Christopher Freshfields Bruckhaus
DAVIS Steven SJ Berwin & Co	MARTIN Charles Macfarlanes
MURRAY-JONES Allan Lovells	SHEACH Andrew CMS Cameron McKenna
SHELDON Jeremy Ashurst Morris Crisp	WAYTE Peter DLA
WHITE Graham SJ Berwin & Co	
UP AND COMING	
BAIRD Derek Dickson Minto WS	HOWARD Susan Allen & Overy
SINGH Daljit Jones, Day, Reavis & Pogue	

CORPORATE FINANCE: DEBT • London	Ptnrs
❶ Allen & Overy	4
Clifford Chance	8
❷ Ashurst Morris Crisp	4
Lovells	3
❸ Denton Wilde Sapte	⚐
Dickson Minto WS	⚐
DLA	*
Norton Rose	3

LEADING INDIVIDUALS	
✪ JOHNSON James Clifford Chance	
❶ GILLESPIE Stephen Allen & Overy	STEWART Mark Clifford Chance
VICKERS Mark Ashurst Morris Crisp	
❷ BARRON Michael Dickson Minto WS	COTTIS Matthew Lovells
GORRIE Euan Allen & Overy	SPENDLOVE Justin Ashurst Morris Crisp
❸ KEAL Anthony Allen & Overy	MORLEY David Allen & Overy
POLGLASE Timothy Norton Rose	POPHAM Stuart Clifford Chance
WARD Anthony Shearman & Sterling	WHALE Philip Norton Rose
❹ CAMPBELL Mark Clifford Chance	
UP AND COMING	
EVANS Jacqueline Allen & Overy	
ONE TO WATCH	
FREEMAN Adam Lovells	

⚐ *Figures unavailable at time of going to press.* *See **Profiles** on page 240*
* *See editorial entries for explanations of team sizes.*

a steady deal flow from Europe has been well served by the firm's recent mergers. Rogers & Wells is perceived to offer closer links with US-based private equity houses (and the high yield market,) with the team increasing the number of transactions for KKR. The *"terrific"* **James Baird** is *"unflappable"* and is praised for developing relations with influential equity houses. **Matthew Layton** is *"energetic and bright"* and **Julia Clarke** is said to have *"the right attitude."* Collectively, clients appreciate the firm as *"excellent deal-doers."* Advised CVC Capital Partners Ltd on the £550 million buy-out of fibres business of Akzo Nobel. **Debt:** With *"strength in depth"* and a heavy deal flow, the debt team is a favourite of clients and peers alike. **James Johnson** is a huge boost for the team; he is *"popular"* and said to add that *"extra vote of confidence"* to a *"firmly established"* team. **Mark Stewart** is *"a larger than life character"* who handles cross-over work well. **Stuart Popham** is said to be slightly removed from transactional work but an important senior figure for clients. *"Personable"* **Mark Campbell** has a strong banking background and offers *"commercial expertise."* The international capabilities have led to transactions such as advising Chase on the buy-outs of the Electrolux Zanussi vending business (€228 million) and CIBC on the Philips passive components business (€430 million.) **Clients: Equity:** CVC Capital Partners; Schroder Ventures; NatWest Private Equity; PPM Vantures; Industri Kapoital; Candover; KKR; Apax. **Debt:** Citigroup; Chase; Bankers Trust/Deutsche Bank; Barclays Capital; Merrill Lynch; CSFB.

Allen & Overy **Equity:** Eclipsed somewhat (and occasionally conflicted) by a strong hold in debt financing, the equity team is pushing forward on the back of a strong international presence. **Alan Paul** is *"excellent"* but is in danger of being *"spread too thinly."* **Susan Howard** has a *"sensible attitude"* towards the deal process and has increased her profile with *"outstanding work"* for Morgan Stanley on its acquisition of the CIBA Speciality Chemicals business. The team has a reputation for complex, cross-border deals, but lacks the depth of the market leaders. Advised KKR on its £627 million buy-out of conglomerate Wassell, the team's first transaction for the US-based private equity house. **Debt:** The *"natural choice"* for clients with a network of leveraged finance specialists across Europe. The team is set to recruit a further high yield specialist from US firm Sullivan & Cromwell and currently benefits from a London-based team of 15 US securities lawyers. **Stephen Gillespie** is *"more inclined to the biggest"* deals, building on his outstanding banking practice. **Euan Gorrie** mixes *"fantastic technical skills"* with low key *"studious"* deal management. **David Morley** acts from the wider acquisition finance group and is perceived to be a figurehead for clients. **Tony Keal** is a major figure, although some find his manner *"abrasive."* New partner **Jacqueline Evans** joins our up and coming lists, praised by clients as *"thorough"* and *"pleasant to work with."* Advised Banque Nationale de Paris on the MBO of Interdean, a transaction covering seven European jurisdictions. **Clients: Equity:** Morgan Grenfell Private Equity; KKR; CVC; Lafarge Platres International SA. **Debt:** Barclays Deutsche Bank; Fuji Bank; Goldman Sachs International; Salomon Smith Barney; JP Morgan; Lehman Brothers; Chase Manhattan.

Dickson Minto WS (Four partners undertake a mix of debt and equity buy-out work.) **Equity:** A small team seen to offer *"high quality solutions."* Though lacking the fire-power of an international network or a strong banking practice, this team is praised for its *"clear focus."* **Alistair Dickson** is envied by peers for inspiring client loyalty and is said to be *"an excellent deal-maker."* **Derek Baird** enters our lists, recommended as *"hardworking"* and *"with a keen grasp of technical issues."* A high point for the team has been advising Cinven on the IBO of AstraZeneca Specialities (£1.3 billion.) **Debt:** A *"safe pair of hands"* for the middle market, this side of the practice has a lower profile, yet is still seen to master complex, domestic transactions. *"Personable"* **Michael Barron** is seen as *"highly skilled"* and clients like his *"easy-going manner."* Advised Royal Bank of Scotland on the IBO of Laporte Hygiene (£35 million) and advised Commerzbank on the MBO of Epwin (£45 million.) **Clients: Equity:** Mercury Private

Equity; Cinven; Apax Partners; Charterhouse Development Capital. **Debt:** Royal Bank of Scotland; Commerzbank West LB Leveraged Finance.

Lovells Equity: The merger with Boesebeck Droste has been met with approval by the market for the stability and concerted effort this presence will bring to its private equity clients based in Germany. **Allan Murray-Jones** is recommended for developing relationships with key clients. The main focus for the equity team remains the *"energetic"* **Marco Compagnoni**, *"sharp, intelligent and quick-witted."* He acted for Doughty Hanson on the cross border MBO of Umbro International (£98 million) and for January Investments Ltd on the MBI of Sears plc (£519 million.) **Debt:** The sad loss of John Penson (head of banking) has been perceived as a blow to the ambitions of the debt team. **Matthew Cottis** is highly respected for his *"easy, user-friendly manner"* but some feel he is personally overstretched, lacking senior figures to share the burden of a growing practice. Acted for Deutsche Bank on the £230 million financing of the acquisition of Pipetronix. **Clients: Equity:** Doughty Hanson & Co Ltd; Mercury Asset Management; 3i Group plc; PPM Ventures; Mercury Private Equity. **Debt:** CSFB; Bank of Scotland; Barclays Bank plc; Crédit Agricole Indosuez.

Macfarlanes Capitalising on strengths in the domestic market but said to be hampered by the lack of a strong debt finance team. This *"quality"* team is starting to build on its international contacts in overseas law firms. **Kevin Tuffnell** brings a *"great presence"* to deals which are *"always extremely well managed."* **Charles Martin** is a *"major asset"* to the private equity team and is widely respected for advising Alchemy Partners on its failed bid for Rover. **Clients:** Cinven Ltd; Candover; Legal & General Ventures; Alchemy Partners.

Travers Smith Braithwaite A leading firm for private equity, it is seen as an *"active"* buy-out team with a sound base of institutional clients such as Candover and NatWest. **Chris Hale** is *"technically sound and practical"* and is seen as the mainstay of the team. **Charles Barter** runs deals with a *"pleasant manner"* and *"inspires confidence."* Although perceived as having a primarily domestic focus, the firm is establishing relationships in key European markets (most successfully in Paris) to undertake cross-border transactions. Highlights of the year include advising the management team on the £220 million MBO of Thomson Directories and acting for Denitz Media Ltd on its £92 million public to private MBI of Adscene group. **Clients:** NatWest Equity Partners; Candover; 3i plc; DLJ Phoenix.

CMS Cameron McKenna A *"sizeable"* and well regarded team with an *"international reach which lacks the penetration of the leaders."* The firm's CMS network is thought not to have provided the transactional depth required. **Andrew Sheach** is *"going from strength to strength"* as he builds up a solid following with the equity houses. He *"controls deals well,"* but is thought to lack support. Highlights for the team include acting for Legal and General Ventures on the £120 million MBO/merger of the Young's/Bluecrest Seafoods Business. **Clients:** NatWest Equity Partners; Advent International; Mercury Asset Management plc; Legal & General Ventures; Lloyds TSB Development Capital Ltd.

DLA (7 partners undertake a mixture of both) **Equity:** *"A fine but limited practice"* which is seen to build on its national base with *"big ticket regional buy-outs as its bread and butter."* **Peter Wayte** maintains his reputation as a leading player in the equity market. The team has acted on substantial deals including for HSBC Private Equity/Newco on the institutional buy-out of Col-Art International Holdings (value £100 million.) **Debt:** Said to lack *"gravitas"* since the departure of Mark Vickers (to Ashursts.) The team is perceived to have a *"comfortable"* position in smaller transactions including mezzanine debt, benefiting from *"a substantial deal flow"* across the offices. Acted for RBS and Dresdner Bank AG as senior debt provider on the MBO of The Bertram Group (value £54 million.) **Clients: Equity:** CVC Capital Partners; HSBC Private Equity; Barclays Ventures; Gresham Trust. **Debt:** Bank of Scotland; Royal Bank of Scotland.

SJ Berwin & Co Acting from the base of a strong investment funds practice, this team is admired for its strong following with major private equity houses. This is a young team, *"improving with each transactional experience."* *"Impressive and proactive"* **Steven Davis** is said to be *"valuable for his strategic knowledge."* **Graham White** is *"an asset"* and a *"user-friendly point man"* for the team. He advised Candover on the £210 million MBO of First Leisure's bar and nightclub operation. **Clients:** Apax Partners; Phildrew Ventures; Atlas Venture; Candover; Barclays Private Equity.

Freshfields Bruckhaus Deringer Perceived to be a relatively new entrant to the equity buy-out market, the team has *"an impressive focus"* but lacks a historically loyal client base. **Christopher Bown** is praised for his handling of major client Cinven and is at the forefront of the *"uphill struggle"* the team is thought to face. With a *"bright, positive attitude"* Bown has focused the team towards larger, international deals. The team advised Cinven on the acquisition of the Dynacast precision engineering business from Coats Viyella. **Clients:** Cinven; Compass Partners European Equity Fund.

Hammond Suddards Edge Seen acting for management groups in the bulk of its transactions, this *"sensible team"* has an active role in a highly competitive market. Lacking a figurehead, the equity team has also lost it's brightest junior to US firm Jones, Day, Reavis & Pogue. Acted for Legal & General Ventures Ltd and Syndicate in the £122 million MBO of Bowater Windows Ltd from Rexam plc. **Clients:** Legal & General Ventures Ltd; Apax Partners and management teams.

Nabarro Nathanson Though the team has a fine reputation for handling smaller buy-outs and acting for the management team, it is said to lack the clout of an institutional following. Seen to have scored a major coup in its relationship with Alchemy Partners, the team is felt to have a *"cost effective, commercial attitude."* Significant transactions include acting for the MBI team on the £262 million recommended offer by Canterbury Healthcare Ltd for Westminster Healthcare plc. **Clients:** Alchemy Partners.

Denton Wilde Sapte Formed from the Wilde Sapte strength in banking, the debt buy-out team is seen to have suffered with the loss of James Johnson and consequently has a much lower profile this year. Although peers perceive the team's core market as mid-tier financial institutions and clearing banks, the *"young, eager"* team has worked on major cross-border transactions such as advising Salomon Smith Barney as lead arranger in the financing of the £1.5 billion pan-European buy-out of BSN. The Denton Hall international network may help with market consolidation in central Europe although the market feels that weak relationships amongst major financial institutions need to be addressed. **Clients:** NatWest Bank plc; Bank of Scotland; CSFB; Salomon Smith Barney; SocGen.

Norton Rose The *"strong, commercial focus"* of the debt team has led to a reputation for appearing on big ticket buy-outs, with particular strengths offered from the firm's international network. However, it is perceived to lack the volume of deals needed to dominate the market. **Philip Whale** is said to be *"a classic deal maker"* and his strong international connections have consolidated the Norton Rose profile. He acted for Chase Manhattan and JP Morgan Securities as underwriter (debt provision of £585 million) to the £1.3 billion acquisition of Zeneca Specialties division from Astra Zeneca. While some find **Timothy Polglase** *"abrasive,"* his profile in the market remains solid, with such deals as advising Chase, Citibank and Bankers Trust on the provision of three separate debt facilities (£630 million aggregate) to finance the £920 million acquisition of Hillsdown Holdings plc. **Clients:** Royal Bank of Scotland; Chase Manhattan Bank; Citibank; JPO Morgan Securities; Chase Capital Partners.

Other Notable Practitioners **Daljit Singh** is featured in our up and coming lists due to his reputation for delivering *"excellence"* and his *"sensible attitude"* towards deal management. He has moved from Hammond Suddards Edge to US firm **Jones Day Reavis & Pogue**. **Anthony Ward** of **Shearman & Sterling** is a *"major figure"* in the debt financing market and is admired for his strong following amongst US investment banks.

THE SOUTH

CORPORATE FINANCE • The South	Ptnrs	Assts
❶ **Blake Lapthorn** Fareham, Portsmouth, Southampton	⚐	⚐
Bond Pearce Southampton	7	11
❷ **Stevens & Bolton** Guildford	5	7
Thomson Snell & Passmore Tunbridge Wells	3	2
❸ **Argles Stoneham Burstows** Crawley	5	8
Cripps Harries Hall Tunbridge Wells	4	7
DMH Brighton, Crawley	4	2
Mundays Esher	5	3
Paris Smith & Randall Southampton	3	4
Rawlison & Butler Crawley	2	2
Shadbolt & Co Reigate	5	2
Shoosmiths Solent	3	4
❹ **Brachers** Maidstone	2	3
Clyde & Co Guildford	3	14
Lester Aldridge Bournemouth	⚐	⚐
Thomas Eggar Church Adams Chichester, Horsham, Reigate, Worthing	6	5

LEADING INDIVIDUALS	
❶ **BAXTER Richard** Stevens & Bolton	**MACPHERSON Moray** Bond Pearce
TROTTER Andrew Shadbolt & Co	
❷ **BUTLER-GALLIE Stuart** Brachers	**CHATFIELD James** Rawlison & Butler
HEWES Simon Bond Pearce	**PARTRIDGE James** Thomson Snell & Passmore
WRIGHT Sean Blake Lapthorn	
❸ **HEATHCOCK Andrew** Paris Smith & Randall	**NORCROSS WEBB Sally** Shoosmiths
❹ **MUNDAY Peter** Mundays	**SADKA Tim** Rawlison & Butler

Within each band, firms are listed alphabetically *See **Profiles** on page 240*

** See editorial entries for explanations of team sizes.*

⚐ Figures unavailable at time of going to press.

Blake Lapthorn *"Still top in Southampton,"* Blake Lapthorn has had a busy year. *"Excellent"* **Sean Wright** and his fellow partners take on the full range of corporate finance work, including MBOs, MBIs, debt restructuring and share acquisitions. Highlights of the year include the sale of DSC communications for Alcatel USA, value £25 million; the sale of Premier Marinas for First Leisure/British Aerospace, value £20 million; the MBO of G Costa and Co Ltd acting on behalf of the management, value £10 million; and acting on behalf of Alcatel in a court approved reduction of capital, value £500 million. Caroline Williams' decision to take a less directly active role as non-executive director and business advisor would not seem to have had too adverse an impact on the performance of the team. **Clients:** Alcatel USA; First Leisure/British Aerospace.

Bond Pearce *"Market leaders because they're the biggest,"* Bond Pearce *"have really got motoring this year."* Previously £2-£10 million deal specialists, that figure has moved over £20 million this year. **Moray Macpherson** *("very good, very well known in Southampton")* is just one of a number of partners and assistants with blue-chip corporate backgrounds. Highlights of the year include providing commercial and corporate support for all three divisions of Arjo Wiggins, continuing to advise Solay Healthcare Ltd, and the completion of four logistics agreements handling billions of pounds of goods for Safeway plc. The respected **Simon Hewes** will be taking up a full-time position at the Bristol office later this year. **Clients:** Arjo Wiggins; Chemring Group plc; Solvay Healthcare Ltd; Safeway plc.

Stevens & Bolton *"Pre-eminent in Guildford"* and *"a very good niche firm," "if they're involved in any transaction, I relax." "Quietly confident"* **Richard Baxter** *("excellent technical lawyer")* is generally recognised to provide *"a high quality personal service with a strong financial understanding to complement his corporate legal experience."* Highlights of the year include acting for Hays Distribution Service Ltd on the purchase of EPS Ltd for up to £55 million, acting for the selling shareholders on the £34 million sale of Puntis Consulting plc to Skills Group plc, and advising Gladedale Holdings plc on its recommended offer for Furlong Homes Group plc. **Clients:** Hays plc; Ener-G plc; BOC Distribution Services Ltd.

Thomson Snell & Passmore *"We've used them in a number of cases against City firms and, frankly, I think we get a better service for a better price."* **James Partridge** *("switched on")* heads a team that specialises in out-sourcing, externalisation and venture capital transactions. Highlights of the year include instructions on the acquisition of an AIM quoted company for £15 million, and instructions on a purchase of assets deal for £7 million. Otherwise, the team has handled an increased volume of conventional corporate finance transactions up to £5 million. **Clients:** Local corporates.

Argles Stoneham Burstows Now one of the largest corporate and commercial teams in the South East outside London, *"they provide a very high quality of service and go out of their way to look after the client, but still have a lot of internal issues to sort out."* One partner was singled out as possessing *"a good commercial brain"* and being *"well-connected in this area with a fantastic network of contacts and clients."* The merger has generally been considered *"a good idea, giving them a strong critical mass." "They'll be quite powerful,"* one commentator said. Over the last year, the team has acted on over 35 transactions with deal values mainly in the £1 million to £5 million range. **Clients:** AirMiles Travel Promotions Ltd; Prismo Ltd; First Choice Holidays plc.

Cripps Harries Hall Experts in the technology market, fund management, the health care sector and project finance, they're generally recognised to *"clean up the Kent area." "One of the largest practices in the SE outside London," "they always do a competent job."* Highlights of the year include acting for Fairfield Imaging Ltd on its reverse acquisition by Medical Solutions plc, and the acquisition of a software company involving a corporate reconstruction, acquisition finance from a bank, and an equity investment from a venture capital house. **Clients:** Dencare Management Group plc; Hidden Hearing Ltd; Fairfield Imaging Ltd.

DMH *"A quality firm"* who provide *"professional, efficient advice and support,"* DMH are generally considered to *"have had a quieter year."* Some have gone further and suggested that though *"they have the critical mass to attract good work, they have lost their way a bit."* Speculation is rife as to how the department will perform after Derek Sparrow's retirement at the end of June. Nevertheless, some big deals have been done, and repeat work is recognised in the publishing, hi-tech, IT and pharmaceutical sectors. Highlights of the year include involvement in the MBI of Paragon Publishing Ltd, and instructions on the Cyborg Systems Ltd deal, value c.£12 million. **Clients:** IBL Lighting Ltd; Bank of Scotland plc; Paragon Publishing.

Mundays *"Very strong commercially, not so much corporate, but they're starting to strengthen that area."* **Peter Munday** *("highly professional, friendly, efficient, meets the needs of the client and gets the job done")* and his team are generally considered to be *"quite aggressive and winning quite a bit of work."* Recently advised Alliance Unichem plc and its retail subsidiary E Moss Ltd on the acquisition of SpiralProfile Ltd. Advised the vending shareholder of Genesis Recruitment Ltd in the sale to Aerotek Europe Ltd. Advised the vending shareholder of B & Z Software Technology Ltd, the holding company of RCS Construction Software Ltd in the sale to Mitek Industries Ltd. **Clients:** Alliance Unichem plc; E Moss Ltd; Genesis Recruitment Ltd.

Paris Smith & Randall *"A true local firm"* that provides *"an excellent service,"* although some felt that it was *"treading water"* this year. **Andrew Heathcock** is generally considered to provide sound advice on a range of substantial deals. Highlights of the year include the acquisition of Portsmouth FC from the administrators, and development funding for Southampton FC's new stadium at St Mary's, involving the sale of the Dell and new facilities from construction financiers, 'takeout' funders and a clearing bank aggregating approximately £40 million. **Clients:** Southampton Leisure Holdings plc; Portsmouth City Football Club Ltd.

Rawlison & Butler *"A good niche firm,"* but the departure of the senior partner and a number of others is considered to have damaged the practice. Nevertheless, **James Chatfield** and **Tim Sadka** have held things together, and continue to develop connections with the venture capital market. Highlights of the year include representing the MBO team on the acquisition of the TBC Group, and representing the shareholders in the disposal of Egerton Hospital Equipment Ltd to Getinge Industrier AB of Sweden. **Clients:** Suzuki GB plc; Alan Group Ltd; James Longley and Co Ltd.

Shadbolt & Co *"First-rate," "friendly," "a lively and successful firm,"* Shadbolts has enjoyed a profitable year. **Andrew Trotter** *("a fantastic resource, incredibly efficient and learned, somebody we've grown to rely on")* heads a team with particular experience in the construction and engineering industries and in hi-tech and IT companies. Highlights of the year include handling the acquisition by the German based Heidenhain Group from Bullough plc of its subsidiary, SEM Ltd, for a consideration of £8 million. Also acted for a US based client in its proposed take-over of a quoted plc for in excess of £200 million. **Clients:** Schoolsnet Ltd; Watson Wyatt Systems Ltd.

Shoosmiths *"Sniping round the edges, but haven't progressed much in the last year."* Still, **Sally Norcross Webb** *("a pretty effective lawyer") "gets about"* and has been involved in a number of big deals this year, including the £23 million purchase of the pharmaceutical division of GEA International plc by GEA Group, the disposal of the Deacon Insurance Group to Hercules Property Services plc for £14.25 million, and the acquisition of the business of J Hollingsworth by Birchwood Garages Ltd. **Clients:** H J Heinz Ltd; Birchwood Garages Ltd; GEA Group.

Brachers **Stuart Butler-Gallie** *("a deal maker rather than a deal breaker and one of the best corporate finance lawyers in the region")* heads *"a quality firm"* whose work load has been substantial this year. The corporate finance team has been involved in 11 transactions above £2 million, including 2 above £10 million. The range of work has included 4 MBOs, 7 company sales, acquisitions and disposals, a Lloyds Umbrella Agreement and a £3.5 million placing of shares for Charlton Athletic plc. **Clients:** Charlton Athletic plc; Alloy Wheels International.

Clyde & Co A new entry this year, Clyde and Co *"has been investing in its people, and they are good people."* Considered by some to be *"good, but resourced out of London,"* it has nevertheless been involved in a number of substantial transactions, including acting for Wren plc in its £250 million merger with BRIT Insurance Holdings plc. Also acted on the £30 million MBO on behalf of the management of Euclidian plc taking the company private from the London Stock Exchange. **Clients:** BRIT Insurance Holdings plc; Microgen plc; WS Atkins plc.

Lester Aldridge Looking to expand and, according to some, vigorously head-hunting, this *"very professional"* outfit has had a busy year. Highlights include acting for the Federal Republic of Yugoslavia in negotiations resulting in the Federal Air Traffic Control Authority concluding a contract for the provision of air traffic services for part of the airspace over Bosnia and Herzegovina. **Clients:** Bath Travel; Anders Elite Ltd; Cobham plc; UK Waste Ltd.

Thomas Eggar Church Adams *"An excellent firm"* with *"a reputation more on the private client side,"* it has undertaken a number of important transactions and acquired Wyndeham Press Group plc as a client this year. Highlights include acting for W F Electrical plc on the purchase of two electrical wholesaling companies from a subsidiary of James Crean plc, and acting for Wyndeham Press Group plc on their purchase of C/S/M Impact Limited, a Class 2 transaction where the consideration was in the region of £7 million. **Clients:** W F Electrical plc; Wyndeham Press Group plc; LINK Interchange Network Ltd.

THAMES VALLEY

CORPORATE FINANCE • Thames Valley	Ptnrs	Assts
❶ **Osborne Clarke OWA** Reading	4	9
❷ **Clarks** Reading	4	6
Manches Oxford	4	4
❸ **Kimbell & Co** Milton Keynes	2	2
Nabarro Nathanson Reading	3	5
Pitmans Reading	3	6
❹ **Garretts** Reading	2	8
Morgan Cole Oxford, Reading	2	3
❺ **B P Collins** Gerrards Cross	3	4

LEADING INDIVIDUALS	
❶ **ANGEL Peter** Manches	**GOWANS Andrew** Osborne Clarke OWA
LEE Richard Clarks	**PILLMAN Joe** Brobeck Hale and Dorr
❷ **HUTCHINSON John** Pitmans	**SMERDON Richard** Osborne Clarke OWA
❸ **DREW Dean** Shoosmiths	**JONES Hugh** Osborne Clarke OWA
KIMBELL Stephen Kimbell & Co	**LOAKE Jonathan** Brobeck Hale and Dorr
TAYLOR Glyn Nabarro Nathanson	**WATSON Andrew** Garretts

Within each band, firms are listed alphabetically. *See **Profiles** on page 240*

Figures unavailable at time of going to press.

Osborne Clarke OWA *"A good firm with quality people,"* and generally recognised to be *"the benchmark for other firms,"* Osborne Clarke *"has made quite a big impact"* on Reading and *"is seen to be there, or just about there, in everything which comes up. They're successful, have committed resources to Reading, spent a lot on promoting themselves and been very focused."* The team is headed by *"leading light"* **Andrew Gowans** *("great reputation, good technical skills and very good with clients,")* and has been strengthened by the arrival of **Hugh Jones** *("down to earth, practical and pragmatic.")* **Richard Smerdon** *("the grand old man,")* also maintains his transactional involvement. Highlights of the year include acting for the management in connection with Racal Electronic plc's disposal of its telecoms division to Global Crossing Inc. for approximately £1.2 billion, and the institutional buy-out of the technology driven logistics division of NFC for £29 million. **Clients:** 3i plc; Hurst Publishing plc; Bank of Scotland; Lloyds TSB Development Capital.

Clarks *"A highly professional, very personable" "old-fashioned"* practice, they *"have retained their pre-eminent position,"* largely due to the performance of *"excellent"* **Richard Lee**. Highlights of the year include the sale of Eurostar Network Systems to Diagonal plc, and the £4.3 million refinancing including debt conversion and placing of Shalibane plc. Members of TAGLaw. **Clients:** BMW Financial Services Group; Bunzl plc; Shalibane plc.

Manches *"They're human beings, have both breadth and depth and are of a London standard."* **Peter Angel** *("a charismatic figure")* heads a department with a particular leaning towards the biotech and IT sectors. Since 1990, the firm has acted on the formation or financing of half the technology 'spin-out' companies from the University of Oxford. Highlights of the year include acting for all the shareholders of M&J on the sale of the company to Brake Brothers in a £48 million transaction, and acting for Mayflower on its disposal of its Douglas, Schopf and Dennis Eagle divisions to a new company backed by NatWest Equity Partners. The price was £31 million. **Clients:** Mayflower Group plc; Xenova Group plc; Blackwells.

Kimbell & Co *"Do a very niche form of corporate finance; it's quality work."* Though occasionally appearing *"a bit stretched,"* it is generally considered *"a decent firm"* that *"takes a very sensible approach."* **Stephen Kimbell** is the stand-out player here and, together with one other partner, has seen through a number of important deals this year. These included successfully taking Ushers of Trowbridge and Denby Group public to private in £120 million and £30 million deals respectively. **Clients:** Dawson Group plc; Ushers of Trowbridge plc; Textron Inc.

Nabarro Nathanson Generally considered to have *"geared up this year,"* they *"have a good IT practice, and, therefore, the base for a good corporate practice."* Though a number of commentators suggested that they had *"lost a bit of direction at senior level,"* **Glyn Taylor** was generally recognised to be *"a tough lawyer,"* who *"does some serious work in this area"* and is *"very prominent in AIM listings."* The team focuses primarily on clients in the IT, new media and communications sector. Highlights of the year include acting for NatWest Equity Partners on the Investor Buy-Out of Stewart Plastics Ltd, and acting for Silver Shield Group plc on the Class 1 disposal of its windscreen business to Kwik Fit for a consideration of £8 million. **Clients:** NatWest Equity Partners; Silver Shield Group plc; The European Investment Bank.

Pitmans An *"aggressive"* firm who *"have recognised where there's a niche in the market,"* and *"seem to know where to go as a firm."* Critics have suggested that the department is too dependent on **John Hutchinson** *("an effective negotiator,")* and that it *"doesn't have the strength in depth to do really substantial work."* It has nevertheless managed to complete a number of substantial transactions including advising the vendors of Checkpoint Security Services on its sale to an MBO team backed by Mercury Asset Management for £17.5 million, and advising on the reverse takeover of Microcache in their acquisition by Gladstone plc. **Clients:** Avis; Coca-Cola; Bank of Scotland; Caradon plc; Imagecom; Biocompatibles plc.

Garretts *"There, but not understood,"* Garretts are *"always in a special position being part of Andersens."* The arrival of **Andrew Watson** *("a good operator and a bloody good lawyer")* is generally considered to have filled the gap created by the loss of Adrian Phillips. Significant deals of the last year include acting for NYSE listed United Healthcare Inc on its acquisition of Medical Monitoring and Research Ltd and Clinpharm Ltd, and acting for Greatminster's subsidiary Tenet Ltd on its acquisition of IFA Network Interdependence Group Ltd. **Clients:** United Healthcare Inc; Greatminster Group Ltd; Cardionetics.

Morgan Cole A number of high level defections has left the department severely disabled. First, there was the loss of Hugh Jones to Osborne Clarke then, more recently, the departure of Joe Pillman and Jonathan Loake to form the Oxford arm of Brobeck Hale and Dorr. The new head of corporate is *"a good lawyer, but his plate's overloaded,"* and Morgan Cole has been forced to fall back on the expedient of drawing partners out of South Wales. Nevertheless, the fact that Morgan Cole has such an expedient open to it is a sign of the firm's extensive depth. Major transactions of the year include acting for BP Amoco in connection with a five and a half year $650 million deal with MCI WorldCom, and acting on an IT outsourcing for a major business in the motor industry involving pan-European aspects worth around £200 million. **Clients:** Bank of Scotland plc; Blackwell Ltd; Lloyds Bank plc; Oxford University.

B P Collins *"A smaller outfit, but a decent firm,"* working mainly on small-ticket transactions. Has acted extensively for Mobile Storage (UK) Limited over the last year, including carrying out five acquisitions for them. **Clients:** Mobile Storage (UK) Limited; United Biscuit Holdings Ltd; Data Connection Ltd.

Other Notable Practitioners *"Brilliant"* **Joe Pillman** and **Jonathan Loake**, *"a sound commercial lawyer,"* have left Morgan Cole to form the Oxford arm of US firm Brobeck Hale and Dorr. *"Sensible"* **Dean Drew** (Shoosmiths) is a new addition to our table. He has been widely acknowledged as a player in the field.

SOUTH WEST

Osborne Clarke OWA *"Have pulled ahead of Burges Salmon,"* and are now generally considered to be *"the leading firm in Bristol."* They are *"extremely well focused and particularly successful at developing relationships with IT companies."* The fundamental question is whether Osborne Clarke is now a regional firm with a London office, or a London firm with regional offices. Commentators have already noted that *"there's not enough work for them in Bristol,"* and that *"they're slowly moving the balance of their work to their London office."* What is certain is that they possess some of the best corporate finance lawyers in the region. *"Brilliant"* **Simon Beswick** is *"pre-eminent by a country mile;"* **Paul Cooper** is *"very commercial;" "very sensible"* **Bruce Roxburgh** has *"the right approach;"* **Patrick Graves** is *"a genius; horribly bright;" "very practical"* **Clive Watts** *"suits the older client;"* and **Alisdair Livingstone**, new to our table, is generally regarded to be *"very sound."* Highlights of the year include advising on the sale of Newcourt Automotive Services Limited for £100 million, and advising on the merger of MSF with AF plc to form Countrywide Farmers Holdings plc for £58 million. **Clients:** 3i Group plc; Dalgety Group Ltd; Jacobs Holdings plc; NatWest Equity Partners.

Burges Salmon *"Along with Osborne Clarke, they are head and shoulders above the rest."* More locally focused than their great rivals, the firm has a particularly strong transport client base. *"Very able"* **Alan Barr**, *"excellent"* **Christopher Godfrey**, **Roger Hawes** *("technically very good",)* **David Marsh**, who now spends more time on his managerial duties, and **Richard Spink** *("a good guy, sensible")* make up an excellent team. Typical work handled over the last year includes acting for Newco in its $60 million cross border buyout of US and UK operations of Spear Group, and acting for Bridport plc on its take-over by West Washington in a £30 million public to private transaction. Recently acted for Orange on its acquisition of Ananova for £95 million. **Clients:** Bristol City Holdings plc; Science Systems plc; North Western Trains.

Bevan Ashford Top-tier in Exeter and generally well thought of. **Simon Rous'** *"service is absolutely excellent – when you can get hold of him."* The Bristol office is *"less seen in corporate,"* doing *"mostly PFI work,"* though one commentator noted that it had *"taken on an awful lot of people"* recently. Exeter office highlights include handling the sale of shares to McBride plc by recommended general cash offer for £21.6 million. Bristol office highlights include advising Invicta Leisure Limited on the sale of a group of their companies for over £12 million. **Clients:** Wrafton Laboratories Ltd; MILS Technology plc; Invicta Leisure Ltd.

Bond Pearce Offers *"a broad range of specialists"* who provide *"sound legal advice."* Traditionally *"strong in Plymouth and Exeter,"* there's some speculation that *"the focus of their practice is shifting to Southampton and Bristol."* Given that they have recently doubled their office space in Bristol, it would certainly appear that the Bristol office will be taking an increasingly active role in future. Simon Hewes (Southampton) will be heading up the corporate finance team in Bristol later on this year, while, down in

CORPORATE FINANCE • South West	Ptnrs	Assts
❶ **Osborne Clarke OWA** Bristol	11	32
❷ **Burges Salmon** Bristol	12	26
❸ **Bevan Ashford** Bristol, Exeter	9	15
Bond Pearce Exeter, Plymouth	8	6
TLT Solicitors Bristol	3	12
❹ **Foot Anstey Sargent** Exeter, Plymouth	3	6
❺ **Cartwrights** Bristol	1	3
Charles Russell Cheltenham	3	1
Clark Holt Swindon	2	-
CMS Cameron McKenna Bristol	2	3
Laytons Bristol	2	7
Michelmores Exeter	4	3
Stephens & Scown Exeter, St Austell, Truro	5	2
Veale Wasbrough Bristol	3	5
❻ **Bretherton Price Elgoods** Cheltenham	3	3
Lyons Davidson Bristol	2	4

LEADING INDIVIDUALS	
✪ **BESWICK Simon** Osborne Clarke OWA	
❶ **BARR Alan** Burges Salmon	**COOPER Paul** Osborne Clarke OWA
GODFREY Christopher Burges Salmon	
❷ **PESTER David** TLT Solicitors	**ROUS Simon** Bevan Ashford
ROXBURGH Bruce Osborne Clarke OWA	
❸ **ACOCK Roger** Bond Pearce	**COOMBS Richard** Foot Anstey Sargent
GRAVES Patrick Osborne Clarke OWA	**HAWES Roger** Burges Salmon
LEWIS Mark Foot Anstey Sargent	**MITCHELL Christopher** Cartwrights
❹ **BELLEW Derek** Veale Wasbrough	**JONES Michael** CMS Cameron McKenna
KELIHER James Stephens & Scown	**MARSH David** Burges Salmon
MORSE Stephen Michelmores	**RUNDALL Francis** Charles Russell
WATTS Clive Osborne Clarke OWA	
UP AND COMING	
LIVINGSTONE Alisdair Osborne Clarke OWA	**SPINK Richard** Burges Salmon

Within each band, firms are listed alphabetically. *See **Profiles** on page 240*

Devon, *"there's only one name you ever hear;"* that of **Roger Acock**. Highlights of the year include advising Roach Foods on its £150 million merger with Dalehead Foods to form Flagship Foods. **Clients:** Roach Foods; SITA Holdings UK Ltd; Headworx Ltd; Darlington Crystal Ltd.

TLT Solicitors *"I'd put TLT third, subject to how the merger goes."* Generally considered to be *"doing quite well,"* they're *"a little bit different, very client focused, quite creative, with a hungry, good team."* Rivals suggest that the two merged firms are not *"natural soul mates"* but most of the market seems content to wait and see. Boasts a key player in *"impressive"* **David Pester** who is *"commercial by style and nature."* Recent big deals include handling the admission of Robotic Technology plc to AIM with a market capitalisation of £120 million, and handling the admission of Advanced Technology (UK) plc to AIM with a market capitalisation of £50 million. **Clients:** Avon Rubber plc; Peel Hunt plc; Alfred McAlpine Construction Ltd.

Foot Anstey Sargent Most commentators considered the merger between Anstey Sargent & Probert and Foot & Bowden *"a good, sensible move"* that had created a *"more dynamic, younger partnership"* and generally made them *"more formidable."* **Richard Coombs** and **Mark Lewis** are both well respected members of the field. Possesses a niche strength in e-commerce and IT. Highlights of the year include handling the MBOs of Mountfield-Westwood, CQL and Quasar. **Clients:** Northcliffe Newpapers Group Ltd; Bank of Scotland; Mountfield-Westwood.

Cartwrights *"Absolutely first-rate professionals, a pleasure to deal with and competent in all matters."* A respected niche firm, whose only drawback is that *"they never seem to acquire any critical mass."* **Christopher Mitchell** *"knows what he's doing,"* but *"does he have the resources to back him up?"* Specialisations in the food and drink retailing sector and the transport sector, as one might expect from a firm which has made its reputation in licensing and transport. Highlights of the year include the purchase of a local software house for Graphisoft NV. **Clients:** Inter Company Management LLC; Copperweld Inc.

Charles Russell *"Totally professional and innovative,"* they're *"doers,"* they *"don't watch the clock"* and *"their costs are very reasonable."* **Francis Rundall** *"knows his onions."* Another partner was described as *"an extrovert, superbly professional"* and *"particularly competent on public company work."* Highlights of the year include acting for Howle Holdings plc in their hostile takeover bid for Brooke Industrial Holdings plc, and acting for Trifast plc on the acquisition of a Swedish engineering company for a consideration of over SEK 35 million. **Clients:** YJL; Eagle Star; Howle Holdings.

Clark Holt *"Have cleaned up in Swindon." "They get good write-ups," "go down quite well,"* and have *"quite a history of success in the technology market."* Tend to act for vendors disposing of their company/business, or for management in buyouts. Highlights of the year include acting on the disposal of Kaisha Holdings Ltd, and acting for Equiinet Ltd in raising £5 million from Schroder Venture. **Clients:** AIT Group plc; Equiinet Ltd; Advance Visual Communications plc.

CMS Cameron McKenna A boutique office offering *"Bristol-based City expertise,"* commentators generally consider that *"it's going very well for them."* **Michael Jones**, *"a fine client lawyer,"* heads a small team that, in addition to servicing the needs of Lloyds, tends to specialise in £10 million plus deals. Highlights of the year include acting for W H Brakspear and Sons plc in its joint venture with Brew Securities plc to form Honeypot Inns plc, and acting for Primetime Petfoods Ltd in its acquisition of the trading subsidiaries of Pascoe's Group plc. **Clients:** Appeal Conservatory Blinds Ltd; Primetime Petfoods Ltd.

Laytons *"Very good; have highly regarded individuals and institutions use them for buyouts and corporate work."* Involved in a large number of transactions for Somerfield Stores, various acquisitions and commercial transactions for E H Bennett, and the MBO of Mike Walker Distribution. **Clients:** Somerfield Stores; Zuken-Redac Group; David S Smith Group.

Michelmores *"Have good local clients whom they service well. In Devon, they're major market competitors." "Very much an Exeter firm,"* they *"have increased enormously and had quite a big impact on the region this year."* A number of partners were singled out for praise, of whom *"up and coming"* **Stephen Morse** was most frequently mentioned. The firm is a founding member of Karatkrunch.com, a business network created to promote awareness and understanding of information technology and the internet. Highlights of the year include acting on the acquisition of Derlite Ltd, and acting on the acquisition of Group SMB Ltd, involving a £9 million refranchising. **Clients:** Razorfish Ltd; Helston Garages Ltd; Christows Ltd.

Stephens & Scown *"Have good individuals,"* **James Keliher** being particularly well thought of. Highlights of the year include acting on the sale of a medical consumable business in the UK and Belgium, and handling an equity/loan finance package for a meat production company. **Clients:** Local corporates.

Veale Wasbrough *"Picking up."* Lost a couple of major players last year, but their replacements are deemed to be *"very good." "Sensible, but not earth-shattering,"* seems to be the general market opinion, one commentator noting that *"they're good, but they've no star players."* Nevertheless, **Derek Bellew** is *"a thoroughly decent, honourable and sensible person,"* and, accordingly, earns a place in our table of leading individuals. Highlights of the year include completing a £180 million PFI project to establish Fire Fighters Training Units in England and Scotland, and advising WMF Ltd on a major group merger to form Country Wide Farmers plc. Co-founders of the Association of European Lawyers. **Clients:** Fire Service College; Ministry of Defence; Great Mills.

Bretherton Price Elgoods *"Entrepreneurial,"* they *"go the extra mile,"* but are not yet widely recognised outside Cheltenham. Niche strengths include hi-tech – recently involved in sale of Swan Software Group Ltd to Infor A.G. at a price of £7.5 million plus earn out. AIM work is also covered, including sales of AIM listed companies. The team was recently involved in the sale of Jardinerie International Group plc (an AIM listed company) to PHS Ltd by way of open offer, price £6.3 million. **Clients:** Aram Resources plc; Mears Group plc; John Charlton.

Lyons Davidson *"Suffering from defections"* a bit this year but still *"a great firm,"* it's *"always in the background"* and possesses *"a strong client base."* The company/commercial team advises on a broad range of issues, including company sales and acquisitions, management buy-outs, partnerships, flotations, EC law, intellectual property, banking and securities, receiverships and liquidations. **Clients:** Local corporates.

WALES

CORPORATE FINANCE • Wales	Ptnrs	Assts
❶ Morgan Cole Cardiff	3	8
❷ Edwards Geldard Cardiff	4	4
❸ Eversheds Cardiff	3	3
❹ Berry Smith Cardiff	1	3
Bevan Ashford Cardiff	1	2
M and A Solicitors Cardiff	2	2
❺ Hugh James Ford Simey Cardiff	2	3

LEADING INDIVIDUALS	
❶ MACINTOSH Duncan Morgan Cole	
❷ MORRIS Andrew Edwards Geldard	PEARSON Jeffrey Edwards Geldard
❸ BERRY Stephen M and A Solicitors	BOUND Andrew Berry Smith
CHERRY Robert Morgan Cole	LOWE Paul Eversheds
UP AND COMING	
THOMAS Michelle Eversheds	

Within each band, firms are listed alphabetically. See **Profiles** on page 240

Morgan Cole Still market leaders, but under pressure, the Thames Valley implosion has forced them to *"divert resources from their Cardiff office to Reading."* Smaller firms note that they're *"becoming more of a national practice,"* hence *"leaving gaps in the local market."* Many attribute their pre-eminent position to *"heavyweight"* **Duncan Macintosh** who's *"very prominent and very good at getting the work in."* **Robert Cherry** at the Swansea office is also a recognised name. Highlights of the year include issuing a recommended offer worth £6.36 million on behalf of PHS Group Ltd to acquire all the shares and options of Jardinerie Interiors Group plc, and being retained by British Energy Retail Markets Ltd to purchase Swalec from Hyder. **Clients:** British Energy Retail Markets Ltd; Vivitar (Europe) Ltd.

Edwards Geldard Offers *"a broad spread of expertise."* **Andrew Morris** *("a good mind, very sensible, very practical,")* and **Jeffrey Pearson** *("commercial but careful with the details")* are recognised to be two of the best corporate finance lawyers in Wales. Highlights of the year include acting for Hicking Pentecost plc on the Coats Viyella plc takeover, and acting for Windward Capital Partners, a US $1 billion private equity fund, on its acquisition of Aracomp Ltd's business. **Clients:** Hyder plc; S4C; Pendragon plc.

Eversheds *"Still rebuilding"* after a number of defections over the last couple of years, Eversheds *"needs to do big work to survive; that's how they're structured." "Brought over from banking to head the department,"* **Paul Lowe** is still finding his feet. He *"adopts a very commercial yet human approach to legal matters."* The department has been further strengthened by the arrival of **Michelle Thomas**, *"a thorough and capable lawyer."* Significant transactions of the last year include acting for Solectron (Nasdaq quoted) on the acquisition of various assets from Nortel, and acting for IQE plc on its flotation on the European Stock Exchange, Easdaq, at a market capitalisation of £120 million. **Clients:** IQE plc; The Peacock Group plc; The Travel House.

Berry Smith *"An excellent firm"* and generally perceived to be *"developing their profile quite well,"* but, like most of the smaller corporate finance teams, *"lacking in strength in depth."* **Andrew Bound** *("really top-notch, exceptionally bright, has an astute business sense and attentive to client needs")* is *"an excellent lawyer." "If you want something done in a hurry, he's your man."* Most deals are around the £2 million mark. Highlights of the year include acting on the sale of an internet security magazine to Haymarket Publications, and acting on the sale of Celtic Plant Ltd to a US quoted company. **Clients:** Bayswater Tubes and Sections; CBL Ceramics Ltd.

Bevan Ashford A *"solid, meticulous, careful"* department that *"balances well with the necessary fast-moving attitudes of venture capitalists,"* Bevan Ashford does not possess the strongest team in the field, but is constantly a presence by virtue of the resources it can call on. Significant transactions of the year include an ongoing involvement in substantial equity investments by Celtic House Investment Partners Ltd. **Clients:** Celtic House Investment Partners Ltd; Newbridge Networks Corporation.

M and A Solicitors *"Probably the most talented bunch in Cardiff, but not available for mainstream work"* due to their association with the corporate finance house Gambit, M and A is a newly opened corporate finance boutique comprised of ex-Eversheds lawyers. **Stephen Berry** *("pretty young but fairly sound")* has been involved in a number of substantial deals over the last year, including acting for the management of ESM Ltd on its £100 million buyout and financing, and acting for a local brewery, Tomos Watkin, in a corporate reorganisation and £10 million fund raising exercise. **Clients:** ESM Ltd; Tomos Watkin.

Hugh James Ford Simey A *"strong regional practice" "specialising in private clients"* with *"a residual corporate finance team,"* Hugh James is *"not in the mainstream,"* but possesses a *"sensible"* head of department. Claiming a niche strength in e-business, it has been involved in a number of company disposals and sales, and in raising $5 million by way of a private placement this year. **Clients:** WEB 2U Ltd; Welsh Rugby Union Ltd.

MIDLANDS

CORPORATE FINANCE • Midlands	Ptnrs	Assts
❶ **Wragge & Co** Birmingham	19	50
❷ **Eversheds** Birmingham, Nottingham, Derby	16	46
Pinsent Curtis Birmingham	10	17
❸ **DLA** Birmingham	9	20
❹ **Browne Jacobson** Nottingham	9	24
Gateley Wareing Birmingham	4	12
Hammond Suddards Edge Birmingham	5	19
Martineau Johnson Birmingham	7	14
❺ **Eking Manning** Nottingham	2	2
Freethcartwright Nottingham	6	6
Lee Crowder Birmingham	5	9
Shoosmiths Northampton, Nottingham, Rugby	6	12
❻ **Edwards Geldard** Nottingham	3	8
Garretts Birmingham	4	17
George Green & Co Warley	3	1
Harvey Ingram Owston Leicester	5	5
Hewitson Becke + Shaw Northampton	2	4
Howes Percival Northampton	7	7
Kent Jones and Done Stoke-on-Trent	2	4
Knight & Sons Newcastle-under-Lyme	3	2

LEADING INDIVIDUALS	
❶ **DWYER Maurice** Wragge & Co	**LEWIS Susan** Eversheds
METCALFE Ian Wragge & Co	**MILLINGTON Jeremy** Wragge & Co
PSYLLIDES Milton Eversheds	
❷ **EASTGATE Andrew** Pinsent Curtis	**GREEN Guy** Eversheds
GRONOW Simon Pinsent Curtis	**HAYWARD Paul** Gateley Wareing
HAYWOOD Richard Wragge & Co	**HUGHES David** Pinsent Curtis
HULL David Hammond Suddards Edge	
McHUGH Peter Eversheds	**METCALFE Robin** Browne Jacobson
RAWSTRON Chris DLA	**SEABROOK Michael** Eversheds
WILD David Eversheds	
❸ **BRAITHWAITE Stephen** Wragge & Co	**CHOHAN Baljit** Hammond Suddards Edge
CRABTREE John Wragge & Co	**GARNETT Chris** Eversheds
KITTS Stephen Eversheds	**MOORE Austin** Eking Manning
STILTON Andrew Martineau Johnson	**WARD Michael** Gateley Wareing
❹ **ALLEN Amanda** Pinsent Curtis	**BIRCHALL Roger** Hammond Suddards Edge
CUMMINGS Gavin Browne Jacobson	**JANSEN Karl** Freethcartwright
LAVERY James Pinsent Curtis	
UP AND COMING	
BLACKWELL Nigel Browne Jacobson	**DAWES Edward** Wragge & Co
JOHNSON Ben Eversheds	**LAWTON SMITH Andrew** Wragge & Co

Within each band, firms are listed alphabetically See **Profiles** on page 240

Wragge & Co This firm retains its premier rating as the *"number one firm"* for corporate finance work in the Midlands. The firm is the largest single site corporate practice outside London, and has a strategy of being a 'City' firm based in Birmingham. There are four limbs to the firm's transactional practice. The first is acting for major national and international corporations on M&A's. The second is acting for plc's with significant Midlands presence. The third is acting for IT/telecom businesses, and the fourth is acting in the private equity arena for both investor and investee clients. Overall the firm is seen to be *"very commercial"* and *"willing to get the job done."* The one-office approach seems to be *"paying handsome dividends for them"* at present, although there has been comment in the market that eventually the firm will need to expand into other regions in order to better service its ever-growing client base, which is situated all around the country and increasingly on the Continent.

The *"excellent"* **Maurice Dwyer** is *"able to focus on the key issues rather than trivial details"* and is rated particularly highly for his private equity work, while the *"top notch"* **Ian Metcalfe** is *"seen about in the market place regularly."* **Jeremy Millington** is *"very laid-back but very good,"* while **Richard Haywood** is *"solid as a rock."* **Stephen Braithwaite** and **John Crabtree** *"always acquit themselves well."* **Ed Dawes** has recently arrived from Kent Jones and Done, and is *"able to handle himself,"* while **Andrew Lawton Smith** remains *"an up and coming prospect."* The team recently advised on a £500 million outsourcing project by British Airways and also acted for Preussag AG in its £700 million plus joint venture with West LB and Carlson Inc to form the Thomas Cook Group. **Clients:** AT&T; HJ Heinz Europe; NatWest Equity Partners.

Eversheds As with Wragge & Co, the sheer depth of this corporate finance team and the consistently high quality of its work are seen to be the firm's greatest strengths in both Birmingham and Nottingham, along with its *"blue chip client base."* The firm has niche strengths in IT/internet/e-commerce hi-tech businesses and transport companies, as well as a growing international client base. There was market comment that the departure of the respected Mark Spinner to become an in-house counsel at a dot.com company was a *"blow"* for the firm. However, the recent arrival of the *"cast-iron"* **Guy Green** from George Green & Co should have compensated for *"any resulting shortfall."* Overall, **Milton Psyllides** is almost uniformly regarded as being *"very commercial." "If ever there was a top band man in this line of work, it's him."* Also singled out was the *"outstanding"* **Susan Lewis**, who was described by some as *"simply the best corporate lawyer in Birmingham, no question about it."* Other top operators in the team include the *"conscientious and meticulous"* **Chris Garnett**, as well as **Stephen Kitts**, *"a shrewd operator,"* and **Peter McHugh**, *"so solid it's not true."* The *"practical and user-friendly"* **Michael Seabrook** is also highly rated, as is the head of the firm's Nottingham office **David Wild**, who has been described as *"a man for all seasons."* **Ben Johnson** is seen as *"energetic," "well-liked"* and *"an emerging talent."* Recent highlights for the firm include acting in the £127.5 million disposal of Romeike Group Holdings to Sifo Group, which was the East Midlands' biggest ever deal, and advising the bidder and management in the £126 million public to private takeover of Wyko Group plc. **Clients:** Lucas Varity Ltd; Mentmore Abbey plc; Nutec Group Ltd.

Pinsent Curtis This firm acts for a range of clients, including FTSE 100/250/350 start-up companies, large private companies, international companies, new dot.com start-ups, venture capital providers, financial institutions and major banks. The firm undertakes the full range of corporate finance work from Stock Exchange to private equity deals, and has a particular niche in advising young technology companies and advising on public to private transactions. Overall, the firm is seen to be targeting *"higher value, more complex deals for a demanding client base."* The corporate finance team includes the *"bright"* **Andrew Eastgate**, who *"has done some good deals over the years,"* and **Simon Gronow**, who has been described as *"a bit eccentric, but very good at his job."* **David Hughes**, has been described as *"bookish but clever"* and has a good reputation for doing *"the higher value deals for the bigger clients."* **Amanda Allen** has *"kept a low profile recently,"* but has been *"perfectly sound whenever she's popped up to do a deal,"* while **James Lavery** has continued to make a name for himself in the region. A recent highlight for the firm was acting for Glanbia plc in the £100 million disposal of its UK Dairy business to Express Dairies. The firm has also been active in the flotation market this year, recently acting in the AIM flotations of Goal plc, which was to the value of £55 million, and iSoft plc, which was in the region of £100 million. **Clients:** NHS Supplies; Smith & Nephew; TRW Inc.

DLA This team contains the *"sensible, commercial and highly practical"* **Chris Rawstron**, who recently abandoned his role as Birmingham head of corporate in order to spend more time on client matters, in addition to focusing on his duties as regional managing partner. The practice primarily undertakes shares work, in terms of buying and selling companies and raising finance for companies by issuing shares on the stockmarket or issuing shares to private equity providers. The practice acts for public and private companies which have a market capitalisation of anywhere up to £200 million, and the firm is also in the process of expanding its international client base. Market comment is that this firm is comparatively *"the new kid on the block"* out of the major players in the region, and that *"while it hasn't made as big an impression as it would have liked, it's getting there."* A significant growth area for the firm in the past twelve months has been in relation to dot.com start-up companies. Highlights of the year include acting for JBA Holdings plc in the £90 million recommended bid by GEAC Corporation and acting on a £14 million MBO of Leaderflush and Shapland Ltd out of Whitecroft plc. **Clients:** Albert E Sharp & Co, Inbis Group plc; Wellman Ltd.

Browne Jacobson This firm has been said to stand *"head and shoulders above the other firms in Nottingham"* for corporate finance work. The corporate finance department is said to be *"huge now, and they churn out a phenomenal amount of work."* However, the team's profile is still limited to the East Midlands. Head of department **Robin Metcalfe** is *"still cooking on gas,"* while his *"heir apparent"* **Gavin Cummings** is *"putting himself out and about"* and **Nigel Blackwell** is *"hard-working"* and *"good to deal with."* The firm's focus has changed in the last twelve months, in that while it is still a strong player in private equity work and MBOs/MBIs, it has been handling an increasing number of bigger deals and international M&As, such as the recent sale of Joseph Profession for £100 million. Other highlights include the disposal of Kentons, a subsidiary branch of Utilitec plc, in a £13.1 million deal and the acquisition of Thomas Pink for LVMH. **Clients:** Chemical Leisure; LVMH; Utilitec plc.

Gateley Wareing This firm is seen to have *"a niche in acting for owner-managed businesses,"* particularly in relation to private equity transactions. The *"practical"* **Paul Hayward** is *"able to get things done,"* while **Michael Ward** is *"technically proficient."* Comment in the market has been that the firm is currently *"trying to position themselves as the big fish in the pond"* of owner-managed businesses. It remains to be seen whether they can *"make it into Browne Jacobson's league."* Recent highlights for the firm include the MBO/MBI of Darwell Fabrications Ltd, with a deal value of £10 million, and the IBO of Frank Thomas Ltd, with a deal value of £20 million. **Clients:** Bank of Scotland; Barclays Private Equity; Gresham Trust plc.

Hammond Suddards Edge Prior to the headlining merger with Hammonds Suddards, the former Edge Ellison had been almost universally regarded as *"having had problems for some time."* However, this was counterbalanced by market comment that *"firms that were as good as this one was don't just fall off the face of the planet,"* and that there were still quality people there, most notably the *"stalwart"* **David Hull**, who is seen to have *"weathered the storm well."* The *"pragmatic"* **Roger Birchall** is especially strong for private equity work, while **Baljit Chohan** is a *"shining light"* for M&A work. The firm has primary expertise in Midlands listed plc work, private equity and acquisition finance, M&A (domestic and cross-border) and UK based corporate work. Highlights of the past twelve months include acting for Wyko Group plc in the £92 million public to private takeover by Perdix Investments Ltd. Another highlight was acting for T&S Stores in the £66 million acquisition of One Stop Community Stores Ltd from Portsmouth & Sunderland Newspapers plc. **Clients:** Folkes Group plc; T & S Stores plc; Wilson Bowden plc.

Martineau Johnson This firm acts for fast-growing innovative companies and their investors, including two venture capital trusts and three university-based venture capital funds. The firm provides specialist corporate finance advice to these clients, and has accepted equity in clients in lieu of cash fees for approximately three years. **Andrew Stilton** is seen as *"a good technician"* and handles a large amount of the work concerning fast-growing innovative companies and their investors. The highlight of the past twelve months was acting in the reorganisation and sale of the consumer products business of McKechnie plc for £81.5 million. Another highlight was the £25 million restructuring of Enterprise VCT plc. **Clients:** McKechnie plc; Foresight Technology VCT plc; South Staffordshire Group plc.

Eking Manning This firm has *"an old commercial client base and a well-known corporate lawyer"* in **Austin Moore**. While he is widely regarded as *"a class act,"* particularly on private equity work, he is also seen as *"a bit of a lone wolf."* However, market comment is that one should *"never underestimate"* this firm. Indeed, in the last twelve months the firm has been involved in 28 deals which were individually in excess of £1 million, and the aggregate value of deals in that period was approximately £240 million. The firm has also been bolstering its traditional strength in private equity work with an increasing amount of M&A work. Recent highlights for the firm include the sale of Compass Cleaning Ltd to Pall Mall Support Services Ltd and the sale of Quatrix Holdings Ltd to Mettoni Group plc. **Clients:** e-gosystems.com plc; John Deere Ltd; Vizacom Inc.

Freethcartwright **Karl Jansen** is the head of department in the Nottingham office of this firm. Regarded as a *"very good operator,"* he is widely credited with *"helping to build the corporate profile"* of this firm, particularly in the Nottingham market, although market comment is that the firm *"still has a fair way to go"* before it establishes itself as a real player in the region. The firm has been acting for an increasing number of local and foreign businesses over the past year, and has a niche strength in risk management. One highlight of the past year include the global refinancing of ADLT in the US, Canada and the UK to the value of US$75 million. Another highlight was acting for the Cypher Group Ltd (the UK's largest supplier of books to libraries) in the purchase of Bertram Books Ltd (the UK's largest wholesale supplier of books) to form the Bertram Group, a £54 million deal. **Clients:** Advanced Lighting Technologies Inc (ADLT); Manthorpe Engineering; Nevison (re Souplex Ltd.)

Lee Crowder This firm acts for a wide range of businesses, from listed plcs to SMEs, and also works with a number of banks, including the Royal Bank of Scotland and the Bank of Scotland Co-op Bank. However, to some extent the firm has been perceived in the market as *"the 3i firm."* Therefore, 3i's decision to appoint Wragge & Co as principal Midlands advisor must be considered a setback. Niche strengths in venture capital and e-commerce, sit alongside expertise with SMEs. Highlights of the past twelve months include the AIM flotation of Myratech.net plc and the substantial sale of Nelson Hind, the largest independent contract catering business in the UK, to Elior, a company quoted on the French stock exchange. **Clients:** Myratech.net plc; TGA Industrial.

Shoosmiths This firm has its base in Northampton and is widely regarded as being *"a sizeable fish in this tiny pond"* and *"a good firm at the smaller end of the market."* The firm occasionally does some MBO work as well as listed company work, although it primarily acts for private clients. **Clients:** Retail; food; IT companies.

Edwards Geldard This firm is widely seen to have *"a Nottingham presence but a Derby focus,"* with some market comment that it *"dominates the Derby market."* The firm's corporate finance work includes M&As, MBO/MBIs, disposals and debt and equity financing. A recent highlight for the firm was acting for the MBO team on the £210 million public to private buy-out of Norcros plc. Another highlight was acting for Pendragon plc in the acquisition of the 32 motor dealerships belonging to Lex Service plc for the sum of £95 million. **Clients:** National Westminster Bank plc; Pendragon plc; Stationery Box Ltd.

Garretts The firm has a particular expertise in cross-border transactions and inward investment. However, market comment has been that the majority of corporate finance work comes from its affiliation with Andersen Legal, and while this is of generally good quality, the firm is *"not really* *a player in the external corporate market.*" The highlight of the past twelve months was advising Oneview.net plc, the internet solutions provider, on its share placing and AIM listing, with a subsequent market capitalisation of £155 million. Another success was advising the management team of Adams Childrenswear Ltd on the £87 million buyout from Sears Ltd. **Clients:** Capital Bars plc; Oneview.net plc; Vislink plc.

George Green & Co This firm is seen to remain *"strong in its patch,"* namely the Black Country, although its corporate finance department has been weakened considerably by the recent departure of its former *"big gun"* Guy Green to the Birmingham office of Eversheds. The firm tends to handle work *"at the smaller end of the private equity market,"* and also undertakes some MBO/MBI work. The highlight of the year for the firm was the merger of Brockhouse Forgings with British and Midland Forgings. **Clients:** Include SMEs.

Harvey Ingram Owston This firm is seen as the *"leading player in corporate finance work in Leicester,"* in that it has *"been there since the year dot"* and is *"the only full service law firm based there."* Tends to act for the larger owner-managed businesses and does second-tier work for listed plcs. In this respect, the firm recently obtained the Camden Motor Group as a client, and is now buying and selling forecourt businesses for them. A growth area for the firm in the last year has been in e-commerce work, and the firm has advised a number of internet start-ups. Recent highlights for the firm include the acquisition of NRC for the WR Group and acting for Texon in the £20 million worldwide acquisition of Foss, a New Hampshire-based non-woven textiles manufacturing business. **Clients:** Bland Bankart plc; Everards Brewery Ltd; Mattel UK Ltd.

Hewitson Becke + Shaw This Northampton practice remains mainly active in MBO/MBIs, and owner-managed business work, although there has been market comment that this practice is the *"poor cousin"* of the firm's office in Cambridge. A recent highlight for the Northampton office was the complex sale of a private company client to a US company, which was its first major acquisition in the UK. **Clients:** Ademco Microtech Ltd; Cambridge Research & Innovation Ltd; DMG Information Ltd/Hobsons plc.

Howes Percival The major focus of the corporate finance work undertaken by this firm is M&A work, MBOs and MBIs, with an average deal value of £5 million to £15 million. Over the past twelve months, the firm has done five acquisitions and disposals for David Chrysler UK Ltd, and has also done two deals for Dimension Data Holdings Ltd with a total value of £120 million. The firm has also recently started doing work for the Volkswagen Audi Group in relation to the acquisition of motor dealerships. **Clients:** David Chrysler UK Ltd; Dimension Data Holdings Ltd; Volkswagen Audi Group.

Kent Jones and Done This firm undertakes a variety of corporate finance work, including sales and purchases, MBOs, corporate restructuring, buy-backs, take-overs, estate privates and equity investments. Over the past twelve months, the firm has undertaken a lot more disposal work than in recent years, particularly in relation to the sales of owner-managed businesses. Market comment is that the firm is *"really going to miss"* Ed Dawes, who recently left to join Addleshaw Booth & Co. **Clients:** Alchemy Partners; JCB Group.

Knight & Sons This firm undertakes a small amount of corporate finance work for listed companies, but the majority of its work is for owner-managed businesses of all sizes. A growth area for the firm in the past year has been in relation to dot.com work. Highlights of the past year include acting for the controlling shareholders of Stoke City Football Club in the sale of 66 percent interest to an Icelandic consortium, acting on the demerger of a £5 million property group and acting on the sale of Tekdata Holdings Ltd to a management buyout team. **Clients:** Stoke City Football Club; Tekdata Ltd; University of Keele.

EAST ANGLIA

CORPORATE FINANCE • East Anglia	Ptnrs	Assts
❶ **Eversheds** Ipswich, Norwich	8	8
Hewitson Becke + Shaw Cambridge	4	7
Mills & Reeve Cambridge, Norwich	6	11
Taylor Vinters Cambridge	2	4
❷ **Birketts** Ipswich	2	1
Garretts Cambridge	1	4
Prettys Ipswich	1	2
❸ **Ashton Graham** Bury St Edmunds	*	*
Greene & Greene Bury St. Edmunds	3	-
Greenwoods Peterborough	3	1
❹ **Steele & Co** Norwich	1	2

LEADING INDIVIDUALS	
❶ **ALEXANDER-SINCLAIR Ian** Mills & Reeve	**FISCHL Nicolas** Mills & Reeve
FITZSIMONS Gerard Garretts	**GOULD Terry** Eversheds
KERLE Bridget Hewitson Becke + Shaw	**SHORT John** Taylor Vinters
❷ **CROOME Andrew** Eversheds	**DIX John** Hewitson Becke + Shaw
EVANS Michael Greenwoods	**FALKUS Bryony** Mills & Reeve
SHARRATT Steve Taylor Vinters	**STANFIELD Glynne** Mills & Reeve
THOMSON Christopher Greene & Greene	**WAINE Ian** Prettys
❸ **LUBBOCK Nigel** Steele & Co	**WHITTINGHAM Paul** Ashton Graham
UP AND COMING	
HUNTER James Mills & Reeve	**MARDLE David** Garretts
WHYBROW Annette Birketts	

Within each band, firms are listed alphabetically. *See **Profiles** on page 240*

Figures unavailable at time of going to press.

* *See editorial entries for explanations of team sizes.*

Eversheds Seen as one of the top firms in the region for corporate finance work, it has been commented that due to its *"national profile"* and nationwide link-up, it is the best equipped of all firms in the region to do *"the sort of deal that needs a lot of people and resources thrown at it."* **Terry Gould** heads the team and is described as *"easy to do a transaction with," "sensible"* and *"technically excellent,"* while **Andrew Croome**, primarily known for his banking work, is *"bright, efficient and conscientious."* The highlight of the past twelve months for the firm was when more than 20 lawyers advised NHP plc on the acquisition of 35 care homes comprising 1,843 beds in England and Scotland from Highfield Group Ltd for £67.5 million. The firm also acted for the joint venture company established by TXU Europe Group plc (formerly Eastern Group) and London Electricity. **Clients:** Bertram Books Ltd; Eastern Counties Newspapers Group Ltd; NHP plc.

Hewitson Becke + Shaw The firm has a range of clients including major international software houses, publishing companies, venture capital funds, bio-tech and hi-tech companies. The respected corporate team includes **John Dix**, described as *"sensible, down to earth and someone you can do business with,"* and the *"immensely experienced"* and *"very tough"* **Bridget Kerle**. Niche strengths include business angel funding, financing for early-stage technology companies, share options, Yellow Book work and international deals. *"There is only so much corporate finance work in this region, and they have their fair share of it."* The firm advised on the sale of electronic publisher Chadwyck-Healey to US-based Bell & Howell for more than £30 million. Other highlights included the sale of Internet Protocols Ltd to Teltran International Group for US$17 million and the sale of digital cellular software developer STNC Ltd to Microsoft. **Clients:** Cambridge Research & Innovation Ltd; DMG Information Ltd/Hobsons plc; Ademco Microtech Ltd.

Mills & Reeve The firm's Norwich office is highly rated and is headed by **Ian Alexander-Sinclair**, whose *"name is rightly respected."* **Nick Fischl** still has *"one of the sharpest minds around,"* and the *"simply excellent"* and *"highly under-rated"* **Bryony Falkus** adds yet *"another valuable string to this team's bow."* **James Hunter** is *"a rising star."* At the Cambridge office, **Glynne Stanfield** is said to be *"a bright, tough and effective lawyer"* although he is sometimes felt to *"overdo the aggression."* Recent highlights include the MBO of SLP Engineering Ltd, with a turnover of £40 million, which was purchased from Oderbrecht, a large Brazilian oil and gas company. The firm also acted Sutton Bridge Ltd on its merger with Russells Burgess Ltd to form Solanum. **Clients:** Anglian Group plc; Jarrold & Sons Ltd; The Wiremold Company.

Taylor Vinters **John Short** is *"bright and sensible,"* will *"cut through to the main issues"* and *"understands what's required of a good transaction lawyer."* **Steve Sharratt** is *"a rainmaker," "a great networker"* and *"a real businessman who happens to be a lawyer as well."* The firm acts for a range of clients in the fields of technology, consultancy, software, telecoms and biotechnology, and have done a number of cross-border acquisitions and disposals. Recent work includes a complex deal involving an MBO with a simultaneous acquisition of a company in the electronic golf-buggy market, to the value of £10 million. **Clients:** Assured Information Systems Ltd; Nationwide Cellular Fit Ltd; Automation Partnership Group plc.

Birketts The firm continues to act mainly for owner-managed businesses and SMEs, as well as a small number of plcs. **Annette Whybrow** is said to be *"showing great promise,"* and has a *"a good analytical mind"* which enables her to *"pick up points that others might overlook."* An increased part of the caseload involves work for UK subsidiaries of foreign companies (based in Germany and the US.) Active in the tourism and leisure industry, the team's deal size typically ranges from £1-30 million. Advised on the £25 million sale of a local vacuum pump business to an American company. **Clients:** Local and international corporates.

Garretts Niche strength in venture capital work in the technology sector has been underscored by the firm's acquisition of such weighty regional clients as TTP Group plc and Gateway Venture. The corporate team is headed by the *"unflappable"* **Gerard Fitzsimons**, who has a good reputation for *"cutting to the chase and getting deals done."* **David Mardle** is *"business-like, good to deal with, doesn't take bad points and knows how to move a deal towards a conclusion."* Although the Andersen connection has provided obvious advantages for the firm's client base, it is not yet felt to have made the expected impact on the local market. The team acted for Dalehead Foods Holdings Ltd on its £150 million merger with Roach Foods Ltd. **Clients:** Amadeus Capital Partners Ltd; Generics Group plc; TTP Group plc.

Prettys The *"likeable"* **Ian Waine** heads up the corporate and commercial department. However, he is felt to *"plough a lone furrow"* at a firm which is felt to lack the degree of specialism of the local market leaders. The principal thrust of the practice is owner-managed businesses, and the practice has been particularly strong in the transport sector over the last twelve months, acting for a number of haulage and transport companies. Agribusiness has provided another growth area. Recent work includes completing a substantial merger between two agricultural service businesses, and handling the sale of a private limited company to a multi-national company. **Clients:** Owner-managed businesses.

Ashton Graham This firm continues to handle corporate finance work out of its Business Law Unit, with three partners spending approximately 40-50% of their time on this area. **Paul Whittingham** is *"practical, knows his stuff and gets the job done."* Following the 1998 merger, the firm is considered to have raised its profile among owner-managed business market in Suffolk. However, this is still seen as a heavily localised operation. **Clients:** Local listed companies.

Greene & Greene This firm *"has a good name for the smaller corporate finance work,"* concentrates on private businesses, and continues to have a solid client base in Suffolk. **Chris Thomson** is *"smart, straightforward and commercially aware."* The team handles venture capital investments in local family-owned businesses, as well as trade sales and disposals and some MBOs and MBIs. **Clients:** Private Clients.

Greenwoods This long-established firm has a client base of major plcs, manufacturers, publishers, national charities, schools and colleges, start-up businesses and companies resident both in and out of the country. **Michael Evans** heads the corporate finance team, and is seen to be *"experienced," " sensible"* and *"pragmatic."* The team has particular experience of working with the food industry, the media, information technology and communications and bio-technology organisations. Workload includes M&A, agency agreements, MBOs/MBIs and joint ventures in the UK and overseas. **Clients:** CCC International; Marshall of Cambridge (Holdings) Ltd.

Steele & Co Newly-ranked team which undertakes a variety of M&A work for both local and overseas clients. The department is headed by **Nigel Lubbock**, who is said to have been *"out and about"* and *"raising his profile"* in the region in the past twelve months. Domestically, the team was recently successful in winning a bid to become appointed solicitors for the flagship ECOTech programme in mid-Norfolk. **Clients:** Ionics (UK) Ltd; Pi Group Ltd; Tulip International (UK) Ltd.

NORTH WEST

Addleshaw Booth & Co This firm is still seen as the *"undisputed leader"* in the region, particularly in terms of resources and client base, although it is not as far ahead of the field as in previous years. Possessing a *"treasure trove of plc lawyers,"* and strong on private equity, the team has *"the clients that everyone else wants."* **Keith Johnston** is *"increasingly active,"* venture capital expert **Darryl Cooke** is one of the acknowledged regional rainmakers, and **Richard Lee** is *"one of the most experienced players in town."* **Paul Devitt** *"does a high volume of good quality work"* and **Mark Warburton** has been *"seen out and about"* with greater frequency. Although **Paul Lee** *"has an established profile,"* he is the current chairman of the CBI, which along with his duties as senior partner has led him to be *"less hands-on recently."* The team acted for Airtours plc in the £852 million share exchange offers for the whole of the ordinary and convertible preference share capital of First Choice Holidays plc. Another highlight was acting for BWI plc on the £85.2 million recommended takeover of the company by a German purchaser. **Clients:** Airtours plc; GEHE UK plc; Skillsgroup plc.

DLA Notably strong in the MBO/private equity market, the firm has been said to be *"getting close to Addleshaws for private equity work, if not yet for public company or M&A work."* The corporate finance team is seen to be *"a tight unit, commercial, pragmatic and collectively good to do business with."* **Michael Prince** is widely considered to be *"on top of his game"* and *"a worthy opponent,"* while **Andrew Holt** is said to *"have a firm foothold with a number of private equity players"* and is *"able to keep all the plates spinning during the complex deals."* **Jonathan Brown** is still *"making a name for himself"* in the market, **David Cadwallader** has a *"nice laid-back style"* and *"knows his way around the market"* and **Jonathan Procter** is *"an accomplished operator."* The experienced William Holt has recently retired. A significant growth area for the firm this year has been in e-commerce work, including the establishment of procurement and retail websites for major corporates. Acted for the vendors in the secondary buy-out of Target Express Parcels Ltd to the value of £210 million, and advised Bowthorpe plc on the £80 million disposal of its thermal management business in the UK, US, Germany, Italy, Hong Kong and

CORPORATE FINANCE • North West	Ptnrs	Assts
❶ **Addleshaw Booth & Co** Manchester	23	34
❷ **DLA** Liverpool, Manchester	16	17
Eversheds Manchester	10	29
❸ **Halliwell Landau** Manchester	4	12
Hammond Suddards Edge Manchester	4	10
❹ **Chaffe Street** Manchester	8	10
❺ **Brabner Holden Banks Wilson** Liverpool	4	5
Cobbetts Manchester	5	5
Davies Wallis Foyster Liverpool, Manchester	6	8
❻ **Aaron & Partners** Chester	2	3
Garretts Manchester	2	8
Kuit Steinart Levy Manchester	4	3
Pannone & Partners Manchester	5	5
Wacks Caller Manchester	6	6

LEADING INDIVIDUALS	
✪ **PYSDEN Edward** Eversheds	
❶ **JOHNSTON Keith** Addleshaw Booth & Co	**PRINCE Michael** DLA
❷ **BLOWER Geoffrey** Eversheds	**COOKE Darryl** Addleshaw Booth & Co
CRAIG Alexander Halliwell Landau	**DEVITT Paul** Addleshaw Booth & Co
DOWNS William Hammond Suddards Edge	**GRISEWOOD Rebecca** Halliwell Landau
HALL Daniel Eversheds	**HOLT Andrew** DLA
LEE Richard Addleshaw Booth & Co	**STREET Robert** Chaffe Street
WARBURTON Mark Addleshaw Booth & Co	
❸ **FITZGERALD Sean** Chaffe Street	**HAMILTON Timothy** Garretts
❹ **BRABNER Michael** Brabner Holden Banks Wilson	**BROWN Jonathan** DLA
CADWALLADER David DLA	**GARSTON Clive** Halliwell Landau
HALPIN Peter Eversheds	**HARPER Tony** Brabner Holden Banks Wilson
LEE Paul Addleshaw Booth & Co	**LEVY Robert** Kuit Steinart Levy
LUMSDEN Christopher Chaffe Street	**O'CONNOR Mark** Davies Wallis Foyster
TURNBULL Robert Cobbetts	
UP AND COMING	
BOWCOCK David Eversheds	**PROCTER Jonathan** DLA

Within each band, firms are listed alphabetically. *See **Profiles** on page 240*

Malaysia. **Clients:** Granada Group plc; MS International plc; Parkwood Holdings plc.

Eversheds *"Going from strength to strength in the region,"* particularly in private equity work, the firm has *"recruited good quality people and kept them."* **Edward Pysden** remains *"in a class of his own"* in Manchester. He is *"immensely experienced," "knows his stuff backwards"* and has a *"track record which is second to none."* Admired for his *"ability to get to the main issues quickly,"* he *"looks after a number of large companies and keeps them very happy."* **Geoffrey Blower** is said to have *"been around the block a few times and picked up all the tricks – from a technical point of view, he's always spot-on."* Head of department **Daniel Hall** is *"a go-getting generator of work,"* while **Peter Halpin** has been a *"valuable addition"* from Addleshaws for his venture capital expertise. Recently appointed partner **David Bowcock** is *"definitely going places."* Highlights of the past year include advising on the Stanley Leisure plc bid for Capital Corporation, and the sale of Martin Dawes Telecom to Cellnet for £130 million. **Clients:** Bank of Scotland; Barclays Private Equity; Martin Dawes Networks/Breathe.Net.

Halliwell Landau This firm has developed a niche strength in Ofex flotations and fund-raising for technology companies, and has completed over 130 deals in the past twelve months, each with a value of over £500,000. Head of department **Alexander Craig** has *"been around a long time,"* while **Rebecca Grisewood** is *"a good private equity practitioner"* and **Clive Garston** *("really underrated")* is highly regarded for his M&A work in particular. Considered a *"good, entrepreneurial, regional player,"* the team's influence is still not felt to extend beyond the North West. The team advised on the £200 million market capital flotation of Knowledge Management Software and the £300 million flotation of Knowledge Support Systems plc. **Clients:** Coral Products plc; KMS Ltd; Royal & Sun Alliance.

Hammond Suddards Edge **William Downs** heads the corporate finance team of this recently merged firm, and is said to be *"slick," "commercially-minded"* and *"professional in the way he does business."* However, the firm itself is seen by some to have *"lost its way"* in the region this year, with the loss of *"some quality personnel."* Market consensus indicated that increased concentration on the newly-merged firm's London office had affected its profile in the region. Acted for EJA Engineering Group, the leading manufacturer of machine safety products, on its sale to US company Rockwell for £50 million. Advised on the acquisition of Norsk Hydro ASA's Hydro Coatings Group by BASF Group for approximately £23 million. **Clients:** Allen plc; Guilbert UK Ltd; Ultraframe plc.

Chaffe Street A respected team is headed by *"worldly-wise and perspicacious"* founding-father **Robert Street**. **Sean Fitzgerald** *("affable and able")* and **Christopher Lumsden**, an *"exemplary technician"* who continues to be highly regarded for his *"banking nous,"* offer highly-rated support. Formerly renowned for venture capital work, the firm has developed a broader base, acting inter alia on behalf of Alan Murphy in the disposal of AM Group Ltd to SCA for a total consideration of £192 million. Another highlight was the acquisition of the air and sea transportation business of Securicor Omega International Ltd on behalf of Danzas (UK) Ltd. **Clients:** Bolton Wanderers Football Club; Jungheinrich; Safeguard Systems Europe Ltd.

Brabner Holden Banks Wilson This firm is seen to be an *"old Liverpool firm which gets involved with some sizeable deals"* and has *"a good client base from way back."* The firm's core client base is owner-managed businesses, for which it primarily handles acquisitions and disposals on a transactional basis. Niche strength exists in MBOs and development capital for housing associations, and the team also carries out institutional funding work for Merseyside Special Investment Fund, the Royal Bank of Scotland and the Bank of Scotland. **Michael Brabner** is *"hard-working"* and *"great at what he does,"* while **Tony Harper** *"gets his hands dirty"* and is *"always a pleasure to deal with."* Acted on the disposal of the entire issued share capital of Crawfords Computing Ltd to a subsidiary of Hays plc, a deal worth £13 million with a £5.5 million earn-out. **Clients:** B & M (Pipeline Services) Ltd; Hays Commercial Services Marketing Technology; Rage Software plc.

Cobbetts Although better known for its strong litigation practice, the firm undertakes a variety of corporate finance work, including M&A work, joint ventures, venture capital, MBO/MBIs, yellow book work and corporate governance. Headed by the *"technically adept"* **Robert Turnbull**, the team has particular niche strengths in acting for US multi-nationals on UK transactions, as well as corporate work for housing associations and venture capital. The team acted for CRS on its merger with CWS, with other significant transactions including the sale of Pennine Computers for c£20 million and the acquisition of Sale Rugby Club. **Clients:** Conso/British Trimmings; Murray Johnstone Private Equity Ltd; Sonoco Products Company.

Davies Wallis Foyster *"Improving"* team with niche strengths in handling corporate finance work for manufacturers (particularly food and drink,) technology companies and educational establishments. **Mark O'Connor** has *"a decent profile"* here. Acting for Chance & Hunt Ltd in the £40 million MBO of ICI Chemical & Polymers Ltd and for G.F. O'Brien Ltd in the sale of 40 pharmacies for in excess of £20 million. **Clients:** Acrol Ltd; Logitek Ltd; Woodward Food Service Ltd.

Aaron & Partners The firm is widely regarded as *"the only significant corporate player in Chester,"* in spite of the recent movement to a consultancy role of founding partner, Julian Aaron. Continues to act for small to medium-sized owner-managed businesses and private companies, on a range of work including acquisitions and disposals, MBO/MBI's re-financing, joint ventures and investment agreements. **Clients:** Small to medium-sized owner-managed businesses; private companies.

Garretts **Timothy Hamilton** is *"a good steady corporate lawyer"* and *"the main asset for the firm in this region."* However, the Andersen connection has been unable to prevent more personnel departures. The team acted for the Latium Group in relation to its £40 million acquisition of the Everest Double Glazing Business from Caradon plc. Also represented NatWest Equity Partners on the £50 million institutional purchase of the NES Group. **Clients:** Digital Projection International plc; Euro Sales Finance plc; NatWest Equity Partners Ltd.

Kuit Steinart Levy The team, *"better known for its commercial work,"* is headed by **Robert Levy**, who *"knows what he's doing."* Acts predominantly for an SME client base, although the firm also has a number of high-profile active plcs. Niche strengths are found in brand acquisitions, e-commerce ventures and AIM flotations. The highlight of the year was the joint instruction with Allen & Overy on the Seton Scholl merger with the London International Group, which was valued at £1.45 billion. **Clients:** Manchester City plc; The Medical House plc; SSL International plc.

Pannone & Partners Although comparatively low-profile, the team is said to be *"perfectly competent whenever they have appeared"* in the corporate finance market. Undertakes shareholder disputes, corporate reorganisations and capital reductions. A recent deal was the sale of Key Students Services Ltd to Keycom plc, where the disposal consideration was £1.2 million, and the capital raised was £3 million. **Clients:** MA Hanna Co Inc; Milliken & Co. (and subsidiaries); Newell Rubbermaid.

Wacks Caller The corporate finance team at this firm is said to have *"a great deal of energy about them,"* although market comment is that the firm has *"much more of a focus on litigation."* The team undertakes a broad range of corporate finance work, including flotations, private placings, acquisitions and disposals, and has a number of clients in the recruitment, biotech and health care industries. **Clients:** JWE Telecom plc; Premier Group plc; Travel World Group.

YORKSHIRE

CORPORATE FINANCE • Yorkshire	Ptnrs	Assts
❶ **Addleshaw Booth & Co** Leeds	9	20
❷ **Eversheds** Leeds	10	-
Hammond Suddards Edge Leeds	7	13
❸ **DLA** Leeds, Sheffield	14	24
❹ **Pinsent Curtis** Leeds	14	18
Walker Morris Leeds	4	10
❺ **Irwin Mitchell** Leeds, Sheffield	4	12
Lupton Fawcett Leeds	4	3
Read Hind Stewart Leeds	3	3
Rollit Farrell & Bladon Hull	6	3
❻ **Andrew M. Jackson & Co** Hull	3	5
Garretts Leeds	2	4
Gordons Cranswick Solicitors Bradford, Leeds	4	2
Gosschalks Hull	4	1

LEADING INDIVIDUALS	
❶ **GILBERT Ian** Walker Morris	**LIPPELL Sean** Addleshaw Booth & Co
❷ **DA COSTA Alastair** DLA	**DARWIN Andrew** DLA
EMMETT Paul Walker Morris	**GRAY David** Eversheds
HUTTON Noel Hammond Suddards Edge	**RICHARDSON Ian** Eversheds
SHAW Martin Pinsent Curtis	**WHELDON Tim** Addleshaw Booth & Co
❸ **ARMITAGE David** Hammond Suddards Edge	**CUNNINGHAM Kevin** Irwin Mitchell
JOHNSON Robin Eversheds	**McINTOSH Ian** Addleshaw Booth & Co
PAINTER Nick Garretts	**PITCHER Robert** Eversheds
❹ **GREENFIELD Ian** Hammond Suddards Edge	**HOPKINS Stephen** Eversheds
ROBINSON Michael Pinsent Curtis	**SMART Peter** Walker Morris
UP AND COMING	
HARRISON Wendy DLA	**JONES Jonathan** Hammond Suddards Edge

Within each band, firms are listed alphabetically. *See **Profiles** on page 240*

Addleshaw Booth & Co Maintains its position as *"the team to catch"* through strength across the spectrum of corporate finance activities. Private equity has always been a core capability, and the team's historic relationship with a number of venture capital houses, most notably 3i, provides a substantial volume of work. The corporate finance department's work in leveraged transactions is supported by the firm's pre-eminent reputation in acquisition finance and is boosted by the relationship with Yorkshire Bank. In larger M&A work, the firm has fewer blue-chip clients than its closest competitors, but its strength in the £10-£100 million deal-range make the practice the most rounded in the region. However, it is the group's *"critical mass"* and most notably its ability to attract and retain new talent that gives this team the edge over its main rivals. Just over a year after arriving, **Sean Lippell** has consolidated his position as a leading individual, and while better known for bringing in the deals than his technical skills, he is perceived by his peers as *"top class."* **Tim Wheldon** is *"a bit of a maverick but a great client guy"* while **Ian McIntosh** has a lower profile but is *"an excellent technical lawyer,"* as shown by his leadership of the team acting on the £1.17 billion disposal of shareholdings in the Meadowhall Centre. **Clients:** 3i; Apax; Yorkshire Group plc; Kingfisher plc.

Eversheds After a run of good years, this team *"has lost its sleeping giant tag"* and is generally considered to be *"a lot sharper than it used to be."* The Leeds office has a strong listed client base but the team has also targeted SMEs. The practice has strengthened its presence in private equity, and increasingly acts for finance providers including Murray Johnstone and Lloyds Development Capital. The future of the corporate finance group is likely to revolve around increasing sector specialisation, with the formation of national dedicated groups for industries such as high-tech/e-commerce, telecoms, chemicals and pharmaceuticals. Among a strong group of individuals, **David Gray** retains a reputation as *"a good operator and leading corporate figure,"* but his increasing managerial responsibility as head of the Leeds and Manchester practices has opened the way for a number of other individuals to raise their profiles. **Ian Richardson** is a well-known figure in private equity, while **Stephen Hopkins** straddles the line between corporate and banking, but has a significant influence on both areas. **Robin Johnson** is a leading figure for transactions in the hi-tech sector, while ex-Slaughter and May **Robert Pitcher** is *"easy to work with and technically very good."* The team acted for Kingston upon Hull County Council on the £700 million flotation of Kingston Communications. **Clients:** DuPont (UK) plc; Murray Johnstone; ICI.

Hammond Suddards Edge *"Always formidable,"* this team's strength lies in its strong public company client base and solid reputation for medium-sized M&A transactions. The practice is also developing a reputation for work in the new media sector and is currently advising the management team at Sports Internet on a £350 million bid by BSkyB. In the private equity arena, the corporate group has advised both venture capitalist funds (such as Murray Johnstone & Apax) and management teams. **Noel Hutton** continues to be the team's public face, although some of the younger partners, such as **David Armitage** *("good at client relations")* and **Ian Greenfield** *("technical and personable")* look set to increase their regional profiles. **Jonathan Jones** has a growing reputation based on smaller venture capital deals, and is one to watch for the future. **Clients:** Allied Textile Companies; Halifax plc; Meyer International plc.

DLA Gathering momentum, largely due to *"a good mix of young and experienced partners which gives the practice a sense of energy."* M&A work has been more buoyant than private equity, with the average deal size for the office rising from £10 million to £14 million. However, the recent recruitment of a specialist private equity partner looks set to provide more balance in the practice. Much of the team's vigour stems from the *"young but excellent"* **Alastair Da Costa**, whose mixture of internal management, client handling and technical skills received unanimous market approval. **Andrew Darwin**, who now heads DLA's corporate finance team nationally, provides both experience and expertise, although his national duties have led some to suggest that he can be *"difficult to get hold of."* **Wendy Harrison** is singled out from a talented group of young partners, with commentators suggesting that her work in private equity for clients such as Apax and Bridgepoint put her among the leading up and coming practitioners in the region. The team acted for Sanderson Group plc on the £115 million recommended bid by Sonarsend plc. **Clients:** Filtronic plc; Halifax plc; Alchemy Partners.

Pinsent Curtis This team has an excellent client base of leading public companies, and is felt by a number of commentators to be strongest on larger transactions. The practice is divided along functional lines, with a Stock Exchange team, a private equity team and a banking (acquisition finance) team. The Stock Exchange team is arguably the best in Leeds, with five dedicated partners including the hugely experienced **Martin Shaw** and **Michael Robinson**. This team has been particularly active in the area of debt financing for small caps, as on a £75 million Eurobond issue for BPT plc. However, in the hi-tech sector, equity continues to be the favoured method of financing, and the team completed a £71.2m rights issue for Filtronic plc as well as a number of dot.com flotations. The private equity team does not have such a high profile, and has recently lost a respected partner to DLA. This loss is symptomatic of a *"practice-wide inability to retain talent,"* and the Yorkshire team is currently felt to lack the necessary dynamism to compete outside its existing, albeit impressive client base. **Clients:** Dunedin Capital; Pace Microtechnology; Case Corporation.

Walker Morris Smaller than its main competitors, and the only one of the top six that is a single office practice, this team is nevertheless perceived to have the quality individuals necessary to remain a key player. The practice covers the full range of work from capital markets to M&A and debt and equity buy-outs. Clients include a number of retail companies such as Browne & Jackson, Arcadia and Debenhams, as well as venture capital houses and clearing banks. **Ian Gilbert** is a *"high profile guy,"* particularly well-known for his work in private equity. **Paul Emmett** is viewed as *"one of the best technical lawyers in Yorkshire"* and **Peter Smart** is a *"very competent and experienced performer."* Below partner level, though, the team is seen to lack strength in depth. Highlight transactions include advising Cattles on a £400 million capitalisation issue and acting for IMS Group and Teamtalk on the latter's £375 million demerger and subsequent listing. **Clients:** Caterpillar Inc; Kelda Group plc; ECI Ventures.

Irwin Mitchell *"A good second tier firm but not making much impact beyond that"* is the consensus opinion of a team that has been active in integrating both the systems and people in its Sheffield and Leeds offices. The team has an international focus, and more than half its deals have involved overseas clients in foreign jurisdictions. One of the largest of these deals was the $88 million US purchase of Bran & Leubbe AG by Bomag Unternehmenverswaltung GmbH. **Kevin Cunningham** is a leading player, well regarded by his peers for both his technical and commercial skills. **Clients:** Thyssen Krupp; HSBC; Royal Bank of Scotland.

Lupton Fawcett Establishing a growing, and potentially highly profitable niche in the larger owner-managed/smaller listed companies market. Most of the team's work involves smaller acquisitions and divestitures, including a £23 million sale of an owner-managed business to Airtours last year. The team has also acted for a number of management teams who have secured equity financing from venture capitalists. **Clients:** ICM Computer Group; Universal Vehicles Group Limited; Caldwell Investments

Read Hind Stewart Maintains a fairly low profile but is recognised as a very capable mid-market player by its peers, and is newly ranked this year. Focused primarily in the owner managed business sector, with an average deal-size in the £3-£10 million range. Particularly strong in the hi-tech sector, where it has acted for the shareholders on the sale of Voyager Networks and Voyager Internet to RSL Communications. **Clients:** Owner-managed businesses.

Rollit Farrell & Bladon The leading practice in the Humberside region, the M&A team has been very active in the last 12 months, with deals typically falling in the £7 to £20 million range. On the private equity side, the group primarily acts for management teams, but the corporate finance team occasionally work with banks on debt-funding of buy outs. The practice also acted jointly with Ashurst Morris Crisp on the £700m flotation of Kingston Communications. **Clients:** Barclays; Fenner plc; Kingston Communications.

Andrew M Jackson & Co Best known for its large public company clients in the food sector, this team actually offers a service to a cross-section of clients and much of its client base consists of owner-managed businesses. The department's work involves small and mid-size M&A transactions, acting for management in some private equity transactions, and acting for banks on leveraged buy-outs. **Clients:** Northern Foods plc; Express Dairies.

Garretts Whilst the firm aspires to act on the largest deals for blue chip clients, the Leeds office continues to lose key individuals. However, the firm's links with Andersen Legal provide a steady stream of work, particularly for small and mid-size companies involved in MBOs or AIM listings. The team includes **Nick Painter**, considered by many to be a *"class act."* His expertise in public transport and competition issues has brought in a number of large deals including the sale of Optare Group Ltd for £21 million and advising Nottingham City Transport Ltd on the £240 million Nottingham Light Rail Project. **Clients:** Manchester Building Society; Stagecoach Group.

Gordons Cranswick Solicitors The merger of Gordons Wright & Wright and Cranswick Watson has brought together a Leeds and a Bradford based practice, to create a strong mid-sized player that spreads across Yorkshire. Around 75% of the team's work involves the buying and selling of small businesses. However, the firm does have a flagship client in Morrison supermarkets, for whom the firm undertakes sporadic but substantial activity, such as rights issues. **Clients:** Morrison Supermarkets; British Mohair Holdings; Peter Black Holdings plc.

Gosschalks Better known for its licensing work, a substantial proportion of the corporate department's work comes as a result of the firm's close links with the leisure industry. The corporate practice is growing and has advised a number of management teams on MBOs in the £10-£30 million range. The team has established a particularly good reputation dealing with smaller, entrepreneurial businesses, but also works with more established clients and has a particular niche acting for motor dealerships. **Clients:** Dixon Motors plc; William Hill.

NORTH EAST

CORPORATE FINANCE • North East	Ptnrs	Assts
❶ **Dickinson Dees** Newcastle upon Tyne	12	22
❷ **Eversheds** Newcastle upon Tyne	7	-
❸ **Ward Hadaway** Newcastle upon Tyne	6	6
❹ **Robert Muckle** Newcastle upon Tyne	3	7
❺ **Watson Burton** Newcastle upon Tyne	5	4

LEADING INDIVIDUALS	
❶ **BELLIS Nigel** Dickinson Dees	**DAVISON Andrew** Eversheds
FLYNN John Dickinson Dees	**HULLS Martin** Ward Hadaway
SPRIGGS Michael Eversheds	
❷ **GILTHORPE Ian** Robert Muckle	**PASS Jamie** Dickinson Dees
PHILLIPS Robert Robert Muckle	
❸ **HARKER Chris** Dickinson Dees	**HOYLE Andrew** Watson Burton
ON Nicholas Eversheds	**SPETCH Michael** Eversheds
UP AND COMING	
WILLIAMS Nigel Dickinson Dees	

Within each band, firms are listed alphabetically. *See **Profiles** on page 240*

Dickinson Dees Has the best public company client base in the region and a good mix of capable individuals, which gives this team a slight edge over its main rival. The practice is best known for acting on the larger deals for blue-chip clients, such as this year's sale of Arriva Automotive Solutions to General Motors for £513 million. The team's work for Northern Venture Managers Limited make it the most active Newcastle-based firm in the private equity market, and the practice also do a small amount of capital markets work for Northern Rock and Newcastle Building Society. **Nigel Bellis** is *"a backroom guy, very good technically"* while **John Flynn** has worked on some of the larger deals but also spends time on practice development. **Jamie Pass** is active in the region and *"gets plugged in to many of the bigger corporate deals"* and **Chris Harker** is often found working with Northern Venture Managers Ltd on private equity transactions. **Nigel Williams** has established himself as a rising corporate star. **Clients:** Arriva plc; The Go-Ahead Group plc; Northern Venture Managers Limited.

Eversheds *"Has the edge over Dickinson Dees in terms of national and international presence"* but the distraction of internal restructuring means that the firm has yet to catch its chief rival, although the signs are that it is getting closer. The team is divided into five groups. The Listed Company Group includes a respectable number of blue-chip clients and is led by the nationally recognised **Andrew Davison**. Davison chairs the company law committee of the Law Society and his expertise in reforms to the regulations for take-overs and stock market listings make the Newcastle office a centre of excellence for yellow/blue book work. The private equity group, led by **Michael Spetch**, acts primarily for management teams but also has a relationship with Northern Enterprise Managers. **Michael Spriggs** is *"excellent with clients"* and heads the successful owner managed business team. The acquisition finance team provides support to the other groups in corporate finance and is led by the *"versatile"* **Nick On**, while the public sector team continues to ensure that Eversheds remains pre-eminent in this sector. The team acted for Jennings on its takeover of Café Inns and for Goldsmiths Group on its recent public to private. **Clients:** Greggs plc; Northern Enterprise Managers.

Ward Hadaway Consistently ranked as a top three practice in the North East region, this team's primary focus is on owner managed businesses, although it does have an increasing number of public company clients, and has acted on some major transactions, such as the £85 million BIMBO of Motherwell Information Systems. The practice also has some leading players in the region including **Martin Hulls**, who has an excellent reputation as a deal maker, establishing some important relationships with local accountants and venture capitalists. **Clients:** Motherwell Information Systems.

Robert Muckle Has made a strategic decision not to compete at the top end of the market, and 95 percent of the team's work is for its existing client base, which is mostly owner managed businesses with £2-£8 million in turnover. Subsequently, the majority of the practice's work involves bolt-on acquisitions or divestitures. The corporate practice is not particularly active in the private equity market, but it does have a number of clients that have venture capital invested, and the team frequently advises management on exit strategies, principally secondary buy outs or trade sales. **Robert Phillips** and **Ian Gilthorpe** are the leading practitioners at a team which acted for Quality Software Holdings on a £17.5 million rights issue. **Clients:** Labelling Dynamics Ltd; Brulines Ltd; Sifam Moulded Products Ltd.

Watson Burton Mixed corporate and commercial practice with transactional work constituting around 70 percent of the caseload. Focused principally on middle market transactions, the firm has also worked on transactions in the £100 million range. Though not a particular specialism, the practice does have experience of capital markets work, advising on the AIM flotation of Premier Direct, and some local housing authorities on bond issues. **Andrew Hoyle** is the practice's best-known figure. **Clients:** Arnott Insurance; Premier Direct Group plc; Bank of Scotland.

SCOTLAND

Dickson Minto WS For pure corporate finance work, this firm is widely seen to have *"taken the top spot"* in Scotland. The firm is seen to have made incursions into the London market in a way that no Scottish firm has ever done, such that it is now regarded as a major player in the London corporate finance market and has paved the way for other Scottish firms to also *"break into London."* **Bruce Minto** is regarded as *"incredibly bright"* and *"very driven"* with a *"stratospheric profile,"* and is widely seen to be *"the major force behind their push into London."* **Keith Anderson** is *"increasingly heading up the complex, multi-faceted deals,"* particularly in the venture capital field, and *"can defend his position well without being dogmatic."* **Roderick Bruce** is *"professional and knowledgeable,"* and, although **Kevan McDonald** has *"less of a profile these days,"* he is still *"solid as a rock."*

The firm is the only Scottish firm with a top 20 UK public company practice, and is the leading private equity practice in Scotland. The firm's largest private equity transaction in the past twelve months was the £1.3 billion buy-out of AstraZeneca Specialities, where it advised Cinven and Investcorp. Recent highlights for the firm include acting for the purchaser (as appointed by 3i) in the £85 million Motherwell Information Systems IBO, which was the biggest IBO in Scotland at the time. **Clients:** Belhaven Brewery Group plc; Havelock Europa plc; Quayle Munro plc.

Dundas & Wilson CS The prevalent feeling in the market is that, as with Garretts in the English market, the firm's affiliation with the Arthur Anderson Group has hindered its contacts with the wider corporate finance market. **David Hardie** remains *"an eminent practitioner"* with *"vast experience"* and *"a very sensible approach to transactions,"* while the *"commercial"* and *"practical"* **Kenneth Rose** has been *"heading up more and more high value deals"* in the past twelve months. The firm continues to be increasingly involved in e-commerce and internet transactions. In this respect, recent highlights for the firm include being instructed by The Royal Bank in its internet banking joint venture with Scottish Power and

CORPORATE FINANCE • Scotland	Ptnrs	Assts
❶ **Dickson Minto WS** Edinburgh	9	35
❷ **Dundas & Wilson CS** Edinburgh, Glasgow	7	19
Maclay Murray & Spens Edinburgh, Glasgow	15	21
McGrigor Donald Edinburgh, Glasgow	15	23
❸ **Shepherd & Wedderburn WS** Edinburgh	8	22
❹ **Burness** Edinburgh	6	9
MacRoberts Glasgow	4	17
Paull & Williamsons Aberdeen	11	12
❺ **Biggart Baillie** Glasgow	8	10
Brodies WS Edinburgh	4	5
Ledingham Chalmers Edinburgh	3	6
McClure Naismith Glasgow	6	5
Semple Fraser WS Glasgow	4	8
Tods Murray WS Edinburgh	7	6
❻ **DLA** Glasgow	2	3
Fyfe Ireland WS Edinburgh	2	6
Henderson Boyd Jackson WS Edinburgh	5	5
Iain Smith & Company Aberdeen	3	3
Thorntons WS Dundee	⚐	⚐

LEADING INDIVIDUALS	
❶ **DICKSON Ian** MacRoberts	**HARDIE David** Dundas & Wilson CS
McNEILL Morag McGrigor Donald	**MINTO Bruce** Dickson Minto WS
SWANSON Magnus Maclay Murray & Spens	
❷ **ANDERSON Keith** Dickson Minto WS	**BRUCE Roderick** Dickson Minto WS
CUNNINGHAM Neil MacRoberts	**GRAY Colin** McGrigor Donald
LUMSDEN Ian Maclay Murray & Spens	**PATRICK Bruce** Maclay Murray & Spens
RAFFERTY John Burness	**SLEIGH Andrew** Burness
WILL James Shepherd & Wedderburn WS	
❸ **ALLAN David** Biggart Baillie	**BARRIE Sidney** Paull & Williamsons
BUCHAN Gordon Paull & Williamsons	**DEANE David** Semple Fraser WS
FRIER George McClure Naismith	**GLEN Marian** Shepherd & Wedderburn WS
McDONALD Kevan Dickson Minto WS	**McGINN James** MacRoberts
MEIKLEJOHN Iain Shepherd & Wedderburn WS	
ROSE Kenneth Dundas & Wilson CS	**SIMMONS William** Tods Murray WS
SLOAN Graeme Maclay Murray & Spens	**SMITH Campbell** Biggart Baillie
STEWART Alan Burness	
UP AND COMING	
FEECHAN Catherine Biggart Baillie	**KANE Hilary** Maclay Murray & Spens
MASTERS Richard McGrigor Donald	**SHAND Kenneth** Maclay Murray & Spens

Within each band, firms are listed alphabetically. *See **Profiles** on page 240*
⚐ *Figures unavailable at time of going to press.*

also in The Royal Bank's strategic alliance with CGU, which involved the sale of a 50 percent stake in Royal Scottish Assurance plc for £150 million. The firm also recently acted as UK legal advisers to Planet Payment Group Inc, an American internet payment solutions company, in a private placing for US$6 million. **Clients:** Dawson International; Martin Currie; Scottish Media Group plc.

Maclay Murray & Spens This firm undertakes a broad range of corporate finance work throughout Scotland, with a growing presence in London, and is particularly strong in the venture capital field. The corporate department's mergers and acquisition practice, which is driven by established acquisitive clients, has been consistently busy over the past twelve months. An *"impressive and effective team"* is headed by the *"stellar," "charming"* and *"very bright"* **Magnus Swanson**, who is renowned for his venture capital expertise. **Ian Lumsden** *"knows his way around the market"* and *"always turns in a good performance – he's top-notch across the board."* **Bruce Patrick** has *"seen it all"* and **Graeme Sloan** is *"pragmatic," "commercial"* and *"good at moving deals along to a conclusion."* The *"hard-working"* **Hilary Kane** is *"a sharp cookie"* who is *"coming up through the ranks,"* while **Kenneth Shand** *"knows what he's about"* and is *"doing a lot of good quality work."* The firm acted for Scottish Widows on its £7.2 billion demutualisation, and advised Colonial Ltd on its acquisition of the entire issued share capital of Stewart Ivory Holdings Ltd, valued at £47.2 million. **Clients:** 3i plc; Scottish Amicable; Scottish Widows.

McGrigor Donald The corporate finance department is headed by **Morag McNeill**, who is widely seen to be *"a worthy adversary"* and *"a tough opponent"* with a *"wealth of experience and ability to match."* **Colin Gray** is *"switched-on"* and *"good to deal with – he knows what he's doing and he gets the job done."* **Richard Masters** is *"a capable operator"* who is *"less visible than some, but a real trouper behind the scenes."* The firm's well-established London office, which is now in its eleventh year, continues to attract an ever-increasing number of blue-chip companies. The firm also operates from offices in Belfast and Brussels. Over the past year, the department has successfully completed fund-raising work for a number of key players in the technology/biosciences sector, and recently advised the Bank of Scotland and the management team of CALA plc on one of the most hotly-contested public to private takeover bids of recent years. **Clients:** Hays plc; Iomart Ltd; TBH Trading Ltd.

Shepherd & Wedderburn WS During the year, the firm has been active in M&A transactions, fund-raisings for unquoted companies and listed companies, flotations, Eurobond issues and investment trust issues and organisations. Head of department **James Will** attracts polarised opinions. Although some felt that he was *"very good at promoting James Will"*, the prevailing consensus was that he *"doesn't mess around when it comes to getting the job done and doing deals."* The *"underrated"* **Marian Glen** is widely regarded as being *"very sensible"* while **Iain Meiklejohn**, although lower profile this year, is still an *"on the ball"* lawyer. Recent highlights include the £60 million disposal of Stewart Ivory Ltd and the £44 million disposal of Sigma Technology Management. **Clients:** Bank of Scotland; Scottish Power.

Burness This firm is said to have *"really got its act together"* in the past twelve months and is now *"more focused."* **John Rafferty** is widely regarded as the *"chairman of the board"* and is *"highly proficient in just about any area of corporate finance you can name."* The *"first class"* **Andrew Sleigh** heads the firm's Glasgow corporate finance practice, and is widely regarded to be *"doing a lot of work at the coalface,"* although there has been comment that he *"spreads himself a bit thin"* by doing banking and insolvency work as well. The firm has also recently hired the *"well-travelled"* and *"street-wise"* **Alan Stewart**. As well as undertaking a number of MBOs, the team has increased its private equity work over the past twelve months, particularly in relation to e-commerce companies. Acted for Fife Power in connection with the £58 million senior debt and subordinated facility for Phase 2 of the Fife Power independent power generation project at Westfield, Fife. Also advised a Jersey investment company on the sale of property holding companies for the sum of £67 million. **Clients:** Charterhouse Private Equity Investments; Investec; Royal Bank of Scotland.

MacRoberts The firm undertakes a variety of corporate finance work including acquisitions and disposals, private equity work and yellow book work. **Ian Dickson** heads the corporate group, and is *"down to earth, straightforward and commercial."* **Neil Cunningham** has been *"moving on up"* and *"making his mark"* in the market, while **James McGinn** is *"a safe pair of hands."* Advised ISI Group plc on the £20 million MBO of McLaren Consulting Ltd from ISI backed by Penta Capital. Also acted for Johnston Press plc in its £16 million acquisition from SouthNews of Four Counties Newspapers Ltd and Lincolnshire Standard Group Ltd. **Clients:** Adams Hotels Ltd; Johnston Press plc; Royal Bank Development Capital.

Paull & Williamsons Retains its *"tight grip on the Aberdeen market."* Along with fellow Aberdeen firm Ledingham Chalmers, the firm has the local market *"practically sewn up,"* particularly in the oil and gas industry. Unlike Ledingham Chalmers, however, this firm has no apparent desire to *"go outside its primary stomping ground."* The highly regarded **Sid Barrie** has *"a lot of corporate nous,"* while **Gordon Buchan** is *"a seasoned campaigner"* and *"a sharp operator."* Acted as the Scottish lawyers for ASCO plc on its recent IPO. **Clients:** AsCO plc; First Group; Orwell Group.

Biggart Baillie Head of department **David Allan** is *"someone you can do business with,"* while recently made-up partner **Catherine Feechan** *"quickly making a name for herself"* in the region, particularly for her listed company and equity investment work. **Campbell Smith** also has his share of market support. The firm acts for a wide range of clients, from major corporate organisations like Scottish Power to funders like ADC (Glasgow) and the major banks. Niche expertise exists in equity investment and AIM flotations. Highlights of the past twelve months include acting for the management team in the MBO of Caley Ocean Systems and acting for AorTech International plc in connection with the acquisition of interests in the UK and Australia. **Clients:** ADC (Glasgow); Aortech International plc; Bell Lawrie Wise Speke.

Brodies WS The firm acts for a diverse range of clients including vehicle rental companies, leisure and hotel operators, engineering companies, computer and IT-related companies, biotech companies, banks, fund managers and insurance companies. Niche strength in advising on the regulatory regime for privatised industries such as rail, electricity, coal and defence contracting accompanies a broad range of standard M&A work. However, there has been market comment that the firm's corporate department *"lacks specialist depth,"* and there is no stand-out practitioner here. Acted on the joint venture between IFA Portfolio Ltd and Bankhall Investment Associates Ltd, which included the disposal by IFA Portfolio Ltd of its subsidiary Anglo-Caledonian Affinity plc. **Clients:** Co-operative Wholesale Society Ltd; IFA Portfolio Ltd; Wolseley Centers Ltd.

Ledingham Chalmers Remains *"a force in Aberdeen"* for its corporate finance work, with a particularly strong oil industry client base, although the firm's Edinburgh office is said to *"have been a bit quiet lately."* In spite of recent personnel losses, the firm *"still churns out some good quality work"* in Aberdeen, although it is not felt to have caught Paull & Williamsons locally. The team acted for Newco and 3i plc on the £8.6 million IBO of AFOS International Limited. **Clients:** Agricultural Mortgage Corporation; Clydesdale Bank plc; Scottish Woodlands Ltd.

McClure Naismith Act for a wide range of owner-managed businesses, and an increasing number of high-profile companies in the drinks, manufacturing, engineering and leisure sectors. **George Frier** is becoming *"more of a name in corporate finance circles,"* particularly for M&A work. However, market comment was that the firm was *"full of good generalists, but lacking specialised expertise."* Recent work has included acting for the management team in the MBO of McLaren Consulting Ltd from ISI Group backed by Penta Capital Partners. **Clients:** First Engineering Ltd; Ridgmount International Ltd; Unicorn Leisure Group plc.

Semple Fraser WS Particularly involved in the M&A market, the firm has niche strength in IT-related matters, and has an increasing number of e-commerce clients. Considered to be doing *"reasonably well in their locality,"* the team is active on small and medium-ticket deals. **David Deane** is *"an impressive operator"* who has the ability to *"complete deals during banking hours on the day they were meant to be completed."* Acted for various vendors on the £5 million sale of the entire issued share capital of First Press Publishing Ltd to Scottish Daily Record and Sunday Mail Ltd. **Clients:** Anderson Precision Gears Ltd; Georgeson Office Interiors Ltd; Thomson Pettie Tube Products Ltd.

Tods Murray WS Act for a broad range of corporate clients over most industry sectors, including fully listed companies, AIM listed companies, merchant banks, manufacturing companies and leisure-related companies. The corporate finance team has a particular niche in the acquisition and disposal of companies and businesses, as well as joint ventures. **William Simmons** is *"the corporate partner you hear about"* here, although he is felt to lack comparable support. The team acted as Scottish legal advisers to Goldman Sachs International, who were the sponsors, financial advisers, brokers, lead underwriters and global co-ordinators of the flotation of Thus plc, the biggest ever Scottish corporate flotation. **Clients:** Bank of Scotland; Dobbies Garden Centres plc; Melrose Resources plc.

DLA This newly constituted firm has been concentrating on handling acquisitions for its plc clients and disposals for its private company clients. The new entity *"can only benefit from the broader resource base"* that DLA can offer. The firm now does all the work for Vivendi in the west of Scotland, and has also been helping the expansion of City Refrigeration Holdings Ltd up and down the country. Acted for an American corporation in acquiring a privately-owned company in the nursery/health care sector in Scotland. **Clients:** City Refrigeration Holdings Ltd; Universal Scientific Industrial Company; Vivendi.

Fyfe Ireland WS The firm continues to derive the bulk of its corporate finance work from its solid property client base as well as a number of acquisitive investment funds. Market comment is that the firm has *"fallen away a bit"* recently, particularly since the loss of two corporate partners to Shepherd & Wedderburn. **Clients:** Property clients; investment funds.

Henderson Boyd Jackson WS The firm continues to act primarily for small to medium-sized owner-managed businesses with turnovers between £1-£15 million. Highlights of the past year include advising BT Cellnet in Scotland on its £35 million acquisition of DX Communications Ltd and advising BUE Marine Ltd on its £28 million acquisition of the North Sea Standby fleet from Tidewater Inc. **Clients:** Bue Marine Ltd; Highfield Group Ltd; Jarvis plc.

Iain Smith & Company Described as *"a good wee firm,"* prominent in and around Aberdeen for corporate finance work, it generally handles private company work, and is particularly noted for advising on the sale of local receivership businesses. **Clients:** Private clients.

Thorntons WS Remains a locally-based entity, *"not on the radar"* outside its immediate locality. However, *"if you think of corporate finance in Dundee, you think of them – they are without question the strongest there."* The firm continues its involvement with housing associations, and occasionally handles MBO work. **Clients:** Housing associations.

NORTHERN IRELAND

L'Estrange & Brett *"The best place in Northern Ireland"* for corporate finance work, this is *"a very good firm with a highly competent team." "Excellent"* **John Irvine** is *"an extremely high quality operator;" "very few will deliver as good a deal for their client as him."* **Richard Gray** is *"technically good and easy to get on with."* **Paul McBride** *"can put things across in layman's language."* Highlights of the year include completing a number of significant transactions for SX3, a subsidiary of Viridian plc, and acting for BetterCare Group in its acquisition of the Extendicare Group of Nursing Homes. **Clients:** SX3; BetterCare Group; Ulster Television plc; Global E-Mail Company Ltd.

Carson & McDowell *"Efficient, responsive and proactive."* **Michael Johnston** *("has a lot of common sense, and doesn't score points unnecessarily")* and **David Jamison** head a formidable team. They have been involved in a number of e-commerce transactions, acted for Open and Direct, a subsidiary of Viridian, on insurance business buy-ins, and worked with the University of Ulster on the Springvale Project this year. **Clients:** Open and Direct; The University of Ulster; The Bank of Ireland.

CORPORATE FINANCE • Northern Ireland	Ptnrs	Assts
❶ **L'Estrange & Brett** Belfast	3	7
❷ **Carson & McDowell** Belfast	3	4
❸ **Mills Selig** Belfast	3	2
Tughan & Co Belfast	3	4
❹ **Arthur Cox** Belfast	2	1
Elliott Duffy Garrett Belfast	3	3
❺ **Cleaver Fulton Rankin** Belfast	2	3
Johns Elliot Belfast	2	1
Johnsons Belfast	1	-
McKinty & Wright Belfast	1	2

LEADING INDIVIDUALS	
❶ **IRVINE John** L'Estrange & Brett	
❷ **JOHNSTON Michael** Carson & McDowell	
❸ **BOYD Frederick** McKinty & Wright	**FULTON Richard** Mills Selig
GRAY Richard L'Estrange & Brett	**JAMISON David** Carson & McDowell
❹ **BUTLER Maurice** Johns Elliot	**CANAVAN Kerry** Arthur Cox
MARSHALL John Johnsons	**McBRIDE Paul** L'Estrange & Brett
WILLIS John-George Tughan & Co	
UP AND COMING	
STAFFORD Peter Arthur Cox	

Within each band, firms are listed alphabetically. *See* ***Profiles*** *on page 240*

Mills Selig *"Small, have their own niche market,"* and *"are quite active."* **Richard Fulton** is *"easy to get along with"* and *"very pragmatic."* Acted for Landmark G.P. Ltd, the Masstock Group and a number of VC houses. **Clients:** Landmark G.P. Ltd; the Masstock Group; VC houses.

Tughan & Co *"Up and coming firm,"* noted for its hi-tech clientele. **John-George Willis** is *"an aggressive figure in the market-place."* Highlights of the year include acting for Glenfarm Holdings in relation to the acquisition of Fats & Protein, a rendering business in Lancaster, for £14.5 million; acting for Tesco Stores on the acquisition of the trade and related assets of the Co-op Yorkgate Superstore, Belfast; and acting for Lamont Holdings plc in the disposal of the trade and related assets of Hollybank Bleach and Dye works. **Clients:** Tesco Stores; ABN; Lamont Holdings plc; Glenfarm Holdings.

Arthur Cox *"More on the banking side,"* according to one commentator, but frequently cited as a player in the field, the firm includes **Kerry Canavan** *("technically very good")* and *"up and coming"* **Peter Stafford.** The team has been involved in a number of important transactions this year, including a private placing raising funds of £7 million, and another placing relating to a property venture. **Clients:** Local and international corporates.

Elliott Duffy Garrett *"Suffering a bit,"* due to the retirement of Brian Garrett, who retains a consultancy position, and the departure of Jacqueline Kerr to an in-house position elsewhere. The firm has advised on a number of acquisitions and disposals, and is active in the fields of securitisation, PFI work, and project finance. **Clients:** Local corporates.

Cleaver Fulton Rankin *"Aspiring to be corporate,"* and, to a certain extent, succeeding, it has established links with a network of international law firms and other advisors. The highlight of the year was advising on Lindsay Cars Ltd's acquisition of Knockdene Garages Ltd. This involved the acquisition by Lindsay Cars of a Ford Dealership with a network of 4 garages in the Belfast region for a consideration of £3.5 million. **Clients:** Lindsay Cars Ltd; The Bank of Ireland.

Johns Elliot *"Present in the market, but to a lesser extent than before." "Old-school"* **Maurice Butler** is *"sensible to deal with"* and *"intelligent."* He heads a team that is currently advising on a joint venture in the textile industry between Samuel Lamont (Holdings) Ltd and Valley Dyeworks Ltd. **Clients:** Samuel Lamont (Holdings) Ltd; Valley Dyeworks Ltd.

Johnsons *"Picking up a bit,"* and *"starting to make a niche for themselves."* **John Marshall** *"a pragmatic generalist,"* is the stand-out practitioner at a firm which continues to advise on small-ticket M&A activity. **Clients:** Local corporates.

McKinty and Wright *"Historically 3i's choice,"* but *"increasingly less evident in the market-place,"* due to the defection of a key player to Carson & McDowell. *"Excellent"* **Eric Boyd** *"does a mix"* of work and, though considered by some to do *"more property than corporate,"* is generally recognised to be *"a decent lawyer."* Highlights of the year include handling the sale of a feed company, the purchase of a bleaching works and a pair of venture capital transactions. **Clients:** 3i.

LEADERS IN CORPORATE FINANCE

ACOCK, Roger
Bond Pearce, Exeter (01392) 211 185
xrja@bondpearce.com
Specialisation: Partner in the Corporate Group specialising in corporate finance. Regularly leads *Bond Pearce* teams on many high profile MBO, MBI, IBO and other corporate finance transactions across the southern region. Recent deals include £35m buy out of British International from CHC Helicopter Corporation and £150m merger of Flagships Foods. Special interest and experience in waste management and aviation law.
Prof. Memberships: Member of the International Bar Association and Solicitors European Group. Chairman of the Devon and Cornwall Branch of the Institute of Directors. Director of Environmental Trust and PLC Employee Share Trust. Member of the British Venture Capital Association.
Career: Qualified 1980. Partner 1985. Previous firm *Durrant Piesse* (now *Lovell White Durrant*).

ALEXANDER-SINCLAIR, Ian
Mills & Reeve, Norwich (01603) 693 212
ian.alexander-sinclair@mills-reeve.com
Partner in Company Department.
Specialisation: Main area of practice is company law, covering mergers and acquisitions, disposals, schemes of arrangement and listed company work. Other area is commercial including joint ventures.
Prof. Memberships: Law Society, Norfolk and Norwich Law Society.
Career: John Mackrell Prize and City of London Solicitors' Company Prize 1971. At *Slaughter and May* from 1969 to 1977. Joined *Mills and Reeve* in 1977, becoming a partner in 1979.
Personal: Christ's Hospital and St John's College Oxford (M.A.) Leisure: History, reading, walking, cricket.Family: Married, 2 sons. Resides Norwich.

ALLAN, David S.
Biggart Baillie, Glasgow (0141) 228 8000
dallan@biggartbaillie.co.uk
Specialisation: Specialist in Corporate Finance. ATM/Listed Company Work. Equity Investments Acquisitions and Disposals. Major deals in 2000 - sale of Atlantech Technologies Ltd to Cisco Systems Inc. For US$180 million. Placing & Open offer for Aortech International plc to raise £18 million.
Prof. Memberships: Law Society of Scotland.
Career: Glasgow University LLB. Trained at *Wright Johnston & Mackenzie*, assistant at *Maclay Murray & Spens*, Group Legal Adviser at Allenwest Group. *Biggart Baillie* since 1982.
Personal: Married with 2 children. Interests golf and sailing. Lives in Troon.

ALLEN, Amanda
Pinsent Curtis, Birmingham (0121) 200 1050
amanda.allen@pinsents.com
Partner in Corporate Finance Department and Head of Automotive Team.
Specialisation: Handles all types of corporate finance work including mergers and acquisitions, disposals, joint ventures, take overs, business and corporate reorganisation etc.

Career: Qualified in 1986. Partner at *Pinsent Curtis* since 1992.
Personal: Born 1960. Leisure interests include golf, skiing and travel.

ALLEN-JONES, Charles
Linklaters (A member firm of Linklaters & Alliance), London (020) 7456 3720
charles.allen-jones@linklaters.com
Senior Partner of Linklaters. Co-chairman Linklaters & Alliance.
Specialisation: Specialist in corporate matters, particularly equity issues, public and private acquisitions, privatisations and projects. Responsible for managing the firm's relationships with several key clients.
Career: Partner in charge of *Linklater's* International Finance Department 1981-83; Partner in charge of Corporate Department 1985-91. Qualified 1963.
Personal: Born 1939.

ANDERSON, Keith T.
Dickson Minto WS, Glasgow (0141) 229 4455)
keith.anderson@dmws.com
Partner in Corporate Department, based in Glasgow.
Specialisation: Corporate and commercial; mergers and acquisitions, management buy-ins and outs, institutional buy-outs, sale and purchase of companies and businesses, refinancings. Recent deals include the £40m IBO of Antler Limited for Royal Bank Development Capital; the £72m IBO of Donprint Limited for Bridgepoint Capital and the £14m IBO of McLaren Consulting Limited for Penta Capital Partners.
Prof. Memberships: Law Society of Scotland; Society of Writers to the Signet.
Career: Qualified in 1981. Joined *Dickson Minto W.S.* as Senior Assistant in 1989 and assumed as a Partner in 1994.
Personal: Born 24th January 1957. Attended George Watson's College 1962-1975; University of Edinburgh 1975-1979 (LLB(Hons)). Leisure interests include rugby, golf, football and music.

ANGEL, Peter G.
Manches, Oxford (01865) 722106
peter.angel@manches.co.uk
Partner in the Company & Commercial Department.
Specialisation: General corporate finance and venture capital work, with particular interest in corporate and regulatory aspects of the Lloyd's insurance market. Regular speaker at seminars on corporate finance topics.
Career: Qualified 1970.
Personal: Born 27th July, 1946. Attended Maidstone Grammar School 1959-64 and then University College London. Board member of The College of Estate Management. Lives in Oxford.

AP SIMON, Charles
Freshfields Bruckhaus Deringer, London (020) 7936 4000
capsimon@freshfields.com
London (020) 7832 7125 direct line. Partner in corporate department.
Specialisation: Main area of practice is corporate and corporate finance. Advises corporate and merchant banking clients on corporate, stock exchange and take-over related issues, including securities issues, joint ventures and private acquisitions and disposals.
Prof. Memberships: Law Society and City Solicitors' Company. Listing Authority Listing Rules Committee member.
Career: Qualified in 1977. Joined *Freshfields* in 1977, becoming a partner in 1982.
Personal: Born 28th June 1947. Attended Epsom College 1960-65 and Christ's College Cambridge 1966-69 (MA, LLB).

ARMITAGE, David W.K.
Hammond Suddards Edge, Leeds (0113) 284 7000
david.armitage@hammondsuddardsedge.co.uk
Specialisation: Corporate Finance partner for the firm operating out of its Leeds and London offices and specialising in national and international merger and acquisition work, MBOs and MBIs, joint ventures, competition issues, commercial and sports sponsorship and endorsement work; corporate restructuring; capital issues and Yellow Book and Blue Book work for plc clients. Leads *Hammond Suddards Edge's* Engineering Sector group and Sports group. Recent highlights include: acting for Halifax plc in its multiple estate agency disposal programme and its rightmove.co.uk joint venture; acting for FKI plc on its £131 million recommended bid for Bridon plc; acting for Umbro International in its £90 million disposal of Umbro to Doughty Hanson.
Prof. Memberships: Law Society.
Career: Rydal School, Colwyn Bay; Queens' College, Cambridge (1980 BA, 1983 MA). Articled *Alexander Tatham*, Manchester; qualified 1983; Ferranti plc 1985-86; joined *Hammond Suddards* 1986; partner since 1988.
Personal: Born 1958; resides Harrogate; married with three children. Leisure interests include golf, rugby, motor sports.

ASHWORTH, Chris John
Ashurst Morris Crisp, London (020) 7638 1111
Specialisation: Mergers and acquisitions, corporate finance, insolvency, transactional work and finance. Clients include investment banks and corporates such as United News & Media, Thuraya, Deutsche Telekom, British Telecom, AMVESCAP, Northern Foods plc and Henlys.
Prof. Memberships: LLB graduate of Southampton University. Lectured at Manchester University. Joined *Ashurst Morris Crisp* in 1982 and became a partner in 1986.

AUDLEY, Max
Hobson Audley, London 020 7450 4500
maudley@hobsonaudley.co.uk
Specialisation: Head of company department. Specialises in corporate finance, IPOs, MBOs, takeovers, mergers and acquisitions.
Prof. Memberships: International Bar Association - Company Law Committee. Associate of American Bar Association - Business Law Section. Association of German-speaking lawyers.
Career: Qualified 1980. Co-founded *Hobson Audley* 1983. Has built up a team of experienced corporate lawyers.

BAIRD, Derek W
Dickson Minto WS, London (020) 7628 4455
derek.baird@dmws.com
Specialisation: Mergers and acquisitions (public and private), particularly institutional and leveraged buy-outs; advising major financial institutions.
Career: Qualified with *Dickson Minto WS* in 1992, becoming a partner in 1999.

BAIRD, James
Clifford Chance, London (020) 7600 1000
jamesbaird@cliffordchance.com
Specialisation: Partner specialising in general company and corporate finance matters including company acquisitions, venture capital, takeovers and listings. Since 1983 major specialisation in leveraged and management buy-outs.
Career: University College, Oxford (BA Jurisprudence 1975). Articled *Pinsent & Co* (Birmingham); qualified 1978; partner *Clifford Chance* 1985.
Personal: Born 1954.

BAKER, Andrew P.
Wedlake Bell, London (020) 7395 3000
Partner. Head of corporate finance.
Specialisation: Corporate. Acts for a wide range of listed companies, brokers and venture capitalists with regard to mergers and acquisitions, equity issues and flotations. Speaker at seminars and conferences with regard to corporate governance and buying and selling companies.
Career: Articled with *Slaughter and May* in 1970. Qualified 1972 joining the commercial department of *Slaughter and May*. Joined *Wedlake Bell* 1979 becoming a partner in 1982. Head of corporate finance 1985 to date. President of the international alliance of independent commercial law firms, TELFA (Trans European Law Firms Alliance). Member of legal and tax and corporate governance committees of European Association of Securities Dealers.
Personal: Born 12th October 1946. LLB(Hons) Birmingham 1969. Lives in Surrey. Also a Director of The Global Group plc, The Egyptian-British Chamber of Commerce and Lambeth Building Society.

BARNARD, Stephen G.
Herbert Smith, London (020) 7374 8000
Partner in Corporate Division.
Specialisation: Heads one of the firm's corporate groups and deals with a broad range of company and commercial work including corporate finance, mergers and acquisitions, venture capital and leveraged transactions, privatisations and major projects. His work involves acting for a number of listed clients as well as financial intermediaries, institutions and government. Deals include the London Stock Exchange demutualisation and European alliances and mergers, the establishment of the global arrangements for the governance of PricewaterhouseCoopers and local PwC mergers in Europe and Africa and the reorganisation of the renewables energy structure in the UK.
Career: Qualified in 1974. Partner at *Herbert Smith* since 1983.
Personal: Educated at Southampton University.

BARNES, Oliver W.A.
Travers Smith Braithwaite, London (020) 7295 3000
Oliver.Barnes@TraversSmith.com
Specialisation: Head of *Travers Smith Braithwaite's* company department. Corporate and corporate finance. Public takeovers, mergers and acquisitions, flotations and secondary issues. Corporate governance.
Prof. Memberships: Member of Law Society's Company Law Committee; International Bar Association.
Career: Articled at *Travers Smith Braithwaite*. Qualified 1976. Partner 1980.
Personal: Born 1950. Educated at Eton College and Trinity Hall, Cambridge.

BARR, Alan
Burges Salmon, Bristol (0117) 939 2255
alan.barr@burges-salmon.com
Specialisation: Company law and corporate finance including: business and company acquisitions and disposals, public company flotations and reversals, equity financing and takeovers, corporate restructuring and management buy-outs and buy-ins, for clients such as Brandon Hire plc FirstGroup plc, Orange plc, Rotork plc, Science Systems plc, Transport Development Group plc. Alan acts for and is company secretary of Bristol City Football Club.
Prof. Memberships: Law Society's Standing Committee on Company Law.
Career: Trained with *Slaughter and May*, joined *Clifford Chance* for 4 years, joined *Burges Salmon* in 1986 and became a partner in 1988.
Personal: Brought up in Northern Ireland, graduated in law from University of Wales. Keen runner, hill walker, cyclist and swimmer.

BARRIE, Sidney
Paull & Williamsons, Aberdeen (01224) 621621
sbarrie@paull-williamsons.co.uk
Specialisation: Partner in the Corporate Department specialising in MBOs and acquisitions and disposals. Also advises on general corporate law, including reconstructions, investment documentation and contractual work.
Prof. Memberships: Law Society of Scotland; Society of Advocates in Aberdeen.
Career: James & George Collie 1971-73. Joined Paull & Williamsons 1973, partner 1978.
Personal: Educated at Robert Gordon's College, Aberdeen 1962-68 and at Aberdeen University 1968-71. Leisure pursuits include golf and watching football. Lives in Aberdeen. Born 14th June 1950.

BARRON, Michael J.
Dickson Minto WS, London (020) 7628 4455
michael.barron@dmws.com
Specialisation: Management buy-outs and buy-ins, especially structured debt finance and other credit facilities. Acts for major financial institutions and banks active in the venture capital and development capital market.
Career: Qualified as a solicitor in Scotland 1977 and in England 1986. Educated University of Edinburgh. Solicitor with 3i plc 1984 to 1987 then with *Dickson Minto WS*, as a partner since 1989.

BARTER, Charles S. J.
Travers Smith Braithwaite, London
(020) 7295 3000
Charles.Barter@TraversSmith.com
Partner in corporate finance department
Specialisation: Corporate finance, in particular private equity, buyouts, buyins, disposals and reconstructions.
Prof. Memberships: Law Society, City of London Solicitors Company.
Career: Articled Clerk 1985; Partner 1995.
Personal: Motorcycling, gardening, natural history, Church.

BAXTER, Richard
Stevens & Bolton, Guildford (01483) 734 213
Specialisation: All aspects of company law, including acquisitions, disposals, MBOs and other venture capital transactions, reorganisations, joint ventures and new issues. Recent transactions include a number of purchases for Hays plc with deal values up to £55 million and the £24 million recommended cash offer by Gladedale Homes plc for AIM-listed Furlong Homes Group plc. Contributor to 'Tolley's Company Law'.
Career: St Paul's School; Exeter University (LLB Hons). 1985 *Clifford-Turner* (now *Clifford Chance*). Specialised in corporate finance before joining *Stevens & Bolton*, becoming partner in 1990. Head of company/commercial department.
Personal: Born 5 May 1962. Married with 2 children. Leisure interests include golf (Hankley Common Golf Club), fishing, other sport, cinema, gardening and family.

BEDDOW, Simon D. J.
Ashurst Morris Crisp, London (020) 7638 1111
Specialisation: UK and cross-border Corporate and Corporate Finance and venture capital.
Prof. Memberships: City of London Solicitors' Company.
Career: 1987-1989 *Pinsent & Co* (Birmingham) (Articled Clerk), 1989-1996 *Travers Smith Braithwaite* (Assistant), 1996- *Ashurst Morris Crisp* (Partner Since 1998).
Personal: Married with two daughters and one son.

BEHARRELL, Steven
Coudert Brothers, London (020) 7248 3000
beharrells@london.coudert.com
Specialisation: Senior partner, *Coudert Brothers*, London. Specialises in energy, oil, gas and power and natural resources, infrastructure investment, project finance, transportation and privatisation. Has 30 years experience advising on oil and gas law in the Middle East, Asia, North Sea and Russia. Also involved in electricity and other privatisations since the late 1980s. Regularly addresses conferences and seminars on the subject of energy and privatisation law.
Prof. Memberships: International Bar Association.
Career: Assistant solicitor, Denton Hall 1966-72 and partner 1972-90. Partner, *Coudert Brothers* since 1990.
Personal: Educated at Sorbonne University, Paris 1961-62 and the College of Law, London 1964-66. Lives in London. Born 22nd December 1944.

BELL, Christopher C.
Travers Smith Braithwaite, London
(020) 7295 3000
Specialisation: Corporate and corporate finance - mergers and acquisitions, equity financings, MBO's and MBI's. Corporate governance issues.
Prof. Memberships: Member of the Company Law sub-committee of the City of London Solicitors Company.
Career: Qualified April 1971. Partner at *Travers Smith Braithwaite* since 1975, having joined the firm in 1971 after Articles at *Crossman Block & Keith*.

BELLEW, Derek J.
Veale Wasbrough, Bristol (0117) 925 2020
Partner in Company Commercial Department. Chairman.
Specialisation: Work covers company sales and purchases, MBOs, corporate finance and professional partnerships. Specialist practice in medical partnerships.
Career: Qualified 1967. Managing Partner of *Veale Wasbrough* 1993-98. Chairman since 1998.
Personal: Born 1942. St John's College, Oxford 1961-64. Chairman St George's Music Trust.

BELLIS, Nigel D.
Dickinson Dees, Newcastle upon Tyne
(0191) 279 9250
Partner in Company and Commercial Department.
Specialisation: Handles flotations, share issues, mergers and acquisitions, IT contracts, e-commerce advice and complex commercial agreements. Clients include public companies, utilities and substantial private companies, as well as public sector organisations.
Prof. Memberships: Law Society.
Career: Qualified in 1977. Joined *Dickinson Dees* in 1980 and became a Partner in 1982.
Personal: Born 1953. Educated at Cambridge University 1971-74. Lives in Newcastle upon Tyne.

BELLIS, P.T.
Herbert Smith, London (020) 7374 8000
Specialisation: Partner in Corporate Division. Has concentrated particularly in the areas of mergers and acquisitions, corporate finance, securities offerings and capital markets transactions on international stock exchanges (London, Hong Kong and Luxembourg) and investment and joint venture work.
Career: Qualified in 1981 and became Partner in 1987.

BENNETT, John E.
Berwin Leighton, London (020) 7760 1000
Specialisation: Mergers and Acquisitions, corporate finance, private equity and general company and securities law specialist.
Prof. Memberships: City of London Law Society Company Laws Sub-Committee.
Career: Qualified in 1983 with *Berwin Leighton*. Became a partner in 1987. Head of Corporate.

BERINGER, Guy Gibson
Allen & Overy, London (020) 7330 3000
beringeg@allenovery.com
Specialisation: He has a wide experience of advising major corporations in relation to their commercial affairs. He has been closely involved in major UK and cross-border M&A work arising from public takeover bids as well as purchases and sales of privately-owned companies and businesses. He has been involved in the establishment of joint ventures and strategic alliances and has broad experience of commercial negotiations involving many industrial sectors.
Career: Associate, *Allen & Overy* 1980-1985. Partner, *Allen & Overy* since 1985. Managing Partner, Corporate Development 1994-1998. Head of the Corporate Department 1998-1999. Senior Partner 2000.
Personal: Born 12th August, 1955. MA Cambridge University, admitted as Solicitor 1980.

BERRY, Stephen
M and A Solicitors, Cardiff (029) 2066 5793
Specialisation: Corporate and commercial work. Transactions in the last twelve months include advising the selling shareholders of the "Travel House" on its sale to Thompson Travel plc, the merger of Epitaxial Products Limited and QED Inc to create IQE plc and it subsequent listing on EASDAQ, a major fund raising by Tomos Watkin Limited, and various acquisitions for Peters Food Service Limited.
Career: 1991-1993 *Herbert Smith*; 1993-1999 *Eversheds* appointed partner in 1998; 1999 present *M and A Solicitors* one of the founding partners.
Personal: Married with one daughter. Lives in Cardiff and is a keen sportsman sailing, skiing, windsurfing, rugby and football.

BESWICK, Simon A.
Osborne Clarke OWA, Bristol (0117) 917 4146
simon.beswick@osborneclarke.com
Specialisation: Specialises in management and institutional buy-outs, M&A and technology investments, acting for institutions, companies and management teams. Simon is independently regarded as the leading transactional lawyer in the South West. Recent work includes: advising a syndicate of institutional investors on the $80m second round funding of Kymata; advising the shareholders of Stentorfield Limited on its sale for £20m; advising Ultra Electronics Limited on the acquisition of DF Group Limited for £45m; acting for a syndicate of investors led by 3i Group plc on the flotation of application service provider Netstore plc for £40m.
Career: Simon became a partner at *Osborne Clarke* in 1989 and from 1996-2000 was Head of Corporate, Bristol. He has published a book entitled 'Buying & Selling Private Companies & Businesses' (Wine & Beswick).

BIRCHALL, Roger
Hammond Suddards Edge, Birmingham (0121) 200 2001
Partner with *Hammonds Suddards Edge* and a member of the Company/Commercial Department.
Specialisation: From a background of general acquisition and disposal work, Roger has particular expertise in management buy-out/buy-in transactions and the venture/development capital sector generally. Whilst he is well known for acting for management teams, he has substantial experience in acting for vendors and a number of the major providors of equity finance. Roger's experience ranges from small local, to large cross-border transactions.
Career: Hull University LLB (Hons). College of Law, Chester.

BIRD, Alistair
Simmons & Simmons, London (020) 7628 2020
alistair.bird@simmons-simmons.com
Specialisation: Partner specialising in corporate matters, particularly public and private acquisitions and venture capital.
Prof. Memberships: Law Society and International Bar Association.
Career: Qualified 1980; articled at *Slaughter & May*; Partner at *Simmons & Simmons* since 1986 and Managing Partner of the New York office 1994-98.
Personal: Born 1955; married with two young boys living in London; interests include photography, fly fishing and cycling.

BIRT, Timothy D.
Osborne Clarke OWA, London (020) 7809 1022
tim.birt@osborneclarke.com
Partner in Corporate Department and member of Brandlegal Group.
Specialisation: Corporate, with a bias towards advising clients in marketing services, media, retail and new economies sectors. Has been particularly active in the new issues market over the last few years, handling flotations of leading technology clients including Stepstone and Redstone. Although responsible for managing a team of specialist solicitors, remains very actively involved in transactions. Co-edits Butterworths company law service, contributing to the section on structuring joint ventures and owner-managed business.
Career: Qualified in 1985. With *D.J. Freeman* 1983-87. Joined *Osborne Clarke* in 1987 and became a Partner in 1988.

BLACKWELL, Nigel J.
Browne Jacobson, Nottingham (0115) 976 6000

BLOWER, Geoffrey
Eversheds, Manchester (0161) 832 6666
geoffreyblower@eversheds.com
Partner in Corporate Department, *Eversheds*, Manchester.
Specialisation: Main area of practice is Corporate Finance including mergers and acquisitions, flotations, management buy-outs, disposals, stock exchange and "Blue Book" work and non-contentious corporate work. Sector experience includes dairy industry, pharmaceuticals, leisure, automotive and engineering. Principal transactions include the Co-operative Wholesale Society's £111m disposal of its Food Manufacturing Group; again for the Co-operative Wholesale Society spearheaded the team which dealt with the complex exchange of assets and businesses with Dale Farm Dairy Group where the total assets involved were £30m; Stanley Leisure plc in its £15m recommended take-over of Gus Carter plc and its subsequent casino and betting shop acquisitions; for Kingspan Group in the acquisition of Kooltherm Holdings Limited and for United Northwest Co-operatives Limited in its acquisition of Hanburys Limited and its chain of 30 convenience stores and in the Society's acquisition of Nevins Limited and its 12 convenience store chain and a chain of 26 'Dawn til Dusk' convenience stores. He acted for Quicks Group plc in its acquisition of the Motor Retail Division of Caverdale Group plc (comprising some 30 companies) for £45.5m with its attendant Rights Issue and Placing and for Granville Private Equity in its £20m MBI of Ora Electronics UK Limited. His more recent deals include acting for Holidaybreak plc (formerly Eurocamp plc) in its £37.5m recommended take-over of Baldwins plc and the subsequent disposal of Baldwins restaurant division; for the United Northwest Co-operatives and West Midlands Co-operative Society in the joint venture with First Choice PLC in relation to the development 'Holiday Hypermarkets'; for Stanley Leisure plc in its attempted £350m acquisition of the Coral betting business and the subsequent disposal of this interest for E4SM; and in its successful £86.4m recommended take-over of Capital Corporation PLC, and the acquisition of two internet casinos; for Holidaybreak in its £30m acquisition of Explore Worldwide Limited and for United Norwest Co-operatives in its acquisition of SCI's Funeral Business in Northern Ireland.
Prof. Memberships: Law Society, Securities Institute.
Career: Qualified in 1972 and became a Partner in 1974.
Personal: Born 14th March 1948. Leisure pursuits include walking, cricket and theatre.

BOARDMAN, Nigel
Slaughter and May, London (020) 7600 1200
Specialisation: M&A, Corporate Finance, Corporate and Commercial. Advises UK and overseas companies and investment banks on the full range of corporate transactions, including acquisitions, disposals, takeovers, joint ventures, financings, flotations, MBOs and general corporate advice.
Career: Qualified in 1975 while with *Slaughter and May*. Joined the Corporate Finance Department of Kleinwort Benson Limited before returning to *Slaughter and May*, becoming Partner in 1982 and Head of Corporate in 1996.

BOND, Richard
Herbert Smith, London (020) 7374 8000
richard.bond@herbertsmith.com
See under Energy & Natural Resources, p.356

BOTT, Adrian J.A.
Olswang, London (020) 7208 8888
ajb@olswang.com
Partner and Head of Corporate Group.
Specialisation: Main areas of practice are corporate and finance. Since 1980, has been consistently involved in activities ranging from M&A, MBOs and MBIs, through flotations (including many on AIM), rights issues, placings and other means of financing, to private equity (acting for both providers and consumers), both in domestic and international transactions. Clients are predominantly quoted or subsidiaries of multinationals. Many have an electronics, internet or media bias. Also active in significant corporate joint ventures (such as BBC Worldwide/Flextech and Carphone Warehouse/AOL) and a broad spectrum of commercial contracts and employee share schemes. Has handled numerous consortium arrangements, leading a variety of consortia in bids for various TV and radio broadcasting licences.
Prof. Memberships: Law Society, British Venture Capital Association.
Career: Qualified in 1980. *Rooks Rider* 1978-87, from 1984 as a Partner. Partner at Olswang from 1988.
Personal: Born 9th June 1956. Charterhouse School 1969-73, Manchester University 1974-77 and Guildford Law School 1977.

BOUND, R.A.
Berry Smith, Cardiff (029) 2034 5511
Specialisation: Full range of corporate and commmercial work including acquisitions, MBOs, refinancing and joint venture arrangements.
Prof. Memberships: Law Society.
Career: Qualified in 1989. Articled at *Eversheds*, Cardiff. Joined *Berry Smith* in 1984 as a partner.
Personal: Born 25 March 1965. Educated at Reading University and Guildford College of Law. Interests: travelling and motor sports.

BOWCOCK, David
Eversheds, Manchester (0161) 832 6666
davidnbowcock@eversheds.com
Specialisation: IPO's, acquisitions, takeovers and fund raising. In 1999-2000 acted for Stanley Leisure plc on its recommended offer for Capital Corporation plc, Landround plc on its acquisition of Travel Offers Limited and Crona Group plc on its OFEX quotation.
Prof. Memberships: Law Society, Institute of Directors.
Career: 1990-1994 *Eversheds*, Birmingham. 1994-1997 *Bowcock Guerden*, Chester. 1998-2000 *Eversheds*, Manchester.
Personal: Education: Birmingham University, Chester College of Law. Interests: cricket, golf, public speaking, scuba diving.

BOWN, Christopher
Freshfields Bruckhaus Deringer, London (020) 7936 4000

cbown@freshfields.com
Specialisation: Partner in corporate department specialising in private equity and cross-border M&A transactions. Recent transactions include major multi-jurisdictional private equity purchase of chemical business, and other major acquisitions.
Prof. Memberships: Law Society
Career: Qualified 1981, partner *Baker & McKenzie* 1987-1998; partner *Freshfields* since 1998.
Personal: Born 1956, educated Queens' College, Cambridge.

BOYD, Frederick W.J.
McKinty & Wright, Belfast (028) 9024 6751
post@mckinty-wright.co.uk
Specialisation: Corporate and commercial law and practice (including corporate acquisitions and disposals, venture capital, lending, commercial property).
Prof. Memberships: Law Society of Northern Ireland.
Career: Graduated from Queen's University Belfast, in Law (LLB) in 1976 and in Business Studies (MBA) in 1977. Admitted to the role of Solicitors in Northern Ireland in 1978. Became partner in *McKinty & Wright* in 1983.

BRABNER, Michael G.
Brabner Holden Banks Wilson, Liverpool (0151) 236 5821
michael.brabner@bhbw.co.uk
Specialisation: Corporate/Corporate Finance.
Prof. Memberships: Law Society.
Career: Shrewsbury School; Liverpool University; qualified 1974. Worked in Corporate Department of *Herbert Oppenheimer Nathan & Van Dyke* 1974-76. Partner *Brabner Holden Banks Wilson* 1976 to date.

BRAHAM, Edward
Freshfields Bruckhaus Deringer, London (020) 7936 4000
Specialisation: Partner in *Freshfield's* corporate department specialising in major cross-border mergers and acquisitions and corporate finance matters. In addition to the UK and USA, he has worked on transactions in many European countries and on various multi-jurisdictional acquisitions and disposals.
Prof. Memberships: Law Society.
Career: Qualified 1987, Partner 1995.
Personal: Born 1961. Educated at Worcester College, Oxford 1980-1984 (BA, BCL).

BRAITHWAITE, Stephen
Wragge & Co, Birmingham (0121) 214 1026
stephen_braithwaite@wragge.com
Partner in Corporate Group.
Specialisation: Handles corporate finance work and mergers and acquisitions for public companies, acquisition and disposals and joint ventures.
Prof. Memberships: Law Society.
Career: Qualified in 1973. Articled with *Turner Kenneth Brown* 1971-73, worked with *Freshfields* 1973-76, joined *Wragge & Co* in 1976, and became a Partner in 1980.
Personal: Born 1947. Interests include sailing, theatre, films, fishing and walking.

BROWN, Jonathan A.
DLA, Liverpool (08700) 111111
jonathan.brown@dla.com
Partner.
Specialisation: Main area of practice is corporate finance work. Work includes acquisitions, disposals, flotations, joint ventures and venture capital. Major transactions include: (acquisition) ALB (Holdings) Limited (£33m); (flotation and rights issue) Cammell Laird Holdings PLC and Dawn Til Dusk Holdings PLC; (acquisition) Connacht Court Group Limited for Johnson Service Group PLC (IR£38m); (joint venture) Benfield Sports International Limited; (acquisition) The Gibraltar Dockyard from the Government of Gibraltar; (acquisition) Topjobs.net plc of JOBBDIREKT.SE; (acquisition) Premium Petcare of Vetstream plc.
Prof. Memberships: Law Society.
Career: Sheffield University 1984-87 LLB (Hons), SOL (Hons). Chester College of Law 1988. Admitted October 1990 *Addleshaw Sons & Latham* (1990-93), *Dibb Lupton Alsop* (*Alsop Wilkinson*) 1993 to date. Partner 1996.
Personal: Born 18 September 1966. Golf (Caldy G.C. & Formby Hall Golf Club). Cricket (Neston C.C.), Hockey (Neston C.C.). The Liverpool Racquet Club.

BROWNLOW, Jeremy
Clifford Chance, London (020) 7600 1000
jeremy.brownlow@cliffordchance.com
Specialisation: Main area of work is company and commercial including corporate finance and mergers and acquisitions. Principally advising public companies and investment banks on recommended and hostile public takeovers and domestic and international corporate transactions.
Career: MA (Camb). Qualified 1970; partner 1973.

BRUCE, Roderick L.
Dickson Minto WS, Edinburgh (0131) 225 4455
roderick.bruce@dmws.com
Specialisation: General corporate, mergers and acquisitions, venture capital, re-organisation.
Prof. Memberships: Law Society of Scotland; Writer to the Signet.
Career: Boroughmuir Secondary School; Edinburgh University (LLB (Hons 2.1)).
Personal: Wife: Jane; Four children: 3 girls, 1 boy. Squash, skiing, golf, rugby (spectating), theatre.

BUCHAN, Gordon A.
Paull & Williamsons, Aberdeen (01224) 621621
gabuchan@paull-williamsons.co.uk
Specialisation: General corporate law, (particularly acquisitions and disposals) and oil and gas law.
Career: Qualified 1976; Partner in corporate department at *Paull and Williamsons* since 1981.
Non-executive director of Aberdeen Football Club plc.
Personal: Born 1952.

BURGESS, Patrick
Gouldens, London (020) 7583 7777
Senior Partner.
Specialisation: Corporate finance and international specialist. Speaker at numerous conferences and seminars. Recent activities include advising on drafting of the new Stock Exchange Yellow Book, membership of the Stock Exchange's Working Party on smaller companies and Alternative Investment Market Panel and tax and legislation advice to the Unquoted Companies Group, besides involvement in a number of high profile bids and M&A transactions.
Career: Qualified in 1972. Joined *Gouldens* in 1968 and became a Partner in 1974.
Personal: Born 31st October 1944. Recreations include sailing, shooting, rowing, reading and opera. Lives in London and Chichester.

BURNS, Richard
Hammond Suddards Edge, London
(020) 7655 1000
richard.burns@hammondsuddardsedge.com
Partner.
Specialisation: Specialises in corporate finance work and, in particular, domestic and international mergers and acquisitions for listed companies and rights issues.
Prof. Memberships: Law Society.
Career: Articled *Last Suddards*; qualified 1983; Partner *Hammond Suddards* 1986.
Personal: Born 1958; resides Knightsbridge and Burley-in-Wharfedale. Enjoys sailing. Prior to retirement played rugby, football and cricket for a number of clubs, now relegated to the role of spectator; member of Sandmoor Golf Club.

BURROW, Robert P.
SJ Berwin & Co, London (020) 7533 2222
robert.burrow@sjberwin.com
Partner in Corporate Finance Department.
Specialisation: Main area of practice is domestic and international merger and acquisition work.
Prof. Memberships: Law Society.
Career: Qualified in 1975. Joined *S J Berwin & Co* as a Partner in 1985. Managing Director of J Rothschild & Co Ltd 1982-85.
Personal: Born 24th March 1951. Educated at Fitzwilliam College, Cambridge 1969-72. Leisure interests include cars, tennis, and skiing. Lives in London.

BUTLER, Maurice R.
Johns Elliot, Belfast (028) 9032 6881
Specialisation: All aspects of company and commercial work including corporate finance and mergers and acquisitions. Construction Claims/Arbitrations. Involved in two recent landmark appeals by way of Cases Stated to High Court from an arbitrator.
Prof. Memberships: Law Society of Northern Ireland.
Career: Graduated QUB 1965. Qualified 1968. Partner 1972, Senior/Managing Partner 1997. Appointed to Solicitor's Disciplinary Tribunal in 1986. Appointed President of Solicitors' Disciplinary Tribunal in 1999. Appointed Deputy County Court Judge in 1990.
Personal: Sailing (National Judge) and Bridge. Abbeyfield Society - Member of Regional Council and Chairman of Abbeyfield NI Development Society Limited. Married with two daughters.

BUTLER-GALLIE, Stuart
Brachers, Maidstone (01622) 690691
Specialisation: Concentrates on M&A work, debt and equity funding, listed company work, (acted on AIM flotation of Charlton Athletic plc March 1997 and Placing and Open Offers November 1998 and June 2000) joint ventures (UK and international), corporate reorganisations and reconstructions, MBOs/MBIs, all aspects of general company law and full range of commercial advice.
Career: Articled: *Denton Hall* 1988-90. Qualified: *Denton Hall 1990. Joined Brachers* Jan 96, Partner May 97.
Personal: Born 1.3.64. St. Dunstan's College Catford. Sheffield University (LLB). Law School Chester. SSVC in Regular Army 1PWO (Prince of Wales' Own Regiment of Yorkshire). Married, 4 children. Local Borough Councillor. Cross country running, military history.

CADWALLADER, David H.
DLA, Liverpool (08700) 111111
david.cadwallader@dla.com
Head of Liverpool Corporate Department.
Specialisation: Main area of practice: Corporate Finance. Work includes mergers and acquisitions (cross border transactions), (with particular expertise in sub-Saharan Africa), MBO/MBI's (advising institutional investors and management teams), venture and development capital, flotations, joint ventures. In addition to transactional work has advised upon and negotiated 'key' commercial contracts and project agreements.
Prof. Memberships: Law Society.
Career: Qualified in 1987. Joined *Alsop Stevens* in 1985. Became partner in 1990.
Personal: Attended Liverpool University and Chester College of Law. Leisure interests include family, golf and football. Lives in Newburgh, West Lancashire.

CAMPBELL, Mark
Clifford Chance, London (020) 7600 1000
mark.campbell@cliffordchance.com
See under Banking, p.116

CANAVAN, Kerry
Arthur Cox - Northern Ireland, Belfast (028) 9023 0007
kcanavan@arthurcox.ie
Specialisation: Company commercial including M&A's, fundraisings, commercial agreements.
Prof. Memberships: Law Society of Northern Ireland.
Career: Trained with Slaughter and May, post-qualification experiance in a general company and commercial department; joined Norman Wilson & Company in Belfast 1993, which merged with Arthur Cox Northern Ireland in 1996.
Personal: Educated: Coleraine High School and St Catherine's College Cambridge.

CANN, Anthony
Linklaters (A member firm of Linklaters & Alliance), London (020) 7456 3592
anthony.cann@linklaters.com
Specialisation: Partner and Co-head of Linklaters & Alliance M&A and corporate practice; specialist in UK corporate finance and company law, advising both corporate clients and investment and merchant banks; main areas of practice include public and private mergers and acquisitions, issues, joint ventures and general corporate advice.
Career: Articled *Linklaters*, 1970-72; qualified 1972; *Linklaters*, New York, 1975-82; assistant solicitor, *Linklaters*, 1972-78 and partner since 1978; and head of corporate department since 1995 and co-head of the M&A and corporate practice area of *Linklaters & Alliance* since 1998; author, chapter on private company and business acquisitions, 'Mergers and Acquisitions', published by Gee & Co, and chapter on UK, 'Mergers and Acquisitions in Europe', published by Gee & Co.
Personal: Educated Shewsbury School; Southampton University (1969 LLB Hons). Born 1947.

CARPANINI, Fabrizio A.
Olswang, London (020) 7208 8888
fcp@olswang.com
Specialisation: Specialising in private equity/venture capital transactions acting for institutions and management teams on buy-outs, buy-ins, institutional buy-outs and development capital deals. Institutional clients include F&C Ventures, Granville Private Equity, Gresham Trust, Lloyds TSB Development Capital and Nash Sello & Partners.
Prof. Memberships: British Venture Capital Association. British Halier Law Association. Law Society.
Career: Joined [IT]Berwin Leighton[IT] as a partner in1994 from *Turner Kenneth Brown*. Joined *Olswang* in February 2000 as a partner in the corporate finance group.
Publications: A regular speaker at conferences on private equity and management buyouts.
Personal: Belmont Abbey School, Hereford & Bristol Poly. Leisure:- Family, golf cycling & skiing.

CHARNLEY, William
McDermott, Will & Emery, London (020) 7577 6900
WCharnley@europe.mwe.com
Head of Corporate/Managing Partner.
Specialisation: Principal area of practice is corporate finance covering flotations, mergers and acquisitions and capital raising for companies acting for underwriters and issuers of securities, private equity transactions and general corporate advice.
Prof. Memberships: Law Society, Institute of Chartered Secretaries and Administrators, The Drapers Company.
Career: Articled at *Slater Heelis* in Manchester 1985-87, then joined *Booth & Co* and became a Partner in 1990; joined *Simmons & Simmons* as a Partner in 1994; joined *McDermott, Will & Emery* in November 1998.
Personal: Born 21st August 1960. Attended Rivington and Blackrod Grammar School 1971-78, Bolton Institute 1978-80, Sheffield Hallam University 1980-81, Lancaster University 1981-83 and Manchester Metropolitan University 1984-85. Trustee of Children's Heart Surgery Fund, Killingbeck Hospital. Non-executive director Sanderson Bramall Motor Group plc 2000-. Leisure pursuits include country sports, art, opera and wine. Lives in London.

CHATFIELD, James H.T.
Rawlison & Butler, Crawley (01293) 527744
Senior partner and member of corporate department
Specialisation: Extensive experience of UK and international corporate and cross-border work, particularly USA. Advising companies on exit strategies and strategic investments in the UK and Europe.
Prof. Memberships: IBA and UIA.
Career: *Linklaters & Paines* 1974-1984. Joined *Rawlison & Butler* as a partner and head of corporate department in 1984. Senior partner since 1999.
Personal: Born in 1952. Educated at Ardingly College and Trinity College, Oxford. Leisure interests: cricket, literature, history and gardening. Member of MCC.

CHERRY, Robert
Morgan Cole, Swansea (01792) 634634
robert.cherry@morgan-cole.com
Specialisation: Corporate transactions and corporate finance. Acted on a number of recent number of recent AIM flotations and reverse takeovers, including HACAS, General Industries, The Celttalk Group and Mazaran Leisure as well as several public takeovers, including Royal Borough of Kensington and Chelsea Assured Homes plc and Jardinerie Interiors Group plc. Other corporate clients include BP Chemicals, TBI plc, PHS and Content Technologies.
Prof. Memberships: Institute of Directors.
Career: MA in law from Cambridge University. Law School in Chester. Articles and 3 years PQE with *Herbert Smith*. Moved back to South Wales in 1995 - joined *Morgan Cole*.
Personal: Married, three sons, enjoys all sports activities.

CHESTER, Martin G.
Theodore Goddard, London (020) 7606 8855
martinchester@theodoregoddard.co.uk
Specialisation: Corporate finance, including mergers and acquisitions, public offerings, flotations, share capital and debt restructuring, investment trusts, corporate governance and general corporate advice. Recent major transactions include the Lloyds TSB merger, reorganisation of the 5 classes of share capital of the Signet Group plc into a single class, the disposals by Blagden plc of its packaging division, chemical manufacturing and distribution businesses and its winding up.
Career: Qualified 1967. Partner in *Theodore Goddard* since 1972. Chairman of the Company Law Sub-Committee of the City of London Law Society 1990-93 and of the Law Society's Company Law Committee 1993-96 (remains a member of each and leads a number of their working parties). Outside expert on the working party on corporate capital maintenance of the UK Company Law Review. Educated at St. Albans School and Exeter University.
Personal: Leisure interests include swimming, scuba diving and enjoying good food and wine.

CHEYNE, David W.
Linklaters (A member firm of Linklaters & Alliance), London (020) 7456 3174
david.cheyne@linklaters.com
Head of Linklaters Corporate Department.
Specialisation: Involved in a wide range of corporate transactions including M&A work, flotations, general corporate finance work and Stock Exchange related matters.
Career: Qualified 1974. Became a Partner in 1980. Partner, *Linklaters*, Hong Kong office, 1981-1986.

CHILDS, David
Clifford Chance, London (020) 7600 1000
david.childs@cliffordchance.com
Specialisation: Head of Global Corporate Practice. Specialises in corporate finance particularly M&A and equity securities issues.
Career: Sheffield University; University College, London (LLB, LLM). Articled *Clifford Chance*; qualified 1976; partner *Clifford Chance* since 1981.
Personal: Born 1951.

CHOHAN, Baljit
Hammond Suddards Edge, Birmingham (0121) 200 2001
Specialisation: Specialises in corporate finance work and has a broad range of experience in acting for private and publicly quoted companies as well as financial institutions and management teams. He is also a member of the Association of Partnership Practitioners and has set up and heads the Partnership Unit of the firm, acting for new and existing partnerships and entrants to existing partnerships. Baljit is also leading the firms e-business initative in the Midlands, advising e-business companies and investors in them on the legal and business implications of operating in the new economy.
Prof. Memberships: Association of Partnership Practitioners.

Career: University of Essex LLB (Hons) 1985-88; College of Law, Chester 1988-89.

CLARK, Adrian S.
Ashurst Morris Crisp, London (020) 7638 1111
Specialisation: Company Department.
Career: Educated - Peterhouse, Cambridge (MA). Qualified 1983. *Slaughter and May* 1981-86; *Ashurst Morris Crisp* 1986 onwards. Partner 1990. Seconded to Take-over Panel 1988-90.

CLARK, Tim
Slaughter and May, London (020) 7600 1200
Specialisation: Principal area of practice is UK and international corporate work, corporate finance and mergers and acquisitions (including public takeovers, flotations, international equity offerings), advising corporate and investment bank clients. Practice also involves demutualisations (building societies and insurance companies). Joint Head of E-commerce Group.
Prof. Memberships: The Law Society.
Career: Qualified 1976 with *Slaughter and May*. Became Partner in 1983.
Personal: Born 9 January 1951. Educated at Sherborne School and Pembroke College, Cambridge. Interests include theatre, sport, Italy and flying. Lives in London.

CLARKE, Julia
Clifford Chance, London (020) 7600 1000
julia.clarke@cliffordchance.com
Specialisation: Partner specialising in private equity and management buy-outs and buy-ins including cross-border European deals and with broad experience of general corporate and corporate finance transactions.
Career: Guildford County School; St Hugh's College, Oxford (MA Oxon 1984). Articled *Clifford Chance*; qualified 1989; partner 1994.
Personal: Tennis, sailing, skiing, travel, theatre. Born 1962.

CLARKE, Tim
Linklaters (A member firm of Linklaters & Alliance), London (020) 7456 3304
tim.clarke@linklaters.com
Specialisation: Partner, Corporate Finance Department specialising in public M&A, takeovers and joint ventures. Recent transactions include National Power's demerger and Wickes successful defence of hostile bid from FDIA. Head of International Privatisation with particular experience of UK and international privatisations, both primary and secondary, including British Aerospace, Rolls-Royce, National Power, British Telecom, Cable & Wireless, Railtrack, AEAT and Associated British Ports. International privatisations experience includes South African Airways, Kenya Telecoms and Montenegro Electricity.

COMPAGNONI, Marco
Lovells, London (020) 7296 2000
marco.compagnoni@lovells.com
Specialisation: Specialises in a range of mergers and acquisitions work and corporate law. A particular specialisation is private equity transactions (MBOs and MBIs) acting primarily for institutional investors. Equity institutions for whom he has acted regularly include Mercury Asset Management and Doughty Hanson. He also has extensive experience of joint ventures, purchase and sales of companies and businesses (both domestic and cross border). Significant recent transactions include acting for ING in its purchase of Barings and advising Doughty Hanson on its purchases of the BTR Aerospace Business and Umbro Sportsware Business.
Prof. Memberships: Member of the British Venture Capital Association, the British Italian Law Association and the City of London Solicitors Company.
Career: Articled at *Lovells*; qualified in 1987 and became a partner in 1993.

COOKE, Darryl J.
Addleshaw Booth & Co, Manchester (0161) 934 6000
djc@addleshaw-booth.co.uk
Partner in Corporate Finance Group; Head of ABC Private Equity.
Specialisation: Principal areas of practice are venture capital, management buy-outs and corporate finance. Author of 'Management Buy-outs' (Sweet and Maxwell); 'Venture Capital: Law and Practice' (Sweet and Maxwell) and 'Due Diligence: A Practical Guide' (Sweet & Maxwell).
Career: Joined firm as a Partner in 1995.
Personal: Educated at Leeds University (LLB, LLM). Plays golf, squash and tennis in his spare time as well as fell and marathon running. Lives in Kerridge, Cheshire.

COOKE, Stephen
Slaughter and May, London (020) 7600 1200
Partner in Company/Commercial Department.
Specialisation: Principal area of practice is company and commercial work with a particular emphasis on M&A.
Prof. Memberships: The Law Society.
Career: Qualified in 1984 while with *Slaughter and May*. Worked in the New York office 1989-90, and became a Partner in 1991. Publications include 'Takeovers' (Legal & Commercial Publishing, 1997).
Personal: Born 7 March 1959. Educated Lincoln College, Oxford (1978-81). Lives in London.

COOMBS, Richard
Foot Anstey Sargent, Exeter (01392) 411221
richard.coombs@foot-ansteys.co.uk
Partner in charge of company commercial team.
Specialisation: Corporate finance, mergers, acquisitions, MBOs, MBIs, share schemes, FSA compliance, friendly societies.
Prof. Memberships: IOD, Chamber of Commerce. External Examiner in Corporate Finance for Exeter University.
Career: Qualified 1979. *Clifford Chance* 1977-80, *Turner Kenneth Brown* 1980-81, *British Coal* 1981-85, *Bond Pearce* 1985-94 (Partner from 1988). Joined *Foot Anstey Sargent* as partner in 1994.
Personal: Born 16th March 1954. Attended Kings School Chester, Cardiff High School, Downing College, Cambridge (First in Law). Interests: walking and music. Lives in Ivybridge.

COOPER, Paul
Osborne Clarke OWA, Bristol (0117) 917 4252
paul.cooper@osborneclarke.com
Specialisation: Specialises in corporate work, including acting for investment venture capitalists; MBO's; company sales and purchases; flotations and other Stock Exchange related company work and joint ventures. Recent work includes acting for NatWest Development Capital in 3 investments and for Barclays Bank Plc on its loan to Mears Group on the acquisition by Mears of United Fleet Distribution Limited. Paul floated Alterian plc, with an opening market capitalisation of £80m in July 2000 and is currently working on a £135 million management buy-out.
Career: Qualified at *Boodle Hatfield* in 1977, joined *Norton Rose* in 1978, moved to *Bevan Ashford* in 1980, becoming a partner in 1981. Joined *Osborne Clark* 1997.

COPPIN, Jonathan
Norton Rose, London (020) 7283 6000
coppinjds@nortonrose.com
Specialisation: Main area of practice is corporate finance in particular mergers and acquisitions, flotations and international securities offerings. Recent transactions include Texas Utilities/The Energy Group, AXA/GRE, AXA/Sun Life and Provincial Holdings, and P&O's disposal of Bovis to Lend Lease.
Prof. Memberships: Member of the Law Society's Company Law Committee.
Career: Articled at *Norton Rose* 1987-1989, Partner Corporate Finance Department *Norton Rose* 1996.
Publications: Author of numerous articles in professional publications.
Personal: Married (Lucy). Hobbies include sailing and running.

COTTIS, Matthew J.
Lovells, London (020) 7296 2000
matthew.cottis@lovells.com
Specialisation: Expertise in management buy-outs/buy-ins, bids and takeovers and other types of acquisition finance, property development finance and general syndicated loans.
Career: Articled *Lovells* 1985-87, partner 1993.

CRABTREE, John
Wragge & Co, Birmingham (0121) 233 1000

CRAIG, I. Alexander
Halliwell Landau, Manchester (0161) 835 3003
Partner, Head of Corporate Department.
Specialisation: Work includes MBOs and MBIs, and flotations, mergers, sales and acquisitions. Specialist in institutional fundraising in the technology area. Has spoken at numerous seminars and conferences.
Prof. Memberships: Law Society, Institute of Management, Securities Institute.
Career: Qualified in 1985, joining *Halliwell Landau* in the same year. Became a Partner in 1989.
Personal: Born 28th September 1957. Attended Sheffield University 1979-82 then College of Law, London 1983. Public Company non executive director. Leisure interests include football, squash and fell walking. Lives in Alderley Edge.

CRANFIELD, Richard
Allen & Overy, London (020) 7330 3000
Specialisation: Head of Corporate Department. Has a wide range of corporate finance experience including domestic and cross-border mergers and acquisitions, privatisations and buy-outs and capital markets work for equity and debt financings. He lead the *Allen & Overy* team which advised the DTI on the privatisation of British Energy, the team which advised Cable and Wireless on the formation of Cable & Wireless Communications in 1996 and its division into two in 1999/2000, the sale of one2one to Deutsche Telekom and the sale of Hong Kong Tele-

com to PCCW. He is currently advising DFID on the public/private partnership for Commonwealth Development Corporation.
Career: Articled 1978, qualified 1980, Partner 1985, Head of Corporate Department 1999 at *Allen & Overy*.
Personal: Born 19/01/56. Educated at Winchester College and Fitzwilliam College, Cambridge. Married with four children.

CROOME, Andrew
Eversheds, Norwich (01603) 272727
See under Banking, p.

CROSTHWAITE, Charles M.
Bird & Bird, London (020) 7415 6000
Specialisation: Partner in the Corporate Department with over 20 years experiance in domestic and international business transactions, principally in the fields of mergers and acquisitions and debt and equity securities offerings.
Career: Qualified 1977; Partner *Ashurst Morris Crisp* 1980; Partner *Bird & Bird* 1994
Personal: Downside School, University of York (1973 Economics). Born 1952; resides London. Member, City University Club.

CUMMINGS, Gavin
Browne Jacobson, Nottingham (0115) 976 6000
gcummings@brownej.co.uk
Specialisation: Corporate finance specialising in MBI's, MBO's, IBO's, disposals, mergers and acquisitions and private equity. Recent transactions include the £98.5m disposal of the Joseph retail chain.
Prof. Memberships: Law Society
Career: Articled – *Browne Jacobson*. Qualified – 1994. Partner – 2000.
Personal: Born 1970, Stamford; educated at Stamford School and Nottingham University (BA Hons Law) Interests: Football, cricket, golf.

CUNNINGHAM, Kevin G.
Irwin Mitchell, Leeds (0113) 234 3333
Specialisation: Corporate finance, mergers and acquisitions and venture capital. Acting in particular for MBO teams and funds. Buy-outs include Viscount, Gloystarne, Baldwin & Francis, Three Star, RFS, Cowen Barrett and Marc Wheatley. Trade deals include the acquisition of the Multi-Compact Group for John Mowlem & Co plc, the Clarkson Osborn group for Hydra Tools International and Wescol Group plc for Salzgitter AG.
Prof. Memberships: The Law Society.
Career: Qualified 1979. Joined *Irwin Mitchell*1983. Partner 1985 and appointed to Management Board in 1989.
Personal: Born 1956. Interests include tennis and skiing.

CUNNINGHAM, Neil
MacRoberts, Glasgow (0141) 332 9988
neilc@macroberts.co.uk
Specialisation: Corporate Finance, Mergers and Acquisitions, Reconstructions and Partnership Law. Recent deals include acting for: Omnia Books Ltd in acquisition of the Business of Caledonian International Book Manufacturing Ltd. from its receivers; sharholders in Feather Brooksbank (wirr Ltd) sale to Carat Group; Ramage Distribution Ltd in acquisition of Eemtrans (UK) Ltd
Prof. Memberships: Law Society of Scotland, Institute of Chartered Accountants in England & Wales, Institute of Chartered Accountants of Scotland, Member of the Investigations Committee of the Institute of Chartered Accountants of Scotland.
Career: Price Waterhouse, Chartered Accountants, London and Glasgow 1984-1988; *Ledingham Chalmers*, Solicitors, Aberdeen 1989-1991; *MacRoberts*, Solicitors, Glasgow 1991 – to date (became a Partner in 1995).
Personal: Born August 6, 1964. Married with three daughters. Leisure interests include golf, football and squash.

DA COSTA, Alastair J.
DLA, Leeds (08700) 111111
alastair.dacosta@dla.com
Specialisation: Corporate finance lawyer specialising in mergers and acquisitions and public company work, including Stock Exchange and takeover code work.
Prof. Memberships: Law Society; Institute of Directors; Director and Company Secretary of Leeds Financial Services Initiative Limited.
Career: Ripon Grammar School; Leeds University (LLB Hons); Articled with *Slaughter and May*; qualified 1990; joined *Dibb Lupton Alsop* in 1992; Partner in 1995, Head of Leeds Corporate Group from 1997.
Personal: All sports, particularly football, tennis, rugby union and golf.

DARWIN, Andrew D.
DLA, Sheffield (08700) 111111
andrew.darwin@dla.com
Also at Leeds and London .
Specialisation: Corporate finance (flotations, secondary issues, takeovers and mergers) venture capital (UBOS/ UBIS; acting for institutions and management) and mergers and acquisitions.
Career: 1981 to date *Dibb Lupton Broomhead.*
Personal: Education – Queens' College, Cambridge.

DAVIDSON, John
Lovells, London (020) 7296 2000
john.davidson@lovells.com
Specialisation: Is a member of Lovells' corporate finance group, specialising in public and private UK and cross-border mergers and acquisitions and joint ventures, international equity offerings and private equity investments, and is a member of the firm's market-leading corporate insurance and Lloyd's practice. Recent major transactions have included advising South African Breweries plc on its £4 billion listing on the London Stock Exchange and its admission to the FTSE 100 Index in March 1999, AEGON UK plc on its £759 million acquisition of Guardian Life in September 1999, and Goldman Sachs International as sponsor of the £1.4 billion IPO of Egg plc in June 2000.
Career: Articled *Lovells*, qualified 1985; partner 1991; resident partner New York office 1991-95.

DAVIS, James P.L.
Freshfields Bruckhaus Deringer, London (020) 7936 4000
Specialisation: Corporate finance, acting for companies and investment bank on M&A and equity issues. Clients include Cinven, Compass, Hays, Logica, Scottish and Southern Energy and Wolseley.
Career: Balliol College, Oxford. Partner since 1976.
Personal: Wife (Sally) and four children. Interests include golf and fishing.

DAVIS, Steven
SJ Berwin & Co, London (020) 7533 2222
steven.davis@sjberwin.com
Specialisation: A diversified corporate practice covering mergers and acquisitions (private and public), leveraged buy-outs, venture and development capital investments, flotations, corporate finance and corporate reconstructions, albeit with a particular focus on private equity transactions acting primarily for financial institutions. Equity institutions for whom he acts regularly include Apax Partners and Phildrew Ventures. Significant recent transactions include the flotation of The Future Network plc, the public to privates of Appollo Metals plc, The Denby Group plc, UPF Group plc and advising NM Rothschild on the take private of United Biscuits.
Prof. Memberships: Member of the New York Bar.
Career: Qualified in 1987 with *SJ Berwin & Co*. Seconded to *Debevoise & Plimpton*, New York office 1992-93 and became a partner in 1994.
Personal: Born 1965. Educated Clifton College, Bristol and Manchester University. Married with one child. Leisure pursuits include golf, squash and cooking. Lives in London.

DAVISON, Andrew J.
Eversheds, Newcastle upon Tyne (0191) 261 1661
Partner in Corporate Department.
Specialisation: General Company Law with particular reference to public company, corporate finance, and mergers and acquisitions work.
Prof. Memberships: Chairman of Law Society Standing Committee on Company Law. Member of DTI Company Law Review Consultative Committee.
Career: Qualified in 1985, becoming a Partner in 1986.

DAWES, Edward
Wragge & Co, Birmingham (0121) 233 1000
edward_davies@wragge.com
Specialisation: Public Company Corporate Finance: takeovers, public to private transactions, M&A, flotations and share issues. Recent Transactions include £1.8 billion recommended order for Thompson Travel Group; several public to private buy outs including Jones Stroud Holdings, Avonside, United Industries recommended offer for Channel Holdings and associated rights issue; McLeod Russel Holdings' purchase of Vokes from Invensys; and AT&T's sale of ACC Europe.
Career: Malvern College; Exeter University. Qualified 1988. *Wragge & Co* 1986-1994; *Kent Jones & Done* 1994-1999 (partner 1995-1999; Head of Corporate Department 1995-1998); Returned to *Wragge & Co* as Partner 1999.
Publications: Regular Contributor to legal Journals.
Personal: DOB. 2/4/63. Married with Three children. Intrests: fly fishing, sailing, shooting.

DEAN, Kevin J.
Sinclair Roche & Temperley, London (020) 7452 4000

DEANE, David
Semple Fraser WS, Glasgow (0141) 221 3771
david.deane@semplefraser.co.uk
Specialisation: Corporate finance, Venture Capital, Acquisitions, Joint Ventures.
Prof. Memberships: Law Society of Scotland.
Career: Articled *Bird Semple Fyfe Ireland* 1986-88; Legal Assistant *Bird Semple Fyfe Ireland* 1988-90; Legal Assistant *McGrigor Donald* 1990-94; Partner

Henderson Boyd Jackson 1994-98; Partner *Semple Fraser* 1998.
Personal: Born 26 August 1964. Educated at Kelvinside Academy and Aberdeen University. Interests include golf, rugby and Partick Thistle Football Club. Married with two children. Lives in Glasgow.

DEVITT, Paul
Addleshaw Booth & Co, Manchester
(0161) 934 6000
pyd@addleshaw-booth.co.uk
Partner in Corporate Finance Group.
Specialisation: Company and Corporate Finance, with particular specialisation in public company and public issue work: flotations; public issues; takeovers; other public company/stock exchange-related advice; acquisitions and disposals of companies and businesses.
Prof. Memberships: Law Society; London Stock Exchange Regional Advisory Group – North West.
Career: Qualified 1988. Joined the firm in 1993. Partner from 1995.
Personal: Educated at University of Bristol (LL.B). Lives in Wilmslow.

DICKSON, Alastair R.
Dickson Minto WS, London (020) 7628 4455
alastair.dickinson@dmws.com
Specialisation: Mergers and acquisitions; leveraged buy-outs; acting for major financial institutions and banks. Deals in the last 12 months include Mergers of Autotrader businesses (£950 million); Sale of Somerfield Stores; Zeneca Speciality Chemicals (£1.3 billion).
Prof. Memberships: Member of Law Society of Scotland; Writer to Her Majesty's Signet.
Career: Educated Edinburgh University 1971. *Dundas & Wilson* 1971-73. *Maclay Murray & Spens* 1973-76. *Dundas & Wilson* 1976-85 (partner from 1978). Founding partner of *Dickson Minto WS* 1985.
Personal: Golf, squash, hill walking.

DICKSON, Ian
MacRoberts, Glasgow (0141) 332 9988
id@macroberts.co.uk
Partner in corporate group.
Specialisation: Although principal area of practice is corporate law and corporate finance, also practises in electricity (and in particular) nuclear energy law. Acts for British Energy.
Prof. Memberships: Law Society of Scotland, International Bar Association, American Bar Association, Institute of Directors.
Career: Qualified 1971. Joined *MacRoberts* in 1973. Partner in 1977, now its Senior Corporate Partner. Non-executive Director of Johnston Press plc.
Personal: Born 10th April 1950. Attended Hillhead High School, Glasgow 1962-68; then Strathclyde University 1968-71. Chairman of Friends of the Beatson Oncology Centre. Leisure interests include music, golf and football. Lives in Glasgow.

DILLON, Martin L.G.
Taylor Joynson Garrett, London (020) 7300 7000
Qualified 1965. Partner 1970. Corporate Commercial Department. Main areas of practice are corporate acquisitions, sales and reorganisations, international tax, international note issues, funding, equity financings, finance leases and reinsurance disputes. Educated at Downside and The Queen's College, Oxford (Morel Scholar, 1st Class Hons. Law).

DIX, John T.
Hewitson Becke + Shaw, Cambridge
(01223) 461155

DOWNS, William N.
Hammond Suddards Edge, Manchester
(0161) 830 5000
william.downs@hammondsuddardsedge.com
Specialisation: Merger and acquisition work, flotations and Yellow Book work generally. Recent transactions include acting for Ultraframe PLC on its flotation, acting for Co-operative Wholesale Society Limited on the merger with CRS, acting for Torotrak plc on its demerger from BTG plc.
Prof. Memberships: Law Society, RSA.
Career: Bradford Grammar School; Downing College, Cambridge.
Personal: Golf, tennis, gardening. Married with three children.

DREW, Dean
Shoosmiths, Reading (0118) 965 8765
dean.drew@shoosmiths.co.uk
Specialisation: Mergers and acquisitions, venture and development capital, MBO's and joint ventures, particularly in the technology and life science sectors. Advises dot-com and other emerging companies and has also acted for Thames Water on M&A work. Acted for the sellers of a software company to Great Plains Software, Inc for $38million in cash and shares, closing the deal in under a week.
Prof. Memberships: Law Society
Career: Trained in London, qualified in 1990 and joined Shoosmiths in 1995 becoming a partner in 1997 and head of the Thames Vally corporate team in 1998.
Personal: Educated at Leeds University. Leisure intrests include music, swimming and gardening. Married with 3 children. Lives in Newbury.

DWYER, Maurice J.
Wragge & Co, Birmingham (0121) 214 1052
maurice_dwyer@wragge.com
Specialisation: Head of Private Equity. Corporate finance, mergers and acquisitions. Structuring of equity and debt finance.
Career: Articled *Freshfields*. Qualified 1983. *Wragge & Co* 1983-86 and 1987 to date. *3i plc* 1987. Partner at *Wragge & Co* from 1990.
Personal: Born 1957. Author of 'Management Buy-outs' (Sweet & Maxwell 1997)and 'Private Equity Transactions' (Sweet & Maxwell 2000).

EASTGATE, Andrew
Pinsent Curtis, Birmingham (0121) 200 1050
andrew.eastgate@pinsents.com
Specialisation: Partner and Head of Corporate in Birmingham. Acts predominantly for quoted companies including Glanbia, Severn Trent, Castings, Booker, Misys and Fountain Forestry. Deals in 2000 include acting for iSOFT Group plc on its flotation on the London Stock Exchange which valued the company at £123 million and for Deloitte & Touche on the AIM flotation of Compass Software.
Prof. Memberships: Law Society.
Career: Qualified in 1980. Assistant Solicitor with *Stephenson Harwood* 1980-83. *Pinsent & Co.* from 1983. Partner in 1985 and Head of Corporate, Birmingham in 1997.
Personal: Born 1956. Attended Uppingham School and Mansfield College, Oxford.

ELLARD, John
Linklaters (A member firm of Linklaters & Alliance), London (020) 7456 3324
john.ellard@linklaters.com
See under Transport, p.799

EMMERSON, Tim
Freshfields Bruckhaus Deringer, London
(020) 7936 4000
Specialisation: Mergers and acquisitions, IPOs, securities and derivatives law. Legal adviser to the Takeover Panel (on Takeover Code issues) and to numerous investment bank's and companies on a wide range of commercial matters. Recent deals include Bass' sale of its worldwide brewing interests, UBS' acquisition of Global Asset Management, Rank's disposal of Rank-Xerox, IPOs of Railtrack plc and of Thomson Travel Group Plc and takeover proposals by T-Online for freeserve, WPP for Young & Rubicam, Akzo-Nobel for Courtaulds, Rhodia for Albright & Wilson, Slough Estates for Bilton, BSkyB of Manchester United plc (referred to MMC). Also acted for Greenalls on its capital reorganisation and for sponsors on mergers of Anglo American with Minorco and of British Steel with Hoogovens.
Career: BA(Hons) Law (First), Sussex University; MA EC Law (First), College of Europe, Bruges.
Personal: Collector of Scottish Colourists, keen opera-goer and gardener. Occasional attendance at Rolling Stones concerts.

EMMETT, Paul D.
Walker Morris, Leeds (0113) 283 2500
pde@walkermorris.co.uk
Partner in Corporate Department.
Specialisation: Principal area of practice is corporate finance, mergers and acquisitions. Work includes flotations, rights issues, other forms of equity financing, acquisitions and disposals. Other main area of practice is general corporate advice. Important transactions have included the £300 million demerger of TeamTalk.com from IMS Group plc, £190 million flotation of Newcastle United plc, £150 million offer by TOTAL for the minority shareholdings in Kalon Group plc, £35 million acquisition of Sheffield Forgemasters Group Limited, £41 million acquisition of The Decorative Holding Company Limited by Roseby's Plc, £23 million acquisition of North Shoe Limited by Brown & Jackson Plc and £75 million offer by BUPA for Goldsborough Healthcare plc. Author of several articles in the *Yorkshire Post* and legal journals. Has spoken at seminars on Stock Exchange listing rules and director's duties.
Prof. Memberships: Law Society.
Career: Qualified in 1987. With *Slaughter and May* 1985-91. Joined *Walker Morris* in 1991 and became a Partner in 1993.
Personal: Born 7th November 1961. Educated at Cheadle Hulme School, Cheshire 1974-80 and King's College, London University 1981-84. Lives in Leeds.

EVANS, Jacqueline
Allen & Overy, London (020) 7330 3000
Specialisation: Advising banks and private equity houses on debt financing of leveraged acquisitions including public bids.
Career: Joined *Allen & Overy* 1990 (September). Qualified 1992 (September). Partner 1999 (May).

EVANS, Michael
Greenwoods, Peterborough (01733) 887700

EVANS, Stuart J.
Simmons & Simmons, London (020) 7628 2020
Head of Corporate Finance at *Simmons & Simmons*.
Specialisation: In the twelve months up to July 2000 he led teams advising: Interbrew on its £2.7 billion acquisition of the beer businesses of Whitbread and Bass; Pacific Century CyberWorks on its US$27 billion acquisition of Cable and Wireless HKT; Wal-Mart on its £6.8 billion acquisition of Asda.
Career: Qualified in 1972. With *Slaughter and May* 1972-79. Joined *Simmons & Simmons* in 1979, Partner since 1981.
Publications: Chapter on Transactions in 'A Practitioner's Guide to the FSA Listing Rules' 12th edition. Formerly Chairman of the Patrons of New Art at the Tate Gallery; director of Hackney Business Venture, an enterprise zone company, supporting small business start-ups and a trustee of st.art 2000, a registered charity.
Personal: Born 31st December 1947. Educated Royal Grammar School, Newcastle-upon-Tyne 1956-66, Leeds University 1966-69. Leisure interests include contemporary art.

FAGELSON, Ian B.
Warner Cranston, London (020) 7403 2900
ian-fagelson@warner-cranston.com
Partner in Company/ Commercial Department.
Specialisation: Handles corporate and financial transactions, including corporate finance, mergers and acquisitions and banking. Wide experience of both public and private corporate and financial transactions, including complex international mergers and acquisitions, disposals, financings, restructurings, debt and equity issues (public and private) and joint ventures. Also deals with insurance and reinsurance, including the establishment of innovative structured reinsurance programmes. University lecturer 1977-79. Subsequently regular conference and seminar lecturer on corporate and banking topics.
Prof. Memberships: Law Society, American Bar Association.
Career: Qualified in 1980, having joined *Warner Cranston* in 1979. Became a Partner in 1981 and Senior Partner in 1997.
Personal: Born 22nd April 1952. Educated at the University of Southampton 1970-73 (LLB) and Oxford University 1973-75 (BCL). Enjoys theatre, reading and loafing. Lives in London.

FALKUS, Bryony J.
Mills & Reeve, Norwich (01603) 693 225
bryony.falkus@mills-reeve.com
Partner in corporate department.
Specialisation: Work covers corporate insolvency generally and in particular receiverships and administrations, acting for banks, specialised lending institutions and insolvency practitioners. Major clients include PricewaterhouseCoopers, KPMG and other accountants. Also handles acquisitions and sales, reconstructions, offers of securities and yellow book work.
Prof. Memberships: Law Society.
Career: Qualifed 1976; Partner *Pickering Kenyon* 1980; Partner *Mills & Reeve* 1992.

FEECHAN, Catherine
Biggart Baillie, Glasgow (0141) 228 8000
cfeechan@biggartballie.co.uk
Specialisation: Specialist in Corporate Finance, Aim/Listed Company Work, Equity Investments Acquisition and Disposals. Major deals in 2000 – sale of Attentech Technologies Ltd to Asco Systems Inc for U$180million, placing an open offer for Actech Onternational plc to raise £18million.
Prof. Memberships: Law Society of Scotland, Law Society of England & Wales.
Career: Glasgow University LLB (Hons) 1991. Trained at *Dickson Minto* 1991-1993. Assistant at *Dundas & Wilson* 1993-1995. *Biggart Ballie* 1995 to date.
Personal: Born 12/4/68, attended Wellington School, Ayr and Glasgow University. Married in 1996, interests include cinema, food and travel.

FISCHL, Nicolas J.
Mills & Reeve, Norwich (01603) 693 223
nick.fischl@mills-reeve.com
Specialisation: MBOs, MBIs, private equity, joint ventures. Also facilities management and other computer/IT agreements.
Prof. Memberships: Law Society, Norfolk and Norwich Law Society.
Career: Qualified with *Clifford Turner* 1979. Joined *Mills & Reeve* in 1984. Partner *Mills & Reve*1986.
Personal: MA (Cantab)

FITZGERALD, Sean
Chaffe Street, Manchester (0161) 236 5800
Specialisation: Corporate finance including mergers and acquisitons, venture and development capital and management buy-outs and buy-ins.
Prof. Memberships: Law Society.
Career: Articled at *James Chapman & Co.* Qualified in 1984. Joined *Chaffe Street* in 1988. Became a partner in 1991.
Personal: Born 22nd January 1960. Attended St Bede's College, Manchester and Hull University. Leisure interests include golf, cricket and football. Lives in Greenmount, Lancashire.

FITZSIMONS, Gerard
Garretts, Cambridge (01223) 355977
gerry.fitzsimons@glegal.com
Specialisation: Corporate transactions with particular specialism in private equity. Has led a number of substantial transactions in 1999 including, in particular, the £150 million merger of Dalehead Foods Limited with Roach Foods Limited. Acts for a number of Cambridge technology funds including Amadeus, TTP Ventures and First Cambridge Gateway Fund. Has wide experience of private equity transactions in the technology sector in which these funds specialise. Also acts for investee companies such as Metris Therapeutics Limited in its recent £11 million financing led by Schroder Ventures.
Prof. Memberships: The Law Society.
Career: 1982-84 Trainee *Coward Chance*; 1984-85 *Shearman & Sterling*, New York; 1986-87 [I T+]Clifford Chance; 1987-96*Taylor Vinters*; 1996-present Senior Partner*Garretts*.
Personal: Born 28.8.59. Educated Cranbrook School, Kent. Oxford University.

FLYNN, John
Dickinson Dees, Newcastle upon Tyne (0191) 279 9252
Partner in Corporate Department.
Specialisation: Work includes mergers and acquisitions, flotations, rights issues and similar related Stock Exchange work, as well as joint ventures. Acted in the acquisition of Thameslink and Thames Trains rail franchises, the £300 million acquisition by Arriva of British Bus and the £513 million sale by Arriva of AAS. Led the team voted U.K. Regional Corporate Team of the Year by Legal Business Magazine.
Prof. Memberships: Law Society.
Career: Qualified in 1979. Joined *Dickinson Dees* in 1981, becoming a Partner in 1986.

FRANCIES, Michael
Weil, Gotshal & Manges, London (020) 7903 1000
michael.francies@weil.com
Specialisation: Head of the London office and a member of the firm's thirteen-member management committee. His practice is in both the UK/US axis and across Europe. He specialises in public and private mergers and acquisitions, equity issues (IPOs and secondary), private equity/venture capital/MBOs and joint ventures. His clients span the telecommunications and new technology sectors, and include major corporates as well as financial advisers and private equity funds.

FRIER, George W.
McClure Naismith, Glasgow (0141) 204 2700
gfrier@mcclurenaismith.com
Specialisation: Partner, Corporate finance and commercial /Tax – VAT. Handles complex negotiations for commercial contracts specialising in MBOs/MBIs, mergers, banking, trade acquisitions and sales, insolvency and shareholder disputes. Recent deals include acting for management in the £20m IBO of McLaren Consulting Limited from ISI Group plc; acting for a vendor shareholder in the £19.5m sale of Anchor International Limited to an IBO led by 3i Group plc; acting for Plexus Corp (USA) in its £17.5m acquisition of Keltek (Holdings) Limited.
Career: Trained Dorman Jeffrey, qualified 1987, assistant Maclay Murray & Spens 1987-1993, associate McClure Naismith 1993-1994, partner 1994.
Personal: Born 1962, resides Glasgow. Educated at Morrison's Acadamy, Glasgow University (1984 LLB Hons Private Law). Leisure pursuits include hill walking, family, theatre, cycling and bad golf.

FULTON, Richard
Mills Selig, Belfast 028 9024 3878
richard.fulton@nilaw.com
Specialisation: Main areas of practice are mergers, acquisitions and disposals, joint ventures, corporate finance generally and distribution and agency agreements. Represents three major venture capital houses. Has extensive experience in mergers and acquisitions and joint ventures both locally and internationally.
Prof. Memberships: Law Society of Northern Ireland.
Career: Queens University, Belfast LLB 1976. Qualified England and Wales 1980. Qualified Northern Ireland 1990. Formerly Senior Company/Commercial Partner with *Blaser Mills*. Joined *Mills Selig* 1991.
Personal: Windsurfing, countryside, literature. Lives outside Belfast.

GARNETT, Chris J.
Eversheds, Birmingham (0121) 232 1000
Specialisation: Mergers and acquisitions for private and public company clients and public company transactions, including flotations, takeover offers and rights issues.
Prof. Memberships: Law Society.
Career: Birmingham University. Articled to *Eversheds* (formerly *Evershed & Tomkinson*) 1983-85, Associate 1989, Partner 1992.
Personal: Married to Kathryn; with 2 children,

Daniel (aged 7) and Anna (aged 5). A keen interest in natural history, particularly ornithology, and enjoys playing tennis and watching football and cricket.

GARSTON, Clive

Halliwell Landau, Manchester (0161) 835 3003

Specialisation: Specialises in all aspects of corporate finance and commercial work, particularly Yellow Book work, mergers & acquisitions and flotations.

Prof. Memberships: Law Society, International Bar Association, American Bar Association, Institute of Directors.

Career: Articled at *Hall Bryden* qualified 1968, partner 1971, partner *Halliwell Landau* 1978. Senior Partner (1989-1995).

Personal: Education: Manchester Grammar School, Leeds University (1965 LL.B). Born 1945, resides Hale, Cheshire, enjoys cricket & golf.

GEE, Tim

Baker & McKenzie, London (020) 7919 1000

Specialisation: Public and private company M&A, privatisation and equity capital markets transactions, acting for underwriters and issuers. Extensive cross-border and emerging markets experience. Identified as one of the UK's leading privatisation lawyers in Euromoney's Guide to the World's Leading Privatisation Lawyers and as one of the UK's leading M&A lawyers in Euromoney's Guide to the World's Leading Mergers and Acquisitions Lawyers. Head of *Baker & McKenzie*'s Global M&A Practice Group.

Prof. Memberships: The Law Society; City of London Solicitors Company.

Career: Educated at Worcester College, Oxford. Qualified in 1986 with *Baker & McKenzie*. 1989-90 *Baker & McKenzie*, Hong Kong. 1991 *Baker & McKenzie*, Budapest. Partner in 1992.

Personal: Married with two sons. Interests include rugby and fly fishing.

GEFFEN, Charles S.H.

Ashurst Morris Crisp, London (020) 7638 1111

Specialisation: General corporate and corporate finance.

Career: Head of Private Equity.

Personal: Married, four children.

GILBERT, Ian M.

Walker Morris, Leeds (0113) 283 2500
img@walkermorris.co.uk

Specialisation: Partner in Corporate Department. Main area of practice is corporate finance, management buy-outs and venture capital. Has been involved in venture capital and development capital for 17 years, acting on both sides. Involved in numerous MBOs of varying size and complexity, including take privates, as well as public and private company acquisitions and disposals, flotations, joint ventures, and share issues.

Career: Qualified in 1981. With 3i Group Plc 1979-85. Joined *Walker Morris* in 1985 and became a Partner in 1986.

Personal: Born 22nd July 1957. Educated at Sheffield University 1975-78. Recreations include tennis, walking, golf and unpaid taxi driver for children. Lives in Follifoot.

GILLESPIE, Stephen

Allen & Overy, London (020) 7330 3000

Specialisation: Partner at *Allen & Overy* in 1995. Has extensive experience in all types of international financing, including acquisition financing, structured financing, project financing, and a number of multi-source financings. Led/is leading the teams advising the underwriters/arrangers/lenders on the leveraged acquisitions of Bosch Telecom, Giraudy, IPC Magazines, Panta Electronics and Newmond Holdings. Also advised the arrangers/underwriters on the api Energia IGCC financing (and refinancing) in Italy, the £1.5 billion Bouygues Telecom third mobile telecommunications financing in France and the Euro595 million financing for KPN Orange Belgium N.V., the third Belgian mobile telecommunications operator. Is currently leading the team advising the arrangers/underwriters of the Euro2.43 billion financing for WIND Telecommunicazioni, the third Italian mobile operator. Recently led the team advising Chase, Deutsche and IBJ as lead arrangers of the £1.725 billion financing for the acquisition of the Drax Power Station by AES from National Power. In the rail sector, he led the team advising Virgin Rail Group in connection with the financing of its rolling stock procurement programme for the UK's West Coast and Cross-Country Passenger rail franchises (the largest single rolling stock procurement ever undertaken in the UK). Also has extensive expertise in PFI transactions: Advised the sponsors/project company in connection with the Law Hospital PFI financing and is currently leading the teams advising the sponsors/project company in connection with the King's College hospital, St George's Hospital and Dumfries and Galloway Hospital PFI financings. Is also leading the team advising the financiers on the Scottish/Northern Irish electricity interconnector project.

Prof. Memberships: Law Society. City of London Solicitors Company.

Career: Articled *Stephenson Harwood* 1985-87, Solicitor *Freshfields* 1987-91, Solicitor *Allen & Overy* 1991-95, Partner 1995.

Personal: Born 1962. Educated at Foyle and Londonderry College and Trinity College, Oxford (MA (Hons) Jurisprudence 1984). Interests include family, reading, outdoor pursuits and music. Lives in St. Albans.

GILTHORPE, Ian M.

Robert Muckle, Newcastle-upon-Tyne (0191) 232 4402

Partner in Commercial Department. Managing Partner.

Specialisation: Main area of practice is corporate finance, including MBOs, acquisitions, disposals, sources of finance, debt re-structuring and flotation.

Career: Qualified in 1978. Partner 1979. Current non-executive directorships: QSP Group plc; Vald Birn (UK) Ltd.

GLEN, Marian

Shepherd & Wedderburn WS, Glasgow (0141) 566 9900
marion.glen@shepwedd.co.uk

Specialisation: Partner and head of corporate finance in Glasgow, specialising in mergers and acquisitions, and joint ventures; recent deals include sale by ScottishPower and Martin Dawes Telecommunications (a BT Cellnet subsidary) of their joint venture company Vodafone Distribution (November 1999) (acting for ScottishPower).

Prof. Memberships: Institute of Directors; British/German Jurists Association.

Career: Trained at *Dundas & Wilson*, Edinburgh; qualified 1989; solicitor *Linklaters & Paines*, London, 1989-94; joined *Shepherd& Wedderburn* 1994; partner 1996.

Personal: Education: Notre Dame High School, Glasgow/Glasgow Unisversity (1983 MA Hons French and German); Edinburgh University (1987 LLB). Born 1960; resides Edinburgh. Lesure: Hill walking, golf and travel. Languages: French and German.

GODDEN, Richard

Linklaters (A member firm of Linklaters & Alliance), London (020) 7456 3610
richard.godden@linklaters.com

Partner. Corporate Department. Has wide experience both in general corporate advisory work and corporate transactions. Advises a wide range of corporate clients and merchant and investment banks in connection with public mergers and takeovers, the establishment of joint ventures, private merger and acquisition transactions, flotations, other corporate equity fund raising, and advises corporations of various sizes in relation to their on-going affairs (e.g. issues connected with general meetings, scrip dividend schemes, removal of directors, etc.)

GODFREY, Christopher

Burges Salmon, Bristol (0117) 939 2219
chris.godfrey@burges-salmon.com

Specialisation: Corporate finance. Chris also heads *Burges Salmon*'s practice in the field of investment funds, where the firm has a specialism, unique among English regional firms, in the area of collective investment schemes, ranked 6th nationally by number of client groups served.

Prof. Memberships: Law Society.

Career: Trained with *Linklaters*, qualifying in 1986, and joining *Burges Salmon* later that year, becoming a partner in 1990.

Personal: Jurisprudence, Hertford College, Oxford 1980-83.

GODFREY, Keith G.

Allen & Overy, London (020) 7330 3000

Specialisation: Partner in the corporate department, specialising in corporate finance, mergers and acquisitions, joint ventures and securities offerings.

Prof. Memberships: Member of Law Society's Standing Committee on Company Law since 1988.

Career: Articled Allen & Overy, qualified 1976, Partner 1981.

Personal: London University 1972. Born 1951.

GOODALL, Caroline

Herbert Smith, London (020) 7374 8000

Specialisation: Specialises in corporate work in particular corporate finance and mergers and acquisitions. She has been involved, as adviser to both companies and to investment banks, in numerous takeovers, international mergers and acquisitions, international share issues, IPOs, rights issues and placings. She has also advised on a number of cross border transactions and complicated international joint ventures. Most recently she has acted for Koninklijke Hoogovens N.V. in relation to its merger with British Steel. She has acted for Lazard Brothers, financial advisers to Electra Investment Trust plc, on the hostile £1.2bn bid by 3i Group plc and the alternative proposals by Electra for a share buy back and related restructuring, for BSkyB in relation to its £623m offer for Manchester United plc and for Friends Provident in relation to its £744m offer for the London and Manchester Group.

Prof. Memberships: City of London Solicitors' Company.
Career: Admitted in 1980 and became a partner in 1987. Head of the corporate division.

GORRIE, Euan
Allen & Overy, London (020) 7330 3000
Specialisation: He specialises in acting for banks or borrowers, in connection with acquisition finance, public bid and other leveraged or structured finance transactions, restructurings, syndicated loans, secured lending and lending to partnerships. He spent a year on secondment to the Mitsubishi Bank in 1992, providing in-house advice on loans, workouts and bilateral transactions.
Career: Glenalmond; New College Oxford; Articled *Allen & Overy*, Partner 1996.
Personal: Married; two children.

GOULD, Terry
Eversheds, Norwich (01603) 272727
terrygould@eversheds.com
Specialisation: Head of Corporate Finance with particular experience in M & A and private equity. Within last 12 months worked on the Bertram/Cypher £54m merger and the scale of Thompson & Morgan to IGI inc. Has worked increasingly on developing business in North America. Addresses seminars.
Prof. Memberships: Law Society.
Career: Qualified 1977 with *Freshfields*. Joined present firm in 1978 and became a Partner in 1981.
Personal: Born 7th March 1952. Attended Downing College, Cambridge 1971-74. Governor Norwich School. Leisure pursuits: golf and football. Lives in Norwich.

GOWANS, Andrew
Osborne Clarke OWA, Reading (0118) 925 2012
andrew.gowans@osbourneclarke.com
Head of Corporate Department in Thames Valley Office.
Specialisation: Specialises in M & A and corporate finance work, mainly with companies in business sectors which rely heavily upon intellectual property rights, such as information technology and publishing. Recent deals include acting for Torex Group PLC in connection with their acquisitions of AAH Meditel Ltd and Peak Systems Ltd.
Career: St Edmund Hall, Oxford MA; Trinity Hall, Cambridge LLM; *Freshfields* (1990-95); *Dallas Brett*, Oxford (1996-97); *Osborne Clarke* 1998 to date.

GRAVES, Patrick
Osborne Clarke OWA, Bristol (0117) 917 4122
patrick.graves@osborneclarke.com
Specialisation: Patrick specialises in corporate finance work, covering all aspects of public and private company mergers, acquisitions, disposals and fundraisings, with a particular emphasis on listed work and financial services regulation. Recent deals include: MBI of Churngold Group Limited; placing and open offer by Science Systems plc; placing and open offer by Pennant International Group plc; institutional and private fundraising by Opsys Limited; private fundraising by Soup Opera; reverse takeover of Tethys Limited by AIM listed Cambridge Mineral Resources Plc; recommended cash offer by Pensa Limited for aspen Group; numerous e-business start-ups/early stage fundraisings (Ezeehelp, Eclecticom and BlueU.com).
Career: Qualified at *Linklaters & Paines* 1989, *Maclay Murray & Spens 1991*; *Ashurst Morris Crisp*1992-95; Partner *Bevan Ashford* 1996-97; partner *Osborne Clarke* 1997 to date.

GRAY, Colin F.
McGrigor Donald, Glasgow (0141) 248 6677
coling@mcgrigors.com
Head of Corporate Unit.
Specialisation: Acquisition and Sales of businesses/companies (both listed and non-listed). Acting on Institutional Investments (on both debt and equity sides). General Corporate (including inward investment franchise agreements, etc).
Prof. Memberships: Law Society of Scotland; Law Society of England and Wales; Society of Scottish Lawyers in London.
Career: 1980-84 Glasgow University (LLB, DipLP), 1987 to date *McGrigor Donald* (Partner – November 1991).
Personal: Married June 1993 to Lee (nee Robertson). Two children, Hannah and Oliver. Leisure interests include golf and trying to keep fit by cycling to and from work.

GRAY, David
Eversheds, Leeds (0113) 243 0391
davidgray@eversheds.com
Managing Partner, *Eversheds* Leeds and Manchester. Chairman of the *Eversheds* National Corporate Group 1998-2000.
Specialisation: Handles all aspects of corporate finance work with a particular emphasis on international work. Clients include Premier Farnell, McCains, Peter Black, Heywood Williams and Waddington. Independent comments include: "a good business adviser highly rated by his competitors", "considered an outstanding player in the Leeds market . . . widely regarded as a class act."
Personal: Age 45. Leisure interests include golf and horse racing.

GRAY, Richard
L'Estrange & Brett, Belfast (028) 9023 0426
richard.gray@lestrangeandbrett.com
Partner, Corporate Department.
Specialisation: Main areas of practice are corporate, corporate finance and banking work. Also active in project finance and PFI work.
Prof. Memberships: Law Society of Northern Ireland; Law Society of England and Wales.
Career: Called to the Northern Ireland Bar in 1989. Admitted as a solicitor in England and Wales in 1992 and in Northern Ireland in 1992. Assistant solicitor with *Cameron Markby Hewitt* (now *Cameron McKenna*) 1989-1992. Partner in *L'Estrange & Brett* since 1996.
Personal: Born 1966. Education: Queen's University of Belfast (LLB). Course Adviser (Company Law): Institute of Professional Legal Studies, Belfast.

GRAYSTON, Clare
Lewis Silkin, London +44 (0) 20 7227 8004
graystonc@lewissilkin.com
Specialisation: Head of Corporate Department. Practice area covering mergers and acquisitions and corporate finance. Practice is predominantly in mergers and acquisitions, public and private, acting for both buyers and sellers and in IPOs and secondary issues on the main market and AIM, frequently representing the sponsor/NOMAD and boker.
Prof. Memberships: Active in l'Association Internationale des Jeunes Avocats.
Career: Qualified in 1985. Other interests: Director (Chair of Finance Committee) of Women in Film and Television (UK) Limited (1992-1998), Director of Living Earth Foundation (environmental charity) (1995-1996). Published author on a number of comparative law texts. French speaker.
Personal: Born 1960. Lives in central London.

GREAVES, Adam
Gouldens, London (020) 7583 7777
Partner in company/commercial department.
Specialisation: Very diversified practice covers venture capital, management buy-outs and buy-ins, mergers and acquisitions (private and public), flotations, corporate finance, corporate reconstructions and commercial agreements and joint ventures.
Career: Qualified in 1982. Joined *Nabarro Nathanson* in 1980, joining and becoming a Partner of *Gouldens* in 1986.
Personal: Born 9th July 1958. Attended Bradfield College 1972-76, Selwyn College, Cambridge 1976-79 and Guildford College of Law 1979-80. Leisure interests include fly fishing (member of the Red Sea Casters), bridge, hockey, walking and cooking. Lives in London.

GREEN, Geoffrey S.
Ashurst Morris Crisp, London (020) 7638 1111
geoffrey.green@ashursts.com
Senior Partner.
Specialisation: Principal area of work is mergers and acquisitions, including cross-border mergers and acquisitions and corporate finance generally, including new issues. Other main area of work is buy-outs acting primarily for equity institutions.
Prof. Memberships: Law Society.
Career: Qualified in 1975 while with *Ashurst Morris Crisp* and became a Partner in 1979.
Personal: Forest School; St. Catharine's College, Cambridge. Leisure pursuits include tennis, golf and riding. Lives in London.

GREEN, W. Guy
Eversheds, Birmingham (0121) 232 1000
Specialisation: Corporate finance with a private equity bias, mergers and acquisitions for both private and public companies advising buyers, sellers and funders.
Career: Qualified at *Bird & Bird* in 1982. Partner at *George Green & Co* 1989 to 1999. Became partner at *Eversheds* in January 2000 heading up *Eversheds* private equity team.
Personal: Leisure interests include sailing, hockey, skiing and golf.

GREENFIELD, G.N. Ian
Hammond Suddards Edge, Leeds (0113) 284 7000
ian.greenfield@hammondsuddardsedge.co.uk
Specialisation: Head of corporate finance in Leeds. Specialises in merger and acquisition work, flotations and secondary issues, stock exchange and take-over code work for plc and substantial private companies. Significant transactions have included the £750 million FKI/Babcock demerger, £68 million acquisition of Hero Drinks Group (UK) Limited by Cott Corporation of Canada, the £26 million bid by Genus plc for VDC plc, the flotation of DBS Management plc on the Official List, acting for Great Lakes Chemical Corporation on the $300 million demerger of Octel Corp on the New York Stock Exchange and the £99 million public to private bid for Allied Textile Companies plc.

Prof. Memberships: Law Society.
Career: Educated at Hymers College, Hull and Emmanuel College Cambridge (MA Cantab). Articled *Coward Chance* London; Qualified 1978. Solicitor *Coward Chance* 1978-80; Solicitor and Associate, *Brooke North & Goodwin* Leeds 1980-83; Solicitor and partner *A V Hammond & Co.* 1984-88; Partner *Hammond Suddards* 1988 to date.
Personal: Born 1953; resides Ikley; married with two children. Leisure interests include golf, tennis and rugby.

GREGORY, Lesley
Memery Crystal, London (020) 7242 5905
lgregory@memerycrystal.com
Specialisation: Corporate and commercial matters, including corporate finance, acquisitions and disposals, Official List and AIM, capital raising, joint ventures and commercial sports law, including licensing and sponsorship. Acted for Wembley Stadium in the negotiations for the first sponsorship of the F.A. Cup Final. Involved with various football clubs. Advised Wembley on the sale of Wembley Stadium and related issues. Advises event owners, agents and event hospitality companies such as Keith Prowse on various sponsorship, licensing and ticketing issues.
Prof. Memberships: The Law Society, Women in Management, CISCO and the British Association for Sport and Law.
Career: Articled *Courts & Co.* Qualified 1983; solicitor *Memery Crystal* 1983-1988; partner since 1988.
Personal: Born 1960; resides London.

GRISEWOOD, Rebecca
Halliwell Landau, Manchester (0161) 835 3003
Specialisation: Handles a range of corporate finance work principally mergers, acquisitions, venture and development capital transactions, MBOs and MBIs.
Career: Articled *Halliwell Landau.* Qualified 1988. Partner 1995, Corporate Department.
Personal: Born 1963. Liverpool University 1981-84 (LLB). Lives in Saddleworth. Enjoys theatre & travel.

GRONOW, Simon D.V.
Pinsent Curtis, Birmingham (0121) 200 1050
simon.gronow@pinsents.com
Partner in Corporate Finance Department.
Specialisation: Principally engaged in general corporate work for UK and International public companies and investment banks/brokers, including flotations, rights issues, takeover offers, capital reconstructions, acquisitions and disposals.
Prof. Memberships: Law Society.
Career: Qualified 1986. Joined *Pinsent Curtis* in 1984, Partner in 1991.
Personal: Born 1961. Educated at King's College Cambridge 1979-83.

HALE, Chris
Travers Smith Braithwaite, London
(020) 7295 3000
Chris.Hale@TraversSmith.com
Specialisation: Main area of practice: Head of Travers Smith Private Equity Group. Advises leading buy-out houses in the UK. Also advises on new issues and a number of listed companies, financial advisers and larger private companies on equity raising and mergers and acquisitions. Known particularly for working on more complex, larger buyouts and cross-border transactions
Prof. Memberships: Hon. Treasurer and Executive Committee member of Society of Advanced Legal Studies.
Career: Qualified as a solicitor in 1981 with *Kingsley Napley*, joined *Travers Smith Braithwaite* in 1983 and became partner in 1987.
Personal: Educated at King's College School, Wimbledon, Emmanuel College, Cambridge (MA) and Wolfson College, Cambridge (LLM). Leisure interests include football, reading, gardening, walking and legal history.

HALL, Daniel C.J.
Eversheds, Manchester (0161) 832 6666
danielhall@eversheds.com
Head of Corporate.
Specialisation: Mergers and acquisitions and corporate finance for public and private companies. Expertise in Takeover Code offers. Visiting lecturer in law at Manchester University. Regular speaker at seminars and conferences.
Prof. Memberships: Law Society. British American Business Group. Committee member of Fiscal Studies Institute.
Career: Trainee Solicitor, *Eversheds* (Manchester) 1985-87, Solicitor (Company Dept.) *Clifford Chance* 1987-92. Partner *Eversheds* (Manchester) 1992. Head of Corporate – January 1999.
Personal: Born 29th August 1962. Educated Repton Preparatory School, Repton School, Bristol University and London College of Law. Leisure pursuits include golf, shooting and fishing. Lives in Wilmslow, Cheshire. Married. Son Benjamin and daughter Isabel.

HALPIN, Peter
Eversheds, Manchester (0161) 832 6666
peterhalpin@eversheds.com
Specialisation: Mergers and Acquisitions with a specialism in private equity and venture capital. National Head of private equity and venture capital. Recent transactions include listing and global offer of Telecity plc (Essom) and institutional buyout of ANC Group (E75M).
Prof. Memberships: Law Society and Wine Society.
Career: Liverpool University (LLB). Partner at *Addleshaw Booth & Co* (1995). Joined *Eversheds* as Partner in 1998.
Personal: Born 19 October 1964. Leisure pursuits include rugby (league and union). Lives in Warrington. Married.

HAMILTON, Timothy
Garretts, Manchester (0161) 228 0707
Specialisation: Senior Partner, Manchester Office (Corporate Department). Advises on a wide range of corporate transactions, including mergers and acquisitions, MBO's, Yellow Book, City Code and international transactions. In 1999 has led a number of substantial transactions including advising NatWest Equity Partners on the £50 million investment in NES Group and advising Latium Group on its £47 million acquisition of the Everest double-glazing manufacturing and installation businesses from Caradon plc.
Prof. Memberships: Law Society.
Career: 1984 to 1996 *Alsop Wilkinson* (Partner from 1990). 1996 *Garretts* (Senior Partner).
Personal: Born 12 January 1962. Educated Durham School, University of Manchester (1980-1983) (LLB (Hons)) and Chester College of Law. Interests: rugby, golf, football, theatre, sailing. Married, 3 children.

HANTON, Bruce
Ashurst Morris Crisp, London (020) 7638 1111
Specialisation: Principal area of work is corporate finance particularly private equity transactions. Recent transactions include the acquisition of William Hill (Cinven and CVC) and the European operations of Safety-Kleen (Electra Fleming) and the acquisition of RoadChef Plc (Nikko Europe).
Prof. Memberships: Law Society.
Career: Qualified in 1988 with *Ashurst Morris Crisp.* Became Partner in 1996.
Personal: Born 7 February 1962. Educated Alleyn's School and Bristol University (LL.B and LL.M). Married with two children.

HARDIE, David
Dundas & Wilson CS, Edinburgh (0131) 228 8000

HARKER, Chris
Dickinson Dees, Newcastle upon Tyne
(0191) 279 9254
chris.harker@Dickinson-Dees.com
Partner in company and commercial department.
Specialisation: Main areas of practice are acquisition finance and venture capital. In addition to working for banks, has acted for Northern Venture Managers Limited in some 18 venture capital investments and disposals over the last year with a value of approximately £20m. Also handled the MBI of Hugh Mackay Carpets.
Career: Qualified in 1978, having joined *Dickinson Dees* in 1976. Became a partner in 1981.
Personal: Born 25th January 1954. Attended Rossall School, Fleetwood 1962-71, then The Queen's College, Oxford 1972-75. Leisure interests include cricket, golf, skiing and other sports. Lives in Ponteland.

HARPER, Tony
Brabner Holden Banks Wilson, Liverpool
(0151) 236 5821
tony.harper@bhbw.co.uk
Specialisation: Partner in Corporate Department. Work includes corporate finance, MBOs, MBIs, venture and development capital, mergers, acquisitions and disposals, housing association funding.
Prof. Memberships: Law Society, Liverpool Law Society.
Career: Educated at St. Ambrose College, Altrincham; University of Liverpool. Articled at Brabner Holden 1981-83 becoming Partner in 1986.
Personal: Born 1959. Interests include golf, fell walking, Round Table. Married with three children. Lives in Stockton Heath.

HARRISON, Wendy A.
DLA, Leeds (08700) 111111
wendy.harrison@dla.com
Specialisation: Corporate finance work including mergers and acquisitions for both public and private companies. Advising on private equity transactions including MBOs, MBIs and Institutional purchases and start-ups (particularly internet related). Matters dealt with include; IBO of Autowindscreens on behalf of HSBC Private Equity (£97,000,000) MBO of Paramount Hotels Limited on behalf of Alchemy Partners (£64,000,000).
Prof. Memberships: Law Society
Career: Joined *DLA* as trainee solicitor in 1989 (qualifying in 1991). Promoted to partnership in 1998.
Personal: Married – 2 children.

HATCHARD, Michael E.
Skadden, Arps, Slate, Meagher & Flom LLP, London (020) 7519 7000
MHatchard@skadden.com
Partner specialising in corporate finance and M&A.
Specialisation: Principally mergers, acquisitions and joint ventures and the full range of securities distribution transactions, particularly where significant UK/US implications arise.
Career: Qualified 1980 with *Theodore Goddard*, partner 1985. Joined *Skadden, Arps* as a partner in 1994 with responsibility for the English legal and regulatory aspects of global securities offerings and cross-border transactions.
Personal: Born 21st November 1955.

HATTRELL, Martin
Slaughter and May, London (020) 7600 1200
Specialisation: Corporate Department. Principal area of practice is corporate and commercial law, in particular mergers and acquisitions.
Prof. Memberships: The Law Society.
Career: Qualified in 1987 with *Slaughter and May* and became a Partner in 1994.
Personal: Born 9 August 1961. Educated at Ampleforth College, Yorkshire and The Queen's College, Oxford.

HAWES, Roger
Burges Salmon, Bristol (0117) 939 2243
roger.hawes@burges-salmon.com
Specialisation: Venture capital and corporate finance. Has recently advised on the £135m takeover of Overview.net plc by freecom.net plc, the £21m disposal by Lumination plc of its wholesale lighting division and the £15m start-up of fibre optic semiconductor foundry specialist, Optical Micro Devices.
Prof. Memberships: Law Society.
Career: Qualified in 1984, joined *Burges Salmon* in 1988 from *Linklaters*, became a partner in 1990.

HAYWARD, Paul A.
Gateley Wareing, Birmingham (0121) 234 0000
phayward@gateleywareing.co.uk
Specialisation: Corporate Finance, General Corporate, mergers and acquisitions and corporate reconstruction.
Prof. Memberships: Law Society, Society of Practitioners of Insolvency.
Career: Alleyne's School; Nottingham Trent University; Chester Law College; Articles *Edge & Ellison* – Assistant Solicitor 1982-1985; *Needham & James* – Assistant/Associate 1985-1988; Partner *Gateley Wareing* 1988 to date.
Personal: Member of Edgbaston Golf Club and Moor Hall Golf Club. Interests: All sport, music.

HAYWOOD, Richard
Wragge & Co, Birmingham (0121) 214 1038
richard_haywood@wragge.com
Specialisation: Wide range of M&A experience; acts for H.J. Heinz, Marconi, Powell Duffryn, PowerGen, Severn Trent, Tomkins, TRW, Wagon Plc.
Career: Qualified 1980; Partner *Wragge +Co* 1986.
Personal: Born 1955. Chairman of the NSPCC Birmingham Business Group.

HEATHCOCK, Andrew E.
Paris Smith & Randall, Southampton (023) 8048 2482
Partner in charge of Company and Commercial Department.
Specialisation: Main area of practice includes over 20 years experience in company and corporate finance work in the private sector.
Prof. Memberships: Law Society.
Career: Qualified with *Bird & Bird* 1977; *Lovell White & King* 1979-81. Partner in charge of Commercial Department of *Boodle Hatfield* in Southampton 1981-90. Joined *Paris Smith & Randall* as a Partner in October 1990.

HENDERSON CBE, Giles
Slaughter and May, London (020) 7600 1200
Senior Partner and Partner in Corporate Department.
Specialisation: Corporate, corporate finance and commercial law, with particular experience in privatisations.
Prof. Memberships: The Law Society. Member, Financial Reporting Council; Chairman, Law Committee, UK/China Forum; Member, Hampel Committee on Corporate Governance.
Career: Qualified 1970. Partner since 1975. Senior Partner since 1993.
Personal: Born 1942. Educated at Michaelhouse School, South Africa and at Witwatersrand University, South Africa (BA) and Magdalen College, Oxford (MA, BCL).

HEWES, Simon P.
Bond Pearce, Southampton (01179) 299197
sph@bondpearce.com
Partner in the Corporate Group.
Specialisation: Corporate finance, particularly acquisitions, disposals and mergers, private equity, including MBO's, MBI's and IBO's and shareholder arrangements. Recent deals include £35m buy-out of British International from CHC Helicopter Corporation and private equity investment in Bowman Power Systems Ltd of £8.5m.
Prof. Memberships: Member of the British Venture Capital Association.
Career: Qualified in 1987 with *Pinsent & Co.*, Birmingham (now *Pinsent Curtis*). Joined *Hepherd Winstanley & Pugh* in 1992, becoming a Partner in 1994 and joining *Bond Pearce* in 1998 on merger.

HOLLAND, Peter Rodney James
Allen & Overy, London (020) 7330 3000

HOLT, Andrew D.
DLA, Manchester (08700) 111111
andrew.holt@dla.com
Specialisation: Qualified – 1984 – Partner since 1990 – Specialises in company acquisitions and disposals, corporate finance, MBOs, MBIs and private equity investments.

HOPKINS, Stephen Martyn
Eversheds, Leeds (0113) 243 0391
stephenhopkins@eversheds.com
Specialisation: Principal commercial lending transaction this year was acting for HSBC in relation to Yorkshire Group's acquisition of business CK Witco. The deal involved facilities of £50 million, with seven jurisdictions involved. Has edited the financial assistance chapter of Tolley's 'Company Law'. Corporate finance practice continues to develop. Led the *Eversheds* team who advised on the break up and disposal of Australian National Industries steel interests in the UK- a project which took nearly six months and raised nearly £100m. With the elevation of David Gray to managing partner, now runs the day to day operation of the corporate team in Leeds and Manchester.
Prof. Memberships: Law Society.
Career: Qualified in 1984. Joined *Eversheds* in 1988. Became a partner in 1991.
Personal: Born 17th March 1960. Attended Sheffield University 1978-81. Leisure interests include golf, cricket and rugby. Lives near Wetherby.

HOWARD, Susan
Allen & Overy, London (020) 7330 3000
susan.howard@allenovery.com
Specialisation: Experience of all aspects of corporate finance work specialising in larger management buy-outs/ins, private equity work of all sizes (from smaller venture capital investments to large cross-border deals for financial purchases) and mergers and acquisitions.
Prof. Memberships: The Law Society
Career: Articled with *Allen & Overy* 1985-87, qualified in September 1987 and became a partner in May 1994.
Personal: Born 7th May, 1962. Attended Pates Grammar School (1973-8), Cheltenham Grammar School (1978-80) and Freter College, Oxford (1981-4). Lives in London.

HOYLE, Andrew C.
Watson Burton, Newcastle upon Tyne (0191) 244 4444
Specialisation: Wide range of corporate & insolvency work involving transactional and security issues arising from instructions received from banks and insolvency practitioners.
Prof. Memberships: Law Society.
Career: Qualified as a solicitor in 1985. Joined *Watson Burton* as a partner in March 1992.

HUGHES, David J.
Pinsent Curtis, Birmingham (0121) 200 1050
david.hughes@pinsents.com
Partner in Corporate Finance Dept.
Specialisation: Corporate finance, including mergers and aquisitions, takeovers and primary and secondary equity issues. He is a senior corporate partner for a number of the firm's major listed clients and also acts for a number of US, German and other multinational companies on UK transactions.
Career: Qualified in 1980. Partner in 1987. Worked at *Nabarro Nathanson* 1978-82, then *Slaughter and May* 1982-85, before joining *Pinsent & Co* in 1985.
Personal: Born 1955. Attended Wolverhampton Grammar School 1966-73, then Jesus College, Oxford 1973-77.

HULL, David Julian
Hammond Suddards Edge, Birmingham (0121) 200 2001
david.hull@hammondsuddardsedge.com
Partner in the Corporate Department and Chairman of the International Task Force of the Firm, *Hammond Suddards Edge.*
Specialisation: Specialises in corporate finance and company commercial work. Primary expertise is mergers and acquisitions, Stock Exchange work, international cross-border transactions and entertainment and leisure contracts.
Prof. Memberships: LL.B (Hons) (Sheff'd). Is responsible for many of the firms large corporate clients. Regular writer of legal articles and visiting lecturer at the Universities of Wolverhampton and Aston.
Career: Qualified 1986. *Dibb Lupton Broomhead* 1984-86, *Hammond Suddards* 1986-87, *Edge Ellison* 1987 to date (Partner from 1990).

Personal: Born 18th October 1961. Educated at Banbury School and Sheffield University. Interests include theatre and West Bromwich Albion FC. Lives in Knowle Solihull.

HULLS, Martin A.
Ward Hadaway, Newcastle upon Tyne (0191) 204 4000
Specialisation: Corporate finance; private equity transactions; MBOs/MBIs.
Prof. Memberships: Law Society.
Career: LLB from Birmingham University. Practised in Birmingham and Nottingham before moving to the North East in 1993. Became Head of Commercial Department in 1994.
Personal: Keeping fit, mountain biking, fast cars, motor racing. Married with two young daughters.

HUNTER, James
Mills & Reeve, Norwich (01603) 693 267
james.hunter@mills-reves.com
Specialisation: Company sales and acquisitions and general corporate finance matters. Acted on acquisitions worth £45 million over two years for one US client. Recently involved in a number of dot.com start ups and fund raising.
Prof. Memberships: Law Society.
Career: Trainee at *Mills & Reeve* (1993-1995). Solicitor at *Mills & Reeve* (1995-2000). Associate at *Mills & Reeves* 2000 to date.
Personal: Married. Cycling, sailing, fishing. LL.B (UEA)- College of Law, York.

HUTCHINSON, John C.
Pitmans, Reading (0118) 9580224
Specialisation: Company/Commercial specialist whose main areas of work include MBO/MBIs, acquisitions, disposals, venture capital and bank funding.
Career: Qualified 1990. Partner 1994.
Personal: Born 7th December 1961. Lives in Oxford. Interests include golf, football and opera.

HUTTON, C. Noel
Hammond Suddards Edge, Leeds (0113) 284 7000
noel.hutton@hammondsuddardsedge.com
Partner in Corporate Finance Department.
Specialisation: Specialises in mergers and acquisitions (principally by and on behalf of listed companies) and new issue work. Also involved in the development of prime contracting for the MoD.
Career: Qualified in 1973. Partner at *Hammond Suddards* since 1977.
Personal: Born 4th November 1949. Interests include sailing, motor sports and sport generally. Lives in Ilkley.

HYMAN, Neil
Slaughter and May, London (020) 7600 1200
Specialisation: Partner specialising in mergers, acquisitions and disposals; joint ventures and general company commercial; particular emphasis in the drinks, pubs and leisure industry and in the telecommunications and media fields.
Career: Articled *Slaughter and May*; qualified 1988; Hong Kong office 1990-92; partner 1995.
Personal: Born 1962; educated at Arnold School and Birmingham University (LLB Hons 1st class); resides in London; Member Dyrham Park Golf & Country Club.

IRVINE, John W.
L'Estrange & Brett, Belfast (028) 9023 0426
john.irvine@lestrangeandbrett.com
Partner and head of corporate department.
Specialisation: Main area of work: Corporate and commercial law.
Prof. Memberships: Law Society of Northern Ireland.
Career: Lecturer in law: Queen's University, Kingston, Ontario; University of Central Lancashire. Tutor in law, University of Exeter; Course tutor, Institute of Professional Legal Studies, Belfast. Qualified 1986. Partner in *L'Estrange & Brett* since 1988.
Personal: Born 1957: Education: Queen's University, Belfast (LLB), Queen's University, Kingston, Ontario (LLM.)

JAMES, Glen William
Slaughter and May, London (020) 7600 1200
Specialisation: Practice covers all work in the fields of company, corporate and finance, including mergers and acquisitions, issues and flotations and corporate restructurings. Additional interest in non-contentious insurance and reinsurance work.
Prof. Memberships: The Law Society; Securities Institute.
Career: Qualified 1976. Articled at *Slaughter and May* 1974-76. Assistant solicitor 1976-1983. Partner since 1983.
Personal: Born 22 August 1952. Educated at King's College School, Wimbledon and New College, Oxford.

JAMISON, David
Carson & McDowell, Belfast (028) 9024 4951
david.jamison@carson-mcdowell.com
Specialisation: Emphasis on mergers acquisitions and disposals.
Prof. Memberships: Law Society of Northern Ireland and Law Society of England and Wales.
Career: Born 1964. Qualified 1989. University of Manchester. Articled and practised in London and latterly in North of England prior to returning to Northern Ireland in 1995. Partner 1998.

JANSEN, Karl
Freethcartwright, Nottingham (0115) 9369 369
karl.jansen@freethcartwright.co.uk
Specialisation: Corporate transactional work including mergers and acquisitions, management buyouts/buyins and refinancing, acting for buyers, seller and equity/debt funders. Highlights of last year include the £54million acquisition of Bertram Books Limited by Cypher Group Limited, the £9million sale of the Way Ahead Group Limited to Flextech plc and the sale of the Data Base Group of Companies to the Ramesys Group.
Career: Articles with *Davies Arnold Cooper*, London. Joined present firm on qualification in 1990. Appointed partner in 1994. Appointed Head of Corporate in 1999.
Personal: Educated at Loughbrough Grammar School and the London School of Economics. Season ticket holder at Leicester City FC. Married with two children.

JOHNS, Michael S.M.
Nicholson Graham & Jones, London (020) 7648 9000
Managing Partner and Partner in the Company and Commercial Department.
Specialisation: Main area of practice is corporate finance. Work includes acquisitions, mergers, venture capital, buy-outs, equity issues, yellow book work and general corporate work for public listed companies. Member of sports group; acts for organisations and individuals in the sports field including sponsors and sports organisers. Has spoken at seminars both in the UK and USA on subjects such as buy-outs, international strategic activities, law firm management and sports sponsorship. Non-Executive Director of Merchant Retail Group Plc since 1979.
Prof. Memberships: Institute of Directors, Law Society. Chairman of Globalex.

JOHNSON, Ben
Eversheds, Nottingham (0115) 950 7000
benjohnson@eversheds.com
Specialisation: Corporate finance, predominantly private equity, mergers and acquisitions. Deals in 2000 include the MBO of Royal Crown Derby Porcelain, the equity investment in MBO of Pauls Fabrications and the sale of part of the Wade Furniture Group.
Prof. Memberships: Law Society.
Career: Qualified 1988; *Burgess Salmon*. 1986 to 1998 (seconded to *Wragge & Co* 1988/89) a partner from 1996. *Eversheds* as a partner 1998 to date.

JOHNSON, James
Clifford Chance, London (020) 7600 1000
Partner, general banking group, banking department.
Specialisation: Advises on all forms of corporate banking but in particular is a leading specialist in acquisition finance, workouts, structured finance and housing assocation finance.
Career: Articled at *Wilde Sapte* and qualified in 1987. Partner at *Wilde Sapte* 1991-2000. Partner at *Clifford Chance* since 2000.
Personal: Born 1963. Educated: Roundhill College, Thurmaston, Leicester 1974-77, Wreake Valley College, Syston, Leicester 1977-81, Collingwood College, Durham University.

JOHNSON, Robin
Eversheds, Leeds (0113) 243 0391
robinjohnson@eversheds.com
Specialisation: A Corporate Finance and Commercial Partner specialising in M&A, purple book and joint venture work with a strong emphasis on technology. Member of the Regional Advisory Group for the Stock Exchange. Robin is client partner for a number of US corporates including Parker Hannifin Corporation, Waters Corporation, SPX Corporate and Geo Corporate as well as leading advisors to UK listed companies such as AEA Technology plc, Sanderson Bramall Motor Group plc, Chapelthorpe plc Intechnology plc and RAP Group plc. Extensive experience on public takeover bids, having been involved in 15 since March 1998. Voted one of "40 under 40" to watch by the Yorkshire Business Insider in 1999.
Career: Qualified 1987, partner 1994.
Personal: Born 1963, resides Leeds, married with two children.

JOHNSTON, Keith T.
Addleshaw Booth & Co, Manchester (0161) 934 6000
byj@addleshaw-booth.co.uk
Partner in Corporate Finance Group.
Specialisation: Principal area of practice is corporate finance mainly for listed companies including mergers and acquisitions, takeovers and general

transaction and corporate advice. Other main areas of work include public/private sector partnerships and project work (see separate entry).
Prof. Memberships: Law Society. Chairman: North West Company Secretaries' Forum. Head of Projects Group at the firm.
Career: Qualified in 1976. Became a Partner in 1981. 1991-94 Member of Board of *Norton Rose* M5 Group. Board member of *Addleshaw Booth & Co.*
Personal: Educated at London University 1970-73 (External). Governor of The Grange School, Hartford, Cheshire. Company Secretary API Group plc. Leisure pursuits include badminton, chess and tennis. Lives in Hale, Cheshire.

JOHNSTON, Michael C.
Carson & McDowell, Belfast (028) 9024 4951
michael.johnston@carson-mcdowell.com
Partner Company/ Commercial Department.
Specialisation: Work includes mergers and acquisitions, PFI/PPP, project finance, management buy-outs and management buy-ins, venture capital, joint ventures and general corporate/ commercial advice.

JONES, Arfon
CMS Cameron McKenna, London
(020) 7367 3333
aj@cmck.com
Specialisation: Corporate finance, including M&A, flotations and equity and debt capital issues. Major transactions include the Luminar/Northern Leisure offer, the £9 billion Glaxo/Wellcome take over and the US$1billion Exchangeable Capital units issue by National Australia Bank.
Prof. Memberships: Law Society; Company Law Sub-Committee; City of London Solicitors Company.
Career: Bristol Grammar School, Clare College, Cambridge. Joined *Markbys* 1968. Partner 1970 to date in *Markbys, Cameron Markby, Cameron Markby Hewitt, CMS Cameron McKenna.*
Personal: Married, 2 sons, 1 daughter. Interests: skiing, golf.

JONES, Hugh
Osborne Clarke OWA, Reading (0118) 925 2094
hugh.jones@osborneclarke.com
Specialisation: Hugh advises on a range of corporate banking matters, with particular emphasis on acquisition finance. His experience includes advising and leading transactions involving banks, merchant banks, UK public and private companies, foreign companies and venture capitalists.
Career: Hugh qualified in1989 with *Norton Rose*, London. He then joined *Cole and Cole* (now *Morgan Cole*) in the Thames Valley, and was made a partner in 1996. He joined *Osborne Clarke* as a partner in1999.

JONES, Jonathan
Hammond Suddards Edge, Leeds (0113) 284 7000

JONES, Michael
CMS Cameron McKenna, Bristol (0117) 930 0200
mgj@cmck.com
Specialisation: Partner in charge of the Bristol corporate practice. The practice covers all company and corporate finance work with particular emphasis on mergers and acquisitions, private equity and venture capital, flotations, takeovers, financings, joint ventures and general corporate advice.
Career: Qualified with *McKenna & Co* in 1987; *McKenna & Co* 1987-89; Investment Banking Division of Samuel Montagu & Co. Ltd1989-92 and HSBC Investment Bank (Asia) Limited 1992-97, becoming a Director; Partner *CMS Cameron McKenna* 1997.
Personal: Born 23 November 1960. Educated at Haberdashers' Aske's School, Elstree; Durham University and College of Law, Guilford. Married with 3 children, lives in Bath.

KANE, Hilary
Maclay Murray & Spens, Glasgow
(0141) 248 5011
hak@maclaymurrayspens.co.uk
Partner specialising in mergers and acquisitions (including cross-border), corporate finance and project finance.
Specialisation: Recent transactions include advising 3i and the management shareholders of Phillips Auction Group in the sale of the Group to LVMH; advising Robert Wiseman Dairies in its £235m unilateral offer to acquire Unigate Daries' dairy & cheese activities which it had previously conditionally agreed to sell to Unigate and advising Candover in a £55m institutional buyout of companies in the UK and US. Has been particularly involved in public to privates including 3i/Redwood Group's £66.1m offer for Clyde Blowers, Harrock plc's £88.1m offer for Wainhomes and advising Scottish Highland on competing offers to take it private, including Paramount Hotel's successful £30m offer.
Prof. Memberships: Mergers and Acquisitions Committee of AIJA (International Lawyers Association).
Career: Articled *Maclay Murray & Spens*; qualified 1985; partner, *Maclay Murray & Spens*, since 1991; established London office where partner in charge before returning to Glasgow office in 1997.
Personal: Craigholme School; Glasgow University (LLB 2(1) Hons, Dip LP). Born 1962; resides Glasgow. Enjoys good food and wine, spinning, watching football, skiing.

KEAL, Anthony C.
Allen & Overy, London (020) 7330 3000
Specialisation: Partner at Allen & Overy in 1982. He specialises in domestic and cross-border acquisition finance and other structured finance products. Recent transactions include financing (for Barclays) the successful public bid for Westminster Healthcare plc and its subsequent acquisition of the Priory Group; (for Deutche Bank) the LBO of TA Health GmbH and a series of subsequent acquisitions by that company (creating the Domus Healthcare Group); (for Credit Suisse First Boston) the LBO of Reed Regional Newspapers Ltd and Westminster Press by KKR and affiliates (creating the Newsquest Group) and refinancings, the LBO of Frida Alimentaria SA and the public takeover of Triplex-Lloyd plc by Doncaster plc; (for Goldman Sachs) the LBO of Cartiere del Garda SpA and its subsiquent acquisition of Smurfit Condat S.A., the original Pacificorp bid for The Energy Group plc and the LBO of Swebus AB; (for Rabobank International) the LBO of BOCM Pauls Ltd and the leveraged acquisition of The Tetley Group by Tata Tea (for BNP) the LBO of Interdean International; (for Merita) the LBO of ColArt International; (for WestLB) the leveraged joint venture of the Thorn and Granada consumer rentals businesses. Tony also acts frequently for investors on the debt side of LBOs for example, for Morgan Grenfell Private Equity in a number of LBOs over a long period; for Investcorp in the LBOs of Welcome Break and Helly-Hansen, the public bid for Watmoughs plc and private acquisition of BPC (creating the Polestar Group); and for KKR, the public bid for Wasssall plc.
Prof. Memberships: Law Society and City of London Solicitors Company.
Career: Articled *Allen & Overy*, qualified 1976; legal adviser/CoSec, Libra Bank plc 1976-78. Assistant Solicitor *Allen & Overy* 1979-81; Partner 1982.
Personal: Born 1951. Educated Stowe School and New College, Oxford (1973). Resides in Surrey. Interests: sailing, skiing, opera and wine.

KELIHER, James
Stephens & Scown, Exeter (01392) 210700
commerce.exeter@stephens-scown.co.uk
Specialisation: Partner dealing with corporate finance, mergers and acquisitions, venture capital, consumer credit; handled a sale by tender of Terry Adams Limited, a private landfill company, to South West Water for £105m.
Career: Educated Worth Abbey, University of Liverpool (1979 LLB); articled *Farrer & Co*; qualified 1983; *Richards Butler* 1984; partner 1988; *Stephens & Scown* 1995; partner 1998; trustee of Jean Sainsbury Animal Welfare Trust.

KERLE, Bridget A.
Hewitson Becke + Shaw, Cambridge
(01223) 461155

KIMBELL, Stephen
Kimbell & Co, Milton Keynes (01908) 668555

KING, Peter
Linklaters (A member firm of Linklaters & Alliance), London (020) 7456 3448
peter.king@linklaters.com
Partner. Corporate Department. Co-Head of Linklaters' International Equities Practice.
Specialisation: Experienced in all aspects of corporate finance, including, in particular, international equity offers, privatisations, mergers and acquisitions and advice to financial institutions on regulatory matters.
Career: Articled at *Linklaters*, Solicitor 1981-90, becoming Partner in 1990.
Personal: Educated, St John's College, Cambridge. Born 1960.

KITTS, Stephen
Eversheds, Nottingham (0115) 9507000
stephenkitts@eversheds.com
Specialisation: Corporate finance, private equity and acquisition finance for banks and mezzanine lenders and venture capitalists as well as general mergers and acquisitions.
Prof. Memberships: Law Society.
Career: Joined *Eversheds* in 1987 and became a partner in 1994. Qualified 1987. Head of Corporate *Eversheds* East Midlands.
Personal: Lives in Derbyshire with his wife and two children, enjoys golf and cycling.

KNAPP, Vanessa
Freshfields Bruckhaus Deringer, London
(020) 7936 4000
Partner in corporate department.
Specialisation: Main area of practice is company/ commercial, covering corporate finance and general corporate work. Also handles financial services. Chairman of the City of London Law Society Company Law Sub-Committee and Member of Law Society, Company Law Committee.

Prof. Memberships: Law Society.
Career: Qualified in 1981. Joined *Freshfields* in 1979, becoming a Partner in 1988.
Personal: Born 3rd November 1956. Attended Exeter University (LLB) 1975-78. Member of the London Symphony Chorus. Lives in London.

KNIGHT, Adrian G.
Shearman & Sterling, London (020) 7655 5000
AKnight@shearman.com
Partner in M&A and Corporate Finance.
Specialisation: Specialises in mergers and acquisitions, corporate finance and private equity transactions.
Career: Qualified in March 1984. Became a Partner at *Ashurst Morris Crisp* in 1992. Resigned from *Ashurst Morris Crisp* becoming a partner at *Shearman & Sterling* in June 1999.
Personal: Graduated from Cambridge University in 1980.

KNIGHT, William
Simmons & Simmons, London (020) 7628 2020
Senior Partner.
Specialisation: Main area of practice involves corporate finance and company work. Author of Acquisition of Private Companies (7th ed.) and member of Editorial Board of PLC magazine.
Prof. Memberships: Chairman Law Society Company Law Committee 1990-93, Institute of Advanced Legal Studies Research Committee, CCBE (Conseil Barreaux de la Communaute Europeenne) Company Law Committee.
Career: Qualified in 1969. Partner at *Simmons & Simmons* 1973. Admitted as Hong Kong Solicitor 1979, and Head of Hong Kong office 1979-82. Leader of one of the corporate finance groups 1984-94. Appointed head of corporate department 1994. Appointed Senior Partner in September 1996.

LAVERY, James
Pinsent Curtis, Birmingham (0121) 200 1050
jim.lavery@pinsents.com
Partner. Head of Private Equity, Birmingham.
Specialisation: Main practice areas are private equity principally acting for venture capital funders and management, and M&A work for private and public companies. Recent deals include the Gresham Trust backed IBO of Alstom's Automation business, the Barclays Private Equity backed MBO of Edotech from Barclays Bank and the recent development funding for 2 technology companies, Intercede and Safix.
Prof. Memberships: Law Society.
Career: Educated at King Edward's School, Birmingham and Exeter University. Qualified 1990. Joined *Pinsent Curtis* in 1994. Partner 1996.
Personal: Born 1964. Leisure interests include golf and music.

LAWES, William P.L.
Freshfields Bruckhaus Deringer, London (020) 7936 4000
Specialisation: Main practice areas are mergers and acquisitions, demergers, joint ventures, restructurings, international offerings and UK domestic issues of all types. Acts for a range of corporate clients (with a media bias) and investment banks. Recent significant M&A transactions include acting for Pearson on the merger of its televsion division with CLT-UFA and the offer for Dorling Kindersley, Amoco on its merger with BP, AirTouch on its merger with Vodafone, GEC/ Marconi on its defence deal with BAe, Capital Radio on its acquisition of a number of radio stations, Scottish Media on its bid for Grampian TV and Amersham on the mergers with Nycomed and the life science business of Pharmacia & UpJohn.
Prof. Memberships: Law Society, City of London Solicitors Company.
Career: Qualified as Barrister and Solicitor in New Zealand in 1986. Judges' Clerk at New Zealand Court of Appeal 1985. Joined *Freshfields* in 1986. Partner in Corporate Department 1994.
Personal: Born 2 January 1964. Educated in England and New Zealand. Victoria University, Wellington N.Z. 1981-85. Gonville and Caius College, Cambridge 1985-86. Leisure pursuits include golf and family.

LAWTON SMITH, Andrew
Wragge & Co, Birmingham (0121) 685 2730
andrew_lawton_smith@wragge.com
Specialisation: Head of M&A Team working with entrepreneurs and large private businesses. Highlights. Acquisition of National Nuclear Corporation from GEC (Marconi) for 3i plc and managers; IBO of Bowater Windows for management; establishment and growth of new focused team
Prof. Memberships: British Venture Capital Association. Law Society. Birmingham Law Society.
Career: Education: Bristol Polytechnic. Guildford College of Law. Trained at Eversheds. Secondment at 3i Legal. Joined *Wragge & Co* in 1990. Non-exec on Midlands housebuilder in which Close Bros VCT funds are invested.
Personal: Skiing, golf, travel, gourmet food and wine.

LAYTON, Matthew
Clifford Chance, London (020) 7600 1000
matthew.layton@cliffordchance.com
Specialisation: Particular emphasis on domestic and international management, leveraged buy-outs and venture capital transactions as well as general corporate and corporate finance work.
Career: LL.B (Hons) Leeds 1982. Qualified 1986; partner 1991.

LEE, Paul
Addleshaw Booth & Co, Manchester (0161) 934 6000
pal@addleshaw-booth.co.uk
Senior Partner and Chairman of the Board of *Addleshaw Booth & Co*, Partner in the Corporate Finance Group.
Specialisation: Work covers acquisitions and disposals for both listed and non-listed companies. MBOs and venture capital specialising in strategic advice and business planning. Addresses conferences and seminars.
Career: Qualified 1970. Joined the firm in 1970, becoming a Partner in 1973, Managing Partner in 1991 and Senior Partner in 1997.
Personal: Attended Clare College, Cambridge. Director of several companies, both public and private, including banking and property: Chairman of the CBI -North West. Chairman of the Royal Exchange Theatre; Chairman of the Board of Governors of Chetham's School of Music and a Board member of the Royal Northern College of Music. Director of Opera North and Northern Theatre Ballet. Leisure interests include the arts, sport and wine. Lives in Manchester.

LEE, Richard
Clarks, Reading (0118) 958 5321
Partner in Company Department.
Specialisation: Work covers company law, corporate finance and venture capital, public issues, company acquisitions, banking and employee share schemes. Advises large corporates, financiers and buy out teams in management buy out and buy in transactions.
Prof. Memberships: Thames Valley Commercial Lawyers Association (Co-Founder 1987, Committee Member 1987-1994, Chairman 1991-93).
Career: Qualified in 1976. Held various marketing positions with Shell International 1969-72; trained with *Norton Rose* specialising in corporate finance until 1980. A Partner at *Simpson Curtis* 1981-1986. Head of Company Department at *Clarks* since 1986.
Personal: Born 16th June 1947. BSc (Economics and Politics) from Bristol University 1969. Leisure interests include golf, music and theatre. Lives in Reading.

LEE, Richard N.F.
Addleshaw Booth & Co, Manchester (0161) 934 6000
rnl@addleshaw-booth.co.uk
Partner in Corporate Finance Group.
Specialisation: Work covers mergers and acquisitions, City Code takeovers, flotations and secondary issues. Also deals with general corporate work including Stock Exchange compliance.
Prof. Memberships: Law Society, Manchester Law Society.
Career: Qualified in 1983 before joining the firm in 1986. Became a Partner in 1988.
Personal: Educated at Trinity College, Cambridge 1977-80. Leisure interests include sport and family. Lives in Wilmslow.

LETH, Mary H.
Macfarlanes, London (020) 7831 9222
Specialisation: Partner Company Commercial and Banking Department. Deals with corporate finance including acquisitions, mergers, demergers and corporate reconstructions.
Career: Educated in United States: University of Colorado. Attorney, *Holland and Hart*, Denver Colorado, USA (1978-1984). Articled at *Macfarlanes*; qualified 1988; Partner 1995. Admitted States of Colorado 1977; New York 1984.
Personal: Born 1952. Resides London. Interests include music, opera, walking, cycling.

LEVY, Graeme
Olswang, London (020) 7208 8888
Partner and Head of Insolvency Unit.
Specialisation: Specialises in corporate, finance and insolvency matters, acting for corporates, institutions, insolvency practitioners and banks. Work includes mergers and acquisitions, joint ventures and public issues, as well as all aspects of funding and insolvency. Co-author of 'Practical Insolvency Precedents' (Sweet & Maxwell) and consulting editor to Butterworths Encyclopedia of Forms and Precedents.
Career: Qualified 1985. Previously at *Herbert Oppenheimer, Nathan & Vandyk, Richards Butler* and *SJ Berwin & Co* (partner there from 1990). Joined *Olswang* as a partner in 1995.
Personal: Born April 1959. Educated at Trinity Hall, Cambridge. Interests include tennis, theatre (musicals) and playing the guitar.

LEVY, Robert A.
Kuit Steinart Levy, Manchester (0161) 832 3434
robertlevy@kuits.com
Specialisation: Corporate finance; corporate and commercial; tax investigation.
Prof. Memberships: Manchester Law Society.
Career: Articled *Kuit Steinart Levy*; Qualified 1984; Partner *Kuit Steinart Levy* 1988.
Personal: Born 1959. Manchester Grammer School & University College London – 1981 LLB Hon. Resides Manchester. Interests – tennis, theatre, amateur dramatics, member Royal Exchange Theatre special events committee, active involvement in the Starlight Foundation.

LEWIS, David T.R.
Norton Rose, London (020) 7283 6000
lewisdtr@nortonrose.com
Partner in Corporate Finance Department; Senior Partner.
Specialisation: Main area of practice is corporate finance, including take-overs (public and private), flotations, stock exchange work of all types, MBOs, schemes of arrangement, international global offerings, all types of commercial agreements, and debt restructurings. Has handled over 100 listings and numerous take-overs including HSBC Holdings/ Midland, GEC Siemens/ Plessey, Imperial Group/ Hanson/ UB, BA/ B-Cal, BMW/ Rover, Redland/ Steetley, Ladbroke/ Hilton, Dixons/ Currys, Guinness/Grandmet, Ciba/Allied Colloids, BMW/Rolls Royce. Has chaired and spoken at numerous conferences.
Prof. Memberships: Member of the Law Society of London Company Law Committee 1982-97. Hon. Fellow Jesus College Oxford.
Publications: Author of articles in Gazette and PLC; also the Norton Rose Guide to Take-overs.

LEWIS, Mark R.L.
Foot Anstey Sargent, Plymouth (01752) 675000
mark.lewis@foot-ansteys.co.uk
Partner. Leader of Commercial Services Division Practise covers a wide range of domestic corporate finance activities including mergers and acquisitions and public and private fund raisings. Also handles company and commercial work, including joint ventures and other strategic commercial agreements and has very substantial experience of public takeovers, flotations and secondary issues on the London Stock Exchange, and privatisations.
Prof. Memberships: Law Society
Career: Qualified in 1978. Joined *Foot & Bowden* as a Partner in 1995.
Personal: Born 1953. Attended Millfield School 1965-71 and Exeter College, Oxford 1972-75 (Exhibitioner). Lives near Exeter.

LEWIS, Susan
Eversheds, Birmingham (0121) 232 1000
Specialisation: Work for listed companies and mergers and acquisitions. The M&A work has become increasingly multi jurisdictional. Used to heading a large team of lawyers (where the job demands) on substantial transactional work.
Career: Oxford University 1976-79. Articled at *Evershed & Tomkinson*, became a partner in 1988. Has been with *Eversheds* throughout career.
Personal: Married with 2 small children. The time for non-work related external interests is almost non-existent, and limited to children and Aston Villa!

LIPPELL, C. Sean
Addleshaw Booth & Co, Leeds (0113) 209 2081
csl@addleshaw-booth.co.uk
Partner in Corporate Department.
Specialisation: Principal area of practice is corporate finance. Work includes public issues, takeovers, MBO/MBIs and private equity, mergers and acquisitions (including cross-border/international transactions), demergers and corporate reconstructions and corporate joint ventures.
Prof. Memberships: Law Society.
Career: Qualified in 1979. Joined June 1999.
Personal: Educated at Kelly College, Tavistock and Durham University. Leisure interests include keeping fit, walking, reading, wine and films.

LIVINGSTONE, Alisdair
Osborne Clarke OWA, Bristol (0117) 917 4128
alisdair.livingstone@osborneclarke.com
Specialisation: Specialises in private equity, M&A's and MBO's and has acted for many venture capitalists, management teams, vendors and purchasers of businesses. Recently acted for management on the MBO of Advance International and for the company and institutional investors on the IBO's of British International (£35.5 million), Eurotel (£38 million), and Mermaidlogic (£41 million) also acted for the company on the sale of Aethos (£40 million), the sale of various parts of the Dalgety business and the sale of the Westinghouse Brakes business of Invensys plc (£65 million).
Career: Alisdair trained at *Osborne Clarke*,qualifying in 1995 and being promoted to partner in 1999.

LOAKE, Jonathan
Brobeck Hale and Dorr, Abingdon, Oxfordshire (01235) 834447
loake@bhd.com
Partner
Specialisation: Company mergers and acquisitions, group reorganisations, MBOs, venture capital subscriptions, corporate transactions in the music industry. Clients include a wide range of technology companies, publishers and record companies.
Prof. Memberships: IBA; Thames Valley Commercial Lawyers' Association (former Chairman).
Career: Editor with Hodder & Stoughton. Qualified with *Denton Hall* in 1979; left after four years to co-found *Dallas Brett*.Partner at *Morgan Cole* from 1997-2000.
Personal: Born 21 March 1951. Educated at Rugby School and Trinity College, Oxford. Married with three children. Leisure pursuits include sport, reading and music.

LONG, Julian
Freshfields Bruckhaus Deringer, London (020) 7936 4000
Specialisation: Is a corporate partner based in London and is a member of *Freshfield's* European M&A Group. Sector experience includes pharmaceuticals, food, publishing and water.
Career: Partner at *Freshfields* since 1995.

LOWE, Paul
Eversheds, Cardiff (02920) 471147
paullowe@eversheds.com
Specialisation: UK and international corprate finance including flotations, public and private company mergers, acquisitions and disposals; joint ventures; MBO's, MBI, etc., together with general corporate advice.

Prof. Memberships: The Law Society. Institute of Bankers. Solicitor qualified in Hong Kong.
Career: *Phillips & Buck* 1982-1987. *Richards Butler* Hong Kong 1988-1991. *Eversheds* 1991 to date.
Personal: Interested in tennis, golf and water sports.

LUBBOCK, Nigel
Steele & Co, Norwich (01603) 274 700
commercial@steele.co.uk
Specialisation: Corporate and commercial work for both national and international businesses specialising particularly in sales and acquisitions, merger and company restructuring. Domestic clients include Pi Group Ltd, Tulip Int. (UK). Ltd and Ionics (UK) Ltd. The team also deal with tendering, procurement and PFI contracts for their local authority clients and draft a wide variety of commercial agreements for use by the authorities.
Career: Trained Bristol, *London and Norwich*, qualified 1975, partner *Steele & Co*1979.
Personal: Married, have a son and daughter; enjoys opera/cricket.

LUMSDEN, Christopher
Chaffe Street, Manchester (0161) 236 5800
See under Banking, p.119

LUMSDEN, Ian G.
Maclay Murray & Spens, Edinburgh (0131) 226 5196
igl@maclaymurrayspens.co.uk
Partner in Corporate Finance Department.
Specialisation: Partner specialising in corporate finance and mergers and acquisitions. Work includes flotations, rights issues and other fund raising activity for plcs as well as acquisitions and disposals for listed and unlisted companies and investment trust reconstructions. Advised Motherwell Bridge Holdings Limited in the £75m disposal of its Information Systems Division in the largest deal funded by 3i in Scotland.
Career: Qualified in 1976. University of Cambridge (BA 1972), University of Edinburgh (LLB 1974). Spent two years working with *Slaughter and May* in London 1978-80.
Personal: Born 1951.

MACAULAY, Anthony D.
Herbert Smith, London (020) 7374 8000
Partner in Corporate Division.
Specialisation: Experienced in company and commercial matters, especially corporate finance work, including takeovers and flotations. Has particular expertise in relation to the Takeover Code (having spent two years as Secretary of the Takeover Panel) and insider dealing.
Career: Qualified in 1974. Became a Partner at *Herbert Smith* in 1983.
Personal: Educated Keble College, Oxford.

MACFARLANE, David J.
Ashurst Morris Crisp, London (020) 7638 1111
Specialisation: General Corporate. Corporate Finance.
Career: Head of Company Department.

MACINTOSH, Duncan J.G.
Morgan Cole, Cardiff (029) 2038 5385
duncan.macintosh@morgan-cole.com
Specialisation: Main area of practice is corporate finance. Work includes mergers and acquisitions and venture capital based transactions, including management buy-outs, management buy-ins and

institutional investments. Acted for management in the MBIs of Regent and Postern to form The Assembly Group of Companies Limited, and of Parker Plant International Limited. Also, the MBO of TIS Software Limited and other venture capital financings.
Prof. Memberships: Member of the Law Society of England and Wales, the Law Society of Scotland, Society of Writers to H M Signet. Qualified in Scotland in 1984, becoming a Partner in an Edinburgh legal practice before joining 3i plc; and then in England and Wales in 1992. Joined *Morgan Bruce* in 1990.
Personal: Born 11 October 1957. Attended Glenalmond College in Perthshire and Glasgow University. Leisure interests include cricket and golf. Director of Davesons Lives in Llanblethian, Vale of Glamorgan.

MACKIE, Chris A.
Olswang, London (020) 7208 8888
cam@olswang.com
Specialisation: Corporate finance, specialising in private equity and venture capital advising management teams and institutions.
Prof. Memberships: Law Society.
Career: 1987-1994 *Turner Kenneth Brown*. 1994-2000 *Berwin Leighton*, partner 1996. Feburary 2000- joined *Olswang* as a partner.
Personal: Married with 3 children. Lives in London.

MACPHERSON, Moray
Bond Pearce, Southampton (023) 8063 2211
xmcm@bondpearce.com
Partner in the Corporate Group.
Specialisation: Specialises in corporate finance: M&A, MBOs etc for management, equity investors and banks. Recent deals include: acquisition FBM Marine Limited for Babcock International Group plc; Equity funding for Flagship Foods Limited in £150m merger deal; sale of business for Chemring Group plc; Equity funding for Sport Business International Limited.
Prof. Memberships: Member of the British Venture Capital Association.
Career: Qualified 1985, becoming partner with *Boodle Hatfield* 1990. Joined *Bond Pearce* 1995 on the firms acquisition of the Southhampton office of *Boodle Hatfield.*

MAHER, Paul J.
Rowe & Maw, London (020) 7248 4282
Head of Corporate Group.
Specialisation: Corporate finance including specifically flotation/new issues, M & A and joint ventures. Main focus in recent years has been transactional and private equity work in both the telecoms and chemicals sectors.
Prof. Memberships: Law Society.
Career: Articled to *Boodle Hatfield* 1982-1984, Solicitor ICI Group Legal Department, 1984-90. *Rowe & Maw* 1990 to date.
Personal: Born 30th July 1959. London Law Degree, LLB Bristol. Interested mainly in books, politics and travel. Other leisure pursuits include running, football and squash. Lives in Wandsworth Common.

MARDLE, David
Garretts, Cambridge (01223) 355977
david.x.mardle@glegal.com
Specialisation: Partner, Cambridge office (Corporate Department). Advises on a wide range of corporate transactions, including private equity transactions and mergers and acquisitions. In 1999, he advised the shareholders in the Dalehead Group on the £50 million merger with Roach Foods.
Prof. Memberships: Law Society.
Career: 1990-1994 *Denton Hall*/1994-1999 *Allen & Overy*/1999 – Garretts.
Personal: Worcester College, Oxford (1985-1988) (BA) and Guildford College of Law. All sport, married, two children.

MARSH, David
Burges Salmon, Bristol (0117) 939 2288
david.marsh@burges-salmon.com
Specialisation: Main area of practice is company/commercial and corporate finance work, and partnerships. Director of Lumination plc.
Prof. Memberships: Law Society.
Career: Joined *Burges Salmon* in 1971, became a Partner in 1972, Managing Partner in 1990 and Senior Partner in 1995 to date.
Personal: University College, Oxford 1962-65. Leisure interests include skiing, music and golf.

MARSHALL, John
Johnsons, Belfast (028) 9024 0183

MARTIN, Charles D.Z.
Macfarlanes, London (020) 7831 9222
cdzm@macfarlanes.com
Specialisation: MBOs/Venture capital. M&A (especially cross-border), private equity and Corporate finance/securities.
Career: Bristol University 1982. Qualified 1985. Partner 1990. Worked in the US 1988-9.
Personal: Married with three children. Lives in London.

MASTERS, Richard
McGrigor Donald, Glasgow (0141) 248 6677
Specialisation: Corporate acquisitions/sales/fund raisings. Successes so far in year 2000: acted for: Abacnet UK in its sale to Netromedia Fiber Networks, the Lombard Group in its £20m AIM flotation and Realty Group in its sale to Great Universal Stores.
Prof. Memberships: Law Society of Scotland.
Career: Associate *McGrigor Donald*, 1993. Partner Corporate Finance, 1996.
Personal: Educated at Wallace High School, Northern Ireland and Strathclyde University. Married with two children, Tom (7) and Michael (4). Main intrests, hill walking, motor racing, football, fine food and wine.

MCBRIDE, Paul
L'Estrange & Brett, Belfast (028) 9023 0426
paul.mcbride@lestrangeandbrett.com
Specialisation: Corporate and commercial including mergers and acquisitions, management buy-outs, venture capital and project finance.
Prof. Memberships: Law Society of Northern Ireland.
Career: Queens University, Belfast (LLB), Cambridge University (LLM). Called to the Northern Ireland Bar in 1990. Admitted as a Solicitor in Northern Ireland in 1993. Partner in *L'Estrange & Brett* since 1998.

MCDONALD, Kevan
Dickson Minto WS, Edinburgh (0131) 225 4455
Kevan.mcdonald@dmws.com
Specialisation: Partner in Corporate Department. Main areas of practice are corporate and commercial: mergers and acquisitions, management buy-ins and outs, sales and purchases of companies and businesses, refinancings and corporate finance. Recent deals include the £85 million institutional buy-out of the information systems division of Motherwell Bridge.
Prof. Memberships: Law Society of Scotland, IBA.
Career: Qualified in 1982. Joined *Dickson Minto WS* as Senior Assistant in 1985 and assumed as a Partner in 1987.
Personal: Born 7th July 1958. Attended Aberdeen University 1976-79 (LLB) and Dundee University 1979-80 (Diploma in Petroleum Law). Leisure interests include fishing, swimming and squash. Lives in Edinburgh.

MCGINN, James
MacRoberts, Glasgow (0141) 332 9988
jamesm@macroberts.co.uk
Specialisation: Corporate finance including mergers and acquisitions and management / institutional buy-outs / buy-ins.
Prof. Memberships: Law Society of Scotland. Law Society (England and Wales)
Career: Qualified 1986 with *Levy & McRae* Glasgow. Joined *Taylor Vinters* Cambridge,1988, *Dickson Minto* London 1990 and *MacRoberts* Glasgow 1997. Partner 1998. University of Glasgow 1980 – 85.

MCHUGH, Peter J.
Eversheds, Birmingham (0121) 232 1000
petermchugh@eversheds.com
Head of Corporate Services, Birmingham.
Specialisation: Handles mainly public company work, share acquisitions and disposals and general corporate advice.
Prof. Memberships: Birmingham Law Society.
Career: Qualified in 1982. Became a Partner in *Eversheds Wells & Hind* in 1989.
Personal: Born 23rd July 1958. Lives in Hartlebury, Worcestershire. Fellow of the RSA.

MCINTOSH, Ian W.
Addleshaw Booth & Co, Leeds (0113) 209 2000
iwm@addleshaw-booth.co.uk
Partner in Corporate Finance Group.
Specialisation: Corporate finance and company law including mergers and acquisitions, joint ventures, MBOs and private and public capital raisings. Acts for a range of public and private companies, banks and venture capitalists.
Prof. Memberships: Law Society.
Career: Qualified 1983. Joined the firm in 1988, becoming a partner in 1989.
Personal: Leisure interests include golf, cinema and walking.

MCNEILL, Morag
McGrigor Donald, Glasgow (0141) 248 6677

MEIKLEJOHN, Iain M.C.
Shepherd & Wedderburn WS, Edinburgh (0131) 228 9900

METCALFE, Ian
Wragge & Co, Birmingham (0121) 214 1074
ian_metcalfe@wragge.com
Specialisation: Corporate Finance: Flotations, public takeovers, company mergers and acquisitions. Important Cases: Acting for BI Group Plc on recommended offer for Cortworth Plc; acting for GKN in joint venture between GKN and Dana Corporation; acting for W.Canning plc on the recommended offer by Macdermid Inc; acting for NIC Holdings (Guernsey) Ltd on the sale of NIC (UK); acting for Specialist Computer International Limited on acquisition of information products division of Buhrmann B.V.; acting for company on flotation of ITNET plc; acting for British Airways Plc on formation of GO.
Career: King Edward's School; St Catharine's Col-

lege, Cambridge (MA Hons Law). Articled O'Dowd & Co; qualified 1983; Partner *Wragge & Co* 1992.
Personal: Born 1958. Leisure: Rugby, Cricket, Golf. Vice president Moseley FC(RU); Warwickshire CCC General Committee; General Purposes and Finance Sub-Committee; Chairman Catering Board; Chairman, West Midlands region of the Lord's Taverners; Member Edgbaston Golf Club.

METCALFE, Robin H.
Browne Jacobson, Nottingham (0115) 976 6000
rmetcalfe@brownej.co.uk
Specialisation: Corporate/corporate finance. Wide experience of transaction oriented work heading unit which advises buyers, sellers and funders (equity and debt).
Prof. Memberships: Law Society.
Career: Articled *Eking Manning*. Qualified 1980. Partner *Browne Jacobson* 1985.
Personal: Born 1956; Educated Barnard Castle School, Co. Durham and Nottingham University (LLB Hons). Resides Nottingham. Interests: football, cricket, squash, watersports, climbing and trekking, travel and music.

MIDDLEDITCH, Matthew
Linklaters (A member firm of Linklaters & Alliance), London (020) 7456 3144
matthew.middleditch@linklaters.com
Partner. Corporate Department.
Specialisation: Specialises in UK corporate finance and company law. Main areas of practice include advising companies and merchant banks on: mergers and acquisitions, including public takeovers and private acquisitions of shares and businesses; flotations; secondary issues, including acting on rights issues, vendor placings and open offers; reorganisations; joint ventures and general corporate work.
Career: Articled with *Linklaters* and qualified in 1982. Born 1958.

MILLINGTON, Jeremy S.
Wragge & Co, Birmingham (0121) 214 1090
jeremy_millington@wragge.com
Specialisation: Partner in corporate group specialising in flotations, takeover offers, securities offerings, acquisitions and disposals.
Prof. Memberships: Member of The Law Society and The Birmingham Law Society; Member of the Birmingham Law Society Company and Commercial Law Sub-Committee.
Career: Qualified 1988. Joined *Wragge & Co* in 1986; Partner in 1995.
Personal: Born 1964. Lives in Harborne, Birmingham.

MINTO, Bruce
Dickson Minto WS, Edinburgh (0131) 225 4455
bruce.minto@dmws.com
Founding Partner in Corporate Department.
Specialisation: Work includes Stock Exchange listings, Yellow Book work generally, mergers and acquisitions and institutional finance.
Prof. Memberships: Law Society of Scotland.
Career: Qualified in 1981. Formed *Dickson Minto WS* in 1985.
Personal: Born 30th October 1957. Attended Edinburgh University 1975-79. Leisure interests include golf, shooting and music.

MITCHELL, Christopher J.
Cartwrights, Bristol (0117) 929 3601
cjmitchell@cartwrights.com
Partner and Head of Commercial Client Department.
Specialisation: Main area of practice is corporate finance work, handling mergers and acquisitions, venture capital, joint ventures; commercial agreements particularly beer supply agreements. Transactions include £17.25m (2000) and £30m (1999) banking facilities for two pub companies, a £1.2m private equity placing for Clarity Commerce Solutions plc, followed by its £2.25m acquisition of Clarity Retail Systems plc and £1.5m acquisition of Microtrain Limited (all in 2000); subsequent flotation of Clarity Commerce Solutions plc on AIM (2000); negotiating a management agreement for an estate of 430 pubs (2000) and various substantial beer supply agreements for a major regional brewer (2000).
Prof. Memberships: Law Society, SBO.
Career: Qualified in 1981. Joined *Cartwrights* in 1986 and became a Partner in 1987.
Personal: Born 3rd October 1957. Educated at Portsmouth Grammar School 1969-73. Brockenhurst College, Hampshire 1973-75 and St. Catherine's College, Oxford 1975-78. Recreations include sport, hill walking, horse riding and all things French. Lives in Bristol.

MOORE, Austin John
Eking Manning, Nottingham (0115) 840 4499
austin@ekings.co.uk
Specialisation: General corporate finance. In the last year, advised on over 20 transactions exceeding £1,000,000 (aggregate deal value £150,000,000), including public offers and acquisitions by e-gosystems plc plus sales of Charles Manson Group Limited, Compass Cleaning Limited and Quatrix Holdings Limited.
Prof. Memberships: Council Member, Nottinghamshire Law Society.
Career: *Shoosmiths & Harrison* 1986 – 1991, *Eversheds* 1991 – 1995, *Eking Manning* 1995 to date.
Publications: Contributing Editor to Encyclopaedia of Forms & Precedents (Business Sales). Author of 'Business Purchase' and 'The Owner Managed Business' published by Butterworths in 1998.
Personal: Married with three children. Music, tennis, karate.

MORLEY, David H.
Allen & Overy, London (020) 7330 3000
Specialisation: Banking and Corporate Finance: Debt. Partner acting for banks and financial institutions, as well as borrowers, on all types of debt and structured finance transactions with particular emphasis on syndicated loans, project finance, telecommunications finance, public bid and other acquisition finance, property and asset finance.
Career: Articled *Allen & Overy*, qualified 1982, trainee solicitor Brussels 1981, assistant solicitor 1982-88. One year on secondment at Chase Investment Bank Limited 1985, partner 1988. Managing Partner, Banking Department 1998.
Personal: St John's College, Cambridge (1979 MA). Born 1956, enjoys cycling, sailing, skiing, family.

MORRIS, Andrew
Edwards Geldard, Cardiff (029) 2023 8239
andrew.morris@geldards.co.uk
Specialisation: Corporate finance, company and business acquisitions and disposals, management buy-outs and buy-ins, joint ventures and reorganisations, acts for clients receiving venture capital and bank funding and for banks and venture capital organisations on the provision of such funding.
Prof. Memberships: Law Society.
Career: Assistant Solicitor at *Edwards Geldard* between 1989 and 1995. Partner in *Edwards Geldard* since 1995.
Personal: Born 1965. Educated at Lady Mary High School, Cardiff and University of Glamorgan. Lives in Cardiff.

MORSE, Stephen
Michelmores, Exeter (01392) 436244

MUNDAY, Peter J.
Mundays, Esher (01372) 809000
peter.munday@mundays.co.uk
Head of Corporate Department and Senior Partner.
Specialisation: Mergers, acquisitions and disposals. Clients include: Alliance UniChem Plc, The BOC Group plc. Photo-Me International Plc, Corporate Express Inc, Air Express International (UK) Ltd, E. Moss Ltd, Fine Frangrances & Cosmetics Ltd, Morgan Elliott Group Ltd, Granger Telecom (Holdings) Plc, Kewill Systems Plc. Has undertaken lecture tours of USA under the title "Building a Bridge To The United States of Europe".
Career: Qualified in 1968 – Notary Public 1975.
Personal: Born 31.10.1938. Educated: College of Law Guildford. Leisure interests include playing hockey, squash and cricket – member of the MCC. Lives in Oxshott, Surrey.

MURPHY, Frances
Slaughter and May, London (020) 7600 1200
Specialisation: General practice consists principally of acting for corporate clients and investment banks on corporate finance and M&A transactions, both in England and overseas, and generally on corporate matters. Wide experience of acquisitions and disposals (both public and private), joint ventures and of equity and debt financing structures. Also has a significant practice in relation to demutualisation of building societies.
Prof. Memberships: The Law Society.
Career: Qualified in 1983 after articles with *Slaughter and May*. Became a Partner in 1990, after a year in the Hong Kong office.
Personal: Born 24 September 1957.

MURRAY-JONES, Allan G.
Lovells, London (020) 7296 2000
allan.mjones@lovells.com
Specialisation: Private equity including cross border mergers and acquisitions, and fund raising.
Prof. Memberships: The Law Society.
Career: Qualified in Australia and moved to England in 1980. Partner 1986.

NEWHOUSE, Anthony
Slaughter and May, London (020) 7600 1200

NEWMAN, Iain
Nabarro Nathanson, London (020) 7524 6000
i.newman@nabarro.com
Specialisation: Head of public Equity Group. Diversified practice inluding floatations, fundraisings, private equity transactions, mergers and acquisitions, mergers and acquisitions. Significant recent transactions include acting for NewMedia SPARK plc on its flotation and subsequent fundraisings, acquisitions and investments and acting for Investec Henderson Crosthwaite on numerous flotations and fundraisings.

Prof. Memberships: The Law Society.
Career: Qualified in 1990 with *Nabarro Nathanson*. Became a partner in 1997.
Personal: Born 1966. Attended St. Bees School and Mansfield College, Oxford. Principal leisure interest is spending time with my wife (Vicki) and two chilren (Anna and Peter).

NORCROSS WEBB, Sally
Shoosmiths, Solent (01489) 881010
sally.norcrosswebb@shoosmiths.co.uk
Specialisation: Company and corporate finance work, especially acquisitions and disposals of companies, MBOs, MBIs, banking, joint ventures, corporate transactions generally, commercial work and business strategy; recent transactions include sale of Deacon Insurance Group to Hercules Property Services plc for £14.25 million. Head of Corporate at Solent office.
Prof. Memberships: Past Chairman Hampshire CBI. Governor of Portsmouth University.
Career: MA LLB (Cantab). Articled *Allen & Overy*; one year *Allen, Allen & Hemsley*, Sydney Australia; *Slaughter and May*; partner in small firm *Norcross Hill* which merged with *Shoosmiths* in 1992.
Personal: Sailing, gardening. Married with two sons. Lives Chichester.

NORMAN, Guy T.D.
Clifford Chance, London (020) 7600 1000
guy.norman@cliffordchance.com
Specialisation: Principal area of practice is corporate and corporate finance. Advises corporate and investment banking clients on takeovers and mergers, capital raising, stock exchange issues, joint ventures, private acquisitions and disposals. Has particular expertise in relation to the Takeover Code and related matters.
Prof. Memberships: Law Society.
Career: Articled with *Clifford Chance* 1989-91, qualified in September 1991 and became a Partner in 1998. *Schroders* corporate finance (on secondment) 1994. Secretary of Takeover Panel (on secondment) 1997-99.
Personal: Born 1966. Educated Sevenoaks School and Downing College Cambridge. Interests include cars, tennis and golf. Lives in London.

O'BRIEN, Barry
Freshfields Bruckhaus Deringer, London (020) 7936 4000
Partner in corporate department: head of corporate department.
Specialisation: Specialises in mergers and acqusitions and securities work much of which has an international element. Acts for a number of the firm's key investment banking clients as well as a wide range of corporate clients. In 1996 led a team of 200 lawyers on the implementation of the Reconstruction and Renewal plan and reinsurance into Equitas.
Prof. Memberships: Law Society.
Career: Qualified in 1978. Joined *Freshfields* in 1983 and became a partner in 1986.
Personal: Born 27th October 1952. Educated at University College, London. Enjoys sport. Lives in London.

O'CONNOR, Mark I.
Davies Wallis Foyster, Liverpool (0151) 236 6226
moc@dwf-law.com
Specialisation: Corporate finance transactions, business structuring, commercial advice, corporate governance, public company work and the establishment of regional investment funds.
Prof. Memberships: Law Society.
Career: Articled *Cuff Roberts North Kirk*; qualified 1980; Partner *Davies Wallis Foyster* 1984; Head of Corporate.

ON, Nicholas
Eversheds, Newcastle upon Tyne (0191) 261 1661
nicholason@eversheds.com
See under Banking, p.120

PAINTER, Nick
Garretts, Leeds (0113) 207 9000
nicholas.painter@glegal.com
Partner in Corporate/Commercial Department.
Specialisation: Principal area of practice is corporate finance. Work includes flotations, UK and cross-border mergers and acquisitions, demergers and corporate reconstructions, management buy-outs, transport infrastructure projects and corporate joint ventures. Other areas of practice are competition law, employee share schemes and local authority law. Represents clients in monopolies and mergers enquiries and Competition Act investigations, advises on employee share ownership plans, especially in relation to employee buy-outs, and advises on local authority statutory powers. Important assignments include management/employee buy-out of London United Busways Ltd from London Regional Transport (1994), representing Stagecoach Busways in the North East of England buses-monopoly enquiry (1995/6), the sale of Humberside International Airport (1999), and representing Nottingham City Transport in relation to the Nottingham Express transit tram project (1997-2000). Major clients include quoted and unquoted companies, particularly in the transport and chemical sectors, and Passenger Transport Authorities and Executives. Regular seminar speaker. Fixed fees by prior arrangement.
Prof. Memberships: Law Society, Leeds Law Society.
Career: Qualified in 1983. With *Howes Percival*, Northampton 1983-85, then *Simpson Curtis* 1985-94 (Partner from 1988). Joined *Garretts* as a Partner in May 1994.
Personal: Born 3rd February 1959. Educated at Gowerton Comprehensive School 1970-74, Haverfordwest Grammar School 1974-77 and Keble College, Oxford 1977-80. Leisure interests include cricket, squash, badminton, films, outward bound activities and hill walking. Lives in Ilkley, West Yorkshire.

PALMER, James E.
Herbert Smith, London (020) 7374 8000
Specialisation: Principal areas of work are mergers and acquisitions, corporate finance and general corporate, including takeovers, UK and international equity offerings, demergers, schemes of arrangement and joint ventures. Also formation/restructuring of international banking and financial services businesses.
Prof. Memberships: City of London Solicitors Company, Company Law Sub-Committee.
Career: Joined 1986, qualified 1988, Partner 1994.
Personal: Born 10.9.1963. Educated at Winchester College and Queens' College Cambridge 1982-85.

PARSONS, Chris
Herbert Smith, London (020) 7374 8000
Specialisation: Extensive corporate finance experience acting for leading investment banks and major corporate clients. One of the key relationship partners for CSFB. Practice includes cross border M&A and international equities work. Also head of *Herbert Smith*'s Italian Practice Group; he advised Olivetti on its successful bid for Telecom Italia. He has also recently been acting for BBVA/Terra Networks on their proposed global internet banking operations.

PARTRIDGE, W.M. James
Thomson Snell & Passmore, Tunbridge Wells (01892) 510000
jpartridge@ts-p.co.uk
Partner in commercial department.
Specialisation: Deals with all company and commercial matters but specialises in the sale and purchase of companies and businesses, management buy-outs, the establishment of joint ventures and corporate finance.
Career: Qualified in 1983. Trained and practised in London before joining *Thomson Snell & Passmore* in 1986. Became a partner in 1987.
Personal: Born 14 March 1958. Educated at Lancing College and Trinity College, Cambridge BA (CANTAB) 1977-80. Other interests: member of the Territorial Army. Lives in Tunbridge Wells.

PASS, Jamie
Dickinson Dees, Newcastle upon Tyne (0191) 279 9285
Specialisation: Mainstream corporate finance, mergers & acquisitions, new issues and private equity work.
Prof. Memberships: Law Society.
Career: Educated Doncaster Grammar School & Jesus College, Cambridge. *Clifford Chance* 1986-92. Joined *Dickinson Dees* in 1992. Partner 1995.
Personal: Born Doncaster, resides Newcastle upon Tyne.

PATRICK, Bruce R.
Maclay Murray & Spens, Edinburgh (0131) 226 5196
brp@maclaymurrayspens.co.uk
See under Insolvency/Corporate Recovery, p.

PAUL, Alan D.
Allen & Overy, London (020) 7330 3000

PEARSON, Christopher
Norton Rose, London (020) 7283 6000
pearsoncc@nortonrose.com
Specialisation: Main area of practice is public company and stock exchange transactions, including public company takeovers, other mergers and acquisitions, flotations, securities offerings, and company reconstructions and institutional investments. Also international transactions, including cross-border mergers and acquisitions and joint ventures. Important public company transactions include Guinness/Grand Metropolitan (£22 billion); Texas Utilties/The Energy Group (£4.45 billion); Ciba Specialty Chemicals/Allied Colloids (£1.42 billion); Trinity/Mirror Group (£2.1 billion); Mannesmann/Orange (£20 billion) and Airtours/Carnival, a subscription and partial offer involving Carnival acquiring 29.5% of Airtours for some £200 million. Securities transactions include the flotation of Beeson Gregory and the "trombone" rights issue by Trinity International Holdings to raise £182 million in connection with the acquisition of regional newspaper interests of The Thomson Corpo-

ration and the HSBC Holdings Enhanced Scrip Dividend Scheme. Other mergers and acquisitions include the linked disposal by Siemens of its shareholding in GPT Holdings to GEC and acquisition of GEC's shareholding in Siemens GEC Communication Systems (£700 million). International transactions include the formation of a cross border joint venture between Redland and Koramic in respect of brick products in Belgium and Holland (to create the largest facing brick manufacturer in continental Europe) and the establishment of a joint venture, Sun International Investments (owned by Royale Resorts, Caledonia Investments and World Leisure Group) to invest over US$100 million in the billion dollar Paradise Island resort project in the Bahamas.
Prof. Memberships: Member of the Law Society, the City of London Solicitors Company and the Royal Automobile Club; also the Firm's representative on the City of London Law Society Company Law Sub-Committee.
Personal: Family status: married. Hobbies/interests: squash, tennis, rugby, theatre and cinema.

PEARSON, David
Clifford Chance, London (020) 7600 1000
david.pearson@cliffordchance.com
Specialisation: Partner specialising in corporate finance, takeovers, flotations, mergers and acquisitions and secondary issues, also venture capital, management buy-outs and buy-ins.
Career: Ashville College, Harrogate; Downing College, Cambridge (MA Law). Articled *Clifford Chance*; qualified 1989; made partner 1996.
Personal: Golf, skiing, running. Born 1964; resides London.

PEARSON, Jeffrey
Edwards Geldard, Cardiff (029) 2023 8239
jeff.pearson@geldards.co.uk
Specialisation: Corporate finance, public takeovers, mergers and acquisitions and multi-jurisdictional joint ventures. Recent work includes a number of transactions for Hyder plc, Hicking Pentecost plc. Pendragon plc, Chevron in the quoted company sector and a number of MBO's and acquisition and disposal work in the private company sector.
Prof. Memberships: Law Society.
Career: *Slaughter and May*, London between 1984 and 1991. Partner in *Edwards Geldard* since 1991.
Personal: Born 1961. Educated at Bishop Gore SC, Swansea and University College of Wales, Aberystwyth. Married with two children. Lives in Cardiff.

PECK, Andrew
Linklaters (A member firm of Linklaters & Alliance), London (020) 7456 3454
andrew.peck@linklaters.com
Specialisation: Partner in the Corporate Department of *Linklaters* since 1983 and Group Leader with the Corporate Practice. Deals with a wide range of company law matters, including new issues, takeovers and mergers, sales and purchases of private companies and company reorganisations, with extensive experience in the financial services sector, for example, insurance companies and building societies.
Career: Corporate Finance Department, N.M. Rothschild & Sons Limited 1976-81. Articled *Linklaters* 1973. Cambridge University – MA, LLB 1967-71.

PELL, Marian
Herbert Smith, London (020) 7374 8000
marian.pell@herbertsmith.com
See under Insurance, p.496

PESCOD, Michael
Slaughter and May, London (020) 7600 1200
Partner 1977.
Specialisation: Corporate Department. Main areas of practice are corporate finance, commercial and corporate law.

PESTER, David P. L.
TLT Solicitors, Bristol (0117) 917 7777
dpester@TLTsolicitors.com
Head of Corporate Finance Team
Specialisation: Mergers, acquisitions and disposals, other corporate finance and company law. Particular experience of OFEX, AIM, EASDAQ and other listings. Led the disposal of Bakers Dolphin to First Choice Holdings for £16m; disposal of the retail operation of Fowlers Bristol for £8m; admission of Advanced Tecnology plc to AIM (£50m initial market cap).
Prof. Memberships: Company Secretary of Salinity (UK) Ltd, Company Secretary of Bristol Tourism and Conference Bureau. Employment Lawyers Association, Bristol Chamber of Commerce and Initiative.
Career: Manchester University, BA (1st), Bristol University, LLM (Employment and Corporate Law); articled at *Lawrence Tucketts (now TLT Solicitors*, the merged firm of *Trumps* and *Lawrence Tucketts*), admitted 1988.
Personal: Sailing, hillwalking, football.

PHILLIPS, Robert
Robert Muckle, Newcastle-upon-Tyne (0191) 232 4402
Specialisation: General Corporate Finance. Partner – quality commercial work for both public and private companies. Specialisation in corporate sales and acquisitions and investment venture capital.
Career: Articled *Denton Hall*; work in corporate finance sector; 2 years with *Memery Crystal*. Qualified 1990. Joined *Robert Muckle* as an associate in 1994; became a partner in 1997.

PILLMAN, Joe
Brobeck Hale and Dorr, Abingdon, Oxfordshire (01235) 834447
pillman@bhd.com
Partner
Specialisation: Handles general company law for technology companies including flotations, mergers and acquisitions, MBOs, MBIs and reconstructions. Important matters handled include several acquisitions by Xerox and Amey, various investments in Bookham Technology, including private placements by Intel and CISCO, the sales of Carfax Publishing to Routledge and Supergas to Centrica, the dual listings of QXL and Bookham Technology on the LSE and NASDAQ and the listings of Screen and Tricorder Technology on AIM.
Career: Qualified in 1977. Partner with *Cole & Cole* from 1983-2000.
Personal: Born 7th July 1952. Educated at Rugby School 1965-69 and Cambridge University 1970-74. Lives in Northumberland.

PITCHER, Robert
Eversheds, Leeds (0113) 243 0391
robertpitcher@eversheds.com
Specialisation: Corporate Finance Lawyer specialising in recommended and contested takeover bids, flotations, secondary offerings and M&A work generally, with a particular focus in the area of telecoms. Acted on eighteen takeovers in the last 24 months, including the take privates of John Haggas plc (12.5m) Evans of Leeds plc (350m) and the recommended takeover of Waddington plc (300m). Acted for Kingston upon Hull City Council on the flotation of Kingston Communications (circa £700m) and acted for Telecity plc on its recent flotation (circa £600m).
Career: BA (Jurisprudence) Brasenose College, Oxford; qualified *Slaughter & May* in 1989, became partner at *Eversheds* in 1996.
Personal: Married with two children. Leisure interests include hunting, shooting and fishing.

POLGLASE, Timothy
Norton Rose, London (020) 7283 6000
polglaset@nortonrose.com
See under Banking, p.121

POPHAM, Stuart
Clifford Chance, London (020) 7600 1000
stuart.popham@cliffordchance.com
See under Banking, p.121

PRINCE, Michael J.
DLA, Liverpool (08700) 111111
michael.prince@dla.com
Corporate and Regional Managing Partner.
Specialisation: Main area of practice is corporate finance. Work includes MBOs, venture and development capital, mergers and acquisitions and flotations. Also handles corporate joint ventures. Author of various articles in local and national newspapers and in Investors Chronicle. Has addressed numerous conferences and seminars.
Prof. Memberships: Law Society.
Career: Qualified 1979. Worked with *Addleshaw Sons & Latham* 1977-81, then for 3i plc 1981-86 as Legal Adviser. Joined *Alsop Wilkinson* as a Partner in the Corporate Department in 1986.
Personal: Born 20th December 1954. Attended Birmingham University. Committee Member of Fairbridge Trust (charity), council member and director of Liverpool Chamber of Commerce and secretary of Liverpool Vision Limited (urban regeneration company). Non-executive director of various companies. Recent deals include the takeover of MTL services plc and the takeover of AF plc. Leisure interests include golf, tennis, squash and skiing. Lives in Aughton, Lancashire.

PROCTER, Jonathan
DLA, Manchester (08700) 111111
jonathan.procter@dla.com
Specialisation: Corporate finance and acquisitions and disposal work for quoted and private companies. E-commerce, especially primary and secondary securities issues on the internet.
Prof. Memberships: Law Society
Career: Trainee solicitor at *Eversheds*, Manchester. Joined *DLA* in1987, and made partner in 1992.
Personal: Educated at Queen Elizabeth's Grammar School, Blackburn, and Brasenose college, Oxford (BA Jurisprudence). Married with two children. Leisure: Family, mountain-biking, fell walking and trout fishing.

PSYLLIDES, Milton N.
Eversheds, Birmingham (0121) 232 1000
Partner.
Specialisation: Public company transactions, including flotations, mergers and acquisitions, new issues and funding transactions.
Prof. Memberships: Chairman of the Midlands & North Wales Stock Exchange Regional Advisory Group. Member of the Law Society and the Birmingham Law Society. Treasurer of the Birmingham Law Society. Member of the Birmingham Law Society Company and Commercial Law sub-committee. Council Member West Midlands CBI.
Career: Qualified March 1978 with *Evershed & Tomkinson*. Partner May 1984 with *Evershed & Tomkinson*. *Eversheds* national firm created May 1989.
Personal: Born 30th October 1953. Brockley County Grammar School and Liverpool University. Married with one daughter and one son.

PYSDEN, Edward
Eversheds, Manchester (0161) 832 6666
edwardpysden@eversheds.com
Senior Partner specialising in Corporate and Commercial work.
Specialisation: Corporate finance covering flotations, acquisitions, MBOs and Yellow Book work, recently with a great deal of international flavour. In the last 18 months he has led Bodycote's £60 million acquisition of HIT s.a., a French company listed on the Lyon Stock Exchange and the sale of Martin Dawes Telecommunications Limited for £130 million. For five years he has been voted top North West Corporate Lawyer by readers of Insider Magazine. Lectures on Company Law at the Manchester Business School and the Henley and Ashridge Schools of Management. Director of Brukens Thermotreat AB and Marketing Manchester.
Prof. Memberships: Chairman of the HallÈ Concert Society.
Career: Articled at *Alexander Tatham*1970-72 and became a Partner in 1974. Appointed Senior Partner of the firm (now *Eversheds, Manchester*) in 1993.
Personal: Born 6th May 1948. Attended Dulwich College 1959-60, King's School, Macclesfield 1960-66, and Manchester University 1966-69. Leisure pursuits include golf, classical music, food and wine. Lives in Alderley Edge.

RAFFERTY, John C.
Burness, Edinburgh (0131) 473 6000
jcr@burness.co.uk
Chairman and Partner in Corporate Department.
Specialisation: Main areas of practice are company law and corporate finance. Particular experience in AIM work, flotations of football clubs and venture capital investments (including EIS and reinvestment relief schemes). Has also worked on numerous capital reconstruction schemes and refinancings, especially debt roll-over and receivership acquisitions. Has developed various executive incentive schemes, including ESOPs. Member of the Securities Institute. Director, Martin Currie Capital Return Trust plc.

RANDELL, Charles
Slaughter and May, London (020) 7600 1200
Specialisation: Company/Commercial.
Career: Articled *Slaughter and May*; qualified 1982; partner 1989.
Personal: Educated at Trinity College, Oxford.

RAWLINSON, Mark S.
Freshfields Bruckhaus Deringer, London (020) 7936 4000
Specialisation: Partner in the corporate department specialising in mergers and acquisitions, particularly international and cross border. Also covers general corporate finance (including IPOs, rights issues and other issues) and joint ventures. Publications include 'A Practitioners Guide to Corporate Finance and the Financial Services Act 1986' (contributor) and 'Rights Issues Practice Manual' (contributor and editor).
Career: Qualified 1984. Assistant solicitor, *Freshfields* 1984-90. Partner since 1990. Listed as one of the top fifteen 'Best Business Lawyers' in Chambers' 1998 survey.
Personal: Educated at Haberdashers' Aske's School, Elstree and Sidney Sussex College, Cambridge 1976-80. Interests include family and sport. Born 3rd May 1957. Lives in London.

RAWSTRON, C.D.
DLA, Birmingham (08700) 111111
chris.rawstron@dla.com
Regional managing partner (Birmingham).
Specialisation: Main area of practice is corporate finance. Work includes mergers and acquisitions, flotations, rights issues, MBOs, MBIs, disposals and general corporate advice.
Prof. Memberships: Law Society.
Career: Qualified in 1986. Joined *Edge & Ellison* in 1984, becoming a partner in 1990. Joined *Dibb Lupton Alsop* as a partner in November 1997. Head of corporate (Birmingham) until April 2000.
Personal: Born 29th July 1962. Attended Clitheroe Royal Grammar School 1978-80, Birmingham University 1980-83 and College of Law 1983-84. Holds various trusteeships and directorships. Leisure interests include golf, Burnley FC and cricket. Lives in Hagley, near Stourbridge.

READ, Nigel P.L.
Lovells, London (020) 7296 2000
nigel.read@lovells.com
Specialisation: Mergers & acquisitions, corporate finance, securities and general corporate law. Particular expertise in public takeovers, both recommended and hostile, and Stock Exchange flotations and secondary issues. Advises corporate clients across a wide range of industry sectors, particularly media, leisure and property. Also acts for a number of invesment banks in their capacity as sponsors, financial advisers and underwriters.
Prof. Memberships: Law Society, City of London Solicitors Company.
Career: Qualified at *Freshfields* in 1984. Investment banker at Lazard Brothers & Co., Limited 1990-93. Joined *Lovells* in 1993 and became a partner in 1996.
Personal: Educated at Marlborough College and St Catharines College, Cambridge. Leisure interests include golf, tennis, skiing and watersports.

RICHARDS, Philip
Freshfields Bruckhaus Deringer, London (020) 7936 4000
prichards@freshfields.com
See under Insurance, p.

RICHARDSON, Ian A.
Eversheds, Leeds (0113) 243 0391
ianrichardson@eversheds.com
Specialisation: Handles all aspects of corporate finance work, in particular transactions of an international and multi-jurisdictional nature. Acquisitions and Disposals. Peterhouse Group plc, a fully listed company. He is joint author of 'Running a Partnership', published by Jordans.
Prof. Memberships: Law Society.
Career: Qualified in 1983 and became a Partner in 1989.
Personal: Born on 23rd April 1959. Lives near Boroughbridge, North Yorkshire. Leisure interests: running, sport and history.

ROBINSON, Michael
Pinsent Curtis, Leeds (0113) 244 5000
michael.robinson@pinsents.com
Specialisation: Specialises in corporate finance and company law with a particular emphasis on public company work including primary and secondary issues. Major transaction include: the £300 million bid for Polypipe plc by IMI plc; the acquisition of Perstorp Pharma of Sweden by Smith & Nephew plc for £8 million. Various AIM and full listings.
Prof. Memberships: Institutute of Directors
Career: Articles: *Linklaters & Paines* 1983-1985. Assistant solicitor, *Linklaters & Paines* 1985-1987. Assistant solicitor, *Simpson Curtis* (now *Pinsent Curtis*) 1987-1990. Partner *Pinsent Curtis* 1990-to date.
Personal: Education: Northallerton Grammar School, St Edmund Hall Oxford University (1st class honours Jurisprudence). Leisure: Football (watching Middlesborough!) all kinds of music and family.

ROSE, Kenneth
Dundas & Wilson CS, Edinburgh (0131) 228 8000

ROSEFIELD, Stephen M.
Paisner & Co, London (020) 7353 0299
Managing partner and partner in corporate department.
Specialisation: Main area of practice is mergers and acquisitions and corporate finance including takeovers (both public and private), purchase and sale of businesses, MBO's, joint ventures and reconstructions. Acts for a wide range of listed property, trading and investment companies. Writes and speaks widely on the purchase and sale of companies and businesses, and joint ventures including having contributed to Butterworths Encyclopaedia of Forms & Precedents Vol. 11.
Prof. Memberships: Law Society.
Career: Qualified in 1977, having joined *Paisner & Co* in 1975. Became a Partner in 1980. Appointed as the firm's first Managing Partner in 1999.
Personal: Born 19th December 1952. Educated at St. Paul's School 1965-70 and St. Edmund Hall, Oxford 1971-74. Recreations include theatre, music, tennis and soccer. Lives in London

ROUS, Simon R.
Bevan Ashford, Exeter (01392) 663333
Specialisation: Heads *Bevan Ashford's* Corporate & Banking Team. Simon is active in corporate finance, MBO's, mergers and acquisitions and new issue work particularly for IT, financial services and e-commerce PLCs. Simon has as spent 25 years specialising on corporate transactions. Much of his work is London based or international, especially from Germany, the USA and the Middle East. *Bevan Ashford's* London Office at No 1 Chancery Lane, enables him to deliver on London based and international transactions at regional charge-out rates. Simon regularly lectures both in the UK and abroad, most recently on 'Acquisitions & Divestitures in the UK' (delivered in Paris), 'Developments in Minority Shareholder Issues' and

'EBT Financed Investor Exits'. His seminars have quite a reputation, commanding fee-paying audiences of over 200. His home ISDN link enables him to stay in contact with his clients' affairs even while notionally off duty. For more details see www.bevan-ashford.co.uk/corporate.
Prof. Memberships: He keeps his memberships to a few influential bodies, such as the Council of the CBI (Southwest) and Exeter University Business Forum, so as to be able to concentrate on his clients.
Career: Simon read Law at Trinity College Cambridge and then spent 11 years with *Clifford Chance* in London, Paris, Brussels, the Middle East and New York before joining *Bevan Ashford* in 1985.

ROXBURGH, Bruce O.
Osborne Clarke OWA, Bristol (0117) 917 4204
bruce.roxburgh@osborneclarke.com
Specialisation: Experienced in a wide variety of corporate finance and other corporate transactional work for private and public companies. This includes MBOs; MBIs; share and asset sales and purchases; private and public take-over offers; flotations, rights issues and other share offers. Recent deals include acting for Marlborough Stirling plc in connection with further investment in the company by 3i plc; acting for Haynes Publishing Group plc on its acquisition of Sutton Publishing Limited and acting for the incoming management team on the Bikes-UK.Com Holdings Limited BIMBO.
Career: Qualified at *Freshfields* in 1986. Joined *Osborne Clarke* 1988 and became a partner 1991.

RUNDALL, Francis R.S.
Charles Russell, Cheltenham (01242) 221122
francisr@cr-law.co.uk
Specialisation: Corporate finance, acquisitions and disposals, public and private. Also advises on flotations and other capital raising projects. Recent work includes acting for Britannia Group plc on its sale; acting for Pennant International Group plc on its placing and open offer; acting for YJL plc on the sale of Birchwood Concrete Limited. Additionally advises on charity law. Is acting for the Countryside Animal Welfare Group in their challenge to the RSPCA's attempt to exclude pro-hunting people from membership.
Career: Marlborough College; University College, Durham. Qualified 1975; Assistant Solicitor at *Slaughter & May* 1975-78; joined *Charles Russell* 1978, becoming a partner in 1981.
Personal: Secretary to the Link Group (Gloucestershire) Limited; Secretary of The Compton Verney Opera and Ballet Project. Leisure interests include hunting and shooting.

RYDE, Andy
Slaughter and May, London (020) 7600 1200
Specialisation: Partner specialising in general corporate and corporate finance; acts for a number of listed companies and investment banks in connection with mergers and acquisitions and corporate finance transactions.
Career: Articled *Slaughter and May*: qualified 1989: partner 1996.
Publications: Author of 'Share Dealings – Restrictions and Disclosure Requirements', a chapter in the 'Practitioner's Guide to the City Code on Takeovers and Mergers'.
Personal: Born 1964. Educated at the Minster School, Southwell, Nottinghamshire, and Wadham College, Oxford (1986 MA Hons Jurisprudence). Resides Northwood. Interests: sports.

SACKMAN, Simon
Norton Rose, London (020) 7283 6000
Partner and Head of Corporate Finance.
Specialisation: Main area of practice is mergers and acquisitions (both public and private), flotations and other equity issues, demergers and other restructurings and investment trusts. Also experienced in regulatory investigations and the hotel sector. Important transactions handled include the sale of Hambros Bank to SociÈtÈ GÈnÈrale and the subsequent restructuring of Hambros plc, the restructuring of GPA Group, the flotation of Harvey Nichols, the enquiry into Lanica's bid for CWS and numerous hotel acquisitions, including the Caledonian in Edinburgh and the Landmark of London. Clients include merchant banks (Samuel Montagu, Hambros, Morgan Grenfell and Charterhouse), hotel groups and investment trusts.
Prof. Memberships: Law Society, City of London Solicitors Company, International Bar Association.

SADKA, Tim
Rawlison & Butler, Crawley (01293) 527744
Specialisation: Partner and head of the corporate department, main areas of work include company and business sales/acquisitions, corporate reorganisations and reconstructions, insolvency based transactions, joint ventures including cross border transactions and corporate succession/governance. Leads teams on outsourcing transactions and on MBO/MBI's.
Prof. Memberships: Solicitors European Group, Law Society, UIA and IBA.
Career: Articled at *Leo Abse & Cohen*. Joined *Rawlison & Butler* in 1987 becoming a partner in 1990 and head of corporate 1999.
Personal: Born 2nd May 1961. Attended Belmont Abbey School, Hereford and Bristol Polytechnic. Leisure interests include art, skiing, golf and member Royal Automobile Club.

SALZ, Anthony M.V.
Freshfields Bruckhaus Deringer, London
(020) 7936 4000
Senior partner and partner in corporate department.
Specialisation: Main area of practice is mergers and acquisitions and all aspects of corporate finance work, both in the UK and internationally.
Prof. Memberships: Law Society.
Career: Qualified 1974. Joined *Freshfields* in 1975. 1977/8 *Davis Polk & Wardwell*, New York. Partner in corporate department 1980. Senior partner 1996. Chair, Tate Gallery Corporate Advisory Group.
Personal: Born 30th June 1950. Attended Summerfields 1958-63, Radley College 1964-67. Exeter University 1968-71. Leisure pursuits include golf, family and fishing and supporting Southampton FC.

SEABROOK, Michael R.
Eversheds, Birmingham (0121) 232 1000
Deputy Senior Partner (Birmingham) in Corporate Services Department.
Specialisation: Corporate finance specialist. Work includes MBOs/ MBIs, mergers and acquisitions (both domestic and international) and venture capital.
Prof. Memberships: Law Society, Securities Institute.
Career: Qualified in 1976. Assistant solicitor at *Clifford Turner* 1977-79. With *Needham & James* 1980-86 (Partner from 1981). Joined *Evershed & Tomkinson* as a Partner in 1986. Now Deputy Senior Partner (Birmingham).
Personal: Born 24th March 1952. Educated at King Edward's School, Birmingham 1963-70 and Exeter University (LL.B) 1970-73. Recreations include cricket, golf, soccer, rugby, and horse racing. Lives in Dorridge, Solihull.

SHAND, Kenneth D.
Maclay Murray & Spens, Glasgow
(0141) 248 5011
kds@maclaymurrayspens.co.uk
Specialisation: Principally mergers and acquisitions, MBOs/MBIs and institutional finance; spent much of 1999 leading the team which advised The Edrington Group Limited on its £600 million bid (through a joint venture with William Grant & Sons Limited) for Highland Distillers plc. Other recent deals include advising 3i on its MBI of Dawson Fur Fabrics from the Dawson International Froup and as a 3i Panel Solicitor, on a number of 3i investments (including several in Ireland) and portfolio disposals. Kenneth advised the shareholders of Elm Holdings on its disposal to Honey Systems, Landmark Retail Group on the acquisition of assets from Essex Furniture plc (in administration) and related financing exercise and Travis Perkins plc on a number of Scottish acquisitions. He also advised innovative time ownership operator Residence International Limited on its acqusition of new locations for development in Paris and Glasgow; Kenneth leads the firm's inward investment team and advises a number of foreign headquartered companies including Compaq, Dupont Photomasks, Mack Technologies and MSA.
Prof. Memberships: Law Society of Scotland, Scottish Solicitors European Group.
Career: *Maclay Murray & Spens* 1982-84 (trainee) *Maclay Murray & Spens* 1984-88 (assistant solicitor) *McKenna & Co* 1988-89 (assistant solicitor) *Maclay Murray & Spens* 1989-date (partner)
Personal: Education: Glasgow Academy (1969-77) University of Glasgow (1981 LLB Hons) University of Glasgow (1982 Diploma in Legal Practice.) Leisure interests: Most sports, especially golf, rugby, tennis and football. Family: Married with one son and one daughter.

SHARRATT, Steve
Taylor Vinters, Cambridge (01223) 423444
ss@taylorvinters.com
Specialisation: Corporate Finance – MBOs/MBIs/senior debt and private equity funding.
Prof. Memberships: Law Society.
Career: Qualified 1989 with *Edge & Ellison*, worked in industry (BP) and private practice before joining *Taylor Vinters* as a partner in 1997. Has been on secondment with a client group in the telecoms sector and currently splits time as a non-legal director between that role and consultant to *Taylor Vinters*.
Personal: Born 1964, interests include music (playing and listening), fast motorbikes and Manchester Utd.

SHAW, Martin
Pinsent Curtis, Leeds (0113) 244 5000
martin.shaw@pinsents.com
Head of Corporate Department, Leeds.
Specialisation: Specialises in corporate finance and company law including M&A, stock exchange prima-

ry and secondary issues and company re-organisations primarily for public listed companies. Major transactions include: sale of SIG Architectural Products Limited for £65 million; the £25.9 million bid by SIG plc for Roskel plc; the £9.18 million sale of Prospect Industries plc; the £52.9 million bid for the CODA Group plc by Baan Company NV; the £11.1 million acquisition and associated £8.6 million placing and open offer by BLP Group plc; the major group reorganisation of BPT plc and its £75 million London Stock Exchange listing of Eurobanks; the £13 million share subscription and strategic media alliance with BSkyB; the OFEX flotation of Square Sum plc and the £14.5 million sale of a Yule Calto & Co plc subsidiary.
Prof. Memberships: Member of the Solicitors European Group; the American Bar Association and the International Bar Association.
Career: Articled *Simpson Curtis* (now *Pinsent Curtis*) 1966-69. Qualified 1969. Lecturer in law (part-time) Leeds Metropolitan University. Partner 1971. Former managing partner at *Simpson Curtis[IT+- until 1994.*
Personal: Member of Headingley Rotary Club (past council member and Chairman of International Services Committee); Chairman of Governors of Gateways School. Hon. Secretary of Yorkshire Regional Committee of the Variety Club of Great Britain.

SHEACH, Andrew
CMS Cameron McKenna, London
(020) 7367 2969
ajs@cmck.com
Specialisation: Specialises in all types of private equity transactions (management buyout/buyin and development capital and exit work), mergers and acquisitions and Yellow and Blue Book work. In the last year he has acted on a number of management buyouts/buyins for both equity investors and management teams and also for Luminar plc on its recent acquisition of Northern Leisure plc.
Career: BA (Law) Pembroke College, Cambridge 1981-84; Joined *Cameron Markby* 1985; Partner 1993.

SHELDON, Jeremy Nigel
Ashurst Morris Crisp, London (020) 7638 1111
jeremy.n.sheldon@ashursts.com
Partner in Company Department.
Specialisation: Principal area of practice is U.K. and international buyouts acting primarily for equity providers, including Cinven Limited, Candover Investments plc and BZW Private Equity Limited. Other areas of practice include establishing and marketing quoted and unquoted investment funds, mergers and acquisitions, flotations and other Stock Exchange transactions.
Prof. Memberships: Vice-president of the mergers and acquisitions commission of the Union Internationale des Avocats.
Career: Qualified in 1980. Became a Partner in 1987.
Personal: Born in 1952.

SHORT, John
Taylor Vinters, Cambridge (01223) 423444
Partner in Company/ Commercial Department.
Specialisation: Work covers acquisitions and sales, reconstructions, venture capital, investment, and MBO/MBIs. Also handles insolvency and banking, advising receivers and liquidators. Advises on taking and enforcing security.
Prof. Memberships: Law Society, Associate Member of Society of Practitioners of Insolvency.
Career: Qualified 1974. Trainee and solicitor at *Prettys*, Ipswich, 1972-75; Assistant Solicitor at *Coward Chance*, London, 1976-78. Joined *Taylor Vinters* in 1979. Became a Partner in 1982. Secretary of Cambridgeshire and District Law Society, 1983-87 and Vice President 1999-2000. President 2000-2001.
Personal: Born 28th December 1949. Attended Sheffield University 1968-71. Leisure interests include walking, music and photography.

SIGNY, Adam
Clifford Chance, London (020) 7600 1000
adam.signy@cliffordchance.com
Specialisation: Partner specialising in corporate finance, M&A, takeovers.
Career: City of London School; Sussex University (Economics). Articled *Clifford Chance*; qualified 1982; partner *Clifford Chance* since 1987.
Personal: Born 1955; married, three children; resides Suffolk and London.

SIMMONS, William G.
Tods Murray WS, Edinburgh (0131) 226 4771
william.simmons@todsmurray.co.uk
See under Projects/PFI, p.700

SINGH, Daljit
Jones, Day, Reavis & Pogue, London
(020) 7236 3939
dsingh@jonesday.com
Fax: (020) 7236 1113
Specialisation: All aspects of corporate finance including Blue & Yellow Book, M & A (UK and cross border); private equity, principal finance transactions (whether for the equity house, management or other funders) and securities work.
Prof. Memberships: Law Society, IOD.
Career: London University, Law College (Chancery Lane), *Baker McKenzie, Alsop Wilkinson, Hammond Suddards, Jones Day, Reavis & Pogue.*
Personal: Football (especially Chelsea Football Club), entertaining, music, business, and the family (married, 2 girls and 1 boy).

SLEIGH, Andrew F.
Burness, Glasgow (0141) 248 4933
afs@burness.co.uk
Specialisation: Has significant experience in all aspects of private company corporate finance, including acting for management, venture capital houses and vendors involved in MBO and MBI transactions. Notable recent deals include acting for Royal Bank Development Capital in investment in Holiday Inn Express, acting for Big Beat International in additional round of equity funding from a leading venture capital house; acting in the acquisition of a significant regional soft drinks manufacturer; acting in the sale of Beat 106 to Capital Radio plc; representing interests of SFA in rescue of Hampden Stadium, Glasgow.

SLOAN, Graeme E.C.
Maclay Murray & Spens, Edinburgh
(0131) 226 5196
gecs@maclaymurrayspens.co.uk
Specialisation: Partner specialising in corporate finance, mergers and acquisitions and joint ventures. Has extensive experience in public company work, advising both companies and financial advisers. Principal clients include Bank of Scotland, Candover, John Menzies, McDermott International and Scottish Widows.
Career: *Balfour & Manson*, trainee solicitor, 1985-87, Arthur Young, tax senior, 1987-88, *Maclay Murray & Spens*, assistant solicitor, 1998-1989, *Freshfields*, manager, 1990-1992, *Maclay Murray & Spens*, partner 1992 to date.

SMART, Peter C.
Walker Morris, Leeds (0113) 283 2500
pcs@walkermorris.co.uk
Head of Corporate.
Specialisation: Main areas of practice are corporate finance, M & A work, venture capital and (because they're interesting) the resolution of shareholder disputes. Recent deals include the £120 million acquisition of 3C Waste Limited by Yorkshire Water plc.
Prof. Memberships: Law Society.
Career: Qualified in 1979, having joined *Walker Morris* in 1977. Became a Partner in 1981, Managing Partner 1993-98, returning to the "front line" in 1998 as Head of Corporate. A director of several companies including BWD Aim VCT plc and Allied Textile Companies plc.

SMERDON, R.W.
Osborne Clarke OWA, Reading (0118) 925 2010
richard.smerdon@osborneclarke.com
Specialisation: Richard is the Corporate Department's senior partner in the Thames Valley office. He specialises in all aspects of corporate finance, in particular, MBOs and M&A work, corporate governance and directors' duties and liabilities. Richard was co-editor of Butterworth's Company Law service and is the author of 'A Practical Guide to Corporate Governance' by Sweet & Maxwell 1998.
Career: Having trained at *Slaughter & May* and lectured at Western Reserve Law School in Ohio, he joined *Osborne Clarke* in Bristol in 1970 before moving to found the firm's London office in 1988 and its Thames Valley office in 1998.

SMITH, Campbell
Biggart Baillie, Glasgow (0141) 228 8000
csmith@biggartbaillie.co.uk
Managing Partner and Partner in Corporate Department.
Specialisation: Main area of practice is corporate transactions. Work includes acquisitions and disposals of private companies and assets. Also insurance companies and friendly societies. Former Director of the Joint Insolvency Examination Board; member of several Law Society Committees.
Prof. Memberships: Law Society of Scotland, International Bar Association.
Career: Qualified in 1972. Assistant at *Herbert Smith & Co.* 1972-73 and *Biggart Baillie & Gifford* (now *Biggart Baillie*)1973-74. Became Partner there in 1974.
Personal: Born 17th May 1946. Attended Glasgow Academy 1951-65, St Catharine's College, Cambridge 1965-68 and the University of Glasgow 1968-70. Member of Convocation, University of Strathclyde; ex-Deacon Incorporation of Barbers, Glasgow. Leisure interests include golf, croquet, barbershop and choral singing. Lives in Glasgow.

SPENDLOVE, Justin
Ashurst Morris Crisp, London (020) 7638 1111
See under Banking, p.121

SPETCH, Michael
Eversheds, Newcastle upon Tyne (0191) 261 1661
Specialisation: Corporate finance, mergers and acquisitions.
Prof. Memberships: Law Society.
Career: Qualified Oct 1988. Three years in corporate

department of *Hammond Suddards*. Then (1991) joined *Williamson Maughan* and then *Eversheds* in 1997.
Personal: University of Leicester – LLB (Hons). Married, 2 children.

SPINK, Richard
Burges Salmon, Bristol (0117) 939 2218
richard.spink@burges-salmon.com
Specialisation: Venture capital and corporate finance. Numerous venture capital transactions include acting for management and Spear Group Holdings on its $60m cross-border buy out of US and UK businesses backed by PPMV; Scottish and Southern Energy plc on its £10m e-commerce investment in Simple2, the first web based company to offer virtual employee financial services; Murray Johnstone in its investment in Basys Marine Ltd and ABN Amro on its investment in Atlantic Technology Ltd. Other recent transactions include acting for Motion Media on its admission to the Official List, various acquisitions by Transport Development Group plc and acting for National Car Parks Ltd on acquisitions of Langdale Systems and Park and Ride Ltd, Housego Plc and subsequent acquisition of US subsidary.
Prof. Memberships: Law Society
Career: Trained and worked with *Freshfields* including a 6 month secondment in New York. Qualified in 1989. Joined *Burges Salmon* in 1994 becoming a partner in 1999. Has had two secondments – one with *Steele Hector & Davis* in Florida and the other with *Transport Development Group plc* as in-house counsel. Downing College, Cambridge 1984-88, Masters in Public International Law.
Personal: Cricket, golf and rowing.

SPRIGGS, Michael I.
Eversheds, Newcastle upon Tyne (0191) 261 1661
michaelspriggs@eversheds.com
Executive Senior Partner *Eversheds* North East. Head of North East Corporate Group.
Specialisation: Corporate finance, covering venture capital, mergers and acquisitions, joint ventures and shareholder disputes.
Prof. Memberships: Law Society.
Career: Banker with Standard Chartered Bank, Hong Kong 1979-81. Trained at *Frere Cholmeley*, London. Qualified as a solicitor in 1985. Joined *Wilkinson Maughan*, becoming Partner in 1987. Executive senior partner 2000.

STAFFORD, Peter
Arthur Cox – Northern Ireland, Belfast (028) 9023 0007
pstafford@arthurcox.ie
Specialisation: General corporate finance including M & A, takeovers, fundraisings, buyouts and shareholders agreements. Also financial services work.
Prof. Memberships: Law Society of Northern Ireland; Law Society of England and Wales.
Career: Qualified 1995. Assistant Solicitor Herbert Smith, London 1995 – 1997. Corporate finance executive IBI Corporate Finance, Belfast 1997 – 1999. Assistant Solicitor with Arthur Cox Northern Ireland since 1999.
Personal: Educated at Royal Belfast Academical Institution and Jesus College, Cambridge. Interested in most sports.

STANFIELD, Glynne
Mills & Reeve, Cambridge (01223) 222 250
glynne.stanfield@mills-reeve.com
See under Education, p.310

STEINFELD, Michael
Dechert, London (020) 7583 5353
advice@dechertEU.com
Partner in Corporate Finance Group, Business Law Department.
Specialisation: Corporate finance, mergers and acquisitions, and general company and commercial work, involving mainly Stock Exchange listed and overseas companies.
Career: Qualified in 1970, having joined *Titmuss Sainer & Webb* (now *Dechert*) in 1968. Became a Partner in 1972.
Personal: Born in 1943. Educated at Pembroke College, Oxford. Interests include skiing, football, good food and France. Lives in London.

STELLA, Keith G.
Paisner & Co, London (020) 7353 0299
Partner and head of Corporate Finance.
Specialisation: Practice covers the full range of corporate finance activities, including flotations, secondary offerings, bids and takeovers (both public and private). Acts for wide range of listed and private companies, as well as for banks, brokers and other intermediaries.
Career: Qualified 1978. Partner from 1980. Educated at City of London School and University College, London (LL.B 1st Class Hons). First Class Hons in Law Society Finals.
Personal: Living in Hertfordshire. Interests include classical music, antiques and wine.

STEPHENSON, Barbara
Norton Rose, London (020) 7283 6000
stephensonb@nortonrose.com
Specialisation: Main area of practice is public company and Stock Exchange transactions, including public company takeovers, other mergers and acquisitions, initial public offerings, securities offerings and company reconstructions and institutional investments. Also international transactions, including cross-border, mergers and acquisitions and joint ventures. Important transactions handled include the £2.5 billion takeover of Eastern Group by Hanson, the £1.4 billion acquisition of the investment banking business of Schroders by Citigroup by way of scheme of arrangement and non Code offer and the flotation of Fox Kids Europe on the Amsterdam Stock Exchange. Corporate clients include Taylor Woodrow, Pillar Property, Fox Kids Europe, Old Mutual, QBE, Blacks Leisure Group, Matsushita Electric Europe and TBI. Investment banks include Schroders Salomon Smith Barney, Credit Agricole Indosuez, HSBC, SG Hambros, Credit Lyonnais, West LB and ABN Amro.
Prof. Memberships: Member of the Law Society.
Personal: Married with three daughters.

STERN, Robert
Slaughter and May, London (020) 7600 1200
Specialisation: General practice consists principally of acting for corporate and investment bank clients on corporate finance and M&A transactions, both in England and overseas and generally on corporate matters. Wide experience of acquisitions and disposals (both public and private), joint ventures and of equity and debt financing structures.
Career: BA in French and German at The Queen's College, Oxford. Qualified as a solicitor in 1986. Became a Partner in 1993.

STEWART, Alan
Burness, Glasgow (0141) 2484933
ajs@burness.co.uk
Specialisation: Main area of practice is in corporate department. Particular experience in private company acquisitions and disposals, equity fundings; listed company flotations and transactions.
Prof. Memberships: Mamber of the Law Society of Scotland.
Career: Legal apprenticeship *McGrigor Donald & Co*, 1977-79; assistant solicitor *McGrigor Donald*, 1979-82; *Herbert Smith*, 1982-84; *McGrigor Donald*, 1984-85. Partner *McGrigor Donald* 1985-94; *Semple Fraser*, 1994-96. Head of legal services, Clydesdale Bank plc 1996-98. Director of various companies 1998-2000. Partner and Head of Corporate, *Burness* April 2000.
Personal: Married with three children. Educated Glasgow Academy and University of Glasgow. Directorships – John R Weir Limited, Eden Bridge Carriage Limited, Image and Print Group Limited.

STEWART, Mark
Clifford Chance, London (020) 7600 1000
mark.stewart@cliffordchance.com
Specialisation: Partner dealing with general corporate banking with an emphasis on acquisition financings.
Career: University College School, London; Bristol University. Articled *Richards Butler*; qualified 1983; trainee and assistant solicitor 1983-1986; *Clifford Chance* 1986-1990; partner since 1990.
Personal: Born 1958; resides London.

STILTON, Andrew J.
Martineau Johnson, Birmingham (0121) 200 3300
andrew.stilton@martjohn.com
Specialisation: Corporate finance: buy-outs, buy-ins and general merger and acquisition work as well as venture capital and flotation work. Also some banking work.
Prof. Memberships: Law Society, Securities Institute, member of the Law Society's Company Law Committee.
Career: Qualified in 1981. Partner in *Ryland Martineau* in 1985. Partner in *Martineau Johnson* on merger in 1987.
Personal: Born 31st October 1957. Educated at Trinity Hall, Cambridge. Leisure interests include cricket, football, music and travel until parenthood intervened.

STORAR, Michael J.
Lawrence Graham, London (020) 7379 0000
Head of Company/Commercial Department.
Specialisation: Main area of practice is corporate finance, covering mergers and acquisitions, flotations, listings and venture capital. Also handles advertising and marketing. Advised the Government and the Director General of the National Lottery on its structure and start up.
Career: Qualified in 1981. Worked at *Ashurst Morris Crisp* 1978-83. Joined *Blyth Dutton* in 1983, which merged to become *Lawrence Graham*.
Personal: Born 25th October 1955. Attended Cranleigh School 1963-73, Camberwell 1973-4 and Birmingham 1974-7. Lives in Suffolk.

STREET, Robert H.
Chaffe Street, Manchester (0161) 236 5800
Partner in Company/ Commercial Department.
Specialisation: Handles all areas of company commercial work including corporate finance, company and business acquisitions and disposals, intellectual property and commercial contracts.
Prof. Memberships: Law Society.
Career: Qualified in 1975. Articles at *Coward Chance*. Became a Partner at *Harold Chaffe & Co* in 1978. Partner at *Chaffe Street* since 1983.
Personal: Born 25th May 1951. Involved with North West Kidney Research. Leisure interests include golf, cricket, fell walking and skiing. Lives in Pott Shrigley, Cheshire.

SULLIVAN, Michael
Linklaters (A member firm of Linklaters & Alliance), London (020) 7456 3166
michael.sullivan@linklaters.com
Partner, Corporate Department.
Specialisation: Specialist in corporate law including mergers and acquisitions, initial and secondary public offerings, corporate reorganisations and demergers and privatisations.
Career: Qualified 1988. Became a Partner 1994.
Personal: Attended King's College, University of London, LL B (Hons).

SUMMERFIELD, Spencer
Travers Smith Braithwaite, London
(020) 7295 3000
Spencer.Summerfield@TraversSmith.com
Specialisation: Corporate finance; Company; Highlights of the year: £8 billion acquisition of Consumer Co operations of Cable & Wireless Communications plc.
Prof. Memberships: Law Society.
Career: Chigwell School; Cambridge University, Gonville & Caius College; College of Law, London; Joined *Travers Smith Braithwaite* as a trainee solicitor in 1987; made a partner in 1997.
Personal: Interests include cinema/theatre, aerobics, rugby. Married to Karen.

SUTTON, Robert H.
Macfarlanes, London (020) 7831 9222
rhs@macfarlanes.com
Senior Partner.
Specialisation: Work covers mergers and acquisitions, corporate finance, securities law, take-overs (private and public, friendly and hostile), flotations and corporate reconstructions, representing corporate and investment banking clients.
Prof. Memberships: Law Society.
Career: Qualified in 1979 while with *Macfarlanes*. Spent a year on secondment to *White & Case*, New York 1980-81. Became Partner in *Macfarlanes* in 1983 and Senior Partner in 1999.

SWANSON, Magnus P.
Maclay Murray & Spens, Glasgow
(0141) 248 5011
mps@maclaymurrayspens.co.uk
Partner in corporate department.
Specialisation: Partner and head of corporate department. Principle areas of work are MBOs/MBIs, mergers and acquisitions and joint ventures. Led the team on the £30m MBI of Phillips International Auctioneers and its subsequent sale to LVMH group; acted for Stagecoach Holdings Plc in its acquisition of Prestwick Airport; led the team acting for Redwood Group in the taking private of Clyde Blowers Plc, the first significant take private completed in Scotland and in recent times with £61m of funding provided by 3i and the Bank of Scotland in relation to the funding of the £500m hostile and subsequently recommended bid for Sears Group Plc by January Investments Limited. MBO of Pelican Hardcopy – a multinational business bought from a US parent, the subject of Chapter II Insolvency Proceedings. Winner of 1998 Legal Dealmaker of the Year Award.
Career: Qualified in 1982. University of Edinburgh (LLB 1980). Spent 18 months working in New York with *Paul Weiss Rifkind Wharton & Garrison*. (1986-87).
Personal: Born 1958.

SWEET, Jon
Marriott Harrison, London (020) 7209 2000
Partner in Corporate Department.
Specialisation: Main area of practice is corporate and commercial, principally venture capital, mergers and acquisitions and general corporate finance. Handles a mix of private and public company work, but primarily private company. Has a broad range of experience in company/ business sales and purchases, complex company and group restructurings, financings (debt and equity) and joint ventures as well as more general commercial advice such as agency and distribution. Past experience has included the full range of stock exchange and take over code work. Also handles banking and insolvency.
Prof. Memberships: Law Society, Associate Member of BVCA.
Career: Qualified in 1982. Worked at *Slaughter and May* 1980-90 (including 1986-88 in the Hong Kong office). Partner at *Iliffes* 1990-93, and at *Marriott Harrison* since 1993.
Personal: Born 7th March 1956. Attended Trinity College Glenalmond 1969-74, Brunel University 1975-79 and Guildford Law College 1979-80. Leisure interests include target rifle shooting, motor sport and classic cars. Lives in Hertfordshire.

TAYLOR, Glyn
Nabarro Nathanson, Reading (0118) 925 4637
g.taylor@nabarro.com
Specialisation: Corporate Finance particularly flotations, fundraisings, and mergers and acquisitions.
Prof. Memberships: Law Society; Oxford University Business Alumni.
Career: *Nabarro Nathanson* – trainee 1985-87, assistant solicitor 1987-1994, equity partner 1994 -to date.
Publications: Numerous magazine articles.
Personal: Dartford Grammar School pre 1979. Oxford University (Hertford College) 197901982. M.A. (English). College of Law 1983-85. Cricket, tennis, football (supports Arsenal F.C.). Theatre and music concerts.

THOMAS, Michelle
Eversheds, Cardiff (02920) 471147
michellethomas@eversheds.com
Specialisation: Partner specialising in corporate and corporate finance. Advises UK and international clients on corporate transactions including mergers and acquisitions, private equity, joint ventures, corporate funding and restructurings. In addition to the UK and United States, she has worked on transactions in South Africa, France, Spain, Austria, Sweden and The Netherlands.
Prof. Memberships: The Law Society; Member of New York Bar.
Career: Joined *Eversheds* as a partner in 1999 following 8 years practice in London with *Baker & McKenzie* and *Freshfields*.
Personal: Born 3 November 1966. LLB, University College Eversheds. LLM – University College Berkeley. Fulbright and John Rankin Scholar. Admitted to NewYork State Bar 1994.

THOMSON, Christopher
Greene & Greene, Bury St. Edmunds
(01284) 762211
ChristopherThomson@Greene-Greene.com
Specialisation: Acts mainly for privately owned, institution backed companies in London and East Anglia. Specialises in advising technology based businesses, including Pharmaceutical Multi-National Schering-Plough and Medical Device Company Weston Medical Group plc. Most work completed over the past year remains confidential to the clients concerned but some highlights that have entered the public domain were advising the management team of the successful flotation of Weston Medical on the London Stock Exchange, handling the sale of Software Comapny Systemware plc to Anglian Water, the sale of TEC Electronic Components Limited to US group Litton Industries and the sale of Electronic Component Manufacturers Syfer Technology Limited to US based Dover Corporation.

THORNEYCROFT, Max
Gouldens, London (020) 7583 7777
mbt@gouldens.com
Specialisation: Advises a range of public and private companies, banks and brokers on mergers and acquisition transactions and equity and debt financings. Throughout the 1980's and 90's, he has been involved in all of Hanson plc's major acquisitions and disposals culminating in its four way demerger in the mid 90's. In addition, he advises Tomkins, TT Group, Mid Kent Holdings, Sibir Energy and Severn Trent Water plc as well as a number of private companies and entrepreneures from the United Kingdom and abroad such as Kingston Metals Limited, which acquired the stainless steel and aliminium distribution business of Glynwed International plc for £100 million, UK Plant Limited, which disposed of its plant hire business to Ashtead Group plc for £20 million, the shareholders of Eurotel Telecom Holdings Limited which was sold to a 3i backed MBO for £30 million and Integralis Limited which reversed into Neuer Markt quoted Articon Information Systems AG for £171 million. On the financing side, he led the corporate aspects of the firm's advice to Bankers Trust on its loan of $2.1 billion to Huntsman to fund the acquisition of part of the business of ICI as well as advising houses such as Investec Henderson Crosthwaite, Campbell Lutyens, Strand Partners and Bulldog Partners.
Prof. Memberships: The Law Society and the CBI Corporate Law Committee.
Career: After reading law at Oxford, he qualified at *Macfarlanes* in 1975 and then spent six years in the Corporate Finance Department of *Norton Rose* before joining *Gouldens* in1981 and becoming a partner in 1983. Managing Partner 1987-1997. Head of the Company Department 1997 to date.
Personal: Educated King's School Macclesfield, Cheshire. Member of the Fund Raising Committee of Lincoln College, Oxford. Leisure pursuits include skiing, rugby, opera and gardening. Lives Holland Park and Gloucestershire.

TROTTER, Andrew
Shadbolt & Co, Reigate (01737) 226277
Andrew_Trotter@shadboltlaw.co.uk
Partner and head of Corporate Department.
Specialisation: Main area of practice is company sales and purchases and corporate finance, including MBOs, MBIs, venture capital, joint ventures and cross-border transactions. Leads a team which also handles general company commercial work, including franchising, IT contracts and intellectual property. Regular lectures on his subject, including a series of seminars 'Buying and Selling Unquoted Companies' and an address to US lawyers on UK and EU competition law.
Career: Qualified in 1981. At *Withers* 1977 – 1983, *Norton Rose* 1983-85, *Donne Mileham & Haddock* 1985-1997 and*Shadbolt & Co* from May 1997.
Personal: Born 5th August 1954. Educated at Lancing College and Oxford. Lives in Cuckfield in Sussex. Interests include football and golf.

TUFFNELL, Kevin
Macfarlanes, London (020) 7831 9222
kat@macfarlanes.com
Partner in Corporate Commercial & Banking Department.
Specialisation: Venture capital, corporate finance, mergers and acquisitions and flotations. Acted on the Allders and LLP Group flotations and on many substantial buy outs and financial purchases, including recently acting for management in relation to the financial purchases of IPC Magazines and William Hill.
Career: Qualified in 1984 while with *Macfarlanes*. Became a Partner in 1989.
Publications: Author of articles, e.g. in 'Company Law' in 1993.

TURNBULL, Robert
Cobbetts, Manchester (0161) 833 3333
robert.turnbull@cobbetts.co.uk
Specialisation: Mergers & Acquisitions, MBOs & MBIs, venture capital, joint ventures, corporate finance.
Career: Partner with *Cobbetts* since 1992.
Personal: Educated at: King Edward VII School, Lytham and Cambridge University.

TWENTYMAN, Jeff
Slaughter and May, London (020) 7600 1200
Specialisation: Mergers and acquisitions, corporate finance, public and private equity finance, joint ventures and commercial contracts, acting for listed and unlisted companies and investment banks; also acts extensively for companies and investors in the telecommunications and technology sectors, significantly in the last twelve months advising Bell Atlantic on the demerger of Cable & Wireless Communications, the SpectrumCo consortium in the UK 3G licence auction and Reuters on its telecommunications networking joint venture with Equant to create Radianz.
Career: Articled *Slaughter and May*; qualified 1991; *Morgan Grenfell & Co. Limited* (1993-94); *Slaughter and May* 1994; partner 1998.
Personal: Born 1965. Educated at Sackville School, East Grinstead and the University of Newcastle-upon-Tyne (1987 LL.B). Resides London; one daughter.

UNDERHILL, William
Slaughter and May, London (020) 7600 1200
Specialisation: Specialises in corporate finance, including acting for underwriters and issuers of securities, M&A, London Stock Exchange rules and regulations and FSA compliance. Also experienced in mortgage and other asset securitisation, and other mortgage-backed financing. Editor of Weinberg and Blank on Takeovers and Mergers.
Career: Qualified 1983 with *Slaughter and May*. Partner 1990.

VICKERS, Mark H.
Ashurst Morris Crisp, London (020) 7638 1111
mark.vickers@ashursts.com
Partner banking and capital markets group.
Specialisation: Corporate banking and international finance: specialising in UK and cross-border acquisition finance and leveraged acquisitions, particularly management buy-outs/buy-ins and institutional purchases; structured finance; and global syndicated lending. Is one of the market's leading experts on the debt funding of public to private takeovers.
Career: Joined *Ashurst Morris Crisp* in 1999 having been Head of european acquisition finance at a top 10 UK law firm (1980-1999).
Publications: Author: 'Senior Debt Market for Management Buy-outs' and 'Public to Private Takeovers: The New Paradigms'.
Personal: Helicopter pilot.

VON BISMARCK, Nilufer
Slaughter and May, London (020) 7600 1200
Specialisation: Partner specialising in corporate finance, general company and commercial work and some banking.
Career: Articled *Norton Rose* 1986-90; qualified 1988; *Slaughter and May* 1990 to date; partner 1994.
Personal: Born 1961. Educated at James Allen's Girls' School and Trinity College, Cambridge (1983 BA Law 2 (1)). Resides London.

WAINE, Ian
Prettys, Ipswich (01473) 232121
lmw@prettys.co.uk
Specialisation: Main areas of work include company law, mergers, acquisitions and reorganisations, MBO's corporate finance, insolvency and advice on directors' liabilities. Works with both private and public companies. Work has also included advice on Private Finance Initiatives projects and privatisations.
Career: Qualified 1986. Partner at *Prettys* since 1989.
Personal: Born 1961. Educated at Walton School, Stafford and Southampton University. Interests include golf and cricket. Lives in Great Finborough, Suffolk.

WARBURTON, Mark
Addleshaw Booth & Co, Manchester (0161) 934 6000
mww@addleshaw-booth.co.uk
Specialisation: Expert in all aspects of corporate transactions involving SMEs and owner-managed businesses in particular. This is complemented by his experience in funding and security matters.
Career: Qualified 1975. Joined firm as Partner 1998.
Personal: Education: Kings School, Chester and Selwyn College, Cambridge. Resides Wilmslow. Leisure: golf, walking and reading.

WARD, Anthony
Shearman & Sterling, London (020) 7655 5000
AWard@shearman.com
Specialisation: Partner specialising in acquisition finance. Advises a variety of leading financial institutions and equity sponsors. Recent transactions include advising Cinven and Investcorp in connection with the debt financing of the acquisition of Zeneca Specialities from Zeneca Plc. Advising Deutsche Bank and Merrill Lynch in connection with debt financing of the acquisition of Ineos Acrylics from ICI. Advising Morgan Stanley in connection with the debt financing of the acquisition of the Paper Technology Business of Invensys Plc.
Career: Qualified in1988. Partner *Ashurst Morris Crisp* in 1996. Partner *Shearman & Sterling* in 1998.
Personal: Education: School of Slavonic and East European Studies, London University, BA in Russian language and literature.

WARD, Michael J.
Gateley Wareing, Birmingham (0121) 234 0000
mward@gateleywareing.co.uk
Specialisation: Corporate finance, disposals, mergers and acquisitions.
Career: Birmingham University; trained at *Pinsent & Co* Birmingham (now *Pinsent Curtis*. Joined *Gateley Wareing* in 1987.
Prof. Memberships: Vice President of Birmingham Law Society; Previously Deputy Vice President and Treasurer of the Birmingham Law Society.
Personal: Member of Edgbaston Golf Club; plays football for University Barbarians.

WATSON, Andrew
Garretts, Reading (0118) 949 0000

WATSON, Sean M.
CMS Cameron McKenna, London (020) 7367 2802
smw@cmck.com
Partner in Corporate Department.
Specialisation: Advises corporate, merchant banking and venture capital clients on all areas of corporate finance including reconstructions, takeovers, mergers and acquisitions, flotations and venture capital transactions, with primary specialisation in stock exchange transactions.
Prof. Memberships: Law Society, City of London Solicitors Company.
Career: Qualified in 1972. Joined *McKenna & Co* in 1979, becoming a Partner in the same year.
Personal: Born 5th April 1948. Attended The Leys School, Cambridge, 1961-66 and Manchester University 1966-69. Leisure interests include tennis, golf, skiing, gardening and family. Lives in Weybridge, Surrey.

WATTS, Clive
Osborne Clarke OWA, Bristol (0117) 917 4110
clive.watts@osborneclarke.com
Specialisation: Specialist in all types of corporate governance and corporate finance transactions. In particular, has handled corporate and commercial aspects of privatisation of a number of general utilities, including handling the flotation and subsequent bids for 10 separate passenger rail franchises for Prism Rail Plc during the privatisation of British Rail. Also acted for LTS Rail Ltd, WAGN Railway Ltd, Railplus Ltd and STVA (UK) Ltd, following privatisation.
Career: Clive joined *Osborne Clarke* in 1987 as a partner after 24 years in the legal department of *Imperial Group plc* and *Imperial Tobacco Limited*, culminating in his appointment as Deputy Solicitor of Imperial Tobacco Limited.

WAYTE, Peter B.
DLA, London (08700) 111111
peter.wayte@dla.com
Specialisation: Corporate Finance, Equity: Mergers & Acquisitions, Corporate Finance, MBOs/ MBIs. Acted for DrKB Private Equity in its investment in and establishment of the Business of Ora Dental Group; for Ramesys Holdings in its second round development capital financing and acquisition of the Database Ltd and for BG Kapital and Bank of America in the provision of development capital to a Swedish company. Corporate Finance, 125-250 Fee Earners: Mergers & Acquisitions, Corporate Finance, MBOs/ MBIs. Acted for Tempus Group plc, Keller Group plc and Altodigital Ltd in a number of aquisitions in the UK and overseas for Xyratex in the placing of its substantial shareholding in a Neuer Markt company, for Melrose Resources plc in its Stock Exchange Listing and Share placing and for Druid Group plc in the recommended offer by F.I. Group.
Prof. Memberships: Law Society.
Career: LL.B Sheffield. Articled *Wilkinson Kimbers & Staddon*; Partner *Dibb Lupton Alsop* (and Predecessor firms) 1976 to date.
Personal: Married; three children. Outside interests: squash, skiing, walking and gardening.

WEBSTER, Martin
Biddle, London (020) 7606 9301
Partner in Company Commercial Department.
Specialisation: Main areas of practice are corporate finance and commercial advice to company clients. In recent years, has particularly specialised in MBOs/MBIs etc. Acted in the establishment of Parliamentary Broadcasting Unit Ltd, the vehicle for the dissemination of Parliamentary broadcasting, which is owned by the major broadcasters but ultimately controlled by Parliament. Is secretary of that company.
Prof. Memberships: Institute of Taxation, Law Society.
Career: Qualified in 1983. ATII 1986. Joined *Biddle* in 1981, becoming a Partner in 1987.
Personal: Born 1st July 1958. Attended Christ's College, Cambridge, 1976-79. Leisure interests include music, theatre and gardening. Lives in London SE11 and Norfolk.

WHALE, Philip
Norton Rose, London (020) 7283 6000
Specialisation: Advises on: a broad range of structured finance transactions including, in particular, on the financing of leveraged acquisitions (MBOs, MBIs, institutional buy-outs, public takeovers, increasingly involving complex cross-border transactions and innovative debt structures) and infrastructure projects; syndicated and bilateral credit facilities and restructurings.
Prof. Memberships: Member of the Law Society Banking Law Sub-Committee.
Career: Qualified in New Zealand; worked in commercial law in Auckland for five years; joined *Norton Rose* in 1986; partner in *Norton Rose* in 1992.

WHELDON, Tim
Addleshaw Booth & Co, Leeds (0113) 209 2000
tjw@addleshaw-booth.co.uk
Partner in Corporate Finance Group.
Specialisation: Corporate/commercial; venture capital.
Prof. Memberships: Law Society.
Career: Qualified 1983. Joined the firm as partner in 1990. Member of the firm's Partnership Board.
Personal: Educated at Hymers College, Hull; Manchester Polytechnic BA(Hons) Law and French. Leisure interests include sailing and skiing.

WHITE, Graham
SJ Berwin & Co, London (020) 7533 2222
graham.white @sjberwin.com
Specialisation: Partner in the corporate department specialising in Private Equity transactions.
Prof. Memberships: Law Society of Scotland.
Career: 1984-86, *Iain Smith & Co* Aberdeen, 1987 *Simmons & Simmons* London. 1999 *SJ Berwin & Co.*

WHITTINGHAM, Paul
Ashton Graham, Ipswich (01473) 232425
paul.whittingham@ashtongraham.co.uk
Specialisation: Specialises in corporate work particularly private company acquisitions and disposals.
Prof. Memberships: Law Society
Career: Trained with City firm *Paisner & Co*. Qualified in 1988. Worked in corporate department until 1991. Gap year in which crossed Africa by Motorcycle. Joined *Graham & Oldham* in 1993. Became a partner in 1995. Now partner in *Ashton Graham* following merger with *Banks Ashton* in 1998. Member of *Ashton Graham* Management Board.
Personal: 1962. Attended Swansea University. Interests include travel, motorcycling, swimming and sailing. Married. Lives in Grundisburgh, Suffolk.

WHYBROW, J. Annette
Birketts, Ipswich (01473) 232300
Specialisation: Principal areas of practice are mergers and acquisitions and disposals, MBO/MBI's, joint ventures, venture capital and bank funding. Also member of the Copyright Tribunal and Chairman of the Insolvency Practioners Tribunal.
Prof. Memberships: Law Society.
Career: University College of Wales, Aberystwyth: (1st Class Hons). Articled and trained at *McKenna & Co* (1974-1980). Partner *Birketts* 1981.
Personal: Married with 2 children. Governor: Suffolk College. Main leisure activity: parenthood.

WILD, David W.
Eversheds, Derby (01332) 360992
Specialisation: Corporate Finance, MBO's, Insolvency.
Prof. Memberships: Council Member, Derby Law Society.
Career: Articled *Wells & Hind*, Nottingham. Qualified 1981. Partner *Eversheds*, 1985.
Personal: Born 1956. Educated Nottingham High School and Jesus College, Cambridge.

WILL, James R.
Shepherd & Wedderburn WS, Edinburgh (0131) 228 9900
james.will@shepwedd.co.uk
Partner in Corporate Department.
Specialisation: Main areas of practice are Stock Exchange work, company law, mergers and acquisitions, major start-ups and development capital, with emphasis on the technology sector.
Prof. Memberships: Law Society of Scotland, Society of Writers to Her Majesty's Signet.
Career: Qualified in 1978. With *Tods Murray WS* 1978-79 and *Clifford Chance* 1980-81. Joined *Shepherd & Wedderburn* in 1981 and became a Partner in 1982.
Personal: Born 30th April 1955. Educated at Merchiston Castle and Aberdeen University.

WILLIAMS, Christine J.
Fox Williams, London (020) 7628 2000
Partner in Corporate Department.
Specialisation: Principal area of practice is corporate finance. Work includes mergers and acquisitions, capital raising, joint ventures, restructurings and partnership law. Has acted on many purchases and sales of companies, both quoted and unquoted, including management buy-outs and buy-ins. Regular adviser to a number of boards of directors. Past member of Company Law Sub-Committee of City of London Law Society. Was listed by Euromoney as one of the world's leading mergers and acquisitions lawyers.
Prof. Memberships: Law Society, City of London Law Society, International Bar Association, Association of Partnership Practitioners.
Career: Qualified in 1977. Partner at *Oppenheimers* 1981-88. Formed and joined *Fox Williams* as a Partner in 1989.
Personal: Born 15th February 1953. Educated at St Anne's College, Oxford 1971-74. Leisure interests include theatre and cinema. Lives in Buckinghamshire.

WILLIAMS, Nigel
Dickinson Dees, Newcastle upon Tyne (0191) 279 9000
Specialisation: M & A work, particularly owner managed business sales and disposals for corporate clients. Tasked with spearheading Dickinson Dees' new Tees Valley Office.
Prof. Memberships: Newcastle upon Tyne Law Society, Durham & North Yorkshire Law Society.
Career: Trained with Cameron Markby Hewitt (now CMS Cameron McKenna), qualifying in 1991. Spent five years with Eversheds before moving to Dickinson Dees.
Personal: Newcastle University and Chester College of Law. One psychiatrist wife and two cats. Leisure interests include any form of sport and frequent trips to Ibiza.

WILLIS, John-George
Tughan & Co, Belfast (028) 9055 3300
Specialisation: Handles all types of company and commercial work including mergers and acquisitions. MBO's/MBA's, joint ventures and public and private share issues.
Career: Qualified 1984. Assistant Solicitor at *Tughan & Co* 1987-92. Partner since 1992.
Personal: Educated at The Royal School, Dungannon and Queen's University Belfast. Interests include family and sport.

WINTER, Martin A.S.
Biddle, London (020) 7606 9301
Senior Partner.
Specialisation: Main areas of practice are private equity, joint ventures, M & A.
Prof. Memberships: British Venture Capital Association (by firm).
Career: Qualified in 1978. Assistant Solicitor at *Norton Rose*, 1979-84. Joined *Biddle* in 1984. Partner in 1985.
Personal: Born 13th April 1954. Graduated in English from St Edmund Hall, Oxford, 1975. World and Nationally ranked waterskier, twice a Conservative Parliamentary Candidate.

WIPPELL, M.A.
Allen & Overy, London (020) 7330 3000
Specialisation: Specialises in corporate finance, mergers and acquisitions and securities offerings, advising investment banks and major international quoted companies. Has particular expertise in transactions involving US companies and transactions in the financial sector.
Career: Educated at Oxford University (MA) 1979; LLM Tulane University, USA (1980); admitted as Solicitor (1983); admitted attorney in New York (1987); became *Allen & Overy* partner in 1999. Previously a partner in *Ashurst Morris Crisp* (1990-1998).
Personal: Born 1958.

WOOTTON, David
Allen & Overy, London (020) 7330 3000
Specialisation: Specialises in corporate finance, in particular mergers & acquisitions, flotations, public and private takeovers, joint ventures, corporate restructurings. Led the teams advising the sponsors and underwriters on the flotation of Canary Wharf Group and The Carphone Warehouse Group, Celltech plc on its merger with Chiroscience Group plc, Admiral on its acquisition by CMG, Thomson Travel Group on the offer by Preussag and Singapore Airlines on its acquisition of 49% of Virgin Atlantic Airways.
Career: BA Cambridge University 1972. MA Cambridge University. Admitted as solicitor 1975. Associate *Allen & Overy* 1975-79; Partner *Allen & Overy* since 1979.

WRIGHT, Sean
Blake Lapthorn, Southampton (023) 8063 1823
sbwright@blakelapthorn.co.uk
Specialisation: Practice covers all company and corporate finance work with a particular emphasis on the sale and purchase of companies and businesses, MBOs/MBIs and venture capital. Recent deals include the sale of a mobile phone company for £62m, the secondary buy-out of Key Industrial Group for £15m and MBO of Duco International for £22m.
Prof. Memberships: Law Society.
Career: Born 16 June 1966. Attended Wolverhampton G.S. and Sheffield University. Qualified in 1990. Became a Partner at *Blake Lapthorn* in 1995.
Personal: Golf, skiing and travel. Married. Lives in Bishops Waltham.

CRIME

OVERVIEW: Firms listed in our tables cover a wide variety of criminal practice ranging from road traffic and shoplifting to murder and professional or white collar crime. Many top band London firms specialise in certain areas of criminal law and have therefore acquired national reputations for excellence in particular niches. In the regions, firms tend to be more generalist, acting for any criminal matter that comes through the door. Many such firms report feeling pressured by the low legal aid remuneration rates and the expected institution of legal aid block-contracting for criminal work. We have this year omitted to rank firms in the south-east as it was found that the volume of criminal cases were referred to London firms.

RESEARCH APPROVED BY BMRB: *For this edition,* Chambers' *researchers conducted 6083 interviews – 4408 with law firms, 598 with barristers and 1077 with clients.*

The validity of the research was scrutinised by BMRB International, who audited both the methodology and the results at our offices in July 2000. They interviewed Chambers' *researchers and cross-checked sample interviews. Details of the audit appear on page 7.*

LONDON

Bindman & Partners This *"impressive"* practice, led by **Neil O'May**, has a widespread reputation for civil liberties work and crime with political facets, namely race-related crimes, cases against environmental and animal rights activists, extradition, and terrorist charges. Recently represented a number of journalists and media clients against charges of violating the Official Secrets Act.

CRIME • London
❶ Bindman & Partners
Birnberg Peirce & Partners
Edward Fail Bradshaw & Waterson
Hodge Jones & Allen
Kingsley Napley
Offenbach & Co
Powell Spencer & Partners
Saunders & Co
T.V. Edwards
Taylor Nichol
Thanki Novy Taube
Whitelock & Storr
❷ Andrew Keenan & Co
Christian Fisher
Duthie Hart & Duthie
Fisher Meredith
Hallinan, Blackburn, Gittings & Nott
Henry Milner & Co
Hickman & Rose
Russell-Cooke, Potter & Chapman
Simons Muirhead & Burton
Venters Reynolds
Victor Lissack & Roscoe
❸ Alistair Meldrum & Co
Claude Hornby & Cox
Darlington & Parkinson
Dundons
J.B. Wheatley & Co
Joy Merriam & Co
Magrath & Co
McCormacks
Russell Jones & Walker
Tuckers

Within each band, firms are listed alphabetically.

Birnberg Peirce & Partners *"Has a corner of the market sewn up"* for high profile political and terrorist cases. It is widely felt that *"you couldn't get a better lawyer for terrorist offences"* than *"pre-eminent"* **Gareth Peirce**.

Edward Fail Bradshaw & Waterson A *"top firm"* particularly noted for armed robbery cases. *"An experienced villain's lawyer,"* **Edward Preston** handles a large volume of heavyweight crime including murders, large drug cases, corruption, and bigamy.

Hodge Jones & Allen A large team under the leadership of the highly regarded **Mark Studdert**, who is *"respected in the local magistrates court."* Represented a defendant in the Stephen Lawrence murder case.

Kingsley Napley Rises in the tables for the quality of its caseload. Although better known for its serious fraud practice, the firm also handles a substantial number of high profile general crime cases for private clients. Well-known for defending General Pinochet, the team is also active in the Bloody Sunday inquiry and Marchioness disaster inquiry.

Offenbach & Co General criminal practice with an emphasis on civil liberties. Particularly noted for expertise in drug related conspiracies. Recently defended an academic researcher against computer obscenity charges.

Powell Spencer & Partners A busy north-west London practice handling a volume of traditional crime for a community client base. Maintains dedicated police station and youth justice teams. Partners **Greg Powell** and **Richard Spencer** were both recommended for their *"efficiency"* and *"reliable judgement."*

Saunders & Co. Criminal practice with a *"reputation for quality work."* **James Saunders** is a *"serious criminal practitioner"* who concentrates on heavyweight drugs, murder, rape and arson cases. Involved in leading case relating to voluntary bills of indictment.

T.V. Edwards A volume practice with *"an intelligent approach to court."* Team includes two solicitor advocates with higher court rights. Although increasingly dedicated to lecturing, **Anthony Edwards** continues to receive outstanding recommendations as an *"absolute star"* in his field, offering clients a *"deluxe service."*

Taylor Nichol A *"committed"* team with a recognised niche in cases involving miscarriage of justice. *"Top quality"* **James Nichol** is *"one of the best solicitors around for ground breaking appellate work." "Absolutely brilliant"* **Carolyn Taylor** defends criminal charges against offenders with mental disorders. Assistant solicitor **Mark Ashford** was praised as *"the leading youth lawyer in the country."*

LEADING INDIVIDUALS • London	
❶ **HASLAM Mark** Burton Copeland	**NICHOL James** Taylor Nichol
PEIRCE Gareth Birnberg Peirce & Partners	
❷ **ASHFORD Mark** Taylor Nichol	**BROWN Robert** Darlington & Parkinson
EDWARDS Anthony T.V. Edwards	**FISHER Michael** Christian Fisher
HICKMAN Jane Hickman & Rose	**KEENAN Andrew** Andrew Keenan & Co
MERRIAM Joy Joy Merriam & Co	**POWELL Greg** Powell Spencer & Partners
PRESTON Edward Edward Fail Bradshaw & Waterson	
SPENCER Richard Powell Spencer & Partners	
TAYLOR Carolyn Taylor Nichol	**THANKI Girish** Thanki Novy Taube
VENTERS June Venters Reynolds	**ZANI John** Whitelock & Storr
❸ **ALMOND Richard** Victor Lissack & Roscoe	
BUTLER Michael Claude Hornby & Cox	
CADMAN Peter Russell-Cooke, Potter & Chapman	
HALLAM Richard Claude Hornby & Cox	
HEWITT Stephen Fisher Meredith	**HUBER Bernard** Duthie Hart & Duthie
MILNER Henry Henry Milner & Co	**MURPHY Shaun** Duthie Hart & Duthie
NOTT Colin Hallinan, Blackburn, Gittings & Nott	
NOVY Rod Thanki Novy Taube	**O'MAY Neil** Bindman & Partners
ROSCOE Robert Victor Lissack & Roscoe	
RYAN Ian Russell-Cooke, Potter & Chapman	
SAUNDERS James Saunders & Co	**STUDDERT Mark** Hodge Jones & Allen

*See **Profiles** on page 275*

Thanki Novy & Taube An *"avant-garde"* practice known for its extradition work and actions against the police. Handled Mardi Gras bomber and Regent's Canal twins murder cases. *"Hard-working"* **Girish Thanki** and *"conscientious"* **Rod Novy** were both recommended.

Whitelock & Storr This small practice maintains a *"high standard of client care and preparation."* Covers the range of traditional crime with noted expertise in extradition work. *"Lively"* **John Zani** has a loyal client following, and is reported to be particularly popular within the Italian community.

Other Notable Firms and Solicitors

Andrew Keenan & Co maintains a strong reputation for general and professional crime under the leadership of name partner **Andrew Keenan**. **Michael Fisher** and his firm **Christian Fisher** were recommended for substantial crime with a political slant. **Duthie Hart & Duthie** is recognised for a solid caseload in drugs, murder, and robbery charges. *"Go getters"* **Bernard Huber** and **Shaun Murphy** *"give good advice sensibly within the perameters of legal aid."* **Stephen Hewitt** manages a *"committed"* team at **Fisher Meredith**, handling a volume of traditional crime in South London. **Hallinan, Blackburn, Gittings & Nott** have a long established reputation as a heavyweight crime practice under the direction of well respected **Colin Nott**. **Henry Milner** of **Henry Milner & Co** *"represents old fashioned big villains"* and is well known for his recent defence of Kenneth Noye. **Jane Hickman** *"takes no prisoners"* in her defence work in drugs and homicide charges and police actions. Her team *"with a vision"* at **Hickman & Rose** emphasises human rights issues and recently acted in the John Drew art fraud case. **Russell-Cooke Potter & Chapman** undertakes both routine crime and police federation work. *"Understated"* **Ian Ryan** and *"academic"* **Peter Cadman** were commended for their ability to *"bring clients to recognition of a realistic position."* In addition to its high profile fraud practice, **Simons Muirhead & Burton** maintains a respected dedicated general crime unit with a stronghold in the Wandsworth area. The team received praise for its Privy Council work in Caribbean Island death row cases. The group at **Victor Lissack & Roscoe** have a recognised specialism in extradition work, with practitioners **Robert Roscoe** and **Richard Almond** receiving general recommendation for a broad based practice. **Alistair Meldrum & Co** and **Tuckers** were rated for their enormous turnover of legal aid work. Both **Dundons** and **J.B. Wheatley & Co** retain substantial shares of the South London market. **Claude Hornby & Cox** continues to be recommended for a range of general crime, with *"enthusiastic"* **Richard Hallam** noted for his *"in your face style"* and **Michael Butler** praised as a *"young solicitor who's going places."* **Robert Brown** maintains a strong local following at the Acton-based firm **Darlington & Parkinson**. **Joy Merriam** runs a *"young firm with a marvellous way of presenting cases"* at **Joy Merriam & Co**. **Russell Jones & Walker** enters the tables for its reputation in representing police officers at criminal and disciplinary trials. **McCormacks** was rated for general crime at Magistrates Court level, as was the *"proactive"* **June Venters** of **Venters Reynolds**. The latter firm is the product of a merger with dedicated crime firm Reynolds Dawson, and should now benefit from an increased focus on extradition work. West End firm **Magrath & Co** handles routine crime and recently persuaded a judge to dismiss a guilty plea in a charge of conspiracy to supply counterfeit ecstasy, on the basis of psychological profile evidence. **Mark Haslam**, *"well versed in the constraints of legal aid"* stands out at fraud-oriented Burton Copeland for his patience with clients and dedication to general crime advice.

SOUTH WEST

CRIME • South West
❶ **Bobbetts Mackan** Bristol
Douglas & Partners Bristol
John Boyle and Co Redruth
❷ **Crosse & Crosse** Exeter
Stephens & Scown Exeter
Stones Exeter
Wolferstans Plymouth
Woollcombe Beer Watts Newton Abbot

LEADING INDIVIDUALS	
❶ **BOYLE John** John Boyle and Co	**FANSON David** Douglas & Partners
MILES Anthony Bobbetts Mackan	**NUNN Stephen** Stephens & Scown
ROSE Timothy Douglas & Partners	

Within each band, firms are listed alphabetically. *See **Profiles** on page 275*

Bobbetts Mackan maintains its share of the Bristol market and thus retains its top band position. **Tony Miles**, considered *"pivotal"* in the field, leads a young team of solicitors, two of whom exercise higher court advocacy rights. Miles himself is heavily involved in courts martial work.

Douglas & Partners receives high ratings for both the quality and size of its criminal practice. **David Fanson** *"has had an exceedingly good year"* and heads a team of experienced solicitors. Maintains a dedicated youth court department and recently acted in a number of road-protester aggravated trespass cases. **Tim Rose** enters the tables this year on the strength of general recommendation.

"Outstanding" **John Boyle** of **John Boyle & Co** is a market leader in the Cornwall area. Active in Police Federation work and court of appeal cases involving death row inmates. Also commands extensive expertise in drug importation charges.

Partner led **Crosse & Crosse** was recommended for its youth court work, as well as its defence of DTI, RSPCA, and DSS prosecutions.

Stephens & Scown continues strongly in the area with its Exeter base now supplemented with a year-old Plymouth "LawDirect" office. *"Conscientious"* **Stephen Nunn** brings *"panache"* to criminal work. The firm is on the CCRC referral panel and includes two solicitors with higher court rights.

Stones, a newcomer to the tables, **Wolferstans**, and **Woollcombe Beer & Watts** have solid reputations for general crime.

WALES

CRIME • Wales	
❶	**Gamlins** Rhyl
	Graham Evans & Partners Swansea
	Huttons Cardiff
	Martyn Prowel Solicitors Cardiff
	Robertsons Cardiff
	Spiro Grech & Co Cardiff

LEADING INDIVIDUALS		
❶	**HUTTON Stuart** Huttons	**PROWEL Martyn** Martyn Prowel Solicitors
❷	**BIRD Jeremy** Hugh James Ford Simey	
	GREEN Christopher Geoffrey Williams & Christopher Green	
	JONES Gwyn Gamlins	
	WILLIAMS Ian Robertsons	

Within each band, firms are listed alphabetically. *See **Profiles** on page 275*

Cardiff firms dominate our table of Welsh leaders in crime. **Huttons** handles a large volume of criminal work with **Stuart Hutton** continuing to *"attract a number of high profile cases,"* particularly miscarriage of justice matters. **Martyn Prowel Solicitors** is known for its advocacy work. Senior practitioner **Martyn Prowel** *"specialises in serious cases,"* both violent and white-collar crime. *"Effective"* **Ian Williams** of **Robertsons** is involved in both prosecution and defence work. At **Spiro Grech & Co** a *"dynamic"* team covers a volume of work, and was particularly recommended for its youth court division. Outside the capital **Gwyn Jones** of **Gamlins** was once again rated for his broadly based practice while Swansea's **Graham Evans & Partners** *"stand out"* in the area for the volume and quality of their criminal work. **Jeremy Bird** of **Hugh James Ford Simey** is well known in the valleys and continues to be rated as *"a solid criminal practitioner."* **Christopher Green** of **Geoffrey Williams & Christopher Green** continues to be ranked as a leader in his field.

MIDLANDS

CRIME • Midlands	
❶	**Banners Jones Middleton** Chesterfield
	Barrie Ward & Julian Griffiths Nottingham
	Fletchers Nottingham
	Glaisyers Birmingham
	Kieran & Co Worcester
	Nelsons Nottingham
	The Johnson Partnership Nottingham
	The Smith Partnership Derby
	Woodford-Robinson Northampton
❷	**Brethertons** Rugby
	Eddowes Waldron Derby
	Elliot Mather Chesterfield
	George, Jonas & Co Birmingham
	Hawley & Rodgers Loughborough
	Parker & Grego Birmingham
	Purcell Parker Birmingham
	Rees Page Wolverhampton
	Silks Oldbury
	Tyndallwoods Birmingham

LEADING INDIVIDUALS		
❶	**GOULBORN Caroline** Fletchers	**GREGO Kevin** Parker & Grego
	GRIFFITHS Julian Barrie Ward & Julian Griffiths	
	MATHER Bertie Elliot Mather	**PURCELL Michael** Purcell Parker
	TOMLINSON Kevin Kieran & Co	
	WARD Barrie Barrie Ward & Julian Griffiths	

Within each band, firms are listed alphabetically. *See **Profiles** on page 275*

Unsurprisingly, Nottingham and Birmingham criminal firms absorb the greatest amount of the Midlands market, although many firms in smaller towns continue to make a strong showing in the tables.

"Committed defenders" **Barrie Ward** and **Julian Griffiths** are particularly accomplished in representing minorities and members of the gay or lesbian community against criminal charges. **Caroline Goulborn** of **Fletchers** was commended as a *"sensible, persuasive advocate"* who *"deals with clients in an understanding way."* **Nelsons**, said to *"rank first in terms of quality,"* divides itself into general crime and business defence units and has recently been involved in several drug conspiracy and murder cases. Also in Nottingham, **The Johnson Partnership** is recognised as having *"enormous turnover"* and a *"police station presence."* **Glaisyers** leads the field in Birmingham. In Chesterfield, **Keiran & Co** is a small but busy criminal practice, with **Kevin Tomlinson** once again rated for *"a good mix of quality work."* **Banners Jones Middleton**, a larger firm, is seen to handle a greater proportion of the local work. In Derby, **The Smith Partnnership** is seen as a *"good quality criminal firm."* **Woodford-Robinson** also continues to be highly rated. *"A slick operator,"* **Kevin Grego** heads an able team at ranked firm **Parker and Grego**. **Tyndallwoods** handles a range of criminal work with a civil liberties slant. **Michael Purcell** is said to be a *"presence in the courts;"* he and his firm **Purcell Parker** are newcomers to the list this year. **George, Jonas, & Co**, also in Birmingham, retains its long-established reputation for criminal work. **Brethertons, Hawley & Rogers** and **Eddowes Waldron** are all seen as busy criminal practices. **Bertie Mather** of **Elliot Mather** once again received strong recommendations. **Rees Page** and **Silks** also enjoy solid reputations for criminal defence work.

EAST ANGLIA

CRIME • East Anglia

Band	Firm
1	**Copleys** Huntingdon
	Gepp & Sons Chelmsford, Colchester
	Hatch Brenner Norwich
	Hunt & Coombs Peterborough
	Overbury Steward Eaton & Woolsey Norwich
	Twitchen Musters & Kelly Southend-on-Sea
2	**Belmores** Norwich
	David Charnley & Co Romford
	Fosters Norwich
	Gotelee & Goldsmith Ipswich
	Hegarty & Co Peterborough
	Lucas & Wyllys Great Yarmouth
	Thomson Webb Corfield & Masters Cambridge

LEADING INDIVIDUALS

Band		
1	**BECKFORD Trevor** Beckford & Co	**COLE Michael** Cole's
	FISHER Ian Overbury Steward Eaton	**KELLY Philip** Twitchen Musters & Kelly
	MASTERS Peter Thomson Webb Corfield	**MUSTERS Patrick** Twitchen Musters & Kelly
	NICHOLLS Simon Belmores	
	WARBOYS Kevin Copleys	

Within each band, firms are listed alphabetically. *See **Profiles** on page 275*

The East Anglia criminal market remains relatively static. *"All-rounder"* **Kevin Warboys** of **Copleys** receives high ratings in the area. **Gepp & Sons** covers a large client base in the southernmost portion of East Anglia. In addition to the general range of criminal work, the *"skilled practitioners"* at **Hatch Brenner** undertake a substantial number of private road traffic matters and prosecution work for Norfolk agencies. In Peterborough, **Hunt & Coombes** receives instructions in violent, white-collar crime, and motoring cases, as well as health and safety criminal prosecutions. **Ian Fisher** of **Overbury Steward Easton & Woolsey** was deemed a *"safe pair of hands"* for general defence work. Partners **Patrick Musters** and **Philip Kelly** of **Twitchen Musters & Kelly** employ their higher court advocacy rights in defences of serious or complex criminal cases, including drugs charges, sexual abuse, white collar crime and post-conviction appeals.

Belmores are seen to be consolidating their position in Norwich, with **Simon Nicholls** rated as a substantial asset to the firm. Niche criminal firm **David Charnley & Co** offers *"high standards of client care"* and recently acted for a number of defendants in the Stansted Hijacking case. The team at **Fosters** have specialisms in professional and mental health related crime and recently dealt with an attempt to evict 70 immigrants from Great Yarmouth. **Gotelee & Goldsmith** also has a mental health interest; although its broad, defence-oriented practice is supplemented by prosecution work for local government agencies. **Hegarty & Co** covers the general range of drugs, child abuse, rape, and murder charges; recent work includes a multiple sex abuse charge and a female stalker case. **Lucas & Wyllys** has a loyal local following while **Peter Masters'** recognised *"experience and ability"* ensures **Thomson Webb Corfield & Masters'** place in the tables.

Ranked individuals **Trevor Beckford**, previously of Leathes Prior, and **Michael Cole** from Cole & Co have left their former firms to set up on their own. Both continue to be recommended but it remains to be seen what impact their new practices, Beckford & Co and Cole's respectively, will make in the area.

NORTH WEST

CRIME • North West

Band	Firm
1	**Burton Copeland** Manchester
2	**Garstangs** Bolton
	Jones Maidment Wilson Manchester
	Maidments Manchester
	Russell & Russell Bolton
	Tuckers Manchester
3	**Betesh Fox & Co** Manchester
	Brian Koffman & Co Manchester
	Cunninghams Manchester
	Forbes Blackburn
	R.M. Broudie & Co Liverpool
	The Berkson Globe Partnership Liverpool
4	**Draycott Gibbon More & Wright** Manchester
	Farleys Blackburn
	Jackson & Canter Liverpool
	Linskills Solicitors Liverpool

LEADING INDIVIDUALS

Band		
1	**GROGAN Peter** Jones Maidment Wilson	
	MAIDMENT Allan Maidments	**SINCLAIR Franklin** Tuckers
2	**BROUDIE Robert** R.M. Broudie & Co	**CUNNINGHAM Martin** Cunninghams
	CUTTLE Barry M.B. Cuttle & Co	**DRAYCOTT Shaun** Draycott Gibbon More
	FREEMAN Nicholas Freeman & Co	**MACKEY Michael** Burton Copeland
	PETER Charles The Berkson Globe Partnership	

Within each band, firms are listed alphabetically. *See **Profiles** on page 275*

In the north west **Burton Copeland** remains the *"premier"* firm for both fraud work and serious traditional crime. The general crime unit contains a *"fund of talent,"* including **Michael Mackey** who is widely respected for his *"expertise and knowledge of the law."* **Peter Grogan** runs a *"well-organised, progressive"* criminal team at **Jones Maidment Wilson**, handling a volume of general blue-collar crime. **Allan Maidment** is seen to be developing **Maidments**' presence as a *"national criminal firm"* with serious crime and fraud offices in Manchester, Liverpool, Birmingham, Bristol, and London. **Tuckers** in Manchester is well known for the sheer volume of its criminal work, with **Franklin Sinclair** highly regarded as a *"strong personality"* with *"an admirable ability to market his firm."* **Garstangs** and **Russell & Russell** both command substantial proportions of the Bolton market. While better known on the fraud side, **Betesh Fox & Co** continue to draw praise for general criminal work in the Salford area. **Brian Koffman & Co** has a long established reputation for serious criminal cases, particularly those involving armed robbery or drug offences. **Robert Broudie** heads a highly regarded criminal practice at **R.M. Broudie & Co**. **Martin Cunningham** enters the tables this year due to widespread recommendation of his legal expertise. His firm **Cunninghams** has recently acted in Moss Side firearms related charges and a charity fraud investigation. In Liverpool, **Charles Peter** of **The Berkson Globe Partnership** continues to be recommended. **Forbes** and **Farleys** are both busy in the Blackburn area. *"Professional"* **Shaun Draycott's** fledgling firm **Draycott, Gibbon, More & Wright** has already made itself felt in the Manchester market and is a new entrant to the tables. Liverpool firms **Jackson & Canter** and **Linskills Solicitors** enjoy strong reputations for criminal work.

Nicholas Freeman operates a niche practice in privately funded road traffic cases, notably for Manchester United members and regional celebrities. Practitioner **Barry Cuttle** of MB Cuttle & Co continues to be rated for his *"strong personality at court"* and *"loyal client following."*

NORTH EAST

CRIME • North East
❶ **Sugaré & Co** Leeds
❷ **David Gray & Company** Newcastle upon Tyne
Grahame Stowe, Bateson Leeds
Howells Sheffield
Irwin Mitchell Sheffield
Levi & Co Leeds
Max Gold & Co Hull
❸ **Gosschalks** Hull
Henry Hyams & Co Leeds
Myer Wolff & Manley Hull

LEADING INDIVIDUALS
❶ **SUGARÉ Anthony** Sugaré & Co

Within each band, firms are listed alphabetically. *See **Profiles** on page 275*

Anthony Sugaré of **Sugaré & Co** remains a central figure in Leeds and our only ranked individual for the North East. His firm maintains a solid reputation for general crime, with a specialism in road traffic matters. **Howells** receives a substantial volume of youth crime, prison, and public order work. **Irwin Mitchell's** criminal department is regarded by competitors as a *"good solid outfit"* although better known on the fraud front. In Leeds, **Graham Stowe, Bateson** and **Levi & Co** maintain a strong position for local work, followed closely by the *"popular"* **Henry Hyams & Co**. **David Gray & Co**, leaders in Newcastle, show a *"commitment to legal aid"* and act frequently in sexual offences and charges brought against overseas nationals. **Max Gold & Co**, *"the first name in Hull"* have a *"reputation as specialists in the field"* with particular experience in drug smuggling cases. Other Hull firms to be recommended are **Gosschalks** and **Myer Wolff & Manley**.

SCOTLAND

CRIME • Scotland
❶ **Beltrami & Co** Glasgow
❷ **George Mathers & Co** Aberdeen
Gilfedder & McInnes Edinburgh
Gordon & Smyth Glasgow
McCourts Edinburgh
More & Co Edinburgh
Ross Harper & Murphy WS Glasgow
❸ **Adams** Edinburgh
Blair & Bryden Greenock
Condies Perth
Gallen & Co Glasgow
Hall & Haughey Glasgow
HBM Sayers Glasgow
Levy & McRae Glasgow
Livingstone Browne Glasgow
McKay & Norwell WS Edinburgh
Ness Gallagher Wishew

Within each band, firms are listed alphabetically.

Beltrami & Co retains its top band position with **Joseph Beltrami** ranked as the pre-eminent criminal practitioner in Scotland, supported by the highly regarded **Murray Macara**. **Alexander Prentice, Douglas Main**, and

LEADING INDIVIDUALS	
❶ **BELTRAMI Joseph** Beltrami & Co	
❷ **DUFF Alistair** McCourts	**GILFEDDER Brian** Gilfedder & McInnes
MACARA Murray Beltrami & Co	**MAIN Douglas** McCourts
McINNES John Gilfedder & McInnes	**MORE George** More & Co
PRENTICE Alexander McCourts	**SMYTH Maurice** Gordon & Smyth

*See **Profiles** on page 275*

Alistair Duff of **McCourts** are well known for their defence of Lockerbie suspects. **Maurice Smyth** is noted for his advocacy work and ensures **Gordon & Smyth**'s place in the tables. **George More** at **More & Co** maintains his hold on the Edinburgh market. Also in Edinburgh, partners **Brian Gilfedder** and **John McInnes** run a well respected criminal practice at **Gilfedder & McInnes**. **Ross Harper & Murphy** continue to draw recommendations while **George Mathers & Co** remain the leading firm in Aberdeen.

Adams has just undergone a merger that is expected to boost their profile in the field. **McKay & Norwell WS** also retain a wide measure of support. A number of Glasgow firms were rated for comprehensive criminal practices, including **Gallen & Co, Hall & Haughey, HBM Sayers,** and **Livingstone Browne.** Also in Glasgow, **Levy McRae** enters our leaders lists this year. In other areas, **Ness Gallagher** in Motherwell, **Condies** in Perth, and **Blair & Bryden** in Greenock were seen to excel in criminal defence work.

NORTHERN IRELAND

CRIME • Northern Ireland
❶ **Babington & Croasdaile** Londonderry
Bogue and McNulty Belfast
Brendan Kearney Kelly & Co Derry
Donnelly & Wall Belfast
Flynn & McGettrick Belfast
J.J. Rice Belfast
Madden & Finucane Belfast
McClenahan Crossey & Co Coleraine
Millar Shearer & Black Cookstown
Richard Monteith Portadown
Trevor Smyth & Co Belfast

Within each band, firms are listed alphabetically.

A steady decrease in terrorist activity is changing the nature of criminal practice in Northern Ireland. Many firms which have historically acted in high profile terrorism cases such as **Donnelly & Wall** and **Madden & Finucane** are turning to general criminal petit sessions work, although the latter firm is still heavily involved in the ongoing Saville Inquiry. While the work may be changing, the names remain the same and our Northern Ireland leaders tables stand unaltered. **Bogue and McNulty** are seen to handle a large volume of work in Belfast, with **Trevor Smyth and Co** and **Flynn & McGettrick** also recommended. In Derry, **Babington & Croasdaile** and **Brendan Kearney Kelly & Co** receive strong recommendations. **J.J. Rice** is a newcomer to the lists. Other featured firms include **McClenahan Crossey & Co, Millar Shearer & Black,** and **Richard Monteith**.

LEADERS IN CRIME

ALMOND, Richard John
Victor Lissack & Roscoe, London (020) 7240 2010
Richardalmond@victorlissack.co.uk
Specialisation: Managing partner, partner in crime department. Main areas of practice, serious crime, white collar fraud, extradition and general crime.
Prof. Memberships: L.C.C.SA, CLSA, Westminster Law Society, Law Society Mental Health Panel (1998).
Career: Qualified 1984, at *Victor Lissack and Roscoe,* partner (1988). LCCSA Committee since 1993. LCCSA News Letter Editor since 1995. LAB (CLS) Area Committee since 1995.
Publications: Editor 'The London Advocate' since 1995. Submissions to House of Lords European Affairs Sub Committee on EEC Corpus Juris fraud against Budget (Tampere) provision. Various submissions/responses as sole/co-author to Government and Law Commission White Papers on Criminal/fraud topics.

ASHFORD, Mark
Taylor Nichol, London (020) 7272 8336

BECKFORD, Trevor
Beckford & Co, Norwich (01603) 660 000

BELTRAMI, Joseph
Beltrami & Co, Glasgow (0141) 221 0981
Specialisation: Consultant and Solicitor advocate specialising in criminal law. Instructed in more than 350 murder and manslaughter cases. Acted in the only two Scottish Royal Pardons this century on matters of substantive crime–Maurice Swanson in 1975 and Pat Meehan in 1976. In each case compensation was awarded. Also acted in the cases of W.S.Ellis, A.Thompson, D. Boyle, Howard Wilson, Johnny Ramensky, James Boyle and Alan Hasson. First solicitor advocate to appear before the Criminal Appeal Court (1993) and the first to lead in a successful murder acquittal (June 1994). Author of 'The Defender' (1980), 'Beltrami's Tales of the Suspected' (1988), 'A Deadly Innocence' (1989) and 'A Scottish Childhood' (1998). Has written numerous articles for 'New Law Journal', 'Scottish Law Journal'.
Prof. Memberships: Solicitor Advocate, Solicitor to the Supreme Court.
Career: Qualified in 1953. Detachment Commander in the Intelligence Corps 1954-56. Founding Partner of *Beltrami & Co*, established in 1958.
Personal: Born 15th May 1932. Educated at St. Aloysius's College, Glasgow and Glasgow University. Recreations include bowls, soccer, snooker and writing. Lives in Bothwell.

BIRD, Jeremy S.
Hugh James Ford Simey, Blackwood (01495) 223328
Specialisation: All areas of criminal work undertaken, particularly legal aid work and agency. Duty solicitor scheme administrator.
Prof. Memberships: The Law Society.

BOYLE, John
John Boyle and Co, Redruth (01209) 213507

BROUDIE, Robert
R.M. Broudie & Co, Liverpool (0151) 227 1429

BROWN, Robert T.J.
Darlington & Parkinson, Acton (020) 8752 8910
Specialisation: Practice encompasses all areas of criminal defence work, mainly in London but also in the Provinces.
Prof. Memberships: Law Society, Central and South Middlesex Law Society, Secretary of the London Criminal Courts Solicitors Association.
Career: Qualified 1983, Partner *Darlington and Parkinson*1985. Has lectured on Criminal Justice in England and overseas.
Personal: Educated at Cambridge University. Resides West London. Interests include literature, painting and sport.

BUTLER, Michael
Claude Hornby & Cox, London (020) 7437 8873
Specialisation: Criminal defence work. His practice covers all aspects of criminal law, with emphasis on serious crime, including drugs importation and other large-scale drugs-related cases, substantial frauds, paedophile/sexual offences and murder. Has successfully represented defendants in a number of recent high-profile and nationally reported cases. Regularly appears as an advocate in Magistrates Courts, Crown Courts, courts martial, and professional disciplinary proceedings.
Prof. Memberships: Law Society.
Career: Qualified 1992. Partner 1997.
Personal: Born in 1965. Lives in London.

CADMAN, Peter H.
Russell-Cooke, Potter & Chapman, London (020) 7405 6566
cadmanp@russell-cooke.co.uk
Specialisation: Highly exerienced solicitor. Personal expertise in defence preparation in cases of murder, money laundering, fraud, extradition and terrorism. Preparation of applications to the Court of Appeal and to the European Court of Human Rights Application and Advocacy in Discretionary Lifer Panel Hearings and Judicial Review proceedings with regard to Prison Law. Regular appearances as advocate in Disciplinary Proceedings either on behalf of the professional body or the individual respondent.
Prof. Memberships: Member of LCCSA. Current Treasurer and past President of the South London Law Society. Solicitor/Advocate with Higher Court Rights of Audience in all Civil & Criminal Courts.
Career: Qualified 1976. Partner 1977.

COLE, Michael
Cole's, Norwich (01603) 441 111

CUNNINGHAM, Martin S.
Cunninghams, Manchester (0161) 833 1600
Specialisation: Purely Criminal Defence work, specialising in the defence of people charged with serious crime. He is currently instructed by various defendants in a number of high profile cases in the North West, Lancashire and the Midlands, involving gangland shootings and related crime. He also specialises in white collar crime involving Inland Revenue investigations, VAT fraud and currently is defending in what has been described by the Prosecution as one of Manchester's largest serious fraud cases. He also continues to practice regularly in the local Magistrates' Courts.
Career: Educated as an external student from London University obtaining an LLB Honours in 1979. Admitted 15 July 1982. Set up in practice in August 1985 as *Martin Cunningham & Co Solicitors* in Moss Side, Manchester, where he practised until the firm moved to Central Manchester in 1995. The firm expanded rapidly, changing its name to *Cunninghams Solicitors* where he is Senior Partner. His career aim is to continue to provide a much needed service in the field in which he practices.
Prof. Memberships: Law Society, Manchester Law Society, Criminal Law Solicitors Association, Manchester Duty Solicitor Scheme.
Personal: Aged 45. Married with three children. Leisure interests include classical music, walking, fine wines and Manchester United. Lives between homes in Cheshire and Derbyshire. ambitions: To walk the Cuillins, the Knoydart, and the Monroe Mountain ranges.

CUTTLE, M. Barry
M.B. Cuttle & Co, Manchester (0161) 835 2050
Specialisation: Criminal Law. Appointed as solicitor in the Strangeways prison riots to negotiate between prisoners and officers towards ending of individual personal disputes in 1990.
Prof. Memberships: Law Society.
Career: Qualified in January 1963. Worked with the Crown Prosecution Service in Manchester. Promoted to new CPS Department in charge of Bolton Borough, thereafter in Lanchashire County Prosecutions. Formed *MB Cuttle & Co.* 1972. Thereafter dealing with much crime of all levels, much fraud conspiricy murders. Now senior partner of *MB Cuttle & Co.*
Personal: Educated at Worksop College in Nottinghamshire. Married with 2 children and upon leaving school at Worksop, became heavily involved in swimming, particularly long distance and raising many thousands for good causes; all sports; became an officer in the Cheshire RGT. Shena (wife) teacher and past president of Soroptimist International Manchester Club; Louise (daughter) bar clerk; Fraser (son) has joined the practice and is an officer with the Cheshire RGT.

DRAYCOTT, Shaun
Draycott Gibbon Moore & Wright, Manchester (0161) 833 1333
Specialisation: Joined the specialist criminal law firm *Maidments* in October 1993. Appointed a partner in 1996. Substantial experience in all types of serious crime with an emphasis upon murder, manslaughter, serious robbery and drug importation. Set up *Draycott, Gibbon, Moore & Wright (inc. Mark D. Browne) Solicitors*, a specialist criminal law firm, on 1.6.98. Duty Solicitor qualified: familiar with all areas of criminal law, practice and procedure.
Prof. Memberships: Member of the Law Society and the Criminal Law Solicitors Association.
Career: Educated Stockport and LLB Manchester Metropolitan University.

DUFF, Alistair
McCourts, Edinburgh (0131) 225 6555

EDWARDS, Anthony
T.V. Edwards, London (020) 7790 7000

FANSON, David
Douglas & Partners, Bristol (0117) 955 2663

FISHER, Ian
Overbury Steward Eaton & Woolsey, Norwich (01603) 610481
Specialisation: All areas of Criminal Defence practice, in particular serious violent crime, major drugs offences and serious fraud. Last year I represented a

police officer charged with sexual offences against colleagues and a fellow solicitor prosecuted for substantial dishonesty offences, both cases attracting national publicity.
Prof. Memberships: Chairman of local Duty Solicitor Scheme.
Career: Qualified in1988; post-qualification experience in general litigation followed by a year with Crown Prosecution Service. With *Overburys* for the past ten years and currently Head of the Criminal Department; a partner on the firms Management Committee.
Personal: Law graduate; married with two children. In limited leisure time enjoys sport, literature, mountaineering and deep-sea diving.

FISHER, Michael
Christian Fisher, London (020) 7831 1750

FREEMAN, Nicholas
Freeman & Co, Manchester 0161 236 7007

GILFEDDER, Brian
Gilfedder & McInnes, Edinburgh (0131) 553 4333

GOULBORN, Caroline
Fletchers, Nottingham (0115) 959 9550

GREEN, Christopher
Geoffrey Williams & Christopher Green (Solicitor Advocates), Cardiff (029) 2034 3377

GREGO, Kevin
Parker & Grego, Birmingham (0121) 633 3031
Specialisation: Serious crime and child care. Successfully disposing of serious cases by ensuring the prosecutionobserve the rules upon proper disclosure.
Prof. Memberships: Law society, Child Care Panel Member.
Career: Qualified 1980, founding partner present firm. Partner 1988 - present.

GRIFFITHS, Julian
Barrie Ward & Julian Griffiths, Nottingham (0115) 941 2622

GROGAN, Peter
Jones Maidment Wilson incorporating Hatton Scates Horton, Manchester (0161) 832 8087

HALLAM, Richard S.
Claude Hornby & Cox, London (020) 7437 8873
Partner in Criminal Litigation Department since 1989.
Specialisation: Crime. Has substantial experience of conducting cases in the Magistrates Courts, Higher Criminal Courts and before Courts Martial in UK and Germany. Normally instructed as a defence advocate, but has experience of prosecuting for the CPS and will prosecute privately for individuals or organisations. Nationwide experience of prosecuting video piracy cases. Defends in professional disciplinary proceedings. Has successfully represented defendants facing allegations of murder, terrorism, large-scale drugs importation and fraud, but equally interested in defending clients charged with less serious offences.
Prof. Memberships: City of Westminster Law Society, London Criminal Courts Solicitors Association, Legal Aid Practitioners Group.
Personal: Born 24th April 1948. Educated at the King's School, Canterbury and Oxford University. Lives in London.

HASLAM, Mark
Burton Copeland, London (020) 7430 2277
Partner in Criminal Litigation Department.
Specialisation: Practice covers all areas of criminal defence work including white collar, large scale drugs cases, serious public order offences and murder and manslaughter cases. Acted successfully in a number of substantial prosecutions brought by Customs and Excise including Charington and Others. Has experience of Court Martial Proceedings and defended Christine Dryland, the wife of Major Dryland, in a highly publicised murder trial in Germany. Also specialises in motoring cases including excess alcohol, careless driving and speeding. Regular broadcaster and lecturer on criminal legal affairs on radio, television and at seminars and conferences.
Prof. Memberships: President of the London Criminal Court Solicitors Association from November 2000. Member of Forces Law, The Criminal Law Committee of the Law Society and the National Duty Solicitor Committee. Sits as a solicitor assessor in the High Court in taxation matters.
Career: Qualified in 1981, worked at *Claude Hornby & Cox* from 1979-1993 and *Magrath & Co* from 1993-1997. Partner at *Burton Copeland* from January 1998.
Personal: Born 16 June 1957. Attended Wellington College, Berkshire 1971-1976 and Pembroke College, Cambridge, 1976 to 1979 (MA). Leisure interests include cricket, horse racing and the theatre. Lives in Cobham in Surrey.

HEWITT, Stephen
Fisher Meredith, London (020) 7622 4468
Specialisation: Managing partner and head of department of one of the largest and most successful criminal defence teams in London. Wide range of criminal defence and associated civil liberties work including advocacy with lengthy experience of major homicide cases, sexual offences and drug trafficking cases as well as a range of business crime experiance. Specialist in sexual offence cases as well as acting for mentally disturbed defendants and undertaking complex appeals to the Court of Appeal. Lecturer on aspects of criminal practice, legal aid franchising, contracting and practice management. Co-author of 'Legal Aid Practice Manual', on committee of London firms negotiating with Legal Aid Board on crime block contracting and on national committee of LAPG.
Prof. Memberships: Law Society, London Criminal Courts Solicitors Association, Criminal Law Solicitors Association, Liberty, Justice.
Career: Qualified 1980. Joined *Fisher Meredith* as partner in 1986.
Personal: Born 14th November 1953. Lives in Brighton.

HICKMAN, Jane
Hickman & Rose, London (020) 7700 2211
Specialisation: Wide range of criminal defence work, particularly murder and serious crime. Creative strategist with particular skill in dealing with complex scientific and medical issues. Special interest in cases of lawyer negligence leading to miscarriages of justice. Writes and lectures on quality assurance in criminal defence firms.
Prof. Memberships: The Law Society, LCCSA, Legal Action Group.
Career: MA (First Class Hons) Edinburgh 1972, qualified 1977. Founded *Hickman & Rose* in 1991. MBA Nottingham Law School 2000. Special Adviser to Lord Justice Auld (Criminal Courts Review) in 2000.

HUBER, Bernard
Duthie Hart & Duthie, London (020) 8472 0138
Partner in Criminal Litigation Department.
Specialisation: Has a large and varied criminal law case load with daily advocacy. Involved in conducting prosecutions on behalf of the North East London Probation Service, London Borough of Barking and the Port of London Authority.
Prof. Memberships: London Criminal Courts Solicitors Association, West Essex Law Society, Child Care Panel, Duty Solicitor Schemes (Newham and Thames).
Career: Qualified in 1980 after articles at *Duthie Hart & Duthie*. Partner since 1982.
Personal: Born 30th October 1955. Educated at Leeds University (LL.B Hons, 1977). Leisure interests, most sports; playing and spectator. Lives in Wanstead, London.

HUTTON, Stuart
Huttons, Cardiff (029) 2037 8621
smch@huttons-solicitors.co.uk
Senior Partner. Criminal Department.
Specialisation: Has been primarily involved in criminal work for over 20 years. Also deals with child care, adoption and fostering. Has been on the Child Care Panel for over 10 years. Has handled some notable murder cases, including the high profile Tooze double Farmhouse murder and the acquittal of Jonathan Jones, another the subject of the 'Bloody Valentine' book, and 'vigilante' killing Penrhys, Rhondda, Mid Glamorgan. Has had continuing success in taking miscarriages of justice to the Court of Appeal. Former part time Chairman of Social Security Appeals tribunals. Has special interest in entertainment and media law.
Career: Qualified in 1975. With *Edwards Geldard* 1973-86 (as a Partner from 1976). Established own practice, *Hutton's*, in August 1986. The practice has a reputation for specialist litigation.
Personal: Born 21st October 1946. Lives in Cardiff.

JONES, Gwyn
Gamlins, Rhyl (01745) 343500
Consultant and Head of Crime and Licencing Unit.
Specialisation: Personally covers and supervises all aspects of serious cases from the outset to their conclusion for both individual and corporate clients. He has extensive experience in representing those charged with sexual abuse and drug trafficking offences and has recently successfully appeared in the Court of Appeal. He regularly appears in the Crown Court and disciplinary proceedings, mostly defending but occasionally prosecuting, both through the medium of English or Welsh. Appears frequently on TV and Radio as legal expert.
Prof. Memberships: Law Society.
Career: Qualified 1984. *Leo Abse & Cohen* 1982-86 (Partner from 1986). Became Higher Court Advocate in 1995. Joined *Gamlins* in 1996.
Personal: Born 22.07.1960. Chair Llamau Housing Society Ltd 1988-91. Duty Solicitor Committee Member. Interests: Travelling, eating out and mountain biking.

KEENAN, Andrew
Andrew Keenan & Co, London (020) 8659 0332

KELLY, Philip L.
Twitchen Musters & Kelly, Southend-on-Sea (01702) 339222
Specialisation: Solicitor Advocate specialising in all areas of Criminal Litigation with particular emphasis on international drugs importations, whites collar fraud, supergrass cases and acting on behalf of Police Officers. Has travelled to USA, West Indies and Pakistan to undertake enquires on behalf of defendants. Has represented defendants attracting national and international notoriety.
Prof. Memberships: Law Society, Criminal Law Solicitors Association, Association of Higher Court Advocates, London Criminal Courts Solicitors Association, Serious Fraud Panel.
Career: Admitted January 1980. Higher Court Advocate April 1994.
Personal: Born 22 February 1951. Avid supporter of Welsh Rugby. Family lives in Stebbing, Essex.

MACARA, J.D. Murray
Beltrami & Co, Glasgow (0141) 221 0981
Specialisation: Solicitor Advocate specialising in criminal law. Has appeared in all courts throughout Scotland. Has appeared in numerous cases in the High Court. In 1999 defended Harvey Good in cellular therapy trial.
Prof. Memberships: Society of Solicitors in the Supreme Court.
Career: Qualified in 1973. Partner in *Beltrami & Co* since 1975.
Personal: Born 22.7.49. Educated at Loretto School Musselburgh & Glasgow University. Interests: most sports, travel, dining out. Lives in Glasgow.

MACKEY, Michael
Burton Copeland, Manchester (0161) 834 7374
Specialisation: Criminal practitioner with experience in all aspects of criminal prosecutions, including road traffic and prosecutions by HSE and Trading Standards. For the past two decades has primarily been involved in the defence of the most serious criminal cases, including numerous murders, serial robbery and sexual offences. Substantial experience of major drug trafficking cases and criminal confiscation proceedings generally. Particular expertise in forensic aspects of investigations, including challenge of DNA evidence and scrutiny of medical expert statements, especially with reference to 'shaken baby' and child abuse prosecutions. Has been involved in many leading Appeal cases including McGarry (adverse inference) and lately, the case of Sally Clark.
Career: Admitted 1974; West Yorkshire County Prosecuting Solicitors' Office 1976; *Glaisyers*, Manchester 1976-80; *Crossley Mackey*, Manchester 1980-87; *Burton Copeland* 1987 to present.
Personal: De La Salle College, Leeds University. Aged 50, married and lives in Altrincham. Interests include music, astronomy and computers.

MAIDMENT, Allan
Maidments, Manchester (0161) 834 0008
Specialisation: Senior Partner of *Maidments* Solicitors. Worked exclusively in Crime and Commercial Fraud. Founded *Maidments* in 1993 as a specialist criminal law practice with particular emphasis on Serious Crime and Commercial Fraud. Developed the firm into one of the country's leading criminal law practices with three offices in Manchester and offices in Birmingham, Liverpool, London, Bolton, Bristol and Leeds.
Prof. Memberships: A member of the Law Society and Local Societies in Manchester and Birmingham. Former member of the Manchester Duty Solicitor Committee. Member of the Criminal Law Solicitors Association. Member of the Serious Fraud Panel.
Career: Educated in Scotland, LLB Leeds University. Qualified in 1976.

MAIN, Douglas
McCourts, Edinburgh (0131) 225 6555

MASTERS, Peter
Thomson Webb Corfield, Cambridge (01223) 578070

MATHER, Bertie J.M.
Elliot Mather, Matlock (01629) 584885

MCINNES, John
Gilfedder & McInnes, Edinburgh (0131) 553 4333

MERRIAM, Joy
Joy Merriam & Co, London (020) 8980 7171
Specialisation: Senior Partner of an East London Criminal Practice established in 1987. Substantial expertise in all areas of criminal law and attributes her firm's success and large client following to giving equal attention to all cases whether involving major crime or not. Works with a professional and dedicated team of criminal lawyers.The firm is a member of the Serious Fraud Panel.
Prof. Memberships: Member of the Law Society, Committee member of the LCCSA and Thames Duty Solicitor Committee.

MILES, Anthony
Bobbetts Mackan, Bristol (0117) 929 9001

MILNER, Henry
Henry Milner & Co, London (020) 7831 9944
Principal of firm.
Specialisation: Sole area of practice is criminal defence work. Has twenty-five years specialist experience defending in serious criminal cases of all types. High Court bail applications a speciality. Defence solicitor in all Brinks Mat robbery trials and many other important trials of the 1980s and 1990s. Subject of an interview regarding his particular specialist criminal practice in the Sunday Times News Review (September 6th, 1998).
Prof. Memberships: Law Society.
Career: Qualified in 1975. Established *Henry Milner & Co.* in 1978.
Personal: Born1947. Holds a law degree from London School of Economics. Leisure interests include bridge, football and traditional American music. Lives in London.

MORE, George M.
More & Co, Edinburgh (0131) 557 1110

MURPHY, Shaun
Duthie Hart & Duthie, London (020) 8472 0138
Partner in Criminal Litigation Department. Assistant Crown Court Recorder.
Specialisation: Criminal law specialist. Advocate in criminal proceedings on a regular basis in courts throughout the London area. Qualified as a Higher Courts Advocate. Also a Privy Council Agent. Other areas of practice are care proceedings and civil litigation. Involved in prosecution work on behalf of North East London Probation Service, London Borough of Barking and the Port of London Authority. Member of Duty Solicitor Schemes (Newham and Thames) and Child Care Panel. Member of Legal Aid Board Area Committee.
Prof. Memberships: London Criminal Courts Solicitors Association, Criminal Law Solicitors Association, West Essex Law Society.
Career: Qualified in 1979 after articles at *Duthie Hart & Duthie*. Became a Partner in 1982.
Personal: Born 10th June 1956. Educated at Warwick University 1974-77 (LL.B Hons). School Governor. Enjoys most sports. Lives in Wanstead, London.

MUSTERS, Patrick H.A.
Twitchen Musters & Kelly, Southend-on-Sea (01702) 339222
pmusters@tmksols.co.uk
Specialisation: Solicitor Advocate specialising in all areas of criminal litigation especially serious crime (murder, armed robbery and sexual offences), prison mutiny and escape, large drug importations and serious white collar fraud. Cases have attracted national and international notoriety. Substantial experience on advice on appeal against conviction.
Prof. Memberships: Law Society, Criminal Law Solicitors Association, Association of Higher Court Advocates, London Criminal Courts Solicitors Association, Serious Fraud Panel, British Academy of Forensic Scientists. Member of Legal Services Commission Funding Committee.
Career: Admitted June 1978. Higher Court Advocate April 1994.
Personal: Born 20 July 1952. Educated Allhallows School, Lyme Regis. Interests include Law Society Golf Club, running and skiing. Consultant to both BBC Radio Essex and Essex Radio on criminal law matters.

NICHOL, James
Taylor Nichol, London (020) 7272 8336

NICHOLLS, Simon J.
Belmores, Norwich (01603) 617947

NOTT, Colin
Hallinan, Blackburn, Gittings & Nott, London (020) 7233 3999
Specialisation: Specialist in criminal Defence Work, Extradition and Judicial review.
Prof. Memberships: LLB (Hons).
Career: Qualified 1978. Sole practitioner 1979-82. Joined *Hallinan Blackburn Gittings & Nott* as a Partner–1982.
Personal: Born 27.6.52. Educated Weymouth Grammar School, London University. Interests: sport, rugby and football in particular, theatre and travel.

NOVY, Rod
Thanki Novy Taube, London (020) 7833 5800
Specialisation: Head of Criminal Department. Workload comprising first tier criminal cases, particularly homicide and drugs offences. Has wide experience of handling complex and weighty cases. Specialist knowlege of Triad crime in the Vietnamese community in the UK and expert knowledge of Commission Rogatoire process. Has travelled widely on behalf of clients. Fought the first Anti-Social Behaviour Order application brought by the Metropolitan Police, arguing legal status in the context of the Human Rights Act 1988. Growing extradition practice.
Prof. Memberships: LCCSA, Law Society.
Career: Co-founded the practice with Girish Thanki

and Martin Taube in 1992. Educated in Langley, Berkshire and University of Southampton.
Personal: Married with two children. Leisure interests include juggling, philosophy, gardening.

NUNN, Stephen
Stephens & Scown, Exeter (01392) 210700
Specialisation: Criminal law specialist in all aspects of defence work, with substantial experience of trial advocacy and Youth Court. Partner in charge of firm's criminal litigation departments. Caseload ranging from murder to summary cases. Acted in large MOD land fraud conspiracy and other white collar cases. Granted Higher Court rights in June 1994, experience of jury trials.
Prof. Memberships: Area Criminal Justice Liaison Committee, Magistrates & Crown Court user groups, council member Devon & Exeter Law Society (past chairman litigation committee). Committee Member of Exeter & Devon duty solicitor schemes. 24 hour and court duty solicitor.
Career: Qualified 1981. 1979-85 *Trump & Partners*, Bristol. 1985 to date, *Stephens & Scown*. Partner, 1990. Joint Winner of Law Society centenary 'My favourite Solicitor' competition for pro bono work in high profile miscarriage of justice case. Regular television appearances on this and other legal issues.
Personal: Born 24.12.55. Married with children. Lives in Exeter. Leisure interests include cinema and computer technology, including programming, Internet and games.

O'MAY, Neil
Bindman & Partners, London (020) 7833 4433
Specialisation: Wide range of criminal defence work from murder and terrorist cases to more general crime. All types of serious fraud (including SFO cases), particularly those involving professionals (solicitors and accountants) as defendants. Particular expertise in large-scale public order arrests and multi-defendant trials. Specialist in cases involving complex scientific and expert evidence including computer and internet crime. Extensive experience in defending journalists on civil liberties issues (the 'AUP' trial in Manchester) and other "professionals in trouble" (including professional body disciplinary proceedings). Defending against top prosecution teams, including the Anti-Terrorist Squad (in the Israeli Embassy bombing case and the IRA mortar attack on Heathrow airport) and special Branch on Official Secrets Actions cases. Experience in the defence of complex drugs cases and sex abuse cases. Fresh evidence appeals in the Court of Appeal and investigations of miscarriages of justice. Inquests including deaths in police custody and judicial review. Supervisor status for the Legal Services Commission Serious Fraud Panel of approved solicitors. Groundbreaking cases in the House of Lords (R v Doody & Others, R v Aziz & Others and Pinochet). Recent involvement on behalf of Amnesty in the Pinochet case, Human Rights Act specialist. Writer, lecturer, and broadcaster on legal issues.
Prof. Memberships: Law Society, London Criminal Courts Solicitors Association, Criminal Law Solicitors Association.
Career: Qualified 1985. Joined *Bindman & Partners* as Head of Criminal Department in 1990.
Personal: Degree in Biochemistry, BSc (Hons). Londoner.

PEIRCE, Gareth
Birnberg Peirce & Partners, London
(020) 7911 0166

PETER, Charles
The Berkson Globe Partnership, Liverpool
(0151) 236 1234

POWELL, Greg
Powell Spencer & Partners, London
(020) 7624 8888
Specialisation: Criminal defence; especially murder, conspiracies to import and supply drugs, armed robbery. Magistrates Court advocacy. Acting for an increasing number of professional clients; accountants, doctors, estate agents, solicitors.
Prof. Memberships: Law Society, Haldane Society, Liberty.
Career: Qualified 1973. Degrees in Law (LSE) and Psychology (Birkbeck) and co-author of a Practical Guide to the Police and Criminal Evidence Act.

PRENTICE, Alexander
McCourts, Edinburgh (0131) 225 6555

PRESTON, Edward
Edward Fail Bradshaw & Waterson, London
(020) 7790 4032

PROWEL, Martyn
Martyn Prowel Solicitors, Cardiff (029) 2047 0909
mprowel@mped.globalnet.co.uk
See under Fraud, p.420

PURCELL, Michael
Purcell Parker, Birmingham (0121) 236 9781

ROSCOE, Robert
Victor Lissack & Roscoe, London (020) 7240 2010
robertroscoe@victorlissack.co.uk
Partner in crime department.
Specialisation: Main areas of practice are white collar fraud, serious criminal offences, extradition and general criminal practice.
Prof. Memberships: Law Society, City of Westminster Law Society, London Criminal Courts Solicitors' Association, Criminal Law Solicitors' Association.
Career: Qualified in 1976. Higher Courts (Criminal Proceedings) Qualification 1994. Joined *Victor Lissack & Roscoe* in 1969, becoming a Partner in 1978. Law Society Council Member 1992-1998; Chairman of Criminal Law Committee 1995-1998; LCCSA: President 1996-1997, Committee Member and Advocacy Training Officer 1983-93; Chairman of no. 14 Regional Duty Solicitor Committee (1991-1997), Legal Aid Board Costs Appeals Committee (1993-4).

ROSE, Timothy
Douglas & Partners, Bristol (0117) 955 2663

RYAN, Ian
Russell-Cooke, Potter & Chapman, London
(020) 8788 0005
ryani@russell-cooke.co.uk
Specialisation: Head of the criminal department leading a team of five fee earners; deals with the full range of criminal defence work but specialises in larger and more complex cases including murder, armed robbery, sexual offences, drugs cases, extradition, and all types of fraud including VAT fraud and diversion frauds. Has a particular interest in cases involving forensic or medical issues. Successfully defended Colin Stagg and has been involved in a number of other high profile cases that have attracted national attention. More recently has specialised in representing professional people (particularly solicitors) in criminal and disciplinary proceedings. Solicitor Advocate in the Crown Court and regular appearances as an advocte at professional disciplinary tribunals.
Prof. Memberships: Member of the LCCSA.
Career: Qualified 1987. Partner from 1995. Head of department 2000.

SAUNDERS, James
Saunders & Co, London (020) 7404 2828
Senior Partner.
Specialisation: Criminal Law; Legal Aid Franchise and Private Client. Covers all aspects of Criminal Law, particularly complex and heavy trials including fraud, (Member LSC Fraud panel), serial murder, drugs, sexual offences, robbery, official secrets and civil liberties. Also deals with scientific, medical and other expert issues; DNA, computers, firearms, confiscation of assets, motoring and London Agent matters.
Career: Articled at the North Kensington Neighbourhood Law Centre. Qualified 1972. Established *Saunders & Co* in 1974.
Personal: Born 1948. Attended King Edward VII School, Sheffield and University of Leicester (LLB).

SINCLAIR, Franklin
Tuckers, Manchester (0161) 233 4321
Senior partner.
Specialisation: In overall control of large criminal practice dealing in all aspects of criminal defence work. Particular specialisation as an advocate defending the rights of clients in a robust manner and dealing with many serious cases, including extensive involvement in preparation from the outset of a case to its conclusion. Has dealt with numerous murder cases and specialises, particularly, in large scale drugs importation and armed robbery cases. Has previously dealt with the first case involving challenge to D.N.A. evidence which initially was successful at the Court of Appeal.
Prof. Memberships: Manchester Law Society. Chairman of Criminal Law Solicitors' Association (C.L.S.A.).
Career: Qualified 1982. Partner with Barry Tucker in *Tuckers Solicitors* since 1984.
Personal: Manchester Grammer School; Manchester University; College of Law, Chester. Married with three children. Interests include golf, environmental issues. Born 28th June 1958. Lives in Cheshire.

SMYTH, Maurice T.
Gordon & Smyth, Glasgow (0141) 332 5705

SPENCER, Richard
Powell Spencer & Partners, London
(020) 7624 8888
Specialisation: A Criminal Law Specialist for over 20 years covering the whole range of defence work, but particularly murder and possession of cannabis offences. Excellent Magistrates Courts defence advocate practising throughout the London area.

STUDDERT, Mark
Hodge Jones & Allen, London (020) 7482 1974
Specialisation: Partner in large franchised criminal department dealing with wide range of offences. Own specialisation–homicide, drug importation, fraud.
Prof. Memberships: Member Liberty, Haldane Society, Prisoners Advice Service. Organiser and administrator of Highbury and Old Street Duty Solic-

itor scheme. Committee member London Criminal Courts Solicitors' Association
Career: Qualified 1979. Joined *Hodge Jones & Allen* 1985, partner 1987.
Personal: Lives in Stoke Newington with partner and young son. Interests: film, popular culture, food.

SUGARÉ, Anthony
Sugaré & Co, Leeds (0113) 244 6978
Senior partner and founder of firm 1974.
Specialisation: Experienced advocate specialising in criminal and road traffic matters. Recommended by leading motoring organisation. Provides representation for defendants in all areas of criminal law, both legal aid and private. Wide expertise in representing sportsmen and sporting associations.
Prof. Memberships: President of the Leeds Law Society; Member of the Leeds Duty Solicitor Committee; Chairman of Solicitors Representatives on the Leeds Court Users Group.
Career: Qualified in 1970. Founded and became senior partner of *SugarÈ & Co.* in 1974.
Personal: Born 16th July 1943. Attended Leeds Grammar School and Manchester University. Leisure pursuits include rugby league, golf and horse racing. Lives in Leeds.

TAYLOR, Carolyn S.
Taylor Nichol, London (020) 7272 8336

THANKI, Girish
Thanki Novy Taube, London (020) 7833 5800
Specialisation: Wide range of criminal defence and civil liberties work including murder, armed robberies and white collar crime with considerable experience of handling complex and weighty cases. Specialist knowledge of forensics and scientific issues. Active extradition practice with particular emphasis on the USA. Recent case involved arguing fairness of trial for black defendants in the State of Missouri. Judicial reviews and appellate work including the House of Lords and the Privy Council.
Prof. Memberships: LCCSA, BAFS, Medico-Legal Society, IBA, Liberty, Justice (Criminal Justice Panel Member), Prisoners' Advisory Service, Inquest, Law Society.
Career: Co-founded the practice with Rod Novy and Martin Taube in 1992. Educated Dame Alice Owen's School and University of East Anglia.
Personal: Lives in London with barrister wife and two children. Leisure interests confined to food, wine, travelling and armchair politics and cricket.

TOMLINSON, Kevin
Kieran & Co, Worcester (01905) 28635

VENTERS, June
Venters Reynolds, London (020) 7839 2373
j.venters@ventersreynolds.co.uk
Specialisation: The two main areas of specialisation are General Crime and Public Law Child Care. CRIME: Representation in all areas of Criminal Law. Most notable cases include sexual offences cases involving a referral from the Home Secretary resulting in an eventual re-trial and acquittal; large scale vat fraud; large scale conspiracy to rob which was a well publicised "yardie" case and conspiracy to defraud invoving a large scale national football scam. CHILD CARE: Serious and complex cases involving High Court advocacy. One such case forming a Court of Appeal Law Report on the rules of disclosure.
Prof. Memberships: Honourary Treasurer & Junior Vice President of the London Criminal Courts Solicitors Association; Regional Chairman of the South Eastern Legal Aid Committee; Law Society accredited trainer; Grays Inn Advocacy Trainer; Member of the Child Care Panel and Duty Solicitor, Assessor for the Childcare Panel
Career: Grammar school education; Qualified as a solicitor in 1984 and since that date has specialised in Crime and Child Care. Became Equity partner in a Soutn East London practice in 1986 and in 1991 commenced *Venters & Co. Venters & Co* has grown from a sole practice to a partnership employing in excess of 35. *Venters & Co* was formed to help local families improve their situation through the practical and prompt application of the law. The firm is now well respected. It acquired a legal aid franchise in 1996 and is currently participating in the Criminal Block Contract pilot scheme. In 1994 published a book on standard letters and forms for the criminal practitioner. In 1996 was the subject of a BBC1 documentary entitled 'Law Women' which focused on the life of a criminal lawyer. Since then has made various television and radio appearances. In November 1998 presented a speech to a central London Conference of the subject of "Legal Aid Block Contracting" which was video linked to America and has written an article for LAG on the same subject which is due to be published in August. In 1998 appointed Assistant Recorder. Appointed Recorder 2000
Personal: Reading; keep fit; theatre; music; walking the dogs and socialising with friends and family.

WARBOYS, Kevin
Copleys, St. Ives (01480) 464515

WARD, Barrie A.
Barrie Ward & Julian Griffiths, Nottingham (0115) 941 2622

WILLIAMS, Ian
Robertsons, Cardiff (029) 20237777

ZANI, John
Whitelock & Storr, London (020) 7242 8612
Specialisation: White collar fraud, extraditions, drugs offences & general crime. Successful extradition appeals Div. Court. (Cavallo v. Govt. of Italy 1996) and (Barone v. Govt. of Italy 1997) and (Div. Court Judicial Review R v. Cropper ex parte City of London Magistrates' Court May 1999) and (R v. Baxter murder retrial acquittal 1999) and (Urru v. Govt. of Italy May 2000) and ongoing extradition appeal to House of Lords (Kumar v. Govt. of Germany). Successful Court of Appeal high profile fraud case R v. Lombardi and Others June 2000.
Prof. Memberships: British Italian Law Association Committee Member. A.I.J.A. Member; Higher Courts Advocate (Crime).
Career: Highgate (Public) School; Qualified as solicitor 1977; Acting Stipendiary Magistrate (Metropolitan) 1994 to date; Senior Partner of *Whitelock & Storr* since 1992.
Personal: Married. Fluent speaker of Italian, Spanish and French. Social interests: Football, cricket, theatre & the Arts.

CUSTOMS & EXCISE

Customs and Excise – National: 280; *Profiles*: 281

OVERVIEW: Practitioners have cited customs and excise work as an expanding area of business. Work has been generated both by the increasing number of investigations carried out by the prosecuting authories and the greater scope for appeal to the customs and excise tribunal. Burgeoning volumes of e-commerce are also raising issues of relevance to customs and excise lawyers – both due to the increased volumes of cross-border trade it entails and the often ambiguous VAT and customs status of internet-based knowledge services.

The firms themselves usually specialise in either advisory and technical roles, or white collar crime and civil litigation work; the nature of the practice is clarified in the editorial comment. The high volume of work in this area undertaken by the major accountancy firms also deserves recognition.

RESEARCH APPROVED BY BMRB: *For this edition,* Chambers' *researchers conducted 6083 interviews – 4408 with law firms, 598 with barristers and 1077 with clients.*

The validity of the research was scrutinised by BMRB International, who audited both the methodology and the results at our offices in July 2000. They interviewed Chambers' *researchers and cross-checked sample interviews. Details of the audit appear on page 7.*

CUSTOMS & EXCISE - NATIONAL

CUSTOMS & EXCISE • National	Ptnrs	Assts
❶ **Dechert** London	3	6
❷ **Baker & McKenzie** London	2	1
❸ **Berwin Leighton** London	1	1
Burton Copeland London, Manchester	2	6
KLegal London	1	3
Peters & Peters London	1	1
Russell Jones & Walker London	1	4
Tarlo Lyons London	3	2
❹ **Clifford Chance** London	2	3
DLA London	1	1
Irwin Mitchell Sheffield	1	3
Kingsley Napley London	2	2
Lovells London	1	1
McClure Naismith Glasgow	2	1
Pannone & Partners Manchester	2	2
Stephenson Harwood Lonon	2	-
Watson, Farley & Williams London	1	1

LEADING INDIVIDUALS	
❶ **CORNWELL-KELLY Malachy** Titmuss Sainer Dechert	
HART Andrew Baker & McKenzie	
❷ **HANMAN David** Russell Jones & Walker	
❸ **GERRARD Neil** DLA	**KENYON Michael** Burton Copeland
HODGKINSON Milly Berwin Leighton	**WHITE Jeremy** KLegal

Within each band, firms are listed alphabetically *See **Profiles** on page 281*

Dechert Still perceived as the top firm in the London market for its range and quality of customs and excise work. The highly regarded and *"technically expert"* **Malachy Cornwell-Kelly** heads a team of three people which has been recently been concentrating on back-duty claims, anti-dumping duty, and classification issues. Some work is carried out in collaboration with major City accountants. Cornwell-Kelly's team is complemented by a white collar crime unit which is equipped to deal with the overlap between alleged fraud and customs and excise issues.

Baker & McKenzie Another key customs and excise practice – whose reputation in this area rests largely on the presence of **Andrew Hart**, commended as *"on top of the field"* by one commentator. The firm specialises in non-contentious customs and duty advisory work, with a transfer pricing/valuation aspect. They do not do criminal defence work for non-commmercial clients. Their major recent clients include several large high-tech companies.

Berwin Leighton The *"increasingly business focused"* **Milly Hodgkinson** joined the firm from HM Customs & Excise in January 1999 and has worked to create a niche in e-commerce issues as they impact on customs and excise law. She has published in this area and is regarded as expert on it. The firm's major clients include multi-national retail companies such as Tesco.

Burton Copeland The firm is rated for its expertise in contentious and criminal matters. It has represented defendents following major NIS investigations that have led to prosecutions. One of several firms selected by the Customs & Excise solicitors office to represent their lawyers in front of the Butler enquiry, which is investigating the collapse of a major criminal investigation. The firm also undertakes customs and excise work from its Manchester office, where **Michael Kenyon** has been recommended as a *"safe pair of hands."* Kenyon has particular expertise in handling delicate NIS investigations.

KLegal The legal arm of KPMG has set up a trade and customs group comprised of three people, headed by **Jeremy White**, who is hotly tipped for the depth of his technical knowledge. The department advises other law firms as well as general clients. They specialise in classification disputes, trade barriers and international trade preference regulations – with reference to WTO and OECD directives. The firm deals both with civil and criminal cases, although so far it is noted more for its advisory and civil expertise.

Peters & Peters Noted for its litigation and criminal fraud work, the practice is thought to have a strong team. Prominent recent cases have involved allegations of diversion fraud and carousel fraud. The firm does not advise on export/import procedures or classification. Litigation and criminal work rather than advisory consultation is the core of this practice.

Russell Jones and Walker The *"formidable"* and *"expert"* **David Hanman** has started to build an impressive client base at Russell Jones Walker, where he heads a new tax and investigation unit. The unit has worked on allegations of sanctions busting, and diversion and import quota disputes.

Tarlo Lyons The firm, reckoned to be *"going places"* by one of its peers, has gained a strong reputation for its white collar crime and litigation work. The practice has worked in collaboration with HM Customs and Excise and CJA Receivers on restraint orders issued by the Customs Authority.

Alleged diversion frauds and contentious grey market imports have also been referred to the practice.

Clifford Chance This international firm is another that deals in customs and excise work mainly as an adjunct to its VAT work. It has advised large banks on the duty implications of financial restructuring being carried out at cigarette manufacturers and large brewers. The leverage enjoyed by such a large practice, rather than the reputation of individual lawyers specialising in this field, warrants the firms inclusion in the tables.

DLA Although there is a perception that the firm's Manchester office was hit by the departure of David Hanman, the London office continues to attract major corporate custom due to the expertise of **Neil Gerrard**, who acted for executive defendents implicated during the huge Anchor Butter case in 1998. Gerrard often fields referrals from the big five accountants, who have commended his experience in contentious customs and excise matters.

Irwin Mitchell The Sheffield office has been commended for its white collar crime work, and is best known for its work on the protracted arms-to-Iraq affair. The practice continues to work on contentious arms exports and it has also defended against prosecutions for drug smuggling bought by Customs and Excise.

Kingsley Napley This well respected firm conducts civil litigation work but is more noted for its white collar crime work. The practice fields referrals from smaller accountants and acts for small to medium sized businesses, freight forwarders, retailers and restaurateurs.

Lovells Commercial and tax expertise are brought to bear on the firm's involvement in a number of duty free and VAT matters. Mixture of contentious and non-contentious work has included appearances before the VAT and Duties Tribunals as well as the High Court.

McClure Naismith The practice has advised US high-tech companies on transfer pricing inquiries and has represented distillers in relation to excise duty matters. It has established itself in Scotland as the only practice with specialist knowledge of customs and excise law.

Pannone & Partners The practice has gained a reputation for its work on alleged diversion frauds, and VAT frauds. Their specialist business crime unit has been strengthened by recent arrivals, and the team undertakes both criminal work and civil litigation.

Stephenson Harwood The firm has gained a reputation for the white collar crime work carried out by its solicitor-advocate senior partner. Recent work has involved classification disputes, representing a defendant accused of duty evasion on spirits, and representing a defendant accused of the illegal import of prohibited goods.

Watson Farley & Williams The firm does no criminal work, but undertakes advisory work on indirect tax matters. Diversion disputes and some civil litigation are also dealt with.

LEADERS IN CUSTOMS & EXCISE

CORNWELL-KELLY, Malachy

Dechert, London (020) 7583 5353
malachy.cornwellkelly@dechertEU.com
Partner and Head of the International Trade and Customs Practice in London.
Specialisation: Negotiates and handles disputes with Customs and Excise and IBEA on all VAT, customs and excise duty matters. Work covers investigation cases, tariff classification, valuation and transfer pricing issues, origin, duty preference, export rebates, CAP questions, import and export licensing, anti-dumping duties, and appeals to and appearances before the VAT and Duties Tribunal and the European Court. Cases have included agricultural levy disputes and CAP export refunds, tariff classification, origin disputes, customs duty panel, VAT liability, Single Market excise liabilities, collateral insurance rights, judicial review of Customs & Excise and United Nations trade sanctions. Author of 'European Community Law', 2nd edition, a regular column in CCH Indirect Tax News and articles in Taxation, The Law Society's Gazette and Exporting Today. Frequent conference speaker.
Prof. Memberships: Law Society Revenue Law Committee, Customs Practitioners Group, Institute of Indirect Taxation, Law Society representative on Joint Customs Consultative Committee, UKWA representative on the Joint Alcohol and Tobacco Consultation Group.
Career: Qualified in 1971. Worked at Customs and Excise Solicitor's Office 1972-77, then *Richards Butler* 1977-83. Joined the Law Society as Revenue Law Committee Secretary in 1983 before becoming Director of Tax Investigations for the Parliamentary Ombudsman in 1988. Joined *Titmuss Sainer & Webb* (now *Dechert*) in 1993.
Personal: Born 11th May 1947. Attended King's College, London, 1965-68 (LLB), then College of Law, London, 1968-69, Ecole Nationale d'Administration, Paris, 1975. Secretary of the Tax Law Review Committee at the Institute for Fiscal Studies 1993-95, chairman of the VAT and Duties Tribunal and deputy special commissioner. Leisure interests include cider and beer making and collecting Customs memorabilia. Lives in Sevenoaks, Kent.

GERRARD, D. Neil

DLA, London (08700) 111 111
neil.gerrard@dla.com
See under Fraud, p.418

HANMAN, David

Russell Jones & Walker, Manchester
(0161) 832 8877
d.i.hanman@rjw.co.uk
Specialisation: Partner in the tax investigations department of *Russel Jones & Walker*. Represents clients involved in criminal tax investigations conducted by National Investigation Service of HM Custom & Excise, Special Compliance Office of HM Inland Revenue, Serious Fraud Office and also investigations by the Department of Trade and Industry and Trading Standards.
Career: Qualified in 1992 and is a member of the Chartered Institute of Taxation (CIOT). Also a member of the Institute of Direct Taxation, (AIIT), VAT Practitioners Group (VPG) and Customs Practitioners Group (CPG).

HART, Andrew

Baker & McKenzie, London (020) 7919 1000
Partner in EU, Competition and Trade Law Department.
Specialisation: Principal area of practice is commercial and trade law, notably customs and VAT law. Advises multinational and domestic companies on practice and procedures relating to their business, especially the impact of customs duties and other taxes, and maximizing the benefit to be derived from various customs regimes and reliefs. Assists clients in responding to enquiries and investigations into compliance with customs and VAT obligations, including negotiation and settlement of investigations by the Customs National Investigation Service and other parts of H.M. Customs & Excise. Clients include Compaq, Seagate, IBM and Informix. Writes Customs Update for Butterworth's monthly 'De Voil's Indirect Tax Intelligence'. Author of Customs and VAT sections of Sweet & Maxwell's 'Encyclopedia of Information Technology Law'. Has undertaken speaking engagements in the US, UK and India on various aspects of UK and EU trade, customs, VAT and tax law and practice. Charge-out rate is £350-400 per hour.
Prof. Memberships: Customs Practitioners Group (Hon. Secretary); Law Society (Formerly a Member of VAT and Duties Sub-Committee of Revenue Law Committee).
Career: Qualified in 1972. Partner at *Baker & McKenzie* since 1980.
Personal: Born 2nd August 1947. Educated at Nottingham University 1966-69 (LL.B Hons). Leisure interests include football and squash. Lives in London.

HODGKINSON, Milly

Berwin Leighton, London (020) 7760 1000
Specialisation: E-commerce, VAT, Excise & Customs duties. *Berwin Leighton* specialises in e-commerce for both start-up and major international retailing clients.Has developed a particular specialisation in advising on cross-border VAT and Customs duties issues and customs & excise warehousing in Europe.
Prof. Memberships: The International Bar Association, The American Bar Association, World Trade Law Association, British Importers Association, United Kingdom Association for European Law, The CBI, The Enterprising Women Network.
Career: Qualified at *Kingsley Napley* in 1991, joined the Solicitors' Office of Customs & Excise in 1992 spe-

cialising in European law, customs duties, VAT and international advisory work, seconded to MAFF in 1998 before joining City law firm *Berwin Leighton* as Head of Indirect Tax at the beginning of 1999.
Publications: A regular contributor to journals including the 'Tax Journal', 'Tornado-Insider.com', 'Legal Week', 'The Institute of Indirect Taxation', 'The Evening Standard' and 'The Financial News'.
Personal: Educated at SOAS London University, leisure interests include gardening and opera.

KENYON, Michael J.
Burton Copeland, Manchester (0161) 834 7374
Specialisation: Acts on behalf of numerous corporate clients under investigation by Customs for VAT & Excise duty irregularities and also defends individuals subject to prosecution. Wider practise includes commercial fraud investigation and Defence including Prospectus Fraud, loan and leasing fraud, insider dealing, fraudulent tradings, frauds on investors, property and mortgage fraud, corruption and tax investigations.
Prof. Memberships: Law Society, Criminal Law Solicitors Association.
Career: Qualified in 1980. Partner at *Chafes*, Stockport 1985-1986 Senior Crown Prosecutor in Manchester 1987-1989. Partner at *Burton Copeland* from 1990.
Personal: Born 1956. Attended Manchester Grammar School and University of Kent. Leisure interests include salmon fishing, game shooting, military and political history and opera. Lives in Cheshire and Scotland.

WHITE, Jeremy
KLegal, London (020) 7694 2500
jeremy.white@kpmg.co.uk
Specialisation: Trade and Customs law; trade barriers (indirect taxes, anti-dumping duty, prohibitions and restrictions); trade preferences (CAP, e-business, WTO). Highlights include: Commissioners of Customs and Excise v Anchor Foods Ltd; expert witness in CAP regime arbitration; legal adviser to the Collector of Customs, Bermuda in customs legislation project.
Prof. Memberships: Bar Council, Customs Practitioners Group.
Career: Called to the Bar (Gray's Inn) in 1976. Barrister in private practice until 1983. Solicitor's office, HM Customs and Excise 1983-1996. Senior Lawyer, KPMG's European Customs Practice 1996-2000. Senior Lawyer, *KLegal's* Trade and Customs Practice from 1 February 2000.
Publications: Consultant Editor of Butterworths 'Customs Duties Handbook' since 1995; Contributor to Halsbury's Statutes since 1996.
Personal: Married with three children.

DEBT RECOVERY

London: 283; Thames Valley: 283; The South: 284; South West: 284; Wales: 285; Midlands: 285; East Anglia: 286; North West: 286; North East: 287; Scotland: 287; Northern Ireland: 288

OVERVIEW: In an increasingly polarised area, the firms recommended in this edition of Chambers profile both the growing trend towards high volume computerised debt collection and the strong commercial litigation teams who service the needs of existing clients. This section has been renamed as Debt Recovery to reflect the importance of added value and tailor-made packages for all client bases in the face of competition from debt collection agencies. As ever, developments in IT software packages and the transparency brought by web based systems are streamlining this process and making investment in this area more important for continued success.

RESEARCH APPROVED BY BMRB: *For this edition,* Chambers' *researchers conducted 6083 interviews – 4408 with law firms, 598 with barristers and 1077 with clients.*

The validity of the research was scrutinised by BMRB International, who audited both the methodology and the results at our offices in July 2000. They interviewed Chambers' *researchers and cross-checked sample interviews. Details of the audit appear on page 7.*

LONDON

DEBT RECOVERY • London
❶ Braby & Waller
❷ Wilde & Partners
❸ Hammond Suddards Edge
Jeffrey Green Russell
Salans Hertzfeld & Heilbronn HRK

Within each band, firms are listed alphabetically.

Braby & Waller *"Nationally the most prominent firm"* with a specialism in bulk collection work. Since the merger with Irwin Mitchell in 1998 this practice has retained its established brand name and focus. An experienced team of twenty-five in the London office (which can also pass work to the Sheffield office) services large commercial clients including utilities, financial institutions, accountants and trade retail. Also offer bespoke packages, fixed fees and credit management training for clients. **Clients:** Crédit Lyonnais Commercial Finance, Penninsula Business Systems Ltd, Mazars Neville Russell.

Wilde & Partners This specialist debt recovery team of fifteen is considered *"big on the factoring side"* also servicing related sectors where debt is a fundamental part of their security. Has expertise in the assignment of debts and set-off defences. Regarded as *"highly skilled,"* this firm acts for major factoring companies and finance houses. **Clients:** Factoring Industry.

Hammond Suddards Edge Operating a *"well-regarded"* national recoveries unit under the wing of finance law, this team is also supported by a strong office in the Midlands. Provide on-line access for clients to view ongoing cases. Niche strength in collect out situations, notably in insolvency and client failures for factors and invoice discounters. **Clients:** Eurosales Finance plc, Horwath Clark Whitehill & Co.

Jeffrey Green Russell *"More aggressive than most"* this firm operates three rival teams of debt collectors and has partners to pick up defended cases. Has attracted clients previously sued by them, and also acts for banks, plant hire, electrical and construction companies. Focus on high volume recovery including a mix of commercial and consumer debt. **Clients:** Citibank, Diners Club, American Express.

Salans Hertzfeld & Heilbronn HRK This *"prominent"* debt recovery team includes eight qualified assistants and twenty paralegals. The bulk of the undefended volume work is carried out in Bromley, which is increasing its capacity for simple contested cases. Has a reputation for consumer credit recovery in the motor finance industry and also acts for banks and building societies. Undertake mortgage repossession, recovery of vehicles and recovery of outstanding loans for banks. **Clients:** Barclays Bank; Bank of Scotland; Britannia Building Society; Nissan Finance.

THAMES VALLEY

DEBT RECOVERY • Thames Valley
❶ **Shoosmiths** Reading
❷ **Boyes Turner & Burrows** Reading
Clarks Reading
Denton Wilde Sapte Milton Keynes
Morgan Cole Reading
❸ **Fennemores** Milton Keynes
Matthew Arnold & Baldwin Watford

Within each band, firms are listed alphabetically.

Shoosmiths This *"highly rated, very strong"* stand alone unit has twenty-three debt recovery specialists undertaking high volume undefended trade debt recovery. The team refers contested cases to the large commercial litigation team where each client has a pre-allocated solicitor. Act for commercial debtors, with strong focus on recruitment agencies, computer and construction companies. The Northampton office also recovers consumer debt for large credit houses. This *"first-class"* practice has a highly-regarded reputation across the UK.

Boyes Turner & Burrows A team of four assistants and one active partner devoted to debt recovery benefit from a large insolvency and commercial practice. The practice has a wide ranging client base including recruitment agencies, white goods manufacturers, spread betting and freight forwarding companies. **Clients:** Kelly Services UK Ltd; IG Index plc.

Clarks Although traditionally this firm has not focused on volume debt recovery, developments in its IT systems are bringing changes to the client base. Based within the litigation department, this team of four associate solicitors and five fee earners acts for academic institutions, recruitment agencies, IT companies, building contractors and finance houses. Recently acquired volume factoring and debt recovery work from Euro Sales Finance. **Clients:** BMW Finance Services Group, Euro Sales Finance plc.

Denton Wilde Sapte The February 2000 merger between Denton Hall and Wilde Sapte has not diminished the former's profile in debt recovery. Based within the commercial litigation department, this *"effective, user-friendly* *team"* of four mainly work on sale of goods and rent recoveries and are also involved in debt collection work across Europe, South Africa, Korea and Japan. Act for NCM, the large trade debt insurer based in Holland, collecting UK debt. **Clients:** CNT (English Partnerships), NCM.

Morgan Cole This firm's substantial debt recovery practice is now centralised in the Reading office and includes twelve fee-earners. Acts for large corporate clients, computer companies and has a specialism in factoring and invoice discounters.

Fennemores With recognised experience in debt recovery, this firm is seen to be servicing its significant commercial client base with a niche strength in invoice discounting. The practice offers pre-legal telephone and written collections, where the pre-summons telephone calls are set by an automatic predictive IT system. Specialist solicitors take up defended cases, and the firm issues County Court summons and enforces judgments with a full trace and debt surveillance service. **Clients:** Factoring Industry.

Matthew Arnold & Baldwin The debt collection team (one assistant, two paralegals) is based within commercial litigation and acts for accountants, manufacturers, publishers and lettings agencies. Undertakes the full range of debt recovery including defended actions and negotiation to settlement. The varied client base which includes plcs and SMEs, mirrors the commercial base of the firm as a whole. **Clients:** Barclays Bank, Robert Bosch, Zurich Financial Services, Eagle Star, Hamerville Magazines.

THE SOUTH

DEBT RECOVERY • The South
❶ **Brachers** Maidstone
❷ **Blake Lapthorn** Portsmouth
❸ **Lester Aldridge** Bournemouth
❹ **Cripps Harries Hall** Tunbridge Wells, Kent
DMH Brighton
Trethowans Southampton
❺ **Clyde & Co** Guildford
❻ **Moore & Blatch** Southampton

Within each band, firms are listed alphabetically.

Brachers This joint debt recovery and insolvency practice has a *"good, strong, dedicated"* team of twenty-five, focusing on bulk debt recovery and post invoice credit management. Wide-ranging client base includes utilities, hauliers, building suppliers, IT, credit card and transport companies. *"Highly rated,"* the team are seen as *"aggressive players"* in the market. The firm has a subsidiary company based in Milton Keynes, which is outsourced as a credit management operation for a single, large commercial client.

Blake Lapthorn This stand alone debt recovery unit is a *"good strong practice with a deserved reputation."* A team of seven including one partner who acts for large multinationals and smaller companies in both commercial and consumer debt recovery. Recently gained new clients in IT and equipment leasing and was appointed by SGB Services for transactions covering nineteen branches. Has a reputation for *"good IT systems"* which service the high volume processing of instructions. **Clients:** SGB Services plc, Key Industrial Equipment.

Lester Aldridge Sixteen fee earners and two partners operate from this rebranded (as *"Lester Aldridge Fast Track"*) and *"high profile"* department which has embraced the volume market. The firm services collection agencies, utilities, accountants, retailers, manufactures, credit insurance companies and financial services. This *"good little operation"* is seen to have raised its profile recently with heavy marketing, and is extending its client base accordingly.

Cripps Harries Hall Well regarded as a *"strong traditional practice,"* this team of five includes a high level of partner involvement. Steering away from the bulk volume debt collection, the team has matured into servicing a strong commercial client base with a specialism in high net worth recoveries. Acting from within the large private client department, the wide range of clients includes manufacturing companies, insurance commissions and the service industry. **Clients:** National Provident Institution, Duncan Web Offset Ltd, regional newspaper group.

DMH The dedicated commercial debt recovery practice has a *"strong reputation"* acting for corporate and institutional clients, including retail, road haulage and construction companies. The firm has a focus on owner-managed SMEs, operating a small business section which offers fixed price debt recovery work. With increased investment in IT systems, volume debt recovery is a growth area. The firm is also able to undertake tracing and status enquiries and offers credit control seminars to clients. **Clients:** Credit Acceptance Ltd, Atalink, GMAC.

Trethowans The debt recovery practice is *"increasingly high profile"* and includes a team of five in Andover with the support of five paralegals in Southampton. Act for a broad range of clients including large multinationals, financial houses, small local companies and local councils in the north of England. The *"efficient"* staff undertake all aspects of debt recovery, including disputed actions, judgments and enforcements.

Clyde & Co This specialist firm has a strong tradition in international, high value debt recovery. Act for major credit risk insurers on a global basis, as well as exporters of varying sizes. The firm specialises in acting for credit insurers who provide cover in countries suffering debt crises. Teams also operate in London and Cardiff and are seen to dominate the international scene, although the firm is yet to make a similar impact on the local market. **Clients:** NCM, Coface, Euler Trading, Charterers Mutual.

Moore & Blatch Acting for a range of clients from large retailers to individuals, this practice operates a well-regarded team of five, perceived by the market as a minor player. The firm undertakes all levels of debt recovery including bespoke packages for individuals.

SOUTH WEST

DEBT RECOVERY • South West
❶ **Bond Pearce** Plymouth
Burges Salmon Bristol
Clarke Willmott & Clarke Taunton
Osborne Clarke OWA Bristol
❷ **TLT Solicitors** Bristol

Within each band, firms are listed alphabetically.

Bond Pearce The stand alone credit management services team of seven includes two dedicated advocates and is the result of an amalgamation of the Plymouth and Southampton operations. With niche strength in retail and education, this firm also acts for smaller plcs, limited companies and financial institutions recovering consumer and trade debt. The firm has a recognised profile with a *"strong client base,"* last year securing bulk recovery work from Friends Provident. **Clients:** B&Q, University of Southampton, Friends Provident.

Burges Salmon Based within the litigation department, this team of two dedicated legal executives handles all aspects of debt recovery including pre-legal work. Perceived by the market as not promoting this practice area, the firm does manage large caseloads for its existing clients. Also advises on the establishment of internal procedures for debt management within a client's organisation.

Clarke Willmott & Clarke This *"increasingly high profile"* team of eleven has traditionally acted for existing clients including individual traders, and is now focusing on banks, building societies and factoring companies. The volume debt recovery practice has seen an increase, due in part to success with conditional fee arrangements. Work has included augmented transactions for banks and building societies, including mortgage shortfalls. **Clients:** BOCM Pauls Limited, Amtrak Express Parcels Ltd, Portman Building Society, National Westminster Bank.

Osborne Clarke OWA This firm services its *"excellent blue chip clients"* with a debt recovery practice of one partner and three fee earners. The team does not attempt to compete on scale. Client base includes a mixture of professional, industrial and general business plcs and smaller limited companies. The firm also acts for German firms collecting debts from UK companies and for Danish companies through a dedicated London based Danish team. **Clients:** Danish Bacon, Mobil Gas Marketing plc, Bristol & West plc.

TLT Solicitors The merger of the active debt recovery practices of Trumps and Lawrence Tucketts has bolstered the team and provided a well rounded client base. A wide offering of debt recovery services includes pre-legal work and a strengthened specialist litigation team. The firm has a foothold in the recovery of consumer debt including mortgage repossessions and receives praise for its bank recoveries work.

WALES

DEBT RECOVERY • Wales
❶ **Eversheds** Cardiff
❷ **Edwards Geldard** Cardiff
❸ **John Collins & Partners** Swansea

Within each band, firms are listed alphabetically.

Eversheds This *"well-run"* team of three partners, one qualified assistant and ninety-three fee earners is by far the pre-eminent debt recovery outfit in Wales. The commercial recoveries unit undertakes work from telephone collections through to High Court actions with a team of eight dedicated litigation lawyers. Within the unit are teams specialising in mortgage enforcements, shortfall recoveries and commercial debt. This practice benefits from a national presence and reputation, and is well regarded for its dedication to the area. **Clients:** Abbey National plc, Cheltenham and Gloucester, Bank of Scotland, Legal & General.

Edwards Geldard *"Active"* team of one partner, one associate solicitor and six fee-earners, which has recently hired senior figures from Eversheds and the relocated Morgan Cole. The firm has registered a limited liability company branded 'Call First.' This will handle pre-legal volume transactions, specifically dealing with the growth in shortfall collections and the insurance client base. Particularly well regarded for acting on behalf of a large commercial client base. **Clients:** CWS Ltd, Headlam Floorcovering Distributors Ltd, Midland Electricity Board.

John Collins & Partners With a team of 18 fee earners and one partner this *"strong practice"* is considered *"a senior figure"* in debt collection. The firm has a client base focusing on banks, building societies and smaller local companies, and has a reputation for aggressively seeking new business. Has acted for Lloyds TSB since 1983, handling substantial volume debt recovery including high court and county court enforcements. Also have a dedicated business services team channelling work across the firm. **Clients:** Lloyds TSB.

MIDLANDS

DEBT RECOVERY • Midlands
❶ **Hammond Suddards Edge** Leicester
Hewitson Becke + Shaw Northampton
Wragge & Co Birmingham
❷ **Eversheds** Nottingham, Birmingham
Freethcartwright Nottingham
❸ **Browne Jacobson** Nottingham
Shakespeares Birmingham
Warner Cranston Coventry
❹ **Howes Percival** Northampton

Within each band, firms are listed alphabetically.

Hammond Suddards Edge This *"sharp and impressive"* team of two partners and eight paralegals has niche strength in the factoring and invoice discount sector. The national recoveries unit acts for a wide range of commercial clients. The firm's web based IT systems have led to a growth in volume debt recovery. Handles client failures for factoring companies and low value high volume debt for Thomas Cook. **Clients:** Thomas Cook Group Ltd, Euro Sales Finance plc, Capital Bank Cashflow Finance, Oxwen Ltd.

Hewitson Becke + Shaw Recognised to have a strong reputation in debt recovery, the firm is noted for its sizeable client base which includes the steel, gas, water and insurance industry sectors. A team of twelve based in Northampton handles volume debt recovery focused on commercial trade. Defended actions are handled by litigation specialists in each relevant section of the firm, with associates based in the Cambridge office receiving particular praise.

Wragge & Co This team of one partner and 15 fee earners is seen to benefit from the firm's *"exceptional overall reputation."* Undertakes consumer credit actions, pre-legal work and enforcement of judgments, and recently acted for a local council on rent arrears repossession. The client base includes the construction industry, hire companies and debt recovery agencies. **Clients:** Croydon Council, Solaglas Ltd (trade as SRG), Dun & Bradstreet.

Eversheds A broad range of consumer (40%) and commercial (60%) debt recovery is undertaken by this team of 25 fee earners, supervised by one partner. The firm has recently launched the Everdebt web based IT system to handle volume debt recovery for a broad range of industry sectors including, telecoms, financial houses, manufacturing and education. **Clients:** Credit Acceptances Corporation, Online Finance Ltd, Pirelli, Raleigh Industries Ltd.

Freethcartwright Debt recovery forms part of the commercial litigation team and includes one legal executive and three fee earners recovering both commercial and consumer debt. Also provides a High Court and County Court information service on all UK business. Seen to have a strong commercial client base, including credit reference agencies, large national and smaller local companies. **Clients:** Bass Brewers Ltd, Top Service Ltd.

Browne Jacobson A recent senior recruit from Eversheds has strengthened this team of three legal executives and two paralegals who also draw on three assistant solicitors for defended cases. The team's client base mirrors the firm as a whole, and includes major IT companies, publishing and local businesses. Able to receive instructions over the web this team covers a wide range of debt recovery services with the capability to handle volume transactions.

Shakespeares Working from within the commercial litigation department, this team (two partners, two assistant solicitors, three paralegals) runs an automated debt recovery system able to act on small ticket litigation, from letters before action to High Court judgments and enforcement procedures. Acting for a broad range of clients including high street banks, computer companies, manufacturers and small local owner-managed companies. The firm also has experience of overseas debt recovery.

Warner Cranston Focusing on small value, high volume corporate debt recovery, this *"good team with strong clients"* has seven fee earners in bulk issuing and a further five assistant solicitors for defended cases. The firm acts for major wholesalers, trade finance companies, manufacturers and electrical component suppliers. Credit management advice is offered, as well as a full range of debt recovery services from pre-litigation to enforcement proceedings and High Court and County Court actions.
Clients: Courtaulds Textiles, Anchor Homes.

Howes Percival A small team which acts out of commercial litigation has two partners and one fee-earner to service its existing client base with tailored solutions to debt recovery. In recent years has moved away from the high volume banking sector and now is most active amongst medium sized local business. Offers the full range of debt recovery options including litigation, but perceived to lack the case management systems necessary for bulk recoveries.

EAST ANGLIA

DEBT RECOVERY • East Anglia
❶ **Eversheds** Norwich
❷ **Ashton Graham** Bury St Edmunds
Birketts Ipswich
Greenwoods Peterborough
❸ **Gotelee & Goldsmith** Ipswich
Prettys Ipswich

Within each band, firms are listed alphabetically.

Eversheds *"Always active with a good client base,"* the team of four paralegals services corporate clients as part of the general litigation team. The firm also undertakes instructions from international creditors for enforcements in the UK. High Court judgments for enforcement are passed to the Under Sheriff who then instructs the team. As one of the main offices for debt recovery, the practice benefits from this pre-eminent firm's focus on this area. **Clients:** GE Capital Global Consumer Finance, Halifax plc.

Ashton Graham This medium sized practice comprises a *"good little team"* of two but is perceived to shy away from volume debt recovery. The commercial client base is serviced by seasoned recovery executives who offer a bespoke package including pre-legal letters before action through to enforcements. A wide ranging client base includes plcs and sole traders and is focused on the East Anglian region.

Birketts Small department with one partner and one other fee earner dedicated to debt recovery, which is respected for its client care. Able to handle high volume debt collection work, the team acts for a major regional newspaper group and for a commercial vehicle parts supplier recovering debts on a national scale.

Greenwoods This team of one legal executive (with twenty years of experience) and three legal assistants act from within the commercial dispute resolution department. The debt recovery team services foreign banks, building societies and insurance companies as well as the local business sector. The latter includes manufacturing companies and professionals. Operates a volume recovery IT system and has created bespoke packages for referrals from the Electrical Contractors Association. **Clients:** Electrical Contractors Association, Thomas Cook.

Gotelee & Goldsmith This team of four handles a variety of work and has a well regarded reputation with large haulage companies and local authority work. The department services its local client base with a range of services, including pre-legal letters before action as well as High Court and County Court actions. The firm also offers advice on credit control and debt management procedures.

Prettys Two paralegals and one partner work closely with the commercial litigation team which handles any contested cases. The firm has some volume debt recovery work but mainly focuses on higher value commercial debts. The client base reflects the local economy with particular growth in the transport sector. Other work has been completed for insurance brokerage firms, hospitals, insolvency practitioners and East Anglian based traders.

NORTH WEST

DEBT RECOVERY • North West
❶ **Thomas A. Higgins & Co** Wallasey
❷ **Bermans** Liverpool
❸ **Davies Wallis Foyster** Liverpool
Lees Lloyd Whitley Liverpool
❹ **Cobbetts** Manchester
Cuff Roberts Liverpool
Halliwell Landau Manchester

Within each band, firms are listed alphabetically.

Thomas A.Higgins & Co One of the most prominent practitioners of debt collection, this *"efficient"* large team has a national reputation which rests with its pure focus on uncontested, high volume debt collection. Perceived to be a specialist niche practice in the market, there is genuine praise for its *"streamlined IT systems,"* the ability to handle *"massive volume"* and their *"national client base."*

Bermans The commercial recoveries department with a team of ten operates a complete package from pre-litigation to advanced proceedings and *"client friendly"* credit management systems. *"Still going strong,"* the firm has a client base which includes banks, breweries, factoring companies and advertising agencies. A long standing name in this field, the team is said to have *"stolen a march in the early 1980s"* and continues to be regarded as a pre-eminent practice.

Davies Wallis Foyster A respected stand alone unit that operates with a team of twelve in both the Liverpool and Manchester offices, and is *"always a recognisable player."* Both offices run the same systems and act as a single operation. The range of clients includes finance, factoring and leasing companies, large plcs and a variety of smaller local clients. Growth is assisted by cross over from corporate and property practices and the team appears on a national basis.

Lees Lloyd Whitley This practice has a good profile within debt recovery and is known primarily for its work for HM Customs & Excise. Is recognised for its *"vast set of paralegals"* who undertake bulk debt recovery work and service a range of local businesses including those with only occasional requirements.

Cobbetts Small team of two paralegals (and four assistant solicitors for defended actions) which has undergone a year of consolidation since its merger with the Slater Heelis team. Acting from within the commercial litigation and insolvency department this team undertakes general trade debt recovery for the motor trade, industrial and mechanical companies. With 70% of its clients based in the North West, the firm is seen to be servicing an active client base without following the bulk collection route. **Clients:** Hill Hire plc, Protec Fire Detection plc.

Cuff Roberts Last year this firm merged two teams to form its insolvency & debt recovery practice which act as complementary areas feeding work across the team (twelve fee earners in debt.) The work is varied, specialising in consumer credit, agricultural based suppliers and insolvency related book debts for a client base which ranges from medium sized companies to sole traders.

Halliwell Landau Stand alone commercial debt recovery team practice with a varied institutional client base including building societies, clearing banks and commercial clients such as hire plants. Mortgage repossessions and shortfalls are seen as a growth area for this practice which handles volume debt to litigation.

NORTH EAST

DEBT RECOVERY • North East
❶ **Hammond Suddards** Bradford
❷ **DLA** Bradford
Eversheds Leeds
❸ **Carrick Read Insolvency** Leeds
Lupton Fawcett Leeds
Walker Morris Leeds
❹ **Braby & Waller** Sheffield
Ford & Warren Leeds

Within each band, firms are listed alphabetically.

Hammond Suddards This *"successful"* team of thirty is led by a litigation partner and is seen by some as *"the leading firm in the country"* across the UK. The branded commercial 'Debtline' team handles six hundred commercial clients including financial houses, builders merchants and recruitment agencies as part of a separate business unit. Seen to have been the main beneficiary of Addleshaw Booth & Co's departure from this field, this firm is also supported by a former DLA senior manager. **Clients:** BSS plc, Abbey National Building Society, Blue Arrow Recruitment.

DLA The high profile debt recovery team, which draws on ten qualified assistants and 159 fee-earners across the business services group, is perceived by the market to have lost ground recently. Comment was made on a move away from unsecured debt recovery, and the recent loss of a leading figure in the team. The team retains its high profile in the market and offers high volume, pre-legal collection with a *"no success, no fee option"* as well as a comprehensive litigation service. The firm has a strength in recovery of secured debts from the financial sector including sale and realisation of assets. **Clients:** Halifax plc, Abbey National plc, Standard Life Bank plc.

Eversheds The *"always active"* team of seventy undertake both commercial and consumer debt recovery for large financial institutions, building societies, credit care providers and large commercial operations. Renowned for a *"national presence in consumer debt recovery,"* the firm operates a Collections Call Centre for the bulk recovery strategy. **Clients:** GE Capital Global Consumer Finance Ltd, Halifax plc, Akzo Nobel.

Carrick Read Insolvency Formed from the merged insolvency and debt recovery units of Read Hind Stewart and Garwood Devine, this team of thirty is *"active, focused specifically on debt."* Has a strong reputation in bulk debt collection, including tracing of debtors and telephone collection work. With a national client base, this firm acts for large corporate clients on significant consumer debt recovery. **Clients:** Vodafone Airtouch, Marks & Spencer Financial Services, Greenflag.

Lupton Fawcett This *"old style firm"* has a significant client base and is driving forward with bulk debt recovery. A team of forty acts for major clients including large plcs, insurance, high tech companies, trade associations and owner-managed businesses. Recently acquired major bulk collection transactions from Sun Microsystems. **Clients:** Sun Microsystems, West Yorkshire Trade Protection Association, Dun & Bradstreet.

Walker Morris The firm has re-engineered its debt recovery practice recently and is no longer focusing solely on high volume low coupon debt. The team of five fee earners (part of the dispute resolution department) undertake institutional debt including shortfall recoveries on mortgages, insolvency book debt recovery and general suppliers who require a full service of pre-litigation and defended case work.

Braby & Waller Retaining the brand name of the merged debt recovery specialists, this team of fifteen fee earners continues the strong reputation of the London office. Operating common IT systems, work is passed from London as well as servicing a strong commercial client base. **Clients:** Poppleton & Appleby.

Ford & Warren This *"classic middle-sized"* firm is seen to be servicing a long established client base rather than pushing forward its reputation in debt recovery. A recognised strength in the field of transport.

SCOTLAND

McClure Naismith With an established reputation in consumer debt recovery, the team containing one partner, two associates and twelve paralegals goes from strength to strength. A dedicated department deals with both contentious issues and documentation. Has a very strong focus on volume debt recovery and has recently acquired the tender for Bank of Scotland business litigation. Also acts for major finance houses and motor dealerships in hire agreements. **Clients:** Birmingham Midshires Mortgage Services Ltd, Capital Bank, Bank of Scotland, RoyScot Trusts.

Yuill & Kyle This practice of three qualified solicitors and two paralegals acts for a wide range of clients including multi-nationals and smaller companies with a 60-40 percent commercial to consumer bias. It is perceived to have benefited from a major marketing push as a result of campaigning within the Scottish Parliament. With *"the right package and the right attitude,"* this practice offers the full range of debt recovery options and a strong commercial client base. **Clients:** Coca-Cola, B&Q, MFI.

Morison Bishop Last year saw the merger of Alexander Morison and Bishop & Robertson Chalmers, perceived as a *"defensive move by two solid firms."* The debt recovery practice (*"reliable and cost effective"*) acts for major commercial clients, often in high volume debt recovery. Also offers an asset recovery division for secured lenders from their Edinburgh office. **Clients:** BP Oil UK Ltd, Your Move, Transco, Alliance & Leicester plc.

DEBT RECOVERY • Scotland
❶ **McClure Naismith** Glasgow
Yuill & Kyle Glasgow
❷ **Morison Bishop** Glasgow
Morton Fraser, Solicitors Edinburgh
Nolan Macleod Glasgow
❸ **Blacklock Thorley** Edinburgh
Bonar Mackenzie WS Edinburgh
Brodies WS Edinburgh
Golds Glasgow
Henderson Boyd Jackson WS Edinburgh
Macdonalds Glasgow
❹ **McGrigor Donald** Glasgow
Miller Samuel & Co Glasgow
Wright, Johnston & Mackenzie Glasgow

Within each band, firms are listed alphabetically.

Morton Fraser Solicitors A strong practice in debt factoring, acting for major banks, building societies, academic institutes and small businesses. The firm is widely regarded for its specialism in debt factoring and has a *"comprehensive legal offering."* Interlaw membership allows access to clients on a global basis and has resulted in substantial transactions from Spain.

Nolan Macleod Two partners and a team of twenty are *"pre-eminent in consumer debt recovery"* and undertake the spectrum of legal offerings, with a focus on volume collections including tracing. Act for blue chip clients including major banks, factoring companies, leasing and hire purchase companies and English solicitors.

Blacklock Thorley Newly recognised by the market as *"a well-known name"* with a focus on volume debt recovery. This practice has received praise from solicitors in both England and Scotland and is praised for its commerciality and client care.

Bonar MacKenzie WS Still *"active in this field"* yet perceived to be lacking some focus, this team of two legal executives supported by two partners handles mainly consumer debt recovery for building societies, banks and smaller businesses.

Brodies WS A *"well-established practice"* with a solid traditional client base and a strong reputation for commercial litigation. The team is perceived to be active in the market although lacking the focus of some of the leaders, but is recommended as an *"old favourite with fine service."*

Golds A recognised specialist in commercial debt recovery, this team of five is *"very hot on IT"* offering an online case management system. Acts for retailers, manufacturers, financial institutions and IT companies covering a broad range of debt recovery options.

Henderson Boyd Jackson WS A team of two assistant solicitors and three paralegals acts for factoring companies, financial institutions and English solicitors, as well as servicing the firm's existing client base. With a clear focus on volume recovery this practice acts as part of a highly regarded commercial litigation team.

Macdonalds Within the commercial litigation team three solicitors and five supporting staff form a team with a reputation as *"strong on factoring."* Acts for large factoring companies in Scotland, and leasing and hire purchase specialists including major plcs. Perceived to be benefiting from an association with factoring specialists Bermans (based in Liverpool) this firm also acts for the Glasgow Sheriff's Court.

McGrigor Donald This *"solid commercial firm"* has a large client base including major banks, building societies and property companies undertaking mainly uncontested cases. The team of three paralegals act for PPL in recovering copyright licensing fees and recovery of rent arrears for managing agents. **Clients:** Phonographic Performance Ltd, major banks.

Miller Samuel & Co This well respected team of twelve has significant partner involvement and a recognised focus on debt recovery. The client base includes referrals from existing clients of the commercial litigation team, accountants and English solicitors.

Wright, Johnston & Mackenzie This *"sizeable, experienced"* team of six fee earners supported by four assistant solicitors runs a volume debt recovery practice for large companies including major banks. The firm also services smaller local business and can operate on behalf of private individuals. **Clients:** Student Loans Company Ltd, Clydesdale Bank plc.

NORTHERN IRELAND

DEBT RECOVERY • Northern Ireland
❶ **Comerton & Hill** Belfast
❷ **Bigger & Strahan** Belfast
SJ Diamond & Son Belfast
❸ **Cleaver Fulton Rankin** Belfast
John McKee & Son Belfast
McKinty & Wright Belfast

Within each band, firms are listed alphabetically.

Comerton & Hill This small practice has a high profile reputation for debt recovery. The *"dedicated team"* of three partners and two paralegals is well respected for the service it offers to major finance houses. Concentrate on the volume side of debt recovery. **Clients:** HSBC, NWIB.

Bigger & Strahan This team of four paralegals supported by a strong commercial litigation and insolvency department has a good reputation derived mainly from its work with large financial houses. Consequently the firm is ranked for the first time. Acts mainly for factoring companies and high street banks in Northern Ireland and England. Also undertakes referrals from the Mainland to handle European debt recovery.

SJ Diamond & Sons A recent recruit from Comerton & Hill has strengthened this debt recovery practice which now has one partner, one assistant solicitor and an experienced legal executive. Acts for Ulster Bank in repossession orders, judgment enforcements and bankruptcy proceedings. Also recovers advertising debts for major newspapers and acts for hire companies as part of a large commercial client base. **Clients:** Ulster Bank, leading newspapers.

Cleaver Fulton Rankin Although not seen to specialise in this area, this team of two paralegals supported by one partner services a wide ranging client base including financial institutions, schools and construction companies. At present does not focus on volume debt recovery and attracts work from an existing client base, as well as through membership of LawNet and referrals from English solicitors. **Clients:** Bank of Scotland, Royal Sun Alliance.

John McKee & Sons *"A substantial practice doing good work nationwide."* Two solicitors and one paralegal handle high volume work for financial institutions, credit agencies, construction companies, debt recovery agents and solicitors based in England. This stand alone unit also offers tailor made packages for smaller businesses or those seeking higher value recoveries.

McKinty & Wright Recommended as having a *"good active practice"* focusing on this area. This firm represents major financial houses which includes undertaking building society mortgage repossession work.

DEFAMATION

OVERVIEW: 1999-2000 has been another bumper year of headline-grabbing libel trials. It appears that reputation remains a prized commodity. Nevertheless, the vast majority of disputes now settle, a process hastened by the Woolf reforms, a draft pre-action protocol and new summary procedure. As a result, those few cases which do reach trial are more carefully selected and harder-fought. Anther perceived threat is the increasing role of in-house lawyers at the major media groups. However, the looming presence of the Human Rights Act should ensure a steady flow of work, particularly in the related fields of contempt, breach of confidence, privacy and official secrets.

RESEARCH APPROVED BY BMRB: *For this edition,* Chambers' *researchers conducted 6083 interviews – 4408 with law firms, 598 with barristers and 1077 with clients.*

The validity of the research was scrutinised by BMRB International, who audited both the methodology and the results at our offices in July 2000. They interviewed Chambers' *researchers and cross-checked sample interviews. Details of the audit appear on page 7.*

LEADING IN-HOUSE LAWYERS

John BATTLE, Group Legal Adviser, *Associated Newspapers Ltd*

Patricia BURGE, Company Solicitor, *Times Newspapers*

Siobhain BUTTERWORTH, Head of Legal Affairs, *Guardian Newspapers Ltd*

Charles COLLIER-WRIGHT, Group Legal Manager, *Trinity Mirror plc*

Tom CRONE, Legal Manager, *News International*

Martin CRUDDACE, Head of Legal Department, *Trinity Mirror plc*

Louise HAYMAN, Legal Manager, *Independent Newspapers Ltd*

Marcus PARTINGTON, Solicitor, *Trinity Mirror plc*

Justin WALFORD, Legal Adviser, *Express Newspapers*

"*Tough*" **John Battle** knows what he can get away with but always "*seeks to find a consensus.*" "*Terrific*" **Patricia Burge** is the "*engine room of the Times legal department*" and has "*good judgement.*" "*Vigorous*" **Siobhain Butterworth** has built up the legal department at The Guardian-Observer from scratch and "*does a good job.*" "*Excellent*" **Charles Collier-Wright** is "*very experienced.*" **Tom Crone** is "*one of the most capable*" and "*could do this work in his sleep.*" Able to relate to both journalists and editors, he "*has a profound understanding of the business*" but "*you can never get one over on him.*" "*Whizzkid*" **Martin Cruddace** is "*tough and aggressive*" and he is "*well-respected*" for his commercial approach. "*Astute*" **Louise Hayman** does an "*impossible job*" but is "*very pragmatic and professional.*" "*Steady*" **Marcus Partington** is "*bright and enthusiastic.*" He "*knows the law*" and "*understands what editors want.*" "*Impressive*" **Justin Walford** is "*clever, articulate, sensitive, thinking and tremendous.*"

In-House lawyers profiles: page 1177

LONDON

Farrer & Co Top-flight outfit whose behind-the-scenes, commercial approach has given it a reputation for being *"discreet enough to act both for the News of the World and the royal family."* Particularly well-known is the *"analytical and pragmatic"* **Robert Clinton**, who remains popular among fellow practitioners for his *"excellent judgement and perspective; he never pulls stunts or takes partisan points."* On the defendant side, the team acts for several major newspaper titles and publishing groups, while claimant clients include high-profile individuals, institutions and corporations. Recent work has included an increasing number of cases with an international element, particularly in relation to e-mail and internet libel issues. The *"reliable and immensely able"* **Penelope Gorman** enters the rankings this year after repeated recommendations from the market. **Clients:** NewsGroup; Daily Telegraph; Haymarket.

Olswang Despite a year marked by fewer front-page cases than in previous years, this *"small but perfectly formed"* team maintains its reputation for *"getting on with it"* for its large bank of *"extremely loyal clients."* **Geraldine Proudler** is the driving force of the practice *("she's constantly fighting, extremely busy and absolutely top-class,")* but **Julia Palca**, although seen less on the circuit, is still rated a *"fine libel lawyer."* The firm is most notable for its formidable defendant practice, with major clients including national newspapers, magazine groups, companies and charities. In addition, the team has a strong reputation in issues relating to the nascent field of internet and e-mail libel and content, and has a smaller claimant practice. Acted for The Guardian and The Sunday Times in the libel action brought by Keith Schellenberg, the former laird of the Scottish Isle of Eigg. **Clients:** Julie Andrews; Guardian Newspapers Ltd; Freeserve plc.

Peter Carter-Ruck and Partners Large team still thought to be *"in a class of its own"* for claimant work in terms of sheer volume, profile and quality. Many in the market praised the team's *"entrepreneurial approach,"* the most notable example being the continuing success of the firm's conditional fee system for certain defamation cases. Lead players are the *"tough and commercial"* **Nigel Tait**, who *"has the skin of a rhino,"* the *"formidable litigator"* **Alasdair Pepper** and **Andrew Stephenson** *("good on erudite legal argument.")* On the defendant side, the team acts for book, magazine and newspaper publishers and television companies. Acted for Victor Kiam in his successful action against Mirror Group Newspapers. **Clients:** United Broadcasting and Entertainment; Express Newspapers; National Magazine Company.

Davenport Lyons *"Steady"* practice, whose increasing stature, prolific volume of work and experience in the field leads it to rise in the rankings this year. The team is particularly rated for its negotiating ability, commercial approach and relationships with clients, which include major tabloid newspapers, book publishers, Private Eye and high-profile individuals. **Kevin Bays** heads up the practice, which includes the *"sensible and straight-talking"* **Philip Conway**. Acted for Penguin Books in Irving v Penguin Books. **Clients:** Private Eye; Mirror Group Newspapers Limited; Centaur.

DJ Freeman A memorable year for the firm was highlighted by its involvement on behalf of Mohammed al-Fayed in his successful case against Neil Hamilton. **Susan Aslan** is the *"extra-competent, diligent"* face of the practice, which earns particularly high marks for its work on behalf of television companies. Although some expressed doubt about the depth of the team, market consensus was that *"this is a firm on the up."* **Clients:** Channel 4; Mohammed al-Fayed.

Schilling & Lom and Partners *"The first stop for film stars,"* this mainly claimant practice has made its niche in acting for celebrities in defamation and related media matters. Despite a reputation for aggression, team head **Keith Schilling** is recognised as a *"tough but realistic"* negotiator, and has a string of high-value settlements under his belt. The rise of the internet has led to a noted increase in cases with an international dimension. The practice also handles some defendant work for clients including TV companies and entertainment organisations. Acted for Marco-Pierre White in his libel action against the New York Times, the first time that journal had been successfully sued in this country. **Clients:** Marco-Pierre White; Formula 1; LWT.

DEFAMATION • London	Ptnrs	Assts
❶ Farrer & Co	3	2
Olswang	3	3
Peter Carter-Ruck and Partners	6	5
❷ Davenport Lyons	3	5
D J Freeman	3	6
Schilling & Lom and Partners	4	2
❸ Biddle	3	2
Crockers Oswald Hickson	4	5
David Price & Co	1	1
Reynolds Porter Chamberlain	4	5
Theodore Goddard	2	2
❹ Goodman Derrick	3	2
H_2O	2	3
Lovells	2	3
Russell Jones & Walker	3	5
Simons Muirhead & Burton	2	-
Swepstone Walsh	3	2
❺ Bindman & Partners	*	*
Harbottle & Lewis	1	3
❻ Clifford Chance	-	1
Finers Stephens Innocent	1	3
Lewis Silkin	1	1
Manches	*	*
Mishcon de Reya	2	5

LEADING INDIVIDUALS	
✪ **CLINTON Robert** Farrer & Co	**HOOPER David** Biddle
PROUDLER Geraldine Olswang	
❶ **ASLAN Susan** D J Freeman	**BAYS Kevin** Davenport Lyons
HARTLEY Elizabeth Reynolds Porter Chamberlain	
KRAMER Martin Theodore Goddard	
SCHILLING Keith Schilling & Lom and Partners	
SHILLITO Richard Crockers Oswald Hickson	
TAIT Nigel Peter Carter-Ruck and Partners	
❷ **CONWAY Philip** Davenport Lyons	**GREY Rupert** Crockers Oswald Hickson
MIRESKANDARI Razi Simons Muirhead & Burton	
PRICE David David Price & Co	
PEPPER Alasdair Peter Carter-Ruck and Partners	
STEPHENSON Andrew Peter Carter-Ruck and Partners	
❸ **ARMSTRONG Nicholas** Goodman Derrick	
BINDMAN Geoffrey Bindman & Partners	**DADAK Roderick** Lewis Silkin
FOX Paul H_2O	**GORMAN Penelope** Farrer & Co
MATHIESON Keith Reynolds Porter Chamberlain	
MAUNSELL Jeffery Goodman Derrick	**McCUE Jason** H_2O
PALCA Julia Olswang	**RIMELL Katherine** Theodore Goddard
ROBERTSON Rhory Swepstone Walsh	**RUBINSTEIN John** Manches
SMYTH Michael Clifford Chance	**STEWART Patrick** Swepstone Walsh
WEBB Sarah Russell Jones & Walker	
ONE TO WATCH	
THOMPSON Mark Schilling & Lom and Partners	

Within each band, firms are listed alphabetically.
** See editorial entries for explanations of team sizes.*

See ***Profiles*** *on page 293*

Biddle An *"exceptional"* reputation is founded on the expertise of *"heavy-weight performer"* **David Hooper**, described as *"an incredibly tough opponent."* The team has noted expertise in pre and post-publication defendant work for book publishers and broadcasters, and received praise for its strength in contentious work. A year dotted with high-profile cases was highlighted by advice to ITN on their successful libel action against Living Marxism Magazine. **Clients:** Michael Ashcroft; Little Brown Publishers; Forbes Magazine.

Crockers Oswald Hickson Mainly defendant practice which looks after a large number of newspapers, and has a *"big slice of the insurance and regional pie."* The team is known as much for its *"constructive and common sense"* approach to dispute resolution as its *"good double act"* of big hitters. The *"charming and flamboyant"* **Rupert Grey**, who *"provides the theatre,"* and the *"get on with it man"* **Richard Shillito** both command a high level of market support. The team has made several notable forays into the claimant market, including acting for Neil Hamilton and the former Taoiseach of Ireland, Albert Reynolds (in his action against the Sunday Times.) **Clients:** The Law Society; Trinity Mirror's regional titles; Financial Times.

David Price & Co Niche practice which continues to build its profile with gusto. The *"positive, dynamic and tenacious"* **David Price** (a *"swashbuckling hero"*) is qualified as a solicitor-advocate, and undertakes a substantial proportion of the practice's court work. The firm is known as one of the few to offer defamation work on a conditional fee basis. Although some defendant work is handled, the firm is most notable for its large volume of claimant work *("the newspapers hate them!")*. Experienced in making applications to the European Court of Human Rights in relation to Article 10 of the European Convention on Human Rights, the team acted for 'Vanessa' researcher Debbie Price in her successful claim against the Daily Mirror. **Clients:** EuroBusiness; Punch Magazine; Daily Telegraph.

Reynolds Porter Chamberlain Expanded team overwhelmingly seen as a *"force to be reckoned with,"* which rises high in the rankings this year. The recruitment of *"wily operator"* **Keith Mathieson** and the entire Davies Arnold Cooper team (and their large insurance client base) boosts an already impressive defendant practice, which has a strong relationship with major media groups. Team head **Elizabeth Hartley** is highly rated as a libel litigator *("brilliant analytical skills and a great strategist,")* and also rises in the ratings. Acted for human rights activist Ralph Schoenman in his libel victory against the author Bryan Magee, The Orion Publishing Group and Orion Books Ltd. **Clients:** Associated Newspapers Ltd; HTV Ltd (Cardiff); BMIF Ltd.

Theodore Goddard Operating out of the firm's well-regarded Media Litigation and Public Law Group, the team is said to have *"flair."* Known in the market for its long-standing relationship with The Times and Sunday Times and its leading edge profile in questions of corporate defamation. **Martin Kramer** heads up the practice and is a *"determined negotiator,"* while the *"meticulous and dogged"* **Katherine Rimell** rises in the rankings this year after recommendations from solicitors and the Bar. The bulk of the team's work is for defendant newspaper, book publisher and corporate clients, with an increasing ISP practice. Acted for the Sunday Times in its successful appeal to the House of Lords on the ambit of the qualified privilege defence available to the media in defamation actions (arising from the Reynolds case.) **Clients:** Givenchy; Western Provident Association; The Times and The Sunday Times.

Goodman Derrick *"Quiet"* but highly-rated practice, which handles a large amount of pre-broadcast and pre-publication clearance work for TV companies and publishing companies. Key players are the *"aggressive"* but *"clever"* **Jeffery Maunsell** and *"sound operator"* **Nick Armstrong**, who makes his rankings debut this year and is building up a substantial claimant practice for TV company and celebrity clients. Recently acted for Granada in its action against the News of the World relating to an article criticising the Tonight programme. **Clients:** Granada TV; Yorkshire TV.

H_2O Particularly known for the strong niche practice of **Jason McCue**, who specialises in defendant work for newspapers with political and/or cross-border dimensions, notably on Irish cases. The team handles pre-publication work for magazines and book publishers, while *"safe pair of hands"* **Paul Fox** continues to build up the claimant practice. Recent trends of practice include corporate defamation and internet libel. Acted for The Sunday Times in their unsuccessful defence of the libel action brought by Sean McPhilemy in connection with his book 'The Committee.' **Clients:** Times Newspapers Ltd; Express Newspapers; IPC.

Lovells Still recognised as a *"serious defamation practice,"* the team is subsumed within a wider media litigation and public law group. Acts for claimants and defendants, with corporate defamation and reputation management remaining a substantial part of the workload. Over the last year, the practice has been instructed on a succession of high-profile matters, with a noticeable growth in defendant work for newspaper clients. Currently acting for Express Newspapers Ltd in their attempt to overturn Jeffrey Archer's 1987 libel verdict against the Daily Star. **Clients:** Sunday Business; The Observer.

Russell Jones & Walker Primarily claimant practice which is known in the market for its Police Federation work and its *"thorough"* litigation style. Undertakes an increasing amount of work for individual claimants, and some defendant work for individuals, unions and companies. **Sarah Webb** is seen by many practitioners as *"easily the best at the firm"* and enters the rankings this year. Successfully settled a claim brought by the Prince of Wales' protection officer, Detective Chief Superintendent Colin Trimming, against the Mail on Sunday. **Clients:** Police Federation; Dr Julian Lewis MP; Lord Brook of Alverthorpe.

Simons Muirhead & Burton Small but respected practice whose claimant clients range from celebrities to those with conditional fee arrangements. The team also has an expanding defendant client base, including major magazine and book publishers. **Razi Mireskandari** is well known among fellow practitioners and is seen as *"sensible"* and *"determined on behalf of his clients."* **Clients:** Time Out; Random House; Channel 4.

Swepstone Walsh A *"traditional name in the field"* perceived to be doing less defamation work than previously, but retaining a degree of expertise. A predominantly defendant firm, most of the team's time is taken up with pre-publication work for newspaper groups and publishers. **Rhory Robertson** and **Patrick Stewart** are both *"capable players."* **Clients:** Mirror Group Newspapers Ltd; Associated Newspapers Ltd.

Bindman & Partners (1 partner, 1 assistant part-time) Although less visible than in previous years, **Geoffrey Bindman** retains his *"low key, effective"* reputation and his capacity for winning high-profile cases. The practice acts largely for individuals, some on a conditional fee basis, often in cases with a human rights dimension. The recent success in acting for the claimant in the McPhilemy case highlights the advice of one solicitor to *"treat them with care."* **Clients:** New Statesman; Linford Christie; Members of Parliament.

Harbottle & Lewis Well-known for its media and entertainment expertise, the firm's recognised defamation capabilities spring largely from this niche. Acts for a number of publishing companies, UK and foreign media companies and individuals drawn from the sports and entertainment sectors. The majority of the workload is pre-publication advice. **Clients:** Richard Branson; Lawrence Dallaglio; Kate Moss.

Recent High Profile Defamation Cases

Parties	Lawyers	Significance
David Irving v Penguin Books	• Lipstadt – Mishcon De Reya; James Libson; Anthony Julius • Penguin – Davenport Lyons; Heather Rogers. Richard Rampton QC as lead counsel for Penguin & Lipstadt	Historian David Irving loses libel case against Penguin Books, the publishers of Professor Deborah Lipstadt's book in which she claimed he was a holocaust denier. Of legal interest are issues concerning truth in history and case management.
Hamilton v Al Fayed	• Al Fayed – D J Freeman; George Carman QC; James Price QC; Heather Rogers • Hamilton– Crockers Oswald Hickson; Desmond Browne QC; Adrienne Page; Godwin Busuttil	Hamilton loses libel action against Al Fayed over allegations of accepting payment in return for asking questions in Parliament. The case concerned whether an MP may waive privilege and the consequences of such a waiver under section 13 of 1996 Defamation act.
Reynolds v Times Newspapers	• The Times – Theodore Goddard; Lord Lester QC; James Price QC; Pushpinder Saini; Emma Dixon • Reynolds – Crockers Oswald Hickson; Andrew Caldecott QC; Benjamin Hinchliffe	Qualified privilege does not extend to politicians and public figures on matters of public concern. The case concerned reports in The Times about former Irish Prime Minister Albert Reynolds. A very important case in terms of legal significance and the questions of press freedom and the rights of public figures to privacy.
Godfrey v Demon Internet	• Godfrey – Bindman & Partners; Gordon Bishop; Justin Rushbrooke • Demon – Olswang ; Desmond Brown QC; Manuel Barca	ISP liable for publication of libel. Demon Internet hosted defamatory postings about Dr Godfrey. The court held that this was publication, one of the necessary ingredients of defamation.
Grobelaar v Sun Newspaper	• The Sun – Daniel Taylor (Sun in–house counsel); George Carman QC; Richard Speerman • Grobelaar – Cuff Roberts; Richard Hartley QC; Giles Crown	Bruce Grobelaar was awarded £85,000 damages after a High Court libel action over allegations of match fixing.
McPhilemy v Times Newspapers	• Times – H_2O; Andrew Caldecott QC; Caroline Addy • McPhilemy – Bindman & Partners; James Price QC; Matthew Nicklin	Mc Philemy sued The Times over allegation that a TV documentary alleging conspiracy to murder Republicans in Northern Ireland was a hoax. £145,000 damages awarded.
Berezovsky v Forbes	• Berezovsky – Carter Ruck; Desmond Browne QC; Justin Rushbrooke • Forbes – Biddle; Geoffrey Robertson QC; Adrienne Page QC; Tom Beazley	The plaintiff who lived in Russia, wished to sue an American magazine with a small distribution in England. Both sides had real connections with England. The case addresses the test for locus of foreign parties to sue in England.
Garfoot v Walker	• Garfoot – Anthony T. Bryson & Co; Edward Garnier QC; Timothy Atkinson • Walker – David Grey & Co; Andrew Monson	The Boots chemist case in which a £400,000 award of damages for false allegations of sexual harassment was made.
LM v ITN Marshall & Williams	• LM – Christian Fisher; Gavin Millar • ITN – Marshall & Williams– Biddle; Thomas Shields QC; Manuel Barca	ITN journalists awarded damages following allegations of fabrication of Serb detention camp reports. £375,000 damages awarded.

Clifford Chance Defamation practice largely consists of reputation management for corporate clients, with some work undertaken for newspapers, often with a foreign dimension. Clients include libel insurers, broadcasters, ratings agencies, book publishers and MPs. Acted for Mirror Group Newspapers in libel proceedings brought by Sir Elton John and his former manager John Reid. The *"professional"* **Michael Smyth** remains respected by the market. **Clients:** Reuters; Standard & Poor's; The Independent (Paris.)

Finers Stephens Innocent Despite a reputation for being seen *"more in the media than at the coal-face,"* this newly-merged team has a strong client base of US media groups, internet content providers and high profile celebrity claimants. Has particular experience in the area of human rights and free speech. **Clients:** Dow Jones; Wall Street Journal; CNN.

Lewis Silkin **Roderick Dadak** heads this respected team which acts for both claimants and defendants. In addition to defamation and regulatory work for the firm's marketing and advertising agency clients, the practice provides pre- and post-publication advice to a range of clients including newspaper and book publishers, companies and accountants. Recent work has included winning high profile retractions and damages for politicians defamed in local and national newspapers. **Clients:** Express Newspapers Ltd; Southern Magazines Limited (Newscom;) JEM Marketing.

Manches (all part-time) Operating out of the IP department, the *"intelligent"* **John Rubinstein** retains his reputation in the field. The practice largely revolves around defendant work for publishing clients and corporate reputation management. Acted in Coleridge and the Condé Nast Publications Ltd v Eurobusiness and Rubython. **Clients:** Condé Nast Publications Ltd; Victor Gollancz; Speakeasy Media Ltd.

Mishcon de Reya Involved in several substantial headline cases over the past year, although market doubts linger over its concentration of resources in the field. The team handles clearance work for publishers and a regular stream of claimant work, with particular experience in complex jurisdiction issues and e-mail/internet libel. Acted for Deborah Lipstadt in her successful defence of the libel action brought by author David Irving. **Clients:** Book publishers; business newspapers; individuals; internet companies.

THE REGIONS

DEFAMATION • The Regions	Ptnrs	Assts
❶ **Foot Anstey Sargent** Exeter	2	2
Wiggin & Co Cheltenham	1	2
❷ **Brabner Holden Banks Wilson** Liverpool	1	2
Cobbetts Manchester	*	*
❸ **Bevan Ashford** Bristol	-	2
❹ **Pannone & Partners** Manchester	1	1
Wragge & Co Birmingham	*	*

LEADING INDIVIDUALS	
❶ **JAFFA Anthony** Foot Anstey Sargent	**KEAN Caroline** Wiggin & Co
❷ **MANLEY Mark** Brabner Holden Banks Wilson	**STONE Peter** Cobbetts

Within each band, firms are listed alphabetically. *See **Profiles** on page 293*
** See editorial entries for explanations of team sizes.*

Foot Anstey Sargent Long established defamation practice which acts for a large number of regional newspapers and is *"particularly good at reporting restricted material."* Some work is also handled for book publishers and radio stations. **Anthony Jaffa** has a high profile in the field. Recently defended a libel action based on 110 articles. **Clients:** Northcliffe Newspapers Group Ltd.

Wiggin & Co **Caroline Kean** continues to build up her first-class reputation at this largely defendant practice, which has an expanding client base. The team is seen to be competing increasingly with London firms. Handles a wide range of work including corporate defamation, TV clearance and cases referred from insurers. **Clients:** Magazines; regional newspapers; book publishers.

Brabner Holden Banks Wilson Headed by the well-regarded **Mark Manley** *("clearly a specialist")* the team acts for major radio stations and publishers. Has niche expertise in using mediation in defamation disputes and boasts an increasing claimant practice, which offers some work on a conditional fee basis and counts several celebrities amongst its clients. **Clients:** All 18 EMP plc Radio Stations; Newsco Publications Ltd.

Cobbetts While not full-time in the area, the *"bright, incisive"* **Peter Stone** is a respected libel lawyer, with a *"tremendous common sense approach."* In addition to regular defendant work for newspaper and corporate clients, he acts for the occasional claimant, usually referred from other law firms. **Clients:** Manchester Evening News.

Bevan Ashford Reputation derives largely from substantial defendant work for NHS Trusts. The practice is also skilled in advising companies on issues such as trade libel and malicious falsehood. Acted for a leading hospital in connection with a defamation action brought by a former senior member of staff. **Clients:** NHS.

Pannone & Partners Mainly defendant practice which is known particularly for its local authority and political clients. The last year has seen a growth on the claimant side of the practice, which has included several high profile matters. **Clients:** Local authorities; sports personalities; companies.

Wragge & Co (1 partner, 2 assistants part-time) Based within the IP department, this mainly claimant practice *"knows the business"* and acts for a range of insurers, and individuals referred from the Law Society. **Clients:** St Paul Insurance Co; major care providers.

SCOTLAND

DEFAMATION • Scotland	Ptnrs	Assts
❶ **Levy & McRae** Glasgow	1	3
❷ **Bannatyne, Kirkwood, France & Co** Glasgow	2	1
DLA Glasgow	1	-

LEADING INDIVIDUALS	
❶ **CURRIE Derek** DLA	**SCOTT Niall** McGrigor Donald
SMITH Martin Bannatyne, Kirkwood, France & Co	**WATSON Peter** Levy & McRae

Within each band, firms are listed alphabetically. *See **Profiles** on page 293*

Levy & McRae The leading libel practice in Scotland, with a heavy workload and strong client base of newspaper, broadcasting and publishing defendant clients. Also operates a limited pursuer practice. **Peter Watson** is *"as tough as old boots."* **Clients:** Scottish Media Group; Trinity Mirror; ITV.

Bannatyne, Kirkwood, France & Co Making up a substantial part of the firm's work, the specialist and *"robust"* team acts largely for Scottish and English newspaper titles, with some pursuer clients. Team head **Martin Smith** has an established reputation. **Clients:** The Scotsman Publications Ltd; Associated Newspapers Ltd; The Guardian.

DLA The *"experienced and straightforward"* **Derek Currie** heads up this respected practice. Handles pre-publication advice and litigation for newspapers and book publishers in addition to corporate defamation issues. **Clients:** News International; DC Thomson & Co Ltd.

Other Notable Practitioner Though doing less defamation work than in previous years, the *"courteous but determined"* **Niall Scott** of McGrigor Donald is *"knowledgeable about his subject"* and remains highly rated by the market.

NORTHERN IRELAND

DEFAMATION • Northern Ireland	Ptnrs	Assts
❶ **Elliott Duffy Garrett** Belfast	*	*
Johnsons Belfast	*	*
McKinty & Wright Belfast	1	2
Mills Selig Belfast	1	1

LEADING INDIVIDUALS	
❶ **DEENY Brian** Elliott Duffy Garrett	**SPRING Paul** Mills Selig
TWEED Paul Johnsons	

Within each band, firms are listed alphabetically. *See **Profiles** on page 293*
** See editorial entries for explanations of team sizes.*

Elliott Duffy Garrett (1 partner part-time) **Brian Deeny** continues to handle pre-publication work for book publishers and litigation for important newspaper clients. The practice is also building an increasing profile in acting for claimants, which include lawyers and corporate clients. **Clients:** Mirror Group Newspapers Ltd.

Johnsons (1 partner, 2 assistants part-time) *"Capable, experienced and tenacious operator"* **Paul Tweed** heads the team which handles *"a large proportion of the claimant work in Northern Ireland."* Acts for a large number of professionals and high-profile individuals drawn from politics, sport and entertainment. **Clients:** Liam Neeson; Natasha Richardson; The Corrs.

McKinty & Wright One of the leading defendant practices in the province, with an impressive client base of major newspapers. Maintains a limited claimant practice, largely for clients with a commercial background. **Clients:** Belfast Telegraph; Sunday Life; Telegraph Group.

Mills Selig Substantial defendant practice with well known Irish and English newspaper, broadcasting and publishing clients. **Paul Spring** *"knows the lie of the land"* and is seen as *"thorough and efficient"* by fellow practitioners and clients. **Clients:** Associated Newspapers Ltd; RTE; WH Smith.

LEADERS IN DEFAMATION

ARMSTRONG, Nicholas

Goodman Derrick, London (020) 7404 0606
narmstrong@goodmanderrick.co.uk
Specialisation: Media litigation for clients in UK and France; especially defamation: defending media organisations against action (including pre-broadcast/publication clearance); securing remedies for claimants (especially against tabloid press). Also: contempt; confidentiality; copyright and passing off; harassment protection; obscenity; also: public and human rights law, judicial review; French-related litigation and company matters. Recent activity: advising Granada Television (e.g. libel action vs. News of the World over Lawrence suspects); advising makers and cast members of television programmes including Coronation Street, Emmerdale, EastEnders, Tonight with Trevor McDonald.
Prof. Memberships: Royal Television Society. Law Society
Career: Qualified 1986. Trained + qualified with *Theodore Goddard (London + Paris)*. Joined *Goodman Derrick* Media Group 1994.
Publications: Numerous in-house seminars + related paperwork for clients and contacts on media law issues.
Personal: Educated Nottingham High School and Jesus College Cambridge. Hobbies: music; cars; French and English Literature; cinema; food and drink.

ASLAN, Susan

D J Freeman, London (020) 7583 4055
saa@djfreeman.co.uk
Partner in Media & Communications Department.
Specialisation: Principal area of practice is advising terrestrial and satellite broadcasting companies in relation to libel, contempt of court, breach of copyright and other programme content issues. Also undertakes a smaller amount of claimant work and covers breach of confidence and contractual disputes including claims in relation to programme format rights. Important cases handled include Thames Television v. Dixons (libel trial); Channel 4 v. Jani Allan (libel trial); Press Alliance v. Sherill (libel jurisdiction case before the European Court of Justice); Channel 4 v. Dr Nixon (libel trial), Hamilton v Fayed (libel trial). Clients include Channel 4, BSkyB, Thames and Carlton. Co-author of 'A Short Guide to Small Screen Law'. Has appeared on ITV, radio, etc on libel matters.
Prof. Memberships: Media Society.
Career: Qualified in 1985. Partner at *D J Freeman* since 1991.

BAYS, Kevin

Davenport Lyons, London (020) 7468 2600
kbays@davenportlyons.com
Fax: (0171) 437 8216 Partner in 1982.
Specialisation: Defamation, publishing and media law. Principal solicitor for 'Private Eye' for over 13 years. Other publisher clients include Mirror Group Newspapers, Express Newspapers, Centaur Communications, Northern Shell and major book and magazine publishers. Also acts for plaintiffs in defamation cases and media related disputes such as breach of confidence. Handles general commercial litigation with an entertainment bias. Recently acted for Penguin Books in a major libel action brought by revisionist historian David Irving arising out of a book entitled 'Denying the Holocaust'.
Prof. Memberships: Law Society.
Career: Qualified 1979, having joined *Wright Webb Syrett* in 1977. Became a Partner in 1982.
Personal: Born 24th April 1955. Leisure interests include skiing, golf, cricket, football and travelling. Member of The Media Society and The Groucho Club.

BINDMAN, Geoffrey

Bindman & Partners, London (020) 7833 4433
See under Human Rights, p.433

CLINTON, Robert

Farrer & Co, London (020) 7242 2022
Partner. Head of Media.
Specialisation: Main areas of practice are defamation and publishing related litigation. Involves extensive range of claimant and defendant work for prominent individuals, institutions and companies, including newspaper and publishing companies. Pre- and post-publication advice involving breach of confidence, contempt etc. Intellectual property work, covering general trademark and passing off work for commercial clients.
Prof. Memberships: Media Society. International Bar Association.
Career: Joined *Farrer & Co.* in 1972. Became Partner in 1979.
Personal: Born 19th August 1948. Attended Brasenose College, Oxford 1967-71. Lives in London.

CONWAY, Philip

Davenport Lyons, London (020) 7468 2600
pconway@davenportlyons.com
Fax: (0171) 437 8216
Partner in Litigation Department.
Specialisation: Main area of practice is defamation, especially with regard to the newspaper and entertainment industries. Acted for Gorden Kaye (against the Sunday Sport), The Daily Star (against Gillian Taylforth) and Carmen Proetta (against The Sunday Times). Sunday Mirror (against Barry Jones). John Prescott (against Daily Telegraph). Chris Bodker (against The Mail on Sunday). The Sunday Express (against Ian Brady).
Prof. Memberships: Law Society (Member of Pri-

vacy and Defamation Working Committees).
Career: Qualified in 1984. Joined *Wright Webb Syrett* in February 1986. Became Partner in August 1988. Joined *Davenport Lyons* as a Partner on Merger with *Wright Webb Syrett* in March 1995.
Personal: Born 15th April 1959. Attended Aldenham School 1972-77. Former Director Southend United Football Club. Member of The Media Society, Groucho Club and a Barker of The Variety Club of Great Britain.

CURRIE, Derek
DLA, Glasgow (08700) 111111
derek.currie@dla.com
Specialisation: Defamation: Acts for Times Newspapers Limited, publishers of The Times, The Sunday Times and The Sunday Times Scotland; News Group Newspapers Limited, publishers of The Sun and The News of the World, and D C Thomson & Co Limited, publishers of The Sunday Post, for all pre-publication advice and any subsequent litigation; The Press Association as well as for a number of publishers.
Prof. Memberships: Member of The Law Society of Scotland Industrial Law Group. British Member of the Labour & Employment Law Committee of Lex Mundi, a worldwide organisation of lawyers. Member of Employment Law Committee of UIA (Union Internationale des Avocats).
Career: Graduated LLB (Hons) Glasgow University 1977. Assumed as a Partner in the Litigation Department in 1983.
Personal: Married with two children. Golf, hillwalking, sport in general.

DADAK, Roderick
Lewis Silkin, London (020) 7227 8000
Head of Defamation.
Specialisation: Main areas of practice are defamation–libel, slander and malicious falsehood and handling complaints to the Press Complaints Commission and the Broadcasting Standards Commission. Wide experience acting for the media and, in particular, newspapers and publishers. Undertakes both plaintiff and defendant work, and pre-publication libel reading. Has represented national newspapers in major libel trials (e.g. Kiffin, Sethia, and Lucas Box); judicial reviews (e.g. AN v Pickering); and major Plc companies in relation to trade libel actions; confidence actions (e.g. Stephens v Avery); copyright actions (e.g. Associated Newspapers v News Group Newspapers Ltd); contempt actions (e.g. acted for the Daily Star in successfully defending contempt proceedings brought by the Attorney General concerning Geoff Knights, and prior to that A.G. v ITV and Express Newspapers PLC) and passing off actions (e.g. Associated Newspapers v Insert Media, Associated Newspapers v News UK Ltd) also in important wardship cases (e.g. Re: W). Acted for many celebrities and high profile individuals in libel actions (e.g. Clare Latimer in Scallywag/New Statesman cases, John Cleese, Jenny Pitman, James Hewitt and numerous M.P.s). Acts for Express Newspapers PLC, Newscom News Communications & Media Plc and other newspaper, book and magazine publishers. Lectures regularly on defamation matters.
Prof. Memberships: Law Society.
Career: Qualified in 1972. Articled *Theodore Goddard*, Partner *Swepstone Walsh* in 1983, becoming Senior Partner in 1991. At *The Simkins Partnership* 1996-1998. Joined *Lewis Silkin* 1998.

Personal: Attended Lancing College and King's College, London. LLB (Hons). Leisure pursuits include tennis, cinema, theatre and holidaying in Provence. Lives in Farnham. Married with three sons.

DEENY, Brian
Elliott Duffy Garrett, Belfast (028) 9024 5034

FOX, Paul
H_2O (Henry Hepworth Organisation), London (020) 7539 7200
Specialisation: Media Law: Defamation, Confidentiality, Intellectual Property, including pre-publication advice and High Court advocacy, Privacy, Copyright (including music), Publishing, Trade Mark, Advertising, Contempt. Acted and advised on all aspects of media law (pre-publication/broadcast clearance, injunctions and litigation)) for broadcasters, national newspapers and magazines, journalists, authors, public figures and corporations.
Career: Qualified 1986. Also qualified to practice in Hong Kong. Joined Henry Hepworth (H_2O) in 1999.
Personal: Cycling, football (QPR supporter) and political history.

GORMAN, Penelope J.
Farrer & Co, London (020) 7242 2022
pjg@farrer.co.uk
Partner, Media Team.
Specialisation: Main area of practice is media-related litigation (chiefly print or internet based) for corporate, individual and institutional clients, both claimants and defendants. Work includes defamation, malicious falsehood, contempt, reporting restrictions, confidentiality, passing off, copyright and trademarks, and regular copy clearance for magazine clients. Involved over the past year in Law Society committees on the Defamation Pre-action Protocol and the implementation of the outstanding sections of the Defamation Act 1996.
Prof. Memberships: Media Society, The Intellectual Property Lawyers Organisation.
Career: Joined *Farrer & Co* in 1986. Became partner in 1996.
Personal: Born 1962. Attended Emmanuel College, Cambridge 1981-1984 (MA English) and King's College, London 1992-1994 (LLM). Lives in London.

GREY, Rupert
Crockers Oswald Hickson, London (020) 7353 0311
Joint Senior Partner; Head of Media Department.
Specialisation: Principal area of practice is defamation and copyright. Retained by leading magazine and newspaper publishers and their insurers to advise on libel and allied matters prior to publication and post publication complaints. Also by leading photographic/syndication agencies to handle matters connected with literary and artistic copyright. Lectures, writes and gives seminars. Also retained by high profile individuals in advisory, preemptive and plaintiff work. Clients include: The Financial Times, Telegraph Group, Emap, Hello! Limited, Centaur Communications Limited, The Liverpool Institute for Performing Arts and Members of Parliament.
Prof. Memberships: Fellow of Royal Geographical Society.
Career: Qualified in 1975, served articles with *Farrer & Co*. Joined *Crockers* in 1981, Partner in 1983, Head of Department in 1989, Senior Partner in 1997. Previous lives include prospecting for copper in the Fiji Islands, for nickel in Australia, as a roughneck in the Yukon and freelance photo-journalism.
Personal: Born 8th September 1946. Educated Wellington College and UCL. Principal leisure activities are expeditions to wild places and building barns. Married to Jan Sinclair, three daughters; lives in the South Downs.

HARTLEY, Elizabeth
Reynolds Porter Chamberlain, London (020) 7242 2877
ebh@rpc.co.uk
Partner and Head of Media and Technology Group.
Specialisation: A very experienced litigation practitioner with wide knowledge of the media, in particular the newspaper industry. Principal areas of practice are defamation and media related litigation, including contempt of court, breach of confidence, malicious falsehood, reporting restrictions, content issues, PCC and BSC complaints and copyright infringement. Also provides pre-publication clearance and advice. Acts for several national newspaper groups as well as magazines and insurers and undertakes some claimant work. Her group's clients include Associated Newspapers Ltd, Times, Express Newspapers Ltd and Telegraph Group Limited. High profile cases include Shoenman v Orion (libel trial) and libel actions brought by Lawrence Dallaglio, Kate Moss and Paula Yates against newspapers. Also experienced in information technology disputes and has represented both users and suppliers of IT products and services. Has advised on IT disputes in banking, manufacturing, publishing, health, aviation and in privatisations.
Prof. Memberships: The Media Society; Honorary Fellow of the American Bar Association; The Society for Computers & the Law.
Career: Qualified 1982. Chairman of London Young Solicitors Group 1987-88. Partner, *DJ Freeman* 1987, Head of Commercial Litigation from 1996. Joined *RPC* as a partner 1997. Education: Royal Masonic School for Girls; University of Sheffield (LLB Hons).
Personal: Born 1957, resides Surrey. Leisure: music, reading and walking.

HOOPER, David
Biddle, London (020) 7606 9301
Partner in Media Department.
Specialisation: Main area of practice is media and defamation. Also handles entertainment, copyright matters, publishing and broadcasting and issues involving multimedia. Acted for Peter Wright and the publishers in the Spycatcher case. Successfully involved in defending libel actions brought by Robert Maxwell. Acted for John Major in his libel action and prevented attempt by the Government to injunct Andy McNab's book. Acted for Chris Patten against HarperCollins. Publications include 'Public Scandal Odium and Contempt', 'Official Secrets: The Use and Abuse of the Act' and 'Reputations Under Fire' (Little, Brown 2000) 'a survey of the law of libel in the last 10 years'. Has contributed many articles on defamation and media matters in periodicals and the national press and regularly addresses conferences.
Prof. Memberships: Law Society, American Bar Association, International Bar Association.
Career: Qualified in 1971 as a Barrister and in 1977 as a Solicitor. Joined *Biddle* as a Partner in 1986.
Personal: MA (Oxon). Leisure pursuits include cricket, theatre and country activities. Lives in London and Wales.

JAFFA, Anthony
Foot Anstey Sargent, Exeter (01392) 203 992
arj@foot-ansteys.co.uk
Fax: (01392) 203 981 Partner. Head of Media Team and Commercial Litigation Division.
Specialisation: Handles libel, contempt of court, court secrecy orders and related law for media clients. Author of articles and reviews on all aspects of media law. Speaker at conferences for the Newspaper Industry.
Prof. Memberships: Law Society, Society of Notaries.
Career: Qualified in 1980. Articled at *Boyce Hatton & Co.* 1978-80. Worked at *Wilde Sapte* 1980-83, before joining *Foot & Bowden* in 1983. Became a Partner in 1987. Chairman of the Devon Young Solicitors Group 1989-90; Member of National Committee of Young Solicitors Group 1988-89. Notary Public 1989.
Personal: Born 6th August 1956. Attended St Boniface's College, Plymouth 1967-74 and Oxford University 1974-77. Leisure interests include windsurfing, sailing and cycling. Married with two children. Lives in Torquay.

KEAN, Caroline
Wiggin & Co, Cheltenham (01242) 224 114
caroline.kean@wiggin.co.uk
Partner, head of litigation department.
Specialisation: Main areas of practice are defamation and media related commercial litigation. Includes contentious work for plaintiffs, defendants and insurers, advising on copy pre-publication and broadcast, confidence, copyright and passing off. Specialises in private seminars to companies and organisations on issues which include media handling/damage limitation and systems.
Prof. Memberships: Law Society, The Media Society (Council Member). Legal Adviser to Women in Journalism.
Career: Articled *Rubinstein Callingham*. Qualified 1985. Partner 1987. Partner *Olswang* 1989-1995. Joined *Wiggin Co* 1995 as a partner and head of litigation. Author of 'Considerations for the Libel Defendant', 'International Media Law: Ideas in the Need of Protection'. Television; Obscenity: Have the New Kids Come of Age?', International Media Law; 'Protection Rackets', 'Director' magazine, 'Libel Damages: literally the cost of an arm and a leg?', International Media Law.
Personal: Born 1960. Burford School 1971-78, Newnham College, Cambridge 1978-81. College of Law, Lancaster Gate 1981-82.

KRAMER, Martin
Theodore Goddard, London (020) 7606 8855
Specialisation: Media-related litigation for corporate and individual clients, both plaintiffs and defendants. Main newspaper clients are The Sunday Times and The Times. Areas of expertise include libel and slander; malicious falsehood; contempt of court; human rights cases relating to freedom of expression; confidentiality and official secrets; copyright and passing off. Recent and current cases include acting for The Sunday Times in its appeal to the House of Lords arising out of the libel action brought by the former Prime Minister of Ireland, Albert Reynolds; and in defence of an action brought by President Charles Taylor of Liberia; for Western Provident Association, the medical insurance company, which successfully sued Norwich Union in the first major e-mail libel action and in internet and e-mail disputes.
Prof. Memberships: Law Society.
Career: Main areas of practice are media-related litigation and administrative and public law. Qualified 1969. Partner 1978.

MANLEY, Mark
Brabner Holden Banks Wilson, Liverpool
(0151) 236 5821
mark.manley@bhbw.co.uk
Partner and Head of Commercial Litigation Department.
Specialisation: Main area of practice is defamation, acting for radio stations, newspapers, broadcasters and publishers. Also acts for claimants in libel cases. Panel member on Lloyd's Syndicate 702 Libel Panel. Prefered EMAP Radio advisor. Also handles general commercial litigation. Has acted in libel actions against several MPs, the ex-Lord Mayor of Liverpool, and in several commercial libel cases both for and against newspapers. Author of numerous articles on mediation sevices. Spent two years as Partner in Lawyers Planning Services lecturing on financial services, practice management and defamation. Acredited mediator with both CEDR and ADR Group.
Prof. Memberships: Law Society, British Association for Sport and the Law.
Career: Qualified in 1987, becoming an Assistant Solicitor at *Loosemores*. Partner in Lawyers Planning Services since 1989. Joined *Brabner Holden* in 1991, and appointed Partner in 1992.
Personal: Born 17th August 1962. Attended St Nicholas and De La Salle Schools, then Liverpool University and Christleton College of Law. Leisure interests include his family, Everton FC, sports (squash and snooker) and writing music. Lives in Chester.

MATHIESON, Keith
Reynolds Porter Chamberlain, London
(020) 7242 2877
Partner in IP and Media Department.
Specialisation: Main area of practice is media law, particularly defamation, but including contempt of court, reporting restrictions, copyright and passing off. Has acted for and against numerous national and regional newspaper and magazine groups and their insurers. As well as litigation, advises a wide range of publishers on copy clearance. Has written various articles for legal and other publications.
Career: Qualified 1983 with *Lovell White & King*. Joined *Oswald Hickson Collier* 1990. Partner 1992. Partner *Davies Arnold Cooper* 1997-2000. Joined *Reynolds Porter Chamberlin* May 2000.
Personal: Born 1959. Caius College, Cambridge 1977-80. Postgraduate diploma in UK and European law of copyright, King's College, London 1997.

MAUNSELL, Jeffery
Goodman Derrick, London (020) 7404 0606
Specialisation: Intellectual property, defamation, copyright and all aspects of media law. Is one of the most experienced practitioners in libel and general litigaton. Specialises in representing television companies and undertaking work requiring pre- and post-transmission expertise. Has acted in many celebrated and successful cases involving films (Oscar Wilde; Oliver!; The Charge of the Light Brigade) and politicians including Harold Wilson (-v- The Move pop group); Reginald Maudling (-v- Granada Television); Jonathan Aitken (both for him in 1970 in his Official Secrets case and against him in the libel trial of Aitken -v- Granada Television which collapsed so bizarrely in June 1997). Enjoys the cut and thrust of litigation and getting to the nub of the intractable problems facing the client.
Career: Joined *Goodman Derrick* in 1956 and has been a Partner since 1972.
Personal: Born 1936. Lives in London.

MCCUE, Jason
H_2O (Henry Hepworth Organisation), London
(0207) 539 7200
Partner in Media Litigation department.
Specialisation: Media Law: Defamation, Confidentiality, Privacy, Copyright (including music), Publishing, Trade Mark, Advertising, Contempt. Acted and advised (on all aspects of media law (pre-publication/broadcast clearance, injunctions and litigation)) for national broadcasters (e.g. Carlton Television), national newspapers (e.g. Express Newspapers, The Sunday Times), publishers (e.g. IPC), journalists, authors, public figures (e.g. politicians, businessmen, celebrities and musicians) and corporations. Defamation Speciality: Complex case investigation (particularly in relation to politics, matters of investigative journalism, security forces, organised crime and international terrorism); internet libel/"cyber policing"; reputation management (media PR); advising and managing Irish and Northern Ireland litigation; managing media litigation on behalf of insurers; cross-border libel. Acted in many leading cases.
Prof. Memberships: The usual!
Career: Queen Mary College, London University. Worked at *Mishcon de Reya*, *Goodman Derrick*. One of the founding partners of *Henry Hepworth* in May 1997.
Personal: Born 1969. Spends time writing, painting, skiing, driving, and enjoying folk music, Ireland and travel.

MIRESKANDARI MA, Razi
Simons Muirhead & Burton, London
(020) 7734 4499
razi@smab.co.uk
Partner 1988. Head, Civil Litigation Department.
Specialisation: Main areas of practice are media-related. Particularly noted for defamation. Acts for book/newspaper/magazine/internet publishers, broadcasters, authors' agents, writers, journalists and a wide variety of clients in the media and entertainment world, ranging from rock bands to restaurants.
Career: Qualified in 1986. Member Groucho club.

PALCA, Julia
Olswang, London (020) 7208 8888
See under Employment, p.342

PEPPER, Alasdair
Peter Carter-Ruck and Partners, London
(020) 7353 5005
Partner in Media Litigation Department.
Specialisation: Main area of practice is media law, with emphasis on defamation and related areas, contempt and copyright. He acts for both claimants and defendants and also undertakes election law (acted for the Referendum Party), advertising law and more general areas of litigation. He has experience in preparing submissions to regulators such as the Medicines Control Agency, Advertising Standards Authority and Broadcast Advertising Clearance Centre and appearing before the Broadcasting Standards Commission.

Prof. Memberships: Law Society, IBA.
Career: Qualified in 1984. Has remained with *Peter Carter-Ruck and Partners* since qualification. Became a Partner in 1986.
Personal: Born 13th May 1960. Attended Radley College, then Guildford College of Law. Leisure interests include riding, tennis, squash and walking. Lives near Alton, Hampshire.

PRICE, David
David Price & Co, London (020) 7916 9911
Specialisation: A solicitor-advocate who offers a "one-stop" service, including representation at trial. Principal area of practice is defamation and media litigation, representing both claimants and a wide range of publishers. Has acted in many high profile and landmark cases. Author of 'Defamation: Law, Procedure and Practice' published by Sweet & Maxwell 2000.
Career: Qualified as a solicitor (1990). Barrister (1991). Principal of *David Price & Co* since 1993.
Personal: Born 16th October 1963. Educated at Haberdashers' Aske School (1970-82) and Harvard High School, Los Angeles (1982-83). Manchester University (1983-86).

PROUDLER, Geraldine
Olswang, London (020) 7208 8888
Head of Defamation
Specialisation: Main area of practice is media law including defamation, contempt of court, breach of confidence, broadcasting complaints and associated matters. Acts for both plaintiffs and defendants including national and regional newspapers and magazines. Acted for the Guardian in its successful defences against Jonathan Aitken, Neil Hamilton, Stoke Newington police officers and Keith Schellenberg, Laird of the Isle of Eigg (acting for both The Guardian and The Sunday Times). This represents four victories in three years on behalf of The Guardian. Acted for Mirror Group in defending the action by Broadmoor patient Peter Oates (1p damages recovered by Oates), and acted for Mirror in the Victor Kiam case. Acted for Demon Internet in defending an internet libel action. Acting for Associated Newspapers in defending a claim by the former editor of Tatler, Jane Proctor. Also acted for Marks and Spencer Plc as Plaintiff in its successful action against Granada Television.
Prof. Memberships: Law Society, Media Society.
Career: Qualified 1980. Became a partner with *Lovell White & King* (now *Lovell White Durrant*) in 1987. Joined *Olswang* as a partner 1995.
Personal: Born 2 July 1956. BA Law at Nottingham University 1974-1977. Lives in London.

RIMELL, Katherine
Theodore Goddard, London (020) 7606 8855
Specialisation: Main areas of practice are media related litigation, particularly defamation, malicious falsehood, confidence, human rights and public law. Acts for a variety of corporate and individual clients, both plaintiffs and defendants. Recent cases include acting for The Sunday Times in its appeal (in the Reynolds action) to the House of Lords to extend the defence of qualified privilege, defending The Sunday Times in a libel action brought by the Barclay brothers and defending The Mirror in the retrial of the action brought by Rupert Allason for malicious falsehood.
Prof. Memberships: Law Society
Career: Qualified in 1985. Partner of *Theodore Goddard* in 1997.

ROBERTSON, Rhory
Swepstone Walsh, London (020) 7304 2100
Specialisation: Practice covers full range of media and commercial litigation; in particular defamation and intellectual property. Acts for substantial Newspapers and Publishing Groups; independent production companies, authors and broadcasters.
Prof. Memberships: Law Society.
Career: Qualified 1977. BBC Solicitor 1978-84. Mirror Group Legal Adviser 1987. Joined *Swepstone Walsh* 1988.
Personal: Born 31st July 1952. Educated Ardingly College and Southampton University (LLB).

RUBINSTEIN, John
Manches, London (020) 7404 4433
Specialisation: All aspects of media law and electronic publishing; defamation, malicious falsehood, copyright, obscenity, trade mark infringement, passing off, rights of privacy and personality. Also practices in publishing, multimedia and computer law. Has appeared on BBC and Sky TV. Recent cases include Stern v Piper (CA) 1998, Bremner v Westview Press Inc, Cardata Ltd v RAC Motoring Services Ltd and representation of Southwest Water in the leading computer law case against ICL. Also led a 22 person team Anton Piller search for Business Software Alliance against The Mirror Group.
Prof. Memberships: International Bar Assocations (Co-Chairman of Art and Cultural Property Law Committee), Media Society, TIPLO, Association of the Bar of the City of New York.
Career: Admitted in 1977; admitted to New York Bar and Federal Courts ED and SD New York 1979; with *Manches* since 1994 on merger with *Rubinstein Callingham Polden & Gale*.

SCHILLING, Keith
Schilling & Lom and Partners, London (020) 7453 2500
Senior Partner
Specialisation: Main area of practice is media and internet litigation especially libel. Represents insurers, broadcasters, publishers, film producers, film distributors, sportsmen, internet users and many leading celebrities. Other areas of practice in media litigation include copyright, breach of confidence, passing off and divorce. Contributor on libel, breach of confidence and copyright in the Entertainment Law Review.
Prof. Memberships: Law Society, City of Westminster Law Society.
Career: Qualified in 1981. Articled at *Wright Webb Syrett* before forming *Schilling & Lom* in 1984.
Personal: Born 25 July 1956. Attended Bromley Technical High School Boys 1967-72, Master of Arts (European Business Law), City of London Polytechnic 1980-82. Member of 'Groucho's' and Chelsea Arts Club. Leisure interests include reading, music, mountaineering. Lives in Hampstead.

SCOTT, Niall
McGrigor Donald, Glasgow (0141) 248 6677
Head of Commercial Litigation Unit.
Specialisation: Pre and post publication editorial advice in relation to contempt of court and defamation. Advised the BBC in relation to the Zircon Affair and the raid by Special Branch on the headquarters of BBC Scotland. Has acted for most of the the main newspaper publishers in Scotland in a career spanning 1979 to 2000. Now also acts for individuals and corporations in defamation claims.
Prof. Memberships: Law Society of Scotland. Royal Faculty of Procurators, Glasgow.
Career: Jordanhill College School, Glasgow. LLB University of Aberdeen. Qualified as a solicitor in 1975. 1991-1993 External examiner for diploma in legal practice, University of Glasgow. Managing Partner, *McGrigor Donald* from April 1994 to August 1997.
Personal: Married to Judith with four children Edward, Antonia, Virginia and Nicholas. Hill walking, golf, tennis, skiing and swimming.

SHILLITO, Richard A.
Crockers Oswald Hickson, London (020) 7353 0311
Partner in Media Department.
Specialisation: Main area of practice is defamation. Acts for a large number of national, regional and trade press clients and their insurers. Other areas of expertise are contempt, reporting restrictions and copyright. Contributor to the Yearbook of Copyright and Media Law (OUP, 1999).
Career: Qualified in 1976, having joined *Oswald Hickson, Collier & Co.* in 1973. Became a Partner in 1984. Previously a trainee journalist at Yorkshire Weekly Newspaper Group Limited, 1970-72.
Personal: Born 13th March 1948. Attended Westminster School, then Magdalen College, Oxford (1970, PPE (Hons)). Leisure interests include music and sailing. Lives in London. Married, with three daughters.

SMITH, Martin B.
Bannatyne, Kirkwood, France & Co, Glasgow (0141) 221 6020
martin@b-k-f.demon.co.uk
Specialisation: The practice, which was established in Glasgow in 1785, covers the full range of intellectual property work and includes all aspects of defamation and media law with particular reference to Scotland. The practice numbers amongst its clients major newspaper and publishing companies and also acts for British Actors Equity Association in Scotland.
Prof. Memberships: A former journalist who graduated in Law at The University of Edinburgh and is admitted as a Notary Public in Scotland.
Career: Qualified in 1971 and joined *Bannatyne, Kirkwood, France, & Co* in 1973 attaining the position of senior partner in 1995. Also a consultant with Messrs. *Peter Carter-Ruck & Partners* in London, being a registered foreign lawyer.
Personal: Educated at the High School of Glasgow and University of Edinburgh. Interests include writing on media matters and lecturing on the subject. In addition, he is a former Chairman of the Scottish Second Division Football Club, Queen's Park F.C. and has represented the Club at Scottish Football League and Scottish Football Association levels.

SMYTH, Michael
Clifford Chance, London (020) 7600 1000
michael.smyth@cliffordchance.com
Specialisation: Partner with extensive experience in all kinds of commercial disputes, including media litigation and public law cases. Clients include public authorities, newspapers, book publishers and news agencies. Heads pre-publication unit providing advice on 24-hour basis. Also ranked in the annual

International Commercial Litigation survey. Author of 'Business and the Human Rights Act'. Runs firm's pro bono practice.
Prof. Memberships: Law Society, City of London Solicitors' Company, Administrative Law Bar Association. Member of the Law Society's Human Rights Act Task Force and of the Liason Group to the Home Office's Human Rights act Task Force. Member of the Law Society's Defamation Pre-action Protocol Committee.
Career: Royal Belfast Academical Institution; Clare College, Cambridge (MA Law). Qualified 1982; partner *Clifford Chance* 1990; also admitted in Hong Kong and Northern Ireland.

SPRING, Paul
Mills Selig, Belfast 028/9024/3878
Litigation partner, specialising in libel.
Specialisation: Main area of practice is libel. Represents several national newspapers, broadcasting organisations and book and magazine publishers in Northern Ireland litigation. Extensive experience of libel litigation for both defendants and plaintiffs. Areas of practice include breach of confidence, contempt of Court, press complaints, copyright and pre-publication work. Other major areas of practice are commercial litigation and product liability litigation. (Clients include British American Tobacco.)
Prof. Memberships: Law Society of Northern Ireland.
Career: Qualified 1983. Formerly litigation partner since 1988 at *Cleaver Fulton & Rankin*; Belfast. Joined *Mills Selig* March 1988.
Personal: Educated Belfast Royal Academy and London School of Economics (graduating in Law in 1981). Leisure interests include cycling, architecture and the countryside. Lives near Belfast.

STEPHENSON, Andrew
Peter Carter-Ruck and Partners, London (020) 7353 5005
Partner in Litigation Department.
Specialisation: Main area of practice is defamation. Extensive experience acting both for claimants, including government ministers, members of Parliament and sports and music personalities, and for defendants including book, magazine and newspaper publishers and television companies. Also experienced in media law generally, including the law of contempt, copyright and passing off work.
Prof. Memberships: Law Society, Media Society.
Career: Joined *Peter Carter-Ruck & Partners* in 1982. Qualified 1983. Became Partner in 1986.
Personal: Born 11th September 1956. Attended University College, London 1975-78. Council of Stock Exchange 1979-81. Leisure pursuits include literature and theatre. Lives in Wokingham, Berkshire.

STEWART, Patrick
Swepstone Walsh, London (020) 7404 1499
Specialisation: Media law including defamation, Contempt of Court, copyright, breach of confidence, passing off and pre-publication clearance. Acts for national newspapers, book and magazine publishers, video production companies and plaintiffs. Also does some general commercial litigation.
Prof. Memberships: Law Society and Media Society
Career: Qualified 1973. Legal Adviser Mirror Group Newspapers 1985-90. Joined *Swepstone Walsh* 1990.
Personal: Born 6th July 1948. Educated Stonyhurst College and Durham University.

STONE, Peter
Cobbetts, Manchester (0161) 833 3333
peter.stone@cobbetts.co.uk
Specialisation: Over 20 years experience in litigation for national and regional blue-chip clients. Particular expertise in commercial property litigation (forfeiture, dilapidations, covenants, contested lease renewals, Brewery/Licensed Retailer work) and in defamation (Plaintiff and Defendant) for individual and media clients.
Prof. Memberships: Law Society. Notaries Society.
Career: Educated at Rossall School and Liverpool University (LLB Hons 1st class). Articled at *Cobbetts*, 1974. Qualified 1976, Partner 1979.
Personal: Born 1951. Leisure interests include fell-walking, climbing and mountain biking.

TAIT, Nigel
Peter Carter-Ruck and Partners, London (020) 7353 5005
Partner in Media Department.
Specialisation: Main area of practice is media law, acting for claimants and defendants and giving pre-publication advice. Cases of interest include Beta Construction v. Channel 4 (award of £568,000: highest ever libel award paid to a company); Vladimir Telnikoff v. Vladimir Matusevitch (first libel case to go to House of Lords for over a decade. Award of £240,000); Jack Slipper v BBC (£50,000 damages: a leading case on liability for republication); Jonathan Hunt (aged 6) v. The Sun (settlement of £35,000 plus costs to mother and son; youngest ever libel plaintiff); Farargay v. Al Hayat (award of £170,000 plus costs); Scholar v. Mail (award of £100,000 plus costs; Gorman v. Mudd (award of £150,000 plus costs); Morelli v. Times (award of £45,000; first CFA libel action to go to trial); Kirby Harris v. Baxter; CA (leading case on trial by Jury; Victor Kiam v. Sunday Times £45,000 damages–the first and only libel award to be upheld by the Court of Appeal since the Courts and Legal Services Act 1990; Shah v. Standard Chartered Bank (the leading case on reasonable grounds to suspect); Kiam v. The Mirror (award of £105,000 plus costs). Has won over 90% of cases that have gone to trial. Also conducts personal injury work, acting for plaintiffs (highest award £755,000). Contributor to 'Carter-Ruck on Libel and Slander', 4th & 5th editions. Regular lecturer on media law and defamation. Has spoken at the Oxford Union Debating Society on 3 occasions on law reform. Member of Law Society Privacy, Defamation and Pre-action Protocol working committees.
Prof. Memberships: Law Society. International Bar Association.
Career: Qualified in 1988, having joined *Peter Carter-Ruck and Partners* in 1986. Became a Partner in 1990. Managing Partner 1997.
Personal: Born 5th April 1963. Attended Nottingham University 1981-84. Leisure interests include family and football. Lives in Clapham, London.

TWEED, Paul
Johnsons, Belfast (028) 9024 0183
pt@johnsonslaw.co.uk
Specialisation: Defamation (the most well known case being for B J Eastwood against the boxer Barry McGuigan–£450,000 award, and more recently has acted for the actors Liam Neeson and Natasha Richardson against a number of Irish newspapers in relation to false reports regarding the state of their marriage and also for Robert McCartney QC, the MP for North Down, who was awarded £80,000 in a high profile case against the Irish Times on the eve of the General Election). Acts for a number of other media, political, public, business and legal personalities and also on the Defence side for several newspapers and publications. Other areas of practice include copyright and related media work.
Prof. Memberships: Incorporated Law Society of Northern Ireland (1978). Law Society of England and Wales (1993).

WATSON, Peter B.
Levy & McRae, Glasgow (0141) 307 2311
Specialisation: Media; Defamation; Libel; Aviation; International Claims and Litigation; Personal Injury Litigation; Public & Fatal Accident Inquiries; civil and criminal litigation; Inland Revenue and Customs & Excise Investigation; employment law; partnership law; Secretary of the Lockerbie Air Disaster Group; Secretary of Braer Disaster Group; Member of the Steering Committee of the Piper Alpha Disaster Group; 'Gecas v. Scottish Television plc'; 'Cavendish v. The Scotsman Publications & Others'; representing the Dunblane Families at the Dunblane Public Inquiry; involved in litigation in more than 12 countries other than the UK.
Prof. Memberships: Law Society of Scotland; SSC Society; APIL; ATLA; President of the Society of Solicitor Advocates; Chairman of the Scottish Mediation Bureau; Member of the IBA.
Career: BA in Economics, University of Strathclyde; Bachelor of Law, University of Edinburgh; research at Scandinavian Maritime Institute and thereafter at Dundee University, Centre for Petroleum and Mineral Law Studies; Visiting Scholar in International Law, Nova University, Florida, USA; on the Board of Anglia Sports Law Research Centre.
Personal: Horseracing; travel; married with two daughters, Anna and Sophie.

WEBB, Sarah L.
Russell Jones & Walker, London (020) 7837 2808
s.l.webb@rjw.co.uk
Specialisation: Partner in the litigation business and private client group specialising in defamation and commercial litigation. Acted for Stephen King solicitor v Daily Telegraph and Mr Justice Garland in his claim against Channel 4. Represented former MP Tim Smith in connection with the Hamilton libel action against The Guardian and in his appearance before the Downey Committee. Also represented the first postmenopausal woman to receive IVF treatment for twins in Italy to protect the identity of her twins, herself and her family from the media. Advised the Jockeys Association on defamation and acting for Lord Harris and supporters of Neil Hamilton's libel action against Mr Al Fayed in the defence of Mr Al Fayed's claim for costs following his successful defence of the claim.
Prof. Memberships: Equine Lawyers Association
Career: Articled *McDonald Stacey*; qualified 1983; joined *Russell Jones & Walker* in 1983, partner since 1990.
Publications: A number of articles in Solicitors Journal, The Lawyer and the Law Society Gazette and a regular column in an equestrian magazine.
Personal: Born 1956, educated at Malvern Girls College, College of Law, Lancaster Gate. Resides in Kent. Interests include family and horse riding.

E-COMMERCE

London: 298; *Profiles*: 300

OVERVIEW: Bowing to the inevitable, this year we recognise e-commerce as a separate sector. This table is designed to recognise the high-profile regulatory practitioners who formerly constituted part of the IT section, as well as those corporate practitioners with particular expertise in overseeing the booming number of IPOs of the dot.com start-up companies. The list of firms and practitioners is expected to grow, as increasing numbers of lawyers specialise in one of the most lucrative areas of current practice. Mention should be made of market leaders Bird & Bird and Olswang, whose comparatively long-term focus on this area continues to pay dividends.

RESEARCH APPROVED BY BMRB: *For this edition,* Chambers' *researchers conducted 6083 interviews – 4408 with law firms, 598 with barristers and 1077 with clients.*

The validity of the research was scrutinised by BMRB International, who audited both the methodology and the results at our offices in July 2000. They interviewed Chambers' *researchers and cross-checked sample interviews. Details of the audit appear on page 7.*

LEADING IN-HOUSE LAWYERS

Tim KUSCHIALL, Associate Counsel, *LibertySurf*

Anisa DHANJI, Company Secretary, *QXL*

Clare GILBERT, Vice President and General Counsel, *AOL Europe*

John KENBURY, Director of Legal and Business Affairs, *Open Interactive*

Marijke REID, Legal/Compliance Manager, *Open Interactive*

Clare Gilbert at AOL really stands out for having *"a solid reputation and a very good grasp of the field."* **John Kenbury** at Open Interactive has been through the hoops and is *"very commercial."* **Anisa Dhanji** at QXL is fairly new but is *"picking it up very fast."* Other newcomers of note include **Tim Kuschiall** at LibertySurf who has *"good all-round IT experience"* and **Marijke Reid** at Open Interactive who is *"responsible, fair and intelligent."*

In-House lawyers profiles: page 1177

LONDON

E-COMMERCE • London
❶ Bird & Bird
Olswang
❷ Clifford Chance
❸ Baker & McKenzie
Denton Wilde Sapte
Field Fisher Waterhouse
❹ H2O
Harbottle & Lewis
Herbert Smith
Kemp & Co
Paisner & Co
Taylor Joynson Garrett
❺ Osborne Clarke OWA
Pinsent Curtis
Theodore Goddard

LEADING INDIVIDUALS	
❶ **ENSER John** Olswang	**HAFTKE Mark** KLegal
McNEIVE Liam McNeive Solicitors	**MILLARD Christopher** Clifford Chance
SMITH Graham Bird & Bird	
❷ **CHISSICK Michael** Field Fisher Waterhouse	**KEMP Richard** Kemp & Co
SMALL Harry Baker & McKenzie	
SUMMERFIELD Spencer Travers Smith Braithwaite	
❸ **CALOW Duncan** Denton Wilde Sapte	**COWAN Matthew** Olswang
EDWARDS Gareth Pinsent Curtis	**HENRY Michael** H2O
KAYE Laurence Paisner & Co	**NICHOLSON Kim** Olswang
PHILLIPS Mark Harbottle & Lewis	**ROSEFIELD Stephen** Paisner & Co
TURNER Mark Herbert Smith	**WILLIAMS Alan** Denton Wilde Sapte
UP AND COMING	
WINTON Ashley Osborne Clarke OWA	

Within each band, firms are listed alphabetically. *See **Profiles** on page 300*

Bird & Bird *"Tremendous commercial lawyers who get the deal done,"* though some felt the quality of their work was, on occasion, of a *"variable"* standard. One of the first firms to venture in to the internet/e-commerce arenas, they are currently active in the fields of digital distribution and media, internet joint ventures and dot.com start-ups. The team is especially noted for its advice to venture capitalists. *"Original thinker"* **Graham Smith** is one of the pre-eminent e-commerce practitioners, although the loss of the Mark Haftke, to KLegal will deal the group's client base an obvious blow. Offering a well established corporate finance service, and seen as "hard negotiators, expanding dramatically," the firm is broadening its client base to include acting for internet investors such as GE Capital and Global Retail Partners on equity financing. Advised Orchestream on four rounds of VC funding leading to its £200 million IPO. **Clients:** Amazon.co.uk; Demon Internet/Thus plc; Carlton Online; Emap; Loot.com; The Electronic Telegraph; lastminute.com.

Olswang *"Head and shoulders above the rest,"* in the view of several interviewees, the firm certainly has one of London's premier Internet/e-commerce practices. A genuine full service 'convergence' practice with a focus on internet content (a real forte), digital TV and WAP related issues. Key hitters in the team include **John Enser** *("he really stands out from the crowd")* and the well known **Kim Nicholson**, who hails from a corporate background. **Matthew Cowan** was also recommended. The firm has recently recruited two private equity specialists from Berwin Leighton to bolster its capacity to assist funding start-up and pre-flotation clients. Advising Freeserve on the launch of its women's portal, iCircle, and on content deals including People Bank and lastminute.com. Also acting for Demon Internet in a leading defamation case concerning on-line libel. In what is seen as an innovative service to attract internet based start-ups, the firm has launched Long Acre Partners, a corporate finance house, in conjunction with JP Morgan. The corporate team has a well established reputation for AIM listings and advised Gameplay.com and VitualInternet on their floats. Also acts for internet incubator funds such as Bain Lab and AntFactory. **Clients:** peoplesound.com; sportal.net; Freeserve; Demon Internet; BBC Worldwide; BSkyB; Granada Media; Dixons; worldpop.com; First Tuesday.

Clifford Chance None of the 'Magic Circle' City firms, are felt to have established themselves in the internet/e-commerce sphere as successfully as Clifford Chance. *"Thoroughly intelligent,"* **Chris Millard** *("amongst the best")* is not only *"one of the UK's leading data protection lawyers,"* he is also known as an academic in the sphere. Particularly noted for its work on IPOs, and often chosen for its global capacity, the team advised Orchestream on the bulk of its £214 million flotation on the London Stock Exchange. **Clients:** Orchestream; dot.com start-ups.

Baker & McKenzie *"Its international contacts are key to the firm's success,"* and the team also benefits from the firm's strengths in the 'hard' IT and telecommunications sectors. Seen to have upped their profile over the past year, online data protection and IP/IT related matters are this full-service team's key specialities in the internet/e-commerce field. *"Intelligent and personable,"* **Harry Small** is still *"the best at Baker Mac"* though generally perceived to be more of a 'pure' IT man. Advising Hewlett Packard on the supply of servers to Stelios Hadji-Ioannou's new online venture EasyEverything Stores. **Clients:** Hewlett Packard; Oracle; Orange; Sony; Cisco Systems; Compaq.

Denton Wilde Sapte While rated by some as *"incredibly impressive on e-commerce,"* especially for internet start-ups, others felt that the firm's profile simply wasn't what it used to be. *"Bright bloke"* **Duncan Calow** is tipped as *"definitely one to watch,"* while **Alan Williams** continues to be recognised for his niche forte in publishing related e-issues. Building on the Wilde Sapte banking reputation and Denton Hall's entertainment business, the firm has *"ridden the dot.com wave"* with an increase in IPOs, acting for institutional investors. **Clients:** Tadpole Technology, Apax Partners.

Field Fisher Waterhouse Seen to have *"made a splash"* in the internet/e-commerce arena, thanks partly to the superlative marketing skills of **Michael Chissick**, a *"very good ambassador for his firm in the e-commerce space."* Venture capital funding, website development and online data protection matters are the department's primary areas of activity. Has successfully capitalised on its traditional profile in this market (which includes taking equity stakes in clients), *"aggressive growth"* includes advising Level 3 Communications LLC. **Clients:** Boo.com, Thomas Cook, BAT, Doubleclick.com.

H20 Perhaps best known for its strength in the content and copyright ('soft IP') arenas, the firm was one of the very first to venture into the e-commerce space. **Michael Henry** was the man behind this pioneering move and remains a known name in the field, though his profile is held to have faded somewhat over the past year. Advised Hay & Robertson on a number of e-commerce deals, including online merchandising agreements for Manchester United and the English Cricket Board. **Clients:** UFI (University for Industry); Arena Leisure plc; Hay & Robertson plc.

Harbottle & Lewis *"Astute"* firm, best known for its superb computer games practice. Has expanded its client base beyond its traditional media and charities focus to embrace clients from all walks of the internet/online industry, from Major ISPs and key web and content providers, to incubator funds, network clubs and 'e-channels.' Particularly active in the fields of interactive television, domain names and WAP related matters. Also currently acting for around 100 internet start-ups (dot.coms and dot.co.uks.) **Mark Phillips** is the best known name in the team. The firm has advised Chrysalis on its JV with rivals.com to form the world's largest network of sports speciality web sites, and advised Dawnay, Day & Lander, the UK's first privately financed internet incubator fund, on its alliance with FBR a US technology focused investment bank (total funds £30 million.) **Clients:** Chrysalis; Virgin.com; Amazon Online; Virgin.net.

Herbert Smith A respectable internet/e-commerce practice, though some felt the firm's *"confrontational approach"* might not go down too well in the 'e-arena.' Offer an across the board service to clients in the sector, with internet financings considered a real forte. Also currently active on behalf of US dot.coms setting up in the UK. **Mark Turner** is the team's best known name. Acting for Time Warner on the UK/European aspects of its merger with AOL and advising WH Smith on an agreement with Microsoft to develop a fully fledged free access internet portal containing a range of educational and entertainment material. Established a strong reputation in the IPO field by acting for the global co-ordinators for the £2 billion listing of Freeserve (Credit Suisse First Boston and Cazenove & Co) and the £263 million placing of QXL.com (Credit Suisse First Boston.) **Clients:** Time Warner; CSFB; BSkyB; WH Smith; Network Solutions.

Kemp & Co Definitely on an upward curve, this specialist convergence 'boutique' has increased its standing in the e-arena over the past year. Concentrating solely on IT, telecoms and internet matters, the firm is led by *"driven"* name partner **Richard Kemp** *("very bright")* who will do *"absolutely anything for his clients."* Continue to advise Microsoft on a range of issues relating to its MSN portal and have been instructed by US based internet infomediary AllAdvantage (known for their 'viral marketing') on the launch of their UK and European operations. **Clients:** Microsoft; Expedia; AllAdvantage Inc.; FTSE International; Primark; Cognotec.

Paisner & Co *"Noteworthy"* practitioners in the field, who entered the e-arena with a background in electronic publishing. On-line financial services, data protection advice and delivery of entertainment and information are considered the team's fortes. So too is lobbying, the firm having industry involvement with the new e-commerce related EU Directives. Well-known *"veteran"* **Laurence Kaye** is *"good on newspaper-related internet issues."* *"Excellent"* corporate partner **Stephen Rosefield** is seen to provide an impetus to the firm's entrepreneurial client base which sits well with its strong private equity practice. The firm acted for Apax Partners on its investment in QXL.com. The practice is currently providing contractual, regulatory and other advice to the FT on the establishment of its new personal finance site – FTYourMoney.com – and the launch of the revised FT.com site. Also acting for Beenz.com in various strategic alliances, including those with Excite UK Ltd and leading Italian portal Kataweb. **Clients:** Point Four Consulting; FTYourMoney.com; FT.com; Espresso Productions; Virtual Jukebox.com; UpMyStreet.com; Fish4; This is Britain.

Taylor Joynson Garrett *"Pulling ahead with a strong private equity offering"* and some *"serious US clients"* in the internet/e-commerce sphere, the firm enters our tables this year as *"something of a rising star."* Its client portfolio is not held to be as impressive, however, when it comes to European clients. Advised Digital Ventures II Ltd and ePartners on their investments in London based e-commerce start-up Eyestorm.com, and 365 Corporation plc on its $1.65 million agreement and merger plan to acquire US based sports content company e-Merchants. **Clients:** Digital Ventures II Ltd; ePartners; 365 Corporation plc.

Osborne Clarke OWA *"Developing a good name for themselves,"* thanks partly to having recruited *"a fine group of people,"* and possessing an impressive client base. One new recruit who has particularly impressed both his peers and the market, is up and comer **Ashley Winton**, snaffled from Bird & Bird. In addition to acting for Yahoo! On-line Service on a number of matters, the department is currently advising Brokat, the world's largest internet banking software company on the creation of the Co-op bank's 'Smile' internet bank. Advised the recently established Internet Investment Trust on its aim to raise up to £100 million for hypergrowth internet companies. **Clients:** Yahoo! On-line Service; Electronic Arts; Brokat; VeriSign; Infobank; Indicii Salus; Netscape Corp; Activision; Sony Computer Entertainment Europe.

Pinsent Curtis With extensive e-commerce work being undertaken by both the corporate and commercial departments of this firm, they enter our rankings on the back of a *"practical, commercial internet focus."* **Gareth Edwards** is said to be *"trustworthy and supportive"* and has a growing reputation acting for the corporate needs of start-ups and established players alike. Acted for Just2Clicks on its £130 million AIM floatation and for Blakes Clothing plc on its transference to AIM to form e-xentric plc (market capitalisation £280 million.) **Clients:** Arlington Group (an internet incubator.)

Theodore Goddard While not one of the leading lights of the e-arena, the e-commerce Group's technical range of skills are said to be good. The firm's media experience is considered particularly relevant. Advise on a range of on-line activities, including cyberliability, dot.com start-up financings, the establishment and running of ISPs and full flotations. Acted for Peel Hunt on the AIM flotation of NewMedia Spark and on the placing and open offer of Sci Entertainment Group plc (the online entertainment group.) **Clients:** News Network Ltd; Kickon plc; Nutravida.

Other Notable Practitioners The *"superb"* **Liam McNeive**, of McNeive Solicitors, *"certainly knows his onions"* and is a well-known name in his field. Seen by some to *"semi-house"* for long-standing client AOL, he advised QXL on all the legal strategic aspects of its European expansion. **Mark Haftke** *("knows all the relevant people")* has joined KLegal from Bird & Bird. Regarded as one of the leading players in the sector, he takes with him a slew of impressive clients, including Amazon.com. In a corporate finance capacity, **Spencer Summerfield** of Travers Smith Braithwaite is said to *"know his stuff."* He acted for NTL on its acquisition of the cable business of Cable & Wireless Communications (value £9.8 billion.)

LEADERS IN E-COMMERCE

CALOW, Duncan

Denton Wilde Sapte, London (020) 7242 1212
dcc@dentonwildesapte.com

Specialisation: Senior solicitor specialising in digital media work. Advises content owner, producer and distributor clients on a wide range of projects including Internet, on-line and e-commerce services; print, CD-Rom, DVD and video games publishing; broadband, interactive television and mobile services. Written and spoken widely on the legal issues of digital media including contributions to specialist and legal press, national newspapers, radio and television. Contributor (with Alan Williams) to Halsburys Laws on Internet Publishing, Butterworths (1999) and author (with Alan Williams and Nicholas Higham) of Digital Media: Contracts, Rights and Licensing, Sweet & Maxwell Second Edition (1998).

Career: University of Nottingham; joined *Denton Hall* 1992; qualified 1994.

Personal: Born 1970; leisure interests include art, sport, comedy and politics.

CHISSICK, Michael

Field Fisher Waterhouse, London
(020) 7861 4000
mpc@ffwlaw.com

See under Information Technology, p.454

COWAN, Matthew

Olswang, London (020) 7208 8888

Specialisation: Commercial and corporate work in the Internet and telecommunications fields. Acted on the establishment of Worldpop.com and flotation of Netstore plc. Practice includes venture capital funding and acquisitions in the Internet and telecommunications fields.

Career: Joined *Olswang* in 1993 upon qualification and became a partner in 1999. Attended Bristol Grammar School 1979-86, then Exeter University 1986-90.

Personal: Born 31.3.67. Lives in Surrey.

EDWARDS, Gareth

Pinsent Curtis, London (020) 7418 7000
gareth.edwards@pinsents.com

Specialisation: Head of Corporate Department, London Corporate finance and company law including M&A, Stock Exchange and AIM primary & secondary issues and City Code take-overs. Major transactions: Flotations of Intrinsic Value plc; Just2Clicks plc; Fulcrum Pharma plc; secondary issues for e-xentric; Transacsys plc.

Prof. Memberships: Solicitors European Group

Career: Articles: *Daultry & Keen* 1983-1985. Assistant solicitor: *Reynolds Porter Chamberlain* 1985-87: *Lewis Silkin* (partner 1988): *Pinsent Curtis* 1998 to date.

ENSER, John

Olswang, London (020) 7208 8888

Specialisation: Principal area of practice: commercial, regulatory and competition law advice for Internet, interactive TV, television and music industries. Specialises in all aspects of e-commerce solutions in business to business and consumer markets. Clients include free and pay ISPs, leading websites, digital TV platform operators, internet technology providers, major film and record companies, retailers and insurers.

Prof. Memberships: ICC.

Career: Qualified: 1989. *Frere Cholmeley* 1987-94 (Brussels 1993-94). *Olswang* 1994 to date. Partner since 1996. School: Queen Elizabeth's Hospital, Bristol 1975-82. Pembroke College, Oxford 1982-85.

Personal: Born 21 October 1964. Married (one son). Lives in London.

HAFTKE, Mark

KLegal, London (020) 7694 2500

Specialisation: Partner, head of eBusiness and Digital Media practice. Internet specialist since 1995 when he co-founded *Bird& Bird's* digital media practice. Negotiates and drafts contracts for the complete e-enabled supply chain, advises on all related issues: e-payment, privacy and data protection, technology licensing, consumer protection legislation, copyright and trade mark/domain name infringement, digital distribution of content (including rights clearances and collecting societies), defamation, regulatory compliance and the EU initiatives covering the regulation of E-commerce, distance selling and electronic signatures. Clients mainly blue chip, analogue and Internet including retailers and fulfillers, newspapers and publishers, ISPs, banks and media conglomerates. Also works with dotcom startups and on major technology JVs. Recent work includes many agreements for interactive digital television platforms and WAP deals.

Publications: Author of Internet chapter in 'Copyright & Designs Law' by Merkin & Black (Sweet & Maxwell) and chapters on Contract and Copyright in CFI's 'Practitioner's Guide to the Internet'.

Career: Joined *KLegal* as Partner June 2000; *Bird & Bird* (1995-2000 made partner 1997); *Russells* (1988-1995 made partner 1992); Qualified as barrister 1986; re-qualified as solicitor1992; BA Jurisprudence St Edmund Hall (1982-1985) MA (Oxon).

HENRY, Michael

H2O (Henry Hepworth Organisation), London (020) 7539 7200

KAYE, Laurence M.

Paisner & Co, London (020) 7353 0299

Partner in computer, media & intellectual property group.

Specialisation: Advises a wide range of clients in the publishing, digital media and e-commerce industries. Clients range from internet start-ups to multinationals. Recent work has included e-commerce, joint ventures and partnership agreements in the information, financial services, and e-tailing sectors, site licences for the use of electronic journals, media joint ventures, co-publishing agreements, agreements for interactive television services and "due diligence" advice on copyright ownership issues. Was a member of the evaluation team which formally evaluated the ground-breaking UK Pilot Site Licence Initiative under which several publishers granted site licences allowing web-based access to their materials to the higher education sector. In addition to transaction-based work, also advises a number of media industry bodies on digital media and e-commerce legal issues, including the European Publishers Council, the Directory Publishers Association and the Periodical Publishers Association. Advised the Cross-Industry Working Group which made representations to the UK government on behalf of the publishers on the implementation of the Database Directive into UK law. Also legal adviser to the European Publishers Council – a member of the Brussels-based Rightsholders Alliance which is actively involved in representing media owners' interests on proposed new copyright and regulatory laws, particularly the forthcoming EU Copyright Directive.

Prof. Memberships: Law Society, Society for Computers & the Law, VISTA Editorial Board.

Career: Qualified in 1975, having joined *Brecher & Co.* in 1973. Left in 1980 to co-found company and commercial department at *Saunders Sobell.* Joined *The Simkins Partnership* in 1994. Joined *Paisner & Co* in 1998.

Personal: Born 1st September 1949. Attended Haberdashers' Askes School, Elstree, then the Sorbonne, and then Sidney Sussex College, Cambridge. Leisure interests include tennis, jogging, yoga, playing the saxophone, cinema, theatre and family life.

KEMP, Richard
Kemp & Co, London (020) 7710 1610
richardk@comlegal.com
Specialisation: Practice covers intellectual property, competition/EU regulatory and general business law for the full range of IT, e-commerce and telecoms sectors, acting for both suppliers and acquirers.
Prof. Memberships: Law Society; Chartered Institute of Patent Agents; Computer Law and Security Reports – Editorial Board Member. Guide to the World's Leading IT Lawyers (1999); one of top 20 global IT lawyers ('Best of the Best') (2000).
Career: *Clifford-Turner* (1978-1984); *Hopkins & Wood* 1984-1991 (Partner 1985); *(Hammond Suddards* (1991-1995 (head of IT Group; Founder Partner London Office)); *Garrett & Co.* (Partner 1995, IP/IT London Office Group Head 1996; IP/IT European Service Line Head, 1997). Set up *Kemp & Co* in November 1997 to specialise in IT, e-commerce and telecoms work – firm now has 15 lawyers and 24 staff.
Personal: Born 8th July 1956. Educated Oakham School, St. Catharine's College Cambridge, Universite Libre de Bruxelles.

MCNEIVE, Liam
McNeive Solicitors, London (020) 7253 0535
liam@mcneive.com
Specialisation: Clients include QXL (www.qxl.com), AOL (www.aol.co.uk), Real Media UK (www.realmedia.com), Crunch (www.icrunch.com), infobank (www.infobank.com), whatsonwhen (www.whatsonwhen.com), Inter Digital Networks (www.interdigital.net) and Good Technology (www.goodtech.co.uk). Founded *mcneive solicitors* in March 1998 to provide an informal, responsive service to fast-growing businesses operating in these industries. The firm has aggressive expansion plans, but will remain focused on servicing new economy enterprises, large, medium and small.

MILLARD, Christopher
Clifford Chance, London (020) 7600 1000
christopher.millard@cliffordchance.com
See under Information Technology, p.457

NICHOLSON, Kim
Olswang, London (020) 7208 8731
kan@olswang.com
See under Telecommunications, p.794

PHILLIPS, Mark D.
Harbottle & Lewis, London (020) 7667 5000
Specialisation: Partner and head of both the Interactive and New Media Group and the Publishing Group specialising in commercial and corporate work for media, leisure and arts industries.
Prof. Memberships: Law Society, Society for Computers and Law.
Career: Qualified in 1986. Worked at *Clifford-Chance* 1984-88. Joined *Harbottle & Lewis* in 1988, became a Partner in 1990.
Personal: Born 3rd April 1961. Attended Manchester Grammar School 1972-78, University College, London 1979-82. Trustee of Performing Arts Lab. School Governor and member of Board of Deputies.

ROSEFIELD, Stephen M.
Paisner & Co, London (020) 7353 0299
See under Corporate Finance, p.262

SMALL, Harry
Baker & McKenzie, London +44 20 7919 1000
harry.small@bakernet.com
See under Information Technology, p.459

SMITH, Graham
Bird & Bird, London (020) 7415 6000
Partner.
Specialisation: Computer project disputes, commercial litigation in computer and telecommunications industries. Evidence, document imaging and computer records. Internet law including domain name disputes, website advice, internet/e-mail use policies and regulatory issues. Intellectual property disputes. Gave evidence to the House of Lords Science and Technology Select Committee on Digital Images as Evidence. Advised Guernsey on its e-commerce legislation. Contributes a section on Non-Contractual Liability to the looseleaf 'Encyclopedia of Information Technology Law' (Sweet & Maxwell). Editor and a co-author of the book 'Internet Law and Regulation' (Sweet & Maxwell, 2nd edition December 1997). Speaks and writes regularly in the UK and abroad mainly on IT and Internet legal issues.
Prof. Memberships: American Intellectual Property Law Association. Council Member, Society for Computers and Law. Computer Law Association. E centre UK Legal Advisory Group. Fellow of the Society for Advanced Legal Studies.
Career: Qualified 1978. Joined *Bird & Bird* 1983. Partner 1985.
Personal: Born 1953. Educated Uppingham School, Rutland; Bristol University (LLB. 1975). Lives London.

SUMMERFIELD, Spencer
Travers Smith Braithwaite, London
(020) 7295 3000
Spencer.Summerfield@TraversSmith.com
See under Corporate Finance, p.266

TURNER, Mark
Herbert Smith, London (020) 7374 8000
Specialisation: Partner specialising in transactional and advisory work in the IT and digital media industries. Works regularly for government departments and agencies, multinationals and leading edge internet and new media businesses. Most of his work has a strong international element. Is at the forefront of developments in e-commerce, advising on on-line exchanges, contracts and payment on the internet, regulation of business on-line and e-commerce issues generally. Work includes acting for BSkyB on new technologies; Freeserve on the acquisition of Smartgroups.com and the joint venture with Barclays Bank, clearlybusiness.com; Credit Suisse First Boston, Goldman Sachs, Bear Stearns and Schroeders on IT and e-commerce issues arising from IPOs, listings and other transactions by their clients.
Personal: Born 1956. Educated Latymer Upper School and University College, Oxford (Exhibitioner).

WILLIAMS, Alan
Denton Wilde Sapte, London (020) 7320 6249
apw@dentonwildesapte.com
Head of Digital Media practice.
Specialisation: Work includes digital media and e-commerce, electronic publishing, copyright, libel, commercial contract, traditional publishing and theatre. Co-author with Michael Flint and Clive Thorne of 'Intellectual Property: the New Law'; contributes to Publishing Agreements edited by Charles Clark. Author with Duncan Calow of 'Digital Media: Contracts, Rights and Licensing' (second edition 1998 Sweet & Maxwell). Lectures for Hawksmere, PIRA and others.
Prof. Memberships: Law Society, Publishing Law Group of the Publishers Association.
Career: Qualified in 1969, having joined *Denton Hall & Burgin* in 1967. Became a Partner in 1972.
Personal: Born 1944. Attended Merchant Taylors' School 1957-63, then Exeter University 1963-66. Clubs include MCC, Groucho, Whitefriars, Omar Khyyam, Magic Circle, Richard III Society, City Law Club, Liveryman of the Worshipful Company of Pewterers; Fellow of the Royal Society of Arts. Leisure interests include theatre, music, cricket and walking. Married, one daughter. Lives in London.

WINTON, Ashley
Osborne Clarke OWA, London (020) 7809 1268
ashley.winton@osborneclarke.com
Specialisation: Advises with a practical approach on the application of e-business, competition and data protection regulation. Specialist advice relates to e-business infrastructure, intangible assets, risk management, cryptology and technology development and international exploitation.
Prof. Memberships: SCL, ABA, CLA, BCS and IEE
Career: Formerly a computer designer. Qualified at *Clifford Chance*, moved to *Garretts* in 1993 and was a founding partner of *Kemp & Co* in1997/8. Moved to *Osborne Clarke OWA* in 1999.
Publications: Computer Law Association Bulletin, European editor; 'International Internet Law Review', 'Lobbywatch' editor; 'eLawFocus', news editor.

EDUCATION

OVERVIEW: Ranked firms in the education sector are divided between those acting for individuals and those acting for institutions. The former is largely litigation work for individual pupils or parents regarding matters such as special education needs, exclusions and bullying. The incorporation of the Human Rights Act, and potential new tort of educational negligence (at the time of writing awaiting a decision of the House of Lords) has led to increased interest and activity in this field, and there are several new firms and individuals listed around the country this year. On the institutional side, clients include higher education (HE), further education (FE) or schools (usually in the private or voluntary-aided sectors). Services offered range from constitutional, governance and student issues to broader employment, projects and commercial work. There remain few firms with real commitment to the sector, but the market is more nationally based than London-centric. Thus while the national Eversheds practice remains pre-eminent, particularly in the FE sector, strong competition comes from Martineau Johnson and Mills & Reeve, with regional heavyweights such as Addleshaw Booth & Co, DLA and Pinsent Curtis beginning to knock on the door. Veale Wasbrough remains the leading firm for independent schools, while Farrer & Co is new to the London rankings to reflect its A-list clients.

RESEARCH APPROVED BY BMRB: *For this edition,* Chambers' *researchers conducted 6083 interviews – 4408 with law firms, 598 with barristers and 1077 with clients.*

The validity of the research was scrutinised by BMRB International, who audited both the methodology and the results at our offices in July 2000. They interviewed Chambers' *researchers and cross-checked sample interviews. Details of the audit appear on page 7.*

LONDON

FIRMS ACTING FOR INSTITUTIONS

EDUCATION (INSTITUTIONS) • London	Ptnrs	Assts
❶ Eversheds	3	4
❷ Beachcroft Wansbroughs	4	7
Winckworth Sherwood	3	4
❸ Lawfords	4	2
Lee Bolton & Lee	2	1
❹ Reynolds Porter Chamberlain	3	3
Witham Weld	2	1
❺ Farrer & Co	*	*

LEADING INDIVIDUALS	
✪ HALL John Eversheds	THATCHER Michael Winckworth Sherwood
❶ BEESLEY Peter Lee Bolton & Lee	GIZZI Julian Beachcroft Wansbroughs
❷ BOYD-CARPENTER Henry Farrer & Co	RICHENS Nicholas Lee Bolton & Lee
❸ HAWTHORNE Peter Witham Weld	

Within each band, firms are listed alphabetically. *See **Profiles** on page 308*

** See editorial entries for explanations of team sizes.*

Eversheds The largest education practice in the country, with *"more FE clients than anyone else"* and a growing portfolio of HE institutions and representative bodies. Seen as *"pre-eminent"* in the field, the London team is able to provide support to its large national network. The *"ubiquitous"* **John Hall** heads up the practice and is a noted constitutional expert. In addition to related property/project and commercial work, core education services include university and college governance (including mergers and joint ventures), employment, student issues and higher education franchising/overseas collaboration. One highlight of the last year was advising the University of Surrey and Roehampton University on the establishment of a new federal structure. **Clients:** London School of Economics, Lambeth College, Royal Institution of Chartered Surveyors.

Beachcroft Wansbroughs Well-known education practice which acts for a large number of public bodies, particularly on the funding side, in addition to several higher education institutions. Team leader **Julian Gizzi** *"has done a lot in the sector"* and was appointed to the Dearing Committee which looked into the future of Higher Education. Recent work includes advising UCAS and CVCP on handling applicants with criminal convictions and providing legal support for the establishment of a new e-university. The team also includes a respected academic consultant. **Clients:** Further Education Funding Council, Higher Education Funding Council, Qualifications and Curriculum Authority.

Winckworth Sherwood Maintains its position in the school sector with a strong reputation for acting for Church voluntary-aided schools and foundation schools. The *"experienced"* **Michael Thatcher** *"knows his subject"* and heads up the team which provides a full range of education legal services including vetting service contracts, employment and student discipline issues, property and commercial work. Recent work includes acting for a consortium led by the Centre of Education Management, which is on the Government approved list for contracting out the services of failing local education authorities. **Clients:** Diocesan Boards of Education for London and Southwark, St Paul's Cathedral School, Roman Catholic Archdiocese of Westminster.

Lawfords Wide-ranging practice based mainly in the FE and HE sectors which receives referrals on specialist education issues from a number of universities and colleges. A full range of services is offered from property and commercial issues (such as protection of IP rights, joint ventures and overseas courses) to employment and student-related issues. A consultant at the practice is able to provide specific expertise in university and college administration. One highlight of the last year was acting for Nottingham University in its successful breach of contract claim against infertility expert Dr Simon Fishel concerning work done abroad without telling the university (University of Nottingham v Dr Simon Fishel). **Clients:** Universities, HE and FE colleges.

Lee Bolton & Lee Highly rated team which is *"known in the schools sector"* and rises in the rankings owing to the strength of recommendation from the market. The *"sound"* **Peter Beesley** heads the team which includes **Nicholas Richens**, who enters the rankings to reflect his reputation for *"expertise in church schools".* Work covers charity and governance issues, property, employment, student issues and setting up trading subsidiaries. **Clients:** Independent and church schools.

Reynolds Porter Chamberlain Known particularly for its employment work for institutions and teaching unions, the team is well-versed in educational negligence and other litigation matters related to its insurance practice. Specialist advice is also available on rights and liabilities of governors, constitutional matters, commercial agreements, property and funding issues for a portfolio of clients including HE and FE colleges and independent schools. **Clients:** ATL, University of Hertfordshire, NASUWT.

Witham Weld **Peter Hawthorne** heads up this respected team which is notable for its strong presence in the Roman Catholic schools sector. Work extends to acting for pupils and parents in religious disputes with institutions and special education needs appeals. Acting for schools in admissions and exclusions disputes is an important recent trend of practice. **Clients:** Roman Catholic schools (public and private) and university colleges.

Farrer & Co New to the rankings this year owing to the strength of its independent school clients, the practice is increasingly active in the tertiary sector. Acknowledged schools specialist **Henry Boyd-Carpenter** chairs the cross-departmental education group which provides its institutional clients with advice ranging from general commercial work to litigation matters such as exclusions and educational negligence. Highlights of the last year include acting on the incorporation of an ancient grammar school and advising the London Business School on a range of IP matters. **Clients:** Eton College, Westminster School, Kings College, Cambridge.

FIRMS ACTING FOR INDIVIDUALS

EDUCATION (INDIVIDUALS) • London	Ptnrs	Assts
❶ Teacher Stern Selby	1	2
❷ Bindman & Partners	1	1
David Levene & Co	1	2
Gills	1	2
John Ford Morrison Solicitors	1	1
❸ Coningsbys	2	-
Fisher Meredith	1	1

LEADING INDIVIDUALS	
✪ RABINOWICZ Jack Teacher Stern Selby	
❶ FORD John John Ford Morrison	GILL Jaswinder Gills
RUEBAIN David David Levene & Co	
❷ CONRATHE Paul Coningsbys	GROSZ Stephen Bindman & Partners
WILKINS Patricia Fisher Meredith	

Within each band, firms are listed alphabetically. *See **Profiles** on page 308*

Teacher Stern Selby Maintains its leading position owing to its size and expertise in the area, as highlighted by the large number of referrals it receives from other London and regional solicitors. Known particularly for its reputation for acting for pupils and parents on matters such as admissions, bullying and special education needs, the team is developing its student practice. **Jack Rabinowicz** is *"obviously a big fish"* and has been involved in several high profile cases over the last year, including the landmark education negligence case Phelps v LB Hillingdon which has moved to the House of Lords.

Bindman & Partners Known for its human rights experience, which some in the market predict *"will take them to centre stage"* after the advent of the Human Rights Act. Handle admissions and exclusions issues for pupils/parents and disputes over exam results and funding for higher education students. **Stephen Grosz** remains rated in the field.

David Levene & Co Highly respected education and disability law practice with a particular reputation in special education needs and related community care and disability discrimination issues. All aspects of education litigation are covered, from admissions, exclusion and bullying to educational negligence and curriculum matters. The well-known **David Ruebain** heads up the team, who have recently acted in R v The Governing Body of Whitefields School, which concerned the relevance of certain provisions of the European Convention of Human Rights to a disabled child refused admission to a mainstream school.

Gills Maintains its strong profile in acting for individuals in education disputes, particularly for HE students. Particular areas of expertise are quality of education issues, educational negligence and judicial review. **Jaswinder Gill** is known as *"quite a specialist"* in the area. Acted in Towns v The Bar Council, which concerned the application of alleged different standards of assessment of the Bar Vocational Course at different colleges.

John Ford Morrison Solicitors Rises in the rankings owing to the practice's increasing profile in the sector. Primarily acting for parents and children in special education needs matters, often with a community care overlap, the team has recently been strengthened with a lateral hire from an LEA background. Pupil and student disputes are a further area of practice. **John Ford** jumps up the rankings after widespread recommendation, and is seen as *"outstanding on the detail."*

Coningsbys Emerging as a respected and competitive player in the market, the team enters the rankings this year, along with its *"efficient and proficient"* head **Paul Conrathe**. Known most for its special education needs expertise (notably in the areas of autism and ADHD), the practice handles a variety of work for pupils and students, including educational negligence, disciplinary matters, bullying and student grants.

Fisher Meredith Also new to the rankings, the practice has a large caseload in the area of special education needs and has noted expertise in profound and multiple disabilities and in the overlap with community care. **Patricia Wilkins** is *"well known in the field"* and makes her debut in the rankings this year.

THAMES VALLEY

FIRMS ACTING FOR INSTITUTIONS

EDUCATION (INSTITUTIONS) • Thames Valley	Ptnrs	Assts
❶ Manches Oxford	1	1
Morgan Cole Oxford	1	4
❷ Winckworth Sherwood Oxford	1	1

Within each band, firms are listed alphabetically.

Manches Particularly known in the HE sector for its large number of Oxford college clients, the practice maintains its position in the rankings. Other clients include a significant number of universities, several FE colleges, independent schools and scientific research councils. Services offered to its institutional clients include constitutional work, student and staff discipline matters, employment and property work. On the commercial side the practice has expertise in joint ventures, research contracts, technology transfers and spin-off companies. **Clients:** University of Oxford, University of Surrey, 24 Oxford colleges.

Morgan Cole Substantial education practice which acts for a range of universities, FE colleges and private schools. The team is well-versed in public sector issues and has particular experience in outsourcing and funding arrangements, college take-overs and setting up hi-tech companies. **Clients:** Oxford Brookes, Oxford University, Dragon School.

Winckworth Sherwood Notable for its strong niche practice acting for religious schools. Clients include the trustees and governors of 250 Church of England schools, several private schools and theological colleges. Handles the full range of education work from admissions and exclusions to employment issues. Recent trends include acting for university visitors in disciplinary matters and outsourcing school management from local authority control. Involved in a major reorganisation of Oxford schools and related land transfers. **Clients:** Oxford Diocesan Board of Education, 3Es.

THE SOUTH

FIRMS ACTING FOR INSTITUTIONS

EDUCATION (INSTITUTIONS) • The South	Ptnrs	Assts
❶ **Bond Pearce** Southampton	2	3
DMH Brighton	⚐	⚐
Steele Raymond Bournemouth	2	-
Thomas Eggar Church Adams Chichester	2	-

Within each band, firms are listed alphabetically. *See* ***Profiles*** *on page 308*

⚐ *Figures unavailable at time of going to press.*

Bond Pearce The practice provides a full range of legal services to a variety of FE and HE colleges and has particular strengths in the employment and procurement fields. An in-house clerking service has recently been introduced to assist college administrators with day-to-day governance issues. Highlights of the last year include involvement in the PPP arrangements for the consolidation of two college sites of Weymouth College. **Clients:** University of Southampton, Farnborough College, Bournemouth Arts Institute.

DMH Recommended practice with longstanding constitutional, governance and funding expertise in the higher education and schools sectors. A cross-departmental group offers property, construction, commercial and IP/IT work. Advised on the extensive revision of a university prospectus to take account of new fee regulations and the law relating to contracting. **Clients:** University of Sussex, Diocese of Arundel and Brighton, Windlesham School.

Steele Raymond Still felt to have a strong local presence in the sector, the practice acts for both institutions and individuals. Handles a range of contentious and non-contentious matters, including employment, property and contract work. Acted in several recent high profile tribunal claims. **Clients:** Higher and further education institutions, independent schools and pupils.

Thomas Eggar Church Adams Maintains a broad practice across the FE, HE and independent schools sectors and has won several significant new clients over the last year. In addition to employment, commercial and property work, the team is able to provide specific education law advice on pupil and student issues. Recent work includes advising on a joint marketing venture between a number of Sussex sixth form colleges. **Clients:** University College, Chichester, Hastings College, Christ's Hospital.

SOUTH WEST

FIRMS ACTING FOR INSTITUTIONS

EDUCATION (INSTITUTIONS) • South West	Ptnrs	Assts
❶ **Veale Wasbrough** Bristol	3	10
❷ **Stone King** Bath	2	-
❸ **Michelmores** Exeter	⚐	⚐
Rickerby Watterson Cheltenham	3	-
❹ **Tozers** Exeter	2	1
❺ **Bevan Ashford** Bristol	⚐	⚐
Bond Pearce Plymouth	2	-
Osborne Clarke Bristol	⚐	⚐

LEADING INDIVIDUALS	
❶ **BOYD Robert** Veale Wasbrough	**GOLD Richard** Stone King
KING Michael Stone King	
❷ **DICKINSON Malcolm** Michelmores	
UP AND COMING	
CASTREY Alison Veale Wasbrough	

Within each band, firms are listed alphabetically. *See* ***Profiles*** *on page 308*

⚐ *Figures unavailable at time of going to press.*

Veale Wasbrough Acting for 600 independent schools, the practice maintains its *"pre-eminent"* national reputation in that field. Its core Schools Unit is headed up by **Robert Boyd** who is seen to *"have the market sewn up"* and whose recent book on the subject received widespread praise in the market. The *"knowledgeable"* **Alison Castrey** enters the rankings as an up and coming player on the recommendation of several respondents. Specialist education advice is available on such matters as pastoral policy, rebuilding internal structures, regulatory authority compliance, employment and discipline disputes. Commercial and property issues from joint ventures and mergers to PFI projects are handled by a cross-departmental team. One significant piece of last year's work was involvement in the setting up of the first Open Access school at Belvedere GDST. **Clients:** Independent Schools, Bristol University, several FE colleges.

Stone King *"A recognised force in the education field,"* the practice rises in the rankings to reflect its presence in the schools sector and the strong reputation of its two leading partners. **Richard Gold** is seen as a *"highly regarded expert,"* whose broad practice extends to advising parents and **Michael King**, who is particularly known for his work with Roman Catholic diocesan schools, *"knows complex areas well."* All aspects of education work are handled for independent and maintained schools, from admissions, exclusions and staff discipline to mergers and redevelopments. One recent highlight was advising a large number of governing bodies on an LEA-wide PFI scheme. **Clients:** Independent schools, Maintained Schools and FE colleges.

Michelmores Respected part-time team headed up by **Malcolm Dickinson** which looks after a broad range of clients including HE and FE institutions and private and Anglican schools. Provides a full range service, with particular experience in property matters, fund-raising, joint ventures, commercial spin-off arrangements, employment and student complaints. Recently advised on partnership arrangements between universities and local business schemes. **Clients:** University of Exeter.

Rickerby Watterson *"Chunky"* practice with a strong portfolio of independent school clients, and a small but growing FE and HE practice. Work for schools includes employment law, constitutional/trust issues and policy advice. In the tertiary sector the last year has seen an increase in EC procurement and competition issues and the team has advised several FE colleges on incentive schemes to increase student numbers. **Clients:** Cheltenham Ladies College, GLOSCAT, Edgbaston Girls School.

Tozers Known for its schools practice which counts foundation, independent and voluntary-aided schools as clients and offers experience in financial rescue, employment, charity and child protection work. The team also acts for parents on special education needs matters, on which it receives referrals from leading education organisations. Its lower profile in the sector leads the team to drop in the rankings this year. **Clients:** The Diocese of Plymouth, several foundation schools and independent schools.

Bevan Ashford Well-established education practice with particular strengths in complex property and PFI work for the FE sector. Other services offered include specialist employment and commercial work (including IT and procurement.) The team recently won a tender to advise Canterbury College on the relocation and re-development of college facilities under PFI. **Clients:** Newbury College, Canterbury College, Farnborough Sixth Form College.

Bond Pearce Solid education team which dispenses a range of legal services to mainly FE clients. Work handled includes outsourcing and procurement, employment, debt collection, corporate governance, charity issues and property management. One highlight of last year was advising a university on honorary contract issues relating to a medical school. **Clients:** University College of St Mark & St John, St Austell College, Cornwall College.

Osborne Clarke OWA Commercial firm seen by the market as *"strong on the education side."* The team is active in the HE sector and acts for several public agencies on education matters. Advice to its institutional clients ranges from public law, contractual issues and exploitation of IP rights to compliance, constitutional matters, taxation and property. Recent work includes drafting and negotiating funding agreements between the NHS Executive South West and universities in the region. **Clients:** University of Plymouth; University of Bath; Avon, Gloucestershire and Northern Wiltshire Education Purchasing Consortium.

FIRMS ACTING FOR INDIVIDUALS

EDUCATION (INDIVIDUALS) • South West	Ptnrs	Assts
❶ **AE Smith & Son** Stroud	1	1
❷ **Bobbetts Mackan** Bristol	-	1

LEADING INDIVIDUALS
❶ **LOVE Robert** AE Smith & Son
❷ **COX Brian** Bobbetts Mackan

Within each band, firms are listed alphabetically. *See **Profiles** on page 308*

AE Smith & Son Highly rated practice which is seen by many as *"first stop for parents"* and receives many referrals from solicitors throughout the region. **Robert Love** maintains his reputation for expertise in the field of special education needs, particularly acting for dyslexic children. Other areas of practice include exclusion and admission appeals and educational negligence. The team is currently acting for the applicant in the test case of G v Bromley which is deciding whether or not Local Authorities can be sued for educational negligence.

Bobbetts Mackan Newly recommended individuals' practice particularly known for its judicial review expertise and work for higher education students. **Brian Cox** is rated in the field.

WALES

FIRMS ACTING FOR INSTITUTIONS

EDUCATION (INSTITUTIONS) • Wales	Ptnrs	Assts
❶ **Eversheds** Cardiff	1	-
Morgan Cole Cardiff	5	4

Within each band, firms are listed alphabetically.

Eversheds Maintains its leading firm position and acts for one third of FE and one half of HE colleges in Wales. In addition to core employment, constitutional and student work (contracts, complaints and discipline,) the team is handling an increasing amount of IP/IT and PFI/property work. Acted for Ceredigion County Council in the completion of Wales' first PFI school. **Clients:** University of Wales Cardiff, University of Wales Glamorgan, University of Wales Institute Cardiff.

Morgan Cole Long-established education practice with clients across the HE, FE and independent school sectors. A wide range of work is covered, from constitutional issues (such as trading, funding and student issues) to commercial and IP work, employment and PFI/PPP. Recent work includes advising the University of Wales at Swansea on a joint venture with its Local Authority to develop an Olympic standard swimming pool. **Clients:** University of Wales, Swansea, Aberdare College, Monmouth School for Boys.

FIRMS ACTING FOR INDIVIDUALS

EDUCATION (INDIVIDUALS) • Wales	Ptnrs	Assts
❶ **Hugh James Ford Simey** Cardiff	1	-
Russell Jones & Walker Cardiff	1	-
Sinclairs Penarth	1	-

LEADING INDIVIDUALS
❶ **IMPERATO Michael** Russell Jones & Walker
JONES Michael Hugh James Ford Simey

Within each band, firms are listed alphabetically. *See **Profiles** on page 308*

Hugh James Ford Simey Recommended practice for special education needs, admissions and educational negligence work for parents. **Michael Jones** is particularly known for his work for Welsh language school pupils. The practice is increasingly taking instructions from students in the tertiary sector challenging academic results.

Russell Jones & Walker Fledgling education practice with a legal aid franchise. The respected **Michael Imperato** acts for pupils in cases of special needs, admissions and educational negligence.

Sinclairs Highly rated franchised practice which handles the full range of education work for pupils/parents, from special education needs to bullying and transport matters.

MIDLANDS

FIRMS ACTING FOR INSTITUTIONS

EDUCATION (INSTITUTIONS) • Midlands	Ptnrs	Assts
❶ **Martineau Johnson** Birmingham	2	2
❷ **Eversheds** Nottingham	1	7
❸ **Shakespeares** Birmingham	2	1
Wragge & Co Birmingham	⚐	⚐

LEADING INDIVIDUALS
❶ **ARROWSMITH Simon** Martineau Johnson **PHARAOH Paul** Martineau Johnson
❷ **STERNBERG Nigel** Eversheds
UP AND COMING
HART Nicola Jane Martineau Johnson

Within each band, firms are listed alphabetically. *See **Profiles** on page 308*

⚐ *Figures unavailable at time of going to press.*

Martineau Johnson Highly rated education practice which competes strongly in the national HE market, in addition to handling some significant work for FE institutions and acting for schools and examination boards. A full-range service deals with student litigation and appeals, as well as exploitation of research, college mergers and major projects work. Up and coming **Nicola Hart** leads the team and specialises in HE work, constitutional issues and discipline disputes, while **Simon Arrowsmith** heads the property side. The well-regarded **Paul Pharaoh** deals with FE clients, mergers and trading subsidiaries. Recent work includes advising Wulfrun College on its take-over of the assets of Bilston College to form the new Wolverhampton College. **Clients:** Birmingham University, De Montfort University, Warwick University.

Eversheds Notable for its *"huge FE practice"* the firm's Midlands practice is highly rated in the market, particularly on employment issues. Other strengths include PFI projects and high-tech spin off ventures. A full-range education service is offered to the firm's wide local institutional client base which also includes several universities and HE colleges, local authority schools, LEAs and private businesses in the sector. **Nigel Sternberg** remains a recommended practitioner. **Clients:** Derby University, Stoke on Trent LEA, Bournville College.

Shakespeares Acts for a number of FE colleges and foundation schools. In addition to employment issues, contractual advice and property work, the team has been involved in several litigation matters for their institutional clients, including a recent case concerning access to school records for criminal proceedings. The practice has also developed a niche acting for ethnic schools and colleges in the region. One highlight of last year was advising the University of Central England on the relocation of one of its faculties to the Millennium Point development. **Clients:** University of Central England, Technology and Innovation Centre, Great Barr Foundation School.

Wragge & Co Solid education practice specialising in property work for the local FE sector. Other services offered include statutory transfer, setting up trading subsidiaries, employment, EU law implications and mergers. One highlight of the last year was the disposal of a site for an FE college subject to rights imposed under the School Sites Reverters Act. **Clients:** Walsall College, Tameside College, Sutton Coldfield College.

FIRMS ACTING FOR INDIVIDUALS

EDUCATION (INDIVIDUALS) • Midlands	Ptnrs	Assts
❶ **Young & Lee** Birmingham	1	-

Within each band, firms are listed alphabetically.

Young & Lee Respected firm which handles special education needs tribunals and exclusions/admissions judicial reviews for pupils, parents and some local authorities.

EAST ANGLIA

FIRMS ACTING FOR INSTITUTIONS

EDUCATION (INSTITUTIONS) • East Anglia	Ptnrs	Assts
❶ **Mills & Reeve** Cambridge, Norwich	5	10
❷ **Eversheds** Norwich, Ipswich	3	8
❸ **Birkett Long** Colchester	2	-
Wollastons Chelmsford	2	-

LEADING INDIVIDUALS
❶ **STANFIELD Glynne** Mills & Reeve
❷ **GEORGE Philip** Birkett Long

Within each band, firms are listed alphabetically. *See **Profiles** on page 308*

Mills & Reeve *"The dominant player"* in the local HE market with a national reputation in the field and a large proportion of its work drawn from outside the region. Involved in several high profile mergers and joint ventures over the last year, including acting for the University of Cambridge in its joint venture with Massachusetts College of Technology. This highlights the team's success in winning big clients and undertaking significant commercial projects for its institutional clients. The team of *"talented people"* is headed by corporate lawyer **Glynne Stanfield**, a *"good salesman,"* who is respected in the education field. A full range of legal services is available from property, employment, student disputes and tax schemes. The practice also runs an Academic Advisory Board. **Clients:** Quality Assurance Agency, Imperial College, UEA.

Eversheds The leading FE practice in the region, which acts for 20 out of 28 local FE colleges, in addition to a number of independent schools and HE clients. Alongside mainstream employment, property, governance and commercial contract work, the team has particular expertise in advising on mitigation of VAT and IT matters. Recent work includes challenging FEFC inspection findings and significant property disposals for their college clients. **Clients:** College of West Anglia, Oaklands College, Association of Colleges in the Eastern Region (ACER.)

Birkett Long Maintains its reputation in acting for local institutions across the HE, FE and school sectors. Work handled for schools includes exclusions, admissions and appeals, while statutory interpretation and general commercial work is provided across the board. The team also does some special educational needs work for individuals/parents, often on referral from organisations such as the Education Law Association. One highlight of the last year was advising Colchester Institute on the development of a retail park on land adjoining their site. **Philip George** is recommended at the practice. **Clients:** University of Essex, Colchester Institute, Thurrock College.

Wollastons Retains a strong presence in the local FE college market for which it provides legal services including employment and property work and commercial and franchising contracts. Recent work includes a major campus relocation worth in excess of £56 million. **Clients:** Anglia Polytechnic.

THE NORTH

FIRMS ACTING FOR INSTITUTIONS

EDUCATION (INSTITUTIONS) • The North	Ptnrs	Assts
❶ **Eversheds** Manchester, Newcastle, Leeds, Middlesbrough	2	5
❷ **Addleshaw Booth & Co** Manchester	℞	℞
DLA Liverpool, Sheffield, Leeds	1	3
Pinsent Curtis Leeds	9	12

LEADING INDIVIDUALS
❶ **BOARDMAN John** Eversheds

Within each band, firms are listed alphabetically. *See **Profiles** on page 308*

℞ *Figures unavailable at time of going to press.*

Eversheds Based around its Manchester and Newcastle hubs, the practice remains *"by far the largest in the market"* with a substantial number of HE and FE clients, and a strong reputation for acting for LEAs in schools work. Work handled ranges from employment, student issues, governance and commercial issues (such as spin off companies and IP exploitation) to sensitive governor issues and major PFI/PPP schemes. The *"excellent"* **John Boardman** heads up the team and drew praise from practitioners outside the region. Highlights of the year included introducing risk management and property consultancy services for the sector. **Clients:** University of Manchester, UMIST, City College, Manchester.

Addleshaw Booth & Co Centred on the firm's projects group, the practice remains rated in the field and acts for independent schools, FE colleges and HE institutions in addition to a smattering of public boards and bodies. The focus of the practice lies in major PFI and local authority outsourcing arrangements, with a recent high profile success being its appointment to advise Nord Anglia in its bids to manage Hackney and Islington LEA services. In addition a cross-departmental team provides a range of advice on matters including corporate governance, finance, employment, commercial contracts and grant funding. **Clients:** University of Sheffield, Royal Northern College of Music, Victoria University of Manchester.

DLA Rises in the rankings to reflect the increasing recognition in the market of its top level HE clients within and outside the region. A cross-site team offers advice on all issues, including IP rights, employment, student disputes, governance, property (including VAT schemes for construction and refurbishment) and finance. Recent work includes advising Tower Hamlets on a bundled school project and a single school PFI project. In addition, some work is done for FE colleges, schools and individuals. **Clients:** University of Liverpool, Department of Education in Northern Ireland, University of Wales, Bangor.

Pinsent Curtis Known in the market particularly for its employment expertise, the practice has a substantial and growing university client base. Also experienced in PFI projects for FE and HE institutions. Recently advised on a £43 million IT project for the Schools Pathfinder PFI scheme. **Clients:** Department for Education and Employment, University of Leeds, University of Durham.

FIRMS ACTING FOR INDIVIDUALS

EDUCATION (INDIVIDUALS) • The North	Ptnrs	Assts
❶ **Elaine Maxwell & Co** Lancaster	1	–
❷ **Ridley Hall Drabble & Co** Huddersfield	2	–

LEADING INDIVIDUALS
❶ **MAXWELL Elaine** Elaine Maxwell & Co

Within each band, firms are listed alphabetically. *See **Profiles** on page 308*

Elaine Maxwell & Co Niche education practice which acts for pupils/parents on special education needs issues and HE and FE students in exclusions, admissions and disciplinary disputes. Former barrister **Elaine Maxwell** is known as a *"feisty fighter"* and is respected nationally for her work in the area.

Ridley Hall New to our rankings this year, the practice is highly rated in the special education needs field, and is particularly known for its expertise in acting for pupils with severe disabilities.

SCOTLAND

FIRMS ACTING FOR INSTITUTIONS

EDUCATION (INSTITUTIONS) • Scotland	Ptnrs	Assts
❶ **Dundas & Wilson CS** Edinburgh	4	25
❷ **Anderson Strathern WS** Edinburgh	3	1
Maclay Murray & Spens Glasgow	3	7

Within each band, firms are listed alphabetically.

Dundas & Wilson CS Maintains its position as the leading education practice in Scotland, praised for its *"volume and quality of work."* It boasts a range of significant clients in the HE, FE and schools sectors, in addition to several professional bodies and local authority education departments. The experience of the team in handling large scale projects is highlighted by its appointment to advise Glasgow City Council on its flagship PPP to upgrade all the buildings and IT facilities of its secondary school estates. Other strengths include employment, funding and commercialisation issues (such as spin-out of research and technology.) **Clients:** University of Glasgow, University of Stirling, Dollar Academy.

Anderson Strathern WS Enters the rankings this year to reflect its established presence in the schools market. Specialist employment, disciplinary and constitutional advice is provided for its independent school clients, while a full range of property and commercial advice is available to several HE institutions. The practice continues to receive referrals of complex pupil cases from the Law Society of Scotland. One highlight of last year was advising Edinburgh College of Art in relation to its proposed merger with Heriot Watt University. **Clients:** Napier University, Fettes College, Mary Erskine College Edinburgh.

Maclay Murray & Spens Particularly strong on commercial matters for HE and FE institutions, the firm is new to the rankings. Examples of the team's work include exploitation of IP rights in relation to high-tech projects, acting for university spin-out companies, outsourcing, joint ventures and employment issues. **Clients:** Glasgow School of Art, Robert Gordon University, Higher Education Quality Council.

FIRMS ACTING FOR INDIVIDUALS

EDUCATION (INDIVIDUALS) • Scotland	Ptnrs	Assts
❶ **Campbell Smith WS** Edinburgh	-	1

Within each band, firms are listed alphabetically.

Campbell Smith WS Well-known special education needs practice which acts for individuals in record of needs appeals and refusal of placement requests appeals. Other expertise includes general education judicial review work, exclusions and bullying reparation claims.

LEADERS IN EDUCATION

ARROWSMITH, Simon
Martineau Johnson, Birmingham (0121) 200 3300

BEESLEY, Peter
Lee Bolton & Lee, London (020) 7222 5381
Senior partner in ecclesiastical education and charity department.
Specialisation: Particular expertise in Church of England work. Joint registrar of the Diocese of Ely; registrar of the Diocese of Guildford; joint registrar of the Diocese of Hereford; registrar of the Faculty Office of the Archbishop of Canterbury; a member of the Legal Advisory Commission of the General Synod of the Church of England. Also handles education and charity work. Solicitor to the National Society and to the Board of Education of the General Synod; Registrar of the Woodard Corporation. Joint Contributor to Volume 13 (2) 'Encyclopaedia of Forms and Precedents- Ecclesiastical Law'. Speaker at and promoter of several conferences and seminars on ecclesiastical charity and education matters.
Prof. Memberships: Law Society, City of Westminster Law Society (ex-President), Ecclesiastical Law Association (Vice-Chairman), Ecclesiastical Law Society (Secretary), Charity Law Association (member of Executive Committee).
Career: Qualified 1967. Joined *Lee Bolton & Lee* in 1968, becoming a partner in 1969.
Personal: Born 30th April 1943. Attended Kings School Worcester, then Exeter University 1961-64 and College of Law 1964-65. Lives in London.

BOARDMAN, John
Eversheds, Manchester (0161) 832 6666
johnboardman@eversheds.com
Leeds (0113) 243 0391
Partner in education law department.
Specialisation: Principal area of work is education law advising higher education, further education and schools. Also advises other non-profit making bodies. Contributes articles to various specialist education law journals and gives numerous lectures and seminars on these areas.
Prof. Memberships: ELAS, Charity Law Association, Justice, Affiliate of Institute of Risk Management.
Career: Qualified 1979 while at *Alexander Tatham*, now *Eversheds* and became a partner in 1986.
Personal: Born 26th July 1955. Attended Manchester Grammar School 1966-73 and Downing College, Cambridge 1973-76. Former Governor of a further education college. Forum Member of an EAZ. Leisure pursuits include pottery, bats, films, books, music and guinea pigs. Lives in Mellor, Derbyshire.

BOYD, Robert P.
Veale Wasbrough, Bristol (0117) 925 2020
rboyd@vwl.co.uk
Partner and head of schools team.
Specialisation: Partner in charge of the education department which has advised more than 600 independent schools in the UK and abroad and some special and grant maintained schools in the last decade. Author of textbook 'Independent Schools: Law, Custom and Practice' (Jordans, 1988) and 'Running a School Boarding House' (BSA, 2000) and of the Parent Contract and numerous other education templates and articles on education issues. Advises schools in matters of governance, management, structural change, incorporation, charity and trust issues, the parent contract and many other concerns. An invited speaker at seminars all over the country for HMC, GBA, IAPS, GSA, and SHMIS.
Prof. Memberships: Bristol Law Society; Bristol Medico-Legal Society; Education Law Association.
Career: Qualified 1972. Joined *Veale Wasbrough* as a partner in 1988. Council of Bristol Law Society 1986-88; Council Member of Academy of Experts 1989; Co-opted to Judicial Committee 1992.
Personal: Born 1946. Attended Stonyhurst College 1960/65 and Birmingham University 1966/69.

BOYD-CARPENTER C.V.O., Henry
Farrer & Co, London (020) 7242 2022
Senior Partner and Head of *Farrer & Co's* Education Group.
Specialisation: Acts for educational institutions in the secondary and tertiary sectors.
Prof. Memberships: Law Society, Holborn Law Society.
Career: Joined *Farrer & Co* in 1962. Qualified in 1966, became a partner in 1968. Private Solicitor to the Queen since 1995, Solicitor to the Duchy of Cornwall 1976-1994.
Personal: Born 11th October 1939. Educated at Charterhouse 1953-58 and Balliol College, Oxford 1959-62. School governor and Charity Trustee. Member of the Board of the British Library since 1999 and Chairman of the Board of Governors of Charterhouse. Enjoys reading, music, hill walking and gardening. Lives in Ascot, Berkshire.

CASTREY, Alison
Veale Wasbrough, Bristol (0117) 925 2020
acastrey@vwl.co.uk
Specialisation: Practises in the field of commercial dispute resolution with particular emphasis on professional partnership disputes, professional liability and commercial and construction disputes.
Prof. Memberships: Member of Association of Partnership Practitioners; Secretary Manchester Professional Forum; Past President Manchester Law Society; Member of Society of Construction Lawyers; Member of CEDR.
Career: Admitted 1975. Practised in North West all working life. Co-founder of *Kershaw Abbott* as niche practice in 1991. Appointed Tax Commissioner in 1995.
Personal: Lives in Ribble Valley with judicial husband and son. Music lover and devoted gardener.

CONRATHE, Paul
Coningsbys, Croydon (020) 8680 5575
Specialisation: Education law, in particular: 1. Special Educational Needs. Appeals to the Special Educational Needs Tribunal, Judicial Reviews and Statutory Appeals in the High Court. 2. Exclusions and admissions. 3. Community care (children).
Prof. Memberships: The Education Law Association. Is the convenor of the Special Educational Needs Tribunal Users Group for the Education Law Association.
Career: Qualified in October 1995 with *Graham Pearce & Co*, Solihull, West Midlands. Moved to *Coningbys*, solicitors, Croydon, in January 1998. Became a partner in *Coningbys* in July 1998 and the senior partner in February 2000.

COX, Brian
Bobbetts Mackan, Bristol (0117) 929 9001

DICKINSON, Malcolm K.
Michelmores, Exeter (01392) 436244

FORD, John
John Ford Morrison, London (020) 7288 1066
Specialisation: Education, community care, personal injury, administrative law, actions public authorities and against police, professional negligence. Works closely with the children and criminal departments to provide holistic approach to overlapping legal problems. The department can provide independent advice to schools and LEAs.
Prof. Memberships: ELAS (former convenor of Children Act special interest group), APIL, Inquest Lawyers Group, MIND, NACRO, Legal Action Group.
Career: Admitted 1975. Strong civil rights background. Author of 'Education Law and Practice'. (Legal Action Group, November 1999)
Personal: School governor.

GEORGE, Philip W.
Birkett Long, Colchester (01206) 217300
philipg@birkettlong.co.uk
Partner in company commercial department.
Specialisation: Advises a university, further education and sixth form colleges and a wide range of foundation and independent schools on contractual and constitutional issues, and upon the interpretation of statutes.
Prof. Memberships: Education Law Association. Fellow of the Society for Advanced Legal Studies.
Career: Qualified April 1975. Partner since 1976. Heads the firm's education unit.

GILL, Jaswinder
Gills, Southall (020) 8893 6869
Specialisation: Offers expert legal advice in protecting and promoting students' legal rights in the law of higher education. Has gained a nation-wide reputation as the leading lawyer in the country in this area in challenging local authorities and universities; previously being unfamiliar territory. Set up his own firm to offer specialist guidance and advice for students aggrieved by decisions made by the above bodies. Also involved in bringing about a greater sense of awareness of legal remedies available to students within a complex framework of education law. Many cases involve novel issues and will have a strong element of wider public importance issues for all students. Specialises in challenging (a) local authorities' decisions refusing discretionary and mandatory awards in the area of student funding and (b) decisions made by universities/colleges regarding examination results, by way of judicial review proceedings. In respect of the latter, also handling cases involving damages for breach of contract and/or negligence. Also focusing on judicial review proceedings within the education field embracing statements of special educational needs and appeals, exclusion appeals and admissions.

GIZZI, Julian
Beachcroft Wansbroughs, London (020) 7242 1011
jgizzi@bwlaw.co.uk
Partner, head of education department.
Specialisation: All aspects of education law including funding matters, incorporations, mergers, learning difficulties, enquiries, judicial reviews and the private finance initiative.
Prof. Memberships: Law Society.
Career: Qualified in 1981, having joined *Beachcroft Stanleys* in 1979. Became a partner in 1986. Member of the Structure and Governance Working Group of the National Committee of Inquiry into Higher Education. Fellow of the Royal Society of Arts. Member of the Admissions and Exclusions Appeals Panel of the Schools' Commission.
Personal: Born 13 February 1957. Educated at Downside School and Cambridge University. Lives in Little Chart, Kent.

GOLD, Richard
Stone King, Bath (01225) 337599
Partner specialising in education work.
Specialisation: Education Law. Acts for schools and parents in all aspects of education law including governor training and PFI projects. Addresses conferences and seminars organised by IBC and Education Law Association and others. Co- author of 'Running a School 2000-2001 - Legal Duties and Responsibilities.' Member of Advisory Board "Education, Public Law and the Individual." Author of 'The Education Act Explained' (The Stationery Office).
Prof. Memberships: Education Law Association (ELAS) (Member of Executive Committee and Treasurer).
Career: Qualified 1968. Joined *Stone King* in 1999 as a partner.
Personal: Born 21st October 1941. Attended William Ellis School 1953-61, then Trinity College, Cambridge 1961-65. Chair of Governors, William Ellis School 1978-87. Chair of Trustees, William Ellis School 1978-present. Governor, Ravenscroft School 1992-1996. Governor, Jews Free School 1994-present. Leisure pursuits include music, theatre, reading and sport.

GROSZ, Stephen
Bindman & Partners, London (020) 7833 4433
See under Human Rights, p.433

HALL, John T.
Eversheds, London (020) 7919 4500
hallj@eversheds.com
Partner and chairman of *Eversheds* education group.
Specialisation: Work includes governance, the Education Acts, employment law, industrial relations, judicial review, the student relationships, commercial law, funding and asset management. Clients include in excess of two hundred education institutions, mainly universities and colleges of higher and further education. Also handles company/commercial and employment and constitutional advice for professional and other bodies. General Editor 'Education Case Reports' (Sweet & Maxwell). Contributor to 'Education and the Law', the 'Times Education Supplement' and education press. Author of further and higher education module in University of Buckingham Postgraduate Diploma in Education Law and contributor on 'Higher Education and the Law' (Open University Press).
Prof. Memberships: Law Society, Chair of the Further and Higher Education Group of Education Law Association, Fellow of the Royal Society of Arts. Fellow of the Institute of Continuing Professional Development.
Career: Qualified in 1975. Partner at *Wedlake Saint* 1978-93. Chair, London Young Solicitors' Group, 1985; Company Secretary, Polytechnics and Colleges Employers' Forum, 1988; Governor, Barnet College of Further Education, 1992; Company Secretary, Colleges' Employers' Forum, 1992., council member of the Royal College of Music (1999) and governor of Lochinver House School (1999). Joined *Eversheds* in 1994 as a partner.
Personal: Born 23rd December 1948. College Governor. Leisure interests include walking, music, history, art and Spain. Lives in Hadley Wood, Barnet, Herts.

HART, Nicola Jane
Martineau Johnson, Birmingham (0121) 678 1311
nicola.hart@martjohn.com
Specialisation: Partner and head of education. Leads specialist education team and co-ordinates a full in-house service to higher and further education clients. Practice covers a wide range of work, from institutional mergers, joint ventures and international work, to disputes with students and academic staff and judicial review. A regular speaker at education sector conferences and seminars, and contributes articles to education law and trade publications.
Career: Qualified 1988, *Le Brasseurs*; joined *Martineau Johnson* 1989; partner since 1995; head of education since 1997.
Publications: Introduction and chapters on student issues in 'Higher Education and the Law: A Guide for Managers' 1998. 'Teacher Stress: the consequences of harrassment and bullying', 2000.
Personal: Born 1962. Educated Worcester Girls Grammar School and Jesus College, Oxford. Director, Midlands Arts Centre.

HAWTHORNE, Peter J.M.
Witham Weld, London (020) 7821 8211

IMPERATO, Michael
Russell Jones & Walker, Cardiff (029) 20262 800
Specialisation: Education law and claimant personal injury. Acts particularly for children with special educational needs. Receives referrals from several charities. Recently represented parents group which successfully challenged Cardiff Councils New Schools Admissions Policy. Also instructed in exclusion cases and by university students challenging College Authorities. Undertakes legal aid work with Education Law franchise. Written articles, presented seminars and lectures on Education Law at University of Glamorgam. Member of Law Society Personal Injury Panel.
Prof. Memberships: ELAS - Convenor for Wales & West, APIL, PEOPIL, ATLA, Law Society.
Career: Qualified 1990 with *Hugh James*, Cardiff. 1994-97 *Gabb & Co.*, Abergavenny. Joined *RJW* 1997. Partner from 1999.
Personal: Born 24 May 1962. Education at Whitchurch High School, Cardiff and Reading University 1980-84. Taught history for 2 years. School Governer. Interests include sport, politics and young family. Lives in Cardiff.

JONES, Michael L.N.
Hugh James Ford Simey, Cardiff (029) 2022 4871
See under Litigation (Commercial), p.563

KING, Michael
Stone King, Bath (020) 7796 1007
michaelking@stoneking.co.uk
See under Charities, p.142

LOVE, Robert J.
AE Smith & Son, Stroud (01453) 757444
Partner. Special educational needs.
Prof. Memberships: Law Society, Convenor of Special Needs Interest Group of Education Law Association, member of Advisory Board - Education & Public Law Journal.
Career: Qualified 1975. Partner in *A.E. Smith & Son* since 1988.
Personal: Has been practising in this area for the last eleven years.

MAXWELL, Elaine
Elaine Maxwell & Co, Lancaster (01524) 840810
Specialisation: Now running own specialist firm handling solely education law and community care. Area of practice covers admissions, exclusions, employment in education, transport cases, with particular expertise in special educational needs and tribunal appeals, and claims by students. Provides seminars and advice to parent groups and professional advisors on statementing system, and higher education law. Recent cases include challenges on statementing policies of local education authorities, group action against school closure, actions by students for breach of contract, and disciplinary and admission problems.

Prof. Memberships: Education Law Association (Regional Co-ordinator), Employment Lawyers Association.
Career: Called to Bar 1974, has advised on education law since 1990, admitted as solicitor 1991, Partner *Marsden Huck* 1995-98, set up *Elaine Maxwell & Co* 1998.
Personal: Born 1951, attended Nottingham High School for Girls, then Manchester University.

PHARAOH, Paul
Martineau Johnson, Birmingham (0121) 678 1314
paul.pharaoh@martjohn.com
Partner in Education Department.
Specialisation: Handles contractual, property-related and constitutional issues for higher and further education institutions and schools. Author of articles in various legal journals, chapters on judicial review in 'Higher Education and the Law' and on due diligence in 'Managing Mergers', and module on law affecting pupils in school for University of Buckingham Diploma in Education Law. Speaker on education law and judicial review at various conferences and seminars. Member of editorial advisory board, 'Education Law Journal'.
Prof. Memberships: Law Society, ELAS.
Career: Qualified in 1971. Joined *Bettinsons* in 1969, becoming partner in 1973. Partner in *Shakespeares* on merger 1990. Partner in *Martineau Johnson* 1996. Law Society Council Member since 1990. Midlands convenor for Education Law Association. Member of West Cumbria College Corporation.
Personal: Born 1947. Attended Manchester University 1965-68 and Liverpool College of Commerce 1968-69. F.R.S.A.

RABINOWICZ, Jack
Teacher Stern Selby, London (020) 7242 3191
Partner in litigation department.
Specialisation: Main areas of practice include education, medical negligence, and personal injury work.
Prof. Memberships: Director of Disability Law Service, Chair of Education Law Association (ELAS), Steering Committee of Whooping Cough Claims, Action for Victims of Medical Accidents (AVMA), American Trial Lawyers Association (ATLA), Medico-Legal Society, Association of Personal Injury Lawyers (APIL), Law Society's Group for the Welfare of People with a Mental Handicap, Council of Registration of Schools teaching Dyslexia (CresTeD).
Career: Qualified in 1977. Currently a partner with *Teacher Stern Selby.*

RICHENS, Nicholas J.
Lee Bolton & Lee, London (020) 7222 5381
Specialisation: Education law and charity law, particularly with reference to church schools and school sites. Advised the General Synod Board of Education on the School Standards and Framework Bill. Joint contributor to Volume 13(2) 'Encyclopaedia of Forms and Precedents - Ecclesiastical Law'. Joint author of 'Charity Land and Premises' (Jordans 1996). Deputy registrar, Diocese of Guilford.
Prof. Memberships: Ecclesiastical Law Society (Deputy Secretary); Ecclesiastical Law Association (Secretary); Charity Law Association.
Career: Admitted 1985. Joined *Lee Bolton & Lee* in 1991.
Personal: Born 1960; Educated Marple Hall High School, Stockport and Downing College Cambridge. Lives in East London.

RUEBAIN, David
David Levene & Co, London (020) 8881 7777
info@davidlevene.co.uk
Head of Education and Disability Law Department.
Specialisation: The Department specialises in all aspects of education law, health law, community care law and disability discrimination. The work of the department has an expanding human rights dimension. He has published and taught extensively on education and disability law and is author of the Code of Practice on Admission, Exclusion and Reinstatement Appeals for Maintained Schools in England and Wales; co-author of the 1995 and 1997 Disabled Persons' (Civil Rights) Bills; consultant editor to Disability Discrimination: Advising on the Law and Practice; author of Notes on the Disability Discrimination Act; co-author of Taking Action, a guide for parents of children with Special Educational Needs and of Education Law & Practice; an editorial board member of Disability and Society; and co-author of the Legal Action Group's Education and the Law.
Prof. Memberships: Trustee of the Disability Discrimination Act Representation and Advice Project, a trustee of the Disability Law Service, Vice Chair of the Rights Now Campaign, a member of the Law Society's Mental Health and Disability Committee, Vice Chair of Disability Equality in Education and a member of the Advisory Board of the Disablement Policy and Law Research Unit.

STANFIELD, Glynne
Mills & Reeve, Cambridge (01223) 222 250
glynne.stanfield@mills-reeve.com
Specialisation: Advises on wide range of corporate and commercial matters for higher education clients. This year he has advised on the merger between Imperial and Wye Colleges and the joint venture between the University of Cambridge and MIT. He also advises extensively on commercialisation of technology and this year has been involved in, for example, the spin outs of Ilotron for the University of Essex (£6 million start up), Gendel from the University of Ulster (£5 million start up) and the establishment of three University Challenge funds. He has a particular interest in the funding of higher education by conventional and unconventional/innovative financing methods including tax based schemes.

STERNBERG, Nigel P.
Eversheds, Nottingham (0115) 950 7000
nigelsternberg@eversheds.com
Head of Commercial.
Specialisation: Practice covers intellectual property work, with specalisation in IT, data and distance learning. Extensive experience of outsourcing and large system developments, both in the public and private sectors. Specialist knowledge of the Higher Education and Banking sectors.
Prof. Memberships: Licensing Executive Society and ELAS.
Career: Lecturer at University of Durham (1977 to 1980); qualifed 1982 *Branson Bramley*, Sheffield (partner 1984); joined *Eversheds* (then *Wells and Hind*) as partner 1987; sometime Chairman of the Evershed Computer IT BDU. Part-time lecturer University of Durham (1977 to date).
Personal: Born November 1954; educated at Staveley-Netherthorpe Grammar School, Staveley and Oriel Oxford. MA in Jurisprudence. Interests include mountain biking, food and wine. Lives Chesterfield.

THATCHER, Michael C.
Winckworth Sherwood, London (020) 7593 5000
mcthatcher@winckworths.co.uk
Partner in education, ecclesiastical and charities department.
Specialisation: Acts for voluntary aided schools, foundation schools, voluntary controlled schools, Church of England and Roman Catholic boards of education and finance, further education colleges and local education authorities. Also acts for charities, airlines, and in general commercial and property law. Has acted in Judicial Review of Appeal Committee decisions, all types of disciplinary and appeal hearings, and Commission for Racial Equality proceedings against Governors. Author of various editorials in the specialist press. Has spoken at a wide range of conferences and seminars on various aspects of education and employment law.
Prof. Memberships: Law Society; Ecclesiastical Law Association; Ecclesiastical Law Society; Education Law Association.
Career: Qualified in 1968. From 1969 to 1989 was clerk to the Governors of St Clement Danes School, to St Clement Danes Parochial Charities and to Isaac Ducketts Trustees. Registrar to the Diocese of Rochester, Joint Registrar to the Diocese of London, Chapter Clerk St Paul's Cathedral.
Personal: Born 19th May 1943. Attended Ardingly College 1956-60, then King's College, London 1961-64, and College of Law 1964-65. Clerk to the Worshipful Company of Cooks, Secretary to the Reunion des Gastronomes, Parish Councillor. Leisure interests include running, shooting, fishing and gardening. Lives outside Guildford.

WILKINS, Patricia
Fisher Meredith, London (020) 7564 2900
central@fismer.co.uk
Specialisation: Head of Education and Community Care Department. Department specialises in Education Law, Health Law and all aspects of Community Care. She has a particular specialisation in special educational needs. Recent cases include R v Lambeth LBC exp N. inadequate consultation on the closure of a special school. R v EFC and Bradford M.B.C. exp. Parkinson on overlapping responsibilities of L.E.A's and F.E.F.C.'s. Chairperson Lambeth Parents Advocacy Project; Management Committee member of Parents for Inclusion.
Prof. Memberships: Education Law Association; Community Care Practitioners Group, Legal Action.
Career: Admitted 1992. Developed specialism in Education and Community Care before joining *Fisher Meredith* in 1997.
Personal: School governor.

EMPLOYEE SHARE SCHEMES

OVERVIEW: ESS is an area growing in prominence and set to increase with the implementation of Government Legislation announced in the March 2000 budget which includes large cuts in capital gains tax for employees owning shares, the introduction of the All Employee Share Options and the Enterprise Management Incentives Schemes. Although most firms operate from within an integrated Tax, Pensions and Employment department this specialist practice area has benefited from the demand for share options by high-tech companies.

Linklaters, under the guidance of Janet Cooper, continues its reign as the most prominent practice with a tightly packed group of City firms chasing them. In the regions, the Pinsent Curtis team continue to build on their enviable national reputation and client base. As the UK market matures, the globalisation of share schemes and e-commerce start-up equity options is set to increase the work load. Firms are increasingly working with and competing against accountants and remuneration consultants. While accountancy firms such as Arthur Andersen and KPMG are actively recruiting share scheme lawyers, the law firms remain protected by this area's increasing complexity and specialism.

RESEARCH APPROVED BY BMRB: *For this edition,* Chambers' *researchers conducted 6083 interviews – 4408 with law firms, 598 with barristers and 1077 with clients.*

The validity of the research was scrutinised by BMRB International, who audited both the methodology and the results at our offices in July 2000. They interviewed Chambers' *researchers and cross-checked sample interviews. Details of the audit appear on page 7.*

LONDON

EMPLOYEE SHARE SCHEMES • London	Ptnrs	Assts
❶ Linklaters	2	16
❷ Clifford Chance	2	8
Herbert Smith	1	4
Slaughter and May	2	2
❸ Freshfields Bruckhaus Deringer	2	4
❹ Allen & Overy	2	2
Norton Rose	1	3
❺ Ashurst Morris Crisp	1	5
Lovells	1	4
Travers Smith Braithwaite	1	2
❻ Baker & McKenzie	1	2
Field Fisher Waterhouse	1	2
Nicholson Graham & Jones	1	1

LEADING INDIVIDUALS	
❶ **CHAMBERLAIN Colin** Herbert Smith	**COHEN David** Norton Rose
COOPER Janet Linklaters	
❷ **CODRINGTON Eddie** Slaughter and May	**EVANS Simon** Freshfields
FENN Jonathan Slaughter and May	**ROWLANDS-HEMPEL Graham** Linklaters
TREMAINE Robin Clifford Chance	
❸ **CHATER Stephen** Allen & Overy	**CROFT Anne** Linklaters
MITCHELL Jocelyn Freshfields	**NICHOLL Victoria** Travers Smith Braithwaite
RANDALL Paul Ashurst Morris Crisp	**WHITEWRIGHT Louise** Lovells
❹ **INGLE Michael** Baker & McKenzie	**JACOBS Michael** Nicholson Graham & Jones
NUTTALL Graeme Field Fisher Waterhouse	

Within each band, firms are listed alphabetically. See **Profiles** on page 314

Linklaters With over 100 active clients, including 40 dot.coms, this practice continues to tower over the ESS market. The *"excellent team"* offers a *"5 star business package,"* mainly to FTSE 250, and increasingly Euro 300 and Fortune 500 clients. **Janet Cooper** *("outstanding;" "an ambassador for Linklaters")* continues to raise the team's international profile. She is ably supported by key players including **Graham Rowlands-Hempel** *("impressive")* who has increased his profile with a recent secondment to the Treasury, advising on NI options and new legislation. **Anne Croft** *("outstanding technical specialist;" "hard hitting, a challenge")* also shines. Linklaters launched the online database Blue Flag ESP, attracting global share scheme work from Vivendi and Pinault Printemps-Redoute. Acted on executive and employee incentive arrangements for newly merged Vodafone Airtouch and ProShare award-winning schemes for NatWest and RMC. **Clients:** BA, Vodafone Airtouch, lastminute.com, Freeserve.

Clifford Chance Still at the forefront, with a strong corporate client base and a growing international ESS service also attracting clients in its own right (Debenhams, Standard Chartered.) The Employee Benefits Unit works closely with New Bridge Street remuneration consultants, a separate entity who monitor the top 500 listed companies, (6 Assistant Solicitors.) Team leader **Robin Tremaine** is *"technically strong"* and has a long standing reputation, but the team as a whole *"have lost that edge,"* with interviewees questioning its failure to capitalise on the mergers and acquisition market. Active on the international stage, advising Diageo on granting stock options to senior managers in 47 countries and Getronics (Dutch based ICT services provider) to roll out options to 40 countries. **Clients:** Diageo, Canary Wharf Group plc, Cookson Group plc.

Herbert Smith A substantial reputation in this field, due mainly to the *"friendly and approachable"* **Colin Chamberlain**, *("always held in high regard, technically an expert.")* The firm handles all aspects of transactional and advisory employee share scheme work, and Chamberlain himself *"handles the two sides more successfully than most."* Recently established De La Rue's Share Price Improvement Plan on an international basis and advised BG on the impact of capital reorganisation. A strong track record in corporate re-organisation and structure of share schemes but the practice as a whole is not felt to have the international strength or critical mass of its immediate competitors. **Clients:** De La Rue, British Gas, Securicor, BAA.

Slaughter and May Renowned for the strength of its commercial client base, this practice advises on major transactions for listed companies. Operating from within the Pensions & Employment Department both partners spend a significant portion of their time on Pensions and have two assistants devoted to ESS. The *"reliable and efficient"* **Eddie Codrington** *("the share schemes lawyer's lawyer, top level but discreet")* continues as a leading practitioner with the increasingly active **Jonathan Fenn**, said to be *"a good chap with a relaxed style."* Concerns are raised over the firm's devotion of resources to this specialism but there is no doubt about the calibre of work. This includes new schemes designed for Schroders and Corus advising on the British Steel/Hoogovens merger and the Reckitt and Colman merger with Benckiser. **Clients:** Norwich Union, Glaxo Wellcome, Schroders.

Freshfields Bruckhaus Deringer Operates an integrated Employment, Pensions & Benefits practice and can draw on specialist ESS practices in Spain, Italy and Germany. Both partners have a strong background in tax and over 12 years of benefits work. **Simon Evans** has a high profile and is *"experienced in this field and responsive to the needs of the client."* **Jocelyn Mitchell** continues to make a name for herself: *"she's good and Simon is lucky to have her."* Offering advice on a wide range of private equity cases, public transactions and mergers & acquisitions, the practice *"has a very commercial approach."* Developed incentive plans for Pearsons and Reed Elsevier, and advised Scottish Power on Share Scheme aspects of its £12.5 billion agreed merger with Pacificorp and the flotation of its Telecoms business. **Clients:** Pearson, Royal Bank of Scotland, Hewlett Packard, Marconi, Scottish Power.

Allen & Overy The Employment, Pensions and Incentives Group has a solid reputation for its share scheme work which is drawn mainly from a large corporate practice. The team is lead by the *"client friendly"* **Stephen Chater** and is *"ready to respond to business practicalities."* Seen to benefit from a network of overseas offices, the firm has acted for UK and Overseas companies in relation to service contracts and remuneration packages. A comparatively low profile in ESS has not improved this year, within the practice perceived as, *"more of a tax focused group."* Advised WPP Group on Leadership Equity Acquisition Plan which required investments by participants and acted on merger of Celltech Plc with Chiroscience Group, valued at £330 million. **Clients:** Celltech, WPP, Sage Group

Norton Rose With leading light **David Cohen** at the helm, this practice has dramatically increased in stature and the extent of its stand-alone work. The team strength includes a new recruit from Baker & McKenzie, Singapore. Chairman of the Share Scheme Lawyers Group and an advisor to the Inland Revenue on the development of employee share schemes, David Cohen is a *"senior figure"* and *"a much respected, charming man."* Dealt with the ESS aspects of Mannesmann's £20 billion acquisition of Orange plc and placed share incentives arrangements for General Cable Corporation's employees in 13 countries. Although limited by a smaller transactional base than the market leaders, the firm is universally considered to be an emerging force in this area of practice. **Clients:** GUS, Monks Partnership, Allied London Properties, Mannesmann.

Ashurst Morris Crisp Advises on all aspects of share schemes and benefits, including tax support to corporate clients, as well as growing a significant base of stand-alone clients. Head of the Employee Benefits practice **Paul Randall** is still ranked but widespread opinion is that *"Ashursts are less prominent than last year."* The firm is recommended for its inroads into the mergers and acquisition market. International share scheme work includes advice on the retrospective changes in Belgian social security charges on share options. Transactions include acting on the flotation of Kingston Communications and the reverse of Fife Indmar into Northern Leisure, following the latter's acquisition of Rank Entertainment. **Clients:** Kingston Communications, Northern Leisure, Coca-Cola Beverages plc.

Lovells Dedicated Share Scheme Unit with strong links to the tax team. Mixture of transactional work and new scheme design including private equity for venture capitalists, although perceived by the market as lacking the complex FTSE 100 corporate transaction. **Louise Whitewright** *("enthusiastic and knows her stuff")* has a high profile, due in part to her role as Secretary to the Share Scheme's Lawyers Group. Implemented the MCI Worldwide share option scheme which covered 17 jurisdictions. Acted for Racal on the special dividends and compensation for non-particpating option holders as a result of the disposal of its telecoms business. **Clients:** Barclays, Mirror Group plc, Racal.

Travers Smith Braithwaite Has a strong reputation in the area of private equity transactions including MBO's and reconstructions. The team operates from within the Tax department and works closely with the additional resources in Employment and Pensions. Although smaller in size, the team is seen as *"a strong practice"* and is headed by the *"effective"* **Victoria Nicholl** who *"sees to the heart of the matter."* Advised Hays Ingredients and Earls Court & Olympia on share schemes while involved in management buy-outs and ntl Inc on their acquisitions. The group also advises clients on a consultancy basis including trustees, executive directors and non-executive directors. **Clients:** ntl Inc, Kier Group plc, The Greenalls Group plc.

Baker & McKenzie *"Active on a global scale"* for multi-national corporations implementing and monitoring UK plans, and also work with a network of offices on international schemes. Perceived by the market to mirror the firm overall, the practice is recommended for its cross border alliances with foreign consultancies. Work includes establishing tax-approved share option plans for major UK multinationals. Team head **Michael Ingle** *("charming")* has one assistant but maintains a low profile in the UK market. Advised Kuoni AG in its proposed friendly merger with First Choice plc and Swiss based Clariant AG on employee benefits issues arising from takeover of BTP plc. **Clients:** Kuoni AG, Japan Tobacco, Unova Inc.

Field Fisher Waterhouse A small niche practice which owes it prominence to a high profile involvement in associate worker ventures and genuine employee ownership of private companies. **Graeme Nuttall** with his *"strong tax background"* heads the team which also draws on expertise within the Employment, Intellectual Property and Corporate Finance departments. His profile was augmented by his presence on the Treasury's Employee Ownership Advisory Group. The first firm to take equity in clients, FFW are building a base within e-commerce. Designed and rafted new employee share ownership legislation for the Federation of Trade Unions of Macedonia (CMM). **Clients:** Steering Wilkins & Sons, CMM, ComputerLand, Zoom, London Regional Transport.

Nicholson Graham & Jones Known for its associations with smaller quoted companies, this firm is also acting for a number of unquoted companies in the financial services industry and offering due diligence consultancy for individual clients. The *"avuncular"* **Michael Jacobs**, *"can deal with the most complex areas,"* and is well-known as Vice Chairman of the SSLAG and Chairman of the CISCO Share Schemes Committee. He is said to have a *"commercial outlook"* but concerns exist that *"ESS is not his bread & butter work."* The team acted for management in taking Goldsmiths plc private and Peel Hunt on new Employee Share Schemes and flotation on AIM. **Clients:** Peel Hunt, Union Group plc, Merrydown plc.

THE REGIONS

EMPLOYEE SHARE SCHEMES • The Regions	Ptnrs	Assts
❶ **Pinsent Curtis** Leeds, Birmingham	2	4
❷ **Eversheds** Birmingham	-	2
Wragge & Co Birmingham	1	1
❸ **Addleshaw Booth & Co** Leeds, Manchester	1	1
Osborne Clarke Bristol	2	-
Walker Morris Leeds	1	1
Wrigleys Leeds	1	-

LEADING INDIVIDUALS	
✪ **PETT David** Pinsent Curtis	
❶ **GREAVES Judith** Pinsent Curtis	
❷ **GREEN Lawrence** Eversheds	**HAYES Richard** Addleshaw Booth & Co
❸ **LYNCH Malcolm** Wrigleys	**POOLE Kevin** Wragge & Co

Within each band, firms are listed alphabetically. *See* ***Profiles*** *on page 314*

Pinsent Curtis By far the leading firm outside London, with over 50 listed companies from FTSE 100, FTSE 350 and overseas, it also has a substantial client base of private companies, including high-techs. Department Head **David Pett**, based in Birmingham has a *"national reputation without parallel."* He is active with the SSLAG Group and sat on the ESS advisory committee for the Inland Revenue. *"Safe pair of hands"* **Judith Greaves** in Leeds has an outstanding profile in her own right, *"easy to get on with."* Advised Babcock International on approved and unapproved executive share options and new approved profit-sharing schemes for their subsidiary. Recently gained an increased number of overseas clients, including advising PanCanadian and Level 3 Communications on UK plans, and Nortel on the UK aspects of their new global plans. **Clients:** Pace Micro Technology plc, Babcock International Group plc, J Rothschild Assurance plc.

Eversheds Acted on mainly transactional work, including advising fledgling e-commerce businesses on tailored share incentives packages and share schemes for established FTSE 250 companies. Two Birmingham associates work closely with the Leeds office, and benefit from the National Human Resources consultancy in Cardiff. Senior associate **Lawrence Green** *"stands out from the pack."* Formulated the structure of the MBO of Computer Answers International, partly funded by rolling over the value in existing share incentives. The firm has international experience in advising US clients on the implementation of stock option plans in the UK. This year the team has continued the renewal and revamp of Britax International's long term incentives for its world-wide subsidiaries. **Clients:** Britax International Plc, Computer Answers, Vision Express, I B Net Ltd.

Wragge & Co Integrated with a wider human resources team, including Tax, Employment and Pensions, the small practice undertakes standardised schemes for listed companies and bespoke tailored packages for companies with no formal market in their shares. **Kevin Poole** *("capable and solid individual")* spends 70% of his time on ESS and has replaced Peter Smith, who now concentrates on tax work. The team arranged pre-floatation bespoke options and post AIM floatation unapproved executive schemes for channelfly.com. Also advised on new executive approved and unapproved share option schemes for freecom.net and eDefined, which also included restructuring of pre-existing options. **Clients:** Richardsons Westgarth, channelfly.com, Bowater Windows.

Addleshaw Booth & Co Operating from the Commercial Services department, this firm draws upon a strong tax team and has experience of design of remuneration packages and share based incentives. **Richard Hayes** *("pretty good in drafting and technical issues")* concentrates exclusively on ESS and is designing a share scheme administration system to assist clients. Unit advised 3i plc on employee benefit aspects of investments and successfully acted for Baxi Partnership Limited in piloting the Baxi Partnership Trusts Act 2000 to Royal Assent. **Clients:** Airtours, Baxi Partnerships Limited, 3i plc.

Osborne Clarke Operating a Pensions and Benefits unit, both partners integrate the two fields with a higher proportion of employee share scheme work. A significant reputation for work within the IT, telecoms and media sector including internet start-ups. The team has also advised offshore trustees on share scheme projects. Acted for 3i on an investment which included due diligence drafting and ongoing maintenance of employee share options. **Clients:** Chesterton International, 3i Group plc.

Walker Morris Firmly rooted in the tax practice, the team can also draw on corporate lawyers bringing in ESS work from an existing client base. Reputed for their work on smaller take-overs this practice also has international experience through implementation of Sigma Kalon's share schemes involving global tax and corporate regimes. Established approved and unapproved share options schemes for Tay Homes and a group wide incentive plan for Rosebys plc. **Clients:** Rosebys plc, Sigma Kalon, Tay Homes.

Wrigleys *"A niche practice"* which attracts private companies forming share scheme employee buy-outs. Practice head **Malcolm Lynch** has a strong tax background. Acted for UBH International Ltd where the company sought majority employee ownership as a route for succession. Has built on the success of its telephone advisory service by launching a web site to advise smaller private companies on the benefits provided by employee share option schemes. **Clients:** Mainly smaller private companies.

SCOTLAND

EMPLOYEE SHARE SCHEMES • Scotland	Ptnrs	Assts
❶ **Dundas & Wilson CS** Edinburgh	-	2
MacRoberts Glasgow	1	1

LEADING INDIVIDUALS
❶ **TROTTER Peter** MacRoberts

Within each band, firms are listed alphabetically. *See* ***Profiles*** *on page 314*

Dundas & Wilson CS Works with AIM and EASDAQ quoted companies and venture capitalists and as part of Arthur Andersen's world wide-network of legal firms has acted for companies listed on NYSE and NASDAQ. The firm has significant listed company experience and also provided advice to private companies on compliance issues and remuneration of non-executive directors. Currently dominating silicon glen, the team has acted for Kymata (on the largest equity placing in Scotland,) Memory Corporation and Digital Animations. **Clients:** Memory Computers plc, Kymata Ltd.

MacRoberts From within a large employment team, the Pensions and Employment Benefits Group has raised its profile with work mainly focusing on smaller plcs and private companies, especially those planning for flotation. Team Leader **Peter Trotter** *("good draftsman,")* is *"accepted as the expert north of the border"* and can draw on a strong tax capacity within the group. Working closely with Employee Ownership Scotland, he is a regular speaker at conferences and the first Scottish member of the Society of Share Scheme Practitioners. Significant high-tech work includes approved option schemes for Keydata Ltd and employee share options for Initiative software. Advised L.A.W. Holding Ltd in buying out 10% of the business, and restructuring with share options. **Clients:** Initiative Software, Keydata Ltd.

LEADERS IN EMPLOYEE SHARE SCHEMES

CHAMBERLAIN, Colin
Herbert Smith, London (020) 7374 8000
colin.chamberlain.@herbertsmith.com
Partner in employment department.
Specialisation: Specialises in employee share schemes and employee benefit arrangements in the UK and overseas including employee cash incentives, ESOPs. He is author of Tolley's 'Practical Guide to Employees' Share Schemes', and a regular speaker at conferences.
Career: Qualified in 1977. Between 1985 and 1989 he worked as a director of the former CC&P, now part of Bacon & Woodrow. Became a partner at *Herbert Smith* in 1989.
Personal: Educated at Sussex University. ATII.

CHATER, Stephen
Allen & Overy, London (020) 7330 3000
Specialisation: Specialises in employee tax and share incentives in an international context. Deals with flotations, privatisations, mergers and acquisitions and management buy-outs and advises on the establishment, operation, variation and termination of employees' share schemes. Has acted for UK public and private companies domestically as well as internationally. Advises UK listed companies on the UKLA Listing Rules, Institutional Investor Protection Committee Guidelines, the City Code on Takeovers and Mergers and corporate governance issues. Also advises senior executives and companies in relation to service contracts and remuneration packages.
Prof. Memberships: Law Society; Share Scheme Lawyers Group; Society of Share Scheme Practitioners.
Career: Joined *Allen & Overy* 1979. Qualified 1981. Partner 1989.
Personal: Educated at Hartlepool Grammar School and Christ Church, Oxford. Lives in Surrey.

CODRINGTON, Eddie
Slaughter and May, London (020) 7600 1200
Specialisation: Main areas of practice are employee benefits, pensions and employment. Deals with the establishment of all types of employee benefit plans, both cash and share based, ESOPs and profit related pay. Also handles pensions work including setting up, merger and termination of pension schemes.
Prof. Memberships: The Law Society, Association of Pension Lawyers, Share Scheme Lawyer Group.
Career: Joined 1974, qualified 1976, partner 1985.
Personal: Born 12 April 1951. St Benedict's School, Ealing 1957-1970. Birmingham University 1970-73. Interests include family and sport (watching).

COHEN, David
Norton Rose, London (020) 7283 6000
cohendhj@nortonrose.com
Partner in employment pensions and incentives department. Head of employee incentives group, Visiting Fellow in Employee Share Ownership Law at London University's Centre for Commercial Law Studies.
Specialisation: Specialises in employee share schemes and employee benefits work. Author of 'Employee Participation in Flotations 1987-1998'. Contributor to the 'Encyclopaedia of Forms and Precedents'. Regular contributor to the Financial Times.
Prof. Memberships: Fellow of the Chartered Institute of Taxation, Chairman of the Share Scheme Lawyers Group. Member of editorial board of Palmer's Company Law. Member of the advisory group set up by the Government in March 1999 to work with the Inland Revenue on the development of the new employee share schemes.
Career: Qualified in 1980. With *Titmuss Sainer & Webb* 1978-82. Assistant Solicitor and Partner at *Nicholson Graham & Jones* 1982-86. Partner at *Paisner & Co.* 1986-98. Joined *Norton Rose* as a partner in May 1998.
Personal: Born Cardiff 15th December 1955. Educated at Jesus College, Oxford. Governor of Independent Jewish Day School. Lives in London.

COOPER, Janet
Linklaters (A member firm of Linklaters & Alliance), London (020) 7456 3662
janet.cooper@linklaters.com
Partner 1991. Employment and Employee Benefits Group, Head of the Employee Share Plans team.
Specialisation: Specialises in employee share plans, executive incentives and corporate governance. On qualification was a general corporate lawyer before specialising in employee and executive plans and therefore familiar with how corporate transactions affect employee share plans. Her work includes advising on, designing and drafting documentation for a variety of employee and executive plans, advising on corporate governance implications for executive plans and generally on codes of conduct.
Prof. Memberships: Committee member of the Share Schemes Lawyers Group, Director of the Employee Share Ownership Centre, Founder member of the Share Schemes Advanced Studies Group.

CROFT, Anne
Linklaters (A member firm of Linklaters & Alliance), London (020) 7456 3706
anne.croft@linklaters.com
Specialisation: Specialises in tax, in particular employee-related tax and national insurance contributions. Practice areas include employee share schemes, ESOPs (including ESOP financing techniques), unapproved pension arrangements, employment contracts and flexible remuneration packages, termination of employment and international employment contracts. Recent transactional work includes demergers and schemes of arrangement (Tarmac, Allied Domecq) and flotations (Anglo American, Freeserve).
Prof. Memberships: Fellow of the Chartered Institute of Taxation, Share Scheme Lawyers Group.
Career: Called to the Bar 1975; LLM, tax and company law (University of London) 1976. Requalified as a solicitor 1990; Consultant 1998.

EVANS, Simon
Freshfields Bruckhaus Deringer, London (020) 7936 4000
Partner in Employment Pensions and Benefits Department.
Specialisation: Specialises in share option, restricted share plan and ESOP arrangements, relating both to establishment of schemes and advice on the impact of corporate transactions on schemes. Also handles employment law, notably executive appointments and dismissals. Devised numerous long term incentive plans and other tailor-made incentive schemes. Regularly lectures on share scheme topics.
Prof. Memberships: Share Scheme Lawyers Group.
Career: Qualified in 1983. Joined *Freshfields* in 1981, becoming a Partner in 1991.
Personal: Born 16th June 1957. Attended Rugby School 1970-75; MA from Sidney Sussex College, Cambridge, 1976-79. Lives in Staplehurst, Kent.

FENN, Jonathan
Slaughter and May, London (020) 7600 1200
Specialisation: Principal area of practice is employees' share schemes, both Inland Revenue approved and unapproved, including deferred bonus and long-term incentive schemes and ESOPs. Also advises on pensions, including in particular the pensions aspects of M&A and corporate transactions, as well as general pensions advice.
Prof. Memberships: The Law Society, Association of Pension Lawyers (member of Legislative and Parliamentary Sub-Committee), Share Scheme Lawyers Group (member of Committee), Society of Share Scheme Practitioners.
Career: Qualified 1986. At *Slaughter and May* 1984 to date. Became a Partner in 1995.
Personal: Born 30 May 1961. Educated at Maidstone Grammar School and King's College, London. Lives in Kent.

GREAVES, Judith
Pinsent Curtis, Leeds (0113) 244 5000
judith.greaves@pinsents.com
Partner in tax and pensions department.
Specialisation: Main areas of practice are employee share schemes: approved and unapproved schemes (including the new Enterprise Management Incentives and AESOPS), long term incentive plans, employee trusts, employee buy outs and international schemes; and corporate tax, covering acquisitions and disposals, group reorganisations, financing and property transactions and MBOs.
Prof. Memberships: Share Schemes Lawyers Group; the Global Equity Organistaion.
Career: Qualified 1986 with *Linklaters & Paines.* Joined *Simpson Curtis* in 1988, becoming partner in 1991.

GREEN, Lawrence
Eversheds, Birmingham (0121) 232 1000
lawrencegreen@eversheds.com
Senior Associate. Head of Share Incentives Team.
Specialisation: Advises on planning and implementation of all types of employee share incentive arrangements. Acts for a range of quoted and private companies on UK and overseas implications and for overseas companies implementing share schemes in the UK. Charge-out rate is £220 per hour.
Career: Trained with *Evershed & Tomkinson* and qualified in 1988. Senior Associate at *Eversheds* since 1996.
Personal: Born 8th March 1964. Educated at Queen Elizabeth Grammar School, Trinity Hall, Cambridge and Chester Law School. Leisure interests include cycling and mountain walking.

HAYES, Richard
Addleshaw Booth & Co, Manchester (0161) 934 6000
Partner in commercial tax department, commercial group.

Specialisation: Specialises in employee share schemes including ESOPs, option schemes and long term incentive schemes for both public and private companies.
Prof. Memberships: Law Society, Manchester Law Society; Society of Share Scheme Practitioners.
Career: Qualified in 1972. Joined the firm in 1973, becoming a partner in 1975.
Personal: Trinity Hall, Cambridge (MA 1969, LLB 1970). Leisure interests include railways, opera, classical music and sheep.

INGLE, Michael
Baker & McKenzie, London (020) 7919 1000
Specialisation: Practice covers the full range of employee benefits and employment taxation. Co-ordinates the firm's practice in the area of share schemes and incentive plans, including the related transactional issues. Works closely with share schemes colleagues in other *Baker & McKenzie* offices around the world in designing and implementing cross-border schemes. Clients include banks and numerous multinational companies. Is a contributing editor of the Gee publication 'Practical Tax Planning'.
Prof. Memberships: Share Schemes Lawyers Group; Employee Share Ownership Centre.
Career: Qualified 1981. At *Dunham Brindley & Linn* 1979-84, Engineering Employers Federation 1984-85 and *Baker & McKenzie* from 1985 (Partner from 1990).
Personal: Born 27 April 1951. Educated in Canada and obtained LLB degree from the University of Western Ontario in 1974. Lives in London.

JACOBS, Michael
Nicholson Graham & Jones, London (020) 7648 9000
michael.jacobs@ngj.co.uk
Head of Private Client Department.
Specialisation: Tax; employee share schemes; international tax, trusts, charities, and public sector bodies. Author of 'Tax on Take-overs' (7 editions) and 'Rewarding Leadership' (published by CISCO, February 1998); contributor to 'Tolley's Tax Planning' and 'Tolley's VAT Planning'. Consultant editor of Tolley's Trust Law International.
Prof. Memberships: Trust Law Committee (Founder Member and (1994-97) Secretary); Share Scheme Lawyers Group (Founder Member and Vice-Chairman); Employee Share Schemes Committee (Chairman) Quoted Companies Alliance; STEP; IFA; IFS; Charity Law Association; FRSA; Academician of the Academy for the Social Sciences.
Career: Articled at *Nicholson Graham & Jones* 1970; Partner 1976. Head of Private Client Department 1981.

LYNCH, Malcolm
Malcolm Lynch, Leeds (0113) 242 9600
law@malcolmlynch.com
See under Charities, p.142

MITCHELL, Jocelyn
Freshfields Bruckhaus Deringer, London (020) 7936 4000
jmitchell@freshfields.com
Specialisation: Main areas of practice are share schemes and employee benefits. Deals with the establishment and ongoing advisory work relating to share option schemes, long term incentive plans, ESOPs, QUESTs and international share schemes. Has extensive experience of share schemes and employment issues on mergers and acquisitions and flotations. Also advises on senior executive terminations, employment tax and the law relating to directors and corporate governance.
Prof. Memberships: Share Scheme Lawyers Group.
Career: Qualified in 1985. *Freshfields* 1995 (partner 1997).

NICHOLL, Victoria
Travers Smith Braithwaite, London (020) 7295 3000
Victoria.Nicholl@TraversSmith.com
Specialisation: Advises on design and operation of UK and international employee incentives and employee taxation. Specialises in employee share schemes, employee benefit trusts and QUESTs (including financing), corporate governance and employee benefits both generally and in relation to MBOs, flotations and other corporate transactions.
Prof. Memberships: Share Scheme Lawyers' Group; Society of Share Scheme Practitioners; ESOP Centre.
Career: Qualified 1987. Joined *Travers Smith Braithwaite* 1989. Partner 1995.

NUTTALL, Graeme
Field Fisher Waterhouse, London (020) 7861 4000
Specialisation: Partner in the Tax Department specialising in all aspects of business taxation. Particular interest in employee share schemes and intellectual property taxation. Has advised on the employee ownership aspects of privatisations both in the UK and overseas in Bulgaria, Macedonia, Romania and Slovenia. Regularly addresses conferences both in the UK and internationally on tax and employee share schemes. Frequently called on to assist in lobbying Government for tax and other changes to encourage employee ownership and now a member of the HM Treasury advisory group involved in helping the Inland Revenue develop new share schemes.
Prof. Memberships: Associate of the Institute of Taxation since 1985; member of the Share Schemes Lawyers Group since 1989; member of the Taxation Committee of the Intellectual Property Institute; Member of HM Treasury employee ownership advisory group (1999).
Career: Qualified 1984. Assistant solicitor, *Field Fisher Martineau* 1984-88. Partner since 1988. Spent six months on secondment to Touche Ross & Co. in 1987. Non-executive director of Job Ownership Ltd.
Publications: 'Employee Ownership–Legal and Tax Aspects' (co-author) 1987; 'Share Incentives for Employees' (co-author) 1990; 'Butterworths Tax Planning' (looseleaf service) (contributor); 'Butterworths UK Corporate Finance' (2nd edition 1992) (contributor); 'Nelson-Jones and Nuttall's Tax Tables' (5 editions) (co-author); 'Nuttall's Tax Tables 1994-95'; 'Sponsorship Endorsement and Merchandising' (co-author) (2nd edition 1998); 'Electronic commerce-law and practice' (co-author) 1998; 'Essential law for the tax practitioner' (contributor) (3rd edition 1998).
Personal: Educated at Price's Grammar School, Fareham, Hants. and Peterhouse, Cambridge (MA law) 1978-81. Lives in Blackheath, London.

PETT, David
Pinsent Curtis, Birmingham (0121) 200 1050
david.pett@pinsents.com
National practice head of tax and pensions.
Specialisation: Leader of a team of acknowledged specialists in the fields of corporate tax , of whom eight specialise in all aspects of employee share schemes. Responsible for devising many of the more innovative share schemes for public and private companies including long-term incentive plans; the use of QUEST, with SAYE option schemes; the tax efficient buyout of companies using employee trusts; and international schemes. Author of 'Employee Share Schemes' (Sweet and Maxwell two volume updated looseleaf).
Prof. Memberships: Active member of The Share Scheme Lawyers Group, the Global Equity Organisation and the Society of Share Scheme Practitioners. Member of Government Advisory Group on Employee Share Schemes.
Career: Qualified 1980, became a partner in 1985.
Personal: Educated at Lincoln College, Oxford.

POOLE, Kevin J.
Wragge & Co, Birmingham (0121) 214 1062
kevin_poole@wragge.com
Specialisation: Share schemes and corporate tax.
Prof. Memberships: Law Society; Birmigham Law Society.
Career: Articles at *Rowe & Maw* 1981-83. Solicitor there 1983-83 (property and commercial litigation). *JCH Bowdler & Sons, Shrewbury 1986. Wragge & Co* 1987, corporate solicitor. Corporate partner 1990. 1993 Tax, financial services and special projects including share schemes.
Personal: Reigate Grammar School and Jesus College, Cambridge. Married, two sons, residence Worcester. Leisure interests photography, Munro collecting and wine.

RANDALL, Paul
Ashurst Morris Crisp, London (020) 7638 1111
paul.randall@ashursts.com
Partner and head of employee benefits.
Specialisation: Designs and implements domestic and international employee share schemes and incentives. These include long term plans, ESOPs, QUESTs, profit sharing, executive and all-employee share options, restricted share schemes and bonus arrangements. Transactional experience covers MBOs, flotations, bids, mergers and privatisations. Advises on tax, corporate, stock exchange and governance aspects. Major clients include Albert Fisher, Amvescap, Coca-Cola Beverages, Exel, Fairey Group, Legal & General, National Express, Royal & Sun Alliance and Taylor Nelson Sofres.
Prof. Memberships: Law Society and Share Scheme Lawyers Group.
Career: Qualified in 1984. Joined *Ashurst Morris Crisp* 1987, partner 1995.

ROWLANDS-HEMPEL, Graham
Linklaters (A member firm of Linklaters & Alliance), London (020) 7456 3680
graham.rowlands-Hempel@linklaters.com
Specialisation: Specialises in employee share plans and executive incentives. On qualification was a corporate tax lawyer. Work includes advising on the design and operation of many international share plans including supervising and co-ordinating the overseas legal advice for companies like BP Amoco, British Airways and Blue Circle, and dealing with employee share plans on various major corporate reorganisations and transactions. Recently returned from secondment to the Inland Revenue as policy advisor on the Government's new share scheme.

Prof. Memberships: Member of Society of Share Scheme Practitioners and the Share Schemes Lawyers' Group.
Career: 1998 to date–Partner, Employment & Benefits Group, *Linklaters*. 1994-98–Senior Assistant, Employment & Benefits Group, *Linklaters*. 1987-94–Assistant Solicitor, Tax Group, *Simmons & Simmons*. Education–University of South Bank–LLB.

TREMAINE, Robin
Clifford Chance, London (020) 7600 1000
robin.tremaine@cliffordchance.com
Specialisation: Partner, head of the employee share schemes unit, options, corporate and international tax.
Prof. Memberships: Member Share Schemes Lawyers Group; Society of Share Scheme Practioners; Share Scheme Advanced Studies Group.
Career: Plymouth College; Trinity Hall, Cambridge (MA (Cantab) 1978). Qualified as barrister in 1979; requalified as a solicitor in 1986; partner 1989.
Publications: 'Employee Share Ownership in the UK' (Butterworths).

TROTTER, Peter A.A.
MacRoberts, Glasgow (0141) 332 9988
PAAT@macroberts.co.uk

WHITEWRIGHT, Louise L.
Lovells, London (020) 7296 2000
louise.whitewright@lovells.com
Specialisation: Principal area of practice is employee share schemes and employee benefits advising on all aspects of the design, structure, establishment and operation of approved and unapproved employee share schemes (including ESOPS, restricted share schemes and international share schemes) for private and public companies. Deals with all aspects of these schemes on flotations, takeovers, privatisations etc. Contributor of section in CCH Editions Employment Manual and to other publications, including Tolley's 'Tax Planning'.
Prof. Memberships: Law Society; Share Scheme Lawyers Group (Secretary and member of Executive Committee). ESOP Centre; City of London Lawyers.
Career: Articled *Rakisons* 1984-1986; qualified 1986 with *Lovells* as an assistant solicitor in the tax group. Specialised in employee share schemes from 1987 and became a partner in 1996.

EMPLOYMENT

RESEARCH APPROVED BY BMRB: *For this edition,* Chambers' *researchers conducted 6083 interviews – 4408 with law firms, 598 with barristers and 1077 with clients.*

The validity of the research was scrutinised by BMRB International, who audited both the methodology and the results at our offices in July 2000. They interviewed Chambers' *researchers and cross-checked sample interviews. Details of the audit appear on page 7.*

LEADING IN-HOUSE LAWYERS

Sally BOYLE, Executive Director and Counsel, *Goldman Sachs International*

Mark COOPER, Senior Legal Counsel, *Nortel Networks plc*

Julia HARRISON, Employment Lawyer, *British Airways*

Melanie JONES, Director of Legal & Business Affairs, *Warner Brothers Productions Ltd*

Hilary SCHRADER, Solicitor, *Nestlé UK Ltd*

Jane STABLES, Group Legal & Personnel Director, *United News & Media plc*

John TUPMAN, Deputy Chief Solicitor, *Woolwich plc*

A new face at Goldman Sachs is the *"commercially-minded"* **Sally Boyle** who focuses solely on employment law. **Mark Cooper** has a *"good knowledge"* of the issues involved and **Julia Harrison** *"heads a significant team."* The *"very experienced"* **Melanie Jones** is known for her *"excellent pan-European work."* **Hilary Schrader** is *"particularly recommended"* while the *"very impressive"* **Jane Stables** is a *"fantastic manager of people"* who is able to *"command great loyalty."* At the Woolwich, **John Tupman** is praised for being *"very good."*

In-House lawyers profiles: page 1177

LONDON

RESPONDENT FIRMS

Simmons & Simmons This *"quality practice can't be ignored."* Disruptions affecting the rest of the firm have made no impact on this *"well structured and well managed department which delivers results."* The group maintains its *"top of the tree"* position largely thanks to its *"first class client list"* of employers in FTSE and plc companies, financial services, arts organisations, and high profile public bodies. The team is said to contain *"no weak links"* and is lead by the *"doyenne of employment law"* **Janet Gaymer.** Although seen to be heavily involved in a marketing role, Gaymer still ranks as the *"top employment lawyer in Europe."* She is supported by *"assiduous"* **William Dawson** who takes a *"humane and sensible"* approach to employment negotiations. *"Shrewd"* **Simon Watson** has a *"fantastic legal mind"* and extensive experience of applying for interlocutory relief, injunctions, and Anton Pillar orders both in the employment tribunal and High Court. **Clients:** Deutsche Bank; Tokai Bank Europe plc; The Telegraph.

Baker & McKenzie Reputed to have ably weathered the loss of Fraser Younson although still seen to be lacking a big hitter personality. *"New kidette on the block"* **Christine O'Brien** has made the *"meteoric climb"* to department head and has apparently marshalled tremendous *"confidence and authority"* in motivating her team. The practice acts for major UK and multi-national companies and has a developed European dimension. Members are frequently called upon to advise clients in connection with European Works Council issues. Acted successfully for defendants in Wheatley v Conrol Techniques and Emerson Electric Co against a wrongful dismissal claim for over £9 million. **Clients:** Emerson Electric Co.; JP Morgan; Reckitt & Colman.

Eversheds A multifaceted practice with links throughout the UK. In addition to a fair share of heavyweight contentious work, the practice advises clients on impending EU legislation and business risk analysis. A large team gives them the capability to act on large corporate mergers, overseeing the project management employment aspects of change management. The team has a reputation for a *"confrontational"* approach to litigation and rates highly for its *"national coverage."* Department head **Elaine Aarons** *"knows her onions"* and has a dedicated client following. Over the past year the group was active in advising on the employment aspects of the creation of the Financial Ombusdman Scheme. **Clients:** McDonalds; HSBC Investment Bank; Queen Mary & Westfield College, University of London.

Lovells This *"steady"* team maintains a good balance and spread of work for a number of quality blue-chip clients. The practice is divided equally between contentious tribunal work, corporate support and advisory work. The firm's German connection has also increased the group's activity in pan-European employment projects. An *"energetic"* team, reputed to be *"committed to providing good client service." "Gentlemanly"* **David Harper** is a *"solid all rounder"* who *"never loses his cool." "Crisp"* **Naomi Feinstein** is said to be an *"organised, details person,"* while **Andrew Williamson** is rated as *"eminently practical"* and *"good at looking at the big picture."* The firm has been involved in the employment aspects of a number of corporate transactions including the merger between Trinity and Mirror. **Clients:** Barclays Bank plc; Trinity Mirror Group plc; Ford Motor Company.

Fox Williams Although a predominantly respondent firm, the practice also undertakes work on behalf of employees and has a particularly strong reputation for acting for senior executives. Seen by many as a *"boutique"* practice, the group maintains a high profile in the area. The department undertakes an increasing amount of international work and acts for a number of clients in the financial, industrial and IT sectors. This *"feisty group of individuals"* is lead by *"delightful"* **Jane Mann,** a *"blunt"* lawyer said to be *"in great demand for sex discrimination cases."* Senior partner **Ronnie Fox** is an *"old hand"* at negotiating payments on termination of employment. The team acted for Charman Underwriting Agency Ltd in relation to a discrimination claim of several millions of pounds brought by an employee who did not receive an allocation of shares during maternity leave. **Clients:** The Body Shop International; GMB; Winterthur International.

Rowe & Maw An *"effective"* group said to *"crop up all over the place"* on employment matters. The department acts for a broad spectrum of employers across a range of sectors. Advises clients on the Employment Rights Act, parental leave, data protection and works councils. Interviewees particularly praised the team's strength at the assistant solicitor level. Department head **Julian Roskill** is an *"incisive"* practitioner who knows the ins and outs of the *"art, mystery and science of employment law." "Rising star"* **Nicholas Robertson** is reckoned an *"extremely hardworking young Turk."* The firm advised the Marsh Group on integration issues following the acquisition of the Sedgwick Group. **Clients:** Independent News & Media; Marsh Group (formerly Sedgwicks) including Mercers; Prebon Yamane.

Allen & Overy Acting primarily for financial institutions, the department is divided between stand alone employment work and corporate support. A *"quality act,"* the group rises in the tables due to an *"excellent client base and interesting work both on the collective and individual side."* Advises increas-

EMPLOYMENT: RESPONDENT • London	Ptnrs	Assts
❶ Simmons & Simmons	4	17
❷ Baker & McKenzie	5	21
Eversheds	4	14
Lovells	4	13
❸ Fox Williams	4	11
Rowe & Maw	2	9
❹ Allen & Overy	1	13
CMS Cameron McKenna	2	9
Herbert Smith	3	9
Lewis Silkin	4	9
❺ Beachcroft Wansbroughs	2	10
Charles Russell	2	12
Clifford Chance	3	17
Denton Wilde Sapte	5	8
Linklaters	2	16
McDermott, Will & Emery	2	7
Osborne Clarke OWA	3	12
Pinsent Curtis	2	6
Slaughter and May	1	5
Stephenson Harwood	Fu	Fu
❻ Boodle Hatfield	2	3
Dechert	1	4
Freshfields Bruckhaus Deringer	2	10
Langley & Co	3	4
Macfarlanes	4	7
Norton Rose	1	10
Olswang	2	9
Paisner & Co	2	7
Richards Butler	2	4
Salans Hertzfeld & Heilbronn HRK	1	2
Speechly Bircham	2	3
Theodore Goddard	3	6
Travers Smith Braithwaite	2	6

EMPLOYMENT: APPLICANT • London	Ptnrs	Assts
❶ Pattinson & Brewer	5	4
❷ Rowley Ashworth	4	7
Thompsons	4	7
❸ Bindman & Partners	2	2
Russell Jones & Walker	6	5
❹ Hodge Jones & Allen	1	2
Irwin Mitchell	4	–
Lawfords	2	3

Within each band, firms are listed alphabetically.
Fu Figures unavailable at time of going to press.

ingly on pan-European disposals and employment issues and has particular strength in unfair dismissal and discrimination claims. *"Proactive"* **Mark Mansell** *"sticks to his guns"* in negotiations involving multi-jurisdictional employment issues. The team is bolstered by the recent addition of *"ambitious"* **Karen Seward** from Pinsent Curtis who is recommended as *"one to watch."* Recently advised Mobil on the employment aspects of their merger with Exxon and dissolution of a joint venture with BP. **Clients:** Pitney Bowes; Warburg Dillon Read.

CMS Cameron McKenna A *"good all round team"* with a *"traditional approach"* to employment matters. This specialist department acts for an extensive client base of large corporates and smaller quoted or unquoted companies. Practice contains a mediation expert and emphasises ADR in employment disputes. Over the past year, the team has been particularly active in issues relating to the Public Interest Disclosure Act and breach of contract/share options matters. Department head **Simon Jeffreys** is *"extremely good at boardroom bust-ups"* and is rated for his *"clarity of thought and expression."* The group has represented clients at a number of arbitration hearings in relation to the termination of senior executive contracts. **Clients:** Lloyds TSB; Nestle; British Aerospace.

Herbert Smith This *"feisty"* group has a distinguished reputation for contentious respondents' work. The advisory practice is nevertheless growing, as is the department's representation of high profile individuals. The team has extensive experience of executive severances, team moves, employee fraud and senior executive discrimination claims. *"Stately"* **John Farr** is a *"smooth litigator"* and a *"pleasure to do business with." "Responsive"* **Peter Frost** is known to be *"on the ball"* and take a *"commercial approach."* The group advised the Government Office for London on employment implications of transfer of its scheme to the Financial Services Ombudsman Scheme. **Clients:** CSFB; Credit Lyonnais; Univar plc.

Lewis Silkin Carry out the full range of contentious and non-contentious work for employers and employees with an emphasis on work for individual directors and senior-level staff. A *"dynamic"* group of lawyers with the *"chutzpah"* to take on complicated sex discrimination and harassment cases. The team has notable expertise in TUPE and maternity/paternity rights. Also provides advice to law firms in relation to their internal employment issues. *"Outgoing"* **James Davies** is *"very good at working out the practical ramifications of agreements." "Intellectual"* **Michael Burd** rates as a *"good clinical black letter lawyer"* and specialises in negotiating senior executive severances. Acted for Kamlesh Bahl in her dispute with the Law Society regarding allegations of bullying and harassment. **Clients:** BAA; Harrods Ltd; Dell Computer Corporation.

Beachcroft Wansbroughs This niche NHS sector firm is seen to be *"doing well"* on the employment front. Approximately 80 percent of the department's clients come from the firm's health sector connection while the remainder are spread across a range of educational institutions, local authorities and private sector clients. The group has particular expertise in specialist disciplinaries involving doctors and consultants and is experienced in advising on protection of confidential information and enforcement of restrictive covenants. It also covers employment issues from a PI angle, addressing stress claims from within the firm's insurance litigation department. *"Thoughtful and articulate"* **Elizabeth Adams** heads a *"successful"* team. **Rachel Dineley** is *"always prepared for a scrap."* Provided employment law advice in connection with the South Tees PFI Project, acting for the South Tees Acute Hospitals NHS Trust. **Clients:** South Tees Acute Hospitals NHS Trust; Capital Business Services; Lynx Express Limited.

Charles Russell A broad based department with a reputation for discrimination cases and boardroom disputes. Although seen by some to be *"lacking in critical mass,"* the team is reputed to be *"thorough and asks the right questions."* Draws upon the skills of two support lawyers and a specialised Pensions and Employee Benefits team. Provides advice on the Transfer of Undertaking Regulations and represents employers and employees in injunctions to enforce restrictive covenants. *"Understated"* **David Green** is widely respected for his *"subtle judgement"* and his way of *"quietly dealing with an operation without a lot of fuss."* The department acted for Suresh Anisetti in a successful racial discrimination case against Tokyo Mitsubishi Bank. **Clients:** HJ Heinz Co Ltd; Arthur Anderson; Lambert Heath.

Clifford Chance A sizeable team seen frequently acting for employers in financial institutions and industrial clients. Handles a substantial amount of high profile litigation including unfair dismissal and discrimination cases in the Employment Tribunal, as well as injunctions and wrongful dismissal claims in the High Court. The group also manages work on a pan-

LEADING INDIVIDUALS	
✪ **GAYMER Janet** Simmons & Simmons	
❶ **AARONS Elaine** Eversheds	**AUERBACH Simon** Pattinson & Brewer
COCKBURN David Pattinson & Brewer	**JEFFREYS Simon** CMS Cameron McKenna
MANSELL Mark Allen & Overy	**YOUNSON Fraser** McDermott, Will & Emery
❷ **ADAMS Elizabeth** Beachcroft Wansbroughs	
BURD Michael Lewis Silkin	**DAVIES James** Lewis Silkin
FARR John Herbert Smith	**FLANAGAN Tom** Stephenson Harwood
FROST Peter Herbert Smith	**JACOBS Howard** Slaughter and May
JULYAN Alan Speechly Bircham	**OSMAN Christopher** Clifford Chance
ROSKILL Julian Rowe & Maw	**SHORT Michael** Rowley Ashworth
❸ **BREARLEY Kate** Stephenson Harwood	**DALE Stephanie** Denton Wilde Sapte
DAWSON William Simmons & Simmons	**GREEN David** Charles Russell
HARPER David Lovells	**JEFFERS Raymond** Linklaters
MANN Jane Fox Williams	**O'BRIEN Christine** Baker & McKenzie
ROBERTSON Nicholas Rowe & Maw	**THOMPSON Tony** Macfarlanes
WATSON Simon Simmons & Simmons	**WYNN-EVANS Charles** Dechert
❹ **ANDREW Jill** Langley & Co	**CAVALIER Stephen** Thompsons
COOPER Edward Russell Jones & Walker	
DALGARNO David McDermott, Will & Emery	
DINELEY Rachel Beachcroft Wansbroughs	
FEINSTEIN Naomi Lovells	**FOX Ronald** Fox Williams
KEANE Georgina Lawrence Graham	**LANGLEY Dale** Langley & Co
MOORMAN Jane D J Freeman	
MORDSLEY Barry Salans Hertzfeld & Heilbronn HRK	
SEWARD Karen Allen & Overy	**WHINCUP David** Hammond Suddards Edge
WILLIAMSON Andrew Lovells	
UP AND COMING	
LILLEY Andrew Travers Smith Braithwaite	
PALCA Julia Olswang	**TAYLOR Catherine** Olswang

See *Profiles* on page 332

European basis for multi-national clients. *"First-rate"* **Chris Osman** *"runs a tight ship."* The firm acted for General Accident in relation to its merger with Commercial Union, involving the transfer and harmonisation of two large workforces. **Clients:** Manpower plc; Salomon Smith Barney; Cola Cola.

Denton Wilde Sapte Denton Hall's merger with Wilde Sapte is seen to have increased the firm's employment law capacities. Acts for employers drawn from media, banking, finance and aviation industries as well as non-corporate entities such as Amnesty International. *"Practical"* **Stephanie Dale** is described as *"responsive to the client's needs."* The group acted for Old Mutual plc in respect of all employment aspects of its establishment as a Listed Company in London. **Clients:** British Airways plc; Capital Radio; NatWest.

Linklaters Seen to be *"cropping up more often,"* the employment unit has a reputation for quality work but is perceived to derive the bulk of its work from corporate support. This *"academic"* group advises on employment aspects of multi-national mergers and acquisitions and has particular expertise in corporate governance, European Works Councils, Working Time Regulations, and whistle-blowing. *"Intellectual"* **Raymond Jeffers** is especially *"clever at knotty legal subjects."* Acted for Zeneca Limited in the sale of its global speciality chemicals business, involving a transfer of over 6,000 employees across 25 jurisdictions. **Clients:** Leading multi-nationals.

McDermott, Will & Emery The arrival of *"powerful operator"* **Fraser Younson** has launched the firm into a high profile position both in the market and Chambers' employment tables. The *"energetic"* Younson is said to *"live and breathe employment law"* and comes highly recommended for European Works Council issues. Thanks to his leadership, the group has made a *"considerable splash"* and is seen to be rapidly building itself up through *"demonstrable recruitment."* Another recent addition is *"mischievous"* **David Dalgarno** whose *"outward bonhomie and easy manner conceals a hard negotiator."* Acts for a client base of multi-nationals, hi-tech start up companies, charities and quasi-government organisations such as the Sports Council. The team acted for a global fashion company on UK closures involving large scale redundancy. **Clients:** Dresdner Kleinwort Benson; Levi Strauss & Co; J Sainsbury plc.

Osborne Clark OWA A *"traditionally strong practice"* working in tandem with the firm's Bristol and Reading branches. Represents employers in a range of sectors including financial services, transport, hi-tech companies and government agencies. Perceived to be *"beefing up the London office,"* the department is reportedly *"recruiting good people and building up a good team."* Recently launched the Osborne Clarke HR Directors Forum of director level professionals. Notably acted for the Professional Golfers Association in the high profile sex discrimination case of a woman manager dismissed for wearing trousers. **Clients:** Prudential Corporation; P&O Stena Line; British Airways.

Pinsent Curtis This *"responsible"* group covers the spectrum of contentious and non-contentious employment work including boardroom disputes, executive terminations, stress at work, executive immigration, discrimination and drafting and enforcement of restrictive covenants. The group is reputed to *"take employment law seriously"* but it is expected that the loss of Karen Seward to Allen & Overy will prove to be a substantial setback to the practice. The team is particularly noted for its expertise in TUPE, discrimination cases and occupational health and safety, and acted for LSG Sky Chefs in relation to an industrial action involving 276 applicants. **Clients:** Nikko Principal Investments Ltd; Thistle Hotels plc; Marks & Spencer plc.

Slaughter and May Perceived to carry on employment work largely under the steam of corporate support, this small team nevertheless rates highly for quality. A combined pensions and employment department advises on a number of corporate transactions and has particular expertise in employee benefits matters. A *"hugely entertaining and charismatic individual,"* **Howard Jacobs** takes a *"no-nonsense approach"* to employment law and is considered to be the *"rock around which the practice is built."* The team advised on employee share schemes in the merger between British Steel and Hoogovens. **Clients:** Blue-chip corporates and senior executives.

Stephenson Harwood A *"successful"* practice with recognised strength and depth. Seen to have built up a *"carefully chosen"* niche in restrictive covenants and confidentiality injunctions. In addition to a large body of corporate clients, the group also advises a number of senior executives, traders and CEOs in relation to employment packages and termination settlements. Other areas of practice include advising European Works Councils, race and disability discrimination, and the outsourcing and application of TUPE. Also handles a fair amount of corporate support work. Ex-barrister **Kate Brearley** is a *"whiz on restrictive covenants"* while *"sensible"* **Tom Flanagan** *"knows how to reach a deal and go forward."* Acted for HSBC in test cases of part-time employees claiming access to occupational pension schemes. **Clients:** Charing Cross & Westminster Medical School, KPMG, Vodafone Airtouch Group Services Ltd.

Boodle Hatfield A comprehensive employment practice acting chiefly for employers but also for a number of employees and staff associations. Rated for expertise in TUPE advice and executive terminations. Practice contains employment litigation and employment tax specialists. Successfully acted for Computacenter on a major sex discrimination case and won two share options cases for the same client. **Clients:** Computacenter; Blockbuster Video; MTV.

Dechert A small team seen to be going through a process of *"rejuvenation."* Involved in all aspects of employment litigation including restrictive covenant disputes, fraud claims and poaching and conspiracy issues. Acts for respondents in the insurance, retail, education, advertising, aviation, publishing and engineering industries. *"Reasonable"* **Charles Wynn-Evans** was commended for his *"handling of sensitive issues in a sympathetic way."* Acted for Mandi Norwood, editor of a well-known magazine, on her contested departure. **Clients:** Mandi Norwood.

Freshfields Bruckhaus Deringer A *"quality department"* seen frequently on employment aspects of corporate transactions. Shares a large blue-chip client base with the firm's corporate departments. Advises on the structure of remuneration arrangements, termination of employment, severance packages, and conducts employment related litigation. Also draws upon the strength of a European Labour Law Group to advise on European Works Councils. Acted for Hewlett-Packard on its recent demerger involving the transfer of over 50,000 employees to a new company, Agilent Technologies. **Clients:** Hays; Hewlett-Packard; Tyco.

Langley & Co This *"pioneer firm"* has *"shot up in the employment firmament."* With a recognised niche in executive termination and restrictive covenants, the practice is split between employer respondent work and representation of individuals at all levels. **Dale Langley** *"shoots from the hip"* while *"optimistic"* **Jill Andrew** is said to have a *"bijoux practice."* Acted in a high profile sex discrimination claim on behalf of former employee Aysling Sykes against JP Morgan. **Clients:** Virgin Airways; Thistle Hotels; Penna Holdings.

Macfarlanes A small and *"solid"* team said to maintain a *"nice balance between City and pure employment work."* Acts principally for employers but also for senior executives in negotiating contracts and severance packages. *"Tough litigator"* **Tony Thompson** is *"switched on and prepared to fight."* Advised several clients on major collective redundancy exercises, each involving hundreds of employees. **Clients:** Carlton Communications plc; Anheuser Busch; KF/ Tricon Restaurants.

Norton Rose Although moving away from corporate support work, some of the practice's best work is handling employment aspects of corporate transactions. Key areas of work include drafting contracts and service agreements, employment policies, collective issues, international advice and executive immigration. Acted for BMW in all employee issues relating to the disposal of Rover Group. **Clients:** AA; Saga Petroleum UK; Citigroup.

Olswang Enters the Chambers' tables for quality employment work for clients in media and financial services. Seen to be a growing practice with niche expertise in restrictive covenants and team moves. **Catherine Taylor** and **Julia Palca** were both recommended as *"impressive"* up and coming employment lawyers. Advised Thus plc on the employee aspects of a business re-organisation involving 2,500 employees. **Clients:** Thus plc; Cantor Fitzgerald International General Motors.

Paisner & Co Interviewees consider this *"steadily reliable"* group to be hard hit by the recent departure of senior practitioner Steven Levinson. It remains to be seen whether the firm will be able to regain its former profile in the field. Team has particular experience in executive termination and immigration matters, collective bargaining, and advising professional and government bodies. Acted for National Power plc in its successful House of Lords action (Carmichael v National Power), relating to rights of casual workers. **Clients:** First Leisure Corporation plc; Royal College of Surgeons of England; ALPHA Catering Services.

Richards Butler A competent practice seen to have slipped in the market following the loss of Georgina Keane to Lawrence Graham. Acts for a range of corporate clients in key industry sectors of banking, finance, insurance, leisure and media. The practice is strongest in collective labour law, restrictive covenants, confidentiality clauses and TUPE work. Handled employment aspects of acquisition by Direct Line of Green Flag. **Clients:** The Rank Group plc.

Salans Hertzfeld & Heilbronn HRK Practice built largely around the reputation of *"mover and shaker"* **Barry Mordsley**, who is reputed to have a *"nice touch with clients."* Handles a large volume of work for employers and a small percentage of employees in city institutions, the motor industry and retail companies. Advised William Baird on mass redundancy following cancellation of a contract by Marks & Spencer. **Clients:** Rotary Watches Ltd; William Baird; Remploy Ltd.

Speechly Bircham A *"balanced"* practice with developed specialisms in employment and corporate governance issues arising from the recruitment, retention and termination of senior executives and the management of organisational change. Clients drawn from financial services companies, management consultancies, employment agencies and employers in manufacturing, telecoms and charities sectors. **Alan Julyan** is *"extremely good news."* His *"calm"* exterior complements his *"encyclopaedic legal knowledge."* **Clients:** Employment agencies; management consultancies.

Theodore Goddard Handles the range of contentious and non-contentious respondent's work with particular strength in tribunal and high court litigation, including interlocutory applications for injunctive relief. This *"sound"* team successfully acted for SBJ Stephenson Ltd on an injunction application against a former employee. **Clients:** SBJ Stephenson Ltd; Oracle Corporation Ltd; Signet Group plc.

Travers Smith Braithwaite This *"professional outfit"* enters Chambers' tables upon general recommendation for quality work. Covers the full range of employment immigration and industrial relations issues, with particular emphasis on resolving board-room disputes, TUPE, enforcing restrictive covenants and collective consultation issues. **Andrew Lilley** ranks as up and coming for his *"superb judgement and excellent preparation."* Advised Geest plc on the establishment of its European Works Council. **Clients:** J Rothschild Assurance Holdings plc; SGB Service plc; Armor Holdings Group.

Other Notable Practitioners *"Old hand"* **Georgina Keane** has left Richards Butler to join Lawrence Graham. This is expected to galvanise the latter's moribund employment practice. Other respected practitioners include the *"able"* **Jane Moorman** of DJ Freeman and *"solution-driven"* **David Whincup** of Hammond Suddards Edge.

APPLICANT FIRMS

Pattinson & Brewer The *"first port of call"* for applicant work, these *"collective labour law specialists"* are *"good people to have batting for you"* in the employment tribunal. Team members have extensive experience of executive severances, disability discrimination cases, human rights and transfer regulation issues. This *"innovative"* team handles a large volume of work for trade unions, voluntary associations, charities and senior executive applicants. Practice contains a number of heavy hitters. A *"likeable but shrewd lawyer,"* **David Cockburn** has a reputation as *"deeply committed to trade union work."* *"Detailed"* **Simon Auerbach** takes an *"academic approach"* to employment law but maintains a professional distance from the politics of trade union work. Acted for former employees in Everson & Ors v Bell Lines in relation to UK's responsibility for insolvency payments. **Clients:** TGWU; RMT; private applicants referred by other solicitors in the area.

Rowley Ashworth This sizeable team acts for major industrial trade unions, undertaking a range of sector work. Recommended for offering *"a high standard of advice,"* this *"approachable"* group *"thinks about problems and drafts helpful instructions."* **Michael Short** is highly regarded as a *"clear thinking"* advocate, *"always on top of his stuff."* Acted in a substantial number of claims for holiday pay calculated in accordance with Working Time Regulations. **Clients:** TGWU; AEEU; GMB.

Thompsons Acts exclusively for trade unions and trade union members. An *"approachable"* team handling a wide range of cases with particular expertise in European employment law, Working Time Regulations, TUPE and equal opportunities law. *"First class"* **Stephen Cavalier** is noted as a TUPE expert and *"effective public relations agent."* Acted for Broadcasting Entertainment and Cinamatographic and Theatre Union in a European Court challenge to the UK government on Working Time Regulations. **Clients:** UNISON; GMB; PCS.

Bindman & Partners An active group with a *"strong commercial edge"* and high profile for discrimination work. Practice split between respondent work for local public bodies, local authorities, charities and campaigning groups, and applicant work for individual employees. Acted in a discrimination case in the European Court of Justice on behalf of Belinda Coote against Granada, concerning failure to give a reference after the end of employment (£120,000 award). **Clients:** The Law Society; National Lottery Charities Board; Equal Opportunities Commission.

Russell Jones & Walker Handles a broad spectrum of applicant work for clients in industry, finance, service and public sectors. Maintains a significant private client practice in addition to its union-funded work. Well known for acting for the Police Federation, the group has particular strengths in TU law, sex, race and disability discrimination claims. *"Cerebral"* **Edward Cooper** leads a team of *"flexible"* employment specialists. The firm secured an award in the employment tribunal of over £190,000 for injury to health in Stubbs v Chief Constable of Lincolnshire. **Clients:** Police Federation; Connect (formerly Society of Telecom); Transport Salaried Staff Association.

Hodge Jones & Allen An applicant-based practice best known for racial and disability discrimination work. Also conducts a smaller proportion of respondent work for voluntary and public sector organisations and an educational institution. **Clients:** Mainly individual applicants.

Irwin Mitchell Undertakes trade union-sponsored work with particular expertise in dealing with equal opportunities and human rights issues. Recently launched a national Human Rights and Discrimination Law Unit. Continues to act for speech therapist plaintiffs in Enderby v Frenchay NHS Trust, settling 351 cases for a total of £12 million. **Clients:** MSF; UNIFI; Association of University Teachers (AUT).

Lawfords Deals principally with trade unions and some commercial clients in engineering, banking, printing and charity industries. Also undertakes a substantial amount of employment work for universities and educational institutions. Acted in private sector test cases Fletcher & Others v HSBC, regarding claims by employees denied access to Occupational Pension Schemes due to their part time status. **Clients:** UNIFI; AEEU; CWU.

THE SOUTH

EMPLOYMENT • The South	Ptnrs	Assts
❶ **DMH** Brighton	3	1
❷ **Blake Lapthorn** Portsmouth	2	4
Cripps Harries Hall Tunbridge Wells, Kent	2	3
Paris Smith & Randall Southampton	1	2
❸ **Argles Stoneham Burstows** Crawley	4	7
Brachers Maidstone	1	1
Clarkson Wright & Jakes Orpington	1	1
Pattinson & Brewer Chatham	5	4
Stevens & Bolton Guildford	1	2

LEADING INDIVIDUALS
❶ **BARRY Quintin** DMH
❷ **ROSS Malcolm** Paris Smith & Randall

Within each band, firms are listed alphabetically. *See **Profiles** on page 332*

DMH A *"well-organised department"* seen to have the *"inside track"* on a range of employment matters. Clients range from individual employees to national chains to NHS Trusts. Although now in a consultant role, **Quintin Barry** still rates highly for his *"mature, constructive approach to achieving settlements."* His *"informal style"* is particularly *"well suited to tribunals,"* as it *"puts everyone at ease and gets results."* The *"efficient"* team *"gives added value to clients"* in the public sector and sports and leisure domains. The group acts for both sides in Disability Discrimination Act cases before the Employment Appeals Tribunal and is frequently instructed by employers in multi-applicant cases and large scale collective redundancy situations. **Clients:** London Borough of Croydon; HFC Bank; Thistle Hotels.

Blake Lapthorn This *"sound and expanding team,"* said to offer a *"reliable service,"* is a new entrant to Chambers' tables. Undertakes a full range of contentious and non-contentious work on behalf of companies, partnerships and charities, ranging from individual employees to multinational plcs. Department members have wide experience of industrial and trade union matters. Acted for Kerry Food in a multi-handed, TUPE-related claim concerning defences and protective awards by several employees, and is pursuing an appeal in the Court of Appeal. **Clients:** Lockheed Martin; Hampshire Training and Enterprise Council; Alcatel Networks Ltd.

Cripps Harries Hall A client base consisting largely of employers in new technology/ IT and start-up company sectors gives the practice considerable strength in corporate transactional work. Advises on pensions aspects of employment and working time regulations, particularly with regard to holiday pay and minimum wage. Also handles business reorganisations, tribunal claims for unfair/wrongful dismissal and discrimination claims. Advised employer in one of the first prosecutions for breach of minimum wage regulations. **Clients:** Dencare Group Management plc; Hidden Hearing plc; Hoverspeed Ltd.

Paris Smith & Randall A newcomer to the Chambers' employment rankings, this *"focused"* group is highly recommended as a specialist in discrimination law. Does a range of contentious and non-contentious work for a number of clients in the manufacturing and service provision industries. Ranked practitioner **Malcolm Ross** has *"been around a long time"* and built up a respected employment practice. Advised on employment aspects of acquisition of the Portsmouth Football Club by the new purchaser. **Clients:** Millbrook Furnishings; Southampton Football Club; Southampton Institute.

Argles Stoneham Burstows Following its November 1999 merger, the group has strengthened its position in the area and enters Chambers' tables for the first time this year. This large group is divided into three specialist areas: transfer work, discrimination issues and high court litigation. The firm's proximity to Gatwick Airport brings them a large base of airline and related service industry clients. Bespoke services to clients include an employment manual, 24-hour helpline and legal expenses insurance policy. The firm recently represented a major educational establishment in the Court of Appeal, relating to job share claim. **Clients:** Airlines, related industry clients.

Brachers Best known for handling advisory work for respondents, the team shares employment work between the London and Maidstone offices. Undertakes a broad spectrum of work with niche strength in restrictive covenants. Clients include paper manufacturers, port and rail operators, retailers, automotive manufacturers, shop fitters, healthcare sector and road haulage. Acted in Dartford and Gravesham NHS Trust v Skidmore involving dismissal of a consultant. **Clients:** Kimberley-Clark; Eurotunnel; FirstAssist.

Clarkson Wright & Jakes Acts for local regional employers in a range of sectors including manufacturing, transport, healthcare, insurance, engineering and further education. Operates a bespoke 'retainer' service which aims to provide clients with access to prompt advice over the telephone following preparation of an initial survey report. Recent highlights include the representation of a business link in connection with the termination of employment of two senior employees. **Clients:** Maunsell; SOLOTEC; Fairhurst Ward Abbot.

Pattinson & Brewer A satellite of the firm's London office, the group is widely recognised for its employment work for trade unions. Also acts for voluntary associations and charities, mostly in relation to contentious matters. Team possesses strengths in executive severances, discrimination, particularly disability, human rights and transfer regulations. **Clients:** TGWU; RMT; private applicants referred by other solicitors in the area.

Stevens & Bolton Seen to be *"building up the employment team,"* the group acts predominantly for employers, including multi-nationals and their subsidiaries, owner-managed businesses and individuals. All three dedicated practitioners have experience in city firms and particular expertise in TUPE, trade union law, restrictive convenants and confidential information. **Clients:** Novartis Pharmaceuticals UK Ltd; Computeraid Services Ltd; Hays plc.

THAMES VALLEY

EMPLOYMENT • Thames Valley	Ptnrs	Assts
❶ **Morgan Cole** Oxford, Reading	2	10
❷ **Clarks** Reading	2	9
Henmans Oxford	1	1
❸ **Underwoods** St Albans	1	6
❹ **Pickworths** Watford	2	-

LEADING INDIVIDUALS
❶ **ASHTIANY Sue** Morgan Cole
❷ **HENNEY Colin** Henmans
❸ **UNDERWOOD Kerry** Underwoods

Within each band, firms are listed alphabetically. *See **Profiles** on page 332*

Morgan Cole Remains pre-eminent in the area due to a *"breadth of expertise rarely found outside City firms."* The firm's employment reputation is largely built around *"unquestioned leader"* **Sue Ashtiany**. Seen regularly in the Employment Appeals Tribunal, this *"big name player" "doesn't beat around the bush"* and was noted for her expertise in hi-tech matters. The group acts for institutional clients including universities and NHS trusts. Corporate clients include a number of hi-tech and computer companies. Also undertakes a significant amount of work on behalf of senior executives. Recently acted for the respondent in a House of Lords decision on redundancy payments, indirect discrimination and community law in Barry v Midland Bank plc. **Clients:** HSBC Bank plc; Unipart Ltd; University of Oxford.

Clarks A team of *"well-informed specialists"* able to *"cut to the quick."* Acts largely for employers in a range of sectors including transport, logistics, media, catering, manufacturers, IT, construction and professional services. Skilled at *"seeing things from all perspectives,"* the group possesses niche strengths in training and HR issues, specifically in relation to discrimination, employer's liability and collective bargaining/recognition issues. **Clients:** Manufacturers; newspapers groups.

Henmans A *"sound but low-key practice"* with particular emphasis on in-house advocacy. Client base includes employers from pharmaceuticals, healthcare, IT and related industries, construction, agriculture and charities sectors and employees at all levels. Team is recommended for its *"commercial attitude"* which makes it *"easy to deal with while protecting the client's interests."* **Colin Henney** is a *"safe pair of hands"* for tribunal advocacy. **Clients:** EDS Ltd; British Bio-Tech; Baxter Healthcare

Underwoods *"Affable"* **Kerry Underwood** was recommended for his *"energy and enthusiasm,"* especially in relation to CFA matters. His team, known for a *"flexible approach,"* has pioneered no win-no fee arrangements, fixed and menu pricing, and reverse CFAs for employers. *"Always well-prepared,"* the group has particular strengths in advocacy, discrimination cases, TUPE, and high level executive terminations. Client base consists of plcs, substantial limited companies and local authorities as well as high profile individuals and senior executives. Acted for claimant in Feeney v IPC Magazines Ltd, concerning a woman's right to work part-time. **Clients:** Gardner Merchant plc; Construction Federation; De La Rue plc.

Pickworths Although not seen to be as specialised as the other high-ranking firms, Pickworth's small employment department has distinguished itself from other local firms by the quality of its work. Handles general contentious and non-contentious employment work and provides training on employment tribunal work. Practice weighted towards advising employers, with employees comprising only 25 percent of the client base. Due to the firm's niche in caravan work, the group has extensive experience in employment matters within the leisure industry. **Clients:** Bourne Leisure Group Ltd; Leisure Great Britain plc; Employee Advisory Resource Ltd.

SOUTH WEST

Bevan Ashford *"Pre-eminent in public sector work,"* this large team is renowned for employment advice on behalf of a number of NHS trusts throughout the South West. Acts largely for applicants in hi-tech, PFI and public sectors. This *"realistic"* team *"talks the right language"* and was highly rated for having both *"resources in terms of numbers"* to draw on, and a varied client base that includes multi-national and nationally-based companies. **Sarah Lamont** and her ex-Veale Wasbrough team complete their first full year in practice at Bevan Ashford. As anticipated, her presence at Bevan Ashford has done much to raise the group's profile in the area. **Jean Sapeta** and **Julian Hoskins** were both recommended as up and coming practitioners. Acted successfully for Kay Swinburne in her sex discrimination/unfair dismissal claim against Deutsche Bank. **Clients:** Orange PCS Ltd; St George's NHS Trust; Allied Domecq.

Bond Pearce *"Clearly a presence in Plymouth,"* the group is geared primarily towards employers and undertakes a substantial amount of work in retail and education sectors. The firm offers specialist in-house counsel and in-house HR support services relating to immigration, health and safety, asset management, and family crisis assistance. *"Careful and considered"* **Nikki Duncan** *"runs a well-organised team"* with experience in tribunal advocacy and high profile executive terminations. Acted for the Post Office in relation to a test case concerning normal retirement age, and dealt with the employment aspects of the £150 million merger of Roach Foods and Dalehead Foods. **Clients:** The Post Office; The National Trust; Virgin Group.

Burges Salmon An employer-oriented department acting for bigger plcs and some public sector organisations. This *"sensible"* team *"gives effective advice and looks after clients well"* and was noted for its *"clear, commercial way of putting things forward."* Commands expertise in employment law specific to transport, finance, sports/leisure, education and hi-tech sectors. Group includes a dedicated support lawyer and offers clients training and

EMPLOYMENT • South West	Ptnrs	Assts
❶ **Bevan Ashford** Bristol	3	8
Bond Pearce Plymouth	2	5
Burges Salmon Bristol	1	6
Osborne Clarke OWA Bristol	2	9
❷ **Cartwrights** Bristol	3	3
Eversheds Bristol	2	3
Thompsons Bristol	1	2
❸ **Pattinson & Brewer** Bristol	1	-
Veale Wasbrough Bristol	1	5
❹ **Michelmores** Exeter	⚐	⚐
Stephens & Scown Exeter	2	-
Stone King Bath	2	1
Thrings & Long Bath	1	1
TLT Solicitors Bristol	⚐	⚐

LEADING INDIVIDUALS	
❶ **DUNCAN Nikki** Bond Pearce	
❷ **HEMMING Julian** Osborne Clarke OWA	**MOORE Nigel** Stephens & Scown
❸ **LAMONT Sarah** Bevan Ashford	
❹ **BROWN Anthony** Eversheds	**RANKIN Claire** Eversheds
UP AND COMING	
BENSON Nick Michelmores	**HOSKINS Julian** Bevan Ashford
SAPETA Jean Bevan Ashford	**SEATON Chris** Burges Salmon

Within each band, firms are listed alphabetically. *See **Profiles** on page 332*

⚐ *Figures unavailable at time of going to press.*

employment document audits. Although still felt to be suffering from the loss of George Dyson, *"approachable and well regarded"* **Chris Seaton** enters the tables as an up and coming practitioner. Involved in the seeking of a three-site Anton Pillar injunction for US-based company. **Clients:** Standard Chartered Bank; New Zealand Milk; Bristol Water plc.

Osborne Clarke OWA Acts for employers in the transport, energy, financial services, IT and technology sectors. Receiving a substantial amount of employment work from the firm's corporate departments, the team handles a fair share of deal-oriented transactional work. This *"professional"* team, *"always on top of the facts,"* was particularly noted for its drafting skills. *"Personable"* **Julian Hemming** is said to *"have a good grasp of the subject"* and continues to rank highly in the tables. Instructed to give specialist employment and industrial relations advice for electricity supply companies Eastern Group and London Electricity in relation to their distribution joint venture. **Clients:** Imperial Tobacco plc; P&O; Lane Group.

Cartwrights Undertakes a wide range of work on behalf of employers based on contentious aspects including TUPE, executive termination and restrictive covenants. Acts for clients in retail, transport, leisure and utilities sectors. A *"good steady employment team,"* seen to be making an impact on the regional market. The group has recently been involved in a number of multi-million pound settlements in the IT sector and a successful challenge to the imposition of restrictive covenants in the IT industry. **Clients:** Safeway; Tibbett & Britten plc; Newscom plc.

Eversheds Despite the firm's national reputation, the Bristol employment group *"has not made much of a splash"* in the South West. Nevertheless, the firm's network system means the group can draw upon the necessary manpower to handle a volume of work. Acts primarily for employers with strengths in the food, financial services and heavy manufacturing industries. Partners **Anthony Brown** and **Claire Rankin** remain highly regarded for their work in severance, restructuring, TUPE and its application to outsourcing. Advised a borough council in connection with a long-running sex discrimination, victimisation and unfair dismissal claim. **Clients:** The Stationery Office Ltd; Walkers Snack Foods; Ecclesiastical Insurance.

Thompsons A *"good hard-hitting employee firm"* with a team that *"clearly knows what they're talking about."* The firm's employment group is integrated with the personal injury practice and acts exclusively for employees and a large proportion of trade unions. Rated an *"efficient practice for volume applicant work."* **Clients:** UNISON; Manufacturing Science & Finance Union (MSFU); Graphical Paper Media Union (GPMU).

Pattinson & Brewer An *"applicant's firm,"* the department acts predominantly for trade unions, members and private clients. Group maintains particular expertise in health and safety and equal pay-related employment matters. Recently acted for a woman police constable on behalf of the Police Federation on a claim of indirect sex discrimination based on a requirement to work shifts. **Clients:** PCS; RMT; Police Federation.

Veale Wasbrough Seen to be trying to regroup following the en masse departure of a number of team members over a year ago. Hasty recruitment has created a rather young team who have still to prove themselves in the local market. However, the group is said to take a *"business-like approach"* and is slowly rebuilding the firm's previous reputation. Work focuses on three specific sectors: employment law for business clients ranging from small owner managed businesses to partnerships and plcs, employment disputes for independent schools, and public sector/local authority work. Also offers mediation services. Acted for the claimant in the case of Levett v Biotrace plc in the Court of Appeal and subsequently in the High Court for assessment of damages. **Clients:** Avon Rubber plc; PB Kennedy & Donkin Ltd; Mole Valley Farmers Ltd.

Michelmores Strong recommendations for **Nick Benson** and his team prompt the entry of Michelmores into the tables this year. *"Sensible, commercial and a good speaker,"* Benson is *"popping up increasingly often"* and is perceived to be a rising star in the South West. Handles the usual range of employment matters. Recently succeeded in a five-day unfair dismissal claim for a group of 27 employees. **Clients:** Local plcs.

Stephens & Scown Better known in the local market than across the South West, the practice undertakes predominantly employer-based work in sectors ranging from small locally-based clients to large multi-nationals. Handles mostly contentious issues, mainly unfair dismissal redundancies and sex discrimination cases. **Nigel Moore** is *"a real details man,"* noted for his skill in looking after clients. **Clients:** Imerys Minerals Ltd; Trago Mills; Cornwall Care.

Stone King *"Quite strong in Bath,"* the group acts for a number of large private clients, in-house human resource departments, schools, colleges and hospitals in private or grant maintained sectors. The firm has a strong client base among charities, particularly educational institutions. Receiving increasing numbers of disability, racial and sex discrimination claims, and is frequently called upon to advise clients on the adoption of pre-emptive internal procedures. **Clients:** Amtrak Express Parcels Ltd; William Mercer Ltd; St John's Rigby College.

Thrings & Long A *"practical"* team with an *"upbeat approach"* to employment law. Culls work mainly from local employers in agricultural, education and IT sectors. *"Straightforward to deal with,"* the group was also noted as having substantial experience of acting in sports-related employment disputes. **Clients:** City of Bath College; Longleat Estate; Cooper Avon Tyres; Bath Rugby Club.

TLT Solicitors Interviewees anticipate that the recent merger between Lawrence Tucketts and Trumps will create a new force to be reckoned with in the area, and on this expectation the group enters the Chambers tables for the first time. The group will combine Lawrence Tucketts' *"aggressive commercial focus"* with Trumps' *"old money client base."* Practice provides contentious and non-contentious legal services as well as HR training and consultancy services. Involved in drafting and negotiating executive service agreements, the firm also advises on risk management in relation to new legislation governing working time, minimum wage and the employment rights bill. **Clients:** Allied Dunbar, C&J Clark International, UPS Ltd.

WALES

EMPLOYMENT • Wales	Ptnrs	Assts
❶ **Eversheds** Cardiff	3	10
❷ **Morgan Cole** Cardiff	2	8
❸ **Edwards Geldard** Cardiff	2	3
❹ **Hugh James Ford Simey** Cardiff	1	4
Palser Grossman Cardiff Bay	2	1

LEADING INDIVIDUALS	
❶ **DU-FEU Vivian** Eversheds	**WARREN Martin** Eversheds
WILLIAMS Audrey Eversheds	
❷ **REES Anthony** Morgan Cole	
❸ **CLARKE Michael** Morgan Cole	
UP AND COMING	
DAVIES Joanne Morgan Cole	**LOVE Alison** Hugh James Ford Simey
NOTT Chris Palser Grossman	

Within each band, firms are listed alphabetically. See **Profiles** on page 332

Eversheds The depth of experience of this large *"proactive"* team and the reputation of its three leading partners keep the group far ahead of its nearest Welsh competitors. Acts principally for employers in sectors ranging from food processing to financial services and electronics manufacturing. The group, *"very good at marketing themselves and turning things around quickly,"* are said to *"put a lot of effort into their written work."* Offers a specialist HR and training consultancy. Clients are impressed by the team's *"pragmatic approach"* and *"the extent to which they are up to date with the issues."* **Viv Du-Feu** is said to be *"commercially minded and realistic with negotiations."* **Martin Warren** is *"sought after for advocacy work"*; he divides his time between employment and environmental practice, but is particularly recommended for unfair dismissal cases. **Audrey Williams** is *"switched on to discrimination issues"* and was noted for her ability to *"translate complex legal matters."* Highlights of the past year include advising clients in the distribution sector on employment and industrial relations implications of major contractual change issues. **Clients:** JC Bamford Excavators Ltd; Cargill plc; Emerson Electric Company.

Morgan Cole Covers contentious and non-contentious employment work for a base of public sector clients and private, owner-managed businesses and support work for corporate clients of other departments. A group of *"good technical lawyers with a good grip on commercial and technical reality."* In Cardiff, **Anthony Rees** *"plays a straight bat." "Pragmatic and down to earth,"* he is known to *"get down to commercial issues very quickly."* Swansea-based **Michael Clarke** is rated for his *"quiet"* ability to deal with a range of contracts and collective disputes. **Joanne Davies** enters the tables as an up and coming practitioner after general recommendation. The group recently defended proceedings on behalf of an employer who has received several hundred tribunal complaints following disposal of a business. **Clients:** University of Wales Swansea; University of Wales Healthcare Trust; PHS.

Edwards Geldard *"A solid bunch of citizens"* acting predominantly for employers in small to medium manufacturing concerns, international plcs, banks and public sector organisations. Maintains a strong base of corporate clients shared between various departments. Recommended as giving good advice and feedback to clients. The firm has experience in large scale reorganisations, TUPE, and harassment cases. Notably, acted as the independent solicitor for the Gwent Police Authority in relation to disciplinary proceedings taken against its Chief Constable. **Clients:** Citibank; Williams plc; Hyder plc.

Hugh James Ford Simey A new entrant to the tables, the firm is seen to be building up its employment department, particularly in relation to racial, sexual and disability discrimination cases. Practice is weighted slightly towards the employee, although the group undertakes a substantial amount of work on behalf of large and medium sized employers and senior executives. Department head **Alison Love** is both *"personable and well-known in the marketplace,"* and is a rising force in Wales. Her team acted for the applicant in a sex discrimination case concerning alleged discrimination on grounds of gender reassignment. **Clients:** G E Capital Equipment; Julian Hodge Bank; Christ Church, Brecon.

Palser Grossman Another newcomer to the lists, this *"small but competent"* group is said to be *"going places"* through their representation of employers in contractual disputes. Acts largely for Welsh companies ranging from individual owner-managed businesses to major plcs. Noted for expertise in advocacy. **Chris Nott** *"does a lot in the market"* and was recommended for his client care. Acting for TRW over claims by collective unions (TNG, AEU, MSF) in relation to the company's contractual redundancy scheme and the method of incorporating collective agreements to employment contracts. **Clients:** TRW Steering Systems; Dyson; International Greetings plc.

MIDLANDS

Eversheds Maintains its established market position and high profile despite intensified competition in the top rank. The team provides a full range of employment services, and includes a group dedicated to work on training. The *"extremely bright"* **David Beswick** heads the large Eversheds team alongside **Martin Hopkins**, another *"leading light."* The firm's client base is as impressive as ever, with niche expertise in the retail sector. The team is also expanding its international operation and now counts 25 hi-tech US West-Coast firms as clients. Advised OFFER on the employment issues of its merger with Ofgas. **Clients:** Alliance & Leicester; The Post Office; WH Smith News Division.

Wragge & Co The fastest growing employment team is able to call on an enormous commercial client base, which has led some to suggest that they are in fact a support facility for the corporate team. However, most feel that the *"very clued-up"* **Martin Chitty** leads a strong partner-led team which is seen to match that of Eversheds in terms of size and quality. The group has advised on a variety of unfair dismissal and discrimination claims, and has niche strength in TUPE, restrictive covenants, maternity and working time. **Jonathan Chamberlain** enjoys a rising profile and is thought to be *"academic and pragmatic with a sound grasp of the law."* Recently outsourced a £350 million computer services contract. **Clients:** Lloyds TSB; PowerGen; Britannic Assurance.

Hammond Suddards Edge A smaller team which fields some of the *"region's best quality lawyers,"* the team has avoided the malaise which has afflicted other areas of the firm's Midlands operation. A well-regarded spearhead comprises *"solid and experienced"* **Veronica Dean** and the highly-rated newcomer **Julia Edwards**, who is perceived to be *"sensible and reasonable."* The team acts on a range of matters, covering drafting employment policies, disciplinary processes and defending tribunal claims. Particular areas of expertise are retail and leisure, financial services and manufacturing. **Clients:** The Football League; Cheltenham & Gloucestershire plc; Delphi Automotive Systems.

Pinsent Curtis *"Top class"* **Colin Goodier**'s *"intellectual vigour and technical excellence"* are once again almost unanimously praised. However, his employment team continues to be hit by the loss of associates. The firm deals with contentious and non-contentious work for an international client base, and is particularly adept at executive immigration work.

EMPLOYMENT • Midlands	Ptnrs	Assts
❶ **Eversheds** Birmingham	2	24
Wragge & Co Birmingham	4	17
❷ **Hammond Suddards Edge** Birmingham	3	8
Pinsent Curtis Birmingham	2	5
❸ **DLA** Birmingham	2	-
Higgs & Sons Brierley Hill	2	2
Martineau Johnson Birmingham	1	4
❹ **Browne Jacobson** Nottingham	1	3
Mills & Reeve Birmingham	2	8
Shakespeares Birmingham	3	2
Shoosmiths Nottingham	1	2

LEADING INDIVIDUALS	
❶ **BESWICK David** Eversheds	**FIELD Roger** Higgs & Sons
GOODIER Colin Pinsent Curtis	
❷ **CHITTY Martin** Wragge & Co	**DEAN Veronica** Hammond Suddards Edge
HOPKINS Martin Eversheds	**MARSHALL Ian** Martineau Johnson
WOFFENDEN Sara Shoosmiths	
❸ **BENSON Edward** Browne Jacobson	**EDWARDS Julia** Hammond Suddards Edge
JONES Alan DLA	
UP AND COMING	
CHAMBERLAIN Jonathan Wragge & Co	

Within each band, firms are listed alphabetically. *See **Profiles** on page 332*

Advised Misys plc on the establishment of a European Consultative Forum, covering employees in 14 countries in the EC and Eastern Europe. **Clients:** Smith & Nephew; HSBC; University of Wolverhampton.

DLA Perceived by the market to be losing profile, the DLA team are felt, with the exception of the *"brusque"* **Alan Jones**, to be relatively untested. Noted for work on DDA claims and maternity issues. The highlight of the year came when in a recent Tesco bid for around 40 Somerfield stores, Tesco hived off the employment due diligence from the corporate, instructing the firm to undertake the former. **Clients:** Johnson & Johnson; Abbey National plc; Makro.

Higgs & Sons This niche firm continues to *"punch way above its weight"* and to be the first port of call for local referrals. The team, led by *"highly regarded and supremely learned"* **Roger Field**, typically handles the full range of employment issues for a range of national and local clients. Recently dealt with employment matters relating to the takeover of two companies by a local brewer. **Clients:** Allied Carpets Group Ltd; Wolverhampton & Dudley Breweries plc; Magnet Ltd.

Martineau Johnson Particularly rated for the quality of their work in the educational sector, Martineaus are held to be *"extremely technical"* lawyers who are not *"pushy marketeers."* The department is led by **Ian Marshall**, who is regarded as *"intellectually first-rate,"* and has greatly expanded its provision of Employment Law-related training services over the past year. **Clients:** De Montfort University; Galliford plc; Community Hospitals Ltd.

Browne Jacobson A leading Nottingham employment firm which continues to flourish under the direction of the respected **Edward Benson**. Although the team's size makes it difficult to handle massive litigation, it deals with the full range of employment issues for clients in the public and commercial sectors. **Clients:** Derbyshire Constabulary, Nottinghamshire & Leicestershire Fire & Rescue Service, Wilkinson Hardware Store.

Mills & Reeve A niche practice, which is rated for its work for NHS trust and health authorities. The team is consolidating its national reputation in this sector. It recently acted for an NHS trust in a high profile race discrimination case on appeal to the Court of Appeal. **Clients:** North Birmingham Mental Health NHS Trust, North Staffs. Hospital NHS Trust.

Shakespeares Acknowledged to be *"trying hard with some success,"* Shakespeares has recently raised its profile, with one partner being appointed Visiting Professor of Employment Law at the University of Central England. **Clients:** University of Central England; Brintons Ltd; Paxar UK Ltd.

Shoosmiths **Sara Woffenden**'s move to Shoosmiths has paid off. Her ability as a *"good marketeer,"* combined with her widely acknowledged expertise on the recent developments of maternity and family law, has given the firm a *"recognised employment team."* Handled the start-up employment issues of the Nike Town flagship store in London. **Clients:** Nike.

EAST ANGLIA

EMPLOYMENT • East Anglia	Ptnrs	Assts
❶ **Eversheds** Ipswich, Norwich	5	6
Hewitson Becke + Shaw Cambridge, Northampton	3	6
Mills & Reeve Cambridge, Norwich	2	9
❷ **Steele & Co** Norwich	1	1
❸ **Taylor Vinters** Cambridge	1	3
❹ **Greenwoods** Peterborough	1	5
❺ **Prettys** Ipswich	1	1

LEADING INDIVIDUALS
❶ **LAMB Norman** Steele & Co
SAYER Nicholas Hewitson Becke + Shaw
WARNOCK Owen Eversheds
❷ **BROWN Nicola** Mills & Reeve
HEMMINGS Richard Richard Hemmings
YATES Tracy Eversheds
❸ **DILLARSTONE Robert** Greenwoods
❹ **LYNE Amanda** Taylor Vinters
PRYKE Oliver Taylor Vinters
TYNDALL Timothy Hewitson Becke + Shaw

Within each band, firms are listed alphabetically. *See **Profiles** on page 332*

Eversheds Rated by competitors as *"worthy opponents,"* the team acts for employers in the public and private sectors throughout East Anglia. The Ipswich office tends to concentrate on manufacturing and education clients while the Norwich branch is more focused on employers in the manufacturing and processing, financial services and health sectors. The firm also has a relatively young Cambridge office with a hi-tech company client base. The team is said to be *"sensible to deal with"* and *"give quality advice."* **Owen Warnock** is a *"front runner"* in the field of disability discrimination. He and **Tracy Yates** are both reckoned to have a *"sound understanding of the law."* The group was one of many of the Eversheds branches to participate in a two-day National Eversheds Employers Convention concerning current human resources issues and employment matters. **Clients:** Cambridgeshire Constabulary; Addenbrooke's NHS Trust; Bernard Matthews plc.

Hewitson Becke + Shaw Maintains its leading profile for quality employment work. Practice is spread over two offices and acts predominantly for employers and some senior executives in public limited companies, professional bodies, educational establishments, hospitals and private limited companies. *"Approachable"* **Nick Sayer** *"knows exactly what he's talking about."* Partner **Tim Tyndall** was recommended as *"a safe pair of hands"* for Employment Tribunal applications and advising on employment aspects of mergers, acquisitions and disposals. The group has particular expertise in injunctions to enforce post-termination of employment restrictions. Acted on behalf of a household name client in a race discrimination case in the Court of Appeal, currently under consideration for appeal to the House of Lords. **Clients:** TNT International; Johnson Matthey Group plc.

Mills & Reeve A *"lawyerly"* group, with the *"strength and depth to allocate their resources"* to address a range of employment concerns for local businessmen, plcs, education institutions, local authorities and NHS trusts. *"Delightful"* **Nicola Brown** is described as *"easy to deal with"* and was praised by peers for her *"practical approach."* The team advises on TUPE in relation to PRI and sales of business and on employee's rights under the Disability Discrimination Act. Successfully defended a local authority against a claim issued by 180 employees in relation to wage deductions. **Clients:** Local authorities; NHS trusts; agricultural concerns.

Steele & Co *"Charismatic"* **Norman Lamb**'s chief strength is that he *"knows when to push and when to settle."* He heads a *"quality"* department noted for its *"customer focus"* and *"understanding of clients' needs."* Practice includes an in-house barrister to conduct tribunal advocacy. While acting primarily for employers in the food sector, public bodies and a variety of businesses, the group also has a reputation for applicant work. Recently acted on behalf of Wymondham College at the hearing of first instance and in the appeal in a sex discrimination case. **Clients:** Canon (UK) Ltd; Bird's Eye Walls Lts; Bowater Windows Ltd.

Taylor Vinters While well known for acting for employers in hi-tech, telecommunications and pharmaceutical industries, the group has also been active in advising clients in the agricultural and farming sectors on new employment legislation. Building up a strong reputation within the bloodstock industry. Practice provides training services and operates the Personnel Practitioners' Forum for local human resources practitioners. **Mandy Lyne** continues to rank as a leader in the field; her experience as a chemist gives her an understanding of the requirements of the firm's scientific and hi-tech client base. *"Personable"* **Oliver Pryke** was described as a *"rising star"* in the field. The team recently acted for an employer on a multi-million pound claim under a health insurance scheme. **Clients:** The University of Cambridge; English Nature; Sodastream.

Greenwoods Noted for its strength in employment tribunal advocacy work, the firm acts almost entirely for employers within the media, construction, oil and charity sectors. The team draws upon the expertise of an in-house pensions and share options specialist in advising clients in contract negotiations. Department head **Robert Dillarstone** was praised as being *"very enthusiastic about his work."* His team recently acted for the respondent in connection with a wrongful dismissal/defamation claim worth approximately £400,000. The claim was settled with the claimant receiving only a fraction of the total claim. **Clients:** Emap plc; Enterprise Oil plc; Railtrack plc.

Prettys Rated as a comprehensive employment practice typically acting for smaller owner-managed businesses and locally-based companies in Suffolk and Essex. A *"technically good"* team with a particular focus on transport and agricultural sectors. Notably strong in equal opportunities work. The firm was recently appointed to the NFU panel, representing six counties in the East Anglian region. **Clients:** Regional business concerns.

Other Notable Practitioner Sole practitioner **Dick Hemmings** has a longstanding name in employment law, and is ranked for the first time this year.

NORTH WEST

EMPLOYMENT • North West	Ptnrs	Assts
❶ **Addleshaw Booth & Co** Manchester	2	9
DLA Liverpool, Manchester	2	11
Eversheds Manchester	2	8
Hammond Suddards Edge Manchester	3	15
❷ **Mace & Jones** Liverpool, Manchester	6	6
Whittles Manchester	2	2
❸ **Cobbetts** Manchester	3	7
Thompsons Liverpool, Manchester	2	3
❹ **Davies Wallis Foyster** Liverpool, Manchester	4	3
Halliwell Landau Manchester	2	3
❺ **Beachcroft Wansbroughs** Manchester	1	1
Pannone & Partners Manchester	3	3

LEADING INDIVIDUALS	
❶ **NICKSON Susan** Hammond Suddards Edge	
❷ **CHAMBERLAIN Andrew** Addleshaw Booth & Co	
CLARKE Mary DLA	**EDWARDS Martin** Mace & Jones
HANTOM Charles Whittles	**MALONE Michael** Mace & Jones
NORBURY Peter Eversheds	**PIKE Malcolm** Addleshaw Booth & Co
WATSON Judith Cobbetts	
❸ **HILLS Stephen** Halliwell Landau	**PARKINSON Helen** Whittles
UP AND COMING	
JACKS David Weightmans	**RESTON Vincent** DLA
THOMPSON Michael Eversheds	

Within each band, firms are listed alphabetically. *See **Profiles** on page 332*

Addleshaw Booth & Co A *"household name"* in employment law, the firm commands a *"sizeable employment team"* with a *"good spread"* of clients across the leisure, pharmaceuticals, banking, media, retail, and healthcare sectors. The team has a national reputation, particularly in relation to transfers of businesses, executive terms, conditions and severance, and sex, race, or disability discrimination claims. *"Robust"* **Andrew Chamberlain** is recognised as an able practitioner but is seen to be spending an increasing amount of time on management issues. *"Academic"* **Malcolm Pike**, known as a *"good technical lawyer,"* heads the group. Recently advised DJ Ryan & Sons Ltd (subsidiary of Allen plc) on issues in litigation arising from the North West Maintenance and Replacement Contracts with Transco, a multiple action against the client constituting approximately 110 employment tribunal cases. **Clients:** GEHE (UK) Group; Airtours; AstraZeneca.

DLA A *"quality team with a high calibre reputation,"* the practice is recommended for discrimination advice, reorganisation and executive termination issues. Practitioners reportedly know how to be *"tough without being difficult"* in acting for a client base of plcs, professional partnerships, local and national government organisations, TECs and education bodies. Group conducts its own advocacy and has niche expertise in advising on corporate issues in new e-commerce ventures. *"Understated"* **Mary Clarke** is sometimes accused of *"hiding her light under a bushel."* She has a *"get on with the job"* attitude towards employment matters and has been commended for her ability *"to recognise the relevant issues."* Another *"self-effacing"* practitioner, **Vincent Reston** is an *"excellent technician"* and remains rated as an up and coming employment lawyer. Over the past year the Manchester branch advised the Spring Group plc on all employment aspects of establishing its e-recruitment business, while the Liverpool office has been acting for Cammell Laird in relation to national partnership agreement with two trade unions. **Clients:** Manchester: TNT; Liverpool: MTL Services plc; Cammell Laird Group; Department of Education Northern Ireland (DENI).

Eversheds Rises in the tables following general recommendation as a *"straightforward"* and *"well-organised"* group of accomplished advocates. Reputed to have consistently high standards of support at the assistant solicitor level. Department head **Peter Norbury** is a *"serious player"* in the area with a reputation as an *"aggressive litigator."* Partner **Michael Thomp-**

son brings a *"sensible and measured approach"* to employment matters and remains rated as an up and coming practitioner. Client base consists mainly of employers in the UK, international plcs and public sector organisations. The team has particular expertise in TU-related advice, large restructuring exercises, and executive terminations. Acted in a major Court of Appeals case for Express Dairies plc on the employment status of franchises. **Clients:** Asda; United Utilities; Express Dairies plc.

Hammond Suddards Edge Practice's profile is said to have grown rapidly over the past few years due to energetic marketing efforts and a varied employer client base of banks, manufacturing companies and airlines. Sometimes described as *"confrontational"* in approach, the employment unit is the largest in the North West. Provides clients with an IOD employment helpline and *"In-Tuition"* in-house training services. Clients and solicitors alike *"doff their caps"* to **Sue Nickson,** *"a good all-round lawyer"* with the *"gravitas and charisma"* to reach settlements. The team is well-regarded for its work on drafting and enforcing restrictive covenants, advising on TUPE, and handling discrimination and harassment claims. The group was appointed by the Inland Revenue to train its national compliance managers for the task of co-ordinating the enforcement of the National Minimum Wage. **Clients:** Motorola Ltd; First Choice Holidays plc; Credit Lyonnais.

Mace & Jones The employment practice is the firm's *"jewel in the crown,"* with a substantial team of *"focused employment specialists"* acting for a diverse base of employers. Group is spread over two offices, with the Liverpool branch slightly more visible in the region. Acts for a significant number of public sector clients. The team's expertise extends to health and safety and equal opportunities matters. The practice is commended for offering clients both *"good value for money"* and *"straightforward, quality service." "Star"* practitioner **Martin Edwards** retains a high profile in the field. Although well-known for his academic articles, he still maintains a *"hands-on approach"* to employment law. *"Sensible"* **Michael Malone** *"works towards a common end"* and was recommended for discrimination cases. **Clients:** Local authorities; leisure organisations; public sector bodies.

Whittles *"Undoubtedly the strongest applicant firm in the North West,"* the practice represents employees in all aspects of employment and labour law including dismissal, redundancy, discrimination, equal pay, transfer of undertakings, TU and human rights law. Conducts the bulk of its work for blue collar trade unions and staff association members. The sheer volume of work has led some competitors to wonder whether the firm is somewhat *"overstretched." "Experienced"* **Charles Hantom** commands *"tremendous loyalty and respect from clients."* **Helen Parkinson** ranks as a *"solid"* employment lawyer with a *"practical"* view towards negotiations. **Clients:** GMB (2 regions); Bakers' Union (several regions); ISTEC.

Cobbetts *"Bright and technically sound,"* **Judith Watson** heads a young employment team with a *"good workmanlike approach."* Group acts for 60 percent employers (mostly in owner-managed businesses across a spread of sectors) and 40 percent employees. Also undertakes applicant work in tribunals and representation of senior executives. Offers advice on management structure and corporate governance. Recently advised on executive contracts in the context of a £2 billion merger. **Clients:** Royal Ordnance; Sonoco Products Ltd; Loot Limited.

Thompsons Remains ranked as an employee firm acting exclusively for trade unions throughout the region, covering white collar and public service sectors. Frequently represents nurses and fire fighters in employment tribunals and has particular expertise in equal opportunities and TUPE-related work. Individuals are said to *"carry weight with union officials."* Successfully acted in Keen v Halton College discrimination case concerning redundancy on the grounds of TU activity in the EAT. **Clients:** UNISON; GMB; The Fire Brigade's Union.

Davies Wallis Foyster Practice seen to be *"heading back in the right direction"* after Andrea McWatt's retirement over a year ago. Operates mainly in the commercial sector, acting for owner-managed businesses, local plcs and small professional firms. This *"unaggressive"* team is noted for its strength in employment issues relating to corporate transactions. **Clients:** Liverpool John Moores University; Telewest Communications plc; Capital Bank plc.

Halliwell Landau A competent practice split between contentious and non-contentious employment work. Handles a large proportion of corporate support work for corporate sector employers. Recognised as a specialist team, but not seen to be as visible in the market recently. Department head **Stephen Hills** *"certainly knows his onions,"* but tends to be personally quite *"self-effacing."* He is known to be an accomplished advocate before employment tribunals. **Clients:** Kwik Fit Holdings plc; Warburtons Ltd; Ladbrokes Ltd.

Beachcroft Wansbroughs Retains its place in the rankings as a small but able group of employment lawyers offering clients *"good practical advice."* Undertakes both contentious and non-contentious work for national private and listed companies of all sizes. Seen to have a commercial slant, but is considered to lack the resources of firms higher up on the tables. **Clients:** United Friendly Group; P&O Shopping Centres Ltd; Lynx Express Ltd.

Pannone & Partners Although better known for applicant work, the firm also acts for employers in smaller and second tier unquoted companies as well as a number of blue chip and household name companies. While most of the department's work consists of stand-alone employment matters, the group also conducts a fair share of corporate support work, and has specific expertise in employment issues relating to management transfers. During the past year the group advised a client on employment law implications of its purchase of the Humberside International Airport. **Clients:** The Bank of England; Milliken Industrials Ltd; Hay Management Consultants Ltd.

Other Notable Practitioner Although his firm is not seen to have created a big enough impact on the local market to warrant ranking in the tables, **David Jacks** of Weightmans ranks individually as an up and coming practitioner. *"Quite a catch for the firm,"* this *"affable and knowledgeable"* practitioner is expected to *"shake up"* the team.

YORKSHIRE

Pinsent Curtis *"Few can touch"* this *"first-class"* team of *"sound and courteous"* practitioners. Deemed to be the strongest in the area in terms of manpower and technical experience. The firm's high profile in the region is largely due to the superb reputation of department head **John McMullen,** who has been described as having *"unsurpassed academic qualifications and a unique grasp of the law."* The *"first name"* in the field, McMullen has a *"prodigious reputation"* in relation to TUPE work and transfer of undertakings. He is surrounded by an experienced team which includes *"client-friendly"* **Chris Booth,** who *"takes a sensible point of view"* in employment negotiations. *"Constructive"* **Martin Brewer** was also recommended for *"heavyweight employment work."* The group acts for a number of universities and blue-chip UK and international corporates, and conducts Working Time training seminars. Particularly distinguished in the field of European Works Councils, the practice was instrumental in setting up and advising on the second wave of voluntary European Works Councils for major multi-national companies prior to the December 1999 implementation deadline. **Clients:** AstraZeneca; University of Leeds; Lloyds TSB.

Hammond Suddards Edge This *"modern"* practice is seen to be playing down a formerly aggressive reputation. The firm's client base is weighted towards employers in large plcs, financial services, engineering, chemicals

EMPLOYMENT • Yorkshire	Ptnrs	Assts
❶ **Pinsent Curtis** Leeds	3	10
❷ **Hammond Suddards Edge** Leeds	2	12
❸ **Addleshaw Booth & Co** Leeds	1	4
DLA Leeds, Sheffield	3	9
❹ **Beachcroft Wansbroughs** Sheffield	1	5
Eversheds Leeds	1	10
Read Hind Stewart Leeds	2	–
Walker Morris Leeds	1	4
❺ **Ford & Warren** Leeds	2	4
Nabarro Nathanson Sheffield	2	2
Rollit Farrell & Bladon Hull	4	1
❻ **Gordons Cranswick Solicitors** Bradford	1	1
Irwin Mitchell Sheffield	1	2
Lupton Fawcett Leeds	1	2

LEADING INDIVIDUALS	
✪ **McMULLEN John** Pinsent Curtis	
❶ **BOOTH Christopher** Pinsent Curtis	**PREST Catherine** Hammond Suddards Edge
SHRIVES Mark Hammond Suddards Edge	
❷ **BRADLEY David** DLA	**BREWER Martin** Pinsent Curtis
GORAJ Ann Beachcroft Wansbroughs	**MOLYNEUX Pauline** Rollit Farrell & Bladon
ROBERTSON Stuart Gordons Cranswick Solicitors	
❸ **DRAKE Ronald** Read Hind Stewart	**HEARN Keith** Ford & Warren
HILL David DLA	**PUGH Keith** Nabarro Nathanson
TWEEDIE Colin Addleshaw Booth & Co	
UP AND COMING	
EMMOTT Jeremy DLA	

Within each band, firms are listed alphabetically. *See **Profiles** on page 332*

and printing industries. Clients appreciate the quality of the team's risk assessment advice and its *"upbeat"* attitude. The department's strength is linked to the presence of two *"motivated and ambitious"* partners. *"Academic"* **Mark Shrives** rates highly for *"sheer depth of knowledge and capabilities." "Down to earth"* **Catherine Prest** *"takes a strong line"* in employment tribunals and is reckoned a considerable *"asset"* to the team. Typical work includes defending employers under TUPE, handling senior executive terminations to training and drafting European Works Council agreements. Advised the Inland Revenue on the application of the National Minimum Wage legislation. **Clients:** ICI; The Post Office; CGU Life.

Addleshaw Booth & Co While seen to be recovering from the mass of departures of over a year and a half ago, the practice still has some rebuilding work left to do in order to reclaim its previous high-ranking position. **Colin Tweedie** has made strides in re-establishing both his own and the firm's profile in the region following his move from Mills and Reeve. The practice shares the services of a professional support lawyer with the Manchester office and acts for clients across a range of industry sectors. The firm's advantages unit advises companies and organisations on employee pay, incentives, benefits and related HR issues. Advises various clients, including MoD, Yorkshire Electricity and CGU, on employment aspects (TUPE) of outsourcing contracts. **Clients:** International Paper Company; Leeds Metropolitan University; Lambeth Building Society.

DLA Of the two Yorkshire offices, the Sheffield branch is felt to have a substantially higher profile than the Leeds office. Both departments act predominantly for employers in retail, financial services, manufacturing and public sectors. **David Bradley** in Sheffield is described as *"hard-nosed and pragmatic,"* while his Leeds counterpart **David Hill** *"commands a lot of respect"* from peers and clients. **Jeremy Emmott** was recommended as an up and coming employment lawyer. The group is particularly strong in industrial relations and has reportedly *"gone into training and HR consultancy in a big way."* Over the past year the group acted for a substantial Yorkshire-based company in the restructuring of its HR department and delivery of HR services. **Clients:** Provident Financial Services plc; The Employment Service; Dixons Stores Group plc.

Beachcroft Wansbroughs Conducts a large proportion of work for local authorities, with particular expertise in employment issues specific to health authorities and NHS trusts. **Ann Goraj** continues to rank as a leader for her *"technical ability"* and *"extensive health service experience."* The group also substantial work on TUPE matters. Acted for John Beckett in relation to discrimination claim in ECJ. **Clients:** Health authorities; NHS trusts.

Eversheds A *"big team and good brand name"* keep this firm high on the tables for employment work. The group is particularly well-known in the education sector and is said to provide *"tried and tested"* advice. Nevertheless some interviewees express concern that the current team is somewhat *"green"* and lacking in leadership since Catherine Prest's move to Hammond Suddards. The Newcastle and Leeds offices interact in a network system, although the Newcastle branch is considered somewhat stronger in education and health areas while the Leeds office excels at PFI-related employment work. The practice has particular strengths in foreign inward investment, contentious advocacy, and senior executive terminations. Notably advised on employment issues in relation to $1 billion international joint venture between DuPont and Sabanci, a Turkish-based multi-national company. **Clients:** Excell plc (previously NFC plc); Grattan plc; Asda.

Read Hind Stewart A small but competent team that *"pops up"* frequently on employment issues. Client base consists largely of employers in private limited companies. Handles a substantial amount of work for German inward investors and clients in the printing industry. **Ron Drake** was recommended as a *"first-class employment lawyer"* and enters the rankings this year. The team has recognised strength in advising on employment aspects of immigration and IP. **Clients:** Employers, particularly plcs.

Walker Morris Known for contentious employment work for a corporate client base shared with the firm's commercial departments. Prosecutes and defends major wrongful dismissal actions for plc clients and former Chief Executives, and advises large plcs and educational institutions in relation to Working Time and Minimum Wage Legislation. Represented a client in the EAT in a case establishing that an unfairly dismissed employee's period of employment could be extended to provide them with sufficient continuity of employment to present a claim. **Clients:** Caterpillar Inc; Redcasts (UK) plc; Rosebys plc.

Ford & Warren A capable employment department said to *"punch above their weight."* Maintains a varied white-collar client base of national plcs, engineering companies and NHS trusts. Known particularly for work in the transport industry, with niche specialisms in employment issues specific to trains, buses and road haulage. **Keith Hearn** was recommended as an able employment lawyer. The practice acted for Wakefield & Pontefract Hospital in relation to an internal inquiry into alleged misconduct by and capability of general surgeon Christopher Ingleby. **Clients:** First Group plc; North West Trains; various hospital trusts.

Nabarro Nathanson A respondent practice praised for its *"team-based approach"* and eagerness to *"pick up issues and jump in."* Acts chiefly for a varied base of employers from owner-managed businesses to plcs. *"Responsive"* **Keith Pugh** was commended for his work in building up the department. The group is particularly strong in collective matters and complex TUPE issues. Acted for British Fuels Ltd in follow-up application to the House of Lords case (Meade and Baxendale v British Fuels Limited and Wilson v St. Helens). **Clients:** HSBC.

Rollit Farrell & Bladon Highly regarded in the local market, the practice provides specialist advice to employers on all aspects of employment law, including employment rights, dismissal, maternity rights and equal pay discrimination. Said to *"give value for the money,"* the firm also provides bespoke training courses and has particular expertise in TUPE work.

"Measured" **Pauline Molyneux** *"combines common sense with good legal ability."* Defended employers against class actions brought by employees under Working Time Regulations. **Clients:** Andersen Consulting; William Jackson & Sons Limited.

Gordons Cranswick Solicitors Gordons Wright & Wright's recent merger with Cranswick Watson has resulted in an enlarged team with greater visibility in the market. Acts principally for regional employers in textiles, engineering and service sectors. *"Down to earth"* **Stuart Robertson** reputedly *"does his damnedest for clients."* The firm acted for a Chief Executive in a contested £250,000 claim following termination of employment. **Clients:** William Morrison Supermarkets plc; Peter Black Holdings plc; Baird Menswear Brands.

Irwin Mitchell This *"estimable"* firm is considered to have a slightly stronger employment team at Sheffield than at the Leeds office. The practice is focused on contentious work and is known to have particular expertise in trade union work and restrictive covenants. Clients appreciate the team's ability to *"handle sensitive cases"* and *"obtain results better than their original expectations."* Acts for a number of clients in higher education, football and local industries. Provided strategic advice to a Training and Enterprise in relation to the transfer of post-16 training. **Clients:** Sheffield College; Sheffield TEC; Sheffield Wednesday FC.

Lupton Fawcett This expanding employment practice is a new entrant to Chambers' tables. Principally a respondent's practice acting for employers in locally-based owner-managed businesses and small plcs. Handles all aspects of contentious and non-contentious employment work but has particular strength in restrictive covenant matters. **Clients:** Premier Custodial Service Ltd; The Symphony Group plc; Hunters Armley Ltd.

NORTH EAST

EMPLOYMENT • North East	Ptnrs	Assts
❶ **Dickinson Dees** Newcastle upon Tyne	3	3
Eversheds Newcastle upon Tyne	2	5
Short Richardson & Forth Newcastle upon Tyne	2	2
Thompsons Newcastle upon Tyne	1	1
❷ **Jacksons** Stockton on Tees	2	2
❸ **Ward Hadaway** Newcastle upon Tyne	3	2
❹ **Crutes** Newcastle upon Tyne	Fu	Fu

LEADING INDIVIDUALS	
❶ **CROSS Stefan** Thompsons	**SHORT Michael** Short Richardson & Forth
❷ **FLETCHER Kevin** Jacksons	**LOY Simon** Eversheds
UP AND COMING	
LANGRIDGE Sharon Short Richardson & Forth	
SMITH Tim Crutes	

Within each band, firms are listed alphabetically. *See* ***Profiles*** *on page 332*
Fu *Figures unavailable at time of going to press.*

Dickinson Dees Rises in the tables following widespread recommendation as an *"efficient"* practice with evident quality and depth. Team strengthened by the recruitment of a recognised tribunal advocate from Jacksons. Acts primarily for employers in plcs, and health and local authorities. The group offers comprehensive human resources services and has particular expertise in TUPE, employee incentives and collective bargaining issues. Represented Carlisle Hospitals NHS Trust in an equal value claim brought by 369 nurses. **Clients:** Northern Electric plc; Reg Vardy plc; Go-Ahead Group plc.

Eversheds Retains its top band rating for respondent work for a varied client base of manufacturers, national plcs, retailers, higher education institutions and public and health authorities. The team *"doesn't muck around pursuing ludicrous issues and are willing to concede if they know they're on a sticky wicket."* Has niche strengths in contentious advocacy, foreign inward investment, senior executive terminations and managing organisational change. *"Level-headed"* **Simon Loy** is noted as *"reliable"* and *"straightforward"* in approach. Acted for several claimants in connection with multi-handed High Court proceedings brought against a national trade union by former lay-breach treasurers of the union. **Clients:** British Polythene; University of Newcastle; Nissan.

Short Richardson & Forth A substantial employment practice with a *"boutique image."* Acts for both individual employees and employers in a range of companies from plcs to small owner managed-businesses. Team members are *"courteous, civilised and easy to deal with,"* and are particularly accomplished in Employment Tribunal representation work and Compromise Agreement work. Department head **Michael Short** has a *"richly deserved reputation"* as an *"astute-minded advocate"* able to *"pick up key issues quickly."* His number two **Sharon Langridge** has developed a focus on discrimination and maternity issues and was recommended as an up and coming practitioner. **Clients:** Greggs plc; St Regis Paper Company Ltd; Nissan Motor Manufacturing (UK) Ltd.

Thompsons The leading applicant firm in the region, this *"professional"* team acts on behalf of trade unions and their members in matters of equal pay, redundancy and consultancy requirements. Rated as particularly attuned to the *"implications of collective labour issues,"* employer-based firms consider the group *"formidable, respectable opponents." "Perceptive and determined"* **Stefan Cross** has a *"thorough knowledge of European and domestic employment law"* and is considered *"particularly hot on discrimination."* The firm acted successfully for the applicant in a high profile disability discrimination case in the Employment Tribunal (Hedley v Aldi.) **Clients:** UNISON; GMB; GPMU.

Jacksons Acts for employers across the UK in a range of sectors. Seen as the *"dominant firm in Teeside,"* the group undertakes its own tribunal advocacy and handles all aspects of employment law issues from discrimination and pensions to redundancy and TUPE. While some worry about the impact of a recent partner departure, *"polished"* **Kevin Fletcher** maintains his reputation as *"someone to be reckoned with."* The group acted for a multi-national engineering firm in a multi-applicant unfair dismissal case involving elements of disability and sex discrimination. **Clients:** British Bakeries; British Steel; Environment Agency.

Ward Hadaway A *"good operation"* with a mixed client base of respondents and applicants. The practice is seen to be expanding and has a solid reputation for employee claims and TUPE work. Undertakes both contentious and non-contentious work for national and North-East based clients and NHS Trusts. Recently acted for South Tyneside Healthcare Trust in a race/sex discrimination case involving a consultant. **Clients:** South Tyneside Healthcare Trust; City Electrical Factors Ltd; Komatsu (UK) Ltd.

Crutes A comprehensive employment practice active in the local market, although perceived to be overshadowed by regional firms of greater strength and depth. *"A dogged competitor,"* **Tim Smith** *"gets stuck in"* and is a *"regular at tribunals." "A thoughtful advocate,"* he enters the tables as an up and coming practitioner. **Clients:** Public sector entities.

SCOTLAND

EMPLOYMENT • Scotland	Ptnrs	Assts
❶ **Mackay Simon** Edinburgh	7	2
MacRoberts Glasgow	4	3
❷ **Brodies WS** Edinburgh	2	4
Burnside Kemp Fraser Aberdeen	Fu	Fu
Dundas & Wilson CS Edinburgh	3	8
Harper Macleod Glasgow	2	6
McGrigor Donald Glasgow	3	4
Paull & Williamsons Aberdeen	2	-
Shepherd & Wedderburn WS Edinburgh	4	5
❸ **Kidstons & Co** Glasgow	3	2
McClure Naismith Glasgow	1	2
Raeburn Christie & Co Aberdeen	1	1
❹ **Brechin Tindal Oatts** Glasgow	2	1
Maclay Murray & Spens Glasgow	4	2
Thompsons Edinburgh	Fu	Fu
❺ **Blackadder Reid Johnston & Carltons** Dundee	Fu	Fu
Maxwell MacLaurin Glasgow	Fu	Fu
Morison Bishop Glasgow	1	2
Morton Fraser, Solicitors Edinburgh	1	2

LEADING INDIVIDUALS

❶
- **MACKAY Malcolm** Mackay Simon
- **SIMON Shona** Mackay Simon
- **WILLIAMSON Raymond** MacRoberts

❷
- **ATACK Iain** Kidstons & Co
- **BURNSIDE David** Burnside Kemp Fraser
- **COCKBURN Alistair** Maxwell MacLaurin
- **CULLEN Joyce** Brodies WS
- **KEMP Sandy** Burnside Kemp Fraser
- **MACLEOD Euan** Dundas & Wilson CS
- **MILLER Stephen** Harper Macleod
- **SPEIRS William** Brechin Tindal Oatts
- **YOUNG James** McGrigor Donald

❸
- **CHRISTIE Reginald** Raeburn Christie & Co
- **GRIFFITHS John** Shepherd & Wedderburn WS
- **GUNN Sheila** Shepherd & Wedderburn WS
- **MACLEOD Ian** Shepherd & Wedderburn WS
- **McKENZIE Rod** Harper Macleod
- **NICOL Diane** McGrigor Donald
- **SALUJA Sean** Paull & Williamsons
- **THOMSON Alan** McClure Naismith
- **WALKER David** Dundas & Wilson CS

UP AND COMING
- **HAY Emma** MacRoberts

Within each band, firms are listed alphabetically. *See **Profiles** on page 332*

Fu *Figures unavailable at time of going to press.*

Mackay Simon The only specialist employment law firm is still regarded as *"top of the tree."* However, the rest of the field seems to be closing on them as the larger firms dedicate teams to employment. Powerful, partner-led team continues to shine, counting not only the *"superb"* **Malcolm Mackay** amongst its number, but also **Shona Simon**, *"an excellent lawyer, especially strong at discrimination work."* The team acted on behalf of a prison officer in relation to a claim of discrimination on the grounds of age. **Clients:** CGU; United Distillers & Vintners; Christian Salveson plc; The Educational Institute of Scotland.

MacRoberts Now the clear leader among the traditional firms in the employment field, MacRoberts are thought to have become *"better and stronger."* This is because of the strength of the team that backs *"flamboyant"* **Raymond Williamson** who, despite having become senior partner, has not suffered any diminution of profile. The younger partners are *"good and straightforward to work with,"* and up and coming **Emma Hay** is highly rated for *"impressive representation of her clients' interests."* The group acts on the full spectrum of employment matters, and has niche strength in the power industry. **Clients:** Clydebank College; Scottish & Southern Energy plc; Scottish Power.

Brodies WS A firm felt to be on the up, this is a team of *"well-known specialists with a long tradition of good work."* **Joyce Cullen** is *"straight-talking and knows her stuff."* The team has been appointed as Scottish External Advisors under a 'whistle-blowing' policy by a major national banking institution. Particularly renowned for work in the contentious field, the team acted for Melville Craig in a case relating to the employment status of an agency worker. **Clients:** The Royal Bank Of Scotland; Tate & Lyle plc; Scottish Legal Aid Board.

Burnside Kemp Fraser An Aberdeen practice that is considered *"sound"* on employment law, which it has made a specialism. Both **David Burnside** and **Sandy Kemp** are held in high regard, and are considered *"first-class employment lawyers."* The firm's forte is in contentious tribunal work, and it has a niche in acting for major oil companies. **Clients:** Oil and gas companies.

Dundas & Wilson CS A strong team of all-rounders who marry advocacy skills with a non-contentious practice, while working closely with the firm's corporate departments. The Andersen Legal link renders the firm particularly adept at advising clients who wish to place employees in Europe on European employment law. **Euan MacLeod** is *"a canny operator,"* while **David Walker**'s arrival from McGrigor Donald has *"definitely strengthened them."* The team advised the Bank of Scotland in relation to an internal audit of working time across the Bank's 20,000 staff. **Clients:** Bank of Scotland; Standard Life Group; University of Glasgow; Scottish Daily Record & Sunday Mail Ltd.

Harper Macleod Seen to be *"doing well with a good range of clients and great publicity,"* the firm is growing in stature and handling a greater volume of respondent work than in previous years. *"Able and well-prepared"* **Stephen Miller** is now seen as a leading player, and handles the bulk of employment cases with a team of well-regarded assistants. Although **Rod McKenzie**'s profile has diminished this year, he is still regarded as an asset in the litigation field. Acted for the appellants in a precedent-setting appeal to the House of Lords in the equal pay case, Marshall & others v Glasgow City Council & others. **Clients:** Thus Ltd, Motherwell College, First Ford.

McGrigor Donald The employment team is now established as a core part of McGrigor Donald's operation, and it enjoys an especially high reputation in Glasgow. David Walker's departure has proved not to affect them unduly. The team retains the *"knowledgeable"* **James Young**, while **Diane Nicol**'s profile has grown appreciably: she is considered *"technically excellent."* Handles all the employment work in Scotland for The Post Office. The team conducts its own advocacy, and has niche strength in negotiating termination packages and advising on sex, race and disability discrimination. **Clients:** Forth Ports plc; Scottish Daily Record and Sunday Mail Ltd; National Australia Group Ltd.

Paull & Williamsons Another Aberdeen firm which has a good reputation for conducting employment work of a commercial bent for an eclectic client base. Jim Tierney has left to become a Sheriff, but the consensus is that **Sean Saluja** is *"bloody good"* and more than able to make good the departure. **Clients:** Oil industry clients; educational establishments; health care trusts.

Shepherd & Wedderburn WS Considered a *"high-profile team"* that is *"active in the market,"* especially in the boom area of training provision. Has made innovative moves into consultancy and deals with both contentious and non-contentious work. The team, spearheaded by **Sheila Gunn**, is thought to be *"particularly good at drafting"* and has acquired accredited employment specialist and litigator **John Griffiths** from Simpson & Marwick WS. **Ian Macleod** is seen as a generalist who lays particular emphasis on the health & safety aspects of employment law. **Clients:** KSCL; Orange PCS Ltd; Scottish Amicable; Edinburgh Fund Managers plc.

Kidstons & Co A smaller firm which largely owes its position in the rankings to the solid reputation of its head of department, **Iain Atack**. The firm advises a preponderance of small company clients, amongst whom it has been consolidating its position. **Clients:** Scottish Power; Dixons Group plc; 3M Health Care Ltd.

McClure Naismith Handles the broad spectrum of employment work from the employer's side. **Alan Thomson** is held to be *"sound"* but *"without a team behind him."* The department recently won at an employment tribunal hearing of an unfair dismissal/sex discrimination case against Mackay Simon. **Clients:** Stagecoach Scotland Ltd; First Engineering Ltd.

Raeburn Christie & Co A respectable employment department for its size, the firm conducts the greatest volume of its respondent work for companies in the oil industry. **Reginald Christie** has a sound reputation as a general litigator. **Clients:** Shell.

Brechin Tindal Oatts A *"reasonable practice"* felt to be moving up the rankings on the strength of accredited specialist **William Speirs**' reputation. The firm represents plcs and small private companies, financial institutions, educational institutions and charities. It is regarded as solid in its handling of TUPE and discrimination matters. **Clients:** Financial institutions; charities.

Maclay Murray & Spens The employment team is regarded as *"more a corporate support facility than pure employment lawyers."* It does boast impressive clients, but is seen to lack a big-hitter. Acting primarily for applicants, the team recently advised a client in the education sector on a discrimination/harassment claim. **Clients:** Compaq; BBC Scotland; Allied Distillers.

Thompsons A highly regarded *"quality"* niche firm, with a strong union employment practice. They are felt to be so niche as to occupy a different market-place, but *"as far as unions are concerned they are THE team."* **Clients:** UNISON.

Blackadder Reid Johnston & Carltons Felt to have a decent reputation in the smaller market-place of Dundee, the practice is considered to be *"sound, if not dynamic."* Primarily acts for respondents.

Maxwell MacLaurin **Alistair Cockburn** is the sole reason why this small employment practice is rated. Accordingly, the team is regarded as something of a *"one man band"* although many felt that Cockburn is *"as good as you can get."*

Morison Bishop Although some have felt that the employment team's profile is slipping, the team is still acknowledged for its non-contentious work, both for respondents and applicants. However, the firm's merger is yet to convince the market in this area of practice. **Clients:** Capability Scotland; Enable; Moray College.

Morton Fraser, Solicitors Both firm and individuals have made less impact on the market this year, but the firm is nonetheless regarded as having a solid employment practice, with niche ability in advising on working time directives and a variety of contentious claims.

NORTHERN IRELAND

EMPLOYMENT • Northern Ireland	Ptnrs	Assts
❶ Jones & Cassidy Belfast	2	1
❷ Elliott Duffy Garrett Belfast	2	1
❸ Cleaver Fulton Rankin Belfast	—	—
L'Estrange & Brett Belfast	1	2
❹ Carson & McDowell Belfast	1	3
Culbert and Martin Belfast	—	—
❺ C & H Jefferson Belfast	—	—

LEADING INDIVIDUALS	
❶ JONES Beverley Jones & Cassidy	
❷ BRETT Adam L'Estrange & Brett	CASSIDY Fiona Jones & Cassidy
COLL Henry Elliott Duffy Garrett	
❸ BROCK Adrienne Elliott Duffy Garrett	GRAY David Culbert and Martin
PRYTHERCH Rosalie Cleaver Fulton Rankin	
TURTLE Brian Carson & McDowell	

Within each band, firms are listed alphabetically. *See **Profiles** on page 332*
— *Figures unavailable at time of going to press.*

Jones & Cassidy The premiere specialist employment firm, regarded as a *"dedicated and experienced niche practice."* The team now handles approximately 75 percent respondent cases, working in conjunction with its clients' own in-house legal teams. The firm's speciality is seen to be discrimination work, in which area **Beverley Jones** is regarded as *"a pre-eminent authority."* **Fiona Cassidy** is also well-regarded in this field. Currently representing the applicants in a high-profile case heading to the House Of Lords that will have a UK-wide impact in terms of judicial appointments. **Clients:** Individuals; financial institutions; public sector; manufacturers.

Elliott Duffy Garrett A *"good mixed practice,"* with clients in the commercial, public and voluntary sectors, Elliott Duffy Garrett is beginning to see at last the impact of the large Queens University contract won some time ago. Their position in the rankings is maintained by the recognition that the firm wields two big-hitters: **Harry Coll**, thought to be *"aggressive but very good,"* who sits on the Employment Commission, and the *"thoroughly reliable"* **Adrienne Brock**. **Clients:** The Arts Council of Northern Ireland; Leck Patrick.

Cleaver Fulton Rankin Although the employment team is perceived to be losing profile, **Rosalie Prytherch's** *"grand"* leadership is still as well respected as ever. Still most respected for its expertise on restraint of trade matters.

L'Estrange & Brett The loss of long-standing client Queens University has not appeared to have knocked back the firm for long. Instead it has been broadening the scope of its employment practice by recruiting clients in Telecoms and IT. **Adam Brett** is *"really knowledgeable"* on discrimination and equal pay cases. **Clients:** Ford Motor Co; Merchant Ferrys; NTL.

Carson & McDowell A mixed practice which is particularly strong on employment law issues in the education and health sectors. This year the firm handled its first race discrimination case. **Brian Turtle** is a *"solid and versatile litigator."* **Clients:** University of Ulster; Hospital Trusts.

Culbert & Martin Known to handle applicant work and referrals from the Equality Commission, the firm is seen as *"strong on discrimination."* A respected niche practice is led by **David Gray**, particularly esteemed for his advice on sex discrimination cases. **Clients:** Equal Opportunities Commission.

C&H Jefferson The employment practice at C & H Jefferson is felt to have been knocked back by the departure of highly-regarded Alana Jones, who was seen to handle most of the employment workload. However, the firm is still respected for its advice on insurance-based employment matters.

LEADERS IN EMPLOYMENT

AARONS, Elaine
Eversheds, London (020) 7919 4500
aaronse@eversheds.com
Partner in Employment and Pensions Group.
Specialisation: Advises public and private companies and senior executives. Specialises in all aspects of employment law, including service agreements, bonus schemes, restrictive covenants, business reorganisations, board room disputes, senior executive severances and discrimination. Well known conference speaker, regularly appearing on radio and television. General editor of Tolley's 'Termination of Employment'.
Prof. Memberships: Employer's Forum on Statute and Practice (Chair), International Bar Association (Labour Law committee), London Law Society (Employment Law Sub-Committee), Employment Lawyers Association (Member, having been an officer 1997-2000, Management Member Committee 1992-2000).
Career: Qualified in 1982 with *Norton Rose*specialising in employment law since then. Has been Head of Employment at*Eversheds* London (and its predecessor firms) since 1989.

ADAMS, Elizabeth
Beachcroft Wansbroughs, London (020) 7242 1011
eadams@bwlaw.co.uk
Specialisation: Partner and departmental leader of employment; practice covers contentious and non-contentious employment work undertaken for both public and private sector clients including discrimination claims on the grounds of sex, race, disability and trade union activities including harassment claims. Has also developed a particular expertise in industrial relations disputes and interlocutory relief. Has in-depth knowledge of the Transfer of Undertakings (Protection of Employment) Regulations 1982 (TUPE). Particular interest in EU social policy aspects and working time. Lectures extensively on all aspects of expertise; regular contributor to the firm's Employment focus and contributor to "Strategic Procurement for the NHS" (The NHS Confederation). Member of the City of London Solicitors Employment Sub-Committee, CBI Competing for Quality Advisory Group, Member of the Employer Lawyers Association Management Committee, Chair of its International Committee, Member of Employment Lawyers Working Parties on Working Time and Employment Relations Bill, Employment Lawyers Association and Industrial Law Society.
Prof. Memberships: LLB (Hons) Law 1977.
Career: Admitted 1980 at *Beachcroft Hyman Isaacs* (now *Beachcroft Wansbroughs*) from 1981. Partner 1986 to date.
Personal: Born 15th April 1955. Interests include reading and travel. Lives in Horsley.

ANDREW, Jill
Langley & Co, London (020) 7397 9650
Partner.
Specialisation: Handles all aspects of contentious and non-contentious employment law. Acted in Payne & others v Port of London Authority (then the longest ever Industrial Tribunal). Frequent contributor to legal and personnel publications. Regular lecturer. Media contributions have included Newsnight, Panorama, Business Breakfast and Kilroy.
Prof. Memberships: Employment Lawyers Association.
Career: Qualified in 1981. Joined *Langley & Co* in 1995. Formerly partner and Head of Employment Law at *Masons* and the London Employment Department of *Dibb Lupton Broomhead*. Director of London Chamber of Commerce 1992-98. Chairman of Social Legislation Committee of London Chamber of Commerce 1989-94. Chairman Employment Lawyers Group 1987-89 and 1991-94. Director – Business Link London South 1995-98.
Personal: Born 8th March 1956. Attended Exeter University (LLB(Hons)) and London School of Economics (MSc in Industrial Relations and Personnel Management). Councillor (1994-98) and Deputy Leader of London Borough of Bromley (1997-98). School Governor (1994-98). Married, two children. Lives in Chislehurst.

ASHTIANY, Sue
Morgan Cole, Reading (0118) 955 3000
sue.ashtiany@morgan-cole.com
Partner in Employment and Discrimination Law Department.
Specialisation: Heads a specialist department in employment discrimination law operating out of 5 offices across the Thames Valley, London and South Wales. Acts for several major clients in the public and private sector. These include: HSBC Bank plc, University of Oxford, Amey plc, Oxford Radcliffe NHS Trust, Unipart and Xerox Ltd. Major cases included: Barry v Midland Bank plc, Bonna v Oxford City Council, Marshall v CPS. Writes and lectures extensively on employment law and discrimination matters and organisational change issues. This includes training for Cabinet Office and Civil Service as well as project management on cultural change. Contributing Editor to the Tolley loose-leaf encyclopaedia on Employment Law: author of chapter on Race Discrimination. Contributing Editor to CCH on line Employment Law Service. Co-author of Butterworths Employment & Discrimination Compensation Calculator.
Prof. Memberships: Law Society; Fellow, Institute of Advanced Legal Studies; Industrial Law Society. Employment Lawyers Association.
Career: Qualified in 1986, having joined *Cole & Cole* in 1984. Became a Partner in 1989. Previously worked extensively in human rights and immigration, including for the UN High Commissioner for Refugees.
Personal: Educated in Iran and the UK. Chair, Advisory Board Oxford Common Purpose: Member, Oxford Brooks University Court: Non-Executive Director Oxfordshire Ambulance Trust. Languages, English, French, Farsi.

ATACK, Iain F.
Kidstons & Co, Glasgow (0141) 221 6551
mail@kidstons.co.uk
Senior partner.
Specialisation: Main area of practice is employment law: accredited as a specialist by the Law Society of Scotland. Advises mainly employers on all aspects of Employment law. Represents at Tribunals in Scotland and England. Also handles general civil litigation and factoring law. Advises invoice factors on all commercial matters. Major clients include several large Plc's operating both in England and Scotland, banks, financial institutions and many medium sized companies. Lectures at conferences. Formerly Tutor in Advocacy & Pleading at Glasgow University.
Prof. Memberships: Law Society of Scotland, Royal Faculty of Procurators in Glasgow, Employment Law Group. Member Law Society of Scotland Employment Law Committee.
Career: Qualified in 1971. Joined *Kidstons & Company* in 1972, becoming a Partner in 1975 and Senior Partner in 1993. Council Member of Royal Faculty of Procurators 1989-92. Committee Member of Employment Law Group since 1984. Chairman of NHBC Appeal Tribunal since 1990.
Personal: Born 22nd November 1947. Attended Kelvinside Academy, Glasgow, then St Andrew's University. Leisure interests include walking and skiing.

AUERBACH, Simon
Pattinson & Brewer, London (020) 7400 5100
Partner in Employment Department.
Specialisation: Practises in all areas of labour, employment and discrimination law. Particular interest in transfers of undertakings, industrial conflict and trade union law. Co-author of 'A Guide to The Employment Act 1988' and author of 'Legislating for Conflict' (OUP, 1990) and 'Derecognition and Personal Contracts' (IER, 1993). Has had articles published in *Industrial Law Journal* and *Political Quarterly*. Regular writer in specialist publications and conference speaker. Has addressed meetings of the Industrial Law Society, Employment Lawyers' Association and the Institute of Employment Rights. Occasional media commentator.
Prof. Memberships: Industrial Law Society, Institute of Employment Rights, Employment Lawyers' Association.
Career: Qualified in 1985. Partner with *Pattinson & Brewer*.
Personal: Born in 1961. Educated at Oxford University (BA in Jurisprudence, 1st Class Hons, 1982 and D.Phil, 1988). Lives in London.

BARRY, Quintin
DMH, Brighton (01273) 744 268
Partner 1961-97. Consultant 1997 to date. Employment Group.
Specialisation: Advises on all aspects of employment law and conducts employment related litigation, including advocacy before industrial tribunals and EAT. Also advises on general commercial law. Major clients include TM Group Ltd., Vosper Thornycroft (UK) Ltd., East Sussex Health Authority, various NHS Trusts, University of Sussex. Regularly addresses conferences and seminars.
Prof. Memberships: ELA, Law Society, Sussex Law Society, Legal Aid Practitioners Group.
Career: Qualified 1958. Assistant solicitor, *Cronin & Son* 1959-60. Assistant solicitor, *Mileham Scatliff & Allen* 1960-62. Partner, *Mileham Scatliff & Allen* 1962-70. Managing Partner, *Donne Mileham Haddock* (now *DMH*)1970-91, Chairman 1991-97. Part-time Chairman Industrial Tribunal 1994 to date.
Personal: Born 7th March 1936. Educated at Eastbourne College and Open University. Principal hobby is the study and writing of history. Chairman Southern FM, Chairman South Downs Health NHS Trust. Lives in Shoreham-by-Sea, West Sussex.

BENSON, Edward
Browne Jacobson, Nottingham (0115) 976 6000
Specialisation: Practice covers full range of employment law services including drafting contracts of employment, general employment advice, representation at employment tribunals in complaints relating to unfair dismissal, redundancy pay, discrimination, equal pay, etc. Contributor and General Editor of Employment Law Service for IPD, published by Jordans. Member of Industrial Law Society.
Career: Admitted 1980. *Slaughter and May* 1978-1982. Assistant Editor of Handbooks and supplements at IDS (1982-1984). Editor of Industrial Relations Legal Information Bulletin (1985-89). Joined *Browne Jacobson* 1989, Partner since 1993.

BENSON, Nick
Michelmores, Exeter (01392) 436244

BESWICK, David
Eversheds, Birmingham (0121) 232 1000
Specialisation: Contentious and non-contentious employment law, advising mainly employers, including education institutions, with strengths in Executive Severance packages, TUPE issues, restructuring and restrictive covenants.
Prof. Memberships: Law Society. Employment Lawyers' Association. Education Lawyers' Association.
Career: Joined *Eversheds* in 1985, Partner 1996.
Personal: Born: 18.2.63. Attended Newcastle University 1981-84. Leisure interests include badminton and tennis.

BOOTH, Christopher
Pinsent Curtis, Leeds (0113) 244 5000
chris.booth@pinsents.com
Specialisation: Specialises in employment law dealing with high-profile executive terminations, trade union recognition, TUPE, restrictive covenants and discrimination cases.
Prof. Memberships: Management Committee of Employment Lawyers Association (ELA) as North East representative (including membership of ELA International Committee). Leeds Law Society.
Career: Educated at Hull University (LLB 1984). Joined former *Simpson Curtis* in 1987 on qualification. Partner 1993.
Personal: Born 1963. Leisure interests: golf, skiing, cooking, family and personal computer.

BRADLEY, David John
DLA, Sheffield (08700) 111111
david.j.bradley@dla.com
Specialisation: All areas of Employment Law, primarily on behalf of employers with particular experience in Senior Executive disputes, Transfers of Undertakings, managing change through contract variation, redundancy programmes and Industrial Relations issues, and is the Co-author of the annual Industrial Relations Survey. David has been involved in a number of high profile matters involving variations to working terms and conditions, strategic redundancy programmes, the construction of union agreement including negotiating with Trade Unions alongside senior management teams, boardroom restructures and dealing with high profile takeovers including in the area of sports.
Prof. Memberships: Law Society; CBI; Employment Lawyers Association.
Career: National Head of the Human Resources Group at *Dibb Lupton Alsop*. Articled with *Broomheads* (predecessor firm of *Dibb Lupton Alsop*). Former President of T.S.G. (Sheffield). Nottingham University. South East Essex Sixth Form College, Greensward School Essex.
Personal: Mainly sport – Rugby Union, mountain biking and golf. Married with two sons.

BREARLEY, Kate
Stephenson Harwood, London (020) 7809 2107
kate.brearley@stephensonharwood.com
Partner, Head of Employment & Pensions Practice Group.
Specialisation: Handles all aspects of contentious and non contentious Employment Law acting on behalf of clients in both the public and private sectors and for high profile Senior Executives/Directors and teams of employees seeking to join competitors. Leading expert on competition in the employment field and co-author of the key textbook on this subject. Regularly advises on all aspects of employee competition including drafting and enforcement of restrictive covenants. Work includes preparation of Service Agreements, handling Employment Tribunal, County and High Court claims, boardroom disputes, stress and discrimination claims, employment aspects of business mergers/takeovers/mbo's (in particular the application of the Transfer of Undertaking Regulations) and establishment of European Works Councils. Cases of note include representing Charing Cross and Westminster Medical School (now Imperial College School of Medicine) in the fixed term contract case Bhatt v Charing Cross and Westminster Medical School and Another. Co-author of Brearley & Bloch, 'Employment Covenants and Confidential Information; Law Practice and Technique' (Butterworths). Chairs conferences and lectures for IBC, EuroForum, CLT and QDos on employment related topics.
Prof. Memberships: City of London Solicitors Company (Member of the Employment Law Sub-Committee), Employment Lawyers Association, Industrial Law Society and United Kingdom Environmental Law Association.
Career: Called to the Bar 1979 and has specialised predominantly in employment law since qualification. Joined *Stephenson Harwood* in 1986 and qualified as a solicitor in 1989. Became a Partner in 1989.
Personal: Born 1957. Educated Harrogate Ladies College and Exeter University 1975-78, LLB Hons.

BRETT, Adam
L'Estrange & Brett, Belfast (028) 9023 0426
adam.brett@lestrangeandbrett.com
Partner. Main area of work: employment law, discrimination law and commercial litigation.
Prof. Memberships: Law Society of Northern Ireland.
Career: Qualified 1981. Partner in *L'Estrange & Brett* since 1985.
Personal: Born 1957. Education: Oxford University (MA). Committee Member Employment Lawyers Group in Northern Ireland and member Employment Lawyers Association. Contributor to two Sweet and Maxwell publications on employment law.

BREWER, Martin
Pinsent Curtis, Leeds (0113) 244 5000
martin.brewer@pinsents.com
Specialisation: All aspects of employment law including advocacy in large multi-party disputes, non-contentious employment law including advice on TUPE and PFI.
Prof. Memberships: Employment Lawyers' Association; IPD; Industrial Law Society.
Career: Nottingham University (BA) Politics. Studied law at Nottingham Trent University. Qualified 1991. Joined *Pinsent Curtis* in 1993. Partner 1997.
Personal: Photography, guitar, books.

BROCK, Adrienne M.
Elliott Duffy Garrett, Belfast (028) 9024 5034

BROWN, Anthony
Eversheds, Bristol (0117) 929 9555
tonybrown@eversheds.com
Specialisation: Partner with extensive experience of all contentious and non-contentious employment law, including drafting employment contracts and disciplinary procedures, employee remuneration and discrimination. Extensive experience of TUPE, especially in its application to outsourcing. Considerable experience of Employment Tribunal work. Lectures and writes widely.
Prof. Memberships: Member of Industrial Law Society; Employment Lawyers' Association; Industrial Tribunal Users Consultative Committee.
Career: Qualified 1983. *Laytons* 1981-83, *Osborne Clarke* 1983-84; *Wansbroughs Willey Hargrave* 1984, Partner 1988; Partner *Eversheds* 1999.

BROWN, Nicola
Mills & Reeve, Cambridge (01223) 222 282
nicola.brown@mills-reeve.com
Specialisation: Specialises in all aspects of employment law acting mainly for employers both in the public and private sector. Deals with contract drafting, advice on dismissals and industrial tribunal claims. Increasing emphasis on discrimination claims and advice on the Transfer of Undertaking Regulations.
Career: 1983 – LLB University of Southampton; 1987 – Qualified as a solicitor; 1987-90 – Assistant solicitor *Kennedys*, Chiswell Street, London; 1990-95 – Senior solicitor *Mills & Reeve*, Cambridge; 1995 to date – Partner *Mills & Reeve*, Cambridge.

BURD, Michael
Lewis Silkin, London (020) 7227 8000
burdm@lewissilkin.com
Partner.
Specialisation: All aspects of employment law. Particular areas of interest include contested dismissals and redundancy, business transfers, Employment Tribunal claims and advice aimed at preventing employment disputes and ensuring compliance with statutory regulations.
Prof. Memberships: Employment Lawyers Association. Committee Member, London Solicitors Litigation Association. Consultant Editor: Croner's "Managing Termination of Employment". Section Editor: Employment Section, Gee Practical Tax Planning and Precedents. President of City of Westminster Law Society (1995/96).
Career: Qualified 1986. Partner at *Lewis Silkin* 1988. Head of Employment at *Lewis Silkin*.
Personal: Born 07/02/58. BA Columbia University 1980. MPhil Cambridge University 1982.

BURNSIDE, David
Burnside Kemp Fraser, Aberdeen (01224) 327500
Senior Partner in Court Department.
Specialisation: Main area of practice is employ-

ment. Has handled employment tribunal cases since 1967 in the fields of redundancy, unfair dismissal, sexual and racial discrimination and Transfer of Undertakings. Acts for a number of major clients in these matters. Accredited by the Law Society of Scotland as an Employment Law Specialist since 1990. Also handles personal injury work. (Member of Personal Injury Panel.) Since 1970 has worked predominantly for claimants. Has substantial experience of offshore cases, although also deals with many cases involving injury at work or in road traffic accidents and medical negligence. Joint lead negotiator in Piper Alpha for claimants. Group spokesman for steering committees involving major helicopter crashes. Gives occasional lectures for Aberdeen University, the Law Society, IPM and other outside bodies. Has considerable media experience arising from matters of local and national interest.
Prof. Memberships: Law Society of Scotland, Society of Advocates in Aberdeen, Association of Personal Injury Lawyers, Aberdeen Bar Association, Employment Law Group, A.T.L.A.
Career: Qualified in 1966. Established *Messrs Burnside Advocates* as Senior Partner in 1989; firm became *Burnside Kemp Fraser* in 1994. President of Junior Chamber of Commerce, Aberdeen, 1978-79; President of Aberdeen Bar Association 1987-89; Board Member of Legal Defence Union since 1990; Scottish convenor and member of National Executive Committee of APIL 1990-1996. Treasurer of Employment Law Group. Treasurer of Society of Advocates in Aberdeen 1990-2000.
Personal: Born 5th March 1943.

CASSIDY, Fiona
Jones & Cassidy, Belfast (028) 90642290

CAVALIER, Stephen
Thompsons, London (020) 7637 9761

CHAMBERLAIN, Andrew
Addleshaw Booth & Co, Manchester (0161) 934 6000
ajc@addleshaw-booth.co.uk
Partner in Employment Department, firm's Graduate Recruitment Partner, member of firm's Partnership Board.
Specialisation: All aspects of employment law including the drafting of service agreements, Transfer of Undertakings Regulations, restrictive covenant injunctions, executive terminations and all contentious employment matters (including advocacy at the Industrial Tribunals), employment aspects of M & A work, and immigration matters.
Prof. Memberships: Employment Lawyers Association, Manchester Industrial Relations Society.
Career: Joined the firm in September 1995.
Personal: Educated at the University of Nottingham. Interests: golf, rugby, cricket and squash.

CHAMBERLAIN, Jonathan
Wragge & Co, Birmingham (0121) 685 2781
jonathan_chamberlain@wragge.com
Specialisation: All aspects of employment law including outsourcing and business protection litigation.
Prof. Memberships: Law Society
Career: *Slaughter and May*, Trainee-Assistant 1990-95, *Warner Cranston*, Associate 1995-98, *Wragge & Co* Associate-1998, Partner-1999
Publications: Contributes regularly to 'Personnel Today'.
Personal: University: Trinity Hall, Cambridge. Resides Warwickshire.

CHITTY, Martin
Wragge & Co, Birmingham (0121) 214 1096
martin_chitty@wragge.com
Head of Employment Team.
Specialisation: Interests include TUPE in public and private sector, collective disputes, senior executive contracts, severance and use and abuse of restrictive covenants.
Career: Articled *Pinsent & Co.*. Qualified 1986. Partner *Pinsent & Co* 1993-1995. Partner *Wragge & Co* from 1995.
Personal: Born 1961.

CHRISTIE, Reginald
Raeburn Christie & Co, Aberdeen (01224) 640101

CLARKE, Mary
DLA, Manchester (08700) 111111
mary.clarke@dla.com
Specialisation: Main areas of practice – employment law-contentious including actions on restrictive covenants and confidential information, share option schemes, boardroom disputes; group tribunal claims; non-contentious including business transfer issues, drafting. Lectures widely on employment law issues.
Prof. Memberships: Employment Lawyers Association.
Career: Qualified 1985 at *Pannone & Partners*. Joined *Alsop Wilkinson* 1988. MSc Employment Studies 1995.

CLARKE, Michael H.
Morgan Cole, Cardiff (029) 2038 5385

COCKBURN, Alistair
Maxwell MacLaurin, Glasgow (0141) 332 5666
acockburn@maxwellmaclaurin.co.uk
Partner in Litigation Department.
Specialisation: Main area of practice is employment law, primarily the representation of employers in relation to proceedings before employment tribunals throughout the whole of the UK including representation before the Employment Appeal Tribunal. Also represents individual employees before tribunals in Scotland and to both in relation to the formation of service agreements and the implications at termination, particularly with regard to covenants. Also handles litigation generally.
Prof. Memberships: Law Society of Scotland, Royal Faculty of Procurators in Glasgow, Glasgow Bar Association.
Career: Qualified in 1972. Joined *Tilston MacLaurin* in 1970, becoming a Partner in 1974. Accredited as a Specialist in Employment Law by the Law Society of Scotland in 1992.
Personal: Born 8th March 1950. Attended High School of Glasgow 1961-67, then University of Glasgow 1967-70 (LLB). Solicitor member of the Scottish Solicitors Dicipline Tribunal. Leisure interests include golf. Lives in Brookfield, Renfrewshire.

COCKBURN, David
Pattinson & Brewer, London (020) 7400 5100
Partner in Employment & Trade Union Law Department.
Specialisation: All areas of trade union, employment and discrimination law.
Prof. Memberships: Immediate past Chair of Employment Law Committee of the Law Society. Former Chair and Vice-President of the Employment Lawyers Association. Vice-President of the Industrial Law Society. Chair of EAT Users Group. Treasurer of the Institute of Employment Rights. Co-author of Know-How for Employment Lawyers.
Career: Joined *Pattinson & Brewer* in 1972. Qualified 1975, Partner 1978.
Personal: Born 30.11.48. Educated at Kings School, Pontefract, and at LSE for LLB and MSc (Econ) Industrial Relations (distinction).

COLL, Henry A.
Elliott Duffy Garrett, Belfast (028) 9024 5034

COOPER, Edward J.O.
Russell Jones & Walker, London (020) 7339 6435
Partner and head of national employment department.
Specialisation: Principal area of practice is trade union and employment law. Advises on a wide range of industrial employment and constitutional issues. Also covers administrative and public law. Advises on police terms and conditions of service, acts on union mergers, major privatisations, terms and conditions reviews, new legislation, health and safety, pensions, disputes, discrimination and other employment cases. Clients include the TUC, Police Federation and trade unions in the public and private sectors. The department (now of over twenty executives and with a national presence) has growing employee private client practice. Author of the trade union section of CCH Employment Law Service and trade union section Butterworths Encyclopaedia of Forms and Precedent.
Prof. Memberships: Industrial Law Society.
Career: Qualified in 1984. With *Simmons & Simmons* 1982-85. Joined *Russell Jones & Walker* in 1985 and became a Partner in 1988.
Personal: Born 12th June 1959. Educated at Bristol University 1977-80. Leisure interests include family, jazz, saxophone, cricket, theatre and tennis. Lives in London SW15.

CROSS, Stefan
Thompsons, Newcastle-upon-Tyne (0191) 261 5341

CULLEN, Joyce
Brodies WS, Edinburgh (0131) 228 3777
jcullen@brodies.co.uk
Specialisation: Partner within Litigation Department's Employment Law Group providing a full range of advice to companies, institutions, partnerships and individuals, including a major Scottish Bank, national retailers, colleges, professional firms and clients in the industrial and manufacturing sectors. Specialises in employment contracts, change management policies, business transfers and redundancies. Extensive experience as an advocate in Employment Tribunals, EAT and the Court of Session.
Prof. Memberships: Member of the Management Committee of the Employment Lawyers Association, Industrial Law Group, Institute of Directors.
Career: Qualified 1981. With *Brodies*, initially as an Assistant Solicitor and as a Partner since 1986. Management Board Member. Accredited Specialist in Employment Law and Solicitor-Advocate with extended rights of audience in the Civil Courts.
Personal: Born 1958. Educated Leith Academy, Edinburgh and Dundee University. Married with three children. Interests include travel and politics.

DALE, Stephanie
Denton Wilde Sapte, London (020) 7320 6438

DALGARNO, David
McDermott, Will & Emery, London (020) 7577 6900
DDalgarno@europe.mwe.com
Partner in Employment group of nine specialist lawyers.
Specialisation: Undertakes all types of advisory employment work, contractual and statutory, contentious and non-contentious; primarily for employers, but also acts for senior executives: principal interests include management of integration, employee consultation and organisational change programmes, collective and trade union issues, discrimination, trial advocacy. He also advises on employee benefits and share scheme issues. He frequently speaks on employment law issues; the author of the CCH Employment Contracts manual. Clients include UK and global financial institutions, major industrial concerns, airlines, major retail businesses, inward investors and 'Fortune 500' companies.
Prof. Memberships: Employment Lawyers Association, City of London Law Society Employment Law Sub Committee, Industrial Law Society.
Career: Called to the Bar at Inner Temple 1978; in-house lawyer specialising in employment and labour law at*Courtaulds plc* 1979-87; Head of Employment *Warner Cranston* 1987-1999. Joined *McDermott, Will & Emery* 1999.
Personal: Born in 1955. Educated at Hatfield School 1969-74 and Warwick University 1974-77. ICSL 1977-78.

DAVIES, James
Lewis Silkin, London (020) 7227 8000
daviesj@lewissilkin.com
Partner. Joint Head of Employment Department
Specialisation: All areas of employment law and business immigration. Particular interests include EC employment law, discrimination law, TUPE and sports law.
Prof. Memberships: Employment Lawyers Association (Treasurer, Management Committee for seven years, Chair of Working Groups on TUPE and Age Discrimination), European Employment Lawyers Association, ILS, IPD, ILPA, and BASL. Management Committee of the AIRE Centre. Member Advisory Group of the Employers Forum on Age.
Career: Qualified in 1988. At *Denton Hall* 1986-90. Joined *Lewis Silkin* in 1992.
Personal: Born 26th February 1962. Educated at Ysgol Gyfun, David Hughes, Menai Bridge; Leicester University (L.L.B. and L.L.M.); and Strasbourg University (Dip. Ed. Jr. Fr.). Interests: long-suffering supporter of Glamorgan Cricket and Welsh rugby; most sports and travel.

DAVIES, Joanne
Morgan Cole, Cardiff (029) 2038 5385
joanne.davies@morgan-cole.com
Specialisation: An experienced employment lawyer with particular expertise in corporate support work, outsourcing, large scale reorganisations, executive service agreements and termination arrangements. Advises on the employment aspects of mergers, acquisitions and disposals involving complex Transfer Regulations issues and post transfer organisational change. Regularly lectures and provides training on a wide area of employment law issues. Is retained by a major client of the firm to provide stategic employment law advice and training to their managers.
Prof. Memberships: Member of The Law Society and Employment Lawyers Association.
Career: Spent 7 years at *Rowe & Maw*, London before joining *Morgan Cole* in 1997 where she is team leader in the Cardiff employment team.
Personal: Married with 2 children. Leisure interests include swimming and golf.

DAWSON, William S.
Simmons & Simmons, London (020) 7628 2020
Specialisation: Has advised on numerous acquisitions, disposals and mergers and transfers of undertakings, both UK and internationally, for major corporations and institutions. He has a strong City-based practice acting for insurance, banking and financial services institutions covering a wide range of complex issues associated with 'high flyers' and has a strong focus on cases involving 'reputational risk'. He acted in the Allied Dunbar v Frank Weisinger case, a leading case on post termination restrictive covenants and has handled many interlocutory matters. Has been voted a 'leading expert' in employment law for several years.
Prof. Memberships: Law Society.
Career: He joined the Employment Law Department at *Simmons & Simmons* in 1981 and became a partner in 1986. He is an employment law practitioner and the Department's Managing Partner. He gained his MA (Hons) Law degree from Cambridge University in 1977 and admitted as a solicitor in England and Wales in 1980.

DEAN, Veronica
Hammond Suddards Edge, Birmingham (0121) 200 2001
veronica.dean@hammondsuddardsedge.com
Head of Midlands Employment Unit
Specialisation: All areas of contentious and non-contentious employment law with a particular interest in Trade Union and Labour relations, TUPE and discrimination issues. A regular tribunal advocate.
Prof. Memberships: Law Society, Employment Lawyers Association, Birmingham Industrial Tribunal Users Group.
Career: Qualified 1984, Joined *Edge Ellison* 1986, partner 1993.
Personal: Born 1959, Graduate of University of Wales, Cardiff. Interests include art, gardening and entertaining. Lives in Worcestershire.

DILLARSTONE, Robert
Greenwoods, Peterborough (01733) 887700

DINELEY, Rachel
Beachcroft Wansbroughs, London (020) 7242 1011
rdineley@bwlaw.co.uk
Specialisation: Practice in both contentious and non-contentious employment work on behalf of employers and individuals in the public and private sectors. Regularly deals with commercial transactions and preparation/negotiation of executive service agreements as well as board room disputes, dismissals and executive termination packages. Has developed a particular expertise in the field of protection of confidential information and enforcement of restrictive covenants. Has an in depth knowledge of discrimination law and is a member of the Editorial Board of Croner's 'Discrimination Law Briefing' in addition to writing the chapter on race discrimination and contributing to two other chapters of Croner's book 'Discrimination Law'. Regularly lectures on these and other topics.
Prof. Memberships: Member of the Employment Law Association and Chartered Institute of Personnel and Development.
Career: University of Exeter Scholar LLB (Hons) 1979. Admitted in 1983. Solicitor and then Partner at *Denton Hall* before joining *Beachcroft Stanleys* in December 1994.
Personal: Married and lives in the Chiltern Hills. Interests include theatre (and occasional amateur dramatics), extensive travel, photography, skiing and walking.

DRAKE, Ronald S.
Read Hind Stewart, Leeds (0113) 246 8123
Specialisation: Unfair/Wrongful dismissal, redundancy, equal pay, discrimination and harrasment industrial action., TUPE transfer and contracting out. Involved as lead Solicitor in 'Tanks & Drums v T & GWU', 'Kelman v Care', 'Jancuik v Winerite', and the Staffordshire Legionnaires' Disease Public Inquiry.
Prof. Memberships: Associate of the Chartered Institute of Arbitrators, Affiliate of the Institute of Personnel & Development, Member of the Employment Lawyers Association, Industrial Law Society, Competition Law Association and The British-Nordic Lawyers Association.
Career: Bradford GS, Manchester University and Chester College of Law. Articles to J Aucott at *Edge & Ellison*, Birmingham. Partner *Last Suddards* (later *Hammond Suddards*) 1981-1990. Partner *Read Hind Stewart* 1990 to date. Part-time Chairman of Industrial Tribunals (Newcastle Region) 1997.
Personal: Married to ex-Solicitor Teacher, two children. Interests in Choral singing and classical music. Scandinavian Culture and Music. Director of Yorkshire & Humberside Business in The Arts.

DU-FEU, Vivian
Eversheds, Cardiff (02920) 471147
vivdufeu@eversheds.com
A Partner and Head of the Employment Law Department at Cardiff.
Specialisation: Head of the *Eversheds* national Employment Law Group of over 130 lawyers. Has wide experience in providing advice on all aspects of contentious and non-contentious employment law. Lectures and writes regularly on various employment issues and is a member of the Editorial Advisory Board for Croners.
Prof. Memberships: A Fellow of the Chartered Institute of Personnel and Development (IPD); Director of Principle Training Limited.
Career: Graduate of University of Wales College of Cardiff. Qualified in 1979. Became a Partner in 1984.
Personal: Married and resides in Cardiff.

DUNCAN, Nikki S.
Bond Pearce, Plymouth (01752) 266633
xnsd@bondpearce.com
Partner and Head of Employment Law Group.
Specialisation: All aspects of employment law. Considerable experience in employment law litigation, advocacy and the employment aspects of corporate transactions and discrimination law issues. Regularly speaks at, or chairs, both regional and national employment law seminars and conferences. Has had published numerous articles and given radio and television interviews on topical employment law issues.

Prof. Memberships: Elected Secretary of the Employment Lawyers Association and, for the last 2 years, their UK Training Co-ordinator – first time anyone outside London has been appointed to this key role. Member of the European Employment Lawyers Association and the Regional IT Users Consultative Committee.
Career: Qualifed in 1979. Joined *Bond Pearce* in 1982, becoming partner 1985. Previous firm *McKenna & Co.*

EDWARDS, Julia C.
Hammond Suddards Edge, Birmingham (0121) 200 2001
julia.edwards@hammondsuddardsedge.com
Specialisation: All aspects of employment law including unfair, wrongful and constructive dismissal, sex, race and disability discrimination, executive severance and injunctive proceedings.
Prof. Memberships: Employment Lawyers Association. Association of Women Solicitors.
Career: Articled *Edge & Ellison*. Admitted 1992 becoming an Associate 1996 and a Partner in 1998.
Personal: Born 1968. Alice Ottley School, Worcester, 1973-1986 and Bournemouth University 1986-1989. Lives in Worcestershire.

EDWARDS, K.Martin
Mace & Jones, Liverpool (0151) 236 8989
Head of Employment Law Department.
Specialisation: Employment law specialist with extensive advocacy experience. Advises on all aspects of industrial relations law and acts for major clients in the public and private sectors throughout the UK. Also expert in relation to computer contracts. Major cases include 'Lavery v. Plessey Telecommunications' (maternity leave). Advised on film 'Letter to Brezhnev'. Author of 'Dismissal Law', 'Managing Redundancies', 'Careers in the Law', 'How to get the Best Deal from your Employer', 'Understanding Computer Contracts' and numerous articles. Founder member of Law Society's Employment Law Committee.
Prof. Memberships: Law Society, Liverpool Law Society, Employment Lawyers Association, Society for Computers and Law, Society of Authors, Crime Writers Association.
Career: Qualified in 1980 while at *Mace & Jones.* Became a Partner in 1984.
Personal: Born 7th July 1955. Attended Balliol College, Oxford 1974-77. First Class Honours Degree in Law. Leisure pursuits include writing crime novels about Liverpool Solicitor Harry Devlin, the first of which was nominated for the award for best first crime novel of 1991. Lives in Lymm, Cheshire.

EMMOTT, Jeremy D.
DLA, Leeds (08700) 111111
jeremy.emmott@dla.com
Specialisation: Employment, Industrial Relations.
Prof. Memberships: Law Society, Leeds Law Society, Employment Lawers Association.
Career: Qualified at Hepworth and Chadwick (now Eversheds) Leeds 1979, Legal/Industrial Relations Adviser EEF Leeds 1979-1990, DLA 1990 to date, 1995 Partner.
Personal: Leeds Grammer School, Nottingham University. Married with one son and two daughters. Interests apart from family life include triathlon and historic architecture.

FARR, John
Herbert Smith, London (020) 7374 8000
Partner in employment and trusts department.
Specialisation: Well known for his representation of companies and senior individuals in contentious matters, including High Court applications in connection with restrictive covenants, confidential information and group defections. He deals with corporate governance and boardroom disputes; bonus issues; dismissals and redundancies; pension disputes; discrimination and harassment claims. He also advises on partnership disputes. Non-contentious work covers, inter alia, business transfers and reorganisations, the devising and introduction of new terms of employment and the implementation of new UK and European employment and trade union legislation. He covers immigration and work permit matters.
Career: Qualified in 1974. Became a Partner at *Herbert Smith* in 1982. Member of the City of London Solicitors' Company Employment Law Committee.
Personal: LL.B. (London).

FEINSTEIN, Naomi M.
Lovells, London (020) 7296 2000
naomi.feinstein@lovells.com
Specialisation: Deals with all aspects of employment law, both contentious and non contentious, including advice on employment contracts, restrictive covenants, termination packages, wrongful and unfair dismissal, redundancies and reorganisations, discrimination and the employment aspects of corporate transactions.
Career: Articled *Osborne Clarke* and *Lovells.* Qualified 1987. Partner 1997.

FIELD, Roger
Higgs & Sons, Dudley (01384) 342000
Specialisation: All aspects of employment law, 80% employer – 20% employee. Emphasis on national retailer clients. Contentious and non-contentious. Part-time Chairman of Employment Tribunals.
Prof. Memberships: Law Society, Birmingham Law Society, Employment Lawyers Association.
Career: Qualified in 1970. Joined *Higgs & Sons* in 1968, becoming a Partner in 1974.
Personal: Born 13th January 1946. Educated at Dudley Grammar School and The London School of Economics. Interests include crosswords, railways and cricket. Lives in Stourbridge.

FLANAGAN, Tom
Stephenson Harwood, London (020) 7809 2148
tom.flanagan@shlegal.com
Managing Partner Employment & Pensions Practice Group.
Specialisation: Employment law, providing a full range of advice to individuals, partnerships, companies and institutions including clearing and merchant banks, insurance companies, a major accountancy practice, recruitment consultants, professional bodies and clients in the IT, telecommunications, education, leisure, property, publishing, shipping, industrial, manufacturing and voluntary sectors. Also has strong experience in acting for high profile individuals, negotiating both employment and termination packages. Tom is one of the country's leading experts on the application of TUPE to corporate transactions and outsourcing, and has taken an early lead in advising on the changing law of employee consultation. Chapters on Transfer of Undertakings Regulations and Employment and Self-employment in 'Tolley's Employment Law'. Has written and given seminar presentations on numerous topics including the application of TUPE to PFI transactions and the introduction of European and national works councils. Cases to note include representing the UK banking sector, through HSBC, in the part-time pensions cases in the European Court of Justice and House of Lords in Fletcher v Midland Bank, Preston v Wolverhampton Borough Council, representing the managers of the Rover Group in its sale to Phoenix.
Prof. Memberships: Employment Lawyers Association (Management Committee); Industrial Law Society; Institute of Personnel and Development; Institute of Directors.
Career: Qualified 1979. At *Brian Thompson & Partners*, Manchester 1980-84; *Barlow Lyde & Gilbert* 1984-85; *Speechly Bircham* 1985-92 (Partner 1988); Partner in *Booth & Co* (then *Addleshaw Booth & Co*) 1992-98; joined *Stephenson Harwood* as Partner in July 1998.
Personal: Born 16 January 1954. Educated at Ushaw College, Durham; St Mary's College Middlesborough; University College London. Interests include playing guitar, theatre, blues and jazz. Languages: speaks a little French and German. Resides in London.

FLETCHER, Kevin J.
Jacksons, Stockton-on-Tees (01642) 643643
genquiry@jacksons.law.co.uk
Senior Partner and head of Company / Commercial Department.
Specialisation: Principal area of practice is employment law advising and representing mainly employers in all aspects, both contentious and non-contentious. Advocates in tribunals throughout the country. Also handles company/commercial work and commercial litigation. Major clients include British Steel Plc, British Bakeries Ltd, Black and Decker and the National Farmers Union. Part-time chairman of Industrial Tribunals in 1991. Regularly gives seminars to clients, local professional bodies and employers' associations.
Prof. Memberships: Law Society and Employment Lawyers' Association.
Career: Qualified in 1971. Appointed a Partner at *Jacksons* in 1972. Became Senior Partner in 1995.
Personal: Born 6th March 1947. Educated at Hull Grammar School 1958-65; St Catharine's College, Cambridge 1965-68 and The College of Law, Guildford 1968-69. Leisure interests include music, sport, art, reading and travel. Lives in Middlesbrough.

FOX, Ronald D.
Fox Williams, London (020) 7628 2000
rdfox@foxwilliams.co.uk
Specialisation: Main areas of practice are employment law and partnership law. Specialises in advising on the calculation and taxation of payments on termination of employment. Frequently negotiates on behalf of the boards of listed companies on the departure of senior executives. Author of "Payments on Termination of Employment" (now in its third edition). Past Master of the City of London Solicitors' Company, Past Chairman of the Practice Management Sub-Committee of the IBA; Past Member of the Law Society Law Management Section Advisory Group. Frequently broadcasts and is the author of numerous articles in the professional and national press on employment, partnership and management topics.

Prof. Memberships: IBA, Law Society, City of London Law Society, Employment Lawyers' Association.
Career: Qualified 1972. Senior Partner at *Fox Williams.*

FROST, Peter
Herbert Smith, London (020) 7374 8000
Partner in employment section
Specialisation: Deals with both contentious and non-contentious employment matters with expertise in transactional work, including cross-border matters, TUPE issues, executive severances, team defections, the drafting and enforcement of special arrangements for executives (including incentive arrangements and restrictive covenants), proceedings in the employment tribunal (particularly discrimination) and the High Court (including injunctive relief), collective matters (including works councils, union recognition and industrial action), human rights issues and internal investigation/inquiries.
Career: Emmanuel College, Cambridge. Qualified in 1985. Became a partner at *Herbert Smith* in 1994.

GAYMER, Janet
Simmons & Simmons, London (020) 7628 2020
Head of Employment Law Department.
Specialisation: Employment. Work covers collective and individual, contentious and non-contentious matters and occupational health and safety. Acted for the Ministry of Defence on the contractorisation of the Royal Dockyards and for Railtrack on the British Rail privatisation. Written numerous articles on employment law and is a frequent lecturer on employment law topics. Founder Chairman of the Employment Lawyers Association and (in 1998) of the European Employment Lawyers Association. Given "The Times" Woman of Achievement in the Law Award in 1997 and in 1998 "The Lawyer/HIFAL Partner of the Year Award".
Prof. Memberships: UIA, IBA, Institute of Advanced Legal Studies (Honorary Fellow). Visiting Law Fellow, St Hilda's College, Oxford (1998). Member of the Chartered Institute of Arbitrators, Member of the Council of ACAS and the Executive Board of "Justice". Member of the Council of Governors of the Royal Shakespeare Company. Patron of the Association of Women Solicitors.
Career: Articled with *Simmons & Simmons* in 1971, qualified in 1973 and became a Partner in 1977. Currently Head of Employment Law Department.
Personal: Born 11th July 1947. Attended Nuneaton High School for Girls 1958-65, then St Hilda's College, Oxford 1966-70. Read LLM at London School of Economics 1976-78. Leisure pursuits include watercolour painting, theatre, music and learning to play the flute. Lives in Effingham.

GOODIER, Colin
Pinsent Curtis, Birmingham (0121) 200 1050
colin.goodier@pinsents.com
Head of Employment Department, Birmingham.
Specialisation: Employment law including contentious and non-contentious work, advice on individual and collective rights and heavy involvement in TUPE, employee consultation and employment aspects of M&A.
Prof. Memberships: Chairman of Employment Tribunals (England & Wales). Founder member of managing committee of Employment Lawyers' Assoc. Member of Birmingham Industrial Tribunal Users' Group and of Employment Law Committee of Birmingham Law Society.
Career: Admitted 1972. Specialist in Employment Law throughout career. Partner *Bettinsons* Birmingham 1976. Partner *Pinsent & Co* (now *Pinsent Curtis*) 1987. Head of Litigation (Birmingham) 1995. Head of Employment (Birmingham) 1996.
Personal: Born 1947. Educated Hertford College, Oxford. Interests include renovation of timber-framed cottage; walking; old prints. Elected FRSA 1996.

GORAJ, Ann
Beachcroft Wansbroughs, Sheffield
(0114) 209 5000
agoraj@bwlaw.co.uk
Head of Employment in our Sheffield office
Specialisation: Partner acting for both major commercial and public sector clients. Specialised solely in employment law for over fifteen years. Recognised as a leading individual in the field of employment law, according to the Chambers Guide. Recent instructions include advising on large-scale changes in terms and conditions including the introduction of reward, and productivity arrangements. Also acts in complex race and sex discrimination cases, drafts contracts of employment, and advises on the applicability of TUPE in relation to contracting out exercises.
Prof. Memberships: She is a part-time chairman of the Birmingham Employment Tribunal and a member of the Employment Lawyers' Association and the Industrial Law Society.
Career: Articled *Clifford Chance*; qualified 1982; *Wragge & Co* 1982; *Dibb Lupton* 1986; *Oxley & Coward* 1990; *Wansbroughs* 1995.

GRAY, David J.
Culbert and Martin, Belfast (028) 9032 5508

GREEN, David
Charles Russell, London (020) 7203 5000
Partner in Employment, Pensions and Employee Benefits Unit.
Specialisation: Handles all aspects of employment law, including individual employment rights, employee benefits, contractual and policy documentation, discrimination, health and safety, equal opportunities, wrongful dismissal, redundancy, protection of confidentiality and goodwill, collective labour law, immigration and employment issues resulting from mergers and acquisitions. Member of editorial board of Croners Employer, Industrial Relations and Discrimination Briefing Notes. Author of various articles in a range of publications, including Management Consultancy and Tolleys Employment Law. Author of 'Business Basics Staff'. Has spoken at and chaired a number of seminars.
Prof. Memberships: Association of Employment Lawyers.
Career: Qualified in 1978. Worked at *Taylors Newmarket* 1976-83 (from 1981 as a Partner); then *McKenna & Co.* 1983-85 and *Clifford Chance* 1985-91. Joined *Charles Russell* in 1991 as a Partner.
Personal: Born 1953. Attended John Lyon School, Forest School and University of London. Committee Member of Downham Town FC. Follows all forms of sports. Leisure interests include gardening. Lives in Downham Market, Norfolk.

GRIFFITHS, John
Shepherd & Wedderburn WS, Edinburgh
(0131) 228 9900
john.griffiths@shepwedd.co.uk
See under Clinical Negligence, p.162

GUNN, Sheila M.
Shepherd & Wedderburn WS, Edinburgh
(0131) 228 9900
sheila.gunn@shepwedd.co.uk
Specialisation: Head of employment unit of *Shepherd & Wedderburn.* Accredited as an employment specialist by the Law Society. Advising on employment aspects of (i) the re-organisation of Scottish Amicable; (ii) the transfer of operatorship by Cairn Energy plc of a gasfield in Bangladesh to Shell; (iii) the sale of Scotish Telecoms by ScottishPower UK plc; (iv) recent outsourcing for ScottishPower UK plc in its £420 million outsourcing and joint venture relating to its IS Division; (v) the City of Edinburgh's current IT PPP outsourcing of the entire IT division to achieve the 'Smart City' vision; and (vi) the drafting and implementation of Bank of Scotland's policy under the Public Interest Disclosure Act and other corporate activities of Bank of Scotland. Also engaged in delivering management training for mangers of many Scottish companies, including KSCL, Scottish Amicable, Scottish Ambulance Service, Baillie Gifford, NMT plc, Marriot Hotels.
Career: Hutchisons' Grammar School; Glasgow University (1985 LLB Hons; 1986 Dip. L.P.)
Personal: Born in 1963; resides in Strathaven. Leisure interests: skiing and walking.

HANTOM, Charles C.
Whittles, Manchester (0161) 228 2061
Senior Partner.
Specialisation: Main areas of practice are employment, trade union and industrial. Handles Employment Tribunal and EAT work. Undertakes advocacy for employment tribunals. Also handles High Court Injunctive proceedings. Predominantly Trade Union practice. Gives occasional seminars for Trade Union clients.
Prof. Memberships: Employment Lawyers Association.
Career: Qualified 1967. Joined *Whittles* in 1969, becoming a Partner in 1972.
Personal: Born 24th January 1942. Attended Windermere Grammar School 1954-60, Nottingham University 1960-63, and College of Law 1966. Leisure interests include walking, classic cars and outdoor pursuits. Lives in Bowdon.

HARPER, David A.
Lovells, London (020) 7296 2000
david.harper@lovells.com
Specialisation: Deals with all aspects of employment law both collective and individual, including executive contracts and severance packages (plus tax, pension and employee benefits aspects), all tribunal litigation, redundancies, discrimination, restrictive covenants, works councils and employment policies and practices such as working time and pay issues. Handles all employment aspects of transactional work, particularly TUPE. Regularly appears as an advocate in industrial tribunals. Substantial experience of collective labour law issues and injunction proceedings. Principal editor of CCH Employment Manual, member of editorial board of Employment Lawyer and regular writer on employment matters.
Prof. Memberships: Employment Lawyers' Association, City of London Solicitors Employment Law Sub-committee.
Career: Articled with *Lovell White & King* (now *Lovells*); qualified 1978; partner 1986.
Personal: Born 1954. Educated Stowe School and

Keble College Oxford. Lives in Richmond. Married with four children.

HAY, Emma J.
MacRoberts, Glasgow (0141) 332 9988
emmab@macroberts.co.uk
Specialisation: Partner in Employment Law Group. Significant experience in conducting Employment Tribunal and Employment Appeal Tribunal hearings and in negotiating exit and entrance packages at senior executive level. Advises on disability, sex and race discrimination issues and the implications of collective redundancies, business transfers and business re-organisations.
Prof. Memberships: Law Society of Scotland.
Career: Trained with *John Wilson & Co.* Qualified 1993. Assistant, Associate and Partner (2000) with *MacRoberts* in Employment Law Group.
Personal: St Josephs College, Dumfries; University of Strathclyde LLB (Hons), Dip LP, NP. Leisure intrests include walking, skiing, hockey. Lives in Glasgow.

HEARN, Keith
Ford & Warren, Leeds (0113) 243 6601
clientmail@forwarn.com
Managing Partner and Head of Employment Law.
Specialisation: Experienced since 1973 in all aspects of employment law. Acted as labour relations adviser on construction of Sullom Oil Terminal and other major projects. Deals with competition issues arising out of human resources matters. Extensive experience in full range of applications before Industrial Tribunals including unfair dismissal, sex and race discrimination. Regularly appeared before the Employment Appeal Tribunal. Practice includes High Court employment based work – injunctions, damages against directors, and restrictive covenants. Wide experience of developing and delivering management training for health service and numerous commercial clients, especially in the area of change management. Received degree of Masters of Laws in European Management and Labour Law in 1995, the subject matter of the dissertation being Fair Competition in the Road Haulage industry. Works closely with his fellow specialists in transport and led the multi national group claiming damages in respect of the 1996 French Lorry Drivers Blockade. Principal clients including PSV, train and HGV operators, hospital trusts and other public health bodies.
Prof. Memberships: Industrial Law Society.
Career: Joined *Ford & Warren* in 1974. Became Partner in 1976. Became Managing Partner in 1989. Leeds University LL.B 1967-70. Leicester University LL.M 1995.
Personal: Leisure interests include scuba diving instruction and racing cars.

HEMMING, Julian
Osborne Clarke OWA, Bristol (0117) 917 4348
julian.hemming@osborneclarke.com
Specialisation: Partner specialising in all aspects of employment law including business transfers, Board level issues, discrimination law and industrial relations. Julian is the SouthWest Representative of the Employment Lawyers Association, sitting on the ELA's management committee.
Prof. Memberships: Employment Lawyers Association.
Career: Articled *Simmons & Simmons*; qualified 1989. *Nicholson Graham & James* in 1997.
Publications: Editor of 'Discrimination in the Workplace' published by John Wiley. Contributor to Tolley's 'Employment Law' and to Croner's 'Discrimination Law Briefing'. One of his cases reported in Butterworths 'Company Law Cases 1997' under the title 'Re A Company (No 002015 of 1996)'.

HEMMINGS, Richard
The Law Offices of Richard Hemmings LLM Solicitor, Ipswich 01473 833 844

HENNEY, Colin C.
Henmans, Oxford (01865) 722181
Partner and Head of Employment Department.
Specialisation: Sole area of practice is employment. Handles the full range of employee and employer work, both contentious and non-contentious. Has appeared before EAT as well as undertaking almost all advocacy in cases before ETs. Involved in ACAS training, giving seminars at individual conciliation officer workshops since 1990. Also provides training to major employer clients and insurers.
Prof. Memberships: Employment Lawyers' Association, Industrial Law Society.
Career: Qualified in 1982. Articled with *Rickerby Watterson* 1980-82; joined *Henmans* in 1983, becoming a Partner in 1987; Managing Partner 1991-3.
Personal: Born 25.11.1957. Attended Daniel Stewart's and Melville College, Edinburgh 1962-75, and Oxford University 1976-79 (Law, BA). Leisure interests include music, golf and languages. Lives in Eynsham, Oxfordshire.

HILL, David G.
DLA, Leeds (0113) 241 2620
david.hill@dla.com
Partner and head of employment department, Leeds.
Specialisation: Deals with all aspects of employment law for private and public sector clients. Specialises in business transfers, employment contracts, policies and procedures, contract variation, restrictive covenants and handling redundancies. Experienced advocate in the Employment Tribunals.
Prof. Memberships: Member of the Employment Lawyers Association. Part-time lecturer on Employment Law, University of Bradford.
Career: Qualified 1978. Partner since 1982.
Personal: Born 1954. Educated at Worcester College, Oxford.

HILLS, Stephen
Halliwell Landau, Manchester (0161) 835 3003
Partner in Employment Department.
Specialisation: Handles all aspects of contentious and non-contentious employment matters. An experienced advocate who regularly appears in the Employment Tribunal in England and Scotland. Particular experience in transfer of undertakings and discrimination. Regularly presents seminars.
Prof. Memberships: Law Society, Employment Lawyers Association, Industrial Law Society.
Career: Qualified in 1986. Joined *Halliwell Landau* in 1990, becoming a Partner in 1992. Previously with *Mills & Reeve*, Norwich.
Personal: Born 20th September 1959. Attended University of East Anglia 1980-83. Leisure interests include walking and gardening. Lives in Appleton, Cheshire.

HOPKINS, Martin W.
Eversheds, Birmingham (0121) 232 1000
Partner and Head of Employment.
Specialisation: Main area of practice is Employment and Industrial Relations Law. Has wide experience of handling all types of contentious and non-contentious employment work in both the public and private sector. Has an international practice and advises many US businesses on UK start up issues. Leads team of 25 specialist employment lawyers, trainers and HR professionals. Co-author of 'Health and Safety: Are You at Risk?' (1993), 'The Maternity Manual' (1994), 'The Law of Harrassment' (1998) and EU and International Employment Law (2000). Speaks frequently on employment issues and regularly delivers in-house tailored training courses for clients.
Prof. Memberships: Member of Institute of Personnel and Development and Employment Lawyers Association.
Career: Joined *Eversheds* 1980, qualified in 1982, and made Partner and Head of Employment in 1989.
Personal: Born 28th October 1957. Attended Warwick School 1971-76 and Coventry University 1976-79. Leisure interests include family and travel. Lives in Lighthorne, near Warwick.

HOSKINS, Julian
Bevan Ashford, Bristol (0117) 923 0111
Specialisation: Acts primarily for employers in the private sector, advising on all aspects of employment and discrimination law, both contentious and non-contentious. Has extensive advocacy experience in the higher courts and appears regularly in the EAT and Employment Tribunals as advocate for clients of the firm's various offices. Frequent speaker at seminars, both internal and external, and provides tailored training for clients.
Prof. Memberships: Employment Lawyers Association.
Career: Called to the Bar in 1987, practised at 1 Serjeants Inn, Fleet Street, 1987 until 1995. Joined *Bevan Ashford* 1995. Re-qualified as a solicitor and became a partner in 1998.
Personal: Born 1962.

JACKS, David
Weightmans, Manchester (0161) 833 2601
david.jacks@weightmans.com
Specialisation: Practice in both contentious and non-contentious employment work and industrial relations law. Principally acts for employers but also for senior executives to negotiate severance packages. Experienced advocate in the employment tribunals. Strengths also in advising companies on contracts of employment/service agreements, re-structuring/redundancy strategies, TUPE and discrimination matters.

JACOBS, Howard
Slaughter and May, London (020) 7600 1200
Specialisation: Executive engagements and dismissals. TUPE.
Prof. Memberships: City of London Solicitors Company Employment Law Sub-committee.
Career: Winchester College. Pembroke College, Cambridge. *Slaughter and May* since 1975.
Personal: Married, three children. Interests: family and gardening.

JEFFERS, Raymond
Linklaters (A member firm of Linklaters & Alliance), London (020) 7456 3702
raymond.jeffers@linklaters.com
Specialisation: Partner and head of employment and benefits group and co-chair of labour practice group of *Linklaters & Alliance* specialising in the field

of employment law since 1978; while covering all aspects of this area, principle roles have been advising publice sector and private sector clients of the firm (national, multinational and foreign) an all aspects of employment law.
Career: Articled at *Linklaters*, becoming Partner in 1986.
Personal: Oxford University (1977 BCL.) Born 1954.

JEFFREYS, Simon
CMS Cameron McKenna, London (020) 7367 3000
Partner Employment Group.
Specialisation: Has specialised in employment and labour relations law since qualifying, advising predominantly employer clients in the public and private sectors on all aspects of their legal relationship with employees and trade unions. Work includes contractual documentation, corporate policies towards employees, workforce reductions, negotiations with trade unions, anti-discrimination law, employee and trade union aspects of acquisitions, disposals and PFI deals together with general advice on all aspects of the day to day employment relationship and the resolution of disputes with employees and trade unions. Has appeared as an advocate in the Employment Tribunal and has conducted litigation for clients in the Employment Appeal Tribunal, County Court, High Court and Court of Appeal. Frequently advises clients on interpretation of legislation and the impact of proposed legislation. Has spoken at numerous conferences and seminars. Contributor of employment precedents to Sweet & Maxwell's 'Practical Commercial Precedents' and 'Commercial Checklists', joint editor of their 'Employment Precedents and Company Policy Documents' and 'Transfer of Undertakings' and author of 'Hiring and Firing Senior Executives' 1995. Also Legal Editor for FT Management's 'HR Expert' on-line service.
Prof. Memberships: Employment Lawyers Association, Industrial Law Society, City of London Law Society, Member Law Society of England and Wales Employment Law Committee.
Career: Joined *McKenna & Co* in 1980 and qualified in 1982. Became a Partner in 1988.

JONES, Alan G.
DLA, Birmingham (08700) 111111
alan.jones@dla.com
Employment Law Partner and Head of Employment in Birmingham office.
Specialisation: Principal area of practice is the whole spectrum of employment law including unfair dismissal, discrimination, executive severance and restrictive covenant work. Both contentious and non-contentious but with an emphasis on the former. A regular and experienced advocate primarily on behalf of such clients as Makro, Tesco, Employment Service, and AMEC Group Plc amongst others. Also acts for senior executives in dispute with their employer. Occasional speaker at conferences, and does a lot of in-house training on related subjects.
Prof. Memberships: Law Society, Employment Lawyers Association.
Career: Qualified with *Needham & James* in 1978 becoming a Partner in 1983. Originally a criminal lawyer, moving to employment from 1985. Partner with *Dubb Lupton Broomhead* upon merger in November 1993, and *Dibb Lupton Alsop* since October 1996.
Personal: Born 17 May 1953. Interests include most sports, particularly rugby, skiing and wind surfing. Lives in South Warwickshire.

JONES, Beverley
Jones & Cassidy, Belfast (028) 90642290

JULYAN, Alan
Speechly Bircham, London (020) 7427 6400
alan.julyan@speechlys.co.uk
Specialisation: Practice covers full range of employment and labour law specialising in the employment and corporate governance issues arising on the recruitment, retention and termination of senior executives, TUPE and the management of organisational change. Author "Key Employees-Drafting Service Agreements" published by Sweet & Maxwell and joint Editor of "Employment Precedents and Employment Policies" published by Gee Publishing Ltd..
Prof. Memberships: Law Society. Committee member of the Employment Law Subcommittee of the City of London Law Society. Member of the Industrial Law Society, and the Employment Lawyers Association.
Career: Qualified 1974. Joined *Speechly Bircham* and became partner in 1977.
Personal: Born 14th October 1949. Educated at Bristol Grammar School and Lanchester Polytechnic. Interests include tennis, painting and jazz. Lives in New Malden.

KEANE, Georgina
Lawrence Graham, London (020) 7379 0000
Partner and Head of Employment Unit. Handles all aspects of employment law, discrimination and trade unions, as well as employee benefits including share option schemes and ESOPS. Has conducted numerous speaking engagements at conferences and training for a wide variety of organisations and for clients.
Prof. Memberships: Employment Lawyers Association, Industrial Law Society, American Bar Association.
Career: Qualified in 1988. Called to the Bar in 1975, practised at the common law Bar until 1984. Then became Employment Law Adviser to the Confederation of British Industry. Joined *Titmuss Sainer Dechert* in 1986 as Head of Employment Unit; requalified as a solicitor and became a Partner in 1988. Joined *Richards Butler* in 1996 as Head of Employment.
Personal: Born 3rd February 1954. Married with two sons. Leisure interests include theatre and music.

KEMP, Sandy
Burnside Kemp Fraser, Aberdeen (01224) 327500
Specialisation: Has specialised in employment law and personal injury claims throughout career. Accredited as an Employment Law Specialist by the Law Society of Scotland and member of Assessment Committee for Personal Injury Panel. Advises employers and individuals on all aspects of employment law, particularly in relation to offshore oil industry. Has lectured for Law Society and others on employment law, negotiation and on personal injury claims, both generally and arising from offshore industry.
Prof. Memberships: Law Society of Scotland, Society of Advocates in Aberdeen, Employment Law Group, European Employment Lawyers Association, Association of Personal Injury Lawyers, Association of Trial Lawyers of America.
Career: Qualified 1983. Partner at *Philip and Kemp* 1986. Joined *Burnside* 1994 and established *Burnside Kemp Fraser.*
Personal: Born 8 February 1959.

LAMB, Norman
Steele & Co, Norwich (01603) 274 700
noremp@steele.co.uk
Specialisation: Main areas of practice: Employment and discrimination. Tribunal advocacy, drafting and advising on terms and conditions, and reorganisations of companies, trade unions recognition issues, collective redundancy consultation, works councils, Working Time, Minimum Wage, Commercial Agents Regulations. Regularly lectures and presents training sessions on Employment Law. Publication: 'Remedies in the Employment Tribunal' (Sweet & Maxwell, 1998).
Prof. Memberships: Employment Lawyers Association, Discrimination Law Association.
Career: Qualified in 1984.
Personal: Born 16.9.1957.

LAMONT, Sarah
Bevan Ashford, Bristol (0117) 923 0111
Specialisation: Partner in Employment Law Department dealing with all aspects of contentious and non contentious employment law. Including: employment aspects of corporate transactions; TUPE; service agreements; sex, race, disability discrimination; equal pay; restrictive covenants; trade unions/industrial action; and employment litigation including tribunals and advocacy. Co-author of Jordan's Secretarial Administration, Jordan's/IPD Employment Service and Sweet & Maxwell's Public and Private Partnerships. Regularly publishes articles and speaks at employment seminars/courses, including tailored training for clients, and lectures on the Legal Practice Course.
Prof. Memberships: Law Society, Institute of Personnel and Development, Employment Lawyers Association, Industrial Law Society, Bristol Law Society Equal Opportunities Committee, National Employment Tribunal Users Consultative Committee.
Career: MA Cambridge University, trained *Macfarlanes*, London. Qualified 1992.
Personal: Astronomy, painting and sketching.

LANGLEY, Dale
Langley & Co, London (020) 7397 9650

LANGRIDGE, Sharon E.
Short Richardson & Forth, Newcastle upon Tyne (0191) 232 0283
sel@short-richardson-forth.co.uk
Specialisation: Has a number of years' experience in employment law, acting for both Respondents and Applicants. Deals with all areas including contracts, reorganisations, TUPE, and a full range of Tribunal claims. Conducts own advocacy in Tribunals locally and nationally, including complex multi-day hearings. Particular interest in sex descrimination and maternity cases, and participates in a maternity advice helpline through the Association of Women Solicitors. Presents seminars to clients and also TV/radio/press involvement.
Prof. Memberships: Employment Lawyers Association; Industrial Law Society; Newcastle Employment Tribunal Users Group; Chair of Association of Women Solicitors North East region; member of Maternity Alliance.
Career: BA (Hons) German and French, London

University (1984). Joined *Baker and McKenzie*, London after graduating. Diploma in Industrial Relations, PCL (University of Westminster) (1988). Admitted 1994 after completing legal qualifications while at *Latimer Hinks*, Darlington. Joined *Short Richardson & Forth* in October 1995, becoming a partner in March 1997.
Personal: Married and lives in Newcastle upon Tyne. Interests include books, music, hill-walking and Languages.

LILLEY, Andrew
Travers Smith Braithwaite, London (020) 7295 3000
Andrew.Lilley@TraversSmith.com
Specialisation: Advises on UK/EC employment law and employee relations. Experience includes executive employment contracts, severance arrangements, corporate issues (Transfer of Undertakings Regulations, managing integration etc.) employee consultation (including European works councils), trade union issues, restrictive covenants, redundancy programmes and all aspects of employment litigation and industrial disputes.
Prof. Memberships: Employment Lawyers Association; Industrial Law Society; Law Society.
Career: Qualified at *Freshfields*. Joined *Travers Smith Braithwaite* in 1995, partner from 1997.
Publications: 'Tolley's Employment Law' (contributing author). Other current year publications include articles in 'The European Lawyer' and 'Employment Law Journal'.

LOVE, Alison
Hugh James Ford Simey, Cardiff (029) 2022 4871
alison.love@hjfs.co.uk
Specialisation: Employment law, including both contentious and non-contentious work. Particular interest and experience in discrimination claims. Recently pursued a claim, on behalf of a transsexual, under the Sex Discrimination (Gender Reassignment) Regulations in relation to less favourable treatment in the provision of vocational training. Regularly conducts training seminars for a variety of organisations including the Chamber of Commerce, ABTA and the Law Society as well as in house and external seminars for clients.
Prof. Memberships: Employment Lawyers Association. Member of the Chartered Institute of Personnel and Development.
Career: Prior to qualifying as a solicitor, worked for a number of years in personnel within the public and private sector. Since qualifying in 1992, specialised in employment work acting for a broad range of clients. Joined *Hugh James Ford Simey* in April 1999 as a Partner and Head of the Employment Law Group.
Publications: Regular contributor to national newspapers and business journals and BBC Wales Radio commentator.
Personal: Ex-county swimmer. Any spare time now spent with her two young sons.

LOY, Simon
Eversheds, Newcastle upon Tyne (0191) 261 1661
Specialisation: Collective and individual employment law. Equal pay, discrimination, tupe and trade union law. Involved in several reported cases involving collective consultation, tupe, equal pay and trade union discrimination.
Prof. Memberships: Industrial Law Society, Employment Law Association.
Career: Degree: University College, London. Research Assistant: University College, London. Joined *Eversheds* 1992; Partner 1995; Head of Employment *Eversheds* North East.
Personal: Newscastle United Football Club, cinema, literature. Married with two young daughters.

LYNE, Amanda
Taylor Vinters, Cambridge (01223) 423444
aml@taylorvinters.com
Partner and head of employment department
Specialisation: All aspects of employment law, national and European, contentious and non-contentious for companies, institutions and individuals. Contracts and benefits. Reorganistaions and redundancies. Dismissals. Transfers of undertakings. Discrimination. Restrictive Covenants. In-house training. Tribunal advocacy. Clients include major high tech, biotech, telecoms, education (including Cambridge University and many colleges, and major schools).
Prof. Memberships: Law Society, Employment Lawyers Association, Industrial Law Society.
Career: Called to the bar in 1969. Qualified as a solicitor in 1981. Joined *Vinters* in 1986 (becoming *Taylor Vinters* after merger in 1988). Became partner in 1989.
Personal: Educated at Adelaide, Australia and Cambridge (MA, LLB). Keen sailor, tennis player, theatre, film and concert goer.

MACKAY, Malcolm
Mackay Simon, Edinburgh (0131) 240 1400

MACLEOD, Euan
Dundas & Wilson CS, Edinburgh (0131) 228 8000

MACLEOD, Ian
Shepherd & Wedderburn WS, Edinburgh (0131) 228 9900
ian.macleod@shepwedd.co.uk
See under Administrative & Public Law, p.

MALONE, Michael
Mace & Jones, Manchester (0161) 236 2244
Partner in Employment Department.
Specialisation: Extensive advocacy experience notably in complex sex discrimination and equal pay cases. Deals with the whole range of employment work acting mainly for employers. Recent publications include "Your Employment Rights", "Discrimination Law – A Practical Guide" and the Employment Law Section of "Butterworths Guide on Law for Accountants". Has also spoken regularly at conferences and seminars.
Prof. Memberships: Law Society; International Bar Association; Associate Member of Institute of Personnel & Development.
Career: Admitted in 1968; partner at *Henry Fallows & Co* in Bolton from 1968-1991; Partner in *Mace & Jones* since 1991.
Personal: Born Bury 1943, educated at Brasenose College, Oxford. Leisure pursuits include tennis, bridge, walking, theatre. Lives in Bolton.

MANN, Jane E.
Fox Williams, London (020) 7628 2000
jemann@foxwilliams.co.uk
Partner in Employment and Immigration Department.
Specialisation: Advises a number of large employers in relation to employment law issues and business immigration. Works closely with in-house legal and personnel departments to provide an integrated service to line management. Has handled a number of difficult and high profile cases. Also acts for senior executives in relation to the termination of employment. Discrimination law is a particular interest. Legal contributor to ExeComp, software to calculate executive compensation. Member of several editorial boards.
Prof. Memberships: Co-founder of Employment Lawyers Association and currently its Chairman. Former Treasurer of the Immigration Law Practitioners Association. Member of the International Bar Association; Member of the Industrial Law Society; the Employment Law Sub-Committee of the City of London Law Society; and The American Immigration Lawyers Association. Associate Member of the Institute of Personnel and Development.
Career: Qualified 1981. Worked at *McKenna & Co* 1979-86, then at *Denton Hall* until 1994, where became a Partner. Joined *Fox Williams* in 1994 as a Partner.
Personal: Born 1957. Attended Cambridge University 1975-78.

MANSELL, Mark
Allen & Overy, London (020) 7330 3000
Partner
Specialisation: Partner in the employment and pensions department, specialising in employment law and dealing with the full range of contentious and non-contentious matters. His experience includes advising on major redundancy and restructuring exercises, including changing terms and conditions of employment and working practices, designing and implementing redundancy procedures and negotiating and consulting with recognised trade unions. He has experience in advising on and drafting service agreements, terms and conditions of employment and other employment policies. He has experience of European law and its implementation in the UK. He has advised on outsourcing employment issues for many clients including contractors, government agencies and companies outsourcing out services and changing contractors.
Prof. Memberships: Member of the Employment Law Sub-Committee of the City of London Solicitors Company and the European Employment Lawyers Association.
Career: LLB (Hons) London University. Admitted as Solicitor 1985. Legal Advisor, CBI Employment Affairs. Directorate 1985-87, Assistant Solicitor *Allen & Overy* 1987-91, Partner *Allen & Overy* since 1992.
Personal: Born in 1961.

MARSHALL, Ian
Martineau Johnson, Birmingham (0121) 200 3300
Specialisation: All aspects of Employment law, contentious and non-contentious, largely for employers. Trial experience includes actions against a trade union, injunctions, contempt of court, and wrongful dismissal. Advice on TUPE, severance agreements, restrictive covenants and equality issues in the private and educational sectors.
Prof. Memberships: Employment Lawyers Association, Birmingham Law Society, Birmingham Employment Tribunal Users Group.
Career: Rugby School and Magdalene College, Cambridge. Articled *Ryland Martineau & Co.*; Partner in *Ryland Martineau & Co.* 1976; *Martineau Johnson* 1987; Head of Employment Department 1994.
Personal: Born 1947. Married, 4 children. Lives in

Edgbaston, Birmingham. Council Member, Edgbaston High School, Birmingham and Edgbaston Debating Society. St Paul's Club, Birmingham. Fell Walking.

MCKENZIE, Rod
Harper Macleod, Glasgow (0141) 221 8888
See under Sport, p.

MCMULLEN, John
Pinsent Curtis, Leeds (0113) 244 5000
john.mcmullen@pinsents.com
Partner and National Head of Employment Department, based in Leeds.
Specialisation: Acts for a wide range of household name plcs, national and multinational, universities and public sector organisations. Leading authority on transfer of undertakings. Expert on European Works Councils. Part-time Professor of Labour Law at University of Leeds. Author 'Business Transfers and Employee Rights', 'Butterworths Employment Law Guide', 'Aspects of Employment Law', 'Acquired Rights of Employees', 'Tolley's Employment Law' (Joint), 'Redundancy: The Law and Practice', 'Jordans/IPD Employment Law Service'. Contributes widely to legal journals such as Modern Law Review, Industrial Law Journal, Company Lawyer, Civil Justice Quarterly, New Law Journal and Cambridge Law Journal. Also contributes to human resources and business journals such as PLC, People Management and Personnel Today.
Prof. Memberships: FCIPD. FRSA. Founder member Law Society's Employment Law Committee. Industrial Law Society Executive Committee, International Bar Association, Member, Fellow, Society for Advanced Legal Studies.
Career: Qualified in 1978. With *Rotheras* 1978-80. Fellow in Law at Girton College, Cambridge 1980-86. Bye Fellow since 1986. Partner, *Rotheras* 1986-91. Partner and Head of Employment, *Simpson Curtis* 1991. National Head of Employment, *Pinsent Curtis* 1995.
Personal: Born 1954. Educated Emmanuel College, Cambridge (BA 1975, double 1st Class (Hons), MA 1979, PhD 1993).

MILLER, Stephen C.
Harper Macleod, Glasgow (0141) 221 8888
stephen.milller@harpermacleod.co.uk
Partner in commercial litigation.
Specialisation: Main areas of practice are employment and sport. Employment cases include Dryden v Greater Glasgow Health Board, Reid v Camphill Engravers and Brown v JBD Engineering. Largely Respondent client base including: Scottish Coal, Thus Ltd, Scottish Area Tourist Boards, Lloyds TSB, Lidl, Schlumberger, hbg Construction and Optical Express. Lead solicitor for Scottish Premier League. Sport work includes McGuire v Scottish Football Association (Judicial Review). Managerial clients include Tommy McLean, Iain Munro, Alex McLeish, Jock Brown and Eamonn Bannon. Handled Paul Gascoigne's Scottish legal affairs. Acts for Licensed Players' Agents. Assisted in re-draft of Scottish Rugby Union's Disciplinary Procedures. Frequent lecturer.
Prof. Memberships: Born 5th January 1965. Attended Aberdeen University 1983, LLB (Hons) DipLP. Law Society of Scotland accredited specialist in Employment Law. Lives in Glasgow.

MOLYNEUX, Pauline
Rollit Farrell & Bladon, Hull (01482) 323239
Partner in Commercial Department.
Specialisation: Head of Employment Law Unit. Covers all aspects, contentious and non-contentious, including Working Time Regulations, boardroom disputes and negotiation of severance arrangements, review and drafting of documentation, the conduct of High Court cases and advising on employment consequences of commercial sales, specialising in matters involving TUPE. Has been involved in a variety of Tribunal cases including sex, race and disability discrimination claims and equal pay claims; cases involving the application of the Transfer of Undertakings Regulations and cases involving injunctions to enforce post-termination employment restrictions. Author of articles in local press and various law journals. Speaker at external and internal seminars for clients and employers' organisations.
Prof. Memberships: Employment Lawyers Association, Industrial Law Society, Law Society.
Career: Qualified in 1977. *Clifford Turner* 1977-79, *Field Fisher and Martineau* 1979-84. Senior lecturer at the College of Law, Lancaster Gate, 1984-86; *Clifford Chance* 1986-89. Joined *Rollit Farrell & Bladon* as a Partner in 1989. Part-time Chairman of Industrial Tribunals (appointed 1995).

MOORE, Nigel
Stephens & Scown, Exeter (01392) 210700
civil.litigation.exeter@stephens-scown.co.uk
Specialisation: All aspects of contentious employment law, acting mainly for employers as regular advocate in Employment Tribunals and the Employment Appeal Tribunal, advising on corporate aspects of employment law including TUPE and Service Agreements, executive terminations and restrictive covenants.
Prof. Memberships: Law Society.
Career: Called to the Bar in 1978, Harmsworth Scholar, Middle Temple. 1982-86 Assistant Editor IDS Brief; 1986-1990 Assistant, *Simmons & Simmons*, December 1989, admitted as solicitor. Joined *Stephens & Scown* in 1990 becoming a partner in 1994.
Personal: Educated Plymouth College and Southampton University 1974-1977.

MOORMAN, Jane
D J Freeman, London (020) 7583 4055
Partner and Head of the Employment Law Group.
Specialisation: Practice covers the full range of employment law work and in particular transfer of undertakings issues arising on transactions, policy advice, particularly in the context of equal opportunities, advising on changing contracts of employment in the context of industrial relations and flexible working. Restrictive covenant enforcement, injunctions and executive level dismissals. Wide experience of media related employment work. Speaks regularly at conferences and writes on the subject of employment law.
Prof. Memberships: Member of the Law Society, the Employment Lawyers Association and a member of its Legislative and Policy Sub-Committee, and the CBI Employee Relations Panel.
Career: Qualified 1984. At *D J Freeman* 1982 to date. Partner 1992.
Personal: Born 12 May 1958. Educated at the London School of Economics and Political Science. Interests include theatre, gardening and swimming. Lives in Wimbledon.

MORDSLEY, Barry
Salans Hertzfeld & Heilbronn HRK, London (020) 7509 6000
BMordsley@salans.com
Partner and Head of Employment Department.
Specialisation: Deals with all employment law issues, contentious and non-contentious, including contracts and handbooks, restrictive covenants, discrimination, transfer of undertakings, executive terminations and collective representation issues. Advocate in the Employment Tribunal. Co-author of Butterworths Emploment Law Guide and Butterworths Older Clients Service and Croners Discrimination law. Regularly contributes to People Management and is on the Editorial Board of Croners Discrimination Law Briefing. Lectures regularly to conferences, professional organisations, educational institutions and clients.
Prof. Memberships: Former member of Employment Lawyers' Association Management Committee, the Law Society's Employment Law Committee, a Member of the Employers' Forum on Age Members' Advisory Group, a Fellow of the Institute of Personnel and Development and of the Institute of Continuing Professional Development.
Career: Qualified 1972. Academic career: Principal Lecturer London Guildhall University; Visiting Professor, Cornell University, USA; Visiting Lecturer Queen Mary & Westfield College. Ran own practice specialising in labour law before joining *Harris, Rosenblatt & Kramer* as a Partner in 1989. A Chairman of Employment Tribunals (England and Wales) since 1984.
Personal: Born:19.01.47. Interests include theatre, music and travel. Avid cricket and football fan (Middlesex and Chelsea respectively). Plays squash frequently.

NICKSON, Susan C.
Hammond Suddards Edge, Manchester (0161) 830 5000
susan.nickson@hammondsuddardsedge.com
Prof. Memberships: Head of National Employment Unit with a team of more than 50 specialist employment lawyers working from the firm's four main offices in Manchester, Leeds, Birmingham and London. Handles the full range of contentious and non-contentious employment law issues acting for companies within the public and private sectors including retail, manufacturing and construction companies. Her particular speciality is advice in relation to the Transfer of Undertakings Regulations. Regularly contributes to journals and lectures frequently. Also runs the Employment Unit's training company 'In-Tuition' which provides in-house training on a wide variety of employment law topics.
Prof. Memberships: Law Society, Employment Lawyers Association, European Employment Lawyers Association, Industrial Law Society.
Career: Qualified in 1988. Worked at *Pannone & Partners* 1986 to 1994 as a Partner from 1991 and as Head of Employment Department from 1992. Joined *Hammond Suddards* as a Partner in 1994 and became Head of National Employment Unit in 1998.
Personal: Born 1st January 1964. Holds a First Class

Honours Degree from Caius College, Cambridge (1982-85) with a TAPP postgraduate scholarship. Associate Member of Institute of Linguists. Interests include motor bike riding, ball room dancing, theatre and Manchester United. Lives in Hale, Cheshire.

NICOL, Diane
McGrigor Donald, Glasgow (0141) 248 6677
www.mcgrigors.com
Specialisation: Partner in the firm's employment law unit. Advises on all aspects of employment law and has considerable experience in appearing at Employment Tribunal. Activities in the recent past have included providing high level strategic advice to major (Scottish) financial institutions, tailored training for major multi-nationals and as ever dealing with severance packages, problems associated with large outsourcing contracts and dealing with a range of discrimination issues.
Prof. Memberships: Associate Member of the Institute of Personnel and Development; Law Society of Scotland.
Career: Qualified in 1989. Spent one year with Australian law firm *Blake Dawson Waldron* and two years at *Maclay Murray & Spens* before joining *McGrigor Donald* in 1992. Became a partner in 1997.
Publications: Contributor to the Employment Law Journal and other publications.
Personal: Born 2nd September 1965; Educated Shawlands Academy, Glasgow and Glasgow University (LLB (Hons) (First Class)). Married. Interests include running, hillwalking and travel.

NORBURY, Peter
Eversheds, Manchester (0161) 832 6666
peternorbury@eversheds.com
Head of Employment for Leeds and Manchester.
Specialisation: Experienced advocate before Employment Tribunals throughout the UK and Employment Appeal Tribunal, together with representation at Joint Industries Board hearings. Particular expertise in trade unions executive terminations, TUPE and discrimination. Key work on collective issues including recognition agreements. Regular speaker at seminars and conferences and contributor to publications. Reported cases include Stoker v Lancashire County Council, Monsanto v TGWU, Roevin BP v Gillick, Akzo Coatings v Thompson and others, Rock Refrigeration v Seward, Merchant Ferries v Brown and Atlas Wright v Wright.
Prof. Memberships: Employment Lawyers Association, Industrial Law Society, RSA, EFSP.
Career: Qualified in 1978 and stayed with the firm before being made partner in 1984.
Personal: Born 12.1.53. Educated at Manchester Grammar School and Sheffield University. Interests include rugby and golf. Lives in Saddleworth.

NOTT, Christopher
Palser Grossman, Cardiff Bay (029) 2045 2770
Specialisation: Represented a major US motor manufacturer defending claims brought by its unionised work force for contractual redundancy pay. Negotiating literally dozens of termination agreements for senior executives (for both employers and the executives). Handled the class action mounted by several hundred members of Roadchef ESOP against its former Managing Director arising from his mishandling for his own benefit of its share option allocation. Dealing with the internal NHS appeal against the dismissal of a consultant and the subsequent internal inquiry. Handled a major constuctive dismissal claim brought by directors of a company against its parent, whose directors froze them out of day to day involvement after acquiring the business (including advocating the case at a 10 day trial). Advised a listed public company on the application of the Minimum Wage Regulations to its several thousand homeworkers. Advised on the application of TUPE to a business acquisition by a multinational company of its 'sister' company in the UK. Handled constructive dismissal/unfair dismissal cases against a National Car Dealership. Advised an International plc on immigration/employment issues of employing persons from outside UK and EEA.
Prof. Memberships: Wales representative on Employment Lawyers Association. Member of the Industrial Tribunal User Group. Tutor to trainee solicitors studying legal skills course. Lecturer on advocacy. External examiner University of Wales.
Career: 1981-83 Articles *Loosemores* solicitors, Cardiff (1983) Assistant solicitor. 1986-89 Assistant solicitor *Simmons & Simmons*, London. 1989-92 *Edward Lewis & Co*, Cardiff. Assistant solicitor (1989) – Partner (1990). 1992 Founding Partner of *Palser Grossman*.
Personal: Skiing, travel, the Arts, WRU referee, food and wine.

O'BRIEN, Christine
Baker & McKenzie, London (020) 7919 1000
Partner at *Baker & McKenzie* and Head of the Employment Law Department, which is one of the leading employment practices in the UK.
Specialisation: Contentious and non-contentious employment law, including corporate re-organisation, advice on European Works Councils and collective issues. Has acted in high profile discrimination cases for public and private sector clients, including investment banks and other financial institutions. Frequent speaker at external conferences, contributor to various publications and televison appearances commenting on employment law issues.
Prof. Memberships: Law Society, Employment Lawyers Association (management committee member), Industrial Law Society.
Career: Qualified 1987 with *Simmons & Simmons*. Joined *Baker & McKenzie* in 1989 and became a partner in 1995.
Personal: Born 6 September 1959.

OSMAN, Christopher
Clifford Chance, London (020) 7600 1000
chris.osman@cliffordchance.com
Specialisation: Partner and head of employment unit specialising in all aspects of employment law.
Career: Ramsden School; Southampton University (LLB 1973). Articled *Coward Chance*; qualified 1976; partner *Clifford Chance* since 1981; editor of 'Harvey on Industrial Relations and Employment Law'; advisory editor 'Butterworths Employment Law Guide'.
Personal: Hot air ballooning. Born 1951; resides Westerham.

PALCA, Julia
Olswang, London (020) 7208 8888
Specialisation: Main areas of practice are media and employment litigation. Represents both print and broadcast defendants, and some plaintiffs, in defamation, breaches of copyright and other media and entertainment-related disputes including judicial review of decisions of media regulatory and quasi-regulatory bodies. Also advises mainly employers on all aspects of employment law, including unfair and wrongful dismissal, discrimination and the application of restrictive covenants. Author of 'Employment Law Checklists' and numerous articles on media and employment issues and editor of Copyright and Media Yearbook. Acted as an in-house libel litigator to a major newspaper group 1985-86. Speaks on both media and employment law issues.
Career: Qualified in 1980. Joined *Olswang* in 1986, becoming Partner in 1987.

PARKINSON, Helen L
Whittles, Manchester (0161) 228 2061
helenparkinson@whittles.com
Specialisation: Specialises in all aspects of contentious employment law including advocacy at employment tribunals and the Employment Appeal Tribunal, acting mainly for trade unions and employees.
Career: Qualified 1989. Joined *Whittles* in 1990, became a partner in 1996 and manager of the firm's employment department in April 2000.

PIKE, Malcolm J.
Addleshaw Booth & Co, Manchester
(0161) 934 6000
mjp@addleshaw-booth.co.uk
Partner
Specialisation: Main areas of practice are employment and industrial relations. Includes drafting and advising on terms and conditions of employment, personnel policies and collective agreements, industrial relations and other trade union matters, discrimination and equal pay, board room disputes, defending and prosecuting High Court and Employment Tribunal proceedings and advising on employment aspects of the sale and reorganisation of companies and businesses. Various publications include 'The Lawyers Factbook', 'Essential Facts Employment,' Butterworths' 'Encyclopaedia of Forms and Precedents,' 'Workplace Discrimination' and Jordan's 'IPD Employment Law Service.' Regular speaker at seminars and conferences.
Prof. Memberships: Law Society, Employment Lawyers Association, Industrial Law Society, Manchester Industrial Relations Society, IBA, ABA.
Career: Qualified in 1984. Joined the firm as a Partner in 1992.
Personal: Attended Leicester University 1978-81.

PREST, Catherine
Hammond Suddards Edge, Leeds (0113) 284 7000
catherine.prest@hammondsuddardsedge.com
Specialisation: Advises on all areas of contentious and non-contentious employment work. Particular experience in discrimination law, strategic employment advice and transfer of undertakings. Experienced Tribunal advocate. Speaks regularly on a wide range of employment law issues. Acted on a number of high profile terminations, mergers and business transfers including BWAT plc, Grattan plc, ASDA, CGU and former National & Provincial Building Society.
Prof. Memberships: Employment Lawyers Association, Secretary West Riding Oxford and Cambridge Club.
Career: Qualified as a Barrister in 1988. Tenant 8, King Street Chambers, Manchester 1988-90. In-House Lawyer with Alliance & Leicester Building Society. Joined *Eversheds* in Leeds in 1993, became a

Partner and Head of Leeds Employment Team in May 1997. Joined *Hammond Suddards* as Partner in April 1999.
Personal: Born 22nd May 1966. Educated Notre Dame High School, Leeds, St Hilda's College Oxford University BA Law 1987, Hardwicke Scholar Lincoln's Inn 1988. Married Charles Prest. Resides in Ilkley.

PRYKE, Oliver
Taylor Vinters, Cambridge (01223) 423444
ocpp@taylorvinters.com
Specialisation: Specialises in all aspects of employment law, both contentious and non-contentious. Acts for private and public sector organisations and senior employees with a particular emphasis on clients in high-tech, bio-tech and pharmaceutical industries. Provides in-house training to clients and other HR professionals.
Prof. Memberships: Employment Lawyers Association.
Career: Qualified as a solicitor in 1996. Joined *Taylor Vinters* in January 1998.
Personal: Born 30 July 1971. Educated at The Judd School, Tonbridge and Oxford University (BA Hons in Law 1989-1992). A keen tennis player and pianist. Lives in Suffolk.

PRYTHERCH, Rosalie
Cleaver Fulton Rankin, Belfast (028) 9027 1322
r.prytherch@cfrlaw.co.uk
Specialisation: Acting almost exclusively for employers, practice includes all aspects of employment law including general advice, drafting, claims handling, advising in area of restraint of trade clauses and advice to companies with regard to dismissal of senior executives. Interactive approach with commercial dept, regarding TUPE implications arising in sales and acquisitions.
Prof. Memberships: Employment Lawyers' Group (NI). Law Society of Northern Ireland.
Career: Qualified 1987. Partner in *Cleaver Fulton Rankin* 1996.

PUGH, Keith
Nabarro Nathanson, Sheffield (0114) 279 4000
k.pugh@nabarro.com
Specialisation: Employment law specialist for 17 years dealing with both contentious and non-contentious issues ranging from drafting employment contracts policies and procedures; Tribunal claims; restrictive covenants and garden leave; trade union recognition and collective issues; industrial action and transfer of undertaking. Instructed by BFL in BFL v. Meade (House of Lords).
Prof. Memberships: Law Society. Employment Lawyers Association. Industrial Law Society.
Career: Admitted 1980. British Coal Legal Department 1980-1990. Joined *Nabarro Nathanson* as a partner in 1990. Head of Employment Department.
Personal: Music, food, wine and gardening.

RANKIN, Claire
Eversheds, Bristol (0117) 929 9555
clairerankin@eversheds.com
Specialisation: Handles all aspects of employment law and is an experienced Employment Tribunal advocate. Has particular expertise in dealing with large scale redundancy, contract change and TUPE issues. Regular speaker at regional and national conferences for organisations including the IPD and Croners. Writes frequently for employment law publications and updates the Unfair Dismissal section of the Croner Case Law Index. Co-author of 'The Working Time Regulations 1998 – A Practical Guide', published by The Stationery Office.
Prof. Memberships: IPD; Institute of Directors.
Career: Birmingham University. Qualified and joined *Eversheds* in 1993, became a Partner in 1999.

REES, Anthony
Morgan Cole, Swansea (01792) 634634
anthony.rees@morgan-cole.com
Partner based in the Swansea Office, Head of Employment and Discrimination Team, Wales.
Specialisation: Advises on the whole range of employment issues. Anthony is an extremely experienced advocate and has appeared before all relevant tribunals including EAT and conducted proceedings involving employment issues before the Courts. Anthony was instructed by the State of Guernsey Board of Industry in connection with the introduction of its employment protection legislation. Clients include BP AMOCO, Elf Oil UK, Dalkia plc, TIMET UK, Human Fertilisation and Embryology Authority (HFEA), Morgan Crucible Group as well as several universities and NHS Trusts.
Prof. Memberships: Employment Lawyers Association. Committee member of Employment Tribunal Users group.
Career: Partner since 1994, a regular lecturer in and designer of workshops, speaking at IPD, ACAS, CBI conferences.
Personal: Three children, rugby, golf, horse racing.

RESTON, Vincent J.
DLA, Liverpool (08700) 111111
vincent.reston@dla.com
Specialisation: An experienced and well respected advocate in Employment tribunals. Major transactions: advising Colleges of Further and Higher Education on re-organisation, advising on employment law aspects of PFI projects. Dealing with boardroom appointments and terminations and handling re-organisations, redundancies, business transfers, discrimination claims and advising on general employment matters.
Career: University: London, King's College: BA Honours Spanish; Articles: *Mace & Jones*, Date of admission 1.11.87. 1987 -1996 *Mace & Jones.* 1996 to date: *Dibb Lupton Alsop.*
Personal: Having qualified and practised as a teacher Vincent chose a career change in 1985 to employment law.

ROBERTSON, Nicholas
Rowe & Maw, London (020) 7248 4282
Specialisation: Nicholas Robertson qualified in 1998. He joined *Rowe & Maw* in 1991 and became a partner in 1995. He has advised on employment matters since he qualified. He has recently been involved in providing advice on the Transfer Regulations, advising on European law measures, agreeing termination packages for employers and senior executives and dealing witha wide range of issues arising on termination of employment. He has also represented employers before the Employment Tribunal and the Employment Appeal Tribunal. He has provided advice on collective redundancy exercises and on fair procedures, consultation issues and the best way to avoid claims for unfair dismissal. He is also advising on the potential impact on employers of the recent changes in employment law, in particular the challenges facing employers as a result of the compulsory union recognition rights in the Employment Relations Act. He is a member of the Editorial Committee of Croner's Discrimination Law Briefing, and the Employment Lawyer Association Sub-Committee on the Transfer Regulations.

ROBERTSON, Stuart D.
Gordons Cranswick Solicitors, Bradford (01274) 202202
stuart.robertson@gordonscranswick.co.uk
Specialisation: All aspects of employment law. Extensive experience of Employment Tribunal Advocacy. Particular knowledge of sex and race discrimination, restrictive covenants and major redundancy/ reorganisation exercises. Regular presenter of seminars to clients and to outside bodies including Chamber of Commerce and ACAS.
Prof. Memberships: Employment Lawyers Association.
Career: Bradford Grammar School. Trinity Hall, Cambridge. Articled: *Durrant Piesse*. Qualified: October 1982. *Hepworth & Chadwick*, Leeds 1982-86. *Dibb Lupton* 1986-92. Joined *Gordons Wright & Wright* as Partner in 1992. Part-time Employment Tribunal Chairman 1994. Deputy Registrar, Bradford Diocese (Church of England) 1997.
Personal: Born 1 May 1957. Married with 2 children. Church activities, hill walking, rugby league.

ROSKILL, Julian
Rowe & Maw, London (020) 7248 4282
jroskill@roweandmaw.co.uk
Specialisation: Has been specialising in employment law since he qualified in 1974. He deals with the full range of employment and industrial relations law and practice for businesses and senior individuals. His special interests are European employment law, discrimination, collective issues, garden leave and restrictive covenants, moves of key employees and team moves, outsourceing and business transfers. Recent reported cases include 'Credit Suisse v Armstrong' (1996); 'AEEU v Thorn' (1997). Regular speaker and writer on a variety of employment topics.
Prof. Memberships: Law Society, City of London Solicitors Company, Employment Lawyers Association, Industrial Law Society.
Career: Qualified in 1974. Joined *Rowe & Maw* in 1986, became a partner in 1988. Member of Editorial Advisory Board of Croners Industrial Relations Briefings. Chairman of Employment Sub-Committee of City of London Solicitors Company.
Personal: Born 22nd July 1950. Attended Horris Hill 1958-63, then Winchester College 1963-69. Leisure interests include tennis, photography and music, theatre and opera (listening!). Lives in London.

ROSS, Malcolm D.
Paris Smith & Randall, Southampton (023) 8048 2482
Specialisation: All aspects of employment law both contentious and non-contentious. Appears regularly as an advocate in Employment Tribunals and the EAT. Acts for many business clients and has a particular interest in TUPE and severance packages.
Prof. Memberships: Employment Lawyers Association. Law Society.
Career: Qualified in 1980. Assistant solicitor with *Paris Smith & Randall*. Partner since 1984. Head of Employment Department. Part-time Chairman of Employment Tribunals in the Bristol Region since 1996.

Personal: Educated at Reading School and Southampton University. Lives in the New Forest and is a keen walker and gardener.

SALUJA, Sean A.
Paull & Williamsons, Aberdeen (01224) 621621
sasaluja@paull-williamsons.co.uk
Specialisation: Almost exclusive area of practice is employment. Advises mainly employers on all aspects of employment and collective relations matters both contentious and non-contentious. Appears regularly in tribunals in both Scotland and England. Has dealt with a number cases involving transfer of undertakings and contracting issues in the offshore oil industry. Lectured on employment law from 1991 to 1995 at Aberdeen University. Regularly presents seminars and training programmes for clients.
Prof. Memberships: Law Society of Scotland, Employment Law Group. Accredited by the Law Society of Scotland as a specialist in Employment Law.
Career: Graduated in 1998, LL.B Hons (First Class); Diploma in Legal Practice, 1989; qualified 1991.
Personal: Born 1967. Interests include golf, walking and travel.

SAPETA, Jean
Bevan Ashford, Bristol (0117) 923 0111
Specialisation: Advises on all aspects of the employment relationship and industrial relations across private and public sectors. Experience includes advising on major restructuring and reorganisation, extensive advice on transfers and changing terms and conditions of employment, wide experience of advocacy and has particularly wide experience in discrimination. Has dealt with a number of high level difficult public sector terminations.
Prof. Memberships: Employment Lawyers Association, Industrial Law Society.
Career: Qualified 1989. Articled at Bevan Ashford, became a partner in 1995.
Personal: Born 15 May 1949. Educated at Sheffield University and University of West of England.

SAYER, Nicholas T.
Hewitson Becke + Shaw, Cambridge (01223) 461155

SEATON, Chris
Burges Salmon, Bristol (0117) 939 2000
chris.seaton@burges-salmon.com
Specialisation: Head of Employment Group dealing with full range of contentious and non-contentious employment work. Experianced Tribunal advocate and frequent user of Bristol Mercantile Court for wrongful dismissal and other contractual claims as well as employment related injunctions. Adviser to a number of multi-national companies based in USA and Europe. Recently advised a Canadian based multi-national company on the setting up of a European Works Council. Acting for a bank in relation to race/disability claims. Acting for a European Government in relation to an alleged breach of Article 12 of the Treaty of Rome. Advised a PLC in relation to the restucturing and contracting out of 3 divisions and associated TUPE implications. Handled a multi-million pound secerance of Senior Executive from a Merchant Bank.
Prof. Memberships: Empolyment Lawyers Association, European Employment Lawyers Association, Bristol Employment Tribunal Users Committee, Regional Committee of IPD.
Career: Royal Navy Officer 1979-1990. Trainee at *Burges Salmon* 1991-1993. Specialised in employment law beggining of 1993, Associate in 1997 and appointed Head of Employment Group in July 1999. One of three partners on the firm's International Steering Committee.
Publications: Contributor to the 'Employment Law Journal'. Author of a chapter on European Works Councils for 'International Employment Law' published by the Centre for International Legal Studies.
Personal: Married with 2 daughters. Intrests include sailing, skiing, music and squash.

SEWARD, Karen
Allen & Overy, London (020) 7330 3000
karen.seward@allenovery.com
Head of Employment. Partner.
Specialisation: Employment law for City clients, in particular boardroom disputes, executive terminations, team moves, harassment and stress at work. Lectures and publishes widely.
Prof. Memberships: Employment Lawyers Association: Legislative and Policy sub committee.
Career: LLB (Hons) Bristol 1987. LSF College of Law 1988. 1988-94 *Simmons & Simmons*. 1994-97 *Stephenson Harwood* (Partner 1996). 1997 to 2000 *Pinsent Curtis*.

SHORT, Michael
Rowley Ashworth, London (020) 8543 2277
mshort@rowley-ashworth.co.uk
Specialisation: Handles trade union and employment law for employees and unions. Work includes trade union constitution, rules, amalgamations etc., collective employment law (including industrial action) and individual employment law (including discrimination). Also deals with defamation and pensions litigation.
Prof. Memberships: Law Society, Industrial Law Society.
Career: With *Lovell White & King* 1977-80. Qualified in 1979. With *Lawford & Co* 1980-87 (Partner from 1983). Joined *Rowley Ashworth* as a Partner in 1988.
Personal: Born 2nd May 1951. Educated at St. Philips Grammar School, Birmingham 1962-69 and Sussex University 1970-73 (BA in Philosophy).

SHORT, Michael C.
Short Richardson & Forth, Newcastle upon Tyne (0191) 232 0283
mcs@short-richardson-forth.co.uk
Founder Partner in Employment Law Department.
Specialisation: Has twenty-five years' experience in employment law, acting on both sides of industry and dealing with the full range of employment law matters including appearing before Employment Tribunals regularly throughout the country and lecturing regularly on employment law matters to Companies. Extensive experience in senior executive terminations.
Prof. Memberships: Member of the Law Society's Employment Law Committee, Employment Lawyers Association, Industrial Law Society and is the Secretary of the Newcastle Employment Tribunal Users Group.
Career: Senior Partner and founding Partner of *Short Richardson & Forth* since 1978.
Personal: Leisure interests include theatre. Lives in Newcastle-upon-Tyne.

SHRIVES, R. Mark
Hammond Suddards Edge, Leeds (0113) 284 7000
mark.shrives@hammondsuddardsedge.com
Specialisation: Partner – employment unit. Specialising in all aspects of contentious and non-contentious employment and discrimination law acting predominately for multi-national and large corporate clients and senior executives. Conducts all own advocacy before employment and employment appeal tribunals. Also handles work permit and other employment-related immigration issues. Speaks regularly on a wide-range of employment issues.
Prof. Memberships: Law Society; Fellow of the Society for Advanced Legal Studies; European Employment Lawyers Association; Employment Lawyers Association.
Career: Articled at *Cameron McKenna*. Qualified 1990. *Eversheds* (Manchester) 1990-1992. *Hammond Suddards* 1992 onwards. Partner 1995.
Personal: Born 13 April 1964. Educated Downing College, Cambridge, BA (Hons) 1986. LLM (1st Class honours) 1987. Law Society Finals (1st Class honours) 1988. Resides in Calderdale. Interests include gardening, DIY, music & cinema.

SIMON, Shona M.W.
Mackay Simon, Edinburgh (0131) 240 1400

SMITH, Tim
Crutes, Newcastle-upon-Tyne (0191) 281 5811
Head of Empolyment Law
Specialisation: Acting Predominatly for NHS, Local Authority and company clients. Particular interest in contentious employment law and TUPE.
Prof. Memberships: Member of The Employment Lawyers Association. Member of The Employment Tribunals User Group.
Personal: Born 4th April 1959. Educated at Whitby Grammar School. Masters degree in Employment Law.

SPEIRS, William Stewart Colin
Brechin Tindal Oatts, Glasgow (0141) 221 8012
Specialisation: Accredited as Employment Specialist by Law Society of Scotland since 1990 when certification was first awarded. Advises mainly employers – from a number of spheres including retail, insurance, leisure, financial and charity – on all areas of industrial relations and employment law. Specialist areas: transfer of undertakings, redundancy schemes, race and sex discrimination and director's service contracts. Seminar speaker on topical employment issues.
Prof. Memberships: Law Society of Scotland, The Society of Solicitors to the Supreme Court, The Royal Faculty of Procurators in Glasgow.
Career: Graduated in 1972, LLB (Hons) Public Law, Glasgow University, Notary Public. Practised Employment Law since 1978. Partner 1984.
Personal: Golf and Travel.

TAYLOR, Catherine
Olswang, London (0207) 7208 8711
cjt@olswang.com
Specialisation: Employment law, specialising in both contentious and non-contentious. Recent cases/matters include advising on all the employment aspects of the floatation of Times plc and defending a claim for PHI benefit worth £1 million. The latter case is now being appealed to the Court of Appeal.
Prof. Memberships: ELA; ILS; IPD

Career: Trained at *Norton Rose* qualifying in 1993. Moved to *Olswang* in 1995 and became a partner in1998.
Publications: 'Employment Law Checklists' – Joint Author with Julia Palaca.

THOMPSON, Michael
Eversheds, Manchester (0161) 832 6666
michaelthompson@eversheds.co.uk
Specialisation: Deals with all aspects of employment law work both contentious and non-contentious acting mainly for employers. Extensive experience both in the public and private sectors. Experienced advocate before the Employment Tribunal and the Employment Appeal Tribunal. Particular expertise in executive terminations, TUPE and injunctive relief. Regularly provides training to clients both in-house and on external courses. Reported cases include Atlas Wright v Wright.
Prof. Memberships: Employment Lawyers Association, The Law Society and the Industrial Society.
Career: Qualified with the firm in 1992, became Senior Solicitor in 1997 and has been promoted to partner this year.
Personal: Born 8.10.65. Educated at Leeds University. Interests, all sports, particularly football and golf. Lives in Rochdale.

THOMPSON, Tony
Macfarlanes, London (020) 7831 9222
Specialisation: Contentious and non-contentious employment law. Drafting and advising on employment contracts, service agreements, secondments and consultancies. Employment policies and procedures. Transfers of undertakings. Drafting and enforcement of restrictive covenants. Negotiation of severance packages.
Prof. Memberships: Law Society. Employment Lawyers Association. City of London Solicitors Company Employment Law Sub-Committee. Currently secretary of the Committee.
Career: Oundle School. MA Cantab (St Catharine's College). Articled at *Markbys* (now part of *Cameron McKenna*). Admitted as a Solicitor June 1976. Joined*Macfarlanes* 1980, Partner 1986, Head of Litigation 1989. Head of Employment Group.

THOMSON, Alan S.
McClure Naismith, Glasgow (0141) 204 2700
athomson@mcclurenaismith.com
Specialisation: Lead partner in Employment Unit. Almost exclusively engaged in employment law practice. Principally advising employers but has a growing practice in pursuing claims for senior executives and negotiating severance arrangements. Regularly appears before Employment Tribunals. Heads a growing team of lawyers in the firm's Glasgow and Edinburgh offices focusing on employment law matters.
Prof. Memberships: Law Society of Scotland, Employment Law Group (Scotland) and Employment Lawyers Association.
Career: Trained at McGrigor Donald, qualifying in 1976. Joined McClure Naismith in 1976 and became a partner in 1979.
Personal: Born in 1952 and lives in Glasgow. Educated at The High School of Glasgow (1957-70) and Edinburgh University (1970-74), LLB (Hons). Enjoys ski-ing, and escaping from employment law to remote croft on west coast of Scotland.

TURTLE, W. Brian W.
Carson & McDowell, Belfast (028) 9024 4951
See under Litigation (Commercial), p.569

TWEEDIE, Colin
Addleshaw Booth & Co, Leeds (0113) 209 2032
cqt@addleshaw-booth.co.uk
Partner in Employment Law Department.
Specialisation: Has specialised exclusively in employment law and industrial relations since qualification. Deals with all aspects, mainly for employers, including employment contracts, procedures and policies, restrictive covenants, discrimination, the employment aspects of the sale and reorganisation of companies and business and contentious matters including appearing before employment tribunals throughout the country. Conducts seminars for clients, lectures and has appeared on local radio. Author of occasional articles.
Prof. Memberships: Employment Lawyers Association.
Career: Qualified in 1978. Joined firm as Partner in 1998.
Personal: Educated at Fitzwilliam College, Cambridge 1972-75. Leisure interests include sports, railways and Scottish history.

TYNDALL, Timothy D.V.
Hewitson Becke + Shaw, Cambridge (01223) 461155

UNDERWOOD, Kerry
Underwoods, Hemel Hempstead
underwoods@compuserve.com
Specialisation: Senior Partner of *Underwoods*. Practice covers full range of Employment Law acting for employers and employees. Well known for advocacy in employment tribunals and the EAT where he is a member of the Employment Law Advisors Appeal Scheme. Clients include Plc's and a number of Directors of Plc's . Lectures regularly for University of Cambridge, Law Society and others. Appears regularly on radio, television and in the national press in relation to legal topics. Conducts in-house training for Government Departments, Local Authorities and major companies. Was successful appellant's advocate, pro bono, in leading pregnancy rights case of Day v T Pickles Farms Ltd (1999) IRLR 217. Advocate in other reported cases.
Prof. Memberships: Fellow Chartered Institute of Arbitrators. Association of Trial Lawyers of America. Law Society. Employment Tribunal Chairman. Employment Law Advisors Appeal Scheme. Transport and General Workers Union. Equal Opportunities Commission Panel.
Career: Qualified in 1981. Set up *Underwoods* in 1991. Pioneered Contingency Fees, Fixed Fees and menu-pricing in Employment Tribunals. Author of Best Seller "No Win No Fee No Worries". Editor of Employment Litigation. Editorial Board Member of Litigation Funding. Editor, Costs Production Section of Butterworths Personal Injury Law Service. Part-time Employment Tribunal Chairman since 1993. London Borough Councillor 1978-1982. Parliamentary Candidate 1979. Member Law Society's Lawyers for Business User Group. Member Law Society's Working Party on Conditional Fee Agreements.
Personal: Born in 1956. Leisure interests include cricket, football and literature, especially the poetry of T S Eliot. Has travelled extensively around the world.

WALKER, David James
Dundas & Wilson CS, Glasgow (0141) 222 2200

WARNOCK, Owen
Eversheds, Norwich (01603) 272727
Specialisation: Has specialised in employment law for 18 years and heads the Eversheds East of England employment department, consisiting of 14 lawyers and one human resources consultant. He has considerable Employment Tribunal advocacy experience and has particluar strength in discrimination law and Health Service employment law. He is Consultant Legal Editor to the CCH Disability Manual and co-author of 'Employment Law in the NHS' (Cavendish 1995). A regular speaker on employment law issues at events ranging from local IPD groups to CBI and similar national conferences. Employment law is main area of practice, but also advises on food and drink law.
Prof. Memberships: Employment Lawyers Association, Industrial Law Society, The Food Law Group.
Career: Qualified 1982 with *Daynes Hill & Perks* (partner 1985).
Personal: Born 5 April 1957. Graduated in Law from Cambridge University in 1979. Lives in Norwich.

WARREN, Martin
Eversheds, Cardiff (02920) 471147
Partner and head of the industrial relations unit at *Eversheds* Cardiff.
Specialisation: An experienced employment lawyer with particular expertise in strategic and re-organisational issues, trade union rights, redundancies and business transfers, industrial action, balloting, and in the area of collective labour law generally. Acted successfully for employer clients in reported cases including O'Dea v ISC Chemicals (Court of Appeal 1995) and Alcan Extrusions v Yates (EAT 1996). Advises multi-national companies, in particular in the US, on the implications of developments in UK labour and employment law.
Prof. Memberships: Member of the Employment Lawyers Association; member of Cardiff Employment Tribunal User Group; Fellow of the Royal Society of Arts; member of the Reform Club.
Career: Qualified in 1985. Joined *Phillips & Buck* in 1986 (now *Eversheds*). Became a partner in 1989.
Personal: Director of Principle Training Limited. Resides in Magor, Gwent.

WATSON, Judith
Cobbetts, Manchester (0161) 833 3333
judith.watson@cobbetts.co.uk
Specialisation: Partner and head of Cobbetts' 10-strong Employment Law Team. Handles the whole spectrum of employment and industrial relations issues. Specialist interest in discrimination and executive recruitment contracts and severance packages. Also acts as a regular media spokesperson for the firm and manages training for clients on all issues concerning human resources and employment.
Prof. Memberships: Secretary of Eurolegal, a network of 30 European law firms. Member of and NW Representative of the Employment Lawyers Association.
Career: Educated at Sheffield High School for Girls and Sheffield University (1981-4). Articled with *Leak Almond & Parkinson* which subsequently became *Cobbett Leak Almond* and then *Cobbetts*. Qualified in 1987. Became a Partner in January 1997.

WATSON, Simon
Simmons & Simmons, London (020) 7628 2020
Specialisation: Employment Law. Simon has a strong City-based Employment Law practice acting for insurance and major corporations and regularly advises on the employment aspects of acquisitions, disposals and mergers including the Transfer of Undertakings Regulations and recently advised on the employment aspects of a £383 million public offering. In addition, Simon has extensive experience of handling litigation both in the industrial tribunal and the High Court, including applying for interlocutory relief, injunctions and Anton Piller orders and has acted in the Court of Appeal case Abrahams vs PRS, which is now the leading authority on termination payments/payments in lieu of notice.
Prof. Memberships: Law Society.
Career: St. Catherines's College, Oxford, College of Law, *Simmons & Simmons.*
Personal: Bridge, Opera.

WHINCUP, David
Hammond Suddards Edge, London (020) 7655 1000
david.whincup@hammondsuddards.co.uk
Partner & Head of Employment Unit – London.
Specialisation: Dealing with a wide variety of employment-related issues, including recruitment issues, policy documents and contracts of employment at all levels, disciplinary and grievance procedures, the defence of employee discrimination claims and other litigation, particularly for Square Mile clients; non-contentious experience includes advising on TUPE, warranties and indemnities and union-related matters. Speaks and writes regularly on employment matters. Chapter author of FT Law and Tax 'Guide to Pensions'; HS/Jordans 'Pensions Disputes'; CILS 'Guide to International Employment Law'; and Jordans/IPD 'Employment Law Services'. Member of editorial board and chapter author of Croners 'Managing Termination of Employment'. Member of editorial board of Croners ''Diversity and Discrimination in Practice', monthly legal columnist for 'Education Law' briefing. Reported cases include 'Clark v. BET', 'Wallace v. Cantor Fitzgerald' and 'Wakeman v. Quick Corporation'.
Prof. Memberships: Law Society.
Career: *Clifford Chance* 1984-1994, *Hammond Suddards* 1994-1995; Partner *Hammond Suddards* 1995 to date.
Personal: Born 1962. Oriel College, Oxford 1980-1983. Chester Law School 1983-1984. Lives in Blackheath, SE London.

WILLIAMS, Audrey M.
Eversheds, Cardiff (02920) 471147
audreywilliams@eversheds.com
Specialisation: A Partner in the Employment Law Department at *Eversheds* Cardiff. Specialises in all aspects of employment law. Particular experience of sex discrimination, race discrimination and disability discrimination. Advises on equal opportunities, maternity, parental leave, harassment and bullying policies; providing advice and training for establishing such policies; grievance procedures and counselling. Author of a number of publications.
Prof. Memberships: Member of the Chartered Institute of Personnel and Development.
Career: Graduate of Southampton University; qualified in 1989, joined *Eversheds Phillips and Buck* in 1989 (now *Eversheds* Cardiff); became a partner in 1993.
Personal: Married and resides in Cardiff.

WILLIAMSON, Andrew P F
Lovells, London (020) 7296 2000
andrew.williamson@lovells.com
Specialisation: Employment and labour law.
Prof. Memberships: Prof. Membership: Past chairman and current member of City of London Law Society Employment Law Sub-Committee.
Career: Career: Partner *Bowman Gilfillan & Blacklock* Johannesburg 1971-1978 practising in insurance and general commercial litigation and political criminal cases; articled *Lovells* 1978; qualified England 1980, Partner 1982.

WILLIAMSON, Raymond
MacRoberts, Glasgow (0141) 332 9988
Partner in Employment Group.
Specialisation: Specialist in employment law since the early 1970's. Advises on the drafting of contracts of employment, on management of staff, on redundancies and disciplinary matters. Also experienced in representing clients' interests before empolyment and other tribunals. Holder of Specialist Authorisation from the Law Society of Scotland in Employment Law. Convener of the Law Society's Employment Law Committee and Chairman of the Employment Law Specialisation Committee. Lectures extensively on employment matters for various course giving bodies and has been an external examiner on employment law at Glasgow University. Author of the chapter on employment law in Greene & Fletcher's 'The Law and Practice of Receivership in Scotland'.
Prof. Memberships: Law Society of Scotland, Royal Faculty of Procurators in Glasgow.
Career: Joined *MacRoberts* Solicitors in 1966 and qualified in 1968. Became a Partner in 1972.
Personal: Born 24th December 1942. Educated at the High School of Glasgow 1949-60 and the University of Glasgow 1960-66. Governor of the Royal Scottish Academy of Music and Drama, Governor of The High School of Glasgow, Chairman of the John Currie Singers Ltd. Chairman Scottish Childrens Music Foundation in Scotland, Chairman National Youth Choir of Scotland, Deputy Chairman Scottish International Piano Competition. Leisure interests include music and gardening. Lives in Glasgow.

WOFFENDEN, Sara
Shoosmiths, Nottingham (0115) 906 5000
Head of Employment Team – Nottingham.
Specialisation: All aspects of employment law but mainly business transfers, re-organisations, trade union recognition and severance agreements.
Prof. Memberships: Part time Chairman of Employment Tribunals (England and Wales); Midlands representative on Management Committee of Employment Lawyers Association 1995-2000; Member of Training Committee of Employment Lawyers Association.
Career: Educated Leeds University. Admitted 1985. 1985-89 *Bettinsons*, Birmingham; 1989-94 *Pinsent & Co* (now *Pinsent Curtis*); 1994-98 *Wragge & Co*; 1998 *Shoosmiths* – Partner.
Personal: Born 1959. Leisure interests currently limited to chauffeuring children (seven and three).

WYNN-EVANS, Charles
Dechert, London (020) 7583 5353
charles.wynnevans@dechertEU.com
Partner and Head of the Employment Unit.
Specialisation: Deals with all aspects of contentious and non contentious employment law, including discrimination, transfers of undertakings, share option and incentive schemes, senior executive appointments and departures and restrictive covenant matters. Regularly writes on employment law for a variety of journals.
Prof. Memberships: Industrial Law Society, Employment Lawyers' Association, Law Society.
Career: Joined *Titmuss Sainer & Webb* (now *Dechert*) in 1990. Qualified 1992. Appointed partner 1997.
Personal: Born 1967. Educated at King Henry VIII School Coventry; Bristol University (LL.B 1988) and Merton College Oxford (BCL 1990). Interests include cricket, rugby and current affairs. Married with one daughter. Lives in Kennington, London.

YATES, Tracy
Eversheds, Norwich (01603) 272727
Specialisation: Employment, handling unfair and wrongful dismissal claims, including advocacy in the employment tribunals and courts. Advising commercial clients and senior employees in respect of compromise agreement/severage packages; and on all aspects of employment law (TUPE, redundancy, dismissals etc). Drafting, and advising on Service Agreements and Statements of Main Terms and Conditions of Employment. Immigration: – Advising on applications for entry clearance (and appeals against refusal), work permits and naturalisation.
Prof. Memberships: Law Society and Employment Lawyers Association.
Career: Qualified October 1986. 1984-86 – Trainee Solicitor, *Daynes, Chittock & Back*; 1992 to date Partner, *Eversheds.*
Personal: Two daughters – Helena and Sophia.

YOUNG, James
McGrigor Donald, Edinburgh (0131) 226 7777
Head of Employment Unit.
Specialisation: Has been involved in Employment Law since the initiating UK legislation in the 1970's. Head of *McGrigor Donald*'s Employment Law Unit and provides advice on a full range of Employment Law issues. Particular concerns of clients in the past year have included working time regulations; trade union issues; the increase in discrimination claims; post-termination restrictions and the impact of new legislation. Has represented and continues to represent a large number of clients at Employment Tribunals. Member of the Law Society Committee of Employment Law; member of Institute of Personnel and Management; speaker at conferences on various aspects of employment law; Scottish contributor to Employment Precedents and Company Policy documents.
Prof. Memberships: Law Society of Scotland; Institute of Personnel and Management.
Career: Qualified in 1975 at *McGrigor Donald & Co.* After two years as Legal Officer West Lothian District Council and two years as Assistant Solicitor at *Moncrieff Warren Patterson & Co.*, became Partner in 1979 and joined *McGrigor Donald* as Partner in 1985.
Personal: Born 26 February 1950. Educated at Hutchesons' Boys Grammar School and the University of Glasgow. Leisure interests include watching and

participating in sport (now mainly golf), Contemporary Scottish Art and Theatre. Lives in Edinburgh.

YOUNSON, Fraser

McDermott, Will & Emery, London
(020) 7577 6992
FYounson@europe.mwe.com

(Bar 1975) Partner and Head of Employment Group.

Specialisation: Main area of practice is employment law, covering executive termination, employment aspects of mergers and acquisitions, sex, race and disability discrimination, restrictive covenants, unfair dismissal and redundancy, wrongful dismissal, union recognition claims law, industrial disputes, worker representation and European Work Councils, EC labour law, Employment Tribunal advocacy and compensation claims, transnational reorganisation and collective redundancies. Author of 'Employment Law Handbook', 'Employment Law and Business Transfers – A Practical Guide', 'Croner's Industrial Relations Law', and contributor to PLC and the Law Society Gazette on employment law issues. Lectures extensively on labour law; 'Transfers of Undertakings' (Sweet & Maxwell).

Prof. Memberships: Law Society, Industrial Law Society, Former Chairman and now life Vice-president of Employment Lawyers Association.

Career: Qualified for the Bar in 1975, and as a Solicitor in 1987. Previously Employment Law Adviser to British Aerospace Group HQ, and previously Editor of IDS Brief. Joined *Baker & McKenzie* in 1983-99, becoming a Partner in 1990. Joined *McDermott, Will & Emery* 1999.

Personal: Born 11th November 1952. Attended Oxford University. Lives in Houghton, Cambs.

ENERGY & NATURAL RESOURCES

London: 348; The South: 353; Midlands: 353; The North: 354; Scotland: 355; *Profiles*: 356

RESEARCH APPROVED BY BMRB: *For this edition,* Chambers' *researchers conducted 6083 interviews – 4408 with law firms, 598 with barristers and 1077 with clients.*

The validity of the research was scrutinised by BMRB International, who audited both the methodology and the results at our offices in July 2000. They interviewed Chambers' *researchers and cross-checked sample interviews. Details of the audit appear on page 7.*

LONDON

Denton Wilde Sapte Many say *"it's the best energy firm in London."* With energy forming almost 20 percent of the firm's workload, this is a key focus. Respected for its *"breadth and depth,"* this large team is encountered at every turn: on technical and industrial as well as corporate matters. Financing aspects are felt to have benefited from February's merger with Wilde Sapte. In short, it is a *"very, very solid practice, difficult to knock."*

Strength in the power sector centres on regulatory and restructuring matters. Although involved at management level, the *"commercial"* **David Moroney** maintains an excellent reputation as *"a good deal doer."* The team's recent work in the sector includes advising OFGEM on the new electricity trading arrangements, notably drafting the new balancing and settlement code. Also advised London Electricity on its proposed joint venture with Eastern Electricity in connection with the distribution businesses of two public electricity suppliers. Extensive regulatory and restructuring work has also been done for the Governments of Ireland and Lesotho and the Sultanate of Oman, while corporate work includes advising London Electricity on its £160 million acquisition of SWEB and involvement in EDF's acquisition of London Electricity.

A broad upstream oil practice, which is also strong on gas issues, comprises a host of established names. *"Tremendously reliable"* **Myles Cave-Browne-Cave** is renowned as *"tenacious and understanding of clients' needs"* as well as for his relationships with Total-Fina and big players in the UK gas industry. He remains *"one you want on your team."* The *"grade A quality"* **Charles Wood** has a strong reputation for his gas regulatory work: *"he eats, sleeps and drinks it."* Senior figure **James Dallas** *"knows when to take a commercial point"* and is a *"vital element"* of the team. During the year the firm set up a new independent UKCS gas company, Consort Resources, where ex-group head Malcolm Groom has gone to play a management role. His *"huge experience"* is expected to be a loss to the team. However, the *"well-connected"* **Doran Doeh** is considered to have settled in well in the year following his move from Allen & Overy's Moscow office.

The team advised Petronas on its investment in Premier Oil (with Amerada Hess) and acted for Premier Oil on the West Natuna gas production and pipeline project. Downstream, the firm has advised on the introduction of the New Gas Trading Arrangements (effective from 1 October 1999) and continued to advise British Gas on the Network Code. Abroad, there has been a notable role in advising the sub-Caucasus states and Central Asian republics on the legal requirements of the Energy Charter Treaty. A successful year for the firm's work in the water sector has been led by the newly-ranked **Chris McGee-Osborne.** This included acting for the Ministry of Defence on Project Aquatrine, the largest water/sewerage project underway in the UK, and for the Sultanate of Oman on the privatisation and regulation of the water industry, involving three independent power projects. **Clients:** Gazprom; Commission for Electricity Regulation; Northumbrian Water Group plc; Petronas; Premier Oil.

LEADING IN-HOUSE LAWYERS

Electricity

Robert HIGSON, Group Solicitor & Company Secretary, *London Electricity plc*

Paul SIMONS, Assistant General Counsel, *Enron*

The *"very effective"* **Robert Higson** is highly recommended *"for his management qualities"* and because he has the *"capacity for sheer hard work."* **Paul Simons** is *"very focused"* and praised for being *"up-to-date in a changing regime."*

Oil & Gas

David BATE, Legal Manager, *Enterprise Energy Ireland Ltd*

Justin BOYD, Senior Legal Adviser, *Enron*

Ian CHITTY, Solicitor, *BG Group*

Alan DUNLOP, Head of Legal and Public Affairs, *Amerada Hess*

Paul MCGOLDRICK, Senior Legal Adviser, *BP Amoco plc*

Eldon PETHYBRIDGE, Director of Legal & Regulatory Affairs, *Centrica*

Despite being fairly junior, **David Bate** is widely regarded for his *"solid work." "Top of the tree"* is **Justin Boyd** who is *"more on the trading side"* and is a *"very good lawyer."* He is *"very focused on the market aspects."* At the upstream end, the *"very bright"* **Ian Chitty** is *"extremely able"* and *"operates to a high standard,"* displaying *"sound judgement, commercially and technically."* **Alan Dunlop** is seen as a *"leading light"* and is *"very commercially minded."* The *"very co-operative"* **Paul McGoldrick** is *"very experienced and very good."* He was noted for being *"co-operative"* and for his *"interesting ideas."* **Eldon Pethybridge** is *"very outstanding and impressive"* and well recommended for his *"very thorough"* work. He *"understands the industry inside out."*

Water

David BADCOCK, Company Secretary & Legal Director, *Thames Water*

Keith DONALD, General Counsel, *International Water*

David HOSKER, Legal Service Manager, *North West Water*

Michael KNIGHT, Company Solicitor, *Severn Trent Water*

David Badcock is a *"very wise owl"* who is praised for being a *"businessman as well as a lawyer."* **Keith Donald** operates with a global outlook. He comes well recommended and is *"very commercial"* in his approach. The *"very professional"* **David Hosker** is *"very bright"* and *"leading in the field."* Praised as an *"excellent lawyer,"* **Michael Knight** is *"very commercially minded"* and has a *"very detailed knowledge of the industry."*

In-House lawyers profiles: page 1177

Herbert Smith *"Undoubtedly right up at the top,"* this is one of the best all-round energy firms. Of special note are its power expertise, a healthy oil and gas practice, a leading profile in water and a litigation track record which stands alone. The energy team is felt to combine *"know-how with bloody hard work."*

The client base includes many electricity companies. *"At the heart of the new trading arrangements,"* the team is currently acting for the 14 PESs on the introduction of supply competition in the UK, and for 10 RECs concerning the new wholesale trading arrangements to replace the Electricity Pool. Here the *"reasonable"* **Adrian Clough** is *"heavily involved,"* although some in the market have commented that the London office has suffered from the departure of *"serious player"* Mark Newbery to Singapore.

Other recent work includes advice to Northern Ireland Electricity/Viridian on the restructuring of the electricity industry in the Republic of Ireland. The team is also acting for the MRA Executive Committee on the administration of the retail electricity market in the UK, as well as the Karnataka Electricity Board (India) on its restructuring. Clearly, the depart-

ENERGY & NATURAL RESOURCES • London	Ptnrs	Assts
❶ Denton Wilde Sapte	19	64
Herbert Smith	18	38
❷ CMS Cameron McKenna	28	47
❸ Allen & Overy	20	40
Clifford Chance	17	68
Linklaters	15	30
Norton Rose	11	47
❹ Freshfields Bruckhaus Deringer	24	37
Slaughter and May	⚐	⚐
❺ Ashurst Morris Crisp	9	22
Coudert Brothers	3	4
Lawrence Graham	3	3
Lovells	7	16
Nabarro Nathanson	6	8
Simmons & Simmons	15	25
Vinson & Elkins LLP	7	9
❻ Baker & McKenzie	4	5
Beachcroft Wansbroughs	7	4
Clyde & Co	8	6
Eversheds	5	5
Field Fisher Waterhouse	3	3
Holman Fenwick & Willan	9	12
Ince & Co	14	15
LeBoeuf, Lamb, Greene & MacRae	5	12
Masons	5	10
Richards Butler	1	2
Watson, Farley & Williams	8	10

Within each band, firms are listed alphabetically. *See **Profiles** on page 356*
⚐ *Figures unavailable at time of going to press.*

ment has an outstanding litigation profile, and has capitalised on the recent upturn in oil and gas litigation to act in some high-profile cases. Among them was one for BP Amoco concerning litigation arising from a drilling contract for the world's largest jack-up rig.

On the oil and gas transactional side, experienced *"first class operator"* **Richard Bond** is widely respected. Also known for his gas expertise, as well as retaining a name in the power industry, is **Henry Davey**, who is helping to *"drive the practice forward."* The recent acquisition of **Paul Griffin** from Cadwalader Wickersham & Taft emphasises the strength in depth of the team. Traditionally strong in North Sea oil financing, the team recently advised Chase Manhattan on a number of deals, including a US$220 million refinancing facility for Intrepid Energy North Sea, and a limited recourse financing for an oil and gas field in Burma. M&A work remains a focus: Davey advised Petroplus on its Cressier oil refinery acquisition and Bond represented Amerada Hess in its strategic alliance with Petronas for a £136m equity stake in Premier Oil.

A leading water practice spans pure regulatory work, corporate and commercial matters and international water projects. **Trevor Turtle** *"features everywhere,"* with his regulatory background and contacts in the UK water industry. He deals with competition aspects in the course of advising on numerous domestic restructurings, including that of British Water. Other work included acting for Anglian Water and Severn Trent on a number of financing transactions. On the corporate side the team advised Bechtel Enterprises on the sale of its 50 percent stake in the International Water Group. Overseas, the firm has advised on water projects in the Philippines and South Africa for International Water. **Clients:** St Clements Services; Enterprise Oil plc; Yorkshire Water; Petroplus.

CMS Cameron McKenna *"One has to hand it to them; they have a great profile."* The energy team won widespread accolades and is now ranked alone just behind the two market leaders. Known for technical expertise, the department is considered to have *"made a virtue out of energy – especially power."* Rated as the *"first port of call"* for power privatisations, the group is headed by **Fiona Woolf**, who has *"a name that goes before her"* in regulatory matters. She is felt to have *"done wonders"* in exporting the UK grid model to the rest of the world, and is commended for *"going in and getting the work."* Both she and the *"sensible"* **Robert Lane** are strong on industry market structures, and act for a number of transmission companies. The power work for the past year has been seasoned with international highlights. In Canada, the team represented the municipal and distribution utilities in preparation for the new Ontario electricity markets, while it advised the Mexican regulator on the development of that country's new electricity trading system. The group has also acted for developers in power projects in Africa. Now held to possess *"a sound mainstream North Sea practice,"* the firm has been aided by an office in Aberdeen. In London, the *"extremely competent"* **Sally Tyne** is rated for her North Sea upstream work by peers and clients alike. The *"pragmatic"* **Rafique Khan** also has a good name for his work in the developing oil and gas markets. The team worked on the Catchment Area Project to finalise the Neptune Field Agreements. Other work has included advice in connection with the acquisition of Soco UK Onshore for Star Energy. In contentious matters, the firm has acted in North Sea litigation concerning the Banff Field.

Closely involved with the International Private Water Association, **Richard Temple** is considered *"an absolute guru in water projects."* He devotes his time to international water projects, public and private, such as Bulgaria's groundbreaking Sofia Water & Sewerage Project (for the Municipality and the EBRD.) **Clients:** Mobil North Sea Ltd; Transgas SA; World Bank; Star Energy.

Allen & Overy *"Commercial and rational, this is a group that knows its business."* Particularly feared when energy transactions involve the use of *"their terrifically skilled finance lawyers,"* the firm recently established an 85-lawyer European Energy Group. This is led by the high profile **Ian Elder** *("a good intellect with a real grasp of his subject")* who is best known for his project finance ability. The group as a whole covers all aspects of the energy sector: corporate, regulatory, trading and finance.

In power deals, the group advised South Western Electricity plc on the sale of its electricity supply business to London Electricity plc, TXU-Europe Group plc on its joint venture with EdF London Investments Ltd; and acted on several international power projects for National Grid Company plc.

"A name from way back," the head of the oil and gas team is *"internationally experienced lawyer"* **Roger Davies**. Upstream work has seen the group acting for Hungarian giant MOL Rt on its proposed merger with the Croatian INA, as well as advising Eastern Power & Energy Trading on the acquisition of interests in the North Sea Oil Fields. Davies was also the lead partner advising Mobil on the European aspects of its merger with Exxon. Abroad, the team has handled gas and petrochemicals privatisations in Oman and Poland.

The water practice's profile has improved greatly, and includes the *"expert"* **John Scriven**, who makes his debut in the tables this year. He is particularly known for his work for the North of Scotland Water Authority, advising on the £120 million Tay Waste Water Project and the Aberdeen Waste Water Project. BOT water projects are a speciality, and have ranged from China and South Africa to Croatia and India. **Clients:** TXU-Europe Group; Western Power Distribution.

Clifford Chance *"Ubiquitous in the domestic power market,"* the team is best known for its energy projects both domestically and abroad (particularly India.) Here **Peter Blake** has a huge IPP reputation and is recognised for his advice to the British Energy Group. **Paul Simpson** also retains his position among the leading lights in power. Generally seen more on the financing side, the perception is that *"they're making an effort to ensure they understand the energy business."* Clients have particularly commented on

LEADING INDIVIDUALS: Oil and Gas	
❶ **BOND Richard** Herbert Smith	
CAVE-BROWNE-CAVE Myles Denton Wilde Sapte	
DALLAS James Denton Wilde Sapte	**GRIFFIN Paul** Herbert Smith
SALT Stuart Linklaters	**TAYLOR Michael** Norton Rose
WOOD Charles Denton Wilde Sapte	
❷ **BEHARRELL Steven** Coudert Brothers	**DAVIES Roger** Allen & Overy
PICTON-TURBERVILL Geoffrey Ashurst Morris Crisp	
ROBERTS Martin Slaughter and May	**STANGER Michael** Lovells
❸ **CARVER Jeremy** Clifford Chance	**DAVEY Henry** Herbert Smith
HIGGINSON Tony Baker Botts	**JONES Gareth** Nabarro Nathanson
KHAN Rafique CMS Cameron McKenna	**REES Jonathan** Freshfields Bruckhaus
SAUNDERS Mark Dewey Ballantine	**TYNE Sally** CMS Cameron McKenna
VERRILL John Lawrence Graham	
❹ **BRETTON Linda** Lawrence Graham	**BROWN Douglas** Eversheds
COFFELL Howard Field Fisher Waterhouse	**DOEH Doran** Denton Wilde Sapte
PEGG Garry LeBoeuf, Lamb, Greene & MacRae	

LEADING INDIVIDUALS: Electricity	
✪ **WOOLF Fiona** CMS Cameron McKenna	
❶ **LANE Robert** CMS Cameron McKenna	**SALT Stuart** Linklaters
❷ **BLAKE Peter** Clifford Chance	**CLOUGH Adrian** Herbert Smith
ELDER Ian Allen & Overy	**MORONEY David** Denton Wilde Sapte
PICTON-TURBERVILL Geoffrey Ashurst Morris Crisp	
STACEY Paul Slaughter and May	
❸ **DAVEY Henry** Herbert Smith	**ROWEY Kent** Freshfields Bruckhaus
SIMPSON Paul Clifford Chance	**TUDWAY Robert** Nabarro Nathanson
WALLACE Patrick Freshfields Bruckhaus Deringer	

LEADING INDIVIDUALS: Mining	
❶ **HURST Philip** Ashurst Morris Crisp	
❷ **CUTHBERT Michael** Clifford Chance	**TAYLOR Michael** Norton Rose
UP AND COMING	
KELLY Christopher Linklaters	

LEADING INDIVIDUALS: Water	
❶ **TURTLE Trevor** Herbert Smith	
❷ **SCRIVEN John** Allen & Overy	**TEMPLE Richard** CMS Cameron McKenna
❸ **LANE Mark** Masons	
McGEE-OSBORNE Christopher Denton Wilde Sapte	

Within each band, firms are listed alphabetically. See **Profiles** on page 356

the group's levels of experience in projects. Apart from their role for InterGen, lead sponsor of Egypt's US$480 million Sidi Krir Project, they acted for the sponsors in Hungary's BorsodChem Industrial Power Plant Project and for the arrangers in the Budapest US$110 million Ujpest CHP Power Project. In addition, the London team acted for the arrangers of a US$11 billion securitisation of stranded costs in the Spanish electricity sector.

In oil and gas, where the firm's profile is not as high, it has still been involved in its share of big-ticket work. The group is acting for Petrobras in the financing of gas separation facilities and oil fields in the Campos Basin, and represented Royal Dutch Shell, as part of a successful US$992 million bid for a controlling stake in Comgas.

Contentious matters are also a feature of the department. Here, the respected **Jeremy Carver** has been involved in a number of matters, including sanctions, decommissioning and oil trading. The team is currently advising Ireland's Bord Gais on a number of issues, including the establishment of that country's energy trading operations and Network Code.

Newly-ranked **Michael Cuthbert** is well-regarded in the mining and minerals sector. His team's work for the Zambian government in its privatisation of Zambia Consolidated Copper Mines earned particular market approbation. The firm is also advising Chase Manhattan on its US$800 million restructuring of Ashanti Goldfields. **Clients:** Mount Isa Mines; InterGen; IVO; Royal Dutch Shell.

Linklaters The market knows this energy team primarily for an *"across the board"* service, its work on behalf of BP Amoco and for key partner, the *"first-class"* **Stuart Salt**. He is felt to combine an understanding of the financial and technical aspects of both oil and gas and electricity in a manner which *"few others emulate."* His team of assistants has also been mentioned for its *"obvious potential." "Strong corporate relationships"* are the key to the group's success, with large volumes of overseas deals. *"Adversarial"* in style, the team is seen as *"a potent force on the other side of the table,"* particularly in power project development. The team has acted for National Power in numerous disposals, the most high profile of which was the US$3 billion disposal of the Drax Power Station.

Oil and gas work has been dominated by M&A and projects/PFI deals. The team acted on the US$26 billion BP Amoco-Arco merger and BP Amoco's US$4.7 billion acquisition of Burmah Castro. In addition, the group advised the sponsors of the US$400 million exploration and development of oil and gas reserves in the Caspian Sea. Numerous downstream gas projects occupy the team from India to Brazil. Involved in many water PFI deals, recent projects included work for Asurix in its bids for water distribution and waste water concessions in Egypt and Morocco.

In mining the team has a fine name, maintaining a host of blue-chip corporate relationships. M&A work in the sector has included advice on the merger of AngloAmerican with Minorco. Significant project work is also being done, where newly-ranked, up and coming assistant **Chris Kelly** has developed an enviable reputation. **Clients:** Enron; British Gas; International Water; Rio Tinto; BHP; Billiton.

Norton Rose A rising energy department has earned high marks for its projects work, in addition to being *"sound on the financing angles"* and having a recognised M&A capacity. **Michael Taylor** is *"a major player in a number of areas,"* and is still comfortably the pre-eminent name here.

In electricity the group is known for its early and consistent involvement in IPP projects, which plays to the firm's strengths in project finance. The client base is evenly split between lenders and developers. New projects in the sector – including the first coal-fired IPP in the country, Fifoots Point and waste to energy PFI projects – are particular niches. Overseas, independent power project advice has been given to the National Electricity Company of Bulgaria. Transactionally, the team acted for AES on the £1.875 billion acquisition of Drax UK from National Power plc.

"A fine upstream oil and gas practice" includes FPSO financing. Downstream, the team advised Nigeria LNG on the US$2 billion expansion of its gas project and LUKOIL Petrol on the US$101 million acquisition of the Neftochim oil refinery in Bulgaria. In contentious matters, the firm acted for Teeside Gas Transportation (an Enron subsidiary) in its Court of Appeal action over send or pay payments relating to the CATS sub-sea pipeline.

In mining, the firm's niche is in African transactions, advising Ashanti Goldfields in a number of cases, and De Beers as majority shareholder in AngloAmerican plc. **Clients:** Mobil Services Company; Scottish Power; Archangel Diamond Company.

Freshfields Bruckhaus Deringer Although many consider that the firm *"hasn't yet fully turned its mind to the sector,"* the department has *"some good people"* and takes advantage of an expanding network of international offices. London partners include group leader **Jon Rees**, who has *"all the technical and commercial skills – he's taken the trouble to get to know the industry"* and **Patrick Wallace** (*"he can see the wider picture"*) who is known for his power station work. There is a large projects and corporate finance component in the group's case-load, as well as notable power privatisation experience. **Kent Rowey** has *"great projects expertise,"* and recently acted for Enron on Croatia's first IPP. The highly-rated energy litigation team is acting for National Grid in an arbitration against National Power over charges for connection to the transmission grid.

In oil and gas the team is well-known for litigation and arbitration, acting for the owners of the North Sea Hewett field in a £70 million dispute with British Gas Trading. For Arco the team acted in a dispute against Chevron over Venezuelan oil operations. Elsewhere, it acted for co-venturers Gazprom and Wintershall in the development and financing of the Prirazlomnoye oil project off the coast of Northern Russia. Downstream work has included the development and financing of a trans-Caspian gas pipeline. The team can call on the services of a specialist tax partner who devotes all his time to oil and gas tax issues. **Clients:** Enron; PSG International Ltd; Goldman Sachs.

Slaughter and May *"Never underestimate them,"* warn competitors, while clients *"don't like them acting against us."* Although not as specialised as other teams *("but if a deal changes, they can handle it")* the year has seen significant work in electricity, oil and gas and mining. In electricity, much of the firm's advice has been on acquisitions and disposals. The team acted for SWALEC on the disposal of its electricity and gas supply business to British Energy and for Entergy in the sale of London Electricity. Advice was also given to the Electricity Pool and other clients on the introduction of the new electricity trading arrangements in England and Wales. Here, the *"efficient"* **Paul Stacey** is *"synonymous with quality."* The group advised the Estonian Eesti Energia on the privatisation of the Eesti and Balti oil shale-fired power stations.

In oil and gas, the experienced **Martin Roberts** is respected on the financing side. Upstream, the team handled privatisation work in Poland, Nigerian development financing and advised Premier Oil on its joint venture with Shell Exploration in Pakistan. The firm also acted for Lasmo in its £600 million bid for Monument Oil & Gas. In mining, the group has a heavyweight roster of mining and minerals houses clients, which it has represented on a number of M&A transactions. Acted for Shell in the sale by auction of its worldwide coal business and for Alcan Aluminium in the sale of its Aughinish alumina refinery in Ireland to Glencore. **Clients:** Shell; AngloAmerican; Midlands Electricity.

Ashurst Morris Crisp Hard-hit by a number of high profile departures recently, the firm is not yet considered to have recovered its former lustre. While the team's energy litigation is highly praised and the corporate transactions continue to pay their way, the market view is that *"there's no real industry partner at the moment." "Solid, dependable, all round good guy"* **Geoffrey Picton-Turbervill** is currently the major name at a department with a traditionally strong gas practice. Increasingly active abroad, the firm has been noted *"developing the international dimensions of the practice."*

In upstream oil and gas last year the group acted for Hunt Oil in selling its interest in the Beatrice Field and associated decommissioning arrangements. In addition, it advised Lundin Oil AB to finance oil fields in Libya. Downstream, the team continues to act as UK counsel to the Azerbaijan IOC in developing export pipelines from Baku to Western markets.

Less recognised in the electricity sphere, the firm nevertheless advised NRG Energy, Inc on its $410 million acquisition of the Killingholme power station from National Power.

With the well-known **Philip Hurst** at the helm of the mining practice, the group has one of the most recognised exploration and development operations. It is especially well-known in *"highly politicised"* climates. The team has acted for AngloAmerican on matters including the Zarshuran Project, a greenfield precious and base metals mining project in Iran – the first foreign investment in Iran since the revolution and the result of four years' work. The practice has also advised CDC Group plc on its acquisition of stakes in Indian power stations and Zambian copper mines. **Clients:** SOCO International plc; Unocal Corp.; Anglo American.

Coudert Brothers Possessing *"genuine energy and project capability"* and the *"personable"* **Steven Beharrell**, the team surprises some in the market by its comparatively low profile in London. The geographical spread of the firm's network of offices gives this team extensive experience of advising on issues relating to Russia and the CIS. Project and trade finance are the primary areas of focus, especially in oil and gas, where they generally act for sponsors. The team are also held to be knowledgeable on production sharing agreements. Recent work includes advising the Williams Companies Inc on its acquisition of a controlling stake in a Lithuanian oil refinery and advising the sponsors on project financing a power plant in Mombasa. In the ongoing Sakhalin LNG project in Russia, the team is now advising on the next phase. Currently, the group is advising the Irish State Electricity Board on gas supply issues, as well as Electricité de France (which supplies England with 5 percent of its power) on sales and contractual matters. **Clients:** EDF; Mitsui & Co Ltd; Conoco Inc.

Lawrence Graham A low profile oil and gas practice which is seen principally in Middle East work, UKCS matters and on a variety of deals for key client Lasmo. However *"they do pop up"* and have also acted for Burlington Resources, as well as handling overflow work from in-house teams. Head of the practice, **John Verrill**, *"understands the problems and has a no-nonsense approach to negotiation."* **Linda Bretton**, *"loved at Lasmo for day to day work"* is also recommended as *"good, solid and dependable,"* and moves up the rankings. Recent work has included acting for Lasmo on the £90 million sale of gas assets to Gaz de France, as well as upstream oil and gas financing for CIBC, pipeline agreements, assignment of oil and gas interests and decommissioning work.

In the water sector, the firm acts for the trade association and advises the Water Grid on a number of issues. **Clients:** Lasmo; Water Grid.

Lovells Although still felt to be a *"solid corporate-focused energy team,"* market perception is that the loss of Tony Higginson to Baker Botts leaves a gap that will be difficult to fill. Known for acting as principal counsel in the UK to Exxon, the group advised on the secondary London listing of Exxon Mobil shares following that merger. Respected for its expertise in finance aspects of the industry, the firm represented JP Morgan on its financial advice to BP during the BP-Amoco merger. In contentious matters, the team has been occupied with extensive litigation and arbitration on FPSOs, dealing with, inter alia, construction and decommissioning. Other contentious work involved advising on a production sharing and joint operating agreement in South America, and contractual disputes over quantity obligations.

On the transactional and regulatory side, as well as continuing to handle claims validation arrangements, for which the team has a long-standing reputation, advice has been given to energy companies on the liberalisation of the European gas market, Interconnector and Network Code issues. Well known to the UK gas community, the *"excellent"* **Michael Stanger** is held in high regard. At home, the group acted for an international oil and gas company on an Irish power station joint venture and the construction of a power station in England. **Clients:** Exxon Corporation; JP Morgan.

Nabarro Nathanson Domestically-focused energy group, which has been perceived to suffer from the consolidation of the industry and consequent stiffer competition. More positively, the team has carved out a niche (around 15-20 percent of the market) in CHP power projects, advising on both industrial heating and district heating schemes. Clients like Pilkington Glass, Hays Chemicals and London Electricity have kept the practice as one of the most focused in this area. **Robert Tudway** continues to be recognised for his abilities as a projects-oriented lawyer. In regulatory issues, the group has advised Slough Heat & Power and others on the licensing and regulation of distribution systems. Importantly, the firm is one of four on the panel of regulator OFGEM. **Gareth Jones** has solid regulatory expertise and is *"a clever guy."*

The oil and gas team has a new group head, and recently advised Dragon Oil on its EBRD financing for an oil and gas development in Turkmenistan. It also advised BP Amoco on compliance with international trade sanctions imposed by the UN, EU and UK. **Clients:** English Partnerships; Elf; OFGEM.

Simmons & Simmons (23 partners and 40 assistants worldwide) Broadly based energy practice with a strong regulatory and corporate base and an international presence. In spite of the lateral hire of three new partners, the group does not have as high a profile as might be expected. When the market did comment, however, it was generally positively. *"They advise OFGAS and have done a really good job."* Leading light Charles Bankes is currently on a two-year secondment to OFGEM, and the practice is now one of four on the OFGEM panel.

In non-contentious matters, the highlight was advising government venture capital house UAE Offsets Group on the Project Dolphin joint venture, developing a cross-border gas pipeline project to connect Qatar, the UAE and Oman. The team is regularly involved in litigation on behalf of Esso and Shell and received a boost to its profile by representing ten major oil and gas companies involved in hydrocarbon exploration in the North Atlantic in judicial review proceedings brought by Greenpeace. In the water sector, the firm acted for Spanish company Union Fenosa in its recent acquisition of Cambridge Water and has acted for many years for General Utility (now part of Vivendi.) **Clients:** OFGEM; UAE Offsets Group; Shell International.

Vinson & Elkins LLP A global energy presence which joins the rankings for the first time after 25 years in London. Described as *"the only sensible US energy practice in London,"* this is *"a first-class outfit"* which has gained in visibility recently. An expansion drive has netted six additions to the team, mainly from City firms. Renowned for its strong link with Enron, the firm's breadth of work has ushered it into the spotlight. It acts for numerous developer clients on energy-related projects, M&A transactions and capital markets work.

Expertise in pipeline projects has been highlighted by advice on cross-border pipelines in the Baltics, Russia and Central Asia. Downstream the team handles refinery and petrochemicals work, representing a Finnish company to divest its chemicals business to a European private equity fund. The power industry has seen the team on projects in West Africa, Andalucia and India, primarily on behalf of developers. It has also advised on credit and commodity derivative contract securitisations and private equity fund energy investment into Europe. **Clients:** Enron Corp; Fortum; EBRD.

Baker & McKenzie A team more active on the international side, it liaises with offices in key energy areas. Rather low-profile, the London group is known primarily for its oil and gas competition law advice to Shell UK and the UK Offshore Operators' Association. Other recent work includes the farm-out of certain interests for Lonrho plc in Africa. The firm acted for Petrobras in the Barracuda and Caratinga offshore oil projects, in addition to advising on the expansion and upgrade of the REFAP Refinery. **Clients:** Shell UK; Petrobras; Lonrho.

Beachcroft Wansbroughs Cross-departmental group which is best known for catering to the legal needs of the domestic water industry. The practice has a long history of involvement, resulting in strength in the regulatory, M&A and planning sides of the sector. The team acts for 60 percent of the UK's water only companies, plus a number of water and sewerage companies. The firm represented a client on an appeal to the Competition Commission against the recent two year price-fix in the water sector, the first such appeal. **Clients:** Cambridge Water; Mid Kent Water; Foundation for Water Research.

Clyde & Co *"Definitely a factor,"* say peers, who have particular respect for the team's track record on contentious matters within the oil and gas sphere. Said to be *"aggressive players,"* they are often seen in oil trading disputes, a natural progression to the firm's shipping and commodities expertise. On the non-contentious side, where the firm's reputation is less well-established, clients include exploration, production and operating companies and offshore construction concerns. Long-term supply contracts are a speciality, and the team handles bank and trade financing for clients such as Glencore. Acted for BG in the Bacton-Zeebrugge Interconnector joint venture. **Clients:** Glencore; BG plc; Fortum Group; Amerada Hess.

Eversheds A group with *"good national coverage"* which has lately been active in the international market. More a transactional operation, the team has a sound reputation for electricity work, and acted for the South African Electricity Utility, Eskom, on a joint venture to organise Gambia's electricity, water and sewage sectors. Closer to home, the team has been advising RECs, generators and other members of the Electricity Association on the impact of the new Competition Act.

In oil and gas, where practice leader **Douglas Brown** remains a name to conjure with, there is a niche in rig design work. The team advised the Rig Design Services Group on a series of oil tanker conversions, drilling operations and farm-in prospects in Turkmenistan, Algeria & Azerbaijan. The London office also advised Terra Nitrogen (UK) Ltd on three gas purchase contracts. **Clients:** Eskom SA; Rig Design Services Group; Electricity Association.

Field Fisher Waterhouse A small team with a low profile, led by the respected **Howard Coffell** who is known for his expertise in energy-related property issues. Primarily a niche pipeline practice, *"they've been active for years in that field."* The team is well-known for its relationship with Interconnector (UK) Ltd and advised on the construction of a variety of gas pipelines. **Clients:** Air BP; Britoil plc; Interconnector (UK) Ltd.

Holman Fenwick & Willan A firm known for its strong work in shipping and litigation, which flavour both its contentious and non-contentious energy practices. These revolve around international work, where an offshore case-load is especially noticeable. Currently, the team is handling a large arbitration for a Hong Kong power project concerning gas quality, and has also advised on decommissioning claims and oil and gas supply disputes. On the non-contentious side, the practice has been appointed by Enron to advise on worldwide trading of coal. **Clients:** Maersk Oil & Gas; Shell; British Gas.

Ince & Co A team known for lending its maritime expertise to all aspects of litigation in the offshore industry. Predominantly an oil and gas group, it handles contractual advice, litigation and arbitration in its own *"aggressive style."* Arbitration is a major part of the work; the team recently handled a number of subcontractor claims on the late delivery of drilling rigs. **Clients:** Global Marine Inc; McDermott/ETPM; Baker Hughes; Occidental.

LeBoeuf, Lamb, Greene & MacRae An energy/power projects group with a focus on Africa and a name in energy insurer work. **Garry Pegg** is especially known for his work for Claims Validation Services. Although the team is not considered to have an especially high profile, it is regarded as *"still a player."*

In oil and gas the team acted for Summit Oil on its purchase of oil fields and exploration licences. Increasingly, advice has been given on the provision of gas to power projects, especially on behalf of project companies. This includes closing the first two phases of the Takoradi 600MW power project in Ghana – the only successful project in West Africa to date. **Clients:** Volta River Authority; Zambia Electricity; US Filter.

Masons In May 2000 the firm created a dedicated, nine-partner energy practice group to combine the firm's work (domestically and internationally) in electricity, nuclear, renewables and oil and gas. The highest profile continues to exist in construction, an area of expertise which strongly flavours the firm's energy work. Specific strength is found in FSPO, pipeline and process contracting issues.

In power matters, the team worked for the Indonesian State Electricity Utility and Government in an UNCITRAL arbitration and for Thomassen UK on disputes arising from a turnkey contract for the construction of a power plant. Significant non-contentious instructions came from Independent Energy, which the firm advises on all corporate and regulatory matters, including its recent acquisition of York Gas.

In oil and gas, FSPO and pipelines issues stand out. A majority of these have been in the contentious sphere, in line with the overall market trend. The team handled a dispute for Bonatti SpA concerning pipeline contracts. In water, the team is said to be *"focused and growing,"* with **Mark Lane** joining the rankings this year for his work in the area. Water PFI has been a growth area, and the team advised the bidders on the Levenmouth Wastewater PFI project. **Clients:** Independent Energy; North Sea Production Company Ltd; Amey Construction Ltd.

Richards Butler Better known in London for Middle Eastern, including Omani LNG work, this team has eclectic experience in energy finance, the sale, carriage and insurance of oil, and production and concession agreements. Other work has included advising overseas governments on legislative policy, reform and drafting. Lack of a big-hitting partner, however, is felt to be a check to the firm's progress in this area. **Clients:** Government of Kyrgyzstan; ESB International.

Watson, Farley & Williams Part of the group forms an electricity practice which focuses on advising sponsors such as AES on power generation projects and M&A on the continent. Highlights include advising AES Horizons on a 650MW coal fired power plant in Bulgaria, the largest project financing of a power plant in the region. The group has also been seen on CHP/renewables deals both in the UK and Eastern Europe.

The firm's well-known shipping capability complements the practice's involvement in upstream offshore oil and gas work. It is notable for its work in financing floating production systems (FSPOs.) Recently handled the contractual aspects of the North Sea Banff Field development and FSPO lease financing. The team also advised on significant acquisitions of natural gas companies and storage facilities on behalf of TransCanada. **Clients:** AES; National Grid; Sithe Energy; Petroleum Geo-Services ASA.

Other Notable Practitioners Much interest has been occasioned by the departure of **Tony Higginson** *("has a good bedside manner")* from Lovells to Baker Botts. His challenge is to build a recognised practice at the firm, which hitherto, has not shone in London. The high-profile **Mark Saunders** of Dewey Ballantine also continues to have his champions in the market.

THE SOUTH

ENERGY & NATURAL RESOURCES • The South	Ptnrs	Assts
❶ **Bond Pearce** Plymouth	5	4
❷ **Deborah Mills Associates** Marlow	1	2
Veale Wasbrough Bristol	1	3

LEADING INDIVIDUALS
❶ **TRINICK Marcus** Bond Pearce
❷ **MILLS Deborah** Deborah Mills Associates
SMITHERS Tim Veale Wasbrough

Within each band, firms are listed alphabetically. *See **Profiles** on page 356*

Bond Pearce Still the leaders in the region, the energy group remains heavily involved in the renewable energy industry – particularly wind energy – driven by the high profile, *"in demand,"* **Marcus Trinick**. He sits on the Renewable Energy Advisory Committee advising the Minister; recent work includes advising on all the contracts for the sale of electricity to the Millennium Dome and acting for the Crown Estate on specimen leases for offshore energy development. Last year was a busy one for the practice, with advice on the legal framework for monopile 2MW wind turbines at sea and planning and property work for onshore wind farms and other renewables plants. **Clients:** Crown Estates.

Deborah Mills Associates A niche gas outfit with a national focus. The practice capitalises on the experience of ex-British Gas lawyer **Deborah Mills**, working on upstream and downstream gas issues, transportation and topical issues of converting gas to power at an earlier stage in the process. This work is done both domestically and in places such as Namibia. Now handling increasing in-house 'overflow' work via secondments to such companies as Esso, Ranger and Mitsubishi. **Clients:** Leading oil and gas companies.

Veale Wasbrough Pipeline expertise is the firm's major energy focus. 'Linear projects,' both pipeline and cable-related, are a niche specialism. The team handles planning, environmental, DTI consent and bulk easement acquisition issues, as well as encroachment disputes. **Tim Smithers** maintains a respected local reputation. The group recently advised on disputes concerning 'take or pay' provisions in pipeline contracts. **Clients:** Esso; Garrad Hassan Ltd.

MIDLANDS

ENERGY & NATURAL RESOURCES • Midlands	Ptnrs	Assts
❶ **Martineau Johnson** Birmingham	2	4
Wragge & Co Birmingham	2	9
❷ **Edwards Geldard** Derby	2	2
Eversheds Birmingham	1	2
Hammond Suddards Edge Birmingham	2	-
Kent Jones and Done Stoke-on-Trent	1	1
Knight & Sons Newcastle-under-Lyme	2	4
Pinsent Curtis Birmingham	-	1

LEADING INDIVIDUALS	
❶ **HAMLETT David** Wragge & Co	
WHITEHEAD Andrew Martineau Johnson	
❷ **BELL Tony** Knight & Sons	**BRENNAN Paul** Martineau Johnson
REEVES Tony Kent Jones and Done	**UPTON Neil** Wragge & Co
WILLIAMS Gwyn Hammond Suddards Edge	

Within each band, firms are listed alphabetically. *See **Profiles** on page 356*

Martineau Johnson A high profile team with a sophisticated electricity, gas and water practice which is seen to be *"keeping up with industry developments."* Transco-experienced **Paul Brennan** is *"knowledgeable"* on gas transportation issues, while the *"quietly confident"* **Andrew Whitehead** *"understands details and works documents well."*

Much of the electricity work concerns the underlying nature and structure of the industry: for the National Grid, the firm has acted on issues such as electricity transmission, advising on new trading arrangements, licences and industry contractual issues. The oil and gas side saw advice on the Within Day Gas Commodity Market, a new trading market, in line with last year's amended gas regulations. **Clients:** East Midlands Electricity; National Grid; South Staffordshire Water.

Wragge & Co A team with great strength in depth in the total utilities sector. Often seen on projects deals, the group works on gas, electricity and water cases. The *"straightforward"* **David Hamlett** is *"the sort of person who will actually get the deal done."* He recently acted for PowerGen in its acquisition of Yorkshire Electricity CHP company, and is also known for his CHP project work. **Neil Upton**, an *"out and about sort of chap,"* is also well regarded. The team is acting for PowerGen Energy on distribution, supply and metering issues, and has been particularly involved in the disposal of metering businesses over the first half of 2000. Regulatory advice is another string to the group's bow, acting on both gas and electricity issues. **Clients:** PowerGen; Transco.

Edwards Geldard A *"competent, helpful"* team involved in electricity, gas and water and said to *"know a lot about supply side issues."* Market perception has detected a decrease in profile in the wake of recent restructurings in the sector, but the firm has developed a customer practice (acting for such clients as Rank Hovis and RocOil Ltd) and expanded its team. In electricity, the team advises on infrastructure, connection and supply agreements, as well as renewables projects. Work includes a niche in metering issues. A good relationship with Welsh water company, Hyder, means that the firm is actively involved in the water sector in its heartland of South Wales. **Clients:** SWALEC; Hyder.

Eversheds Although the Birmingham office is known for its mining work, it is felt to lack the profile of the firm's London and Leeds offices. The team also handles wind, water, landfill gas, and straw burning renewables work for power projects, generally acting for the developer. During the past year, the firm has advised on the acquisition of landfill gas sites for US companies. **Clients:** Cinergy Global Power; Energy Power Resources Limited; Wedgewood Power Corp.

Hammond Suddards Edge In energy, the firm is associated above all with mining and quarrying. Well connected ex-Tarmac lawyer **Gwyn Williams** is known for being *"down to earth"* and *"a member of the minerals club."* The team's client base contains a vast range of leading minerals concerns. In the water sector, the team has given advice on treatment, supply and management issues, as well as the use of waste in electricity generation. **Clients:** Hanson; Lafarge Redland; Castle Cement.

Kent Jones and Done *"Solid and respected"* practice that is known for coal and minerals work. This includes gold and other mining interests in Wales, leases, prospecting licences and exploration licences. Act for some operator clients, such as Laporte Industries, for which the practice disposed of a flowerspa business in Derbyshire. Senior partner **Tony Reeves** – newly ranked – is well known for his involvement as Chair of the Law Society Committee for mining subsidence, and for his prowess in related litigation. **Clients:** Laporte Industries.

Knight & Sons *"Heavily involved in minerals,"* this is an energy practice with an agricultural/minerals bias, handling a lot of work for ARC/Hanson as well as landowners. **Tony Bell** *"commands the respect of clients"* and has long experience in the sector. **Clients:** ARC/Hanson.

Pinsent Curtis A practice with a waste management/PFI niche and a traditional public sector client base, providing the practice with newly privatised local clients. Known for renewables, the team has been involved in some waste to energy matters for Vivendi and are acting on the Tyseley waste disposal work. Generally, however, this is regarded as a team with *"limited scope."* **Clients:** Vivendi.

THE NORTH

ENERGY & NATURAL RESOURCES • The North	Ptnrs	Assts
❶ **Nabarro Nathanson** Sheffield	4	6
❷ **Eversheds** Leeds	1	2
❸ **Dickinson Dees** Newcastle upon Tyne	7	6
Pinsent Curtis Leeds	3	1
Wake Dyne Lawton Chester	3	1
Wrigleys Leeds	1	-

LEADING INDIVIDUALS	
❶ **BROWN Neil** Eversheds	**LOGAN Niall** Nabarro Nathanson
RENGER Michael Nabarro Nathanson	**WAKE Brian** Wake Dyne Lawton
WHITAKER Neil Pinsent Curtis	

Within each band, firms are listed alphabetically. *See **Profiles** on page 356*

Nabarro Nathanson This Sheffield team has *"a ton of experience in the coal industry,"* and is now felt to be the pre-eminent energy group in the region. The largest coal practice in England and Wales, it will act for the Coal Authority for a further 5 years, having won the 1999 tender. The group also works for major private companies in England and Wales such as RJB Mining, for whom they are principal external counsel, and Celtic Energy. These briefs mean that the team advises on environmental work, waste to power work and supply contracts for the sale of coal to power stations. *"Mr Coal"* **Michael Renger** *"knows his stuff,"* especially environmental aspects of the industry. Newly-ranked **Niall Logan** (client care partner for the Coal Authority,) is *"second to none"* on mineral rights issues.

In other matters, the firm acts for UK Nirex (the body responsible for handling and disposing of nuclear waste) and handles downstream work for Conoco. Internationally the team is acting for a Swiss client purchasing copper mines in rapidly privatising Zambia, while in the water sector, the team is handling specialist litigation for Northumbrian Water. **Clients:** The Coal Authority; Conoco Inc; Celtic Energy plc; RJB Mining.

Eversheds *"I've got respect for them."* Part of an increasingly integrated national energy team, the Leeds office is primarily known as an electricity and projects practice, with notable strength on the finance side. Complementary involvement in gas and water supply issues acting for generator clients, the most well known of which is Yorkshire Electricity. The firm is increasingly involved in infrastructure and supply issues. **Neil Brown** maintains his reputation. Act for the electricity retailer 3A, and have advised the British Waterways Board on environmental, energy and utilities hydropower issues. **Clients:** Yorkshire Electricity; British Waterways Board.

Dickinson Dees A broad-based general minerals team which acts for a number of Northumberland landowners and minerals companies. The firm is less well known for, but active in, waste and utilities work, acting for quarrying and waste disposal company Thompsons, for whom they do planning, extraction, environmental and litigation work. For local generator Northern Electric, the firm advises on contracts for the sale and purchase of gas and electricity to commercial and retail customers and small scale generating projects. However, the firm suffers from the absence of a recognised heavyweight within the department. **Clients:** Northern Electric; H J Banks; Thompsons.

Pinsent Curtis They *"have minerals muscle"* and energy work grows from this base. Led by the *"straight-talking"* **Neil Whitaker**, the team is backed by strong planning and commercial property departments. Advice has been given on mining, quarrying and landfill cases. The electricity practice focuses mainly on on-site power generation, most recently for a hospital in the area. **Clients:** Hanson; HJ Banks.

Wake Dyne Lawton Highly regarded former Tarmac lawyer, **Brian Wake**, has *"a good idea of the nuances of mines and minerals."* He heads a team which has advised extensively on mineral extraction issues. The group conducted specialist mining and waste due diligence for Parkhill Group on a £41 million acquisition. **Clients:** Parkhill Group.

Wrigleys Small group with a reputation for *"thinking global, acting local."* Known for its specialist renewables and energy efficiency niche, it is developing a position in wind power. Work covers the spectrum from property concerns over the siting of wind farms to security and financing work, production tenders and contracts. The team has acted on the financing of energy efficiency measures (eg insulation,) as well as grants and research projects for the Energy Savings Trust. The firm is on the Panel of Experts for ESCOs (energy service companies.) **Clients:** Energy Savings Trust.

SCOTLAND

ELECTRICITY

ENERGY: ELECTRICITY • Scotland	Ptnrs	Assts
❶ **Biggart Baillie** Glasgow	7	6
Dundas & Wilson CS Edinburgh, Glasgow	5	6
MacRoberts Glasgow	1	2
Shepherd & Wedderburn WS Edinburgh, Glasgow	4	10
❷ **Burness** Edinburgh	5	4
Harper Macleod Glasgow	3	1
McGrigor Donald Glasgow	4	3

LEADING INDIVIDUALS
❶ **CUMMING Donald** Dundas & Wilson CS
DICKSON Ian MacRoberts
ROSS David Biggart Baillie
SAUNDERS James Shepherd & Wedderburn WS
THOMSON Gordon MacRoberts

Within each band, firms are listed alphabetically. *See **Profiles** on page 356*

Biggart Baillie A top-ranked energy practice, strong in the complementary areas of electricity and gas, with a reputation built around the time of privatisation and an excellent client base which includes Scottish Power. Practice mainstay, the *"excellent"* **David Ross** *("he's got a presence and attracts a following")* is devoting his time to Scottish Power work. Renowned for *"a good understanding of industry issues,"* the team recently acted on a project for the construction and operation of a power station in Lancashire. **Clients:** Scottish Power; BP.

Dundas & Wilson CS This broadly-based electricity practice is often seen acting for banks in energy-related transactions, but also earns plaudits for its power expertise, representing a number of leading Scottish clients. The firm's workload is varied: power project advice forms one third and includes English law capacity, commercial energy work a further third (this encompasses gas contracts and tie-ins,) with regulatory and corporate work making up the remainder. The *"sensible, thoughtful"* **Donald Cumming** has drawn attention in the PFI area, acting for a number of public water companies. **Clients:** Scottish Hydro; Scottish and Southern Electricity; East of Scotland Water Authority.

MacRoberts The practice's historical involvement with Scottish Nuclear gives them a high profile in the energy sector, particularly as the company produces some 50 percent of Scotland's power. The highly rated **Ian Dickson** is praised for his technical ability, and it is said that *"his clients swear by him."* The firm acts for TXU Europe Power (the old Eastern Electricity,) the UK's fourth largest generator, as well as undertaking more general work for a number of smaller open cast mining operators. Newly-ranked **Gordon Thomson** is well-known both here and for his work on PFI issues in the water sector. **Clients:** British Energy plc; Scottish Nuclear Ltd.

Shepherd & Wedderburn WS *"A practice with astute people and good clients."* Sharing Scottish Power as a client with Biggart Baillie, the firm has its primary reputation in electricity, as well as doing a little work in gas and renewables cases. **James Saunders** *"has been around since privatisation"* and combines *"technical knowledge with a commercial approach."* The team advised on the £150 million upgrade to the Northern Ireland Undersea Interconnector and acted for Scottish Power in a public enquiry into their objection to a proposed power station at Westfield, Fife. Overseas, the firm advised Cairn Energy on its joint venture with Shell in Bangladesh and India. **Clients:** Scottish Power plc; Cairn Energy plc.

Burness Small energy team which is seen to be moving increasingly towards the PFI side of the energy sector. In the industry, the team has undertaken notable PFI work for lenders in the North of Scotland, as well as acting on social infrastructure and waste management matters in Edinburgh. Advised Fife Power on issues concerning Scotland's first power station. **Clients:** Fife Power; Ramco Energy; Magnox Electric.

Harper Macleod Traditional favourite of the extractive industries, the natural resource practice group is known especially for its coal expertise, representing the Scottish Coal Company, which supplies the group with 50 percent of its workload. The firm also handles general corporate matters for energy companies, as well as providing aggregates advice to operators. Work includes land and land option acquisitions and disposals, coal licensing and planning advice and coal extraction and transportation agreements. Highlight of the year was successfully obtaining planning consent for the Glen Taggart open cast mine site. **Clients:** Scottish Coal Company.

McGrigor Donald *"Steeped in electricity"* from its privatisation experience acting for the Government, this *"high quality"* practice is felt to suffer from the lack of a mainstay energy client and a high profile partner. Nevertheless, the team is *"picking up work around the edges,"* acting on behalf of exploration and production companies. **Clients:** Conargo Energy.

OIL & GAS

ENERGY: OIL AND GAS • Scotland	Ptnrs	Assts
❶ **CMS Cameron McKenna** Aberdeen	3	-
Ledingham Chalmers Aberdeen, Edinburgh	2	*
Paull & Williamsons Aberdeen	1	4

LEADING INDIVIDUALS
❶ **RUDDIMAN Robert** Ledingham Chalmers
WARNE Penelope CMS Cameron McKenna

Within each band, firms are listed alphabetically. *See **Profiles** on page 356*

CMS Cameron McKenna Established in 1993, this is *"a notable English presence"* known for its oil work and respected for its client base and long-term investment in the Scottish market *("they're stayers.")* **Penelope Warne** has a high profile and was involved in advising oil companies on the Spring 2000 First Licensing Round for oil and gas exploration activities in the Faeroe Islands.

Work under English and Scottish law has included advising BP on the Catchment Area Project. The group advised OMV AG on its sale of Cultus Petroleum and continued to represent DSND Subsea on North Sea litigation in connection with the Banff Field. **Clients:** BP; OMV AG.

Ledingham Chalmers (2 partners full-time, 12 assistants part-time) *"Dedicated to the oil industry,"* this is a long established, traditional oil and gas practice known for its *"pragmatic"* upstream work. The team capitalises on contacts with exploration, production and service companies from its Aberdeen base, both in the North Sea and further abroad. The firm is a recognised presence in Azerbaijan, acting for Ramco and small service providers in the sector. The respected **Bob Ruddiman** heads the oil and gas practice, which in the past year has seen transactional work, buying and selling assets, exploration, licensing, oil and gas sales and joint venture arrangements. **Clients:** Ramco Energy plc; Conoco (UK) Inc.

Paull & Williamsons An oil and gas team with *"a good niche in Aberdeen,"* and a reputation that *"if they do something, they generally do it well."* Noted for excellent corporate back-up, the firm acts for 3i and the Bank of Scotland in upstream oil and gas transactions. However, the main emphasis of the group is on acting for Aberdeen-based oil service companies, for which they service the range of corporate and legal requirements. In contentious matters, the firm acted for Occidental on the long-running Piper Alpha matter. **Clients:** Occidental; Bank of Scotland.

LEADERS IN ENERGY & NATURAL RESOURCES

BEHARRELL, Steven
Coudert Brothers, London (020) 7248 3000
beharrells@london.coudert.com
Specialisation: Senior partner, *Coudert Brothers*, London. Specialises in energy, oil, gas and power and natural resources, infrastructure investment, project finance, transportation and privatisation. Has 30 years experience advising on oil and gas law in the Middle East, Asia, North Sea and Russia. Also involved in electricity and other privatisations since the late 1980s. Regularly addresses conferences and seminars on the subject of energy and privatisation law.
Prof. Memberships: International Bar Association.
Career: Assistant solicitor, Denton Hall 1966-72 and partner 1972-90. Partner, *Coudert Brothers* since 1990.
Personal: Educated at Sorbonne University, Paris 1961-62 and the College of Law, London 1964-66. Lives in London. Born 22nd December 1944.

BELL, Tony
Knight & Sons, Newcastle-under-Lyme
(01782) 619225

BLAKE, Peter M.W.
Clifford Chance, London (020) 7600 1000
peter.blake@cliffordchance.com
Specialisation: Partner specialising in general company and commercial work, energy, oil, gas, natural resources and project finance.
Career: Partner *Clifford Chance* 1983.

BOND, Richard
Herbert Smith, London (020) 7374 8000
richard.bond@herbertsmith.com
Senior partner.
Specialisation: Wide ranging experience of corporate transactions, particularly in the fields of energy and natural resources, utilities and privatisations.
Career: Qualified in 1969. Partner with *Herbert Smith* since 1977.

BRENNAN, Paul
Martineau Johnson, Birmingham (0121) 678 1527
paul.brennan@martjohn.com
Specialisation: Advises energy companies and major users on energy and generation, also advises on competitive water supply. Editor: 'Code Update'. Career highlights include international litigation involving production assets in Kazakhstan, de-merger of British Gas plc and associated gas purchase and transportation arrangements, drafted Network Codes for Phoenix Natural Gas and East Midlands Pipelines Ltd, advised on the establishment of EnMo, an on-line energy market.
Prof. Memberships: Law Society, UK Energy Lawyers Association, Society for Computers & Law.
Career: Stonyhurst College, Durham University, Leeds University, College of Law, Articled *TV Edwards & Co.* Various positions BG plc, Partner, *Martineau Johnson Solicitors* 1997.
Personal: Born 1961, resides Warwick with daughter and wife. Interest/Pastimes - cricket, football and the other arts.

BRETTON, Linda
Lawrence Graham, London (020) 7379 0000
linda.bretton@lawgram.com
Partner in Company Commercial Department.
Specialisation: Main area of practice is energy law, mainly upstream oil and gas and in particular asset sales and purchases, swaps, farm-ins, and reorganisations. Worked in-house by way of a long-term placement at a major oil company during which advised on a range of oil industry contracts and issues.
Prof. Memberships: The Law Society, UK Energy Lawyers' Group, International Bar Association (section on Energy and Resources Law).
Career: Reading University (BA Psychology). Qualified as a solicitor in 1991.
Personal: Lives in Hertfordshire. Enjoys the gym, reading, wine, dancing and family.

BROWN, Douglas
Eversheds, London (020) 7919 4500
browndr@eversheds.com
Specialisation: Oil and gas exploration, JOAs PSAs, farm ins/outs, drilling and services contracts; gas purchasing and PPAs; onshore and offshore construction, pipelines, partnering. Currently involved in inward investment mining project in the West Indies and electricity/water infra-structure projects in Africa and a variety of oil and gas transactions in the C.I.S.
Prof. Memberships: IBA Section on energy and natural resources law; UK Energy Lawyers; Institute of Petroleum; Member of the Pipelines Industries Guild; Companion of the Institution of Chemical Engineers.
Career: Senior legal adviser British Gas plc 1981-88; partner 1990.

BROWN, Neil
Eversheds, Leeds (0113) 243 0391
neilbrown@eversheds.com
See under Telecommunications, p.

CARVER CBE, Jeremy
Clifford Chance, London (020) 7956 0123
jeremy.carver@cliffordchance.com
Specialisation: Head of international law group, representing states, government agencies and international organisations in relation to proceedings in England and elsewhere. Representing Kuwait and its Oil Sector companies in claims to the United Nations Compensation Commission. Areas of expertise include state and diplomatic immunity; status, privileges and immunities of international organisations; upstream oil and gas operations; international economic sanctions; maritime and territorial boundary issues; world trade law, jurisdiction, conflicts of laws, extraterritoriality.
Prof. Memberships: International Law Association, British Branch, Hon Treasurer 1981-1998, Vice-President since 1998; Executive Council, International Law Association since 1991; ILA International Trade Law Committee since 1996; Executive Committee, British Institute of International and Comparative Law since 1996; Council of Management since 1998; American Society of International Law since 1977; Fellow Royal Geographical Society since 1971; Advisory Council, RefAid (UNHCR-UK) since 1997; Board Member, International Rescue Committee; Chairman, British Invisibles CIS Panel 1993-1995; Kazakh-British Trade and Industry Council since 1994; Uzbek-British Trade and Industry Council since 1994; British Export Promotion Forum since1996; City Promotion Panel since 1995.
Career: Trinity College, Cambridge (MA Engineering). Qualified 1969; made partner 1974; *Coward Chance* 1969-1987; *Clifford Chance* since 1987; resident manager Brussels 1973-1974; resident partner Singapore 1982-1983; contributions to numerous books and professional publications.
Personal: Born 1943; resides London.

CAVE-BROWNE-CAVE, Myles
Denton Wilde Sapte, London (020) 7242 1212

CLOUGH, Adrian
Herbert Smith, London (020) 7374 8000
adrian.clough@herbertsmith.com
Specialisation: Partner in *Herbert Smith*'s Projects Group, specialising in privatisation, major restructurings, infrastructure projects and complex commercial contracts, particularly in the electricity sector. Involvement with the electricity sector began when part of the team advising the Area Boards of England and Wales on the 1990 restructuring and their subsequent privatisation. Continues to advise various members of the industry on contractual and regulatory issues. Had day to day responsibility for the *Herbert Smith* team advising the 14 Public Electricity Suppliers in Great Britain on the major revisions to the industry's contractual and regulatory structure which were necessary to enable full supply competition to be introduced. Has also advised British Gas in relation to the Northern Ireland electricity privatisation and the Magnox division of Nuclear Electric on the restructuring that preceded the privatisation of British Energy. Currently advising a group of RECs on implementation of the New Electricity Trading Arrangements and a new entrant generator in relation to the restructuring of the electricity sector in the Republic of Ireland. Regular speaker at electricity related conferences.

Career: Educated at Christ Church, Oxford (MA); qualified as a solicitor 1988; partner of *Herbert Smith* 1995. Seconded for two years as an Assistant Director of the Office of Passenger Rail Franchising, leading the development of the new contractual and regulatory structure of the railway industry as it developed.

COFFELL, Howard
Field Fisher Waterhouse, London (020) 7861 4000
Partner Commercial Property Department. Head of Pipeline Services Unit.
Specialisation: Practice covers acquisition, disposal and development of commercial property including industrial sites, oil and gas terminals and facilities and the construction of cross-country pipelines. Acts for a number of major UK oil and gas companies, pipeline operators and other industrial concerns.
Prof. Memberships: Law Society.
Career: Qualified 1974, having joined *Field Fisher Waterhouse* in 1972. Became a Partner in 1978.
Personal: Born 23rd November 1948. Attended King Henry VIII School, Coventry and Magdalen College, Oxford.

CUMMING, Donald
Dundas & Wilson CS, Edinburgh (0131) 228 8000

CUTHBERT, Michael
Clifford Chance, London (020) 7600 1000
michael.cuthbert@cliffordchance.com
Specialisation: Corporate and capital markets; specialist in energy and natural resources matters with particular emphasis on mining and oil and gas. Advised Government of Republic of Zambia on privatisation of copper industry. Advisor to other mining houses.
Prof. Memberships: Solicitor of the Supreme Court of England and Wales; solicitor of the Supreme Court of Hong Kong; licensed legal consultant, State of New York. Member of Law Society, City of London Solicitors Company, International Bar Association.
Career: Partner *Clifford-Turner* 1986; *Clifford Chance LLP* 1986 to date (managing partner New York 1990-1993).
Personal: Enjoys opera, food and wine. Married with one child.

DALLAS, James
Denton Wilde Sapte, London (020) 7242 1212

DAVEY, Henry
Herbert Smith, London (020) 7374 8000
henry.davey@herbertsmith.com
Specialisation: Electricity: Involved in the privatisation and restructuring of the UK electricity industry in 1990, acting on behalf of the 12 Regional Electricity Companies and in the restructuring of the electricity industry in Northern Ireland. Continues to advise on the UK electricity industry, including UK power projects (for example Humber Power, Teesside, Sutton Bridge, Kingsnorth, Salt End, South Denes), and advises on innovative electricity and gas trading contracts. Advises on international power projects and on electricity transmission projects including in Europe, India and the Middle East.
Oil and Gas: Advises on UK and international oil and gas projects, including UK oil and gas field developments and asset acquisitions and disposals (for example the Alba, Beryl, Boulton, Brae, Britannia, Elgin & Franklin, Everest, Gallahad, Hudson, Hutton, Audrey & Johnston, Markham and Victor fields), refinery contracts and on all aspects of oil and gas contracts, including joint ventures and joint operating agreements; advises on gas sales and transportation agreements, including sales of gas to power stations and gas to gas trading and the Network Code. Advises on upstream and downstream acquisitions and disposals of energy assets, production sharing agreements, licensing and concession agreements and development contracts in various jurisdictions (including Europe, Russia and the former C.I.S. countries, the Middle East and India).
Prof. Memberships: Member of IBA. Member of the United Kingdom Energy Lawyers Group. Representative on the SERL Oil Committee.
Career: Partner in *Herbert Smith.* Joined *Herbert Smith* as a trainee in September 1986; qualified in 1988. MA Cantab (Queens' College), Law; Nottingham High School.

DAVIES, Roger
Allen & Overy, London (020) 7330 3000
Specialisation: He more than 25 years' experience in general operational, acquisition and financing matters relating to the oil and gas industry, both upstream and downstream. He has represented Mobil on its European downstream joint venture with BP over the past 5 years.
Career: Articled *Allen & Overy*, qualified 1972, Partner 1976, Partner in charge of Dubai office 1980-83.
Personal: Fitzwilliam College, Cambridge 1969. Born 1946. Speaks French.

DICKSON, Ian
MacRoberts, Glasgow (0141) 332 9988
id@macroberts.co.uk
See under Corporate Finance, p.

DOEH, Doran
Denton Wilde Sapte, London (020) 7242 1212

ELDER, Ian
Allen & Overy, London (020) 7330 3000
Specialisation: Corporate partner and head of Allen & Overy's European Energy Group. Extensive experience of mergers, acquisitions and joint ventures, as well as a large number of energy transactions, both in the UK and internationally. He has acted for a number of major industrial companies including ICI, BG, Enron, Mobil, Zeneca, Courtaulds and SWEB. He has also acted on a number of UK IPPs, including Teeside Power, Barking Power, Derwent Power, Humber Power and Seabank Power. He co-led the A&O team on the UK nuclear privatisation (British Energy). He is advising a number of clients on the implication of the de-regulation of the European Energy Markets and on the new electricity trading arrangements in the UK.
Prof. Memberships: Law Society (England and Scotland), IBA, City of London Solicitors Company.
Career: Apprenticed *Dundas & Wilson*; qualified Scotland 1977, England 1984; Solicitor ICI legal department 1977-87; Assistant Solicitor, *Allen & Overy* 1987-89; Partner 1989.
Personal: St Andrew's University (1972 MA); Edinburgh University (1974 LLB). Born 1951.

GRIFFIN, Paul
Herbert Smith, London (020) 7374 8000
Partner in energy and project finance.
Specialisation: Wide experience in energy and project finance, in particular the oil, gas and power sectors, both in the UK and overseas. Deals with a variety of projects and transactions in both the energy and infrastructure fields, together with privatisations. Involved in the re-negotiation of long term contracts in liberalised gas and electricity markets and has also been much involved in energy related disputes in court and before experts and arbitrators. Experience in the related areas of competition and regulation. Writes and lectures widely.

HAMLETT, David
Wragge & Co, Birmingham (0121) 214 1044
david_hamlett@wragge.com
Specialisation: Head of Energy/Utilities Team and has a very wide experience of corporate and commercial matters for utility clients, particulary in the energy and water sectors. His experience includes CHP and waste to energy projects, sludge plants, water treatment plants, energy supply agreements, supply contracts, outsourcing contracts, joint ventures, financing, acquisitions and disposals, both in the UK and internationally.
Career: Articled *Linklaters & Paines.* Qualified 1980. Joined *Wragge & Co* 1983. Became a partner 1988.

HIGGINSON, Tony J.
Baker Botts, London (020) 7778 1400
Specialisation: Energy & Natural Resources: advising both in the UK and internationally on energy projects, including: concession and production sharing contracts; corporate and asset transactions; gas supply and marketing contracts; LNG; transportation and tariffing; downstream refining and product sales and power generation.
Prof. Memberships: International Bar Association; Institute of Petroleum; Association of International Petroleum Negotiators.
Career: Articled *Herbert Smith*; legal adviser Vickers Plc, 1974-76; attorney Phillips Petroleum Company Europe–Africa and Phillips Petroleum Company, Oklahoma 1976-84; General Counsel Sun Oil International; Managing Director Sun Oil Britain Limited, Far East Regional Manager, Sun Oil, 1984-92; partner *Lovell White Durrant* 1996-99. Partner *Baker & Botts* from 1 January 2000.
Personal: MA, Emmanuel College, Cambridge (1971); Graduate PMD Harvard Business School 1987.

HURST, Philip
Ashurst Morris Crisp, London (020) 7638 1111
Partner in projects group and energy & natural resources group.
Specialisation: Heads mining team and electricity team. Leading practitioner in natural resources law, especially in Africa, Middle East and South Asia. Extensive experience in advising sponsors of independent power projects, particularly in India and Pakistan. Currently advising on a major greenfield mining project in Iran, and on power/mining project in Zambia. Visiting lecturer in natural resources law, Imperial College, London, and Ecole des Mines, Fontainebleau.
Career: BA, LLB(ANU), MA, LLM (Virginia) FRGS. 1981-85 associate *White & Case*, New York; 1985-87, Counsel, The World Bank, Washington DC; 1988-92, solicitor *Linklaters & Paines*, London.

JONES, Gareth
Nabarro Nathanson, London (020) 7524 6209
g.jones@nabbarro.com
Energy law specialist. Acts for developers/ other contract parties of power station and infrastructure projects. Advises on power and gas supply, upstream petroleum issues and electricity and gas licensing.
Prof. Memberships: Law Society, Institute of Petroleum.
Career: Qualified in 1980. *Nabarro Nathanson* in 1983 onwards (partner in 1986).

KELLY, Christopher
Linklaters (A member firm of Linklaters & Alliance), London (020) 7456 3600
christopher.kelly@linklaters.com
Specialisation: Partner, co-head of the e-commerce business group. Specialist in corporate law, including M&A, takeovers, privatisations, joint ventures, securitisations & corporate reorganisations. Key focus on the technology sector. Also specialist in mining related corporate and projects work.
Prof. Memberships: Solicitor of Supreme Court of England and Wales. Solicitor of Supreme Court of Queensland, Australia.
Career: 2000–to date partner, corporate department, *Linklaters*. 1995–2000 Solicitor, corporate department, *Linklaters*. 1992-1995 solicitor, corporate department *Feez Ruthning*(now *Allen, Allen & Hemsley*), Australia. 1990-1992 Articles, *Feez Ruthning*.

KHAN, Rafique
CMS Cameron McKenna, London
(020) 7367 2469
rzk@cmck.com
Specialisation: Specialises in oil and gas particularly in the areas of natural gas production, transportation and supply with an additional emphasis on project-financed CCGT Power Projects. He has extensive experience of the European natural gas industries both in the commercial and regulatory field. Speaker on legislative, regulatory and commercial issues facing the gas industries in the UK, elsewhere in the European Union and Central and Eastern Europe.
Prof. Memberships: Law Society of England and Wales; The Institute of Petroleum.
Career: Graduated in 1982 from the University of Leeds; articled clerk and senior legal adviser at *British Gas* 1984-1992. In 1992 joined the firm as Assistant Solicitor and since 1994 a partner in the Energy, Projects and Construction Group.
Personal: Cinema, opera, eating, walking and climbing.

LANE, Mark
Masons, London (020) 7490 6214
mark.lane@masons.com
Partner in infrastructure group. Head of water group.
Specialisation: Principally contract drafting and dispute resolution. Includes ICC arbitrations, domestic litigation and contract drafting for international and UK infrastructure projects. Also handles EU public procurement advising contracting authorities (including government departments, agencies and utilities) on tendering procedures and structuring tendering procedures under PFI schemes. Acted for Eric Cumine Associates on Harbour City litigation in Hong Kong. Member of the firm's team on Channel Tunnel and Canary Wharf projects and on a number of PFI projects including hospitals (procurement issues) and water and waste water treatment works (project agreements and construction issues). Contract drafting on other water related projects in the recent past includes projects in India, the Philippines, Australasia, and Scotland. Editor-in-chief of Mason's 'Water Yearbook'. Has extensive African experience (much of it FIDIC related) including matters in Nigeria, Gambia, Ghana, Mozambique, Kenya and Mali. Has recently worked on projects in Maldives (airport) and Belgium. In March of 1998, led Masons' team acting for the Government of Ukraine in negotiations to establish the Project Management Unit to manage the project to render the Chernobyl Nuclear Reactor No4 safe. (The project is ongoing.) Experienced conference speaker nationally and internationally.
Prof. Memberships: Society of Construction Law; IBA (Committee T) Chairman of sub-committee on International Procurement in Construction Projects; European Construction Institute (Member of Executive Committee) (Chairman of European Legislation Task Force).
Career: Qualified in 1975. Partner at *Masons* since 1988.
Personal: Born 18th March 1950. Educated at Cranleigh School 1962-67 and Trinity College, Cambridge 1968-72. Lives in London.

LANE, Robert
CMS Cameron McKenna, London
(020) 7367 3000
Partner specialising in utilities law and regulation.
Specialisation: Extensive experience of electricity projects and restructurings in the UK and overseas with over 12 years experience. Adviser to The National Grid Company plc. From 1988 to 1990 advised on the restructuring of the England and Wales electricity industry, including drafting the Grid Code for the England and Wales system, with extensive involvement in the design of the regulatory regime and pooling arrangements and in drafting and advising on many of the documents (e.g. those dealing with connection to and use of the system). Continues to advise on these topics and on the development and reform of the market structure. Is heavily involved in the introduction of the 'New Electricity Trading Arrangements'. Also adviser to Northern Ireland Electricity plc on its re-structuring and privatisation and on the further recent restructuring in the Northern Ireland markets to introduce the requirements of the European IME Directive, which introduced bi-lateral trading and balancing mechanisms. Further afield he advised the ESI Reform Unit of the State Government of Victoria on the restructuring of the electricity market there, which involved consideration of and scoping of the regulatory, contractual and code structures and critiquing the licences, codes and contracts. Has also advised on power purchase agreements for Electricidade de Portugal and the Public Power Corporation of Greece and advised on all aspects of the restructuring of the electricity supply industry in Orissa, India. Advised Electricity Supply Board in Eire and Ontario Hydro in Canada. Advising in a number of jurisdictions on the implementation of the European IME Directive, including drafting legislation for Greece and transitional regimes, which has also involved advising a major Western European integrated utility on its compliance with the Directive including advising on Grid Code, connection and use/access agreements, legislation, licensing and ancillary services. Regular speaker at conferences throughout the world.
Prof. Memberships: International Bar Association (Member of Section on Energy and Natural Resources Law and co-chairman of Utilities Law Committee).
Career: Qualified in 1982. Joined *McKenna & Co.*, now *Cameron McKenna*, in 1988.
Personal: Educated at University College, London.

LOGAN, Niall
Nabarro Nathanson, Sheffield (0114) 279 4000
n.logan@nabarro.co.uk
Specialisation: Mineral development and extraction, royalty agreements, post extraction landfill schemes, coalbed methane gas exploitation. From 1992 to 1995 worked on the restructuring and privatisation of the UK coal industry. Recent projects include advising mineral owners on large scale extension to workings at Boulby Potash Mine in North Yorkshire, advising the Coal Authority in relation to colliery closures and advising on the acquisition of copper mines in Zambia.
Career: Qualified 1981; British Coal Legal Dept. 1982-1990; Partner, *Nabarro Nathanson* 1990.

MCGEE-OSBORNE, Christopher
Denton Wilde Sapte, London (020) 7242 1212

MILLS, Deborah
Deborah Mills Associates, Marlow
(01628) 487 711

MORONEY, David
Denton Wilde Sapte, London (020) 7242 1212

PEGG, Garry
LeBoeuf, Lamb, Greene & MacRae, London
(020) 7459 5000
Specialisation: Main areas of specialisation are corporate and commercial work focussing on projects, particularly in the Energy and Natural Resources Sector, and Private International Law generally.
Prof. Memberships: Law Society, International Bar Association (SERL), Association of International Petroleum Negotiators and the UK Energy Lawyers Sub Group. Numerous articles published in Legal and energy publications and has been a frequent speaker at conferences and seminars.
Career: Qualified as a Barrister in 1981 and requalified as a solicitor in 1994. Began his career with the West of England P & I Club, was staff legal adviser at Chevron UK Limited between March 1986-1990, and Senior International Counsel at BHP Petroleum Limited between 1990–1992. Was with *Clifford Chance* between 1992-1995 and joined *LeBoeuf, Lamb, Greene & MacRae* as a partner in June 1996. Currently acts as a Director of a number of energy companies including Claims Validation Services Limited.
Personal: Born 1958. BA (Hons) Law Class 2.1 University of Kent 1981. Lives in London.

PICTON-TURBERVILL, Geoffrey
Ashurst Morris Crisp, London (020) 7638 1111
geoffrey.picton-turbervill@ashursts.com
Partner in energy and projects groups.
Specialisation: Commercial lawyer specialising in energy and natural resources law, in particular upstream and downstream oil and gas and power both in the UK and overseas. His work covers all aspects of oil and gas and electricity industries, and he has particular expertise in mergers and acquisitions and project work. Represents many UK and International energy clients on corporate, project and regulatory matters.
Prof. Memberships: India Editor of 'Oil & Gas Law

& Taxation Review', and the author of the chapter on 'Oil and Gas Acquisition Agreements' for Sweet & Maxwell.

REES, Jonathan
Freshfields Bruckhaus Deringer, London (020) 7936 4000
Specialisation: Head of the Freshfields Energy Group; specialises in M&A, commercial and regulatory work in the oil and gas, electricity and natural resource sectors. Clients include oil companies, government, utilities and investment banks.
Prof. Memberships: International Bar Association (Section on Energy and Natural Resources Law), Member Institute of Petroleum, Vice Chair of the American Bar Association, Section on International Energy and Resources.
Career: *Freshfields* 1982, qualified in 1984 and became a partner in 1992.
Personal: Educated at Wadham College, Oxford (MA).

REEVES, Tony
Kent Jones and Done, Stoke-on-Trent (01782) 202020

RENGER, Michael
Nabarro Nathanson, Sheffield 0114 279 4130 m.renger@nabarro.com
Partner and head of environment department.
Specialisation: Extensive energy, industrial and property client base. Projects include privatisation of coal industry, construction and modification of power stations, waste to energy plants, CHP Schemes. Clients include UK Nirex, all major UK coal operators, US and UK owned oil companies and regional electricity companies.
Prof. Memberships: Legal Associate of RTPI; Associate of Institution of Mining Engineers; Member of the Law Society's Planning Panel; contributor to 'Energy Law and Regulation in the European Union'.

ROBERTS, Martin J.D.
Slaughter and May, London (020) 7600 1200
Specialisation: Has been involved in more than fifty oil & gas and energy-related projects (acting for purchasers, sellers, sponsors and financiers) since the mid 1970s and more recently power station and other infrastructure projects (including road and rail) in the UK and overseas. Has acted for both sponsors and banks on major PFI projects.
Prof. Memberships: The Law Society, City of London Solicitors Company, International Bar Association.
Career: *Slaughter and May* 1967, qualified in 1969 and became partner 1975.
Personal: Born 20 March 1944, attended Shrewsbury School and Trinity Hall, Cambridge.

ROSS, David
Biggart Baillie, Glasgow (0141) 228 8000 dross@biggartbaillie.co.uk
Head of corporate department.
Specialisation: Leads team of several lawyers working extensively in this field. Main areas of practice are electricity and gas law. Widely involved in the drafting and negotiation of a wide variety of contracts relating to the Electricity Industry, including Connection, Use of System, Supply and Sales Agreement for Electricity Companies. Work covered both the vertically integrated industry in Scotland and the industry in England and Wales. Advised on the review of the Agreement for the Nuclear Industry to supply 50% of Scotland's electricity. Adviser on Scottish aspects of the contracts required for all the Public Electricity Suppliers in Great Britain post-1988. Advised on first Energy PFI contract in Health sector in England. Advising on a range of CHP and energy PFI projects throughout Great Britain. Also extensively involved in gas law matters. Particularly drafting and negotiating contracts for the purchase and sale of gas from the field to the domestic customer, including contracts for use throughout Great Britain in the domestic gas market. Separately advises those holding Transporters, Shippers and Suppliers licences on porous and non-porous gas storage in the UK. Author of texts for internal circulation in the firm on energy matters; lectures on energy and PFI topics.
Prof. Memberships: Law Society of Scotland, International Bar Association Section Energy and Natural Resources Law, Insolvency Lawyers Association.
Career: Qualified in 1972. Worked at *Maclay Murray & Spens* 1970-75. Joined *Biggart Baillie & Gifford* in 1975, becoming a Partner in 1977.
Personal: Born 14th January 1948. Attended Trinity College, Glenalmond 1961-65, then Glasgow University: Engineering 1965-66 and Law 1966-70. Business Committee, University of Glasgow 1990-96, Law Society representative, Scottish Council Development and Industry 1995 to date. Director, Glasgow Chamber of Commerce 1996 to date. Chairman Euro-American Lawyers Group 1997 to date. Leisure interests include gardening and windsurfing. Lives in Glasgow.

ROWEY, Kent
Freshfields Bruckhaus Deringer, London (020) 7936 4000
See under Projects/PFI, p.

RUDDIMAN, Robert J.A.
Ledingham Chalmers, Aberdeen (01224) 408515 bob.ruddiman@ledingham-chalmers.co.uk
Specialisation: Oil and gas exploration and production. Bidding agreements, licence applications, joint operating agreements, production sharing agreements, unitisation, pipeline and transportation agreements, trading in field and licence interests, onshore/offshore construction agreements, drilling contracts, integrated services agreements, logistics agreements and all aspects of contracting and operational philosophy.
Prof. Memberships: Law Society of Scotland, The Law Society.
Career: Qualified in Scots Law 1989, English Law 1994. Articled and assistant with *Shepherd & Wedderburn W.S.* 1987-1991. Legal counsel Elf Exploration 1991-1993. *Cameron Markby Hewitt* 1993-1997. Partner *Ledingham Chalmers* 1997.

SALT, Stuart
Linklaters (A member firm of Linklaters & Alliance), London (020) 7456 5912 stuart.salt@linklaters.com
See under Projects/PFI, p.700

SAUNDERS, James
Shepherd & Wedderburn WS, Edinburgh (0131) 228 9900 james.saunders@shepwedd.co.uk
Partner in corporate department.
Specialisation: Main areas of practice are energy law and I.P. (including computer law). Advises on electricity agreements and on I.P. agreements including licensing and turnkey.
Prof. Memberships: Intellectual Property Committee of Law Society of Scotland.
Career: Qualified in 1984. Trainee with *McClure Naismith*, Glasgow 1983-85. Worked for ICI plc 1986-87 and *Freshfields* 1987-93. Joined *Shepherd & Wedderburn WS* in 1993.

SAUNDERS, Mark
Dewey Ballantine, London (020) 7456 6121 msaunders@deweyballantine.com
Specialisation: Partner specialising in all aspects of energy law and corporate law. A London-based partner in the firm's energy and projects group specialising in all aspects of energy law, particularly oil and gas. Seconded to a major oil and gas company in the mid 1980s. Outside counsel to a number of the integrated majors as well as service companies within the sector. Also solicitor to oil industry environmental response collective. An editor of OGLTR, frequent speaker at energy conferences worldwide, contributed to Sweet & Maxwell's 'Upstream Oil and Gas Agreements' and to 'Energy Law & Regulation in the European Union'. Listed in Chambers Survey of Leading UK Commercial Lawyers as one of the eight leading commercial lawyers in the United Kingdom 1997-1998. Listed in 'The Best of the Best: 2000–Energy & Natural Resources' as one of the world's leading 20 energy lawyers–June 2000.

SCRIVEN, John
Allen & Overy, London (020) 7330 3000
Specialisation: Specialises in advising on BOT Schemes, concessions and privatisations, acting for governments, project sponsors, lenders and contractors. Has extensive experience advising on water projects in Europe, Africa, India, South America and the Far East.
Career: Articled *Allen & Overy* 1977, Partner 1988.
Publications: Editor and co-author of 'A Contractual Guide to Major Construction Projects', Sweet & Maxwell (1999). Contributor to 'Future Directions in Construction Law' (1992) and to 'Risk Management and Procurement' (1995), Kings College, London.
Personal: Born 1953; married two daughters. Leisure; family, church, tennis, ski-mountaineering.

SIMPSON, Paul
Clifford Chance, London (020) 7600 1000 paul.simpson@cliffordchance.com
Specialisation: Partner specialising in infrastructure projects and project financings, particularly oil and gas, electricity, transport and Public Private Partnership projects.
Career: Edinburgh University (2(1) LLB Hons 1974). Articled *Norton Rose*; qualified Scotland 1976, England and Wales 1980; assistant solicitor *Fox & Gibbons* 1980-1982; assistant solicitor *Clifford-Turner* (now *Clifford Chance*) 1982-1988; partner 1989.
Personal: Born 1952; resides London.

SMITHERS, Tim M.D.
Veale Wasbrough, Bristol (0117) 925 2020 tsmithers@vwl.co.uk
See under Property (Commercial), p.735

STACEY, Paul
Slaughter and May, London (020) 7600 1200
Qualified with *Slaughter and May* 1983. Partner 1990. Main areas of practice include electricity-related work, banking and project finance. Member of The Law Society. Born 1959.

STANGER, Michael A.
Lovells, London (020) 7296 2000
michael.stanger@lovells.com
Specialisation: Practice covers a wide range of energy and projects work; energy work related primarily to the gas industry; heavily involved in the structural changes in the UK, acting on behalf of gas shippers in relation to the drafting of the Network Code and the 'Claims Validation' agreements; and acting for the Bacton Agent's Group in relation to gas flows through the Interconnector to Continental Europe. Practice also covers gas trading agreements, gas supply agreements, gas storage and work related to the development of independent gas pipeline systems.
Prof. Memberships: Law Society, City of London Solicitors Company, Institute of Petroleum, UK Energy Lawyers Group.
Career: Field Engineer in the oil industry for SPE Schlumberger, mainly in Africa, 1975 to 1978; articled *Lovells*; qualified 1981; partner 1986.

TAYLOR, Michael
Norton Rose, London (020) 7283 6000
taylormpg@nortonrose.com
See under Projects/PFI, p.701

TEMPLE, Richard
CMS Cameron McKenna, London
(020) 7367 3000
rxt@cmck.com
Specialisation: Richard Temple is head of Water in the Energy Projects and Construction Group at *CMS Cameron McKenna*. Richard advised the World Bank on the water and sanitation toolkit: a manual on how to implement water and sewerage projects. He has advised on water projects in Romania, Bulgaria, India, the Czech Republic, Panama, Oman, Bolivia, Poland, Peru, Ghana, Kazakhstan, Hungary and Scotland.
Prof. Memberships: Vice President Europe, Africa and Middle East of the International Private Water Association; Committee Member of the Overseas Forum of British Water; Committee Member of the British Czech and Slovak Law Association; International Bar Association; Project Finance Law Sub-Committee of the IBC; Law Society of England and Wales.
Career: Partner, *Cameron McKenna* 1997. Articled Clerk 1987-89 *Lovell White Durrant*, Solicitor 1989-95 *Lovell White Durrant*, 1996-97 *Ashurst Morris Crisp*.
Personal: Tennis and squash.

THOMSON, Gordon M.
MacRoberts, Glasgow (0141) 332 9988
gmt@macroberts.co.uk
Specialisation: Partner, commercial property group. Deals with all manner of work in commercial property field, including commercial leases; mineral exploration; railway industry; commercial property litigation.
Career: Assistant, *McGrigor Donald*, Glasgow, partner with *MacRoberts* commercial property group since 1978.
Personal: University of Aberdeen (LLB), cars and motorsport, gardening, travel, family.

TRINICK, G. Marcus
Bond Pearce, Plymouth (01752) 266633
xgmt@bondpearce.com
See under Planning, p.668

TUDWAY, Robert
Nabarro Nathanson, London (020) 7524 6421
r.tudway@nabbarro.com
Head of Energy Group Nabarro Nathanson
Specialisation: Energy Law. Advises developers and other parties on electricity distribution and generation contracts, electricity
Prof. Memberships: International Bar Association. Statute Law Society. General Editor, Energy Law and Regulation in the European Union (Sweet & Maxwell). Qualified in 1973. Joined *Nabarro Smith* as a partner 1995.

TURTLE, Trevor W.
Herbert Smith, London (020) 7374 8000
trevor.turtle@herbertsmith.com
Partner since 1987 in company department, with general corporate and commercial practice. Head of firm's water practice.
Specialisation: Specialisations include regulatory, privatisation, project and corporate work in water sector. One of two core partners on team acting for water companies on water privatisation in England and Wales. Since then increasingly involved in water project work in UK and overseas. Member of IBA Water Law Committee, member of management board of British Water.

TYNE, Sally M.
CMS Cameron McKenna, London
(020) 7367 2693
smt@cmck.com
Specialisation: Specialises in oil and gas, with particular emphasis on acquisitions and disposals of UKCS and international petroleum interests via share or asset deals. Extensive experience of oil industry contracts and joint venture issues. Speaker on licensing, unitisation, JOAs and oil & gas acquisition agreements. Co-author of second edition of Taylor & Winsor on Joint Operating Agreements (standard industry textbook).
Prof. Memberships: United Kingdom Energy Lawyers Group (IBA); Law Society.
Career: Educated Trinity College, Oxford. Joined the firm as an oil & gas partner in London, reinforcing its strong existing energy practices in London and Aberdeen. Previously specialised in oil & gas for ten years at *Norton Rose*.
Personal: Married with three children.

UPTON, Neil
Wragge & Co, Birmingham (0121) 214 1005
neil_upton@wragge.com
Specialisation: Interests include power projects and project financing; utilities regulation. Has advised on the setting up of a major UK gas trading business including risk management structure, IPE trading and contracts. He has advised on CHP and Renewables Projects with a value in excess of £1 billion as well as IPPs and is experienced in both UK and overseas BOT projects. Advised on refinancing of £50 million portfolio of windfarms. Currently advising on various NETA and separation of business matters. He has been engaged in the re-organisation of one of the UK's largest PES and advises in Pan-European gas transportation, trading and downstream activities. He is a regular contributor at conferences on utilities matters.
Career: Dover Grammar School 1970-1997; Ran a leasing company before college. 1984-1985 North East London Polytechnic 1st Class Degree LL.B (Hons). Winner of Sweet & Maxwell Law Prize. Articled *Slaughter & May* 1989. Qualified 1991. Partner at *Wragge & Co* May 1996.
Personal: Ex Youth International Golfer; Cricket; Squash; Operetta and Cookery.

VERRILL, John
Lawrence Graham, London (020) 7379 0000
john.verrill@lawgram.com
Partner in Company Commercial Department.
Specialisation: Significant area of practice is oil and gas law. Head of Oil and Gas Team. Work covers all aspects of upstream asset management, including sales and purchases, farm-ins and earn-ins, transportation and joint ventures. Recent work has included advice on decommissioning and security therefor and also advice on public procurement issues in abandonment. Has worked in the UK, Netherlands and Norwegian sectors of the North Sea and on first major offshore gas development in Bangladesh in the summer of 1996, a project structured around the industry's new "alliancing" concept. Also has an insolvency practice.
Prof. Memberships: UK Energy Lawyers Group, International Bar Association Section on Energy and Resources Law. Insolvency Practitioners Association, Insolvency Lawyers Association (Council Member R3).
Career: Qualified in 1981. Licensed Insolvency Practitioner 1990. Joined *Lawrence Graham* in 1983, becoming a Partner in 1986.
Publications: Author of Butterworths 'Insolvency Meetings Manual'. Frequent speaker and writer on insolvency topics.
Personal: Born 25th March 1954. Attended University College School Hampstead, then University College, London (LLB Hons.). Leisure interests include shooting, rowing and gardening. Lives in South Oxfordshire.

WAKE, Brian
Wake Dyne Lawton, Chester (01829) 773100
bdw@wdl.co.uk
See under Environment, p.379

WALLACE, Patrick
Freshfields Bruckhaus Deringer, London
(020) 7936 4000
Specialisation: Advised on establishing the UK electricity market structure at privatisation. Acted on a wide range of electricity projects in the UK and internationally. Advises on energy and natural resources, project financing, regulatory issues, privatisation, commercial contracts and corporate transactions. Speaks English, German and French.
Career: Holds degrees from London, Paris and Harvard Universities. Qualified in 1986. Partner since 1992. Now in Frankfurt with *Deringer Tessin Herrmann & Sedemund* in association with *Freshfields*.

WARNE, Penelope
CMS Cameron McKenna, Aberdeen
(01224) 622002 ex 4412/4437
spw@cmck.com
Specialisation: Practice covers commercial agreements and advice of all types associated with oil & gas exploration and production; dealings in oil and gas interests, farm-ins and farm-outs; unitisation and joint operating agreements; partnering, alliances and joint ventures; and service contracts including pipleline, construction and drilling contracts.
Career: Qualified in English Law in 1981. Articled and assistant solicitor with *Slaughter and May* 1976-

83. Thereafter in-house legal adviser to Marks & Spencer plc before establishing own practice in Aberdeen. 1993 joined *CMS Cameron McKenna* to establish the Aberdeen office. Became a partner in 1994. Also qualified in Scots law.

WHITAKER, Neil

Pinsent Curtis, Leeds (0113) 244 5000
neil.whitaker@pinsents.com

Specialisation: Partner in commercial property dept. Head of mines, minerals and landfill unit, specialising in transactions involving minerals extraction and utilisation of airspace. Acts for nationally known clients in this field.

Career: University of Leeds; qualified 1987; partner *Pinsent Curtis* 1996.

WHITEHEAD, Andrew R.

Martineau Johnson, Birmingham (0121) 678 1528
andrew.whitehead@martjohn.com

Specialisation: Head of Utilities Department acting for a broad client base of electricity, gas and water companies. Heavily involved in ongoing reviews of electricity and gas trading arrangements for several major utilities. Leads a team advising The National Grid Company plc on contractual, regulatory and pool issues affecting its transmission services business, in particular the procurement of ancillary services. Also leads a team advising on a variety of CHP projects. Advised on creation of the world's first reactive power market.

Prof. Memberships: Law Society.

Career: South Hunsley School, Birmingham University (1985 LLB). College of Law, Chester (1986). Articled *Ryland Martineau* (now *Martineau Johnson*). Qualified 1988; Partner 1994.

Personal: Born 1963, resides Warwick with wife and daughter. Music (plays piano and oboe). Member UK Energy Lawyers Association. Associate London College of Music, piano, curries.

WILLIAMS, Gwyn

Hammond Suddards Edge, Birmingham
(0121) 200 2001
gwyn.williams@hammondsuddardsedge.com
See under Environment, p.380

WOOD, Charles

Denton Wilde Sapte, London (020) 7242 1212

WOOLF, Fiona

CMS Cameron McKenna, London
(020) 7367 3000
cfw@cmck.com
Energy Projects and Construction Group.

Specialisation: Main areas of practice are electricity restructurings and privatisations, regulation and the introduction of wholesale and retail competitive markets in the power sector, projects and financings. Worked exclusively on banking and project finance transactions in Bahrain, 1982-85. Acted in the Channel Tunnel project as one of the lead negotiators on the Concession Agreement and the Treaty with British and French Governments. Led a team of 40 people acting for The National Grid Company plc on the privatisation of the Electricity Supply Industry in England and Wales and advised on the Northern Ireland Electricity restructuring and privatisation. Advised Electricidade de Portugal on the Tapada do Outeiro and Pego power projects and the project to bring natural gas to Portugal. Worked on independent transmission projects in Pakistan and Malaysia and the privatisation of the transmission system of Argentina. Has worked on power sector restructurings, utility regulation and privatisations in Australia, Canada, India, California, South Africa, the Republic of Ireland and Central America. Contributor to 'Utilities Law Review' and the Electricity Journal; regular speaker at conferences.

Prof. Memberships: Council Member of the Law Society.

Career: Qualified in 1973. Worked at *Coward Chance* 1973-78 before joining *McKenna & Co.* in 1978. Became a Partner in 1981.

Personal: Born 11th May 1948. Attended Keele University 1966-70. Leisure interests include wine and opera. Lives in Esher, Surrey.

ENVIRONMENT

OVERVIEW: The environmental law market remains well defined, to the extent that the firms who have well established practices continue to dominate, with only limited opportunities for new entrants to reap rewards. After a few false dawns, momentum has gathered behind the introduction of the government's new contaminated land regime (part 2a) which is set to provide increased opportunities to offer environmentally-related advice.

In London, there are few key changes in a market dominated by a handful of City firms. In the smaller teams, environmental advice is often confined to the expertise of a particular individual, or else is subsumed as a cross-departmental service to corporate and property transactions. Freshfields Bruckhaus Deringer, as last year, are threatening to establish themselves as the environmental practice.

As this relatively youthful area of law finally matures, a whole generation of younger practitioners are making their presence felt as partners.

LEADING IN-HOUSE LAWYERS

Simon BOYLE, Environmental Lawyer, *Marconi*

Jeff DURKIN, Senior Legal Adviser, *BP Amoco*

Richard WISEMAN, UK General Counsel, *Shell International Ltd*

Simon Boyle focuses *"one hundred per cent on environmental law"* and is *"the best in the UK"* in this small field. Also highly rated is **Jeff Durkin** who *"knows his stuff,"* as is Richard Wiseman who *"has a fair amount of expertise."*

In-House lawyers profiles: page 1177

RESEARCH APPROVED BY BMRB: *For this edition,* Chambers' *researchers conducted 6083 interviews – 4408 with law firms, 598 with barristers and 1077 with clients.*

The validity of the research was scrutinised by BMRB International, who audited both the methodology and the results at our offices in July 2000. They interviewed Chambers' *researchers and cross-checked sample interviews. Details of the audit appear on page 7.*

LONDON

Allen & Overy The team is unanimously felt to be operating at the highest level, muscling in on an increasing number of major transactions for corporate and banking clients. Positioned in the corporate department, the practice does not follow the land-based approach of other practices. Instead it exploits a vast quantity of M&A-driven work, as well as the firm's advantages in banking and lender liability. Complemented by environmental litigation, stand-alone work is also increasingly apparent.

Owen Lomas is credited with being one of the few magic circle partners to have successfully created a thriving environmental practice. His greatest asset is felt to be his technical knowledge, boosted by a solid track record in academia. A good public speaker and marketeer, he also has the *"ability to settle clients down."* He is felt to have *"outstanding analytical skills"* and *"ferrets out difficult points."* He is particularly active in advising on waste and packaging. Increasingly visible and prolific on transactions, **Ross Fairley** has been the recipient of substantial praise. He is *"intelligent, commercial and doesn't mess about on transactions."* A recent recruit from CMS Cameron McKenna, *"client-friendly"* young assistant **Matthew Townsend**'s arrival was *"quite a coup."* Advice in the chemical industry is a particular forte, and the team acted for ICI on environmental liability issues arising from its major programme of industrial asset disposal. Acting for the financiers (several international banks) of the purchase of Western Europe's largest coal-fired power station, the Drax site in Yorkshire. **Clients:** Enron Power Operations; EVC International; Mobil Oil Corporation.

Freshfields Bruckhaus Deringer The well-oiled Freshfields machine motors on, and is considered by some to offer the most comprehensive full-service environmental team. Famed both for defence litigation and big-ticket transactional work, the contentious and non-contentious departments were recently fused to create an integrated internal structure – a *"holistic approach"* seen by the market as a precursor to a more streamlined operation.

Defence litigator **Paul Bowden** has consolidated his early BNFL reputation, and has carried this forward into a series of toxic tort and judicial reviews where he has *"unrivalled experience."* A *"tough but fair battler,"* he is *"thorough, commercial and always tries to solve problems."* Big personality and *"showman"* **Paul Watchman** is *"the anchor"* – the principal deal maker, he is noted for his expertise on international project finance and infrastructure developments. Regarded by peers as *"a fierce negotiator,"* his planning and environmental expertise *"carries the transactional practice."* The *"father figure of environmental law,"* and still regarded as a *"formidable character,"* **Malcom Forster** carries *"a lot of gravitas."* His mixed practice includes corporate support as well as large prosecution cases. Young litigation partner **Jonathan Isted** continues to cement his reputation for toxic tort defence cases. The team's caseload is increasingly multinational and comprises a number of cross-border litigation matters and major international projects. Acting for One2One in the successful defence of Mohammed al Fayed's appeal relating to the alleged health implications of a mobile phone base station at Oxted in Surrey. In addition, the group advised BNFL on obtaining injunctions against Greenpeace in the UK, France and the Netherlands, following direct action against nuclear transport operations. Recent key transactions include the acquisition of the acrylics division of ICI for Charterhouse on behalf of INEOS. **Clients:** BAe Systems; UK Atomic Energy Authority; National Grid Company; LUL.

Simmons & Simmons The original 'pure' environmental City practice may have lost a little of its lustre with the departure of original spearhead Stephen Tromans to the bar. However, the team is still a favourite with peers. Although the group is unable to compete with the corporate and transactional might of their principal competitors, it is perceived to offer the best balance between transaction support, contentious and stand alone regulatory and advisory work. **Kathy Mylrea** continues to be highly rated for her transactional acumen. *"Versatile"* and possessing *"sound instincts"* she has the *"ability to deal with a range of situations."* **Mike Nash** is similarly popular, has a *"diligent manner"* and is tipped to go far. The firm's workload extends from waste, contaminated land and litigation to water, landfill and human rights. Clients are drawn primarily from the industrial, waste and energy sectors. Acting for George Wimpey plc, the practice successfully settled a complex nuisance case involving contaminated land and statutory nuisance allegations. Also advised Shell International on a multi-jurisdictional transaction involving refinery and pipeline assets. **Clients:** Owens Corning; George Wimpey plc; Cleanaway; Railtrack plc.

ENVIRONMENT• London	Ptnrs	Assts
❶ Allen & Overy	1	6
Freshfields Bruckhaus Deringer	4	16
Simmons & Simmons	2	6
❷ CMS Cameron McKenna	2	5
❸ Ashurst Morris Crisp	1	4
Denton Wilde Sapte	1	2
Lawrence Graham	2	6
Leigh, Day & Co	3	5
Linklaters	2	-
❹ Barlow Lyde & Gilbert	3	2
Berwin Leighton	1	5
Clifford Chance	1	6
Herbert Smith	-	1
Lovells	1	4
Nabarro Nathanson	1	2
Norton Rose	1	3
Slaughter and May	1	3
❺ Gouldens	1	2
Nicholson Graham & Jones	2	1
Rowe & Maw	1	3
SJ Berwin & Co	1	3
Stephenson Harwood	1	-
Theodore Goddard	1	1
Trowers & Hamlins	-	2

LEADING INDIVIDUALS

❶ **BOWDEN Paul** Freshfields Bruckhaus Deringer
CASTLE Pamela CMS Cameron McKenna
FAIRLEY Ross Allen & Overy
FORSTER Malcolm Freshfields Bruckhaus Deringer
LOMAS Owen Allen & Overy
MAY Caroline Lawrence Graham
MYLREA Kathy Simmons & Simmons
O'KEEFFE Jacqui Denton Wilde Sapte
WATCHMAN Paul Freshfields Bruckhaus Deringer

❷ **CUCKSON David** Stephenson Harwood
DAY Martyn Leigh, Day & Co
FOGLEMAN Valerie Barlow Lyde & Gilbert
GREENWOOD Brian Norton Rose
HAVARD-WILLIAMS Vanessa Linklaters
KEEBLE Ed Slaughter and May
LOOSE Helen Ashurst Morris Crisp
NASH Mike Simmons & Simmons
SHERIDAN Paul CMS Cameron McKenna
WAITE Andrew Berwin Leighton

❸ **DEANESLY Clare** Gouldens
DEVAS Hugh Boodle Hatfield
DOOLITTLE Ian Trowers & Hamlins
GARBUTT John Nicholson Graham & Jones
ISTED Jonathan Freshfields Bruckhaus Deringer
REDMAN Michael Clifford Chance
RICE Paul Denton Wilde Sapte
SHEPPARD Claire Theodore Goddard
WISEMAN Andrew Trowers & Hamlins

UP AND COMING
HOBLEY Anthony CMS Cameron McKenna
HUTCHINSON Michael Rowe & Maw
LLOYD Deborah Herbert Smith
MARSHALL Anna Nabarro Nathanson
TOWNSEND Matthew Allen & Overy

Within each band, firms are listed alphabetically. *See **Profiles** on page 372*

CMS Cameron McKenna Felt by many observers to possess a superior stand-alone practice, not excessively shaped by ties to either corporate or property departments. Although some corporate support is a feature of the practice, it is felt that the firm's chief expertise rests in advising medium-sized plcs on a stand-alone basis. Increasing work on contamination-related civil litigation has been evident this year, as well as advice on regulatory and compliance matters in the waste and water fields. High profile **Pamela Castle** is closely associated with her committee and government advisory work. Her strength to the team lies in her strategic client-getting abilities and the *"sheer weight of reputation that she carries."* **Paul Sheridan** *("an absolute professional")* has assumed a greater role at the firm and is widely recommended by the market. *"Unflappable and sensible,"* he *"doesn't posture or score cheap points."* Junior assistant **Anthony Hobley** continues to be praised and maintains his standing. The firm also has a specialist environmental information service which provides advice to European multi-nationals.

On contentious matters, the team has advised the Atomic Weapons Establishment on a number of regulatory enforcement issues relating to water, waste and radioactive substances. Acted for a multi-national food and drinks manufacturer in connection with a hydrocarbon spillage on an adjacent site, polluting the water source for its production lines. Advised Delphi Automotive Systems on its £538 million acquisition of Lucas Diesel Systems from the US based group, TRW Inc. **Clients:** Aventis Crop Science Ltd; BG plc; Alba Life Ltd; United Waste Ltd.

Ashurst Morris Crisp The recent award of partnership to rising star **Helen Loose** was warmly greeted by the environmental fraternity as a sign that the firm had finally thrown their weight behind the dedicated environmental risk management group. *"Bright and persistent,"* she is described as a *"punchy and forceful negotiator."* The mainstay of the practice is the provision of advice on corporate transactions – the majority stemming from the manufacturing, industrial and chemical sectors. There is additionally some pure regulatory work and a separate contentious department dealing with environmental litigation. Energy to waste advice is an area of particular expertise. Transactionally, the group acted for NRG on the acquisition of Killingholme gas-fired power station from National Power plc. Also acted for Victrex plc in relation to its joint venture arrangements with Laporte plc. Stand-alone work includes advice to Enviros and The Albert Fisher Group. **Clients:** Albert Fisher Group; McBride; Soco International plc; Berkeley Group.

Denton Wilde Sapte The firm is most commonly recommended for a substantial regulatory stand-alone component with particular expertise in the energy industry and on PFI projects. Landfill and packaging waste are felt to be additional strings to the bow. Hard-working partner **Jacqui O'Keeffe** has *"enormous personal drive"* and a *"phenomenal capacity for work."* Assistant **Paul Rice** *("bright and personable")* is also frequently recommended by peers. Corporate transactions have included environmental advice to Shell International Chemicals in relation to their joint venture with Exxon, involving sites in 25 jurisdictions. On the regulatory side, handled negotiations for BHP on the disposal of processed waters for offshore installations. Also advised on the implications of the establishment of the Commission for Electricity Regulation in the Republic of Ireland. **Clients:** Entrust; Wellcome Foundation; Thames Waste Ltd; London Electricity.

Lawrence Graham Although this medium-sized practice has been recognised in the past for its litigation strength and operates from the firm's commercial litigation department, the emphasis has recently become more transaction-oriented. Corporate and property support now account for the lion's share of the practice, the rest coming from stand-alone compliance work and some litigation. Contaminated land cases and oil, gas and chemical industry transactions are prime features of the caseload. Much hinges on the fine reputation of *"energetic and enthusiastic"* **Caroline May**. Originally a litigator, her individual standing is felt to be crucial to attracting new clients to the roster. She has a *"sensible and pragmatic approach"* and *"doesn't miss a trick."* However, her reputation rather overshadows her colleagues, and question-marks have been raised over the team's strength in depth.

A recent highlight was the successful completion of a commercial property transaction for a major retailer, stalled for over two years because of environmental difficulties. It involved negotiating with British Gas for an ex-gasworks site and issues of water contamination and environmental impairment insurance. Currently, the team is advising BT on a $40 million nation-wide remediation programme for a cabling network. **Clients:** J Sainsbury Developments Ltd; Crest Nicholson plc; property developers; chemical companies.

Leigh, Day & Co Any of the City environmental defence litigation practices will invariably have come across this firm in its capacity as a leading public law claimant practice. *"Pioneering"* and *"always on the other side,"* the team frequently takes on potent judicial reviews and tort actions on behalf of individuals and aggrieved groups. **Martyn Day** is *"assiduous, persistent and highly pro-active."* Most significant recent case is the ongoing Cape asbestos case from South Africa (at House of Lords stage) which has implications for the environmental liability of British companies operating in the developing world. Acting for a local residents group in Runcorn in a case involving alleged pollution from a nearby ICI facility. The team has also acted on cases connected with electromagnetic fields and microwaves emitted from mobile phones. **Clients:** claimants; residents groups.

Linklaters Not surprisingly, the firm has profited in the past year from a market-led increase in corporate transactions. This accounts for around half the practice. Litigation and environmental planning comprise the remainder. The environmental litigation and transactional practice has recently been fused with the planning group to create a single unit. The firm is felt by the market to be challenging the other City practices for premium transactional environmental work, especially internationally. Energy, power and mining clients feature heavily. The *"shining light"* is **Vanessa Havard-Williams**, whose profile continues to rise. *"Accessible,"* she has a friendly and easy manner, and *"doesn't lay claim to knowledge she doesn't have."*

Key corporate highlight was advice to AngloAmerican in connection with the acquisition by one of their subsidiaries of copper mines previously owned by the Zambian Consolidated Copper Mines Ltd. Also advised on the environmental aspects of the corporate restructuring of BG plc. Contentious work includes defending a major industrial company from issues arising from radioactive contamination. **Clients:** AstraZeneca; AngloAmerican; Trelleborg; Azurix.

Barlow Lyde & Gilbert Considered one of the leading environmental insurance practices, the team is widely recommended for its level of applied expertise in this field. Head of the environmental liability group is *"enigmatic"* **Valerie Fogleman**, who commands a healthy level of market respect. Insurance, re-insurance and professional indemnity are the practice's bread and butter. Corporate transactions are a minor complementary feature. Advised a major international insurer in respect of various claims in several states of the US concerning insurance cover for environmental liabilities. Valerie Fogleman has also been instructed by foreign law firms as an expert witness on English environmental insurance law in two large US pollution insurance coverage actions. **Clients:** insurers; reinsurers.

Berwin Leighton Pre-eminence in planning is the springboard for the firm's environmental practice. Possessing an impeccable client base of retailers, industrials and property developers, a land-based approach is the hallmark of the team. Contaminated land cases, noise abatement and waste management issues are frequently conducted. **Andrew Waite** is a traditional specialist, and a *"quintessential"* environment lawyer. Major recent cases include the Southern Water case relating to an appeal against refusal of planning permission for a major waste water treatment plant. Advised BG on an appeal to obtain the surrender of waste management licences, resulting in a policy change by the Environment Agency. Also acting for a leading chipboard manufacturer, Kronospan Ltd, on several regulatory air pollution issues relating to the operation of their new UK site. **Clients:** Robinsons; Schenectady Europe Ltd; Wood Panel Industries Federation; Tesco.

Clifford Chance The environmental function is intertwined with that of the planning practice, with the majority of client instructions coming as referrals from the corporate department. Energy and utilities are a particularly active area of involvement. The firm's size, resources and international connections stand the practice in good stead to receive a continuous supply of transactional work, the area of greatest visibility. Ex-barrister and solicitor-advocate **Michael Redman** is again recommended for his technical abilities. A traditional planning and environmental lawyer, and a *"real work-horse,"* he has a *"good feel for the nitty-gritty of the business."* The team advised stand-alone clients such as TIP Ltd and Troy Corporation. Advised British Energy on the environmental issues connected with the acquisition of coal-fired power stations, including Eggborough Power Station. Acting for CVC Capital Partners Ltd, Amsterdam in acquiring the Accordis Division of Akzo Nobel bv. **Clients:** GE Capital Europe Ltd; American Standard Inc; Coca-Cola Company; Kvaerner Corporate Development Ltd.

Herbert Smith The practice continues to be rated for its spread of clients in the energy and utilities industries, although it appears to lack a big-hitting individual now that planning and environmental specialist David Brock has left for Mills & Reeve. However, a number of recommendations were received for Australian-trained assistant **Deborah Lloyd**. Well liked by clients and a *"robust negotiator,"* she is considered a practitioner of great potential. The environment team continues to draw its impetus from the planning, property and corporate departments.

On the contentious side, there is noted strength in insurance and environmental defence litigation. Transactionally, the team acted for Petroplus in its acquisition of an oil refinery in Switzerland from Shell. Advised Severn Trent Water in a number of high-profile litigations, including the ongoing Worcestershire and Gloucestershire water pollution incident, and British Waterways Board v Severn Trent (October 1999) concerning the statutory powers of sewerage undertakers. **Clients:** Johnson Matthey; Simon Storage; Royal & Sun Alliance; St Paul International Insurance Co.

Lovells The environment practice is fused with health and safety and headed by a full time partner. This is given extra weight with input from the planning and property departments. The range of clients takes in companies from the manufacturing, waste, power and banking industries. The bulk of the practice revolves around corporate support and technical due diligence on cross-border transactions, although there is also a sizeable litigation and stand-alone capability. The latter includes advice given to a large international company in connection with a Drinking Water Inspectorate (DWI) investigation into a drinking water pollution incident. Significant transactions include advice to BE Aerospace on environmental liabilities and contractual protection in connection with its acquisition of CF Taylor from the TI Group. **Clients:** Quintain Estates plc; Cinven; Cory Environmental Ltd; Bank Of Scotland.

Nabarro Nathanson The small environmental team in London works in close tandem with the larger Sheffield office. The practice's client base comprises a large number of US corporations requiring advice on managing the environmental aspects of multi-national transactions. Much of this is handled by former management consultant and corporate lawyer **Anna Marshall**, who is newly recommended. Clients have praised her *"understanding of our needs and objectives." "Not overly lawyerish"* she *"finds solutions."*

The team acts for large numbers of the firm's property clients, primarily on contaminated land issues. Have acted for the US Dana Corporation in relation to the acquisition and subsequent management of multi-site portfolios across Europe. Also assisted Mercury Asset Management on the acquisition and management of their development sites, including advice on contaminated land issues and remediation strategies. **Clients:** Security Capital Group; Access Storage Centres; Dana Corporation; GKN.

Norton Rose A small but acclaimed unit headed by the *"gentlemanly and professional"* **Brian Greenwood**. His fine reputation has been established largely in planning although he is devoting increasing energy to the firm's environmental practice. Felt to be strong on regulatory issues (notably in waste licensing) he is rated as a tactician and also as an accomplished and thorough litigator. As well as assisting the firm's banking and corporate practice, stand-alone work focuses on contractor regulatory work for commercial clients. Handled all the environmental due diligence for BMW on its recent sale of the Rover Group to the Phoenix Consortium. Advised Castle Cement Ltd on all environmental issues, including representation at public inquiries in relation to appeals against decisions made by the Environment Agency. **Clients:** AES; General Cable Corporation; Chase Manhattan; New Millennium Experience Company Ltd.

Slaughter and May More than most, the firm's environmental team provides a near-exclusive corporate transactional support service, including large numbers of company consolidations and disposals. Stand-alone capability is limited, although contaminated land advice and multi-party clean-ups are increasingly common. **Ed Keeble** is *"thorough and workmanlike"* and rated highly for his input into transactions. An *"effective deal-doer"* he is occasionally felt to *"veer towards the over-robust."* The team recently provided advice to Blue Circle on packaging matters. **Clients:** ICI; Blue Circle; large plcs.

Gouldens Property-based partner **Clare Deanesly** is the recommended name at a firm that *"shouldn't be underestimated."* Her team has particular expertise in the waste management industry, and also acts for minerals, landfill and water clients. The commercial property department also generates substantial levels of contaminated land-related issues for development clients. The bar commented on the practice's *"clear instructions, identification of the issues and fantastic client care."* Highlight of the year was advice offered in the sale of Hughes Waste Management Ltd to United Waste. For Hanson Waste Management, the team advised on the establishment of a joint venture company, Gamble Waste Ltd, with FL Gamble & Sons Ltd – a waste recycling operation at Newhaven. Acted for Mid-Kent Water in respect of a prosecution by the Drinking Water Inspectorate on drinking water quality issues. **Clients:** Hanson Waste Management; Biffa Waste; SITA GB Ltd; Enstone plc.

Nicholson Graham & Jones The vastly experienced **John Garbutt** has a long track record in local government, the minerals industry and private practice. The firm continue to be active in the cement, concrete and minerals industry for core clients such as Blue Circle Industries plc and UK Nirex Ltd, although its profile is not felt to have expanded far beyond this. Still regarded as *"sound on waste management,"* the team also acts for food processing companies and local authorities, and have acted in a number of judicial reviews. Acted in the Hillingdon Hospital Incineration case where the planning authority challenges were successfully resisted in the High Court. The team also conducted public inquiries for meat industry clients under the Environmental Protection Act 1990. **Clients:** Blue Circle Industries plc; UK Nirex Ltd; Strong & Fisher Holdings Ltd; London Waste Ltd.

Rowe & Maw The small environmental team is based in the corporate department and acts as an additional support function to property, banking and projects transactions. Substantial levels of regulatory work complement this. Overlaps to a great degree with the chemical practice where the firm acts for several leading industrials. Expertise also exists in waste management and landfill sites. The departure of Hugh Devas to Boodle Hatfield at the end of May was a setback, although it has acquired the services of rising practitioner **Michael Hutchinson** from Freshfields. Represented the Waste Recycling Group plc in its acquisition of 3C Holdings Ltd for approximately £120 million. The team is currently handling the environmental aspects of the £82 million cross-border disposal of ICI's Fluoropolymers division, as part of a large scale divestment programme. **Clients:** Marley plc; Monsanto plc; ICI plc; Waste Recycling group plc.

S J Berwin & Co The environmental practice is linked closely with the planning department and generally provides support to property development clients seeking advice on land contamination. Stand-alone advice is given to clients in the water, sewerage and waste treatment industries. Act on a number of instructions from the Environment Agency concerning water-related matters. Highlights have included negotiations over threatened litigation for pollution arising from an industrial work-wear cleaning facility. For a large American manufacturing company the practice acted on the environmental aspects of the sale of an aerospace products company. Also advised on the upgrade of a sewerage treatment facility required to comply with EU sewerage treatment directives. **Clients:** Marylebone Warwick Balfour; Foster Pepper & Shefelman; Delancey Estates; Environment Agency, Southern Water.

Stephenson Harwood **David Cuckson** heads the practice and is still widely known and respected in his capacity as head of the UK Environmental Law Association (UKELA.) A *"name to be reckoned with,"* he is *"bright and able,"* although his practice is felt to be *"slightly low-key."* The practice embraces property and contaminated land work, M&A transactions and waste management regulation. A large cross-departmental team assists on other specialist areas such as shipping collisions and spillages, insurance and regulatory offences. Major deals include advice to Hepworth plc on environmental liabilities in relation to the disposal of part of its business, including the sale of a landfill site, a quarry subject to site restoration obligations and water discharge arrangements. Also assisted AEA Technology plc on a project for a local authority to provide an energy from waste facility. **Clients:** Sorin Biomedica SpA; Caird Group plc; Accor Business and Leisure Hotels; Elementis plc.

Theodore Goddard Recently made partner, **Claire Sheppard**'s rise continues in concert with a practice that *"promises much for the future."* The work is a mixed bag of transactional, regulatory and litigation matters. Corporate, banking, PFI and property-related support rubs shoulders with contentious civil cases. Niche focus is felt to centre around the provision of advocacy and advice at inquiry stage for the waste industry. Examples here include acting for the leading promoters of waste-fired incinerators over a number of sites across the south of the country. Also acted for Delta plc on the disposal of its cable business to Draka Sarphati BV, and for Blagden plc in the sale of its chemicals division to Borden International Holdings Ltd. **Clients:** National Westminster Bank plc, PricewaterhouseCoopers; Lansbury Group.

Towers & Hamlins The firm's acknowledged strengths in local authority and housing work are evident on the environmental front, where contaminated land advice is the main thrust of the practice. Client base comprises housing associations, the public sector and the waste industry. **Andrew Wiseman** is again recommended for his specialist focus in waste and contaminated land. Partner **Ian Doolittle** spreads himself rather more thinly, mixing environmental advice with a housing and local authority caseload. The practice recently acted for Wellingborough Borough Council concerning contamination issues and the third-party liabilities of a closed landfill site. **Clients:** Haleport Limited; SERM; local authorities.

Other Notable Practitioners **Hugh Devas** has recently moved to Boodle Hatfield from Rowe & Maw. A practitioner of long experience, he has a particular name for waste management issues.

THE SOUTH

ENVIRONMENT • The South	Ptnrs	Assts
❶ **Blake Lapthorn** Portsmouth, Southampton	2	4
Bond Pearce Southampton	-	2
Brachers Maidstone	2	-
DMH Brighton	1	1
Stevens & Bolton Guildford	1	-
❷ **Fynn & Partners** Bournemouth	2	1

LEADING INDIVIDUALS	
❶ **ABRAHAM Henry** Brachers	**ALLEN Tony** DMH
BARLOW Colin Blake Lapthorn	**DAVEY Catherine** Stevens & Bolton
HORNER Douglas Brachers	

Within each band, firms are listed alphabetically. *See **Profiles** on page 372*

Blake Lapthorn Considered to be *"making a push"* in the market, the environmental group contains a number of individuals with specialist expertise based in the Southampton and Portsmouth offices. It overlaps with the planning and property departments, in addition to offering stand-alone capability. **Colin Barlow** is particularly recommended. The nature of the workload is varied and includes packaging, development and waste. There is also an environmental management and auditing consultancy. Recently called out by a client to contain a pollution incident and manage the clean-up. The team advised a US multi-national in meeting its waste packaging obligations. Currently instructed by Planned Maintenance Engineering Ltd to implement an environmental management system for ISO accreditation. **Clients:** Hillier Nurseries; Horticultural Trades Association; Goodmans Loudspeakers Ltd.

Bond Pearce The environmental and planning unit has been most noted this year for acting on the large container port extension outside Southampton for Associated British Ports. Considerable projects and infrastructure development expertise has been necessary for this project, which has substantial environmental implications. Wider ability exists in waste, landfill sites, renewable energy and urban regeneration. The practice also provides transactional support to the firm's locally-based corporate clients. **Clients:** Devonport Management Ltd; Scottish Power plc; Musgrove; Enron Corporation.

Brachers Associated as much with the firm's planning practice, **Henry Abraham** and **Douglas Horner** are well-regarded by the market. Both engage in corporate support and the defence of land-owning clients in environmental damage cases. Defended a historic farming practice alleged to have polluted a private waterway. Clients include individuals and organisations from the manufacturing, waste disposal, agriculture, tourism and development sector. Represented a major tourist attraction in noise abatement proceedings concerning audio visual displays. **Clients:** Paper manufacturers; truck repair business; farmers; waste disposal operators.

DMH Provides a cohesive specialist planning and environmental unit that contains both professional consultants and qualified lawyers. Although planning represents the weightier aspect of the practice, **Tony Allen** sustains a fine reputation and is felt to be particularly *"dominant and influential"* in the southern half of the region. Advises predominantly on environmental planning and liability for a series of local industrial clients, often in the waste and incineration sector, and NHS trusts. Contentious work revolves around statutory nuisance appeals, environmental prosecution defence and judicial review. A highlight was a ten-day local public inquiry concerning the refusal of planning permission for an animal remains incinerator for Crawley Abattoir. **Clients:** Friends Provident Life; Crawley Abattoir (Sussex); Cory Environmental; NHS trusts.

Stevens & Bolton **Catherine Davey**'s reputation as one of the few leading environmental specialists in the region appears to have been further strengthened. Maintaining a split planning and environmental practice, she *"always has a lot of work"* and is regarded as a proactive and visible local practitioner. The bulk of the workload is the application of environmental due diligence on corporate transactions. There is a steady stream of waste licensing work for waste to energy and CHP (combined heat and power) clients. Lesser amounts of work are undertaken on statutory nuisance, landfills and on behalf of local authorities. Recently undertook a combined property, planning and environmental case for a large West London-based hospital trust. **Clients:** Waste operators; hospital trusts; local authorities; medium-sized companies.

Fynn & Partners Largely as a spin-off from the planning practice, environmental matters stem from planning advice given to leisure operators, engineering and manufacturing clients. Noise pollution and abatement and statutory nuisance issues are key areas for the practice. On behalf of a local authority, a highlight included mounting an appeal to the Court of Appeal to determine the existence of statutory nuisance. **Clients:** SFI Group plc; Hall & Woodhouse Ltd; Wessex Leisure Group.

SOUTH WEST

ENVIRONMENT • South West	Ptnrs	Assts
❶ **Bond Pearce** Plymouth	1	4
Burges Salmon Bristol	2	2
Osborne Clarke Bristol	2	1
❷ **Bevan Ashford** Bristol	1	2
Clarke Willmott & Clarke Bristol, Taunton	*	*
❸ **Lyons Davidson** Bristol	*	*
Stephens & Scown Exeter	3	-
Veale Wasbrough Bristol	1	-

LEADING INDIVIDUALS	
❶ **GIBBS Kevin** Osborne Clarke	**HOLMES Sarah** Bond Pearce
JOHN Alan Osborne Clarke	**SALTER Ian** Burges Salmon
TRINICK Marcus Bond Pearce	
❷ **BAKER Neil** Clarke Willmott & Clarke	**HAYDEN Tim** Clarke Willmott & Clarke

Within each band, firms are listed alphabetically. *See **Profiles** on page 372*
** See editorial entries for explanations of team sizes.*

Bond Pearce For some time, the firm's environmental image has been epitomised by the renewable energy and wind practice of **Marcus Trinick.** As the pre-eminent expert in this niche area, he maintains a high regional profile, although there have been suggestions that he appears less in the commercial and regulatory mainstream. However, he is seen as an *"energetic"* practitioner and possesses considerable *"flair and presence."* Associate **Sarah Holmes** runs a far broader practice, including work for waste, industrial and development clients, and is considered a *"sparky and punchy operator."*

The practice is rounded out with corporate due diligence and some litigation. The team has acted on some major transactions in the waste and mineral sector, acting for waste companies entering into gas agreements with electricity generators, on landfill schemes and the impact of European legislation. Continue to assist on the development of a legal framework for offshore wind energy development through a contract with the DTI. Successfully defended Devonport Management Ltd and a subsidiary of County Environmental Services Ltd on an environmental prosecution. **Clients:** Renewable Energy Systems; National Wind Power Ltd; Pennon Group; SITA (GB) Ltd.

Burges Salmon The corporate base of the firm has recently been bolstered by the emergence of a definite specialist environmental capability. This has been widely attributed to the highly experienced **Ian Salter**. *"Affable"* and *"easy to work with,"* he focuses on environmental regulation, and has niche nuclear expertise. Additionally acts for clients in the transport, food, minerals and agricultural sectors. The wider remit of the practice involves due diligence for corporate transactions and land contamination issues. Advising the Ministry of Defence on a multi-billion pound contract involving a number of nuclear sites and the transfer of over 100 environmental consents. On behalf of transport client FirstGroup plc, the group continues to advise on prosecutions brought by the Environment Agency and contaminated land risk assessment. **Clients:** Ministry of Defence; FirstGroup plc; UK Nirex Ltd.

Osborne Clarke OWA The stand-alone capability was given a boost with the cross-town recruitment of specialist **Kevin Gibbs** from Lyons Davidson in March. A well-established regional player, his planning, regulatory and waste expertise are frequently cited. *"Energetic"* partner **Alan John** *"knows his stuff."* In addition to supporting M&A transactions, the team is noted for specific expertise in waste management and renewable energy. Acting for Amgen Rhondda in the acquisition of a landfill site in administration and the subject of enforcement proceedings. For a large petrol retailer, the team is acting on chemical contamination threatening surface and ground waters. **Clients:** Aggregate Industries plc; Churngold Waste Management; Manweb plc; SITA Holdings (UK) Ltd.

Bevan Ashford The practice intertwines with planning and health and safety departments. The firm's client base and spread of work is broad, and includes contaminated land advice, environmental prosecutions, NHS trusts, renewable energy and waste disposal. Acting for the Isle of Man Government on the operation of a waste to energy plant. The team assisted in establishing a joint venture for a water effluent plant at an industrial site in Wales, and advised on the development of renewable energy plants across England, securing consents and the construction of facilities. **Clients:** Rolls Royce; Aeron Valley Cheese Ltd; Border Biofuels Ltd; NHS trusts.

Clarke Willmott & Clarke (2 partners 50%, 1 associate and 2 assistants up to 50%) First-rate planning team applies environmental expertise from this perspective. Environmental prosecutor **Tim Hayden** is again recommended for his advocacy in criminal prosecutions. His practice extends into the south of the region and involves acting for agricultural and commercial clients on waste disposal, contaminated land and water pollution. Bristol-based **Neil Baker**, formerly of Nicholson, Graham & Jones, has considerable experience of waste and industrial matters and is rapidly raising his profile as a rising regional name. Acting more for manufacturing and industrial clients, he has a broad contentious and non-contentious practice, dealing with appeals, water pollution offences, statutory nuisance proceedings and corporate transactions. The firm acts for a number of clients in the food and drink sector. A highlight of 1999 was the successful defence of the first prosecution brought under the 1997 BSE regulations. **Clients:** NFU South-West region; Matthew Clark plc; JV Richards plc; government agencies.

Lyons Davidson (2 partners part-time, 1 assistant part-time) The practice has apparently suffered due to the departure of its only recognised specialist, Kevin Gibbs, to Osborne Clarke. The caseload is now spread between two partners with both contentious and non-contentious experience. The former involves a number of environmental prosecutions and multi-party liability claims on waste, nuisance and pollution matters. The latter revolves around increased amounts of property-led contaminated land advice for development, healthcare and institutional clients. Acted recently for a large High Street bank in the sale of a site based on a former industrial land. **Clients:** Property developers; health trusts; universities; residential developers.

Stephens & Scown The practice exerts its influence over the far south-west of the region and is best-known for its agricultural-related practice and core client English China Clays. The joint planning and environmental unit also advises in the mineral, mining and quarrying industries. Highlight of the year was dealing with substantial claims for compensation arising from new environmental protection conferred by the Birds Directive and Habitats Directive. **Clients:** Aggregate Industries plc; ECC International Ltd; Trago Mills.

Veale Wasbrough Two strands characterise the environmental practice. Firstly, a particular expertise in waste, which includes management planning and licensing issues, financial provision for after-care of sites and land/lease acquisition for landfill purposes. Secondly, the regeneration of contaminated sites, which feeds off work originating from the commercial property department's development clients. Continue to be involved in acting for a consortium of landowners on the remediation of Bristol's Harbourside development. **Clients:** Hemming Waste Management; Esso Petroleum Co Ltd; Bristol City Council.

WALES

ENVIRONMENT • Wales	Ptnrs	Assts
❶ **Edwards Geldard** Cardiff	*	*
Eversheds Cardiff	Fb	Fb
Morgan Cole Cardiff	2	1

*Within each band, firms are listed alphabetically. Fb Figures unavailable at time of going to press. * See editorial entries for explanations of team sizes.*

Edwards Geldard (1 partner part-time, 1 assistant part-time) The environmental capability is part of a wider public law, local authority and planning team and contains few specialists. In addition to general public law advice with an environmental dimension, the team undertakes corporate support work and environmental prosecutions. Advised on the environmental consequences of the acquisition for a US client of ANACOMP, a manufacturer of data tape with a UK facility at Brynmawr, South Wales. **Clients:** Central Trains; ANACOMP; motor dealerships; local authorities.

Eversheds The Cardiff office works closely with the regulatory unit at the Bristol office, forming an environment unit which overlaps with health and safety and consumer protection. The property department also provides non-contentious advice on planning and environmental matters. Advised a chemical manufacturing client following a chemical spill and fume release, leading to prosecutions undertaken by the HSE and Environment Agency. **Clients:** Retail and leisure companies; construction and aggregates groups; manufacturers; financial institutions.

Morgan Cole Last year's ranked individual Luke Bennett left in March 2000 to join Nabarro Nathanson in Sheffield. This is felt to leave the practice revolving around the litigation partners who conduct a substantial proportion of environmental advocacy work. In addition, the firm's industrial client base generates regulatory and advisory matters, dealt with by the joint planning and environmental team. Advise a number of waste businesses in Wales including LAS Waste Ltd on compliance issues relating to the collection, transportation and disposal of waste. Acted in a joint venture between BP Oil UK Ltd and Mobil Oil Ltd, covering a portfolio of 900 sites, dealing with the environmental liability issues associated with disposing of storage sites and pipelines. **Clients:** PHS Group Ltd; NFU services Ltd; Rockwool Ltd; UK Atomic Energy Authority.

MIDLANDS

ENVIRONMENT • Midlands	Ptnrs	Assts
❶ **Eversheds** Birmingham	1	5
Pinsent Curtis Birmingham	*	*
Wragge & Co Birmingham	*	*
❷ **Hammond Suddards Edge** Birmingham	*	*
❸ **Kent Jones and Done** Stoke-on-Trent	1	2

LEADING INDIVIDUALS	
❶ **SHINER Philip** Public Interest Lawyers	**TURNER John** Wragge & Co
❷ **MACKINLAY Hannah** Pinsent Curtis	
WILLIAMS Gwyn Hammond Suddards Edge	

Within each band, firms are listed alphabetically. *See **Profiles** on page 372*

** See editorial entries for explanations of team sizes.*

Eversheds The firm's Midlands office is still considered a key regional player, and the work is divided up between a large team dealing with a range of contentious and non-contentious matters. Much of this eminence derives from the firm's client base. The *"terrific"* property department is a notable source of work, generating clients who are advised on contaminated land/urban regeneration issues for house-building and institutional development clients. On the contentious side, lawyers handle defence litigation, notices issued by statutory authorities and civil disputes involving environmental issues. Recent examples of transactional support include the provision of environmental due diligence for BMW's sale of the Rover Group to the Phoenix consortium. Advised Energy Power Resources Ltd on the new IPPC regime in respect of a purpose built-plant to recover electricity, steel and carbon from used or rejected tyres. Also acted for Aldec Ltd in respect of an industrial explosion. **Clients:** British Gypsum; Artex Blue Hawk; Lucas Varity; Ryland Group plc.

Pinsent Curtis (3 partners part-time, 2 contentious, 1 non-contentious, 1 assistant part-time) The wider practice has a reputation for its institutional and public sector work, although the individual remit of *"flourishing"* associate **Hannah Mackinlay** is largely restricted to non-contentious advice on corporate transactions. Her profile is mushrooming and she is held to be *"straightforward to deal with."* Her influence has extended to expanding activity within UKELA and the local professional community. Land contamination and waste are central themes of the practice, while additional partners handle judicial review, regulatory work and prosecutions in the packaging and water industry. Advised on the sale of Premco, a waste disposal company owned by Staffordshire County Council. Acted for Onyx on the tendering-out of Surrey County Council's waste disposal service, and implemented the Herefordshire and Worcestershire integrated waste management contract (for Severn Waste Services.) **Clients:** Onyx / Vivendi; Daventry District Council; Staffordshire County Council; property developers.

Wragge & Co (1 associate full-time, 1 commercial property partner 20%, 1 planning asst 20%, 1 property asst 20%) Although no longer alone at the zenith, the firm retains a leading environment profile. This rests largely on the individual expertise of **John Turner**, who *"really stands out"* and is still considered *"the name"* in the Midlands. Felt to be stronger on the contentious side, he acts for corporate and property development clients in regulatory, transactional and litigious matters. Extra resources at both partner and assistant level are available from the property department. Air pollution control is a specific area of expertise. Acted for Tarmac on its purchase of the environmentally sensitive Marley Block Paving Business, a transaction involving matters concerning air pollution authorisations, water drainage rights and contaminated land issues. Acting for the directors of BMEC on a prosecution by HM Customs and Excise for the non-payment of landfill tax. **Clients:** Albright & Wilson; Alumasc; Lacks Enterprise; TRW.

Hammond Suddards Edge (1 consultant full-time, 2 assistants part-time) The practice has suffered a slight slip in fortunes, in keeping with a difficult year in the Midlands. The effect of the recent merger, of course, remains to be seen. **Gwyn Williams** has an acknowledged reputation for waste, mining and minerals work. Although this accounts for the main thrust of the practice, the team also acts for a number of property development clients and manufacturers, primarily on non-contentious matters. Acted for the Government of Ireland on the authorisation of a mixed oxide facility at Sellafield. The team advised Brintons plc on the negotiation of new effluent discharge arrangements for its textile factories in the Midlands. **Clients:** Aggregate Industries; Viasystems (UK); Government agencies.

Kent Jones and Done A traditional name in minerals and coal work is seen to have progressed to embrace advice on environmental compliance, waste management licensing and contaminated land. The spread of clients mixes mineral operators and commercial clients with landowners and developers. Advised on a range of environmental issues following the closure of Fluorspar mining division of a mineral operator, and its subsequent disposal. Also gave advice on a matter connected with the acquisition of a chemical manufacturer in Suffolk. **Clients:** Laporte plc; Shraff Tip Ltd; Epichem Ltd.

Other Notable Practitioners **Phil Shiner** of Public Interest Lawyers is *"enormously dedicated"* and widely respected for his human rights flavoured claimant practice in environmental matters, planning and public law. Formerly at Tyndallwoods, his *"bravery and commitment"* in cutting-edge cases and judicial reviews are frequently admired. Acting for pressure group Nuclear Awareness in a legal aid case challenging the manufacturers of new Trident warheads at Aldermaston.

EAST ANGLIA

ENVIRONMENT • East Anglia	Ptnrs	Assts
❶ **Mills & Reeve** Norwich, Cambridge	1	3
Richard Buxton Cambridge	1	1
❷ **Eversheds** Norwich	2	-
Hewitson Becke + Shaw Cambridge	1	2

LEADING INDIVIDUALS	
❶ **BRYCE Andrew John** Andrew Bryce & Co	**BUXTON Richard** Richard Buxton
❷ **BROCK David** Mills & Reeve	**CARRIAGE Rebecca** Mills & Reeve
JEWKES Penny Eversheds	

Within each band, firms are listed alphabetically. *See **Profiles** on page 372*

Mills & Reeve Blessed with a particularly strong complement of environmental and planning *"all-rounders"* now that former Herbert Smith planning lawyer **David Brock** has made East Anglia his new professional home. He runs a successful minerals practice. Unlike Brock, **Rebecca Carriage** has a greater emphasis on stand-alone environmental work, both litigious and regulatory. Client base stretches from mineral operators and local authorities to landed estate owners and some commercial clients. Although there is substantial cross-over with the planning practice, stand-alone advice is given on waste management issues, packaging regulations, statutory nuisance and water pollution. Currently acting on a major lands tribunal case for two large corporate clients against the DETR and Highways Agency. **Clients:** NHS Trusts; universities; landowners; minerals operators.

Richard Buxton Few practitioners in the field are as renowned as the determined *"maverick"* **Richard Buxton**, who has carved out a formidable space of his own acting exclusively for claimants in nature conservation, airport noise and environmental impact assessment cases. He is said to *"judicially review everyone," "puts spanners in the works"* and is always *"chipping away and making law."* His strategy is felt to be based on *"playing it all at an instinctive level"* and *"taking a punt."* He and a qualified assistant are currently engaged in a long series of judicial reviews against the government, acting for a number of local residents concerned with the noise caused by night flights into Heathrow. Won the Huddlestone case in the Court of Appeal, concerning the interpretation of the environmental impact assessment directives for old quarrying permissions. Also acted for an eco-protestor in the Tugwell development. **Clients:** Individual applicants; resident groups.

Eversheds Advises a series of commercial clients in due diligence on their corporate mergers and acquisition transactions. Feeding off a large property practice, typical advice centres on contaminated land issues and brownfield site developments for property and house-building clients. Additionally, there is expertise in pollution control, waste disposal and regulatory compliance. Ex-lecturer **Penny Jewkes** is the recognised specialist. Her style has been described as *"academic and precise."* Advising John Rannoch Ltd on their proposals to construct broiler units in Suffolk. Advise a number of property clients on clean-up liabilities, dealing with the Environment Agency and local authorities. **Clients:** Bernard Matthews plc; Atlas Aggregates (RMC) Group; Technigraph Products Ltd.

Hewitson Becke + Shaw The practice is more widely known for its planning work, although it does advise on matters including waste management and disposals, contaminated land and corporate transactional support. The team also represent clients in civil and criminal proceedings. Advising Shanks Waste Services on the development of a large waste landfill site on the outskirts of Milton Keynes, involving negotiations to secure the construction of an £87 million link road by-pass. **Clients:** Shanks Waste Services; university colleges; Norfolk Homes; Comer Group.

Other Notable Practitioners **Andrew Bryce**, an influential sole practitioner working from home, continues to evoke admiration for his *"remarkable consistency and longevity."* He specialises in compliance issues, acting for large corporates in the waste and oil and gas sectors.

NORTH WEST

ENVIRONMENT • North West	Ptnrs	Assts
❶ **DLA** Manchester	1	2
Eversheds Manchester	1	4
Leigh, Day & Co Manchester	1	1
Wake Dyne Lawton Chester	2	2
❷ **Addleshaw Booth & Co** Manchester	1	2
Hammond Suddards Edge Manchester	2	3
Masons Manchester	℞	℞

LEADING INDIVIDUALS	
❶ **DAWSON Andrew** DLA	**SHEPHERD Elizabeth** Eversheds
WAKE Brian Wake Dyne Lawton	

Within each band, firms are listed alphabetically. *See **Profiles** on page 372*

℞ *Figures unavailable at time of going to press.*

DLA Contentious-focused practice which deals primarily with environmental criminal defence cases. Enthusiastic livewire and litigator **Andrew Dawson** *"really knows what he's doing"* and is again recommended for his work in defending chemical and manufacturing companies from the regulatory authorities. Successfully defended a subsidiary of BTP on a number of charges in a case against the Environment Agency where they were alleged to have caused a major fish-kill in the Calder Valley. **Clients:** Avecia; BTP plc; pharmaceutical companies; food companies.

Eversheds **Elizabeth Shepherd** *("can deal with most problems")* is widely recognised and heads what is regarded as the strongest non-contentious environment practice in Manchester. Although some prosecution work is conducted, the bulk of the caseload involves supporting an extensive roster of property development and corporate clients. Some chemical and manufacturing clients receive independent environmental compliance advice. Highlights include an appointment to act for the Waste Recycling Group, whom they have advised on the delivery of an integrated waste management system for councils in Yorkshire. Acting on behalf of Dupont in relation to the environmental aspects of the transfer of their polyester and films business to Turkish and Japanese joint venture companies. **Clients:** Australian National Industries Ltd; AEA Technology plc; Tilcon (South) Ltd; Chapelthorpe plc.

Leigh, Day & Co Acting almost exclusively for claimants, the firm maintains a *"deservedly high reputation."* The claims department covers individual and multi-party actions concerned with product liability, public law and environmental cases. The work typically involves actions on behalf of people exposed to noxious fumes such as carbon monoxide. Acting on behalf of a husband and wife poisoned over a ten-year period by a defective gas fire, where allegations centred on lack of care by the landlord. **Clients:** Individual claimants.

Wake Dyne Lawton *"Putting together an effective team of lawyers."* The firm's profile is perceived to be on the up, following recent boosts to the planning and environmental teams. The firm has noted expertise in minerals-related matters. *"Affable"* and *"switched-on"* **Brian Wake** continues to be recommended. Recently formed the Land Resource Alliance, a joint venture with Manchester property firm Mace & Jones, intended to capitalise upon contaminated land issues. Client base is mainly drawn from the industrial areas of the North West. The team is representing an objectors' group in an inquiry concerning a cement kiln manufacturer in North Wales burning hazardous waste. **Clients:** RTZ; Castle Cement.

Addleshaw Booth & Co This large commercial practice is again rated by the market, although is not felt to offer a fully specialised environmental unit. Instead, the firm's environmental capacity feeds off substantial planning and commercial property departments. Provided environmental advice to Scapa Group plc in connection with the sale of the Speciality Materials Division to Duke Street Capital Ltd. **Clients:** 3i Group plc; Berkeley Group plc; Lancashire Waste Services; North West Water Ltd.

Hammond Suddards Edge This sizeable environmental practice offers both contentious and non-contentious advice, although the former is considered to predominate. One commercial litigation partner acts in civil and criminal defence cases for clients in a spread of industries such a as pharmaceuticals, foodstuffs and utilities. A recently-made partner provides full-time support for corporate transactions. The firm acted for a large chemical corporation on its purchase of a polystyrene business from a major oil company. **Clients:** Chemical companies; utilities; oil companies; food producers.

Masons Personnel changes have not altered the firm's market standing as an environmental practice which makes skilful use of its nationally recognised construction expertise. The firm's client base is primarily focused on major house builders and waste management groups. **Clients:** House builders; construction companies.

NORTH EAST

ENVIRONMENT • North East	Ptnrs	Assts
❶ **Eversheds** Leeds	2	6
Nabarro Nathanson Sheffield	2	3
❷ **Addleshaw Booth & Co** Leeds	1	3
❸ **Dickinson Dees** Newcastle upon Tyne	1	1
DLA Sheffield	1	1
❹ **Hammond Suddards Edge** Leeds	2	2
Pinsent Curtis Leeds	1	1

LEADING INDIVIDUALS	
✪ **SMITH Paul** Eversheds	
❶ **RENGER Michael** Nabarro Nathanson	
❷ **BELL Stuart** Eversheds	**BERESFORD Amanda** Addleshaw Booth & Co
BURNLEY Paul Eversheds	**CLARKE Ray** Nabarro Nathanson
DOWEN Denise Dickinson Dees	**HITCHCOCK Teresa** DLA
PIKE John Addleshaw Booth & Co	

Within each band, firms are listed alphabetically. *See **Profiles** on page 372*

Eversheds Felt by one prominent City solicitor to be *"opening up a clear lead nationally,"* the Leeds headquarters represents the fulcrum from which the firm's other offices pivot. Founded on a bed-rock of litigation, the practice has developed to embrace corporate transactional support, compliance and dispute management, although its strength and reputation continues to derive from its excellent defence litigation record. Criminal claims, insurance cases, toxic torts and judicial review are all fixtures on the contentious side. An extensive industrial, chemical and manufacturing client base is also greatly admired by peers. Defence litigator **Paul Smith** is widely regarded throughout the country. *"Immensely charismatic"* and a *"terrific showman,"* he has *"no equal"* as a client getter. His *"first class negotiation skills"* are recognised by solicitors, barristers and clients alike. **Stuart Bell** provides *"superb"* support from an academic perspective, and is considered a *"valuable resource."* Partner **Paul Burnley** is also renowned for his litigation strength. The firm has acted for the British Waterways Board in a High Court national test case against Severn Trent Water in relation to discharges of drainage into the canal network. Currently representing the English, Welsh and Scottish railways in civil proceedings brought by Esso Petroleum relating to contaminated railway land. **Clients:** Associated Octel; Alco Waste Management Ltd; Dupont.

Nabarro Nathanson The firm has built upon the foundation of expertise in the coal and energy field, and developed a genuine environment unit, providing stand-alone advice on strategic and regulatory matters. Particular expertise is felt to exist in contentious issues, notably on waste-related matters, where the firm acts for major industrial clients. **Mike Renger** is a *"leading northern figure,"* although he still spends a proportion of his time in London. His track record and experience in energy, mining, planning and environmental work are considered prime assets to the team. Litigator **Ray Clarke** continues to be recommended for environmental defence work, although he has also undertaken prosecutions on behalf of the Environment Agency. The group is providing policy advice to UK Nirex on the storage and disposal of radioactive waste, and acted for Union Railways (South) in its acquisition of a former landfill site, forming part of the route of the Channel Tunnel Rail Link. **Clients:** Coal Authority; County Environmental Services; Parkwood Landfill Ltd; Humberside Wastewise.

Addleshaw Booth & Co The Leeds office is perceived as the strongest piece of the firm's environmental jigsaw. It is also seen as largely non-contentious and transactional, and is felt to provide a high-class corporate support service. Head of the environmental law unit and *"all-rounder"* **Amanda Beresford** is the major name here, while **John Pike**, head of the commercial property group also assists with issues arising from property transactions, such as waste and contaminated land. The expertise of the practice stretches to planning matters, covering pollution compliance and environmental risk minimisation on urban regeneration projects. The team also includes an environmental consultant. Advised Yorkshire Group plc on environmental issues arising from a £53 million acquisition of the world-wide Textiles Dyes Business and European Industrial Dyes Business of CK Witco Corporation. The team also represented the MoD on environmental issues in connection with a £225 million PPP project for the rationalisation of the Royal Military School of Engineering's estate. **Clients:** Akcros Chemicals Ltd; Kvaerner Estates; Morrison Developments.

Dickinson Dees No major competition has emerged in the far North East to rival this practice. Acting almost exclusively for environmental defendants in prosecution cases, **Denise Dowen** has made litigation her forte. She is described as a true specialist who is *"thoroughly efficient, tenacious and someone who gets down to detail."* Waste and minerals clients are prominent features of the client base, while due diligence and property/contaminated land transactions round out the practice. Increasingly, the firm provides legal risk assessment for companies, acting on environmental regulatory matters and insurance. Acting on the waste licensing arrangements for a clinical waste incinerator. **Clients:** Ship repairer; transport operator; large retailer; automotive manufacturer.

DLA **Teresa Hitchcock**, a former environmental regulator and national head of the firm's non-contentious commercial regulatory group, is well known for her advisory and compliance practice. The practice is active in the traditional economic regions of the north where it advises a number of steel industry and chemical companies on both environmental and health and safety matters. Acted for Petrus Oils, an oil refining company caught in a dispute with the Environment Agency, after allegations that they committed pollution crimes. After judicial review proceedings, the case was successfully concluded with no summons brought. **Clients:** Whitbread plc; Rhodia Holdings plc; ANI Aurora plc; B Elliot plc.

Hammond Suddards Edge The practice is balanced across contentious and non-contentious work, with perhaps slightly more emphasis on litigation. The non-contentious aspect of the practice is frequently planning related, and also supports property and corporate transactions. Clients are drawn from the utilities, manufacturing and engineering sectors. Acted for CGU Insurance in relation to multi-party claims against it, following a chemical pollution incident in Cumbria. Advised a substantial client in the chemical waste re-processing sector on a number of pollution incidents and breaches of its waste licence. **Clients:** Debenhams plc; Manweb plc; Cable & Wireless Communication plc; Tioxide.

Pinsent Curtis Recommended again this year for environmental litigation, primarily on the defence side acting for large retailers and manufacturing companies. Non-contentious advice is provided by a regulatory unit which also deals with health, safety and food matters. This sits alongside traditional areas such as contaminated land and water and air pollution cases. The team also assists in negotiating environmental warranties on corporate deals. **Clients:** Case Corporation; Tesco plc; Smith & Nephew; Schneider Electric.

SCOTLAND

ENVIRONMENT • Scotland	Ptnrs	Assts
❶ **Brodies WS** Edinburgh	1	*
❷ **Morison Bishop** Glasgow	1	1
Morton Fraser, Solicitors Edinburgh	*	*
❸ **Dundas & Wilson CS** Edinburgh	1	3
❹ **Maclay Murray & Spens** Glasgow	1	1
McGrigor Donald Glasgow	1	4
❺ **Burness** Edinburgh	1	1
MacRoberts Glasgow	1	1
Tods Murray WS Edinburgh	⚐	⚐

LEADING INDIVIDUALS	
❶ **SMITH Charles** Brodies WS	
❷ **REID Donald** Morton Fraser, Solicitors	**ROSS Kenneth** Morison Bishop
❸ **PRIMROSE Andrew** Maclay Murray & Spens	
❹ **BROWN Vincent** Dundas & Wilson CS	**GRANT James** MacRoberts
McPAKE Ian Tods Murray WS	**SALES Martin** Burness

Within each band, firms are listed alphabetically. *See **Profiles** on page 372*

⚐ Figures unavailable at time of going to press.

** See editorial entries for explanations of team sizes.*

Brodies WS (2 assistants 20%) Still top of the pile. The firm has an enviable array of clients in a range of industries, including utilities and manufacturing, and is also felt to be *"a cut above the rest"* on the non-contentious side. **Charles Smith** is as close to a pure environmental specialist as one will find in Scotland. A *"good corporate lawyer with an environmental bent,"* he is *"sober, sound and commercial."* Niche strengths include contaminated land, waste management licensing and water and sewerage law. Highlights include advice to British Steel in respect of the negotiation and conclusion of Heads of Agreement concerning the redevelopment of the Ravenscraig Steelworks site in Lanarkshire. **Clients:** Tilbury Douglas Homes; Crop Chemicals Ltd; Tarmac Quarry Products Ltd.

Morison Bishop Commercial property partner **Kenneth Ross** *("incredibly knowledgeable")* is the acknowledged environmental specialist at this recently merged firm. His property background boosts the land contamination work which is the mainstay of the practice. The team also provides transactional support and general advice on contracts, legal liability, discharge consents and prosecutions. **Clients:** Transorganic Ltd; Greenpeace.

Morton Fraser, Solicitors (1 consultant part-time, 1 partner part-time) The practice is considered to be a reliable all-rounder that spans the range of environmental advice from transactional support, contaminated land cases, some litigation and increasingly, a nuclear specialisation. Clients originate inter alia from the brewing, chemicals and industrial development sectors. The reputation of the practice has traditionally rested on the eminent shoulders of **Donald Reid**, still a rated player, although now less visible than in previous years. The practice still undertakes substantial work related to the Landfill Tax Credit Scheme. **Clients:** UK Atomic Energy Authority; United Distilleries; Scottish & Newcastle.

Dundas & Wilson CS The sheer size and extensive corporate client base of the firm is felt to provide the practice with *"great exposure to transactions,"* although the team is not considered to be a specialist unit. **Vincent Brown** is the key player. The team acts on a number of cross-border corporate transactions for clients in the chemicals, explosives and engineering sectors. Highlight was assisting Silvermines Group plc in negotiation of environmental warranties and indemnities relevant to a major corporate sale. Provides full environmental advice to the West of Scotland Water Authority on PFI projects, notably on contaminated land. Advising BG plc on waste management liabilities arising from a contract with an on-site waste contractor. **Clients:** NSK-RHP Europe Ltd; Brady Corporation; Bank of Scotland; Donside Paper Co.

Maclay Murray & Spens In the newly structured planning and environmental department, **Andrew Primrose** is the partner responsible for contaminated land, packaging and waste, and mixes his practice with commercial property work. *"Old-fashioned and charming,"* he *"really knows his stuff."* The practice provides a service to existing commercial and private clients as the drafters of risk management. Stand-alone work includes advice to the whisky industry on what constitutes a definition of packaging. Also conduct some civil defence litigation work. Advising DuPont (UK) in connection with the environmental issues involved in the transfer of a chemical plant to an international joint venture company. Additionally, acted for the Kvaerner Group in relation to the sale of their shipyard at Govan, Glasgow. **Clients:** British Waterways Board; Compaq; Tullis Russell Papermakers Ltd; Wilson Bowden.

McGrigor Donald Environmental advice originates from the commercial property department, and is now headed up by a commercial property partner supported by a full time associate. Former specialist partner and face of the practice, Patricia Hawthorn, has left the law, and there is a view in the market that time is required to adequately fill the void. The practice is especially respected for its advice on statutory nuisance work, and draws its clients from the water industry, minerals and waste management concerns. The team was recently appointed to act for a number of local authorities, and advised the MoD on Project Aquatrine, the outsourcing of water and sewage facilities serving all MoD sites in the UK. **Clients:** Dumfries and Galloway Council; Renewable Energy Systems Ltd; Pioneer Group; Tilcon Northern.

Burness Property based department head and ex-litigator **Martin Sales** is perhaps more closely associated with his planning practice, but nevertheless continued to receive recommendation for his environmental expertise. Has a particular niche in waste management and 'bad neighbour' (waste/landfill) developments where there is an identifiable environmental angle such a contaminated land. The team receives a number of instructions from PFI and capital projects. Advised on the environmental implications of the share sale of Hamish Morison Ltd to Grampian Country Chicken (Rearing) Ltd. Also continue to act on landfill and contaminated land issues for J Fenton & Sons (Contractors) Ltd. **Clients:** Lafarge Redland Aggregates Ltd; Taylor Dalgleish Associates; Alldays plc.

MacRoberts Expertise here rests with **Jamie Grant**, also a noted planner, who is considered a *"sound technician"* and a *"real details man."* Chief areas of expertise include water and sewage PFI, although advice extends to clients in the nuclear, engineering, NHS trusts and quasi-public sector matters. Highlights include advice to a whisky company on a threatened prosecution concerning discharges into a salmon river. Also advised a construction company on its obligations in respect of development of a large tract of potentially contaminated land. **Clients:** B&S Visual Technologies; Yorkshire Environmental Solutions Ltd; Scottish Nuclear Ltd; Glasgow Development Agency.

Tods Murray WS Provides an integrated planning and environmental law service which supports other departments in the firm. *"Bright guy"* **Ian McPake** is recognised for his broad-based approach which includes charities and PFI work, *"but when he's involved, he's good."* Continues to advise Dundee Energy Recycling Ltd on all environmental matters relating to the Baldovie Waste to Energy project, including waste disposal and waste transport contracts. Acted for North of Scotland Environmental Services on UK and EC water quality requirements and sludge disposal, in connection with two wastewater treatment PFI projects. Continues to act for a number of land-owning clients and charities. **Clients:** RSPB; WWF; Forestry Commission; Woodland Trust.

NORTHERN IRELAND

ENVIRONMENT • Northern Ireland	Ptnrs	Assts
❶ **Cleaver Fulton Rankin** Belfast	1	2
LEADING INDIVIDUALS		
❶ **FARIS Neil** Cleaver Fulton Rankin		

Within each band, firms are listed alphabetically. *See **Profiles** on page 372*

Cleaver Fulton Rankin **Neil Faris** heads the joint environmental and planning unit. Advises clients on the new environmental legislation in Northern Ireland and Environmental Impact Assessment. In particular, supports the property department on its transactions. Advising on a detailed site appraisal for a sewerage treatment works. The team is acting for a leading NGO on the implications of the Habitats Directive on a development proposal. **Clients:** Water Service (Department Of Regional Development); Local authorities; BT plc; Charities.

LEADERS IN ENVIRONMENT

ABRAHAM, Henry
Brachers, Maidstone (01622) 690691
See under Planning, p.660

ALLEN, Tony
DMH, Brighton (01273) 744451
Partner.
Specialisation: Areas of practice: town planning, environmental highways and compulsory purchase law. Head of *DMH* Planning and Environmental Law Unit. Has acted in applications and appeals relating to housing and all types of commercial development, incinerators, waste transfer stations, waste to power plants, mineral extraction, listed buildings, statutory nuisance prosecutions, Structure and Local Plan Policy representations. Author of various articles and books on planning topics. Recent seminar topics have included Environmental Law - The European Background, Contaminated Land - The New Code and Planning Traps for Conveyancers.
Prof. Memberships: LMRTPI, Environmental Law Foundation, European Environmental Law Association, British Nordic Lawyers Association, UK Environmental Law Association.
Career: MA (Cantab). Qualified in 1970, having joined *Donne Mileham & Haddock* (now *DMH*) in 1969. Became a Partner in 1976. Member of the Law Society Planning and Environmental Law Committee.

BAKER, Neil
Clarke Willmott & Clarke, Bristol (0117) 941 6600
nbaker@cw-c.co.uk
Specialisation: Specialises in environmental and planning law including planning and other development applications, agreements, appeals, public inquiries, High Court proceedings such as judicial review, pollution control under the Environment Acts and related legislation, defending environmental prosecutions and advice on minerals, waste and contaminated land. Recent experience has included advising the Countryside Agency on environmental issues arising from the potential overlap between the Habitats Directive and Regulations and the emerging legislation relating to acess to open countryside, acting for an animal by-produce rendering company in connection with potential High Court challenge to an Inspector's decision to refuse planning permission for waste water treatment plant and advising a major food manufacturer on the application of Integrated Pollution Prevention and Control to the business.
Prof. Memberships: Law Society. Committee Member, UKELA, South West branch.
Career: Articled with *Nicholson Graham & Jones*; qualified in 1994. Joined *Clarke Willmott &Clarke* in 1999 as Senior Associate.
Personal: Born 19 September 1967. Attended Queen Elizabeth's School and Bristol University (BSc Hons Biochemistry). Leisure interests include golf; squash, and the theatre. Lives in Bristol.

BARLOW, Colin
Blake Lapthorn, Fareham (01489) 579990
cpbarlow@blakelapthorn.co.uk
Partner 1968. Head of Planning and member of the firm's Environmental Law Group.
Specialisation: Main area of practice is planning and environmental law. Also a senior member of the employment team. Involved in appeals re: mineral extraction, landfill and "wind farm" development, hazardous substances and statutory nuisance. Lectures frequently to architects, surveyors and planning consultants on environmental law matters.
Prof. Memberships: Royal Town Planning Institute (Legal Associate), Law Society (Member of Planning Panel), Law South Group of Solicitors.
Career: Qualified in 1959. Joined *Blake Lapthorn* in 1967 and became a Partner in 1968.
Personal: Born 18th August 1935. Attended Nottingham University 1953-56. Member of MCC. Leisure pursuits include cricket and walking. Lives in Havant.

BELL, Stuart
Eversheds, Leeds (0113) 243 0391
stuartbell@eversheds.com
Consultant.
Specialisation: Main area of practice is environmental law. Advises on the whole range of environmental issues with particular emphasis on commercial and regulatory matters. Institutional clients include the Environment Agency, the Australian Commonwealth Environmental Protection Agency, the World Health Organisation and the European Commission. His commercial clients include chemical companies, utilities and retailers. Editor of the Environmental Law Reports and Water Law. Editorial board member of the Journal of Planning and Environment Law. *Eversheds* Professor of Environment Law at Nottingham Law School.

BERESFORD, Amanda
Addleshaw Booth & Co, Leeds (0113) 209 2000
aqb@addleshaw-booth.co.uk
Head of Environmental Law; Leeds.
Specialisation: All planning work including retail, leisure, industrial, residential and advocacy at Public Inquiries. Comprehensive environmental advice including pollution control, energy, waste, transport, contaminated land and due diligence. Clients advised include major development and manufacturing companies, utilities, banks and local authorities. Particular expertise in environmental and planning issues in urban regeneration projects. Recognised authoress and speaker at conferences.
Prof. Memberships: Qualified planner. Member U.K.E.L.A.
Career: Qualified in 1985, joined *Addleshaw Booth & Co* in 1997.

BOWDEN, Paul
Freshfields Bruckhaus Deringer, London (020) 7936 4000
See under Litigation (Commercial), p.558

BROCK, David M. J.
Mills & Reeve, Cambridge (01223) 222 438
david.brock@mills-reeve.com
Partner in Planning and Environmental Group.
Specialisation: Has a wide ranging environmental, planning and minerals law practice. Work includes judicial review, integrated pollution control, contaminated land, defence, waste, power generation and oil and gas. Advises on all aspects of planning law. Contributor to 'Commercial Environmental Law and Liability' 1993-98.
Career: Qualified in 1980. Partner at *Herbert Smith* 1989-2000, *Mills & Reeve* 2000 to date.
Personal: Born in 1954. Educated at Dame Allan's Boys School, Newcastle, Marylebone Grammar School and University College, London (LL.B). Practising Christian. Enjoys opera, skiing, modern art and architecture. Lives near Saffron Walden.

BROWN, Vincent
Dundas & Wilson CS, Glasgow (0141) 222 2200

BRYCE, Andrew John
Andrew Bryce & Co, Coggeshall (01376) 563123
andrewbryce1@compuserve.com
Specialisation: A specialist in environmental and health and safety law, including waste management, contaminated land, water law, criminal defence, corporate, banking and property due diligence and environmental training programmes. The practice also includes planning and environmental assessment on major projects. Author of numerous magazine articles and papers. Has spoken at many conferences in the UK and abroad.
Prof. Memberships: Law Society, UK Environmental Law Association (Chairman 1988-91).
Career: Qualified in 1971, having joined *Cameron Markby Hewitt* in 1969. Became a Partner in 1973. Vice-Chair of UKELA 1987-88, and Chairman of UKELA 1988-91. Vice Chair of City of London Law Society, Planning and Environmental Sub-Commit-

tee, 1990-96. Convenor of UKELA Waste Working Party.
Personal: Born 31st August 1947. Attended Thorpe Grammar School, Norwich to 1965, then Newcastle University 1965-68. Leisure interests include bird-watching, tennis, walking, decorative arts and music. Lives in Coggeshall, Essex.

BURNLEY, Paul
Eversheds, Leeds (0113) 243 0391
paulburnley@eversheds.com
Specialisation: Principal area of practice is acting for corporate/commercial clients and other directors in complex health and safety litigation. Known for his extensive experience of crisis management, having represented clients in major incidents, large scale disasters and product recall. He and his team article all their own advocacy where possible. Experienced in all aspects of health and safety issues including Coroner's Court. A "no-nonsense" advocate! Invited to many venues as a guest speaker on corporate and individual Director liability.
Prof. Memberships: UKELA.
Career: Qualified April 1980. Nine years as a Prosecuting Solicitor, he joined *Eversheds* in 1989 becoming a Partner in May 1996. A gamekeeper turned poacher!
Personal: Born 31 August 1955.

BUXTON, Richard
Richard Buxton, Cambridge (01223) 328933
law@richardbuxton.co.uk
Sole Practitioner, environmental lawyer, with associate Susan Ring
Specialisation: Environmental assessment, noise (esp. aircraft noise) and other nuisance work; water (esp. abstraction licensing); nature conservation. Context: judicial review, human rights, other litigation, planning inquiries and appeals, general advice, lectures. Clients: statutory agencies, local authorities, charities, groups, private clients and other solicitors. Cases include Heathrow night flights in the domestic courts and European Court of Human Rights, Lappel Bank for RSPB, several current cases and appeals on environmental assessment, including Berkeley and Brown and Cartwright (both won in the House of Lords), and Huddleston (won in CA); Tugwell in relation to land possession orders and protestors' rights (won in CA); Hewlings v McLean Homes (won in Divisional Court) in relation to statutory nuisance; and Cambridge trishaws.
Prof. Memberships: UK Environmental Law Association. Institute of Environmental Assessment.
Career: Qualified 1978 with *Farrer & Co. Sinclair Roche & Temperley* 1978, shipping disputes work. Legal adviser, Japan Line, Tokyo 1981-84. Environmental consultancy, Nova Scotia 1986-89, marine and fisheries issues. *Mills & Reeve*. Cambridge 1989. Independent since 1990.
Personal: Born1953. Lives and works in Cambridge.

CARRIAGE, Rebecca
Mills & Reeve, Norwich (01603) 693 228
rebecca.carriage@mills-reeve.com
Specialisation: Environmental and Compulsory Purchase/ Compensation Law and Town and Country Planning. Recent work includes major mineral and waste planning appeals and development plan work; defence of a number of statutory nuisance prosecutions; referrals to the Lands Tribunal involving questions of law and valuation; enrolment of environmental bodies under the Landfill Tax Regulations 1996.
Prof. Memberships: Member of Steering Group of East Anglian Business Environment Club. Associate member of Quarry Products Association and Environmental Services Association.
Career: Articled *Hill & Perks* (now *Eversheds*, Norwich). Moved to *Mills & Reeve* 1988.

CASTLE, Pamela
CMS Cameron McKenna, London
(020) 7367 2335
pmc@cmck.com
Partner, Head of Environmental Law Group.
Specialisation: Handles a range of environmental law matters. Provides compliance advice on all areas of UK and EC environmental law, in particular the regulatory control of emissions to air and water, the transport, labelling and disposal of waste, contaminated land issues, the handling and storage of hazardous substances and health and safety at work.
Prof. Memberships: Law Society, Vice Chairman UK Environmental Law Association, UK Round Table on Sustainable Development, Chairman Environment Agency, Thames Region, Environmental Protection Advisory Committee, Port of London Authority, NERC, NRPB, City of London Solicitors Company, Institute of Wastes Management, Institute of Environmental Assessment (accredited environmental auditor), Royal Society of Chemistry, Fellow of the Royal Society of Arts.
Career: With Shell Chemical Company, New York 1965-67. Head of European Operations of Paul de Haen Inc, New York (research company associated with the pharmaceutical industry) 1967-84. Joined the firm in 1986 and became a Partner in 1994.
Personal: Born 7th September 1941. Educated at the University of London (Queen Mary College) 1960-63 (BSc, 1st Class Hons in Chemistry) and the College of Law 1984-86. Interests include music, reading, theatre and walking. Lives in London.

CLARKE, Ray
Nabarro Nathanson, Sheffield (0114) 279 4000
r.clarke@nabarro.com
Specialisation: Civil and criminal environmental litigation including advocacy. Advised on minewater pollution litigation and strategic policy, nuisance emission from power stations and industry, Prosecutions and appeals, defending high profile multi-party actions. Land Tribunal Reference re landfill business. Acquisitions and disposals. Privatisation - mines and chemicals. Urban regeneration including developments on gas works sites, chemical site for international nature reserve and landfill, petro-chemicals sites with pollution of groundwater. Management of large development schemes including town centres, sub-regional shopping centre (Trafford Centre). Judicial review and Public Inquiries. Crisis and awareness training for Directors and other personnel.
Prof. Memberships: Member of UKELA Council. Fellow of the Institute of Quarry. Visiting Tutor, on Environmental and Regeneration, International Development Law Institute, Rome.

CUCKSON, David M.
Stephenson Harwood, London (020) 7809 2505
david.cuckson@shlegal.com
Partner, Property Department, Head of Environmental Law Group.
Specialisation: David's early legal career was spent working in Local Government, latterly as the Council's principal legal adviser. As a result he gained extensive experience of advising members and officers on relevant legal issues. As head of the Environmental Law Group, he covers most aspects of environmental law. Specific work includes issues relating to contaminated land, corporate mergers and acquisitions and waste management. He also handles property law work relating to education, local government and other public bodies, including PFI projects. Has written articles and lectured extensively on environmental law topics. Has contributed chapters to 'Conveying Contaminated Land', 'Issues in Environmental Geology - A British Perspective' and 'Waste Prevention in the EEC'. Reports on energy - from - waste issues have been published by ETSU on behalf of the Department of Trade & Industry.
Prof. Memberships: Chairman of UK Environmental Law Association, also member of Contaminated Land and Waste Working Parties..
Career: Qualified October 1978. Held various posts in different local government authorities, most recently as Borough Secretary and Solicitor for Test Valley Borough Council 1988-89. Joined *Stephenson Harwood* in 1989 and became partner in 1992.
Personal: Born 30 November 1942. Educated at Nottingham High School, Fitzwilliam College, Cambridge. MA 1967 (Law and Theology). Interests include travel, photography, swimming. Minister United Reformed Church. Resides Winchester.

DAVEY, Catherine
Stevens & Bolton, Guildford (01483) 734 234
Specialisation: All aspects of environmental law including contaminated land, statutory nuisances, waste disposal, corporate support. Highways and commons law. Town & Country Planning. Contributor to Sustainable Architecture, European Directives & Building Design (Butterworths).
Prof. Memberships: Law Society; Council Member United Kingdom Environmental Law Association; Executive Committee Environment Law Foundation, FRGS.
Career: Woking County Grammar School for Girls, University of Exeter (BA Hons). Joined *Stevens & Bolton* 1988 from local government, becoming a partner in 1989.
Personal: Leisure interests are foreign travel, photography, sailing, film, theatre, the arts and virtual reality gardening.

DAWSON, Andrew W.
DLA, Manchester (0161) 830 4321
andrew.dawson@dla.com
Partner within Regulatory Group.
Specialisation: Practice covers the full ambit of environment and health and safety law, investigations and prosecutions, and includes advice and representation before criminal Courts. Has handled many high profile reported cases. Pollution matters waste and the chemical and construction industries are particular specialisms.
Career: Qualified in 1988 in Local Government before joining *Alsop Wilkinson* in 1991 (Partner 1996).
Personal: Born 10th November 1963. Educated St Margaret's High School and Liverpool University (LLB).

DAY, Martyn
Leigh, Day & Co, London (020) 7650 1200
See under Product Liability, p.674

DEANESLY, Clare
Gouldens, London (020) 7583 7777
chd@gouldens.com
Partner and Head of Environmental Law Group.
Specialisation: Member of UKELA Waste Working Party. Member of ICC Committee on Environment, ESA Commercial Contracts Sub-committee and ESA Policy and Development Sub-commitee. Principal area of practice is environmental law, dealing with minerals, waste management, landfill and contaminated land cases. Also handles general commercial property work including landlord and tenant matters and retail and development work. Acted for the Landfill Division of ARC (Greenways) in their acquisition of Econowaste from Tarmac plc 1993; 1993 and 1996 acted for London Brick Property Limited on sale of substantial landfill void to Shanks & McEwan; 1996 acted for minerals division of ARC in Midlands joint venture with Tarmac plc. Other major clients include Hanson plc, SITA, Biffa Waste Management and Thames Waste Management. 1998: acted on landfill and minerals sites in connection with sale of Hanson Properties. 1999: acted on the sale of Hughes Waste Management Limited. Advised on landfill tax and environmental bodies. Author of 'Badlands: Essential Environmental Law for Property Professionals' (1993) and author of various articles on waste management property issues for professional publications. Contributor to ESA training seminar on Duty of Care. Speaker on waste management issues at conferences and seminars. Individual charge-out rate varies depending on type of job, degree of complexity and other relevant factors.
Prof. Memberships: Law Society, UKELA, ESA.
Career: Qualified in 1977 while at *Field Fisher Martineau.* Joined *Gouldens* in 1978 and became a Partner in 1980.
Personal: Born 30th May 1953. Attended Edgbaston C of E College for Girls, Birmingham 1957-71, then Southampton University 1971-74 (LLB Hons). Leisure pursuits include family, skiing, walking, tennis, travel and theatre. Lives in London.

DEVAS, Hugh E.
Boodle Hatfield, London (020) 7318 8174
hdevas@boodlehatfield.co.uk
Partner, Property Department
Specialisation: Urban regeneration, brownfield redevelopment and contaminated land issues, infrastructure projects, the waste sector and related funding work. Advises a wide range of clients on regulatory and sustainable development issues, including the preparation of environmental policy documents. Lectures and writes widely on environmental topics. Author of industry guide 'The Impact of Environmental Legislation on the European Paper Industry' (1994).
Prof. Memberships: United Kingdom Environmental Law Association (Member of the Waste Working Party).
Career: Spent two years as a transaction lawyer before taking up a partnership outside London. Joined *Rowe & Maw* as a partner in1988, specialising increasingly in the environmental aspects of property transactions. Seconded to Corporate Department in 1994 to head up specialist Environment Group. Joined *Boodle Hatfield* in May 2000 as part of its property infrastructure team to handle major development projects.
Personal: Married with four children, living in Hampshire. Leisure interests: tennis, skiing, sailing and the performing arts.

DOOLITTLE, Ian
Trowers & Hamlins, London (020) 7423 8000
idoolittle@trowers.com
Partner, public sector. Head of environmental law.
Specialisation: Specialist in environmental law, especially transactional and regulatory work (including contaminated land and waste management). Editor of 'Garner's Environmental Law'. Author of 'Butterworths Environmental Regulation'. Former Vice Chairman of the International Bar Association's sub-committee on European Environmental Law. Also specialist in public sector law.

DOWEN, Denise
Dickinson Dees, Newcastle upon Tyne
(0191) 279 9215
Specialisation: Practice covers all aspects of environmental law in relation to company and property transactions including EIAs, waste management, water pollution, process authorisations and contaminated land. Acts for developers, lending institutions and waste management companies.
Prof. Memberships: Law Society. Member of CBI Environment Committee.
Career: Qualified in 1990. Trained with Avon County Council before moving to private practice. Joined *Dickinson Dees* in 1994.
Personal: Born July 1965. Read Law at the University of Leeds.

FAIRLEY, Ross
Allen & Overy, London (020) 7330 3000
ross.fairley@allenovery.com
Environmental Law
Specialisation: Involved in all aspects of UK and EU environmental and health and safety law particularly in areas such as policy, management and audit, contaminated land, power and renewables projects and lender liability. Works closely with environmental consultants advising on the findings of detailed site and management audits, writes and speaks regularly on environmental matters and is a contributor to Sweet and Maxwell's 'Commercial Environmental Law and Liability' and Legal Editor of Gee's 'Environmental Risk Manager' and 'Premises, Health and Safety' and Tolley's 'Environmental Law and Procedures Management'.
Prof. Memberships: Law Society, Council Member of the United Kingdom Environmental Law Association, Associate Member of the Institute of Environmental Management and Assesment.
Career: Born 11.10.68, educated at Leicester University LLB Law; qualified with *Allen & Overy* in 1993.
Personal: Interests include all sports, particularly hockey, cricket and driving an old Austin Healey 'Frogeye' Sprite.

FARIS, Neil C.
Cleaver Fulton Rankin, Belfast (028) 9024 3141
n.faris@cfrlawonline.com
Specialisation: Environmental Law.
Prof. Memberships: Council Member of the United Kingdom Environmental Law Association; Founder Member and Chair 1998-99 Environmental & Planning Law Association of Northern Ireland.
Career: Qualified in 1977 and Managing Partner and Head of Consultancy Department.
Personal: Born 1950, educated in Belfast and at Trinity College Dublin and University of Cambridge.

FOGLEMAN, Valerie
Barlow Lyde & Gilbert, London (020) 7247 2277
vfoleman@blg.co.uk
Specialisation: All aspects of environmental law including environmental liability matters, particularly contaminated land and water pollution, specialist environmental insurance policies, environmental insurance coverage claims, due diligence, criminal and civil environmental litigation, lender liability. Numerous books and articles on environmental liabilities and environmental insurance in UK and US publications including monthly article in Insurance Day; frequent speaker in UK and overseas.
Prof. Memberships: Convenor, United Kingdom Environmental Law Association (UKELA) Insurance and Liability Working Party; Chair, Construction Industry Research and Information Association Contaminated Land and Urban Regeneration Working Party. Memberships include: RICS Environmental Appraisal Practice Panel; Lloyd's European Environment Working Group; UKELA Council.
Career: Solicitor and member of Texas State Bar; practised environmental and insurance law in Texas before joining *Barlow Lyde & Gilbert* in 1992; became a partner in 1998. University of Illinois (1992 LLM); Texas Tech University (1989 MSc, 1989 JD, 1983 BLA).

FORSTER, Malcolm
Freshfields Bruckhaus Deringer, London
(020) 7936 4000
Litigation department (environment group).
Specialisation: Advises and represents on regulatory challenges and liability disputes in the environmental field. Manages preparation of environmental statements for major projects and ensures statutory compliance. Handles corporate indemnity and warranty disputes over environmental issues. Gives environmental support for international investment, including project financing. Has special interest in matters with transnational elements including public international law issues relating to environment and natural resources; supervising partner Pan-European environmental practice; advises international organisations. Editor of Environmental Law & Management, Editor, author or contributor to numerous books and articles in legal journals. Professor of International Environmental Law at the Durrell Institute for Conservation and Ecology, at the University of Kent. Sometime Deputy Chairman, United Kingdom Environmental Law Association.
Prof. Memberships: International Bar Association, Selden Society.
Career: Qualified in 1992, having joined *Freshfields* in 1991. Partner 1995. Director of the Centre for Environmental Law at the University of Southampton 1973-84 and 1987-91. General Counsel for the Commission on Environmental Law at the International Union for Conservation of Nature and Natural Resources, Bonn, Germany, 1984-87.
Personal: Born 22nd October 1948. Attended University of Southampton 1967-70. Interests include ecclesiastical law, naval history, legal history and equestrianism. Lives in,Crow Hill, Hants.

GARBUTT, John
Nicholson Graham & Jones, London
(020) 7648 9000
john.garbutt@ngj.co.uk
Head of Planning and Environment Unit.
Specialisation: Planning and environmental law,

including appeals, development plans, environment disputes, audits and policy, compulsory purchase, rating, Lands Tribunal, major planning inquiries concerning minerals, waste management, leisure developments, and judicial reviews. Author 'Environmental Law- A Practical Handbook', 'Waste Management Law: A Manager's Handbook'. Contributor 'Commercial Environmental Law and Liability'. The firm is a member of the Land Pollution Consortium.
Prof. Memberships: UKELA, CBI Minerals Committee and Environment Protection Panel, Mining & Mineral Law Group.
Career: Qualified in 1963. Local government 1965-69. Blue Circle Industries (1978-85) and Chief Executive, Blue Circle Industrial Minerals 1986-88 and Blue Circle Waste Management 1989. *Nicholson Graham & Jones*, Partner 1991.

GIBBS, Kevin
Osborne Clarke OWA, Bristol (0117) 917 4222
kevin.gibbs@osborneclarke.com
Specialisation: Expert in Environmental and Planning law. Has experience in renewable energy projects, particularly CHP projects, environmental due diligence and corporate transactions, environmental authorisations and licensing and advice on all forms of planning applications and appeals including advocacy.
Career: Qualified 1990. Local Government Planner from 1980-84; Principal Legal Officer, London Borough of Camden 1984-88. Joined *Lyons Davidson* in 1988, became Partner in 1994, joined *Osborne Clarke* in 1999 as a partner.

GRANT, James R.
MacRoberts, Glasgow (0141) 332 9988
jamieg@macroberts.co.uk
See under Planning, p.663

GREENWOOD, Brian J.
Norton Rose, London (020) 7283 6000
greenwoodbj@nortonrose.com
Head of Environment and Planning Law Group.
Specialisation: Corporate acquisitions, disposals and funding; environmental due diligence (including BMW sale of Rover and Land Rover), project finance, waste, water and IPC including appeals and advocacy (acted for Castle Cement in judicial review of Environment Agency re alternative fuels); international practice with considerable experience in Eastern Europe.
Career: Qualified in local government, with posts at Westminster, South Yorkshire and Kent before being appointed Chief Solicitor at Bedfordshire County Council. Joined *Norton Rose* in 1985, partner in 1988.
Prof. Memberships: Chairman Law Society's Planning and Environmental Law Committee, CBI Environmental Protection Panel; UKELA.
Publications: Author "Butterworths Planning Law Service", Co-author "Environment Regulation and Economic Growth", Editor Butterworths Planning Law Handbook.

HAVARD-WILLIAMS, Vanessa
Linklaters (A member firm of Linklaters & Alliance), London (020) 7456 4280
vanessa.havard-williams@linklaters.com
Specialisation: Member of the firm's environmental unit since 1990 and founding partner of the Environmental Law Group. Specialist in all aspects of environmental and health and safety work, (including corporate and property transactions, projects, advisory and EHS litigation).

HAYDEN, Tim
Clarke Willmott & Clarke, Taunton
(01823) 442266
thayden@cw-c.co.uk
Partner in Advocacy Department.
Specialisation: Main area of practice is environmental. Work includes prosecution and defence of industrial pollution cases, agricultural pollution and noise abatement. Also handles commercial criminal work, including health and safety, trade descriptions, food and drugs, road haulage and licensing. Lectures on legal aspects of pollution and waste disposal. Solicitor-Advocate.
Prof. Memberships: UKELA.
Career: Qualified in 1981. Joined *Clarke Willmott & Clarke* in 1979, becoming a Partner in 1985. Qualified as a Higher Courts Advocate in 1995.
Personal: Born 10th December 1956. Attended Bristol Grammar School 1968-74, University College Cardiff 1974-78 and College of Law Guildford 1978-79. Leisure interests include golf and cricket. Lives in Taunton.

HITCHCOCK, Teresa C.
DLA, Sheffield (08700) 111111
teresa.hitchcock@dla.com
Specialisation: Environmental Law: a) Advice to industrial organisations on compliance issues; b) Environmental input into corporate finance transactions; c) Regulatory Investigations and d) Involvement in environmental litigation. Also advice on Health & Safety at Work, Crisis Management, Product Safety and Food Safety. A significant proportion of this work comprises projects for high profile, blue chip companies and major plcs.
Prof. Memberships: Institute of Environmental Health. Law Society. UKELA.
Career: Environmental Health Degree 1981. 12 years in local government as a principal environmental health officer dealing with enforcement of environmental pollution, health & safety and food safety issues. Honours Law Degree 1988.
Personal: Equestrian activities. Netball. Walking.

HOBLEY, Anthony
CMS Cameron McKenna, London
(020) 7367 2759
arh@cmck.com
Specialisation: Senior solicitor in the Environmental Law Group. Handles a wide range of environment law matters with particular emphasis on the environment aspects of national and international corporate, banking and property transactions. Advises regularly in relation to contaminated land and its redevelopment. Regularly advises in connection with regulatory and enforcement issues in connection with many industries and with regard to major infrastructure projects. Other issues about which he has advised are the definition and regulation of waste, producer responsibilty obligations and packaging; trading of economic environment instruments such as packaging recovery notes; lender liability issues; environmental liability in the context of insolvency; landfill tax; alleged radioactive contamination of groundwater and the availability, terms and coverage of environment insurance products. Increasingly advising on matters with international aspects such as climate change issues, permit trading, climate change levy energy efficiency agreements and related matters. Has advised on a number of marine pollution matters and various mining related issues. He has spoken at public conferences on topics such as contaminated land, environmental law in Central Europe and environmental taxation. He has had a number of articles published in the Environment Times, the Royal Society of Chemistry Newsletter and the Institute of Chemical Engineers Environmental Protection Bulletin and the International Company & Commercial Law Review. He is currently the co-ordinator for his firm's Central European Environmental Law group and travels regularly to Central Europe in this capacity. He recently spoke at a high profile conference in Budapest on contaminated land issues in Central Europe.
Prof. Memberships: Law Society, UK Environmental Law Association, Graduate of the Royal Society of Chemistry, Mining & Mineral Group.
Career: First Class Honours Degree in Chemistry with Physics. Qualified as a solicitor in 1994. Joined *Cameron McKenna* (formerly *McKenna & Co* in 1996.
Personal: Born 24th November 1966.

HOLMES, Sarah C.
Bond Pearce, Plymouth (01752) 266633
xsch@bondpearce.com
Associate in the Planning and Environmental Group.
Specialisation: Specialises in planning and environmental law. MA (Oxon) and Master of Arts in Environmental Law (1997), national reputation for work in renewable energy having been at the forefront of the industry since 1991. Advises on all stages of planning process, including environmental impact assessment (advised on over 40 such renewable, waste, commercial and other projects), with clients in public and private sector. Extensive environmental practice includes contaminated land remediation, risk minimisation and allocation, environmental insurance, complex landfill tax issues, European Sites (nature conservation) and consents/permits. Active involvement in major waste, minerals, food and motor deals with due diligence on many further transactions. Runner-up Assistant Solicitor of the Year (The Lawyer, 1995), Council Member of UK Environmental Law Association, Secretary of UKELA South West and member of British Wind Energy Association.
Career: Qualified in 1991. Joined *Bond Pearce* in 1989 becoming an Associate in 1997.

HORNER, Douglas G.
Brachers, Maidstone (01622) 690691
See under Agriculture, p.75

HUTCHINSON, Michael
Rowe & Maw, London (020) 7248 4282
Specialisation: Environmental aspects of corporate, property and finance transactions, as well as stand-alone UK and EU advisory work. Recent clients from a variety of sectors including energy, engineering, motor manufacturing, chemicals, retail and banking.
Career: Qualified and practised for three years at *Linklaters & Paines*. Assistant solicitor, *Freshfields* (1996-2000). Joined *Rowe & Maw*, 2000.

ISTED, Jonathan
Freshfields Bruckhaus Deringer, London
(020) 7936 4000
Specialisation: Defence of multi-party toxic tort claims, including Sellafield childhood leukaemia cases, electromagnetic field cases, judicial review and product liability actions, disaster litigation and contaminated land liability claims. Also general

commercial litigation. Member of Lord Woolf's Advisory Group on Multi-Party actions.
Prof. Memberships: Law Society, UKELA.
Career: Articled with *Freshfields* 1987-89. Qualified as an assistant solicitor in *Freshfields'* Litigation Department in 1989. LLM (with Distinction) in Advanced Litigation from Nottingham Trent University in 1996. Partner in *Freshfields* 1998. CEDR Accredited Mediator in 2000.
Personal: Born 5 May 1964. Educated at Newport Free Grammar School and Durham University, College of Law (Chester) 1987. Leisure activities include golf, squash, running and travel. Reform Club.

JEWKES, Penny
Eversheds, Norwich (01603) 272727
Specialisation: Handles a broad range of environmental matters including due diligence audits arising in the course of major transactions, regulatory compliance (advisory and defence), civil liability, waste management and packaging issues. Also practices on the planning/ environment interface. Major clients include machinery manufacturers, food producers, government bodies, charities and premier car dealerships. Regular speaker at conferences and seminars. Has published in the Journal of Occupational Safety and Health on 'Corporate Killing'. Article published in the Journal of Planning and Environment Law on Light Pollution frequently referred to in planning and committee meetings.
Prof. Memberships: Barrister (non-practising). United Kingdom Environmental Law Association (UKELA), Chair, East Anglian Branch.
Career: Called to the English Bar in 1974 and the Hong Kong Bar in 1976. Crown Counsel in Hong Kong. Lecturer in law at Hong Kong University and from 1990 at the University of East Anglia specialising in planning and environmental law. Returned to practice in 1997.

JOHN, Alan
Osborne Clarke OWA, Bristol (0117) 917 4240
alan.john@osborneclarke.com
Specialisation: Alan specialises in all areas of environmental law, particularly waste management, contaminated land, water pollution, contractual protection and renewable energy projects (including wind, biomass, water, landfill gas and waste to energy). He advises on the environmental aspects of corporate and property transactions, and the making and defending of environmental claims. Clients include SWEB, MANWEB, St Regis Paper Company and Pasminco.
Career: He qualified as a solicitor in 1984 and joined *McKenna & Co* in London, moved to *Osborne Clarke* in 1987 and became partner and head of Environmental Group in 1990.

KEEBLE, Ed
Slaughter and May, London (020) 7600 1200
Specialisation: Wide range of environmental matters, including major transactions, due diligence, contaminated site litigation and general environmental law advice.
Prof. Memberships: United Kingdom Environmental Law Association.
Career: Ipswich School, Cambridge University. Qualified in 1988 and became a Partner at *Slaughter and May* in 1995.

LLOYD, Deborah
Herbert Smith, London (020) 7374 8000
Specialisation: Advising on the full range of environmental issues arising in corporate and property transactions, PFI projects and litigious matters. Areas of speciality include contaminated land, waste, water and energy related matters.
Prof. Memberships: United Kingdom Environmental Law Association.
Career: Admitted as a barrister and solicitor of the Supreme Court of Victoria, Australia, April 1995, practising in environmental law. Commenced work in the UK in March 1997.

LOMAS, Owen
Allen & Overy, London (020) 7330 3000
Partner and Head of Environmental Law Group.
Specialisation: All aspects of UK and EU Environmental and Health & Safety law notably contaminated land, air and water pollution, waste management, product responsibility and stewardship (including packaging, electrical and electronic and other product recycling obligations) and corporate environmental policy, management and audit. Acted for VALPAK, the industry organisation set up to negotiate the packaging industry's recycling obligations with HMG, the DTI on environmental aspects of the privatisation of the nuclear power industry and for a wide range of major industrial companies and banks on environmental aspects of their businesses and on acquisitions and disposals. Co-author of 'Packaging Recycling Obligations - An Industry Guide to the British Regulation, 'Frontiers of Environment Law' and an Editor of Commercial Environmental Law and Liability (1994). Editor of Environmental Law, journal of the UK Environmental Law Association 1989-1997 and author of numerous articles on environmental law.
Prof. Memberships: Vice Chairman, International Environmental Law Committee; Member of the UK Government's 'Producer Responsibility Forum'; Member of the Editorial Board of Water Law and the Utilities Law Review; Past Chairman of the UK Environmental Law Association standing committee on air pollution and member of the standing committees on integrated pollution control and environmental liability. The Council of Management of the UK Environmental Law Association 1987-1996. Law Society.
Career: Articled *Simons, Muirhead & Allen*, London; qualified 1980; lecturer in Law, University of Birmingham 1979-88; Lecturer in Law University of Warwick 1988-91; Professor in Law, University of Trier, Germany 1991-92. Joined *Allen & Overy* 1992; Partner 1995.
Personal: London University (1976 LL.B); University of Birmingham (1987 LL.M). Born 1955. Lives near Saffron Walden.

LOOSE, Helen
Ashurst Morris Crisp, London (020) 7638 1111
helen.loose@ashursts.com
Specialisation: Head of the Environmental Risk Management Group which specialises in both transactional and advisory environmental and health and safety matters. Helen specialises in all aspects of environmental law in corporate, major projects, banking and property transactions and advises in either a transactional or standalone context on all aspects of current and proposed UK and EU environmental and health & safety legislation, regulation and compliance, environmental insurance and claims, non-high court contentious matters including prosecutions, regulatory actions and planning issues from an environmental perspective. Helen acts regularly for The Polestar Group, Newmond PLC, Unipoly Managers Ltd, Automotive Products, BT Property and Enviros in both a transactional and advisory role.
Prof. Memberships: Council Member of United Kingdom Environmental Law Association; Member of the air pollution Working Group of the Sustainability Unit of London First; Chair of the Local Government Working Group of the Energy from Waste Association; UK representative of the Environmental Law Association; Member of the editorial board, Asbestos Risk Management (Croners.CCH); Director of the National Waste Awareness Initiative.
Career: Trained at *Freshfields*, qualified in 1992, Partner in 2000.
Personal: Resides in London; enjoys opera; skiing; reading; travel.

MACKINLAY, Hannah
Pinsent Curtis, Birmingham (0121) 200 1050
hannah.mackinlay@pinsents.com
Specialisation: Advising in relation to the environmental issues involved in: corporate mergers and acquisitions, handling UK and multinational matters, negotiating warranties and indemnities, often in transactions involving many properties and various jurisdictions, advising on risks and compliance issues. Recent significant deals for IMI plc; 3i and Onyx. Property transactions, including contaminated land and advising waste industry companies on issues such as licensing and landfill developments.
Prof. Memberships: Graduate member of Institute of Wastes Management. Member National Council of the UK Environmental Law Association and author of its Internet website. Co-author of 'What Every Manager Needs to Know about Environmental Law'.
Career: LLB (Hons) Sheffield. Qualified 1981. MA (Environmental Law) Distinction, De Montfort University. Partner *Shoosmiths & Harrison*, Northampton 1986-95. 1995, Associate *Pinsent Curtis*.
Personal: All aspects of new technology.

MARSHALL, Anna
Nabarro Nathanson, London (020) 7524 6000
a.marshall@nabarro.com
Specialisation: Non-contentious environmental work with particular emphasis on: risk assessment and apportionmant in context of corporate and property transactions; advice on contaminated land issues in context of developments, property portfolio management and landlord and tenant issues; advice on environmental policy and management systems. Clients include a wide range of UK property investment companies seeking advice on environmental risk on cross-border transactions.
Prof. Memberships: CBI Environmental Protection Panel, UKELA.
Career: 1983-1987: *Freshfields* (qualified 1985); 1988-92: *Hay Management Consultants* working as a management consultant specialising in strategy and organisation); 1992-94: *Norton Rose*; 1994-Present: *Nabarro Nathanson*.
Personal: Education: Girton College, Cambridge (MA(Hons)); University of Bath (MBA). INtrests include tennis, skiing, football, ballet, opera and gardening.

MAY, Caroline
Lawrence Graham, London (020) 7379 0000
Specialisation: Partner specialising in all aspects of environmental law, with particular specialisation in contentious issues but increasingly involved in transactional work including acquisitions and disposals, planning and property development issues. Her work has an international flavour with multi-national and transatlantic corporations with varied environmental concerns. Particular specialisms include dioxin and methane emission problems, chemical waste managment issues and contaminated land. One the development side, she has become increasingly involved in the liability issues arising from brownfield site remediation on behalf of commercial property developers, institutional investors and banks. Regular speaker at public seminars and trade association events. Also undertakes in-house training tailored to client needs and contributes articles to various legal and environmental publications.
Prof. Memberships: Member of the National Council of the United Kingdom Environmental Association and member of its Noise and Finance Working Parties. Freeman of the City of London and winner of the Institute of Energy Roscoe Prize 1995.
Career: Articled Beachcroft Stanley 1985-1987; qualified October 1987. *Clifford Chance* solicitor 1988-1994. Joined *Lawrence Graham* 1994, made partner November 1995.
Personal: Trevelyan College, Durham University BA Hons.

MCPAKE, Ian A.H.
Tods Murray WS, Edinburgh (0131) 226 4771
ian.mcpake@todsmurray.co.uk
Partner in Capital Projects Department.
Specialisation: Work includes PFI, commercial property and environmental law.
Prof. Memberships: Member of United Kingdom Environmental Law Association.
Career: Qualified in 1971. Articled *J & W Buchan, Peebles* 1969-72. *Ranken & Reid SSC* 1972-90, Partner 1973. Joined *Tods Murray WS* as a Partner in 1990.
Personal: Born 1948. Attended George Watson's College, Edinburgh and St Andrew's University (LLB 1969). Leisure: golf, walking, skiing, reading. Lives in Edinburgh.

MYLREA, Kathy
Simmons & Simmons, London (020) 7628 2020
Head of Environmental Law Department.
Specialisation: Advises on all aspects of UK and EU environmental law including transaction work involving allocation of environmental liabilities and co-ordination of due diligence, advice on authorisations and permits, criminal and civil litigation, in particular defence of criminal prosecutions. Particular expertise in contaminatied land, water pollution, IPPC and waste management issues. Organises and conducts training seminars on the application of environmental law to individual businesses and business sectors. Major clients include Rohm & Haas, Owens Corning, Vivendi Water UK, BASF and Railtrack.
Prof. Memberships: Law Society, International Bar Association, UK Environmental Law Association.
Career: Qualified in Ontario, Canada in 1986 and in England & Wales in 1992. With *McKenna & Co* 1988-1992. Joined *Simmons & Simmons* in May 1992.
Personal: Born 6th November 1958. Educated at Brown University, Providence, Rhode Island, USA (BA 1980) and the University of Toronto (LL.B, 1984). Outside interests include skiing, scuba diving and ballet. Lives in London. Married with one son.

NASH, Mike
Simmons & Simmons, London (020) 7628 2020
Specialisation: Practises in all areas of UK, EU and international environmental law with particular emphasis on waste, contaminated land, chemicals and water law and its application to commercial transactions and contracts and in litigation. Mike is an Editor of the Encyclopaedia of Environmental Law and co-author of The Environment Acts 1990-95 (annotated). Significant recent matters include: civil litigation in relation to a closed landfill and contaminated land; compliance advice on PPC (pollution prevention and control); Channel Tunnel Rail Link; landfill planning appeal inquiries; decommissioning and sale of major industrial installations and equipment across Europe. Clients over the last year include English Partnerships, SmithKline Beecham, British Sugar, Railtrack, Invensys, Country Landowners' Association, National Farmers' Union, London Electricity, Owens Corning, Caird Group, VSEL.
Prof. Memberships: Law Society of England and Wales.
Career: BA (First Class Honours) New College, Oxford University. Joined *Booth & Co*, Leeds in 1991. Joined *Simmons & Simmons* in 1994.
Personal: Married with two children. Interests - football, reading, travel.

O'KEEFFE, Jacqui
Denton Wilde Sapte, London (020) 7242 1212
jok@dentonwildesapte.com
Head of Environment, Health & Safety Team
Specialisation: Principal areas of work covers environmental, health and safety and related planning law. Main areas of practice include waste management issues including transfrontier shipments of waste, packaging waste and landfill tax, corporate and property due diligence, environmental auditing, contaminated land, regulatory compliance, and advice on applications for transfer or appeals of environmental permits, environmental and health and safety litigation (in particular judicial reviews) and the preparation and co-ordination of environmental statements for major projects. Advice covers UK, EU and international legislation and conventions. An increasing amount of work also involves projects in Central and Eastern Europe. Recent projects include drafting the training manual for local authorities containing advice on the implementation of the Contaminated Land Regime and acting for Mayer Parry Recycling Limited in a judicial review of the Environment Agency's decision not to accredit it as a reprocessor. Has also advised a number of environmental trade associations and associated bodies such as the British Metals Federation, Entrust, Valpak and Wastepack. Widely published and has spoken at many conferences both in the UK and abroad.
Prof. Memberships: Law Society, International Bar Association and Institute of Wastes Management.
Career: Qualified in 1982. Local government solicitor until 1987, *Field Fisher Martineau* 1987-1989, *S J Berwin* 1989-1995, *Denton Hall* 1996
Personal: Born in Canada in 1955, attended University of South Bank 1974-1977 (LLB Hons). Enjoys white water rafting, wilderness camping and motorcycling.

PIKE, John D.
Addleshaw Booth & Co, Leeds 0113 209 2000
jdp@@addleshaw-booth.co.uk
Head of Commercial Property Group (includes Commercial Property, Environmental, Construction, Planning and Property Litigation).
Specialisation: Main area of practice is commercial property work, in particular development, banking, investment and private sectors. A particular specialism is land pollution and he frequently advises on land contamination and remediation, waste and lender risk.
Career: Qualified 1972. Partner 1976.
Personal: Jesus College Cambridge (MA: Hons). De Montfort University (MA: Environmental Law). Governor Moorlands School, Leeds and Governor of St Peters School, York. Director of Urban Mines Limited and heavily involved in the Brownfields project as a member of the Advisory Group. Interests include sports and family.

PRIMROSE, Andrew H.
Maclay Murray & Spens, Glasgow
(0141) 248 5011
ahp@maclaymurrayspens.co.uk
Specialisation: Senior commercial property and environmental law partner. Qualified to practise in both Scotland and England. In-depth experience of all property and environmental issues, including those relating to acquisitions, waste management and risk assessment. Currently advising on water abstraction project, packaging waste in the whisky industry and environmental indemnities for old industrial sites. Author of numerous publications. Chairman elect IBA's Section on Legal Practice.
Prof. Memberships: UK Environmental Law Association, Scotland Europa Environmental Group, Scottish Environmental Industries Association.
Career: Oxford University (BA 1961) and Glasgow University (LL.B 1964).
Personal: Married with two children.

REDMAN, Michael
Clifford Chance, London (020) 7600 1000
michael.redman@cliffordchance.com
Specialisation: Solicitor advocate (qualified in criminal and civil jurisdiction). He has experience in dealing with the environmental aspects of corporate, banking and property transactions and infrastructure projects. Appeared in judicial review proceedings. A considerable depth of expertise in energy sector going back to his time at the bar, he has been involved in British Coal and Nuclear Electric privatisation as well as recently a number of independent power projects.
Prof. Memberships: UKELA.
Career: Barrister (1975); solicitor (1986).
Personal: Rugby referee.

REID, Donald A.
Morton Fraser, Solicitors, Edinburgh
(0131) 247 1000
dar@morton-fraser.com
Consultant and Head of Environmental Law Group.
Specialisation: Advises on all aspects of environmental law and liability including legislative compliance, property transactions, civil litigation and corporate environmental strategy, with a particular emphasis on European and international environmental law. Frequent contributor to environmental law journals and conferences. Lecturer to universities and industrial groups throughout the UK and abroad.

Prof. Memberships: Immediate past Chairman of the UK Environmental Law Association, and currently Chairman of the Scottish Contaminated Land Forum, CBI (Scotland) Environment Committee. Director ENTRUST.
Career: Qualified in 1968. Joined *Morton Fraser WS* as a Partner in 1975.
Personal: Born 14th February 1945. Educated at George Watson's College 1949-62 and Edinburgh University 1962-66. Leisure interests include sailing, hill walking and music. Lives in Aberdour, Fife.

RENGER, Michael
Nabarro Nathanson, Sheffield 0114 279 4130
m.renger@nabarro.com
Partner and head of environment department.
Specialisation: Extensive industrial, energy, waste and property client base. Projects include construction and modification of power stations, waste to energy plants, regional waste facilities, major commercial property and mineral developments. Privatisation of coal industry. Practice includes environmental regulation, due diligence and litigation (both civil and criminal). Chaired Environment Agency/CIRIA project 'Building a Cleaner Future'. Legal Member of Environment Steering Group of Institute of Chartered Accountants.
Prof. Memberships: Legal Associate of RTPI; Law Society's Planning Panel; UKELA.

RICE, Paul
Denton Wilde Sapte, London (020) 7242 1212
Specialisation: Specialises solely in environment and health and safety law. Recent work includes redevelopment of former power stations, judicial review of Environment Agency, water prosecutions and sale of Rentokil service companies. Clients include BHP, Entrust, Mayer Parry, Sainsbury's, Thames Waste and Totalfina.
Prof. Memberships: UKELA Waste and Liability Working Groups, ICC Wastes Committee.
Career: LLB (Hons) Queen's University Belfast with DJ Hill Memorial Prize (1992). University of London LLM (Environmental Laws). King's College (1993). *Denton Hall* (1994).
Publications: Contributing author of 'A-Z Guide to Environmental Practice' and monthly column in 'Wastes Management'. He was awarded the first UKELA Andrew Lees Prize in 1997.
Personal: Interests include travel, performing arts, mountain biking and running.

ROSS, Kenneth C.
Morison Bishop, Glasgow (0141) 248 4672
Partner in Charge of Commercial Property Division. Head of Environmental Law Group.
Specialisation: All aspects of environmental law, with particular reference to contaminated land and waste. Frequent lecturer to conferences, and author of articles regarding a variety of environmental law topics, particularly contaminated land and its connection with commercial property transactions, waste management licences and other waste issues. Author of chapter on Contaminated Land in Second Edition of Greens Guide to Environmental Law in Scotland.
Prof. Memberships: Convenor of Law Society of Scotland Environmental Law Committee, Convenor and Member of National Council of UK Environmental Law Association and Member of Editorial Board of Scottish Planning and Environmental Law. Qualified in1982, Partner since 1984.
Personal: Born 30th September 1958. Graduate of Glasgow University (LLB 1st Class Hons 1980). Spare time interests include archaeology. Lives in Glasgow.

SALES, Martin
Burness, Edinburgh (0131) 473 6000
Specialisation: Martin Sales has for many years acted for a wide range of environmental interests, particularly in relation to the legal aspects of environmental assessment, the disposal of non-waste and waste materials using available exemptions from UK Licensing requirements, waste water and sewerage projects, the scope and conditions attaching to environmental consents including planning permissions, discharge consents, license transfer and modification and the registration of waste carriers. For corporate acquisition work, Martin is well placed to advise on the need for and scope of environmental warranties especially in the context of corporate recovery.

SALTER, Ian
Burges Salmon, Bristol (0117) 939 2225
ian.salter@burges-salmon.com
Specialisation: Environmental regulation. Particular expertise in the transport, chemical, nuclear and food/agricultural sectors. Advises on all aspects of waste management licensing, radioactive waste and nuclear licensing, IPC and LAAPC, water law and abstraction licensing, contaminated land and remediation notices, packaging waste, related criminal prosecutions and corporate due diligence.
Prof. Memberships: Legal Associateship Royal Town Planning Institute, Law Society's planning panel, UKELA, International Nuclear Law Association.
Career: Joined *Burges Salmon* 1990, partner 1999.
Publications: Joint author Tolley's 'Environmental Law' and Butterworths 'Forms and Precedents' (Agriculture and the environment).
Personal: Ian enjoys golf and spending time with his family.

SHEPHERD, Elizabeth
Eversheds, Manchester (0161) 832 6666
elizabethshepherd@eversheds.com
Specialisation: Environmental and Health and Safety. Head of Manchester Environmental, Health and Safety Team advising on corporate and property transaction related environmental issues and general environmental compliance, carrying out legal environmental audits and formulating on behalf of clients corporate environmental policies and management systems.
Prof. Memberships: UKELA (United Kingdom Environmental Law Association). CBI North West Environment Business Forum, GMEA (Greater Manchester Environmental Association) and Law Society Environmental Law Sub-Committee.
Career: Cambridge University, Churchill College M.A. First Class Honours. Admitted as a Solicitor in October 1984. Articled with *Eversheds Alexander Tatham* in Manchester and appointed partner of Eversheds in 1988.
Personal: Elizabeth lives near Knutsford, Cheshire. Her interests include classical music, skiing & gardening.

SHEPPARD, Claire
Theodore Goddard, London (020) 7606 8855
Specialisation: All areas of environmental law with particular emphasis on the environmental aspects of corporate, banking, PFI and property transactions, toxic tort and contaminated land litigation, contaminated land insurance and regulatory and compliance advice.
Prof. Memberships: Land and Water Committee of the Society of Chemical Industry.
Career: Articled *Linklaters & Alliance* (1989-91), assistant in the Environmental Unit and litigation department of *Linklaters & Alliance* (1991-98), joined *Theodore Goddard* 1999 and made a partner in November 1999.

SHERIDAN, Paul
CMS Cameron McKenna, London
(020) 7367 2186
pfs@cmck.com
Partner in Environment Law Group.
Specialisation: Partner of a team dedicated to providing a full environment law service. He advises numerous national and international clients on a wide range of domestic and international contentious and non-contentious matters. Non-contentious matters include transactional services in share and asset transactions, joint ventures, PFI/PPPs, major infrastructure projects, contaminated land transfers and developments, lenders transactions and businesss recoveries; advice on the insurance of environment risks; regulatory compliance advice; economic environment instruments; packaging and producer responsibilities; and the compilation of databases on both domestic and international environmental laws. He is very active in contentious environment matters both civil and criminal. He has, for instance, acted for parties in high profile test cases. He is regularly involved in water, waste and licence/permit related prosecutions. He is particularly involved with environment issues relating to waste, water, contaminated land, IPPC and APC energy, nuclear installations and construction. He is a regular speaker at UK and overseas conferences, has contributed to several environment law textbooks and is the author of several articles.

SHINER, Philip
Public Interest Lawyers, Birmingham
(0121) 777 5187
phil_shiner@publicinterestlawyers.co.uk
Specialisation: Specialises in enviromental protection work especially judicial review for individuals and communities. Particular emphasis on landfill/incineration/mineral planning/ nuclear installations. Instructed in a number of reported cases: R v Rochdale MBC ex parte Brown; R v Derbyshire CC ex parte Woods; R v North Somerset DC ex parte Garnett; R v Somerset CC ex parte Dixon; R v Bolton MBC ex parte Kirkman; R v environment Agency ex parte Leam et al. Has also been instructed in cases about the storage of BSE waste and the manufacture of trident warheads.
Prof. Memberships: Law Society's Planning Panel, Council Member of UKELA, Member of Crown Office Users Group, ELF, CATS, Friends of the Earth and Labour Party.
Career: Solicitor, *Robin Thompsons* 1981-2; Small Heath Law Centre 1982-4; Birmingham Council Estates Project 1985-8; Birkenhead Resource Unit 1992-5; *Tyndallwoods* 1995-9. Also worked in community development for Barnardos.
Publications: Has written and spoken extensively on environmental and planning law.

Personal: Born 25 December 1956. Educated, Bishop Ullathorne RC School, Coventry 1968-75; Birmingham University 1975-8; Warwick University 1984-6 (LLM by research). Married with three children. Leisure interests include contemporary music especially indie, cycle racing, running, fell walking and real ale.

SMITH, Charles

Brodies WS, Edinburgh (0131) 228 3777
csmith@brodies.co.uk
Partner in Corporate Department.
Specialisation: Advises on environmental law and liability generally and in respect of land, water and air pollution, sales and purchases of land, assets and shares, leases and security/banking transactions. Also handles major commercial contracts (including PFI and privatisations) and banking transactions. Advises companies on environmental compliance, housebuilders on environmental liability, contractors on waste management licensing and the landfill tax, and numerous clients on contaminated land. Continues to advise on Ravenscraig Steelworks Site. Co-author of "Pollution Control: The Law in Scotland", published in November 1997.
Prof. Memberships: Law Society of Scotland, United Kingdom Environmental Law Assocation, Royal Society of Arts, Manufactures and Commerce, Scottish Environmental Industries Association.
Career: Qualified in 1987 having joined *Brodies WS* in 1985. Became a Partner in 1990.
Personal: Born 21st October 1960. Attended Perth Academy 1972-78, Exeter College, Oxford 1978-82, then University of Edinburgh 1982-85. Lives in Edinburgh.

SMITH, Paul A.

Eversheds, Leeds (0113) 243 0391
paulsmith@eversheds.com
Partner in Commercial Litigation Department.
Specialisation: Main area of practice is Environment and Health and Safety Law. Heads *Eversheds'* National Environmental Law Group, having established the unit in 1988. Acts principally for major industrial companies in the UK, US and Europe in civil and criminal proceedings. Successfully took the River Derwent test case to the House of Lords. In the crisis management field he acted in the Hickson & Welch Castleford incident, the Hickson International Cork incident and the Associated Octel fire at Ellesmere Port. Co-author of College of Law Environment Law and Environmental Manual published by CCH Publications. Regular contributor to BBC radio programmes. *Eversheds* client partner for Du Pont in the UK. Visiting Professor in Environment Law at the Nottingham Law School.
Prof. Memberships: UKELA, Law Society, ABA, IBA.
Career: Qualified in 1982, having joined *Freshfields* in 1980. Joined *Eversheds Hepworth & Chadwick* in 1984 and became a Partner in 1987.
Personal: Born 14th November 1956. Attended Warwick University 1975-79. Governor of Richmond House School. Director Nottingham Law School Limited. Member Reform Club. Professional Puppeteer. Lives in Menston, West Yorks.

TOWNSEND, Matthew

Allen & Overy, London (020) 7330 3000
matthew.townsend@allenovery.com
Specialisation: Specialises in all aspects of environmental law with particular experience in advising on environmental issues arising from domestic and international acquisitions and disposals, new issues, projects (including PPP) and financing. Advises regularly in relation to waste issues (in particular, on a number of recent landfill acquisitions and disposals), IPC/IPPC, contaminated land, securing environmental insurance and producer responsibility in relation to electrical equipment and packaging. He has advised a major UK land holder on its contaminated land and remediation strategy and on various divestments by a major chemical company. He has also advised leading packaging waste compliance schemes on various matters including the trading of packaging waste recovery notes. He has particular experience in environmental, health and safety litigation (both civil and criminal) including high profile prosecutions arising from radioactive contamination and recent environmental test cases. he has also represented a major trade association in negotiating a voluntary agreement under the climate change levey.
Prof. Memberships: Law Society, UKELA (sitting on a number of UKELA working groups) and the Environmental Industries Commission (waste management and contaminated land working groups).
Career: Articles *Morgan Cole* (1994-1996), solicitor in the environmental group at *CMS Cameron McKenna* (formerly *Cameron Markby Hewitt*) (1996-2000) and joined as an associate in the environmental law group at *Allen & Overy* in early 2000.
Publications: Contributor to and reviwer of 'Environmental Law and Procedures Management Handbook', contributor to 'Health, Safety and Environment Cases' and 'Environmental Assessment'. Regular speaker on environmental matters and has published a number of articles including providing the environmental law update section of the Law Society Gazette.
Personal: Born 18th February, 1971 in Sheffield. Educated at Birmingham University 1989 - 1992 (BA Hons in History). Interests include theatre, history, reading and most sports particularly tennis, golf and marathon running. Regular Diver.

TRINICK, G. Marcus

Bond Pearce, Plymouth (01752) 266633
xgmt@bondpearce.com
See under Planning, p.668

TURNER, John R.

Wragge & Co, Birmingham (0121) 214 1050
john_turner@wragge.com
Specialisation: Has wide experience in all aspects of air pollution, water, contaminated land and waste law for commercial clients. Specialises in litigation and regulatory law as well as advising on corporate acquisition and due diligence matters.
Prof. Memberships: Chairman, Midlands Environmental Business Club Limited; Director, Birmingham Groundwork; Member, Chartered Institution of Water and Environmental Management (C.I.W.E.M.), Member, UKELA. Member Environment Agency Midlands Regional Environmenta Protection Advisory Committee.
Career: Articled *Mills and Reeve.* Qualified 1980. Joined *Wragge & Co* 1982. Partner at *Wragge & Co* from 1989. Consultant from 2000.
Personal: Born 3.7.55.

WAITE, Andrew

Berwin Leighton, London (020) 7760 1000
andrew.waite@berwinleighton.com
Partner Planning & Environment Department and Co-ordinator of the Environment Group.
Specialisation: Specialist in environmental liability and pollution controls, dealing principally with contaminated land, waste management, noise, water resources issues, integrated pollution controls and air pollution. Advises on environmental liabilities in corporate and property transactions, lender liability issues, environmental litigation and legal issues involved in establishing and operating environmental management systems. Clients advised include English Partnerships, Blue Circle, BG Plc, Tesco, Royal Bank of Scotland, Girobank, Prudential Property Management, Philips and Drew Fund management, Legal & General, Kronospan, W.H.Smith, Harnischfeger Industries and Transamerica. Advises Waste Facilities Audit Association on waste management issues and the Brownlands Group on law and policy developments relating to contaminated land. Has advised the Bulgarian and Ukrainian governments with regard to their proposed environmental legislation and has drafted forestry legislation for Sierra Leone as well as contributing to the Environmental Protection Act 1990 and the Environment Act 1995. Co-author of Environmental Law in Property Transactions (Butterworths 1997); Editor of Butterworths' Environmental Handbook (2nd edition 1997) and author of numerous articles on environmental law. Frequent speaker at national and international conferences on environmental law, with TV and radio experience.
Prof. Memberships: President of the European Environmental Law Association, Co-founder and former Secretary of the UK Environmental Law Association, Member of the IUCN Commission on Environmental Law, Member of the International Court of Environment Arbitration and Conciliation, Member of CBI ad hoc working party on environmental liability and former Chairman of the UKELA working party on contaminated land.
Career: Qualified 1975, Lecturer in law at Southampton University from 1980-88; acting director of the Centre for Environmental Law at Southampton University 1984-87; visiting Professor in Environmental Law at the University of Georgia 1987. Head of Environmental Law Group at *Masons* 1988-90 and Co-ordinator of the Environment Group at *Linklaters & Paines* 1990-93. Joined *Berwin Leighton* in 1993.
Personal: Born 25th February 1950. Attended Lincoln College, Oxford, 1969-72, BA (Hons) 1972, MA 1977. Leisure interests include history, archaeology, wildlife, theatre, cinema and walking in the countryside. Lives in Chandlers Ford, Hampshire.

WAKE, Brian

Wake Dyne Lawton, Chester (01829) 773100
bdw@wdl.co.uk
Specialisation: Mineral extraction, waste management, land reclamation and environmental law. Acts for major mineral companies and landowners, and advises regularly on contaminated land and pollution control matters.
Prof. Memberships: Fellow of the Institute of Quarrying. Founder, United Kingdom Environmental Law Association North West Section.
Career: Qualified 1978 with *Linklaters & Paines.* Tar-

mac Quarry Products 1981-86.
Personal: Born 19.9.53 Hong Kong. Speaks Cantonese. LLB Liverpool 1975.

WATCHMAN, Paul Q.
Freshfields Bruckhaus Deringer, London (020) 7936 4000
Property department: environment group.
Specialisation: Principal area of work is environmental law, including contaminated land, water pollution, waste management, energy and minerals. Other main area of work is planning law, covering mineral developments (including coal mining and coastal superquarries), planning inquiries and retail office and business developments. Author or co-author of books and articles on environmental planning and public law. Lectures regularly on planning and environmental law.
Prof. Memberships: Law Society, Law Society of Scotland.
Career: Qualified as a Scottish Solicitor in 1977 and as an English Solicitor in 1994, partner *Freshfields*, 1995.
Personal: Born 17th November 1952. Lives in Surrey.

WILLIAMS, Gwyn
Hammond Suddards Edge, Birmingham (0121) 200 2001
gwyn.williams@hammondsuddardsedge.com
Partner.
Specialisation: Main areas of practice are in energy and natural resources law including the environmental and financing aspects of the mineral exploration and development, power generation, waste to energy and liabilities regulation. Also has experience of rail privatisation and the development of large rail terminals and railway infrastructure projects.
Prof. Memberships: Law Society.
Career: Qualified in 1970, Tarmac Group Legal Department 1972. Company Secretary and Solicitor Tarmac Quarry Products 1981-89. Partner with *Edge Ellison* since 1990.
Personal: Educated at Liverpool University. Leisure interests include industrial archaelogy.

WISEMAN, Andrew
Trowers & Hamlins, London (020) 7423 8000
awiseman@trowers.com
Specialisation: Practice covers the full range including noise, waste, contaminated land, pollution and planning. Former member of London Waste Regulation Authority. Visiting lecturer at Brunel University. Has addressed numerous conferences and been interviewed on TV and radio.
Prof. Memberships: Treasurer UK Environmental Law Association, City of London Law Society (Planning and Environmental Law Sub-Committee), Environmental Law Foundation, Members Institute of Waste Management.
Career: Qualified in 1989. Former Partner at *Shindler & Co*, *Finers* and *Wiseman*Solicitors.
Personal: Fellow of the Royal Society of Arts.

FAMILY/MATRIMONIAL

London: 381; The South: 383; Thames Valley: 383; South West: 384; Wales: 385; Midlands: 385; East Anglia: 386; North West: 387; Yorkshire: 387; North East: 388; Scotland: 389; Northern Ireland: 390; *Profiles*: 390

RESEARCH APPROVED BY BMRB: *For this edition,* Chambers' *researchers conducted 6083 interviews – 4408 with law firms, 598 with barristers and 1077 with clients.*

The validity of the research was scrutinised by BMRB International, who audited both the methodology and the results at our offices in July 2000. They interviewed Chambers' *researchers and cross-checked sample interviews. Details of the audit appear on page 7.*

LONDON

FAMILY/MATRIMONIAL • London	Ptnrs	Assts
❶ Manches	7	11
Withers	7	9
❷ Charles Russell	9	6
Farrer & Co	4	6
Gordon Dadds	6	5
Levison Meltzer Pigott	3	2
Miles Preston & Co	3	3
❸ Bates, Wells & Braithwaite	3	6
Sears Tooth	⚐	⚐
❹ Clintons	3	3
Dawson Cornwell	6	4
Kingsley Napley	2	3
Mishcon de Reya	2	7
The Family Law Consortium	6	3
❺ Barnett Sampson	2	2
Bindman & Partners	2	3
Collyer-Bristow	3	4
Dawson & Co	4	2
Goodman Ray	3	4
Hodge Jones & Allen	4	3
International Family Law Chambers	2	-
Reynolds Porter Chamberlain	2	4
Russell-Cooke, Potter & Chapman	3	2
Stephenson Harwood	1	2
❻ Anthony Gold, Lerman & Muirhead	2	2
Fisher Meredith	1	8
Forsters	1	1
Osbornes	3	3
Payne Hicks Beach	3	2
The Simkins Partnership	1	-

Within each band, firms are listed alphabetically.
⚐ Figures unavailable at time of going to press.

Manches *"Exceedingly well-resourced"* and receiving widespread praise from its peers, the size and strength of the team means that its big money clients are able to receive a *"luxury service."* The firm consequently remains in the front rank. Big-hitters include the *"clever, able and well-connected"* **Helen Ward** who is seen as *"a real star on the tougher money cases,"* the *"honest and sensible"* **Richard Sax** and **Jane Simpson** *"who brings an approach of experience and fairness to her work."* Last year's up and coming **William Massey** moves into the main rankings this year. The team specialises in complex and high value financial cases, and high profile highlights of last year included acting for Sir Ian McEwan and continued involvement in the Paloma Picasso divorce, in which they introduced the use of litigation support technology. Other services offered include the full range of private children work and abduction as well as cohabitation issues and pre-nuptial agreements.

Withers Seen by the market as a *"pre-eminent"* team in the field, offering *"a better spectrum of service"* with leading partners supported by *"competent assistants."* The firm continues to vie with Manches for the the leading position. High value, high profile and often international ancillary relief is the focus of the practice, with clients able to take advantage of the firm's complementary tax and trust expertise. Other increasing areas of practice include cohabitation (**Mark Harper** is an acknowledged expert), surrogacy and pre-nuptial agreements. Leading players at the firm include the respected **Andrew Gerry**, the *"first rate"* **Diana Parker** who continues to practice in addition to her role as managing partner, the *"full-on"* **James Harcus** and the *"charming"* **Gill Doran** who is seen as *"a great talent."* One particular highlight of the last year was the team's involvement in the landmark 'stolen' sperm case Von Schonburg v London Gynaecology and Fertility Centre.

Charles Russell In the process of expansion, with the arrival of **Erica Shelton** and three assistants from Rooks Rider building on the existing large team of *"excellent people."* Leading players at the firm include pensions expert **David Davidson**, **Maryly La Follette**, **William Longrigg** and the *"quiet but top class"* **Grant Howell** who has recently become managing partner. The team deals with all aspects of complex financial settlements and private children work, with international expertise including forum shopping and child abduction. The highly respected Peter George has now become a consultant.

Farrer & Co Acting for many well-known entertainment, royal and professional clients, the team remains a strong player in matrimonial finance. **Fiona Shackleton** is seen by many as a *"stylish operator"* whose *"big personality"* and reputation as a *"brilliant strategic manager"* draws many clients to the firm, while team head **Richard Parry** is respected as *"outstanding, quietly efficient, intelligent and pragmatic."* In addition to the *"big money"* work, which often has an international dimension including jurisdiction disputes and advising people abroad, the full range of private children work is undertaken.

Gordon Dadds Well known and expanding team which handles a large amount of high value and often high profile ancillary relief and private children work. International issues such as forum shopping, abduction and foreign trusts make up a significant part of the practice's work. **Douglas Alexiou** is recognised by many as a *"gentleman,"* whose *"polished and organised"* style attracts many well known clients, including the Spice Girl Melanie Gulzar. Young partners **Susan Philipps** and **Jeremy Fisher**, who won his name when acting in the Picasso case, are also recommended.

Levison Meltzer Pigott A small specialist practice seen in the market as *"quite a team,"* whose clients range from the *"more zany, arty people"* to high net worth individuals drawn from industry, commerce and the professions. Aspects of specialisation include divorce, high net worth financial settlements and private children work. The *"individualistic"* **Jeremy Levison** *"can be tough when he needs to be,"* and fellow partners **Clare Meltzer** and the *"capable"* **Simon Pigott** were also recommended.

Miles Preston & Co Niche firm widely praised in the market as handling *"good quality work in a tough and constructive way."* The *"charming and businesslike"* **Miles Preston** leads a well regarded team which includes **Julia Stanczyk**, who is new to the leaders' table this year. Work covers financial matters for a range of clients, often of high net worth and with international connections, and private children work.

LEADING INDIVIDUALS • London	
✪ ALEXIOU Douglas Gordon Dadds	SHACKLETON Fiona Farrer & Co
WARD Helen Manches	
❶ DAVIS Sandra Mishcon de Reya	DORAN Gill Withers
HUGHES Frances Bates, Wells & Braithwaite	
LEVISON Jeremy Levison Meltzer Pigott	PARKER Diana Withers
PRESTON Miles Miles Preston & Co	SAX Richard Manches
SIMPSON Jane Manches	TOOTH Ray Sears Tooth
❷ DAVIDSON David Charles Russell	FISHER Jeremy Gordon Dadds
HARCUS James Withers	HUTCHINSON Anne-Marie Dawson Cornwell
PARRY Richard Farrer & Co	RAE Maggie Clintons
RAY Peggy Goodman Ray	
❸ COLLIS Pamela Cawdery Kaye Fireman & Taylor	
DRAKE Michael Collyer-Bristow	FOWLER Pauline Bates, Wells & Braithwaite
GERRY Andrew Withers	HARPER Mark Withers
HOWELL Grant Charles Russell	KEIR Jane Kingsley Napley
LA FOLLETTE Maryly Charles Russell	LEVERTON David Payne Hicks Beach
LONGRIGG William Charles Russell	MARCO Alan Collyer-Bristow
PEARSON Philippa Family Law Consortium	PHILIPPS Susan Gordon Dadds
PIGOTT Simon Levison Meltzer Pigott	ROBINSON Sara Family Law Consortium
RUTTER Geoffrey Collyer-Bristow	TRUEX David International Family Law Chambers
❹ BAKER Miranda Kingsley Napley	BEATSON Kim Anthony Gold, Lerman & Muirhead
CHAPMAN Elspeth Barnett Sampson	CLARK Peter Dawson Cornwell
CORNWELL John Dawson Cornwell	CROWTHER Felicity Bindman & Partners
GIEVE Katherine Bindman & Partners	HODSON David Family Law Consortium
MASSEY William Manches	MELTZER Claire Levison Meltzer Pigott
MONRO Pat Wilford Monro	PEMBRIDGE Eileen Fisher Meredith
PIRRIE James Family Law Consortium	RODGERS Hilary Forsters
SHELTON Erica Charles Russell	STANCZYK Julia Miles Preston & Co

See *Profiles* on page 390

Bates, Wells & Braithwaite City-based team which is known for its diverse practice and international profile. The *"outstanding"* **Frances Hughes** received praise from many in the market as *"someone you can always get a straight answer from"* while **Pauline Fowler** is known as a *"very good lawyer"* and a *"safe pair of hands."* On the financial side, the practice has a stong City client base with an increasing number of IT, software and media millionaires and it runs a separate "big money" mediation practice. Complex children's work is another specialism, with expertise in international child abduction and cases involving cults.

Sears Tooth Small niche practice known particularly for the *"feisty"* and *"energetic"* **Ray Tooth** who *"likes an argument"* but *"knows his stuff without a doubt."* Highly rated for contentious ancillary relief work, the team can also be constructive when needs be. Some private children work is also handled.

Clintons West End team with a significant number of sport, media and entertainment clients and a growing reputation in matrimonial work, which takes it up in the rankings this year. Private children work and abduction make up an important part of the practice, with offshore trusts, foreign tax domiciles, jurisdiction issues, prenuptial contracts and offshore assets being some of the international work on offer. **Maggie Rae** remains a *"serious player with a huge following,"* and the team structure and quality of assistants was also praised.

Dawson Cornwell *"A good cross-section of specialists,"* which combines a high value ancillary relief practice with a separate children department. The latter has a top class reputation in international child abduction and disputes. The *"enormously experienced and knowledgeable"* **Anne-Marie Hutchinson** is *"pre-eminent"* in the children field while **John Cornwell** and **Peter Clark** are recommended on the money side.

Kingsley Napley Led by the *"able"* **Jane Keir** following the departure of Pamela Collis, with **Miranda Baker** also recommended, the practice maintains its reputation for strength and diversity. In addition to high value matrimonial work, the firm's longstanding abduction expertise has led to an increase in its international instructions, particularly on jurisdiction issues. Recent interesting cases have included the question of a solicitor's duty of confidentiality to his client and when it can be overriden.

Mishcon de Reya Known particularly for its *"phenomenal client base"* of high profile individuals, often with a media angle, the team remains a strong player in the family field and handles all elements of matrimonial and private children work. International work includes forum shopping, trust and tax advice, jurisdiction issues and enforcement, while on the children side, specialisms include complex domestic disputes and child abduction. **Sandra Davis** has a *"well deserved reputation"* and continues to act for Jerry Hall.

The Family Law Consortium A large and expanding practice known for its variety of work, and its *"imaginative approach"* to mediation and non court-based matrimonial dispute resolution. This is enhanced by an in-house counselling and marriage support service. Work ranges from ancillary relief to complex private children work with an increasing amount of applications to remove from the jurisdiction and international abduction cases, often outside the ambit of the Hague Convention. Recommended individuals are **Philippa Pearson**, **James Pirrie**, the *"extremely good"* **Sara Robinson** and the *"high profile"* **David Hodson**, and the firm rises in the tables this year as a result of its depth of practitioner.

Other Notable Practitioners

Among other rated firms, **Collyer-Bristow** is a respected matrimonial outfit with a strong client base and noted specialism in abduction. Partners **Michael Drake**, **Alan Marco** and **Geoffrey Rutter** are all recommended. New outfit **International Family Law Chambers** is known for its expertise in Australian jurisdiction issues and is expanding its US and European practices. Team head **David Truex**, is seen as a *"hugely energetic practitioner"* and rises in the rankings this year. **Goodman Ray** is particularly rated on the children side, with a strong reputation in childcare work, and **Peggy Ray** maintains her *"outstanding"* reputation; *"what she doesn't know on public law, no-one knows."* **Reynolds Porter Chamberlain** is known as a *"quality"* and *"widely-based"* practice, with a strong reputation for international child abduction for which it acts for the Lord Chancellor's Department, Reunite, Relate and other public bodies. **Bindman & Partners** (where **Katherine Gieve** is a recommended children practitioner and **Felicity Crowther** heads up the ancillary relief team) and **Hodge Jones & Allen** are respected mixed practices with a significant number of legal aid clients and noted public law expertise. **Barnett Sampson** (where **Elspeth Chapman** is seen as a *"competent and experienced lawyer,"*) **Dawson & Co** and **Russell-Cooke Potter & Chapman** also remain highly regarded and act for middle to high net worth individuals on matrimonial issues, in addition to handling children and international work. Unique amongst the large City firms in retaining a family practice, the team at **Stephenson Harwood** is also recommended, and receives significant work by referral from its international and City connections. **Anthony Gold Lerman & Muirhead** (where **Kim Beatson** is recommended), **Fisher Meredith** (where **Eileen Pembridge** heads the matrimonial team) and **Osbornes** are well-regarded, broad-based practices, while the reputation of the family team at **Payne Hicks Beach** is seen to rest on the shoulders of the *"very experienced"* managing partner **David Leverton**. **Forsters** (where **Hilary Rodgers** is well-regarded) and **The Simkins Partnership** are smaller, but respected teams, the latter known particularly for its media and entertainment clients. **Pamela Collis** of **Cawdery Kaye Fireman & Taylor** remains respected by the market though her new firm has not yet made a big enough impact to warrant inclusion in the table. **Pat Monro** of niche children practice **Wilford Monro** is new to the rankings this year to reflect her position as *"a pre-eminent individual in public law children work."*

THE SOUTH

FAMILY/MATRIMONIAL • The South	Ptnrs	Assts
❶ **Lester Aldridge** Bournemouth	1	2
❷ **Paris Smith & Randall** Southampton	2	3
Thomson Snell & Passmore Tunbridge Wells	2	2
❸ **Brachers** Maidstone	1	-
Coffin Mew & Clover Portsmouth	6	5
Cripps Harries Hall Tunbridge Wells, Kent	2	4
DMH Brighton	1	3
Max Barford & Co Tunbridge Wells	2	1

LEADING INDIVIDUALS
❶ **FOSTER Stephen** Lester Aldridge
❸ **WRIGHT Barbara** Thomson Snell & Passmore

Within each band, firms are listed alphabetically. See **Profiles** on page 390

Lester Aldridge More active on the London circuit, this Bournemouth practice led by the *"ambitious"* and *"well-informed"* **Stephen Foster** handles big money cases with assets ranging from £1 million to £10 million. Foster acts in a substantial number of international cases and has carved a particular niche for himself in handling ancillary relief for expatriots in the Tokyo money markets. Also operates a mediation practice.

Paris Smith & Randall A *"competent"* and *"well-rounded"* team covering all aspects of family work. Currently expanding its high net worth client base, the practice offers a private financial mediation service. Also possesses considerable expertise in international child abduction cases.

Thomson Snell & Passmore The presence of **Barbara Wright**, a *"dynamic force," "able to see both sides,"* continues to attract media and sports celebrity clients to this ancillary relief dominated practice. Highly accomplished in complex agricultural divorces and ancillary relief cases involving foreign property.

Other Notable Firms

Brachers, **Coffin Mew & Clover**, **Cripps Harries Hall**, **DMH**, and **Max Barford & Co** were all commended as having *"sound"* family teams covering general family law.

THAMES VALLEY

FAMILY/MATRIMONIAL • Thames Valley	Ptnrs	Assts
❶ **Blandy & Blandy** Reading	4	2
Manches Oxford	1	1
❷ **Darbys Mallam Lewis** Oxford	2	2
Morgan Cole Oxford	2	4
❸ **Henmans** Oxford	1	1
Iliffes Booth Bennett Uxbridge	2	7
Linnells Oxford	1	2
❹ **Boodle Hatfield** Oxford	1	1
Rowberry Morris & Co. Reading	1	2

LEADING INDIVIDUALS	
❶ **DON Andrew** Blandy & Blandy	**EDDY Catherine** Darbys Mallam Lewis
MITCHELL Jane Manches	**SIMPSON Barbara** Boodle Hatfield
UP AND COMING	
BLORE Sian Blandy & Blandy	

Within each band, firms are listed alphabetically. See **Profiles** on page 390

Blandy & Blandy Under the direction of senior partner **Andrew Don**, a man *"not afraid of confronting the issues,"* this team of recognised strength and depth maintains its top band position. Equally strong in public and private children work and high net worth financial settlements, the practice is also making a name for itself on the mediation front with its STEPahead counselling program. The group's strength is bolstered by the addition of 'up and coming' **Sian Blore** from Farrers & Co.

Manches Strong connections with the firm's main London office give this Oxford branch a high profile on complex and high level ancillary relief cases. **Jane Mitchell,** said to *"fight for her clients,"* handles financial and private child care matters for a private client base of medics, academics, media professionals, and marketing directors.

Darbys Mallam Lewis With considerable strength in public care children cases acting for both guardians and parents, the team maintains a substantial legal aid practice. *"Calm"* **Catherine Eddy** was recommended for her *"willingness to work things out"* in ancillary relief cases and mediation.

Morgan Cole The departure of Barbara Simpson and outsourcing of legal aid work to the Oxford Family Law Group are perceived as substantial losses to the practice. The team still handles high value ancillary relief cases over the £1 million mark as well as a considerable number of cases with international elements.

Henmans Commended as *"a safe pair of hands"* in matrimonial matters, the department is moving away from legal aid work to concentrate on high value financial settlements. Has particular expertise in cases where there is a family owned business. Team includes a trained mediator.

Iliffes Booth Bennett A large practice covering the full range of family law, the group is particularly well-respected in child care matters, both public and private. Also handles a number of high value ancillary relief cases in excess of £1 million and maintains a specialist domestic violence unit to deal with emergency injunctions.

Linnells Practice dominated by legally aided public law but developing its profile in high net ancillary relief and financial advice for Oxford academics.

Boodle Hatfield Enters the tables this year on the back of *"gutsy"* **Barbara Simpson**, highly accomplished in big money financial cases. Although the firm has yet to establish its reputation in the field, Simpson's arrival in December 1999 from Morgan Cole is expected to boost the firm's profile in family practice.

Rowberry Morris Highly regarded in the area, covers the middle range market with approximately half of its caseload legally aided. Handles full range of child care and adoption cases, divorce cases and large financial settlements.

SOUTH WEST

FAMILY/MATRIMONIAL • South West	Ptnrs	Assts
❶ Bond Pearce Plymouth	1	2
Burges Salmon Bristol	1	2
Foot Anstey Sargent Exeter	3	4
Gill Akaster Plymouth	1	2
TLT Solicitors Bristol	3	2
Tozers Torquay, Plymouth, Exeter	5	5
Wolferstans Plymouth	4	6
❷ Clarke Willmott & Clarke Yeovil, Taunton	4	2
Stephens & Scown Exeter	5	1
❸ Hooper & Wollen Torquay	3	1
Ian Downing Family Law Practice Plymouth	1	1
❹ E. David Brain & Co St. Austell	2	-
Hartnell & Co Exeter	2	3
Stones Exeter	2	5
❺ Hugh James Ford Simey Exeter	3	-
Stone King Bath	3	3
Veale Wasbrough Bristol	1	2
Withy King Bath	2	2
Woollcombe Beer Watts Newton Abbot	1	3

LEADING INDIVIDUALS	
❶ ASHLEY Jacqueline Gill Akaster	BONNER Margaret Foot Anstey Sargent
BOYCE Wendy Bond Pearce	HALLAM Catherine Burges Salmon
KIDD Philip Tozers	THORNEYCROFT Philip Wolferstans
WOODWARD David TLT Solicitors	
❷ DOWNING Ian Ian Downing Family Law	LAMBERT Tracy Tozers
PAYNE Peter Stephens & Scown	SCOFIELD Ian Hooper & Wollen
SHAKESPEAR Felicity Clarke Willmott & Clarke	
WOODS Paul Wolferstans	
❸ BROOKES Alan Hooper & Wollen	DODD Andrew Tozers
HARTNELL Norman Hartnell & Co	JURY Susan Wolferstans
SHRIMPTON Julie Tozers	
UP AND COMING	
ALLEN Elizabeth Stephens & Scown	

Within each band, firms are listed alphabetically. *See **Profiles** on page 390*

Bond Pearce A team of specialists handling heavyweight financial settlements. *"Academic"* **Wendy Boyce** is a *"leading light"* within the SFLA and adds an in-depth knowledge of pensions and insolvency to the family practice. Acts for a range of professional clients from senior civil servants, to farmers, business owners, and company chairmen. Also handles private children matters relating to divorce.

Burges Salmon Financially focused practice receives referrals from the firm's large private client base. **Catherine Hallam**, *"at home with big money cases,"* acts largely for landed gentry, farming clients, and entrepreneurs, frequently advising clients on the implications of pension sharing legislation. One associate has particular expertise in cohabitation issues.

Foot Anstey Sargent A February 2000 merger combines the strengths of the Foot & Bowden and Anstey Sargent teams and is widely thought to compensate for the loss of Cathryn Smith to the firm's media division. **Margaret Bonner** maintains a *"formidable"* reputation for child care work while additions from the Exeter based Ansteys team concentrate on heavyweight financial cases.

Gill Akaster Handles large amounts of public law children work and ancillary relief. *"Tenacious"* **Jacqueline Ashley** is recognised as *"committed to child care."* The appointment of a mental health specialist within the family department strengthens the group's profile in public care work.

TLT Solicitors Trumps recently merged with Lawrence Tucketts to form a sizeable family practice of considerable repute in the area. The team, led by *"tactician"* **David Woodward**, focuses primarily on high net worth ancillary relief cases for professionals, gentry, and celebrities in the southwest, with a substantial proportion of work involving international assets or foreign partners. However, the team is also active in mediation and has recruited one new partner to undertake public law children cases.

Tozers A large child care and public law practice said to *"have the monopoly on care from local authorities."* **Philip Kidd**, known for his *"encyclopaedic memory of cases"* has a particular speciality in international adoption, and handles several cases of direct child representation. His colleagues **Tracy Lambert**, **Andrew Dodd**, and **Julie Shrimpton** were all recognised for their excellence in public child protection.

Wolferstans Jeremy Bennett has left Wolferstans to chair a tribunal but leaves behind a competent team covering the full spectrum of family law. *"On the ball"* **Philip Thorneycroft** and *"reliable"* **Paul Woods** handle high value ancillary relief of £1 million plus while *"effective"* **Susan Jury** has been building up the public and private child care practice. The team also has a specialised unit dealing with emergency injunctions in instances of domestic violence and possesses a franchise for mental health work.

Clarke Willmott & Clarke Strong on public law child work, but also handles private children matters and ancillary relief. *"Well respected"* **Felicity Shakespear** was described as a *"specialist in an area where there are few specialists"* and has considerable experience in cases involving the break-up of farming partnerships.

Stephens & Scown Operate a number of offices throughout the southwest and respected for general family practice. **Peter Payne**, described as *"a smooth operator"* and the *"ebullient"* **Elizabeth Allen**, a newcomer to the rankings, specialise in high net worth financial settlements, often acting for farming clients. Other partners have particular experience in adoption, child abduction and surrogacy. The team also has a welfare benefits practitioner and offers mediation services.

Hooper & Wollen Equally split between matrimonial and public care work. *"Sensible"* **Ian Scofield** is active in SFLA mediation while *"professional"* **Alan Brookes** is almost exclusively a child care lawyer, receiving instructions from both guardians ad litem and children permitted to represent themselves.

Ian Downing Family Law Practice Specialist niche practice concentrating on private ancillary relief. *"Approachable and well-liked,"* **Ian Downing** has an impressive command of pensions and insurance issues, as well as a particular interest in Inheritance Act claims of partners wishing to contest the will of a deceased ex-spouse or cohabitant. His assistant handles private child cases and is a trained mediator.

Other Notable Practitioners

Niche family practices **Hartnell & Co** and **E. David Brain & Co** were recognised for their breadth of expertise in family law with **Norman Hartnell**, of the former firm, identified as a *"leading light"* in mediation. **Stones** were particularly recommended for their accomplishments in child care and public law work.

Veale Wasbrough, **Woollcombe Beer Watts**, **Stone King**, **Withy King**, and **Hugh James Ford Simey** also elicited market commendation for their broad based family departments.

WALES

FAMILY/MATRIMONIAL • Wales	Ptnrs	Assts
❶ **Hugh James Ford Simey** Cardiff	5	4
Larby Williams Cardiff	2	1
Martyn Prowel Solicitors Cardiff	1	2
Nicol, Denvir & Purnell Cardiff	2	2
❷ **Wendy Hopkins & Co** Cardiff	3	1
❸ **Granville-West** Newbridge (nr. Newport)	2	3
Harding Evans Newport	1	1
Leo Abse & Cohen Cardiff	-	4
Robertsons Cardiff	2	1

LEADING INDIVIDUALS	
❶ **NICOL Frazer** Nicol, Denvir & Purnell	**POWELL Mark** Hugh James Ford Simey
WILLIAMS Jane Larby Williams	**WILLIAMS Frances** Larby Williams
❷ **EDWARDS Robert** Martyn Prowel Solicitors	**GREGORY-JONES Rosemary** Leo Abse & Cohen
HOPKINS Wendy Wendy Hopkins & Co	**WILLIAMS Gail** Robertsons
WILLIAMS Ian Robertsons	

Within each band, firms are listed alphabetically. *See **Profiles** on page 390*

Hugh James Ford Simey Operating a number of offices throughout the region, the firm is a recognised presence in South Wales. Has taken the lead in mediation in Wales through the team's involvement in the mediation pilot scheme. *"Larger than life"* **Mark Powell** is considered the *"top man in child care,"* but also spends considerable time on mental health tribunal work. The group maintain a domestic violence hotline and acts frequently for women's aid refuges. Have a niche speciality in international child abduction and receive referrals through membership on the Reunite panel in Wales.

Larby Williams Heavy emphasis on high value ancillary relief and private adoption work. *"Trustworthy"* **Jane Williams** brings with her from Morgan Cole considerable experience as a mediator while **Frances Williams** is *"known for being exceptionally thorough"* and frequently deals with divorce cases of £1 million plus.

Martyn Prowel Solicitors A broad based practice handling property and financial settlements for clients of all means. **Robert Edwards** has built up a reputation in heavyweight ancillary relief cases. The practice is de-emphasising children work but still handles some care work for parents.

Nicol Denvir & Purnell A largely legal aid practice renowned for expertise in care proceedings. *"Upbeat"* **Frazer Nicol** *"takes an even-handed approach"* to his child care work representing guardians ad litem, parents, and local authorities. The team also handles a number of adoption cases. One partner undertakes private family law, specialising in ancillary relief and mediation for legally aided as well as high income clients.

Wendy Hopkins & Co A substantial all-female practice that specialises in high value divorce. *"A doughty opponent,"* **Wendy Hopkins** takes an *"aggressive approach"* in ancillary relief proceedings for wealthy clients.

Other Notable Practitioners

Leo Abse & Cohen also received recommendations, particularly for **Rosemary Gregory-Jones**'s *"sensible"* approach to litigation. At **Robertsons,** lead partners **Gail Williams** and **Ian Williams** have built a reputation for themselves in care work. Both **Granville-West** and **Harding Evans** cover a mix of ancillary relief and public and private child care.

MIDLANDS

FAMILY/MATRIMONIAL • Midlands	Ptnrs	Assts
❶ **Blair Allison & Co** Birmingham	3	6
Challinors Lyon Clark West Bromwich	6	5
Nelsons Grantham, Derby	4	8
Rupert Bear Murray Davies Nottingham	3	6
Tyndallwoods Birmingham	1	2
❷ **Freethcartwright** Nottingham	5	2
Wace Morgan Shrewsbury	1	2
❸ **Hadens** Walsall	3	2
Lanyon Bowdler Shrewsbury	1	1
Morton Fisher Kidderminster	-	3
Young & Lee Birmingham	1	2
❹ **Blythe Liggins** Leamington Spa	2	1
Varley Hibbs Coventry	2	1
Warren & Allen Nottingham	4	2

LEADING INDIVIDUALS	
❶ **CARTER Barbara** Barbara Carter	**DAVIES Murray** Rupert Bear Murray Davies
❷ **BENUSSI Diane** Benussi & Co	**FLINT Peter** Lanyon Bowdler
McDONALD Roberta Sole Practitioner	**MEISEL Mari** Blair Allison & Co
MESSENGER Mercy Sole Practitioner	**YOUNG Hugh** Freethcartwright
YOUNG Ian Young & Lee	

Within each band, firms are listed alphabetically. *See **Profiles** on page 390*

Blair Allison & Co A large group of specialised family lawyers maintain a solid reputation for high value ancillary relief work. Franchised for mediation and involved in the mediation pilot scheme. **Mari Meisel** enters our tables this year for her strength in negotiation and *"considered approach"* to divorce settlements. Receive an increasing number of co-habitation cases. Practice also handles care work for guardians and parents.

Challinors Lyon Clark A young and diverse team cover the full range of family law. Undertakes both high net and legal aid ancillary relief cases. Considerable expertise in public and private children work with particular experience in adoption, abduction, and Hague Convention cases. Possess a legal aid block contract and offer advice to domestic violence victims at the local women's refuge. Also very involved in training both for police officers and guardians ad litem.

Nelsons Recent merger with Trumans has increased the firm's presence throughout the East Midlands. Emphasizes higher value ancillary relief cases in excess of £1 million, receiving many referrals from the firm's commercial practice. Handle divorce proceedings for British nationals abroad and have a particular niche in advising clients on the relevance of new pensions regulations. Also acts for children in public care cases.

Rupert Bear Murray Davies A focused niche family practice led by *"realistic"* **Murray Davies**, particularly experienced in big money divorce settlements. Receiving an increasing amount of farming cases and offers the services of an in-house conveyancer for family cases relating to wills. Team also includes child care, adoption, and mental health specialists and covers all aspects of family law.

Tyndallwoods Reputed for child care work, acting for guardians and occasionally parents. Receives an unusual amount of international adoption cases due to the firm's top class immigration practice. The practice is largely legal aid focused but also undertakes high value ancillary relief.

Freethcartwright A significant family team with a reputation for high value ancillary relief matters over the £1 million mark. Highly regarded **Hugh**

Young acts for wealthy sports figures in the Midlands and in cases with international complications. Team also includes public and private child care specialists as well as two trained mediators.

Wace Morgan Covers the full range of family law with a particular interest in SFLA mediation. Experienced in representing children and guardians ad litem in care work. Also very active in domestic violence injunction work, operating a 24 hour TraumaLine service offering immediate legal advice to victims of abuse.

Other Notable Practitioners

Hadens and **Morton Fisher** were recognized as highly regarded in the area. **Peter Flint** at **Lanyon Bowdler** was recommended for his *"cooperative"* approach to mediation and high value ancillary relief while **Ian Young** at **Young & Lee** has a *"solid reputation"* in child care matters.

Blythe Liggins, **Varley Hibbs & Co**, and **Warren & Allen** also possess estimable general family law teams.

There are a number of high profile sole practitioners operating in the Midlands. *"Open-minded"* **Barbara Carter** and *"sensible"* **Roberta McDonald** have built up a considerable reputation for private and public law children work. Sole practitioner **Mercy Messenger** also enters our tables this year for her expertise in high level divorce settlements. **Diane Benussi** of Benussi & Co whose impressive reputation for nigh net ancillary relief work does not yet extend to the practice as a whole, is also ranked for the first time.

EAST ANGLIA

FAMILY/MATRIMONIAL • East Anglia	Ptnrs	Assts
❶ **Greenwoods** Peterborough	1	1
Hunt & Coombs Peterborough	3	2
Mills & Reeve Norwich, Cambridge	2	5
Silver Fitzgerald Cambridge	2	9
❷ **Miller Sands** Cambridge	4	1
❸ **Buckle Mellows** Peterborough	3	3
Eversheds Cambridge, Norwich	1	1
Fosters Norwich	3	1
Leonard Gray Chelmsford	2	1
Ward Gethin King's Lynn	2	1
❹ **Cozens-Hardy & Jewson** Norwich	2	2
Hatch Brenner Norwich	2	3
Overbury Steward Eaton & Woolsey Norwich	2	2
Rudlings & Wakelam Thetford	2	1

LEADING INDIVIDUALS	
❶ **CARMICHAEL Graeme** Graeme Carmichael	
❷ **BAMBER Roger** Mills & Reeve	**HENSON John** Hunt & Coombs
PROCTOR Jane Greenwoods	**SANDS Rosemary** Miller Sands
SILVER Raphael Silver Fitzgerald	**SISSON David** Eversheds
❸ **FIFE Peter** Ward Gethin	**ILIFF Catherine** Fosters
O'DONNELL Caroline Miller Sands	**O'REGAN Timothy** Rudlings & Wakelam
RANDALL Richard Leonard Gray	**WHITE Iain** Cozens-Hardy & Jewson
WILSON Bruce Mills & Reeve	

Within each band, firms are listed alphabetically. *See **Profiles** on page 390*

Greenwoods A small family department handling private ancillary relief cases for professional clients, receiving referrals from other departments of this largely commercial firm. **Jane Proctor** is known to *"dig her heels in"* in local authority work and is highly respected for her accomplishments in child care proceedings.

Hunt & Coombs The team is firmly committed to legal aid work with three partners handling public law children cases for parents and guardians as well as legally aided divorce proceedings. **John Henson** *"doesn't mind getting his hands dirty"* in complex child care cases, representing children and guardians ad litem. Team also undertakes private ancillary relief cases for clients of all means.

Mills & Reeve Considered *"big players"* in high net worth ancillary relief cases involving landed estates and large farming businesses. Have a commanding experience of tax, trust, chattel, and pension problems associated with divorce settlements. **Roger Bamber** works out of the Cambridge office and is commended as being both *"personable"* and *"good with figures and finance."* His Norwich-based colleague **Bruce Wilson**, *"a skilful technician"* is also *"red hot on divorce settlements."* The team also has a specialist in international child abduction and offers mediation services.

Silver Fitzgerald An expanding family practice, well known for its public law child work, also handles a considerable amount of private family law in a middle range market. **Raphael Silver** was recognized for his advocacy skills and for being *"good on his feet"* in care work representing local authorities, guardians and parents. The team is experienced in adoption issues and cases involving sexual abuse, drawing upon the expertise of an in-house social worker in Children's Act applications and care proceedings.

Miller Sands Handles a mixture of private and public family law, including ancillary relief cases for a range of clients from legally-aided individuals to farmers and business owners. **Rosemary Sands**, long considered a *"leading light in Cambridge"* for her mediation work and SFLA involvement, also directs *"tremendous enthusiasm"* towards representing guardians and local authorities in child care cases. She is assisted by *"rising star"* **Caroline O'Donnell,** who covers a similar range of work. The team is also experienced in adoptions, private child matters, and Inheritance Act claims.

Other Notable Practitioners

Specialist sole practitioner **Graeme Carmichael** received sweeping recommendations as a *"measured"* practitioner *"idolised by guardians ad litem in Suffolk."* Has carved a niche for himself in complex child care proceedings and is universally liked for his *"enormous integrity"* and *"ability to deal well with disadvantaged clients and psychiatrists."*

Buckle Mellows maintains a large, well-respected family team active in high value divorce settlements involving agricultural properties and owner-managed businesses. *"Trustworthy"* **David Sisson** picks up **Eversheds**' heavyweight matrimonial cases at both the London and Brussels offices in addition to cases coming into the firm's East Anglia branches, and was lauded for his excellent client manner. **Catherine Iliff** at **Fosters** is reputed for her involvement in and enthusiasm for mediation. **Richard Randall** at **Leonard Gray** also runs a mediation practice and is well known as an advocate for guardians ad litem. *"Amiable but firm"* **Peter Fife** at **Ward Gethin** is well regarded for his extensive experience acting for parents in private law children cases.

"Mellow" **Iain White** at **Cozens-Hardy & Jewson** and *"highly articulate"* **Tim O'Regan** at **Rudlings & Wakelam** are regarded as leading child care lawyers acting for children, guardians, and local authorities. **Hatch Brenner** and **Overbury Steward Eaton & Woolsey** were both deemed to have comprehensive family departments offering quality services in both public and private family work.

NORTH WEST

FAMILY/MATRIMONIAL • North West	Ptnrs	Assts
❶ **Pannone & Partners** Manchester	7	5
❷ **Farleys** Blackburn	2	8
Laytons Manchester	1	1
❸ **Addleshaw Booth & Co** Manchester	1	2
Cobbetts Manchester	1	2
Cuff Roberts Liverpool	1	2
Green & Co Manchester	1	5
Jones Maidment Wilson Manchester	1	3
Stephensons Salford	4	7
❹ **Burnetts** Carlisle	2	7
Forbes Blackburn	-	4
Morecroft Urquhart Liverpool	3	1
Rowlands Manchester	4	5

LEADING INDIVIDUALS	
❶ **DEVLIN Michael** Stephensons	**JONES Catherine** Pannone & Partners
WILKINS Beth Pannone & Partners	
❷ **BARKER Christine** Laytons	**COTTRELL Patricia** Cuff Roberts
GREEN Michael Green & Co	**HUGHES Kathryn Lesley** Farleys
MILBURN Paula Jones Maidment Wilson	**SHEPHERD Nigel** Addleshaw Booth & Co

Within each band, firms are listed alphabetically. *See **Profiles** on page 390*

Pannone & Partners Viewed by many as *"clear market leaders,"* the practice rises to the leading firm spot this year to reflect its acknowledged size, strength, client base and reputation for *"good service and good results."* Ancillary relief and private children work is provided by a large team in a *"tightly controlled house style"* for a range of clients which include many high value professional and business individuals and some media personalities. **Catherine Jones** is seen as *"effective"* and *"good to deal with"* and **Beth Wilkins** is known for her *"enormously appealing way with clients."*

Farleys A broad-based team with a strong reputation which handles all aspects of matrimonial and children work and can draw on further family specialists from several branch offices. Ancillary relief clients range from high net worth individuals through to legally aided clients. A significant children practice deals with all elements of private children work and represents children and guardians in care proceedings. **Kathryn Hughes** is seen as an *"accomplished"* lawyer who *"puts people at their ease."* The last year has seen a notable rise in the use of mediation at the practice.

Laytons New to the rankings this year due to widespread market recognition of the firm's *"high quality, high value work"* for the region's business community and referrals from the firm's London office. The practice has a legal aid franchise and handles all aspects of children work, from contact and residence through to care work. It is particularly known in the market for its abduction expertise. **Christine Barker** is also new to the tables, and is seen as *"a major player in the ancillary field."*

Addleshaw Booth & Co Small and relatively young practice led by **Nigel Shepherd** whose main focus is divorce and ancillary relief work for high net worth business people, professionals and individuals from the sport and entertainment fields. Some private children work is also undertaken. The general view of the market is that the team has not yet developed enough to share the leading firm status of its counterpart in the North West.

Cobbetts Commercial firm with a strong reputation in ancillary relief and *"excellent clients"* which are garnered from its corporate connections. The practice, known for its *"aggressive approach,"* enters the rankings this year.

Cuff Roberts The top firm in Liverpool for matrimonial finance, team leader **Patricia Cottrell** is respected as a *"name"* who *"knows what she is doing."* Ancillary relief for small to high net worth individuals is the main focus of the practice with some private children work also handled, including abduction and adoption.

Green & Co Small specialist practice with a top notch reputation for childcare work. **Michael Green** is *"held in high regard"* by his fellow practitioners and represents children instructed by guardians in care proceedings, while assistants in the team represent parents.

Jones Maidment Wilson Mixed practice with a legal aid franchise whose reputation largely derives from its strength in public law children work. Other work includes private children, a significant amount of ancillary relief for small to high net worth individuals and specialisms in domestic violence and adoption. **Paula Milburn** is recommended and works in both the money and children fields. The highly respected Iain Hamilton has now joined the judiciary.

Stephensons *"Big and succesful practice"* based in a network of branch offices which handles the full range of family law issues for a mixture of legal aid and private clients. Children specialist **Michael Devlin** is recognised as an *"excellent care practitioner and a true adoption specialist"* and rises in the rankings.

Other Notable Firms

Burnetts, Forbes, Morecroft Urquhart and **Rowlands** are recommended for broad-based practices, which have noted expertise in children law.

YORKSHIRE

Addleshaw Booth & Co A *"strong," "well-resourced"* and *"extremely experienced"* practice which has achieved a *"pre-eminence"* in the region and *"gets all the mega stuff."* Work focuses largely on ancillary relief and private children work for high net worth clients including local landed gentry, business and professional people and an increasing number of instructions are received from elsewhere in the UK and abroad. **David Salter,** who heads the team, is a *"superb lawyer and a superb presenter"* and is known for his specialism on pension issues in family breakdowns, while his deputy **Philip Way** is seen as a *"good negotiator"* and an *"able technical lawyer."*

Irwin Mitchell Large family practice with *"pretensions at stardom"* and *"a good spectrum of work"* spread across its Sheffield and Leeds offices. In addition to its high value ancillary relief practice, which receives a significant number of referrals from its corporate department, the firm has a legal aid franchise and childcare expertise. While no individuals are listed in the rankings, the team as a whole is recommended for its *"depth"* and remains a leading firm.

Jones Myers Gordon Niche practice with experience in all areas of family work and an interdisciplinary counselling referral service. **Peter Jones** handles the higher net worth ancillary relief cases and is recognised in the market as *"technically knowledgable, a good advocate and good with clients."* The firm is also known for its children work, both private and public, and handles a number of complex legal aid cases. The last year has seen an increasing amount of international work.

Zermansky & Partners Known originally in the market for the strength of its childcare work, the practice *"is now pursuing money matters with some success."* The *"experienced"* **Norman Taylor** leads the ancillary relief team, which acts for clients across the wealth scale and has a significant legal aid

FAMILY/MATRIMONIAL • Yorkshire	Ptnrs	Assts
❶ **Addleshaw Booth & Co** Leeds	1	3
❷ **Irwin Mitchell** Sheffield	3	4
Jones Myers Gordon Leeds	4	2
Zermansky & Partners Leeds	4	2
❸ **Andrew M. Jackson & Co** Hull	2	4
Gordons Cranswick Solicitors Leeds, Bradford	3	2
Grahame Stowe, Bateson Leeds	3	5
Lee & Priestley Leeds	2	3
❹ **Crombie Wilkinson** York	3	1
Henry Hyams & Co Leeds	2	3
Kirbys Harrogate	1	2

LEADING INDIVIDUALS	
❶ **SALTER David** Addleshaw Booth & Co	
❷ **FOSKETT Peter** Gordons Cranswick	**JONES Peter** Jones Myers Gordon
STAKES John Anthony Gordons Cranswick	**TAYLOR Norman** Zermansky & Partners
WAY Philip Addleshaw Booth & Co	
❸ **BRAITHWAITE Anne** Lupton Fawcett	**PREST Charles** Lee & Priestley
STOWE Marilyn Grahame Stowe, Bateson	

Within each band, firms are listed alphabetically. See **Profiles** on page 390

practice. Highly-rated childcare and domestic violence specialists complete the team.

Andrew M. Jackson & Co *"The top firm in Hull"* with *"a good reputation"* across the range of family work. Divorce settlements for both high value and legal aid clients, public and private children work and domestic violence are all handled by the team. The firm also maintains a separate inter-disciplinary mediation service, including a probation officer, counsellor and children's mediator.

Gordons Cranswick Newly merged firm which brings together two leading individuals and teams. With its increased size and geographical reach the team may become a major player in the region. A broad-based family practice, it undertakes ancillary relief work for legally aided to high value individuals in addition to private and public children work. International child abduction, often outside the ambit of the Hague Convention, is a particular specialism and the firm is on the Reunite panel. **John Stakes** is widely respected as a "good clients man," while the *"experienced, approachable and friendly"* **Peter Foskett** is particularly known for his expertise on pensions restructuring on divorce.

Graham Stowe, Bateson Particularly notable for its growing portfolio of high net worth clients, with assets often in the millions and featuring a significant international dimension. As a result, the firm rises in the rankings this year, though many in the market felt that its *"belligerent"* style is an acquired taste. The *"very astute"* **Marylin Stowe**, who is the Chief Assessor of the Law Society's Family Panel, leads the team which is based across six branch offices and maintains a childcare and legal aid practice, in addition to its high value work.

Lee & Priestley New to the rankings this year on the recommendations of several in the market, the practice offers a wide-ranging family law service from financial settlement to private children and care work. **Charles Prest**, who also enters the tables this year, is a noted care specialist, and on the ancillary relief side acts for many high net worth clients, some with assets exceeding £10 million.

Other Notable Practitioners **Crombie Wilkinson** and **Henry Hyams & Co** are recommended local practices, while **Kirbys** enters the rankings this year due to its strong reputation in matrimonial finance.
Anne Braithwaite at **Lupton Fawcett** also enters the individuals' rankings, and was particularly praised for being *"a sound tactician."*

NORTH EAST

FAMILY/MATRIMONIAL • North East	Ptnrs	Assts
❶ **Dickinson Dees** Newcastle upon Tyne	2	2
❷ **Mincoffs** Newcastle-upon-Tyne	1	1
Sinton & Co Newcastle upon Tyne	2	1
❸ **Hay & Kilner** Newcastle-upon-Tyne	3	2
Samuel Phillips & Co Newcastle upon Tyne	1	3
❹ **Askews** Redcar	1	2
Jacksons Stockton-on-Tees	1	2
Ward Hadaway Newcastle upon Tyne	2	1

LEADING INDIVIDUALS	
❶ **GRAY Tim** Sinton & Co	**RUTHERFORD Lyn** Dickinson Dees
SMITH Michael Mincoffs	**SPEKER Barry** Samuel Phillips & Co
❷ **CARLISLE Kenneth** Hay & Kilner	

Within each band, firms are listed alphabetically. See **Profiles** on page 390

Dickinson Dees Remains *"the highest profile"* practice in the region with a reputation for high value work, often referred from its commercial practice. Based in the firm's substantial private client department, the team has particular expertise in divorces involving business assets and is also well-versed in child support work. **Lyn Rutherford** *"has his own style"* which is *"good if you want a fight,"* but is recognised as *"a man who knows the ins and outs of the job."*

Mincoffs New to the rankings this year on the recommendation of its peers, this specialist family practice looks after a wide client base from legal aid to high net worth. **Mike Smith** also enters the rankings and is *"an experienced practitioner who deserves to be up there."*

Sinton & Co The *"well-connected"* **Tim Gray** "has built up a major caseload" over recent months, and the firm rises in the rankings this year. The team handles divorce, financial settlements and related private children work for an increasing number of high net worth clients, and maintains a legal aid practice.

Hay & Kilner Large and broad-based practice spread across three offices which covers all aspects of family law from childcare and mental health expertise through to complex and high value ancillary relief work. **Kenneth Carlisle** *"knows his stuff"* and enters the individuals' rankings this year. The last year has seen the practice take on an increasing amount of England/Scotland cross-border work and unusual cases, including an ongoing case where a mother is accused of Munchausen's syndrome.

Samuel Phillips & Co Long-established, wide-ranging family practice with a particular reputation in care work and abduction, for which the firm is on the Reunite panel and receives referrals from a number of adoption agencies and local authorities. Team head **Barry Speker** is seen as a *"decent lawyer"* and *"very good at children work,"* and acts as legal advisor to Barnardo's adoption panel. On the matrimonial side, the firm receives referrals from other professionals and handles a large number of complex ancillary relief contested cases for both legally aided and private clients.

Other Notable Firms

Askews and **Jacksons** remain highly regarded local practices which offer the full spectrum of family law services, while commercial firm **Ward Hadaway** enters the rankings due to its reputation for good quality ancillary relief work.

SCOTLAND

FAMILY/MATRIMONIAL • Scotland	Ptnrs	Assts
❶ Anne Hall Dick & Co. Glasgow	2	2
Balfour & Manson Edinburgh	1	4
Loudons WS Edinburgh	3	1
❷ Brodies WS Edinburgh	1	4
Drummond Miller WS Edinburgh	6	7
Erskine MacAskill & Co Edinburgh	2	2
Iain Smith & Company Aberdeen	-	2
Morton Fraser, Solicitors Edinburgh	1	2
Russells Gibson McCaffrey Glasgow	4	2
❸ Burnett & Reid Aberdeen	1	1
Mowat Dean & Co WS Edinburgh	1	2
Walker Laird Paisley	5	3

LEADING INDIVIDUALS	
❶ DICK Anne Anne Hall Dick & Co.	GIBB Andrew Balfour & Manson
LOUDON Alasdair Loudons WS	SMITH Caroline Loudons WS
❷ BALLANTINE Tom Mowat Dean & Co WS	BRUCE LOCKHART Karen Brodies WS
CATTO Joan Burnett & Reid	ERSKINE Sarah Erskine MacAskill & Co
FOTHERINGHAM John Ross & Connel	MAIR Leonard Morton Fraser, Solicitors
PATIENCE Iain Iain Smith & Company	SCANLAN Margaret Russells Gibson McCaffrey
SHEEHAN Wendy Balfour & Manson	TAIT Fiona Drummond Miller WS
❸ GRAHAM Caroline Macleod & MacCallum	JAMIESON George Walker Laird
MacBRIDE Caroline Quinn Martin & Langan	McTAGGART Anne Stronachs

Within each band, firms are listed alphabetically. See **Profiles** on page 390

Anne Hall Dick & Co With a high reputation in family work, this specialist practice undertakes matrimonial finance and private children work across the wealth spectrum and is known for its strong commitment to mediation. The team also has a significant legal aid practice and is run from two offices. **Anne Dick** is highly regarded by the market.

Balfour & Manson Known as a *"technically good"* practice with an *"ethical approach,"* the team handles ancillary relief, often of high value and with an increasing international dimension, in addition to public and private children work. The firm's acknowledged court expertise (it acts as agent for many firms in the Court of Session) is supplemented by mediation experience. **Andrew Gibb** heads up the team and *"knows what he's doing,"* while **Wendy Sheehan** is recommended as *"competent and thorough."*

Loudons WS An exclusively family law practice seen as a *"good team of experienced lawyers"* with an established reputation in matrimonial finance and private children work for a broad range of clients. **Alasdair Loudon** is known for his *"negotiating expertise"* on financial matters and **Caroline Smith** deals with the full range of court work, negotiation and mediation.

Brodies WS Particularly known for their involvement in large contested ancillary relief cases in the Court of Session, the firm is seen to have *"a huge range of expertise to draw on"* and rises in the rankings this year. **Karen Bruce Lockhart** is new to the individuals' table this year, and is regarded as *"technically excellent at negotiation,"* although she is seen to delegate a lot of work to her well-regarded team. Private children work, including child abduction, is also handled.

Drummond Miller WS Spread across seven offices, the practice handles a broad range of family work, from high profile Court of Session divorce work through to children law and protection. **Fiona Tait** deals mainly with high value ancillary relief work, which has an increasing international element, and her *"reputation is growing all the time."*

Erskine MacAskill & Co Highly regarded family practice which is particularly known for its childcare expertise and legal aid work including abduction and domestic violence. **Sarah Erskine** is respected as a *"very steely"* operator who *"brings a great deal of energy to representing young people."*

Iain Smith & Company *"A sound family team"* which is seen by many as *"the first choice in Aberdeen"* for matrimonial and children work. **Iain Patience** is known as a *"fighter"* and remains highly rated by the market.

Morton Fraser, Solicitors *"Technically good"* family practice which *"tends to be involved in high net worth cases"* while continuing to act for the full spectrum of clients. **Leonard Mair** is seen by many in the market as a *"huge strength"* and deals mainly with financial settlements. Children work is another area of expertise and runs from residence and contact through to adoption and care. Reported highlights of last year included a major Court of Session divorce case with implications for the breaking up of companies on divorce and 'Dosoo,' a case concerning rights of access of a parent to their child.

Russells Gibson McCaffrey Well thought of practice which covers divorce settlements (from legal aid to high value) and public and private children work.The team is particularly known for its court work and **Margaret Scanlan** is seen as a *"formidable opponent"* in financial disputes.The last year has seen an increasing amount of international work, such as enforcement of alimony.

Other Notable Practitioners

Burnett & Reid is a respected mixed practice and the *"conciliatory approach"* of **Joan Catto** won praise in the market. **Mowatt Dean & Co WS** is known for its children expertise, but is increasingly moving into lucrative ancillary relief work, and team leader **Tom Ballantine** is highly rated in both fields as *"thorough and diligent; he brings a lot of concern to what he's doing."* **Walker Laird** is recommended on the children side, in which new entry **George Jamieson** is an acknowledged expert.

John Fotheringham at **Ross Connel** continues to be rated in the children and domestic violence fields and well-regarded matrimonial specialists **Caroline McBride** at **Quinn Martin & Langan**, **Caroline Graham** at **Macleod & MacCallum** and **Anne McTaggart** at **Stronachs** enter the rankings for the first time this year.

NORTHERN IRELAND

FAMILY/MATRIMONIAL • Northern Ireland	Ptnrs	Assts
❶ **Babington & Croasdaile** Londonderry	1	1
Flynn & McGettrick Belfast	1	1
Peden & Reid Belfast	1	-
Thompsons Newtownards	-	1
❷ **Carnson Morrow Graham** Bangor	1	-
Wilson Nesbitt Belfast	-	2

LEADING INDIVIDUALS	
❶ **CALDWELL Anne** Flynn & McGettrick	**PALMER George** Peden & Reid

Within each band, firms are listed alphabetically. *See **Profiles** on page 390*

Most family law services in the province are provided by local general practices. The firms listed have a noted specialism in the field. **George Palmer** at **Peden & Reid** is the most well-known big money matrimonial practitioner, while **Anne Caldwell** at **Flynn & McGettrick** is "*a capable operator*" who handles family issues across the board.

LEADERS IN FAMILY / MATRIMONIAL

ALEXIOU, Douglas
Gordon Dadds, London (020) 7493 6151
Senior Partner and Head of Family Law Department.
Specialisation: Covers all areas including divorce, judicial separation, financial disputes, co-habitation, children (including Children Act applications, Child Support Act) and international aspects (including recognition and enforcement). Lectures, gives TV, radio, magazine and newspaper interviews; workshop leader at the 'Big Money' conference.
Prof. Memberships: Law Society, Solicitors Family Law Association (Chairman of London Regional Group 1992-1996), President-elect International Academy of Matrimonial Lawyers (President, European Chapter 1998-2000), City of Westminster Law Society, Member of the Family Mediators Association.
Career: Qualified in 1970. Joined *Gordon Dadds* in February 1971, and was made a Partner later that year. Became Senior Partner in 1986. Director of Tottenham Hotspur Football Club from 1980-1998. Chairman 1982-84. Director of Tottenham Hotspur Plc 1983-91 and 1993 to 1998. Member of 1996 British Olympic Appeal Council.
Personal: Born 24th May 1942. Attended St Paul's School 1955-59, Kings College, London (LLB Hons) 1965 and College of Law. Leisure interests include golf, tennis, association football and collecting old fountain pens. Lives in Kingston-upon-Thames.

ALLEN, Elizabeth
Stephens & Scown, Exeter (01392) 210700
family.exeter@stephens-scown.co.uk
Specialisation: Partner specialising in divorce and family work - matrimonial finance and business cases. Is an accredited Mediator and is recognised by the Legal Aid Board. Also a co-trainer in mediation for a national training organisation.
Prof. Memberships: A full member of the UK College of Family Mediators and the Law Society's Family Law Panel.
Career: Articled *Bevan Ashford*, qualified 1986; *Stephens & Scown* 1989, partner 1993.
Personal: Educated University of Nottingham; Awarded the Sir George Fowler Prize.

ASHLEY, Jacqueline S.
Gill Akaster, Plymouth (01752) 203500

BAKER, Miranda
Kingsley Napley, London (020) 7814 1200
mbaker@kingsleynapley.co.uk
Specialisation: All aspects of family law, including complex children and ancillary relief applications. Advice in relation to the legal implications of surrogacy arrangements. Occasional writer and lecturer on family law. SFLA trained mediator. Law Society Family Law Panel member.
Career: Qualified 1981. With *Collyer-Bristow* 1983-86, *Rubinstein Callingham* 1986-94 (partner from 1989) and *Manches & Co* (following the merger with *Rubinstein Callingham*) 1994-95. Joined *Kingsley Napley* as a partner in 1995.
Prof. Memberships: SFLA (member of Children Committee since 1989 and chair of its Surrogacy subcommittee), National Council for Family Proceedings.
Personal: Born 16/05/56. Attended Wimbledon High School, then New Hall, Cambridge (1974-77). Leisure interests include travel, opera, football and swimming. Lives in London.

BALLANTINE, Tom
Mowat Dean & Co WS, Edinburgh (0131) 555 0616
Specialisation: Main area of practice is family law covering separation, divorce, children, financial issues and protection. Accredited by Law Society of Scotland as a specialist in family law and a family mediator. On Law Society Mediation Accreditation Committee and Management Councils of Lothian Marriage Counselling Service and Scottish Adoption Association.
Prof. Memberships: Law Society of Scotland, Family Law Association, CALM.
Career: Qualified 1986, set up *Mowat Dean & Co* family law department in 1994.
Personal: Born 3rd May, 1959, obtained MA at Cambridge University 1978-1981, LL.B at Edinburgh University 1982-1985. Leisure interests include walking, football and reading. Lives on outskirts of Edinburgh.

BAMBER, Roger
Mills & Reeve, Norwich (01223) 222 203
roger.bamber@mills-reeve.com
Partner in family department.
Specialisation: With partner Bruce Wilson, leads the largest and most specialised team in the region. Has lectured extensively within the profession as well as appearing on radio and television. Work includes mainly financial provision, in particular complex financial cases involving businesses, trusts and pensions. Author of divorce.co.uk - a comprehensive website dealing with all aspects of family breakdown, including a guide to the law. Practises as a mediator with the Family Mediation Association and is a member of the UK College of Family Mediators.
Prof. Memberships: Law Society, SFLA.
Career: Qualified in 1981. Joined *Mills & Reeve* as a partner in 1989. Member of the Training Committee of SFLA 1988-91; Chairman of the Cams and West Suffolk SFLA 1989-98.
Publications: Co-author of 'Pensions and Insurance on Matrimonial Breakdown'. Editor of 'The Family Through Divorce', which is a comprehensive guide to the personal, financial and legal aspects of family breakdown, with marital therapist Dr Janet Reibstein, and colleagues, Jackie Wells, Sarah Attle, and Dr Jeannette Josse.
Personal: Born 5th February 1955. MA Cantab. Leisure interests include family, rowing and art. Lives in Cambridge.

BARKER, Christine E.
Laytons, Manchester (0161) 834 2100
Specialisation: Divorce, ancillary relief (high value cases), contact and residence disputes; Fournier v Fournier.
Prof. Memberships: SFLA member.
Career: Family lawyer for past 20 years. Qualified October 1978. Law degree, Nottingham University. Moved to *Laytons* 1992, set up department.
Personal: Married to hotelier and resturanteur. Two children aged 11 and 13. Hobbies; travel, food and wine.

BEATSON, Kim
Anthony Gold, Lerman & Muirhead, London (020) 7940 4000
kim.beatson@anthonygold.co.uk
Partner and head of matrimonial department.
Specialisation: Exclusively family law particularly financial disputes. Occasional lecturer and accredited family mediator.
Prof. Memberships: SFLA, Chair of SFLA Mediation Committee, member of Family Mediators Association and UK College of Family Mediators.

Career: Qualified in 1984. Became a Partner and Head of family law department, *Russell-Cooke, Potter & Chapman* 1986. Joined *Anthony Gold, Lerman & Muirhead* as a Partner in 1996. Head of family department.

BENUSSI, Diane
Benussi & Co, Birmingham (0121) 248 4001
diane@benussilaw.co.uk
Specialisation: Divorce and ancillary relief, high net worth cases. Acting for CEOs/chairmen of private companies with growing international practice.
Prof. Memberships: SFLA; Birmingham Law Society; Assoc. Women Sols.
Publications: Various articles in journals, Times, Birmingham Law Society Bulletin.
Career: Prior to qualifying as a solicitor, trained as a teacher; systems analyst; civil servant. Founded *Benussi & Co* in 1994 as a niche practice specialising in divorce.
Personal: 1969 University of London & Cert. Ed. (Business Studies); 1974 University of Birmingham LLB (Law). Divorcee, two children. Leisure interests: cycling, concerts (eclectic tastes).

BLORE, Sian
Blandy & Blandy, Reading (0118) 958 7111
Specialisation: All areas of family and matrimonial law with particular emphasis on complex financial issues (including those with an international element) for high net worth clients.
Prof. Memberships: SFLA, Law Society Family Law Panel.
Career: Qualified 1985. Specialised in family law at *Theodore Goddard*; joined *Farrer & Co* in 1989 and became partner in 1993; joined *Blandy & Blandy* as partner in 1996 having decided to leave London to work nearer home and family.
Personal: Born 1961. Attended University College of Wales, Aberystwyth. Lives in Henley-on-Thames with husband and three small sons.

BONNER, Margaret
Foot Anstey Sargent, Plymouth (01752) 675000
margaret.bonner@foot-ansteys.co.uk
Partner. Head of Legal Aid Division.
Specialisation: Acts in cases involving children, in both public and private law. Work includes adoption and child abduction. Past National Secretary SFLA 1994-2000. Conference Chairman at the SFLA fifth National Conference in 1993.
Prof. Memberships: Member of Children Panel. Association of Lawyers for Children. Association of Women Solicitors, Plymouth Child Care Support Group.
Career: Qualified in 1985. Joined *Foot & Bowden* in 1986, becoming a Partner in 1987. Previously Nursing Auxiliary in Geriatric Hospital, Trainee Assistant Editor of Cookery magazine and personal assistant to Clinical Psychologist.
Personal: Born 31st August 1946. Attended University of Sussex 1965-68. Leisure interests include opera, gardening, yoga, walking, food and wine.

BOYCE, Wendy
Bond Pearce, Plymouth (01752) 266633
xwab@bondpearce.com
Partner and head of the Family Law Group.
Specialisation: Experienced practitioner skilled in dealing with complicated and commercial cases, substantial assets, pensions and insolvency related problems. Lectures extensively on a wide range of topics.
Prof. Memberships: Member of the Devon & Cornwall Solicitors Family Law Association and of the Law Society Family Law Panel.
Career: Qualified in 1980. Joined *Bond Pearce* in 1978, becoming partner in 1987.
Publications: Co-author of 'Debt and Insolvency on Family Breakdown' and 'Pensions and Insurance on Family Breakdown' (Jordans) and general editor of the former.

BRAITHWAITE, Anne
Lupton Fawcett, Leeds (0113) 280 2000

BROOKES, Alan
Hooper & Wollen, Torquay (01803) 213251
Specialisation: Has specialised in child law since the mid 1980's, is committed to Public Law proceedings under the Children Act and is a very experienced practitioner for children, guardians ad litem and parents. Maintains a heavy caseload of complex cases including work in the Family Procedures Court, County Court and High Court. Has acted in several substantial cases where network abuse has been alleged and where evidence gathering has been crucial. Experienced in child abduction cases and in acting for children who have become "Gillick" competent. Legal Aid Specialist.
Prof. Memberships: Law Society Child Care panel since its inception.
Career: Admitted 1978. Practicing in Child Care since mid 1980's

BRUCE LOCKHART, Karen
Brodies WS, Edinburgh (0131) 228 3777
kblockhart@brodies.co.uk
Partner in litigation department.
Specialisation: Main areas of practice are personal injury and professional negligence. Handles serious injuries, often arising from medical negligence, including paraplegia, tetraplegia and brain damage. Also handles divorce work, mostly in the Court of Session and of high monetary value. Lectures on preparing personal injury cases for court.
Prof. Memberships: IAML, WS Society. Law Society of Scotland Personal Injuries Panel, Family Law Association.
Career: Qualified in 1970. Partner in *Courtney Crawford & Co.* 1974-77; joined *Brodies WS* as a Partner in 1978. Member of VAT Tribunal since 1992.
Personal: Born 28th October 1942. Attended Nga Tawa, New Zealand 1954-59 and Edinburgh University 1966-70. Leisure interests include walking, reading and skiing. Lives in Edinburgh.

CALDWELL, Anne I.M.
Flynn & McGettrick, Belfast (028) 90244212

CARLISLE, Kenneth
Hay & Kilner, Gosforth (0191) 284 2818
Partner and head of family law department
Specialisation: Leads a team of eight. Specialises in dealing with substantial financial and property matters within divorce and cohabitee proceedings including inheritance tax claims and contact/residence applications. Also a trained mediator.
Prof. Memberships: Founder and Chairman of Solicitors Family Law Association (N.E. Region). Member of the Law Society Family Law Panel.
Career: Qualified 1972. Partner 1975.
Personal: Born 28/1/44. Married with two children. Interests include cycling, walking, reading and travel.

CARMICHAEL, Graeme
Graeme Carmichael, Ipswich (01473) 252159
Specialisation: Principally work concerning children in public and private law, including advocacy. Balance of caseload divorce and related issues.
Prof. Memberships: Law Society Children Panel; Law Society Family Law Panel, SFLA (Regional Chairman); Association of Lawyers for Children.
Career: Qualified 1976. Previously family law Partner at *Eversheds* (Norwich) and *Prettys* (Ipswich).
Personal: Born 1950. Educated Fettes College and Newcastle University.

CARTER, Barbara
Barbara Carter, Birmingham (0121) 441 3238

CATTO, Joan
Burnett & Reid, Aberdeen (01224) 644333
Partner in court department.
Specialisation: Main area of practice is family law. Deals with numerous divorce cases including ancillary issues such as financial arrangements and residence and contact orders. Also handles child law: acts as curator ad litem and reporter in adoptions, residence and contact disputes. Was for ten years safeguarder to the Children's Panel and to the Sheriff Court. Acted as safeguarder in W. which went to the Inner House of the Court of Session. Acted on behalf of the petitioners in K Petitioners and for child in Cameron v Cameron. Has participated in and organised numerous family law seminars in Aberdeen and elsewhere.
Prof. Memberships: Member of Family Law Association, member of Family Mediation (Grampian).
Career: Qualified in 1968. Joined *Burnett & Reid* in 1988, becoming a partner in 1991.
Personal: Born 30th April 1946. Attended Aberdeen High School for Girls and Aberdeen University. Member of Business Committee, General Council, Aberdeen University; committee member, Aberdeen Civic Society. Leisure interests include needlework, walking and foreign travel. Lives in Aberdeen, and Glenbuchat.

CHAPMAN, Elspeth
Barnett Sampson, London (020) 7831 7181
Specialisation: Partner in the expanding family department. Specialises in substantial ancillary relief applications, often with an international, trust or offshore aspect for both married and cohabiting clients. Also undertakes private children's applications. Has written a number of articles and book reviews.
Prof. Memberships: Founder member and current Treasurer of the Solicitors Family Law Association; accredited member of the Family Mediators Association.
Career: Qualified in 1972. Partner at *Barnett Sampson* since 1984.
Personal: Educated at Howells School, Denbigh 1957-63 and University College, London (LL.B 1968). Leisure pursuits include travel, horse riding, cooking, reading and gardening.

CLARK, Peter
Dawson Cornwell, London (020) 7242 2556
Specialisation: Exclusively family law, mainly financial settlements. Co-author of Sweet & Maxwell's 'Practical Matrimonial Precedents' and Gee Publishing's 'The Lawyer's Factbook - Family Law section.'
Prof. Memberships: Solicitors Family Law Association (SFLA).
Career: Qualified 1974. Partner *Edwin Coe* 1980 and

Dawson Cornwell 1993.
Personal: Born Yorkshire 19 December 1947. Married, 2 children, lives in London.

COLLIS, Pamela
Cawdery Kaye Fireman & Taylor, London (020) 7431 7262
Head of family department.
Specialisation: International and domestic family law work; particularly financial aspects of marriage and cohabitation breakdown, pre-nuptial contracts and Children Act work. Contributor to legal journals and speaker on matters relating to family law.
Prof. Memberships: International Academy of Matrimonial lawyers, SFLA (Committee Member London Regional Group), Member Principal Registry Family Division Users Group.
Career: Qualified 1981. Partner and head of family law at *Kingsley Napley* 1984-99. Joined *Cawdery Kaye Fireman & Taylor* in 1999 as partner and head of family.
Personal: Born 9th March 1957. Attended Rosemead School for Girls, then Bristol University (LLB 1978). Leisure pursuits include sailing, books and family life. Lives in London.

CORNWELL, John
Dawson Cornwell, London (020) 7242 2556
Specialisation: Has practised in family law as a specialist since 1970; particular specialism in ancillary relief and pensions on divorce. Has practised as a mediator in family law since 1985. Practises as a sole mediator under the auspices of the SFLA and as a comediator under the auspices of the Family Mediators Association. Spent the summer term of 1999 at Wolfson College, Oxford as visiting fellow at the Institute for Socio-Legal Studies. Lectures on pension in divorce.
Prof. Memberships: Solicitors' Family Law Association, Founder, Chairman 1982-87; Femily Mediators Association, co-founder 1988; has chaired the SFLA Children Committee and the SFLA Mediation Committee; member of the Law Society Family Law Committee 1993-99; Deputy District Judge at the Principal Registry of the Family Division, 1986 to date.
Career: Qualified in 1969. Founding Partner of *Dawson Cornwell* in 1972. Founder of the SFLA, Chairman 1982-87 and returned to the Committee in 1994. Co-founder of FMA, Vice Chairman 1992-93 and Board Member from inception until 1994. Deputy District Judge since 1987.
Personal: Born 21st September 1943. Educated at St. Paul's School 1957-62 and Bristol University 1962-65. Leisure interests include theatre and cricket. Lives in London.

COTTRELL, Patricia A.
Cuff Roberts, Liverpool (0151) 237 7777
Partner in family department
Specialisation: Deals with high-profile matrimonial work principally for clients in the Corporate and Professional sectors, invariably involving complex high value pension and share valuation issues. The practice deals with all aspects of Family Law, particularly divorce, separation, ancillary relief, co-habitation and private law children cases, including child abduction.
Prof. Memberships: Member of Law Society Family Panel; Solicitors Family Law Association (SFLA), Merseyside Legal Services Commission Appeals Committee; former Chair of Merseyside SFLA; Solicitor to Liverpool branch of Relate; appointed deputy District Judge in 1997.
Career: Qualified 1983; joined *Cuff Roberts* in 1981, now franchise Partner and Head of Family Department.
Personal: Leisure interests include walking, theatre, gardening, reading and travel. Lives on the Wirral Peninsula.

CROWTHER, Felicity
Bindman & Partners, London (020) 7833 4433
Partner in family department.
Specialisation: Work includes ancillary relief, residence and contract, cohabitation disputes and international child abduction.
Prof. Memberships: Solicitors Family Law Association, Family Mediators Association. Deputy District Judge of the Principal Registry of the Family Division, Law Society Family Law Panel, SFLA accredited specialist.
Career: Qualified in 1974. Joined *Bindman & Partners* in 1974, becoming a partner in 1976.
Personal: Born 14th January 1947. Lives in London. Married with three children.

DAVIDSON, David
Charles Russell, London (020) 7203 5114
davidd@cr-law.co.uk.
Partner in Family Law Department.
Specialisation: Handles all areas of family law with emphasis on substantial financial applications, frequently with an international aspect. Author of 'A Guide to Pensions and Marriage Breakdown'. Writes, lectures and broadcasts on Taxation and Pension issues relating to separation and divorce. Joint author latest edition of Solicitors Family Law Association Precedents for Consent Orders and forthcoming edition of 'SFLA Precedents for Seperation Agreements and Pre-marital Agreements'.
Prof. Memberships: Solicitors Family Law Association, International Academy of Matrimonial Lawyers. Gave evidence to parliament on behalf of SFLA on Welfare Reform and Pensions Bill.
Personal: Born 30th January 1947. Educated Winchester College and Edinburgh University. Leisure pursuits include hill walking in the Highlands.

DAVIES, Murray
Rupert Bear Murray Davies, Nottingham (0115) 924 3333
Specialisation: All aspects of family law with emphasis on financial aspects to divorce and separation.
Prof. Memberships: SFLA.
Career: Qualified in 1978. Formerly a partner at *Freeth Cartwright Hunt Dickins* - Joined *Rupert Bear* January 1996.
Personal: Born in 1951. Married, 4 children. Interests: walking, bird watching, bricklaying.

DAVIS, Sandra S.
Mishcon de Reya, London (020) 7440 7000
Head of Family Department.
Specialisation: Work includes international and domestic 'big money' cases with a specialisation in high profile and high net worth individuals attracting media attention, international child abduction, divorce and separation, cohabitation disputes and contact and residency disputes. Author of 'International Child Abduction' and numerous articles. Frequently lectures at various national and international events. Lord Chancellor's Department panel solicitor; Radio 4 'You & Yours' panel member.
Prof. Memberships: Solicitors Family Law Association, Holborn Law Society, Law Society. Fellow of the International Academy of Matrimonial Lawyers; Fellow of the RSA.
Career: Qualified with *Mishcon de Reya* in 1981, becoming a Partner in 1984.
Personal: Born 3rd July 1956. Attended University of Sussex 1974-78 and Université Aix-en-Provence, France, and studied European Studies/ Law. Languages: French and German. Leisure interests include travel, painting and photography. Lives in London. Married with two children.

DEVLIN, Michael
Stephensons, Leigh (01942) 777777

DICK, Anne
Anne Hall Dick & Co., Glasgow (0141) 636 0003

DODD, Andrew J.
Tozers, Plymouth (01752) 206460

DON, Andrew M.W.
Blandy & Blandy, Reading (0118) 958 7111
Andrew_Don@blandy.co.uk
Specialisation: Head of one of the largest family departments in the Thames Valley region consisting of seven specialist lawyers. Involved with substantial financial/property matters and children issues arising from divorce and separation. An experienced mediator having trained with the FMA in 1990. In the past has trained other solicitors to be mediators. Member of the UK College of Mediators.
Career: Parachute regiment 1976-1979. Qualified with *Blandy & Blandy* in 1981 and became a partner in 1984.
Prof. Memberships: Solicitors Family Law Association. Family Mediators Association
Personal: Born 1.12.52. Educated at Malvern College and Liverpool University. Lives in Hampshire. Married with four sons. Enjoys outdoor and sporting activities which include playing rackets and rough gardening.

DORAN, Gill
Withers, London (020) 7936 1000
Partner in and head of the family law department.
Specialisation: Has specialised in family and matrimonial work for 20 years. Has written articles about family matters, addressed conferences and done committee work for the Solicitors Family Law Association (SFLA).
Prof. Memberships: International Academy of Matrimonial Lawyers (IAML), Family Mediators Association (FMA).
Career: Qualified in 1974. Joined *Gordon Dadds* (1979-96). Joined the family law department at *Withers* in 1996.
Personal: Born 28th September 1949. Educated at The Abbey School 1960-68 and Manchester University 1968-71. Leisure interests include music, opera and horses. Lives in London.

DOWNING, Ian
Ian Downing Family Law Practice, Plymouth (01752) 226224
ian.downing@virgin.net
Specialisation: Family law generally, and particularly: high asset ancillary relief claims involving company/business matters and pensions; Inheritance Act claims; cohabitee disputes.
Prof. Memberships: Chairman, Devon & Cornwall SFLA.

Career: Qualified 1984. Family law partner, *Bond Pearce*, 1990. Left to set up specialist family practice 1997. Contributing writer to 'Pensions and Insurance on Family Breakdown', 'Debt and Insolvency on Family Breakdown', and 'Humphreys Family Proceedings'.
Personal: Born 20.09.59. Newcastle-upon-Tyne University LLB (Hons). Married. Interests include windsurfing, skiing, scuba diving, theatre, travel.

DRAKE, Michael J.
Collyer-Bristow, London (020) 7242 7363
Head of Matrimonial Department.
Specialisation: Handles all areas of matrimonial and family law, particularly where there is a commercial, financial or international element. Also advises on litigation and business law, including contract and commercial advice and employment issues. Author of various textbooks, SFLA publications, articles. Co-author of 'Divorce and the Family Business', published in 1997 by Jordans. On the editorial board of 'The Family Practitioner'. Has lectured and broadcast on radio and television.
Prof. Memberships: SFLA (National Committee 1987 to 1994).
Career: Qualified in 1971. Joined *Collyer-Bristow* as a partner in 1984.
Personal: Born 14 August 1947. Educated at Haberdasher's Askes's Elstree (to 1965) and Selwyn College, Cambridge (to 1968). Recreations include travel, arts reading and tennis. Lives in London.

EDDY, Catherine
Darbys Mallam Lewis, Oxford (01865) 811700
Specialisation: Practice is exclusively family law and mediation and covers all aspects, but with particular emphasis on the resolution of financial issues on marriage/relationship breakdown.
Prof. Memberships: Law Society's Family Law Panel, Solicitors Family Law Association, Family Mediators Association.
Career: Qualfied 1970, Partner, Head of Family Department, Family Law specialist for 20+ years.
Personal: Lives in Oxford. Married with 2 children.

EDWARDS, Robert N.
Martyn Prowel Solicitors, Cardiff (029) 2047 0909

ERSKINE, Sarah R.
Erskine MacAskill & Co, Edinburgh (0131) 557 1520
Partner.
Specialisation: Main area of practice is family law covering matrimonial separation agreements, cases involving violence, all aspects of the law of the child including children in care and children's hearings, child sexual abuse, non-accidental injury cases and abduction cases. Acts for Shakti Women's Aid and works on cases concerning marital disputes amongst ethnic minorities. Also handles other civil court work and criminal work.
Prof. Memberships: SSC (Solicitor to the Supreme Court), Notary Public.
Career: Qualified in 1980. Joined *Erskine Macaskill & Co* in 1984 as a Partner.
Personal: Educated at Edinburgh University LL.B.

FIFE, Peter R.G.
Ward Gethin, King's Lynn (01553) 773456

FISHER, Jeremy
Gordon Dadds, London (020) 7493 6151
Partner.
Specialisation: Specialises in the problems arising out of the breakdown of family relationships. Particular expertise in complex financial structures both domestic and international .

FLINT, Peter
Lanyon Bowdler, Shrewsbury (01743) 236400 shrewsbury@lblaw.co.uk
Specialisation: Head of Family Law Department, *Lanyon Bowdler*–based in firm's Shrewsbury office, specialising in all aspects of Family Law. Articled to *J.C.H. Bowdler & Sons*, Shrewsbury, in 1967. Qualified in 1971. Admitted into partnership with *J.C.H Bowdler & Sons* in 1972.
Prof. Memberships: Member of Legal Aid Area (No 12) Committee. Member of S.F.L.A. and of Family Mediators Association and of SALM (Shropshire Associated Lawyer Mediators).
Career: Educated at St Martin's Preparatory School, Northwood, Haileybury and I.S.C, Hertford and College of Law. Passed Law Society Pt II exams with 2nd class honours.
Personal: Married, with 3 daughters. Lives in Bayston Hill, near Shrewsbury. Interests include golf and tennis.

FOSKETT, Peter W.
Gordons Cranswick Solicitors, Bradford (01274) 202202 peter.foskett@gordonscranwick.co.uk
Partner in the family department.
Specialisation: All aspects of privately funded family law, but especially complex/high value ancillary relief claims involving business and pension issues. Lectures extensively to the legal profession.
Prof. Memberships: SFLA, FMA.
Career: Qualified 1981. At *Addleshaw Sons & Latham* 1979-1982. Joined *Gordons* in 1983. (Partner from 1985).
Personal: Born 27 May 1957. Educated at Leeds University (LLB). Interests revolve around Manchester City F.C.

FOSTER, Stephen
Lester Aldridge, Bournemouth (01202) 786161
Specialisation: Head of Family Law Unit, leading a team of six specialist lawyers dealing with all areas of family law work, financial and children. Specialises in dealing with substantial financial and property matters within divorce and cohabitee proceedings, including related shareholding and other company disputes. Cases often involve an international element. Team includes 2 SFLA qualified Mediators. Also specialises in solicitors' negligence covering all areas of family law.
Prof. Memberships: Solicitors Family Law Association. (Good Practice Committee Member).
Career: Qualified 1986. *Bircham & Co Westminster* 1986-92 as lead family lawyer and member of the commercial litigation team. Joined *Lester Aldridge* in 1993 as a partner to head up large Family Law unit. Qualified SFLA Mediator 1998.
Personal: Born 1959. Educated at Newport High School and University of Wales, University College Swansea (1980 BA History). Lives near Dorchester, Dorset. Interests include his two young daughters, English and American literature, swimming and tennis.

FOTHERINGHAM, John M.
Ross & Connel, Inverkeithing Tel:01383 414104
Specialisation: Accredited specialist in child law. Also specialises in general family law. Author of articles in JLSS on child and family law. Lectures to CPD courses. Extensive experience of Child Support Act cases.
Career: Qualified 1977. Partner with *Ross & Connel* since 1983. Writer for the Signet since 1986.
Personal: Born 24th July 1953. Educated at Edinburgh University.

FOWLER, Pauline J.
Bates, Wells & Braithwaite, London (020) 7551 7777
Specialisation: Partner, Family Law Department. Work includes complex financial settlements, regularly with an overseas element; all aspects of children's law including international adoption; mediation; cohabitation and Inheritance Act cases.
Prof. Memberships: SFLA (serves on mediation committee); FMA (Vice Chair); BAAF legal group.
Career: Liverpool University (1972-75); College of Law (1979-81); articled to Henry Hodge, *Hodge Jones & Allen* (1981-83) and then stayed on after qualification; *Bates Wells & Braithwaite* from 1985 where became a partner in 1990. Trained as mediator with FMA 1992 and now practises as FMA accredited sole and co-mediator. Lectures and writes on family law.
Personal: Born 1955; lives in London; leisure interests include Chamber music.

GERRY, Andrew
Withers, London (020) 7936 1000
Consultant in family law department.
Specialisation: Practises only family law.
Prof. Memberships: Founding Fellow International Academy of Matrimonial Lawyers (IAML), American Bar Association (ABA) (Family Law Section), Founding member Solicitors Family Law Association (SFLA).
Career: Factory Manager from 1964 to 1969. Management Consultant from 1969 to 1974. Qualified in June 1977, having joined *Withers* in 1974.
Personal: Born 27th March 1938. Cambridge University 1958-61. Enjoys golf, fishing and walking. Lives in London.

GIBB, Andrew T.F.
Balfour & Manson, Edinburgh (0131) 2001250 atg@balfour-manson.co.uk
Partner in Litigation Department.
Specialisation: Has a substantial practice in family law in both the Court of Session and Sheriff Court, also involving drafting of separation agreements with particular regard to financial provision. Is involved in all aspects of education law including contract disputes, disciplinary matters, criminal prosecutions and accident cases. Provides employment law advice to both employers and employees. Solicitor to The Educational Institute of Scotland, the main teaching union in Scotland. Joint editor of 'The Family Law Bulletin' and regular contributor to 'Update' (Education Department of Law Society of Scotland) on family law matters.
Prof. Memberships: Law Society of Scotland, Family Law Association.
Career: Qualified in 1971. Became a partner in *Balfour & Manson* in 1975. Member of Council of Law Society of Scotland 1981-93 and President of Law Society of Scotland 1990-91.

Personal: Born 17th August 1947. Educated at Perth Academy 1959-65 and Edinburgh University 1965-69. Chairman, Management Committee Lothian Allelon (Probation hostel); Leisure interests include golf and music. Lives in Edinburgh.

GIEVE, Katherine

Bindman & Partners, London (020) 7833 4433

Specialisation: All aspects of work concerning children, both private and public law cases; adoption; abduction; consent to treatment. On Law Society Children Panel. Member of Nuffield Child Protection and Family Law and Justice Committee. Co-author, 'Co-habitation Handbook'.

Prof. Memberships: Solicitors Family Law Association (on Children Sub-committee); Association of Lawyers for Children; National Council for Family Proceedings.

Career: Qualified 1978, *Bindman & Partners* 1988, partner 1991.

Personal: Born 1949, attended Merchant Taylor's School and Oxford University.

GRAHAM, Caroline J.M.

Macleod & MacCallum, Inverness (01463) 239393

Partner in court department. Specialist in Family Law. Accredited Family Law Mediator.

Specialisation: Extensive experience in Family Law: divorce, separation, child law. Curator ad Litem in court proceedings and Reporting Officer. Safeguarder to children in Children's Panel proceedings and Sheriff Court referrals and appeals. Accredited as a Family Law Mediator: has made presentations at family law seminars and been involved in training for Children's Panel members. A member of the Scottish Partnership on Domestic Abuse.

Prof. Memberships: Member of Family Law Association. Member and former convenor of CALM (Family Law Mediators in Scotland)

Career: Qualified in 1977.Worked in Inverness since 1976. Previous experience in criminal court work leading to full time speciality in family law.

Personal: Born 9 March 1954. School education–Glasgow. Edinburgh University. Married, three children.

GRAY, Tim

Sinton & Co, Newcastle upon Tyne
(0191) 212 7800
t.gray@sinton.co.uk

Specialisation: Substantial ancillary relief work especially involving particators in limited companies, professional partnerships etc. Has handled a large number of cases involving assets in excess of £1,000,000 and settlements of similar size particularly in the last 2 years. Considerable work load in dealing with cases under the Inheritance (Provision for Family & Dependants) Act 1975.

Prof. Memberships: Member of SFLA. Member of the Law Society Family Law Panel.

Career: MA (Cantab). Qualified 1978. Articled clerk, assistant solicitor and then partner in the firm of *Sinton & Co* (1980). Specialist in family law work and especially ancillary relief throughout that time.

Personal: Married with one child. Devotee of Newcastle United Football Club and the Times crossword puzzle.

GREEN, Michael

Green & Co, Manchester (0161) 834 8980

GREGORY-JONES, Rosemary

Leo Abse & Cohen, Cardiff (029) 2038 3252
rosemaryg@leoabse.co.uk

Specialisation: Family Law, particularly practising in the area of complex ancillary relief cases, also Children Act applications and claims under the Inheritance (Provision for Family and Dependant) Act. Also practises as a family mediator and is a member of the Law Society's Family Law Panel.

Prof. Memberships: Degree in Economic History from Leicester University. Thereafter qualified as a solicitor. At *Morgan Bruce*, Cardiff, for 15 years, 9 of which as a partner.

HALLAM, Catherine

Burges Salmon, Bristol (0117) 939 2000
catherine.hallam@burges-salmon.com

Specialisation: Advice about separation, divorce and related financial/children issues. Particular specialist knowledge of high asset value and complex financial settlements, restructuring of family businesses and pensions on marriage breakdown. Also settlements with an offshore element.

Prof. Memberships: Fellow, International Academy of Matrimonial Lawyers, SFLA, Accredited Specialist (Pensions and Substantial Asset Cases). Family Mediators Association, Member of Law Society Family Panel.

Career: Qualified 1984. Worked in London until 1988. Partner at *Burges Salmon* since 1990. Regular contributor to legal journals and lecturer on family law issues. Co-author of 'Pensions and Insurance on Family Breakdown'. (Jordans 1999).

Personal: Jesus College, Oxford 1977-80. Married with two children.

HARCUS, James

Withers, London (020) 7936 1000

Partner in family law department.

Specialisation: Specialises in divorce, matrimonial finance and taxation, children and cohabitation (including international cases) and pre-marital contracts. Acted in Robinson v Robinson 1982 (case involving setting aside for material non-disclosure) and Cornick v Cornick 1994 (Barder principles). Author of articles in Family Law, (Pre-Nuptials/Term Maintenance). Has lectured for the Solicitors Family Law Association and the Institute of Financial Planning.

Prof. Memberships: Fellow of the International Academy of Matrimonial Lawyers (IAML). Treasurer of the Solicitors Family Law Association (SFLA) 1982-87.

Career: Qualified in 1974. Partner of *Gordon Dadds* (1981-96). Joined family law department at *Withers* in 1996.

Personal: Born 15th April 1949. Educated at Exeter University 1968-71. Leisure interests include riding, skiing, sailing and gardening. Lives in London.

HARPER, Mark

Withers, London (020) 7936 1000

Partner in family law department.

Specialisation: Exclusively family law and, in particular, in substantial financial cases including those with an international element and child abduction. Author of articles in Family Law and SFLA Newsletter. Author of Model Letters for Family Lawyers (Jordans). Has broadcast on TV and radio and been quoted regularly in national press.

Prof. Memberships: SFLA National Committee 1992-98, SFLA Family Law Bill team, SFLA Cohabitation Working Group Chairperson 1995-97, SFLA Press Officer 1997-98, Law Society, Family Law Committee 1998 to date.

Career: Qualified in 1988. Became a partner in 1990 at *Anthony Gold* after articles with the firm. Head of family law department 1991-99. Joined *Withers* February 1999.

Personal: Born 2 February 1962. Educated at Malvern College and Pembroke College, Oxford. Enjoys travel, architecture and classic cars. Lives in Balham, South London

HARTNELL, Norman A.

Hartnell & Co, Exeter (01392) 421777

Senior partner in specialist family law practice.

Specialisation: Main areas of practice are substantial ancillary relief/children issues, care proceedings and family mediation. Member of Law Society Children Panel; accredited mediator with FMA; FMA trainer and supervisor; SFLA mediator supervisor. Involved in promotion of interdisciplinary training; Manager of Devon Family Mediation Agency.

Prof. Memberships: Family Mediators Association; Devon and Cornwall SFLA (past Secretary); Devon & Exeter Law Society. U.K. College of Family Mediators.

Career: Qualified in 1979. Established own specialist family law practice in 1991, now has staff of 15. Previously partner with *Dunn & Baker* from 1988.

Personal: Born 1st October 1953. Attended Aylesbury Grammar School, then Selwyn College, Cambridge (1974-76) MA, MCFM and Chester College of Law 1978.

HENSON, John S.

Hunt & Coombs, Peterborough (01733) 565312

HODSON, David

The Family Law Consortium, London
(020) 7420 5000
dh@tflc.co.uk

Specialisation: Partner, family law solicitor and mediator, specialises in financial disputes involving families with middle/high income/capital resources, international or other complex aspects, sole and joint mediation.

Prof. Memberships: Deputy district judge, Principal Registry of Family Division; SFLA Accredited Specialist (portfolios in Substantial Assets and International Cases); accredited family mediator; elected governor and vice-chairman of UK College of Family Mediators; member, LCD's Family Proceedings Rule Committee; chairman, Solicitors Family Law Association Ancillary Relief Reform Committee and member, SFLA International Committee; Fellow, International Academy of Matrimonial Lawyers; trustee, Marriage Resource; member, Lawyers Christian Fellowship; trustee, Surrey Mediation Forum; member, Society for Computers and the Law.

Career: Articled *Hepherd Winstanley & Pugh*, Southampton; qualified 1978; *Anthony Collins & Co.*, Birmingham; *Theodore Goddard*, 1985-91, *Frere Cholmeley Bischoff*, 1991-95, *The Family Law Consortium*, 1995;

Publications: Publications include co-author 'Divorce Reform: A Guide for Lawyers and Mediators' (Sweet & Maxwell) and 'The Business of Family Law' (Jordans); consulting editor 'Family Law in Europe' (Butterworths); co-author SFLA's 'Guide to Family Law in Europe'; regular writer and speaker (England and abroad) on family law issues.

Personal: King Edward VI Grammar School, Southampton; Leicester University (LLB Hons). Born 1953; resides Guildford.

HOPKINS, Wendy
Wendy Hopkins & Co, Cardiff (029) 20342233
Specialisation: Divorce and high value financial claims for spouses and cohabitees. Children including contact and residence. Adoptions including inter country.
Prof. Memberships: S.F.L.A.
Career: Private client partner with *Eversheds*, Cardiff from 1980 to 1996. Member of board of *Eversheds*, Cardiff 1991 to 1996. Senior Partner in *Wendy Hopkins & Co*, Cardiff, specialist family law practice 1996 to date.
Personal: Own children aged 15 and 13. Fitness, golf and design.

HOWELL, Grant
Charles Russell, London (020) 7203 5000
granth@cr-law.co.uk
Specialisation: Handles all areas of family law. Lectures and writes on the subject. Author 'Family Breakdown and Insolvency' (Butterworths).
Prof. Memberships: Member National Committee Solicitors Family Law Association (SFLA) (1993-98). Member Training Committee SFLA. (1991 to date: Chairman 1993-98). Member Family Justice and Training Committee. Fellow of the Institute of Advanced Legal Studies.
Career: Qualified 1980. At *Batchelor Street Longstaffe* till 1985; then *Bennett Taylor Tyrrell* till 1990 when joined *Charles Russell* as a partner.
Personal: Born 4th February 1956. LLB from Birmingham University. Leisure interests include Chelsea Football Club and music.

HUGHES, Frances
Bates, Wells & Braithwaite, London (020) 7551 7777
Partner and head of family law department.
Specialisation: Practice covers the full range of family law, especially international cases, and cases involving trust law or complex offshore corporate entities, also complex children's work. Clients include City professionals, entertainment clients and other lawyers. Writes, lectures and broadcasts on family law, nationally and internationally, former contributing editor Butterworths Family Law Service.
Prof. Memberships: International Academy of Matrimonial Lawyers; Vice President of the European Chapter of IAML; SFLA; Co-ordinator of SFLA Mediation Training (1996-99). Accredited SFLA and FMA Mediator.
Career: Qualified in 1981. Assistant at *Theodore Goddard*. Joined *Bates Wells & Braithwaite* to establish the Family Department in 1983 and became a partner in 1984.
Personal: Born 15th June 1954. Oxford 1973-76. School Governor. Enjoys opera and gardening. Lives in London and Wiltshire.

HUGHES, Kathryn Lesley
Farleys, Blackburn (01254) 606060
klh@farleys.com
Partner in family law department.
Specialisation: Main areas of practice are child care and ancillary relief in divorce, together with the law relating to cohabitants. Handles all aspects, privately paid and legal aid and public and private law cases. Children Panel Member. Law Society Family Law Panel Member also. Has acted in instances from the most straightforward ancillary relief case to cases involving very substantial assets; from uncomplicated children matters to the most difficult; and adoptions with a foreign element. Past contributing author to Butterworths 'Family Law Service'.
Prof. Memberships: Law Society Family Law Committee Member; SFLA, Child Concern.
Career: Qualified in 1985. Past member of the Bar (called 1977). Joined *Farleys* in 1983, becoming a partner in 1985. Recorder, sitting on Crime, Civil, and Family.
Personal: Born 5th June 1954. Leisure interests include walking, swimming and reading. Lives in Hale, Chesire.

HUTCHINSON, Anne-Marie
Dawson Cornwell, London (020) 7242 2556
Specialisation: Practises exclusively in family law, with particular specialism in international family law, international custody disputes and child abduction. SFLA accredited specialist. Is currently engaged in extensive research into Forced Marriage. Awarded the inagural UNICEF Child Rights Lawyer Award, 1999.
Prof. Memberships: Chair of Reunite, International Child Abduction Centre, Solicitors' Family Law Association, International Society of Family Law, International Bar Association, Association of Lawyers for Children, National Council for Family Proceedings, The Society for Advanced Legal Studies.
Publications: Consultant Editor Hershman and McFarlane 'Children Law and Practice' and co-author 'International Parental Child Abduction'. International correspondent: 'International Family Law'.

ILIFF, Catherine
Fosters, Norwich (01603) 620508
Bungay (01986) 895251
Specialisation: Partner in *Fosters'* substantial family law department. Highly experienced in all aspects of family work for private clients. Accredited as a family mediator in 1991 and now has substantial mediation practice across East Anglia.

JAMIESON, George
Walker Laird, Paisley (0141) 887 5271

JONES, Catherine E.
Pannone & Partners, Manchester (0161) 909 3000
Partner and Joint Head of Family Department.
Specialisation: Work includes divorce, separation, financial provision, children including contested adoption and cohabitation, with special emphasis on financial matters for corporate, other business and high net worth clients.
Prof. Memberships: Law Society, Manchester Law Society, SFLA.
Career: Qualified 1977. Joined *Pannone & Partners* in 1982, now Client Care partner. North West SFLA secretary and Regional Representative, and solicitor representative Greater Manchester Circuit Adoption Committee.
Personal: Leisure interests include walking, sailing, theatre and travel. Lives in Altrincham.

JONES, Peter
Jones Myers Gordon, Leeds (0113) 246 0055
Specialisation: Main areas of practice Divorce and high value Ancillary Relief together with Cohabitation Disputes and Mediation.
Career: Qualified 1980. Founded 8 years ago a Specialist Family Law Practice.
Prof. Memberships: Former National Chairman of the Solicitors Family Law Association, Lecturer and Member of the UK College of Family Mediators.
Personal: Born 4th June 1948. Married with 2 daughters. Lives in Harrogate.

JURY, Susan N.
Wolferstans, Plymouth (01752) 663295
Family/Matrimonial
Specialisation: Family Law– all areas of divorce work; ancillary relief; children, private and public law; cohabitee and domestic violence.
Prof. Memberships: Member of SFLA and special accredited member–childrens matters; member Law Society, Children Panel, Trained SFLA family mediator.
Career: Tavistock School; Huddersfield University; Chester College of Law; LL.B. Articled *Wolferstans* 1987, qualified 1990, became a partner 1995.
Personal: Year of birth: 1964; town of residence: Christow. Main leisure activities: skiing, aerobics, reading and caring for 2 small children.

KEIR, Jane
Kingsley Napley, London Mobile: 07887 371050
Partner and head of family law department.
Specialisation: Specialises in financial and children cases, often with an international element. Workload is split between financial cases, domestic and international custody disputes and child abduction. Such matters frequently give rise to issues of which jurisdiction is the more appropriate. Writes and lectures on family law and is a contributing author to 'Evidence in Family Proceedings'.
Prof. Memberships: Former Chair of the international committee of the Solicitors Family Law Association. Fellow of the Institute of Advanced Legal Studies and member of its working group looking at the issues arising from the cross border movement of children; SFLA and Law Society accredited family lawyer; Member of Reunite; the National Council for Family Proceedings and the International Bar Association.
Career: Qualified December 1987. Joined *Kingsley Napley* in September 1989 and became a partner in the family law department in November 1992.
Personal: Born 4th March 1962. Lives in London. Leisure interests include horses and National Hunt racing, tennis and travel.

KIDD, Philip E.
Tozers, Torquay (01803) 291898

LA FOLLETTE, Maryly
Charles Russell, London (020) 7203 5000
marylyl@cr-law.co.uk
Partner in the Family Department.
Specialisation: International Divorce, ancillary relief and child related work (private law).
Prof. Memberships: Solicitors Family Law Association; Family Mediators Association.
Personal: Born 18 October 1942; Attended San Francisco University, University of California at Berkeley, Columbia University (New York). Interests include tennis, skiing, reading, music and charitable work.

LAMBERT, Tracy
Tozers, Torquay (01803) 407020

LEVERTON, David. J.
Payne Hicks Beach, London (020) 7465 4300
Head of Family Law Department.
Specialisation: Founder member of International Academy of Matrimonial Lawyers. Very experienced specialist in all aspects of matrimonial law with particular expertise in complex financial matters and in negotiating financial settlements.

Career: Qualified 1958 at *Ridsdale & Son* of Westminster: joined *Payne Hicks Beach* in 1959. Became Partner in 1963. Managing Partner of firm. Member of Solicitors Disciplinary Tribunal.
Personal: Born 8th September 1935. Educated at The Haberdashers' Askes' School, Hampstead. Enjoys fine art, music and rugby. Lives in London.

LEVISON, Jeremy I.

Levison Meltzer Pigott, London (020) 7556 2400
jlevison@lmplaw.co.uk
Specialisation: Along with leading practitioners Claire Meltzer and Simon Pigott has opened the specialist divorce and family law firm, *Levison Meltzer Pigott*. Handles all aspects of matrimonial work, with particular interest in high worth clients, cohabitation, cases with a foreign element, children and, particularly more recently, pre-nuptial contracts.
Prof. Memberships: International Academy of Matrimonial Lawyers. Solicitors' Family Law Association. American Bar Association (Family Section).
Career: Qualified in 1974 and worked for *Theodore Goddard* until 1980. *Collyer-Bristow* 1980-98. *Levison Meltzer Pigott* from 1st June 1998.
Personal: Born 3rd February 1952. Educated at Charterhouse School 1965-1969 and the University of Kent 1970-73. Enjoys fine art, music, cricket, classic cars and France. Lives in London.

LONGRIGG, William

Charles Russell, London (020) 7203 5000
williaml@cr-law.co.uk
Partner in Family Department.
Specialisation: Main areas of practice are divorce, ancillary relief and child-related work (private law).
Prof. Memberships: Solicitors Family Law Association (Former member SFLA Mediation Committee; Chairman SFLA London Regional Group since 1996).
Career: Qualified in 1987. Joined *Charles Russell* in 1985, becoming a Partner in 1992.
Personal: Born 6th July 1960. Attended Dragon School, Oxford 1968-73, Shrewsbury School 1973-78 and Warwick University 1979-82. Leisure interests include drawing, writing and junk shops. Lives in London.

LOUDON, Alasdair

Loudons WS, Edinburgh (0131) 662 4193
loudons@btconnect.com
Founding partner.
Specialisation: Sole area of practice is family law, including divorce cases, particularly those involving claims for capital payments or property transfer orders. Also handles substantial number of cases involving the negotiation of separation agreements. Acts in Court of Session and Sheriff Court. Former tutor in criminal advocacy at Edinburgh University. Accredited by the Law Society of Scotland as a specialist in family law.
Prof. Memberships: WS Society, Edinburgh Bar Association (Past President), Family Law Association. Member of Sheriff Court Rules Council for Scotland.
Career: Qualified in 1978. Apprentice at *Tods, Murray & Jamieson WS* 1978-80. Qualified assistant at *Warner & Co.* 1980-82 and partner 1982-92. Founded *Loudons WS* in 1992.
Personal: Born 7th April 1956. Attended Dundee University 1974-78. Leisure interests include golf (member of Bruntsfield Links and Luffness New) and football (Hearts Season Ticket holder). Lives in Edinburgh.

MAIR, Leonard

Morton Fraser, Solicitors, Edinburgh
(0131) 247 1000
lm@morton-fraser.com
Partner in Civil Litigation Division. Head of Family Law Team.
Specialisation: Main areas of practice are family law, negotiating financial divorce settlements, Child Law, ADR and mediation and defamation. Has covered a wide range of work over a 27 year period and has developed mediation skills since 1993. Mediator with Family Mediation Service; Accredited 'solicitor-mediator' with Law Society of Scotland.
Prof. Memberships: Law Society of Scotland, Writers to the Signet, UK College of Family Mediators.
Career: Qualified in 1975. Joined *The Morton Fraser* in 1973, becoming a Partner in 1977.
Personal: Born 5th September 1949. Attended Stirling University 1967-71 and Edinburgh University 1971-73. Former Vice Chairman of Lothian Marriage Counselling Service. Former part-time Chairman CSAT. Former board member Family Mediation Lothian. Council Member Step Family Scotland. Leisure interests include fly fishing, sailing and the arts. Lives in East Lothian.

MARCO, Alan

Collyer-Bristow, London (020) 7242 7363
Partner, Matrimonial Department.
Specialisation: Handles all areas of family and matrimonial law with emphasis on financial provision applications. Deputy District Judge at Principal Registry of the Family Division
Prof. Memberships: Solicitors Family Law Association.
Career: Qualified in 1965. Partner at *Baileys Shaw & Gillett* 1972-1996. Partner *Collyer-Bristow* 1996.
Personal: Born in Devon. Married with three children.

MASSEY, William

Manches, London (020) 7404 4433
william.massey@manches.co.uk
Specialisation: Practises exclusively in family and matrimonial law.
Prof. Memberships: Solictor's Family Law Association, SFLA London Regional Committee, SFLA Accredited Specialist (Big Money and International Cases).
Career: Qualified in 1990 at *Freshfields. Penningtons* 1991-94. Joined *Manches* in 1994, became partner 1999.
Personal: Born 3rd May 1964. Educated at Oundle School and Exeter University. Married with three young children. Enjoys sports, outdoors and sleep.

MCBRIDE, Carolyn

Quinn Martin & Langan, Glasgow
(0141) 429 4354

MCDONALD, Roberta

Roberta McDonald–Sole Practitioner,
Birmingham (0121) 449 6821

MCTAGGART, Anne

Stronachs, Aberdeen (01224) 845845
anne.mctaggart@stronachs.co.uk
Specialisation: Family and child law. Family mediation (all issues). Accredited by the Law Society of Scotland as family law specialist and comprehensive lawyer mediator. Sheriff court and court of session cases.
Prof. Memberships: Law Society of Scotland. Aberdeen Bar Association. Family Law Association. C.A.L.M (Comprehensive Accredited Lawyer Mediators). Safeguarders Association. Aberdeen Business Womens Network.
Career: Qualified 1976. Partner in *Stonarchs* joined firm in 1986. Specialised in family law for over 10 years. Regularly appointed by sheriffs court to report on child related disputes and as safeguarder for children.
Personal: Educated at High School of Dundee. Law degree at Aberdeen University. Married with two teenage children.

MEISEL, Mari

Blair Allison & Co, Birmingham (0121) 233 2904

MELTZER, Claire

Levison Meltzer Pigott, London (020) 7556 2400
cmeltzer@lmplaw.co.uk
Specialisation: Along with leading family practitioners Jeremy Levison and Simon Pigott opened specialist family and divorce law firm, *Levison Meltzer Pigott*. Handles all aspect of family work. Special knowledge of high profile financial and children's cases and pensions on divorce. Regular broadcaster and lecturer.
Prof. Memberships: Solicitors Family Law Association. American Bar Association (Family Section). Family Mediators Association.
Career: Qualified 1979. Partner in *Theodore Goddard* 1983-85. Partner in *Collyer-Bristow* 1985-98. Partner in *Levison Meltzer Pigott* 1998.
Personal: B.A. Hons (Eng. Lang. & Lit.). Lives in London.

MESSENGER, Mercy

Mercy Messenger–Sole Practitioner, Solihull
(01564) 779 427

MILBURN, Paula

Jones Maidment Wilson incorporating Hatton Scates Horton, Manchester (0161) 832 8087
paulam@jmw.co.uk

MITCHELL, Jane

Manches, Oxford (01865) 722106
jane.mitchell@manches.co.uk
Specialisation: Advises on all areas of family law, particulary complex financial and children issues arising from matrimonial and relationship breakdown.
Prof. Memberships: Solicitors Family Law Assocaition, Law Society.
Career: Qualified in 1988. Has practised at *Manches* since then, first in London and then, in 1995, moving to their Oxford office to set up its family law department. Partner since 1997.
Publications: Contributing editor to 'Current Law Weekly.'
Personal: Born 17th May 1963. B.A. Hons (English and Related Literature). Married with three children. Leisure interests include theatre and gardening.

MONRO, Pat

Wilford Monro, London (020) 7582 6002

NICOL, Frazer

Nicol, Denvir & Purnell, Cardiff (029) 20796311

O'DONNELL, Caroline
Miller Sands, Cambridge (01223) 366741
miller.sands@dial.pipex.com
Specialisation: Children (private and public law), divorce and ancilliary relief. SFLA Mediator.
Prof. Memberships: SFLA member. Legal Aid Committee member (SFLA). Association of Lawyers for Children, National Committee member. Member of the Law Society's Children Panel.

O'REGAN, Timothy
Rudlings & Wakelam, Thetford (01842) 754151
Specialisation: Specialises in child law, particularly child care and adoption. Original member of the Children Panel. Head of Child Law Department at *Rudlings & Wakelam.*
Prof. Memberships: Secretary to Children Committee of the Solicitors Family Law Association, National Committee member of the Association of Lawyers for Children, member of British Agencies for Adoption and Fostering, associate member of National Association of Guardians ad Litem and Reporting Officers, solicitor representative on the Suffolk Family Court Business Committee, member Law Society Child Law sub-committee.
Career: Admitted as solicitor in 1975, partner since 1978. Writes and lectures regularly on child law and adoption.

PALMER, George
Peden & Reid, Belfast (028) 9032 5617

PARKER, Diana C.
Withers, London (020) 7936 1000
Partner in family law department.
Specialisation: Exclusively family law. The senior partner of *Withers* but still handling heavy caseload of complex cases. Co-author of 'Longman's Practical Matrimonial Precedents' and 'Know How for Family Lawyers'. Author of articles in professional journals and elsewhere. Occasional lecturer, speaker at conferences and contributor to the media.
Prof. Memberships: Solicitors Family Law Association (SFLA); Family Mediators Association (FMA); International Academy of Matrimonial Lawyers (IAML).
Personal: MA (Cantab) MPhil (Cantab). Lives in London and Oxford.

PARRY, Richard
Farrer & Co, London (020) 7242 2022
Specialisation: Partner in family team. Main area of practice is family law.
Prof. Memberships: Solicitors Family Law Association.
Career: Qualified in 1976. Joined *Farrer & Co.* in 1974, becoming a partner in 1983.
Personal: Born 6 December 1951. Educated at Eton College (1964-1969) and Balliol College, Oxford (1970-1973). Governor of Downe House. Leisure interests include golf, bridge and music. Lives in London.

PATIENCE, Iain
Iain Smith & Company, Aberdeen (01224) 645454

PAYNE, Peter
Stephens & Scown, Exeter (01392) 210700
family.exeter@stephens-scown.co.uk
Specialisation: Partner and head of the firm's Family Department specialising in divorce, finance, children, child care and adoption.
Prof. Memberships: Law Society; SFLA; Child Care Panel; Family Lawyers.
Career: Articled *Stephens & Scown*; qualified 1975; partner 1980.

PEARSON, Philippa
The Family Law Consortium, London
(020) 7420 5000
pp@tflc.co.uk
Specialisation: Main aim is to deal with family issues in a conciliatory but firm manner so that, particularly where children are involved, the parties are able to communicate effectively after the legal process is over.
Prof. Memberships: Member of the SFLA National Committee and chair of its Legal Aid Committee for six years.
Career: Qualified 1988, previously head of family law at *Osbornes.*
Publications: Regularly writes (including Butterworths 'Family Law Service' and 'Cohabitation Law and Precedents'), lectures and appears in the media to talk about family law matters.

PEMBRIDGE, Eileen
Fisher Meredith, London
(020) 7924 9124 (Family Dept.)
central@fismer.co.uk
Senior Partner and Head of Family Department.
Specialisation: Deals with all aspects of family law, but especially complex ancillary relief on divorce and other financial matters. Has always taken on legal aid work. Has written various opinion pieces on family law and the legal profession, lectured and addressed sessions on Family Law at the Solicitors Annual Conference.
Prof. Memberships: Law Society (Council Member for London South since 1990, Family Law Committee 1990 to date (chair 1990-94), Courts and Legal Services Committee from 1987, now Access to Justice Working Party. International Human Rights working party for five years from 1993 and Equal Opportunities Committee since 1994, (Chair from 1999). LAPG (Committee Member since 1982 and Chair 1987-88), SFLA (member Legal Aid Committee), International Family Law Association, Chair of Law Society Reputation Working Party (1990-date)
Career: Worked as a freelance interpreter for the UN 1967-73 and casually thereafter until 1983. Qualified in 1975. Co-founder of *Fisher Meredith* in 1975, now 100 strong. Challenged Law Society convention by standing for election as President, July 1995.
Personal: Born 15th March 1944. Educated at Worcester Girls' Grammar School; Newnham College, Cambridge (Natural Sciences degree and postgraduate French and Russian), and Bath University (postgraduate language studies). FRSA. Interests include sailing, animal welfare, childrens' activities, hill-walking, vegetable-growing and reading novels in French, Russian and Spanish. Lives in Dulwich Village, London with her two young children and husband (a judge).

PHILIPPS, Susan
Gordon Dadds, London
(020) 7493 6151
Partner.
Specialisation: Covers all areas of family and matrimonial law. SFLA Trained Mediator.
Prof. Memberships: Solicitors Family Law Association. Serves on Education Committee of the SFLA.
Career: Qualified in 1984. Joined *Ward Bowie* in 1982 and became a partner in 1986 on merger with *Penningtons.* Head of family law department since 1994 until joined *Gordon Dadds* in 1999.
Personal: Born 9th April 1957. Lives in London.

PIGOTT, Simon
Levison Meltzer Pigott, London (020) 7556 2400
spigott@lmplaw.co.uk
Specialisation: Along with leading practitioners Jeremy Levison and Claire Meltzer opened *Levison Meltzer Pigott.* Handles all aspects of matrimonial work including cases involving complex financial issues and children. Practising family mediator. Lecturer and broadcaster.
Prof. Memberships: Solicitors Family Law Association. American Bar Association (Family Section). Family Mediators Association. United Kingdom College of Family Mediators.
Career: Qualified 1982. *Wright Webb Syrett* 1978-83; *Theodore Goddard* 1983-85; *Collyer-Bristow* 1985-98 (partner from 1987); *Levison Meltzer Pigott* 1998.
Personal: Born October 1956. Mill Hill School 1970-74. University of Southampton 1974-77. Lives in Wolverton, Hants. Married with three daughters.

PIRRIE, James
The Family Law Consortium, London
(020) 7420 5000
flc@tflc.co.uk
Specialisation: Aiming to help clients find solutions before cost and trauma of the process can begin to put them out of reach.
Prof. Memberships: SFLA accredited specialist ('substantial assets' and cohabitation; accredited mediator, and voice on the CSA.
Career: Qualified 1985

POWELL, J. Mark H.
Hugh James Ford Simey, Bargoed (01443) 822022
mark.powell@hjfs.co.uk
Partner and Head of Family Group.
Specialisation: Public Childrens Law, Mental Health.
Prof. Memberships: Association of Lawyers for Children (Past Chair).
Career: Rugby School. University College, London. Admitted as Solicitor 1977. Barrister and Solicitor of the High Court of New Zealand (admitted 1990). Assistant Recorder 1995. Made Recorder in the year 2000.

PREST, Charles
Lee & Priestley, Leeds (0113) 243 3751
Specialisation: Selected divorce/ancillary relief cases and some education law cases. Mostly complex children matters.
Prof. Memberships: SFLA, ELAS.
Career: MA (Cantab), DipLG. Qualified 1988. Joined *Lee & Priestley* 1994. McMahon Law Studentship; winner–Local Government Legal Society prize; silver award in 'The Lawyer' pro bono category.
Publications: Editor–Butterworths Family Law Service. 'Not Alone: A Children's Guide to Care Proceedings' (HMSO).
Personal: Married to Catherine Prest. Interests include archaeology, football, contemporary art and children's stories.

PRESTON, Miles
Miles Preston & Co, London (020) 7583 0583
Founding partner 1994.
Specialisation: Practises exclusively in matrimonial and family law.
Prof. Memberships: Solicitors Family Law Association, International Academy of Matrimonial Lawyers.
Career: Qualified in 1974. Partner with *Radcliffes & Co.* 1979-94. Served on Sir Gervaise Sheldon's Family Law Liaison Committee 1982; founder member SFLA 1982; served on Main Committee of SFLA 1982-88; chaired working party on procedure 1982-88; founder member of IAML 1986; Governor IAML 1986-89; Parliamentarian to Main Committee 1989; president of English Chapter 1989; president of European Chapter 1989-92; president Elect of Main Academy 1992-94. President of Main Academy 1994-96. Member of the President's International Family Law Committee (chaired by Lord Justice Thorpe) since 1994.
Personal: Born 1950. Educated Shrewsbury School 1963-68. Leisure interests include food, travel and classic cars. Lives in Greenwich, London.

PROCTOR, E. Jane
Greenwoods, Peterborough (01733) 887700

RAE, Maggie
Clintons, London (020) 7379 6080
Partner. Family Department.
Specialisation: Work includes divorce, children, adoption, employment and education. Also all aspects of family and children work. Author of 'Women and the Law', 'Children and the Law', 'First Rights' and 'Child Care Law'. Lectured at Warwick University. Undertakes frequent teaching, lecturing and writing assignments.
Prof. Memberships: Solicitors Family Law Association, Education Law Association, British Association for Adoption and Fostering, Inter Country Adoption Lawyers Association, International Academy of Matrimonial Lawyers, member of the Government's consultation panel on Pensions and Divorce, the President of the Family Division's International Committee and special advisor to the Social Security Select Committee in relation to Pensions and Divorce, Fellow of the RSA.
Career: Qualified in 1973. Barrister 1973-77. Partner at *Hodge Jones & Allen* 1978-92. Joined *Mishcon de Reya* in 1992, becoming a Partner in 1993.
Personal: Born 20th September 1949. Attended Great Yarmouth High School 1961-68 and University of Warwick 1968-71. Leisure interests include walking, cooking and gardening. Lives in London.

RANDALL, Richard M.
Leonard Gray, Chelmsford (01245) 251411
Specialisation: All aspects of family law including complex cases involving substantial financial assets or children. Particular specialisation in contact cases involving hostile parents and the representation of teenage children in legal proceedings. Broadcasts, lectures and writes on family law and related issues.
Prof. Memberships: Solicitors Family Law Association. Founder member British Association of Lawyer Mediators.
Career: Qualified 1972. Partner *Leonard Gray* 1975. Head of Family Law Department 1984. Senior Partner 1991. Sole Family Mediator 1996.
Personal: Born 17th May 1948. Educated at Brentwood School, LLB London. Lives and works in Chelmsford. Enjoys performing choral music and opera, cricket, cycling.

RAY, Peggy
Goodman Ray, London (020) 7254 8855
Specialisation: Practice covers all areas of child care work including both public and private law cases, adoption and associated areas such as judicial review, education law, and administrative law. Speaker and trainer in child care. Former member of the Law Society Family Law Committee, current member of Solicitors Family Law Association children committee, member of the Expert Witness Group, former member of the Inner London Children Act Business Committee. Member of the Law Society Children Panel since 1985. Member of Funding Review Committee, member of President's Interdisciplinary Committee, member of Family Appeals Review Group.
Prof. Memberships: Solicitors Family Law Association, Association of Lawyers for Children, NaGALRO, National Council for Family Proceedings, BAAF.
Career: Qualified 1980. Established own practice with Judith Goodman in Hackney in 1985.

ROBINSON, Sara
The Family Law Consortium, London (020) 7420 5000
scr@tflc.co.uk
Specialisation: Twenty-one years of practice spent pursuing assets and children around the globe interested in giving team-work support to those experiencing life-changing times. Founded FLC in 1995 to provide a spring-board for these services and to promote the multi-disciplinary approach to finding solutions that are cost-effective in financial and emotional terms.
Prof. Memberships: Member of the SFLA International Committee; Accredited sole and co-mediator and consultant for the Family Mediators Association and SFLA.

RODGERS, Hilary
Forsters, London (020) 7863 8333
hrodgers@forsters.co.uk
Specialisation: Head of family law practice, specialising in complex financial divorce settlements. Also experienced in issues of jurisdiction, taxation, trusts and pensions in relation to matrimonial matters.
Prof. Memberships: Solicitors Family Law Association Member, also SFLA Procedure Committee and Chair of the Cohabitation Working Group, International Bar Association, and International Academy of Matrimonial Lawyers.
Career: Admitted 1987. Assistant at *Theodore Goddard.* Joined *Frere Cholmeley Bischoff* 1991. Partner 1994. Founder partner of *Forsters*, August 1998.
Personal: Born 1962. Married, lives in North London.

RUTHERFORD, Lyn
Dickinson Dees, Newcastle upon Tyne (0191) 279 9229
Partner and head of family law department.
Specialisation: The practice covers a full range of family law matters. In particular specialisation in high net worth private clients and major ancillary matters.
Career: Qualified 1972. Thereafter one year at *Clayton Mott* in Nottingham. Joined *Dickinson Dees* in January 1974. Became a partner in 1976.
Personal: Born 20 January 1948. Educated at Hookergate Grammar School and Liverpool University–LLB Degree. Interests include sports, particularly horse racing, football and reading. Lives in Newcastle upon Tyne.

RUTTER, Geoffrey M.
Collyer-Bristow, London (020) 7242 7363
geoffrey.rutter@collyer-bristow.co.uk
Specialisation: Many years experience in family law, principally involving substantial financial issues resulting from marriage breakdown. Considerable knowledge of and experience in the investigative elements of domestic and international work including offshore trusts and structures. Regularly advises on the commercial and tax considerations involved in financial negotiations and settlements.
Prof. Memberships: Solicitors Family Law Association, International Academy of Matrimonial Lawyers. Committee member of the London Regional Committee of the Solicitors Family Law Association.

SALTER, David A.
Addleshaw Booth & Co, Leeds (0113) 209 2000
das@addleshaw-booth.co.uk
Partner and head of family law department.
Specialisation: Handles all aspects of family law, but principally financial relief with an emphasis on pensions. Author or joint author of 'Humphreys Family Proceedings', 'Matrimonial Consent Orders and Agreements', 'Family Finance and Tax' and 'Family Courts: Emergency Remedies and Procedures'. Editor of 'Pensions and Insurance on Family Breakdown' and 'Longman Litigation Practice'. Contributor to 'Insolvency on Family Breakdown' and 'Butterworths Family Law Service'. Frequent lecturer on family law topics.
Prof. Memberships: SFLA (Chairman 1997-99). Chairman of SFLA Accreditation and Pensions Committees. International Academy of Matrimonial Lawyers (Fellow).
Career: Qualified in 1972. Joined the firm in 1975, becoming a Partner in 1978. Recorder (North Eastern Circuit); Member of Supreme Court Procedure Committee Family Division Sub-committee; Member of the Family Committee of the Judicial Studies Board.
Personal: Educated Pembroke College, Cambridge.

SANDS, Rosemary
Miller Sands, Cambridge (01223) 366741
miller.sands@dial.pipex.com
Senior partner, heads family law department.
Specialisation: Work includes divorce, ancillary relief, adoption and children (public and private law). FMA mediator. Hon Adviser for local CAB.
Prof. Memberships: Law Society, SFLA, FMA, ALC, BAAF, Chair of Cambridgeshire Guardian ad litem advisory panel. Member Children Panel. Law Society Family Law Panel. Member UK College of Family Mediators.
Personal: LLB 1954. Barrister (Middle Temple) 1956-64.

SAX, Richard
Manches, London (020) 7404 4433
richard.sax@manches.co.uk
Partner in family department.
Specialisation: Advises on all areas of family law, particularly complex financial and children issues arising from matrimonial and relationship breakdown including International, Trust and Tax aspects.
Prof. Memberships: Solicitors Family Law Association. International Academy of Matrimonial Lawyers, Law Society.
Career: Qualified in 1967. 1968 Partner and subse-

quently Managing Partner at *Rubinstein Callingham* (which merged with *Manches* in 1994). Sits as a Deputy District Judge at the Principal Registry. Past Chairman of the Solicitors Family Law Association. Governor and Secretary/Treasurer International Academy of Matrimonial Lawyers European Chapter. Member of the DSS Consultation Panel on Pension Sharing and Council Member Family Policy Studies Centre. Co-Author 'Know how for Family Lawyers', published by Longmans. Joint General Editor Butterworth's 'Family Law Service'.

SCANLAN, Margaret
Russells Gibson McCaffrey, Glasgow (0141) 332 4176
Specialisation: Family law and child law, including negotiating settlements and court work. Law Society of Scotland accredited specialist in family law.
Prof. Memberships: Family Law Association, Sheriff Court Rules Council, Scottish Legal Aid Board.
Career: Qualified 1972 after apprenticeship with *Flowers & Co.* Thereafter wide general practice, specialising in Family Law for last 10 years. Founder member and past chair of Family Law Association.
Personal: Bad golf, good food.

SCOFIELD, Ian D.
Hooper & Wollen, Torquay (01803) 213251
Specialisation: Senior Partner & Head of department advising on all aspects of family law and child care. Specialises in financial and property issues and has a substantial case load of high value divorces involving complex negotiation. Accredited mediator with the Family Mediators Association and one of the few mediators in the South West with a regular case load. Member of the Solicitors Family Law Association and a member of the Law Society's Child Care Panel.

SHACKLETON, Fiona
Farrer & Co, London (020) 7242 2022
Partner in family team.
Specialisation: Principal area of practice is family law. Author of 'The Divorce Handbook'.
Prof. Memberships: SFLA, IAML.
Career: Qualified in 1980. Became a partner with *Brecher & Co* in 1982. Joined *Farrer & Co* in 1984 and became a partner in 1987.
Personal: Born 26th May 1956. Attended Benenden School and Exeter University. Governor of Benenden School since 1985. Leisure pursuits include opera and bridge. Lives in London.

SHAKESPEAR, Felicity
Clarke Willmott & Clarke, Taunton (01823) 329 845
fshakespear@cw-c.co.uk
Specialisation: Partner, head of family department. Has specialised in family law since qualification and is now Leader of eight specialist lawyers. All areas of family law are covered, in particular, high asset ancillary relief claims involving companies, pensions and farmers, and also public law child care. Acting for Mr White in a case pending in the House of Lords regarding the interest of spouses in a farming partnership on dissolution of the marriage.
Prof. Memberships: Member of Children Panel. SFLA Regional Committee Member, Family Law Panel Assessor, Law Society.
Career: Qualified in 1973. Partner with *Darlington & Parkinson* (Ealing, London) 1985/1986. President of Central and South Middlesex Law Society. Joined *Clarke Willmott & Clarke* in 1986, becoming a partner in 1989.
Personal: Born 1948. LLB Southampton. Leisure interests include gardening, bridge and running a large apple orchard.

SHEEHAN, Wendy
Balfour & Manson, Edinburgh (0131) 200 1200
ws@balfour-manson.co.uk
Specialisation: Practises solely in Family Law both in the Sheriff Court and Court of Session dealing with inter alia financial provision on divorce, parental rights, residence and contact cases, spousal maintenance/CSA and separation agreements. Appointed as an independent court reporter in child residence and contact cases. Also accredited by the Law Society of Scotland as a family law specialist and mediator with a substantial mediation practice.
Prof. Memberships: Family Law Association, Notary Public, vice convenor of C.A.L.M.
Career: Born 26th December 1968. Educated at St. George's School for Girls and University of Aberdeen. Admitted as a solicitor in 1991.
Personal: Lives in Edinburgh. Author for Butterworths Family Law Service, Chair of Couple Counselling Lothian. Leisure interests include music and water sports.

SHELTON, Erica
Charles Russell, London (020) 7203 5000
ericas@cr-law.co.uk
Specialisation: Family law, ancillary relief, particularly experienced in dealing with cases where there are trusts involved, and children. Acted for wife in Conran v Conran.
Prof. Memberships: Law Society, SFLA, Association of Contentions Trust and probate practitioners.
Career: Articles *Gregory Rawcliffe & Co* 1982-84. Admitted March 1984. 1984-86 at *Birkseck Montagues*–assistant. 1986–April 2000 at *Rooks Rider*, assistant then partner and head of family law from 1991. April 2000– *Charles Russell.*
Personal: History and Politics–Queen Mary College London University, then College of Law. Married with 7 year old son, Edward. Enjoy reading, theatre, entertaining, tennis and swimming.

SHEPHERD, Nigel G.
Addleshaw Booth & Co, Manchester (0161) 934 6000
ngs@addleshaw-booth.co.uk
Partner in family law practice
Specialisation: Main areas of practice are financial issues with particular emphasis on medium to high net worth cases, and private Children Act work; lectures on family law topics; regular contributor to family law publications, print and broadcast media.
Prof. Memberships: SFLA (National Chairman 1995-97, North West Chairman 1987-91); Law Society; National Council for Family Proceedings.
Career: BA (Hons) Manchester Polytechnic 1978; Married: two daughters; Lives in Stockport; Leisure interests include sport, music and wine.

SHRIMPTON, Julie E.
Tozers, Plymouth (01752) 206460

SILVER, Raphael
Silver Fitzgerald, Cambridge (01223) 562001
Senior litigation partner.
Specialisation: Childcare, crime.
Career: Admitted 1984. Litigator/advocate. Dealt with all types of serious crime before turning to Childcare work in 1991. Now handles mainly public law children work acting for children, parents and local authority: adoptions and related litigation for those who have been in care.
Prof. Memberships: Law Society Children Panel. SFLA. Associate Member NAGALRO and BAAF.
Personal: Born 1960, Liverpool. Graduated Durham University. Married. Lives in Saffron Walden. Interests include cricket, gardening and wine.

SIMPSON, Barbara
Boodle Hatfield, Oxford (01865) 790744
bsimpson@boodlehatfield.co.uk
Specialisation: All types of privately funded children law and ancillary relief issues. In particular dealing with substantial financial cases including those with an international element or complex commercial or pension issues. Experienced in emergency work including injunctions and strong contacts with London office.
Prof. Memberships: First chair of Solicitors Family Law Association Oxford.
Career: Qualified 1974. Head of family law teams in *Cole & Cole* since1984. Deputy District Judge in Principal Registry of Family Division. Became a partner at *Boodle Hatfield* in 1999.
Personal: Born 31 March 1948. Educated at Durham University. Leisure pursuits include skiing, books and family life.

SIMPSON, Jane
Manches, London (020) 7404 4433
jane.simpson@manches.co.uk
Partner and head of family law department.
Specialisation: Deals in particular with divorce and complex financial issues, children, tax, and the commercial implications of divorce and separation; international aspects of divorce and separation and forum shopping. Has addressed and chaired many family law conferences and seminars, and appeared on radio and television. Member of the Lord Chancellor's Family Law Advisory Board.
Prof. Memberships: Solicitors Family Law Association, International Academy of Matrimonial Lawyers, Law Society. Non-executive director of the Tavistock Portman NHS Trust.
Career: Qualified in 1967. Marriage Guidance Counsellor 1972-77. Joined *Manches* as a partner and head of family law Department in 1977. Member of Management Board from 1990. Founder member of Solicitors Family Law Association (1982), Chairman of its Education Committee 1982-90, Chairman 1993-95. Member of Lord Chancellor's Advisory Committee 1991-2000.
Personal: Born 15th July 1942. Educated at Channing School, Highgate, and London University 1961-64. Leisure interests include reading, walking, music and food. Lives in London. Two adult daughters and son.

SISSON, David
Eversheds, Norwich (01603) 272727
Specialisation: Exclusively family law, with emphasis on finance.
Prof. Memberships: SFLA; SFLA International Committee.
Career: Qualified 1977. Partner *Eversheds* 1985. Head of *Eversheds* family law department since 1991.
Personal: Born 5th May 1951. Leisure interests include bridge and golf.

SMITH, Caroline
Loudons WS, Edinburgh (0131) 662 4193
loudons@btconnect.com
Partner dealing with family law .
Specialisation: Fifteen years experience dealing exclusively with family law. Accredited by Law Society of Scotland as specialist in family law and as a family mediator. Member of local panel of reporting officers/curators ad litem for adoption proceedings. Prepares child welfare reports for Sheriff Court.
Prof. Memberships: Family Law Association, Edinburgh Bar Association. W.S. Society, Comprehensive Accredited Lawyer Mediators.
Career: Qualified MB.Ch.B 1979 and worked as hospital doctor 1979-82. Assistant *Warner & Co.* 1985-88. Qualified LLB 1986. Assistant (Litigation) *Morton Fraser Milligan WS* 1988-93. Joined *Loudons WS* as an associate in October 1993. Partner July 1994.
Personal: Born 23rd June 1955. Educated St. Denis School, Edinburgh 1960-73 and Edinburgh University 1973-79 and 1982-85. Leisure interests include horses, swimming, reading. Lives in Edinburgh.

SMITH, Michael
Mincoffs, Newcastle-upon-Tyne (0191) 281 6151
Specialisation: Family Law.
Prof. Memberships: Secretary of the North East Region SFFA, member of Family Law Panel.
Career: Qualified in 1974.
Personal: Jogging, keeping fit and speedway racing. Together with Mary Smith probably representing the only husband and wife family law team in the country.

SPEKER, Barry N.
Samuel Phillips & Co, Newcastle upon Tyne (0191) 232 8451
Senior partner and head of litigation department.
Specialisation: Medical negligence, personal injury, family (including child care and adoption) and employment law. Legal adviser for Newcastle Health Authority and various NHS trusts, NSPCC and Barnardo's North East. Regular lecturer on child care law, medical negligence and employment law. Affiliate of Institute of Risk Management.
Prof. Memberships: Law Society (Medical Negligence and Children Panels). President Newcastle Law Society 2000.
Career: Qualified 1971 while with *Leigh Gold & Co*, then joined *Samuel Phillips & Co*. Partner 1973, senior partner 1987. Part time Employment Tribunal Chairman.
Personal: Born 28th June 1947. Heaton Grammar School, London University. Member of Mensa. Leisure pursuits include golf, debating and the Times Crossword.

STAKES, John Anthony
Gordons Cranswick Solicitors, Leeds (0113) 245 2450
mail@gordonscranswick.co.uk
Specialisation: Family Law: Divorce, Finance, Cohabitation and Abduction.
Career: Qualified 1971. Partner 1975
Prof. Memberships: Former National SFLA Regional Press Officer and currently Chairman of West and North Yorkshire SFLA.
Personal: Married with two children and three step-children. Leisure interests include walking, amateur dramatics and cricket.

STANCZYK, Julia
Miles Preston & Co, London (020) 7583 0583
milespreston@aol.com
Specialisation: Financial cases, often involving complex and international issues; pre-marriage contracts; cohabitation cases and private Children Act cases. Instructed in the leading case on reciprocal enforcement of maintenance orders: K v. M, M and L (Financial Relief: Foreign Orders) 1998 2 FLR 59.
Prof. Memberships: SFLA
Career: Articled *Radcliffes & Co*; partner 1990; partner *Miles Preston & Co* 1994. One of the first SFLA accredited specialists (complex financial cases/ emergency relief) 1999.
Personal: Educated Haberdashers' Aske's Girls' School, Elstree and Southampton University.

STOWE, Marilyn J.
Grahame Stowe, Bateson, Leeds (0113) 260 6191
famlaw@grahame-stowe-bateson.co.uk
Specialisation: Deals in particular with divorce and complex financial issues, children, tax, commercial implications of divorce and separation.
Prof. Memberships: The Law Society, The Law Society Family Law Panel.
Career: Qualified in 1980. Former lecturer in English Law at University of Le Mans, France. Partner in *Grahame Stowe Bateson* 1982. Chair Child Support Appeals Tribunal 1993 to date. Chair Social Security Appeals Tribunal 1994 to date. Chief Assessor and Chief Examiner of the Law Society's Family Law Panel 1998 to date.
Publications: Author; 'Divorce–A New Beginning' published 1993.
Personal: Born 30/4/54. Attended Leeds Girls High School 1965–1972 and University of Leeds 1973-1976. Leisure interests include distance running. Married with one son. Lives in Leeds.

TAIT, Fiona
Drummond Miller WS, Edinburgh (0131) 226 5151
ft@drumil.demon.co.uk
Partner.
Specialisation: Head of *Drummond Miller*'s family law team which deals with divorce, financial provision, child law, child abductions and children's hearings. Accredited specialist in family law. Tutor at the University of Edinburgh LLB Course in commercial law (1990-97).
Prof. Memberships: Law Society of Scotland, Edinburgh Bar Association Council Member (1993-96).
Career: Qualified in 1991. Joined *Drummond Miller* in 1989, becoming a Partner in 1996.
Personal: Born 9th January 1966. Attended University of Edinburgh: LLB (Hons) 1988, DipLP 1989. Lives in Edinburgh.

TAYLOR, Norman S.
Zermansky & Partners, Leeds (0113) 245 9766
norman@zermansky.demon.co.uk
Specialisation: Ancillary relief in divorce and cohabitation disputes.
Prof. Memberships: West and North Yorkshire S.F.L.A. Committee.
Career: Qualified July 1975. With *Zermansky & Partners* since February 1974, Head of family department. Educated at University of Newcastle upon Tyne (LL.B)
Personal: Born 14 January 1951. Married with three children. 1st Dan Black Belt Japan Karate Association (retired). Lead guitarist in charity rock band.

THORNEYCROFT, Philip M.
Wolferstans, Plymouth (01752) 663295
Partner 1990. Head of Matrimonial Department.
Specialisation: Main areas of practice are child-care and family law. Acts on behalf of parents and children in care proceedings and related matters. Acts for private and legally aided clients in divorce, ancilliary relief, injunctions and domestic violence matters. Head of the firms mediation unit. Has made a number of appearances on local radio dealing with such issues as sexual abuse, cohabitation contracts and the effect of pensions on divorce.
Prof. Memberships: Solicitors Family Law Association, local committee memberMember of Children Panel, a founder member of the Plymouth Child-care Support Group. Associate member of the National Association of Guardians ad Litem and Reporting Officers. SFLA trained family mediator.
Career: Qualified in 1982. Joined *Wolferstans* in 1982, becoming a Partner in 1990. Member of the Plymouth Hockey Club.
Personal: Born 2nd December 1957. Attended Chesterfield Grammar School 1970-76, Hull University 1976-79 and Chester Law College 1979-80. Leisure interests include hockey, skiing, music and Sheffield Wednesday. Lives in Plymouth.

TOOTH, Ray
Sears Tooth, London (020) 7499 5599
Specialisation: All aspects of matrimonial matters with particular emphasis on financial cases, often of an international nature. Has habitually been involved on difficult cases.
Prof. Memberships: The Law Society.
Career: Dragon School. Oxford. Kings School, Canterbury. Univeristy College Oxford.
Personal: Extensive horse racing interests, including breeding.

TRUEX, David
International Family Law Chambers, London (020) 7583 5040
truex@internationalfamilylaw.com
Specialisation: SFLA accredited specialist family lawyer (1999). Particular expertise in multi-jurisdictional disputes involving forum, recognition, enforcement and analysis of foreign laws.
Prof. Memberships: Chair, SFLA International Committee; Chair, UK Host Committee 2001 World Congress on Family Law and the Rights of Children and Youth. Member: SFLA; Law Society; NCFP; ABA; AFCC; Law Council of Australia Family Law Section; Law Institute of Victoria.
Career: Qualified Australia 1974; England and Wales 1990. Founded *David Truex and Company* (now *International Family Law Chambers) 1990.*
Personal: Born 7 March 1949 Washington, DC. Educated USA and Australia. Enjoys creative thinking, problem solving and fracturing French and German grammaticals.

WARD, Helen
Manches, London (020) 7404 4433
helen.ward@manches.co.uk
Partner in family law department.
Specialisation: Handles all areas of family law, particularly complex financial aspects of matrimonial and relationship breakdown involving an international element.
Prof. Memberships: Solicitors Family Law Association, International Academy of Matrimonial Lawyers, Law Society.

Career: Qualified in 1978. Partner at *Ward Bowie* from 1978, which subsequently became *Penningtons*. Joined *Manches* as a partner in July 1994. Deputy District Judge in the Principal Registry and Recorder.
Personal: Born 28th May 1951. Attended King Alfred School, London 1955-69 and Birmingham University 1970-73. Family come first but leisure interests include music, theatre, tennis and gardening.

WAY, Philip
Addleshaw Booth & Co, Leeds (0113) 209 2000
Solicitor in Family Law Department.
Specialisation: Deals with all aspects of privately funded family law, in particular high value applications for ancillary relief. SFLA trained mediator. Contributor to 'Humphreys Family Proceedings', 'Pensions on Family Breakdown', 'Insolvency on Family Breakdown' and 'Family Finance and Tax'. Regular author of articles for legal journals.
Prof. Memberships: SFLA. Accredited SFLA specialist family lawyer with particular specialisms in dealing with substantial assets on divorce and emergency financial procedures on divorce. Associate of UK College of Family Mediators.
Career: Educated at Durham University. Joined firm in September 1990.
Personal: Married. Lives in Wakefield.

WHITE, Iain
Cozens-Hardy & Jewson, Norwich (01603) 625231
Family department.
Specialisation: Specialises in child-related work, divorce and matrimonial finance.
Prof. Memberships: Original member of the Children Panel. Member of the Family Law Panel and Solicitors Family Law Association. Representative on the Norwich Family Court Business Committee.
Career: Qualified 1977. Partner 1986.

WILKINS, Beth D.
Pannone & Partners, Manchester (0161) 909 3000
Partner and Joint Head of Family Department.
Specialisation: Handles all aspects of marriage breakdown, matrimonial finance and private law relating to children. Advises on co-habitation and pre-nuptial agreements. A large percentage of work comprises acting for professionals and high-net-worth individuals, and in cases with a corporate/business element.
Prof. Memberships: Member of SFLA National Committee and Chair of Good Practice Committee; SFLA North West Branch press officer. Regular speaker, lecturer and broadcaster on family law topics.
Career: Qualified in 1981. Formerly partner and head of Family Department *Maurice Rubin Clare* (now *DAC*); partner *Pannone & Partners* 1995.
Personal: Leisure interests include gluttony, theatre, cinema, the arts and travel. Lives in Manchester.

WILLIAMS, Frances
Larby Williams, Cardiff (029) 20472100

WILLIAMS, Gail
Robertsons, Cardiff (029) 20237777

WILLIAMS, Ian
Robertsons, Cardiff (029) 20237777

WILLIAMS, Jane R.
Larby Williams, Cardiff (029) 20472100

WILSON, Bruce
Mills & Reeve, Norwich (01603) 693 207
bruce.wilson@mills-reeve.com
Specialisation: High value and complex applications for ancillary relief with emphasis on landed estates. Partner deals with high net worth individuals seeking advice on divorce and family matters; has vast experience in large landed estates and farming cases supported by the private client, tax and agricultural departments. Has written and lectured on pensions and divorce.
Prof. Memberships: Solicitors' Family Law Association.

WOODS, Paul L.
Wolferstans, Plymouth (01752) 663295
Family/Matrimonial
Specialisation: Specialising in divorce for private and legally aided clients, including ancillary relief and advocacy.
Career: Qualified in 1975; Became partner with *Rundle McDonald & Rendle* 1979; Became partner with *Wolferstans* following merger in 1992; Part time Chairman Social Security Appeal Tribunal 1988 to date; President Plymouth Law Society 1996-97; Founder member & past committee member Devon & Cornwall SFLA.
Personal: Year of birth: 1949; town of residence: Plymouth. Wellford Grammer School, Durham; Liverpool University; LL.B. 1972. Main leisure activities, clubs: Past Chairman, Plymouth Albion Rugby Football Club; member St Mellion and Yelverton Golf Clubs; golf, rugby, theatre.

WOODWARD, David W.
TLT Solicitors, Bristol (0117) 917 7501
dwoodward@TLTSolicitors.com
Partner in Family Law Department.
Specialisation: Main areas of practice are divorce, ancillary relief and children. Acted in Richardson 1994 1FLR 188, B v. B 1995 IFLR 9 and Richardson (No2) 1996 2 FLR 617. Contributor to Western Daily Press. Experience includes cable television work, LNTV and occasional lecturing.
Prof. Memberships: SFLA, Law Society, Chairman Bristol SFLA. Member of Family Law Panel. Accredited member of SFLA
Career: Qualified in 1975. Joined *Trumps* in 1979, becoming a partner in 1981. *Trumps* merged with Bristol law firm *Lawrence Tucketts* to become *TLT Solicitors* on May 1 2000. Heads up family law team of twelve.
Personal: Born 10th January 1950. Holds an LLB from Bristol. Leisure interests include cycling, badminton and cricket. Lives in Bristol.

WRIGHT, Barbara J.
Thomson Snell & Passmore, Tunbridge Wells (01892) 510000
bwright@ts-p.co.uk
Partner and head of family department.
Specialisation: Deals with all areas of family breakdown. Particular interest in financial aspects.
Prof. Memberships: Member of the College of Family Mediators and Solicitors Family Law Association. Founding Chair of Kent Solicitors Family Law Association and member of National Committee of SFLA from March 1997 to 1998.
Career: Qualified 1979. Joined *Thomson Snell & Passmore* in 1987. Equity partner from 1995. Honorary Legal Adviser to West Kent Relate. Accredited mediator and supervisor trained by the Family Mediators Association.
Personal: Born 16th March 1955. Honours Law degree Sheffield University. Second Class Honours in Part II Law Society's examinations. Interests include English and French history, current affairs, cuisine. Lives in the Tunbridge Wells area.

YOUNG, Hugh
Freethcartwright, Nottingham (0115) 9369 369
Specialisation: Partner in the family law department and head of private client services specialising in matrimonial work.
Career: Articled *Simmons & Simmons*. Qualified 1970. Partner in *Freeth Cartwright* (now *Freeth Cartwright Hunt Dickins*) since 1973.
Personal: Born 1943. Educated at Ampleforth and Pembroke College, Cambridge. Resides in Nottingham. Married with four children. Interests include all sports, principally now as spectator.

YOUNG, Ian
Young & Lee, Birmingham (0121) 633 3233

FINANCIAL SERVICES

London: 402; South West: 404; Midlands: 404; The North: 404; Scotland: 405; *Profiles*: 406

OVERVIEW: With the eventual passing of the Financial Services & Markets Act in June and the growth of online financial services, this has been a busy year for financial services lawyers. Lawyers' opinions have been sought on the implications of the new Act throughout its tortuous evolution. Some of the problems lawyers foresee include new penalties relating to promotional issues, and the impact of the new Human Rights Act. In addition, there is a fear that the relationship between the business community and the FSA will become more confrontational, leading to more US style litigation.

RESEARCH APPROVED BY BMRB: *For this edition,* Chambers' *researchers conducted 6083 interviews – 4408 with law firms, 598 with barristers and 1077 with clients.*

The validity of the research was scrutinised by BMRB International, who audited both the methodology and the results at our offices in July 2000. They interviewed Chambers' *researchers and cross-checked sample interviews. Details of the audit appear on page 7.*

LEADING IN-HOUSE LAWYERS

Mitchell CALLER, Senior Vice-President & Associate General Counsel, *The Chase Manhattan Bank*

Brian HARTE, Head of Compliance for Europe, Middle East & Africa, *The Chase Manhattan Bank*

Therese MILLER, Managing Director & General Counsel, *Goldman Sachs International*, US qualified only

Andrew WHITTAKER, Deputy General Counsel, *Financial Services Authority*

The widely recommended **Mitch Caller** has *"good commercial acumen"* and *"understands the legal risks and difficulties."* The *"fearfully good"* **Brian Harte** is acknowledged as a *"well organised thinker"* and a *"man with presence."* He is praised for his regulatory work and for being the *"only lawyer on top of the new FSM Act."* **Therese Miller** is known to be *"very practical"* undertaking *"very thorough and no nonsense"* work. The *"first-rate"* **Andrew Whittaker** is *"held in high regard"* and praised for the *"public service ethos"* imbuing his work at the FSA.

In-House lawyers profiles: page 1177

LONDON

LEADING FIRMS

FINANCIAL SERVICES • London	Ptnrs	Assts
❶ Clifford Chance	22	66
Linklaters	3	20
❷ Allen & Overy	8	12
Freshfields Bruckhaus Deringer	24	55
❸ Norton Rose	6	*
Simmons & Simmons	4	6
SJ Berwin & Co	4	5
❹ CMS Cameron McKenna	8	15
Lovells	5	-
Slaughter and May	9	10
Travers Smith Braithwaite	4	5

LEADING INDIVIDUALS
❶ **ABRAMS Charles** SJ Berwin & Co
HERRINGTON Timothy Clifford Chance
MORTON Guy Freshfields Bruckhaus Deringer
NELSON Paul Linklaters
❷ **CHAMBERLAIN Margaret** Travers Smith Braithwaite
MORRIS Simon CMS Cameron McKenna
❸ **BAGGE James** Norton Rose
STONES Richard Lovells
SYKES Annabel Freshfields Bruckhaus Deringer
❹ **FOX Ruth** Slaughter and May
LITTLE Tamasin SJ Berwin & Co
MARSDEN Tim Norton Rose
PHILLIPS Paul Allen & Overy
SLATER Richard Simmons & Simmons

Within each band, firms are listed alphabetically. See **Profiles** on page 406

Clifford Chance *"Moving away to become a global entity."* As in other areas, the financial services work of this colossus is a feature of its global, particularly European reach. The international financial markets group combines lawyers based in offices in Western and Eastern Europe, America, Asia and the Middle East. The mergers with Rogers & Wells, Pünder, Volhard, Weber & Axter and Faltz & Kremer have added leading financial services practices in three jurisdictions. The firm therefore has an integrated global advisory capacity at an impressive level. While the London office is generally mentioned in the same breath as Linklaters as the leading pair, a minority sees evidence of a gap. *"They've just got so many resources."* In advisory work, **Tim Herrington** is widely praised by peers as *"an excellent financial services generalist, who is very sensible and can cover just about any area."* The investigation/disputes side can draw upon the experience of a former director of the Serious Fraud Office. Most work is on multi-jurisdictional projects for global financial institutions. Workload includes e-commerce and retail business, financial infrastructure and strategic advice. Clients are drawn from financial regulation bodies, investment and commercial banks, asset management companies and investment companies. The team advised CEDEL International on the merger of its custody, clearing and settlement business with Deutsche Clearing to create Clearstream International, the first merger between an international and a national central securities depository. **Clients:** Merrill Lynch; International Swaps and Derivatives Association; Futures and Options Association; Financial Services Authority; Clearstream International; International Petroleum Exchange.

Linklaters *"A leading firm, no dispute."* Acknowledged alongside Clifford Chance in the premier division for financial services, particularly for its regulatory advice. While not possessing the dedicated numbers of Clifford Chance, the department can call upon FMG representatives in Hong Kong and New York. The recent merger with German alliance partner Oppenhoff & Rädler should add to the firm's global coverage. *"Individualistic"* partner **Paul Nelson**, who is "intellectually agile," drives the practice. The firm is distinctive for its Blue Flag service, a screen-based information data base for use by financial markets participants doing business in Europe,

Asia Pacific and South America. Its success has led some to wonder whether the focus is more on a *"commoditised than transactional"* operation. A highlight for the firm was providing extensive advice on the establishment of new electronic exchanges and interdealer brokers such as Brokertec and E-Crossnet. Clients are drawn from investment banks, broker-dealers, and portfolio management clients. The workload is split between internal services provided by financial institutions, global custody and collateral management derivatives products, foreign exchange, and stock loans. **Clients:** Investment Companies; banks; broker-dealers.

Allen & Overy The firm is highly rated in this area in recognition of the size of its general banking practice, which is seen as its base for regulatory and contentious work. The financial services group provides cross-disciplinary advice from the banking, capital markets, corporate, tax and litigation departments. However, there is some concern that the team is spread too thinly. **Paul Phillips** leads the team and is *"strong"* on Lloyds and Takeover Panel work. Recent work has focused on bank capital regulation, e-finance and e-banking, UK retail regulation, financial exchanges, the restructuring of the UK financial regulatory system, swaps and derivatives markets, and sovereign and governmental work. A highlight deal in e-banking was advising the Co-operative Bank on its banking venture. On the regulation side, the regulations investigations and proceedings group comprises nine fee earners and handles investigations and disciplinary proceedings, principally advising banks and financial institutions. Recent work has involved dealing with major investigations by the SFA and IMRO. Also advised Credit Suisse Financial Products on matters arising from regulatory inspection of its Tokyo branch by the Japanese Financial Services Agency. An international regulatory capability has been developed due to the regulatory clients; regulatory and investments products being a notable feature of its Asia Banking Practice. **Clients:** ABN Amro; Bank of Scotland; Deutsche Bank; Barclays Capital; British Gas Pensions Funds; Chase Asset Management; CSFB; Salomon Brothers; Allied Carpets plc; Avon Cosmetics Ltd; Britannia Building Society; the Financial Services Authority; Merrill Lynch; UBS; Phillips & Drew.

Freshfields Bruckhaus Deringer *"First-rate firm which works well as a team."* Noted especially for regulation work, its financial services client base is served by a large team which includes a non-contentious advisory group encompassing the investment funds team, a contentious team and the newly formed financial institutions group which deals with transaction work for institutional clients. Head of the financial services group **Guy Morton** is rated by peers as a *"lawyer you can do business with."* His work this year has included advising Salomon Smith Barney on its joint venture with Nikko Securities and Morgan Stanley on the establishment of a UK bank. He is among a number of lawyers who gave evidence before the joint committee of the House of Lords and House of Commons on the Financial Services & Markets Bill. Partner **Annabel Sykes** is respected amongst practitioners as *"a good details person."* The group advised Bank of England on the merger of the CGO and CMO services with CREST and the Royal Bank of Scotland on an unincorporated, contractual joint venture for financial services to be marketed globally to British Airways customers. **Clients:** AIG; Alliance & Leicester; Bank of England; British Bankers Association; Deutsche Bank; Goldman Sachs; ISMA; Merrill Lynch; Nomura International; Prudential Corporation; Takeover Panel; UBS; Zurich.

Norton Rose *"Solid and cohesive"* firm with an impressive client base whose key focus is on regulatory investigation and enforcement work, marketing of collective investment schemes, and acquisitions and mergers in the fund industry. Recent work has included advising (in conjunction with Skadden Arps) Salomon Smith Barney on its acquisition of Schroders. A significantly smaller practice than firms higher in the list, it is nevertheless acknowledged for the speed of its progression. *"They put a lot of work in, and it is amazing how quickly they have moved up."* One of the five core non-contentious partners, **Tim Marsden** has a focus in collective investment schemes although he is seen by some as more of an investment funds man. The non-contentious side has recently been bolstered by a new recruit from Pinsent Curtis. While there are no full-time assistants, the group can call upon 25 core non-contentious and five contentious assistants as the occasion demands. Sole contentious partner, **James Bagge** is considered *"good on enforcement."* A member of the consulting group advising the FSA on financial reform, he has acted for the Board of Banking Supervision and LIFFE and conducted inquiries under the Banking Act. **Clients:** Collins Stewart; Foreign & Colonial; Merrill Lynch; Salomon Smith Barney; Employees of CSFB; PIA Complaints Commissioner; Amerindo Investment Inc; Energy Investments; Bank of Ireland; Gartmore Investment; LIFFE, HSBC.

Simmons & Simmons For observers, Simmons & Simmons financial services practice is a *"curious animal,"* closely combining its regulatory practice with its well-regarded investment funds capacity. It is known particularly for its hedge funds advice, and in common with other firms, has seen a sharp increase in IT related work for traditional clients such as banks. The firm presents a clearer picture in contentious work, and is held to be *"very capable on sticky assignments."* The disparate elements of the firm's financial services groups will be grouped as a one floor financial markets department later this year. Partner **Richard Slater** receives a good following, and is held to be *"top class"* although his talents are more closely associated with investment funds work. The investment team, alongside SJ Berwin, advised the Shadow Front Bench Treasury team on the Financial Services & Markets Act during its passage through Parliament. Other work includes acting for Metalgesellschaft (MG) in setting up a world-wide trading platform for metals. **Clients:** MG; financial institutions.

SJ Berwin & Co Financial services work for this firm is seen to be leveraged from its strength in corporate finance, venture capital and private client work. *"Top class"* out and out financial services campaigner **Charles Abrams** drives the practice. *"He lives for it."* He has spent much of the last year as an unpaid advisor to the Shadow Treasury Team on the recently passed Financial Services & Marketing Bill specialising in financial promotion, the proposed office of market abuse and the single European passport. Partner **Tamasin Little** is noted for advisory and venture capital work. The financial services and marketing group is augmented by the cross-departmental finance division. It has a strength in regulation issues and advises on e-commerce initiatives, SRO rules and lobbying, disputes with regulators, structuring of financial products, and Stock Exchange rules. Recent work has included the establishment and authorisation of internet brokers Sharepeople.com and advising on the MBO of the NatWest Equity Partners Group from NatWest Bank. **Clients:** Interactive Investor International; DLJ; Quilters; Virgin Direct; Sharepeople.com; Electra; Brewin Dolphin; SLK Global Markets; NatWest Equity Partners Group.

CMS Cameron McKenna Said to be performing *"top level FSA work,"* the firm *"definitely has credibility."* Predominantly transaction-driven practice with UK investment fund manager client base and *"strong"* pension mis-selling work. Partner **Simon Morris**, who *"knows his stuff,"* is experienced in the fund management and life assurance industries and is noted for regulatory enforcement work, having been instructed in over sixty FSA disciplinary proceedings. The team recently won headline work from Norton Rose to act for HSBC on the $1 billion joint venture with Merrill Lynch to create a global internet bank. Also acted on the acquisition by KBC Bank NV of the global financial products business of DE Shaw & Co. The team has referred an increasing amount of work to its overseas offices, particularly in South East Asia. **Clients:** Abbey Life; Abbey National; Aon Group; Argyll Asset Managers; BUPA; Commerzbank; HSBC; Legal & General; Nationwide Building Society; Old Mutual.

Lovells Leading individual **Richard Stones** heads the financial services group which specialises in securities and market regulation, product marketing issues and investment funds. He is rated as a good generalist with *"sound technical skills,"* particularly in retail asset management and insurance matters. *"A quietly sensible lawyer, I treat his opinion with respect."*

Through its international offices the firm has financial markets lawyers in the USA, Germany and Asia. The financial services group liaises with lawyers in the corporate finance, capital markets, pensions, banking, intellectual property and information technology, City litigation and tax departments. Other work conducted by the firm includes advice on retail banking and consumer credit law and regulation. Clients include fund managers, securities dealers, banks, lenders and insurance companies. **Clients:** Financial institutions; insurance companies.

Slaughter and May Although this is not perceived as a core area for the firm, commentators acknowledge that *"they are starting to build."* Partner **Ruth Fox** is recognised for her finance skills, and is felt to possess a *"good intellect and a sound grasp of the issues."* The team reports an increase in instruction for internet start-up clients, having acted on the flotation of Prudential's internet bank, Egg. Work over the last year has included advising a number of banks and other financial institutions on the regulatory aspects of proposed take-overs and mergers, proposed offerings of products and services over the internet. Other work included advising on the establishment of a new investment exchange. **Clients:** Abbey National plc; JP Morgan; Prudential.

Travers Smith Braithwaite Renowned for its *"attentive client service,"* the firm is also notable for the quality of its leading lawyer and its key client CRESTCo. Chairman of the British Venture Capital Association Regulatory Committee, **Margaret Chamberlain** has been principally responsible for negotiations between the venture capital community and the FSA and the Treasury concerning the regulation of venture capital firms under the FSMA. *"Personable and not over aggressive,"* she has a good knowledge of settlement issues and *"sees the problems quickly."* The team advises CREST-Cow on all aspects of its business development, and has a niche in trading, securities settlement and payment systems issues as well as being active in advising pension fund clients on settling their investment management, custody and related business. **Clients:** CRESTCo Ltd; Bloomberg LP; Bank Brussels Lambert; Pension Funds.

SOUTH WEST

FINANCIAL SERVICES • South West	Ptnrs	Assts
❶ **Burges Salmon** Bristol	⚐	⚐

Within each band, firms are listed alphabetically.
⚐ Figures unavailable at time of going to press.

Burges Salmon Still the leading practice in the region, it acts for a number of management groups, advising on compliance issues, OEIC issues, amalgamations and conversions. **Clients:** J. Rothschild Assurance plc; Exeter Investment Group plc.

MIDLANDS

FINANCIAL SERVICES • Midlands	Ptnrs	Assts
❶ **Pinsent Curtis** Birmingham	2	3
❷ **Wragge & Co** Birmingham	1	5

Within each band, firms are listed alphabetically.

Pinsent Curtis Cross-departmental unit rather than unified department is renowned for its pensions mis-selling work. The team advises on corporate finance transactional advice, compliance and enforcement advice in relation to the FSA and pension mis-selling review work. Clients comprise financial institutions including Fortune 100 company New York Life. The latter results in advice to clients in corporate, insurance, broking and intermediary fields. The contentious workload in particular is a bulk phenomenon with over 3,300 pensions mis-selling instructions on the books. Work handled this year has included recovering a multi-million pound sum on a pension mis-selling warranty claim. Currently involved in four contentious mis-selling matters in each case of the value of £10 million. **Clients:** New York Life; DBS; Britannic Assurance.

Wragge & Co The firm's clientele centres on Midlands based financial companies including building societies, banks, regional life associations and insurance companies. Additionally it has advised a utility setting up a futures exchange and the regional subsidiaries of national concerns. The team's lawyers all come from in-house financial services positions and their work includes Treasury and capital markets work for balance sheet management, interest rate exposure management and ISDA swap agreements. Clients are advised on all aspects of the financial services regulation regime, consumer credit and data protection issues. This year the team has advised the Derbyshire Building Society on its £125 million floating rate note debut issue. Also advised a building society on a euro medium term note in excess of £650 million. **Clients:** Chelsea Building Society; Lloyds TSB Life Assurance; West Bromwich Building Society; Lloyds TSB; Exiode Corporation; British Energy; Police Mutual Society; Norwich and Peterborough Building Society.

THE NORTH

FINANCIAL SERVICES • The North	Ptnrs	Assts
❶ **Addleshaw Booth & Co** Leeds	2	1
Dickinson Dees Newcastle upon Tyne	1	2

LEADING INDIVIDUALS
❶ **GERVASIO James** James Kendall
LUMSDEN Christopher Chaffe Street
LYNCH Malcolm Wrigleys

Within each band, firms are listed alphabetically See **Profiles** on page 406

Addleshaw Booth & Co Financial services team split between the advisory/regulatory department and the finance litigation team. The team acts for banks, building societies, friendly societies, finance companies and insurance companies. Advised Leek Building Society on its defence against carpetbaggers and has advised housing associations on finance facilities totalling £3.75 billion over seven years. Matters covered include industry specific regulation, Ombudsman matters, Codes of Conduct lending and investment product documentation. The finance litigation team has a particular strength in asset finance and leasing, and advises banks, building societies and other financial institutions on claims for and against financial providers. **Clients:** NatWest; Royal Bank of Scotland, 3i; Abbey National; Bradford and Bingley Society; National Australia Group Ltd; HSBC.

Dickinson Dees Team advises a number of banks, building societies, brokers and insurers in financial services under the related legislation and rules promulgated by relevant regulatory authorities. Areas covered include structuring financial products and terms and conditions of business. The private client team has recently expanded to form the financial planning group which advises on investment business using an in-house team of financial services professionals. **Clients:** Financial institutions; insurance companies.

Other Notable Practitioners Three practitioners in the region maintain a reputation for their work on compliance issues. **James Gervasio** at James Kendall, **Christopher Lumsden** at Chaffe Street and **Malcolm Lynch** of the newly-merged Wrigleys have all come in for their share of market support.

SCOTLAND

FINANCIAL SERVICES • Scotland	Ptnrs	Assts
❶ **Dundas & Wilson CS** Edinburgh	4	9
❷ **Dickson Minto WS** Edinburgh	2	3
Maclay Murray & Spens Glasgow	4	4
McGrigor Donald Glasgow	2	3
Shepherd & Wedderburn WS Edinburgh	2	7
Tods Murray WS Edinburgh	3	2

LEADING INDIVIDUALS
❶ **ATHANAS Christopher** Tods Murray WS
MACKAY Philip Dundas & Wilson CS
❷ **DORAN Frank** McGrigor Donald
LIVINGSTON Michael Maclay Murray & Spens
MINTO Bruce Dickson Minto WS
THURSTON SMITH Martin Tods Murray WS
WATT James Dundas & Wilson CS

Within each band, firms are listed alphabetically. *See **Profiles** on page 406*

Dundas & Wilson CS Renowned for its *"strength in depth,"* the firm has traditional strength acting for Scotland's blue chip corporates. Financial services work operates out of the banking and services department. Leading individual is **Philip Mackay** who is a *"good technical lawyer."* **James Watt** is also highly regarded in this area. The focus is on the financial services industry as a whole including banking, retail, insurance, asset management and work for building society clients such as Abbey National. A recent recruit from Slaughter and May will assist with expanding the asset and fund management client base. This year the team has acted for Bank Assurance advising on the selling of financial policies in their branches using a network of arrangements with third party operators. Other work has included major advice to the Royal Bank of Scotland on the takeover of NatWest and subsequent restructuring. **Clients:** Abbey National; Scottish Widows; Britannia Asset Management.

Dickson Minto WS Firm known for its work on demutualisations. *"They are starting to make their presence felt."* **Bruce Minto**'s work on demutualisations is seen as *"top-class."* Although the firm is involved in some contentious and FSA disciplinary matters, it focuses mainly on investment funds. Financial services work is divided between compliance advisory work, mainly for IMRO regulated clients, and advice for a wider range of clients in relation to investment business, fund raising and promotion. It also approves investment advertisements in matters such as offer documents for issue by clients who are not authorised under the FSA. In recent months the firm acted as lead adviser to RBDC and Penta Capital Partners in relation to obtaining IMRO membership. **Clients:** BlackRock; JO Hambro Capital Management; Aberforth Partners; Scottish Amicable Unit Trust Managers; Royal Bank Development Capital; Penta Capital.

Maclay Murray & Spens **Michael Livingston**, regarded as a *"totally reliable guy,"* heads a team which specialises in advice on the development of financial products, as well as compliance with, and enforcement of, legislation and SRO rulebooks. Also acts on investment management agreements, in particular for pension funds. **Clients:** Scottish Amicable Life Assurance Society; Scottish Widows Edinburgh Investment Trust.

McGrigor Donald The firm has met with some success in gaining work from new clients. A growing client base is advised on limited partnership funds, FSA rulebook work, and e-commerce issues. **Frank Doran** is highly regarded in the field. Clients include institutions, banks and fund managers. In e-commerce work, the firm has advised on Halifax's internet bank Intelligent Finance. **Clients:** Royal Bank of Scotland; Clydesdale Bank; Direct Line; Standard Life; Abbey National; Scottish Mutual; Scottish Friendly Association; Murray Johnstone.

Shepherd & Wedderburn WS Particularly noted for its work on unit trusts, the team also handles financial services regulation and compliance, including specialist transactional advice. The group also advises on retail investment products. Dealt with the launch of a number of portfolio bond products for Scottish Life International. **Clients:** Baillie Gifford & Co; Scottish Life International.

Tods Murray WS Equally well-known for its work for investment funds, the team has advised clients on a variety of financial services matters, including compliance issues. Advised a leading bank in relation to the disposal of its share registration operations. Also acted for another bank on its establishment of a centralised and enhanced share dealing service for customers, including outsourcing arrangements. The *"outstanding"* **Christopher Athanas** and **Martin Thurston Smith** remain recommended practitioners. **Clients:** Royal Bank of Scotland plc; State Street Trustees Limited.

LEADERS IN FINANCIAL SERVICES

ABRAMS, Charles
SJ Berwin & Co, London (020) 7533 2222
charles.abrams@sjberwin.com
Specialisation: Advises almost exclusively on securities law and regulatory issues including EU Directives, the marketing of investment funds, insider dealing, market abuse and the disclosure of interests in shares, primarily to investment and private banks, venture capital fund managers, stockbrokers, and corporate finance houses. Has developed a niche specialisation in advising clients on how to reorganise group structures or activities to minimise regulation and financial resources requirements, often as a result of persuading regulators to agree with helpful interpretations of EU and UK rules. Was a legal adviser to the Conservative Party's Shadow Treasury Team in relation to the Financial Services and Markets Bill from June 1999 to June 2000, especially in relation to the provisions relating to financial promotion (including on the internet), cross-border issues including the used of the 'single European passports' and market abuse. Member of the editorial advisory board of European Financial Services Law (Kluwer Law International). Writes and lectures frequently on regulatory issues. Is a member of the CBI's Financial Services Group and the APCIMS FSA Committee, and was formerly an arbitrator for SFA's Consumer Arbitration Scheme and a special adviser to IMRO on Venture Capital.
Prof. Memberships: Chartered Institute of Arbitrators.
Career: Qualified in 1976 with *Linklaters & Paines* and moved to *S J Berwin* in 1985. Became a partner in *S J Berwin* in 1988.
Publications: Co-author of a leading text book on the Financial Services Act, 'Guide to Financial Services Regulation' (CCH, 3rd Edition 1997) and contributor to 'Bond Market Compliance' (IFR) for which he wrote an analysis of the FS Act's money market exemption, 'Futures Trading Law and Regulation' (Longmans) for which he wrote an analysis of SFA's customer categorisation rules and 'International Survey of Investment Advisor Regulation' (Kluwer, 2nd Edition 1999) for which he wrote an analysis of UK regulatory law relevant to investment and fund managers.

ATHANAS, Christopher
Tods Murray WS, Edinburgh (0131) 226 4771
chris.athanas@todsmurray.co.uk
See under Investment Funds, p.

BAGGE, James
Norton Rose, London (020) 7283 6000
baggeajs@nortonrose.com
See under Fraud, p.416

CHAMBERLAIN, Margaret
Travers Smith Braithwaite, London
(020) 7295 3000
margaret.chamberlin@trowerssith.com
Specialisation: Specialist in trading, clearance, settlement, investment management and custody issues. Part of team at *Travers Smith Braithwaite* which advised The Bank of England and CREST Co Limited on the legal arrangements for the introduction of CREST and continues to advise CREST Co, including on links to overseas settlement systems, central counter party development, dematerialisation of money-market instruments and central bank money. Advises on commercial and risk issues arising out of custody relationships; on the legal and regulatory requirements relevant to the establishment and management of funds; and on a wide range of general regulatory and legal issues arising from the conduct of financial services business.
Prof. Memberships: Chairman Regulatory Committee of the British Venture Capital Association and member of BVCA Council. Member of City of London Law Society Regulatory Working Party. Contributor to Tolley's Company Law and Palmer's Company Law. Chairman of sub-Committee Q6 (Settlement and Clearance), International Bar Association.
Career: Qualified September 1985. Partner *Travers Smith Braithwaite* 1991.
Personal: Educated at University College, Oxford. Married.

DORAN, Frank
McGrigor Donald, Glasgow (0141) 248 6677
Partner in Corporate Unit.
Specialisation: Advises on securities law and regulatory issues generally including compliance with FSA Rule books, insider dealing legislation, global custody and insurance law. Also involved in the development and marketing of retail financial products and establishment and management of investment funds.
Prof. Memberships: Member of the Law Society of Scotland Investor Protection Committee.
Career: Qualified in 1985 with *Maclay Murray & Spens* and then moved to *McGrigor Donald*. Became a partner in *McGrigor Donald* in 1991.

FOX, Ruth
Slaughter and May, London (020) 7600 1200
Specialisation: Practice covers a wide range of commercial work, with an emphasis on banking and capital markets, now focusing on financial regulation. Has acted extensively for banks and also for building societies, including in relation to conversions, and for corporate trustees.
Prof. Memberships: The Law Society.
Career: Qualified in 1979 with *Slaughter and May*. Became a partner in 1986.
Personal: Born 3 October 1954. Educated at St Helena School, Chesterfield and University College, London. Married with three sons. Lives in London and Hertfordshire.

GERVASIO, James
James Kendall, Leeds (0113) 294 5059
email@keeblehawson.co.uk
Specialisation: Regulatory compliance, with particular reference to IMRO.
Prof. Memberships: Member of the Securities Institute.
Career: BSc Econ. (Hons); LLB; IMRO Compliance Officer.
Personal: Married–two adult daughters. Walking, theatre.

HERRINGTON, Timothy
Clifford Chance, London (020) 7600 1000
tim.herrington@cliffordchance.com
Specialisation: Partner specialising in financial services including mutual funds, asset management and investment trust work, securities and derivatives trading and regulatory issues, insurance, mergers and acquisitions, Stock Exchange and other corporate work for the financial services industry. Head of the firm's Global Asset Management Group.
Prof. Memberships: Member Law Society's Company Law Committee (past chairman); Vice Chairman, Investment Funds Committee; International Bar Association.
Career: Queen Mary's Grammar School, Basingstoke; Bristol University (LLB). Articled *Clifford Chance*; qualified 1978; partner Clifford Chance since 1985.
Personal: Cricket, travel, walking, gardening and wine. Born 1954; resides Sevenoaks.

LITTLE, Tamasin
SJ Berwin & Co, London (020) 7533 2222
tamasin.little@sjberwin.com
Specialisation: Specialises in financial markets and regulatory matters including structuring derivatives, funds and other investment products and advising investment managers, banks, brokers, venture capitalists and insurance companies on regulatory and related matters.
Prof. Memberships: City of London Law Society, International Bar Association, EASD Legal and Tax Committee, Futures and Options Association Legal Scrutiny Committee, Financial Services Authority Internal Advisory Committee on Authorisation Manual.
Career: First class BA Jurisprudence, Oxford, LLM London School of Economics. Legal Associate seconded to the Bank of England's Legal Risk Review Committee 1991/2. Partner *Stephenson Harwood* 1992-1996. Partner *S J Berwin & Co* Financial Services Group 1996 to date.
Publications: Editor of Bond Markets: 'Law & Regulation' (Sweet & Maxwell 1999).

LIVINGSTON, Michael B
Maclay Murray & Spens, Glasgow
(0141) 248 5011
mbl@maclaymurrayspens.co.uk
Specialisation: Partner specialising in corporate finance and financial services. Particular experience working with public companies and in the insurance sector. Advises on listings, rights issues and takeovers and financial services regulatory matters. Has also advised on insurance demutualisations.
Career: Strathclyde University (LL.B First Class Hons 1979, LLM 1981). After qualifying, spent 7 years working in corporate finance and asset finance with Noble Grossart and with Edinburgh Financial Trust. Corporate Development Director of Lilley plc (1990-92). Joined *Maclay Murray & Spens* in 1992.
Personal: Born 1958.

LUMSDEN, Christopher
Chaffe Street, Manchester (0161) 236 5800
See under Banking, p.119

LYNCH, Malcolm
Malcolm Lynch, Leeds (0113) 242 9600
law@malcolmlynch.com
See under Charities, p.142

MACKAY, Philip
Dundas & Wilson CS, Edinburgh (0131) 228 8000

MARSDEN, Tim
Norton Rose, London (020) 7283 6000
See under Investment Funds, p.524

MINTO, Bruce
Dickson Minto WS, Edinburgh (0131) 225 4455
bruce.minto@dmws.com
See under Corporate Finance, p.524

MORRIS, Simon
CMS Cameron McKenna, London
(020) 7367 2702
sm@cmck.com
Partner in Financial Services Group.
Specialisation: Advises financial institutions on acquisitions, joint ventures, new funds and products, distribution and regulatory issues; and advises and represents institutions in their dealings with FSA regulators, including over 50 investigations and disciplinary cases. Author of 'Financial Services: Regulating Investment Business' (Third edition forthcoming). An advisor to HM Opposition on FSM Bill.
Prof. Memberships: Compliance Institute.
Career: Qualified in 1982, having joined *Cameron Markby* in 1980. Became a Partner in 1988.
Personal: Born 24th January 1958. Attended Cambridge University. Member of Council, London Topographical Society. Leisure interests include travel and cartography. Lives in Islington.

MORTON, Guy
Freshfields Bruckhaus Deringer, London
(020) 7936 4000
Specialisation: Head of the financial services group. Practice covers a wide range of financial services, regulatory and banking work. Specialises in banking and securities regulation, payment systems and trading law, repos and securities lending. Is particularly experienced within the banking, securities dealing, investment trading and insurance sectors. Has given evidence to the Joint Committee on Financial Services and Markets on the Financial Services and Markets Bill.
Prof. Memberships: Chairman of the City of London Law Society Regulatory Sub-Committee, which is reviewing and commenting on the Financial Services and Markets Bill and the associated regulatory reforms in the UK.
Career: Became partner in *Freshfields* in 1986. Corpus Christi College, Oxford.

NELSON, Paul M.
Linklaters (A member firm of Linklaters & Alliance), London (020) 7456 3766
paul.nelson@linklaters.com
Partner, Head of Financial Markets Group
Specialisation: Specialises in markets and financial institutions including investment banks, securities houses and their affiliates in the UK and internationally.
Career: Articled *Linklaters*; Solicitor Corporate Department 1981; Partner Corporate Department 1987; Head of Financial Markets Practice 1992.

PHILLIPS, Paul
Allen & Overy, London (020) 7330 3000
Specialisation: Partner specialising in financial services and the regulatory field, including the Financial Services Act, Banking Act, SRO Rules–restrictions on marketing investments, prospectuses, advertisements, collective investment shares, internet investment services, regulatory aspects of acquisitions, reorganisations, drafting and negotiating terms of business for investment activities, investment management, custody arrangements, capital adequacy requirements, conduct of investment business, cross-border regulatory practice, bank-customer duties.
Career: MA Cambridge University (first class honours) 1982; Barrister 1983-87; admitted as a Solicitor 1988; Assistant Solicitor, *Allen & Overy* 1987-1994.

SLATER, Richard E.H.
Simmons & Simmons, London (020) 7628 2020
Partner in Corporate Department.
Specialisation: Corporate and regulatory work with a particular emphasis on the financial services industry. Work covers regulatory advice on the formation and promotion of investment vehicles of all types, the acquisition and disposal of financial services businesses and the reconstruction and merger of investment trust companies, unit trusts and other investment entities. Transactional advice includes public and private company take-overs and acquisitions, joint ventures, initial share offerings and flotations.
Career: Qualified in 1977, after joining *Simmons & Simmons* as an articled clerk in 1975. Became a Partner in the Corporate Department in 1981.
Personal: Born 9th November 1950. Attended City University 1979-82, then Cambridge University 1982-84. Lives in London.

STONES, Richard J.L.
Lovells, London (020) 7296 2000
richard.stones@lovells.com
Specialisation: Advises financial services businesses, mostly on regulatory matters, the establishment and marketing of unit trusts and other investment funds and other legal issues affecting the industry. Has a general corporate and commercial training, and deals with corporate transactions involving businesses in his sector. Also advises a number of major pension funds on investment management issues. Has contributed to the CCH *Financial Services Reporter* and Securities Transactions in Europe. Regularly speaks at seminars on regulatory and investment fund topics.
Prof. Memberships: Is a member of the Securities Institute, and of the City of London Law Society Regulatory Working Party.
Career: Joined *Lovells* 1977; qualified 1980; Partner 1987.

SYKES, Annabel
Freshfields Bruckhaus Deringer, London
(020) 7936 4000
Specialisation: Partner dealing with regulatory and other issues for asset managers, custodians, broker-dealers and other institutions in the financial services and insurance sectors. Has advised Lloyd's on various regulatory matters including the admission of corporate capital and the market's reconstruction and renewal and the 1998 premiums trust deeds revision.
Prof. Memberships: Law Society; Member of the Financial Services Working Party of the Law Society Company Law Committee; Member of the Financial Services Authority's advisory group on its rules and guidance handbook.
Career: Trinity College, Cambridge; University of Auckland.
Personal: Born 1961.

THURSTON SMITH, Martin
Tods Murray WS, Edinburgh (0131) 226 4771
martin.thurston.smith@todsmurray.co.uk
See under Investment Funds, p.524

WATT, James P.
Dundas & Wilson CS, Edinburgh (0131) 228 8000

FRANCHISING

National: 408; *Profiles*: 409

OVERVIEW: Reflecting the fact that franchise business is conducted all over the country, there is a single national table this year. This table focuses on those that advise both franchisors and franchisees and is limited to those considered to have specialist franchising expertise.

RESEARCH APPROVED BY BMRB: *For this edition,* Chambers' *researchers conducted 6083 interviews – 4408 with law firms, 598 with barristers and 1077 with clients.*

The validity of the research was scrutinised by BMRB International, who audited both the methodology and the results at our offices in July 2000. They interviewed Chambers' *researchers and cross-checked sample interviews. Details of the audit appear on page 7.*

NATIONAL

FRANCHISING • National	Ptnrs	Assts
❶ **Eversheds** London, Newcastle upon Tyne	6	23
Field Fisher Waterhouse London	6	11
❷ **Mundays** Esher	5	2
Pinsent Curtis Birmingham	1	4
Wragge & Co Birmingham	1	1
❸ **Brodies WS** Edinburgh	1	2
Hammond Suddards Edge Manchester	1	3
Owen White Slough	5	4
❹ **Chambers & Co** Norwich	1	-
Dundas & Wilson CS Edinburgh	1	3
Leathes Prior Norwich	3	1

LEADING INDIVIDUALS	
❶ **ABELL Mark** Field Fisher Waterhouse	**BATES Anton** Owen White
ISHANI Manzoor Mundays	**MENDELSOHN Martin** Eversheds
PRATT John Pinsent Curtis	
❷ **CHADD Jonathan** Leathes Prior	**CHAMBERS John** Chambers & Co
COWIE Pauline Hammond Suddards Edge	**HARRIS Gordon** Wragge & Co
VOGE Julian Brodies WS	**WORMALD Chris** Eversheds

Within each band, firms are listed alphabetically. *See* ***Profiles*** *on page 409*

Eversheds Consistently mentioned as a first choice. The team advises a number of well known international franchisors on their global structuring arrangements, as well as on inbound deals. Advise major franchisors on buy-backs, acquisitions and disposals and represent franchisee associations. Acted for Swinton and Bodyshop franchisee groups in their multi-million pound buy-back deals, represented Alldays in its buy-back of its regional operations and handled two acquisitions of UK-franchised restaurant chains by overseas clients. Perceived to be particularly expert in multi-jurisdictional deals. The nationwide practice is led by the acclaimed **Martin Mendelsohn** who is considered to be *"the grandfather of franchise lawyers."* The London team is led by **Chris Wormald** who is praised for his technical ability and the ability to *"think laterally"* about his clients' needs. **Clients:** Mainly franchisors; both UK and international household names.

Field Fisher Waterhouse Acting for around 350 franchisors and master franchisees, the team is headed by **Mark Abell**, respected for his knowledge of IP-related franchising matters. The team has been involved in roll-outs in the US, Middle and Far East and South America recently, as well as advising US companies on franchising in the UK and Europe. Defending a large family restaurant chain in an ICC arbitration against a multi-million pound suit brought by a Fortune 100 company in respect of non-performance of the German master franchise business. **Clients:** Thirstquench; Finnings; National Rent-a-Car.

Mundays The team has helped UK companies such as Early Learning Centre, Durex Vending and Jigsaw franchise their businesses into 24 countries. Also act for inbound franchisors and have advised Impress Promotions from Australia, Mailboxes etc. from Canada and q.b. Vision from Austria. Led by the *"highly visible"* **Manzoor Ishani**, the group has been described as *"just about the best outside London."* Advised foreign companies on their operations outside the UK such as First Active Bank in connection with a new Irish product. **Clients:** Clarks Shoes; Pret A Manger; the New Covent Garden Soup Company.

Pinsent Curtis Acting for large quoted companies and small franchisors alike, the team is especially noted for its advice to international clients bringing their franchises to the UK. *"They really know what they're doing, and you can get to the essentials quickly."* Led by the *"personable"* **John Pratt**, the group acted for Countrywide on the franchising of its 800 unit estate agent chain. **Clients:** Countrywide Assured Group plc; Kall Kwik Printing (UK) Ltd; ANC Ltd.

Wragge & Co Seen to be gaining an increasing reputation and to be *"good competition"* for Pinsent Curtis. The practice is headed by **Gordon Harris**, who although now seen less on the front line, remains the team's *"eminence grise."* Acted for Premier Hotels in negotiating and acquiring the master franchise rights from Cendant Global Services for the Howard Johnson Hotel brand for Austria, Belgium, Germany and several other European countries. **Clients:** Premier Hotels; Inn Partnership; Autosmart International.

Brodies WS The *"competent and practical"* **Julian Voge** is generally accepted as the foremost franchising lawyer in Scotland. The practice acts mainly for franchisees on contentious matters. Act for hotel developers and continue to advise OPRAF. **Clients:** OPRAF; hoteliers; franchisees.

Hammond Suddards Edge Led by the *"very bright"* **Pauline Cowie**, this team operates out of the enterprise and technology group and maintains a high profile in the north. Advising disaster/trauma support organisation ICAS NL on franchising in Argentina, Germany, Sweden and Switzerland. Also acting for Bradford & Bingley on the franchising of their branch network. **Clients:** Mainly from the service sector and including a number of FTSE 100 companies.

Owen White The team is led by **Anton Bates**, who is legal counsel to the British Franchise Association and *"knows his franchising."* Delivered a presentation to a Fédération Française de la Franchise conference, and act for a number of franchisors. **Clients:** Saks Hair and Beauty; Humana; Dyno Group.

Chambers & Co **John Chambers**, formerly of Pinsent Curtis, runs this niche practice that specialises in franchise work and acts for around 80 franchisors. Said to be *"highly pragmatic,"* he oversees a team which provides advice on complex franchise arrangements and has advised Northcliffe Retail on a new retail licensing arrangement. **Clients:** French Connection Ltd; Dyno Group; Eastern Counties newspapers.

Dundas & Wilson CS Advise master franchisors and franchisees on the preparation, review, negotiation and enforcement of franchise and licence documentation. Continue to advise Scotwork International on their establishment of a network of franchisees that has expanded into countries in Africa, Asia and continental Europe. **Clients:** Scotwork International; Toni & Guy (Scotland); Airtec International.

Leathes Prior *"Proactive"* firm led by **Jonathan Chadd**, which offers a fixed fee report service to franchisees. Acts for franchisors on both inbound and outbound international franchises, in addition to UK deals. Advised on two franchise business acquisitions of franchise networks. **Clients:** Metal Supermarkets; Belvoir Property Management; Restaurant Systems International.

LEADERS IN FRANCHISING

ABELL, Mark
Field Fisher Waterhouse, London (020) 7861 4000
Partner heading the Brands Technology and Communications Department.
Specialisation: Main areas of practice are franchising and licensing of intellectual property rights. Work covers negotiating, drafting and advising generally on international and domestic master, area and unit franchises, development agreements, concessions, subordinated equity arrangements, technology transfers, merchandising, endorsement and sponsorship. Advises the United Nations WIPO on the appropriate legal regime for franchising and trademark licensing and evaluation of IP in developing countries. Other area of practice is the negotiating, drafting and advising generally on the distribution of branded products internationally and domestically. Acted in the Moosehead decision of the EC Commission, an important trademarks and anti-trust case. Visiting lecturer and external examiner at University of London. Lectures regularly in the USA, Japan, PRC and Europe. Editorial Board Member of Trade Mark World and Franchise Law and Business Review, I.P World and I.P Business. Creator of europeanfranchising.com
Prof. Memberships: IFA, IBA, INTA, UIA, LES, Society of Franchising, British Franchise Association (BFA).
Career: Worked for Japanese company in Japan 1980-81. Qualified in 1984. Joined *Field Fisher Waterhouse* in 1985 and became a Partner in 1987.
Publications: Author of 'The Franchise Option', 'The International Franchise Option', 'European Franchising- Law and Practice in the European Community Vol. I & II', 'International Technology Transfer for Profit', 'Franchising in India', chapters in ten textbooks and over 300 articles on franchising, licensing and I.P.
Personal: Born 19th February 1957. Attended Southampton University 1975-78. BFA Legal Committee Member. Leisure interests include Japanese, Chinese and Thai culture (Japanese speaker), scuba diving, keeping fit, opera, travelling and his family.

BATES, Anton B.
Owen White, Slough (01753) 536846 Fax: (01753) 691360
Partner leading the Commercial Department.
Specialisation: Main area of practice is franchising. Legal Advisor to British Franchise Association since advising founder members and drafting constitution in 1977. Chairman of BFA legal committee and BFA representative on European Franchise Federation legal committee. Has advised scores of franchisors and franchisees including companies engaged in international franchising. Acts for many household names in the franchising industry. Author of many articles in various specialist magazines and newspapers. Organiser and speaker at numerous seminars in the UK (for the BFA) and abroad.
Prof. Memberships: Law Society, Chartered Institute of Arbitrators.
Career: Qualified in 1967. After 5 years as a Partner in a large city firm, joined *Owen White* as a Partner in 1973.

CHADD, R. Jonathan
Leathes Prior, Norwich (01603) 610911
Partner in Commercial Department.
Specialisation: Principal area of practice is franchising and intellectual property including drafting and advising on documentation for franchisers, negotiation and drafting of master licence agreements, advice to franchisees, I.P. licences and distribution agreements. Other main area of work is international commercial agreements and joint ventures, agency, distribution, entertainment, e commerce and planning and environmental law. Acts for UK and international franchisers with particular expertise in relation to USA, Middle East, and FSU. Contributor of articles to Franchise Link and other professional journals. Seminar speaker at National and International Franchise Events.
Prof. Memberships: British Franchise Association, Society of Notaries, European Solicitors' Group, International Franchise Association.
Career: Qualified 1980. Admitted as a Solicitor New South Wales, 1983. Notary Public 1994. Formerly with Norton Rose. A partner with *Leathes Prior* since 1986.
Personal: M.A. Oriel College, Oxford. Leisure pursuits include sailing, skiing and tennis.

CHAMBERS, John
Chambers & Co, Norwich (01603) 616 155
Principal of *Chambers & Co.*
Specialisation: Franchising. Twelve years specialisation. Drafts agreements, handles disputes. Particular expertise in new start franchises, regional franchises and international masterlicence transactions. Clients include UK public companies and overseas based licensors. Said to be very 'user friendly' because of working in industry. Writes and lectures extensively.
Prof. Memberships: Law Society; BFA; IoD.
Career: Twelve years commercial experience in industry in UK and overseas. Qualified 1993. Associate at *Eversheds* then *Pinsent Curtis*. Started *Chambers & Co* in 1998.
Personal: Born 1954. Educated at Bradford Grammar School and University College London.

COWIE, Pauline
Hammond Suddards Edge, Manchester (0161) 830 5000
pauline.cowie@hammondsuddardsedge.com
Specialisation: Partner in Enterprise and Technology unit providing advice on franchising, commercial contracts, outsourcing and e-commerce. Leads the national franchise team and specialises in franchising on a national and international basis for listed PLC's and large corporates. Has personally advised clients on over 150 franchised systems and developed a substantial computerised franchising database. Contributes articles on franchising and speaker at seminars on how to franchise, its benefits and legal structures.
Prof. Memberships: Affliate member of the British Franchise Association, Solicitors European Group, Institute of Directors, Institute of Logistics and Transport, Instiitute of Purchasing and Supply, Computers and the law.
Career: Qualified in 1985 joining *Janet Scowcroft & Co* on qualification. Became a partner in 1988 and remained a partner on merging the practice with *Coleman & Co* to form *Colemans* Solicitors in 1991. Joined *Hammond Suddards* as a Partner in 1998.
Personal: Born 1961, resides Wilmslow, married, two children.

HARRIS, Gordon D.
Wragge & Co, Birmingham (0121) 265 2200
gordon_harris@wragge.com
See under Intellectual Property, p.511

ISHANI, Manzoor G.K.
Mundays, Esher (01372) 809000
Manzoor.ishani@mundays.co.uk
Partner and Head of Franchising Unit.
Specialisation: Principal area of practice (for over 20 years) in UK and international franchising, including franchise dispute resolution and joint ventures with overseas companies. Over past three years has helped UK companies franchise into more than 24 countries. Other main area of work is EU Competition Law. Has advised Clarks International, TDK, London International Group Plc, Pret à Manger, Redland Roofing Systems, Ribbon Revival, Stagecoach Theatre Arts, Securicor Pony Express, Early Learning Centres, John Menzies [UK] Ltd, The Meteorological Office, Jigsaw Menswear and E. Moss Chemists (Alliance UniChem Plc). Regular columnist on legal and commercial aspects of franchising for Business Franchise Magazine, Franchise World and Business Money Magazine. Author of 'The European Community' (Fourmat Publishing [Tolley] 1992) and co-author of 'Franchising in the UK'; (Second Edition, Franchise World Publications 1989); 'Franchising in Europe' (Second Edition, Cassey Publications 1993); 'Franchising in Canada' (MacMillan Canada 1992); and 'The Business Franchise Guide-Franchise Handbook' (Seventh Edition, CGB Publishing 1994). European Contributing Editor. Advisory Editor: Journal of International Franchising and Distribution Law (1986-1991). Lectures frequently on legal and commercial aspects of franchising to businessmen, academics and lawyers worldwide; Legal Advisor to the Franchise Consultants Association; Fellow of the Royal Society of Arts.
Prof. Memberships: British Franchise Association

(Legal Committee), International Bar Association (Franchise Committee–Section of Business Law), American Bar Association (Forum Committee on Franchising), International Association of Lawyers (Franchising Committee), Fellow of the Society for Advanced Legal Studies, Association of Swiss Arbitrators.
Career: Qualified 1976. Previously a Partner with City practice. Joined *Mundays* as a partner in 1992.
Personal: Born 6th October 1949. Attended St. Edmund's School Canterbury 1963-68, then the University of St. Andrews 1969-72. Leisure pursuits include classic cars, reading and jazz. Lives in Oxshott, Surrey.

MENDELSOHN, Martin
Eversheds, London (020) 7919 4500
mendelm@eversheds.com
Specialisation: Has 40 years experience of handling a wide range of commercial, corporate and international transactions. Has particular expertise in franchising, distribution, agency and licensing transactions, both domestic and international, as well as UK and EC competition law. Obtained a Doctorate from Middlesex University in 1999 on Effective Business and Professional practice in Franchising. Has been active in many parts of the world in providing support and assistance to Franchise Associations. Has advised Governments. Visiting Professor of Franchise Management, Middlesex University Business School where he introduced an undergraduate course and a Masters Degree course in Franchising. Member of the UNIDROIT study group on franchising. Current publications include 'The Guide to Franchising' (6th edition), and 'How to evaluate a Franchise' (6th edition) and `The Ethics of Franchising' (2nd edition), 'How to Franchise Internationally' (3rd edition). He is also co-author of several publications, including 'How to Franchise your Business' (4th edition) `Franchising and the Block Exemption Regulation' and `Franchising'. Editor of the 'International Journal of Franchising and Distribution Law' and editor of and contributor to 'Franchising in Europe' and the Canadian Franchise Guide; Co-editor of the International Encyclopaedia of Franchising. His works have been published in ten languages. Legal consultant to the British Franchise Association. Assisted in the introduction of a franchising law course by Queen Mary & Westfield College, London University as a subject for the University's Master of Law Degree. Frequent lecturer at conferences and seminars world-wide. Regular contributor to journals and publications. Was first chairman of the International Franchising Committee of the International Bar Association.
Prof. Memberships: Fellow of the Chartered Institute of Arbitrators, Law Society, International Bar Association, American Bar Association (and Forum on Franchising).
Career: Qualified in 1959. Joined *Jaques & Lewis* (now *Eversheds*) as a partner in 1992.
Personal: Born 6th November 1935. Lives in Stanmore, Middlesex.

PRATT, John
Pinsent Curtis, Birmingham (0121) 200 1050
john.pratt@pinsents.com
Managing Partner, Birmingham office.
Specialisation: Main area of practice is franchising. Drafts franchise agreements, advises on international franchising and prepares documentation. Expertise also in competition law including anti-trust compliance programmes, notifications and general advice. Has prepared franchise agreements for 100 UK franchisors including FT 100 companies. Author of 'Franchising Law & Practice', and 'Franchising'. Contributor to 'New Frontiers in Competition Law' and 'Il Franchising Internazionale'. Lectures in the UK and overseas.
Prof. Memberships: Law Society; Birmingham Law Society.
Career: Qualified in 1976. Worked at *Lovell White Durrant* from 1974-83, then *Needham & James* 1983-93. Joined *Pinsent & Co.*as a Partner in 1993. Previously Chairman of Young Solicitors of England and Wales.
Personal: Born 1951. Attended Dulwich College 1960-69; Oxford University 1969-72 and Universite D'Aix-Marseille 1972-73. Interests include theatre, wine, food and sport.

VOGE, Julian C.A.
Brodies WS, Edinburgh (0131) 228 3777
jvoge@brodies.co.uk
Partner 1987. Corporate Department.
Specialisation: Main areas of practice are corporate and contract law, including franchising and licensing. Author of chapters on Scots law for 'Franchising Law and Practice' and 'International Franchising Law'.
Prof. Memberships: Law Society of Scotland, Writer to the Signet. Also admitted as a solicitor in England and Wales.
Career: Qualified 1982. Articled at *Tods Murray*. Then worked at *Brodies* and *Berwin Leighton*, before re-joining *Brodies* as a Partner in 1987.
Personal: Born 3rd February 1958. Attended Daniel Stewarts & Melville College 1964-76, then University of Edinburgh 1976-80. Lives in Edinburgh.

WORMALD, Chris
Eversheds, London (020) 7919 4500
wormaldc@eversheds.com
Specialisation: Main areas of practice for over 19 years - franchising and other variants of business system expansion; substantial volume of international work in addition to domestic UK practice; related EC competition law; acts primarily for franchisors, master franchisees and franchisee associations. Joined McDonald's European headquarters in 1984 as their first European General Counsel and became a Vice-President of McDonald's Europe two years later. During 10 years with McDonald's played a key role in developing the local teams as the system grew to 2000 restaurants in Europe. Hired and managed outside lawyers; negotiated Master, Development and Joint Venture Franchise arrangements throughout Europe, North Africa and the Middle East; and designed and implemented franchise arrangements for new jurisdictions. Trained European real estate and franchising teams and was responsible for the legal side of the property acquisition programme. General Counsel role also involved him in trouble-shooting, litigation, lobbying, and multi-national group restructuring. In 1996 joined Martin Mendelsohn to strengthen Eversheds' experienced franchising group as it began its international joint venture with Horwath International to form a global franchise consultancy. Today he leads the firm's London team. Specialises in strategic advice to major corporations considering re-engineering and international expansion, and to government organisations. Works across commercial sectors - from hotels, restaurants and retail to IT, insurance and financial services, manufacturing, distribution and the public sector. Writes and speaks frequently worldwide on legal and business aspects of 'system expansion', most recently co-authoring for specialist UK publishers 'The Guide to Franchising in UK Pubs and Restaurants'. He speaks French and German and has lived and worked in Brussels and Frankfurt.
Prof. Memberships: IBA, American Bar Association, International Franchise Association, British Franchise Association, Law Society.
Career: Qualified with *Simmons & Simmons* 1979 - international tax and commercial structuring for 6 years. McDonald's Europe - European General Counsel and Vice-President; partner *Eversheds* London 1996.
Personal: Born 1954. Law degree from Sidney Sussex College, Cambridge University. Leisure interests include sailing, fishing, travel and family.

FRAUD

OVERVIEW: Two important changes coming up over the next year will alter the way fraud is dealt with. On the criminal side, the Legal Services Commission is establishing a Serious Fraud Panel of firms with established experience in fraud work, to whom high cost cases will be referred. The criteria for receiving legal aid will be broadened.

On the civil side, the Financial Services and Markets Act will increase the regulations surrounding the financial services industry, particularly in connection with takeovers.

RESEARCH APPROVED BY BMRB: *For this edition,* Chambers' *researchers conducted 6083 interviews – 4408 with law firms, 598 with barristers and 1077 with clients.*

The validity of the research was scrutinised by BMRB International, who audited both the methodology and the results at our offices in July 2000. They interviewed Chambers' *researchers and cross-checked sample interviews. Details of the audit appear on page 7.*

LONDON

CRIMINAL

FRAUD: CRIMINAL • London	Ptnrs	Assts
❶ Burton Copeland	9	5
Kingsley Napley	5	5
Peters & Peters	9	6
❷ Irwin Mitchell	2	6
Simons Muirhead & Burton	6	2
❸ Dechert	2	10
Russell Jones & Walker	4	6
❹ Oury Clark Solicitors	2	1
❺ Claude Hornby & Cox	2	3
DLA	2	5
Garstangs	1	4
Offenbach & Co	3	2
Ralph Hume Garry	2	3
Victor Lissack & Roscoe	3	3

LEADING INDIVIDUALS	
✪ **BURTON Ian** Burton Copeland	**RAPHAEL Monty** Peters & Peters
❶ **COLHOUN Aileen** Oury Clark Solicitors	**CORKER David** Peters & Peters
KIRK David Simons Muirhead & Burton	**OLIVER Keith** Peters & Peters
POLLARD Stephen Kingsley Napley	**TRAVERS Harry** Burton Copeland
❷ **BYRNE David** Dechert	**CAPLAN Michael** Kingsley Napley
COWELL Adam Irwin Mitchell	**DELAHUNTY Louise** Peters & Peters
FLETCHER Rod Russell Jones & Walker	**HUME John** Ralph Hume Garry
SPIRO Brian Simons Muirhead & Burton	
❸ **BINNING Peter** Peters & Peters	**CARNELL Bernard** Offenbach & Co
CORNTHWAITE Richard Garstangs	**FRANKLAND Matthew** Dechert
HARDING John Kingsley Napley	**MURRAY Christopher** Kingsley Napley
PEACOCK Karen Burton Copeland	

Within each band, firms are listed alphabetically. *See **Profiles** on page 416*

Burton Copeland Widely recognised as one of the leaders in this field, the firm's pre-eminence has been questioned by some in the market who have noted *"weaknesses"* at assistant level. However, *"great front man"* **Ian Burton**, the *"dynamic and bright"* **Harry Travers** and **Karen Peacock** still constitute a formidable spearhead.

Kingsley Napley Also maintaining their position in the top division, this firm remains *"the leader"* in defending the big SFO frauds, including Morgan Grenfell and Wickes. Now that John Clitheroe is undertaking consultancy work, the team is led by the *"measured and tactical"* **Stephen Pollard**, who is ably assisted by established name **Christopher Murray**, *"the exceptionally thorough"* **Michael Caplan**, and rising star **John Harding**.

Peters & Peters Considered by some to be *"first among equals,"* the firm undertakes a full range of fraud work, led by *"quality lawyer"* **Monty Raphael**. He is helped by **Keith Oliver** and **David Corker** who *"always do a first-class job,"* together with **Peter Binning** and *"responsive"* **Louise Delahunty**.

Irwin Mitchell Climbing a division this year, the London branch of the firm is *"making a huge impact." "Full of ambitious young men"* such as the *"conscientious"* **Adam Cowell**, the team's position has been boosted by recent recruits taken from other leading firms. Work is directed through the business crime unit, and current cases include an involvement with the first dot.com fraud, as well as instructions in several major DTI prosecutions.

Simons Muirhead & Burton This well-established firm has been involved in a wide range of civil and criminal work, including the Morgan Grenfell case, and the successful Jubilee Line Extension case. **David Kirk** is a *"first-class lawyer"* who may be *"a bit dry but knows his onions."* Highly rated colleague **Brian Spiro** *"knows how to win the confidence of clients."*

Dechert Seen as a *"superb"* practice which is *"riding the crest of the wave,"* the firm is renowned for its work on Inland Revenue, Customs & Excise and SFO cases. The firm's criminal investigations department provides both civil and criminal advice, as it did for Geoffrey Robinson MP, the former Paymaster General when he was investigated by the DTI. Noted here is **Matthew Frankland**, recommended as a *"bright and conscientious lad"* who is *"thorough and capable."* However, he is overshadowed by **David Byrne**, who is *"a dream to deal with."*

Russell Jones & Walker The focus here is on medium-sized criminal frauds with a number of referrals coming from City firms. Although the firm do few SFO prosecutions, the team did act on the Jubilee Line Extension case during the past year. Regarded as a *"reliable, middle-ranking firm,"* the team includes the *"capable"* **Rod Fletcher**.

Oury Clark Solicitors This firm enjoys a sound name for its work in the criminal defence field. It has been involved in some big SFO cases and also represents clients whilst under SFO investigation. Mortgage fraud cases are also undertaken. The big name here is **Aileen Colhoun**, *"a very clever lawyer who is good with clients."*

Claude Hornby & Cox Undertakes middle-ranking frauds of £100,000 – £200,000 in both criminal and civil proceedings but this is essentially a criminal specialist practice with a strong fraud component. The team was involved in the Wickes case and has also acted on mortgage fraud work.

DLA Enters the tables for the first time in the criminal section. The firm's corporate defence team is currently involved with a number of SFO, Inland Revenue and Customs & Excise prosecutions as well as undertaking civil investigatory work.

Garstangs Recent work includes defending the Richmond Oil & Gas Co against an SFO prosecution, and much work is derived from Customs & Excise investigations into VAT fraud and money-laundering. A current case involves fraudulent trading and case values range from £1-100 million. Although the move south is not unanimously considered to have increased the firm's profile, **Richard Cornthwaite** remains *"a tower of strength."*

Offenbach & Co *"Good on crime broadly,"* although *"not a massive player"* in fraud per se, this practice is headed by the *"thorough"* and highly respected **Bernard Carnell**. Work includes a number of VAT fraud cases, and the firm is currently representing an internet start-up which is subject to an SFO inquiry.

Ralph Hume Garry Some in the market questioned the extent of the fraud caseload of this *"old school"* firm, but it has acquired a niche in advising professionals on the edge of big criminal prosecutions. Partner **John Hume** is *"an exceptionally talented player."*

Victor Lissack & Roscoe Another general crime practice with a *"good name,"* cases include defending solicitors against fraud charges. However, the firm is felt to lack the critical mass for big-ticket SFO cases and civil investigations.

CIVIL, REGULATORY & INVESTIGATORY

FRAUD: CIVIL • London	Ptnrs	Assts
❶ Allen & Overy	3	14
Clifford Chance	9	25
Herbert Smith	8	6
Linklaters	4	6
Lovells	4	12
Norton Rose	1	4
❷ Peters & Peters	8	6
Simmons & Simmons	8	16
Slaughter and May	8	40
Stephenson Harwood	6	10
❸ CMS Cameron McKenna	6	12
DLA	6	9
Eversheds	4	5
Kingsley Napley	3	3
Richards Butler	5	2
❹ Ashurst Morris Crisp	5	12
Dechert	2	8
Denton Wilde Sapte	12	5
Freshfields Bruckhaus Deringer	13	12
Macfarlanes	1	2
Mishcon de Reya	4	5
SJ Berwin & Co	4	8
Theodore Goddard	3	5
❺ D J Freeman	5	5
Jeffrey Green Russell	3	2

LEADING INDIVIDUALS	
❶ BAGGE James Norton Rose	STAPLE George Clifford Chance
❷ FORDHAM John Stephenson Harwood	GAINES Keith Lovells
GERRARD Neil DLA	HUNTER Robert Allen & Overy
MAYHEW David Clifford Chance	MYERS Sidney Allen & Overy
NATALI David Herbert Smith	OLIVER Keith Peters & Peters
POLLARD Stephen Kingsley Napley	RAPHAEL Monty Peters & Peters
WALLS Alan Linklaters	WOODCOCK Tony Stephenson Harwood
❸ BARRETT Elizabeth Slaughter and May	BYRNE David Dechert
FINKLER Deborah Slaughter and May	POTTS John Clifford Chance
SANDELSON Jeremy Clifford Chance	
SPARROW Edward Ashurst Morris Crisp	

Within each band, firms are listed alphabetically. *See **Profiles** on page 416*

Allen & Overy • **Civil Fraud:** Decidedly the *"top of the tree"* as far as its civil fraud work is concerned, this is the only City firm offering a specialised fraud, asset-tracing and trust practice. Exclusively handling this work is a dedicated team of partners, headed by the *"knowledgeable"* **Robert Hunter**. Actions are often multi-jurisdictional and involve off-shore jurisdictions, money tracing and retrieval. Further work is carried out for the Public Trustee, and the team continues to act in the Grupo Torras case.

• **Reg/Inv:** The firm is also highly recommended in this area, and boasts a specialist regulatory investigations and proceedings group. This handles contentious regulatory cases including investigations and disciplinary hearings, advising not only institutions but also regulatory authorities. **Sidney Myers** is a stand-out name in the field. **Clients:** HSBC; FSA; Ministry of Sound; Phillips & Drew; SFA; Warburg Dillon Read.

Clifford Chance • **Civil Fraud:** A broad range of multi-jurisdictional corporate fraud work is undertaken, including acting for claimants in asset recovery and offering specialist advice to governments and financial institutions on the discovery of fraud and regulatory breach. A strong team is led by **George Staple QC**, and includes **David Mayhew** *("an expert litigator,")* the *"exceptionally bright"* **Jeremy Sandelson** and **John Potts** who is *"switched on."*

• **Reg/Inv:** Investigations are carried out on behalf of regulatory and other official bodies. The team also represents clients before official inquiries and regulatory disciplinary tribunals, and has advised companies accused of mis-selling pensions.

Herbert Smith • **Civil Fraud:** Mostly advisory work is undertaken for a range of corporate clients, as well as some claimant work, and the caseload has a multi-jurisdictional flavour. New cases have included an Ecuadorian banana fraud and a case of light bulb theft at Heathrow.

• **Reg/Inv:** Growing regulatory work has been noted in the market, and is felt likely to increase with the new FSM Act as the regulator becomes more muscular. The team has advised extensively on Inland Revenue and Customs & Excise investigations, typically acting on behalf of financial institutions. *"Robust"* partner **David Natali** received particular mention for his *"subtle, lateral but devastating approach to litigation."* **Clients:** Codelco; London Stock Exchange; Westpac.

Linklaters • **Civil Fraud:** Widely recognised to be one of the market leaders, the team acts for an *"imposing"* array of corporate clients. The firm's multi-jurisdictional capabilities make it particularly popular for international work, where advising clients on fraud prevention is a particular area of expertise. **Alan Walls** has earned notable market approval in the civil litigation field.

• **Reg/Inv:** The team were selected by the Bank of England to act on an investigation into a major bank. Particularly noted for advice on disciplinary procedures and risks of criminal liability.

Lovells • **Civil Fraud:** This *"top tier"* firm has seen an increase in the amount of civil fraud work undertaken, with matters deriving especially from Russia and Eastern Europe following the firm's recent merger with the former Boesebeck Droste. Cases have also occurred in relation to the financial operations of the European Commission. The team has inter alia acted for the liquidators of BCCI and for HRH Prince Jefri Bolkiah. The department is headed by **Keith Gaines** who is lauded as an *"exceptionally tough litigator."*

• **Reg/Inv:** Frequent investigatory matters are undertaken, often as a result of asset tracing work. Owing to the firm's successful insolvency practice, this type of work is regarded as an area of particular strength.

Norton Rose • **Civil Fraud:** This firm of *"smooth operators"* is well recommended in this area, especially for the litigation work, undertaken by its civil fraud litigation unit. The team advises Credit Agricole Indosuez and other large investment banks.

• **Reg/Inv: James Bagge** is commended for being *"authoritative but unstuffy."* He is widely recognised for being *"a true specialist"* in the investigative field. **Clients:** Credit Agricole Indosuez; Komercni Bank; Merrill Lynch.

Peters & Peters • **Civil Fraud:** The firm's civil fraud work has been growing steadily and the firm is now gaining a reputation to match its profile in the criminal area. **Keith Oliver** is said to be *"brilliant,"* while **Monty Raphael** remains *"a name to get work in."*

• **Reg/Inv:** The practice continues to handle parallel investigations.

Simmons & Simmons • **Civil Fraud:** Most of the firm's work is for financial institutions, governments and existing multi-national clients. Acted for Fiba Nordic Securities and has advised similar institutions which have suffered fraud. The team is also seen acting for individuals. Only the lack of an individual big-hitter is felt to hold the firm back from a still higher profile.

• **Reg/Inv:** The practice has undertaken a number of recent investigatory cases, acting most notably on the Morgan Grenfell investigation.

Slaughter and May • **Civil Fraud:** Both corporate fraud and white collar crime is undertaken from within the commercial litigation department. **Deborah Finkler** is perceived as a *"hugely able litigator,"* while **Elizabeth Barrett** is renowned as *"tough and impressive."*

• **Reg/Inv:** The firm is considered to have developed a strong investigations practice acting both for regulatory authorities and its existing blue-chip corporate client base. Acted on investigatory work subsequent to the Morgan Grenfell case and also handle FSA, IMRO and PIA investigations. Advised a number of overseas governments on asset recovery.

Stephenson Harwood • **Civil Fraud:** Cases in the past year have included acting for the Arab International Bank and recovering $50 million from Merrill Lynch. The market reputation of the firm's in-house advocacy team were underlined when acting for McGraw-Hill and obtaining emergency freezing orders within five hours of instruction. Also involved in proceedings against the late Nigerian President Abacha.

• **Reg/Inv:** The firm has acted for the FSA and for two large accountancy firms in this area. Asset tracing and recovery are areas of strength. **Tony Woodcock** and **John Fordham** have *"plenty of experience"* and are *"obvious choices."* **Clients:** KPMG; RZB; HSBC; RBS.

CMS Cameron McKenna • **Civil Fraud:** The firm is felt to have slipped this year, with market opinion questioning the volume of work in this area, and commenting on the absence of a high-profile practitioner. Nevertheless, a range of civil fraud work is covered, including client investigations, causes of fraud, recovery, financial services and money-laundering for individuals and companies. Acting for a major US bank and a major clearing bank on a multi-million pound cheque fraud, as well as conducting substantial advisory work.

• **Reg/Inv:** Conducted an investigation into share dealing and acted for a defendant in disciplinary proceedings before the SFA. Particular expertise in financial services matters.

DLA • **Civil Fraud: Neil Gerrard** heads the commercial regulatory team and is praised as *"a real dynamo with great energy."* The practice has specialists in asset-tracing and other dispute linked work, often with an international element.

• **Reg/Inv:** The team has acted for corporate defendants under investigation, also offering advice to regulators and undertaking prosecutions.

Eversheds • **Civil Fraud:** Although not recognised as specialists in this area, nor having the high-profile clients of firms in the higher divisions, this firm is conceded to have increased its involvement over the past year, including FSA cases and arbitrated disputes.

• **Reg/Inv:** The firm represents those companies under investigation by the DTI and undertakes advisory work for those being investigated.

Kingsley Napley • **Civil Fraud:** Often getting referrals from City firms, the firm has established its name in both claimant and defendant cases. Typically acts for banks and other financial institutions, for whom the group provides a full service, notably including asset tracing.

• **Reg/Inv:** Acts on a number of regulatory matters as a consequence of the firm's pre-eminent reputation in criminal fraud. The *"versatile"* **Stephen Pollard** tends to represent individuals rather than companies in SFA investigations. Work also includes extradition cases and money-laundering advice.

Richards Butler • **Civil Fraud:** This firm is seen as *"possessing a solid team ethic."* Much of this year's caseload has involved purely advisory work, such as its involvement on behalf of the firms acting on the Sumitomo Copper trading scandal.

• **Reg/Inv:** More involved with regulatory and investigatory matters, including fraud prevention matters and tightening procedures. Undercover asset-tracing work is also covered, as well as representations before the operators. Held to have been *"more prominent this year,"* the firm advises regulators on fraud prevention and money-laundering cases.

Ashurst Morris Crisp • **Civil Fraud:** A new entry this year, the team is led by the highly-rated **Ed Sparrow**. Acted for Sirte, the Libyan State Oil Company, on matters including asset tracing and asset freezing. Last year, were instructed by the former partners of Phillips & Drew and also acted for the liquidators of Barings Singapore. Also a force on the defendant side, the team was involved in the Grupo Torras affair.

Dechert • **Civil Fraud: David Byrne** is recommended here as a *"bullish"* litigator and the civil arm of the firm's fraud department is felt to complement its extensive and well-reputed criminal work. In this area, the team concentrates on defendant cases and does a substantial amount of legal aid work. Clients include medium-sized companies and plcs.

• **Reg/Inv:** The firm is currently involved in the SFO investigation of Wickes, on behalf of a defendant.

Denton Wilde Sapte • **Civil Fraud:** The recent merger has broadened the combined client base in significant areas, providing large banking clients, such as the State Bank of South Australia. The firm has experience in banking fraud and asset recovery, acting on the Ostrich Farming Corporation Limited case. Other prominent areas include confiscatory work and matters arising from insolvency cases.

• **Reg/Inv:** Commended for its client base, the firm has handled instructions on behalf of the FSA relating to asset freezing and regulatory injunctions.

Freshfields Bruckhaus Deringer • **Civil Fraud:** Another new entry, the firm has earned recognition for its work for the FSA and the Bank of England, in connection with such high-profile cases as Barings and BCCI. Often seen on multi-jurisdictional cases, the team has been advising the State of Brunei and the Brunei Investment Agency on the Prince Jefri case. This has involved proceedings in Brunei, the UK and the US, and is thought to be one of the largest ever civil claims for misappropriation of funds.

• **Reg/Inv:** The team acts for a large corporate clientele on investigations and disciplinary matters, including SFO and DTI enquiries and SFA and Stock Market investigations.

Macfarlanes **Civil Fraud:** Fraud work here is carried out from within the commercial litigation department. They represent both individuals and companies and are often referred matters by the DTI, as well as doing asset-tracing work.
Reg/Inv: Current work includes an SFO enquiry and advising a firm of accountants on the periphery of an investigation.

Mishcon de Reya **Civil Fraud:** Newly ranked this year, the firm do both claimant and defendant work for a clientele primarily comprising international financial institutions. Characterised as *"proactive and aggressive litigators."*
Reg/Inv: Specialises in the investigation and prosecution of fraud claims, generally liaising with the authorities over prosecutions and regulatory matters.

S J Berwin & Co **Civil Fraud:** Current cases in the firm's defendant-focused caseload include the Abacha case and the Pirate of Prague case. 50 % of the work has an international dimension and involves asset-tracing, often on behalf of individuals.

Theodore Goddard **Civil Fraud:** Has a noteworthy practice in this area, acting for governments, major banks and individuals. Particular strengths are felt to lie in money-laundering cases and asset-freezing on a global basis. Currently advising in connection with such an enquiry at the Bank of New York.
Reg/Inv: Undertakes complex investigatory work in foreign jurisdictions and remedial action in international fraud.

DJ Freeman Civil Fraud: Not widely noted in the market but nevertheless acting for the Department of International Development on asset recovery and involved with a DTI investigation.

Jeffrey Green Russell **Civil Fraud:** This firm undertakes both civil and criminal fraud with the focus on a range of civil work including Customs & Excise, Inland Revenue and DTI cases.
Reg/Inv: Investigatory work forms a large part of the practice here and a niche has been built up in money-laundering cases. **Clients:** Nissan UK; Monarch Assurance.

THE SOUTH & SOUTH WEST

FRAUD: CRIMINAL • The South	Ptnrs	Assts
❶ **Bobbetts Mackan** Bristol	1	3
❷ **Blake Lapthorn** Fareham	1	2
DMH Brighton	2	1
Wolferstans Plymouth	2	2

LEADING INDIVIDUALS
❶ **GABBITASS David** Wolferstans
MITCHELL John Blake Lapthorn

Within each band, firms are listed alphabetically. *See **Profiles** on page 416*

Bobbetts Mackan Considered to possess a *"first-class reputation,"* this firm is well-respected for its range of fraud work, including Customs & Excise investigations and DTI investigations, but it does not undertake purely civil cases.

Blake Lapthorn Work includes both regulatory matters and civil fraud, generally in medium-ticket cases. The team acts for insurers, recoverers for companies and individual professionals. **John Mitchell** working on the regulatory side helps to maintain the reputation that this is *"a definite player."*

DMH Well-known in the South East, a small amount of white-collar crime work is undertaken, but the group's focus is on business defence and commercial fraud matters. Acting from the commercial litigation department, the team advises public bodies, including local authorities, quangos and charities, as well as for companies and individuals.

Wolferstans The firm has an established name in the South West, largely thanks to **David Gabbitass**, esteemed for his abilities as a solicitor-advocate.

WALES

FRAUD: CRIMINAL • Wales	Ptnrs	Assts
❶ **Martyn Prowel Solicitors** Cardiff	2	2
❷ **Huttons** Cardiff	4	8
❸ **Gamlins** Rhyl	-	1

LEADING INDIVIDUALS
❶ **PROWEL Martyn** Martyn Prowel Solicitors

Within each band, firms are listed alphabetically. *See **Profiles** on page 416*

Martyn Prowel Solicitors This *"respectable and experienced practice"* deals with white-collar crime and is involved with Customs & Excise and Inland Revenue investigations. After twenty years, the *"shrewd"* **Martyn Prowel** is considered to have *"a real breadth of experience."* Frequently, cases have included conspiracies to defraud and mortgage fraud cases.

Huttons A broad litigation practice, work here includes criminal and civil matters. Advises professionals, medical practices, companies and individuals. Recent growth areas have been computer fraud and database thefts.

Gamlins Although felt to be less prominent than in past years, the practice continues to be noted acting for corporate defendants, often in mortgage and post office frauds.

MIDLANDS

FRAUD: CRIMINAL • Midlands	Ptnrs	Assts
❶ **Cartwright King** Nottingham	2	-
Nelsons Nottingham	2	17
❷ **Hammond Suddards Edge** Birmingham	⚐	⚐
Varley Hadley Siddall Nottingham	1	-
❸ **George, Jonas & Co** Birmingham	2	3
Glaisyers Birmingham	4	4

LEADING INDIVIDUALS	
❶ **NELSON Richard** Nelsons	**THURSTON Michael** Cartwright King
WILSON Mark Cartwright King	
❷ **JONAS Steven** George, Jonas & Co	
❸ **ROYLE Charles** Glaisyers	

Within each band, firms are listed alphabetically. *See* ***Profiles*** *on page 416*

⚐ *Figures unavailable at time of going to press.*

Cartwright King Having split from the former Freeth Cartwright Hunt Dickins, this new firm continues to service the same clients and is currently running a small number of big-ticket fraud cases. Both **Mark Wilson** and **Mike Thurston** are known to be *"efficient and easy to deal with."*

Nelsons A wide range of work is dealt with at this *"excellent outfit"* under the leadership of **Richard Nelson**. Matters handled include regulatory and investigatory matters, as well as SFO cases.

Hammond Suddards Edge Doing a *"fair amount"* of white-collar crime work, the firm benefits from being the only commercial operation in Birmingham with a criminal department.

Varley Hadley Siddall Another newly-formed firm, this specialist general crime outfit is the result of a schism with Berryman & Co. Current cases include DTI prosecutions and a CPS prosecution into pension fraud.

George, Jonas & Co The work at this firm involves advising on professional fraud. **Steven Jonas** maintains an enviable local reputation.

Glaisyers Another firm which derives most of its fraud work from a renowned general crime practice. **Charles Royle** is the stand-out practitioner.

THE NORTH

FRAUD: CRIMINAL • The North	Ptnrs	Assts
❶ **Burton Copeland** Manchester	4	3
❷ **Betesh Fox & Co** Manchester	3	2
Irwin Mitchell Sheffield	1	5
Pannone & Partners Manchester	5	2
❸ **DLA** Manchester	2	7
Garstangs Bolton	1	-
McCormicks Leeds	3	-
❹ **Russell Jones & Walker** Manchester	1	1

LEADING INDIVIDUALS	
✪ **KENYON Michael** Burton Copeland	**SMYTH Richard** DLA
❶ **BURROWS Lesley** Burton Copeland	
❷ **BARNFATHER Anthony** Pannone & Partners	
COOPER Ian Burton Copeland	**TAYLOR Paul** Pannone & Partners
❸ **FOX Stephen** Betesh Fox & Co	**HANMAN David** Russell Jones & Walker
KENYON Andrew Betesh Fox & Co	**McCORMICK Peter** McCormicks
ROBINSON Kevin Irwin Mitchell	

Within each band, firms are listed alphabetically. *See* ***Profiles*** *on page 416*

Burton Copeland Widely seen to be riding head and shoulders above other competitors in the North. More Customs & Excise work has been undertaken than in previous years, but white-collar crime and civil litigation remain the practice's staple. The *"experienced"* **Michael Kenyon** leads the way, supported by *"direct"* **Ian Cooper** and **Lesley Burrows** *("so good at what she does.")*

Betesh Fox & Co Highly respected team, among which **Stephen Fox** and **Andrew Kenyon** are the leading lights. Work involves several current SFO cases, including acting for the lead defendant in the Alliance Resources case and in the Smith Robinson case. Handles criminal as well as civil matters.

Irwin Mitchell **Kevin Robinson** oscillates between the London and the Sheffield offices but remains *"pre-eminent in Yorkshire."* The group's most notable current case is its involvement with Donnygate, acting for the Doncaster councillors in one of the most high-profile local authority corruption cases in UK history.

Pannone & Partners Rising up the rankings, this *"small but perfectly formed"* team is led by **Paul Taylor** *("has exacting standards")* who, together with former Bermudan policeman **Tony Barnfather**, is *"doing quality work."* Caseload is predominantly white-collar fraud, including SFO investigations, but the firm operates both a civil and a criminal practice.

DLA Slipping this year, despite undertaking SFO, investigatory and regulatory work, this firm are widely seen to have suffered from recent defections. However, **Richard Smyth** remains, rated as *"an absolutely top man"* who is *"efficient, hard-working and has sound judgement."*

Garstangs This widely rated Bolton practice focuses on criminal fraud cases. The firm's London office, however, is now felt to take the lion's share of big-ticket cases.

McCormicks Rated as *"one of the best in the North East,"* the firm advises on investigatory and asset-tracing work. **Peter McCormick** is a universally-known figure, and although his practice extends far beyond fraud cases, *"when he does the work, he does it well."*

Russell Jones & Walker A new presence in the northern section this year, although a regular feature in the London rankings, the investigations department at the firm has been up and running for just over a year. The work concentrates exclusively on white-collar crime, acting for corporate or individual defendants. Seen to be *"building a niche in the region,"* former DLA lawyer **David Hanman** heads the department and is praised as a *"shrewd operator."*

LEADERS IN FRAUD

BAGGE, James
Norton Rose, London (020) 7283 6000
baggeajs@nortonrose.com
Partner in Commercial Litigation Department.
Specialisation: Practice focuses on fraud and the regulation of investment and banking business, in particular advising on all forms of investigations, statutory or private, and associated legal proceedings involving the SFO, DTI, SRO and Revenue authorities. Advised the Board of Banking Supervision on the Barings inquiry. Has acted for LIFFE in relation to market investigations and enforcement actions. Conducted the Banking Act inquiry into Hambros involvement with the aborted bid for the Co-operative Wholesale Society. Is representing the Trustees of the Thyssen Bornemisza Trust in action commenced by Baron Thyssen in Bermuda. Acts for three global investment banks in relation to ongoing regulatory investigations.
Prof. Memberships: International Bar Association.
Career: Qualified 1979. Spent eight years at the Criminal Bar and two years on secondment to the Serious Fraud Office. Joined *Norton Rose* in 1990 and became a Partner in 1993.

BARNFATHER, Anthony
Pannone & Partners, Manchester (0161) 909 3000
anthony.barnfather@pannones.co.uk
Specialisation: Main area of specialisation encompasses all aspects of business crime. Prime areas of expertise include representation of corporations and individuals subject to investigation by regulatory agencies. Present/recent case load includes Customs & Excise, F.S.A., Inland Revenue, Office of Fair Trading and SFO work. Also assists a number of corporations including multi-nationals regarding quasi-criminal investigations brought by such agencies as the Environment Agency and Health and Safety Executive. (Presently advising on a number of fatal accidents). Lectures to the profession and Industry in these areas, Acts for professional clients in respect of allegations of serious/complex crime. Recent high profile cases include successful outcomes for members of the pharmacy profession.
Prof. Memberships: The Law Society
Career: Initial involvement with criminal litigation was in his role as a police officer. He served with the West Yorkshire Police and thereafter continued this investigative role in the tax haven of Bermuda. He gained his law degree in Leeds, later becoming a partner in a Leeds practice. He joined Pannone & Partners in 1998 and is now a partner in their Business Crime and Corporate Defence Unit.
Personal: Interests include Rugby League, motorcycling and hillwalking.

BARRETT, Elizabeth
Slaughter and May, London (020) 7600 1200
Partner in Litigation Department.
Specialisation: Principal area of practice is commercial litigation (including defamation) with particular emphasis on civil and commercial fraud and corporate crime, and extensive experience of a broad range of statutory, regulatory and disciplinary investigations and enquiries.
Prof. Memberships: The Law Society.
Career: Qualified 1981. Partner *Peter Carter-Ruck and Partners* 1982-1986. Joined *Slaughter and May* 1986; Partner 1989.
Personal: Born 23 November 1956. Attended University College, London (LLB Hons 1978).

BINNING, Peter
Peters & Peters, London (020) 7629 7991
pbinning@petersandpeters.co.uk
Specialisation: All aspects of business crime and other complex criminal cases, including extradition, tax and customs fraud, money laundering and data protection. Current cases include first ever extradition request from the UAE.
Prof. Memberships: JUSTICE Executive Board, London Criminal Courts Solicitors Association and IBA.
Career: Called to the Bar: 1985. Crown Prosecution Service: 1989 -1994. Serious Fraud Office: 1994–1996. Joined *Peters & Peters*: 1996–partner 1998.
Publications: Articles in legal journals and responses to consultation papers. Also numerous broadcasting appearances.
Personal: Resides London. Sailing, ski mountaineering. Member of Royal Ocean Racing Club, Royal Geographical Society.

BURROWS, Lesley
Burton Copeland, Manchester (0161) 834 7374
Specialisation: Commercial fraud defence work including liquidation, banking, stock market, loan and leasing and mortgage and property fraud. Considerable experience of SFO investigations and prosecutions having acted for the first defendants in the Arrows and Butte Mining prosecutions.
Prof. Memberships: Law Society and Criminal Law Solicitors Association.
Career: Qualified 1980. Partner at *Burton Coplend* from 1990.
Personal: Attended Arnold School in Blackpool and the University of Sheffield.

BURTON, Ian
Burton Copeland, London
(020) 7430 2277 & (0161) 834 7374
Commercial Fraud Department.
Specialisation: All aspects of national and international white collar crime. Advising and representing both prior to and during investigation by bodies such as the DTI, SFO, Customs & Excise, and following charge. Extensive experience in major cases involving fraud, tax and Customs investigations including general financial regulatory problems, advising professionals facing disciplinary proceedings and cross jurisdictional cases.
Career: Qualified in 1971.
Prof. Memberships: Law Society, London Criminal Courts Solicitors' Association. International Bar Association.
Personal: Born 1947. Resides Cheshire and London.

BYRNE, David
Dechert, London (020) 7583 5353
david.byrne@dechertEU.com
Partner and head of Commercial Litigation, London.
Specialisation: Responsible for all aspects of investigation work ranging from disciplinary hearings and insurance disputes to serious fraud. He specialises in civil and criminal commercial fraud for both plaintiff and defendant. In particular, he has specialised in cases brought by the SFO, City regulators, Inland Revenue and Customs & Excise. He has acted for clients involved directly and indirectly in Barlow Clowes, BCCI, Resort Hotels, Polly Peck, Guinness, Blue Arrow, Hinchcliffe, Hamilton Wines, Leyland Daf and Hare Wines. He has acted for the only successful defendant in the Jyske Bank case in the Chancery Division. He also deals with investigations arising from Insolvency matters.
Prof. Memberships: Law Society, Society Practitioners of Insolvency.
Career: Qualified in 1978. Articled at *Norton Rose.* Solicitor *Norton Rose* 1978-1983. *Clifford Turner* (now *Clifford Chance*) 1983-1985. Partner *Titmuss Sainer & Webb* (now *Dechert*) since 1987.
Personal: Born 1951. Attended Kings College London, Masters degree in insurance law, Sweet & Maxwell prize for company law. Interests include golf and fell walking.

CAPLAN, Michael
Kingsley Napley, London (020) 7814 1200
mcaplan@kingsleynapley.co.uk
Partner in Criminal Litigation Department.
Specialisation: Work includes criminal law, advocacy, extradition, casino applications, gaming and licensing, and prosecuting for and advising professional and regulatory bodies. Sits as a Recorder. Rights of audience in the Crown Court. Vice-Chairman of the Solicitors Association of Higher Court Advocates
Career: Qualified in 1977. Joined *Kingsley Napley* in 1978 and became a Partner in 1982.
Personal: Born 3rd May 1953. Attended Kings College, London: LLB (Hons), AKC. Leisure interests include family, sport and reading. Lives in London.

CARNELL, Bernard
Offenbach & Co, London (020) 7434 9891
Senior Partner in Criminal Department.
Specialisation: Work includes commercial fraud, insider dealing, drug related crime, obscene publications and all areas of general crime. Particular experience of legal aid regulations and international and financial investigations. Acted in R v. Kellard and Others (Britannia Park Fraud trial, the longest in English history); BCCI Investigation; R v. Fisher (the first insider dealing trial); R v. Adelaja and Others (the first trial using computers); R v. Howard Marks and others (one of the largest and well-publicised drug cases); the inquest of Cynthia Jarrett (Tottenham riots); and R v Gay News Ltd and Lemon (Blasphemy trial) and numerous Divisional Court, Court of Appeal and House of Lords proceedings. Individual charge-out rate is usually £150-£220 per hour, depending on nature and seriousness of case.
Prof. Memberships: Law Society.
Career: Qualified in 1972. Joined *Offenbach & Co* in 1976, becoming a Partner in 1982.
Personal: Born 1947. Attended LSE (1966-69) and Law College. Lives in London. Former Board Director of Release.

COLHOUN, Aileen
Oury Clark Solicitors, London (020) 7629 8844
Partner specialising in criminal litigation.
Specialisation: Practice covers all areas of criminal work, particularly large scale white collar criminal defence work. Advises in investigations conducted by

other regulatory bodies.
Prof. Memberships: Law Society, London Criminal Courts Solicitors Association, International Bar Association, British Academy of Forensic Sciences, Chairman of Criminal Law Sub-Committee, City of Westminster Law Society, Justice.
Career: Qualified in 1983. Worked at *Kingsley Napley* 1981-87, then *Powell Magrath & Spencer* 1987-90. Partner at *Magrath & Co.* 1990-97. Founding partner of *Oury Colhoun and Co* 1997 (now *Oury Clark*).
Personal: Born 14th September 1957. Attended University of Bristol 1976-79 (LLB), then University of Cambridge (MPhil in Criminology 1979-80). Leisure interests include reading and live music. Lives in London.

COOPER, Ian
Burton Copeland, Manchester (0161) 834 7374
Specialisation: Partner specialising in business and corporate fraud, investment, offshore and tax fraud, mortgage and property fraud, professional misconduct matters, share and securities fraud.
Career: Articled *Copeland Glickman*; qualified 1987; Assistant Solicitor *Hugh Pond & Co* 1987-1989; Assistant Solicitor *Burton Copeland* 1989-1991, Partner 1991. King Edward VII School. Liverpool University (1973 BA Hons).

CORKER, David
Peters & Peters, London (020) 7629 7991
Partner in white collar crime/general crime.
Specialisation: Specialist in fraud, regulatory and general crime. Author of 'Disclosure in Criminal Proceedings' (Sweet and Maxwell, 1998) and 'Abuse of Process and Fairness in Criminal Proceedings' (Butterworths, 2000). Lectured to, inter alia, the Judicial Studies Board, SFO, CPS, DTI, Criminal Bar Association. Recent fields of interest include the impact of Human Rights law on crime and on the FSA and money laundering. Recent major cases include DTI-v-Maxwell, Wickes and a major miscarriage of justice case before the CCRC.
Career: BA from Oriel College Oxford, MA from University of Sheffield. Police Officer 1984–1987. Qualified in 1990 and been at *Peters and Peters* thereafter.
Personal: Born 1961.

CORNTHWAITE, Richard
Garstangs, London (020) 7242 4324
r.cornthwaite@garstangs.co.uk
Specialisation: Specialises in the defence of fraud cases, including SFO, Inland Revenue, HM Customs and Excise and D.T.I. prosecutions. Also handles ancillary commercial litigation, particularly in relation to fraud and asset recovery in the Chancery Division. Acted in the Guinness, Eagle Trust, Thermastor and Brent Walker cases. Also secured the acquittal of Kevin Taylor in the 'Stalker Affair'. Recently represented a principal defendant in Chancery proceedings brought by Jyske Bank (Gibraltar) Limited. During last twelve months represented defendants acquitted in cases prosecuted by HM Customs and Excise. Currently acting in Alpine Double Glazing and Richmond Oil & Gas PLC (SFO prosecutions) and three major HM Customs and Excise investigations.
Prof. Memberships: Law Society.
Career: Qualified in 1977. Joined *Garstangs* as a Partner in 1990.
Personal: Born 12th November, 1951. Keele University 1970-74. Lives in London and Manchester.

COWELL, Adam
Irwin Mitchell, London (020) 7250 1884
cowella@irwinmitchell.co.uk
Specialisation: Partner in Business Crime Group, specialises in SFO and DTI investigations and advises on regulatory matters including S447 enquires, CDDA proceedings and FSA investigations. Currently instructed in Jubilee Line Extention Fraud and SFO prosecution of internet company, BCCI related litigation (Gokal-v-UK) and numerous DTI and FSA investigations and civil cases.
Prof. Memberships: Hon. Secretary of International Criminal Law Association; Committee member LCCSA; Law Society.
Career: Qualified 1989. Solicitor *Bindman & Partners*, then partner at Moss & Co. 1993 to 1998. Partner *Irwin Mitchell*1998.
Publications: Regular lecturer on Company Investigations (including White Collar Crime Conferences 1999 & 2000) Business Crime and Internet (ICLA Conference 2000) and Business Crime and Human Rights (various)).
Personal: Lives in London. Enjoys golf.

DELAHUNTY, Louise
Peters & Peters, London (020) 7629 7991
ldelahunty@petersandpeters.co.uk
Partner in Business Crime.
Specialisation: Her principal area of practice is white collar crime, dealing with prosecutions and enquiries by the SFO, DTI, Customs & Excise and Inland Revenue. She also deals with regulatory and disciplinary proceedings. Extensive experience in acting for professionals, including solicitors. In 1998 she defended Judge Richard Gee. She currently represents Peter Young.
Prof. Memberships: Law Society, The City of Westminster Law Society, London Criminal Courts Solicitors Association (LCCSA), International Bar Association, Hong Kong Law Society. She is a member of the Law Society Money Laundering and Serious Fraud Task Force.
Career: Joined *Peters & Peters* in 1982 and qualified in 1984. Spent 4 years in Hong Kong between 1986 and 1990, practising in both criminal and commercial litigation. Returned to *Peters & Peters* in 1990 and became a Partner in 1991. Lectures on mortgage fraud, money laundering and human rights. In 1998 lectured on behalf of the Law Society to lawyers in the Middle East.

FINKLER, Deborah L.
Slaughter and May, London (020) 7600 1200

FLETCHER, I. Rod
Russell Jones & Walker, London (020) 7837 2808
Partner and Head of Criminal and Business Investigations Department.
Specialisation: Main area of practice is criminal defence. Has particular involvement with white collar/ business crime and major miscarriage of justice cases. Also regularly instructed in disciplinary cases. Represents individuals attending a number of government and other public inquiries: examples include the Scott Inquiry, the Stephen Lawrence Inquiry, the Marchioness Inquiry and the Bloody Sunday Inquiry. Acted in many miscarriage of justice cases, including the representation of the police officers prosecuted following the Birmingham Six, Guildford Four and Broadwater Farm investigations. Acted in the Maxwell, Barings and Bute Mining cases. Currently acting in a series of major corruption cases.
Prof. Memberships: Law Society, LCCSA, IBA
Career: Qualified in 1981. Worked with *Kingsley Napley*, 1979-83. Left to join *Russell Jones & Walker* in 1983, becoming a Partner in 1985.
Personal: Born 21st April 1957. Attended Berkhamstead School, then Birmingham University 1975-8. Leisure interests include sailing, golf, cricket and music. Lives in London.

FORDHAM, John
Stephenson Harwood, London (020) 7809 2300
john.fordham@shlegal.com
See under Litigation (Commercial), p.560

FOX, Stephen
Betesh Fox & Co, Manchester (0161) 832 6131
stephen.fox@fraud.co.uk
Senior Partner.
Specialisation: International and UK Fraud, Commercial Crime and Defendant injunctive work including defence of DTI, Excise and Revenue prosecutions, Solicitors Tribunal and professional proceedings. Defence of Extradition proceedings.
Prof. Memberships: The Law Society, The Manchester Law Society
Career: Instructed by Defendants in Eagle Trust, BCCI, Arrows, IRL Group Australia (Malcolm Johnson), Kevin Taylor (the Stalker Affair), Jyske Bank, Alliance Resources, Hamilton Wines, Harrovian Property, G Grosberg, A Mandelberg and other Solicitor Defendants.
Personal: Born 8 October 1948. Educated Manchester G.S. College of Law. Interests: Rugby League and writing.

FRANKLAND, Matthew
Dechert, London (020) 7583 5353
matthew.frankland@dechertEU.com
Partner in the Investigations Department.
Specialisation: Specialises in defence of national and international fraud/white collar crime cases, including those brought by the SFO, DTI, CPS, Inland Revenue and Customs & Excise. Particular experience of High Court confiscation and restraint proceedings. Also handles regulatory investigations including those by the FSA and advises on investigations by professional institutes and insurers. He has conducted litigation arising from Criminal Law in the House of Lords and European Court of Human Rights. He also advises on transatlantic investigations and prosecutions and this work is set to increase following the firm's merger with US practice, *Dechert Price & Rhoads.*
Prof. Memberships: Law Society, Criminal Law Solicitors' Association.
Career: Qualified in September 1991. Joined *Titmuss Sainer Dechert (now Dechert)* in 1995.
Personal: Born 1964, attended University of Wales, resides London and Sussex. Leisure interests include sport, travel and art.

GABBITASS, David J.L.
Wolferstans, Plymouth (01752) 663295
Partner specialising in criminal advocacy.
Specialisation: Regular advocate for prosecution and defence in the Crown Court and Magistrates' Courts and for the defence at Courts Martial for all branches of the services. Represents police officers at disciplinary hearings, solicitors at Solicitors' Disciplinary Tribunals and also appears at inquests. Former agent for the DPP, Treasury Solicitor and Bank of England. Currently agent solicitor for the DTI. Mem-

ber of Justice Committee on Fraud Trials. Appears on television and radio, as well as regularly having articles published in the local press. Chairman S.S.A.T., Adjudicator Criminal Injuries Compensation Panel. Member Criminal Injuries Compensation Board.
Prof. Memberships: Law Society, Fellow of the Chartered Institute of Arbitrators, Higher Courts Advocates Association.
Career: Plymouth City Police 1956-59. Joined practice in 1959, became Partner in 1965, Senior Partner in 1980 and Managing Partner in 1986. President of Plymouth Law Society, 1987. Obtained Higher Court advocacy rights in 1994.
Personal: Born 19th July 1935. Attended Huish's Grammar School, Taunton 1945-51. President of Plymouth Albion RFC, 1985-90. Past President of Rotary Club of Drake, Plymouth. Member of Management Committee of Somerset County Cricket Club and ECB Discipline Committee. Lords Taverner. Leisure interests include cricket and rugby.

GAINES, Keith
Lovells, London (020) 7296 2000
keith.gaines@lovells.com
Specialisation: Principal areas of work: contentious insolvency, commercial fraud, asset tracing. Wide experience with emphasis on cross border situations encompassing many jurisdictions from USA through Caribbean to Europe and Far East. Advised on several key legal developments in last 10 years; acted on several high profile cases, including liquidation of BCCI. Advises UK accountants, overseas lawyers, UK and overseas financial institutions. Experienced in dealings with Serious Fraud Office and other regulatory bodies. Worked for the administrators of British and Commonwealth, ING in the Barings collapse, the receivers of Rosehaugh, and for the court-appointed receivers. Much of his work before the courts has advanced legal principles, particularly in leading the Derby v. Weldon case.
Prof. Memberships: The Law Society, International Bar Association, Society of Practitioners of Insolvency, AEPPC. Author of several articles and talks on insolvency.
Career: Qualified 1981; seconded to New York 1984-86; partner 1986, London; admitted Hong Kong solicitor 1986.

GERRARD, D. Neil
DLA, London (08700) 111 111
neil.gerrard@dla.com
Specialisation: Partner and Head of the Regulatory Group specialising in the defence of companies under investigation from the various Regulators but particularly in respect of Inland Revenue and Customs & Excise investigations. His most notable case was acting for Anchor Butter and the New Zealand Dairy Board in the largest ever Customs & Excise investigation. He is increasingly called upon to act for large multi-nationals involved in the full panoply of Customs and duty issues including IPR/OPR, CAP and GSP issues. DLA Corporate Defence team, which is part of the Regulatory Group, has a 24 hour, 7 days a week emergency call out number from which the team of 27 defence lawyers can cover the country from DLA's 8 offices.
Personal: Neil, formerly of the Metropolitan Police, joined DLA in April 1995 from Pannone & Partners. He now works out of the London office residing in East Sussex. He enjoys sailing, golf and skiing.

HANMAN, David
Russell Jones & Walker, Manchester
(0161) 832 8877
d.i.hanman@rjw.co.uk
See under Customs & Excise, p.281

HARDING, John
Kingsley Napley, London (020) 7814 1200
jharding@kingsleynapley.co.uk
Specialisation: Partner in Criminal Litigation Department dealing with white collar and general crime. Recent cases include SFO and Inland Revenue Investigations, and International case work involving sanctions legislation and fraud and mutual legal assistance. Currently involved in the Jubilee Line Extension case and the criminal prosecutions of the staff and partners of Robinson's, solicitors.
Prof. Memberships: Law Society; LCCSA; CLSA; BAFS.
Career: Qualified in October 1988. Joined *Kingsley Napley* in 1990 and became a partner in 1994.
Personal: Born 9th April 1963. Educated at Derby School and Brunel University.

HUME, John
Ralph Hume Garry, London (020) 7831 3737
Specialisation: Partner specialising in corporate litigation civil and criminal with an emphasis on fraud related shareholder and partnership disputes. Experience encompasses international fraud actions, large white collar crime trials, takeover battles, post company acquisition claims, directors disqualification applications and Commonwealth capital appeals. Represents professionals in all disciplinary regulatory inquiries, tribunals and criminal matters.
Prof. Memberships: Liveryman and member of the Court of the City of London Solicitors' Company, past Committee member of the London Litigation Solicitors' Association and member of London Criminal Courts Solicitors Association. Solicitor Advocate All Higher Courts.
Career: Qualified in 1970. Articled at *Titmuss Sainer & Webb*. Partner in 1973. Partner *Ralph Hume Garry* August 1997.
Personal: Born 1945. Educated at Cranleigh School and College of Law, Lancaster Gate. Interests include shooting, scuba diving, watching cricket, rugby, motor racing and rallying classic cars.

HUNTER, Robert
Allen & Overy, London (020) 7330 3000
Specialisation: Litigation Partner and Head of the Trust, Asset Tracing and fraud Group. Has extensive experience in trust, asset tracing and fraud claims and is known as one of the leading practitioners in this area.
Prof. Memberships: He is currently Secretary of the Association of Contentious Trust and Probate Specialists. Lectures internationally on trust and fraud litigation.
Career: Admitted as a solicitor 1984; assistant solicitor, *Allen & Overy* 1984-1990; partner since 1991.
Publications: Contributor to: 'Halsbury's Laws' 4th Edition.

JONAS, Steven
George, Jonas & Co, Birmingham (0121) 212 4111
info@georgejonas.co.uk
Partner specialising in crime and personal injury work.
Specialisation: Deals with all areas of crime, from the most serious (e.g. murder) to minor traffic offences, with particular development recently in white collar and commercial crime. Acts for both legal aid and private clients. Also handles civil actions against the police and compensation claims to the Home Office. Increasing practice also in applications to the Criminal Cases Review Commission and to the Court of Appeal. Now developing a reputation for his knowlege of the European Convention of Human Rights and the Human Rights Act. Acts for both legal aid and private clients in this area also. Has been involved with several high profile criminal cases (e.g. 'Home Alone' Heidi Colwell) and personal injury cases (e.g. 'failed vasectomy', Mr & Mrs Stobie). Author of publications in the 'New Law Journal' on costs in criminal cases. Has a large amount of media experience involving newspapers, radio and television, both local and national.
Prof. Memberships: Law Society, Birmingham Law Society, Personal Injury Panel, AVMA, APIL, Liberty.
Career: Qualified in 1981. Joined *George Jonas & Co.* as a Partner in 1982. Became senior partner in 1993. Chairman of Birmingham Young Solicitors Group 1989-90. Member of Birmingham Law Society's Council since 1990 (Library Committee since 1990, Civil Litigation Committee 1991-1995 and Criminal Litigation Committee since 1995). Member of Legal Aid Board No.6 Area Committee and of the Law Society Personal Injury Panel from 1994.
Personal: Born 30th December 1956. Educated at Moseley School, Birmingham until 1975, then Manchester University 1975-78. School Governor in 1974. Enjoys mountaineering, listening to music and good food and wine. Lives in Birmingham.

KENYON, Andrew
Betesh Fox & Co, Manchester (0161) 832 6131
andrew.kenyon@beteshfox.co.uk
Specialisation: Partner in Serious and Commercial Crime Department. Commercial Fraud and Business Crime including defence of cases instituted by SFO, DTI, Inland Revenue and Customs and Excise: and other areas of white collar crime.
Prof. Memberships: The Law Society and the Manchester Law Society.
Career: Qualified 1970. Practised in both Private Practice and Crown Prosecution Service. Joined *Betesh Fox & Co* as Partner in 1993. Instructed by Defendants in Arrows, Financial Services Group plc, Ahmed (British Telecom Fraud), Herr Peter Tuegel, Allgemeine Handels and Effectenbank AG, BancEurope, Robinsons (Legal Aid Fraud).
Personal: Born 13th March 1946. Educated Oundle School and Leeds University. Interests include sport, walking, theatre and cinema.

KENYON, Michael J.
Burton Copeland, Manchester (0161) 834 7374
Specialisation: Commercial fraud investigation and including prospectus fraud, loan and leasinf fraud, insider dealing, fraudulent trading, frauds on investors, property and mortgage fraud, corruption and tax investigations. Considerable recent experience of advising and defending in Customs, Duty and VAT cases. Defends numerous solicitors charged with mortgage and other frauds.
Prof. Memberships: Law Society, Criminal Law Solicitors Association.
Career: Qualified in 1980. Partner at *Chafes*, Stockport 1985-1986 Senior Crown Prosecutor in Manchester 1987-1989. Partner at *Burton Copeland* from 1990.

Personal: Born 1956. Attended Manchester Grammar School and University of Kent. Leisure interests include salmon fishing, game shooting, military and political history and opera. Lives in Cheshire and Scotland.

KIRK, David
Simons Muirhead & Burton, London
(020) 7734 4499
Head. Fraud Department.
Specialisation: Commercial Fraud (including SFO, DTI, Inland Revenue and Customs & Excise investigations), Regulation, Investigations. Co-author of 'Serious Fraud–Investigation and Trial' (2nd Edition, Butterworths 1997).
Prof. Memberships: Law Society, LCCSA, IBA.
Career: Qualified in 1989. Called to the Bar 1974. Worked at the office of the DPP 1976-85, and the Law Officers Department 1985-88. Partner at *Stephenson Harwood* 1989-94; joined *Simons Muirhead & Burton* as a Partner in 1994.

MAYHEW, David
Clifford Chance, London (020) 7600 1000
david.mayhew@cliffordchance.com
Specialisation: David Mayhew has been a partner in *Clifford Chance* since 1987, specialising in complex financial litigation and regulatory proceedings, acting as litigation partner and as solicitor advocate in all forums. Recent experience includes investigations, including multi-jurisdictional investigations, and appearing in SFA disciplinary proceedings; representing the FSA in litigation under the Financial Services Act 1986; and acting as legal advisor in disciplinary tribunals in London futures markets. He is a member of the FSA's Lawyers Consultative Group and Practitioner Group on Regulation of Market Abuse. He also sits as a Recorder in the Crown Court.

MCCORMICK, Peter D.G.
McCormicks, Leeds (0113) 246 0622
Senior partner.
Specialisation: Over 20 years experience of complex fraud cases of all types–defending white collar fraud; DTI investigations, prosecutions and applications to disqualify Directors; Inland Revenue, VAT, back duty and other Customs and Excise prosecutions and inquiries on an international basis including appearing in the High Court on Mareva and other restraining order hearings; conducts cases before the VAT Tribunals and Commissioners of Inland Revenue. Holds the Higher Courts (Criminal Proceedings) Qualification, conducting cases in the Magistrates and Crown Courts and the Court of Appeal. Has conducted a number of substantial and high profile cases internationally including the first case of extradition from Uruguay (the bullion dealer Harvey Michael Ross–alleged £20m fraud), the first G.P. to be prosecuted for conspiracy to defraud the Health Service, the largest fraud case ever prosecuted by the West Yorkshire Fraud Squad and taxation cases where the tax involved has exceeded £25m; founder member of the Complex Case Practitioners Group; Supervisor for Serious Fraud Panel Work, Criminal Defence Service. Other areas of practice include: Sports Law and Media and Entertainment Law (Leader in the Field in both–see elsewhere) and Commercial. Lectures widely. Resident legal expert on Radio Leeds, Yorkshire Television and the Yorkshire Post. Also writes for the Gazette, the Lawyer and other legal and business journals. Author of 'Sport, Business and the Law' published by Jordans.
Prof. Memberships: Associate Director and Legal Counsel Leeds United F.C. Chairman of the Yorkshire Young Achievers Awards. Member of the Advisory Board, Sports Law Centre, Anglia University; Vice-President of The Outward Bound Trust; Solicitor to The Duke of Edinburgh's Award; Member of the Legal Working Party of The F.A. Premier League; Patron of the Harrogate Junior Chamber of Commerce; Trustee, Friends of War Memorials.

MITCHELL, John
Blake Lapthorn, Fareham (01489) 579990
jjmitchell@blakelapthorn.co.uk
Partner in Regulatory Unit.
Specialisation: Main areas of practice are white collar and corporate fraud. Has practised criminal law since qualification and now concentrates on defending all types of commercial fraud prosecutions, especially tax fraud. Defends businesses against regulatory investigation, sanction and prosecution by local and national Government Departments and by Tax authorities, and is a member of the firm's Environmental Law Group.
Prof. Memberships: Law Society.
Career: Qualified in 1979. Joined *Blake Lapthorn* in 1977, becoming a Partner in 1984.
Personal: Born 2nd March 1954. Attended Portsmouth Grammar School 1962-72, Pembroke College, Cambridge, 1973-76, and Guildford College of Law 1977. Lives in Hampshire.

MURRAY, Christopher
Kingsley Napley, London (020) 7814 1200

MYERS, Sidney A.
Allen & Overy, London (020) 7330 3000
Specialisation: Litigation Partner and Head of the Regulatory Investigations and Proceedings Group. Deals with all types of contentious financial regulatory matters, principally for major international banks, investment banks and other financial sector clients, as well as investigations carried out by the DTI, SFO Inland Revenue and Customs and Excise. Acts for both firms and individuals in handling investigations and defending disciplinary proceedings brought by all of the major City regulators. Has extensive experience of litigating and negotiating a broad range of commercial disputes, including judicial review proceedings involving decisions of financial regulatory bodies and the UK tax authorities. Reported cases include R v Commissioners of Customs & Excise ex p Kay and Others. Admitted as a solicitor in England (1984) and Hong Kong (1995). Assistant solicitor, *Allen & Overy* 1984-1990; partner, *Allen & Overy*, London since 1991; partner, *Allen & Overy* Hong Kong (1994-1996). CEDR accredited mediator.

NATALI, David P.
Herbert Smith, London (020) 7374 8000
See under Litigation (Commercial), p.656

NELSON, Richard
Nelsons, Nottingham (0115) 958 6262
richard.nelson@nelsons-solicitors.co.uk
Specialisation: Leads substantial Business Crime Department comprising in-house Solicitors and Barristers covering full range of business related investigation and prosecution, acting for companies and individuals. Practice involves cases over wide geographical area throughout England and Wales often with international element. Current case work of Fraud (including computer fraud), Revenue and Customs & Excise investigations (including tax and duty evasion), Trading Standards (including for nationwide retail chain), HSE, Environmental, Companies Act, DTI and Insolvency offences, also corporate and other individual crime and SFO prosecutions (this year including Ostrich Farming case and instructed by Tim Robinson before Bristol Crown Court). Casework often involves pursuit and consideration of large volumes of evidence in various forms (several million documents in one case) and liaison with technical and forensic experts. The firm also has a separate department dealing with civil law implications and further department dealing with general and other serious crime.
Prof. Memberships: Notts Crim Justice Strategy Committee. Notts Law Society Criminal Business Committee (former chairman). Former Council Member Notts Law Society.
Career: Qualified 1975. 1972-77 *J A Bright Richards & Flewitt*. 1977-83 *Freeth Cartwright & Sketchley* (Partner from 1980). 1983 Formed *Nelson, Johnson & Hastings* (now *Nelsons*) with two partners and no staff in 1983. *Nelsons* is now one of the largest firms in the region, based in several cities.
Personal: Born 14.06.50. Educated Nottingham High School and Bristol University. Interests include sport and comedy.

OLIVER, Keith
Peters & Peters, London (020) 7629 7991
Partner in Commercial & Regulatory/ Business Crime Litigation.
Specialisation: Main areas of expertise are commercial, regulatory and business crime litigation, both domestically and internationally. Has extensive experience in this area and acted for Kevin Maxwell following the collapse of the Maxwell Group of Companies and for Anthony Parnes in the Guinness proceedings. Has done considerable work involving the powers of the SFO and the privilege against self-incrimination both at Common Law and under insolvency legislation. Wide experience of DTI Companies Act and various regulatory enquiries. President of AIJA Business Crime Sub-commission. Lectures, and has delivered papers on regulatory, jurisdictional and human rights issues.
Prof. Memberships: Association Internationale de Jeunes Avocats (AIJA), International Bar Association, Law Society, British Italian Law Association.
Career: Qualified in 1980, having joined *Peters & Peters* in 1978. Became a Partner in 1983.
Personal: Lives in London.

PEACOCK, Karen
Burton Copeland, London (020) 7430 2277
Partner in Commercial Fraud Department.
Specialisation: All types of commercial fraud and white collar crime. City background in commercial litigation particularly banking. Extensive experience in SFO investigations and prosecutions including George Walker, BCCI and Morgan Grenfell.
Prof. Memberships: Law Society, LCCSA.
Career: Qualified 1990. At *Slaughter and May* 1988-1992; *McKenna & Co* 1992-1993; *Harkavys* 1993-1994; *Burton Copeland* 1995, partner December 1995.
Personal: Educated at Longsands College and London University.

POLLARD, Stephen
Kingsley Napley, London (020) 7814 1200
spollard@kingsleynapley.co.uk
Partner in Criminal and Regulatory Department.
Specialisation: Practice covers all criminal work, but particularly white collar fraud and 'city crime'. Also handles regulatory work including disciplinary proceedings before the SFA. Acted for Lou Macari in the revenue prosecution of Swindon Town FC, and in the SFO prosecution of the directors of DPR Futures. Currently represents Nick Leeson, the ex-Barings trader, parties in the Deutsche Morgan Grenfell and Hambros enquiries and Lord Saville's Inquiry into 'Bloody Sunday'. Appears regularly on TV and radio on criminal law matters.
Prof. Memberships: AIJA, London Criminal Courts Solicitors' Association, City of London Solicitors.
Career: Qualified 1985. Worked at *Payne Hicks Beach* 1982-87, including 1984-5 as a Member of Secretariat of the European Commission of Human Rights, Strasbourg. One year with the Crown Prosecution Service 1987-88. Joined *Kingsley Napley* in 1989, becoming a Partner in 1990.
Personal: Born 5th September 1958. Attended Manchester Grammar School 1972-77, and Pembroke College, Oxford 1977-80. Leisure interests include reading, sport, theatre and family. Lives in Putney, London. Married with four children.

POTTS, John
Clifford Chance, London (020) 7600 1000
john.potts@cliffordchance.com
Specialisation: Managing partner Litigation. regulatory disputes and tribunals, statutory enquiries, white-collar crime, fraud and asset recovery and financial services.
Career: Worksop and Exeter Schools; Manchester University (BSc Hons 2.1) 1968. Articled *Clifford-Turner*; qualified 1982; partner *Clifford Chance* since 1987.
Personal: Born 1946.

PROWEL, Martyn
Martyn Prowel Solicitors, Cardiff (029) 2047 0909
mprowel@mped.globalnet.co.uk
Specialisation: Complex fraud trials, commercial and VAT/revenue fraud and other serious crime trial defences. Prosecutions undertaken for RSPCA. General crime, magistrates and crown court defence.
Prof. Memberships: Law Society.
Career: LL.B (Hons) Wales 1962-1965. European Law Studies 1965-1966 Nancy Univ. France. Qualified 1970. Former senior partner Hallinans solicitors.
Personal: Married, 2 children.

RAPHAEL, Monty
Peters & Peters, London (020) 7629 7991
Senior Partner.
Specialisation: Main area of practice is business crime and associated litigation. Handles major cases involving fraud, tax and securities offences, customs infractions and general financial regulatory problems. Has specialised in commercial fraud for 30 years. Author of numerous articles and publications on the subject. Has spoken widely at conferences held by, among many others, the American Bar Association, American Bankers Association, American Society of Criminology, The Crown Agents, Commonwealth Secretariat, Jesus College, Cambridge, British-German Jurists Association, the Anglo-French Law Society and the Bank of England.
Prof. Memberships: Law Society, The City of Westminster Law Society, London Criminal Courts Solicitors' Association, British Academy of Forensic Science, International Bar Association, International Fiscal Association, International Association of Penal Law.
Career: Qualified 1962; Senior Partner of *Peters & Peters*. In 1979 became the first Advocacy Training Officer appointed by the London Criminal Courts Solicitors' Association, (President 1982-84). Provided detailed written and oral evidence on the prosecution and trial of commercial fraud to the Roskill Committee and to the Royal Commission on Criminal Justice. Founder and past Chairman of the Business Crime Committee of the Section on Business Law of the International Bar Association. Served as a member of the Home Office Working Party advising on the proposed alterations to 'right to silence' in 1988-89. Chairman of the White Collar Crime Unit at the Liverpool Business School. Assisted the Council of Europe in its programme to help the emergent economies of Eastern Europe in their transition to a market economy. Has advised a number of offshore jurisdictions on money laundering measures. Honorary Solicitor to the Howard League for Penal Reform. Member ICAEW Fraud Advisory Panel. Chair IBA Anti-Corruption Working Group.
Personal: Lives in London.

ROBINSON, Kevin
Irwin Mitchell, Sheffield (0114) 276 7777
Partner heading Business Crime Unit. Based in London.
Specialisation: Acted in the major Iraqi arms export cases and also Astra/BMARC disqualification proceedings. Involved in arms export prosecutions in this country and the US. Represents Company directors, managers and professionals subject to investigation or charged with fraud, particularly JFO prosecution, fraudulent trading, VAT Inland Revenue and like offences. Also represents Corporations including multi-nationals and Plc's in criminal proceedings arising out of their commercial activities. Additionally acts in Local Authority Corruption Cases.
Prof. Memberships: Member International Bar Association. Legal Reds. Committee member Solicitors Associates of Higher Court Advocates, London criminal Courts Solicitors Association.
Career: Qualified in 1973. Joined *Irwin Mitchell* in 1974 became a partner in 1975. Former Treasurer of Criminal Law Solicitors Association. Higher Courts Rights of Audience 1995.

ROYLE, Charles P.
Glaisyers, Birmingham (0121) 233 2971
Specialisation: Crime, all areas including Youth & Motoring, Licensing–liquor & gaming.
Prof. Memberships: Law Society, Birmingham Law Society, Duty Solicitor.
Career: Palmers School Grays, George Dixon Grammar School Birmingham, Sheffield University. Articled *George Jonas*, Partner with *Jonas Grove & Co*, Partner with *Glaisyers* since 1979, now Senior Partner.
Personal: Keen Sportsman & Fan; Cricket, Tennis, Golf, Soccer, Rugby. Married with 3 children; President of Edgbaston Nursery School.

SANDELSON, Jeremy
Clifford Chance, London (020) 7600 1000
jeremy.sandelson@cliffordchance.com
See under Litigation (Commercial), p.567

SMYTH, Richard
DLA, Manchester (08700) 111111
richard.smyth@dla.com
Specialisation: Representation of companies and individuals defending enquiries and prosecutions commenced by Customs and Excise, Inland Revenue, DTI and Serious Fraud Office. Played a major part in Barlow Clowes Seil Trade Finance and Butte Mining litigation. Currently involved in a multi-million pound Inland Revenue prosecution, several Serious Fraud Office enquiries and the discreet representation of several national/international companies. Also represents solicitors and accountants in professional Disciplinary Tribunal proceedings.
Prof. Memberships: The Law Society.
Career: Qualified 1977. *Millers Solicitors* 1977-1987. *Burton Copeland* 1987-1996 (Founder member of Commercial Fraud Department). 1996 joined Commercial Regulatory Group of *Dibb Lupton Alsop*.
Personal: Born 4/1/53. Lives in Todmorden. Interests: wooden boats/sailing.

SPARROW, Edward C.A.
Ashurst Morris Crisp, London (020) 7638 1111
See under Litigation (Commercial), p.568

SPIRO, Brian
Simons Muirhead & Burton, London
(020) 7734 4499
brian.spiro@smab.co.uk
Partner.
Specialisation: Criminal defence litigation, specialising in business crime, drugs law and serious offences against the person. Also fraud investigation and international consultancy work. Regular contributor to legal journals and broadcaster.
Prof. Memberships: Law Society, LCCSA, I.B.A, A.I.J.A.
Career: Qualified in 1984, having joined *Simons Muirhead & Burton* in 1982. Became Partner in 1986. Author of 'Police Station Adviser's Index' (Sweet & Maxwell).

STAPLE, George
Clifford Chance, London (020) 7600 1000
george.staple@cliffordchance.com
Specialisation: Partner in London office specialising in all forms of commercial litigation and arbitration in the UK and abroad but especially fraud and regulatory investigations.
Prof. Memberships: Member of the Council of the Law Society; Fellow of the Chartered Institute of Arbitrators; Fellow of the Society of Advanced Legal Studies.
Career: Qualified as a solicitor in 1963; Queens Counsel, Honoris Causa, 1997. Joined *Clifford Turner* in 1964; made partner in 1967; Member Commercial Court Committee 1977-92; appointed by the Secretary of State for Trade & Industry as a Companies Act Inspector 1986 and 1988; partner *Clifford Chance* 1987; a Chairman of the Authorisation and Disciplinary Tribunal of The Securities Association and Securities and Futures Authority 1987-91; Treasurer

of the Law Society 1989-92; Director of the Serious Fraud Office 1992-97; partner *Clifford Chance* 1997; Chairman Fraud Advisory Panel. Member, Senior Salaries Review Body 2000. Hon Bencher, Inner Temple 2000.

TAYLOR, Paul J.
Pannone & Partners, Manchester (0161) 909 3000
paul.taylor@pannone.co.uk
Specialisation: All aspects of business crime.fraud and related proceedings. Advising and representing individuals & Corporations at all stages of investigation and litigation by the SFO, Customs & Excise, DTI, Fraud Investigation Group, Trading Standards, Health and Safety Executive, and other regulatory authorities. Significant experience in representing Solicitors and Accountants in a wide range of fraud cases, including those with an international dimension, money laundering and in serious/complex criminal cases generally. Successfully acted in a number of recent major cases for the Chief Executive of a former PLC charged with fraudulent trading; a Director facing multi million pounds VAT & Excise duty proceedings; a number of Solicitors under investigation for perverting the course of justice & high profile proceedings against pharmacy professionals.
Prof. Memberships: Law Society of England & Wales and Hong Kong; former member of the Criminal Law Sub-committee Hong Kong; Complex case Practitioners Group; Serious Fraud Panel Supervisor.
Career: Admitted in England & Wales 1980; admitted in Hong Kong 1985: Head of Business Crime *Alsop Wilkinson* Hong Kong 1989-93; Head of Business Crime *Pannone & Partners* 1995 to date.
Personal: Born 1955; graduated University College of Wales 1977; Keen sportsman and enjoys travelling.

THURSTON, Michael
Cartwright King, Nottingham (0115) 958 7444
Specialisation: All types of fraud for over 20 years defending businesses, directors and professionals. Experience in SFO, Fraud Squad, DTI, Customs & Excise, Inland Revenue fraud cases and regulatory investigations and prosecutions by the HSE, Environment Agency, Trading Standards, etc. Consultancy advice to commerce to prevent and detect fraud, and deal with the aftermath of it. Cartwright King is a specialist corporate crime (and general criminal defence) practice, and is a member of the LSC Serious Fraud Panel.
Career: Engineering graduate and worked in industry prior to qualification. Criminal Litigation partner in Freeth Cartwright Hunt Dickins from 1976. Involved in White Collar Crime department from 1990 to 1999 and remains a consultant to freethcartwright. Founding partner in Cartwright King which de-merged on 1 January 2000.
Personal: Born 1948. Leisure: tennis, shooting, golf, skiing.

TRAVERS, Harry
Burton Copeland, London (020) 7430 2277
Commercial Fraud Department
Specialisation: Partner specialising in white-collar crime, often with an international element, including tax fraud, corruption, insolvency/banking/insurance fraud/insider dealing and money laundering. Also specialises in regulatory and disciplinary work (e.g. Lloyds, FSA), Inland Revenue and Customs & Excise investigations, directors' disqualifications, and prosecutions for breach of environmental protection/health and safety legislation. Acted for Darius Guppy, Dieter Abt, George Hendry (the European Leisure case), Hisham Alwan (R v Allcock & Others) and Victoria Aitken. Disciplinary work has included acting for Derek Walker (Lloyd's Disciplinary Proceedings relating to Gooda Walker), and for barrister acquitted of professional charges arising from Cook Report. Fluent French speaker.
Career: Qualified as a barrister in 1986, a solicitor in 1990. 1987-1991: *Berwin Leighton* Tax & Trusts Dept specialising in tax investigations, trusts and tax avoidance litigation including Craven v White up to House of Lords. 1991 joined *Burton Copeland* Commercial Fraud Dept. Partner February 1995. Educated at Manchester Grammar School and St Edmund Hall, Oxford (BCL MA).
Prof. Memberships: LCCSA (sub-committees relating to fraud), BISLA.
Personal: Leisure interests include Manchester United, golf, languages and music.

WALLS, Alan
Linklaters (A member firm of Linklaters & Alliance), London (020) 7456 4258
alan.walls@linklaters.com
Specialisation: Partner, litigation department, specialising in contentious commercial practice, principally fraud investigation and asset recovery, insolvency and banking, encompassing regulatory investigations and other types of commercial dispute.
Career: Qualified *Linklaters* 1981; Partner 1987. Born 1957.

WILSON, Mark
Cartwright King, Nottingham (0115) 958 7444
Specialisation: Commercial and professional fraud and regulatory crime. LSC Serious Fraud Panel Supervisor. Recent experience of investigations and prosecutions by all fraud investigation agencies, DTI, Revenue, HMC&E, Trading Standards, HSE, Environment Agency, for corporations and individuals. Mainly defence representation but also prosecutions for regulatory bodies and advice to commerce the subject of fraud. Cartwright King is a niche commercial crime (and general criminal defence) practice, and is a member of the LSC Serious Fraud Panel.
Career: Partner in Freeth Cartwright Hunt Dickins White Collar Crime department 1990 to 1999. Demerged to set up Cartwright King on 1 January 2000. Remains a consultant to freethcartwright.
Personal: Born 1961. Leisure: family, motor racing, mountain biking.

WOODCOCK, Tony
Stephenson Harwood, London (020) 7809 2349
tony.woodcock@shlegal.com
Partner - Litigation Department; Head of Investigation and Regulation Group.
Specialisation: Main area of practice is white collar crime and business and professional regulation, including fraud, insider dealing, and directors liability. Has extensive experience of prosecuting and defending before professional and statutory disciplinary tribunals. Also deals with financial and professional investigations, conducting investigations for regulatory bodies in financial services, accounting and insolvency and advising institutions on launching procedures. Tony is one of the leading business regulatory lawyers in the UK and has acted in many high profile matters, including representing several directors of Barings Bank in the inquiries and litigation which followed the collapse of the Bank in 1995, the Banking Act enquiry into the aborted bid for the Co-operative Wholesale Security Business. Co-author of 'Serious Fraud: Investigation and Trial' (Butterworths). Regular television appearances in relation to fraud and regulatory issues and regularly presents seminars to those working in the financial services industry.
Prof. Memberships: Law Society; International Bar Association.
Career: Called to the Bar in 1976. At the Office of the DPP 1979-85 and the Office of the Treasury Solicitor 1985-87. *Slaughter and May* 1987-90. Admitted as a solicitor in 1989. Joined *Stephenson Harwood* 1990, became partner in 1994. Solicitor-Advocate (All Courts) 1996.
Personal: Educated at University College, London. LLB (Hons), LLM; Joseph Hume Law Scholar (UCL); Montague Prizeman & Harmsworth Scholar (Middle Temple); School Governor. Interests include reading, cycling, running, swimming and music. Languages: French. Resides London.

HEALTH & SAFETY

London: 422; The South & South West: 422; Wales: 423; Midlands and The North: 423; *Profiles*: 424

OVERVIEW: While few firms have distinct health and safety practices, contentious and non-contentious employment, environmental, personal injury, and insurance claims and transactions often encompass important health and safety issues. The need to comply with EU health and safety law and new UK regulations, as well as the increased publicity of large-scale industrial accidents and work-place fatalities have raised public and corporate awareness of health and safety obligations. All firms have reported tremendous growth in health and safety litigation and many have taken on a variety of pro-active roles in advising clients on liability, risk assessment, due diligence, and compliance obligations.

RESEARCH APPROVED BY BMRB: *For this edition,* Chambers' *researchers conducted 6083 interviews – 4408 with law firms, 598 with barristers and 1077 with clients.*

The validity of the research was scrutinised by BMRB International, who audited both the methodology and the results at our offices in July 2000. They interviewed Chambers' *researchers and cross-checked sample interviews. Details of the audit appear on page 7.*

LONDON

HEALTH & SAFETY • London	Ptnrs	Assts
❶ CMS Cameron McKenna	2	5
❷ Masons	3	1
❸ Nabarro Nathanson	1	1
Simmons & Simmons	5	5

LEADING INDIVIDUALS
❶ **TYLER Mark** CMS Cameron McKenna
❷ **BROWN Alison** CMS Cameron McKenna
SCOGGINS Mark Elborne Mitchell
❸ **SYMES Thomas** Nabarro Nathanson

Within each band, firms are listed alphabetically. *See **Profiles** on page 424*

CMS Cameron McKenna Handles both contentious and non-contentious work for a large blue-chip corporate client base from industries ranging from transport and construction to chemical and medical. *"Pragmatic"* **Mark Tyler** has particularly distinguished himself in regulatory and due diligence work relating to product liability. In criminal and civil defence work and public health and safety inquiries, he is assisted by the *"highly skilled"* **Alison Brown**. The two head a team which is widely respected for its comprehensive knowledge and dedication to health and safety issues. **Clients:** Various industrial clients.

Masons Considered particularly strong in construction-related health and safety law, this specialist team operates from both London and Leeds offices. Acts for builders and construction companies in a range of cases including an on-site death of a sub-contractor, breach of asbestos regulations, and inadequate welfare facilities. **Clients:** HBG Construction Limited, The Berkeley Group Plc, Bovis Lendlease Limited.

Nabarro Nathanson **Thomas Symes** heads the health and safety department of the firm's London branch and remains rated as a *"corporate lawyer who knows his stuff."* Involved in non-contentious aspects of health and safety, providing ongoing legal advice to construction, transportation and property companies. **Clients:** Great Portland Estates.

Simmons & Simmons Combines expertise in employment, construction, and environmental law to address occupational health and safety issues in railway and construction sectors. Advises Railtrack on health and safety implications, regulatory compliance, and risk management in the aftermath of the Paddington rail crash. **Clients:** Railtrack, theatre clients.

Other Notable Practitioners **Mark Scoggins** of Elborne Mitchell advises clients on risk-avoidance in industries such as water, transport, and chemicals. This complements his defence work in a number of health and safety prosecutions. His recent involvement in the Balfour Beatty Heathrow Tunnel collapse prosecution and Paddington rail crash inquiry promises to bring his firm a higher profile on health and safety matters.

THE SOUTH & SOUTH WEST

HEALTH & SAFETY • The South & South West	Ptnrs	Assts
❶ **Osborne Clarke OWA** Bristol	1	3
❷ **Bevan Ashford** Bristol	1	1
Lester Aldridge Bournemouth	2	1
❸ **Bond Pearce** Plymouth	5	5
Lyons Davidson Bristol	4	4
Veale Wasbrough Bristol	2	2

LEADING INDIVIDUALS	
❶ **BRETTON Richard** Osborne Clarke	
❷ **BYRNE Richard** Lester Aldridge	**COOPER Jonathan** Bond Pearce
WOOD David Bevan Ashford	

Within each band, firms are listed alphabetically. *See **Profiles** on page 424*

Osborne Clarke OWA **Richard Bretton**, with his *"deep, global understanding of the issues involved"* in health and safety law, places emphasis on non-contentious work, largely on behalf of quarry industries. Particularly active in fire law issues, Bretton also handles numerous due diligence transactions and is currently involved in a major police inquiry into a legionnaire's disease outbreak. **Clients:** National Britannia, SITA, CB Hillier Parker.

Bevan Ashford Acting equally on private and public sector claims, the firm's health and safety practice is chiefly engaged in litigious work. *"Reliable"* **David Wood** regularly prosecutes for the HSE on a local level. He has also acted on behalf of health trusts and housing associations in cases involving injury to vulnerable persons. **Clients:** Guy's Hospital, HSE.

Lester Aldridge **Richard Byrne** is *"easy to get on with"* and was noted for his expertise in regulatory matters. Handles both prosecution and defence work with considerable overlap with the firm's employment practice. Instructed by Health and Safety Executive in a prosecution relating to breach of pesticide regulations, resulting in fines amounting to £220,000. **Clients:** Health and Safety Executive.

Bond Pearce This insurance-driven practice handles HSE prosecutions for the South West as well as non-contentious work in risk-assessment, corporate due diligence and disaster planning advice. **Jonathan Cooper**, commended for his *"excellent rapport with clients,"* is a recognised expert in asbestos prosecutions for local authorities, and makes his debut in the new ratings. Recently acted in a prosecution following the demolition of a hospital. **Clients:** Nippon Electric Glass, Post Office, HSE: Offshore Safety, Chemical and Hazardous Installations.

Lyons Davidson The recent appointment of a former health and safety environmental practitioner and HSE inspector is expected to shift the focus of Lyons Davidsons' PI and employment practices towards health and safety issues. **Clients:** Insurance and road traffic companies.

Veale Wasbrough Handle both litigious health and safety work and advice to corporate directors on risk-avoidance and health and safety liability in contracts. These are dealt with from within the firm's insurance practice. Particular experience of Crown body procedures and expertise on the impact of EC regulation on everyday activities. **Clients:** Great Mills Retail Limited, EW Beard Ltd, Kleeneze.

WALES

HEALTH & SAFETY • Wales	Ptnrs	Assts
❶ Eversheds Cardiff	1	2
❷ Hugh James Ford Simey Cardiff	3	3

LEADING INDIVIDUALS
❶ WARREN Martin Eversheds
❷ HAVARD Robin Morgan Cole

Within each band, firms are listed alphabetically. See **Profiles** on page 424

Eversheds Reputed for his *"problem-solving"* attitude, **Martin Warren** handles a variety of health and safety matters in connection with his work in environmental and employment law. Although the practice predominantly handles criminal prosecutions in the coroner's court, Warren also advises directors of US multi-national corporations on management of labour relations and trade union strategy. The firm is currently conducting investigatory work following the discovery of radioactive waste in a public area. **Clients:** Luxfer, General Electric, Solutia.

Hugh James Ford Simey Acquired notable experience in health and safety issues through long-standing insurance and PI practices. Engaged chiefly in contentious work on behalf of insurers and health authorities. Acted for Hyder Welsh Water in a Crown Court insurance case on a damages claim further to the accidental electrocution of an employee. **Clients:** Hoover, AIG, CGU.

Other Notable Practitioners The *"effective"* **Robin Havard** at Morgan Cole has received favourable mention for his strength in regulatory matters and experience in accident-related criminal prosecutions.

MIDLANDS & THE NORTH

HEALTH & SAFETY • Midlands and The North	Ptnrs	Assts
❶ Eversheds Leeds	2	2
Hammond Suddards Edge Manchester, Birmingham	3	6
Nabarro Nathanson Sheffield	2	3
❷ Addleshaw Booth & Co Leeds	2	2
Halliwell Landau Manchester	2	2
Hill Dickinson Chester	2	1
Weightmans Liverpool	1	-

LEADING INDIVIDUALS	
❶ SHEPHERD Michael Hammond Suddards Edge	
WATKINS Gareth Nabarro Nathanson	
❷ BURNLEY Paul Eversheds	ELLIKER Michael Addleshaw Booth & Co
PARRINGTON Simon Hill Dickinson	PHILLIPS Christopher Halliwell Landau

Within each band, firms are listed alphabetically. See **Profiles** on page 424

Eversheds A strong corporate client base has given Eversheds' employment and environmental practices ample experience in health and safety matters. Particular expertise in chemicals and transport. **Paul Burnley** draws upon considerable environmental experience in prosecutions and inquiries into asbestos contamination and gas explosions. **Clients:** A range of clients in the chemical industry.

Hammond Suddards Edge Acting primarily for uninsured or self-insured companies, the firm has earned a reputation for dedicated customer service and impressive in-house advocacy. **Michael Shepherd**, commended for his ability to get problems resolved quickly, participates in a large number of fatal accident proceedings and offers training seminars for crisis management in chemical, power, and construction industries. **Clients:** ICI, Rank.

Nabarro Nathanson A *"go-getter"* reputed for *"acting in the clients' best interests,"* **Gareth Watkins** divides his dedicated health and safety unit between litigious enforcement of health and safety regulations, drafting health and safety policies for management systems, and advising on corporate liability and due diligence in company acquisitions. Recently secured a not guilty verdict for Hanson Brick in charges brought by the HSE following a work-place accident. **Clients:** Hanson Brick, Coal Authority.

Addleshaw Booth & Co Carries out both defence and prosecution of claims for large company client base. *"Conscientious"* **Michael Elliker** was recommended for his ease with both regulatory and criminal litigation, and enters Chambers' rankings this year. Recently involved in Food Act and asbestos-related prosecutions. **Clients:** Manufacturing, transport and construction clients.

Halliwell Landau A growing practice, handling manslaughter, pollution and disease prosecutions from within its insurance litigation department. Defence lawyer **Christopher Phillips** is currently deploying his *"rapid personal style"* in a pollution litigation with 3000 claimants in the North-West. **Clients:** AIG, CGU, AstraZeneca.

Hill Dickinson **Simon Parrington** is known for his courtroom *"flair"* in chemical-escape prosecutions and accident litigation. Currently engaged in prosecution against local authority, contractors, and a water company in a black damp case concerning the escape of coal-mine gas into industrial estate sewers. **Clients:** Health and Safety Executive.

Weightmans Have earned a mention in Chambers for their heavy involvement in health and safety matters throughout the North. Possess wide insurance-based experience in handling employee claims, particularly over factory accidents. **Clients:** Local companies and individuals.

LEADERS IN HEALTH & SAFETY

BRETTON, Richard
Osborne Clarke OWA, Bristol (0117) 984 5298
richard.bretton@osborneclarke.com
Specialisation: Main areas of expertise are health and safety and personal injury. Advises a wide range of corporate clients, private and public on health, safety and fire issues and risk management and related due diligence matters. Also advises on criminal enforcement procedures in the retail and food sectors. He has a reputation as a litigator and lectured in all aspects of health, safety and fire compliance, risk management and facilities management..
Career: Qualified in 1978; partner *Veale Wasborough* 1987-93; partner and head of Health & Safety unit *Osborne Clarke*1993.

BROWN, Alison
CMS Cameron McKenna, London
(020) 7367 3000
afb@cmck.com
Assistant Solicitor in Healthcare Department.
Specialisation: Advises on civil and criminal aspects of a wide range of health and safety matters and acts for companies faced with criminal prosecutions, inquests and claims for damages. Also handles related litigation, including product liability litigation. Has written several articles for legal journals and spoken at conferences and seminars. Editor of the Enforcement Law chapter of Tolley's Health and Safety at Work Handbook. Holds the NEBOSH National General Certificate in Occupational Safety and Health.
Career: Joined *McKenna & Co* in 1988 and qualified in 1990.
Personal: Born 12th June 1966. Educated at Latymer Grammar School, Edmonton 1977-84 and Bristol University 1984-87.

BURNLEY, Paul
Eversheds, Leeds (0113) 243 0391
paulburnley@eversheds.com
See under Environment, p.424

BYRNE, Richard
Lester Aldridge, Bournemouth (01202) 786161
richard.byrne@lester-aldridge.co.uk
Specialisation: Advises on all aspects of health and safety legislation, company health and safety policies and their management. Provides representation in connection with Health and Safety at Work Act and associated regulatory prosecutions. Advises and represents the Health and Safety Executive in prosecutions. Part time employment tribunal chairman. Visiting lecturer at Bournemouth University in Health and Safety Law.
Career: Qualified in 1978. Joined *Lester Aldridge* 1983 becoming a partner in 1984.
Personal: Born 1955. Lives near Romsey, Hampshire.

COOPER, Jonathan J.
Bond Pearce, Plymouth (01752) 266633
xjc@bondpearce.com
Partner and head of the Health and Safety Group.
Specialisation: Specialises in all aspects of health and safety including prosecutions in all Courts, and advisory work in relation to health and safety policies and risk management and increasingly health and safety due diligence issues in corporate transactions. The work arises from all sectors of industry and commerce ranging from the nuclear industry to agriculture.
Prof. Memberships: Member of the Law Society Personal Injury Panel.
Career: Qualified in 1984, becoming a partner in 1989.

ELLIKER, Michael
Addleshaw Booth & Co, Leeds (0113) 209 2000
Senior solicitor in litigation and dispute resolution group.
Specialisation: Specialises in health and safety matters but also deals with trading standards and environmental cases. An experienced advocate who frequently conducts prosecutions on behalf of the Health and Safety Executive.
Prof. Memberships: Law Society and Leeds Law Society.
Career: Articled at *Booth and Co.* and qualified in 1974; with *R.C. Moorhouse and Co.* from 1977 to 1984; rejoined *Booth & Co.* in 1984. Deputy District Judge from 1988 to 1998.
Publications: Contributor to 'Litigation Practice' (Sweet and Maxwell).
Personal: Born 11 December 1949. Educated at St. Michael's College Leeds and University of London (Queen Mary College). Lives in Leeds.

HAVARD, Robin
Morgan Cole, Cardiff (029) 2038 5385
Partner in General Insurance Department.
Specialisation: Handles all aspects of contentious matters involving health and safety legislation and environment law, having advised and represented a wide range of both private and public companies on compliance with environmental law and health and safety legislation, including defence of high profile prosecutions, conduct of Appeals against prohibition, improvement, and enforcement notice. Provides advice and representation in relation to numerous water pollution prosecutions for manufactuing industry clients; including a number of pollution incidents arising from multi-party errors during chemical loading and unloading operations. Representation of both directors and company in prosecution by Health and Safety Executive following continued breaches of health and safety legislation and serious injuries (including fatalities) to employees covering such matters as access to confined spaces; workplace exposure to lead; mine safety regulations and transport safety.
Prof. Memberships: Law Society, FOIL, the first solicitor in private practice in \Wales to gain Higher Courts (all proceedings), qualification in 1995.
Career: Qualified in 1981. Partner at *Morgan Cole* since May 1987.
Personal: Born 7th May 1957. Educated at the Cathedral School, Cardiff, Epsom College and University College, Cardiff. Lives in Cardiff.

PARRINGTON, Simon
Hill Dickinson, Chester (01244) 896600
Specialisation: Personal injury specialist with an interest in Health and Safety. Much of his work is with the handling of Employer's Liability and Public Liability for insurers but a significant portion of his work is in the handling of prosections brought by Health and Safety Executive. He has been involved in a number of high profile prosecutions of major industrial companies including the Associated Octel case which settled law in relation to sections 2 and 3 of the Health & Safety at Work Act 1974 and the prosecution of Monsanto plc in connection with their breach of the terms of their licence for growing genetically modified oilseed rape.
Prof. Memberships: Law Society.
Career: Law Society's Civil Litigation Committee member. Formerly member of Lord Woolf's working group on the Fast Track. Deputy District Judge. Admitted 1975. Partner *Wayman Hales* 1980, Partner *Hill Dickinson*, following merger, 1997.
Personal: Gardening, all sports including country sports and skiing. Music, theatre.

PHILLIPS, Christopher
Halliwell Landau, Manchester (0161) 835 3003
Specialisation: Head of Insurance Litigation Department. Has considerable experience of Defendant personal injury issues, both within the Industry and private practice. Currently regarded as one of the leading UK specialists in Industrial Disease and Environmental Litigation. He writes articles and gives seminars on many specialist disease issues. He has a reputation for success in a number of leading disease cases.
Career: Articled Greater London Council; Qualified 1986; Partner *Hammond Suddards* 1992 – 1994; Partner *Halliwell Landau* 1994.
Personal: Born 1953, resides Halifax.

SCOGGINS, Mark
Elborne Mitchell, London (020) 7320 9000
scoggins@elbornes.com
Specialisation: Commercial dispute resolution: health and safety and environmental regulation; defence of civil and criminal proceedings; acted (1998-99) for Balfour Beatty in prosecution over collapse of the Heathrow Express tunnels and for Albright & Wilson in the HSE proceedings following explosion of their Avonmouth works. Represents Thames Trains in the aftermath of the Ladbroke Grove collision of 5 October 1999. Acts for a number of UK water companies in regulatory and environmental claims. Experienced advocate in public inquiries, inquests and court. Insurance: coverage, claims and industry regulation. Product liability and personal injury defence, principally mass tort. International (mainly EEA) commercial litigation and arbitration. Firearms law.
Career: Nottingham High School; Cambridge University (MA 1984); Inns of Court School of Law 1981-82; barrister of Gray's Inn 1983-93; qualified as solicitor 1993; *Davies Arnold Cooper* 1989-99 (partner 1993-99); joined *Elborne Mitchell* 1999. Visiting lectureships at the Police Staff College Bramshill and Fire Service College Moreton-in-March. Regular conference speaker and contributor to professional journals.
Personal: Leisure interests include target shooting, DIY and family. Born 1957. Resides in Dulwich, London. Member of Hawks Club, Cambridge.

SHEPHERD, Michael L.
Hammond Suddards Edge, Manchester
(0161) 830 5000
michael.shepherd@hammondsuddardsedge.com
Partner in commercial dispute resolution unit.
National Head of Safety Health and Environment Group.

Specialisation: Main areas of practice are Environmental, Health and Safety, Food Safety and Trading Standards.
Prof. Memberships: Law Society. Member of UKELA, CBI Environment Committee, Construction Industry Safety Group and European Food Law Association.
Career: Qualified in 1969. Worked in Town Clerk's office, Manchester 1966-72. Joined *Hammond Suddards* in 1972, becoming a partner in 1974.
Personal: Born 26th September 1944. Attended Bradford Grammar School 1954-1963, then The Queen's College, Oxford 1963-66. Leisure interests include cricket, football, golf and foreign languages (Portuguese, French and Spanish).

SYMES, Thomas
Nabarro Nathanson, London (020) 7524 6000
Specialisation: Partner, commercial property department specialising in shopping centres and general investment projects. In addition, advises on health and safety policy and legislation, particularly on structuring contractual arrangements to allocate responsibility for health and safety risks.
Prof. Memberships: Law Society. Anglo American Real Property Institute.
Career: LLB, Reading University. Joined *Nabarro Nathanson* 1982, partner 1986.
Personal: Resides London. Hobbies: Skiing, running, family.

TYLER, Mark
CMS Cameron McKenna, London
(020) 7367 3000
mlt@cmck.com
Partner in Product Liability and Health & Safety.
Specialisation: Main areas of practice are product liability and health and safety. Co-author of 'Product Safety' and 'Safer by Design'; Consultant Editor of Health and Safety Liability and Litigation; legal reviewer for Croner's Management of Construction Safety. Contributor to 'Buildings and Health: The Rosehaugh Guide to the Design Construction and Management of Buildings', 'A New Balance: A Guide for Property Owners and Developers', 'Environmental Issues in Construction' – CIRIA Special Report, CIOB Handbook Facilities Management and 'Medicines, Medical Devices and the Law', 'PLC Legal Risk Management Manual'.
Prof. Memberships: Law Society, Institution of Occupational Safety and Health (IOSH), CBI Health and Safety Panel, CBI Consumer Affairs Panel, Forum of Insurance Lawyers, International Association of Defense Counsel.
Career: Joined *McKenna & Co* in 1984 and qualified in 1986. Became a Partner in 1992.
Personal: Born 10th October 1960. Educated at Sir William Borlase's Grammar School, Marlow, Worcester College, Oxford and Kings College, London.

WARREN, Martin
Eversheds, Cardiff (02920) 471147
See under Employment, p.345

WATKINS, Gareth
Nabarro Nathanson, Sheffield (0114) 279 4000
Head of Sheffield litigation department.
Specialisation: Main area of practice is health and safety. Gives advice to clients on health and safety policies, organisation, inquests, public inquiries and Health and Safety at Work Act prosecutions. Lead partner for defendant in the Coal Industry Respiratory Disease Litigation, the largest multi party trial to come before the English courts. Has published numerous papers and articles in professional journals, magazines and newspapers. Regular conference speaker. Edits the 'Encyclopedia of Health & Safety at Work' and published the 'Health and Safety Handbook' in 1997.

WOOD, David R.
Bevan Ashford, Bristol (0117) 923 0111
Partner in planning and energy department.
Specialisation: Main area of practice is planning and environmental. Handled local authority planning work in Essex 1972-76; specialised in planning and advocacy at Public Inquiries while a Partner in Bristol. Now Head of Planning and Energy at *Bevan Ashford*. Lead Partner on privatisation of Port of Bristol including the environmental issues and parliamentary procedures arising. Author of an article in 'Urban Regeneration'. Wrote planning law section for NHS Estates 'Estate Code' guidance to land transactions by Health Authorities and Trusts. Lectured for NHS Training Authority, University of the West of England, CBI and others.
Prof. Memberships: Law Society, UK Environmental Law Association.
Career: Qualified in 1969. Worked at *Hatten, Jewers & Mephan* in Basildon, Essex 1969-76. Partner at *Harris & Harris*, Bristol 1976-88, then partner at *Bevan Ashford* since 1988.
Personal: Born 7th January 1946. Attended Taunton School, Somerset 1957-62.

HEALTHCARE

OVERVIEW: Firms listed here specialise in providing a comprehensive service to the main healthcare institutions, predominantly NHS Trusts and Health Authorities. Around 60 per cent of the work by volume is clinical negligence related, and most of the firms listed here are on the NHSLA panel. The rest of the work typically includes employment, PFI, property, commercial, construction and judicial review.

Mental Health: Practitioners fall into two broad categories: those representing patients and those advising Health Authorities and NHS Trusts. On the hospital side, many providers listed under general healthcare will have a small number of dedicated mental health specialists. Firms who have a particular niche in mental health include Hempsons and Capsticks, where John Taylor and Lyndsey Gee have developing reputations. In addition there are sole practitioners who deal only with Mental Health issues for Healthcare institutions.

RESEARCH APPROVED BY BMRB: *For this edition,* Chambers' *researchers conducted 6083 interviews – 4408 with law firms, 598 with barristers and 1077 with clients.*

The validity of the research was scrutinised by BMRB International, who audited both the methodology and the results at our offices in July 2000. They interviewed Chambers' *researchers and cross-checked sample interviews. Details of the audit appear on page 7.*

LONDON

HEALTHCARE • London	Ptnrs	Assts
❶ Capsticks	20	19
❷ Beachcroft Wansbroughs	12	47
❸ Hempsons	11	8
Le Brasseur J Tickle	13	25
❹ Bevan Ashford	3	4
❺ Trowers & Hamlins	3	25

LEADING INDIVIDUALS
❶ **FRANCIS Barry** Buchanan Ingersoll
HOLMES John Beachcroft Wansbroughs
MASON David Capsticks
❷ **BROADHURST Marisa** Beachcroft Wansbroughs
DINGWALL Christian Bevan Ashford
LEIGH Bertie Hempsons
SMITH Janice Capsticks
SUMERLING Robert Le Brasseur J Tickle
❸ **BARBER Janice** Hempsons
BLACKWELL Hilary Capsticks

Within each band, firms are listed alphabetically. *See **Profiles** on page 428*

Capsticks *"A comprehensive team able to demonstrate capacity in a wide range of issues including primary care, nursing homes and staffing issues."* Particularly strong in clinical negligence work, where the *"original"* **David Mason** and **Janice Smith** are leading figures. The *"responsive"* **Hilary Blackwell** heads a growing property and commercial department. A highlight of the firm's work this year has been advising approximately 20 Health Authorities on reviewing their eligibility criteria for continuing care in the light of the Coughlan decision, including how joint funding arrangements can be structured lawfully. **Clients:** Approximately 100 NHS Trusts and Health Authorities.

Beachcroft Wansbroughs Recognised as a leading healthcare practice in London, the team benefits from being able to call on the wider expertise of the national firm in areas outside the traditional health sector. **John Holmes** received widespread approval as an *"effective litigator"* with a *"reasonable approach,"* while the employment team has supported NHS bodies over the dismissal of five Chief Executives/Chairs in the last 12 months. Recognition was also given to **Marisa Broadhurst** who specialises in property. The loss of the firm's pre-eminent PFI team has *"left a hole,"* and some observers remain *"unsure exactly how the merger has settled down."* **Clients:** 100 NHS Trusts and 19 Health Authorities.

Hempsons Act for both institutions and individuals across the healthcare spectrum, including most of the Royal Colleges, the BMA, the BBA, the MDU, NHS Trusts and Health Authorities. Perceived to be *"reliable, if a little old- fashioned."* Possess strength in depth, particularly in clinical negligence, where **Bertie Leigh** remains the department's senior figure. **Janice Barber**, was also noted by the market. **Clients:** 7 NHS Trusts and 8 Health Authorities.

Le Brasseur J Tickle *"Undeniably experts,"* the team maintains a similar reputation in the market to Hempsons. Represents individual doctors alongside NHS Trusts and Health Authorities. The *"excellent"* **Robert Sumerling** is active across a number of different areas, and is a leading light in the firm's *"well respected"* clinical negligence practice. Property, PFI, employment and commercial matters form the remainder of the team's work. **Clients:** Approximately 45 NHS Trusts and Health Authorities.

Bevan Ashford Described by one client as *"thorough, quick to respond and approachable,"* the profile of the London office has been raised significantly by the recruitment of popular clinical negligence specialist **Christian Dingwall** (formerly of Le Brasseur J Tickle). The market suggests that Bevan Ashford are the *"ones to watch"* in the coming year. The team acts for a diverse client base, comprising inter alia health authorities and local GPs. **Clients:** 4 Acute Trusts and a number of Community Health Trusts.

Trowers & Hamlins Now entering its third year, the healthcare department has received the bulk of its work acting as both corporate lawyers and gatekeepers for the NHSLA. The firm also has particular expertise in staff accommodation projects, advising amongst others Great Ormond Street Hospital for Children NHS Trust. Other areas covered by the practice include PFI, employment, and mental health. **Clients:** Over 50 healthcare bodies

Other Notable Practitioners

Barry Francis (formerly of Beachcroft Wansbroughs) retains his excellent reputation among fellow practitioners in healthcare-related PFI work. His London-based team at American firm Buchanan Ingersoll will be looking to compete on the larger healthcare PFI projects in 2001.

THE SOUTH, SOUTH WEST, WALES & THAMES VALLEY

HEALTHCARE • South, South West, Wales & Thames Valley	Ptnrs	Assts
❶ **Bevan Ashford** Bristol, Cardiff	20	50
❷ **Beachcroft Wansbroughs** Winchester, Bristol	4	20
❸ **Morgan Cole** Reading, Oxford, Cardiff	15	15
❹ **Brachers** Maidstone	5	8

LEADING INDIVIDUALS
❶ **ANNANDALE Richard** Bevan Ashford
BARBER Paul Bevan Ashford
BROADHEAD Jill Bevan Ashford

Within each band, firms are listed alphabetically. *See **Profiles** on page 428*

Bevan Ashford This large healthcare practice has a national reputation as *"a class outfit."* Strong in clinical negligence, where the trio of **Richard Annandale, Paul Barber** and **Jill Broadhead** are recognised as *"aggressive and successful litigators."* Often chosen to work on complex, high-profile matters including the BRI Inquiry, where the team is advising Avon Health Authority. The firm has recently split its practice into clinical negligence and general healthcare departments. The latter will focus on PFI schemes for trusts, re-financing of residential care homes, employment cases and inquiry work. **Clients:** Approximately 120 NHS Trusts and Health Authorities.

Beachcroft Wansbroughs Established Bristol-based PFI practice now supported by growing clinical negligence groups in Winchester and Bristol. Represented the United Bristol Healthcare NHS Trust in the BRI inquiry, and successfully opposed an application for judicial review in Glass v Portsmouth Hospitals NHS Trust. **Clients:** 50 NHS Trusts and Health Authorities.

Morgan Cole Not on the NHSLA panel but nevertheless regarded as *"well-established"* in Wales. Clients viewed the team as *"responsive and timely"* and *"competitively priced."* Successful in tenders for the newly formed Pontypridd & Rhondda NHS Trust and the Bro Morgannwg NHS Trust. Although not possessing a similar profile in the Oxford and Reading offices, the firm is regarded as one of the few in the region to have any degree of healthcare specialism. **Clients:** 8 NHS Trusts, 2 Health Authorities.

Brachers A panel firm recognised as a *"class act,"* but far smaller than its main competitors. Favoured by some Trusts and Authorities in Kent and Sussex because of their *"accessibility."* **Clients:** 12 NHS Trusts, 3 Health Authorities.

MIDLANDS & EAST ANGLIA

HEALTHCARE • Midlands & East Anglia	Ptnrs	Assts
❶ **Mills & Reeve** Cambridge, Birmingham, Norwich	17	50
❷ **Beachcroft Wansbroughs** Birmingham	4	7
❸ **Browne Jacobson** Nottingham, Birmingham	⚐	⚐

LEADING INDIVIDUALS
❶ **KING Stephen** Mills & Reeve
❷ **PICKUP Raith** Mills & Reeve

Within each band, firms are listed alphabetically. *See **Profiles** on page 428*

⚐ *Figures unavailable at time of going to press.*

Mills and Reeve Since the merger with The Lewington Partnership, this large team has established a *"solid reputation"* in healthcare across the region. **Stephen King** has a national reputation as a leader in clinical negligence, while **Raith Pickup** is *"well known and well liked"* in healthcare-related PFI. **Clients:** Over 150 NHS clients across the country.

Beachcroft Wansbroughs Predominantly involved in clinical negligence and PFI work. Recently acquired South Warwickshire General Hospitals Trust as a client. **Clients:** 12 NHS Trusts, 3 Health Authorities.

Browne Jacobson Recently joined the NHSLA panel and noted by a number of competitors as *"up and coming."* Known largely for its strength in clinical negligence, the firm has also witnessed an increase in employment-related work. **Clients:** Approximately 20 NHS Trusts.

THE NORTH

HEALTHCARE • The North	Ptnrs	Assts
❶ **Beachcroft Wansbroughs** Leeds, Sheffield	6	20
Hempsons Harrogate, Manchester	11	49
❷ **Eversheds** Newcastle upon Tyne	3	1
❸ **Crutes** Newcastle-upon-Tyne	6	-
Hill Dickinson Manchester, Liverpool	⚐	⚐

LEADING INDIVIDUALS	
❶ **HALLATT Diane** Beachcroft Wansbroughs	
❷ **BRADBEER Ronald** Eversheds	**EVANS John** Beachcroft Wansbroughs
HARRISON Frances Hempsons	**SLACK Richard** Eversheds

Within each band, firms are listed alphabetically. *See **Profiles** on page 428*

⚐ *Figures unavailable at time of going to press.*

Beachcroft Wansboroughs Recognised by its competitors as *"a major player"* in the North, this large healthcare team is led by the widely praised **Diane Hallatt**, ably supported by **John Evans**, who drew particular praise from competing law firms. The strong clinical negligence practice is supported by a respected employment team, while the office is also noted for its health-related PFI work. **Clients:** Over 70 NHS Trusts.

Hempsons The largest healthcare practice in the North, this team has strength in depth across both offices. The experienced **Frances Harrison** maintains a reputation as *"a good negotiator"* and leads the Manchester practice. A Manchester partner acted for the defence in the high profile trial of Dr Harold Shipman. In Harrogate, the year's highlight was conducting a successful defence for both the Health Authority and the Scarborough & NE Yorkshire Health Care NHS Trust in the alleged nurse bullying case, Sally-Anne Chamberlain v North Yorkshire Health Authority. **Clients:** 73 Trusts and 26 Health Authorities.

Eversheds Smaller than Hempsons and Beachcroft Wansboroughs but increasingly dominant in the North East, Eversheds' Newcastle *"centre of excellence"* for health care won seven out of nine competitive tenders in the region during the last 12 months. The practice was strengthened by the recruitment of **Richard Slack** (formerly of Crutes) who joins qualified mediator **Ronald Bradbeer** among the leading individuals. **Clients:** Numerous NHS Trusts and Health Authorities including Newcastle and North Tyneside Health Authority.

Crutes Continues to be well thought of by its clients who appreciate the firm's strengths in clinical negligence. Suffered a setback with the departure of former head of healthcare Richard Slack. **Clients:** Gateshead and South Tyneside Health Authority.

MENTAL HEALTH

REPRESENTING PATIENTS

INDIVIDUALS (REPRESENTING PATIENTS) • Nationwide
❶ SCOTT-MONCRIEFF Lucy Scott-Moncrieff, Harbour & Sinclair
❷ EDWARDS Peter Peter Edwards & Co
MACKINTOSH Nicola Mackintosh Duncan

See *Profiles* on page 428

Hill Dickinson A large department, providing the main competition to Hempsons in the North West. Dominates the Merseyside region, but its influence spreads north to Cumbria and east into Manchester. Specialises in clinical negligence work, but also has expertise in mental health, nursing home registration and employment. Successfully defended all the hospital prescribers in the Benzodiazepine class action. **Clients:** 45 NHS Trusts and Health Authorities.

Lucy Scott-Moncrieff This *"feisty"* performer remains the pre-eminent practitioner according to her peers. Tribunal work is the main element of the practice's business but Scott-Moncrieff also acts for the mentally disordered on a number of judicial reviews.

Peter Edwards Maintains an *"excellent reputation"* built on 30 years experience in the specialism. Areas of work include tribunal representation, habeas corpus, negligent psychiatric treatment and the legal right to care in the community.

Nicola Mackintosh Recognised for her community care work, she is often prominent when there is an overlap between community care and mental health. Acted on the ground-breaking Coughlan case. Occasionally does tribunal work.

REPRESENTING INSTITUTIONS

INDIVIDUALS (REPRESENTING INSTITUTIONS) • Nationwide
❶ ELDERGILL Anselm Anselm Eldergill
IRONS Ashley Reid Minty
PARSONS Andrew Radcliffes

See *Profiles* on page 428

Anselm Eldergill Sole practitioner who specialises in providing independent advice to public sector institutions and charities on issues related to mental health. In particular, provides advice on interpreting the effects of the Human Rights Act and changes to the Mental Health Act. Has acted as legal chairman in five independent NHS and social services inquiries into homicides committed by psychiatric patients in the last 12 months.

Ashley Irons Specialises in acting on behalf of hospitals housing patients detained under the Mental Health Act. Provides a comprehensive service to the Special Hospital Authorities as well as private hospitals such as Cheadle Health Care. High profile cases this year include Brady v Ashworth Hospital Authority.

Andrew Parsons Has developed a leading reputation in mental health issues, and 40 percent of the healthcare team's work is mental health-related. His team produces a specialist brochure for mental health providers, a monthly mental health law briefing note and a 24-hour advice line. Currently advising a neighbouring country on the drafting of its new mental health legislation.

LEADERS IN HEALTHCARE

ANNANDALE, Richard H

Bevan Ashford, Bristol (0117) 923 0111

Specialisation: Partner in the health and social care group specialising in clinical litigation, medical law and risk management, particularly for hospitals with acute services. Handled a large number of compensation claims arising from a serious and widely publicised radiotherapy incident and succeeded in reaching over 100 settlements without a single writ being issued by using a novel method of mediation. Now involved in a high profile series of claims arising from the breast screening programme and with nationally sensitive issues relating to the retention of childrens' organs.

Career: Qualified 1977. Partner since 1993. Director of QRM Healthcare Limited (*Bevan Ashford's* healthcare risk management company) since 1993.

Personal: Educated at Manchester University (LL.B) 1968-71.

BARBER, Janice C.

Hempsons, London (020) 7836 0011
jcb@hempsons.co.uk

Managing Partner.

Specialisation: Has an enormous experience in all areas of Healthcare Law, though she specialises in employment law, contract law and the law relating to hospital and general practice. Has undertaken variously: medico-legal advice to and representation of defendant Health Authorities, NHS Trusts and individual practitioners covering all areas of hospital and general practice; professional disciplinary and other Tribunals and statutory Inquiries; defence of serious criminal charges and employment law, particularly in relation to hospital practice. Leading cases include R v. Cox 1992: manslaughter, euthanasia, acting for the defendant; Howard v. E Dorset Health Authority 1993: hospital, negligence, applicability of res ispa loquitur principle in medical negligence cases, for the defendant; Thomson v. Blake-James CA 1997: re. forseeability; WG Dick v. Brookmount Estates Limited & Ford Sellar Morris Developments Limited CA 1992: successful recovery of fees, under Order 14, acting for Plaintiff, a quantity surveyor; Colley v. Canterbury Council: House of Lords decision on planning law and compensation due to following compulsory purchase order; Stanley Royd Hospital Inquiry: Salmonella Inquiry, led to the lifting of Crown Immunity for hospital kitchens; United Leeds Hospital v. Duncan Walker 1997: Disciplinary Inquiry under HSG(95)25 and subsequent appeal to the Secretary of State.

Career: Graduated with a 1st Class Hons BA at the University of Reading. Was articled at *Hempsons* and admitted in 1983. Has been a partner since 1984. Often conducts seminars and lectures in all the specialist areas of practice set out above.

BARBER, Paul H

Bevan Ashford, Bristol (0117) 923 0111

Specialisation: Head of the firm's health and social care group. Is widely experienced in all areas of hospital litigation, in particular major obstetric cases. Pre-eminent area of work in recent years has been the handling of multi-party medical negligence actions (such as the haemophiliac HIV, Debedox and Benzodiazipine claims and the Myodil litigation on which he was the lead solicitor for Health Authorities nationally). In addition, has specialist experience of mental health law.

Prof. Memberships: Law Society.

Career: Trained with *Bevan Ashford*. Admitted 1976; Partner 1979.

BLACKWELL, Hilary

Capsticks, London (020) 8780 2211
h.blackwell@capsticks.co.uk

Specialisation: Partner in property department comprising five partners and four solicitors specialising in NHS property and contracts issues, including the private finance initiative special interest in community care and pioneered the Lewisham Partnership

approach to joint commissioning. Is currently working on a number of schemes under the Government's new 'Partnership in Action' agenda to enhance collaboration between the NHS and local authorities. Contributor to 'The Provision of Staff Accommodation in the NHS - Problems Issues & Opportunities'. Research Report prepared for the Regional Estates Management Group.
Prof. Memberships: Law Society.
Career: LL.B (Hons) University of Bristol, College of Law, Guildford. Articles *Veale Benson* (now *Veale Wasborough.*) 1992 joined *Capsticks* to head property and commercial department, 1993 partner. Member of firm's management committee.
Personal: Lives Wimbledon.

BRADBEER, Ronald
Eversheds, Newcastle upon Tyne (0191) 261 1661
bradeer@eversheds.com
See under Alternative Dispute Resolution, p.81

BROADHEAD, Jill F.H.
Bevan Ashford, Bristol (0117) 923 0111
Partner in the health and social care group.
Specialisation: Has over 20 years' experience in the medical negligence and medical law fields dealing with a wide variety of cases for the NHS and has been actively involved in multi-party litigation affecting the NHS. Was admitted in 1978, becoming a Partner at *Bevan Ashford* in 1986. Is advising Avon Health Authority regarding the Bristol Royal Infirmary Inquiry into the management of care of children receiving complex heart surgery at the Bristol Royal Infirmary. The Inquiry is considering the adequacy of the management and delivery of service. As the largest Inquiry ever set up to look into the NHS it is also looking at its organisation and culture, as well as the action taken both within and outside the hospital to deal with the concerns raised about the surgery. It is to make recommendations to secure high quality care across the NHS. Other important cases acting for health service bodies include Nash v. Southmead Health Authority and Taylor v. Somerset Health Authority, which was the successful defence of the first reported claim for nervous shock in medical negligence litigation, limiting the exceptions where such claims are allowed. Lectures widely to managers and clinicians on a wide range of medico-legal issues affecting the NHS and provides consultancy advice to NHS Trusts.

BROADHURST, Marisa
Beachcroft Wansbroughs, London (020) 7242 1011
Specialisation: All aspects of estates and commercial property transactions, with particular emphasis on developments. Currently lead Partner for the redevelopment of Guy's Hospital, Lambeth Hospital and St Thomas' Hospital. Also, the property partner on a number of other hospital redevelopments under the private finance initiative such as the Barts & London hospital PFI. Regular speaker at both internal seminars held for clients and external public conferences.
Prof. Memberships: Law Society.
Career: Admitted 1970, articles at *Max Bitel Greene & Co*, a Partner from 1970-71, the Greater London Council from 1971-76, the London Residuary Body from 1988-89 and *Beachcroft Stanleys* from 1989 to present, a Partner from 1991.
Personal: Born in Spain. Educated in Spain, France and at The Convent of Our Lady of Sion London. Interests include cinema and theatre, travelling and reading. Lives in Wimbledon, London.

DINGWALL, Christian
Bevan Ashford, London (020) 7421 4400
Partner handling defendant medical negligence dispute resolution. Head of the NHS Claimants Department at *Bevan Ashford.*
Specialisation: Principal area of practice is medical negligence. Handles a wide range of medical negligence claims on behalf of defendants. Important cases include Poynter v Hillington HA and Jenkins v Lambeth Southwark & Lewisham HA. Other past cases include R v Managers of South Western Hospital ex p. M. R v NW London Mental Health Trust ex ps and R v Brent & Harrow HA ex p. LB of Harrow. Clients include the NHSLA. Has addressed conferences and seminars.
Prof. Memberships: Law Society.
Career: Qualified in 1986. Partner at *Le Brasseur J Tickle* 1988-2000 and *Bevan Ashford from April 2000.*
Personal: Born 28th December 1959. Educated at Bristol University 1979-82 and the College of Law 1982-84. Leisure activities include gardening. Lives in Raynes Park, London.

EDWARDS, Peter Charles
Peter Edwards & Co, Hoylake, Wirral
(0151) 632 6699

ELDERGILL, Anselm
Anselm Eldergill, London (020) 7284 1006
Specialisation: Specialist in mental health law. Inquiries, conferences, lecturing, policy drafting, and training for NHS trusts and local authorities. Chairman, Mental Health Act Commission Legal & Ethical Committee, 1997-98. Discussant, xxiiird International Congress on Law and Mental Health, Sorbonne (1998). Chairman, IBC Conference, Mental Health Law, Regents Park (1998). Keynote speaker, 1st National Conference on Risk Management in Mental Health, Royal College of Physicians (1998). Main speaker, Institute of Mental Health Law Conference on Mental Health Review Tribunals, Law Society's Hall (1998). Speaker, Institute of Mental Health Act Practitioners Conference on the Code of Practice, Royal College of Physicians (1999). Legal chairman of five independent NHS and Social Services inquiries into homicides committed by psychiatric patients (1999). Advising foreign states on the reform of their mental health legislation (1999).
Publications: 'Mental Health Review Tribunals - Law and Practice' (Sweet & Maxwell, 1998, lxxviii, 1333pp); 'The Falling Shadow and the Deteriorating Patient' Mental Health Act Commission Discussion Paper, 1998. 'The Law and Individual Rights' in 'The Treatment of the Personality Disordered Offender' (ed. R Blackburn, et al., Butterworth-Heinemann, 1998); 'Psychopathy, the Law and Individual Rights' (Princeton University Law Journal, Summer 1999). 'The Legal Logistics of Independent Inquiries: Common Steps and Principles for Navigating through Tragedy' (British Journal of Health Care Management, May 1998). 'Reforming Independent Inquiries' (Journal of Mental Health Law, September 1999).
Career: London School of Economics, Oxford University and The College of Law; Mental Health Act Commissioner; Alexander Maxwell Law Trust Scholar; member of, and interviewer for, the Mental Health Review Tribunal panel; David Hallett Prize for Government.

EVANS, John
Beachcroft Wansbroughs, Sheffield
(0114) 209 5000
jevans@bwlaw.co.uk
Work department: Health Advice.
Specialisation: Partner. Specialises in health service and medical law. Recent experience has been concentrated on corporate issues and clinical governance issues. This has encompassed administrative law, matters of powers/duties, advising in relation to Notices issued by the external auditor, internal administrative arrangements, in particular, relating to procurement, standing orders and standing financial instructions. Has wide knowledge of professional negligence, consent, mental health and confidentiality issues as they affect health care professionals across the disciplines. Has wide experience of advising on the handling of high profile untoward incidents and of working with Public Relations in this context. Has advised and lectured extensively on clinical and corporate governance and related risk management issues. This builds on his extensive experience in advising on disaster handling, for instance in the aftermath of Hillsborough, Kegworth, Allitt and the Abbie Humphries abduction. Continues to act as the Secretary to the Queen's Medical Centre Trust in Nottingham. For some years he has been chairman of the regional Legal Advisors Group. Has also chaired and spoken at many local and national conferences on NHS-related legal matters.
Career: Qualified 1968. Private practice 1968-1973. Solicitor and assistant director of administration, Cotswold District Council 1974-1977. Regional solicitor/legal adviser, Trent Regional Health Authority 1977-1996. Secretary to the Trust, Queen's Medical Centre 1994 to date. *Wansbroughs Willey Hargrave*, (now *Beachcroft Wansbroughs*) 1996.

FRANCIS, Barry
Buchanan Ingersoll, London (020) 7920 3800
francisb@buchananingersoll.com
Specialisation: Public/private interface transactions including PPP, PFI projects and other commercial transactions in the health and other public sectors including public sector/private sector joint ventures outsourcing contracts and procurement and administrative law advice. Current projects include major hospital building and services projects (PFI). Managing Partner *Buchanan Ingersoll.* Regular speaker at conferences and seminars. Contributor to a range of specialist publications including Butterworths PFI Manual. A member of the Editorial Board of 'The PFI Report'.
Prof. Memberships: Law Society.
Career: Admitted 1977, at *Beachcroft Hyman Isaacs* (now *Beachcroft Wansbroughs*). Associate 1979-80, Partner 1980-1999, Managing Partner *Buchanan Ingersoll* 2000.
Personal: Born 14th March 1953. Educated at Enfield Grammar School and University of Bristol. Interests include travel, history and food. Lives in North London.

HALLATT, Diane
Beachcroft Wansbroughs, Sheffield
(0114) 209 5000
dhallatt@bwlaw.co.uk
Partner and national head of health law advice group.
Specialisation: Specialises in defendant medical negligence and health service related law. Has detailed knowledge of medical negligence, risk management,

inquests, the Children Act, the Mental Health Act, complaints handling, ethical issues, class actions and major untoward incidents. Has experience of a wide range of health service and public administrative law issues and has defended several Judicial Reviews. Advised in the Beverley Allitt case and was involved in overseeing the HIV haemophilia litigation and in the Myodil and Benzodiazepine class actions.
Career: Qualified 1980. Trent Regional Health Authority 1986-89. Partner at *Oxley & Coward* 1989-95 and at *Wansbroughs Willey Hargrave* from February 1995. 1999 Partner in *Beachcroft Wansbroughs.*

HARRISON, Frances A.
Hempsons, Manchester (0161) 228 0011
fah@hempsons.co.uk
See under Clinical Negligence, p.163

HAVARD, Robin
Morgan Cole, Cardiff (029) 2038 5385
robin.havard@morgan-cole.com
Partner in General Insurance Department.
Specialisation: Handles all aspects of contentious matters involving health and safety legislation and environmental law, having advised and represented a wide range of both private and public companies on compliance with environmental law and health and safety legislation, including defence of high profile prosecutions, conduct of Appeals against prohibition, improvement, and enforcement notices. Provides advice and representation in relation to numerous water pollution prosecutions for manufactuing industry clients; including a number of pollution incidents arising from multi-party errors during chemical loading and unloading operations. Representation of both directors and comapny in prosecution by Health and Safety Executive following continued breaches of health and safety legislation and serious injuries (including fatalities) to employees covering such matters as access to confined spaces; workplace exposure to lead; mine safety regulations and transport safety.
Prof. Memberships: Law Society, FOIL, the first solicitor in private practice in Wales to gain Higher Courts (all proceedings), qualification in 1995.
Career: Qualified in 1981. Partner at *Morgan Cole* since 1987.
Personal: Born 7th May 1957. Educated at the Cathedral School, Cardiff, Epsom College and University College, Cardiff. Lives in Cardiff.

HOLMES, John
Beachcroft Wansbroughs, London (020) 7242 1011
jholmes@bwlaw.co.uk
See under Clinical Negligence, p.163

IRONS, Ashley
Reid Minty, London (020) 7318 4444

KING, Stephen
Mills & Reeve, Norwich (0121) 454 4000
stephen.king@mills-reeve.com
See under Clinical Negligence, p.164

LEIGH, Bertie
Hempsons, London (020) 7836 0011
mamsl@hempsons.co.uk
Senior Partner.
Specialisation: Principal area of practice is medical law, with particular interest in cases involving obstetrics, anaesthesia, paediatrics, orthopaedics, neurosurgery and general practice. Other main area of expertise is National Health Service Acts and associated Regulations. Has dealt with a number of Court of Appeal cases including Gregory v. Pembrokeshire (1989), Forest (1991), and Bull & Wakeham v. Devon Health Authority (1989), DeFreitas v. O'Brien (1994), R v Nottingham HA (1996), Re MB (1997) and Thomas v. Brighton HA in the House of Lords (1998). Major clients include the Association of Anaesthetists and the Royal College of Paediatrics and Child Health of which he is an Hon. Fellow. Author of chapters in 'Ethics & Obstetrics & Gynaecology' (RCOG 1994) and 'Safe Practice in Obstetrics & Gynaecology' (1994), Dewhursts 'Obstetrics' 1999 and 'Neonatology' (Ed Roberton & Rennie) 1997. Lectures regularly to lawyers and doctors. Delivered the John Snow Lecture 1999
Prof. Memberships: Medico-Legal Society.
Career: Qualified in 1976, having joined *Hempsons* in 1973. Became a Partner in 1977.
Personal: Born 30th August 1946. Educated at St. Christopher School, Letchworth 1960-65 and the University of East Anglia 1966-69. Lives in Clapham.

MACKINTOSH, Nicola
Mackintosh Duncan, London (020) 7357 6464
admin@mackdunc.co.uk
See under Administrative & Public Law, p.59

MASON, David
Capsticks, London (020) 8780 2211
See under Clinical Negligence, p.165

PICKUP, Raith
Mills & Reeve, Cambridge (01223) 222 283
raith.pickup@mills-reeve.com
Specialisation: Head of PFI at *Mills & Reeve.* Considerable experience of advising on capital projects in the NHS. Completed PFI schemes for several NHS trusts and the NHS Executive with projects including acute facilities, mental health schemes, staff accommodation, nurse training facilities and car parks. Work includes joint ventures between NHS trusts and other public sector bodies or the private sector; EC procurement and tendering; CIM and Concode compliance, income generation schemes. Is a regular speaker at NHS seminars.

SCOTT-MONCRIEFF, Lucy
Scott-Moncrieff, Harbour & Sinclair, London (020) 7485 5588

SLACK, Richard
Eversheds, Newcastle upon Tyne (0191) 261 1661
See under Clinical Negligence, p.166

SMITH, Janice
Capsticks, London (020) 8780 2211
See under Clinical Negligence, p.166

SUMERLING, Robert W.
Le Brasseur J Tickle, London (020) 7836 0099
rsumerli@lbjt.co.uk
See under Clinical Negligence, p.167

HUMAN RIGHTS (CIVIL LIBERTIES)

London: 431; Midlands: 432; The North: 432; *Profiles*: 433

OVERVIEW: This year signals a transition, with the implementation of the Human Rights Act in October casting an increasing shadow on this area of law. We recognise shifting ground by renaming this section. In this context we define human rights as where the rights of the individual or collection of individuals are impinged by public bodies covering inter alia immigration, crime, education and freedom of speech.

Unusually, with the ground breaking formation of Matrix Chambers, it is the bar that has made the initial running. Amongst solicitors, while new human rights departments mushroom, market opinion for now continues to recognise the experienced civil liberties firms as remaining ahead of the field.

RESEARCH APPROVED BY BMRB: *For this edition,* Chambers' *researchers conducted 6083 interviews – 4408 with law firms, 598 with barristers and 1077 with clients.*

The validity of the research was scrutinised by BMRB International, who audited both the methodology and the results at our offices in July 2000. They interviewed Chambers' *researchers and cross-checked sample interviews. Details of the audit appear on page 7.*

LONDON

HUMAN RIGHTS (CIVIL LIBERTIES) • London	Ptnrs	Assts
❶ Bindman & Partners	4	4
❷ Bhatt Murphy	4	1
❸ Birnberg Peirce & Partners	⚐	⚐
Christian Fisher	3	12
Deighton Guedalla	2	1
❹ Winstanley-Burgess	2	-
❺ Hickman & Rose	1	6
Simons Muirhead & Burton	⚐	⚐
❻ Irwin Mitchell	7	4
Taylor Nichol	2	5
Thanki Novy Taube	3	8

LEADING INDIVIDUALS	
❶ BHATT Raju Bhatt Murphy	BINDMAN Geoffrey Bindman & Partners
GROSZ Stephen Bindman & Partners	
❷ CHRISTIAN Louise Christian Fisher	DEIGHTON Jane Deighton Guedalla
KHAN Sadiq Christian Fisher	MURPHY Fiona Bhatt Murphy
PEIRCE Gareth Birnberg Peirce & Partners	
❸ LESKIN Nigel Birnberg Peirce & Partners	LESLIE Sara Irwin Mitchell
MACHOVER Daniel Hickman & Rose	NICHOL James Taylor Nichol
SCHWARZ Michael Bindman & Partners	

Within each band, firms are listed alphabetically. *See **Profiles** on page 433*

⚐ *Figures unavailable at time of going to press.*

Bindman & Partners *"Bindmans are the ones covering the whole spectrum, they are possibly unique."* The breadth and quality of its work is widely accepted to give Bindmans an edge and an unrivalled human rights perspective. Its larger resources are deployed in a range of areas including immigration, criminal, mental health, judicial review, animal rights, inquest, discrimination and freedom of speech. **Geoffrey Bindman**, *"although not as busy as he once was,"* is still widely acknowledged to be at the top of his profession, particularly for his recent work for Amnesty International in the Pinochet case. **Stephen Grosz** who is *"exceptional in judicial review"* handled the judicial review over General Pinochet's medical report. He rises in the rankings in recognition of his Strasbourg experience and a wide portfolio of current human rights cases. New entrant **Michael Schwarz**, who underlines the strength in depth at the firm, advised Greenpeace on genetically modified crop protests.

Bhatt Murphy Last year's civil law breakout from Birnberg Peirce has won widespread praise for its *"consistent"* police and prisons work. *"They are always at the forefront. I admire their dedication."* Despite *"some criticism"* of the firm's narrow range of work, it is nevertheless considered very good at what it does. *"They are top rate if you are going to sue the police or a public authority."* **Raju Bhatt** is held in high esteem by his peers. Acknowledged for his *"depth of knowledge and experience"* he is elevated into the leading tier of lawyers. He is currently at the Divisional Court challenging the DPP's decision not to prosecute the death of Alton Manning who was killed at Blakehurst Prison under police restraint. **Fiona Murphy**, a founding member of British Irish Rights Watch, enters the lists in what for many was previously an omission. Both she and Raju Bhatt are *"tough and highly intelligent."* Current work includes, judicial review, deaths in custody, and challenges under the new Human Rights Act.

Birnberg Peirce & Partners Attracts a mixed review from fellow lawyers. For acolytes, it is still *"unquestionably"* top, with a pedigree for attacking the excesses of state power. The more common response, however, sees the split with Bhatt Murphy as only entrenching the firm's criminal focus, (*"it is mainly crime now."*) **Gareth Peirce** equally polarises debate. Garnering widespread acknowledgement, she is *"exceptional in the cases we use her in,"* but is increasingly viewed through a mainstream criminal prism. She is currently acting for Satpal Ram who is claiming physical abuse in prison and wrongful imprisonment on the grounds of racism. The human rights workload is perceived to have fallen off because there is less cross-over criminal work. Equally, the heady days of set piece Irish terrorist cases may have abated, but Algerian and Iraqi terrorist work has recently been undertaken *"and they are doing them well."* **Nigel Leskin** is seen to have *"done a good job"* on the Campsfield case.

Christian Fisher Well known for its work on disasters such as the Marchioness and the Ladbroke Grove rail crash. Also rated for its more broad ranging actions against the police, deaths in custody, inquests, and asylum refugee work. Although for some *"a great marketeer,"* **Louise Christian** has had a dedicated and successful involvement in a number of noteworthy cases. She is currently acting for eight bereaved families in relation to lost children following the Paddington rail crash. Also involved in actions against the police and deaths in prison. Due to market recommendation, **Sadiq Khan**, who has *"done well to get where he is,"* rises in the ranks this year. He has a case pending in ECHR in Strasbourg on Articles 2, 6 and 8 in relation to a man shot dead by police in Bedfordshire. Also won a House of Lords case which involved claiming negligence against the Metropolitan Police on behalf of a man who committed suicide in Kentish Town police station.

Deighton Guedalla *"Immensely talented firm, very specialised in actions against the police and discrimination."* Deighton Guedalla is well regarded for its human rights work, particularly in discrimination, immigration, police protection and criminal issues. Partner **Jane Deighton** has a niche in discrimination work and is widely recognised for acting on behalf of Jane Coker against the Lord Chancellor. *"She is a fiery lady.... barristers I speak to say she is knowledgeable and gets results."* Also represented a woman referee refused a licence and in another leading case achieved one of the highest awards (£300,000) of damages against the Metropolitan Police.

Winstanley-Burgess Immigration specialists who are *"pretty good on police actions."* This small firm has a good reputation for refugee and asylum cases, and police action work. Its lawyers are seen by peers to *"hold the interests of clients as paramount."* Also undertake pro bono inquest work, and domestic worker immigration cases. Recently instructed by Free Tibet Campaign on a judicial review in relation to the handling by the Metropolitan Police of the demonstrations against the visit of the Chinese premier Jiang Zemin.

Hickman & Rose *"Fine lawyers,"* seen to be heavily involved in actions against the police, miscarriages of justice, and judicial review. The firm has a special unit for miscarriage of justice cases and in addition to the headline Wormwoods Scrubs cases, is working on prison violence at Wandsworth and Portland juvenile units. **Daniel Machover** who has *"made a name for himself,"* is widely credited with exposing the violence by prison officers at Wormwood Scrubs Prison. Currently cases are pending against twenty seven prison officers and are due to be heard in the Crown Court in mid-March. Machover is acting on behalf of Harry Stanley who was shot dead by armed police in Hackney, and is also being instructed on two police restraint death in custody cases. The firm has recently acquired two assistants one who will assist with death in custody and prison violence cases and the other who will work in employment and discrimination issues. Act for Newham Monitoring Project who monitor racial incidents, Liberty, and the Close Supervision Centre.

Simons Muirhead & Burton *"The leaders for death row cases."* The firm is recognised as having a firm commitment in particular to Privy Counsel Caribbean death row cases. 90% of the firms work in this area is on a pro bono basis. Human rights activities are split between the more renowned death row work in the Caribbean and civil litigation in miscarriage of justice cases arising out of the work of the Criminal Cases Review Commission (CCRC.) Also act for organisations such as Greenpeace.

Irwin Mitchell Irwin Mitchell are among a group of firms to open a new human rights department. However, it drops in the rankings due to a reduced profile and a feeling that *"the new department will be aspirational until they start producing. But when they do they will do it well."* Also possessing a highly regarded Sheffield office it is for some a national human rights firm, particularly for employment issues. Represent a wide range of private individuals in human rights issues, including hunt saboteurs, road protesters and animal rights activists. Head of the new human rights unit, **Sara Leslie**, is noted for discrimination based employment law. She successfully acted for Jo Hayes in contending that secret soundings militated against women barristers in selection for the Government for civil proceedings. The firm also represented ten hunt saboteurs against Cheshire Police for unlawful arrest, false imprisonment, and assault and battery.

Taylor Nichol Small criminal firm recommended for its cross-over human rights work particularly in juvenile crime. Well regarded by some of the field's notables, one of whom stated *"I have nothing but respect for an exceptional team."* Recently led the appeal against length of sentence for Myra Hindley. Solicitor advocate **James Nichol** is *"Mr Energy."* He is currently instructing at the Court of Appeal on the conviction of a mentally impaired man for the murder of two women on Aldershot Common.

Thanki Novy Taube Ranked this year in recognition of its human rights work from a traditional crime base. *"Coming onto the scene for crime and police misconduct."* Work includes inquests, miscarriages of justice, rights of prisoners and the rights of the fugitive. Additional work derives from human rights issues for mental patients. The firm is a nominated member of the Criminal Cases Review Commission for cases such as unsafe convictions.

MIDLANDS

HUMAN RIGHTS (CIVIL LIBERTIES) • Midlands	Ptnrs	Assts
❶ **Tyndallwoods** Birmingham	2	6
❷ **McGrath & Co** Birmingham	†	†

LEADING INDIVIDUALS
❶ **PHILLIPS Mark** Tyndallwoods

Within each band, firms are listed alphabetically. *See **Profiles** on page 433*

† *Figures unavailable at time of going to press.*

Tyndallwoods *"If I had a conflict judicial review with a civil liberties bent, I would choose them for family or immigration."* Known mainly for immigration work Tyndallwoods is picked out for human rights in a region without the dedicated practitioners of the North or London. **Mark Phillips** is considered *"absolutely excellent"* by peers.

McGrath & Co Highly regarded firm known for immigration and criminal work in this area. The firm has recently established a human rights department, which has yet to capture a public profile. The respected Graham McGrath no longer works in this area.

THE NORTH

HUMAN RIGHTS (CIVIL LIBERTIES) • The North	Ptnrs	Assts
❶ **A S Law** Liverpool	1	1
Harrison Bundey & Co Leeds	3	1
Howells Sheffield	2	8
Robert Lizar Manchester	†	†
❷ **David Gray & Company** Newcastle upon Tyne	†	†
Irwin Mitchell Sheffield	2	4

LEADING INDIVIDUALS
❶ **BUNDEY Ruth** Harrison Bundey & Co
❷ **ABRAHAMSON Elkan** A S Law
SIMPSON Danny Howells
❸ **PURCHAS Simon** Harrison Bundey & Co

Within each band, firms are listed alphabetically. *See **Profiles** on page 433*

† *Figures unavailable at time of going to press.*

A S Law Good reputation beyond the Pennines, notably for prisoners rights work. Additional work in immigration/asylum issues, housing and mental health. There is a growing awareness of the firm's *"courageous and skilled"* work with women offenders, for example in liaising with Justice for Women in the cases of women who murder violent partners. In prisoners' rights, **Elkan Abrahamson** is praised by top flight London counsel for *"unearthing miscarriages, commitment and a certain originality."* Active on judicial reviews, the firm advised on access to condoms and the right of a prisoner to artificially inseminate his wife. Act for UNLOCK, a prisoners support group.

Harrison Bundey & Co Harrison Bundey, and **Ruth Bundey** in particular, are picked out by both London and regional practitioners. Ruth Bundey *"has a long standing profile in civil liberties."* She is responsible for the firm's work on death in police and prison custody cases and related inquests which commonly do not attract legal aid funding. **Simon Purchas** who covers complaints against the police is ranked this year in recognition of his judicial review work on prison governors' decisions on prison release dates. The firm is well known for work in prisoner's rights cases and public order issues. Other related work derives from immigration and family matters. Recently represented a same-sex couple in relation to a child custody case whilst one partner was in prison.

Howells *"Still up there for general work."* Sheffield firm seen primarily in criminal related human rights work for legal aid funded individuals covering civil liberties, public law, prisoners cases, judicial review and actions against the police. *"Know them for pro bono work, exceptional client care and being willing to go the extra inch, unlike many."* Also known locally for drawing on a *"number of strong departments"* such as personal injury, employment, education and immigration. **Danny Simpson**, *"a good criminal defence guy"* while not recognised by all for human rights work is admired by local counsel for miscarriages of justice cases and his legal argument. He acts for all twelve Asian youths charged with public order offences after riots in Darmal, South Yorkshire.

Robert Lizar Newcastle based criminal firm praised by national commentators for its human rights work. For fans, it is *"the Birnbergs of the north"* due to its dedicated approach. *"You have to go through hoops to do this work, and they do it."*

David Gray & Company *"Known and respected"* nationally, this Liverpool-based firm with a crime focus is also highly rated for its human rights-related work.

Irwin Mitchell *"Should be there, the fact is that what they do is excellent."* Being a commercial firm, it suffers a little from market prejudice but the Sheffield office in particular is an acknowledged player for its human rights work. The civil department is seen as more focused on human rights work than the criminal side. Act for a range of private individuals, including demonstrators (hunt saboteurs, road protesters, animal rights activists), ethnic minorities and those in dispute with public or regulatory authorities. Represented ten hunt saboteurs against Cheshire Police for unlawful arrest, false imprisonment and assault and battery en route to a hunt in 1995. The first case, that of Michael Peterkin, was settled for £3,500.

LEADERS IN HUMAN RIGHTS (CIVIL LIBERTIES)

ABRAHAMSON, Elkan
A S Law, Liverpool (0151) 707 1212

BHATT, Raju
Bhatt Murphy, London (020) 7253 7744

BINDMAN, Geoffrey
Bindman & Partners, London (020) 7833 4433
Senior partner.
Specialisation: Specialises in civil liberties and human rights, media law, defamation, anti-discrimination and general litigation. Author of numerous articles in the professional and national press on these subjects, and has broadcast frequently. Has represented the ICJ, IBA, Amnesty International, and other bodies in human rights missions in many countries.
Prof. Memberships: Law Society. President, Discrimination Law Association. Honorary fellow Society of Advanced Legal Studies.
Career: Established *Bindman & Partners* in 1974. From 1966 to 1976 was Legal Adviser to the Race Relations Board and thereafter until 1983 to the Commission for Racial Equality. Visiting professor, U.C.L.A (1982). Visiting Professor of Law at University College London; Hon. LL.D (De Montfort University).
Personal: Born 3rd January 1933. Attended Newcastle RGS and Oriel College, Oxford.

BUNDEY, Ruth
Harrison Bundey & Co., Leeds (0113) 200 7400
Partner specialising in crime and immigration.
Specialisation: Main areas of practice since 1980: crime, immigration and inquests. Acted in the Helen Smith inquest, the case of the Bradford 12 and of Anwar Ditta, and various Yorkshire drug operations, and involving women and violence. Contributor to the Liberty Guide 'Know Your Rights' and member of the Liverpool 8 Inquiry which published 'Loosen the Shackles'. Involved more and more with inquests into deaths and custody and currently instructed by the sister of Christopher Adler who died on video in Hull Police Station on 1 April 1999.
Prof. Memberships: Law Society, Leeds Law Society, Liberty. Chairs Law Society Immigration Sub-Committee.
Career: Qualified in 1980. Formed *Ruth Bundey & Co* in 1986. Merged in 1993 to form *Harrison Bundey & Co.*
Personal: Educated at the University of Kent (BA Hons in English & American Literature). Awarded Honorary Master of Arts Degree for services to law in November 1995: University of Kent. Management member of Chapeltown CAB and of Umoja House (hostel) and a member of West Yorkshire Justice for Women. Lives in Chapeltown, Leeds.

CHRISTIAN, Louise
Christian Fisher, London (020) 7831 1750
louisec@christianf.co.uk
Partner in civil litigation department.
Specialisation: Main area of practice is administrative law/judicial review, public inquiries, inquests, medical negligence, personal injury and disaster law, actions against government departments, and Human Rights Act litigation.
Prof. Memberships: Civil Liberties Trust, Law Society Human Rights Committee, Association of Personal Injury Lawyers, Immigration Law Practitioners Association, Inquest Lawyers Group, British Panel of the International Federation of Human Rights, Advisory Boards of Kurdish Human Rights Project and the Redress Trust. Law Society Personal Injury and Clinical Negligence Panel member.
Career: Qualified in 1978 while at *Lovell White & King*. Solicitor, Plumstead Community Law Centre 1979-81, then Advisor to the GLC Police Committee 1981-84. Co-founded *Christian Fisher* with Michael Fisher in November 1985.

DEIGHTON, Jane
Deighton Guedalla, London (020) 7359 5700

GROSZ, Stephen
Bindman & Partners, London (020) 7833 4433
Partner in public law and litigation department.
Specialisation: Specialises in public and administrative law handling applicant work on behalf of pressure groups and individuals in civil liberties and environmental cases including European Community law. Also handles respondent work on behalf of the Law Society and the Office for the Supervision of Solicitors. Major clients include Friends of the Earth, the World Development Movement (the Pergau Dam case) and Amnesty International. Frequently writes articles on public law and human rights. Contributor to 'A Practitioner's Guide to the Impact of the Human Rights Act 1998'. Co-author, with Jack Beatson QC and Peter Duffy QC, of ['*Human Rights: The 1998 Act and the European Convention*'] (Sweet & Maxwell, 2000).
Prof. Memberships: Administrative Law Bar Association, United Kingdom Environmental Law Association, Solicitors European Group, Executive Committee of Public Law Project and Governor of British Institute of Human Rights, Member of the Council of JUSTICE. Member of the Advisory Board of Judicial Review quarterly; Member of the Advisory Board of Education, Public Law & the Individual; Member of the Advisory Board of the Human Rights Incorporation Project.
Career: Qualified in 1978. Entire career spent at *Bindman & Partners*. Partner since 1981.
Personal: Born April 1953. Graduate in Law of Cambridge University and in European Law of Université Libre de Bruxelles.

KHAN, Sadiq
Christian Fisher, London (020) 7831 1750
Partner in Civil Litigation Department.
Specialisation: Main area of practice is actions against the police, employment law, personal injury work, judicial reviews, Inquests. Involved in all areas of civil liberties work. Sadiq has given oral evidence to the Home Affairs Select Committee. He has also authored various submissions to the Lord Chancellors Department on legal reform and writes extensively on civil liberties issues.
Prof. Memberships: Police Action Lawyers Group, Executive Committee of Legal Action Group, Inquest Lawyers Group, Society of Labour Lawyers. Executive Committee of Liberty, APIL. Member of The Law Society's Equal Opportunities Committee.
Career: Trainee Solicitor with *Christian Fisher & Co* where he is now a partner. He is a visiting lecturer in Employment Law at the University of North London.
Personal: Awarded Sweet & Maxwell Law Prize,

Governors Award, Windsor Fellowship, Esso Law Bursary and Awarded Society of Black Lawyers bursary. Labour Councillor in Wandsworth since 1994. Deputy leader of the Labour Group since 1996. Representative on Police Consultative Committee and Racial Incidents Panel. Involved in human rights visits to Turkey and has lectured in Poland on the ECHR on behalf of Justice. Member of Institute of Advanced Legal Studies Advisory Committee examining civil legal aid and Advisory Committee of Liberty examining independent police complaints system.

LESKIN, Nigel
Birnberg Peirce & Partners, London (020) 7911 0166

LESLIE, Sara
Irwin Mitchell, London (020) 7250 1749
Specialisation: Head of *Irwin Mitchell*'s human rights unit and the firm's London employment team. Specialises in human rights and discrimination law. Last year in particular was involved in two notable cases–Couch v The British Boxing Board of Control, Hayes v The Attorney General. She received the Wainwright Trust Breakthrough Award for her conduct of Enderby v Frenchay Health Authority and the Secretary of State for Health and the speech therapists' equal value litigation.
Prof. Memberships: Justice, Liberty, ILF, ELA, Maternity Alliance and the TUC Equal Value Working Party.
Career: Qualified as a solicitor in 1984 and employed at *Thompsons*, becoming a partner in 1986. Moved to *Irwin Mitchell* in 1995 to open *Irwin Mitchell*'s London office.
Personal: Born 1956, resides London. Interests include skiing and opera.

MACHOVER, Daniel
Hickman & Rose, London (020) 7700 2211
dmachover@hickmanandrose.co.uk
Specialisation: Civil remedies to all problems experienced by people within the criminal justice system, including actions against the police, judicial review of chief officers of police, magistrates, prison governors and the Home Secretary, inquests and claims arising out of assaults by prison officers. Represents over fifty alleged victims of assaults at HMP Wormwood Scrubs.
Prof. Memberships: Founder of Lawyers for Palestinian Human Rights, convenor of the Working Group of Lawyers for Liberty, member of Council of Liberty, Inquest Lawyers Group, Prisoners' Rights Legal Group and APIL.
Career: Qualified 1988, worked at North Kensington Law Centre, Liberty's legal department (locum) and *Christian Fisher* before joining *Hickman and Rose* in January 1997 as head of the civil litigation department. Partner since March 1998.
Personal: LL.B., LL.M. in International Human Rights Law.

MURPHY, Fiona
Bhatt Murphy, London (020) 7253 7744

NICHOL, James
Taylor Nichol, London (020) 7272 8336

PEIRCE, Gareth
Birnberg Peirce & Partners, London (020) 7911 0166

PHILLIPS, Mark
Tyndallwoods, Birmingham (0121) 624 1111
Mark_Phillips@tyndallwoods.co.uk
See under Immigration, p.444

PURCHAS, Simon R.
Harrison Bundey & Co., Leeds (0113) 200 7400
Specialisation: After more than ten years in criminal defence practice now specialising in related civil law aspects of criminal defence work, principally actions against police, prisoners' rights, judicial review and a range of civil liberties.
Career: BA (Hons) History and Philosophy, Leeds University. Qualified as a solicitor in 1985. Joined *Ruth Bundey & Co* as a partner in 1988 and since 1993 as a partner in the merged practice of *Harrison Bundey & Co.*
Prof. Memberships: Law Society.

SCHWARZ, Michael
Bindman & Partners, London (020) 7833 4433
Specialisation: Specialist in criminal defence work, including fresh evidence appeals to the Court of Appeal. Acts often for political activists and campaigners on environmental, animal rights, peace/disarmament, race, social justice issues. Particular experience of public order arrests and multi-defendant trials. Has represented anti-roads protestors at Twyford Down, the M11 and Newbury. Represents Greenpeace campaigners against GMOs and charges at London demonstrations on June 18th 1999, November 30th 1999 and 1st May 2000. Represents family of Michael Menson set alight by racists in North London, at inquest, Old Bailey Prosecution and police complaint. Represented Animal Defenders in successful prosecution of Chipperfields for animal cruelty. Also inquests, extradition, police complaints, complaints to the European Court of Human Rights.
Career: Qualified in 1992. Partner at Bindmans since 1995.
Personal: Degree in law (Oxford) and postgraduate degree in European Law (College of Europe, Brugge, Belgium).

SIMPSON, Danny
Howells, Sheffield (0114) 249 6666
Partner and Head of Criminal Law Department.
Specialisation: All aspects of criminal law, including miscarriage of justice cases and a range of civil liberties issues.
Prof. Memberships: Law Society.
Career: BA (Hons) Degree, Exeter College, Oxford, Politics, Philosophy and Economics, qualified as a solicitor in 1984 and employed at *Bindman & Partners* solicitors becoming a partner in 1989, before moving to Sheffield in 1990 as a partner, Head of Department at *Howells* solicitors.
Personal: Lives in Sheffield, married to GP practising locally, with 3 children. Member of Labour Party.

IMMIGRATION

OVERVIEW: The distinction in London between business and personal immigration (usually legal aid/asylum work) continues to be maintained. The larger City departments tend to provide higher volume work permit services for commercial and corporate clients, whereas further down the lists, the smaller London practices often embrace a more varied mixture of private client work, investor applications and less routine applications. A major feature across all business immigration departments is the proliferation of IT/e-commerce start-up applications as highly trained specialists from abroad are brought in to develop this burgeoning sector of the economy.

The business/personal distinction is not made in the regions where our lists incorporate firms spanning the immigration spectrum. Many traditional legal aid firms have been forced to rethink their commercial strategy in the light of falling income, and contemplate an expanding portfolio of business services.

The recently introduced asylum dispersal programme is a government initiative designed to ease the burden on traditional immigration entry points such as the south coast ports and airport surrounds. The effect of the programme will be to increase the volume of asylum cases in the regions of Britain, particularly those in the North with an abundance of cheap housing.

RESEARCH APPROVED BY BMRB: *For this edition,* Chambers' *researchers conducted 6083 interviews – 4408 with law firms, 598 with barristers and 1077 with clients.*

The validity of the research was scrutinised by BMRB International, who audited both the methodology and the results at our offices in July 2000. They interviewed Chambers' *researchers and cross-checked sample interviews. Details of the audit appear on page 7.*

LONDON

BUSINESS

BUSINESS IMMIGRATION • London	Ptnrs	Assts
❶ CMS Cameron McKenna	1	7
Kingsley Napley	2	6
❷ Bates, Wells & Braithwaite	1	2
Magrath & Co	2	10
Warner Cranston	2	3
❸ Eversheds	1	5
Gherson & Co	1	2
Sturtivant & Co	1	1
❹ Baker & McKenzie	1	2
Gulbenkian Harris Andonian	3	1
Mishcon de Reya	2	-
Norton Rose	1	1
Pullig & Co	-	4
❺ DJ Webb & Co	1	4
Fox Williams	1	1
Penningtons	-	1
❻ Campbell Hooper	-	1
Harbottle & Lewis	-	1

Within each band, firms are listed alphabetically.

LEADING INDIVIDUALS	
❶ **BELCHAK Hilary** Kingsley Napley	**GUILD Elspeth** Kingsley Napley
ONSLOW-COLE Julia Cameron McKenna	**STURTIVANT Karen** Sturtivant & Co
TROTT Philip Bates, Wells & Braithwaite	
❷ **ALFANDARY Peter** Warner Cranston	**BARTH Philip** Mishcon de Reya
DEVINE Laura Eversheds	**KEMP Lesley** Warner Cranston
❸ **ANDONIAN Bernard** Gulbenkian Harris Andonian	
HAQUE Tony Baker & McKenzie	**MAGRATH Christopher** Magrath & Co
MANN Jane Fox Williams	**MEHMET Gülay** Penningtons
MOSS Peter Bates, Wells & Braithwaite	**WEBB David** DJ Webb & Co
❹ **BALCOMB Anne** Pullig & Co	**GHERSON Roger** Gherson & Co
POPE Caron Norton Rose	**RIVIERE Susanna** Harbottle & Lewis
UP AND COMING	
ROLLASON Nicolas Kingsley Napley	

*See **Profiles** on page 440*

CMS Cameron McKenna The most high-profile and productive business immigration team in London, with a spread of international office links. Has attracted a number of large corporate blue-chips *("they've tied up the market in terms of clients.")* The emphasis here is on a high volume of work permit applications for mainstream corporate inter-company transferees. Media-friendly department partner **Julia Onslow-Cole** is a *"consummate PR person"* and a *"real doer"* and has *"a superb knowledge of immigration, as well as being ultra-commercial."* She has aggressively marketed and developed a successful City practice and is credited by contemporaries with *"doing wonders for immigration by giving it a reputation it never had before."* A large number of assistants add resources to the team. Advises multi-nationals, financial organisations, entrepreneurs and high net worth individuals. Advised on the rights of a homosexual couple to bring an adopted baby to the UK. Negotiated on behalf of a leading financial services client an unusual series of MBA hires which resulted in changes to the way MBA hires are treated under the Work Permit Scheme. Has advised Premier League and first division football clubs on a number of urgent immigration matters. **Clients:** corporate multi-nationals; investment banks; IT/software houses; football clubs.

Kingsley Napley Since the Simmons bolt-on in early 1999 expanded the team size, the firm has settled down and is considered to have the greatest collective strength in depth of any of the business practices. *"They have a great level of experience and tremendous assistants."* A triumvirate of varied but effective personalities lead the charge. Key department head and business immigration specialist, the *"self-deprecating"* **Hilary Belchak** is a *"hardworking lawyer."* She is *"thorough, and really cares about the clients."* The *"cerebral"* and *"professorial"* **Elspeth Guild** applies an academic and intellectual approach, and is universally regarded as the expert for European immigration. *"Her EEA countries' regulation knowledge is unsurpassed."* **Nick Rollason** makes an appearance in the up and coming list after a number of favourable comments. Straddling business and personal immigration, he is *"outstanding; a first class brain."* Lesley Kemp left the practice in March for Warner Cranston, and it remains to be seen what effect this will have on the immigration department. The firm acted for a new e-commerce business challenging the work permit rule stating that permits are not granted to anyone with a significant shareholding in the company. Pursuing an appeal for a sole representative in the UK on whether immigration rules are required to be met at the end or beginning of their first year's residence. **Clients:** pharmaceutical multi-nationals; banks and financial services companies; technology and internet sites.

Bates, Wells & Braithwaite Well-known, high-quality practice with an immigration department that straddles the business and personal divide. *"Good lateral thinker"* **Philip Trott** is *"very approachable"* and rises in the tables, while hands-on full-time assistant **Peter Moss** is *"quieter, but sharp."* Both are considered *"excellent representatives and highly knowledgeable."* Offers low volume, more complex immigration advice to business and private clients. Recently processed a number of corporate work permits for large oil multi-nationals and several e-commerce and telecommunication European start-ups for large US companies. Involved in the deportation issue surrounding Lennox Lewis' Ghanaian right-hand man. **Clients:** Shell; BP; EMI.

Magrath & Co Substantial West End immigration practice with a sizeable team and prestigious client list. *"A good professional firm, hardworking, with some big corporate clients."* The firm is driven by hands-on partner **Chris Magrath**, and competes in the lucrative corporate work permit market for a series of major organisations in banking, industry and the media. **Clients:** international banks; media organisations; retailers.

Warner Cranston Broad-ranging and expanding commercial practice offering work permit and investor application services to a largely corporate client base. Headed by *"calm and balanced"* experienced ex-corporate lawyer **Peter Alfandary** *("he's got nothing to prove, he's bright, fair, not possessive of clients and not competitive,")* the department is strengthened by *"good international links and a global client base."* The firm scored a major coup with the acquisition of the *"quiet, gentle and effective"* partner **Lesley Kemp** from Kingsley Napley. Continues to work for major US, Japanese and Middle Eastern corporations and financial institutions. Increasing amount of work for IT and e-commerce start-ups. Recently processed permits for a number of international Hitachi executives, an American millionaire investor and a US mobile telecoms service expanding its European operations. **Clients:** Hitachi; TI Group; Saudi International Bank; Ogilvy & Mather.

Eversheds The London office services existing corporate clients with permit applications, operating under the guidance of the *"bubbly"* **Laura Devine** who is employed on a consultancy basis and *"gets decent private clients as well as the corporate clients."* Her individual reputation is perceived to be more prominent than the firm itself, but she *"always seems to be busy, and has a young and hardworking team."* Client base is drawn from sectors including manufacturing, financial and management consultancy. Increasing e-commerce and US visa work. Closely involved with a number of business schools where high profile individuals and professionals are seeking to stay in the UK. **Clients:** Fidelity Group; Boston Consulting Group; Deloitte & Touche; Cable & Wireless.

Gherson & Co Small and mixed niche immigration practice headed by the idiosyncratic *"enthusiastic and energetic,"* **Roger Gherson** *"a mover and shaker and an interesting character."* Tends not to compete in the mass-volume corporate work permit market, opting for an esoteric mix of smaller businesses, some private client work and some personal immigration. Recent case-load included a major national security case as well as a series of work permits for computer programmers and salespeople from India, Russia and South Africa. **Clients:** banks; film companies; internet/e-commerce concerns.

Sturtivant & Co Experienced and well-established. Sole practitioner **Karen Sturtivant**, *"an effective and efficient one-man band,"* maintains this quality niche immigration practice among the leaders. Size limits the firm to low volume corporate and private client work. Although *"she's got ideas and interesting angles,"* and the practice is seen as perpetually busy and active, it is sometimes felt to be somewhat over-worked. Client base comprises private clients, sole representatives and commercial companies. **Clients:** commercial companies; private clients.

Baker & McKenzie A historically sound immigration department keeps its place in the rankings, although the firm is *"not seen to be actively promoting it."* The US corporate leviathan employs a small team to serve its multinational client base, largely from the US, Japan and Asia. Well-liked and *"academic,"* **Tony Haque** *"got there very quickly – a great find for Baker & McKenzie."* He advises a number of clients in the software and IT sectors. The small team is strengthened by a Japanese speaking case-worker who has brought in extra corporate clients. Recently obtained over forty work permits for technical specialists and management at Honda Racing Development Ltd, a new Formula 1 Racing Team developed in conjunction with British American Racing. Assisted Kvaerner Process UK Ltd to obtain 13 work permits for senior engineers working on a new construction project. **Clients:** Toyota Manufacturing UK Ltd; Elsevir Science; Towers Perrin Forster & Crosby Inc; Novell UK Ltd.

Gulbenkian Harris Andonian Experienced and broad-ranging immigration practice with three full-time partners and substantial collective experience. Conducts a mixture of corporate work permit applications and private client work, much of it with a European dimension. **Bernard Andonian** is ranked for his business immigration expertise. Recently handled a series of permit applications from small IT and technology companies from the Indian sub-continent and Bulgaria. **Clients:** BAT; Coca-Cola; L'Oreal.

Mishcon de Reya The firm is felt to be on the rise this year, and the highly experienced commercial lawyer **Philip Barth** is regularly singled out by contemporaries as an emerging force *("Philip has stabilised, developed and grown the practice.")* The firm is felt to have acquired a higher immigration profile under his stewardship and has amassed a healthy client list. Recently processed all the work permits for a $12 million foreign telecoms start-up. Expertise in the IT/e-commerce arena, with a number of clients from the Indian sub-continent and the Middle East. Handled a same-sex appeal case for a diagnosed AIDS sufferer, where the government conceded the application within four months and granted the applicant leave to remain. **Clients:** television/film companies; model agencies; technology companies.

Norton Rose The *"professional and ambitious"* assistant **Caron Pope** oversees Norton Rose's small sub-employment commercial immigration department. Clients are drawn from the existing internal commercial base as well as stand-alones. The clientele includes companies in a range of financial and corporate sectors, including airlines, sports clubs and shipping operators. Highlights have included handling sole representative applications for a Japanese broadcasting company, a tourist complex in the Maldives and a US fund management group. Recently provided the immigration services for a £100 million Dutch cineplex start-up. **Clients:** Credit Agricole; Eidos Group; Eva Airways; Budweiser.

Pullig & Co Broad-based immigration practice which focuses on business and commercial private client work, but offers refugee and asylum services via its legal aid franchise – with full-time assistants devoted to both. The *"experienced"* **Anne Balcomb** is well-liked by peers and enters the individuals list. Client base is less corporate, comprising a range of smaller and medium-sized organisations and investor applications in a range of sectors. Involved in obtaining a number of permits for IT employees originating from Eastern Europe and the Indian sub-continent. **Clients:** media companies; financial services; travel agents; charities.

D J Webb & Co Despite being formerly associated with personal immigration and legal aid work, **David Webb** *("thoroughly committed and very capable")* is *"pretty well equipped to deal with anything that is thrown at you – he just knows everything."* He runs a niche immigration practice embracing all aspects of immigration, which has produced *"good work across the board."* Focus has switched recently to commercial immigration and private client work, with an eclectic client mix stretching from Japanese corporates and IT/e-commerce start-ups to million-pound applications, NHS trusts, writers and artists. **Clients:** IT/software companies; Rolls Royce; Towers Perrins.

Fox Williams The firm retains a ranking due to the efforts and high reputation of *"persuasive and articulate"* employment partner, **Jane Mann**, *"an original visionary,"* and a recent assistant recruit from Magrath's. The pervading view is that the *"immigration department is heading upwards."* Currently processing large numbers of permits for US software houses which are expanding UK operations. **Clients:** IT/technology companies; financial advisors.

Penningtons Not regarded as high profile, but nevertheless *"a sound all-round immigration firm."* Ex- JCWI, **Gülay Mehmet** started out in legal aid and personal asylum but has effectively made the transition to business immigration. *"She developed the practice very quickly and is able to take on the tricky cases."* A wide range of new clients includes North American internet start-ups, South African musicians and video producers. **Clients:** IT/software companies; private clients.

Campbell Hooper The firm has recently undergone a number of internal personnel changes, but continues to offer the range of immigration services to existing clients in the media and entertainment industries. Recently processed a US national tier 1 work permit application. **Clients:** PR companies; Advertising agencies; Deutsche Bank; Bank of Nova Scotia.

Harbottle & Lewis The firm exploits its competitive advantage in the media/entertainment sphere to provide commercial and individual immigration services to a variety of clients in the entertainment, sports and aviation industries. **Susanna Riviere** has a lower immigration profile these days but remains recommended for her niche client base. Obtained a work permit at short notice for the travel author Bill Bryson in time for the filming of 'Notes From A Small Island.' Advised a leading actress on possible routes for staying in the UK after the breakdown of her marriage. **Clients:** New Millennium Experience Company (NMEC); The Virgin Group; Wasps Rugby Football Club; Youth At Risk.

LONDON

PERSONAL

PERSONAL IMMIGRATION • London	Ptnrs	Assts
❶ Bindman & Partners	1	2
Birnberg Peirce & Partners	1	2
Deighton Guedalla	1	-
Wesley Gryk	1	3
Winstanley-Burgess	4	1
❷ Coker Vis Partnership	1	-
Glazer Delmar	-	2
❸ Bartram & Co	1	-
Gill & Co	2	4
Luqmani Thompson	2	-
Powell & Co	1	4
❹ Christian Fisher	-	2
Stuart Miller	-	2
Wilson & Co	2	5

LEADING INDIVIDUALS	
❶ **COKER Jane** Coker Vis Partnership	**GRYK Wesley** Wesley Gryk
GUEDALLA Vicky Deighton Guedalla	**LINDSLEY Fiona** Birnberg Peirce & Partners
RANDALL Christopher Winstanley-Burgess	
STANLEY Alison Bindman & Partners	
❷ **BURGESS David** Winstanley-Burgess	**DAVIES Matthew** Wilson & Co
HANLEY Michael Wilson & Co	**HUSSAIN Belayeth** Powell & Co
JONES David Rhys Glazer Delmar	**LUQMANI Jawaid** Luqmani Thompson
RIPLEY Fiona Winstanley-Burgess	**SMITH Graham** Bindman & Partners
❸ **BARTRAM Peter** Bartram & Co	**LESKIN Nigel** Birnberg Peirce & Partners
PENROSE Martin Winstanley-Burgess	**SMITH Lisa** Stuart Miller
THOMPSON Sally Luqmani Thompson	

Within each band, firms are listed alphabetically. *See Profiles on page 440*

Bindman & Partners Top flight human rights and civil liberties practice which is seen as *"almost unassailable."* Acts on a range of personal immigration including asylum, refugee, nationality and family work. The immigration portfolio is felt to *"feed into the general reputation for human rights."* **Alison Stanley** *"enhances the firm's reputation immeasurably"* and is acknowledged universally as a leading light. *"She will push at every opportunity with the Home Office – very dedicated and thorough."* Bengali-speaking **Graham Smith** is less high profile but his reputation is based on specialism in India/Bangladeshi cases and family reunions *("he's so committed and an expert in that area of the world.")*

Birnberg Peirce & Partners A contender for top-tier status, the firm continues to win praise and has acquired some key personnel. **Fiona Lindsley** is *"the most sophisticated immigration practitioner, and is utterly meticulous in her approach."* She is highly regarded for asylum, detainee and habeas corpus work. Both she and the firm rise a notch this year. **Nigel Leskin** *("idiosyncratic and excellent in his way – never gives up")* handles crime in addition to immigration, with a focus on *"esoteric"* student cases and illegal overstayers. A full time Turkish caseworker handles Kurdish asylum cases at the firm.

Deighton Guedalla Small niche immigration practice *("they're not huge but high quality")* headed by **Vicky Guedalla** who *"works tremendously hard"* and *"shows enormous dedication – never lets go."* The firm is strong on a range of asylum and children's cases. Guedalla is also known for *"her excellent work with the Turkish Kurd community"* and *"takes on more work than many others would."*

Wesley Gryk The team remains in the upper tier despite the loss of two ranked individuals from last year. The internal changes have been offset by new acquisitions and are not felt to have lowered the standing of the firm which is individually driven by the outstanding **Wesley Gryk**, *("analytical, human and sympathetic to his clients.")* The firm is closely associated with high profile AIDS and gay rights work, as well as asylum cases. *"Wesley himself has always been at the pinnacle, and he still remains there."* New personnel includes an ex-Terence Higgins trust assistant.

Winstanley-Burgess Large personal immigration practice with a fine reputation for asylum and human rights and tremendous strength in depth. *"Each practitioner has extra capacity and ability to handle volume; each has 'knots' of speciality."* Several lawyers continue to be highly ranked including **David Burgess** who has worked on a number of national security cases. He is seen as *"creative and tenacious in the way he tackles problems."* **Christopher Randall** has *"tremendous knowledge,"* is *"genuinely interested in the clients"* and *"slogs away"* on asylum cases. Community-focused **Fiona Ripley** continues to get *"good results"* and works on asylum cases from Turkey, Iraq and Afghanistan. The *"quieter personality"* **Martin Penrose** has a case-load which runs the gamut of personal immigration.

Coker Vis Partnership Small and committed firm driven by the *"magnetic and determined," "fiery and committed"* personality of high profile **Jane Coker**. She has been described as *"extremely inventive, constantly searching for imaginative solutions."* The team has a strong reputation for children's cases and undertakes a high volume of critical asylum work.

Glazer Delmar The firm rises a tier this year on the back of several good reviews. *"Their reputation is based on intelligence and commitment,"* and they are especially well known for detention and children's cases. **David Rhys Jones** is *"thorough"* and has *"brought a new professionalism to the firm."* He continues to build his reputation for Latin American asylum and refugee cases and rises in this year's tables.

Bartram & Co Small immigration team headed by **Peter Bartram**, who has *"years of experience in different sorts of practice and the voluntary sector."* Conducts not only asylum work for Afghanistani and Algerian refugees, but a number of family/children's cases and also non-legal aid business work. Recently handled an unusual case involving a Bulgarian pretending to be a lesbian.

Gill & Co A new entry to this years lists, the firm have been described as *"committed, hard-working and experienced."* A number of assistants have been mentioned as potential stars of the future but collectively the firm has won praise for its active and committed asylum work.

Luqmani Thompson Newly-established firm which has earned excellent reviews. *"Each partner has their own following, they're good individuals and they've established themselves well."* **Jawaid Luqmani** is *"not afraid to be innovative without being unrealistic"* and continues to enjoy a respected and quality reputation *("his analysis and identification of issues are good.")* Partner **Sally Thompson** also has a respected immigration track record.

Powell & Co Strong community and legal aid-flavoured practice, conducting the full range of personal immigration services. Recently made partner, *"hardworking and thorough"* **Belayeth Hussain,** *("his experience goes way back")* remains a ranked individual. A former focus on Kosovan and Somali cases has expanded to include much of Africa, Latin America and Eastern Europe.

Christian Fisher The firm is associated with high profile work across the civil liberties field, but has less of an immigration focus nowadays. The emphasis is more on occasional cases rather than consistent levels of regular work. Asylum and HIV cases are still the main areas of expertise here.

Stuart Miller The firm has been less active than usual, but is still operating in the asylum field, notably on Turkish Kurd cases. **Lisa Smith** remains a recommended practitioner. Heavily involved in the much publicised case in 1999 involving the prosecution of alleged asylum seekers for holding false documents.

Wilson & Co The firm is felt by many to have raised its profile this year. Experienced *"front-line"* partner **Matthew Davies** is *"intellectually top-rate"* and has grown his own reputation through work in the gay rights and HIV field. **Michael Hanley** *("a steady hand on the helm")* keeps a lower profile, but is highly respected. Handles a variety of asylum work for Somali, Turkish and Kosovan refugees. Acted for the applicant in ex parte M, an asylum seeker diagnosed with AIDS who had a deportation order to Uganda overturned after a High Court judicial review.

THE SOUTH

IMMIGRATION • The South		
❶ **Eric Robinson & Co** Southampton	-	1
Trethowans Southampton	1	-

LEADING INDIVIDUALS
❶ **DENSON Gordon** Trethowans

Within each band, firms are listed alphabetically. *See **Profiles** on page 440*

Eric Robinson & Co Small immigration practice dealing largely in asylum for Kosovan, South American and Indonesian clients. Other private client work such as marriage, reunion and naturalisation sits alongside limited amounts of business work permit applications.

Trethowans Mixed personal and business practice headed by part-time adjudicator, **Gordon Denson.** Conducts business work permit applications for South African and Zimbabwean clients, European association applications and asylum and marriage cases.

THAMES VALLEY

IMMIGRATION • Thames Valley	Ptnrs	Assts
❶ **Darbys Mallam Lewis** Oxford	-	2
Linnells Oxford	1	1

LEADING INDIVIDUALS
❶ **HARVEY Jenny** Darbys Mallam Lewis
TURPIN Philip Linnells

Within each band, firms are listed alphabetically. *See **Profiles** on page 440*

Darbys Mallam Lewis Associate partner **Jenny Harvey** is praised for having *"built up the practice."* She leads a full time team of three at this well-respected and very busy *("they're turning work away due to the explosion in asylum work")* immigration department. Specialises in family reunion and asylum cases drawn heavily from the Kosovan community and Syrian and Sudanese applicants.

Linnells Mirroring the local pattern, commercial firm Linnells have benefited from huge rises in asylum applications recently. *"Linnells are incredibly busy"* but *"appear to be building their commercial immigration operation"* as a diversification measure alongside traditional asylum and legal aid cases. **Philip Turpin** is *"very knowledgeable, not a slapdash character, very accurate."* Clients on the business side include charities, a number of university colleges and technology companies.

SOUTH WEST

IMMIGRATION • South West	Ptnrs	Assts
❶ **Bobbetts Mackan** Bristol	-	2

Within each band, firms are listed alphabetically.

Bobbetts Mackan Bristol community firm that advises a predominantly local client base on asylum and family reunion work. The department's clientele is drawn largely from the area's local Somali population.

WALES

IMMIGRATION • Wales	Ptnrs	Assts
❶ **Eversheds** Cardiff	*	*

Within each band, firms are listed alphabetically.
** See editorial entries for explanations of team sizes.*

Eversheds (Assistants from the employment department available as required) The Welsh office provides business immigration services as an adjunct to the employment department for existing commercial clients. These include large corporate multi-nationals in the financial services sector. Act for large numbers of technology workers from the Indian sub-continent requiring UK work permits.

MIDLANDS

IMMIGRATION • Midlands	Ptnrs	Assts
❶ **Tyndallwoods** Birmingham	1	3
❷ **McGrath & Co** Birmingham	-	2
Nelsons Nottingham	1	2

LEADING INDIVIDUALS	
❶ **PHILLIPS Mark** Tyndallwoods	**SMITH David** Nelsons
❷ **CONLAN Sue** Tyndallwoods	**FINCH Margaret** Tyndallwoods

Within each band, firms are listed alphabetically. See **Profiles** on page 440

Tyndallwoods Still regarded as the region's premier immigration practice, it has a reputation that stretches nationwide. Partner **Mark Phillips** *"a high profile manager"* is only one of two non-London lawyers to sit on the Law Society's immigration panel and applies a human rights angle to immigration work. Ex-JWCI **Sue Conlan** has a *"good track record"*, and with **Margaret Finch** *("active in court, gets the work done")* continues to be highly rated. Workload is mainly asylum, with clients drawn from Africa, Eastern Europe and Asia. The rest is split between family, student and limited business work permit applications.

McGrath & Co The firm are not perceived to have fully recovered from the loss of former department head Manjit Singh in May 1999 to a smaller Leicester practice. Still seen as a productive immigration practice, it manages a caseload of asylum, family and marriage cases, many drawn from well-established local Bangladeshi communities. Also act for sizeable numbers of Kosovan and Albanian refugees.

Nelsons Beyond Birmingham, regarded as one of the Midlands' best personal immigration practices *("a very able bunch.")* **David Smith** is well known and regarded nationally for his policy and training input *("he's very committed,")* and heads the East Midlands' leading firm. He mixes personal and business immigration, focusing on complex, non-routine work permit applications, while the assistants process asylum applications. Involved in major judicial review cases.

EAST ANGLIA

IMMIGRATION • East Anglia	Ptnrs	Assts
❶ **Gross & Co** Bury St. Edmunds	1	-
Leathes Prior Norwich	1	-
Wollastons Chelmsford	-	1

LEADING INDIVIDUALS	
❶ **CARY Tim** Leathes Prior	**KIRK Graeme** Gross & Co.

Within each band, firms are listed alphabetically. See **Profiles** on page 440

Gross & Co Bolstered by a small West End office, this Suffolk-based general practice offers business immigration services to a varied client base, many originating in London and internationally. Acts for a number of corporates including the South African INVESTEC banking group, ING Barings and wealthy private clients seeking investor applications. Full time partner and department head **Graeme Kirk** *("a good representative of this part of the profession")* is the leading name.

Leathes Prior Full time partner **Tim Cary** offers a mix of business immigration services as part of the firm's commercial base, alongside asylum and family cases. Due to proximity to the east coast, handle a large number of East European refugee cases.

Wollastons Essex-based commercial practice specialising in business immigration for predominantly London-based clients in the television, advertising and film production industry. Provides work permit and other immigration services to UK commercial production companies seeking to bring US actors, directors and technicians to the country. Also private client work for local based businesses. Clients include AFVPA Advertising Film Videotape Production Association.

THE NORTH

David Gray & Co Continues to be Newcastle's leading immigration practice, and in this area, the firm has a national reputation that transcends the confines of the North East. Senior partner **David Gray** is a well-respected specialist and has *"given a notable immigration focus to the office."* He is described as *"committed and helpful, with a manner that suggests he is very on the ball."* Involved personally in complex non-asylum work, family settlements and deportations, while his assistants concentrate on asylum cases for a mixture of clients including Kosovans, Croatians and Afghanis.

Howells Well respected and well-resourced Sheffield legal aid firm with broad expertise in civil, family and housing law. Immigration practitioners straddle all these departments, devoting extra resources to immigration when required. *"They're professionally tuned in, provide representation and advice at all levels."* **John Donkersley** is *"experienced over a range of work and administers an effective department."* The firm are felt to be adequately equipped to handle large volumes of asylum cases as well as other personal immigration issues.

A S Law Huge Liverpool legal aid practice offering the spectrum of personal immigration services, mainly refugee, family and asylum cases and many judicial reviews. *"Their integrity is utterly unquestionable."* **Peter Simm** is *"a real fighter,"* in his commitment to winning difficult cases with the authorities.

Harrison Bundey & Co **Ruth Bundey**, chair of the Law Society immigration committee is *"a good operator, knows her stuff and is very committed."* She continues to be highly thought of in the fields of crime and human

IMMIGRATION • The North	Ptnrs	Assts
❶ **David Gray & Company** Newcastle upon Tyne	1	2
Howells Sheffield	-	3
❷ **A S Law** Liverpool	1	2
Harrison Bundey & Co Leeds	⚐	⚐
Jackson & Canter Liverpool	1	1
James & Co Bradford	1	-
❸ **Davis Blank Furniss** Manchester	1	1
Samuel Phillips & Co Newcastle upon Tyne	-	1
Thornhill Ince Manchester	3	-

LEADING INDIVIDUALS
❶ **GRAY David** David Gray & Company
JAMES Charles James & Co
SIMM Peter A S Law
❷ **BUNDEY Ruth** Harrison Bundey & Co.
DONKERSLEY John Howells
HOLROYD Andrew Jackson & Canter
INCE Robin Thornhill Ince

Within each band, firms are listed alphabetically. *See **Profiles** on page 440*

⚐ *Figures unavailable at time of going to press.*

rights, but the practice as a whole has been seen less frequently this year. Assistants continue to provide asylum and refugee services, *"the people are very effective,"* and the overall quality of the practice remains high.

Jackson & Canter Known in Liverpool for its broad range of services including small business applications, as well as the usual legal aid diet of asylum, although African and Asian refugee cases form the bulk of the case-load. *"They do the work very efficiently."* Acts for a number of small level business applications drawn from the local Asian community. Partner **Andrew Holroyd** has done *"thorough work, he's conscientious and hard-working."*

James & Co Personal practice dealing primarily with asylum and deportation. Strong links to Bradford's Asian community creates core business, and a Serbo-Croat speaking assistant deals with ethnic Serb refugees from Croatia. Partner **Charles James** has *"a hell of a lot of work"* and recently helped to bring in a troupe of Pakistani entertainers.

Davis Blank Furniss Mixed practice offering business services such as sole representatives, investor applications and work permits alongside a body of asylum and marriage immigration work. The latter work primarily involves East European, Afghan and Algerian cases. Acts for a number of local IT/computer software companies seeking to introduce foreign staff.

Samuel Phillips & Co Conducts a broad range of work which includes business immigration services such as investor applications to local clients and asylum cases. Strong links to the local Chinese community developed by a full-time Cantonese speaking member of staff. Processed a number of work permits for Hong Kong, Chinese and Japanese electronics and technology companies. Recently processed an investor application for a Shanghai-based electronics company seeking to establish a marketing representative in the UK.

Thornhill Ince *"We would recommend them as the best Manchester firm,"* commented another regional practitioner. One commentator had *"the highest regard"* for partner **Robin Ince** who sits as a part-time adjudicator. The firm conducts a steady stream of legal aid asylum work.

LEADERS IN IMMIGRATION

ALFANDARY, Peter

Warner Cranston, London (020) 7403 2900
Peter-Alfandary@Warner.Cranston.com

Partner and head of corporate immigration department.

Specialisation: Corporate immigration. 17 years of experience advising national and multinational corporations on work permits and related immigration issues with the Home Office and Department of Education and Employment. Advice on nationality law, overseas investor rules and business related immigration for individuals. Author of chapter on immigration in 'CCH Employment Contracts Manual.'

Prof. Memberships: Law Society; Immigration Law Practitioners Association.

Career: Articled *Lovell White & King*; qualified 1983. Spent a year in industry and a year with a leading firm of French advocates. Joined *Warner Cranston* as a partner in 1982. Managing partner 1991-1993.

Personal: Born 10 January 1953, resides in London. Educated at LycÈe Francais de Londres, University of Kent and London School of Economics. Interests include Theatre, Music and Anglo-French relations. Deputy-President French Chamber of Commerce; decorated by the French Government as a *Chevalier dans L'Ordre Nationale du MÈrite* in 1991.

ANDONIAN, Bernard

Gulbenkian Harris Andonian, London (020) 7937 1542

Partner in Immigration Department.

Specialisation: Principal areas of practice are UK and US business immigration for multi national companies and foreign business executives. Deals with work permit applications and business insolvency inter applications; preparation, submission of business and investor plans; independent means. Contributor to numerous business immigration articles. Lectures on business immigration. Has recently reviewed 'Law and Practice' by Michael Supperstone QC and Declan O'Dempsey; appointed by the Lord Chancellor as part-time Immigration Adjudicator and Special Adjudicator.

Prof. Memberships: Member of Immigration Law Practitioners Association, and former Executive Committee Member, the International Bar Association, Law Society, Holborn Law Society.

Career: Qualified 1985 while at *Gulbenkian Harris Andonian*, and became a Partner in 1986.

Personal: Born 11th September 1949. Attended City of London and Thames Valley Universities. Obtained Distinction in Intellectual Property for the MA Degree. Leisure pursuits include reading, rambling, table tennis, snooker, swimming. Lives in Osterley, Middlesex.

BALCOMB, Anne

Pullig & Co, London (020) 7353 0505

Specialisation: All aspects of immigration and nationality law; advising corporate and personal clients, in particular on employment and business-related matters.

Prof. Memberships: Law Society; Immigration Law Practitioners' Association

Career: Worked as a teacher from 1964 to 1978; qualified as a solicitor in 1982; practised in immigration and nationality law since 1986; worked for *Simmons and Simmons* from 1990 to 1993 and for *Pullig & Co* from 1993 to date.

Publications: Three articles in professional journals.

Personal: St Anne's College Oxford 1960-1963; BA Hons Modern Languages 1963. College of Law 1978-1979. Fluent in french. Lives in London and Devon

BARTH, Philip

Mishcon de Reya, London (020) 7440 7000

Specialisation: Specialises in all aspects of immigration and nationality law other than asylum. Having a background as an experienced company/commercial lawyer, his combination of expertise is of particular benefit for all businesses, corporates and persons who wish to move to the UK to pursue economic activities. He is regulary involved in cases at the cutting-edge of business immigration practice and has many years experience in providing practical immigration advice within the wider commercial context to meet the needs of business. Writes and speaks regularly on business immigration topics.

Prof. Memberships: Immigration Law Practitioners Association–Treasurer and Co-chair of the Employment & Business Sub-committee. Law Society.

Career: Rugby School; Magdalene College, Cambridge University. 1980-1982 articles with *Malkin Cullins & Sumption*; 1983-1986 Assistant solicitor at *Clintons*; 1986-1988 Assistant solicitor at *Walters Fladgate*; 1988-1998 partner in successor firm, *Fladgate Fielder*; 1998-present: partner *Mishcon de Reya*.

BARTRAM, Peter
Bartram & Co, Hounslow (020) 8814 1414
Specialisation: Head of Practice near Heathrow Airport devoted to all aspects of UK immigration and asylum law with Community Legal Service contract in immigration law.
Prof. Memberships: Law Society Immigration Law Panel; Immigration Law Practioners Association.
Career: Qualified 1981. Immigration specialist since 1984. Has worked in law centres, advice centres and in private practice. Established own firm, *Bartram & Co*, in 1994.
Personal: Born 21 August 1957. Bristol University (LLB, 1978) and Brunel University (MA, 1988). Spanish and French speaker.

BELCHAK, Hilary
Kingsley Napley, London (020) 7814 1200
Partner and head of immigration department.
Specialisation: Main areas of practice are UK immigration and nationality law. Has sixteen years experience in this field. Presently covering corporate immigration such as work permits, immigration advice to entrepreneurs and high net worth individuals wishing to invest and settle in the UK, and nationality issues.Numerous articles including in the 'International Quarterly', 'Offshore Investment', the new quarterly publication 'Immigration and Employment Law', as well as being deputy editor of that journal. Has spoken at ILPA and the immigration committees of AILA, IBA and IPBA annual conferences as well as conferences of CBI Employee Relocation Council, IBC UK, Employment Lawyers Association, the Japan Institute for Overseas Investment and In-house Seminars. Recently prepared contribution for the Croner's publication 'Managing Internationally Mobile Employees', as well as articles for its monthly bulletin.
Prof. Memberships: ILPA, IPBA, AILA. Chair IPBA's Immigration Committee 1997-1999. Secretary of ILPA 1995-1997.
Career: Qualified in 1984. Senior lecturer at North London Polytechnic 1971-1981; worked at *Winstanley Burgess* 1982-1984 and *Clinton Davis & Co.* 1984-1988. Joined *Simmons & Simmons* in 1988, becoming a partner in 1994. Joined *Kingsley Napley* February 1999.
Personal: Born 17th March 1949. Holds an LLB (1970) and LLM (1971). Leisure interests include opera and cinema. Lives in London and Suffolk.

BUNDEY, Ruth
Harrison Bundey & Co., Leeds (0113) 200 7400
See under Human Rights, p.433

BURGESS, David C.W.
Winstanley-Burgess, London (020) 7278 7911
Partner in immigration department.
Specialisation: Main area of practice is immigration, including refugee work. Acted in Re M (H.L.), asylum case involving Ministers' liability to contempt; Re Sivakumaran (H.L. and European Court of Human Rights), 'refugee' definition case and Chahal (European Court of Human Rights) national security case establishing the absolute nature of Article 3. Has acted in other national security cases including NSH, Gulf War detainees and cases before the Special Immigration Appeals Commission. Acted in the Ben James case. Has conducted cases before the European Court of Human Rights and the European Court of Justice. Other areas of practice include transsexual cases including cases before the European Court of Human Rights. Author of articles and book reviews concerning immigration matters. Has appeared on television and radio, as well as teaching at seminars in Europe.
Prof. Memberships: Law Society, Immigration Law Practitioners Association, Refugee Legal Group, European Legal Network on Asylum (Joint UK Representative).
Career: Qualified in 1972. Partner at *Winstanley-Burgess* from 1975.
Personal: Born 25th September 1947. Attended Cambridge University (MA, 1969). Lives in London.

CARY, Tim
Leathes Prior, Norwich (01603) 610911

COKER, Jane
Coker Vis Partnership, London (020) 8885 1415
Partner specialising in immigration.
Specialisation: Work includes deportation, asylum, appeals representation and judicial review, and contempt of court. Cases have included National Security, Deportation of EC Nationals, Association Agreements and the inter-relation between the Children Act and immigration law. Author of numerous articles for Immigration Nationality Law Journal, LAG and Socialist Lawyer. Lectures on ILPA, LNTV and LAG courses. Addresses WNS, UKCOSA and medical conferences. Numerous TV and radio interviews.
Prof. Memberships: Immigration Law Practitioners Association, Law Society
Career: Qualified 1980. Set up *Jane Coker & Partners* in 1982. Now *Coker Vis Partnership.*
Personal: Born 11th July 1954. Holds a BSc in Biological Sciences. Trustee to Haldane Educational Trust.

CONLAN, Sue
Tyndallwoods, Birmingham (0121) 624 1111
Specialisation: All aspects of immigration, including asylum, family reunion, illegal entry, deportation and detention. Experienced and special interest in advocacy before Adjudicators and Immigration Appeal Tribunal. Experienced in Judicial Review (including emergency cases) and in preparing appeals for Court of Appeal. Visiting lecturer in Immigration Law (with particular emphasis on asylum law and practice) for MA in Immigration Law, Policy and Practice at University of Central England (UCE) and the Legal Practice Course at UCE.
Prof. Memberships: Immigration Law Practitioners' Association. Immigration Panel of the Law Society.
Career: Graduated with a B.A. (Hons.) Law degree from Kingston Polytechnic (1980) and with an LLM (Welfare Law) from Leicester University (1990). Specialised in immigration law since July 1987. Joined *Tyndallwoods* in March 1996.
Personal: Born 14 November 1958, Birmingham.

DAVIES, Matthew
Wilson & Co, London (020) 8808 7535
Specialisation: All areas of immigration, refugee and nationality law including appeals to the Immigration Appeals Tribunal, Court of Appeal and Judicial Review.
Prof. Memberships: Law Society, Immigration Law Practitioners Association. Member of the Law Society Immigration Law Panel.
Career: Joined *Wilson & Co* in 1990 and qualified 1992. Partner since 1998.
Personal: Born 1965. Manchester University (1987) & College of Law (1990). Chair of Stonewall Immigration Group (1998-1999) and co-Chair of Inquest (1997-1998)

DENSON, Gordon F.
Trethowans, Southampton (023) 8032 1000
Partner in immigration department.
Specialisation: Work covers all areas of immigration, nationality and asylum law. Conducts own appeals before adjudicators. Other areas of practice are commercial and conveyancing. Has undertaken personal visits to India to organise visas for children on compassionate grounds.
Prof. Memberships: JCWI.
Career: Qualified 1975. Joined *Woodford & Ackroyd* 1976 (now *Trethowan Woodford*). Partner 1980. Deputy Coroner for Southampton and New Forest District 1993. Appointed part-time Immigration Adjudicator 1995.
Personal: Born 22nd May 1950. Rotary member. Leisure interests include road running, walking, ornithology and foreign travel.

DEVINE, Laura
Eversheds, London (020) 7919 4856
devinel@eversheds.com
Specialisation: Laura heads the immigration and nationality group at *Eversheds*. Laura qualified as a solicitor at *Cameron Markby Hewitt* (now *CMS Cameron Mckenna*). She established the immigration unit at *Coopers & Lybrand* (now *PricewaterhouseCoopers*). She has an LLM from the London School of Economics, where she specialised in immigration law. Laura advises clients on immigration to the UK for work and business including work permits, sole representatives, business persons and innovators. Additionally, Laura advises on family reunion, settlement and nationality. She has a growing practise in US immigration law. She lectures on immigration and is author of 'Key Techniques in Employing Oversea Nationals Under the Work Permit Scheme, Immigration for Employment–Practical Guidance to the Law' published by Palladian in 2000. Laura contributes to 'Croners'. She is a visiting lecturer at Hull University. She is featured in 'An International Who's Who of Corporate Immigration Lawyers' and the 'Legal Experts Directory' as being one of the top ten executive immigration solicitors in the UK.

DONKERSLEY, John
Howells, Sheffield (0114) 249 6666
Specialisation: All aspects of immigration, in particular Kosovan, Yemeni and Somali asylum cases, family reunion cases and judicial review. Teaches immigration courses for NACAB, local authorities etc. Recently dealing with large numbers of dispersal asylum cases, Commissions on benefits, support and immigration and had reported case of Traore (CA).
Prof. Memberships: Law Society, ILPA, Stonewall.
Career: Welfare Rights worker and freelance trainer 1985-1988. Articled, and qualified 1991 at current firm where cut teeth representing detained Iraqis during Gulf War.
Personal: Born 1st December 1961. Attended London School of Economics (University of London), LLB (Hons) 1985. Leisure interests include computers and internet.

FINCH, Margaret
Tyndallwoods, Birmingham (0121) 624 1111
Specialisation: Has practised immigration exclusively since qualification in 1993. Asylum work forms approximately 80% of current case-load, but other personal immigration work also handled. Conducts own advocacy when possible, including pro bono on occasion. Has strong track-record of investigating and substantiating asylum cases which have previously been rejected. Has taught on the Legal Practice Course of the University of Central England.
Prof. Memberships: ILPA, Law Society, member Law Society Immigration Law Panel.
Career: Graduated 1984. Taught English in Palestinian refugee camps in the Gaza Strip & worked in Switzerland before undertaking law conversion course. Trained at *John Howell & Co* before moving to *Tyndallwoods* in 1993.
Personal: Born 22.2.62. BA English Literature 1984. Fluent French speaker. Leisure interests include music (piano and flute player) & hillwalking.

GHERSON, Roger M.
Gherson & Co, London (020) 7724 4488

GRAY, David
David Gray & Company, Newcastle upon Tyne (0191) 232 9547
lawyers@davidgray.co.uk
Founding principal.
Specialisation: Main areas of practice are immigration and mental health. Handles a wide range of casework including family settlement, nationality, illegals, students, political asylum and refugees, including judicial review (deportation) and European Convention cases. Member of Law Society MHRT Panel. Contributor to local radio, TV and press on current legal issues, with particular reference to immigration law.
Prof. Memberships: Law Society, Immigration Law Practitioners Association, Legal Action, LAPG.
Career: Qualified in 1970. Worked at the University of Malawi 1970-1973, Newcastle Law Centre 1974-1979, and established *David Gray & Company* in 1979.
Personal: Born 16th November 1944. Attended University of Manchester (LLB Hons, 1963-1966). Member of Liberty, Amnesty, Greenpeace, the Labour Party. Part time chair ITS. Solicitor member Northern Legal Services Committee. Leisure interests include family, walking, cycling and Newcastle United. Lives in Newcastle upon Tyne.

GRYK, Wesley
Wesley Gryk, London (020) 7240 8485
Specialisation: All areas of UK immigration and nationality law.
Prof. Memberships: Law Society, Immigration Law Practitioners Association, Association of the Bar of the City of New York.
Career: Qualified in 1990, admitted to the Bar of New York in 1976. Federal Judicial Clerk, Southern District of New York, 1975-1976; Associate, *Shearman & Sterling*, New York and Hong Kong, 1976-1980; Deputy Representative and Legal Advisor, UN High Commissioner for Refugees, 1980-1981; Deputy Head of Research Department, Amnesty International, 1981-1986; *B.M. Birnberg & Co*, London, 1988-1994; established own firm 1995.
Personal: Born 12th May 1949; attended East Catholic High School, 1963-1967; Harvard College, 1967-1971, BA; Warsaw University, 1971-1972, Fulbright Scholar; Harvard Law School 1972-75, JD. Trustee of the Redress Trust. Active in the work of Stonewall and the Terrence Higgins Trust. Has travelled widely on human rights missions for Amnesty International, Human Rights Watch, and Article 19.

GUEDALLA, Vicky
Deighton Guedalla, London (020) 7359 5700

GUILD, Elspeth
Kingsley Napley, London (020) 7814 1200
Partner, immigration department.
Specialisation: Primarily specialises in European Community law relating to free movement of persons including the transfer of staff from companies in one Member State to another Member State, the right of self-employment and provision of services. Wide expertise in UK immigration and nationality law generally. Frequent lecturer and has written many articles on UK immigration and nationality issues. Author of two textbooks on Free Movement of Persons in the European Union and the Developing Immigration and Asylum Policy of the European Union. A further book is to be published on the Position of the European Convention on Human Rights in the Community Legal Order.
Prof. Memberships: Chair of the Immigration Law Practitioners' Association European Group; Member of the Council of Justice; UK Expert to the European Commission's Network: Free Movement of Persons; British representative of the European Sections of the International Commission of Jurists; Member of the Executive Committee, Centre of European Law, Kings College London; Legal Expert to Migrant's Forum. Coordinator, Centre of Migration Law, University of Nijmegen.
Career: 1989 to 1997 *Baileys Shaw & Gillett*: head of immigration department; joined *Kingsley Napley* as a partner in March 1997.

HANLEY, Michael
Wilson & Co, London (020) 8808 7535
Specialisation: All aspects of Immigration and Asylum law. Personal Injury litigation.
Prof. Memberships: Law Society Immigration Panel, Immigration Law Practitioners Association and Association of Personal Injury Lawyers.
Career: Qualified 1985. Partner in *Wilson & Co.* since 1990. Specialised in Immigration law since 1988.
Personal: Born 1959. Pembroke College Cambridge (1978-1981). Married, 2 children.

HAQUE, Tony
Baker & McKenzie, London (020) 7919 1000
tony.haque@bakernet.com
Solicitor, Immigration Department
Specialisation: All areas of UK immigration and nationality work and related European Community law with emphasis on employment and business related applications. Acts principally for multinational companies and other corporate clients, entrepreneurs and high net worth individuals offering creative solutions to effect international transfers as expediently and cost effectively as possible. Client base is particularly strong in the information technology sector. Also extensively involved with the firm's leading Japanese practice. Works closely with *Baker & McKenzie's* worldwide network of offices, particularly in the North America and Asia Pacific regions, to assist clients who require advice upon relocation issues outside of the UK. Member of the firm's International Executive Transfer Practice Group which provides advice on a broad range of related corporate, tax and labour law issues. Has published articles and spoken at seminars on a wide number of immigration issues.
Prof. Memberships: Law Society, Immigration Law Practitioners' Association.
Career: 1994-97 *Baileys Shaw & Gillett*; qualified at *Kingsley Napley*; joined *Baker & McKenzie* as an Associate in November 1997.

HARVEY, Jenny
Darbys Mallam Lewis, Oxford (01865) 811700
Specialisation: All aspects of immigration work including family reunion, work permit applications and other business/employment matters. Extensive experience in the field of asylum law, with large case load of Kosovan asylum seekers in recent months. Have developed close links with Asylum Welcome, a local charity set up to help asylum seekers, and have worked with a large number of detainees at Campsfield Detention Centre.
Prof. Memberships: Law Society, Immigration Law Practitioners Association, Joint Council for Welfare of Immigrants.
Career: Degree in modern history at Lady Margaret Hall, Oxford (2:1). Worked in Sydney Legal Centre, Australia upon completion of law finals. Completed articles at *Darbys Mallam Lewis* and qualified in October 1994.
Personal: Involved in Oxford Amnesty International Group, travel, sport.

HOLROYD, Andrew
Jackson & Canter, Liverpool (0151) 282 1700
Partner in immigration department.
Specialisation: Covers all aspects of immigration law including business immigration matters.
Prof. Memberships: Law Society Council Member and member of Law Society Immigration Sub-Committee. Past President of Liverpool Law Society. ILPA. Immigration Law Panel member.
Career: Qualified 1974 in Liverpool, joined *Jackson & Canter*. Became a partner in 1977.
Personal: Born 13th April 1948. Attended Nottingham University.

HUSSAIN, Belayeth
Powell & Co, London (020) 8854 9131

INCE, Robin
Thornhill Ince, Manchester (0161) 839 2550

JAMES, Charles
James & Co, Bradford (01274) 729900

JONES, David Rhys
Glazer Delmar, London (020) 7639 8801

KEMP, Lesley
Warner Cranston, London (020) 7403 2900
Lesley-Kemp@Warner-Cranston.com
Partner, business immigration department.
Specialisation: Primarily specialises in business/employment related immigration. Advises both small and large scale global organistions in the relocation process for expatriates transferring to the UK; individual entrepreneurs and overseas firms seeking to establish a business in the UK; professionals in the entertainment, arts and media fields. Expertise in all aspects of UK immigration and nationality law including personal applications for investors; retired persons of independent means; spouse and family applications.

Prof. Memberships: Lectures and has published articles on immigration issues. City of London Law Society. Member of Immigration Law Practioners' Association (ILPA) (past treasurer and member of the Executive Committee of ILPA 1995-1997.
Career: Qualified February 1989. Assistant solicitor 1989-1993, *Kingsley Napley*; assistant solicitor and partner 1993-1995, *Magrath & Co*; returned to *Kingsley Napley* as a partner, 1995-2000, to establish the firm's immigration department. Joined *Warner Cranston* as a partner in March 2000.
Personal: Born 1960. Tiverton Grammar School; University of Kent at Canterbury (BA Hons); College of Law, Chancery Lane.

KIRK, Graeme
Gross & Co., Bury St. Edmunds
(01284) 763333 and (020) 7935 5541
gdk@gross.co.uk
Senior Partner and Partner in Immigration and Commercial Department.
Specialisation: Principal area of practice is immigration and nationality law. Also deals with company/commercial work for private companies and businesses, including foreign businesses seeking to establish a UK presence. Handles work permit, self-employment, investor, business sole representative independent means and all other immigration cases. Addressed IBA conferences regularly since 1991 and has given seminars throughout the world. Acts as Consultant in immigration law to solicitors firms throughout the UK. Has lectured on business immigration for CLT. Client base includes international banks, foreign and UK corporations, entrepreneurs and high net-worth individuals.
Prof. Memberships: Law Society, IBA, ILPA.
Career: Qualified in 1981. Assistant solicitor with *Radcliffes & Co.* 1981-1984, then joined *Gross & Co.* in 1984 becoming a partner in 1986. Currently senior vice-chairman of the Immigration & Nationality Committee of the International Bar Association, and recently chaired session at IBA Boston conference.
Personal: Educated at Westminster School and University of East Anglia. A member of Bury St. Edmunds Rotary Club. Leisure pursuits include cricket, badminton, opera and the violin. Lives in Bury St. Edmunds.

LESKIN, Nigel
Birnberg Peirce & Partners, London
(020) 7911 0166

LINDSLEY, Fiona
Birnberg Peirce & Partners, London
(020) 7911 0166

LUQMANI, Jawaid
Luqmani Thompson, London (020) 8365 7800
luqthom@btinternet.com
Partner specialising in immigration.
Specialisation: Work includes judicial review and habeas corpus at High Court and Court of Appeal in immigration law and related fields of education, crime and civil actions against the immigration service. Cases include interrelationships between asylum and terrorism, asylum and crime and free movement entitlements for non EU nationals in particular rights of Eastern European nationals. Co-author of 'Recent Developments in Immigration' for Legal Action Group and author of immigration sections in 'Defending Suspects at Police Stations'. Lecturer for ILPA, LAG and CAB. Numerous TV and Radio interviews in respect of topical immigration issues.

Prof. Memberships: Executive Committee Member of ILPA since 1992, appointed by Law Society as Immigration Assessor 1999, member of the Law Society.

MAGRATH, Christopher
Magrath & Co, London (020) 7495 3003
chris.magrath@magrath.co.uk
Senior partner and head of immigration and employment department.
Specialisation: Practice has substantially specialised in immigration and nationality law since 1985, primarily in the corporate field of executive expatriate transfer on a global basis, as well as for numerous individual clients over the last fifteen years. Also practises employment law in both contentious and non-contentious circumstances. Co-author of 'Practitioners Guide to the Police and Criminal Evidence Act 1984' (Longmans) and 'Working in the United Kingdom–A Guide for Foreign Nationals' (Handbook). Has published numerous articles in both professional and commercial magazines. Has made many conference addresses worldwide on immigration and employment related issues arising from expatriate transfer and relocation. Regular broadcaster on legal affairs since 1983.
Prof. Memberships: Law Society, ILPA, American Immigration Lawyers Association, International Bar Association, London Criminal Courts Solicitors' Association, Employment Lawyers' Association.
Career: Qualified in 1975. Admitted to New York Bar in 1986. Set up *Magrath & Co* as senior partner in 1990.
Personal: Born 12th May 1948. Attended Campbell College, Belfast, 1961-1966 and Trinity College Dublin (BA degree) 1972. Leisure interests include tennis, restaurants, dogs and skiing. Lives in London.

MANN, Jane E.
Fox Williams, London (020) 7628 2000
jemann@foxwilliams.co.uk
Partner in Employment and Immigration Department.
Specialisation: Specialises in immigration related to business and employment. Advises multi-national companies relocating employees to the UK, overseas companies establishing an office in the UK for the first time and overseas nationals wishing to establish a UK business. Handles problems with both immigration and employment law aspects.
Prof. Memberships: Founder Member of Employment Lawyers Association and currently its Chairman. Former Treasurer of the Immigration Law Practitioners Association. Member of The International Bar Association and The American Immigration Lawyers Association. Associate Member of the Institute of Personnel and Development.
Career: Qualified 1981. Worked at *McKenna & Co.* 1979-1986, then at *Denton Hall* until 1994, where became a Partner. Joined *Fox Williams* in 1994 as a Partner.
Personal: Born 1957. Attended Cambridge University 1975-78.

MEHMET, Gülay
Penningtons, London (020) 7457 3000
mehmetg@penningtons.co.uk
Specialisation: Immigration nationality and related European Community Law. Corporate/business and private client work including judicial review, and appeals. Acts for three of the India's top ten public companies.

Prof. Memberships: Law Society Immigration Committee, ILPA European Group, Trustee to the Immigration & Nationality Research and Infomation Charity, International Bar Association.
Career: Liverpool University, College of Law. 1991-94 Assistant Director, Joint Counsel for Welfare of Immigrants. Consulted with Home Office, House of Commons Home Affairs Committee and House of Lords Select Committee on immigration law issues.
Personal: Bilingual Turkish. Trustee of Refugee Legal

MOSS, Peter
Bates, Wells & Braithwaite, London
(020) 7551 7777
p.moss@bateswells.co.uk
Immigration and nationality Advisor.
Specialisation: Advises on immigration and nationality matters and conducts advocacy in appeals. Main area of practice covers commercial immigration: work permits and applications for entry clearance as businessmen, overseas representatives, and under the Europe Agreements with Eastern European countries. Also specialises in applications outside the immigration rules for long term residents and couples who cannot marry. Other main area of work for private clients including persons of independent means, self-employed artists and family settlement cases. Author of articles for 'Immigration Law and Practice' and the 'Hong Kong Law Society Gazette'.
Prof. Memberships: Treasurer of Immigration Law Practitioners' Association, 1992-1996. Many years service on the Executive of I.L.P.A., and its European sub-committee.
Career: HM Immigration Officer, Dover 1973-1975. Immigration Counsellor with the United Kingdom Immigrants Advisory Service 1975-1976, then Senior Counsellor 1976-1989. Immigration and Nationality Advisor with *Thomson Snell & Passmore* 1989-1992, then joined *Bates Wells & Braithwaite.*
Personal: Born 11th July 1949.

ONSLOW-COLE, Julia
CMS Cameron McKenna, London
(020) 7367 3000
Partner and head of immigration and nationality group.
Specialisation: Partner responsible for the firm's global immigration and nationality group, the largest in the UK and ranked number one by all the legal directories. *CMS Cameron McKenna* is the only City firm to offer a US immigration law service. The group deals with all the aspects of immigration and nationality law (except asylum and refugee) and advises principally on applications for work permits, business persons, sole representatives, investors, retired persons of independent means and applications for British citizenship; on the US side specialising in international transfers, professionals and investors. The group also provides advice on immigration to China, Singapore and Hong Kong through its Hong Kong Office. Offices in Germany and Poland cater for clients moving individuals to Central and Eastern Europe. The group has an extensive international client base, principal clients being multinational businesses and financial intitutions whose employees need to be able to move rapidly. In 1999, the group launched a dedicated UK immigration sports and entertainment practice–advising football clubs and sports associations and individual entertainers and artists. In addition the group has a specialised practice for high net worth individuals and entrepreneurs, particularly in the field of e-commerce, from all parts

of the world. The group makes several applications at the cutting edge of European immigration law. The Group has an impressive track record, taking an innovative approach to solve client problems and offers tailored in-house training to corporate clients on immigration issues.
Prof. Memberships: Chairman of International Bar Association, Immigration & Nationality Committee, Member of Immigration Law Sub-Committee of Law Society, Secretary of Immigration Law Practitioners Association and co-convenor of Immigration Law Practitioners Association's Business and Employment Sub-Committee, Member and Assessor of the Law Society's Immigration Law Panel, Member of the UK Association for European Law, Fellow of the Society for Advanced Legal Studies, member of Home Office User Panel, member of American Immigration Lawyers Association.
Career: Qualified 1984. Worked for British Coal 1982-1986, then *Simmons & Simmons* as head of UK immigration and nationality department 1986-1990. Joined *Cameron Markby Hewitt* in 1990 as head of immigration and nationality group, partner from 1991.
Personal: Born 30th September 1959. Took an LLB(Hons) in 1981, Law Society exams in 1982.

PENROSE, Martin

Winstanley-Burgess, London (020) 7278 7911
Specialisation: Partner in the immigration department specialising in refugee law, Judicial Review and general immigration law. Has experience of teaching for ILPA and community organisations and has appeared on radio and television. Has travelled to Turkey for Amnesty International and the Law Society to monitor Human Rights trials. Specialist interest and experience in Sudanese casework.
Prof. Memberships: Immigration Law Practitioners Association; Refugee Legal Group.
Career: Graduate of Balliol College, Oxford. Qualified at *Winstanley-Burgess* in 1992. Partner since 1998.

PHILLIPS, Mark

Tyndallwoods, Birmingham (0121) 624 1111
Mark_Phillips@tyndallwoods.co.uk
Partner and head of civil liberties department.
Specialisation: Main area of practice is immigration and public law, mainly refugee, marriage and family reunion cases. Undertakes advocacy and judicial review work. Author of 'Tenants Control' (Council Housing Co-operatives). Has lectured for LIBERTY on civil liberties issues (especially policing and Human Rights Act) and for ILPA and IISA on judicial review and immigration appeals advocacy. Member of Amnesty International and Joint Council for the Welfare of Immigrants. Member of the Law Society Immigration Law Committee, Chairperson Midland Immigration Practitioners (MIP). Member of Region 6 Legal Services. Commission Review Committee.
Prof. Memberships: Law Society, Birmingham Law Society, Immigration Law Practitioners Association, Assessor and Member Law Society Immigration Law Panel.
Career: Paralegal advisor at Stepney Green Law Centre 1973-1975. Action/ research project on tenant's co-operatives 1975-1977. Articled clerk at *T.V. Edwards* 1978-1981. Assistant solicitor at *Geffens* 1981-1983. Senior solicitor at Handsworth Law Centre, Birmingham, 1983-1985. Joined *Tyndallwoods* in 1985, becoming a partner in 1988.
Personal: Born 10th May 1947. Educated at Lymm Grammar School, Cheshire, 1958-1964; Dame Allen's School, Newcastle-on-Tyne, 1964-1966, Hull University 1967-1970; then London School of Economics 1970-1971. Married with two children. Leisure interests include mountain biking. Lives in Walsall.

POPE, Caron

Norton Rose, London (020) 7283 6000
popecp@nortonrose.com
Specialisation: Caron has specialised in UK business immigration law since qualification in 1990 and has extensive experience in all types of business immigration applications. Particular areas of expertise include work permit applications, particulary obtaining permits for outside hires which have not been advertised or which do not fully meet the requirements of the work permit scheme and "switches" from training and work experience permits to full work permits. The team has a 100% success rate over the last four years. In addition, Caron has made numerous applications for sole representatives and other permit free employment categories, applications for businessmen, applications under Home Office concessions and settlement and naturalisation applications. She also advises on marriage and student applications and the application of European Law.
Prof. Memberships: Immigration Law Practitioners Association. Associate member–Canada / UK Chamber of Commerce; Member Inter Pacific Bar Association (IPBA).
Career: Croydon High School for Girls 1977-1984. University of East Anglia, Norwich 1984-1987 (LLB Hons). Guilford College of Law. *Cameron Markby Hewitt* 1988-1996. Articled Clerk (1988-1990). Solicitor, Immigration & Nationality Law Group (1990-1996). *Norton Rose* Head of Business Immigration Team August 1996 to date. Caron has lectured and written on UK immigration issues in the UK and overseas.

RANDALL, Christopher W.

Winstanley-Burgess, London (020) 7278 7911
wb@gn.apc.org
Partner in Immigration Department.
Specialisation: Handles refugee law, judicial review and general immigration law. Solicitor in the cases of R v Special Adjudicator ex parte Mehari and R v SSHD ex parte Radiom. Author of 'An Asylum Policy for the UK' in 'Strangers and Citizens', published by IPPR in 1994 and co-author of the trimonthly article 'Recent Developments in Immigration Law' in Legal Action. Has experience of teaching for ECRE, ILPA, the Refugee Council and community organisations, and has appeared on radio and television.
Prof. Memberships: Immigration Law Practitioners Association executive committee member for 9 years, (with special responsability for refugee and legal aid matters).
Career: Joined *Winstanley-Burgess* in 1985 and qualified 1987. Partner since 1990.
Personal: Born in 1959. Attended Oxford University 1978-1981 and the City of London Polytechnic 1983-1985. Lives in South East London.

RIPLEY, Fiona

Winstanley-Burgess, London (020) 7278 7911
Partner in immigration department.
Specialisation: Specialises in refugee law, judicial review and all aspects of immigration law. Has organised and participated in human rights delegations and seminars relating to Turkey and Kurdistan. Has appeared on television. Co-founder of the Refugee Legal Group. Provides training for and works closely with refugee community organisations particularly Turkish Kurdish refugee groups.
Prof. Memberships: Immigration Law Practitioners Association, Refugee Legal Group.
Career: Qualified at *Winstanley Burgess* in 1987. Partner since 1990.
Personal: Born in 1961. Attended SOAS (University of London) 1981-1984.

RIVIERE, Susanna

Harbottle & Lewis, London (020) 7667 5000
sriviere@harbottle.co.uk
Joint head of the Immigration section of the Employment and Immigration Group.
Specialisation: Practices exclusively in immigration and nationality work covering the full spectrum of business/employment related immigration and most personal immigration. Particular expertise in corporate and personal immigration work for clients in *Harbottle & Lewis*' key industry areas of Media, Entertainment, Travel and Leisure.
Prof. Memberships: Law Society; Immigration Law Practitioners Association; British Institute of Human Rights; Stonewall.
Career: Attended Churchill College, Cambridge. Joined *Harbottle & Lewis* in 1977. Qualified in 1979. Head of Immigration Group 1996.
Personal: Married with three children. Leisure interests include sailing.

ROLLASON, Nicolas

Kingsley Napley, London (020) 7814 1200
nrollason@kingsleynapley.co.uk
Specialisation: All areas of business and personal immigration and nationality law with particular emphasis on EU free movement law and the rights of establishment under the EC Asssociation Agreements with central and eastern Europe. Substantial experience of immigration appeals, judicial review and proceedings before the ECJ and Court of First Instance in Luxembourg. Reported cases before the ECJ include Case C-356/98 Kaba v SSHD and C-416/96 El Yassini v SSHD. Frequent lecturer on EU free movement and related human rights issues. Member of the Editorial Board of the Immigration and Employment Law Journal. Rapporteur to the European Commission on free movement 1996-2000.
Prof. Memberships: Member of the ILPA European Subcommittee since 1996, Law Society.
Career: Qualified in 1996. Assistant in immigration department *Baileys Shaw and Gillet* 1996-1997. Joined *Kingsley Napley* in March 1997.
Personal: Born 1968. Attended Oxford University 1986 to 1989. Lives in London.

SIMM, Peter

A S Law, Liverpool (0151) 707 1212

SMITH, David

Nelsons, Nottingham (0115) 958 6262
david.smith@nelsons-solicitors.co.uk
Partner, head of immigration unit.
Specialisation: Developed immigration work from scratch at *Nelsons* since 1989. Works across full range of individual and corporate immigration cases.
Prof. Memberships: Law Society, Immigration Law Practitioners Association. Panel solicitor for

Stonewall and Refugee Legal Centre. Member of and Assessor for Law Society Immigration Panel.
Career: After ten years in social work qualified as a solicitor in 1989. Partner at *Nelsons* since 1995.
Personal: Born 5/3/54. BA Philosophy 1976, Master in Social Work 1978.

SMITH, Graham
Bindman & Partners, London (020) 7833 4433
Specialisation: All areas of immigration and nationality law, especially family settlement appeals and applications outside the rules for South Asian and African clients; advocacy before Adjudicators and the Tribunal.
Career: Educated Barry Grammar School and SOAS, graduating in 1973 with a degree in Marathi and Hindi. After 3 years' research in Hindu Law, joined *Bindmans* in 1977 as immigration adviser. Visits South Asia regularly (since 1980) conducting enquiries for clients in immigration and family cases. Speakes Sylheti, and translates Bengali literature. Gives training courses for ILPA.

SMITH, Lisa
Stuart Miller, London (020) 8881 7440
Specialisation: Work covers all aspects of immigration, particularly asylum and work with unaccompanied minors.
Prof. Memberships: ILPA, Refugee Legal Group.
Career: Qualified at *Bindman & Partners* in 1994. Became head of immigration department at *Stuart Miller & Co* in 1997.
Personal: Born 1963. Graduate of Sussex University.

STANLEY, Alison
Bindman & Partners, London (020) 7833 4433
Specialisation: Practice covers all aspects of immigration, asylum and nationality law.
Prof. Memberships: Member of the Law Society's Immigration Law Sub-Committee, Immigration Law Practitioner's Association, the JUSTICE administrative law panel and the Refugee Women's Legal Group.
Career: Articled at *Winstanley-Burgess.* Subsequently worked for 4 years as the solicitor to the Joint Council for the Welfare of Immigrants. Joined *Bindman & Partners* in July 1994. Became partner and head of immigration department in May 1995.

STURTIVANT, Karen L.
Sturtivant & Co, London (020) 7486 9524
visas@sturtivant.co.uk
Principal.
Specialisation: Runs a practice devoted entirely to UK Immigration and Nationality law. Emphasis on business clients, but covers the full range of private client immigration work, although legal aid not undertaken. Author of numerous articles and has spoken widely at seminars in the UK and abroad.
Prof. Memberships: Immigration Law Practitioners Association, American Immigration Lawyers Association, International Bar Association, Law Society Immigration Law Sub-Committee, Deputy Assessor Immigration Law Panel.
Career: Qualified in 1980. Founded *Sturtivant & Co.* in 1985.

THOMPSON, Sally
Luqmani Thompson, London (020) 8365 7800
luqthom@btinternet.com
Specialisation: All aspects of immigration and nationality law with emphasis on human rights issues, and increasing social security law for persons from abroad.
Prof. Memberships: ILPA, Law Society.
Career: Articled in London and Reading, qualified in 1991. Working exclusively in immigration since qualifications. Founding member of *Luqmani Thompson* & Partners from December 1998.

TROTT, Philip
Bates, Wells & Braithwaite, London
(020) 7551 7777
p.trott@bateswells.co.uk
Partner in immigration and employment department.
Specialisation: Commercial Immigration law, advising individuals and corporations on how they can be economically active in the UK and advising on Home Office and Department of Employment unpublished practices and concessions. Regular lecturer on professional courses on immigration and employment law issues. Regular contributor for TV and radio broadcasts on immigration and extradition issues. Editor of 'Immigration and International Employment Law'.
Prof. Memberships: Immigration Law Practitioners' Association, Joint Chair of its Business and Employment sub-committee, Employment Lawyers Association, American Immigration Lawyers' Association, Law Society.
Career: Qualified in 1979. Assistant Solicitor *Lawford & Co* 1979-1982. Partner *Lawford & Co* in 1982. Joined *Thomson Snell & Passmore* as Head of Immigration and Employment Law Department in 1989, and moved to *Bates, Wells & Braithwaite* in 1992, Head of Immigration Department.
Personal: University College, London 1973-1976. Fluent in French.

TURPIN, Philip B.C.
Linnells, Oxford (01865) 248607
pt@linnells.co.uk
Partner and head of immigration department.
Specialisation: Handles exclusively immigration and nationality matters, involving work permits, investors, business people, visitors, students, academics, family settlement and asylum and representing both private and corporate clients. Regular course lecturer for ILPA and steering committee member for "Breaking Down the Barriers" ILPA 1999.
Prof. Memberships: ILPA.
Career: Attended the Inns of Court Law School 1981-1982, followed by pupillage at 2 Paper Buildings. Employed by UKIAS 1983-1986, Paddington Law Centre 1986-1988 and *McGrath & Co* in 1988-1995. Joined *Linnells* 1995.

WEBB, David J.
DJ Webb & Co, London (020) 7253 2400
djwebb@webbimmigration.com
Specialisation: Heads a specialist firm entirely devoted to immigration and nationality law. David advises on a wide range of immigration matters in a business and commercial context, with particular emphasis on the operation of the Work Permit Scheme and the establishment/ expansion of businesses in the UK. In addition to his corporate clients, he advises individuals as to how they may enter or remain in the UK either to be economically active or for other purposes. In this context, he has prepared applications in respect of investors, self-employed business persons (including writers and artists), family reunion (entry clearance and variation applications in respect of immediate and extended family members), and retired persons of independent means.
Career: In a 20 year career, he has experienced the full breadth of his chosen subject spending time at an inner London law centre and a multinational law firm. Previously a partner in a Central London practice, he established his own firm in 1997. A founder member of the Immigration Law Practioners Association, he was an elected Committee Member for several years. In December 1998 he was appointed Chief Assessor of the Law Society Immigration Law Panel.
Publications: David has published many articles on immigration law in legal and popular journals and is the co-author of 'Immigration & Asylum Emergency Procedures'. An experienced advocate and lecturer, he frequently appears before the Immigration Appelate Authority.
Personal: To relax David studies history and comparative religion and enjoys spending time with his children.

INFORMATION TECHNOLOGY

OVERVIEW: This year, the section takes on a new appearance. The e-commerce rankings now appear under a discrete heading, and this year's IT tables are intended to identify the leading specialist practitioners. Lawyers with a substantially IP-oriented practice now feature solely in that area of practice. Of particular note this year is the performance of the leading convergence firms, with Olswang now emerging as the principal threat to the dominance of the leading three, who remain unchanged this year. Other strong showings have come from Osborne Clarke OWA, Field Fisher Waterhouse and niche firm Kemp & Co.

LEADING IN-HOUSE LAWYERS

Graham ALLAN, Managing Attorney, *Cisco Systems*

David HOFFMAN, General Counsel UK & Ireland, *Oracle*

Christopher PARKER, Director of Legal Services, *Compaq*

Jane REEVES, Company Lawyer, *Primark Financial Data*

Graham Allan at Cisco is *"very organised and very responsive."* **David Hoffman** at Oracle is a *"very competent manager."* **Christopher Parker** at Compaq is described as a *"leading cutting-edge lawyer."* **Jane Reeves** at Primark is very *"high quality."*

In-House lawyers profiles: page 1177

RESEARCH APPROVED BY BMRB: *For this edition,* Chambers' *researchers conducted 6083 interviews – 4408 with law firms, 598 with barristers and 1077 with clients.*

The validity of the research was scrutinised by BMRB International, who audited both the methodology and the results at our offices in July 2000. They interviewed Chambers' *researchers and cross-checked sample interviews. Details of the audit appear on page 7.*

LONDON

INFORMATION TECHNOLOGY • London	Ptnrs	Assts
❶ Baker & McKenzie	5	15
Bird & Bird	7	33
Clifford Chance	8	38
❷ Lovells	6	12
Olswang	5	11
❸ Allen & Overy	3	15
Masons	7	15
Osborne Clarke OWA	7	22
Taylor Joynson Garrett	15	17
❹ Denton Wilde Sapte	10	22
Field Fisher Waterhouse	6	14
Kemp & Co	3	2
❺ Freshfields Bruckhaus Deringer	5	23
Herbert Smith	4	15
Linklaters	3	15
Rowe & Maw	6	16
Slaughter and May	2	13
Tarlo Lyons	7	10
❻ Ashurst Morris Crisp	4	20
Berwin Leighton	5	36
Bristows	11	14
CMS Cameron McKenna	2	13
D J Freeman	2	5
DLA	6	19
Hammond Suddards Edge	3	4
Nabarro Nathanson	4	9
Simmons & Simmons	-	3
Theodore Goddard	2	4

Within each band, firms are listed alphabetically

Baker & McKenzie *"Well-known, established practice"* that is one of London's finest and is seen to benefit from a *"good European geographic spread"* (especially in Germany.) Also said to treat IT as *"less of a corporate service arm than many other large firms."* Active across the entire span of IT work, the practice's centres of excellence are in outsourcing agreements, IT litigation, digital media and IT/telecommunications convergence matters. The practice's key hitters remain **Don Jerrard** *("an outstanding reputation in the field")* and **Harry Small**, best known for his litigating skills, who is a frequent speaker at conferences and seminars. **Michael Hart** also comes recommended. Large soft/hardware suppliers, many of them American, form a substantial part of the practice's extensive client portfolio. Advised Compaq over the provision of software systems, over the Internet, to Cable & Wireless' new Triangle venture. **Clients:** Sony (all corporate); 3com; Apple; Cisco Systems; Oracle; Compaq; Orange; Symbian; Nortel Networks; Viasoft.

Bird & Bird *"Focused"* team with a massive reputation in the field and *"strong US connections."* Despite its superlative name however, quality is sometimes seen to be *"patchy,"* in part due to the perception that recent junior recruits do not match the ability of the firm's leading lights. The stand-out name here is *"public sector guru"* **Hamish Sandison** who *"went in with all guns blazing and turned the practice around."* Other recommended practioners include **Roger Bickerstaff**, whose forte is in public sector procurement, litigator **Hilary Pearson** *("dry but nice")*, *"super all-rounder"* **Christopher Rees**, who earns promotion this year, and the *"bloody good"* **Graham Smith**. The team advised BA/POCL on the restructure of contracts between DSS, POCL and ICL and acted for SEMA on contracts for supplying systems integration services (including for the International Olympic Committee) and service provider agreements for outsourced IT. **Clients:** SEMA Group; CCTA; BA/POCL.

Clifford Chance With *"great all-round expertise"* across the 'convergence' spectrum (IT, e-commerce, telecoms, media and corporate), the City leviathan certainly has *"the power to make it"* in the field, where it has long been a distinguished combatant. While some see the IT practice as intimately linked to the firm's corporate activities (though less so than at other

LEADING INDIVIDUALS • London	
❶ **KEMP Richard** Kemp & Co	**MILLARD Christopher** Clifford Chance
SANDISON Hamish Bird & Bird	
❷ **JERRARD Donald** Baker & McKenzie	**McCALLOUGH Robert** Masons
REES Christopher Bird & Bird	**RENDELL Simon** Osborne Clarke OWA
SMALL Harry Baker & McKenzie	
❸ **ARCHER Quentin** Lovells	**BICKERSTAFF Roger** Bird & Bird
CHISSICK Michael Field Fisher Waterhouse	**GARDNER Nick** Herbert Smith
GRAHAM Rory Osborne Clarke OWA	**GRIFFITHS David** Clifford Chance
JACOBS Laurence Allen & Overy	
MAHONY Michael Hammond Suddards Edge	
MAUGHAN Alistair Shaw Pittman	**NICHOLSON Kim** Olswang
PEARSON Hilary Bird & Bird	**ROWE Heather** Lovells
SEGAL Arnold Theodore Goddard	**SINGLETON Susan** Singletons
SMITH Graham Bird & Bird	**SWYCHER Nigel** Slaughter and May
WARD Conor Lovells	
WEBSTER Michael Nicholson Graham & Jones	
❹ **BURNETT Rachel** Masons	**DAVIES Clive** D J Freeman
GARDNER Paul Osborne Clarke OWA	**HART Michael** Baker & McKenzie
HIGHAM Nicholas Denton Wilde Sapte	
LISTER Richard Freshfields Bruckhaus Deringer	
LUBBOCK Mark Ashurst Morris Crisp	**MONAGHAN Iain** Masons
ROBERTSON Ranald Robertson & Co	**TURNER Mark** Herbert Smith
WESTMACOTT Philip Bristows	**WILDISH Nigel** Field Fisher Waterhouse
WORTHY John Denton Wilde Sapte	

*See **Profiles** on page 453*

'magic circle' firms), *"you can never, never discount them – they have a lot of top clients."* The mainstay of the practice remains **Christopher Millard**, "an absolute leader and one of the best IT lawyers in London." Another key player is **David Griffiths**, while Vanessa Marsland, a highly respected IT litigator, moves to our IP section, where the bulk of her practice now rests. **Clients:** Large financial institutions and banks; equipment suppliers; internet start-ups.

Lovells Although possessing a comparatively low-key profile, (the team is considered *"safe if not that dynamic"*) the firm's quality is beyond dispute. *"They're a real blue chip organisation with quality people."* A broad-based department specialises on advising clients in the insurance and financial services industries on IT-related matters. The team is headed by **Quentin Archer**, who has extensive industry experience from his time in-house at Acorn. Other key players include **Heather Rowe** *("Ms Data protection")* and **Conor Ward** *("knowledgeable, personable and always impressive")*. The group recently advised on the IT aspects of three significant acquisitions in the insurance sector: Britannia Life by Britannic, Scottish Equitable by Aegon and National Provident Institution by AMP. **Clients:** Nintendo; Barclays; Pearson Group; Prudential Corp.; Union America; Aegon; Scottish Equitable.

Olswang *"Extremely go-ahead, trendy"* firm with an impressive breadth of experience in 'convergence' practice areas. Commonly perceived to be the *"media darling,"* the firm has successfully expanded beyond those roots into 'pure' IT, internet/e-commerce, digital mixed media and telecoms work. Active across the IT spectrum, the firm's clients include both suppliers and users from home and abroad. Work conducted ranges from procurement contracts and software distribution agreements to outsourcing and IT litigation. **Kim Nicholson**, who hails from a telecoms background, is seen to be *"raising her profile"* in the IT field. Currently advising Warner Music International in respect of the outsourcing of its billing systems throughout Europe to Cap Gemini. The team advised Tao Group Ltd in respect of a Sony Investment in that group and the licensing of Tao Technology to Sony. **Clients:** Thus plc (formerly Scottish Telecom); Motorola; RSPCA; BBC Worldwide Ltd; Bloomberg LP; Warner Music (International and UK); MCI WorldCom; Viacom.

Allen & Overy *"Quality outfit"* with a *"down to earth"* and professional approach who *"don't haggle too much – they want to get the deal done."* Renowned for its *"innovative approach,"* the firm is *"becoming a serious player"* in the IT field, especially on corporate-related matters, and rises in the rankings this year. **Lawrence Jacobs** *"picks up on points straight away"* and is considered *"quite a guru."* Outsourcings are a major source of revenue for the practice, which was involved in over 15 transactions with an individual value of over £100 million each. This includes advising EDS on a wide range of outsourcing and other IT-related projects, and acting for Unisys on a major outsourcing and on the acquisition of City Lifeline Systems Ltd. **Clients:** Natwest; Chase Manhattan; Lloyds; Unisys; Nestle; Mobil; EDS; Fage Business Pages.

Masons Renowned for IT litigation, the firm is held to lack similar punch on the non-contentious front. Non-contentious activities do include IT system procurements, data protection, computer games, outsourcings, software supply/services contracts, distribution and licensing. Group head **Rob McCallough** is a *"great communicator at all levels,"* **Rachel Burnett** is known for contract negotiation and drafting and outsourcing and **Iain Monaghan** retains a strong reputation for computer and communications projects. Advising Standard Chartered Bank on an agreement to relocate all IT systems in one location, and ICL Group and ICL Pathway in relation to the £1 billion Pathway/Horizon project with Post Office Counters Ltd. **Clients:** ICL Group; ICI; Bank of Ireland; Standard Chartered Bank; CGU; The Law Society; Kingston Technology.

Osborne Clark OWA Respected team that is *"edging ever upwards"* in this area. With offices in Reading and Bristol, in addition to London, the firm is held to be in a *"geographically ideal"* situation and reputedly enjoys *"great non-City work."* Act for a broad range of clients from major suppliers to company users, with fortes in the e-commerce and computer games arenas. **Simon Rendell** *("on the ball and on top of developments")* is the best known name at the firm, though **Rory Graham** *("tough to be up against")* is also a respected practitioner. Computer games specialist **Paul Gardner** completes a sound front line. The firm advised accounting giant KPMG on its accounting and payroll management contracts with several clients and on its back-to-back agreement with Compaq for data centre services. **Clients:** Communications & Control Electronic; Prudential Corp plc; Infobank; Carlton Screen Advertising; KPMG.

Taylor Joynson Garrett *"Cracking"* team with *"good people and a great client-base."* Although lacking a 'star' practitioner, the team is said to *"exceed the sum of its parts."* The department is particularly strong on outsourcing, IT supply/procurement, computer games and US in-bound investments. Clients range from IT suppliers and overseas software suppliers to computer games companies. Advising Britannia Airways on the outsourcing of procurement, support and maintenance of desk-top computing operations. In contentious matters, the firm is acting for Sony Computer Entertainment on its anti-piracy programme, a process concerning the re-chipping of PlayStations to allow the playing of counterfeit discs. **Clients:** Alliance & Leicester plc; Eidos; Genesys; Britannia Airways; Hiscox; Rank Group plc; Citrix Systems; NCR; Sony Computer Entertainment Europe.

Denton Wilde Sapte The firm has been less visible than in previous years, although it acts across the IT spectrum, including contentious, retail and public sector work and projects. The past year has also seen an increase in the number of IT suppliers for which the firm acts. The *"aptly named"* **John Worthy** and **Nick Higham**, who hails from a satellite/media background, are the group's key players. The team acted for a leading IT supplier on a range of projects, including strategic acquisitions for wireless data operating systems, and have advised on numerous IT disputes, including database infringement cases. **Clients:** IT suppliers; retail groups; public sector organisations.

Field Fisher Waterhouse The firm is seen as one of the *"success stories"* of recent years in the field, and has specific expertise in IT procurement and outsourcing agreements. **Michael Chissick**, a frequent speaker on the conference circuit, is *"developing a great following"* and continues to be perceived as the firm's leading name. *"Nice guy"* colleague **Nigel Wildish** is seen as a *"safe pair of hands."* Currently advising Thomas Cook Longhaul on a systems integration system for holiday reservations. **Clients:** London Transport; London Underground; Sun Microsystems; Granada Media; Pizza Hut.

Kemp & Co Niche firm that concentrates on IT, internet/e-commerce and telecoms. *"Clearly a player,"* the practice is said to offer *"competitive services and prices."* Ex-Garretts man and *"visionary,"* **Richard Kemp** is *"truly innovative"* and is seen to have *"done a really good job"* with an *"extremely loyal"* client base. Clients include major IT buyers, software developers, service suppliers/software houses and equipment suppliers. Work highlights of the year include advising Deloitte Consulting on a large scale public sector development contract and on-going advice to the AFR Consortium (of 34 UK Police Authorities) on various projects. These include the AFIS (automatic fingerprint identification system) services contract with SAGRM SA. **Clients:** Microsoft Europe; AFR Consortium; Deloitte Consulting.

Freshfields Bruckhaus Deringer The firm has consolidated its IT reputation, thanks in part to the acquisition of the *"dependable and sensible"* **Richard Lister** from Berwin Leighton. Although best-known for its role in providing support to the firm's vast existing corporate client base, the department has also advised on outsourcing work and restructuring for a high-profile IT clientele. The team advised on the IT and data protection aspects of the demerger of Hewlett-Packard, and acted for Deutsche Bank on outsourcing its payroll systems to KPMG. **Clients:** GEC; Logica; Quadriga.

Herbert Smith With what is *"probably the largest IT litigation group in the country,"* the firm is also making a *"big splash"* in e-commerce and internet start-ups. Large IT PFI/PPP projects are another forte. **Nick Gardner** is considered a *"highly effective litigator,"* and **Mark Turner** is also recommended. The team is currently advising the Civil Aviation Authority on the implementation of major new air traffic control facilities, reportedly one of the largest IT projects in the UK. **Clients:** IBM; Capita Group; Amstrad; BSkyB; Network Solutions; Vodafone; Jardine Matheson; Cable & Wireless.

Linklaters *"Corporate driven"* with *"loads of quality clients,"* the firm *"does not appear terribly serious about stand-alone IT,"* and lacks an outstanding individual player. However, *"one always has to take them into account,"* and the team acts on outsourcing, dispute resolution, and IT-related railway/transport systems work. Advised Microsoft UK on all its Y2K problems. **Clients:** ICL; Microsoft; BP Amoco; BBC; BA; Dixons; Freeserve; Ernst & Young.

Rowe & Maw Respected unit with an especially good name for big-ticket outsourcing projects. However, the high-profile departure of Michael Webster to Nicholson, Graham and Jones is considered to be a setback to the team's profile. The team has an established reputation for advice on outsourcing, internet start-ups and data protection. Advised on the restructuring of Cable & Wireless Communications' IT outsource arrangements with IBM and acted for Zeneca Agrochemicals on the strategic outsourcing of elements of their systems to Cap Gemini, Compaq and BT. **Clients:** Cable & Wireless; M&G; Vignette.

Slaughter and May *"The blue chip solicitors"* are *"moving in"* on the IT sector. While some argue that they *"only care about the big ticket M&A work,"* most acknowledge that these *"quality generalists"* can *"turn their hand to anything." "Extremely bright, outgoing and forthright,"* **Nigel Swycher** is a *"class act"* credited with *"putting Slaughters on the IT map."* The team is acting for the DETR on the proposed PPP of National Air Traffic Services and advising the New Scottish Centre on systems procurement. **Clients:** Symbian; Psion; Cambridge Positioning Systems; HSS; Abbey National; Enron; Colgate Palmolive; Inchcape; Reuters; JP Morgan.

Tarlo Lyons *"Have made a big effort in the IT sector."* Some have characterised this ambitious group as excessively *"pushy,"* but many sources others comment on the team's depth, one source even describing it as a *"smaller Bird & Bird."* Active across the 'convergence' areas, the practice's forte lies in high-level software patent disputes. Other work covered includes outsourcing and procurement issues. **Clients:** Internet suppliers; financial institutions.

Ashurst Morris Crisp *"Ace firm"* that *"has the skill set"* required of a genuine IT practice. The team is noted in particular for its *"good IT float work."* **Mark Lubbock** heads the group and enters the rankings this year on the back of substantial positive market comment. Advised Big Flower on its acquisition of the mailing services business of the Reader's Digest Association. In addition, acted for Hoare Govett on the flotation on the LSE of the Terence Chapman Group plc, a specialist provider of IT services and software solutions to the financial services industry. **Clients:** Savills; Royal Sun Alliance; Acorn; Big Flower; Nomura; Amey plc; Hoare Govett.

Berwin Leighton *"Making a stab"* in the sector though the loss of Richard Lister to Freshfields is an undoubted blow. Primarily active on big IT outsourcings, software development agreements and systems integrations. Advised the London Borough of Enfield on the outsourcing of all its IT services to ITnet UK Ltd. Over the past twelve months, the firm has been instructed by some of the UK's top ten IT outsourcing suppliers including ICL, Capital and Andersen Consulting. **Clients:** GAP; Tesco: NatWest; SDL; FDS; Andersen Consulting; Capital; ICL; London Borough of Enfield.

Bristows Still generally perceived to be an IP/patents firm, some interviewees believe that *"after the new management changes, the firm is now more forward-looking."* **Philip Westmacott** is an *"excellent"* IT lawyer, though some believe that he ploughs a lonely furrow here. Active across the IT spectrum, the firm is at its strongest on 'technically heavyweight' IT litigation. In non-contentious matters, the team acted for British Airways on a substantial outsourcing deal to support all the company's pc procurement. **Clients:** Litigation clients include NEC; IBM; Motorola; Ericsson; UMC; KPM; Pony Computer Entertainment.

CMS Cameron McKenna Seen to have *"done well"* this year, although the departure of key practitioner Jeremy Newton, who is going in-house at client Sun Microsystems, will undoubtedly be a loss. However, a *"sensible, deal-driven team"* is expected to keep the practice above water in the post-Newton era. Clients are principally drawn from large IT users, with less activity on the supplier side. Fortes lie in the provision of regulatory advice, commercial/private equity-related transactions and internet start-ups. Advising National Bank of Australia on the outsourcing of a back-office IT system. **Clients:** Lloyds Bank; NGC; Commerce Bank; British Gas; Abbey National; Home Office; Treasury; Sun Microsystems; EDS; NSB.

DJ Freeman **Clive Davies** is the stand-out figure at a team which enters the rankings following strong support for its quality and client base. Work covers the gamut of the IT field, with particular ability in corporate support, contractual joint ventures and venture capital investments. The firm advised Bull Information Systems on the Accord project, where the client was one of the successful consortia bidding for the DSS's IT service requirements. **Clients:** Bull Information Systems.

DLA The firm is still not perceived to have compensated for the substantial personnel losses of the last two years. However, the team is still recognised for its capacity to work on outsourcing, data protection and procurement issues in both contentious and non-contentious spheres. The team advised NTL on the development and launch of its electronic programme guide. **Clients:** NTL; Intec Systems; RM plc.

Hammond Suddards Edge Small, *"workmanlike"* team with strength in the commercial and venture capital-related aspects of IT transactions and a growing presence in the e-commerce field. The respected **Michael Mahony** is the practice's leading light and a regular on the conference circuit. Clients are primarily drawn from the corporate and financial services sectors. Currently advising SGB on the outsourcing of its IT systems and 7C on a variety of call centre outsourcing arrangements (including e-commerce applications). **Clients:** One2One; Virgin Mobile; SCB Bank; SGB plc; Aircom International; Barclays Capital.

Nabarro Nathanson The national IT practice's strength is still seen to lie in Reading. However, the London office boasts a sturdy clientele of IT suppliers and services, with a niche in acting on behalf of venture capitalists investing in the IT industry. E-commerce is an area of expansion, as are IT sector joint ventures. Advising Deloitte Consulting on a major systems implementation project. **Clients:** Deloitte Consulting; Lockheed Martin Information Systems; CMG; Olivetti; Safety Net.

Simmons & Simmons Not considered to have advanced in the past year, the department is still acknowledged to have a sound client base, highlighted by a long-term association with Railtrack. The merged communications practice acts on corporate support and outsourcing matters, and negotiated an outsourcing arrangement on behalf of Riyad Bank for the provision of IT services and personnel, a transaction worth in excess of US$50 million. **Clients:** Railtrack, Riyad Bank.

Theodore Goddard Although it has suffered departures in recent times, the team can still call on the services of **Arnold Segal** who *"gets into things and doesn't let go – he's a bulldog."* In addition to extensive corporate experience in IT-related transactions, the firm focuses on outsourcing and computer games. The team acted for Peel Hunt plc on the AIM flotation and placing of shares for a start-up internet incubator company. **Clients:** Peel Hunt plc.

Other Notable Practitioners Singleton's *"phenomenal"* **Susan Singleton** is *"eminently sensible and knows her stuff."* She advised this year on two large outsourcing agreements, in addition to writing several highly respected publications. **Ranald Robertson** (*"he's seen it all"*) of Robertson & Co continues to offer a *"practical low-cost service"* to his *"client base of well-known names."* He regularly advises one of North America's largest IT services companies on various UK projects and is currently representing a worldwide consortium of banks on a software development contract. **Alistair Maughan** of Shaw Pittman is held to be *"an impressive guy who knows his stuff."* **Michael Webster**, who left Rowe & Maw for Nicholson, Graham & Jones, is considered a *"smooth, commercial lawyer"* and is *"seen a lot"* in IT legal circles.

THE SOUTH

INFORMATION TECHNOLOGY • The South	Ptnrs	Assts
❶ **DMH** Brighton	2	5
❷ **Clyde & Co** Guildford	3	6
Lester Aldridge Bournemouth	2	3

Within each band, firms are listed alphabetically.

DMH *"Expanding"* IT practice that rules the roost unchallenged in Kent and its native Sussex. At home in both the contentious and non-contentious spheres, the bulk of the practice's workload stems from 'hard' IT systems supply agreements. Internet/E-commerce is also a major new focus for the firm, accounting for roughly three fifths of the practice's current clients. Acting for Eyretel in connection with a system supply agreement with a major telecommunications company. **Clients:** Eyretel; Digital View; Seaboard plc.

Clyde & Co Continuing to build up its IT profile, the firm's Surrey outpost is active in the fields of IT outsourcing and litigation and in the new growth area of internet/e-commerce. The firm's higher profile in the telecoms arena has enabled it to act for some impressive telecommunications industry clients in the IT sphere. Advising Microgen in relation to its e-billing project, a software package concept to be sold to other companies enabling them to set up their own e-billing programmes. **Clients:** Dell Europe; Ericsson; Nokia; Psion; Comax; Microgen plc; Catalyst Solutions; WS Atkins; Aztec.

Lester Aldridge Niche firm whose mixed IT/IP practice (contentious and non-contentious) *"certainly has clients and people."* Clients include both buyers and suppliers, with software licensing and development agreements the primary fields of activity. Currently acting for a client in a £25m multi-jurisdictional claim relating to IT research and development for an IT development company. **Clients:** Hugh Symons Group plc; Wham!Net UK Ltd; Meggitt Petroleum Systems; Teachers Assurance Group; Sunseeker International Boats; Portsmouth University.

THAMES VALLEY

INFORMATION TECHNOLOGY • Thames Valley	Ptnrs	Assts
❶ **Law Offices of Marcus J. O'Leary** Bracknell	4	2
Nabarro Nathanson Reading	3	6
❷ **Garretts** Reading	2	6
Manches Oxford	2	3
Osborne Clarke OWA Reading	1	4
Willoughby & Partners Oxford	3	3
❸ **Clark Holt** Swindon	1	1
❹ **Boyes Turner & Burrows** Reading	1	1

LEADING INDIVIDUALS	
❶ **BAILES Tony** Nabarro Nathanson	
O'LEARY Marcus Law Offices of Marcus J. O'Leary	
TIGHE David Manches	
❷ **GOODGER Ben** Willoughby & Partners	**HARRINGTON Alison** Garretts
HOLT Jeremy Clark Holt	
❸ **ELLACOTT Sara** Nabarro Nathanson	

Within each band, firms are listed alphabetically. See **Profiles** on page 453

Law Offices of Marcus J O'Leary 'Boutique' practice with a *"wonderful reputation"* and a *"traditional focus on M4 corridor IT firms"* (*"a strategy that has worked"*.) *"Dynamic"* name partner **Marcus O'Leary** oversees a *"superb"* client portfolio. The firm is active across the IT spectrum (software, hardware and outsourcings), and has an emerging specialism in IT/music convergence issues. Clients are drawn from across the IT/internet/multimedia spectrum and include numerous household names from around the world. **Clients:** IT suppliers and users.

Nabarro Nathanson *"At or near the number one slot,"* Nabarro's clearly enjoys *"pride of place in the South."* The *"serious and commercially-minded"* **Tony Bailes** is credited with bringing *"Nabarro's City style and high-calibre clients to Reading."* The *"driven and tremendously organised"* **Sara Ellacott** comes newly recommended this year.

Active across the board in the IT sector, the practice has particular expertise in dealing with large projects disputes (including PFI), IT-related EU Competition Commission claims, and internet/e-commerce matters. Also enjoy good relations with venture capitalists active in the IT sector. Recent highlights for the practice include advising Commerce One on the commercial and regulatory aspects of its on-line procurement venture with BT, the MarketSite product. Also acted for the SPV in the provision of IT and

Managed Technical Services for the Barnet Hospital and for Siemens Healthcare Services on the provision of equipment services for the Worcester Royal Infirmary, both first wave PFI schemes. **Clients:** Sun Microsystems; Oracle; Siemens; EDS; Commerce One; Wincor; Nixdorf.

Garretts IT practice seen to derive some benefit from its membership of the Andersen International network and with some impressive international clients. While active throughout the IT sector, its fortes are in e-commerce and in acting on behalf of IT suppliers (competition, licensing, retail arrangements). Departmental head **Alison Harrington** is thought to be *"on her way up."* Currently advising Motorola Inc. on e-business strategies. **Clients:** Motorola (Ltd & Inc); Wireless Application Protocol (WAP); Network Appliance (Ltd & Inc); Microsoft.

Manches *"Small, quality outfit"* which maintains its reputation for conducting *"City level"* work. Alongside a traditional focus on systems procurement and acting for IT suppliers (over 50 at present), the team has been increasingly active in outsourcing contracts work. The *"quietly-spoken"* **David Tighe** (formerly in-house at Logica) *"invariably knows what he is doing."* Acted for Rebus Group on a multi-million pound outsourcing project for the Employment Services Agency, and a New York bank on a $9 million development project. **Clients:** Rebus Group Ltd; Deutsche Bank; Nominet; Numerical Algorithms Group; Reed Business Information.

Osborne Clarke OWA Already well established in the IT sector in London and Bristol, the firm's new Reading office is active in corporate support work, internet start-ups, facilities management outsourcings and telecoms/IT convergence matters. Advised Kompass International on the establishment of a website and its relations with 70 franchisees worldwide. Also represented 3i on the IBO of the technology-driven logistics division of NFC, now called Isotrak. **Clients:** 3i; Mycom; Vanco; CDT; Kompass International; NatWest Equity Partners; Lloyds Development Capital.

Willoughby & Partners With a *"lot of experience"* in the sector, the firm enjoys a fine reputation for its IT work, though some see the practice as IP-driven. *"Serious player"* **Ben Goodger** heads the team. The team still acts for a variety of business service providers and IT users. **Clients:** Corporates and other IT users.

Clark Holt With an *"excellent reputation and practice,"* this is *"a firm one is always happy to work with on the other side." "Enthusiastic IT man"* **Jeremy Holt** is a well-known name on the conference and lecture circuit and *"very industry-savvy."* Internet start-ups have been a growth area this year, especially in the field of computer-related employment policies. Currently assisting in the drafting of documentation for the establishment of a 'real time' electronic market for commodities trading. **Clients:** Advance Visual plc; AIT Group plc; Phoneme Ltd; Shift 7 Ltd; Star Internet Ltd; British Computer Society; PHH Europe.

Boyes Turner & Burrows Small, local Reading outfit whose clientele is largely on the supply side (hardware and software). Outsourcing agreements and electronic publishing work are the firm's principal strengths. Clients appreciated the firm's *"hands on, commercial approach – they know their clients' business needs."* Acting for i-Way Ltd (an internet service provider) for the establishment of a free internet mail service, involving a telephone operating company and a large retail chain. Also advising on software licensing agreements for IMS with IBM USA for the installation and support of the Real 32 product in the Coco/Carrows and Denny's restaurant chain across the USA. **Clients:** GEAC Computer Systems Ltd; Information Resources; Kyocera Electronics (UK) Ltd.

SOUTH WEST

INFORMATION TECHNOLOGY • South West	Ptnrs	Assts
❶ **Osborne Clarke OWA** Bristol	2	7
❷ **Laytons** Bristol	3	2
❸ **Beachcroft Wansbroughs** Bristol	1	2
Burges Salmon Bristol	3	5
Foot Anstey Sargent Exeter	1	1

Within each band, firms are listed alphabetically.

Osborne Clarke OWA *"Hugely energetic and aggressive"* firm that has *"made a big impact"* in the IT and internet/e-commerce field this year. For some they even *"come top."* The practice is principally occupied with systems sales purchases, outsourcing agreements, corporate support and internet/e-commerce issues (especially US start-ups in the UK). Clients include both users and suppliers. Highlight transactions include advising on the sale of Aethos Communication Systems to Logica plc for c.£40 million and the sale of Knowledge Technology to Sysnstar plc for c.£12 million. **Clients:** Easier.co.uk; Free2Give; Stepstone; Lucent Technologies.

Laytons *"Working very hard"* on upping their profile in the IT sector, and have partially dispelled the market perception that this is fundamentally an IP group. Have advised the Zuken-Redac Group on numerous software and IT related transactions. **Clients:** ITAS (Business Link); Mayrise; Smoby UK; Somerfield Stores; Zuken-Redac Group; Oxford Instruments plc; Edgecombe Investments.

Beachcroft Wansbroughs Practice with a strong profile for PFI and public sector procurement projects. Also had a good name in Y2K litigation (especially for the NHS.) Clients tend to be IT users. Advising the CPS in relation to an IT PFI project for the modernisation of its computer systems nationwide. In addition, acted for Norwich City Council on a major outsourcing project intending to ensure IT systems can make local government more accessible. **Clients:** West Wiltshire County Council; CPS; Norwich City Council; various NHS Trusts.

Burges Salmon Most often seen in the IT arena in a corporate support role, the firm also has a niche specialism in PFI/PPP for both public and private sector clients. Best known of the firm's clients in this field are the MoD and the London Fire Brigade, with others drawn from the rail, water and telecoms utilities sectors. Continue to act for the MoD on its high-profile Defence Fixed Telecommunications System. **Clients:** First Group; United Biscuits; Matthew Clarke; MoD; Insigma Technology; London Fire Brigade.

Foot Anstey Sargent Mixed IT/IP practice with a specialism in the internet/e-commerce field. Work in this area includes advising clients on ISP problems with domain disputes and e-mail policies, setting up internet training and web design contracts, as well as data protection matters. Software licensing agreements are another area of strength for the practice. Currently assisting a client in setting up, taking through to the patents stage and putting on the market a new software innovation. **Clients:** The North Face; Vettrac.

WALES

INFORMATION TECHNOLOGY • Wales	Ptnrs	Assts
❶ **Edwards Geldard** Cardiff	1	3
❷ **Eversheds** Cardiff	1	1
Morgan Cole Cardiff	4	6

LEADING INDIVIDUALS
❶ **DELEMORE Ceri** Edwards Geldard

Within each band, firms are listed alphabetically. See **Profiles** on page 453

Edwards Geldard Wales' premier IT practice, with particular fortes in facilities management and IT public procurement contracts. Clients include software developers, IT service providers, plcs, academic institutions, broadcasters, software and hardware suppliers and the Welsh Development Agency. **Ceri Delemore** "*thinks very quickly*" and is rated the principality's finest IT practitioner. **Clients:** Citibank; Hyder plc; Salomon Smith Barney.

Eversheds Mixed IT/IP practice with a good name in outsourcing agreements on behalf of financial institutions and insurance companies. Also act on behalf of website providers in connection with internet start-ups. Acting for major client the DVLA in relation to the outsourcing of its IT systems, which involves negotiating an interim contract and helping in the search for a new service provider. **Clients:** DVLA; London Life Assurance; National Museums & Galleries of Wales; First Plus Financial; Permanent Health Insurance Ltd.

Morgan Cole Best known for work on behalf of the Welsh authorities. Other activities include software licensing support, outsourcings, e-commerce transactions, distribution agreements, and telecoms supply agreements. Recently acted for BP Amoco in a major outsourcing deal worth £560 million with MCI WorldCom, who will manage BP's telecoms infrastructure across six continents and 85 different countries. **Clients:** BP Amoco.

MIDLANDS & EAST ANGLIA

INFORMATION TECHNOLOGY • Midlands & East Anglia	Ptnrs	Assts
❶ **Eversheds** Birmingham, Nottingham	3	9
Wragge & Co Birmingham	10	20
❷ **Hewitson Becke + Shaw** Cambridge, Northampton	4	4
Pinsent Curtis Birmingham	3	5

LEADING INDIVIDUALS	
❶ **JONES Bill** Wragge & Co	**YATES John** V-Lex
❷ **ARNOLD Michael** Eversheds	**SASSE Sarah** Wragge & Co
❸ **PARK Charles** Pinsent Curtis	

Within each band, firms are listed alphabetically. See **Profiles** on page 453

Eversheds The firm offers a full IT service with notable strengths in public sector IT work, e-commerce, IT outsourcings (for both the public and private sectors), and 'e-government' matters, including IT PFIs. Clients range from suppliers and software processors to banks and venture capitalists looking to invest in e-business start-ups. The leading light in the department is national IT head **Michael Arnold**. Advising Lincolnshire County Council on a complex outsourcing and the business process consequences thereof. **Clients:** Lincolnshire County Council; Baron Software; Midlands Software (a subsidiary of Zeda); Driving Standards Agency.

Wragge & Co "*Technically very good*" and possessing a "*substantial client-base,*" the firm is led by **Bill Jones**, who remains the "*eminence grise*" of Midlands IT law. He is supported by **Sarah Sasse** *("competent, reliable and liked by clients")*. Outsourcing and IT-related corporate, commercial, insurance, telecoms and financial services work form the bulk of the practice's workload. E-commerce and internet start-ups transactions, especially those with a private equity component, are another area of expertise. Currently advising BA on the outsourcing of its key Next Steps IT system, reportedly one of the largest in the private sector in the UK. **Clients:** British Airways; BT.

Hewitson Becke + Shaw "*Took advantage of what is going on in Cambridge and you can't ignore that.*" The premier firm in East Anglia's 'Silicon Fen', it is said to make "*good commercial use*" of its clients in the field. With a focus on all 'convergence' practice areas (IT, Internet-e-commerce, multimedia, telecoms), the firm has a niche speciality in matters relating to software access via mobile telephones (WAP), the web (including litigation as a part of sell-outs) and e-commerce. Advised local client STNC, which develops products granting web access via wireless telephony, on its sale to Microsoft. **Clients:** STNC; Pegasus Software; Novell.

Pinsent Curtis "*Serious firm*" that has made a "*sensible contribution to public sector IT*" in the West Midlands. Public sector IT projects, IT procurements for PFI deals and e-commerce are the firm's fortes and form the bulk of its practice. **Charles Park** is "*definitely a name*" in Birmingham's IT circles. Currently advising Dudley Council on the £70 million Dudley PFI Education Project. **Clients:** Dudley Council; NHS Supplies (national); ISS; NEC; TRW; Sema Group; Lanner Group; Bull Information Systems; Sapint; Smith & Nephew.

Other Notable Practitioners The biggest shake-up in the region is the decision of Rotherham-based Oxley & Coward's first-class IT team to set up their own specialist IT 'boutique', V-Lex , in Worksop. The high profile and "*enthusiastic*" **John Yates**, one of the region's finest practitioners, will head the new outfit.

THE NORTH

INFORMATION TECHNOLOGY • The North	Ptnrs	Assts
❶ **Masons** Leeds, Manchester	4	13
❷ **Eversheds** Leeds	3	8
❸ **Addleshaw Booth & Co** Leeds, Manchester	5	12
Halliwell Landau Manchester	3	5
❹ **Irwin Mitchell** Leeds	1	–
Pinsent Curtis Leeds	5	10
❺ **DLA** Leeds, Manchester, Sheffield	2	5

LEADING INDIVIDUALS	
❶ **GASKILL Shelagh** Masons	
❷ **MOAKES Jonathan** Halliwell Landau	**PARRY Rex** Eversheds
❸ **OLLERENSHAW Zoe** Masons	**PEETERS Michael** Pinsent Curtis
SAMPSON Ian Addleshaw Booth & Co	
❹ **DAVIS Dai** Nabarro Nathanson	

Within each band, firms are listed alphabetically. *See **Profiles** on page 453*

Masons Niche IT practice with an especially good name for government IT projects and data protection matters. Whilst Leeds is seen to have an edge over Manchester, the gap has definitely closed, with the latter office acknowledged to be *"competent, if low-profile."* The star of Masons' northern practice remains **Shelagh Gaskill** who *"runs a tight ship"* and is *"probably the UK leader in data protection."* She is assisted by the *"efficient"* **Zoe Ollerenshaw**. In addition to public sector PFI/PPP work, Leeds is known for its expertise in global data flows and e-commerce, while Manchester has a good reputation for IT outsourcings. The northern offices share the national practice's high profile for IT litigation. Currently advising numerous public and private clients and government agencies on compliance with the new Data Protection Act and annotating the statute for Sweet & Maxwell's Encyclopaedia of Data Protection. Also involved in the IT aspects of the divestments of the polyurethanes and petrochemical business of ICI to Huntsman Group and the ICI Acrylics business to Ineos. **Clients:** Leeds: Bradford & Bingley Building Society; Hilton International Hotel Group; Express Dairies; Rolls Royce Power Engineering Co.; Dixons Group plc. Manchester: Metropolitan Police Service; South Gloucestershire Council; The Co-operative Bank plc; Rockcliffe Computers.

Eversheds Mixed IT/IP practice that benefits from the firm's extensive client portfolio in the corporate sector. Active across the 'convergence' spectrum, the practice is primarily involved in the e-commerce/internet and IT outsourcing arenas. *"Well-rounded lawyer"* **Rex Parry**, who took over the practice from Dai Davis, has raised his profile this year to join the ranks of the North's leading IT practitioners. Currently advising Asda Group plc on a major website development. **Clients:** Asda Group plc; Martin Dawes; Telecity; National Computing Centre; U-Net.

Addleshaw Booth & Co Largely non-contentious, mixed IT/IP practice that does well out of the firm's extensive corporate client base. Internet/e-commerce matters, often on behalf of financial institutions, computer software licensings and IT outsourcings are the firm's principal areas of activity. The *"commercial, pragmatic and down-to-earth"* **Ian Sampson** is also *"irritatingly good"* and heads up the Leeds office. The Manchester office has advised on IT procurement transactions with an aggregate value in excess of £300 million in the last eighteen months. Yearly highlights include Leeds acting for the MoD on the outsourcing of IT services relating to the management of its entire housing stock. The Manchester office has acted for Airtours plc on consultancy, development tendering and hardware and software contracts. **Clients:** Leeds: Time Retail Finance; MoD; ESM Ltd. Manchester: Airtours plc; ADS Anker Group; Skillsgroup plc.

Halliwell Landau **Jonathan Moakes** *("straightforward and friendly")* is a well known name in the northern IT legal arena. The firm covers a broad range of IT work, including litigation, e-commerce, technology licences and IT systems agreements. **Clients:** Ninja Corporation; Reflec plc; Telecity Ltd.

Irwin Mitchell Equally strong on contentious and non-contentious work, the firm undertakes high-value, complex bespoke software deals. Advising PanCredit systems on the proposed termination of a £5 million software development and supply agreement with General Motors, and Bewise Ltd (retail chain) on the implementation of a new computer system valued at £500,000. **Clients:** The Bay Trading Company Ltd; Bewise Ltd; Chess Logistics Ltd; Delta Engineering Holdings; PanCredit Systems Ltd; Square-Sum plc.

Pinsent Curtis Though best known for their PFI/public sector projects practice, the Technology Group is also strong in the fields of e-commerce, 'e-pharmaceuticals' and digital signatures/encryption. Clients are frequently drawn from the retail and financial services industries. **Michael Peeters** is the best known name for IT work. Advising the Metropolitan Police on a £1 billion IT outsourcing project and acting for Planet Online on all its contractual work. **Clients:** Sema plc; Groupe Schneider; Planet Online; Tesco; Argos; MAFF; DETR: DSE; Metropolitan Police; London Fire Brigade; Spring Group plc.

DLA Although hit by recent departures, the group still remains an important part of the national set-up. The team deals with start-ups, data protection issues, e-commerce, procurement and outsourcing. The team has advised a number of financial institutions and service providers on the financial regulatory implications of taking their businesses on-line. **Clients:** NTL.

Other Notable Practitioners Peripatetic *"techie"* **Dai Davis** of Nabarro Nathanson is still regularly seen *"on the circuit"* and remains a regional name to conjure with.

SCOTLAND

INFORMATION TECHNOLOGY • Scotland	Ptnrs	Assts
❶ **Maclay Murray & Spens** Edinburgh, Glasgow	3	8
❷ **MacRoberts** Glasgow	3	5
McGrigor Donald Glasgow	3	8
Shepherd & Wedderburn WS Edinburgh	2	7
❸ **Dundas & Wilson CS** Edinburgh	3	8

LEADING INDIVIDUALS	
❶ **FLINT David** MacRoberts	**MACPHERSON Shonaig** McGrigor Donald
NICOLSON Fiona Maclay Murray & Spens	
❷ **BYATT Lorne** Dundas & Wilson CS	**CAMERON Gillian** Maclay Murray & Spens
SAUNDERS James Shepherd & Wedderburn WS	
❸ **McROBB Elizabeth** Shepherd & Wedderburn WS	
ORR Alistair Maclay Murray & Spens	

Within each band, firms are listed alphabetically. *See **Profiles** on page 453*

Maclay Murray & Spens *"Big time"* practice with an excellent client base and a team who are *"all highly regarded, good people."* Active across the IT spectrum, including IT litigation, internet start-ups, anti-piracy matters and outsourcing agreements for large financial institutions. Departmental head **Fiona Nicolson** is *"brilliant"* on licensing and technology transfer agreements, while colleagues **Gillian Cameron** and **Alistair Orr** are both *"doing some very interesting work on the software front."* Currently handling multi-million pound outsourcing transactions for Scottish Power's information services division. In addition, acting for Adobe Systems Europe on an outsourcing deal and for Microsoft on anti-piracy work in Scotland. **Clients:** Adobe; Microsoft; Scottish Widows; Bank of Scotland, Scottish Power; Scotland On-line.

MacRoberts The firm's current lack of transactional visibility is thought to be due to its *"heavy involvement in some big IT/PFI projects."* In addition to PFI projects, have a focus on the internet/e-commerce/cyberlaw and multimedia sector. International regulation, licensing and trade agreements are another forte. **David Flint**, the group's on-line expert, is well known as a writer and publisher and *"invariably good on IT matters."* Advising the Scottish Internet Exchange on setting up and putting operating contracts in place. Other work includes advising 3Ed on the ICT contract for the Glasgow Schools PFI Project and SCET on the Learning Schools Project. **Clients:** Venturedome.com; Calligrafix; Giltech; University of Strathclyde; Railtrack plc; British Energy plc; Scottish Internet Exchange; NetGame Ltd; Rampant Multimedia.

McGrigor Donald Another *"long-standing, highly respected"* full service IT department. Technology work is its speciality. *"Definitely a leader in Scotland,"* **Shonaig MacPherson** is increasingly focusing on the internet/e-commerce arena. Assisting the Virtual Component Exchange (VCX) in its efforts to establish a self-regulating environment to facilitate the trading of 'virtual components', used in the design of systems on chip. This is the latest advance in the semiconductor industry. Continue to work with 3i plc, Scotland's leading technology investor, on a variety of cutting-edge projects. **Clients:** Axis Shield plc; 3i plc; Vis Interactive plc; Virtual Component Exchange; Indigo Active Vision Ltd.

Shepherd & Wedderburn WS Upwardly mobile IT department (*"they clearly want to focus on IT"*), best known for its systems acquisitions and outsourcing work. Other areas of expertise include IT litigation, internet/e-commerce (including fund-raising for start-ups and advising financial services clients) and IT/telecoms convergence issues. *"Talented"* **James Saunders** has an *"interesting practice – he's essentially a corporate lawyer who excels at advising IT clients."* Colleague **Liz McRobb** deals primarily with public sector procurements and outsourcing projects. Advising the MoD's Defence Procurement Agency in connection with the high profile Surgeon General's Information Services Project. In addition, advising the City of Edinburgh Council on its outsourcing projects. Both these two IT PPP outsourcing projects are valued in excess of £100 million. **Clients:** MoD; Institute of Chartered Accountants of Scotland; Thus plc; City of Edinburgh Council; Scottish Power UK plc; Friends Ivory & Sime; Edinburgh Fund Managers; Bank of Scotland; Data Protection Office.

Dundas & Wilson CS Andersen Legal's respected Scottish member firm lack the profile of others ranked in these tables. Niche fortes in IT outsourcing agreements, internet/e-commerce matters and software licensing, maintenance and development agreements. Though *"technically very able,"* **Lorne Byatt** is seen to be *"more academic than commercial."* Big systems acquisitions and outsourcings are his specialities. Advising Glasgow City Council on an IT procurement to supply managed IT services to all of its schools. Also advising Digital Animations on its joint venture with the PA to develop a 'virtual newscaster', Ananova. **Clients:** Bank of Scotland; Royal Bank of Scotland; Glasgow City Council; CCT; Memory Corporation; Digital Animations.

LEADERS IN INFORMATION TECHNOLOGY

ARCHER, Quentin D.R
Lovells, London (020) 7296 2000
quentin.archer@lovells.com
Specialisation: Partner specialising in all aspects of IT law, both contentious and non–contentious, particularly computer contracts (including projects under the Private Finance Initiative), electronic commerce and the introduction of new technology. One of the first lawyers to move (in 1985) from the IT industry back into private practice. Most clients outside the IT sector are in the financial services, defence, and media fields.
Prof. Memberships: Law Society; US Computer Law Association; Treasurer, British Czech and Slovak Law Association.
Career: Qualified 1981. In-house solicitor at Acorn Computer Group PLC, 1984–1985. Rejoined *Lovells* in 1985, partner 1987.

ARNOLD, Michael R.
Eversheds, Birmingham (0121) 232 1000
michaelarnold@eversheds.com
Specialisation: System development, outsourcing, e-commerce. Head of *Eversheds* IT Group.
Prof. Memberships: Society for Computers and Law.
Career: MA (Cantab). Qualified with *Eversheds* 1984. Partner 1990.
Personal: Cricket.

BAILES, Tony
Nabarro Nathanson, Reading (0118) 925 4602
a.bailes@nabarro.com
Partner and Head of IT Communications and New Media Group.
Specialisation: Sole area of practice is in IT disputes of all types, acting for a wide range of major US and European owned multi–national computer and communication companies, including Sun Microsystems and Siemens. Jointly led the team acting for the major complainant in the landmark Digital case before the EC Commission. Acted with a fast growing specialist team in relation to over 30 substantial high-value disputes arising from systems integration and software development contracts, outsourcing contracts and PFI based projects.
Personal: Born 15.05.51

BICKERSTAFF, Roger
Bird & Bird, London (020) 7415 6000
Partner in Company Department.
Specialisation: Principal area of practice is information technology. Particular work focus is large-scale IT–infrastructure projects, including outsourcing, partnering and PFI projects. Other specialities include dispute resolution, protection of rights, e-commerce, the impact of EC legislation and impact of

new technology. Also advises on all aspects of EC/GATT procurement law. Clients include many government departments and major private sector IT purchasers.
Prof. Memberships: Society for Computers and Law. Works on a part-time secondment basis as head of CCTA's legal services.
Career: Qualified in 1990. At *Linklaters & Paines* 1990–1992. Joined *Bird & Bird* in 1992 and became a Partner in 1995.
Personal: Born 1961. Attended King's College, Cambridge 1980–1984. Lives in London.

BURNETT, Rachel
Masons, London (020) 7490 4000
rachel.burnett@masons.com
Partner, Information & Technology Group.
Specialisation: Practice covers contract negotiation, drafting and related commercial advice for the full range of IT and e-commerce industry transactions. Acts for major vendors, system integrators, software publishers, dot.com companies, data licensors, service providers, resellers, major corporate and financial services sectors. Co-author of "Drafting and Negotiating Computer Contracts" (Butterworths, 1994), author of "Outsourcing IT-The Legal Aspects" (Gower, 1998). Editor of the IT Law Guides Series for the institute of Chartered Accountants. Writes and lectures widely on IT–related matters.
Prof. Memberships: Institute for Information Systems Management Vice-Chairman; Worshipful Company of Information Technologists (Livery Member); British Computer Society (Security Committee and Legal Affairs Committee Member); Society for Computers & Law; Law Society.
Career: Qualified 1980. Former IT professional. Joined *Masons* in 1990. Partner in 1994.
Personal: Exeter University (BA Soc. Studies, Hons). Associate, Institute of Linguists (French). Chair, Association of Women Solicitors, 1990–1991.

BYATT, Lorne
Dundas & Wilson CS, Edinburgh (0131) 228 8000

CAMERON, Gillian J.
Maclay Murray & Spens, Glasgow
(0141) 248 5011
gjc@maclaymurrayspens.co.uk
Partner in Intellectual Property Department.
Specialisation: Specialises in IP generally and non-contentious IT/ internet work in particular for a wide range of clients, including advising Scotland's largest dotcom startup and various ISPs. Accredited as an IP specialist by the Law Society of Scotland and an honorary lecturer in Strathclyde's Entrepreneurship Initiative.
Prof. Memberships: Member of Licensing Executives Society.
Career: LLB (Hons) Edinburgh University (1987); Dip LP (1988); Joined *Maclay Murray & Spens* in 1996; previously Head of Technology Law Unit at *Bird Semple*.

CHISSICK, Michael
Field Fisher Waterhouse, London (020) 7861 4000
mpc@ffwlaw.com
Specialisation: Head of IT and E-commerce Law Group which comprises a team of 6 partners and 14 specialist lawyers. Main areas of practice include: outsourcing projects, data protection, digital mixed media, electronic commerce and m-commerce contracts, linking agreements, software contracts and internet law. In the past year has advised on several major outsourcing projects, including advising London Underground on an outsourcing to ITNET and Thomas Cook on its e-commerce project.
Prof. Memberships: Law Society; Solicitors European Group; FAST Legal Advisory Group; Computer Law Association.
Career: 1st Class Degree in Law (LLB); Law Society Finals 1st Class; Masters Degree in IT and Telecommunications.
Publications: Author of 'Internet Law' published in October 1997 by FT Publications and co-author of 'Electronic Commerce Law and Practice' published in 1999 and 2000 by Sweet & Maxwell.

DAVIES, Clive
D J Freeman, London (020) 7583 4567
cld@djfreeman.co.uk
Partner Media & Communications Department
Specialisation: All aspects of information technology and communications law particularly PFI, major procurement contracts, outsourcing and software development. Internet and e-commerce work includes web site development, content and linking agreements and contracts with ISP's. Regularly advises on related competition and European issues. Acts for a variety of computer, telecommunications and media clients including Bull Information Systems Limited, The Post Office, Channel Four, the British Phonographic Industry (BPI) and Energis.
Prof. Memberships: Member of CBI Intellectual Property Working Group.
Career: Qualified 1977. Joined D J Freeman 1990. Partner 1991.
Publications: Author of publications on the internet, 'E-mail and the Law', and 'E-commerce Start Ups' and a chapter of copyright and the internet in a Unicom Electronic Commerce Report. On editorial team of 'Tolleys Communications Law'.
Personal: Born 30.9.52. Educated Royal Grammar School Worcester and Manchester University (LLB Hons). Leisure activities include family, skiing, sailing and tennis.

DAVIS, Dai
Nabarro Nathanson, Sheffield (0114) 279 4000
d.davies@nabarro.com
Consultant.
Specialisation: Main areas of practice are computer, internet and technology law. Advises on sale of computer systems, licensing of computer systems, intellectual property, joint ventures, development agreements and facility management agreements. Expert in internet and e-commerce legal issues. Clients range from start-up dot.coms to large PLCs. Also advises on the safety of technological products, and on compliance with technology related European Union legislation such as Electromagnetic Compatibility Directive. Contributor to and consultant editor to Croner's Electronic Commerce and to Croner's Industrial Equipment Safety. Speaker at many national and international conferences; co-opted legal expert to BSI committee DS/1/1 and convenor of IEC Committee TC56 Legal Working Group.
Prof. Memberships: Solicitor; Member of Institution of Electrical Engineers; Chartered Engineer; Member of Royal Academy for the Arts, Manufacture and Commerce; Honorary Scientific Member of International Association of Cybernetics; Honorary Member of Centre for International Legal Studies; Member of Licensing Executives Society.
Career: Joined *Eversheds Hepworth & Chadwick* in 1987; became a Partner in 1992; head of *Eversheds* National IT Law practice 1995–1998.
Personal: Born 2nd March 1958. Took a Physics MA at Keble College, Oxford 1976–1979; then MSc Computing Science at Newcastle University 1981–1983. Leisure interests include tennis, reading and cooking. Lives in Boston Spa.

DELEMORE, Ceri
Edwards Geldard, Cardiff (029) 2023 8239
ceri.delemore@geldards.co.uk
See under Intellectual Property, p.510

ELLACOTT, Sara
Nabarro Nathanson, Reading (0118) 950 4700
s.ellacott@nabarro.com
Specialisation: Internet related and e-commerce issues, with particular expertise in e-mail issues cybersquatting, domain names and Meta-tags; largescale IT disputes, mainly acting for large IT suppliers; advising internet start ups on aspects of setting up and running their businesses.
Prof. Memberships: TIPLO. Thames Valley Commercial Lawyers Association.
Career: *Turner Kenneth Brown*: Trainee Solicitor (March 1989–1991), Solicitor (March 1991–May 1995). *Nabarro Nathanson*: Solicitor (May 1995–May 1998), Partner (May1998).
Publications: 'Email scanning may breach privacy'–Computing (May 2000). 'IT companies need to prepare for new email privacy rights' – Corporate Briefing (April 2000). 'Private Lives – privacy, human rights and e-mail' – IT Consultant (March 2000). 'Use of e-mails within the working environment' (Charity Finance Yearbook 2000). 'Domain names explained' – The Business Magazine (October 1999). The Year 2000: issues of conformity, discovery and legal privilege' – IT, Communications and Law (February 1999) Commercial Litigation (January 1999).
Personal: Lincoln College Oxford – BA Hons in Jurisprudence. Post Graduate Diploma in UK and European Copyright and Related Rights – Kings College London. Married, one child.

FLINT, David
MacRoberts, Glasgow (0141) 332 9988
df@macroberts.co.uk
Partner in corporate and commercial group.
Specialisation: Corporate and commercial matters including commercial contracts, patents, trade marks, copyright and other intellectual property licensing, computer and technology contracts, agency and distribution agreements, restrictive practices and competition law in terms of both EU and UK law. Author of 'Liquidation in Scotland' (Jordan & Sons Ltd, 2nd edition 1990); EU Competition Law Section of Stair Memorial Encyclopaedia of the Laws of Scotland. Extensive lecturing experience on a variety of legal and IT subjects. Member of Joint Working Party of Scottish, English and Northern Irish Law Societies and Bars on Competition Law (since 1981). Member of CBI Competition Panel; Member of Law Society of Scotland Intellectual Property Law and International Relations Committees. Licensed Insolvency Practitioner.
Prof. Memberships: Licensing Executives Society, Insolvency Practitioners Association, Society of Practitioners of Insolvency, Institute of Credit Management, The Computer Law Association Inc., Union Internationale des Avocats, UK Association for European Law. American Bar Association (Associate).
Career: Qualified in 1979. Assistant in *MacRoberts*

Company and Commercial Department 1979–84 and Partner from May 1984. Admitted Notary Public 1980. Chairman of Scottish Lawyers European Group 1985 – 1995.
Personal: Educated at the High School of Glasgow 1964–73, the University of Glasgow (LLB 1976 and LLM 1982), and the Europa Instituut, Universiteit van Amsterdam (Diploma in European Integration 1978). Director of Giltech Ltd, The Shareholding & Investment Trust Ltd, and Advoc Ltd.

GARDNER, Nick
Herbert Smith, London (020) 7374 8000
Partner in intellectual property and information technology department.
Specialisation: Deals with intellectual property and technology, specialising in matters involving technical issues in the computing and electronics field. Contentious and non–contentious work. Admitted as a Solicitor Advocate with rights of audience in all civil proceedings. Appointed expert for internet domain name determinations by the World Intellectual Property Organisation.
Career: A number of years experience in the electronic and computing industries before becoming a solicitor. Qualified in 1988 and became a partner at *Herbert Smith* in 1994. Handled the first Internet domain name case in front of the English courts, acting for Harrods. Acted for Amstrad in its record breaking £50 million plus judgment against Seagate Technology. Acted for Dyson Appliances Limited in its litigation against Electrolux. Also deals with data protection matter and has advised a number of utilities in relation to Data Protection Tribunal Proceedings. Handles a wide range of internet and e-commerce work as well as traditional hardware and software contracts.
Personal: Educated at the University of Nottingham.

GARDNER, Paul
Osborne Clarke OWA, London (020) 7809 1062
paul.gardner@osborneclarke.com
Partner in IT & Telecoms.
Specialisation: Specialises in intellectual property and commercial law relating to interactive media and e-business. Works with several leading interactive media publishers and developers. Has also advised a variety of organisations in connection with e-business projects including retailers, interactive media publishers and advertising agencies.
Prof. Memberships: Member of the Executive Committee of the British Interactive Media Association (BIMA) and works closely with the European Leisure Software Publishers Association (ELSPA).
Career: Joined *Titmuss Sainer Dechert* as trainee in 1985 and made partner in 1992. Joined *Osborne Clarke* as partner in 1998.

GASKILL, Shelagh
Masons, Leeds (0113) 233 8905
Partner and Head of Data Protection Group.
Specialisation: Industrial and commercial IT outsourcing deals, information law, data protection law, database design, international data flows, electronic and new media and major infrastructure projects.
Prof. Memberships: Associate Member of BCS.
Career: Lecturer – Faculty of Law, University of Leeds 1979-84. Qualified 1986. At *Dibb Lupton Broomhead* 1984–1994 (Partner from 1993). Joined *Masons* as a Partner in 1994.
Personal: Interests: opera and bridge.

GOODGER, Ben
Willoughby & Partners, Oxford (01865) 791990
ben@iprights.com
Partner in intellectual property department.
Specialisation: All aspects of internet, e-commerce and IT law; trade marks and brand management; technology transfer, patenting and biotechnology; other general I.P. and commercial law, including advertising and trading standards.
Prof. Memberships: Past President of Licensing Executives Society; Secretary: Society for Computers & Law (Thames Valley Group); IPI; INTA, on Editorial Boards for 'Global eCommerce' and 'Euro Watch' journals.
Career: Exhibition to Keble College, Oxford; *Frere Cholmeley* 1986–90; *Denton Hall* 1990–93; *Dallas Brett*1993–97. *Willoughby & Partners* 1997 to date.
Personal: Married with three children; plays the bassoon; architecture; drama; drawing.

GRAHAM, Rory
Osborne Clarke OWA, London (020) 7809 1116
rory.graham@osborneclarke.com
Partner in IT & Telecoms.
Specialisation: Leading practitioner in commercial work in the technology sector, covering IT, telecommunications and e-business. Has advised on over 40 outsourcing transactions for data processing, call centres, voice and data services and billing systems. Also acts on large–scale software development and procurement projects, telecoms privatisations and venture capital work. Has advised financial institutions, content owners and service providers on e-business and EDI work. Much of the work is international in nature, with an emphasis on the US and European jurisdicitions.
Prof. Memberships: The Network Outsourcing Association (Director, Legal Affairs), British Computer Society committee on IP law.
Career: Articled at *Stephenson Harwood* (London) and *Stephenson Harwood & Lo* (Hong Kong). Assistant at *Bird & Bird* from May 1990; partner from January 1994. Joined *Osborne Clarke* 1998. Co–author of 'Internet Law & Regulation'.

GRIFFITHS, David
Clifford Chance, London (020) 7600 1000
david.griffiths@cliffordchance.com

HARRINGTON, Alison
Garretts, Reading (0118) 949 0000
alison.harrington@glegal.com
Specialisation: Practice covers all aspects of computer and technology law including media and communications. Areas of practice include electronic commerce, computer software development, systems integration, network maintenance, information provision, IT distribution, internet and new media related work. Work also includes the protection and exploitation of copyright, trade marks, designs, patents and confidential information.
Prof. Memberships: Law Society, Committee Member Thames Valley Branch of the Society for Computers and Law, Federation Against Software Theft.
Career: Qualified in 1989 - *Denton Hall* (1987–1994). *Garretts* 1994 to date (Head of Technology Group – *Garretts* Reading), Partner from September 1997.
Personal: Born 13 July 1963. Educated at Harrogate College/Harrogate Grammar School and St Edmund Hall, Oxford University. Lives in Henley-on-Thames. Leisure interests include sailing and hill walking.

HART, Michael
Baker & McKenzie, London (020) 7919 1000
Specialisation: Contentious and non–contentious information technology lawyer. Has conducted software and hardware infringement actions, computer fraud cases and numerous computer contract disputes and has drafted and negotiated a wide variety of computer and IT related agreements ranging from distribution and licensing agreements to networking and interactive communications contracts. Clients he has represented include Sony, Nortel, Apple Computer and Canon and the European Association of Consumer Electronics Manufacturers. He has recently written and spoken at seminars on legal aspects of the Internet, on–line services and email/Internet policy and on IT and ADR.
Career: Qualified in 1983. With *Linklaters & Paines* 1983–87. Joined *Baker & McKenzie* in 1987 and became a Partner in 1990.
Personal: Born 12th August 1959. Educated at City of London School 1970–77 and Exeter College, Oxford 1977–80. Leisure activities include theatre, cinema, horse racing and tennis. Lives in London.

HIGHAM, Nicholas
Denton Wilde Sapte, London (020) 7242 1212
nach@dentonwildesapte.com
See under Telecommunications, p.793

HOLT, Jeremy
Clark Holt, Swindon (01793) 617444
Partner specialising in computer law.
Specialisation: Advises on all aspects of non–contentious work including internet related contracts, software rights, system purchase agreements and maintenance contracts.
Prof. Memberships: Society for Computers and Law, British Computer Society.
Career: Qualified in 1980, co–founded *Clark Holt* Commercial Solicitors in 1995.
Personal: Born 1956. Leisure interests include military history, five–a–side football and reading computer magazines.

JACOBS, Laurence
Allen & Overy, London (020) 7330 3000
Specialisation: Contentious and non–contentious information technology, e-commerce and related intellectual property matters. Advising suppliers and customers on outsourcing and electronic commerce projects, joint ventures, advising on development of new digital products and services. Also advised on major contract and copyright disputes in the IT sector.
Career: Qualified *Clifford Chance* 1990. Partner *Allen & Overy* 1997.
Personal: Born 1960. Educated Queens College and Kings College, Cambridge University.

JERRARD, Donald
Baker & McKenzie, London (020) 7919 1000
Senior Partner of Intellectual Property and Information Technology Law Department.
Specialisation: Main areas of practice are intellectual property, information technology and competition law, including patent, trade mark and copyright litigation, technology transfer, computer contracts, computer disputes, and competition law (domestic and EC). Has acted for many leading companies in

the Computer and Consumer Electronic industries (including Sony, Lotus, 3Com, Mitsubishi Electric) in corporate acquisitions and major infringement actions. Has written numerous articles on IP and IT law. Member of the editorial board of 'Computer Law and Security Report'. Editor 'Protecting Computer Technology' (Longmans, 1985) and contributor to 'Guide to Intellectual Property in the IT Industry' (Sweet & Maxwell, 1998) and 'Encyclopaedia of Information Technology Law' (Sweet & Maxwell). Speaker and Chairman at many conferences, especially on IT law, in the UK and abroad.
Prof. Memberships: Law Society, London Computer Law Group.
Career: Qualified in 1976 and joined *Baker & McKenzie* in 1977. Became Head of Department in 1983 and a Partner in 1985. Board Member, Federation against Software Theft (1988–1991). Chairman, Fast Legal Advisory Group (1988–1991).
Personal: Born 21st March 1950. Educated at Winchester College (1963–1968) and Emmanuel College, Cambridge (1969–1973). Leisure pursuits include swimming, tennis, watching most sports and landscape gardening. Lives in Greatham, near Liss, Hampshire.

JONES, Bill
Wragge & Co, Birmingham (0121) 265 2201
bill_jones@wragge.com
Partner and head of Information Technology Group (ITG)
Specialisation: Principal area of practice is information technology, including contract negotiation, outsourcing and facilities management, data protection, dispute resolution, Year 2000, Internet and intellectual property issues. Also communications, telecommunications, multimedia and broadcasting. Acted for one of defendants in 'IBCOS' in Court of Appeal. Acts for a wide range of well known supply side and user clients, both nationally and internationally. Frequent speaker at conferences and seminars. Author of numerous articles. Co–author: 'The TRIPS Agreement', chapter in 'International Protection of Intellectual Property', Sweet & Maxwell, 1997, and of confidentiality section in 'Commercial Contracts Practice Manual', Vol 2 PLC, 1999.
Prof. Memberships: British Computer Society; The Society for Computers and Law; FAST Legal Advisory Group; Institute of Trade Mark Agents; Chartered Institute of Patent Agents.
Career: Qualified in 1984 at *Wragge & Co*. Partner 1990.

KEMP, Richard
Kemp & Co, London (020) 7710 1610
richardk@comlegal.com
Specialisation: Practice covers intellectual property, competition/EU regulatory and general business law for the full range of IT, e-commerce and telecoms sectors, acting for both suppliers and acquirers.
Prof. Memberships: Law Society; Chartered Institute of Patent Agents; Computer Law and Security Reports – Editorial Board Member. Guide to the World's Leading IT Lawyers (1999); one of top 20 global IT lawyers ('Best of the Best') (2000).
Career: *Clifford–Turner* (1978–1984); *Hopkins & Wood* 1984–1991 (Partner 1985); *(Hammond Suddards* (1991–1995 (head of IT Group; Founder Partner London Office)); *Garrett & Co.* (Partner 1995, IP/IT London Office Group Head 1996; IP/IT European Service Line Head, 1997). Set up Kemp & Co in November 1997 to specialise in IT, e-commerce and telecoms work – firm now has 15 lawyers and 24 staff.
Personal: Born 8th July 1956. Educated Oakham School, St. Catherine's College Cambridge, Université Libre de Bruxelles.

LISTER, Richard
Freshfields Bruckhaus Deringer, London
(020) 7936 4000
Specialisation: IT/Telecoms transactional work (procurement, outsourcing,joint ventures) for customers and suppliers. Advises on e-commerce projects and on–line services generally (contract, intellectual property, data protection, security.)
Prof. Memberships: Law Society. American Bar Association. Society for Computers and Law.
Career: Joined *Berwin Leighton* 1989 and became a partner in 1997. Partner at *Freshfields* 1999.
Personal: Born 21 April 1966. Educated Manchester Grammar School and University College, Cardiff. Married with two children.

LUBBOCK, Mark
Ashurst Morris Crisp, London (020) 7638 1111
mark.lubbock@ashursts.com
Specialisation: IT/E-Commerce/IP.
Prof. Memberships: Law Society; Society for Computers & Law; Associate Member of Trade Mark Agents; and Computer Law Group.
Career: Articles *McKenna & Co IT–] (1982–1984) McKenna & Co* (1984–1988); and *Ashurst Morris Crisp* (1988–date).
Publications: Intellectual Property Section of Sweet and Maxwell's 'Practical Commercial Precedents'; Intellectual Property Section of Sweet and Maxwell's 'Practical Commercial Checklists'; 'E-Commerce – Doing Business Electronically, A Practical Guide'. Published by The Stationery Office, 2000.
Personal: Education: Cranleigh and Peterhouse, Cambridge. Interests: Rugby, cricket, tennis, modern art and lately, babies.

MACPHERSON, Shonaig
McGrigor Donald, Edinburgh (0131) 226 7777
Edinburgh Office Managing Partner and Head of Technology Unit.
Specialisation: Handles all aspects of intellectual property and information technology work. Advises on protection strategies, funding for technology projects, licensing, research contracts, litigation and dispute resolution, expertise on software licensing, systems developments and procurement, outsourcing and facilities management contracts. Speaker at Glasgow IT summits in 1993 and 1994, and at the International Science Festival in Edinburgh in 1992, 1993 and 1994, Chicago 1996.
Prof. Memberships: Law Society (England & Wales), Law Society (Scotland), Licensing Executives Society, Royal Society, Scottish Biomedical Association, Scottish Biomedical Research Trust. Visiting Professor at Heriot–Watt University, Society for Computers and the Law.
Career: Qualified in 1984 in England & Wales with *Norton Rose*. Assistant Company Secretary (Legal) Storehouse plc, then Legal Director of Harrods 1987–1989. Partner at *Calow Easton* in London 1989–1991. Qualified in Scotland 1991. Joined *McGrigor Donald* in 1991 and became a Partner in 1992.
Personal: Born 29th September 1958. Director of Edinburgh Chamber of Commerce and Enterprise. Recreations include theatre, opera and reading. Lives in Edinburgh.

MAHONY, Michael
Hammond Suddards Edge, London (Lloyd's)
(020) 7655 1000
michael.mahony@hammondsuddards.co.uk
Specialisation: All aspects of legal work for users and suppliers of information technology products and services including e-commerce, licensing and distribution, development, systems integration, outsourcing, telecommunications and dispute resolution.
Career: Articled Clerk at *Ashurst Morris Crisp* 1986 and Assistant Solicitor in 1988. Counsel *IBM United Kingdom Limited* 1990 to 1993. Assistant Solicitor 1993 and then Partner 1996 at *Hammond Suddards.*
Personal: Born 1964. Resides in London.

MAUGHAN, Alistair
Shaw Pittman, London (020) 7337 9400
Partner in Global Technology Group.
Specialisation: Acts for major technology users and vendors, government departments, banks and manufacturing entities. Focus on complex and strategic technology projects, particularly outsourcing and e-commerce. Involved in major IT PFI projects (BA - POCL, Inland Revenue – NIRS2, Home Office – Police mobile radio replacement project), DSS – ACCORD. Specialises in IT, e-commerce and technology acquisition supply contracts. Work is mainly non–contentious and divided equally between major government contracts and contracts for private sector clients. Assisted in the Inland Revenue Information Technology Office outsourcing and the DVOIT privatisation (first privatisation of a UK government executive agency). Author of several articles on computer law. Lectures on outsourcing, e-commerce and acquiring computer systems. Contributing author to Sweet and Maxwell's 'Outsourcing Practice Manual'.
Prof. Memberships: Law Society, New York State Bar, NY State Bar Association, Society for Computers and Law, Computer Law Association.
Career: Qualified in 1987. With *Boodle Hatfield* 1985–89, then *Crowell & Moring* in Washington D.C, 1989–92. Qualified in New York in 1990. At *Theodore Goddard* 1992–93, before joining *Dibb Lupton Broomhead* in 1993. Became a Partner in 1994. Joined *Shaw Pittman* in 1998.

MCCALLOUGH, Robert
Masons, London (020) 7490 4000
Partner and Head of Information & Technology Group.
Specialisation: International experience in handling large commercial and technology–related disputes involving arbitration, litigation and Alternative Dispute Resolution relating to hardware and software procurement, project management, product liability, licensing, outsourcing and PFI contracts. Specialises in legal risk management and dispute resolution for the computer, telecommunications and other technology–related industries. Also lectures widely upon commercial and legal issues relevant to the IT industries.
Prof. Memberships: Hong Kong Law Society; English Law Society; the N.C.C.; European workshop for resolution of telecommunications disputes and the Worshipful Company of Information Technologists.
Career: Qualified in 1975. At *Hill & Perks*, Norwich 1975–1978. Member of Attorney General's Chambers

in Hong Kong 1978–1983. Joined *Masons* (Hong Kong) in 1983. Became a Partner in 1984.

MCROBB, Elizabeth M.M.
Shepherd & Wedderburn WS, Glasgow
(0141) 566 9900
liz.mcrobb@shepwedd.co.uk
Specialisation: Head of the firm's Technology and Intellectual Property Group which combines specialists in IT, Intellectual Property and Corporate Finance for young technology companies. Experienced in advising on all aspects of intellectual property protection and exploitation. Particular interest over recent years in advising public and private sector clients in procurement of IT, outsourcing arrangements, software development and support including recent engagement on major MoD project and leadership of Scottish Electricity Settlements organisation's contractual arrangements to procure systems required for the deregulated electricity market. Also acted recently for Scottish Power UK plc in its £420 million outsourcing and joint venture relative to its IS Division and acting for City of Edinburgh Council in its current IT PPP outsourcing of the entire IT division to achieve the "Smart City" Vision.
Prof. Memberships: Law Society of Scotland.
Career: Joined *Shepherd & Wedderburn* WS in 1993 and became a partner in 1996. Qualified in English Law 1995.

MILLARD, Christopher
Clifford Chance, London (020) 7600 1000
christopher.millard@cliffordchance.com
Specialisation: Partner in the Media, Computer and Communications Group, specialises in online services and the Internet, telecommunications regulation and contracts, data protection, outsourcing, computer procurement and distribution arrangements, software development and licensing, intellectual property rights in software and data.
Prof. Memberships: Senior visiting fellow University of London teaching LLM courses in IT Law and Telecommunications Law; joint chairman Society for Computers and Law, president International Federation of Computer Law Associations; general editor OUP 'International Journal of Law and Information Technology'; board member Computer Security Research Centre LSE; board member 'Cyberspace Lawyer' and many other IT and telecoms journals.
Career: Manchester Grammar School; University of Sheffield (LLB Hons 1980); University of Toronto (MA 1982, LLM 1983). Articled *Clifford Turner*; qualified 1986; partner *Clifford Chance* since 1992.
Personal: Music. Born 1959; married with two children; resides London.

MOAKES, Jonathan
Halliwell Landau, Manchester (0161) 835 3003
See under Intellectual Property, p.514

MONAGHAN, Iain
Masons, London (020) 7490 4000
Partner Information & Technology Group
Specialisation: Continues to be involved in innovative transactions in the services arena, having drafted contracts for major systems procurements in the UK and elsewhere and advised on some of the UK's earliest and largest ICT outsourcing transactions. In the past few months, has led teams handling the first PFI-funded ICT procurement and the first private sector property outsourcing. In e-commerce, deals with procurement of services for prospective businesses and advises clients, particularly in the financial sector, upon the customer/commercial interface. Recently led a team advising on the establishment of the first off-shore internet bank in Europe and is involved in various projects relating to the development of e-banking and e-procurement.
Prof. Memberships: Law Society
Career: MA (Cantab)

NICHOLSON, Kim
Olswang, London (020) 7208 8731
kan@olswang.com
See under Telecommunications, p.794

NICOLSON, Fiona
Maclay Murray & Spens, Glasgow
(0141) 248 5011
fmmn@maclaymurrayspens.co.uk

O'LEARY, Marcus
The Law Offices of Marcus J. O'Leary, Bracknell
(01344) 303044
Specialisation: IT: Main area of practice is IT, including the drafting and negotiation of computer and software distribution, development, tpm, outsourcing, evaluation, VAR and licensing arrangements. All areas covered especially internet and e-commerce issues, (including cybersquatting), multimedia, disaster recovery, database, software piracy, data protection, matters and disputes generally. IP: Other principal area of practice is intellectual property where experience encompasses copyright and designs generally, patents, biotechnology, trade marks, branding, passing off, confidential information, trade libel, music, media and entertainment (particularly the new methods of music delivery), franchising and character merchandising, as well as intellectual property health checks and IP litigation. Advertising and Sales Promotion: Healthy advertising and marketing practice involving copy advice on marketing/ advertising and promotional campaigns on TV, in print, on the Internet and in direct marketing - including multimedia material. Dealing with agency/client relationships including drafting suitable contracts. Acts for some of the world's leading international technology companies.
Prof. Memberships: Law Society, Society for Computers and the Law, British Japanese Law Association and member of the legal advisory group to FAST.
Career: Over 20 years experience in the IT industry. Previously an accountant, then qualified as a barrister, later requalifying as a solicitor, Manager of Legal Affairs at Hewlett Packard and was negotiating IT contracts for them as long ago as 1978. In-house as an Intellectual Property Lawyer for the United Biscuits Group in the mid 1980s, moving to *Pitmans* in 1989 and forming their IP/IT department. With two others founded the Reading office of *Garrett & Co* in 1994 and set up *Garrett's* IP/IT function including a worldwide network of IP/IT lawyers. Launched *The Law Offices of Marcus J O'Leary* in 1995, which has gone from strength to strength since that date.
Personal: Born 31st October 1952. Educated at London University and the Inns of Court School of Law. Enjoys sailing, writing, and scrambling in the mountains. Lives in Eversley, Hampshire.

OLLERENSHAW, Zoe
Masons, Leeds (0113) 233 8905
Specialisation: All types of computer, intellectual property and telecommunications agreements for both end users and suppliers; from advising on the terms of outsourcing and facilities management contracts, software licence, procurement and distribution agreements and the IT aspects of mergers and acquisitions, to advising on the acquisition of intellectual property, multimedia titles and technology transfer licences.
Prof. Memberships: Member of British Computer Society and the Society for Computers and Law.
Career: Qualified in 1987. Helped to establish the Intellectual Property Department of *Dibb Lupton Alsops'* Sheffield office in 1991. Joined *Masons* on the opening of its Leeds office in August 1994.
Personal: LLB University of Sheffield. Interests include travelling, hiking, mountain biking and antiques. Lives in Sheffield.

ORR, Alistair C.
Maclay Murray & Spens, Edinburgh
(0131) 226 5196
aco@maclaymurrayspens.co.uk
Specialisation: Heads up the Edinburgh side of the firm's IP department and specialises in IP and IT issues; recent experience includes large scale internet projects for blue chip clients; advising Motherwell Bridge on the scale of its information services division; acting in Scotland for Nominet, the UK domain name authority; other clients include 3i, British Aerospace, Greig Middleton, the Royal Observatory, Edinburgh, Scottish Widows and a variety of growing high–tech companies.
Prof. Memberships: Secretary of The Internet Society–Scotland; member of Licensing Executives Society; member of IMAS (Interactive Media Alliance Scotland).
Career: Trained *Dundas & Wilson CS*; Qualified October 1992; assistant solicitor *Dundas & Wilson* 1992–1994; assistant solicitor 1994–1996; associate 1996–1998; partner since 1998 *Maclay Murray & Spens.*
Personal: Born 1964. Educated at University of Glasgow, Balliol College Oxford (LLB, Dip LP, MLitt). Enjoys rugby, swimming, reading. Resides Edinburgh.

PARK, Charles
Pinsent Curtis, London (020) 7418 7000
charles.parke@pinsents.com
Specialisation: Information Technology, e-commerce, intellectual property. Has headed up PC's e-commerce initiative in 2000, organising and speaking at Law Society C&I group's seminars on the subject.
Prof. Memberships: Computer Law Association. International Bar Association. Society for Computers & Law.
Career: Trained *Veale Wasborough*, Bristol; Qualified 1989, *Nabarro Nathanson* 1991, *Pinsent Curtis* 1992–date. Moved from Birmingham to London summer 2000 to establish PC technology group. Head of Group of 4/5 lawyers by September 2000.

PARRY, Rex
Eversheds, Leeds (0113) 243 0391
Specialisation: All aspects of IT and digital media work except litigation, with particular emphasis on outsourcing, e-commerce, the Internet and related agreements.
Prof. Memberships: Society for Computers and Law and Computer Law Association.
Career: Qualified in 1989; *Frere Cholmeley* from 1987 to 1992. Joined *Eversheds* in 1992, becoming a

partner in 1996.
Personal: Born 1965. Fanatical trout fisherman. Interests also include walking and wine.

PEARSON, Hilary
Bird & Bird, London (020) 7415 6000
Partner in Information Technology and Intellectual Property Groups.
Specialisation: Main areas of practice are intellectual property and computer law. Barrister in patent chambers then worked in Silicon Valley 1980–1983, becoming involved in the start of the personal computer industry. Since then has represented a wide range of hardware, software and component suppliers. Work includes intellectual property and computer contract litigation and non–contentious issues. Author of 'Computer Contracts' (1983) and 'Commercial Exploitation of Intellectual Property' (1990). Contributor to 'Internet Law and Regulation' (1996, 1997).
Prof. Memberships: American Bar Association, Computer Law Association (Board Member), Licensing Executives Society, American I.P. Law Association.
Career: Qualified 1976. New Court, Temple 1977–80; *Rosenblum, Parrish & Bacigalupi*, San Francisco 1980–83; *Arnold White & Durkee*, Houston 1983–90. *Simmons & Simmons*, London 1990–95. Joined *Bird & Bird* in 1995. Member of the Californian Bar 1981 and Texas Bar 1985; US Patent Attorney.
Personal: Born 1943. Holds BA/ MA (Oxon) Hons Physics 1965–69, and LLB (London) 1975.

PEETERS, Michael
Pinsent Curtis, Leeds (0113) 244 5000
michael.peeters@pinsents.com
Head of Commerce, Trade and Technology Department in Leeds.
Specialisation: Principal area of practice is information technology law including major I.T. procurement contracts, data protection, telecommunications, electronic trading, software licensing and distribution, and dispute resolution. Other main area of work is intellectual property law, particularly international software copyright. Frequently addresses seminars and conferences. Registered Trade Mark Agent.
Career: *Clifford Chance* 1986 until 1992, then became Head of I.T. Law Unit at *Simpson Curtis* in Leeds.

REES, Christopher W.
Bird & Bird, London (020) 7415 6000
Specialisation: Advises on all IT–related issues. Practice covers: system supply contracts; national and international outsourcing; sale and purchase of IT–based companies and joint ventures. Acts for both users and suppliers for some of the world's leading system houses, content providers and SMEs from from start–up through to IPO. Also has unrivalled expertise in protection and use of content (data protection, privacy and database and copyright ownership). In addition to this transactional and advisory practice, is involved in contentious work. He has overseen cases in the English and Scottish courts: successful applications for injunctive relief and damages for software and trademark infringement – including one of the first court–sponsored mediations of a damage system supply contract dispute carried out under the new English Civil Procedure.
Prof. Memberships: Freeman; Worshipful Company of Information Technologists. Since 1996, Chairman, Legal Affairs Committee of the National Computing Centre. Chairman, Computer and Database Committee. Member of the International Bar Association.
Career: Qualified in 1979. In–house European Council and Director; Data General. 1990 Partner *Bird & Bird* – founder and co–chair of IT Group (Managing Partner 1993–1996)
Personal: Born 1955; resides London; married with two daughters. Hobbies include all ball games; skiing; music and philosophy. Attended Christ's College, Cambridge 1973–1976.

RENDELL, Simon
Osborne Clarke OWA, London (020) 7809 1018
simon.rendell@osborneclarke.com
Specialisation: Advises on the Internet, multimedia software development, intellectual property, contractual negotiations, outsourcing and systems integration. For telecommunications, advises carriers, service providers and re–sellers and users of telecom services on legal and regulatory issues and developments. Consultant editor for IT Law Today and International Computer Law Adviser. Lectures on all aspects of IT law.
Prof. Memberships: FAST Legal Advisory Group, Public Network Operators Interest Group, Competition Law Association.
Career: Qualified in 1991 at *Hopkins & Wood.* Appointed Partner and Head of Department in 1991. Previously qualified as a Barrister in 1986. Joined *Osborne Clarke* as Head of Department in 1996.

ROBERTSON, Ranald
Robertson & Co, Technology Law Practice, London (020) 7731 4626
Specialisation: Focus of practice is IT law, with over 18 years experience in this field within the computer industry and private practice. Advises an international client base of users and vendors. Work includes major IT procurement projects (outsourcing, software development, systems integration), distribution agreements, software licensing, e-commerce/internet issues, international data protection and hi–tech start ups. Author of 'Legal Protection of Computer Software' and Computer Contracts section of Butterworths Forms and Precedents. Co–author of 'European Computer Law' and Sweet & Maxwell 'Outsourcing Practice Manual'. Editorial Panel of IT Law Today.
Prof. Memberships: British Computer Society. Computer Law Association, Worshipful Company of Information Technologists, London Computer Law Group, Founder Chairman of 13 country pan–European IT Law Group/Europe network of which *Roberston & Co* is UK member.
Career: Legal Services Manager with CAP/SEMA (1980–87); Partner and head of IT groups at *Stephenson Harwood*, *Field Fisher Waterhouse* and *Taylor Johnson Garrett* (1987–97). Set up *Robertson & Co* in September 1997 to provide clients with senior expertise and experience on computing, software and Internet matters at an affordable and reasonable cost. Qualified 1980.
Personal: Born 1948. Graduated Auckland University, New Zealand 1972. Married with 2 children.

ROWE, Heather
Lovells, London (020) 7296 2000
heather.rowe@lovells.com
Specialisation: Non-contentious information technology, telecommunications and multimedia work, including matters relating to electronic commerce, electronic banking, electronic data interchange and agreements and regulation of the IBA; Chairman UK editorial board 'Droit de l'Informatique et des Telecoms'; consultant editor, 'IT Law Today' and 'Computer Law and Security Report'; correspondent 'Computer and Telecommunications Law Review'; editorial panel 'World Telecoms Report', and 'World Internet Law Report', 'Communications Law' and 'Banking Technology'; editorial Board Butterworths Journal of International Banking and Financial Law.
Prof. Memberships: Co-Chairman of Committee R (technology and e-commerce), IBA; Chairman ICC International Working Party on Data Protection and Privacy; Chairman ICC UK Computing, Telecommunications and Information Policies Commission; member International Telecommunication Users Group and Telecommunications Users Association.
Career: Articled *Wilde Sapte*, London: Qualified 1981 with *Wilde Sapte*; Assistant Solicitor, *S J Berwin & Co*: Assistant Solicitor, *Lovells*; Partner 1988.

SAMPSON, Ian
Addleshaw Booth & Co, Leeds (0113) 209 2000
ics@addleshaw–booth.co.uk
Partner in trade and regulatory department.
Specialisation: Advises on all non–contentious aspects of information technology contracts, including outsourcing, e-commerce and systems procurement.
Prof. Memberships: LES, IBA, Society for Computers and Law.
Career: Qualified in 1987. Joined the firm in 1988, partner in 1992.
Personal: Educated at University of Kent. Enjoys competitive distance running.

SANDISON, Hamish
Bird & Bird, London (020) 7415 6000
Partner in Company Department and Co–Chair of Information Technology Group.
Specialisation: Main area of practice is IT law. Acts for both public bodies and private sector companies on IT procurement, including major IT PFI projects. Heads team representing CCTA (the Government's Central Computer and Telecommunications Agency). Member of DSS and BBC legal advisers panels. Intellectual property, e–commerce and multimedia work is also covered, especially advising on copyright law. Clients include Motion Picture Export Association of America and numerous scientific and technical publishers. Co–author of 'Computer Software Protection Law', 1989. Contributing Editor 'International Copyright and Neighbouring Rights', 1990. Lectures frequently in both UK and US. Often interviewed on TV and Radio.
Prof. Memberships: Council of Intellectual Property Institute, FAST Legal Advisory Group, Intellectual Property Committee of the British Computer Society.
Career: Admitted to Washington DC Bar 1980. Qualified in UK 1989. Joined *Bird & Bird* 1992 as a Partner.
Personal: Born 1952. Attended University College School, London 1960–1970, Jesus College, Cambridge 1971–1974, then University of California, Berkeley 1974–1975. Lives in Usk, Monmouthshire.

SASSE, Sarah
Wragge & Co, Birmingham (0121) 265 2205
sarah_sasse@wragge.com
Specialisation: Specialist in non contentious computer and IT related matters within the Computer and Communications Team. Wide experience of system supply agreements, software development, maintenance and support arrangements outsourcing agreements and facilities management. Other interests include Internet trading, domain name disputes, and data protection.
Prof. Memberships: Member of Licensing Executives Society, Society for Computers and Law, memeber of International Bar Association.
Career: Articled at *Macfarlanes*. Qualified 1992. Associate *Wragge & Co* 1996. Partner *Wragge & Co* 1999.
Personal: Born 1967.

SAUNDERS, James
Shepherd & Wedderburn WS, Edinburgh (0131) 228 9900
james.saunders@shepwedd.co.uk
See under Energy & Natural Resources, p.359

SEGAL, Arnold
Theodore Goddard, London (020) 7606 8855
arnoldsega@theodoregoddard.co.uk
Head of IT Law Group
Specialisation: Over 20 years' experience in the IT law field. Leads a team of specialists in IT and e–commerce transactions. These include complex systems integration, outsorcing and facilities management arrangements, managed services, ASPs, software and hardware agreements, IT issues in coporate transactions, and upstream and midstream IT arrangements for the firm's e-commerce group. Also has an established reputation in the computer games area. The group operates a cross–firm skills matrix to ensure seamless advice from experts with wide experience of IT and e-commerce business in their relevant fields. Examples of recent work include credit card processing arrangements; outsourcing of a data warehouse; managed services for a large retail group, a bank, and a utility company; ASP arrangements for a financial software supplier, software supply for an internet travel agent and for a new internet bank; ITTs for and from private and public organisations; various infrastructure and and operating agreements for e-commerce B2B and B2C ventures and games defvelopment agreements with major publishers. A frequest speaker on IT issues, particularly relating to systems integration and computer games.
Prof. Memberships: Law Society, FAST Legal Advisory Group, Society for Computers and Law, BCS, FRSA.
Career: Assistant Legal Adviser/Company Secretary Alcan Aluminium. Legal Adviser Morgan Crucible. Partner *Spark & Co*. Established *Arnold Segal* in 1986. Joined *Theodore Goddard* in 1997.
Personal: Born 17th July 1943. Attended King's College, London. Leisure pursuits include travel, theatre, cinema and reading. Lives in London.

SINGLETON, E. Susan
Singletons, London (020) 8866 1934
susan@singlelaw.com
Principal of firm since 1994.
Specialisation: Main areas of practice are Commercial law, Competition law and IT/IP law. Handles compliance, competition law, litigation and complaints, and EU law generally. Advises on internet law, copyright, trade marks and patents, ownership of rights, licences, EU IT/IP directives, general commercial law, agency (particularly Commercial Agents (Council Directive) Regulations), distribution and contract law. Author of 20 books including 'Business, Internet and the Law' (Tolley 1999), 'Commercial Agency' (Butterworths 1998) 'Blackstone's Guide to the Competition Act 1998', 'Jordan's Data Protection' (1998) and contributor to Croner's 'I.T. Guide', 'Europe' and 'Model Business Contracts', and Gee's 'Factfinder' CD–ROM. Editor of 'Comparative Law of Monopolies' looseleaf and journal I.T. Law Today. Writes and speaks widely on legal issues.
Prof. Memberships: Competition Law Association, Licensing Executives Society, Law Society, Society of Computers and Law and Computer Law Association.
Career: Qualified 1985, having joined *Nabarro Nathanson* in 1983. Joined *Slaughter and May* in 1985, then *Bristows* in 1988. Established *Singletons* in 1994.
Personal: Born 14th December 1961. Attended Westfield School, Newcastle upon Tyne 1972–79, then Manchester University 1979–1982 and Chester Law College 1982–1943. Married with five children. Lives on Pinner Hill.

SMALL, Harry
Baker & McKenzie, London +44 20 7919 1000
harry.small@bakernet.com
Partner in Intellectual Property and Information Technology Law Department.
Specialisation: Principal area of practice is IT Law including computer litigation, software protection and IT contracts (especially e-commerce and outsourcing). Other main area of work is IP law, covering enforcement of IP rights, copyright and designs law and multimedia contracts. Acted in many significant computer systems and high technology disputes including, amongst others, Exel - v - Dun & Bradstreet Software and Vodafone -v- Orange. Contributor to Sweet & Maxwell 'IT Encyclopaedia' and Sweet & Maxwell 'Outsourcing Practice Manual.' Author of numerous articles on IP and IT law for various legal periodicals. Regularly addresses conferences and is lecturer on designs on Bristol University Intellectual Property Diploma course. Expert to EU Economic and Social Committee on various IT and IP related draft legislation. Chair, Society for Computers & Law.
Prof. Memberships: Law Society, Computer Law Group, Patent Solicitors Association.
Career: Articled with *Linklaters & Paines* 1979–1981 and then Assistant Solicitor 1981–1986. Joined *Baker & McKenzie* in 1986 and became a Partner in 1989.
Personal: Born 20th April 1957. Attended St. Alban's Grammar School 1968–1975, then Oriel College, Oxford 1975–1978. Leisure pursuits include travel, railways, computers, books and sleeping. Lives in London.

SMITH, Graham
Bird & Bird, London (020) 7415 6000
Partner.
Specialisation: Computer project disputes, commercial litigation in computer and telecommunications industries. Evidence, document imaging and computer records. Internet law including domain name disputes, website advice, Internet/e-mail use policies and regulatory issues. Intellectual property disputes. Gave evidence to the House of Lords Science and Technology Select Committee on Digital Images as Evidence. Advised Guernsey on its e-commerce legislation. Contributes a section on Non–Contractual Liability to the loose–leaf 'Encyclopedia of Information Technology Law' (Sweet & Maxwell). Editor and a co–author of the book 'Internet Law and Regulation' (Sweet & Maxwell, 2nd edition December 1997). Speaks and writes regularly in the UK and abroad mainly on IT and Internet legal issues.
Prof. Memberships: American Intellectual Property Law Association. Council Member, Society for Computers and Law. Computer Law Association. E centre UK Legal Advisory Group. Fellow of the Society for Advanced Legal Studies.
Career: Qualified 1978. Joined *Bird & Bird* 1983. Partner 1985.
Personal: Born 1953. Educated Uppingham School, Rutland; Bristol University (LLB. 1975). Lives London.

SWYCHER, Nigel
Slaughter and May, London (020) 7600 1200
Specialisation: Intellectual property and information technology law; including the IP and IT aspects of acquisitions, disposals, flotations and privatisations; involved in technology, licensing and transfer, franchising and sponsorship and IT procurement and development. Co–head of the firm's Electronic Commerce Group.
Prof. Memberships: ITMA.
Career: Admitted 1987 with *Slaughter and May*. Partner 1994.
Personal: Born 6 June 1962. Educated at Denstone College, Staffordshire and Durham University. Magician.

TIGHE, David P.
Manches, Oxford (01865) 722106
Specialisation: Main area of practice is IT, dealing with all types of non–contentious IT related agreements. These include software licensing, distribution and marketing agreements, software development contracts, facilities management and computer bureau agreements, system supply agreements, supply agreements for hardware and other equipment and support and maintenance contracts. An increasing amount of Internet related work. Corporate finance work, ranging from start–ups and venture capital deals to acquisitions/disposals and flotations, concentrating in the IT field. Also writes articles on IT issues.
Prof. Memberships: Society for Computers and Law.
Career: Attended Marist College, Hull and Trinity College, Cambridge. Qualified as a solicitor in 1982. At *Boodle Hatfield* from 1980–1985. Head of Legal Services at Logica plc from 1986–1988. *Manches* since 1989. Partner since 1990.

TURNER, Mark
Herbert Smith, London (020) 7374 8000
Specialisation: Partner specialising in transactional and advisory work in the IT and digital media industries. Works regularly for government departments and agencies, multinationals and leading edge internet and new media businesses. Particular expertise in major systems procurement and software development projects, outsourcing and IT service provision. Recent work includes acting for the Civil Aviation Authority in the development of a new Scottish air traffic control centre; the Jigsaw project (consumer marketing), a consortium of Unilever,

Cadbury–Schweppes and Kimberly–Clark; for Jardine Matheson on the supply of the baggage handling system for the new Hong Kong airport. Also acting for the fourteen electricity supply companies in the UK on the supply of IT and telecoms services to them and advising on the IT aspects of PFI projects for major NHS trusts.
Career: Qualified 1983. *Macfarlanes*, 1981–1985. *Denton Hall*, 1985–1995 (partner from 1989). *Garrett & Co.*, 1995–1997. Joined *Herbert Smith* as a partner in 1998.
Publications: Co–author of Butterworths' 'Encyclopaedia of Competition Law', chapter on licensing of intellectual property rights. Co–author of a chapter on complex licensing issues in 'International Technology Transfer' (Kluwer). Correspondent for 'Computer Law and Security Report'. Many articles in national, legal and trade press.
Personal: Born 1956. Educated Latymer Upper School and University College, Oxford (Exhibitioner).

WARD, Conor
Lovells, London (020) 7296 2000
conor.ward@lovells.com
Specialisation: Partner in the firm's computer, communications and media unit. Work includes advising on the contentious and non–contentious aspects of systems acquisition and development; facilities management and outsourcing (including telecommunications services); electronic commerce, electronic data interchange; encryption technologies, anti–piracy and computer crime. Practises exclusively in the information technology field, often where the technological issues are most complex. Recent work includes advising in relation to the setting up of the e-commerce protection scheme in the UK and various matters including a major strategic alliance, relating to WAP technology.
Prof. Memberships: The British Computer Society Legal Affairs Committee (where he sits on its Year 2000 Working Group), The Computer Law Association, member of editorial board of the Computer and Telecommunications Law Review published by Sweet and Maxwell. Appointed a Director of the Federation Against Software Theft (FAST) and Chairman of the legal advisory group of FAST.
Career: 1980–84 The Queen's University, Belfast (Law LL.B (Hons)); 1984–88 IBM United Kingdom Laboratories Limited – development programmer; 1987 called to the Bar of England & Wales; 1988–1990 *Heald Nickinson* – assistant; 1990 to date *Lovells White Durrant*, assistant solicitor.

WEBSTER, Michael
Nicholson Graham & Jones, London
(020) 7648 9000
Specialisation: Computer & telecoms, software & service supply contracts, ranging from software development & distribution contracts, VAR & franchising, turnkey supply and systems integration agreements, Internet, EDI, e-commerce and web site issues, multi–media rights, joint ventures, technology transfer, outsourcing & long term supply of services agreements.
Prof. Memberships: Society for Computers & the Law, British Computer Society, Computer Law Group, Software Business Network, Worshipful Company of Information Technologists.
Career: Articled Herbert Smith, qualified in 1967, partner *Rowe & Maw* 1973. Long term involvement with specialisations has led to many invitations to speak and write articles on a number of topics such as outsourcing, joint ventures and liability arising from computer contracts.
Personal: Born 1942. Educated at Berkhamsted School and Bristol University (LLB hons). Interests include tennis, golf, long distance walking and tree felling. Member of The Honourable Artillery Company and Liveryman of the Worshipful Company of Upholders.

WESTMACOTT, Philip G.
Bristows, London (020) 7400 8000
philip.westmacott@bristows.com
Partner in intellectual property department.
Specialisation: The full range of intellectual property work, contentious and non–contentious, with an emphasis on disputes involving, and advice to, the IT and computer industries. Has given evidence as an expert on UK IP law in US proceedings. Cases include, for the plaintiff, Philips v VDC, IBM v Phoenix, Monsanto v Maxwell M Hart and Monsanto v Stauffer and, for the defendant, Smith Myers Communications Ltd v Motorola, Iomega v Nomai, and Intel v VIA Technologies. Lecturer and marker on the Bristol University Diploma in Intellectual Property Law and Practice.
Prof. Memberships: Law Society, Associate of Chartered Institute of Patent Agents, London Computer Law Group, AIPPI, Society for Computers and Law.
Career: Undergraduate trainee at Tube Investments Ltd 1971–1974. Joined *Bristows* on qualification in 1978 and became a partner in 1985.
Personal: Born 15th April 1954. Educated at Cambridge University 1972–1975 (Engineering and Law). Enjoys sailing, walking, skiing and cycling. Lives in London.

WILDISH, Nigel D.
Field Fisher Waterhouse, London (020) 7861 4000
ndw@ffwlaw.com
Specialisation: IT Law: acting for suppliers and customers in relation to a wide range of IT contracts, including systems and software development and procurement, networking, marketing and distribution agreements, outsourcing contracts and service level agreements. Electronic Publishing, Electronic Commerce and Internet Law: drafting and negotiating all kinds of e-commerce contracts including web development and exploitation agreement, and linking affinity agreements; advising on all legal aspects of the Internet, including contracts over the Internet, cross–jurisdictional liability and name/brand protection. Mergers and Acquisitions in IT, Telecoms and E-commerce: due diligence, joint ventures, acquisitions and sales.
Prof. Memberships: IBA (Technology and Intellectual Property Committees) National Computing Centre (Member, Law Group) Computer Law Association. Information and Communications Industries Association.
Career: Clare College, Cambridge. Partner: Turner Kenneth Brown (1974–1995); Nabarro Nathanson (1995–1997); Osborne Clarke (1997– 1999). *Field Fisher Waterhouse* (1999–date).
Personal: Married with 2 teenage children. Active in squash, golf, cricket. Active member of Church of England. Member: MCC.

WORTHY, John
Denton Wilde Sapte, London (020) 7242 1212

YATES, John
v–lex ltd., Worksop (01909) 544 000
Chief Executive Officer
Specialisation: Main area of practice is computer law, including computer contracts and disputes. Author of numerous articles on all aspects of computer law. Regular speaker on outsourcing and computer disputes.
Prof. Memberships: Council member of Society of Computers and Law.
Career: Qualified in 1984. IBM In–house lawyer 1984–87. Partner at *Theodore Goddard* in Computer Group, 1987–1993. Joined *Oxley & Coward* as a Partner in 1993. Co–founder of *v–lex limited* in June 2000.
Personal: Born 8th May 1959. Attended Leeds University (LLB) and Oxford University (BCL). Leisure interests include mountaineering and rock climbing. Lives near Sheffield.

INSOLVENCY / CORPORATE RECOVERY

London: 461; The South: 465; Thames Valley: 465; South West: 466; Wales: 467; Midlands: 467; East Anglia: 468; North West: 468; Yorkshire: 469; North East: 471; Scotland: 471; Northern Ireland: 472; *Profiles*: 473

RESEARCH APPROVED BY BMRB: *For this edition,* Chambers' *researchers conducted 6083 interviews – 4408 with law firms, 598 with barristers and 1077 with clients.*

The validity of the research was scrutinised by BMRB International, who audited both the methodology and the results at our offices in July 2000. They interviewed Chambers' *researchers and cross-checked sample interviews. Details of the audit appear on page 7.*

LONDON

INSOLVENCY / CORPORATE RECOVERY • London	Ptnrs	Assts
❶ Allen & Overy	Fu	Fu
❷ Denton Wilde Sapte	12	19
Lovells	11	25
❸ Clifford Chance	4	13
CMS Cameron McKenna	10	14
Freshfields Bruckhaus Deringer	4	12
Linklaters	9	12
❹ Cadwalader, Wickersham & Taft	2	5
Herbert Smith	2	7
Lawrence Graham	8	10
Norton Rose	4	10
Stephenson Harwood	5	11
❺ Ashurst Morris Crisp	9	8
DJ Freeman	7	9
DLA	4	12
Hammond Suddards Edge	7	10
Isadore Goldman	3	1
Nabarro Nathanson	8	11
Nicholson Graham & Jones	3	12
Simmons & Simmons	2	4
Slaughter and May	7	6
Travers Smith Braithwaite	2	4
❻ Berwin Leighton	12	16
Eversheds	1	5
Osborne Clarke OWA	8	19
Richards Butler	2	4
Sprecher Grier Halberstam	3	1
Taylor Joynson Garrett	8	10

Within each band, firms are listed alphabetically.
Fu Figures unavailable at time of going to press.

Allen & Overy A *"fabulous practice"* which *"continues to set the standard"* and is *"in an undisputed position at the top."* Part of the finance team, the Business Reconstruction Group works on non-contentious, bank-driven matters with a global element. Driven from London, the firm's international reach is exemplified by large work such as advising a rating agency on the analysis of the impact of defaults in the European high-yield debt market, advising on the Uneximbank restructuring in Russia and on the Thai Telecom restructuring in Asia.

The *"first class"* **Gordon Stewart** is commended for his *"strong technical ability,"* while **Nicholas Segal** is simply regarded as *"outstanding,"* with strong experience in the Far East. Whilst some expressed concern over the retirements over the past two years of Peter Totty and Judith Naylor, the market is generally bullish on the practice's mid-level strength. The team has also expanded significantly. Personal insolvency work is dealt with but the overwhelming majority of work is of a corporate nature. Cross-border rescues and insolvencies across the globe include Guangdong Enterprises (advising the international steering committee,) the restructuring of VSZ, a Slovakian steel company, and advising the company in the TransTec workout and receivership. Other examples of major international work includes Ocean Marine, Daewoo, Ashanti, Unexim, CAP Securities and the World Telecom receivership. A continuing shift towards corporate rescue in the market has seen the team busy on turnarounds and workouts. **Clients:** the big five accountants and top clearing banks; international investment banks.

Denton Wilde Sapte Operational head of the group (and Deputy Chairman of the firm) is the *"client friendly"* **Mark Andrews.** He is *"a great leader with tremendous knowledge,"* who began life as a banking litigator before moving to insolvency, an area in which *"he would be part of anybody's dream team."* Head of the group is the *"bright"* **Michael Steiner.** He is an insolvency all-rounder, working on personal and corporate, reconstruction and procedural and cross-border matters. Well known for contentious work (although they are also involved on the non-contentious side) are the *"charming and commercial"* **Mark Gill** (who has also been involved in banking-related litigation), and the *"experienced and effective"* **Nigel Barnett.** *"Real gentleman"* **Richard Scopes** straddles the line between banking and insolvency and is *"very experienced on the non-contentious side."* **Richard Bethell-Jones,** is well regarded on the restructuring side, coming from a transactional and regulatory banking and finance background. New to the lists is recovery and turnaround specialist **Howard Morris,** recommended for being *"commercial and technically sound."*

Although it is the practice with the most recommended practitioners, it is not yet perceived to be up with Allen & Overy in terms of global expertise. That may well change this year as the merger comes to fruition and the practice takes advantage of the firm's newly expanded global reach (work this year has already seen the team active in Asia, Eastern Europe, the CIS and Africa). Work of an international nature this year includes the provisional liquidation of a global financial services group (Princeton Economics International) with a £1 billion loss. On domestic matters though, with work on the prominent mandates of TransTec (for Arthur Andersen) and the Versailles Group (for PricewaterhouseCoopers), the group can justifiably claim a place at the top. Other domestic highlights this year include the administration of Crystal Palace FC, and the liquidation of The Automobile Association as part of its demutualisation and sale. **Clients:** The big five accountancy firms and other insolvency practitioners; NatWest; HSBC; RBS.

Lovells A leader in the receivership market and in the insurance insolvency sector, the team's litigation work covers asset chasing and fraud-connected matters. Internationally strong in Asia the firm is seen to be expanding in Europe. A well balanced team containing many top-notch lawyers includes **Christopher Grierson,** particularly active on banking and litigation matters. Departmental head **Nicholas Frome** has a *"strong banking background and has enormous experience in handling big corporate rescue cases."* **Deborah Gregory** displays *"solid technical skills and a sense of humour,"* and **Keith Gaines** is an experienced litigator.

LEADING INDIVIDUALS • London	
❶ **ANDREWS Mark** Denton Wilde Sapte	**GALE Stephen** Herbert Smith
HYDE Mark Clifford Chance	**SEGAL Nicholas** Allen & Overy
STEWART Gordon Allen & Overy	**WHITE John** CMS Cameron McKenna
❷ **ANDERSON Hamish** Norton Rose	**ELLIOTT Robert** Linklaters
FOSTER Stephen CMS Cameron McKenna	**FROME Nicholas** Lovells
GREGORY Deborah Lovells	**GRIERSON Christopher** Lovells
SCOPES Richard Denton Wilde Sapte	**STEINER Michael** Denton Wilde Sapte
WRIGHT Richard Linklaters	
❸ **BARNETT Nigel** Denton Wilde Sapte	**BERRY Christopher** Edwin Coe
BETHELL-JONES Richard Denton Wilde Sapte	
BUGG Anthony Linklaters	**FLETCHER Ian** Stephenson Harwood
GAINES Keith Lovells	**GILL Mark** Denton Wilde Sapte
GORDON-SAKER Paul Stephenson Harwood	
HAMILTON Dan CMS Cameron McKenna	**HIGHAM John** Stephenson Harwood
HOUGHTON John Simmons & Simmons	**MALLON Christopher** Freshfields Bruckhaus
RAJANI Shashi Nicholson Graham & Jones	
ROOME James Bingham Dana & Gould LLP	
SCHAFFER Danny Isadore Goldman	
SHANDRO Sandy Freshfields Bruckhaus Deringer	
VERRILL John Lawrence Graham	**WOOLF Geoffrey** SJ Berwin & Co
❹ **ANGEL Nick** Ashurst Morris Crisp	**COHEN Adrian** Clifford Chance
GRIER Ian Sprecher Grier Halberstam	**LEWIS Jonathan** Finers Stephens Innocent
MANNING Peter Simmons & Simmons	**MORRIS Howard** Denton Wilde Sapte
OUGHTON Paul Nicholson Graham & Jones	
PEARSON Stephen Travers Smith Braithwaite	
POPE Timothy Hammond Suddards Edge	
PRIOR Michael Nabarro Nathanson	
RUSHWORTH Jonathan Slaughter and May	
WALSH Jeremy Michael Travers Smith Braithwaite	
UP AND COMING	
PIKE Nick Lawrence Graham	**WITHYMAN Tom** Lawrence Graham

LEADING INDIVIDUALS: INSURANCE INSOLVENCY	
❶ **SPENCER Robin** Lovells	**STEINBERG David Jeremy** Clifford Chance
❷ **FIDLER Peter** Stephenson Harwood	**FRENCH Matthew** Lovells
MONTGOMERY Nigel DLA	**TYRELL Vivien** DJ Freeman
WILKINSON Andrew Cadwalader, Wickersham & Taft	
YORKE Jonathan Richards Butler	
UP AND COMING	
HERTZ Philip Clifford Chance	

*See **Profiles** on page 473*

On the insurance side, clients commend the team for offering *"professional, helpful and responsive services."* **Robin Spencer**, who is said to be *"exclusively committed to this sector,"* is *"friendly and cautious, with a thorough understanding of the market."* The *"intelligent"* **Matthew French** is also known in this field, although he is set to have a broader remit. Joe Bannister has moved to work in Hong Kong. As well as advising on various schemes of arrangement in the insurance sector the team acted on the New Cap Reinsurance insolvencies and on Ocean Marine Mutual Insurance Association Ltd's provisional liquidation. Work on restructurings and insolvencies includes TransTec plc, AY Bank Ltd, Cyberdesk Ltd, BCCI and Debonair Airways Ltd. Also active this year in the nursing home sector. International assignments include the Japan Leasing insolvency and work in other parts of Asia and in Eastern Europe. **Clients:** the big five accountancy firms and Barclays.

Clifford Chance Back from a two-year stint in Hong Kong leading the team advising the Peregrine liquidators, a case on which he acquired a *"fabulous reputation,"* **Mark Hyde** is the global practice leader of the firm's insolvency group. **Adrian Cohen** is highly rated for the *"technical competence and creative ideas"* that have won clients difficult cases. With its traditionally strong bank connections, a mix of banking and insolvency partners lead the major deals.

Clients are *"totally satisfied"* with a practice that is *"big and eminent."* Particular strengths are in international matters and insurance insolvency. On the international side, the practice has developed a solid insolvency and workout capability in New York, Germany, Moscow, Bangkok and Hong Kong. Led by London, the team has been *"particularly visible"* in Asia and Russia over the past year. Three cases in particular highlight the international expertise of the practice. The Harnischfeger assignment, involving a company in US Chapter 11 proceedings where the practice advised on English, French, German, Italian and Polish matters; the Ashanti Goldfields case, advising the banks, and the debt restructuring of First Commercial Bank of Latvia, advising the private and NGO finance houses. Closer to home, the team has been acting for the two principal creditors of Air Bristol.

The *"AAA"* insurance insolvency team is composed of the *"impressive"* **David Steinberg** *("a big man in insurance")* and the *"able"* and much-touted **Philip Hertz**, who arrived this year from Cadwalader. Work this year includes advising the provisional liquidators of Anglo American Insurance company Ltd, the liquidators of Bermuda Fire & Marine Insurance company and the administrators of English & American Insurance company Limited. **Clients:** KPMG; PricewaterhouseCoopers; Ernst & Young; Chase Manhattan; Citigroup; Barclays; NatWest; HSBC; Fuji Bank; Bank of America; Nomura International.

CMS Cameron McKenna The *"excellent and attentive"* team is well regarded for its restructuring practice, which has noted connections with clearing banks such as Lloyds TSB and Royal Bank of Scotland. Considered to be a *"healthy"* insolvency group, its areas of focus include the IT and life science sectors. The *"charismatic"* **John White** is considered a *"veteran in banking and insolvency."* Clients highly appreciate the *"tough and personable"* **Stephen Foster**'s *"technical skills, commercial advice and hands-on approach."* He is known for his work in insurance insolvency, where the practice is regarded as one of the best by accountancy firms. Back from Hong Kong, **Dan Hamilton** is *"an impressive operator."*

Work this year includes acting for the administrators of Debonair Airways Ltd, the largest administration of the year, and for the administrators of Axis Genetics plc. Russia and Central and Eastern Europe continue to be active areas for the practice, with deals including advising on the debt restructuring of Rossiyskiy Kredit Bank. Asia is also an active source of work, working on matters associated with Peregrine and on the GZITIC debt restructuring. **Clients:** Lloyds TSB; the big five accountancy firms; Grant Thornton.

Freshfields Bruckhaus Deringer Market perception is that this *"first-class"* firm has successfully built up a rounded practice and a global presence based on its solid banking and corporate practices. One competitor even felt that Freshfields deserved *"a special mention as a firm that seems to be growing an international practice aggressively." "Smooth and sensible operator"* **Sandy Shandro** *"makes an impact with his intelligence."* Shandro forms a *"very strong team"* with the internationally experienced **Chris Mallon**. Working mainly on matters of a cross-border nature (from Asia to the US), the practice advised Astra International (Indonesia) on its debt restructuring, the first complete work-out in Indonesia since the crisis began and said to be the largest debt structuring to have been completed in Asia during 1999. Other work includes bank restructuring in Latvia and Russia, advising one of the hedge bank counterparties in connection with the Ashanti Goldfields restructuring and acting on the winding up of Albion Films for the liquidator. The firm advises on the purchaser side, a recent case being advising Wella AG on its acquisition of the trade marks and stocks associated with the bath luxury products range of the Yardley Group, which went into receivership in August 1998. Major litigation includes acting for the Bank of England in defending claims brought by depositors in

BCCI. Insurance insolvency work includes advising on matters pertaining to the insolvencies of the Bermuda Fire & Marine Insurance company, North Atlantic Insurance company and EMLICO. **Clients:** Lloyds TSB; ICO; Goldman Sachs; Deloitte & Touche; the Brunei Government; KPMG; ABN Amro.

Linklaters Considered a newcomer to the domestic market but strong internationally, the group has a well-established pre-insolvency practice through its solid bank relationships, and rises in this year's table. With his *"strong banking background"* **Robert Elliott** is a *"sensible deal-maker,"* experienced in workouts. Both **Anthony Bugg** (*"aggressive"*) and **Richard Wright** (*"hard-working and extremely clever"*) are solid all-rounders. Bugg advises on pre-insolvency matters and insolvency litigation, whilst Wright advises on both personal bankruptcy and corporate insolvency. The team has grown this year with a notable arrival from Wilde Sapte. Ongoing work includes the Eurotunnel debt restructuring, and advising the banks on co-ordinating the Ashanti restructuring. The practice acted for the administrators of Ionica plc and for the banks on the Harnischfeger Industries proceedings. Restructuring work has seen the firm busy on work with the Thai Petroleum Industry and for the Slovakian VSZ. **Clients:** NatWest; HSBC; Barclays; Chase Manhattan; Grant Thornton; Pricewaterhouse Coopers; KPMG.

Cadwalader, Wickersham & Taft A *"commercial, direct and abrasive"* firm. committed to and *"dominant"* in the high yield market, acting primarily for bondholders. **Andrew Wilkinson** is a *"heavy-hitter"* in the insurance insolvency market who has branched out his insolvency activities. However, *"pragmatic all-rounder"* James Roome has recently left to join Bingham Dana LLP. Junk bonds handled included those issued by One Finsbury Circus, Ionica and ICE. Also played a lead role in the Alpha Shipping case. **Clients:** bondholders; hedge funds; banks; accountants and IPs.

Herbert Smith A solid corporate client base and the traditionally strong litigation practice are particular assets of the corporate recovery and insolvency team. Advise on a broad range of contentious and non-contentious issues, with a strong cross-border element. Work this year includes the reorganisation of London and continental Railways and the continuing Eurotunnel debt restructuring. The practice also acted on the administration of Solvera plc, the liquidation of CAP Securities (in Hong Kong) and for the creditors of Crystal Palace FC. **Stephen Gale** is *"clearly very good and high-profile"* and is the new President of the R3 (the ex SPI). However the firm suffered a loss with the departure of recognised figure Richard Obank to DLA in Leeds and was overall perceived to have a lower profile this year. The team is also proficient in insurance insolvency, this year advising the provisional liquidators of Ocean Marine Mutual Insurance on the world-wide implications of the failed insurance company. Other work in the sector ranges from advice on schemes of arrangement to acting for the Policyholders Protection Board in connection with various insurance companies in liquidation. **Clients:** PPB; Eurotunnel; Westpac; the big five accountancy firms.

Lawrence Graham Clients rate the *"attentive team"* for its *"first class technical competence"*. **John Verrill** has a broad practice and is considered to be *"commercially and technically strong."* He has been well supported by the *"experienced and user-friendly"* **Nick Pike** and the *"bright and industrious"* **Tom Withyman**. Focuses on mid-market to large insolvencies. Areas of expertise include the travel trade, oil and gas and partnership insolvency. Amongst the 33 administrations, 12 receiverships and 42 liquidations the practice acted on this year are the administrations of PEX plc, Osmosis Ltd and Deans Furniture Ltd and the receivership of M&N Group Ltd. **Clients:** Pannell Kerr Forster; Ernst & Young; RBS.

Norton Rose The transition from the retired Sandy Pratt to **Hamish Anderson** has widely been perceived as a smooth one. Anderson is focused on formal insolvency proceedings and is currently advising the National Audit Office on its second study of directors disqualification. He commands immense respect as a *"miracle mind"* and is *"well-versed in the application of the law."* Another partner concentrates on restructuring in the UK and internationally. The team advised the Export-Import Bank of the US on the restructuring of Indonesian corporates, and has been busy on debt restructuring in Moscow. This year the practice has acted on the administrations of AB Airlines and Falmers Jeans and on the receivership of Metro Trading International Inc. **Clients:** all the big five accountancy firms, particularly PricewaterhouseCoopers and Deloitte & Touche; BDO Stoy Hayward; Moore Stephens Booth White. Clearing banks including HSBC; RBS and Bank of Scotland; Exim Bank of Japan; FSA and DTI.

Stephenson Harwood Has devoted a lot of resources to beef up its insolvency practice, and market perception is that the team has the potential to be a strong contender. With the arrival of **John Higham QC** from 3-4 South Square, the firm has boosted its in-house advocacy skills. The department has a significant regulatory practice and works on both corporate and personal matters. **Paul Gordon-Saker** is *"highly respected and technically strong,"* **Ian Fletcher** has strong academic ability and **Peter Fidler** has a long-standing name in insurance insolvency. The firm continues to act for the administrators of Polly Peck International plc. Work this year also includes advising RBS on its position in relation to The Versailles Group plc, and acting for the trustee in the bankruptcy of Jonathan Aitken. **Clients:** StanChart; Nordes Bank; HSBC; Deloitte; PricewaterhouseCoopers; Grant Thornton; Baker Tilly; Smith & Williamson; IPs; banks; regulators.

Ashurst Morris Crisp Working at the *"quality end"* of insolvency work, the team is populated by corporate and banking generalists with an insolvency bias. With such a background, the team's lawyers have been active in restructuring and reconstruction work, particularly **Nick Angel**, who made his name on the Eurotunnel restructuring. With the firm's general high profile in private equity, recovery work is an area which could still grow. However the firm does not neglect the traditional insolvency side, and this year has seen it involved in the administrations of Rackwood Mineral Holdings plc, Axis Genetics and Ford Sellar Morris Group, as well as the receivership of Luton Town FC. On the contentious side work includes the ongoing Barings Singapore matter. **Clients:** Arthur Andersen Singapore; Ernst & Young; Buchler Phillips; Levy Gee.

DJ Freeman A force in insurance and property insolvency. **Vivien Tyrell** is well regarded on the insurance side. The firm acted for Bermuda Fire and Marine itself on its liquidation, for PricewaterhouseCoopers on the ongoing continental assurance case, and for the creditor in the Richbell case. **Clients:** major accountancy firms such as PricewaterhouseCoopers; Bermuda Fire and Marine.

DLA **Nigel Montgomery** remains a leading figure in insurance insolvency. He has been involved in high profile cases such as those of the Protection and Indemnity Club and Ocean Marine. However, the team is not perceived to be as strong in other areas. Renamed the Business Support and Restructuring department, business recovery is an area which has seen the firm busy this year, an example being the restructuring of a dairy company over five jurisdictions. Work this year includes advising on the administrative receiverships of Crowded House Pub Company Ltd and Grampian Nursing Home Group and on the administration of Portsmouth Football Club. **Clients:** Royal Bank of Scotland; Barclays; NatWest; major accountants/IPs.

Hammond Suddards Edge Big on the national scene, the practice is *"steadily developing"* itself. **Timothy Pope** is a well-regarded veteran insolvency and restructuring practitioner. The team is notably busy in the SME market. This year has seen the practice involved on turnarounds in the private equity field and on several UK-based multi-creditor workouts, acting for Barclays Bank, RBS and large corporates. The market is divided as to whether the establishment of a business recovery consultancy (staffed by accountants and bankers) will reinforce the legal practice. Work this year includes continuing to act for the liquidators in Leyland DAF, on the Tiger Books administration and on receiverships including those of restaurant groups and magazine publishers. The recent merger with Edge Ellison strengthens connections with finance houses, notably the asset-based lending industry, including institutions such as Bank of America and Capital Bank Cashflow Finance Ltd. Work this year includes advising on the administrations of Crystal Palace FC and Shaw Carpets plc. **Clients:** KPMG; Deloitte & Touche; Ernst & Young; Grant Thornton; Barclays; Lloyds TSB; Begbies Traynor; BDO Stoy Hayward; Levy Gee; GE Capital Commercial Finance.

Isadore Goldman Strong reputation built around its niche of personal insolvency where it has a national profile. commended by the market for offering *"extremely good quality services."* Aside from personal insolvency, **Danny Schaffer** is experienced in directors disqualification proceedings. Clients like his *"clear-cut opinions"* and *"efficient manner."* **Clients:** NatWest; KPMG.

Nabarro Nathanson Although the firm is still highly regarded by clients for its *"attentive"* approach, its long-time guru **Michael Prior** is now a consultant at the firm, and thus spends less time 'at the coal-face'. Market concern exists over the lack of a big-hitting successor. The team acts on a mixture of domestic and international transactions. Work this year includes acting on the administrations of Mondi (UK) Ltd, AB Airlines Ltd, Crystal Palace FC and Sondhi Kellar plc. The practice also advised on the reorganisation of Planet Hollywood. **Clients:** HSBC; Barclays; Bank of Scotland; GE Capital; PricewaterhouseCoopers; Ernst & Young; Begbies Traynor and some creditors.

Nicholson Graham & Jones Busy in the mid-range market, and active in restructuring. Licensed IP **Shashi Rajani** is an *"all-round great intellect"* who is highly respected on formal and informal insolvency work. The *"commercial and thorough"* **Paul Oughton** has *"good banking connections"* and is seen more on the contentious side. The team advised Norfill Ltd on its insolvency and the office holder on the administration of Fashion Café (UK) Ltd. Other work includes advising a shareholder/director on the Ocean Marine case. **Clients:** KPMG; BDO Stoy Hayward; Baker Tilly; Lloyds TSB; Barclays.

Simmons & Simmons The team works on a balance of restructuring and mainstream insolvency work. *"High profile"* **John Houghton** is an insolvency all-rounder who has teamed up with IPs' favourite **Peter Manning** (who has recently moved to London from the North West). They head a broad domestic practice, working in all industries, from nursing homes to sports. It could almost be said to have a niche in the latter category, having worked this year on the Oxford and Portsmouth FCs and Richmond RFC matters. On the international side, the team advised the Bank of Latvia on the reconstruction of Rigas Komercbanka plc. Other cross-border work includes advising parties concerned with the Ashanti Goldfields and Debonair matters. **Clients:** Deloitte & Touche; KPMG; Robson Rhodes; Singer & Friedlander.

Slaughter and May The firm's generalist corporate approach means that in insolvency, as in other areas, their UK rivals (with specialised practices) perceive the firm to be *"not seriously playing the game."* However, the practice's involvement in one way or another on almost every high profile domestic and international case (such as the ongoing Peregrine, Barings, Debonair and TransTec matters) would suggest that the practice deserves more credit that the market would grant it. *"Extremely professional"* **Jonathan Rushworth** delivers *"solution-oriented advice."* Other work over the past year includes advising on the Lion Group of companies in Malaysia and Singapore and advising on the refinancing of a Slovakian oil company (Slovnaft). **Clients:** major accountants; IPs; banks and corporate clients.

Travers Smith Braithwaite Its lawyers are considered *"dedicated and commercial"* in presenting a broad insolvency practice. *"Hard-working and straight forward"* **Stephen Pearson** has a solid contentious practice whilst **Jeremy Walsh** has a track record in restructuring. Recent work includes advising on the GEI International plc and Channel Holding plc matters. **Clients:** GEI International; Channel Holding; Deloitte & Touche; PricewaterhouseCoopers.

Berwin Leighton The firm has a well-established domestic insolvency and business regeneration practice acting principally for management teams. Prominent in the property sector, the firm has worked on a number of administrations this year, including those of Cadoro plc, Cherokee Group plc and Ionica Group plc. **Clients:** BDO Stoy Hayward; Begbies Traynor; Buchler Phillips; Grant Thornton; RBS.

Eversheds With recognised regional expertise, the insolvency practice has sound national coverage (as well as international presence in places such as Eastern Europe). New arrivals have been effective in building up a corporate recovery practice. Refinancings and restructuring experience this year have seen the practice active in the leisure industry. Recent work includes acting for Bank One in the TransTec case and being involved in the Goodman International and Alldays matters. **Clients:** KPMG; Grant Thornton; PricewaterhouseCoopers; Bank One; Barclays.

Osborne Clarke OWA Respected department which is active on the non-bank side and is experienced in the IT and communications sectors. Acted for Brown Shipley in a receivership case and for ABN Amro in recovering non-performing debts. **Clients:** NatWest; ABN Amro; insolvency practitioners.

Richards Butler The team is commended for having *"a good insurance insolvency team – commercial and responsive."* **Jonathan Yorke**, who has a continuing involvement in the North Atlantic and Black Sea and Baltic cases, is considered *"an expert"* in insurance insolvency on which he works full-time. On more mainstream insolvency, the departure of Ian Fletcher to Stephenson Harwood is perceived to have weakened the department's profile. The firm acted on the receivership of Wessex Dairies and on the liquidation of Comtim SA, the Romanian pig farm. **Clients:** PricewaterhouseCoopers; Deloitte & Touche; RBS.

Sprecher Grier Halberstam Evenly divided between corporate and personal work, this specialist insolvency firm is especially well regarded for its SME work. The practice is also active on larger corporate work acting for a wide range of IPs, from sole practitioners to the big five. Licensed IP **Ian Grier** has a tremendous reputation in the area and writes extensively. Work is also sourced from banks (including secondary lenders) and corporates directly. Well known for general contentious insolvency work – administrations, receiverships, liquidations, voluntary arrangements, bankruptcies and directors disqualification proceedings. Has an association with an insolvency practice in Scotland, Anderson Fyfe. **Clients:** big five accountancy firms; IPs; clearing banks and corporates.

Taylor Joynson Garrett Insolvency strengths in this practice are found in property, real estate, IP and IT. It has experience in advising banks on reconstruction/recovery work. Work this year includes numerous manufacturing receiverships, the Advantage Group receivership and the Crystal Palace FC administration **Clients:** KPMG; PricewaterhouseCoopers; Smith & Williamson.

Other Notable Practitioners **Christopher Berry** of Edwin Coe is active in the personal insolvency market and principally works for trustees in bankruptcy. **James Roome** is an experienced practitioner who has left Cadwalader, Wickersham & Taft for Bingham Dana LLP. Recent experience includes the bankruptcy cases of Elizabeth Emmanuel and Jonathan Aitken. **Jonathan Lewis** of Finers Stephen Innocent is a *"strong technician"* and has a track record of advising on business turnaround for SMEs. **Geoffrey Woolf** moved from Stephenson Harwood to S J Berwin & Co at the end of 1999. He is highly rated and has long experience in both formal and informal insolvency work.

THE SOUTH

INSOLVENCY / CORPORATE RECOVERY • The South	Ptnrs	Assts
❶ **Argles Stoneham Burstows** Brighton	3	6
Blake Lapthorn Southampton	2	3
Sherwin Oliver Solicitors Portsmouth	5	3
❷ **Bond Pearce** Southampton	3	4
Cripps Harries Hall Tunbridge Wells, Kent	2	2
Lester Aldridge Bournemouth	3	4
❸ **Paris Smith & Randall** Southampton	2	3
❹ **Paul Davidson Taylor** Horsham	3	2
Thomas Eggar Church Adams Chichester	2	1

LEADING INDIVIDUALS	
❶ **DOBSON Julian** Cripps Harries Hall	**KEITLEY Nicholas** Blake Lapthorn
TAYLOR Andy Argles Stoneham Burstows	
❷ **BROCKMAN Christopher** Sherwin Oliver	**LE BAS Malcolm** Paris Smith & Randall
NIEKIRK Malcolm Lester Aldridge	**OLIVER David** Sherwin Oliver
❸ **COOK Nigel** Paul Davidson Taylor	**CRAIG Nigel** Sherwin Oliver Solicitors
JEFFRIES Graham Bond Pearce	
UP AND COMING	
MUNRO Rick Lamport Bassitt	

Within each band, firms are listed alphabetically. See **Profiles** on page 473

Argles Stoneham Burstows Stamping its regional authority through merger, the firm's insolvency practice now covers Sussex, Surrey, Kent and South Essex. The *"competent and sensible"* **Andy Taylor** is a recognised figure considered to have wide experience. He heads the group which is regarded as the *"first choice department in Brighton."* It has a market reputation for directors' disqualification work, where it acts for the DTI. The practice advises on the technical side of insolvencies, with the corporate department coming in on turnaround work. Both personal (bankruptcies and particularly IVAs) and corporate work are handled, with recent work involving plant hire and haulage businesses and a yachting company. **Clients:** major regional IPs.

Blake Lapthorn A major player in Hampshire, covering corporate as well as personal insolvency. The *"fine and sensible"* **Nicholas Keitley** *("knows his stuff")* is a licensed IP who heads a team which is developing its turnaround practice, and is particularly active in refinancings and CVAs. Work on a mix of corporate and personal matters. Cases dealt with this year include the administrative receivership of Hadrian PMC International Ltd and the liquidation of the Lightning Group of companies. **Clients:** big five accountancy firms; other IPs.

Sherwin Oliver Solicitors very well regarded for their contentious work, the team is considered a capable one, peopled by specialists who *"know their stuff."* **Christopher Brockman** has a good name, **David Oliver** is the departmental *"sage,"* whilst **Nigel Craig** *"gets things done."* The team is considered to have *"strength in depth."* **Clients:** IPs; accountants; corporates.

Bond Pearce The Southampton office *"has status"* as a leading insolvency practice, complementing the firm's Plymouth and Bristol competence. Work consists of bank-driven receivership work, and there is increased emphasis on turnaround work. **Graham Jeffries** is well regarded. **Clients:** IPs; accountants; corporates.

Cripps Harries Hall **Julian Dobson** *"knows the subject,"* has a good reputation among clients and is considered *"technically very good."* The practice's work extends to Sussex, Kent and London. Working on an even mix of corporate and personal work, the majority of the firm's work is IP-originated. Dobson has a specialisation in partnership insolvency, although this does not exclude contentious matters and corporate recovery work. **Clients:** major accountants and IPs.

Lester Aldridge The *"sensible and commercial"* **Malcolm Niekirk** has his reputation particularly on non-contentious matters. The team has acted on several receiverships, ranging from private receiverships to routine bank appointments. Recognised areas of expertise are found in football club insolvencies (particularly where supporters' groups are involved) and in the health care sector, where the team advised lenders on the insolvency of two private hospitals. **Clients:** major accountants and IPs.

Paris Smith & Randall The bulk of the firm's work comes from regional and national IPs, with whom **Malcolm Le Bas** has a strong following. The team acts on both contentious and non-contentious matters, with an increase in work on the recovery side. Work this year includes acting for the purchaser of Portsmouth Football Club Limited in Administration. **Clients:** IPs and accountants.

Paul Davidson Taylor **Nigel Cook** is known for his insolvency and banking work, and is considered a leading individual for his non-contentious experience. The practice has a good reputation in trading receiverships. **Clients:** IPs; major accountants.

Thomas Eggar Church Adams A player in Sussex, well considered for both contentious and non-contentious work. The firm is active in international litigation, partnership liquidation, administrations and defending directors' disqualification proceedings. The practice is also involved in restructuring work, and has been active in the IT sector. **Clients:** IPs; accountants.

Other Notable Practitioner **Rick Munro** of Lamport Bassitt is considered to have a notable track record as an insolvency litigator.

THAMES VALLEY

INSOLVENCY / CORPORATE RECOVERY	Ptnrs	Assts
❶ **Boyes Turner & Burrows** Reading	4	3
❷ **Darbys Mallam Lewis** Oxford	3	-
Morgan Cole Reading	4	5
Pitmans Reading	3	4

LEADING INDIVIDUALS	
✪ **BRANSON Christopher** Boyes Turner & Burrows	
❶ **TAYLOR Elizabeth** Darbys Mallam Lewis	
❷ **ARCHER David** Pitmans	**POTTER Bruce** Morgan Cole
SMITH Phillip Boyes Turner & Burrows	

Within each band, firms are listed alphabetically. See **Profiles** on page 473

Boyes Turner & Burrows Team head, **Chris Branson** has a national reputation for his insolvency work. A licensed IP, he is *"universally well thought of"* and respected for his experience, primarily as a litigator. **Phil Smith** enters our lists this year following strong market recommendation. The team works from Gloucester to Guildford (and is involved abroad), and has a general reputation as the *"lawyers' lawyers"* – *"technically, they have a huge level of expertise."* Case-load includes personal and corporate work, both contentious and non-contentious. Work this year in personal insolvency has included acting for the trustee in bankruptcy in the Hellyer and Jimmy White cases, and on the bankruptcy of Jack Dunnett (former MP, solicitor and chairman of the football league). On the corporate side, work has included acting for the administrators of AMI and converting the administration into a creditors voluntary liquidation, then representing the liquidators. **Clients:** main accountancy firms.

Darbys Mallam Lewis **Elizabeth Taylor** is considered *"highly capable,"* with a reputation outside the area. More than half of the practice's work is on the personal insolvency side. On corporate side, the team is increasingly involved in turnaround work. **Clients:** main accountants and IPs.

Morgan Cole **Bruce Potter** is *"well known and well thought of."* The team acts for a wide client base, including large accountants. **Clients:** big five accountancy firms and major IPs.

Pitmans Considered *"a presence in Reading,"* the team, led by **David Archer**, has a broad insolvency practice. Work on contentious and non-contentious, corporate and personal matters. Administrations, partnership insolvencies, defending directors disqualification proceedings and rescue work are all part of the department's case-load. **Clients:** main IPs.

SOUTH WEST

INSOLVENCY / CORPORATE RECOVERY	Ptnrs	Assts
❶ **Osborne Clarke OWA** Bristol	5	17
❷ **Bond Pearce** Bristol, Plymouth	3	13
Foot Anstey Sargent Exeter	⚐	⚐
❸ **Laytons** Bristol	2	3
❹ **Burges Salmon** Bristol	⚐	⚐
CMS Cameron McKenna Bristol	⚐	⚐
TLT Solicitors Bristol	4	8
❺ **Clarke Willmott & Clarke** Taunton	2	-
Meade-King Bristol	1	2

LEADING INDIVIDUALS	
❶ **COOK Patrick** Osborne Clarke	**LAWSON Stephen** Foot Anstey Sargent
TETTMAR Victor Bond Pearce	
❷ **ALLINSON Stephen** Clarke Willmott & Clarke	**BON Gordon** Laytons
HARRIS Anthony Laytons	**HARRIS Clare** Meade-King
MAY Philip TLT Solicitors	**STOBART Guy** Burges Salmon
❸ **AGAR Nick** CMS Cameron McKenna	**BOOBIER Nigel** Osborne Clarke
SMITH Gillian Foot Anstey Sargent	**WALD Matthew** Stephens & Scown
WILTSHIRE Peter CMS Cameron McKenna	

Within each band, firms are listed alphabetically. *See **Profiles** on page 473*

⚐ *Figures unavailable at time of going to press.*

Osborne Clarke OWA **Patrick Cook** is now seen more on banking transactions, yet remains well regarded for his insolvency work. **Nigel Boobier** is a new entry to the tables after strong market recommendation. The banking and insolvency departments are now being brought together. A *"busy team"* works a lot on the banking side, in traditional receivership and administration work. Considered *"practical and technical"* the team is the agent for the DTI in the M4 corridor on directors' disqualification work. Turnaround work is increasing. Work this year includes the Fownes Hotel plc and Craftworld Trading Ltd receiverships, and the BMI Electronics, Select Software Tooling plc and Christies Fitted Bedrooms administrations. **Clients:** NatWest; 3i Group; big five accountancy firms; IPs; major clearing banks.

Bond Pearce The Bristol office has so far been a success for this regional firm. *"All-rounder"* **Victor Tettmar** is *"quietly effective."* He leads a team considered *"very pleasant to work with"* by major City firms and is considered to have *"good back-up people."* The practice covers a wide range of work, in sectors such as financial services and agriculture. **Clients:** Portman Building Society; BNP; Lloyds TSB; Grant Thornton; PricewaterhouseCoopers.

Foot Anstey Sargent *"The leader in Exeter."* considered a good team for personal work, the firm is also active on the corporate side, where it has a reputation for being *"innovative." "The elder statesman"* **Stephen Lawson** is considered *"technically accurate,"* and has a massive regional profile. He is recognised for his personal insolvency expertise. **Gillian Smith** is also a leading name. The practice acts for the Disqualification Unit of the Insolvency Services. **Clients:** national and local IPs.

Laytons *"Hard litigator"* **Gordon Bon** is one of two leading names in a locally respected practice. As well as traditional litigation work, he is involved on non-procedural activities. **Anthony Harris** is considered to have *"broad insolvency knowledge,"* and is active on the non-contentious side, extending into restructurings. **Clients:** main IPs; corporates.

Burges Salmon **Guy Stobart** is the leading name in a practice considered to be *"good at what they do,"* although he is perceived by local solicitors as more involved in banking and corporate matters. Work has included nursing home insolvencies and personal workouts and increased corporate rescue, particularly in the agricultural sector. **Clients:** major accountants; Lloyds TSB; UCB Group Ltd.

CMS Cameron McKenna **Nick Agar** is active in the recovery sector, while the newly-ranked **Peter Wiltshire** *("does good work")* concentrates on pure insolvency and banking work. Known for their strong links with Lloyds TSB, the firm is *"building a sound practice,"* acting mainly for the banks and IPs, occasionally advising trade creditors and purchasers. **Clients:** local IPs; Lloyds TSB.

TLT Solicitors *"They are solid in this area, and one to watch."* **Philip May** is the main name in the newly merged firm's insolvency practice. The firm has a good reputation on small-to-medium sized work, and is popular with the banks and IPs, as much for contentious as non-contentious work. **Clients:** accountants; national clearing banks; IPs.

Clarke Willmott & Clarke Based in Taunton, the firm's insolvency practice is headed by **Stephen Allinson**, who is a *"good name in the region."* He is a licensed IP, considered *"bright,"* and works with the ABRP (ex-SPI) on the teaching side. Working on the contentious and non-contentious side, the firm advises on an even mix of corporate and personal work. Over half of the practices work is sourced from IPs, whilst the remainder is equally split between banks and companies. Rescue work is increasing and the firm is involved in defending directors' disqualification proceedings. **Clients:** IP; banks; companies.

Meade-King **Clare Harris** *("she's good, she knows her stuff")* has a great reputation in the field. Previously perceived to lack support, she has strengthened her team over the past year. Whilst turnaround work is getting more popular, most of the department's work is concentrated in pure insolvency. Working on an even mix of corporate and personal matters, the majority of the practice's work is sourced from IPs, with the team having a particularly good reputation in personal insolvency. **Clients:** IPs.

Other Notable Practitioner **Matthew Wald** of Stephens & Scown in Plymouth was recommended, primarily for his litigation prowess. During the past year, he has been involved on the liquidation of a shipyard and a major hotel receivership.

WALES

INSOLVENCY / CORPORATE RECOVERY • Wales	Ptnrs	Assts
❶ **Eversheds** Cardiff	1	2
❷ **Edwards Geldard** Cardiff	6	4
Hugh James Ford Simey Cardiff	3	2
Morgan Cole Cardiff	4	5

LEADING INDIVIDUALS	
❶ **VAUGHAN Philip** Eversheds	
❷ **REES Bleddyn** Morgan Cole	**THOMAS Catrin** Hugh James Ford Simey
WILKINS John Dolmans	

Within each band, firms are listed alphabetically. *See* ***Profiles*** *on page 473*

Eversheds considered pre-eminent for insolvency work in the region, both due to the size of the group and to the *"personable"* **Philip Vaughan**. He has a general reputation in the area and is considered to *"stand-out on the non-contentious side."* The practice's work is concentrated on receiverships, administrations, corporate restructurings and refinancings, and its remit extends to the Bristol region. Work this year includes acting on the receivership of the Welland Group and on the insolvencies of Newport Wafer Fab and the Advantage Group. **Clients:** major accountants/IPs; clearing banks; finance houses and surveyors.

Edwards Geldard Felt to be *"running along smoothly"* this year, the firm has been busy acting on administrations. Recent work includes acting for the administrators of Newport Wafer Fab Ltd and ASAT UK Ltd. **Clients:** big five accountancy firms; IPs and accountants.

Hugh James Ford Simey The reputation of **Catrin Thomas** continues to give the firm a good name on the contentious side. This year the practice has beefed up the non-contentious side, acting on recovery and voluntary arrangement work. The team acts for a broad range of clients on a spread of insolvency work. Cases this year includes the Sunrise Homes Ltd, Jaymart Construction Ltd and Advantage Healthcare Group receiverships. **Clients:** big five accountancy firms and IPs.

Morgan Cole **Bleddyn Rees** maintains his reputation, although is not widely perceived to be as active this year. The team's work has included the receiverships of GKR construction, Dumbarton Properties Ltd and W. Hosp & Co. **Clients:** big five accountancy firms and IPs.

Other Notable Practitioners Although his firm is no longer considered to rank among the elite in Wales, **John Wilkins** of Dolmans still has a name for both contentious and non-contentious insolvency.

MIDLANDS

INSOLVENCY / CORPORATE RECOVERY	Ptnrs	Assts
❶ **Eversheds** Birmingham	2	7
❷ **Martineau Johnson** Birmingham	2	2
❸ **Wragge & Co** Birmingham	3	18
❹ **DLA** Birmingham	4	2
Irwin Mitchell Birmingham	1	4
❺ **Gateley Wareing** Birmingham	3	9
Hammond Suddards Edge Birmingham	3	2
❻ **Actons** Nottingham	2	2
Pinsent Curtis Birmingham	1	2
Shoosmiths Northampton	7	8

LEADING INDIVIDUALS	
✪ **DREW Jeff** Eversheds	
❶ **BAKER Ian** Martineau Johnson	
❷ **BOWDEN Jeremy** DLA	**PALLETT Julian** Wragge & Co
McGEEVER Brendan Gateley Wareing	
PHEASANT Louise Eversheds	
❸ **DOLPHIN Huw** DLA	**READETT Helen** Martineau Johnson
SULLIVAN John Hammond Suddards Edge	
❹ **COOKE David** Pinsent Curtis	

Within each band, firms are listed alphabetically. *See* ***Profiles*** *on page 473*

Eversheds A dedicated, *"capable and straightforward"* team focused solely on insolvency. The non-contentious side of the practice is considered very strong, working on a large amount of restructuring work for banks and being *"prominent in turnaround work"* in both the West and the East Midlands. *"Pure insolvency man"* **Jeff Drew** has *"the brightest reputation of anyone."* He is well regarded nationally for his experience, gained through being someone who was *"in at the start and has never moved out." "Practical to deal with,"* **Louise Pheasant** retains consistent market respect. Work this year out of Nottingham includes acting on an administration for Century International Limited. The Birmingham office advised the administrative receivers of Dudley Drop Forging Company Ltd. Other work has included acting on the receiverships of William Barlow & Son Ltd, Abco Engineering Ltd and En Tout Cas plc. **Clients:** major UK and Irish clearing banks; IPs and companies.

Martineau Johnson The team combines banking and insolvency, working on corporate and personal work (around a quarter is on work for individuals), in contentious and non-contentious situations. **Ian Baker** is a *"popular choice,"* someone who is *"good to work with."* Also *"able and popular"* is **Helen Readett**, who is an all-rounder, working on turnarounds, contentious work and on the property insolvency side. Because of the firm's strong connections with banks, the insolvency team is considered to have a practice oriented towards bank-driven turnarounds and receiverships. The team does work for IPs, has been active in administrations and voluntary arrangements, and also includes a litigator. Advised on the receivership of S Jones Industrial Holdings plc and the administration and sale of Cadoro, a high street fashion store. **Clients:** Lloyds TSB; big five accountancy firms; other accountants; IPs.

Wragge & Co As with other teams, the firm runs the banking and insolvency sides together, and is perceived to have *"taken steps to reinforce its position in insolvency."* The broad consensus is that the practice has already *"re-established its capabilities."* The *"excellent"* **Julian Pallett** is a *"good operator"* who is well regarded for bank-driven pre-insolvency and receivership work. Focused more on corporate recovery and turnaround, mainly for banks, the firm nevertheless keeps an eye on traditional work. Matters handled this year include the receiverships of Apollo Group, Perma Led, Smallshaw Group, Victor Cast Ware Ltd and Brookside Dyers and Finishers. Also handles work from the DTI. **Clients:** Lloyds TSB; HSBC; IPs; including most of the big five accountancy firms.

DLA Works on pure insolvency and pre-insolvency work for an even mix of IPs and banks. Corporate support and turnaround work is increasing, particularly in distressed MBO situations. **Huw Dolphin** and **Jeremy Bowden** are considered *"sound players,"* particularly on the contentious side. Work this year includes acting on the administrative receiverships of National Homecare Group plc, AE Clutterbuck Ltd, P Summerfield, Holbruck Products Ltd and Eastbourne Auto Productions Ltd. **Clients:** major clearers and accountants/IPs.

Irwin Mitchell This *"small but effective"* practice has a *"good transactional presence."* The majority of the firm's work comes from IPs, with the rest coming from banks and companies (directors/creditors/purchasers). The team has advised on the receivership of a company in the Potteries, as well as receiverships in the seed and foodstuff market. **Clients:** Lloyds TSB

Gateley Wareing From the Leicester and Birmingham bases the firm is well regarded for its voluntary arrangement and liquidation/bankruptcy work. Appreciated by clients for its cost-effectiveness. *"Super bloke"* **Brendan McGeever** is regarded as an *"easy going and effective lawyer,"* who is well liked by IPs. The firm acted on the receiverships of PCG Glass Ltd, Maxpower (Auto) Ltd and Rheanco Foods plc, and the acquisition out of receivership of National Homecare plc. **Clients:** Deloitte & Touche; Grant Thornton; AIB; Clydesdale Bank.

Hammond Suddards Edge Well known for cross-border international insolvency litigation work, an area where **John Sullivan** is highly regarded. This international reputation has overshadowed the work of the rest of the team, which continues to work on pure domestic insolvency matters. The majority of work comes from IPs, the remainder being made up of bank-driven work. Work this year includes the administration of Blakedown Nurseries Ltd and involvement in connection with the insolvency of the British Athletic Federation and the completion of its reconstruction. **Clients:** Capital Bank.

Actons Based in Nottingham, the firm's insolvency practice is considered to be a leading player in the East Midlands. Having been *"around a long time"* it is generally viewed as a favourite of local IPs (the practice acts for four of the big five accountants). The team has two IPs at partner level. Work is received from local accountants, solicitors and national and foreign banks. **Clients:** IPs; major accountants.

Pinsent Curtis The firm maintains a reputation for insolvency work, yet is perceived to have no individuals earmarked specifically for it. **David Cooke**, who is regarded as a *"solid player"* in insolvency, is seen more on banking matters. Works for a wide range of banks and IPs, as well as corporates and insurers on insolvency related IP claims. **Clients:** main accountants; clearing banks.

Shoosmiths Generally well regarded in Northampton for local insolvency work. Handles a wide range of corporate and personal insolvency work, including directors' disqualification matters. **Clients:** IPs; major accountants.

EAST ANGLIA

INSOLVENCY / CORPORATE RECOVERY	Ptnrs	Assts
❶ **Eversheds** Cambridge, Ipswich, Norwich	4	8
❷ **Mills & Reeve** Cambridge, Norwich	2	6
❸ **Prettys** Ipswich	3	2
Taylor Vinters Cambridge	2	3
❹ **Nicholsons** Lowestoft	1	1

LEADING INDIVIDUALS	
❶ **McGURK Anthony** Eversheds	**SHORT John** Taylor Vinters
WAINE Ian Prettys	
❷ **NICHOLSON Mark** Nicholsons	**WHEATLEY Jamie** Mills & Reeve
❸ **FALKUS Bryony** Mills & Reeve	

Within each band, firms are listed alphabetically. *See* ***Profiles*** *on page 473*

Eversheds Operates through three offices in the region. The practice has a *"good following"* and a *"fair share of receiverships."* **Anthony McGurk** enjoys a high profile locally. The firm works on contentious and non-contentious sides, for both IPs and banks. Work this year includes the administrative receiverships of Eaton International and of Laserpoint Communications Ltd. **Clients:** big five accountancy firms and other major accountants, corporates.

Mills & Reeve With **Bryony Falkus** perceived to have shifted towards more corporate work, **Jamie Wheatley** is considered the firm's main insolvency practitioner. He has a contentious background, exemplified by involvement in the Metro Trading International litigation. Banking and property insolvency specialists complement the team. In Cambridge, the emphasis is on voluntary arrangements and turnaround work for biotechnology and new technology companies. **Clients:** Allsop & Co; RBS; Deloitte & Touche; Panos Eliades; KPMG.

Prettys Considered the leading firm in Ipswich for insolvency. **Ian Waine** is *"perfectly competent."* Advises on a range of corporate and personal insolvency issues. **Clients:** local accountants.

Taylor Vinters *"Up at the top"* in Cambridge, the local market has perhaps been too buoyant over the past year (especially the high tech sector) for the insolvency practice to have been excessively active. **John Short** is well regarded for his expertise. Despite the relatively sluggish market for insolvency work, the practice has worked on restructurings, turnarounds, voluntary arrangements, receiverships and liquidations. **Clients:** Ernst & Young; Grant Thornton; Lloyds TSB

Nicholsons **Mark Nicholson** is recommended by the market for his personal insolvency skills. A licensed IP, he also works on the corporate side. **Clients:** local accountants.

NORTH WEST

Addleshaw Booth & Co The firm is perceived to have strong connections for insolvency work, especially since the merger with Slater Heelis. It has accordingly achieved *"the lion's share of the big-ticket market,"* and is seen as particularly active in restructuring work. Its practice covers a broad range of industries including retail, agricultural, health care and manufacturing sectors. *"Just about the best,"* **Egan Brooks** is a *"doyen in the market"* – a *"superb lawyer"* who *"delivers well-researched opinions."* **Julia Burrows** is *"extremely approachable and a safe pair of hands,"* and is well regarded for her property insolvency and turnaround work. **John Joyce** is an all-round insolvency lawyer who has been involved in many big cases in the region and is regarded as *"a solid player."* Work this year included the administrative receiverships of Dawn til Dusk plc (involving 80 convenience stores in the North) and of Fearnley Construction Ltd. Another transaction was the administration of the UK subsidiary (Beloit Walmsley Ltd) of a US parent in Chapter 11 proceedings. The department works on turnaround issues along with the firm's strong corporate team. **Clients:** the main UK clearing banks; factoring companies and secondary lenders; leading accountants and IPs.

Hammond Suddards Edge Identified by Manchester rivals as a major competitor. In Manchester the *"prominent"* **Duncan Haymes** is a *"sensible, experienced and commercial operator."* He is the *"dominant figure"* in a *"big team which is successful even in a flat market."* More active in the recovery and business support area, the team maintains strong relationships with banks and IPs. Work this year includes the administrations of Chester City FC, Fine Art Wallcoverings Ltd, Wilson Wilcox Furnishings Ltd and Cramlington Textiles Ltd. The firm was involved in the administrations and subse-

INSOLVENCY / CORPORATE RECOVERY	Ptnrs	Assts
❶ **Addleshaw Booth & Co** Manchester	9	9
❷ **Hammond Suddards Edge** Manchester	2	8
❸ **DLA** Liverpool, Manchester	3	9
Halliwell Landau Manchester	1	6
❹ **Chaffe Street** Manchester	4	3
❺ **Davies Wallis Foyster** Liverpool	3	4
Eversheds Manchester	1	4
❻ **Cuff Roberts** Liverpool	2	2
Mace & Jones Manchester	2	3

LEADING INDIVIDUALS	
✪ **BROOKS Egan** Addleshaw Booth & Co	
❶ **SPENCER Shân** Chaffe Street	
❷ **BURROWS Julia** Addleshaw Booth & Co	**HAYMES Duncan** Hammond Suddards Edge
❸ **BUCHANAN Andrew** Halliwell Landau	**COATES Philip** DLA
GOODMAN Nick NJ Goodman & Co	**GREGORY Andrew** Davies Wallis Foyster
JOYCE John Addleshaw Booth & Co	**JUMP Graeme** Mace & Jones
WALLER Simon Eversheds	

Within each band, firms are listed alphabetically. See **Profiles** on page 473

quent voluntary arrangements leading to the survival of Philip Johnstone Group Ltd and its subsidiaries. Work on the personal side includes continuing to act for trustees on the bankruptcy of former Lloyds names. **Clients:** Royal Bank of Scotland; Lloyds TSB; Co-op Bank; KPMG; Begbies Traynor.

DLA Still perceived to be affected by the loss of Peter Manning, the practice is nevertheless seen as one of the *"largest and most experienced."* A balanced North West presence, with a strong office in Liverpool, the firm registered strong approval ratings from clients. **Philip Coates** is well regarded. Good on the contentious side, the team also has a profile for non-contentious work. The firm has acted on high-visibility reconstruction deals, most recently in the leisure and transport industries. Work this year includes acting for the joint liquidators on Millwest Ltd, advising on the receivership of Principal Distribution Ltd, the administration of Etcetera Reject Shops, the liquidation of Tom Finney Group and the administrative receivership of Clay Construction Ltd. A busy year in Liverpool included work on the administrations of Falcroft Ltd, Christopher Haydn Ltd, Leonelle Blouses Ltd and Delaway Ltd. **Clients:** major clearers; big five accountancy firms; IPs; corporates.

Halliwell Landau A large and dedicated team serving clearing banks and insolvency practitioners. *"Commercially-minded"* **Andrew Buchanan** enters our lists this year. Andrew Livesey has left the firm. The department acts across a range of sectors and peers perceive the group to be *"dominant in the brewery sector."* Work this year includes the administrations of Curtina, Wills Group and Standish Van Hire. **Clients:** main clearing banks and big five accountancy firms; IPs.

Chaffe Street A small, partner-heavy and *"visible"* practice populated with *"good people."* All-rounder **Shân Spencer** is *"competent, thorough and practical."* The first lawyer to become the North West Regional Chairman of the Association of Business Recovery Professionals she is perceived as a *"well-connected"* and has been involved in a number of high-profile matters. Strengthened by the arrival of a partner from Addleshaws, the practice is active in procedural work (mainly on the corporate side) and corporate recovery. Recent work includes the administrative receiverships of the Overlander Group of companies, Universal Bulk Handling Ltd, Darmac Ltd and Paramount Engineering Ltd. **Clients:** clearing banks; big five accountancy firms; IPs.

Davies Wallis Foyster *"Growing well"* as a balanced North West practice with strength in Manchester and Liverpool. Considered *"helpful"* by clients **Andrew Gregory** is *"an excellent lawyer."* The team includes a licensed IP. Recent sectors of activity include the leisure and catering industries, while corporate rescue is an area of increased activity. Acted for the administrators of the Stuart Group. **Clients:** major clearers; big five accountancy firms and other accountants and IPs; corporates.

Eversheds With its national banking connections and powerful regional presence, the relatively recently formed insolvency team in Manchester is now considered to have *"emerged."* Led by the *"respected and reliable"* **Simon Waller**, the *"growing practice"* has been active on both procedural and turnaround work. Areas of activity include nursing homes, manufacturing, the accident management industry (where it has an important profile), and IT start-up companies. Work this year includes advising banks in their exposure in the accident management industry in the Dimond v Lovell case, advising the administrative receivers of Knockdene Garages Ltd and the receivers of Nationwide Self Drive Ltd. **Clients:** main UK clearing banks; accountants and IPs.

Cuff Roberts Well connected and active in Liverpool, the firm also has a certain amount of activity sourced from Manchester. Recognised for its technical ability, the department is perceived to be active on non-bank liquidation work. **Clients:** AIB Bank; Nationwide; KPMG; Grant Thornton; Begbies Traynor.

Mace & Jones A leading practice in Liverpool. A solid litigation practice advises on both personal and corporate insolvency. **Graeme Jump** enters our lists this year following market recommendation. Cases have included work in the agricultural sector, where the Liverpool practice works with the Knutsford office. **Clients:** Co-op Bank; RBS, mid-size accountancy firms and IPs.

Other Notable Practitioners **Nick Goodman** has left Addleshaw Booth & Co to set up as a sole practitoner. He is best known for his work in insolvency procedures.

YORKSHIRE

DLA *"First class"* **Peter Cranston** leads *"an aggressive and hard hitting"* practice regarded as the *"most well-established in the North East."* Cranston himself is *"very good both technically and commercially,"* is viewed as *"excellent for complex issues"* and has an influence which extends beyond Leeds. **Mark Jackson** is appreciated by clients for his *"hard working, hands-on, incredibly commercial approach."* These two heavy hitters offer a *"great pool of experience and know-how"* and can count on the support of a team with *"strength in depth,"* including 7 licensed IPs. Additionally, the practice received a major boost with the arrival of **Richard Obank**, a highly regarded insolvency all rounder, from Herbert Smith in London. Work on a wide range of insolvency and bankruptcy issues, though the emphasis has shifted to corporate turnaround and reconstruction work, where the practice now spends most of its time (and has accordingly be renamed as the Business Support and Restructuring Group). The team advises a mix of banks and IPs, as well as the DTI in directors' disqualifications. Work this year includes the Moorfield Holding and Advantage Healthcare Group receiverships. The team has been retained by NatWest as regional panel lawyers on corporate recovery and debt work and is on the Barclays panel for corporate business support and debt recovery work nationally. Work this year includes acting on the administrative receiverships of Moorfield Holdings Group, Wahlco Engineering Group and Advantage Healthcare Group and on the on administration of Full Circle Industries plc. **Clients:** Barclays; NatWest; RBS; Bank of Scotland; wide range of accountants/IPs.

INSOLVENCY / CORPORATE RECOVERY	Ptnrs	Assts
❶ **DLA** Leeds, Sheffield	8	9
❷ **Walker Morris** Leeds	5	15
❸ **Addleshaw Booth & Co** Leeds	3	7
Hammond Suddards Edge Leeds	5	10
Pinsent Curtis Leeds	3	6
❹ **Eversheds** Leeds	3	7
❺ **Brooke North** Leeds	5	5
Keeble Hawson Sheffield, Leeds	3	-
❻ **Carrick Read Insolvency** Leeds	3	5
Irwin Mitchell Sheffield	1	5

LEADING INDIVIDUALS	
❶ **CRANSTON Peter** DLA	**MUDD Philip** Walker Morris
RHODES Paul Hammond Suddards Edge	
❷ **CORR Patrick** Pinsent Curtis	
❸ **BALLMANN William** Addleshaw Booth	**FRITH Stuart** Brooke North
HINCHLIFFE David Walker Morris	**JACKSON Mark** DLA
JEFFRIES Jonathan Pinsent Curtis	**OBANK Richard** DLA
RIDLER Graham Eversheds	
❹ **BENNETT Jeremy** Hammond Suddards Edge	
BRIGGS Graham Addleshaw Booth	**BROWN Robert** Keeble Hawson
TAYLOR Michael Walker Morris	
UP AND COMING	
FERGUSSON Richard Keeble Hawson	

Within each band, firms are listed alphabetically. *See **Profiles** on page 473*

Walker Morris A *"solid"* practice with depth, which clients appreciate for its *"calm and considerate approach."* The *"quiet and level-headed"* **Philip Mudd** is one of the area's recognised leaders. Some in the market commented that his new role in management would result in reduced involvement on the fee-earning side, yet he *"still does the stuff."* A qualified insolvency practitioner with a corporate background, Mudd is involved mainly in complex insolvencies, turnarounds and bank-related work along with **Michael Taylor. David Hinchcliffe** is well regarded on the contentious/procedural side. Recent work includes the Peterhead Group plc and Total Office Group plc receiverships, both of which contained cross-border elements. **Clients:** Lloyds TSB; RBS; Barclays; the big five accountancy firms.

Addleshaw Booth & co IP work is the practice's bread and butter, yet with more work in turnaround and reconstruction work the practice is increasingly creditor (bank) driven. The *"committed"* **William Ballmann** is the firm's key figure on the traditional insolvency side. He is ably assisted by the *"practical and user-friendly"* **Graham Briggs** who enters our lists this year following strong recommendation, especially on 'intensive care' work. Clients regard the *"in-form"* practice as *"commercial and receptive."* On pre-insolvency and insolvency procedural matters, an important source of work for the firm is still Yorkshire Bank. Work this year includes the Grampian Care Limited (nursing and residential care homes) and York Vale Pig Co receiverships. **Clients:** 3i Group; HSBC; RBS; Lloyds TSB; leading accountants and IPs.

Hammond Suddards Edge Through the *"experienced strategist"* and *"national figure,"* **Paul Rhodes**, the firm is seen to be building a strong turnaround/reconstruction practice to complement its *"strength in litigation."* He is supported by the able **Jeremy Bennett** who enters our lists this year following strong market recommendation. A varied practice which goes beyond traditional insolvency, major work this year includes the T&D Industries and Silvercross Prams administrations. **Clients:** leading accountancy firms.

Pinsent Curtis Appreciated by clients for its *"proactive and forward looking approach."* The team spends much of its time on complex turnaround work, liaising closely with the corporate and private equity teams. considered strong in pre-packaged receiverships and administrations. The *"outgoing"* and *"brilliant"* **Patrick Corr** gets *"very involved in client matters."* **Jonathan Jeffries** is *"experienced and highly respected"* and is developing expertise in the financial services sector. Administrative receiverships this year include O'Hare Ltd and Chamberlain Phipps Ltd. The team advised on the administration of Bradlor Developments Ltd. **Clients:** banks; accountants.

Eversheds The firm is well known for its litigation work and has been expanding its non-contentious practice and non-bank/IP clientele. Work for corporates, such as creditors, purchasers or companies and directors in difficulty now takes up around 40% of the practice's workload. Julian Horrocks has retired, but **Graham Ridler**, also considered to be a heavyweight, has come to Leeds from the firm's Newcastle office. He is perceived to have more of a contentious background, although he is also involved in reconstruction work. His expertise extends to debt reconstruction, recognition and workout. The international dimension of the practice is also increasing, with recent cross border work including US Chapter 11 elements. On the contentious side, the practice has increased its contingency fee work and recently successfully advised the liquidator in the Hollicourt litigation. Acted for Sanderson Bramall Motor Group in its acquisition of Albany Lease Ltd from the receivers of The J. Blake Group Ltd. **Clients:** accountants/IPs; banks; corporates.

Brooke North The firm has an established bankruptcy and liquidation practice and is considered a *"leader for middle market work."* **Stuart Frith** is considered to be *"a strong litigator"* and the team has a strong profile in both personal and corporate insolvency. **Clients:** accountants/IPs; banks; corporates.

Keeble Hawson **Richard Fergusson**, formerly at Addleshaw Booth & Co, has joined the firm and is regarded as a practitioner of potential. Team head **Robert Brown** is regarded as *"a bulldog, who simply will not let go,"* and the insolvency group is regarded as a *"bunch on the up."* Have established a particular reputation for working on behalf of leading accountants. **Clients:** accountants/IPs; banks; corporates.

Carrick Read Insolvency A firm entirely focused on insolvency and recovery work. Considered to be specialists in matters connected to office holders' roles and directors' disqualification proceedings. Recent work includes the liquidation of PSD and the administration of Advantage Healthcare. **Clients:** accountants/IPs; banks; corporates.

Irwin Mitchell The practice is considered to have *"grown considerably"* in the last year, predominantly on insolvency procedural work rather than the turnaround/recovery side. Clients regard them as *"an up and coming force."* Notable for recent advice on professional firm insolvencies. **Clients:** large accounting firms.

NORTH EAST

INSOLVENCY / CORPORATE RECOVERY	Ptnrs	Assts
❶ **Dickinson Dees** Newcastle upon Tyne	4	3
❷ **Eversheds** Newcastle upon Tyne	3	-
❸ **Robert Muckle** Newcastle upon Tyne	1	-
Ward Hadaway Newcastle upon Tyne	1	1
❹ **Hay & Kilner** Newcastle upon Tyne	2	1
Watson Burton Newcastle upon Tyne	2	-

LEADING INDIVIDUALS	
❶ **ANDERSON John** Eversheds	**SANDERSON Gordon** Dickinson Dees
❷ **BLAIR Jonathan** Dickinson Dees	**PENNIE John** Dickinson Dees
❸ **DALLOW Sally** Dickinson Dees	**JAMES Jim** Ward Hadaway

Within each band, firms are listed alphabetically. *See **Profiles** on page 473*

Dickinson Dees With a dedicated team the firm is considered to be the *"leader in Newcastle"* for insolvency related matters. Department head **John Pennie** covers more than the insolvency discipline, yet remains highly regarded for his capabilities in the area. The *"sensible"* **Gordon Sanderson** is regarded as *"great to work with"* and is active on bank work. **Jonathan Blair** is well regarded for his work in directors' disqualification matters, where the firm is the sole agent for the DTI in the North East region and shares the appointment in the North West region. **Sally Dallow** enters our lists this year following strong market support; and heads the personal insolvency unit which the team is developing. IPs and banks form the bulk of clients, with the practice also working for corporates, such as purchasers. Work this year includes advising on the Hallcam Engineering, North Timber and Shepherd's Scrap Metal Newcastle receiverships. **Clients:** major accountancy firms and DTI.

Eversheds The practice is a respected component of Eversheds' tri-partite Northern insolvency coverage. With a *"good base of work"* and *"critical mass,"* the team is deemed to be *"catching up with Dickinson Dees."* Possessor of a *"sound intellect,"* the *"technical stalwart"* **John Anderson** would be part of *"anyone's Newcastle insolvency dream-team."* He has a corporate background and an expertise in pension problems. Graham Ridler has left for the firm's Leeds office. The practice works on a wide range of insolvency issues, including the personal side, though it concentrates more on corporate, where it is also involved in turnaround work. Work this year includes acting on the receiverships of Teeside Wholesale Meat Company Ltd. and the Varley Walker group of companies. **Clients:** major accountancy firms.

Robert Muckle The insolvency group has a wide remit working on corporate and personal matters of both contentious and non-contentious nature. Most of the work is of a corporate bent, with the firm working on bank-led and non-bank led matters. The team has increasingly advised companies and directors on turnaround/reconstruction work. **Clients:** big five accountancy firms; Lloyds TSB; HSBC; Bank of Scotland.

Ward Hadaway A general insolvency practice working on matters from corporate insolvency to personal bankruptcy. The team is making a push in creditor-led work, which has brought the firm work outside the region. **Jim James** won market plaudits for his non-bank work. **Clients:** major accountancy firms.

Hay & Kilner The firm is a player in the small-to medium sized market, considered to work mainly on IP-led work. With a licensed IP within the team it has an emphasis on investigation work. Strengths are found in personal bankruptcy, voluntary arrangements, creditor insolvency work and directors' disqualification work, where the practice successfully defeated disqualification proceedings brought by the DTI on behalf of three directors. **Clients:** Ernst & Young.

Watson Burton A broad practice which includes a licensed IP and an insolvency lawyer with a commercial background. The team handles the full range of insolvency services, both corporate and personal. **Clients:** the main accountants.

SCOTLAND

Dundas & Wilson CS *"Always strong, they majored on insolvency and are still market leaders on their own."* The firm is considered to be *"far and away the leader,"* so much so, that notwithstanding the Arthur Andersen connection, the firm is the number one port of call for all the accountants on large jobs. **Ian Cuthbertson** has *"the biggest reputation of all"* and although his fee earning time is cut back by management responsibilities, his *"innovative approach"* means that he is still active on big turnarounds and strategic planning work. The *"pragmatic"* **Yvonne Brady** is considered the firm's main insolvency expert. Sources of work include public and private companies, yet the bulk of the practice's time is spent advising IPs and banks. The department is called the corporate recovery (CR) group, reflecting the increased focus on turnaround work. Receiverships this year include those of Pillans and Wilson Ltd, the Basford Group Ltd, Seed Crushers Ltd and Lewis Offshore Ltd. Administrations this year include those of Victoria Offshore Ltd and Ocargo Ltd. The team advised the administrators appointed to the Queens Park Football Club Ltd in finalising the refinancing of the club. **Clients:** RBS; Deloitte & Touche; Grant Thornton; KPMG; PricewaterhouseCoopers; Arthur Andersen.

Burness The high profile **Andrew Sleigh** is considered *"meticulous and client driven."* He *"knows what he's doing"* and is appreciated for his approach where *"clients' interests always remain paramount to him."* The practice has a focus on corporate insolvency work. **Clients:** main accountants and financials.

MacRoberts As a negotiator **David Flint** remains *"extra astute,"* and he is still highly regarded for his insolvency work though he is well known in the intellectual property area as well. He is a licensed IP and is considered to have long experience in the sector. The firm has *"always had a reputation in insolvency"* and covers the whole gamut of insolvency work, from advice to directors to intensive care and workouts. **Clients:** Grant Thornton; Deloitte & Touche.

Shepherd & Wedderburn WS **Paul Hally** is a licensed IP whose new role as managing partner will lead to slightly less visibility in the area, yet he remains *"excellent,"* combining *"youth with gravitas."* The practice covers a broad range of insolvency matters, being traditionally creditor-driven, although working increasingly on the banking side now with an increased emphasis on rescue work. The firm is known for its work for Customs and Excise and for its directors' disqualification work for the DTI. Additionally the practice advises overseas banks in relation to the enforcement of securities and general debt recovery work. **Clients:** Customs & Excise; HSBC; DTI; RBS; Bank of Scotland

DLA The firm's merger with Bird Semple builds on its existing strengths. Work predominantly on the corporate side, with an increased emphasis on restructuring work. **Gordon Hollerin** is *"good fun to work with,"* being both *"constructive and amicable."* **Joan Devine** enters our lists this year, with her *"negotiating maturity"* especially recognised by the market. **Clients:** IPs; accountants and corporates.

INSOLVENCY / CORPORATE RECOVERY• Scotland	Ptnrs	Assts
❶ **Dundas & Wilson CS** Edinburgh, Glasgow	4	8
❷ **Burness** Edinburgh, Glasgow	5	5
MacRoberts Glasgow	1	3
Shepherd & Wedderburn WS Edinburgh	-	3
❸ **DLA** Glasgow	4	-
Iain Smith & Company Aberdeen	3	-
Maclay Murray & Spens Glasgow	*	*
❹ **Biggart Baillie** Glasgow	1	1
McGrigor Donald Glasgow	1	-
Morison Bishop Glasgow	1	1
❺ **Paull & Williamsons** Aberdeen	4	3

LEADING INDIVIDUALS	
❶ **BRADY Yvonne** Dundas & Wilson CS	**CUTHBERTSON Ian** Dundas & Wilson CS
ROXBURGH Roy Iain Smith & Company	**SLEIGH Andrew** Burness
❷ **FLINT David** MacRoberts	**HOLLERIN Gordon** DLA
❸ **HALLY Paul** Shepherd & Wedderburn WS	**LANG Russell** Morison Bishop
MACFARLANE John McGrigor Donald	**MERSON James** Stronachs
PATRICK Bruce Maclay Murray & Spens	**SHAW Murray** Biggart Baillie
SWANSON Magnus Maclay Murray & Spens	
UP AND COMING	
DEVINE Joan DLA	

Within each band, firms are listed alphabetically. *See **Profiles** on page 473*

** See editorial entries for explanations of team sizes.*

Iain Smith & Company The *"technically super"* **Roy Roxburgh** remains the name in the Granite City for insolvency work. His patch extends to Inverness and Dundee. Known as a *"proactive, specialised"* outfit, the firm works mainly for the accountants, on the full range of insolvency work, including receiverships and voluntary arrangements. **Clients:** IPs; accountants and corporates.

Maclay Murray & Spens *"Gent of insolvency,"* **Bruce Patrick** is a *"class act"* who can *"do a £5m deal in half an hour."* His remit extends beyond insolvency. **Magnus Swanson** is admired for his *"purposeful"* approach and is well regarded for his corporate negotiating skills. They are supported on the insolvency side by partners from the litigation and property sides. Works for a mix of IPs, companies, directors, shareholders, accountants and clearing banks. Work this year includes the receiverships of Printhaus plc, Calchou Electronics and Nordvik Salmon Farms and the liquidations of Lockerbie Meat Packers and Sutherland Air Cargo Ltd. **Clients:** IPs; accountants and corporates.

Biggart Baillie The *"technically sound"* **Murray Shaw** is *"a name for insolvency."* The team's focus is on rescue type work and a general advisory role rather than formal insolvency. **Clients:** IPs; accountants and corporates.

McGrigor Donald **John MacFarlane** in Edinburgh works on the whole gamut of insolvency work. This includes corporate restructuring and Anglo-Scottish cross-border matters. Acted for the liquidator of Sheraton Caltrust Group. **Clients:** banks and accountants.

Morison Bishop **Russell Lang** is the *"technical master"* of this partner heavy practice. Works on a broad range of matters and is capable of handling the larger transactions. Have been active on PHARE funded projects, recently advising on the drafting of Lithuanian bankruptcy laws. Advised on the receivership of Knoydart Peninsula Ltd. **Clients:** big five accountancy firms and others.

Paull & Williamsons Based in Aberdeen, the firm's *"sheer size"* relative to others in the area means that its insolvency team stands out . **Clients:** IPs; accountants and corporates.

Other Notable Practitioner **James Merson** of Stronachs is well-regarded for his work in contentious matters, although the firm lacks a similar profile.

NORTHERN IRELAND

INSOLVENCY / CORPORATE RECOVERY	Ptnrs	Assts
❶ **Napier & Sons** Belfast	4	1
❷ **John McKee & Son** Belfast	⚐	⚐
❸ **Elliott Duffy Garrett** Belfast	3	1
McManus & Kearney Belfast	1	-

LEADING INDIVIDUALS
❶ **GORDON John** Napier & Sons
❷ **ROSS Alexander** John McKee & Son
❸ **KEARNEY Mary** McManus & Kearney
WILSON Michael Elliott Duffy Garrett

Within each band, firms are listed alphabetically. *See **Profiles** on page 473*

⚐ *Figures unavailable at time of going to press.*

Napier & Sons *"Northern Ireland's premier insolvency practice."* Perceived as a niche firm which is *"doing a lot of insolvency work"* and *"has been doing it for years,"* the practice is composed of the *"lawyers' lawyers"* in the region. **John Gordon** is the first name for insolvency work. A licensed IP, he has been increasingly involved on advisory work in the context of troubled businesses. Voluntary arrangement work is the practice's main thrust, with around 70 ongoing voluntary arrangements a year, the majority of which are of the individual kind. Matters with international elements are also a part of the practice's workload, and the practice advised Global Marine (a large US offshore drilling company) on potential local supplier insolvency difficulties. **Clients:** IPs; accountants and corporates.

John McKee & Son Known for his specialisation in receiverships, **Lex Ross's** practice is *"ticking over nicely."* He mixes receivership work with his day-to-day banking and corporate work. Other members of the firm work on voluntary arrangements, particularly IVAs. **Clients:** IPs; accountants and corporates.

Elliott Duffy Garrett **Michael Wilson** was recommended for his general insolvency work, mainly for the IPs. **Clients:** IPs; accountants and corporates.

McManus & Kearney **Mary Kearney**, a licensed IP, was recommended for her work on personal and corporate insolvencies. **Clients:** IPs; accountants and corporates.

LEADERS IN INSOLVENCY / CORPORATE RECOVERY

AGAR, Nick
CMS Cameron McKenna, Bristol (0117) 930 0200
nsda@cmck.com
Specialisation: Advises banks and insolvency practitioners on all aspects of corporate and personal insolvency and on debt recovery.

ALLINSON, Stephen
Clarke Willmott & Clarke, Taunton
(01823) 445207
sallinson@cw-c.co.uk
Specialisation: One of a select number of lawyers in the UK who is also a licenced insolvency practitioner. Head of both commercial services department and corporate recovery and insolvency department (a member of the firm's Management Board). Experienced in all aspects of insolvency law (corporate and personal). Acting for major banks and accountants (national firms and niche practices). Also undertakes general insolvency advocacy (for creditors and debtors, with particular experience in defendant director disqualification work.) Over the last twelve months developed the department in terms of insolvency rescue actions, acting with other professionals in this regard. Balance of other professional work is commercial banking litigation and professional negligence in the banking and insolvency fields. Recommended defendant solicitor by the Institute of Chartered Accountants in England and Wales in respect of accountants facing professional disciplinary proceedings. Has extensive lecturing experience with Lowe & Gordon Seminars and others.
Prof. Memberships: Law Society; Fellow of the Association of Business Recovery Professionals; The Institute of Credit Management (South West Branch Committee Member); The Insolvency Lawyers Association; Chairman of the ACCA Authorisation Appeals Tribunal Committee.
Career: Joined and trained with *Clarke Willmott & Clarke* in September 1982, admitted in October 1984. Became a partner in January 1989 and member of the firm's Management Board in May 1999.
Publications: Author of 'Debt Recovery' two editions (Cavendish Publishing) and regular contributor of professional articles to insolvency and debt recovery journals. Member of the editorial board of 'Insolvency Bulletin'.
Personal: Sport (Director of Yeovil Town Football Club); church activities; charity and school work; amateur dramatics.

ANDERSON, Hamish
Norton Rose, London (020) 7283 6000
andersonh@nortonrose.com
Partner in the insolvency group.
Specialisation: His work covers all aspects of insolvency under the Insolvency Act 1986 and cross–border insolvency. Recent assignments include acting for the court appointed receivers of Metro Trading International Inc. and for the administrators of the Falmer Jeans Group, AB Airlines, Knickerbox and K&H Options. Assignments frequently involve knowledge of insolvency law in other jurisdictions. Recent examples include: US, France, Germany, Greece, Russia, Indonesia, Singapore and Thailand. Has acted as an expert witness on english insolvency law in US chap II proceedings.
Prof. Memberships: Past president and council member, Insolvency Lawyers' Association. Council member, R3. Editor of R3 journal 'Recovery'. Member, Law Society Insolvency Sub-Committee. Publications Officer, Committee J (creditors' rights) International Bar Association. Member, editorial board 'Insolvency Law & Practice'.
Career: Admitted 1973. Licensed insolvency practitioner since 1987. Partner, *Bond Pearce* 1977-1996. Partner, *Norton Rose* since 1996. Author of several insolvency textbooks and numerous articles.

ANDERSON, John
Eversheds, Newcastle upon Tyne (0191) 261 1661
andersj@eversheds.com
Specialisation: All aspects of insolvency, corporate and personal; acting for secured and unsecured creditors, office holders and debtors; banking; asset tracing and recovery. Particular interests include landlord and tenant, pensions in bankruptcy and directors disqualification. Ensuring the conversion of the technicalities into results.
Prof. Memberships: The Law Society. Incorporated Law Society of Newcastle upon Tyne.
Career: Education: Royal Grammar School, Newcastle upon Tyne 1976-83. Newcastle University 1983-86. Articles: *Wilkinson Maughan* 1987–89. Partner: 1997 (when *Wilkinson Maughan* joined *Eversheds*).
Personal: Interests include cricket, ancient history and legal history.

ANDREWS, Mark B.
Denton Wilde Sapte, London (020) 7242 1212

ANGEL, Nick
Ashurst Morris Crisp, London (020) 7638 1111
nick.angel@ashursts.com
Specialisation: Corporate turnaround and insolvency law. Nick's practice is divided between mainstream corporate work and reconstruction and insolvency. On the reconstruction and insolvency side Nick's practice tends towards rescues and reconstructions of larger, often international, corporate groups but he also advises on formal insolvency appointments.
Prof. Memberships: Insolvency Lawyers Association. Society of Practitioners of Insolvency.
Career: Southend High School for Boys; Bristol University. Joined *Ashurst Morris Crisp* in 1993. Partner 1997.

ARCHER, David B.
Pitmans, Reading (0118) 9580224
darcher@pitmans.com
Specialisation: All aspects of commercial and personal insolvency including insolvency litigation and insolvency/pensions issues. Acts as an independent trustee to corporate pension schemes.
Prof. Memberships: Insolvency Lawyers Association. Member of AEPPC (European Insolvency Practitioners Association). Associate Member of R3. Law Society.
Personal: Christianity and Skiing.

BAKER, Ian P.
Martineau Johnson, Birmingham (0121) 678 1575
ian.baker@martjohn.com
See under Banking, p.116

BALLMANN, William
Addleshaw Booth & Co, Leeds (0113) 209 2000
wb@addleshaw-booth.co.uk
Partner in banking and financial services group.
Specialisation: Specialises in corporate reconstruction and turnaround work as well as contentious and non-contentious corporate and personal insolvency and related banking issues. German national with extensive contacts in Europe, a substantial proportion of the work is international. Licensed Insolvency Practitioner. Author of articles and legal updates on corporate recovery issues.
Prof. Memberships: Law Society, ABRP (Fellow), ILA (Council Member), AEPPC.
Career: Qualified in 1983. Joined the firm as Partner in 1992.
Personal: Educated at the University of Leeds (LLB 1978). Leisure interests include golf, skiing and scuba diving.

BARNETT, Nigel
Denton Wilde Sapte, London (020) 7242 1212

BENNETT, Jeremy M.
Hammond Suddards Edge, Leeds (0113) 284 7000
Specialisation: Advising banks and IPs on all types of insolvency and corporate recovery (both corporate and personal), advice to financial institutions (lending banks, secondary lenders, factors and invoice discounters). Dealt with many mayor cases in the last year including the administration of Silver Cross Prams, receivership of the Billam group of companies in Sheffield, the liquidations of Tudor Caravans and ODI plc and continuing to advise on the liquidation of the Lola Formula One racing company.
Prof. Memberships: Law Society, Insolvency Practitioners Association.
Career: Been with *Hammond Suddards* since qualification twelve years ago, partner four years, head of the insolvency and corporate recovery department in Leeds, qualified by passing the JIEB in November 19997 as an insolvency practitioner.
Publications: Various seminars, articles and flysheets.
Personal: Ashten Grammar School, 2(i) degree Cardiff University, College of Law Chester, insolvency practitioner exams. Outside interests–watching and playing sport, particularly football, tennis and golf. Travelling the world and looking after my two year old daughter.

BERRY, Christopher R.
Edwin Coe, London (020) 7691 4000
Specialisation: Personal insolvency and all other areas including disciplinary licensing and disqualification proceedings.
Prof. Memberships: Law Society. Association of Business Recovery Professionals, AEPPC, Insolvency Lawyers Association (Technical Committee).
Career: Partner *Edwin Coe*. Crown Court Recorder. Chartered arbitrator. Law Society Nominee, Insolvency Court Users–Committee. Several books, numerous articles.
Personal: Early morning squash. Chairman, Warman Sports Trust.

BETHELL-JONES, Richard J.S.
Denton Wilde Sapte, London (020) 7242 1212

BLAIR, Jonathan
Dickinson Dees, Newcastle upon Tyne
(0191) 279 9219
Partner, insolvency group, head of Directors Disqualification Team.
Specialisation: Work includes: corporate recoveries, administrations and receiverships as well as individual insolvency work. Jonathan heads up the seven man strong Directors Disqualification Team working for the Insolvency Service across the North of England. Treasury Solicitor's Northern Agent for Disqualification cases.
Prof. Memberships: Law Society; Committee Member of SPI (North East Region)
Career: LLB; training with *Wragge & Co* 1987-1989; 1989 to date *Dickinson Dees*. Partner at *Dickinson Dees* 1997.
Personal: Married, two children; keen mountaineer and rock climber.

BON, Gordon E.
Laytons, Bristol (0117) 930 9500
gordon.bon@laytons.com
Specialisation: Partner and Head of Bristol Insolvency department, specialising in insolvency (contentious and non–contentious). Acting for major, medium–sized and small accountancy firms with insolvency practitioners as well as for British and foreign banks and other commercial clients. Cases include refinancing and restructuring businesses in financial crisis.
Career: Torquay Boys' Grammar School; Queen Mary College, London. Called to the bar 1983, qualified as a solicitor 1986. Joint insolvency exam 1995. Partner at *Laytons* since 1994.
Personal: Born 1959. Lives in Bristol.

BOOBIER, Nigel
Osborne Clarke OWA, Bristol (0117) 917 3000
nigel.boobier@osborneclarke.com
Specialisation: Advises on all areas of insolvency and recovery work both contentious and non-contentious. Acts for insolvency practitioners, banks and other lenders together with commercial clients needing solutions in this area. Passed the Joint Insolvency Examination Board examinations in 1998 and is now a licensed Insolvency Practitioner.
Career: Qualified 1994. Joined Osborne Clarke in 1997 from *Dibb Lupton Alsop* in Leeds.

BOWDEN, Jeremy
DLA, Birmingham (0121) 262 5946
jeremy.bowden@dla.com
Specialisation: Head of Business Services and Reconstruction Birmingham. All aspects of contentious and non-contentious corporate and individual insolvency, Corporate rescue and reconstruction. Bank security enhancement.
Prof. Memberships: Law Society, Society of Practitioners of Insolvency, Insolvency Lawyers Association, Institute of Credit Management.
Career: Qualified 1987. Partner 1992. Licensed Insolvency Practitioner. (Passed JIEB exams.) JIEB examiner.
Personal: Country pursuits.

BRADY, Yvonne T.
Dundas & Wilson CS, Glasgow (0141) 222 2200

BRANSON, Christopher
Boyes Turner & Burrows, Reading
(0118) 959 7711
Partner in insolvency.
Specialisation: Principal area of practice is corporate and individual insolvency. Acts for receivers, liquidators and administrators in corporate insolvency situations and for trustees in bankruptcy as well as nominees and supervisors in CVAs and IVAs. Acts for office-holders in areas of fraud and asset tracing, often abroad. Advises banks and financial institutions on security and lending issues. Clients include all the major accountancy firms, plus many smaller regional firms. Has lectured at IBC Conferences, SPI South conferences as well as giving internal lectures and talks to accountancy firms. Charge-out rate of £180 per hour.
Prof. Memberships: Law Society, IPA, 3R. Insolvency Lawyers Association.
Career: Qualified in 1981. Partner at *Boyes Turner & Burrows* from 1988.

BRIGGS, Graham M.
Addleshaw Booth & Co, Leeds (0113) 209 2000
Specialisation: Insolvency, turnaround and banking law. Grahams broad based skills as an advisor to banks and insolvency practitioners were further enhanced by a one year secondment to a major UK bank as lead advisor to a commercial debt management project. Highlights of last year include advising the receivers of Grampian Care Limited, Scotland's largest nursing home operator.
Prof. Memberships: Leeds Law Society. Insolvency Lawyers Association. Association of Business Recovery Professionals.
Career: Joined *Addleshaw Booth & Co* upon qualifying as a solicitor in 1984. Developed his expertise from a background in bank litigation and bank advisory work.
Personal: Married with 3 children, lives in Menston near Ilkley. He is the holder of a Motor Sports Association competition license and competes in the Thoroughbred Sportscar Championship in a race prepared MGB.

BROCKMAN, Christopher C.
Sherwin Oliver Solicitors, Portsmouth
(023) 9283 2200
christopher.brockman@sherwinoliver.com
Specialisation: Deals with all aspects of individual and corporate insolvency, from administration to voluntary arrangements, particularly on the contentious side. Acts for many of the leading and smaller insolvency practitioners on the South Coast. Also prosecutes for the DTI and acts for directors facing disqualification proceedings. Regularly gives talks at professional seminars. Has a particular interest in the effect of the incorporation of the European Convention on Human Rights into UK law on insolvency proceedings.
Prof. Memberships: Law Society, Society for Practitioners of Insolvency, LawNet Insolvency Unit, Insolvency Lawyers Association.
Career: Called to Bar 1985, transferred to solicitors 1988, joining *Sherwin Oliver Solicitors* in 1992 from a leading London firm.
Personal: Born 1962, lives in Broughton, Hampshire. Sailing.

BROOKS, Egan R.
Addleshaw Booth & Co, Manchester
(0161) 934 6000
Specialisation: Head of corporate recovery practice.
Prof. Memberships: The Law Society (Chairman, Insovency Law sub-committee 1999-). Licensed Insolvency Practitioner, Society of Practitioners of Insolvency and Notary Public.
Career: Qualified 1966. *Slater Heelis* 1964–1998. Partner 1969. Joined firm 1998 as Partner.
Personal: Educated at Manchester Grammar School and Manchester University (LLB Hons). Lives in Hale. Leisure interests include motoring, architecture and walking.

BROWN, Robert
Keeble Hawson, Leeds (0113) 244 3121
Specialisation: Partner and Head of Department dealing with all aspects of insolvency and recovery both personal and corporate. Also acts for Respondents in disqualification proceedings.
Prof. Memberships: The Law Society, SPI, ILA, IPA and Licensed Insolvency Practitioner.

BUCHANAN, Andrew
Halliwell Landau, Manchester (0161) 835 3003
Specialisation: Corporate and personal insolvency and Turnaround Administrative Receivership of Cooperheat (UK) Limited and Cooperheat International Limited on behalf of Arthur Andersen. Administrative Receivership of Manchester Abattoir on behalf of Pannel Kerr Foster.
Prof. Memberships: Law Society.
Career: Partner with *Haliwell Landau* since joining in March 1999.
Publications: Accountancy books: 'Corporate Recovery Health Check'.
Personal: Stockport Grammar School, Sheffield University, Trent Polytechnic. Golf, cricket, rugby, walking. Father, retired medical practitioner.

BUGG, Anthony
Linklaters (A member firm of Linklaters & Alliance), London (020) 7456 4470
tony.bugg@linklaters.com
Specialisation: Principal area of practice is corporate insolvency and business reorganisations. Wide experience of all aspects of contentious and non-contentious insolvency work acting for insolvency practitioners, banks and other financial institutions. Recent assignments include acting for the liquidator of Toshoku Finance UK PLC and the adminisitrator of Tulip Computers UK PLC and Administrators of Ionica plc.
Prof. Memberships: Insolvency Lawyers' Association (Council Member), SPI (Member of PR Committee), Law Society, AEPPC, IPA, IBA.
Career: Qualified 1981. Partner *William Prior & Co* 1982. Partner *Dibb Lupton Broomhead* 1990. Joined *Linklaters* 1997; became partner 1998. Licensed Insolvency Practitioner since 1987.

BURROWS, Julia K.
Addleshaw Booth & Co, Manchester
(0161) 934 6000
jkb@addleshaw-booth.co.uk
Partner Corporate Recovery Department.
Specialisation: Specialising in insolvency banking and corporate recoveries.
Prof. Memberships: Law Society; Insolvency Lawyers Association; Society of Practitioners of Insolvency.

Career: Educated at Leicester University (1977 LLB Hons). Articled with *Addleshaw Booth & Co.* Qualified 1980. Made Partner in 1992.
Personal: Leisure interests include theatre, skiing and walking. Resides Bolton.

COATES, Philip B.
DLA, Manchester (08700) 111 111
philip.coates@dla.com
Specialisation: Licensed Insolvency Practitioner specialising in business support and reconstruction. Involved in numerous leading cases including Charnley Davies, re International Bulk Commodities and re Cosslett Contractors.
Prof. Memberships: SPI and Insolvency Lawyers Association.
Career: BA Politics and Economics, Newcastle upon Tyne 1977. LLB Leeds 1979. Qualified 1982. Trained Mediator. Partner: *Simpson Curtis* 1988-1994; Consultant: 1994–1997. Solicitor: *Hammond Suddards*, 1997–1999. May 1999 onwards: Partner *Dibb Lupton Alsop.*

COHEN, Adrian Leon
Clifford Chance, London (020) 7600 1000
adrian.cohen@cliffordchance.com
Specialisation: Finance practice partner specialising in all aspects of domestic and international non-contentious insolvency and corporate reconstruction, including negotiation of standstill, inter-creditor and security documentation, advising on counter-party risk, security enforcement, asset realisation, directors' duties and officeholders' duties.
Career: London School of Economics; Queen Mary and Westfield College, London (LLB (Hons) 1985, LLM 1987). Called to the Bar 1988; Barrister at law 1988–90; joined *Clifford Chance* corporate practice 1990; the firm's insolvency group 1991 to date.
Personal: Born 1963.

COOK, Nigel C. S.
Paul Davidson Taylor, Horsham (01403) 262 333
Specialisation: Corporate insolvency, particularly administrative and LPA receiverships. Within past year has acted for receivers in respect of insolvencies in the motor trade, education, music industry and retail. Also specialises in advice to directors facing disqualification proceeds.
Prof. Memberships: Associate Member of the Insolvency Lawyers Association.
Career: Assistant Solicitor: commercial department *Clifford–Turner* (1976-1981). Head of Legal Department First National Commercial Bank (1982-1989); Partner: *Paul Davidson Taylor* (1995-).
Personal: B.A (Oxon) Jurisprudence. Keen golfer and cricketer. Trustee of penal affairs charity, The Inside Out Trust.

COOK, Patrick D.
Osborne Clarke OWA, Bristol (0117) 984 5225
patrick.cook@osborneclarke.com
Head of Insolvency Department.
Specialisation: Main areas of expertise are banking and corporate recovery work where he is a leader in these fields. He is appointed as a company inspector under Section 177 of the Financial Services Act to investigate allegations of insider dealing. His clients include banks, insolvency practitioners, the DTI, the Disqualification Unit of The Insolvency Service, life insurance companies and pension fund trustees.
Prof. Memberships: SPI, IPA, ILA, Law Society.
Career: Trained: *Denton Hall & Burgin*; qualified 1981 and joined *Norton Rose*. Moved to *Osborne Clarke* 1983, became a partner 1986. 1989 became a licensed insolvency practitioner.

COOKE, David J.
Pinsent Curtis, Birmingham (0121) 200 1050
david.j.cooke@pinsents.com
See under Banking, p.117

CORR, Patrick
Pinsent Curtis, Leeds (0113) 244 5000
patrick.corr@pinsents.com
Specialisation: Head of corporate recovery, Leeds. Advises insolvency practitioners and turnaround specialists on all aspects of corporate recovery and turnarounds. Also advises banks and other financial institutions on security issues. Recently acted in relation to the turnaround of a company with a turnover in excess of £200 million and advised the Administrators of Bradlor Developments Ltd. Has presented seminars to accountants and banks on corporate recovery, turnaround and banking issues and regularly presents seminars on behalf of the Association of Business Recovery Professionals.
Prof. Memberships: Young Solicitors Group. The Insolvency Lawyers Association. Subscriber to the Society of Practitioners of Insolvency.
Career: LLB (Hons), Leeds Metropolitan University. Joined *Pinsent Curtis* in 1988. Qualified in 1990. Partner 1996.

CRAIG, Nigel S.
Sherwin Oliver Solicitors, Portsmouth
(023) 9283 2200
nigel.craig@sherwinoliver.com
Partner in corporate/commercial and corporate rescue department.
Specialisation: Principal area of practice is corporate restructuring, mergers, acquisitions and disposals, with and without insolvency related issues. Approximately half of the department's cases are insolvency-related and involve acting for the Insolvency Practitioner on a restructuring/hive down prior to sale, and subsequently on the sale, or acting for the clients acquiring from receivers, administrators or liquidators. Has dealt with twenty to thirty group re-structurings for groups of various values, the acquisition and disposal of insurance companies and insurance brokerages and the acquisition, disposal and re-structuring of major cross-channel ferry companies and shipping companies. Also handles management buy-outs and provides management and general corporate advice. Has advised on the setting up of nationwide franchise operations and re-structuring of a franchise group. Author of a number of articles published in legal journals and newspapers. Lectures regularly and has been interviewed and spoken on radio on legal topics. Charge out rate for normal work is in the region of £160 per hour plus VAT.
Prof. Memberships: Law Society, Insolvency Lawyers' Association (Associate Member), LawNet Insolvency Unit.
Career: Qualified 1981. Shortly afterwards set up with David Oliver as *Oliver & Co.* The firm merged with *Sherwins* to produce *Sherwin Oliver* in May 1989.
Personal: Born 16th December 1956. Educated at Southern Grammar School, Portsmouth 1968–1975, Kingston-upon-Thames Polytechnic 1975–1978 and Guildford Law College 1978–79. Leisure pursuits include sailing (racing two-man catamarans), and motor biking (including track days). Lives in Emsworth, Hampshire.

CRANSTON, Peter E.
DLA, Leeds (08700) 111 111
peter.cranston@dla.com
Licensed insolvency practitioner.
Specialisation: Partner and national group head of Business Support and Restructuring Group of *DLA*, dealing with a full range of issues arising from distressed lending and commercial insolvency, with emphasis on taking and enforcement of security, restructuring and asset recovery.
Prof. Memberships: Member Law Society; R3.

CUTHBERTSON, Ian
Dundas & Wilson CS, Glasgow (0141) 222 2200

DALLOW, Sally
Dickinson Dees, Newcastle upon Tyne
(0191) 279 9000
sally.dallow@dickinson-dees.com
Specialisation: Senior associate–insolvency team. Handles all aspects of insolvency work-personal and corporate, contentious and non-contentious. Senior role in directors disqualification team working for DTI in North East and North West regions.
Prof. Memberships: Law Society.
Career: Qualified November 1992 with *Dickinson Dees.* Associate since April 1997.
Personal: Interests include travel, music, food and drink.

DEVINE, Joan Gabriel
DLA, Glasgow (08700) 111111
joan.devine@dla.com
Specialisation: Insolvency–accredited by the Law Society as an insolvency specialist. Advises mainly banks and insolvency practitioners on all aspects of mainly corporate insolvency.
Prof. Memberships: Law Society of Scotland. Insolvency Lawyers Association.
Career: Joined *Bird Semple* 1987. Partner at *Bird Semple* 1997. On merger between *Bird Semple* and *DLA*, became partner in *DLA* 2000.
Publications: Writes quarterly law review in 'Impecunias' and sits on editorial board. 'Impecunias' is a joint publication by the Law Society and the Institute of Chartered Accountants. Assists with training for the Joint Insolvency Exam.

DOBSON, Julian C.
Cripps Harries Hall, Tunbridge Wells, Kent
(01892) 506273

DOLPHIN, J.Huw
DLA, Birmingham (08700) 111111
huw.dolphin@dla.com
Partner
Specialisation: Advises on all areas of insolvency and recovery work both contentious and non-contentious but with particular emphasis on liquidation and receiverships. Acts for insolvency practitioners, banks and other lenders and commercial clients needing solutions in this area.
Prof. Memberships: Member of the Association of Insolvency Business Professionals (AIBP). Insolvency Lawyers Association.
Career: Manchester University 1985–1988. Qualified 1991. *Dibb Lupton Broomhead*–London office 1992–1993. *Dibb Lupton Broomhead*, then *Dibb Lupton Alsop* – Birmingham office 1993 to date. Partner 1999. Licensed insolvency practitioner since 1995.

Personal: Married with two children. Lives near Shrewsbury. Interested in sport particularly football and motor racing.

DREW, Jeff
Eversheds, Birmingham (0121) 232 1000
Partner in insolvency and banking group. Chairman of *Eversheds* insolvency group.
Specialisation: Advises insolvency practitioners and banks in connection with all aspects of insolvency law and banks in connection with the taking and realising of charges. Speaks widely at conferences and seminars.
Prof. Memberships: Association of Business Recovery Professionals.
Career: Qualified in 1980. Worked at *Wragge & Co* 1978–1982, then *Edge & Ellison* 1982–1992 (from 1984 as a partner). Joined *Eversheds* as a partner in 1992.
Personal: Born 12th October 1954. Attended Solihull School and St Edmund Hall, Oxford 1974–1977. Leisure interests include tennis, squash and badminton. Lives in Birmingham.

ELLIOTT, Robert
Linklaters (A member firm of Linklaters & Alliance), London (020) 7456 4478
robert.elliott@linklaters.com
Specialisation: Partner in the banking department of *Linklaters* since 1990. Co–head, Corporate Recovery and Insolvency *Linklaters & Alliance*. Recent significant transactions include the £1.5billion acquisition financing of Southern Electric/Southern Water, GUS/Argos $1.6 billion takeover financing and the British Land Universal £300 million mortgage bond issue.
Career: Leeds Grammar School; London University; Qualified in 1976. *Wilde Sapte* 1976–1990; joined *Linklaters* 1990–date as a partner.

FALKUS, Bryony J.
Mills & Reeve, Norwich (01603) 693 225
bryony.falkus@mills-reeve.com
See under Corporate Finance, p.249

FERGUSSON, Richard
Keeble Hawson, Leeds (0113) 244 3121
Specialisation: Licensed insolvency practioner dealing with all forms of corporate and personal insolvency and recovery on behalf of practitioners, banks and building societies and debtors. Deals with a full range of contentious and non-contentious insolvencies from bankruptcy to trading receiverships and administrations. Also has experience of court appointed, agricultural and LPA receiverships as well as director disqualification proceedings.
Prof. Memberships: Law Society and ABRP.
Career: Trained at *Dibb Lupton Broomhead* 1989 to 1991, joined *Booth & Co* (now *Addleshaw Booth & Co*) September 1992, partner *Keeble Hawson* June 2000.
Personal: Educated at Batley Grammar School and Leeds University. Interests include hill walking, reading, travelling, food and wine.

FIDLER, Peter J. M.
Stephenson Harwood, London (020) 7809 2003
peter.fidler@shlegal.com
Partner, Litigation Department (Recovery and Insolvency Group).
Specialisation: Has specialised in banking since 1967 and in insolvency for some 25 years. In the last eight years has specialised in schemes of arrangement for insolvent insurance companies. Has been involved in recovery of assets from abroad using compulsory interrogation techniques in the UK and abroad. One of the high profile cases this year was acting for the trustee in the Hadkinson bankruptcy which featured twice in The Times Law Report. Main Editor, Sheldon & Fidler's Practice and Law of Banking, 11th Edition, 1982. Lectures regularly at conferences on a variety of banking and insolvency topics.
Prof. Memberships: City of London Law Society Insolvency Law Sub-Committee. SPI International.
Career: Qualified in June 1967. Solicitor at *Clifford Chance* (previously known as *Coward Chance*) in 1967–72. Partner at *D J Freeman* in 1972–84. Joined *Stephenson Harwood* in 1984 as partner.
Personal: Born 16 March 1942. Educated at Bradford Grammar School; St John's College, Oxford. Interests include music, theatre, the arts and sports. Languages: speaks French. Resides London.

FLETCHER, Ian
Stephenson Harwood, London (020) 7809 2025
ian.fletcher@shlegal.com
Specialisation: Partner, Banking Group, Corporate Restructuring, Corporate Recovery and insolvency work and MBO/MBI work against a general corporate law background.
Prof. Memberships: Council of the Law Society of Scotland (currently convener Insolvency Solicitors Committee and Insolvency Practitioners Adjudication Panel), Council of the Association of Business Recovery Professionals (R3), member of the Government Working Party on Insolvency Regulation which reported in 1998; Law Society of England & Wales; Council Insolvency Lawyers' Association Ltd; President of the Insolvency Lawyers' Association 1995/96; IBA Member Committee J (Joint Chairman of Sub-Committee on Remedies under Security Interests: Section on Business Law); the Society of Scottish Lawyers, London (past president); Institute of Directors; LTCL, LRAM, ARCO, MinstD, MIPA, FSPI, FSALS (Fellow of Society for Advanced Legal Studies), WS. Joint author 'The Law and Practice of Receivership in Scotland' (1987 2nd ed. 1992) and 'The Law and Practice of Corporate Administrations 1994, 1st ed., joint contributor to a chapter on Insolvency and Finance in the Transportation Industry (1993). Joint author of contribution on UK Corporate Insolvency Law for Norton Annual Bankruptcy Serving–International Section. Joint Editor of 'Cross Border Insolvencies' incorporating contributions from 35 jurisdictions to be published by Oceana Publications Inc in late 1999. Member of the Government Working Party on Insolvency Regulation which reported in 1998.
Personal: Educated Glasgow University (LLB). Qualified Scotland 1971, England 1978. Interests include music, golf and swimming.

FLINT, David
MacRoberts, Glasgow (0141) 332 9988
df@macroberts.co.uk
See under Information Technology, p.494

FOSTER, Stephen J.
CMS Cameron McKenna, London
(020) 7367 3000
sf@cmck.com
Partner in Banking & Insolvency Department.
Specialisation: Principal areas of practice is banking, reconstruction and insolvency. Work includes advising banks and corporates on domestic and international banking questions and pre-insolvency issues, including options to maximise recovery and advising Insolvency Practitioners in receiverships, administrations and liquidations. Other main area of practice is UK and US distressed debt issues, advising on documentation and insolvency issues. Has lectured to the Institute of Bankers, R3 and for various commercial lecture providers on banking and insolvency topics.
Prof. Memberships: Law Society, Insolvency Lawyers Association, AEPPC.
Career: Qualified in 1989. Became a Partner at *Cameron Markby Hewitt* in 1991.
Personal: Born 4th January 1958. Educated at Pembroke College, Cambridge. Interests include walking, music and film. Lives in London.

FRENCH, Matthew
Lovells, London (020) 7296 2000
matthew.french@lovells.com
Specialisation: Business restructuring and insolvency. Particular expertise in (re)insurance run-off and insolvency. Broad experiance of default and credit risk management in financings and commercial contracts. Recent assignments include a multi-bank workout of a major UK manufacturing business, advice to merchant services creditors of Air Bristol (in administration), advising the liquidators of Caribbean International Insurance, the provisional liquidation and implementation of a scheme of arrangement for Pine Top Insurance and restructuring issues for providers of corporate capital at Lloyd's.
Prof. Memberships: The Association of Business Recovery Professionals. The International Association of Insurance Receivers. The Association of Run-off Companies. The Insolvency Lawyers Association.
Career: Churchhill College, Cambridge University 1984-87 MA (Law). Qualified as a barrister 1988 (Lincoln's Inn and 3/4 South Square, Chambers of Michael Crystal Q.C.). Associate at *Wilde Sapte*, solicitors 1989-96 (co-qualified as a solicitor 1994). Partner at *Wilde Sapte* 1997-9. Joined *Lovells* in November 1999.
Publications: Contributing editor to Butterworth Tolley's 'Insolvency' loose-leaf. A regular conference speaker. Features published in several journals.
Personal: Married with two children, resides London. Interests include oriental philosophy and contemporary arts. Born 1966.

FRITH, Stuart J.
Brooke North, Leeds (0113) 283 2100
Specialisation: Contentious insolvency of all types with particular interest in the environmental consequences of insolvency; acting on behalf of Respondents in directors disqualification proceedings. Recent cases include Secretary of State v Cleland (acceptability of undertaking in disqualification proceedings) [1997] BCC 473; Re Double S Printers Ltd [1999] BCC 303 (fixed charge on book debts); Yorkshire Water Services Ltd v Jarmain & Sons Ltd [1997] EULR 577 (applicability of Article 86 Treaty of Rome to water undertakers); Hollicourt (Contracts) Ltd v Bank of Ireland [2000] 2 All ER 45 (s.127 Insolvency Act 1986- availability of agency as a defence to a bank).
Prof. Memberships: Law Society; Vice-President of Insolvency Lawyers' Association 2000-2001; R3; IPA.
Career: Qualified October 1983; Articled at *Jacksons*

Monk & Rowe, Middlesbrough; Joined *Brooke North* in 1984; Partner 1989; Licensed Insolvency Practitioner 1989.
Personal: Born 6 December 1957; Educated Spalding Grammar School; Leeds University.

FROME, Nicholas P.
Lovells, London (020) 7296 2000
nicholas.frome@lovells.com
Specialisation: Business restructuring and insolvency; adviser to the banks in relation to the restructurings of Heron, Wickes and Ashanti; English Law adviser to the bondholders in relation to Tiphook (CTRL) restucturings; adviser to the banks in relation to certain aspects of the Queens Moat restructuring; advised ING in relation to the acquisition of Barings Bank from administrators and attempted City Disputes Panel settlements with subordinated noteholders; advised co–ordinating banks and steering committees in relation to numerous confidential restructurings of nternational groups including a number of technology comanies. Recently advised the receivers of the Hollas Group plc and Yorkshire Foods plc; advising in relation to Ionoca plc, TransTec plc, the administrators of Japan Leasing, the administrators AY Bank Limited and in relation to restructurings llinked to the russian debt crisis and of a quoted technology group based in Hong Kong.
Prof. Memberships: Licensed insolvency practitioner. Member of the Association of Business Recovery Professionals; INSOL; Insolvency Lawyers' Association; Insolvency Practitioners Assocaition.
Career: Marlborough College, University College London. *Durrant Piesse*, now *Lovells*, since 1975.
Personal: Fly-fishing, golf, cricket, military history and music. Married with three children.

GAINES, Keith
Lovells, London (020) 7296 2000
keith.gaines@lovells.com
See under Fraud, p.418

GALE, Stephen
Herbert Smith, London (020) 7374 8000
stephen.gale@herbertsmith.com
Partner and head of corporate recovery at *Herbert Smith.*
Specialisation: Principal area of practice is corporate rescue and company reorganisation. Has wide experience of acting for banks and other financial institutions in work-outs and reorganisations. Also has considerable insolvency related experience, particularly in corporate insolvencies. Recent cases include BCCI, Paramount, Leyland Daf, Peregrine, Knickerbox, Solvera, Ocean Marine, Ionica. President of R3, the Association of Business Recovery Professionals. Lectures widely on insolvency-related issues.
Prof. Memberships: Law Society, Institute of Credit Management, SPI, IPA, AEPPC.
Career: Qualified in 1982. Associate with *Simpson Curtis* 1984, then Partner with *Masons & Marriott* in Hong Kong, 1985. Joined *Hammond Suddards* in 1987 as a Partner. Partner *Herbert Smith* January 1998.
Personal: Born 15th October 1957. Attended Blackpool Grammar School and Sixth Form College, then Sheffield University. Leisure pursuits include fell walking, windsurfing, horseriding, skiing and classical music. Married with three children.

GILL, Mark S.
Denton Wilde Sapte, London (020) 7242 1212

GOODMAN, Nick
NJ Goodman & Co, Altrincham (0161) 928 0990
nick@njgoodman.co.uk
Specialisation: Specialist with wide experience acting for officeholders in all types of insolvency cases, both personal and corporate, gained as a partner within the banking and insolvency groups of 2 Top 20 law firms. Undertakes director defence work including disqualification proceedings.
Prof. Memberships: ABRP; Law Society.
Career: Qualified 1982; N J Goodman & Co (2000); Addleshaw Booth & Co (1995–2000); Dibb Lupton Broomhead (1989–1995); Hong Kong (1982–1988). Member of the North West Regional Committee of SPI (1994–1996)
Personal: Attended Southampton University. Leisure pursuits: golf and family. Lives in Cheshire.

GORDON, John Gerard
Napier & Sons, Belfast (028) 90244602
Managing Partner.
Specialisation: Licensed Insolvency Practitioner. Presents seminars for Law Society and lectures at Institute of Professional Legal Studies. Contributor of Northern Ireland chapter to Grier & Floyd Personal Insolvency. Main area of practice is rescue and recovery of small businesses.
Prof. Memberships: Law Society N.I. Treasurer and council member A.B.R.P.
Career: LL.B. Queen's University Belfast. Certificate Professional Legal Studies, Queen's University Belfast. Qualified 1981. Managing Partner *Napier & Sons* 1985. Member of the Lord Chancellor's Advisory Rules Committee on Insolvency.

GORDON-SAKER, Paul D.
Stephenson Harwood, London (020) 7809 2367
paul.gordon-saker@shlegal.com
Partner, Litigation Department. Head of Recovery and Insolvency Group.
Specialisation: Has specialised in insolvency work for the last 29 years and has substantial experience in all types of insolvency procedures operating in the UK together with more general experience of procedures in the United States, Europe and Hong Kong. Has special expertise in cross border insolvency disputes and is heavily involved in reconstruction and workouts for banking clients. Acts for all the major accountancy practices and the major banks and building societies. Is involved with many reported decisions of the High Court, Court of Appeal and House of Lords and has a prestigious reputation throughout the insolvency world. Has been involved in many of the headline cases of the last few years including acting for the liquidator of Charge Card Services Limited, the liquidators of some of the Maxwell companies and the receivers of Brent Walker Group. Has a continuing involvement acting for the administrators of Polly Peck International in the international asset recovery work associated with that particular case. Is currently acting for the trustee in Bankruptcy of Jonathan Aitken.
Prof. Memberships: The Insolvency Practitioners Association; The Society of Practitioners of Insolvency; The Insolvency Lawyers' Association; The American Bar Association; The International Bar Association; The American Bankruptcy Institute; Association Europeenes des Practices des Procedures Collectives; The Law Society.
Career: Qualified as a Solicitor in 1970 and as a licensed insolvency practitioner in 1989. Trainee/Assistant Solicitor at *Alsop Stevens* 1962–1973; Became partner in 1973–88 in Litigation Department; Partner and Head of Litigation at *Alsop Wilkinson* 1988–1996; Partner in Corporate Recovery/Insolvency Group at *Dibb Lupton Alsop* 1996–1999. Joined *Stephenson Harwood* as Partner and Head of Recovery and Insolvency Group in June 1999.
Publications: Co-author of 'Insolvency Procedure Notes', which is a guide to insolvency procedures in the United Kingdom. He is author of a number of articles on insolvency topics for the specialist legal and insolvency magazines. He is a frequent lecturer on insolvency topics at various conferences.
Personal: Born 6 August 1944. Educated at Stonyhurst College, Lancashire. Interests include theatre, opera and wine. Married with two children. Languages: speaks a little French. Resides: London and Devon.

GREGORY, Andrew
Davies Wallis Foyster, Manchester
(0161) 228 3702
ahg@dwf-law.com
Specialisation: Insolvency; banking; corporate recovery; developed the practice and procedure on the transfer of Insolvency Practioners' appoitments, removal from office and change of firms.
Prof. Memberships: Law Society; Association of Business Recovery Professionals.
Career: Partner *Davies Wallis Foyster* 1992 (Head of Insolvency and Banking); Deputy District Judge 1997.
Publications: Editorial board 'The Insolvency Lawyer' (Sweet & Maxwell).
Personal: Paramount Secondary School; St Helens College of Technology; Liverpool John Moores University; walking; reading; theatre; resides Macclesfield.

GREGORY, Deborah A.
Lovells, London (020) 7296 2000
deborah.gregory@lovells.com
Consultant in the insolvency and business restructuring department.
Specialisation: Insolvency and business restructuring; dealing with corporate and personal insolvency and insurance insolvency including individual and corporate voluntary arrangements, schemes of arrangements, administrations, receiverships, liquidations, and corporate restructuring; advising in relation to the Insolvency Act and related provisions. A licensed insolvency practitioner. Major cases include acting for the Administrators of The British & Commonwealth Group, Proton on the acquisition of Lotus, ING on the Barings acquisition of a proposed scheme of arrangement, the Receivers of Yorkshire Food Group Plc and its 27 subsidiaries and recently for a bank on two multi million pound reschedulings, one linked to the collapse in Russia and one linked to the indebtedness of a finance house and a restructuring and receivership of two groups of nursing homes.
Prof. Memberships: Law Society; Law Society's Insolvency Law Sub-Committee; Fellow of and Council Member of R3 (Association of Business Recovery Professionals); AEPPC; Insolvency Lawyers' Association; International Women's Insolvency & Restructuring Confederation; British Insurance Law Association; International Association of Insurance Receivers.
Career: Qualified in 1984 *Lovells.*

GRIER, Ian Stephen
Sprecher Grier Halberstam, London
(020) 7544 5555
iang@sprgr.co.uk
Head of litigation and insolvency department.
Specialisation: Deals with all aspects of corporate and individual insolvency, principally working for administrative receivers, liquidators and trustees in bankruptcy as well as for banks and creditors. Substantial involvement in rescue schemes for limited companies, partnerships and individuals by way of corporate and individual voluntary arrangements. Also has considerable experience in relation to court appointed receiverships and LPA receiverships. Other main area of practice is corporate litigation including contractual disputes, construction work, intellectual property, banking litigation and debt recovery. Important cases have included Re Brightlife Limited (leading case on fixed and floating charges); Re Cranley Mansions Limited (leading case in relation to individual voluntary arrangement); Scottish Enterprise v. Bank of East Asia Limited. Clients include merchant banks, a substantial number of firms of insolvency practitioners and major firms of accountants, international employment agencies and many companies in the IT and technology sectors. Lectures widely to the Association of Business Recovery Professionals (R3), firms of chartered accountants and other professional bodies in relation to the law and practice of insolvency. Co–author of three published works on corporate and individual insolvency and of numerous articles.
Prof. Memberships: Law Society, Fellow of the Society of Practitioners of Insolvency.
Career: Qualified in 1972. Joined with *David Sprecher* to form *Sprecher Grier* in 1984.
Personal: Born 23rd February 1945. Educated at London University (LL.B 1967, LL.M 1968). Former local councillor. Leisure interests include theatre, playing poker and bridge. Lives in London.

GRIERSON, Christopher K.
Lovells, London (020) 7296 2000
christopher.grierson@lovells.com
Specialisation: International and domestic litigation with particular emphasis on insolvency, fraud and asset recovery matters, and insurance and reinsurance. Has acted in a number of prominent cases, including Laker Airways, Mentor Insurance, BCCI, Barings and EMLICO. Has recently been acting for Prince Jefri of Brunei in the KPMG "Chinese Walls" litigation in defence of the proceedings brought by the governor of Brunei. Licensed insolvency practitioner.
Prof. Memberships: International Bar Association (Vice-Chairman of Committee J (Insolvency)), American Bar Association, American Bankruptcy Institute, European Association of Insolvency Practitioners, London Solicitors Litigation Association, The Law Society (England), City of London Solicitors' Company.
Career: 1976–1980 Assistant Solicitor in *Durrant Piesse*; 1980 Partner *Lovells*; 1991–1994 partner in New York office and 1992–1994 managing partner of that office.

HALLY, Paul W.
Shepherd & Wedderburn WS, Edinburgh
(0131) 228 9900
paul.hally@shepwedd.co.uk
Chief executive and partner in corporate department.
Specialisation: Main area of practice is corporate finance. Work includes PFI, mergers and acquisitions, MBOs, banking and insolvency.
Prof. Memberships: Law Society of Scotland, Society of Writers to the Signet, Institute of Directors.
Career: Qualified in 1983. Worked at *Fyfe Ireland WS* 1982–1984 and joined *Shepherd & Wedderburn WS* in 1984, becoming a partner in 1987.
Personal: Born 23rd June 1959. Holds an LLB (Hons) Dip LP Edinburgh (1977–1984).

HAMILTON, Dan
CMS Cameron McKenna, London
(020) 7367 3000
djh@cmck.com
Partner in Banking Group.
Specialisation: Principal area of practice is insolvency and reconstruction. Has wide experience of insolvency and rescue work including receiverships, administrations, liquidations, corporate and individual voluntary arrangements and schemes of arrangements. Also has wide experience of advising directors of troubled companies, banks and creditor groups on restructuring and rescues. The firm acts for the leading firms of accountants and insolvency practitioners and has numerous banks among its clients. During Summer 1998 he was a member of the team establishing the firm's corporate rescue and recovery practice in Hong Kong and South East Asia. Now working on restructuring the foreign debt of a major Russian bank. Recently completed restructuring of debts of Russian Industrial Company. Regular lecturer to clients and occasional conference speaker.
Prof. Memberships: Society of Practitioners of Insolvency (Associate Member), Insolvency Lawyers Association.
Career: Qualified in 1988. Joined *Cameron Markby* in 1986 and became a partner at *Cameron Markby Hewitt* in 1994.
Personal: Educated at Reigate Grammar School 1973–1980 and Worcester College, Oxford 1981–1984.

HARRIS, Anthony
Laytons, Bristol (0117) 930 9500
Specialisation: Bristol managing partner and part of the Company, Commercial & Insolvency department. Specialises in all aspects of insolvency law and is a licensed insolvency practitioner. Practice also covers company and commercial work including mergers and acquisitions, corporate finance and banking.
Prof. Memberships: Association of Business Recovery Professionals; Insolvency Lawyers Association.
Career: Qualified 1971. Partner at *Laytons* since 1977. Editor of 'Laytons Insolvency'.
Personal: Educated at Kings School, Rochester and St. Johns College, Cambridge 1962–1966. Born 14th May 1946. Lives near Bath.

HARRIS, Clare
Meade-King, Bristol (0117) 926 4121
ch@meadeking.co.uk
Specialisation: Personal and Corporate Insolvency.
Prof. Memberships: MABRP, ILA.
Career: Qualified (at *Meade-King*) 1989. Partner from 1994.

HAYMES, Duncan R.
Hammond Suddards Edge, Manchester
(0161) 830 5000
duncan.haynes@hammondsuddards.co.uk
Partner in insolvency and corporate recovery department.
Specialisation: Banking, corporate turnaround and insolvency. Has addressed conferences and seminars.
Prof. Memberships: Law Society; Association of Business Recovery Professionals, Insolvency Lawyers Association.
Career: Joined *JW Hollows & Co* in 1975, moving to *Pilkington Brothers* in 1980. From 1983–1990, was at *William Prior & Co* and from 1990–1992, was at *Addleshaw Sons & Latham*. Joined *Hammond Suddards* as a partner in 1992.
Personal: Born in 1953. Lives in Manchester.

HERTZ, Philip
Clifford Chance, London (020) 7600 1000
philip.hertz@cliffordchance.com
Specialisation: Senior associate in insolvency group specialising in insurance reconstruction and insolvency, general restructuring and general insolvency including advising on derivature–related products, securitisations and structured financings.
Prof. Memberships: International Association of Insurance Receivers. Association of Run–Off Companies, FSA Sub–Committe member. R3 and ILA.
Career: *Clifford Chance* (1991–1997). *Cadwalader, Wickershaw & Taft* (1997–1999) and *Clifford Chance* (1999–to date).
Publications: Co–author of chapter entitled 'Insurance Insolvency' in Tolley's 'Insolvency Law' (July 1999) as well as numerous insurance insolvency and insolvency-related articles in 'Insurance Day' and Healey's 'Insurance Insolvency Report'.
Personal: City of London School, University College, London, Downing College, Cambridge. Interested in all types of sport, wine tasting and relaxing with family and friends. Married with one daughter.

HIGHAM QC, John
Stephenson Harwood, London (020) 7329 4422
Specialisation: Commercial Litigator with particular experience in the fields of corporate insolvency, company law, banking, financial services, personal insolvency and professional negligence. Has acted as an advocate or specialist advisor in virtually every major UK corporate insolvency in recent years.
Prof. Memberships: Insolvency Lawyers' Association.
Career: Partner *Stephenson Harwood* 2000. Called to the Bar in 1976. From 1978 to 1999 he was a practising barrister and a member of a leading insolvency set of chambers. He was appointed a QC in 1992. In 1999 he requalified as a solicitor advocate. He is also a Recorder attached to the Midlands and Oxford Circuit.
Publications: The Law and Practice of Appropriate Administrations (Joint Editor/Published 1994). MA, LL.M Churchill College, Cambridge (1971–1975).

HINCHLIFFE, David
Walker Morris, Leeds (0113) 283 2500
Specialisation: Advises insolvency practitioners on all aspects of insolvency with particular emphasis upon company and individual rescue, often through voluntary arrangements and administrations. Also specialises in liquidations and bankruptcies. Significant instructions have included acting for the liquidators of Medchoice Holidays, Sir James Hill and Dunn & Co. Speaker at Regional SPI Conference.
Prof. Memberships: Society of Practitioners of Insolvency, Insolvency Lawyers Association.
Career: Qualified 1989. Became a partner at *Walker Morris* immediately upon joining the firm from *Ever-*

sheds in 1996.
Personal: Born 1965. Played rugby for Otley RUFC. Leisure pursuits include supporting Bradford Bulls, food (preferably lots), generally being noisy and heavy rock music.

HOLLERIN, Gordon Craig
DLA, Glasgow (08700) 111111
gordon.hollerin@dla.com
Scottish Regional Managing Partner.
Specialisation: Main areas of practice are corporate recovery and insolvency, including administrations, receiverships, liquidations and company voluntary arrangements. Also specialises in commercial litigation. Accredited as ADR Mediator by Centre for Dispute Resolution and the Law Society of Scotland. Head Partner on receivership of Lilley plc and Group Companies and on Scottish aspects of receivership of Rush & Tompkins Group. Contributor to 'ADR in Scotland', published in 1995. Has widespread experience as seminar speaker on ADR and Insolvency.
Prof. Memberships: Joint Convenor of Scottish Insolvency Discussion Group, Member of AIJA, Property Litigation Association.
Career: Qualified in 1980. Joined *Bird Semple* in 1978, becoming a Partner 1985.
Personal: Born 23 January 1957. Attended University of Glasgow 1974–1978 (LLB with Honours in Private Law). Leisure interests include mini–rugby coaching. Lives in Glasgow.

HOUGHTON, John
Simmons & Simmons, London (020) 7628 2020
Head of Corporate Recovery.
Specialisation: Rescues and reconstructions, administrations, receiverships and liquidations and cross–border insolvencies, including Booker plc's standstill and refinancing and Brent Walker's work–out. Advising Deloittes on the receivership of a hotels group and KPMG on the Receivership of a multinational polyester manufacturer. Advised the administrators of Richmond Rugby Club, the supervisors of Oxford United FC's CVA and Portsmouth FC on its administration application. Receiverships (Colorvision plc; the de Savary companies) and adminisrations (Team Lotus; Travers Morgan).
Prof. Memberships: R3, Insolvency Lawyers' Association, European Insolvency Practitioners Association and City of London Law Society Insolvency Committee.
Career: Partner 1994.
Personal: LL.B, LL.M.

HYDE, Mark
Clifford Chance, London (020) 7600 1000
mark.hyde@cliffordchance.com
Specialisation: Partner and head of the insolvency group specialising in both contentious and non–contentious insolvency work and restructuring work often with a cross-border element.
Prof. Memberships: Member of the Association of Business Recovery Professionals; Council member and past president of The Insolvency Lawyers Association.
Career: Bootham School, York; Birmingham University (LLB Hons1980). Articled *Philip Conway Thomas*; joined *Clifford Turner* on qualification in 1984; made partner *Clifford Chance* 1993; licensed insolvency practitioner; admitted to practice in Hong Kong and Brunei.
Personal: Born 1958; resides London; married with three children.

JACKSON, Mark S.
DLA, Leeds (08700) 111 111
mark.jackson@dla.com
Specialisation: Banking, corporate reconstruction and insolvency.
Prof. Memberships: Society of Practitioners in Insolvency.

JAMES, Jim
Ward Hadaway, Newcastle upon Tyne (0191) 204 4000
Specialisation: (i) Extensive experience in advising lenders, companies, directors, individuals and creditors on the options available when a business is in crisis or has failed. Has advised Banks, Insolvency Practitioners, Directors and creditors on issues as diverse as receiverships of quoted companies, voluntary arrangements for "ex" multi-millionaires and negotiations with Banks when businesses are in financial difficulty. Has also been involved in major litigation involving complex construction frauds. (ii) Experience in dealing with Director's disqualification and attending creditors' meetings on behalf of creditors. (iii) Is also the Partner responsible for the management of the firm's Debt Collection Unit.
Prof. Memberships: Member of Law Society, Associate Member of Society of Practitioners in Insolvency.
Career: University of Bristol BSc in Politics. Qualified 1990. Employed at *Walker Morris* 1988–1998. Joined *Ward Hadaway* 1998 as a partner.

JEFFRIES, Graham
Bond Pearce, Southampton (023) 8033 2001
gdj@bondpearce.com
See under Banking, p.118

JEFFRIES, Jonathan D.
Pinsent Curtis, Leeds (0113) 244 5000
jonathan.jeffries@pinsents.com
Partner, Licensed Insolvency Practitioner and Head of Finance Services Group, Leeds.
Specialisation: Advises insolvency practitioners on all aspects of insolvency, and banks and other financial institutions on re–financing and security. Acted for the Receivers of O'Hare Limited, the Administrator of Evans Group Limited and the Administrators of Charnley Davies Limited, James Ferguson Holdings Plc (of which Barlow Clowes was a subsidiary). Advises a number of banks on financial recovery strategies. Lectures to banks and accountants on corporate recovery, debt recovery and banking law.
Prof. Memberships: Fellow of the Association of Business Recovery Professionals–R3; Fellow of the Insolvency Practitioners Association; Member of the Education Courses and Conference Committee of R3.

JOYCE, John
Addleshaw Booth & Co, Manchester (0161) 934 6180
joj@addleshaw-booth.co.uk
Specialisation: Partner specialising in Banking and Insolvency work, dealing with non-contentious and contentious corporate recovery work.
Career: Qualified 1988. Joined firm as Partner in 1998.
Personal: Educated at De La Salle College Salford and Manchester University (1985 LLB Hons). Law Society Finals (1986 Second Class Hons). Resides Chorley.

JUMP, G.K.
Mace & Jones, Manchester (0161) 236 2244
Specialisation: Senior partner. Head of insolvency and recovery department. Licensed insolvency practitioner (1989). Insolvency assessor to the Law Society's Post–Qualification Case Work Committee (1992). President of the Insolvency Lawyers Association (1997/1998). A fellow of the Society of Practitioners of Insolvency (1998). Member of the American Bankruptcy Institute (1998). Member of AEPPC.
Prof. Memberships: Member of the Association of Partnership Practitioners; President, Manchester Law Society, 1991/92; Honorary Treasurer, Manchester Law Society 1995/98; Founder member and honorary secretary of the Northern Arbitration Association (1990); Associate of the Chartered Institute of Arbitrators (1997). Member of the Chartered Institute of Arbitrators (1999).
Career: Admitted 1969. Joined *Mace & Jones* in 1971. Partner, 1973.

KEARNEY, Mary Frances
McManus & Kearney, Belfast (028) 9024 3658
law@mcmk.co.uk
Specialisation: Licensed Insolvency Practitioner. Specialised in all aspects of personal and corporate insolvency. Also handles general corporate work. Advisor to Insolvency Practitioners.
Prof. Memberships: Law Society of Northern Ireland and Member of the Association of Business Recovery Professionals.
Career: Qualified in April 1986. Partner in the firm of *McManus & Kearney* in 1990. Authorised by Law Society of Northern Ireland to carry on insolvency practice since 1996.

KEITLEY, Nicholas
Blake Lapthorn, Southampton (023) 8063 1823
njrkeitley@blakelapthorn.co.uk
Specialisation: Partner and head of insolvency and business rescue group; acts for insolvency practitioners in relation to all types of insolvency procedures; advises companies and individuals about their financial problems and is increasingly involved in turnaround and business rescue work; advises creditors about their rights and remedies and acts for purchasers of businesses and assets from insolvency practitioners; also advises on company reorganisations and solvent liquidations and does some banking and factoring work.
Prof. Memberships: Law Society, Fellow of the Association of Business Recovery Professionals
Career: Articled *Stoneham Langton & Passmore*; qualified 1985; assistant solicitor at *Lovell White Durrant* (formerly *Durrant Piesse*) 1985–1993; assistant solicitor *Hammond Suddards* 1993–1995; joined *Blake Lapthorn* 1995; partner *Blake Lapthorn* 1996. Educated at Epsom College and Leeds University; Bachelor of Laws (Hons) 2:1; Insolvency Practitioners Licence obtained in 1990.

LANG, J. Russell
Morison Bishop, Glasgow (0141) 248 4672
Specialisation: Partner in corporate division. Has specialised in all aspects of personal and corporate insolvency and corporate rescue work since 1976. Has been involved in all aspects of corporate and commercial law since 1990. Licensed Insolvency Practitioner since 1987. Accredited as a specialist in insolvency law by the Law Society of Scotland. Member of Joint Discussion Group for insolvency specialists set up by the Law Society of Scotland and

the Institute of Chartered Accountants of Scotland. Lecturer on courses run by the Law Society of Scotland, Institute of Chartered Accountants of Scotland and Strathclyde University. Appointed Moderator (Personal Insolvency–Scotland) by Joint Insolvency Examination Board in September 1993. Appointed member of the Scottish Technical Committee of the Association of Business Recovery Professionals; Appointed member of the Insolvency Law Acreditation Panel of the Law Society of Scotland.
Prof. Memberships: Law Society of Scotland, Insolvency Lawyers Association, the Association of Business Recovery Professionals, European Insolvency Practitioners Association.
Career: With *McGrigor Donald, Solicitors* in Glasgow 1974–1980. Qualified in 1976. Joined *Bishop & Co, Solicitors*, Glasgow in 1980 and became a Partner in 1982. Firm became *Bishop and Robertson Chalmers, Solicitors* in 1986 and more recently merged to form the firm *Morison Bishop*. Partner in the Litigation department 1986–1990. Partner in the corporate division from 1990.
Personal: Educated at Edinburgh University 1970–1974.

LAWSON, Stephen A.
Foot Anstey Sargent, Exeter (01392) 411221
stephen.lawson@foot-ansteys.co.uk
Partner in insolvency department.
Specialisation: Handles all areas of corporate and personal insolvency, including LPA receiverships. Also handles bank litigation and professional negligence, including acting as expert witness in these fields. Author of 'Individual Voluntary Arrangements' and 'LPA Receivers'. Has extensive lecturing experience for *Jordans*, College of Law and others.
Prof. Memberships: Law Society, IPA, SPI, Institute of Credit Management.
Career: Qualified in 1969. Partner in 1973. Former President and Secretary of Devon and Exeter Law Society. Deputy High Court Bankruptcy Registrar.
Personal: Born 27th August 1945. Attended Queens College Taunton 1956–64.

LE BAS, Malcolm H.
Paris Smith & Randall, Southampton
(023) 8048 2482
Senior Partner in commercial department.
Specialisation: Principal area of practice since 1972 has been insolvency and sales and purchases of businesses, including MBO's. Has an extensive practice acting for both vendors and purchasers. Clients include national firms of insolvency practitioners, the Insolvency Service and a significant number of local companies. Acts for Southampton Football Club, Portsmouth Football Club and Hampshire County Cricket Club. Increasingly involved in sports law.
Prof. Memberships: Law Society. Insolvency Lawyers Association.
Career: Qualified in 1964. Became a partner at *Paris Smith & Randall* in 1969. Managing partner 1993–1998. Senior partner from 1998.
Personal: Born 28th October 1941. Educated at Worksop College 1955–59. Governor, Southampton Institute; Hon. Solicitor to Hampshire County Cricket Club; Director, Mayflower Theatre Trust; Chairman Newscom plc Pension Fund; Chairman Alldays Pension Fund. Past President Trojans Sports Club. Trustee of Wessex Cancer Trust. Interests include cricket, rugby union, cinema, theatre and jazz. Lives in Southampton.

LEWIS, Jonathan
Finers Stephens Innocent, London
(020) 7323 4000
Specialisation: All aspects of corporate recovery and insolvency work, corporate and personal, together with a corporate law practice. Advises lenders, debtors, and insolvency practitioners. Emphasis on cross-border insolvency and on strategic planning. Most recently, has acted for the liquidators of the English and Cook Island subsidiaries of the *Australian Bond Corporation* and for the company in a significant cross-border turnaround assignment particularly involving the Far East. Speaker and author on insolvency topics. Authorised insolvency practitioner.
Prof. Memberships: Law Society Company Law Sub–Committee; Insolvency Lawyers Association; AEPPC; Society of Practitioners of Insolvency; International Bar Association (Creditors' Rights Committee J); Insol International.
Career: Qualified 1971. Head of Insolvency Group at *Finers Stephens Innocent.*
Personal: Born 1946. Educated at Harrow County Grammar School and Downing College Cambridge. Interests include walking, theatre and family.

MACFARLANE, John
McGrigor Donald, Edinburgh (0131) 226 7777
See under Banking, p.119

MALLON, Christopher
Freshfields Bruckhaus Deringer, London
(020) 7936 4000
cmallon@freshfields.com
Manager in restructuring and insolvency group.
Specialisation: All areas of Insolvency law and asset tracing. Particular expertise in cross–border insolvency and complex bank fraud.
Prof. Memberships: Insolvency Lawyers Association, City of London Solicitors Company.
Career: Qualified in Australia in 1982. Practised at *Jackson McDonald*, Perth, 1982–1985, *Allen & Overy* 1985–1986. Joined *Lovell White & King* 1987. Admitted in England 1987. Joined *Biddle* as a partner in July 1995.
Personal: Born 6th May 1956. Attended Aquinas College, Perth, Western Australia and the University of Western Australia. Lives in Stockwell.

MANNING, Peter R.
Simmons & Simmons, London (020) 7628 2020
Partner, Corporate Recovery.
Specialisation: Corporate insolvency and reconstructions, banking and security reviews. Regular lecturer on insolvency matters.
Prof. Memberships: Law Society, Association of Business Recovery Professionals, Insolvency Lawyers Association.
Career: Qualified 1986. Partner *Alsop Wilkinson* 1990 to 1999.
Personal: Born 1959. Attended Hertford College, Oxford 1978–1982.

MAY, Philip N S
TLT Solicitors, Bristol (0117) 917 7777
pmay@TLTSolicitors.com
Specialisation: Principal area of practice is business breakdown and insolvency. Acts for Official Receivers and Insolvency Practitioners nationally, particularly in connection with corporate insolvency and contentious matters. Acts for Lloyds TSB in business lending recoveries. Also acts in relation to corporate restructuring and recovery. Has acted personally as court appointed receiver. Charge-out rate is £150 per hour.
Prof. Memberships: Law Society, Bristol Law Society, Insolvency Lawyers Association, Association of Business Recovery Professionals.
Career: Educated Southend-on-Sea, Essex and Lincoln College, Oxford Articled *Osborne Clarke* Bristol 1982–1984. Assistant solicitor to partner *Osborne Clarke* Bristol 1984–1995. Joined *Trumps* as partner 1995. *Trumps* merged with Bristol law firm*Lawrence Tucketts* to become *TLT Solicitors* on May 1 2000.
Personal: Born 16th March 1959; married with two children; lives in Bristol. Leisure pursuits include golf, snooker and skiing.

MCGEEVER, Brendan G.
Gateley Wareing, Birmingham (0121) 234 0000
bmcgeever@gateleywareing.co.uk
Senior Partner and Partner in Banking and Insolvency Department.
Specialisation: Main areas of practice are insolvency, banking and commercial litigation. Acts for administrative receivers, liquidators, administrators and trustees in bankruptcy on all aspects of insolvency law. Also advises banks and other financial institutions in relation to securities and realisations.
Prof. Memberships: Law Society.
Career: Qualified in 1983. Joined *Gateley Wareing* in 1984, becoming a Partner in 1986 and Senior Partner in 1993.
Personal: Born 1958. Attended St Mary's College, Middlesbrough 1971–1976 and Birmingham University 1976–1979. Leisure interests include golf, soccer and rugby. Lives in Birmingham.

MCGURK, Anthony J.G.
Eversheds, Cambridge (01223) 224 204
anthonymcgurk@eversheds.com
Specialisation: Handles all aspects of corporate insolvency and reconstruction work, including acting for insolvency practitioners in connection with administrative receiverships, LPA receiverships, administrations, IVA's and liquidations. In addition, specialises in company/ corporate work, including mergers and acquisitions and banking.
Prof. Memberships: Eastern Region Committee member of ABRR; Institute of Directors.
Career: Qualified in September 1989. Became a Partner at *Eversheds* in May 1995 and relocated to the Cambridge office in December 1998.
Personal: Educated at Downside School, Nr. Bath, Graduated in Law from Hull University. Obtained First Class Honours in Law Society finals.

MERSON, James T.
Stronachs, Aberdeen (01224) 845845
james.merson@stronachs.co.uk
Partner in commercial litigation department.
Specialisation: Specialist area of practice is insolvency. Licensed insolvency practitioner and certified by Law Society of Scotland as a specialist in insolvency law. Also handles civil litigation, spanning all types of commercial disputes and litigation and employment tribunals.
Prof. Memberships: Law Society of Scotland. Aberdeen Bar Association.
Career: Qualified in 1974. Joined *Stronachs* in 1974, becoming a partner in 1978.
Personal: Born 24th April 1951. Attended Aberdeen University 1969–1972. Leisure interests include travel and golf. Lives in Aberdeen.

MONTGOMERY, Nigel W J
DLA, London (08700) 111111
nigel.montgomery@dla.com
Partner in charge of financial services and insurance reconstruction.
Specialisation: Principal area is advising on exit routes and schemes of arrangement for solvent and insolvent insurance and reinsurance companies and pools. Current insurance schemes and insolvencies include RMCA Re; ICS Re; Charter Re; MGI; ICS UK; Pan Atlantic; UIC; Hawk Insurance Company; HIR (UK) Ltd; Marina Mutual; English & American Group plc; English and American Insurance Holdings plc; Pacific & General. Nigel is advising the surety market in relation to a P&I Club insolvency, Ocean Marine Mutual Insurance Association and is acting for participants in the English & American and WFUM Pools. Nigel and his colleagues are also advising on the restructuring of a number of Financial Services Companies. Frequently lectures and writes on insurance insolvency in UK and internationally. Is a licensed Insolvency Practitioner and has previously acted as receiver, liquidator and administrator of a wide variety of companies while a partner in an accounting firm.
Prof. Memberships: Law Society; Association of Business Recovery Professionals; International Association of Insurance Receivers; AEPPC.
Career: Qualified 1981.

MORRIS, Howard
Denton Wilde Sapte, London (020) 7242 1212

MUDD, Philip J.
Walker Morris, Leeds (0113) 283 2500
Managing Partner and Head of Banking and Insolvency Department.
Specialisation: Deals with insolvency and banking issues for lenders, insolvency practitioners and corporate clients with an emphasis on debt restructuring and corporate rescue in addition to mainstream insolvency, lending and realisation work. Acted for lender in reconstruction of UK Land plc. Recent work includes administration of Transperience Limited, the receiverships of Listed companies On Demand Information plc, Peterhead Group plc, Total Office Group and the liquidations of Dunn & Co and Greenfield Hotels. Contributor to 'Insolvency Law and Practice'. Speaker at local and regional SPI conferences.
Prof. Memberships: Fellow of Association of Business Recovery Professionals, Insolvency Lawyers Association.
Career: Qualified 1983, and joined *Walker Morris* the same year. Became a Partner in 1985. Licensed insolvency practitioner.
Personal: Born 19th January 1959. Attended Bristol University 1977–1980. Leisure interests include music, skiing and sailing. Lives in Huddersfield.

MUNRO, Rick
Lamport Bassitt, Southampton (023) 8083 7777
rick.munro@lamportbassitt.co.uk
Specialisation: All aspects of corporate and personal insolvency, particularly in liquidations and bankruptcies; fraud/asset tracing work; acting primarily for insolvency practitioners. Recent work includes acting for liquidators of construction company in preference claim against former directors, acting for receivers of property company in enforcement of their equitable charge over shares, acting for trustees in bankruptcy in realising assets such as the matrimonial home and personal pension policies. Contributor to 'Tolley's Insolvency Law and Practice'.
Prof. Memberships: Hampshire Incorporated Law Society; Association of Business Recovery Professionals.
Career: Qualified in 1992 following articles with *Lovells*; Assistant Solicitor with *Lovells*, London (1992 to 1994) and in Hong Kong (1994 to 1997); joined *Lamport Bassitt* in January 1998. Partner in January 2000.
Personal: Born 19 April 1967. Educated at Birmingham University (Law Degree) 1985–1988. Married with two children. Interests include cricket, golf, diving.

NICHOLSON, Mark
Nicholsons, Lowestoft (01502) 532300
Specialisation: Bankruptcy and personal insolvency and liquidations. Acts for insolvency practitioners.
Career: Qualified May 1977. Licensed insolvency practitioner.
Personal: Born 14.6.52.

NIEKIRK, Malcolm
Lester Aldridge, Bournemouth (01202) 786161
malcolmniekirk@lester-aldridge.co.uk
Specialisation: Head of the corporate recovery and insolvency unit. Licensed insolvency practitioner. Deals almost exclusively with non–contentious corporate insolvency, including turnaround work and restructuring as well as the full range of formal insolvency procedures. Usually advises banks and other financial institutions, insolvency practitioners and sometimes businesses buying assets from receivers and companies in financial difficulties. He has received public attention for his work with insolvent football clubs. Occasional conference speaker. Supports plain English drafting. One of his documents was commended in the 1999 Clarity awards.
Career: Articled *Moore & Blatch*, Southampton; qualified 1987. Joined *Lester Aldridge* 1990. Partner 1994. Insolvency practitioners licence 1998.
Personal: Born 1963. Educated Royal Grammar School, High Wycombe; Southampton University (1984 LL.B Hons). Lives in Lyndhurst.

OBANK, Richard
DLA, Leeds (08700) 111111
richard.obank@dla.com
Specialisation: Partner handling a wide range of corporate advisory matters including restructuring/ reorganisations and all forms of recovery procedure, frequently of an international nature.
Prof. Memberships: Law Society (City of London Society); Association of Business Recovery Professionals; Insolvency Lawyers' Association; INSOL; AEPPC; Committee J, International Bar Association; Chancery Bar Association; IPA (licensed property receiver).
Career: Trained *A.V Hammond & Co*; assistant solicitor in national corporate recovery department of *Hammond Suddards* (Leeds and London). Joined *Herbert Smith* (international and banking litigation) end of 1994; partner (corporate recovery) 1997; successful candidate in JIEB examinations (November 1997); licensed insolvency practitioner.
Personal: Age 36. Educated at Fulneck School for Boys, Pudsey, West Yorkshire; University of Manchester 1986 LLB Class 2: 1 (2 subject prizes for Jurisprudence); Guildford College of Law (1987); Honorary Fellow to the Institute of Advanced Legal Studies at the University of London; Member of the Advisory Board for the Centre for Law and Business at the University of Manchester. General Editor of BJIBFL; Editorial Board for Insolvency Lawyer. Married with 3 children. Lives in Leeds.

OLIVER, David C.
Sherwin Oliver Solicitors, Portsmouth
(023) 9283 2200
david.oliver@sherwinoliver.com
Senior partner in insolvency and litigation department.
Specialisation: Practice covers all areas of corporate and individual insolvency, acting for all of the major insolvency practitioners in the Southern region and some outside. Acts for various firms of chartered surveyors in relation to LPA receiverships. Also handles general civil litigation and major fraud prosecutions. Work includes construction arbitration contract disputes, involving claims in excess of £5 million each (obtained an Administration Order in relation to a Lloyds managing agent company with claims against it of approximately £90 million) and major fraudulent trading cases, representing a company with a deficiency in excess of £12 million. Has lectured for Portsmouth University, LawNet, Chambers of Commerce, 3Rs and others. Written articles on insolvency; radio and TV appearances.
Prof. Memberships: Law Society, Insolvency Lawyers Association, AEPPC, Chartered Institute of Arbitrators, R3.
Career: Senior litigation partner at *Sherwin Oliver* since 1985. Fellow of Chartered Institute of Arbitrators since 1993. Appointed Deputy District Judge in June 1993. Past Chairman Lawnet Insolvency Unit.
Personal: Born 13th March 1944. Leisure interests include golf, tennis, walking, swimming, films and theatre. Trustee of three national charities and member of NHS Research Ethics Committee. Lives in Portsmouth.

OUGHTON, Paul
Nicholson Graham & Jones, London
(020) 7648 9000
Specialisation: Traditional insolvency/corporate recovery/corporate rescue areas such as liquidations, receiverships, administrations, corporate voluntary arrangements, bankruptcies, individual voluntary arrangements and structured moratoriums and schemes of arrangement. He has specialist knowledge in media-related work particularly in film/television post-production and the music business. Paul is active in corporate litigation/project finance and development/corporate breakdown and re–financing and corporate work-outs.
Prof. Memberships: R3, ILA, AEPPC, IBA and Law Society.
Career: Partner in the Corporate Rescue and Insolvency Group since July 1997. He joined from *Hill Taylor Dickinson*. Previously practised through to partnership at *William Prior & Co* and *Dibb Lupton Broomhead*.

PALLETT, Julian C.
Wragge & Co, Birmingham (0121) 233 1000
julian_pallett@wragge.com
Specialisation: Banking: Lending and security arrangements, intercreditor arrangements, project and acquisition finance, transaction funding. Insolvency: Receivership, liquidations, administration, troubled companies, refinancing, restructuring.
Career: Articled *Wragge & Co.* Qualified 1983. Partner at *Wragge & Co* from 1990.
Personal: Born 1958.

PATRICK, Bruce R.
Maclay Murray & Spens, Edinburgh
(0131) 226 5196
brp@maclaymurrayspens.co.uk
Specialisation: Senior partner experienced in all areas of corporate law but most notably in venture capital, MBO's/ MBI's, receiverships and ship finance. Vice–Convenor of the Company Law Committee of the Law Society of Scotland. Has been a panel solicitor for 3i plc for over 20 years. Head of the firm's Scottish Parliamentary Group.
Career: Qualified 1973. University of Oxford (BA 1967) and University of Edinburgh (LLB 1971). Former Managing Partner of *Maclay Murray & Spens* (1991–1994). Senior partner (2000–).
Personal: Born 1945.

PEARSON, W Stephen
Travers Smith Braithwaite, London
(020) 7295 3000
Stephen.Pearson@TraversSmith.com
Specialisation: Specialises in insolvency litigation, acting for insolvency practitioners, banks and creditors. Has particular expertise in relation to claims for wrongful and fraudulent trading, preferences and transactions at an undervalue.
Prof. Memberships: Law Society, Law Society of Scotland, Association of Business Recovery Professionals (Associate), ILA, AEPPC, IBA.
Career: Qualified in Scotland in 1985. Requalified in England in1989. Made partner in *Travers Smith Braithwaite* in 1994. Seconded to Deloitte & Touche in 1988.
Personal: Born 25 March 1961. University of Glasgow. Leisure interests include music (piano and singing), tennis, family.

PENNIE, John A.
Dickinson Dees, Newcastle upon Tyne
(0191) 279 9255
Specialisation: A specialist in both personal and corporate insolvency, leading a team of nine lawyers. JIEB Moderator in personal insolvency. Member of the Law Society Insolvency Authorisation Casework Committee. Licensed insolvency practitioner.
Prof. Memberships: Law Society.
Career: MA (Cantab). Partner with *Dickinson Dees* since 1985.

PHEASANT, Louise A.
Eversheds, Birmingham (0121) 232 1000
Specialisation: Banking and insolvency. Acts for lenders and insolvency practioners on all aspects of insolvency law, security and asset realisations.
Prof. Memberships: SPI – Society of Practitioners of Insolvency, Law Society.
Career: Birmingham University (1st Class Hons) Midland Bank plc 1979–83, BBC 1983–84, *Eversheds* 1988 becoming partner 1997.
Personal: Cinema, contemporary art, West Bromwich Albion.

PIKE, Nick
Lawrence Graham, London (020) 7379 0000
nick.pike@lawgram.com
Partner in Litigation Department.
Specialisation: Specialist in all aspects of insolvency, recoveries and reconstruction. Instructions over the last year include the receivership of the M&N Group of Companies, together with a large number of liquidations, administrations and bankruptcies.
Prof. Memberships: Law Society. Insolvency Practitioners' Association. Institute of Credit Management. American Bankruptcy Institute, Insolvency Lawyers' Association.
Career: 1987–qualified as a solicitor (*Alsop Williamson*, later *DLA*. 1992– partner. 1996–partner and head of insolvency, London (*DLA*) 1999–partner, banking and corporate recovery group, *Lawrence Graham.*
Publications: Numerous insolvency articles; Editorial Board Member of Finance and Credit Law.
Personal: Educated Bristol University (LLB).

POPE, Timothy J.
Hammond Suddards Edge, London
(020) 7655 1000
tim.pope@hammondsuddardsedge.com
Specialisation: Specialising in all types of insolvency both non–contentious and contentious. Particular specialism is non–contentious receivership and administration work. Also experienced in advising banks and other financial institutions on restructuring and workouts and debt equity swaps. Highlights of the Past Year: Acting for the Joint Liquidators of Leyland Daf Limited, Messrs Kroll Buchler Phillips and PricewaterhouseCoopers, in respect of litigation involving a £50m surplus arising from the Receivership in relation to an action bought by the Dutch bondholders of Leyland Daf limited. Acting for Levy Gee as Receivers of the China Jazz Restaurant Group in London. Acting for Arthur Andersen as Administrators of Essex Furniture Plc, a listed plc with 30 leasehold shops. Recent reported cases include (1) Homepower Trading Ltd and Powerstore Stores Ltd, (2) C E King Limited.
Prof. Memberships: Licensed Insolvency Practitioner (licence held since 1990), Fellow of Association of Business Recovery Professionals (R3), Member oft the AEPPC and Committee J of the International Bar Association (Insolvency and Creditors Rights).
Career: Qualified 1982. 1985 – joined what is now *Dibb Lupton Alsop* in the Leeds office, partner 1988. 1990–partner in London office of *Dibb Lupton Alsop.* October 1996–joined *Hammond Suddards London office*
Personal: BA Hons Law. Leisure interests include ballet, opera, theatre, horse racing, travelling. Single, resides in London.

POTTER, Bruce J.
Morgan Cole, Reading (0118) 955 3008
bruce.potter@morgan-cole.com
Specialisation: Corporate Insolvency, particularly Administrations, Receiverships and Professional Partnership VAs. Also specialist insolvency, reconstruction and recovery advice to lenders, including banks and factoring/invoice discounting clients and other asset based lenders.
Prof. Memberships: Chairman Thames Valley Commercial Lawyers Association 1998–1999.
Career: Qualified 1985. Joined *Cole & Cole* 1986. Partner 1989.
Personal: Born June 1958. Oxford University 1977–1980. Married. Rugby and skiing.

PRIOR, Michael
Nabarro Nathanson, London (020) 7524 6205
m.prior@nabarro.com
Specialisation: Insolvency, corporate recovery, national/international. Cases include: Maxwell Personal Bankruptcy, Epic Group, Dallhold (Alan Bond), Olympia & York. 1996/97: Facia Group, YC Group, Administration & CVA Millwall Football Club; Melita Group of Shoe Companies; Lister Group of Textile Companies (1998). Falmers Jeans Group Administration (1998/1999).
Prof. Memberships: COMMJ, IBA; INSOL, Council ABRP (R3), SPI, IPA, ILA, Various Technical Committees (ILA, SPI, CBI). Chairman Int'l Comm. ABRP (R3).
Career: Epsom College, England; Sorbonne University, France.
Personal: Heli–skiing, cricket, opera, Peninsular War History. Large growing family.

RAJANI, Shashi H.
Nicholson Graham & Jones, London
(020) 7648 9000
Specialisation: All aspects of corporate rescue and insolvency matters, acting for accountants and banking and corporate clients. Also advises banking and individual clients on personal insolvency matters, particularly skilled in director disqualification cases and international aspects of turnarounds and insolvencies. Acts as consultant to the other departments and groups of the firm on insolvency matters. Licensed Insolvency Practitioner since 1986.
Prof. Memberships: The Law Society, including Chief Insolvency Assessor; The City of London Solicitor's Company; The City of London Law Society and its Insolvency Law Sub–Committee; Association of Business Recovers Professionals (R3) and its Membership Committee; European Insolvency Practitioners Association (AEPPC).
Career: Partner and head of corporate rescue and insolvency group from 1994 to date. In practice as an advocate in Dar es Salaam, Tanzania and Tabora (1956–1964). Appointed (1964) to the Tanzanian Civil Service as Assistant Administrator General. Promoted to Senior Assistant Administrator General (1967). *Coopers & Lybrand*, London as manager in insolvency department (1970–1977). *Linklaters & Paines*, senior assistant solicitor (1977–1988). *Cameron Markby Hewitt*, partner (1989–1993); *Nicholson Graham & Jones*, partner since 1994.
Publications: Author of: Tolley's 'Corporate Insolvency Law Handbook' (1990); Tolley's 'Corporate Insolvency' (1995); chapters in Tolley's 'Company Law on Insolvency'; chapter in 'Theory & Practice' (Sweet & Maxwell 1993) on "Equitable Assistance in the Search for Security" in insolvency law; and Tolley's 'Insolvency Fees and Costs' (1995–1997). Joint chief editor of Tolley's 'Insolvency Law & Practice' and joint consulting editor of Tolley's 'Insolvency Law'–1996. Writes for a number of international journals.

READETT, Helen A.
Martineau Johnson, Birmingham (0121) 678 1576
helen.readett@martjohn.com
Specialisation: Advises insolvency practitioners on all types of insolvency work and banks and lending institutions on putting security in place and maximising realisations.
Prof. Memberships: Licensed insolvency practitioner and member R3. Law Society member.
Career: Qualified 1982. *Edge Ellison* partner until 1998. Now with *Martineau Johnson.*
Personal: Married with young son.

REES, Bleddyn
Morgan Cole, Cardiff (029) 2038 5385
bleddyn.rees@morgan-cole.com
Partner in Business Services Division.
Specialisation: Principal area of practice is corporate insolvency and commercial. Work includes

administrations, receiverships, liquidations and advising borrowers and lenders on lending security and guarantees. Major receiverships have included Baker Group plc (a private company with three Ford main dealerships and a substantial contract hire business with debts in excess of £45 million); Tern Group plc (a USM listed property company); John Williams Industries plc (a quoted property, steel foundry and garage business); Wyndham Group plc (a listed property and motor dealership group) and Parrott Group Ltd (a floppy disk manufacturer including an important Court of Appeal decision–WDA v Export Finance Company Ltd). He leads a team which has handled over 250 receivership appointments.
Prof. Memberships: Law Society.
Career: Joined *Morgan Cole* in 1984 and qualified in 1986. Became a Partner in May 1989.
Personal: Born 28th June 1961. Educated at Llandovery College 1973–80, UWIST 1980–83 and Guildford College of Law 1983–84. Leisure pursuits include skiing. Lives in Cardiff.

RHODES, Paul
Hammond Suddards Edge, Leeds (0113) 284 7000

RIDLER, Graham
Eversheds, Leeds (0113) 243 0391
ridlerg@eversheds.com
Partner and head of insolvency for Leeds, Newcastle and Teesside.
Specialisation: Advises insolvency practitioners on both contentious and non–contentious insolvency work. Advises banks on security and intensive care issues. Particular specialism in receivership and adminstration work. Recent receiverships include Crestdale Limited (£8m sale), Penguin Group of Companies, Verler Walker Group, Teeside Wholesale Meat Co Ltd. Recent administrations include Meldron Tena Plc , Extrusions Limited and BNH Construction Limited.
Prof. Memberships: Law Society, SPI.
Career: Leicester University LLB (Hons), qualified 1987–joined *Pinsent Curtis*, made partner 1993, joined *Eversheds* as partner in 1996.
Personal: Resides Durham City, leisure interests include golf, shooting and weight training.

ROOME, James H.D.
Bingham Dana LLP, London (020) 7375 9770
Partner in financial restructuring group.
Specialisation: Corporate law, including insolvency and reconstructions. Specialist experience in corporate insolvency, including work-outs and reconstructions and advising company directors. Particular experience in multinational insolvencies including a central role in the BCCI liquidation. James is a licensed insolvency practitioner and has spoken at conferences on topics ranging from professional liability to financial institution insolvency.
Prof. Memberships: Society of Practitioners of Insolvency, the Law Society, London Law Society, Insolvency Lawyers Association, European Insolvency Practitioners Association.
Personal: Born 7th October 1958.

ROSS, Alexander T.
John McKee & Son, Belfast (028) 9023 2303
Specialisation: Advises banks and financial institutions on lending and security matters and has particular expertise in acting for funders in private finance initiative work. Also advises insolvency practitioners, particularly administrative receivers, on all legal matters arising from corporate recovery and insolvency including sales of businesses and assets and claims by creditors.
Prof. Memberships: Law Society of Northern Ireland.
Career: Qualified 1967; Partner in *John McKee & Son* from 1972.
Personal: Born 23.12.1942. Educated at Strathallan School, Perthshire and Queens University, Belfast.

ROXBURGH, Roy
Iain Smith & Company, Aberdeen (01224) 645454
roy@iainsmith.com
Partner in Company & Commercial Department.
Specialisation: Main areas of practice are mergers and take-overs, MBO's, MBI's and corporate insolvency, acting for both purchasers and vendors of businesses, investors both private and institutional, and receiverships. Involvement in insolvency is generally on a specialist basis. Author of a chapter on diligence for the ICAS 'Insolvency Case Book'. Convener 1993 to 1995 of the Law Society/ ICAS's Insolvency Specialist Group.
Prof. Memberships: Law Society of Scotland (Member of Insolvency Solicitors Committee since 1992, and Insolvency Specialist Accreditation Panel since 1994), S.P.I. (Member of Scottish Technical Committee).
Career: Qualified in 1974. Joined *Iain Smith & Co* as a Partner in 1977. External Examiner JIEB since 1993 (administration and Receiverships). Notary Public.
Personal: Born 29th September 1950. Educated at Dunfermline High School 1961–1968 and Edinburgh University 1968–1972. Recreations include skiing, golf, bridge, chess and football. Lives in Aberdeen.

RUSHWORTH, Jonathan E.F.
Slaughter and May, London (020) 7600 1200
Partner.
Specialisation: Has a wide-ranging company, corporate finance and capital markets practice, acting in particular for listed and other companies, for partnerships and also for corporate trustees in capital markets issues. He has a particular interest and specialisation in corporate recovery and insolvency work, advising companies and their directors, banks and other creditors and also insolvency practitioners on refinancing and insolvency issues. His practice involves domestic, overseas and cross-border insolvency matters. He has been involved in many of the recent large insolvencies, in particular acting for the administrators of the Barings Group. He has lectured extensively on the subjects of corporate recovery and insolvency, written numerous papers on the subject and has written a book on receivership.
Prof. Memberships: Creditors' Rights Committee of the International Bar Association.The Law Society's Standing Committee on Company Law.

SANDERSON, R. Gordon
Dickinson Dees, Newcastle upon Tyne (0191) 279 9348
Specialisation: Practice covers advising banks and other leading institutions on all aspects of personal and corporate recovery, term loan and other security documentation, enforceability of directors guarantees and other third party security and general banking issues.
Career: Qualified 1985. After qualification spent three years at *Robert Muckle*, Newcastle before moving to *Dickinson Dees* in January 1990. Became Partner in 1993 and Head of firm's Banking Unit in 1995. Former lecturer in Banking Law at the University of Northumbria.

SCHAFFER, Danny
Isadore Goldman, London (020) 7242 3000
Partner.
Specialisation: Specialises in all aspects of insolvency including related litigation and bank recovery. Licensed insolvency practitioner.
Prof. Memberships: Society for Practitioners of Insolvency, Insolvency Practitioners Association, Insolvency Lawyers Association.
Career: Qualified in 1975. Partner at *Isadore Goldman* since 1978. Appointed Deputy Registrar in Bankruptcy at High Court in February 1992.
Personal: Born 2nd September 1950. University of Birmingham 1969–1971. Spare time activities include being a football referee. Lives in London.

SCOPES, Richard H.
Denton Wilde Sapte, London (020) 7242 1212

SEGAL, Nicholas A.
Allen & Overy, London (020) 7330 3000
Specialisation: Insolvency. In recent years worked on a number of international restructurings including the attempt to rescue and restructure BCCI; the worldwide restructuring of the Heron Group; restructuring of the Queens Moat House Group; the workout and refinancing of a major Danish multinational corporate; and the restructurings of the Thai telecom and Uneximbank of Russia. Extensive experience of insolvency proceedings in England and abroad; recent assignments include advising the receivers of Layland Daf Finance and the provisional liquidators of the IWG Group.
Prof. Memberships: Fellow of the Society for Advanced Legal Studies; Fellow of the Association of Business Recovery Professionals; International Insolvency Institute.
Career: Articled *Cameron Markby*, qualified 1982, assistant solicitor *Cameron Markby*, Partner *Cameron Markby*; Partner *Allen & Overy*. A visiting lecturer in the University of London and an occasional lecturer in the University of Oxford. Member of the editorial board of 'Insolvency Intelligence' and on the advisory board of various other journals. Editor of the insolvency chapters in 'Gore-Brown on Companies' and the joint author of the 'International Recognition' chapter in Totty and Moss', 'Insolvency'. Recently contributed chapters to 'Current Developments in International and Comparative Corporate Insolvency Law' (ed Ziegel, OUP 1994); 'Insolvency of Banks: Management of Risks' (ed Oditah, FT Law and Tax 1996) 'Restitution and Banking Law' (ed Rose Hart Publishing, 1998).
Personal: Educated at St Peter's College, Oxford (1979 MA First Class). Born 1956. Married with one son. Interests include opera and golf.

SHANDRO, Philip Alexander (Sandy)
Freshfields Bruckhaus Deringer, London (020) 7936 4000
Partner in Restructuring and Insolvency Group
Specialisation: Advises on all aspects of insolvency from risk-avoidance to restructuring. Also advises officeholders in formal insolvency proceedings. Much cross-border experience. Fluent French. Frequent speaker and author. Member of editorial board of Receivers, Administrators & Liquidators Quarterly.
Prof. Memberships: Vice Chairman, City of London Law Society Insolvency Sub–Committee, Insolvency Lawyer's Association, AEPPC, INSOL, Canadian Bar Association.
Career: Qualified in 1978 (British Columbia) and 1992 (England & Wales). Solicitor Advocate. CEDR

Accredited Mediator.
Personal: Born 14th July 1951. Educated in Canada (BA, Alberta, 1972; MA McGill, 1974) and at Oxford University (BA 1976, BCL 1978). President, Canada–UK Chamber of Commerce. Lives in London.

SHAW, Murray W.A.
Biggart Baillie, Glasgow (0141) 228 8000
mshaw@biggartbaillie.co.uk
See under Litigation (Commercial), p.567

SHORT, John
Taylor Vinters, Cambridge (01223) 423444
See under Corporate Finance, p.264

SLEIGH, Andrew F.
Burness, Glasgow (0141) 248 4933
afs@burness.co.uk
Specialisation: Acts for many insolvency practitioners and financial institutions in all aspects of company rescue; insolvency related legal issues and procedures. Acted for PricewaterhouseCoopers in Scotland's largest agricultural insolvency–Simmers Group and for major Scottish banks in confidential rescue arrangements; acted for SFA in rescue of Hampden Stadium, Glasgow.

SMITH, Gillian C.
Foot Anstey Sargent, Exeter (01392) 411221
gillian.smith@foot-ansteys.co.uk
Partner in Insolvency department.
Specialisation: Handles all aspects of personal and corporate insolvency, particularly personal contentious work. Acts for Insolvency Practitioners in the West Country and for national firms. Acts for the Insolvency Service in bringing disqualification proceedings under the CDDA 1986. Law Society CPD course assessor.
Prof. Memberships: Law Society.
Career: BA Birmingham University. Qualified in 1981. LLM at University College London, before moving to Devon in 1982. Partner with Anstey Sargent & Probert since 1989. Licensed Insolvency Practitioner since 1990.
Personal: Leisure interests include riding, skiing, water sports and energetic teenage family.

SMITH, Phillip
Boyes Turner & Burrows, Reading
(0118) 959 7711
psmith@b-t-b.co.uk
Specialisation: All aspects of insolvency work, corporate and personal. Particular experience in dealing with administrations, administrative receiverships and large-scale bankruptcies involving cross-border investigations and asset tracing.
Prof. Memberships: Association of Business Recovery Professionals. Insolvency Lawyers Association, Law Society.
Career: With *Boyes Turner & Burrows* since articles: qualified 1994, associate 1998, partner April 2000.
Personal: Born 1970. Leisure interests: golf, football and the guitar.

SPENCER, Robin G.N.
Lovells, London (020) 7296 2000
robin.spencer@lovells.com
Specialisation: Insolvency and business restructuring group specialising in insolvent insurance and reinsurance companies, insurance–related insolvency matters and troubled financial services companies, as well as other more general types of insolvency and restructuring. Major assignments include Mentor Insurance Limited; Drexel Burnham Lambert Group; British & Commonwealth Merchant Bank plc; OIC Run-Off (formerly The Orion Insurance Company plc); The London and Overseas Insurance Company PLC; Gooda Walker Limited; Dawnay, Day Securities Limited; the scheme administrators of Sovereign Marine & General Insurance Company Limited; New Cap Reinsurance Corporation (Bermuda) Limited and New Cap Re (Australia).
Career: Qualified as Barrister 1981; solicitors' office HM Customs & Excise 1983–1986; joined *Lovells* 1987 (including two year secondment to *Appleby, Spurling & Kempe*, attorneys, Bermuda); requalified as solicitor 1991; partner 1994; member of International Association of Insurance Receivers, Society of Practitioners of Insolvency.
Personal: Born 1958. Educated at Birkenhead School (1969–1976); Pembroke College, Cambridge (1980 BA Hons (Cantab)); 1984 MA (Cantab)). Resides Chesham, Buckinghamshire.

SPENCER, Shân
Chaffe Street, Manchester (0161) 236 5800
Specialisation: Deals with the full range of insolvency matters with the emphasis on corporate insolvency including administrative receiverships, administrations, liquidations and CVAs. Also acts for banks in recovery matters and risk positions. Has acted in cases including Keith Prowse, ELS, Kumar Brothers, Doctus plc, Habit Group, Paddy Hopkirk Limited, Australia House Limited and Production Steel Group. Addresses SPI conferences.
Prof. Memberships: Society of Practitioners of Insolvency, (Chairman North West Region), Insolvency Lawyers Association, Insolvency Practitioners Association, Association Europeene des Practiciens des Procedures Collective.

STEINBERG, David Jeremy
Clifford Chance, London (020) 7600 1000
david.steinberg@cliffordchance.com
Specialisation: Insolvency group partner specialising in insurance reconstruction and insolvency, general restructuring and general insolvency.
Prof. Memberships: CBI Insolvency sub-panel.
Career: King Edward VI Grammar School, Southampton; St John's College, Cambridge. Articled *Clifford Chance*; qualified 1988; partner 1994.
Personal: Born 1960; resides London.

STEINER, Michael
Denton Wilde Sapte, London (020) 7320 6887

STEWART, Gordon C.
Allen & Overy, London (020) 7330 3000
Partner in Banking Department and Head of Business Reconstruction and Insolvency Group.
Specialisation: Practice covers the full range of rescue and insolvency work. Recent and current jobs include acting for banks on a confidential but high profile workout in the retail sector and in the restructuring of Slovakian steel manufacturer, VSZ, through to acting for the receivers of World Telecom and secured creditors in the insurance collapse, Ocean Marine. Past highlights include acting for the Maxwell administrators, the Farranti receivers and the Facia liquidators. Also advised foreign governments on law reform and represented the insolvency profession in connection with Paramount in the House of Lords.
Career: Qualified in 1980. Joined *Allen & Overy* as a Partner in 1989. The first lawyer to become President of what is now called R3 or the Association of Business Recovery Professionals (formerly Society of Practitioners of Insolvency–SPI) in 1996–1967, and remains a council member. Council Member of INSOL International and from 1993–1999 was the solicitor member of the Lord Chancellor's Insolvency Rules Committee. Author of 'Administrative Receivers and Administrators' (1987) and contributor to 'Leasing Law in the European Union' (1994). Prolific lecturer and author of various articles in this field including the legal update column in 'Recovery', the R3 journal.
Personal: Born 1956. Attended Hutcheson's Boys Grammar School, Glasgow 1970–74 and University College, Oxford 1974–77. Leisure interests include running, golf and humour. Lives in London.

STOBART, Guy W.
Burges Salmon, Bristol (0117) 939 2241
guy.stobart@burges-salmon.com
Specialisation: Corporate rescue and recovery and head of this unit. He is also involved with the financing aspects of a number of PFI projects. Major clients include Lloyds TSB, Bank of Scotland and Standard Chartered Bank. His finance work also covers a diverse spectrum of banking transactions and general banking law.
Prof. Memberships: Law Society, member of the Association of Business Recovery Professionals and the Insolvency Lawyers Association and a licensed insolvency practitioner.
Career: Trained and worked at *Slaughter and May* for five years before joining *Burges Salmon* in 1983, becoming a partner in 1986. He was managing partner from 1995–1999.

SULLIVAN, John C.P.
Hammond Suddards Edge, Birmingham
(0121) 200 2001
Partner in Insolvency and International Litigation Departments.
Specialisation: Handles banking and insolvency work of all types with international work as a specialist skill.
Prof. Memberships: Member of Society of Practitioners in Insolvency.
Career: Qualified in 1980. Joined *Edge Ellison* in 1978, becoming a Partner in 1987.
Personal: Born 10th August 1956. Attended Oxford University 1974-77.

SWANSON, Magnus P.
Maclay Murray & Spens, Glasgow
(0141) 248 5011
mps@maclaymurrayspens.co.uk
See under Corporate Finance, p.266

TAYLOR, Andy
Argles Stoneham Burstows, Brighton
(01273) 828000

TAYLOR, Elizabeth
Darbys Mallam Lewis, Oxford (01865) 811700
Specialisation: Deals with all aspects of individual and corporate insolvency, from administration to IVAs. Acts for a number of insolvency practitioners. Recently joined this leading Oxford firm to enhance their already expanding insolvency practice.
Prof. Memberships: Law Society, LawNet Insolvency Unit. Licenced insolvency practitioner.
Career: Born 18th March 1967. Oxford University. Partner *Parrott & Coales* 1997–1999. Joined *Darbys Mallam Lewis* as a Partner September 1999.

TAYLOR, Michael F.
Walker Morris, Leeds (0113) 283 2500
Specialisation: Work includes all aspects of non-contentious corporate insolvency, restructuring and work outs.
Career: Qualified 1986; Partner *Walker Morris* 1991.
Personal: Attended King Edward VI School, Lichfield and University of Bristol 1980–83. Leisure interests include hockey and fly-fishing. Lives in Leeds.

TETTMAR, Victor
Bond Pearce, Bristol (0117) 929 9197
xvst@bondpearce.com
Partner and Head of the Banking and Insolvency Group.
Specialisation: Licensed insolvency practitioner specialising in all aspects of insolvency, bank recovery and rescue. Particular expertise in corporate insolvency, security issues, restructuring and the agribusiness sector.
Prof. Memberships: Full member of the Association of Business Recovery Professionals (R3), the Insolvency Lawyers Association and Non Administrative Receivers Association, and Vice Chairman of South West and South Wales region of R3.
Publications: Editor of Jordans Agricultural Lending: Security and Enforcement published 1999.
Personal: Manchester University. Remained with *Bond Pearce* on qualifying in 1985, becoming a partner 1991.

THOMAS, Catrin Wyn
Hugh James Ford Simey, Cardiff (029) 2022 4871
catrin.thomas@hjfs.co.uk
Partner and Head of insolvency and debt recovery unit.
Specialisation: Handles all aspects of personal, partnership and corporate insolvency. Acts on behalf of a variety of clients including insolvency practitioners, banks and other financial institutions, directors, shareholders and many professional individuals (mainly architects and accountants). Deals with contentious and non-contentious insolvency work and also commercial litigation including banking litigation and litigation between directors and shareholders.
Prof. Memberships: Law Society, Insolvency Lawyers' Association.
Career: Qualified in 1983. Became a Partner at *Hugh James* in 1986. Licensed Insolvency Practitioner since 1989, the only one in Wales amongst the legal profession.
Personal: Born 26th September 1956. Educated at the University of Wales, Aberystwyth 1975–78 (LL.B) and Emmanuel College, Cambridge 1980–81 (LL.M). Leisure interests include reading, music, theatre, travel and watching rugby and cricket. Lives in Cardiff.

TYRELL, Vivien M.
D J Freeman, London (020) 7583 4055
vmt@djfreeman.co.uk
Partner in the Insurance Department.
Specialisation: Authorised insolvency practitioner. Acting for officeholders and advising in relation to all aspects of insolvency. The largest proportion of her work is insurance insolvency involving drafting international schemes of arrangement. She has unwound joint venture agreements and vehicles, pursued actions for the repatriation of assets using injunctions and officeholders' interrogation procedures both here and abroad. Wrongful trading, directors' misfeasance and other directors' liability issues. Advice in relation to exit routes to creditors and shareholders whose interests are in insurance companies in run-off.
Prof. Memberships: International Association of Insurance Receivers, AEPPC (European Insolvency Practitioners Association), INSOL, ILA and ABRP.
Career: Qualified 1980. Joined *D J Freeman* 1981 (Partner from 1985).
Personal: Educated at South Shields Grammar School for Girls and Somerville College, Oxford (BA Hons Jurisprudence). Interests include opera, skiing, sailing, hot air ballooning.

VAUGHAN, Philip D.
Eversheds, Cardiff (02920) 471147
Partner.
Specialisation: Practice covers a wide–range of non-contentious banking and finance work and includes transactional work (including acquisition finance), regulatory advice and drafting of standard documentation for banks, building societies, centralised mortgage lenders and finance companies. Has a particular expertise in consumer credit work. Also involved in a wide range of non-contentious insolvency work acting for receivers, administrators and liquidators and advising lenders on enforcement of security and restructuring/refinancings.
Career: Qualified 1984. Formerly with *Clifford Chance* and *National Westminster Bank* Legal Department. Joined current firm in 1987 and became Partner in 1988.
Personal: Born 14th December 1958. Educated at Haverfordwest Grammar School, St. Edmund Hall, Oxford (M.A.) and Emmanuel College, Cambridge (LL.M.).

VERRILL, John
Lawrence Graham, London (020) 7379 0000
john.verrill@lawgram.com
Partner in Company Commercial Department.
Specialisation: Significant area of practice is insolvency. Acted in the company voluntary arrangement of London Securities PLC and gave advice to boards of British and Commonwealth and Polly Peck after administration orders made. Author of Butterworths 'Insolvency Meetings Manual'. Frequent speaker and writer on insolvency topics. Recent work includes restitution and wrongful trading actions arising out of ultra vires local authority contracts. Has also been involved in elements of Thailand's restructuring and the 'Bangkok Principles'. Also has significant area of practice in oil and gas law. Work covers all aspects of upstream asset management, and Council Member Association of Business Recovery Professionals or R3.
Prof. Memberships: Insolvency Practitioners Association, Fellow of Society of Practitioners in Insolvency, Insolvency Lawyers Association (Council Member and Vice-President). UK Energy Lawyers Group, International Bar Association Section on Energy and Resources Law.
Career: Qualified in 1981. Licensed Insolvency Practitioner 1990. Joined *Lawrence Graham* in 1983, becoming a Partner in 1986.
Personal: Born 25th March 1954. Attended University College School Hampstead, then University College, London (LLB Hons). Leisure interests include shooting, rowing and gardening. Lives in South Oxfordshire.

WAINE, Ian
Prettys, Ipswich (01473) 232121
lmw@prettys.co.uk
Specialisation: Acts for insolvency practitioners, banks, corporate and unincorporated clients on corporate reconstructions and rescues, administrations, receiverships, liquidations, bankruptcies and voluntary arrangements.

WALD, Matthew
Stephens & Scown, Plymouth (01752) 213 850
commerce.lawdirect@stephens-scown.co.uk
Specialisation: Partner specialising in insolvency and bank recovery; licenced High Court Advocate; cases include AMC Woodward [1994] BCC and Re Rae [1995] BCC.
Career: Called to the Bar in 1982; solicitor 1990; Inland Revenue Solicitors Office 1984–1988; *Bond Pearce* 1988–1994; *Stephens & Scown* 1994, partner 1996.

WALLER, Simon
Eversheds, Manchester (0161) 832 6666
simonwaller@eversheds.com
Specialisation: Partner; head of corporate recovery and insolvency, Leeds and Manchester; specialises in insolvency and corporate reconstruction. Acts for all of the main accountancy practices and for a number of banks and secondary lenders; previously acted (whilst at *Wilde Sapte*) for the Receivers of Leyland Daf Limited and the Administrators of Paramount Airways Limited amongst others. Currently advising a number of clearing banks on their exposure to the accident management industry and the Receivers of Tudor Properties Ltd (the largest RBS appoitment this year in the North West).
Prof. Memberships: SPI.
Career: Articled *Booth & Co*; qualified 1989; *Wilde Sapte* to 1996; partner *Halliwell Landau* 1996–98; partner *Eversheds* 1998; sits on editorial board of Receivers, Administrators and Liquidators quarterly.
Personal: St Cuthbert's School; Durham University (BA Hons Law); sport, cinema, reading; resides Didsbury; one daughter.

WALSH, Jeremy Michael
Travers Smith Braithwaite, London
(020) 7295 3000
Jeremy.Walsh@TraversSmith.com
Specialisation: Partner specialising in corporate rescue, reconstruction and insolvency, acting for banks, companies, insolvency practitioners, creditors and investors. Has wide experience including rescues, reconstructions, administrations, receiverships, liquidations, voluntary arrangements and schemes of arrangement. Licensed insolvency practitioner since 1994.
Prof. Memberships: Law Society, Association of Business Recovery Professionals, Insolvency Lawyers Association, European Insolvency Practitioners Association and International Bar Association.
Career: Qualified in 1985. Partner in *Travers Smith Braithwaite* since 1994.
Personal: Born 4 November 1960. University of Manchester. Interests include family, films, theatre, swimming and music.

WHEATLEY, Jamie G.
Mills & Reeve, Cambridge (01223) 222 206
jamie.wheatley@mills-reeve.com
Specialisation: Practices in commercial and insolvency litigation.
Career: Articled *Ryland Martineau & Co*; qualified 1987; partner *Mills & Reeve* 1993.
Personal: Rugby School; Southampton University (1983 LLB).

WHITE, John J.
CMS Cameron McKenna, London (020) 7367 3000
jjw@cmck.com
Partner and head of banking and insolvency group.
Specialisation: Insolvency work includes multi–bank support operations, administrations and administrative receiverships. Banking work includes clearing bank lending, property and project finance, trade finance and syndicated facilities. Acted for the administrators of Polly Peck, the examiner of the Maxwell Communication Corporation and the administrators of Air Europe. Addresses around twenty conferences per year.
Prof. Memberships: Law Society, Chartered Institute of Bankers, Society of Practitioners in Insolvency, Insolvency Lawyers Association, International Bar Association, City of London Solicitors Company, Association Europeene des Practiciens des Procedures Collectives.
Career: Qualified in 1963. Having joined *Cameron Markby Hewitt* in 1957, became a partner in 1964. Fellow of the Chartered Institute of Bankers.
Personal: Born 6th July 1938. Leisure interests include hockey, cricket and port. Lives in London. Clubs: Athenaeum and West Herts.

WILKINS, John R.
Dolmans, Cardiff (029) 2034 5531
Qualified 1969 partner in insolvency and commercial litigation department.
Specialisation: Advises administrators, administrative receivers, liquidators, supervisors and trustees in bankruptcy on all aspects of insolvency practice both contentious and non–contentious and assists in the realisation of assets and sales of business. Advises directors on their responsibilities and potential liabilities both before and after insolvency. Advises individuals and partnerships on their business and other financial matters.

WILKINSON, Andrew J.O.
Cadwalader, Wickersham & Taft, London (020) 7456 8500
Partner in financial restructuring group.
Specialisation: Wide experience in both insurance restructuring and general restructuring and insolvency. He has pioneered the use of schemes of arrangement for the work out of troubled insurance companies and is currently acting for investment banks, related hedge funds and insolvency practitioners on general restructuring and insolvency matters. Mr Wilkinson is a licensed insolvency practitioner. He also writes and lectures extensively on all aspects of restructuring and insolvency.

WILSON, Michael W.C.
Elliott Duffy Garrett, Belfast (028) 9024 5034

WILTSHIRE, Peter
CMS Cameron McKenna, Bristol (0117) 930 0200
Specialisation: All aspects of insolvency related work advising banks and other financial institutions and insolvency practitioners. Includes rescue and work outs, concentrating on non-contentious insolvency.
Prof. Memberships: Insolvency Lawyers Association. Associate Member 3R's.
Career: Articled *Cameron Markby/Cameron Markby Hewitt* 1988–1990. Qualified *Cameron Markby Hewitt*, London, 1990. Bristol *Cameron Markby Hewitt* to date (now *CMS Cameron McKenna*). Partner 1999.
Personal: Regular provider of seminars for SPI (3R's). Church. Armchair sports critic. Singing. Married, five children.

WITHYMAN, Tom
Lawrence Graham, London (020) 7379 0000
tom.withyman@lawgram.com
Specialisation: Partner handling all aspects of corporate insolvency and reconstructions with particular specialisation in administrations. Recent non-contentious work includes acting for the Administrators of Pex Plc and the Receivers of Luton Town Football Club. Acted for Liquidators of ASRS Establishment Ltd in reported case on validity of fixed charges. Frequently lectures and writes on insolvency topics.
Prof. Memberships: Law Society, Insolvency Practioners Association, Association of Business Recovery Professionals, Insolvency Lawyers' Association.
Career: *Lawrence Graham* 1990-1995, Senior Crown Counsel Turks and Caicos Islands 1995-1997, *Lawrence Graham* 1997 to date (Partner 2000); Licensed Insolvency Practitioner 1999.
Career: Born 1966. Educated at Spalding GS and Emmanuel College, Cambridge. Interests: hiking and golf. Married with two children.

WOOLF, Geoffrey
SJ Berwin & Co, London (020) 7809 2012
Partner in Banking Department (Insolvency & Asset Recovery Group).
Specialisation: Principal area of practice is corporate insolvency and reconstruction. Also handles banking and financial services work and debt restructuring. Advises a clearing bank on its standard forms and procedures. Has acted as an expert witness in a number of cases. Regularly speaks at conferences and publishes articles.
Career: Qualified in 1970 after articles at *Stephenson Harwood*. Former Head of the Property Department and former Finance Partner.
Personal: Born 1946. Educated at Harrow County Grammar School and King's College, London (LL.B 1967).

WRIGHT, Richard W.
Linklaters (A member firm of Linklaters & Alliance), London (020) 7456 3477
richard.wright@linklaters.com
Specialisation: Has acted in all areas of insolvency most recently on contentious and investigatory matters. Presently acting for the liquidators of Japan Leasing (Hong Kong) Ltd. Also practises in the field of fraud and financial services malfeasance.
Prof. Memberships: Member of the Insolvency Practitioners Association, R3 and the Insolvency Lawyers Association. Former President and Council Member of the Insolvency Lawyers Association. Member of the Justice Committee on Bankruptcy in the mid-1970s.
Career: Bryanston School, Dorset; MA (Cantab) – articled and at *Simmons & Simmons* 1964–1967, partner *William Prior & Co* 1968–1990, partner *Dibb Lupton Broomhead* 1990–1996, Of Counsel to *Linklaters* 1996 to date.

YORKE, Jonathan
Richards Butler, London (020) 7247 6555
Specialisation: Specialises in all aspects of corporate insolvency in particular receiverships, administrations, liquidations and voluntary arrangements. He has been involved in a number of larger insolvencies over the last decade with particular involvement in cross border cases. In recent years he has specialised in the insolvency of insurance companies acting for PricewaterhouseCoopers in the North Atlantic and Black Sea and Baltic provisional liquidations.
Prof. Memberships: Society of Practitioners of Insolvency, Law Society European Insolvency Practitioners Association, Insolvency Lawyers Association.
Career: University of Essex LLB (Hons). Qualified as a solicitor 1986, Licensed Insolvency Practitioner 1990, Partner at *Richards Butler* 1992.
Personal: Cycling, skiing, sailing, paragliding and trying to get fit. Married with two children.

INSURANCE

OVERVIEW: Our London section continues to be divided into General Claims, Reinsurance and Non-contentious work, while Insurance Insolvency is included in the Insolvency section. No individuals' table has been included in this year's regional section, due to the feeling that most work is team-based. Individuals have also been reduced in London, although it is perceived here that *"the very top names do open doors."*

Reinsurance is almost all carried out in London. The specialist companies and Lloyds Syndicates are served by firms with dedicated re-insurance teams and broader practices with a strong interest in the field. The Woolf reforms have not had a major impact in this area.

Non-contentious work includes demutualisations, mergers, take-overs and flotations of insurance companies. It is with this type of work that the major corporate firms come into their own.

RESEARCH APPROVED BY BMRB: *For this edition,* Chambers' *researchers conducted 6083 interviews – 4408 with law firms, 598 with barristers and 1077 with clients.*

The validity of the research was scrutinised by BMRB International, who audited both the methodology and the results at our offices in July 2000. They interviewed Chambers' *researchers and cross-checked sample interviews. Details of the audit appear on page 7.*

LEADING IN-HOUSE LAWYERS

Bob BRITTON, In-House Solicitor, *Hiscox Syndicate 33*

Victoria COCHRANE, Partner, *Ernst & Young*

Paul JAFFE, Solicitor and Attorney at Law, *Brockbank*

Jane OWEN, Senior Lawyer, *Aon UK Holdings Limited*

Vyvienne WADE, Group Legal Director, *Jardine Lloyd Thompson*

Rhic WEBB, Head of Legal, *Brockbank*

Bob Britton at Hiscox has *"a very good handle on the commercial needs of the market."* **Victoria Cochrane** at Ernst & Young is a *"most highly respected lawyer."* **Jane Owen**, who has built up an extremely impressive legal team at Aon has *"very good commercial acumen."* **Vyvienne Wade** at Jardine Lloyd Thompson is *"a force to be reckoned with."* **Rhic Webb** at Brockbank *"brings both market and legal expertise to the job."* Also with Brockbank is **Paul Jaffe** who is *"excellent."*

In-House lawyers profiles: page 1177

LONDON

GENERAL CLAIMS

Barlow Lyde & Gilbert By a short head this is the leading firm in the field. Commended universally by other law firms, clients and barristers, and seen as having real technological expertise. Acts for all types of insurance carriers, including Lloyd's Syndicates, risk managers and most of the major insurers. The firm's workload ranges from small claims to high volume and major international deals. It is strongly recommended for its professional negligence work. During the past year, the team defended the broker Minet in a claim for over $250m following a smelter explosion in Utah, and acted as overall co-ordinating advisor to Lloyds on Y2K for non-US jurisdictions. Known more for team strength than individual excellence, the firm boasts **Tim Hardy** who is a *"real heavyweight"* and *"nice to deal with."* **Clients:** AXA Reinsurance (UK) Plc; Lloyd's Claims Office; Churchill Insurance Co Ltd.

Clyde & Co A real player at the top end of the market, and noted by peers for its *"excellent marine and energy insurance work."* The work is handled at the London and Guildford offices, which receive considerable support from the firm's overseas offices. Much of the firm's workload derives from Lloyd's syndicates and the Lloyd's Claims Office, but it also received commendations from major insurance companies. Highlights of the past year include representing London insurers in disputes over extended warranty disputes in the US and Canada, and representing international traders over oil losses in the Middle East. The most notable figures in a strong team are **Michael Payton**, seen by many as *"the best of the bunch,"* **Rod Smith**, who is considered good on international issues, and **Peter Farthing**, who is a *"substantial player."* **Clients:** Lloyd's Syndicates; insurance companies.

CMS Cameron McKenna An excellent practice with *"a very good name"* on larger claims work. Best known for its work for the major accountancy companies on liquidations and commended for its personal injury and brokers' financial services work. Also advise various Lloyd's Underwriter's brokers and insurers on insolvency. *"Flamboyant"* **Mark Elborne** is considered to be *"the firm's rainmaker"* and is *"very good with clients."* **Belinda Schofield** has a *"good reputation"* and is considered *"a class act"* by her peers. The team acted for the Association of British Insurers in connection with the hearing of eight test cases, during which the Court of Appeal considered recommendations made by the Law Commission for increased payments to accident victims. **Clients:** Insurance Companies; Lloyd's Syndicates.

Ince & Co Another firm at the top end of the market, *"a major player"* with *"a long-standing name."* Known for handling lots of energy, non-marine, political risk and property work. The team has been involved in the insurance drafting and regulatory aspects of projects to securitise project finance up to investment grade with the use of political, credit and contingency risk insurance. **Clients:** P&I clubs; insurance companies.

Davies Arnold Cooper General market perception is that the practice has not suffered as badly as it could have done following the firm's trials and tribulations of the past year. It continues to work for composite insurers, Lloyd's syndicates and a motor direct insurer. Nevertheless, it is not considered to be one of the elite and its position is under some pressure. Work ranges from high volume, low value claims in personal injury to highly complex matters in professional indemnity. The practice is also noted by clients for its specialisation in property and construction insurance. Highlights of the past year include defence of the West Midlands Fire Brigade accused of negligent fire fighting resulting in a £11m loss. Despite a troubled year, **Nicholas Sinfield** *"remains very sound on insurance"* and is widely perceived by the market to be a major player. **Clients:** Zurich, Independent, R&SA.

Kennedys Considered to be a firm on the up, particularly with regard to bulk work. Particularly liked by regional firms and clients, it is frequently seen in the marketplace. Has attracted a number of new partners over the past year, partly by securing the Zurich/Eagle Star insurance litigation team

INSURANCE: GENERAL CLAIMS • London	Ptnrs	Assts
❶ Barlow Lyde & Gilbert	55	109
❷ Clyde & Co	33	56
CMS Cameron McKenna	13*	32*
Ince & Co	14*	24*
❸ Davies Arnold Cooper	26	58
Kennedys	43	57
Reynolds Porter Chamberlain	27	52
❹ Freshfields Bruckhaus Deringer	8*	20*
Herbert Smith	8	20
Lovells	8	20
Vizards, Staples & Bannisters	14	23
❺ Beachcroft Wansbroughs	7	14
Berrymans Lace Mawer	3	5
Clifford Chance	8*	31*
DJ Freeman	6	15
Holman Fenwick & Willan	7*	10
Rowe & Maw	5	7
❻ Elborne Mitchell	⚐	⚐
Eversheds	4	13
Hextall Erskine	19	14

LEADING INDIVIDUALS	
❶ BAKES Martin Herbert Smith	ELBORNE Mark CMS Cameron McKenna
GREENLEY Simon Reynolds Porter Chamberlain	
HIGGINS David Herbert Smith	PAYTON Michael Clyde & Co
SCHOFIELD Belinda CMS Cameron McKenna	
SINFIELD Nicholas Davies Arnold Cooper	SMITH Roderick Clyde & Co
❷ CONNOLEY Mark Richards Butler	FARTHING Peter Clyde & Co
HARDY Tim Barlow Lyde & Gilbert	

Within each band, firms are listed alphabetically. *See **Profiles** on page 493*

** Figures are totals for Insurance and Reinsurance teams*

⚐ Figures unavailable at time of going to press.

from disintegrated Edward Lewis. Clients include Lloyd's Syndicates and many of the major composites. On a lot of panels and *"does an awful lot of work."* In professional liability, and personal injury, it attracts a high volume of work, but this can range from 'slip and trip' work to a rail crash. Also handles general and public liability, property and employers' insurance. **Clients:** Lloyd's Syndicates.

Reynolds Porter Chamberlain A strong practice which is felt to be making progress. Made its name in professional indemnity, within which it is still considered *"top rank,"* but clients praised the team across the board. The firm works for major insurance companies and mutuals, and there has been a significant increase in work undertaken under pre-action protocols following the introduction of the Woolf reforms. Highlights of the year include defending Countess Spencer's claim against her ex-solicitors, and advising Lloyd's on property matters arising from Y2K. **Simon Greenley** is the star name; he is *"a solid performer in everything he does"* and *"he does everything."* **Clients:** Wren Insurance Services; John Hancock; Lloyd's Syndicates.

Freshfields Bruckhaus Deringer Not considered an insurance specialist, the firm has *"carved a reputation for company work"*, and is *"excellent at the top end of the market, where money is no object."* Known for international and technically difficult work, and one of the leading corporate insurance firms. The firm continues to represent the Equitas Group on various matters associated with the reconstruction and renewal of Lloyd's. **Clients:** Lloyd's; Equitas; CE Heath plc.

Herbert Smith *"Good on the big stuff,"* it is largely considered to be a broker practice, but also acts for UK insurance institutions. Highlights of the year include advising Amey and its insurers regarding the Ladbroke Grove and Southall train crashes. The firm also did the advocacy work in the Southall train crash. Not a large outfit, but *"those who do it, do well."* The team is known for having its *"tough characters"*: **Martin Bakes** *("a noted litigator")* and **David Higgins,** who is known for the breadth of his work in the industry. **Clients:** CGU; Royal & Sun Alliance; Willis.

Lovells Another firm acting at the top end of the market, but not seen as a specialist outfit. During the past year, it resolved the Mirror Group litigation and represented a major US insurance company in arbitration proceedings. It also worked on a variety of Y2K exposures. Continued to handle a large volume of claims for the Solicitors Indemnity Fund, the company market and Lloyd's. **Clients:** Mirror Group.

Vizards, Staples & Bannisters This *"quality"* practice handles a mixture of large and small scale work and *"is becoming a player."* Generally considered by the market to be making progress, it was highly praised by its peers. It specialises in employers' and public liability work for a clientele ranging from charities to multinationals, and clients also noted its expertise in industrial disease and motor liability. **Clients:** CGU; Iron Trades; Royal & Sun Alliance.

Beachcroft Wansbroughs This national player is beginning to attract some higher value work. The merger is seen to have consolidated the firm's position in the market. The office handles work for London and the South-East, and undertakes some work with an international flavour. Apart from the standard personal injury and professional negligence work which is handled by the firm nationally, the office is also noted for coverage work. The clientele consists of Lloyd's Syndicates, large corporates and corporate insurers. **Clients:** ICI.

Berrymans Lace Mawer A solid national practice with a substantial London presence. Works for many of the leading insurance companies, and specialises in the recovery of insurance funds following fire, flood and other disasters. Other work includes pensions mis-selling, tobacco litigation and coverage issues. Highlights of the past year include a derailment breakdown cover dispute and the development of a schools insurance policy. **Clients:** Royal & SunAlliance; CGU; Independent Insurance Company.

Clifford Chance Best known for its insurance insolvency work, the practice is well known by the top accountancy firms. Not seen a great deal in the marketplace, the firm *"appears exclusively for the big cases."* Does a lot of work for Anglo American Insurance Company, and acted for the liquidators on the litigation in Bermuda against the Bermuda Fire and Marine Insurance Company Ltd. **Clients:** Anglo American Insurance Company.

DJ Freeman Maintaining its ranking, the firm has a good name in the market, both for high volume and high value claims work. The team acted for six insurance companies and 1000 shareholder defendants in the Bermuda Fire & Marine case. **Clients:** Insurance companies.

Holman Fenwick & Willan A well known marine insurance practice which *"handles masses of claims."* The practice is heavily influenced by Lloyd's and the company market. Advised managing agents on mechanisms for portfolio tranfers into Lloyd's from overseas insurers. **Clients:** Quincy Mutual Fire Insurance Corp; Liberty Syndicate Management Limited.

Rowe & Maw A middle sized practice that is *"on its way"* and is *"punching well above its weight."* Clients and London rivals consider that the firm has done *"an awful lot in raising its profile,"* and that slick marketing has been accompanied by a growing workload. The firm is currently working for London Market Insurers and Reinsurers in a number of countries. It is also recognised for its professional indemnity work, and often deals with fraud and forensic investigations. Highlights of the past year include work on the pension mis-selling scandal. **Clients:** RJ Wallace & Others; The Chartwell Underwriting Group; Axa Insurance

Elborne Mitchell The firm acts in a number of areas, including marine and construction insurance, but is not considered to have as high a profile as previously. **Clients:** Insurance companies.

Eversheds The practice is not considered a player by the market as a whole, but several clients were impressed by its work and so the practice is worth ranking. It is keen to make an impact and has attracted clients including major insurance composites, Lloyd's Syndicates and self insurers. The firm's strengths lie in construction and property damage claims, and regulatory investigations of insurance brokers. One of the highlights of the past year was advising insurers on a £4.5 million claim over the construction of an office block. **Clients:** Insurance composites; Lloyd's Syndicates.

Hextall Erskine An insurance specialist with a broad range of work. Although seen somewhat less in the market over the past year, the firm continues to handle professional indemnity, public and product liability. **Clients:** Underwriters; Lloyd's Syndicates.

Other Notable Practitioner Mark Connoley is an exception to the prevailing climate in insurance. Although his firm, Richards Butler, has a lower profile this year, he is still recognised as a *"consistently reliable"* performer.

REINSURANCE

INSURANCE: REINSURANCE • London	Ptnrs	Assts
❶ Barlow Lyde & Gilbert	15	22
❷ Clyde & Co	5	7
Ince & Co	14*	24*
❸ Clifford Chance	8*	31*
CMS Cameron McKenna	13*	32*
Holman Fenwick & Willan	7*	10*
❹ DJ Freeman	5	13
Freshfields Bruckhaus Deringer	8*	20*
Lovells	6	12
❺ Elborne Mitchell	⚐	⚐
Herbert Smith	8	20
Paisner & Co	3	3
Reynolds Porter Chamberlain	4	9
Richards Butler	2	4

LEADING INDIVIDUALS	
✪ ROGAN Peter Ince & Co	
❶ CROLY Colin Barlow Lyde & Gilbert	
❷ DUFF John Holman Fenwick & Willan	
❸ BANDURKA Andrew Holman Fenwick & Willan	
BROOK Nigel Clyde & Co	DOBIAS Michael Davies Arnold Cooper
ELBORNE Mark CMS Cameron McKenna	
O'NEILL Terry Clifford Chance	PAYTON Michael Clyde & Co
❹ AKEROYD Tim Elborne Mitchell	HEPWORTH Allan Ince & Co
KENDALL David DJ Freeman	LEWIS Stephen Clifford Chance
MACKIE Francis Norton Rose	McKENNA Ian Holman Fenwick & Willan
MENDELOWITZ Michael Barlow Lyde & Gilbert	
MUNDAY Nicholas Clifford Chance	WHEATLEY Vere CMS Cameron McKenna

Within each band, firms are listed alphabetically. *See Profiles on page 493*
** Figures are totals for Insurance and Reinsurance teams*
⚐ Figures unavailable at time of going to press.

Barlow Lyde & Gilbert Considered *"definitely the number one firm"* by a majority of players in the market, the firm is considered *"a cut above"* the other heavyweight runners in the field. Its range of UK and international clients and the size of its department and workload, *"mark the firm out as something special."* Its clientele includes major British and foreign insurance and re-insurance companies. During the past year the firm advised the International Underwriting Association on Y2K and worked on claims arising out of the Indonesian riots. One of the firm's highlights of the past year was its work on the disputed reinsurance cover of Kennecott mining operations. *"High profile"* **Colin Croly** is considered to be *"a real leader,"* who runs his team with *"a rod of iron."* Of the other impressive members of the practice, **Michael Mendelowitz** proves particularly popular with clients. **Clients:** Bavarian Re; SVB Syndicates Limited; CGU.

Clyde & Co A leading player and considered by the market as a whole to be *"on a par with Inces."* Its main fields of activity are marine, professional indemnity, credit, aviation and energy work. Clients include most of the major managing agents at Lloyd's, and leading London and overseas Insurance companies, particularly those in Scandinavia. Seven overseas offices offer considerable support to a practice, known for handling a large amount of multi-party international disputes. Highlights of the past year include work for Sphere Drake in the workers' compensation reinsurance affair and the continuing saga of the Exxon Valdez. Of the leading figures in the team, **Nigel Brook** *"has a reputation for being solid and straightforward,"* while *"figurehead"* **Michael Payton** still *"gets his hands dirty"* and is *"damn good at what he does."* **Clients:** Sphere Drake.

Ince & Co One of the leading practices, the firm is well known for the quality of its work among peers, and commended for the *"excellence"* of its lawyers by clients. During the past year it has advised Crown Life on the PA spiral and has attracted praise for its work for brokers. **Peter Rogan** is *"the real star"* of the outfit. Although active in a number of areas, he is an expert on reinsurance who is perceived as being *"hands on in the marketplace."* Peers consider his talents rate *"way up the scale."* **Allan Hepworth** is *"a civilised human being"* who *"thinks he's good and is good."* **Clients:** Crown Life.

Clifford Chance Market perception of the firm is rather confusing; it is not considered to be a specialist practice, yet is considered to be gaining work and increasing its profile. The firm's huge resources regularly attracts work from liquidators. During the past year, the firm has worked for major North Amercian Life companies concerning Unicover and the PA LMX Spiral. Also worked on the Bermuda Fire & Marine case, and won the Sphere Drake v Orion case in the Court of Appeal. **Terry O'Neill** is considered to be *"bright and talented,"* but his *"reputation for being aloof"* can sometimes mask this. **Nick Munday** is noted for work on political risks and **Stephen Lewis** is also a recommended practitioner. **Clients:** AON; Sun Life (Canada); Lloyd's Underwriters.

CMS Cameron McKenna *"Now have more bodies and so are getting a higher profile."* The *"realistic"* **Mark Elborne** is considered *"the driving force"* and **Vere Wheatley** is also *"well known in this area."* Particularly renowned for work on film, finance and contingency, the team achieved a notable coup when acting on behalf of Aneco and its liquidators on its successful Court of Appeal case, when a damages award was increased by $32 million to encompass the whole of the losses suffered as a result of entering into a reinsurance treaty. **Clients:** Aneco.

Holman Fenwick & Willan A solid traditional reinsurance practice, respected by peers and clients alike. *"Focused on marine"* the firm also attracts work outside its area of specialism. The outfit boasts three noted performers. **John Duff** is *"extremely able"* and handles the highest profile cases, **Andrew Bandurka** is seen to have made *"great strides"*, and *"is heading for the top"* with his good relations with clients. **Ian McKenna** is *"a nice guy"* and *"a good litigator."* Have won a number of recent high-profile arbitrations. **Clients:** P&I Clubs; Lloyd's Underwriters.

DJ Freeman Warmly recommended, the firm is a secure mid-table performer. Market perception is that it is not seen as much as formerly, although it is noted for the quality and quantity of *"liquidation work"* which it attracts. **David Kendall** is seen *"all over the place;"* he *"has a very good name and a very good practice."* **Clients:** Insurance companies; underwriters.

Freshfields Bruckhaus Deringer A big City practice which attracts big City work in the form of liquidators. The team is perceived as *"only involved in the big action,"* but has great resources and *"do have a real expertise."* The team has won high level cases over the past year, including acting for C.E. Heath plc in defence of a claim by Companhia de Seguros Imperio, arising from the latter's participation in an underwriting pool set up and managed by Heath in the 1970s. **Clients:** KWELM; C.E.Heath.

Lovells Another big city practice which is known for its work on liquidations, and has an outstanding reputation for big-ticket litigation. The team advised a leading insurance client on a facultative reinsurance obtained by the client from the London Market. **Clients:** OIC Run-off Limited.

Elborne Mitchell A practice with undoubted reinsurance expertise, it is perceived to have had a consistent year. **Tim Akeroyd** ensures the practice's ranking. *"A doughty fighter,"* he is the *"star of the day"* having just won two big arbitrations. **Clients:** Insurers; underwriters.

Herbert Smith A small team with *"good lawyers"* which attracts much of its reinsurance work from existing clients. In one of the main cases of the past year, the practice acted for Willis Faber on the collapse of Sovereign Marine & General Insurance Company Ltd. It also advised on a number of issues arising from the Jakarta riots. **Clients:** Willis Faber; Assuransi Central Asia; Provisional Liquidators of Ocean Marine.

Paisner & Co A presence in the sector, but perceived to be less high-profile than last year. Noted for its work for a variety of medium and large-scale insurance companies, as well as for a number of Lloyd's Syndicates. The practice worked on various aspects of the Unicover Worker's Compensation reinsurance problems in the US and London. **Clients:** AON; Equitas Limited; Lloyd's.

Reynolds Porter Chamberlain One of the best of the smaller specialist teams. The practice receives a number of instructions from the London market's reinsurance of foreign insurers. The firm represents John Hancock's interests in personal accident disputes, emanating from London market business and workers' compensation claims in the United States. Worked for two banks involved in one of the biggest losses of the year on the London market. Also represented the London market over losses caused by the Indonesian riots. **Clients:** Lambert Fenchurch Group; Lloyd's Syndicates.

Richards Butler Considered by peers to have a profile in war and political risk insurance, the team is particularly noted for its marine expertise, and has conducted a number of recent arbitrations and mediations. **Clients:** PricewaterhouseCoopers; Stirling Cooke Brown; Willis Corroon.

Other Notable Practitioner **Francis Mackie** *"IS reinsurance at Norton Rose"* and has a high market profile, representing a variety of Lloyd's Syndicates and insurance companies. **Michael Dobias** has retained a favourable reputation at Davies Arnold Cooper, although the firm is said to have had a *"trying year."*

NON-CONTENTIOUS

INSURANCE: NON-CONTENTIOUS • London	Ptnrs	Assts
❶ Lovells	5	17
❷ Clifford Chance	4	34
Herbert Smith	11	20
❸ Freshfields Bruckhaus Deringer	9	24
Linklaters	11	11
Slaughter and May	11	20
❹ Barlow Lyde & Gilbert	8	21
❺ Clyde & Co	11	15
Eversheds	5	4
Norton Rose	3	11
❻ Ashurst Morris Crisp	9	9

LEADING INDIVIDUALS	
✪ YOUNG John Lovells	
❶ COATES Katherine Clifford Chance	PELL Marian Herbert Smith
❷ HOLDERNESS Andrew Clyde & Co	JAMES Glen Slaughter and May
MIDDLEDITCH Matthew Linklaters	RICHARDS Philip Freshfields Bruckhaus
SOUTHEY Verner Barlow Lyde & Gilbert	
❸ BARKER Alan Linklaters	BATESON James Norton Rose
DUNLOP Leah Lovells	EVENETT Hilary Clifford Chance
HILL Jeremy Ashurst Morris Crisp	MADDOCK Geoffrey Herbert Smith
RONALDSON Cheryl Norton Rose	

Within each band, firms are listed alphabetically. *See **Profiles** on page 493*

Lovells Continues as the top ranked firm. Its corporate expertise married with insurance know-how makes the practice a real power in the field. Rated by peers for being *"focused and specialised," "a dedicated practice"* was established early in the demutualisation era, and has maintained its lead. **John Young** is the star man. He *"really knows the industry,"* and is *"best for work of the highest level."* **Leah Dunlop**, who does substantial work for Lloyd's, is also considered a major name in the sector. The team acted for AMP Ltd on its successful bid in the demutualisation of NPI. **Clients:** AEGON UK plc.

Clifford Chance A leading firm which does a lot of big corporate work for insurance companies. It *"does a lot of deals"* and *"may be ready to challenge at the top."* Highlights of the past year include acting for CGU plc on its offer for Hibernian Group plc and acting for Britannia Building Society on the sale of Britannia Life. **Katherine Coates** is *"the stellar figure in the practice."* She is *"technically very good,"* but seen by some as *"abrasive."* **Hilary Evenett** is *"young and relatively new,"* but has a fine reputation for non-life and Lloyd's work. **Clients:** CGU; Britannia Building Society.

Herbert Smith The outfit *"has real expertise in its small team."* Most noted for its work for major UK insurance companies. Several clients used it for the more *"day-to-day issues,"* although others consider the firm *"top notch"* for big deals. Highlights of the past year include acting for AXA in connection with the restructuring of the inherited estate of AXA Equity & Law. The firm also continued to advise NPI in relation to its demutualisation. **Marian Pell** is *"a real specialist,"* while **Geoffrey Maddock** is considered by some clients to be *"a real trouper."* **Clients:** AXA; NPI; Friends Provident.

Freshfields Bruckhaus Deringer *"Excellent on the heavyweight corporate deals"* where the firm benefits from its corporate strength. The practice is also known for its work for Lloyd's. **Philip Richards** is felt to have *"his fingers in a number of pies,"* and is considered *"a mover and shaker"* on the big insurance deals. The team advised Prudential Corporation on its £1.9 billion recommended cah offer for M&G Group, and acted for Scottish Widows Fund and Life Assurance Society on its demutualisation and merger with Lloyds TSB. **Clients:** Generali; Prudential Corporation; Scottish Widows.

Linklaters The practice is *"becoming a heavyweight."* Clients, including leading insurance companies, listed and mutual, from the UK and overseas, felt that it was *"good for specific big deals."* Also represents insurance brokers and participants in the Lloyd's market. Highlights of the year include acting for Lloyds TSB in its acquisition of Scottish Widows, and acting for National Westminster on its recommended offer for Legal & General. **Matthew Middleditch** is a *"generalist who has done a lot for Sun Life"* and is felt to be *"becoming a player"* in this and a number of other sectors. **Alan Barker** has also received market commmendation. **Clients:** Lloyds TSB; NatWest.

Slaughter and May *"Has a number of the prestige deals,"* but are still *"some way behind the leaders."* The practice is considered to attract the top deals because of its corporate expertise rather than as the result of any insurance specialism. Acts for a large number of insurance clients, including reinsurers, brokers and life companies. Highlights of the past year include acting for Guardian Royal Exchange on the £3.4 billion bid for it by Sun Life and Provincial Holdings. Also worked on Zurich Group's securitisation of the profits on hurricane insurance, and advised on the design of a number of new products. **Glen James** is the stand-out name here. **Clients:** Guardian Royal Exchange; Zurich Group.

Barlow Lyde & Gilbert With its knowledge and specialists, this is *"the best of the non-corporate firms."* It is *"focused on insurance as a whole,"* and is considered to have had a good year. Clients include Lloyd's Underwriters and major insurance companies. During the past year, the team has advised the Corporation of Lloyd's on aspects of alternative risk, transfer regulation, and has worked on the establishment of two integrated Lloyd's vehicles. **Verner Southey** is considered by some to be *"doing less now."* Many, however, view him as the *"doyen of the non-contentious field"* and *"as one of the best lawyers in the field."* He is perceived to be most active in the small to medium size market around Lloyd's. **Clients:** Corporation of Lloyd's.

Clyde & Co Perceived to suffer from a comparative lack of corporate expertise, the practice is nevertheless a noteworthy player. Works for several major UK and European insurers and reinsurers, Lloyd's brokers and retail insurers, and is also recognised by the market for its work on syndicate start-ups. The firm is advising Wren on a number of transactions, including the merger with BRIT. One of the highlights of the year was acting for Swiss Reinsurance in its $700 million Princess insured private equity investment structure. Although the firm has lost several weighty figures in recent years, it retains some substantial talent. *"Impressive"* **Andrew Holderness** is a noted figure in all aspects of insurance, and is enjoying a growing profile in this sector. **Clients:** Wren; Swiss Reinsurance.

Eversheds Recommended warmly by those who have worked with the firm, it is considered a moderate force in the sector. Deals with the establishment of authorised insurance companies and the transfer of insurance portfolios. Highlights of the year include acting for Admiral Group Limited on its acquisition of Admiral Insurance Services. Represents insurance companies operating both inside and outside the Lloyd's market, life and non-life insurers, insurance agents and self insured businesses. **Clients:** Cox Insurance; Liberty Mutual Insurance; Lloyd's of London.

Norton Rose The firm has made a big push and has taken a couple of substantial figures from other firms. With a workload which includes general insurance, life insurance, Lloyd's and insurance broking, the team has solid knowledge of insurance matters, which has enabled it to develop its practice in this area. Highlights of the past year include advising AXA on the acquisition of Guardian Royal Exchange. Two names are deemed worthy of ranking. **James Bateson** is *"charming and affable,"* and gets on well with clients. **Cheryl Ronaldson** is *"young and bright"* and has a *"good future ahead of her."* **Clients:** HSBC Insurance; AIG Inc; SVB Holdings plc.

Ashurst Morris Crisp The team is a recognised corporate player, but hitherto has not been rated as a notable insurance player. The acquisition of a new lawyer from Barlow Lyde & Gilbert is considered to be a step in the right direction. **Jeremy Hill** is seen as *"a Lloyd's expert."* The team acted on the A$445 million sale of Iron Trades to QBE and the £125 million disposal of NIG by Skandia. **Clients:** Royal & Sun Alliance; Skandia; Iron Trades.

THE REGIONS

Beachcroft Wansbroughs A firm with nationwide coverage and a good reputation amongst peers and clients alike. It has a strong client base and has fared well during the recent round of panel-cutting in the industry. Leeds, Manchester, Birmingham and Bristol are the main regional offices, handling employers', public and product liability, professional indemnity and property based insurance. The Winchester and Sheffield offices specialise in health litigation. Particularly strong in the North-West, the team is expanding rapidly in the West Midlands, and is noted for doing *"bucket loads of PI-related work."* **Clients:** Insurers; NHS trusts.

Berrymans Lace Mawer Widely perceived by the market to be an *"excellent practice,"* particularly in the North-West. Its main offices outside London are Manchester and Liverpool, and there are also offices in Southampton, Birmingham and Leeds. The Liverpool office specialises in company commercial work, while all the other offices do a range of work. The firm as a whole is particularly noted for PI, professional indemnity, construction and insurance liability, and has maintained its position on a large number of panels. The PI work of every office was commended. Acts for a high proportion of top insurance companies. **Clients:** CGU; ACE; AXA.

Keoghs *"Pound for pound the strongest players in the country."* An insurance specialist, the practice is on the up and *"has a steadily growing reputation."* Respected by its peers and loved by its clients, the firm is attempting to extend its geographical reach with the acquisition of a Southampton practice and the opening of a Coventry office. One major insurance company said that the firm was *"the first name to be written on our panel list."* The firm has generally been well placed on the new panels, although it was dropped from the new Royal & Sun Alliance panel. It also works for the vast majority of UK composite insurers. The firm's specialist interests include fraud-related claims, disease, professional indemnity, motor insurance, and employers' and public liability. **Clients:** Zurich Commercial; Eagle Star Direct.

Weightmans Generally perceived to be *"near the top of the tree,"* the firm is making a major push for the top with new offices, strong marketing and substantial investment in IT. Although known for its Liverpool and Birmingham offices, the firm also has offices in Manchester, Leicester and Dudley. Fields of expertise include employers liability, industrial disease, motor and catastrophic injury. Also has the largest private practice police unit in the UK. The firm merged with William Hatton on 1st May 1999, thereby acquiring eight new partners. Acts for the majority of the top insurance companies in the country, and was another winner in the panel reviews. **Clients:** Zurich Commercial; Eagle Star.

Bond Pearce The strongest outfit in the South-West, the firm is considered to be *"a significant player"* and *"talented"* on professional indemnity. It is also noted for its personal injury, product liability and defendant professional indemnity. The firm has recently opened a Leeds office to handle the insurance requirements of one of its key clients, Sumitomo Marine & Fire. The firm as a whole survives on the Solicitors Indemnity Panel, does work for Royal & Sun Alliance, and does professional indemnity work for Countrywide Surveyors, the largest surveyors in the UK. **Clients:** Countrywide Surveyors; Royal & Sun Alliance; Sumitomo Marine & Fire.

Browne Jacobson An *"excellent firm for its size,"* the practice is *"a large player in the region"* and has a *"sensible commercial approach."* Well known for its local authority work, particularly on child abuse scandals and fostering and adoption cases. Works for Lloyd's Syndicates and strong on professional indemnity. **Clients:** Lloyd's Syndicates.

INSURANCE • The Regions	Ptnrs	Assts
❶ **Beachcroft Wansbroughs** Birmingham, Bristol, Leeds, Manchester	30	84
Berrymans Lace Mawer Birmingham, Liverpool, Southampton	4	7
❷ **Keoghs** Bolton	18	56
Weightmans Birmingham, Liverpool	40	102
❸ **Bond Pearce** Bristol, Exeter, Plymouth	12	20
Browne Jacobson Nottingham	10	26
❹ **Hill Dickinson** Liverpool	28	25
Jacksons Gateshead, Stockton-on-Tees	9	6
❺ **Cartwrights** Bristol	3	18
Crutes Newcastle-upon-Tyne	⚐	⚐
James Chapman & Co Manchester	29	22
Mills & Reeve Cambridge, Norwich	6	27
❻ **Buller Jeffries** Birmingham	6	15
CMS Cameron McKenna Bristol	2	8
Davies Arnold Cooper Manchester	4	5
DLA Leeds, Liverpool	8	104
Eversheds Cardiff, Ipswich, Newcastle upon Tyne	7	13
Hammond Suddards Edge Leeds	2	3
Merricks Chelmsford, Ipswich	10	13
Peter Rickson and Partners Preston	12	10
Wragge & Co Birmingham	8	17

Within each band, firms are listed alphabetically.
⚐ *Figures unavailable at time of going to press.*

Hill Dickinson A substantial, traditional insurance practice in the North-West. Acts for many of the UK's leading insurers and Lloyd's Underwriters, and has benefited from mergers within the industry. Works for major British corporates and recently gained a substantial contract from Rolls Royce. Undertaking an increasing amount of Insurance Brokers' Professional Indemnity work for the London Insurance Market. The firms also represents insurers of local authorities, church bodies and charities on sex abuse claims. **Clients:** AGF; Guardian Insurance; Rolls Royce; British Gas.

Jacksons An *"excellent"* defendant insurance litigation practice. Noted for its disease, RSI and local government work, but also handles most standard types of general insurance work. The firm was included on the new Zurich Commercial, CGU and Iron Trades panels, and *"must be seen as successful."* **Clients:** CGU; Zurich; Iron Trades.

Cartwrights A defendant-oriented firm, its personal injury expertise is perceived to attract work in a number of other sectors. Insurance work makes up a sizeable one third of this notable regional practice, although it is perceived as being hit by panel cutting. The firm is part of a litigation consortium with Jacksons and Hextall Erskine. Clients include major insurance and self-insured companies, for whom the team handle property risks, public, motor and employers' liability. It also has a niche strength in occupational disease. **Clients:** AXA.

Crutes A *"good outfit in the North-East,"* but *"hasn't grown outside the region."* The practice has been one of the most successful regional operations for staying on the insurance panels. Considered to *"do a mixed bag,"* the firm is particularly noted for its professional indemnity, local authority and location-sensitive work. **Clients:** Insurance panels.

James Chapman & Co A substantial player in the North-West, the practice is considered to be *"highly focused on insurance litigation"* and was praised by regional peers. The team is particularly praised for its professional indemnity and personal injury work. **Clients:** AXA, NFU/Avon; Zurich Commercial.

Mills & Reeve Considered to be the biggest of the East Anglian outfits, the firm has set its sights higher and has embarked upon an aggressive expansion policy in the insurance sector. With a substantial clinical negligence department in Birmingham and a newly opened London office, it is attracting an increasing volume of more complex risks. The market commended the firm's professional indemnity work and the quality of the practice's solicitors. **Clients:** Imperial College; NHS Litigation Authority.

Buller Jeffries A *"competitive, niche practice"* with *"a good reputation,"* this is another of the survivors of the panel cuts. Having developed as an employers' liability practice, personal injury is still the most active area of work. The firm handles a wide range of cases, from road and industrial accidents and disasters, to occupational and environmental diseases. Clients include major insurers, loss adjusters and claims handlers. Also noted for product claims and policy disputes. **Clients:** Zurich Commercial and Eagle Star Direct.

CMS Cameron McKenna An unusual and *"highly rated"* niche offshoot of the respected London outfit. Considered *"top flight"* for professional indemnity work, it also handles professional negligence and a limited amount of reinsurance work. Noted for work on substantial material damage losses, such as fires and floods and commended for its policy wording disputes. **Clients:** Lloyd's Syndicates; corporate insurers.

Davies Arnold Cooper Although the firm is perceived to have had a *"traumatic year,"* it has maintained its position on several panels and has been able to attract several new partners. Areas of specialism include fraud against insurers, ADR, accountants' professional indemnity, and insurance policy disputes and advice. **Clients:** Insurers.

DLA Insurance work for a number of impressive clients makes up a considerable part of the workload of this large national firm, yet the practice is not considered by the market to have a strong national profile. The firm specialises in motor and disease work. Clients of this defendant insurance practice include major insurance and self-insured companies, policy holders, loss adjusters and brokers. **Clients:** Insurance companies.

Eversheds Although acting for insurance companies, the firm is better-known for its work for self-insurers. Handles medical, motor and fraudulent insurance claims work. Birmingham is the most respected of the regional offices. **Clients:** Northumbria Water plc; Transco; Norwich Union.

Hammond Suddards Edge This respected practice has had a worrying year and faces an uncertain future. Following a thorough review, the panel work division – which works for insurance companies, large self-insurers and Lloyd's Syndicates – is to be hived off. Professional indemnity, political risk and fraud, areas where the firm maintains a fine reputation, will be kept by the firm. **Clients:** Direct Line; Iron Trades; Eagle Star.

Merricks *"A jolly good insurance firm,"* the market is divided over whether it can maintain its position with the ongoing process of panel cutting. Strong in East Anglia, the firm is noted for its general liability and recovery work. **Clients:** Insurers.

Peter Rickson & Partners An insurance specialist which is perceived to have maintained its market share in the face of strong competition in the North-West. Its niche strengths include disease work and fraudulent motor claims. Achieved a notable success in being kept on the Iron Trades panel. **Clients:** Iron Trades panel.

Wragge & Co *"Competitive"* and with a good reputation at the higher end of the market, the firm is nevertheless not felt to have the breadth of work to make it a major player. Noted for construction and professional indemnity work. Does a range of contentious and non-contentious work for UK and overseas insurers, several Lloyd's Underwriters and loss adjusters. Known for personal injury and professional indemnity work. One highlight of the year involved acting for the employer's liability insurers of the local authority in a claim for stress and psychological injury. **Clients:** Lloyd's Underwriters.

REINSURANCE

INSURANCE: REINSURANCE • The Regions	Ptnrs	Assts
❶ **Humphreys & Co** Bristol	2	1

Within each band, firms are listed alphabetically.

Humphreys & Co An unusual niche practice run by former lawyers of top London practices, and probably the only regional firm to specialise in reinsurance. Clients include major national insurers, managing agents and Lloyd's Syndicates. Competes with City firms by offering much more economical rates. Noted for arbitration and litigation expertise. **Clients:** Insurance companies.

SCOTLAND

INSURANCE • Scotland	Ptnrs	Assts
❶ **Simpson & Marwick WS** Edinburgh	13	40
❷ **Biggart Baillie** Glasgow	5	8
Brechin Tindal Oatts Glasgow	2	1
Dundas & Wilson CS Edinburgh	3	14
HBM Sayers Glasgow	13	14

Within each band, firms are listed alphabetically.

Simpson & Marwick WS With the greatest volume and widest range, this is undoubtedly the top insurance practice in Scotland. A defendant litigation practice, known for the strength of its team-work. Work ranges from policy interpretation to employers' liability, motor and professional indemnity policy. Acts for the majority of the major composites, Lloyd's Underwriters, and some United States' and European companies. It is the only Scottish firm on the revamped Iron Trades panel. **Clients:** Iron Trades panel.

Biggart Baillie A substantial mid-ranking insurance practice which is recommended by clients and peers alike. The firm is particularly well-known for its non-contentious work. It has experience in demutualisation and handles a substantial volume of policy interpretation work. The practice is also noted for its work on industrial disease, and employers' and public liability. Clients include major insurance companies, composites and self-insured companies. **Clients:** Insurance companies; composites.

Brechin Tindal Oatts A new entry to this year's table, this is a solid insurance practice which, although it does not handle a massive volume of work, is known for its professional indemnity and other general liability work. **Clients:** Insurance companies.

Dundas & Wilson CS A defendant firm which remains a player despite the perception by some that it is *"losing ground."* Best-known for professional indemnity and professional negligence work, and is instructed by brokers in relation to engineers, doctors and architects. Works for one of the major national insurance clients. **Clients:** Insurance companies.

HBM Sayers The newly merged firm is seen to have established itself as an insurance player, and is particularly commended for its *"pragmatic outlook."* Act for a number of leading insurance companies. **Clients:** Norwich Union.

LEADERS IN INSURANCE

AKEROYD, Tim
Elborne Mitchell, London (020) 7320 9000
akeroyd@elbornes.com
Qualified 1971. Partner 1973. Specialist areas of practice are insurance and reinsurance litigation.

BAKES, Martin
Herbert Smith, London (020) 7374 8000
martin.bakes@herbertsmith.com
Partner in litigation department (insurance section).
Specialisation: Has expertise in a wide range of insurance work, including policy disputes between insureds and insurers, subrogated actions against all types of professionals, local authorities, banks and many others, acting for major UK brokers and their errors and omissions insurers.
Career: Qualified in 1980. Became a partner at *Herbert Smith* in 1987.
Personal: Educated at Downing College, Cambridge.

BANDURKA, Andrew A.
Holman Fenwick & Willan, London (020) 7488 2300
Andrew.Bandurka@hfw.co.uk
Partner in insurance/reinsurance department.
Specialisation: Principal area of practice is insurance and reinsurance related. Work covers insurance and reinsurance and professional negligence (insurance/reinsurance brokers and managing agents). Author of numerous articles in 'Lloyd's List', 'Mealey's' and other publications. Regular speaker at seminars world wide. Sits as an arbitrator.
Prof. Memberships: British Insurance Law Association.
Career: Degrees in Mathematics and Statistics. Masters degree in Operational Research. Called to the Bar in 1985. Qualified as a solicitor in 1989. Became a Partner at *Holman Fenwick & Willan* in 1993.
Personal: Born 31st December 1956.

BARKER, Alan V.
Linklaters (A member firm of Linklaters & Alliance), London (020) 7456 3388
alan.barker@linklaters.com
Partner 1986. Corporate Department.
Specialisation: Responsible for insurance companies practice, dealing with a wide range of corporate work including acquisitions, disposals, demutualisations, joint ventures, reconstructions, regulatory problems, etc., particularly in relation to insurance companies. Advises a number of leading UK insurance companies, both life and non-life and both listed and mutual. In addition, advises many non-UK insurance companies on UK and European legal matters.

BATESON, James
Norton Rose, London (020) 7283 6000
batesonjgd@nortonrose.com
Specialisation: Advises on the establishment, regulation, sale and purchase of insurance companies and related business in the UK and Europe and in relation to Lloyd's matters. A member of the Insurance Law sub-committee, City of London Solicitors Company. Part of the team which advised AXA on its takeover of Guardian Royal Exchange plc for £3.4 billion. Led the team advising the Law Society in relation to the new Professional Indemnity Scheme.
Prof. Memberships: Law Society; City of London Solicitors Company.
Career: Aldenham School; Southampton University (LLB). Articled *Norton Rose*. Qualified 1986; Partner since 1995.
Personal: Born 1961. Resides Harpenden.

BROOK, Nigel
Clyde & Co, London (020) 7623 1244
Partner; Head of Reinsurance
Specialisation: International disputes, mainly for London market; on the direct side, credit insurance, brokers' professional indemnity, and regulatory. Drafts and advises on wordings. Author of various articles and many of Clydes' "Reinsurance Updates".
Career: Qualified 1981, partner 1985.

COATES, Katherine
Clifford Chance, London (020) 7600 1000
katherine.coates@cliffordchance.com
Specialisation: Partner in corporate finance group specialising in non-contentious insurance matters including UK and European regulation, start-ups, mergers and acquisitions, demutualisations, ART capital raising, distribution arrangements, product development, Lloyd's, investment funds including in particular private equity funds and other financial services matters.
Career: King Edward VI High School for Girls, Edgbaston, Birmingham; Somerville College, Oxford

(MA Jurisprudence); Law Society Finals. Articled *Coward Chance/ Clifford Chance*; qualified 1983; partner *Clifford Chance* since 1990.
Personal: Born 1959. Resides Godalming, two children.

CONNOLEY, Mark F.
Richards Butler, London (020) 7247 6555

CROLY, Colin V.
Barlow Lyde & Gilbert, London (020) 7247 2277
ccroly@blg.co.uk
Partner and Head of Reinsurance and International Risks.
Specialisation: Advises on all areas of reinsurance and international risks, including contract wording and dispute resolution. Joint Editor 'Reinsurance Practice and the Law', published by LLP. Speaks regularly on a number of aspects relating to reinsurance/insurance at various conferences, including such matters as drafting and construction of reinsurance contracts and coverage issues in respect of asbestos, environmental, tobacco and Y2K issues.
Prof. Memberships: Secretary General of AIDA (Association Internationale de Droits des Assurances), and Chairman of the AIDA Reinsurance Working Party. Chairman, International Section, Federation of Insurance and Corporate Counsel (FICC), Vice Chairman Reinsurance Section (FICC). Government Appointed member Insurance Brokers Registration Counsel (IBRC) 1997-1998.
Career: Qualified in 1971 in the Republic of South Africa. Practising attorney in Transvaal 1974-75. Qualified in England and Wales 1980. Joined *Barlow Lyde & Gilbert* 1976, Partner 1980.
Personal: Born 9th October 1949. Read economics and law at Cape Town University, followed by a Masters Degree in International Law at London University. Recreations include gardening, reading, theatre, gym. Lives in Central London.

DOBIAS, Michael
Davies Arnold Cooper, London (020) 7936 2222
Partner and Head of Reinsurance Interest Group.
Specialisation: Main areas of practice in insurance, particularly professional indemnity, financial institutions and Directors & Officers: also reinsurance matters, both domestic and international, covering arbitration and litigation. Includes facultative and treaty contracts. Represents insurers, reinsurers and brokers. Author of 'The Trials of Treaty Disputes' jointly with David McIntosh and 'The Scales of Justice: the Need for a Defence Bar Representation Body'. Lectured extensively at conferences and seminars on insurance and reinsurance issues.
Prof. Memberships: Law Society, International Association of Defence Counsel, London Solicitors Litigation Association.
Career: Joined *Davies Arnold Cooper* in 1973. Qualified in 1975. Partner 1980. Head of Reinsurance Interest Group.
Personal: Born 28th September 1950. Attended Birmingham University 1969-1972. Leisure pursuits include sport, cinema and wine tasting. Lives in Chigwell, Essex.

DUFF, John
Holman Fenwick & Willan, London
(020) 7488 2300
John.Duff@hfw.co.uk
Partner in Insurance/Reinsurance Department.
Specialisation: Main area of practice is non-marine and marine reinsurance. Author of various articles and a frequent speaker worldwide.
Career: Qualified in 1982. Joined *Holman Fenwick & Willan* in 1983, becoming a Partner in 1987.

DUNLOP, Leah R.
Lovells, London (020) 7296 2000
leah.dunlop@lovells.com
Specialisation: Specialises in corporate finance and mergers and acquisitions, including in the Lloyd's market; the structuring, establishment and financing of Lloyd's corporate capital vehicles; advice to participants in the Lloyd's market on corporate and regulatory issues. Advised ACE Limited on its acquisition of the Tarquin Group; acted for Federal Insurance Company, a member of the Chubb Group, on its acquisition of a 27% interest in Hiscox plc; advised ACE, LIMIT plc and New London Capital plc on the purchase/sale of various corporate capital vehicles; advised Capital re Corporation and UnumProvident on their withdrawal from Lloyd's.
Prof. Memberships: Is the firm's representative in the Lloyd's Market Association and is a member of the City of London Solicitors' Company, the British Italian Law Association and the British Venture Capital Association.
Career: Articled *Lovells*; qualified 1985; partner 1991.
Personal: Born 1959; educated at Tiffin Grammar School for Girls, Kingston upon Thames; Southampton University (LLB 1981); Law Society Finals (1982). Fluent in Italian.

ELBORNE, Mark E.M.
CMS Cameron McKenna, London
(020) 7367 3057
me@cmck.com
Partner in Insurance and Reinsurance Department.
Specialisation: Principal areas of practice involve acting in claims and disputes for insurers and reinsurers of banks and financial institutions, directors and officers, accountants, financial advisers and stockbrokers, Lloyd's agents and Lloyd's brokers; advising insurers and reinsurers on policy wordings and construction in insurance and reinsurance contracts; acting in major reinsurance arbitration and litigation disputes and advising reinsurers generally with clients in the London market, Europe, Middle and Far East, USA and Bermuda. Lectured in Bermuda at International Reinsurance Congress and in Hong Kong and London at various conferences on financial institutions insurance, Directors' and Officers' liability cover and on reinsurance.
Prof. Memberships: Law Society, Chartered Institute of Insurers, Society of Insurance Receivers.
Career: Qualified 1983 while at *Cameron Markby Hewitt* and became a Partner in 1988.
Personal: Born 22nd January 1958. School Trustee. Leisure pursuits include golf, swimming, tennis, shooting and opera. Lives near Uppingham, Rutland. Married with five children.

EVENETT, Hilary
Clifford Chance, London (020) 7600 1000
hilary.evenett@cliffordchance.com
Specialisation: Partner specialising in non-contentious insurance matters, including UK and European regulation, new authorisations, mergers and acquisitions, portfolio transfers, demutualisations, Lloyd's corporate capital transactions, and other financial service matters.
Prof. Memberships: Life Assurance Legal Society.
Career: King Edward VI High School for Girls, Birmingham; Merton College, Oxford (MA Jurisprudence). Called to Bar 1986; requalified as solicitor with *Clifford Chance* 1990; made partner *Clifford Chance* 1997.

FARTHING, Peter
Clyde & Co, London (020) 7623 1244
Partner in Insurance and Reinsurance Department.
Specialisation: Has covered almost every aspect of insurance and reinsurance: marine: hull, cargo, war and liability, contract frustration; non-marine: property, jewellers' block, fine art, goods in transit, kidnap and ransom, E & O, D & O, pollution, personal accident, personal stop loss, employers' liability, product liability, performance guarantee, contractors' all risks; reinsurance: excess of loss, quota share, run-off covers, LMX, pools, commutations; brokers' liabilities; issues involving Lloyd's Names, Managing and Members' Agents; recent cases include 'Napier v. Kershaw' (1993) (subrogation) andCommercial Union v. NRG Victory (1998) ('follow the fortunes'). Member of Council of Law Society (non-constituency, insurance matters); worked on implementation of open market for solicitors' professional indemnity insurance.
Career: *Clyde & Co.* 1973 to date. Became a Partner in 1977.

GREENLEY, Simon K.P.T.
Reynolds Porter Chamberlain, London
(020) 7242 2877
Partner in insurance, reinsurance and professional indemnity department.
Specialisation: Main area of practice is reinsurance and coverage litigation and arbitration, 1st party property and professional liability litigation. Work includes litigation for London market class Underwriters, including banks and other financial institutions, Directors and Officers, Bankers' Bond, financial services industry, insurance brokers, accountants, engineers and surveyors. Acts in a wide range of non-marine insurance and reinsurance disputes for Lloyd's syndicates and company underwriters, including commercial property risks, liability and contingency. Special studies of financial institutions and 1st party property risks; also e-commerce risks. Handles international insurance and reinsurance and liability litigation (US, South America, European).
Prof. Memberships: Law Society. British Insurance Law Association.
Career: Qualified in 1980. Became a partner in 1983.
Personal: Born 29 January 1957. Leisure interests include golf, tennis, rackets, squash, 20th century art, antique furniture. Hurlingham Club and Walton Heath Golf Club. Married with two children and lives in London.

HARDY, Tim
Barlow Lyde & Gilbert, London (020) 7247 2277
thardy@blg.co.uk
Specialisation: For over 17 years has advised and represented participants in the insurance and reinsurance markets in London and around the world upon policy coverage issues and resolution of disputes in multi-national litigation, arbitration or other forms of dispute resolution in most leading jurisdictions. Extensive experience of London Market pooling and underwriting agency problems and coverage issues associated with North American and other long-tail liabilities, insolvencies and commutations. Additional wide experience of insurance cases with an international element in respect of liability/ property

programmes, bond and credit and political risk insurance, mortgage indemnity, contingency/ cancellation coverage and overseas binders and other schemes. Presently serving on London Market committees advising upon policy drafting in wake of leading insurance and reinsurance cases and in anticipation of new risk transfer problems. In 1998 became CEDR accredited mediator.
Prof. Memberships: Immediate Past Chairman of the British Insurance Law Association; Chartered Insurance Institute; British Exporters Association.
Career: *Barlow Lyde & Gilbert* since qualification in 1982, partner since 1987.
Publications: In addition to conference presentations and published articles, contributing author of 'Reinsurance Practice and the Law' (LLP 1993, looseleaf).
Personal: Educated at RGS High Wycombe and Balliol College, Oxford graduating in Jurisprudence. Lives in London.

HEPWORTH, Allan
Ince & Co, London (020) 7623 2011
Specialisation: Specialises in marine, non-marine and aviation reinsurance litigation. In recent years his practice has had particular emphasis on London market reinsurance problems arising out of the marine, aviation and personal accident LMX spirals. He has also handled major reinsurance disputes such as the 'Pan Atlantic v. Pine Top' litigation and the dispute arising out of the death of Robert Maxwell. His practice also extends to dealing with numerous direct insurance problems involving in recent years major disputes arising out of loss of hire open covers, cargo insurances and political risk contracts.
Career: Educated at Rugby School and obtained a Law with French degree from Birmingham University. He joined *Ince & Co* as an articled clerk in 1986, qualified in 1988 and became a partner in 1995. In the early 1990s, spent 15 months on secondment to the Legal Department of the reinsurance division of a major US insurance and reinsurance company.

HIGGINS, David E.A.
Herbert Smith, London (020) 7374 8000
Partner and head of insurance litigation section.
Specialisation: Specialises in insurance and reinsurance law. Many of his cases have an international element requiring advice on jurisdiction and choice of law.
Prof. Memberships: Recorder of the Crown Court. He is a solicitor advocate with higher court rights in all courts in all proceedings both civil and criminal, Chairman of the Insurance Law Sub-Committee of the City of London Law Society and member of the Committee of the City of London Law Society.
Career: Qualified in 1970 and joined *Herbert Smith* in 1971. Became a partner of the firm in 1977.
Personal: Educated at St. Peter's School, York and Newcastle University.

HILL, Jeremy G.
Ashurst Morris Crisp, London (020) 7638 1111
Partner in company/commercial department. Head of insurance.
Specialisation: Lloyd's of London and London Market: handles all non-contentious matters, particularly policy wordings; acquisition, disposal, flotation of agencies, brokers and insurance and reinsurance companies; regulatory issues; captive insurance vehicles; insurance reconstructions and insolvencies; and creation and registration of Lloyd's Corporate Members. Has advised on numerous capacity offers in the Lloyd's market (both for cash and securities) as well as conversion schemes. Acted for Iron Trades on the disposal of Iron Trades Insurance Company to QBE; acted for CBS on the largest conversion scheme at Lloyd's, CBS 2000. Acted in the flotation of Delian Lloyd's Investment Trust PLC, HCG Lloyd's Investment Trust PLC and Archer Dedicated PLC; advised on the agreed merger of Angerstein Underwriting Trust PLC with Delian Lloyd's Investment Trust PLC and the establishment of London Processing Centre; acted for the St Paul Companies on the sale of Minet to Aon and for Goshawk Insurance Holdings plc on its takeover of Matheson Lloyds Investment Trust plc. Acted for Ockham Holdings PLC on its takeover of New London Capital PLC, and for Royal & Sun Alliance in connection with its joint venture with ACE and AON. Author of 'Willis Corroon Guide to Directors' and Officers' Liability', and of articles in publications on Lloyd's and the London Insurance market.
Prof. Memberships: Chartered Insurance Institute, Law Society.
Career: Qualified in 1984. Joined *Ashurst Morris Crisp* in 1982, spending a year seconded to Lloyd's of London in 1985, and becoming a Partner in 1992.
Personal: Born 4th November 1958. Attended Bootham School, York 1972-1977 and Pembroke College, Oxford 1977-1980. Leisure interests include sailing, fishing and antiques. Lives in London and Suffolk.

HOLDERNESS, Andrew
Clyde & Co, Guildford (01483) 555 555
Specialisation: Principal area of practice is corporate finance covering flotations, mergers, acquisitions and disposals (both public and private), MBOs/MBIs, joint ventures, private equity transactions and general corporate advice for the Lloyd's and the Companies Market. Also specialises in the introduction and structuring of corporate capital to Lloyd's, formation of new Lloyd's Managing Agents and Syndicates. Acted in 1999 for Wren plc on the £250 million merger with BRIT Insurance Holdings plc; Fairfax Financial Holdings on the US$600 million takeover of TGI Holdings, Inc; management of Euclidian plc on the £30 million MBO; Chartwell Re, Swiss Re and Thomas Miller on the new US$50 million joint venture marine hull syndicate and Wren plc on the £130 million group reorganisation.
Prof. Memberships: Law Society, Institute of Directors, Chamber of Commerce.
Career: Articled at *Titmuss Sainer Dechert* 1985-1987, became a Partner in 1992, joined *Clyde & Co* as a Partner in 1997.
Personal: Born 15th February 1962. Educated Marlborough College 1975-80, Exeter University 1981-1984. Leisure pursuits include golf and skiing.

JAMES, Glen William
Slaughter and May, London (020) 7600 1200
Specialisation: Practice covers all work in the fields of company, corporate and finance, including mergers and acquisitions, issues and flotations and corporate restructurings, with a specific interest in non-contentious insurance and reinsurance work.
Prof. Memberships: The Law Society; Securities Institute.
Career: Qualified 1976. Articled at *Slaughter and May* 1974-1976. Assistant solicitor 1976-1983. Partner since 1983.
Personal: Born 22 August 1952. Educated at King's College School, Wimbledon and New College, Oxford.

KENDALL, David R.
D J Freeman, London (020) 7583 4055
drke@djfreeman.co.uk
Partner and head of insurance department.
Specialisation: Main area of practice is insurance and reinsurance. Acts for major UK and overseas insurers and reinsurers, for scheme administrators and for Lloyd's brokers in litigation and arbitration. Has particular experience of advising on pool and syndicate group reinsurance programmes and on insurance coverage. Advises on regulatory, structural and management issues affecting Lloyd's, particularly in relation to run-off and corporate capital. Lloyd's panel arbitrator. Cases have included 'PCW Syndicates v PCW Reinsurers' (reinsurance), 'Suncorp v Milano' (pools/reinsurance), 'DR Insurance v Central National' (jurisdiction), 'Munich Re v Weavers' (reinsurance), 'Milano v Walbrook' (reinsurance) and Bermuda Fire & Marine v BF&M (insurance insolvency). Regularly contributes articles to ReActions, Lloyd's List and other insurance publications. Speaks regularly at conferences and *D J Freeman* seminars.
Prof. Memberships: Law Society, Federation of Insurance and Corporate Counsel, BILA, ARIAS, LMAA, British-German Jurists and SEG.
Career: Qualified in 1981. Worked at *Hedleys* 1979-87, from 1985 as a Partner. Joined *D J Freeman* in 1988 as a Partner, becoming Head of Department in 1993.
Personal: Born 17th September 1955. Holds an LLB (Hons) 1976, and MA (Business Law) 1982.

LEWIS, Stephen
Clifford Chance, London (020) 7600 1000
stephen.lewis@cliffordchance.com
Specialisation: Partner specialising in insurance and reinsurance, ADR, arbitration, litigation and advisory work, including reinsurance treaty and policy drafting and review.
Prof. Memberships: Insurance Law Sub-Committee of the Law Society, editorial committee 'International Insurance Law Review'.
Career: St Catherine's College, Oxford (1st class Hons Philosophy, Politics and Economics 1970); University of London (LLB 1980). Qualified 1974; partner *Clifford Chance* 1985; worked with the Law Commission, a branch of the British Government concerned with law reform 1975-1980 concentrating particularly on reform of insurance and reinsurance law and the law concerning liability for defective products; written numerous articles on insurance and reinsurance law and on the London insurance market generally.

MACKIE, Francis
Norton Rose, London (020) 7283 6000
mackiefo@nortonrose.com
Specialisation: Partner practising in the international commercial insurance and reinsurance market, with clients being London market insurers (Lloyd's and the company market) and the international insurance market, with clients from Europe, USA, Middle East and the Far East. The practice involves both contentious matters and policy advisory work as well as regulatory matters and advising on the creation of the insurance companies. High profile cases are–acting for the Plaintiffs in the continuing 'SAIL v Farex' litigation in London, acting for the successful

Lloyds Syndicate Plaintiffs in the Aggregate Extension Clause/MIPI Lineslip litigation, acting for a section of reinsurers (and successfully) in a London Arbitration concerning the major property loss/damage claim arising out of Iraq's invasion of Kuwait, acting for reinsurers in the ongoing large and complex Eastern European ship building disputes/arbitrations, also continuing to act on behalf of the Plaintiffs in the ongoing 'Syndicate 947 v Black Sea & Baltic' litigation which may go to the House of Lords on the question of recovery of legal costs from reinsurers.
Career: Admitted 1976. After qualification practised for two years in Newcastle and then moved to London, becoming a partner at *Clyde & Co.* in 1984. In November 1993 he moved over to *Norton Rose* to become a partner in the Insurance Group.

MADDOCK, Geoffrey C.
Herbert Smith, London (020) 7374 8000
geoffrey.maddock@herbertsmith.com
Partner in the insurance section of the company department.
Specialisation: In addition to general company law and corporate finance experience, has expertise in corporate insurance and reinsurance work involving mutual and proprietary life and general insurance companies, including mergers and acquisitions, joint ventures, demutualisation and restructuring of insurance businesses.
Career: Qualified in 1990 and became a partner in 1997.
Personal: Educated at Gonville & Caius College, Cambridge.

MCKENNA, Ian
Holman Fenwick & Willan, London
(020) 7488 2300
Ian.Mckenna@hfw.co.uk
Specialisation: Partner specialising in all aspects of insurance and reinsurance dispute resolution on behalf of cedants, reinsurers and brokers in both the London and overseas insurance and reinsurance markets. Also specialises in brokers' E & O disputes, and more recently disputes arising from the operation of underwriting agencies/reinsurance pools.
Prof. Memberships: British Insurance Law Association; The Law Society.
Career: Belfast Royal Academy; University of Birmingham; University of Limoges (France); Munich Re (London) 1985 to 1987; trained and qualified *Holman Fenwick & Willan*; *Barlow Lyde & Gilbert* (1992 to 1994); rejoined *Holman Fenwick & Willan* in 1994. Became partner in 1997.
Personal: Family, reading, watching sport. Resides Hertfordshire.

MENDELOWITZ, Michael
Barlow Lyde & Gilbert, London (020) 7247 2277
Partner in Reinsurance Division.
Specialisation: All aspects of insurance and reinsurance, with emphasis on complex reinsurance claims, environmental and other long-tail problems, insurance insolvency and disputes concerning intepretation of contracts.
Prof. Memberships: Association Internationale de Droit des Assurances (Assistant Secretary-General), British Insurance Law Association, UK Enviromental Law Association, Law Society and Chartered Insurance Institute.
Career: Practised as a barrister in South Africa before joining *Barlow Lyde & Gilbert* in 1987. Re-qualified as a solicitor in 1989 and became a partner in 1990. Frequent speaker at conferences in UK and overseas on topics ranging from arbitration and alternative dispute resolution in reinsurance to liability for pollution and toxic torts. Numerous articles published in legal and market journals. Co-author and co-ordinating editor of 'Reinsurance Practice and the Law' (Lloyd's of London Press, 1993).
Personal: Born 1952. Educated at University of the Witwatersrand (B.A., LL.B.) and Oxford University (B.C.L.) as a Rhodes Scholar. Lives in North London. Interests include his family, music and skiing holidays.

MIDDLEDITCH, Matthew
Linklaters (A member firm of Linklaters & Alliance), London (020) 7456 3144
matthew.middleditch@linklaters.com
See under Corporate Finance, p.259

MUNDAY, Nicholas
Clifford Chance, London (020) 7600 1000
nicholas.munday@cliffordchance.com
Specialisation: Partner resident in Lloyd's office and specialises in insurance and reinsurance. Practice focuses on re-insurance, project finance insurance and political risk and Lloyd's matters including Lloyd's regulatory issues.
Career: Forest School, Snaresbrook; BA Law London–South Bank. Qualified 1985; articled *Barlow Lyde & Gilbert*; joined *Clifford Chance* 1990; made partner 1995.
Personal: Horse riding, tennis, motor racing, golf. Born 1959; married two children.

O'NEILL, Terry
Clifford Chance, London (020) 7600 1000
terry.oneill@cliffordchance.com
Specialisation: Partner specialising in contentious and non-contentious insurance, reinsurance, Lloyd's and professional indemnity.
Career: Ratcliffe College, Leicester; University College, London (LLB 1965, PhD 1973). Barrister Lincoln's Inn 1973; joined *Clifford Turner* 1977; qualified 1978; partner *Clifford Chance* since 1980; solicitor advocate (Civil) 1994; co-author (with Jan Woloniecki) 'The Law of Reinsurance', (Sweet & Maxwell 1998).
Personal: Born 1944; resides London.

PAYTON, Michael
Clyde & Co, London (020) 7623 1244
Partner in Insurance and Reinsurance Dept.
Specialisation: Adviser to Insurers worldwide on most of the major International Insurance problems of recent years, notably (and in no particular order) "PIPER ALPHA"; the invasion of Kuwait; collapse of US Savings & Loans Banks; breast implants; US environmental and pollution claims; break up of the former Yugoslavia; Scandinavian credit reinsurance; loss of Sleipner GBS; the kidnap of' 'SHERGAR' the ships 'BRAER', 'ESTONIA', and 'SEA EMPRESS'; Chernobyl related contamination of food crops; and the Lloyd's litigation including Reconstruction and Renewal, in particular the Reinsurance aspects; implications of the break up of the former USSR for the Oil and Gas Industries from an insurance perspective. US and Canadian Extended Warranty Insurance problems.
Prof. Memberships: Chairman, Solicitors' Indemnity Mutual Insurance Association. Chairman, British Maritime Law Association. 1995-1996 Member of the working party of the President of the Law Society on professional indemnity insurance. 1997 Chairman–Energy Employers Mutual Insurance Association.
Career: 1984 to date: Senior Partner, *Clyde & Co.*

PELL, Marian
Herbert Smith, London (020) 7374 8000
marian.pell@herbertsmith.com
Partner and head of insurance section of company department.
Specialisation: Has expertise in corporate insurance and reinsurance work involving mutual and proprietary life and general insurance companies, including mergers and acquisitions, demutualisation, restructuring of insurance businesses and the establishment, authorisation and regulation of insurance businesses and insurance intermediaries, as well as many years experience in general company law.
Career: Qualified in 1976 and became a partner at *Herbert Smith* in 1984.
Personal: Educated at Southampton University.

RICHARDS, Philip
Freshfields Bruckhaus Deringer, London
(020) 7936 4000
prichards@freshfields.com
Partner in corporate department. Head of financial institutions group.
Specialisation: Deals with corporate and securities law including public and private mergers and acquisitions and joint ventures. Specialises in transactions involving financial institutions especially mutual and proprietary life and general insurance companies and fund managers, and regulatory matters.
Prof. Memberships: Law Society.
Career: Qualified in 1980, becoming a partner in 1987.
Personal: Born in 1956. Attended Lincoln College, Oxford.

ROGAN, Peter J.H.
Ince & Co, London (020) 7623 2011
Peter Rogan, who became Senior Partner of the firm in May 2000, is the current Chairman of the International Bar Association Insurance Committee. He specialises in advising in the insurance and reinsurance fields and is joint Chairman of the *Ince & Co* Insurance Business Group. His reinsurance practice is litigation oriented and diverse, acting for clients both in London and abroad on high profile non-marine, aviation and marine reinsurance disputes, including, such high profile matters as the PA LMX Spiral & Unicover. Past cases included a number setting important precedent in areas of legal difficulty, such as Pine Top, on non disclosure, and PCW on moral hazard. In direct insurance work, his practice is almost as broad, again encompassing a variety of classes, most significanty professional indemnity insurance matters for brokers, accountants, banks and solicitors and others in a range of high value cases arising from major market losses and disputes since the late 1980s.
Prof. Memberships: Aside from the IBA, he is a Committee member of ARIAS (UK).
Career: Educated at Stellenbosch University and Kings College, London, he spent two years at London brokers *Willis Faber* before joining *Ince & Co* in 1977, to become a partner in 1982.
Personal: Born 1950, resides London, leisure interests include family, theatre, tennis, golf and skiing. Lives in London.

RONALDSON, Cheryl
Norton Rose, London (020) 7 444 3323
ronaldsonca@nortonrose.com
Partner, insurance group
Specialisation: Partner within the corporate insurance group at *Norton Rose*. Has a strong reputation for corporate and regulatory insurance, particularly within the Lloyd's market. Experience covers a broad range of private and public company transactions for insurance companies, Lloyds' managing agencies, brokers and corporate members in all sectors of the insurance industry. Also has expertise in advising participants in the market on a wide variety of insurance regulatory matters–both life and non-life, and on alternative risk products and structures.
Prof. Memberships: The Law Society.
Career: Partner *Norton Rose* Jan. 1999. Solicitor *Clifford Chance* 1994-1998. Solicitor *Barlow Lyde & Gilbert* 1990-1994. Trainee *Barlow Lyde & Gilbert* 1988-1990. King's College London–LLB (Hons). Leicester High School for Girls.

SCHOFIELD, Belinda
CMS Cameron McKenna, London
(020) 7367 3000
Partner in insurance and reinsurance group.
Specialisation: Principal areas of practice are handling professional indemnity claims against accountants, actuaries, financial instituirons, insurance brokers and directors' and officers' liability. Acting for insurers and insureds. Growing and significant area of practice is in the field of regulation and risk management acting for professionals and insurers in risk control and avoidance projects, due diligence exercises and advising on the impact of regulatory controls, including representing individuals in regulatory proceedings and monitoring such proceedings for insurers. Work also includes general insurance and reinsurance advice and drafting and construction of policy wordings. Experienced in handling large commercial disputes. Speaks at numerous market seminars.

SINFIELD, Nicholas
Davies Arnold Cooper, London (020) 7936 2222
Specialisation: Partner leading the practice's Insurance Services and Corporate Risk teams, specialising in professional indemnity, coverage and reinsurance litigation. Practice also covers fire and property insurance coverage disputes. Interesting cases include the JD Wood consequential insurance litigation; Asbestos London Market Coverage disputes; defence of RMH Outhwaite (Underwriting) Agency in Names litigation; Judicial Review process of PIA Pensions; Daichi and Kobe reinsurance litigation and Spanish D&O cases relating to the Banesto scandal. Regularly addresses conferences and has lectured as a guest of Stamford Law School on catastrophe excess of loss insurance. Has written various articles on insurance and fraud, and insurance/reinsurance coverage issues.
Prof. Memberships: Law Society; British Insurance Law Association, Arson Prevention Bureau.
Career: Qualified 1984. *Reynolds Porter Chamberlain* 1984-1987. *Davies Arnold Cooper* since 1987, partner since 1989.
Personal: Educated at Bedford School 1965-1977, University College, London 1977-1980 and at the College of Law 1981. Leisure pursuits include ergometer and fitness training. Born 22nd March 1959. Lives in Chiswick. Married with four children

SMITH, Roderick
Clyde & Co, London (020) 7623 1244
Partner in Insurance & Reinsurance Department
Specialisation: Acts for London market and overseas insurers in a wide range of insurance and reinsurance disputes, frequently of an international nature. Work areas include marine and non-marine insurance including cargo, goods in transit, jeweller's block, Fine Art, contingency, business interruption, credit political and financial risks, and personal accident including Key Man insurance. Handles all aspects of reinsurance disputes including excess of loss, quota share, run-off reinsurance and commutations, and has extensive involvement in the drafting and review of insurance and reinsurance wordings including new product development. Experienced in ADR, particularly mediation. Represents parties in relation to Lloyd's Disciplinary Investigations and proceedings.
Career: 1976, qualified as an attorney in South Africa. 1977, joined *Clyde & Co*. 1980, qualified in England and Wales. 1982, partner in *Clyde & Co*.

SOUTHEY, Verner
Barlow Lyde & Gilbert, London (020) 7247 2277
vsouthney@blg.co.uk
Consultant with *Barlow Lyde & Gilbert*.
Specialisation: Corporate insurance work in all its aspects for public and private corporations and partnerships engaged in insurance activities at Lloyd's and in the London, European and international insurance markets.
Career: Formerly practised as attorney in Rhodesia (now Zimbabwe). Practised in the City and admitted as a solicitor in England in 1977 and joined *Clyde & Co*. as Head of Corporate in 1986. From September 1996 until March 1999 acted as Consultant to *Clyde & Co* and to entities in the insurance industry. Joined *Barlow Lyde & Gilbert* as Consultant in 1999.
Personal: Born 1st October 1942. Educated Grahamstown and University of Cape Town, South Africa. Lives in London and the Dordogne and devotes leisure to wife, wine, sport, music and international commuting.

WHEATLEY, Vere A.
CMS Cameron McKenna, London
(020) 7367 3045
vw@cmck.com
Partner in Insurance and Reinsurance Group.
Specialisation: Main area of practice is insurance and professional indemnity insurance.
Career: Qualified in 1982. Practised in New York 1985-1989. Admitted as a lawyer in New York state 1987. Joined *CMS Cameron McKenna* in 1989, becoming a partner in 1992.

YOUNG, John T.
Lovells, London (020) 7296 2605
john.young@lovells.com
Specialisation: Advises on the formation, regulation, sale and purchase of insurance companies and businesses in the UK and internationally. Co-ordinates the activities of *Lovells* lawyers who advise the insurance industry on non-contentious matters. Has acted on numerous transactions within the industry, including several recent life assurance demutualisations. Author of various articles on insurance; author of the insurance chapter in the CCH Common Market Reporter (1996). Regularly speaks on topics relating to the regulation of insurance and mergers and acquisitions in the industry.
Prof. Memberships: Law Society. Member ICC Committee on Insurance. President of the Society of Scottish Lawyers in London.
Career: Articled *Lovells* 1979-1981: qualified 1981; partner 1987.

INTELLECTUAL PROPERTY

RESEARCH APPROVED BY BMRB: *For this edition,* Chambers' *researchers conducted 6083 interviews – 4408 with law firms, 598 with barristers and 1077 with clients.*

The validity of the research was scrutinised by BMRB International, who audited both the methodology and the results at our offices in July 2000. They interviewed Chambers' *researchers and cross-checked sample interviews. Details of the audit appear on page 7.*

LEADING IN-HOUSE LAWYERS

Mary Ann ALFORD, Associate General Counsel, Intellectual Property, *Diageo plc*

Sheila HENDERSON, Marketing Property Manager, *Mars Confectionery*

Richard HEATH, Head of Department, Corporate Trademarks, *Unilever*

Stephen JENNINGS, Trade Mark Manager E Hemisphere, *Gillette*

Frederick MOSTERT, Intellectual Property Counsel, *Richemont International*

David ROBERTS, Director and Senior Vice President, Corporate Intellectual Property, *SmithKline Beecham*

Mary Ann Alford at Diageo is *"one of the major players in the international trade mark world."* **Stephen Jennings** at Gillette has international trade mark experience and is *"an outstanding litigator."* **Richard Heath** at Unilever has *"a very broad spectrum of knowledge."* **Sheila Henderson** at Mars is *"absolutely excellent and manages huge jobs very well."* **Frederick Mostert** at Richemont International has written the definitive trade mark text book and is *"best of the best."* **David Roberts** at SmithKline Beecham is admired for being *"a great strategist."*

In-House lawyers profiles: page 1177

LONDON

Bird & Bird *"No rubbish or time-wasting"* from this powerhouse of IP. Perceived to be edging more to a technology base by some whilst also acknowledged to have a growing commercial side to the firm. Litigation, however, is what the team is best known for and they sit without question at the top of both the patent and general league tables. Why? One expert explained it quite simply in terms of *"quality of solicitors and quality & quantity of work. It is a whole firm dedicated to this area of law."* Bird & Bird were in on IP ahead of almost everyone else in the game and the same can be said of the emerging technology sectors. Any talk in the market about a diminished profile is largely explained by the fact that some of their really big patent cases in the last couple of years have now settled. *"Smooth operator"* **Trevor Cook** *"has a realistic approach to litigation"* whilst senior partner **David Harriss** is described as *"a fantastic lawyer and an elder statesman in the business."* **Morag MacDonald** and **Miles Gaythwaite** each have a fearsome reputation, she as a *"tough opponent"* and he as a *"fierce litigator."* The well known focus areas of biotech, hi-tech and pharmaceuticals belie a thoroughly impressive client list across the board. Conducted trade mark and passing off litigation for Associated Newspapers in relation to the METRO trade mark against the Guardian Group and Modern Times Group. **Clients:** Pfizer; Nestlé; One 2 One.

Bristows If Bird & Bird are still perceived as a niche firm, Bristows are doubly so. Finally free of the *"old family firm image,"* Bristows has emerged once more as an all round leader and a truly *"class act."* It occupies the position of overall joint leader despite the fact that it does not have a giant-sized commercial practice behind it and as a result has an overwhelming bias towards litigation. A common sentiment of the department's work is that it is *"first rate and you know it will always be incredibly thorough."* The fact that so many of them are so well known speaks volumes. *"Clients are guaranteed to like"* **Sally Field**: *"she's very amenable"* and *"gets on with things."* **Ian Judge** is a man *"looked up to"* by the profession. **David Brown** *"is a very experienced and competent patent lawyer"* who does *"wonderful work."* Effective **Edward Nodder**, who is seen to be *"involved in so much,"* is promoted in this year's rankings. On the brands side, **Paul Walsh** *"speaks a lot of sense and he's got – and he keeps – good clients."* In addition to the team size shown, the firm fields two senior IP consultants. Plenty of grey goods actions and a thriving brands prosecution practice has helped see the non-patent work increase at an even faster pace in the last year than the patent work. The numbers of overseas clients instructing on litigation continues to grow. Advising United Distillers & Vintners on brand protection, transactions and co-ordination of foreign litigation. **Clients:** Monsanto/Searle (Pharmacia); Sara Lee UK; Sony Computer Entertainment Europe.

Simmons & Simmons Whatever has been happening in the rest of the firm, the IP team has remained immune and they are as strong as ever. Traditionally very good on soft IP, on the patents side, it is now recognised as an equally potent force and is involved in plenty of big cases. **Kevin Mooney** has put together a *"superb department"* and has a *"strong reputation"* which attracts work to the firm. Other patent litigators commended **Rowan Freeland** for being *"easy to deal with"* and perhaps *"the backbone of the operation"* at Simmons. He is one of only three lawyers that rose in our leaders' table and now joins the enthusiastically endorsed **Helen Newman**. *"She's quick and efficient and you can't pull a fast one on her!"* **Gerry Kamstra** heads the firm's pharmaceuticals and biotechnology practice. The pharmaceuticals sector is clearly behind much of Simmons' success but chemicals and electronics are also significant. The practice now manages big-ticket European litigation rather than concentrating purely on domestic bound disputes. The firm has a TM filing practice. Acted for Proctor & Gamble on the CA interlocutory hearing concerning disclosure in the patent amendment action with Kimberley-Clark. **Clients:** SmithKline Beecham; 3M; Time Warner Entertainment Co LP.

Taylor Joynson Garrett Seen to be really *"holding their own"* and working on *"great cases."* A large department which has come from a smaller start than the other three leaders, the style is seen as distinctively aggressive, and for this reason a few practitioners commented that they were not always the easiest opponents. Others went no further than acknowledging a *"firm but fair"* approach. Litigation is the engine room to the IP practice and there is a self proclaimed preoccupation with winning. Leading name, *"top notch"* **Mark Hodgson** *"shows common sense"* and falls squarely within the *"firm but fair"* category. **Gary Moss** *"is a good operator and he'll fight hard"* and **Richard Price** is both *"great for PR"* and a tough litigator. **James Marshall** who specialises in patents holds a Higher Courts Advocacy Certificate. All the assistants on the patent side have science or technology qualifications. Clients vary enormously from tobacco, food and pharmaceuticals manufacturers through to charities, oil and computer games. The emphasis is on contentious work, but the broader nature of the firm also ensures a modest helping of corporate support work. **Clients:** Eli Lilly; Amgen; Hoechst; Hasbro; Reckitt & Benckiser plc.

Herbert Smith On a roll at the moment, and clearly more visible than a few years ago. Head of the combined IP/IT department **Bill Moodie** shows *"intelligence and common sense"* but some question whether his time is spent more on IT matters these days. Nick Gardner who has performed well in our tables and whose IP record is greatly admired, appears in our IT table, indicating that this now comprises the larger part of his work. *"Effec-*

INTELLECTUAL PROPERTY: PATENT • London	Ptnrs	Assts
❶ Bird & Bird	7	16
Bristows	11	20
❷ Simmons & Simmons	⚐	⚐
Taylor Joynson Garrett	4	7
❸ Herbert Smith	*	13
Linklaters	4	13
Lovells	5	18
Wragge & Co incorporating Needham & Grant	3	4
❹ Clifford Chance	2	9
❺ Baker & McKenzie	2	5
Eversheds	3	7
❻ Allen & Overy	*	*
Hammond Suddards Edge	2	6
Roiter Zucker	⚐	⚐
Stringer Saul	4	4

INTELLECTUAL PROPERTY: GENERAL • London	Ptnrs	Assts
❶ Bird & Bird	17	22
Bristows	19	33
❷ Clifford Chance	5	21
Linklaters	7	25
Simmons & Simmons	6	15
Taylor Joynson Garrett	8	19
❸ Baker & McKenzie	5	10
Eversheds	6	11
Herbert Smith	3	17
Lovells	2	8
Willoughby & Partners	6	12
❹ Allen & Overy	4	18
Denton Wilde Sapte	3	8
Llewelyn Zietman	7	7
Olswang	2	7
Slaughter and May	2	13
Stephenson Harwood	2	3
Wragge & Co incorporating Needham & Grant	3	4
❺ Ashurst Morris Crisp	3	20
CMS Cameron McKenna	2	12
DLA	4	7
Field Fisher Waterhouse	11	67
Freshfields Bruckhaus Deringer	3	21
Hammond Suddards Edge	4	11
Roiter Zucker	⚐	⚐
Rowe & Maw	6	13
❻ Briffa	1	5
Charles Russell	2	6
Dechert	4	5
Gouldens	3	7
H2O	5	7
Macfarlanes	⚐	⚐
Norton Rose	3	8
SJ Berwin & Co	3	6

Within each band, firms are listed alphabetically. See **Profiles** on page 508

⚐ *Figures unavailable at time of going to press.*

* *See editorial entries for explanations of team sizes.*

tive" **Mark Shillito** and **Andrew Rich** are both involved in massive biotech and pharmaceuticals actions. Rich is running the Erythropoietin patent litigation for Roche Diagnostics and Genetics Institute. Shillito is, in addition to the patent work, keeping his profile on softer matters. There is also strength in counterfeit work and transactional and advisory matters, including handling all the TM work on the BSkyB bid for Manchester United. **Clients:** Harrods; Vodafone; Formula One Administration.

Linklaters The strength of Linklaters' recent reputation in IP is unsurprising. An acknowledged *"steady flow of work"* has involved the very highest profile cases. It is seen to be *"getting the kind of clients every firm would want"* and has *"endless reams of top quality lawyers"* to look after them. In particular, at partner level, **Jeremy Brown** is unshiftable in the upper reaches of our rankings. He shares this elevated status with **Robin Whaite**, a *"very capable academic lawyer who knows his stuff"* and rises accordingly. At the bar, Whaite is known to *"be thorough in preparation and always has all points of evidence covered – there are never any surprises."* Some regard **Ian Karet** as *"the most talented young IP lawyer in the City today."* His focus is a very commercial one and he *"gets things done."* An *"established character,"* **Robert Swift** displays great sense and *"a close understanding of all the issues"* on a case. **Nigel Jones** concentrates on pharmaceuticals and biotechnology and chairs the firm's Healthcare Group. Further down the line, the practice is felt to have a stack of *"good youngsters."* 23 of the assistants have science or engineering degrees. The integrated TM filing practice is admired by others who operate in that particular field. Acted for the successful patentee in American Home Products v Novartis and on the Davidoff v A&G Imports grey goods case. **Clients:** Microsoft; Johnson & Johnson; 3M.

Lovells Some high profile patent work has kept Lovells in the limelight and there is a distinct feeling that they have consolidated their position in the biotech/pharmaceuticals and chemicals sectors. Of those specialising in patent work, nine have scientific degrees. Two names stand out; head of department **Robert Anderson**, who is seen to be a tough litigator and can be a *"devil in the detail"* and **Nick MacFarlane**, who leads on many of the firm's high profile patent cases. Certain of the more junior members of the department have been noted for their contribution to mediation work. Lovells' merger with German firm Boesebeck Draste is expected to pay dividends in the IP field. The new millennium brought them success on one of the biggest biotech patent trials to date, Monsanto v Merck. Instructed on piracy and other matters by the PRS/MCPS. **Clients:** Exxon; BBC; Reuters.

Wragge & Co incorporating Needham & Grant Until its recent merger with Birmingham powerhouse Wragge & Co, Needham & Grant was an established boutique firm. It was felt to be *"excellent at handling small to medium sized litigation,"* particularly patents, with a really *"sensible"* approach. That market perception didn't quite factor in the size of many of the clients. In terms of size they may have been *"a minnow"* but they were swimming with the big fish daily. Big City players were often surprised that Wragge & Co didn't have a London presence. Their activity in Birmingham rippled through anyway and the marriage with Needham & Grant looks set to provide each of the two firms with what they were looking for. *"Wonderful man"* **Gregor Grant** *"is getting superb results with a minimalist style."* *"Effective"* **Adam Cooke** is seen to have an *"aggressive"* style, whilst **David Gibbins** is an excellent draftsman and *"fair to deal with."* Acting for Unilever in the action against Nestlé & Ors. **Clients:** Thames Water; Kone; Yamanouchi Pharmaceuticals.

Clifford Chance Strong in IP work for the IT sector, including domain names and database rights issues, the team is also recognised for financial services branding, software and confidential information issues. A Goliath in brand management and TM filing, it manages some 30,000 marks. It has embraced the EC trademark office, becoming one of the largest filers in that venue. The firm's foreign offices in Europe have placed CC in a good position to handle multi-jurisdictional disputes. Thought to have been

LEADING INDIVIDUALS • London	
✪ COOK Trevor Bird & Bird	FIELD Sally Bristows
GRANT Gregor Wragge & Co	HODGSON Mark Taylor Joynson Garrett
JUDGE Ian Bristows	MOONEY Kevin Simmons & Simmons
WILLOUGHBY Anthony Willoughby & Partners	
❶ ANDERSON Robert Lovells	BROWN David Bristows
BROWN Jeremy Linklaters	DAVIES Isabel Eversheds
FREELAND Rowan Simmons & Simmons	HARRISS David Bird & Bird
MacDONALD Morag Bird & Bird	MacFARLANE Nicholas Lovells
MARSLAND Vanessa Clifford Chance	MOSS Gary Taylor Joynson Garrett
NEWMAN Helen Simmons & Simmons	NODDER Edward Bristows
PERKINS David Clifford Chance	STARR Ian Ashurst Morris Crisp
WALSH Paul Bristows	WHAITE Robin Linklaters
❷ COHEN Laurence McDermott, Will & Emery	COOKE Adam Wragge & Co
HICKSON Chris Slaughter and May	INGLIS Andrew Olswang
JONES Stephen Baker & McKenzie	KARET Ian Linklaters
LLEWELYN David White & Case	MacDONALD SMITH Catriona Allen & Overy
PRICE Richard Taylor Joynson Garrett	SWIFT Robert Linklaters
SWYCHER Nigel Slaughter and May	
❸ GAYTHWAITE Miles Bird & Bird	GIBBINS David Wragge & Co
HARRIS Paul Eversheds	HART Michael Baker & McKenzie
IRVINE James Llewelyn Zietman	JONES Nigel Linklaters
KAMSTRA Gerry Simmons & Simmons	MacDONALD-BROWN Charters Gouldens
MARSHALL James Taylor Joynson Garrett	MARTINDALE Avril Freshfields Bruckhaus
MOODIE Bill Herbert Smith	RICH Andrew Herbert Smith
SHILLITO Mark Herbert Smith	TAYLOR Peter Clifford Chance
❹ BARRY Robert Allen & Overy	BRIFFA Margaret Briffa
GOLD Tibor Stephenson Harwood	RAWLINSON Paul Baker & McKenzie
THORNE Clive Denton Wilde Sapte	WOOD Ian Rowe & Maw

See *Profiles* on page 508

spending a fair amount of time in the US, **David Perkins** is a *"good ambassador for the firm."* He's *"very commercial and clients love him." "Thorough and meticulous"* **Vanessa Marsland** is often perceived as an IT lawyer, but her time is more devoted to IP work and not exclusively for IT clients. **Peter Taylor** is highly regarded for his TM work. Acted for HSBC in its defence of passing off proceedings by HFC which went to the CA in January 2000. On the patents side, the team battled in the so-called 'Kettle Wars' and visited the CA four times in January on the litigation that has arisen from the Bourns v Raychem dispute. **Clients:** Allergan; Volvo; Nike.

Baker & McKenzie This is a practice which is remarkably strong in the telecoms/IT sector, and as such, its reputation in IP can be somewhat overshadowed. However, the department deals with a lot of counterfeiting work and numerous fashion, perfumes and pharmaceuticals clients. Big brand names rest side by side on a long and impressive client roster. *"As long as their people are there they will be doing good work,"* we were told. *"Charming man"* and ex-patent agent **Stephen Jones** has given them *"a big plus"* on the patent side. Harry Small is ranked in our IT and e-commerce tables as it is in these areas that he spends most of his time. **Michael Hart** and **Paul Rawlinson** each have a good name in brand work, particularly in fashion. The department includes a TM filing practice. Acted for co-claimant Pfizer in the patent infringement action against Merck brought by Monsanto and Searle. **Clients:** Sony Corp/Sony UK; Calvin Klein Inc; L'Oréal.

Eversheds The deepest root in the Eversheds national IP practice. Strong in media-related copyright and TM work and exerting a presence in patent litigation on matters such as the Boston Scientific dispute with various Johnson & Johnson subsidiaries and the defence of Hewlett Packard on infringement proceedings. It is for TMs that the team is better known though, and *"high performer"* **Isabel Davies** is a *"tough cookie"* who commands recognition in this area. Both Davies and **Paul Harris** (who is also commended for being an exceptionally good speaker on IP matters) conduct patent work in addition to a heavy workload of brand issues, passing off and confidential information cases. It is sometimes said that the London office gets the pick of the best cases attracted to the firm nation-wide, and certainly clients of different regional departments are served by the capital's lawyers on many occasions. Advised Unilever companies on its OXO TM litigation with General Housewares. **Clients:** Nabisco; Porsche; Mothercare.

Allen & Overy Generally felt to be still in need of a heavyweight patent litigator but superb for transactional work. It is said of the team that *"they understand deals and have good people who understand IP and the value of it to a deal."* **Catriona MacDonald Smith** is *"someone you can do business with."* Praised for sense, calm and versatility, she *"turns her hand to many things."* The team has very recently been expanded at partner level as a result of **Robert Barry**'s defection from one of Eversheds' northern offices. Acted for Nestlé on the disposal of the Findus brand and for Beckman Coulter in their fight with Oxford Gene Technology. **Clients:** Nestlé; Beckman Coulter.

Hammond Suddards Edge From the Hammonds side of this recently merged firm, there has been an unquestionably strong patent litigation practice, although some find the style a little aggressive and unforgiving. The Edge input is an unquantifiable factor at present. Most work is patents based for the electronics, biotech and pharmaceuticals/agrochemicals markets. The *"serious and established"* Laurence Cohen, however, has left for US firm McDermott, Will & Emery, a move which must be considered a drastic blow. As a whole, the IP team is noted as *"prepared to put itself out"* for clients. Most advocacy is conducted in-house and the firm is looking more to pan-European issues. Acted for the defendant in the OXO TM litigation, Unilever v General Housewares. **Clients:** Aventsis; Thomson Licensing SA; Imprint Systems Ltd.

Roiter Zucker This niche firm which acts for a number of pharmaceutical clients, including generic drugs companies, has built up a splendid reputation through a number of well known patent actions. It features in our Patent table as well as our General IP table this year. It has a focused team, which given its size, associates freely with far bigger outfits. Regarded as a paradigm of a high-achieving niche practice. **Clients:** Pharmaceutical companies.

Stringer Saul *"A nice little niche outfit"* which is *"highly focused"* in pharmaceuticals and biotech work. New to our Patent table following appointments to major biotech and pharmaceuticals names for patent litigation and licensing work. Involved in multi-jurisdiction litigation for large clients. **Clients:** Celltech Medeva; British Biotech Plc; Antisoma.

Willoughby & Partners *"A lovely practice"* with a *"pretty impressive range of clients."* This firm has *"an element of sexiness to it,"* with its Docklands location and collection of ex-City lawyers now working together purely on IP for big brand names. The main man **Tony Willoughby** attracts the comment *"Tony is who he is!"* and he is one of IP's most recognisable names. Others describe him as *"best of breed,"* a true TM specialist who has made the firm the equivalent in TM work to Needham & Grant in patent work. Willoughby leads a band of youngsters deemed to be *"competent and enthusiastic."* Acted in the parallel imports litigation between SmithKline Beecham and GlaxoWellcome and in the well publicised Mont Blanc pens litigation. The team additionally includes two full time senior consultants and a barrister. **Clients:** The Ford Motor Company; Cadbury Schweppes; Coca Cola.

Denton Wilde Sapte In the short term, the Denton Hall/Wilde Sapte merger is not felt to have altered DH's previous IP capability. However, with fresh talent now bubbling under, it is thought unlikely that **Clive Thorne** will remain the firm's sole entrant in our leading individuals table indefinitely. He heads the combined department. A burgeoning media practice sits alongside the IP/IT contentious team and non-contentious technology team. From each of these three focal points, IP work is drawn. Strong in the financial services industry, media and brand clients, DWS cover all aspects of IP work. Acted for Sony Corporation in its registered design action against Manwa over the 'Sports' personal stereo. **Clients:** Abbey National; Mattel Inc; Honda Motors (Europe) and (Japan).

Llewelyn Zietman In the aftermath of the departure of big names from the firm last year, notably David Llewelyn and followers to White & Case, the remaining team has maintained a good profile and a substantial portion of its client base. **James Irvine** has impressed on some significant litigation. **Clients:** GlaxoWellcome; Ryanair.

Olswang Although still having to deal with a *"more media"* image, in reality media clients provide just a portion of the IP work. **Andrew Inglis** packs a *"fair old punch"* in litigation. The caseload can be split into four almost equal servings; TM litigation, patent litigation, licensing and TM filing. Clients come from manufacturing, retail (including internet) media and financial services. Acting for the Czech brewer in the CA litigation over the Budweiser TM. **Clients:** De Beers; The Guardian; RSPCA.

Slaughter and May *"Very commercial"* deal man **Nigel Swycher** splits his time between IP and IT related matters. He is ranked in both tables but in a lower band to reflect the fact that he is not exclusively devoted to either. Litigator **Chris Hickson** has been described as *"laid back"* with a *"good attitude."* On the transactional side, S&M is deeply respected, but it is felt that it needs to bring on the litigation in order to compete at a higher level all round. Its clients are essentially all large plcs in a broad range of sectors. It advised Cadbury Schweppes on the disposal of its beverage business in several countries to Coca-Cola and concluded and settled patent proceedings for APV (Siebe Group) against Tetrapak. **Clients:** Stena Lines; EMAP; Richemont.

Stephenson Harwood A TM filing and management practice of repute with significant client names in media, telecoms and other wide ranging areas. Head of department **Tibor Gold** is a *"competent practitioner"* and patent agent who *"certainly deserves to be ranked."* On the contentious side, the firm acted for a famous name clothing brand in multi-jurisdiction passing off and TM infringement actions. The firm manages the world wide TM portfolio of the BBC. **Clients:** Kraft Jacobs Suchard; British Aerospace Plc; Sony Computer Entertainment Inc.

Ashurst Morris Crisp A busy practice perceived to be occupied with a large volume of transactional work and parallel imports cases, but in reality covering a fairly extensive range of brand related litigation. **Ian Starr** is the team's big name. Acting for Johnson & Johnson in the 'no more tears' TM litigation. **Clients:** Nike Inc; Motorola Inc; Galen Holdings Ltd.

CMS Cameron McKenna Heavily involved with pharmaceuticals, biotech and medical devices clients. Also dealing with a volume of IP related matters pertaining to the internet. The team (which additionally includes a consultant) divides its time equally between corporate support and contentious instructions, most matters are on the softer side although four of the lawyers deal with patent litigation. Acting for Eli Lilly in a High Court case on the repackaging of Prozac, which is now being referred to the ECJ. **Clients:** Asari Medical; Amazon.com; The Post office.

DLA Part of the Communications & Technology group, this is a somewhat lesser known London IP practice. Clients from the media and publishing worlds make up a healthy proportion of the client base on the trade marks side. This side of the practice is counterbalanced by the activity of the patent specialists within the team. The firm offers a TMs One Stop Shop and the number of marks under management has again leapt up this year. Acting for Unilever in relation to the protection of TMs for PERSIL and DOVE. **Clients:** B Elliott plc; NTL Group plc; Yorkshire Television.

Field Fisher Waterhouse Best known for their serious TM filing and prosecution practice, it is the recent victim of a break up between the two heads of this element of the practice. The firm's original head has left to join Nabarro Nathanson. This is a department that carries out almost no corporate support work whatsoever; its various focus groups are kept busy on stand-alone work. Split into non-contentious (licensing, merchandising and sponsorship) and contentious (mostly TM, design and domain name disputes) in addition to the TM filing practice, the firm also separates out its very successful IT and online unit. Instructed by Ordnance Survey in proceedings against the AA in relation to Crown Copyright in maps. **Clients:** Laura Ashley Ltd; Logica plc; Coca-Cola.

Freshfields Bruckhaus Deringer *"Serious people"* who have *"strengthened their corporate support role."* The team is one part of a larger IP network of teams world wide. The name in London is **Avril Martindale**. Advised Hewlett-Packard in the IP aspects of the demerger, including issues in 40 jurisdictions. **Clients:** AstraZeneca; Wella AG; Microsoft.

Rowe & Maw A very decent practice which has historically come from a corporate support base. Patent and TM litigation now features more prominently. Patent clients tend to be more on the mechanical than pharmaceutical side but the team has done some chemicals work for ICI and some biotech matters for Monsanto. **Ian Wood** may appear *"relaxed and laid back"* but *"he knows his onions."* Has acted for BP Amoco in the protection of its 'green' TM registrations. **Clients:** AstraZeneca; C&A; Corning Communications.

Briffa Viewed as *"catering for a different market"* to the other ranked firms, often acting for the under-dog. It is unafraid of selling standard form agreements to clients over the internet or by way of CD-ROM. For such a small and young practice, it has had a remarkable number of CA appearances, although some question whether or nor certain cases should have reached that venue. **Margaret Briffa** gives a strong and unconventional image to the firm. Acted for film director in the Norowzian v Arks and Guinness CA copyright action.

Charles Russell A small team servicing a broad range of clients with hotspots in entertainment, the toy trade and technology transfer. Acted for Rocky Mountain Traders Ltd in patent infringement action RMT v Hewlett Packard. **Clients:** Sun Nutritional Inc ('Slim Fast'); Cable & Wireless Communications plc.

Dechert Part of a wider global network, the London team additionally includes a consultant and a barrister. Known to be strong in TM filing and management, this work is carried out by qualified solicitors. Much of the patent and TM litigation is multi-jurisdictional. Carries out international opposition work in relation to the mark 'Diana, Princess of Wales,' acting for client Franklin Mint. **Clients:** Thomas Cook; Vauxhall/General Motors; Asprey & Garrard.

Gouldens **Charters MacDonald-Brown** *"leads a young team"* of *"competent"* lawyers. Acting on quality work, the firm moves up a band in our rankings this year. It also offers a TM filing and management service. Advised GlaxoWellcome and Boehringer Ingelheim AG in relation to parallel imports cases. **Clients:** Plato Technology; Eidos Interactive.

H20 Henry Hepworth has rebranded as H20, having acquired the IP team of Davies Arnold Cooper last summer. The firm holds its own in the tables in spite of Michael Henry's increased concentration on IT/e-commerce work. The team has a long-standing name for acting on behalf of retailers. **Clients:** Major retailing names.

Macfarlanes A brands oriented practice which takes advantage of its strength in advertising and marketing work. Parallel importation cases have been high on the team's agenda, including the landmark decision of Zino Davidoff v A&G Imports in which the firm acted for the importer. The team also handles contentious patent work. **Clients:** Casio Electronics; Tricon (KFC and Pizza Hut); DC Thomson ('The Beano.')

Norton Rose A softer IP practice focusing primarily on TM and copyright infringement matters and working alongside sports and IT lawyers. Acting for Anheuser-Busch Inc in CA proceedings relating to the on-going disputes with Ceske Podovice over the 'Budweiser' TM. Also advised on the new collective brand and licensing structure for the ATP tennis tour. **Clients:** Coflexip Stena Offshore Ltd; P&O; Honeywell Inc.

SJ Berwin & Co No longer offering the TM filing service for which they were as well known up to two years ago, but the most popular of the prospects to feature as a new firm in this year's tables. Primarily copyright and TM work but also covering a decent volume of R&D and technology transfer agreements. Benefiting from the firm's strong commercial client base on the IP aspects of commercial transactions. Acted on the sale by Merck of a company specialising in the R&D of active pharmaceutical ingredients and a related technology and supply agreement. **Clients:** Britt Allcroft (Thomas) Ltd; Hilton Hotels; UDV/Diageo.

Other Notable Practitioners **David Llewelyn**, now with White & Case, holds onto his reputation following his move from Llewelyn Zietman. The strong figure at Hammonds Suddards Edge, **Laurence Cohen**, *("one of the most industrious lawyers you'll ever meet")* has now moved to McDermott, Will & Emery.

THE SOUTH

INTELLECTUAL PROPERTY • The South	Ptnrs	Assts
❶ **Lochners Technology Solicitors** Godalming	⚐	⚐
❷ **DMH** Brighton	4	2
❸ **Lester Aldridge** Bournemouth	3	3

LEADING INDIVIDUALS	
❶ **ASPINALL Tim** DMH	**LOCHNER Ludi** Lochners Technology Solicitors

Within each band, firms are listed alphabetically. *See **Profiles** on page 508*

⚐ *Figures unavailable at time of going to press.*

Lochners Technology Solicitors Some pretty high profile litigation in both TMs and patents for this small and purely niche partner-dominated practice. The Remington-Philips 'shape' litigation now moves to the ECJ. Well known **Ludi Lochner** heads the group. Acted recently for United Wire in its successful action against Screen Repair Services, which is due to go to appeal in the coming year. Also carrying out licensing work for, inter alia, academic institutions. **Clients:** Remington; Stoves plc.

DMH A primary focus on contentious work draws DMH apart from other sizeable commercial practices in the region. The contentious part of the team are moving to the firm's Crawley office whilst the commercial lawyers will remain in Brighton. IT and hi-tech engineering are growth areas but the firm also has a profile amongst pharmaceuticals clients. Managing partner **Tim Aspinall** is ranked for his contentious work. The team recently acted for the successful defendants in Eventures Ltd v New Vision International and Anor, a passing off case and in several parallel imports actions. **Clients:** Avid plc; Europharm Group; Thomson CSF Group.

Lester Aldridge New in to our IP section this year, lawyers from the firm's Technology and IP Unit have impressed the market with their work. Presently instructed on a design infringement case relating to a raiding craft constructed for the Royal Marines. **Clients:** RK Marine Ltd; Paragon Publishing Ltd.

THAMES VALLEY

INTELLECTUAL PROPERTY • Thames Valley	Ptnrs	Assts
❶ **The Law Offices of Marcus J. O'Leary** Bracknell	2	2
Willoughby & Partners Oxford	2	4
❷ **Nabarro Nathanson** Reading	2	5
❸ **Garretts** Reading	1	1
❹ **Manches** Oxford	3	7
Osborne Clarke OWA Reading	1	5

LEADING INDIVIDUALS
❶ **BOOY Anna** Willoughby & Partners
NORTCLIFF Celia The Law Offices of Marcus J. O'Leary

Within each band, firms are listed alphabetically. *See **Profiles** on page 508*

The Law Offices of Marcus J. O'Leary An IP/IT focused firm that also offers a broader range of work for a client base which is the envy of many IT/technology oriented outfits. Work is growing in all areas and the client base reaches into manufacturing, music and sport. Patent actions now account for a sizeable proportion of a largely contentious work-load. **Celia Nortcliff** is the stand-out name. In addition to the team size shown, other members of the firm work on IP matters. **Clients:** Include the top names in IT.

Willoughby & Partners This firm is known to be just *"so cool."* The Oxford sibling of the London niche IP practice is the venue for much of the firm's non-contentious work. Retail, publishing and IT clients dominate. **Anna Booy** heads a *"slick operation,"* which also includes a consultant in addition to the team shown. She is described as *"up there."* The team has advised a number of publishers in relation to online publishing and internet content and has seen an increase in domain name instructions. These include multinational filings and retrievals of well known names from opportunists. **Clients:** The Stationery Office; Universal Music.

Nabarro Nathanson A client base that is overwhelmingly dominated by IT companies but also encompassing manufacturers now selling through the internet. Some large charity clients also provide a volume of work. Advised and issued proceedings on behalf of Tetra International Ltd against MIH Associates in relation to claims of passing off and TM infringement within the defendant's website. **Clients:** Direct Wines; Guide Dogs for the Blind; Sun Microsystems Ltd.

Garretts Work here includes technology transfers and R&D agreements for biotech and pharmaceuticals companies, plus branding and patent matters for manufacturers. In addition to the team size shown, a further two assistants also cover a mix of IT/IP work. The team acts for the Committee of Vice Chancellors and Principals in its action for passing off, copyright and TM infringement against a Mr Quinn, who is selling degree certificates over the internet. **Clients:** R P Scherer; Hallmark Cards; Motorola Ltd.

Manches The client base of this newly ranked department is packed with IT, hi-tech and biotech names and the firm takes advantage of its ideal geographical location in one of the hottest spots in the UK for new technology. Act for investors, academics and companies exploiting technology on a host of activity spawned by the universities and other research institutes. The firm has been involved in a number of copyright and database infringement actions and passing off cases, including the 'One in a Million' domain name case for Nominet, the registry for such names. **Clients:** Oxford Gene Technology; Oxagen; National Trust (Enterprises) Ltd.

Osborne Clarke OWA Growing fast from a fairly recent start in the region in August 1998, the firm has been gaining new business and bulking up the IP team. Particular growth in the vehicle sector where the firm acts for a number of top brand names. Advised Glyko Inc on its purchase of the biochemical research gene business of Oxford GlycoSciences. **Clients:** Porsche; 3i; Vtech Electronics.

SOUTH WEST

INTELLECTUAL PROPERTY • South West	Ptnrs	Assts
❶ **Osborne Clarke OWA** Bristol	1	3
❷ **Bevan Ashford** Bristol	2	3
❸ **Beachcroft Wansbroughs** Bristol	2	4
Burges Salmon Bristol	2	4
Humphreys & Co Bristol	1	3
Laytons Bristol	*	*

LEADING INDIVIDUALS	
❶ **BRAITHWAITE Andrew** Osborne Clarke	**HUMPHREYS Robert** Humphreys & Co
JONES Gareth Bevan Ashford	
❷ **BROWN Richard** Laytons	**WOOD Alan** Beachcroft Wansbroughs

Within each band, firms are listed alphabetically. *See **Profiles** on page 508*
** See editorial entries for explanations of team sizes.*

Osborne Clarke OWA Significant corporate and commercial deals and a new thrust in branding work has characterised the IP activities of the firm this year. The team has *"stacks of IP capability"* and is led by **Andrew Braithwaite** *("good and slick presentation style")* who *"gets out into the market and wins a high profile."* In addition to the team size shown, there is an active and well-regarded litigation partner and two assistants. Strong showing from IT clients, media, retail, motor and sports sectors. The firm won work from motor manufacturer Morgan and acted for Ryder Cup Ltd dealing with injunctive proceedings in relation to TM infringement, particularly on the internet. **Clients:** Allied Domecq; GWR Group plc; Mulberry Group plc.

Bevan Ashford It is acknowledged in several circles that **Gareth Jones** has largely been responsible for the position of the IP team in the marketplace. This is a man described as *"commercial and focused in terms of where he wants to go and energetic in getting the firm on the map."* The firm's Health Trust clients provide a volume of licensing and copyright protection instructions and the team has recently been appointed as IP advisers to English Heritage. **Clients:** Orange PCS Ltd; Biotrace International plc; Pittards plc.

Beachcroft Wansbroughs The IP team follows the firm's focus in healthcare but serves a client base that is comprised only of 50 percent healthcare clients. Increasingly, R&D work and collaborative projects between the NHS and universities or domestic or overseas companies are the major contributors to the case-load. **Alan Wood** exudes a calmness which has not escaped the attention of his clients, many of whom refer to the benefits he brings to a project. Acting for Dualit on TM litigation on the registerability of 3D shapes. **Clients:** Geodetic Services Inc; Sotherby's; Daimler Chrysler.

Burges Salmon Strong in service based industries and engineering, most work is non-patent related and in the non-contentious arena. The IP lawyers practice from within the firm's commercial unit and handle a moderate amount of IP audits and due diligence exercises. This accompanies a wide range of IP transactional work which is quite distinct from the activities of the corporate department. IT, food, transport and financial services all feature. In addition to the team size shown in the table, litigators include those with significant experience on IP cases. Carried out IP due diligence, financing and domain name work for e-commerce technology client Insigma Technology. **Clients:** Ministry of Defence;

Humphreys & Co An even balance between contentious and non-contentious work for a team covering both patents/designs and brand issues in equal measure. **Robert Humphreys**' team has *"substance"* and is well known despite shying away from much publicity. Humphreys is described as having IP *"in his blood."* Clients are rarely locally based. **Clients:** Food and drinks manufacturers; financial services sector.

Laytons (3 ptnrs & 2 assts spend up to 50 percent of their time on IP work.) Another firm that has tightened up links with the IT sector, particularly with ITAS (Business Link.) **Richard Brown**, while practising in other areas of general commercial law *"holds his own with regional specialists."* The team all devote part of their time to IP work. Acted for the makers of Red Bull Stimulation on various types of rights infringement cases against a number of other manufacturers. **Clients:** Somerfield Stores; Oxford Instruments plc; Zuken-Redac Group.

WALES

INTELLECTUAL PROPERTY • Wales	Ptnrs	Assts
❶ **Edwards Geldard** Cardiff	1	3
❷ **Eversheds** Cardiff	1	1
Morgan Cole Cardiff	1	1

LEADING INDIVIDUALS	
❶ **DELEMORE Ceri** Edwards Geldard	**McNABB Heather** Eversheds
❷ **LINDSEY Michael** Morgan Cole	

Within each band, firms are listed alphabetically. *See **Profiles** on page 508*

Edwards Geldard Concentrating on non-contentious work, the IP team is seen as the established name in the region. A leading light in Wales for some time, **Ceri Delemore** is widely praised as one of those lawyers that gives *"straightforward, practical and clear advice to clients"* as well as an indication of costs. In addition to TM licensing and disposal work for an impressive list of household name clients, the team has seen a number of TM and registered design infringement actions this year. Acted for the University of Wales in a pharmaceutical licensing deal with GlaxoWellcome. **Clients:** Williams plc and subsidiaries (Chubb, Yale, Union); Newmond plc (Valor gas fires, Pulse Home Products); University of Wales, Cardiff.

Eversheds Another non-contentious TM-based practice, working on building up the litigation aspect to the caseload. Litigation is dealt with by lawyers outside the IP unit. Part of the national Eversheds IP group, the client base includes a number of IT and software companies but a small local market has prevented concentration in any one market sector. **Heather McNabb** is an acknowledged leader and many would be *"happy to have her on side."* She and her assistant acted for Black Cat on its disposal to Granada TV of special educational software. **Clients:** UGCS (a subsidiary of the University of Glamorgan); Swansea Institute.

Morgan Cole A team seen as less formal than the other two firms, Morgan Cole's IP capability is spearheaded by *"young gun"* **Michael Lindsey**, who is felt to be a rising star. His enthusiasm appears to count for a lot and the firm's client base is potentially more IP-rich than those of its competitors. The appointment in September 1999 of a lawyer with a PhD in molecular immunology can only serve to strengthen the firm's ripeness for the biotech/pharmaceuticals market. Involved in a cross-border patent infringement dispute with a German company and the High Court Tynant Spring Water TM infringement and passing off dispute. **Clients:** Rockwool; Girus plc; Teneco.

MIDLANDS

INTELLECTUAL PROPERTY • Midlands	Ptnrs	Assts
❶ Wragge & Co incorporating Needham & Grant Birmingham	4	26
❷ Martineau Johnson Birmingham	3	6
Pinsent Curtis Birmingham	3	8
❸ Hammond Suddards Edge Birmingham	3	6
❹ Eversheds Birmingham, Nottingham	2	7
Freethcartwright Nottingham	2	2
Hewitson Becke + Shaw Northampton	*	*
Shoosmiths Northampton	2	2
❺ Browne Jacobson Nottingham	2	4

LEADING INDIVIDUALS
✪ BARRON David Wragge & Co incorporating Needham & Grant
❶ BARKER William Martineau Johnson
HARRIS Gordon Wragge & Co incorporating Needham & Grant
❷ LUCKMAN Michael Hammond Suddards Edge
WYN DAVIES Cerys Pinsent Curtis
❸ ELLIS Peter Browne Jacobson
UP AND COMING
DRISCOLL Helen Freethcartwright
HEAD-RAPSON Niall Eversheds

Within each band, firms are listed alphabetically. *See **Profiles** on page 508*

** See editorial entries for explanations of team sizes.*

Wragge & Co incorporating Needham & Grant Such a strong practice across the spectrum of IP work that many of the London opposition forget that Wragges is not a City firm. In April this year it scooped up IP boutique Needham & Grant, thereby giving geographical reality to its London presence. There appears to be little in the way of regional competition for the Birmingham giants and both its leading individuals **David Barron** and **Gordon Harris** (who now splits his time between the region and London) still sit at the top of the tree. Both are commended because they *"get on with it and conduct business pleasantly."* The Midlands provides a ready-made client base in the engineering and manufacturing sectors and the firm has enhanced its skills in the pharmaceuticals and agrochemical sectors through the recruitment of specialists at degree and PhD level. In addition, the team now boasts a solicitor with nine years experience within one of the largest pharmaceuticals companies in the world. A niche in toys is also developing. In the last year, the firm worked on a huge brand splitting exercise for Heinz and saw the completion of Hadley Industries v Metal Sections. **Clients:** British Airways; B.I. Group plc (Cinpres Ltd); AstraZeneca.

Martineau Johnson Not up there in size with Wragges but a leading regional presence. **William Barker** *("terribly nice chap")* commands a team of *"good young people"* who are taken seriously. A broad client base has been strengthened of late, and of particular interest are the education and biotech sectors. The focus is primarily contentious and the firm acted for the successful defendant in the High Court design right case of Scholes Windows Ltd v Magnet Ltd. The firm now covers the BMW TM portfolio in the UK. An interesting case involving chocolate bar lookalikes is looming. **Clients:** Glynwed International plc; McKechnie plc; Manganese Bronze Holdings Ltd.

Pinsent Curtis Historically, Pinsent's reputation in the Midlands has been built on non-contentious work, and has hitherto sat in the shadow of the litigation work carried out by its Leeds office. It is one of the few practices to take on the TM agents and offer a filing service as part of a one-stop approach to IP work. **Cerys Wyn Davies** earns great respect in the market place and is now building up the litigation limb of her team. At the same time, some top new IP clients, outside the traditional regional industry sectors of automotive and engineering, point to a busy period ahead. Defended the Taiwanese manufacturer in Mont Blanc Simplo GmbH v Sepia Products Ltd. **Clients:** People's Dispensary for Sick Animals; Breed Automotive Technology; TRW Inc (Lucas Varity Diesels Div.)

Hammond Suddards Edge Bigger on litigation than many in the region, contentious work accounts for about 50 percent of the team's time. On the patents side, biotech work is coming through, and amongst the raft of brand led clients, there is a strong prevalence of retail/wholesale and engineering/manufacturing companies. The firm is acquiring significant sports-related work. Ex-City lawyer **Michael Luckman** is well established as a leader in the region. Acted for Dunkin' Donuts in their US/UK litigation and for Premier Brands Ltd in the 'Typhoo' TM case against Typhoon Europe Ltd. **Clients:** Apollo Leisure; Quadrant Healthcare; Alvis plc.

Eversheds Birmingham and Nottingham offer up two peas in the national Eversheds IP pod. Whilst the philosophy is built on unity and homogeneity, each of these regional offices still retains an individual character. Birmingham is seen to be *"making efforts to crank it up,"* having acquired a partner from Manchester firm Cobbetts to head the team. Manufacturing and engineering clients sit with a number of brewers on the Birmingham client roster. Licensing and merchandising work for Pedigree is just one example of the office's involvement in the toys and leisure sector. In Nottingham, Up and Coming young player **Niall Head-Rapson** is seen as *"confident, commercial and pragmatic,"* and appears to be making headway in the East Midlands, albeit that he was still seen as relatively junior on the Hadley Industries v Metal Securities plc case last year. **Clients:** Boots plc; Bell Fruit Ltd; Novara.

Freethcartwright **Helen Driscoll** is another Up and Coming department head from Nottingham. This brand-led practice is now seen to be developing a dedicated team of IP specialists whose work leans marginally more towards contentious matters. In addition to a healthy quota of mid-sized local clients, a number of designer label clothing manufacturers instruct the firm on both the domestic and international aspects of their brand protection. Grey goods actions have featured significantly in the last year. **Clients:** Paul Smith; Helly Hansen; Plasplugs.

Hewitson Becke + Shaw In a departmental link up with the top ranked Cambridge office of the firm, the reputation of HB+S is uniformly Cambridge driven. Partners and assistants are confirmed to operate out of either office depending on client requirements. See the East Anglia section for further details.

Shoosmiths *"Fairly major on decent-sized patent cases"* with involvement in hi-tech and biotech work. Referrals of work from both solicitors and patent attorneys confirm an established regional reputation for expertise in patent work. Up to half the work, however, involves TMs and passing off. Carrying out an increasing amount of work for the PRS/MCPS. **Clients:** TKMaxx; Games Workshop.

Browne Jacobson The non-contentious bias of the practice perhaps fuels the perception in the market that the team led by **Peter Ellis** is comprised of more general commercial practitioners rather than 100 percent IP specialists. A significant growth in IP work in the last year has perhaps made this a redundant issue. Fashion, food and health have been partly responsible for the increase in work, but more traditional sources in engineering and manufacturing have also played a part. Has retained the legal work for the Joseph fashion group after its sale. **Clients:** NHS Trusts; French fashion houses; Premier and First Division football clubs.

EAST ANGLIA

INTELLECTUAL PROPERTY • East Anglia	Ptnrs	Assts
❶ Hewitson Becke + Shaw Cambridge	3	5
❷ Mills & Reeve Cambridge, Norwich	4	6
❸ Eversheds Cambridge, Ipswich, Norwich	2	1
❹ Greenwoods Peterborough	1	1
❺ Taylor Vinters Cambridge	1	2

LEADING INDIVIDUALS	
❶ CRAIG Ian Hewitson Becke + Shaw	
❷ ACKERMANN Niel Hewitson Becke + Shaw	FARRANT Patrick Eversheds
NAPPER Isabel Mills & Reeve	POORE Alasdair Mills & Reeve
SLOAN Philip Greenwoods	

Within each band, firms are listed alphabetically. *See **Profiles** on page 508*

Hewitson Becke + Shaw In a region that is bursting into life with new technology, HB+S remain clearly at the top of the pile in the Cambridge area for IP work. The firm is now targeting US clients. Unsurprisingly, **Ian Craig** and **Niel Ackermann** maintain their leading reputations in IP; they have each been dedicated to the work for a long time now. The team has attained a superb reputation for litigation and has been involved in many recent important decisions. Particularly active on biotech patent litigation in the last year, it also acted on landmark TM disputes relating to product shape and labelling issues. **Clients:** DaimlerChrysler; Novell Inc; South African Rugby Union

Mills & Reeve This strong commercial practice is well positioned to use its wider strengths to make the best of the requirement to link funders with those developing new technology. Long held relationships with Cambridge colleges provide the route into many new spin-out companies arising from academic research. **Isabel Napper** is well known and seen as *"pretty commercial."* Fellow partner **Alasdair Poore** is also qualified as a Patent Attorney and a barrister. His strength is seen to come from both his technical and intellectual skills. Clients reach nation-wide and are not pooled exclusively around Cambridge, despite rich seams of work locally. **Clients:** Imperial College; NHS Executive.

Eversheds Cambridge is the lead office in this trio, with a smaller volume of work being carried out in Norwich and Ipswich. The team size shown in the tables does not include a further 6 lawyers who work for part of their time on IP. **Patrick Farrant** is a name mentioned outside the region by virtue of his being head of the firm's national bioscience practice. It is believed that he will indeed *"make an impression on the biotech side"* and that Eversheds see Cambridge as a place to *"make a big mark."* However the impression locally is that the firm is still the new kid on the Cambridge block and needs a little more time to establish its turf. In addition to the biotech and internet related work, a broader client base is developing. Carried out IP and R&D advisory work for Dairycrest. **Clients:** Du Pont; Morley Research; Sue Ryder.

Greenwoods **Philip Sloan** has a reputation for being somewhat of a David in a world of patent Goliaths. No-one forgets how this East Anglian practitioner managed to *"change the face of patent law"* on the Gerber case. Some say that *"no-one touches him"* in the region while others wonder if his practice is large enough to keep him at the top for high quality IP work. The fact is that the Gerber case brought Sloan's talents to the attention of those who now instruct him, and these include large US corporations. Sloan and his assistant have been working on a range of patent, design, TM and copyright litigation matters. Recent client wins have included two US manufacturers. **Clients:** Manufacturers.

Taylor Vinters The number of software, internet and telecoms clients using the firm's services has shot up. Certain biotech suppliers pass many of their instructions to the compact team rather than feeding all work to London. The firm acted on the sale of Olivetti/Oracle's IP assets to AT&T, for whom it now continues to act. Also acted on the spin-out of wireless internet access provider Cambridge Broadband Ltd from Adaptive Broadband Corporation. **Clients:** University of Cambridge; One Ltd; Symbionics.

NORTH WEST

INTELLECTUAL PROPERTY • North West	Ptnrs	Assts
❶ Addleshaw Booth & Co Manchester	2	5
Halliwell Landau Manchester	3	5
❷ Hill Dickinson Stockport	2	2
❸ DLA Liverpool, Manchester	2	6
Hammond Suddards Edge Manchester	2	5
❹ Eversheds Manchester	2	4
Kuit Steinart Levy Manchester	3	2
Lawson Coppock & Hart Manchester	*	*
Taylors Blackburn	2	2
❺ Philip Conn & Co Manchester	2	2

LEADING INDIVIDUALS	
❶ BOARDMAN Richard Halliwell Landau	MOAKES Jonathan Halliwell Landau
STOKER Robert Addleshaw Booth & Co	WOODS Philip Hill Dickinson
❷ BENTHAM Paul Addleshaw Booth & Co	ORCHISON Graeme DLA
UP AND COMING	
JONES Patricia Hammond Suddards Edge	

Within each band, firms are listed alphabetically. *See **Profiles** on page 508*
** See editorial entries for explanations of team sizes.*

Addleshaw Booth & Co A *"quality"* firm with *"tons of work,"* Addleshaws are known primarily in the non-contentious arena. Clients range from chemicals and engineering through to food manufacturing, education and sport. **Robert Stoker** *"knows his stuff."* **Paul Bentham** has the added specialisation of competition law. Two of the team are Trade Mark Agents and the firm has a filing practice. Acting for a number of university spin-out companies entering into joint venture arrangements as well as advising one of the world's largest paint manufacturers on a TM and passing off matter. **Clients:** University of Central Lancashire; Manchester 2002 Ltd; Clayton Plant Protection Ltd.

Halliwell Landau *"A lot of good commercial work"* from this *"acknowledged IP presence."* **Richard Boardman** is described as *"delightful"* to work with whilst **Jonathan Moakes** is also strongly recommended. Aiming to provide a package of advice together with their corporate department colleagues, the IP team are focusing attention on business start ups in the hi-tech sector, tying in with funders on 'business angel' schemes. Around half of the IP work is now contentious with a number of being dealt with in the Patent's Court in London. Acting for the Ninja Corporation, licensees of a patent for children's pop-up tents who are suing UK manufacturers and retailers. **Clients:** Trinity Pharmaceuticals; Osmetech; Tepnel Life Sciences.

Hill Dickinson (incorporating Philip Woods & Co) A practice little understood by the market and operating as an IP oasis in Stockport, away from the firm's main offices in Manchester. This is indicative of the independence preferred by the four practitioners, headed by **Philip Woods** (*"exceptionally nice, pragmatic and a very pleasant litigator"*). There is little that the team doesn't take on and the client base ranges from TV companies to textiles. It has been advising on hi-tech joint ventures between universities and hospitals. **Clients:** Medical; pharmaceutical; mobile phone and clothing manufacturer companies.

DLA **Graeme Orchison** has been dubbed *"the man"* in the north and, consequently, earns a place in the tables for his *"commercial and pragmatic approach."* Although not as visible as some of its competitors, the firm has a reputation for *"getting a decent result without having to go to court."* These reports belie the image of the team displaying a *"rottweiler"* style of litigation, and emphasise a flexible approach. Acting on the case of Charlesworth v Relay Roads (in liquidation.) **Clients:** JJB Sports; sports clubs; mail order retailers.

Hammond Suddards Edge A younger team than others in the North West, and one recently joined by Up & Coming **Patricia Jones** from Wacks Caller (a lady with *"Oomph!"*) The team's profile still suffers from being in the shadow of its London group but the tide could be about to turn. The practice is noted for mediated settlements, and such an approach to dispute resolution does not result in high profile cases. Around half of the work is contentious, however, and this covers both patents and brands. With three PhDs between them, the team members are ideally qualified for complicated patent work. Acting on anti-counterfeiting work for Kappa and three domain name disputes for a major household name pharmaceuticals chain. **Clients:** Ultraframe plc; JSB plc; Torotrak plc.

Eversheds A softer focus to the Manchester office in comparison to colleagues east of the Pennines. Passing off, confidential information copyright and TM matters dominate here in a 50/50 contentious/non-contentious practice. The team handled four sets of injunctive proceedings in the last year and were involved in an eight week High Court trial relating to the ownership of £40 million of goodwill. Of late, funders have been approaching the firm for advice on how to tap into the spin out ventures from the educational sector. Handles all aspects of the world wide enforcement of the Woolmark certification mark. **Clients:** UMIST Ventures Ltd; GR & MM Blackledge plc; University of Wales; Bangor.

Kuit Steinart Levy *"A good firm involved with good work,"* mainly on the non-contentious side in brands. Clients include those in healthcare, toys, textiles and sports.

Lawson Coppock & Hart This small team of three partners working part time on IP concentrate on design rights, registered designs and TMs for a client base that includes textiles and mail order companies. Work centres around licensing and infringement issues. The firm is seen to have *"an incredibly loyal client base"* and *"whilst many have tried to dislodge them, all have failed."* The partners are reputed to be *"extremely likeable."* **Clients:** Includes textile companies and mail order companies.

Taylors A tight operation respected for its long standing work for textiles clients. Some feel that the firm has an aggressive style but is stocked with *"good people who know what they are doing."* The client base brings with it plenty of design related work and some patents and has now stretched beyond textiles into other areas of manufacturing. Went to the House of Lords recently with 'Designers Guild v Russell Williams Textiles Ltd.' **Clients:** The Tensar Group; Graham & Brown; Beckers.

Philip Conn & Co Perceived to have a *"very, very aggressive"* style and a reputation concentrating very much on its head of department, the firm has two cases in the CA in the last 12 months, one of which is the 'Russell Williams Textiles Ltd v Designers Guild,' which recently went up to the House of Lords. **Clients:** Clients range from engineering to textiles and computers.

NORTH EAST

INTELLECTUAL PROPERTY • North East	Ptnrs	Assts
❶ Addleshaw Booth & Co Leeds	1	7
DLA Leeds, Sheffield	1	7
Eversheds Leeds	2	8
Pinsent Curtis Leeds	2	9
❷ Hammond Suddards Edge Leeds	1	4
❸ Lupton Fawcett Leeds	1	4
Walker Morris Leeds	2	3
❹ Irwin Mitchell Leeds	1	4
❺ Dickinson Dees Newcastle upon Tyne	1	4

LEADING INDIVIDUALS	
❶ KEMPNER Richard Addleshaw Booth & Co	
❷ CANTRILL Patrick Walker Morris	CHANDLER Stephen Pinsent Curtis
CLAY Andrew Hammond Suddards Edge	SYKES John Lupton Fawcett
TULLEY Christopher DLA	
❸ LOVE James Irwin Mitchell	

Within each band, firms are listed alphabetically.

*See **Profiles** on page 508*

Addleshaw Booth & Co A contentious profile to the Leeds IP practice of the firm. *"On the ball"* **Richard Kempner** is a *"deal broker who acts with common sense and co-operation."* He is also praised for *"bringing goodwill with him to a case."* A further partner spends 50 percent of his time on IP. The clients are top notch and include household names from diverse sectors. On the non-contentious side, investors such as 3i instruct the firm on investigation projects and warranties issues. Plenty of IP work for Airtours and a unique application to the court on behalf of Asda for a declaration of non-infringement of the Gillette three-bladed razor. **Clients:** Ferrari; Reckitt Benckiser; Jacobi & Perani for the Consortium of Lambrusco Wine Growers.

DLA The army of nine patent attorneys has recently been sold off leaving a much smaller IP team of solicitors and three Trade Mark Agents plus technical assistants. The change is too recent to ascertain the effect on what had clearly become a very successful practice combining filing with litigation and transactional work. **Christopher Tulley** is a *"quiet and unassuming"* lawyer but what he does is respected in several corners of the UK legal profession. The client base is broad covering manufacturing, brands and financial services. Acting for PortaKabin in a multi-national TM dispute with US company Porta-Camp Inc. **Clients:** Early Learning Centre; Dimplex; ICI.

Eversheds Has been carefully and methodically rebuilding a team in Leeds. The departure of head of department Robert Barry to Allen & Overy after less than two years, however, must be seen as a severe blow to the practice. The practice is evenly split between the contentious, which covers the full gamut of patents, TM and design rights work and the non-contentious, which includes TM and patent licensing, confidentiality agreements plus sponsorship, R&D and strategic brand advice. Responsible for the management of the international patents and TMs portfolio of Pipeline Integrity International. **Clients:** Woolmark; Du Pont; Philips NV.

Pinsent Curtis The firm has taken a decision to home in on emerging technologies (both digital and biotech/medical.) The *"smooth and charismatic"* **Stephen Chandler** heads a team whose practice is based increasingly on international clients, transactions and cases. As with many firms across the country, the educational sector is providing opportunities for work pertaining to spin-out ventures. The team of three Trade Mark Agents run a busy filing practice. Advising on an important licence agreement for the purchase of technology to produce the human clotting protein in sheep. The firm is acting for a client that is taking the lead role in a technical review of patents for a group of digital TV companies. **Clients:** Specsavers; PACE; Smith & Nephew.

Hammonds Suddards Edge **Andrew Clay** is *"someone you don't want on the other side of a case – he doesn't miss a trick."* In spite of the dominance of the London office, the Leeds team is self-sufficient in its client base and workload. Primarily a softer practice with a decent minority of patent work. This year has seen two major pieces of litigation, including Parsons v Parsons, a passing off action between two book supplier brothers. **Clients:** Halifax plc; Automotive Products Group Ltd; Linpac Plastics Ltd.

Lupton Fawcett Catering primarily to medium-sized business in the region, Lupton Fawcett act for manufacturers, chemical, pharmaceuticals and computer companies. *"Diplomatic"* **John Sykes** *"represents clients in a non-confrontational manner"* and is *"good at smoothing a path through litigation."* He has just co-authored a book for Sweet & Maxwell on the valuation and commercial assessment of IP rights. Two of the team's cases are going to the CA this year; 1-800 Flowers Inc and the Scholes Windows Ltd v Magnet plc case. **Clients:** Tyco Industries.

Walker Morris A broad spread of work covering patents, TMs, copyright and database protection from a team lead by well known **Patrick Cantrill.** In addition to the team size shown in the table, the busy Walker Morris TM filing and prosecution unit is managed by two trade mark attorneys. One of the solicitors is also dual qualified in TMs. Last year the firm conducted a major chemical patent infringement and revocation action with associated cross-border proceedings in two other jurisdictions – Th. Goldschmidt & Ors v EOC Belgium NV & Ors. **Clients:** Toyota; Northern Foods Group plc; ICI.

Irwin Mitchell Rising in the tables this year primarily as a result of the work of *"excellent client-handler and very commercial"* **James Love**, who is seen to have done the firm a lot of good and given them a far higher profile in the region. Not shy of the Anton Piller order in previous years, last year it obtained one for a client against a competing manufacturer of metal joints. Other work ranges from patent issues on oil rig components to cybersquatting for an overseas sports manufacturer. With a broad client base and strategy, the firm is seen to be popping up on the other side of patent and brand disputes with increasing regularity. **Clients:** Minit UK plc; The Rugby Football League; Gripple Ltd.

Dickinson Dees Industrial IP work dominates the Dickinson Dees practice. There is currently an increased pool of clients in that sector in the North East, and the firm, as one of the strongest regional commercial players, is in prime position to scoop up much of that work. Two thirds of the IP work is non-contentious, but the firm has just won anti-counterfeiting, TM infringement and passing off work from a major sports wear company. Involved in on-going litigation between Waste Systems International Incorporated v Eurocare Environmental Services. **Clients:** Applied Optical Technologies; Northern Electric; Formica Ltd.

SCOTLAND

INTELLECTUAL PROPERTY • Scotland	Ptnrs	Assts
❶ **Maclay Murray & Spens** Glasgow	4	12
McGrigor Donald Edinburgh	3	5
❷ **Dundas & Wilson CS** Glasgow	3	8
MacRoberts Glasgow	2	4
❸ **Shepherd & Wedderburn WS** Edinburgh, Glasgow	2	7
❹ **Burness** Edinburgh, Glasgow	*	1

LEADING INDIVIDUALS	
❶ **MACPHERSON Shonaig** McGrigor Donald	
NICOLSON Fiona Maclay Murray & Spens	
❷ **BYATT Lorne** Dundas & Wilson CS	**FLINT David** MacRoberts
❸ **GRASSIE Gill** Maclay Murray & Spens	**McLEAN James** Burness
SAUNDERS James Shepherd & Wedderburn WS	

** See editorial entries for explanations of team sizes.* *See* ***Profiles*** *on page 508*

Maclay Murray & Spens A massive team which is doing well with technology clients and funders and acting on quite a number of joint venture arrangements. A majority of the IP work is non-contentious. **Fiona Nicolson** has many years of experience and is thought by some to be *"the doyenne of the profession"* while ranked **Gill Grassie** is the name in litigation. Acts for Scottish Enterprise in a number of investment projects. **Clients:** Scottish Widows; Davidoff; Kodak.

McGrigor Donald The loss of a partner to Dickson Minto in 1999 appears not to have dented the standing of the firm in IP. The work of the dedicated team is characterised by *"significant clients"* and *"high profile lawyer"* **Shonaig MacPherson** who enters our top band of individuals this year. **Clients:** Axis Shield plc; 3i plc.

Dundas & Wilson CS The Scottish arm of Andersen Legal and, for many, the most successful limb. IP work is spearheaded by respected **Lorne Byatt.** Interestingly, the team is exclusively a non-contentious one, with any disputes being handled by the firm's commercial litigation department. A huge proportion of the work comes from university clients. Last year it acted on nine successful technology transfers to joint venture spin-out companies. Provided legal services to the shareholders in the £45 million sale of the Roslin Bio-Med (Dolly the sheep technology) to the Geron Corporation. **Clients:** University of Glasgow; Geron Bio-Med Ltd; Buck Chemicals (UK) Ltd.

MacRoberts *"Growing a lot and pushing hard, especially in online work."* In terms of the big value and high volume work, not seen to be doing as much as the largest practices, but congenial **David Flint** is a well recognised name who can *"cover a few bases."* Clients range from universities through to medical device manufacturers. Much licensing work and advice on spin out ventures from educational establishments. **Clients:** Dundee and Strathclyde Universities; Scottish Council for Educational Technology.

Shepherd & Wedderburn WS General IP work for major organisations in Scotland including funding, brand work and IP aspects of major transactions and flotations. Partner **James Saunders** leads the team. Acting for Strakan Pharmaceuticals in relation to patents, licensing and joint venture arrangements for skin and bone therapeutic medicines. **Clients:** Scottish Enterprise; Scottish Power UK plc; Performing Rights Society (Scotland.)

Burness Technology transfer and licensing accounts for much of the non-contentious work. On the contentious side, the firm handles passing off, and software disputes relating to domain names, licences and proprietorship. *"Intellectual"* **James McLean** heads the department from Edinburgh and spends part of his time on IP and the rest on e-commerce matters. **Clients:** Scottish Football Association; Harris Tweed Authority; Clyde & Forth Press.

LEADERS IN INTELLECTUAL PROPERTY

ACKERMANN, Niel
Hewitson Becke + Shaw, Cambridge
(01223) 461155

ANDERSON, Robert J.
Lovells, London (020) 7296 2000
robert.anderson@lovells.com
Specialisation: Intellectual property and technology. Patent litigation–he has particular experience of cases with a chemical, pharmaceutical and biotechnological content. Designs, copyright, trade secrets and trade marks. R&D agreements and acquisitions and joint ventures involving technology based businesses. Also other matters involving computers, pharmaceuticals, biotechnology or otherwise having a high technology content. Lectures on patent litigation for the Bristol University IP Diploma.
Prof. Memberships: AIPPI, Associate Member Chartered Institute of Patent Agents, Solicitors European Group, City of London Law Society Intellectual Property Sub-Committee, IPLA.
Career: BSc Edinburgh (Natural Sciences), 1968. Articled *Bristows Cooke and Carpmael*, admitted 1972; joined *Lovells* 1974; partner 1978.

ASPINALL, Tim J.M.
DMH, Brighton (01273) 744 319
tim.aspinall@dmh.co.uk
Managing partner.
Specialisation: Practice focuses on intellectual property and computer related litigation. Particular experience of heavyweight commercial litigation cases concerning high technology products and services, in addition to dealing with the full range of commercial disputes. Work covers the full range of intellectual property litigation including copyright, design rights, trademarks, patents, passing off and breaches of confidential information. Also handles information technology disputes. Acted for the successful defendant in the reported patent dispute Hughes Rediffusion v Link-Miles (a multi-million pound patent infringement claim concerning visual displays on flight simulators). Clients include national and international companies, fast growing private companies and academic institutions. Regularly speaks at conferences and lectures to other lawyers around the country on the tactics and strategy of winning cases, contributor to new book on litigation.
Prof. Memberships: Society for Computers and Law, Law Society.
Career: Qualified in 1982. Spent a year at West Sussex County Council before joining firm in 1983. Appointed partner in 1987 and head of litigation department in 1994. Appointed managing partner 1997.
Personal: Born 30th June 1956. Educated at Huddersfield New College 1967-1974, York University 1975-1978 (BA Hons, History) and Leeds Law School 1979-1980 (CPE and LSF). Plays golf and enjoys cricket and theatre. Trustee of local charity. Lives in Brighton.

BARKER, William
Martineau Johnson, Birmingham (0121) 678 1632
william.barker@martjohn.com
Partner, Head of Intellectual Property Department.
Specialisation: Areas of practice include contentious and non-contentious intellectual property and computer law. Experienced in anti-counterfeiting and has particular experience of trade marks, copyright and patents. Has written various articles on the protection and enforcement of intellectual property rights and has addressed seminars in Birmingham, Singapore, Sydney, Seattle, Munich and Cincinatti. Experienced in the application and execution of Anton Piller Orders and is on the Birmingham Law Society list of supervising solicitors.
Prof. Memberships: Anti-counterfeiting Group; Licensing Executives Society; T.I.P.L.O. (the Intellectual Property Lawyers Organisation).
Career: Articled: *Laces & Co*, Liverpool; Qualified 1986; Assistant Solicitor, *Pinsent & Co* 1986-1990; Associate, 1990-1991; Partner, *Martineau Johnson* 1992.
Personal: Born 4th January 1962. Educated at Merchant Taylors School, Crosby, Liverpool. BSc in Law and Mathematics. Leisure interests include tennis, member Edgbaston Priory LTC and golf, member Moor Hall Golf Club.

BARRON, David
Wragge & Co, Birmingham (0121) 265 2203
david_barron@wragge.com
Specialisation: All aspects of intellectual property with an emphasis on litigation. Particular expertise in multinational patent litigation and also anti-counterfeiting campaigns. Led the successful *Wragge & Co* team in Hadley v Metsec, the first ever Patents Court trial outside London. Reported cases include NRDC v Wellcome, Beloit v Valmet, GGHB v Montgomery, Pioneer Oil Tools Ltd's Licence of Right application, French v Mason, Abeco v Tavismanor, Hadley v Metsec. Regular speaker at IP Conferences in UK and abroad. Published papers in most IP Journals.
Prof. Memberships: Intellectual Property Lawyers Association, Chartered Institute of Patent Agents, Institute of Trademark Attorneys, American Intellectual Property Law Association, Law Society. Member of Advisory Board of World Intellectual Property Report.
Career: University of Birmingham LLB (1986), College of Law (Guildford) 1987. *Bird & Bird* 1990-1996. Partner at *Wragge & Co* since 1996.
Personal: Interests: family, sport and travel.

BARRY, Robert
Allen & Overy, London (020) 7330 3000
Specialisation: Considerable experience of the full range of intellectual property litigation with a particular emphasis on patents and trade marks. Acted in many major patent disputes in both High Court and Patents County Court, as well as oppositions in the European Patent Office, covering a number of different technologies and industry sectors. Reported cases include OCLI v Pilkington, STEP v Emson, Exxon v Lubrizol, Symbol v Opticon. Currently acting for Philips Electronics against Remington in the three headed shaver shape mark litigation, which has been referred to the European Court of Justice.
Prof. Memberships: Member of the Royal Pharmaceutical Society of Great Britain; International Bar Association; Associate member of the Chartered Institute of Patent Agents; The International Association for the Protection of Industrial Property; INTA.
Career: Kings College Chelsea (B Pharmacy). City University (Dip Law). Called to the Bar 1983. Pupil to Nicholas Pumfrey at 11 South Square, Gray's Inn. Joined *Bird & Bird* December 1985, partner 1991. Joined *Eversheds* in September 1997 as partner and Head of Intellectual Property Litigation North. Joined *Allen & Overy* May, 2000.
Personal: Resides Surrey. Leisure interests include running, sailing, golf and football; season ticket holder at Middlesbrough Football Club.

BENTHAM, Paul
Addleshaw Booth & Co, Manchester
(0161) 934 6000
Specialisation: Intellectual property and technology including patents, trade marks, passing off, copyright and designs, trade secrets and confidential information and related areas of competition law. Particular expertise in information technology contracts including the acquisition of computer systems, the licensing of computer software and outsourcing agreements. Also has considerable experience in technology licensing and advising on intellectual property matters in respect of corporate acquisitions and joint ventures.
Prof. Memberships: Licensing Executives Society, Solicitors European Group and The Society for Computers and Law.
Career: Qualified in 1989 and became a partner in 1995.
Personal: Educated at the University of Leicester (1984-1987), (LL.B Hons, Law with French) Universite de Strasbourg (Diplome d'Etudes juridiques francaises). Leisure interests include foreign travel and supporting Manchester United.

BOARDMAN, Richard
Halliwell Landau, Manchester
(0161) 831 2905 / 0467 790 981
rboardman@halliwells.co.uk
Partner in the intellectual property and information technology department.
Specialisation: Has extensive experience of managing large scale, often international, commercial and dispute related IP & IT projects and related anti-trust work, helps clients to design and implement risk managed solutions to commercial issues or opportunities where IP & IT issues are significant. Projects have included multi-jurisdictional brand litigation (with strategy facilitiation and the construction of commercial risk models), commercial patent based technology exploitation within the Indian sub-continent, risk managed software delivery into a life-critical environment and global music collecting society comparative benchmarking to balance revenue maximisation with exploitation control. Increasingly, works with clients operating within the internet and e-commerce environments.
Prof. Memberships: The Chartered Institute of Patents Agents (Associate), The Society for Computers and the Law, The Licensing Executives Society, The British Interactive Multimedia Association, The Law Society and The International Association of Entertainment Lawyers.
Career: Qualified in 1989. Employed as trainee solicitor, assistant and associate at *Simpson Curtis* 1987-1994. Joined *Garrett & Co* in 1994. Appointed partner in 1995. *Halliwell Landau* 1998 as partner.

BOOY, Anna
Willoughby & Partners, Oxford (01865) 791990
anna@iprights.com
Consultant in intellectual property department.
Specialisation: All transactional intellectual property work especially in the industry areas of computer software, the internet, multimedia, publishing, music and entertainment, the fine arts, advertising and brand management.
Prof. Memberships: SCL, IPI, SEG.
Career: Qualified both UK and Australia.
Personal: Born 19th June 1962. Educated at the University of Queensland (BA LLB Hons.) and University College, London. (LLM in Intellectual Property).

BRAITHWAITE, Andrew
Osborne Clarke OWA, Bristol (0117) 917 4178
andrew.braithwaite@osborneclarke.com
Specialisation: Main areas of expertise are IP and Sports law. Experience drafting and negotiating commercial contracts with a focus on IP exploitation, principally technology licensing, manufacturing and merchandising arrangements; and advising on brand protection and exploitation. Also has experience in trade marks and merchandising, sponsorship and TV production. Has acted as sole legal adviser to the Professional Golfers Association for the past 7 years, handling all its commercial affairs, including venue agreements, media rights, trade marks and merchandising for, among other things, Ryder Cup 2001. Other clients include: Bristol Rugby Football Club, Gloucestershire County Cricket club, Professional Event Riders Association and Professional Cricketers Association.
Career: Qualified, 1985. Moved to *Osborne Clarke* in 1997 as head of Commercial and IT/IP.

BRIFFA, Margaret
Briffa, London (020) 7288 6003
Principal of niche intellectual property practice *Briffa & Co.*
Specialisation: All aspects of Intellectual Property and Information Technology law. Acts for a wide range of clients across all industries.
Career: Qualified in 1987. *Boodle Hatfield* 1987-1991, *Clifford Chance* 1991-1992, *Rouse & Co.*1992-1995, Established *Briffa & Co.* in 1995.
Personal: Born 18 September 1961. Educated Ursuline High School, East London and London School of Economics. Enjoys dancing, boats, travel, gardening and family pursuits. Lives Crouch End, North London.

BROWN, David
Bristows, London (020) 7400 8000
david.brown@bristows.com
Partner in intellectual property department.
Specialisation: Practice covers the full range of intellectual property and includes disputes in relation to patents, copyright, design rights, trade secrets and antitrust issues. Co-ordinates multi-forum disputes. Acts for international companies in the manufacturing, pharmaceutical, electronic and engineering industries. Had conduct of major cases such as Pilkington v. PPG and Glaxo v. Generics. Recent cases include Electrolux v. Dyson, Texas Instruments v. Hyundai, and Novartis v. AHP.
Career: Member Royal Corps of Naval Constructors 1960-1966. Joined *Bristows* 1966. Qualified as Solicitor in 1973; Partner from 1974; Member of Editorial Board of Patent World.
Personal: Born 8 May 1942. Educated at Royal High School Edinburgh, Royal Naval Engineering College Plymouth and Royal Naval College Greenwich (Honours Degree in Naval Architecture). Interests include the Turf.

BROWN, Jeremy
Linklaters (A member firm of Linklaters & Alliance), London (020) 7456 5748
jeremy.brown@linklaters.com
Specialisation: Head of *Linklaters'* Intellectual Property and co-head of the IP Practice Group of *Linklaters & Alliance*. Technology Department. Jeremy has degrees in chemical engineering and law and is an English solicitor and a South African patent attorney. He has over 28 years experience in IP practice, with particular reference to issues affecting the pharmaceuticals, chemical, electronics and luxury goods industries. His experience includes UK and multi-jurisdictional patent and trademark litigation, combating unlawful parallel imports, advising on exhaustion of IP rights in Europe and internationally, and advising on EC competition law implications of patent and technology licences and other IP related collaborations.

BROWN, Richard
Laytons, Bristol (0117) 930 9500
richard.brown@laytons.com
Partner in Company and Commercial Department.
Specialisation: Work includes mergers and acquisitions, corporate finance (including banking and venture capital), pensions, employment, employee incentive schemes, commercial contracts, agency and distribution, and export law. Also handles intellectual property work, including computers, patents, trade marks, design rights copyright, confidential information and licensing of intellectual property rights, covering both contentious and non-contentious work. Author of several articles in local business magazines. Gives DTI computer licensing seminars.
Prof. Memberships: Consular agent for France, Representative of Law Society's Solicitors' European Group for the South West of England, Law Society International Working Group, Member of Council for Bristol Chamber of Commerce, Chairman of Franco-British Business Club South West, Commercial and European Committee of Bristol Law Society.
Career: Qualified in 1976. Worked at *Norton Rose* 1974-79, BAT Industries 1979-84 and joined *Laytons* in 1984, becoming a Partner in 1986.
Personal: Born 11th April 1952. University College, London 1970-73 and College of Law 1973-74. Lives in Bristol.

BYATT, Lorne
Dundas & Wilson CS, Edinburgh (0131) 228 8000

CANTRILL, Patrick
Walker Morris, Leeds (0113) 283 2500
Specialisation: Practice covers the full range of contentious and non contentious intellectual property and information technology work including advice on the securitisation the management of IP and e-commerce issues. Case load relates to a broad client base. Has acted in a number of infringement disputes and high profile IT procurement and technology licensing deals. Has lectured extensively in the UK and abroad on IT, e-commerce and IP issues.
Prof. Memberships: Chairman of the North East chapter of Licensing Executives Society; Anti-Counterfeiting Group; Chairman of the Parallel Imports Committee of International Trademark Association.
Career: Qualified 1984. Also admitted in Hong Kong in 1986. Joined *Walker Morris* as a partner and head of the Intellectual Property Group in 1992.
Personal: Educated at Wycliffe College and University College, London. Lives in York.

CHANDLER, Stephen
Pinsent Curtis, Leeds (0113) 244 5000
stephen.chandler@pinsents.com
National head of commercial and partner in commercial department, Leeds.
Specialisation: Intellectual property, including protection, exploitation and enforcement of patents, trade marks, copyrights, design rights and trade secrets, as well as consultancy in the management of IP. Acted in PLM v Redfearn; for Smith & Nephew plc in healthcare patent matters; Pace Microtechnology in telecoms matters; worked for the NHS in developing a framework for the management of its intellectual property; Case Corporation and a number of NHS Hospital Trusts. Currently handling two large scale patent litigation actions, both for US clients.
Career: Qualified in 1980. Partner in 1985.
Personal: Born 1955. Educated St. John's College, Cambridge 1974-1977.

CLAY, Andrew J.
Hammond Suddards Edge, Leeds (0113) 284 7000
Specialisation: The commercial exploitation and enforcement of intellectual property rights, e-commerce and data protection. Particular specialisation in heavyweight patent, design right, copyright, breach of confidence and passing-off litigation as well as the laws relating to the internet. Cases include Re GEC's Patent, Haifax Building Society v Urquarht-Dykes & Lord, Halifax Building Society v Sutcliffe (domain name infringement), eFax.com, Inc v efax (domain name passing-off), Luk v Automotive Porducts plc (patents), Netlon Ltd v The Tensar Corporation, Single Buoy Moorings v Brown Brothers Ltd (patent), Degler v M&J Polymers Ltd (breach of confidence).
Prof. Memberships: Chartered Institute of Patent Agents, Institute of Trade mark Agents, Solicitors' European Group, Licensing Executive Society, Society for Computers and Law, member of anti-counterfeiting group.
Career: Harrogate Grammar School, St Andrew's University (First Class Honours BSc. Degree), Law School in Leeds, Bristol University (Diploma in Intellectual Property), certificates in EU Competition Law, Open University (Certificate in Analogue and Digital Electronics). *Herbert Smith* 1989-1992. 1992 to date *Hammond Suddards*. Partner 1997.
Personal: Resides in Harrogate. Hobbies include cinema, theatre, cycling and reading.

COHEN, Laurence J.
McDermott, Will & Emery, London (020) 7577 6900
Partner–Intellectual Property Unit.
Specialisation: Contentious and non-contentious intellectual property matters including patents, trademarks, copyright, design right and trade secrets. Also deals with regulatory law, particularly in the area of agrochemicals and medicines and genetically modified organisms. Acted in Chiron v. Murex (client), Harrods Limited (client) v. Harrods (Buenos Aires) Limited, GEC v. FKI (client), Coin Controls (client) v. Suzo and Philips Electronics v. Ingman (client); R v DETR ex p Watson (Adventa Seeds intervening-

client); Author of 'World Litigation Law and Practice: Unit B1 England and Wales' (1986) and CIPA/ ITMA Trademarks Handbook section on Civil Litigation (1992). Contributor of numerous articles to a variety of specialist publications on intellectual property topics and regular conference speaker.
Prof. Memberships: CIPA, ITMA, INTA, IBA, Law Society.
Career: Qualified 1976. Assistant Solicitor with *Bristows Cooke & Carpmael* from 1976, and became a Partner in 1981. Joined *Hammond Suddards* in 1992. Joined *McDermott, Will & Emery* in 2000 and is currently Head of Contentious Intellectual Property.
Personal: Born 12th September 1951. Attended Emmanuel College, Cambridge 1970-1973. Leisure pursuits include tennis, cycling and skiing. Lives in Radlett, Hertfordshire.

COOK, Trevor
Bird & Bird, London (020) 7415 6000
Partner in Intellectual Property Department.
Specialisation: Main areas of practice are litigation, transactional and advisory work in relation to patents, copyright, trademarks and other intellectual property rights and associated regulatory law issues, particularly in the information technology and pharmaceutical/biotechnology sectors. Contributor to 'Information Technology and the Law', 'CIPA Guide to Patents Act' and 'European Patents Handbook'; co-author of 'Pharmaceuticals Biotechnology and the Law' and 'Practical Intellectual Property Precedents'; author of 'The Protection of Regulatory Data'. Frequent writer and speaker on various intellectual property and regulatory topics.
Prof. Memberships: Treasurer of the International Association for the Protection of Industrial Property (AIPPI) (British Group), member of Licensing Executives Society, associate member of Chartered Institute of Patent Agents, Secretary of British Copyright Council Working Group on Copyright & Technology.
Career: Qualified in 1977. Joined *Bird & Bird* in 1974, became a Partner in 1981.
Personal: Born 1951. Attended Southampton University (BSc Chemistry, 1973).

COOKE, Adam N.
Wragge & Co, London (020) 7242 5866
adam_cooke@wragge.com
Partner.
Specialisation: All aspects of intellectual property law across the full range of patents, trade marks, copyright, designs and trade secrets, both litigation and non-contentious work. Leading cases include Wellcome v Genentech, Unilever v Gillette, Glaverbel v British Coal and Gerber v Lectra.
Prof. Memberships: CIPA, ITMA, AIPLA, AIPPI, LES (member of EEC Laws Committee).
Career: Qualified in 1986 at *Bristows Cooke & Carpmael.* Seconded to *Arnold White & Durkee* Houston, Texas, US patent attorneys 1989-1990. Assistant with *Stephenson Harwood* 1991-1993. Joined *Needham & Grant* in 1993, partner from 1994, partner at *Wragge & Co.*
Personal: Born 1960. Attended Durham University (BSc 1981). Married with 3 children. Interests include travel, gardening and architecture. Lives in London.

CRAIG, Ian R.
Hewitson Becke + Shaw, Cambridge (01223) 461155

DAVIES, Isabel
Eversheds, London (020) 7919 4500
daviesi@eversheds.com
Partner and head of intellectual property at *Eversheds*, London. Head of *Eversheds* national intellectual property group.
Specialisation: Work includes patents, trademarks, copyright, designs, competition and EC law. Cases have included Jif, Boston Scientific v Palmaz 1998, Prince Internet Litigation 1998, Tommy Hilfiger v Tesco 1998 and Elvis TM appeal (CA) 1999, Denny v Instance 2000, Unilever v American Housewares Inc (Oxo). Editor of Sweet and Maxwell's 'European Trade Mark Litigation Handbook'. Co-editor of *Eversheds* 'IPEye'. Legal Editor of 'Journal of Brand Management', Editorial Board of Trademark World and Country Correspondent for EIPR. Has spoken widely at conferences on IP issues, often taking the Chair.
Prof. Memberships: ITMS, CIPA, INTA, ACG. Member of Intellectual Property Sub-committee of the Law Society.
Career: Qualified in 1976. Partner at *Wragge & Co*, 1979-1985. Joined *Woodham Smith (Taylor Joynson Garratt)* as Partner in 1986, then *Jaques & Lewis* (now *Eversheds*) in 1994.
Personal: Born 30th May 1952. Attended St Albans Girls' Grammar School, Leicester University and Guildford College of Law. Leisure interests include travel, theatre, squash, skiing, food and wine. Lives in Chelsea.

DELEMORE, Ceri
Edwards Geldard, Cardiff (029) 2023 8239
ceri.delemore@geldards.co.uk
Partner, Head of Intellectual Property/Information Technology
Specialisation: All aspects of intellectual property and information technology law including transactional work, research and collaboration agreements, licensing, assignments, trade mark applications, IT procurement, FM contracts, bespoke software developments and IP and IT related litigation. Also handles media work.
Prof. Memberships: The Intellectual Property Lawyers Organisation. The Law Society's Solicitors' European Group. Society for Computers & the Law.
Personal: B.A. (Hons.) English and French Law Class 1, University of Kent at Canterbury: Diplome de droit francais de l'universitÈÇ de Paris-Sud. Articled *Slaughter and May*; qualified 1986; *Slaughter and May* 1984-88; joined *Edwards Geldard* 1988: partner 1991. Author of 'Copyright Explained' published by RIBA.

DRISCOLL, Helen
Freethcartwright, Nottingham (0115) 9369 369
helen.driscoll@freethcartwright.co.uk
Specialisation: Intellectual Property Specialist, principally dealing with contentious work. Particular expertise; trade mark, and passing off actions, design right and copyright actions, injunctions and contempt.
Prof. Memberships: AIPPI. Law Society's European Group.
Career: Articled *Eversheds*, qualified 1993, associate 1996, *Freeth Cartwright, Hunt Dickins* 1997; partner 1998. Education: University College, Cardiff; Leicester University.

Personal: Interests include Choral singing, fast cars, and languages.

ELLIS, Peter
Browne Jacobson, Nottingham (0115) 976 6000
pellis@brownej.co.uk
Specialisation: Practises in all aspects of Intellectual Property litigation and dispute resolution including patents, copyright and design rights (registered and unregistered), confidential information, passing off trade secrets; acting for computer software and hardware companies, telecommunications, engineering and clothing companies. In 1998 involved in the trademark for major fashion house, assisting/representation with clients in US patent litigation.
Prof. Memberships: TIPLO, LES, AIPPI.
Career: Qualified 1976. At *Wells & Hind* 1976-1980. *Browne Jacobson* 1981 to present (Partner from 1984).
Personal: Born 3.6.52. Interests include family, golf, cricket and sports generally. Lives in Nottingham.

FARRANT, Patrick
Eversheds, Cambridge (01223) 355 933
patrickfarrant@eversheds.com
Specialisation: A commercial lawyer specialising in the exploitation of intellectual property, biotechnology and competition law. Head of national biosciences group.
Prof. Memberships: Solicitors European Group, AIPPI, AIJA, Licensing Executive Society, BIA.
Career: Trained with *Frere Cholmeley*; qualified in 1989; joined *Eversheds* in 1990; partner in 1995.
Personal: Three children; Swiss and British national; fluent French speaker.

FIELD, Sally
Bristows, London (020) 7400 8000
sally.field@bristows.com
Partner in intellectual property department.
Specialisation: Sally is one of over 50 lawyers handling intellectual property matters in the firm together with 18 other intellectual property partners; Ian Judge, David Brown, John Allcock, Philip Westmacott, Edward Nodder, Paul Walsh, Kevin Appleton, Alan Johnson, Pat Treacy, Tim Powell, Dr Penny Gilbert, Matthew Warren, David Wilkinson, Simon Ayrton, Christine Hore, Laura Anderson, Justin Watts and Andrew Lykiardopoulos Intellectual Property litigation. Work covers advising on full range of intellectual property including patents, trade marks, copyright, designs and confidential information. Cases include Allen & Hanbury's (Glaxo) v. Generics, IBM v. Phoenix and Kimberly-Clark v. Procter & Gamble, Writes articles for specialist periodicals. Regular speaker at intellectual property conferences and seminars.
Prof. Memberships: Law Society, Associate Member Chartered Institute of Patent Agents, Associate Member Institute of Trade Mark Agents.
Career: Articled with *Clifford Turner* 1979-1981, then moved to *Bristows* in 1983. Became a Partner in 1987.
Personal: Born 16th May 1957. Attended Durham University 1975-78. Leisure pursuits include golf, tennis and skiing. Lives in London.

FLINT, David
MacRoberts, Glasgow (0141) 332 9988
df@macroberts.co.uk
See under Information Technology, p.454

FREELAND, Rowan
Simmons & Simmons, London (020) 7628 2020
Specialisation: Intellectual Property litigation particularly patents and designs. Major cases include Texas Instruments v. Hyundai Electronics, Allied Colloids v American Cynamid, General Instrument v Intel, Southco v Dzus and Hallen v Brabantia. Also IT law. Commissioning Editor, then Editorial Board Member, 'Patent World'.
Prof. Memberships: AIPPI, AIPLA, TIPLO.
Personal: Born 1956. Education Wellington, St Catherines College Oxford (BA 1978). Joined *Simmons & Simmons* 1980, qualified 1982, partner 1988. Married with three daughters. Interests reading, gardening, opera.

GAYTHWAITE, Miles
Bird & Bird, London (020) 7415 6000
Consultant to Intellectual Property Group.
Specialisation: Principal area of practice is patents, patent and know-how licensing, trade marks and copyright. Also pharmaceuticals and software. Important cases handled include L.B. Plastics v Swish; Holtite v Jost; Unilever v Gillette; Societe Francaise Hoechst v Allied Colloids Ltd; Kakkar v Ferring; BICC plc v Burndy Corporation; Amersham v Corning; H%ssle v SmithKline Beecham, Cynamid and Knoll; Connaught Laboratories v SmithKline Beecham and Napro Biotherapeutics v Bristol Myers Squibb.
Prof. Memberships: Chartered Institute of Patent Agents, Licensing Executives Society, APRAM.
Career: With *Elkington & Fife*, Chartered Patent Agents 1967-74. Qualified as a Chartered Patent Agent in 1972. Joined *Bird & Bird* in 1974 and became a Partner in 1978.
Personal: Born 1943. Educated at Glasgow University 1960-64 (BSc, Chemistry) and Cambridge University 1964-67 (PhD, Organic Chemistry). Lives in London.

GIBBINS, David
Wragge & Co, London (020) 7242 5866
david_gibbins@wragge.com
Specialisation: Intellectual property litigator. Main technical areas are electronics, computers, mechanical and electrical engineering; also significant experience in passing off and trademarks.
Career: Practised at patent bar 1969-79 (chambers of J Whitford QC); director of anti-piracy operations at IFPI for 3 years; re-qualified as solicitor, partner in *Needham & Grant* since 1984; consultant for *Wragge & Co*, 2000.
Personal: MA (Cantab), lives in Kent. Married, 3 children. Interests include astronomy, playing golf and fast cars.

GOLD, Tibor Z.
Stephenson Harwood, London (020) 7329 4422
Specialisation: Intellectual Property. A large number of contentious and non-contentious trademark matters for the BBC. Major branding exercise worldwide for a FT-SE top 25 company.
Prof. Memberships: Law Society; Chartered Institute of Patent Agents (President, 1998/1999); ECTA; INTA; AIPPI; LES; ITMA (Fellow); UNION. Fellow of Royal Society of Arts.
Career: Chartered Patent Agent 1969; European Patent Attorney 1977; Registered Trade Mark Attorney 1990; European Trade Mark Attorney 1996; Solicitor 1993; *J. Miller & Co* 1964-1970 Patent Agent; *T.Z. Gold & Co* 1970-1991; with *Stephenson Harwood* since 1991; partner since 1994.
Publications: Co-Editor: The Trade Mark Handbook (Sweet & Maxwell, looseleaf) and contributor. Contributor: The C.I.P.A. Guide to the Patents Act. Many articles in IP journals such as European I.P. Review, Trademark World, Copyright World, CIPA Journal, ITMA Newsletter, ECTA Newsletter.
Personal: Budapest schools 1948-1956; Surbiton C.G.S. 1958-61; Oxford Univ. 1961-1964 (BA; MA 1967); London Univ. 1978-1982 external LLB. Married, two children; live in West Hampstead. Main interests: films, reading, current affairs, travel, wine (on firm's wine committee!).

GRANT, Gregor
Wragge & Co, London (020) 7242 5866
gregor_grant@wragge.com
Head of intellectual property.
Specialisation: Patent litigator. Main technical areas are mechanical, chemical and biotechnology. Long hand-on experience in numerous patent actions in these fields, many cases reported in RPC and FSR. Also deals with trademark and design litigation.
Prof. Memberships: CIPA, AIPPI, IPLA.
Career: Articled with *Hempsons*, assistant solicitor with *Bird & Bird*, co-founder of *Needham & Grant* in 1971, which merged with *Wragge & Co* in April 2000.
Personal: Born in Glasgow, lives in North London. Married, 4 children. Interests include jazz, piano, sketching, cooking, riding bikes.

GRASSIE, Gill
Maclay Murray & Spens, Edinburgh (0131) 226 5196
gg@maclaymurrayspens.co.uk
Specialisation: Contentious IP litigation partner specialising in trade marks, patents, copyright and confidential information/trade secret disputes, recent cases included House of Lords copyright appeal case–Redrow Homes v Bett; parallel imports trade marks case Davidoff/Joop v M&S Toiletries, multi-jurisdictional patent/trade secret case.
Career: Edinburgh University (LL.B Hons 1984). Writer to the Signet. Law Society IP Committee member; LawSociety specialist accreditation in IP law; Associate member of CIPA; member of TIPLO and INTA; Scottish correspondent for CIPA guide. Member of Editorial Committee for Sweet & Maxwell European Trade Mark Reports; author of Scottish chapters of Sweet & Maxwell European Trade Mark Litigation Handbook and of Monitor Press IT 2000 Handbook. Worked for *Bristows* IP litigation department, London (1991-92) and *Drostes*, Munich (1992-93).
Personal: Born 1963. Interests: running; skiing; scuba diving; travelling.

HARRIS, Gordon D.
Wragge & Co, Birmingham (0121) 265 2200
gordon_harris@wragge.com
London (020) 7242 5866
Partner in Commercial Group and team leader of Intellectual Property Team.
Specialisation: Practices largely in intellectual property litigation and defamation work. Principally works in the field of patents, but is experienced in all aspects of IP work and handled the Motor Car spare part litigation culminating in the landmark Veng v Volvo European Court decision. He has written and spoken widely on the subject of IP and as a member of the International Chamber of Commerce IP Commission he is involved in the political and policy issues surrounding the area of parallel trade and exhaustion of rights.
Prof. Memberships: Intellectual Property Lawyers Association; Associate of Chartered Institue of Patent Agents; Associate of Institute of Trade Mark Agents; International Trade Marks Association; Licencing Industry Merchandisers Association; Anti-Counterfeiting Group; mediator accredited by CEDR and WIPO; Licencing Executives Society; International Chamber of Commerce; IP Commission.
Career: Joined *Wragge & Co* 1982; qualified 1984; partner 1990.
Personal: Born in London, 1959; lives in Worcestershire.

HARRIS, Paul
Eversheds, London (020) 7919 4500
harrisp@eversheds.com
Partner *Eversheds* London Intellectual Property Group.
Specialisation: Patents, trademarks, copyright, designs. Notable cases include Coloplast [1993]; Wagamama v City Centre Restaurants [1995]; Electrolux v Black & Decker [1996]. Author of various IP articles; regular lecturer including Bristol University: IP Diploma course.
Prof. Memberships: ITMA; CIPA; INTA (Chair of the European Legislation Analysis Sub-committee); AIPPI; UNION; Royal Society of Chemistry; Chariman of the Whittington Committee of the City of London Law Society.
Career: Qualified in 1987. *Bristows Cooke & Carpmael; McKenna & Co [1988-92]; Taylor Joynson Garrett* [1992-94]; *Eversheds* formerly *Jaques & Lewis[* [1994-], became Partner in 1995.
Personal: Born 17th May 1961; Keele University; Leisure interests include fitness; running; theatre; Italian wine. Lives in Westminster.

HARRISS, David
Bird & Bird, London (020) 7415 6000
Specialisation: Partner in Intellectual Property Department. Main area of practice is intellectual property litigation. Includes UK and international patent infringement litigation, trademark infringement, passing off, copyright infringement, design infringement and breach of confidence. Acted in Akzo/ Du Pont, PLG/Ardon, BP/Hoechst Celanese, BP/Union Carbide and Exxon/ Lubrizol. Member of Editorial Board of Patent World. Chairman of Law Society I.P. Working Party
Prof. Memberships: Law Society, Chartered Institute of Patent Agents (Fellow).
Career: Qualified as Patent Agent 1969. Worked for AA Thornton & Co. 1965-1970, then Langner Parry from 1970-1973 (Chartered Patent Agents). Joined *Bird & Bird* in 1973. Qualified as a Solicitor 1977. Partner 1977. Senior Partner 1993.
Personal: Born 1943. Attended Epsom College 1956-1961, then Christ's College, Cambridge 1961-1964. Lives in Chobham, Surrey.

HART, Michael
Baker & McKenzie, London (020) 7919 1000
Partner in Intellectual Property and Information Technology Law Department.
Specialisation: Principal area of practice is contentious and non-contentious IP and IT Law. Work includes copyright, trade marks and passing off, patents and trade secrets, computer copyright disputes, broadcasting and media law. Also deals with government regulations and trade libel. Has repre-

sented various trade bodies in lobbying activities relating to UK and EU legislative proposals, including the copyright in the Information Society Directive. Has acted in numerous IP court actions representing companies such as Fila, McLaren, Seiko, Versace, Apple Computer and Sony.
Prof. Memberships: Anti-counterfeiting Group, AIPPI, Intellectual Property Lawyers Association.
Career: Qualified in 1983. With *Linklaters & Paines* 1983-1987. Joined *Baker & McKenzie* in 1987 and became a Partner in 1990.
Personal: Born 12th August 1959. Educated at City of London School 1970-1977 and Exeter College, Oxford 1977-1980. Leisure activities include theatre, cinema, horse racing and tennis. Lives in London.

HEAD-RAPSON, Niall
Eversheds, Nottingham (0115) 950 7000
Specialisation: Senior Associate, Intellectual Property. First patent case outside London, Elvis case at first instance.
Prof. Memberships: AIPPI, INTA, LES, AVRIL.
Career: CPE/LSE Nottingham Law School; Kings College, London–Biotechnology BSc (Hons) 2:1; Diploma in intellectual property–Queen Mary's College, London; Articled and qualified *Gouldens. Freshfields; McKennas.*

HICKSON, Chris
Slaughter and May, London (020) 7600 1200
Specialisation: Head of group specialising in contentious and non-contentious intellectual property and information technology matters. Practice comprises principally litigation and advice on patents, trade marks, passing off, copyright and designs, the protection of trade secrets, and advertising. Has a wide experience of IP in the context of corporate transactions, intellectual property licensing and general litigation.
Prof. Memberships: ITMA, ACG, INTA, AIPPI.
Career: Admitted 1977. With *Slaughter and May* since 1975. Became a Partner in 1984.
Personal: Born 10 December 1951. Educated at St. Joseph's College, Beulah Hill and Birmingham University (LLB). Interests include stamps, books and mountaineering. Lives in Surrey.

HODGSON, Mark
Taylor Joynson Garrett, London (020) 7300 7000
mhodgson@tjg.co.uk
Partner in intellectual property department. Head of pharmaceutical and medical group.
Specialisation: Specialises in patent litigation in the U.K. courts and in the European Patent Office. Also handles pharmaceutical, medical device and biotechnology matters, including regulatory issues, product liability, advertising, parallel importation and clinical trial contracts. Acted in respect of Smith Kline and French Laboratories Ltd.(Cimetidine) Patents, Bonzel v. Intervention, R v. Licensing Authority ex parte Smith Kline and French Laboratories Ltd. Merck/SB v. Primecrown, Smithkline Beecham v. Norton/LEK, Eli Lilly & Co v. Novo Nordisk and Biogen v. Medeva. Currently acting for Lilly ICOS in action against Pfizer concerning the patent for sildenafil (Viagra) to be heard in October. Has written articles for legal and pharmaceutical journals and lectures extensively on matters such as E.C. medical device regulations, patent term restoration and parallel importation.
Prof. Memberships: Member Law Society, AIPPI, IBA and Secretary of Intellectual Property Lawyers Association.
Career: Qualified in 1983 whilst at *Woodham Smith* 1981-85. Joined *Simmons & Simmons* in 1985 where he became a partner in 1989. Joined Taylor Joynson Garrett in 1998.
Personal: Educated at Barnard Castle School 1969-1977 and at Emmanuel College Cambridge 1977-1980. Chester Law School 1981. Leisure interests include Newcastle United F.C. and chauffeuring his children to parties. Lives near Gamlingay, Cambs.

HUMPHREYS, Robert
Humphreys & Co, Bristol (0117) 929 2662
Senior partner in commercial department.
Specialisation: Intellectual property, commercial and reinsurance.
Prof. Memberships: Law Society.
Career: Qualified 1981. With *Simmons & Simmons* 1979-85. Partner *Cartwrights* 1985-1986. Co-founded *Humphreys & Co* 1986.
Personal: Born 1953. Educated Dr Morgan's School, Bridgwater and New College, Oxford. Leisure interests include cricket. Lives near Bristol.

INGLIS, Andrew
Olswang, London (020) 7208 8888
api@olswang.com
Specialisation: Partner specialising in intellectual property, particularly patents and trade marks. He also deals with copyright issues for media clients of the firms. Heads *Olswang*'s Intellectual Property Group which comprises 16 lawyers. The practice spans substantial patent and trade mark practices (including patent and trade mark filing practices), as well as meeting the needs of the more traditional clients of the firm in the areas of media, IT and e-commerce. Splits his time between litigation and commercial matters and through his practice in relation to trade marks and branding he has considerable expertise in advertising and marketing. Important reported cases he has handled include British Coal Corporation v Glaverbel SA, R Bance & R Bance & Co Ltd's Licence of Right (copyright) Application, Mecklermedia v DC Congress and the most recent "Budweiser" trade mark appeal on behalf of the Czech Brewery.
Career: Originally qualified in Australia in 1981 where he practised before moving to England. After qualifying in England in 1990 he was a partner at *Nabarro Nathanson* from 1991-1997, and has been a partner at *Olswang* since 1997. Active in contributing articles to publications such as the European Intellectual Property Review and public speaking on intellectual property issues.

IRVINE, James
Llewelyn Zietman, London (020) 7842 5400
Partner.
Specialisation: Specialises in IP litigation, particularly major patent and trademark litigation and anti-counterfeiting work for international companies. Clients in industries ranging from computer software to fashion accessories. Co-author of chapter on Hong Kong in book about IP rights in Hong Kong and other countries. Lectures on IP issues. Regular contributor of articles to IP magazines.
Prof. Memberships: Institute of Trade Mark Agents (Associate Member), Chartered Institute of Patent Agents, Marques, Law Society of Scotland, AIPPI, INTA.
Career: Admitted in Scotland in 1983, Hong Kong in 1984 and England and Wales 1995. With *Johnson Stokes & Master* in Hong Kong 1984-88. Joined *Denton Hall* in 1988 and became a partner in 1990. In their Hong Kong office 1988-92. Joined Llewelyn Zietman in November 1997.
Personal: Born 24th August 1959. Educated at Aberdeen University 1977-82 (LL.B Hons, DLP). Interests outside the law include golf and bridge.

JONES, Gareth
Bevan Ashford, Bristol (0117) 923 0111
Specialisation: Technology transfer agreements, all aspects of IT procurement in public and private sectors including framework agreements, software licencing agreements, Private Finance Initiative funded transactions, and advice on national guidance issued by public sector bodies.
Prof. Memberships: Licensing Executives Society; Society for Computers and Law; The Intellectual Property Organisation.
Career: University College Wales, Aberystwyth–LLB Hons. Qualified 1980. 1985-1991 Partner *Eversheds* Cardiff (formerly *Phillips & Buck*). 1991 to date Partner–*Bevan Ashford.*
Personal: Golf, rugby, skiing.

JONES, Nigel
Linklaters (A member firm of Linklaters & Alliance), London (020) 7456 5804
nigel.jones@linklaters.com
Specialisation: Specialist in intellectual property and technology related matters, particularly in the pharmaceuticals field. Chairman of *Linklaters*' Healthcare Group. Main areas of practice include IP aspects of corporate transactions and IPOS; drafting and negotiating technology agreements; IP litigation, including patent litigation (particularly in the biotech and general healthcare fields), breach of confidence actions and trade mark and copyright disputes.
Prof. Memberships: Fellow of the Chartered Institute of Arbitrators; Licensing Executives Society, International: Chair, European Committee. Licensing Executives Society, Britain & Ireland: Member of Council and Chairman of EEC Laws Committee. Associate Member of the Chartered Institute of Patent Agents and American Intellectual Property Lawyers Association. Member of Editorial Board of BioScience Law Review.

JONES, Patricia
Hammond Suddards Edge, Manchester (0161) 830 5000
patricia.jones@hammondsuddardsedge.com
Specialisation: Contentious and non-contentious intellectual property, including patents, trade marks, passing off, copyright, designs and confidential information. Particular expertise in patent litiagtion and biotechnology.
Prof. Memberships: Licensing Executives Society.
Career: Qualified 1995. *Eversheds* (1993-1996), *Wacks Caller* (1996-2000), joined *Hammond Suddards* January 2000.
Personal: Strathclyde University–Applied Physics BSc (Hons) (1st class). Manchester University pHD–Structure of Proteins Using X-Rays. Interests include watching rugby union.

JONES, Stephen
Baker & McKenzie, London (020) 7919 1000
stephen.jones@bakernet.com
Specialisation: Intellectual property litigation and advice work including patents, trade marks, designs

and copyright; passing off; technology related litigation and dispute resolution; IP aspects of corporate transactions; commercial agreements, in particular in the pharmaceuticals and healthcare industries; partner in charge of Trade Marks Unit, responsible for applications for trade marks and registered designs.
Prof. Memberships: CIPA (Fellow); EPI; ITMA; INTA; ECTA; LES; AIPPI (British Group); PTMG; Royal Society of Chemistry (Associate).
Career: BSc (Chemistry) Imperial College; ARCS; LLB (London); Chartered Patent Agent; European Patent Attorney; Registered Trade Mark Agent; European Trade Mark Attorney; solicitor; partner *Baker & McKenzie*, London.
Personal: Born 22 January 1956; married with three children.

JUDGE, Ian
Bristows, London (020) 7400 8000
ian.judge@bristows.com
Partner in intellectual property department.
Specialisation: Work covers litigation and licensing of the full range of intellectual property, including patents, trade marks, copyright, designs and confidential information. Has had conduct of major patent cases such as Bristol-Myers ats Beecham and Du Pont v. Akzo (both H.L.), Chiron v. Organon Teknika and Chiron v. Evans Medical. Speaker at seminars on specialist intellectual property topics.
Prof. Memberships: Law Society, Chartered Institute of Patent Agents (Associate Member), Chairman–Intellectual Property Lawyers Association, AIPPI, AIPLA.
Career: Joined *Bristows* 1964, became a partner in 1969.
Personal: Born 4th December 1941. Attended Cambridge University (BA 1963, MA 1967).

KAMSTRA, Gerry
Simmons & Simmons, London (020) 7628 2020
Partner in Intellectual Property Department.
Specialisation: Principal area of practice is intellectual property law, including financings, commercial transactions and litigation within the pharmaceutical and biotechnology industries. Clients include Astra Zeneca, 3M, Bayer, Bristol-Myers Squibb, Guidant Corporation, Alizyme plc and Inhale Therapeutic Systems. Has written numerous articles and lectures widely.
Prof. Memberships: Member Intellectual Property Advisory Committee of BioIndustry Association and Associate Member of Chartered Institute of Patent Agents.
Career: Qualified in 1986. Joined *Simmons & Simmons* 1986 where he became a Partner in 1992.
Personal: Born 13th May 1954. Educated at Hymers College, Hull, Keble College, Oxford (Psychology & Physiology), Leicester University (Ph.D in Neuroendocrinology) and Trent Polytechnic.

KARET, Ian
Linklaters (A member firm of Linklaters & Alliance), London (020) 7456 5800
ian.karet@linklaters.com
Specialisation: Specialist in IP and technology related matters, particularly in patents. Main areas of practice include IP aspects of major acquisitions and disposals, corporate fund raising and licensing (including drafting and reviewing patent, know-how, trade mark and software licences, both from the commercial and EC anti-trust viewpoints); drafting and negotiating IP licences, manufacturing agreements and distribution agreements and general advisory work. IP litigation, including patent litigation (biotech, pharmaceutical and chemicals), trade mark and copyright disputes and software exploitation.
Prof. Memberships: Assistant Reporter General of AIPPI. Associate Member of the Chartered Institute of Patent Agents. Member of the Royal Society of Chemistry and Chartered Chemist.

KEMPNER, Richard
Addleshaw Booth & Co, Leeds 0113 209 2000
Partner and joint head of intellectual property, commercial group.
Personal: Handles both disputes and transactions involving patents, copyright, trade marks, designs, confidential information and IT. Voted the UK's 'Top Trade Marks Rising Star' for 2000 by the 'Insider Guide to Brands and Trade Marks' and as being 'very knowledgeable' and 'bright, friendly and highly proactive'. Clients include Asda, Airtours and Ferrari. Speaks and writes extensively on protection, licensing and enforcement.
Prof. Memberships: LES, INTA, CIPA, IPLA, ITMA.
Career: Joined the firm in 1990. Partner 1992.
Personal: Educated at Durham University 1981-1984 (BA 1st class Hons Law).

LINDSEY, Michael
Morgan Cole, Cardiff (029) 2038 5385
micheal.lindsey@morgan-cole.com
Partner in intellectual property/IT group.
Specialisation: Intellectual property and information technology Law, advising on all aspects of IP law including copyright, patents, designs, trade marks, trade secrets and digital media law. Practice split evenly between contentious and non-contentious matters.
Prof. Memberships: The Intellectual Property Lawyers Organisation; The Intellectual Property Institute; The Law Society.
Career: LLB (Hons) University of Birmingham 1983; *HCL Hanne & Co* , London 1985-1988; qualified 1987; joined *Morgan Cole* 1988; Partner 1999.
Personal: Born 9th December 1960. Married with two children. Lives in Caerphilly. Leisure interests include walking, cricket and cooking.

LLEWELYN, David
White & Case, London (020) 7600 7300
Dllewelyn@whitecase.com
Partner in *White & Case's* London office specialising in intellectual property law.
Specialisation: Main area of practice is intellectual property. Deals with all aspects, both contentious and non-contentious. Also covers information technology, e-commerce and pharmaceutical law. Has been involved in a number of major IP related transactions and cases, many cross-border. Clients come principally from the cosmetics, food and drink, pharmaceuticals and retail sectors. Also computer companies (especially software) and multimedia. Author of numerous articles published in legal journals, Editor, IIC. Has also delivered many conference papers in the UK and abroad. Senior Visiting Fellow in Intellectual Property, Centre for Commercial Law Studies, Queen Mary and Westfield College, London.
Prof. Memberships: Law Society, Pharmaceutical Trade Marks Group, International Trademark Association.
Career: Research Fellow at Max Planck Institute for Patent, Copyright and Competition Law, Munich 1980-81. Qualified in 1985. With *Linklaters & Paines* 1982-87, then Partner at *McKenna & Co* 1987-94. Founded *Llewelyn Zietman* in July 1994. Joined *White & Case's* London office in September 1999.
Personal: Born 15th July 1956. Educated at Wallingford Grammar School 1967-74, Southampton University 1974-77 (LL.B) and Worcester College, Oxford 1978-79 (BCL, 1st Class Hons). German speaker. Lives in London SW7.

LOCHNER, Ludi
Lochners Technology Solicitors, Godalming (01483) 414588

LOVE, James
Irwin Mitchell, Leeds (0113) 234 3333
lovej@irwinmitchell.co.uk
Specialisation: Intellectual Property. Handling an oil industry patent dispute which is set to become one of only half a dozen cases since 1977 to reach the House of Lords in connection with the Patents Act 1977. Handling defence of dispute featured on national television concerning the extent of Dyno-Rods alleged monopoly in Day-Glo painted vans. Major international litigation in US and throughout Europe.
Prof. Memberships: Chartered Institute of Patent Agents. Institute of Trade Mark Agents.
Career: 1989-1994: *Bristows*, London. 1994-1996: *Eversheds*, Leeds. 1996- : *Irwin Mitchell*, Leeds (Partner from 1997). Named as one of Yorkshire's top three lawyers under 40 in 1999 and as one of the regions leading young professionals.
Publications: Articles in a wide variety of general and specialist press.
Personal: 1984-1987: Queens College, Cambridge (Sciences). 1987-1989: The College of Law, Chancery Lane. 1992-1993: Diploma in Intellectual Property, Bristol University.

LUCKMAN, Michael
Hammond Suddards Edge, Birmingham (0121) 200 2001
michael.luckman@hammondsuddardsedge.com
Specialisation: Complete range of commercial and contentious intellectual property and information technology work. Specialist areas of advice include biotechnology and technology, the Internet and the retail sector–brands and counterfeit issues.
Prof. Memberships: Licensing Executives Society. The Intellectual Property Lawyers Organisation. British In Vitro Diagnostics Association.
Career: St Brendan's College, Bristol. Exeter University (LLB Hons). *Simmons & Simmons* (1983-88). *Slaughter and May* (1989-94). Qualified 1985. Partner *Edge Ellison* 1995.
Personal: Interests include fly fishing, watching rugby, reading, skiing.

MACDONALD, Morag
Bird & Bird, London (020) 7415 6000
Partner in Intellectual Property Department.
Specialisation: Work includes litigation, transactional and advisory work in relation to patents, trade marks, copyright and other intellectual property rights. Also handles electronics and computer law. Acted in Mentor/Hollister, Compaq/Dell, Richardson Vicks/Reckitt & Colman, Chocosuisse/Cadbury, Unilever/Johnson Wax, Research Corporations SPC, Swiss Miss, Baxter/Pharmacia Upjohn and Genetics Institute, Cartonneries de Thulin/White Knight, Stolt Comex Seaway/Coflexip, Novo Nordick/DSM.

Prof. Memberships: CIPA, ITMA, INTA, ECTA, British Computer Society.
Career: Called to the Bar in 1984. Qualified as a Solicitor in 1988, having joined *Bird & Bird* in 1985. Became a Partner in 1989. Contributor on IP issues to 'Internet Law and Regulation' (Sweet & Maxwell, 2nd edition, December 1997), UK section of 'The New Role of Intellectual Property in Commercial Transactions' (Wiley 1994) and the Legal Aspects chapter of 'Essential IT' (Gee Publishing 1996). Co-author of 'Designs & Copyright Protection of Products: World Law & Practice' (Sweet & Maxwell).
Personal: MA in Mathematics, Physics and Law from Cambridge.

MACDONALD SMITH, Catriona
Allen & Overy, London (020) 7330 3000
Specialisation: Partner dealing with patent, trade mark, copyright, designs and trade secrets litigation, with emphasis on pharmaceuticals, computers and hi-tech products; banking and insolvency related IP, in particular post-insolvency asset disposal; dispute resolution and malicious falsehood.
Prof. Memberships: Honorary Secretary Union of European Practitioners in Industrial Property; Council Member Intellectual Property Lawyers Association, Member of The Intellectual Property Lawyers Organisation, American Intellectual Property Lawyers Association, Association of Intellectual Property Practitioners in Industry.
Career: Articled *Clifford-Turner* (now *Clifford Chance*); qualified 1982; *Clifford Turner* (Clifford Chance) 1980-89; *Allen & Overy* 1989 to present; partner 1992.
Personal: St Andrew's University (MA). Interests include mountain climbing, music and languages.

MACDONALD-BROWN, Charters
Gouldens, London (020) 7583 7777
cmb@gouldens.com
Specialisation: Head of Intellectual Property Group. Advised in numerous patent, copyright, design, trade mark and other IP cases. Executive Council of AIPPI (UK). Honorary adviser to the Legal and Parliamentary Committee of the Royal Society of Chemistry. Regular conference speaker. Lectures on IP courses at Bristol University and QMW (part of London University).
Prof. Memberships: Law Society, IBA, CIPA, ITMA, AIPPI, ABA, AIPLA, INTA, ECTA, LES, Pharmaceutical Trademark Group.
Career: Qualified 1974. Partner from 1977.

MACFARLANE, Nicholas R.
Lovells, London (020) 7296 2000
nicholas.macfarlane@lovells.com
Specialisation: Patents; trade marks; passing-off; copyright; misuse of confidential information; trade libel and other allied areas of competition law; largely involved in litigation. Involved in many leading intellectual property cases concerning inter alia; patentability of software; the movement of patented pharmaceuticals within the EU; extent of relief in Anton Piller Orders; comparative advertising and counterfeiting.
Prof. Memberships: Founder Member of and former Secretary of Intellectual Property Lawyers Association; Council Member British Group of AIPPI; associate member Chartered Institute of Patent Agents and Institute of Trade Mark Agents; member European Trade Mark Association (Anti-Counterfeiting Committee).
Career: Lancaster University 1974 BA (Hons). Articled *Richards Butler*; qualified 1977. *Faithfull Owen & Fraser* partner 1980. 1985 amalgamated with *Durrant Piesse*. Now *Lovells*.

MACPHERSON, Shonaig
McGrigor Donald, Edinburgh (0131) 226 7777
Edinburgh Office Managing Partner and Head of Technology Unit.
Specialisation: Handles all aspects of intellectual property and information technology work. Advises on protection strategies, funding for technology projects, licensing, research contracts, litigation and dispute resolution with particular expertise in biosciences. Speaker at Glasgow IT summits in 1993 and 1994, and at the International Science Festival in Edinburgh in 1992, 1993 and 1994, Chicago 1996.
Prof. Memberships: Law Society (England & Wales), Law Society (Scotland), Licensing Executives Society, Royal Society, Scottish Biomedical Association, Scottish Biomedical Research Trust. Visiting Professor at Heriot-Watt University, Society for Computers and the Law.
Career: Qualified in 1984 in England & Wales with *Norton Rose*. Assistant Company Secretary (Legal) Storehouse plc, then Legal Director of Harrods 1987-89. Partner at *Calow Easton* in London 1989-91. Qualified in Scotland 1991. Joined *McGrigor Donald* in 1991 and became a Partner in 1992.
Personal: Born 29th September 1958. Director of Edinburgh Chamber of Commerce and Enterprise. Recreations include theatre, opera and reading. Lives in Edinburgh.

MARSHALL, James
Taylor Joynson Garrett, London (020) 7300 7000
jmarshall@tjg.co.uk
Specialisation: All areas of intellectual property, both contentious and non-contentious. In particular, patent, trade mark, copyright and breach of confidence litigation; licences and other agreements concerning exploitation of intellectual property including in competition law context.
Prof. Memberships: Solicitor's Association of Higher Courts Advocates; Associate of Chartered Institute of Patent Agents; AIPPI; IP Advisory Committee of BioIndustry Association.
Career: BSc (Mathematics and Physics), University of Bristol. Called to the Bar in 1986 with pupillage in Chambers of (then) Stephen Gratwick QC. 1987 joined *Lovell White Durrant*, subsequently requalifying as a solicitor. 1995 obtained Solicitor-Advocate (Higher Courts Civil) qualification. 1997 joined partnership of *Taylor Joynson Garrett*.

MARSLAND, Vanessa
Clifford Chance, London (020) 7600 1000
vanessa.marsland@cliffordchance.com
Specialisation: Partner specialising in intellectual property including copyright, patents, trademarks, and designs.
Career: St Leonard's, Mayfield; King's College Cambridge. Admitted 1981; intellectual property partner in *Clifford Chance* since 1987; director of the Computer Law Association Inc. and of the Federation Against Software Theft (FAST) the UK's software anti-piracy body; specialist editor of 'Copinger & Skone James on Copyright' (14th Edition).
Personal: Born 1957; resides London.

MARTINDALE, Avril
Freshfields Bruckhaus Deringer, London
(020) 7936 4000
amartindale@freshfields.com
Partner specialising in intellectual property.
Specialisation: Main area of practice covers non-contentious intellectual property and information technology. Deals with commercial, advisory and transactional aspects of intellectual property and information technology.
Prof. Memberships: Law Society of England & Wales, Law Society of Scotland, Licensing Executives Society, Competition Law Society, INTA.
Career: Qualified in Scotland in 1985. With Scottish firm *Dickson Minto WS* 1985-88, then *McKenna & Co.* 1988-92. Qualified in England & Wales in 1992. Joined *Bristows Cooke & Carpmael* and became a partner in 1993. Joined *Freshfields* August 1997.
Personal: Born 1st June 1961. Educated at Glasgow University 1978-83.

MCLEAN, James
Burness, Edinburgh (0131) 473 6000
Specialisation: Graduated in English and Scots Law at Cambridge and Edinburgh Universities. Is Convenor of the Law Society of Scotland's Intellectual Property Committee. Practice covers assignation disposal and licensing of intellectual property including property and insolvency aspects.

MCNABB, Heather
Eversheds, Cardiff (02920) 471147
Partner and head of intellectual property and information technology unit.
Specialisation: Specialises in all aspects of Intellectual Property and IT work. Practice covers the full range of contentious and non-contentious IP. Advises on the protection, maintenance and exploitation of intellectual property rights. Particular interest in trade mark issues, technology-based businesses and the internet. Extensive experience of exploiting and protecting IP and drafting and negotiating all types of IT contracts, including agreements for licensing and maintenance, turnkey, facilities management, and outsourcing arrangements, (including PFI work). Also particular interest in e-commerce dealing with clients on the supplier and customer side.
Prof. Memberships: Member of the Licensing Executives Society; member of the Society for Computers and Law; Member of the Intellectual Property Lawyers Association and the New Media Development Group.
Career: University of Wales, Cardiff (LLB Hons. 1986). Qualified in 1989. Joined *Eversheds* in 1994, becoming a partner in 1995.
Personal: Married and resides in South Wales.

MOAKES, Jonathan
Halliwell Landau, Manchester (0161) 835 3003
Partner and head of intellectual property department.
Specialisation: Work includes patents, copyright, designs, trade secrets, technology transfer and exploitation agreements, trade marks and disputes. Particular experience in acting for high tech businesses–member of the firm's high tech/biotech unit. Other area of practice is computer law, including software licensing, supply contracts and disputes. Author of International Information Technology Law–England and Wales and the Encyclopaedia of Information Technology Law–Export Licensing Control. Has addressed numerous conferences on intellectual property and computer law issues.

Prof. Memberships: Committee Member of North West Branch of the Licensing Executives Society, Society for Computers and Law, Solicitors European Group.
Career: Qualified 1984. Worked at *Baker & McKenzie* 1982-88, then *Halliwell Landau*, becoming a Partner in 1989.
Personal: Born 1960. Attended Queens' College, Cambridge 1978-1981. Leisure interests include sailing, skiing, fell walking, tennis and playing the violin. Lives in Wilmslow.

MOODIE, Bill

Herbert Smith, London (020) 7374 8000
bill.moodie@herbertsmith.com
Head of the intellectual property and technology department.
Specialisation: Specialises in intellectual property law, particularly patents, copyright and trade marks involving the electronics, communications and the IT and digital media industries. Extensive litigation experience but also substantial non-contentious practice. Clients include Quantel, Cable & Wireless, Guinness, Formula One, BSkyB, Bridgestone/Firestone, PriceWaterhouseCoopers, Warner, Vodafone, Bourns, WH Smith, BAT.
Career: South African patent agent and attorney–1975; Solicitor in England and Wales–1979; Partner at *Herbert Smith*–1984; Head of IP Group–1996.
Personal: Education–University of Cape Town (B.Sc Elec. Eng.) First Class Honours–1969; University of South Africa (LL.B)–1975.

MOONEY, Kevin

Simmons & Simmons, London (020) 7628 2020
Senior Partner in Intellectual Property Department.
Specialisation: Principal area of practice is patent litigation. Clients include Smith Kline Beecham, Eli Lilly, Bristol Myers Squibb, Pharmacia & Upjohn, 3M, Union Carbide, Procter & Gamble, Intel Inc and Norsk Hydro. Member of Nuffield Bioethics Council Working Party on Human Tissue (April 1995). Experienced speaker at conferences.
Prof. Memberships: ABA, AIPLA, AIPPI, City of London Solicitors Company (Member of Intellectual Property Sub-Committee).
Career: Qualified in 1971. Partner at *Simmons & Simmons* since 1973.
Personal: Born 14th November 1945. Educated at Bristol University (LL.B 1968). Leisure activities include gardening and supporting Q.P.R. Lives in Ealing, West London.

MOSS, Gary

Taylor Joynson Garrett, London (020) 7300 7000
gmoss@tjg.co.uk
Member of *Taylor Joynson Garrett's* intellectual property department.
Specialisation: Practice covers all areas of intellectual property, but with particular emphasis on patents, biotechnology, information technology and technology transfers. Also handles both contentious and non-contentious matters within the field of information technology including licence disputes, fitness for purpose disputes and copying/ plagiarism disputes. Examples of important cases handled are Pall Corporation v Commercial Hydraulics, SKM v Wagner Spraytech, Single Buoy Moorings v Brown Brothers and Vickers plc, Brugger v Medic-Aid Limited, Amgen v Roche Diagnostics & Genetics Institute (major litigation relating to biotechnology patents) Amgen v Aventis (ditto) and Taylor v Ishida Co Limited. Clients include Amgen Inc, Visa, Pall Corporation, Norcros plc, Haberman Associates, Avery Denison, Geron Corporation and Biocompatibles plc. Member of the Editorial Boards of *The Biotechnology Law Report*and the Journal of Brand Management. Has spoken at seminars on life sciences and information technology, both protection and issues arising on acquisitions of technology based companies.
Prof. Memberships: Law Society (Member of Intellectual Property Sub-Committee).
Career: Qualified in 1977. With *Clifford Turner* 1977-1979, then *Woodham Smith* 1979-1990 (partner from 1981). Joined *Taylor Joynson Garrett* as a partner in 1990.
Personal: Born 7th April 1953. Educated at the University of Leicester 1971-1974 (1st Class Hons) and the College of Law (1st Class Hons). Recreations include theatre, opera and golf. Lives in London.

NAPPER, Isabel

Mills & Reeve, Cambridge (01223) 222 379
isabel.napper@mills-reeve.com
Specialisation: Strong City background dealing in all aspects of intellectual property law. Her move to Cambridge, where she has acquired a substantial reputation, enables her to use that experience to the advantage of clients. Enjoys handling a wide variety of IP issues relating to patents, designs, trade marks and confidential information, including advising companies of all sizes on how to deal with their intellectual property in order to protect and exploit it efficiently. Frequently lectures and gives seminars to clients and professional bodies. Extensive practical experience of litigation and licensing. Has a particular interest in technology transfer and biotechnology.
Prof. Memberships: Chartered Institute of Patent Agents, Society for the Application of Research, Licensing Executives' Society.
Career: Masters Degree (London). Qualified 1984. Specialist IP lawyer with *Lovell White Durrant*. 1991 IP partner *Hopkins & Wood*. 1994 to 1998 IP team at *Taylor Vinters*. 1998 Partner in IP team *Mills & Reeve*.
Personal: Born 1958. Keen on good food, wine and enjoying life.

NEWMAN, Helen

Simmons & Simmons, London (020) 7628 2020
Partner and Managing Partner of Intellectual Property Department.
Specialisation: Principal area of practice is advising on a wide range of contentious and non-contentious intellectual property matters. Conducts litigation involving patents, know-how, copyright, designs and trade marks in the UK, and co-ordinates or instructs corresponding litigation overseas. Other main area of work is advising on the acquisition, disposal, re-structuring and exploitation of intellectual property rights portfolios.
Prof. Memberships: International Trademark Association, Institute of Trade Mark Agents, MARQUES, Anti-Counterfeiting Group, European Communities Trade Mark Association.
Career: Articled with *Simmons & Simmons*. Qualified 1980 and became a Partner in 1985.

NICOLSON, Fiona

Maclay Murray & Spens, Glasgow
(0141) 248 5011
fmmn@maclaymurrayspens.co.uk
Partner and head of intellectual property department.
Specialisation: Specialises in Intellectual Property and Information Technology work for clients both national and international, including start-ups, listed companies, venture capitalists and educational institutions.
Prof. Memberships: Immediate past president–Licensing Executives Society, 'Britain and Ireland' Council Member. Chairman of the Law Society of Scotland panel for accreditation of intellectual property.
Career: Joined *Maclay Murray & Spens* in 1993. Previously partner and Head of IP at *Bird Semple, Fyfe Ireland.*
Personal: Glasgow University MA (1974) LLB (1983). Born 1954.

NODDER, Edward

Bristows, London (020) 7400 8000
edward.nodder@bristows.com
Partner in intellectual property department.
Specialisation: Advises on the full range of contentious and non-contentious intellectual property, including patents, trade marks, copyright, designs and confidential information, computers and IT, pharmaceuticals and biotechnology. This includes advice on European competition and harmonisation laws as they impact on intellectual property, including the European Patent Office and the Community Trade Mark Office. Amongst numerous reported cases, acted for the plaintiff in 3M v. Rennicks (patent infringement and licensing) and Gillette v. Edenwest (trademark infringement and passing off) and for the defendant in Kastner v Rizla (patent claim contructions). Has been involved in opposition proceedings at European Patent Office for 3M, British Gas and other clients. Currently responsible for High Court and Appeal Court patent and brands litigation on behalf of 3M, Novatis, Sara Lee (Douwe Egberts), Rizla (Imperial Tobacco) and Th. Goldschmidt AG (Veba /Viag). Author of articles for specialist periodicals such as 'Patent World'. Regular speaker at intellectual property conferences and seminars.
Prof. Memberships: Law Society, Associate Member of Chartered Institute of Patent Agents, AIPPI.
Career: Joined *Bristows* in 1978. Became a Partner in 1986.
Personal: Born 29th June 1956. Educated at Cambridge University 1974-77 (MA in Natural Sciences and Law). Enjoys opera, chamber music, tennis, gardening and the Languedoc.

NORTCLIFF, Celia

The Law Offices of Marcus J. O'Leary, Bracknell (01344) 303044
Specialisation: Full range of intellectual property and information technology work with emphasis on computer industry; advice includes software licensing and distribution; hardware sales and distribution; competition; advertising and marketing; facility management; e-commerce; CCTA contracts; public procurement; disaster recovery; acts for a number of world renowned companies.
Prof. Memberships: Law Society
Career: Qualified 1971. Ten years in City finally as partner at *Rowe & Maw*; 1982 onwards in Reading becoming partner and head of intellectual property at *Brain & Brain* in 1991; joined *The Law Offices of Marcus J O'Leary* as a partner in 1996.
Personal: Educated Lowestoft Grammar School then Manchester University. Leisure interests–plays flute and piano; enjoys travel and reading.

ORCHISON, Graeme W.E.
DLA, Manchester (08700) 111111
graeme.orchison@dla.com
Specialisation: All aspects of contentious intellectual property including patent, copyright, design, trade mark, passing off and confidential information disputes. Particular experience in the law of the internet and in the obtaining and enforcing of asset freezing injunctions and search and seizure orders.
Prof. Memberships: Law Society, Licensing Executives Society; Solicitors European Group.
Career: Qualified 1988. Partner *Philip Conn & Co* 1989-1996. Joined *DLA* 1996. Partner *DLA* 1998. Head of *DLA's* North West communications and technology team.
Personal: Victoria University of Manchester 1981-1984 (LLB. Hons). Lesiure interests include Far Eastern travel and cooking, films and reading and watching Liverpool FC.

PERKINS, David
Clifford Chance, London (020) 7600 1000
david.perkins@cliffordchance.com
Specialisation: Partner and head of intellectual property department specialising in patents, trademarks, designs and pharmaceuticals.
Prof. Memberships: The Law Society; City of London Solicitors Company; The Intellectual Property Lawyers Association [IPLA]; International Bar Association; Chartered Institute of Patent Agents (Associate Member); Institute of Trade Mark Agents (Associate Member); European Communities Trade Mark Practioners' Association; Union of European Practioners in Industrial Property (Council Member of the British Group); AIPPI (Associate Internationale pour la Protection de la Propriete Industrielle); International Trade Mark Association (Foreign Member); American Bar Association (Foreign Member); American Intellectual Property Law Association (Foreign Member): International Sub-CommitteeChair of Anti-trust Law Committee and Co-Chair of International Developments Sub-Committee of the ADR Committee; Common Law Institute of Intellectual Property (Council Member); World Intellectual Property Organisation: listed as WIPO Mediator/Arbitrator; The Intellectual Property Lawyers Organisation [TIPLO]: Council Member.
Career: Newcastle Preparatory School; Uppingham School; Newcastle University. Partner *Clifford Chance* 1975.
Personal: Golf; tennis. Born 1943; married; three sons, one daughter; resides London.

POORE, Alasdair
Mills & Reeve, Cambridge (01223) 222 248
alasdair.poore@mills-reeve.com
Specialisation: Wide range of intellectual property work including commercial (licensing and other agreements, computer contracts, competition law and M&A) and litigation and dispute resolution. Experience and particular interest in high-tech areas including electronics, computers and software, and also chemicals and biotechnology. Recent work has included a substantial patent action involving electronic copy protection technology, a multi-million pound refunding of recognition software, licensing and advice on a significant web browsing technology, negotiation of Pathfinder PFI project in the IT sector.
Prof. Memberships: Chartered Patent Agent, Registered Trade Mark Agent, Former Council Member of CIPA and Chairman General Laws' Committee, Patent Litigators' Association, Licensing Executives' Society, INTA.
Career: MA (Cantab) Law and Natural Sciences; Shell International Petroleum Co; *Lovell White Durrant; Clyde & Co; Mills & Reeve*, partner 1996.
Personal: Squash, real tennis, mountaineering, music.

PRICE, Richard
Taylor Joynson Garrett, London (020) 7300 7000
rprice@tjg.co.uk
Partner in intellectual property department.
Specialisation: Intellectual property specialist dealing with patents, trade marks, copyright, confidential information and trade libel litigation, IP intensive acquisitions and disposals and licensing. Important cases handled include successful appeal to House of Lords concerning Asahi Chemical's Patent Application in 1991 (cancer inhibiting genetic engineering; priority of competing patent applications and the need for an enabling disclosure; brought UK back into line with Europe; first IP case ever taken to House of Lords by a Japanese company); Reckitt & Colman plc v Borden Inc [1990] (successful prevention of JIF lemon lookalike. House of Lords). Also acted for Canon in the last civil appeal to the Privy Council from Hong Kong (patent issues successful; copyright issues re spare part for PC printer also successful.) Latest heavy cases included two for Hoechst Celanese Corporation against BP Chemicals (patents for more efficient production and decontamination of acetic acid). The main case was successful at trial in February 1997 and on appeal in 1998. It proceeded to the first account of profits hearing in September 1998, the first in a patent case for over 100 years. This litigation settled successfully before judgment in the account. Also Healing Herbs v Bach Flower Remedies (biggest trade mark trial in 1998, complementary medicines successful at trial; and on appeal). Also Sara Lee v Johnson Wax (successful defence of patent infringement action in December 1999).
Prof. Memberships: Chairman, 1994-1997 The Intellectual Property Lawyer's Association (formerly Patent Solicitors Association), City of London Solicitors' Company, Law Society's Intellectual Property Working Party, Solicitors European Group, AIPPI (UK). Lecturer Bristol University IP Diploma.
Career: Qualified in 1970. With *Joynson-Hicks & Co* 1968-1975 (partner 1973-75), then partner at *Courts & Co* 1975-1977 and at *Woodham Smith* 1977-1990. Joined *Taylor Joynson Garrett* as a partner in 1990.
Personal: Born 7th January 1946. Educated at Kingston Grammar School 1957-64 and Bristol University (LLB) 1964-1967. Leisure interests include natural history, tennis and sailing. Trustee, British Ornithologist's Union. Lives in Berkshire. Married with three sons.

RAWLINSON, Paul
Baker & McKenzie, London (020) 7919 1000
paul.rawlinson@bakernet.com
Specialisation: 'Soft' intellectual property litigation including trade marks, copyright, unfair competition: particular emphasis on 'brand' industries where anti-counterfeiting/infringement work is undertaken for clients such as inter alia, Calvin Klein, Polo/Ralph Lauren, Tommy Hilfiger, L'Oreal, Lancome and Stussy.
Prof. Memberships: Steering Committee of the Anti-Counterfeiting Group. International Anti-Counterfeiting Coalition. French Chamber of Commerce.
Career: Trainee with *Baker & McKenzie*; qualified 1988; partner 1995; also admitted Hong Kong; lecturer for ITMA.
Publications: Written articles for 'European Intellectual Property Review'; contributor 'Encyclopedia of Information Technology Law' (Sweet & Maxwell); editor *Baker & McKenzie* 'Guide to Intellectual Property Laws in Central & Eastern Europe'; co-editor of 'Guide to Famous Marks'; editor 'Trade Marks in Europe' and 'Global Brand Protection' publications.
Personal: Born 1962, resides London. Education: St Peter's Grammar School; University of Kent (1983 BA Law); University of Paris XI (1984 Licence en Driot). Enjoys football, golf, wining and dining and waterskiing. Speaks fluent French and some Spanish and Italian.

RICH, Andrew
Herbert Smith, London (020) 7374 8000
andrew.rich@herbertsmith.com
Specialisation: All areas of intellectual property law, contentious and non-contentious. Has been involved in a number of the leading cases in this area including the Boehringer-Mannheim-Amgen patent litigation (recombinant erythropoietin), the SKB v Connaught appeal, the Sandvik v Iscar and Sandvik v Emporia patent actions, an action for Hoffmann-La Roche concerning the PCR patents, actions brought by the owners of the UK Quiksilver trade marks to prevent parallel imports, the patent action between Carter-Wallace and Unilever relating to pregnancy test kits, a contested application by BASF for a supplementary protection certificate and a number of oppositions in the European Patent Office.
Prof. Memberships: Member of the Intellectual Property Advisory Committee of the UK BioIndustry Association. Member of British Group Committee of AIPPI, member of IPLA and associate member of CIPA and ITMA.
Career: Degree in Biology from Liverpool University (First Class Honours)–1984. Articled at *Lovell White Durrant*–1987-1989. Joined *Hammond Suddards* in Yorkshire in 1992. Joined *Herbert Smith* in 1994. Partner 1996.

SAUNDERS, James
Shepherd & Wedderburn WS, Edinburgh (0131) 228 9900
james.saunders@shepwedd.co.uk
See under Energy & Natural Resources, p.

SHILLITO, Mark
Herbert Smith, London (020) 7374 8000
mark.shillito@herbertsmith.com
Specialisation: All aspects of intellectual property work, contentious and non-contentious; extensive trial experience; has acted in a number of the leading cases in the fields of patents (Chiron v Organon Teknika; Strix v Otter; Fort Dodge v Akzo); trade marks (Vodafone v Orange); plant variety rights (Germinal v Fell & Rowsell); copyright (BSkyB v. PRS; Newspaper Licensing Agency Ltd v Marks & Spencer plc); and breach of confidence (Berkeley Administration v McClelland). Specific expertise in law relating to genetically modified organisms.
Prof. Memberships: AIPPI; AIPLA; CIPA; ITMA; INTA; IPLA; TIPLO.
Career: Articled at *Herbert Smith*; qualified 1989; partner 1996. University College London (LLB Hons). Queen Mary & Westfield College, London (Dip.IP).

SLOAN, Philip
Greenwoods, Peterborough (01733) 887700

STARR, Ian
Ashurst Morris Crisp, London (020) 7638 1111
ian.starr@ashursts.com
Specialisation: Patent, trade mark, confidential information and copyright, particularly litigation in the UK and across Europe. Clients range from a number of multi-national telecommunications, computer and healthcare companies to both large and small UK and foreign companies in the general engineering and fmcg industries.
Prof. Memberships: Active member of, and speaker at, a wide range of specialist intellectual property and competition law organisations. Chairman of City of London Solicitors' Company, IP sub-committee.

STOKER, Robert
Addleshaw Booth & Co, Manchester (0161) 934 6000
Partner in intellectual property department, commercial group.
Specialisation: Work includes the acquisition, exploitation and enforcement of patents, trade marks, copyright and designs, confidential information and related areas of competition law. Head of sport and entertainment unit. Other areas of practice are information technology, disposal or licensing of software, hardware purchase and maintenance, facilities management and computer bureau agreements. Appointed to advise the Organising Committee of the 2002 Commonwealth Games. Has spoken on various intellectual property/ information technology related topics in the UK and USA and bradcast on radio on sports issues.
Prof. Memberships: Licensing Executives Society, INTA, LIDC, Solicitors European Group, Law Society, British Association for Sport and Law, Member of the Board of Governors of Sports Aid North West.
Career: Qualified in 1981. Joined firm in 1989; partner since 1991.
Personal: Educated at St Catharine's College, Cambridge 1972-1975 and 1976-1977. Leisure interests include angling, music, journalism, photography and Sunderland A.F.C.

SWIFT, Robert
Linklaters (A member firm of Linklaters & Alliance), London (020) 7456 5806
robert.swift@linklaters.com
Partner, Intellectual Property and Information Technology Department.
Specialisation: Specialist with over 30 years experience in the intellectual property field. Typical matters include: resolving disputes about trade marks, copyright, designs and unfair trading through negotiations and litigation where necessary, interim injunctions and damages assessments against 'pirates' and 'counterfeiters'; protection of computer software; drafting and negotiating licence agreements of various IP rights; EC and UK competition law issues arising out of complex licensing structures; IP aspects of major corporate deals.

SWYCHER, Nigel
Slaughter and May, London (020) 7600 1200
Specialisation: Intellectual property and information technology law; including the IP and IT aspects of acquisitions, disposals, flotations and privatisations; involved in technology, licensing and transfer, franchising and sponsorship and IT procurement and development. Co-head of the firm's Electronic Commerce Group.
Prof. Memberships: ITMA.
Career: Admitted 1987 with *Slaughter and May.* Partner 1994.
Personal: Born 6 June 1962. Educated at Denstone College, Staffordshire and Durham University. Magician.

SYKES, John
Lupton Fawcett, Leeds (0113) 280 2000

TAYLOR, Peter D
Clifford Chance, London (020) 7600 1000
peter.taylor2@cliffordchance.com
Specialisation: Partner dealing with intellectual property, patents, trade mark, copyright, registered design and design right law, contentious and non-contentious, related aspects of competition law, passing off, trade libel and misuse of confidential information.
Prof. Memberships: ECTA; INTA; AIPPI
Career: LLb Hons Law, Birmingham. Articled *Needham & Grant*; qualified 1984; made partner at *Clifford Chance* 1990.
Personal: Born 1959; resides London.

THORNE, Clive
Denton Wilde Sapte, London (020) 7320 6953
cdt@dentonwildesapte.com
Partner and head of intellectual property litigation group.
Specialisation: Specialises in contentious intellectual property work, including copyright law, patents, trade marks, passing off, marketing law, computer law and trade secrets. Also commercial litigation, arbitration and employment law. Fellow of the Chartered Institute of Arbitrators. Co-author of 'Intellectual Property–the New Law,' joint author of 'Sony Guide to Home Taping' and 'Users Guide to Copyright.' Lectures on and has written numerous articles about intellectual property. Leading cases have included: Alan Clark v. Associated Newspapers; Halifax B.S. v. Urquhart DyRes; Interlego A.G. v. Tyco Industries; Sony Corporation v. Saray Electronics; Robin Ray v. Classic FM; Dormeuil v. Nicolian; Dormeuil v. Ferlaglow; Karoon v. Bank of Tokyo.
Prof. Memberships: A founding member of The Intellectual Property Lawyers Organisation. Member of Patent Solicitors Association, International Trade Mark Association, Institute of Trade Mark Agents (Associate Member,) Anti-counterfeiting Group, Computer Law Group, Chartered Institute of Patent Agents (Associate Member,) panel of arbitrators WIPO and Patents County Court.
Career: Qualified in 1977. Articled *Clifford Turner.* Admitted in Hong Kong in 1984 and Victoria, Australia in 1985. Joined *Denton Hall* as a partner in 1987.
Personal: Born 1952. Educated at Trinity Hall, Cambridge 1971-1974 (BA Hons in Law.) Interests outside the law include politics, flute playing, opera and English music.

TULLEY, Christopher T.
DLA, Leeds (08700) 111 111
chris.tulley@dla.com
Specialisation: Full range of intellectual property litigation including patents, trade marks, copyright and design right, passing off and breach of confidence.
Prof. Memberships: Chartered Institute of Patent Agents (Associate), Intellectual Property Lawyers Association, Patent Litigators Association, Law Society.
Career: Qualified 1985. Joined *Dibb Lupton* in 1987. Partner in 1992. Head of the Yorkshire IP Group 1995.
Personal: Born 1961. Attended Leeds University. Lives in Harrogate.

WALSH, Paul
Bristows, London (020) 7400 8000
paul.walsh@bristows.com
Partner in intellectual property department.
Specialisation: Practice spans both contentious and non-contentious intellectual property matters including computer contracts and related disputes. Legal adviser to the British Brands Group, an alliance of leading manufacturers in the FMCG industry concerned with lookalike products. Also interested in emergency interlocutory applications, search and seizure and asset freezing orders, and has been appointed by the High Court to supervise in the conduct of such orders. Cases include Pilkington v PPG (confidential information arbitration), PPG v Pilkington (anti-trust arbitration), Assidoman Multipack v Mead Corporation and Altertext Inc. v Advanced Data Communications Ltd. Lecturer on technology transfer litigation, trade mark law, biotechnology law and Anton Piller Orders. Author of various articles for 'Trade Mark World' and 'Corporate Briefing'.
Prof. Memberships: Licensing Executives Society, Associate Member of the Institute of Trade Mark Agents, European Community Trade Mark Association, Law Society.
Career: Qualified and joined *Bristows* in 1983. Became a partner in 1988.
Personal: Born 21st December 1956. Educated at Salvatorian College 1968-1975 and Oxford University 1976-1979. Leisure interests include tennis, squash, literature and wine. Lives in London.

WHAITE, Robin
Linklaters (A member firm of Linklaters & Alliance), London (020) 7456 5828
robin.whaite@linklaters.com
Partner, Intellectual Property and Technology Department, since 1989.
Specialisation: Considerable experience in commercial and litigious matters involving IP rights and technology. Particular knowledge of issues in the healthcare and computer industries. Main areas of practice include patent, copyright, trade marks and trade secrets litigation; technology joint ventures and IP aspects of corporate finance and restructurings; technology transfer generally, including European anti-trust and competition law considerations; pharmaceutical law, including regulatory affairs. Member of IP panel of the London Chamber of Commerce and Industry and the Government's Standing Advisory Committee on Intellectual Property; editorial board, 'Managing Intellectual Property'; committee of the IP Lawyers Association.

WILLOUGHBY, Anthony
Willoughby & Partners, London (020) 7345 8888
tony@iprights.com
Senior Partner.
Specialisation: All areas of Intellectual Property, but particularly litigation relating to trade marks, passing off, copyright, designs and confidential information.
Prof. Memberships: ITMA, INTA, LSLA, TIPLO, SALS.

Career: Qualified 1970. At the Distillers Co Ltd 1970-1973, *Herbert Smith* 1973-1994. Partner from 1977. Joined present firm as a Partner in 1994.
Personal: Born 29th September 1944. Educated at Westminster School. Interests include music, sport and wine. Member of the Governing Body of Westminster School.

WOOD, Alan

Beachcroft Wansbroughs, Bristol (0117) 918 2000
awood@bwlaw.co.uk
Partner in commercial department.
Specialisation: Main areas of practice are computer and IT, competition and public procurement, and intellectual property. Acts for both public bodies and private sector companies. IT projects range from complex, high-value IT system procurements, with advice on tendering procedures, review and incorporation of technical specifications, contract drafting and award and ongoing contract support, to advice on standard supply, licence and maintenance terms. Also includes advice on public procurement rules, the Private Finance Initiative, out-sourcing and facilities management. Intellectual property advice includes both contentious and non-contentious aspects of IP protection, licensing agreements both national and international, technology led joint ventures and technology transfer generally.
Career: Qualified at *Linklaters & Paines* in 1975. With *Linklaters & Paines* 1975-1987. *Osborne Clarke* 1987-1997. Joined *Wansbroughs Willey Hargrave* May 1997. 1999- Partner in *Beachcroft Wansbroughs.*

WOOD, Ian

Rowe & Maw, London (020) 7248 4282
Partner intellectual property department.
Specialisation: All aspects of intellectual property law, including patents, trade marks and copyright and allied rights, although primarily involved in the area of dispute resolution. Acts for a broad range of clients from large multinational corporations to smaller more locally based businesses, covering a broad spectrum of industries and services extending from those involved in newly emergent technologies to those in more established areas of business. Responsible for the conduct of several notable actions in the High Court, including the following leading reported patent infringement actions: Molnlycke v. Procter & Gamble; Nidek v. VISX; Unilever v. Akzo and Chefaro; Honeywell v. ACL. Other leading cases include Burton v. Burton Snowboards and BP Amoco v. Kelly. Also (with *Rowe & Maw's* WTO team) advising the European Commission in connection with WTO disputes regarding international obligations on patents. Author of several articles and regularly invited to speak at conferences and seminars (including those attended by fellow professionals).
Prof. Memberships: CIPA; ITMA; INTA; AIPPI; IPLA.
Personal: Born 1950. Attended Durham University (BSc Physics and MSc Nuclear Physics). Qualified as a solicitor in 1977.

WOODS, Philip

Hill Dickinson, Stockport (0161) 429 6767
Specialisation: Partner in Technology and Intellectual Property Group of *Hill Dickinson* specialising in all aspects of intellectual property and computer law, both contentious and non-contentious.
Prof. Memberships: Chartered Institute of Patent Agents (Associate); Institute of Trade Mark Agents (Associate); UNION; FICPI; AIPPI; Society for Computers and Law; Committee Member of LES (North West Group); TIPLO (founder member).
Career: Qualified 1974. Admitted Hong Kong 1975. *Deacons* (Hong Kong) 1975-1981. Partner, *Wilkinson & Grist* (Hong Kong) 1981-1989. Partner, *Eversheds Alexander Tatham* (head of IP Department) 1989-1994. Chairman of Eversheds National IP Group until 1994. Partner, *Philip Woods & Co* 1994-1997. Presently Partner *Hill Dickinson.*
Personal: Leisure pursuits include classic cars, wines, walking, reading and gardening. Lives in Prestbury, Cheshire. Born 23rd December 1950.

WYN DAVIES, Cerys

Pinsent Curtis, Birmingham (0121) 200 1050
cerys.wyn-davies@pinsents.com
Technology partner.
Specialisation: Full range of intellectual property, information technology and e-commerce/e-business and data protection work, emphasis on non-contentious matters including technology and biotechnology licensing; multimedia licensing; research and development and collaboration agreements; confidentiality arrangements; trade marks licensing and advice and IP/IT due diligence in connection with transactions.
Prof. Memberships: Licensing Executives Society. TIPLO. FAST. Intellectual Property Lawyers Association. ICC.
Career: Qualified 1985. *Coward Chance* 1983-1987 and *Clifford Chance* 1987-1995. Joined *Pinsent Curtis* in 1995 as partner.
Personal: Born 1961. Graduated from Exeter University 1982 (LLB) First Class Honours and Sweet and Maxwell prize winner. Diploma in intellectual property law, University of London 1991–Distinction in all four heads. Interests include theatre, walking and skiing.

INVESTMENT FUNDS

London: 519; The Regions: 521; Scotland: 521; *Profiles*: 522

OVERVIEW: A busy area for practitioners this year, with the investment fund market no longer seen as a "minority sport." The most successful firms are those which can provide large, experienced teams on demand and are seen to offer the broadest coverage of both domestic and off-shore investment funds.

The Financial Services and Markets Bill will provide a further incentive to push resources at this area. The Bill extends the range of authorised unit trusts able to be converted to open-ended investment companies (OEICs), and increases the level of regulatory expertise required of leading firms in this area.

RESEARCH APPROVED BY BMRB: *For this edition,* Chambers' *researchers conducted 6083 interviews – 4408 with law firms, 598 with barristers and 1077 with clients.*

The validity of the research was scrutinised by BMRB International, who audited both the methodology and the results at our offices in July 2000. They interviewed Chambers' *researchers and cross-checked sample interviews. Details of the audit appear on page 7.*

LEADING IN-HOUSE LAWYERS

Kylie EDWARDS, Head of Legal & Controls, *Schroder Investment Management*

Kenneth GREIG, Head of Legal Services, *Axa Investment Managers Ltd*

Lucy LYNCH, Head of Law & Compliance for Europe, *Morgan Stanley Dean Witter Investment Management Ltd*

Alexander MARSHALL, Executive Director & Counsel, *Goldman Sachs Asset Management International*

Simon MARTIN, Legal Manager, *Gartmore Investment Management plc*

Michelle SORRELL, Company lawyer, *Newton Investment Management*

Jonathan THOMAS, Divisional Director of Legal Services, *Henderson Investors*

Jane THORNTON, Head of Legal, *Gartmore Investment Management plc*

Josephine TUBBS, Head of Legal & Secretariat, *Framlington Group Ltd*

Progenitor of the industry's 'Legal Discussion Group' is **Michelle Sorrell** who is well recommended as a *"safe pair of hands."* Focusing on UK institutions is the *"incisive and smart"* **Kylie Edwards** who has *"a good capacity for complex issues and a high work output."* *"Switched on"* **Kenneth Greig** enjoys a *"good commanding presence"* and is *"proactive"* within the industry. *"Robust"* **Lucy Lynch** is *"very experienced and a good commercial lawyer."* She *"knows when to stand her corner."* Widely recommended was **Alex Marshall** who *"knows his stuff"* and enjoys a *"good reputation."* **Simon Martin** enjoys a *"growing reputation"* although he lacks a high profile as junior to the *"well-experienced"* **Jane Thornton**. She received a wide range of recommendations, acknowledging her *"good technical ability"* and the fact that *"her finger is on the pulse."* The *"nettle-grasping"* **Jonathan Thomas** is praised for his *"very good commercial knowledge,"* for being *"pragmatic"* and having *"good business sense."* The *"forthright"* **Josephine Tubbs** is perceived to *"grasp the issues well."*

In-House lawyers profiles: page 1177

LONDON

Clifford Chance *"A strong, broad"* team seen to dominate a substantial part of the market. *"Outstanding"* **Tim Herrington**, recommended for his *"great brain,"* leads a team which includes the *"impressive"* **James Barlow** and new partner **Andrew Hougie**. Covers all areas of practice with recognised strengths in investment trusts, private equity and hedge funds. The team is seen to benefit from its strong banking practice and its link up with US firm Rogers & Wells. Acted for Industri Kapital on its €3 billion private equity fund which included limited partnerships, and for Clerical Medical on the conversion of its unit trust range to OEICs. **Clients:** Credit Suisse Asset Management; Gartmore Split Capital Opportunities Trust plc.

Linklaters This *"excellent"* team has a number of high-profile personalities: *"Fantastic lawyer"* **Matthew Middleditch**, is seen as a *"corporate heavy hitter,"* praised for his investment trust work, **Tim Shipton** *"handles complex documentation with ease"* and is seen to be *"a provider of solutions,"* and **Paul Harris** has an overseas focus with strengths in offshore funds, real estate funds and OEICs. They are accompanied in the rankings by the fast-rising and *"level-headed"* **Jonathan Perkins**. Cross-border transactions are a growth area, with the Alliance firms providing *"well co-ordinated support."* Acted for ProLogis Trust in the establishment of the ProLogis European Properties Fund to acquire distribution facilities across Europe, and advised Lend Lease Europe Ltd on the formation of the UK's largest limited partnership to invest in property (includes Bluewater Shopping Centre). **Clients:** PIMCO; AIB Govett Asset Management; Lend Lease Europe Ltd.

Eversheds A practice growing in strength on the domestic front with a traditional expertise in the retail investment fund market including OEICs, and an increasing base of closed-end funds and regulation work. *"Knowledgeable and personable"* **Richard Millar** is rated as the *"mainstay of the old unit trust market,"* and **Pamela Thompson** is recommended for leading an *"experienced, practical"* team. Advised on the restructuring of the Henderson European Income Fund and on the conversion of Colonial's unit trusts, life and pension assets to an OEIC (value £3 billion.) **Clients:** AXA Sun Life Investment Fund Managers Ltd; Philips & Drew; Finsbury Smaller Quoted Companies Trust Plc.

Herbert Smith A strong practice recommended for its work in the split-capital investment fund market and on the reconstruction and reorganisation of investment funds. *"Commercial and client friendly"* **Nigel Farr** is praised across the board as one of the most active players in the listed investment trust market. Although not traditionally a strength, the team has a growing reputation in property limited partnerships with **Dominic Clarke** particularly recognised for his private equity work. Advised Fleming Income & Growth Investment Trust plc on its £350 million reorganisation and fund raising, and acted for Close FTSE 100 Trust plc on the £136 million launch of a split-capital investment trust. **Clients:** Henderson Investors; Gartmore Scotland Investment Trust plc; Exeter Asset Management.

Norton Rose Considered to be *"hugely active"* in the OEIC market with a good mix of off-shore and on-shore work and a growth in collective investment scheme transactions. Highly rated **Tim Marsden** is *"an out and out investment trusts man"* and the *"delightful"* **Simon Cox** is recognised for his work in unit trusts and limited partnerships. New funds launched include Mercury Asset Allocator plc as part of the take-over of Mercury Asset Management by Merrill Lynch (value £200 million). The team also established an English limited partnership for Bayerisch Hypo- und Vereinsbank AG to invest in UK retail and commercial property. **Clients:** Foreign & Colonial; Collins Stewart; Jupiter Enhanced Income Investment Trust plc.

Macfarlanes *"Commercial and quick to respond,"* the team is praised for its strength in the retail market, with niche ability in unit trusts and private equity. **Tim Cornick** is seen as a retail specialist and department head **Bridget Barker** is recommended for her unit trust work. Growth areas for the practice include private equity and property funds, with the firm acting on the conversion of unit trusts to OEICs. Acted for Morgan Grenfell Private

INVESTMENT FUNDS • London	Ptnrs	Assts
❶ Clifford Chance	12	40
Linklaters	10	30
❷ Eversheds	4	6
Herbert Smith	3	8
Norton Rose	4	12
❸ Macfarlanes	3	5
Simmons & Simmons	5	9
❹ Ashurst Morris Crisp	3	7
SJ Berwin & Co	8	11
Slaughter and May	6	15
❺ Dechert	2	8
Field Fisher Waterhouse	3	4
Freshfields Bruckhaus Deringer	2	6
Lovells	4	7
Stephenson Harwood	3	9
Travers Smith Braithwaite	2	4
❻ Allen & Overy	*	*
Lawrence Graham	3	1
Rowe & Maw	2	2
Speechly Bircham	3	2

LEADING INDIVIDUALS	
❶ **FARR Nigel** Herbert Smith	**MIDDLEDITCH Matthew** Linklaters
SHIPTON Timothy Linklaters	
❷ **CORNICK Timothy** Macfarlanes	**CRIPPS James** Slaughter and May
HARRIS Paul Linklaters	**HERRINGTON Timothy** Clifford Chance
MARSDEN Tim Norton Rose	**MILLAR Richard** Eversheds
SLATER Richard Simmons & Simmons	
❸ **ASTLEFORD Peter** Dechert	**BLAKE Jonathan** SJ Berwin & Co
CLARKE Dominic Herbert Smith	**CULLEN Iain** Simmons & Simmons
STONES Richard Lovells	**SUTCH Andrew** Stephenson Harwood
THOMPSON Pamela Eversheds	
❹ **BARKER Bridget** Macfarlanes	**BARLOW James** Clifford Chance
BROUGH Gordon Brough Skerrett	**COX Simon** Norton Rose
IVE David Rowe & Maw	
McWHIRTER Anthony Freshfields Bruckhaus Deringer	
PERKINS Jonathan Linklaters	
WALSOM Roger Ashurst Morris Crisp	
WATTERSON Mark Freshfields Bruckhaus Deringer	
UP AND COMING	
BAILLIE Kirstene Field Fisher Waterhouse	
HOUGIE Andrew Clifford Chance	

Within each band, firms are listed alphabetically. *See **Profiles** on page 522*

** See editorial entries for explanations of team sizes.*

Equity in its pan-European private equity fund (value €1 billion) and advised on the conversion of Lazard's range of unit trusts to an OEIC. **Clients:** Morgan Grenfell Private Equity; Legal & General Ventures; HSBC Private Equity.

Simmons & Simmons Recognised for its traditional specialism in hedge funds and investment trusts. Department head **Richard Slater** *("a real gent")* is the guiding light of the firm's open-ended unit trust team, and is praised for his client friendly attitude. He is supported by *"workaholic"* **Iain Cullen**, seen as a hedge funds specialist. Advised Salomon Smith Barney on the establishment of Pendragon Fund Limited, the Cayman Islands feeder hedge fund, and advised Arisaig Partners (off-shore fund client) on a BVI feeder fund listed on the Irish Stock Exchange. **Clients:** Henderson Investors; Arisaig Partners.

Ashurst Morris Crisp Well known for its work for Invesco and Carlyle Group, the team is seen to have a primary focus on the investment trusts market with strengths in limited partnerships. Team head **Roger Walsom** is highly regarded for his private equity work structuring funds both in the UK and off-shore, although the team does not have the profile of some of the market leaders. Acting in the high-tech growth area for Ernst & Young on its incubator fund for new e-commerce businesses. Advised on the Carlyle Internet Partners Europe fund (based in the Cayman Islands, value Euros 770 million and on the launch of an Invesco-leveraged high yield fund (Jersey-domiciled, investing principally in European high-yield bonds). **Clients:** Carlyle Group; Invesco; JZ Equity Partners.

SJ Berwin & Co Perceived to lead the market in venture capital technology funds, the team owes much to the leadership of **Jonathan Blake.** He is also noted for his advice on establishing and structuring private equity funds. The opening of offices in Germany and Spain has strengthened the firm's pan-European influence, and cross-border transactions now comprise a substantial proportion of the workload. Advised on the establishment of Apax Europe IV (value €1.8 billion) and the Electra European Fund LP, including the buy-out of the management company. **Clients:** Natwest Equity Partners; Schroder Ventures; UBS Capital; B&S Electra SpA.

Slaughter and May Despite lacking the focus of a specific department, this team is well regarded for its work in private equity and its strong institutional client base. Growing influence in OEIC-based retail product launches and reorganisations. **James Cripps** is the most prominent player and draws his team from a wide range of departments. Advised 3i on the establishment of 3i Eurofund III, a limited partnership for investment in European venture capital opportunities, and acted for the co-ordinators (including Goldman Sachs Asia, Jardine Fleming Securities Ltd and ING Barings Asia Ltd) on the Tracker Fund of Hong Kong which involved an institutional and public offer. **Clients:** 3i; Commonwealth Development Corporation.

Dechert A traditional reputation for off-shore work assisted by a high profile US link up. **Peter Astleford** is recommended for his *"robust advice"* and his experience in alternative products including hedge funds. The team has offered advice to US houses on investment products and services across Europe. Assisting four major East European private equity finds on ongoing acquisitions (includes Baltic Republic Fund) and advised Fleming Investment Management Ltd on new fund launches. **Clients:** Fleming Investment Management; Morgan Grenfell; Gartmore Investment Management.

Field Fisher Waterhouse *"Proactive"* **Kirstene Baillie** is recommended for establishing the team, capturing *"juicy deals"* and raising her own profile with specific strengths in the retail market. Cross-border advice is notable on off-shore funds (Cayman and Guernsey) and EU collective investment funds. Advises Electricity Pensions Trustees, one of the largest unitised funds for occupational pensions and have acted for Shell on limited partnership investments (includes BAA Partnership). **Clients:** Société Générale Asset Management; Johnson Fry; Phillips & Drew.

Freshfields Bruckhaus Deringer Recommended for its off-shore work and particularly active in the structuring of UK authorised unit trusts, the team also has a growing reputation for private equity fund work and the formation of limited partnerships. The firm is acknowledged for its strength in tax and regulatory issues. **Mark Watterson** is seen on off-shore work, often acting in conjunction with the Hong Kong office. **Anthony McWhirter** is another experienced investment funds player. Advised State Street Global Advisors on the formation of the Tracker Fund of Hong Kong. Also acted for the placement agents in relation to the ProLogis European Properties Fund (Luxembourg) led by Morgan Stanley. **Clients:** State Street Global Advisors; Morgan Stanley.

Lovells A respected team seen as active in the retail market with a specialism in limited partnerships. It is led by **Richard Stones**, *"a reliable techni-*

cal man." Growth areas for the team include a surge in property-related funds and OEIC launches. The recent merger with Boesebeck Droste is expected to provide a substantial boost to the firm's pan-European retail capacity. Launched Egg Investments' online supermarket and the Bank of Scotland's in-house range of investment products and services. Also advised AMP Ltd on the regulatory aspects of the demutualisation of National Provident Institution. **Clients:** Prudential Banking; ING Barings; Mercury Asset Management.

Stephenson Harwood A recognised strength in split-capital and investment fund reconstructions. Led by *"effective"* **Andrew Sutch**, an investment trusts expert. Has advised on Channel Islands' London-listed fund launches and seen a growth in OEIC conversion and registering funds in European jurisdictions. Investment trust reconstructions include Framlington Dual Trust and Aberdeen High Income. Advised Gartmore Fledgling Investment Trust on a successful hostile bid for Themis Fledgling Investment Trust. **Clients:** Hoare Govett Ltd; Collins Stewart Ltd; Gartmore.

Travers Smith Braithwaite *"A friendly and flexible team"* with a particular reputation in limited partnerships and venture capital work. The department has focused on building up its private equity practice and has recently overseen new investment fund launches. Advised on GMT Communications II private equity fund (value €200 million) and the Stella Eclipse Hedge Fund. **Clients:** GMT Communications; Ulster Bank; Baring Private Equity Partners.

Allen & Overy (Can draw upon 11 ptnrs and 20 assts.) The firm's Investment Structures Group is not perceived by the market to have a strong focus on this area. However, the firm's international network of offices (particularly Luxembourg) and an undeniably strong banking practice have led to involvement in structuring investments, off-shore funds (both close-ended and open-ended) and limited partnerships. Advising a wide range of UK and overseas banks and investment funds, and acted on the winding-up and reconstruction of German Smaller Companies Investment Trust plc. **Clients:** Centennier Ltd, Schroder Exempt Property Unit Trust.

Lawrence Graham A strong team, seen *"to punch above its weight,"* which is recommended for its *"strong grasp of technical issues."* Well-known for its split-capital investment trust work (floatations and reconstructions) and the take-over of investment trusts. Advised on the Gartmore High Income Trust Plc and on the reconstruction of Fulcrum Investment Trust. **Clients:** Gartmore Investment Management; Second St David's Investment Trust plc; Brewin Dolphin & Co Ltd.

Rowe & Maw **David Ive** is recommended for his focus in the area of tax, particularly the taxation of unit trusts, OEICs and off-shore funds. A high profile in the market is due in part to a sound client base featuring major names such as M&G Securities. **Clients:** M&G Securities.

Speechly Bircham Recognised for its unit trust expertise and seen to have an entry into the OEIC market. A smaller player in the market, the team advises on the structuring of unit trusts, OEICs and investment trusts. Advised Ecclesiastical Insurance Group on the St Andrew Trust and the launch of the Group of Allchurches Investment Funds, an umbrella OEIC with five sub-funds. **Clients:** Ecclesiastical Insurance Group; Royal Bank of Scotland; Singer & Friedlander Unit Trust Management Ltd.

Other Notable Practitioner *"Fabulous"* **Gordon Brough** of Brough Skerrett is recommended as a leading figure in this market, with a personal profile greater than the firm itself. Commended for his *"excellent insight,"* he is seen principally on the launches of new investment funds.

THE REGIONS

INVESTMENT FUNDS • The Regions	Ptnrs	Assts
❶ Burges Salmon Bristol	2	2

Within each band, firms are listed alphabetically.

Burges Salmon Acting in isolation, the team has had little impact on the city firms, but is recognised as the one and only regional firm in this market. Recommended as a *"cost-effective department,"* the team has secured a small number of active clients, with a focus on unit trusts and a growth in new OEIC issues and conversions. Advised on the OEIC conversion and amalgamation for Premier Portfolio Managers Ltd and amalgamation for St James Place Unit Trust Management Ltd. **Clients:** Nationwide Unit Trust Management; Exeter Investment Group Plc; Asset Management Investment Company plc.

SCOTLAND

INVESTMENT FUNDS • Scotland	Ptnrs	Assts
❶ Dundas & Wilson CS Edinburgh	3	6
Tods Murray WS Edinburgh	3	2
❷ Dickson Minto WS Edinburgh	4	4
McGrigor Donald Glasgow	2	2
❸ Maclay Murray & Spens Glasgow	1	1
Shepherd & Wedderburn WS Edinburgh	2	6

LEADING INDIVIDUALS	
❶ ATHANAS Christopher Tods Murray WS	MACKAY Philip Dundas & Wilson CS
❷ DORAN Frank McGrigor Donald	MINTO Bruce Dickson Minto WS
❸ DUNSIRE David Tods Murray WS	POLSON Michael Dundas & Wilson CS
THURSTON SMITH Martin Tods Murray WS	
TODD Andrew Dickson Minto WS	WATT James Dundas & Wilson CS

Within each band, firms are listed alphabetically. *See **Profiles** on page 522*

Dundas & Wilson CS Nationally a highly respected team, dealing with all types of fund work and particularly praised for its involvement in the retail market. **Philip Mackay** is a prominent player and a *"good technical open-ended funds lawyer,"* and **Michael Polson** is praised for his investment trust reconstructions. **James Watt** is recommended for his technical acumen, although he is set to take a consultancy role with the firm at the end of August. Advised Scottish Equitable Fund Managers Ltd on the conversion of 16 authorised unit trusts (value £850m) into sub-funds of SEAM Investment Company ICVC. Advised on reconstruction of St Andrew Trust plc (value c£140m) involving a new UK- authorised investment company and split-capital investment trust. **Clients:** Martin Currie Investment Management; Scottish Equitable Fund Managers; Scottish Widows Fund Management.

Tods Murray WS A firm seen to be growing with the reputation of the *"talented and trustworthy"* **Christopher Athanas** who is said to dominate the OEIC market. The team itself has a *"realistic approach"* and is recommended for building strong relationships with clients. **David Dunsire** is praised for his OEIC trustee work and **Martin Thurston Smith** has *"sound technical ability."* Acted for Baillie Gifford & Co Ltd and Royal Bank of Scotland in establishing Baillie Gifford UK & Balanced Funds ICVC, its first umbrella OEIC and is acting for Scottish Equitable Asset Management plc on the integration of 12 authorised unit trusts. **Clients:** Chase Manhattan

Trustees Ltd; Edinburgh Unit Trust Managers Ltd; Royal Bank of Scotland plc.

Dickson Minto WS A leading financial services team is seen by the market to be more focused on investment trusts with comparatively minor involvement in OEICs and unit trusts. **Bruce Minto** has a high profile and is considered *"commercial and pragmatic."* He is ably supported by **Andrew Todd**, recommended for his reconstruction of investment trusts. Advised Aberdeen Asset Managers on the establishment of the ADC Fund limited partnership which acquired the Clydesdale Bank Equity portfolio and advised Penta Capital Partners on its first limited partnership. **Clients:** Scottish Amicable; Edinburgh High Income Trust; Aberdeen Scotland Investment Company; The Scottish Investment Trust plc.

McGrigor Donald *"Technically strong,"* easy to work with and appreciated by his clients, **Frank Doran** is the heartbeat of this team, and a universally respected practitioner. Seen to be lacking the financial clout offered by a substantial Edinburgh presence, the team is nevertheless recommended for its strength in the unit trust OEIC market. The team also advises on limited partnership trusts and the listing of investment trusts on the London Stock Exchange. Acted for Saracen Value Trust plc and Murray Ventures plc on their reconstruction schemes. **Clients:** Murray Johnstone Ltd.

Maclay Murray & Spens Recognised by the market as an active player, the firm is still felt to lack the individual big-hitter needed to challenge the leaders. The team advises on investment trusts, OEICs, limited partnerships and private equity funds and is seen to benefit from a booming corporate practice. Acted for Scottish Widows on its demutualisation and for Brewin Dolphin on its investment trust reorganisations. **Clients:** Edinburgh Investment Trust; Scottish Widows; Brewin Dolphin.

Shepherd & Wedderburn WS Still not perceived by the market to have replaced Sue Inglis adequately, the team is felt to have lost ground this year. However, it retains an enviable client base with a bias towards investment trust work. Recent work includes advising Friends Ivory & Sime plc on its acquisition of London & Manchester Group's asset management subsidiaries, and acting for Britannia Investment on the launch of exempt unit trust funds. **Clients:** Baillie Gifford & Co; Friends Ivory & Sime; Edinburgh Fund Managers.

LEADERS IN INVESTMENT FUNDS

ASTLEFORD, Peter
Dechert, London (020) 7583 5353
peter.astleford@dechertEU.com
Partner and Head of the Financial Services and Investment Management Group, London.
Specialisation: Specialises in all aspects of onshore and offshore mutual funds and attendant legal and regulatory issues applicable to the funds and their promoters/ investment managers/ other service providers. His unit also provides a one-stop-shop dealing with UK and US regulatory issues including dual purpose compliance manuals. Frequent contributor to the financial press and speaker at related conferences.
Career: Qualified in 1986. Specialised in financial services/ investment funds with a leading City of London law firm and subsequently became Group Legal Advisor and then Head of Corporate Services at the London listed holding company to a major international financial services group. In 1997, appointed a dual partner of the integrated practices of *Dechert Price & Rhoads* and *Titmuss Sainer Dechert* which this year merged to form one firm called *Dechert*.
Personal: Born 1962.

ATHANAS, Christopher
Tods Murray WS, Edinburgh (0131) 226 4771
chris.athanas@todsmurray.co.uk
Specialisation: Specialises in Corporate Financial Services and Investment Funds; all aspects of collective investment schemes including open-ended investment companies (OIEC's), unit trusts, investment trust companies, investment products (including PEPs and ISAs), related regulatory and compliance law.
Prof. Memberships: Law Society of Scotland.
Career: Qualified 1966 *Paull & Williamsons*; *Dundas & Wilson* 1968; Partner 1969-1996; Partner *Tods Murray* 1996.
Personal: Born 1941. Attended Fettes College, Edinburgh; Aberdeen University (1962 MA) 1964 (LLB); WS. Leisure: the arts, collecting, walking, golf, angling.

BAILLIE, Kirstene M.
Field Fisher Waterhouse, London (020) 7861 4000
kmb@ffwlaw.com
Specialisation: Financial services – Head of Investment Funds and Products Group. Advises fund managers, insurance companies, and brokers on a wide range of investment products, with expertise in the inter-related areas of collective investments, financial services, insurance and pensions.
Prof. Memberships: City of London Solicitors Company; Association of Pension Lawyers; Life Assurance Legal Society.
Career: Qualified 1987; partner *Frere Cholmeley Bischoff* 1995-1998; partner *Field Fisher Waterhouse* 1998 to present.
Publications: Financial Services Chapter of 'E-Commerce: Law and Practice' written by fellow partner Michael Chissick and published by Sweet and Maxwell (currently in its second edition). Article in 'FT Trust and Oeic Yearbook 2001' on Financial Services and Markets Act and its impact on collective investment schemes.

BARKER, Bridget
Macfarlanes, London (020) 7831 9222
Partner in Company, Commercial and Banking Department.
Specialisation: Specialises in investment funds and financial services, acting for a number of on-shore and off-shore investment funds, covering a range of investment areas. Also experienced in corporate finance work, acting for a number of listed companies. Recent matters include advising on pan European venture capital fund for Morgan Grenfell Private Equity. Author of articles on investment funds, financial services and money laundering.
Prof. Memberships: Law Society, International Bar Association. Vice Chairman of IBA Committee on Specialised Investment Funds. Association of Women Solicitors.
Career: Qualified with *Macfarlanes* in 1983. Became a Partner in 1988.

BARLOW, James
Clifford Chance, London (020) 7600 1000
james.barlow@cliffordchance.com
Specialisation: Partner specialising in financial services and investment funds.
Prof. Memberships: Chartered Institute of Taxation (Associate).
Career: Mill Hill School; Nottingham University (LLB). Partner *Clifford Chance* since 1980.
Personal: Born 1943.

BLAKE, Jonathan E.
SJ Berwin & Co, London (020) 7533 2222
jonathan.blake@sjberwin.com
Specialisation: Partner in the Corporate Finance Department and Head of Private Equity advising generally on mergers and acquisitions of private and public companies and specialising in the establishment of private equity and other funds, the structuring of companies, venture capital investment, MBOs as well as reorganisations, flotations and associated taxation matters.
Prof. Memberships: Associate of the Chartered Institute of Taxation (ATII); British Venture Capital Association; International Bar Association; European Venture Capital Association.
Personal: Educated at Haberdashers' Aske's School, Elstree and Queens' College, Cambridge (MA LL.M). Qualified 1979. Born 7th July 1954.

BROUGH, Gordon
Brough Skerrett, London (020) 7253 5505
gordon@broughskerrett.co.uk
Specialisation: Corporate with emphasis on Fund management and Fund transactions including flotations, acquisitions and mergers. Specialist interest in partnership law.
Prof. Memberships: Association of Partnership Practitioners.
Career: Founded *Brough Skerrett* in 1994. Formerly a partner with *Bird Semple Fyfe Ireland WS* and prior to that, *Thorntons WS*.
Publications: Private Limited Companies: Forma-

tion and Management. The Law of Partnership in Scotland.
Personal: An enthusiastic socialiser and writer (resting). Married with two children.

CLARKE, Dominic
Herbert Smith, London (020) 7374 8000
dominic.clarke@herbertsmith.com
Partner in corporate division
Specialisation: Specialises in investment funds within the UK and overseas and in the regulation of the financial services and insurance industries. His work in connection with investment funds includes the formation and restructuring of unit trusts, open-ended investment companies, investment trusts, limited partnerships, common investment funds for charities, off-shore funds and other investment vehicles. His regulatory practice covers the application of regulations governing the financial services and insurance industries.
Career: Qualified in 1975. Became a partner at *Herbert Smith* in 1987.
Personal: Educated at Leeds University.

CORNICK, Timothy
Macfarlanes, London (020) 7831 9222
Partner in Company/Commercial Department.
Specialisation: Practice covers Financial Services Act regulatory and securities work. Main area of practice is investment management and collective investment schemes. Substantial involvement in matters on behalf of investment managers, custodians and trustees. Particular experience of unit trusts and open ended investment companies onshore and offshore. Speaker at conferences and seminars for IBC, Cadogan and Oracle.
Prof. Memberships: Law Society.
Career: Qualified in 1982, having joined *Kenneth Brown Baker* in 1980. Became a Partner of *Turner Kenneth Brown* in 1988. Joined *Macfarlanes* as a Partner in 1995.
Publications: Contributor to Butterworths Financial Services Law and Practice and Encyclopaedia of Forms and Precedents. Lead editor, Sweet & Maxwell's 'Collective Investment Schemes Law and Practice'. Author of articles in International Business Lawyer, Journal of International Banking and Financial Law and Compliance Monitor.
Personal: Born 1st November 1957. Attended Weymouth Grammar School 1969-76, then Worcester College, Oxford 1976-79 and College of Law Guildford 1979-80. Society of Dorset Men; Primary Club, MCC. Leisure interests include cricket, wine, jogging, reading history. Lives in Kent.

COX, Simon F.T.
Norton Rose, London (020) 7283 6000
Partner in Corporate Finance Department.
Specialisation: Has a wide-ranging securities and corporate practice with an emphasis on collective investment and international and domestic corporate finance, particularly in relation to emerging markets. Contributor to 'A Practitioner's Guide to the Stock Exchange Yellow Book' and author of various articles. Has spoken at a number of UK and overseas conferences on funds, stock exchange and Financial Services Act issues and on investment in the former Soviet Union.
Prof. Memberships: Securities Institute, IBA, Law Society, City of London Solicitors Company.
Career: Qualified in 1980, having joined *Norton Rose* in 1978. Became a Partner in 1988.
Personal: Born 17th January 1956. Attended Eton College 1967-73 and Trinity College, Oxford 1974-77. Trustee of two Charitable Trusts. Lives in London.

CRIPPS, James
Slaughter and May, London (020) 7600 1200
Partner in Commercial Department.
Specialisation: General and international corporate and corporate finance practice with emphasis on listed and unlisted collective investment schemes (including private equity and emerging markets) and advice (including regulatory advice) to providers of financial services and financial products.
Prof. Memberships: Co-ordinator of Asset Management practice.
Juvenile Diabetes Foundation UK (director).
The Law Society, Securities Institute, Worshipful Company of Fullers (Court Member), City of London Solicitors' Company.
Career: Joined *Slaughter and May* 1978, qualified 1980, Partner 1989.
Personal: Born 15 March 1956. Educated Eton and St. Catharine's College, Cambridge. Married, three sons, two daughters. Lives in London and Buckinghamshire. Leisure interests include farming, forestry, opera and golf.

CULLEN, Iain
Simmons & Simmons, London (020) 7628 2020
See under Commodities, p.171

DORAN, Frank
McGrigor Donald, Glasgow (0141) 248 6677
See under Financial Services, p.406

DUNSIRE, David
Tods Murray WS, Edinburgh (0131) 226 4771
david.dunsire@todsmurray.co.uk
Partner in Corporate Department.
Specialisation: Specialises in financial services particularly unit trusts, acting principally for trustee. Also handles corporate finance and general corporate work, with an emphasis on acquisitions and disposals, MBOs and start-ups.
Prof. Memberships: Law Society of Scotland.
Career: Qualified 1982, having joined *Tods Murray WS* in 1980. Partner *Tods Murray WS* 1986. Departmental Managing Partner 1998.
Personal: Born 1958. Attended Buckhaven High School, Fife 1970-76, then Edinburgh University 1976-80 (LLB). Leisure: family, gardening and music.

FARR, Nigel J
Herbert Smith, London (020) 7374 8000
nigel.farr@herbertsmith.com
Specialisation: Main areas of practice are transactional and advisory work in the investment funds sector, general corporate finance and M & A. Particular expertise in relation to investment trusts but with increasing involvement with UK and offshore limited partnerships and offshore funds generally. Has extensive experience of acting for funds, fund management groups and financial advisers, with particular emphasis on the structuring, launch, take-over and merger, reorganisation and reconstruction of funds. Also advises on acquisitions and disposals in the financial services sector.
Career: Joined *Herbert Smith* in 1985; partner in 1994.
Personal: Educated at Wimbledon College and Gonville & Caius College, Cambridge. Interests include food and wine, sport, cinema and travel.

HARRIS, Paul
Linklaters (A member firm of Linklaters & Alliance), London (020) 7456 3104
paul.harris@linklaters.com
Partner, Corporate Department and Head of Investment Funds Group.
Specialisation: Specialises in investment funds matters. Has over 25 years experience in structuring, creating and organising funds for investment in property of all types (securities, derivatives, financial instruments, real estate, etc) onshore and offshore, domestic and international, public and private, retail and institutional.
Career: Articled at *Linklaters*, and made Partner in 1976.
Personal: Born 1943.

HERRINGTON, Timothy
Clifford Chance, London (020) 7600 1000
tim.herrington@cliffordchance.com
Specialisation: Partner specialising in financial services including mutual funds, asset management and investment trust work, securities and derivatives trading and regulatory issues, insurance, mergers and acquisitions, Stock Exchange and other corporate work for the financial services industry. Head of the firm's Global Asset Management Group.
Prof. Memberships: Member Law Society's Company Law Committee (past chairman); Vice Chairman, Investment Funds Committee; International Bar Association.
Career: Queen Mary's Grammar School, Basingstoke; Bristol University (LLB). Articled *Clifford Chance*; qualified 1978; partner *Clifford Chance* since 1985.
Personal: Cricket, travel, walking, gardening and wine. Born 1954; resides Sevenoaks.

HOUGIE, Andrew
Clifford Chance, London (020) 7600 1000
andrew.hougie@cliffordchance.com
Specialisation: Partner specialising in investment companies, closed end funds and other collective investment funds as well as transactional and advisory work in the funds, financial institutions and asset management sectors generally and general corporate finance. He has extensive experience of acting in relation to the design, launch, take-over and merger, reorganisation and reconstruction of funds. Recent work included the reconstruction of Biotechnology Investment Limited and the establishment of its successor, 3i Bioscience Investment Trust plc.
Career: Articled *Slaughter and May* 1984, qualified 1986. Joined *Clifford Chance* 1996, partner 1999.
Personal: Stockport Grammar School; Gonville & Caius College, Cambridge. Married. Interests include cycling, walking and bridge.

IVE, David
Rowe & Maw, London (020) 7248 4282
Partner in Corporate Taxation Department.
Specialisation: Experienced in all aspects of taxation, especially in relation to financial services, collective investment schemes, unit trusts, offshore funds, life assurance taxation and also taxation matters relating to trusts generally, and tax litigation. Author of articles in various tax journals, including 'British Tax Review' and 'Tax Journal'. Lecturer on tax topics, especially collective investment schemes and unit trusts. Former member of the Taxation Committee of the Associators of Unit Trusts and Investment Funds. Member Law Society Revenue Law Stamp Duty Committee.

Prof. Memberships: Law Society.
Career: Qualified in 1972. Worked with *Allen & Overy* 1976-84. Spent 6 months at the Tax Bar (1984-85), then joined *Rowe & Maw* in June 1985. Became a Partner in 1986.
Personal: Born 2nd January 1950. Attended Highgate School 1963-68, then Birmingham University 1968-71. Chairman of the Association of Liberal Democrat Lawyers. Joint author of a number of Liberal Democrat publications on constitutional reform. Parliamentary candidate for 1979, 1983 and 1987 General Elections. Leisure pursuits include opera and swimming. Lives in London.

MACKAY, Philip
Dundas & Wilson CS, Edinburgh (0131) 228 8000

MARSDEN, Tim
Norton Rose, London (020) 7283 6000
Partner in Corporate Finance Department.
Specialisation: Corporate finance with particular emphasis on financial services operations and collective investment schemes, both on-shore and off-shore. Advises on acquisitions and disposals in the financial services sector and advises both public and private sector entities on financial services regulation generally. Commonly advises on corporate and collective investment transactions involving emerging markets. Lectures on financial services, investment trusts and unit trusts.
Career: Qualified 1984; Barrister 1984-85. Joined *Norton Rose* 1986. Partner in 1993.
Personal: Born 9th September 1961. Honorary solicitor to DEBRA. Leisure interests include sport and social activities.

MCWHIRTER, Anthony
Freshfields Bruckhaus Deringer, London (020) 7936 4000
Partner in tax department.
Specialisation: Main practice area is investment funds. Advises on all aspects of the structuring, operation and winding up of investment funds and other collective investment arrangements including tax planning and regulation. Author of various articles; has spoken widely at conferences.
Prof. Memberships: Law Society of City of London, AUTIF.
Career: Qualified in 1979, having joined *Freshfields* in 1977. Became a Partner in 1985.
Personal: Born 5th October 1954. Attended Downing College, Cambridge 1973-76.

MIDDLEDITCH, Matthew
Linklaters (A member firm of Linklaters & Alliance), London (020) 7456 3144
matthew.middleditch@linklaters.com
See under Corporate Finance, p.259

MILLAR, Richard
Eversheds, London (020) 7919 4500
richardmillar@eversheds.com
Specialisation: Main area of practice is collective investment schemes, acting for managers of unit trusts, promoters of offshore funds and open-ended investment companies. Also advises generally on financial services law as well as broader company law. Regular speaker at conferences. Advises ANTIF.
Prof. Memberships: Law Society, IBA. Member of Law Society's Company Law Committee and Chairman of its Sub-committee on Collective Investment Schemes.
Career: Qualified in 1963. Joined *Bischoff & Co* in 1965, becoming a Partner in 1967 and Senior Partner and Managing Partner in 1990. Firm merged with *Frere Cholmeley* in 1993 and with *Eversheds*, London, in 1998.

MINTO, Bruce
Dickson Minto WS, Edinburgh (0131) 225 4455
bruce.minto@dmws.com
Founding Partner in Corporate Department.
Specialisation: Work includes Stock Exchange listings, Yellow Book work generally, mergers and acquisitions and institutional finance.
Prof. Memberships: Law Society of Scotland.
Career: Qualified in 1981. Formed *Dickson Minto WS* in 1985.
Personal: Born 30th October 1957. Attended Edinburgh University 1975-79. Leisure interests include golf, shooting and music.

PERKINS, Jonathan M. J.
Linklaters (A member firm of Linklaters & Alliance), London (020) 7456 3049
jonathan.perkins@linklaters.com
Partner in Corporate Department.
Specialisation: Principal areas of practice are all aspects of investment fund work for managers, promoters and investors, including the structuring, establishment and reorganisation of different forms of collective investment vehicles (open and closed companies, unit trusts and limited partnerships), in both domestic and offshore domiciles and for institutional and retail investors. Also advises on general corporate law matters.
Career: Trainee solicitor at *Linklaters*; qualified 1992.
Personal: Born 1967. Corpus Christi College, Oxford.

POLSON, Michael
Dundas & Wilson CS, Edinburgh (0131) 228 8000

SHIPTON, Tim
Linklaters (A member firm of Linklaters & Alliance), London (020) 7456 3100
tim.shipton@linklaters.com
Partner in Corporate Department.
Specialisation: Specialist in offshore fund work advising domestic and foreign clients on the corporate, regulatory and tax aspects of structuring, creating, organising and marketing funds for investment in property of all types (securities, derivatives, financial instruments, debt, real estate, onshore and offshore, domestic and international, public and private, retail and institutional). Has been involved in international capital market issues of debt and equity securities joint ventures and project financing work.

SLATER, Richard E.H.
Simmons & Simmons, London (020) 7628 2020
Partner in Corporate Department.
Specialisation: Corporate and regulatory work with a particular emphasis on the financial services industry. Work covers regulatory advice on the formation and promotion of investment vehicles of all types, the acquisition and disposal of financial services businesses and the reconstruction and merger of investment trust companies, unit trusts and other investment entities. Transactional advice includes public and private company take-overs and acquisitions, joint ventures, initial share offerings and flotations.
Career: Qualified in 1977, after joining *Simmons & Simmons* as an articled clerk in 1975. Became a Partner in the Corporate Department in 1981.
Personal: Born 9th November 1950. Attended City University 1979-82, then Cambridge University 1982-84. Lives in London.

STONES, Richard J.L.
Lovells, London (020) 7296 2000
richard.stones@lovells.com
See under Financial Services, p.407

SUTCH, Andrew
Stephenson Harwood, London (020) 7809 2100
andrew.sutch@shlegal.com
Partner, Head of Corporate Department, Head of Funds and Financial Services Group.
Specialisation: Specialises in investment funds, both UK and offshore, and has considerable depth of experience in his specialist field of financial services regulation. Transactional work has involved a number of investment fund flotations, takeovers and restructurings. Has been involved in a number of split capital investment and trust reconstructions, including the first Channel Islands funds to issue zero dividend preference shares. Also has considerable experience of emerging market funds and advises on open-ended funds in the UK, including unit trusts and OEICs. Lectures on open-ended investment companies (OEICs) and other aspects of financial services law.
Prof. Memberships: Law Society, IBA.
Career: Qualified October 1979. Grindlays Bank (1974-76) trained for 5 months in Beirut; Assistant Operations Manager in Calcutta; *Stephenson Harwood* 1979 as Assistant Solicitor; seconded *Stephenson Harwood & Lo*, Hong Kong 1982-86. Partner in 1984 and Head of Corporate Department in 1997.
Personal: Born 10 July 1952. Educated at Haileybury College; Oriel College, Oxford (1970-74) 1974 Literae Humanoires (MA Oxon). Interests include running, theatre, former member of the TA (Intelligence Corps). Languages: French and some Russian. Resides London.

THOMPSON, Pamela
Eversheds, London (020) 7919 4500
thompspm@eversheds.com
Partner and Head of Financial Services Group.
Specialisation: Main areas of practice are collective investment schemes, pooled investments and financial services regulatory work. Handles onshore schemes including authorised and unauthorised unit trusts open ended investment companies and limited partnerships and offshore schemes such as trusts, open ended companies and closed ended funds. Also handles general financial services work, including regulatory advice, structuring, taxation and marketing investment schemes.
Prof. Memberships: Association of Women Solicitors.
Career: Qualified in 1982, having joined *Bischoff & Co.* in 1980. Became a Partner in 1986.
Personal: Born in 1956. Attended St Hilda's College, Oxford 1975-78.

THURSTON SMITH, Martin
Tods Murray WS, Edinburgh (0131) 226 4771
martin.thurston.smith@todsmurray.co.uk
Partner in Corporate Department.
Specialisation: Specialises in collective investment schemes, financial services and pension schemes. Also handles corporate and commercial work including other commercial applications of trusts.

Prof. Memberships: Law Society of Scotland.
Career: Joined *Tods Murray* 1974. Qualified 1977. Partner 1978.
Personal: Born 1951. Attended The Edinburgh Academy 1957-69 and Christ's College Cambridge 1970-1974. Leisure: family, hillwalking, wine, classical music and jazz. Fluent German and French.

TODD, Andrew G.
Dickson Minto WS, Edinburgh (0131) 225 4455
andrew.todd@dmws.com
Specialisation: Main areas of practice are Stock Exchange work, financial services and venture capital work.
Prof. Memberships: Law Society of Scotland, Writer to the Signet.
Career: Joined *Dickson Minto* in 1987; Partner 1995.
Personal: Born 1964. Edinburgh University 1982 - 1987.

WALSOM, Roger
Ashurst Morris Crisp, London (020) 7638 1111
Specialisation: A partner in the company department involved in a wide range of corporate work including corporate finance and investment funds. Advises on all aspects of investment fund work, including in particular investment trusts and venture capital funds, and has been involved in the launch and restructuring of numerous investment vehicles. Also has substantial experience of a wide range of other corporate transactions, particularly in relation to the raising of capital, mergers and acquisitions and capital restructuring.
Prof. Memberships: Law Society.
Career: Qualified in 1980. Joined *Ashursts* in 1983. Became a Partner in 1988.

WATT, James P.
Dundas & Wilson CS, Edinburgh (0131) 228 8000

WATTERSON, Mark
Freshfields Bruckhaus Deringer, London (020) 7936 4000
Specialisation: Specialises in transactional and advisory work in the investment funds sector, including the structuring, marketing and taxation of investment funds, including property funds and joint ventures, and structuring fund-based financial products and tax-driven financing transactions.
Prof. Memberships: Law Society, City of London Solicitors Company.
Career: Attended Wymondham College 1974-81, Churchill College, Cambridge 1982-85. Joined *Freshfields* 1986, qualified 1988 and became a partner 1997.
Personal: Born 1963. Leisure interests include golf and motor racing (Le Mans 24 hours).

LICENSING

London: 526; South: 527; Thames Valley: 528; South West: 528; Wales: 529; Midlands: 529; East Anglia: 530; North West: 531; Yorkshire: 532; North East: 532; Scotland: 533; Northern Ireland: 534; *Profiles*: 534

OVERVIEW: 'Licensing' encompasses a variety of work, but primarily refers to liquor licensing, public entertainment licensing and betting and gaming work. Liquor and public entertainment work are closely intertwined, and make up the bulk of most licensing practices, with betting, gaming and other licensing work tending to be more adjunct or niche practice areas. A significant growth area in licensing work in the past twelve months has been in internet-related matters, particularly in regard to betting, gaming and retail.

RESEARCH APPROVED BY BMRB: *For this edition,* Chambers' *researchers conducted 6083 interviews – 4408 with law firms, 598 with barristers and 1077 with clients.*

The validity of the research was scrutinised by BMRB International, who audited both the methodology and the results at our offices in July 2000. They interviewed Chambers' *researchers and cross-checked sample interviews. Details of the audit appear on page 7.*

LONDON

LICENSING • London	Ptnrs	Assts
❶ Field Fisher Waterhouse	1	1
Jeffrey Green Russell	2	2
Joelson Wilson & Co	2	1
Kingsford Stacey Blackwell	1	1
Paisner & Co	1	3
Richards Butler	3	5
❷ Allen & Fraser	1	2
Davenport Lyons	8	6
Pullig & Co	1	1
❸ Biddle	5	3
Loxleys	1	*

LEADING INDIVIDUALS	
✪ LAVENDER David Davenport Lyons	
❶ CLIFTON David Joelson Wilson & Co	DAVIES Suzanne Joelson Wilson & Co
EDNEY Robert Kingsford Stacey Blackwell	
GLAZEBROOK Peter Field Fisher Waterhouse	
SOUTHORN Elizabeth Richards Butler	
❷ BAYLIS Craig Paisner & Co	HALLIWELL Tilly Jeffrey Green Russell
HARRIS Graeme Loxleys	HARRIS Julian Biddle
HEPHER Christopher Pullig & Co	SKEENS Julian Jeffrey Green Russell
WALTER Robin Allen & Fraser	

Within each band, firms are listed alphabetically. *See* ***Profiles*** *on page 534*

* *See editorial entries for explanations of team sizes.*

Field Fisher Waterhouse This practice is headed by the *"sharp"* **Peter Glazebrook**, who is seen to have *"extensive experience"* in licensing work. The licensing department has a primary area of practice in liquor and entertainment, and also handles some betting, gaming and lotteries work. In addition, the department advises on ancillary matters such as planning law, food safety and health and safety legislation. The workload includes a heavy flow of applications to Licensing Justices throughout England and Wales for liquor licenses for public houses, hotels, clubs, wine bars, restaurants, off-licences, supermarkets and convenience stores. The firm has also advised on the licensing of historic castles and palaces. An increasing part of the practice is entertainment licensing involving contentious public hearings in front of local authorities. The department also provides support to the Hotel and Leisure Property Group on the acquisition of existing licensed sites and new sites for development. **Clients:** First Quench Retailing Limited; Jamies Wine Bars Limited; Unwins.

Jeffrey Green Russell Licensing work at this firm is undertaken by the *"combined firepower"* of **Julian Skeens** and **Tilly Halliwell**, although each of them have their own client base and work independently of each other. The former *"handles a lot of work for breweries"* and is seen as being *"good at getting results,"* while the *"extremely affable"* and *"switched-on"* Halliwell acts for a range of clients in liquor and entertainment. Recent work includes handling all the licensing matters for the second Rainforest Cafe at the Trafford Centre, Manchester, and obtaining the licence on appeal for Fish!, a new restaurant development in Borough Market for BGR plc. **Clients:** Glendola Leisure Ltd; Hard Rock Cafe; Gioma BV.

Joelson Wilson & Co This firm is considered to take a *"fresh new approach"* to licensing work, and has been seen to be *"doing more and more"* of it in the past twelve months. The *"always well prepared"* **David Clifton** continues to handle gaming matters while the *"very capable"* **Suzanne Davies** continues to act for both applicants and objectors in liquor licensing matters involving hotels, restaurants and casinos. **Clients:** Grosvenor Casinos; Rank Group plc; Regent Inns plc.

Kingsford Stacey Blackwell The firm maintains its good reputation in liquor licensing and public entertainment work in particular, with the *"practical"* **Robert Edney** continuing to act for both large and small companies as well as individual operators. **Clients:** Fuller Smith & Turner; Oddbins; Pitcher & Piano; Punch Retail; Tootsies Restaurants.

Paisner & Co Licensing work at this firm is undertaken by the regulatory law department, which is headed by the *"pragmatic"* and *"commercially-minded"* **Craig Baylis**. The department handles all aspects of licensing including liquor, public entertainment and gaming prosecutions, and is regularly asked to comment on licensing issues for media and television. Over the past twelve months the firm has seen an increase in the work undertaken for commercial property developers. This work has resulted from developers wishing to secure site licences for a large number of leisure units within a single development before letting those units to recognised operators. **Clients:** Bhs plc; City Restaurants; Parisa Group.

Richards Butler There is an extensive licensing practice at this firm presided over by **Elizabeth Southorn**, who is regarded as being *"pleasant to deal with."* The practice covers liquor, public entertainment, late night licences, multi-leisure sites, gaming, betting and ongoing management of clients' licensed estates. The clients range from hotels and nightclubs to cinemas and restaurants, as well as developers. Highlights of the year include the provision of internet gaming advice to international clients, advising the Royal Opera House on licensing issues and acting for Coral in a landmark Court of Appeal case on 'judicial bias post-Pinochet.' **Clients:** Marylebone Warwick Balfour; Conran Restaurants; Rank Group.

Allen & Fraser This practice is known for its licensing expertise, particularly on liquor and entertainment, but also in betting and gaming work. Its clients range from pubs, clubs and restaurants to cinemas, casinos, hotels and off-licences. With the recent departure of leading practitioner

David Lavender to Davenport Lyons, the licensing department is now headed by **Robin Walter**. The full effect of Lavender's departure is yet to be seen, although a number of his clients have left with him. Recent work has included doing the licensing for a major property development involving three building sites in the Greater London area. **Clients:** Scottish & Newcastle; Chelsea Football Club; Slug and Lettuce Group.

Davenport Lyons This firm has always had a focus on the media, entertainment and leisure industry, which is now extending to cover licensing work. The team now acts for a wide range of clients including breweries, hotels and multi-site restaurant chains. The client base has been increased considerably with the recent addition of the highly esteemed **David Lavender**, who is seen as *"London's licensing guru."* Indeed, the prevalent view in the market is that *"any firm which has David Lavender working for them is going to attract clients."* Recent work has included the opening of the 'Sugar Reef' restaurant. In addition, the firm was recently involved in the high profile dispute between 'The Titanic' and 'The Atlantic Bar & Grill' where its client, 'The Titanic', was successful. **Clients:** Breakfast Group; Capital Radio Restaurants; Stringfellows.

Pullig & Co Run by the *"understated and underrated"* **Christopher Hepher**, this is a *"comparatively small"* but still well-regarded licensing practice, with niche areas of expertise in liquor, licensing-related crime and entertainment work. The firm acts primarily for small to medium-sized operators. **Clients:** Off-licences; pubs; nightclubs.

Biddle The gaming and leisure group at this firm is the City's only specialist group dedicated to gaming and leisure. The *"astute"* **Julian Harris** heads up the group and *"doesn't miss a trick"* with his *"extensive experience"* in advising gaming operators on a variety of legal issues. The firm has a close working relationship with the Gaming Board of Great Britain, and obtains many clients on the Board's recommendation. In addition, the firm advises clients worldwide on gaming in the UK and the rest of Europe. A recent highlight for the firm was acting for a private client on the acquisition of the Corals chain of betting shops from Ladbroke plc. **Clients:** The A & S Leisure Group Ltd; Fantasy League Ltd; Stanley Leisure plc.

Loxleys (1 ptnr full-time, 1 ptnr part-time, 1 asst part-time) **Graeme Harris** is recommended for his work in this area, particularly in relation to liquor licensing. He is regarded as *"a solid practitioner,"* and has been referred to as *"about the only person on the licensing circuit who's never had anything bad said about them – an absolute pleasure to deal with."* **Clients:** Include brewing industry clients.

THE SOUTH

LICENSING • The South	Ptnrs	Assts
❶ **Blake Lapthorn** Portsmouth	3	6
Fynn & Partners Bournemouth	2	1
Trethowans Southampton	1	1
❷ **Argles Stoneham Burstows** Maidstone	2	8
Lester Aldridge Bournemouth	2	-
❸ **DMH** Brighton	2	*
Girlings Herne Bay	3	-
Lamport Bassitt Southampton	2	-
❹ **Penningtons** Basingstoke, Godalming, Newbury	2	2

LEADING INDIVIDUALS	
❶ **FYNN Lionel** Fynn & Partners	**MESSENT Michael** Trethowans
❷ **CHA Walter** Blake Lapthorn	**PALMER Julia** Fynn & Partners
❸ **GOVER Graham** Fynn & Partners	**PATRICK Colin** Lester Aldridge

Within each band, firms are listed alphabetically. *See* ***Profiles*** *on page 534*

** See editorial entries for explanations of team sizes.*

Blake Lapthorn This team is headed by **Walter Cha**, who is seen as *"a big mover and shaker in licensing circles."* The team handles a range of licensing applications with a particular focus on liquor licensing and new applications. Cha himself specialises in licensing and licensed property work, covering the full range of applications including contested applications for new grants of on-licences and off-licences. The team acts for breweries, retail operators, supermarkets, convenience stores, leisure developers and private individuals. **Clients:** Alldays Stores plc; Lidl UK GmbH; Whitbread plc.

Fynn & Partners **Lionel Fynn** is seen to have *"vast experience"* in the licensing field and is said to be *"a wonderfully eloquent advocate."* He heads this *"licensing dream team"* in which **Julia Palmer** and the *"increasingly prominent"* **Graham Gover** *"get results and get them often."* The team undertakes all types of liquor, entertainment, betting and gaming, cinema and night cafe licence applications on a national scale, for the entire range of licensed premises. Particular experience lies in applications for off-licences at sites selling petrol. Recent highlights for the firm include achieving various licences for all leisure operators at the new IMAX cinema site in Bournemouth, and a successful appeal against a refusal of a public entertainment licence by the Borough of Poole. **Clients:** Hall & Woodhouse Ltd; SFI Group plc; Wessex Leisure Group plc.

Trethowans **Michael Messent** is seen as being *"a class act"* and *"on top of his game,"* particularly on betting work in the region. He continues to orchestrate the firm's betting work across England and Wales, as well as handling a variety of licensing matters for a number of football clubs. **Clients:** Ladbroke Racing Ltd; Tower Casino Group; Pizza Hut.

Argles Stoneham Burstows The newly-merged firm is seen as *"one of the leading licensing practices in the South-East."* The team has niche strengths in liquor and entertainment, acting primarily for pub chains, historic houses and leisure centres. **Clients:** Larkfield Leisure; Leeds Castle; Sevenoaks Leisure.

Lester Aldridge This firm is headed by the *"on the ball"* **Colin Patrick**, who is widely regarded as *"the nightclub man"* in the region. The firm undertakes licensing work for the Greenalls Group, a number of large nightclubs, country house hotels and restaurants. In addition, the firm are the appointed solicitors to the Bournemouth Hotels and Restaurants Association. The highlight of the past twelve months for the firm was a series of successful appeals against refusals by the local authority licensing sub-committee. **Clients:** Greenalls Group; Bournemouth Hotels and Restaurants Association; a number of large nightclubs.

DMH (2 ptnrs full-time, 4 assts part-time) This team has expertise in all areas of liquor and entertainment licensing, as well as betting and gaming licensing and the niche areas of sports ground licensing and taxi licensing. The team is instructed in a wide variety of licensing matters throughout Sussex, Surrey and Kent, and acts for hotel chains, national and regional brewers, off-licence chains, sports and leisure facilities, betting offices, theatres and sports facilities. **Clients:** Sarumdale Ltd; Scottish and Newcastle.

Girlings This firm handles a range of licensing work including bookmakers' permits, gaming machines and betting offices, with a client base that *"extends well outside (the firm's) immediate catchment area."* **Clients:** Breweries; individual licensees.

Lamport Bassitt This firm continues its traditional focus as a licensing and leisure practice, handling agency work for leading national firms, section 77 certificates, revocation proceedings, public entertainment licence applications and appeals. The firm handles licensing work for a variety of local and regional companies and private individuals. A recent highlight was being appointed by C & L Mathison Ltd to do the licensing work for a new hotel which has just opened in Eastleigh. **Clients:** Alehouse Company; Syaybar Ltd; Meridian Taverns.

Penningtons Licensing work is undertaken by this firm's Basingstoke, Godalming and Newbury offices. Recently the firm acted for David Bruce, one of the country's leading pub entrepreneurs, in relation to a joint venture with the brewing company W H Brakspear & Sons plc. Further, the firm has been appointed to act for the resultant joint venture company, Honeypot Inns, on the acquisition of future licensed premises. **Clients:** Honeypot Inns.

THAMES VALLEY

LICENSING • Thames Valley	Ptnrs	Assts
❶ **Morgan Cole** Oxford	2	2
❷ **Allan Janes** High Wycombe	*	-
Blandy & Blandy Reading	2	1
Field Seymour Parkes Reading	-	3
Turbervilles with Nelson Cuff Uxbridge	1	1

LEADING INDIVIDUALS	
❶ **HAY David Leslie** Allan Janes	**ROCHE Paddy** Morgan Cole
❷ **SMITH David** Turbervilles with Nelson Cuff	
UP AND COMING	
DAY Philip Field Seymour Parkes	**DOWLING Susan** Blandy & Blandy

Within each band, firms are listed alphabetically. *See* ***Profiles*** *on page 534*

** See editorial entries for explanations of team sizes.*

Morgan Cole **Paddy Roche** heads up this licensing practice, and is widely regarded as being *"top of the tree"* in licensing in Oxford. He handles applications on a national basis for Morland Brewery and acts regularly for Granada plc as well as other smaller operators in the Thames Valley area. The bent of the practice is towards liquor licensing, with some public entertainment work. The firm also does substantial local agency work in Oxford for regional and national firms. Recent highlights include new licence applications at the Oracle Centre in Reading for Granada and the Imax Centre in Bournemouth for Morland Brewery. **Clients:** Century Inns; Food Mountain Ltd; Sound Exchange Banbury.

Allan Janes (1ptnr part-time) **David Hay** remains *"very good at what he does"* in licensing work in the region. He continues to act for independent licensees as well as a number of clients in the leisure and hotel industry. **Clients:** Independent licensees; the leisure and hotel industry.

Blandy & Blandy This practice is historically strong in sports-related licensing, and frequently deals with licensing issues for premises such as football grounds. **Sue Dowling** is said to be *"making an impact"* in the region with her licensing work for this firm, particularly in the realms of liquor and public entertainment. **Clients:** Sports stadia.

Field Seymour Parkes This firm is still seen as the leading player on the Reading licensing scene, with a particularly large practice in betting and gaming work which is headed by the *"rising star"* and *"slick operator"* **Philip Day**. It also handles liquor licensing for a number of off-licences and department stores in the South East region, as well as dealing with public entertainment licensing, sporting events licensing, track betting licensing and section 68 certificates. **Clients:** Dick Brunton; Grosvenor Casinos; Taylor's Racing Services.

Turbervilles with Nelson Cuff This practice is headed by the *"highly professional"* and *"polished"* **David Smith**, who handles *"the whole gamut"* of licensing work including liquor licensing, public entertainment licensing, gaming and betting work. The practice acts on a national basis for World Duty Free, the largest duty free company in the country, as well as Budgens Supermarkets in the South East and Home Counties and the Radisson Edwardian Hotel Group in London. **Clients:** Booker plc; Nuance; Sheraton Heathrow Hotel.

SOUTH WEST

LICENSING • South West	Ptnrs	Assts
❶ **Cartwrights** Bristol	3	2
Eversheds Bristol	1	4
❷ **Clarke Willmott & Clarke** Taunton	1	5
Crosse & Crosse Exeter	1	*
Foot Anstey Sargent Exeter	2	1
Gregg Galbraith Quinn Bristol	*	*
❸ **Bevan Ashford** Bristol	2	1
Stephens & Scown Exeter	2	2
Stones Exeter	1	1
❹ **Rickerby Watterson** Cheltenham	3	3

LEADING INDIVIDUALS	
✪ **PHILLIPS Jeremy** Eversheds	
❶ **DAVIES Timothy** Cartwrights	
❷ **EARDLEY Kathryn** Cartwrights	**PARROTT Michael** Cartwrights
❸ **GREGG Andrew** Gregg Galbraith Quinn	

Within each band, firms are listed alphabetically. *See* ***Profiles*** *on page 534*

** See editorial entries for explanations of team sizes.*

Cartwrights This practice is widely respected for the *"tremendous ability and experience"* of its team, headed by **Timothy Davies**, who is *"ever-present, reliable and thorough"* as well as being *"a good advocate."* **Kathryn Eardley** is *"switched-on,"* while **Michael Parrott** *"always goes the distance for his clients."* The department has a core business of liquor, gaming and entertainment licensing, and has niche strength in defending prosecutions arising from consumer protection and food safety legislation. The department also provides advice and training in respect of licensing legislation and best practices. One of the highlights for the practice in the past twelve months was acting for Ladbroke Casinos (formerly Stakis Casinos) in five major contested casino battles involving a total of 36 court days in 1999. Also acted on a series of successful applications for Safeway/BP and Tesco/Esso for their growing chain of convenience shops at petrol filling stations. **Clients:** Greene King; Tesco Stores plc; Ladbroke Casinos.

Eversheds **Jeremy Phillips** is the head of licensing at this firm's Bristol office, and is also head of the firm's national licensing law team, which is the largest of its kind in the country. On top of his *"unparalleled licensing knowledge"* Mr Phillips possesses *"considerable advocacy skills,"* and is widely regarded to be *"in a league of his own"* in the region. The team handles all types of liquor licensing applications, from public entertainment licences for retail shops to justices' licences for service stations. The firm also has a presence in each major retail sector, and acts for a number of national property companies which are involved in the development of leisure and retail parks. **Clients:** City Centre Restaurants; Eldridge Pope; Unique Pub Co.

Clarke Willmott & Clarke This unit deals with all types of liquor licensing for breweries, public houses and catering businesses and remains responsible for all the Co-operative Wholesalers Services licences for the South West region. The unit also handles licensing work for major food and drink multiples and licensees of nightclubs. In the last twelve months, the unit has secured several new licences on the basis of the Good Practice Guide. The highlight of the year for the firm was securing an off-licence in Cornwall on appeal. **Clients:** Co-operative Wholesale Society Ltd; Sutcliffe Catering Ltd; Ushers of Trowbridge Ltd.

Crosse & Crosse (1 ptnr full-time, 2 assts part-time) This firm is *"fairly active locally"* in licensing work, and is used for local agency work by a number of firms in the licensing field. **Clients:** Include nightclubs and festivals.

Foot Anstey Sargent The merged firm continues to undertake licensing applications in the realms of liquor, entertainment, betting and gaming. **Clients:** Major breweries; the local licensing victuallers association.

Gregg Galbraith Quinn (1 ptnr part-time, 1 asst part-time) The *"always proficient"* **Andrew Gregg** heads up this niche licensing practice which is *"relatively small but has a number of significant clients."* As he has handled substantial food law work alongside his duties as President of the Bristol Law Society, it has been said that this firm *"hasn't been seen around as much"* in licensing work over the past twelve months. **Clients:** Include pubs, clubs and shops.

Bevan Ashford This department has niche practice areas in public entertainment licensing and obtaining new licences in respect of public houses and supermarket chains. The department acts for a range of clients including retailers, supermarkets, breweries, large multinational drinks companies and pop festivals. The highlight of the past twelve months for the department was gaining the brewery company SA Brains and Co. Ltd as a new client, and expanding their current operations from Wales into the South-West region. **Clients:** Glastonbury Festivals; Lidl UK GmbH; SA Brains and Co. Ltd.

Stephens & Scown This *"small but impressive"* practice acts for numerous small companies and individuals involved in the leisure/holiday industry, including proprietors of holiday complexes, hoteliers and restaurants. The practice has particular expertise in dealing with contested licensing applications for both applicants and objectors from the leisure/holiday industry, including the police. **Clients:** Haven Holidays Ltd; Primex UK Ltd; Walkers Foods.

Stones This practice undertakes applications primarily for new on-licences and off-licences, but also for gaming licences. In addition, the practice handles club registration applications and the acquisition and disposal of public houses. **Clients:** On and off-licences.

Rickerby Watterson This practice has seen a growth in public outdoor entertainment work over the past twelve months, during which time it has acted for the organisers of several major pop concerts and open air events. The practice has also hosted two major licensing forums. **Clients:** Gloucester Rugby Football Club; Whitbread plc.

WALES

LICENSING • Wales	Ptnrs	Assts
❶ **Eversheds** Cardiff	1	2
Morgan Cole Cardiff	3	5
❷ **Cartwrights Adams & Black** Cardiff	*	*

LEADING INDIVIDUALS	
❶ **RAWLE Claire** Morgan Cole	
❷ **CHILDS Christopher** Cartwrights Adams & Black	
FREEMAN Bill Freemans Solicitors	**MORGAN Rosemary** Morgan Cole
MORSE John John Morse Solicitors	**PHIPPS Matthew** Eversheds

Within each band, firms are listed alphabetically. *See* **Profiles** *on page 534*
** See editorial entries for explanations of team sizes.*

Eversheds The Cardiff office provides a *"dedicated licensing practice,"* and handles a full range of licensing applications throughout Wales, from public entertainment licences for retail shops to justice's licences for service stations. The firm has a presence in each major retail sector, and also acts for a number of national property companies involved in the development of major leisure and retail parks. **Matthew Phipps** receives instructions from a number of major clients based in London and throughout the UK. Highlights for the year include obtaining and maintaining all licences in relation to Piers Adam's nightclub ventures in London, as well as obtaining a contested 'occasional licence' which established a fundamental principle of the consumption of alcohol in the seats of a sports stadium in Wales. A further highlight for the firm was handling a successful application for a major operator of table-side dancing venues. **Clients:** SWALEC; SFI (Surrey Inns); Cardiff National Ice Rink; Threshers.

Morgan Cole This firm continues to act for major breweries, but in the last twelve months it has been increasingly acting for individual operators such as local entrepreneurs and club-owners, particularly in the Cardiff area. The firm remains the appointed panel solicitors for the Southern Region of Allied Domecq and also handles a broad range of licence applications in Wales and the West for Whitbread Severn Inns, including transfers, section 20 alterations, new public entertainment alterations and section 77 certificates. **Rosemary Morgan** has *"a wealth of experience"* and remains *"an eminent licensing practitioner"* in the region, while the *"affable"* **Claire Rawle** has become *"more and more prominent"* in the last twelve months and is now seen to be doing *"the bulk of the licensing work"* for the firm. Recent projects for the practice include advising on all licensing issues for the Cardiff Hilton Hotel and doing the licensing work for a number of athletic/rugby football clubs throughout Wales. **Clients:** Apollo Leisure UK Ltd; Spar; Wolverhampton & Dudley.

Cartwrights Adams & Black (1ptnr, 1 asst part-time) This practice is headed up by the *"high calibre"* **Christopher Childs**, who spends approximately 30 percent of his time on licensing work and undertakes a wide range of liquor licensing and public entertainment work throughout Wales. The practice acts for a well-known Cardiff brewery and also handles licensing work for a number of national hotel chains. **Clients:** A Cardiff brewery, national hotel chains.

Other Notable Practitioners Sole practitioner **Bill Freeman** is regarded as *"a seasoned licensing campaigner,"* who often acts for individual clients in the Cardiff area. **John Morse**, based in Swansea, has a particularly good name for betting and gaming work.

MIDLANDS

Poppleston Allen It has been said that *"anyone who works in licensing in the region will inevitably come across, lock horns with or trip over"* this practice, which is seen as *"an excellent niche practice"* both in the Midlands and around the country. The firm is unanimously seen as remaining *"at the top by itself"* for licensing work in the region, if anything having increased its lead over its competitors over the past twelve months, particularly in the realm of late night licences. **Jeremy Allen** is seen as *"a superb advocate"* who has *"been around forever"* and *"knows most of the tricks of the trade."* **Susanna Poppleston** is known for being *"proactive"* and for *"getting results,"* especially on club licensing. Both **Kirsty Pearson** and **Lisa Sharkey** have been prominent in licensing work in the past twelve months, with the former seen as *"determined"* and *"a formidable opponent"* and the latter renowned for her persuasiveness. The firm was recently successful in a contested licence application for a development in Sunderland City Centre, the first new contested licence granted in that locality for many years. **Clients:** Allied Leisure; Pizza Express; Punch Taverns.

LICENSING • Midlands	Ptnrs	Assts
❶ **Poppleston Allen** Nottingham	2	5
❷ **Anthony Collins Solicitors** Birmingham	1	2
Hammond Suddards Edge Birmingham	3	2
❸ **Berryman Shacklock** Nottingham	1	1
Kenneth Curtis & Co Birmingham	1	-
Young & Pearce Nottingham	4	-
❹ **Challinors Lyon Clark** West Bromwich	*	*
Freethcartwright Nottingham	2	1
❺ **Eversheds** Nottingham	1	2
Lanyon Bowdler Shrewsbury	1	1

LEADING INDIVIDUALS	
❶ **ALLEN Jeremy** Poppleston Allen	
COLLINS Anthony Anthony Collins Solicitors	
CURTIS Anthony Kenneth Curtis & Co	
POPPLESTON Susanna Poppleston Allen	
POTTS Andrew Hammond Suddards Edge	
SHAW Deborah Anthony Collins Solicitors	
❷ **PEARCE John** Young & Pearce	**RADCLIFFE Malcolm** Freethcartwright
WILSON Robin Berryman Shacklock	
❸ **CRIER Phil** Hammond Suddards Edge	**LEE Trevor** Challinors Lyon Clark
ONIONS Robin Lanyon Bowdler	**PEARSON Kirsty** Poppleston Allen
PERRATON Stephanie Hammond Suddards Edge	**SHARKEY Lisa** Poppleston Allen
YOUNG David Eversheds	

Within each band, firms are listed alphabetically. *See **Profiles** on page 534*

* *See editorial entries for explanations of team sizes.*

Anthony Collins Solicitors At this highly regarded firm, **Anthony Collins** and **Deborah Shaw** reportedly make *"an impressive and effective licensing team,"* who *"go out of their way to make things work."* Anthony Collins is seen as *"a fine advocate"* and *"the elder statesman of licensing law in the Midlands,"* while Deborah Shaw is seen to be *"on the ball"* and *"a real scrapper"* in court. The firm has a niche practice in pub licensing applications, with a number of high profile clients, particularly in the entrepreneurial field. A recent highlight for the firm was obtaining 22 outline licences for the Birmingham Mailbox, a multi-leisure complex encompassing 240 apartments, two hotels and a number of retail shops. The firm has been retained by the Mailbox for the purposes of providing ongoing licensing advice. **Clients:** Capital Radio Restaurants; City Centre Restaurants; Northern Leisure Restaurants.

Hammond Suddards Edge Perceived to have had *"a number of problems"* this year, the firm's merger is too recent to judge. However the practice is still highly rated in the licensing field in the region. The firm acts for a range of clients from national plcs and leisure companies to private individuals. Niche expertise exists in liquor licensing, and the team is particularly well-known for obtaining special hours certificates. **Andrew Potts** has a *"wealth of experience"* and acts for *"an impressive array of clients"* while **Stephanie Perraton** is *"a capable advocate."* The *"likeable"* **Phil Crier** has substantially increased his profile this year and is now said to be *"one of the most promising licensing lawyers in the region."* Recent highlights for the firm include obtaining five new licence applications for Millennium Point, Birmingham, a new licence application for Birmingham Airport and a number of successful applications for special hours certificates for venue bars in the City of Birmingham. **Clients:** Aston Villa Football Club; Compass Group plc; T&S Stores plc.

Berryman Shacklock The firm predominantly handles liquor licensing and public entertainment licensing work. Formerly known as Shacklocks, the firm recently merged with Nottingham firm Berryman & Co, thus increasing its portfolio of licensing clients, particularly individual operators. The firm now has a range of licensing clients in an area encompassing a large swathe of the Midlands and Eastern Counties. **Robin Wilson** is prominent in regional licensing work. **Clients:** Nottinghamshire Police; Punch Taverns; Off-licences, Clubs and individual operators.

Kenneth Curtis & Co This firm is felt to have an *"excellent"* and *"well established"* licensing practice, particularly expert in acting for off-licences. **Tony Curtis** is seen as a *"tenacious and passionate advocate"* who handles a number of licensing applications for small off-licence operators in Birmingham. **Clients:** Include off-licences.

Young & Pearce **John Pearce** *"knows his stuff"* and heads a team which handles a range of licensing applications for pubs, nightclubs, casinos and off-licences. **Clients:** Include pubs, nightclubs, casinos and off-licences.

Challinors Lyon Clark (1 ptnr part-time, 2 assts part-time) This licensing practice is currently *"not as high-profile as it used to be,"* although the respected **Trevor Lee** is *"still seen around and about"* the West Midlands area. The licensing work is now primarily for off-licences, clubs and supermarkets in the area, with some local agency work coming in from Bass. **Clients:** Minnesota Fats; off-licences; clubs; supermarkets.

Freethcartwright This firm has a niche strength in off-licence work and revocations, and continues to specialise in supermarket licensing and police objections. **Malcolm Radcliffe** is said to be *"a well-travelled man"* and continues to handle licensing work for Aldi on a national basis, acting for the Leicestershire Police in a number of high profile objections and revocations. The highlight of the past twelve months for the firm was progressively obtaining licences for 22 new Aldi stores, at an average of one licence per fortnight. **Clients:** Leicestershire Police; Aldi Supermarkets.

Eversheds This licensing practice is headed by the respected **David Young.** The practice handles a wide variety of licensing work, including new builds for on-licences (pubs and hotels,) conversions, interim authorities, transfers, special hours certificates and multi-unit developments. It has niche strengths in licensing-related development and acquisition work. **Clients:** Bass Leisure Retail; Carillion; Eldridge Pope plc.

Lanyon Bowdler **Robin Onions** heads up this licensing team, and is seen as a *"genuine heavy hitter."* He continues to handle a high volume of off-licence work, particularly for A F Blakemores, the largest Spar wholesalers in the country, and also acts for a number of independent traders and local developers. **Clients:** Include pubs; nightclubs and garage forecourts.

EAST ANGLIA

Howes Percival **Alan Kefford** is said to have *"been around a long time"* and remains the ne plus ultra for licensing work in the region. The firm has a wide range of clients in the liquor, entertainment and gaming industries, and is said to handle *"the vast majority of the licensing work"* in East Anglia, with other firms doing *"bits and pieces of whatever's left."* A recent highlight was obtaining twelve liquor licences for a complicated property development in Norwich. **Clients:** Scottish & Newcastle; Ryan Elizabeth Holdings plc.

Belmores (1 ptnr part-time, 1 asst full-time) The *"prominent"* **Simon Nicholls** continues to handle all the licensing at the practice, and is renowned as a *"skilful player."* He has a particular niche in securing pub licences. **Clients:** Hotels and pubs.

Eversheds The firm is still widely regarded to be *"doing a lot of work in the region."* **Malcolm Partridge** is the stand-out practitioner here. The firm continues to handle liquor licensing matters, including new special hours certificates for public houses and club premises as well as bingo licensing.

LICENSING • East Anglia	Ptnrs	Assts
❶ **Howes Percival** Norwich	1	1
❷ **Belmores** Norwich	*	1
Eversheds Ipswich, Norwich	1	3
Kenneth Bush King's Lynn	*	*
❸ **Greenwoods** Peterborough	1	1
Mills & Reeve Norwich	1	1
Steele & Co Norwich	3	2

LEADING INDIVIDUALS	
❶ **KEFFORD Alan** Howes Percival	
❷ **PARTRIDGE Malcolm** Eversheds	
❸ **NICHOLLS Simon** Belmores	
❹ **BUSH Kenneth** Kenneth Bush	**HYDE Philip** Steele & Co

Within each band, firms are listed alphabetically. *See **Profiles** on page 534*
** See editorial entries for explanations of team sizes.*

Recent work for the firm includes obtaining a number of new licences including a special hours certificate for Kafe Da in Norwich, a new licence at the Hills Road Sixth Form Centre in Cambridge and gaming licensing matters for Newport Caravan Park (Norfolk) Ltd. **Clients:** Henry Watt & Partners; Norwich Airport; University of East Anglia Students Union.

Kenneth Bush & Co (1 ptnr & 1 asst part time) This practice continues to spend approximately 40 percent of its time handling gaming and liquor licensing matters. **Kenneth Bush** is a respected regional figure. He acts principally for pub, hotel and off-licence operators, many of which are on-site at holiday parks, and two leisure companies which have holiday sites around England and Wales. **Clients:** Leisure companies; off-licences; hotels.

Greenwoods This practice is involved in liquor and entertainment work for a range of organisations, including the Vaux Group plc, First Leisure Corporation plc and the Haycock, one of Peterborough's premier hotels. The practice has also handled liquor and entertainment work for a number of local sports and social clubs. **Clients:** Arcadian Group; The Cresset; Dawe Media.

Mills & Reeve This firm has worked on a number of new projects and premises advising extensively on liquor (including liquor trading on the internet,) bingo, public entertainment and gaming licences. The firm also does licensing work for a number of private clients and local and national leisure and holiday property companies. **Clients:** The National Trust; Norwich City FC.

Steele & Co **Philip Hyde** has raised his profile as a licensing practitioner in the region as the author of *"Licensing Precedents and Procedures"* and *"Local Authority Licensing and Registration."* He is known as the firm's *"drawcard."* A substantial amount of the firm's licensing work arises from its public sector and institutional work in the region. **Clients:** Norwich District Council; Lambeth Borough Council.

NORTH WEST

LICENSING • North West	Ptnrs	Assts
❶ **Cobbetts** Manchester	2	2
❷ **Weightmans** Liverpool	2	5
❸ **Elliotts** Manchester	1	1
❹ **Addleshaw Booth & Co** Manchester	2	-
Pannone & Partners Manchester	1	1
❺ **A. Halsall & Co** Birkenhead	1	3
Davies Wallis Foyster Liverpool	2	6
Halliwell Landau Manchester	2	2

LEADING INDIVIDUALS	
❶ **HOLLAND Barry** Elliotts	**LAWSON Hamish** Cobbetts
LYONS Anthony Addleshaw Booth & Co	
OWEN Mark Weightmans	
❷ **DICKINSON Nicholas** Pannone & Partners	
HORNE Anthony Weightmans	**JONES Simon** Cobbetts
❸ **JOHNSON Christopher** A. Halsall & Co	
UP AND COMING	
BRUDER Carl Davies Wallis Foyster	

Within each band, firms are listed alphabetically. *See **Profiles** on page 534*

Cobbetts The *"awesome team"* of **Hamish Lawson** and **Simon Jones** reputedly handles *"the lion's share of the licensing work"* in the North West. The firm acts in all aspects of liquor and public entertainment licensing for a range of clients, including small local breweries, regional breweries and property developers. The firm also handles acquisition-related licensing for a wide variety of licensed premises. Recent highlights include handling the multiple licensing applications for The Lowry in Manchester, which is a National Landmark Millennium Project for the Arts. **Clients:** De Vere Group plc; Devonshire Pub Co Ltd; Whitbread plc.

Weightmans This team retains its high rating in the North West, which is due in no small part to the efforts of the *"highly skilled and dependable"* **Mark Owen** and **Anthony Horne**. Recent highlights for the firm include being instrumental in the relaxation of the special conditions for lap dancing bars in Liverpool and the successful completion of the Queen Square development in Liverpool involving eight new trading licences. In addition, the firm also recently obtained the first Sunday night extension (until 2am) for Cream nightclub in Liverpool. **Clients:** Cream; First Quench Retailing Ltd; Liverpool Football Club.

Elliotts **Barry Holland** *"knows his stuff"* and is *"one of the personalities in liquor licensing."* He leads a licensing department which continues to have a niche in petrol stations and convenience stores, for both on-licensing and off-licensing. The department has recently been appointed to handle all of the national licensing work for the Pelican Group and for Woolworths (involving a growing chain of off-licences.) The department also continues to do some betting and lotteries work, mainly for Coral Racing. **Clients:** Pelican; Majestic Wine Warehouses; Cellar 5.

Addleshaw Booth & Co With the addition of nationally recognised *"licensing machine"* **Anthony Lyons** from Pannone & Partners, the reputation of this firm's Licensing Unit has continued to grow in the North West region. The clients include store and restaurant chains, property developers, concert halls, arts centres, the tertiary education sector, public houses, nightclubs, off-licences, restaurant multiples, hotel groups, leisure site developers, petrol forecourt retailing and golf clubs. The firm has a niche strength of liquor licensing along with expertise in other local authority licensing such as entertainment licences and other relevant approvals. One recent highlight was obtaining nine provisional justice's on-licences for The Light, a flagship hotel/retail/leisure development in Leeds including nightclubs, where the firm acted for Halifax plc. The team was also recently successful in obtaining an internet betting and casino licence for an existing client in Gibraltar. **Clients:** FLVA; Inventive Leisure Ltd; Yesteryear Pub Co Ltd.

Pannone & Partners The prevalent feeling in the market following the recent departure of Anthony Lyons to Addleshaw Booth & Co, is one of scepticism. However, there has also been comment that the subsequent recruitment of the *"top-notch"* **Nick Dickinson** from Davies Wallis Foyster to replace him may *"go some way to making good the shortfall."* The practice continues to handle predominantly liquor licensing and a smaller amount of betting and gaming applications in the region, acting for breweries, pub operators, club operators and an oil company. Over the past twelve months, the team has secured several petrol station forecourt liquor licences. **Clients:** Texaco; Jennings Brothers; Fox Group.

A. Halsall & Co In this practice, **Chris Johnson** is said to be an *"all-round nice guy"* and *"fine lawyer,"* as well as being *"a pretty good scrapper who doesn't mess around."* The practice has traditionally been localised in terms of its client base, but has handled an increasing amount of licensing work for large national co-operatives over the past twelve months. **Clients:** Large national co-operatives.

Davies Wallis Foyster This practice has recently lost respected practitioner Nick Dickinson to Pannone & Partners. However, they do have an excellent licensing practitioner in *"perfectly sound"* **Carl Bruder**. The firm's niche strengths are in off-licensing, on-licensing, public entertainment licensing and casino licensing. Continues to handle all the licensing and property acquisition work for Blackburn-based brewers Daniel Thwaites. **Clients:** Daniel Thwaites plc; Kwik Save Stores Ltd (Somerfield); Swallow Inns & Restaurants Ltd.

Halliwell Landau This practice has continued to expand into the leisure industry, now handling ongoing licensing work for a number of hotel chains in the region such as Arcadian Hotels, Handpicked Hotels and Virgin Hotels. The practice also continues to do a number of betting and gaming applications for Done Brothers Cash Betting Ltd, and recently did the licensing work for a new five-star hotel in Manchester. **Clients:** Marbury Taverns; Burlington Dining Rooms & Bars; Scottish & Newcastle.

YORKSHIRE

LICENSING • Yorkshire	Ptnrs	Assts
❶ **DLA** Sheffield	1	3
Gosschalks Hull	2	1
John Gaunt & Partners Sheffield	3	1
❷ **Lupton Fawcett** Leeds	1	3

LEADING INDIVIDUALS	
❶ **COWELL Martin** DLA	**GAUNT John** John Gaunt & Partners
❷ **JOHNSON Clare** Gosschalks	**WOODS Andrew** Gosschalks

Within each band, firms are listed alphabetically. *See **Profiles** on page 534*

DLA **Martin Cowell** heads this practice, and is known as a *"solid and dependable lawyer."* He handles licensing work for a number of major clients, primarily in relation to liquor, public entertainment and cinemas, with a small amount of betting and gaming work. The practice recently relicensed a Sheffield Football Ground, and also did the licensing for a new £4m nightclub which recently opened in Sheffield. **Clients:** Punch Retail Ltd; UCI Cinemas; York Co-operative Ltd.

Gosschalks With the recent untimely death of *"licensing legend"* Les Green, the prevalent feeling in the market is that while this firm remains *"top notch,"* with **Andy Woods** and **Clare Johnson** both highly regarded licensing practitioners, it is *"no longer up the top of the tree by itself."* The practice continues to handle licensing matters for a wide range of clients all over the country, including First Leisure Nightclubs, Northern Leisure Nightclubs, Yates's Wine Lodges and other pub operators, entertainment venues and restaurants. A recent highlight for the firm was being appointed to do the licensing work for the redevelopment of the Crystal Palace site in South London, which is planned to be the most substantial leisure park in the country. **Clients:** Yates's Wine Lodges Ltd; Greenalls Pubs & Restaurants; Northern Leisure plc.

John Gaunt & Partners Liquor licensing work in relation to leisure premises is the forte of this highly successful practice, headed by the *"first class"* and *"ubiquitous"* **John Gaunt**, who also handles public entertainment licensing and a smaller amount of gaming and betting work. He now lodges well over 3,000 licensing applications every year connected with leisure premises and city centre sites. The firm is exclusively retained by Wolverhampton & Dudley Breweries for licensing work, involving over one thousand pubs. **Clients:** Debenhams Department Stores; Enterprise Inns; Whitbread plc.

Lupton Fawcett The firm continues to develop its practice in major leisure developments and works for various breweries. The Licensing and Leisure Division advises entrepreneurs on liquor licensing issues and has been successful in obtaining liquor licences for petrol stations. **Clients:** Pubs; clubs and petrol station forecourt retailers.

NORTH EAST

LICENSING • North East	Ptnrs	Assts
❶ **McKenzie Bell** Sunderland	1	*
❷ **Dickinson Dees** Newcastle upon Tyne	1	2
Mincoffs Newcastle upon Tyne	2	1
❸ **Freemans** Newcastle upon Tyne	2	1
❹ **Eversheds** Newcastle upon Tyne	1	1

LEADING INDIVIDUALS	
❶ **TEMPERLEY William** McKenzie Bell	
❷ **ARNOT Richard** Dickinson Dees	**SCIENCE Austen** Mincoffs
❸ **FREEMAN Keith Michael** Freemans	
UP AND COMING	
ROBINSON Sarah Mincoffs	

Within each band, firms are listed alphabetically. *See **Profiles** on page 534*

McKenzie Bell (1 ptnr full-time, 1 ptnr part-time) **William Temperley** stands out in the region, with a *"knowledge of licensing law that is without parallel."* The firm is felt to be as *"dominant as ever"* in the region, and has a niche practice area of liquor licensing, with some public entertainment and betting work. Recently handled a multiple licence development for Land Securities and has also done transactional licensing work for Northumbria Police and AMEC Developments in Durham. **Clients:** Scottish & Newcastle; Whitbread plc.

Dickinson Dees The licensing department of this firm has undergone rapid growth over the past twelve months. With its central focus on liquor licensing work, which in turn gives rise to ancillary gaming and betting work, the department is guided by *"safe pair of hands"* **Richard Arnot**, who is said to give *"good value for money."* The department provides legal advice and representation on all aspects of liquor licensing, including applications for new licences for pubs, restaurants, hotels, off-licences and clubs. The department also handles applications for extensions of hours, either permanent or temporary, and the purchase of licensed premises. **Clients:** Castle Eden Inns; Sir John Fitzgerald Ltd; St James Group.

Mincoffs This firm has a particular niche strength in the gaming machine industry, but also handles public entertainment and leisure industry licensing work, acting for a range of individuals, local companies and national operators. Senior partner **Austen Science** is renowned for his *"tenacious* *and uncompromising advocacy.*" Recently appointed partner **Sarah Robinson** has also been *"steadily making a name for herself."* The firm regularly makes applications for new licences for public houses, nightclubs, hotels, off-licences and amusement centres. A recent highlight was leading the first successful appeal for a new public house in Newcastle in ten years, the appeal being run against police opposition. **Clients:** Absolute Leisure; Ultimate Leisure plc; Wessex Taverns Ltd.

Freemans **Keith Freeman** is seen as a *"genuine licensing specialist in a field in which many practitioners only dabble."* Particularly noted for handling licensing applications on behalf of breweries. **Clients:** Breweries.

Eversheds The practice deals mainly with liquor licensing matters, but also handles substantial public entertainment licensing work. It handles applications for new on-licences and special hours certificates, as well as licensing for restaurants, pubs, clubs and music and theatre venues. Recent work has included a number of successful applications for new on-licences in Newcastle City Centre. **Clients:** Mills Newsagents; Scottish & Newcastle; Victoria Wine.

SCOTLAND

LICENSING • Scotland	Ptnrs	Assts
❶ **Brunton Miller** Glasgow	3	-
R. & J.M. Hill Brown & Co Glasgow	2	3
❷ **Dundas & Wilson CS** Edinburgh	1	4
McGrigor Donald Glasgow	-	5
❸ **Harper Macleod** Glasgow	2	4
Hasties Edinburgh	1	*
Lindsays WS Edinburgh	1	2
❹ **Blackadder Reid Johnston & Carltons** Dundee	Fu	Fu
Johnston & Herron Lochgelly	1	*

LEADING INDIVIDUALS	
❶ **BATTERS John** John Batters & Co	**CUMMINS Jack** R. & J.M. Hill Brown & Co
DALGLEISH Douglas Brunton Miller	**LOUDON John** Dundas & Wilson CS
❷ **FERRIE Audrey** McGrigor Donald	**JOHNSTON Tom** Johnston & Herron
LAWSON Peter R. & J.M. Hill Brown & Co	
MACIVER Archibald Brunton Miller	**MORTON Robin** Brunton Miller
UP AND COMING	
BRYNES Joanna Harper Macleod	

Within each band, firms are listed alphabetically. *See **Profiles** on page 534*

Fu *Figures unavailable at time of going to press.*

* *See editorial entries for explanations of team sizes.*

Brunton Miller This practice has expertise in licensing across the board, from large corporate clients to individuals and small local operators throughout Scotland. The *"hugely experienced"* **Douglas Dalgleish** has a primary focus on liquor licensing, while the *"first-rate"* **Archie MacIver** handles more of the gaming work. **Robin Morton** is also reckoned to be *"a valuable part"* of the team. **Clients:** Bass Retail; JD Wetherspoon; Whitbread plc.

R & J M Hill Brown & Co This firm predominantly handles liquor licensing and public entertainment work, with a niche practice area of leisure and late-night venues. However the firm also does some gaming and betting work. **Jack Cummins** is seen to be a *"true specialist in licensing,"* while **Peter Lawson** is said to *"know his stuff"* and *"doesn't mess around."* **Clients:** First Leisure; Northern Leisure; Tesco.

Dundas & Wilson CS The profile of this licensing department has grown considerably with the addition of *"four-star player"* **John Loudon**, such that the firm is now *"a force to be reckoned with"* in liquor licensing, gaming, leisure and hospitality. Recent highlights include being retained to do the licensing work on an exclusive basis for ABC Odeon, the entity which resulted from the merger between ABC Cinemas and Odeon Cinemas. **Clients:** Festival Inns; Morrisons; Scottish Highland Hotels.

McGrigor Donald The firm's licensing team regularly appears at licensing boards throughout Scotland in relation to gaming, betting and liquor licensing work. Accredited as a specialist in liquor licensing law by the Law Society of Scotland since 1994, **Audrey Ferrie** represents a wide range of interests in the licensed trade, and is seen as being *"a top notch lawyer and well-liked to boot."* The firm's licensing team continues to act for Yates Brothers Wine Lodges plc as the company expands it portfolio in Scotland. A recent highlight for the team was successfully securing licences for Wine Lodges in Falkirk and Dundee in the face of local objections. **Clients:** Hilton International; Ladbroke Casinos; PizzaExpress (Restaurants) Ltd.

Harper McLeod The practice group maintains its representation of 1,700 members of the Scottish Licensed Trade Association (SLTA). As well as representing the members of the SLTA, the Group also acts for a number of major brewers and a portfolio of both corporate and owner-operated businesses. **Joanna Brynes** is responsible for all licensing matters for the STLA members for whom the firm acts, and is widely regarded as a *"rising star."* **Clients:** Alloa Brewery Company Ltd; Colin Wiseman Inns Ltd; Mercury Management (UK) Ltd.

Hasties (1 ptnr full-time, 1 asst part-time) This firm has a *"small but solid"* licensing practice which deals with a range of licensing matters, primarily in and around Edinburgh.

Lindsays WS The firm represents a broad range of clients from large national retailers and hoteliers to local publicans. It has a niche strength in licensing *"out-of-the-ordinary"* venues such as sports stadiums and golf courses, in particular the British Open Golf Championship when it takes place in Scotland. **Clients:** Whitbread plc; Granada plc.

Blackadder Reid Johnston & Carltons Competent Dundee-based practice which continues to be *"very localised"* in its area of practice, dealing predominantly with liquor licences. **Clients:** Small businesses; pubs.

Johnston & Herron (1 ptnr full-time, 1 asst part-time) **Tom Johnston** is said to run a *"one-man licensing show,"* and continues to feature on a number of licensing boards. He is described as *"extremely able, very professional and well respected"* by his peers. **Clients:** Private clients.

Other Notable Practitioners

John Batters runs a specialist licensing practice in Glasgow. He does the licensing work for a number of high profile corporate clients such as Aldi GmbH & Co, as well as advising on gaming and betting work in the west of Scotland. **Clients:** Scottish & Newcastle plc; Booker Cash & Carry Ltd; G1 Group.

NORTHERN IRELAND

LICENSING • Northern Ireland	Ptnrs	Assts
❶ E & L Kennedy Belfast	1	-
Shean Dickson Merrick Belfast	2	-
❷ McCann & Greyston Belfast	*	1
O'Reilly Stewart Belfast	*	1

Within each band, firms are listed alphabetically

E & L Kennedy This firm handles licensing matters for a variety of pubs and clubs in Northern Ireland. **Clients:** Tesco; Boots.

Shean Dickson Merrick This team deals with a large number of club registrations and other general licensing matters such as supermarket off-licences. **Clients:** Guinness; Sheridan Restaurants Ltd; Northern Ireland Federation of Clubs.

McCann & Greystoke (1 ptnr part-time and 1 asst full-time) This firm acts for a range of clients from public houses to conference centres in various licensing matters, particularly liquor licensing. **Clients:** Pubs; conference centres.

O'Reilly Stewart (1 ptnr part-time and 1 asst full-time) This firm is known particularly for its licensing work pertaining to the hotel and catering industries. **Clients:** Hotels.

LEADERS IN LICENSING

ALLEN, Jeremy
Poppleston Allen, Nottingham (0115) 953 8500
Partner and Co-Founder.
Specialisation: Specialises in licensing and leisure work, including liquor, public entertainment, betting and gaming. Also handles associated crime work, including trades descriptions and breach of conditions. Legal Director of B.E.D.A. (British Entertainment and Discotheque Association). Major clients include Allied Leisure, Bass Leisure Entertainment, Belgo, Chorion Plc, Luminar Plc, PizzaExpress, Scottish and Newcastle, Wolverhampton & Dudley Breweries, XS Leisure and many university student unions.
Prof. Memberships: Law Society. Secretary Nottinghamshire Law Society 1977-84; President East Midlands Association of Local Law Societies (Secretary 1981-86). Founder Chairman Law Society's Child Care Working Party; member Law Society Council 1986-92; member Magistrates' Courts Rule Committee since 1982; Chairman Law Society's Criminal Law Committee 1987-1991; member Lord Chancellor's Efficiency Commission 1987-89; member of Home Office Review of Procedure Committee. First Higher Courts (crime) Advocacy course leader, current Chairman of Advocacy Training Sub-Committee.
Career: Qualified in 1970. Articled at *Johnstone Sharp & Walker* 1962-68. *Raleigh Industries* 1968-72. Joined *Hunt Dickins* in 1972, becoming a Partner in 1973 and Managing Partner in 1987. Co-founded *Poppleston Allen Licensing Solicitors* in 1994, which won 'Lawyer' Small Firm of the Year Award 1999.
Personal: Born 5th July 1944. Attended Bedales and College of Law. Leisure interests include theatre, hockey and running. Lives in Nottingham.

ARNOT, Richard
Dickinson Dees, Newcastle upon Tyne (0191) 279 9000
richard.arnot@dickinson-dees.com
Specialisation: Specialises in liquor licensing law and has presided over a rapidly expanding licensing practice which is well on its way to becoming a national presence.
Prof. Memberships: British Institute of InnKeepers. Association of Licensing Practitioners.
Career: Articled at *Mincoffs* and qualified in1992. Spent a number of years specialising in criminal advocacy before being recruited by the Chief Constable of Northumbria Police to represent the force in licensing matters. In 1998 he was asked to join *Dickinson Dees* to establish and develop a licensing department.
Personal: Enjoys most sports and was a keen but untalented boxer.

BATTERS, John A.
John Batters & Co, Glasgow (0141) 427 6884
jonbatters@aol.com
Founding Partner.
Specialisation: Main areas of practice are licensing, principally gaming and liquor; and commercial conveyancing. Regular contributor to licensing seminars and conferences. Member Law Society of Scotland Licencing Law Working Party, and Accreditation Panel for Specialists in Licensing Law; Consultant Editor Scottish Licensing Law & Practice.
Prof. Memberships: Law Society of Scotland.
Career: Qualified in 1971. Partner in *Andrew & J M Aitken* 1974-1978, *Aitken Malone & McKay* 1978-1988, *Hamilton Burns & Moore* 1988-1991. Set up *John Batters & Co.* in 1991.
Personal: Born 19th June 1946. Educated Hamilton Academy and Glasgow University; Various directorships, including House for an Art Lover; Glasgow and Member Board of Governors, drawing, music making, collecting books etc. Lives in Glasgow.

BAYLIS, Craig
Paisner & Co, London (020) 7353 0299
Partner in regulatory department and head of the business regulation unit.
Specialisation: Main area of practice is licensing and leisure. Handles all aspects for the leisure, retailing and brewing industries including advocacy at all levels throughout the UK. Other area of expertise is business protection and environmental law. Advises and represents on all regulatory matters, health and safety, food safety, trading standards and environmental health. Author of 'Food Safety: Law and Practice' and 'Environmental Regulation- Its Impact on Foreign Investment'.
Prof. Memberships: Food Law Group.
Career: Qualified 1981. Solicitor for the Metropolitan Police 1981-84; Partner at *Field Fisher Waterhouse* 1984-92. Joined *Paisner & Co.* in 1992 and became a Partner in 1993.
Personal: Born 9th February 1957. Attended Exeter University 1975-78. Lives in London.

BRUDER, Carl
Davies Wallis Foyster, Liverpool (0151) 236 6226
ceb@dwf-law.com
Specialisation: All aspects of liquor licensing including applications and appeals, consultancy and licensing management throughout England, Wales and Scotland.
Prof. Memberships: Law Society; Association of Licensing Practitioners.
Career: Articled *Davies Wallis Foyster*; qualified 1990; Partner *Davies Wallis Foyster* 2000.
Personal: Cardinal Allen Grammar School; Liverpool John Moores University; Squash; Everton Football Club.

BRYNES, Joanna
Harper Macleod, Glasgow (0141) 221 8888
joanna.brynes@harpermacleod.co.uk
Specialisation: Licensing and leisure. Represents The Scottish Licensed Trade Association, OKO Restaurants in the first sushi conveyor belt restaurant in Scotland, Cairngorm Chairlift Company in the highest restaurant in Scotland, Lidl, and RW Cairns Ltd.
Prof. Memberships: Law Society of Scotland.
Career: Qualified 1996; trained at *Harper Macleod*; associate August 2000.
Personal: Educated at Balfron High School, Stirlingshire; University of Glasgow 1991 - 1996; lives in Glasgow; enjoys visiting some of the licensed premises she represents; cinema, IT, gardening and reading.

BUSH, Kenneth
Kenneth Bush, King's Lynn (01553) 692737

CHA, Walter
Blake Lapthorn, Portsmouth (023) 9222 1122
wjbcha@blakelapthorn.co.uk
Managing Partner
Specialisation: Specialist area of practice is licensing. He acts for national and regional brewers and undertakes his own advocacy. He is also a member of the firm's leisure and retail group providing licensing support for the firm's leisure and retail clients.
Career: Joined *Blake Lapthorn* 1981, qualified in 1983, partner 1987 and head of Commercial Department 1998.
Personal: Born 9th August 1959. Married with two children and lives in Southsea. Leisure interests include rugby, golf, tennis and theatre.

CHILDS, Christopher
Cartwrights Adams & Black, Cardiff
(029) 2046 5959
cgc@cablaw.co.uk
Specialisation: Partner specialising in all aspects of liquor and entertainment licensing, betting and gaming. Clients include regional brewery and hotels, as well as individual licensees. Advises commercial department on licensing issues arising from acquisitions and disposals. Also handles general regulatory work including health and safety and trading standards prosecutions and public enquiries.
Career: LL.B Southampton 1977. Qualified 1980. Seven years with Hampshire Magistrates Courts Committee. Joined [IT+Cartwrights Adams & Black in 1987, becoming a partner in 1990. Clerk to the General Commissioners of Income Tax for Cardiff 1989.
Prof. Memberships: Member of Law Society.
Personal: Born 1957.

CLIFTON, David R.G.
Joelson Wilson & Co, London (020) 7580 5721
drgc@joelson-wilson.co.uk
Partner in Charge of Licensing/Leisure Department.
Specialisation: Liquor, betting, gaming and late-night entertainment licensing and lotteries. Acts for a range of leading public companies, appearing as advocate in magistrates courts and crown courts and before local authorities throughout England and Wales. Advises two of the leading trade organisations in the leisure field which has resulted in involvement in the drafting of national licensing legislation and membership of working parties on licensing law reform. "Legal Expert" for 'The Publican' Newspaper and featured on Sky Television's 'Inn Business' programme. Regularly speaks at seminars and conferences. Clients include leaders in the casino, bingo, betting, internet gaming, pub, hotel, resturant and nightclub fields.
Prof. Memberships: Law Society. International Association of Gaming Attorneys, Association of Licensed Multiple Retailers.
Career: Attended Wellingborough School (1963-74) and University of Reading (1974-78). Articled at *Joelson Wilson & Co* in 1979; Appointed Partner in 1983, Head of Litigation Department 1988 and Head of Licensing/Leisure Department in 1993.
Personal: Born 14th March 1955. Lives in West Sussex. Leisure interests include family, theatre and cricket.

COLLINS, Anthony Ralph
Anthony Collins Solicitors, Birmingham
(0121) 200 3242
Specialisation: Heads up the licensing and leisure law department of the firm. Specialises in licensing applications of all types, particularly for national brewers and entrepreneurs. The majority of the applications are concentrated within the West Midlands conurbation but clients are also advised throughout England & Wales. The firm also arranges secured lending for breweries.
Prof. Memberships: Co. Chairman Association of Licensing Practitioners 2000. Deputy Vice President Birmingham Law Society.
Career: Articled *Wragge & Co* and qualified 1970, joined *Tilley Carson & Finlay* in Toronto 1970 and admitted as a Barrister and Solicitor to the Law Society of Upper Canada 1972. Founded *Anthony Collins Solicitors* in 1973.
Personal: Married. Three children. Bradfield College. Family history and fly fishing.

COWELL, Martin E.
DLA, Sheffield (0114) 2833474
martin.cowell@dla.com
Partner in litigation department.
Specialisation: Main area of practice is licensing - has specialised since 1979. Established and became head of firm's licensing unit in 1989. Deals with all types of liquor licensing, as well as public entertainment, gaming and bingo licensing and lotteries. Acts for National and Regional brewers, various companies operating public houses, major hotel chains, restaurant operators, leisure groups and supermarket operators together with individual entrepreneurs and licensees. Also handles white collar and corporate crime, covering fraud, health and safety, food safety and trading standards prosecutions. Has given various seminars on Licensing and Food Safety, including IBC conferences on Revocations.
Career: Qualified in 1975, having joined *Dibb Lupton Alsop* in 1973. Became a partner in 1979.

CRIER, Phil
Hammond Suddards Edge, Birmingham
(0121) 200 2001

CUMMINS, Jack
R. & J.M. Hill Brown & Co, Glasgow
(0141) 332 3265/333 0636
Partner in Licensing Department.
Specialisation: Handles licensing, gaming, leisure and retail matters, representing a wide range of brewing, restaurant, retail and entertainment interests in the licensed trade. Author of 'Licensing Law in Scotland' (Butterworths, 1993); contributor to 'Scots Law Times', 'Journal of the Law Society of Scotland' and 'Scottish Licensed Trade News'. Reporter for 'Scottish Civil Law Reports' and Editor of 'Scottish Licensing Law and Practice'. Contributed chapter on Scottish Licensing Law to 'Licensing Law Guide' (Butterworths, 1998). Accredited as a specialist in liquor licensing law by The Law Society of Scotland. Keynote speaker, National Conferences for Licensing Boards 1994, 1995 and 1996, Chairman 1997 and 1998. Contributor to various radio programmes. Law Society of Scotland 'Update' speaker. Convenor of Certificate in Liquor Licensing Course, Central Law Training/ University of Glasgow 1995, 1998 and 1999; Convenor and keynote speaker Annual Licensing Conference, Central Law Training 1996, 1997, 1998,1999 and 2000. Keynote speaker 'ACPOS' Conference, York, November 1998. Member of Licensing Law Committee of the Law Society of Scotland.
Prof. Memberships: Law Society of Scotland.
Career: Joined *R & JM Hill & Brown & Co.* in 1976. Qualified in 1978 and became a Partner in 1980.
Personal: Born in 1952. Educated at the University of Glasgow (M.A., 1974, LL.B. 1976) and University of Montpellier (1972-1973). Leisure pursuits include motoring. Lives in Glasgow.

CURTIS, Anthony G.
Kenneth Curtis & Co, Birmingham
(0121) 356 1161

DALGLEISH, Douglas S.
Brunton Miller, Glasgow (0141) 337 1199
Senior Partner.
Specialisation: Has been involved in licensing work for over thirty years. Widely experienced, acting for several major breweries and supermarket chains. Also handles general commercial work. Regular contributor to various licensed trade publications. Has addressed numerous conferences and seminar groups. Scottish Legal Adviser to B.E.D.A. and to Scottish Golf Union, lives in Helensburgh.
Prof. Memberships: Law Society of Scotland.
Career: Qualified in 1956. Became Senior Partner of *Brunton Miller* in 1974. Member of Law Society Working Party on licensing law.
Personal: Born 26th December 1927. Attended Glasgow University 1949-55. Chairman of Dumbarton FC; Past President of Scottish Golf Union; Chairman of Caledonian Golf Travel Limited. Leisure interests include golf and football. Lives in Helensburgh.

DAVIES, Suzanne
Joelson Wilson & Co, London (020) 7580 5721
scd@joelson-wilson.co.uk
Partner in Licensing/Leisure Department.
Specialisation: Liquor, betting, gaming and late night entertainment licensing, together with associated compliance and regulatory matters, including health and safety, food safety, trading standards and criminal prosecutions. Appears as advocate in courts throughout England and Wales. Acts for, amongst others, Regent Inns plc, IG Index plc, Grosvenor Casinos Limited, Association of Licensed Multiple Retailers and NMEC (Millennium Dome). One of the firm's legal experts who writes for 'The Publican'.
Prof. Memberships: Hotel Property Network.
Career: Manchester University, American Studies BA (Hons) 1982-86, Pennsylvania State University, USA 1986-87, College of Law, Chester - CPE and LSF 1987-89.
Personal: Interests include theatre, cinema and travelling.

DAVIES, Timothy L.
Cartwrights, Bristol (0117) 929 3601
tldavies@cartwrights.com
Specialisation: 16 years continuous specialisation in Liquor, Gaming and Entertainment Licensing. Advises on strategy and specific issues and appears as advocate nationally. Examples of clients: Labroke Casinos, Tesco Stores, Hilton Hotels. Co-ordination with commercial partners on licensed property acquisitions and disposals. Consultant to British Retail Consortium.
Personal: Educated at Clifton College, Bristol and University College, London. Clubs: RAC and Aberaeron Yacht Club

DAY, Philip J.
Field Seymour Parkes, Reading (01189) 516200
licensing@fieldseymour.co.uk
Specialisation: Head of licensing department acting mainly for independents but including regional chains of bookmakers and national department store. Was responsible for the Noquet Betting case and all licensing for the Madejski Stadium. Undertakes liquor, betting, gaming and public entertainment licensing. Prosecutes for the RSPCA throughout the Thames Valley.
Career: Qualified 1982 having joined Government Legal Service (HM Customs and Excise) in 1978. Joined *Brain and Brain*, Reading 1984, partner 1989. Consultant, *Field Seymour Parkes* since 1997.
Personal: Born 8 November 1957. Trinity College, Cambridge 1975-78. Leisure interests include computing, reading, photography and motor sport.

DICKINSON, Nicholas H.
Pannone & Partners, Manchester (0161) 909 3000
nick.dickinson@pannone.co.uk
Specialisation: Represents major clients throughout

the United Kingdom, one of very few English solicitors regularly appearing before Licensing Boards in Scotland. Special interest in petrol station forecourt licensing. Has lectured extensively on licensing related matters. Has written staff training manuals and written and produced training videos for clients.
Prof. Memberships: Law Society and Association of Licensing Practitioners.
Career: Qualified in 1975. Partner since joining *Pannone & Partners in 2000* in 2000, previously Head of Licensing at *Davis Wallis Foyster*
Personal: Born 3rd June 1943. Educated at Uppingham School 1956-61. Leisure interests include shooting and sailing.

DOWLING, Susan
Blandy & Blandy, Reading (0118) 951 6829
Sue_dowling@blandy.co.uk
Partner in charge of licensing and gaming department.
Specialisation: The department has considerable experience in sports related liquor licensing, often dealing with licensing issues for football and cricket grounds. Currently on the licensing panel for Wembley National Stadium Ltd and continues to appear on licensing applications relating to Wembley Stadium. Also acts for Wembley plc/Wembley (London) Ltd on licensing matters relating to the Wembley Exhibition Halls, Arena and Conference Centre. Over the last year, has also acted for Debenhams Plc, on numerous licensing applications for its stores in London and in the South of England.
Prof. Memberships: The Law Society. Thames Valley Commercial Lawyers Association.
Career: Articled at *Blandy & Blandy*. Associate (1991), partner 1992 to date.
Personal: LLB (Hons) Business Law (Coventry), College of Law (Guildford). Leisure interests include family, travel, dance, renovation of antique furniture.

EARDLEY, Kathryn A.
Cartwrights, Bristol (0117) 929 3601
kaeardley@cartwrights.com
Partner in Licensing Department.
Specialisation: Specialises in the administration of licensed estates particularly for national retailers and breweries. Has recently been involved in the development of pioneering licensing case management and database systems for *Cartwrights*. The objective is to automate licensing processes, whilst providing clients with enhanced information on their licensed properties.
Career: Qualified in 1978, while articled with *George Brown & Co* and then moved to *Blatch & Co*. Spent six years with Hampshire Magistrates' Court Committee. Joined *Cartwrights* in 1988 and became a Partner in 1990.
Personal: Educated at University of Sheffield, 1971. Lives in Bristol.

EDNEY, Robert
Kingsford Stacey Blackwell, London
(020) 7447 1200
Partner in Licensing Department.
Specialisation: Acts for major brewery clients and others in the leisure industry at all levels in relation to liquor and entertainment licensing and related work.
Career: Qualified in 1970, having joined *Kingsford Stacey* in 1968. Became a Partner in 1972.
Personal: Born 8th September 1946. Educated at Cambridge University (MA 1968). Chairman of local tennis club. Enjoys tennis, food and wine. Lives in Aston, near Stevenage with his wife and family of five.

FERRIE, Audrey
McGrigor Donald, Glasgow (0141) 248 6677
Specialisation: Liquor, betting and gaming licensing throughout Scotland, acting for a hotel and casino operator, several English pub chains expanding into Scotland and two bookmakers. Highlights - licensing for the new Tom Cobleigh in Stirling and for two Yates Wine Lodges in Dundee and Falkirk.
Prof. Memberships: Accredited as a specialist in liquor licensing by Law Society of Scotland.
Career: Educated Notre Dame High School, Glasgow and Glasgow University, trained with well-known criminal litigation firm in Glasgow (*Hughes Dowdall & Co*) then to *Moncrieff Warren Paterson* who merged with *McGrigor Donald*.
Personal: Married to Glasgow lawyer, two children. Leisure interests include travel and attempting to keep fit - when time permits.

FREEMAN, Bill
Freemans Solicitors, Lower Chepstow
(01291) 623 225

FREEMAN, Keith Michael
Freemans, Newcastle-upon-Tyne (0191) 222 1030

FYNN, Lionel C.
Fynn & Partners, Bournemouth (01202) 551991
Partner and head of environmental, licensing and planning department.
Specialisation: Regular advocate in a wide range of planning, environmental and licensing matters. Has personally conducted numerous cases involving liquor licensing, betting and gaming and noise related proceedings at Magistrates Court and Crown Court level, as well as many Town Planning Inquiries. Specialises in High Court Challenges/Judicial Review.
Prof. Memberships: Member of BISL, Associate Member of The Institute of Acoustics.
Career: Lectures at national seminars on licensing and planning matters. Produced "cassette law" audio series with Oyez IBC and Law Society. Has produced two licensing videos and a third on children's certificates; to wide acclaim. Currently involved in the production of a town planning video on urban design.

GAUNT, John R.T.
John Gaunt & Partners, Sheffield (0114) 266 8664
Specialisation: Main area of Practice is Licensing & Leisure with over 20 years experience in this field. Has developed a wide client base including many plcs and operates nationally. Exclusively retained by many clients. Has handled a number of high profile licence applications (including the licensing of multi-faceted leisure centres) attracting significant media attention and coverage, particularly in recent years.
Career: Qualified in 1976. Became a partner in *Wake Smith* in 1977 and latterly a member of the firm's Management Committee. Co founded *John Gaunt & Partners* in 1995, a specialist commercial litigation and property practice particularly for the liquor and leisure industries. The practice now handles in excess of 3,200 licence applications per annum and has over fourteen people dedicated to the field of licensing.

GLAZEBROOK, Peter G.
Field Fisher Waterhouse, London (020) 7861 4000
Partner and head of the Licensing Department.
Specialisation: Main area of practice is liquor and entertainment licensing law. Work includes applications to the licensing justices for liquor licences for public houses, hotels, clubs, wine bars and off-licences including supermarkets. Also advises clients on food safety legislation, the Health & Safety at Work Act and related statutory provisions.
Career: Qualified in 1970. Joined *Field Fisher Waterhouse* in 1974 and became a partner in 1977.

GOVER, Graham
Fynn & Partners, Bournemouth (01202) 551991
Associate in environmental, licensing and planning department.
Specialisation: Advocate specialising in every aspect of liquor and public entertainment licensing, particularly for the outdoor events industry and sports and leisure operators. Acts for a major convenience store and leisure plc, both represented nationally, has obtained numerous off-licences at petrol stations. With a background as a prosecutor and local authority solicitor, also conducts appeals and defends criminal proceedings and advises on all local authority, environmental and planning matters. A regular speaker on the national circuit, at major seminars on liquor and public entertainment licensing and planning issues.
Prof. Memberships: FSELP and Member of: BISL's Liquor Licensing Working Group, Law Society, UKELA and Food Law Group.

GREGG, Andrew
Gregg Galbraith Quinn, Bristol (0117) 925 8123
Specialisation: All aspects of law concerning food, licensing, employment and health and safety. Acts for wide variety of food and drink manufacturers, processors and retailers. See R v Gateway Foodmarkets Ltd C.A. TLR 2.1.97.
Prof. Memberships: Secretary Food Law Group, President Bristol Law Society, Council Member Notaries Society.
Career: The Dragon School Oxford, The Kings School Canterbury. Solicitor D.o.A. 1970, Notary Public D.o.A. 1984. For 20 years partner with a leading Bristol firm before setting up own niche practice in 1992.
Personal: Born 12.9.43. Interests include rugby, sailing, motor racing and restoration of vintage cars. Owns and campaigns a 1933 Lagonda. Chairman of Young Bristol.

HALLIWELL, Tilly
Jeffrey Green Russell, London (020) 7339 7000

HARRIS, Graeme
Loxleys, London (020) 7377 1066
Partner in Licensing Department.
Specialisation: Acts for major companies and individuals on liquor licensing and Gaming Act matters. Also advises on entertainment licensing. Other area of practice is commercial property, acting for companies and individuals with particular reference to licensing and attendant matters. Has acted in a wide range of licensing cases related to liquor and entertainment licensing.
Prof. Memberships: Law Society, London Brewery and Licensing Solicitors Association (Chairman).
Career: Qualified in 1960. Joined *Loxleys* in 1960, becoming a Partner in 1965.
Personal: Born 27th September 1936. Attended Westminster School 1950-54, then College of Law. Leisure interests include theatre, bowls and watching other sports. Lives in Eltham, London.

HARRIS, Julian A.
Biddle, London (020) 7606 9301
Partner in Litigation Department
Specialisation: Main area of practice is gambling and licensing law. Most recently with particular emphasis on internet gambling, advising internet businesses and obtaining the necessary regulatory permits. The firm has advised sports betting operators moving their internet operations offshore and it advises Fantasy League and several gambling and other sporting web sites. The firm acts for several major casino, leisure and food/catering groups, and recently obtained an internet liquor licence for CERT Group Plc. Spent six years with the solicitors for the Gaming Board. In the past year has represented the British Casino Association. Well known regular contributor to gambling and particularly internet related seminars and international conferences.
Prof. Memberships: International Association of Gaming Attorneys, International Internet Gaming Association, European Forum for the Study of Gambling and the Food Law Group.
Career: Qualified 1980; partner *Nicholson Graham Jones* 1986-88 and *Shoosmiths* 1988-93 where he was Head of Litigation. Joined *Biddle* 1993 where he is head of the Gaming & Leisure Group.
Personal: Born 15 May 1955. Magdalene College, Cambridge. Enjoys the good things in life. Lives in Richmond, Surrey and Mayfair, London.

HAY, David Leslie
Allan Janes, High Wycombe (01494) 521301

HEPHER, Christopher
Pullig & Co, London (020) 7353 0505

HOLLAND, Barry K.
Elliotts, Manchester (0161) 834 9933

HORNE, Anthony
Weightmans, Manchester (0161) 833 2601
anthony.horne@weightmans.com
Specialisation: Sole area of practice is licensing and leisure. Work includes liquor, gaming and public entertainment. Currently handling 16 site licenses at the Great Northern Warehouse, Manchester - a substantial £100 million leisure development. Major clients include Morrison Merlin plc (Great Northern Warehouse), Westport developments Ltd (currently handling 6 site licences), Rank Leisure Division Ltd, Menzies Hotels plc, Grosvenor Casinos Ltd, UMIST and Bargain Booze.
Prof. Memberships: Law Society. Fellow to the Society of Entertainment Licensing Practitioners.
Career: M.A. (Cantab.) 1983. Admitted 1985. Articled at *Nigel Copeland*, which merged with *Burton & Co.* in 1985 to become *Burton Copeland.* Appointed head of licensing *Davies Arnold Cooper* (Manchester) 1993. Joined *Halliwell Landau* as licensing partner. Progressed to Weightmans as a licensing partner March 1999.
Personal: Born 29 July 1957. Leisure interests include swimming, reading and dining out.

HYDE, Philip
Steele & Co, Norwich (01603) 274 700
phyde@steele.co.uk
Specialisation: Local authority/licensing and gaming.
Prof. Memberships: Notary Society. Norfolk and Norwich Incorporated Law Society Chairman - Norwich Business Group.
Career: Trained in local government; qualified 1981; partner *Steele & Co* 1989; Public Notary 1994.
Publications: Author and editor of 'Local Authority Licensing and Registration' and 'Licensing Procedures and Precedents' (both Sweet & Maxwell)
Personal: Resides Norwich. Leisure: Golf, theatre, football, most sport.

JOHNSON, Christopher R.
A. Halsall & Co, Birkenhead (0151) 647 6323
Head of Licensing Department.
Specialisation: All aspects of Liquor licensing including Off Licence work. Acting for National Companies England and Wales.
Career: Qualified 1971. Partner 1973.

JOHNSON, M. Clare
Gosschalks, Hull (01482) 324 252

JOHNSTON, Tom
Johnston & Herron, Lochgelly (01592) 780421
tjg@johnston-herron.co.uk
Partner specialising in Liquor Licensing.
Specialisation: Main area of practice is liquor licensing. Accredited Liquor Licensing Specialist. Advises on and attends at Licensing Boards. Deals with purchase, sale and finance of licensed properties. Author of 'How Not to Lose Your Licence', published in April 1994. Has lectured extensively to solicitors and to licensees. Regular contributor to Scottish Licensing Law and Practice.
Prof. Memberships: Law Society of Scotland (Member of Specialist Accreditation Committee on Liquor Licensing).
Career: Apprentice and assistant at *Allan McDougall & Co.* 1976-79. Qualified in 1978. Partner *Johnston & Herron* in 1979. Past Dean of Dunfermline District Society of Solicitors. Member of Law Society Council 1989-92.
Personal: Born 10th July 1954. Educated at Edinburgh University 1972-76. Leisure interests include reading, cooking and wine. Lives in Edinburgh.

JONES, Simon
Cobbetts, Manchester (0161) 833 3333
simon.jones@cobbetts.co.uk
Partner in Commercial Property Department.
Specialisation: Specialises in licensing and leisure work including all aspects of liquor licensing, public entertainment and Gaming Act matters, representing a wide range of brewing, restaurant and retail interests in the licensed trade. Also provides assistance and representation in related prosecutions - food safety, consumer protection, trading standards, environmental protection, weights and measures and health and safety legislation. Has extensive experience in appearing before courts and committees throughout the North of England and in negotiating with enforcing authorities.
Prof. Memberships: Law Society, Manchester Law Society, Food Law Group.
Career: Articled with *Leak Almond & Parkinson* which subsequently became *Cobbett Leak Almond* and qualified in 1978. Became a Partner in 1982.
Personal: Born 28th March 1953. Educated at Birkenhead School 1965-71 and Oxford University 1972-75.

KEFFORD, Alan
Howes Percival, Norwich (01603) 762103
Managing Partner for East Anglian office and Head of firm's Liquor and Leisure Division.
Specialisation: Main area of practice covers all aspects of liquor and entertainment licensing. Also includes gaming matters. Alan is a staunch believer in the principle of providing a one-stop service to the leisure sector. He has made applications throughout East Anglia and the South East on a regular basis. He acts for two major breweries on licensing matters in East Anglia and counts amongst his clients a number of major hotels in Norfolk. Instrumental in *Howes Percival* being licensed by the Awarding Body of the British Institute of Innkeeping to run courses and examinations for the National Licensee Certificate in four centres: Lowestoft, Great Yarmouth, Thetford and Ipswich. Alan is a director of two companies - Anglian Archives plc and The Leisure Stop Ltd - and his family have close links with the hotel industry. He has spoken at various seminars for representatives of the leisure industry.
Personal: Born 1st May 1944. Attended University College, London 1963-66. Leisure pursuits include walking, cricket and Norwich City F.C. Lives in Norwich.

LAVENDER, F. David
Davenport Lyons, London (020) 7468 2600
dlavender@davenportlyons.com
Specialisation: Liquor and entertainment licensing for public houses, restaurants, clubs, discotheques, off licences, hotels and casinos. Acts for several national companies as well as for individual applicants.
Career: Qualified 1966. Partner since 1968. Clerk to Board of Green Cloth Verge of the Palaces since 1984. Clerk to General Commissioners of Taxes. Partner, *Allen & Fraser* until May 2000, consultant *Davenport Lyons* to date.
Personal: Born 23 August 1942. Educated at St Peter's School York and Worcester College Oxford.

LAWSON, Hamish K.
Cobbetts, Manchester (0161) 833 3333
hamish.lawson@cobbetts.co.uk
Partner in Commercial Property Department.
Specialisation: Main area of practice is licensing. Acts for most of the breweries and major licensed retail operators represented in the north west, especially with regard to new site applications. Also handles food law, acting for two major national food manufacturers. Acted in Drury & Samuel Smith Old Brewery (Tadcaster) v. Scunthorpe Licensing Justices on surrender of licences. Firm advises North West Brewers and Licensed Retailers Association. Has addressed numerous conferences and seminars including 'The 24 Hour City' in Manchester in 1993.
Prof. Memberships: Law Society of England and Wales, Manchester Law Society.
Career: Qualified in 1978. Joined *Cobbett Leak Almond* in 1976, becoming a Partner in 1981.
Personal: Born 23rd June 1951. Attended Oxford University 1969-72. Leisure interests include theatre (acting and directing) and sport. Lives in Bramhall, Cheshire.

LAWSON, Peter J.
R. & J.M. Hill Brown & Co, Glasgow (0141) 332 3265/333 0636
plawson@hillbrown.co.uk
Partner in licensing department.
Specialisation: Principal area of practice is licensing. Deals with new licence applications, provides an advice service to multiple operators and individuals, court representation (including trading standards, consumer protection, etc.) and renewal/ review service for existing clients. Also handles commercial/ employment matters, providing a full commercial service,

advice and representation in relation to employment law. Clients include most national brewers, supermarket chains and national entertainment companies. Has written various articles for trade magazines and lectured on Glasgow University Licensing Course. Co-presenter of licensing seminars throughout Scotland.
Prof. Memberships: Law Society of Scotland.
Career: Qualified in 1981. Partner at *McSherry Halliday, Irvine* 1984-90. Joined *Hill Brown* as a partner in 1990.
Personal: Born 25th March 1958. Educated at Glasgow University. Holds various directorships. Director of Tron Theatre, Glasgow. Leisure interests include theatre. Lives in Glasgow.

LEE, Trevor A.
Challinors Lyon Clark, Edgbaston (0121) 455 6333
Specialisation: Licensing (gaming, betting and liquors). Leisure. Heads an enlarged licensing team with wide client base throughout West Midlands in all forms of licensed premises. Undertakes work for Bass Taverns Enterprise Inns and instructed by Richardson Brothers for licensing work at prestigious development of Merry Hill Waterfront.
Prof. Memberships: Past President of Birmingham Law Society.
Career: Admitted 1969. Worked in licensing since then with present firm where he is Senior Partner.
Personal: Married, sons 18 and 20. Golf, cricket, skiing, good wines.

LOUDON, John A.
Dundas & Wilson CS, Edinburgh (0131) 228 8000

LYONS, Anthony S.
Addleshaw Booth & Co, Manchester (0161) 934 6000
axl@addleshaw-booth.co.uk
Partner and Head of Licensing Department.
Specialisation: Specialist Liquor Licensing Solicitor handling all aspects of liquor and entertainment licensing law including agency work. Particular strengths in Public House, Nightclub, Theatre, Off licence and Restaurant work. Council Member of the British Institute of Innkeeping and Solicitor to the Federation of Licensed Victuallers Associations. His firm has been accredited by the British Institute of Innkeeping as a training and examination centre for licensees seeking their National Licensee's Certificate. Client base includes City Centre Restaurants Plc., Whitbread, Inventive Hersom Plc, Hatchersure Ltd and many other household names.
Career: Former partner of *Lyons Wilson*. October 1993 formed *Copeland Lyons* which practice merged with *Pannone & Partners* in 1997.
Personal: Resides in Manchester. Leisure interests include cycling, snow skiing, fell walking and classic cars.

MACIVER, Archibald D.
Brunton Miller, Glasgow (0141) 337 1199
Partner.
Specialisation: Main area of practice is licensing. Extensive experience in all aspects of liquor licensing work. Also involved heavily in licensing under Civic Government (Scotland) Act such as public entertainment licences, street traders and late hours catering licences. Regular columnist in various trade papers. Has addressed many seminar groups on licensing matters.
Prof. Memberships: Law Society of Scotland, Scottish Law Agents Society, Glasgow Bar Association.
Career: Qualified in 1982. Worked at *Levy & McRae* 1981-88, from 1984 as a Partner. Joined *Brunton Miller* in 1988 as a Partner. Accredited by the Law Society of Scotland as a Specialist in Liquor Licensing Law in 1993.
Personal: Born 13th December 1959. Attended Hutchesons' Grammar School 1972-77 and University of Strathclyde 1977-81. Leisure interests include sport (especially football), cinema and reading. Lives in Glasgow.

MESSENT, Michael J.
Trethowans, Southampton (023) 8032 1000
Partner in Licensing Department.
Specialisation: Head of Department with extensive experience as advisor and advocate in betting, gaming and liquor licensing law.
Career: Qualified 1971. Joined *Woodford & Ackroyd* 1973. Partner 1976.
Personal: Born 15th August 1947. Court Member of the Cooks Company. Leisure interests include golf, walking and world travel.

MORGAN, Rosemary
Morgan Cole, Swansea (01792) 634634
rosemary.morgan@morgan-cole.com
See under Property (Commercial), p.732

MORSE, John
John Morse Solicitors, Swansea (01792) 648 111
mail@johnmorse.co.uk
Specialisation: Licensing, Leisure and Commercial work.
Prof. Memberships: The Law Society, past President of the Swansea Law Society.
Career: Admitted 1967. Formed own practice in 1970. Experienced in all forms of licensing including liquor, betting and gaming. Acted for major brewers in the acquisition of new liquor licenses in Wales, West Country London and Northern England. Represented 3 of the major bookmaking firms in betting and gaming applications and objections and represented casino operators in Wales, the Midlands and other areas.
Personal: Educated at Swansea Grammar School and The College of Law. Married with three grown up children. Horse racing, rugby and golf.

MORTON, Robin J.M.
Brunton Miller, Glasgow (0141) 337 1199
Mobile Telephone No: 07970 272953. Consultant in Licensing Department.
Specialisation: Handles liquor licensing, leisure and entertainment law. Acts for major organisations as well as individuals in obtaining and operating liquor licences, appearing at many boards throughout Scotland. Also acts for banks, purchasers and sellers in the property and commercial aspects relating to licensed premises. Has been involved in a number of reported cases, including one which resulted in a change of law (Mount Charlotte Investments v. City of Glasgow District Licensing Board). Accredited by the Law Society of Scotland as a specialist in liquor licensing. Regular contributor to 'Scottish Licensed Trade News' Legal Clinic. Frequently lectures on liquor licensing law and is on the panel of lecturers for the First Annual Advanced Licensing Seminar.
Prof. Memberships: Law Society of Scotland.
Career: Qualified in 1975. With *Brunton Miller*, Solicitors 1975-1978. Assistant Director of Legal Aid for the Hong Kong Government 1978-81. Partner with *Brunton Miller* 1981-88. Joined *McClure Naismith Anderson & Gardiner* as a Partner in 1988, established *Robin Morton Solicitors* in 1995. Consultant with *Brunton Miller*, 1996-Date.
Personal: Born 1st October 1951. Educated at Glasgow Academy 1961-69, then Glasgow University 1969-72. Leisure pursuits include music and football. Lives in Glasgow.

NICHOLLS, Simon J.
Belmores, Norwich (01603) 617947

ONIONS, Robin W.
Lanyon Bowdler, Shrewsbury (01743) 236400

OWEN, Mark D.
Weightmans, Liverpool (0151) 227 2601
mark.owen@weightmans.com
Specialisation: Head of the firm's licensing department - handles all areas of liquor licensing as well as public entertainment and betting and gaming. Represents most of the major breweries and major licensed retail operators - particular expertise in new site applications. Acts for the sixth largest bookmaker in the country, and represents other smaller independents. Regularly appears before Committees across the country. Clients include First Quench, Done Brothers, Merseyside Police, University of Liverpool and Liverpool Football Club.
Prof. Memberships: Law Society.
Career: Qualified 1987 - Partner 1992.

PALMER, Julia C.
Fynn & Partners, Bournemouth (01202) 551991
Partner and head of licensing department.
Specialisation: Specialising in advocacy for all aspects of liquor and public entertainment licensing, betting and gaming licensing, and local authority matters affecting the leisure industry. Also advises on allied matters, including: food law, health and safety, noise and environmental legislation. Julia is highly experienced in new site licensing, with a good record of obtaining "superpub" licences on previously unlicensed sites. Enjoys a national reputation and appears regularly before Courts and Committees throughout England and Wales. Her clients include: major Leisure Plc's, Breweries, entire Managed Estates, Stadia operators and Vineyards.
Career: A former legal adviser to the Licensing Justices, Julia qualified in 1980.

PARROTT, Michael Kindersley
Cartwrights, Bristol (0117) 929 3601
mkparrott@cartwrights.com
Specialisation: Partner specialising in all aspects of licensing law including liquor, gaming, entertainment and cinema licences on behalf of major Plcs. Practice has involved applications for judicial review of interpretation and implementation of licensing justices' policy. Also acts for national food retailers on food law matters.
Career: Articles in Magistrates Courts Service, *Cartwrights* in 1985, appointed Partner in 1987.
Personal: Educated at Exeter School 1965-71 and Leicester University 1972-1975. Leisure pursuits include golf, tennis, skiing and photography. Born 1953. Lives in Bristol.

PARTRIDGE, Malcolm
Eversheds, Norwich (01603) 272727
Specialisation: Specialisations include all aspects of liquor and entertainment licensing for both indepen-

dent operators and national concerns. Contributor to monthly licensing section of 'In-House Lawyer'.
Prof. Memberships: Norfolk and Norwich Law Society (Former President), Employment Lawyers Association.
Career: Qualified 1970. Partner in Norwich since 1976. Considerable advocacy experience. Specialist in licensing law for twenty years.
Personal: Born 16th January 1945. University of Sheffield 1964-67.

PATRICK, Colin
Lester Aldridge, Bournemouth (01202) 786161
Specialisation: Chairman of the firm, Partner and specialist in licensing law. Practice covers liquor, public entertainment (especially night-clubs), betting and gaming. Has written a number of articles on licensing matters for Hotel and Restaurant Association publications.
Prof. Memberships: The Law Society.
Career: Qualified 1957. Partner, *Lester Aldridge* 1962. Chairman, *Lester Aldridge* since 1990.
Personal: Educated at Canford School, Wimborne 1948-1952. Law Society Finals 1957 (2nd Class honours). Hampshire Law Society Prize 1957. Bournemouth Law Society Prize 1957. Chairman, Board of Trustees Bournemouth Orchestras Endowment Trust and Bournemouth Orchestras' board of Directors. Governor of Canford School, Wimborne and of Portchester School Bournemouth. President, Summer Music Society of Dorset. Leisure pursuits include music, theatre, food and wine, antiques, art, gardening, architecture, travel and the countryside. Born 28th August 1934. Lives in Poole, Dorset.

PEARCE, John
Young & Pearce, Nottingham (0115) 959 8888

PEARSON, Kirsty
Poppleston Allen, Nottingham (0115) 953 8500
Specialisation: Specialises in licensing and leisure work, including liquor and public entertainment and related criminal matters. Writes regular articles for firms' website. Major clients include Allied Leisure, Bass Leisure Entertainment, Belgo, Chorion Plc, Luminar plc, PizzaExpress, Scottish and Newcastle Wolverhampton & Dudley Breweries and XS Leisure and works for an increasing number of student unions.
Prof. Memberships: Law Society; Nottinghamshire Law Society.
Career: Joined *Poppleston Allen* in March 1998 having worked for *Eversheds*, Birmingham for six years. Educated at Manchester University (law degree) and Chester College of Law.
Personal: Holidays spent exploring and trekking. Leisure time devoted to outdoor pursuits, food and sport. Lives in Solihull.

PERRATON, Stephanie
Hammond Suddards Edge, Birmingham (0121) 200 2001
stephanie.perraton@hammondsuddardsedge.com
Partner with Edge Ellison since May 1996.
Specialisation: Key member of a specialist team operating exclusively on behalf of the Licensed Trade. Acts on a day to day basis for a wide range of operators from listed companies to individual entrepreneurs, advising and making applications on behalf of theatres, cinemas, concert halls, entertainment venues, breweries, stores, hoteliers, sports facilities, pub and club owners, off-licences, post offices and newsagents. She has considerable experience in acting on behalf of receivers of licensed premises.
Prof. Memberships: Member of the Law Society (local and international), BEDA (British Entertainment and Disco Association).

PHILLIPS, Jeremy
Eversheds, Bristol (0117) 929 9555
jeremyphillips@eversheds.com
Specialisation: Main area of practice is licensing and regulation, acting on behalf of licensed retailers throughout England and Wales. Also regulatory work, defending companies concerning food safety, trade descriptions, weights and measures and environmental legislation. Advisor to industry groups on law reform and a member of the National Licensing Forum. Conducts seminars on licensing law for conference organisers, operators, financial institutions and professional practices. Chairman of *Eversheds'* National Licensing Group.
Prof. Memberships: A.B.I.I.
Career: Partner in 1982, Co-founder of *Holt Phillips* in 1984.
Publications: Joint editor of Paterson's Licensing Acts. Author of 'Phillips: Licensing Law Guide' published by Butterworths; contributor to 'Halsbury's Laws of England' (Vol 26, 'Intoxicating Liquor') and 'Lawyers Rememberances'.
Personal: Lives in South Gloucestershire

PHIPPS, Matthew
Eversheds, Cardiff (02920) 471147
mattewphipps@eversheds.com
Specialisation: Head of the Licencing Unit in Cardiff, which is recognised as the leading liquor and entertainment licensing practice in the region. Has an established national profile and receives instructions from a significant number of major clients throughout England and Wales. Handled a successful application for a major operator of table-side danceing venues, which established a fundamental principle that was critical to the success of the entire industry.
Prof. Memberships: Barrister (general council of the bar; retained barrister status). The Law Society. Affiliate Member of the B.I.I.
Career: *Temple*, London 1991-1994. *Eversheds* 1994 to date.
Publications: Contributor, 'Halsbury's Laws of England (Vol. 26)'
Personal: Born 1966. Resides Cardiff. Reading University (1988). Westminster University (1990 CPE). Bar Finals (1991). Solicitor conversion exams (1999)

POPPLESTON, Susanna
Poppleston Allen, Nottingham (0115) 953 8500
Partner and Co-founder.
Specialisation: Main area of practice is licensing and leisure. Work includes liquor, betting and gaming, public entertainment for clubs and big special events. Legal correspondent and columnist for Licensee and Morning Advertiser, a trade paper for the licensed trade. Former Notts advocacy training officer and trainer with the National Law Society. Major clients include Allied Leisure, Bass Leisure Entertainment, Belgo, Luminar Leisure, PizzaExpress, Scottish and Newcastle, Wolverhampton & Dudley Breweries XS Leisure and many university student unions.
Prof. Memberships: Past President Nottinghamshire Law Society, Law Society.
Career: LLB. Bristol 1969. Qualified in 1972. Articled at *Shacklocks* (subsequently merged with *Ashton Hill & Co.*) 1969-72, setting up own criminal department in 1972 and becoming a Partner in 1974. Set up and ran the first legal aid suburban branch office in Nottingham. Co-founded *Temple Wallis* in 1979, which merged to create *Hunt Dickins* in 1987. First woman Vice-President of the Nottingham Law Students' Society. Co-founded *Poppleston Allen* in 1994, which won 'Small Law Firm of the Year' Award 1999.
Personal: Born 24th June 1948. Educated Nottingham and Bristol University. Leisure interests include reading, cooking, fell walking and eating. Lives in Nottingham.

POTTS, Andrew J.
Hammond Suddards Edge, Birmingham (0121) 200 2001
Specialisation: Advises on liquor, gaming and betting licenses, with 27 years' experience in the field. Acts for a number of public company clients as well as numerous private companies and individuals. His experience includes licensing airports, football clubs, public houses, night clubs, off-licenses, pop concerts, betting offices and gaming applications.
Prof. Memberships: Law Society, Birmingham Law Society.
Career: Qualified in 1971. Joined *Edge Ellison* in 1970, becoming a Partner in 1976. Part time Industrial Tribunal Chairman from 1983-95.
Personal: Born 7th September 1944. Attended Aldenham School 1958-63 and Bristol University 1963-66. Leisure interests include tennis, hockey and cricket. Lives in Leamington Spa.

RADCLIFFE, Malcolm
Freethcartwright, Leicester (0116) 201 4000
malcolm.radcliffe@freehcartwright.co.uk
Partner in Licensing and Commercial Department.
Specialisation: Principal area of practice is licensing. Also handles commercial conveyancing. Major clients include Leicestershire Police. Individual charge-out rate is normally £148 per hour.
Prof. Memberships: Law Society, Solicitors Benevolent Association.
Career: Qualified in 1972. With *Ironsides* from qualification and became a Partner in 1974. Partner in *Freeth Cartwright Hunt Dickins* 1998.
Personal: Born 22nd November 1948. Educated at Oakham School 1959-66. Parish Councillor and Vice Chairman of local primary school governors.

RAWLE, Claire
Morgan Cole, Cardiff (029) 2038 5385
claire.rawle@morgan-cole.com
Specialisation: Specialist advocate and specialises in all aspects of liquor and public entertainment licensing for major breweries, independent operators and specialist off licenses and convenience stores. She attends before court and council nationally and also advises in relation to trade descriptions, weights and measures and food safety issues.
Career: Articles and PQE with *Morgan Cole.*
Personal: Educated - Cardiff, Leicester and Bristol. Lives in Cardiff. Married.

ROBINSON, Sarah
Mincoffs, Newcastle-upon-Tyne (0191) 281 6151
Specialisation: Licensing, covering liquor, entertainments, gaming, amusements and planning.
Career: Qualified in1994 and became Partner in 2000. Extensive previous experience in civil litigation.
Personal: Born 12th September 1969. Interests in sport, leisure and maintaining personal awareness of developments in the leisure trade.

ROCHE, Paddy
Morgan Cole, Oxford (01865) 262600
paddy.roche@morgan-cole.com
Specialisation: Leads firms Thames Valley licencing practice specialising in all forms of licence application and health and safety work as well as criminal advocacy. Significant following in Oxford area. Acts for local licensees as well as public house management companies.
Career: Partner in Insurance Litigation division. Has developed advocacy department of *Morgan Cole* which now comprises six advocates dealing with crime, road traffic, licensing and health & safety matters.
Personal: Born 4.1.51. Educated at Magdalen College School Oxford and Exeter University. Married - 3 sons. Intrests - sport - hockey - fell walking.

SCIENCE, Austen
Mincoffs, Newcastle-upon-Tyne (0191) 281 6151
Leisure Department Head.
Specialisation: Main area of practice is licensing, covering liquor, gaming, amusements, and planning. Acted in numerous leading cases including R v Herrod, ex parte Leeds City District Council; R v Newcastle Gaming Licensing Committee, ex parte Whiteheart Enterprises Ltd and R v Burt & Adams. Major clients included Rank, Mecca, Scottish & Newcastle, Century Inns and Pubmaster. Editor of sections on Clubs in Halsbury's Laws of England and in Encyclopaedia of Forms and Precedents.
Prof. Memberships: Law Society Planning Panel, National Vice President of the British Amusement Caterers Trade Association.
Career: Qualified in 1961.
Personal: Born 11th August 1938.

SHARKEY, Lisa
Poppleston Allen, Nottingham (0115) 953 8500
Specialisation: Specialises in licensing and leisure work, including liquor, public entertainment, pay parties and related criminal matters. Writes legal column for 'Trading News', a magazine for Student Unions. Major clients include Allied Leisure, Bass Leisure Entertainment, Belgo, Chorion Plc, Luminar plc, PizzaExpress, Scottish and Newcastle Wolverhampton & Dudley Breweries, XS Leisure and works for an increasing number of student unions. Involved with B.E.D.A. and the campaign to Legalise Sunday dancing.
Prof. Memberships: Law Society; Nottinghamshire. Law Society; Committee Member of Society of Entertainment Licensing Practitioners.
Career: LLB: (Hons) Leeds 1989. Lectured Law at the University of Derby 1991. Articled at *Hunt Dickins* 1992. Left *Hunt Dickins* in 1994 with Jeremy Allen and Susanna Poppleston when they formed *Poppleston Allen* Licensing Solicitors.
Personal: Leisure interests include drinking and dancing, eating, and Tae Kwon Do.

SHAW, Deborah
Anthony Collins Solicitors, Birmingham (0121) 200 3242
Specialisation: Deborah Shaw is an Associate in the firm's licensing and leisure department specialising in licensing applications of all types, particularly for national breweries and entrepreneurs. Applications are made throughout England and Wales but with a special concentration in the West Midlands. Deborah has wide experience of handling betting and gaming licensing. The firm's licensing expertise incorporates a licensing property department with a substantial secured lending emphasis.
Career: Qualified in 1984. Deborah has 15 years experience with two leading licensing practices.
Personal: Educated at Birmingham University; interests include mountaineering, fell walking, films and theatre, reading, travel when time and family permit.

SKEENS, Julian M.
Jeffrey Green Russell, London (020) 7339 7000
Partner in charge of Licensing and Gaming Law Department with another partner, two assistant solicitors, three paralegals and other support staff. Works closely with other departments which have specialist knowledge of the leisure industry.
Specialisation: Specialist in liquor licensing, betting, gaming, public entertainment and lotteries: undertakes cases nationwide. Described as being at the cutting edge of licensing; known for his creative approach. Last year he represented the industry in the leading case of Shipley and obtained a new licence for a 3,000 capacity nightclub in Leicester Square, London. Cases successfully handled include the UK's first multi-activity centre, the UK's first 24-hour public entertainment licence and the UK's largest licensed premises.
Prof. Memberships: Law Society, Business in Sport and Leisure (Director), Society for the Study of Gambling, International Association of Gaming Attorneys, European Society for the Study of Gambling, Society of Entertainment and Licensing Practitioners (Fellow).
Career: Qualified 1980. Joined *Jeffrey Green Russell* in 1987 as a Partner to establish the now thriving specialist Licensing and Gaming Department.
Personal: Born 26th December 1951. LLB (Hons) (1974).

SMITH, David
Turbervilles with Nelson Cuff, Uxbridge (01895) 201700
david.smith@turbervilles.co.uk
Specialisation: Head of licensing dept., joint head litigation dept. Specialises in all aspects of licensing. Clients include major retailers & wholesalers, health clubs, hotel groups and airport retailers. Defends in criminal proceedings, prosecutes for RSPCA. Advises the Association of Licenced Free Traders.
Prof. Memberships: Law Society, Association of Licensing Practitioners.
Career: Qualified in Magistrates Courts Service. Admitted 1981, Private Practice from 1984, Partner at *Turbervilles* from 1986.
Publications: Columnist in Licensing for London Restaurant News.
Personal: Born 1st Feb. 1953. Married with 2 children. Lives in Ickenham. Leisure, - football, music, fine wines.

SOUTHORN, Elizabeth
Richards Butler, London (020) 7247 6555
es@richardsbutler.com
Specialisation: Licensing of liquor, betting, gaming, late night entertainment , large new multi-leisure sites, lotteries and Internet gaming. Acts for major players in the leisure industry such as the Rank Group, national bookmakers Coral, Sir Terence Conran, the BBC, the Royal Opera House and many of the most active developers including THI plc. and Marylebone Warwick Balfour. Lectures in all aspects of licensing.
Prof. Memberships: Business in Sport and Leisure; Association of London Brewery Solicitors; the Law Society.
Career: Articled *Oswald Hickson Collier & Co.*; Qualified in 1974; *Clyde & Co* 1980-82; *Crossman Block & Keith* 1982-88; Partner and Head of Licensing at *Penningtons (London)* 1988-93. Joined *Richards Butler* in 1993. Currently Partner and Head of Licensing Unit.
Personal: St Anne's College, Oxford 1968-71; (MA Jurisprudence) 1975. Leisure interests include family, sailing, opera and reading.

TEMPERLEY, William B.
McKenzie Bell, Sunderland (0191) 567 4857
Partner in Licensing and Leisure Department.
Specialisation: Principal area of work covers liquor and public entertainment licensing including sports grounds, betting and theatre licences and all types of applications and offences under the Licensing Act 1964. Handles applications to Justices and local authorities and Appeals to Crown Court throughout five North Eastern counties. Handles objections and applications for late licences, revocations and opposed renewals on behalf of police and licensees.
Prof. Memberships: Lawyers for Licensing North. Fellow of the Society of Entertainment Licensing Practitioners.
Career: Articled with *McKenzie Bell* and became a Partner in 1966.
Personal: Born 1940. Attended Bristol University 1958-61. Leisure pursuits include theatres and railways. Lives in Sunderland.

WALTER, Robin
Allen & Fraser, London (020) 7437 4001
Partner in Licensing Department.
Specialisation: Main area of practice is liquor and entertainment licensing. Has acted for several major national companies engaged in the entertainment and leisure industry.
Prof. Memberships: Law Society.
Career: Qualified in 1975. Joined *Allen & Fraser* as a Partner in 1983.
Personal: Leisure interests include cricket and real tennis.

WILSON, Robin K.
Berryman Shacklock, Nottingham (0115) 941 0789

WOODS, Andrew
Gosschalks, Hull (01482) 324 252

YOUNG, David A.
Eversheds, Birmingham (0121) 232 1000
See under Product Liability, p.677

LITIGATION (COMMERCIAL)

London: 541; The South: 545; Thames Valley: 546; South West: 547; Wales: 548; Midlands: 548; East Anglia: 550; North West: 550; Yorkshire: 552; North East: 554; Scotland: 555; Northern Ireland: 557; *Profiles*: 558

OVERVIEW: This year's section has been altered considerably following our search for the UK's top general commercial litigators. The London leading individuals table has been dramatically expanded to reflect the best litigation talent amongst those who have not chosen to specialise to any significant degree. We have also omitted reference to many of the firms which appeared in this section of previous editions of the Chambers Guide. Many firms which do not appear excel in particular types of litigation, for example, Masons for Construction, Kennedys for Insurance and Harbottle & Lewis for Media & Entertainment. The aim of this section is to focus on those practices that have received the warmest market recognition for their work in areas not covered elsewhere in the Chambers Guide. In the regions there is less of a tendency for litigators to specialise to the same degree.

It is clear that no two firms define their commercial litigation practices in the same way. Our researchers have taken pains to identify team sizes by excluding specialist litigation groups. In London we have highlighted commercial litigation teams that contain at least one individual who received sufficient market feedback to be named in the leading individuals table. However, other firms are included as an acknowledgement of nearly 100 London litigators who also received positive and spontaneous recommendations (albeit not of the same quality or frequency) from barristers, clients and other solicitors. Commendations for a team as a whole were noted in addition to feedback on individuals. For London, the four tables of firms by size have been reduced to two, following discussions with practitioners.

RESEARCH APPROVED BY BMRB: *For this edition,* Chambers' *researchers conducted 6083 interviews – 4408 with law firms, 598 with barristers and 1077 with clients.*

The validity of the research was scrutinised by BMRB International, who audited both the methodology and the results at our offices in July 2000. They interviewed Chambers' *researchers and cross-checked sample interviews. Details of the audit appear on page 7.*

LONDON

40+ LITIGATORS

LITIGATION (COMMERCIAL): 40+ LITIGATORS • London	Ptnrs	Assts
1 Herbert Smith	28	71
2 Freshfields Bruckhaus Deringer	14	50
Lovells	27	77
3 Linklaters	14	58
4 Allen & Overy	15	54
Clifford Chance	Fu	Fu
5 CMS Cameron McKenna	25	69
Norton Rose	13	*
Simmons & Simmons	14	41
6 Barlow Lyde & Gilbert	*	*
Denton Wilde Sapte	21	44
DLA	25	33
Richards Butler	23	34
Slaughter and May	8	32

Within each band, firms are listed alphabetically.
Fu Figures unavailable at time of going to press.
** See editorial entries for explanations of team sizes.*

Herbert Smith Seemingly untouchable as the premier team, producing consistently high quality across a very large department. Its reputation has definitely changed. *"It used to be the endless letters on a Friday afternoon, but not now."* It can still *"generate a situation which you just can't get out of,"* but whilst *"the letters are tough"* they are *"realistic, clever formidable litigators,"* not offering a plain *"red meat"* diet all of the time. A good choice of firm, *"particularly for cases where the cost is not an issue and requires a team to be working on it."* There is no shortage of 50+ aged partners, who are felt by some to be *"very individualistic"* and certainly the most senior figures have almost unmatched standing. *"Master tactician"* **David Gold** is *"diligent"* and *"hasn't rested on his laurels. He keeps a good watching brief over his assistants"* and *"knows when to delegate and when to intervene."* Another *"hard working"* senior name is that of **Ted Greeno**, for whom feedback has meant a rise in our table to the star band. Both he and confident **Campbell McLachlan** were endorsed strongly by other practitioners. *"The grand old man"* in the team is **David Natali**. Noted as *"active and very thorough," "he puts in a lot of time"* ensuring that assistants get the right support. **Harry Anderson**, as head of the group, is involved with the formulation and implementation of the firm's international litigation strategy. **Charles Plant** has *"great wisdom and is a great negotiator – he pins down points."* This year the market has identified two young female partners worthy of the attention they are now receiving. **Christa Band** had a *"scorching victory and did herself proud on Goldman Sachs v Mannesmann,"* while **Paula Hodges** is one of those *"professional" "normal, sensible people who put games to one side."* Key matters have included Bairds v Marks & Spencer and instructions from the Law Society concerning Kamlesh Bahl. **Clients:** Vodafone; BSkyB; Royal & Sun Alliance.

Freshfields Bruckhaus Deringer *"Involved in lots of areas"* and *"really motoring."* The bar confirms that they give *"fantastic back up"* and overall, the team is seen to be *"more consistent than some others"* with a *"stronger intellect."* One of the leading names is **Paul Leonard**, a man recognised by other top litigators. Interviewees have assumed that **Raj Parker** has *"lived his life doing Lloyd's,"* such are the levels of energy that he has put into the work. He's *"a cool cookie; incredibly calm and unflappable."* **Paul Bowden** is an extremely well regarded solicitor advocate, although now known primarily for his environmental cases. The established names are joined by the newly recommended and *"somewhat dry"* **Paul Lomas**, who *"has the ability to turn his hand to a whole range of disputes."* Acting for the Government of Brunei in matters including claims against Prince Jefri. **Clients:** RJB Mining; Lloyd's.

Lovells *"First class – we enjoy working with them"* was a fairly representative comment on the good-natured and *"gentlemanly"* Lovells litigators. Barristers gush about the quality of instructions and support given. *"They do*

LEADING INDIVIDUALS: LITIGATION (COMMERCIAL) • London	
✪ GOLD David Herbert Smith	GREENO Ted Herbert Smith
STYLE Christopher Linklaters	
❶ DAVIES Valerie Norton Rose	FAGAN Neil Lovells
FORDHAM John Stephenson Harwood	LEONARD Paul Freshfields Bruckhaus
MACKIE David Allen & Overy	MCLACHLAN Campbell Herbert Smith
NATALI David Herbert Smith	PARKER Raj Freshfields Bruckhaus
PLANT Charles Herbert Smith	SANDELSON Jeremy Clifford Chance
TURNBULL John Linklaters	
❷ ANDERSON Harry Herbert Smith	BOWDEN Paul Freshfields Bruckhaus
GOLDSPINK Robert Morgan, L & Bockius	PEARSON Nick Baker & McKenzie
SPARROW Edward Ashurst Morris Cris	TAYLOR Tim SJ Berwin & Co
TROTTER John Lovells	
❸ CANNON Lista Richards Butler	GOOD Diana Linklaters
HOUSE Tim Allen & Overy	KELLY Jonathan Simmons & Simmons
NICHOLSON Brinsley Linklaters	SLEIGH Russell Lovells
❹ ARCHER Nick Slaughter and May	BACON Gavin Simmons & Simmons
DE WALDEN Ludovic Lane & Partners	ELDER Hugh Gordon Dadds
FRASER David Baker & McKenzie	GRIERSON Christopher Lovells
HEARN Andrew Dechert	HENDERSON Guy Allen & Overy
HUMPHRIES Mark Linklaters	KING Ronnie Ashurst Morris Crisp
LOMAS Paul Freshfields Bruckhaus	MAGNIN John Nicholson Graham & Jones
MAYHEW David Clifford Chance	MICKLETHWAITE Neil Philip DLA
RANDS Harvey Memery Crystal	REYNOLDS John McDermott, Will & Emery
SHERRINGTON Patrick Lovells	SKREIN Michael Richards Butler
TOUT Liz Denton Wilde Sapte	WATSON Peter Allen & Overy
YORK Stephen Hammond Suddards Edge	
UP AND COMING	
BAND Christa Herbert Smith	HODGES Paula Herbert Smith
POLLACK Craig SJ Berwin & Co	

See *Profiles* on page 558

a huge amount of work and allow the bar to get on with the barristering." **Neil Fagan** has *"extraordinary wisdom"* and *"gets his sleeves rolled up."* **John Trotter** is *"quite reserved but effective."* Head of department **Russell Sleigh** is greatly admired by the bar, has *"incredible contacts"* and reputedly the dedication that leads him to *"stay up until 4am on his cases."* **Patrick Sherrington** has also been praised. New entrant to the Up and Coming table this year is *"class act"* **Christopher Grierson**, who has performed *"admirably"* for Prince Jefri. Achieved a swift decision on Young v Robson Rhodes, where it acted for the defendant in this case examining the erection of Chinese walls. **Clients:** Liquidators of BCCI; Nortel Networks plc; Merck & Co Inc.

Linklaters *"Consistent standard and always professional."* The approach is to breed assistants as generalists of an increasingly self-sufficient nature. International work continues to increase in significance. The financial services sector remains a particular strength. Mr *"common-sense-no-nonsense"* **Christopher Style** is particularly well liked by his peers and is a calm and *"well-rounded"* individual. **John Turnbull** *("extremely capable, canny"* and *"amusing")* rises up the table this year. He's *"outrageously good"* as well as *"tactically astute"* and *"comfortable on a range of cases."* Senior figure **Brinsley Nicholson** is also *"good fun."* The senior figures typify the pleasant approach displayed by the team. **Diana Good** sees high profile work. **Mark Humphries** is newly recommended. He pioneers in-house advocacy at the firm. Last year it obtained the largest ever freezing order (US$1 billion) for a foreign state and has been managing a prospectus liability claim for Paribas in the Danish courts arising out of the collapse of insurance company Hafnia. **Clients:** BG; LB Hillingdon; Republic of Panama.

Allen & Overy On first appearances, the litigation practice is linked inextricably with the finance practice but take away the self contained banking and finance litigation group and the remaining, larger part is to be found acting on all manner of instructions thrown up by the firm's strong corporate client base. Has the strength to *"muscle its way through disputes."* **Guy Henderson**'s cases are *"well put together"* and *"he takes responsibility for setting them and putting them to bed."* Counsel find him *"supportive and free thinking."* **Tim House** *("What more could you want?")* enters our table with quite superb feedback. He *"deals very well with clients and counsel"* and *"provides realistic views on tactics and strategy."* Distinguished **David Mackie QC** has been *"making a really big push to do pleadings in-house"* and is *"excellent in an arbitration context."* **Peter Watson** has also been recommended. Successfully acted for Queens Moat Houses plc in its £40 million action against four former directors concerning liability for misleading practices. **Clients:** BAe Systems plc; UBS; CSFB.

Clifford Chance Undeniably a presence. The already *"worthwhile transatlantic litigation capacity"* has just had the biggest boost possible, having teamed up with the US litigation powerhouse of Rogers & Wells. *"Big and around a lot,"* the department is not felt to contain any great *"sparkles."* Its strong reputation in international arbitration work and overseas cases overshadows the English court litigation. **Jeremy Sandelson** is widely acknowledged to have *"done a good job"* and, whilst not actually head of the London practice, he is seen almost as a de facto head. **David Mayhew** *"has a profile through advocacy,"* impressing those who see him performing without counsel. The team has had a high profile in both of the big Bermudan cases, Thyssen and Bermuda Fire & Marine. **Clients:** HSBC; Source Informatics; Philip Morris.

CMS Cameron McKenna Regularly encountered on a variety of important cases for big and household name clients. While some interviewees tell us that there is *"no house style,"* others feel that elements of the practice carry a reputation for being rather *"unexciting."* This is not to be mistaken for lack of talent; on the whole the team is praised for its *"all-round very sensible and measured"* approach, perhaps a more Woolfian style. Last year it hit the headlines on cases such as Spice Girls Ltd v Aprilia World Service BV, in which it was instructed by the defendant, Europe's second largest motorcycle manufacturer. **Clients:** Coca-Cola & Schweppes Beverages Ltd; Aventis CropScience; Essex & Suffolk Water plc.

Norton Rose Has moved away from its old shipping litigation image and is now established as a real player on serious mainstream work. The team of eight core partners is assisted by an army of assistants and other partners. Certain interviewees believed that *"they are what Herbert Smith were five years ago,"* and many felt that a little extra finesse would not go amiss. The Norton Rose style has been likened to one in which *"blunt instruments"* are used, where there is more call for use of the rapier. *"Mover and shaker"* **Val Davies** is politically well connected and knows how to be *"a snappish operator."* Continuing to act for Enron Europe Ltd in a complex North Sea dispute against six other companies relating to the termination of a CATS transportation system for North Sea Gas. **Clients:** Thybo Trustees Ltd; Siemens Group; Jurong Shipyard.

Simmons & Simmons A mixed bag of feedback for this group, but there are those who cite them as the firm to whom they always prefer to refer conflict work. Why? It emphasises *"strategy and keeps the level and the quality high."* Although putting his main focus on banking litigation, **Jonathan Kelly** is also handling a wider spread of contentious corporate matters. He's *"young, sensible and able."* **Gavin Bacon** joins the ranks of profiled litigators. *"He's hands-on and really applies due diligence to his work. Things don't go awry; never half baked."* Railtrack accounts for around 10 percent of the litigation work. Acting for Merrill Lynch Mercury Asset Management in the defence of claims brought by Unilever plc's pension fund. **Clients:** Mercury One2One; Gallaher; Society of Lloyd's.

Barlow Lyde & Gilbert *"A phenomenal amount of work and they do it well."* For a firm which *"does nothing else but litigate – their whole attention is turned to it,"* a lesser reputation would be a problem. Insurance/reinsurance/professional negligence is still a clear focus. Of the firms of the insurance ilk, it is perceived to be more broad based. Although one interviewee implied that a team of Amazon warriors dwelt at Barlows, others felt that its litigators had *"changed their style of late."* No team size is shown in the table to denote that all of the team (25 partners and 52 assistants) handle both professional negligence and insurance work in addition to more general commercial litigation. Currently acting for the principal defendant in the Metro Trading case. **Clients:** Dixons; Bank of America; Kelda Group plc.

Denton Wilde Sapte *"Top class litigation"* and *"realism"* from this new, improved practice produced from the merger of two well-established litigation groups earlier this year. The ingredients for success are *"hard -working and straightforward"* litigators, who are *"switched on and really deserve a plug,"* plus an interesting client base in a number of areas. Energy, finance and media sectors pump in plenty of good quality work. This year, **Liz Tout**, a lawyer with whom you can have *"sensible discussions,"* is the team's stand-out performer. Acting for Equitable Life in connection with its attempts to uphold its policy as to guaranteed annuity rates. **Clients:** Premier League, Total Oil Marine; FSA.

DLA *"Coming up fast"* according to some. Seen to *"have a good commercial attitude; not too legalistic."* Lots of computing cases and banking and *"expanding its profile in both areas,"* but still a perceived absence of the *"large blue-chip disputes."* National head of litigation **Neil Micklethwaite** makes the roll call of leading litigators, being described as *"a deal maker"* who is *"go-getting and expects a lot."* He *"goes to the nth degree to prepare and plays a major part in the case."* Acted for Cable & Wireless Communications in the US$10 million English proceedings brought by US claimant Communications Telesystems Inc t/a WorldChance. **Clients:** EDS; Granada; Henry Ansbacher & Co Ltd.

Richards Butler Attracting *"good cases." "Nice people"* with a *"commercial outlook"* and a number of *"good, younger general litigators"* with *"promise."* **Lista Cannon** is recommended again this year and is now joined by **Michael Skrein**, who deals with more than a dose of media related disputes but has a wider profile than as a *"showbiz"* litigator. Acted for the BBC on the Premier League litigation and for The Express with regard to Elton John and Eversheds. **Clients:** Trillium; Direct Line; Fortis Bank/MeesPierson.

Slaughter and May A team assumed to have *"an easier job than most in attracting clients,"* and, as usual for non-corporate groups at S&M, a recipient of the old charge that it is *"small and an adjunct to the corporate department."* Those who look a little closer at the client base and a little deeper into the performance of the team acknowledge that the litigators have *"brains, experience, back-up and facilities"* and that their cases *"span the range of commercial issues."* Department head **Nick Archer** *"does things the Slaughters' way,"* and is *"very good at what he does – a solid litigator."* Acting for Unilever on its claim against Mercury Asset Management arising from its handling of the Unilever pension fund. **Clients:** Cadbury Schweppes; BOC; Avions de Transport Regional.

FEWER THAN 40 LITIGATORS

LITIGATION (COMMERCIAL): FEWER THAN 40 LITIGATORS • London	Ptnrs	Assts
1 Ashurst Morris Crisp	7	20
Baker & McKenzie	9	18
SJ Berwin & Co	6	16
Stephenson Harwood	14	20
2 Clyde & Co	15	17
D J Freeman	10	12
Eversheds	8	15
Gouldens	5	14
Nabarro Nathanson	5	20
Nicholson Graham & Jones	14	20
3 Dechert	4	⚐
Lawrence Graham	5	7
Reynolds Porter Chamberlain	6	12
Travers Smith Braithwaite	5	9
4 Hammond Suddards Edge	5	18
5 Berwin Leighton	7	16
Charles Russell	7	11
Lane & Partners	⚐	⚐
Lewis Silkin	6	4
Memery Crystal	⚐	⚐
Mishcon de Reya	8	8
Taylor Joynson Garrett	7	10
6 Biddle	3	3
LeBoeuf, Lamb, Greene & MacRae	2	11
Macfarlanes	7	16
Rowe & Maw	8	17
Theodore Goddard	6	10
Warner Cranston	5	8

Within each band, firms are listed alphabetically.
⚐ Figures unavailable at time of going to press.

Ashurst Morris Crisp *"Good quality work,"* which ranges from the City and financial to oil and gas, and covers a multitude of jurisdictions. **Ed Sparrow** has a double-sided, nice guy/tough guy image. *"He has good judgement"* and *"provides realistic views on tactics and strategy."* Newly ranked **Ronnie King** *"really has his eye on the ball, displays a lot of common sense and can turn his hand to the range of commercial litigation."* He is, however, best recognised for his oil and gas work. Acting for Sumitomo Corporation in proceedings against Credit Lyonnaise Rouse to cover part of the £2 billion losses suffered as a result of Yasuo Hamanaka's unauthorised copper trading. **Clients:** Royal & SunAlliance; National Power; British Gas Trading.

Baker & McKenzie *"A great name for international clients"* and running heavy pieces of litigation. Matters such as the Grupo Torras case have *"lifted them."* **Nick Pearson**'s reputation is going through the roof, following his spell in the limelight on that dispute. He displays *"highly competent organisation of cases." "He thinks about technical issues ahead of time"* and is *"unflappable"* with clients. **David Fraser** (*"switched on and hands on"*) is newly ranked this year. The team is now active internationally in its enforcement of the judgments handed down in last year's Grupo Torras litigation. **Clients:** Dr Andrew Millar; Stafford-Miller; Asprey & Garrard.

S J Berwin & Co *"Lots of good clients with money – a really different firm."* It *"understands and respects litigation as a key part of the practice."* The team is *"big on personality"* and displays a *"tough, no nonsense attitude with the right level of aggression turned on and off as required."* Plenty of international work and good links with the US. Rising up the rankings this year, *"charismatic"* **Tim Taylor** *"does the most extraordinary amount of work."* His younger sidekick **Craig Pollack** has also been endorsed and together they are gaining a reputation as a dynamic duo. It acts in the Nigerian Noga litigation for the Abacha family and in the Eastern Agents matter in which it is bringing a claim for five companies against Eastern Electricity plc concerning the application and construction of Commercial Agents regulations. **Clients:** Fyffes plc; Hilton Group; Elegant Hotels.

Stephenson Harwood *"Gets around a bit"* and has the *"contacts and support"* which allows it to *"run huge cases."* If *"litigation is the jewel in their crown,"* then this is in no small part due to **John Fordham** (*"bloody thorough and a normal, nice guy"*) who commands widespread respect amongst his peers for his sense of *"fairness and propriety."* He is *"a natural leader and great motivator."* Acted on Noga v Abacha concerning the theft of Nigerian promissory notes. **Clients:** Christies; Royal Albert Hall; Wang (UK) Ltd.

Clyde & Co *"A traditional shipping firm with more of a commercial base than the other shipping firms."* Its qualification for this section relies on that broader base. Usually *"on the ball"* with *"the right measure of aggression."* The department as a whole is involved in a considerable number of the cases that pass through the Commercial Court and in a number of claims in other jurisdictions, including the US and Indonesia. Aside from insurance clients, it acts for the hi-tech sector, Government departments and a variety of plcs. The Metro litigation continues, pertaining to matters relating to an oil refinery in UAE. **Clients:** ECGD.

DJ Freeman The team has had a good year and *"been in some interesting headline cases."* The department has concentrated on developing links with in-house counsel. Also sees some interesting international public law cases. One observer pointed out that the firm *"has a tendency to win its cases."* One such victory was for British Steel in BHP v British Steel & Anor in April 2000, when the firm was successful in striking out a £200 million claim. **Clients:** Shell; the Governments of Nigeria and Botswana; Invensys plc.

Eversheds To say that Eversheds handles a *"broad work load,"* is greatly to understate the case. It deals with a range of matters so wide and for clients of such diverse nature that it simply cannot be pigeonholed. The interaction between London and the firm's regional litigation groups is in evidence: Bloody Sunday and other high profile enquiries being examples. Acting for Grupo Torras/Torras Papal on its various disputes. **Clients:** PSInet; Du Pont; Thomson CSF.

Gouldens The firm maintains a good grip on its reputation. Has seen plenty of distressed debt activity for US Hedge Funds. Has been acting for Old English Inns plc in proceedings which followed the publication of a trading statement to the Stock Exchange. **Clients:** Cargill plc; Standard Bank; London Forfaiting.

Nabarro Nathanson An *"interesting balance of experience and breadth of work"* and described as *"nice people."* Acted for an Isle of Man liquidator (KPMG) and OMV Supply & Trading AG in three separate proceedings in the High Court against 14 defendants. The case included eight worldwide freezing orders and eventually settled. **Clients:** Granada Group; Maxwell Pension Fund Trustees; United Mizrahi Bank.

Nicholson Graham & Jones *"Cropping up a lot and seem to know what they are doing."* **John Magnin**, who is newly ranked this year, is *"good at team building."* The one he has built has been recognised as *"a well-integrated team of litigators"* with a *"good client list of wealthy individuals and businesses."* Indeed the team participates in regular brainstorming sessions on its cases. These have included Manoukian v Prince Jefri, Grupo Torras and the benzene litigation. **Clients:** Kazakhstan Mineral Resources Corporation; Bass Group; Windsor Life/G Financial Services.

Dechert *"Getting better and catching up with certain other strong firms."* Another firm thought to be *"not in the usual mould."* **Andrew Hearn** is a general commercial litigator who often ends up on product/supply oriented cases, such as that concerning benzene contamination of fizzy drinks. His forte is client relationships and he *"has a good feel for litigation and knows when to fight and when to settle."* **Clients:** Sears Ltd; William Hill; Banner Homes Ltd.

Lawrence Graham Strong with institutional clients, the team has advised PPP Healthcare plc in respect of matters arising from its merger with Guardian Healthcare. **Clients:** 3i; Cash Converters; Scottish & Newcastle plc.

Reynolds Porter Chamberlain *"Doing their best to broaden the base from solicitor related professional negligence work."* Has a good measure of pure commercial disputes in addition to a host of more specialist cases. Tipped as *"interesting to watch"* by pundits. *"You can talk to them – they take a commercial view."* Advised Symonds, the minority shareholder of Trillium, in Dalkia plc v Trillium plc. **Clients:** Associated Newspapers Ltd, Vivendi plc, The Morgan Crucible Company plc.

Travers Smith Braithwaite A traditional practice with *"good work – they know their stuff."* Has a strong base of commercial and finance clients. The case it is running for Orbis plc, following the sale of one of its divisions by way of management buy-out, is an example of an increase in the work arising out of the business disposal market. **Clients:** MGN Pension Trustees; Voest Alpine Industrienlagenbau GmbH; Lloyd's Disciplinary Committees.

Hammond Suddards Edge Of the two merging practices, Hammonds has had the strongest reputation. It has been *"getting big work and getting well-known"* although a perception exists that the slickest blue-chip disputes are not yet in their grasp. The new outfit doubles the commercial litigation capacity of either of its constituent parts. People see **Stephen York** as *"the chief rainmaker in the department."* The Hammonds practice has taken a distinctly international direction of late with clients and disputes in several continents. Has been acting for Sahara India Airlines in a multi-million pound claim against Polaris Aircraft Leasing Corporation. **Clients:** The Government of Bolivia; Woolworths plc; British Energy plc.

Berwin Leighton *"Straight forward"* and *"direct"* in its approach. It acts for huge names in retail, aviation, utilities and banking. Acted for one of the two investment consortia in defending the attempt to wind up the Johannesburg Stock Exchange listed company Del Monte Royal Holdings Ltd. **Clients:** Oasis Stores plc; Summit Financial Group plc; Tesco.

Charles Russell *"Exhibit a down to earth attitude,"* the firm has impressed enough in our survey to enter the table in a season which has seen the relegation of nearly half the firms previously ranked. They have *"won through on quality."* Last year acted for Gary Kemp and Reformation Publishing Company Ltd in the Spandau Ballet litigation. **Clients:** Cable & Wireless; ntl; Reichold Chemicals.

Lane & Partners **Ludovic de Walden** is a *"hands on work generator"* and has generated much more than the commonly perceived aviation workload. **Clients:** Financial institutions; airlines.

Lewis Silkin Clients range from media and publishing through utilities to professional partnerships. It offers *"good quality and good work"* but its general commercial litigation reputation is still stifled by the firm's status as a leading employment practice. Where there is a crossover in these two areas the firm steps out with top-ranking opposition, such as in the Kamlesh Bahl / Law Society affair, in which the litigation team dealt with the administrative law and constitutional aspects of the former Vice President's claim against the Society. **Clients:** London Electricity plc; Telegraph Group Ltd; House of Fraser plc.

Memery Crystal **Harvey Rands** is a *"superb operator"* with *"a tough image,"* and is one of the principal reasons for this small firm's continued ranking.

Mishcon de Reya Hanging on to its position, having come through bad times and back into the limelight. Praised for issuing *"reasoned responses"* to the opposition. In Alcock & Ors v Phildrew Nominees Ltd, UBS AG & Eaves, it is defending tracing and constructive trust claims against Emma Eaves, whose husband allegedly lost £15m of a retirement fund belonging to ex partners of Phildrew. **Clients:** Commercial Acceptances; European Healthcare Group; 31 investors in Royal & Sun Alliance.

Taylor Joynson Garrett A *"mainstream traditional"* group of *"bright, commercial and team players"* handling *"really large cases."* It is *"very quick to see the commercial angle."* Instructed to act for the NFU in proceedings against France over the beef ban and for National Bus Company Pension Trustees in its claim against the Government resulting in a £350 million settlement. **Clients:** NCR; Toyota (GB)plc; Crane Co.

Biddle Securing high quality work through strong personal relationships and client care. Represented the General Council of the Bar as Intervener in Hall v Simons in the House of Lords, arguing that immunity for advocates should remain. **Clients:** H M Salaam (Dubai Aluminium case); Independent Trustees of Maxwell Private Side Pension Schemes; Speciality Care plc.

LeBoeuf, Lamb, Greene & MacRae Forged a strong relationship with Royal & Sun Alliance following the acquisition of a partner from Davies Arnold Cooper. It conducts a spread of interesting work and *"asks all the right questions."* **Clients:** Telecoms, insurance, aviation and e-commerce clients.

Macfarlanes Successful in the Court of Appeal on behalf of Thomson Holidays Ltd in its JR challenge arising out of the MMC report into the foreign package holiday industry. **Clients:** Patterson Belknap Webb & Tyler; Southwood Working Party (BSE); R&B Falcon Corporation Inc.

Rowe & Maw Standing comfortably alone from other departments and growing its turnover and team size. Multi-jurisdictional cases now account for nearly a third of its work. It is presently acting for client United Pan-European Communications in attempts to restrain the disposal of substantial assets over which its client has a claim. **Clients:** EMI Group plc; Unilever plc; Metro Media Group.

Theodore Goddard A smaller team, but *"into a broad range of cases."* Clients come from the media, finance, transport and aviation. Around half the work is for international clients. Those handling product liability litigation receive particular praise. Presently acting for The Law Debenture Trust Corporation plc which, as trustees of a US$150 million convertible bond issue in 1994, is suing Tanayong plc, the Thai public transport company. It also continues to act for that client in the Barings litigation. **Clients:** Commerzbank; Glaxo Wellcome; Oracle.

Warner Cranston A small and successful team with a big turnover. They are *"fun to deal with," "tough"* litigators with whom you'll have *"all kinds of ding-dongs."* The team, enhanced by new names from DAC and Nabarro Nathanson, still takes its lead from its namesake consultant. Continue to act in the Dubai litigation. **Clients:** The Government of Dubai; Petrotrade; Brierley Investments.

Other Notable Practitioners As practitioners in the smallest of firms sometimes point out, there is considerable value to be found amongst those who provide a personal service to clients. The market agrees and accordingly we highlight **Hugh Elder** at Gordon Dadds *("good with clients," "you can pit him against the best.")* With a year and a half in the saddle, **John Reynolds** at McDermott, Will & Emery receives praise for his handling of cases and progress in building a London team at the firm. Also recommended is **Robert Goldspink** of Morgan, Lewis & Bockius.

THE SOUTH

LITIGATION (COMMERCIAL) • The South	
❶	**Blake Lapthorn** Fareham
	Cripps Harries Hall Tunbridge Wells, Kent
❷	**Bond Pearce** Southampton
	DMH Brighton
	Thomas Eggar Church Adams Chichester, Worthing
❸	**Argles Stoneham Burstows** Crawley
	Brachers Maidstone
	Clyde & Co Guildford
	Stevens & Bolton Guildford
❹	**Barlows** Guildford
	Paris Smith & Randall Southampton
	Thomson Snell & Passmore Tunbridge Wells
❺	**Lester Aldridge** Bournemouth

LEADING INDIVIDUALS	
❶ **ASPINALL Tim** DMH	**HIGHAM David** Blake Lapthorn

Within each band, firms are listed alphabetically. *See **Profiles** on page 558*

Figures unavailable at time of going to press.

Blake Lapthorn Operating in tandem with its London office (European export and export credit work,) the firm has consolidated its rise up the table last year. The team is comprised of *"good people" "who know what they are doing."* This year it has won work across the board from leisure sector organisation Queensborough Holdings plc. From a solid base amongst UK clients, especially in manufacturing, telecoms and hi-tech, it is expanding into international arbitration work and professional disciplinary proceedings. **David Higham** has focused on professional negligence work of late but is still regarded as a top general commercial litigator. Depending on how redistribution of SIF work affects the firm, the market expects to see him on a broader range of cases in 2001. **Clients:** General Optical Council; Pirelli UK plc; Alcatel.

Cripps Harries Hall This is a firm that everyone expects to do well, implying that it has the requisite ingredients in terms of experience and clients. It carries out wide ranging work for both national and regional clients, particularly in financial services, insurance and housebuilding. Construction, insolvency, IP and SIF work is handled in addition to a plump general commercial caseload. Has been acting on two interesting cases of fraud, one relating to conspiracy to defraud a major plc, another to defrauding investors. **Clients:** NPI; Alba Life Ltd; HM Customs & Excise.

Bond Pearce Having transferred fast track, smaller claims and partnership disputes to the Plymouth office, Bond Pearce's Southampton office concentrates on more substantial claims, its retail clients, EU/competition cases and public law litigation. It has *"made and established a market presence"* and is acknowledged by the south coast players as *"the competition."* Has been appointed by the independent wholesalers who sell Wall's Ice Cream to challenge the current arrangement which is the subject of a DTI and LST enquiry and which is now going to Europe. **Clients:** Woolworths plc; B&Q plc; The National Trust.

DMH Seen regularly by regional players and maintaining an established reputation, handling cases from the quirky to the complex. *"Prominent"* **Tim Aspinall** is the best known of the South's litigators and has *"an incredible talent."* He leads a team instructed by IT, engineering, telecoms, manufacturing and pharmaceuticals clients. Its Innovation and Media team litigators now operate from the new Croydon office. The Mandy Allwood/Max Clifford battle continues and it has acted recently for a high-tech client concerning the right to equity in a company reversed into an AIM floated internet portal. **Clients:** Wandsworth & Croydon Borough Councils; Thomson CSF; Airtel plc.

Thomas Eggar Church Adams Has four offices in the region and one in London. The Chichester and Reigate offices serve their local business communities, with the latter recently handling a £3.5 million computer dispute. Worthing deals with insolvency litigation, debt work and European fraud actions. London handles mortgage-related work and operates an agency practice. **Clients:** Nationwide BS; Levy Gee Kidsons Impey; MJ Gleeson & Co.

Argles Stoneham Burstows A tripartite merger of firms in Crawley, Maidstone and Croydon has more than piqued the interest of our interviewees. The Burstows element seems to have brought the real strength in general commercial litigation and it is the Crawley office which handles the major work, with Maidstone concentrating on property and planning cases. Gives litigation support to the corporate department (also in Crawley) in the form of company and shareholder disputes, derivative actions and s459 petitions. Aviation and travel is an expanding area. Last year it was successful in its Court of Appeal attempt to reduce a US$1.4 million damages award to US$365,000. The original claim had been issued for US$4 million. Also successful in the CA in Thornton Springer v NEM Insurance Co. Ltd and Ors. **Clients:** First Choice; Virgin.

Brachers A good practice which has traditionally been seen as *"the firm that the agricultural community and moneyed country people use."* Admittedly, it is now the sole NFU panel firm in the south east, but this impression is only a part of the story. The corporate department spins off work for the litigators and computer and IT disputes are on the increase. Continues to handle Eurotunnel BAA Terminals work. **Clients:** 12 NHS Trusts and two Health Authorities; Eurotunnel; Travis Perkins.

Clyde & Co If Clyde & Co's Guildford office were independent of the main London office of the firm it might receive considerably more attention in the region. The clients and cases occupying the litigators are both big and international in nature and come from several industry sectors, including energy, high-tech, food and distribution. Judgment is currently awaited on a US$100 million dispute in the US against manufacturer General Dynamics. **Clients:** NCM; ECGD; SkyNet Worldwide Express.

Stevens & Bolton Corporate work and Company Court actions keep this Guildford outfit busy. Seen to be *"very professional"* with *"decent clients"* and *"plenty of bravado."* Selected also for smaller product liability actions by a major pharmaceuticals manufacturer. Acting on telecoms claims and credit insurance matters. Successful strike out action for client Bestfoods Inc in a claim for negligent misstatement and breach of warranty. **Clients:** Hays plc; Gerling Namur Insurances of Credit; IAF Group plc.

Barlows Handles many types of case for a spread of client sectors, including education, insurance, public authorities and construction. Has seen injunctive activity and some cross-border instructions in the last year. It acted recently for a provisional liquidator of an insurance company obtaining the recovery of money from a Greek defendant. It is part of the Surrey Mediation Forum. **Clients:** Public authorities.

Paris Smith & Randall General commercial litigation including a modest proportion of insolvency cases, for which it is well known. Recently acted in a claim on behalf of a local plc for damages for breach of contract and unpaid commission as a result of the termination of a Mercantile Agency Agreement. **Clients:** Regional plcs.

Thomson Snell & Passmore Cover breach of warranty claims, directors and shareholder disputes, s459 and s122 actions and contractual work. Has been instructed on claims in Europe and the Far East. Recently took shareholder agreement dispute McPherson v DSP to the Court of Appeal. Certain partners take on the role of Supervising Solicitor under Search Orders. **Clients:** Aspinalls Ltd; Colas Ltd.

Lester Aldridge New into the table this year, having been seen to have *"come together in the last few years."* Known to have a number of international clients as well as acting for insurers, the food industry and waste management companies. It is presently handling a US$25 million claim. **Clients:** Insurers; waste management companies.

THAMES VALLEY

LITIGATION (COMMERCIAL) • Thames Valley
❶ **Clarks** Reading
Morgan Cole Oxford, Reading
❷ **Boyes Turner & Burrows** Reading
Garretts Reading
Nabarro Nathanson Reading
Shoosmiths Reading

LEADING INDIVIDUALS
❶ **ROWE Claire** Shoosmiths

Within each band, firms are listed alphabetically. See **Profiles** on page 558

Clarks Felt to be a *"rising star"* in the region and to be *"acquiring good clients,"* the firm moves upwards in the tables for a second year running. The client base includes a number of significant corporations, many of whom are multi-nationals, and they are derived from both public and private sector. In the past year the team has carried out a number of seven-figure High Court actions, and has seen a marked increase in its work for BMW Financial Services Group. **Clients:** Blue Circle Industries plc; BMW Financial Services Group; Bunzl plc.

Morgan Cole *"A good firm who deserve to be at the top and who should be respected,"* the firm takes on high volume work of a *"major commercial calibre."* In the last year the firm has made new law on cross-examination on assets under a freezing order and successfully defended the same. Particularly strong client base in the financial sector. **Clients:** Financial institutions.

Boyes Turner & Burrows Thought to count *"a number of good people"* in commercial litigation, the firm enters the rankings this year. Its clients are drawn in the main from the IT and property sectors, although it acts for a range of companies on commercial matters. Has a real strength at directors' disqualification work and in the last year has successfully defended proceedings in a fully contested directors' disqualification case. **Clients:** Barratts Construction; Grenco Ltd; FLS Aerospace; Kelly Services.

Garretts A firm that draws mixed comment: Garretts is felt to do *"some quality commercial litigation,"* but this is seen to come through the connection with the Andersen Legal network and leads people to question their ability to generate high-calibre work independently. However, the team has handled some notable *"independent"* cases, including acting for CVCP (The Committee of Vice Chancellors & Principals of the Universities of the United Kingdom) and virtually all UK Universities in proceedings seeking an injunction to restrain the production and sale over the internet of fake degree certificates. **Clients:** Timberland; Quorum Systems; Wordsworth Holdings plc; CVCP.

Nabarro Nathanson Acting largely for blue-chip and multi-national companies, the commercial litigation team has seen its workload increase from its initial raft of work, garnered from the firm's IT clients. Respected by firms from outside the region as often as firms within it, the team advised Bank Of Ireland, Singer & Friedlander Ltd, and Brown, Shipley & Co Ltd on a range of banking, bills of exchange and trade finance-related matters throughout the year. **Clients:** Siemens plc; Osram Ltd; Singer & Friedlander Ltd; Swansea City AFC Ltd.

Shoosmiths The team's reputation in the region rests largely on the shoulders of **Claire Rowe**. Head of Shoosmiths' national commercial litigation team, she is felt to be a *"good litigator"* to whom rival firms would *"happily refer."* The Thames Valley practice has an insurance bias, although it handles the broad spectrum of Commercial Litigation work and has seen a particular growth in IT and IP work arising from disputes related to e-business. **Clients:** Insurance companies; IT service providers.

SOUTH WEST

LITIGATION (COMMERCIAL) • South West
❶ **Burges Salmon** Bristol
Osborne Clarke OWA Bristol
❷ **Beachcroft Wansbroughs** Bristol
Bevan Ashford Bristol
Bond Pearce Bristol, Exeter, Plymouth
Eversheds Bristol
TLT Solicitors Bristol
Veale Wasbrough Bristol
❸ **Cartwrights** Bristol
Foot Anstey Sargent Exeter, Plymouth
Laytons Bristol
❹ **Clarke Willmott & Clarke** Yeovil
Lyons Davidson Bristol

LEADING INDIVIDUALS	
❶ **CLOUGH Peter** Osborne Clarke OWA	**HAGGETT Paul** Burges Salmon
MAY Philip TLT Solicitors	**MORRIS Peter** Eversheds
PIZZEY Simon Veale Wasbrough	
❷ **METCALFE Stephen** Beachcroft Wansbroughs	
OWENS David Bevan Ashford	**PUDDICOMBE Nigel** Cartwrights
❸ **WILLIAMS Peter** Burges Salmon	

Within each band, firms are listed alphabetically. See **Profiles** on page 558

Burges Salmon Almost universally held to be *"extremely professional litigators"* with a *"quality practice,"* the team continues to put in a strong performance. New to the rankings, **Paul Haggett** is felt to be *"the region's brightest star in this field,"* while **Peter Williams** is *"thoughtful and astute"* and *"a joy to be instructed by."* Provides a broad range of commercial litigation services, but has a particular niche in transport. The team acts for First Great Western in relation to all aspects of the Ladbroke Grove train crash. Notably acts for a number of financial institutions. **Clients:** First Group plc; St Paul International Insurance Company Ltd; Nationwide Building Society.

Osborne Clark OWA Felt by many interviewees to be *"pre-eminent for company and commercial work,"* the team is *"highly regarded,"* with special mention being made of strength in banking work. The firm is seen to offer *"a full service and to offer a wide variety of skills."* **Peter Clough** is described as a *"really hot general commercial litigator,"* by people from outside as well as within the region. Acted for Greek Cypriot interests in R v Maff ex parte S P Anastasiou (Pissouri) Ltd. The matter was referred by the House Of Lords to the European Court Of Justice. **Clients:** Abbey National plc; British Airways plc; European Telecom plc; Mulberry & Co Design.

Beachcroft Wansbroughs Acknowledged as *"the best for insurance work,"* the commercial litigation team suffers from the market perception of them as merely a SIF firm. However, it handles a broad range of disputes, from the high-value to the everyday contractual and banking disputes, and a vociferous lobby feel that they are, in fact, since the merger, *"coming on more than anyone else,"* and doing *"a tremendous amount of work and doing it well."* **Stephen Metcalfe** joins the rankings this year. Acted for one of the parties in a reported case (A&J Fabrications v Grant Thornton) concerning whether the solicitor acting for a liquidator owes a duty of care to a creditor. **Clients:** Equifax plc.

Bevan Ashford A year of consolidation for this firm sees them move up a band. The Exeter office is felt to do *"as much commercial litigation as NHS work,"* while the Bristol team struggles rather more to be recognised for its commercial litigation work. **David Owens,** whose commercial litigation work for NHS & private sector clients is conducted under the aegis of the Healthcare team, is deemed to be *"switched on."* The Bristol team is involved in some exciting commercial litigation for multi-nationals, nation states and global professionals and has been acting for a former Soviet Republic in a multi-million pound banking related international UNCITRAL arbitration. **Clients:** Allied Domecq; Orange PCS Ltd.

Bond Pearce The Bristol office is still perceived as embryonic by the market, and is thought to *"revolve around insolvency work."* It has, however, enough commercial litigation acumen to be dealing with a novel and multi-million pound derivative action on behalf of a shareholder in several different companies. Exeter and Plymouth, which operate as a tightly co-operative unit, are thought to be *"excellent."* Have just completed a five-year fraud case litigation on behalf of a major car manufacturer. **Clients:** Volkswagen Group UK; Peugeot Wholesale Ltd; The National Trust; St. Merryn Meat Ltd.

Eversheds A firm which polarises the market. The majority view is that they field a *"strong team"* for commercial litigation while a minority see them as no longer having a *"credible practice"* now that the Bristol & West work is *"drying up."* **Peter Morris** is unanimously voted a *"respected, competent and quality player."* Typically handles professional negligence claims, bank recoveries, and one-off commercial cases, and is seen to have particular expertise in banking and finance work. **Clients:** Bristol & West plc; Lloyds TSB; Skipton Building Society; Rhodia Ltd.

TLT Solicitors It is generally believed that the merger has *"enhanced the position"* of the original firms by allowing them to offer a *"new size and quality,"* to clients. The firm is felt to possess *"commercially minded"* and *"aggressive litigators,"* with banking a particular forte. **Philip May** is highly respected for possessing *"good judgement and experience,"* and for offering *"a constructive approach."* Have seen a significant increase in cross-border work as a result of development through the European Law Firm network. **Clients:** Hanson Quarry Products Europe.

Veale Wasbrough Acting for a variety of clients in the private and public sector, the firm advised on the defence of a £1 million claim for damages for alleged breach of warranties relating to share purchases in hi-tech business. **Simon Pizzey** is rated as an *"aggressive"* practitioner, although now has to combine fee-earning work with his position as Managing Partner. **Clients:** Bristol & West plc; SWEB; Great Mills (Retail Ltd); Institute of Physics Publishing Ltd.

Cartwrights Continues to handle commercial litigation work primarily as a service department (although carrying out independent work as well.) **Nigel Puddicombe**, who is held to be *"sensible,"* enjoys a healthy profile, no doubt boosted by his being made this year's President of the Bristol Law Society. Have carved a distinct niche in transport litigation. **Clients:** Dalgety Group Ltd; Railtrack PLC; Standard Life Assurance.

Foot Anstey Sargent Another firm seen to have consolidated its position through a merger which the market believes to have placed them *"marginally ahead"* of the other firms in their band. The firm acts for a number of owner-managed companies, as well as property developers, publishing companies and banks. **Clients:** Property developers; financial institutions.

Laytons *"Dependable"* general commercial litigation practice with two noted strengths in construction and insolvency. A highlight of their year was acting for a major supermarket chain in a claim against it by a potential supplier in excess of £1.5 million. **Clients:** World Kitchens; Hamptons International; Merlett Plastics; Gullivers Group.

Clarke Willmott & Clarke A practice that is adept at dealing with the food and drink sector, the construction industry and , more generally, EC Regulations. The Taunton team is perceived by the market to be the hard-hitter amongst the firm's commercial litigation outfits, offering a *"well-thought-of"* general service and *"good banking support."* **Clients:** Gloucestershire County Council; Chartered Trust plc; Beaufort Western Ltd.

Lyons Davidson Although not felt to be especially high-profile, the firm contains *"approachable and commercially minded"* litigators. Its litigation skills were felt to show rather more in specialist areas, such as insurance, than in all-round general commercial work. **Clients:** Insurance companies.

WALES

LITIGATION (COMMERCIAL) • Wales
❶ **Edwards Geldard** Cardiff
Eversheds Cardiff
Hugh James Ford Simey Cardiff
Morgan Cole Cardiff, Swansea
❷ **Palser Grossman** Cardiff Bay

LEADING INDIVIDUALS	
❶ **HOPKINS Paul** Edwards Geldard	**JEFFERIES Michael** Hugh James Ford Simey
❷ **JONES Michael** Hugh James Ford Simey	**JONES Peter** Eversheds
WILLIAMS Gareth Hugh James Ford Simey	**WILSON Allan** Morgan Cole
UP AND COMING	
RHYS-JONES Mark Eversheds	

Within each band, firms are listed alphabetically. *See Profiles on page 558*

Edwards Geldard Moving up for the second year running, Edwards Geldard is looking good. Somewhat smaller than some of its rivals, the team is nevertheless seen to possess a *"good client base who bring them quality commercial work."* A highlight of the year was advising the Welsh Development Agency and three individual defendants in a high profile, complex and significant litigation initiated by Landare Investments Ltd. Their *"thorough"* handling of this *"monster"* case drew the admiration of their competitors. The team boasts *"very good individuals,"* including the *"respected"* **Paul Hopkins,** described as a *"sensible litigator who gets results."* **Clients:** Williams plc; Hyder plc; Citibank NA; Welsh Development Agency.

Eversheds *"Always there or thereabouts,"* the team is clearly a leading local player. **Peter Jones** is *"very good, but tied up in the Bloody Sunday enquiry,"* and he heads the firm's national team devoted to this enquiry. He is also joint lead partner of the team appointed as sole legal advisors to the National Assembly for Wales. **Mark Rhys-Jones** is still seen as an up and coming figure in this department. The team continues to advise on the full spectrum of contentious matters for a large number of organisations in the private and public sectors. Currently acting on behalf of a client in defending a multi-million claim brought by Eurostar. **Clients:** Welsh Development Agency; National Assembly for Wales.

Hugh James Ford Simey The firm's commercial litigation work is seen to be driven by its strong insurance practice. Nonetheless, the team is highly rated, and fields no fewer than three litigators whose skills were commented on by their competitors. **Michael Jefferies,** more a construction specialist than a general commercial litigator, is *"impressive,"* while **Michael Jones** and **Gareth Williams** are *"lawyers for whom we have a lot of time."* **Clients:** Insurance companies

Morgan Cole An impressive practice, seen to be *"a pure commercial litigation department."* Not only admired by their Welsh rivals but also commended by practitioners in the South West and London, the team's profile is evidently growing, notably in IP and e-commerce. *"Professional"* team leader, **Allan Wilson,** is thought to be *"an able litigator."* Instructed in a major Customs and Excise investigation involving pan-European customs fraud, estimated to be in excess of £30 million. **Clients:** National Farmers Union.

Palser Grossman Although not historically one of the major players, the firm is seen to be *"coming up."* Has good links with insurers. Also acts for the mid-range corporations, and in the last year has acted for a club against the Welsh Rugby Union, as well as handling a large litigation for The American Furniture Group. **Clients:** The American Furniture Group; TRW inc; Brunswick Construction.

MIDLANDS

LITIGATION (COMMERCIAL) • Midlands
❶ **Pinsent Curtis** Birmingham
Wragge & Co Birmingham
❷ **Eversheds** Birmingham, Nottingham
Martineau Johnson Birmingham
❸ **Browne Jacobson** Nottingham
DLA Birmingham
Hammond Suddards Edge Birmingham
❹ **Freethcartwright** Nottingham
Gateley Wareing Birmingham
Lee Crowder Birmingham
❺ **Bell Lax Litigation** Birmingham
Challinors Lyon Clark West Bromwich
Kent Jones and Done Stoke-on-Trent
Moran & Co Tamworth
Shakespeares Birmingham
Shoosmiths Northampton
The Wilkes Partnership Birmingham

Within each band, firms are listed alphabetically.

Pinsent Curtis A well-thought of team, held to be *"organised, sensible, good-quality and professional."* Undertakes high value work, typically multi-million breach of warranty claims, financial services misselling cases, IT disputes and claims under the Restrictive Trade Practices Act. **Carl Garvie** maintains his strong reputation as a *"switched on and commercially astute lawyer."* Recently acted on a breach of EC directive on free movement of goods case on behalf of Optident Ltd/ Ultradent Products Inc against the Secretary of State for Trade and Industry and the Secretary of State for Health. **Clients:** Axa Sun Life; Alstom UK Ltd; United Kenning Group.

Wragge & Co The firm's commercial litigation team capitalises on its *"size and profile"* with a *"straightforward"* approach that is commended as *"professional."* Thought by some to be *"the quality act in Birmingham,"* the team includes **Andrew Manning Cox**, an *"extremely professional litigator and a strong performer,"* while *"top flight and tenacious"* **Paul Howard** is an admired *"team-player"* and felt to be the nearest thing to a regional *"star."* **Nicola Mumford** is admired by the bar for her *"intelligence"* and *"formidable ability"* in court. Handle a broad spectrum of cases, many of which are characterised by an international flavour. Currently acting in a multi-million pound tracing action involving Swiss, Guernsey and English jurisdictions. **Clients:** BG Transco; Lloyds TSB; British Airways; Department of Trade & Industry.

Eversheds Consolidated traditionally strong areas of practice such as transport, manufacturing and engineering, while expanding newer areas in litigation: IT, Telecoms and Education. **Justin Byrne**, a senior associate, has impressed the London Bar with his ability to *"run a big case expertly."* The Nottingham team, too are described as *"consummate professionals."* Among

LEADING INDIVIDUALS	
❶ HOWARD Paul Wragge & Co	
❷ GARVIE Carl Pinsent Curtis	MANNING COX Andrew Wragge & Co
WILLETTS Jayne Hammond Suddards Edge	
❸ DAVIES Peter Gateley Wareing	ROSE Digby Hammond Suddards Edge
SINGLETON Bernard Gateley Wareing	
❹ BERWICK Guy Freethcartwright	BOWKER Neil DLA
GILLESPIE Michael Gateley Wareing	MUMFORD Nicola Wragge & Co
SPOONER Andrew Nicolas Martineau Johnson	
UP AND COMING	
BYRNE Justin Eversheds	JAMDAR Smita Martineau Johnson

See *Profiles* on page 558

many high-value cases, handled an SSRA dispute with a rail operator for the sum of £65m. **Clients:** NatWest Bank plc; Rolls-Royce plc; Ryder plc; Birmingham International Airport.

Martineau Johnson *"A match for any of the big guns,"* this strongly endorsed team is perceived to be on the up. Admired for their *"consistent rather than aggressive"* style of litigation, as well as for a method of operation which allows easy access to partners, and individual management of cases. The *"excellent"* **Andrew Spooner** makes an *"efficient and fair"* opponent, and the up and coming **Smita Jamdar** appears to have struck all those who have come across her as being *"extremely clever and a highly competent litigator."* Act for multinationals, plcs, universities, local authorities, banks, and wealthy individuals and professionals. **Clients:** Alstom UK Ltd; Britannic Assurance plc; Birmid Holdings Ltd; Equifax.

Browne Jacobson The leading commercial litigation player in the East Midlands is felt to have an *"excellent"* team – *"solid, professional, bright and co-operative."* Popular for referrals, especially for professional negligence cases, the firm clearly maintains its convincing position in the marketplace. **Clients:** Siemens Communications Ltd; Nottingham City Hospital.

DLA *"Tough but professional,"* DLA divides the opinion of the market. Some see the resolutely expanding commercial litigation team as demonstrating *"skill, efficiency and professionalism."* Others take the view that the aggression which characterises the DLA style is *"decidedly unhelpful."* All seem agreed that DLA has yet to *"crack the local market"* as successfully as they have elsewhere in the UK. **Neil Bowker** is highly rated, but possibly *"lacks support."* Have developed a close working relationship with a world-wide supplier of commercial software solutions whom the firm advised on a multi-million pound dispute. **Clients:** DSG Retail (Dixons); Conoco; Kodak.

Hammond Suddards Edge The team is regarded to have *"stayed strong"* despite the losses and uncertainty that have beset the firm. **Digby Rose** is universally considered a *"shrewd and sensible performer"* and **Jayne Willetts**, current president of the Birmingham Law Society, is deemed *"likeable, tough and pioneering."* Count among their clients large plcs, small local companies, professional partnerships and individuals. The last year has been characterised by a marked increase in the number of appeals and applications to the Court of Appeal. **Clients:** Allied Domecq; Wagon plc; Singer Europe.

Freethcartwright A solid outfit which has developed a particular niche in working for the regional textile and clothing industry. **Guy Berwick**'s approach to litigation (with a construction bent) *"still impresses."* Has handled five claims in the past year of between £1.6 and £4.4 million, and offers a long-established risk-management service. **Clients:** British Gas Energy Centres Ltd; Polestar; Helly Hansen.

Gateley Wareing Perceived to have *"invested in commercial litigation,"* and to have invested wisely. The team is perceived as *"young and aggressive"* and includes **Peter Davies**, who is seen to do general commercial work on the back of his construction work. He is even thought by some to be *"Birmingham's best litigator."* *"Reliable"* **Michael Gillespie** *"prepares the best instructions you ever get,"* while **Bernard Singleton** *"is effective and pragmatic."* The team acts for a number of the firm's existing commercial clients. **Clients:** Commercial clients.

Lee Crowder An outfit that is *"characterised by an old-school charm"* fields a *"very able"* team that brings in *"good commercial cases for a smaller firm."* Now employs two barristers in its new in-house advocacy unit. Handles work for a variety of international, national and regional commercial clients. **Clients:** Euromoney Publications; William M. Mercer; MPO; Wesleyan Financial Services.

Bell Lax Litigation An outfit which is *"capable of inspiring fear"* in its opponents. However, market opinion is that the team can be erratic – they are *"either brilliant or bored."* Their clients, gathered from all over the country, consist inter alia of owner-managed businesses, individuals and some large plcs. **Clients:** Owner-managed businesses.

Challinors Lyon Clark An expanding department, reputed to act for a surprisingly high calibre of clients for its size. Many remarked that for a small firm it *"handles some extraordinarily big cases."* Acts for a large range of medium sized local industrial and engineering companies, and espouses an objective of resolving disputes at the earliest possible stage. Recently completed defence of claim worth £6.23 million for a large local company. **Clients:** Local plcs.

Kent Jones and Done This firm maintains its robust reputation for *"perfect efficiency,"* and is noted for acting in a variety of areas including environment, property and planning. **Clients:** JCB Group.

Moran & Co New to the rankings this year, the firm has been widely recommended by the market, especially for work with a financial bias. Thought to deal with *"big work for a small firm,"* their litigation skills are felt in some quarters to *"rival the best."* **Clients:** Financial institutions.

Shakespeares Acknowledged to have a healthy profile for commercial litigation, the team is a well-regarded local player. The firm is particularly commended for banking litigation. Handled a Restraint of Trade in European Competition Law matter which involved goods worth millions of pounds. **Clients:** Ash & Lacy plc; University of Central England; Concentric plc.

Shoosmiths Widely perceived as a broad practice handling high-volume work of a financial bias, the commercial litigation group has a developed niche in banking and building society work. Act for national and international clients, including a sizeable number of local manufacturers. **Clients:** NatWest Bank plc; TK Maxx; Radstone Technology plc; Games Workshop.

The Wilkes Partnership The firm has expanded significantly, having recently taken over Blunts, a specialist debt recovery firm, and, bringing in a number of new clients. **Clients:** ATS Midlands; Avis Rentacar; EMI Records; Bank Of Ireland.

EAST ANGLIA

LITIGATION (COMMERCIAL) • East Anglia
❶ **Eversheds** Ipswich, Norwich
Mills & Reeve Cambridge, Norwich
❷ **Hewitson Becke + Shaw** Cambridge
Taylor Vinters Cambridge
❸ **Greenwoods** Peterborough
Prettys Ipswich
❹ **Birketts** Ipswich

LEADING INDIVIDUALS	
❶ **CALLAGHAN Edward** Mills & Reeve	**ROESSLER Max** Eversheds
❷ **HOPKINS Dominic** Hewitson Becke + Shaw	**PERROTT Edward** Taylor Vinters
❸ **BLAKE Peter** Prettys	

Within each band, firms are listed alphabetically. *See **Profiles** on page 558*

Eversheds Highly-rated in all their East Anglian offices, the firm goes from strength to strength. While it is perceived that *"most of the work they do isn't regional work,"* their profile in the region itself remains high, with some commentators seeing them as *"marginally ahead of the rest."* Much of the caseload has an international flavour. **Max Roessler**, team leader in the Norwich office, is considered to be *"the name at Eversheds"* and is widely recognised as a *"talented all-rounder"* for whom people have a *"lot of time."* Acted for international freight forwarders in a multi-million pound, multi-partner, multi-jurisdictional breach of contract/conversion/bailment case. **Clients:** Ransomes plc; Argentaria; Zurich Municipal; Fortis Aviation Group Ltd.

Mills & Reeve Seen to handle *"the lion's share"* of the region's commercial litigation work, the firm is clearly Eversheds' *"main competitor"* in the region. **Edward Callaghan** not only has a *"good team working for him"* but comes highly-recommended himself as a *"very relaxed, business-like lawyer."* Handles regional corporate work, often for hi-tech and bio-tech companies, and has a growing portfolio of foreign clients. **Clients:** Neopost; Cooper Roller Bearings; Fenner plc; UCLES.

Hewitson Becke + Shawe Described by competitors as *"business-like in their approach and easy to deal with"* and by the bar as *"providing quality instructions,"* they are widely held to have a *"good reputation and a good client base."* They are also seen by some as *"first choice"* in the event of a conflict. **Dominic Hopkins**, new to the rankings, is rated, notably by the London bar, who describe him as *"a fantastic general commercial litigator of a City standard."* **Clients:** IT companies; regional plcs.

Taylor Vinters **Edward Perrott** attracts wide praise as an *"all-round commercial litigator"* and *"has excellent judgement."* The team continues to have a strong reputation for technology and engineering-based litigation. Successfully acted for Benfica Football Club against its former manager, Graeme Souness, who had obtained a freezing order worth £1.8m over Benfica's British assets. **Clients:** Benfica football Club; University of Cambridge; Philips Electronics UK Ltd.

Greenwoods Felt to be the most significant of the Peterborough firms for commercial litigation. Works for a range of clients including newspaper and magazine publishers, retail distributors and manufacturers in various fields. In the last year, the team has advised on architects' negligence, solicitors negligence, agricultural contracts, manufacturing and legal contracts. **Clients:** Farmers; local plcs.

Prettys The team is led by the respected **Peter Blake** who is regarded as a *"safe pair of hands."* The noticeable progress observed last year, is felt to have *"levelled off"* this year, although the team itself has seen a growth in its IT and ADR work. Clients consist of owner-managed businesses and the local subsidiaries of foreign-owned businesses. The firm maintains its niche in transport and shipping related work. **Clients:** Transport and shipping companies.

Birketts The other leading firm in Ipswich for commercial litigation, Birketts is thought of as a *"solid outfit."* Has handled some high-profile cases in the last year, including representing former England manager Bobby Robson in connection with a claim against FC Porto for unpaid remuneration. **Clients:** Regional clients including brewers; manufacturers; building societies and local authorities.

NORTH WEST

LITIGATION (COMMERCIAL) • North West
❶ **Addleshaw Booth & Co** Manchester
DLA Liverpool, Manchester
Eversheds Manchester
❷ **Cobbetts** Manchester
Halliwell Landau Manchester
❸ **Hammond Suddards Edge** Manchester
❹ **Hill Dickinson** Liverpool
❺ **Berg & Co** Manchester
Berrymans Lace Mawer Liverpool, Manchester
Brabner Holden Banks Wilson Liverpool, Preston
Chaffe Street Manchester
Davies Wallis Foyster Liverpool
❻ **Cuff Roberts** Liverpool
Kershaw Abbott Manchester
Mace & Jones Liverpool
Pannone & Partners Manchester
Rowe & Cohen Manchester
Wacks Caller Manchester
Weightmans Liverpool

Within each band, firms are listed alphabetically.

Addleshaw Booth & Co The practice holds its position well among the upper echelon of leading firms. Powered by a *"fundamentally great corporate client base,"* this is the engine that drives the practice, although this competitive advantage is supported by a clutch of individual litigators, who *"work effectively in teams, with lots of hands-on input."* Described as a *"traditionalist,"* **John Gatenby** is *"extremely analytical, considers all the points,"* and picked up recommendations at a national and regional level. Specialises in high-value cross-border transactional disputes with an emphasis on ADR and mediation. Department head **John Gosling** *("sensible and easy to deal with")* is noted for his general commercial litigation practice, embracing a degree of professional negligence and insurance work. Formerly of Slater Heelis, Australian lawyer **Mark Amsden** was a frequent recommendation among the local legal fraternity. Exhibiting a *"positive and direct approach,"* he's *"incisive, popular with clients"* and *"knows how to take the heat out of litigation."* The firm has a broad litigation practice with particular expertise in computer/IT and construction disputes. Financial services and pensions litigation remain additional core areas of strength. Highlight of the last year was the successful outcome of a 6 week High Court trial in favour of client Derbyshire College. Involved defending a £3m claim by Link Organisation plc, concerning the franchising of educational provision. **Clients:** Airtours plc; Tyco International Inc; ADT Fire And Security plc; Wedgwood plc.

LEADING INDIVIDUALS	
❶ **CLAVELL-BATE Michael** Eversheds	**HARRIS Andrew** DLA
MATTISON Mark Eversheds	**ROPER Robert** Cobbetts
THOMAS Paul Halliwell Landau	
❷ **GATENBY John** Addleshaw Booth & Co	**GOLD Antony** Eversheds
GOSLING John Addleshaw Booth & Co	**SORRELL Christopher** Wacks Caller
WINTERBURN Anthony DLA	
❸ **AMSDEN Mark** Addleshaw Booth & Co	**GRAY David** DLA
KERSHAW Anne Kershaw Abbott	**KHAN Charles** Berg & Co
MEREDITH Ian Hammond Suddards Edge	**TRANTER Ian** Chaffe Street
❹ **BLAKEMORE Craig** Mace & Jones	**GAUL Patrick** Weightmans
MANLEY Mark Brabner Holden Banks Wilson	
RAWLINSON David Cuff Roberts	**SMALL Graham** Rowe & Cohen
WHITTELL Mark Cobbetts	

See *Profiles* on page 558

DLA *"A continuing force putting real effort into the team."* Roundly praised this year, a reflection of a high quality team, involvement in substantial disputes and a tangible litigation ethos which is readily identifiable externally. Active in a number of large corporate, shareholder, company law and civil fraud disputes. The practice is subject to an increasing synergy between the regulatory and commercial litigation functions. **Andrew Harris** is *"great at taking on big detailed cases with lots of factual considerations."* Considered *"cerebral"* in his approach, he nevertheless has a *"firmness and persistence – with all the force of inevitability,"* and a professional judgement well-respected by peers. *"Vigorous"* **Tony Winterburn** also scored highly. He has *"emerged to make a real name for himself,"* acting for a rich mix of local businesses, wealthy entrepreneurs and football clubs. Now the national head of commercial litigation, **David Gray** is still visible, and specialises in ADR, arbitration and breach of confidence matters. Acting for Brother Int. Europe in a pan-European product recall of 160,000 potentially defective sewing machines. Currently immersed in a 16 week trial surrounding an engineering process plant dispute. **Clients:** BWB; British Waterways; Brother Int. Europe; Cable & Wireless Communications.

Eversheds In keeping with the wider trend of toning down the stress on aggressive litigation, Eversheds' robust reputation appears to have moderated with increasing attention paid to dispute resolution and mediation. With three ranked individuals, they sit comfortably in the upper reaches of the ranks. A mainstream reputation in broad commercial litigation is beefed up with expertise in contentious construction, IP and defamation. The latter is a feature of **Michael Clavell-Bate**'s practice. Held in the highest regard by other lawyers, this *"modern, smooth and urbane"* solicitor is *"really on top of the commercial issues"* and *"seems to pull in a lot of work."* An *"efficient and polished litigator,"* **Mark Mattison** still knows how to *"beat the hell out of the other guy – he's technically brilliant."* He has a construction bias to his practice, while IP/commercial litigator **Antony Gold**, the *"old campaigner"* is *"still as strong as ever"* and *"knows how to give an opponent a hard time."* Recent success (February 2000) was Arrow Nominees v Blackledge, the department's largest case in recent years. It involved a series of multi-party claims (passing off and unfair prejudice petitions) relating to a national chain of shops. Acted for a large food manufacturer in relation to an allegation of breach of contract for failure to meet food production requirements. The claim was valued in excess of £10m. **Clients:** North West Water Ltd; BAe Systems; GR & MM Blackledge plc.

Cobbetts The practice is not felt to be a threat to the pre-eminence of the leading trio, yet is *"individually impressive"* with several litigators *"positioned at the forefront."* Performance this year rested primarily on the reputation of **Robert Roper**, who commanded a sizeable chunk of support from the market. He is *"customer friendly, and clients invariably like him."* His *"downright technical knowledge"* is also pinpointed – *"he really knows the minutiae of the law."* Felt to be *"creative and constructive in his approach to finding solutions,"* he embodies the new style litigator who *"always talks but never falls out."* Caseload includes a number of IT and IP cases in addition to mainstream commercial disputes. Head of department **Mark Whittell** is *"dynamic in his approach"* and *"inspires faith in his clients."* Felt to demand high standards all-round, he's *"approachable, sensible and won't bail out on his clients."* He mixes insolvency into the commercial litigation caseload, while firm-wide, expertise covers property litigation, banking, defendant insurance and professional negligence. Many clients are drawn from the North West region, such as local co-operatives, banks and plcs. Currently involved in a 6-week case involving allegations of a cartel in the motor dealership industry not supplying parts to certain wholesalers. **Clients:** Royal Bank of Scotland; Lookers; Cheshire Building Society; Royal & Sun Alliance Insurance.

Halliwell Landau Despite the trend towards mediation, the firm's litigation department retains its image as robust and adversarial, with individual litigators to match, albeit one that always provides a *"slick professional performance."* Head litigator **Paul Thomas** is felt to be chiefly responsible for having raised the profile of the department. An *"unflamboyant, quiet type,"* he's seen as a *"tough negotiator who's prepared to take on a case and get on with it."* The firm's client base comprises almost an equal split between developer/entrepreneurs and institutional clients. Areas of special expertise include professional negligence and partnership. Highlights include a major piece of strategic litigation for Liverpool City Council concerning a £200 million site. Reported cases include Whitbread plc v UCB Corporate Services Ltd. **Clients:** AMEC Developments; Kwik Fit (GB) Ltd; Reebok; Time Computers.

Hammond Suddards Edge Newly merged firm has the benefit of a Midlands presence and expanded London office. In Manchester, they fit into the general pattern of a greater move towards mediation. *"Their approach is now more conciliatory – there's less of the red meat litigation of old."* The firm's *"no-nonsense businesslike approach"* is personified by **Ian Meredith** who enters the tables this year. He is noted for *"impressive organisational skills,"* and an ability *"to really get his team up and running well."* The mainstream commercial dispute practice acts for a number of corporates and banks, while the litigation group also takes in fraud, defamation, media, sports and environmental litigation. Key recent case was a multi-million commercial fraud recovery action involving international asset tracings with search and worldwide freezing orders, and supporting proceedings in a range of other jurisdictions. Resolved a number of high profile disputes through the use of ADR techniques. **Clients:** Gencor Industries Inc; Ultraframe plc; ICI plc; BASF plc.

Hill Dickinson The litigation capabilities of the firm continue to be prolific. Market commentary still focuses on insurance (largely defendant), and to a lesser degree, admiralty and construction litigation. There are also small amounts of banking, property litigation, insolvency and shareholder disputes. Have recently acted both for and against a number of banks. Retained on the Barclays Bank panel to act for them in business debt and recovery disputes. A separate insurance litigation department handles a large number of claims. **Clients:** Barclays Bank; Insurance companies.

Berg & Co A four partner team combine to produce a well-regarded unit, although **Charles Khan** continues to enjoy the most acknowledged market reputation. Well respected by fellow layers, he is felt to *"suit the small firm environment."* He is rated as a *"good tactician"* and possesses a *"real poker-face."* Aside from commercial contractual disputes, his practice comprises insolvency and professional negligence work. **Clients:** A broad spread client base includes textile manufacturers and IT/computer companies.

Berrymans Lace Mawer Most commonly viewed by the market as an insurance defence practice, there is nevertheless capability to handle other commercial disputes at both the North West offices. The Manchester based partner has been described as offering a *"client friendly, common sense approach."* Niche strengths include partner disputes and minority shareholder disputes. Also handle breaches of confidentiality, contentious IP and professional negligence (surveyors and accountants.) Highlight of the year (Liverpool) was a defamation action involving members of the Welsh Conservative party. **Clients:** NWF plc; BPB Paperboard Ltd; Abbey Holdings; MKD Holdings.

Brabner Holden Banks Wilson Epitomised by the defamation credentials of *"great litigator"* **Mark Manley**, this compact unit is held in high esteem by north-west solicitors. Inevitably, defamation disputes constitute the core slice of the practice, although employment, property, professional negligence and debt recovery all feature to a lesser extent. The general commercial caseload includes copyright, injunction and IP work. Currently acting for a radio station in a libel action brought by eleven claimants. Also involved in a £11.5 million breach of warranty claim. Defended a large plc client in a trading standards prosecution regarding allegedly unsafe goods involving issues of European law and safety standards. **Clients:** Business and Community Services Ltd; Stoves plc; Riverside Housing Association.

Chaffe Street *"Certainly a force,"* albeit within the category of a *"smaller but attractive niche practice."* Several partners were recommended for their litigation efforts, including **Ian Tranter**, who is seen only occasionally by the market, but is still widely respected. Characteristically, banking and insolvency litigation typify the core of the work. The practice has a good spread of corporate clients and financial institutions for whom it acts on a range of contentious matters. **Clients:** Tuchenhagen UK Ltd; Veka plc; Boss Group Ltd; Recticel.

Davies Wallis Foyster The Liverpool office picked up a number of recommendations, particularly from the local bar, although there is a lingering hint in some quarters that they are living off a historical reputation, particularly in view of Kit Sorrell's departure to Wacks Caller in Manchester. However, the corporate advisory department is felt to be adequate to generate a good throughput of litigation work. Several of the lawyers are *"prepared to take tough negotiated stances"* but *"willing to look at other ways of resolving disputes."* Across the spread of litigation, conduct cases in asset finance, banking, construction, IP and professional negligence. Acted for a finance company in a substantial claim against an insurance company for breach of trust. Also defending a company from a £1.2 million claim relating to an alleged unlawful dividend. **Clients:** Acrol Ltd; Allied Domecq; Lloyds TSB Bank; Van Leer (UK) Ltd.

Cuff Roberts *"Always do a decent job."* The four-partner litigation department touches on the insolvency and debt recovery practices. This broad-ranging practice also conducts a number of construction and partnership disputes. **David Rawlinson** is new to this year's list. He was singled out by the bar in particular for his *"thorough handling of big cases."* Also handle employment, property litigation and professional negligence cases. **Clients:** The Littlewoods Organisation; Littlewoods Pools; Johnson Cleaners UK Ltd.

Kershaw Abbott A small commercial practice who are *"really targeting commercial litigation."* The practice makes an appearance in this year's list, largely because of *"fearsome litigator"* **Anne Kershaw**'s high reputation locally as a *"worthy opponent."* The broad composition of the practice extends to insurance, construction, professional indemnity and partnership disputes. The practice is considered a prime choice of many solicitors for professional disputes. Client base stretches from owner managed businesses to national plcs. **Clients:** Railtrack plc; Cruden Construction plc.

Mace & Jones This medium sized firm has a spread of north-west offices and picked up a number of endorsements for its commercial litigation practice, which overlaps insolvency to a considerable degree. Also instructed in engineering, IT, IP, professional negligence and shareholder disputes. **Craig Blakemore**, head of commercial litigation and insolvency in the Liverpool office, was singled out by interviewees. He was described as *"level headed and streetwise with good judgement."* Assisted in the liquidation of the Nigerian National Shipping Line, and advised the Administrative Receivers of Biltons Tableware Limited, Stoke. **Clients:** Regularly instructed by 'big five' accountancy firms, as well as mid and smaller firms.

Pannone & Partners The team collectively are felt to bring *"lots of experience and real focus,"* while not having the benefit of a corporate client base to rival their cross-town competitors. The department covers property disputes, insolvency, banking, IP and cross-border litigation. Notable cases include a multi-million pound dispute over the ownership of a world-famous antique/art collection. Acting for Jennings Brothers (Lake District Brewers) in a dispute over ownership of stock. Acting for a household company in a large sum claim dealt with using ADR. **Clients:** Granada Group; Texaco; Jennings Brothers plc.

Rowe & Cohen Newly recommended **Graham Small** *"runs a good little litigation practice"* and is *"really making an impression there."* In addition to some claimant/personal injury, insurance and a well known reputation for commercial legal expense work, the solidity of the commercial department is felt to stand the practice in good stead. The practice is involved in an increasing number of international commercial disputes including a multi-million pound US fraud case, and is advising a Dubai-based client over a dispute in Yemen. **Clients:** Small and medium sized enterprises; wealthy businessmen; trade/professional associations.

Wacks Caller Boosted by the arrival of **Kit Sorrell** from Davies Wallis Foyster, who in the last six months, *"has really kicked some life into the practice and moved it forward a lot."* Considered an *"aggressive litigator but amazingly streetwise – he doesn't know all the legal analysis, but knows how to get good results."* Niche strengths here include multi-jurisdictional commercial disputes, property litigation and judicial review. Notable highlights include a £6 million commercial fraud involving proceedings in England and abroad. Also acting for North West Properties Ltd in action involving a £5 million commercial shopping development at Bury. **Clients:** Total Fitness UK Ltd; Anglo International Holdings Ltd; Liverpool and Lancashire Properties Ltd; John Smiths Brewers Ltd.

Weightmans The practice is felt to be skewed primarily towards insurance litigation, and this constitutes as much as 80% of all contentious work. Some therefore have questioned the team's ability to handle broader general commercial litigation, although disputes in the employment, leisure, brewing and licensing practices are increasing. **Patrick Gaul**, best known for his professional negligence work, is felt to be *"particularly good."* Acting for Hoover in a major IP litigation against Dyson. **Clients:** Major brewers; manufacturers.

YORKSHIRE

Addleshaw Booth & Co The team is felt to adopt a lower-key stance than some of its tougher Leeds counterparts, but can rely on some fine individual reputations and its perennially healthy corporate client base. **Simon Kamstra** *("a commercial litigation generalist in the truest sense")* is the star of the show. He *"impresses with his knowledge of obscure areas of law,"* and is considered *"a cunning strategist."* Not aggressive, he *"holds his own and fights his corner but can still reason well."* Acts for many of the firm's corporate, banking and building society clients in resolving contractual disputes. The experienced **Peter Cherry** handles a number of litigation and arbitration matters. Recently dealt with two disputes in the opencast mining industry on behalf of a contractor, worth £12 million and £6.5 million respectively. Also has an active defamation and media/television practice. The practice brings additional specialist expertise in financial services litigation, pensions, pharmaceuticals, minerals and railways. Acted successfully in judicial review proceedings for Asda against Bromsgrove District Council in a challenge to planning decisions threatening a £30 million turnover superstore. Also acted for Leek Building Society in connection with a hostile takeover bid by Murray Finan-

LITIGATION (COMMERCIAL) • Yorkshire
❶ **Addleshaw Booth & Co** Leeds
DLA Leeds
Eversheds Leeds
Hammond Suddards Edge Leeds
Pinsent Curtis Leeds
❷ **Irwin Mitchell** Sheffield
Walker Morris Leeds
❸ **Gordons Cranswick Solicitors** Bradford, Leeds
Lupton Fawcett Leeds
Rollit Farrell & Bladon Hull
❹ **Andrew M. Jackson & Co** Hull
Beachcroft Wansbroughs Leeds
Ford & Warren Leeds
Keeble Hawson Leeds, Sheffield
❺ **Brooke North** Leeds
Gosschalks Hull
Russell & Creswick Sheffield

LEADING INDIVIDUALS	
❶ **HEAPS John** Eversheds	**KAMSTRA Simon** Addleshaw Booth & Co
SINCLAIR Jonathan Eversheds	
❷ **CHAPMAN Stuart** Pinsent Curtis	**CROSSLEY Peter** Hammond Suddards Edge
GILBERT Ralph Rollit Farrell & Bladon	**KISSACK Nigel** Pinsent Curtis
STONE Paul DLA	
❸ **CHERRY Peter** Addleshaw Booth & Co	**CROSSE Damian** DLA
DAVIES Gwendoline Walker Morris	**EVANS Hugh** DLA
HAWKSWELL Jonathan Pinsent Curtis	
❹ **ROTHWELL Charles** Keeble Hawson	**SMITH Hugh** Andrew M. Jackson & Co
WOOD Ashley Russell & Creswick	

Within each band, firms are listed alphabetically. *See* ***Profiles*** *on page 558*

Figures unavailable at time of going to press.

cial. **Clients:** Miller Group Ltd; CGU Life Services; GEHE UK plc; Yorkshire Group plc.

DLA A large team with many ex-City lawyers is felt to be expanding its litigation profile and building on its *"red-meat"* litigation ethos of the 90s, while tempering it with a more conciliatory post-Woolf approach – *"they're more in tune with the market."* Leeds head of litigation, ex-Clifford Chance **Paul Stone** was widely recommended. Thoroughness and tenacity are his characteristic hallmarks, although *"he's laid back with it."* The London bar rated him *"top drawer in his own particular way – he's an all round thinker who makes time to cover everything."* Specialises in corporate and shareholder disputes, cross-border litigation and acts for a number of the firm's media clients in defamation work. Formerly at Herbert Smith, **Damian Crosse** has a *"commercial attitude that isn't too legalistic."* Conducts a number of IT/e-commerce, telecoms and media related cases. On the banking/finance litigation side, **Hugh Evans** is *"felt to run a good team."* Successfully defended Yorkshire Post Newspapers from a defamation claim brought by GKR Karate Ltd. Acting for Newcastle United plc in a claim by UEFA Sports GmbH (German/European television broadcaster) in a dispute over broadcasting rights for UEFA Cup games. **Clients:** Beazer Group plc; Brooke Group plc; L'Oréal (UK) Ltd; Shepherd Construction.

Eversheds *"Will never let you down."* The team is sizeable and runs the gamut of litigation from corporate and shareholder matters to IT and negligence disputes. Large single quality pieces of litigation are best exemplified by involvement in the Bloody Sunday Inquiry, although there are suggestions that the kudos and profile has been a mixed blessing, inevitably sucking in resources deployed elsewhere. Gary Pellow, ranked last year, has been a notable casualty of almost full-time involvement in the case. National head of litigation **John Heaps** is a *"brilliant strategic manager"* and noted for his experience in handling the weighty pieces of litigation. He is seen as *"one of the best litigators in Leeds."* **Jonathan Sinclair** is younger and has a greater emphasis on dispute management and early case assessment. A *"thorough technician,"* he would *"always be recommended for his commercial nous"* and *"has clearly benefited from his London training."* Major case handled was on behalf of Terra Industries Inc, the defendants in a substantial product liability case involving the carbonated drinks industry (lead case brought by Coca-Cola.) Involved in further proceedings against leading drugs manufacturers in connection with ASDA's ongoing campaign in relation to OTC pharmaceuticals. **Clients:** Terra Industries Inc; DuPont; BBA

Hammond Suddards Edge Seen to offer a collectively strong pool of litigators, who are *"well-trained and sharp, if sometimes slightly aggressive."* The *"effective and no-nonsense"* **Peter Crossley** *("an out-and-out litigator")* commands a healthy body of admirers. Key areas of activity for the commercial dispute resolution practice are contractual warranty claims, shareholder and director disputes, and increasing amounts of fraud and pre-trial injunction work. Also conduct large scale recovery work and professional negligence cases for institutional lender clients. Successfully advised NatWest Home Loans in a managed mediation against the Solicitors Indemnity Fund (SIF) involving claims for millions and over 200 firms of solicitors. This is the largest mediation ever handled against SIF. Handled a large multi-million pound case for Quantica plc, involving the obtaining and execution of two search and seizure orders, resulting in the recovery of the client's losses. Acting for Cott Beverages Ltd in a multi-party claim arising out of contaminated carbon dioxide in soft drinks. **Clients:** Dimon Incorporated; Tontarelli SpA; Gillette Company; Yorkshire Electricity Group plc.

Pinsent Curtis Widespread commendation of a number of individual lawyers saw the practice edge into the upper bracket this year. Market consensus supports the view that the practice has regained lost ground conceded over the last few years and is *"now well and truly back as a contender."* Foremost is *"active coal-face litigator"* **Stuart Chapman** who is a *"straightforward operator, very sensible on the general commercial side"* and a *"real mover."* Conducts a number of IT disputes in addition to a general commercial practice. National head of litigation, **Nigel Kissack**, is less visible given managerial commitments but is acknowledged by the market as a quality litigator. **Jonathan Hawkswell** *("a quick, astute lawyer")* picked up several endorsements from the London bar. Mixing a general commercial litigation practice with construction and IP disputes, he is *"diligent and hard-working," "extremely commercial,"* and *"always has the client's best interests at heart."* Key strengths include expertise in the retail sector, IT disputes, regulatory work, the food industry and competition issues. A large number of multi-million pound IT disputes have been handled in the last year, including advice given to some major retailers in respect of highly-publicised web-site retailing issues. Involved in a big-sum settlement of an exclusive supplier for the unlawful termination of a supply contract by a national retailer. **Clients:** Tesco; Eurocopy plc; Maxima Information Group plc; MD Foods plc.

Irwin Mitchell *"Making more of a noise these days"* and still acknowledged by the premium Leeds market as a significant player. Rated across a wide range of disputes from smaller, lower value legal aid cases to larger oil and gas disputes. The Leeds and Sheffield offices are becoming increasingly fused and collectively offer additional expertise in mergers and acquisitions, IT disputes, warranty and shareholder disputes, property litigation and legal expense insurance, often serving Yorkshire based medium sized plcs. Partners in both offices were mentioned by the larger firms as more than capable of managing weighty pieces of litigation, and as recipients of referred work. Highlight case was reported in the Court of Appeal, Parkes v Esso Petroleum (acting for Esso.) Also successfully recovered £2.3 million for the claimant in Strongforth Investments Ltd and Others v Probus Estates plc. **Clients:** Harveys Furnishings plc; PanCredit Systems Limited; AXA Sun Life Services; Telewest.

Walker Morris The practice is not felt to be quite the same force in general commercial litigation as the larger Leeds commercial firms, but is felt to compete more forcefully in insolvency and property litigation. **Gwen Davies** has *"always maintained a historically high reputation,"* although has not been so visible this year. The team includes partners with specialisms in media and construction matters. Successfully represented Swallow Hotels Ltd in their case against the Commissioners of the Inland Revenue over the rates of applicable stamp duty. Acting for a major event company in a £600,000 dispute involving one of the leading sporting events. **Clients:** Acting for the plaintiff companies in receivership, in connection with the reported case of On Demand Information plc v Michael Gerson (Finance) plc.

Gordons Cranswick This newly merged pan-Yorkshire unit scored several recommendations for its work on sizeable pieces of litigation. The principal commercial litigators will be based in the Leeds office, where the firm is attempting to gain an increasing foothold in the local market. The lion's share of the client base comprises regionally based companies in industries such as textiles, retailing and technology. Also engage in a number of property and construction disputes. **Clients:** William Morris Supermarkets plc; Peter Blacks; motor dealerships; menswear chain.

Lupton Fawcett Well-rated by medium-tier peers in Leeds, the practice is *"smooth and well-run."* Felt to present the *"next choice down"* for local commercial clients seeking a lower cost quality alternative to the city's big guns. Collectively offer partners providing expertise in engineering disputes, IP/e-commerce, banking, property, debt and professional negligence. A sizeable contentious insurance practice completes the litigation picture. The practice has bought heavily into Woolf with several mediators on board. Recently processed a £2.5 million dispute through the courts. **Clients:** T & N Federal Mogul; High Street banks and building societies; engineering and manufacturing companies.

Rollit Farrell & Bladon Of a number of commercial litigation partners, **Ralph Gilbert** managed to leave a lasting impression on a number of interviewees, both solicitors and barristers who drew attention to his *"extremely capable and through litigation style."* He *"thinks heavily about cases, doesn't just manage them but gets into the nitty-gritty."* His practice embraces a degree of insolvency work while colleagues tackle construction litigation, property, IP and product liability. The practice largely services the contentious needs of its regional commercial client base, acting in most cases for the defendant companies. Recently involved in a major construction law case. **Clients:** Cranswick plc; Eagle Star; Kingston Communications (Hull) plc; Marr Foods Ltd.

Andrew M. Jackson & Co The practice is felt to be driven by **Hugh Smith** who has *"built a good team,"* and is considered a *"solid, slightly aggressive litigator."* Perceived to handle higher-value lower volume disputes. Commercial property, partnership, professional negligence and IP are all characteristics of the litigation practice. Recently acted in a highly contentious matter on behalf of a foreign manufacturing company supplying machinery to Africa. Also involved in a complex building arbitration, and another contentious construction matter in relation to a dispute over subcontracted work. **Clients:** De Smet; MFI; Willoughby Holiday Homes.

Beachcroft Wansbroughs Not felt to have the breadth to be a considered a definitive general litigation practice, but continues to be rated for its insurance and professional indemnity litigation, where are a number of partners operate. The nature of the contractual disputes handled frequently involves insurers having paid out and seeking to recover costs. **Clients:** Large numbers of major corporate insurers.

Ford & Warren Another Leeds practice rated by the bigger boys for smaller and medium sized regional claims. *"Great for localised clients – a good reference point after the top tier firms."* Contentious expertise spans contractual disputes in construction, property, professional negligence, insolvency and debt recovery. Niche areas include brewery leasing and transport dispute. **Clients:** Transport companies.

Keeble Hawson New entrant on the back of some positive endorsements from interviewees, including the regional bar. A two-office Yorkshire structure contains eight litigators. Both units run a general commercial litigation caseload with additional emphasis on construction, property, IT and IP litigation. Practice is felt to possess a *"youngish, sensible attitude to litigation."* Partner **Charles Rothwell** is *"switched on and detailed."* He *"maps out courses of action"* and *"thinks both conceptually and practically."* Act predominantly for Yorkshire-based companies, both defendant and claimant. Recently handled a number of search orders (formerly Anton Pillers) and passing-off actions. **Clients:** Several regional based companies in the building, demolition and retail industries.

Brooke North *"A down to earth litigation practice with good judgement."* Seen to provide an economical and reliable alternative to Leeds' larger and more expensive firms. Handle the spread of commercial litigation with emphasis on ADR. Construction litigation, property, IP and insolvency disputes are particular areas of expertise. Recent reported cases include Rowe v Glenister and Dennison v Krasner. **Clients:** Evans Of Leeds; Bank of Ireland; Linpac Containers Ltd; Illingworth Morris Ltd.

Gosschalks Another of Hull's leading contenders, the practice has moved on from its high street roots and now acts for a number of local commercial clients, both for defendant and claimant. Among a clutch of litigators, *"there is no one there that is less than competent."* Areas of core expertise are clinical negligence and insurance defendant litigation. Also serve a number of national clients, many in the leisure/licensing industry, where contentious property matters have been a significant feature. Acted on Clarke v Cato (House of Lords), an insurance defence case. **Clients:** Privilege; Direct Line; Groupama; CGU.

Russell & Creswick Newly recommended this year as *"a small but competent litigation practice."* Partner **Ashley Wood** is *"proactive, knows the procedures and how to achieve the right results for the client."* His general commercial litigation bias is towards insolvency, while two of the partners handle construction and employment disputes. Acting for TW Ward Machinery Ltd in a Court of Appeal case concerning an unsuccessful winding-up petition. **Clients:** Ballast Wilshire; Billington Structures; Kiveton Park Steel & Wireworks Ltd.

NORTH EAST

Eversheds Felt to have *"attracted a lot of work from the local area"* as well as the inevitable spread of national corporate and commercial clients drawn nationally. A number of *"good, hard, intelligent litigators"* were recommended. Newcastle insurance firm Linsley & Mortimer were subsumed into the Eversheds' empire in May 2000 adding another potent string to their bow. Handle a variety of contractual disputes including notable IP, product liability and cross-jurisdictional matters. Involved in a multi-million pound dispute arising from the termination of a European Agency agreement. Recently involved in several contentious intellectual property matters including advice given in relation to cross-jurisdictional questions of ownership, copyright infringement and passing off. **Clients:** Northumbrian Water Ltd; PII plc; Invensys plc.

Ward Hadaway The litigation practice continues to be highly ranked on account of two singled-out individuals **Bob Elliott** is *"switched-on, not superman, but a solid reliable and trustworthy lawyer."* His approach was described as *"more academic"* by one observer, who paid tribute to his *"firm, solid negotiation ability."* Felt to have most interest and expertise in IP and IT contentious matters. **Ian Collinson** also received praise for his handling of some big local disputes. Seen as well established and influential locally, the firm is considered to have a *"more regionally based clientele, but they've built themselves up well."* The practice covers most litigation bases including insurance, professional negligence, property, banking, IP and fraud. Key cases include a professional negligence claim on behalf of Pride Valley Foods Limited claiming sums in excess of £10 million. Also acting for Able UK

LITIGATION (COMMERCIAL) • North East
❶ **Eversheds** Newcastle upon Tyne
Ward Hadaway Newcastle upon Tyne
❷ **Dickinson Dees** Newcastle upon Tyne
Watson Burton Newcastle upon Tyne
❸ **Hay & Kilner** Newcastle upon Tyne
Robert Muckle Newcastle upon Tyne

LEADING INDIVIDUALS	
❶ **ELLIOTT Robert** Ward Hadaway	
❷ **COLLINSON Ian** Ward Hadaway	**SOLOMAN Martin** Hay & Kilner

Within each band, firms are listed alphabetically. *See **Profiles** on page 558*

Ltd in a £25 million injunctive relief and damages claim, relating to chemical leaks affecting Able's property. **Clients:** Safeway Stores plc; Pride Valley Foods; Able UK.

Dickinson Dees Has the luxury of a substantial corporate client base which generates a steady supply of business disputes. A number of partners were mentioned for their quality reputations this year, particularly in the insolvency field and general contractual claims. *"They know where they're going and target the end result well."* The client base tends to be more national and internationally focused than their north-east competitors. Increasing emphasis on problem avoidance and dispute mediation. Involved in various claims under the commercial agents regulations. Major profile case is acting on behalf of Thames Trains in relation to the Paddington rail crash disaster. **Clients:** Transport, utility and IT companies.

Watson Burton Primarily recommended for their well known contentious construction practice, there is a sense from the market that *"there are more strings to their bow."* The firm is also noted for shareholder and other commercial disputes. Insurance, engineering, banking, professional negligence and employment round out the bigger litigation picture. As much as half the practice falls under the banner of commercial litigation. The overall flavour and ethos of the practice is felt to be *"slightly robust, but on the right side of aggressive."* Acting for a Brazilian client, Odebrecht, in a £25 million dispute concerning an allegedly defective oil field. **Clients:** Co-operative Wholesale Society; Premier Direct Group; AAF/McQuay; local banks and accountants.

Hay & Kilner **Martin Soloman** is still acknowledged by the market as an accomplished litigator, but is increasingly seen on insurance litigation work, the area of law with which the practice continues to be most closely associated. He also conducts construction, IP and media related disputes. The practice has an insurer led institutional client base but acts increasingly for a range of regional commercial entities, owner managed businesses and partnerships. Have handled a number of commercial judicial reviews in the last year. Acted in a claim by a landowner that tree root penetration has caused £224 million worth of damage to his property. **Clients:** Commercial companies; insurers and partnerships.

Robert Muckle The department handles commercial contract disputes, insolvency-related litigation and construction. Adopting a greater focus on early dispute solution, the team includes a qualified mediator. Shareholder, partnership and IP/e-commerce disputes represent a growing feature of the caseload. Act for a series of owner-managed businesses (in the £5 million – £10 million range), manufacturing and technology companies. **Clients:** Sunderland FC; QSP plc.

SCOTLAND

LITIGATION (COMMERCIAL) • Scotland
❶ **Brodies WS** Edinburgh
Dundas & Wilson CS Edinburgh, Glasgow
McGrigor Donald Edinburgh, Glasgow
❷ **Maclay Murray & Spens** Edinburgh, Glasgow
Shepherd & Wedderburn WS Edinburgh
Simpson & Marwick WS Edinburgh
❸ **Anderson Strathern WS** Edinburgh
Burness Edinburgh
MacRoberts Edinburgh, Glasgow
Morison Bishop Glasgow
❹ **Balfour & Manson** Edinburgh
Biggart Baillie Edinburgh, Glasgow
Henderson Boyd Jackson WS Edinburgh
Morton Fraser, Solicitors Edinburgh
❺ **DLA** Glasgow
Levy & McRae Glasgow

LEADING INDIVIDUALS	
✪ **WILLIAMSON David** Brodies WS	
❶ **ANDERSON Peter** Simpson & Marwick WS	**MACLEOD Colin** Dundas & Wilson CS
MACLEOD Ian Shepherd & Wedderburn WS	
❷ **CONNAL Craig** McGrigor Donald	**EASTON Ewan** Maclay Murray & Spens
HOLLIGAN William Brodies WS	**SWANSON Alayne** Maclay Murray & Spens
❸ **CULLEN Joyce** Brodies WS	**DONALD Hugh** Shepherd & Wedderburn WS
HAYWOOD Brent Burness	**SHAW Murray** Biggart Baillie
STEWART David Morton Fraser	**TYLER Alfred** Balfour & Manson
WATSON Peter Levy & McRae	

Within each band, firms are listed alphabetically. *See **Profiles** on page 558*

Brodies WS There are few things more certain than **David Williamson**'s status as Scotland's leading commercial litigator – *"you don't look further than him when searching for the best in Scotland."* Popular with other solicitors, he commands a huge amount of respect from professional peers, is *"intellectually top drawer," "drives things to conclusions"* and *"isn't easily pushed around."* He also provides *"skilled commercial advice for his clients"* and *"isn't blinkered in his approach."* Wide experience in handling contractual disputes, insolvency, partnership and IP contentious matters. Far from being a one-man band, the firm also includes **William Holligan**, well known for his court and judicial review work, who is considered *"another excellent litigator."* Equally, **Joyce Cullen**, particularly for property and land related disputes, received a number of recommendations. All three partners are solicitor-advocates. The last year has seen the department deal with a number of major contractual disputes, partnership disputes, large negligence claims and a variety of landlord and tenant property disputes. **Clients:** Numerous Scottish companies.

Dundas & Wilson CS There is speculation and a degree of confusion in the marketplace as to how the Arthur Andersen's tie-in will impact upon the growth potential of commercial litigation. The firm remains strong in a number of contentious areas, namely professional indemnity, insurance, insolvency, banking, construction and property. **Colin MacLeod** continues to be routinely identified as a leading practitioner. He's a *"good opponent to have and always plays by the rules,"* and is noted for his banking and insurance work. He is regarded as a *"capable and decent lawyer"* who attracts *"reasonable, interesting and substantial work."* The practice exploits its voluminous corporate client base, and has acted on behalf of Boots plc in four successful judicial reviews. There has been an upturn in the amount of IT/IP litigation handled by the practice. Recently involved in a number of high-profile administration orders, contentious banking disputes and professional negligence claims. **Clients:** Boots plc; Stirling Council; Scottish Widows; Rangers Football Club.

McGrigor Donald A *"good name in litigation and our closest competitor"* was a comment from a leading practice, signifying McGrigor's reasonably high profile in the market, albeit one where fewer litigators than expected are regularly seen appearing in court on general commercial matters. The marked exception is *"thorough, competent and sensible"* **Craig Connal**, probably best known for planning appeals and inquiries. The firm serves a number of large corporate clients while health and safety litigation and product liability have been prevalent recently. The unit's main service lines are contentious IP, contractual disputes and property litigation. Recently completed a successful passing-off action by William Grant & Sons Ltd against Glen Catrine Bonded Warehouse. Other big litigations have included acting for M & S toiletries against the pursuers, JOOP, a reported case dealing with entitlement to sell in Scotland. Also acted for chocolate manufacturers Tunnocks in King v Tunnocks. **Clients:** Imperial Tobacco Ltd; BP Amoco; William Grant & Sons Ltd; Phonographic Performance Ltd.

Maclay Murray & Spens Strong on solicitor-advocacy, the firm is especially noted for its prowess in, IP, property and fraud-related disputes. **Ewan Easton**, best known for his property litigation practice, is a *"tough battler and difficult to have on the other side."* Undeterred by a challenge, he *"won't roll over and play dead when you tell him your clients are marvellous."* He is felt to handle a lot of the pre-litigation preparation and negotiation, but appears in court less frequently than others. Glasgow based solicitor-advocate **Alayne Swanson** is *"absolutely terrific"* and is active in the Scottish Court of Session. Instructed by the CAA in connection with the civil airliner crash at Glasgow airport. Handled a corporate fraud investigation for Thomas & Betts Inc, and acted for Reuters plc in connection with a large European cross-border litigation. **Clients:** Haslemere; Schlumberger; KPMG; Scottish Widows.

Shepherd & Wedderburn WS The practice continues to be well regarded for its activity in key practice areas, such as clinical negligence and aviation, where former chief executive of the practice **Hugh Donald**, now back on fee-earning duty has *"got his drive back"* and is recommended for his *"sensible and commercial approach to disputes."* The vastly experienced **Ian MacLeod**, a *"first class litigator,"* is *"frequently on the other side,"* and *"always takes a commercial view of things."* His practice is wide-ranging and includes work for government departments (including HM Customs and Excise) and local authorities. Other partners handle employment, company, construction, property, planning and environmental litigation. Acted on behalf of J C Decaux Ltd, respondents in a petition for judicial review brought by More Group UK Ltd, concerning a £43 million 15 year contract for the provision of bus shelters. Acted on behalf of Bristow Helicopters and their insurers in a fatal accident inquiry in Shetland. Handled an internet/IP case on behalf of Scottish Power challenging an individual using a similarly named website. **Clients:** General Accident; HSBC plc; Orange plc; Miller Group Ltd.

Simpson & Marwick WS Giving David Williamson a run for his money, **Peter Anderson** *("head and shoulders above most people")* is the nearest challenger to the Brodies lawyer's pre-eminence at the summit. Although it is rightly observed that insurance represents the overwhelming bulk of his practice, he has enough experience (PI/professional negligence) and is felt to be *"so skilled a litigator"* that *"he's an expert in everything he does."* For opponents, *"he's a fearsome competitor if you're against him."* Some solicitors have paid tribute to the perceived success of a structural business model in which most emphasis is placed on high volume and throughput of cases. Aside from defenders' insurance reparation work (up to 80% of litigation), the team advises on construction, product liability, employment and other business disputes. Ross Harper v Banks – a professional negligence claim dealing with the liabilities of partners in a law firm. Currently acting for a Finnish company on a heavy mechanical engineering dispute concerning the building of petro-chemical facility. **Clients:** Insurers; engineering companies.

Anderson Strathern WS Well known for banking, financial services, construction and other general commercial disputes, small teams of partners operate in all these divisions. Act for a series of Scotland's major banks, insurance companies and leisure groups. IP disputes in particular are felt to be increasing in scope. A number of partners in financial service and construction litigation were noted by the market for their *"sensible and pragmatic approach."* Acted for a major Scottish bank defending actions based upon allegations of negligence through fraudulent misuse of foreign language Power of Attorney. Also dealing with a major dispute between two insurance companies, in particular, the demise of one them. **Clients:** Bank of Scotland; Zurich Commercial; Royal Bank of Scotland; Scotmid.

Burness The practice is seen to be emerging from a transitional period onto a bigger commercial stage, albeit a process that has not quite reached maturity. In keeping with this, *"bright and able"* **Brent Haywood**, head of the 'e-com' IT/IP dispute group, is one of the *"newer breed,"* who has a *"good grip and hits the right notes."* He has also been commended for his commercial dispute work involving competing football clubs. Structurally, there is a new dispute resolution initiative headed up by a corporate/commercial litigator joined from Alexander Stone and Co in last year's merger. The employment and product liability departments also contain dedicated practitioners with litigation expertise. Acted on Rubislaw Land Co Ltd v Aberdeen Construction Group Ltd, advising the defendants in a dispute over servitude right of access relative to a former quarry site in Aberdeen. **Clients:** The Wise Group; Reith Lambert; Ashtead Group; Scottish Football Association.

MacRoberts Excluding construction litigation, the practice is not considered a heavyweight overall contender, but still has a reputation as a reputable contender. Non-construction litigation (up to a third of overall litigation) embraces IP, IT, property and employment. Also act for a number of insurance companies and loss adjusters on property insurance claims, and also some professional indemnity claims. Acting for a Scottish computer system supplier in relation to a £2.5 million action. **Clients:** British Energy plc; Ford Motor Company; London & Regional Properties Ltd; Texaco.

Morison Bishop *"A reasonable practice"* with a number of partners endorsed by the market for their *"sensible approach."* A healthy insurance (both defenders and claimant) practice has been added to expertise in banking, insolvency and professional indemnity. Witness to an increasing number of IP/e-commerce disputes, including some 'cyber-squatter' cases. Highlights include acting on behalf of the liquidators of Baxter Brothers (Glasgow) Ltd, a high value claim settled extra-judicially. Acting for the pursuers in the commercial court in the reported case of F H Bertling v Tube Developments concerning the recovery of freight charges for freight forwarding agents. **Clients:** Beazer Homes; computer manufacturers.

Balfour & Manson *"You'll never go wrong"* with *"great litigator"* **Fred Tyler** who was newly recommended this year. Rated for a practice that includes civil and PI work alongside general commercial litigation. Core areas, beyond general contractual disputes, include IP, media/defamation, passing-off actions and a sizeable professional negligence practice.

Biggart Baillie **Murray Shaw** is an *"astute litigator"* who is also associated with insolvency and planning work, but is felt to retain the essential qualities of a *"definite commercial litigator."* The department also contains two solicitor-advocates. Highlights include acting for the defenders in a claim brought under section 32D of the Companies Act. Also acted for the subsidiary of a multi-national in respect of claims for alleged breach of joint venture. **Clients:** Scottish Power; County Properties; Highland Council.

Henderson Boyd Jackson WS A practice that is seen to handle *"a reasonably large amount of litigation."* Felt to be *"trying hard"* despite losing its senior litigation partner who has become a sheriff. However, the firm's good reputation for commercial work is felt to assist the team's strength in insolvency, debt recovery and general contractual disputes. Highlights include a major building arbitration for a plc company. Also involved in a £1.5 million Court of Session dispute and the liquidation of a listed IT company. **Clients:** KPMG; HLB Kidsons; Ernst & Young

Morton Fraser Solicitors *"Not to be ignored."* With a *"good blue-chip client list"* and involvement in some high profile disputes, this practice stays in contention. **David Stewart** is a *"good, thoughtful lawyer"* who acts in general commercial disputes as well as conducting some planning and employment litigation. Other partners handle construction, IP and judicial review work. Asset finance, contentious recovery work and employment litigation are felt to be areas of niche expertise. Currently acting for a large construction company in a £250,00 dispute. Acting for SEPA in a judicial review testing the extent of their functions in issuing consent. **Clients:** Halifax; UKAAE; International Oil Pollution Compensation Fund.

DLA The old Bird Semple have been re-packaged under the DLA banner, which has the immediate effect of adding high-level insurance defendant litigation capability. The firm already contains a dedicated construction litigation practice and a more general commercial litigation group. The three partners in the latter handle media, defamation, property litigation and insolvency. Acted on behalf of publishers News International in the high profile Court of Session case involving Govan MP, Mohammed Sarwar. Acted for the Royal Bank of Scotland in its rescue of Hampden Park, and a property/insolvency case for P & O Property Holdings. **Clients:** Northern Rock; Esso Petroleum; Royal Bank of Scotland.

Levy & McRae *"Strong in the marketplace, with good all-round litigation expertise."* Felt to *"have bags of work,"* the firm is newly recommended this year. **Peter Watson** is a *"good all rounder, a fighter who knows his stuff."* His practice is a varied one, taking in media, defamation, criminal work and a track record of notable high profile cases, including Piper Alpha, Dunblane and Lockerbie. **Clients:** Scottish Media Group; Scottish Daily Record; Strathclyde Police Federation.

NORTHERN IRELAND

LITIGATION (COMMERCIAL) • Northern Ireland
❶ **Carson & McDowell** Belfast
Elliott Duffy Garrett Belfast
L'Estrange & Brett Belfast
❷ **C & H Jefferson** Belfast
Cleaver Fulton Rankin Belfast
McKinty & Wright Belfast
Mills Selig Belfast
❸ **Johns Elliot** Belfast
Johnsons Belfast
Tughan & Co Belfast

LEADING INDIVIDUALS	
❶ **BECKETT Samuel** L'Estrange & Brett	**HAM Brian** Mills Selig
LYNCH Michael Elliott Duffy Garrett	**O'DRISCOLL Patrick** Cleaver Fulton Rankin
SPRING Paul Mills Selig	**TURTLE Brian** Carson & McDowell
WILSON Michael Elliott Duffy Garrett	
UP AND COMING	
CRAWFORD Sandra McKinty & Wright	**FOX Brendan** Cleaver Fulton Rankin

Within each band, firms are listed alphabetically. *See **Profiles** on page 558*

Carson & McDowell A generalist commercial litigation practice that includes **Brian Turtle** who has a *"fine reputation that is well deserved."* Intellectual Property matters on copyright and design right have been prominent recently with cases concerning ambulances, bathroom design and railways featuring.

Elliott Duffy Garrett Team includes **Michael Lynch** *("sensible, practical and gets on with it")* and **Michael Wilson.** Firm has a good corporate base which provides a range of litigation clients. Areas covered include professional indemnity, defamation and construction in addition to general commercial litigation. Also handle insolvency, planning appeals and judicial reviews.

L'Estrange & Brett Team includes **Samuel Beckett** who is *"good to deal with."* and *"seeks solutions."* Handle a wide range of work with a particular strength in construction where clients are usually contractors and sub–contractors. Also cover professional negligence and employment areas. **Clients:** Gilbert Ash NI Ltd; various insurers.

C & H Jefferson This practice is heavily construction-oriented especially on professional indemnity cases. Also acts on commercial claims such as commercial agents disputes, public liability insurance and judicial review on planning issues. Involved in a substantial claim in defence of an accounting practice and a case involving the structural collapse of a building.

Cleaver Fulton Rankin Team includes **Patrick O'Driscoll** and **Brendan Fox** who is said to be *"good, he keeps you under pressure."* Among the areas of practice are financial services, construction, IP, employment, personal injury, defamation and commercial agents litigation. The firm has specialists in each of these areas and utilises the London Bar for specialist advice. Acted in the competition and EC law case in the matter of an application for judicial review by Peninsula Securities Ltd. **Clients:** Kingspan Building Products Ltd; Unigate; Capital Bank plc.

McKinty & Wright Another professional negligence-oriented firm. The team has acted in a number of cases concerning accountants negligence and insurer generated construction claims. Also featuring are product liability, defamation and general commercial disputes. Acted in a number of disputes regarding the provision of IT systems. The tragic death of Owen Catchpole has been a setback for the practice but this is mitigated, in professional terms, by the performance of the respected **Sandra Crawford.**

Mills Selig Team includes **Paul Spring** and **Brian Ham.** Act mainly for limited companies and are felt to be *"commercial"* in outlook. Also have expertise in defamation and product liability. **Clients:** News Group Newspapers Ltd; CGU; Northern Bank Ltd.

Johns Elliot This *"well established and respected"* firm acts for a number of public bodies and companies. Among the areas covered are defamation, where the team has acted for a number of newspapers including the FT, personal injury where clients include Belfast Airport and air-law. Also handle insolvency, professional indemnity and employment aspects of the sale and reorganisation of companies. **Clients:** Downtown Radio; NI Housing Executive; Belfast International Airport Ltd.

Johnsons A general commercial litigation practice with strength in defamation. Also handles personal injury and criminal injury and in these three areas the team has reportedly obtained some of the highest awards of damages in Northern Ireland. Act in breach of copyright, an area where they have crossed swords with the likes of the BBC and Sky. Among their clients are the Ministry of Defence and insurers. The team has also acted in applications to the European Court of Justice on Article 82 and 83 references.

Tughan & Co Act mainly for insurers and said to do *"a fair bit."* Also act for private commercial clients. Recent cases include a negligence action in respect of construction supplies, the undermining of a property through excavation and damage to a property by an exploding boiler.

LEADERS IN LITIGATION (COMMERCIAL)

AMSDEN, Mark
Addleshaw Booth & Co, Manchester
(0161) 934 6000
mra@addleshaw-booth.co.uk
Specialisation: I.T. Litigation, Commercial Disputes. Engineering, e-commerce. 1) Won a 3 week, £2million computer supply trial to do with computer software in the travel industry. 2) Lead Partner in a tens of million pound breach of contract software supply case (on going). 3) Various internet related disputes 4) Planned a £ 50 million product liability recall. 5) Extensive experience of warranty and company acquisition related disputes.
Career: Solicitor and Barrister Victoria Australia - admitted 1987, Solicitor admitted England 1992. *Slater Heelis* 1990-1998, partner 1996. *Addleshaw Booth & Co* 1998-date. Partner 1998.
Personal: Educated Melbourne Grammar, Monash University, Melbourne. Married 1 son. Cricket, rugby, travel.

ANDERSON, Harry R.A.
Herbert Smith, London (020) 7374 8000
Head of litigation and arbitration division.
Specialisation: Also heads one of the firm's general commercial litigation groups with substantial experience in litigation arising out of corporate transactions, such as claims for misrepresentation and breach of warranty.
Career: Joined *Herbert Smith* as an articled clerk in 1968. Qualified 1970. Partner since 1976. Started *Herbert Smith's* Hong Kong office in 1982; returned to London 1987.
Personal: Educated at Jesus College, Cambridge.

ANDERSON, Peter
Simpson & Marwick WS, Edinburgh
(0131) 557 1545
Partner in commercial litigation department. Solicitor Advocate 1993.
Specialisation: Work includes professional negligence, personal injury, commercial litigation and aviation litigation. Acted in the Lockerbie inquiry (for Pan-Am) and all related claims, advocacy for C.A.A. in litigation and inquiries including Cormorant Alpha, Brent Spar, for BTA in EL and passenger cases, commercial aviation contract cases.
Prof. Memberships: Law Society of Scotland, International Association Defence Counsel, I.B.A., senior lecturer Edinburgh University.
Career: Qualified 1977, partner since 1980. Solicitor advocate 1993.

ARCHER, Nick
Slaughter and May, London (020) 7600 1200
Principal area of practice is commercial litigation and arbitration.
Specialisation: Handles a wide variety of domestic and international disputes in the commercial context. Has particular experience in banking disputes and has worked extensively on litigation and arbitration both for and against Middle Eastern and Indian banks and corporates.
Prof. Memberships: The Law Society; International Bar Association; Indian Council of Arbitration.
Career: Qualified in 1981 with *Slaughter and May* and became a Partner in 1988.
Personal: Born 15 May 1956. Attended Oakham School and Durham University. Lives in London.

ASPINALL, Tim J.M.
DMH, Brighton (01273) 744 319
tim.aspinall@dmh.co.uk
See under Intellectual Property, p.508

BACON, Gavin
Simmons & Simmons, London (020) 7628 2020
gavin.bacon@simmons-simmons.com
Specialisation: Heavy commercial litigation and dispute resolution; regulatory issues. Acted for the majority shareholders of BCCI, Novastis and Railtrack amonst others.
Prof. Memberships: Law Society of England & Wales; IBA; ABA.
Career: Qualified in1982: partner 1988. Worked in the following *Simmons & Simmons* local offices; Adu Dhabi (1993-5); Hong Kong (1995-7); Shanghai (1997-9). Relocated to *Simmons & Simmons* London office in April 1999.
Personal: Bristol University. Married with two children. Gardening, wine and travel.

BAND, Christa
Herbert Smith, London (020) 7374 8000
Specialisation: Partner in litigation and arbitration division. Specialises in banking and financial services work, including work with an international element. Also has wide experience of general commercial litigation including professional negligence work.
Career: Educated at Tiffin Girls' School; Trinity Hall, Cambridge (BA 1985, MA 1988); Inns of Court Law School (Bar Finals 1986); St. Edmund Hall, Oxford (BCL 1987); qualified 1993; barrister, London, 1987-1990; worked with major solicitors' firm, Sydney, Australia, 1990-1992; solicitor advocate, all Courts (1994); partner, Herbert Smith, since 1996.

BECKETT, Samuel R.
L'Estrange & Brett, Belfast (028) 9023 0426
sam.beckett@lestrangeandbrett.com
Partner.
Specialisation: Main area of work: Civil litigation, including construction, planning law and professional negligence.
Career: Qualified 1980. Partner in *L'Estrange & Brett* since 1986.
Prof. Memberships: Law Society of Northern Ireland. Member Contentious Business Committee, Chancery Division Liasion Committee and Commercial Division Liasion Committee.
Personal: Born 1957. Education: Queen's University, Belfast (LLB.)

BERWICK, Guy
Freethcartwright, Nottingham (0115) 9369 369
Specialisation: Solving problems, especially complex disputes, at the right time, in the right way, ensuring the most realistic result at the right price. Wide experience of all commercial disputes especially construction, engineering and arbitration. Considerable experience of injunctive work, often acts as supervising solicitor in Search and Seizure orders.
Prof. Memberships: Fellow of the Chartered Institute of Arbitrators.
Career: 1979: LLB Nottingham University. 1994: FCIArb. 1996: LLM Advanced Litigation (with Distinction) - Nottingham Law School. Qualified 1982. Joined present firm 1983, Partner, Construction Group.
Personal: Interests include Football and regrettably Blackburn Rovers. Married to Kathy, two daughters, Katrina and Stephanie.

BLAKE, Peter L.G.
Prettys, Ipswich (01473) 232121
plb@prettys.co.uk
Specialisation: Handles a range of commercial litigation including construction and engineering, sale of goods, warranty claims, carriage of goods by road and freight forwarding. Clients include insurance, construction, engineering, road haulier and freight forwarding companies.
Prof. Memberships: Law Society.
Career: Qualified in 1987. Partner in *Prettys* Commercial Litigation Department since 1991.
Personal: Born 1963. Educated at King Edward VI School, Norwich 1973-81, Exeter University 1981-84 and Guildford College of Law. Past Chairman of Ipswich and East Suffolk Hockey Club.

BLAKEMORE, A.C.
Mace & Jones, Liverpool (0151) 236 8989
craig.blakemore@maceandjones.co.uk
Specialisation: Commercial contract disputes, professional negligence actions (particularly solicitors), insolvency, computer/IT law.
Prof. Memberships: Society for Computers and Law. Association of Business Recovery Professionals.
Career: Articled *Mace & Jones* - 1980/1982. Solicitor *Mace & Jones* - 1982/1986. Partner *Mace & Jones* - 1986 onwards. Head of Litigation for the firm.
Personal: Rugby, squash, motorcycling.

BOWDEN, Paul
Freshfields Bruckhaus Deringer, London
(020) 7936 4000
Partner in Litigation Department.
Specialisation: Multi-party litigation and judicial review cases in the environmental and product fields.
Prof. Memberships: Membership: Joint Bar/ Law Society Working Party on Civil Justice (1992-93); Lord Woolf's advisory committee on multi-party actions (1995-96); International Nuclear Lawyers Association; Chairman of Nottingham Law School.
Career: Qualified with *Freshfields* in 1981. Partner in 1987, qualified in Hong Kong, 1986.
Personal: Born 1955. Educated: Bristol University 1973-78.

BOWKER, Neil
DLA, Birmingham (08700) 111111
neil.bowker@dla.com
Specialisation: Complex commercial disputes particularly in the technology, software and computer services, automotive, paper, oil and engineering industry sectors.
Prof. Memberships: The Law Society, Birmingham Law Society and CEDR.
Career: Qualified 1992; Partner 2000
Personal: Born 1968; educated at Altringham Grammar School for Boys and University of Nottingham. Married and living in Sutton Coldfield. Enjoys all types of sport, particularly football, cycling and athletics.

BYRNE, Justin
Eversheds, Birmingham (0121) 232 1000
justinbyrne@eversheds.com
Specialisation: Complex multi-party litigation. Commercial litigation, including IT and professional negligence. Shareholder disputes. Defamation, often as

part of a wider dispute. Reported cases include Investors Compensation Scheme Limited v. West Bromwich Building Society (HL) and West Bromwich Building Society v. Mander Hadley (C/A). Recently a member of the team of *Eversheds* lawyers working on the Bloody Sunday Enquiry. Also has mediation experience, including successful Court Of Appeal mediation.
Career: Articled at *Farrer & Co*, 1990-1992. Joined *Eversheds* in 1995 from *Harbottle Lewis*.
Personal: Born in 1966. Attended Shrewsbury School and Bristol University.

CALLAGHAN, Edward J.
Mills & Reeve, Cambridge (01223) 222 242
edward.callaghan@mills-reeve.com
Partner in Commercial Litigation Department.
Specialisation: Main areas of practice include building and engineering litigation and arbitration, banking and insolvency. Also covered is professional indemnity work relating to architects, surveyors, engineers and solicitors. Has addressed seminars to Barclays Bank and Building Employers' Confederation.
Prof. Memberships: Law Society, Legal Panel Eastern Builders' Federation. Technology & Construction Solicitors' Association.
Career: Qualified with *Mills & Reeve* in 1974. Became Partner in Commercial Litigation Department in 1979.
Personal: Born 25th February 1950 in Middlesex. Attended Franciscan College, Buckingham 1961-68, then Exeter University 1968-71. Member of area board of Norwich Chamber of Commerce. Leisure pursuits include squash, reading and the Internet. Lives Norfolk Broads.

CANNON, Lista
Richards Butler, London (020) 7247 6555
Specialisation: As a lawyer qualified in New York and England & Wales, her practice covers the full range of commercial litigation work with particular emphasis on transnational (cross-border) commercial disputes and litigation, sovereign immunity issues, risk assessment and dispute resoluton and government advisory work. She has a strong banking, finance and regulatory practice. Her work includes ICC arbitration and energy related contract disputes.
Prof. Memberships: In September 1998 she was seconded for six months to the Financial Services Authority as a Senior Legal Advisor and Acting Head of Enforcement. Law Society, admitted to New York State Bar in 1976, Federal Bar Council, ICC UK Environmental Committee.
Career: Litigation lawyer at *Sullivan & Cromwell*, New York, 1975-1980. Established commercial litigation department, (*Boodle Hatfield*), London 1980-1992; Member of the Partnership Board of *Richards Butler* since May 1998.
Personal: Educated at New York University 1969; University of London LLB (hons) 1971. Trustee British American Educational Foundation since 1980, member of India House, New York and Reform Club.

CHAPMAN, Stuart
Pinsent Curtis, Leeds (0113) 244 5000
stuart.chapman@pinsents.com
Specialisation: Partner and Head of Litigation, Leeds. Independently acknowleged expert in resolution of both Commercial and IT disputes.
Prof. Memberships: Chairman, Society for Computers & Law (Northern Group)
Career: *Linklaters* (1989-1994). *Eversheds*, Leeds (1994-1998). *Pinsent Curtis*, Leeds (1998-Date).
Personal: Born (1965) & educated in Grimsby. Leisure interests include family, football, sailing, cricket, most other sports, reading.

CHERRY, Peter J.
Addleshaw Booth & Co, Leeds (0113) 209 2000
pjc@addleshaw-booth.co.uk
Specialisation: Partner in Litigation and Dispute Resolution Group, dealing with delivery of dispute resolution services to clients, including disputes arising on the sale and purchase of businesses, product liability related cases, arbitrations, fraud and judicial review.
Prof. Memberships: Qualified 1978, Partner at the firm 1983.
Career: BA Durham 1975.
Personal: Leisure interests include prehistory, wine and numismatics.

CLAVELL-BATE, Michael
Eversheds, Manchester (0161) 832 6666
michaelclavellbate@eversheds.com
Specialisation: Head of the commercial litigation team in Manchester. All areas of management of commercial disputes including mainstream commercial litigation and ADR. Also specialises in all areas of defamation. Last year received national press coverage following the Football Association's withdrawal of its charges against Brian Clough. Also hit the headlines this year acting for Ros Marks, former nanny to Cherie and Tony Blair. Described in November 1998 issue of North West Business Insider as a 'Young Turk'. Recently contributed to a chapter on 'defamation on the internet' for a legal text published April 2000. Reported cases include Secretary of State v Secure & Provide plc. Current major cases include two very high profile defamation cases and a professional negligence case with a damages claim in excess of £10m.
Prof. Memberships: Chairman of the Civil Litigation Committee of the Manchester Law Society. Council member of the Manchester Law Society. Currently Vice President of Manchester Law Society and President commencing 2001.
Career: Qualified with*Eversheds* in 1990 and became a partner in 1997.
Personal: Born 25 March 1966. Attended Newcastle University and Chester College of Law. Resides in Trawden, North East Lancashire. Leisure interests include all sport.

CLOUGH, Peter
Osborne Clarke OWA, Bristol (0117) 917 4060
peter.clough@osborneclarke.com
Specialisation: Partner, leading a team dealing with commercial and corporate litigation and arbitration. Specialises in large scale commercial and contractual disputes, both in the UK and internationally. Also specialises in shareholder and partnership disputes and professional negligence claims.
Career: *Allen & Overy* 1989-1996. *Osborne Clarke* 1996 to date.

COLLINSON, Ian H.
Ward Hadaway, Newcastle upon Tyne (0191) 204 4000
Specialisation: Head of Commercial Litigation with particular expertise in professional negligence, insurance and defamation.
Career: Birkenhead School and Kings College, London. Qualified in 1982. Articled and subsequently partner with *Dawson & Co*, London. Head of litigation 1989. Moved to Newcastle and *Ward Hadaway* 1991. Partner 1992. Head of litigation 1993.
Personal: Golf, sailing and fishing.

CONNAL, R. Craig
McGrigor Donald, Glasgow (0141) 248 6677
See under Planning, p.661

CRAWFORD, Sandra
McKinty & Wright, Belfast (028) 9024 6751
post@mckinty-wright.co.uk
Partner.
Specialisation: Practice in all types of commercial litigation including claims arising out of the carriage of goods and general marine matters. Also extensive employment law practice both advisory and litigation, acting for employers.
Prof. Memberships: Law Society of Northern Ireland, Northern Ireland Employment Lawyers Group.
Career: Graduated Queen's University of Belfast in Law (LLB) 1985. Qualified 1987. Partner in *McKinty & Wright* since 1995.
Personal: Born 1962. Married, one child.

CROSSE, Damian G.
DLA, Leeds (08700) 111111
damian.crosse@dla.com
Specialisation: Commercial and corporate disputes; particular specialism in IT, Telecoms and media litigation. Extensive experience of various forms of ADR and International Arbitration.
Career: *Herbert Smith* (89-94), *Coudert Brothers* (94-97), *DLA* (1997)
Personal: Becket RC. and Ratcliffe College; Kent University. All sports, particularly cricket and football; Keen follower of Yorkshire County Cricket Club; Dales walking. Married with 2 children.

CROSSLEY, Peter M.
Hammond Suddards Edge, Leeds (0113) 284 7000
peter.crossley@hammondsuddardsedge.com
National Head of Commercial Dispute Resolution Unit.
Specialisation: Specialises in litigation for corporate clients, primarily heavy/light engineering. Particular experience in large scale contractual warranty claims, shareholders disputes and fraud related work and the international sales of goods. Presently dealing with a £20 million warranty claim arising out of an institutional buy-out of a manufacturing group in Belgium.
Prof. Memberships: Law Society, Leeds Law Society.
Career: Kearsney College, South Africa, University of Natal, South Africa (B.Com, LL.B), St Johns College, Cambridge (MA), qualified Attorney in South Africa (1984), Articled *Richards Butler*, Assistant Solicitor *Richards Butler* (1989 - 1992); Assistant Solicitor *Hammond Suddards* (1992-1995), Partner 1995.
Personal: Resides in Ilkley. Leisure interests include cricket, running, theatre, church and family.

CULLEN, Joyce
Brodies WS, Edinburgh (0131) 228 3777
jcullen@brodies.co.uk
See under Employment, p.171

DAVIES, Gwendoline
Walker Morris, Leeds (0113) 283 2500
Specialisation: Partner engaged in a wide range of High Court and commercial dispute resolution for corporate clients and for various institutional clients such as banks and building societies. Emphasis on banking; insolvency; contractual disputes; breach of warranty claims; defective products; member of firm's lender services group; recent cases: successfully acted in a leading case on agency defending a bank's right to charged assets (Triffit Nurseries v Salads Etcetera Ltd) and acted on a landmark case involving relief from forfeiture of

finance leases (On Demand Information plc, On Demand Information International plc v Michael Gerson Finance plc, Michael Gerson Investments Ltd).
Prof. Memberships: Society of Practitioners of Insolvency (subscriber status); Law Society; Leeds Law Society.
Career: Whitland Grammar School; Leicester University (LLB); College of Law, Chester, Articled *Herbert Smith* 1996-98; Qualified 1998 with *Herbert Smith* until December 1992, *Mallesons Stephen Jacques* (Australia - 6 months), Joined *Walker Morris* in 1992 and Partner May 1994.
Personal: Born 1964; resides Luddendenfoot. Leisure interests include reading, walking, sport, travel and family.

DAVIES, Peter G.
Gateley Wareing, Birmingham (0121) 234 0000
pdavies@gateleywareing.co.uk
See under Construction, p.199

DAVIES, Valerie E.M.
Norton Rose, London (020) 7283 6000
Specialisation: Partner in Commercial Litigation Department and Head of Corporate and Banking Litigation with substantial experience in banking, corporate and financial litigation, insolvency and commercial fraud with particular emphasis on the recovery of assets. She has wide experience of cross border international insolvency. She is also a Recorder and a CEDR accredited mediator.
Prof. Memberships: Law Society; City of London Solicitors Company; International Bar Association.
Career: Qualified 1979. Partner at *Norton Rose* since 1986.

DE WALDEN, Ludovic
Lane & Partners, London (020) 7242 2626
dewaldenl@lane.co.uk
Specialisation: Complex multinational litigation and arbitration, art law problems.
Prof. Memberships: Chartered Institute of Arbitrators; IBA; Institution of Art and Law.
Career: Litigation partner since 1985.
Personal: Interests: Opera, theatre, skiing, shooting, golf, reading. Married with 3 children. Lives Chelsea and Oxfordshire.

DONALD OBE, Hugh R.
Shepherd & Wedderburn WS, Edinburgh
(0131) 228 9900
hugh.donald@shepwedd.co.uk
See under Clinical Negligence, p.162

EASTON, Ewan R.
Maclay Murray & Spens, Edinburgh
(0131) 226 5196
ere@maclaymurrayspens.co.uk
Specialisation: Partner and Head of Litigation Department. Specialises in property litigation, planning issues and employment law. Initiated the series of "stay open" clause litigations in Scotland which have resulted in orders requiring banks, a supermarket and numerous other traders to keep trading operations alive, has acted for Haslemere in shopping centre repossession, and for WISCO in environmental judicial review against the Scottish Executive, instrumental in the first Business Petition to the new Scottish Parliament suggesting new Scottish legislation on Landlord and Tenant Law.
Career: University of Glasgow (LL.B 1980). Member of the Arbitration Committee of the Law Society of Scotland. Worked for *Herbert Smith*, London (1984-85).
Personal: Born 1958.

ELDER, Hugh
Gordon Dadds, London (020) 7493 6151
hughelder@gordondadds.com
Specialisation: General commercial litigation. (Recent reported case: Secretary of State for Trade and Industry v _ and Another (2000 2 _.907)).
Prof. Memberships: President London Solicitors Litigation Association 1998-2000 (Honnary Treasurer 1998-2000). Society for Computers and Law; Law Society.
Career: Qualified 1973. Articled clerk and assistant solicitor *Radcliffes & Co* 1971-1976; assistant solicitor *Cammeron Kemm Nulon* 1976-1979; asstsant solicitor *Gordon Dodds* 1980, partner and head of litigation 1981.
Publications: Articles in various legal journals.
Personal: Education: Sherborne School and Edinburgh University (LL.B. 1970); Leisure intrests: family, (married, 2 daughters), golf, music, arts; Resides: London and the West.

ELLIOTT, Robert G.
Ward Hadaway, Newcastle upon Tyne
(0191) 204 4319
bob.elliot@wardhadaway.com
Specialisation: Partner dealing with wide range of commercial litigation, primarily heavy/light engineering, IT/high tech, and other manufacturing businesses. Particular interests in intellectual property, IT sector disputes, company/business sales disputes, faulty machinery/manufacturing processes, EU/international, defamation. CEDR accredited mediator.
Career: Attended RGS Newcastle, then Manchester University. Qualified 1983. Practised in London 1981-93; *Herbert Smith, Clifford Chance, Richards Butler* (Partner), Returned to Newcastle 1994 joining *Ward Hadaway* as Partner in 1996.
Personal: Lives in Wall (nr Hexham); married, two daughters; interests: hill walking, gardening and cooking.

EVANS, H.C.
DLA, Leeds (08700) 111111
hugh.evans@dla.com
Specialisation: Specialises in banking and finance litigation and leads a team of 18 fee earners who act for a wide range of clearing banks, building societies, mortgage banks, finance companies, life assurers, factors and discounters. Has many years experience of advising clients on recoveries, insolvency issues, operational loss claims (breach of mandate, cheque conversion etc) and professional negligence as well as prior title disputes, asset quality claims and ADR procedures. The team has a truly national practice with clients based as far apart as Newcastle and Cardiff. Amongst its recent achievements has been the appointment to the reduced Barclays recoveries panel as well as accreditation by Barclays for general litigation.
Career: Born 1958. LLB (Birmingham) 1979. Articled *Edge Ellison* 1980-82. Assistant solicitor and associate *Edge Ellison* 1982-89. Associate *Dibb Lupton Broomhead* 1989-91. Partner 1991 to date.
Personal: Married with 3 children. Interests include Welsh Rugby and Huddersfield Town Football.

FAGAN, Neil J.
Lovells, London (020) 7296 2000
neil.fagan@lovells.com
Specialisation: Senior partner of 'city litigation group' specialising in financial, 'City' and commercial regulatory issues and commercial dispute resolution. He also heads the firm's public policy practice.
Prof. Memberships: Member of the City of London Solicitors' Company and former Chairman, Employment Law Sub-Committee City of London Solicitors' Company; member International Bar Association Commercial Litigation and Labour Law Committees.
Career: Articled *Lovells*); qualified 1971; partner 1975.

FORDHAM, John
Stephenson Harwood, London (020) 7809 2300
john.fordham@shlegal.com
Partner, Head of Litigation Department.
Specialisation: Extensive litigation and dispute resolution experience. John deals with High Court litigation; international arbitrations; international investigations and asset-tracing; multi-jurisdictional disputes; commercial, banking, insolvency and fraud litigation; judicial review; regulatory enquiries and enforcement litigation; various forms of alternative dispute resolution, both as advocate and mediator.During the 1990's he was the lead partner in the team representing the joint liquidators of Bishopsgate Investment Management Limited, the Maxwell pension trustee company. Recoveries of approximately £400 million have been made for the Maxwell pensioners. Lectures at seminars and conferences on banking and fraud matters.
Prof. Memberships: CEDR - Accredited Mediator.
Career: Qualified in October 1974. Joined *Stephenson Harwood* in 1972 as a trainee and became partner in 1979. Became Head of Litigation Department in 1995.
Personal: Born 15 December 1948. Educated at Dulwich College; Gonville & Caius College, Cambridge BA (Hons), MA. Married with two children. Interests include theatre, cinema, modern art, modern literature, tennis and cricket. Vice-president Sutton Cricket Club. Languages English and French. Resides Cheam, Surrey.

FOX, Brendan
Cleaver Fulton Rankin, Belfast (028) 9027 1325
b.fox@cfrlaw.co.uk
Specialisation: Construction and property litigation, intellectual property and competition law.
Prof. Memberships: The Law Society of Northern Ireland.
Career: Educated at St Patrick's College, Knock, Belfast and The Queen's University of Belfast (LLB). Qualified in 1991. Became a Partner in *Cleaver Fulton Rankin* 1 April 1998.
Personal: Born 7 December 1966. Hobbies include walking, music and sport.

FRASER, David
Baker & McKenzie, London (020) 7919 1000
david.fraser@bakernet.com
International Arbitration
Specialisation: Business disputes with experience in the areas of insurance and reinsurance, trade finance, sovereign immunity, professional liability, and carriage by sea, telecommunications, corporate joint ventures, minority shareholders right and contentious insolvency. Has acted as counsel in and managed several major commercial arbitrations in England and elsewhere and has brought a number of cases to trial in the Commercial Court and the Court of Appeal in London. Has recently represented the owners of the Kazakhstan metals industry in complex arbitration proceedings against former joint venture partners. Led the team acting for Geest in the banana wars with Fyffes. Acts for a number of professional consultancy firms including Tillinghast and LEK. Acts in contentious issues for Camelot. Advis-

er on crisis management and senior management responsibilities. Member of City Disputes Panel Users Committee and LCIA.
Prof. Memberships: The Law Society and New York Bar.
Career: Qualified in 1973. Joined *Baker & McKenzie* in 1975, becoming a partner in 1982.
Publications: Arbitration of International Commercial Disputes Under English Law - The American Review of International Arbitration 1997/vol.8. no.1.
Personal: Born 1948. University of Birmingham. Lives in London. Litigation (commercial)
Specialisation: Business disputes with experience in the areas of insurance and reinsurance, trade finance, sovereign immunity, professional liability, and carriage by sea, telecommunications, corporate joint ventures, minority shareholders right and contentious insolvency. Has acted as counsel in and managed several major commercial arbitrations in England and elsewhere and has brought a number of cases to trial in the Commercial Court and the Court of Appeal in London. Has recently represented the owners of the Kazakhstan metals industry in complex arbitration proceedings against former joint venture partners. Led the team acting for Geest in the banana wars with Fyffes. Acts for a number of professional consultancy firms including Tillinghast and LEK. Acts in contentious issues for Camelot. Adviser on crisis management and senior management responsibilities. Member of City Disputes Panel Users Committee and LCIA.
Prof. Memberships: The Law Society and New York Bar.
Career: Qualified in 1973. Joined *Baker & McKenzie* in 1975, becoming a partner in 1982.
Publications: Arbitration of International Commercial Disputes Under English Law - The American Review of International Arbitration 1997/vol.8. no.1.
Personal: Born 1948. University of Birmingham. Lives in London.

GARVIE, Carl
Pinsent Curtis, Birmingham (0121) 200 1050
carl.garvie@pinsents.com
Partner.
Specialisation: Specialises in corporate and commercial litigation including warranty claims, shareholder disputes, fiduciary duty claims and commercial contractual disputes. Considerable experience in injuctive relief applications, including acting as the court-appointed supervisor of search orders.
Prof. Memberships: Law Society.
Career: MA Trinity Hall, Cambridge. Articled at *Pinsent & Co.* Qualified in 1986. Partner in 1991.
Personal: Soccer, music, gymnasium.

GATENBY, John
Addleshaw Booth & Co, Manchester (0161) 934 6000
Partner.
Specialisation: Advises English and overseas private and public companies on international litigation, arbitration and alternative dispute resolution, including the enforcement of foreign judgements, and arbitral awards, commercial contract disputes and partnership law. Lectures regularly on civil procedure matters including international litigation, arbitration, ADR and documentary evidence.
Prof. Memberships: Law Society, Chartered Institute of Arbitrators (Fellow), Institute of Credit Management, IBA, SEG, LSLA, Commonwealth Lawyers Association, Association of Partnership Practitioners, Non-exec Director of CEDR. CEDR and ADR Group registered mediator.
Career: Qualified in 1975. Joined the firm in 1984; Partner since 1985.
Personal: Educated at Trinity Hall, Cambridge 1968-72. Elder, Poynton Baptist Church.

GAUL, Patrick
Weightmans, Liverpool (0151) 227 2601
patrick.gaul@weightmans.com
Specialisation: Professional negligence, solicitors and doctors in particular and industrial disease litigation (bladder cancer). Regularly lectures on variety of topics in civil litigaiton, especially medical negligence. Very substantial civil practice. Important cases include Ridenhalgh v. Horsefield, Whitley v. Cook Leathes & Bickerton and others, Roberts v. Johnstone, Sa'D v. Robinson.
Prof. Memberships: Law Society.
Career: Oxford University BA Jurisprudence.

GILBERT, Ralph
Rollit Farrell & Bladon, Hull (01482) 323239
rng@rollits.co.uk
Specialisation: Full range of commercial disputes including contentious insolvency and commercial property work.
Career: Qualified at *Rollit Farrell & Bladon* (1990), Partner (1999).
Personal: Born 1965. Educated at University of Hull (1987). Married with 3 children. Interests include church and charity work.

GILLESPIE, Michael
Gateley Wareing, Birmingham (0121) 234 0000

GOLD, Antony
Eversheds, Manchester (0161) 832 6666
antonygold@eversheds.com
Head of Litigation - *Eversheds* Manchester. Former Chairman of *Eversheds* National Litigation Group.
Specialisation: Main current area of practice is Intellectual Property. Specifically, passing off, trade mark, patent and copyright litigation. Other previous experience includes acting in 'Brady v. Brady' (House of Lords, 1988), Barlow Clowes, BCCI, Lancashire and Yorkshire Assurance Society. Most recent reported case is Arrow Nominees v GR+MM Blackledge Plc (Court of Appeal July 2000). Has extensive media experience.
Prof. Memberships: Law Society. International Bar Association, International Arbitration Club, London Court of International Arbitration.
Career: Qualified in 1983, joined *Eversheds Alexander Tatham* in 1984 and became a Partner in 1988. Chairman of *Eversheds'* National Litigation Group 1993-98.
Personal: Born 26th August 1958. Attended Birkenhead School 1969-76, then Manchester University 1976-79 and Chester College of Law 1979-80. Leisure interests include climbing and mountaineering. Lives in Adlington, Cheshire. Married, three children.

GOLD, David L.
Herbert Smith, London (020) 7374 8000
Partner in Litigation and Arbitration Division.
Specialisation: Main area of practice is general commercial litigation, often with an international connection. Also handles company/partnership disputes, local authority law, computer law and injunctions. Led the legal team responsible for pursuing the former owner of Rumasa SA, a large private company expropriated in Spain in 1983, involving litigation in England, Jersey, Switzerland, Holland and the United States. Led the teams dealing with the Hammersmith loan swaps dispute and Le Gavroche health prosecution. Represented Tottenham Hotspur plc, Alan Sugar and others against Terry Venables and led the team representing Amstrad in its successful litigation against US disk drive manufacturer, Seagate. He represented a major Israeli company in its successful claim against insurers arising out of the expropriation of a timber concession in Liberia. He also represented one of the Defendants in the Atlantic Computer/B&C litigation which settled at the beginning of 1999 after a successful mediation. He represented Abbey National Treasury Services in litigation arising out of the Barings collapse. He led the team representing John Reid Enterprises in its claim against Michael Flatley which was settled during the trial. He conducted an independent enquiry for Britannia Building Society in relation to their mortgage to Peter Mandelson. He represented one of the defendants in major proceedings brought in Bermuda following the collapse of Bermuda Fire & Marine Insurance Company Limited. He is currently representing John Duffield in his dispute with Jupiter Asset Management and Commerzbank.
Prof. Memberships: Law Society.
Career: Qualified in 1975. Joined *Herbert Smith* in 1973, becoming a Partner in 1983.
Personal: Born 1st March 1951. Attended LSE 1969-72. Leisure interests include theatre, bridge and family. Lives in Thorpe Bay, Essex and in Hampstead.

GOLDSPINK, Robert A.
Morgan, Lewis & Bockius, London (020) 7710 5500
rgoldspink@morganlewis.com
Partner and head of international litigation.
Specialisation: Main areas of practice are international commercial litigation and arbitration. Has particular experience in heavy, muliti-jurisdictional cases and in advising companies who have been the victims of fraud on how to handle the issues arising and recover their losses. Cases include Alexander Howden, PCW, Lloyds litigation, Lonrho v Fayed, 'Operation Cheetah' (Liverpool and Derek Hatton), Canada Trust Company and Others v W.O. Stolzenberg and Others, and Grupo Torras litigation. Member of joint working party of the general counsel of the Bar and the Law Society which in 1993 reviewed Britain's civil courts and made wide ranging recommendations for the reform of the English Civil Litigation process. Member of the 'Mariott' committee which produced draft legislation for the reform of British arbitration law, eventually taken up by the DTI. Member of steering committee assisting Court of Appeal with mediations, CEDR accredited mediator. Member of the Advisory Board of the Centre of Advanced Litigation of Nottingham Law School. Teaches law regularly at conferences and seminars.
Prof. Memberships: City of London Law Society, London Litigation Solicitors' Association.
Career: Qualified in 1975. Joined *Denton Hall* in 1980, becoming a Partner in 1981. Joined *Morgan Lewis and Bockius* as a partner in 1997.
Personal: Born 8th August 1949. Attended Eltham College 1959-67, then Cambridge University 1968-72 (receiving an MA & LLM). Leisure interests include gardening and fishing.

GOOD, Diana
Linklaters (A member firm of Linklaters & Alliance), London (020) 7456 4328
diana.good@linklaters.com
Partner. Litigation Department. Part time judicial appointment as Recorder. CEDR accredited mediator.

Specialisation: Specialises in commercial litigation, and has extensive experience of advising clients, settling and fighting a wide range of commercial disputes involving banking and insurance, and financial services work. Also specialises in EC law disputes including competition law (both EU and UK); and tax litigation.

GOSLING, John
Addleshaw Booth & Co, Manchester
(0161) 934 6000
jag@addleshaw-booth.co.uk
Head of Litigation and Dispute Resolution Group.
Specialisation: Heavyweight corporate and commercial disputes. Also professional negligence work, particularly financial services industry claims, valuers, surveyors and barristers, predominantly on behalf of insurers.
Prof. Memberships: Law Society, Manchester Law Society.
Career: Qualified in 1984; partner since 1990. Appointed Head of Group in May 1998.
Personal: Educated at Durham University 1978-81. Leisure pursuits include sport and family.

GRAY, David
DLA, Manchester (08700) 111111
Specialisation: All aspects of dispute resolution for commercial organisation acting for plcs, large limited companies, partnerships and financial institutions. Experience of ADR, arbitration as well as traditional litigation. In the circumstances workload covers an extremely wide variety of subject matter. Particular expertise in bringing negligence claims against professionals, in particular solicitors and valuers. Completed at the beginning of 2000 a 16 week trial relating to a multi million pound action arising out of an allegedly defective process plant. Also concluded a Pan-European product recall for defective sewing machines manufactured by a household name.
Prof. Memberships: Law Society and Manchester Law Society.
Career: Admitted in 1986 and joined Sheffield office of *DLA*. Moved to Manchester Office in 1990 and became local head of litigation until 2000 when appointed national head of litigation group.
Personal: 2:1 Law degree from Sheffield University 1983 and Honours at Law college 1984 passing all heads at first attempt. Family, travel and most sports.

GREENO, Ted
Herbert Smith, London (020) 7374 8000
Partner in litigation and arbitration division.
Specialisation: Wide range of experience in both litigation and arbitration work spanning a number of commercial, industrial and professional sectors including the oil and gas industry, engineering and construction, media, product liability and accountancy.
Career: Qualified 1983. Partner at *Herbert Smith* since 1989.
Personal: Educated at King's College, London.

GRIERSON, Christopher K.
Lovells, London (020) 7296 2000
christopher.grierson@lovells.com
Specialisation: International and domestic litigation with particular emphasis on insolvency, fraud and asset recovery matters, and insurance and reinsurance. Has acted in a number of prominent cases, including Laker Airways, Mentor Insurance, BCCI, Barings and EMLICO. Has recently been acting for Prince Jefri of Brunei in the KPMG "Chinese Walls" litigation in defence of the proceedings brought by the governor of Brunei. Licensed insolvency practitioner.
Prof. Memberships: International Bar Association (Vice-Chairman of Committee J (Insolvency)), American Bar Association, American Bankruptcy Institute, European Association of Insolvency Practitioners, London Solicitors Litigation Association, The Law Society (England), City of London Solicitors' Company.
Career: 1976-1980 Assistant Solicitor in *Durrant Piesse*; 1980 Partner *Lovells*; 1991-1994 partner in New York office and 1992-1994 managing partner of that office.

HAGGETT, Paul S.N.
Burges Salmon, Bristol (0117) 939 2262
paul.haggett@burges-salmon.com
Specialisation: Head of Litigation Department. Responsibility for firm's contentious banking and insolvency litigation practice. Lead partner of Nationwide Managed Litigation project and team leader for *Burges Salmon's* involvement in Paragon Managed Litigation Project.
Career: Trained at *Freshfields*. Qualified in 1985. Manager (*Freshfields* Litigation Department) 1985-89. Assistant/Associate *Burges Salmon* - 1989-92. Partner *Burges Salmon* - 1992 to date. Head of Commercial Litigation Unit - 1997 to 2000. Head of Litigation Department 2000 to date.
Personal: Born 1960, resides Bristol. Interests - golf, gardening, reading, family.

HAM, Brian E.
Mills Selig, Belfast (028) 9024 3878
Specialisation: Property based litigation. Acts for a number of major local property developers.
Prof. Memberships: Law Society of Northern Ireland The Environmental & Planning Law Association for Northern Ireland. Other major area of practice is commercial property work (primarily site aquisition and development) and construction law.
Career: Qualified 1969. Joined *Mills Selig* 1971. Became Partner 1984.
Personal: Sailing, Gardening and Architecture.

HARRIS, Andrew D.
DLA, Manchester (08700) 111111
andrew.harris@dla.com
Specialisation: Company law & corporate governance issues; shareholder disputes; matters arising out of mergers & acquisitions, joint ventures & similar. Professional negligence involving solicitors, accountants & independent financial advisers. Fraud & asset recovery actions; executing & supervising search orders.
Career: Archbishop Tenison's Grammar School, Croydon. B.Soc.Sc. Keele University. LL.M. Bristol University. Qualified Nov. 1985. Partner *Alsop Wilkinson* 1990.
Personal: Motoring, wine, jazz.

HAWKSWELL, Jonathan
Pinsent Curtis, Leeds (0113) 244 5000
jonathan.hawkswell@pinsents.com
Specialisation: National head of Construction and Engineering. Specialises in construction and engineering, resolving disputes through adjudication, arbitration, conciliation and the courts.
Prof. Memberships: Member of the Society of Construction Law, the Chartered Institute of Arbitrators.
Career: Qualified 1984, *Simpson Curtis* 1985-1987, *McKenna & Co* 1987-1992, *Dibb Lupton Alsop* partner 1992-1997, Partner *Pinsent Curtis* 1997 to date.
Publications: Guide to Adjudication.
Personal: Born 1960. Educated Ermysteads Grammar School, Leicester University.

HAYWOOD, Brent
Burness, Edinburgh (0131) 473 6000
bwh@burness.co.uk
Specialisation: Partner in Dispute Resolution department handling general commercial litigation and specialising in contractual disputes, insolvency, e-commerce and intellectual property. Particular experience in cross border disputes and interim protective measures.
Career: Qualified in New Zealand (1989), England and Wales (1993), Scotland (1993). Joined Burness in 1994; Became partner in 1999.
Personal: Born 1965. Attended Otago University, New Zealand, and Glasgow University. Long Distance runner and cyclist.

HEAPS, John
Eversheds, Leeds (0113) 243 0391
johnheaps@eversheds.com
Partner. National Head of Litigation. Head of Litigation Department, Leeds and Manchester.
Specialisation: Main area of practice is the management and negotiation of business disputes. Particular expertise in the fields of cross border disputes, information technology, business risks and product liability.
Prof. Memberships: Vice-Chairman to Committee 12 (Civil Litigation SLP) International Bar Association. Fellow of The Chartered Institute of Arbitrators.
Career: Qualified 1978 *Hepworth & Chadwick*, Leeds. *Freshfields* 1978-84. Joined *Eversheds*, Leeds 1984, partner 1985.
Personal: Born 8th July 1953. Ratcliffe College then Liverpool University 1972-75. Lives near Harrogate, North Yorkshire.

HEARN, Andrew
Dechert, London (020) 7583 5353
andrew.hearn@dechertEU.com
Litigation Partner.
Specialisation: Andrew specialises in the resolution of commercial disputes and also in the areas of intellectual property and libel (in which areas his broad client base is well represented in the publishing and retail sectors). His work is both national and international and extends to international arbitrations and mediations. Examples of its range in the past year include: a 53 day commercial court trial and its connected litigation in several other jurisdictions involving claims of over $1 billion (outcome awaited): the successful defence of the Daily Telegraph against Mohammed Al Fayed's attempts to prevent the serialisation of the Trevor Rees-Jones' book 'The Bodyguard's Story'; acting for members of the British Retail Consortium in their pioneering test case to secure the registration of retail service marks in the UK (outcome awaited); and his successful arbitration of a libel dispute against the Sunday Times for a major publishing client.
Prof. Memberships: Fellow of the Chartered Institute of Arbitrators; CEDR Accredited Mediator and on W.I.P.O. List of Mediators; former member of the City of London Law Society's Litigation Sub-Committee.
Career: Andrew graduated in law in 1979 from St John's College, Oxford. He was articled to *Titmuss Sainer & Webb (now Dechert)*, qualified in 1982 and became a partner in 1986.
Personal: Born: 1957. Married with three sons. Skiing, tennis, the arts, member of Old Gowers Club and Campden Hill Tennis Club.

HENDERSON, Guy
Allen & Overy, London (020) 7330 3000
Specialisation: General commercial litigation. Experience spans arbitration, banking and finance, contentious regulatory, M&A, corporate governance, insolvency, security enforcement, commercial fraud and business crime. He is a CEDR accredited mediator.
Prof. Memberships: Member of the Law Society of Hong Kong; Associate of the Chartered Institute of Arbitrators. Member of the Compliance Committee of the Law Society of Hong Kong 1995-97: Member of the Securities and Futures Appeals Panel of Hong Kong 1994-1997; Member of the Editorial Board of Longman's Legal Practice Manuals in Hong Kong 1995-1997; Member of the Hong Kong International Arbitration Centre's sub-committee formed to report to the Attorney General of Hong Kong on amendments to Hong Kong's arbitration law 1996-1997; Appointed a lay member of the Insider Dealing tribunal of Hong Kong, 1995.
Career: Qualified in 1982, and became a partner at *Allen & Overy* in 1990. Head of Litigation and Dispute Resolution, *Allen & Overy*, Hong Kong 1993-97. Head of Corporate and Commercial Litigation Group, *Allen & Overy*, London since 1998.
Personal: Born 1958. Educated at Cambridge University (MA).

HIGHAM, David
Blake Lapthorn, Fareham (01489) 579990
drhigham@blakelapthorn.co.uk
Specialisation: After a first career as a submarine officer in the Royal Navy, David Higham joined *Blake Lapthorn* in 1976, a Partner 1980. Head of Civil Litigation 1991 to 1999. David Higham specialises in complex fraud matters, particularly professional fraud. He also heads Blake Lapthorn's professional indemnity team. He was awarded a LLM in Advanced Litigation at Nottingham Law School in 1996. He is an advocacy trainer with NITA (UK) and a principal tutor in Litigation at Nottingham Law School. David Higham writes and lectures on litigation management topics.

HODGES, Paula
Herbert Smith, London (020) 7374 8000
paula.hodges@herbertsmith.com
Specialisation: Experience in a wide range of commercial litigation and international arbitration with particular expertise in energy, IT and telecommunications disputes. Leading cases in the High Court of London include acting for Amoco, British Gas, Amerada Hess, Agip, Fina and Phillips Petroleum in the renowned dispute with Enron regarding the CATS gas pipeline in the Central North Sea (now on appeal to the House of Lords) (1995-2000); acting for IBM in highly publicised dispute regarding the provision of an Automatic Fingerprint Recognition System to a consortium of UK police forces (1995-1998); acting for MMK UK Limited in a multi-million pound dispute with BT regarding network services provided for the purpose of an on-line lottery system (1999-2000).
Prof. Memberships: Member of the United Kingdom Energy Lawyers Group; member of Institute of Petroleum.
Career: Qualified 1989; partner 1996.
Publications: Contributor to PLC 'Legal Risk Management Manual' (2000).
Personal: Read law at Cambridge University. Undertakes legal pro bono work in the UK and overseas.

HOLLIGAN, William
Brodies WS, Edinburgh (0131) 228 3777
wholligan@brodies.co.uk
See under Administrative & Public Law, p.59

HOPKINS, Dominic A.
Hewitson Becke + Shaw, Northampton (01604) 233233

HOPKINS, Paul
Edwards Geldard, Cardiff (029) 2023 8239
paul.hopkins@geldards.co.uk
Specialisation: Head of Commercial Dispute Resolution at *Edwards Geldard* and also the firm's International Services partner. He specialises in large scale High Court Commercial Litigation and Commercial Dispute Resolution including negotiation, arbitration and ADR. Recent cases include Centrax Ltd v Citibank NA (1999) 1 All ER (Comm) 557.
Prof. Memberships: Member of the Law Society, an associate member of the American Bar Association and a member of the International Bar Association. Officer and Council Member of the Cardiff and District Law Society, responsible for training and coopted to the Council for the Confederation of South Wales Law Societies. Also sits on the Chancery Court Users Committee for the Wales and Chester circuit. Committee member of the South Wales Exporters Association.
Career: Educated at University College, Oxford. Trained at *Slaughter & May*. Joined *Edwards Geldard* in 1988 from *Slaughter & May's* Litigation Department. Made a partner in 1992.
Personal: Interests include: History, Rugby and Music.

HOUSE, Tim
Allen & Overy, London (020) 7330 3000
Specialisation: Partner specialising in commercial litigation and dispute resolution. Acts for listed companies, banks and other financial instructions in complex litigation and regulatory disputes. Reported English cases include: BZW and Others v Asil Nadir, AMF v Hashim, Bankers Trust v Arthur Anderson, GE Capital v Bankers Trust, Ocotal v Credit Suisse First Boston, Boomtime v Goldman Sachs International, Bairstow and Others v Queens Moat Houses plc and Allied Carpets Group plc v Nethercott and others. Acts Predominantly for leading European and US banks. Particular expertise in derivatives disputes. Also acts for quoted companies in English and cross-border litigation. Admitted as a solicitor in England (1986) and in Hong Kong (1988). Assistant solicitor, *Allen & Overy*, London (1985-1992). Partner since 1992.

HOWARD, Paul
Wragge & Co, Birmingham (0121) 214 1010
paul_howard@wragge.com
Specialisation: Commercial litigation.
Career: Articled *Wragge & Co.* Qualified 1975. Partner at *Needham & James* 1980-1993, Partner *Dibb Lupton Broomhead* 1993-94, Partner *Wragge & Co* from 1995.
Personal: Born 1948.

HUMPHRIES, Mark
Linklaters (A member firm of Linklaters & Alliance), London (020) 7456 4250
mark.humphries@linklaters.com
Partner. Litigation Department.
Specialisation: Main area of practice is commercial litigation. Is an experienced solicitor-advocate and practises in the High Court and many other courts and tribunals. Has experience of handling a wide range of commercial disputes but with an emphasis on industrial and insurance cases. Chairman of the Solicitors' Association of Higher Court Advocates. Seconded to Morgan Lewis Bockius, Washington DC in 1988. Educated at Cambridge University.

JAMDAR, Smita
Martineau Johnson, Birmingham (0121) 200 3300
smita.jamdar@martjohn.com
Specialisation: Commercial and statutory disputes for corporate and institutional clients including High Court, arbitration, judicial review and regulatory disputes. Particular interests include breach of warranty/misrepresentation claims and educational litigation. Recent cases include a claim for recission of a share purchase agreement and declaration/rectification proceedings.
Prof. Memberships: Law Society Birmingham, Law Society.
Career: Qualified 1996; Associate 1999
Publications: Author of articles for Court brief and Education Brief. Addressed seminars on ADR, the Woolf Reforms and Health & Safety.
Personal: Born 1970. Educated at Bolton School Girls' Division and Trinity College, Oxford. Interests include Liverpool FC, the cinema and modern literature.

JEFFERIES, Michael
Hugh James Ford Simey, Cardiff (029) 2022 4871
See under Construction, p.202

JONES, Michael L.N.
Hugh James Ford Simey, Cardiff (029) 2022 4871
Partner and Head of Civil Litigation Department.
Specialisation: Handles a wide variety of commercial litigation work including intellectual property. Acts for numerous clients including advertising agencies, building companies and manufacturers. Also handles construction arbitration and litigation matters acting for housing associations and architects amongst others. Cases handled include R v South Glamorgan County Council ex parte Evans concerning parents' choice in education. High Court Advocate. Lecturer on civil advocacy courses at Cardiff Law Society
Prof. Memberships: Chartered Institute of Arbitrators, past President of Cardiff Law Society, Law Society Welsh Spokesman for over 20 years.
Career: Joined *Hugh James* in 1963. Qualified in 1966 and become a Partner the same year. Senior Partner in 1970.
Personal: Born 14th January 1943. Educated at Neath Boys' Grammar School 1953-60 and Jesus College, Oxford 1960-63. School Governor. Past Chairman of Parents for Welsh Education. Leisure pursuits include gardening and music. Lives in Peterston-S-Ely, Cardiff

JONES, Peter
Eversheds, Cardiff (02920) 471147
peterjones@eversheds.com
Specialisation: Commercial litigation, particularly construction and engineering and property related litigation. Has considerable experience in major construction disputes and professional negligence in relation to earthworks design and claims for loss and expense. Also advises on matters of defamation. Is joint lead partner for the provision of legal services to the National Assembly for Wales. Continues to lead *Evershed's* lawyers acting for Lord Saville's Bloody Sunday Inquiry (now entering its third year). Has practised as a mediator and is an accredited mediator with CEDR and the ADR Group.
Prof. Memberships: Fellow Chartered Institute of Arbitrators; member of the Law Society.

Career: Articled with *Phillips & Buck*, now *Eversheds*. Partner 1986.
Personal: Educated University of Wales; University of Aix-en-Provence; has a university doctorate in Comparative Law. Fluent French and Welsh speaker. Is a semi-professional musician.

KAMSTRA, Simon
Addleshaw Booth & Co, Leeds (0113) 209 2000
spk@addleshaw-booth.co.uk
Partner in Commercial Litigation.
Specialisation: Specialising in company and shareholder disputes; sports law; mergers and acquisition related claims; trusts and trustee law; misfeasance and directors duties issues; professional negligence.
Prof. Memberships: IBA. Leeds Law Society.
Career: Educated at University of Manchester (LLB). Partner 1996.
Personal: Leisure: Music; cricket.

KELLY, Jonathan P.
Simmons & Simmons, London (020) 7628 2020
Partner in Financial Markets Department and Head of the Finance Litigation Group.
Specialisation: Main areas of practice are banking and financial services litigation, specialising in asset management, securities, commodities and derivatives disputes, and regulatory issues arising in these areas. Experienced in corporate disputes and large scale commercial fraud actions. Clients include UK, US and European commercial and investment banks, investment institutions, brokers and commodity houses.
Prof. Memberships: Law Society, Society of English and American Lawyers.
Career: Qualified in 1989 after articles at *Simmons & Simmons*. Became a Partner in 1995.
Personal: Born 11th August 1964. Educated at Stonyhurst College 1972-82, Balliol College, Oxford 1983-86.

KERSHAW, Anne
Kershaw Abbott, Manchester (0161) 839 0998
mail@kershaw-abbott.co.uk
Specialisation: Practises in the field of commercial dispute resolution with particular emphasis on professional partnership disputes, professional liability and commercial and construction disputes.
Prof. Memberships: Member of Association of Partnership Practitioners; Secretary Manchester Professional Forum; Past President Manchester Law Society; Member of Society of Construction Lawyers; Member of CEDR.
Career: Admitted 1975. Practised in North West all working life. Co-founder of *Kershaw Abbott* as niche practice in 1991. Appointed Tax Commissioner in 1995.
Personal: Lives in Ribble Valley with judicial husband and son. Music lover and devoted gardener.

KHAN, Charles
Berg & Co, Manchester (0161) 833 9211
Specialisation: Charles Khan is a Partner in the Commercial Litigation Department. He specialises in commercial litigation, including in particular contract disputes (special expertise in disputes in the textile and clothing sector), concerning quality, title, non-payment; professional negligence; landlord and tenant; advising office holders, companies and individuals on insolvency related matters. He was appointed a Deputy District Judge in June 1994.
Prof. Memberships: Law Society; Manchester Law Society.
Career: Qualified in 1980. Joined *Berg & Co* in 1982 and became Partner in 1984. Appointed Deputy District Judge in the Northern Circuit in 1994.
Personal: Born 21 June 1956. Educated Stand Grammar School and Hull University. Enjoys cycling, football, cricket, cinema. Lives in Prestwich, Greater Manchester.

KING, Ronnie
Ashurst Morris Crisp, London (020) 7638 1111
ronnie.king@ashursts.com
Specialisation: Commercial litigation and arbitration, both domestic and international with particular experience in oil and gas, power, engineering and projects. Also acts on general contract claims including warranty claims and disputed completion accounts.
Career: Articled *Ashurst Morris Crisp* 1984-1986. Assistant Solicitor 1986-1994. Partner 1994.
Personal: Educated at the Belfast Royal Academy and St Catherine's College, Cambridge (Simmons Scholar); M.A., LL.M.

KISSACK, Nigel
Pinsent Curtis, Leeds (0113) 244 5000
nigel.kissack@pinsents.com
National Head of Litigation and Managing Partner in Leeds. Commercial Litigation
Specialisation: 1. Product Liabitlity - acted as co-council for European defendant in claim in US Courts for $7m. 2. Defamation - settled claimants case in mediation for £60 + costs. 3. Contract - acted for exclusive supplier for national retailer whose contract was terminated without notice. Settled for £4m + costs.
Career: Partner *Alsop Wilkinson* 80-96. Partner *Dibb Lupton Alsop* 96-97. National Head if Litigation *Pinsent Curtis* 97-date.
Publications: Numerous articles in professional and general media.
Personal: King William's College, Isle of Man. Sheffield University LLB (Hons). Married with two children. Reading, travel, arts and motorcycling.

LEONARD, Paul M.
Freshfields Bruckhaus Deringer, London (020) 7936 4000
Specialisation: Partner in Litigation Department. Main areas of practice are international litigation, arbitration and mediation. Cases include Ocean Island case (Tito v Waddell), Westinghouse Uranium Contract litigation and the Alexander Howden insurance fraud cases. Acting in numerous ICC arbitrations. Also involved in insurance insolvency litigation, acting in the KWELM and Electric Mutual (EMLICO) cases. A CEDR accredited mediator.
Prof. Memberships: Law Society.
Career: Articled at *Freshfields*. Qualified in 1966. Partner in 1972. Head of Litigation Department 1988-91.
Personal: Born 14th January 1942. Educated at Finchley Grammar School and Sheffield University (LL.B.). Leisure interests include cricket, contemporary art and an old Aston Martin.

LOMAS, Paul
Freshfields Bruckhaus Deringer, London (020) 7936 4000
Specialisation: Particular interests: EC and anti-trust; ECHR; financial services and banking; regulatory or economics dominated cases; art law; crises. Previous cases include: Bank of England/JMB/MMB privatisation (ECJ, High Court and arbitrations); Spain v. Christies/Sevso silver/seconded to Sotheby's; a range of art market disputes; European Communities, protecting Lome funds from seizure. Recent matters include; Milk Marque JR of MMC; Reichhold v Goldman Sachs; Lloyds [Names, R&R and related litigation]; PowerGen; various gas/buy down/coal market restructuring/anti-trust/M&A litigation; Bank of England/BCCI; cases for PepsiCo, IBM and Reed Elsevier (Reed Travel Group), Pro Bono; death row defence (for House of Lords) before Florida Supreme Court, Chequepoint v. McClelland (C.A.).
Prof. Memberships: Law Society, Solicitors' European Group, INSEAD Alumni Association.
Career: Sciences and Law, Emmanuel College, Cambridge; Freshfields Litigation Department; MBA INSEAD; Freshfields Brussels office in 1989; partner 1990; Litigation Department, London from 1993.
Personal: Interests: anything that you can do on a mountain, on a beach or in France, music, food and wine, family (one wife and two daughters); not necessarily mutually exclusive or in that order.

LYNCH, Michael P.
Elliott Duffy Garrett, Belfast (028) 9024 5034

MACKIE, Q.C., David L.
Allen & Overy, London (020) 7330 3000
Head of Litigation.
Specialisation: Litigation and arbitration.
Prof. Memberships: Law Society.
Career: Qualified 1971, having joined *Allen & Overy* in 1969. Became a Partner in 1975 and Head of Litigation in 1988. Deputy High Court Judge 1998. Recorder of Crown Court since 1988. Higher Court Advocate (all courts). Queen's Counsel 1998. Fellow Chartered Institute of Arbitrators, CEDR Accredited Mediator.
Personal: Born 1946. Attended various schools 1951-63, then St Edmund Hall, Oxford 1964-7. Leisure interests include climbing. Lives in London.

MACLEOD, Colin
Dundas & Wilson CS, Edinburgh (0131) 228 8000

MACLEOD, Ian
Shepherd & Wedderburn WS, Edinburgh (0131) 228 9900
ian.macleod@shepwedd.co.uk
See under Administrative & Public Law, p.60

MAGNIN, John .D.
Nicholson Graham & Jones, London (020) 7648 9000
Specialisation: Involved in all aspects of commercial litigation, UK and international, including: shareholder disputes; contractual, warranty and agency claims; fraud; defamation; confidential information; boardroom disputes and departures; restrictive covenants; proceedings under the Companies, Insolvency, Financial Services and Company Directors Disqualification Acts; financial services, regulatory and disciplinary proceedings. Recent work includes: the Kazakhstan metals and minerals litigation; substantial warranty claims; and acting for financial services, media and sports companies and organisations.
Career: Joined *Nicholson Graham & Jones* in 1995, qualified in 1997 and became a partner in 1992.
Personal: Attended UCL 1981-4. Interests include family, golf, cricket and football.

MANLEY, Mark
Brabner Holden Banks Wilson, Liverpool (0151) 236 5821
mark.manley@bhbw.co.uk
See under Defamation, p.295

MANNING COX, Andrew
Wragge & Co, Birmingham (0121) 214 1034
andrew_manning_cox@wragge.com
Specialisation: Commercial Litigation/ Dispute Resolution; arbitration; ADR.

Prof. Memberships: Law Society, Notary Public.
Career: MA (Cantab)
Personal: Country Pursuits.

MATTISON, Mark
Eversheds, Manchester (0161) 832 6666
markmattison@eversheds.com
Partner in Commercial Litigation Department.
Specialisation: Main areas of practice are construction litigation, shareholder disputes and contract claims.
Prof. Memberships: Law Society. Past President of Manchester Law Society. Member, Chartered Institute of Arbitrators, Vice Chairman of North West Branch, Member Society of Construction Law. CEDR Accredited Mediator.
Career: Articled at *Alexander Tatham* (now *Eversheds*) 1972-74 and became a partner in 1978.
Personal: Born 26/4/1951. Attended Liverpool College and studied Law in Liverpool. Leisure pursuits include cycling, swimming and overseas travel. Lives in Hale, Cheshire.

MAY, Philip N S
TLT Solicitors, Bristol (0117) 917 7777
pmay@TLTSolicitors.com
Head of commercial dispute resolution team with more than 15 years' experience. Specialises in shareholder and partnership disputes and contentious insolvency. Wide experience of other general commercial disputes including Arbitration and ADR.
Prof. Memberships: Associate of the Chartered Institute of Arbitrators and member of the Bristol Chancery Court users Group. For biographical details see insolvency section.

MAYHEW, David
Clifford Chance, London (020) 7600 1000
david.mayhew@cliffordchance.com
See under Fraud, p.419

MCLACHLAN, Campbell A.
Herbert Smith, London (020) 7374 8000
Partner in litigation and arbitration department.
Specialisation: Specialises in international commercial litigation and arbitration including public and private international law, investment disputes, multinational fraud and cross-border banking. He is Vice-Chairman of the IBA Committee on International Litigation, and Joint Secretary of the British Branch of the ILA. His book, 'Transnational Tort Litigation', is published by OUP.
Career: Qualified New Zealand 1984 and England and Wales 1991. Partner at *Herbert Smith* since 1992.
Personal: Educated at Victoria University of Wellington, New Zealand, the University of London and Hague Academy of International Law (Diploma cum laude).

MEREDITH, Ian
Hammond Suddards Edge, Manchester (0161) 830 5000
ian.meredith@hammondsuddardsedge.co.uk
Specialisation: Commercial Dispute Resolution partner specialising in national and international disputes extending from warranty claims, completion account and related disputes flowing from corporate acquisition activity; shareholder, boardroom and partnership disputes; commercial fraud; commercial trading and trade finance related disputes; defence of claims brought against banks. Recent highlights include two successful appeals before the Court of Appeal on behalf of banks; a series of cases arising from a substantial international fraud which was uncovered after an acquisition by a US corporation of a UK group requiring world-wide freezing orders, search and seizure orders, international asset trace exercise through an extensive range of tax havens; complex recovery proceedings and multi - jurisdictional enforcement action; complex shareholder dispute resolution through a bespoke structured negotiation/expert determination model.
Prof. Memberships: CEDR Accredited Mediator.
Career: Leicester University; articles *Slater Heelis* Manchester, joined *Hammond Suddards* on qualification 1988, partner 1995.
Personal: Born 1963; resides Prestbury. Leisure interests include football, cricket, golf, motor sports and performance kites.

METCALFE, Stephen J.
Beachcroft Wansbroughs, Bristol (0117) 918 2000
smetcalfe@bwlaw.co.uk
Specialisation: Commercial Litigation, particularly involving IT and financial institutions. Reported case in 1999 - A&J Fabrications v Grant Thornton.
Prof. Memberships: Law Society.
Career: *Dussant Piesse* 1981-85. *Beachcroft Wansbroughs* 1985 to date. Partner 1988.
Personal: BA (Hons) New College, Oxford. Married with 4 children. Interests: Music, theatre, literature, walking.

MICKLETHWAITE, Neil Philip
DLA, London (08700) 111111
neil.micklethwaite@dla.com
Specialisation: Auditors negligence, Civil fraud, Companies Acts, Corporate defence, Crisis management, Defamation, Disciplinary tribunals, DTI investigations, Financial Services, Insider dealing, Shareholder disputes.
Prof. Memberships: ABA, IBA.
Career: to date *DLA*, Head of Business Solutions Division and Board Member 1994-2000 *DLA*, Head of Commercial Litigation 1993-1994 *DLA*, Head of Banking Litigation 1992-1993 *DLA*, Partner & Head of Commercial Investigations Unit 1986-1992 *Gouldens* 1984-1986 *Chambers of Colin Ross Munro*, 2 Hare Court
Publications: Various articles and lectures on financial services matters
Personal: University: Warwick University, LLB (Hons) Law 1983. Called to the Bar July 1982.

MORRIS, Peter
Eversheds, Bristol (0117) 929 9555
petermorris@eversheds.com
Head of banking and property litigation in *Eversheds'* Bristol office.
Specialisation: All types of commercial litigation particularly for banks and financial institutions. Professional negligence for financial and commercial clients both as Claimant and Defendant. Heavily involved in recent years in managed litigation against multiple defendants. Also property litigation, mainly Landlord and Tenant, for retail clients.
Prof. Memberships: Bristol Law Society; CBI.
Career: Qualified in 1982. *Kenwright & Cox* 1982-86, partner 1985. *Holt Phillips* 1986-94, partner 1986, becoming *Eversheds* partner in 1994. Senior partner (Bristol) 1999.
Personal: Born 1957. Lives outside Bristol. Interests include hill walking, smallholding and real ale.

MUMFORD, Nicola
Wragge & Co, Birmingham (0121) 214 1078
nicola_mumford@wragge.com
Specialisation: Specialises in commercial dispute resolution including litigation, mediation, arbitration insolvency litigation and international litigation. Extensive experience of urgent applications (freezing and search and seize orders) breach of warranty claims and contractual disputes particularly in the automotive and engineering sectors. She is worldwide chair for membership for the IBA committee on international litigation.
Prof. Memberships: IBA, (International Bar Association), ILPA (Immigration Law Practitioners Association) and 3R (Society for Practitioners of Insolvency).
Career: Articled at *Kingsley Napley*, Partner at *Wragge & Co.* 1993.

NATALI, David P.
Herbert Smith, London (020) 7374 8000
Specialisation: Cross-border fraud; asset tracing in jurisdictions noted for their banking, trust and corporate secrecy laws; commodities disputes; partnership disputes; professional negligence; defamation and major international disputes of all kinds. Currently acting for Codelco, the Chilean state-owned copper company in claims arising from $178m losses on the futures markets; and in other multi-jurisdictional disputes between major corporations; and throughout the 1990s acted for Price Waterhouse in defending claims which arose following the collapse of BCCI.
Career: Articled *Herbert Smith*; qualified 1963; partner 1968. One of the firm's senior litigation partners. Former member of the firm's Management Committee. Former member of Joint Bar/Law Society Working Party on the Civil Courts.
Personal: Born 1940.

NICHOLSON, Brinsley
Linklaters (A member firm of Linklaters & Alliance), London (020) 7456 4364
brinsley.nicholson@linklaters.com
Partner, Litigation Department.
Specialisation: Practised in proceedings before the High Court of Justice and the Commercial Court; experienced in obtaining urgent injunctions (particularly to freeze assets), dealing with jurisdictional issues, questions of conflict of laws and handling substantial disputes. Also experience of arbitration, insolvency, financial services, investigations, banking and white collar crime. Joined *Linklaters*, 1972, became a Partner in 1977.

O'DRISCOLL, Patrick M.
Cleaver Fulton Rankin, Belfast (028) 9027 1311
p.o'driscoll@cfrlaw.co.uk
Specialisation: Commercial litigation, serious fraud, multi-document litigation, intellectual property, product liability and judicial review.
Prof. Memberships: The Law Society of Northern Ireland.
Career: Educated at Glenstal Abbey School, Republic of Ireland and Queen's University of Belfast (BSc Econ). Qualified 1972. Became a Partner in *Cleaver Fulton & Rankin* 1975.
Personal: Born 7 December 1947. Running. Happily married with four children.

OWENS, David .J.
Bevan Ashford, Bristol (0117) 923 0111
Partner in Public Sector Commercial.
Specialisation: After twelve years experience working in the Commercial Litigation Department of Bevan Ashford, his focus on public law issues, particularly Judicial Review, has increased to the extent that he is now working with the Public Sector Commercial team. His work has involved commercial litigation on a wide range

of topics both for NHS and private sector clients, together with a significant degree of advice on more general matters on the law and practice of the NHS and other public sector bodies.Currently main practice areas are Judicial Review within the NHS and associated public law litigation.
Prof. Memberships: Bristol Law Society, Society of Computers and Law.
Career: Joined *Bevan Ashford* in 1982. Qualified 1984. Partner 1990.
Personal: Born 23rd July 1958.

PARKER, Raj D.
Freshfields Bruckhaus Deringer, London (020) 7936 4000
Partner in Litigation Department, Solicitor Advocate.
Specialisation: Main area of practice is insurance and reinsurance work. Regular speaker at insurance industry seminars. Substantial general commercial dispute resolution practice. Also deals with sports law, acting for the Football Association in advisory and contentious work.
Prof. Memberships: Law Society; Society of Solicitor Advocates. Nominated Court of Arbitration for Sport ('CAS') Arbitrator. Member of British Insurance Law Association, British Association for Sport and the Law. CEDR accredited mediator.
Career: Joined *Freshfields* in 1986 and became a Partner in 1993.
Personal: Born 19th September 1960. Educated at Christ's College 1972-79 and Southampton University 1979-82. Recreations include sport, music, theatre and ornithology. Lives in London.

PEARSON, Nick
Baker & McKenzie, London (020) 7919 1000
nick.pearson@bakernet.com
Specialisation: Civil Fraud, insolvency, and international disputes. Significant experience in managing large multi-jurisdictional claims.
Prof. Memberships: Licensed insolvency practitioner. Member of Association of Business Recovery Professionals, Insolvency Lawyers Association, Insolvency Practitioners Association, and European Insolvency Practitioners Association.
Career: Qualified 1976. Articled with and remained at *Herbert Smith* 1974-79. *Baker & McKenzie*, Hong Kong 1979-88. Partner *Baker & McKenzie* 1982. *Baker & McKenzie*, London 1988-date.
Personal: Educated King Edwards School, Birmingham and Lincoln College, Oxford. Keen sportsman. Married, two children.

PERROTT, Edward
Taylor Vinters, Cambridge (01223) 423444
efvp@taylorvinters.com
Partner and head of commercial litigation.
Specialisation: Specialising in leading edge technology, precision engineering and high quality manufacturing clients. Litigation covering infringement of intellectual property rights, contractual disputes and professional negligence.
Prof. Memberships: Law Society.
Career: Jesus College, Cambridge 1965-68; Retail business owner in Beirut 1968-73; Trained and practised in London with *Crossman Block and Keith* 1974-1980; Joined *Taylor Vinters* in 1981.
Personal: Interests include skiing, sailing and cricket.

PIZZEY, Simon F.
Veale Wasbrough, Bristol (0117) 925 2020
spizzey@vwl.co.uk
Managing partner.
Specialisation: Commercial litigation in the fields of banking, commercial fraud, business breakdown (corporate and partnership) and professional negligence. Clients include building societies, banks, local authorities, central government agencies, professional partnerships and corporates.
Prof. Memberships: Bristol Law Society Panel of Supervising Solicitors for the enforcement of Search and Seize Orders.
Career: Qualified 1982. Joined *Veale Wasbrough* in 1987. Partner in 1989. Head of *Veale Wasbrough*'s Litigation Department. Managing partner since 1998.
Personal: Born 1957. Birmingham University.

PLANT, Charles W.
Herbert Smith, London (020) 7374 8000
Specialisation: Principal area of practice is commercial litigation with particular reference to media, oil and gas and construction industries. Also provides expert advice on international arbitration law.
Prof. Memberships: Law Society, International Bar Association (Secretary of the International Litigation Committee).
Career: Qualified in 1969 while at *Herbert Smith*. Became a partner in 1976. Head of Litigation Department 1988-95. Member of Lord Chancellor's Advisory Committee on Legal Education and Conduct (1994 - 1999). Member Legal Services Consultative Panel (appointed December 1999.) Governor of College of Law.
Personal: Born 1944. Attended Cambridge University 1963-66. Lives in Tunbridge Wells.

POLLACK, Craig
SJ Berwin & Co, London (020) 7533 2222
craig.pollack@sjberwin.com
Specialisation: Commercial litigation with an emphasis on contractual disputes, civil fraud and shareholder disputes. Also acts as a mediation advocate. Major cases include: Tamarind International Ltd and Others v Eastern Natural (Retail) Limited and Another (The Times 27 June 2000); Kinstreet Ltd v Balmargo Corporation Ltd (CPR 1.4.11)
Prof. Memberships: Law Society. Israel Bar Association.
Career: BA (Cape Town); LLB (Jerusalem); LLM (London) Qualified as an advocate in Israel 1989. Joined *SJ Berwin* in 1991. Partner Commercial Litigation 1997.

PUDDICOMBE, Nigel R.
Cartwrights, Bristol (0117) 929 3601
nrpuddicombe@cartwrights.com
See under Litigation (Property), p.579

RANDS, Harvey
Memery Crystal, London (020) 7242 5905
dhrands@memerycrystal.com
Specialisation: Head of litigation; leads groups specialising in commercial, commodities, insurance and shipping litigation; company and regulatory enquires and white collar crime; intellectual property; directors' and officers' liability.
Prof. Memberships: Brooks's; Chartered Institute of Arbitrators
Career: Articled *Charles Mazillius & Co*; qualified 1976; solicitor *Rubinstein Callingham* 1977; solicitor *Stilgoes* 1977; partner *Stilgoes* 1978; partner *Memery Crystal* since 1980.
Personal: Pilgrim School, Bedford; The City University (1972 BSc Philosophy and Physics); College of Law (1976 solicitors Finals). Born 1951; resides in London. Leisure interests include family and town and country living.

RAWLINSON, David J.
Cuff Roberts, Liverpool (0151) 237 7777
david.rawlinson@cuffroberts.co.uk
Specialisation: Commercial contract and construction litigation, related professional negligence, arbitration, alternative dispute resolution and defamation.
Prof. Memberships: Law Society, Liverpool Law Society, Member of Chartered Institute of Arbitors, Member of Society of Construction Law, Northern Arbitration Association Council, Member of Council of Society for Computers & Law, Chairman SCL Liverpool Group.
Career: Qualified 1976. Assistant solicitor, then partner (1978) *Banks Kendal Taylor & Gorst*, merged with *Cuff Roberts* 1987. Chariman of firm's Executive Board 1999 to date. Past member of Young Solicitors' Group National Committee. Past Chairman YSG Liverpool Group.
Personal: Nottingham University (1970-73). Married, two children. Lives West Kirby, Wirral. Golf, cycling, walking, local and family history. Suporter Tranmere Rovers F.C.

REYNOLDS, John
McDermott, Will & Emery, London (020) 7577 6900
jreynolds@europe.mwe.com
Specialisation: International commercial litigation and arbitration.
Prof. Memberships: Law Society.
Career:1985-1987: *Lickfolds Wiley & Powles*, London (Articles); 1987-1999: *Herbert Smith*, London (New York 1989-1990; Partner 1994); 1999 to date: *McDermott, Will & Emery*, London (Partner)
Personal: Born 1963. Educated at Clifton College, Reading University and UCL. Married with two children. Lives in Islington. Leisure: rugby, Formula One, cooking, music (loud/quiet/dance). Member of the Groucho Club.

RHYS-JONES, Mark
Eversheds, Cardiff (02920) 471147
markrhysjones@eversheds.com
Partner in the Dispute Resolution and Commercial Litigation Department at *Eversheds'* Cardiff.
Specialisation: Specialises in conducting litigation in all areas of IT, intellectual property, product liability and general contractual disputes of a substantial value; accredited mediator with the Centre for Dispute Resolution (CEDR) and the ADR Group; Chair of the *Eversheds'* IT Litigation Group.
Prof. Memberships: Society for Computers and Law; Cardiff Business Club; Advisory Board of Centre for Professional Legal Studies, Cardiff Law School.
Career: Educated at Merton College, Oxford (1987 BA Hons Jurisprudence). Articled with *Eversheds*; qualified 1990; became a partner in 1995.
Personal: Born 1966 and resides in Cardiff. Leisure pursuits include aerobics, skiing and badminton.

ROESSLER, Max
Eversheds, Norwich (01603) 272727
Specialisation: Professional Negligence, Product Liability.
Prof. Memberships: Law Society
Career: Admitted: 1981. Partner: 1986

ROPER, Robert
Cobbetts, Manchester (0161) 833 3333
robert.roper@cobbetts.co.uk
Specialisation: Principal area of practice is intellectual property. Work includes litigation on all types of trade mark, passing off, copyright and design right matters as well as mechanical and electrical patent proceedings. Also handles commercial litigation and dispute resolu-

tions including large commercial contract disputes with overseas elements and/or competition law issues. Has considerable experience in injunction work including Anton Piller Orders both in intellectual property matters and commercial litigation. Important cases handled include McMillan Graham & Others v. R R UK Ltd (contempt of court for breach of interlocutory undertakings in passing off/ copyright case) and DTI v. D C Wilson and others (acted for the major intermediaries sued by the DTI in the Barlow Clowes collapse). Watson & Watson -v- Duton Forshaw and Others commercial court London, Restrictive Trade Parctice and conspiracy to injure by unlawful means.
Prof. Memberships: Law Society, Manchester Law Society, Licensing Executive Society.
Career: Qualified in 1979 while at *Cobbett Leak Almond*. Became a Partner in 1983.
Personal: Born 11th August 1953. Educated at Altrincham Grammar School 1964-71 and the University of Wales Institute of Science and Technology 1973-76 (LL.B Hons). Married with 2 children. Narrowboating, golf, training.

ROSE, Digby H.
Hammond Suddards Edge, Birmingham (0121) 200 2001
digby.rose@hammondsuddardsedge.com
Specialisation: Commercial dispute resolution and litigation. Has wide experience covering contractual disputes, computer claims and contentious intellectual property work. Other areas of interest include defamation and professional negligence. Also advises on partnership issues. Cases include substantial disputes concerning computer systems, industrial machinery, engineering plant and media contracts as well as patent and design right infringement and claims resulting from the acquisition and sale of businesses. Regular contributor to Current Law Week, providing the focus articles on Civil Litigation.
Prof. Memberships: Law Society, Birmingham Law Society.
Career: Qualified in 1975. Worked in London for four years before joining *Edge Ellison* in 1979. Became Head of Commercial Litigation in 1990.
Personal: Born 16th September 1950. MA Gonville & Caius College, Cambridge. Honorary Secretary of Birmingham Botanical Gardens. Leisure interests include music. Lives in Birmingham.

ROTHWELL, Charles E.S.
Keeble Hawson, Leeds (0113) 244 3121
charlesrothwell@keeblehawson.co.uk
Specialisation: Partner specialising in Commercial Litigation matters, particularly of a heavyweight nature. Main areas of practice are: building and engineering disputes, partnership disputes and professional negligence. The practice covers commercial disputes, construction and property litigation, and expertise in mediation and arbitration.
Career: Articled at, and assistant with *Biddle and Co.* Qualified in 1993. Assistant at *Dibb Lupton Broomhead* 1995 to 1997. Partner at Keeble Hawson 1998.
Personal: Born 1968. Resides at Holmfirth. Educated at Queen Elizabeth Grammar School, Wakefield and the University of Liverpool. Intrests; horse riding, gardening and walking.

ROWE, Claire M.
Shoosmiths, Reading (0118) 965 8959
claire.rowe@shoosmiths.co.uk
Head of Dispute Resolution Unit.
Specialisation: Insurance lawyer advising major insurers, loss adjusters, loss assessors and self-insured companies. Experience in prosecuting and defending claims for business interruption and consequential loss. Also advises on professional negligence claims and commercial contracts disputes. Successfuly acted in connection with the appeal of a decision of the Pension Ombudsman where the value of the claim, had the appeal not succeeded, would have meant a liability of approximately £40 million to the client.
Prof. Memberships: Member of the Law Society
Career: Joined Shoosmiths in 1984 as a trainee. Qualified in 1986. Associate in 1987. Salaried Partner in 1990 and Equity Partner in 1999.

SANDELSON, Jeremy
Clifford Chance, London (020) 7600 1000
jeremy.sandelson@cliffordchance.com
Specialisation: Specialising in commercial litigation, including securities disputes, mergers and acquisitions litigation and regulatory investigations. Regular speaker at seminars. Recently involved in the Thyssen litigation in Bermuda.
Career: Charterhouse School; Cambridge University (scol). Qualified 1981; partner *Clifford Chance* 1988; Secretary Takeovers and Mergers Panel 1982-1984.
Personal: Born 1957.

SHAW, Murray W.A.
Biggart Baillie, Glasgow (0141) 228 8000
mshaw@biggartbaillie.co.uk
Head of Litigation Department.
Specialisation: Partner in the litigation department specialising in construction law (contentious and non-contentious) and planning law. Law Society accredited in both areas as well as Licensed Insolvency Practitioner. Work includes commercial litigation including contract disputes, building contract diputes and arbitration, and planning (with particular reference to the energy industry). Author of chapter on liquidation in 'Scottish Insolvency Casebook', and has written several articles on insolvency for the IBA Journal. Speaker on courses on insolvency and building contracts.
Prof. Memberships: International Bar Association; Law Society of Scotland.
Career: Qualified 1982. Assistant solicitor, *Biggart, Baillie & Gifford* 1982-85 and 1986-87 Assistant *Speechly Bircham*, London, 1985-86. Partner, *Biggart, Baillie & Gifford* since 1987.
Personal: Educated at Dundee University (LL.B Hons 1980).Leisure pursuits include golf, reading and rugby. Born 25th September 1957. Lives in Glasgow.

SHERRINGTON, Patrick P.
Lovells, London (020) 7296 2000
patrick.sherrington@lovells.com
Specialisation: Commercial Litigation. Extensive experience of international commercial litigation, arbitration and ADR, especially in the fields of banking and finance, energy, product liability and professional negligence. Leads the firm's ADR practice and regularly sits as a mediator. Author of: 'Civil Litigation' published in Hong Kong by Longmans, 2nd edition 1996; writes and regularly speaks on his specialist areas of practice.
Prof. Memberships: Admitted in the UK, Hong Kong and Australia (NSW). Law Society of England & Wales, Solicitors' European Group, City of London Solicitors' Company, Fellow of the Chartered Institute of Arbitrators, Law Society of Hong Kong, Inter-Pacific Bar Association, LawAsia, International Bar Association.
Career: Articled *Lovells* 1978-80; resident in New York 1982-84; Partner 1985; resident in Hong Kong 1987-96; CEDR accredited mediator; Higher Courts (Civil proceedings) qualification; Law Society of Hong Kong Council Member 1990-96; Vice President 1993-96; Council Member Inter-Pacific Bar Association 1990-96; Governor Advocacy Institute of Hong Kong 1994-96.

SINCLAIR, Jonathan
Eversheds, Leeds (0113) 243 0391
jonathansinclair@eversheds.co.uk
Partner. Head of Commercial Dispute Management Group for Leeds and Manchester. National Head of Risk Management.
Specialisation: Management and resolution of business disputes for corporate clients. Particular expertise in relation to warranty, product liability and competition matters. Also advises on risk management projects.
Prof. Memberships: Law Society.
Career: Qualified in 1987. *Clifford Chance*, London 1985-89. Joined *Eversheds*, Leeds 1989. Partner 1992.
Personal: Born 1961. Oxford University (1st) 1979-82. Lives in Ilkley. "Leisure" mainly keeping up with son and two daughters at football, tennis etc.

SINGLETON, Bernard
Gateley Wareing, Birmingham (0121) 234 0000

SKREIN, Michael
Richards Butler, London (020) 7247 6555
Partner.
Specialisation: A leading lawyer in intellectual property, media and aviation. Work is mainly litigation, but also advisory, particularly in relation to insurance and advertising and media clearance work. Specialist areas of work include administrative law, aviation, competition, contempt of court, defamation, insurance, intellectual property (the law of confidence, copyright, patents and trade marks), international law and judicial review. Has years of experience in the aviation, food and drink, insurance, leisure (including sports) and media industries as well as many other areas of litigation after over 20 years as a litigation partner in a firm with very broad and notably international scope of practice.
Prof. Memberships: Fellow of the Society for Advanced Legal Studies; Law Society; The City of London Solicitors' Company; Copinger Society, the Baltic Exchange.
Career: Articled *Richards, Butler & Co.* 1971; qualified 1973; Partner since 1976; Head of Litigation Department 1990 to 1996; lectured on advertising law, copyright infringement, intellectual property and defamation implications of the Internet, libel and trade marks; chair of the 'Protecting the Media' series of conferences, the market leader.
Personal: Born 1947. Educated at Oxford University (MA, Modern History) and the University of Southern California (AM *magna cum laude* International Relations). Honor Society of *Phi Kappa Phi*.

SLEIGH, Russell H.P.
Lovells, London (020) 7296 2000
russell.sleigh@lovells.com
Specialisation: Managing partner, litigation and dispute resolution practice. Experienced in wide range of international commercial litigation, in particular corporate, banking and regulatory disputes and multi-jurisdictional fraud issues. Acted on numerous official investigations on behalf of the authorities and of other parties involved. Also experienced in media law issues.
Career: Qualified 1973. Partner 1980. New York office 1977-80. Paris office 1990-93.

SMALL, Graham
Rowe & Cohen, Manchester 0161 830 4600
Specialisation: Commercial litigation and dispute resolution. Head of Department Act mainly for SMEs/OMBs and high net worth entrepreneurs, covering the full spectrum of commercial disputes. Increaseing international dimension to trade disputes and within last 12 months, has handled/advised on issues arising in North America, South Africa, Far East (Hong Kong, Taiwan, Vietnam), Middle East (Dubi, Yemen) and pan-European.
Prof. Memberships: Law Society; British Association for Sport and Law.
Personal: Family, work, sport, art.

SMITH, Hugh E.
Andrew M. Jackson & Co, Hull (01482) 325242
Head of Litigation
Specialisation: Substantial area of practice involves retail law covering Trading Standards, Health and Safety, Consumer Protection and Consumer Safety. Particular specialism in the vitamin and fish industry. Commercial Litigation; contractual disputes both international and domestic, company and partnership disputes, commercial property disputes, professional negligence, defamation and passing off. Represents finance houses in respect of consumer complaints/recoveries.
Prof. Memberships: Member of the Law Society and the Food Law Group. Also an ADR mediator.
Career: Admitted 1983. Joined present firm in 1989 becoming a Partner in 1991 in charge of the Commercial Litigation Division.
Personal: Born 16.01.59. Attended Nottingham University (LLB Hons).

SOLOMAN, Martin
Hay & Kilner, Newcastle-upon-Tyne (0191) 232 8345
lawyers@hay-kilner.co.uk
Specialisation: Full range of commercial disputes including contracts, shareholder disputes, professional negligence, partnership disputes, consturction, mediation, breach of warranty claims arising out of purchase/sales of businesses, defamation, copyright and trademark litigation, litigation relating to development of land.
Prof. Memberships: Law Society, Chairman of a Health Authority Disciplinary Committee.
Career: Educated at University of Kent 1971 - 1974. Joined *Hay & Kilner* in 1984 becomming a Partner that year.
Personal: Born 1953. Lives in Newcastle upon Tyne; leisure pursuits include family, skiing, music and cycling.

SORRELL, Christopher
Wacks Caller, Manchester (0161) 957 8888

SPARROW, Edward C.A.
Ashurst Morris Crisp, London (020) 7638 1111
Specialisation: General commercial litigation and dispute resolution (mergers and acquisitions, Stock Exchange transactions and management and trading of securities/other financial instruments); energy sector disputes (offshore construction, exploration and extraction contracts); professional negligence, insolvency and insurance; financial services and professional regulation; and civil fraud.
Prof. Memberships: Law Society.
Career: Ampleforth College; Lincoln College, Oxford. Articled *Ashurst Morris Crisp*; qualified 1977; partner 1981; head of litigation department 1993.
Personal: Born 1953; resides London.

SPOONER, Andrew Nicolas
Martineau Johnson, Birmingham (0121) 200 3300
andrew.spooner@martjohn.com
Partner and Head of Litigation Department.
Specialisation: Main area of practice is commercial litigation including major claims for breach of contract and tort. In particular, handles claims arising from product liability and defective goods and machinery. Has acted in a variety of large claims involving the engineering industry, including robots, cranes, mining equipment, furnaces, diesel trains, power stations, industrial conveyors, plastic extrusions, computers, boilers, radiators and hi tech safety devices. Author of articles for 'Court Brief'. Addressed seminars on Trading Conditions, the Millennium Bomb, the Woolf Reforms and resolving disputes by mediation.
Prof. Memberships: Chartered Institute of Arbitrators, Centre for Dispute Resolution, Association of Midlands Mediators.
Career: Qualified in 1978. Partner in 1980 and Head of Litigation in 1989. Fellow of the Chartered Institute of Arbitrators in 1995 and Accredited Mediator (CEDR). Solicitor Member of the Solicitors Disciplinary Tribunal.
Personal: Holds an LLB (1975). Leisure interests include golf, cricket, walking the dogs and the Arts.

SPRING, Paul
Mills Selig, Belfast 028/9024/3878
See under Defamation, p.297

STEWART, David L.
Morton Fraser, Solicitors, Edinburgh (0131) 247 1000
dls@morton-fraser.com
Partner in Litigation Department.
Specialisation: Acting for the International Oil Pollution Compensation Fund in all damage claims following upon the Braer Oil Tanker casualty in Shetland. Reparation, Judicial Review.
Prof. Memberships: WS Society.
Career: Partner in *Morton Fisher* since 1971.
Publications: 'Judicial Review in Scotland' for the 'Environmental Judicial Review Bulletin'.
Personal: Attended Cambridge and Edinburgh Universities. Married and living in Edinburgh. Leisure activities include skiing and travel.

STONE, P.B.
DLA, Leeds (08700) 111111
paul.stone@dla.com
Partner, Head of Commercial Litigation, DLA, Leeds Office.
Specialisation: Paul specialises in Corporate/Commercial Litigation including advising on major international disputes involving complex multi-party litigation. He has considerable experience of advising both media clients and corporate/commercial clients on media/marketing law related issues as well as working with PR agencies and other professionals to assist clients in crisis situations. In the past year, the Commercial Litigation Department in Leeds had been involved in a series of defamation, breach of confidence and related disputes including a growing number of cases of trade libel of various types. Paul's team has both pursued and defended a series of complaints to the PCC, BCC and ITC, as well as other associated regulatory bodies such as the ASA. They have, also, been involved in a series of applications to Court for media clients involving challenges to restrictive reporting orders and similar issues.
Career: Born 1960. Read Jurisprudence at Worcester College, Oxford - Upper Second Class Degree. Articled *Charles Russell & Co* 1983-85. Joined *Clifford Chance (Clifford Turner)* April 1986. Joined *Dibb Lupton* in Leeds as Partner in the Commercial Litigation Department in October 1993.
Personal: Hill walking, cricket, reading and music.

STYLE, Christopher J.D.
Linklaters (A member firm of Linklaters & Alliance), London (020) 7456 4286
christopher.style@linklaters.com
Partner and head of litigation and arbitration
Specialisation: Specialises in commercial litigation. Has practised in proceedings before the High Court of Justice and Commercial Court. Has conducted numerous arbitrations, both ad hoc and institutional (ICC, LMAA, LCIA etc). Also advised on questions of public international law before international tribunals. Extensive experience of all forms of urgent injunctive relief and a specialist in jurisdictional issues and questions of conflict of laws. Member of London Solicitors Litigation Association, International Bar Association and the City of London Solicitors' Company. Fellow of Chartered Institute of Arbitrators, Solicitor Advocate (Higher Courts Civil), accredited Mediator.

SWANSON, Alayne
Maclay Murray & Spens, Glasgow (0141) 248 5011
aes@maclaymurrayspens.co.uk
Specialisation: Partner in Litigation Department; Solicitor Advocate with 16 years of experience as a commercial litigator; specialist areas include contractual disputes, arbitration, employment law, media law, debt collection, and insolvency. Major cases include: Three major Court of Session Commercial cases concerning contracts for supply of goods/services; two Commercial Agency cases; Resisting Minority Shareholder's Petition; Challenging retention of title clause for Receivers & Major contractual dispute for Cable & Wireless. Appears regularly in Sheriff Court and Court of Session.
Career: Attended University of Edinburgh (LLB Hons, Dip LP). Articled at *Shepherd & Wedderburn* 1982-84; assistant solicitor Glasgow 1984-85; foreign associate at *Hughes Hubbard & Reed*,New York 1986-87; assistant solicitor *Bird Semple Fyfe* Ireland 1987-90; partner 1990-93; Partner *Dundas & Wilson* 1994-97; Solicitor Advocate 1996.
Personal: Born 1959. Resides Glasgow. Leisure interests include music, playing cello and piano, walking.

TAYLOR, Tim
SJ Berwin & Co, London (020) 7533 2222
tim.taylor@sjberwin.com
Specialisation: Complex commercial litigation with an emphasis on cross-border disputes. Co-author of Sweet and Maxwell's European litigation Handbook. Major cases in the last 12 months include: acting in Federal Republic of Nigeria v General Abacha (deceased), Brunei Investment v Agency Prince Jefri Bolkiah, Ladbroke Clubs v Commissoners of Customs and Excise.
Prof. Memberships: International Bar Association; American Bar Association.
Career: MA Oxon.

THOMAS, Paul
Halliwell Landau, Manchester (0161) 835 3003
pathomas@halliwells.co.uk
Partner, 1981. Head of Litigation and Corporate Recovery Department.

Specialisation: All types of commercial litigation, professional negligence, Interim Remedies & Freezing Orders, landlord and tenant, other property-related disputes.
Prof. Memberships: Law Society of England and Wales.
Career: Qualified 1979, partner at *Halliwell Landau* since 1981.
Personal: Born 1954; squash, rugby, French language and culture.

TOUT, Liz
Denton Wilde Sapte, London (020) 7242 1212

TRANTER, Ian
Chaffe Street, Manchester (0161) 236 5800

TROTTER, John G.
Lovells, London (020) 7296 2000
john.trotter@lovells.com
See under Professional Negligence, p.686

TURNBULL, John
Linklaters (A member firm of Linklaters & Alliance), London (020) 7456 4310
john.turnbull@linklaters.com
Specialisation: Partner, litigation department. Specialising in corporate finance litigation, all contentious aspects of mergers and acquisitions work and professional negligence. After qualifying in 1983, became partner at *Linklaters* in 1989.

TURTLE, W. Brian W.
Carson & McDowell, Belfast (028) 9024 4951
Specialisation: Commercial litigation (30 years of practice in all major areas). Intellectual Property. Professional Negligence. Employment law/Industrial relations to include unfair dismissal, race, religious and sex discrimination claims.
Prof. Memberships: Law Society of Northern Ireland
Career: 1968: LLB - QUB; joined *Carson & McDowell* 1971: Admitted as solicitor 1971: partner in *Carson & McDowell.*

TYLER, Alfred J.
Balfour & Manson, Edinburgh (0131) 200 1210
ajt@balfour-manson.co.uk
See under Personal Injury, p.647

WATSON, Peter B.
Levy & McRae, Glasgow (0141) 307 2311
See under Defamation, p.297

WATSON, Peter M.
Allen & Overy, London (020) 7330 3000
Specialisation: Deals with the full range of contentious commercial work in particular aviation, freezing orders, conflict of laws, professional negligence, banking, finance and commercial fraud, judicial review and trade promotion issues. Member of the Civil Procedure Rules Committee.
Career: Assistant solicitor *Allen & Overy* 1981-86, seconded to *Allen & Overy* Dubai office 1984-86; partner *Allen & Overy* 1987.
Personal: BA Oxford University 1978. Born 1956.

WHITTELL, Mark
Cobbetts, Manchester (0161) 833 3333
mark.whittell@cobbetts.co.uk
Specialisation: Commercial Litigation including banking professional negligence, franchise disputes, insolvency
Prof. Memberships: CEDR, Acredited Mediator
Career: Articled 1980-82. Assistant Solicitor *Glass Bajoheue Miller* 1982-84. Assistant Solicitor *G W Towels* 1984-86. *Cobbetts* 1986-to date - mode partner 1989.
Personal: 43 years old 3 children. Educated Marple Hall Grammer School & Sheffield University. Lacrosse player at international & veteran international level. Interests, enthusiastic sportsman, wine, travel.

WILLETTS, Jayne
Hammond Suddards Edge, Birmingham (0121) 200 2001
jayne.willetts@hammondsuddardsedge.com
Specialisation: Partner. Specialises in professional negligence and pensions litigation. Qualified as first woman High Court Solicitor Advocate 1994.
Prof. Memberships: First female Chairman Law Society National Young Solicitors' Group 1990-91; first woman President of Birmingham Law Society 2000-2001; member Court Users Committees for both Mercantile Court and the Chancery Division in Birmingham.
Career: Qualified in 1982. Joined *Edge Ellison* 1988 - Partner from 1991.
Personal: Born 1958. Educated at Stourbridge High School for Girls and University College London. Leisure interests include equestrian sports.

WILLIAMS, Gareth J.
Hugh James Ford Simey, Cardiff (029) 2022 4871
Partner and Head of Commercial Litigation Department.
Specialisation: Personal injury litigation for insurers. Has acted for insurers for more than 20 years and undertaken the usual range of personal injury work. Has a particular interest in health and safety matters. Also deals with commercial litigation, acting for a number of local companies and partnerships by whom he is regularly instructed to deal with contractual and other disputes. Advises major sports governing body on litigation and constitutional issues.
Prof. Memberships: Law Society; F.O.I.L.
Career: Joined *Hugh James* in 1975 and qualified in 1976. Became a Partner in 1978. First Solicitor in Wales to be appointed a Licensed Insolvency Practitioner. Deputy District Judge from 1991 to date.
Personal: Born 5th September 1951. Educated at Glan Clwyd High School 1962-69 and University College of Wales, Aberystwyth 1969-72 (Morgan Owen Law Prizeman). Leisure pursuits include sport, reading and music. Lives in Cowbridge.

WILLIAMS, Peter Rhys
Burges Salmon, Bristol (0117) 939 2223
peter.williams@burges-salmon.com
See under Agriculture, p.78

WILLIAMSON, David
Brodies WS, Edinburgh (0131) 228 3777
dswilliamson@brodies.co.uk
Partner in Litigation Department.
Specialisation: Solicitor-Advocate handling general commercial litigation and specialising in intellectual property, employment law, partnership disputes and professional negligence. Experienced speaker at conferences and seminars. Lectured for over 5 years at University of Edinburgh in Civil Procedure.
Career: Qualified in 1971. With *Simpson & Marwick* 1969-75, latterly as Partner. Joined *Brodies WS* as a Partner in 1976. Part time Industrial Tribunals Chairman and Temporary Sheriff. Criminal Injuries Compensation Board member.
Personal: Born in 1949. Educated at Royal High School, Edinburgh and University of Edinburgh. Leisure interests include cricket and hill walking. Lives in Edinburgh.

WILSON, Allan E.
Morgan Cole, Cardiff (029) 2038 5385
allan.wilson@morgan-cole.com
Specialisation: Handles a wide variety of commercial litigation work, including substantial, high profile matters. Has acted for a range of institutional and corporate clients concerning competition, professional indemnity and construction claims, as well as buyout/acquisition disputes. Work also covers defamation and transportation related claims. Advised Rugby Clubs on disputes with governing bodies and International Rugby Board on regulatory and competition, matters including dealing with the competition directorate in Brussels. Also dealt with engineering claims resulting from Severn Bridge gantry collapse. Has conducted many mediations and has sat as a mediator.
Prof. Memberships: Law Society, Association of European Lawyers, TECSA, Mediator ADR Net Ltd.
Career: Hutton Grammar School, Preston 1968-75; University of Surrey, BSc Linguistics (German) 1975-79; College of law, Guildford 1979-80; *Slaughter and May* 1980-85; *Morgan Cole* 1985 to date, Partner from 1986. Currently divisional director for litigation.
Personal: Golf, indoor rowing. Married, two sons. Lives near Raglan, Monmouthshire.

WILSON, Michael W.C.
Elliott Duffy Garrett, Belfast (028) 9024 5034

WINTERBURN, Anthony B.
DLA, Manchester (08700) 111111
anthony.winterburn@dla.com
Specialisation: Commercial contract and warranty disputes, corporate litigation, including boardroom and shareholder disputes and professional negligence claims.
Career: Qualified 1988 and rejoined *Alsop Wilkinson* (now *Dibb Lupton Alsop*) in 1989. Partner 1999
Personal: Born 17th November 1962. Attended Hull University 1981-84. Leisure pursuits - sport. Lives in Failsworth, Manchester.

WOOD, Ashley
Russell & Creswick, Sheffield (0114) 276 7481

YORK, Stephen D.
Hammond Suddards Edge, London (020) 7655 1000
stephen.york@hammondsuddardsedge.com
Specialisation: Commercial Dispute Resolution and International Arbitration (both as Counsel and as Arbitrator), principally in the Civil Engineering and Construction Industry, Software Engineering and Gas Contracts Industries.
Prof. Memberships: Fellow, Chartered Institute of Arbitrators. Admitted in Hong Kong and ACT, Australia. Member of ORSA and British Computer Society.
Career: Articled at *Slaughter & May* and *Ledbury, Merry, Bristol*; Assistant at *Masons* (1982-84). *Baker & McKenzie*, Hong Kong (1984-86); *Masons*, Hong Kong (1986-1991), Partner in 1988. Partner at *Hammond Suddards*, London in 1993. Author: 'Practical ADR' published by Sweet & Maxwell, December 1996.
Personal: Married with four children. Interests include fast motor cars, gastronomic enterprises and travelling abroad.

LITIGATION (PROPERTY)

RESEARCH APPROVED BY BMRB: *For this edition,* Chambers' *researchers conducted 6083 interviews – 4408 with law firms, 598 with barristers and 1077 with clients.*

The validity of the research was scrutinised by BMRB International, who audited both the methodology and the results at our offices in July 2000. They interviewed Chambers' researchers and cross-checked sample interviews. Details of the audit appear on page 7.

LONDON

LITIGATION (PROPERTY) • London	Ptnrs	Assts
❶ Nabarro Nathanson	2	13
❷ Berwin Leighton	1	5
Clifford Chance	1	5
Denton Wilde Sapte	2	6
Herbert Smith	2	6
Linklaters	1	8
Lovells	2	7
❸ Ashurst Morris Crisp	1	7
CMS Cameron McKenna	2	5
Dechert	2	6
D J Freeman	1	2
Lawrence Graham	2	4
❹ Masons	3	11
Rowe & Maw	2	2
Simmons & Simmons	1	5
SJ Berwin & Co	1	1
❺ Macfarlanes	2	5
Olswang	1	2
Radcliffes	1	2
Speechly Bircham	2	3
❻ Boodle Hatfield	2	3
Dewar Hogan	2	7
DLA	-	2
Maxwell Batley	2	1

LEADING INDIVIDUALS	
❶ **BRADFORD Katie** Linklaters	**CHEFFINGS Nicholas** Lovells
FRANCIS Penelope Lawrence Graham	**HUTCHINSON Lucy** Herbert Smith
KING Vivien D J Freeman	**MADDEN Michael** Ashurst Morris Crisp
MILLER Wendy Clifford Chance	**PEET Carole** Denton Wilde Sapte
PICKSTON John Clifford Chance	**RICKARD Jennifer** Nabarro Nathanson
WALTHAM Anne Lovells	
❷ **COHEN Roger** Berwin Leighton	**FREYNE Michele** Rowe & Maw
HEWSON Carol Simmons & Simmons	**MASTERS David** Dawson & Co
MOLYNEUX Anne Masons	**TRAVERS Iain** Nabarro Nathanson
WEBBER Lesley Beachcroft Wansbroughs	
❸ **BRIERLEY Ian** Clifford Chance	**COX David** Paisner & Co
CROSS Siobhan Masons	**FOX-EDWARDS Jane** Lawrence Graham
HIGHMORE Robert Radcliffes	**HOGAN Ronald** Dewar Hogan
WALKER Andrew CMS Cameron McKenna	
WILLETTS Guy Theodore Goddard	

Within each band, firms are listed alphabetically. *See **Profiles** on page 576*

Nabarro Nathanson The leaders for their *"sheer presence"* in property litigation. The practice benefits from an enviable list of property clients and is seen to have a wide client base. *"Larger than life"* **Iain Travers** heads the team and *"knowledgeable"* **Jennifer Rickard** is *"good to negotiate with," "committed"* and *"someone to respect."* Acting for Ogilvy & Mather in a £15m claim for damages for misrepresentation against Canary Wharf Ltd. Redevelopment and rent review work have featured heavily at the practice recently. **Clients:** Land Securities; GE Capital; British Land.

Berwin Leighton Well regarded for its professionalism, the team is led by **Roger Cohen** who *"quietly gets on with it."* The practice has particular expertise in retail landlord and tenant matters, often acting for institutional investors. Acted for Tesco Stores Ltd in a contentious rent review determination with British Land. **Clients:** Prudential; Tesco Stores Ltd; Property Advisers to the Civil Estate

Clifford Chance A *"first-class"* team that *"makes things happen."* The practice acts for banks, retailers, developers and property institutions, and is increasingly instructed by US and European clients. Led by *"extraordinarily able"* **John Pickston**, the team also includes **Wendy Miller** *("a valuable asset")* and **Ian Brierley**, described as *"a coming force"* in property litigation. Acting in a major city centre shopping complex redevelopment project involving multiple litigation with tenants. **Clients:** Burford Group plc; CGU plc; Witkoff Group.

Denton Wilde Sapte An *"unstuffy"* team held in high regard by the market. Handles development based work, portfolio management and is known for its expertise in the retail and leisure sectors. The practice is run from both London and Milton Keynes with clients being largely London based. Stand-out practitioner here is **Carole Peet** a *"top person"* who *"knows when to be tough."* Recently appointed by Barclays to act on two of their three regional portfolios. Also handle significant portfolio management for Whitbread, CNT, the Crown Estate and Equitable Life. **Clients:** CNT; J Sainsbury Group plc; Barclays Bank plc.

Herbert Smith **Lucy Hutchinson** may be *"fearsome"* and a *"hard fighter"* but the consensus is that the team is *"firm but fair"* and *"a pleasure to deal with."* Acted in a record-breaking rent review, a £15million trespass claim and corporate recovery aspects of property litigation. **Clients:** Hermes; Standard Life; Queensborough.

Linklaters Perceived to be handling *"quality, high-margin"* work. *"Tough opponent"* **Katie Bradford** leads the team and is reportedly an *"enthusiastic litigator."* The practice still seems, to some, to be focused around her. Acted in Prudential Assurance Co Ltd v Waterloo Real Estate Inc., a widely reported case concerning squatters rights over a party wall in Knightsbridge and in a number of high level rent reviews, an area where they are *"tops."* **Clients:** Canary Wharf; Atlantic Bar & Grill; Merrill Lynch.

Lovells Felt to be *"a force on the big cases,"* the team has drawn positive comment. The approach of the team is reputedly *"hard but not unreasonable."* **Nicholas Cheffings** is *"respected for his legal skills"* and **Anne Waltham** is said to be *"particularly good,"* tough when necessary but *"able to see the broader picture."* Acted in securing timely vacant possession of a redevelopment site with 140 different parties in occupation. **Clients:** Prudential Corp.; Barclays; BAA Lynton.

Ashurst Morris Crisp *"Pragmatic"* **Michael Madden** heads the team and is well regarded. The practice covers all areas of commercial property litigation, acting for landlords, funders, developers and tenants. However, the team is perceived to be going through an unsettled patch, following personnel losses in the property department. Acted in the settlement of a £multi-million break clause dispute. **Clients:** BT plc; British Gas; Thames Water.

CMS Cameron McKenna Viewed as *"solid and dangerous competition."* **Andrew Walker** heads the practice, which acted for a major developer defending claims in relation to tenants' rights of first refusal on sale. Received instructions on property disputes, landlord and tenant disputes, insolvency property matters and debt recovery. **Clients:** The Wellcome Trust; The Crown Estate Commissioners; Heron Land Developments Ltd.

Dechert Continuing to be viewed as *"abrasive litigators,"* the practice is increasingly active in transactional based litigation. Other aspects of the practice include joint venture disputes, professional negligence and insolvency as they relate to property. Acted in the Canary Wharf rent review. **Clients:** PACE; Dixons; Frogmore.

D J Freeman Part of the property services department, this team acted in a leading case regarding derogation of grant before the High Court. The practice is still considered to be a force in the field, acting for both landlord and tenant clients. *"Aggressive"* **Vivien King**, a *"hard fighter"* with *"huge energy"* has maintained her profile among the upper echelons of the sector. **Clients:** Benchmark; Capital & Provident; Post Office.

Lawrence Graham *"Commercially aware"* **Penny Francis** *"cuts to the chase"* and *"comes up with different approaches."* As head of the property department, however, she is less seen in active litigation these days. *"Sound"* **Jane Fox-Edwards** is now team head. The practice is seen to be *"rebuilding"* following Lesley Webber's departure to Beachcroft Wansbroughs, and *"continues to impress."* Acted in the Park Air case in the House of Lords. **Clients:** Legal & General Property Ltd; BT; National Farmers Union.

Masons A *"capable and aggressive"* team which has a *"good feel about it"* and is *"pleasant to deal with."* The team keeps a lower profile than most but acts for the licensed trade and general commercial property clients. Currently acting in an appeal to Luxembourg from the Court of Appeal decision in Courage v Crehan on issues relating to breaches of Article 81. Head of department **Anne Molyneux** is *"praised to the sky"* and **Siobhan Cross** is considered to be *"thoroughly sensible."* **Clients:** Inntrepreneur Pub Co; Unique Pub Co; Portman Family Settled Estates.

Rowe & Maw The team, headed by **Michele Freyne**, has been involved in a number of high profile cases in the last year. An appeal to the House of Lords over a refusal of consent to assignment and a leading case widening the law of trespass of land were notable highlights of the past year. **Clients:** Oliver Ashworth Ltd; Pearl Assurance plc; Unilever plc.

Simmons & Simmons Provides advice on a range of contentious property issues such as landlord and tenant for commercial and residential clients, real property, planning and insolvency disputes. **Carol Hewson** leads the team which has acted in a substantial service charge dispute, breach of covenants cases and ratings appeals over the past twelve months. **Clients:** Scudder Threadneedle Property Investments Ltd; Wereldhave Property Corp plc.

S J Berwin & Co This practice is perceived by the market to have been weakened since the departure of Vivien King. However, the team retains a respectable and diverse client base, and recently settled by mediation a litigated nuisance claim against a private company developer client. **Clients:** British Land; AXA Sun Life; Hilton International Ltd.

Macfarlanes Acts for a range of clients including institutional landlords, commercial occupiers, residential landlords and tenants and agricultural landlords. The contentious property group has been involved in Mareva injunctions, 1954 Act renewals and possession proceedings in relation to Assured and Rent Act tenancies. **Clients:** Cordiant plc; King Sturge; Scottish Life.

Olswang Generally good comments on this *"strong"* practice whose name *"keeps coming up."* Involved in substantial dilapidations cases recently in respect of warehouse premises and industrial space, as well as a claim for arrears of rent and resisting (successfully) a counter-claim for breach of a repairing covenant. **Clients:** Helical Bar plc; Prestbury Group plc; Minerva plc.

Radcliffes *"Knowledgeable"* **Robert Highmore** heads this *"effective"* team. Acts on a substantial volume of residential landlord and tenant cases in addition to its general commercial property litigation work. Acted for the Portman Estate in the Court of Appeal in connection with a claim for possession of valuable residential premises. **Clients:** The Portman Settled Estate; The Crown Estate Commissioners; The Church Commissioners for England.

Speechly Bircham A *"safe pair of hands,"* the practice is sometimes felt to be *"less dynamic"* than some of its competitors. Clients include property companies, institutions and other substantial organisations. Acting in what is believed to be the largest dilapidations claim ever, against a government department. **Clients:** P&O Group.

Boodle Hatfield Provides advice on lease renewals, consents to assignment, dilapidations and enfranchisement claims, rent reviews and service charge disputes. Successfully defended a £750k claim for alleged unpaid commission for introducing tenants to an office block. **Clients:** The Grosvenor Estate.

Dewar Hogan This *"thorough"* firm led by **Ronald Hogan** is a niche property litigation specialist, handling complete cases and acting as litigation support. Advising a developer on contentious issues arising out of conditional agreements to acquire airspace over a railway cutting from a railway company in a substantial development project. **Clients:** Property companies; investment banks.

DLA While general opinion sees the firm as primarily active in the North, the London practice is recommended on the basis of *"competence"* and an impressive client list. Acted in the ground-breaking decision on s37 of the Landlord & Tenant Act 1954 in Sun Life Assurance Society plc v Racal Tracs Ltd and Another. **Clients:** Sun Life Assurance Society plc; Granada Group plc; Greenwich NHS Trust.

Maxwell Batley Considered to possess *"good clients"* and to be *"doing sound work,"* this practice is an adjunct to the commercial property section of the firm and provides dispute resolution support. Handles the bulk of arrears related work and associated litigation for the English portfolio of the BT and Post Office pension schemes. Similar work is undertaken for National Mutual Life Assurance in respect of their property portfolio. **Clients:** Hermes (panel); National Mutual Life.

Other Notable Practitioners **David Cox** from Paisner & Co, **David Masters** from Dawson & Co, **Lesley Webber** from Beachcroft Wansbroughs and **Guy Willetts** from Theodore Goddard are all recommended names for this work.

THE SOUTH & THAMES VALLEY

LITIGATION (PROPERTY) • The South & Thames Valley	Ptnrs	Assts
❶ **DMH** Brighton	2	1
❷ **Coffin Mew & Clover** Portsmouth	1	3
Thomson Snell & Passmore Tonbridge	1	2
❸ **Brachers** Maidstone	3	3
Cripps Harries Hall Tunbridge Wells, Kent	1	2
❹ **Harold Benjamin Littlejohn** Harrow	3	1
Rawlison & Butler Crawley	2	3

LEADING INDIVIDUALS
❶ **ALLEN Martin** DMH

Within each band, firms are listed alphabetically. *See **Profiles** on page 576*

DMH A dedicated property litigation team headed by **Martin Allen**. The *"principal players"* in the region, acting primarily for commercial, institutional and public sector clients. Enfranchisement, environmental and housing association related litigation services are provided in addition to landlord and tenant work. Acted in the complex privity-related action Sun Life v Tantofex, release from liability. **Clients:** Croydon Council; Wandsworth Council; T M Retail Group.

Coffin Mew & Clover Acting for many RSL clients, a healthcare trust, a bank and commercial estate agents. Matters handled include anti-social behaviour, declarations of ownership and adverse possession. **Clients:** Medina HA; Eastleigh HA; Portsmouth HA.

Thomson Snell & Passmore Acts on landlord and tenant building contracts, possession actions, enfranchisement, dilapidations, planning appeals and property-related professional indemnity work. **Clients:** Commercial and agricultural landlords and tenants.

Brachers Property litigation is undertaken by a specialist team in the commercial litigation, town planning and environmental law departments. Agricultural work is perceived to make up the bulk of the litigation undertaken. **Clients:** Investors, developers, estate owners and farmers.

Cripps Harries Hall A dedicated property litigation unit that specialises in planning-related litigation and judicial review work. Advising Union Rail in connection with the Channel Tunnel. **Clients:** A major property portfolio company; Crown Prosecution Service; HM Customs & Excise.

Harold Benjamin Littlejohn Acts in contested renewals under the Landlord and Tenant Act, boundary disputes, repossessions and Housing Association matters. Negotiating the termination of a subtenancy in a commercial lease. **Clients:** A major national house builder; Ladbrokes.

Rawlison & Butler The practice, which has a *"reliable reputation,"* is part of the commercial litigation department. Acts on general landlord and tenant disputes, professional negligence cases, and has a niche specialism in dilapidations. **Clients:** J.T. Davies & Sons Ltd; Amadeus Marketing UK Ltd, subsidiaries of the Crest Nicholson Group.

SOUTH WEST

LITIGATION (PROPERTY) • South West	Ptnrs	Assts
❶ **Burges Salmon** Bristol	6	15
❷ **Osborne Clarke OWA,** Bristol	2	6
❸ **Bond Pearce** Exeter, Plymouth	1	3
Cartwrights Bristol	1	2
Eversheds Bristol	-	2
Lyons Davidson Bristol	1	1
Masons Bristol	1	6
Veale Wasbrough Bristol	-	1
❹ **Beachcroft Wansbroughs** Bristol	1	2
Bevan Ashford Bristol	1	4
Bobbetts Mackan Bristol	1	3
Foot Anstey Sargent Plymouth	1	2
TLT Solicitors Bristol	1	2

LEADING INDIVIDUALS	
❶ **BEDFORD Richard** Burges Salmon	**BRIGGS Leona** Osborne Clarke
MORRIS Peter Eversheds	**ORME James** Osborne Clarke
❷ **BASTOW Martin** Lyons Davidson	**COX Brian** Bobbetts Mackan
HAM Neil Burges Salmon	**MARTIN Bonnie** Masons
PUDDICOMBE Nigel Cartwrights	

Within each band, firms are listed alphabetically. *See **Profiles** on page 576*

Burges Salmon Leading regional firm which undertakes substantial commercial property litigation and maintains a reputation for pre-eminence in agricultural property litigation. **Richard Bedford**, who specialises in professional negligence and insolvency-related disputes, is *"technically excellent."* **Neil Ham** specialises in commercial property and landlord/tenant disputes. Acted in the House of Lords case Barrett v Morgan, a leading case concerning the effect of a notice to quit on sub-tenancies. **Clients:** Transport Development Group plc; Nationwide; UCB Bank plc.

Osborne Clarke OWA A *"professional"* team with a *"strong"* regional presence. Acts for banks in property-related litigation and advises clients on duties to guarantors on disposal of property, disputes relating to mortgage priority, professional indemnity and other property-related issues. Led by **James Orme**, the practice also includes **Leona Briggs**, considered by some in the region to be the *"best in Bristol."* Acting in RBS v Etridge and others in the House of Lords. **Clients:** National Westminster Bank plc; Imperial Investments Ltd; Somerfield Stores Ltd.

Bond Pearce A dedicated team with particular strengths in freehold restrictive covenants, retail and Housing Association property-related disputes. The team is said to *"know their stuff."* Acted in a hotly contested adverse possession trial concerning the running of time under criminal trespass. **Clients:** B&Q plc; Coral Group; The National Trust (Exeter.)

Cartwrights The licensed trade comprises a substantial proportion of this team's practice, led by **Nigel Puddicombe**. Secured lending recoveries, foreclosures, environment and development contract disputes are among the work handled. The transport sector also provides important clients, with the firm continuing to act for Railtrack on renewals of business tenancies and termination of leases. **Clients:** Railtrack plc; Wolverhampton & Dudley Breweries plc; Morrells of Oxford Ltd.

Eversheds Acts for multiple retailers and financial institutions on 1954 Act renewals, breaches of covenant, possessions and injunctions. **Peter Morris** is described as a *"fearsome litigator."* Acting in the repossession of a listed mansion occupied as a conference centre. **Clients:** Forest Enterprise; Bristol and West Estates; BurgerKing Limited.

Lyons Davidson Acts for LPA receivers, universities and private investors, providing advice on landlord/tenant, arbitration proceedings, residential matters and security enforcement. Team head **Martin Bastow** is a *"safe pair of hands."* **Clients:** Lloyds TSB plc; AXA Sun Life Services plc; multiple licensees/brewers, builders.

Masons **Bonnie Martin**, a *"bright lawyer"* with a growing reputation, leads the department which is *"particularly knowledgeable."* The team provides a full service property litigation capacity. Recently appointed to act for Bath & North East Somerset DC in respect of property litigation work, following a competitive tender. **Clients:** Wereldhave Property Corp. plc; Bath & North East Somerset DC; Haven Leisure Ltd.

Veale Wasbrough Julie Exton's elevation to the bench has left an obvious void at this practice, which is, however *"still very visible."* The practice focuses on commercial landlord and tenant disputes. Instructed in relation to a manorial rights dispute for a major quarrying company. **Clients:** Great Mills (Retail) Ltd; PricewaterhouseCoopers; PACE.

Beachcroft Wansbroughs Despite the recent merger, the team is not seen to be substantially strengthened, and is regarded as *"mainly insurance and indemnity"* based. Advises on contested lease renewals, lease rectifications, restrictive covenants. Acted in Holding and Barnes plc v Hill House Hammond Ltd regarding the construction of repairing covenants in a lease. **Clients:** CGU; Bristol & West plc.

Bevan Ashford Acted for the Secretary of State for Health against a residential home developer in a dispute over a payment under a sale agreement. The practice also acts for Housing Associations and consequently is viewed as *"heavily public sector oriented."* Also acts for other landlords on possessions and injunctions, dilapidations, rent arrears and planning claims. **Clients:** Allied Domecq plc; Capitec; Secretary of State for Health.

Bobbetts Mackan A *"prime"* practice – if you are a borrower or tenant. Said to be *"turning away work"* due to popularity and *"really good at what they do." "Effective"* **Brian Cox** is thought of highly and with a measure of discomfort by those who oppose him. **Clients:** Individual tenants and borrowers.

Foot Anstey Sargent Acting primarily for commercial landlords, this dedicated unit is said to be *"solid and reliable."* Acted for a mining exploration firm in relation to contested lease renewal involving disclosure of sensitive commercial information. **Clients:** Ministry of Defence; Housing Associations; Plc's and Limited Companies.

TLT Solicitors The merger between Lawrence Tucketts and Trumps results in a firm that is viewed as *"a competitor"* by the serious players, due to an increased property client base. Felt to be particularly proficient on planning-related matters, the team successfully negotiated a settlement for a client against whom an injunction, specific performance and over £1m damages were raised. **Clients:** GE Capital Equipment Services Ltd; Alexandra plc; Strachan & Henshaw Ltd.

WALES

LITIGATION (PROPERTY) • Wales	Ptnrs	Assts
❶ **Eversheds** Cardiff	1	1
Hugh James Ford Simey Cardiff	1	2
❷ **Edwards Geldard** Cardiff	1	1
Morgan Cole Cardiff, Swansea	1	2

Within each band, firms are listed alphabetically.

Eversheds Advises on complex property litigation, often concerning contaminated land issues, arbitrations and professional negligence, in addition to traditional landlord and tenant matters. Recovered possession from several hundred travellers ensconced at a gas holder. **Clients:** Lloyds Bank plc; BG Property Holdings Ltd; Welsh Development Agency.

Hugh James Ford Simey Heavily involved with Housing Association work, the practice also acts for individuals, clubs and companies. Work includes landlord/tenant, dilapidations and possessions. Successfully defended a multi-million pound dilapidations claim against Companies House. **Clients:** Companies House; Charter HA; Wales & West HA

Edwards Geldard Acts in commercial property disputes on dilapidations, professional negligence, sale options and lease disputes. Handled a complex group action on a self-build development site, where the developer became bankrupt, and a professional negligence claim against his solicitor was successfully pursued. **Clients:** Williams plc; Hyder plc; Powergen plc.

Morgan Cole Seen to be primarily active in Solicitors Indemnity Fund and insurance work, the team still maintains a profile in the principality. **Clients:** Financial Institutions; major plcs; Housing Associations.

MIDLANDS

LITIGATION (PROPERTY) • Midlands	Ptnrs	Assts
❶ **Wragge & Co** Birmingham	1	8
❷ **Eversheds** Birmingham, Derby, Nottingham	1	4
Hammond Suddards Edge Birmingham	1	5
❸ **Pinsent Curtis** Birmingham	1	2
❹ **Martineau Johnson** Birmingham	1	2
❺ **Anthony Collins Solicitors** Birmingham	4	10
Browne Jacobson Nottingham	2	3
DLA Birmingham	1	3
Freethcartwright Nottingham	1	-

LEADING INDIVIDUALS	
❶ **KENT Paul** Pinsent Curtis	**LLOYD HOLT Suzanne** Wragge & Co
O'BRIEN Gary Eversheds	**SCOTT Gordon** Hammond Suddards Edge

Within each band, firms are listed alphabetically. *See **Profiles** on page 576*

Wragge & Co Led by the *"fabulous"* **Suzanne Lloyd Holt** who is *"always on the ball,"* this specialist team is recognised far and wide as leaders in the region. Possessing *"consistently high standards,"* the practice is said to be going *"from strength to strength."* Acts for investors, major developers and end users as well as public sector bodies. Handled a complex contested set of lease renewals for HSBC, complicated by the newly introduced Civil Procedure Rules. **Clients:** Calthorpe Estates; HSBC.

Hammond Suddards Edge About to become part of the firm's national property department integrated with the London team, this practice is praised for its *"efficiency."* Advising on commercial property matters and residential tenancies, the team is headed by the *"personable"* **Gordon Scott**. Acted on a major dilapidations trial for the Secretary of State for Health concerning a listed building. **Clients:** T&S Stores plc; Wilson Bowden plc; Aggregate Industries UK Ltd.

Eversheds **Gary O'Brien** is said to be an *"aggressive knockabout litigator."* He has also reputedly *"knocked the practice into shape."* The team are said to be *"big hitters"* and *"sound opponents."* Acts for blue-chip clients including institutions, commercial tenants, professional partnership and education establishments. Acted in the site clearance of the Bullring indoor market for Hammerson which involved the service of 2000 1954 Act notices. **Clients:** Bass Pensions; The Birmingham Alliance; Partco.

Pinsent Curtis *"Experienced"* **Paul Kent** heads the practice which is perceived to have a lower profile this year. The team advises on rent reviews and lands tribunals, and recently handled three contested lease renewals, a large dilapidations claim over contaminated land and a judicial review. **Clients:** Inland Revenue; Lex Group plc; Manders Group.

Martineau Johnson An *"institutional firm with institutional clients."* The team acts primarily on commercial property matters including boundary and rights of way disputes, actions against squatters, trust property disputes and dilapidations. Advised an international surveying firm on their own dilapidations claim and related issues. **Clients:** Private clients; landed estates; companies and property developers.

Anthony Collins Solicitors Combining the property litigation and social housing departments, the team acts for the licensed and leisure industries and general commercial clients. Reduced a dilapidations claim by negotiation for a commercial client. **Clients:** Halifax plc; Wolverhampton & Dudley Breweries plc; Hanover HA.

Browne Jacobson Part of the property department, this team is *"technically impressive"* and provides *"sound practical advice."* Advise both residential landlords and commercial owners and occupiers. Acted in Mace and others v Rutland Household Textiles Ltd. **Clients:** Fii Group plc; Vision Express.

DLA Acting for retail clients as well as property developers on management, lease renewals, dilapidations and rent reviews, the team is beginning to make a name for itself in the region. Brought proceedings in the High Court for unreasonably withholding consent, on behalf of a large retailing client. **Clients:** Dollond & Aitchison Ltd; Halfords Ltd; SCI Funerals Ltd.

Freethcartwright Advises Housing Associations, investors and landlords, with a speciality in anti-social behaviour cases. Conducted a dilapidations trial concerning a listed commercial property. **Clients:** Notts County Council; North British HA; Nottingham Community HA.

EAST ANGLIA

LITIGATION (PROPERTY) • East Anglia	Ptnrs	Assts
❶ **Eversheds** Ipswich, Norwich	1	2
Mills & Reeve Norwich	1	3
❷ **Hewitson Becke + Shaw** Cambridge	1	2

LEADING INDIVIDUALS
❶ **FALKNER James** Mills & Reeve
SCANNELL John Eversheds

Within each band, firms are listed alphabetically. *See **Profiles** on page 576*

Eversheds Includes a barrister in the team, which is led by the respected **John Scannell**. Provides the full range of property litigation services primarily for commercial landlords and tenants. Advised on a case for a local authority involving mooring rights on a tidal river. **Clients:** Lancaster plc; Ipswich BC; RMC Group plc.

Mills & Reeve **James Falkner** heads this highly regarded team and is felt to be *"pleasant to deal with."* The practice acts for the firm's clients in relation to disputes over commercial, agricultural and residential property. **Clients:** Cambridge colleges; Nokia UK Group; Wherry Limited Partnership.

Hewitson Becke + Shaw This team acts on landlord/tenant disputes, lease renewals, dilapidations and lands tribunals matters for the clients of the firm's commercial property department. Acted in a ransom case for a property developer in a claim arising out of shooting rights. **Clients:** Major property developer; Cambridge University Estate Management Service.

NORTH WEST

LITIGATION (PROPERTY) • North West	Ptnrs	Assts
❶ **Cobbetts** Manchester	1	2
❷ **DLA** Liverpool, Manchester	1	3
Eversheds Manchester	1	4
❸ **Addleshaw Booth & Co** Manchester	1	3
Gorna & Co Manchester	1	-
Hammond Suddards Edge Manchester	1	2
Pannone & Partners Manchester	4	1

LEADING INDIVIDUALS	
❶ **JENNINGS Steven** DLA	**RANSON Lee** Eversheds
STONE Peter Cobbetts	
❷ **HOATH Helen** Gorna & Co	**O'FARRELL Vincent** Pannone & Partners
THOMAS Paul Halliwell Landau	**WALKER Alan** Cobbetts

Within each band, firms are listed alphabetically. *See **Profiles** on page 576*

Cobbetts One of the largest commercial conveyancing practices in the North, with a strong background in brewery work. The team is led by **Peter Stone**, frequently recommended for his abilities on big-ticket cases. Specialises in forfeiture and were asked to comment on the Law Commission's draft proposals on peaceable re-entry and adverse possession. The *"brilliant"* **Alan Walker** joins the team from Addleshaw Booth & Co. **Clients:** Whitbread Property; P&O Properties Ltd; British Rail Property Board.

DLA Now fielding a Liverpool team in addition to Manchester, this practice has litigated cases on break clauses, service charges and dilapidations in the past year. *"High profile"* **Steven Jennings** is said to be *"particularly good with clients."* **Clients:** Abbey National plc; English Partnerships; BP Pension Fund.

Eversheds *"Sensible"* **Lee Ranson** leads this team, and is spoken of as a *"good operator."* Acts for Government and local authority bodies and large developers. Successfully defended a £20m claim arising from a land development programme. **Clients:** North West Development Agency; United Norwest Cooperatives Ltd; Stanley Leisure plc.

Addleshaw Booth & Co The loss of Alan Walker to Cobbetts will be felt by the team which is perceived to be a *"service function"* to the *"splendid"* commercial property group. Advises on residential and landlord/tenant disputes in addition to commercial matters. Acted for a developer in a dispute involving an option to purchase land for inward investment/urban regeneration. **Clients:** Speke Garston Development Corp; Standard life Investments; Sainsbury's Supermarkets Ltd.

Gorna & Co **Helen Hoath**, spoken of as a *"genuine specialist,"* deals with property litigation for the firm, which acts principally on behalf of institutions. Seen as *"a natural choice for smaller cases,"* she is *"someone who tries to find solutions."* **Clients:** Friendly societies; companies and banks.

Hammond Suddards Edge Not a high profile presence in the market, this team is part of the firm's commercial dispute resolution unit. Acting for a major agro-chemicals company on a £500k neighbour dispute in a six week trial in the Technology and Construction Court. **Clients:** Co-operative Wholesale Society; BASF plc; Luxfer Group.

Pannone & Partners **Vincent O'Farrell**, referred to by some as the *"most ruthless litigator in Manchester,"* leads this partner-heavy practice. Act for clients ranging from small corporates to multi-nationals in commercial property disputes. Acted for a large nursing home proprietor in a month-long trial involving setting aside of conveyances and allegations of fraud. **Clients:** Texaco; Jennings Bros; Nursing homes.

Other Notable Practitioners **Paul Thomas** of Halliwell Landau continues to be recommended, although the firm itself is not felt to be a major regional factor in this field.

NORTH EAST

LITIGATION (PROPERTY) • North East	Ptnrs	Assts
❶ **Addleshaw Booth & Co** Leeds	1	4
Pinsent Curtis Leeds	2	2
❷ **DLA** Leeds	1	4
Eversheds Leeds	1	2
Hammond Suddards Edge Leeds	1	4
Nabarro Nathanson Sheffield	2	5
Walker Morris Leeds	1	4
❸ **Dickinson Dees** Newcastle upon Tyne	1	3

LEADING INDIVIDUALS
❶ **BELCHER Penny** Irwin Mitchell
HERBERT Alan Pinsent Curtis
O'LOUGHLIN Philip Addleshaw Booth & Co

Within each band, firms are listed alphabetically. See **Profiles** on page 576

Addleshaw Booth & Co Part of the commercial property group, this team, which is seen to work closely with the Manchester office, is *"active."* **Philip O'Loughlin** is praised for his technical knowledge and *"sensible approach."* Include residential landlord and tenant work and are seen to be *"sophisticated enough to appreciate both their own and the other side's strengths and weaknesses."* **Clients:** Halifax plc; Standard Life Investments; Principal Hotels.

Pinsent Curtis A *"good team"* who *"know their stuff."* This dedicated practice is led by **Alan Herbert** who has a *"good grasp of the law."* Acted in a test case on timing for service of Business Rates demands, for a client who had been in occupation for 17 years before the council demanded payment of rates. **Clients:** Encon Group Ltd; Haemonetics (UK) Ltd; Costcutter Supermarkets.

DLA A *"competent"* practice that is mainly retail-driven. The practice handles property litigation for major portfolio holders and receives a number of referrals from other departments. **Clients:** Arcadia Group plc; Hepworth plc; The Employment Service.

Eversheds *"Seem to have taken their eye off the property litigation ball."* The loss of *"mainstay"* Penny Belcher to Irwin Mitchell was clearly a blow, in spite of the fact that the practice retains a number of household name clients. Advised Guardian Assurance plc in connection with the refurbishment of the Capital Centre Cardiff, on disputes arising from the £50m scheme. **Clients:** Asda Stores plc; Greggs plc; St Martens Property Corp.

Hammond Suddards Edge Recently added an in-house barrister to the practice, but the team still lacks an individual heavyweight name. Advises major companies on injunctions, user of land and other commercial property disputes. Acted for the former landlord of the Arndale Centre in respect of a dispute over substantial rent arrears and service charges, following the IRA bombing in June 1996. **Clients:** Allied London Properties plc; Austin Reed Group plc; Harrods Ltd.

Nabarro Nathanson Ability to draw on the strength of the London practice and links with the mining industry have helped to establish the profile of the Sheffield office. Said to be *"on the way up,"* the team handles portfolio management litigation for the retail and public sectors. Acted in Moss Bros v CSC Properties, defending allegations of unreasonable refusal of consent. **Clients:** GE Capital Ltd; British Waterways; The Coal Authority.

Walker Morris Said to *"know their stuff,"* this practice is felt to *"quietly get things sorted out."* Advises clients in mediation, ADR, lease forfeitures, and general contentious property matters. Defended a £750k dilapidations claim in respect of a city centre retail unit. **Clients:** Halifax plc; Arcadia Group plc; Top Shop Estates plc.

Dickinson Dees Serves the property litigation needs of agricultural and commercial clients of the firm and felt to be active *"on the retail side of things."* Acting in the Court of Appeal relating to the interpretation of a contract involving reservation of rights. **Clients:** Social housing; commercial, agricultural and private clients.

Other Notable Practitioners

Penny Belcher of Irwin Mitchell is a practitioner held in the highest regard. Her move from Eversheds is felt *"highly likely"* to raise her new firm's property litigation profile.

SCOTLAND

LITIGATION (PROPERTY) • Scotland	Ptnrs	Assts
❶ **Dundas & Wilson CS** Edinburgh	1	5
Maclay Murray & Spens Glasgow	1	6
❷ **Brodies WS** Edinburgh	1	1
McGrigor Donald Glasgow	3	4
Semple Fraser WS Glasgow	3	3
Steedman Ramage WS Edinburgh	2	1
❸ **Archibald Campbell & Harley WS** Edinburgh	2	1
Burness Edinburgh	2	1
Shepherd & Wedderburn WS Edinburgh	*	*

Within each band, firms are listed alphabetically.
** See editorial entries for explanations of team sizes.*

Dundas & Wilson CS *"You can't go too far wrong"* with this team which has the *"necessary size and strength,"* and an enviable client base. Acted in the House of Lords in Axis West development Ltd v Chartwell Land Ltd in a boundary dispute on development property concerning whether land was conveyed under title. **Clients:** Scottish Metropolitan Properties plc; Scottish Widows; Standard Life Assurance.

Maclay Murray & Spens *"Forged ahead"* with the keep open cases a few years ago (one of which is now in the House of Lords) and still rated one of the market leaders. Advising clients in the redevelopment of 1970's shopping centres and said to be *"clever and imaginative."* Presented the first business petition to the Scottish Parliament in an attempt to reform the landlord and tenant legislation in the Tenancy of Shops (Scotland) Act 1949. **Clients:** Sears; Stannifer; Hazelmere Estates.

Brodies WS Said to *"rate well"* for their agricultural property litigation work and to be *"efficient litigators."* The firm represents developers, retailers and large estates. **Clients:** Landed estates and agricultural businesses; developers; retailers.

McGrigor Donald The independence of this firm is seen as one of its strengths. So too is the large client base of the property department. Successfully resolved a case for CWS in relation to the development of a supermarket that gave rise to a number of competing interests. **Clients:** Banks and building societies; property developers and managers; retailers.

Semple Fraser A commercial property firm with a wide client base. The property litigation team, which works closely with the non-contentious property department, handles landlord/tenant disputes, dilapidations claims, joint ventures, development agreements and licensing issues. Known for expertise in keep-open cases, the team also advises on ranking disputes. **Clients:** Tesco Stores Ltd; British Land Corp; Clydeport Operations Ltd.

Steedman Ramage WS Bring an *"intelligent commercial approach"* to property litigation that at times can be *"hard-nosed."* Work includes litigation in connection with unreasonable withholding of consent to assignations and a case relating to the difference between experts and arbitrators in rent reviews. Resisted a liquidator's claim for rent for the unexpired portion of a lease. **Clients:** Sears; Next plc; Helical Retail Ltd.

Archibald Campbell & Harley WS A *"good team"* with a comparatively low profile, which handles a number of agricultural property disputes, notably in connection with heritage buildings. **Clients:** Scottish Natural Heritage.

Burness Considered to have a *"definite involvement"* in the sector, the team benefits from the presence of a highly-rated commercial property department. Land values disputes remain a substantial part of the practice's caseload. **Clients:** British Land Universal; Charterhouse Square Finance Co Ltd.

Shepherd & Wedderburn WS The integrated unit of commercial property lawyers and litigators, operating out of the commercial litigation department, continues to be recognised as players in the market. Acts primarily for the firm's commercial property clients, and planning matters feature heavily in the workload. Acted in Seafield Investments Ltd v DCS Mackintosh in the Court of Session, concerning access rights to a retained area of land. **Clients:** Developers; funders; landlords.

LEADERS IN LITIGATION (PROPERTY)

ALLEN, Martin
DMH, Brighton (01273) 744 324

BASTOW, Martin
Lyons Davidson, Bristol (0117) 904 6000
Partner and Head of Property Litigation Group.
Specialisation: Experienced in all aspects of property litigation with particular emphasis on landlord and tenant disputes and complex security enforcement. Work includes dilapidations, forfeiture, 1954 Act renewals, arbitration, possession proceedings, property-related prosecutions and acting for LPA receivers.
Prof. Memberships: Associate of the Chartered Institute of Arbitrators, PACT panel member.
Career: Joined *Lyons Davidson* on qualification in 1988. Partner since 1994. Member of Bristol Housing Lawyers Group, Property Litigation Association and The Legal Aid Area Committee. Bristol County Court Duty Solicitor (possession hearings).

BEDFORD, Richard
Burges Salmon, Bristol (0117) 902 2749
richard.bedford@burges-salmon.com
Specialisation: As a specialist property litigator, he deals with professional indemnity claims, agricultural insolvency related matters and real property disputes. Particular specialism is banking disputes relating to agriculture. He has lectured on numerous subjects including agricultural law, secured lending and specialist areas of landlord and tenant law.
Prof. Memberships: Law Society.
Career: Joined *Burges Salmon* in 1983 as a trainee and became a partner in 1992. Joint author of RICS publication, Farm Receiverships.

BELCHER, Penny
Irwin Mitchell, Leeds (0113) 234 3333
belcherp@irwinmitchell.com
Specialisation: All areas of Property Litigation, Arbitration and Property Dispute Management including Landlord & Tenant disputes, lease renewals, dilapidations, rent reviews, rights of way, boundaries, restrictive covenants. Lands Tribunal, Land Compensation Claims, planning, Judicial Review.
Prof. Memberships: Attorney State Bar of California. Property Litigation Association.
Career: Barrister 1980. Practised as barrister specialising in Property Litigation until 1987. Admitted Attorney State Bar of California 1988. Qualified as solicitor 1993. Joined *Eversheds* 1993. Partner 1997. Joined *Irwin Mitchell* January 2000
Personal: Educated St Hugh's College, Oxford: BA + MA Jurisprudence. Interests include music and theatre, walking, sailing and squash.

BRADFORD, Katie
Linklaters (A member firm of Linklaters & Alliance), London (020) 7456 4234
katie.bradford@linklaters.com
Partner and Head of Property Litigation Unit.
Specialisation: Specialises in all aspects of property litigation and arbitration, including landlord and tenant; solicitors/surveyors negligence; insolvency related disputes; leader in rent review arbitration. Has taken over 60 actions to trial and 12 to CA. Recent cases include: Prudential v Waterloo (CA 1999); CLE v Kato Kagaku (1999). Named as 'Expert's Expert' in property litigation by competitors. Blundell Lecturer on rent review (1998).
Prof. Memberships: Women in Property Litigation. Women in Property. Registered mediator (CEDR accreditation); Fellow of Chartered Institute of Arbitrators.; PACT arbitrator; Member of ARBRIX and MEDRIX; Fellow of Royal Society for Art; and aspirant member of MCC.
Career: Articled *Osmond Gaunt & Rose* (Finchley), *Lovell White Durrant*, commercial litigation, *Linklaters* since 1992. Former Chairman of Property Litigation Association.

BRIERLEY, Ian P.
Clifford Chance, London (020) 7600 1000
ian.brierley@cliffordchance.com
Specialisation: All aspects of property litigation including rent review, business lease renewal, dilapidations, development, insolvency and professional negligence. Acted in Crown Estate Commissioners -v- Town Investments, Bankers Trust Company -v- Namdar, Aquilina -v- Havering London Borough Council. Contributing Editor Sweet & Maxwell's Commercial Property Disputes: practice and procedure.
Prof. Memberships: Chairman of Property Litigation Association's committee for education and training.
Career: Qualified 1994; joined *Clifford Chance* 1991.

BRIGGS, Leona
Osborne Clarke OWA, Bristol (0117) 984 5441
leona.briggs@osbourneclarke.com
Head of property litigation
Specialisation: Practice areas: all aspects of Commercial landlord and tenant disputes but particularly rent reviews, dilapidation and lease renewals. Contentious conveyancing issues and general title problems, boundary disputes, options and easement.
Career: Qualified in1992, joining *Osborne Clarke* on qualification. She was appointed to Partner in 2000.

CHEFFINGS, Nicholas
Lovells, London (020) 7296 2000

COHEN, Roger D.
Berwin Leighton, London (020) 7760 1000
roger.cohen@berwinleighton.com
Partner in Litigation and Dispute Resolution Department.
Specialisation: Main area of practice is property litigation including landlord and tenant, planning-related litigation, environmental claims, rating, ADR, and professional indemnity. Acts as a mediator. Other areas are general commercial litigation and arbitration. Acted for Tesco in high profile rent review dispute with British Land concerning the valuation of a store in Maidstone, and represents Prudential, Legal & General, Central Government and Phillips & Drew. Regular conference presenter and conducts client seminars and regularly contributes articles to the property press.
Prof. Memberships: CEDR Registered Mediator, Fellow Chartered Institute Of Arbitrators, Administrative Law Bar Association, City of London Solicitors' Company, Law Society, Law Reform Sub-Committee, Property Litigation Association, Member London Court of International Arbitration, Associate Fellow, Society of Advanced Legal Studies, Secretary, Association of Mediation Solicitors, panel member, Dispute Mediation Ltd, mediation panel of Chartered Institute of Arbitrators.
Career: Articled with *Donnelly & Elliott* in Gosport, then joined *Matthew Arnold & Baldwin* in Watford. Joined *Berwin Leighton* in 1984 and became a Partner in 1989. Head of Contentious Property Group and Head of Berwin Leighton Israel Desk.
Personal: Born 2nd June 1959. Attended Portsmouth Grammar School 1970-77. Leisure pursuits include soccer, music and reading. Lives in London.

COX, Brian
Bobbetts Mackan, Bristol (0117) 929 9001

COX, David
Paisner & Co, London (020) 7353 0299
Specialisation: Specialises in a whole range of property-related disputes, including rent collection and service charge disputes, forfeitures, rent reviews, lease renewals, dilapidations claims, title and right to light disputes and professional negligence claims. Clients include institutional investors, retail groups, developers and owner-occupiers. Has led seminars on a variety of property topics (most recently on Woolf Reforms) and has had articles published recently in Estates Gazette and Property Law Journal.

Prof. Memberships: Law Society, Property Litigation Association.
Career: Qualified 1979. Partner *Lovell White Durrant* 1985-1997. Partner *Paisner & Co.* 1998.

CROSS, Siobhan
Masons, London (020) 7490 4000
Partner in Property Litigation Department.
Specialisation: Practice covers all areas of property litigation and dispute resolution including landlord and tenant litigation such as rent reviews, dilapidations, possession proceedings, and lease renewals and other property related disputes including disputes over joint venture developments, relevant professional negligence claims and rights of way, light and air. Experienced in alternative methods of dispute resolution including mediation, arbitration and expert determination.
Prof. Memberships: Property Litigation Association.
Career: Qualified in 1987. Joined *Masons* in 1988 and became a partner in 1993.
Personal: Born 21 July 1962 and lives in North London.

FALKNER, James M.G.
Mills & Reeve, Norwich (01603) 693 230
james.falkner@mills-reeve.com
Specialisation: Agricultural, commercial and residential property and landlord and tenant disputes.
Prof. Memberships: Law Society. Property Litigation Association, Agricultural Law Association.
Career: Joined *Mills & Reeve* 1980. Partner 1988.

FOX-EDWARDS, Jane
Lawrence Graham, London (020) 7379 0000
jane.fox-edwards@lawgram.com
Specialisation: Practice covers all areas of property litigation including shopping centre and portfolio management issues, dilapidations, rent reviews. Also deals with insolvency related property issues, residential property problems and restrictive covenant issues. Gives regular seminars and contributes to the Estates Gazette and other property journals.
Prof. Memberships: Property Litigation Association.
Career: Qualified in 1988. Joined *Lawrence Graham* 1989 from *Boodle Hatfield* amd became a partner in 1996. Now head of Property Litigation.

FRANCIS, Penelope J.L.
Lawrence Graham, London (020) 7379 0000
penny.francis@lawgram.com
From 1 May 1998, Head of property department. Partner in property litigation team.
Specialisation: Main area of practice is property litigation, covering rent reviews, insolvency, shopping centre and portfolio management, lease renewals and dilapidations. Lectures for RICS, ARBRIX, Henry Stewart, AdIdem, TBR and other conferences. Qualified as a PACT arbitrator and on the Law Society's panel of arbitrators.
Prof. Memberships: Law Society, Women in Property, Property Litigation Law Reform Group and RICS Dispute Resolution Panel.
Career: Qualified in 1984. Worked at *Beachcroft Stanleys* 1982-88. Joined *Lawrence Graham* in 1989, becoming a Partner in 1991.
Personal: Born 9th November 1959. Attended University of Bristol 1978-81, then College of Law 1981-2. Leisure interests include ballet, eating and travel. Lives in London.

FREYNE, Michele
Rowe & Maw, London (020) 7248 4282
Specialisation: Main area of practice is property litigation. Started first specialist team in 1980 which has grown into team which she heads of 6 including 2 partners. Also specialises in matrimonial law (about 15% of total workload).
Prof. Memberships: Property Litigation Association, Solicitors Family Law Association.
Career: Qualified in 1978. Joined *Rowe & Maw* in 1979, became partner in 1984. Group Managing Partner, Commercial Litigation 1993-94.

HAM, Neil
Burges Salmon, Bristol (0117) 902 2747
neil.ham@burges-salmon.com
Specialisation: Commercial property disputes, including rent and service charge disputes, contested rent reviews, and general dilapidations, contested lease renewals, professional negligence claims, risk assessment for major landowners and developers, and non-litigious dispute resolution.
Prof. Memberships: Law Society.
Career: Qualified in 1987 and continued with *Simmons & Simmons*, joined *Burges Salmon* in 1991 and became a Partner in 1996.
Personal: University of Bristol 1981-84. Interests include tennis and mountain biking.

HERBERT, Alan
Pinsent Curtis, Leeds (0113) 244 5000
alan.herbert@pinsents.com
Specialisation: All aspects of property dispute resolution and litigation including landlord and tenant, development disputes, dilapidations, portfolio management, rent reviews, rating, possession, vendor/purchaser disputes, enforcement and protection of security, enforcement of restrictive covenents. Arbitration, litigation, mediation and Lands Tribunal work.
Prof. Memberships: Property Litigation Association.
Career: Articled with *Ashurst Morris Crisp*. Qualified 1989. Joined *Pinsent Curtis* 1993. Partner and Head of Property Litigation team 1996.
Personal: Walking, fly fishing.

HEWSON, Carol
Simmons & Simmons, London (020) 7628 2020
Partner in Litigation Department.
Specialisation: Main area of practice is commercial litigation, with particular experience in all aspects of commercial property and landlord and tenant litigation. Acts for institutional landlords, property developers and banks, as well as for commercial and retail tenants. Also has extensive experience in rent review disputes, including arbitration, service charge disputes, forfeiture claims and litigation under the Landlord and Tenant Act 1954. Experienced in insolvency litigation, acting primarily for banks and insolvency practitioners. Addressed seminars for Central Law Training on Commerial Property Litigation and at their annual Commercial Landlord and Tenant Conference, also for Euroforum on Commercial Lease Insolvency.
Prof. Memberships: Law Society; City of London Solicitors Company; Member of Property Litigation Association; Member of Women in Property Litigation.
Career: Qualified in April 1980, after joining *Stephenson Harwood* as an articled clerk in 1978. Left for *Simmons & Simmons* in 1983, Partner in 1986.
Personal: Born 8th October 1955. Attended Kings College, London 1974-1977. Deputy Chairman of Broomleigh Housing Association and Chairman of its Audit Committee. Leisure pursuits include fell walking, skiing and horse racing. Lives in London.

HIGHMORE, Robert P.
Radcliffes, London (020) 7222 7040
robert.highmore@radcliffes.co.uk
Litigation Partner and Head of Property Litigation and Dispute Resolution Team.
Specialisation: Principal area of practice covers full range of property and landlord and tenant litigation and dispute resolution including commercial and residential property and professional negligence actions. Acts for both landlords and tenants including major institutions, pension funds, the NHS, banks and life assurance companies.
Prof. Memberships: Chairman 1998-1999 and founder committee member of Property Litigation Association; active member of British Property Federation; Law Society; City of Westminster Law Society.
Career: Qualified 1982, at *Radcliffes & Co* since 1980. Became a partner in 1987.
Personal: Born 9th February 1957. Educated at Cambridge and County High School (1968-71), Beverley Grammar School, East Yorkshire (1971-75), Trinity Hall, Cambridge (1976-79). Leisure pursuits include squash and Ceroc. Lives in Bromley, Kent.

HOATH, Helen
Gorna & Co, Manchester (0161) 832 3651
hmh@gorna.co.uk
Specialisation: Property litigation; dilapidations; rent reviews; contested business tenancy renewals; specific performance; restrictive covenants; easement disputes; rights to light' Allied London Industrial Properties Ltd v Castleguard Properties Inc 1997 EGCS 18. Jolley v Carmel Limited 100 EGC572.
Prof. Memberships: Law Society; Association Women Solicitors; Property Litigation Association; Women in Property; M.C.I.A.
Career: Easingwold School; Worcester College Oxford; Articled *Kramer & Co.* London; *McKenna & Co.*

HOGAN, Ronald D.
Dewar Hogan, London (020) 7822 7400
ronhogan@dewarhogan.co.uk
Specialisation: All types of contentious property matters and related litigation in connection with commercial and residential property. Instructed in relation to property management disputes (including dilapidations, arrears, forfeiture, and rent reviews); professional negligence cases involving solicitors and valuers; enforcement of securities and other insolvency related work; leasehold enfranchisement and estate management schemes. Instructed in a number of reported cases, author of articles in the property press and speaker at conferences on property issues. Chairman of the Property Litigation Association 1995-96.
Career: Formed the niche property litigation practice of *Dewar Hogan* in 1991. Formerly at *Nabarro Nathanson.*

HUTCHINSON, Lucy
Herbert Smith, London (020) 7374 8000
Head of property litigation: partner in litigation and arbitration division.
Specialisation: Deals with specialised property litigation involving major property and landlord and tenant disputes relating to commercial, retail, indus-

trial and residential property. Does rent review work, including acting as legal assessor to Arbitrators. Acts for a number of institutional investors including Hermes and Standard Life. Also does regulatory work and general commercial litigation.
Career: Qualified in 1982. Became a partner at *Herbert Smith* in 1989.
Personal: Educated at Southampton University.

JENNINGS, Steven
DLA, Manchester (08700) 111111
steven.jennings@dla.com
Specialisation: Property litigation, arbitration and advice covering commercial landlord and tenant work (including rent reviews, dilapidations, contested lease renewal and alienation applications, service charge disputes and forfeiture), restrictive covenants, nuisance, easements, professional negligence and disputes relating to development agreements and the like. Regularly advises arbitrators on legal issues. Frequent speaker at seminars run by the RICS and other property related organisations. A member of ARBRIX (the rent review arbitrators club).
Prof. Memberships: Law Society, Chartered Institute of Arbitrators.
Career: Partner with *Gorna & Co*, Manchester 1982-94. Joined *Dibb Lupton Broomhead* as Property partner in 1994. Now Head of Property Litigation *Dibb Lupton Alsop*, Midlands and North West.

KENT, Paul
Pinsent Curtis, Birmingham (0121) 200 1050
paul.kent@pinsents.com
Partner in Property Litigation
Specialisation: All aspects of property dispute resolution including the tactical value of disputes in corporate transactions. Rent review, Lands Tribunal work, dilapidations claims, rates disuptes and all contentious landlord and tenant matters. Recent cases: Banks v Kokkinos [1998] NPC 171. Two major judicial review applications and two major dilapidations including contamination and resolution of a high profile proprietory estoppel claim.
Prof. Memberships: Property Litigation Association.
Career: Fifteen years in wholesale food distribution prior to qualification as solicitor. Several years of commercial litigation and for 7 years specialising in property litigation. Joined *Pinsent Curtis* 1993. Partner 1998.
Personal: Sailing, large scale landscape gardening, English furniture and ceramics.

KING, Vivien M.
D J Freeman, London (020) 7583 4055
vmk@djfreeman.co.uk
Specialisation: Caseload includes all aspects of contentious property matters including real property, mortgage and leasehold concerns. Venues for dispute include the courts, arbitration and mediation. Particular legal interests include trespass, dilapidations and rent reviews. PACT arbitrator and member of Arbrix. Fellow, Institute of Continuing Professional Development.
Prof. Memberships: Lectures extensively. Member, Property Litigation Association and its Law Reform Committee. Member of organising committee for RICS Oxford Study Weekend.
Career: BA in Law. Qualified 1987. Partner at *Turner Kenneth & Brown* 1989 - 1993; partner *Bower Cotton & Bower* 1993-1994; partner at *SJ Berwin & Co* 1995-1999; joined partnership *D J Freeman* 1999.
Publications: Frequent contributor to the property press. Contributed to publications 'Commercial Property Dispute', 'Nuisances' and 'Freemans's Guide to the Property Industry'.
Personal: Old houses, antique glass, cooking and wine. Born 1950. Lives London and South of France.

LLOYD HOLT, Suzanne
Wragge & Co, Birmingham (0121) 214 1046
suzanne_lloyd_holt@wragge.com
Specialisation: Head of Property Litigation Team, specialising in all types of property disputes including dilapidations, rent reviews and site clearance on redevelopment schemes.
Prof. Memberships: French UK Chamber of Commerce - council member, Chartered Institute of Arbitrators - member, Associazione Internazionale Giuristi di Lingua Italiana (Milan) - council member, PACT arbitrator/ expert on RICS/ Law Society specialist panel.
Career: Partner at *Wragge & Co* from 1988.

MADDEN, Michael
Ashurst Morris Crisp, London (020) 7638 1111
Specialisation: Partner in charge of the property litigation group at *Ashursts*. He specialises in development agreement disputes, mortgage and property financing actions, adjoining owner/party wall/adverse possession claims in addition to landlord and tenant, estate management, and other general property disputes. Acts for both landlords and tenants in contested rent review arbitrations and expert determinations. The group advises on both liquor and gaming licensing matters.
Prof. Memberships: Accredited mediator with CEDR. FCIArb. Chairman of Property Litigation Group Law Reform Committee.

MARTIN, Bonnie
Masons, Bristol (0117) 924 5678
bonnie.martin@masons.com
Specialisation: Specialises in property litigation. Acts for a number of companies relating to a range of property disputes arising from their retail and leisure outlets. Advises on numerous landlord and tenant problems arising out of all aspects of commercial leases including dilapidations, forfeiture and the Landlord & Tenant Act 1954. Acts for a number of landlords of industrial estates advising on all aspects of management. Has acted for parties to a number of significant Lands Tribunal appeals, a high profile arbitration concerning the financial effects of boundary changes and arbitrations relating to land values.Has a particular interest in rent review and arbitration law as it relates to property. Is an appointed arbitrator under the Professional Arbitration on Court Terms (PACT) scheme and a Member of ARBRIX.
Prof. Memberships: ARBRIX, BURA, UKELA (UK Environmental Law Association) BPAA (Bristol Property Agents Association), BPF, British Council of Offices, TCPA, Law Society, in the process of setting up the Bristol Branch of Property Litigation Association.
Career: Admitted 1985 - partner *Masons* London before moving to set up property litigation department in Bristol in 1990.
Personal: Lives in Somerset with partner and two small boys.

MASTERS, David C.
Dawson & Co, London (020) 7421 4800
d.masters@dawson-and-co.co.uk
Specialisation: Practice covers full range of property litigation including rent reviews, dilapidations and disrepairs claims, applications under the Landlord and Tenant Act 1954, the Housing Act 1988 and Leasehold Reform Housing and Urban Development Act 1993. Acts for large and small property companies, housing associations, landed estates and private individuals.
Prof. Memberships: Property Litigation Association, The Institute of Continuing Professional Development.
Career: Qualified 1981. *Speechly Bircham* 1988 to 1998 (partner from 1990) *Dawson & Co* since 1999 (partner).
Personal: Born 7.11.56. Educated at Felsted School and Reading University. Married. Interests include skiing, tennis, RHS member. Lives in Coggeshall, Essex.

MILLER, Wendy
Clifford Chance, London (020) 7600 1000
wendy.miller@cliffordchance.com
Specialisation: Consultant (former head) in property litigation unit, specialising in all aspects of property litigation and alternative dispute resolution including professional indemnity and insolvency related property disputes. Also has a growing mediation practice, specialising in property and professional indemnity matters.
Prof. Memberships: Property Litigation Association; CEDR.
Career: University of Sussex (BA Hons 1979). Articled *Clifford Turner*; qualified 1984; partner *Clifford Chance* 1991; CEDR registered mediator.
Personal: Born 1957; married with two children.

MOLYNEUX, Anne
Masons, London (020) 7490 4000
anne.molyneux@masons.com
Partner and Head of Property Litigation Department.
Specialisation: Handles all areas of High Court litigation. Cases have included Passmore v. Morland (House of Lords interpretation of EC Treaty). Courage v. Crehan (reference to Luxembourg - right to damages/illegality), Langton v. Inntrepreneur (House of Lords - set-off), Little v. Courage (covering status of option). Addressed Law Society National Conference on litigation; has addressed conferences on dilapidations, insolvency, litigation and rent review. Worked on a TEN video. Presented programmes for the BBC. Addressed RICS (INDEX) Conference.
Prof. Memberships: Law Society.
Career: Qualified in 1983. Associate at *Lawrence Messer & Co.*, before joining *Masons* in 1987. Became a Partner in 1989. Appointed Recorder in 2000.
Personal: Born 12th January 1959. Member of Ealing and Fulham Book Club. Lives in Ealing. Has two children.

MORRIS, Peter
Eversheds, Bristol (0117) 929 9555
petermorris@eversheds.com
Head of banking and property litigation in *Eversheds'* Bristol office.
Specialisation: Involved in all types of litigation and advice relating to contentious property matters, particularly Landlord and Tenant disputes for retail clients. Also all types of commercial litigation, partic-

ularly for financial institutions. Heavily involved in recent years in managed litigation against multiple defendants.
Prof. Memberships: Bristol Law Society; CBI.
Career: Qualified in 1982. *Kenwright & Cox* 1982-86, partner 1985. *Holt Philips* 1986-94, partner 1986, becoming *Eversheds* partner in 1994. Senior partner (Bristol) 1999.
Personal: Born 1957. Lives outside Bristol. Interests include hill walking, smallholding and real ale.

O'BRIEN, Gary
Eversheds, Birmingham (0121) 232 1000
Specialisation: Head of Property Litigation Team which handles all types of Landlord and Tenant disputes. Gary has particular specialisation in freehold property developments involving difficult restrictive covenants or major boundary and easement disputes as well as enforcement of sale and purchase contracts and clearance of sites for redevelopment schemes.
Career: Qualified in 1985. Joined *Simpson Curtis* in 1987. Partner at *Simpson Curtis* 1990 and at *Eversheds* from 1996.
Personal: Born 1959. Attended KEGS Aston and St. John's College, Oxford. Interests include opera and Aston Villa Football Club.

O'FARRELL, Vincent B.
Pannone & Partners, Manchester (0161) 909 3000
vincent.o'farrell@pannone.co.uk
Partner and Head of Department in Commercial Litigation.
Specialisation: He specialises in land disputes, contentious probate and trust issues, civil fraud, judicial review, defamation, contract and pre-emptive remedies. He is also a notary public.
Prof. Memberships: Member of ACTAPS (Association of Contentious Trust and Probate Specialists).
Career: Vincent was admitted in 1971, when he joined *Howards*, a predecessor to *Pannone & Partners*.
Personal: Leisure interests include theatre, sport and music. Lives in Bury.

O'LOUGHLIN, Philip
Addleshaw Booth & Co, Leeds (0113) 209 2000
pho@addleshaw-booth.co.uk
Head of Property Litigation Department, Commercial Property Group.
Specialisation: Practice covers all landlord and tenant and property litigation, in particular rent reviews, dilapidations, property related professional negligence. Work also includes Landlord and Tenant 1954 applications, forfeiture, tenant default.
Career: Qualified 1986; joined the firm 1991, becoming a Partner in May 1995.
Personal: Attended Cambridge University 1979-1982. Leisure interests include fellwalking, landscape photography, archaeology.

ORME, James
Osborne Clarke OWA, Bristol (0117) 917 3248
james.orme@osborneclarke.com
Specialisation: Specialises in banking and property litigation and deals with a wide range of disputes, dealing particularly with commercial landlord and tenant disputes, contested mortgage possession claims, enforcement of mortgages and guarantees, and consumer credit disputes. James also has a wide experience of disputes relating to security over property.
Prof. Memberships: Fellow of the Royal Institution of Chartered Arbitrators.
Career: Qualified at *Burges Salmon*. Joined *Osborne Clarke* in 1980, becoming a partner in 1984.

PEET, Carole
Denton Wilde Sapte, London (020) 7320 3905 / (01908) 690 260

PICKSTON, John
Clifford Chance, London (020) 7600 1000
john.pickston@cliffordchance.com
Specialisation: Partner. All types of litigation and advice relating to contentious property matters including development issues, rent review, professional negligence and landlord and tenant.
Career: Qualified 1986; partner 1996.

PUDDICOMBE, Nigel R.
Cartwrights, Bristol (0117) 929 3601
nrpuddicombe@cartwrights.com
Specialisation: All aspects of property litigation principally acting for lenders and landlords. Clients include breweries and pub companies, Railtrack, passenger, freight and road transport providers, property companies, and local authorities. Also handles contractual, negligence and passing off disputes.
Prof. Memberships: President, Bristol Law Society. Chairman, Bristol Law Society Civil Courts Committee 1993-98.
Career: Qualified 1979. Partner with *Cartwrights* from 1987.
Personal: Born 10th August 1954. Educated Kings College Taunton and Southampton University (LLB 1976). Interests include sport, theatre and gardening. Lives North Somerset.

RANSON, Lee
Eversheds, Manchester (0161) 832 6666
leeranson@eversheds.com
Specialisation: Property litigation - acting for commercial and institutional landlord clients in Retail, Local Authority and Banking sectors. Specific niche areas include resolution of property disputes in the education and leisure industries. Has a particular interest in property related professional indemnity claims.
Prof. Memberships: Law Society. CEDR qualified mediator. Member of Property Litigation Association.
Career: Qualified - 1990. *Jaques & Lewis* (merged *Eversheds* 1994) 1988-96. Transfered to *Eversheds* Manchester, Jan 1997. Partner.
Personal: Born 16.12.64. Educated - Wilmslow Grammer School & Hull University. Married - 2 children. Interests - golf, football, cricket. Lives in Bramhall.

RICKARD, Jennifer
Nabarro Nathanson, London (020) 7524 6000
j.rickard@nabarro.com
Partner Property Litigation Department.
Specialisation: All aspects of Property litigation. Acted in 'Mannai Investment Company Ltd v. Eagle Star Assurance Ltd', 'Lewisham Investment Partnership v. Morgan', 'Straudley Investment v. Mount Eden Land', 'Grundy v. Summit Group Holdings' and 'Pontsarn v. Kansallis Osake Panke'. Speaker at Blundell Memorial Lectures, Henry Stewart conferences, RICS, ISVA, IBC conferences, Euroforum, Contract Property Training, Central Law Training. Speaker on Owlion cassettes on Dilapidations 1996, Lease Renewals 1998, Rent Reviews 1998 and Property law updates 1997-2000.
Career: Qualified 1983. Partner 1989.

SCANNELL, John
Eversheds, Norwich (01603) 272727
Specialisation: Landlord and tenant - commercial and residential. Other property litigation - squatters, adverse possession, title disputes.
Career: University of East Anglia B.Sc. Articles *Daynes Hill and Perks* 1987-1989. 1989-1992 - non-contentious commercial property/company commercial. 1992-present time - civil litigation, now exclusively property litigation.
Personal: Single. Interests - classical music, jazz guitar, keep fit, food and wine.

SCOTT, Gordon
Hammond Suddards Edge, Birmingham (0121) 200 2001
gordon.scott@hammondsuddardsedge.com
Specialisation: Partner in the Property Litigation Unit, which covers the complete spectrum of property-related disputes and includes landlord and tenant, title disputes, easements and covenants, specific performance, judicial review and professional negligence claims. Particular interest in dilapidations claims. Acts for companies across the property sector, including institutional landlords, major retailers, Housing Associations and development groups.
Prof. Memberships: Member Property Litigation Association. Milk Marque Arbitration Panel.
Career: Joined *Edge Ellison* as a Partner in 1990 from another local firm, having moved to Birmingham in the early 1980s from *MacFarlanes* and earlier, *D.J. Freeman & Co.*
Personal: Born 1951. Educated at Whitgift School and Exeter College, Oxford. External interests include rugby, cricket and walking. Lives in Edgbaston.

STONE, Peter
Cobbetts, Manchester (0161) 833 3333
peter.stone@cobbetts.co.uk
Specialisation: Over 20 years experience in litigation for national and regional blue-chip clients. Particular expertise in commercial property litigation (forfeiture, dilapidations, covenants, contested lease renewals, Brewery/Licensed Retailer work) and in defamation (Plaintiff and Defendant) for individual and media clients.
Prof. Memberships: Law Society. Notaries Society.
Career: Educated at Rossall School and Liverpool University (LLB Hons 1st class). Articled at *Cobbetts*, 1974. Qualified 1976, Partner 1979.
Personal: Born 1951. Leisure interests include fell-walking, climbing and mountain biking.

THOMAS, Paul
Halliwell Landau, Manchester (0161) 835 3003
pathomas@halliwells.co.uk
See under Litigation (Commercial), p.568

TRAVERS, Iain
Nabarro Nathanson, London (020) 7524 6000
i.traver@nabarro.com
Head of Property Litigation.
Specialisation: Property litigation and arbitration generally.
Prof. Memberships: Fellow of Chartered Institute of Arbitrators. Chairman of Property Litigation Association (1999/2000). Member of London Court of International Arbitration. Member of ARBRIX. Member of RICS/ Law Society PACT Panel. Joint author of 'Distress for Rent' (Jordans) 'trained Mediator (ADR Net).
Career: Qualified 1977. Partner 1980.

WALKER, Alan
Cobbetts, Manchester (0161) 833 3333
alan.walker@cobbetts.co.uk
Specialisation: All aspects of property litigation work, with particular emphasis on landlord and tenant matters, including dilapidations, rent reviews, opposed renewal proceedings, breaches of covenant and associated aspects of property management work.
Prof. Memberships: Law Society. Property Litigation Society.
Career: Magdalene College, Cambridge (M.A., LLM). Articled 1989-1991. Admitted 1991.
Personal: Leisure interests include swimming, walking and theatre.

WALKER, Andrew
CMS Cameron McKenna, London
(020) 7367 2710
alw@cmck.com
Partner in Property Litigation Group.
Specialisation: Main area of practice covers all types of property disputes including landlord and tenant (breaches of covenants, rent reviews, statutory renewals of commercial leases, breaches of statutory obligatons, insolvency and applications to the Leasehold Valuation Tribunal for Estate Management Schemes), claims arising out of contracts for the sale and purchase of land/buildings, breach of statutory obligations, disputes on boundaries, trespass, rights of way, professional negligence by surveyors or solicitors in relation to property matters.
Prof. Memberships: Law Society, Property Litigation Association, The City of London Property Association.
Career: Qualified 1986 and became a Partner and Head of Property Litigation Group in 1993.
Personal: Born 8th December 1959. Leisure pursuits include horse-riding, gardening, cars and family life. Lives in London and Ross-on-Wye.

WALTHAM, Anne
Lovells, London (020) 7296 2000
anne.waltham@lovells.com
Specialisation: A partner in the property litigation group. Specialises in property litigation, dealing with a wide variety of landlord and tenant and real property disputes, including advising the firm's property department on potentially litigious matters. Particular expertise in rent review disputes acting for leading institutional landlords. Familiar with running substantial landlord and tenant cases and has also dealt with a number of property related professional negligence cases and arbitrations. Contributes to a number of publications including the Estates Gazette, Property Week, Property Law Journal, Square Foot and Commercial Lawyer. Regularly presents seminars on aspects of property litigation, to clients and externally, most recently on break clauses, service charges and expert witnesses post Woolf.
Prof. Memberships: Law Society; Property Litigation Association.
Career: Qualified in 1982 and joined *Lovells* in 1989; Partner 1998.

WEBBER, Lesley
Beachcroft Wansbroughs, London (020) 7242 1011
lwebber@bwlaw.co.uk
Partner, Head of Property Litigation and Planning Department.
Specialisation: Principal area of practice is property litigation including rent reviews, lease renewals, dilapidations and service charge disputes, possession and forfeiture, rating and professional negligence actions. Also acts as arbitrator and as legal assessor to arbitrators. Other main area of work is town and country planning covering planning applications, agreements and appeals, local planning advice and representation, compulsory purchase orders and environmental assessments. Acted in 'PHIT v Holding & Management', 'Shield Properties v Anglo Overseas Transport Ltd', 'Zubaida v Hargreaves', 'Sterling Estates v Pickard', 'Morgan Sindall v Sawston Farms' and in the original arbitration of 'National Westminster Bank v Arthur Young'. Member of Law Society/RICS Working Party on Landlord and Tenant Act 1954 and draftsman of PACT scheme for lease renewals. Member of Property Advisory Group to the Department of the Environment, Transport and the Regions.
Prof. Memberships: Fellow of the Chartered Institute of Arbitrators, Honorary Member of ARBRIX, Blundell Memorial Lecturer 1999.
Career: Qualified 1980 while with *Freshfields*. Joined *Masons* in 1984 and became a Partner in 1985. Partner London office of *Dibb Lupton Broomhead* from 1993. Joined *Beachcroft Stanleys* in 1997.
Personal: Born 10th April 1956. Attended Birmingham University 1974-77. Winner of SLSS Prize for Planning Law.

WILLETTS, Guy
Theodore Goddard, London (020) 7606 8855
Specialisation: All aspects of property litigation including landlord and tenant disputes, land disputes, nuisance claims and environmental prosecutions.
Prof. Memberships: Member of Property Litigation Association.
Career: LLB with French Law at LSE followed by Articles with *Robert Gore and Company*, Grosvenor Street, to 1988; *McKenna & Co* to 1994. Currently associate at *Theodore Goddard* and Head of Property and Environmental Litigation.
Personal: Family and Music.

LOCAL GOVERNMENT

London: 581; South West: 583; Wales: 583; Midlands: 584; East Anglia: 584; The North: 585; Scotland: 585; *Profiles*: 586

RESEARCH APPROVED BY BMRB: *For this edition,* Chambers' *researchers conducted 6083 interviews – 4408 with law firms, 598 with barristers and 1077 with clients.*

The validity of the research was scrutinised by BMRB International, who audited both the methodology and the results at our offices in July 2000. They interviewed Chambers' *researchers and cross-checked sample interviews. Details of the audit appear on page 7.*

LONDON

LOCAL GOVERNMENT • London	Ptnrs	Assts
❶ Nabarro Nathanson	4	10
❷ Rowe & Maw	2	8
Sharpe Pritchard	7	6
❸ Ashurst Morris Crisp	4	7
Berwin Leighton	4	-
Lawrence Graham	6	14
Léonie Cowen & Associates	1	1
Towers & Hamlins	5	6
❹ Denton Wilde Sapte	2	10
❺ Clifford Chance	*	*
Herbert Smith	*	*
Jenkins & Hand	*	*
❻ Dechert	-	2
D J Freeman	1	*
Winckworth Sherwood	3	2

LEADING INDIVIDUALS
❶ **CHILD Tony** Rowe & Maw
COWEN Léonie Léonie Cowen & Associates
FORGE Anna Rowe & Maw
GRIFFITHS Trevor Sharpe Pritchard
ILEY Malcolm Nabarro Nathanson
❷ **AMBROSE Ray** Nabarro Nathanson
CURNOW Tony Ashurst Morris Crisp
RANDALL Simon Lawrence Graham
❸ **DOOLITTLE Ian** Trowers & Hamlins
HALL Brian Clifford Chance
HAND Catherine Jenkins & Hand
UP AND COMING
SERRELLI Roseanne Sharpe Pritchard
SHARLAND John Sharpe Pritchard

Within each band, firms are listed alphabetically. *See **Profiles** on page 586*

** See editorial entries for explanations of team sizes.*

Nabarro Nathanson *"In a different league."* The firm continues to occupy top spot in London, where *"skilful articulation of cases"* has produced a *"very slick unit."* With a huge local authority client list, they have succeeded where other large commercial firms have not, by developing a strong *"pure local authority practice"* that is *"accessible and affordable."* The firm's traditional strength in property raises some speculation that this is the core of the work, but the dedicated public sector group is felt to be large and resourced enough to offer quality services in town centre regeneration, education/schools, NHS trusts and PFI projects. Group head **Malcolm Iley** (*"a godfather to the practice"*) leads London's largest public sector team. His *"on the ball and enthusiastic manner"* and organisational and project management skills win him consistent praise from all quarters. *"Creative thinker"* **Ray Ambrose** has a *"depth of knowledge"* of local government finance and adopts a *"responsible way of getting things done."* Among the vast local authority case-load, the team acted for the London Borough of Lewisham on the unique Pathfinder project providing schools, social services and catering facilities. Completed major housing regeneration projects for the London Borough of Hackney based on mixed tenure and commercial developments. **Clients:** Sheffield City Council; Cheltenham Borough Council; London Borough of Islington; DTI, DETR; National Audit Office; Housing Associations.

Rowe & Maw Continue to be regarded as one of the leading firms for vires work and *"still the big name for local authority powers."* Traditionally, **Tony Child**'s reputation as the principal figure for audit law and local government finance has obscured further exploration of the public law group's other strengths. However, the impact of **Anna Forge**'s move from Berwin Leighton in April 1999 has had time to be felt, with most commentators suggesting she has brought added dimension and breadth to the firm (*"She's been a real plus to the organisation."*) Regarded as something of a *"stickler for the letter of the law,"* Tony Child nevertheless has an *"astonishing tenacity and grasp of detail,"* and *"really fights his corner for his clients."* Beyond the financial focus, Anna Forge has a wider practice embracing development, regeneration, housing and structural issues. Many local authority clients and district auditors continue to use the firm for due diligence and audit opinion, although PFI, social services and human rights advice are also important. Act for local authorities on matters relating to property regeneration schemes and 'best value' contracts. **Clients:** Local authorities; local government and NHS external auditors.

Sharpe Pritchard There are few local authorities that will not have come across the name of Sharpe Pritchard in their capacity as an agency litigation practice. They are elevated a tier this year on account of their prodigious volumes of local authority work, which comprise a major portion of the overall practice, and the rising reputations of the individual personnel. Not regarded as the most glamorous or cutting edge firm because of their agency status and competitive fees, nevertheless a *"superb public sector client base"* allows them to *"start from a strong platform."* **Trevor Griffiths** (*"a good source of pragmatic advice and strong on technical points"*) is well-known amongst the local government fraternity, particularly in a litigious capacity. He *"knows his way round the Crown Office and the judicial review minefield better than anyone."* Felt to be expanding the range of services that the firm offers to the public sector, he is *"clearly steering them in the right direction with his innovative approach."* Two new names enter the fray this year. **Roseanne Serrelli** (*"exudes a confident air"*) has been praised by fellow solicitors for her hardworking style and ability to *"tune in to the local authority way of doing things."* Among several commendations for his effectiveness, **John Sharland** has impressed clients with his *"local authority background and contacts."* Act for a large number of local authorities in judicial review proceedings as well as advising on vires, planning and community governance. **Clients:** Large numbers of local authorities.

Ashurst Morris Crisp Still regarded as a significant player by the market (*"A well-organised and efficient firm,"*) largely because of a comprehensive team with inter-related expertise in planning and urban development, as well as in public law and pure advisory services. They are felt to be most active in circumstances where purely local government work turns into a commercial deal. This allows the firm to draw on a team with expertise in development and regeneration issues, land disposals and planning enquiries. Clients have commented that when outsourcing to Ashursts, they are good at *"responding to our demands and carrying through their commitments."* The *"relaxed and experienced"* **Tony Curnow** *"conducts himself forcefully and thoroughly"* and is *"reliable for a sensible judgement."* Acting for Wimpey Homes, the preferred bidder selected by The London Borough of Lambeth in Project Vauxhall, one of London's largest housing and community regeneration projects. Acting for Bath and North East Somerset Council on the Southgate town centre leisure and housing re-development. **Clients:** London Boroughs of Hackney, Hounslow and Brent; Surrey Heath Borough Council.

Berwin Leighton Slip slightly this year. Undoubtedly pre-eminent in property and planning, the firm are perceived to have less of a commanding presence in the wider 'pure' local government arena. The team is inevitably weighted in the property and planning direction and contains *"some quality practitioners."* However the firm is still not felt to have replaced Anna Forge who brought broader local government expertise to the practice. The team are best known for recent work on urban town centre developments. Advised Canterbury City Council on a £100 million mixed use development scheme. Acted for Solihull Metropolitan Borough Council on the major Touchwood Court town centre retail and leisure development. **Clients:** Newcastle City Council; Swindon Borough Council; London Borough of Enfield.

Lawrence Graham *"An active and important competitor,"* commented a fellow local government solicitor. There may be question marks over the wider collective strength of the team who are still felt to be in the shadow of the *"well-rated"* **Simon Randall**. He *"gets on well with clients"* and *"gets things done."* The firm boasts a solid roster of local authority clients for whom its reputation rests largely on housing work, including a number of large scale voluntary housing stock transfers. The team advises a number of local authorities on the use of partnering charitable trusts in service delivery. Recently completed the transfer of six leisure centres in South Oxfordshire and three leisure centres in Thurrock to newly established not-for-profit entities. **Clients:** London Borough of Enfield; Local authority regeneration schemes.

Léonie Cowen & Associates Despite their diminutive size, this *"excellent niche specialist"* are frequently *"a competitor that we come up against."* The firm is felt to merit inclusion in the list of leading firms through sheer level of specialisation. **Léonie Cowen** is well-liked by clients and fellow solicitors alike and *"brings her bubbly personality out in her work."* Clients also like her responsiveness and have commented on the *"excellence of her technical skills."* Local authorities have typically called on her specialised services when requiring complex and innovative service delivery solutions. Advising The London Borough of Tower Hamlets on the legal structuring of a charitable trust regarding the £20-30 million multi-purpose Mile End Park millennium project. Also assisting the London Borough of Hackney on evaluating future options for a building maintenance team. **Clients:** Barking Council; Basingstoke and Deane Council; London Borough of Hounslow Community Initiatives Partnership.

Trowers & Hamlins There is no question that as one of the top social housing firms, Trowers are munching on a large chunk of the local authority pie. The only question is whether their singular focus on housing leaves much capacity to tackle other areas of the law for local government clients. Possessing *"deep resources"* in housing, leisure and regeneration, the firm is not felt to provide the more rounded local government practice of the market leaders. However, a long list of clients still keeps the firm high in the pecking order. **Ian Doolittle** is *"friendly, intelligent and hard-working"* and recognised for his expertise in housing finance and stock transfers. Have acted for a number of local authorities on complex housing stock transfers including a 13,000 property deal for Telford & Wrekin Council. **Clients:** North Wiltshire District Council; Coventry City Council; Telford & Wrekin Council.

Denton Wilde Sapte One of the few City firms that have made the effort to compete in the local authority market. Have successfully acquired portions of high level local authority work, although the small cross-departmental team lack the more voluminous client lists and weighty personalities that typify the top tier firms. Strong on public law and commercial regulatory work, the local government team also straddles housing (Milton Keynes office), planning and PFI projects. Scored a minor coup by making an advisory secondment to the government office for London in preparation for the Greater London Assembly and the Mayor for London elections. Acted for Bedfordshire County Council in relation to planning, consortium and vires advice surrounding the Bedford Western by-pass. Also involved in the Chequers Corner Regeneration Scheme for the London Borough of Barking & Dagenham. **Clients:** London Borough of Tower Hamlets; Windsor and Maidenhead Council; English Partnerships.

Clifford Chance Large cross-departmental team utilises lawyers from property, planning, environment and PFI jointly to provide local government assistance. Advising banks on lending to local authorities and related vires issues is also a core feature of the practice. **Brian Hall**'s main reputation is as a planning lawyer, although commentators have observed a definite *"synergy between the firm's local government and planning practices."* Clients were quick to point out the firm's resourcefulness and *"impressive results."* Acting for Spelthorne Borough Council on the administration of three compulsory purchase orders to facilitate the 'Two Rivers' Staines town centre redevelopment. Acting for West Dorset District Council on the development of Dorchester town centre. **Clients:** Corporation of London; Hastings Borough Council; London Borough of Hounslow.

Herbert Smith Reflecting a general upturn in the perceived quality and profile of the whole public law practice, Herbert Smith rises a band this year. Like most of the City firms, local government partners are spread thinly across a range of departments, notably litigation, property and PFI. Advised the Government Office for London on the legislation establishing the Greater London Authority. Acted on behalf of Oxfordshire County Council in relation to the restoration of Oxford Castle and the redevelopment of Oxford Prison to form a luxury hotel and leisure development. **Clients:** Oxfordshire County Council; Audit Commission; Surrey County Council.

Jenkins & Hand (1 partner up to 50%, 1 partner up to 30%) Relatively small practice which sometimes falls prey to the charge that *"they can appear a bit overstretched at times."* Despite the focus on social housing, this is not the only area where local government expertise is offered. Increasingly, district audit services and finance/procurement issues are surfacing alongside the more common housing stock transfers. *"Highly capable"* **Catherine Hand** is well-liked for her *"bright and pleasant"* approach, and is *"not short of a good brain."* Acting for the district auditor in the issue surrounding costs and payments made by Northampton Borough Council to subsidise the Northampton Town football stadium. Involved in a series of local authority housing transfers, including Test Valley Borough Council and £80 million of housing stock. **Clients:** Local authorities; housing associations.

Dechert Last year's ranked individual, Graham McGowan has since departed the firm and it is perhaps too early to assess whether this has had any impact. The firm is felt to offer good commercial property services to local authority clients. Much of the planning work for local authorities relates to large property schemes. The group left an impression upon one London in-house counsel, who chose their bid above many far larger and more established practices. Acting for the Corporation of London in a large property development project and for Mole Valley Council on a shopping centre development. **Clients:** Corporation of London; Mole Valley Council; London Borough of Redbridge; West Sussex County Council.

DJ Freeman The firm's local government practice is slanted heavily towards property, although it incorporates tax, CPO, planning and construction.

Development clients are represented as much as local authorities on the roster. The firm's visibility is perceived to have dipped slightly this year, although one partner occupies a full time public sector role, while other partners are called upon from the property and commercial departments. Acting for Elmbridge Borough Council on the £50-60 million retail/leisure redevelopment of Walton-On-Thames. **Clients:** London Borough of Camden; Fareham and Hertsmere Borough Council.

Winckworth Sherwood The market perceives that housing and vires/powers are the firm's areas of greatest activity in this area of practice. The team is multi-faceted, drawing on partners in planning, housing, education and health. Acting for Hammersmith and Fulham Council in a development and regeneration project involving a new public park, bridge and the demolition of old flats. Advising Leeds City Council on a major infrastructure project involving road express routes and the authorisation for a tramway. **Clients:** Cheshire County Council; Hertfordshire County Council; health trusts.

SOUTH WEST

LOCAL GOVERNMENT • South West	Ptnrs	Assts
❶ **Bevan Ashford** Exeter, Bristol	2	6
❷ **Bond Pearce** Bristol, Exeter	3	4
LEADING INDIVIDUALS		
❶ **JARMAN Chris** Bevan Ashford		

Within each band, firms are listed alphabetically. See **Profiles** on page 586

Bevan Ashford Rated by the London market, the firm is felt to be on an upward curve, with a much expanded profile. A major local authority client instructing them on a PFI project were impressed with their performance and client care. *"They always perform on time and serve you well. We're never left in the lurch."* Expertise filters through the range of departments from projects, health and property to procurement, waste and regeneration. Entering the individual ranks this year, **Chris Jarman** is *"very much the lead man."* Clients have been impressed with his *"wide local authority expertise in NHS, PFI and vires."* Acting for Bournemouth Borough Council in relation to the re-development of the Winter Gardens, involving the construction of residential and leisure developments. Appointed to act for Tamworth Borough Council upon its waste collection, management strategy and proposed partnering arrangements. **Clients:** Bath And NE Somerset Council; Maidstone Borough Council; Bristol City Council; Wiltshire County Council.

Bond Pearce A new face in the local government section, the firm has begun to acquire a more noticeable profile *("trying to muscle in,")* in particular at the London Bar. Much of the public sector work stems from the firm's property profile, although a number of part-time partners from other departments can be called upon. The firm regularly advise local authorities on IP and IT issues. Advise the National Assembly for Wales and continues to act for the Highways Agency under contracts awarded for the Southern region. **Clients:** Government agencies; local authorities, English Heritage; defence estates.

WALES

LOCAL GOVERNMENT • Wales	Ptnrs	Assts
❶ **Eversheds** Cardiff	2	2
❷ **Edwards Geldard** Cardiff	1	2
Morgan Cole Cardiff	*	*
LEADING INDIVIDUALS		
❶ **EVANS Eric** Eversheds		
❷ **COLE Alun** Morgan Cole		
WILLIAMS Huw Edwards Geldard		

Within each band, firms are listed alphabetically. See **Profiles** on page 586
* See editorial entries for explanations of team sizes.

Eversheds The Cardiff office is felt to be one of the national practice's healthier arms. The department acts for a string of local authorities seeking advice on PFI, employment, vires and planning. Ex-local authority **Eric Evans** is described as *"a real star in Cardiff"* and *"very influential in the Welsh goldfish bowl."* His style is felt to be slightly on the aggressive side although he *"gets things done"* and *"if I were a client, I would want him on my side acting for me."* The firm has been appointed as external advisors to the National Assembly of Wales. Acting for Ceredigion County Council in the completion of Wales' first PFI school, a £12 million project which was also the Welsh National Assembly's first local government pathfinder project to complete. Acted for Newport County Borough Council on a major Welsh road scheme. Also advising Wiltshire County Council on vires issues relating to their PFI schemes. **Clients:** Ceredigion County Council; Neath Port Talbot County Borough Council; Cardiff County Council; Assembly-sponsored public bodies.

Edwards Geldard *"Strong on powers, development and planning."* Head of the firm's public sector unit, **Huw Williams** is another well known local authority figure-head who is felt to possess considerable clout in the Welsh public sector. The team is best known for its public law and judicial review expertise, where it has both defended and acted against the decisions of public bodies. Successfully advised Cardiff Bay Development Corporation in a dispute with the environment Agency about the operation of the Cardiff Bay Barrage – one of the most public rows between two public bodies ever seen in Wales. The defence of public bodies. Also act for a number of local authorities and development agencies in planning related cases. **Clients:** Cardiff County Council; Welsh Development Agency; Bay Development Corporation.

Morgan Cole (Up to 8 partners and 32 assistants available from the public law/local authority practice) **Alun Cole** has an impeccable public sector CV, and his credentials have helped to maintain the practice among Welsh leaders. Adopting a strategy of acting for both public and private sector clients, it is common to see the firm active in powers and duties in a range of public law and local authority cases. The focus is on acting in areas such as PFI, development and regeneration, where there is interplay between the public and private sector. Advised the Cardiff Bay Development Corporation on the £120 million Bute Avenue Road and Urban Regeneration scheme. Advising the University of Swansea in relation to a major joint venture with the local authority for the construction of an international swimming pool complex. **Clients:** Local authorities; government departments; port authorities.

MIDLANDS

LOCAL GOVERNMENT • Midlands	Ptnrs	Assts
❶ **Wragge & Co** Birmingham	4	1
❷ **DLA** Birmingham	2	6
Pinsent Curtis Birmingham	3	*
❸ **Anthony Collins Solicitors** Birmingham	3	5
Eversheds Nottingham	3	5

LEADING INDIVIDUALS
❶ **KEITH-LUCAS Peter** Wragge & Co
MATTHEW Stephen Eversheds
ORLIK Michael DLA
❷ **COOK Mark** Anthony Collins Solicitors
KNOX Martin Anthony Collins Solicitors
RANDLE Anthony DLA
WHITE Martin Pinsent Curtis

Within each band, firms are listed alphabetically. *See **Profiles** on page 586*

* *See editorial entries for explanations of team sizes.*

Wragge & Co *"Classy operators."* Now considered major players on the local authority scene with a *"name that appears everywhere."* The firm consistently won commendation from all quarters in a competitive local market. One local authority solicitor felt they had *"gone through the stratosphere in internal expansion,"* arriving on the market this year *"with a wallop!"* Key to this rapidly improved market profile has been the networking and marketing skills of *"heavyweight and persuasive"* **Peter Keith-Lucas** who has *"tried hard to drum up links with all the local authorities."* Well-known in local government circles and with an extensive track record in the public sector himself, he has *"brought valuable inside knowledge"* and *"talks the same language as local authorities."* The firm has developed a strong pure local authority practice that is *"accessible and affordable."* Most commonly associated with town centre regeneration work and development, the firm have a team with expertise in PFI, planning, property and externalisation of social services. Acting on behalf of Croydon Borough Council in undertaking all its housing legal services. Acting on behalf of the DETR Railways Directorate in resolving land ownerships with Railtrack for the Channel Tunnel. **Clients:** Local authorities; government departments; government agencies.

DLA Still regarded as a key member of the *"Birmingham Three,"* the team has expertise in core local government specialist areas such as 'best value', procurement and PFI projects. The view from the market is that they appear to be moving away from *"routine nuts and bolts"* to providing *"more complex and sophisticated services."* One client believed that the firm's flexible approach, negotiation skills and strong personnel and resources were the decisive factors in choosing them. **Michael Orlik**, traditionally known for his reputation as a highway law specialist, was again positively recommended this year by clients and private practitioners alike. **Tony Randle** is considered another *"very active"* component of the team, and brings considerable knowledge of public sector PFI projects. Advised South Gloucestershire council on its £300 million integrated waste project. Acting for The London Borough of Tower Hamlets on its Grouped Schools and Mulberry School project. **Clients:** Coventry City Council; Doncaster Borough Council; Reading Borough Council; police authorities.

Pinsent Curtis (Up to 9 partners and 8 assistants naturally drawn from public sector and PFI practice)The firm's focus is on PFI/PPP, waste disposal, outsourcing, transport infrastructure and urban regeneration. As a fellow private practitioner at a competitor firm in London observed, *"we come across them frequently; they win; they do the work."* Although as active in the planning field, **Martin White** once again received a number of noteworthy comments for his local authority connections *("he's a strong individual in a strong firm.")* Acted for Barnsley Metropolitan Borough Council on the transfer of all its leisure facilities to a non-profit making organisation. Active in completion of a compulsory purchase order for Walsall Council with respect to phase 2 of the Town Wharf development. Acted on the disposal of Premco, the waste disposal company owned by Staffordshire County Council. **Clients:** County councils; Unitary authorities; District councils.

Anthony Collins Solicitors Esteemed as a leading Midlands social housing practice, the firm is not quite felt to have the size and breadth to compete with the leading triumvirate in the Midlands, although their quality standards are well documented. Department head **Martin Knox** possessess a *"strong background"* and adopts a *"practical approach"* to housing related work. **Mark Cook** also continues to win recommendations as a name *"associated with leisure work,"* including best value partnerships, PFI and invariably, housing. Acted for the Pinnacle development organisation, negotiating their best value contract with The London Borough of Lewisham. Active in a number of urban regeneration projects for the Sandwell authority in the West Midlands. **Clients:** Local authorities; development companies.

Eversheds The firm's Nottingham office is felt best placed to make a concerted challenge to the established order in the Midlands. Ex-Shropshire County Council **Stephen Matthew** is an acknowledged PFI specialist, particularly in education and social services-related projects, and is considered by peers a *"good local authority lawyer."* As well as supporting an extended client list of stand-alone local authority clients, there is the advantage of being able to draw upon additional strategic resources from the national operation on the bigger deals. Range of work also includes pioneering best value and partnering arrangements, public procurement, outsourcing and PPP. Highlight of the year was acting on behalf of Walsall Metropolitan Borough Council in a transfer of empty homes to a consortium of housing associations. **Clients:** Stoke City Council; Nottinghamshire County Council; Walsall MBC.

EAST ANGLIA

LOCAL GOVERNMENT • East Anglia	Ptnrs	Assts
❶ **Mills & Reeve** Norwich	2	2
Steele & Co Norwich	2	2

Within each band, firms are listed alphabetically.

Mills & Reeve Led by an ex-local authority solicitor, also spending a portion of his time in developing the Cambridge office, this East Anglian firm have managed to expand westwards and now have a client list including some notable local authorities from the Midlands. Expertise centres around property, litigation and employment issues arising from local government. Recently secured a contract to provide legal services to Leicester City Council. Acting for Norfolk and Norwich Millennium company, a consortium arrangement led by Norfolk County Council and Norwich City Council. **Clients:** East Herts District Council; Bedfordshire County Council; Norfolk County Council; police authorities.

Steele & Co The firm runs a small two-partner local government operation, with an unusual geographic spread of client authorities, including London boroughs. Areas of prime activity include property, housing and litigation. One partner is drawn from the commercial property department while the department head applies a more strategic 'best value' and PPP approach. The firm are retained to provide all legal services for Broadlands District Council. Also act on behalf of the London Borough of Lambeth in all non-contentious conveyancing and property work. **Clients:** London Boroughs of Bromley, Newham and Sutton; Bath and NE Somerset Council.

THE NORTH

LOCAL GOVERNMENT • The North	Ptnrs	Assts
❶ **Eversheds** Leeds	4	13
❷ **Pinsent Curtis** Leeds	6	7
❸ **Masons** Leeds	4	9
❹ **Pannone & Partners** Manchester	5	5
Walker Morris Leeds	1	8

LEADING INDIVIDUALS
❶ **CIRELL Stephen** Eversheds
❷ **BENNETT John** Eversheds
DOBSON Nicholas Pinsent Curtis
❸ **KILDUFF David** Walker Morris

Within each band, firms are listed alphabetically. See **Profiles** on page 586

Eversheds Few disagree that Eversheds' Leeds powerhouse represents the nation's leading local government practice. *"They dominate local government work nationally – everything funnels out of the Leeds office."* The fine reputation in Leeds rests on the ability to provide *"low fees and instant advice"* while breaking new ground by offering *"interesting, cutting edge and progressive services."* Eversheds were seen to have *"got in first ten years ago"* when local government private practices were in the early stages of development. The acquisition of *"entrepreneurial and enthusiastic flagship"* **Stephen Cirell** from Leeds City Council, one of the first major local government lawyers to move into private practice, was a key move in establishing their current position. A *"great salesman"* and a *"lively, rumbustious personality,"* Cirell is noted for his marketing and networking abilities and represents the *"leading name"* in private practice today. Acknowledged as an expert on best value and governance arrangements, he is complemented amongst a large team by the more *"cerebral"* **John Bennett**. The *"thinker and the go-getter"* combine to form an *"effective double act."* The firm offers a well-rounded local authority practice embracing the corporate, commercial and property departments – with a major track record in large PFI deals. Recent highlights include developing strategic waste disposal procurement under PFI terms for East Sussex County Council and Brighton and Hove Council, and a highway options review for Northamptonshire County Council. **Clients:** Large numbers of local authorities; Regional Development Agencies.

Pinsent Curtis We hinted last year that the arrival of **Nick Dobson** from Doncaster Council, a recognised best value advocate, could signal the development of the firm's local authority capabilities. There is evidence that this has occurred, with commentators pointing out that his *"local authority background has been of great benefit to the firm"* in providing strategic direction and impetus. Acknowledged to be strong on PFI (housing, education) projects, the firm's advisory services also include project finance, employment and dispute resolution. Acted in the Cardinal Heenan High School (Leeds) local authority education PFI Pathfinder project, the first voluntary aided schools PFI in the country. Acted on behalf of Dudley Metropolitan Borough Council in the £43 million IT for schools Pathfinder PFI scheme. **Clients:** Hackney Borough Council; Barnsley Metropolitan Council; Brighton and Hove Council; Bolton Metropolitan Borough Council.

Masons Local government work is undertaken across a number of practice areas including construction, projects, IT and property. The firm competes successfully with far more focused local authority practices on construction-related matters, but is not felt to challenge the local market leaders in other areas. Act for a number of prominent authorities on major construction litigation disputes. Advised Leeds City Council on a large delay and disruption claim brought by the contractor who built South Leeds Stadium. Act for the New Millennium Experience Company, the builders and operators of the Millennium Dome on a range of commercial agreements including IT procurement and ticketing services. **Clients:** Hackney Borough Council; Leeds City Council; Harrogate Borough Council.

Pannone & Partners The strength of Manchester as a centre of excellence for local government appears to have suffered by comparison with Leeds. However, clients believe Pannones have an *"understanding and awareness of public sector issues"* and maintain *"high quality standards."* They have a good client base of North West authorities, with particular expertise in corporate transactions, education, transport and private/public partnerships. Advised Manchester Airport plc on its controlling acquisition of Humberside International Airport Ltd – the first purchase of one publicly owned airport company of another. Acted for Tameside MBC on the transfer of their leisure functions to the voluntary sector. **Clients:** Greater Manchester Passenger Transport Executive; Manchester City Council; Oldham Metropolitan Borough Council; North West Regional Assembly.

Walker Morris **David Kilduff's** acquisition is felt to have bolstered the firm's fortunes. A range of comprehensive advice is offered to local authority organisations including a specialist human rights service. Advising Calderdale Metropolitan Borough Council in their partnering arrangements for the outsourcing of the council's transportation requirements, including social services and home-to-school transport. Advising Medway Council in connection with the development of its waste strategy and the suitability of procurement options. **Clients:** Sheffield City Council; Stockton-on-Tees Borough Council; Isle of Wight Council; Liverpool City Council.

SCOTLAND

LOCAL GOVERNMENT • Scotland	Ptnrs	Assts
❶ **Dundas & Wilson CS** Edinburgh	*	*
McGrigor Donald Glasgow	*	*
Shepherd & Wedderburn WS Edinburgh	4	5
❷ **Brodies WS** Edinburgh	2	2
Burness Edinburgh	*	*
Simpson & Marwick WS Edinburgh	3	5
Tods Murray WS Edinburgh	3	4

Within each band, firms are listed alphabetically.
** See editorial entries for explanations of team sizes.*

Dundas & Wilson CS (Up to 12 partners and 25 assistants part-time drawn from projects, PFI and planning) *"The premier local government firm,"* is considered to be *"ahead of the game, with several former local government lawyers on board."* Areas of depth within the government services group are felt to be in planning, PFI projects and property. The list of major Scottish local authority clients is felt to be a notable attribute, in particular an exclusive partnership arrangement with Stirling Council. The firm is felt by the market to have benefited from the relationship with Arthur Andersen in attracting new business. Recent work highlights include the appointment to act for Edinburgh Council on its £90 million schools project. Acting for Stirling on its £50 million Forthside development involving a brownfield site, including retail, leisure and office development. **Clients:** Glasgow City Council; Stirling Council; Orkney Islands Council, West Lothian Council.

McGrigor Donald Felt to *"pitch for a lot of work,"* with *"broad public sector strengths in some key areas,"* the firm enters the rankings this year. Overlapping with administrative and public law work, the work of the public sector team includes advice to local authorities on statutory powers and public procurement. The unit also advises local authorities and public sector clients on the powers and implications of the Scottish Parliament. Acted for the Aberdeenshire housing partnership in the structuring and facilitation of a £20 million 500-house transfer. **Clients:** Local authorities; government departments and agencies; NHS trusts.

Shepherd & Wedderburn WS *"Undoubtedly up there"* was the view of one prominent local government solicitor. One of a small number of Scottish firms who have established a dedicated local government unit, they are particularly well regarded for their projects and PFI expertise. There is great breadth to the practice, with four partners spread across litigation, PFI, employment and planning. Acted for East Dunbartonshire council on the first ever public enquiry into a proposed flood prevention scheme. Advised Edinburgh City Council on proposals to reintroduce trams to the city. **Clients:** East Dunbartonshire Council; East Renfrewshire Council; Angus Council; Commissioner for Local Administration; Accounts Commission for Scotland.

Brodies WS Much of the practice is dedicated to public law and local authority work, particularly advising local authorities on vires and powers issues, and judicial review. Property and planning work are also features of the local government practice. Recently provided substantial levels of employment and regulatory advice to retained local authority clients. **Clients:** North Lanarkshire Council; Shetlands Isles Council; Inverclyde Council.

Burness (All partners and assistants part-time) Well-regarded in the market for development and regeneration projects. Acts for a number of development agencies and local authority commissions seeking to engage in partnering and joint venture arrangements. Acted for the City of Edinburgh Council on the structuring of a joint venture between the council and LEEL for the Waterfront Edinburgh project. Acting for North Ayrshire Council in creating the vehicle for the involvement of the council in a proposed joint venture project with EDI. **Clients:** Local authorities; development agencies; government agencies.

Simpson & Marwick WS Big litigation practice renowned for defending local authorities. The firm is well-known for acting for large numbers of local authorities in a respondent capacity, defending them from judicial review challenges. Housing is regarded as one of the principal areas of expertise. Involved recently in two employment litigation cases at the House of Lords on behalf of Glasgow City Council. Advising Aberdeen City Council on new areas of the law such as stress- related illness. **Clients:** Fife Council; East Ayrshire Council; Highland Council.

Tods Murray WS Provide a range of advice to local authorities in Scotland on private/public partnerships, externalisation of services, economic development, PFI projects and planning litigation. Advised Dundee City Council on the establishment of an economic development company. **Clients:** West Lothian Council; Dumfries & Galloway Council; The Highland Council.

LEADERS IN LOCAL GOVERNMENT

AMBROSE, Ray
Nabarro Nathanson, London (020) 7518 3177
Specialisation: Local government and administrative law (powers and duties, statutory interpretation, capital controls, companies). Formerly at GLC and London Residuary Body. Recently advised on 'best value' housing management contract, PFI for civic accommodation, new-build social housing scheme, regeneration schemes (SRB and others), and partnership structures, Redbridge audit inquiry and establishment of Regional Development Agency.
Prof. Memberships: Law Society.
Career: Qualified 1975; Head of Administrative Law and Parliamentary Branch GLC 1985-86; Deputy Director of Legal Services, London Residuary Body 1986-90. Joined *Nabarro Nathanson* 1991.

BENNETT, John
Eversheds, Leeds (0113) 243 0391
johnbennett@eversheds.com
Consultant in public sector unit.
Specialisation: Work covers all aspects of contracting and tendering, including PFI, Best Value, e-commerce and EC public procurement. General Editor–Local Government Law Reports. Specialist Editor on Competition for the Encyclopaedia of Local Government Law, and Local Government Precedents and Procedures. Co-author of 'Best Value: Law and Practice'; co-author of 'The Private Finance Initiative and Local Government'; co-author of 'EC Public Procurement: Law and Practice'; co-author of 'Municipal Trading'; co-author of over two hundred articles on public sector contracting. Has appeared on TV and addressed numerous conferences and seminars.
Prof. Memberships: Law Society.
Career: Qualified in 1975. Became a Consultant in 1984. Previous appointments include *Malcolm Lynch Solicitors* in Leeds; Head of Public Law Group at Leeds Business School; Solicitor at the Department of Education and Science; Education Assets Board; Senior Contracts Solicitor at Brown & Root (UK) Ltd (Consultant to Esso, Shell, ELF and Mobil); *Peysner & Foley Solicitors* in Sheffield; *John Howell & Co Solicitors* in Sheffield; and Solicitor for Nottinghamshire County Council.
Personal: Born 11th October 1950. Attended Universities of Nottingham and Sheffield. Leisure interests include wife and family, and outdoor pursuits. Lives in Leeds.

CHILD, Tony
Rowe & Maw, London (020) 7248 4282
See under Administrative & Public Law, p.58

CIRELL, Stephen
Eversheds, Leeds (0113) 243 0391
stephencirell@eversheds.com
Partner in public sector unit.
Specialisation: Principal area of practice covers Best Value, Corporate Governance, major commercial transactions such as under the Private Finance Initiative, e-commerce and public sector contracting generally. Co-author of 'CCT- Law & Practice' (FT 1990), 'Municipal Trading' (FT 1992), 'Competitive Tendering for Professional Services' (FT 1994), 'Private Finance Initiative for Local Authorities' (FT 1997) and 'Best Value: Law and Practice' (Sweet & Maxwell 1999). Specialist editor to Encyclopaedia of Local Government Law. Specialist correspondent to the Local Government Chronicle and author of numerous articles for professional publications. Lectures frequently on local government law and related matters for commercial course organisers, professional organisations, local authorities and in-house.
Prof. Memberships: Law Society.
Career: Qualified 1984 while with Stockport MBC. Assistant Solicitor, then Principal Solicitor with Dudley MBC 1984-88, then Head of Common Law/Assistant Director at Leeds City Council 1988-93. Joined *Eversheds Hepworth & Chadwick* as a Partner in the Public Sector Unit in October 1993.
Personal: Born 3rd July 1960. Attended University College of Wales Aberystwyth 1978-81. Leisure pursuits include motorcycling. Lives in Leeds.

COLE, Alun
Morgan Cole, Cardiff (029) 2038 5385
alun.cole@morgan-cole.com
See under Administrative & Public Law, p.58

COOK, Mark
Anthony Collins Solicitors, Birmingham (0121) 200 3242
Specialisation: Public sector commercial lawyer, with particular experience of "public/private partnerships" in the local government, NHS and education sectors. Advising principally upon service delivery, strategic procurements, facilities management and the Private Finance Initiative, with considerable involvement in EC public procurement, UK competitive tendering legislation and vires issues, along with Best Value.
Prof. Memberships: Law Society.
Career: Joined *Anthony Collins* in 1997 as an Associate. Prior to that worked with *Pinsent Curtis* where he was extensively involved in local government work. Has been principally responsible for exploring a legal framework for the "Public Sector Plc" initiative, and contributed to the book of that title.
Personal: Leisure interests–World music, real ale, football and walking. Married with two children.

COWEN, Léonie
Léonie Cowen & Associates, London
(020) 7604 5870
Specialisation: Local Authority professional work and consultancy, especially public private partnerships, companies, joint ventures, PFI, project finance, Best Value, CCT and quality, high level sensitive investigations and inquiries, social services, education, employment and public procurement. Has advised over 70 local authorities. Recent projects include transfers of leisure sevices for Enfield, Hounslow (including a first for libraries) and others, externalisation of theatres in Enfield and elsewhere, acting for the governors of the new Worlds End Lane School (the first new-build school PFI), a sports hall Lottery/ PFI, community-led social and economic regeneration companies in England and Wales, an ESCO, transfers of residential homes for older people and £30 million in capital funding for one of these, drafting procurement and service contracts. Contributor to "The Handbook of Local Authority Legal Practice", author of many articles, and regular speaker at conferences and seminars. Member of Local Government Residuary Body (England), and director of an NHS trust.
Prof. Memberships: Law Society, Assoc. of District Secretaries, Charity Law Association.
Career: 15 years in local government, latterly as Chief Solicitor to Barnet and Director of Law & Admin./ Deputy Chief Executive at Camden. Founded her own practice in 1989.
Personal: Born 1950. Leisure interests include music and her family.

CURNOW, Tony
Ashurst Morris Crisp, London (020) 7638 1111
Partner and head of public sector group.
Specialisation: Advises local authorities and the private sector on planning, regeneration and public infrastructure projects. Major schemes include Channel Tunnel Rail Link, Docklands Highways, Chalkhill Estate for London Borough of Brent, Parkway/M602 inTrafford Park, Hackney Estates Regeneration Strategy, Surrey Heath Borough Council's town centre redevelopment at Camberley, Project Vauxhall in the London Borough of Lambeth, the redevelopment of the Guinness Brewery at Park Royal and the Southgate Shopping Centre in Bath.
Prof. Memberships: Law Society Planning Panel and Legal Associate RTPI.
Career: Qualified 1979. 11 years in local government. Joined *Ashurst Morris Crisp* 1988, Partner in 1996.

DOBSON, Nicholas
Pinsent Curtis, Leeds (0113) 244 5000
nicholas.dobson@pinsents.com
Specialisation: National head of Local Government Law and partner. Advises on local authority, constitutional and administrative law, Best Value and local government modernisation generally. Advises local authorities and others (public and private) and the Improvement and Development Agency for Local Government and the Employers' Organisation for Local Government.
Prof. Memberships: A member of the national TUPE Forum.
Career: Qualified in 1984 (also qualified in teaching and social work). Has worked as a lawyer with six local authorities. In 1999 left Doncaster MBC (Chief Solicitor). 1999 *Pinsent Curtis*, Partner.
Publications: Writes and lectures extensively on local government law. Books: Best Value: Law and Management (Jordan Publishing Limited June 2000); TUPE, Contracting-Out and Best Value (Sweet and Maxwell, December 1998). Conferences: 1999–Law Society in Paris, Association of Council Secretaries and Solicitors (London), 2000. Law Society Local Government Group Weekend School. Contributes to Legal Network Television on training videos.

DOOLITTLE, Ian
Trowers & Hamlins, London (020) 7423 8000
idoolittle@trowers.com
Partner, public sector. Head of public sector.
Specialisation: All aspects of public sector law, especially property and housing law (including housing stock transfers). Specialises in public/private sector partnerships, especially in the context of urban regeneration. Also specialist in environmental law.

EVANS, Eric
Eversheds, Cardiff (02920) 471147
See under Property (Commercial), p.726

FORGE, Anna
Rowe & Maw, London (020) 7248 4282
Specialisation: General local government law. Primarily acts for local authority clients, also for other public sector bodies and parties dealing with them. Provides advice on local government powers and administrative law, finance issues, interests in companies, compulsory purchase; domestic and European grants, particularly in connection with development, regeneration, leisure or housing schemes. Acts in PFI, best value and other 'partnership' projects. Handles a range of unusual or sensitive cases for local authority clients. Speaks at national conferences and seminars; produces plain guides on local government legal issues; writes for a major legal publisher on Local Government finance and the Private Finance Initiative.
Prof. Memberships: Law Society.
Career: Qualified 1982. London Borough of Southwark 1979-1989. Joined *Berwin Leighton* in 1989. Partner 1996. Joined *Rowe & Mawe* as a partner 1999.
Personal: Born 1951. Leisure interests include ballet, theatre, travel, reading. Two children. Lives in Hove.

GRIFFITHS, Trevor
Sharpe Pritchard, London (020) 7405 4600
See under Administrative & Public Law, p.58

HALL, Brian
Clifford Chance, London (020) 7600 1000
brian.hall@cliffordchance.com
See under Planning, p.664

HAND, Catherine
Jenkins & Hand, London (020) 7222 5002
Partner in Housing and Local Government Department. Set up *Jenkins & Hand* in 1996 with Keith Jenkins as a firm specialising in work for the public and not-for-profit sector. Local government work includes advice on local authority powers and district audit issues, numerous housing stock transfers both large scale and estate based, major urban regeneration schemes, procurement issues, tenant management coops and local authority sponsored companies. Also has extensive experience on all aspects of housing association work. Lectures regularly on housing stock transfers and on housing association law.
Career: Qualified 1978. Lecturer in Law at Queen Mary College, London 1978-79 and 1980-84. Lecturer in Law University of Kent 1979-80. In Government Legal Service, Lord Chancellors Department 1984-89. Joined *Winckworth & Pemberton* in 1989, partner 1990. Left to set up new firm 1996.
Personal: Born September 1954. Educated Southampton University 1972-75 (L.L.B 1st Class Hons). Board member of Rosebery Housing Association.

ILEY, Malcolm
Nabarro Nathanson, London (020) 7524 6000
Partner specialising in public sector and local government. Head of *Nabarro Nathanson*'s public sector team.
Specialisation: Main practice area is public law relating to local government, government departments and public sector powers generally. Experience in local authority outsourcings, asset transfer, regeneration, compulsory purchase, planning, education, competition and PFI, including the consideration of wider European involvement. Currently advising on one of the first "best value" partnership joint ventures. Clients have included London boroughs, district and county councils, government departments, local authority related companies, higher and further education, LAWDAC, and urban development corporations. Currently involved in research concerning the proposed regional development agencies. Media advisor and broadcaster on public sector legal issues. Regular contributor to local government and regional press.
Career: Qualified in 1976. Began career in the private sector, transferred to local government and later became a senior lawyer with Leeds City Council. Appointed City Solicitor and Deputy Chief Executive for Plymouth City Council. Held other senior posts in Lancashire, Sussex and Norfolk. Joined *Nabarro Nathanson* in 1997 as a partner.
Personal: Born 12 April 1950. College Governor. F.E. Governor, company director, director of environmental trust and Business in the Community.

JARMAN, Christopher
Bevan Ashford, Bristol (0117) 975 1621
c.jarman@bevanashford.co.uk
Specialisation: Project work. Member of the PFI and Projects Group. Deals with local authorities, NHS Trusts and M.O.D. work for the private sector. Recently: pathfinder local authorities PFI; closed largest NHS PFI in Wales; advising on largest (£9bn) PFI scheme to date.
Prof. Memberships: Law society.
Career: Sidcot School; University College, London (BA History). Articled, qualified 1987 and partner 1989 at *Sharpe Pritchard*; joined *Bevan Ashford* 1997 as associate partner, became partner, *Bevan Ashford*, 1998.
Publications: Editor and contibutor to 'Public Private Partnerships', Sweet & Maxwell. Contributor to 'TUPE and the Acquired Rights Directive', edited by Sharland and Isaacs Q.C.
Personal: Reading, walking, playing with my children, and Axbridge Saxons Football Club.

KEITH-LUCAS, Peter
Wragge & Co, Birmingham (0121) 214 1084
peter_keith_lucas@wragge.com
Specialisation: Local government and public sector law, property and planning. Specialises in administrative law and partnerships and joint ventures between local authorities and other public and private bodies. Highlights include: award of the partnership contract

with Buckinghamshire County Council, Croydon's housing contract and appointment to the DETR property law panel. Regular contributor to local government press and speaker at conferences/seminars.
Prof. Memberships: Former president 1996-97 of the Association of Council Secretaries and Solicitors.
Career: Qualified 1976, initially with Berkshire County Council, then Avon and West Glamorgan. Chief Executive, Medina Borough Council. Director of Legal and Administrative Services, Swansea City Council and Swansea Unitary Authority. Joined *Wragge & Co* as Partner, November 1997.
Personal: Tennis, sailing. Lives in Birmingham and Swansea.

KILDUFF, David
Walker Morris, Leeds (0113) 283 2500
Specialisation: Has experience in a full range of projects across sector and service areas including MOD (vehicles/ship and army foundation college), education (colleges and schools), Home Office (secure accomodation) environment and transport (waste management, highways maintenance). He is a regular speaker at conferences on topical legal and practical issues in the PFI.
Prof. Memberships: Law Society: Member of the specialist Law Society Planning Panel.
Career: Training: Calderdale MBC; Qualified in 1982. Appointments include Assistant Chief Solicitor Stockton on Tees, Deputy Secretary Ashford Borough Council then Borough Secretary and Solicitor 1988-1995. Former secretary and honorary legal adviser to the Kent Association of district Councils. Joined *Walker Morris* as Head of Psctr & PFI in May 1999 from *Eversheds.*
Personal: Born 26 July 1958. Attended the University of Kent. Married with three children. Lives in Shipley.

KNOX, Martin
Anthony Collins Solicitors, Birmingham (0121) 200 3242
See under Social Housing, p.761

MATTHEW, Stephen
Eversheds, Nottingham (0115) 950 7000
See under Projects/PFI, p.699

ORLIK, Michael F.
DLA, Birmingham (08700) 111 111
michael.orlik@dla.com
Partner in property litigation group.
Specialisation: Main area of practice is town and country planning, environmental law, highway law and compulsory purchase. Worked for four local authorities from 1967 to 1989. Currently has a number of local authority and developer clients. Also advises on local authority legislation, powers of local authorities and judicial review. Has represented numerous clients at local inquiries. Acted in the Skypark planning inquiry, the prosecution of a County Council for obstructing a highway and a lengthy Lands Tribunal case for compensation for compulsory acquisition by a Development Corporation. Author of 'An Introduction to Highway Law' (1993); contributes to a regular monthly column for 'The Surveyor'. Has lectured on these topics at a number of seminars.
Prof. Memberships: Law Society. Environmental Law Foundation, Education Law Association.
Career: Qualified in 1970. VSO teacher in West Africa 1965-66. Articled clerk and then solicitor with West Sussex C.C. 1967-77. Assistant County Solicitor at Buckinghamshire C.C. 1977-81. Assistant Chief Executive at Dorset C.C. 1981-84. Chief Executive of Surrey Heath B.C. 1984-89. Joined *Needham & James* as a Partner in 1990; firm merged with *Dibb Lupton Broomhead* in 1993.
Personal: Born 21st September 1943. Attended Oxford University 1962-65. Degree in History.

RANDALL, Simon
Lawrence Graham, London (020) 7379 0000
simon.randall@lawgram.com
Partner, Head of Local Government Services.
Specialisation: Principal area of practice is public sector work advising local authorities on externalisation, charitable trusts, urban regeneration and public procurement, PFI, housing and competitive tendering. Involved in large scale voluntary transfers of housing stock to housing associations and local housing companies. Author of many articles and pamphlets on local government and social issues ranging from the private rented sector, large scale voluntary sector of housing stock, local authority companies, community care and housing finance. Organises many seminars on health service, housing and local government related matters.
Prof. Memberships: Law Society.
Career: Articled with *Lawrence Graham* and became a Partner in 1970. Member, London Borough of Bromley 1968–1994. Chairman London Borough of Bromley Housing Committee 1971-76 and Leader of the Council 1976-81. Member Greater London Council 1981-86. Chairman, London Boroughs Association Housing and Social Services Committee 1978–1994. Non-executive Director Bethlem Royal and Maudsley Special Health Authority 1971-94.
Personal: Born 1944. Attended Westminster School. Appointed CBE in June 1991 for housing work in London. Chairman Kelsey Housing Association Ltd and member of Management Committee of Broomleigh Housing Association Ltd. Member National Housing Federation Council and director H.O.M.E.S. Limited.

RANDLE, Anthony R.
DLA, Birmingham (08700) 111 111
tony.randle@dla.com
See under Projects/PFI, p.700

SERRELLI, Roseanne
Sharpe Pritchard, London (020) 7405 4600
rserrelli@sharpepritchard.co.uk
Specialisation: All areas of public sector contracting but especially public/private partnerships and PFI. Particular specialities–waste management, leisure provision, information technology procurement, schools PFI and housing regeneration.
Prof. Memberships: Law Society.
Career: Articles *Sharpe Pritchard* 1992-1994. Partner *Sharpe Pritchard* 1997.
Publications: Lectures: PFI standardisation documents, waste management, IT contracts and case law.
Personal: Ursuline School; New Hall, Cambridge.

SHARLAND, John
Sharpe Pritchard, London (020) 7405 4600
jsharland@sharpepritchard.co.uk
Specialisation: Partner specialising in local government law including advice on local authority powers, local government finance, public sector contracting, housing regeneration, town and country planning.
Prof. Memberships: Law Society.
Career: Articles *Dale and Newbury* 1980-1982. Solicitor *Fisher Meredith* 1983-1985. London Borough of Croydon 1985-1986. London Borough of Hammersmith & Fulham 1986-1991. Chief solicitor London Borough of Hackney 1991-1994. *Sharpe Pritchard* since 1994. Partner since 1997.
Publications: TUPE and the 'Acquired Rights Directive' (co-editor) 1996. 'A Practical Approach to Local Government Law', Blackstones 1997. Articles in various publications. Lectures and presentations to seminars and conferences.
Personal: Educated Dulwich College, LSE, City of London Polytechnic. Leisure interests include history of art and architecture, swimming, walking and theatre.

WHITE, Martin
Pinsent Curtis, Birmingham (0121) 200 1050
martin.white@pinsents.com
See under Planning, p.61

WILLIAMS, Huw
Edwards Geldard, Cardiff (029) 2023 8239
huw.williams@geldards.co.uk
See under Administrative & Public Law, p.61

MEDIA & ENTERTAINMENT

RESEARCH APPROVED BY BMRB: *For this edition,* Chambers' *researchers conducted 6083 interviews – 4408 with law firms, 598 with barristers and 1077 with clients.*

The validity of the research was scrutinised by BMRB International, who audited both the methodology and the results at our offices in July 2000. They interviewed Chambers' *researchers and cross-checked sample interviews. Details of the audit appear on page 7.*

LONDON

FILM FINANCE/ FILM & TV PRODUCTION/ BROADCASTING

S J Berwin & Co The film finance practice now appears unassailable in its top ranking position. Major sale and leaseback work and a mass of traditional bank lending has allowed a team packed with great partners to shine. Head **Nigel Palmer** is unquestionably one of the top two names in this field. **Tim Johnson**, who is particularly noted for his work for distributors, is seen as *"hard but fair"* whilst **Jacqueline Hurt** is now identified as a clear rising star. *"Pragmatic and easy to deal with, she doesn't take silly points."* On the production side the team advises on both TV and film projects. For TV work, including regulatory advice and the cross-over with sports, **Peter McInerney** is endorsed. The firm advised Société Générale on the funding arrangements for the Anglo-French-Hungarian co-production of 'The Luzhin Defence' and acted for The Britt Allcroft Company on its new film production of 'Thomas the Tank Engine.' **Clients:** Columbia Pictures Industries; Société Générale; Britt Allcroft Company plc; United Artists Films Ltd.

Richards Butler A strong and long-held link with the BBC is viewed as the cornerstone of the broadcasting practice. Instructions range from copyright and content issues through to distribution and transmission matters in both TV and radio. *"Active"* and *"experienced,"* **Stephen Edwards** is the key man in that relationship. Production advice is split evenly between film and TV clients, whilst on the finance side, the firm sees sale and leaseback transactions as well as bank and gap/mezzanine finance. **Richard Philipps** is a *"dedicated"* finance lawyer and ranked equal first for this work. He is joined in our tables this year by **Michael Maxtone-Smith**, another specialist in funding. Production man **Barry Smith**, who *"shows a huge amount of common sense,"* rises in our tables with strong support from the market. Instructed by Société Générale on an insurance-backed revolving credit facility for Intermedia Film Equities, the makers of 'Sliding Doors' and 'Enigma'. **Clients:** FACT; Carnival Films; MTV.

Davenport Lyons *"Commercially sensible and technically knowledgeable,"* this is a firm seen to offer good value advice with a *"responsive"* style. The team has seen a high volume of bank lending for several major players, has advised insurers and acted on sale and leasebacks and EIS schemes. The production caseload is felt to have increased in volume and profile. **Leon Morgan** is the name in finance, whilst **Richard Moxon**, now fully settled into the firm, is *"very reasonable to deal with"* on the production side. The partners are said to be nurturing some real talent at junior level. Acted for the Arts Council of England on their funding of a number of films, including 'Love's Labours Lost.' Advised the British producer of 'Vatel,' the largest Anglo-French co-production in history. **Clients:** Barclays Bank plc; Bank Leumi (UK) Ltd.

Denton Wilde Sapte Superlative for broadcasting, particularly in pay TV, very strong in finance and well regarded in production work. The Denton Hall/Wilde Sapte merger is perceived to have brought particular advantage on the funding side. With ample resources and international reach, DWS is recognized as being amongst the more capable players with real industry background. Its documentation is praised as well as its top lawyers. *"Smooth"* and pleasant **Michael Ridley** is visible on the production side and a clear leader for his broadcasting practice. **Ken Dearsley** is a strong player in finance work. Advised on the launch of The Money Channel including digital distribution and transmission arrangements with BSkyB and others. **Clients:** Universal Television/Sci-fi Channel; Discovery Communications; Sony Pictures Entertainment.

Olswang Top of the range for production and broadcasting work. A perception that clients pay handsomely but get the best quality advice. *"Very corporate, as opposed to a West End approach"* some felt, whilst others commented that the firm now has to work hard to live up to the reputation is has acquired. *"Doyen"* **Mark Devereux** is the key figure in the team and well viewed for production work, for which he is seen as *"tough"* and *"goes in very hard for his clients."* David Bouchier's move in-house to BSkyB is seen to have dented partner strength somewhat. Next in the pecking order come **David Zeffman** for his broadcasting expertise and fierce opponent **Libby Savill** for her finance and production work. Act for terrestrial, cable and satellite broadcasters. Recent work includes the launch of ITN's 24 hour news channel, a joint venture with NTL. On the production and finance side much of the work has been for the distributors and studios,

TOP IN-HOUSE LAWYERS

Television

Deanna BATES, Head of Legal, *BSkyB plc*

Colin CAMBELL, Director of Legal and Business Affairs, *Channel 5*

Antonia DOWNEY, Head of Legal, *The Jim Henson Company*

Svenja GEISSMAR, Vice-President of Business Affairs, *MTV*

Simon JOHNSON, Head of Legal, *ITV*

Sarah TINGAY, Director of Legal and Business Affairs, *Pearson TV*

Deanna Bates at BSkyB is *"precise, detailed and a tough negotiator."* **Colin Cambell** at Channel 5 has *"unrivalled experience in TV."* **Antonia Downey** at The Jim Henson Company has "great people skills." **Svenja Geissmar** has *"good commercial skills."* On the sporting side, **Simon Johnson** at ITV enjoys an excellent reputation for *"managing the politics of the situation well"* and *"can really go to the kernel of the problem."* **Sarah Tingay** at Pearson TV is a *"extremely bright and well-focused."*

Film

Sara CURRAN, Head of Legal and Business Affairs, *Working Title*

Cameron MCCRACKEN, Head of Corporate and Business Affairs, *Pathé Distribution*

Angela MORRISON, Chief Operating Officer, *Working Title*

Andrew HILDEBRAND, Director of Business Affairs, *FilmFour*

James SHIRRAS, Financial Director, *Film Finances*

Mark PYBUS, Head of Business Affairs, *Granada Film*

Andrew Hildebrand at FilmFour *"gets things done."* **Cameron McCracken** now at Pathé Distribution is *"pragmatic and very commercial."* **Angela Morrison** of Working Title has *"very good negotiation and management skills."* **Sara Curran** also at Working Title, is described as *"highly regarded."* The up and coming **Mark Pybus** of Granada, once the *"brightest young media lawyer"* in private practice is already considered to be *"very knowledgeable."* **James Shirras** of Film Finances is *"an institution"* and has *"enormous knowledge and great flexibility."*

In-House lawyers profiles: page 1177

MEDIA & ENTERTAINMENT: FILM FINANCE • London	Ptnrs	Assts
❶ SJ Berwin & Co	4	6
❷ Richards Butler	4	6
❸ Davenport Lyons	3	4
Denton Wilde Sapte	8	10
Olswang	3	5
❹ The Simkins Partnership	3*	1*

MEDIA & ENTERTAINMENT: FILM & TV PRODUCTION • London	Ptnrs	Assts
❶ Olswang	3	10
❷ Davenport Lyons	3	4
Harbottle & Lewis	2	4
Lee & Thompson	2	2
Theodore Goddard	3	8
❸ SJ Berwin & Co	3	5
The Simkins Partnership	3*	1*
❹ Denton Wilde Sapte	7	11
H2O	2	-
Harrison Curtis	1	-
Richards Butler	3	8
Schilling & Lom and Partners	1	2

MEDIA & ENTERTAINMENT: BROADCASTING • London	Ptnrs	Assts
❶ Denton Wilde Sapte	2	4
Olswang	3	8
❷ Clifford Chance	2	9
Wiggin & Co	6	9
❸ Ashurst Morris Crisp	1	7
Goodman Derrick	3	2
Richards Butler	4	5
❹ D J Freeman	3	3
❺ Davenport Lyons	1	-
Field Fisher Waterhouse	2	4
Harbottle & Lewis	4	4
SJ Berwin & Co	2	4
The Simkins Partnership	3*	1*
❻ Allen & Overy	8	10
Herbert Smith	6	15
Lovells	*	*
Travers Smith Braithwaite	2	4

Within each band, firms are listed alphabetically.
** See editorial entries for explanations of team sizes.*

such as the production work on 'The Talented Mr. Ripley' for Miramax. **Clients:** Granada; Channel 4; Sky Productions.

The Simkins Partnership An all round media and entertainment firm that appears in every London table in this section of the book. The firm has one team working on the whole range of film and TV work. This year, the firm makes its debut in the film finance table to acknowledge their involvement in the sale and leaseback market. **Antony Gostyn** is *"quite dry"* but well regarded for his production work for which the Film and Television Group is best known. **Nigel Bennett** also holds his own in our table of leaders. The client roster numbers financiers and a host of major and independent TV and film production companies. A niche is developing with Italian film and TV companies. Advised Picture Palace on their productions of 'Rebel Heart' and 'Patagonia' and Really Useful Group on the full length TV/video productions of 'Joseph & the Amazing Technicolour Dreamcoat' and 'Jesus Christ Superstar'. **Clients:** Channel 4; FilmFour Ltd; Matrix Securities Ltd.

Harbottle & Lewis The team displays a number of similarities to The Simkins Partnership. It has a marvellous all-round reputation in media and entertainment and has always been seen to focus its resources in that area. Some feel it now has aspirations to become *"big, corporate and expensive in production work."* Again, like Simkins, the firm is seen as strongest on the production side, fielding a mid-sized team with experienced players such as *"jolly good producer's lawyer"* **Robert Storer** and TV man **Medwyn Jones**, whose experience crosses into other aspects of broadcasting work. One of this year's two new Up and Coming lawyers is the *"bubbly and helpful"* **Abigail Payne**. There has been an increase in the funding work this year with sale and leaseback deals and litigation arising from insurance-backed schemes. In the last year the team advised Ecosse Films on its production of the TV series 'Monarch of the Glen' and the feature film 'Charlotte Gray'. **Clients:** Merchant Ivory Productions; Chrysalis Visual Entertainment; Ginger Media Group.

Lee & Thompson *"More responsive than some of the others and better value for money."* **Jeremy Gawade** looks after some *"good clients and the firm makes an effort to put itself about."* **Reno Antoniades** *"cuts to the quick sooner than some others."* The list of production clients is almost endless. An interesting sideline is developing in the production of major music TV specials for artists such as the Spice Girls and Robbie Williams. Last year the firm advised on the production of 'Kingdom Come', one of the biggest budget UK independent films for some time. **Clients:** Kudos Productions Ltd; Red Production Company; Revolution Films.

Theodore Goddard Has maintained a strong position for production work this year with an enhanced list of clients. **Jonathan Berger** *"is the driving force"* of the team which seems to be seeking out and acting for the bigger-ticket production clients. Acting for Renaissance Films on new productions including the European co-production 'The Luzhin Defence'. **Clients:** Warner Bros; DNA Films Ltd; September Films.

H2O Media and entertainment team lawyers act for a variety of client types rather than organising in to separate teams. No figures are set out in the tables. **Michael Henry** is rated for his production work although is seen to cover many bases and this may detract somewhat from his reputation in any one particular area of expertise. The team is expanding though the addition of two full time consultants and a barrister. The re-branded firm seems intent on keeping pace with its clients' moves onto the internet. Last year has seen the firm brought in as specialist adviser on litigation and deal construction pertaining to insurance backed film finance. **Clients:** Carlton; Channel 5; Entertainment Rights plc.

Harrison Curtis A small two partner firm which *"offers a good service to clients,"* one of the partners specializes in the film and TV work on both the production and financing side. The firm has advised on a number of production matters for FilmFour in the last year and has given advice to Channel 4 concerning rights over its back catalogue. **Clients:** Zone Vision Enterprises; Diplomat Films Ltd; Ice Media Ltd.

Schilling & Lom and Partners In addition to the team size shown in the table, there are a further two consultants and one of the assistants is a qualified barrister. **Nicholas Lom** has a pretty good reputation for production work, acting for some well known independents as well as major names such as Warner Bros. Finance and production advice for some well known TV programmes, such as reality show 'City Hospital' and drama productions like 'Poirot' and '10th Kingdom'. **Clients:** Castle Communications; Renegade Films; Criminal Productions.

Clifford Chance Consistently positive endorsement for the work of the firm in broadcasting. Seen to have good clients and have particular expertise on the bigger regulatory/corporate issues. **Daniel Sandelson** is well known in

FILM FINANCE/FILM & TV PRODUCTION LEADING INDIVIDUALS	
❶ **DEVEREUX Mark** Olswang	**PALMER Nigel** SJ Berwin & Co
PHILIPPS Richard Richards Butler	
❷ **BERGER Jonathan** Theodore Goddard	**DEARSLEY Ken** Denton Wilde Sapte
GOSTYN Antony The Simkins Partnership	**JOHNSON Timothy** SJ Berwin & Co
MORGAN Leon Davenport Lyons	**SAVILL Lisbeth** Olswang
SMITH Barry Richards Butler	**STORER Robert** Harbottle & Lewis
❸ **ANTONIADES Reno** Lee & Thompson	**GAWADE Jeremy** Lee & Thompson
JONES Medwyn Harbottle & Lewis	
LOM Nicholas Schilling & Lom and Partners	
MAXTONE-SMITH Michael Richards Butler	
MOXON Richard Davenport Lyons	
❹ **BENNETT Nigel** The Simkins Partnership	**HENRY Michael** H2O
MCINERNEY Peter SJ Berwin & Co	
UP AND COMING	
HURT Jacqueline SJ Berwin & Co	**PAYNE Abigail** Harbottle & Lewis

BROADCASTING LEADING INDIVIDUALS	
❶ **JAMES Sean St John** Wiggin & Co	**RIDLEY Michael** Denton Wilde Sapte
ZEFFMAN David Olswang	
❷ **EDWARDS Stephen** Richards Butler	**GHEE Tony** Ashurst Morris Crisp
SANDELSON Daniel Clifford Chance	
❸ **BALLARD Tony** Field Fisher Waterhouse	**LEIFER Tony** D J Freeman
❹ **SWAFFER Patrick** Goodman Derrick	

See *Profiles* on page 596

the field. There has been no shortage of interesting work this year, including activity in Pay Per View. Amongst last year's large deals are the work for UPC on its proposed £2 billion acquisition of European TV broadcaster SBS and on Daily Mail's £146 million consolidation of its UK, Hungarian and Australian broadcasting assets into GWR Group plc. **Clients:** ONDigital; Channel 5; Hearst.

Wiggin & Co The ever popular and highly respected **Sean James** rises in our broadcasting table this year. The firm is seen to have a deep specialisation in cable and satellite work but is all too often linked primarily with Flextech. The market has questioned how the merger of Flextech with Telewest (on which Wiggin & Co gave advice) will affect the firm. It has been advising SDN, one of the four commercial digital multiplexes, on its challenge to get services on air. **Clients:** UKTV; Discovery; Fox Kids.

Ashurst Morris Crisp *"Solid Aussie guy"* **Tony Ghee** *("user friendly and easy to deal with")* is doing well in broadcasting, having built up a thriving distribution practice from a standing start just a few years ago. Advised on the competition and regulatory aspects of the United/Carlton merger and act for Kingston Interactive Television, Europe's first ASDL-based interactive digital television service provider. **Clients:** Yes Television; Grosvenor Park Film Partnership; SBS Broadcasting S.A.

Goodman Derrick Seen as very traditional broadcasting players who have *"been ITV's lawyers forever."* **Patrick Swaffer** leads a compact team which advises a mainly terrestrial client base. Carries out plenty of work for ITV Network Centre on transmission arrangements plus regulatory, legislative and policy issues. Drawing on the strengths of its defamation specialists, the firm offers programming and clearance advice and looks after a number of Granada's major talent. **Clients:** BBFC; Granada; GMTV.

DJ Freeman Seen primarily in this market for corporate and commercial advice. **Tony Liefer** is a *"very bright guy"* and *"the original contact with Channel 4,"* a client closely associated with the firm but not necessarily tied to it. Recently acted for Intertainment Group GmbH on the sale of film rights for broadcast by way of video on demand for US$67 million. **Clients:** Channel 4; Channel 5; Universal.

Field Fisher Waterhouse **Tony Ballard** is a well known name in broadcasting and commands a lot of market respect. The firm has branched out from its traditional terrestrial client base to act for Bollywood Eros Network Ltd on the launch of B4U, the UK Hindi language satellite film channel. Also advised the BBC on a wide range of production agreements, rights agreements and joint ventures. **Clients:** Axel Springer TV International Ltd; BBC; BBC Worldwide Ltd.

Recent High Profile Media Deals & Cases

Parties	Lawyers	Significance
Universal; Andrew Lloyd Webber	• Universal – Theodore Goddard • Andrew Lloyd Webber – Clintons	Universal sells its 30% stake in the Really Useful Group for some £80m.
Universal; Carlton Communications	• Universal – Theodore Goddard • Carlton – Clifford Chance	£157m Sale of ITC library to Carlton.
Windswept Pacific; EMI	• Windswept – Denton Wilde Sapte • EMI – Rowe & Maw	Sale of large part of publishing catalogue to EMI in a deal worth around £120m.
BSkyB; ITV; NTL; FA Premier League	• BSkyB– Herbert Smith • ITV– Goodman Derrick • NTL– Travers Smith Braithwaite • FAPL– Denton Wilde Sapte	Sale of TV broadcast rights of Premier League football. Total value over 3 years is £2.3bn.
Warner Music; EMI	• Warner Music– Herbert Smith • EMI– Freshfields	£12bn merger.
Spice Girls Ltd –v– Aprilia World Service BV	• Spice Girls – Lee & Thompson; Ian Mill QC; Vernon Flynn • Aprilia – CMS Cameron McKenna; Andrew Sutcliffe	Misrepresentation claim and counterclaim over sponsorship. Concerned the promotion of a special edition scooter and the departure of one of the group that made promotional material obsolete.
Disney; Apollo Leisure	• Disney – In-house counsel • Apollo Leisure– Denton Wilde Sapte	Theatre agreement for production of The Lion King.

Allen & Overy New to our broadcasting table the firm is seen increasingly on corporate deals in the broadcasting media and has a focus on regulatory work. Advised Cable & Wireless on the sale to NTL and United News & Media on its proposed merger with Carlton. **Clients:** Cable & Wireless.

Herbert Smith The perceived wisdom that the firm has justified its new ranking in our broadcasting table because of *"the large regulatory/M&A/corporate work"* it does for BSkyB. This is something of an underestimation of the team's capacity. There is certainly a concentration on competition and corporate work, but other work has included acting for the ITV Network on proceedings in the Copyright Tribunal, raising a statutory challenge to the licensing policy of MCPS for its music repertoire in TV programmes. **Clients:** CNN; Time Warner; Capital Radio.

Lovells No team size is shown in the broadcasting table but the firm offers up a large number of lawyers who work on broadcasting matters of all types. This is another firm perceived to be a figure in broadcasting if only for its presence on large M&A work and competition matters. In reality, the team is delivering varied advice to broadcasters. For LWT, the team advises on programme content advice and licensing arrangements. The team advised the BBC last year on carriage arrangements for digital satellite with BSkyB. It also acted on the flotation of Granada Media plc at £7 billion. **Clients:** Granada/LWT; Trinity Mirror; Telewest.

Travers Smith Braithwaite Seen to be really benefiting from *"tremendous client"* NTL in its current acquisitive phase. TSB's profile in the world of cable TV has clearly risen and it was a popular addition to our broadcasting table. Last year advised NTL on its proposed acquisition of Cable & Wireless Communications plc, including the implementation of ongoing arrangements for the sharing of cable, duct and switch assets. **Clients:** Channel 5; NTL Inc; Premium TV Limited.

MUSIC

MEDIA & ENTERTAINMENT: MUSIC • London	Ptnrs	Assts
❶ Russells	10	3
❷ Clintons	9	7
❸ Lee & Thompson	5	3
❹ Eatons	6	6
Sheridans	7	2
❺ Babbington Bray and Krais Solicitors Ltd	3	2
Harbottle & Lewis	4	3
The Simkins Partnership	5	7
Statham Gill Davies	11	-
Theodore Goddard	3	6
❻ Davenport Lyons	2	3
Denton Wilde Sapte	3	4
Eversheds	3	5
Hamlins	3	5
Harrison Curtis	1	1
Searles	2	2
Spraggon Stennett Brabyn	3	2

LEADING INDIVIDUALS	
❶ **GRAFTON GREEN Paddy** Theodore Goddard	
HOWARD Brian Russells	**JONES Howard** Sheridans
LEE Robert Lee & Thompson	**RUSSELL Tony** Russells
SHARLAND Andrew Clintons	**THOMPSON Andrew** Lee & Thompson
❷ **EATON Michael** Eatons	**HARMAN James** Theodore Goddard
LANDSMAN David Clintons	**TURTON Julian** The Simkins Partnership
❸ **ALLAN Robert** Denton Wilde Sapte	
BRAY Richard Babbington Bray and Krais Solicitors Ltd	
GILL Kaz Statham Gill Davies	**GILMORE Laurence** Hamlins
GLICK David Eatons	**HORSFALL Robert** Lee & Thompson
ORGAN Chris Russells	**RENNEY Paul** Theodore Goddard
STATHAM John Statham Gill Davies	**TREGEAR Steven** Russells
❹ **ABRAMSON Lawrence** Harbottle & Lewis	
DAVIS David Clintons	**FREE Dominic** The Simkins Partnership
SEARLE Helen Searles	**SINNOTT Mark** Russells
WARE James Davenport Lyons	**WILLIAMS Gordon** Lee & Thompson
UP AND COMING	
BROOKES Mike Lee & Thompson	**ESPLEN Simon** Russells

Within each band, firms are listed alphabetically. *See **Profiles** on page 596*

TOP IN-HOUSE LAWYERS

Music

Alastair GEORGE, Head of Legal Affairs UK, *Sony*

Paul JONES, Legal and Business Affairs Director, *Polydor*

Dej MAHONEY, Business Affairs, *Sony*

James RADICE, Director of Business Affairs, *EMI*

Clive RICH, Senior Director of Legal and Business Affairs, *BMG Entertainment*

Alastair George at Sony is *"seriously heavy-weight."* He is *"practical and tough enough to take a stand."* **Paul Jones** of Polydor really stands out despite being a newcomer. He readily draws praise for being *"very personable and knowledgeable"* as well as an *"extremely good lawyer."* **Dej Mahoney** at Sony is also recommended for seeing *"the broad commercial picture."* **James Radice** at EMI manages his very busy caseload *"calmly and with a sense of humour."* **Clive Rich** at BMG successfully manages his time between legal, management and creative and *"does it thoroughly well."*

Music Publishing

Grenville EVANS, Director of Commercial Affairs, *BMG Entertainment*

Chris MILESON, Director of Legal and Business Affairs, *EMI Publishing*

Rackesh SANGHVI, General Manager, *Sony Publishing*

In music publishing, **Grenville Evans** of BMG is a good lawyer with the ability to *"take the commercial view to get the deal done."* **Chris Mileson** at EMI is pragmatic and personable and *"knows his music publishing back to front."* **Rackesh Sanghvi** plays both a legal and general management role at Sony Publishing and focuses well on *"the commercial element of a deal."*

In-House lawyers profiles: page 1177

Russells To the surprise of no-one, Russells is still number one. The explanations are clear, consistent and frequent. With this firm clients get *"great ability and no weak links," "you can't ignore them and they are good to do business with."* While there may be litigators to compete on an equal footing, the non-contentious crown remains firmly planted on the collective head of the Russells team. **Tony Russell** is *"phenomenally capable and hard working and couldn't be more loyal to clients."* **Chris Organ** *("a terrific draftsman and a fantastic negotiator")* is seen as Russell's right hand man and *"a very good mentor to the younger lawyers." "Excellent"* **Brian Howard** and newcomers to our tables **Steven Tregear** *("an ideal litigator with a most amazing capacity for work")* and **Mark Sinnott** are viewed as the core of the litigation team. Up and Coming **Simon Esplen** *("very active – good with clients")* is seen to have had a very good year with Travis. The work handled by the firm is comprehensive from artist deals through to management disputes and corporate acquisitions. **Clients:** Major and independent record labels; leading artists.

Clintons Has a litigation department that is equal top with Russells, although doesn't quite match it on the commercial side. If there is a single favourite lawyer in music then it might well be **Andrew Sharland**, who rises into our top band this year. *"He's direct and down to earth"* and some even say that *"he's the outstanding litigator in music. He's not a table thumper; he analyses carefully – the perfect post-Woolf lawyer."* Senior figure **David Landsman** heads the commercial side, where the team is particularly strong in artist representation. **David Davis** is to be found as often these days on film related litigation and his position in the table reflects that music cases are just a part of a broader ranging practice. Some prestigious new clients have been added to their range of major labels, which famously includes Sony. **Clients:** EMI Music; Virgin; Polygram/Universal.

Lee & Thompson Moving up and creating a great impression, this firm has a stack of leading names in our tables. **Robert Lee** *"has a good eye for detail – he's a lawyer's lawyer,"* whilst **Andrew Thompson** is an *"all-rounder."* The *"omnipresent"* **Robert Horsfall** is *"very effective."* Two new names to our tables this year are **Gordon Williams** and his protégé **Mike Brookes**, who has come into his own since his move from Harbottle & Lewis. As with the other leaders, the client base is not limited to either talent or industry or any particular sector of it. **Clients:** Spice Girls; Paul Oakenfold; EMI/Warner.

Eatons One of the well established niche practices that maintains a consistently strong reputation in the market and now enjoys the added bonus of some of the leading artist names of the moment (Craig David, Bush, Gabrielle, Fatboy Slim) to add to a solid back catalogue of stalwart artist clients (Eric Clapton, The Bee Gees, Enya.) *"Top flight"* **David Glick** is *"bright, tenacious and hard working."* **Michael Eaton** has the level of experience that means he is almost seen as a *"self contained unit."* If other lawyers know them best for their artist clients, industry players know them equally well for their commercial work, such as joint ventures and restructuring, for the labels for whom they provide *"tough negotiation, attention to detail and a well thought out approach."* **Clients:** Major music companies.

Sheridans **Howard Jones** is the market leader in senior executive work and this area of his practice *"has gone through the roof."* The last year has seen continued work on artist securitisation, for established acts. The firm is also instructed by new and developing artists, including those in dance and club music. **Clients:** Artists; industry executives; smaller record companies.

Babbington Bray and Krais Solicitors Ltd An adjustment to the name this year to reflect an increase at partner level. *"A tidy little practice"* concentrating heavily on talent but also beginning to pick up the industry work. Has recognised quality across the team, but it is **Richard Bray** *("a hard worker and a tough cookie")* who is best known. The team also includes a consultant. **Clients:** Boyzone; Texas; Skunk Anansie.

Harbottle & Lewis *"A good broad practice and a fantastic client base"* is typical of the comment on the all-round entertainment law capabilities of the firm. The cross-over between departments is seen by some as their great strength, whilst others view it as an absence of commitment to any one aspect of the client base. Whichever view is correct, the firm performs well and is in pole position to exploit its digital media skills as its clients diversify their activities. Andrew Stinson has recently left the firm to pursue other activities in the industry. He was seen as the strength of the department by many. Whilst other litigators may not whoop with joy to see **Lawrence Abramson** on the other side of a case, clients are impressed. The firm were involved in major music webcasts last year, including Netaid and Robbie Williams' Slane Castle Concert. **Clients:** 19 Management; Robbie Williams; K-Tel.

The Simkins Partnership **Julian Turton** presides over a team of experienced music lawyers including newly ranked litigator **Dominic Free**, who is seen as *"pragmatic and bright and a dream to deal with."* There have been some changes at partner level this year but this does not appear to have had a major effect on the team. Acts for artists of all types, publishers and record companies. Advised Crispian Mills on the dissolution of the band Kula Shaker. **Clients:** BMG UK Ltd; Sony Europe; Underworld.

Statham Gill Davies *"Deal makers"* and *"good talent lawyers,"* **John Statham** and **Kaz Gill** are both well endorsed figures in our table. The client base includes a number of independent record companies and publishers, evidence that it is not just an artists' firm. As a litigation force, the firm is perceived to take a very strong but *"overly firm"* line. **Clients:** Major bands; independent labels.

Theodore Goddard *"Terrific – its size gives it something the smaller practices don't have – it can call on all sorts of specialists."* Here lies the firm's major advantage; the ability to pull in and excel at the corporate and tax led work as well as the regular music contract matters. *"Fair, sensible and first rate"* **Paddy Grafton Green** is enormously well liked and quite unmatched in his skills as a tax expert. Our research also revealed continued support for *"fabulously well-rounded"* **James Harman** and new media-oriented **Paul Renney** with his *"solid, common-sense intelligence".* Acted for Roger Ames on his appointment as Chairman and CEO of Warner Music Group and for Warners on their acquisition of London Records. **Clients:** Sony Music; Universal Music International Ltd; many major artists.

Davenport Lyons *"A great, classic entertainment firm"* with music as one of its assets. As a former director of a major record company, **James Ware** brings a lot of experience to the team and is the stand-out name. This year, work has ranged from the conclusion of The Clash's new publishing deal with Universal Music to Copyright Tribunal references. **Clients:** Michael Nyman; VP Records; Mediaeval Baebes.

Denton Wilde Sapte Best known for its involvement in M&A work for media businesses. **Robert Allan** leads a team seen far more for its corporate, particularly international, expertise. Represented Windswept Pacific Entertainment Co (USA) and Windswept Pacific Music Ltd (UK) on the disposal of a large part of their publishing catalogue to EMI. **Clients:** Boxman.com plc; K-Tel Entertainment UK Ltd; Warner/Chappell Music.

Eversheds Preferred lawyers of some superstar names in British pop, such as Sting and The Beatles' organisations. One of the firm's major pieces of work has been on 'Party in the Park' for The Prince's Trust. It has also completed a joint venture for its new client, Virtue Interactive, which puts big music events on the internet. **Clients:** AEI Music; Elton John.

Hamlins *"Has cornered a lot of industry rights work – piracy etc."* It is the firm's work for PPL that is best known, although artist/management litigation will bring the firm to the CA when the Bruce Springsteen case is heard later this year. **Laurence Gilmore** is *"a cut above the average litigator both academically and strategically,"* but some felt *"there's a bit of a self-publicist in him."* On the non-contentious side the range of work for artists and industry clients continues to grow. **Clients:** Sony; BMG International; BPI.

Harrison Curtis A small two partner outfit which *"has a calling card,"* particularly for record companies. Acts for SINE in negotiations for joint ventures and label deals, such as those with Oyster Music and Naive Records Ltd. **Clients:** Courtyard Music; Universal Island Records; Siouxsie & The Banshees/The Creatures.

Searles A firm that is *"reasonably visible"* and very *"artist oriented." "Hand-holder"* **Helen Searle** takes great care to develop good relationships with her clients and is *"wonderful socially."* Has recently renogotiated Moby's recording contract. **Clients:** Jamiroquai; Moby; Sonique.

Spraggon Stennett Brabyn *"Good at getting new bands"* the firm has a longstanding reputation for acting for a stream of *"worthwhile clients,"* **Clients:** The Prodigy; Gomez; Asian Dub Foundation.

THEATRE

MEDIA & ENTERTAINMENT: THEATRE • London	Ptnrs	Assts
❶ Tarlo Lyons	2	1
❷ Campbell Hooper	2	-
Clintons	2	1
❸ Harrison Curtis	2	-
The Simkins Partnership	1	1
❹ Bates, Wells & Braithwaite	1	1
Harbottle & Lewis	-	3
❺ Theodore Goddard	3	2

LEADING INDIVIDUALS	
❶ COHEN John Clintons	ROSE Michael Tarlo Lyons
SHAW Barry Barry Shaw	WILLS David Campbell Hooper
❷ EGAN Sean Bates, Wells & Braithwaite	FRANKS David The Simkins Partnership
HARRISON Lawrence Harrison Curtis	JENNINGS Carolyn Campbell Hooper
❸ MEADON Simon Tarlo Lyons	

Within each band, firms are listed alphabetically. *See **Profiles** on page 596*

Tarlo Lyons *"True specialist"* **Michael Rose** is now joined in our Theatre table by **Simon Meadon**, a man who brings plenty of industry experience to the party. Some feel that the reputation of the theatre practice rests quite heavily on its main client Cameron Mackintosh, but such a view fails to take into account scores of other top productions on which the firm works each year. Recent shows have included 'Witches of Eastwick', 'Gumboots', 'Tap Dogs' and 'Happy Days'. **Clients:** Delfont Mackintosh Theatre; Back Row Productions; AMP Ltd.

Campbell Hooper A firm that really *"knows what it is doing."* **David Wills** *("a pleasure to deal with")* and **Carolyn Jennings**, who is also correctly noted for her TV/film work, both feature strongly in our rankings. The last year's productions include 'Napoleon', 'Prisoner on Second Avenue', 'Rent' and 'Defending the Caveman' plus the TV exploitation of 'Jeffrey Bernard is Unwell'. **Clients:** Stoll Moss; Theatre of Comedy; Bill Kenwright.

Clintons Almost every theatre lawyer we spoke to had some recent experience of acting opposite this firm; surely clear testament to how busy *"committed"* **John Cohen** and his team are. Very talent-oriented, the firm's clients include creators, composers, directors, producers and funders. Advised on the purchase of the Stoll Moss theatres and a range of different productions, including 'Soul Train', 'Cooking with Elvis' and the new production of 'The Graduate'. **Clients:** Andrew Lloyd Webber; Tim Rice; Ben Elton.

Harrison Curtis **Lawrence Harrison** appears in our table of Leaders in Theatre this year for the first time. He is the recognised half of the partnership for this area of work. Acted for Victor Hochhauser in relation to the Bolshoi Ballet & Opera season at the Coliseum. **Clients:** Purecote Ltd; Shakermaker; Drill Hall Theatre.

The Simkins Partnership Really Useful Group work dominates and, by comparison, the rest of the theatre work *"pales into insignificance."* **David Franks** heads the small team that now finds itself instructed as expert counsel to other law firms in relation to the theatre aspects of their commercial work. **Clients:** RUG; Imagination Entertainments; Escape Artists.

Bates, Wells & Braithwaite Before his move to the firm just over a year ago, **Sean Egan** was regarded by many as *"the heir apparent to Lawrence Harbottle."* The move appears not to have dented his standing in theatre work at all and he is known to be *"tapping into his contacts"* and coming up with good instructions. Egan is now building a team and concentrating on developing a range of clients that include, producers, theatres, agents, actors and other talent. **Clients:** ENO; Adventures in Motion Pictures; Green & Lenagan.

Harbottle & Lewis A name *"synonymous with theatre,"* with *"a wealth of experience"* in media and entertainment work generally. Three partners spend a small part of their time working for theatre clients. Lawrence Harbottle still acts as a consultant, but the team now lacks a big partner-level name. Recent productions have included 'Fosse', 'West Side Story' and 'Spend, Spend, Spend'. **Clients:** Pola Jones Associates; SOLT; Almeida Theatre.

Theodore Goddard New in our theatre section this year, having bubbled under for some time. The firm is a strong favourite with a number of theatre-owning organisations for whom they are providing advice on theatre acquisitions and corporate expertise as well as core production advice. Production accounts for as much of the team's work as structuring/acquisition advice. Recent productions have included 'The Pyjama Game' and 'The Weir'. **Clients:** Robert Stigwood Organisation; Ambassador Theatre Group; Associated Capital Theatres.

Other Notable Practitioner **Barry Shaw** is almost a legend in his own lifetime for theatre work. He is *"hugely experienced and a superb contract lawyer."*

PUBLISHING

Denton Wilde Sapte Pulling away from the pack, in no small part due to the efforts of *"reliable and sensible expert"* **Alan Williams** who *"always takes time to understand what his clients are up to and their business."* The rise of e-publishing has added to the group's strengths rather than challenged them. Last year, the firm helped Britannica.co.uk bring Britannica's content online. **Clients:** Macmillan; Random House; John Wiley.

Taylor Joynson Garrett A strong publishing practice which includes all-round media lawyer and *"copyright expert"* **Paul Mitchell**, who has vast experience acting for estates and is someone who *"understands collecting societies."* This year has seen a partner go in-house at the Publishing Association. The team *"gives a personal service"* and is thought to be greatly helped by the firm's good standing in intellectual property and commercial matters generally. **Clients:** Roald Dahl Literary Estate; DACS; Macmillan.

Harbottle & Lewis Act for a number of publishers (especially on-line and in books and magazines), literary agents and authors. **Mark Phillips** is *"practical"* in his negotiations. Last year advised Nick Logan on the disposal

TOP IN-HOUSE LAWYERS

Publishing

Andrew CROMPTON, Business Development Director, *MacMillan*

Cecily ENGLE, Business Affairs Director, *Penguin*

Roger FIELD, Legal Director, *Random House*

Adrian LAING, Director of Legal Affairs/Company Secretary, *HarperCollins*

Andrew Crompton of MacMillan is described as *"on the ball."* **Cecily Engle** at Penguin who has now combined her legal role with business affairs is *"head and shoulders above the rest."* She is *"practical, not overly legalistic and well-liked within the industry."* The more aggressive **Adrian Laing** at Harper Collins also has significant experience and is known as *"quite a tough cookie."* Fairly new to the industry is **Roger Field** at Random House. Coming from a newspaper background, he has the ability to *"explain issues to his Board in clear and simple language."*

In-House lawyers profiles: page 1177

MEDIA & ENTERTAINMENT: PUBLISHING • London	Ptnrs	Assts
❶ Denton Wilde Sapte	3	5
❷ Taylor Joynson Garrett	4	4
❸ Harbottle & Lewis	5	6
Lovells	6	13
❹ H2O	2	-
The Simkins Partnership	4	-

LEADING INDIVIDUALS	
❶ **WILLIAMS Alan** Denton Wilde Sapte	
❷ **MITCHELL Paul** Taylor Joynson Garrett	**NYMAN Bernard** B. M. Nyman & Co
❸ **KAYE Laurence** Paisner & Co	**PHILLIPS Mark** Harbottle & Lewis

Within each band, firms are listed alphabetically

*See **Profiles** on page 596*

** See editorial entries for explanations of team sizes.*

of Wagadon Ltd, publishers of 'The Face', 'Arena' and 'Arena Homme Plus,' to EMAP plc. **Clients:** Aitken & Stone Ltd; Chrysalis Books Ltd; Amazon.com.

Lovells Primarily newspaper and magazine related work for major media groups. The range of instructions handled by the firm is of an extremely varied nature. Last year defended a claim by the NUJ against Guardian Media Group that electronic publishing of freelance journalists' articles is an infringement of copyright. **Clients:** Trinity Mirror; Guardian Media Group; European Press Holdings Ltd.

H2O Media and entertainment team lawyers acting for a variety of client types, including publishing. Recently acted on behalf of The Times newspaper in a case against McPhilemy. Also represented David Trimble in a dispute with Amazon.co.uk, the internet retailer. **Clients:** Times Newspapers Ltd; Express Newspapers plc; IPC Magazines.

The Simkins Partnership E-publishing, literary agents, photographic work and traditional book publishing all add to the Simkins blend of publishing work. The firm was instructed by the authors of three of the biggest selling books of 1999 and now represents a leading creative figure in magazine publishing, hoping to bring four new titles to the market in 2000. **Clients:** Sebastian Faulks; Gillon Aiken; David Campbell Publishers.

Other Notable Practitioners **Bernard Nyman** is a sole practitioner who made the break just over a year ago and now focuses exclusively on publishing work. *"A real expert, he understands the anatomy of a publishing agreement."* Still retained as a consultant to his former firm Manches & Co, he acts for clients such as Consumer's Association, Wrox Press Ltd and Wilbur Smith. **Laurence Kaye** of Paisner & Co is recommended for his e-publishing work.

THE SOUTH & SOUTH WEST

MEDIA & ENTERTAINMENT • The South & South West	Ptnrs	Assts
❶ Wiggin & Co Cheltenham	4	6
❷ Manches Oxford	3	2

Within each band, firms are listed alphabetically.

Wiggin & Co *"Outstanding"* to the extent that *"no one else in the regions compares."* The firm is also ranked in our London Broadcasting section in recognition of the fact that a number of its media partners work from both the Cheltenham and London offices. It has a focus in newer media and television but also publishing expertise. Acts for an increasing number of independent film and TV production companies. **Clients:** TAC (association for independent producers in Wales); Jean Doumanian Productions (Woody Allen films); Scottish Committee for Gaelic Broadcasting.

Manches Seen as a *"sensible choice"* and used by a number of top publishing companies in Oxford and beyond. Offers a full range of advice from Corporate work and employment through to licensing, libel reading and author agreements. **Clients:** Blackwells Group; the Tolkien Estate; Reed Elsevier.

WALES

MEDIA & ENTERTAINMENT • Wales	Ptnrs	Assts
❶ Morgan Cole Cardiff/Swansea	1	-

LEADING INDIVIDUALS
❶ **LEWIS Emyr** Morgan Cole

Within each band, firms are listed alphabetically.

*See **Profiles** on page 596*

Morgan Cole **Emyr Lewis**' name is known by those involved in TV/film production in Wales. It is a small market, which Morgan Cole dominate as a result of his endeavours. Acts for over 20 independent production companies and is developing a niche in animation. **Clients:** Agenda Group; Fiction Factory ('Rancid Aluminium'); Screen Wales.

MIDLANDS

MEDIA & ENTERTAINMENT • Midlands	Ptnrs	Assts
❶ Hammond Suddards Edge Birmingham	1	2
❷ Kent Jones and Done Stoke-on-Trent	*	*

LEADING INDIVIDUALS
❶ **ANDERSON Frances** Lee Crowder

Within each band, firms are listed alphabetically.

*See **Profiles** on page 596*

** See editorial entries for explanations of team sizes.*

Hammond Suddards Edge Coming at media and entertainment work primarily from two angles; sports broadcasting and venue ownership. Both have as a common thread the exploitation of live entertainment. Have also become involved in film financing and negotiations for clients who wish to exploit rights pertaining to TV and radio performances and concepts. Advised Aston Villa FC on its broadcasting deal with NTL. **Clients:** Heart FM; Stoll Moss Theatres; Apollo Leisure Group plc.

Kent Jones & Done The firm is new to our table this year and is turning its hand to many different types of work, including book publishing deals, libel readings, profit/royalty participation for the estates of authors and producers, merchandising advice to musicians such as Nine Inch Nails and a range of smaller work for local clients. **Clients:** David Lean Film Trust; Faraway Productions AG; Estate of Patrick Hamilton.

Other Notable Practitioner **Frances Anderson**, one of the region's leading names in this field, has recently moved to Birmingham firm Lee Crowder, a move that is expected to provide the firm with real credibility in the sector.

THE NORTH

MEDIA & ENTERTAINMENT • The North	Ptnrs	Assts
❶ **McCormicks** Leeds	3	3
❷ **DLA** Leeds	*	*
Eversheds Leeds, Manchester	1	2
Lea & Company Stockport	1	-
❸ **Ramsbottom & Co** Blackburn	1	-

LEADING INDIVIDUALS	
❶ **LEA Stephen** Lea & Company	**McCORMICK Peter** McCormicks

Within each band, firms are listed alphabetically. See **Profiles** on page 596

* *See editorial entries for explanations of team sizes.*

McCormicks Perhaps the strongest profile in the region belongs to **Peter McCormick**. There is a strong sports broadcasting bias to the firm's work. The firm advised FAPL on problems concerning the overseas broadcasting contract with Canal+ and on current and future broadcasting arrangements with, inter alia, BSkyB and the BBC. Also acts for a number of TV personalities and comedians. **Clients:** Leeds United TV; The FA Premier League; The Music Factory Entertainment.

DLA A mainly contentious practice including a volume of defamation and other types of actions for the Yorkshire Post. Also giving broadcasting advice to sporting clients. However, former client Yorkshire TV/Granada now send their work elsewhere. **Clients:** Newcastle United FC; Yorkshire Post.

Eversheds Primarily a non-contentious TV production and finance plus commercial radio practice. The head of department has had substantial in-house/secondment experience in TV companies. **Clients:** Granada/Yorkshire TV; Straight TV Ltd; local radio stations.

Lea & Company **Stephen Lea** is an unashamed specialist and acknowledged music lawyer. He rises in our table of leading individuals this year. Acts for both recording artists/songwriters and record/production companies. Artists include Teenage Fanclub, James and The Charlatans. **Clients:** Engine Records Ltd; Global Underground, R&S Records.

Ramsbottom & Co *"The Circus Man!"* The work carried out at this firm for circus, fairground and ice show clients must make it one of the most unique practices around. The industry throws up an enormous breadth of work and it is becoming ever more international in nature. Advised the parliamentary working group on new legislation relating to the welfare of circus animals. **Clients:** Cottle & Austen Electric Circus; European Entertainment Corp; Cirque Surreal.

SCOTLAND

MEDIA & ENTERTAINMENT • Scotland	Ptnrs	Assts
❶ **Tods Murray WS** Edinburgh	2	2
❷ **Dundas & Wilson CS** Edinburgh	3	4
McGrigor Donald Glasgow	3	3
❸ **Anderson Strathern WS** Edinburgh	4	3
Bannatyne, Kirkwood, France & Co Glasgow	2	1
Levy & McRae Glasgow	4	5
Wright, Johnston & Mackenzie Glasgow	2	2

LEADING INDIVIDUALS
❶ **FINDLAY Richard** Tods Murray WS
❷ **SIBBALD Graham** Dundas & Wilson CS

Within each band, firms are listed alphabetically. See **Profiles** on page 596

Tods Murray WS **Richard Findlay** is *"full time in the media sector in a way that no one else in Scotland is."* From a start in theatre work, the practice now focuses on television, with Findlay acting for most of the film and TV production companies in Scotland. He has also managed to pull some funding work away from London. **Clients:** Scottish Screen; Federation of Scottish Theatres; Wark Clements & Company Ltd.

Dundas & Wilson CS Known for *"commercial deals for Scottish media"* **Graham Sibbald** has plenty of experience in some of the biggest media transactions in the region. He really *"gets to grip with the issues."* Acted for Scottish Radio Holdings plc in its contested bid for Border Television plc for £141 million, including advice on cross-media issues. **Clients:** Scottish Media Group plc; The Scotsman Publications Ltd; The Rangers FC plc.

McGrigor Donald Strong in non-broadcast media, such as pure IP/publishing, the firm is also making headway with independent production companies and smaller television companies. Corporate deals are handled alongside ITC licensing advice and clearance advice for newspaper clients. The firm has seen a rise in independent production work and licence applications for radio. **Clients:** Scottish Daily Record; Glasgow Opportunities TV; Chrysalis.

Anderson Strathern WS Felt to *"have done well to associate themselves with growing businesses."* The last year has seen a growth in publishing work, ranging from start-ups and corporate advice through to contracts and copyright. Acted for the National Trust for Scotland in relation to a television series produced by STV. **Clients:** Scottish Rugby Union; Mackintosh Red Ltd; Scottish Publishers Association.

Bannatyne, Kirkwood, France & Co New into our tables this year, the firm is recommended for its advice to leading newspaper clients, for whom it carries out a range of advisory and contentious work. **Clients:** Associated Newspapers; Scottish & Universal Newspapers; The Scotsman; Observer & Guardian.

Levy & McRae Strong on contentious and clearance advice for newspaper clients and acting for a number of titles. Also acting for major and independent TV production companies and benefiting from an informal relationship with Goodman Derrick in London. Instructed by a group of television companies in their petition to televise the Lockerbie trial. **Clients:** Scottish Media Group; Scottish Daily Record & Sunday Mail Ltd; Borders TV.

Wright, Johnston & Mackenzie Historically involved in public sector film finance, but now beginning to see movement into the private sector, acting for production companies. **Clients:** Glasgow Film Fund; Antonine Films.

LEADERS IN MEDIA & ENTERTAINMENT

ABRAMSON, Lawrence
Harbottle & Lewis, London (020) 7667 5000
Specialisation: Specialist litigator in all areas of the entertainment and media industries, including music, television, film, publishing and sport.
Prof. Memberships: International Association of Entertainment Lawyers.
Career: Education: British School of The Netherlands, University of Manchester, Chester College of Law – LLB 2:1 Professional Career: Trained – *Sheridans*, Solicitor with *Denton Hall* 1988-97, *Harbottle & Lewis* 1996 – to date.
Personal: Married with one child. All sports, music, theatre, travel and entertaining.

ALLAN, Robert
Denton Wilde Sapte, London (020) 7320 6516

ANDERSON, Frances
Lee Crowder, Birmingham (0121) 236 4477
Specialisation: Non-contentious work in music, television, film, the arts, new technology and computer law.
Prof. Memberships: Law Society; Women in Film and Television; PACT; Society for Computers & Law.
Career: Qualified in 1989 at *Wragge & Co*; set up own practice in 1995 and joined *Lee Crowder* in 2000.
Personal: Former chairman and currently a director of Birmingham International Film & Television Festival. Company Secretary and a director of the Grand Theatre, Wolverhampton. Company Secretary and a director of the Media Development Agency for the West Midlands.

ANTONIADES, Reno
Lee & Thompson, London (020) 7935 4665

BALLARD, Tony
Field Fisher Waterhouse, London (020) 7861 4000
jab@ffwlaw.com
Partner.
Specialisation: Main area of practice is communications with a recent focus on network platforms at the leading edge of recent developments in this field; including telecommunications, broadcasting and IT; advising both established operators and new entrants on the new technologies. Other areas of practice include television network and service providers in both public and private sectors, including established broadcasters and new entrants in the satellite, cable, multimedia and general major feature film production and distribution, competition, copyright and administrative law. Arbitrator on International Arbitration panel of American Film Marketing Association and trained mediator for alternative dispute resolution. Frequent speaker at conferences.
Prof. Memberships: International Bar Association, Communication Lawyers Association, Royal Television Society and Chairman of UK branch of European Centre for Space Law.
Career: Qualified in 1974, having joined *Allison & Humphreys* in 1971. Became a Partner in 1975. Merged with *Field Fisher Waterhouse* in 1998.
Personal: Born 21st August 1945. MA (Cantab) 1964-68. Fellow of Royal Anthropological Institute. Leisure interests include astrophysics and painting. Lives in London and Suffolk.

BENNETT, Nigel
The Simkins Partnership, London (020) 7907 3000
Partner in Media and Entertainment Department.
Specialisation: Main areas of practice cover media finance, production and distribution (particularly in fields of film, television and radio). Experience in advising media groups, producers, distributors, broadcasters and financiers on copyright, financing agreements, production contracts and distribution arrangements world-wide. Other areas of practice include sport (particularly the exploitation of sports rights), publishing and mediation of disputes.
Prof. Memberships: Law Society, International Bar Association, American Bar Association, Media Dispute Resolution (Founder Member), Royal Television Society.
Career: Qualified in 1970 with *Rubinstein Nash*. Lecturer in contract and commercial law, College of Law, Lancaster Gate (1971-73). Joined *The Simkins Partnership* in 1973; Partner 1975; Joint Managing Partner 1992-96.
Personal: Educated Dulwich College and Clare College, Cambridge. Leisure pursuits include golf, cricket, sailing, films and the jazz guitar.

BERGER, Jonathan
Theodore Goddard, London (020) 7606 8855
Specialisation: Main area of practice covers legal and business affairs advice on the production, finance and distribution of feature films and television programming. Acts for leading independent producers and distributors. Regular speaker on the film and television industry.
Prof. Memberships: British Academy of Film & Television Arts; Producers Association for Cinema & Television; New Producers Alliance.
Career: Qualified in 1986 with *Bartletts de Reya* and became a partner in *Miscon de Reya* in 1990 and joined *Theodore Goddard* as a partner in the Media & Entertainment Group in 1995.
Personal: Born 1962. Educated Charterhouse and the University of Kent at Canterbury. Leisure interests include supporting Chelsea FC, cooking and golf.

BRAY, Richard
Babbington Bray and Krais Solicitors Limited, London (020) 7493 8840

BROOKES, Mike
Lee & Thompson, London (020) 7935 4665

COHEN, John M.R.
Clintons, London (020) 7379 6080
Partner in Entertainment Department.
Specialisation: Principal area of practice is theatre, representing most of the leading British creators of musical theatre – Andrew Lloyd Webber, Tim Rice, Don Black and the Late Lionel Bart as well as directors, designers and a number of producers. He also continues to represent a number of recording artists and television personalities. In addition handles corporate matters in the entertainment business. This year advised Andrew Lloyd Webber in relation to the acquisition by Really Useful Group of Stoll Moss Theatres.
Prof. Memberships: The Law Society.
Career: Qualified 1970. Joined *Clintons* in 1968 and has remained there throughout career, becoming a Partner in 1972.
Personal: Born 14th February 1946. Attended University College London 1964-67. Trustee of Mercury Workshop and the Arts Foundation. Lives in London.

DAVIS, David W.
Clintons, London (020) 7379 6080
Specialisation: Media/Entertainment including Music, film and sport. Senior Litigator and Head of Department with *Clintons*.
Career: Instructed during the past 25 years in many of the leading cases in this field representing Rod Stewart, Frank Bruno, The Stone Roses, Pete Townshend, Sony (George Michael), Polygram, Decca, Pavarotti, U2(PRS), Polygram Films International. Also my firm *Clintons* acted in the cases of Elton John, Dave Clark and The Cure.
Personal: Educated at Shooters Hill Grammar School. Admitted to the University of London and subsequently articled to *A. E. Hoffman*. Thereafter, joined David Landsman in 1973. Also lectured in law. Interests include sports, classical music and the arts generally.

DEARSLEY, Ken
Denton Wilde Sapte, London (020) 7320 6547
krd@dentonwildesapte.com
Partner in Media and Technology Group.
Specialisation: Specialises in all aspects of film financing with special expertise and reputation in UK sale/leaseback transactions, tax based financing arrangements and working with the major studios, other leading US and European film companies, banks and other lending institutions. Wide experience in film and television production and distribution, video distribution, 'due diligence' reviews in the media industry and copyright matters generally. Has lectured on a wide number of industry subjects in London, America, India and Far East.
Prof. Memberships: International Bar Association.
Career: Has been with *Denton Hall* since articles. Qualified in 1974. Became a Partner in 1979.
Personal: Born 1945. Fitzwilliam College, Cambridge 1965-68 (MA Hons in Economics). Leisure pursuits include tennis and music.

DEVEREUX, Mark J.
Olswang, London (020) 7208 8888
mjd@olswang.com
Senior Partner.
Specialisation: Main area of practice is film and television finance, production and distribution. Responsible for all areas of work covered by entertainment, media and communications. Regular contributor to media trade press.
Prof. Memberships: Law Society, State Bar of California.
Career: Qualified in 1981, joining *Simon Olswang & Co* in the same year and becoming a Partner in 1982.
Personal: Born 2nd August 1956. Attended Lycée Français de Londres 1961-74, then University College London 1975-78. Leisure interests include tennis, skiing, diving and photography. Lives in London.

EATON, Michael C.A.
Eatons, London (020) 8877 9727
Specialisation: All areas of media and entertainment law, including merchandising, touring, television, film and sport, as well as expertise in corporate law.

Career: Qualified in 1967 and became a Corporate Partner in the city firm, *Stephenson Harwood*. Joined Dick James Music in 1977 as Head of Business Affairs to gain further industry experience and was responsible for all business and contractual dealings with a vast roster of clients. Returned to private practice with the formation of *Eaton & Burley* in 1980. In 1990 founded *Eatons* together with Jeremy Wakefield and David Glick.

EDWARDS, Stephen
Richards Butler, London (020) 7247 6555
Specialisation: Broadcasting law including ITC licence applications; satellite and cable transmission and programme contracts; production financing, distribution and co-production agreements and European regulation. Other copyright and media/entertainment work including copyright collecting society transactions; print and multimedia publishing agreements; talent contracts; website agreements; copyright tribunal hearings and music industry agreements. Chairs Hawksmere Conference on 'Rights Clearances for Television Programmes'. Regular speaker at media industry conferences. Author of 'Rights Clearances for Film and Television Production.'
Career: Qualified in 1976. Joined the BBC in 1978, and was Head of Copyright 1981-1990. Joined *Richards Butler* as a Partner in 1990.
Personal: Attended University of the Witwatersrand, Johannesburg 1968-70 and Trinity Hall, Cambridge 1971-73. Leisure pursuits include sailing, cricket and music.

EGAN, Sean
Bates, Wells & Braithwaite, London (020) 7551 7777
s.egan@bateswells.co.uk
Partner and head of the media department
Specialisation: Acts for a large number of theatre, film, and television producers and other media organisations. Specialist areas include copyright law, charity law, film and television production and the exploitation of theatre. Acts for English National Opera and has advised on numerous first class theatre productions including 'Swan Lake', 'Cinderella', the 'Car Man', 'Mindgame', 'A Busy Day', 'Peggy for You', 'Gumboots', the 'Birthday Party', 'Bing Bong' and De La Guarda's 'Villa Villa'. Recently acted for the producers on the films 'East is East' and 'Love, Honour, & Obey'. Regular lecturer and author.
Prof. Memberships: Charity Law Association, Law Society
Career: Qualified in 1988. At *Clifford Chance* 1986-1988, *Harbottle & Lewis* 1988-1998 joined *Bates, Wells & Braithwaite* in 1999.
Personal: Born 19th August 1961. Attended Queens' College, Cambridge 1980-84. Charity trustee. Leisure interests include film, theatre, Fives, and golf.

ESPLEN, Simon
Russells, London (020) 7439 8692

FINDLAY, Richard M.
Tods Murray WS, Edinburgh (0131) 226 4771
richard.findlay@todsmurray.co.uk
Entertainment Law Partner.
Specialisation: Practices exclusively in entertainment and media law acting for a wide range of clients throughout the film, television and music industry sectors and also for companies in the fields of theatre, festival and event management and the arts generally.
Prof. Memberships: International Association of Entertainment Lawyers.
Career: Partner *Ranken & Reid* (1979-90); Partner *Tods Murray* (1990).

FRANKS, David T.
The Simkins Partnership, London (020) 7907 3030
david.franks@simkins.com
Specialisation: Music and theatre.
Prof. Memberships: The Law Society, IAEL.
Career: Qualified 1973, *The Simkins Partnership* 1974 to date.

FREE, Dominic
The Simkins Partnership, London (020) 7907 3000
Partner in Litigation Department.
Specialisation: Main area of practice is disputes in the music industry. Has a particular interest in music technology and new media. Acts for several major record companies, music publishers, a major collecting society and recording and performing artists. Also acts for those in the film and television, print and online publishing and advertising industries and on intellectual property disputes particularly copyright and trade mark matters.
Career: Qualified in 1985. Partner *Richard Butler* 1989-92. Partner *The Simkins Partnership* 1993.
Personal: Born 16th November 1956. Educated in New Zealand (LLB, Auckland 1979) and the USA (LLM, Cornell University 1982).

GAWADE, Jeremy
Lee & Thompson, London (020) 7935 4665

GHEE, Tony
Ashurst Morris Crisp, London (020) 7638 1111
tony.ghee@ashursts.com
Specialisation: Main practice areas: media and entertainment and telecommunications. Regulatory, corporate and commmercial advice for cable and telecommunications operators, terrestrial and satellite broadcasters and film and television production companies. Particular expertise: all aspects of satellite and broadcasting law including digital media. Speaks regularly on the convergence of broadcasting, telecoms and information technology industries and broadcasting regulation.
Prof. Memberships: IBA, Copinger Society.
Career: Worked: *Blake Dawson Waldron* and TEN television network in Australia. *Denton Hall* and partner at *AMC* in UK.
Personal: Married.

GILL, Kaz
Statham Gill Davies, London (020) 7487 5565

GILMORE, Laurence
Hamlins, London (020) 7355 6000
lgilmore@hamlins.co.uk
Specialisation: A Managing Partner and head of the entertainment and intellectual property department. Specialises in all aspects of related litigation including copyright, trademark, contract disputes, monopolies and mergers and EC competition law. Practice also covers defamation and passing off actions. Acts for prominent organisations, corporations and individuals from the world of entertainment.
Prof. Memberships: International Association of Entertainment Lawyers.
Career: Articled at *Davenport Lyons* 1984-86. Assistant solicitor *Taylor Joynson Garrett* 1986-87. Partner, *Hamlins* (previously known as *Hamlin Slowe*) since 1988.
Personal: Educated at Preston Manor Grammar School and Trinity Hall, Cambridge. Writes occasional newspaper articles. Leisure pursuits include theatre, music and sport. Born 17th April 1959. Lives in London.

GLICK, David S.
Eatons, London (020) 8877 9727
Specialisation: All areas of media and entertainment law with particular emphasis on music, television, film and sport. Music client base ranges from new and emerging artists/bands to 'superstar artists' to major record and publishing companies as well as a number of independent record labels and publishing companies in relation to their various spheres of activities. Has developed a specialism in co-ordinating substantial joint venture and other 'label' structures. and bridges the gap between the media business and the City.
Career: Qualified in 1989 and joined *Eatons* at its inception in 1990.

GOSTYN, Antony
The Simkins Partnership, London (020) 7907 3000
Specialisation: Film and television production, finance and distribution agreements. Author of 'Pact Model Contracts' (1991, 1998 and 1999 Editions).
Career: Qualified 1975. With Thorn EMI 1976-82. Partner at *DJ Freeman* 1986-95. Joined *The Simkins Partnership* as a partner in 1995.

GRAFTON GREEN, Paddy
Theodore Goddard, London (020) 7606 8855
Specialisation: Work includes advice on (i) copyright issues in relation to recordings, musical compositions and theatrical productions and (ii) production, distribution, management concert appearance, sponsorship and merchandising agreements. Advice on taxation both within the UK and overseas of income derived by businesses and artists. Cases have included acting as Chairman of BPI Tribunal into chart hyping, and for BMG in the MMC Enquiry into Recorded Music, for PolyGram and Universal Music in relation to a variety of corporate and commercial transactions including PolyGram Filmed Entertainment's acquisition of ITC in 1995 and sale in 1999 and PolyGram's acquisition (1991) and disposal (1999) of its interest in The Really Useful Group, in the sale in 1999 of London Records to the Warner Group, for major companies and artists in structuring international transactions including concert tours (Tina Turner, Michael Jackson, Janet Jackson, Lionel Richie and The Rolling Stones), for David Bowie in relation to the "Bowie Bonds" and Iron Maiden in relation to the securitisation of income. Lecturer and seminar chairman for IBC Legal Studies and others.
Prof. Memberships: Law Society.
Career: Qualified 1967, having joined *Theodore Goddard* in 1966. Became a Partner in 1973. Member of the firm's Management Committee from 1990-93. Currently the firm's Senior Partner and Head of the Media & Entertainment Group.
Personal: Born 30th March 1943. Attended Ampleforth College 1957-62; holds an MA (Oxon), 1963-65. Leisure interests include music and cricket. Lives in London.

HARMAN, James
Theodore Goddard, London (020) 7606 8855

HARRISON, Lawrence
Harrison Curtis, London (020) 7637 3333

HENRY, Michael
H2O (Henry Hepworth Organisation), London (020) 7539 7200

HORSFALL, Robert
Lee & Thompson, London (020) 7935 4665

HOWARD, Brian
Russells, London (020) 7439 8692

HURT, Jacqueline
SJ Berwin & Co, London (020) 7533 2632
Specialisation: Partner in the Media and Communications Group, advising on all aspects of media and communications law specialising in the financing, production and distribution of films and television programmes.
Prof. Memberships: Law Society, Women in Film & Television.
Career: Trained at *SJ Berwin & Co* qualified 1991, partner at *SJ Berwin & Co* 1998.

JAMES, Sean St John
Wiggin & Co, London (020) 7290 2424
Specialisation: Partner specialising in cable, satellite, analogue and digital terrestrial, on-line, internet and other television operations and programming including regulatory compliance, programming acquisitions, licences, co-productions and commissions, telecommunications and satellite agreements including uplink, transponder capacity, encryption and compression, facilities agreements, conditional access and subscriber management contracts and licence agreements, cable affiliation agreements and direct-to-home distribution agreements.
Prof. Memberships: Royal Television Society.
Career: Articled *Wiggin & Co*; qualified 1990; 18 months secondment to United Artists 1991-92; Assistant solicitor with *Wiggin & Co* until May 1996; partner 1996.
Personal: Born 1965. Interests include squash, cars, windsurfing and rowing.

JENNINGS, Carolyn
Campbell Hooper, London (020) 7222 9070
CarolynJennings@campbellhooper.com
Head of the Media Group
Specialisation: Specialist in intellectual property rights and contract law with a detailed knowledge of the theatre, film, music, television and merchandising industries. Her practice covers all fields of the entertainment and media business representing independent television companies, film producers, film financiers, theatre producers and music companies.
Career: Admitted as a solicitor in 1982 having trained at *Campbell Hooper.*

JOHNSON, Timothy A.
SJ Berwin & Co, London (020) 7533 2202
tim.johnson@sjberwin.com
Specialisation: Film production, financing and distribution, satellite communications, digital media, broadcasting and communications. Structuring film projects for financing purposes including co-productions and use of local incentives.
Career: MA, Sidney Sussex College, Cambridge. Denton Hall 1987-1993, *Yusef & Leader* 1993-1994, S J Berwin & Co 1994-date. Partner 1995.
Personal: Married. Interests include rugby, travel, food, history and the West country.

JONES, Howard
Sheridans, London (020) 7404 0444

JONES, Medwyn
Harbottle & Lewis, London (020) 7667 5000
Partner and Head of the Broadcasting Group.
Specialisation: Main area of practice is television production, financing, distribution and broadcasting. Work includes television commissioning, licensing and financing agreements, programme content, sponsorship, broadcasting legislation, carriage and transmission agreements and joint ventures. Also handles film production and financing. Regular lecturer at conferences and seminars.
Prof. Memberships: Law Society, Royal Television Society.
Career: Qualified in 1980. Worked at *Theodore Goddard* 1978-81, then *Walker Martineau* 1981-92 (from 1983 as a Partner). Joined *Cameron Markby Hewitt* as a Partner in 1992 and *Harbottle & Lewis* as a Partner in 1994.
Personal: Born 13th September 1955. Attended Scorton Grammar School, Chester Grammar School, Sheffield University and College of Law. Leisure interests include skiing, regular exercise and good wine. Lives in Richmond.

KAYE, Laurence M.
Paisner & Co, London (020) 7353 0299
See under E-commerce, p.300

LANDSMAN, David M.
Clintons, London (020) 7379 6080
dml@clintons.co.uk
Partner in Entertainment Department.
Specialisation: Deals with music, internet, TV, video, film, merchandising, media and leisure work.
Prof. Memberships: Law Society.
Career: Qualified 1970. Founding partner of *D M Landsman & Co*, which merged with *Clintons* in 1990.
Personal: Born 14th March, 1946. Educated at Haberdashers' Aske's School. Leisure pursuits include music, reading, sport and family. Lives near London.

LEA, Stephen
Lea & Company, Stockport (0161) 480 6691

LEE, Robert
Lee & Thompson, London (020) 7935 4665

LEIFER, Tony
D J Freeman, London (020) 7583 4055
nal@djfreeman.co.uk
Specialisation: Head of Media & Communications Department; both corporate and commercial work for media and hi-tech clients including major start-ups, venture capital, flotations, corporate acquisitions, disposals, joint ventures, programme financing, film distribution agreements and e-commerce internet start-upsand Internet-related broadcasting ventures.
Prof. Memberships: Law Society.
Career: Qualified in 1972, having joined *D J Freeman* in 1970. Became a Partner in 1975.
Personal: Born 17th September 1945. LLB (London) 1968 and LLM (University of California) 1969. Enjoys tennis and cooking. Lives in London.

LEWIS, Emyr
Morgan Cole, Swansea (01792) 634634
emyr.lewis@morgan-cole.com
Specialisation: A highly experienced and verstaile commercial lawyer with experience including media and entertainment law, IT law and public and constitutional law with a particular interest in the developing interface between charity, public and private sectors.
Career: Peterhouse, Cambridge and UCW Aberstwyth. Articles with *Morgan Cole*, admitted 1984. Partner from 1986.
Personal: Literature, languages and theatre.

LOM, Nicholas
Schilling & Lom and Partners, London (020) 7453 2500
nicholas.lom@schillinglom.co.uk
Founder Partner and Head of Entertainment and Commercial Department.
Specialisation: Main areas of practice – non-contentious internet, film, television, video, music, publishing, multimedia and copyright matters.
Career: Qualified in 1982. Articled at *Wright Webb Syrett* before forming *Schilling & Lom* in 1984.
Personal: Born 29th April 1949. Attended Westminster School and Pembroke College, Cambridge (MA Cantab). Member of the Groucho Club. Leisure interests include his children, chess, book collecting.

MAXTONE-SMITH, Michael
Richards Butler, London (020) 7247 6555
Specialisation: Advises banks and financiers in connection with all aspects of financing film and television both in Europe and the USA including the granting of security over intellectual property rights. Clients include National Westminister Bank plc, Coutts & Co, Natexis Banque, DG Bank and MM Media Capital Partners.
Career: Articles at *McKenna & Co.* (1986-88); assistant at *Richards Butler* (1988-98); partner at *Richards Butler* (1998-).
Personal: Educated at Nottingham High School and St. Catharine's College Cambridge. Married with two sons. Leisure interests: playing the piano, cricket and literature.

MCCORMICK, Peter D.G.
McCormicks, Leeds (0113) 246 0622
Senior partner.
Specialisation: Substantial area of practice is media and entertainment (allied to extensive portfolio of Sports Law) with considerable experience in both contentious and non-contentious aspects. Advises a number of sporting bodies, clubs and individuals on contractual matters as well as media and entertainment law issues. Clients include The F.A. Premier League, Leeds United F.C., a number of sporting personalities, Leslie Ash, Lee Chapman, Billy Pearce, Freddie Trueman, Richard Whiteley and a number of television presenters, actors, actresses and journalists. Advises on all aspects of broadcasting legislation. Has advised on three radio franchise bids. Deals with a number of defamation actions and advice on behalf of leading public figures, including politicians and personalities and handles complaints on broadcasting and press issues. Lectures on media and entertainment. Advises a number of clients in the music industry including performers and managers. Considerable experience of broadcast sponsorship and similar issues. Negotiates contracts for personal benefits, corporate sponsorship and ancillary matters. Has twenty years experience of tax investigation and enquiry work, both Revenue and VAT and serious fraud cases. Resident legal expert on Radio Leeds, Yorkshire Television and the Yorkshire Post. Author of 'Sport, Business and the Law' published by Jordans.
Prof. Memberships: Associate Director and Legal

Counsel Leeds United F.C.
Personal: Chairman of the Yorkshire Young Achiever Awards. Member of the Advisory Board, Sports Law Centre, Anglia University; Vice-President of The Outward Bound Trust; Solicitor to The Duke of Edinburgh's Award; Member of the Legal Working Party of the F.A. Premier League. Patron, Harrogate Junior Chamber of Commerce; Trustee, Friends of War Memorials.

MCINERNEY, Peter B.G.
SJ Berwin & Co, London (020) 7533 2521
peter.mcinerney@sjberwin.com
See under Sport, p.770

MEADON, Simon
Tarlo Lyons, London (020) 7405 2000
simon.meadon@tarlolyons.com
Specialisation: Having practised as an Entertainment Lawyer for over ten years both in private practice and in industry, he then worked as a Theatre producer with Bill Kenwright Ltd for five years presentsing over 50 theatrical production in the West End of London and onn Broadway. Principal area of practice is theatre and related work particularly for the Donmar Warehouse, Adventures In Motion Pictures and Cameron Mackintosh Limited. He also acts for Theatrical Agents and Personal Management companies. In addition, his long experiance of film production and financing enables him to advise on these and related matters
Prof. Memberships: Law Society
Career: Qualified in 1983
Personal: Born 25th August 1958, in Staffordshire, England. Educated at North Staffordshire Polytechnic where he graduated in 1979 with a BA, honours in Law. Leisure pursuits include theatre, film, tennis and bridge.

MITCHELL, Paul
Taylor Joynson Garrett, London (020) 7300 7000
pmitchell@tjg.co.uk
Partner in intellectual property department.
Specialisation: Principal area of practice is entertainment and media law including copyright and related work in various areas of the entertainment and media industry including music, books, films, television and multimedia. Other main area involves company law aspects of the acquisition and disposal of companies and joint ventures in the entertainment and media industry. Contributes articles to various professional publications and is co-author of Joynson-Hicks on UK Copyright Law. Addresses various conferences on topics related to entertainment and media law.
Prof. Memberships: Law Society.
Career: Qualified in 1976 while with *Joynson-Hicks* and became a partner in 1978.
Personal: Born 2nd November 1951. Attended Canford School 1965-69, then Bristol University 1970-73. Roald Dahl Foundation (Advisory Board Member). Leisure pursuits include family life, sailing and walking. Lives in London.

MORGAN, Leon R.
Davenport Lyons, London (020) 7468 2600
lmorgan@davenportlyons.com
Specialisation: A specialist in the production, financing and distribution of films, television and other audio visual material and IP rights generally. Advises funds specialising in film and television sale and leaseback transactions and other similar financing or investment schemes. Major clients include Barclays Bank Plc, The Royal Bank of Scotland, Equity Bank, Bank Leumi, MVI and Southern Star Circle Plc, Ed Victor Limited, The Mersey Television Company and many individuals including Phil Redmond, Matthew Vaughn, Guy Ritchie, Douglas Adams, Richard Harris and Sylvie Guillem. Is regularly quoted in industry periodicals.
Prof. Memberships: Law Society
Career: Qualified and joined Davenport Lyons in 1964. Became a partner in 1969.
Personal: Born 3rd July 1939. Educated at Westcliff High School, 1951-1958. Leisure interests include film, books, art, theatre, music and opera. Lives in London

MOXON, Richard
Davenport Lyons, London (020) 7468 2600
rmoxon@davenportlyons.com
Specialisation: Main area of practice is film and television production and finance including animation and children's programming together with involvement in merchandising and character licensing. He has also been particularly active in the area of tax-based financings, film library acquisitions and so-called 'sale and leaseback' tranactions.
Prof. Memberships: PACT Council, BAFTA and a co-opted member of the British Screen Advisory Board.
Career: University of Birmingham LLB (Hons) 1969-1972. Imperial Tobacco Legal Dept, 1975-1977, *Denton Hall & Burgin* 1977-1984 (partner 1982), Lorimar Productions (Head of Legal & Business Affairs, 1984-1986, Partner, *Marriott Harrison* 1986-January 1999. Partner [IT+Davenport Lyons to date.
Personal: Interests: singing, cinema, golf. Lives Sunbury-on-Thames.

NYMAN, Bernard M.
B. M. Nyman & Co, London (020) 8365 3060
bernie.nyman@iname.com
Specialisation: Principal area of practice is non-contentious work in publishing (books, magazines, journals, etc), dealing with contracts for all aspects of publishing including electronic publishing, acting for publishers, authors, literary agents, printers, distributors and learned societies. Libel reading (i.e. pre-publication advice) and dealing with libel complaints post publication. General intellectual property work including advice on copyright, trade marks and passing off, and agreements in the entertainment industry generally. Author of the copyright section of 'The Encyclopaedia of Forms & Precedents' (5th Ed re-issue, 1999, Vol. 21(2)), precedents for Adams: 'Character Merchandising' (2nd Ed., 1996, Butterworths). Regular contributor to 'Entertainment Law Review'. Specialist contributor to the 14th edition of 'Copinger & Skone James on Copyright' (Sweet & Maxwell, 1999).
Prof. Memberships: Law Society, European Communities Trade Mark Association, The Media Society, TIPLO. Trustee of The Enid Blyton Trust for Children (Appointed 2000).
Career: Qualified in 1979. Partner at *Rubinstein Callingham* from 1983. Partner at *Manches & Co* 1994-98. Proprietor *B.M. Nyman & Co* 1999.
Personal: Born 1954. Educated at Royal Liberty School 1965-72 and Sheffield University 1972-75 (BA in Law). Leisure interests include jazz, film and cricket. Lives in North London.

ORGAN, Chris
Russells, London (020) 7439 8692

PALMER, Nigel S.
SJ Berwin & Co, London (020) 7533 2265
nigel.palmer@sjberwin.com
Head of Media and Communications Group.
Specialisation: Main area of practice is media and entertainment work, including film financing, tax shelter financing, merchandising, film and television production, publishing and video distribution. Involved in financing of many notable feature films, and tax based film financing. Lawyer to 'Thomas the Tank Engine' company from back bedroom to public company. Author of Longman's Practical Commercial Precedents on Merchandising. Member of Editorial Board of International Media Law Review.
Prof. Memberships: International Bar Association, Copinger Society, Fellow of Royal Society of Arts.
Career: Joined *Denton Hall & Burgin* in 1976, qualifying in 1979. Partner *Denton Hall Burgin & Warrens* 1983-88. Left to join *S J Berwin & Co.* as a Partner in 1988.
Personal: Born 12th May 1950. Attended St. Edward's School, Oxford 1963-67, then Christ Church, Oxford 1968-71. Leisure pursuits include swimming, reading and music. Lives in Greenwich.

PAYNE, Abigail
Harbottle & Lewis, London (020) 7667 5000
Specialisation: Main areas of practice are film and television production, financing, distribution and copyright issues. Particular expertise in structuring international co-productions to obtain subsidies and tax incentives. Clients include major US production companies and sales agents, leading UK producers, sale and leaseback partnerships, insurance underwriters and talent agencies.
Career: Qualified in 1995, worked at *Theodore Goddard* 1993-95, then BBC (Independent Drama) 1995-97. Joined *Harbottle & Lewis* in 1997. Became senior associate in 2000.
Personal: Born 25th July 1968. Attended Lockleaze School 1981- 86, then Bath University. Leisure interests include tennis, skiing, gym and cinema.

PHILIPPS, Richard P.S.
Richards Butler, London (020) 7247 6555
rpsp@richardsbutler.com
Partner in Media Group.
Specialisation: Specialises almost exclusively in film finance work, acting for leading banks and other financial institutions active in the market, distribution companies and major overseas organisations and also acts for producers.
Career: Qualified 1978. Partner at *Richards Butler* since 1985.
Personal: Born 1952. Educated at Queens' College, Cambridge.

PHILLIPS, Mark D.
Harbottle & Lewis, London (020) 7667 5000
See under E-commerce, p.

RENNEY, Paul
Theodore Goddard, London (020) 7606 8855
paulrenney@theodoregoddard.co.uk
Specialisation: Head of e-commerce group, overseeing the different legal aspects of internet and other digital businesses; co-ordination of Data Protection advice throughout the firm and advice on non-contentious intellectual property and commercial

matters, as well as corporate media acqusitions, disposals and joint venture; advises on theatre rights, acquistions and production arrangements, especially musicals, general sponsorship and sales promotions, book and magazine publishing and commercial and IPR arrangemnets for the horseracing industry.

RIDLEY, Michael
Denton Wilde Sapte, London (020) 7320 6526
mfr@dentonwildesapte.com
Partner in Media and Technology Group.
Specialisation: Practice encompasses all aspects of television industry, especially the establishment of new television channels, and also includes commissioning, distribution, co-production agreements for films and television, sponsorship agreements, broadcasting regulation, satellite agreements, copyright law, artists' contracts and defamation. Frequently lectures on copyright, television production and broadcasting.
Prof. Memberships: Law Society, Copinger Society, Royal Television Society.
Career: Qualified in 1980. Rights Manager, National Theatre 1980-81. Senior Solicitor, London Weekend Television 1981-89. Joined *Denton Hall* in 1989 and became a Partner in 1990.
Personal: Born 1955; Durham University 1974-77 (BA in Law). Chairman of St Paul's Arts Trust and on board of Pop Up Theatre Company.

ROSE, D. Michael
Tarlo Lyons, London (020) 7405 2000
michael.rose@tarlolyons.com
Partner in Entertainment and Media Department.
Specialisation: Principal area of practice is theatre and related work, largely involving stage musicals. Also handles copyright disputes, piracy claims and defamation, as well as most other aspects of entertainment law, with background experience in general company and commercial work. Administration trustee of a large theatre-related charity. Major involvement in contract work (including much international licensing) in respect of over 70 first class stage productions, including such well-known musicals as 'Cats', 'The Phantom of The Opera', 'Les Miserables', 'Miss Saigon', 'Five Guys Named Moe', 'Carousel', 'Follies', 'Moby Dick!', 'Oliver', 'Martin of Guerre', 'Tap Dogs', 'Dance of the Vampires', 'Swan Lake', 'Oklahoma' (1998), 'Cinderella', 'Slava's Snow Show' and Ugly Rumours'. Experience also in high profile copyright and employment disputes, as well as some film and TV work. Solicitor to Sir Cameron Mackintosh and his group of companies since 1977. Writes a monthly column in 'The Stage' newspaper on entertainment law; contributes to various other publications including 'Musical Stages' and 'Entertainment Law Review'. He has also written a section on 'Theatre, Opera and Ballet' for the 1999 edition of 'Copinger & Skone James on Copyright'. Seminar speaker on various theatre-related topics.
Prof. Memberships: Law Society, International Association of Entertainment Lawyers, Charity Law Association and is a fellow of the Society of Advanced Legal Studies.
Career: Qualified in 1958. Partner in *Randall Rose* from 1960 until merger with *Tarlo Lyons* in 1986.
Personal: Born 27th August 1934. Educated at Rugby School 1948-52 and University College, London 1952-55. Chairman of Allied Cavendish Properties Ltd (30 shareholders) since 1985. Trustee/director of the Mackintosh Foundation since 1988 and the Theatre Investment Fund Ltd since 1997. Leisure pursuits include golf, theatre, reading and walking. Lives in London.

RUSSELL, Tony
Russells, London (020) 7439 8692

SANDELSON, Daniel
Clifford Chance, London (020) 7600 1000
daniel.sandelson@cliffordchance.com
Specialisation: Partner in communications and technology group specialising in commercial law relating to the media industries; acts for artists, production companies, distribution networks and financial institutions particularly in the broadcasting field, advises on television and film production and distribution, broadcast start-ups particularly in on-demand pay and terrestrial television, broadcasting regulation, pan-European copyright as it relates to the media industries and media asset acquisitions and disposals including film library acquisitions and disposals.
Career: St Catherines; Oxford University (BA Philosophy, Politics & Economics). Articled *Allen & Overy*; qualified 1988; partner *Clifford Chance* 1996; author of 'UK and EC Broadcasting Law' section in Butterworths Competition Law Handbook; contribution editor to Longmans 'Law and Practice of Multimedia' Handbook; contributor to many trade journals including 'Broadcast' and 'Intermedia'.
Personal: Born 1961; married with two children; resides London.

SAVILL, Lisbeth
Olswang, London (020) 7208 8888
ljs@olswang.com
Partner and Head of Entertainment, Media and Communications Group.
Specialisation: Specialist in the production, financing, distribution and acquisition of feature films and television programmes. Work includes structuring finance therefor, including loans, subsidies, and tax-based leasing deals. Clients include independent producers, television broadcasters, major US studios and film financiers (including banks). Runs the Film Business School in Spain and contributes to the National Film and Television School Finance Module for its Producers Course.
Career: Obtained Arts/Law degree from University of New South Wales in 1980; began her career as a litigation solicitor in Sydney in 1981; followed by international finance work for a major city firm in New York and London 1985-89; and became a partner at *Olswang* in 1991.

SEARLE, Helen
Searles, London (020) 7371 0555
helen@searles-solicitors.co.uk
fax (020) 7371 7722
Specialisation: Joint founding partner of *Searles Solicitors*. The firm represents a large number of successful international artists, as well as independent record companies, publishers and distributors. The recent explosion in brand exploitation, sponsorship and e-commerce has led to much new work. Current clients in the news include Jamiroquai, Sonique, Moby, Jamelia, Chumbawamba and Finley Quaye.
Career: Became a partner at *Siefert Sedley Williams* in her mid-twenties. Represented such diverse clients as The Prodigy, Seal, Nigel Kennedy and Go Discs. When that firm closed, the vast majority of the entertainment client base followed her to the new practice.
Publications: Regularly lectures to both industry and university audiences on the field of agreements relating to the music industry. She contributes articles to the music legal and academic press and is currently commissioned to write on the recording and publishing industries.

SHARLAND, Andrew J.
Clintons, London (020) 7379 6080
jsharland@sharpepritchard.co.uk
Specialisation: A leading partner in the litigation department of *Clintons*. Over the last 12 years, Andrew Sharland's practice has developed from one near-exclusively music-based to one which now encompasses clients within several fields of the entertainment world, including film and video production companies, sporting personalities and representatives, actors and actresses, comedians and television presenters. His interest in popular music and in its creation and production has ensured that his practice retains a strong music bias. Together with David Davis, he represented Sony in the litigation brought by George Michael and has separately brought or defended actions for EMI Music Publishing Limited, Robert Smith (The Cure), Nigel Martin-Smith (the former manager of Take That), Virgin Records and A&M Records. He successfully represented Island Records following the seizure by the Police on the grounds of obscenity of the album 'Niggaz 4 Life' by the band NWA.
Career: Called to the bar 1986. Partner *DM Landsman & Co* 1988, *Clintons* 1990 (upon its merger with *DM Landsman & Co*).

SHAW, Barry
Barry Shaw, London (020) 8297 8899
barhanelth@compuserve.com
Specialisation: Drafting of documents in connection with theatrical presentations not only in and for the United Kingdom but also overseas. Invariably, but not always, acts for the Producer. Normally involved in the negotiation and preparation of all material documents for clients. Thereafter acts on the further licensing of rights in the ventures. Recent projects have included dealing with the arrangements for 'The Lady in the Van'; 'Cressida'; 'Lautrec'; the production documents for 'Mama Mia!'. Additionally specialises in music copyright matters, publishing and defamation.
Prof. Memberships: Associated with a large number of subsidised theatres, has sat on numerous boards and is a Director and the Secretary of Greenwich Theatre. Is also actively involved with Blackheath FC (Rugby Union) (where he is the Honorary Secretary).
Career: Articled to Oscar Beuselinck and followed him when he rejoined *Wright & Webb* in 1963. Stayed in *Wright & Webb* (which in due course merged with *Syrett & Sons*) until *Wright Webb Syrett* decided to join another firm in 1995 at which point he set up practice on his own.

SIBBALD, Graham I.
Dundas & Wilson CS, Glasgow (0141) 222 2200

SINNOTT, Mark
Russells, London (020) 7439 8692

SMITH, Barry
Richards Butler, London (020) 7247 6555
Partner in Media and Entertainment Group.
Specialisation: Advises on all aspects of copyright

law, film and television production, distribution and financing in particular, specialising in advice on sale and leaseback transactions and internet company content providers, character merchandising, multimedia and other forms of publishing and on music agreements.
Personal: Born 1949. Educated at Queen Mary College, London (LLB), 1972. Qualified 1974.

STATHAM, John
Statham Gill Davies, London (020) 7487 5565

STORER, Robert A.
Harbottle & Lewis, London (020) 7667 5000
Partner and Head of the Film & TV Production Group
Specialisation: Main areas of practice are film and television production and finance and copyright issues. Over 25 years' experience representing leading producers including Merchant Ivory Productions, Fragile Films and Kismet Films, financiers, completion guarantors and film finances. Involved in production and financing of numerous films and television series and programmes, recently including Mr Bean, Spice World – The Movie, Ideal Husband, Honest and Golden Bowl. Addressed a number of conferences on media issues.
Prof. Memberships: Law Society, International Bar Association, Director of Association of Independent Producers in early 1980s, Director of Film Finances Ltd 1983-88.
Career: Joined *Harbottle & Lewis* in 1969, qualifying in 1971. Became Partner in 1974, and Senior Partner in 1999.
Personal: Born 29th April 1947. Attended Buxton College 1960-65, then London School of Economics 1965-68. Leisure pursuits include family, golf, tennis and cinema. Lives in Barnes, London.

SWAFFER, Patrick
Goodman Derrick, London (020) 7404 0606
Partner in media department.
Specialisation: Main areas of practice are broadcasting and publishing. Includes pre- and post-publication advice on defamation, contempt, confidence and copyright, rights exploitation, contractual issues and regulatory advice for the broadcasting industry.
Career: Joined *Goodman Derrick* in 1974. Qualified 1976. Became partner in 1979 in media department.
Personal: Born 12th February 1951. Lives in London.

THOMPSON, Andrew J.
Lee & Thompson, London (020) 7935 4665

TREGEAR, Steven
Russells, London (020) 7439 8692

TURTON, Julian M.
The Simkins Partnership, London (020) 7907 3000
Partner in Media and Entertainment Group and of the Management Board.
Specialisation: Main area of practice is media and entertainment, with emphasis on the music industry but also including publishing, art, and new media. Represents artists, composers, publishers and record companies, book publishers, media selling operations, advertising agencies, telecoms companies and internet service providers. Editor of 'Neighbouring Rights, Artists, Producers and their Collection Societies', co-editor of 'Impact of Competition Law on the Music Industry' and past contributor to books on 'Lead and Commercial Effects of Digitisation on the Music Industry' and 'Merchandising and Sponsorship'and 'Moral Rights'. Author of articles in International Media Law, Entertainment Law Review and Business Magazine. Has lectured to the IBA on new media issues and at commercial seminars on music publishing agreements, on the enforceability of contracts, on new technologies and on performance rights.
Prof. Memberships: President and Committee Member of the International Association of Entertainment Lawyers; Founder Member of Advertising Law International; BAFTA.
Career: Qualified 1980 and joined *The Simkins Partnership* the same year. Articled at *Trower, Still & Keeling*. Became a Partner in 1985.
Personal: Born 23rd July 1952. Attended Bristol University (1974). Leisure interests include family, golf, reading, food and Arsenal F.C. Lives in London.

WARE, James
Davenport Lyons, London (020) 7468 2600
jware@davenportlyons.com
Specialisation: Copyright and copyright tribunal, music industry, broadcasting, entertainment, merchandising, rights administration, theatre, computer media. Clients include substantial independent music publishers and specialist entertainment businesses on the one hand and well-known composers and artists on the other.
Prof. Memberships: International Association of Entertainment Lawyers, International Managers Federation. Deputy Chairman of the Guildford School of Acting.
Career: St Johns College, Oxford. Virgin Group, Director, CBS Songs, European Regional Vice-President, Partner, Davenport Lyons since 1986.
Personal: Music, theatre and hill walking. Members: Athenaeum, MCC.

WILLIAMS, Alan
Denton Wilde Sapte, London (020) 7320 6249
apw@dentonwildesapte.com
See under E-commerce, p.301

WILLIAMS, Gordon
Lee & Thompson, London (020) 7935 4665

WILLS, David
Campbell Hooper, London (020) 7222 9070
DavidWills@campbellhooper.com
Consultant in Media Group.
Specialisation: Extensive experience of the law and practice of the theatre. Advises producers, financiers and creative personnel in the West End, on Broadway, off Broadway and all other territories where live theatre is performed. Regularly negotiates production rights, finance agreements, co-production ventures, theatre licences and agreements for the services of creative contributors to theatrical productions. Handles media litigation. Represents writers and performers on stage and screen.
Career: Qualified 1967. Partner at *Campbell Hooper* 1970.
Personal: Lives in London and Wiltshire.

ZEFFMAN, David
Olswang, London (020) 7208 8888
dcz@olswang.com
Partner Entertainment, Media and Communications Group.
Specialisation: Principal area of practice involves commercial and corporate aspects of television, music and e-commerce businesses.
Prof. Memberships: IBA, IAEL.
Career: Qualified 1983 while with *Frere Cholmeley* and became a Partner in 1989. Appointed Head of Company and Commercial Department, *Frere Cholmeley Bischoff* in 1993. Joined *Simon Olswang & Co* as a Partner in 1994.
Personal: Born 28th February 1958. Attended Haberdashers' Aske's School 1969-76, then Brasenose College, Oxford 1977-80. Lives in London.

PARLIAMENTARY & PUBLIC AFFAIRS

RESEARCH APPROVED BY BMRB: *For this edition,* Chambers' *researchers conducted 6083 interviews – 4408 with law firms, 598 with barristers and 1077 with clients.*

The validity of the research was scrutinised by BMRB International, who audited both the methodology and the results at our offices in July 2000. They interviewed Chambers' *researchers and cross-checked sample interviews. Details of the audit appear on page 7.*

LONDON

PARLIAMENTARY AGENCY

PARLIAMENTARY AGENCY • London	Ptnrs	Assts
❶ Dyson Bell Martin (Bircham & Co)	*	*
Rees & Freres	3	3
Winckworth Sherwood	4	1
❷ Sharpe Pritchard	1	-

LEADING INDIVIDUALS	
❶ DURKIN Joseph Rees & Freres	GORLOV Alison Winckworth Sherwood
IRVING Paul Winckworth Sherwood	McCULLOCH Ian Dyson Bell Martin
THOMPSON Paul Dyson Bell Martin	
❷ LANE Peter Rees & Freres	LEWIS Alastair Sharpe Pritchard
OWEN Robert Dyson Bell Martin	
❸ BROWN Nicholas Dyson Bell Martin	PETO Monica Rees & Freres

Within each band, firms are listed alphabetically. *See* **Profiles** *on page 604*

Dyson Bell Martin (Bircham & Co) (6 ptnrs & 4 assts split between Parliamentary Agency and Public Affairs.) *"Lobbyists who affect the way policy works."* Specialist complementary parliamentary and public affairs department, with large firm back up. Handle Transport and General Works Act matters for a wide range of clients including passenger transport executives, local government and harbour trusts as well as commercial and financial companies. A key client group is the niche area of passenger transport executives. *"You couldn't get that experience elsewhere: they manage the process and deal with statutory objectors."* Its offices in Westminster, Edinburgh, Cardiff and Brussels shadow the key sites of the British and European political institutions. The department's strength in depth is signified by the fact that four of its five lawyers are Roll A parliamentary agents. The experienced **Paul Thompson** (*"very thorough, he covers all the angles"*) is respected by clients for his understanding of the statutory issues surrounding Passenger Transport Executives. *"Diplomatic"* **Ian McCulloch** is noted for his *"high intellect."* **Robert Owen** is an *"astute"* practitioner and **Nick Brown** has a *"hands on"* approach. **Clients:** Merseytravel (Merseyside Passenger Transport Executive;) City of Newcastle upon Tyne; West Somerset District Council.

Rees & Freres Features mainly in transport based parliamentary and planning work, and provides advice and drafting assistance on legislation for private members trade associations. Known particularly for railway work, the firm acts for a range of transport and rail clients and is one of Railtrack's principal advisers. It is seen to be becoming more commercial in its orientation. *"Personable and technically very good"* **Peter Lane** is highly rated by industry observers along with *"commercial animal"* **Jo Durkin** for Transport and General Works Act issues. **Monica Peto** (*"extremely clever – good at arguing her corner"*) is generally regarded as a rising star. **Clients:** Railtrack plc; GNER Ltd; Port of Tyne; Felixstowe Dock and Railway Co; Seacontainers.

Winckworth Sherwood Traditionally pre-eminent parliamentary agents who *"act for the objectors."* Advise a diverse client base on parliamentary bills, TWA orders, Harbour orders, Scottish provisional orders and private bills. Infrastructure and projects advice covers rail and light railways, as well as harbours, bridges and tunnels. In the local legislation arena, clients include banks and building societies, local authorities and statutory companies. Additional work is undertaken in planning, environmental assessment and judicial review. Recent work has included the promotion of a bank merger bill, advising a T&W enquiry authorising a guided baseway and acting for Associated British Ports on a trusts parts review. *"Bright and reasonable"* **Alison Gorlov** is highly rated by peers as a *"true academic"* in the field. Widely versed in a full range of parliamentary work, she is noted for the quality of her client care and for *"running a tight ship."* **Paul Irving**, who has experience of local government and the civil service, is *"a leading name in the sector."* **Clients:** Alliance & Leicester plc; Cheshire County Council; Railtrack plc; Bristol County Council; LRT; Harwich Haven Authority.

Sharpe Pritchard Parliamentary agents, operating from Parliamentary and Planning department, considered to have a smaller practice than the other firms in the list. Advise on the legislative process, Private and Hybrid Bills, and Royal Charters. Recently assisted the British Red Cross in obtaining the Act which incorporated the protocols to the Geneva Convention into UK law. Active in promoting private bills for clients notably local authorities such as Westminster City Council and Kent County Council, Medway Council, the Transport Salaried Staff Association, and boiler manufacturers BAXI. *"Personable and bright,"* Roll A parliamentary agent **Alastair Lewis** is rated highly by peers for his *"prolific"* workload. He has acted for the majority of local councils in petitioning for the Channel Tunnel Rail Link Act and promoted and opposed a number of TWA Act Orders and Harbour Revision Orders in connection with railways, harbours and bridges. The retirement of Michael Pritchard is thought to have left a sizeable gap at the firm. **Clients:** Westminster City Council; Transport Salaried Staff Association; BAXI; British Red Cross.

PUBLIC AFFAIRS

Clifford Chance High profile US and German mergers have added an extra dimension to the breadth of advice offered by this leading international firm. Activities range widely including advising clients on UK and EU parliamentary and regulatory developments. Activities such as Network Europe, an EU monitoring device, have raised the firm's profile substantially. About half of the workload derives from public affairs issues relating to work and clients from other departments. Former Office of Fair Trading lawyer **Richard Thomas** has substantial public sector experience, recently writing an introduction to the Human Rights Act. The department helped build and advise a consortium of accounting firms to deal with threats presented by IR35. It is currently acting for a specialist importing company on

PARLIAMENTARY: PUBLIC AFFAIRS • London	Ptnrs	Assts
❶ Clifford Chance	1	1
DLA Upstream	-	1
Dyson Bell Martin (Bircham & Co)	*	*
Lovells	1	4
SJ Berwin & Co	*	*

LEADING INDIVIDUALS	
❶ **BRACKEN Jonathan** Dyson Bell Martin	**CLEMENT-JONES Tim** DLA Upstream
HOLMES Simon SJ Berwin & Co	**INNES Gordon** Lovells
THOMAS Richard Clifford Chance	

Within each band, firms are listed alphabetically. *See **Profiles** on page 604*

UK plans to implement the EU directive on direct marketing. **Clients:** Business Information Providers Association; Diageo plc; Goldman Sachs; The Radio Authority.

DLA Upstream Branded new public affairs arm of national mid-sized firm DLA, which has already gained a degree of market recognition. Headed by Liberal peer and public affairs professional, **Tim Clement-Jones**, who also operates as Chairman of Environmental Context. The practice has recently won a beauty parade to provide European-wide advice to an internet service provider against competition from established public affairs consultancies. Work focuses on e-commerce, financial services, environment and the transport and utility sectors. Advised clients on the Utilities Bill and on road haulage issues. Draw upon DLA's public affairs resources in Brussels and wider international network. The recent addition of Scottish firm Bird Semple to the DLA fold should further add to the geographical reach of the practice. **Clients:** Freeserve.

Dyson Bell Martin (Bircham & Co) (6 ptnrs & 4 assts split between Parliamentary Agency and Public Affairs.) Unique firm in that it is highly rated for both its parliamentary and public affairs work. Clients are drawn from public and private companies, local authorities (including passenger transport executives,) government agencies and non-departmental public bodies, professional bodies, trade associations, charities, regulatory bodies and pressure groups. In common with the other parliamentary firms, it has strength in the transport sector. Offices in London, Edinburgh and Cardiff allows it access to decision makers in the key UK markets. **Jonathan Bracken** is the stand-out practitioner here. **Clients:** BT plc; Passenger Transport Executives Group; Environment Agency Wales.

Lovells *"Have a high regard for them, they are keen competition."* Broad-based practice advising clients across a range of disciplines including transport, financial services, data protection and e-commerce, pharmaceuticals and telecoms. **Gordon Innes** has a *"first-class reputation."* Recently addressed civil servants on the Financial Services and Markets Bill, and represented tobacco interests on advertising and workplace safety and regulation issues. The related EU practice is continuing judicial proceedings challenging the Tobacco Advertising Directive. It has also advised on e-commerce and data protection directives. US public policy is co-ordinated by a partner stationed in the small Washington office. **Clients:** Tobacco firms.

SJ Berwin & Co (9 ptnrs & 11 assts part time.) Commercial firm whose public affairs work originates from its highly rated EU competition practise rather than a bespoke department, cross-department lawyers being brought in as necessary. Consequently serves a diverse client base of companies in the drinks, agrochemical, music, and skiing industries as well as political parties. Rated partner **Simon Holmes** has previously acted for the licensed betting association BOLA. **Clients:** BOLA; British Association of Ski Instructors.

LEADERS IN PARLIAMENTARY & PUBLIC AFFAIRS

BRACKEN, Jonathan
Bircham & Co., London (020) 7222 8044
jonathanbracken@bircham.co.uk
Specialisation: Principal areas of practice are public affairs, lobbying, legislative drafting, parliamentary procedure, research and advice on public policy issues. Over the past year has worked on the Utilities Bill, Financial Services and Markets Bill, Transport and Finances Bill, as well as continuing his involvement in the implementation of the Competition Act 1998.
Prof. Memberships: Law Society; Institute of Public Relations (Government Affairs Group); Administrative Law Bar Association.
Career: Partner *Bircham & Co* 2000.

BROWN, Nicholas
Bircham & Co., London (020) 7222 8044
nicholasbrown@bircham.co.uk
Specialisation: Specialises in infrastructure legislation. Adviser to charities and trustees. Is presently engaged in promoting a new private sector freight railway in Scotland and England, four Harbour Orders and advising on the Thameslink project.
Career: Articled *Bircham & Co* 1979. Qualified as a Solicitor in 1983. Partner and Roll A Agent 1985. Chairman of Executive Committee 1997-to present.
Personal: Attended Westminster School and Jesus College, Oxford. Plays cricket and golf and is a qualified soccer referee. Two children.

CLEMENT-JONES, Tim
DLA, London (08700) 111111
Specialisation: EU and UK Public Affairs.
Prof. Memberships: The Law Society, Institute of Public Relations.
Career: Head of *DLA Upstream*, *DLA*'s public affairs and government relations practice. He was a founding partner of Independent Corporate Mentoring-ICM - the legal management consultancy. Until its sale to Lopex plc in April 1999, he was a founding director of Political Context, the fast growing public affairs consultancy. He is Chairman of Environmental Context, the environmental strategy and communications consultancy. he qualified in 1974, having trained at *Coward Chance*, as it then was. From 1986 until 1995, he was the Group Company Secretary and Legal Adviser of Kingfisher plc, the major retail group. He was responsible for ensuring group compliance with Stock Exchange and other regulatory requirements and group public affairs activity in Westminster and Brussels, led a series of competition cases before UK and EU authorities and was responsible for the legal aspects of many public acquisitions. He also co-ordinated Kingfisher plc's contribution to the Shopping Hours Reform Campaign which led to the Sunday Trading Act 1993. Prior to Kingfisher, he was Legal Director of Grand Metropolitan Retailing and Head of Legal Services at London Weekend Television.
Personal: He was Chairman of the Liberal Party from 1986-1988 and played a major part in the merger negotiations with the SDP to form the Liberal Democrats. He ran Paddy Ashdown's campaign to become leader of the party in 1988. He was Director of the Liberal Democrats' campaign for the 1994 European Parliament Elections and vice chair of the Party's 1997 General Election campaign team. He is a member of the National Executive of the Liberal Democrats and was Chair of the Party's Finance Committee from 1991 to 1998. He was made a life peer in 1988 and is now the Liberal Democrat Health Spokesman in the House of Lords. He was educated at Haileybury and then Trinity College, Cambridge, where he took a degree in Economics (Part 1) and Law (Part 2). He is married to Jean, until recently a financial counsellor in the voluntary sector and is father to Harry, aged 18 months. His main outside interests are cinema, travel, reading, walking, running, modern art and appreciating other people's cooking.

DURKIN, Joseph
Rees & Freres, London (020) 7222 5381
Specialisation: Senior partner and specialist in administrative and public law, railways and tramways, highways and harbours, planning, environmental law and compulsory acquisition. 30 years experience of promoting and opposing legislation on behalf of the Central Government, local authorities, major public and private sector transport operators, port authorities, universities and colleges and major national and multinational corporations. Publications include 'Blackstones Guide To The Transport & Works Act 1992' (co-author). Regularly addresses conferences on the parliamentary and legislative process, Royal Charter, harbour law, infrastructure, and Transport & Works projects.

Prof. Memberships: Society of Parliamentary Agents (President). Law Society.
Career: 1961-70 solicitor in general practice in the City. 1970-73 Government parliamentary draftsman with the Office of the Parliamentary Counsel. Partner, Rees & Freres since 1973, senior partner since 1981.
Personal: Educated at Sheffield University (LL.B). Born 2nd January 1938.

GORLOV, Alison
Winckworth Sherwood, London (020) 7222 0441
amhgorlov@winckworths.co.uk
Specialisation: Senior parliamentary partner and parliamentary agent. Specialist in legislation and legislative drafting, parliamentary and legislative procedures, administrative and public law, transport and other infrastructure (railways, harbours, tramways, utilities), public sector bodies, commercial undertakings. Long experience of acting for central and local government, major transport undertakers, port authorities, utility undertakers, banks, building societies, charities and educational bodies.
Prof. Memberships: Law Society. Society of Parliamentary Agents (past president).
Career: Joined *Sherwood & Co.* in 1971. Qualified as a solicitor in 1975, became a partner and Roll A Agent in 1978.

HOLMES, Simon
SJ Berwin & Co, London (020) 7533 2222
simon.holmes@sjberwin.com
Specialisation: European, competition and trade law. Major cases include some of the largest anti-dumping, competition and single market law cases involving lobbying in Brussels, London and other member state capitals.
Prof. Memberships: Recent Chairman, Solicitors' European Group.
Career: 1st Class Honours, Law and Economics from Cambridge. Grande Distinction, Licence Speciale en Droit Européen, Brussels University.
Personal: Married, 2 daughters. Walking, cycling, tennis, film.

INNES, Gordon
Lovells, London (020) 7296 2000
gordon.innes@lovells.com
Specialisation: Public Policy; government machinery and processes; influencing government policy, regulation and decision making; Parliamentary procedure, European governance.
Prof. Memberships: Law Society; Whitehall and Industry Group.
Career: BA (Hons), LLB (Hons) University of Melbourne 1989-94; MSC (European Studies) (Chevening Scholar) London School of Economics 1997-98; Legal Intern, Australian Mission to the EU 1995; Admitted 1996; Commercial Lawyer, *Deacons Graham & James* 1995-97; Senior Legal and Policy Advisor, Cabinet Office, Victorian Government 1996-97; Public Policy Lawyer, *Lovells* 1998 – present.
Personal: Rowing, skiing.

IRVING, Paul
Winckworth Sherwood, London (020) 7593 5000
pirving@winckworths.co.uk
Specialisation: Partner in Parliamentary department. Specialises in drafting, promoting and opposing legislation in Parliament and delegated legislation (including Orders under the Transport and Works Act and the Harbours Act) and in advising on railways, harbours and other infrastructure projects.
Prof. Memberships: Society of Parliamentary Agents (Secretary). Law Society
Career: Called to the Bar 1986. Requalified as solicitor 1991. Partner at *Sherwood & Co* since 1992.
Personal: Educated at Trinity College, Oxford (MA and D.Phil). Born 7th November 1956.

LANE, Peter
Rees & Freres, London (020) 7222 5381
Specialisation: Partner at *Rees & Freres.* Parliamentary Agent and specialist in public law, transport and infrastructure, and legislative drafting. Experienced in drafting, promoting and opposing legislation, including that for the construction and operation of transport infrastructure projects on behalf of major public sector transport operators, port authorities, local authorities, universities and colleges and major national and multinational corporations. Advises on harbour law, infrastructure and transport and works projects. Publications include 'Blackstone's Guide to the Transport & Works Act 1992' and 'Blackstone's Guide for the Environment Act 1995' (co-author).
Prof. Memberships: Society of Parliamentary Agents. Law Society.
Career: 1977-80, barrister, member of Peter Boydell QC's chambers (2 Harcourt Buildings). 1978-80, Lecturer in Laws, Queen Mary College, University of London. 1980-85, Government parliamentary draftsman with the Office of the Parliamentary Counsel. Since 1985 solicitor at *Rees & Freres,* partner since 1987.
Personal: Educated at Hertford College, Oxford (MA) and University of California, Berkeley (LL.M). Born 26th April 1953.

LEWIS, Alastair
Sharpe Pritchard, London (020) 7405 4600
alewis@sharpepritchard.co.uk
Specialisation: Promotion of and opposition to private and hybrid bills, transport and works orders and harbour revision orders. Is promoting a number of private bills including a major bill for the london boroughs. Work on government bills includes drafting amendments for clients and monitoring progress through parliament. Is acting for the promoters of Transport and Works and Harbour Revision Order.
Prof. Memberships: Society of Parliamentary Agents.
Career: LL.B Trent Polytechnic, College of Law.
Personal: Football, walking, cycling.

MCCULLOCH, Ian
Bircham & Co., London (020) 7222 8044
Specialisation: Parliamentary strategy and procedure, tactics and lobbying. Promoting and opposing primary and subordinate legislation for statutory companies, local authorities, trade associations, transport undertakers, banks, property companies, harbours, charities and sporting and amenity bodies.
Prof. Memberships: Society of Parliamentary Agents (Hon Sec 1989-95; President 1995-98) City of Westminster Law Society (President 1994-95). Law Society. Statute Law Society.
Career: Admitted as a Solicitor 1976. Partner since 1977. Enrolled as a Roll A Parliamentary Agent 1979. Senior Parliamentary Partner since 1992. Senior Partner (1997-).
Personal: Born 13th May 1950. Educated Edinburgh Academy and University of Dundee (LLB Hons. jurisprudence and philosophy).

OWEN, Robert
Bircham & Co., London (020) 7222 8044
robertowen@bircham.co.uk
Specialisation: Main areas of practice continue to be parliamentary and local legislation, town and country planning, transport and environmental law. Over the past year highlights have been: promoting for Merseyside Passenger Transport Authority the Mersey Tunnels private bill to authorise the indexation of tolls payable for use of the Mersey road tunnels and their future operation under a public/private partnership; promoting for Knowsley Metropolitan Borough Council and Docklands Light Railway Limited orders under the Transport and Works Act to authorise, respectively, a rail freight terminal in the Knowsley Industrial Park and an extension of the DLR to Silvertown and London City Airport; acting for objectors in relation to various other orders proposed to be made under the TWA for transport infrastructure; continuing to act for landowners affected by the proposed Channel Tunnel Rail Link; advising in relation to various other light rail schemes and railway re-openings; advising the Environment Agency Wales in relation to Welsh devolution and the National Assembly for Wales; advising various ports, harbours and conservancies on local legislation and the Government's new ports policy.
Prof. Memberships: Law Society; United Kingdom Environmental Law Association; Society of Parliamentary Agents.
Career: University of London: 1983-1986; College of Law: 1986-1987; Qualified as a solicitor: 1989; Partner with *Bircham & Co.* and *Dyson Bell Martin* since 1991.
Personal: Married with two children.

PETO, Monica
Rees & Freres, London (020) 7222 5381
monica.peto@1thesanctuary.com
Specialisation: Partner at *Rees & Freres,* Parliamentary Agent and specialist in public law, transport and infrastructure, and legislative drafting. Experienced in drafting, promoting and opposing legislation, including that for the construction and operation of transport infrastructure projects on behalf of major public sector transport operators, port authorities, local authorities. Publications include Blackstone's guide to the Transport & Works Act 1992, Blackstone's guide to the Environment Act 1995 (co-author).
Prof. Memberships: Society of Parliamentary Agents, Law Society.
Career: 1972 – 1980 solicitor in general practice, 1976 – 1980 Part time lecturer in law at Southampton University, 1978 – 1994 Litigation Examiner for the Law Society. 1994 to date Law Society External Examinter for the University of West of England and Manchester Metropolitan University. Since 1989 solicitor at *Rees & Freres,* partner since 1990. Educated at Bristol University (LLB) and University of Southampton (LLM).
Publications: Publications include Blackstones 'Guide to the Transport & Works Act 1992'; Blackwell's 'Guide to the Environment Act 1995' (co-author).
Personal: Born 16 August 1947.

THOMAS, Richard
Clifford Chance, London (020) 7600 1000
richard.thomas@cliffordchance.com
Specialisation: Director of Public Policy at *Clifford Chance* since 1992. For the previous 18 years he held various legal, policy and regulatory posts in the public sector including 6 years as Director of Consumer

Affairs at the Office of Fair Trading. Helps *Clifford Chance* and its clients to deal with business developments inside Whitehall, Westminster and Brussels. Has in-depth knowledge on governmental structures, procedures and culture and extensive experience of getting legislation onto the statute book and amending Bills. Also has a wide-ranging network of personal contacts - within the civil service, parliament, the media, trade associations, interest groups and the voluntary sector. Writes and speaks extensively on legal and related matters and is regularly used by the media for comment on constitutional, legislative and other pubic sector developments. Is a member of various governmental and self-regulatory committees and schemes.

Prof. Memberships: Law Society; Royal Society of Arts.

Career: *Freshfields* (1971 - 1974); CAB Legal Service (1974 - 1979); National Consumer Council (1979 - 1986); Office of Fair Trading (1986 - 1992); *Clifford Chance* (1992 - present).

THOMPSON, Paul

Bircham & Co., London (020) 7222 8044
paulthompson@bircham.co.uk

Specialisation: Advice on parliamentary and legislative procedures and tactics, legislative drafting, lobbying and public affairs and the promotion of and opposition to local legislation. Has acted for a wide range of public and private sector bodies including national, local, port and transport authorities, banks and other financial institutions, major plcs, utilities, trade and amenity associations and religious and other charitable bodies. Currently, particularly involved in advising various interests on, and assisting them in relation to, new government legislation and devolved matters, whilst also heavily engaged in the promotion of light rail schemes by Transport and Works Order and port-related work.

Prof. Memberships: Law Society, Society of Parliamentary Agents.

Career: Called to the Bar 1977. Partner in *Dyson Bell & Co* 1982. Partner and Solicitor at *Bircham & Co and Dyson Bell Martin* since 1990.

Personal: Born 26th March 1954.

PARTNERSHIP

RESEARCH APPROVED BY BMRB: *For this edition,* Chambers' *researchers conducted 6083 interviews – 4408 with law firms, 598 with barristers and 1077 with clients.*

The validity of the research was scrutinised by BMRB International, who audited both the methodology and the results at our offices in July 2000. They interviewed Chambers' *researchers and cross-checked sample interviews. Details of the audit appear on page 7.*

LONDON

PARTNERSHIP • London	Ptnrs
❶ Allen & Overy	5
Fox Williams	3
Kingsley Napley	3
Rowe & Maw	3
❷ Herbert Smith	2
Reynolds Porter Chamberlain	2
❸ Bristows	3
Field Fisher Waterhouse	3
❹ Finers Stephens Innocent	2
Ralph Hume Garry	2
Wright Son & Pepper	1

LEADING INDIVIDUALS	
❶ **FOX Ronald** Fox Williams	**LINSELL Richard** Rowe & Maw
SACKER Tony Kingsley Napley	**TURNOR Richard** Allen & Overy
❷ **GOLD David** Herbert Smith	**MAYER Stephen** Reynolds Porter Chamberlain
RALPH Stephen Ralph Hume Garry	
❸ **McARTHUR Colin** Field Fisher Waterhouse	**SIMMONS Michael** Finers Stephens Innocent
WILLIAMS Christine Fox Williams	
❹ **LACE John** Bristows	**WRIGHT Nicholas** Wright Son & Pepper

PARTNERSHIP: Large International Mergers • London
❶ Allen & Overy
Herbert Smith
Rowe & Maw
Linklaters
Slaughter and May

LEADING INDIVIDUALS
❶ **FLECK Richard** Herbert Smith
GODDEN Richard Linklaters
TRIGGS Jeffrey Slaughter and May

Within each band, firms are listed alphabetically *See **Profiles** on page 610*

Allen & Overy A private client lawyer by background, **Richard Turnor** is heavily involved in non-contentious partnership work, and was particularly instrumental in the development of the law for LLPs. Acts for professional firms advising on international restructuring and mergers. He has already received instructions to establish LLPs from two professional partnerships in anticipation of its availability. **Clients:** professional partnerships.

Fox Williams At times regarded as top-heavy, this firm relies heavily on the expertise of its *"pretty sharp"* senior partner **Ronnie Fox**, who is widely regarded as *"one of the stars"* in this area. Dipping into a cross-departmental group of six partners, including fellow founding partner **Christine Williams**, who is known for her sound drafting skills. The team advises on all aspects of contentious and non-contentious partnership law. Recently advised on the de-merger of partners from Moores Rowland when the majority of its partners joined BDO Stoy Hayward. **Clients:** solicitors and accountants.

Kingsley Napley *"Streetwise"* **Tony Sacker** is considered to be rather more *"earthy"* than technical in his approach to partnership law. He spends an increasing amount of time on non-contentious issues, where he acted for BDO Stoy Hayward on their merger with Moores Rowland. The team has also advised a number of US law firms, particularly on the enforceability of restrictive covenants. **Clients:** accountants; law firms.

Rowe & Maw Described by some as a *"most fearsome competitor,"* **Richard Linsell** *("highly imaginative")* has a reputation as a top non-contentious practitioner, and has also made a name for himself in the development of LLPs. He continues to lead the corporate-based multi-disciplinary professions group, which offers a broad range of advice from incorporating offshore partnerships to group partnership structures. Recently instructed by three law firms to redo their partnership deeds. The firm has a respected name for dealing with partnership issues raised by major international mergers. **Clients:** accountancy firms and other professional partnerships.

Herbert Smith Although known chiefly for his role as a *"heavy-duty"* commercial litigator, **David Gold** has unwittingly carved himself a reputation as a *"feared but respected adversary"* in the field of partnership litigation. He has been recommended as the man to turn to for partnership break-ups, poaching and restrictive covenants. The firm is renowned for its work in advising the major accountancy partnerships, and can draw on a cross-departmental group of three partners, including **Richard Fleck** who enjoys a reputation as an M&A and EU partnership expert. The firm acted for PricewaterhouseCoopers' global network following its merger and on partnership issues raised by the subsequent completion of local mergers of PwC entities in Europe and Africa. **Clients:** accountancy firms.

Reynolds Porter Chamberlain **Stephen Mayer** has developed contentious and non-contentious partnership work into a niche area of the firm's practice. Along with a commercial litigation partner, Mayer frequently advises partners on restrictive covenants and on their enforcement in partnership agreements. Non-contentious work involving the drafting of partnership agreements is also handled by the team. **Clients:** solicitors, accountants, surveyors.

Bristows **John Lace** continues to practice non-contentious commercial partnership work, a particular niche that he has developed within the corporate department. He draws on the expertise of other partners in the tax and property departments. He advises individual partners within the legal sphere as well as other professional firms on their partnership disputes and agreements, in particular on restrictive covenants. **Clients:** individuals and professional partnerships, in particular solicitors and accountants, but also including surveyors, architects, and veterinary surgeons.

Field Fisher Waterhouse Within the commercial and corporate department, **Colin McArthur**, *("competent and discreet,")* leads a team of one corporate and one tax partner in advising on partnership law. He advises on an assortment of non-contentious partnership issues as well as dealing with the increasing number of contentious partnership exits. If negotiation or mediation fails, he is also able to draw from the litigation department who are experienced in dealing with partnership disputes. **Clients:** accountants, architects and solicitors.

Finers Stephens Innocent *"Nanny to the legal profession"* **Michael Simmons** advises departing groups of professional partners and in doing so *"attempts to find a commercial solution"* to a legal problem. He also draws on the expertise of a partner in the commercial department who specialises in negotiating partnership and shareholder disputes. The firm advises on the full range of partnership issues including formations, mergers, retirements and dissolutions. **Clients:** accountants; solicitors; patent agents.

Ralph Hume Garry **Stephen Ralph** is the stand-out figure at a firm which deals most notably with contentious aspects of partnership law. Acting for a range of surveyors, farming clients and other commercial concerns, his team has acted on a number of arbitrations to settle partnership disputes **Clients:** surveyors and other professionals.

Wright Son & Pepper Senior partner and experienced commercial lawyer **Nicholas Wright** tackles an increasing amount of regulatory and partnership work, particularly now that David Morgan has left the firm. Wright advises on a variety of contentious and non-contentious issues, such as the formation, dissolution and alteration of partnerships, whilst dealing with the discipline and regulation of the practice as well as partnership aspects. **Clients:** solicitors, accountants, surveyors, architects, landscape architects.

Linklaters A general corporate partner, **Richard Godden**'s particular expertise in partnership law has developed from working with multinational professional services organisations. His international structuring of professional partnerships stems from his work in cross-border M&A and other international contractual issues. He frequently draws from a cross-departmental group of partners, including partners from the tax and employment departments. Advised Ernst & Young on the migration of a number of their UK partners to Cap Gemini. **Clients:** accountants.

Slaughter and May Corporate partner **Jeff Triggs** advises major professionals and accounting firms on their partnership agreements as well as on mergers and constitutional issues. He also frequently draws on expertise from five other commercial partners handling partnership work including specialist tax advice. Acted for Price Waterhouse on its merger with Coopers & Lybrand to form PricewaterhouseCoopers, and recently redrafted the Bacon & Woodrow partnership deed. **Clients:** big five accountancy firms; leading actuaries including Bacon & Woodrow; other large professional and commercial partnerships.

THE SOUTH & THAMES VALLEY

PARTNERSHIP • The South & Thames Valley	Ptnrs
❶ **Lester Aldridge** Bournemouth	2
Linnells Oxford	1
Mundays Esher	1
Rawlison & Butler Crawley	1
Rodgers Horsley Whitemans Guildford	3

LEADING INDIVIDUALS	
❶ **IRVING David** Mundays	**MISCAMPBELL Andrew** Linnells
WHITEMAN Martyn Rodgers Horsley Whitemans	

Within each band, firms are listed alphabetically. *See **Profiles** on page 610*

Lester Aldridge The team deals with both contentious and non-contentious matters, and is particularly well known for advising and resolving disputes amongst medical practices, notably such matters as valuation of medical premises. **Clients:** medical practitioners, trading partnerships; lawyers, accountants.

Linnells **Andrew Miscampbell** is the leading name at the firm which deals primarily with non-contentious matters, although the firm deals with several partnership matters arising from the commercial department. **Clients:** professional and commercial partnerships, including medical and veterinary.

Mundays **David Irving** draws on four commercial partners including specialist tax and insolvency practitioners for non contentious advice, and has the back-up of a four partner litigation department when needed. **Clients:** solicitors, architects and accountants and GPs.

Rawlison & Butler The firm's commercial litigation department handles partnership disputes. The firm is well known for acting in the medical sector, and has niche expertise in incorporation issues. **Clients:** mainly professional practices including medical practitioners.

Rodgers Horsley Whitemans **Martyn Whiteman** spends much of his time advising dental partnerships and draws on one other partner for his non-contentious advice. Acts on all aspects of partnership, from formation to dissolution. **Clients:** dental practices.

SOUTH WEST

PARTNERSHIP • South West	Ptnrs
❶ **Burges Salmon** Bristol	2
TLT Solicitors Bristol	2
Veale Wasbrough Bristol	3
❷ **Osborne Clarke OWA** Bristol	2
❸ **Bond Pearce** Bristol	1

LEADING INDIVIDUALS	
❶ **BELLEW Derek** Veale Wasbrough	**LLEWELYN EVANS Adrian** Burges Salmon
MAY Philip TLT Solicitors	
❷ **MARSH David** Burges Salmon	**MOULE Jos** Osborne Clarke
STARKS Brian Bond Pearce	

Within each band, firms are listed alphabetically. *See **Profiles** on page 610*

Burges Salmon The firm is particularly known for its expertise in farming partnerships, stemming from its pre-eminent agricultural and landlord and tenant practices. The experienced **David Marsh** and *"litigation wizard"* **Adrian Llewelyn Evans** comprise a formidable spearhead to the practice. **Clients:** lawyers, accountants, surveyors, engineers and farmers.

TLT Solicitors Leading litigator **Philip May** heads a separate partnership unit specialising in GP partnerships, with one litigation and one commercial partner. Particularly esteemed for work on medical partnerships, although the team handles the gamut of professional partnership matters. **Clients:** GPs.

Veale Wasbrough Although best-known for advice on medical partnerships, partner **Derek Bellew** heads a team expert advice for partnerships generally. The team acts for some 200 GP partnerships across the country. The team has acted on a number of successful mediations this year. **Clients:** GPs, architects and solicitors.

Osborne Clarke OWA Mainly handled by two corporate and two litigation partners; the team has a reputation for sorting out particularly acrimonious disputes without recourse to litigation. Also advise on the tax implications of partnerships. **Jos Moule** retains his reputation. **Clients:** mainly professional, but some business partnerships.

Bond Pearce **Brian Starks** is the respected head of a team which principally handles contentious partnership issues, usually acting for individual professionals. Experienced in dealing with partnership disputes, the team successfully obtained a recent freezing order in a law firm dispute. **Clients:** solicitors; accountants; doctors; farmers.

MIDLANDS

PARTNERSHIP • Midlands	Ptnrs
❶ **Hammond Suddards Edge** Birmingham	2
Pinsent Curtis Birmingham	⚐
❷ **Freethcartwright** Nottingham	1

LEADING INDIVIDUALS	
❶ **CHOHAN Baljit** Hammond Suddards Edge	**COOKE David** Pinsent Curtis
❷ **THOROGOOD Paul** Freethcartwright	

Within each band, firms are listed alphabetically. *See **Profiles** on page 610*

⚐ *Figures unavailable at time of going to press.*

Hammond Suddards Edge Renowned for dealing with both contentious and non-contentious issues, the team is headed by the *"sensible"* **Baljit Chohan**. The team advises on drawing up partnership agreements, as well as their dissolution. Recently advised a law firm on a new partnership deed to take into account new business ventures. **Clients:** professionals, including law firms.

Pinsent Curtis A new entry this year, the firm is said to have had a *"prolific"* year. The *"constructive"* **David Cooke** heads a team which advises on partnership agreements, drafts and interpretation, and acts more for groups than individuals. **Clients:** Solicitors; architects; surveyors.

Freethcartwright Acting on partnership matters arising from mergers of professional practices, the firm maintains its regional reputation. **Paul Thorogood**'s experience in this area is beyond dispute. The team acts on contentious and non-contentious matters, and has noted expertise on tax implications. **Clients:** solicitors; accountants, architects.

THE NORTH

PARTNERSHIP • The North	Ptnrs
❶ **Cuff Roberts** Liverpool	2
❷ **Kershaw Abbott** Manchester	1
Mace & Jones Manchester	2
❸ **Hill Dickinson** Liverpool	2
❹ **Cobbetts** Manchester	1

LEADING INDIVIDUALS	
❶ **TWEMLOW Tony** Cuff Roberts	
❷ **JUMP Graeme** Mace & Jones	**KERSHAW Anne** Kershaw Abbott
❸ **QUINN Michael** Hill Dickinson	
❹ **WALTON Paul** Hill Dickinson	

Within each band, firms are listed alphabetically *See **Profiles** on page 610*

Cuff Roberts The leading firm in the region also has the area's most recognisable partnership lawyer. **Tony Twemlow** is *"one of the doyens of the game,"* and heads a team which acts on both partnership disputes and non-contentious matters. Recently acted for a firm of accountants on an alleged expulsion from the partnership. **Clients:** professional groups.

Kershaw Abbott *"A frightening litigator,"* **Anne Kershaw**'s reputation continues to inspire fear and admiration. The firm acts almost exclusively in the contentious sphere, mainly advising individuals. Successfully mediated a partnership expulsion this year. **Clients:** solicitors; accountants and surveyors.

Mace & Jones Senior Partner and insolvency expert **Graeme Jump** has a well-established reputation in the North. Particularly noted for advice on medical partnerships, the group is experienced in mediation and litigation. **Clients:** GPs, solicitors and accountants.

Hill Dickinson The firm handles both contentious and non-contentious work for a client base of professional partnerships. **Michael Quinn** and **Paul Walton** are both highly respected practitioners. **Clients:** solicitors; accountants; dentists; GPs.

Cobbetts Possessing a strong reputation for advisory work to medical partnerships, the team also deals with drafting commercial and professional partnership agreements in mainly non-contentious matters. **Clients:** medical partnerships.

SCOTLAND

PARTNERSHIP • Scotland	Ptnrs
❶ **Dundas & Wilson CS** Edinburgh, Glasgow	3
❷ **Maclay Murray & Spens** Glasgow	2
McGrigor Donald Edinburgh, Glasgow	2
❸ **Burness** Edinburgh	⚐
Robson McLean WS Edinburgh	1
❹ **Bell & Scott WS** Edinburgh	1
Fyfe Ireland WS Edinburgh	1

LEADING INDIVIDUALS
❶ **STUBBS Ian** Maclay Murray & Spens

Within each band, firms are listed alphabetically. *See **Profiles** on page 610*

⚐ *Figures unavailable at time of going to press.*

Dundas & Wilson CS Limited liability partnerships (LLPs) are a speciality of the team, which deals mainly with the non-contentious, while contentious matters are dealt with by the litigation department. Has a notable niche in dealing with Lloyd's members and investment companies on partnership issues. **Clients:** Lloyd's members.

Maclay Murray & Spens Increasingly active in advising on corporate limited partnerships, the team is headed by **Ian Stubbs**. The firm deals with businesses rather than individuals, and acts on both partnership formations and disputes. LLPs are also taking a higher profile among the firm's caseload. **Clients:** architects; surveyors; dentists.

McGrigor Donald Renowned for acting on limited partnerships and using partnership structures for investment funds, notably on property issues. However, the firm is active on both contentious and non-contentious matters. **Clients:** professional partnerships.

Burness *"Thriving"* practice which advises on partnership dissolutions, formations and disputes, as well as the establishment of limited partnerships for use as fund vehicles. The team advised on the establishment of a £1 billion investment fund for Standard Life, structured using Scottish limited partnerships. **Clients:** limited and professional partnerships.

Robson Mclean WS Advise on partnership formation and dissolution, and still recognised as a player in Scotland, although there is no specialist department here. Act on both contentious and non-contentious matters. **Clients:** professional partnerships.

Bell & Scott WS Partnership matters stem largely from non-contentious issues, and the team has advised a US law firm on a client's investment in Scotland through a limited partnership. The team also advises commercial clients on the use of limited partnership for joint venture. **Clients:** solicitors; surveyors; accountants.

Fyfe Ireland WS The firm retains a reputation for advisory work for medical partnerships, although it has also acted for a range of Scottish commercial partnerships. **Clients:** medical, hotel and farming partnerships.

NORTHERN IRELAND

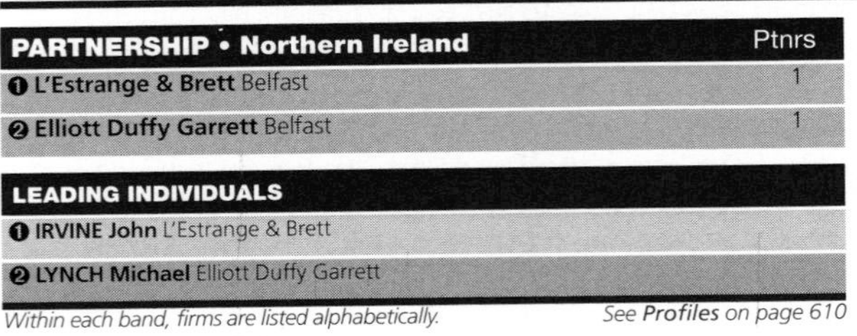

PARTNERSHIP • Northern Ireland	Ptnrs
❶ **L'Estrange & Brett** Belfast	1
❷ **Elliott Duffy Garrett** Belfast	1

LEADING INDIVIDUALS
❶ **IRVINE John** L'Estrange & Brett
❷ **LYNCH Michael** Elliott Duffy Garrett

Within each band, firms are listed alphabetically. *See **Profiles** on page 610*

L'Estrange & Brett Advise on new partnership agreements and have a fine reputation for acting on joint ventures. **John Irvine** is a noted practitioner. The team has recently acted on a petition to wind up a retail chain partnership. **Clients:** solicitors, architects.

Elliott Duffy Garrett Almost exclusively focused on contentious matters, the firm's principal reputation still rests on the shoulders of the respected **Michael Lynch**. **Clients:** professional partnerships.

MEDICAL PARTNERSHIPS - NATIONAL

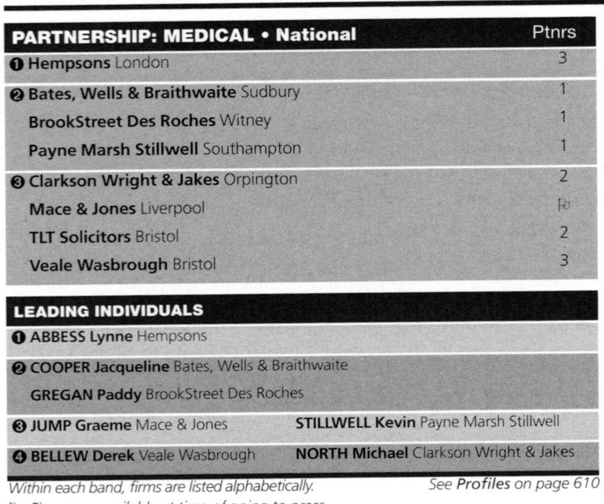

PARTNERSHIP: MEDICAL • National	Ptnrs
❶ **Hempsons** London	3
❷ **Bates, Wells & Braithwaite** Sudbury	1
BrookStreet Des Roches Witney	1
Payne Marsh Stillwell Southampton	1
❸ **Clarkson Wright & Jakes** Orpington	2
Mace & Jones Liverpool	⚐
TLT Solicitors Bristol	2
Veale Wasbrough Bristol	3

LEADING INDIVIDUALS	
❶ **ABBESS Lynne** Hempsons	
❷ **COOPER Jacqueline** Bates, Wells & Braithwaite	
GREGAN Paddy BrookStreet Des Roches	
❸ **JUMP Graeme** Mace & Jones	**STILLWELL Kevin** Payne Marsh Stillwell
❹ **BELLEW Derek** Veale Wasbrough	**NORTH Michael** Clarkson Wright & Jakes

Within each band, firms are listed alphabetically. *See **Profiles** on page 610*

⚐ *Figures unavailable at time of going to press.*

Hempsons *"Committed"* **Lynne Abbess** is widely recognised to have cornered the market in medical partnership, be it a contentious or non-contentious matter. Working closely with the GPC at the BMA, her strong property and commercial background gives her an understanding of the regulations and law peculiar to medical partnerships. She advises Health Authorities on the formation of the new GP Primary Care Groups. Simon Barnes has now retired. **Clients:** GPs and other professionals.

Bates, Wells & Braithwaite **Jacqueline Cooper** continues to be regarded as the major reason for the firm's leading reputation, acting on partnership formations and disputes for both GPs and dentists. **Clients:** medical partnerships; general commercial partnerships.

BrookStreet Des Roches **Paddy Gregan**, an expert on partnership finance, dissolution and incorporation, maintains his high profile at a firm which is best known for acting for GPs. **Clients:** GPs; professional partnerships

Payne Marsh Stillwell Tend to act for partnerships as opposed to individual partners, with niche strength in advising medical and dental partnerships. **Kevin Stillwell** is the stand-out practitioner here. **Clients:** many clients are doctors and dentists.

Clarkson Wright & Jakes Principally active in non-contentious matters, the firm, headed by the experienced **Michael North**, drafts partnership deeds on behalf of GPs and other professionals. The team is also active on commercial property matters pertaining to partnership law. **Clients:** doctors; dentists; surveyors; solicitors.

Mace & Jones See The North editorial.

TLT Solicitors See the South West editorial.

Veale Wasbrough See the South West editorial.

LEADERS IN PARTNERSHIP

ABBESS, Lynne M.
Hempsons, London (020) 7836 0011
Partner and Head of the Professional Services Department.
Specialisation: Principal area of practice is partnership law, encompassing advice on partnership formation, disputes, termination and associated property matters (in particular NHS GP's cost rent schemes and other surgery developments). Acts for doctors, dentists, solicitors, accountants and other professional partnerships. Advises the BMA/GPC on policy issues relating to partnerships and surgery developments affecting all NHS GPs in England and Wales. Author of chapters on partnership in 'The Law and General Practice' and 'When Partners Fall Out' and numerous articles in a variety of professional publications. Co-author of 'Primary Healthcare Premises: An Expert Guide'. Frequent lecturer on partnership issues. Legal correspondent for Medeconomics and regular contributor to the Journal 'GP'.
Prof. Memberships: Law Society. Founder member of Association of Partnership Practitioners.
Career: Qualified 1982 with *Hempsons*. Partner since 1985.

BELLEW, Derek J.
Veale Wasbrough, Bristol (0117) 925 2020
See under Corporate Finance, p.242

CHOHAN, Baljit
Hammond Suddards Edge, Birmingham (0121) 200 2001
See under Corporate Finance, p.245

COOKE, David C.
Pinsent Curtis, Birmingham (0121) 200 1050
david.c.cook@pinsents.com
Specialisation: Partner in Corporate Department. Partnership work including drafting and advising on partnership deeds, partner disputes and retirements, mergers, acquisitions and disposals of professional partnership practices. Clients include a major national firm of chartered accountants, a major national firm of property advisors, accountants, solicitors, actuaries and architects.
Career: Manchester University. Qualified 1961. Partner at *Pinsent Curtis* (then *Pinsent & Co*) since 1969 and Senior Partner 1987-1994.

COOPER, Jacqueline
Bates, Wells & Braithwaite, Sudbury (01787) 880440
solicitors@bateswell-sudbury.co.uk
Recently appointed Commercial Partner.
Specialisation: Specialises in Partnership Law acting in both partnership formations and disputes. Most of her experience has been gained acting for doctors and dentists and also for other professionals including solicitors, accountants, architects and surveyors. With her move to Suffolk, her client base includes doctors and dentists, locally and nationally, and is extended to include farmers and other business clients for whom she provides commercial and property advice. Advising also on clients for whom she provides commercial and property advice. Advising also on related property ownership issues, her background being in property law which she continues to practise enabling her to draw on that experience in the drafting of partnership and other commercial documentation and settlement of partnership disputes.
Prof. Memberships: Law Society. Founder member of Association of Partnership Practitioners.
Career: Lectures to GPs on property and partnership issues and contributes to journals and magazines including 'Doctor' and British Dental Health Foundation – Word of Mouth Year Book on similar matters. Qualified 1987. Worked as an assistant solicitor with *Hempsons* from September 1987 to January 1992 when made a partner. Left in January 1999 to take up her current position as Commercial Partner with *Bates, Wells & Braithwaite.*
Personal: Born 17th April 1962. Lives outside Sudbury, Suffolk.

FLECK, Richard J.H.
Herbert Smith, London (020) 7374 8000
richard.fleck@herbertsmith.com
See under Competition/Anti-trust, p.180

FOX, Ronald D.
Fox Williams, London (020) 7628 2000
rdfox@foxwilliams.co.uk
Specialisation: Main areas of practice are employment law and partnership law. Specialises in advising partnerships and partners in professional firms. Regularly deals with partnership disputes involving the departure of partners. Chairman of the multi-disciplinary Association of Partnership Practitioners. Chairman of *Fox Williams'* Partnership Law Group. Past Master of the City of London Solicitors' Company, Past Chairman of the Practice Management Sub-Committee of the IBA; Past Member of the Law Society Law Management Section Advisory Group. Frequently broadcasts and is the author of numerous articles in the professional and national press on employment, partnership and management topics.
Prof. Memberships: IBA, Law Society, City of London Law Society, Employment Lawyers' Association.
Career: Qualified 1972. Senior Partner at *Fox Williams.*

GODDEN, Richard
Linklaters (A member firm of Linklaters & Alliance), London (020) 7456 3610
richard.godden@linklaters.com
Partner. Corporate Department.
Specialisation: Has wide experience both in general corporate advisory work and corporate transactions. Advises a wide range of corporate clients and merchant and investment banks in connection with public mergers and takeovers, the establishment of joint ventures, private merger and acquisition transactions, flotations, other corporate equity fund raising, and advises corporations of various sizes in relation to their on-going affairs (e.g. issues connected with general meetings, scrip dividend schemes, removal of directors, etc.)

GOLD, David L.
Herbert Smith, London (020) 7374 8000
See under Litigation (Commercial), p.561

GREGAN, Paddy
BrookStreet Des Roches, Witney (01993) 771616
Specialisation: All aspects of business law including company acquisitions and disposals, corporate finance, partnership and joint ventures and company restructuring. Also advising on insolvency law. Particularly regarded for his work on behalf of professional partnerships and individual partners. Acts for a wide range of corporate clients, institutions and professionals.
Prof. Memberships: Law Society, Thames Valley Commercial Lawyers Association, Association of Partnership Practitioners.
Career: Qualified in 1987. With *Linnells* from 1988 to 1997, as a partner from 1990. Joined *BrookStreet Des Roches* in 1997 as a partner.
Personal: Born 23.6.61. Educated at West Park Grammar School, St. Helens. Leisure interests include all kinds of sport, mountains and spending time with his family.

IRVINE, John W.
L'Estrange & Brett, Belfast (028) 9023 0426
john.irvine@lestrangeandbrett.com
See under Corporate Finance, p.254

IRVING, David P.
Mundays, Esher (01372) 809000
david.irving@mundays.co.uk
Partner in the Corporate and Commercial Departments.
Specialisation: Main areas of practice include partnership, commercial agreements, sale and purchase of companies and aviation. Partnership: drafting deeds, advising on deeds, incorporation, departure of partners, advise wide range of professional partnerships.
Prof. Memberships: Director of Fulham Legal Advice Centre; Member of Aviation Club of Great Britain; Chair of Governors at All Saint's School, Putney.
Career: Educated at Downside School and Exeter University. Qualified in 1984. Partner in *Seddons* before joining *Mundays* as a partner in 1998.
Personal: Born 1 November 1958. Married with two children. Leisure interests include wine, walking and cycling.

JUMP, G.K.
Mace & Jones, Manchester (0161) 236 2244
See under Insolvency/Corporate Recovery, p.479

KERSHAW, Anne
Kershaw Abbott, Manchester (0161) 839 0998
mail@kershaw-abbott.co.uk
Specialisation: Practises in the field of commercial dispute resolution with particular emphasis on professional partnership disputes, professional liability and commercial and construction disputes.
Prof. Memberships: Member of Association of Partnership Practitioners; Secretary Manchester Professional Forum; Past President Manchester Law Society; Member of Society of Construction Lawyers; Member of CEDR.
Career: Admitted 1975. Practised in North West all working life. Co-founder of *Kershaw Abbott* as niche practice in 1991. Appointed Tax Commissioner in 1995.
Personal: Lives in Ribble Valley with judicial husband and son. Music lover and devoted gardener.

LACE, John D.
Bristows, London (020) 7400 8000
john.lace@bristows.com
Partner in Company Department.
Specialisation: Main areas of practice are company, corporate finance, partnership and charity law. Extensive experience in mergers, acquisitions, corporate reorganisations and joint ventures, acting particularly for UK and US corporations. Has advised in relation to many partnership agreements, mergers, demergers and disputes, particularly in the accountancy and legal professions. He advises several professional institutions and other learned societies on their corporate and regulatory affairs.
Prof. Memberships: Law Society.
Career: Qualified in 1973 after articles at *Meade-King & Co* in Bristol. Joined *Bristows* in 1974 and became a Partner in 1978.
Personal: Born 11th September 1947. Educated at Malvern College 1961-66. Enjoys sailing, gardening and photography, and is a member of MCC. Lives in London.

LINSELL, Richard
Rowe & Maw, London (020) 7782 8806
Specialisation: Partnership and commercial law. Acts for leading partnerships in all areas of professional practice. Work undertaken ranges from mergers, demergers and strategic alliances, through partnership defections and a wide range of partnership disputes, to partner assessment and remuneration schemes and regulatory and disciplinary issues. Remains closely involved in the LLP movement. Lectures and writes on these and other professional topics. Also regularly advising on the adoption of improved partnership agreements with particular emphasis on partner retention, profit sharing and succession issues. He is also a CEDR Accredited Mediator.
Prof. Memberships: IBA, APP.
Career: Jesus College, Cambridge 1966-69; Articled *Rowe & Maw*; Partner 1976.

LLEWELYN EVANS, Adrian
Burges Salmon, Bristol (0117) 939 2272
adrian.llewelyn-evans@burges-salmon.com
Specialisation: Broadly based heavyweight litigation and arbitration with a bias towards technical subject matter, often with an international element. Recent work includes substantial product liability cases for insurers; corporate finance claims; professional indemnity and liability claims on engineering equipment failure in the defence, marine and aircraft industries; partnership disputes of all description; and a flourishing practice as a mediator.
Prof. Memberships: Registered mediator CEDR and ADR Group, FCI Arb, Law Society, Bristol Mercantile Court Users Committee, Official Referee Solicitors' Association.
Career: Trained at *Linklaters*, qualifying in 1979 and joining *Burges Salmon* in 1982, becoming a partner in 1984.
Personal: University College of Durham 1973-76. Leisure interests include gardening, walking, fishing and music.

LYNCH, Michael P.
Elliott Duffy Garrett, Belfast (028) 9024 5034

MARSH, David
Burges Salmon, Bristol (0117) 939 2288
david.marsh@burges-salmon.com
See under Corporate Finance, p.258

MAY, Philip N S
TLT Solicitors, Bristol (0117) 917 7777
pmay@TLTSolicitors.com
Specialisation: Deals with contentious issues for partnerships. Has recently acted as a Court-Appointed receiver for a dissolving partnership at the request of a major law firm in the UK. Has also acted as an expert in relation to professional partnership issues. Specialises in shareholder and boardroom disputes and professional partnership breakdowns. For biographical details see insolvency section.

MAYER, Stephen D.
Reynolds Porter Chamberlain, London (020) 7242 2877
Specialisation: Head of Commercial Litigation. A substantial and increasing area of his practice consists of advice on partnership disputes and their resolution, including advising on restrictive covenants in partnership agreements. Clients include professional and commercial partnerships. He also acts in employment disputes.
Prof. Memberships: Law Society; International Bar Association; Media Society.
Career: Educated at St Paul's School and Oriel College, Oxford. Qualified in 1974. Partner of *Reynolds Porter Chamberlain* since 1977.
Personal: Married with three children. Leisure interests include erratic golf and slightly less erratic tennis.

MCARTHUR, Colin
Field Fisher Waterhouse, London (020) 7861 4000
Partner in Company and Commercial Department.
Specialisation: Handles all aspects of corporate and partnership law, including establishment, mergers and acquisitions, sales, retirements, dissolutions and joint ventures. Also deals with commercial contracts. Co-author of 'A Director's Guide – Duties, Liabilities and Company Law' (1990), and contributor to 'A Directors Guide to Accounting and Auditing' (1991).
Prof. Memberships: Law Society, I.B.A, Institute of Directors.
Career: Qualified in 1969, having joined *Waterhouse & Co* (now *Field Fisher Waterhouse)* in 1967. Became a Partner in 1974.
Personal: Born 5th November 1944. Educated at Fettes College 1958-63 and Cambridge University 1963-66. Leisure interests include golf and aphorisms. Lives in London.

MISCAMPBELL, Andrew
Linnells, Oxford (01865) 248607
afm@linnells.co.uk
Specialisation: Partnership, especially professional practices including medical practices. Commercial Property. Mediation.
Prof. Memberships: Law Society. Association of Partnership Practitioners.
Career: Qualified 1985; *Anstey Sargent and Probert* 1988-94 (Partner 1990-94); *Linnells* 1995 to date (Partner). Trained Mediator 1993.
Personal: Born 18 June 1959. Educated at St Edwards, Oxford and Nottingham University. Interests: golf, hockey, family. Active church member.

MOULE, Jos
Osborne Clarke OWA, Bristol (0117) 917 4218
jos.moule@osborneclark.com
Specialisation: Advises on all aspects of partnership law, particularly professional practices. Deals regularly with partnership disputes, where his approach is to encourage settlement without resort to formal litigation. Has also advised on partnership mergers and strategic alliances
Career: Qualified at *Osborne Clarke* in 1992 and became a partner in 1998.
Personal: Educated at Bristol University. Born 1960.

NORTH, Michael A.
Clarkson Wright & Jakes, Orpington (01689) 887887
Specialisation: Handles medical partnerships in Kent and the South East with a particular emphasis on formation and property matters. Acted for a practice under the Personal Medical Services pilot scheme. Assisted with publications for medical practitioners and their accontants. Has contributed articles to journals and local medical committee publications. Has addressed GPs on partnership and associated property issues. Also acts for other professional partnerships generally.
Prof. Memberships: Law Society; Notaries Society; Association of Partnership Practitioners.
Career: Educated at Oriel College, Oxford. Qualified in 1972 after training with Central London Practice and a period in industry. Private practice in Orpington since 1978; Partner in the following year. Notary Public since 1987.
Personal: Born 1945. Keen squash player; other interests enjoyed include walking, music and literature.

QUINN, Michael J.
Hill Dickinson, Liverpool (0151) 236 5400
Specialisation: Partner in the Commercial Department heading the Private Client Team. Specialist in Partnership Law and advises on estate and tax planning through the use of partnerships, companies and trusts, both onshore and offshore. Speaks fluent French and is the Honorary French Consul in Liverpool.
Prof. Memberships: Society of Estate and Trust Practitioners, Law Society.
Career: Cardinal Allen Grammar School, Liverpool. Christ's College, Cambridge (Latin, Medieval French and Law).
Personal: Art, literature, cinema, opera, current affairs and sport.

RALPH, Stephen
Ralph Hume Garry, London (020) 7831 3737
Specialisation: Senior partner of firm specialising exclusively in litigation, arbitration and dispute resolution. The firm covers the full range of commercial litigation matters specialising in partnership work, in particular solicitors, accountants, surveyors and medical practices. The firm also has particular expertise in insolvency, white collar crime, fraud, asset recovery work and arbitration matters. Sits as an arbitrator.
Prof. Memberships: Member of Insolvency Practitioners Association, Fellow of the Society of Practitioners of Insolvency, Member of the Insolvency Lawyers Association, Fellow of the Chartered Institute of Arbitrators, Founder Member of the Association of Partnership Practitioners.
Career: Qualified in 1975. Articled at *Payne Hicks Beach.* Senior Commercial Litigation Partner at *Payne Hicks Beach* until 1992. From 1992 to 1995 Senior Commercial Litigation Partner at *Boodle Hatfield.* 1995 to date Senior Partner at *Ralph Hume Garry.* Licensed insolvency practitioner.
Personal: Born 7 April 1946. 1971 BA (Law). 1988 Diploma in Insolvency Law and Administration. 1995 Fellow of the Chartered Institute of Arbitrators. Lives in London, Oxfordshire and Paris. Interests include painting, theatre, sport, member of the RAC.

SACKER, Tony
Kingsley Napley, London (020) 7814 1200
tsacker@kingsleynapley.co.uk
Head of Partnership Unit.
Specialisation: Main area of practice is partnership law. Over 20 years experience advising and negotiating in this area. Also deals with charities. Author: "Practical Partnership Agreements" (Jordans).
Prof. Memberships: Association of Partnership Practitioners, City of London Law Society, Westminster Law Society, Association of Charity Lawyers. STEP.
Career: Qualified in 1963. Partner from 1967 at *Egerton Sandler*, which merged with *Kingsley Napley* 1989. Partner at *Kingsley Napley* since 1989. President Westminster Law Society 1987-88.Chairman City of London Law Society 1998 -. Committee Member Association of Partnership Practitioners 1997 -.
Personal: Born 2nd March 1940. Educated at Owens School to 1958. Recreations include doing communal work and improving computer skills. Lives in London.

SIMMONS, Michael D.
Finers Stephens Innocent, London (020) 7323 4000
Partner in Company and Commercial Department.
Specialisation: Handles general company and commercial work, with particular reference to partnership matters. Deals with partnership formation, growth, management and remuneration issues, consultancy advice, disposal of unproductive partners, partnership disputes and dissolution. Acts for partnerships and for individual partners. Also deals with cross border transactions and other international matters, with particular reference to inward investment into the UK. Has a wide overseas clientele. Author of 'An Anatomy of Professional Practice', published by Gazette Publications, and 'Successful Mergers' published by Waterlows. Also many articles published in UK and overseas law journals. Regular speaker at management and marketing conferences for professionals both at home and abroad. Has appeared many times on television and radio as a legal spokesman on various topics. Standard charge out rate £265 per hour.
Prof. Memberships: International Bar Association (Chairman of Committee dealing with Professional Practice and Technology), Law Society, American Bar Association, College of Law Practice Management.
Career: Qualified in 1958. First Class Honours in Law Society Final and Clements Inn Prize. National Service Commission in Secretarial Branch Royal Air Force 1959-61. With *Malkin Cullis & Sumption* 1961-90, as a Partner and as Senior Partner from 1964. Joined *Finers* as a Partner in 1990.
Personal: Born 19th May 1933. Educated at St. Paul's School 1947-52 and Emmanuel College, Cambridge 1952-56 (MA and LLM). Leisure interests include music, (especially jazz), football, cricket, tennis, eating, cooking and travelling. Lives in Highgate and Italy.

STARKS, Brian D.
Bond Pearce, Plymouth (01752) 266633
xbds@bondpearce.com
Partner in the Commercial Litigation Group.
Specialisation: Specialises in partnership litigation and in particular professional partnerships eg. solicitors, accountants, doctors, surveyors and valuers, and family farming partnerships.
Prof. Memberships: Member of the Association of Partnership Practitioners.
Career: Qualified as a solicitor in 1972 with *Bond Pearce*, Plymouth, becoming a partner in 1977.

STILLWELL, Kevin
Payne Marsh Stillwell, Southampton
(023) 8022 3957
Specialisation: Advising GPs (practices and individuals) constitutes the vast majority of his work: partnership formations and restructuring -admissions and retirements- surgery relocation, leasing and building schemes, interpartner disputes. His approach is practical, drawing on extensive experience of general medical practice.
Prof. Memberships: Law Society; Hampshire Law Society; Association of Partnership Practitioners.
Career: LLB Southampton, London articles, qualified 1979, two years with *Ashford Sparkes* in Exeter then relocated to Hampshire in 1981.
Personal: Born 1954. Married with young family. Carriage driving is his main hobby.

STUBBS, Ian M.
Maclay Murray & Spens, Glasgow
(0141) 248 5011
ims@maclaymurrayspens.co.uk
See under Trusts & Personal Tax, p.825

THOROGOOD, Paul
Freethcartwright, Nottingham (0115) 9369 369
paul.thorogood@freethcartwright.co.uk
Specialisation: Commercial contracts and Partnership.
Prof. Memberships: Law Society.
Career: Articled *Hunt Dickins & Willatt* 1980-1982; Partner *Hunt Dickins & Willatt* 1986; Partner *Freeth Cartwright Hunt Dickins* 1994.
Personal: Theatre and sailing.

TRIGGS, Jeff
Slaughter and May, London (020) 7600 1200
Specialisation: General corporate/commercial practice. Recent matters in the past year include the merger of *Price Waterhouse* and *Coopers & Lybrand*, the takeover of the Savoy Group by Blackstone, the renegotiation of the contracts for the automation of post office counters among ICL, the DSS and the Post Office, the takeover of How Group by Tilbury Douglas and the joint venture between the Post Office, TNT Post Group NV and Singapore Post Pte Limited relating to international cross-border mail business.
Prof. Memberships: The Law Society.
Career: Gorleston Grammar School; University College, London (LLB, Hons).
Personal: Leisure interests include playing trombone in a jazz band, sport and keeping fit.

TURNOR, Richard
Allen & Overy, London (020) 7330 3000
Specialisation: Partner who advises professional partners and partnerships, joint venture partnerships, banks and others who deal with partnerships.
Prof. Memberships: Association of Partnership Practitioners (Deputy Chairman), Chairs APP Working Party in limited liability partnerships, member of City of London Law Society Working Party on limited liability Partnerships.
Career: Articled *Allen & Overy*, qualified 1980, Partner 1985.
Personal: Oxford University 1977. Born 1956.

TWEMLOW, W.A.
Cuff Roberts, Liverpool (0151) 237 7777
tony.twemlow@cuffroberts.co.uk
Specialisation: Insolvency, Partnership, Charities and anything with a 'Chancery' ring to it.
Prof. Memberships: Society of Practitioners in Insolvency. Insolvency Lawyers' Association. Association of Partnership Practitioners.
Career: MA (Cantab). Qualified 1968. Assistant and then Partner (1971) in *Cuff Roberts.* Chairman of the Young Solicitors Group of the Law Society (1978). President, Liverpool Law Society (1995). Managing Partner, *Cuff Roberts* 1988-1994.
Personal: Music, Tennis. Married with three children. Lives in Hoylake, Wirral.

WALTON, Paul
Hill Dickinson, Liverpool (0151) 236 5400
Senior Partner of Firm. Member of Commercial and Insurance Litigation Department.
Specialisation: Principal area of practice is professional negligence acting for insurers of architects, surveyors, engineers, accountants, brokers and other professionals. Also plaintiff work against solicitors and some other professionals and advice to insurers generally. Other main areas of practice are partnership (advising on professional partnership disputes) and Libel. Important cases handled include Liverpool L.R.A.T.I v Sir Frederick Gibberd & Others (Liverpool R.C. Cathedral litigation); Christian Brothers v Eagle Star & Stephensons, Offshore Reinsurers PCI v Evandale and Others (international libel), Rimmer v Storey (political libel action) and Comer v St. Patrick (Occupiers Liability). Clients include major insurers, reinsurers and underwriters, dioceses and religious orders as well as companies and partnerships.
Prof. Memberships: Law Society, Official Referees Solicitors Society, Association of Lawyers for Defence of the Unborn.
Career: Qualified 1969. Became a Partner at *Hill Dickinson Davis Campbell* in 1972, Management Partner in 1989 and Senior Partner in 1994. Member of Board of Faculty of Law, Liverpool University, 1996-present. Currently Senior Partner *Hill Dickinson.*
Personal: Born 18th May 1945. Educated at Exeter University 1963-66 (Lloyd Parry Prize in Constitutional Law and Bracton Law Society Prize) and The College of Law, Guildford 1966-67. Member of Council of the Catholic Union; Knight of the Equestrian Order of St Gregory; Knight of the Holy Sepulchre of Jerusalem. Activities outside the law include herb growing, philately, antiques, opera, shooting and anti-abortion causes. Resides Hoghton, near Preston.

WHITEMAN, Martyn
Rodgers Horsley Whitemans, Guildford
(01483) 302000
martin.whiteman@rhw.co.uk
Specialisation: Has extensive experience in acting for professional and commercial partnerships. A large part of his work is devoted to medical partnerships, acting for partnerships of doctors and dental and veterinary surgeons. Advises on the many structural and management issues facing partnerships, including the introduction of partners, dissolution, and retirement. Is a regular contributor to various professional journals.
Prof. Memberships: Law Society, Chairman of the Association of Service Providers to Dentists Limited.
Career: Qualified in 1970. Became a partner of *Whiteman and Packer* in 1973. Currently Senior Partner of *Rodgers Horsley Whitemans.*
Personal: Born 1946. Married with four children. Active church member in Guildford. Other interests include walking, sailing, art and music.

WILLIAMS, Christine J.
Fox Williams, London (020) 7628 2000
Partner in Corporate Department.
Specialisation: Within the context of her corporate work, has extensive experience in the area of professional partnerships. Work has included drafting partnership deeds, restructuring partnerships, negotiating mergers of firms, advising on and implementing the incorporation of partnerships. Has also undertaken much work in the area of partnership disputes, including negotiating the departure of partners. Member of the working party of the Association of Partnership Practitioners which made representations to the Government on the proposed legislation for limited liability partnerships. Has written and spoken extensively on partnership law.
Prof. Memberships: Law Society, City of London Law Society, International Bar Association, Association of Partnership Practitioners.
Career: Qualified in 1977. Partner at *Oppenheimers* 1981-88. Formed and joined *Fox Williams* as a Partner in 1989.
Personal: Born 15th February 1953. Educated at St Anne's College, Oxford 1971-74. Leisure interests include theatre and cinema. Lives in Buckinghamshire.

WRIGHT, Nicholas J.
Wright Son & Pepper, London (020) 7242 5473
Head of Partnership and Professional Department.
Specialisation: Main area of practice is partnership law. Advises on partnership creation, disputes and dissolutions, including interventions and practice management of other firms. Member of the Solicitors Assistance Scheme and solicitor member of Defendants' Friends (ICA). Has considerable commercial experience and acts for both UK and overseas corporations.
Prof. Memberships: Law Society. Holborn Law Society, Association of Partnership Practitioners.
Career: Qualified in 1970, having joined *Wright Son & Pepper* in 1960. Became a Partner in 1979.
Personal: Born 2nd February 1943. Educated at Charterhouse 1956-60.

PENSIONS

London: 614; Thames Valley: 617; South West: 617; Wales: 617; Midlands: 618; East Anglia: 618; North West: 619; North East: 619; Scotland: 620; *Profiles*: 621

RESEARCH APPROVED BY BMRB: *For this edition,* Chambers' *researchers conducted 6083 interviews – 4408 with law firms, 598 with barristers and 1077 with clients.*

The validity of the research was scrutinised by BMRB International, who audited both the methodology and the results at our offices in July 2000. They interviewed Chambers' *researchers and cross-checked sample interviews. Details of the audit appear on page 7.*

LEADING IN-HOUSE LAWYERS

Mark MCKEOWN, Litigation Counsel UK & Europe, *William Mercer*

Val VARDY, Principal, *Towers Perrin*

Mark McKeown is known to be *"very able"* and is supported by a *"strong team."* **Val Vardy** is *"respected for her knowledge of the industry and the law."* She is well recommended for being *"very competent,"* especially on the technical side.

In-House lawyers profiles: page 1177

LONDON

Freshfields Bruckhaus Deringer *"A competent, energetic focused practice – going great guns."* Still seen to be dominated by transactional work, the firm has noted cross-border expertise. The firm's reputation for academic pre-eminence owes much to the reputations of their three well known leaders. Star performer, the *"colourful and charismatic"* Practice Head, **Kenneth Dierden** is *"a good public face for the firm"* and *"the man to watch."* With *"tremendous enthusiasm for the subject,"* **David Pollard** *"has a compendious knowledge of case law."* Described as *"a dog with a bone"* in negotiations, **Daniel Schaffer** is felt to be an *"astute"* practitioner. Acting for Hewlett Packard in its demerger in over 40 countries involving working out structural applications in all jurisdictions in conjunction with local advisors. **Clients:** Railways Pension Scheme; Hewlett Packard; Scottish Widows.

Linklaters This *"fully rounded department"* has *"expertise on all aspects."* Acts for major corporates and trustees of large schemes. Seen as *"more cohesive"* under **Ruth Goldman**'s *"energetic"* leadership, the team has *"gone from strength to strength with the Alliance."* Among the firm's *"extremely talented players"* are **Tim Cox** *("the best there" – "brilliant, clear, concise, and one of the brightest boys on the circuit")* and **Claire Petheram** *("you know where you are with her – no obfuscation.")* The team acted for National Power plc before the Court of Appeal in a case concerning the arrangements made by National Power and National Grid for dealing with surpluses in the Electricity Supply Pension Scheme. **Clients:** British Coal Staff Superannuation Scheme; BP Amoco; Diageo.

Rowe & Maw *"No nonsense, practical people." "A pretty steady year"* for a practice which still has a considerable reputation. This *"all service"* pensions practice has a distinct niche in stand alone work. Noted for having *"a lot of good historic clients,"* comprising mainly employers and trustees of very large occupational pensions schemes. Some query whether they have adequate succession planning in light of their high partner to assistant ratio, perceived lack of expansion and ultra-seniority of **Stuart James**. *"An old hand and canny operator – unbeatable in a pitch"* he is responsible for having *"laid the foundations for the practice,"* and although seen less these days is *"still a first rate lawyer." "Analytical"* **Andrew White** is *"in the premier league in terms of technical competence"* and *"sparky"* **Anna Rogers** has *"an acute appreciation of things."* Acted for P&O on the proposed flotation and private sale of Bovis to Lend Lease, and for Bovis in setting up a new UK Pension Scheme for 1500 members. **Clients:** BG (part of British Gas); British Steel; P&O; Reed Elsevier.

Sacker & Partners Still *"making good business by being a specialist pensions firm – things are going well."* Their popular ethos is reflected in their *"user-friendly, value for money"* approach. Seen as *"a good solid animal for the UK market,"* they are *"wonderful for scheme advice work"* and a safe option for referral work. Perceived to be *"growing by the day"* with strongly acknowledged depth of senior experience although some are not altogether convinced they have the same standard in their juniors. Ex-Chairman of APL **Mark Greenlees** is *"genial and sensible."* **Ian Pittaway** *"used to be Mr Pensions"* but has a lower profile these days while **Jonathan Seres** is *"seen as one of the greybeards – his experience is invaluable."* With his *"nice, laid-back style,"* **Peter Docking** *"delivers advice in a user-friendly way."* Moving down *"slightly understated"* **Peter Lester** is less well-known but *"has a bunch of really good clients,"* whereas moving up *"effective operator"* **Sarah Tier** *"has a clear idea of what's going on."* New entry into the tables **Chris Close** is *"sound and very practical."* The team acted on the pensions aspects of the merger of GEC's defence interests with British Aerospace. **Clients:** Trustee of Electricity Supply Pension Scheme; National Australia Group Pensions Common Investment Fund; Express Newspapers plc.

Allen & Overy Widely perceived as primarily a *"respectable transaction-driven"* practice. Appearing to be *"under-resourced,"* the firm is possibly over-reliant on *"the master"* **Derek Sloan**. Although as *"superb quality as ever – he has a total focus with a lovely, laid-back but clear style,"* he remains *"low profile"* and often *"almost impossible to contact."* The firm acted for ICI in disposal of its Teesside Utilities and Services Business to Enron. **Clients:** ICI; United News & Media; Queens Moat Houses plc.

Clifford Chance *"Pre-eminent transactionally,"* the team is best known for big-ticket international work. Act for FTSE 100 companies across a range of sectors, the majority being financial institutions, investment banks and private equity product providers. *"Self-deprecating"* **Nick Sherwin** is *"the man to go to for a transaction – he never makes a mistake"* and **Helen Cox** can be both *"commercial and thoughtful."* The team acted for the Bank of New York on the pensions aspects of its acquisition of RBS Trust Bank. **Clients:** British Energy; Safeway; Whitbread.

Lovells *"A first rate practice"* with an *"old blue-blooded pukka image."* Its wide-ranging client base is dominated by blue-chip companies but also includes smaller clients such as arts based charities. Handles some pro bono work. The team is said to have settled down, and works well together under **Jane Samsworth**'s leadership, following previous manpower changes. Appointed this year as president elect of the SPC, she is *"one of the most charming people in the pensions world."* Seen less these days, **Russell Strachan** is *"a shadowy figure who was the stuff of legend" – "very cool and collected,"* while *"new force in the land"* **Stephen Ito** is *"a good driver, very energetic and very focused – a powerhouse."* Moving down, low profile **John Pearson** *"deals with things in a business-like way – no messing around."* Acted on major reorganisation of the PO Pension Scheme including establishment of new DC arrangement. **Clients:** The Post Office; Barclays Bank; Ford.

PENSIONS • London	Ptnrs	Assts
❶ Freshfields Bruckhaus Deringer	7	28
Linklaters	4	20
Rowe & Maw	7	7
Sacker & Partners	16	15
❷ Allen & Overy	3	14
Clifford Chance	2	10
Lovells	4	10
Nabarro Nathanson	7	15
Slaughter and May	1	12
❸ Baker & McKenzie	2	8
CMS Cameron McKenna	2	6
Travers Smith Braithwaite	2	6
❹ Biddle	5	5
❺ Eversheds	4	5
Hammond Suddards Edge	4	10
Herbert Smith	1	5
Simmons & Simmons	3	2
❻ DLA	⚐	⚐

LEADING INDIVIDUALS	
✪ **BENNETT Philip** Slaughter and May	**COX Tim** Linklaters
DIERDEN Kenneth Freshfields Bruckhaus	**SLOAN Derek** Allen & Overy
STANNARD Paul Travers Smith Braithwaite	
❶ **ARTHUR Hugh** Macfarlanes	**GOLDMAN Ruth** Linklaters
GREENLEES Mark Sacker & Partners	**JAMES Stuart** Rowe & Maw
PITTAWAY Ian Sacker & Partners	**POLLARD David** Freshfields Bruckhaus
QUARRELL John Nabarro Nathanson	**SERES Jonathan** Sacker & Partners
SHERWIN Nick Clifford Chance	**WEST Robert** Baker & McKenzie
WHITE Andrew Rowe & Maw	
❷ **BENNEY Belinda** Field Fisher Waterhouse	**COX Helen** Clifford Chance
DOCKING Peter Sacker & Partners	**ELLISON Robin** Eversheds
FENTON Jonathan DLA	**LEWIS Roger** Eversheds
MARSHALL Jane Hammond Suddards Edge	**MOORE Nigel** CMS Cameron McKenna
MULLEN Chris Biddle	**PETHERAM Claire** Linklaters
ROGERS Anna Rowe & Maw	**SAMSWORTH Jane** Lovells
SCHAFFER Daniel Freshfields Bruckhaus	**SMITH Stephanie** Travers Smith Braithwaite
STRACHAN Russell Lovells	**TIER Sarah** Sacker & Partners
❸ **FORD Peter** Nabarro Nathanson	**GAULT Ian** Herbert Smith
ITO Stephen Lovells	**JACOBS Howard** Slaughter and May
LESTER Peter Sacker & Partners	**MURRAY John** Nabarro Nathanson
POWELL Andrew Hammond Suddards Edge	
❹ **ATKINSON Mark** CMS Cameron McKenna	**BERKELEY Christopher** Biddle
CLOSE Chris Sacker & Partners	**COWLEY Michael** Stephenson Harwood
PEARSON John Lovells	
UP AND COMING	
ANDREWS Sue Eversheds	**GRANT Mark** CMS Cameron McKenna
KOWALIK Mark CMS Cameron McKenna	**MEEKS Alastair** Biddle
SAUNDERS Carolyn Taylor Joynson Garrett	

Within each band, firms are listed alphabetically.
⚐ Figures unavailable at time of going to press.

*See **Profiles** on page 621*

Nabarro Nathanson Its reputation for having a strong pensions practice continues. The practice looks set to have *"something of a revival"* with its *"solid, all-round team"* having stabilised and *"refreshing life blood of the department"* **John Quarrell** *"back in the swing of things."* He is *"the man you go to for a judgement call."* Principally advising trustees of large occupational pension schemes and companies, the practice covers public and private sector work acting for insurance companies and trade unions, public bodies, local government schemes, and charities. *"Commercial and rounded"* **Peter Ford** has *"bags of common sense and is very focused"* while **John Murray** is *"low-profile – he's one of the older generation of lawyers."* The firm continues to advise the trustees of the NPI pension scheme. **Clients:** IBM; BTR; NPI.

Slaughter and May *"They don't market – they just get on and do it."* Unsurprisingly, a *"first rate"* client base reflects that of the firm's blue chip corporate clientele. However, the firm is known to have strength in both pure and transactional pensions work. Consistent with their reputation in other fields, they are regarded as *"the quintessential font of excellence,"* although some find their advice overly precise at the expense of a more pragmatic approach. Star performer **Philip Bennett** is *"absolutely top notch intellectually"* and with his *"considerable personality"* and mixed practice (with employment law), **Howard Jacobs** *"brings a fresh approach."* Advised on pension scheme restructurings, including the Hoechst Group pension scheme. **Clients:** Unilever; Blue Circle; Vauxhall Motors.

Baker & McKenzie The firm's major strength is in its international presence where it can draw on the expertise of other offices to act for multinational organisations. Domestically, they are *"always seen popping up in UK transactions for US clients."* A strong team base of *"young, enthusiastic people"* is headed by current APL Chairman **Robert West**, who ably *"balances technical knowledge with a commercial approach."* Advising in connection with settlement of National Bus litigation. **Clients:** Co-Operative Insurance Society; Hanson; National Provident Institution.

CMS Cameron McKenna With a considerably higher profile this year, the firm moves up in the tables. Most consider that the team (*"innovative, stable, pretty solid"*) is coming along well and *"will probably power ahead."* Generally acts for employer or trustee (rarely for trustee alone) across a mix of industries with a strong profile in PO-related work. Head of department **Nigel Moore** *"sees the wider picture."* Notable members of his team include **Mark Atkinson** (*"an astute communicator who can understand that 2+2 can make 5"*) who moves up in the tables and new entrants **Mark Grant** (known for his book on the Pensions Ombudsman) and APL Treasurer **Mark Kowalik**. Acting for Trustees of Ferranti Pension Scheme on a dispute of entitlement of membership, following the multi-million pound disposal of its business to GEC. **Clients:** Ferranti; Hogg Robinson Trustees; House of Fraser Trustees.

Travers Smith Braithwaite *"A strong, cohesive department,"* handling *"good quality work,"* which moves up the tables this year. The firm targets the upper end of the pension scheme fund market and also acts for insurance companies. Possessed of a *"dry, succinct style,"* **Paul Stannard** *"finds creative solutions to seemingly intractable problems"* while his *"distinctive"* colleague **Stephanie Smith** provides *"a breath of fresh air"* with her *"broad, earthy sense of humour."* Acting for NTL on the pensions aspects of its acquisition of Cable & Wireless. **Clients:** Guardian Royal Exchange Pension Fund; Associated British Foods Pension Scheme; British Aerospace Pension Scheme.

Biddle *"Solid and thorough."* Appear to be *"almost like a boutique in relation to their size – pensions is so important to them."* **Chris Mullen** is *"maturing well into the leadership role,"* demonstrating that *"there is life after Hugh Arthur."* Continuing to impress with high profile clients and moving upwards, **Christopher Berkeley** is *"well established, thorough and extremely courteous."* New entry into the tables **Alistair Meeks** has *"an incisive mind."* The group provided advice for Dow Jones on all European pensions issues. **Clients:** Group Trustees of The National Power Scheme; Vivendi; Combined Lloyd's Schemes.

Eversheds *"There's something going on there – they're worth watching."* Seen as a *"lively, progressive practice"* through their involvement in interesting pensions initiatives, and move up the tables accordingly. Currently acting as joint advisors with Linklaters and Mercers in seeking to promote a Brussels test case on challenging tax barriers which prevent pan-European employee pension schemes. Credited with having strength based on their geographical spread which affords genuine resource support. Act for large employer plcs and pensions providers in developing pensions products – the electricity industry comprises 25% of their practice. **Robin Ellison** is *"without equal at developing pensions learning"* and **Roger Lewis** is *"a strong operator in his field"* of old nationalised industrial schemes. New entry **Susan Andrews** is *"energetic and hard-working."* Advising Department of Environment, Transport and the Regions on pensions section of the Transport Bill. **Clients:** National Grid Company.

Hammond Suddards Edge *"Good solid all-rounders."* Although the team has *"cornered the market up north,"* it is generally felt that it is *"not quite as influential as before,"* particularly in view of the lower rating of their leaders this year. National Practice Head **Jane Marshall** is *"well-liked by clients."* **Andrew Powell** is respected, although seen as a *"touch bombastic."* **Clients:** Elementis plc; United Utilities; Hyder plc.

Herbert Smith Failing to attract much distinctive comment this year, although the department appears to have been *"rebuilt with some success"* by **Ian Gault** *("quiet but steady and sure.")* Majority perception persists that the practice is *"virtually entirely corporate support."* The team advised the Government Office for London on pensions aspects of the establishment of the Greater London Authority. **Clients:** Swiss Re; F&IOA.

Simmons & Simmons Suffering from a marked lack of profile this year which seems at odds with their team size, employment expertise and the anticipated exposure afforded by their production of academic publications. Those who have had substantive dealings comment on their *"slightly idiosyncratic approach – they are not the easiest of negotiators."* The team acted for Barclays in reviewing all life and pensions policies, thereby helping them achieve plain English accreditation for all policies. **Clients:** Gallaher Pensions Ltd; Eagle Star Pension Scheme.

DLA The London office suffers from being somewhat *"outshone by the provinces."* **Jonathan Fenton**'s reputation as *"an extremely meticulous and thorough"* individual remains intact – *"he researches a case left, right and centre, leaving no stone unturned."* Acted for HSBC Private Equity in its buyout of Col Art International Holdings. **Clients:** Universities Superannuation Scheme; Allied Domecq Pensions Funds.

Other Notable Practitioners *"The personification of urbanity"* at MacFarlanes, **Hugh Arthur** *"has his work cut out"* in building the practice, together with handling key client British Airways. **Michael Cowley** of Stephenson Harwood *"has a considerable amount of energy – good at meeting deadlines."* In recognition of her considerable ability, **Belinda Benney** of Field Fisher Waterhouse moves up in the tables. *"Always has a very fresh approach, she's an unconventional thinker with bags of energy – she's nobody's pushover."* Having taken over the management at Taylor Joynson Garrett, new entry into the tables **Carolyn Saunders** *"has the potential to lift the practice's profile."*

PENSIONS LITIGATION : NATIONAL

PENSIONS LITIGATION • National	Ptnrs	Assts
❶ Eversheds Derby	1	1
Lovells	7	14
Nabarro Nathanson	3	4
Sacker & Partners	1	2
❷ Biddle	4	4
CMS Cameron McKenna	3	6
Linklaters	3	10
Rowe & Maw	1	1

LEADING INDIVIDUALS	
❶ DIMSDALE GILL Angela Lovells	ORTON Giles Eversheds
❷ CARRUTHERS Andrew Rowe & Maw	LEGRAND Janet DLA
MONTY Craig Lovells	
UP AND COMING	
BLYTH Mark Linklaters	COOMBS Monica Sacker & Partners

Within each band, firms are listed alphabetically. *See Profiles on page 621*

Eversheds *"Serious players"* – *"the only true pensions litigators."* Seen to be evolving from its origins as champion of member bodies' and union causes towards becoming more established in mainstream work. Widely regarded as an *"extremely efficient litigation machine"* on account of **Giles Orton**'s *"unparalleled expertise as a skilled litigator"* and *"good track record"* in high profile cases from Maxwell to date. With a national reputation as *"Mr Big Scheme Litigation,"* he is *"very articulate, and such a colourful character."* Appointed by the Trustees of Melton Medes (Fletchers) Fund, a £42 million fund serving 560 members. Advised an employer on difficulties caused by debt arising on a pension scheme winding-up under the Pensions Act 1995, including the negotiation of compromise of the debt with Trustees of the scheme. Advising the Association of Mirror Pensions on its successful complaint to the Pensions Ombudsman regarding refusal of Mirror Trustees to release an actuarial report. **Clients:** Association of Mirror Pensions.

Lovells Provides a *"first class service."* Involved in many of the major cases – Courage, BC, National Power and Maxwell, from its inception in 1987, the pensions litigation group is comprised of a skilled team of *"aggressive"* commercial litigators who *"certainly play hard – come through a few rounds with them and you know it."* Pensions-related work is cross-fertilised with linked specialisms including professional indemnity, fraud and construction. Acts for a range of clients including insurers, trustees, members and employers, predominantly on large blue-chip schemes. *"Veteran"* team leader/ litigator **Angela Dimsdale Gill** has *"enormous energy. She's a street-fighter who achieves a lot for her clients."* **Craig Monty** has *"strong judgement, is realistic but fights his corner hard."* The team acted for the trustees of the BT pension scheme in high value court proceedings. **Clients:** National Power; BT trustees.

Nabarro Nathanson *"Doing it for a long time."* Has respected pensions litigators who are *"pretty clued up."* A wealth of experience stems from *"a long tradition of pensions litigation"* dating as far back as the Courage case. Their style is described as *"tough"* but imbued with *"a huge amount of common sense; they're reasonable and commercial."* The team achieved the successful resolution of all issues arising from the judgement of Knox J in the HF pension scheme. **Clients:** Trustees of HF Pension Scheme; British Coal.

Sacker & Partners *"Definitely a presence now,"* having *"made a good start"* as *"a relative newcomer to pensions litigation."* Acts mainly for trustees of large schemes, in recent enquiries by OPRA and larger employers and trustees in PO disputes. Department Head **Monica Coombs** is *"hard as nails"* and *"good at getting things organised."* Acting for L&G in appeal against decisions of the Ombudsman which determined that there is no appeal from preliminary point from the PO, and that he has limited jurisdiction to investigate the contractual terms of an insurance contract. **Clients:** Legal & General; Dalgety Group; Merchant Navy.

Biddle *"They have the expertise and are clearly well equipped to deal with the work."* Involved in a number of significant cases including Lansing Linde and Belling, with major clients including Law Debenture and National Power Group Trustees. With *"good pensions knowledge"* from a litigation background, the main partners have at least six years' experience in the field. **Clients:** Trustees of National Power Group; Trustees of Lansing Linde Pensions Scheme.

CMS Cameron McKenna Best known for Pensions Ombudsman work. The *"very young, very bright"* team, comprising the firm's specialist Ombudsman unit, handles referrals from other firms. Acted in the Coloroll case in the European courts and for Law Debenture in reversing the ruling in the Swan Hunter case. **Clients:** Law Debenture; Hogg Robinson Trustees; Ferranti Pension Scheme.

Linklaters *"Made a big splash"* setting up its Pensions Litigation Group in October 1998. Additional resources of three partners and three assistants in the Pensions Department. Known to be involved in large scale litigation, their highest profile case to date is acting for National Power plc in the Electricity Supply Pension Scheme case, currently on appeal in the House of Lords. *"Going places"* at the heart of their pensions team, **Mark Blyth** is *"sparky and intelligent."* **Clients:** British Airways plc; Ferranti Pension Scheme trustees.

Rowe & Maw *"Knowledgeable and can defend their client's interests robustly yet deal with disputes in a civilised fashion."* Involved in the Barnardos and South West Trains cases. Act mainly for trustees of large schemes. *"Agile tactician"* and secretary to the APL Pensions Litigation Committee, **Andrew Carruthers** is *"experienced and well informed."* **Clients:** BG plc; P&O; Sedgwick Group.

Other Notable Practitioner **Janet Le Grand** of DLA has *"an enormous amount of inner steel – not someone you'd want to pick a fight with."*

THAMES VALLEY

PENSIONS • Thames Valley	Ptnrs	Assts
❶ **Clarks** Reading	1	-
LEADING INDIVIDUALS		
❸ **CLARK David** Clarks		

Within each band, firms are listed alphabetically. *See **Profiles** on page 621*

Clarks Not known as a mainstream practice, but rather as having a niche in independent trusteeship work based on the reputation of **David Clark** *("a pretty good litigator.")* Advises mostly on small to medium sized schemes based in the local area. Also advises employers and insolvency practitioners, gives M&A support and documentation work. Acting for the Trustees of the Scientific Investment Pension Plan in High Court case and in the further hearing of Kemble v Hicks (ruling on the ability of one section of a scheme to subsidise another and on a trustee's ability to insure.) **Clients:** The Trustees of the Scientific Investment Pension Plan.

SOUTH WEST

PENSIONS • South West	Ptnrs	Assts
❶ **Burges Salmon** Bristol	1	4
Osborne Clarke OWA Bristol	3	4
LEADING INDIVIDUALS		
❶ **ILLSTON Tim** Burges Salmon		
❷ **WOMERSLEY Mark** Osborne Clarke OWA		
UP AND COMING		
MATTHEWS Paul Osborne Clarke OWA		

Within each band, firms are listed alphabetically. *See **Profiles** on page 621*

Burges Salmon A well respected practice *"providing pragmatic and generally timely advice on most pensions aspects."* Team leader **Tim Illston** *("good for particularly complex matters")* has a strong reputation in the region. Most opine that he has adequately addressed any perceived lack of resource at assistant level. Acts mainly for trustees of pensions schemes of regionally based companies in financial services, manufacturing/services and academic sectors. Advised on the merger of London Life Pension Scheme with AMP Scheme. **Clients:** AT&T Istel; Dalgety Group; University of Oxford.

Osborne Clarke OWA *"Hungry for business and focused on building their practice."* Acts for well known plcs, and household names in industry and financial services sector, servicing London, Reading and Bristol and life companies UK-wide. Developing his practice and moving up the tables, Head of the Pensions and Employee Benefits Unit **Mark Womersley** *"has all the potential to drive the team forward."* New entry into the tables **Paul Matthews** is *"very responsive in a deal."* Dealing with appointment of external investment managers for Imperial Tobacco (£2.2 billion fund.) **Clients:** Imperial Tobacco Pension Fund; Lincoln National; Kier Group Pension Scheme.

WALES

PENSIONS • Wales	Ptnrs	Assts
❶ **Eversheds** Cardiff	1	1
LEADING INDIVIDUALS		
❷ **DAVIES Ian** Eversheds		

Within each band, firms are listed alphabetically. *See **Profiles** on page 621*

Eversheds *"Their fees are competitive and their quality is on par with others."* They would undoubtedly attract more resounding praise were it not for the strong perception that the scale of their work is limited by their size. Additional resource of one part time assistant. Has regional and UK wide presence, acting for major household name plcs. **Ian Davies** has *"a good pensions brain." "He gives advice quickly by getting to the nub of the issue and giving a commercial solution."* Appointed by National Assembly for Wales Member's Pension Fund and by Abbey National Benefit Consultancy as preferred provider of pensions related legal work. **Clients:** Rural Development Commission; Walkers Snack Foods; Hymans Robertson.

MIDLANDS

PENSIONS • Midlands	Ptnrs	Assts
❶ **Wragge & Co** Birmingham	4	12
❷ **Eversheds** Birmingham, Derby	3	12
Hammond Suddards Edge Birmingham	2	8
❸ **Pinsent Curtis** Birmingham	2	1
❹ **Garretts** Birmingham	1	1
Martineau Johnson Birmingham	-	2

LEADING INDIVIDUALS	
❶ **COCKERILL Vivien** Wragge & Co	**FORREST Ian** Hammond Suddards Edge
HINGLEY Gerald Wragge & Co	**ORTON Giles** Eversheds
RYLAND Glyn Wragge & Co	
❷ **DAVIS Richard** Hammond Suddards Edge	**FALLON Liz** Eversheds
MILTON Kevin Garretts	**SHELLEY Daniel** Pinsent Curtis
❸ **BLACK Richard** Wragge & Co	**HUGHES Sara** Wragge & Co
UP AND COMING	
SUTTON Philip Hammond Suddards Edge	

Within each band, firms are listed alphabetically. *See* **Profiles** *on page 621*

Wragge & Co *"They have the advantage in quality."* With *"a lot of high class people, you wouldn't expect to find many mistakes in their work."* Act for an even mix of employers and trustees of group schemes for a clientele which includes FTSE plcs and private companies. In litigation work, the team is currently involved in multi-party actions re applications on surplus and early retirement provisions in High Court. **Vivien Cockerill** is *"vivacious, focused and intellectual,"* although not necessarily seen as being *"head and shoulders above the rest."* **Gerald Hingley** *"tends to be undervalued – in no sense flashy, he handles a lot of quality work." "Not many things are a problem"* for **Glyn Ryland**, *"he just cuts through them – extremely sharp and bright, he gets things right without having to shout about it."* Moving up in the tables are **Sara Hughes** *("still a force, she knows her way around all sorts of things and has long experience")* and new partner **Richard Black** *("will be a shining star.")* Dealing with pensions issues arising from the purchase by HJ Heinz Europe of the frozen and chilled foods businesses of United Biscuits (£190 million transaction.) **Clients:** EMAP; TI Group; GKN Westland.

Eversheds *"They have the contentious side sewn up although they haven't made an impact on the non contentious side."* Two assistants spend approximately 50% of their time handling the latter. Everyone has heard of **Giles Orton**, *"one of the swashbucklers of the legal profession." "He has pushed back the boundaries of pensions law on the litigious side."* Handling a court application in relation to the Melton Medes sex equalisation case. At the Birmingham office, **Liz Fallon** gives *"pretty straightforward and commercial advice and doesn't sit on the fence."* Her team acted for the Trustees of the Works and Staff Final Salary Schemes of the then Tomkinsons plc on the transfer of their assets and liabilities to a new scheme. **Clients:** Melton Medes; Bradstock Trustee Services; Alliance & Leicester.

Hammond Suddards Edge *"Little diminution in profile"* despite division of resource to London headed by Robert Gravill. He accordingly drops out of the tables although he continues to handle and receive instructions from Midlands clients. Undertaking a full management role, Simon Ramshaw also drops out of the tables. Moving up however following consistent praise this year, **Ian Forrest** *"does well in always pushing things forward on behalf of clients – they love him to death!"* Other notable individuals are **Richard Davis** *("friendly, straightforward and doesn't overcomplicate matters")* and new entry into the tables **Phil Sutton** *("a good backbone lawyer")* who is helping to raise the firm's profile. Acts principally for blue-chip entities including insurance companies, listed plcs and trustees of major pensions schemes (85-90%.) Has a strong independent trusteeship business, the largest in the region. Also handles SSAS, trustee training and schemes wind-up work. Acting for Allied Dunbar in cross-border merger of two pensions schemes. **Clients:** Football League; Allied Dunbar Assurance plc; The Heath Consulting Company Ltd.

Pinsent Curtis A small team which is highly rated on the basis of their *"superb client list,"* which is biased towards acting for the trustees of large schemes. **Daniel Shelley** *"pays a lot of attention to detail."* Advising on scheme merger involving assets of £230 million. **Clients:** TI Group; GKN Group; Cadbury Schweppes Pension Fund.

Garretts *"Not really broken into the marketplace."* However, **Kevin Milton** *"seems to be settling in well there"* handling the department's corporate related work. Historically acted more for employers than trustees – now acting increasingly for independent trusteeship clients of small to medium sized plcs. Advising on pensions aspects of the disposal of a number of Silvermines plc businesses. **Clients:** Wagon plc.

Martineau Johnson *"Looking in good form,"* this newly ranked practice has been noted in the market as *"very solid"* and *"one to watch."* Also has a full time consultant who is well known name in the industry. Acts for a broad range of pensions schemes across a range of industry areas including universities, educational institutions and motor trade. Has several plc appointments and also acts for owner-managed businesses and high net worth individuals. **Clients:** Educational institutions; the motor trade.

EAST ANGLIA

PENSIONS • East Anglia	Ptnrs	Assts
❶ **Hewitson Becke + Shaw** Cambridge, Northampton	2	2
❷ **Eversheds** Norwich	1	-

LEADING INDIVIDUALS
❶ **COLACICCHI Clare** Hewitson Becke + Shaw
SCOTT Harry Mills & Reeve

Within each band, firms are listed alphabetically. *See* **Profiles** *on page 621*

Hewitson Becke + Shaw Somewhat diminished in profile this year. Operating from Northampton and Cambridge, the team acts for substantial private companies, small to medium sized plcs and trustees of small to medium sized occupational schemes. Transactional work – particularly advice to trustees on pensions disputes and winding up mergers – has increased this year. With a *"down to earth"* approach, **Clare Colacicchi** is perceived to have a more mixed practice and is also known for financial services/ investment related work. Acting for an independent trustee company in settling a claim against a previous trustee using mediation. **Clients:** St Andrew's Hospital; Travis Perkins plc.

Eversheds Still has practically no profile outside the locality. Handles exclusively non-contentious work mainly for large privately owned companies based in the locality. Typically handles variety of work flowing from review and amendment of pension scheme documentation and rules, and involved in providing independent trusteeship services and winding up of pension schemes. **Clients:** Eastern Counties Newspapers Group; R G Carter; W Vinten.

Other Notable Practitioner **Harry Scott** of Mills & Reeve is *"refined, precise and a real gentleman,"* and has a long-standing name in the sector.

NORTH WEST

PENSIONS • North West	Ptnrs	Assts
❶ **Addleshaw Booth & Co** Manchester	1	2
DLA Liverpool, Manchester	2	3
❷ **Eversheds** Manchester	1	6
❸ **Hammond Suddards Edge** Manchester	1	3
❹ **Masons** Manchester	1	4

LEADING INDIVIDUALS
❶ **WRIGHT David** DLA
❷ **ASHLEY TAYLOR Andrew** Hammond Suddards Edge
GRAHAM Ronald Eversheds
GRIFFITHS David Addleshaw Booth & Co
KENNEDY Patrick Masons
❸ **HARRIS Jeremy** DLA
UP AND COMING
SCHOLEFIELD Stephen Addleshaw Booth & Co
SOUTHERN Steve Hammond Suddards Edge
TIMMINS Jacqueline Eversheds

Within each band, firms are listed alphabetically. *See **Profiles** on page 621*

Addleshaw Booth & Co *"A premier firm – you get the impression they don't have to try too hard."* The image here is of a stable, static practice. **David Griffiths** is *"technically able, and a calm, quiet type."* New entry into the tables **Stephen Scholefield** is *"extremely in tune with pensions law."* Francis Shackleton leaves the tables having retired as a partner in January this year, and retains a connection with the firm as a consultant on an ad hoc basis. Continuing advice to the trustee of the HH Robertson (UK) Ltd Retirement Benefits Plant 1978, including handling the current Pensions Ombudsman's investigation. **Clients:** Cussons (International) Ltd; Kellogg UK Holding Company Ltd; API Group plc.

DLA *"They still have an unassailable position in Liverpool."* The client base is dominated by large occupational pension schemes work, with expanding key client Universities' Superannuation Scheme seen as providing the backbone to the practice. Head of Practice **David Wright** is *"still regarded as pre-eminent in the North West,"* while *"quiet and unassuming"* Manchester partner **Jeremy Harris** *"will always do the job required of him."* Advising in the merger of KwikSave pensions schemes into Somerfield pensions schemes. **Clients:** Universities' Superannuation Scheme (USS); Royal Insurance Group Pension Scheme; Ciba.

Eversheds *"Gathering pace"* with an increase in team numbers and quality. Handles mainstream and merger work for medium to large corporate clients and their pension schemes. Niche in local authority/local government scheme practice involving externalisations and privatisations of government functions. Also experienced in multi-scheme mergers. **Ronald Graham** is *"very intelligent and always gets the law right." "Making an increasing impact on the scene,"* **Jackie Timmins** is a new entry to the tables. Advising trustees of Akzo Nobel Pension Scheme on entire restructuring of investment portfolio following multi-scheme merger. **Clients:** Bodycote; Akzo Nobel; United States Filters.

Hammond Suddards Edge *"A very nice practice beginning to mature nicely – they have interesting people with complex skills."* Acts for wide range of corporates ranging from small private to blue chip plcs. Undertakes a high proportion of work involving mergers of pensions arrangements and rationalisation of schemes. *"Softly spoken"* leader **Andrew Ashley Taylor** *"has a steady hand at the tiller." "Still making his way"* is *"rumbustious"* **Steve Southern**, *"the fighting man's lawyer."* Acted for one of the two representative beneficiaries of a complex industry-wide scheme (over 3,000 potential beneficiaries in total) with respect to under-funding issues. **Clients:** FKI plc; Motorola Ltd; Seddon Atkinson.

Masons *"The team there have stuck together and will be there for a while yet."* Their attitude, said to flow from *"gregarious"* team leader **Patrick Kennedy**, is described as *"very practical – they are keen to achieve a sensible result for all involved."* Act for range of corporates mainly within the manufacturing sector, doing an even mix of trustee work, advisory/documentation work and corporate support work. Acting for ICI in relation to the outsourcing to ICL of information technology involving complex series of pensions transfers across Europe. **Clients:** London Scottish Bank plc pension schemes; ICI; Metropolitan Police.

NORTH EAST

Addleshaw Booth & Co *"They still do good work"* and have maintained their solid reputation at the top of the tables. Advise ongoing schemes for client base comprising mainly banks, financial institutions and insurance companies. Also undertake significant amount of insolvency-related work and independent trusteeship work. Niche strengths in the latter and in-house benefits consultancy. *"Consummate gentleman"* **Neville Peel** *"is the type of lawyer who charms clients." "Doing more at leadership level,"* **Rachel Rawnsley** has a *"serious, committed attitude."* Advising trustees on a major reorganisation and merger involving more than £1 billion in assets. **Clients:** Asda Pension Schemes; Refuge Assurance Pension Scheme; Bradford & Bingley Building Society.

DLA Much stronger this year. Acts for broad range of employers and trustees on variety of schemes with significant quantity of scheme merger work. Notable individuals include consultant **Martin Lee**, **Kate Payne** *("tenacious, she fights like a tiger")* and new entry last year **Vikki Massarano Salt** *("settled down quite nicely, and increasing in experience")* who moves up accordingly. Advising Pendragon plc and the trustees of the Pendragon Pension Plan on the latter's merger with the Evans Halshaw Group Retirement Benefits Scheme. Also advising the former on its joint venture with Ford Motor Company Ltd and establishment of new pension scheme. **Clients:** BASF UK Pensions Trustees Ltd; Trustees (Dupont) UK; Firth Rixon plc.

Eversheds *"A long-running team which is maturing nicely."* Historically acts predominantly for trustees of West Yorkshire plcs. However a couple of extended periods of absence by team leader **Raymond Ainscoe** have raised resourcing issues in the minds of many. He is still regarded as the best technically – *"you can't find a better all round pensions advisor than him." "Growing in stature,"* **Leigh Holmes** is *"pragmatic in transactions, bright but not overly obsessed with technicalities."* She moves up in the tables. Acted for the trustees of a large utilities pension scheme on a partial merger with another scheme. **Clients:** Utilities; pharmaceutical companies.

Hammond Suddards Edge *"A very strong growing pensions team with a lot of depth, which operates at a really consistent level."* Acts mainly for corporate clients in utilities, chemical and civil engineering sectors. Team leader **Catherine McKenna** *("smooth presenter, well prepared")* is joined in the tables by two new entries, **Terry Saeedi** *("involved for a long time")* and ex-Irwin Mitchell **Mark Ridler** *("knows the law like the back of his hand.")* Acting for Kelda Group in exit from two centralised water industry pension schemes. **Clients:** Kelda Group (previously Yorkshire Water plc); Trustees of Northern Electric Pensions Scheme; BBA Group pension schemes.

Dickinson Dees *"Making a mark in the North East"* and moves up in the tables. Also has two assistants who spend up to 50 percent time on litiga-

PENSIONS • North East	Ptnrs	Assts
❶ **Addleshaw Booth & Co** Leeds	2	2
DLA Leeds, Sheffield	1	6
Eversheds Leeds	1	4
Hammond Suddards Edge Leeds	2	5
❷ **Dickinson Dees** Newcastle upon Tyne	2	3
Walker Morris Leeds	1	1
❸ **Nabarro Nathanson** Sheffield	-	3
Pinsent Curtis Leeds	1	1
Wrigleys Leeds	1	1

LEADING INDIVIDUALS	
❶ **AINSCOE Raymond** Eversheds	
❷ **McKENNA Catherine** Hammond Suddards Edge	
PEEL Neville Addleshaw Booth & Co	**RAWNSLEY Rachel** Addleshaw Booth & Co
❸ **JENKINS Martin** Dickinson Dees	**PAYNE Kate** DLA
TURNBULL Andrew Walker Morris	
❹ **ALLISON Margaret** Nabarro Nathanson	**ARCHER Richard** Wrigleys
HOLMES Leigh Eversheds	**KNIGHT Timothy** Wrigleys
LEE Martin DLA	**MASSARANO SALT Vikki** DLA
TAYLOR Anne Irwin Mitchell	
UP AND COMING	
RIDLER Mark Hammond Suddards Edge	**SAEEDI Terry** Hammond Suddards Edge

Within each band, firms are listed alphabetically. *See **Profiles** on page 621*

tion matters (OPRA prosecutions.) Acts predominantly for clients in the region including North Yorkshire, Teesside and Cumbria. Clients range from national plc companies to private limited companies and trustees. Scheme merger work is a growth area. Going up in the tables, team leader **Martin Jenkins** is *"making name for himself in pensions world"* with *"a growing team."* Advising Northern Rock plc in relation to new pension documentation and revision of benefit structure. **Clients:** Railways Pensions Management Ltd; The Go-Ahead Group; Procter and Gamble Ltd.

Walker Morris *"One of the best for practical advice and efficiency,"* this practice moves up in the tables although relatively small in comparison. Provides independent trustee services and advises trustees on winding-up pension schemes, but does not act for plcs. **Andrew Turnbull** is *"succinct and reliable"* – *"co-operatives like him."* Acting on pensions aspects of the 3C Waste acquisition by Yorkshire Water plc **Clients:** Yorkshire Water plc; Trustees of E Timm & Son Ltd Pension Scheme; Trustees of Guilford Europe Pensions Scheme.

Nabarro Nathanson Not seen to be making a significant impact in the locality and still regarded as *"an outpost"* of the London office. With the benefit of the latter's team resource, undertakes the full range of pension work. Acts predominantly for trustees and employers with significant SSAS/SIPs practice. Growth area in PFI related work. Perceived to need back-up, **Margaret Allison** *("bright and constructive")* works with another assistant who works four days a week. Providing complex advice to Lindley Trustees Ltd, an independent trustee company, regarding the legal aspects of winding up various schemes and related matters. **Clients:** Trustees of The Moorland Poultry Pension Scheme; Taylor Nelson Sofres plc; The Audit Commission.

Pinsent Curtis *"Super but niche."* Although they are not proactive in marketing themselves, they have *"good regional coverage"* and move up in the tables in recognition of this. Clients include large non-quoted and FTSE 250 plc companies. Niche in advising schemes in wind-up. Represented North Eastern Farmers in relation to merger of two of their schemes in Court of Sessions case in North Scotland. **Clients:** Clayton Pension Scheme; Bitmac Ltd; CGU Life.

Wrigleys Despite not aiming to be a pure practice, they retain a *"super"* reputation for the work they do, largely on account of their experienced leaders. Predominantly act for and as trustees of pension schemes and in conflict situations. Full time partner **Timothy Knight** *("bags of knowledge and brain")* spends between 20-30 percent of his time on pensions work, together with education, charities and private trusts related work. Part time consultant **Richard Archer** spends 4 days per week doing 50-60 percent pensions related work, together with private trusts and tax planning. *"Faced with a seemingly impossible situation, he can throw it up into the air and come up with solutions with lateral thinking."* **Clients:** Pension scheme trustees.

Other Notable Practitioner **Anne Taylor** has left Halliwell Landau to join Irwin Mitchell's practice in Leeds, and is expected to boost her new firm's pensions reputation.

SCOTLAND

PENSIONS • Scotland	Ptnrs	Assts
❶ **Morison Bishop** Glasgow	3	2
Shepherd & Wedderburn Edinburgh	2	2
❷ **Maclay Murray & Spens** Glasgow	2	4
McGrigor Donald Glasgow	1	3
❸ **Burness** Glasgow	1	3
Tods Murray Edinburgh	1	-

LEADING INDIVIDUALS
❶ **GORDON Ian** McGrigor Donald
HOLEHOUSE Andrew Shepherd & Wedderburn WS
TALMAN Iain Morison Bishop
❷ **CROMBIE June** Morison Bishop
❸ **KNOX Louisa** Shepherd & Wedderburn WS
TROTTER Peter MacRoberts

Within each band, firms are listed alphabetically. *See **Profiles** on page 621*

Morison Bishop *"No discernible change"* following their merger on 1 August 1999 with general commercial practice Alex Morison & Co which may extend their client base in Edinburgh. Still seen as *"more trusts based than a corporate beast."* Acts predominantly for trustees of company schemes ranging in size from very small to over £100 million in value. Other work includes independent trustee work, insolvency, winding up, SSAS, pensions litigation and cases before the Pensions Ombudsman. On OPRA panel and IT on OPDU panel. **Iain Talman** *"probably has the greatest depth of knowledge of pensions legislation of anyone,"* although he can be *"overly thorough."* Taking on more independent trusteeships, **June Crombie** is *"possibly coming out from behind his coat tails."* Advising Trustees of Ellis & McHardy scheme in relation to restructuring of pensions arrangements, use of surplus and application to court for directions on these matters. **Clients:** Law Society of Scotland Staff Pension Scheme; Rosyth Royal Dockyard Pension Scheme; Ellis & McHardy (Part of North Eastern Farmers.)

Shepherd & Wedderburn WS *"A respectable firm with an excellent client base."* Acts for large institutions and public companies and their occupational pensions schemes, providing advice on winding up, reorganisation and documentation. Also acts for smaller corporate clients converting from final salary to money purchase schemes. Rated for his commercial pensions advice, **Andrew Holehouse** is seen as *"unflappable, calm and in control."* Moving up in the tables, **Louisa Knox** *"can handle corporate transactions in her sleep."* Representing Scottish Transport Group pensions schemes in successfully resisting members' claims for over-surplus. **Clients:** Scottish Transport Group; Scottish Power; WM Company Bankers Trust.

Maclay Murray & Spens *"Gone through a lot of upheavals"* with key individuals leaving in recent years. Andrew Fleming has left to replace Keith Wallace as team leader of Richards Butler's practice. The majority are *"reserving judgement until the new department shakes down."* Acts mostly for plc company pension schemes, insurance company advice work and less than 5% SSAS. Niche in pensions and financial services litigation, trustee training, mergers of pensions schemes, advising insurance companies on pension products. Have national pensions team with significant client base in England and Scotland. **Clients:** Coats Viyella plc; John Menzies plc; Bank of Scotland.

McGrigor Donald *"You get a straightforward commercial answer to a legal question – brief and to the point."* Continue to act for larger established companies and also acts for smaller entrepreneurial listed companies. Niche strengths in pensions litigation, scheme wind-ups and mergers. **Ian Gordon** *"has grounding in all the relevant areas"* and is *"not interested in point scoring for the sake of it."* Acting for Stakis trustees following the Hilton merger. **Clients:** Scania Group; Stakis.

Burness Still *"pretty low profile"* despite having a team in place. Acts mostly for business, ranging from owner-managed to medium sized, and provides support to larger corporate commercial clients on various aspects of their occupational pension schemes. Advising Vickers plc on the pension aspects of its acquisitions of Ulstein UK Ltd. **Clients:** Standard Life; Clyde & Forth Press; Tuboscope Holdings Ltd.

Tods Murray WS Seen to provide a service to the firm's corporate clients. Has a generalist approach with pensions work undertaken by a partner spending up to 50% of his time on the work and an assistant (spending 25% time on the area.) Act for wide range of clients including corporate entities of all sizes and universities. Specifically involved in pensions matters relating to corporate and banking transactions (evaluative powers of trustees.) Advised in merger of Don & Low Group Pension Schemes. **Clients:** Bank of Scotland; Bank of Scotland Trustees; Don & Low Group Pensions Schemes.

Other Notable Practitioner Leader **Peter Trotter** moved from Maclay Murray & Spens to MacRoberts last year. He gives *"sound practical advice."*

LEADERS IN PENSIONS

AINSCOE, Raymond
Eversheds, Leeds (0113) 243 0391
raymondainscoe@eversheds.com
Partner in commercial department.
Specialisation: Area of practice is pensions. Contributed to Pensions World and Pensions Management. Lectured to Leeds Metropolitan University. Addressed APL, NAPF and PMI conferences.
Career: Qualified 1980 with *Stephenson Harwood.* 1983 joined *Nicholson Graham & Jones.* Joined *Hepworth & Chadwick* 1985. Partner 1987.
Personal: Born 28th April 1954. Attended Bolton School 1965-72, St. Catherine's College, Oxford (BA) 1972-75, B.C.L. 1977. Trustee of Yorkshire Spinal Deformity Trust, Leeds. Leisure pursuits include Italian racing motorcycles. Author of four books.

ALLISON, Margaret
Nabarro Nathanson, Sheffield (0114) 279 4000
Specialisation: Work covers almost every aspect of pension law, including advising trustees and companies on the re-organisation of schemes and the up-dating of scheme documentation. In the last year, has advised increasingly on the pension aspects of local government PFI projects of disposals by several plcs. Enjoys speaking engagements and trustee training.
Prof. Memberships: Full APL member.
Career: Qualified 1987. Specialised in pensions since 1988. Joined *Nabarro Nathanson* 1994 to establish their Sheffield pension team.
Personal: Born 1962. Has lived and worked in Sheffield since 1985. Interests include horses and cats.

ANDREWS, Sue
Eversheds, London (020) 7919 4500
Specialisation: Advises on all areas of pensions law including trustees duties and liabilities, winding up, investment management and custody and mergers and acquisitions.
Prof. Memberships: Member and secretary of the Association of Pensions Lawyers; Fellow of the Pensions Management Institute.
Career: Qualified as barrister in 1984. Requalified as solicitor in 1991. Worked in-house 1986-1989; *Herbert Smith* 1989-1994, *Charles Russell 1994-19998; Frere Cholmeley Bischoff* 1998 until merger with *Eversheds.*
Personal: Born 1st July 1961 and holds an LLB fromThames Valley University. Leisure interests include squash and golf. Lives in Hertford with her daughter.

ARCHER, J.Richard
Wrigleys, Leeds (0113) 244 6100
Consultant.
Specialisation: Former Head of *Hammond Suddards'* pensions unit and of private trust tax and probate department: still handles such work. Trustee of several plc pension schemes. Joint author of 'Pensions: The New Law'.
Prof. Memberships: Association of Pension Lawyers, NAPF, Society of Pension Consultants (Yorkshire Committee Member).
Career: Qualified 1969 (Law Society Prizeman). Assistant at *Wells & Hind* 1969-71, and at *Linklaters & Paines* 1971-75. Joined *Hammond Suddards* in 1975, becoming a Partner in 1977. Joined *Wrigleys* 1997 as a consultant.
Personal: Born 27th March 1943. Attended Rugby School 1956-61, then Cambridge University 1961-64. Charity Organiser.

ARTHUR, Hugh
Macfarlanes, London (020) 7831 9222
Partner in pensions group.
Specialisation: Advises on all areas of pensions law, including advice to employers, trustees, actuaries and other pensions professionals. Work includes scheme mergers, corporate and business transfers, MFR problems, disputes, and the drafting of complex documentation. Has lectured extensively on pensions topics at all levels. Author of "Pensions and Trusteeship" (Sweet & Maxwell, 1998), a leading textbook on pensions law in the light of the Pensions Act 1995, and of numerous articles in specialist pensions publications.
Prof. Memberships: Association of Pension Lawyers.
Career: Qualified in 1980. Worked at *Lovell White & King* 1978-84. *Biddle* 1984 – 1998, *Macfarlanes* 1999-.
Personal: Born 6th November 1955. Attended Cardinal Vaughan Memorial School, London 1967-74, then Magdalene College, Cambridge (Open Scholarship in Classics) 1974-77 (MA Law).

ASHLEY TAYLOR, Andrew M.
Hammond Suddards Edge, Manchester (0161) 830 5000
Specialisation: The law and practice relating to occupational pension schemes and other forms of retirement provision in the UK. Covers a wide variety of pension disciplines for employers, employees and trustees including corporate transactional work, project and merger advice, documentation and pension dispute resolution. Speaks regularly at seminars and writes articles. Qualified mediator for Alternative Dispute Resolution procedures.
Prof. Memberships: Association of Pension Lawyers, Associate of the Pensions Management Institute, Member of the North West Group of the NAPF.
Career: Qualified November 1984 and became an Associate of the Pensions Management Institute in 1990. Worked in private practice to 1988 then joined *Baker & Mckenzie,* London to specialise in Pensions law.
Personal: Golf, travel, cycling, music and theatre.

ATKINSON, Mark
CMS Cameron McKenna, London (020) 7367 3000
mark.atkinson@cmck.com
Specialisation: Advises trustees and companies on all aspects of pensions law including scheme mergers and de-mergers, Pensions Act compliance, documentation, litigation, issues arising from corporate transactions, Pensions Ombudsman complaints and other member disputes. Established the stakeholder team across pension and financial services groups. Speaks for NAPF, APL and commercial conference organisations. Secretary to Coloroll Pension Trustees Limited. Contributor to Tolleys 'Pensions Handbook'.
Prof. Memberships: Association of Pension Lawyers, associate of the Pensions Management Institute.

Career: Qualified 1994 *Cameron McKenna.*
Personal: Born 1968. Attended Pembroke College, Cambridge.

BENNETT, Philip F. J.
Slaughter and May, London (020) 7600 1200
Partner in Pensions/Employment Department.
Specialisation: Main area of practice is pensions work. Author of 'Pension Fund Surpluses', March 1989, 1994.
Prof. Memberships: Association of Pensions Lawyers, Past Chairman Legislative & Parliamentary Sub-Committee of the Association of Pensions Lawyers, Former Member, Main Committee of the Association of Pensions Lawyers.
Career: Qualified 1979. Partner 1986. Currently with *Slaughter and May* in London.
Personal: Born 2 March 1954.

BENNEY, Belinda
Field Fisher Waterhouse, London (020) 7861 4000
Partner in Pensions Department.
Specialisation: Full-time pensions specialist since 1986 when switched from private client work. Since then has covered full range of pensions work: documentation and rule drafting, sex discrimination, mergers & acquisitions, privatisations, severance terms, application of surplus, trustee duties and liabilities, asset protection, and all aspects of pension investment. Frequent speaker at pensions seminars and trustee training courses. Author of 'A Guide to the Pensions Act 1995' (Butterworths), and the pensions chapter in the 'Administration of Estates' practitioners' manual published by Tolley's. Appointed by the Board of the Occupational Pensions Regulatory Authority (OPRA) in April 2000.
Prof. Memberships: National Association of Pension Funds, Association of Pension Lawyers, Law Society, Institute of Chartered Accountants Pensions Sub-Committee.
Career: Qualified in 1981. Joined *Field Fisher Waterhouse* in 1996 as head of the pensions practice.
Personal: Holds an LL.B from the University of Bristol.

BERKELEY, Christopher B.
Biddle, London (020) 7606 9301
Partner in pensions group.
Specialisation: Acted this last year for the trustees of the Lansing Linde Pension schemes in rule construction proceedings which have been appealed to the Court of Appeal. He is acting for the trustees of the National Power Group of the ESPS in the National Grid/National Power allocation of surplus case that has been appealed to the House of Lords. He has acted for the trustees of the British Airways schemes; advised on the pensions aspects of privatisations such as British Coal, British Rail and AEA Technology; acted for the British Coal Staff Scheme Trustees in the well-known British Coal case regarding use of surplus; acted for the Trustees of both British Coal pension schemes in the major outsourcing of their pensions administration following the privatisation of British Coal and has recently acted for the National Power Group Trustees of the ESPS in the outsourcing of their scheme administration to AON Consulting.
Prof. Memberships: Member of the Association of Pension Lawyers; Member of the Committee of the City & Eastern Group of the National Association of Pension Funds; Co-opted member of the NAPF Investment Committee; City of London Solicitors Company.
Career: Educated at Sherborne School (1967 to 1971) and Brasenose College, Oxford (1972 to 1976) where he gained a Second Class Honours degree in Classics; MA (1980); articled at *Lemon & Co*, Swindon (1977 to 1979); qualified as a solicitor with *Lemon & Co* in May 1980; commercial property solicitor with *Wansbroughs* in Bristol (1981 to 1985); Assistant Parliamentary Counsel (1985 to 1990); assistant solicitor in the Pensions and Employment department of *Lovell White Durrant* (1990 to 1996); Partner in the Pensions Group of *Biddle* (1996 to present). A scenic route career-wise!
Personal: Married with three children; lives in Wimbledon; armchair cricket and rugby union enthusiast as evidenced by his membership of MCC and London Wasps RFC.

BLACK, Richard
Wragge & Co, Birmingham (0121) 685 2760
richard_black@wragge.com
Specialisation: Pensions advice for employers and trustees.
Prof. Memberships: Secretary of Midlands Group of the APL.
Career: Trained *Wragge & Co*; qualified 1995, associate 1998. Partner 2000. Education: King Edward VI Camp Hill, Birmingham; Sheffield University, College of Law.
Personal: Born 1967, resides Moseley. Interests: sport, music.

BLYTH, Mark
Linklaters (A member firm of Linklaters & Alliance), London (020) 7456 4246
mark.blyth@linklaters.com
Specialisation: Consultant, head of pensions litigation group. Full time specialist in all types of pensions litigation, including surplus disputes, trustee applications to court for directions, breach of trust, Pensions Ombudsman complaints, professional negligence of actuaries/professional advisers, administrators and regulatory issues with Opra. High profile cases this year include acting for National Power (Court of Appeal) over arrangements made for dealing with surpluses in the Electricity Supply Pension Scheme (now appealed to the House of Lords).
Prof. Memberships: Association of Pensions Lawyers. Advisory Panel member – The Occupational Pensions Defence Union Limited. Association of Contentious Trust & Probate Specialists.
Career: 1988-1990: Articled to *Allen & Overy*. 1990 – Present: *Linklaters & Alliance.*
Publications: Has written and spoken widely about pensions litigation issues.

CARRUTHERS, Andrew
Rowe & Maw, London (020) 7248 4282
acarruthers@roweandmaw.com
Specialisation: Pensions litigation and domestic and international arbitration and mediation.
Prof. Memberships: Law Society; Association of Pensions Lawyers; CEDR; LCIA; Chartered Institute of Arbitrators; Secretary of Pensions Litigation Committee of the Association of Pensions Lawyers.
Career: Solicitor *Lovell White & King* 1975-1977; Solicitor *Bond Pearce* 1977-1980; Solicitor *Linklaters & Paines* 1980-1983; Solicitor *Rowe & Maw* 1983-present; Partner 1985; Head of Litigation 1995; Managing Partner 1998-1999.
Publications: Pensions Litigation – Tolley's; Pensions Law (2000).
Personal: Music, travel, family, history, gardening, life.

CLARK, David
Clarks, Reading (0118) 958 5321
Partner in company department.
Specialisation: Handles all areas of pensions work but has particular experience of advising trustees in conflict situations, advising independent trustees appointed under s23 Pensions Act 1995 and of acting as independent trustee. Also handles corporate insolvency and banking work, advises on the pensions aspects of mergers and acquisitions and advises trustees in bankruptcy on pensions related issues. Acted in Clark v. Hicks (independent trusteeship) and Kemble v. Hicks (independent trustee v. trustees in bankruptcy), (trustee insurance, part-timers and cross subsidies between final salary and money purchase sections of schemes).
Prof. Memberships: Association of Pension Lawyers.
Career: Qualified in 1983. Admitted as a solicitor and barrister in New Zealand in 1979. Worked at *Coward Chance* 1980-84, *Linklaters & Paines* 1984-86 and British Alcan Aluminium plc 1986-88. Joined *Clarks* in 1988, becoming a partner in 1989.
Personal: Born 20th December 1953. Holds an LLB 1978 and MA (Business Law) 1984. Full time father; mediocre golfer. Lives in Maidenhead.

CLOSE, Chris
Sacker & Partners, London (020) 7329 6699
chris.close@sacker-partners.co.uk
Specialisation: Partner in specialist law firm. All aspects of law relating to pension schemes. Represented the employer in South West trains case. Acted on a number of high profile scheme mergers and demergers. Experienced in transactions including TUPE. Lectures at conferences, seminars and workshops.
Prof. Memberships: Association of Pension Lawyers.
Career: Qualified in April 1987; became a partner at *Sackers* in June 1987.
Personal: Born 14th December 1954, University of York 1973-76. London University (external) 1981-85. Interests: family, cricket, Charlton Athletic, real ale, walking and backgammon. Lives in Sevenoaks.

COCKERILL, Vivien
Wragge & Co, Birmingham (0121) 214 1072
vivien_cockerill@wragge.com
Specialisation: Acting for trustees and employers in relation to approved and unapproved pension arrangements.
Prof. Memberships: Former elected member of main committee of Association of Pension Lawyers. National Association of Pension Funds local group committee, OPAS Adviser.
Career: Articled *Sackers & Partners*. Qualified 1987. Partner at *Wragge & Co* from 1992.
Personal: Born 1961.

COLACICCHI, Clare E.V.
Hewitson Becke + Shaw, Northampton (01604) 233233

COOMBS, Monica
Sacker & Partners, London (020) 7329 6699
monica.coombs@sacker-partners.co.uk
Specialisation: Specialising in pensions litigation and mediation particularly professional negligence, trust law and asset tracing and recovery.
Prof. Memberships: Association of Pension Lawyers. Law Society.
Career: Admitted in Western Australia 1990. Qualified in England 1996. Partner at *Sacker & Partners*

since 1999.
Personal: Educated at the University of Western Australia. Leisure activities include travel, diving and walking.

COWLEY, Michael J.
Stephenson Harwood, London (020) 7809 2108
Partner in Corporate Department and Employment and Pensions Group.
Specialisation: Pensions covering all aspects of pensions law, advising banks, public and private companies, building societies, trustees, charities and individuals. Also share schemes and other employee incentives.
Prof. Memberships: Association of Pensions Lawyers (Member of Legislative and Parliamentary Sub-Committee), National Association of Pension Funds, Society of Pensions Consultants (Member of Financial Services Regulation Sub-Committee), Share Scheme Lawyers Group.
Career: Qualified in 1984. Whole career has been spent with *Stephenson Harwood*, except for 3 years with the firm's Hong Kong office and one year with *Burges Salmon.*
Personal: Born 1954. Attended Bryanston School, then Oxford University (BA in Philosophy, Politics and Economics). Leisure pursuits: family, hill walking and reading.

COX, Helen
Clifford Chance, London (020) 7600 1000
helen.cox@cliffordchance.com
Specialisation: Partner and head of the pensions group specialising in all aspects of pensions law and practice including pension scheme documentation, the establishment, merger and winding-up of pension schemes, the pensions aspects of corporate mergers and acquisitions, sales, flotations and privatisations and international pension arrangements.
Prof. Memberships: Law Society; Liveryman of the City of London Solicitors' Company; Association of Pension Lawyers (APL); International Pension and Employee Benefits Lawyers Association (IPEBLA); former member of the Main Committee of APL; former member of the Legislative and Parliamentary Sub-Committee of APL; former chairman of the International Sub-Committee of APL; former UK representative on the Steering Committee of IPEBLA; former chairman and secretary of the National Association of Pension Funds City and Eastern Group.
Career: Barry County Grammar School for Girls; University College, London (LLB 1st Class Hons 1974). Articled *Coward Chance*; qualified 1977; made partner *Clifford Chance* 1989.
Personal: Travel, cinema, theatre, art and reading. Born 1953; resides London.

COX, Tim
Linklaters (A member firm of Linklaters & Alliance), London (020) 7456 3692
tim.cox@linklaters.com
Partner, Employment & Employee Benefits Department.
Specialisation: Specialises in mainly pension law. Work includes drafting pension scheme documentation, and advising on pensions matters generally.
Prof. Memberships: Association of Pension Lawyers: member since 1987; member of Legislative & Parliamentary Sub-Committee since 1989; Member of Main committee 1991-96.
Career: Articled at *Linklaters* 1985, Assistant Solicitor 1987-96, Partner 1996.
Personal: Educated at Sir John Deane's Grammar School, BA (Law) (Downing College, Cambridge), BCL (Magdalen College, Oxford). Born 1960.

CROMBIE, June
Morison Bishop, Glasgow (0141) 248 4672
Specialisation: Accredited by the Law Society of Scotland as a specialist in Pension Law. Pensions law and practice, including independent trusteeships through directorship of Mitre Pensions Ltd which is involved in a considerable number of schemes including 6000 member, Rosyth Royal Dockyard Pension Scheme.
Prof. Memberships: Law Society of Scotland, Association of Pension Lawyers. Secretary of the Scottish Group and full member of the Association of Pension Lawyers. Local member of the Scottish Group of the Pensions Management Institute.
Career: Qualified 1987, Partner 1991, partner in pensions unit of corporate division.

DAVIES, Ian H.
Eversheds, Cardiff (02920) 471147
Partner in pensions unit, employment, pensions and licensing department.
Specialisation: Handles all aspects of establishing and running pension schemes; documentation; scheme mergers; winding-up; ownership of surpluses; advice to trustees, acting as independent trustee; and pensions aspects of M&As. Has particular experience of handling multi-scheme mergers. Also handles taxation work, including share option schemes, ESOPs, business and capital taxation. Has published several articles on pensions and tax issues.
Prof. Memberships: APL.
Career: Qualified in 1984. Joined *Phillips & Buck* (now *Eversheds Cardiff*) in 1982, becoming a partner in 1988.

DAVIS, Richard G.L.
Hammond Suddards Edge, Birmingham (0121) 200 2001
richard.davis@hammondsuddardsedge.com
Partner in Pensions Department.
Specialisation: Specialises in occupational pension schemes. Covers documentation, transactional work, scheme mergers, reconstructions and wind ups, insolvency advice and independent trusteeship. Has handled several major scheme mergers.
Prof. Memberships: NAPF; APL; Law Society.
Career: Qualified in 1977. At *Overbury Steward & Eaton* 1978-88. Joined *Eversheds (Wells & Hind)* in 1988 and was a Partner 1989-97. Joined *Edge Ellisonin 1997.*
Personal: Born 29th April 1952. Attended Leeds University 1970-73.

DIERDEN, Kenneth N.
Freshfields Bruckhaus Deringer, London (020) 7936 4000
Partner in Employment, Pensions and Benefits Department.
Specialisation: Work covers all aspects of the establishment and operation of pension schemes (both private and public sector). Experienced in pensions litigation and has wide involvement of the pensions aspects of privatisations. Acts for employers and trustees.
Prof. Memberships: Former Chairman of the Association of Pension Lawyers (APL). Current member of the Legislative and Parliamentary Council of APL. Associate of the Institute of Taxation. Books and Articles: Joint editor of Tolley's 'The Guide to the Pensions Act 1995'. Contributor to Tolley's 'Company Law Handbook' and Tolley's 'Director's Handbook'. Other Relevant Experience: Former lecturer at the College of Law. Regular speaker at pensions conferences.
Career: Qualified in 1977. Lecturer at College of Law 1977/80. Joined *Freshfields* 1980. Partner 1987.
Personal: Born 1952.

DIMSDALE GILL, Angela M.
Lovells, London (020) 7296 2000
amdg@lovells.com
Specialisation: Commercial chancery, pension fund disputes, professional negligence and fraud. Significant cases include Re Courage, National Power plc v Feldon, British Coal Corporation v British Coal Superannuation Scheme Trustees Ltd and the largest fraud claim arising out of collapse of BCCI. Extensive experience of high value pension and trust disputes and professional negligence work. Advises OPRA and Solicitors Indemnity Fund.
Prof. Memberships: City of London Law Society Litigation Sub-Committee, Association of Pension Lawyers and Pension Litigation committee of that association, Pensions Litigation Court Users' Committee, City of London Law Society Pro Bono Sub-Committee (Chair), Trustee Solicitor's Pro Bono Group.
Career: Qualified 1982, partner *Lovells* 1988.

DOCKING, Peter J.
Sacker & Partners, London (020) 7329 6699
peter.docking@sacker-partners.co.uk
Partner in specialist pensions law firm.
Specialisation: Principal area of practice is pensions law. Covers all aspects including litigation, sales and purchases, trust law issues and life office matters. Frequent lecturer and contributor to pensions and academic journals. Former Chairman of APL's Education Committee.
Prof. Memberships: Association of Pension Lawyers, Law Society.
Career: Qualified in 1987. Partner at *Nicholson Graham & Jones* 1991 to 1996. Joined *Sacker & Partners* as a partner in 1996.
Personal: Born 1st June 1961. Educated at Sutton Manor High School for Boys and the University of Exeter. Leisure activities include mountaineering, climbing, walking, skiing and travel.

ELLISON, Robin
Eversheds, London (020) 7919 4500
ellisor@eversheds.com
National head of pensions.
Specialisation: Acted in the Maxwell pensions case. Author of 'Pensions Law and Practice'. Editor of Pensions Benefit Law Reports. Has also published 'Pensions and Divorce', 'The Pension Trustee Handbook' and 'Pensions: Europe and Equality'. Regular broadcaster including frequent contributions to BBC Radio 4's 'Moneybox'.
Prof. Memberships: NAPF, Association of Pensions Lawyers, Law Society.

Career: Fellow of Wolfson College, Cambridge 1975-80. Founded *Ellison Westhorp* in 1980, carrying out exclusively pensions work. Managing Director of Finance for Housing Ltd 1982-87 and Director of Baltic plc 1985-87. Chairman, Pendragon.

FALLON, Liz
Eversheds, Birmingham (0121) 232 1000
Partner
Specialisation: Handles all aspects of pensions law including transactional work, scheme reorganisation, advice to insolvency practitioners, establishment of schemes and scheme documentation. Is also a Director of Eversheds Pension Trustees Limited, which has a substantial portfolio of trusteeships. Has spoken at the Institute of Actuaries Annual Conference and is a regular lecturer for a number of professional training organisations. Also regularly involved in Trustee training courses.
Prof. Memberships: Law Society, Association of Pension Lawyers, National Association of Pension Funds.
Career: Qualified 1983. Joined *Eversheds* 1981. Became a partner 1997. Heads up pensions team in Birmingham.
Personal: Born 17.2.1959. Attended University of Kent, BA Law and German. Interests include keeping up with two young sons and horse riding.

FENTON, Jonathan G.
DLA, London (08700) 111111
jonathan.fenton@dla.com
Specialisation: Partner and Head of the firm's national Pensions Group in London. Experienced in establishment, consolidation, review and merger of schemes and in scheme advisory and transactional work of all kinds including advice on legal aspects of scheme investment and advice to industry-wide schemes. He also advises on contentious matters (both at Ombudsman and High Court level) such as investment and surplus disputes, acting for independent trustees, advice on trustee protection and exoneration and acts for insolvency practitioners and independent trustees on pension aspects of company and scheme winding-up. Also advises on the establishment of Investment Funds and other collective investment schemes. Publications include 'Tolley's Small Self-Administered Pension Schemes' (1988) and 'Tolley's Pensions Law' (original co-author).
Prof. Memberships: Association of Pension Lawyers.
Career: Joined *Oppenheimer Nathan & Vandyk* in 1981, qualifying in 1983. Assistant solicitor 1983-88. Associate partner of *Oppenheimers* 1988, Partner *Denton Hall* 1989-92. Senior Associate *Ashurst Morris Crisp* 1992-94. Partner *Alsop Wilkinson* since 1994-96, partner in the merged firm of *Dibb Lupton Alsop* since its formation in October 1996.
Personal: Educated at Haberdasher's Askes' School and St John's College, Oxford (MA Modern Languages).

FORD, Peter
Nabarro Nathanson, London (020) 7524 6000
Partner in pensions department.
Specialisation: Handles all aspects of pensions law, including company sales and purchases, scheme reorganisations and mergers, investment and the preparation of trust documents.
Prof. Memberships: Association of Pensions Lawyers.
Career: Qualified in 1988, having joined *Nabarro Nathanson* in 1986. Became a partner in 1993.
Personal: Born 8th December 1962. Attended John Fisher School, Purley 1974-81 and the University of Hull 1981-84.

FORREST, Ian
Hammond Suddards Edge, Birmingham (0121) 200 2001
ian.forrest@hammondsuddardsedge.com
Head of the Pensions Department.
Specialisation: Practice includes the full range of pensions law work including transactional support, documentation, scheme mergers, trusteeship and 'special projects'. Clients include several public companies, a national sports association, charities and insurance companies.
Prof. Memberships: APL, PMI, IPEBLA.
Career: Qualified with *Edge Ellison* in 1989. Made Associate in 1994 and Partner in 1995.
Personal: Born 2 April 1951. Educated at Loughborough University (1968-71). Law degree gained through part time study.

GAULT, Ian T.
Herbert Smith, London (020) 7374 8000
ian.gault@herbertsmith.com
Senior pensions partner.
Specialisation: Has extensive experience of advising on all aspects of pensions law and practice. Currently on the legislative and parliamentary sub-committee of the Association of Pensions Lawyers, the executive committee of the Pensions Research Accountant's Group and the Council of the Society of Pensions Consultants.
Prof. Memberships: Association of Pensions Lawyers.
Career: Qualified in 1977. Partner at *Herbert Smith* since 1988.
Personal: Educated at Clare College, Cambridge.

GOLDMAN, Ruth T.
Linklaters (A member firm of Linklaters & Alliance), London (020) 7456 3686
ruth.goldman@linklaters.com
Partner. Employment and Employee Benefits Group.
Specialisation: Specialises in pensions law and employee benefits. Considerable experience in all main areas of pension law practice including trust law aspects, documentation, mergers and acquisitions, flotations, privatisations, international benefits and industry-wide schemes.
Career: Chair of the International Committee of the Association of Pension Lawyers, and member of NAPF Benefits Committee. Articled at *Linklaters*, and made Partner in 1992.

GORDON, Ian
McGrigor Donald, Glasgow (0141) 248 6677
Specialisation: Partner in Corporate Unit. Principal area of practice is employee benefits, pension schemes, share incentive schemes, option schemes, and employee share ownership arrangements for listed, AIM and Ofex companies. Also advises employees and trustees on pensions law. Work includes establishment of and ongoing advice in relation to approved and unapproved pension arrangements. Frequent lecturer on pensions and taxation issues. Has given TV and radio interviews on pension issues.
Prof. Memberships: Association of Pension Lawyers.
Career: Joined *McGrigor Donald* as a trainee in 1979. Qualified in July 1979. One year secondment to *Thomson McLintock CA* in 1983. Became a Partner at *McGrigor Donald* in the same year.
Personal: Educated at Edinburgh University 1975-79. Born 15th August 1957. Lives in Glasgow.

GRAHAM, Ronald
Eversheds, Manchester (0161) 832 6666
ronaldgraham@eversheds.com
Specialisation: All aspects of pension law, including trust documentation and advice (approved and unapproved schemes), sales and acquisitions, scheme mergers, dispute resolution, investment matters, statutory schemes and independent trusteeship.
Prof. Memberships: Full member APL, Committee Member NAPF Manchester Group, NWAPL, Law Society.
Career: Qualified 1985 at *Alexander Tatham* (now *Eversheds* Manchester) and became a partner in 1990.
Personal: Attended Kendal Grammar School, Merton College, Oxford (MA in Jurisprudence) and Corpus Christi College, Cambridge (Diploma in Criminology). Interests include theatre, birds and travel. Lives in Hayfield, Derbyshire.

GRANT, Mark
CMS Cameron McKenna, London (020) 7367 3000
msg@cmck.com
Specialisation: Partner in pensions group advising employers and trustees on all aspects of pensions law, including creation of stakeholder schemes. Established firm's Pensions Ombudsman Unit which defends complaints made against employers, trustees and advisers. Acted for trustee of Coloroll schemes in landmark European Court of Justice case on sex equality issues.
Prof. Memberships: APL, IPEBLA (membership secretary and steering committee member since 1997).
Career: Trained *McKenna & Co*, qualified in 1992; secondment to pensions practice of New York firm *Winthrop, Stimson, Putnam & Roberts*, 1995; Law Society working committee on Pensions Bill, 1995; partner *CMS Cameron McKenna* 1999.
Publications: Co-editor 'International Pension Lawyer' 1995-97; assistant editor 'Occupational Pensions Law Reports' 1997-; author of 'The Pensions Ombudsman; Powers, Procedures and Decisions' (Sweet & Maxwell) 1998; numerous articles for trade journals and papers for conferences.
Personal: Hertford College, Oxford 1986-89. married with two children. Interests: football and cycling.

GREENLEES, Mark B.
Sacker & Partners, London (020) 7329 6699
mark.greenlees@sacker-partners.co.uk
Partner in specialist pensions law firm.
Specialisation: All aspects of law relating to occupational pension schemes. Represented the male beneficiaries in the "Coloroll" reference to the European Court. Acted for vendor in what was then the second largest MBO in UK business history. Regular contributor to pensions periodicals; regular speaker at major conferences and seminars. Immediate past Chairman of the Association of Pension Lawyers.
Prof. Memberships: Association of Pension Lawyers.
Career: Qualified in 1979. Joined *Sacker & Partners* in 1977, becoming a partner in 1982. Former chairman of APL. Member of the Main Committee of APL 1991-1996. Chairman of Legislative and Parliamentary Committee of APL 1992-1994. Chairman

of Legislation Committee of SPC 1991-2. Member of SPC Council.
Personal: Born 18th April 1954. Attended Berkhamsted 1964-71 and Oxford University 1972-76. Leisure interests include family, old cars and Watford FC. Lives near Berkhamsted.

GRIFFITHS, David
Addleshaw Booth & Co, Manchester
(0161) 934 6000
Partner in pensions department, commercial group.
Specialisation: Pensions law, covering advice to individuals, employers and/or trustees in relation to the maintenance and conduct of occupational pension schemes, scheme mergers and reconstructions, contentious pensions issues and the pensions aspects of mergers and acquisitions. Provides full legal document service.
Prof. Memberships: Association of Pension Lawyers. Currently serving on their Legislative and Parliamentary Sub-Committee.
Career: Qualified as a solicitor in 1990 with the firm. Associate 1993. Partner 1996.
Personal: Educated at the University of Edinburgh, (M.A. English Language and Literature). Interests include music, literature, hill-walking and badminton. Lives in Bolton.

HARRIS, Jeremy J.
DLA, Manchester (0161) 235 4222
jeremy.harris@dla.com
Specialisation: Full spectrum of pensions work, including pensions aspects of corporate transactions, drafting definitive and other documentation, advisory including Pensions Act 1995, trustee duties.
Prof. Memberships: Member of the Association of Pension Lawyers.
Career: Partner with *DLA*. M.A. Oxon (Jurisprudence) 1986. Admitted as solicitor 1990 (formerly barrister called to the bar 1986). Formerly with Engineering Employers Federation 1987-89.
Personal: Born 1964. Married, one son. Regular churchgoer. Church work. Cinema/theatre. Cricket. Lives in Cheadle, Cheshire.

HINGLEY, Gerald
Wragge & Co, Birmingham (0121) 685 2777
gerald_hingley@wragge.com
Specialisation: Provides advice and documentation for all aspects of pensions, including the pensions aspects of corporate transactions. Acted for the trustees in the case of Davis v. Richards and Wallington (1990). Frequent speaker at seminars.
Prof. Memberships: Association of Pensions Lawyers, Law Society.
Career: Articled *Vizards*. Qualified in 1970. Partner at *Wragge & Co* from 1974.
Personal: Born 1943.

HOLEHOUSE, Andrew N.
Shepherd & Wedderburn WS, Edinburgh
(0131) 228 9900
andrew.holehouse@shepwedd.co.uk
Partner and head of pensions group.
Specialisation: Deals with all legal aspects of pensions law, including establishment, winding up and ongoing advice for major occupational pension schemes, advice to life offices, pensions aspects of company sales, acquisitions, mergers and flotations, pensions litigation and EC aspects. Also handles employee share schemes. Has written journal articles and regularly speaks at seminars on pensions law.
Prof. Memberships: Committee member and immediate past Chairman Scottish Group Association of Pensions Lawyers, Law Society Pensions Law Accreditation Panel, Law Society Working Party on Pensions Law.
Career: Qualified in England & Wales 1981. With *Rooks Rider*, London 1981-87 (Partner from 1984). Joined *Shepherd & Wedderburn* in 1988. Qualified in Scotland 1989. Became an associate at *Shepherd & Wedderburn* in 1990 and a partner in 1992.
Personal: Born 8th December 1955. Leisure activities include malt whisky, fine wines, opera, classical music, rugby. Lives in Edinburgh.

HOLMES, Leigh
Eversheds, Leeds (0113) 243 0391
leighholmes@eversheds.com
Senior solicitor in commercial department.
Specialisation: Advises on all aspects of pensions law. Has recently advised on scheme amendments, wind ups, restructuring of pension arrangements for corporate clients and on pension aspects of sales and acquisitions. A contributor to Butterworths/Tolleys 'Pensions Law' textbook.
Prof. Memberships: Full member of the Association of Pension Lawyers.
Career: Degree in law obtained from St Hilda's College, Oxford University in 1991. Qualified in 1994 with *Eversheds*, Leeds. Worked in the pensions unit since qualifying.
Personal: Born 1970. Leisure interests include photography.

HUGHES, Sara
Wragge & Co, Birmingham (0121) 685 2723
sara_hughes@wragge.com
Specialisation: Associate in the pensions team. Specialises in legal advice to employers and trustees. Experience covers the Local Government Pension Scheme and the National Health Service Pension Scheme, large scale mergers and wind-ups.
Prof. Memberships: Association of Pension Lawyers.
Career: Articled at *Pinsent & Co*. Qualified 1985. Joined *Wragge & Co* in 1985. Associate *Wragge & Co* 1988.
Personal: Born 1961. Lives in Colchester.

ILLSTON, Tim
Burges Salmon, Bristol (0117) 939 2284
tim.illston@burges-salmon.com
Specialisation: Head of pensions unit. Has experience in independent trusteeships, trust law, unapproved retirement benefits schemes, SSASs, ESOPs, share schemes, pension fund trustee training, investment management agreements and establishment, merger and winding-up of pension schemes. Drafts insurance company and pension scheme documentation.
Prof. Memberships: Law Society, Association of Pension Lawyers, NAPF, PRAG, Society of Pension Consultants, PMI and IPEBLA.
Career: Moved from *Freshfields* to *Burges Salmon* in 1988, becoming a partner in 1990.
Personal: University of Manchester 1977-80. Leisure interests include hockey, guitar and cycling.

ITO, Stephen
Lovells, London (020) 7296 2000
stephen.ito@lovells.com
Specialisation: Principal area of practice is pensions law with a particular emphasis on corporate mergers and acquisitions related work including multi-jurisdiction transactions. Otherwise involved in all aspects of UK pensions law acting mainly for UK, US and EU corporate clients.
Prof. Memberships: Law Society, Association of Pension Lawyers.
Career: Former Barrister (qualified 1984): qualified as a solicitor 1992 *Lovells*, partner 1995.

JACOBS, Howard
Slaughter and May, London (020) 7600 1200
Specialisation: Pension scheme restructurings, general pension advice.
Prof. Memberships: City of London Solicitors Company Employment Law Sub-committee.
Career: Winchester College. Pembroke College, Cambridge. *Slaughter and May* since 1975.
Personal: Married, three children. Interests: family and gardening.

JAMES, Stuart C.
Rowe & Maw, London (020) 7248 4282

JENKINS, Martin
Dickinson Dees, Newcastle upon Tyne
(0191) 279 9528
Specialisation: Pensions law in all its aspects and manifestations.
Prof. Memberships: Association of Pensions Lawyers; Chairman National Association Pension Funds (Northern Counties Group).
Career: Studied law at University of Newcastle upon Tyne.
Personal: Mountain biking and walking in the Northumberland countryside – "an undiscovered wilderness".

KENNEDY, Patrick
Masons, Manchester (0161) 234 8234
Head of pensions *Masons* Manchester.
Specialisation: Is accustomed to giving commercial legal advice on all aspects of pensions and is a Director of Masons Trustees Limited. He has served on the Committee of the National Association of Pension Funds, Manchester Group, and was involved in providing assistance to the Legislative and Parliamentary Committee of the Association of Pension Lawyers in connection with the Pensions Act 1995 Regulations. He was also a member of the Barber Committee of the Association of Pension Lawyers until it was eventually disbanded. Patrick has spoken on a variety of pensions law topics at national conferences, and is a Full Member of the Association of Pension Lawyers. He has established a liaison group which involves The Association of Pension Lawyers, The Association of Corporate Trustees and The Society of Practitioners of Insolvency.
Career: Graduated in law from London University, where he was awarded two prestigious academic prizes. He then trained with *Allen & Overy* in their London and New York offices, qualifying as a solicitor in 1990. Patrick, who is 34 and a partner, subsequently gained specialist pensions experience with *Eversheds* in Leeds before joining *Davies Arnold Cooper* for five years in Manchester after which, the team having established itself as the largest pensions team in the North West, he negotiated the transfer of the entire pensions team to *Masons*.

KNIGHT, Timothy
Wrigleys, Leeds (0113) 244 6100
Partner.
Specialisation: Extensive experience in private client law and pensions with a particular emphasis on acting for trustees concerning occupational pension

schemes. Also has estate planning, private client and company/commercial experience.
Prof. Memberships: Association of Pension Lawyers (Former Member of Legislative and Parliamentary Committee).
Career: Computer analyst with Rolls Royce 1966-71. Joined *Dibb Lupton* in 1976 and became a partner in 1978. Moved to *Wrigleys* 1 May 1997.
Personal: Born 1948. Educated Ampleforth College (Scholar) Worcester College Oxford (Exhibitioner).

KNOX, Louisa
Shepherd & Wedderburn WS, Edinburgh
(0131) 228 9900
louisa.knox@shepwedd.co.uk
Specialisation: Partner in pensions group 1998. Deals with all aspects of pensions law, writes journal articles and regularly speaks at seminars.
Prof. Memberships: Committee Member of the Association of Pension Lawyers (Scottish Group), Member of the Association of Pension Lawyers.
Career: Glasgow University (LLB Hons); Qualified 1993; specialised in pensions law since then.
Personal: Hill walking; mountain biking; swimming; socialising – food and drink.

KOWALIK, Mark
CMS Cameron McKenna, London
(020) 7367 3000
mak@cmck.com
Specialisation: Specialises in all aspects of law relating to occupational pension schemes, including trust law, documentation, mergers and acquisitions, privatisations, Ombudsman complaints and scheme wind ups. Handles day to day work for several major pension funds. Recently advised trustees on Halliburton Group Pension Plan merger.
Prof. Memberships: Association of Pension Lawyers (Treasurer of APL since 1996, member of Education & Seminars Committee since 1993).
Career: Qualified in 1988. Whole career has been at *McKenna & Co* and then *CMS Cameron McKenna*.
Personal: Born 17 September 1962. Educated at King Henry VIII School, Coventry (1973 to 1981) and St John's College, Oxford (1982 to 1985). Interests include fine art, international athletics and football (Member of Coventry City London Supporters Club).

LEE, Martin P.W.
DLA, Sheffield (0114) 283 3247
martin.lee@dla.com
Specialisation: Consultant for the firm's Pensions Team. A leading practitioner in pensions law in the South Yorkshire area since the early 1980's. Trustee of a number of pension schemes. A director of Fountain Trustee Ltd, the firm's independent pension scheme trustee company.
Career: Qualified 1966.
Personal: Born 24.5.39.

LEGRAND, Janet
DLA, London (020) 7796 6827
janet.legrand@dla.com
Specialisation: Pensions litigation and professional negligence, including representing the Group Trustees in the National Grid pension surplus litigation in the Court of Appeal (currently pending before the House of Lords), High Court and Ombudsman proceedings and broad range of topics and several substantial professional negligence claims.
Prof. Memberships: Association of Pensions Lawyers. Association of Women Solicitors.
Career: 1981-83: trainee, *Lovell White Durrant.* 1983-91: solicitor, *Lovell White Durrant.* 1991 to date: partner, *DLA.* 1999 to date: Board and Audit Committee member, *DLA.*
Personal: Education: Trinity Hall, Cambridge, Law MA. Family: Married with two children. Leisure: Family.

LESTER, C. Peter
Sacker & Partners, London (020) 7329 6699
peter.lester@sacker-partners.co.uk
Partner in pensions only law firm.
Specialisation: Deals with all areas of pensions law with specialist expertise in relation to FURBS and multinational pension provision. Major clients include BBC and the pension funds of leading companies. Contributor to pensions periodicals and speaker at major conferences and seminars.
Prof. Memberships: Association of Pension Lawyers. For many years a co-opted member of the Parliamentary Committee of the National Association of Pension Funds.
Career: Qualified in 1968. Partner at *Walker Martineau* 1970-83. Joined *Sacker & Partners* as a Partner in 1983.
Personal: Born in 1944. Educated at Christ's Hospital 1954-62 and Birmingham University 1962-65 (LL.B). Leisure activities include golf, music, theatre and walking. Lives in Hove.

LEWIS, Roger
Eversheds, London (020) 7919 4500
lewisr@eversheds.com
Head of London pensions group.
Specialisation: Advises employers and trustees in relation to all aspects of corporate pension arrangements.
Prof. Memberships: Law Society, APL, NAPF.
Career: Qualified 1978. Employed IBM 1966-68, GEC 1968-72 and Commission of the European Communities 1973-75. Joined *Lewis, Lewis & Co.* (now *Eversheds*) in 1976, becoming a partner in 1979.
Personal: Born 14th April 1945. Attended UCS 1958-63, then Balliol College, Oxford 1963-66 (MA, Physics). Governor of Hebrew University of Jerusalem. Married with two children. Leisure interests include golf, tennis and theatre.

MARSHALL, Jane M.
Hammond Suddards Edge, London
(020) 7655 1000
jane.marshall@hammondsuddardsedge.com
Partner and head of pensions unit.
Specialisation: Handles all areas of pension law, with particular emphasis on complex advice work and special projects, including scheme mergers, conflicts, privatisation, outsourcing and similar issues affecting the public sector, and pension surpluses. Handled pensions aspects of water privatisation and acted for the trustees in one of the first large surplus refund cases (£50 million). Contributor to professional journals, including' Pensions Age', 'Professional Pensions' and 'Occupational Pensions Quarterly'. Lectures at conferences and seminars, and is a speaker on radio and TV. Editor and co-author of 'Pensions: The New Law' (Jordans 1995) and 'Pension Disputes: Prevention and Resolution' (Jordans 1998).
Prof. Memberships: Law Society, Association of Pension Lawyers and International Pensions and Employee Benefit Lawyers Association. Member of the Regulatory Sub-Committee of National Association of Pension Funds. OPAS adviser.
Career: Qualified in 1978. Worked abroad after qualifying. Joined *Lovell White & King* in 1980 to specialise in pensions. Founder partner with pensions specialists *Ellison Westhorp* and became partner with *Hammond Suddards* following its merger with *Ellison Westhorp* in 1994, becoming head of the firm's pension practice.
Personal: Born 17th December 1953. Attended March High School for Girls to 1972, then Dundee University 1972-76 (First Class Honours). Leisure interests include gardening, antiques and local history. Mother of four. Lives in Little Bromley, near Colchester.

MASSARANO SALT, Vikki
DLA, Leeds (08700) 111111
vikki.massarano.salt@dla.com
Specialisation: Advising on all aspects of pensions law, including scheme governance, mergers, documentation, restructuring, sales and acquisitions.
Prof. Memberships: Association of Pension Lawyers. Student member of Pensions Management Institute.
Career: Qualified with *Booth & Co* in 1994. Joined *Dibb Lupton Alsop* as an associate in 1998. Partner 2000.
Personal: Born 1970. Educated Loughborough High School for Girls and University College, Oxford. Interests include travel, native American art, books.

MATTHEWS, Paul
Osborne Clarke OWA, Bristol (0117) 917 3000
paul.matthews@osborneclarke.com
Specialisation: Advises on all aspects of pensions law, including pensions aspects of sales and acquisitions, but is his particular specialism is in advising trustees, employers and life companies on contentious or potentially contentious pensions matters. These include OPRA and Pensions Ombudsman's investigations as well main stream High Court pensions litigation.
Career: Trained with *McKenna & Co* and joined *Osborne Clarke* in 1993 and was made a partner in 1999.

MCKENNA, Catherine M.P.
Hammond Suddards Edge, Leeds (0113) 284 7000
catherine.mckenna@hammondsuddardsedge.com
Partner in pensions department.
Specialisation: All work relating to occupational pension schemes. General advice work, including documentation, sales and acquisitions, mergers, insolvency advice, FURBS and trusteeship. Regular speaker at seminars and co-author of 'Pensions – The New Law' (Jordans).
Prof. Memberships: Association of Pension Lawyers, National Association of Pension Funds, Associate of the Pensions Management Institute, Society of Pension Consultants.
Career: Educated at Nottingham University (LLB Hons) and Chester Law School (2nd class honours). Qualified 1989. Joined *Alsop Wilkinson* in Manchester and moved to *Hammond Suddards*, Leeds in January 1994. Committee member NE NAPF and Chairman NE PMI.
Personal: Born 1964. Interests include socialising, food, wine, watching sport. Lives in Ilkley.

MEEKS, Alastair
Biddle, London (020) 7606 9301
a.meeks@biddle.co.uk
Specialisation: Advising trustees and employers on all aspects of the law relating to occupational pension schemes. Clients include the Provincial Pension Fund,

Charter plc and ITN.
Prof. Memberships: APL, Associate of the Pensions Management Institute.
Career: Joined *Biddle* on qualification 1992. Became a partner in 1997.
Publications: Assistant Editor of the occupational Pensions Law Reports, Legal Contributor to 'Occupational Pensions' magazine.
Personal: Born 16 November 1967. BA (Hons) Law Durham 1985-88. Lives in London.

MILTON, Kevin
Garretts, Birmingham (0121) 698 9000
kevin.milton@glegal.com
Specialisation: Advice to trustees, employers and members on the legal aspects of the establishment and operation of occupational pension schemes. This includes preparing the documentation establishing schemes and altering schemes to meet changing circumstances and legislative requirements.
Prof. Memberships: Association of Pension Lawyers; Law Society; National Association of Pension Funds.
Career: Articled at *Davis, Campbell & Co.* Qualified 1984. Joined *Wragge & Co* in 1987 becoming associate in 1990. Joined *Browne Jacobson* as partner in 1995.
Personal: Born 31 March 1960. Married with two children. Hobbies – hockey, skiing and scuba diving.

MONTY, Craig
Lovells, London (020) 7296 2000
craig.monty@lovells.com
Specialisation: Partner in the commercial litigation sector with particular emphasis on professional indemnity work, trust and pensions disputes (important cases include: British Coal Corporation v British Coal Staff Superannuation Scheme Trustees Limited (1995) 1 All ER 912; National Power plc v Hugh Feldon & Others (1999:CA)) and product liability work.
Prof. Memberships: Member London Solicitors Litigation Association; associate member of Association of Pension Lawyers.
Career: Articled *Lovells*; qualified 1988; partner 1998.
Personal: Education: Our Lady and St. Bede's Roman Catholic Comprehensive School, St. Mary's Sixth Form College, University of Newcastle upon Tyne (LLB 1st Class Hons); College of Law, Chester (Law Society Finals). Personal: Born 1964; resides Harpenden. Leisure: All sports, particularly football (Middlesbrough FC) and horse racing.

MOORE, Nigel
CMS Cameron McKenna, London (020) 7367 3000
Partner and Head of Pensions Team.
Specialisation: Main area of practice is pensions. Work includes advising on administration of pension schemes; drafting trust deeds and rules; advising on pension aspects of mergers and acquisitions; advising on mergers of schemes; handling litigation in employment tribunals, High Court and European Court of Justice. Organises and speaks on trustee training courses. Also handles employment law. Acted in Coloroll's application to the European Court. Speaking experience includes NAPF training courses, APL annual conferences and commercial conferences.
Prof. Memberships: Law Society, City of London Solicitors Company, Association of Pension Lawyers (Chairman of International Committee). OPAS advisor. Member of Training Committee of NAPF.
Career: Qualified 1986. Articled at *Radcliffes & Co* 1984-86. Joined *McKenna & Co* in 1986. Partner 1994.
Personal: Born 13th June 1962. Attended St Albans School 1973-80, Warwick University 1980-83, College of Law Chancery Lane 1983-84 and City of London Polytechnic (MA in Business Law) 1984-86. Leisure interests include golf and football. Lives in Welwyn Garden City.

MULLEN, Chris P.
Biddle, London (020) 7606 9301
Partner in and head of pensions group.
Specialisation: Advises companies and scheme trustees on all aspects of pensions law, relating principally to occupational pension schemes. Heavily involved in complex mergers and pension scheme reorganisations; negotiations concerning benefit improvements allied to surplus refunds; advising trustees and employers on member disputes and Ombudsman complaints; documentation advice, drafting and large-value transaction advice. Clients include Heinz, Lloyd's, Costain Group plc, Vivendi Group, Air France and the NSPCC as well as other law firms seeking specialist pensions support.
Prof. Memberships: APL, Member of APL Education Committee, City of London Solicitors Company. Editor of 'Pension Lawyer' Magazine. Conference Speaker for IBC, NAPF, APL.
Career: Qualified in 1986 after articles at *Biddle*. Became a partner in 1990. Head of pensions group since 1998.
Personal: Born 11th September 1960. Educated at Jesus College, Cambridge 1979-82 (MA in Law). Lives in Hertford, Herts. Three children, a beagle and a swimming pool.

MURRAY, John
Nabarro Nathanson, London (020) 7524 6000
Specialisation: Advises employers, trustees and others on all aspects of pensions law; specialises in scheme re-organisation and documentation for approved and unapproved schemes; experienced in pensions litigation and pensions ombudsman enquiries.
Prof. Memberships: Law Society, APL, IPEBLA, former member Association of Pensioneer Trustees Committee 1991-97.
Career: Leeds University (1976 LL.B). Qualified and joined *Nabarro Nathanson* 1979. Partner 1986.
Personal: Born 1953. Resides London.

ORTON, Giles A.C.
Eversheds, Derby (01332) 360992
Head of litigation, East Midlands.
Specialisation: Main area of practice pensions litigation, conducting disputes over pension schemes, particularly regarding surplus and winding up. Acted in Falconer v Aslef and NUR, Imperial Tobacco, Mirror Group, Lloyd's Bank Pension Scheme Cases. Author of numerous articles on pensions law. Addresses a wide range of seminars and conferences, including TV/radio appearances.
Prof. Memberships: Member of main Committee of Association of Pension Lawyers. Chairman of Pensions Litigation Committee of Association of Pension Lawyers. East Midlands Committee, NAPF.
Career: Qualified in 1983. *Broomheads* from 1981, Associate in 1986. Joined *Evershed Wells & Hind* in 1987, Associate 1988, partner in 1989.
Personal: Born 18th August 1959. Attended King Edward VII School, Sheffield 1970-77; The Queen's College, Oxford (Hastings Exhibition) 1977-80 and Chester College of Law 1980-81. Derby City Councillor 1988-92.

PAYNE, E.Kate
DLA, Sheffield (08700) 111 111
kate.payne@dla.com
Specialisation: Advises corporate clients and trustees on all aspects of ongoing pension schemes and schemes in winding-up.
Prof. Memberships: Full member of the Association of Pension Lawyers Law Society.
Career: Qualified with *Rowe & Maw* and left to join *Ashurst Morris Crisp*. Joined *Dibb Lupton Alsop* in 1995.
Personal: Born 12th May 1962. Educated at Oxford University.

PEARSON, H. John H.
Lovells, London (020) 7296 2000
john.pearson@lovells.com
Partner in pensions and employment group.
Specialisation: Advises employers, trustees and others on all aspects of pensions law and documentation relating to occupational and personal pension schemes and pension products; reorganisations; offshore schemes; pensions aspects of company sales, purchases and insolvencies; and pensions litigation. Acted for Mirror Group Newspapers post-Maxwell in sorting out its pensions problems. Has given many pensions related talks, including one in French.
Prof. Memberships: Law Society, City of London Solicitors Company, Association of Pension Lawyers, International Pension and Employee Benefit Lawyers Association.
Career: Qualified in 1971. Joined *Lovells* and became a partner in 1986.
Personal: Attended King's College, London (LLB 1968).

PEEL, Neville
Addleshaw Booth & Co, Leeds (0113) 209 2000
Partner in pensions department, commercial group.
Specialisation: Advises employers and trustees regarding all aspects of ongoing occupational pension schemes. Complete service to insolvency practitioners including independent statutory trusteeships. Co-author of 'Pensions and Insurance on Family Breakdown' (Jordans) and 'Pension Schemes Act 1993' (Sweet & Maxwell).
Prof. Memberships: Association of Pension Lawyers; Law Society.
Career: Qualified in 1967. Joined the firm as pensions partner in 1990, after 25 years in manufacturing industry.
Personal: Educated at Manchester University. Lives in Sheffield. Freeman of the Cutlers' Company; Council Member, University of Sheffield.

PETHERAM, Claire
Linklaters (A member firm of Linklaters & Alliance), London (020) 7456 3676
claire.petheram@linklaters.com
Partner, Employment and Employee Benefits Group.
Specialisation: Specialises in all aspects of pension law including pension scheme mergers, pension aspects of commercial transactions, trust law queries relating to pension schemes, investment management issues and plain English documentation.

PITTAWAY, Ian M.
Sacker & Partners, London (020) 7329 6699
ian.pittaway@sacker-partners.co.uk
Partner in specialist pensions law firm.
Specialisation: Covers all aspects of pension law

including acting as trustee, arbitrator and expert witness. Joint author of 'EC Pensions Law' and numerous articles and lectures. Former Chairman and Secretary of APL.
Prof. Memberships: Law Society, Association of Pension Lawyers, Justice.
Career: Qualified in 1980 and joined *Nicholson Graham & Jones* in 1981. Became a Partner in 1984. Joined *Sacker & Partners* in 1996.
Personal: Born 28th July 1956. Attended the University of Hull 1974-77. Leisure interests include gardening, golf, wine and whisky.

POLLARD, David N.
Freshfields Bruckhaus Deringer, London London (020) 7832 7060
Specialisation: Partner in Employment, Pensions and Benefits Department, and group of over 30 lawyers covering the whole range of pensions, employment and benefits work. Acted for trustees in Drexel pension case. Author of book 'Corporate Insolvency: Employment and Pension Rights' and contributor of chapters to Tolley's 'Employment Law' and Tolley's 'Insolvency Law'. Co-Editor 'Trust Law International' magazine. Editor of 'Guide to the Pensions Act 1995' book. Editorial Board, Occupational Pensions Law Reports. Main Committee of the APL. Awarded APL 'Wallace Prize' in 1998.

POWELL, Andrew M.
Hammond Suddards Edge, London (020) 7655 1000
Partner in Pensions Unit.
Specialisation: Handles all aspects of pensions work, including inter alia documentation, deal based work, financial products, mergers and other complex advice work. Contributor to Trust Law International, Accountancy Age, Acquisitions Monthly and others. Co-author of 'Managing a Company Pension Scheme'. Contributor to 'Pensions: The New Law' (Jordans 1995). Editor 'Pension Law Reports' (IDS).
Prof. Memberships: Law Society, Institute of Directors, the Society for Advanced Legal Studies.
Career: Qualified in 1980. Articled *Granville West Chivers & Morgan*. Then in-house lawyer covering pensions work for DHSS; adviser to OPB, NHS superannuation fund; responsible for pensions work at *Denton Hall Burgin & Warrens*, before becoming a Partner at *Ellison Westhorp* in 1990. Joined *Hammond Suddards* in 1994. Former main committee member of Association of Pension Lawyers; member of APL investment sub-committee, IPEBLA and Director of Trustee Corporation Limited.
Personal: Born 26th January 1955. Attended King Henry VIII Grammar School to 1975. Graduated from the University of Wales in 1978; then attended Lancaster Gate College of Law. Lives in Harrow-on-the-Hill.

QUARRELL, John
Nabarro Nathanson, London (020) 7524 6000
Partner and Head of Pensions Department.
Specialisation: Work covers all aspects relating to occupational and personal pension schemes, including investment legalities, overseas provision, equality issues, litigation matters and dispute resolution. Acts for and advises most leading firms of accountants, many pension providers and a number of firms of pensions consultants and actuaries. Has acted in a large number of leading cases. Author of numerous articles and papers. Lectures at home and abroad. Advises Russian Government.

RAWNSLEY, Rachel
Addleshaw Booth & Co, Leeds (0113) 209 2000
Partner in pensions department, commercial group
Specialisation: Advises corporate clients and trustees on all aspects of ongoing pension schemes, setting up new schemes, winding up and merging established schemes. Advises insolvency practitioners, including on independent statutory trusteeships. Co-author of the pensions chapter of 'The Business Client Handbook' (Sweet & Maxwell). Editor of 'An Introduction to Pensions Law' written and published by the University of Northumbria.
Prof. Memberships: Association of Pensions Lawyers, National Association of Pension Funds.
Career: Joined the firm in January 1993. Partner in 1997.
Personal: Educated at Cambridge University 1983-86 (MA in Law). Lives in Ilkley.

RIDLER, Mark
Hammond Suddards Edge, Leeds (0113) 284 7000 mark.ridler@hammondsuddardsedge.com
Specialisation: Pensions law. Experience includes scheme documentation, trustee and employer advisory work, scheme mergers and legal due diligence and drafting and negotiating documentation for company and business sales and purchases.
Prof. Memberships: Association of Pensions Lawyers.
Career: Qualified with *Bevan Ashford* in 1986. Moved to *Kershaw Tudor*, Sheffield in 1988 and became a partner in 1991. Became a partner in *Irwin Mitchell* in 1994 upon the merger with *Kershaw Tudor*. Joined *Hammond Suddards* in September 1999. Regular speaker at seminars.
Personal: Married with two children. Interests include radio controlled aircraft and jazz.

ROGERS, Anna
Rowe & Maw, London (020) 7248 4282 arogers@roweandmawe.co.uk
Partner in Pensions Department.
Specialisation: Specialises in pensions work including scheme mergers and demergers and all aspects of advisory and documentation work fro trustees and employers in defined benefit, defined contribution, hybrid and umbrella occupational pension schemes of all sizes.
Prof. Memberships: Association of Pensions Lawyers, Fellow and Council Member of Pensions Management Institute.
Career: Articled at *Nabarro Nathanson*. Qualified in 1985. Became a Partner at *Rowe & Maw* in 1989.
Personal: Born 15th May 1961. Educated at Sheffield High School for Girls 1972-79 and Keble College, Oxford 1979-82. Lives in London. Known as Anna Kelly 1991-96.

RYLAND, Glyn
Wragge & Co, Birmingham (0121) 214 1004 glyn_ryland@wragge.com
Partner in Pensions Team, Birmingham Head of *Wragge & Co's* 20 lawyer Pensions Team.
Specialisation: All aspects of UK and Hong Kong pensions law. Scheme set-ups, mergers and wind-ups; statutory compliance advice; FURBS, section 615 schemes and international aspects; pensions litigation and Ombudsman work; documentation and communication; investment management and custody; pensions on corporate deals, pensions and financial services mis-selling.
Prof. Memberships: Association of Pension Lawyers. Admitted in England and Wales and Hong Kong.
Career: Articles *Eversheds*, Cardiff *(Phillips and Buck)*. Qualified Feb 1988. 1988-December 1991 *Herbert Smith*. 1992-94 *Johnson Stokes & Master*, Hong Kong. 1994 to 1998 *Pinsent Curtis*. Partner 1995. Joined *Wragge & Co.* as a partner in 1998.
Personal: Born 1962.

SAEEDI, Terry
Hammond Suddards Edge, Leeds (0113) 284 7000 terry.saeedi@hammondsuddardsedge.com
Specialisation: All aspects of pensions law and practice including general advisory work, scheme establishment and re-organisations, insolvency advice, transaction support, documentation. Director of *Hammond Suddards* Pension Trust Ltd (independent trustee company). Regular speaker at seminars and co-author of *Naborro Nathanson's* 'A Guide to UK Pensions Law'.
Prof. Memberships: Association of Pension Lawyers, Pensions Management Institute, Society of Pension Consultants (Yorkshire Group Committe Member), Society of Computers and Law.
Career: Analyst/Programmer with Sheffield Local Education Authority 1988 to 1990. Trainee and assistant solicitor with *Dibb Lupton Broomhead* 1990-1995. *Nabarro Nathanson* 1995-1997. Joined *Hammond Suddards* in September 1997. Partner on 1 May 2000.
Personal: BA(Hons) Law, Msc Software Engineering. Qualified 1992.

SAMSWORTH, Jane M.
Lovells, London (020) 7296 2000 jane.samsworth@lovells.com
Specialisation: Partner advising on all aspects of pension law and documentation, including establishment, management and termination of occupational pension schemes, (both approved and unapproved and personal pensions); reorganisation and scheme mergers; pension aspects of company sales and acquisitions; pension litigation; pensions in insolvency; advising clients in their relations with the regulatory authorities including the preparation of submissions to the Pensions Ombudsman. Co-author of 'Guide to the Pensions Act 1995'; regular contributor to seminars and conferences on pension issues.
Prof. Memberships: Fellow Pensions Management Institute; Member of main committee of Association of Pension Lawyers, immediate past Honorary Secretary and former member of its Legal and Parliamentary and Education and Training Sub-Committees; Member of the Council of OPAS Ltd; Council Member and president elect SPC; Law Society; City of London Solicitors; director *Lovells* Pension Trustees Ltd, member Institute of Directors.
Career: Qualified 1978. 1978-83 Greater London Council. 1983-87 British Telecommunications plc; 1987 joined *Lovells* partner 1991.

SAUNDERS, Carolyn
Taylor Joynson Garrett, London (020) 7300 7000 csaunders@tjg.co.uk
Specialisation: Partner in employment department and head of the Pensions Group. Has specialised in pensions law since qualifying at *Baker & McKenzie* in 1987 and advises employers, trustees and individuals on all aspects – contentious and non-contentious. Regular conference speaker.
Prof. Memberships: Association of Pension Lawyers (current member of the Association's Educa-

tion and Seminars sub-committee); NAPF Local Group Committee member.
Career: Qualified at *Baker & McKenzie* in 1987, subsequently working at *Travers Smith Braithwaite* before joining *Taylor Joynson Garrett* in February 1995. Became a partner in 1997.

SCHAFFER, Daniel
Freshfields Bruckhaus Deringer, London
(020) 7936 4000
Partner in employment, pensions and benefits group.
Specialisation: Pensions. Advises on all aspects of pensions.
Prof. Memberships: Association of Pension Lawyers (Member of International Committee). Sir John Vinelott Trust Law Committee. Sat on Financial Law Panel working party on "commercial dealings with trustees". Regular speaker.
Career: Joined *Freshfields* in 1988. Part-time tutor in trusts at LSE (1987-88), Merton College, Oxford (1987-90) and Balliol College, Oxford (1988-92).
Personal: Born 13th October 1963. Educated at Haberdashers' Aske's School, Elstree 1971-82, Bristol University 1983-86 (LLB, Simmons Scholar) and Merton College, Oxford 1986-87.(BCL 1st Class). Leisure pursuits include travelling in France. Fluent in French; working knowledge of Spanish.

SCHOLEFIELD, Stephen
Addleshaw Booth & Co, Manchester
(0161) 934 6000
Specialisation: Advises on all aspects of pensions law, including the pensions aspects of corporate disposals and acquisitions, pension scheme mergers, trustee issues, contentious matters and documentation.
Prof. Memberships: Association of Pension Lawyers.
Career: Qualified as a solicitor in 1996 and joined the firm in 1997.
Personal: Educated at Cambridge University. Interests include football, walking and reading.

SCOTT, Harry
Mills & Reeve, Norwich (01603) 693 249
harry.scott@mills-reeve.com
Specialisation: Pensions i.e. law and practice relating to occupational pension schemes including documentation, advice, Pensions Ombudsman Cases and acting as a pension scheme trustee through *Mills & Reeve's* corporate trustee, Francis House Trustees Limited. Full member of the Association of Pension Lawyers.

SERES, Jonathan S.D.
Sacker & Partners, London (020) 7329 6699
Senior Partner of specialist pensions law firm.
Specialisation: Experienced in all aspects of pension schemes, covering establishment, alteration, merger, booklets, related employment law, Financial Services Act work, common investment funds and investment management and custody agreements. Advises employers, trustees, trade unions and charities. Acted in application to the ECJ in the Coloroll matter (*Sacker & Partners* were acting for the four classes of male beneficiaries). Acted in 1998 on £700m transfer from GEC Plan on flotation of Alstom, and in 1999 on £2.5bn separation of MES. Author of 'Pensions: A Practical Guide' (4th edition 1997, FT Law & Tax,450 pages). Appeared as pensions tax expert on Channel 4's City Programme. Now leads the firm of 35 specialist pensions lawyers.
Prof. Memberships: Association of Pension Lawyers, National Association of Pension Funds, Society of Pension Consultants, Law Society.
Career: MA (Oxon). Qualified at *Sacker & Partners* in 1971. Became Partner in 1973. Chairman of the Association of Pension Lawyers 1985-88. APL International Sub-Committee 1992-1997. Member of former Government/ Industry Working Party for Personal Pension Schemes.
Personal: Born 13th June 1945. Oxford University PPE (Hons) 1966. Leisure interests include sailing, history and charities. Lives in London.

SHELLEY, Daniel
Pinsent Curtis, Birmingham (0121) 200 1050
daniel.shelley@pinsents.com
Specialisation: All aspects of pension law.
Prof. Memberships: Association of Pension Lawyers.
Career: Articles – *Slaughter and May*; *Pinsent Curtis* – partner 1995.
Personal: Born 1958.

SHERWIN, Nick
Clifford Chance, London (020) 7600 1000
nick.sherwin@cliffordchance.com
Specialisation: Partner specialising in pensions, also widely experienced in taxation matters, particularly employee share schemes and other benefits.
Career: Manchester Grammar School; St John's College, Cambridge (MA Hons 1982); University of Pennsylvania (LLM 1983); ATII, Gilbert Burr Medal Winner. Articled *Clifford-Turner*; assistant solicitor *Clifford-Turner/ Clifford Chance* 1986-1993; made partner *Clifford Chance* 1993; former committee member of Association of Pension Lawyers; former chairman Legislative & Parliamentary Sub-Committee of Association of Pension Lawyers; NAPF Case Law Standing Group member. Member Pensions Research Accountants Group, Associate Member SIPP Provider Group.
Personal: Born 1961; resides London; married with two daughters.

SLOAN, Derek S.
Allen & Overy, London (020) 7330 3000
derek.sloan@allenovery.com
Partner and head of Employment, Pensions and Incentives Department.
Specialisation: Practice covers all areas of pensions work including establishing, reorganising, merging and terminating schemes, investment management and custody arrangements, the pensions implications of business sales, reorganisations and insolvencies, funding issues and equal treatment. Regular speaker at conferences.
Prof. Memberships: Law Society, Association of Pension Lawyers, Chairman of APL Legislative and Parliamentary sub-committee, Pensions Research Accountants Group.
Career: Qualified 1973, having joined *Allen & Overy* in 1971. Became a Partner in 1977.
Personal: Attended Oxford University 1967-70 (BA Jurisprudence). Born 1948.

SMITH, Stephanie
Travers Smith Braithwaite, London
(020) 7295 3000
Stephanie.Smith@TraversSmith.com
Partner in pensions department.
Specialisation: Handles all aspects of pensions law. Regular public speaker.
Prof. Memberships: Association of Pensions Lawyers.
Career: Qualified in 1986. Joined *Travers Smith Braithwaite* in 1993, becoming a partner in 1994.
Personal: Born 22nd March 1962. Holds an LLB from Queen Mary College, London (1983). Lives in London.

SOUTHERN, Steve
Hammond Suddards Edge, Manchester
(0161) 830 5000
steve.southern@hammondsuddards.co.uk
Specialisation: The law and practice relating to occupational pension schemes and other forms of retirement pensions in the UK. Includes advice to employers and trustees, transactional work, mergers, trusteeship, documentation.
Prof. Memberships: Association of Pension Lawyers and Associate of the Pensions Management Institute.
Career: Qualified in September 1996 and became an Associate of Pensions Management Institute in 1998.
Personal: Football, music.

STANNARD, Paul A.C.
Travers Smith Braithwaite, London
(020) 7295 3000
Paul.Stannard@TraversSmith.com
Partner in pensions department.
Specialisation: All aspects of pensions law.
Prof. Memberships: Hon. Secretary Association of Pensions Lawyers (1991-94), Fellow of the Pensions Management Institute.
Career: Qualified 1982. Joined *Travers Smith Braithwaite* as a partner in 1989.
Personal: Born 1957.

STRACHAN, Russell A.
Lovells, London (020) 7296 2000
russell.strachan@lovells.com
Specialisation: Pension law in all its applications, particularly: negotiating scheme reorganisations and mergers, benefit design, sales and acquisitions, conflicts of interest and trustee problems, winding-up, equal pay and contentious issues, investment and regulatory matters, scheme documentation and member communications. Clients include multi-national and UK employers, trustees, insurance companies, investment companies and professional advisers.
Prof. Memberships: Law Society, Association of Pension Lawyers, National Association of Pension Funds; Pension Research Accountants Group.
Career: Articled *Lovells* qualified 1970; partner 1975.

SUTTON, Philip
Hammond Suddards Edge, Birmingham
(0121) 200 2001
philip.sutton@edge.co.uk
Specialisation: Pensions in particular scheme wind-ups, independent trusteeship, insolvency related pensions issues and scheme mergers.
Prof. Memberships: Association of Pension Lawyers.
Career: 1990-94: *Martineau Johnson*. 1994-96: *Hammond Suddards*. 1996 to present: *Edge Ellison*.
Publications: Various pieces in 'Technical Pensions Press'.
Personal: Birmingham University LLB Honours.

TALMAN, Iain J.S.
Morison Bishop, Glasgow (0141) 248 4672
Partner in corporate division (head of pensions unit).
Specialisation: Accredited by The Law Society of

Scotland as a specialist in pensions law. All aspects of pensions law and practice including pensioneer trusteeships, independent trusteeships through directorship of Mitre Pensions Ltd which acts in relation to a number of schemes including the 6,000 member Rosyth Royal Dockyard Pension Scheme. Acted in Mirror Group Pensions and Lilley Group, Clydesdale Group and Capital Foods independent trusteeships cases. Legal adviser to The Law Society of Scottish Staff Pension Scheme. Author and speaker.
Prof. Memberships: Law Society of Scotland, Association of Pension Lawyers, Association of Pensioneer Trustees, Local Member of the Scottish Group of the Pensions Management Institute, Actuarial Society of Glasgow (Life and Pensions Group). Pensioneer Trustee on the OPRA Panel. Scottish Legal panel member for Occupational Pensions Defence Union.
Career: Qualified in 1976. Partner in 1978. Past Chairman, Scottish Group of Association of Pension Lawyers, PMI Working Group on Pensions and Divorce, Convener of Law Society Pensions Accreditation Panel, Convener of Law Society Working Party on Pensions.
Personal: Born 18th July 1952. Leisure interests include movies, people, travel and ardent liquors.

TAYLOR, Anne
Irwin Mitchell, Leeds (0113) 234 3333
Partner and national head of Pensions Department.
Specialisation: Specialises in winding-up and merger of pension schemes, advice on the pensions aspects of transfers of business and the impact of the Transfer of Undertakings legislation, dealing with litigious pensions issues including claims against companies, advising on potential breaches of the Pensions Act 1995, actions involving the Pensions Ombudsman.
Prof. Memberships: NAPF, PMI, APL.
Career: Qualified 5 September 1990.
Personal: Educated at Bradford Girls' Grammar School. Recreations include sailing, skiing, cars.

TIER, Sarah J.
Sacker & Partners, London (020) 7329 6699
sarah.tier@sacker-partners.co.uk
Partner in specialist pensions law firm.
Specialisation: Deals with all aspects of pensions law including public sector and post-privitisation schemes, scheme mergers, advising trustees and pensions on divorce. Lectures at professional conferences, seminars and workshops. Writes for the professional and specialist press.
Prof. Memberships: Law Society, Association of Pension Lawyers, National Association of Pension Funds.
Career: Qualified in 1986. At *Clyde & Co* 1986-87. Joined *Nicholson Graham & Jones* in 1987 and became a Partner in 1991. Joined *Sacker & Partners* as a Partner in 1996.
Personal: Born 21st November 1960. Educated at the University of Southampton 1980-83. Interests include reading and hill-walking. Lives in West Hampstead, London.

TIMMINS, Jacqueline
Eversheds, Manchester (0161) 832 6666
Partner in commercial department.
Specialisation: Pensions law including scheme mergers, amalgamations, establishment of schemes, documentation, trusteeship matters, sales and acquisitions and dispute resolution. Preserved at APL and external seminars.
Prof. Memberships: Full member APL, secretary to North West APL, Committee Member of anchester NAPF Group and a member of SPC.
Career: Qualified in 1991. Joined *Eversheds* in 1995.
Personal: Born 1965. Married, one son. Leisure interests include wine (vineyard partner 'La Chevaleire' in the Loire Valley), hill walking and windsurfing.

TROTTER, Peter A.A.
MacRoberts, Glasgow (0141) 332 9988
PAAT@macroberts.co.uk
Partner pensions and employee benefits.
Specialisation: Pensions Law (including investment management agreements and acquisitions/disposals) and Employee Share and Management Incentive Schemes (including ESOPs and employee buy-outs).
Prof. Memberships: Associate of Pensions Management Institute (NAPF Prize and Scottish Group Prize 1993), Member of Society of Share Scheme Practitioners and Association of Pension Lawyers, PMI Scottish Group Committee Member.
Career: Joined *MacRoberts* 1998.
Personal: LLB (Birm), LLB (Edin), Dip LP (Strath), APMI.

TURNBULL, Andrew D.C.
Walker Morris, Leeds (0113) 283 2500
Specialisation: Practice covers the full range of pension work and includes creation and administration of schemes, scheme mergers, transactions and wind ups whether acting as an individual independent trustee or through Walker Morris Trustees Limited.
Prof. Memberships: North Eastern Group of the Association of Pension Lawyers.
Career: Qualified 1983. Joined *Walker Morris* after qualification becoming a partner in 1985.
Personal: Born 19th April 1957. Educated at Shrewsbury and Birmingham University. Interests include golf, tennis and keep fit.

WEST, Robert J.
Baker & McKenzie, London (020) 7919 1000
Partner in Pensions Department.
Specialisation: Principal area of practice involves advising on all legal aspects of pensions including trust aspects, litigation, surpluses, sales and purchases, drafting and advice to independent trustees. Other area of work is employee benefits and share schemes. Acted in South West Trains v Wightman, National Bus, The Times Pension Fund litigation, the Drexel Pension Scheme litigation and in the sex discrimination case in the European Court, Neath v. Hugh Steeper. Contributor on pensions to Butterworths' Legal Service and author of articles for Pensions World and Pensions Management. Addressed many conferences in UK, USA and Canada.
Prof. Memberships: Law Society, Chairman of Association of Pension Lawyers, former Secretary of International Employee Benefits Association, Member of the Legal Advice Committee of the Occupational Pensions Advisory Service.
Career: Qualified in 1978. Joined *Baker & McKenzie* in 1982 and became a Partner in 1985.
Personal: Born 1st January 1952. Attended Maidenhead Grammar School 1963-71 and Clare College, Cambridge 1971-74. Leisure pursuits include sport and archaeology. Lives in Wargrave, Berks.

WHITE, Andrew G.
Rowe & Maw, London (020) 7782 8632
awhite@roweandmaw.co.uk
Partner in Pensions Department.
Specialisation: All aspects of law relating to company and personal pension schemes. Also handles life insurance, advising insurance companies on life policies and other products. Author of 'Pensions Issues in Mergers and Acquisitions' (FT Law and Tax, 2nd edition 1996); writes a regular monthly article in PLC Magazine. Frequent speaker at conferences.
Prof. Memberships: Law Society, formerly a member of the Main Committee of the Association of Pension Lawyers.
Career: Qualified 1974. Joined *Rowe & Maw* 1977, becoming a Partner in 1979.
Personal: Born 1st January 1950. Attended Manchester Grammar School 1961-68, then University College, Oxford, 1968-72. Leisure pursuits include reading. Lives in London.

WOMERSLEY, Mark
Osborne Clarke OWA, Bristol (0117) 917 3000
mark.womersley@osborneclarke.com
Specialisation: Head of the Pensions and Benefits Unit. Acts as lead adviser to both trustees and employers of large and medium sized pension schemes and advises on corporate transactional work and pensions litigation. Has developed a "full service" package of advice for corporate clients on executive benefits matters (i.e. encompassing pensions, share schemes, employee tax and, where necessary, employment law).
Career: Trained at *Osborne Clarke*, qualifying in 1992, spent until 1996 in the corporate tax department. Became a member of the Chartered Institute of Taxation in 1993 and Head of the Pensions and Benefits Unit in 1996. A member of the Association of Pension Lawyers and the Share Scheme Lawyers' group.

WRIGHT, David
DLA, Liverpool (0151) 237 4731
david.wright@dla.com
Pensions Partner.
Specialisation: Handles all aspects of pensions law, including advice to industry-wide schemes, plc's, trustees and individuals. Work also includes mergers and acquisitions, corporate and business transfers and pensions litigation. Contributes to pensions periodicals.
Prof. Memberships: Law Society, Association of Pension Lawyers and an Associate of the Pensions Management Institute (APMI).
Career: Qualified in 1986. Articled with *March Pearson & Skelton*. Joined *DLA* in July 1990. Became Partner in 1995 and now responsible for the pensions group in *DLA*. A member of the Legislation Committee of the Society of Pension Consultants and a senior examiner for the PMI.
Personal: Born 19th November 1961. Lives in Orrell, near Wigan.

PERSONAL INJURY

OVERVIEW: This year, we have dispensed with one of our personal injury tables. If a firm has sufficient strength to be ranked for its work on behalf of both claimant and defendant, it will be found in both the relevant tables. The table headed 'both claimant and defendant' therefore vanishes this year. There are fewer ranked firms this year. This reflects the slashing of a number of panels, and the consequent difficulty in gaining high-profile personal injury work.

RESEARCH APPROVED BY BMRB: *For this edition,* Chambers' *researchers conducted 6083 interviews – 4408 with law firms, 598 with barristers and 1077 with clients.*

The validity of the research was scrutinised by BMRB International, who audited both the methodology and the results at our offices in July 2000. They interviewed Chambers' *researchers and cross-checked sample interviews. Details of the audit appear on page 7.*

LONDON

MAINLY CLAIMANT

PERSONAL INJURY: MAINLY CLAIMANT • London	Ptnrs	Assts
❶ Russell Jones & Walker	10	14
❷ Thompsons	4	18
❸ Evill and Coleman	4	3
Irwin Mitchell	3	4
Leigh, Day & Co	4	8
Pattinson & Brewer	5	14
Rowley Ashworth	5	12
❹ Hodge Jones & Allen	7	8
Stewarts	6	7
❺ Anthony Gold, Lerman & Muirhead	3	5
O.H. Parsons & Partners	7	5
❻ Bolt Burdon	4	5
David Levene & Co	5	17

LEADING INDIVIDUALS	
❶ ETTINGER Colin Irwin Mitchell	LEE Terry Evill and Coleman
McCARTHY Frances Pattinson & Brewer	WALKER Ian Russell Jones & Walker
❷ ALLEN Patrick Hodge Jones & Allen	CAHILL John David Stewarts
DAY Martyn Leigh, Day & Co	KITSON Paul Russell Jones & Walker
MARSHALL David Anthony Gold, Lerman & Muirhead	
NELSON-JONES Rodney Field Fisher Waterhouse	

Within each band, firms are listed alphabetically. *See **Profiles** on page 641*

Russell Jones & Walker Historically a trade union firm, and well known for its work for the Police Federation, the team has *"gone from strength to strength"* this year, with a number of defendant firms recognising the practice as *"the best of the bunch."* Effective marketing has raised its profile, but new institutional clients such as the Royal College of Nursing, and the doubling in size of the firm's dedicated private client unit suggests that there is substance behind the *"very positive, proactive"* image presented. Last year the London office of this national firm handled over 3000 personal injury cases over a range of injuries. Particular specialisms include industrial and environmental disease, workplace injury, stress, RSI, multi tort claims and accidents abroad. **Ian Walker** heads the team, and as President of APIL is a well known figure widely admired as a *"great communicator."* **Paul Kitson** also received a number of recommendations, and is seen as an *"imaginative and effective lawyer."* **Clients:** Police Federation; ISPC; PCF; IPMS.

Thompsons The biggest claimant personal injury practice nationwide, the London office retains a loyal following of trade union clients which generate over 75% of the practice's workload. The firm is strong in both the public sector and manufacturing, working with UNISON, the GMB, the MSF and a number of Civil Service unions. The London office received mixed reviews this year, with many commentators noting that it is *"not the force of old,"* and it is generally held that the firm has *"geared up for volume"* and has *"lost a number of its quality practitioners."* Nevertheless, the firm remains popular with its principal clients, and has been active in a number of high profile cases, such as the Paddington Rail Inquiry. **Clients:** UNISON.

Evill and Coleman Received recommendations from a large number of claimant and defendant firms, and is known for handling high value claims, particularly head injuries. **Terry Lee** is a hugely respected individual, although some commentators noted that the practice may be *"over-reliant"* on one individual, and that he might be *"spread a little thin."*

Irwin Mitchell Part of a widely respected national practice, the London office has established a formidable reputation in its own right. Catastrophic injuries, particularly road traffic-related, form the mainstay of the practice, with individual settlements of up to £2 million reached in the past year. Team leader **Colin Ettinger** is one of the most respected personal injury practitioners in London and has particular expertise in spinal and traumatic brain injury cases. Ettinger is also known for his work in occupational health, particularly in handling mesothelioma cases, a key factor in the growing relationships with trade unions such as the MSF and ASLEF.

Leigh, Day & Co Referred to as a *"passionate outfit,"* this firm is known for taking on those claims deemed too risky by more orthodox claimant firms. In particular, the firm has a reputation for conditional fee multi-party actions, and is currently heavily involved in an asbestos case on behalf of South African miners. The dedicated multi-party team is also well known for work with an environmental bent, and this is the area where the much respected **Martyn Day** spends the majority of his time. The London office also has a traditional PI team, acting principally for private clients, which specialises in RTA, horseriding and sports injury related cases.

Pattinson & Brewer Trade union work remains the *"bread and butter"* of the London office, and the strength of the firm's employment practice enables it to provide an all-round service to this client base. The firm also deals with an increasing number of private clients. Head of department **Frances McCarthy** was recognised by her peers as *"extremely talented."* She is the Vice-President of APIL and a member of the Woolf Working Party that drafted the personal injury pre-action protocol. **Clients:** TGWU; RMT; PCS; GMB.

Rowley Ashworth Maintains a fairly low profile, but continues to be considered one of the big four trade union firms. Perceived to be *"good, straightforward litigators,"* who *"put more thought into their cases than the volume merchants."* Although *"not first-choice for more complex issues,"* the team is high on the list for injury at work or road traffic cases. **Clients:** AEEU; TGWU; GMB.

Hodge Jones & Allen The practice specialises in medical accidents, injuries as the result of crime, accidents at work, and road traffic accidents. The team has been particularly active in multi-party litigation, and leading practitioner **Patrick Allen**'s experience in this area includes sitting on the Plaintiff's Steering Committee for both the Kings Cross fire and the Marchioness litigation.

Stewarts Known as *"the head injury specialists,"* this London practice specialises in compensation claims following serious injury, and last year recovered £20 million for clients. The PI practice also acts for those injured in disasters such as the Paddington Rail Crash, the Soho, Brixton and Brick Lane bombings and the Air Kenya crash. **John Cahill** is respected by his peers as an experienced and capable PI practitioner.

Anthony Gold, Lerman & Muirhead *"Good, solid PI practice"* which acts principally for individuals and families, mainly referred by specialist advice and support agencies such as Headway, RoadPeace and the London Cycling Campaign. Serious RTA injuries form a substantial part of the practice's work. The team has a particular expertise in conditional fee agreements, and **David Marshall** is acknowledged as an expert in this area.

O.H. Parsons & Partners A growing practice that defendant firms and barristers say are getting *"an increasing amount of trade union work."*

Bolt Burdon This North London-based PI practice acts purely for individuals and specialises in head injuries, RSI and injuries abroad. The industrial disease team is particularly prominent in the area of upper limb disorders, and has taken on some difficult cases dropped by union firms and brought them to a successful conclusion.

David Levene & Co A national firm, growing rapidly, where personal injury represents 85% of overall turnover. The PI practice covers a range of injuries, including RTA, employer's liability and catastrophic claims. The firm represents private clients and legal expense insurers, and has pursued a number of cases to the Court of Appeal in the past year.

Other Notable Practitioner While **Rodney Nelson-Jones** retains his reputation as a *"terrific PI lawyer"* particularly in the field of asbestos disease claims, his firm, Field Fisher Waterhouse, was not prominent among the market's recommendations.

MAINLY DEFENDANT

PERSONAL INJURY: MAINLY DEFENDANT • London	Ptnrs	Assts
❶ Barlow Lyde & Gilbert	4	26
Beachcroft Wansbroughs	13	40
Berrymans Lace Mawer	13	35
❷ Davies Arnold Cooper	5	-
Kennedys	14	53
Vizards, Staples & Bannisters	12	18
❸ Hextall Erskine	7	13
Watmores	7	3

LEADING INDIVIDUALS
❶ DICKINSON Graham Barlow Lyde & Gilbert
❷ CHERRY Anthony Beachcroft Wansbroughs
SLESS Tania Beachcroft Wansbroughs
STAPLES Martin Vizards, Staples & Bannisters

Within each band, firms are listed alphabetically. *See **Profiles** on page 641*

Barlow Lyde & Gilbert A rapidly growing practice which covers a broad spectrum of personal injury work. Best-known for working with local authorities and their insurers, defending claims of bullying, stress, child abuse and failure to educate. BLG has recently taken on Davies Arnold Cooper's highly respected motor unit and are now able to do volume work alongside more complex and catastrophic claims. **Graham Dickinson** is held in the highest regard by his peers, not least for his management abilities, which have enabled him to bring together disparate elements to form a cohesive and effective team. Dickinson has a particular specialisation in the field of rehabilitation of those claimants suffering catastrophic injuries and was appointed by Swiss Re to advise on and develop their rehabilitation programme. **Clients:** Zurich Municipal.

Beachcroft Wansbroughs *"The leading player nationwide,"* the firm is *"expanding and expanding"* to meet the needs of the large composite insurers that provide 80% of the practice's caseload. While fast-track work provides the volume, the firm has a balanced practice and has retained some quality individuals. **Tony Cherry** is head of the practice and is admired by his peers, as is his colleague **Tania Sless**. **Clients:** Royal Sun Alliance; CGU; AXA; BAe.

Berrymans Lace Mawer While this practice continues to grow, the team does not yet dominate the PI defence market. Indeed, there has been talk of *"growing pains"* and *"patchy quality"* in the market, although its closest competitors still consider Berrymans a threat. A broad-based practice, with a balance of fast-track and multi-track work, the London team maintains a particularly high profile in industrial disease-related work such as stress, asbestos and RSI. **Clients:** Royal Sun Alliance; CGU; AXA.

Davies Arnold Cooper Not an easy year for a practice that used to be acknowledged as pre-eminent in defendant personal injury work. Of the two main teams, the motor practice has suffered most, with many of that group leaving to join Barlow Lyde & Gilbert. Motor is now half the size of the employer's/public liability team which specialises in occupational health, sports, multi-defendant litigation and HSE issues. Overall, while some commentators suggested that DAC has *"lost the heart of its practice,"* competitors noted that the firm *"still has a lot of good people."* **Clients:** Independent Insurance Company.

Kennedys Have recently split the practice into two sections, with the Brentwood office focusing on high-volume motor claims which contribute around a quarter of total PI fees. The City office specialises in asbestos, noise and stress-related complaints, particularly in relation to the railway. This rapidly-growing team has also taken on former employees of Edward Lewis, who have brought an expertise in high value motor claims for clients such as Zurich and Eagle Star. Considered by the market to have a *"robust attitude to litigation,"* Kennedys are consistently counted among the top five or six defendant personal injury practices in London. **Clients:** Railtrack plc.

Vizards, Staples & Bannisters Previously regarded as an *"unknown quantity,"* this team has now firmly established itself among the leading defence practices. The team does very little fast-track work, but its expertise in complex claims is utilised by large composite insurers, smaller insurers and Lloyds syndicates. The firm also has a niche in the area of travel, and is retained by a number of 'self-insured' travel operators such as BAA and Airtours. **Martin Staples** has a high profile, and whilst much of his time is taken up as President of FOIL, he does act in some high profile cases such as the Sheep Dip/Organic Phosphates claims. **Clients:** CGU.

Hextall Erskine Praised by clients for its *"exemplary levels of service,"* the firm's focus is directed towards high-value claims rather than volume work. Divisions include motor, disease, travel and sport. The firm has also identified a growing niche in defending corporate manslaughter claims. Entered a national alliance with Jacksons (Newcastle) and Cartwrights (Bristol) developing compatible case management systems to provide the insurance market with nationwide claims management information. **Clients:** AIG.

Watmores The firm specialises in acting for local authorities and their insurers. Represents six of the new train operating companies, dealing with accident claims pursued by employees or members of the public. **Clients:** Gallager Bassett; Zurich Municipal; St Paul.

THE SOUTH

MAINLY CLAIMANT

PERSONAL INJURY: MAINLY CLAIMANT • The South	Ptnrs	Assts
❶ **Shoosmiths** Basingstoke	12	33
❷ **Amery-Parkes** Basingstoke	4	6
Blake Lapthorn Portsmouth	3	9
George Ide, Phillips Chichester	2	3
Lamport Bassitt Southampton	1	-
Pattinson & Brewer Chatham	2	4
Thomson Snell & Passmore Tunbridge Wells	4	7
Warner Goodman & Streat Fareham	4	-

Within each band, firms are listed alphabetically. See **Profiles** on page 641

Shoosmiths The newly opened 'Claims Compensation Division' is principally focused on processing fast-track claims for legal expense insurers and motoring organisations. The division's focus is national rather than regional, and there are few firms capable of competing with this large outfit. Adopts a *"factory-like"* business model, which sees much of the work conducted by assistants and legal executives. However, a more magnanimous view was that *"they will always secure a settlement quickly and cheaply."* **Clients:** AA; Direct Line; Privilege.

Other Notable Firms Competing with Shoosmiths on fast-track motor work for legal expense insurers, **Amery-Parkes** lacks its competitor's size but has been praised for its *"efficiency."* **Blake Lapthorn** also does fast-track motor claims for the RAC, but has a more balanced practice, and is well regarded locally for its work on catastrophic RTA, industrial diseases, sexual assaults and actions against the police. Another practice that combines volume work for legal expense insurers with complex claims is **George Ide, Phillips**. The multi-track work at this Chichester-based practice is focused on head/brain injury claims, while the fast-track practice is bolstered by two specialist foreign claims handlers, dealing with injuries sustained abroad. **Lamport Bassitt**, **Pattinson & Brewer** and **Warner Goodman & Streat** cater to the needs of trade unions as well as private individuals, and all three have well respected industrial disease groups. **Thomson Snell & Passmore** is an orthodox PI practice with a good reputation for dealing with cases ranging from slipping and tripping to severe brain injuries.

MAINLY DEFENDANT

PERSONAL INJURY: MAINLY DEFENDANT • The South	Ptnrs	Assts
❶ **Beachcroft Wansbroughs** Winchester	2	4
Berrymans Lace Mawer Southampton	5	6
Bond Pearce Southampton	1	6
Davies Lavery Maidstone	3	18
Ensor Byfield Southampton	3	2
❷ **AE Wyeth & Co** Dartford	11	5
Keoghs Southampton	1	2
Palser Grossman Southampton	4	2

LEADING INDIVIDUALS	
❶ **BRUFFELL Martin** Berrymans Lace Mawer	
❷ **EVANS Roderick** Ensor Byfield	**RIGG Bettina** Bond Pearce

Within each band, firms are listed alphabetically. See **Profiles** on page 641

Beachcroft Wansbroughs Although better known as a clinical negligence practice, the Winchester office of this national powerhouse has been developing a reputation for PI work, and is considered to be a *"serious player"* in the southern region by both claimant and defendant solicitors.

Berrymans Lace Mawer The Southampton office of this national firm is a broad based practice with a balance of fast-track and multi-track work. A number of the cases conducted are controlled through London but completed in Southampton to take advantage of the lower cost base. The practice has been bolstered by the arrival from the London office of **Martin Bruffell**, who has a national reputation as a leader in personal injury litigation. He is currently training as a mediator, and is leading his firm in a joint venture with claimant firm Stewarts to do insurance mediation based on a fixed fee/fixed time structure.

Bond Pearce Retained on the panel of Royal & Sun Alliance, and gaining work from self-insureds, particularly in the retail sector, the firm is recognised by local rivals as *"serious competition."* Focused on employer's liability, public liability, policy issues and road traffic, the firm has particular strength in catastrophic injury claims and claims from the health sector. **Bettina Rigg** was noted by claimant firms as being *"pleasant and reasonable to deal with."* **Clients:** Royal & Sun Alliance; Hiscox Insurance Co Ltd; St Paul International Insurance.

Davies Lavery Based in Maidstone so less well known to its South Coast competitors, but retains a reputation as a *"good local firm with a select band of loyal insurers."* The firm targets small and mid-size insurers and has a specialist RTA department. **Clients:** Independent Insurance; ACE Europe.

Ensor Byfield As a thriving local defence practice, this team is something of a rarity given the larger insurer's preference for larger national practices. Quality individuals such as **Rod Evans** have much to do with the continued success of this mixed insurance practice. **Clients:** Zurich, Guardian, Cornhill and Iron Trades.

Other Notable Firms **AE Wyeth & Co** is an established Dartford firm, and has grown in prominence in this area of practice. *"New kids on the block"* **Keoghs** and **Palser Grossman** have both extended their reach into the south from their respective heartlands of Bolton and Cardiff. While the practices may need some time to *"bed down,"* competitors are acutely aware of their presence as excellent national operations.

THAMES VALLEY

MAINLY CLAIMANT

Osborne Morris & Morgan Specialists in catastrophic brain and spinal injuries and cerebral palsy claims, this team provides a comprehensive *"neuro-law"* service including rehabilitation and long term care. **Tom Osborne** is considered to be a leading authority on head injuries. **Clients:** private clients.

Other Notable Firms **Boyes Turner & Burrows** is known for its work on cases of major injury including brain, spinal, neurological, major sensory or skeletal injury, and recovered over £5 million in compensation for its

PERSONAL INJURY: MAINLY CLAIMANT • Thames Valley	Ptnrs	Assts
❶ **Osborne Morris & Morgan** Leighton Buzzard	3	2
❷ **Boyes Turner & Burrows** Reading	2	2
Fennemores Milton Keynes	4	5
Henmans Oxford	3	10
LEADING INDIVIDUALS		
❶ **OSBORNE Thomas** Osborne Morris & Morgan		

Within each band, firms are listed alphabetically. See **Profiles** on page 641

clients in 1999. **Fennemores** *"have cornered a fair part of the local market"* in the Milton Keynes region. 75% of the fees come from the firm's high volume RTA practice for legal expense insurers, with the remainder coming from Employer's and Public Liability including stress claims and head injuries. The firm has also formed a joint partnership with Northants Police Authority to provide advice and guidance for the relatives of victims of fatal accidents. **Henmans** is better known for defence work but is still considered a player in claimant work in the Oxford area. The firm acts for legal expense insurers and increasingly undertakes work under conditional fee agreements.

MAINLY DEFENDANT

PERSONAL INJURY: MAINLY DEFENDANT • Thames Valley	Ptnrs	Assts
❶ **Morgan Cole** Reading	8	30
❷ **Henmans** Oxford	3	10
LEADING INDIVIDUALS		
❶ **TENQUIST Iain** Morgan Cole		

Within each band, firms are listed alphabetically. See **Profiles** on page 641

Morgan Cole A mixed practice conducting both high volume RTA work and multi-track work, including RSI, industrial diseases, and foreign claims. The latter are usually handled out of the Croydon office, where the firm has a number of multi-lingual staff. The firm has bolstered its practice with a number of former Edward Lewis employees who specialise in serious road traffic injuries. **Iain Tenquist** is arguably the best known PI defence practitioner in the region. **Clients:** AXA; Norwich Union; CGU; Tesco.

Henmans Good reputation for RSI, industrial disease, explosions and asbestos-related claims. The firm has a number of lawyers trained at City practices, and this expertise has been valued by a number of insurers. The defendant practice offers a national service to employers and does not charge for travel. **Clients:** 25-30 insurers.

SOUTH WEST

MAINLY CLAIMANT

PERSONAL INJURY: MAINLY CLAIMANT • South West	Ptnrs	Assts
❶ **Bond Pearce** Plymouth	3	19
Lyons Davidson Bristol	⚐	⚐
Thompsons Bristol	2	7
Veale Wasbrough Bristol	3	9
❷ **Rowley Ashworth** Exeter	-	3
Russell Jones & Walker Bristol	1	9
Wolferstans Plymouth	8	13
❸ **Bobbetts Mackan** Bristol	2	1
David Gist & Co Bristol	4	6
LEADING INDIVIDUALS		
❶ **HERBERT Andrew** Thompsons		
ROWE Bernard Lyons Davidson		
WEBSTER John Veale Wasbrough		

Within each band, firms are listed alphabetically. See **Profiles** on page 641

⚐ *Figures unavailable at time of going to press.*

Bond Pearce Although better known for defence work, the team is recognised as having *"a large PI practice with good people on the claimant side."* The firm acts for various Trade Unions, major credit-hire companies and private clients. Particular niche strengths include occupational disease work, RTA claims and employers/public liability.

Lyons Davidson This claimant practice focuses on volume RTA work for legal expenses insurers. The large team of over 60 fee earners is well marshalled by the *"effective"* **Bernie Rowe**. The practice has an in-depth knowledge of all aspects of road accident claims and employs specialist accident investigators. **Clients:** Direct Line.

Thompsons Union work constitutes around 75% of the workload, with the remainder coming from private client references from local solicitors and Accident Line. The Bristol team have a broad spread of work including fast-track RTA and employer's liability. The office has particular expertise in occupational health work, notably stress and asbestosis. The team acted for a teacher who secured £500,000 in compensation for carbon monoxide poisoning. **Andrew Herbert** continues to be recognised as a leader in the market. **Clients:** trade unions.

Veale Wasbrough Now concentrating purely on claimant work, this practice has *"made a strategic priority of getting claimant union work, and have got their fair share."* In addition to major unions such as the TGWU and the Royal College of Nursing, the firm acts for legal expense insurers and private clients. Recovered £1.5 million in damages for a victim of a road traffic accident, part of over £6 million recovered last year. Head of department **John Webster** has a high profile. **Clients:** TGWU; RCN; BRAWU.

Other Notable Firms **Rowley Ashworth** and **Russell Jones & Walker** both have offices in the South West to meet the needs of their union client base. The former has particular niche strengths in chemical poisoning, stress and accidents abroad. **Wolferstans** are one of few claimant practices in the South West that are exclusively focused on individual clients, and have an increasingly strong reputation in this area. The firm has a specialist industrial disease unit in Taunton and Plymouth that deals with a lot of asbestos claims along with Gulf War, dyslexia and psychological (stress/bullying) claims. The firm also has a specialist motorcycle unit with nationwide coverage. **Bobbetts Mackan** have recently taken on Trumps' personal injury practice and are building a reputation in this area. **David Gist & Co** compete with Lyons Davidson for volume RTA work for legal expense insurers.

MAINLY DEFENDANT

PERSONAL INJURY: MAINLY DEFENDANT • South West	Ptnrs	Assts
❶ **Beachcroft Wansbroughs** Bristol	4	18
❷ **Bevan Ashford** Bristol	1	7
Bond Pearce Plymouth	4	2
Cartwrights Bristol	5	6
Hugh James Ford Simey Exeter	3	-
Palser Grossman Bristol	1	2
Veitch Penny Exeter	6	5

LEADING INDIVIDUALS	
❶ **BEALE Robert** Beachcroft Wansbroughs	**DERBYSHIRE Paul** Hugh James Ford Simey

Within each band, firms are listed alphabetically. See **Profiles** on page 641

Beachcroft Wansbroughs The Bristol office is viewed by some to have *"bought market share"* through extremely competitive pricing, and *"nearly has the regional market sewn up."* The practice is divided into a fast-track and a multi-track team, with the latter focused on disease work, back and head injuries and fraudulent personal injury claims. **Bob Beale** leads the practice, and remains active in day to day litigation. **Clients:** composite insurers; Lloyd's syndicates; increasing number of self insureds.

Other Notable Firms **Bevan Ashford** is better known for medical negligence work, but is active in PI work, in particular for the insurers of NHS trusts and medium-sized motor insurers. **Bond Pearce** have a well established reputation for defendant work in Bristol. The majority of the work is multi-track, focused on industrial disease and spinal injuries. Most of the team's fast-track work comes from servicing the Post Office. **Cartwrights** maintains a high-profile name, using specialist units for employer's liability and motor. The practice also has a respected occupational diseases unit which has acted on 27 of the prescribed industrial diseases. **Hugh James Ford Simey** and **Palser Grossman** have both crossed the border from their Welsh heartlands and have met with success, sometimes at the expense of the more established Bristol firms. **Paul Derbyshire** at Hugh James Ford Simey has a particularly strong reputation in this area. **Veitch Penny** do both claimant and defendant work but have a stronger reputation in the latter. Competitors considered the firm to be *"a very good firm at the 'tripper and slipper' end of the market,"* although the practice also has expertise on more complex issues such as post-traumatic stress disorder.

WALES

MAINLY CLAIMANT

PERSONAL INJURY: MAINLY CLAIMANT • Wales	Ptnrs	Assts
❶ **Hugh James Ford Simey** Merthyr Tydfil	9	21
Leo Abse & Cohen Cardiff	6	35
Thompsons Cardiff	4	8
❷ **Loosemores** Cardiff	2	5
Smith Llewelyn Partnership Swansea	2	3

LEADING INDIVIDUALS	
❶ **BENT Roger** Thompsons	**HARDING Andrew** Hugh James Ford Simey
HARVEY Mark Smith Llewelyn Partnership	**HOPKINS Ian** Leo Abse & Cohen
WILLIAMS Robin Leo Abse & Cohen	

Within each band, firms are listed alphabetically. See **Profiles** on page 641

Hugh James Ford Simey Spread throughout Wales and the South West, this firm has a specialist Head Injuries Unit in Cardiff, headed by the *"excellent"* **Andrew Harding**. There is also a Specialist Industrial Disease Unit based in Merthyr which has been active in multi-party cases and has acted for five of the eight lead claimants in the South Wales miners' respiratory claims. As one of only two Welsh firms with a multi-party franchise (along with the Smith Llewelyn Partnership), the firm has also been active in class actions such as the Gerona Air Crash and some cervical cancer cases.

Leo Abse & Cohen Divided into teams for trade unions and private client work, this firm retains a strong reputation for PI work. Private client department includes a serious injury team led by **Ian Hopkins**, and a group dedicated to respiratory-related claims for miners who have now retired. **Robin Williams** retains a high profile for trade union work.

Thompsons Remains exclusively a union firm in the region and does not appear to be moving into private client work. Nevertheless, the team has a strong reputation as *"fierce litigators"* and counts the highly regarded **Roger Bent** amongst its members.

Other Notable Firms **Loosemores** was commended by the market as a *"solid RTA-based practice."* Its principal client is the RAC. The **Smith Llewelyn Partnership** is principally known for its expertise in pharmaceuticals and clinical negligence, but the firm does have a respected PI practice led by one of Wales' leading PI practitioners, **Mark Harvey**. He is on the steering committees of both the Southall and the Ladbroke Grove public inquiries and is co-ordinating the Gerona Air Crash claims jointly with Hugh James Ford Simey.

MAINLY DEFENDANT

PERSONAL INJURY: MAINLY DEFENDANT • Wales	Ptnrs	Assts
❶ **Hugh James Ford Simey** Cardiff	13	11
Morgan Cole Cardiff	4	15
Palser Grossman Cardiff Bay	6	5
❷ **Dolmans** Cardiff	6	12
❸ **Eversheds** Cardiff	2	3

LEADING INDIVIDUALS	
❶ **CRADICK Simon** Morgan Cole	**PRICE Hugh** Morgan Cole
WILLIAMS Gareth Hugh James Ford Simey	

Within each band, firms are listed alphabetically. See **Profiles** on page 641

Hugh James Ford Simey Work for a broad spectrum of insurance firms ranging from local authority specialists like Zurich Municipal, to motor specialists and the major composites such as RSA, CGU and AIG. The firm also has a strong reputation among self-insureds and does a lot of work for Hyder. The *"highly experienced"* **Gareth Williams** does maximum severity claims and health and safety work. **Clients:** Royal & Sun Alliance; CGU.

Morgan Cole A *"professional, competent"* practice with *"strength in depth,"* this firm counts among its clients many of the largest insurance companies including CGU, Independent and AXA. The firm is also looking to expand in the self-insured market and already does work for BP Amoco. Provides a broad service, with particular strength in industrial disease, and recently completed a large action relating to Legionnaires' disease. **Simon Cradick** is *"technically excellent"* while **Hugh Price** is a *"great communicator"* and a good front man for the practice. **Clients:** CGU.

Palser Grossman *"Aggressive in terms of client acquisition and litigation,"* this firm is now clearly one of the leading defendant practices in Wales.

Acts for a number of leading composite insurers. **Clients:** Royal & Sun Alliance; CGU; Zurich/Eagle Star; AXA/GRE.

Other Notable Firms **Dolmans** remains popular in the market, described as *"a nice practice focused on police and local authority work."* The practice has formed particularly good relations with local authorities, who have been known to request that insurers retain the firm as a panel member.

Eversheds *"have tried to crack the insurance market"* in Wales, but are not seen to have had a tremendous impact. However, the firm has a strong presence in the self-insured market, handling all the employer's liability, public liability and motor claims of Invensys plc, Meyer plc and the Forestry Commission.

MIDLANDS

MAINLY CLAIMANT

PERSONAL INJURY: MAINLY CLAIMANT • Midlands	Ptnrs	Assts
❶ **Irwin Mitchell** Birmingham	3	16
Rowley Ashworth Birmingham	5	6
Russell Jones & Walker Birmingham	4	18
Thompsons Birmingham	5	15
❷ **Freethcartwright** Nottingham	3	4
❸ **Barratt Goff & Tomlinson** Nottingham	5	2
Nelsons Nottingham	6	8

LEADING INDIVIDUALS	
❶ **GOODMAN Sarah** Thompsons	**HENDERSON Stuart** Irwin Mitchell
LAWTON Anthony Thompsons	
❷ **BALEN Paul** Freethcartwright	**PRAIN David** Rowley Ashworth
ZINDANI Jeffry Russell Jones & Walker	

Within each band, firms are listed alphabetically. *See **Profiles** on page 641*

Irwin Mitchell A large broad-based practice, which mixes expertise in high-value claims with a volume RTA practice for legal expense insurers. **Stuart Henderson** is a leading practitioner, and his multi-track PI team recently secured one of the highest awards handed out in a personal injury case when road traffic victim Faisal Luhar was awarded £5.1 million. The department is also strong on travel and tourism cases. **Clients:** private clients and various legal expense insurers.

Rowley Ashworth Have a reputation for being *"volume merchants,"* and low value claims from the firm's trade union client base have seen this office remain busy, without creating a high profile for the practice. Nevertheless, the Birmingham office has some experienced practitioners, including **David Prain**, who is highly thought of for his work in this area.

Russell Jones & Walker Have a small fast track team to deal with simple RTA cases, but most of this office's work is multi-track. The practice has an occupational disease group which has dealt with a number of asbestos and stress-related claims, and the team also do a lot of health and safety work, particularly related to death in the workplace. The firm now acts for the Royal College of Nursing and the Police Federation. **Jeffry Zindani** is the managing partner and has a particular interest in back injury/lifting cases. **Clients:** a range of trade unions.

Thompsons Some competitors felt that this large trade union practice had sacrificed some quality in favour of volume, but the Birmingham office still retains two leading players in this area. The *"highly experienced and quietly confident"* **Sarah Goodman** and *"safe pair of hands"* **Anthony Lawton** help the firm to deal with a variety of more complex claims. **Clients:** trade union members.

Other Notable Firms **Freethcartwright** is the most high profile PI claimant practice in the Nottingham area. The firm has niche strength in manual handling work, accidents at work and industrial disease cases, and is led by **Paul Balen**. The firm also has a specialist serious injuries unit. **Barratt Goff & Tomlinson** and **Nelsons** are other noted firms from the Nottingham region. Nelsons handles claims for private clients and has added a specialist motor division for legal expense insurers. The firm is known for its industrial disease work, and also its multi-party team, which has acted in connection with the SwissAir plane crash and the Sun Vista sinking.

MAINLY DEFENDANT

PERSONAL INJURY: MAINLY DEFENDANT • Midlands	Ptnrs	Assts
❶ **Beachcroft Wansbroughs** Birmingham	3	7
Browne Jacobson Nottingham	7	8
Weightmans Birmingham	7	8
❷ **Buller Jeffries** Birmingham	7	5
Everatt & Company Evesham	4	2
❸ **Chapman Everatt** Birmingham	5	2
Hammond Suddards Edge Birmingham	1	7

LEADING INDIVIDUALS	
❶ **ADAMSON Derek** Buller Jeffries	**ARKELL Catherine** Everatt & Company
DACE Nigel Weightmans	
❷ **CHAPMAN Richard** Chapman Everatt	**LEWIS Geoffrey** Buller Jeffries
PERRY Timothy Weightmans	**ROACH Andrew** Beachcroft Wansbroughs

Within each band, firms are listed alphabetically. *See **Profiles** on page 641*

Beachcroft Wansbroughs Known particularly for employer's liability and industrial disease work, this office nevertheless received enough positive feedback to be considered another leading Beachcroft Wansbroughs practice. **Andrew Roach** was the individual most frequently singled out for praise. **Clients:** composite insurers and Lloyd's syndicates.

Browne Jacobson A broad-based practice, by far the strongest in the Nottingham area, known in particular for local authority work. Has a particularly strong reputation in the area of sexual abuse claims. Also counts some of the major composite insurers among its clients **Clients:** St. Paul International.

Weightmans Viewed as a volume insurance practice, Weightmans has a strong Birmingham office headed by the much praised **Nigel Dace**. The merger with William Hatton has been viewed positively by the market, with a number noting quality individuals that have joined the firm as a result, most notably the *"excellent"* **Timothy Perry**. The practice covers employer's liability, industrial diseases, public services (including the police, the fire service and the post office) catastrophic injuries and motor. The firm now acts for eight of the country's top ten insurers.

Buller Jeffries The general consensus is that this firm has *"had a tough year,"* but remains a traditional, highly competent firm. The team has retained its leading figures and is unsurpassed for experience. **Derek Adamson** is one of the most high profile litigators in the region, and his colleague **Geoffrey Lewis**, who specialises in high value motor claims, is also rated highly. The group does a wide range of work, including serious motor injuries, employer's liability for major motor manufacturers' insurers, local authority work (child abuse, education) occupational health (particularly stress/bullying) and novel injuries including fibral neuralgia. **Clients:** insurance companies.

Everatt & Company Smaller than its main competitors but well regarded, this practice specialises in industrial disease work, especially asbestosis, VWF and other work-related upper limb disorders. The firm also has a substantial defendant motor practice. Team leader **Catherine Arkell** is *"a scrapper,"* respected by her competitors. **Clients:** iron trades.

Other Notable Firms **Chapman Everatt** remains a noted firm with particular strength in local authority work, although also doing lower value RTA and employer's liability work. **Richard Chapman** is its stand-out practitioner. **Hammond Suddards Edge** has lost some of its insurance client base but has made some progress in the self-insured market, particularly in the leisure sector, acting for hotels and pubs.

EAST ANGLIA

MAINLY CLAIMANT

PERSONAL INJURY: MAINLY CLAIMANT • East Anglia	Ptnrs	Assts
❶ **Cunningham John** Thetford	5	12
❷ **E. Edwards Son & Noice** Ilford	2	7
Leathes Prior Norwich	2	1
Morgan Jones & Pett Great Yarmouth	3	1
Taylor Vinters Cambridge	3	7

LEADING INDIVIDUALS	
❶ **JOHN Simon** Cunningham John	**JONES David** Morgan Jones & Pett

Within each band, firms are listed alphabetically.

See **Profiles** on page 641

Cunningham John Leading practitioner **Simon John** specialises in brain injuries and is treasurer of the United Kingdom Acquired Brain Injury Society (UKABIS.) Other areas of specialist knowledge for the practice include nursing accidents, amputees and seriously injured children. The firm steers clear of both fast track and multi-party claims. **Clients:** private clients.

Other Notable Firms **E. Edwards Son & Noice**'s claimant practice has retained its links with major trade unions such as the TGWU and the CWU. The firm also has a growing legal expense insurers practice, acting for motor fleet clients such as Hogg Robinson. **Leathes Prior** is largely a volume practice, most of which is RTA-related. The firm also handles back claims and head injuries in the £100-150,000 range. **Morgan Jones & Pett** continue to be highly regarded in this region, with **David Jones** noted for being *"a little terrier but good to deal with."* **Taylor Vinters** are also familiar to defendant firms in the region. The practice specialises in fatal accident claims and catastrophic brain injury cases.

MAINLY DEFENDANT

PERSONAL INJURY: MAINLY DEFENDANT • East Anglia	Ptnrs	Assts
❶ **Eversheds** Norwich	2	5
Mills & Reeve Norwich	2	2
❷ **E. Edwards Son & Noice** Ilford	2	4
Greenwoods Peterborough	2	-
Merricks Ipswich	2	2
Prettys Ipswich	1	4

Within each band, firms are listed alphabetically.

See **Profiles** on page 641

Eversheds Works with a range of clients but with particular strength in local authority work and with self-insured plcs. Areas of expertise include sexual abuse claims, RSI, sports law and police work. **Clients:** Suffolk County Council; British Gas Transco; Royal & Sun Alliance.

Mills & Reeve A recognised player in personal injury, but not dominating the region in the manner of the firm's clinical negligence practice. Specialises in high value head and spinal injury claims, quadriplegic cases and cerebral palsy. **Clients:** Insurers; underwriters; Lloyd's syndicates.

Other Notable Firms **E. Edwards Son & Noice** maintain a reputation for defendant work. **Merricks** have a *"fine insurance practice,"* but are seen to have greater strength in professional indemnity and construction. Both **Greenwoods** and **Prettys** handle a mixture of both claimant and defence work, but were noted in the market for their strength in the latter.

NORTH WEST

MAINLY CLAIMANT

PERSONAL INJURY: MAINLY CLAIMANT • North West	Ptnrs	Assts
❶ **Pannone & Partners** Manchester	5	18
❷ **John Pickering & Partners** Oldham	2	2
Leigh, Day & Co Manchester	3	4
Whittles Manchester	15	15
❸ **Russell Jones & Walker** Manchester	2	-
Thompsons Liverpool	3	4
❹ **Donns Solicitors** Manchester	12	22
Linder Myers Manchester	4	6

LEADING INDIVIDUALS	
❶ **JACKSON Carol** Pannone & Partners	**PATTERSON Frank** Leigh, Day & Co
PICKERING John John Pickering & Partners	
❷ **CHANDLER Pauline** Pannone & Partners	**LEECH Catherine** Pannone & Partners
MANSFIELD Collin. Whittles	**McCOOL Geraldine** Leigh, Day & Co
POTTER Hugh Hugh Potter & Company	

Within each band, firms are listed alphabetically.

See **Profiles** on page 641

Figures unavailable at time of going to press.

Pannone & Partners Consistent recommendations combined with a wealth of leading individuals place this firm ahead of its main competitors. The consensus in the market is that this is a firm that *"does its best for its clients without having to resort to devious tactics."* **Carol Jackson** was viewed to be *"quiet, self-contained and competent"* and *"a leader in the field."* **Pauline Chandler** was noted for her expertise in disease work, and **Catherine Leech** has an established reputation for her catastrophic injury work. The firm acts principally for private clients, and specialises in complex, catastrophic, aviation, child abuse and disease claims. **Clients:** RAC; Eastgate; private clients.

John Pickering & Partners A small, niche practice highly rated principally because of the reputation of **John Pickering** for industrial disease, in particular mesothelioma cases. **Clients:** private clients.

Leigh, Day & Co An unusual practice built around a number of niche areas. Just over half the office's workload comes from the Communication Workers Union. The team serving this client is led by **Frank Patterson**, who is viewed by the market as being *"sound on the law and tenacious."* Another noted individual, **Geraldine McCool**, is principally involved in claims against the Ministry of Defence, and is particularly experienced in cases arising from MoD aviation crashes, and those involving special forces. A final niche area for the firm involves carbon monoxide poisoning. The firm also handles serious spinal injury claims and recently settled a claim worth £3.9 million. **Clients:** Communication Workers Union; Royal British Legion; private clients.

Whittles A large practice built on trade union work, in particular for the GMB. Has a specialist accidents in the workplace team which has expertise from catastrophic and fatal accidents through to minor workplace injuries. The practice also has a specialist industrial disease department with experience in asbestosis, asthma, dermatitis, RSI, deafness, stress, upper limb disorder and industrial cancer. **Collin Mansfield** was commended as a *"sound litigator with good ideas."* **Clients:** GMB and other unions.

Other Notable Firms & Practitioners Both **Russell Jones & Walker** and **Thompsons** have a noted presence in the North West to serve their Trade Union clients. The Russell Jones & Walker office has a serious injuries group, which secured damages of over £2 million for an individual who had suffered severe frontal lobe damage. Thompsons' Liverpool office is best known for its disease work. **Donns Solicitors** was noted as busy at the 'slippers and trippers' end of the market. **Linder Myers** also maintains its regional reputation for claimant work. **Hugh Potter** retains a strong name for personal injury work at his recently formed practice Hugh Potter & Co.

MAINLY DEFENDANT

PERSONAL INJURY: MAINLY DEFENDANT • North West	Ptnrs	Assts
❶ **Berrymans Lace Mawer** Liverpool, Manchester	26	70
James Chapman & Co Manchester	13	16
Keoghs Bolton	18	56
Weightmans Liverpool, Manchester	22	34
❷ **Beachcroft Wansbroughs** Manchester	4	17
Hill Dickinson Liverpool, Manchester	⚐	⚐
❸ **Halliwell Landau** Manchester	5	27

LEADING INDIVIDUALS
❶ **FINNIGAN Kevin** James Chapman & Co
TAZIKER Barry Keoghs

Within each band, firms are listed alphabetically. *See **Profiles** on page 641*
⚐ *Figures unavailable at time of going to press.*

Berrymans Lace Mawer The largest defendant practice in the North West with offices in both Liverpool and Manchester. Act for the larger composite insurers such as Royal & SunAlliance, CGU plc and AXA Insurance. Known principally for the volume of work handled. Maintains specialist departments for industrial disease, RTA, employer's liability and environmental claims. **Clients:** RSA; CGU; Guardian.

James Chapman & Co Very positive feedback from the market place, which perceived the firm as *"proactive, competent and fair to deal with."* **Kevin Finnigan** is a recognised specialist in catastrophic injuries, and heads a *"strong team with good technicians."* Another area of speciality is stress, and the firm recently defended a £100,000 stress claim for Zurich Municipal. **Clients:** Zurich Commercial; AXA; RSA,

Keoghs *"A class outfit,"* the firm has departments specialising in industrial disease, employer's liability, fraudulent claims and motor. Principally work for the major insurers, although the firm has picked up an increasing amount of work from small and medium sized insurers. **Barry Taziker** is considered to be an *"excellent team manager."*

Weightmans Maintains a *"very good reputation,"* for insurance work. However Tony Summers retired in August 2000. **Clients:** 8 out of top 10 insurers.

Other Notable Firms **Beachcroft Wansbroughs** is viewed as *"still processing the merger with Vaudreys"* but is felt to provide *"serious competition"* for the established players. **Hill Dickinson** maintains its reputation, although it is generally felt that the insurance *"lacks the depth of the leaders."* **Halliwell Landau** was characterised as *"up and coming"* by a number of leading claimant practitioners, especially in the area of disease work.

YORKSHIRE

MAINLY CLAIMANT

PERSONAL INJURY: MAINLY CLAIMANT • Yorkshire	Ptnrs	Assts
❶ **Irwin Mitchell** Leeds, Sheffield	13	20
❷ **Pattinson & Brewer** York	3	4
Rowley Ashworth Leeds	3	4
Russell Jones & Walker Leeds, Sheffield	4	6

LEADING INDIVIDUALS	
❶ **PICKERING John** Irwin Mitchell	**TUCKER Andrew** Irwin Mitchell
❷ **ALLEN Simon** Russell Jones & Walker	**CARSON Peter** Rowley Ashworth

Within each band, firms are listed alphabetically. *See **Profiles** on page 641*
⚐ *Figures unavailable at time of going to press.*

Irwin Mitchell Retains its reputation as *"the leading claimant practice in the North."* Best known for acting on behalf of private clients with severe injuries, the firm also has experience in multi-party claims, including the vibration white finger and respiratory disease cases against British Coal. There is also a motor division, which, when combined with the Birmingham Motor practice, provides the only serious competition to Shoosmiths nationally. The office also handles some trade union work, in particular for the MSF. Head of department **John Pickering** is a recognised expert in catastrophic injury claims, while **Andrew Tucker** is *"one of the best technical lawyers around"* and led the claims against British Coal. **Clients:** MSF; legal expense insurers; private clients.

Pattinson & Brewer The only national trade union firm based in York, this team specialises in industrial diseases, with mesothelima claims particularly prevalent. Also experienced in disasters resulting in psychological diseases, such as post traumatic stress disorder. Trade Union work for the RMT, TGWU and the PCS forms the bulk of the practice, although 20% of fee income comes from private client work. **Clients:** RMT, TGWU.

Rowley Ashworth A *"sound team,"* albeit with a low profile. Part of a solid national trade union practice, **Peter Carson** remains recognised for his skills in this area.

Russell Jones & Walker Mixed practice, led by the respected **Simon Allen**, best known for its work for the Police Federation. Also has a serious injury group and an occupational disease group, which has a number of multiple action cases on-going, including aluminium, RSI, asbestos, MDF-Dust, and VWF. Around 70% of the work undertaken is fast track with RTA handled mostly from Leeds, with Sheffield focusing on employer's liability. **Clients:** Iron & Steel Trades Confederation; Police Federation; private clients.

MAINLY DEFENDANT

PERSONAL INJURY: MAINLY DEFENDANT • Yorkshire	Ptnrs	Assts
❶ **Beachcroft Wansbroughs** Leeds	3	18
❷ **DLA** Leeds, Sheffield	8	36
❸ **Irwin Mitchell** Sheffield	⚐	⚐
Nabarro Nathanson Sheffield	3	16
Praxis Partners Leeds	3	28

LEADING INDIVIDUALS	
❶ **ANSON Peter** DLA	**DAYKIN Stephen** Nabarro Nathanson
HOTCHIN Samuel Beachcroft Wansbroughs	

Within each band, firms are listed alphabetically. *See **Profiles** on page 641*

⚐ *Figures unavailable at time of going to press.*

Beachcroft Wansbroughs Another leading office of this national player. Known to be *"a reasonable firm with reasonable people,"* and considered to be the best defendant practice in the region by a number of claimant firms. **Samuel Hotchin** is *"sound on the law"* and *"good to deal with."* **Clients:** Guardian; Royal & Sun Alliance; CGU.

DLA The biggest practice in Sheffield, known for its *"realistic approach."* **Peter Anson** has a long-standing reputation in the field. Has a specialist disease unit focused on stress, VWF, respiratory illnesses, dermatitis and deafness. Also has a motor unit and a small claims motor unit, handling volume claims. The firm has close ties with the coal industry, and along with industrial disease cases, handles a number of catastrophic injuries involving miners and explosions.

Irwin Mitchell Much better known for claimant work, however the defendant practice counts 18 leading insurers among its clients and this part of the practice is a growing presence in the region.

Nabarro Nathanson Best known for acting on behalf of the DTI in connection with the health liabilities of British Coal. The last year saw the firm establish schemed arrangements for over 150,000 Chronic Obstructive Pulmonary Disease and VWF claims brought by former miners. **Stephen Daykin** retains a top regional reputation. However, the firm's *"sensible approach"* has also been popular with some insurers, and the firm has a *"growing profile in Yorkshire"* for employer's liability, public liability and RTA work at all levels and in all courts. **Clients:** DTI; RJB; Crowe Insurance.

Praxis Partners Formerly the insurance practice of Hammond Suddards, this newly independent firm will be looking to retain the strong reputation established under its former parent.

NORTH EAST

MAINLY CLAIMANT

PERSONAL INJURY: MAINLY CLAIMANT • North East	Ptnrs	Assts
❶ **Thompsons** Newcastle upon Tyne	6	10
❷ **Marrons** Newcastle upon Tyne	2	5
❸ **Beecham Peacock** Newcastle upon Tyne	5	-
Browell Smith & Co Newcastle upon Tyne	⚐	⚐
Hay & Kilner Newcastle upon Tyne	8	3

LEADING INDIVIDUALS	
❶ **MADDOCKS Roger** Thompsons	
❷ **ALLAN David** Marrons	**MURPHY Patrick** Marrons
PEACOCK Norman Beecham Peacock	**PORTEUS Stephen** Marrons

Within each band, firms are listed alphabetically. *See **Profiles** on page 641*

⚐ *Figures unavailable at time of going to press.*

Thompsons One of the strongest offices in the Thompsons network, the Newcastle team received widespread approval. It is felt that the team has *"lost its aggressive edge and are now much more sensible."* **Roger Maddocks** has *"good occupational health knowledge"* and is *"down to earth, a bit gruff, but knows how to negotiate and gets a good deal for his clients."* **Clients:** trade unions.

Marrons *"Quieter since they lost some union work but still a good outfit."* The team still has a number of individuals with a high profile in the market. **David Allan** is *"a superb big case litigator,"* while **Patrick Murphy** and **Stephen Porteus** maintain their solid reputations.

Other Notable Firms **Beecham Peacock** is a practice that specialises in serving private clients on a conditional fee basis. Areas of expertise include industrial disease and road traffic accidents, with **Norman Peacock** a well-known local figure. **Browell Smith & Co** specialises in serving trade union clients as well as private clients, and has particular expertise in industrial disease. **Hay & Kilner** is better known as a defendant practice, but its claimant practice serves a number of trade union clients and legal expense insurers, as well as private individuals referred through Headway and the Spinal Injuries Association.

MAINLY DEFENDANT

PERSONAL INJURY: MAINLY DEFENDANT • North East	Ptnrs	Assts
❶ **Eversheds** Newcastle upon Tyne	5	17
Jacksons Stockton-on-Tees	7	6
❷ **Sinton & Co** Newcastle upon Tyne	6	2
❸ **Crutes** Newcastle upon Tyne	⚐	⚐
Deas Mallen Newcastle upon Tyne	7	3
Hay & Kilner Newcastle upon Tyne	⚐	⚐

LEADING INDIVIDUALS	
❶ **DIAS James** Sinton & Co	
❷ **CLARKE Richard** Jacksons	**DREWE David** Crutes
PESCOD Peter Hay & Kilner	**WILLIAMS Alun** Hay & Kilner

Within each band, firms are listed alphabetically. *See **Profiles** on page 641*

⚐ *Figures unavailable at time of going to press.*

Eversheds Swallowed up Linsley & Mortimer and now a more rounded practice. Not traditionally known for acting for composite insurers, the team is nonetheless on the panel for the Royal & Sun Alliance and Norwich Union. Also has an unrivalled client base in the self-insured market, and has purchased Liberty Loss Adjusters to assist with the high volume end of the market. The Linsley & Mortimer Team brought with them particular expertise in industrial diseases, as well as membership of the Iron Trades and CGU environmental panel. **Clients:** RSA; Generali.

Jacksons *"Deserve to be recognised as leaders in the North East"* and developing a national reputation for PI work. The firm has a number of specialist units which include VWF, asbestosis, road traffic and EL/PL litigation. Act on behalf of insurers and an increasing number of self-insured plcs. **Richard Clarke** received a number of recommendations from the market. **Clients:** iron trades; Federal Mogul.

Sinton & Co Suffered a little in the panel culls but retained by some key players such as Norwich Union and AXA. Specialises in disease work and serious spinal injuries. The firm has also set up a dedicated compensation recoveries unit which is gaining a number of instructions to act on appeals. **Jim Dias** continues to be recognised as *"one of the best PI lawyers around."* **Clients:** Norwich Union; AXA; Provident.

Other Notable Firms Traditionally a large insurance practice with a particularly strong grasp on local authority work, the market perception is that **Crutes** may have slipped a little, although the firm remains on the panel of a number of composite insurers and **David Drewe** is still a familiar name in the area. **Deas Mallen** has lost some clients and a senior partner, but *"is still a name"* according to competitors. **Hay & Kilner**'s defendant practice, led by highly respected **Peter Pescod**, has remained largely resilient to the effects of panel reductions, and has received an increased level of instruction relating to industrial diseases, particularly asbestos Partner **Alun Williams** was also noted as a leading practitioner.

SCOTLAND

MAINLY PURSUER

PERSONAL INJURY: MAINLY PURSUER • Scotland	Ptnrs	Assts
❶ **Thompsons** Edinburgh	⚐	⚐
❷ **Balfour & Manson** Edinburgh	8	10
Burnside Kemp Fraser Aberdeen	⚐	⚐
Digby Brown Glasgow	4	15
Lawford Kidd Edinburgh	2	4
❸ **Anderson Strathern WS** Edinburgh	8	10
Drummond Miller WS Edinburgh	4	4
Levy & McRae Glasgow	4	10

LEADING INDIVIDUALS	
❶ **KEMP Sandy** Burnside Kemp Fraser	**SHORT David** Lawford Kidd
SMITH Sid Thompsons	**TYLER Alfred** Balfour & Manson

Within each band, firms are listed alphabetically. *See **Profiles** on page 641*
⚐ *Figures unavailable at time of going to press.*

Thompsons *"Streets ahead of the competition,"* although the firm *"sticks largely to union work, of which there is a lot."* Have a particularly strong reputation for industrial diseases. Possesses *"aggressive litigators"* like **Sid Smith**, who retains a reputation as a *"formidable opponent."* **Clients:** trade unions.

Balfour & Manson More weighted towards high value claims than their competitors and do not have many union clients. Widely admired **Fred Tyler** has expertise in head and spinal injury. The team also handles industrial disease, RTA and employer's liability cases. **Clients:** private clients and agency work through the Court of Session in Edinburgh.

Burnside Kemp Fraser Centred in Aberdeen and specialising in oil industry related claims, the firm is nevertheless a familiar name to competitors in Central Scotland, and both **Sandy Kemp** and the practice in general are well regarded.

Digby Brown A respected union practice, known especially for handling large volumes of small-ticket claims.

Lawford Kidd *"A very capable practice"* felt to be *"easy to deal with"* by defendant firms. **David Short** is a key player.

Other Notable Firms **Anderson Strathern WS**'s pursuer practice does a significant amount of work for the Royal College of Nursing. The team also does a lot of uninsured loss recovery and agency work. **Drummond Miller WS** have an almost exclusively pursuer PI practice and represent a number of trade unions as well as private clients. **Levy & McRae**'s reputation in high-profile litigation is often put to use in personal injury cases, particularly in fatal accident inquiries.

MAINLY DEFENDER

PERSONAL INJURY: MAINLY DEFENDER • Scotland	Ptnrs	Assts
❶ **Simpson & Marwick WS** Edinburgh	12	30
❷ **HBM Sayers** Glasgow	⚐	⚐
❸ **Biggart Baillie** Glasgow	5	7
Dundas & Wilson CS Edinburgh	1	11
Paull & Williamsons Aberdeen	2	5
❹ **Anderson Strathern WS** Edinburgh	4	10

LEADING INDIVIDUALS	
❶ **ANDERSON Peter** Simpson & Marwick WS	**KEYDEN Gordon** Simpson & Marwick WS
MOORE George HBM Sayers	**ROXBURGH James** Biggart Baillie

Within each band, firms are listed alphabetically. *See **Profiles** on page 641*
⚐ *Figures unavailable at time of going to press.*

Simpson & Marwick WS *"Head and shoulders above the competition both in terms of size of practice and the amount of work they get from insurers."* The practice provides a comprehensive national service to the major composite insurers, and has handled a lot of stress-related work this year, alongside RSI and asbestosis claims. **Gordon Keyden** does a lot of EL and lung disease cases and is *"thorough and reliable."* **Peter Anderson** specialises in disaster litigation and high-value, complex claims. **Clients:** Commercial Union; Eagle Star; ITT London & Edinburgh.

HBM Sayers This newly-merged practice is now considered *"the closest competition to Simpson & Marwick."* Acts for a number of major insurers including Royal & SunAlliance and Norwich Union. Specialises in industrial accidents and also has a substantial motor practice. **George Moore** continues to be a leading individual. **Clients:** RSA; Prudential.

Biggart Baillie Almost exclusively a defendant practice, with a balance between high-value and low-value claims. Have a breadth of expertise, but particularly well-known for respiratory illnesses such as asbestosis, with a strong link with the railways. The firm also does a degree of local authority work. **James Roxburgh**, regional president of FOIL, is a well known and much-respected practitioner. **Clients:** iron trades; Zurich Municipal; Scottish Power.

Dundas & Wilson CS Not a particular specialism for the firm, nevertheless the PI practice acts for a number of insurance companies including Royal & Sun Alliance, as well as self-insured corporate bodies. The team handles a broad range of work-related claims such as stress and RSI as well as catastrophic injuries such as paraplegia, tetraplegia and brain damage. **Clients:** Royal & Sun Alliance; Independent Insurance.

Paull & Williamsons *"Tucked away in Aberdeen and doing a tidy business with the oil industry."* Has shown no signs of spreading into Central Scotland, but the firm remains Simpson & Marwick's main competitor in the Grampian region.

Anderson Strathern WS The firm's defender practice acts for a number of insurers including Assicurazioni Generale SpA. The team handles high profile PFI claims including serious head injury cases, RSI, stress and multiple deafness claims.

NORTHERN IRELAND

MAINLY CLAIMANT

Leading Firms At **Agnew, Andress, Higgins, Seamus Agnew** and **Stephen Andress** continue to be recommended by the market, as does **Eamonn McEvoy** at **Eamonn McEvoy & Co. Edwards & Co** retains its reputation. **Francis Hanna & Co** is another recognised firm on the claimant side, whilst **Maurice Diamond**'s practice **SJ Diamond & Son** remains popular with both trade unions and private clients.

PERSONAL INJURY: MAINLY CLAIMANT • Northern Ireland	Ptnrs	Assts
❶ **Agnew, Andress, Higgins** Belfast	3	-
Eamonn McEvoy & Co Lurgan	1	4
Edwards & Co Belfast	2	2
Francis Hanna & Co Belfast	3	1
❷ **S.J. Diamond & Son** Belfast	1	2

LEADING INDIVIDUALS
❶ **AGNEW Seamus** Agnew, Andress, Higgins
ANDRESS Stephen Agnew, Andress, Higgins
McEVOY Eamonn Eamonn McEvoy & Co
❷ **DIAMOND W. Maurice** S.J. Diamond & Son

Within each band, firms are listed alphabetically. *See **Profiles** on page 641*

MAINLY DEFENDANT

Leading Firms C&H Jefferson and **McKinty & Wright** are the two best known insurance practices in Northern Ireland. **Ian Jefferson** and **Derek Taylor** are the names at C&H Jefferson, while **John Cross** is the leading light at McKinty & Wright. **Tughan & Co** are another leading practice, where **Michael Gibson** is a well-known figure, while **Ronnie Bowden** at **Harrison, Leitch & Logan** is also highly regarded. **Brian Stewart** of **O'Reilly Stewart** now deals almost exclusively in defence work, and represents several large British and Irish insurance companies such as Admiral Insurance GB and Privilege.

PERSONAL INJURY: MAINLY DEFENDANT • Northern Ireland	Ptnrs	Assts
❶ **C & H Jefferson** Belfast	6	10
McKinty & Wright Belfast	⚐	⚐
❷ **Harrison, Leitch & Logan** Belfast	3	2
O'Reilly Stewart Belfast	2	6
Tughan & Co Belfast	5	4

LEADING INDIVIDUALS	
❶ **BOWDEN Ronnie** Harrison, Leitch & Logan	**CROSS John** McKinty & Wright
GIBSON Michael Tughan & Co	**JEFFERSON Ian** C & H Jefferson
STEWART Brian O'Reilly Stewart	**TAYLOR Derek** C & H Jefferson

Within each band, firms are listed alphabetically. *See **Profiles** on page 641*

⚐ *Figures unavailable at time of going to press.*

LEADERS IN PERSONAL INJURY

ADAMSON, Derek
Buller Jeffries, Birmingham (0121) 212 2620
Specialisation: Personal injury claims particularly fatal accidents, catastrophic injuries, industrial disease and medical negligence. High profile cases have included motorway disasters, asbestos litigation and products' claims. Other principal areas include professional indemnity, fires, construction claims, policy interpretation and defending civil claims against the police.
Prof. Memberships: Law Society, Birmingham Law Society, FOIL.
Career: Articles *Buller Jeffries* 1979-1981. Partner 1985. Deputy District Judge 1993-1997.
Personal: Born 1956. Birmingham University 1975-78. Leisure Interests: Mainly sport, manager of youth soccer team.

AGNEW, Seamus
Agnew, Andress, Higgins, Belfast (028) 90320035

ALLAN, David
Marrons, Newcastle upon Tyne (0191) 281 1304

ALLEN, Patrick
Hodge Jones & Allen, London (020) 7482 1974
Specialisation: Principal area of practice - clinical negligence, personal injury and miscarriage of justice claims. Member of Steering Committee of Plaintiff lawyers in the Kings Cross Fire and Marchioness litigation and represented many survivors and bereaved in each case. Since April 1998 coordinating and managing the Gulf War, and Sheep Dip multi-party claims, and Kerrin Point group claims. Lecturer on legal aid, personal injury practice and costs.
Prof. Memberships: Law Society, Executive Committee of APIL since 1992, Vice President April 2000. Law Society Personal Injury and Medical Negligence Panels, AVMA referral panel. Society of Labour Lawyers. Legal Services Commission Funding Review Committee.
Career: Articled *Offenbach & Co.* 74-76. Qualified 1977 and simultaneously set up *Hodge Jones & Allen* with Henry Hodge. Senior partner of *Hodge Jones & Allen* and head of personal injury team.
Personal: Born 27.5.50. St Catherine's College, Oxford 1969-72. Married to GP, 2 daughters. Lives Camden Town, London. Interests - windsurfing, sailing, hillwalking, opera, theatre.

ALLEN, Simon J.N.
Russell Jones & Walker, Sheffield (0114) 276 6868
Specialisation: Claimant Personal Injury. Involved specifically in Industrial accidents, RSI cases, Asbestos cases, multi-handed fume and VWF cases and occupational stress cases. Ran the Hillsborough Police PTSD Litigation which was successful before the Court of Appeal in October 1996 and set new law in the House of Lords in 1998. Has been involved in two of the top six RSI settlements ever, winning over £0.5 million in damages in the year 2000.
Prof. Memberships: APIL. American Trial Lawyers Association. Member of Personal Injury Panel. Appointed Assessor for Personal Injury Panel in 2000. Member of Law Society Committee which produced the Pre-Action Protocol and is preparing the Disease protocol for the Lord Chancellors' Dept. Local contact point for Headway. Society of Labour Lawyers. Regular lecturer.

Career: Articled *Favell & Smith*, Sheffield. Qualified 1985. *Brian Thompson & Partners*, Sheffield 1985-89 (Partner 1987). *Russell Jones & Walker* 1989 to date (Partner 1990). Local Managing Partner: Leeds 1996-97. Local Managing Partner: Sheffield (which he opened in 1997). Heads RSI, PTSD, VWF and Asbestos Units within the firm. Set up the firm's National Occupational Disease Group, which is the first of its kind in the UK, to research and develop knowledge of such illnesses.
Publications: Sol. Journal 1993, 1994, 1997, and 2000; New Law Journal 1997 and 2000; PMILL 1996, 1997, 1998 and 1999; APIL Magazine 1995, 1996, 1997, 1998 and 1999; Legal Times 1996. Regular lecturer on PI and in particular on PTSD, RSI, Stress, Employers Liability, Asbestos and procedure. 'PI Update' provider: Law Society Gazette 1996 to date with 4 published articles in 2000. Published Sweet & Maxwell paper on P.T.S.D.
Personal: Family, photography. Trades Union Movement, Manchester United supporter.

ANDERSON, Peter
Simpson & Marwick WS, Edinburgh
(0131) 557 1545
See under Aviation, p.558

ANDRESS, Stephen
Agnew, Andress, Higgins, Belfast (028) 90320035

ANSON, Peter
DLA, Sheffield (0114) 2833406
peter.anson@dla.com
Specialisation: Main area of practice is defendant personal injury with particular reference to mining claims and Construction plant hire claims.
Career: Qualified 1976. Partner 1986.

ARKELL, Catherine
Everatt & Company, Evesham (01386) 47191
Senior Partner CLA
Specialisation: Acts for defendant insurers in a variety of personal injury claims. Has dealt with serious road traffic claims including paraplegia, head injury, etc, and many disease cases including large volume deafness, asbestos-related, RSI, and hand/arm vibration claims. Has also dealt with large (over £1 million) fire-related claims for insurers. Important cases include Rastin v British Steel Plc [1994] (for successful appellant defendants) and Heal v Garringtons Ltd (for defendant's insurers). Contributed to a chapter in 'Hand-arm vibration: A Comprehensive Guide for Occupational Health Professionals' (ed. Pelmear, Taylor & Wasserman).
Prof. Memberships: Law Society.
Career: Qualified in 1979. Became a Partner in *Everatt & Co* in 1980. Now Senior Partner.
Personal: Born 8th November 1954. Educated at Westwood's Grammar School and Bristol University 1973-76. Hon. Legal Advisor to Wychavon Citizen's Advice Bureau.

BALEN, Paul
Freethcartwright, Nottingham (0115) 9369 369
paul.balen@freethcartwright.co.uk
See under Clinical Negligence, p.160

BEALE, Robert L.
Beachcroft Wansbroughs, Bristol (0117) 918 2000
rbeale@bwlaw.co.uk
Specialisation: Partner. Has handled property, fraud and fire damage claims, advising on policy wording and coverage disputes in such claims. Now specialises in public and employer's liability and motor claims, particularly in back injury and malingering cases. Also continues to handle fraud and other policy coverage issues.
Career: Articled *Robins Hay*; qualified 1971; assistant solicitor *Burges Salmon* 1971. *Wansborough Willey Hargrave*, 1974.

BENT, Roger
Thompsons, Cardiff (029) 2048 4136

BOWDEN, James Ronald
Harrison, Leitch & Logan, Belfast (028) 9032 3843
Fax: (028) 9033 2644
Ronnie.Bowden@harrisonll.com
Senior Partner
Specialisation: Road Traffic, Employers Liability. Matters handled recently have included: serious injury (brain damage and quadriplegia); structured settlements; repetitive strain injury; stress in the workplace.
Prof. Memberships: Law Society of Northern Ireland.
Career: Educated at Methodist College, Belfast and Queen's University, Belfast.
Personal: Married: two adult children. Weekend golfer. Soccer fan.

BRUFFELL, Martin
Berrymans Lace Mawer, Southampton
(023) 80236464
martin.bruffell@blm-law.com
Specialisation: Senior partner of the Southampton office and joint national head of the insurance liability group, which includes one of the largest personal injury divisions in the country. Handles personal injury claims for defendants with particular interest in industrial disease cases and employers liability work.
Prof. Memberships: Former President of FOIL (The Forum of Insurance Lawyers), past member of the Editorial Board of JPIL (The Journal of Personal Injury Litigation) and one time contributor to Binghams and Berrymans 'Motor Claims Cases.' Has been involved in working parties for the Law Society and the Lord Chancellors Department, Government bodies (DSS,DETR), and insurance bodies (ABI). These include working parties in the Ogden tables, Woolf, Damages, Conditional Fee Arrangements, the tracing of EL Insurers and Rehabilitation.
Career: Joined *Berrymans* in 1979, qualified in 1981, became an associate in 1982, a partner in 1984. A CEDR accredited mediator.
Publications: Written articles for 'The Lawyer', 'Post Magazine', the 'Law Society's Gazette', and the publications of ILEX and the Association of District Judges. Recently appeared on both Radio 4 and Radio 5 as a commentator on litigation issues.
Personal: Born 1955, educated at RGS High Wycombe and Leeds University.

CAHILL, John David
Stewarts, London (020) 7242 6462
jcahill@stewarts-solicitors.co.uk
Specialisation: Managing Partner and Head of Personal Injury and Clinical Negligence Group. Specialises in foreign personal injury claims and ADR.
Prof. Memberships: Centre for Dispute Resolution; Law Society; Association of Personal Injury Lawyers; Richard Grand Society.
Career: Articled *Kingsford Stacey*; Qualified 1985; Partner 1990; CEDR accredited mediator; member of Personal Injury Panel; Founder of The Richard Grand Society; Trustee of Headway, The Brain Injuries Association; Chairman Headway, London.
Publications: 'Spinal Injuries Case Studies' and 'What Litigation-Happy Culture?' (Wall Street Journal Europe).
Personal: Born 1960; educated at Oratory School and Bristol Polytechnic (1981 LLB Hons.); resides London ;married with two daughters; enjoys fine wines, golf, swimming, and time off in France.

CARSON, Peter
Rowley Ashworth, Leeds (0113) 244 2018
pcarson@rowley-ashworth.co.uk
Specialisation: Personal Injury - specialising in asbestos, head injury and spinal injury cases. Personal Injury Panel member. On approved Headway and SIA list.
Prof. Memberships: APIL.
Career: BA Hons degree (Geography), Manchester University. College of Law, London. *Rowley Ashworth* January 1989, Partner May 1991. Has run Leeds office since January 1992.
Personal: Married with two children. Running, badminton, bridge.

CHANDLER, Pauline
Pannone & Partners, Manchester (0161) 909 3000
pauline.chandler@pannone.co.uk
Specialisation: Plaintiff personal injury work comprising industrial accidents and disease including; asbestos claims (Owen v IMI (bystander asbestos case); Jeromsom v Shell Tankers (asbestos mesolthelioma in marine engineers); asthma; lead welders bronchitis (Knox and Others v Cammel Lairds); lung disease; deafness; vibration; repetitive strain; passive smoking cases; solvent damage (Jenkins v MOD - brain damage from trike); Professional negligence; fatal disease & accident cases (William v Great Ormond Street Hospital).
Prof. Memberships: Law Society Personal Injury Panel Assessor.
Career: Degree at Manchester University. Admitted 1974. Specialised in personal injury and disease work for 25 years at *Thomsons*. Joined *Pannone & Partners* as partner summer of 1999.

CHAPMAN, Richard
Chapman Everatt, Wolverhampton
(01902) 717700
rdc@chapmaneveratt.co.uk
Partner specialising in defendant personal injury.
Specialisation: Specialises in defendant personal injury. The whole firm acts exclusively for insurers and has no private clients. Has appeared on radio and television.
Prof. Memberships: Law Society, Birmingham Law Society, Birmingham Medico Legal Society.
Career: Qualified in 1970. Founding Partner of *Chapman Everatt* in May 1992. Birmingham Law Society Council Member since 1979 and President for 1996/97.
Personal: Born 7th October 1945. Educated at Birchfield School 1952-59, then Denstone College 1959-64. Governor of Birchfield School. Leisure interests include all sports, particularly golf and cricket, as well as theatre and cinema. Lives near Wolverhampton.

CHERRY, Anthony
Beachcroft Wansbroughs, London (020) 7894 6022
acherry@bwlaw.co.uk
Specialisation: Partner specialising in liability insurance claims and related Risk Management issues, handling cases of long-term exposure to chemical, physical and biological agents in the workplace, through products and in the environment. Has a special interest in the Chemical Industry. Lectures regularly on related topics and is on the Editorial Board of JPIL.
Prof. Memberships: On the Editorial Board of JPIL. President of the Forum of Insurance Lawyers from 1995 to 1997. He is a member of the Law Society Civil Litigation Committee and is a member of the Vice Chancellor's working party on Practice Direction.
Career: Admitted May 1979, articles at *Bates & Partners*, Medico Legal section at ICI Legal Department from 1980 to 1983 (developing an expertise in long-term exposure to chemical and physical agents in the work place through products and the environment), *Stanley Simpson North* (then *Beachcroft Stanleys*) from 1983 to date, a Partner since 1985.

CLARKE, Richard P.R.
Jacksons, Stockton-on-Tees (01642) 643643
genquiry@jacksonslaw.co.uk
Specialisation: Principle areas of practice has been a mixture of traumatic injury and disease cases, in the fields of repetitive strain injury, hand arm vibration syndrome and dermatitis. Major clients include eight out of ten of the top insurance firms in the UK.
Prof. Memberships: Law Society and FOIL (Forum of Insurance Lawyers).
Career: Joined *Jacksons* 1977. admitted as a solicitor in 1979 and became a partner in 1982. After gaining initial general experience of legal work, including matrimonial and Magistrates Court work, has specialised in personal injury actions since the early 1980's. Became managing partner in June 2000 after completing intensive management trining at Cranfield.

CRADICK, Simon J.
Morgan Cole, Cardiff (029) 2038 5385
simon.cradick@morgan.cole.com
Partner in Insurance Department.
Specialisation: Main area of practice is insurance litigation, covering all areas of personal injury work including maximum severity claims, industrial disease, RSI, employers' and public liability claims also professional indemnity. Contributes to a regular bulletin on legal update for all insurance clients. Prepared and lectured on all aspects of personal injury litigation.
Prof. Memberships: Member of Cardiff Law Society, Personal Injury Panel and FOIL. Secretary of the Welsh Personal Injury Lawyers Association.
Career: Qualified in 1984, joined *Morgan Cole* in 1985 and become a partner in 1988.
Personal: Interests include skiing and playing squash.

CROSS, John
McKinty & Wright, Belfast (028) 9024 6751
post@mckinty-wright.co.uk
Specialisation: Defending claims for motor insurers and defending medical negligence suits.
Prof. Memberships: Law Society of Northern Ireland and member of Contentious Business Committee of the Society.
Career: Qualified 1970. Partner in *McKinty & Wright* 1975. Graduate of Trinity College Dublin (B.A., LL.B).
Personal: Married with four children. Leisure interests include computers and travel.

DACE, Nigel H.
Weightmans, Birmingham (0121) 233 2601
Specialisation: Partner specialising in personal injury work including motor, employers liability, public liability, local authority and professional and clinical negligence claims. Practice also covers subsidence and other property claims. Acts for insurance companies and Lloyd's syndicates, at both High Court and County Court level. Very considerable experience of cases involving paraplegic and tetraplegic damage, brain damage and cerebral palsy. Has lectured on behalf of Birmingham Law Society and Worcester Law Society on 'The Practice and Procedure in Personal Injury Claims'.
Prof. Memberships: Birmingham Medico-Legal Society.
Career: Qualified 1973. Trained in London. Partner with *George Green & Co* 1982-96. Partner with *Weightmans* since May 1996.
Personal: Educated at Shrewsbury School 1963-67 and Liverpool University 1967-70. Leisure pursuits include playing golf and tennis, watching most sports, particularly football, and also theatre. Born 6th September 1949. Lives in Hagley, Worcestershire.

DAY, Martyn
Leigh, Day & Co, London (020) 7650 1200
See under Product Liability, p.674

DAYKIN, Stephen
Nabarro Nathanson, Sheffield (0114) 279 4000

DERBYSHIRE, Paul A.
Hugh James Ford Simey, Exeter (01392) 274126
pad@fordsimey.co.uk
Partner in Insurance Division
Specialisation: Lead Partner at the Exeter Insurance Division office specialising in all aspects of Defendant Personal Injury work. In the past year has dealt with 3 major brain damage trials up to £1m, 1 tetraplegic action (settlement £2.35m) and several other catastrophic injury claims. Acted for one of the successful Defendants in Rastin v. British Steel (1994). Promotes use of I.T. in dealing with court applications.
Prof. Memberships: Law Society. Past Chairman of Devon & Exeter Law Society Litigation Committee.
Career: Qualified in 1973. Partner in *Ford Simey Daw Roberts* (now *Hugh James Ford Simey*) since 1979. Deputy District Judge 1986 to date. Assistant Recorder 1999.
Personal: Born 13 March 1949. Educated at St Brendans College, Bristol and Exeter University (1967-70). Trustee of Exeter Rugby Club and loves rugby, trout fishing and Dartmoor walking.

DIAMOND, W. Maurice
S.J. Diamond & Son, Belfast (028) 90243726

DIAS, James C.
Sinton & Co, Newcastle upon Tyne
(0191) 212 7800
Partner in Personal Injury Department.
Specialisation: Sole area of practice is personal injury and medical negligence. The personal injury is mainly on behalf of Defendant insurers and the medical negligence on behalf of claimants.
Prof. Memberships: Law Society.
Career: Qualified in 1972 after articles with *John H. Sinton & Co.* Became a Partner in 1974.
Personal: Born 1948. Educated at Austin Friars School, Carlisle 1958-66 and Leeds University 1966-69. Deputy District Judge. Deputy District Chairman Appeals Service. Past President of North of England Medico-Legal Society. Leisure interests where family commitments permit include sport and reading. Lives in Newcastle upon Tyne.

DICKINSON, Graham
Barlow Lyde & Gilbert, London (020) 7247 2277
gdickinson@blg.co.uk
Specialisation: All aspects of insurance liability work but primarily Employers Liability, Industrial Disease, Motor and Public Liability claims. Extensive experience in major injury and loss claims and defence of group action.
Prof. Memberships: Member of the Chartered Insurance Institute.
Career: Qualified 1978. Partner *Robin Thompson & Partners* 1980. Founding Partner *Dickinson Simpson* (Birmingham) 1983. Senior Partner *Rowley Dickinson* (Birmingham) 1989. Appointed Head of General Insurance Division, *Barlow Lyde & Gilbert* 1994.

DREWE, David M.
Crutes, Newcastle-upon-Tyne (0191) 281 5811
Partner in Litigation Department.
Specialisation: Main area of practice is personal injury, acting largely on behalf of insurers and professional negligence, acting exclusively for defendants, including solicitors, surveyors, brokers and accountants making growing use of mediation in both personal injury and professional indemnity matters.
Prof. Memberships: Law Society.
Career: Joined *Crutes* and qualifying in 1981. Became a Partner in 1986.
Personal: Born 15th July 1957. Educated at Merchant Taylor's School, Crosby 1968-75, and Newcastle University 1975-78. Member of Management Board, Newcastle Enterprises for the Deaf and Handicapped (Nefdeaf Ltd). Leisure interests include walking, theatre, cinema and reading. Lives in Newcastle upon Tyne.

ETTINGER, Colin
Irwin Mitchell, London (020) 7250 1884
Specialisation: Partner specialising in Personal Injury and trade union law; conducts catastrophic injury cases of a high value and has particular specialities in workplace accident cases and occupational health matters.
Prof. Memberships: Executive council member Association of Personal Injury Lawyers; convenor Health & Safety Group of the Society of Labour Lawyers; patron for the charity Roadpeace; member of the OSS Professional Negligence Panel. Consultant Editor of J.P.I.L.
Career: Articled *Robin Thompson & Partners*; qualified 1978; partner 1980-95; partner *Irwin Mitchell* 1995. Fellow of College of Personal Injury Law.
Personal: Born 1952, London. Interests: Current affairs, circuit training, football memorabilia collecting, cinema.

EVANS, Roderick M.M.
Ensor Byfield, Southampton (023) 8048 3260
rme@ensorbyfield.com
Specialisation: Injuries of maximum severity and stress related claims and has a special interest in rehabilitation. Also advises in construction disputes and

policy interpretation. Regular contributor of articles to legal journals and conducts training for insurance staff.
Prof. Memberships: FOIL, committee member Rehabilitation Special Interest Group, Law Society.
Career: Qualified 1981. *Deacons Solicitors* Hong Kong 1982-85. *Ensor Byfield* 1985 to date. Senior Partner 1997.
Personal: Running, classic cars.

FINNIGAN, Kevin P.
James Chapman & Co, Manchester (0161) 828 8000 kevin.finnigan@james-chapman.co.uk
Specialisation: Head of Personal Injury Department. He has extensive experience in dealing with severe brain and spine injury claims involving maximum awards. He has pioneered successfully the development of a consensual approach with Claimant's Solicitors resulting in early economic settlement of the largest personal injury claims. He is a frequent speaker at conferences and seminars on the topic of handling largest PI claims. He has assisted Insurers in developing a pro-active approach in true partnership with Insurers.
Prof. Memberships: Manchester Law Society. FOIL.
Career: Educated at St Bedes College. Hull University LLB (Hons) - 1975. Articled at *James Chapman & Co.* Admitted 1978.
Personal: Born: 18.12.53. Married with 3 children. Enjoys hill walking particularly in Ireland, reading and consuming Guinness.

GIBSON, C. Michael H.
Tughan & Co, Belfast (028) 9055 3300
Specialisation: Partner and Head of Litigation Department. Main areas of practice are personal injury, pharmaceutical and asbestos related litigations.

GOODMAN, Sarah
Thompsons, Birmingham (0121) 236 7944

HARDING, Andrew J.
Hugh James Ford Simey, Cardiff (029) 2022 4871 andrew.harding@hjfs.co.uk
Specialisation: Partner and Head of the Plaintiff Personal Injury Litigation Group in the firm's head office. Specialises in catastrophic injury claims with particular interest and speciality in claims involving head injury. Established the firm's Head Injury Unit in 1998. Also undertakes Clinical Negligence work and Solicitors' Negligence claims.
Prof. Memberships: Member of the Law Society's Personal Injury Panel and the Association of Personal Injury Lawyers. Trustee and Chairman of Headway Cardiff and Childrens' Head Injury Trust (CHIT) Cymru.
Career: Born 10.06.61. Graduate of University College Cardiff. Joined the firm in 1982 and qualified in 1984. Partner since 1986.

HARVEY, Mark
Smith Llewelyn Partnership, Swansea (01792) 464444
Specialisation: Personal injury, clinical negligence, product liability; representing victims of transport accidents including; P&O Lifeboat; Maidenhead Rail Fire; the steering committees of Southall and Ladbroke Grove rail crashes as well as household product failures including sanitary and cosmetic items. Head of personal injury in Legal Services Commission multi-party panel practice that has successfully steered mass pharmaceutical liablity actions including Eraldin, Opren, Myodil and the CJD/Human Growth Hormone litigation.
Prof. Memberships: Secretary of APIL; PEOPIL; ATLA; Swansea Law Society PRO; National Back Pain Association and British Association of Sports and the Law; Editorial Board Wales Law Today; Headway.
Career: 1987 Legal Executive *Owen White*; qualified 1990 *Lawford & Co*; Partner *Smith Llewelyn Partnership* 1995.
Personal: Born September 1962; Wine Bluffer; Footballer; Golfer and Skier; resides Vale of Glamorgan.

HENDERSON, Stuart
Irwin Mitchell, Birmingham (0121) 212 1828
Partner in Personal Injury Department.
Specialisation: Particular emphasis on catastrophic spinal cord and brain injury, fatal accident claims, clinical negligence and travel litigation. Heads firm's Plaintiff Personal Injury Department in Birmingham. Acted in a number of cases involving some of the highest awards of damages in personal injury in the UK including the Leung case (a record award of £3.4 million in 1994) and the Luhar (a record award of £5.1 million in 2000). Acting in numerous major group actions for illness suffered by holiday makers against tour Operators. Has extensive media experience and lectures in-house and externally.
Prof. Memberships: APIL, Law Society.
Career: Qualified in 1992. Joined *Robin Thompson & Partners* in 1979, becoming a Partner in 1992. Partner in *Irwin Mitchell* from January 1995.
Personal: Born 20th February 1958. Attended UCE Birmingham.

HERBERT, Andrew
Thompsons, Bristol (0117) 941 1606

HOPKINS, Ian
Leo Abse & Cohen, Cardiff (029) 2038 3252
Partner in Litigation Department.
Specialisation: Personal injury litigation specialist. Member of Law Society PI Panel and Scheme contact for Law Society's Accident Line. Handles large personal injury claims for both plaintiffs and defendants including a substantial case load of industrial disease claims (particularly occupational asthma and asbestosis). Clients include Trade Unions, Insurance companies and the general public. Supervisor in Legal Aid Board Franchised Legal Aid Department. Member of Steering Committee for Severn Tunnel train crash.
Prof. Memberships: Law Society, APIL, Personal Injury Panel.
Career: Qualified in 1987. Became a Partner at *Leo Abse & Cohen* in 1990.
Personal: Born 20th August 1961. Educated at Aberdare Grammar School and Kingston University 1979-82. Lives in Aberdare.

HOTCHIN, Samuel G.
Beachcroft Wansbroughs, Leeds (0113) 251 4700
Consultant in General Insurance Department.
Specialisation: Insurance Litigator. Specialises in personal injury, product liability, and insurance law, including fraudulent claims, policy interpretation and liability.
Career: Qualified and joined *Wansbroughs Willey Hargrave* in 1979. Became a Partner in 1982. Consultant in *Beachcroft Wansbroughs* in 1999.

JACKSON, Carol G.P.
Pannone & Partners, Manchester (0161) 909 3000 carol.jackson@pannone.co.uk
Specialisation: Serious injuries, head, spine and fatal accidents. Settlements: Maidenhead train crash; tetraplegic claim £2.75m; complex liability Clegg v Sunset Holidays diving into swimming pool in Spain; CICA 'baby shaking' case £365k.
Prof. Memberships: Law Society Personal Injury Panel, APIL, Headway, SIA and CHIT.
Career: Admitted as a solicitor in 1981, became a partner with *Pannone & Partners* in 1994. Head of personal injury department.

JEFFERSON, H.L. Ian
C & H Jefferson, Belfast (028) 9032 9545
Specialisation: Senior Partner practising in personal injury work, primarily motor claims, both for Defendants and also Plaintiffs. Clients include major Insurance Companies and Lloyd's Syndicates. Considerable experience of cases involving head injuries including brain damage, spinal injuries and loss of limbs.
Prof. Memberships: Council of the Law Society of Northern Ireland: area representative of FOIL: Headway: Spinal Injuries Association. NI Medico-Legal Society. PEOPIL.
Career: Qualified Northern Ireland 1971. England 1990.
Personal: Fishing, sailing, hockey and theatre.

JOHN, Simon G.
Cunningham John, Thetford (01842) 752401
See under Clinical Negligence, p.163

JONES, David
Morgan Jones & Pett, Great Yarmouth (01493) 334700
See under Clinical Negligence, p.163

KEMP, Sandy
Burnside Kemp Fraser, Aberdeen (01224) 327500
See under Employment, p.339

KEYDEN, Gordon
Simpson & Marwick WS, Edinburgh (0131) 557 1545
Specialisation: Specialises in insurance-based litigation but is principally involved in personal injury claims. Handles claims ranging from catastrophic injury to industrial ailments as well as accidents at work and road traffic cases. Currently the Motor Insurer's Bureau appointed Solicitor in Scotland and has been involved in revising the wording of the new MIB Agreement from a Scottish Viewpoint.
Prof. Memberships: International Bar Association, Forum of Insurance Lawyers, British Insurance Law Association.
Career: Qualified at the English Bar in 1978 before returning to practice in Scotland. Partner in litigation department since 1980.

KITSON, Paul
Russell Jones & Walker, London (020) 7837 2808
Specialisation: Plaintiff personal injury specialist. Has successfully pursued numerous claims for injuries on the sports field for footballers and rugby players. Has spoken at seminars and conferences on sports law and regularly writes for sports magazines and legal journals.
Prof. Memberships: Past committee member of British Association of Sport & the Law; Member of the Association of Personal Injury Lawyers; Co-ordi-

nator of Greater London Regional Group of APIL; Member of Law Society Personal Injury Panel.
Career: Partner with *Russell Jones & Walker* since 1992.

LAWTON, Anthony
Thompsons, Birmingham (0121) 236 7944

LEE, Terry
Evill and Coleman, London (020) 8789 9221
evill@globalnet.co.uk
See under Clinical Negligence, p.164

LEECH, Catherine J.B.
Pannone & Partners, Manchester (0161) 909 3000
catherine.leech@pannone.co.uk
Specialisation: All types of personal injury work especially catastrophic injury claims (particularly spinal), aviation law and disaster litigation, product liability litigation and multi-party actions.
Prof. Memberships: Personal Injury Panel since 1995; APIL Co-ordinator Product Liability and Consumer Affairs SIG; Spinal Injury Association Panel; Association of Trial Lawyers of America. Lectures in PI law for Law Society/AWS Returners course and other continuing education suppliers.
Career: Attended University of Wales, Cardiff and College of Law, Chester. Trained at *Ryland Martineau* then *Pannone and Partners*Admitted September 1987. Became partner with firm May 1991.
Personal: Married with three children, enjoys; running, rowing and being a perfect mother (virtual reality). Member of SIA Ball committee.

LEWIS, Geoffrey
Buller Jeffries, Birmingham (0121) 212 2620
Specialisation: Extensive insurance related practice with some claimant work as well. Catastrophic injury cases. Fatal Accidents Act, Employers' Liability and Property claims. Local authority work and Motor Insurers' Bureau specialist. Policy problems and interpretation. Enjoys unusual or novel accident claims involving points of law.
Prof. Memberships: Law Society, Birmingham Law Society and FOIL.
Career: Articled to Roger Coates at *Buller Jeffries* 1971. Qualified 1973 and partner 1979.
Personal: Born 1949. Graduated 1970 external London University LLB, 2:1 Hons. Leisure interests include running (London Marathon 1996), ballroom dancing, music and DIY.

MADDOCKS, Roger
Thompsons, Newcastle-upon-Tyne (0191) 261 5341

MANSFIELD, Collin. P.
Whittles, Manchester (0161) 228 2061
collinmansfield@whittles.com
Specialisation: Specialises in maximum severity (motor and employers liability) personal injury claims and has lectured on special damages at Manchester Metropolitan University.
Career: Qualified with *Whittles* in 1975, became a partner in 1977, senior litigation partner in 1993, and as of July 2000 became a consultant with the intention of concentration on case handling.

MARSHALL, David
Anthony Gold, Lerman & Muirhead, London (020) 7940 4000
Specialisation: Principal area of practice - personal injury and medical negligence work. Member of the Law Society's Personal Injury and Medical Negligence Panels. Acted in APIL campaigns on Legal Aid, Lord Woolf's Report and on the development of Conditional Fees.
Prof. Memberships: Law Society, APIL (Executive Committee Member since 1996 and Treasurer since 1998).
Career: Joined *Anthony Gold, Lerman & Muirhead* as a trainee Solicitor in 1985, qualifying in 1987 and becoming a partner in 1989. Managing partner 1997.
Personal: Born 5.6.62. Education - Queen's College, Oxford, 1980-1983. Lives in Herne Hill, South London. Honorary Treasurer, Blackfriars Advice Centre. Leisure interests include foreign travel, history and contemporary fiction.

MCCARTHY, Frances
Pattinson & Brewer, London (020) 7400 5100
Partner in Personal Injury Department.
Specialisation: Main area of practice is accidents at work and occupational disease claims. Also handles medical negligence and other areas of personal injury. Has handled successful appeals to the European Court of Justice, on the question of equal treatment in matters of Social Security. Co-author of Know how for Personal Injury Lawyers. Regular lecturer for Legal Action Group and other bodies.
Prof. Memberships: Law Society, Association of Personal Injury Lawyers, Association of Trial Lawyers of America, Environmental Law Foundation.
Career: Qualified in 1981. Joined *Pattinson & Brewer* in 1979, becoming a Partner in 1985. President of APIL, Secretary of the International Practice Section of ATLA, founder member of ELF. Editorial Board of Journal for Personal Injury Law.

MCCOOL, Geraldine M.
Leigh, Day & Co, Manchester (0161) 832 7722
See under Product Liability, p.675

MCEVOY, Eamonn E.
Eamonn McEvoy & Co, Lurgan (028) 3832 7734

MOORE, George K.
HBM Sayers, Glasgow (0141) 353 2121
Specialisation: Litigation for Insurance Companies with particular reference to personal injury, employers and public liability claims. Also specialist in advising on Insurance Company fraud, professional negligence and industrial disease claims. Dealt with the legal aspects of the recent E-Coli outbreak in Scotland including representing the Insurers involved.
Prof. Memberships: Member of the Law Society of Scotland, Solicitor to the Supreme Court, Solicitor/Advocate and Member of FOIL.
Career: Admitted as a Solicitor in 1971, founding partner of *Hamilton Burns & Moore* in 1972, now *HBM Sayers*. Qualified as a Solicitor/Advocate with Rights of Audience in the Court of Session in 1994.

MURPHY, Patrick
Marrons, Newcastle upon Tyne (0191) 281 1304

NELSON-JONES, Rodney
Field Fisher Waterhouse, London (020) 7861 4000
Partner in charge of Personal Injury Litigation Department.
Specialisation: Personal injury work includes asbestosis, aviation and road accidents. Also handles medical negligence work. Cases have included the M1 Air Crash (Steering Committee Member), Bryce v. Swan Hunter Group (Asbestosis), and Pendergast v. Sam & Dee (medical negligence).
Prof. Memberships: Law Society.
Career: Qualified in 1975. Worked at *Prothero & Prothero* 1973-77 and *L Bingham & Co* 1977-83. Joined *Field Fisher Waterhouse* in 1983.
Publications: Co-author of 'Product Liability - The New Law Under the Consumer Protection Act 1987 (2nd ed 1988)', 'Medical Negligence Case Law' (2nd ed. 1995) 'Personal Injury Limitation Law' (1994), 'Computing Personal Injury Damages' (3rd ed. 2000), 'Multipliers' (1998) and 'Butterworths Personal Injury Damages Statistics' (2nd ed. 2000). Contributor to 'Structured Settlements - A Practical Guide', 'Butterworths Personal Injury Litigation Service' and 'The Medical Accidents Handbook'.
Personal: Born on 11 February 1947. Educated at Repton School and Hertford College, Oxford (MA Oxon). Lives in London.

OSBORNE, Thomas R.
Osborne Morris & Morgan, Leighton Buzzard (01525) 378177

PATTERSON, Frank P.
Leigh, Day & Co, Manchester (0161) 832 7722
Specialisation: All areas of personal injury litigation, acting exclusively on behalf of claimants. Handles in particular industrial accidents and industrial disease claims on behalf of trade union clients. Deals with maximum severity damages actions on behalf of plaintiffs with spinal injuries and head injuries and is a member of the Spinal Injuries Association and Headway Specialist Panels. Co-ordinator of large multi-party PI actions. Co-author 'PI Know How' - published by Longmans. Co-author 'Personal Injury Precedents & Pleadings' - published by Sweet & Maxwell, former General Editor 'Personal Injury Precedents + Pleadings.'
Prof. Memberships: Member of the Law Society's Personal Injury Specialist Panel.
Career: Qualified in 1986, having served articles with *Pannone & Partners.*Became a partner in 1990, and head of personal Injury Litigation in 1993. Partner at *Leigh Day & Co* from December 1995.
Personal: Born 6th December 1959, graduated from University of Manchester.

PEACOCK, Norman Douglas
Beecham Peacock, Newcastle upon Tyne (0191) 232 3048
genenquiry@beechampeacock.co.uk
Specialisation: Personal Injury

PERRY, Timothy
Weightmans, Dudley (01384) 211211
Specialisation: Mainly defendant insurance and associated personal injury work. Predominantly deals with employers liability and public liability claims, to include catastrophic injuries and asbestosis, deafness and other industrial diseases.
Prof. Memberships: Law Society and Birmingham Law Society
Career: Educated at Abraham Darby Comprehensive in Telford and then Hull University. After qualifying in 1974, was assistant solicitor at *Browne Jacobson*. Joined *William Hatton* in 1979. Became a partner in 1981.
Personal: Married and lives in Birmingham. Interests include motor sport and football.

PESCOD, Peter
Hay & Kilner, Newcastle-upon-Tyne
(0191) 232 8345
lawyers@hay-kilner.co.uk
Partner in Litigation Department.
Specialisation: Main area of practice is personal injury, acting primarily for major insurers in all types of accident/ disease claims. Handles professional negligence work relating to surveyors, accountants, insurance brokers and architects. Has lectured on medical negligence and special damages and expert evidence.
Prof. Memberships: Law Society, Personal Injury Panel, FOIL (Forum of Insurance Lawyers), FHS Appeals Authority, Deputy District Judge. ADR Mediator.
Career: Joined *Hay & Kilner* in 1973. Qualified in 1975 and became a Partner in 1976.
Personal: Born 29th June 1951. Educated at Queen Elizabeth Grammar, Darlington 1962-69 and Newcastle University 1969-72.

PICKERING, John
Irwin Mitchell, Sheffield (0114) 276 7777
Specialisation: Partner and head of personal injury department; specialist interest in medical negligence; catastrophic injury cases; personal injury specialist with particular interest in medical negligence, foreign claims and catastrophic injury cases (both brain and spinal injury). Important cases include Hepworth v Kerr (medical negligence case in which a patient suffered paralysis after routine ear operation); Bird v Hussain (a record award for chronic pain suffered as a result of a road traffic accident); Thomas v Charles (head injury sustained abroad, damages £750,000 then a record award for the Canary Islands); Ward v Newalls Insulations and Cape Contractors (the highest damages award in this country of £750,000 for an asbestos disease case); Hodgson & Others v Imperial Tobacco Ltd and Gallagher & Hergall Ltd (acting on behalf of smoking-related lung cancer victims against the major UK tobacco manufacturers Court of Appeal decision on conditional fee agreements); Van Oudenhoven v Griffin Inns Ltd (£950,000 damages for closed head injury as a result of pub blackboard accident.), Warren £3.1m damages (test case on multipy) and Annabel, two of the group of cases in the Landmark judgement of Heil v Rankin. Other actions include acting in test cases for industrial deafness and vibration white finger, the latter leading to Irwin Mitchell's involvement in the VWF Solicitor's Steering group and the subsequent £500 million settlement scheme with British Coal. Lectures in the UK and abroad on the subject of medical negligence and personal injury; co-author of clinical negligence pre-litigation protocol.
Prof. Memberships: Member of Board of Governors of The Association of Trial lawyers of America (ATLA); co-chair of International Practice Section, Assessor for any members of Law Society's Personal Injury Panel and Medical Negligence Panel; AVMA panel member; former secretary of APIL; vice-chairman & former executive committee member of the Children's Head Injury Trust; England and Wales representative for The Pan-European Organisation of Personal Injury Lawyers; member of Clinical Disputes Forum.
Career: Articled *Irwin Mitchell*; qualified 1979; partner 1980; head of personal injury department of *Irwin Mitchell*.
Personal: Born 1955, resides Sheffield. Interests in theatre, squash, golf and motor racing.

PICKERING, John
John Pickering & Partners, Oldham
(0161) 633 6667
law@jpicks.u-net.law
Specialisation: Specialist in handling asbestos claims for Plaintiffs. Claims handled throughout the country. Much experience in other industrial disease claims, i.e. asthma, white finger, dermatitis, bladder cancer. Also experience in solicitor's and medical negligence claims. Instructed by trade unions for members. Devised Conditional Fee Agreement for trade unions. Pioneered byssinosis, i.e. cotton dust, claims in England. Acted for Plaintiff in Leeds neighbourhood asbestos trial of 'Margereson v. J.W. Roberts Limited'. Handled many claims for citizens of Australia and for claimants in Malta, Ireland, Canada, South Africa, USA, New Zealand with claims to pursue in UK. One of his cases resulted in a change in the law so that companies no longer in existence can be put back on the register and sued.
Prof. Memberships: APIL. Personal Injury Panel. Legal Aid Franchise.
Career: Qualified 1965. Partner *W.H. Thompson* and *Brian Thompson & Partners* from 1968 until 1979. Founded own firm in Manchester 1979. Now four branches, Oldham, Manchester, Liverpool and Halifax.
Personal: Born 1939.

PORTEUS, Stephen
Marrons, Newcastle upon Tyne (0191) 281 1304

POTTER, Hugh
Hugh Potter & Company, Serious Injury Solicitors, Manchester (0161) 237 5888
Specialisation: Mainly brain and spinal cord injury including medical negligence and professional negligence cases. Has growing caseload of English Plaintiffs injured abroad.
Prof. Memberships: Member of The Law Society Personal Injury and Medical Negligence Panels, The Richard Grand Society and APIL.
Career: Qualified in 1988, became a partner in *Pannone Napier* and *Pannone & Partners* in 1990 and joined *Perkins & Company* as a partner in 1994 and formed *Hugh Potter & Company Serious Injury Solicitors* on 1st May 1998. The firm has franchises for personal injury and clinical negligence.
Personal: Born 8 June 1962. Fund raiser for Headway and Spinal Injuries Association.

PRAIN, David
Rowley Ashworth, Wolverhampton
(01902) 771551
dprain@rowley.-ashworth.co.uk
Partner in Personal Injury Litigation Department. Currently Managing Partner.
Specialisation: Over 25 years' experience of all types of injury and disease work on behalf of leading trade unions and private clients.
Prof. Memberships: Law Society, Birmingham and Wolverhampton Law Societies, member of the Law Society's Personal Injury Panel, Association of Personal Injury Lawyers.
Career: Qualified 1973. Articled at *Rowley Ashworth* 1967-72. Re-joined *Rowley Ashworth* in 1975 and became a partner in 1976.
Personal: Born 20th July, 1948. Attended Silcoates School, Wakefield 1960-66; St John's College of Further Education, Manchester 1966-67; Manchester College of Commerce (L.S. Part 1) 1968-69; College of Law, Guildford 1972. Governor of Halesowen College. Leisure pursuits include wood carving, photography, motor sports, gardening and travel. Lives in Kidderminster.

PRICE, Hugh
Morgan Cole, Cardiff (029) 2038 5385
hugh.price@morgan-cole.com
Partner, Insurance Division.
Specialisation: Main areas of practice are professional negligence for insurance clients. Has handled many maximum severity claims including quadraplegia and serious head injury cases. Professional negligence work for solicitors, brokers, engineers, surveyors and accountants. Frequent lecturer on Woolf changes (CPR); also lectured on adequacy of professional indemnity cover to RICS. Member of SIF Protocol drafting working party and CGU reserving guideliines drafting tream.
Prof. Memberships: Deputy District Judge 1988-1997. President of Cardiff Law Society 1998/9; Member of Law Society Personal Injury Panel and FOIL. Trained ADR mediator.
Career: Articled at *Hardwickes* (now *Morgan Bruce*) and qualified in 1975; partner in 1978.

RIGG, Bettina
Bond Pearce, Southampton (023) 8063 2211
xbar@bondpearce.com
Specialisation: Partner and Head of Insurance Group in Southampton. Specialises in personal injury and medical negligence claims for insurers and self insureds. Work includes a wide range of motor, employers' liability and public liability claims as well as all aspects of Health and Safety. Appears regularly as advocate in the Civil Courts and the Coroners Court.
Prof. Memberships: Member of the British Insurance Law Association, FOIL, the Chartered Insurance Institute and the Council of The Insurance Institute in Southampton.
Career: Qualified in 1982. Joined *Bond Pearce* in 1980, becoming Partner in 1989.

ROACH, W.D. Andrew
Beachcroft Wansbroughs, Birmingham
(0121) 698 5200
ARoach@bwlaw.co.uk
Specialisation: Partner handling all types of personal injury work including serious motor cases and public and employers' liability claims. Specialises in particular in gradual and modern diseases and sports law. Ran the successful defence of the co-defendant in the groundbreaking case of Smoulden v Whitworth & Nolan, the first case where liability attached to a referee for his handling of a rugby game. Also acts on large loss claims, especially arson and product liability, and advises on policy disputes of all types. Has spoken at AIRMIC and numerous other conferences on trends in industrial diseases and sports law.
Prof. Memberships: BILA, FOIL
Career: Qualified 1980; solicitor *Lawrence Graham* 1980-1982. Solicitor *Herbert Smith* 1982-1986. *Wansbrough Willey Hargrave* (now *Beachcroft Wansbroughs*) 1986.

ROWE, Bernard V.
Lyons Davidson, Bristol (0117) 904 6000
Partner and Head of Personal Injury and Insurance.
Specialisation: Principal area of practice is personal injury litigation arising from road traffic accidents. Heads a department of 180 personnel, handling personal injury and road traffic litigation

for plaintiffs and defendants. Has been involved in numerous substantial personal injury cases, including structured settlements. Experienced lecturer at legal conferences and seminars. Organised 3-day international Conferences on Whiplash Injuries 1997, Psychological Injuries 1998 and Whiplash 2000 Conference. Served on Working Party to establish the Disability Assessment Unit and now Treasurer of BICMA (Bodily Injury Claims Management Association).
Prof. Memberships: Treasurer of Motor Accident Solicitors Society (Chairman 1992-94), Member Judicial Advisory Committee to European Whiplash Association. Treasurer of BICMA
Career: Qualified in 1976. Partner at *Iveson Jarratt* in Hull from 1977. Joined *Lyons Davidson* in 1986 and became a Partner in 1987. Managing Partner 1992-94.
Personal: Born 21st December 1951. Educated at Watford Grammar School 1963-70 and Hull University 1970-73 (BA, Politics and Law). Leisure pursuits: fly fishing. Lives in Gloucestershire.

ROXBURGH, James A.R.
Biggart Baillie, Glasgow (0141) 228 8000
jroxburgh@biggartbaillie.co.uk
Specialisation: Leading defence practioner in industrial (particularly lung) disease cases. Scottish Regional Chairman of Forum of Insurance Lawyers and member of Panel of Solicitors advising Law Society's PI Insurers.
Career: Glasgow University BL 1963; partner *Biggart Baillie* 1968; senior partner, *Biggart Baillie* 1990. Acted for claimants in a number of accidents involving oil industry in North Sea.
Personal: Married with two daughters, one son. Leisure interest include skiing, golf, tennis and bridge.

SHORT, David
Lawford Kidd, Edinburgh (0131) 225 5214
law@lawfordkidd.co.uk
Specialisation: Exclusively acts for victims. Extensive practice acting on behalf of Trade Unions including AEEU, UNISON, BALPA and FirstAssist for ULR claims. Main area of practice, work related accidents and disease cases. Particular specialisation in aviation related accidents mainly representing pilots. Past steering committee member of Piper Alpa and Brent Spar disasters.
Prof. Memberships: Law Society of Scotland, Society of Writers to Her Majesty's Signet. Executive Councillor - APIL. ATLA member.
Career: Dundee and Strathclyde Universities, trained at *Lawford & Co*, London for period in 1980s. Qualified 1984.
Personal: Married - one son.

SLESS, Tania
Beachcroft Wansbroughs, London (020) 7242 1011
tsless@bwlaw.co.uk
Partner.
Specialisation: Partner in department, specialising in employers', public and products liability and also serious motor injury claims. Particular expertise in work-related upper limb disorders and stress claims on behalf of retailers and manufacturers. Retains an intrest in Irish claims, and has written and broadcast on comparative levels of compensation between this jurisdiction and Ireland. Prof. memberships: FOIL
Prof. Memberships: FOIL

Career: Admitted as solicitor 1985 Ireland; 1991 England & Wales.
Personal: Trinity College, Dublin (1982 BA Mod in Legal Science) Incorporated Law Society of Ireland 1982-1985. Leisure: reading, cinema, theatre, art.

SMITH, Sid
Thompsons, Edinburgh (0131) 225 4297

STAPLES, Martin R.
Vizards, Staples & Bannisters, London (020) 7400 9999
Specialisation: Insurance law of all descriptions. Thalidomide Litigation in the 1960's. The first industrial deafness case, Berry v Stone Manganese 1972. Numerous high profile cases. Currently farmers' 'sheep dip' organophosphate litigation and McDonalds hot drink claims.
Prof. Memberships: President of foil- forum of insurance lawyers. Founder member BICMA - Bodily Injuries Claims Managers Association.
Career: Began articles in 1962. Insurance litigation in every field ever since. Senior partner of *Vizards* in its bicentenary year, 1997. Currently in the forefront of conditional fees issues on behalf of the insurance community and its practitioners.
Personal: Hounslow College. Interests: travel, wine, sport, reading. Wife. two sons and two stepchildren.

STEWART, Brian J.C.
O'Reilly Stewart, Belfast (028) 9032 1000
oreillystewart@dnet.co.uk
Partner and head of the Litigation Department.
Specialisation: Specialises in product liability defence and insurance defence generally.
Prof. Memberships: Member of the Council of the Law Society of Northern Ireland. Former Chairman of the Belfast Solicitors' Association. Member of the International Association of Defence Counsel.
Career: Qualified 1978. Admitted to the Republic of Ireland Roll of Solicitors 1991.

TAYLOR, Derek T.
C & H Jefferson, Belfast (028) 9032 9545
Specialisation: Main area of practice is all aspects of industrial chest disease acting for Defendants including all asbestos-related conditions and occupational asthma. Has some 15 years experience acting for major insurers who have carried EL and PL risks in industry. Other area of expertise is medical negligence. Has some 13 years experience acting for Health Boards in Northern Ireland in all kinds of medical negligence claims. Has acted for the defence in a number of successfully defended and high-profile obstetric cases.
Prof. Memberships: Law Society of NI, NI Medico-Legal Society.
Career: Qualified in 1975. Assistant Solicitor with *Harrison Leitch & Logan* 1975-1977. *L'Estrange & Brett* 1977-1978. Partner with *C&H Jefferson* 1979 to date.
Personal: Born 17th April 1949. Educated Bangor Grammar School, Co. Down and then Queen's University of Belfast 1968-1972. Leisure interests include hill walking and golf. Member of National Trust.

TAZIKER, Barry
Keoghs, Bolton (01204) 532611
Senior Partner.
Specialisation: Insurance policy interpretation. Insurance fraud. Commercial and personal injury litigation, on the instructions of insurers.
Career: Qualified 1970. Partner since 1971.

Personal: Born 11th January 1945. Educated at St Peters' College, Oxford. Open Exhibitioner. Former Chairman of the Area Legal Aid Board. Former President of the local Law Society.

TENQUIST, Iain R.
Morgan Cole, Reading (0118) 955 3046
iain.tenquist@morgan.cole.com
Specialisation: Catastrophic injuries, in particular brain injuries; public liability claims, led the litigation arising from the 60 vehicle pile-up on the M4 in March 1991 involving 10 fatalities; regular contributor of articles to journals; experienced speaker.
Prof. Memberships: Law Society, Forum of Insurance Lawyers.
Career: 1969-76 Magdalen College School, Oxford. 1977-80 King's College, London (LLB). 1980-81 College of Law, Guildford. 1982-85 *Humfrys & Symonds*, Hereford (qualified 1984). 1985 to date *Morgan Cole.*

TUCKER, Andrew
Irwin Mitchell, Sheffield (0114) 276 7777
See under Product Liability, p.676

TYLER, Alfred J.
Balfour & Manson, Edinburgh (0131) 200 1210
ajt@balfour-manson.co.uk
Partner in Litigation Department.
Specialisation: Main area of practice is personal injury (with special interest in head and spinal injuries) and medical negligence (with a special interest in birth cases). Also handles general commercial (including defamation and professional negligence) and aviation matters. Has been involved in major multi party actions including the 1986 and Mull of Kintyre Chinook disasters, the Piper Alpha disaster, the Lockerbie disaster and the Brent Spar and Cormorant Alpha helicopter crashes, and the Scottish Myodil claims. Represented the pursuer in the House of Lords cases of Herd v Clyde Helicopters and the House of Lords appeal of McFarlane v Tayside Health Board, the failed sterilisation case, which is now the subject of a to the European Couts of Human Rights.
Prof. Memberships: S.S.C, N.P, Association of Personal Injury Lawyers (Scottish Co-ordinator), Spinal Injuries Association, Headway, Scottish Head Injury Forum (Advisor to Management Committee)
Career: Qualified in 1975, having joined *Balfour & Manson* in 1973. Became a Partner in 1978.
Personal: Born 27th January 1951. Educated at Daniel Stewart's College, Edinburgh 1956-69 and Edinburgh University 1969-73. Enjoys golf. Lives in Edinburgh.

WALKER, Ian J.
Russell Jones & Walker, London (020) 7837 2808
Joint Senior Partner in personal injury department.
Specialisation: Has specialised in plaintiff personal injury since 1975. Acted in the then largest CICB award in 1988. Also the then-largest ever court fatal award (£920,000) in 1991. Lead solicitor in the Kings Cross fire cases. Co-Author of 'Tribunal Practice and procedure 1985', 'Know-How for Personal Injury Lawyers 1993 and 1997', and Editor in Chief of the 'Journal of Personal Injury Litigation 1994/5'. Regular lecturer for IBC, Jordans, Euroforum, Hawksmere and others. Immediate past President of Association of Personal Injury Lawyers. Former co-chair, International Section of Association of Trial Lawyers of America. 1993-95 Co-ordinator for Information Technology Group APIL. Member of Board of Governors, Association of Trial Lawyers of America. Member of

ABI and IUA Rehabilitation working parties. Senior Fellow, College of Personal Injury Law. Member of Executive Board, College of Personal Injury Law. Member of Editorial Board, Journal of Personal Injury Litigation. CEDR - accredited Mediator. Vice-President, Bodily Injury Claims Management Association.
Prof. Memberships: Association of Personal Injury Lawyers, Association of Trial Lawyers of America, Law Society, Holborn Law Society, Medico-Legal Society, Association of Plaintiff Lawyers of Australia, Society for Computers and the Law, London Solicitors Litigation Association.
Career: Qualified in 1974. Joined *Russell Jones & Walker* in 1968, becoming a Partner in 1977.
Personal: Born 15th April 1950. Attended Whitgift School 1961-68. Governor of an independent school. Leisure interests include music, golf, gardening, cooking and walking. Lives in Caterham, Surrey.

WEBSTER, John
Veale Wasbrough, Bristol (0117) 925 2020
jwebster@vwl.co.uk
Specialisation: Personal Injury acting for claimants in accident and disease cases. Special interest in head and spinal injury cases and fatal accident cases. Many asbestos injury and post traumatic stress disorder cases. Much experience of employers' liability, road accidents (including multi-party cases, (including Paddington rail crash, South African bus crash, M4 Hungerford multi vehicle and Avonmouth explosion) and product liability. Some interest in sports and holiday injury cases.
Prof. Memberships: Fellow of the College of Personal Injury Law, Chairman of the Civil Courts Committee, Bristol; Member of: Bristol Law Society Council, Association of Personal Injury Lawyers, Bristol Medico Legal Society; Panel Member of: Law Society Personal Injury Panel, Spinal Injuries Association, Headway, MIND, Roadpeace.
Career: Manchester University (LLB Hons) - College of Law, London. Partner 1994 and head of the firm's personal injury team.
Personal: Born 1961.

WILLIAMS, Alun C.
Hay & Kilner, Newcastle-upon-Tyne
(0191) 232 8345
lawyers@hay-kilner.co.uk
Partner in Litigation Department.
Specialisation: Has specialised in personal injury work for plaintiffs and defendants and claimants since 1979. Also handles health and safety and road traffic work. Has a particular interest in stress related and industrial disease claims.
Prof. Memberships: Personal Injury Panel, FOIL.
Career: Qualified in 1979. Joined *Hay & Kilner* in 1977, becoming a Partner in 1982.
Personal: Born 7th August 1955. Attended Newcastle University 1973-76. Leisure interests include military history, football, reading and music. Lives in Newcastle-upon-Tyne.

WILLIAMS, Gareth J.
Hugh James Ford Simey, Cardiff (029) 2022 4871
See under Litigation (Commercial), p.569

WILLIAMS, Robin
Leo Abse & Cohen, Cardiff (029) 2038 3252
Partner in Trade Union Services Department.
Specialisation: Principal area of practice covers personal injury claims, employment and Trade Union law. Advises BFAWU, GMB,TGWU, UNIFI and USDAW business and private clients. Acts in industrial disease cases including asbestosis, deafness, asthma, RSI and dermatitis. Also handles fatal accident claims, employment injunctions and has extensive experience of all complaints to the Employment Tribunal including mass dismissal claims, sex discrimination cases, transfer regulations disputes. Has acted in general Chancery and Commercial cases, particularly contested probate actions, winding up petitions and bankruptcy. Lectures on personal injury, employment and Trade Union Law.
Prof. Memberships: Law Society, Personal Injury Panel, APIL (Regional Co-ordinator of the South Wales and West Regional Group), Fellow of College of Personal Injury Lawyers.
Career: Qualified in 1980 while with *Leo Abse & Cohen* and became a Partner in 1985.
Personal: Born 15th October 1955. Attended Glanafan Comprehensive School 1966-74 and London School of Economics 1974-77. School Governor. Leisure pursuits include sport (rugby, soccer and badminton), theatre, art, cinema, modern music and reading. Lives in Cardiff.

ZINDANI, Jeffry
Russell Jones & Walker, Birmingham
(0121) 643 6800
Specialisation: Main area of practice is personal injury acting for a number of Trades Union clients. Acted in the largest noise induced deafness claim for a Police Firearms Officer. Acted in a number of lifting cases, and in particular in the reported case of Colclough v. Staffordshire County Council 1993. Author of Book entitled 'Manual Handling Law and Litigation' (CLT Professional Publishing) and several articles.
Prof. Memberships: Member of the Personal Injury Panel Law Society; Member of the Birmingham Medico-Legal Society and APIL.
Career: Qualified in 1989; April 1989 joined *Russell Jones & Walker,* in Birmingham, became a partner in July 1994, local managing partner in 1998.
Personal: Born on the 4th July 1963. Attended Moseley Comprehensive School and UCE. LLB (Hons.); The University of Keele, MA (Industrial Relations).

PLANNING

London: 649; South: 652; Thames Valley: 653; South West: 653; Wales: 654; Midlands: 655; East Anglia: 656; North West: 657; Yorkshire: 657; North East: 658; Scotland: 658; *Profiles*: 660

OVERVIEW: The majority of planning solicitors were less circumspect and more positive about the future than this time last year. Although it has become ever more difficult to obtain permission for major developments because of the increasing complexity of the planning rules, the effects of the current buoyant property cycle have been actively felt. The prospering firms appear to be those with strong commercial property departments who can capitalise upon these skills in addition to 'stand-alone' planning capability. This duality of function may well come to represent the future, as planning consultants reap an increasingly large share of the market.

There are signs of an emerging personnel trend away from the capital, perhaps due to the ability to seize attractive pieces of work at more competitive fee levels. The notable departures of David Brock to Mills & Reeve and Iain Gilbey to Shoosmiths hint at this pattern.

RESEARCH APPROVED BY BMRB: *For this edition,* Chambers' *researchers conducted 6083 interviews – 4408 with law firms, 598 with barristers and 1077 with clients.*

The validity of the research was scrutinised by BMRB International, who audited both the methodology and the results at our offices in July 2000. They interviewed Chambers' *researchers and cross-checked sample interviews. Details of the audit appear on page 7.*

LONDON

Berwin Leighton Although the chasing pack has closed, this is still the nation's leading planning outfit. Unquestionably the largest team, three pure planning partners and a never-ending supply of go-getting assistants run a huge caseload of big-ticket work. Critical mass allows the team to project manage large scale retail and development cases. Feeding off a successful and buoyant property department, the firm also has an unsurpassed roster of planning clients.

Ian Trehearne's *"deep knowledge of the subject and commercial approach"* are regularly sought after. **Tim Pugh** is *"meticulous, thorough and works hard to find solutions."* Every inch the technician, he is *"extremely good on detailed agreements."* Clients and fellow lawyers love the *"calm and able"* **Tim Hellier** who flew up the ranks this year after several positive endorsements of his personable, yet *"no-nonsense"* approach. Geoffrey Crighton has now retired. Of the many bright and dogged assistants, *"switched-on"* **Tim Smith** is felt by many to be *"exceptionally promising."* Tescos remain the major client, although recent highlights include acting for Southern Water on the complex Portobello waste water treatment works on the south coast. Also acted for Legal & General in the major public enquiry of the last 12 months at Bracknell concerning the implications of the town centre redevelopment. **Clients:** Tesco; Blue Circle; BAA MacArthur Glen; British Land.

Ashurst Morris Crisp The firm's depth of expertise and widely coveted client base increasingly render it an emerging planning force. Even the departure of top junior Iain Gilbey to Shoosmiths has not had a calamitous effect. Active in the range of development sectors and with associated expertise in local government, the team are frequently mentioned by clients and fellow lawyers as a player on an upward curve. Star partner **Michael Cunliffe** *"rules the roost,"* and is recognised for his *"big-picture thinking."* Good at client relations and negotiating, he also has a *"thorough knowledge of the statutory framework and planning rules."* **Tony Curnow** attacks planning from a local government perspective, his individual strengths being a hard-working attitude and *"real attention to detail."* **Martin Evans** was instrumental in bringing a large slice of Tesco's work with him when exclusivity ended. *"Immensely able"* and *"capable of running a huge amount of work,"* he is a key component of the team and rises this year. New entrant **Karen Howard** was regularly endorsed by the market. Trained at the Berwin Leighton academy, she is considered to be a valuable acquisition for the firm. Acted for Tesco stores in connection with its redevelopment of the Cattle Market and Morton Lane sites at Beverley. Advised the London Boroughs of Brent and Ealing in a major section 106 agreement relating to the Guinness business park development at the Park Royal brewery site. **Clients:** Tesco; BG plc; Thames Water; local authorities.

CMS Cameron McKenna The big question surrounding the firm was whether they would fill the post-T5 void, having been tied up on the most mammoth inquiry of recent years. The practice has risen to the challenge and has particular strength in the construction and energy sectors. Considered to be *"obvious contenders"* for extensive inquiries and major infrastructure projects. **Tony Kitson** is an *"enthusiastic lawyer"* and a *"smooth operator"* who provides *"top quality judgements,"* and is rated as *"one of London's greats."* **Christopher Williams**' reputation also remains intact. Ian Mackay has left to set up his own firm, Innes Mackay. A recent major case was the firm's work on a high profile redevelopment of Bristol harbourside, where it acted for Crest Nicholson. Also acting for The Wellcome Trust in the Hinxton Genome Campus inquiry. **Clients:** Berkeley Group; Crown Estate Commissioners; J Sainsbury plc; Taylor Woodrow plc.

Denton Wilde Sapte The firm's strength is considered to lie in the versatility of a team which can apply planning capabilities to a number of differing projects – leisure, retail and public sector matters are significant components of the practice. Despite assuming managerial responsibilities in the property department, **Stephen Ashworth** has risen to the top tier of practitioners for his *"vast intellect, smooth personality and aggressively commercial approach."* Ex-barrister **Margaret Casely-Hayford** is a *"tremendous worker"* and a *"fearless fighter."* She has been active recently for sports and leisure clients, while **Sandra Banks** still runs a mixed practice incorporating clients from the public sector and local government. Historic retail client Sainsburys still generate substantial planning work, such as the Greenwich Millennium Store advice. Highlight, however, was the obtaining of consent for the redevelopment and expansion of the Chelsea Football Club stadium at Stamford Bridge. Also acting for the Burford Group concerning the development of a large rail freight distribution facility in Manchester. **Clients:** Sainsburys Supermarkets Ltd; Carter Commercial; London Borough of Barking and Dagenham; English Partnerships.

Herbert Smith (Up to 10 assistants can be called upon, many from the property department) Although David Brock has left for Mills & Reeve, the firm is not felt to have suffered unduly. Big-ticket, property-driven planning work continues, and the firm is described as *"still a first class outfit."* The emphasis at the firm is on versatile development and property lawyers with the ability to embrace planning and environmental work on big projects and transactions. Foremost among these is partner **Patrick**

PLANNING • London	Ptnrs	Assts
❶ Berwin Leighton	4	12
❷ Ashurst Morris Crisp	2	7
CMS Cameron McKenna	2	4
❸ Denton Wilde Sapte	3	10
Herbert Smith	2	*
Nabarro Nathanson	3	6
SJ Berwin & Co	2	2
❹ Clifford Chance	1	6
Linklaters	2	9
Lovells	1	3
McGuinness Finch	3	-
Norton Rose	1	5
❺ DJ Freeman	1	2
Gouldens	2	4
Simmons & Simmons	1	2
Slaughter and May	2	1
Stephenson Harwood	1	4
Theodore Goddard	1	2
❻ Dechert	-	3
Fladgate Fielder	3	1
Freshfields Bruckhaus Deringer	1	5
Lawrence Graham	2	2
Macfarlanes	1	2
Olswang	1	2
Travers Smith Braithwaite	1	2

LEADING INDIVIDUALS

✪ **ASHWORTH Stephen** Denton Wilde Sapte	**CUNLIFFE Michael** Ashurst Morris Crisp
GREENWOOD Brian Norton Rose	**KITSON Tony** CMS Cameron McKenna
THOMAS Patricia SJ Berwin & Co	
❶ **DYER Carl** McGuinness Finch	**GALLIMORE Michael** Lovells
GRAVES Gary Nabarro Nathanson	**HALL Brian** Clifford Chance
HELLIER Tim Berwin Leighton	**JACKSON Raymond** Linklaters
MAX Richard D J Freeman	**PUGH Timothy** Berwin Leighton
TREHEARNE Ian Berwin Leighton	
❷ **CASELY-HAYFORD Margaret** Denton Wilde Sapte	
COOPER David Gouldens	**CURNOW Tony** Ashurst Morris Crisp
EVANS Martin Ashurst Morris Crisp	**HAWKINS David** Nabarro Nathanson
HILLEBRON Richard Slaughter and May	**HUGHES Norna** Nabarro Nathanson
RICKETTS Simon SJ Berwin & Co	**ROBINSON Patrick** Herbert Smith
❸ **BANKS Sandra** Denton Wilde Sapte	**EVANS Douglas** Theodore Goddard
FONGENIE Wesley McGuinness Finch	**FRASER Moira** McGuinness Finch
JEEPS Barry Stephenson Harwood	**QUAYLE Sophie** Herbert Smith
SHERLOCK Roger Nabarro Nathanson	**WELLS Martin** Stephenson Harwood
WILLIAMS Christopher CMS Cameron McKenna	
❹ **BLANEY Trevor** Lawrence Graham	**REDMAN Michael** Clifford Chance
TRUE Justin Dechert	**TURNER Angela** Gouldens
WATCHMAN Paul Freshfields Bruckhaus Deringer	
WATKINS David Linklaters	
UP AND COMING	
DRUKARZ Daniel Fladgate Fielder	**HOWARD Karen** Ashurst Morris Crisp
LEA Alison Travers Smith Braithwaite	**SMITH Tim** Berwin Leighton

Within each band, firms are listed alphabetically. *See* ***Profiles*** *on page 660*

** See editorial entries for explanations of team sizes.*

Robinson, considered primarily a commercial property lawyer, but still recognised in planning circles for his indefatigable work-rate. **Sophie Quayle** is known for her public inquiry work, and is considered a *"young and hardworking"* lawyer. She won praise for her handling of the four-month Allied London Properties/Schroder Property Investment Management Ltd inquiry concerning redevelopment proposals for the whole of Bracknell town centre. Advised and obtained planning permission for More London Bridge for a office and retail site on the south side of the Thames including the site for the Mayor of London's office. Also acting for Coventry City Football Club in seeking to obtain permission for a new 40,000 seat arena **Clients:** Stanhope plc; Argent; BG plc ; Fulham Football Club.

Nabarro Nathanson Singled out by the market as a firm who, more than most, have exploited the buoyant property economy to raise their planning profile. Particularly visible on lengthy inquiries and projects such as Brent Cross, Bracknell and the Oracle Shopping Centre in Reading, where a team of nine specialist fee-earners can apply considerable resources. A leading local authority practice, related strength in areas such as compulsory purchase is also a feature of the practice. Several practitioners are recommended, most notably **Gary Graves** *("consistently high quality")* and **Norna Hughes**. **David Hawkins** has always been *"another key player"* while assistant **Roger Sherlock** also maintains his reputation. Continue to act for Hammerson UK Properties plc and Standard Life Assurance Company in seeking to extend Brent Cross Shopping Centre. Acted for THI plc in relation to an inquiry around proposals for a major leisure scheme in Dartford. **Clients:** Dana Corporation; Costco; Land Securities; local authorities.

SJ Berwin & Co For a number of years, leading light **Pat Thomas** has maintained the highest standing and her star continues undimmed. Phenomenally hard working and possessing *"enormous drive"* she was felt by one observer to represent the *"optimum"* in terms of experience and expertise. In addition to mainstream retail and leisure work, an increasing feature of her practice is her airports specialism. Given her larger than life presence *("when Pat enters a room, it's like a whirlwind has arrived!")* it is to **Simon Ricketts**' credit that he has successfully carved out his own reputation. A former barrister, he has experience as an inquiry advocate *("provides quality commercial judgements")* and manages a more property-focused caseload, including acting for British Land on their purchase of the Meadowhall shopping complex outside Sheffield. Among a range of airports cases, advised Christchurch Borough Council on the negotiation of a complex section 106 agreement for a new terminal at Bournemouth International Airport. Also acting on behalf of The Walton Group in connection with their proposed mixed retail and leisure development in Liverpool City Centre. **Clients:** Marks and Spencer plc; J Sainsbury Developments Ltd; London City Airport plc.

Clifford Chance Of the Magic Circle firms, this remains the one most likely to shake off the tag of 'corporate support group.' The team acts for a roster of developer and retail clients, with work overlapping the firm's environment, PFI and local government expertise. Traditionally, the practice has rested on the capable shoulders of sole partner **Brian Hall**, a lawyer equally highly regarded for his environmental and public law abilities. Well-liked professionally and a *"big personality,"* he still shows *"hunger for the work."* Ex-barrister and senior assistant **Michael Redman** is another well known figure synonymous with environment. Work highlights include the obtaining of planning permission for Burford Holdings plc on the redevelopment of land at Avonmouth, Bristol involving a regional business park. Also acting for International Generating Company (UK) Ltd, relating to planning consents for gas energy projects at Stanlow and Aldborough. **Clients:** BHS; Safeway plc; MEPC plc; Hazama Corporation.

Linklaters *"Made real progress lately."* The team fuses planning with environmental law, profiting from the firm's unsurpassed property practice. Many barristers singled out the team for its work on prominent City developments. *"Their input into transactions, identification of the issues, preparation and back-up is first class."* Led by the respected **Ray Jackson**, the team also includes popular choice **David Watkins**. Advised Swiss Reinsurance Company on its redevelopment proposals for the Baltic Exchange site in the City of London. Seeking planning permission and listed building consent for the development of an all seater stadium and ancillary accommodation for Fulham FC. Also acting for Development Securities plc on the planning aspects of the Bishopsbridge site adjacent to Paddington Station in London. **Clients:** AMEC; Royal Opera House; Railtrack plc; John Laing Developments Ltd.

Lovells The *"vastly experienced"* **Mike Gallimore** has a tremendous reputation as a planning specialist *("he knows the system thoroughly,")* and his move to assume managerial responsibility at the head of the property department has prompted speculation about his potential time 'at the coalface.' The focus of the planning practice centres around commercial property and development clients. While the client list remains superb, it is felt that the firm needs more senior planning fire-power to challenge the market leaders seriously. The team acted for Leading Rule Ltd and secured permission from the local authorities in late 1999 for a major office development on a former Ministry of Defence site within the Surrey green belt. On behalf of Waitrose, successfully obtained planning permission for a food superstore in conjunction with a leisure scheme on a regeneration site in Cheltenham. **Clients:** Octagon; Prudential; Church Commissioners; Quintain.

McGuinness Finch *"Really going somewhere,"* commented one lawyer. *"They've carved out a great niche in next to no time."* The firm's roll-call of clients reads impressively, with some big gun retailers sitting alongside commercial developers and other institutional clients. The epithet *"punching above their weight"* may be unoriginal, but it is certainly apt. *"First class operator"* **Carl Dyer** is most highly rated. *"A robust practitioner,"* he is commended for being *"exceptionally thorough."* A leading planning silk rated him as one of the sector's top drafters and inquiry performers. The firm is another to sit on the Tesco panel. Considered an efficient and friendly front person, **Moira Fraser** is *"brilliant with clients."* **Wesley Fongenie**, qualified as a barrister, is one who is felt to have *"blossomed since arriving"* from Berwin Leighton. The firm acts for Carter Commercial Developments Ltd, and has secured a number of planning consents at various national sites in the last 12 months. Acting for Tesco Stores Ltd on a town centre redevelopment scheme at Chester-Le-Street, and for Asda Stores Ltd in connection with their supermarket store proposal at Thurmaston. **Clients:** British Gas plc; Stadium Developments Ltd; Pelham Homes Ltd; Peel Developments Ltd.

Norton Rose Less involved in the planning aspects of large commercial transactions, the firm occupies positions of strength in sectors such as minerals and conservation. The team is led by the experienced and *"suave"* **Brian Greenwood**, an elder statesman well respected by fellow lawyers and institutional clients alike. However, it is felt that the firm lacks the depth of some of its leading rivals. Acting for the New Millennium Experience Company Ltd, the firm co-ordinated and secured planning permission for the Greenwich Millennium Dome. Involved in the project team acting for Castle Cement Ltd who are seeking to develop and expand a cement works in North Wales. Retained as external legal advisers for English Heritage, one aspect of which is co-ordination of the planning aspects of the new visitors' centre at Stonehenge. **Clients:** Arlington Securities; Esso; SmithKline Beecham; Spitalfields Development Group.

DJ Freeman Expanding team which is only felt to lack the depth of resources of the leading players. The *"ambitious"* **Richard Max**, recently made chairman of the City of London Law Society Planning and Environmental Sub-Committee, is noted for his *"boundless enthusiasm"* and *"strong, forthright personality."* Ultimately, as the driving force, his reputation is felt to be greater than that of the firm. Regarded as a *"top-class advocate,"* he leads a team which acted for AXA Equity & Law in a successful appeal to redevelop the brownfield HQ site in High Wycombe for residential purposes. Also acted for Great Portland Estate in the extension of Ranleigh House in Kensington & Chelsea. **Clients:** Shell; GlaxoWellcome; AXA.

Gouldens *"A force to be reckoned with."* An impressive client base includes major organisations in the retail, commercial development, leisure and sports sectors. Much of the credit is attributed to *"maverick"* **David Cooper**, who *"has pulled in a good range of starry clients."* A larger than life character, his *"rogueish personality"* and advocacy skills are well known among peers, and he has conducted over 950 planning inquiries. **Angela Turner** also remains recommended this year. Acting for Pillar Property plc as they seek to expand their out-of-town retail park portfolio in England and Scotland, notably the new consent at Fulham Broadway. Another highlight was advising on Arsenal Football Club's 5 year relocation plan which will include a new football ground for Arsenal FC. Also advised Arlington Securities in relation to a proposed new international business park next to East Midlands airport. **Clients:** Galliard Homes; British Car Auctions; Heron Corporation.

Simmons & Simmons The firm slips a little this year after losing a property and planning partner to Gouldens, while the planning department has become increasingly subsumed into the general commercial property structure. There is now less emphasis on contentious appeals and inquiries and more on negotiated planning agreements. The team works largely for property and development clients. Acting on behalf of Fort James UK Ltd in connection with applications for planning permission for a new warehouse extension for the company. Advising MEPC plc in connection with the renewal of their planning permission for a commercial redevelopment of land and air-space above London Underground's station at Liverpool Street. **Clients:** Viridor Waste Group plc; BP Amoco; Perpetual plc; Kimberley Developments.

Slaughter and May The firm's planning capability comes from a team drawn from the property and litigation departments. The *"refreshingly co-operative"* **Richard Hillebron**, an experienced senior assistant from the litigation department, is the only solicitor to devote 100% of his time to planning. The team acts for London Regional Transport on the White City development scheme which has involved the negotiation of complex section 106 agreements. Acting for Derwent Valley on a number of projects, including the planning application for refurbishment and extension of the former Companies House in London, and the redevelopment of Broadwick House, a Richard Rogers-designed building in Soho. **Clients:** London Regional Transport; Derwent Valley.

Stephenson Harwood The firm is perceived to have raised its profile significantly in the last few years after a series of high profile and lengthy inquiries acting for major client Peel Holdings over the Trafford Centre in Manchester. The client base is drawn from across the development, property, hotel group and local authority spheres. An increasing feature of the practice is a railways specialism. *"Able and thorough"* partner **Barry Jeeps** is singled out for special attention while *"quieter"* senior assistant **Martin Wells** is frequently mentioned in the same breath and is held in equally high regard. Acting for KPMG in their objections to the applications made by Railtrack plc for Transport and Works Act Orders, which will authorise the reconstruction of Blackfriars station and other works. Currently advising St Martins property group in connection with its proposals to expand a shopping centre in Croydon, and in relation to the construction of a new station on the Tramlink system. **Clients:** National Mutual Life Assurance Company; London Regional Transport; Accor Group; University of Greenwich.

Theodore Goddard Definite planning profile due to the combination of a comprehensive range of clients and the leadership qualities of high profile partner **Douglas Evans**. Clients are spread across the housing, retail and utilities sectors with particular emphasis on waste management. Douglas Evans *("efficient and thorough")* is well known by fellow lawyers and highly respected by clients for his ability to be *"aggressive in the right circumstances."* Also known for provision of development advice and advocacy at inquiries for housing development and waste industries. Acted for a leading provider of waste fired incinerators, SITA GB Ltd, in securing the 25 year contract for the disposal of waste in Surrey, and in the promotion of two major waste to energy incinerators. Acting for Bryant Homes to secure planning permission for numerous development sites, ranging from 150 units to 10,000 units. **Clients:** Thames Water Utilities Ltd; Hampshire Waste Services; Beazer Homes; P&O Property Developments Ltd.

Dechert As a support unit to the mainstream commercial property department, the team is active in offering planing advice to a number of developer and housebuilder clients. There is also a local authority dimension to the practice, mainly relating to property schemes. Provide ongoing advice to The Crown Estate in connection with the refurbishment of a London listed building. Acted for PACE (an executive agency of the Cabinet Office) in successfully concluding the planning for a supermarket development in Cambridgeshire and an ongoing compulsory purchase compensation claim in London. **Justin True** is the stand-out practitioner here. **Clients:** FairMeadow Ltd; Freeport Leisure plc; Helical Retail Ltd; local authorities.

Fladgate Fielder The firm fuses planning with environmental and judicial review capability. Commentators have drawn particular attention to impressive key clients in the technology sectors, as well as cutting edge development work, creating the impression that the firm are *"forward-thinking and dynamic."* Lead planning partner, **Daniel Drukarz**, is relatively junior but *"could be up there soon."* One barrister claimed he *"exhibits a positive attitude"* and has the *"real potential to make a name for himself."* Advising Amylum UK on planning issues arising from the regeneration strategy for the Greenwich peninsula, and its likely impact on its UK refining operation near the Millennium Dome and the proposed Meridian Village. Advising a major overseas consortium on the planning aspects of a £40m, 125,000 sq ft mixed use redevelopment scheme in inner London. **Clients:** Sun Microsystems; Mitsubishi Corporation; Safeway Stores plc; Texas Instruments Ltd.

Freshfields Bruckhaus Deringer Planning is only a minor component of the make-up of the environmental and property practice. The team is seen to act as a support function on bigger projects. No lawyers are full time planners, but *"what they do, they do well."* **Paul Watchman** is esteemed by his peers for his involvement on the planning and environmental aspects of large development and infrastructure projects. Advising Edison First Power on the planning aspects of the acquisition of Fiddler's Ferry and Ferrybridge C power stations. Dealing with planning aspects of the new Selfridges hotel development, a major listed building in central London and the Chelsea barracks for Cadogan Estate. **Clients:** Honda; Powergen; Conoco; Scottish Power.

Lawrence Graham **Trevor Blaney** heads the planning unit, working closely with commercial property and environmental partners for developer, housebuilder and local authority clients. Particular expertise is directed toward advocacy at local plan inquiry and appeal stage. Highlights have included the obtaining of consent for a major residential development in a prime area of Kensington for St James Homes. Acting for East Sussex County Council on a lengthy waste challenge. **Clients:** P&O Properties; London & Regional; St George North London Ltd; BT.

Macfarlanes Felt to be providing good quality advice and have registered some *"active successes in health authority cases."* Offer specialist planning capability alongside broader commercial property expertise to developers, housebuilders and the National Health Service. Large scale involvement with London Bridge Holdings, a subsidiary of the CIT group, on the planning aspects of the major development on the south side of the Thames near London bridge – the new home for the Greater London Authority. Offered specialist planning advice to P&O Developments Ltd and Chelsea Harbour Ltd arising from s106 obligations relating to prestige developments at Chelsea Harbour. **Clients:** AXA Sunlife; Chartwell Land; Comet Group plc; Ian Schrager Hotels.

Olswang Transactional support to the property department is supported by stand-alone planning work for developers and landowners, and wider public authority advice. Recent transactions have included major acquisitions for property development clients such as Delancey, Minerva and Helical Bar. Also advised on an urban regeneration project in Dunstable for Charterhouse Shopping Centre Fund. **Clients:** AstraZeneca; Capital & Regional Properties plc; Green Property (UK) Ltd; Healthland UK Ltd.

Travers Smith Braithwaite *"Good potential to build up a quality planning practice."* **Alison Lea** *("has made good progress,")* formerly at Norton Rose, has built a planning team from scratch and is tipped to progress further. Client base reflects commercial property development as well as standalones with particular emphasis on the leisure sector. Advocacy is a major part of the team's appeal. Obtained planning permission for Greenwich Reach 2000 for a big mixed use development incorporating retail, leisure and accommodation. Acted for Clearwater Estates, securing planning permission and listed building consent for a cinema complex in Kingston-upon-Thames. **Clients:** Lend Lease Europe Ltd; Booker plc; London Regional Transport; Thurleigh Estates Ltd.

THE SOUTH

Bond Pearce The team hit the headlines by embarking on the massive container port project at Dibden, outside Southampton, for Associated British Ports, a job which would normally have been expected to land at the doorstep of a big London player. *"An impressive achievement for a regional firm,"* as a leading planning silk confirmed. Coupled with the acquisition of experienced project manger *("a large scale project specialist")* **John Houghton** from Clarke Willmott & Clarke (who learnt much of his trade at Denton Hall where he was formerly head of planning) this has placed the firm at the head of the planning pecking order in the region. The office also has proven expertise in areas such as wind, renewable energy and environmental assessment. Probably the largest infrastructure project in Europe, the 250 hectare Dibden terminal proposal to extend the port of Southampton sees the firm advising on complex planning issues above and below water, integrated transport and process issues spanning planning, environmental and public law. **Clients:** Associated British Ports; Plymouth City Council.

Brachers One of the most prominent firms in the South East manages to combine a *"strong traditional farming clientele"* with a *"good commercial client base"* in the surrounding locale. Key planning partner **Henry Abraham** has a reputation that extends beyond the Kent boundaries, as does the client base which includes nationally known developers and other commercial clients. Two partners manage all planning and environmental matters while part-time assistants are from the litigation department. Represented a major house-builder in local planning objections to a 35 acre site. Acted for two aerodromes concerned with a number of complex planning conditions and enforcement issues. **Clients:** developers; manufacturers; ports; football clubs; parish councils; estate owners; farmers.

DMH The key feature of this specialist unit is the *"legal mix"* of the organisation incorporating four qualified planning professionals in addition to solicitors. This gives them a *"wide remit,"* with the consequence that they are considered *"particularly active"* in The South. The experienced **Tony Allen** is rated highly both by the London bar and other solicitors alike. The firm is felt to possess a strong grip on a number of local clients. The major

PLANNING • The South	Ptnrs	Assts
❶ **Bond Pearce** Southampton	1	1
❷ **Brachers** Maidstone	2	3
DMH Brighton	1	1
❸ **Fynn & Partners** Bournemouth	1	1
Lester Aldridge Bournemouth	2	-

LEADING INDIVIDUALS
❶ **HOUGHTON John** Bond Pearce
❷ **ABRAHAM Henry** Brachers
ALLEN Tony DMH
HIGNETT Andrew Lester Aldridge
❸ **MACKAY Ian** Innes Mackay Solicitors

Within each band, firms are listed alphabetically. See *Profiles* on page 660

clients here come from housebuilding, retail and waste. Highlight of the last year was acting for Compco Holdings plc on a number of planning applications and appeals for the redevelopment of the Aquarium Terraces on Brighton sea front. **Clients:** Reprotech Ltd; Camden and Islington Health Trust; Crest; Bryant.

Fynn & Partners A contentious case-based firm, described as *"good at day-to-day planning appeals,"* but there is a market suggestion that the team is overly dependent on inquiries at a time when fewer are taking place. Clients are drawn from residential developers, commercial businesses, residents' associations, holiday and leisure operators. Worked on a year-long project with a brewing client on an application to expand the size of a grade 2 listed licensed property. Gained planning permission for a hotel client in a Bournemouth conservation area to replace the original with a residential flat scheme. **Clients:** Hall & Woodhouse; UKAEA; Glossbrook Homes.

Lester Aldridge **Andrew Hignett** (*"technically very sound,"*) has established himself since his arrival from Osborne Clarke. His *"organised and robust style"* is at the head of a team which handles a caseload of core developer, utility and institutional clients. Acting for a national utility company in relation to the use of its compulsory purchase powers to develop a six mile gas pipeline in Lancashire. Advised a port authority in relation to the listing of its breakwaters and concluding a management agreement with the planning authority and English Heritage to facilitate future works on the structure. **Clients:** Scottish Power plc; Poole Pottery Limited/Orb Estates plc; Ibstock plc; government agencies.

Other Notable Practitioner The respected **Ian Mackay**, formerly of CMS Cameron McKenna and known for his Heathrow Terminal 5 work has left the firm and now operates as part of Innes Mackay Solicitors in Beckenham.

THAMES VALLEY

PLANNING • Thames Valley	Ptnrs	Assts
❶ **Clarks** Reading	2	1
Jameson & Hill Hertford	1	1
Pitmans Reading	2	1

LEADING INDIVIDUALS	
❶ **DIMMICK Simon** Clarks	**JAMESON Robert** Jameson & Hill
VALENTINE Richard Pitmans	

Within each band, firms are listed alphabetically. See *Profiles* on page 660

Clarks Well staffed planning unit known as much for public sector work as for commercial clients, particularly housing infrastructure cases. The *"business-like"* **Simon Dimmick** is the key player here. He *"really knows how the local government machine works"* and *"helps to foster good working relationships."* The team was recently strengthened by the addition of a Bond Pearce solicitor at partner level. Representing a major landowner in a 12 month public inquiry over plans for a 2,500 home residential development south of Reading. Also offers frequent advice on planning and infrastructure issues for town centre development schemes. **Clients:** University Of Reading; Windsor and Maidenhead Borough Council; NHS trusts.

Jameson & Hill Well-known among the big guns in London, the practice's planning influence extends far beyond the Home Counties. **Robert Jameson** (*"well-respected and top notch"*) handles a client list overwhelmingly comprising local authorities in addition to small numbers of development, retail and private individuals. The team conducts its own advocacy and engages in substantial amounts of enforcement work. Acting for Somerfield supermarkets at inquiry level concerning a development in Horncastle, Lincolnshire seeking to prevent Safeway's encroachment on the town. **Clients:** Local authorities; private clients; property developers.

Pitmans Senior partner **Richard Valentine**, a big name locally, has long maintained a high reputation for his contentious-biased practice which acts for a number of large institutional and developer clients. The department has been occupied recently on major 'new town' development work and substantial town centre refurbishment projects. **Clients:** Insurance companies; retailers; developers; building societies.

SOUTH WEST

Clarke Willmott & Clarke The biggest practice, and *"few would argue with their position as the best."* Still strong in traditional development sectors such as housing, retail and local planning inquiries where they have the capacity to handle the larger 'bread and butter jobs.' The merger with Alsters in October 1999 saw Tom Graham move from that firm to Nabarro Nathanson, but more significantly, John Houghton moved to Bond Pearce, a potentially damaging loss. The remaining individuals, however, appear to have consolidated their positions well. Everyone knows Taunton leader **Nick Engert** (*"well focused and a lateral thinker"*) who commands a high reputation in the southern counties and nationally for his residential, retail and commercial practice and local planning inquiry advocacy. He is *"still very busy"* and has *"great housebuilding contacts."* **Stephen Pasterfield**, who has established his patch in Bristol and is widely regarded as a key acquisition, is *"more of a technician"* and a *"methodical"* rather than flamboyant advocate. He is well connected in the immediate area and has used the *"Bristol launchpad"* to *"make the local market-place his own."* Senior associate **Neil Baker** (*"knows his stuff"*) arrived from London with an environmental focus and has settled in well, although is known rather more for his industrial, waste and pollution specialism than for pure planning. Appeared for Westbury Homes at the Salisbury Local Plan inquiry on a major housing allocation. Advised Matthew Clark plc in connection with the recycling of a factory and brownfield site as part of a comprehensive development scheme for up to 1,000 new homes, shopping centre and employment units. **Clients:** Carter Commercial Developments; Beaufort Western Developments Ltd; Beazer Homes Ltd.

Bevan Ashford *"Polished"* team with a strong client base, notably in health trust planning where they are clear market leaders. Additional sectors where planning expertise is applied include regeneration bodies, local

PLANNING • South West	Ptnrs	Assts
❶ **Clarke Willmott & Clarke** Bristol, Taunton	3	3
❷ **Bevan Ashford** Bristol, Exeter	2	2
Bond Pearce Bristol, Plymouth	2	4
Burges Salmon Bristol	1	2
❸ **Davies and Partners** Gloucester	1	1
Osborne Clarke OWA Bristol	1	2
Stephens & Scown Exeter	2	-
TLT Solicitors Bristol	1	1

LEADING INDIVIDUALS	
❶ **BOSWORTH John** Bevan Ashford	**ENGERT Nick** Clarke Willmott & Clarke
PASTERFIELD Stephen Clarke Willmott & Clarke	
ROBINSON Patrick Burges Salmon	**TRINICK Marcus** Bond Pearce
❷ **BAKER Neil** Clarke Willmott & Clarke	**BIRD Rina** Davies and partners
EVANS Katherine TLT Solicitors	**GIBBS Kevin** Osborne Clarke
HOLMES Sarah Bond Pearce	**WOOD David** Bevan Ashford

Within each band, firms are listed alphabetically. *See* **Profiles** *on page 660*

authorities, developers and retailers. **John Bosworth** has a mixed practice, but is most closely associated with health sector work. **David Wood** has also established his reputation in large hospital PFI planning as well as being noted for his advocacy abilities. Highlights include persuading Mendip Council to review its local plan strategy over the Moorlands site in Glastonbury. Conducted appeals for residential development of Whitchurch hospital in Cardiff and Lord Mayor Treloar hospital, Alton. **Clients:** NHS Executive (South And West); Border Biofuels; Crest Nicholson; Local authorities.

Bond Pearce The string of regional offices combine together well although the core location is still perceived to be in Plymouth, from where the firm has a grip on the far South West. Client base comprises retail, residential and commercial developers, port developers and the public sector. Much of the team's reputation rests on the strengths of the two principal lawyers. **Marcus Trinick** has *"earned his reputation well"* and continues to maintain his specialism for renewables and wind energy, is assisting John Houghton in the Southampton office on the ABP project and also has *"great local authority contacts."* Associate **Sarah Holmes** is regarded nationally for her fusion of environmental and planning work, frequently in sectors such as minerals. The firm has recently been appointed solicitors to English Heritage. Conducted a number of planning appeals for and against Truro airfield concerning wind farms in South Wales, Northumberland and Yorkshire. Acting for the Plymouth & South West Co-operative Society Ltd over substantial retail planning work in South West England. **Clients:** Taylor Woodrow; British Wind Energy Association; Pennon Group; NFU.

Burges Salmon Not felt to be quite as prominent as the other leaders across the region, although considered to be extremely active in the Bristol market. Like other south western firms, commercial and retail clients mix with environmentally focused minerals and energy work. *"Enthusiastic"* **Patrick Robinson** has a high profile in Bristol, both for his transactional ability and his advocacy skills. The team has recently acted on two successful judicial reviews providing decisions in the field of retail planning and minerals planning. Currently have an advocate appearing at a three month call-in inquiry where they are acting for a client promoting a motorway service area for the M42. **Clients:** Foster Yeoman; Orange; Garden and Leisure Group Ltd; Basingstoke and Deane Borough Council.

Davies and Partners Small housebuilding team with a stock of repeat clients in this market. Despite location, the firm is felt to be influential in the wider residential development market. Felt to be less contentious and inquiry based, the group handles enforcement work and private client work for landowners. The *"bubbly"* **Rina Bird** has returned from maternity leave and is a prominent name among local and national housebuilders. The team acted on the demolition deal to build a new settlement on the site on RAF Upper Hayford. **Clients:** Tayward Homes; Wimpey Homes; Westbury Homes; Persimmon Homes.

Osborne Clarke OWA Key acquisitions and cross-departmental critical mass have lifted the planning team's profile. *"Proactive"* planning and environmental specialist **Kevin Gibbs** has arrived from Lyons Davidson and provides specialist expertise here. The team advised E&J Commercial Properties on multiplex cinema schemes in Glasgow and Cardiff. Acting for Somerfield Stores plc in relation to new and existing stores. **Clients:** Close Brothers; HP Bulmer Ltd; Barratt Homes Ltd; Wilson Bowden Properties Ltd.

Stephens & Scown Closely linked with core client English China Clay, the team's principal expertise lies in minerals and waste disposals. The senior partner has now retired to assume consultant status, and two full-time partners across Devon and Cornwall maintain the department. Recently acted in a lengthy inquiry relating to a factory outlet shopping centre at Roche in Cornwall. Also dealing with substantial claims for compensation arising from new environmental protection conferred by the Birds Directive and the Habitats Directive. **Clients:** English China Clays plc; Aggregate Industries plc; South Crofty plc; Viridor Waste Management Ltd.

TLT Solicitors Experienced local government solicitor Nicola Mathiason has made the move back into the public sector, joining Bath and North East Somerset Council. Newly made partner **Katherine Evans** is a specialist planner by trade, cut her teeth on housebuilding cases at Davies and Partners and is highly rated by fellow Bristol practitioners. She is particularly well regarded in the lucrative local property development market. The team acted for Hanson on a site adjacent to the Millennium Dome involving a number of planning and environmental issues. **Clients:** Hanson; Edward Ware New Homes Ltd; Wiltshire County Council.

WALES

PLANNING • Wales	Ptnrs	Assts
❶ **Edwards Geldard** Cardiff	1	2
Eversheds Cardiff	2	2
❷ **Morgan Cole** Cardiff	1	2

LEADING INDIVIDUALS	
❶ **EVANS Eric** Eversheds	**WILLIAMS Huw** Edwards Geldard
❷ **BOSWALL Julian** Morgan Cole	**MANSON Stephen** Eversheds

Within each band, firms are listed alphabetically. *See* **Profiles** *on page 660*

Edwards Geldard Planning is inextricably linked to the wider public law and environmental practice overseen by **Huw Williams**, who regularly receives praise for the application of his extensive public sector experience. The team acts for some housebuilder development clients and rail companies. Have acted for the Welsh Development Agency and Cardiff County Council on procedures under the Local Government Planning & Land Act to wind up the Cardiff Bay Development Corporation. Secured planning consent for the lottery funded Wales Millennium scheme, the £70m Cardiff Arts Centre. **Clients:** Central Trains; Silverlink Trains; Wilcon Homes; Wrexham Borough Council.

Eversheds *"A clearly defined specialism"* acting on some of the biggest PFI and public sector schemes in Wales. Have a slightly tighter grip on traditional commercial developer clients than Welsh competitors, although the practice as a whole mirrors the over-arching public sector structure from which much of Welsh planning work flows. The firm's client base comprises a mixed bag of minerals companies and commercial developers. The *"charismatic"* **Eric Evans** is an established public sector solicitor who has built upon substantial local authority experience in a successful private firm environment. His *"robust manner"* can be slightly excessive for some people, although *"everyone respects his abilities."* **Stephen Manson** *"complements him well"* with a less aggressive negotiating style. A recent planning recruit from Cardiff County Council adds extra punch at assistant level. Secured instructions from a major media group on the planning appeal for the £50 million redevelopment of a television studio site, aiming to provide a large retail centre and associated development. **Clients:** Welsh Development Agency; Hanson Aggregates South Wales Ltd; Macob Construction.

Morgan Cole Without a planning lawyer for a while, the firm's recruitment of **Julian Boswall** from London has provided extra planning impetus. The planning support and development work is applied to clients in an number of sectors including corporates, health and public sector. Much has stemmed from major fire, hospital and police station PFI schemes. Two core clients, Elf and the NFU, have recently generated the major instructions. **Clients:** Elf Oil UK Ltd; NFU; University Hospital Of Wales; Cardiff Bay Development Corporation.

MIDLANDS

PLANNING • Midlands	Ptnrs	Assts
❶ **Marrons** Leicester	4	2
❷ **Eversheds** Birmingham	1	6
Pinsent Curtis Birmingham	2	2
❸ **Hewitson Becke + Shaw** Northampton	1	1
Shoosmiths Northampton	3	3
Wragge & Co Birmingham	2	4
❹ **Browne Jacobson** Nottingham	2	3
Hammond Suddards Edge Birmingham	-	2
❺ **DLA** Birmingham	2	4
❻ **Kent Jones and Done** Stoke-on-Trent	1	2
Knight & Sons Newcastle-under-Lyme	1	2

LEADING INDIVIDUALS	
❶ **BULL Rod** Eversheds	**MARRON Peter** Marrons
❷ **DAMMS Martin** Pinsent Curtis	**EDMOND John** Marrons
GILBEY Iain Shoosmiths	**SMITH Brian** Browne Jacobson
TAYLOR Peter Hewitson Becke + Shaw	**WHITE Martin** Pinsent Curtis
❸ **HEMMING Dan** Wragge & Co	

Within each band, firms are listed alphabetically. *See **Profiles** on page 660*

Marrons *"Full time niche planning practice with a leading edge."* Unquestioned regional top dogs, the team is recognised for its first-rate strategic developer and housebuilding practice, and also acts for some local authorities. Has a *"sharper edge"* than its competitors, and contains some high quality advocates. A leading London barrister felt that they *"always provide a positive input," "understand the issues well"* and have a high level of support and back-up. Experienced **Peter Marron** is universally well regarded (*"an excellent front man"*) while prominent and *"switched-on"* **John Edmond** is seen by the market as the leading figure on day-to-day cases. Involved in a major commercial development at Alconbury acting for a consortium of developers including BAA and Prologic. Also acting for a number of clients at inquiry level seeking to develop motorway service stations along the M25 and M40. **Clients:** David Wilson Homes; Hallam Land Management Ltd; Blaby District Council; Henry Boot Homes Ltd.

Eversheds Nudged ahead of the Birmingham competition this year, largely through its substantial housebuilder practice, additional niche minerals and waste activity and the emergence of a truly national profile. The team is considered to have the resources and capacity to handle the larger plc clients. *"Juicy"* housebuilding client, Bryant Homes, are felt to *"carry the practice a bit"* but beyond this, the firm has a glittering list of commercial, development and public sector clients on the books. Now head of the Eversheds national planning team, *"enthusiastic"* **Rod Bull** has *"really grown the practice"* and *"commands a great presence in the market."* Drawing off existing firm-wide property clients alongside his own stand-alones, he commands a *"great deal of client loyalty."* Also a respected advocate, he runs a core team which serves as the hub of the national network. Acting for a consortium of Bryant and Leech homes in a huge mixed-use development in Newcastle (The Newcastle Great Park). Also acting for a consortium of Jaguar Cars and Coventry City Council on a call-in inquiry for the new Whitley Business Park proposal. **Clients:** Bellway Homes; British Gypsum; Leech Homes Ltd; Huntingdon District Council

Pinsent Curtis Traditionally known more for its local authority flavoured practice, the firm has attempted to diversify into the commercial development arena, with the result that they are still considered a big player, not excessively focused in one area. The practice acts for clients from local authorities, PFI, development, waste and airport operators. **Martin Damms** has been recruited from Edge Ellison to act on town centre development and compulsory purchase cases. He has a good reputation for his work with developer clients and local authorities. A *"steady"* and *"technical lawyer,"* his experience and prominence in the market are still in demand. Advocacy is also a recommended feature of his practice. There is little dispute that **Martin White** is still a regional leader. He is commended for *"getting stuck in"* to big commercial developments, although he is also associated with local government work. The team acted on the Walsall Town Wharf phase 2 project and the Nuneaton town centre redevelopment. Currently involved in High Court litigation involving an extension to the East Midlands Airport runway. Also opposing the London International Freight Exchange proposals on behalf of Three Valleys Water plc. **Clients:** Castlemore Securities; Wolverhamton MBC; IM Properties; Connex Group.

Hewitson Becke + Shaw Now felt to be the more prominent of the two-office planning structure although there is inevitably a degree of fluidity between the two. The reputation of the firm has extended outwards to the point where they are recognised nationally. Regarded more for his local authority practice, *"understated"* **Peter Taylor** *"distinguishes the wood from the trees."* Conducts a high level of advocacy at appeals. Known for his work locally where he is retained as solicitor for Daventry Council, the practice acts for a number of commercial companies and developers, as well as private individuals. Acted for a local residents group, Langford residents, seeking to challenge a consent issued by Bedford Council for a waste transfer site. Acting for Daventry District Council in relation to the calling in of a scheme for the redevelopment of a Royal Ordinance depot at Weedon, Northamptonshire. **Clients:** Persimmon Homes; HSBC Bank; Scottish & Newcastle; Travis Perkins.

Shoosmiths Scored a massive coup when *"pre-eminent planning solicitor of his generation"* **Iain Gilbey** left the capital for Northampton. The team *"now offer a more rounded legal service."* Gilbey arrived with a flattering reputation from his Ashursts days. *"Clear, organised and tactically astute,"* barristers have commented on his ability to *"handle extremely complex inquiries expertly."* Clients have followed him to the Midlands citing his *"smooth operating style"* and *"ability to get the work done quickly."* The client base here includes large residential developers, institutions and public authority clients. A highlight was advising St James Homes Ltd in the Kew

Riverside project, securing consent for 400 residential units on a high profile site adjacent to the River Thames near Richmond. On behalf of Gala Leisure, secured consent on appeal for a major leisure development in Chatham town centre in Kent. **Clients:** Elementis plc; Thames Water Property Ltd; Coats Viyella plc; British Gypsum plc.

Wragge & Co It is a surprise to some that Wragges do not figure more prominently locally, given their eminence in related practice areas such a local government and commercial property. The team works closely with the commercial property department, and are therefore less likely to provide advocacy for stand alone clients at inquiry stage. **Dan Hemming** (*"effective and nice to deal with"*) has assumed more of a strategic development role but is still frequently recommended. *"Made the right impression"* with local solicitors and clients when acting for Cambridge City Council on a town centre redevelopment. Highlight has been Transport and Works Act applications for Rapid Transport International in relation to a guided bus system in Northampton and for a rail link to serve the Land Rover plant at Solihull. **Clients:** Alfred McAlpine Homes; Birmingham International Airport; MEPC; Exeter City Council.

Browne Jacobson One observer felt Nottingham was increasing its position as a thriving planning centre, and this firm is best-placed to exploit an upturn in local fortunes. The practice is overwhelmingly local authority and public sector-dominated, increasingly less for development clients, with a particular niche in nature conservation. *"Key figure"* **Brian Smith** is *"respected by solicitors on the other side."* Recently appointed as planning lawyers for Doncaster Metropolitan Borough Council. Also act for the Countryside Council for Wales in all their planning, property and conservation work. **Clients:** English Nature; Commercial property developers; Local authorities.

Hammond Suddards Edge Slipped this year, partly as a result of Martin Damms' defection across town to Pinsent Curtis and also due to a prevailing uncertainty surrounding the practice. The newly-merged entity has much ground to recover. Compulsory purchases, highways and JR are felt to be niche strengths. Acted for a motorway services operator in successfully opposing a proposed new motorway services site. Also advising Advantage West Midlands in respect of a regeneration scheme. **Clients:** Wilson Bowden Developments; West Midlands Regional Development Agency; Jennings Homes Ltd; Lawson Beaumont.

DLA Although not especially high-profile, the firm is still acknowledged to have particular expertise in highway law. A London barrister was impressed with their efficiency on a major 600 home scheme judicial review challenge in North Yorkshire. Client list is an eclectic mix of commercial, minerals and retail organisations. Highlights include a high court application to quash an inspector's decision in connection with a residential development in Stockton on Tees. **Clients:** Castle Hill Quarry Co; EH Smith Group; Ibstock Brick Leicester Ltd; John David Sports plc.

Kent Jones and Done *"Hard-working and tenacious"* North Midlands outfit. Chunky client JCB has always generated a steady stream of planning-related work and continues to do so. Active in environmentally-related sectors such as minerals and waste, the team is also renowned for 'pure' planning, commercial development and landowning clients. Advising an estate landowner in a case concerning the construction of a country house. Advising a developer on an application to review the decision of Stoke City Council to grant planning permission for an out of town leisure development. **Clients:** Laporte plc; J E Greenall Ltd; JCB Group.

Knight & Sons Planning flows from special attention given to mines, minerals and general property. Partners and assistants from the property department work part time on related planning implications for developer clients. Acting for developers in connection with a leisure development on a mixed-use site, with several planning permissions and a multi-party combined section 106 and section 278 agreement. **Clients:** Hepworth Minerals & Chemicals Ltd; Morrison Developments Ltd; Hanson Quarry Products Europe Ltd.

EAST ANGLIA

PLANNING • East Anglia	Ptnrs	Assts
❶ **Mills & Reeve** Cambridge	2	3
❷ **Hewitson Becke + Shaw** Cambridge	1	2
❸ **Taylor Vinters** Cambridge	1	2

LEADING INDIVIDUALS	
❶ **BRADY Peter** Hewitson Becke + Shaw	**BROCK David** Mills & Reeve
FIRTH Beverley Mills & Reeve	
❷ **KRATZ Philip** Taylor Vinters	

Within each band, firms are listed alphabetically. *See **Profiles** on page 660*

Mills & Reeve Now *"quite a force in planning."* The team acquired a truly national reputation when ex-Herbert Smith planning and environmental partner **David Brock** made his career decision to leave London for Cambridge. Bringing with him key minerals client Hanson, he has added a new dimension to this already highly-rated practice. He joins the *"outstanding"* **Beverley Firth** to form a formidable spearhead to the practice. Firth's practice has assumed a quasi-public sector flavour, acting for NHS health authority, academic, institutional and local authority clients. The firm advised on Hanson's application to build one of the country's largest waste to energy facilities. It has also been involved in a number of judicial reviews on Hanson's behalf on the extension of Whately Quarry. **Clients:** University Of Cambridge colleges; NHS Trusts; local authorities.

Hewitson Becke + Shaw Not felt to be as active as its partner office further West in Northampton, the continued reputation of **Peter Brady** is a prime factor in the Cambridge office's high standing. Particularly noted for advocacy at appeal and local planning inquiry level for residential, landowning and waste clients. Acting for a landowner/funder consortium in promoting a 1200 acre New Town scheme through the draft South Hams Local Plan in Devon. Advising Shanks Waste Services on the development of a large waste landfill site on the outskirts of Milton Keynes. **Clients:** Cambridge University; Medical Research Council; Norfolk Homes; Leech Homes.

Taylor Vinters Experienced ex-local authority solicitor **Philip Kratz** is *"well connected locally"* and a *"real name in East Anglia."* He oversees this regionally focused practice which acts for a number of public and private sector clients. There is close overlap with the large commercial property department. Have acted for the University of Cambridge in negotiating the s106 agreement for an edge of city development on the west side of Cambridge. Also acting for developers Countryside and Kajima on a large development in the middle of Cambridge at Brooklands Avenue. **Clients:** BG Transco; University Of Cambridge; Countryside Properties; Kajima.

NORTH WEST

PLANNING • North West	Ptnrs	Assts
❶ **Halliwell Landau** Manchester	1	2
❷ **Addleshaw Booth & Co** Manchester	1	2
Eversheds Manchester	1	2
❸ **DLA** Manchester	-	2
Wake Dyne Lawton Chester	2	-

LEADING INDIVIDUALS	
❶ **LANCASTER Roger** Halliwell Landau	
❷ **KENWORTHY Michael** Addleshaw Booth	**MORITZ John** Wake Dyne Lawton
WINTER Paul Eversheds	
UP AND COMING	
PIATT Andrew DLA	
RICHARDSON Simon Davies Wallis Foyster	

Within each band, firms are listed alphabetically. *See **Profiles** on page 660*

Halliwell Landau There seems to be no let-up for this advocacy-focused practice, which tops the regional lists once again. The team's high standing owes much to the formidable advocacy talents of **Roger Lancaster** who *"gives you a battering in inquiries."* It is a wonder to fellow lawyers that his role as managing partner has not diminished his remarkable work-rate and consistent appearances at planning inquiries where he has become a permanent fixture. Workload encompasses clients from the housebuilding, retail development, transport and health authorities. Appeals and CPOs are felt to be the core areas of strength. Acted for Peel Holdings in challenging the decisions of Bury Metropolitan Council at local planning level, then at the High Court and Court of Appeal. **Clients:** Fairclough Homes Ltd; Kwik Fit Properties Ltd; Persimmon Homes Ltd (NW); NHS Executive North West.

Addleshaw Booth & Co In tandem with the Leeds practice, the commercial property driven Manchester office was on the receiving end of a bundle of commendations this year. Some of the most prominent nation-wide commentators reserved their praise for *"technically capable"* **Michael Kenworthy**. A *"good administrator of big cases,"* he *"spots problems looming ahead"* and is experienced enough to deal with them. The firm is associated with substantial utility and corporate clients, as well as property developers. Conducted a planning application for Arrowcroft Northwest Limited/United Utilities plc for a 100,000 square foot DIY retail warehouse. **Clients:** Green Property plc; Railtrack plc; Manchester Metropolitan University.

Eversheds The firm has increased its profile in Manchester largely thanks to the efforts of *"proactive"* **Paul Winter**, who has assumed trans-Pennine responsibility for the planning practice. Based partially in Leeds and highly rated nation-wide, he leads a team acting on major local leisure, residential and retail schemes. Acting for AMEC Developments Ltd on a number of urban regeneration projects, including employment and town centre schemes. Advised English Partnerships on the Rochdale Kingsway scheme. **Clients:** Salford City Council; Manchester University; AMEC Developments; English Partnerships.

DLA Run by *"slick operator"* **Andrew Piatt**, the Manchester office is now felt to be a presence in the market, notably acting on a number of national schemes including town centre, commercial development and transport infrastructure projects. Acted successfully for Hampton Trust plc in a call-in inquiry and related agreement for a 2.8 million square foot Birmingham City Centre scheme including a fifty storey tower. Obtained planning permission and opposed judicial review challenge for a multiplex cinema development in Llandudno for Liberty Properties plc. **Clients:** CWS Ltd; Bellway Homes Ltd; Commission for New Towns; East Midlands International Airport Ltd.

Wake Dyne Lawton This small independent specialist firm with niche expertise in minerals, planning and environmental work has benefited from the high-calibre addition of **John Moritz**, who returns to the region after a spell at Masons' London office. The team is felt to be well-placed to exploit opportunities in the North West and Cheshire region. Two full-time planners act for a selection of minerals, quarrying and waste clients. Some commercial clients and private client objector groups comprise the remainder of the clientele. Recently acted for an objectors' group in opposing a proposed new cement works. Acted for Hanson on a planning application for a recycling facility. **Clients:** Objectors' groups; minerals and waste companies.

Other Notable Practitioner **Simon Richardson** of Davies Wallis Foyster has been recommended for his versatility which includes solicitor-advocacy capabilities as well as being qualified as a chartered town planner. Acts at inquiries and appeals for a number of housebuilding and developer clients.

YORKSHIRE

PLANNING • Yorkshire	Ptnrs	Assts
❶ **Wilbraham & Co** Leeds	5	3
❷ **Addleshaw Booth & Co** Leeds	2	3
Eversheds Leeds	1	4
Walker Morris Leeds	3	2
❸ **Hammond Suddards Edge** Leeds	1	3
❹ **Nabarro Nathanson** Sheffield	2	4

LEADING INDIVIDUALS	
✪ **WILBRAHAM Peter** Wilbraham & Co	
❶ **TURNBULL Stephen** Addleshaw Booth	**WILLIAMSON Andrew** Walker Morris
❷ **WADE-SMITH Richard** Wilbraham & Co	**WINTER Paul** Eversheds
❸ **BERESFORD Amanda** Addleshaw Booth	**GOODMAN David** Hammond Suddards Edge
UP AND COMING	
BUTTERFIELD Katharine Wilbraham & Co	**GRIFFITHS Marion** Eversheds
WALTON David Wilbraham & Co	

Within each band, firms are listed alphabetically. *See **Profiles** on page 660*

Wilbraham & Co Arguably one of the nation's supreme planning firms, this is a niche unit with a network of client relationships which have created *"a critical mass which sucks work in."* Geographical reach extends nationally, and the firm is felt able to compete with London firms for the bigger infrastructure projects. Much of the kudos is attached to the pre-eminent **Peter Wilbraham** who *"commands huge respect."* A successful, *"shrewd tactician,"* and *"charming with clients,"* he is now believed to spend more time on non-contentious project management work and on drawing in clients. Advocacy is not a major feature of the practice whose expertise spans a range of commercial development, leisure, energy and utilities projects. Right-hand man **Richard Wade-Smith** has a property background but gets *"stuck in"* on a mixed caseload of planning and environmental work, such as wind and renewable energy. Partners **Katharine Butterfield** and **David Walton** have acquired increased levels of experience and are said to be *"developing well."* Major recent highlights have included acting for National Wind Power on a number of wind power generators. **Clients:** Evans; Land Securities Properties; Leeds Sporting; Yorkshire Water.

Addleshaw Booth & Co Works closely in tandem with the Manchester office, and received favourable reviews this year, both from fellow local solicitors and the London bar. One barrister described them as *"one of the top northern practices."* Feeding off a buoyant property department, the team is led by **Stephen Turnbull**, commended for his *"sharp and focused"* mind and his affable manner. He takes the advocacy lead at planning inquiries, while **Amanda Beresford** continues to be visible for her mixed private and public sector practice. Client base is felt to be a recognised strength, and includes retailers, commercial developers and local authorities. Advising Stockton Metropolitan Council in relation to a town centre regeneration project. Advising Bass plc in relation to a number of compulsory purchases and infrastructure projects in Liverpool, Potters Bar and Blackfriars. **Clients:** Sainsburys Supermarkets; Bryant Homes (Northern) Ltd; Stadium Group plc; East Midlands Development Agency.

Eversheds Despite minding the shop in Manchester, where the firm has formed a trans-Pennine equity partnership, the *"proactive"* and *"highly capable"* **Paul Winter** is frequently cited by top barristers as an outstanding practitioner. Major retail, commercial development, institutional and large commercial companies are all represented on the firm's client roster. **Marian Griffiths** has held the fort in Leeds and is increasingly visible in the local market. Handled a large inquiry on behalf of Asda supermarkets in Bradford in which the developer was proposing to relocate to a more central location. Advised on several PFI projects, including one in West Sussex involving the development of several new waste disposal installations, including energy from waste plants. **Clients:** English Partnerships; Keyland Developments; Bryant Homes; Victor Homes.

Walker Morris The Leeds contentious practice is most visible at inquiry level. Headed by the brash and *"technically superb"* **Andrew Williamson** who *"always questions the status quo"* and has a *"thorough knowledge of the planning system."* The large team includes chartered town planners as well as lawyers. Traditionally associated with housebuilding clients, there are substantial levels of instructions from minerals, waste and general commercial clients. Acting for Asda plc in connection with two major food based retail schemes at Glasshoughton, near Wakefield. Acted on a major case for WRG Group plc for landfill and land reclamation at Bentinck colliery, covering the interests of Midland Mining Ltd against a competing scheme proposed by Viridor Waste Management Ltd. **Clients:** Bellway Homes; David Wilson Homes; Caterpillar UK Ltd; Town Centre Securities plc.

Hammond Suddards Edge The firm has an established practice which has acted for a cross-section of clients from the retail, commercial and property development stables. Have recently emerged with a significant electricity profile through acting for a number of major industry clients. Unfortunately the firm have suffered slightly, due to the illness of mainstay **David Goodman**, a well respected and astute advocate, famed for his *"phenomenal work rate."* Advising Powergen Renewables Ltd and TXU Europe (formerly Eastern Generation) on a number of wind energy proposals in both England and Wales. Acting for The National Grid Company plc in the preparation of a CPO to facilitate the second Yorkshire line. **Clients:** Allied London Properties plc; British Aerospace; Electricity Association; WM Morrison Supermarkets.

Nabarro Nathanson Niche expertise lies in the fields of waste, minerals and reclamation. Better known for its environmental practice, the planning group has been bolstered by a town planning specialist recruited from the South West. Advising Celtic Energy Ltd on compulsory purchase procedures involving common land over the East Merthyr Reclamation Scheme. Acting for Trafford Borough Council in their efforts to redevelop Altrincham Town Centre, advising on planning and road closure procedures including planning agreements. **Clients:** Argyll Property Management; British Waterways Board; Coal Authority Ltd; Hanson Brick.

NORTH EAST

PLANNING • North East	Ptnrs	Assts
❶ **Dickinson Dees** Newcastle upon Tyne	2	3
❷ **Ward Hadaway** Newcastle upon Tyne	1	1

LEADING INDIVIDUALS	
❶ **FINCH Paul** Dickinson Dees	**TAYLOR Paul** Dickinson Dees

Within each band, firms are listed alphabetically. *See **Profiles** on page 660*

Dickinson Dees *"The best law firm in town."* Undeniably the North East's premier practice with a large integrated department. Client base is regarded by competitors as first-class and incorporates a number of large housebuilders and property developers. **Paul Finch** brings a long track record in local authority work, while **Paul Taylor** has been involved at private practice level. An experienced duo, they have *"formed a technically proficient unit."* Associated with advocacy at inquiry and local planning stages. Successfully concluded a planning application in relation to land owned by Grainger Trust, overseeing the development of 3,800 houses on two sites near Basingstoke in Hampshire. Other niche strengths include minerals, compulsory purchase and land compensation. Highlights include a land compensation agreement in Buckinghamshire. **Clients:** National Grid; Grainger Trust plc; Go-Ahead; Miller Homes.

Ward Hadaway Involved largely in *"site-finding and persuading clients to run with sites."* Act for a number of volume residential housebuilders and commercial clients, as well as farming and landowning clients. Have acted for English Heritage in objections to changes to listed buildings. Acted for a large property company in the Dalton Flats development, objecting to an application for commercial and retail development. **Clients:** Coral Racing Ltd; Bellway Homes; Barratt Homes; Duke Of Northumberland.

SCOTLAND

Dundas & Wilson CS Felt to be the premier planning outfit in Scotland, its major planning focus lies in public sector matters. **Ann Faulds** is first port of call for *"esoteric planning issues"* and *"complex points of law."* Without sacrificing practicality or commercial acumen, she is a pure planner with a substantial in-house track record both at local authorities and in private practice. In inquiry situations, her style has been described as *"robust"* where she *"goes in all guns blazing."* **Frances McChlery**, formerly chief solicitor at North Lanarkshire, also brings considerable experience and is felt to have strengthened the team substantially. Client base includes major commercial property developers and retailers, in addition to public authorities. Work highlight of the year was the Kelso Retail Public Inquiry, appearing on behalf of Sainsburys. **Clients:** Carter Commercial Developments; Stirling Council; Land Securities Properties Limited.

Brodies WS Still consistently mentioned as one of the leading firms. The team advises a core of reliable public and private sector clients where housing, retail and leisure development are the main thrusts. **Neil Collar** is one of the most prominent planning figures in Scotland, and wrote the standard academic planning text. His academic credentials are complemented by an acclaimed commercial instinct, and he is considered to *"run a pretty tight ship."* Obtained planning permission for Miller Homes for a 650

PLANNING • Scotland	Ptnrs	Assts
❶ **Dundas & Wilson CS** Edinburgh	2	2
❷ **Brodies WS** Edinburgh	1	1
❸ **Archibald Campbell & Harley WS** Edinburgh	1	2
McGrigor Donald Glasgow	2	1
❹ **Burness** Edinburgh	1	1
Maclay Murray & Spens Glasgow	2	2
Paull & Williamsons Aberdeen	2	-
Shepherd & Wedderburn WS Edinburgh	1	2
❺ **Ledingham Chalmers** Aberdeen	1	3
MacRoberts Glasgow	1	1
Semple Fraser WS Glasgow	2	*

LEADING INDIVIDUALS	
❶ **COLLAR Neil** Brodies WS	**CONNAL Craig** McGrigor Donald
FAULDS Ann Dundas & Wilson CS	
❷ **COCKBURN David** Archibald Campbell	**INNES Colin** Shepherd & Wedderburn WS
SALES Martin Burness	**SMITH Bruce** Paull & Williamsons
❸ **GRANT James** MacRoberts	**McCHLERY Frances** Dundas & Wilson CS
UP AND COMING	
HARRIS Jacqueline McGrigor Donald	

Within each band, firms are listed alphabetically. *See **Profiles** on page 660*

** See editorial entries for explanations of team sizes.*

house development in Hamilton following a public inquiry. Successfully appealed on behalf of Bass Taverns to the Court of Session against the decision by the Secretary of State to refuse an enforcement notice appeal. **Clients:** North Lanarkshire Council; British Steel; Tesco; Asda/Allied Carpets.

Archibald Campbell & Harley WS Traditionally regarded for its retail practice and the advocacy skills of **David Cockburn**, who is a *"tough opponent"* in inquiry situations. Core client, Scottish National Heritage accounts for a substantial portion of the planning caseload. Advice, both contentious and non-contentious is given to residential and commercial developers and retail clients. Recently involved with planning and environmental cases for Scottish National Heritage concerning landfill sites. A major recent case saw the team acting for Hanson on a large quarrying site in Scotland. **Clients:** Scottish National Heritage; Hanson; retailers.

McGrigor Donald Felt to be foremost of the firms who support their planning team through a buoyant commercial property department. A *"litigator at heart"* and regarded as a good inquiry lawyer, solicitor-advocate **Craig Connal** is felt to be as expert on esoteric points of law as he is prominent on inquiries for commercial developers. Newly made up planning and property litigation partner **Jacqueline Harris** has raised her profile significantly, particularly through the high profile Ocean Terminal Waterfront Retail development. Active recently on planning issues for British Gas, including the Granton Waterfront Development Scheme. **Clients:** Forth Ports plc; Tilcon Ltd; Scottish Metropolitan Property PLC; Barratt Southampton.

Burness Formerly part of the litigation department, planning advice is now offered as part of the commercial property department, integrated with the construction and PFI practices. Full time environmental and planning partner **Martin Sales** maintains his traditional rural development caseload incorporating landfill, waste and minerals, although urban schemes and commercial property clients are increasingly prominent. Representing AXA Re at public local inquiries into retail, leisure and sports developments in Ayr. Advising British Nuclear Fuels on the planning aspects of the decommissioning of Hunterston 'A'. **Clients:** Cumbernauld Centre Ltd; Royal Bank of Scotland plc; Lafarge Redland Aggregates.

Maclay Murray & Spens Changes have been afoot as the firm have recently recruited a new department head from Ledingham Chalmers and an additional planning specialist from Edinburgh City Council. The firm is rated highly for commercial property, from where most planning work stems. Client base is comprised overwhelmingly of commercial developers, with a small public sector dimension. Active in the housing development and leisure sector. Acted for Tulloch Bishopcross and Macdonald Hotels in connection with a new luxury hotel at Dundee. Acting for Wilson Bowden on a range of planning instructions including proposals for a 'new town' in Lanarkshire. **Clients:** Barratt Construction; Muir Group; Sun Microsystems; Scottish Enterprise.

Paull & Williamsons A prominent and *"visible practice"* not only in the north of Scotland, but in the more competitive central belt where they are well rated for advocacy at housing inquiries. **Bruce Smith** *"wins for sheer practicality,"* working in tandem with an academic consultant. Three-quarters of the client base are housing developers, with the rest a mixture of retail, industrial and quarrying companies. Acting for multiple developers in the consolidated Aberdeenshire local plan inquiry on substantive housing policy issues. **Clients:** Housing developers; Elmford Ltd; retailers.

Shepherd & Wedderburn WS Highly regarded by the market through providing property-driven planning services for housing clients, retail developers and on PFIs. Partner **Colin Innes**' litigation background is brought to bear on Court of Session challenges where they act for local authorities in judicial review proceedings. Unaggressive, he *"sits back and thinks"* and *"devises good strategies for his clients."* Niche areas of expertise include the energy, telecoms and health sectors. Highlights include acting for Scottish Power plc in a public inquiry objection to a proposed power station at Westfield, Fife. Acted for Pillar Property plc in obtaining consent for the Kinnaird Park retail development in Edinburgh. **Clients:** Bryant Homes (Scotland) Ltd; Orange Personal Communications Services Ltd; Freeport Leisure plc; local authorities.

Ledingham Chalmers Less emphasis on stand alone planning here, with all partners and assistants drawn from the commercial property department. Clients are typically commercial developers and builders. The team is especially recommended for its housebuilding expertise. Highlight was acting for Cala in respect of the new Glasgow headquarters for the Scottish Media Group. Continue to advise on planning issues relating to the Standard Life 140,000 square foot Exchange Crescent development in Edinburgh. **Clients:** Cala Ltd; Morrison Developments Ltd; George Craig Group Ltd; MJ Gleeson Group plc.

MacRoberts The firm is still respected in its particular areas of expertise, namely mining and minerals and large PFI/projects. **Jamie Grant** is the stand-out player here. Advising Sea Container Ferries Scotland Ltd on a contentious enforcement notice and public inquiry involving the local council and the issue of ferry sailings to Northern Ireland. Provided extensive planning advice to First Group plc over the construction of a rapid transit scheme in Edinburgh. **Clients:** Railtrack plc; Texaco Ltd; LAW Mining Ltd; Inverness Air Terminal Ltd.

Semple Fraser WS (Up to 4 assistants part time) A new entrant, largely by virtue of a substantial retail and property development client base. Planning is fused with the property, construction and litigation departments. Have acted this year as advisors to British Land and Royal & Sun Alliance plc in relation to major retailing schemes in Dumbarton and Inverness respectively. Highlights include representing Zeneca Ltd at a public inquiry resisting residential development adjacent to the company's factory at Grangemouth. **Clients:** Tesco Stores Ltd; Lidl UK Ltd; British Land Corporation; Wilcon Homes.

LEADERS IN PLANNING

ABRAHAM, Henry
Brachers, Maidstone (01622) 690691
Partner in Planning & Environmental Law Department.
Specialisation: Experienced in all aspects of planning applications and appeals, enforcement proceedings, development plans, integrated pollution control, all environmental matters under the EPA 1990, private bills procedure, compulsory purchase and highway orders. Occasional contributor to the 'Journal of Planning & Environment Law'.
Prof. Memberships: UK Environmental Law Association, Legal Associate Royal Town Planning Institute, Member of the Law Society's Specialist Planning Panel.
Career: Qualified in 1983. Joined *Brachers* in 1990 and became a Partner in 1994.
Personal: Born 8th June 1957. St. Dunstan's College. University of London. Leisure pursuits include rowing. Lives in London.

ALLEN, Tony
DMH, Brighton (01273) 744451
See under Environment, p.372

ASHWORTH, Stephen
Denton Wilde Sapte, London (020) 7242 1212
Specialisation: Partner, Planning and Public Law Group. Head of Property Department. Experience in planning law, including major development inquiries; judicial review; highway law; compulsory purchase orders; Private Finance Initiative projects; waste proposals. Advises on developing policy issues on retailing; planning benefits; private funding of infrastructure through the planning system; and town centre management.
Prof. Memberships: Member UK Environmental Law Association; Town & Country Planning Association; Urban Land Institute. Council member of City Property Association
Career: Articled *Denton Hall* 1986; qualified 1988; partner 1995; secondment to Sainsbury plc 1992-94; Harkness Fellowship at Lincoln Institute of Land Policy, Cambridge Massachussetts 1995-96 (researching American approaches to regeneration, provision of infrastructure and public participation in the planning process); Member Department of Transport, Private Sector Panel on Developer Contributions and Highways Agreement; Member DETR, Expert Review Group on Town Improvement Zones.
Personal: Born 1963; leisure activities include cycling, 19th century British history, dry-stone walling, cookery.

BAKER, Neil
Clarke Willmott & Clarke, Bristol (0117) 941 6600
nbaker@cw-c.co.uk
See under Environment, p.372

BANKS, Sandra
Denton Wilde Sapte, London (020) 7242 1212
sab@dentonwildesapte.com
Partner in Planning and Public Law Group.
Specialisation: Main areas of practice are development projects (for both the private and public sectors), including transport and regeneration with associated appeals and judicial review. Current projects include the redevelopment of Battersea Power Station and its environs as a visitor attraction with new rail link, housing, hotels, theatres and offices; major improvements at Ascot Racecourse; 3,000 houses at Northampton SW Sector for English Partnerships including new transport infrastructure; judicial review in respect of a Rapid Transport System at Northampton; acting on behalf of clients on the Thameslink 2000 Order, the London International Freight Exchange Order and the Docklands Light Railway extension to City Airport.

BERESFORD, Amanda
Addleshaw Booth & Co, Leeds (0113) 209 2000
aqb@addleshaw-booth.co.uk
Head of Environmental Law; Leeds.
Specialisation: All planning work including retail, leisure, industrial, residential and advocacy at Public Inquiries. Comprehensive environmental advice including pollution control, energy, waste, transport, contaminated land and due diligence. Clients advised include major development and manufacturing companies, utilities, banks and local authorities. Particular expertise in environmental and planning issues in urban regeneration projects. Recognised authoress and speaker at conferences.
Prof. Memberships: Qualified planner. Member U.K.E.L.A.
Career: Qualified in 1985, joined *Addleshaw Booth & Co* in 1997.

BIRD, Rina
Davies and partners, Gloucester (01452) 612345

BLANEY, Trevor
Lawrence Graham, London (020) 7379 0000
Specialisation: Senior Planning Partner, specialising in planning law and associated areas, including compulsory purchase and highways law for both private sector and public authorities. All aspects of planning law undertaken with emphasis on appeal work, particularly advocacy and High Court litigation, including judicial review. Regularly appears as an advocate at planning appeals, local plan inquiries and enforcement appeals. Advocacy undertaken for a wide range of clients. Work also includes negotiating and drafting planning and highways agreements. Inquiries recently conducted as Advocate on behalf of National Car Auctions, British Telecom, St. George North London Limited, & Crest Strategic Projects Limited. Also acts for Health Authorities and has been instructed in relation to the redevelopment of Whipps Cross hospital. Is currently instructed by St James Homes regarding the redevelopment of a redundant reservoir in Kensington for residential use. Has been responsible for the conduct of a number of judicial review proceedings on behalf of NHS Executive, North Thames, Cellnet and London & Regional Properties, the latter in relation to a redevelopment of Crystal Palace. In the London & Regional case he was successful in opposing leave to apply to judicial review set aside, a judgment which withstood appeals to the Court of Appeal and the House of Lords.
Prof. Memberships: Law Society's Planning Panel, Legal Associate Member of the Royal Town Planning Institute, United Kingdom Environmental Law Association. Regular contributor to planning publications and lectures widely on planning issues.

BOSWALL, Julian R.G.
Morgan Cole, Cardiff (029) 2038 5385
julian.boswall@morgan-cole.com
Head of Planning and Environment Unit.
Specialisation: Specialises in Planning, Environmental and Local Government Law.
Career: Qualified 1992. Became a partner 1999.

BOSWORTH, John
Bevan Ashford, Bristol (0117) 923 0111
j.bosworth@bevanashford.co.uk
Specialisation: Planning, urban regeneration and local government law. Special expertise in judicial review, compulsory purchase, and regional government. Projects have included regional shopping centres, Canary Wharf, a new village in South Hampshire, renewable energy schemes, town centre regeneration schemes, Temple Quay, Bristol and many PFI hospitals and the redevelopment of major brownfield sites. Advisor to south west branch of Housebuilders Federation.
Prof. Memberships: Legal Associate of RTPI. Member of Law Society's Planning Panel.
Career: Qualified 1988. Articled Portsmouth City Council. Joined *Bevan Ashford* 1995, after six years working for *Ashurst Morris Crisp.*

BRADY, Peter J.
Hewitson Becke + Shaw, Cambridge (01223) 461155

BROCK, David M. J.
Mills & Reeve, Cambridge (01223) 222 438
david.brock@mills-reeve.com
Partner in Planning and Environmental Group.
Specialisation: Has a wide ranging planning, environmental and minerals law practice. His planning work includes new settlements, urban regeneration, minerals and waste planning and PFI projects. He also advises on all aspects of environmental law.
Career: Qualified in 1980. Partner at *Herbert Smith* 1989-2000, *Mills & Reeve* 2000 to date.
Personal: Born in 1954. Educated at Dame Allan's Boys School, Newcastle, Marylebone Grammar School and University College, London (LL.B). Practising Christian. Enjoys opera, skiing, modern art and architecture. Lives near Saffron Walden.

BULL, Rod
Eversheds, Birmingham (0121) 232 1000
Head of national *Eversheds* Planning Group.
Specialisation: Planning and compulsory purchase/environmental. Experienced advocate. Considerable experience of advising developers on large mixed-use schemes (especially residential). Also specialist in minerals/waste law.
Prof. Memberships: Law Society's Planning Panel, Legal Associate RTPI, UK Environmental Law Association, Associate of Institute of Quarrying.
Career: Educated Rugby, Hull University. Partner of *Eversheds* leading Planning and Environmental Team.
Personal: Married, resides Twycross (Atherstone, Warwick). Interests: walking, computers and reading.

BUTTERFIELD, Kate
Wilbraham & Co, Leeds (0113) 243 2200
kate.butterfield@wilbraham.co.uk
Specialisation: Extensive experience of planning law; recent cases range from advising on planning and

environmental matters for motor racing circuits, dealing with compulsory purchase orders, complex planning and highways matters for major commercial developments and advising on strategic infrastructure projects.
Career: Articled *Hammond Suddards*; Qualified 1992; *Hammond Suddards* London & Leeds 1992-95; *Pinsent Curtis*; *Wilbraham & Co* 1995.
Personal: Born 1967. Horse riding, tennis and motor racing.

CASELY-HAYFORD, Margaret
Denton Wilde Sapte, London (020) 7242 1212
Partner and non-practising barrister, Planning and Public Law Group.
Specialisation: Practice covers the full range of major project property planning and PFI advice (such as housing, multi-purpose stadium and concert venue developments, police station developments, shopping centres, superstores, hospital development and contaminated land redevelopment proposals, as well as major energy installations). Negotiates planning consents and related agreements, carries out planning audits for funders and developers and co-ordinates and advises on compulsory purchase and land assembly matters and public inquiries covering all regulatory matters related to site development, as well as High Court appeals and judicial review proceedings.
Prof. Memberships: Bar (England and Wales), *Grays Inn*, UKELA, Association of Women Barristers, firm's representative on Business in Sport and Leisure.
Career: Called to the Bar by *Gray's Inn* 1984. Pupillage *4-5 Gray's Inn Square* 1985-1987 In house counsel ADC. Joined *Denton Hall* in 1987, partner 1998.
Publications: Author of 'Practical Planning: Permission and the Application' published by FT Law and Tax December 1995.
Personal: Educated at Streatham Hill High (Girl's Public Day School Trust) and Somerville College, Oxford.

COCKBURN, David
Archibald Campbell & Harley WS, Edinburgh (0131) 220 3000
Partner in Commercial Property Department.
Specialisation: Accredited planning law specialist and recognised as one of Scotland's leading planning lawyers. Handles planning inquiries. Contributes book reviews and articles to Law Journal of Law Society of Scotland and Scottish Planning and Environmental Law. Regularly contributes by way of lectures to Law Society Update, Scottish Young Lawyers' Association, Surveyors' bodies and Edinburgh University.
Prof. Memberships: Society of Writers to HM Signet.
Career: Qualified in 1966. Worked with Glasgow Corporation 1966-67, then *Breeze, Paterson & Chapman* 1967-70. Joined *Archibald Campbell & Harley WS* in 1970, becoming a Partner in 1971.
Personal: Born 4th February 1943. Attended Edinburgh University 1961-1964. Leisure pursuits include sport and reading.

COLLAR, Neil A.
Brodies WS, Edinburgh (0131) 228 3777
nacollar@brodies.co.uk
Partner and Head of Planning Law Department, Legal Associate of the Royal Town Planning Institute, LLM for research into use of planning issues 1990.
Specialisation: Handles town and country planning matters – planning applications, appeals and inquiries, planning issues in relation to land acquisition and disposal, Local Authority compulsory purchase, roads etc. Wide experience of private and public sector clients. Author of 'Planning', published by W.Green & Son and Sweet & Maxwell (Concise Scots Law Series) co-author of "Pollution Control in Scotland" published by T&T Clark and a number of articles in journals. Member of Editorial Board of Scottish Planning and Environmental Law. Has regular planning law columns in Greens Property Law Bulletin. Senior tutor for planning law at University of Edinburgh and speaker on aspects of planning law at several conferences.
Prof. Memberships: Law Society of Scotland, Legal Associate of the RTPI, United Kingdom Environmental Law Association.
Career: Qualified in 1992, having joined *Brodies WS* in 1990.
Personal: Born 31st March 1967. Educated at the University of Glasgow 1984-88 and 1989-90 (LLB and Diploma) and Liverpool University 1988-89 (LLM). Enjoys playing the saxophone, lacrosse, hockey and touch rugby. Lives in Edinburgh.

CONNAL, R. Craig
McGrigor Donald, Glasgow (0141) 248 6677
Partner in Commercial Litigation Unit.
Specialisation: Solicitor Advocate. Many years experience of advising on and appearing at Tribunals, Courts and Inquiries in contentious and high profile matters. Cases have ranged from successfully acting for the Respondent before the Inner House of the Court of Session in the landmark case of East Dunbartonshire Council v McTaggart & Mickel, to appearing successfully for FIFA in claims arising from the abortive Estonia v Scotland football match. A regular lecturer and author of many articles, from the general press to, for example, Estates Gazette and JPEL. Contributor, Stair Memorial Encyclopaedia of Scots Law.
Prof. Memberships: Law Society of Scotland, SSC (Solicitor in the Supreme Courts), Council member, Royal Faculty of Procurators in Glasgow 1995-98.
Career: Joined *McGrigor Donald* in 1977 on qualification, becoming a partner in 1980.
Personal: Born 7th July 1954. Educated at Glasgow University (LLB, 1st Class Honours 1975). Rugby referee.

COOPER, David
Gouldens, London (020) 7583 7777
Partner in Planning Department.
Specialisation: Specialises in Local Government work. Has conducted approximately 850 Planning Inquiries on behalf of clients who include ADT; Alton Towers; ARC Properties; Arlington Securities; Arsenal Football Club; Bristol Airport; British Car Auctions; British Aerospace; Citibank; Flairline Properties; GRE Properties; Group Lotus; Hanson Properties Limited; P&O Developments; Pillar Properties; Port Ramsgate; Sally UK; Sir Emmanuel Kay CBE; Sir Robert McAlpine; Southampton Football Group; Tarmac Properties and Virgin, the majority as Advocate. Has also acted on behalf of groups concerned with the conservation of important buildings in London and the Provinces including SAVE Britain's Heritage, the Covent Garden Resident's Association, the Georgian Society and the Victorian Society. He now also has a major practice specialising in Regulatory, White Collar Crime and Fraud.
Prof. Memberships: Law Society Planning Panel, Legal Associate of the Royal Town Planning Institute.
Career: Qualified in May 1967. Gained experience in the planning field with George Wimpey Limited before joining *Gouldens* as a Partner in 1973.
Personal: Born 8th June 1942. Took an LLB(Hons) in 1960. Lives in London SW1.

CUNLIFFE, Michael
Ashurst Morris Crisp, London (020) 7872 7367
michael.cunliffe@ashursts.com
Partner and Head of Planning Group.
Specialisation: Planning law acting for both developers and local authorities. Major clients include British Gas, Chelsfield, Kvaerner, Frogmore and Dartford Borough Council.
Prof. Memberships: Legal Associate of the Royal Town Planning Institute, Member of the Law Society's Planning Panel and Member of the City of London Law Society's Planning and Environmental Law Sub-Committee. Associate Fellow of the Society for Advanced Legal Studies and a Member of the Society's Planning and Environmental Law Reform Working Group.
Career: Qualified 1974. Joined *Ashurst Morris Crisp* 1983. Partner in 1987.

CURNOW, Tony
Ashurst Morris Crisp, London (020) 7638 1111
See under Local Government, p.587

DAMMS, Martin
Pinsent Curtis, Birmingham (0121) 200 1050
Specialisation: Planning and Environmental Law. Covers full range of contentious and non contentious matters including advising and representing public bodies. Planning applications, appeals, development plan representations, judicial review, negotiating/drafting planning agreements, enforcement action, housing, commercial, retail, leisure and minerals development, highways issues, compulsory purchase proceedings, contaminated land issues and waste regulation, hazardous substances consents. Advocate.
Prof. Memberships: Law Society. Birmingham Law Society. Member of the Law Society's Planning Panel. Legal Associate R.T.P.I. Member of the Midlands Environmental Business club.
Career: Qualified 1976. In Local Government to 1989. Joined *Edge Ellison* in 1989. Partner from 1993. *Pinsent Curtis* 2000 to date.
Personal: Born 17th November 1952. Educated at Mexborough Grammar School and University of Birmingham.

DIMMICK, Simon
Clarks, Reading (0118) 958 5321
Specialisation: Town and Country Planning, highways law, environmental work relating to property development. Advice on local authority matters generally. Advocacy. Acts for land owners, developers and local authorities.
Career: Qualified in 1977. 1983-1988 Assistant County Solicitor, Berkshire County Council. Joined *Clarks* in 1988, becoming a Partner in 1989.
Personal: Born 19 January 1952. Educated Kings School, Worcester, and University College, London – LLB 1974. Leisure time interests include family and Church work.

DRUKARZ, Daniel
Fladgate Fielder, London (020) 7323 4747
ddrukarz@fladgate.com
Head of Planning Unit
Specialisation: Partner specialising in all aspects of planning law and practice, including judicial review and major inquiry work. Wide experience in office and business park schemes, urban regeneration initiatives and other large scale retail, residential and mixed use developments. Expertise in negotiating and drafting planning and infrastructure agreements. Acts for a variety of multinationals (including advice on EC wide environmental strategy), investment and development companies and amenity groups.
Prof. Memberships: Law Society; Member Institute of Petroleum.
Career: Articles *Titmuss Sainer & Webb*, qualified 1989, assistant solicitor with *Nabarro Nathanson* and *S J Berwin* before joining *Fladgate Fielder*in 1994 to set up Planning Unit. Partner since 1997.
Personal: Born 1960. Married with two children. Interests include family, Himalayan and African trekking and five-a-side. Lives in London.

DYER, Carl
McGuinness Finch, London (020) 7493 9593
carldyer@mcguinnessfinch.com
Specialisation: Specialises in retail and housing development, regeneration and centre development, including project coordination, inquiry and CPO work and all ancillary aspects including Section 106 and other infrastructure agreements. Judicial Review and High Court Appeals also undertaken.
Prof. Memberships: Law Society.
Career: BA (Hons) Law University of Kent at Canterbury, Anthony London Law Prize, Havant Borough Council (1982-1985), Brighton Borough Council (1985-1986), *Fitzhugh Gates* (1986-1989) Assistant Solicitor, *Norton Rose* (1989-1992) and *Berwin Leighton* (1992-1997), Partner *McGuinness Finch* (1997-).
Personal: Swimming, keep fit, RSC, theatre generally

EDMOND, John
Marrons, Leicester (0116) 289 2200
Partner in planning, development and public law department.
Specialisation: Has 13 years experience of specialist contentious town planning and associated work, including judicial review and high court challenges to planning decisions under the 1990 Act, public law matters and compulsory purchase. Has acted in a wide range of cases including new village schemes, contaminated land proposals, landfill proposals, motorway service areas, retail and leisure applications, applications involving Conservation Areas, Listed Buildings and Registered Parks. Has experience in negotiating Section 106 agreements and related agreements relating to major infrastructure proposals. Major clients include Persimmon Homes, Barratt Homes, David Wilson Homes, Allison Homes, Hallam Land Managements, Forte UK Ltd, Yuill Homes, Stapleford Park plc, Safeways, Wilson Bowden Properties, CWS. Has conducted Local Plan Inquiries on behalf of Local Planning Authorities including Daventry District Council, South Derbyshire District Council and North West Leicestershire District Council.
Prof. Memberships: Law Society, Legal Associate of the Royal Town Planning Institute, Member of the Law Society's Planning Panel.
Career: Qualified in 1983, joined *Marron Dodds* in 1987 becoming a partner in 1988. Prior to joining *Marron Dodds* specialised in Magistrates Court/ Crown Court prosecution and defence work. Educated at Hull Grammar School.
Personal: Born 8th February 1959. Attended Wolverhampton University (BA (Hons) Law 1980). Leisure interests include golf (member of Luffenham Health Golf Club), off-shore sailing, personal fitness and the arts. Lives on the Leicestershire/ Rutland border. Married with four children.

ENGERT, Nick
Clarke Willmott & Clarke, Taunton
(01823) 442266
nengert@cw-c.co.uk
Chairman and Partner heading Planning and Environmental Department now comprising four partners, a consultant on Local Government matters, two associates and a chartered town planner.
Specialisation: Main areas of practice are town and country planning, compulsory purchase and compensation and land development. Recent appearances as an advocate include Local Plan Inquiries for national housebuilders in Bedfordshire, Cheshire, Dorset and Wiltshire. Successful Sectioon 78 appeals in Devon, Gloucestershire and Somerset. A principle adviser to local authorities and other landowners in respect of several substantial development schemes involving such issues as contaminated land, environmental assessment, flood prevention, listed buildings and conservation areas, renewable energy, retail and traffic impact, design and layout and overall sustainability. Currently advising landowners and local authorities on use of compulsory purchase powers and disputed compensation claims. Is on the Urban Advisory Board for the Regional Development Agency. Regular lecturer on planning related matters to regional branches of the Royal Town Planning Institute and RICS. Recognised as one of the highest rated planning solicitors (as chosen by leading solicitors and planners – Magazine Survey 1999).
Prof. Memberships: Member of the Law Society and UKELA.
Career: Qualified in 1973. Joined *Clarke Willmott & Clarke* in 1975, becoming a partner in 1979.
Personal: Born 28th September 1948. Attended Oundle School and Southampton University. A Governor of the West of England School for Children with little or no sight and an official steward at the British Horse Trials Association. Leisure interests include riding, shooting, tennis, golf, choral singing and wine tasting. Lives near Taunton, Somerset.

EVANS, Douglas
Theodore Goddard, London (020) 7606 8855
Specialisation: Advocacy, strategic advice and negotiation of planning permissions and agreements for all forms of property development. Advice on environmental assessment and contaminated land is an important part of the practice. Major clients include national house builders and commercial developers, retailers, institutional developers, power generation companies, waste landfill and incineration companies, utility companies and mining companies. Major current cases include: acting for Thames Water Utilities in the Terminal 5 Inquiry; promoting a 10,000 house development at Stevenage for Persimmon Homes; promoting three major 'waste to energy' incinerators for Hampshire Waste; obtaining planning permission to double the size of the UK's only potashmine for Cleveland Potash; securing planning permission for 1000 dwellings at Banbury for Bryant Homes; advising SITA on the 25 year Surrey Waste Contract and promoting two waste to energy incinerators; promoting three further waste to energy incinerators at various locations; advising on a major landfill site extension; presenting objections to numerous Local Plan Inquiries to secure allocations for retail and housing development.
Prof. Memberships: Member of the Law Society Specialist Planning Panel, Legal Associate of the Royal Town Planning Institute, Affiliate Member of the Institute of Waste Management, Member of the City of London Law Society Planning and Environment Law Sub-Committee, Member of Energy from Waste Association and Chairman of Planning Committee and Member of the UK Environmental Law Association. Awarded the Institute of Waste Management Waste Regulation Award for 1997.
Personal: Leisure interests include: sailing, shooting and (in this order) staying married!

EVANS, Eric
Eversheds, Cardiff (02920) 471147
See under Property (Commercial), p.726

EVANS, Katherine
TLT Solicitors, Bristol (0117) 917 7777
kevans@TLTsolicitors.com
Specialisation: Specialises in all aspects of development including planning, highways, compulsory purchase/compensation, land acquisition. Also environmental law particularly contaminated land and environmental liability in corporate transactions. Experienced in High Court challenges and judicial reviews. Acts for developers, financial institutions, minerals and waste operators, local authorities, private landowners and individuals.
Prof. Memberships: Law Society, Royal Town Planning Institute.
Career: Qualified planner 1987, solicitor 1997. 1986-96 employed by national housebuilders to acquire and project manage major development sites. *Lawrence Tucketts (now TLT Solicitors*, the merged firm of *Trumps* and *Lawrence Tucketts)* since 1998.
Personal: Born 1962. Lives in Bristol. Interests include family and travel.

EVANS, Martin
Ashurst Morris Crisp, London (020) 7638 1111
Senior Assistant Solicitor in the Planning Group.
Specialisation: Town and country planning and related issues. Particular experience in providing strategic advice on major retail and leisure schemes (both in and out of town) and public inquiries acting both for developer and local authority clients. Major clients include Chelsfield, Reuters, Thames Water, Tesco, British Gas, Friends Provident and British Telecom. Also involved in negotiating complex planning and infrastructure agreements on behalf of developers and local authorities.
Prof. Memberships: Law Society, Journal of Leisure Property Forum (Editorial Board).
Career: Qualified 1989.

FAULDS, Ann
Dundas & Wilson CS, Edinburgh (0131) 228 8000

FINCH, Paul
Dickinson Dees, Newcastle upon Tyne (0191) 279 9000
Specialisation: Planning, compulsory purchase and compensation. Involved in major housing projects in Hampshire, Lancashire and London, major urban regeneration schemes in London and the North East and in various PFI schemes. Highlights of last year include negotiation of bus depot relocation agreement & compensation package, representation of public transport provider at Redcar Town Centre CPO Inquiry, negotiation of planning agreements re major development in Basingstoke, successful advocacy in a number of public inquiries.
Prof. Memberships: Law Society. Newcastle Law Society. Member of Law Society Planning & Environmental Committee.
Career: 1979-1982 *Runnymede BC*, 1982-1986 *North Tyneside MBC*, 1986-1990 *Clifford Chance*, 1990-date *Dickinson Dees.*
Publications: Notes to Leasehold Reform Housing and Urban Development Act 1993 (Current Law). Various articles in property and planning law journals, 'Rights of Way Law Review.'
Personal: Educated Omskirk Grammar School and University of Newcastle Upon Tyne. Married, no children. Outside intrests hockey, squash, hill-walking, travel.

FIRTH, Beverley
Mills & Reeve, Cambridge (01223) 222 235
beverley.firth@mills-reeve.com
Specialisation: Partner in the Property Services Department, specialising in all aspects of planning law. Work includes advice on aspects of land development, negotiations with local authorities including planning agreements. Also includes advocacy in planning appeals and in local plan inquiries. Contentious work includes judicial review. Particular environmental expertise in land contamination and waste disposal including clinical waste. Also experienced in health and safety. Consultant editor of Longman's Planning & Environment Law Bulletin. Recent projects include local airfields, new settlement and University campus.

FONGENIE, Wesley
McGuinness Finch, London (020) 7493 9593
Specialisation: Particular expertise in retail, housing, leisure and office developments, compulsory purchase and infrastructure schemes. Activities include project co-ordination, inquiry and CPO work, negotiation of planning and infrastructure agreements together with undertaking planning audits for funders and developers as well as high court appeals and judicial review proceedings.
Career: LLB (Hons) Barrister 1981. Joined *Berwin Leighton* in 1992 after career in local government (GLC, LB Camden and Royal Borough of Kensington and Chelsea). Joined *McGuinness Finch* 1998. Partner 1999 to present.
Personal: Married with two children. Leisure pursuits include motor racing and cricket.

FRASER, Moira A.
McGuinness Finch, London (020) 7493 9593
moirafraser@mcguinnessfinch.com
Partner
Specialisation: Many years specialist experience in planning, CPO and compensation, highway and other infrastructure issues. Emphasis on inquiry work and appeals. Expertise in negotiating and drafting planning and infrastructure agreements. Advises on development plan policies. Acts for public authorities, private sector and amenity groups. Special expertise in large retail.
Prof. Memberships: The Law Society; UKELA; Fellow of the Royal Society of Arts; Town and Country Planning Association.
Career: MA (Hons) Cantab. Articled 1977-79 *Norton Rose*, qualified 1979. *D J Freeman* 1988-99, *McGuinness Finch* 1999-
Personal: Born 1955. Leisure pursuits include golf, art appreciation and family.

GALLIMORE, Michael
Lovells, London (020) 7296 2000
michael.gallimore@lovells.com
Partner in commercial property department and head of planning group.
Specialisation: Principal area of practice is property development with particular expertise in the planning and environmental aspects of major development and infrastructure projects. Wide experience in office and business park developments, retail schemes, new housing settlements, leisure projects and waste management schemes. Also experienced in development site acquisitions. Expertise includes negotiations and appeals for planning and associated consents and drafting and negotiation of s.106 agreements and related development/infrastructure agreements. Has acted on numerous judicial review applications and High Court challenges. Experience also on various PFI projects. Acts as an advocate at planning and local plan inquiries.
Prof. Memberships: Law Society Specialist Planning Panel, Law Society Planning and Environmental Law Committee, City of London Law Society Planning and Environmental Law Sub-Committee.
Career: Qualified 1983, Partner 1988.

GIBBS, Kevin
Osborne Clarke OWA, Bristol (0117) 917 4222
kevin.gibbs@osborneclarke.com
See under Environment, p.375

GILBEY, Iain
Shoosmiths, Northampton (01604) 543000
iain.gilbey@shoosmiths.co.uk
Partner and Head of Planning Group.
Specialisation: Town and Country Planning and environmental law. All aspects of planning development. Specialises in providing strategic advice on residential, retail and other large scale commercial developments. Experienced in conducting major public inquiries and associated High Court litigation. Acts for privatised utilities, major national housebuilders, landowners, retailers and occupiers.
Prof. Memberships: Law Societly and UKELA.
Career: Educated at Royal Grammar School, High Wycombe. Southampton University (LLB). College of Law, Guildford. Trained at *Berwin Leighton*. Qualified 1994. *Ashurst Morris Crisp* 1997-2000. Joined *Shoosmiths* Janurary 2000. Partner May 2000.

GOODMAN, David
Hammond Suddards Edge, Leeds (0113) 284 7000
david.goodman@hammondsuddardsedge.com
Partner and Head of Planning Department.
Specialisation: Main area of practice is town and country planning handling all aspects of planning issues relating to development, including retailing, residential, office, power generation, mineral extraction, waste disposal and leisure uses. Undertakes advocacy at public inquiries. Also deals with environmental law including environmental assessment and environmentally sensitive developments. Has handled a proposal for an overhead transmission line through Cleveland and North Yorkshire, various power generation projects including windfarms, promotion of clinical waste incinerator proposals, and a football stadium in the North East. Author of articles on planning law. Lectures regularly to RTPI and other professional bodies.
Prof. Memberships: Law Society, British Wind Energy Association.
Career: Qualified in 1980. Articled at Surrey County Council 1978-80, then Assistant Solicitor at Oldham Metropolitan B.C 1980-84. Senior Solicitor at Newcastle upon Tyne City Council 1984-88. Joined *Hammond Suddards* in 1988 and became a Partner in 1991.
Personal: Born 15th October 1955. Educated at the Royal Grammar School, Newcastle upon Tyne 1967-74 and Sheffield University 1974-77. Recreations include sport, gardening and theatre.

GRANT, James R.
MacRoberts, Glasgow (0141) 332 9988
jamieg@macroberts.co.uk
Specialisation: Main area of practice in planning and environmental law, although he also does some commercial property work (especially licensed trade).
Prof. Memberships: Law Society of Scotland.
Career: Edinburgh University 1979-84. *Mitchells Roberton* 1984-88 (trainee/assistant). *Maclay Murray & Spens* 1988-91 (assistant/associate). *MacRoberts* 1991 – present (assistant/associate/partner (1993)).
Personal: Born 29 June 1961. Lives Glasgow. Leisure interests include sailing, music and gardening.

GRAVES, Gary
Nabarro Nathanson, London (020) 7524 6000
g.graves@nabarro.com
Specialisation: Partner specialising in all aspects of planning law and practice, including major inquiry work and judicial review.
Prof. Memberships: Member Law Society Planning Panel (1995) and City of London Law Society Planning and Environmental Law Sub-Committee. Legal Associate of RTPI.
Career: Articles: *Russells*; qualified 1983. *Herbert Oppenheimer* (1983-1988); *Lovell White Durrant* (1988-1991); Partner *Nabarro Nathanson* (1991 to date).
Personal: Born 1958. Married with 1 child, resides London.

GREENWOOD, Brian J.
Norton Rose, London (020) 7283 6000
greenwoodbj@nortonrose.com
Specialisation: Areas of expertise include planning applications, environmental assessment, negotiation of planning and infrastructure agreements and hearings and appeals. Appears as advocate at appeals. Recent instructions encompass, industrial processes (Castle Cement), power stations, residential and commercial development, listed buildings (English Heritage) and motorway service areas (Esso).
Prof. Memberships: Chairman, Law Society's Planning and Environmental Law Committee, former Chairman City of London Law Society Planning and Environment Committee; UKELA; Law Society's Specialist Planning Panel.
Publications: Author of 'Butterworths Planning Law Service', co-author of 'Environmental Regulation

and Economic Growth', editor of 'Planning Law Handbook' and 'Butterworths Planning Law Guidance'.

GRIFFITHS, Marian
Eversheds, Leeds (0113) 243 0391
Specialisation: Town and country planning, compulsory purchase. Main areas of practice are retail, minerals and waste disposal and housing, town centre regeneration.
Prof. Memberships: Law Society's Planning Panel. Legal Associate RTPI.
Career: Law degree from Leeds and qualified as a solicitor in 1981. Articled in local government and worked in the public sector until 1991. Joined *Eversheds* in 1996.
Personal: Born Chester, educated in Wolverhampton. Married with twin daughters aged 10. Lives in Leeds.

HALL, Brian
Clifford Chance, London (020) 7600 1000
brian.hall@cliffordchance.com
Specialisation: Partner and head of firm's planning unit specialising in environment, local government and town planning.
Prof. Memberships: Member of the Environmental Law Group.
Career: Rutherford Grammar School; King's College, London (LLB, DMA, FCIS). Articled North Tyneside MBC; qualified 1980; partner *Clifford Chance* since 1988.
Personal: Born 1950; resides London.

HARRIS, Jacqueline
McGrigor Donald, Glasgow (0141) 248 6677
www.mcgrigors.com
Partner in Commercial Litigation Unit.
Specialisation: Principle areas of practice are commercial litigation and planning. Developed expertise in planning through dealing with contentious planning applications, appeals, public inquiries and judicial review. Now advises on all aspects of planning, particularly in relation to major development and infrastructure projects, retail and mineral planning. Conducts advocacy at public inquiries. Clients include: The Post Office, BG Property Holdings, Forth Ports plc, I & H Brown Ltd, Glasgow Harbour Ltd.
Career: Qualified 1990; Partner *McGrigor Donald* 1999.

HAWKINS, David
Nabarro Nathanson, London (020) 524 6261
Partner in Planning Department since 1978.
Specialisation: Covers all aspects of planning and development, particularly large scale commercial developments, public inquiries and judicial review; also administrative law, Parliamentary work and compulsory purchase and compensation. Author of 'Compulsory Purchase' volume of the Encyclopaedia of Forms and Precedents and 'Boynton's Guide to Compulsory Purchase and Compensation'. Addresses seminars regularly.
Prof. Memberships: Law Society; Legal Associate, R.T.P.I.; Law Society Planning Panel.
Career: Member of Planning and Environmental Law Committee of the Law Society, FRSA.
Personal: King's College, London: LLB (Hons).

HELLIER, Tim
Berwin Leighton, London (020) 7760 1000
tim.hellier@berwinleighton.com
Specialisation: Wide experience in retail, housing, leisure, office developments and major urban regeneration schemes, compulsory purchase, contaminated land, risk management and infrastructure schemes and urban regeneration schemes. Acted for AMEC Developments in securing planning permission for the first freight terminal associated with the Channel Tunnel in the Green Belt. Acted for BAA-McArthur/ Glen (UK) Limited, the factory outlet operator in securing planning approvals for over 1.5 million square feet of retail floorspace. Currently acting on major urban regeneration schemes in Bracknell, Hull, Chester and Liverpool. Other major clients: Tesco, Legal and General, London and Amsterdam, Liverpool Council and Warner Village.
Prof. Memberships: Law Society, Associate Fellow of the Society of Advanced Legal Studies, UKELA.
Career: Strode College, Egham. Sheffield University LLB(Hons). Law Society Finals, City of London Polytechnic. Qualified 1986; partner *Berwin Leighton* 1997.
Personal: Married with two children. Interests include rugby, running and general fitness, music, his children.

HEMMING, Dan
Wragge & Co, Birmingham (0121) 214 1082
dan_hemming@wragge.com
Specialisation: Town and Country Planning. Highways. Compulsory Purchase. Land compensation.
Prof. Memberships: Law Society (Member of Law Society's Planning Panel)
Career: Wolverhampton MBC (1976-1978), West Midlands CC (1979-1985), Solihull MBC (1986-1988), *Wragge & Co* (1989 – partner 1993)
Personal: Education, Stourbridge Grammar School, Birmingham Polytechnic (BA Hons) Law). Interests: cricket and family

HIGNETT, Andrew
Lester Aldridge, Bournemouth (020) 7984 5373
Specialisation: Retail and residential developments, development of contaminated land, planning appeals and Local Plan representations, including advocacy at Public Inquiries. He acts for port authorities and has therefore considerable experience in port and marina developments.
Career: Qualified 1978. With Local Authorities until 1988, culminating as a Chief Officer in the South West. A planning specialist in private sector since then. Has advised both local authorities and developers in relation to town centre developments including capital spending restrictions. Compulsory purchase work, including compensation, is a major part of his practice, advising both the public sector and national utilities in relation to the promotion of their compulsory purchase powers, together with businesses/individuals affected by CPO's. Andrew Hignett has also lectured extensively to solicitors and other professionals on planning law issues.

HILLEBRON, Richard
Slaughter and May, London (020) 7600 1200
Specialisation: Specialises in all aspects of Town and Country planning from submission of an application through to decision and appeal, including compulsory purchase, negotiating highways and other agreements with local authorities and Certificates of lawful use or development.

Prof. Memberships: Legal Associate of The Royal Town Planning Institute. Member of The Law Society's Planning Panel. Member City of London Law Society Planning and Environmental Law Sub-Committee.
Career: Qualified 1980.

HOLMES, Sarah C.
Bond Pearce, Plymouth (01752) 266633
xsch@bondpearce.com
Associate in the Planning and Environmental Group.
Specialisation: Specialises in planning and environmental law. MA (Oxon) and Master of Arts in Environmental Law (1997), national reputation for work in renewable energy having been at the forefront of the industry since 1991. Advises on all stages of planning process, including environmental impact assessment (advised on over 40 such renewable, waste, commercial and other projects), with clients in public and private sector. Extensive environmental practice includes contaminated land remediation, risk minimisation and allocation, environmental insurance, complex landfill tax issues, European Sites (nature conservation) and consents/permits. Active involvement in major waste, minerals, food and motor deals with due diligence on many further transactions. Runner-up Assistant Solicitor of the Year (The Lawyer, 1995), Council Member of UK Environmental Law Association, Secretary of UKELA South West and member of British Wind Energy Association.
Career: Qualified in 1991. Joined *Bond Pearce* in 1989 becoming an Associate in 1997.

HOUGHTON, John
Bond Pearce, Southampton (023) 8332 211
jerh@bondpearce.com
Consultant in the Specialist Planning and Environmental Group.
Specialisation: Advocate at Section 78 and Local Plan Inquiries. Past projects include nuclear power, gas terminal and pipelines, wind farms, DBFO projects, retail proposals and airport expansion feasibility studies. Currently involved in proposed expantion of the Port of Southampton.
Prof. Memberships: Member of the UK Environmental Law Association.
Career: Educated Cheltenham College and Lincoln College, Oxford (MA Law). Qualified 1973. Managing Partner *Denton Hall*, Hong Kong 1984-1988; Head of Planning Group, *Denton Hall* 1989-1994; Partner, *Clarke Willmott & Clarke* 1995-2000.

HOWARD, Karen
Ashurst Morris Crisp, London (020) 7638 1111
Specialisation: Advises on Town Planning and related matters, including urban regeneration, compulsory purchase and highway orders, appeals and public inquiries, High Court challenges, and planning and infrastructure agreements. Wide experience in retail, leisure and housing matters and major mixed use development schemes. Acted for English Partnerships in securing permission for the Millennium Dome and the regeneration of the Greenwich Peninsula. Main adviser to Tesco Stores Limited since 1988. Other major clients have included Amec Developments Limited, Lloyds Bank, BG plc, St James Homes, Hemmingway and DLR.
Prof. Memberships: Fellow of Institute of Legal Executives Student member of Law Society
Career: Local Government 1984-1986. Joined *Denton Hall* 1986. Moved to *Berwin Leighton* 1988;

became senior manager left March 2000. Now Legal Manager at *Ashurst Morris Crisp*.
Personal: Born 1964; 1 child. Interests include motorcycling, personal fitness, socialising and family. Lives in Broomfield, Essex.

HUGHES, Norna
Nabarro Nathanson, London (020) 7524 6000
n.hughes@nabarro.com
Heads Planning Department.
Specialisation: Handles all aspects of planning related work, particularly contentious planning. Also handles rating and Judicial Review, covering business rate appeals and local and central government powers. Represents Costco in all planning matters.
Career: Qualified in 1989. Joined *Nabarro Nathanson* in 1987, becoming a Partner in 1989. Previously a Barrister specialising in planning, having been called to the Bar in 1983.
Personal: Leisure interests include family, friends, socialising and tennis. Lives in London.

INNES, Colin
Shepherd & Wedderburn WS, Edinburgh (0131) 228 9900
colin.innes@ shepwedd.co.uk
Specialisation: Partner in Litigation Department. Head of the Planning and Environmental Group specialising exclusively in planning and environmental issues. Has substantial experience of advising on planning or related issues to clients both in the private and public sectors, including on the contentious side representation at public local inquiries, planning appeals and judicial review of planning decisions in the Court of Session. In relation to non-contentious work has extensive experience in providing advice on all types of planning projects and PFI schemes.
Prof. Memberships: Law Society (England and Wales). Law Society (Scotland) and UKELA. WS Society.
Career: LL.B (Hons) University of Aberdeen. LL.M (Environmental Law) University of Aberdeen.

JACKSON, Ray
Linklaters (A member firm of Linklaters & Alliance), London (020) 7456 4884
ray.jackson@linklaters.com
Partner. Planning & Environmental Unit in the Property Department.
Specialisation: Specialises in all aspects of environmental law including town planning, public health, control of pollution, compulsory purchase and highways. Typical matters have included a wide selection of corporate, privatisation and major property transactions where planning, regulatory and environmental issues have been pertinent. Has had extensive involvement in major public local inquiries for motorways, large redevelopment schemes and compulsory purchase orders. Detailed knowledge of the Compensation Code in respect of claims in the Lands Tribunal and as Parliamentary Agent; considerable experience of Private and Hybrid Bill procedures.
Career: Joined *Linklaters* in 1985, made Partner in 1988.

JAMESON, Robert
Jameson & Hill, Hertford (01992) 554881
Specialisation: Main area of practice is Town and Country Planning, handling all aspects of planning issues, including retailing, residential, office, mineral extraction, waste disposal, and leisure uses; acting both for private clients and local authorities. Considerable Local Plan experience. Regular advocate at Inquiries into Local Plans. Planning and Enforcement Appeals. In addition, has extensive experience in negotiating complex Planning Agreements.
Career: Qualified in 1971. Started legal career in Local Government. Was Principal Assistant County Secretary at Hertfordshire County Council before co-founding *Jameson & Hill* in 1982. Over 20 years of planning experience.

JEEPS, Barry
Stephenson Harwood, London (020) 7809 2513
barry.jeeps@shlegal.com
Partner, Head of Town and Country Planning Group.
Specialisation: Extensive experience in all aspects of town and country planning, compulsory purchase and Transport and Works Act applications with particular emphasis on large-scale public inquiries and court litigation. He has wide experience in contested planning decisions, including work in the Crown Office of the High Court, Court of Appeal and the House of Lords. His work involves regular contact with local authorities. Continuing planning advice in relation to London Bridge City (one of the largest urban regeneration projects in the country) and the recently opened Trafford Centre, Manchester (a major sub-regional shopping centre) planning permission for which was defended successfully in the House of Lords.
Career: Qualified November 1982 specialising in Commercial Property. Joined *Stephenson Harwood* as assistant solicitor in the Property Department. Became Partner and Head of Town and Country Planning Group in 1989.
Publications: Written numerous articles for 'Property Law Journal' and *Stephenson Harwood*'s 'Town and Country Planning Bulletin' and has chaired client seminars.
Personal: Born 17 March 1958. Educated Slough Grammar School 1969-76; St Catherine's College, Oxford 1976-79. Interests include swimming, reading, theatre and supporting Tottenham Hotspur FC. Resides London.

KENWORTHY, Michael
Addleshaw Booth & Co, Manchester (0161) 934 6000
mbk@addleshaw-booth.co.uk
Partner in Commercial Property Group.
Specialisation: Specialises in planning, environmental, highways and compulsory purchase matters. Acts for local authorities, utility companies, waste operators, developers and NHS trusts. Advises international companies on environmental due-diligence in land and corporate acquisitions.
Prof. Memberships: Member of the Law Society and UKELA.
Career: University of Keele 1974-1978. Qualified in 1981. Joined the firm in 1986. Partner in 1990.

KITSON, Tony
CMS Cameron McKenna, London (020) 7367 3556
abk@cmck.com
Partner in Planning Group.
Specialisation: Advises on the planning aspects of all sizes and types of property development. Has handled numerous appeals involving retail, office, industrial and residential developments, and appears as an advocate at public local inquiries. Experienced in negotiating and drafting Section 106 Agreements and other development agreements. Advises on all aspects of local authority law and administration, and PFI schemes. Advises on compulsory purchase and compensation, and Transport and Works Act schemes, the clean-up of contaminated industrial sites and disposal for redevelopment. Speaker at seminars on planning and environmental law, local government law. Contributor to Solicitors Journal, Law Society's Gazette, Journal of Planning and Environmental Law and *Cameron McKenna* publications on planning, highways, compulsory purchase and public sector law and finance.
Prof. Memberships: Law Society, Law Society's Panel of Planning Solicitors. City of London Solicitors Company.
Career: Qualified in 1975. Local authority solicitor before joining *McKenna & Co* in 1988; became a Partner in 1990.
Personal: Born 14th February 1952. Lives in London.

KRATZ, Philip
Taylor Vinters, Cambridge (01223) 423444
prk@taylorvinters.com
Specialisation: All aspects of town and country planning and environmental law. Experienced advocate. Work includes agreements, applications, appeals (including local inquiries), local plan and structure plan representations. Recent experience has included acting in connection with large scale residential proposals in Cambridge and the surronding area and commercial proposals throughout the country.
Prof. Memberships: Law Society; member of the Law Society's Specialist Planning Panel; Legal Associate member of the Royal Town Planning Institute.
Career: Qualified in 1982. District Solicitor and head of Legal Services with East Cambridgeshire District Council from 1983-1992; Assistant Chief Executive until joining *Taylor Vinters* in May 1995. Head of planning development and construction team.
Personal: Leisure interests include cricket, Jaguar cars and military engineering.

LANCASTER, Roger
Halliwell Landau, Manchester (0161) 835 3003
rlancaster@halliwells.co.uk
Senior Partner and Head of Planning and Environmental Law Department.
Specialisation: Specialises in town and country planning, environmental law and compulsory purchase matters and local government issues and general advocacy at inquiries. Has substantial house building retail and developer clients and also acts for public sector authorities.
Prof. Memberships: Law Society.
Career: Qualified in 1975. Solicitor with Humberside County Council and Birmingham City Council. Joined *Halliwell Landau* as a Partner in 1982. Senior Partner 1995.
Personal: Born in 1951. Educated at Biddulph Grammar School and Leicester University (LLB 1971). Recreations include cricket, squash and gardening.

LEA, Alison
Travers Smith Braithwaite, London (020) 7295 3000
Alison.Lea@TraversSmith.com
Specialisation: Partner and head of planning and environment group. Specialises in all aspects of planning and environmental law including highway matters and compulsory purchase. Has recently acted

on a number of successful judicial review applications and High Court challenges for Lafarge Redland Aggregates and Clearwater Estates. Particular experience in negotiating consents for large retail, leisure and residential mixed use schemes including the drafting and negotiation of planning and infrastructure agreements.
Prof. Memberships: City of London Law Society Planning and Environment Law Sub-Committee.
Career: Trained *Norton Rose*; qualified 1989. *Norton Rose* 1987-1997. *Travers Smith Braithwaite* 1997 to date; made partner in 1998.
Publications: Author of monthly 'Planning Focus' in 'Property Law Journal', member of contributory board of 'Property Law Journal'. Articles in 'Journal of Planning and Environmantal Law', 'Environmental Law Monthly' and 'Environmental Law Review'.
Personal: Educated at Rainford High School and Girton College, Cambridge. Interests include horse riding and playing classical piano and flute.

MACKAY, Ian
Innes Mackay Solicitors, Beckenham
(020) 8249 2600
innesmackay@yahoo.co.uk
Solicitor specialising in all aspects of town planning and development.
Specialisation: Twenty five years' experience as planner and planning solicitor in advising planning authorities, developers and public sector agencies on all aspects of town planning and development.
Career: Town planner with several local planning authorities, attaining the position of Deputy County Planning Officer. Qualified as a solicitor in 1984. Solicitor (Head of Planning, Highways and Contracts Legal Department), London Borough of Southwark 1986-88. Senior solicitor with CMS Cameron McKenna 1988-1999. Founded niche planning, highways and compulsory purchase practice October 1999.

MANSON, Stephen
Eversheds, Cardiff (02920) 471147
See under Projects/PFI, p.699

MARRON, Peter
Marrons, Leicester (0116) 289 2200
Senior partner in planning, development and public law department.
Specialisation: Has twenty-five years' experience of contentious town planning, together with associated work advising the development industry. Also handles public law matters, compulsory purchase and judicial review. Has acted in cases ranging from new village schemes, landfill proposals and many other applications of strategic importance. Has given talks over the years to a number of bodies. Major clients include national house-builders, major land promoters, commercial developers and local authorities.
Prof. Memberships: Law Society, Chartered Institute of Arbitrators.
Career: Qualified in 1970. Founded *Marron Dodds* as a senior partner in 1978. DOT/ RYA Ocean Yacht Master with commercial endorsement. ACIArb 1990. Fellow of the Royal Society of Arts 1995. Legal Associate of the Royal Town Planning Institute. Member of International Bar Assocation. Member of Law Society's Planning Panel.
Personal: Born 3rd June 1944. Attended Liverpool University (LLB Hons 1966). Leisure interests include the arts and off-shore sailing. Lives in Uppingham, Rutland.

MAX, Richard
D J Freeman, London (020) 7583 4055
rdm@djfreeman.co.uk
Partner in Property Services Department. Head of Planning.
Specialisation: Deals with all areas of planning law and practice as well as compulsory purchase and highways work. Offers full and competitive advocacy service to clients for all planning inquiries. Clients include retailers, local authorities, developers, health authorities, property funds and development companies.
Prof. Memberships: Law Society, Law Society's Planning Panel, Chairman of the City of London Law Society Planning and Environmental Law Sub-Committee, Legal Associate and Council Member of the Royal Town Planning Institute.
Career: Qualified in 1988. Assistant Solicitor at *Macfarlanes* 1988-93. Planning Solicitor, Oxford City Council 1993. At *Radcliffes & Co* 1993-95. Joined *D J Freeman* in April 1995. Made a partner in May 1997.
Personal: Born 1 September 1963. Educated at St Paul's School 1976-82, Oxford Polytechnic 1982-85 and The College of Law, Chester 1985-86. Interests include exhibiting and driving a convertible VW Beetle as well as skiing and cycling. Lives in London.

MCCHLERY, Frances
Dundas & Wilson CS, Edinburgh (0131) 228 8000

MORITZ, John
Wake Dyne Lawton, Chester (01829) 773100
Specialisation: Initially in local government. Has advised on a number of major development projects in the North West and nationally involving urban regenerationn and contaminated land. Advises housebuilders, commercial developers waste management companies and local authorities on planning and infrastructure law, compulsory purchase and environment law.
Prof. Memberships: Member of the Law Society's Planning Panel and a Member of the United Kingdom Environmental Law Association.
Career: Qualified in 1973. Partner at *Lambert Storey* in 1990. Joined *Masons* in 1990 as a Partner.
Personal: Born in Manchester 20th September 1948. LLB Manchester University. Leisure interests include travel, theatre and viewing and appreciating art and architecture.

PASTERFIELD, Stephen
Clarke Willmott & Clarke, Bristol (0117) 941 6600
spasterfield@cw-c.co.uk
Partner in the Planning and Environmental Department.
Specialisation: Specialises in planning, handling all issues relating to development including mineral extraction, waste disposal, urban regeneration, retailing, office and residential uses; also compensation and environmental law including waste management licensing, contaminated land, nuisance and water pollution. Acts for Government Departments, Developers, Financial Institutions, Minerals and Waste Operators and Local Authorities as well as private individuals. Recent appearances as advocate at appeals have been for a national housebuilder in Gloucestershire, a local authority on the South Coast and a national food group in Kent. Has advised housebuilders on strategic planning and on several large schemes involving brownfield sites. Has advised Unitary Authority on its planning gain policy, and an international commercial group on road transport policy. Continues to act on Compulsory Purchase issues. Very experienced advocate and lecturer on techniques at inquiries. Author of numerous articles. Member of Law Society's specialist Planning Panel and Legal Associate of the Royal Town Planning Institute.
Prof. Memberships: Law Society, Royal Town Planning Institute.
Career: Qualified in 1974. Principal Solicitor, Solihull MBC 1976-79. Deputy City Solicitor, Winchester 1979-1988. Partner at *Lawrence Tucketts* from 1994 to 1999. Joined as Partner at *Clarke Willmott & Clarke* 1999 to date.
Personal: Born 30th April 1949. Educated Birkenhead School 1960-67. Leisure pursuits include sport of all kinds, especially golf, fishing and horse racing. Lives in Wrington.

PIATT, Andrew
DLA, Manchester (0161) 235 4024
andrew.piatt@dla.com
Fax: 0161 235 4124
Specialisation: Planning, highways, compulsory purchase & compensation (all aspects) including advocacy. Advises house builders, developers, retailers, landowners & public sector bodies. 1999 – obtained planning permission after a call in inquiry for 2.8 mft sq arena central development in Birmingham including a 50 storey tower.
Prof. Memberships: Called to the bar 1987. Solicitor.
Career: Local government in N.W. England 1987-1996 specialising in planning, highways, compulsory purchase & compensation.
Publications: Articles in 'Journal of Planning & Environment Law' & 'Estates Gazette'. Regular speaker at conferences & seminars.
Personal: Married with two young sons. Interests – gardening & family. LLB (Hons) – University of Southampton (1986)

PUGH, Timothy
Berwin Leighton, London (020) 7760 1000
timothy.pugh@berwinleighton.com
Partner; Co-Head Planning and Environment Department.
Specialisation: Planning and Environmental Law. Particular areas of planning-related expertise: rail and infrastructure projects, urban regeneration, retail, industrial, warehousing, waste disposal, land reclamation and housing projects; compulsory purchase; highway orders; planning and infrastructure agreements; Transport and Works Act Orders. Particular areas of environment-related expertise: contaminated land; waste disposal; environmental impact statements; water law; environmental terms and conditions of contract.
Prof. Memberships: City of London Solicitors Company, IBA, Society for Advanced Legal Studies (SAALS). Member: Planning and Environment Committee of the British Property Federation; Planning and Environment Law-Sub Committee of the City of London Law Society; IBA's Committee on International Environmental Law; and SAALS Planning and Environmental Law Reform Group.
Career: Qualified 1984. Articled at *Donne Mileham & Haddock* 1982-84. Joined *Berwin Leighton* 1984; Partner 1990.
Personal: Born 1959. Duffryn High School, Newport, Gwent; University College, London; and College of Law, Lancaster Gate. Leisure interests include skiing, cycling and lying under old cars. Lives in Hove.

QUAYLE, Sophie Jane
Herbert Smith, London (020) 7374 8000
Specialisation: Wide ranging experience of all matters relating to planning applications and associated documentation; extensive work on section 106 agreements and conditions, implementation of planning agreements, and general planning/property issues; and advising on judicial review and statutory appeals relating to planning matters. Advised ALP/Shroders on their Bracknell proposals and Coventry City Football Club on their new arena.
Career: *Herbert Smith* (1989 to date). Qualified 1991. Partner 1998.
Personal: Born 1964; St. Anthony's Leweston, Dorset; Southampton University. Sporty – especially sailing, diving and skiing; travel.

REDMAN, Michael
Clifford Chance, London (020) 7600 1000
michael.redman@cliffordchance.com
Specialisation: Solicitor advocate (qualified in criminal and civil jurisdiction). Senior member of the planning group of the commercial property practice advising developers on all aspects of planning and development. He is on the DETR Compulsory purchase policy review working group. Appeared in the courts in judicial review proceedings. Negotiating and drafting planning and other statutory agreements. Has advised on the planning aspects of the Canary Wharf development. Has advised power companies in respect of major gas power generating stations. Writes regularly on planning issues and is a contributor to the Journal of Planning Law.
Prof. Memberships: Member of the Law Society's Planning Panel.
Career: Barrister (1975); solicitor (1986).
Personal: Rugby referee.

RICHARDSON, Simon
Davies Wallis Foyster, Manchester
(0161) 228 3702
sfr@dwf-law.com
Specialisation: Planning consultancy, applications and appeals and development services.
Prof. Memberships: Law Society; Royal Town Planning Institute.
Career: Christchurch Borough Council; Thamesdown Borough Council; *Berwin Leighton*; *Chapman Warren*; *Cobbetts*; *Davies Wallis Foyster* 1997.
Personal: Baines Grammar School; The Queen's College, Oxford; Landscape photography; Food and cookery.

RICKETTS, Simon
SJ Berwin & Co, London (020) 7533 2222
simon.ricketts@sjberwin.com
Specialisation: Planning and local government law, advising institutions and developers on major retail/ business/ residential/ leisure schemes, including negotiating related agreements, coordinating appeals and legal challenges. Extensive experience in compulsory purchase and related procedures and Parliamentary work in respect of private and hybrid Bills.
Prof. Memberships: Member of Law Society, Member of British Council for Offices Planning Legislation Committee.
Career: Called to the Bar 1985. Pupillages with 1 Serjeants Inn and 2 Harcourt Buildings. Member of planning group at *Lovell White Durrant* 1988 before moving to *S J Berwin* in 1997. Partner 1999. Requalified as a solicitor 1991.

ROBINSON, E. Patrick G.
Herbert Smith, London (020) 7374 8000
patrick.robinson@herbertsmith.com
Specialisation: Commercial property development and planning work including negotiated planning consents, Inquiries (Appeals and Call-Ins), judicial review, compulsory purchase, and general strategic property and planning advice.
Prof. Memberships: Law Society's Specialist Planning Panel.
Career: Articled at *Herbert Smith* (1978-80). Partner 1986. Joint Editor of Blundell & Dobry's Planning, Applications, Appeals and Proceedings (5th Ed) 1996.
Personal: Born April 1956. Educated at University of Nottingham (LLB 1977). Leisure pursuits include jazz, the CÈvennes and family. Lives in London.

ROBINSON, Patrick
Burges Salmon, Bristol (0117) 902 2740
patrick.robinson@burges-salmon.com
Specialisation: All planning issues including negotiation of planning and other infrastructure agreements and appearing as an advocate at Planning Inquiries. Current projects include: acting for motorway service area provider at tri-partite call-in inquiry; advising on planning application and ES for major expansion of rail-access limestone quarry.
Prof. Memberships: Legal Associate of the Royal Town Planning Institute and a member of the Law Society specialist Planning Panel.
Career: Before joining *Burges Salmon* in 1990, he worked as a planning solicitor with Southampton City Council. Became a partner and head of planning unit in 1995.
Personal: University of Leicester 1982-85. Enjoys his motorbike and yachting.

SALES, Martin
Burness, Edinburgh (0131) 473 6000
Specialisation: As one of Scotland's first Accredited Specialists in Planning Law, Martin Sales is well placed to advise on all aspects of Town & Country Planning specialising in developments involving contentious applications for major projects in environmentally sensitive areas, including brownfield and greenfield sites. Martin has extensive experience of minerals developments in areas of high conservation value, environmental assessment as an integral part of planning applications, the legal aspects of the remediation and disposal of contaminated land, landfill sites and the negotiating of planning and related agreements, management plans and restoration schemes.

SHERLOCK, Roger
Nabarro Nathanson, London (020) 7524 6000
r.sherlock@nabarro.com
Senior Solicitor in Planning Department.
Specialisation: Main areas of practice are planning and compulsory purchase law. Handles all planning aspects of commercial and infrastructure development. Other areas of practice include rating, compensation and highways. Undertakes advocacy at planning inquiries and in Lands Tribunal. Author of articles on rating, compulsory purchase and highways law.
Prof. Memberships: Legal Associate of RTPI, Law Society Planning Panel.
Career: Qualified in 1975. Senior lawyer in local Government 1982-1989. Joined *Nabarro Nathanson* in 1989.

SMITH, Brian
Browne Jacobson, Nottingham (0115) 976 6000
bsmith@brownej.co.uk
Partner. Head of Property Department.
Specialisation: Main area of practice is planning and development acting for developers, local planning authorities and national conservation bodies. Has over 20 years post-qualification experience in this field, in local government, commerce and private practice. Handles environmental work, dealing principally with land contamination and environmental liability in corporate acquisitions and disposals, funding transactions and insolvencies. Also deals with local government law, compulsory purchase and rating.
Prof. Memberships: Member of Law Society Planning Panel, Legal Associate of Royal Town Planning Institute, Law Society Advisory Group on Conservation, Heritage and Rural Issues, Fellow of the Land Institute.

SMITH, G. Bruce
Paull & Williamsons, Aberdeen (01224) 621621
gbsmith@paull-williamsons.co.uk
Partner in Planning and Environmental Law Department.
Specialisation: Main area of practice is planning. Advises on planning applications, appeals, enforcement notice appeals, local and structure plans and the conduct of public inquiries. Also handles environmental law. Advises on waste disposal licences, river purification issues and other issues arising out of the Environmental Protection Act. Has acted in many of the major planning inquiries in Scotland over the last decade. Lecturer in planning law at Aberdeen University.
Prof. Memberships: Law Society of Scotland, Society of Advocates in Aberdeen. Law Society accredited specialist in Planning Law.
Career: Qualified in 1967. Joined *Paull & Williamsons* in 1970, becoming a Partner in 1973.
Personal: Born 15th June 1947. Attended Aberdeen University 1964-67 (LLB). Chairman of Abernethy Trust which runs four residential outdoor pursuit centres in Scotland. Leisure interests include golf, skiing and sailing. Lives in Aberdeen.

SMITH, Tim
Berwin Leighton, London (020) 7760 1000
timothy.smith@berwinleighton.com
Specialisation: Handles all aspects of Planning and Environmetal work including inquires and court work, strategic advice infrastructure agreements, compulsory purchase and highways. Acted for Chatsfield in relation to White City, and in relation to West Quay, Southampton. Other major clients include Tesco, British Land and Ministry of Defence.
Prof. Memberships: Member of Planning Inspectorate's advisory 'user group' panel.
Career: Educated at Thomas Bedock Upper School Northampton, and Nottingham University. Articled and qualified with *Hewitson Becke & Shaw*. Joined *Berwin Leighton* 1996.
Publications: Planning chapter of 'Commercial Transaction Checklists', and environmental chapter of 'CBI European Business Handbook 1999' (with Andrew Waite).
Personal: Leisure intrests include rugby (lifelong supporter of Northampton RFC) and fell walking.

TAYLOR, Paul A.T.
Dickinson Dees, Newcastle upon Tyne
(0191) 279 9534
paul.taylor@dickinson-dees.com
Partner in Planning Department.
Specialisation: Handles all aspects of planning including the preparation of applications, the conduct of appeals (including advocacy at local inquiries), enforcement procedures and development plan work. Also deals with compulsory purchase orders and land compensation. Experience includes advocacy at many local inquiries, particularly involving housing development and mineral extraction.
Prof. Memberships: Law Society, Law Society Planning Panel. Legal Associate RTPI.
Career: Qualified 1971. Assistant solicitor at Nottinghamshire County Council 1971-74; Senior Assistant Solicitor for Leicestershire County Council 1974-77. Worked for Hoveringham Group Ltd 1977-82 before joining *Eversheds* in Newcastle in 1982. Became a Partner in 1983. Joined *Dickinson Dees* 1994.
Personal: Born 19th August 1947. Holds an LLB, 1968. Leisure interests include gardening. Lives in North Shields.

TAYLOR, Peter J.A.
Hewitson Becke + Shaw, Northampton
(01604) 233 233

THOMAS, Patricia
SJ Berwin & Co, London (020) 7533 2222
pat.thomas@sjberwin.com
Specialisation: Principal areas of practice are planning and local government law including highways, land drainage and water matters, conservation issues (natural and built heritage) and environment law including environmental impact assessment, compliance and due diligence audits, advice on IPC authorisations, water abstraction licences, pollution and waste cases. Extensive experience of airport and aviation-related developments. Editor of and main contributor to 'The Planning Factbook'. Editor of 'Environmental Liability' and 'Water Pollution: Law and Liability'. Contributed planning law chapter to 'The Surveyor's Factbook'. Lectures frequently on planning and environmental topics.
Prof. Memberships: Law Society (member of Committee on Planning and Environmental Law), City of London Solicitors' Company (member of Planning and Environment Committee), International Bar Association. Member of Law Society's Specialist Planning Panel. CBI Property Management Forum.
Career: Qualified 1974. Planning Solicitor and Advocate, Greater London Council and London Borough of Southwark 1975-79. Joined *Denton Hall Burgin & Warrens* in 1979 and became a Partner in 1981, then moved to *S J Berwin & Co.* in 1988 as a Partner and Head of Planning and Environment Group.

TREHEARNE, Ian
Berwin Leighton, London (020) 7760 1000
ian.trehearne@berwinleighton.com
Planner and Barrister. Joint Head of Planning and Environment Department.
Specialisation: Principal area of work is planning law covering advice and advocacy on development, including major retail and office schemes, transport related developement, airports, media and entertainment, factory outlet centres, housing, hotels, utility and waste disposal developments and local plan inquiries. Specialist active on conservation, historic building and design issues. Also environment law advising on contamination liability and threats and European Community matters. Advised on Ludgate development, Regents Place, Euston Centre and tower and other major office sites in London, Ebbsfleet Station and 8.5m sq. ft. development surrounding it, major five-star hotel in Bloomsbury, 1.6m sq. ft. shopping in Croydon, the Channel Tunnel Rail Link and environmental cases such as Dartford and Welbeck, as well as Finningley and Manston Airports, station related development for Railtrack PFI issues: redevelopment of DSS estate in Newcastle and Sunderland; rationalisation and rebuilding of University College Hospital, United Medical and Dental Schools and King's College, London. Numerous conferences and seminars. Lectured at City University 1982-84.
Prof. Memberships: Royal Town Planning Institute.
Career: London Borough of Newham, 1972-4, then joined the London Borough of Islington 1974-76. City of Westminster 1977-9. Joined the London Borough of Camden in 1979 and moved to *Berwin Leighton* in 1985. Admitted to Partnership in 1988. Called to the Bar 1980.
Personal: Born 17th May 1950. Attended Durham University 1968-71. Leisure pursuits include sailing, building, books and music. Lives in London.

TRINICK, G. Marcus
Bond Pearce, Plymouth (01752) 266633
xgmt@bondpearce.com
Partner and Head of the Specialist Planning and Environmental Group.
Specialisation: Twenty years experience of project development (often in large teams) in all parts of the UK. Advocate at over 300 public inquiries. Especial experience in energy generation, port development, retail work, nature conservation law, EU environmental law and Environmental Impact Assessment (EIA), as well as commercial, retail and housing development.
Prof. Memberships: Secretary of British Wind Energy Association and member of European, Republic of Ireland and US Wind Energy Associations. Legal Associate member of the RTPI and member of UK Environmental Law Association.

TRUE, Justin
Dechert, London (020) 7583 5353
justin.true@dechertEU.com
Head of the Planning Unit.
Specialisation: Principal areas of practice include inquiry work, highways, environment, local government, CPO and compensation work and judicial review for retailers, housebuilders, developers, corporate and public sector clients. Experienced advocate and professional witness. Negotiates complex planning and infrastructure agreements.
Prof. Memberships: Royal Town Planning Institute.
Career: Has a background in Local Government in London and the Home Counties between 1974 and 1985. Joined *Titmuss Sainer Dechert (now Dechert)* in 1985. Member and former Director of the Association of Town Centre Management (1994-00). Member of the Planning Task Group of the British Retail Consortium (1996-00).
Personal: Born 1955. BA Hons Planning Studies and Diploma in Town Planning, Oxford Brooks University. Leisure pursuits include golf, skiing and cycling. Lives in Surrey.

TURNBULL, Stephen
Addleshaw Booth & Co, Leeds (0113) 209 2000
snt@addleshaw-booth.co.uk
Specialisation: Specialises in town planning and local government work; recent cases include public inquiries into town centre retail developments, compulsory purchase promotion and advice for numerous local authorities; also acts for numerous private sector developers in relation to objections to local plans and UDPs and planning applications and appeals including advocacy.
Prof. Memberships: Member of the Law Society Planning Panel and a Legal Associate of the Royal Town Planning Institute. Visiting lecturer in planning law at Leeds Metropolitan University, regular speaker at RTPI and other seminars, and author of articles in press and professional journals.
Career: Hull University 1980; admitted 1984. Joined the firm in 1989 and made a partner in 1995.
Personal: Walking, swimming and tennis.

TURNER, Angela
Gouldens, London (020) 7583 7777
Specialisation: Wide range of planning, environmental and local government law including appeals, inquiries, judicial review and agreements. During 12 years in local government (Royal Borough of Kensington & Chelsea), has great experience of planning law from the local government perspective and particularly in relation to listed building and conservation area law and enforcement related matters. During 15 years in private practice has an equivalent depth of experience of advising developers and others on planning strategies relevant to their proposals. Has acted as Advocate at Public Inquiries and other tribunals including the Magistrate and County Courts.
Prof. Memberships: Law Society Planning Panel; Legal Associate of the Royal Town Planning Institute; City of London Law Society's Planning & Environmental Law Sub-Committee; UKELA Town Planning.
Career: Qualified in 1973. Principal Solicitor, Royal Borough of Kensington & Chelsea. Partner at *Gouldens* from 1985.
Personal: Sheffield University (LLB). Co-author of 'Badlands, Essential Environmental Law for Property Professionals'. Many interests.

VALENTINE, Richard
Pitmans, Reading (0118) 9580224
rvalentine@pitmans.com
Specialisation: The co-ordination and implementation of strategies and tactics employed in relation to major planning proposals, particularly in connection with inquiries and judicial reviews. In the last five years, he has increasingly specialised in the judicial review process as a means of challenging planning decision and in the statutory appeal procedures.
Prof. Memberships: Law Society.
Career: Partner *Stephenson Harwood* 1973-77. Partner *Pitmans* 1977-.
Personal: Travel, fishing and shooting, classic cars and any lawful intellectual challenge.

WADE-SMITH, Richard
Wilbraham & Co, Leeds (0113) 243 2200

WALTON, David
Wilbraham & Co, Leeds (0113) 243 2200
david.walton@wilbraham.co.uk
Specialisation: Partner with wide breadth of practice including housing, retail, leisure and employment applications. Retains strong local government practice including compulsory purchase, Transport and Works Act and other public utility projects.
Career: Qualified 1982; Hereford Council (articled clerk); Oxfordshire Council (assistant solicitor environment); Shewsbury Council (principal solicitor planning); Leeds City Council (assistant chief legal officer); *Wilbraham & Co* (partner).
Publications: 'Development Plans: Law and Practice', Sweet & Maxwell (1998). Lectured on the post-graduate diploma for planning & environmental law at Leeds Metropolitan University.
Personal: Born 1958.

WATCHMAN, Paul Q.
Freshfields Bruckhaus Deringer, London (020) 7936 4000
See under Environment, p.380

WATKINS, David
Linklaters (A member firm of Linklaters & Alliance), London (020) 7456 4852
david.watkins@linklaters.com
Specialisation: Partner, environmental law, experienced in town planning & development activity included requisite planning. Environmental law expertise includes advising on the contaminated land regime & the development of brownfield sites & environmental implications of corporate disposals.
Career: Partner – 1997 to date. Assistant solicitor 1987-97 (*Linklaters*). Assistant solicitor 1985-87 (*Shepperd & Wedderburn*).

WELLS, Martin
Stephenson Harwood, London (020) 7809 2529
martin.wells@shlegal.com
Senior Associate in Property Department: Town and Country Planning Group.
Specialisation: Advises on a wide range of town planning and related matters, including agreements, appeals, public inquiries and High Court challenges. Cases have included advising on a series of major developments for the University of Greenwich, Stakis plc, the Godinton Estate, Wimpey Homes, the Bristol Port Company, the London Borough of Hackney, Skandia Property (UK) Limited, Martin International Holdings plc, Wonder World plc, the Accor Group, Chiltern District Council, Den norske Bank ASA, the Royal Albert Hall, Canterbury College and London Transport Property. Also advises on transport and works orders for major railway schemes, including Thameslink 2000 and the East London Line extension. Occasional speaker at external seminars and a regular speaker at internal training seminars.
Prof. Memberships: Legal Associate of Royal Town Planning Institute, Law Society's Planning Panel, City of London Law Society's Planning and Environmental Law Sub-Committee, UKELA's Planning Law Working Party.
Career: Qualified in 1972. Legal Assistant at Luton CBC 1965-71; Solicitor at St Albans CC 1972-73, then Watford BC 1973-79; Principal Planning Administrator, Hertsmere BC 1979-81 and Solicitor to the Council to 1986; Borough Secretary at Runnymede BC 1986-87; Assistant Solicitor with *Denton Hall Burgin & Warrens* 1987-88. Joined *Stephenson Harwood* in 1988 and became Senior Associate in 1989.
Publications: Has contributed to 'Property Week', 'Planning Week', 'Planning Journal', 'Housing & Planning Review' and 'Planning in London'.
Personal: Born 12 September 1944. Educated at Exeter University, 1965 LLB (Hons). Married with two children. Interests include music and travel. Resides Woking, Surrey.

WHITE, Martin
Pinsent Curtis, Birmingham (0121) 200 1050
martin.white@pinsents.com
Partner in property department. Head of planning and environment.
Specialisation: Handles planning and related areas including environmental issues, with emphasis on town centre regeneration, planning appeal work, development plans, compulsory purchase, issues of planning gain, Section 106 agreements, rail related scheme and waste matters. Has acted in appeals relating to major inward investment, airports and business parks, for local Planning Authorities and private sector clients. Also handles local government and public law generally. Involved generally in advice given to local authorities. Author of articles, speaker at conferences and seminars on planning gain and environmental issues.
Prof. Memberships: Law Society (Member of Planning Panel), Legal Associate of Royal Town Planning Institute.
Career: Qualified in 1979. Articled at Solihull Council 1977-79. Joined *Pinsent & Co.* in 1981. Partner in 1987.
Personal: Born 1953. Attended Cambridge University 1972-76; Newcastle Polytechnic 1976-77. Interests include drama and music.

WILBRAHAM, Peter
Wilbraham & Co, Leeds (0113) 243 2200
peter.wilbraham@wibraham.co.uk
Specialisation: Acts for public and private sector clients, who are involved in a wide range of development issues, including housing, employment, retail and infrastructure projects. Also undertaking sensitive listed buildings and conservation area projects on behalf of the National Trust and various public bodies. Leading teams involved in the planning process, formulating strategy and, normally negotiating a successful conclusion to meet client's requirements.
Prof. Memberships: Honorary Solicitor and Secretary to the Royal Town Planning Institute; a member of the Council of the RTPI; and a member of the Law Society's Specialist Planning Panel. Lectures regularly on planning law issues at professional conferences as well as at Leeds Metropolitan University; and gave the main paper at the planning law conference at the University of Ulster.
Career: Specialist in planning law for over 30 years. In1994 founded *Wilbraham & Co* – a niche planning and environmental law practice which is consistently ranked as one of the leading firms in its specialism.

WILLIAMS, Christopher J.C.
CMS Cameron McKenna, London (020) 7367 3000
Specialisation: Partner in the Planning Group. Specialising in Town and Country planning aspects of all sizes and types of property development, including retail, residential, office, and industrial development; compulsory purchase and compensation; Transport and Works Act schemes; planning related aspects of environmental law, particularly environmental assessments relating to major projects; infrastructure projects; advocacy at public inquiries. Specialist in major infrastructure projects, including airport and airport related development. Advising BAA plc in connection with proposals for a fifth terminal at Heathrow Airport. Speaker at seminars on Planning and Environmental Law.
Prof. Memberships: Law Society of England and Wales.
Career: St John's College, Cambridge University. Joined *McKenna & Co* 1987; Partner 1996.
Personal: Born 1962. Resides London. Leisure interests: skiing, mountaineering.

WILLIAMS, Huw
Edwards Geldard, Cardiff (029) 2023 8239
huw.williams@geldards.co.uk
See under Administrative & Public Law, p.61

WILLIAMSON, Andrew J.
Walker Morris, Leeds (0113) 283 2500
ajw@walkermorris.co.uk
Partner in Planning and Environment Department.
Specialisation: Handles all aspects of planning law with an emphasis on advocacy at s.78 appeals, Local Planning Inquiries, compulsory purchase order and enforcement. Also handles Lands Tribunal and CPA Licensing and Environmental Protection Act authorisation appeals.
Prof. Memberships: Corporate Member of Royal Town Planning Institute, Law Society Planning Panel.
Career: Articled at *Race & Newton* in Burnley 1981-83, then joined *Walker Morris* in 1984 and became a Partner in 1985.
Personal: Born 16th February 1957. Lives in Leeds.

WINTER, Paul E.A.
Eversheds, Leeds (0113) 243 0391
paulwinter@eversheds.com
Partner in Property Department.
Specialisation: Main areas of practice are planning and environmental law. Experience includes major town centre schemes, large urban regeneration projects and residential development. Enjoys both the advocacy and the negotiation aspects. Particularly handles environmental aspects of property transactions (especially contaminated land), waste management and development. Handled City Challenge projects, and Mixed Leisure and Commercial Development, involving the second largest city grant at the time. Contributed 'Contaminated Land' and 'Planning and the Environment' chapters in College of Law Environmental Law Book. Also, contributed 'Contaminated Land' chapter of the CCH Environment Manual.
Prof. Memberships: Law Society, Town & Country Planning Association (Policy Council). Member of Specialist Planning Panel of the Law Society. Legal Associate of the Royal Town Planning Institute. Notary Public. Accredited Mediator (working on Planning Inspectorate's pilot study on mediation). Also, member of the Oxford Joint Planning Law Conference Committee.
Career: Qualified 1976. Joined *Eversheds Hepworth & Chadwick* as a Partner in 1989.
Personal: Born 24th April 1949. Attended Leeds University 1968-72. Leisure interests include music and opera, walking, travelling and reading. Lives near Leeds.

WOOD, David R.
Bevan Ashford, Bristol (0117) 923 0111
See under Health & Safety, p.425

PRODUCT LIABILITY

OVERVIEW: Dispersed, but not destroyed, the tobacco litigation rumbles on, largely in other countries now. Instead, a series of major pharmaceutical and multi-party cases have taken centre stage. MMR, sheep dip, Gulf War Syndrome, Ritalin, Variant CJD and LSD have all been making the headlines this year. Speculation continues as to whether group actions might also be brought by mobile phone users and 'passive smokers.' Critical to the long term viability of group actions is the issue of funding. Legal Aid is no longer generally available and legal aid certificates are fiercely fought over. Further complications are threatened by the EU Commission's proposed changes to the Product Liability Directive and the General Product Safety Directive. These, if adopted, will increase the burden on manufacturers and suppliers to ensure product safety and encourage more product liability litigation.

This year, we have decided to split up the leading product liability firms into those that act for the defendant and those that act for the claimant. In the regions, only claimant firms are listed, as there were no notable defence firms mentioned by the market. In Scotland and Northern Ireland, only defence firms are listed for the same reason.

RESEARCH APPROVED BY BMRB: *For this edition,* Chambers' *researchers conducted 6083 interviews – 4408 with law firms, 598 with barristers and 1077 with clients.*

The validity of the research was scrutinised by BMRB International, who audited both the methodology and the results at our offices in July 2000. They interviewed Chambers' *researchers and cross-checked sample interviews. Details of the audit appear on page 7.*

LONDON

MAINLY DEFENDANT

PRODUCT LIABILITY: MAINLY DEFENDANT • London	Ptnrs	Assts
❶ CMS Cameron McKenna	7	10
❷ Davies Arnold Cooper	6	13
❸ Ashurst Morris Crisp	2	10
Lovells	8	20
Theodore Goddard	2	3
❹ Kennedys	5	8
Simmons & Simmons	2	6
❺ Clifford Chance	3	5

LEADING INDIVIDUALS	
❶ DODDS-SMITH Ian CMS Cameron McKenna	
HODGES Christopher CMS Cameron McKenna	
PEARL Simon Davies Arnold Cooper	TYLER Mark CMS Cameron McKenna
❷ KELLEHER John Theodore Goddard	MELTZER John Lovells
WARE Anne Davies Arnold Cooper	
❸ ELVY Mark Ashurst Morris Crisp	McDOUGALL Arundel Rowe & Maw

Within each band, firms are listed alphabetically. *See **Profiles** on page 674*

CMS Cameron McKenna Experience, strength in depth and excellent connections have once again made them the leaders of the field this year. **Ian Dodds-Smith**, still recognised as the *"doyen"* of product liability, *"excellent"* **Mark Tyler** and **Christopher Hodges**, who possesses an *"encyclopaedic knowledge"* of the subject, combine to make Cameron McKenna *"a Rolls Royce outfit."* The bulk of the work still consists of defending product liability claims against manufacturers and suppliers or their insurers, risk management, product regulation, product safety, product recall and product liability risk management training. It remains to be seen whether the loss of Gary Hickinbottom to the circuit bench will in any way affect the performance of the team. **Clients:** Leading pharmaceuticals companies, international insurers.

Davies Arnold Cooper DAC's much publicised 'streamlining' campaign has had no direct impact on the product liability team so far, which continues to perform to a high standard. **Simon Pearl** is regarded as *"first-class,"* and **Anne Ware** *"a sharp, effective professional."* The firm has enormous in-depth experience of group action, personal injury and related claims in the pharmaceutical and healthcare field, and incorporates a specialist health and safety unit and a specialist occupational health unit. Highlights of the year include winning the imposition of a stay of proceedings on the Lubbe v Cape plc case, and the successful defence of London Rubber Company Products Limited over the alleged manufacture of a defective condom. **Clients:** Cape plc; Rio Tinto plc; SmithKline Beecham.

Ashurst Morris Crisp Widely recognised to possess *"excellent people in depth,"* and ably headed by **Mark Elvy**, the team has built on its success in last year's tobacco litigation to become a major contender in the field. Currently advising on a potential group action arising from an outbreak of Legionnaires' Disease, and in connection with two major public inquiries dealing with health, safety and environmental issues. **Clients:** Manufacturers of tobacco, pharmaceuticals.

Lovells **John Meltzer** (*"bloody good"*) heads a team that is generally considered to *"provide succinct and pragmatic advice."* The firm boasts an enviable client list that includes numerous major players in the fields of tobacco, pharmaceuticals, food and beverages. It offers extensive advice on regulatory matters, and has advised clients in relation to several product recalls from toys to food and bottled drinks. **Clients:** Pharmaceutical companies including Merck & Co, tobacco companies including British American Tobacco.

Theodore Goddard One of a small number of firms with group action experience. Demonstrated it by ensuring that The Wellcome Foundation was removed from the MMR litigation at an early stage. Though accused by some of depending on a single client for the majority of work in this field, the client in question is a considerable one, and *"phenomenal"* **John Kelleher** has demonstrated himself more than active in other areas. MDU members, mobile phone manufacturers and toy manufacturers have all benefited from his *"straight down the line"* advice. **Clients:** Manufacturers of mobile phones, oral contraceptives, diet drugs and toys.

Kennedys Newcomers to this year's table, the team has impressed onlookers with an increasing presence in the product liability market. The product liability team draws a great deal of its work from representing major manufacturers in pharmaceutical and medical cases, but there is also a considerable involvement in risk management, particularly in the pharmaceutical sector. It continues to act on the committee for the industry response to Organo-Phosphate claims. **Clients:** Johnson and Johnson; Novartis; Medeva; NHSLA.

Simmons & Simmons Boasts an experienced team that has been less active this year following its well-publicised successes in the tobacco litigation last year. Still, new instructions from a pair of large pharmaceutical companies have re-animated the department and much work is currently being done in the fields of pre-litigation, risk anticipation and risk awareness. **Clients:** Telecommunications, manufacturers of tobacco, healthcare products.

Clifford Chance More involved in the advisory than the litigious side of product liability, the firm has been especially active in the fields of transport and pharmaceutical products this year. Distinguished by international reach, the firm specialises in offering pan-EU advice, but has also just enjoyed a major success in the Court of Appeal representing Source Informatics in a case relating to the use of anonymous information from medical prescriptions. **Clients:** Best Foods UK Ltd; H J Heinz Company Limited; Source Informatics Limited.

Other Notable Practitioner Although Rowe & Maw does not possess a strong market profile in this area, **Arundel McDougall** has caught the eye of a number of good judges, acting for a range of clients in the bioscience and chemicals industry.

MAINLY CLAIMANT

PRODUCT LIABILITY: MAINLY CLAIMANT • London	Ptnrs	Assts
❶ Leigh, Day & Co	3	6
❷ Alexander Harris	1	2
Hodge Jones & Allen	4	4
❸ Field Fisher Waterhouse	1	2

LEADING INDIVIDUALS
❶ DAY Martyn Leigh, Day & Co
❷ BARR Richard Alexander Harris
❸ NELSON-JONES Rodney Field Fisher Waterhouse

Within each band, firms are listed alphabetically. *See* **Profiles** *on page 674*

Leigh, Day & Co Has once again succeeded in dividing the field. Many consider **Martyn Day** *"a top rank practitioner"* and *"a tough opponent."* Others maintain that the firm's attitude can be *"excessively gung-ho."* The firm nevertheless continues to possess an audacious reputation, and is currently involved in the pill litigation, a number of hip replacement claims and various latex allergy cases.

Alexander Harris Altrincham-based Ann Alexander, generally reckoned to be the behind the scenes driving force at Alexander Harris, oversees a department run by **Richard Barr** that *"treats cases as causes"* and has built its reputation by combining compassion and understanding with real determination. Dubbed *"crusaders"* by some, with *"evangelical zeal,"* the firm is generally regarded as one of the highest profile claimant firms in the field. Currently leading the investigation into the much publicised MMR/MR vaccine.

Hodge Jones & Allen Our research suggests that the loss of Richard Barr to Alexander Harris last year has had no visible effect on the quality of the team, which continues to enjoy a high profile and has retained the generic contract for the Organo-Phosphate litigation. Multi-party action specialists, they have been heavily involved in the Gulf War illness litigation and represented a number of MMR claims and DPT claims.

Field Fisher Waterhouse The *"very thorough"* **Rodney Nelson-Jones** heads a small team with a specialisation in asbestos claims, aircraft engines and defective medical devices.

THE REGIONS

MAINLY CLAIMANT

PRODUCT LIABILITY • The Regions	Ptnrs	Assts
❶ Irwin Mitchell Sheffield	5	5
❷ Freethcartwright Nottingham	1	2
❸ Alexander Harris Altrincham	1	1
❹ Leigh, Day & Co Manchester	2	1
❺ Smith Llewelyn Partnership Swansea	2	2

LEADING INDIVIDUALS	
❶ BALEN Paul Freethcartwright	
❷ BODY David Irwin Mitchell	PICKERING John Irwin Mitchell
TUCKER Andrew Irwin Mitchel	
❸ ALEXANDER Ann Alexander Harris	HARRIS David Alexander Harris
HARVEY Mark Smith Llewelyn Partnership	
McCOOL Geraldine Leigh, Day & Co	

Within each band, firms are listed alphabetically. *See* **Profiles** *on page 674*

Irwin Mitchell With their unparalleled experience, judicious use of Counsel, excellent IT skills and capacity not to be fazed by big cases, market consensus almost unanimously dictates that this is *"the best claimant firm by miles."* **John Pickering** is *"a man of huge knowledge and good connections,"* **Andrew Tucker** is *"completely unflappable"* and has *"extremely good judgement and loads of experience,"* and **David Body** is *"excellent."* The team is currently representing all the families of victims of the new variant CJD at the BSE inquiry, following their heavy involvement in the tobacco litigation and the human growth hormone CJD cases.

Freethcartwright *"Respected"* **Paul Balen** heads a team that is widely perceived to be one of the best in the field. Though dubbed by some *"too much of a crusader,"* the *"bright"* Balen is widely sought after for his intellect and experience, and continues to be heavily involved in 3M hip cases, silicone/soya breast implant claims, the Hepatitis C litigation and work on the widely publicised MMR vaccination.

Alexander Harris Recently reported to be co-ordinating the action against Novartis' alleged failure to warn of the adverse impacts of Ritalin, it is widely considered that **David Harris**' department has enjoyed a much greater degree of activity this year. Vigilantly supported by **Ann Alexander**, the managing partner, it has led cases in Myodil, Persona and LSD.

Leigh, Day & Co **Geraldine McCool**, *"an extremely competent litigator with loads of experience,"* has continued to build on her specialisation in product liability with a military/aviation context, and is widely regarded as the leading expert in this field. In 1999, work continued on the design of the Tornado, Hawk and Lynx aircraft, and, in the civilian context, on the 1998 Swissair crash.

Smith Llewelyn Partnership Despite the loss of Peter Llewelyn to the circuit bench, the team continues to be well-regarded by competitors, and **Mark Harvey**'s team has been successful in recovering damages in Eraldin, Opren, Myodil and Gammagard. The team has also won the tender to obtain the Legal Aid Certificate in the drug Roaccutane.

SCOTLAND

MAINLY DEFENDANT

PRODUCT LIABILITY • Scotland	Ptnrs	Assts
❶ **Burness** Edinburgh	2	4
McGrigor Donald Glasgow	2	1
Simpson & Marwick WS Edinburgh	4	6

LEADING INDIVIDUALS
❶ **MURRAY Marsali** Burness

Within each band, firms are listed alphabetically. *See **Profiles** on page 674*

Burness **Marsali Murray** continues to lead one of the most extensive defendant product liability practices in Scotland. The team currently represents a number of multi-national companies in the pharmaceutical, agrochemical and consumer product fields. **Clients:** Manufacturing and pharmaceutical companies.

McGrigor Donald New to our table this year. Possesses a reputation for thoroughness, and the head of department is a well-respected figure in the profession. Acts for one of the major tobacco companies, a range of manufactures and wholesalers and a number of whisky companies. **Clients:** Manufacturers and wholesalers.

Simpson & Marwick WS Boasts a very focused team with a specialisation in pharmaceuticals, motor vehicles and their components, and construction works. **Clients:** Manufacturers of pharmaceuticals and other products.

NORTHERN IRELAND

MAINLY DEFENDANT

PRODUCT LIABILITY • Northern Ireland	Ptnrs	Assts
❶ **Elliott Duffy Garrett** Belfast	2	2
McKinty & Wright Belfast	1	-
Mills Selig Belfast	1	1
O'Reilly Stewart Belfast	1	2

LEADING INDIVIDUALS	
❶ **WILSON Michael** Elliott Duffy Garrett	
❷ **SPRING Paul** Mills Selig	**STEWART Brian** O'Reilly Stewart

Within each band, firms are listed alphabetically. *See **Profiles** on page 674*

Elliott Duffy Garrett **Michael Wilson** with *"perhaps more experience in the field of product liability than anyone else in Northern Ireland"* heads a team that has been less high-profile this year, following the developments in tobacco litigation in England. He continues to defend a number of large pesticide companies against apple growers. **Clients:** Gallaher Group plc; SmithKline Beecham.

McKinty & Wright Predominantly a defence firm, it has once again been active in the field this year, representing major high-street retailers, and pesticide, agrochemical and lawn mower manufacturers. **Clients:** Retailers and manufactures.

Mills Selig **Paul Spring**, a recognised specialist in this field, does the majority of his work for multi-national manufacturers and tobacco companies, although some claimant work is also taken on. **Clients:** A major tobacco company.

O'Reilly Stewart *"Well respected"* **Brian Stewart** is *"the first port of call for anyone in product liability"* in Northern Ireland. The bulk of his work this year has been primarily taken up with the tobacco litigation, but he is also involved in the Nicotine Patch litigation and some commercial libel work as well. **Clients:** Tobacco and pharmaceuticals manufacturers.

FOOD LAW

LONDON

FOOD LAW• London	Ptnrs	Assts
❶ **Paisner & Co**	1	3
❷ **Simmons & Simmons**	2	2
❸ **Covington & Burling**	1	4
Taylor Joynson Garrett	2	2
❹ **Barlow Lyde & Gilbert**	3	7
Biddle	1	2
Bird & Bird	2	3

LEADING INDIVIDUALS	
❶ **BAYLIS Craig** Paisner & Co	**DAVIES Gareth** KLegal
❷ **CODY Nick** Taylor Joynson Garrett	**FREER Gary** Barlow Lyde & Gilbert
GILBERTSON Kathryn Paisner & Co	**ROSS Hilary** Paisner & Co

Within each band, firms are listed alphabetically. *See **Profiles** on page 674*

Paisner & Co Recognised as leaders once again this year, Paisners boasts an impressive team with a high international profile. **Craig Baylis** is widely regarded as one of the leading figures in the field, **Hilary Ross** *"has made a niche for herself with GM foods,"* and is *"a force to be reckoned with, with a very impressive CV,"* and **Kathryn Gilbertson** is *"responsive and proactive."* The team has a close relationship with the EU Commission, extensive links with the USA and Canada, and all members of the group regularly lecture the industry on law, food trends and novel issues. Business is split between contentious and non-contentious work. **Clients:** Tropicana; Pizza Hut; Whitbread; BHS plc; Tesco Stores Ltd.

Simmons & Simmons Despite the loss of Gareth Davies to KLegal, Simmons continues to possess a *"good practice with great strength."* A member of the Food Law Group, its work focuses on labelling regulations and defence of food/drinks companies. It has recently been invited by Leatherhead Food RA to write a book on environmental law for the food industry, and is heavily involved in the effects of environmental and health and safety laws on the food industry. One of its members has just been appointed to the Agriculture and Environment Biotechnology Commission. **Clients:** British Sugar; Cadbury Schweppes; the National Farmer's Union.

Covington & Burling A *"successful transatlantic practice"* with a *"predatory"* attitude, the team acts for McNeil Consumer Nutritionals, which markets Benecol cholesterol-reducing margarine, plus several major producers of dietary supplements and marketers of other foods and cosmetics. They possess a *"good specialist at Brussels and good clients on the trade side."* **Clients:** McNeil Consumer Nutritionals.

Taylor Joynson Garrett Though it does not have a separate food department, and is considered *"less strong than it used to be"* in the field, the firm is still a member of the Food Law Group, maintains a good reputation, and conducts the majority of its food law work through its excellent intellectual property department. The respected **Nick Cody** works extensively with food suppliers and other organisations that are involved in the food chain. **Clients:** Food manufacturers.

Barlow Lyde & Gilbert Litigation specialists, Barlows draws most of its work from disputes between manufacturers and their suppliers, though the direction of the practice has taken a recent turn towards 'prevention' work rather than direct defence work in court. **Gary Freer** is a well-respected figure in the industry and a regular speaker at food law seminars. **Clients:** Manufacturers, a major chain of fast food restaurants.

Biddle Continues to advise a number of manufacturers, retailers and caterers on crisis management and regulatory issues. **Clients:** Include HJ Heinz.

Bird & Bird A new entry to this year's table, Bird & Bird is now a recognised name in the field. It does a wide range of regulatory work, has recently represented Nestlé over allegations made against its 'healthy heart' campaign, acts for a number of alcohol producers and gives frequent advice concerning nutraceuticals. **Clients:** Nestlé.

Other Notable Practitioner A *"brilliant regulatory lawyer,"* **Gareth Davies** has moved from Simmons & Simmons to KLegal. He is very highly regarded by the rest of the field.

THE REGIONS

FOOD LAW • The Regions	Ptnrs	Assts
❶ **DLA** Birmingham	2	1
Elliotts Manchester	1	1
Eversheds Birmingham, Norwich	5	5
Gregg Galbraith Quinn Bristol	1	3
Margetts & Ritchie Birmingham	1	1
Shoosmiths Northampton	3	2
❷ **Andrew M. Jackson & Co** Hull	2	3
Bevan Ashford Bristol	2	-
Cartwrights Bristol	1	1
Hammond Suddards Edge Birmingham	-	2

LEADING INDIVIDUALS	
❶ **EDMONDS Steven** DLA	**GREGG Andrew** Gregg Galbraith Quinn
HOLLAND Barry Elliotts	**REID Ron** Shoosmiths
WARNOCK Owen Eversheds	
❷ **HETHERINGTON David** Margetts & Ritchie	**SMITH Hugh** Andrew M. Jackson & Co
TOZER Roy DLA	**YOUNG David** Eversheds

Within each band, firms are listed alphabetically.

*See **Profiles** on page 674*

DLA *"Seasoned campaigner"* **Steven Edmonds** and **Roy Tozer** form a formidable team whose excellent knowledge of food law is incorporated within a wider range of expertise that covers environmental, product liability, and health and safety issues. Involved in both contentious and non-contentious work, the firm carries out almost all its own advocacy. **Clients:** Allied Domecq Ltd.

Elliotts A *"one-off legend in his own right,"* **Barry Holland** has built up his expertise in food law around a strong liquor-licensing practice. Still chairman of the Food Law Group, he finished rewriting the procedures for catching out of code products for Safeway last year, and has been engaged in defending a number of retailers against prosecution this year. **Clients:** Pelican; meat producers and supermarkets.

Eversheds New to our list of leading individuals this year, **David Young**'s time is mostly taken up defending clients challenged by local authorities. The emphasis of the Birmingham practice is on food safety and hygiene and is of a fundamentally litigious character, as opposed to the practice in Norwich which specialises in offering regulatory and labelling advice. In the latter office, **Owen Warnock** *"knows his stuff."* He is a contributor to Halsburys Laws on Food, heads a team of advisory specialists, and has been particularly involved in ensuring that US products meet European labelling requirements this year. **Clients:** McDonalds Restaurants Ltd; Bass Leisure Retail; Brown-Forman Corporation; Greggs plc.

Gregg Galbraith Quinn Like many of the best food lawyers, *"very bright"* **Andrew Gregg**'s roots are in liquor licensing. Work this year has included licensing various restaurants and the first internet off-license in Ramsey. The practice continues to advise on new EC regulations. **Clients:** Restaurants, food manufacturers.

Margetts & Ritchie *"Superb"* **David Heatherington** heads *"a tailor-made consumer law defence firm with a particular emphasis on food."* The firm works closely with, and is instructed by, Law Laboratories and is currently involved in a salmonella case. It also acts for restaurants and supermarkets. **Clients:** Restaurants, supermarkets.

Shoosmiths Specialising in the needs of the food industry generally, *"excellent"* **Ron Reid** is widely considered to *"know what he's talking about."* Now advisor to the London Food Clubs, and a long-term member of the Food Law Group, he continues to be actively involved in crisis management, and has also branched out into offering consumer care department training courses. **Clients:** Just Juice; The Catering Forum; various US and European food manufacturers.

Andrew M Jackson & Co Widely recognised as specialists in fish and vitamins, the concentration of the work has been on fish this year. **Hugh Smith** is a well-respected member of the industry. **Clients:** Seven Seas.

Bevan Ashford Specialists in food labelling law, the firm is a member of the Food Law Group, and has experience in advising on food law in relation to EU regulations, health and safety regulations, and food hygiene. **Clients:** Allied Domecq Ltd; Meridian Leisure.

Cartwrights New to the table this year, Cartwrights has been widely acknowledged as an active participant in the field. The vast majority of its work is of a litigious character, coming under the Food Safety Act and the Environmental Protection Act, and it does most of its own advocacy. **Clients:** Restaurants, food manufacturers.

Hammond Suddards Edge *"Still a presence"* despite the loss of Steven Edmonds and Roy Tozer, it has gone on to pick up a number of important clients. The team does both advisory and litigious work and has added to its staff a couple of ex-local authority prosecutors. Clients include the biggest food manufacturers in the country. **Clients:** Hazelwoods; Woolworths; Superdrug; hotels.

LEADERS IN PRODUCT LIABILITY

ALEXANDER, Ann
Alexander Harris, Altrincham (0161) 925 5555
ann@alexharris.co.uk
See under Clinical Negligence, p.160

BALEN, Paul
Freethcartwright, Nottingham (0115) 9369 369
paul.balen@freethcartwright.co.uk
See under Clinical Negligence, p.160

BARR, Richard
Alexander Harris, London (020) 7430 5555
Specialisation: Main areas of practice - personal injury and product liability. Cases: Opren, currently co-ordinating generic MMR vaccine cases at *Alexander Harris*. Co-author of the Penguin Guide to the Law. Writes regular light-hearted column for the Solicitors Journal. Regular live slot as 'Legal Eagle' on BBC Radio Norfolk. Lectures on personal injury, pharmaceutical product and multi party actions to legal and medical audiences. An expert regularly called upon to contribute to news and current affairs programmes, who is frequently quoted in the press.
Prof. Memberships: Panel solicitor for AVMA, Law Society National Personal Injury Panel, Society of Authors.
Career: July 1999 joined *Alexander Harris* – Partner. April 1998 – July 1999 *Hodge Jones & Allen* – Partner. 1974 – April 1998 *Dawbarns*. Qualified 1971.

BAYLIS, Craig
Paisner & Co, London (020) 7353 0299
See under Licensing, p.534

BODY, David
Irwin Mitchell, Sheffield (0114) 276 7777
Bodyd@irwinmitchel.co.uk
See under Clinical Negligence, p.160

CODY, Nick
Taylor Joynson Garrett, London (020) 7300 7000
ncody@tjg.co.uk
Specialisation: Advises on a wide range of consumer law issues, including consumer protection, consumer safety and trading standards. Also advises on advertising, sales promotions and related issues. Particular experience in advising clients operating in the food, cosmetics and toy industries.
Prof. Memberships: Member of Food Law Group.
Career: Joined firm in 1967 and has been advising clients on consumer law issues since 1972.
Personal: Leisure – watching cricket and football, walking, local community and family life.

DAVIES, Gareth
KLegal, London (020) 7694 2500
Partner in Corporate Commercial Department.
Specialisation: Specialises in the food and drink industry. Scientific and technical adviser to EU Commission (DGVI) on Designations of Geographic Origin and Specific Character. Advises on all matters relating to composition labelling and regulation of food and drink. Has handled various acquisitions and disposals of food processing and distribution businesses, advice and compliance with compositional regulations, labelling regulations and free circulation of products in the EU and relations with the EU Commission, MAFF and local regulatory authorities, including prosecutions. Contributor (re sale of goods) to Butterworth's 'Encyclopedia of Forms & Precedents'. Lectures regularly on all aspects of food law.
Prof. Memberships: Law Society, Food Law Group (Committee Member).
Career: Qualified in December 1979 (England & Wales) and May 1981 (Hong Kong). Partner at *Simmons & Simmmons* from 1989 until earlier this year.
Personal: Born 5th July 1955. Educated at the University of Sheffield 1973-76 (LL.B Hons) and the City of London Polytechnic 1978-81 (MA, Business Law). Leisure interests include sailing, cookery, board games and history. Lives in Burnham-on-Crouch.

DAY, Martyn
Leigh, Day & Co, London (020) 7650 1200
Partner in environment and product liability department.
Specialisation: Main area of practice is environmental and product liability law. Heads team of 14 lawyers specialising in representing groups of injured people in complex actions. Co-Author of 'Toxic Torts', 'Personal Injury Handbook', 'Multi-Party Actions' and 'Environmental Action: A Citizens Guide'. Regularly addresses lectures, seminars and media on environmental issues.
Prof. Memberships: APIL, Executive Committee Member of Society of Labour Lawyers, Director of Greenpeace.
Career: Qualified in 1981 with *Colombotti & Partners*. Moved to *Clifford Chance* and then *Bindman & Partners* in 1981. Left to join *Leigh Day & Co* as a partner in 1987.
Personal: Born in 1957.

DODDS-SMITH, Ian C.
CMS Cameron McKenna, London (020) 7367 2509
ids@cmck.com
Partner and Head of Healthcare Group.
Specialisation: Main area of practice is healthcare relating to pharmaceuticals and products in the medical, cosmetics and food sectors. Specialist in both licensing and related regulatory affairs (see separate Healthcare section), and product liability. Practice includes product liability and personal injury litigation. Has handled very many multi-claimant product liability cases, often with international elements and has coordinated cases in Europe as a whole. Major cases include those relating to hormone pregnancy tests, oral contraceptives, blood products, benzodiazepines, IUCDs, breast implants, baby drinks, pesticides, heart valves and vaccines. Has also dealt with many judicial reviews in the regulatory and NHS sector (some with references to the E.C.J.).
Prof. Memberships: Include the American Bar Association, Federation of Insurance & Corporate Counsel, Fellow of the Royal Society of Medicine.
Career: Joined the firm in 1974 and qualified in 1976. Became a Partner in 1984. Member of various working parties on research and medical law issues for Royal College of Physicians, Medical Research Council and Royal College of Pathologists. Temporary Adviser (1987) to W.H.O. on law relating to clinical trials. Previously member of Clinical Sciences Ethics Committee of the University of London and University College Hospital.
Publications: Author of 'Product Liability for Medical Products' in 'Medical Negligence' (Butterworths) and 'Legal Liabilities in Clinical Trials' in 'Early Phase Human Drug Evaluation' (CRC). Author of various articles on liability issues. Frequent lecturer in the UK and abroad. Consultant Editor to the Personal and Medical Injuries Law Letter.
Personal: Born 31st July 1951. Educated at Solihull School and Downing College, Cambridge 1969-72.

EDMONDS, Steven James
DLA, Birmingham (0121) 262 5954
steven.edmonds@dla.com
Specialisation: A Partner, qualified 1978. His practice covers all aspects of regulatory work in food safety, consumer protection, health and safety, retailing, trading standards, sports law and contentious environmental law. Very experienced in tax, Customs & Excise and fraud investigations acting for individuals and businesses. Highly experienced in representing individuals charged with professional disciplinary offences. Experienced advocate in courts and tribunals of all types.
Prof. Memberships: Law Society and Food Law Group.
Personal: Educated at Bromsgrove and Warwick University (Upper Second). Higher Court Advocate (Criminal) since 1994.

ELVY, Mark
Ashurst Morris Crisp, London (020) 7638 1111
Specialisation: Main areas of practice are product liability and risk management in the health, safety and environment fields. Particular expertise in the defence of multi-party product related claims and co-ordinating the defence of multi-jurisdictional claims. Represented Imperial Tobacco in the Tobacco Litigation, Hodgson v Imperial Tobacco and advises clients in the food, beverage and retail industries on developing effective risk management procedures. Participated in numerous seminars and a contributing author on risk management and group actions.
Prof. Memberships: Law Society, International Association of Defence Council and Defence Research Institute.
Career: Joined *Ashurst Morris Crisp* in 1987; partner 1994; qualified in both the UK and Australia.
Personal: Born 20 April 1961; attended University of N.S.W. (B Comm 1982, LLB 1984). Married with two children, Resides London.

FREER, Gary
Barlow Lyde & Gilbert, London (020) 7247 2277
gfreer@blg.co.uk
Specialisation: Commercial litigation of all kinds, including employment, food safety, defamation and professional negligence.
Prof. Memberships: Food Law Group, Employment Lawyers Association. City of London Solicitors Company, Member of Employment Law Sub-committee.
Career: Articled with *Barlow Lyde & Gilbert*, qualified 1986, Partner May 1993.
Personal: Born 16th April 1961, Educated at Nottingham High School and St. Catharine's College Cambridge (M.A.). Interests include hockey (West Hampstead Hockey Club), cricket (Flamstead Cricket Club), choral singing and sport of all kinds.

GILBERTSON, Kathryn
Paisner & Co, London (020) 7353 0299
Specialisation: Senior solicitor in the business regulation unit. Practice focuses on food law including defending enforcement prosecutions and advising retailers on compliance strategies. Has extensive experience in due diligence protocols and health and safety risk assessment matters. Lectures throughout Europe and UK.
Prof. Memberships: Food Law Group, Chartered Institute of Environmental Health, Society of Food Hygiene Technology.
Career: Educated in Wales. BSc(Hons) Environmental Health from Bristol Polytechnic. Diploma in Health and Safety at Work North East London Polytechnic. Qualified Mediator. Practised as a local authority Environmental Health Officer for 9 years before qualifying as a Solicitor. Admitted 1994. Joined *Paisner & Co.* in 1996.
Personal: Born 14 July 1962. Lives in Standon Hertfordshire. Married. Interests include Italian sports cars, fine wine and visiting sites of historical interest.

GREGG, Andrew
Gregg Galbraith Quinn, Bristol (0117) 925 8123
See under Licensing, p.536

HARRIS, David N.
Alexander Harris, Altrincham (0161) 925 5555
Joint Senior Partner and Partner in charge of the Pharmaceutical Product and Disaster Litigation Department.
Specialisation: All areas of pharmaceutical product litigation, concentrating on multi party action litigation. Lead Solicitor in Myodil litigation and member of Steering Committees in Opren, Human Insulin, and Hillsborough Disaster. Lead Solicitor in Listeriosis claims against the Government and instructed by families of victims of BSE/ CJD. Lead Solicitor in the investigation of Septrin claims and in the action for underdosing of Radiotherapy at the North Staffordshire District Hospital. Considerable experience in litigation in the USA, including Shiley Heart Valves, Telectronic Pacemakers and Breast Implant claims. Contributes regularly to television news and current affairs programmes and is an expert frequently consulted by radio reporters and producers, and has been extensively quoted in the Press. Lectures on pharmaceutical product and multi party actions to legal and medical audiences. Investigating claims for 'Persona' multi party action. Responsible for all generic work in LSD multi party action. One of two firms nominated by Legal Aid Board to carry out preliminary investigations into ECT treatment. Lead solicitor investigating claims of overtreatment by Manchester orthodontist, Melvyn Meggitt.
Prof. Memberships: Law Society, APIL, ATLA.
Career: Qualified in 1979 and then became co-founder of *Alexander Harris* in May 1989. First practice in this country specialising exclusively in clinical negligence and pharmaceutical product liability. The practice has now added a specialist personal injury department. Deputy District Judge on the Northern Circuit since 1988. Assessor to Law Society Personal Injury Panel. CEDR Accredited mediator.
Personal: Born 23rd May 1949. Attended Hull University (LL.B 1972).

HARVEY, Mark
Smith Llewelyn Partnership, Swansea (01792) 464444
See under Personal Injury, p.644

HETHERINGTON, David
Margetts & Ritchie, Birmingham 0121 236 5517
Specialisation: Defends businesses prosecuted by Local Authority and Government Departments under Regulatory Law relating to Food Safety, Trading Standards, Environmental Health, Consumer Protection, Product Safety, Health & Safety and Directors' personal liability. Has represented: meat producers, scotch egg producer, poultry producer, ice cream producer, yoghurt producer, restaurant chains, butchers retail chains, butchers, bakers, brewery, vineyard, cafÈ and shop proprietors, delicatessen proprietor, various supermarkets, fish processors and suppliers, fish importer, shellfish distributor, nut importer, tinned foods importer, general food importers, electrical retailer, electrical distributors, furnishing retail chains, toy importer and retail chain, holiday camp operator, doors kitchens and conservatories producer, golf professional and university. Has had ten recent cases dismissed with defendants costs orders: delicatessen proprietor acquitted of salmonella contamination; supermarket and butchers retail chain acquitted of unfit poultry; wrong supermarket company charged and acquitted of insects in marmalade; two meat producers acquitted of misleading food labelling following representations; vineyard proprietor acquitted of adding peach flavouring to wine following successful Criminal Cases Review Commission referral; two furniture retailers and conservatory installer acquitted of misleading prices following representations or trials.
Career: With *Margetts & Ritchie:* articles (1975 - 1977), assistant solicitor (1978 - 1984), and partner (1984 - 2000). As a Prosecution Solicitor agent: West Midlands Trading Standards, Environmental and Fire Service Departments (1981-1986), West Midlands Probation Service (1986 - 1991), Crown Prosecution Service (1987 - 1991), Birmingham Trading Standards (1988 - 1989) and M.A.F.F. (1990). As a Defence Solicitor: general criminal law offences (1978 - 1999), duty solicitor (1979 - 1996), West Midlands Fire Service drivers (1981 - 1987), Trading Standards, Environmental Health and M.A.F.F. cases (1987 - 2000).

HODGES, Christopher J.S.
CMS Cameron McKenna, London (020) 7367 3000
Specialisation: Main areas of practice are product liability, product regulatory and safety law and product recall across a wide range of sectors, including medical devices, pharmaceuticals, automotives and electronics. Editor of 'Product Liability: European Laws and Practice', and 'Product Safety', Chapters in 'Product Liability: Law and Insurance', 'The Textbook of Pharmaceutical Medicine' and various other books. Author of 1995 European Commission Study on the Product Liability Directive.
Prof. Memberships: Law Society, CBI Consumer Affairs Committee and Working Parties on Product Liability and General Product Safety, ABHI Council and Legal Committee, International Association of Defense Counsel, Vice-Chair of International Bar Association Committee on Product Liability and Consumer Affairs.
Career: Worked at *Slaughter and May* and *Clifford Chance* before becoming Partner at *McKenna & Co* in 1990.
Personal: Born 19th March 1954. Educated at King Edward's School, Birmingham. Academical Clerk at New College, Oxford. Founder member and Trustee of 'The Sixteen'.

HOLLAND, Barry K.
Elliotts, Manchester (0161) 834 9933

KELLEHER, John R.
Theodore Goddard, London (020) 7606 8855
Specialisation: Product liability litigation, particularly for clients in the pharmaceutical industry. Represented Glaxo in the Myodil litigation and The Wellcome Foundation Limited in the MMR Vaccine Litigation. Has acted for pharmaceutical manufacturers in defending claims arising out of a range of therapeutic products including corticosteroids. Has recently advised major electronics company and electrical cable manufacturing companies on product recalls and related issues.
Prof. Memberships: Law Society, City of London Solicitors Company, IBA.
Career: Uppingham, Sheffield University, trained with *Theodore Goddard*, qualified in 1978, partner 1984, Head of litigation 1990.
Personal: Married, three children.

McCOOL, Geraldine M.
Leigh, Day & Co, Manchester (0161) 832 7722
Specialisation: Main area of practice is aviation for plaintiffs, product liability and MOD claims. Cases have included Lockerbie, British Midland at Kegworth, Piper Alpha and Chinook Mull of Kintyre crash 1994. Co-Author of Longmans Know How PI and Multi Party Actions by LAG.
Prof. Memberships: APIL, ATLA, past Chairman of Young Solicitors Group. Member of Law Society's Personal Injury Panel. On Panel of Mediators in Personal Injury for Court of Appeal cases. Council Member Manchester Law Society.
Career: Joined *Leigh Day & Co.* in 1994 as a Partner.
Personal: Born 20th April 1961.

McDOUGALL, Arundel
Rowe & Maw, London (020) 7248 4282

MELTZER, John
Lovells, London (020) 7296 2000
john.meltzer@lovells.com
Specialisation: Main areas of practice are product liability litigation and product safety regulation. Particular experience in defending multi-party claims. Currently representing pharmaceutical companies in the MMR vaccine group action. Also has experience defending cross-border product liability claims. Has assisted UK companies in the co-ordination of the defence of claims in jurisdictions outside the UK including the US, Canada and Australia. As well as defending claims, advises on non-contentious issues such as product safety, risk management, labelling, product recalls, crisis management and media handling. This work is often for clients who have to deal with high profile 'public health' issues, such as EMF (mobile phones), dioxin contamination, ETS ('passive smoking') and BSE. Has also acted in several judical reviews of the actions of governmental authorities at national and EU levels. Currently acting for the principal UK tobacco companies in a judicial review of the EU Directive banning tobacco advertising and sponsorship. Partner in the firm's product liability group whose clients include manufacturers and retailers of motor vehicles (and components), aircraft engines, tobacco, pharmaceutical products, electronic goods, food, guns, toys and beverages.
Prof. Memberships: London Litigation Solicitors Association; International Association of Defence Counsel.

Career: Qualified New South Wales, Australia 1982. Qualified England & Wales 1991. Solicitor at *Freehill Hollongdale & Page* 1984-1986. Joined *Lovells* in 1987 and became a partner in 1997.

MURRAY, Marsali C.
Burness, Edinburgh (0131) 473 6000
mcm@burness.co.uk
Specialisation: Partner dealing with commercial litigation and specialising in product liability (including multiple claims) and employment law.

NELSON-JONES, Rodney
Field Fisher Waterhouse, London (020) 7861 4000
See under Personal Injury, p.645

PEARL, Simon
Davies Arnold Cooper, London (020) 7936 2222
Partner in Healthcare Unit.
Specialisation: Main areas of practice are product liability and negligence. Defends pharmaceutical companies and healthcare professionals and their insurers. Also handles pharmaceutical regulatory work. Co-ordinating solicitor for the NHS in HIV Haemophilia litigation and Hepatitis C litigation. Defended in the whooping cough vaccine test case, Loveday v. Renton. Represents SB in the MMR vaccine litigation. Author of Product Liability Insurance and European Product Liability Publishing Monitor Press. Writes and speaks widely at conferences.
Prof. Memberships: Law Society. Law Society's Working Party on Group Actions, Medico-legal Society.
Career: Qualified in 1977. Joined *Davies Arnold Cooper* in 1975, becoming a Partner in 1980.
Personal: Born 30th April 1953. Attended Horace Mann School, New York and Birmingham University (LLB(Hons) 1974). Leisure interests include road running, theatre, music and family. Lives in Harpenden, Herts.

PICKERING, John
Irwin Mitchell, Sheffield (0114) 276 7777
See under Personal Injury, p.646

REID, Ron F.
Shoosmiths, Northampton (01604) 543000
Specialisation: Main areas of practice are food law, including advice on product liability, trading standards matters and consumer claims. Also advises on health and safety, environmental law and liquor licensing. Under matters of health and safety, Ron has led the launch of *Shoosmiths* Occupational Safety, a department dedicated to offering straight forward advice on all safety matters. Has set up specialist training department to handle the requirements of national and international companies for in-house training and is a regular speaker at conferences and seminars in his areas of specialisation.
Prof. Memberships: Honorary Member of Executive Committee of Inter-Company Consumer Affairs Association, a trade association of Consumer Care Managers in the food and drinks manufacturing industry. Member of The Food Law Group. Secretary to both the Food Industry Regional Safety Team and Northamptonshire Occupational Safety & Health Association. Director of the Radon Council. Independant Board Member of Huntingdon Housing Partnership.
Career: Qualified in 1983, having previously been a F.I.L.Ex. Joined *Shoosmiths & Harrison* in 1974. Became a Partner in 1985.

ROSS, Hilary
Paisner & Co, London (020) 7353 0299
Specialisation: Senior solicitor in Regulatory Department. Advises on EU and UK regulatory compliance issues for foods. Specifically advises US and Canadian manufacturers about how to successfully launch their products in the EU. This includes providing advice on composition, labelling, packaging, claims and advertising. Also advises clients about defending prosecutions for non-compliance issues and represents clients in Court. Has extensive experience in obtaining pre-market approval for novel foods and advises US and Dutch companies on this matter. Hilary advises many US companies about compliance issues particular to nutraceuticals and food supplements. In the last year has also advised several e-commerce businesses on compliance issues. A specialist in the regulation of GM foods advising manufacturers, retailers and caterers on this topic. Has also been invited to address the Canadian Ministry of Agriculture and the Ontario Ministry of Agriculture on several occasions. Was also asked to address the 8th Asian Congress of Nutrition in Korea on this topic. Regularly participates in the PAGB's one day training course on food supplements.
Publications: Has recently authored a report for Monitor Law Press called 'Novel Foods: A guide to the Law & Technology of GMOs in Europe'.
Prof. Memberships: Food Law Group, European Food Law Association. Food & Drink Federation, President of the London Young Solicitors Group 1996-1997.
Career: Qualified in Scotland in 1993; Obtained English Practicing Certificate in April 1994; Solicitor in pharmaceutical department of *McKenna & Co* 1993-1995; Associate in Litigation Department of International law firm *Sonnenschein* 1995-1998; Joined *Paisner & Co* in 1998.
Personal: Born 25 April 1969; Graduated from Glasgow University 1991 with an Upper Second Class Honours Degree in Medical Law and Ethics. Lives in London and enjoys dining out, socialising with friends, hunting for antiques and going to the cinema.

SMITH, Hugh E.
Andrew M. Jackson & Co, Hull (01482) 325242
Head of Litigation
Specialisation: Substantial area of practice involves retail law covering Trading Standards, Health and Safety, Consumer Protection and Consumer Safety. Particular specialism in the vitamin and fish industry. Commercial Litigation; contractual disputes both international and domestic, company and partnership disputes, commercial property disputes, professional negligence, defamation and passing off. Represents finance houses in respect of consumer complaints/recoveries.
Prof. Memberships: Member of the Law Society and the Food Law Group. Also an ADR mediator.
Career: Admitted 1983. Joined present firm in 1989 becoming a Partner in 1991 in charge of the Commercial Litigation Division.
Personal: Born 16.01.59. Attended Nottingham University (LLB Hons).

SPRING, Paul
Mills Selig, Belfast 028/9024/3878
See under Defamation, p.297

STEWART, Brian J.C.
O'Reilly Stewart, Belfast (028) 9032 1000
oreillystewart@dnet.co.uk
Partner and head of the Litigation Department.
Specialisation: Specialises in product liability defence and insurance defence generally, including pharmaceuticals.
Prof. Memberships: Member of the Council of the Law Society of Northern Ireland. Former Chairman of the Belfast Solicitors' Association. Member of the International Association of Defence Counsel.
Career: Qualified 1978. Admitted to the Republic of Ireland Roll of Solicitors 1991.

TOZER, Roy C.
DLA, Birmingham (0121) 262 5939
roy.tozer@dla.com
Specialisation: An experienced Associate with *DLA* and a member of the Commercial Regulatory Group. Specialises in criminal litigation. A former prosecuting solicitor, he has invaluable experience of both sides of a criminal prosecution. Has wide experience in dealing with corporate crime and regulatory prosecutions. Undertakes fraud and Customs & Excise enquiries and acts for a large number of retail, manufacturing, transport and leisure service clients on all trading standards, product liability and health & safety issues.
Career: Admitted 1990. Prosecuted for Birmingham City Council until 1993 when joined *Edge & Ellison* in Birmingham. Joined *DLA* in August 1998.

TUCKER, Andrew
Irwin Mitchell, Sheffield (0114) 276 7777
Specialisation: Litigation in respect of products giving rise to injury, particularly pharmaceutical products, medical devices, experience of multi-party litigation both product related and arising from transport disasters and occupational disease. Acted for Plaintiffs in many high profile cases including: Opren, Dalkon Shield, Benzodiazepines, Manchester Aircrash, "Herald of Free Enterprise", Kegworth Aircrash, "Marchioness"/Bowbelle" collision, North Cornwall Water Pollution, Armley Asbestos, Human Growth Hormone/Creutzfeldt-Jacob Disease, tobacco, silicone implants, Mineworkers V.W.F. and Mineworkers Respiratory Disease.
Prof. Memberships: Law Society, Association of Personal Injury Lawyers, South Yorkshire Medico Legal Society, American Trial Lawyers Association, Secretary to The Environmental Law Foundation.
Career: Articled *Wallace Mitchell*, Nottingham. Qualified 1985. Partner, *Irwin Mitchell*, 1988.
Personal: Born October 1960, University of Liverpool, LL.B. Lives North Derbyshire.

TYLER, Mark
CMS Cameron McKenna, London
(020) 7367 3000
mlt@cmck.com
Partner in Product Liability and Health & Safety.
Specialisation: Main areas of practice are product liability and health and safety. Co-author of 'Product Safety' and 'Safer by Design'; Consultant Editor of Health and Safety Liability and Litigation; legal reviewer for Croner's Management of Construction Safety. Contributor to 'Buildings and Health: The Rosehaugh Guide to the Design Construction and Management of Buildings', 'A New Balance: A Guide for Property Owners and Developers', 'Environmental Issues in Construction' – CIRIA Special Report, CIOB Handbook Facilities Management and 'Medi-

cines, Medical Devices and the Law', 'PLC Legal Risk Management Manual'.
Prof. Memberships: Law Society, Institution of Occupational Safety and Health (IOSH), CBI Health and Safety Panel, CBI Consumer Affairs Panel, Forum of Insurance Lawyers, International Association of Defense Counsel.
Career: Joined *McKenna & Co* in 1984 and qualified in 1986. Became a Partner in 1992.
Personal: Born 10th October 1960. Educated at Sir William Borlase's Grammar School, Marlow, Worcester College, Oxford and Kings College, London.

WARE, Anne
Davies Arnold Cooper, London (020) 7936 2222
Specialisation: Specialist in product liability litigation with particular expertise in mass tort claims. Major pharmaceutical related litigation experience includes Pertussis, Opren, Benzodiazepines; current caseload includes medical device claims; environmental and multi-jurisdictional litigation. Other areas include medical negligence; complex or unusual medically related and personal injury actions; work related stress, sexual harassment and abuse claims; veterinary, cosmetic and food product related claims.

WARNOCK, Owen
Eversheds, Norwich (01603) 272727
See under Employment, p.345

WILSON, Michael W.C.
Elliott Duffy Garrett, Belfast (028) 9024 5034

YOUNG, David A.
Eversheds, Birmingham (0121) 232 1000
Partner in Litigation Department.
Specialisation: Acts principally for retail and leisure clients. Work covers all aspects of food, environment, health and safety, product liability and trading law. Acts for a number of recognised operators.
Prof. Memberships: Law Society, Food Law Group.
Career: Qualified in 1984. Became a Partner at *Eversheds* in 1993.
Personal: Born 11th October 1959. Educated at Solihull School 1971-78, University College, London 1978-81 and The College of Law, Chancery Lane 1981-82. Leisure time devoted to his children and partner, sport and travel. Lives Warwick.

PROFESSIONAL NEGLIGENCE

OVERVIEW: The London section of professional negligence work continues to be divided into legal, financial, insurance and construction specialisms, although the market as a whole is becoming gradually more diluted. The level of legal and construction cases has fallen over recent years, while the number of IT instructions is increasing, as are cases against a variety of more traditional professions. A source of particular growth has been the pensions' misselling saga.

With solicitors' work continuing to provide the greatest amount of instructions, the market is awaiting the winding down of the SIF panel on the 1st September this year. This may allow a larger number of firms to enter the field, from the current slimmed down SIF panel of fourteen firms.

There has been less work about, largely because of Woolf, although some claimants have been waiting for the conditional fee arrangements which are now in force. In addition, the more widespread use of ADR and the improvement in the national economy over recent years are widely credited with reducing the motivation for making claims.

RESEARCH APPROVED BY BMRB: *For this edition,* Chambers' *researchers conducted 6083 interviews – 4408 with law firms, 598 with barristers and 1077 with clients.*

The validity of the research was scrutinised by BMRB International, who audited both the methodology and the results at our offices in July 2000. They interviewed Chambers' *researchers and cross-checked sample interviews. Details of the audit appear on* *page 7.*

LONDON

LEADERS ACROSS THE BOARD

Barlow Lyde & Gilbert *"Unceasingly successful,"* this is the most recognised professional negligence practice in the country. *"Bore you to death with the law, but they are almost always right."* Rated highly for their technical ability and knowledge by peers and clients alike. Recognised as a major player in all sectors apart from construction, although they also have a presence there. Clients include various professional organisations and insurers, including accountants, solicitors and stock brokers. Highlights of the past year include working for PricewaterhouseCoopers on a claim against them by Elton John, and the successful settlement of the MCC litigation on behalf of Coopers & Lybrand. **Stuart Hall** is noted for his work on some massive cases. He worked on several large accountancy negligence cases, including the MCC litigation and acted in the Bermuda Fire & Marine litigation. **Ian Jenkins** is a respected and senior figure in the field while **David Arthur** received plaudits for his work on Y2K. **Richard Dedman**, known for mediation and construction work, is another member of a large and impressive team. Financial expert **Michael Wilson** *"takes on a lot of cases and usually wins them."* He is seen as a valuable acquisition from Berwin Leighton. **Clients:** PwC.

Reynolds Porter Chamberlain A clear second overall, this *"hugely respected"* firm has a varied professional negligence practice, and is noted for an *"original approach."* Handles claims against solicitors and barristers, acting for SIF, top-up insurers, Lloyd's syndicates and commercial insurers. During the past year, the firm represented Countess Spencer in her claim against the solicitors who acted for her during her divorce. Received a large number of instructions from independent financial advisors on pensions related work, and has also advised on internet defamation claims. **Paul Nicholas** is *"one of the key players"*, and is loved by peers, who rate his work as *"unfailingly good."* **Barney Micklem** *"makes friends wherever he goes."* His knowledge of the sector is considered to be *"outstanding."* **Simon Greenley** is considered a knowledgeable and respected player. **Clients:** Lloyd's syndicates; Royal & Sun Alliance; AIG.

FIRMS IN ALPHABETICAL ORDER

The editorial for the other firms listed in the tables follows in alphabetical, rather than ranking order.

Beachcroft Wansbroughs *"A pleasure to deal with,"* the firm is felt to have made *"a serious push across the board and across the country."* A leading SIF panel firm, it also acts for a range of Lloyd's syndicates and composite insurers. Represent a diverse range of professional disciplines including accountants, architects, computer consultants and engineers. The London office also has a niche interest in fraud cases, policy interpretation and market disputes, while the Construction Risks Group acts for a number of large insurers. **Clients:** Insurance companies.

Beale and Company A leading construction practice which is respected by clients and peers alike. It is now expanding into management consultants, film industry and acting against solicitors. Has experienced notable growth in IT and new media, particularly with computer consultants. Known for its construction work on the ACE scheme for engineers, and also for its work for CGU. **John Ward** and **Antony Smith** are both highly rated specialists on construction cases. **Clients:** CGU; Wren.

Berrymans Lace Mawer With a broad practice, the firm is recognised as a solid player in the sector. Particularly noted for construction expertise, the team also acts for professional indemnity underwriters, surveyors, accountants, local authorites and in-house solicitors. Handles a growing number of claims against schools and universities by former pupils involving learning difficulties, bullying, abuse and discrimination. Also works on a large number of more eclectic claims, such as those from vets and photographers. Acted for City of London Police in connection with the City of London riots. **Clients:** Underwriters, police forces.

Clyde & Co Insurance work has developed as an offshoot of the firm's noted shipping practice. Clients range from the insurers of the big five accountants and the top ten law firms to firms of architects, surveyors and accountants. The practice is largely known for high value, lower volume work, and highlights of the past year have included working on the BCCI cases. **Clients:** Equitas; Swiss Re; AON.

PROFESSIONAL NEGLIGENCE: LEGAL • London	Ptnrs	Assts
❶ Barlow Lyde & Gilbert	29*	53*
Reynolds Porter Chamberlain	27*	50*
❷ Lovells	15*	33*
❸ Beachcroft Wansbroughs	8*	25*
Herbert Smith	16*	40*
Pinsent Curtis	5	15
❹ Davies Arnold Cooper	15*	20*
Ince & Co	8*	15*

PROFESSIONAL NEGLIGENCE: FINANCIAL • London	Ptnrs	Assts
❶ Barlow Lyde & Gilbert	29*	53*
Reynolds Porter Chamberlain	27*	50*
❷ CMS Cameron McKenna	12*	43*
Herbert Smith	16*	40*
❸ Lovells	15*	33*
Rowe & Maw	9*	20*
❹ Berrymans Lace Mawer	2	3

PROFESSIONAL NEGLIGENCE: INSURANCE • London	Ptnrs	Assts
❶ Barlow Lyde & Gilbert	29*	53*
❷ Reynolds Porter Chamberlain	77*	50*
❸ CMS Cameron McKenna	12*	43*
❹ Herbert Smith	16*	40*
Rowe & Maw	9*	20*
❺ Clyde & Co	3	6
Fishburn Morgan Cole	11*	16*
Ince & Co	8*	15*
Squire & Co	8	9
❻ Beachcroft Wansbroughs	8*	25*
Davies Arnold Cooper	15*	20*
Holman Fenwick & Willan	6	15

PROFESSIONAL NEGLIGENCE: CONSTRUCTION • London	Ptnrs	Assts
❶ Beale and Company	6	5
CMS Cameron McKenna	3	10
Kennedys	6	18
Rowe & Maw	9	20
❷ Berrymans Lace Mawer	3	5
Fishburn Morgan Cole	11*	16*
Reynolds Porter Chamberlain	27*	50*
❸ Davies Arnold Cooper	4	6
Hextall Erskine	8	7
❹ Vizard Oldham	4	2
❺ Barlow Lyde & Gilbert	29*	53*
Williams Davies Meltzer	4	6

Within each band, firms are listed alphabetically. *See **Profiles** on page 684*
** Figures are totals for all four professional negligence sectors.*

CMS Cameron McKenna A widespread perception exists that the firm has lost steam in the sector during the past year. This has been most marked in the insurance and finance areas, where the loss of Geoff Barrett to Mills Reeve has come as a particular blow. However, the firm is still ranked close to the top in most areas, notably its specialist field of construction. The *"talented"* generalist **Stephen Tester** is one of the leading names in professional indemnity work while **Mark Elborne's** broad practice also gains market plaudits. **Belinda Schofield** is particularly rated as a player in insurance cases. The practice has acted for Lloyd's syndicates, accountants and engineers and other professionals associated with the construction industry. **Clients:** Accountants, engineers, underwriters.

Davies Arnold Cooper The decreasing influence of this former powerhouse has been one of the notable features of the past year. The firm's clients, however, consider it to be a *"solid and knowledgeable practice."* Acts for London and international market insurance and reinsurance professionals, including companies, brokers, composites and Lloyd's syndicates. Highlights of the past year include work for Drysdales Syndicate and others in Arab Bank v Zurich Insurance & Others. Worked on the ongoing Lloyd's names litigation, and was heavily involved in Y2K and IT related work. As with much of the market, the firm has seen a reduction in the level of construction work, but has attracted a small but growing level of work from IT professionals. **Clients:** R E Brown & Others; R J Wallace; Eastgate Syndicate Management Ltd.

Fishburn Morgan Cole Although not generally considered one of the leading lights in the sector, the firm is considered to have a particular niche in the construction industry, notably acting for architects. The team also acts for insurance brokers, and continues to be recognised for a *"professional"* service. **Clients:** Architects, insurance brokers.

Herbert Smith *"An impressive outfit with loads of expertise"* on accountancy and surveyor-related work. Does well in the Lloyd's market and is well respected by peers. Highlights of the past year include representing PricewaterhouseCoopers Singapore in defending proceedings brought against them following the collapse of Barings. Also advised Arthur Andersen on claims surrounding the collapse of the Bond Group in Australia. **Clients:** KPMG; Arthur Andersen; PWC.

Hextall Erskine A respected construction practice which is felt to rely heavily upon its leader's name. The linchpin of the practice is **Stuart White**, rated by peers as a *"commercially-minded"* leader with *"long experience."* The firm's client base is mainly insurance-related, but includes an increasing amount direct from professionals. Becoming increasingly involved in international work, and has a niche strength in legal expenses. **Clients:** G E Lloyd-Roberts & Others; Wren Managers; First Assist.

Holman Fenwick & Willan Noted shipping firm with a long-standing name in insurance, although it has assumed a lower profile this year. Typically acting on the defendant side, the practice has a substantial international dimension. **Clients:** Insurance brokers.

Ince & Co A substantial player, particularly on legal work. During the past year, the firm worked on a Court of Appeal decision on the construction of a Tomlin Order (Line Trust v Fielding.) Also involved in a long-running dispute representing the insurers of a major accountancy firm which was accused of negligence following a major city scandal. **Clients:** Insurance brokers.

Kennedys Recognised by peers, particularly for its work on construction. Works for surveyors, architects, engineers, accountants and other professionals. Heavily involved with mediation. Worked on several fire and structural claims over the past year, and was employed by a firm of architects on the redevelopment of Sadler's Wells theatre. In one high profile case, acted for an independent expert in an action brought against him by Currys over the rent of some commercial property. The firm's individuals are considered *"very reasonable; they cut to the chase and don't get bogged down in the detail."* **Nick Thomas** is a name which carries particular weight. **Clients:** Architects, engineers, accountants.

LEADING INDIVIDUALS • London	
❶ **HALL Stuart** Barlow Lyde & Gilbert	**NICHOLAS Paul** Reynolds Porter Chamberlain
TESTER Stephen CMS Cameron McKenna	**WARD John** Beale and Company
WHITE Stuart Hextall Erskine	
❷ **ARTHUR David** Barlow Lyde & Gilbert	**BARRETT Geoff** Mills & Reeve
CONNOLLY Sean Rowe & Maw	**ELBORNE Mark** CMS Cameron McKenna
HARTFIELD David Vizard Oldham	**JENKINS Ian** Barlow Lyde & Gilbert
MICKLEM Barney Reynolds Porter Chamberlain	
SMITH Antony Beale and Company	**TROTTER John** Lovells
❸ **DEDMAN Richard** Barlow Lyde & Gilbert	**GREENLEY Simon** Reynolds Porter Chamberlain
REGAN Michael Rowe & Maw	**SCHOFIELD Belinda** CMS Cameron McKenna
SEYMOUR Michael Lovells	**THOMAS Nicholas** Kennedys
WILSON Michael Barlow Lyde & Gilbert	**WYLDE Peter** Irwin Mitchell

Within each band, firms are listed alphabetically. *See **Profiles** on page 684*

Lovells A major player on *"particularly intricate SIF work."* Handled a number of claims against solicitors during the year; many were dealt with through mediation. Involved in various matters on behalf of accountants, including the defence of a big five firm in a tax negligence claim. **John Trotter** and **Michael Seymour** are the outstanding practitioners here. **Clients:** SIF, insurers.

Pinsent Curtis Considered to be *"steady and efficient,"* this is another London firm on the SIF panel, with niche strength in handling claims against solicitors and insurance brokers. Receives instructions to defend claims against professionals from Lloyd's, company market and mutual insurers. In one of the highlights of the past year, the practice successfully defended a major Lloyd's broker from a large scale Commercial Court litigation arising from the Personal Accident LMX spiral dispute. **Clients:** Solicitors Indemnity Fund; Benfield Greig Group plc; Marsh Group of Companies.

Rowe & Maw A growing practice that is making progress *"on several fronts."* Particularly recommended by peers for its construction and architects' work, the firm's client base includes accountants, brokers, financial institutions and foreign lawyers. Known for work involving fraud and complex forensic investigations, the firm has noted expertise in offshore jurisdictions. At home the team has continued to act on a number of large scale surveyors' negligence claims. **Sean Connolly** is *"enjoyable to work with,"* and is famed for his work for Lloyd's syndicates, while **Michael Regan's** reputation encompasses a number of areas, most notably construction. **Clients:** RJ Wallace & Others; The Chartwell Underwriting Group; David Marshall & Ors

Squire & Co A respected litigation practice, known for its strong-willed attitude, for handling the more difficult cases, and for *"flexing its muscles when necessary."* Works for insurers on architects' and accountants' cases. Felt to have an *"utterly loyal client base,"* the team has represented several Lloyd's syndicates. **Clients:** Insurers and re-insurers.

Vizard Oldham The *"top-quality"* Hartfields team is now a part of this newly-constituted firm, and maintains its presence as a major player in the construction sector. **David Hartfield** is respected for his commercial approach and is considered one of the leaders in his field. The group's clientele is defendant-based and includes surveyors and architects, as well as insurance brokers and accountants from its non-construction department. A particular niche interest is in licensed conveyancing. **Clients:** Insurance composites; Lloyd's and the London market.

Williams Davies Meltzer A small niche professional negligence outfit, representing various professionals, including the traditional accountants, lawyers and marine surveyors, as well as new media professionals. During the past year it has dealt with a number of pension mis-selling claims. **Clients:** Accountants, surveyors.

Other Notable Practitioners

Geoff Barrett, formerly of CMS Cameron McKenna, is moving to Mills & Reeve to operate at the highly-rated East Anglian firm's London office. **Peter Wylde** of Irwin Mitchell is *"open, effective and practical."* He works in London on the claimant side, handles class actions, and is considered by peers to be *"good to work with."*

THE SOUTH

PROFESSIONAL NEGLIGENCE • The South	Ptnrs	Assts
❶ **Blake Lapthorn** Fareham	3	4
Cripps Harries Hall Tunbridge Wells	6	6
Thomson Snell & Passmore Tunbridge Wells	6	3

Within each band, firms are listed alphabetically.

Blake Lapthorn A substantial solicitors' negligence practice despite being dropped from the SIF panel. Handles defence of all types of claims against solicitors including fraud, claims by lenders and 'lost opportunity' cases. Also works on accountants', surveyors' and financial advisors' negligence. Related work includes disciplinary proceedings against professionals and pensions litigation. **Clients:** Solicitors and barristers.

Cripps Harries Hall Another strong solicitors' practice, although the firm survived the recent SIF cull. Most clients are solicitors, although the team also handles cases for surveyors, accountants, architects and management consultants. One highlight of the past year has been the appointment of the firm to co-ordinate around 150 claims against solicitors brought by a major high street residential property lender. **Clients:** Solicitors, accountants, surveyors.

Thomson Snell & Passmore The firm's niche strength is solicitors' negligence claims in relation to litigation, conveyancing, company commercial, trust and probate, personal injury and employment. Suffered blow when it was dropped from the SIF panel. **Clients:** Nelson Hurst Marsh.

THAMES VALLEY

PROFESSIONAL NEGLIGENCE • Thames Valley	Ptnrs	Assts
❶ **Henmans** Oxford	4	11

LEADING INDIVIDUALS
❶ **SUMMERFIELD Neil** Lightfoots

Within each band, firms are listed alphabetically. *See **Profiles** on page 684*

Henmans A large, almost purely defendant negligence practice which has maintained its position on the SIF panel. Also deals with accountants, surveyors and insurance brokers' work, as well as a growing level of new media professionals. The firm has attracted a large number of solicitors from City firms and major regional practices. **Clients:** RE Brown; Drysdales.

Other Notable Practitioners

Neil Summerfield of Lightfoots continues to be rated for his work on building society cases.

SOUTH WEST

PROFESSIONAL NEGLIGENCE • South West	Ptnrs	Assts
❶ **Beachcroft Wansbroughs** Bristol	5	13
Bond Pearce Plymouth, Bristol, Exeter	5	9
❷ **CMS Cameron McKenna** Bristol	2	8
SJ Cornish Tiverton	3	1
❸ **Burges Salmon** Bristol	4	10
Veale Wasbrough Bristol	2	3

LEADING INDIVIDUALS	
❶ **CHALLANDS Richard** Bond Pearce	**CORNISH Sarah** SJ Cornish
HEGARTY Simon CMS Cameron McKenna	**SALOMONSEN Erik** Bond Pearce

Within each band, firms are listed alphabetically. *See **Profiles** on page 684*

Beachcroft Wansbroughs A leading player in the South West, several commentators consider this to be the strongest office of a firm which is strong nationwide. *"The pie is getting smaller but they are maintaining their market share."* Best known for its solicitors' work, but clients come from the accountancy, legal and property-related professions, as well as including medical, education, media and environmental consultants. Act for over fifty insurance companies, Lloyd's syndicates and self-insureds. Also carry out big-ticket defendant work. **Clients:** RE Brown; DJ Newman; CGU.

Bond Pearce One of the leading regional practices, highly respected by City firms and a strong SIF player. The firm's range of clients includes major corporate insurers, Lloyd's syndicates and self-insureds. Known for its work for solicitors, financial services professionals and construction related claims, including claims against surveyors. **Erik Salomonsen** *"stands out from the crowd,"* and is *"an impressive lawyer with an easy manner."* His colleague **Richard Challands** is considered to be *"experienced and knowledgable."* **Clients:** Royal & Sun Alliance; Chartwell Underwriting Limited; Solicitors' Indemnity Fund Ltd.

CMS Cameron McKenna The largest non-SIF practice in the South West, it acts on behalf of financial advisors, surveyors and engineers, as well advising a number of IT professionals. Clients include Lloyd's syndicates and companies, and the practice acts for AIG on professional indemnity and directors' and officers' claims. **Simon Hegarty** remains respected for his all-round technical ability. **Clients:** AIG; Norwich Union; CGU.

S J Cornish A niche practice which handles a range of work, for architects, surveyors, accountants, brokers and engineers, although it is not involved in solicitors' cases. A defendant practice, it is currently handling a large volume of construction disputes. Half a dozen Lloyd's syndicates are the firm's main clients, and it also works for loss adjusters. The firm boasts the highly rated **Sarah Cornish**, who *"certainly knows what she's doing."* **Clients:** Construction professionals, accountants.

Burges Salmon A solid regional practice, acting in both claimant and defendant negligence work, in the agricultural, banking and finance sectors. The highlight of the past year was the settlement of the Nationwide Building Society-managed litigation case and appointment to the Paragon Finance plc panel. In addition, the practice was the lead firm acting on claims against regional solicitors over negligent tax advice, a case involving several jurisdictions. **Clients:** Noel Riossi; Nationwide Building Society; Paragon Finance plc.

Veale Wasbrough Considered by the market to have had a successful year in this area, the firm's niche strength lies in work for construction indemnity professionals. Clients include professionals, brokers, composites and syndicates. During the past year, it has defended consulting civil and structural engineers in a variety of cases involving traditional and alternative approaches to dispute resolution. **Clients:** Griffiths and Armour; Bar Mutual Indemnity Fund; CGU Insurance.

WALES

PROFESSIONAL NEGLIGENCE • Wales	Ptnrs	Assts
❶ **Morgan Cole** Cardiff	8	26

Within each band, firms are listed alphabetically.

Morgan Cole The top Welsh operation and a survivor on the SIF panel, the firm continues to possess a leading defendant practice. During the past year, it has acted for a solicitor in defending possession proceedings brought by a bank against the claimant. **Clients:** SIF.

MIDLANDS

PROFESSIONAL NEGLIGENCE • Midlands	Ptnrs	Assts
❶ **Browne Jacobson** Nottingham	5	10
❷ **Pinsent Curtis** Birmingham	4	16
❸ **Beachcroft Wansbroughs** Birmingham	3	8
Wragge & Co Birmingham	6	7
❹ **THM Tinsdills** Stoke-on-Trent	3	2
❺ **Wright Hassall** Leamington Spa	4	3*

LEADING INDIVIDUALS	
❶ **RIDGWELL Robert** Browne Jacobson	
❷ **LONG Andrew** Pinsent Curtis	**MURRAY Paul** Beachcroft Wansbroughs
PATON Andrew Pinsent Curtis	
❸ **HICK Mark** Wragge & Co	**McKECHNIE Robert** Wright Hassall
WAREING Diana Shakespeares	

Within each band, firms are listed alphabetically. *See **Profiles** on page 684*

* *See editorial entries for explanations of team sizes.*

Browne Jacobson The firm's principal main area of work continues to be solicitors' work, within which *"it is invariably outstanding."* Also acts for insurance brokers and financial intermediaries on pensions and endowment mortgages. The firm has handled fewer claims this year, but has advised a number of underwriters on risk management. Other work has been undertaken for London insurance companies, and the firm is listed on various panel schemes. *"Open, sensible and excellent,"* **Robert Ridgwell** is *"brilliant to work with"* and is universally considered to be the region's leading practitioner. **Clients:** SIF; CGU; St Paul Insurance.

Pinsent Curtis A SIF firm which is said to be *"big on mediation."* Handles multiple claims arising from the pensions' review, including dishonesty claims. Expertise lies in tax-related work and claims against solicitors stemming from complex corporate deals. During the past year, the firm has mediated settlement of 200 claims brought by NatWest Home Loans against various firms of solicitors worth a total of £8.5 million. Clients include insurers, Lloyd's underwriters, domestice and overseas life offices and IFA networks. **Andrew Paton** is *"a mediation star,"* while **Andrew Long** is *"the guy who makes the practice tick."* **Clients:** SIF; PYV Ltd; Equitas.

Beachcroft Wansbroughs The other firm in the West Midlands on the SIF panel, the practice also handles some accountants, financial services, construction and architects' defence instructions. Its main clients are major insurance companies. A recognised force in the legal market in the City, the firm has been increasingly prominent in mediation. Currently handling a large number of claims over £1m. Although considered to have a lower profile this year, **Paul Murray** is still a recognised name. **Clients:** CGU; RSA.

Wragge & Co A *"growing practice which could threaten the leaders."* Has attracted a considerable amount of work in emerging industries such as financial services, IT and outsourcing. Gained appointments on Y2K policy coverage and advises a number of insurers. During the past year, the firm advised a Bermuda-based reinsurer on a major claim against a firm of accountants. **Mark Hick** is considered to be *"a sound performer."* **Clients:** Chubb Insurance; St Paul International Insurance; RJ Wallace.

THM Tinsdills An omission from the SIF panel, the firm continues to handle solicitors' work, as well as cases on behalf of includes architects, quantity surveyors and veterinary work. **Clients:** Construction professionals.

Wright Hassall Historically a force in solicitors' defence cases, the firm is gaining a growing reputation for acting in accountancy matters. Although primarily a defence practice, the team does undertake building society work for claimants. **Robert McKechnie** is an *"old hand in this line of work."* **Clients:** Insurance brokers, banks.

Other Notable Practitioners

Diana Wareing of Shakespeares is considered to be the personification of her firm in this area of practice, to which she brings *"long years of experience."*

EAST ANGLIA

PROFESSIONAL NEGLIGENCE • East Anglia	Ptnrs	Assts
❶ **Mills & Reeve** Cambridge, Norwich	4	12
❷ **Merricks** Chelmsford	5	5

LEADING INDIVIDUALS
❶ **HODGSON Guy** Mills & Reeve

Within each band, firms are listed alphabetically. *See **Profiles** on page 684*

Mills & Reeve The key players in East Anglia, the firm is expanding into London and is considered to have the potential to become a force in the wider market. SIF claims form the backbone of the practice. **Guy Hodgson** *"is one of the most recognised names in East Anglia."* **Clients:** SIF.

Merricks Continues to be rated as a player, despite its demotion from the SIF panel. The practice acts predominantly on the defendant side for a clientele which includes accountants, surveyors and architects. **Clients:** Construction professionals, accountants.

NORTH WEST

PROFESSIONAL NEGLIGENCE • North West	Ptnrs	Assts
❶ **James Chapman & Co** Manchester	10	9
Weightmans Liverpool	8	14
❷ **Hill Dickinson** Liverpool	3	8
❸ **Elliotts** Manchester	2	7
Halliwell Landau Manchester	3	3
Keoghs Bolton	3	2

LEADING INDIVIDUALS	
❶ **McKENNA John** James Chapman & Co	**TAYLOR Elisabeth** James Chapman & Co

Within each band, firms are listed alphabetically. *See **Profiles** on page 684*

James Chapman & Co A specialist niche practice which has survived on the SIF panel. The firm handles claims against a variety of professions, including solicitors, architects, auctioneers and engineers. During the past year, the firm defended a multi-million pound claim against a North East district council by a major supermarket, arising from a revocation of planning permission by the Secretary of State. The team has also handled a number of key product liability cases for the NFU. **Elisabeth Taylor** and **John McKenna** are the stand-out names of a group which is considered to have *"a good all-round track record."* **Clients:** SIF; AXA; Zurich Municipal.

Weightmans SIF firm which also acts for a number of other professions, including bankers and accountants. The Liverpool office has its principal reputation for solicitor work, while Manchester handles the majority of non-solicitor work. **Clients:** Solicitors Indemnity Fund; Bar Mutual; Norwich Union.

Hill Dickinson Best-known for its engineers and construction work, the firm has attracted a growing level of financial liability work from CGU. Also handles claims for the Association of Consulting Engineers and their insurers. Other clients include architects, engineers, accountants, estate agents and travel agencies. During the past year, the firm has defended a £20 million claim brought against architects and engineers by the University of East Anglia. **Clients:** Construction professionals.

Elliotts A defence firm which principally works for engineers, brokers and architects. Also represents advertising agencies, trade unions and local authority officers. Over the past year, however, the practice has seen a particularly notable surge in construction cases, usually for engineers and architects. As well as its work for London-based insurance companies, the firm is noted for its advice on defence cases in Ireland. **Clients:** Construction professionals, insurance companies.

Halliwell Landau A plaintiff practice, often representing banks, which also takes referrals from the Law Society. The practice's principal growth area has been in the pensions sector. **Clients:** AIG.

Keoghs Noted for strength in insurance, the team works for more than forty insurers and has a heavy bias towards acting for defendants. **Clients:** Insurance companies.

YORKSHIRE

PROFESSIONAL NEGLIGENCE • Yorkshire	Ptnrs	Assts
❶ **Beachcroft Wansbroughs** Leeds	5	16
❷ **Irwin Mitchell** Sheffield	6	11
❸ **Hammond Suddards Edge** Leeds	2	3

Within each band, firms are listed alphabetically.

Beachcroft Wansbroughs Long established regional practice, which handles the gamut of professional indemnity work. Noted for its work on risk assessment, the team acts for a wide range of insurers, construction professionals, insolvency practitioners and accountants. **Clients:** CGU; RSA; Lloyd's syndicates.

Irwin Mitchell Strong claimant firm with a diverse client base which includes public and private companies, Legal Expenses Insurers, Unions and private individuals. During the past year the team has acted on a number of claims against solicitors relating to personal injury cases. Claims against surveyors, structural engineers and independent financial advisors are other growth areas. One highlight of the past year was the firm's advice to a manufacturing company on a claim against its tax advisors. **Clients:** Unions, individuals, public and private companies.

Hammond Suddards Edge Defendant firm which operates from the insurance unit and acts for insurers, financial advisors and computer and IT-related professionals. Pensions cases have also become a growth area here. However, the construction sector provided one of the highlight cases of the past year, with the firm's advice on the Holbeck Hall Hotel affair, where a hotel in Scarborough collapsed into the sea. The case was won in the Court of Appeal. **Clients:** Chartwell; Independent; AIG.

NORTH EAST

PROFESSIONAL NEGLIGENCE • North East	Ptnrs	Assts
❶ **Crutes** Newcastle-upon-Tyne	7	-
❷ **Hay & Kilner** Newcastle-upon-Tyne	4	2

Within each band, firms are listed alphabetically.

Crutes Widely rated SIF panel firm acknowledged to be the regional leader in terms of both size and quality *("they're a pleasure to deal with.")* The team acts for a varied professional client base, almost exclusively on the defendant side. **Clients:** SIF, accountants.

Hay & Kilner Acts for both claimants and defendants, and advises on brokers' negligence claims and coverage issues. During the past year the firm has handled a claim against a quantum specialist firm relating to the Piper Alpha disaster. The firm also acts on behalf of a mixture of insurance brokers, surveyors and banks. **Active Clients:** Financial institutions, surveyors.

SCOTLAND

PROFESSIONAL NEGLIGENCE • Scotland	Ptnrs	Assts
❶ **Simpson & Marwick WS** Edinburgh	5	7
❷ **Dundas & Wilson CS** Edinburgh	2	4
❸ **Balfour & Manson** Edinburgh	8	1
Morison Bishop Glasgow	4	3
❹ **Brechin Tindal Oatts** Glasgow	1	2
Brodies WS Edinburgh	1	1

LEADING INDIVIDUALS	
❶ **ANDERSON Peter** Simpson & Marwick WS	**MACLEOD Colin** Dundas & Wilson CS
WELSH John Morison Bishop	
❷ **ALLAN Derek John** Brechin Tindal Oatts	**ROXBURGH James** Biggart Baillie
WILLIAMSON David Brodies WS	

Within each band, firms are listed alphabetically. *See Profiles on page 684*

Simpson & Marwick WS Felt to be *"definitely near the top"* in Scotland, this largely defendant-oriented firm enjoys particular renown in the insurance field, where *"anyone who says they are not the leading practice is lying."* **Peter Anderson** is regarded as *"the main man in Scotland,"* and the firm also has a niche in acting on construction-related litigation. **Clients:** Solicitors, insurance brokers, construction professionals.

Dundas & Wilson CS Primarily acting on the defendant side, the firm acts for a mixture of engineers, doctors, architects and insurance companies. Considered to be challenging for the top spot in Scotland, the firm is on the engineers' panel and boasts the services of **Colin MacLeod**, who *"has a huge reputation."* **Clients:** Insurers, architects and engineers.

Balfour & Manson *"Certainly doing the work,"* the firm acts both for defenders and pursuers in a variety of professions, most notably acting for insurance brokers, solicitors and architects. **Clients:** Solicitors, architects.

Morison Bishop Work here comes principally from major insurance companies, loss adjusters and self-insureds. Two thirds of the caseload is on the defendant side, and the client base includes major insurance companies and several trade unions. **John Welsh** has a historically renowned reputation in the sector. **Clients:** Insurance companies, trades unions.

Brechin Tindal Oatts Said to *"do rather a lot,"* the firm acts for surveyors, solicitors and accountants. **Derek Allan** maintains a reputation for his defendant-based work. **Clients:** Solicitors, accountants.

Brodies WS The firm acts for both pursuers and defenders and handles a broad range of claims arising from solicitors, chartered accountants and surveyors' errors and omissions. **David Williamson** is the stand-out practitioner here. **Clients:** Law Society of Scotland; professional indemnity insurers.

Other Notable Practitioners

James Roxburgh of Biggart Baillie is considered to have a reputation which transcends the comparatively low profile of his firm.

NORTHERN IRELAND

PROFESSIONAL NEGLIGENCE • Northern Ireland	Ptnrs	Assts
❶ McKinty & Wright Belfast	6	3
❷ Carson & McDowell Belfast	2	4
Tughan & Co Belfast	3	1

LEADING INDIVIDUALS • Northern Ireland
❶ TURTLE Brian Carson & McDowell

Within each band, firms are listed alphabetically. *See **Profiles** on page 684*

McKinty & Wright In spite of the tragic loss of Owen Catchpole, the firm is still considered to be an *"impressive player,"* and is on the solicitors' Professional Indemnity Scheme for Northern Ireland. **Clients:** Solicitors, architects, accountants.

Carson & McDowell **Brian Turtle** is seen as the leading local light for professional indemnity work. The firm is also a member of the solicitors' Professional Indemnity Scheme. **Clients:** Solicitors.

Tughan & Co Handles solicitors' and construction claims, predominantly, although not exclusively, on the defendant side. Most work comes directly from insurance companies. **Clients:** Insurance companies.

LEADERS IN PROFESSIONAL NEGLIGENCE

ALLAN, Derek John
Brechin Tindal Oatts, Glasgow (0141) 221 8012
Specialisation: Principal area of practice is professional negligence, acting on behalf of insurance companies and corporate lenders in professional indemnity claims against solicitors, accountants and surveyors. Mainly defender orientated, but some pursuer/claimant work.
Prof. Memberships: The Law Society of Scotland. The Scottish Law Agents Society.
Career: Joined *Brechin Robb* as apprentice in 1978. Partner since 1984.
Personal: Golf, Tennis, Walking. Married with two sons.

ANDERSON, Peter
Simpson & Marwick WS, Edinburgh (0131) 557 1545
See under Aviation, p.558

ARTHUR, David
Barlow Lyde & Gilbert, London (020) 7247 2277
darthur@blg.co.uk
Specialisation: Professional negligence disciplinary and regulatory experience involving accountants, insurance brokers, solicitors and financial institutions. Also insurance and reinsurance matters including drafting and construction of policy wordings.
Prof. Memberships: Law Society, International Bar Association, B.I.L.A.
Career: Qualified in 1978. Joined *Barlow Lyde & Gilbert* in 1981. Became a Partner in 1984.

BARRETT, Geoff
Mills & Reeve, London (020) 7891 2670
geoff.barrett@mill-reve.com
Partner in Insurance and Reinsurance Group.
Specialisation: Principal areas of practice involve acting in claims and disputes for Insurers and Reinsurers. Has acted in numerous disputes involving accountants, financial advisers, insurance brokers, members' agents, surveyors and loss adjusters and Directors' and Officers' liability cover, both for the Lloyd's and company market. Also advises on general insurance and reinsurance matters including drafting and construction of policy wordings.
Prof. Memberships: Law Society.
Career: Read Law at University College London following which he obtained articles with *Hewitt Woollacott & Chown*, as it then was, in 1979. Was admitted as a solicitor in April 1981 and has been a partner since 1986. Joined *Mills & Reve* as a partner on 1st February 2000.

CHALLANDS, Richard
Bond Pearce, Plymouth (01752) 266633
xrc@bondpearce.com
Partner in the Insurance Group.
Specialisation: Specialises in professional indemnity and insurance litigation. Handles work on behalf of accountants, brokers, solicitors, barristers and surveyors. Also deals with policy and coverage disputes and has wide experience of claims involving fraud.
Prof. Memberships: Member of the International Bar Association Insurance Group and the British Insurance Law Association.
Career: Qualified 1975. Joined *Bond Pearce* in 1973, becoming partner 1978.

CONNOLLY, Sean
Rowe & Maw, London (Lloyd's) (020) 7327 4144

CORNISH, Sarah
SJ Cornish, Tiverton (01884) 243377

DEDMAN, Richard H.J.
Barlow Lyde & Gilbert, London (020) 7247 2277
rdedman@blg.co.uk
Specialisation: Professional liability; commercial litigation and arbitration; insurance.
Prof. Memberships: CEDR accredited mediator; Society of Computers & Law; Member of Society of Construction Law.
Career: Trained at *Lovell White & King*; since 1979 at *Barlow Lyde & Gilbert* where currently joint head of Professional Liability and Commercial Litigation Department.
Personal: Born 1954; educated at Felsted School and Cambridge University (Clare College - modern languages and law); interests include tennis, golf, football, music and languages.

ELBORNE, Mark E.M.
CMS Cameron McKenna, London (020) 7367 3057
me@cmck.com
Partner in Insurance and Reinsurance Department.
Specialisation: Principal areas of practice involve acting in claims and disputes for Insurers and Reinsurers of Banks and Financial Institutions, Directors and Officers, Accountants, Financial Advisers and Stockbrokers, Lloyd's Agents and Lloyd's Brokers; advising Insurers and Reinsurers on policy wordings and construction in insurance and reinsurance contracts; acting in major reinsurance arbitration and litigation disputes and advising Reinsurers generally with clients in the London market, Europe, Middle and Far East, USA and Bermuda. Lectured in Bermuda at International Reinsurance Congress and in Hong Kong and London at various conferences on financial institutions insurance, Directors' and Officers' liability cover and on reinsurance.
Prof. Memberships: Law Society, Chartered Institute of Insurers, Society of Insurance Receivers.
Career: Qualified 1983 and became a Partner of *CMS Cameron McKenna* in 1988.
Personal: Born 22nd January 1958. School Trustee. Leisure pursuits include golf, swimming, tennis, shooting and opera. Lives near Uppingham, Rutland. Married with five children.

GREENLEY, Simon K.P.T.
Reynolds Porter Chamberlain, London (020) 7242 2877
See under Insurance, p.494

HALL, Stuart
Barlow Lyde & Gilbert, London (020) 7247 2277
shall@blg.co.uk
Specialisation: Professional Indemnity, especially Accountants, and Commercial Litigation.
Prof. Memberships: English and Hong Kong Law Societies.
Career: Cambridge University; admitted 1975; partner *Dawson & Co* 1976-1985; partner *Barlow Lyde & Gilbert* 1985 to date.

HARTFIELD, David
Vizard Oldham, London (020) 7663 2222
david.hartfield@vizold.co.uk
Partner specialising in professional negligence, insurance and construction work.
Specialisation: Main area of practice is professional negligence, acting for professional indemnity insurers and their insureds in claims against architects, surveyors, engineers, insurance brokers, accountants and licensed conveyancers. Also handles insurance and construction work, acting for (and occasionally against) insurers in respect of policy disputes and for developers in building and contractual disputes.
Prof. Memberships: Law Society.
Career: Qualified in 1972. Previously a Partner at *Alastair Thomson & Partners.* Set up *Hartfields* in 1997.

HEGARTY, Simon
CMS Cameron McKenna, Bristol (0117) 930 0200
Specialisation: Specialises in insurance litigation (particularly professional indemnity and directors'

and officers' liability) and banking litigation.
Career: Trained and qualified with *Cameron Kemm Norden* (1979-81), served with the Royal Navy (1981-86), re-joined *Cameron Markby* (1987) becoming a Partner in *Cameron Markby Hewitt* in 1992. Managing Partner of *CMS Cameron McKenna*'s Bristol office from 1994.
Personal: Children, amateur dramatics, folk dancing, beer and butterflies are repacing rapidly deteriorating performances on the sports field.

HICK, Mark
Wragge & Co, Birmingham (0121) 685 3652
mark_hick@wragge.com
Specialisation: Leads Professional Indemnity Team. Defends cases against Accountants, Surveyors, Actuaries and many other professionals. Cases include £100 million claim arising from construction of factory, £15 million insurance brokers professional indemnity claim; acting in £10 million venture capitalists professional indemnity claim.
Prof. Memberships: The Chartered Insurance Institute. The British Insurance Law Association. The Liabilities Society.
Career: Called to the Bar 1979. Admitted as Solicitor 1985. Partner at *Wragge & Co* from 1991.
Personal: Born 1957.

HODGSON, Guy
Mills & Reeve, Norwich (01603) 693 221
guy.hodgson@mills-reeve.com
Specialisation: Partner, board member and head of the firm's insurance group of over 50 lawyers covering professional indemnity, general liability and health risks. Specialises in professional indemnity risks and coverage disputes for insurers, mutual funds and professional firms. Acts for all professions dealing with claims brought against them and any related insurance issues. Joined *Mills & Reeve* in 1984 to develop their professional indemnity practice after gaining a number of years' experience working in the London market. Regular speaker on professional indemnity matters.
Prof. Memberships: British Insurance Law Association. Law Society.

JENKINS, Ian
Barlow Lyde & Gilbert, London (020) 7247 2277
ijenkins@blg.co.uk
Specialisation: Insurance, Brokers, Accountants. Directors' and Officers' Liability.
Prof. Memberships: International Bar Association.
Career: Partner, *Barlow Lyde & Gilbert*, 1974. Elected Senior Partner, 1989. Non -Executive Director of Kiln Plc, Crowe Insurance Group Ltd, CEDR accredited mediator.
Personal: Born 1946. Educated at Denstone College and King's College, London. Leisure interests include family and sailing. Member of Royal Thames Yacht Club. Ocean Cruising Club.

LONG, Andrew P.
Pinsent Curtis, Birmingham (0121) 200 1050
andrew.long@pinsents.com
Partner in Insurance Litigation and Head of Financial Services Litigation.
Specialisation: Professional indemnity defendant work, specialising in acting for solicitors and for the financial services industry. Author, speaker and leading expert on pension mis-selling claims. Acts for mutuals, Lloyd's Underwriters, insurers and the financial services industry. Also sits as a Deputy District Judge.
Career: Qualified in 1980. Joined *Pinsent & Co.* in 1986 becoming a Partner in 1989.
Personal: Born 1955. Lives in Worcestershire. Educated at Exeter School and Pembroke College, Oxford. Interests include village sport and bridge.

MACLEOD, Colin
Dundas & Wilson CS, Edinburgh (0131) 228 8000

MCKECHNIE, Robert
Wright Hassall, Leamington Spa (01926) 886688

MCKENNA, John
James Chapman & Co, Manchester (0161) 828 8000
Specialisation: Professional Indemnity cases on behalf of Insurers and Indemnifiers.
Prof. Memberships: The Law Society and The Manchester Law Society.
Career: Admitted–January 1966. Senior Partner–1976 to 1999. Working Consultant–1999.

MICKLEM, Barney
Reynolds Porter Chamberlain, London (020) 7242 2877
Partner in Professional Indemnity Litigation Department.
Specialisation: Professional indemnity litigation specialist. Work relates principally to solicitors, barristers and surveyors. Has addressed various professional indemnity seminars.
Prof. Memberships: Law Society.
Career: Qualified in 1974. Became a Partner in 1977.

MURRAY, Paul C.
Beachcroft Wansbroughs, Birmingham (0121) 698 5200
pmurray@bwlaw.co.uk
Specialisation: Partner and Head of *Beachcroft Wansbroughs* Litigation Department; handles all aspects of professional negligence work, acting primarily for solicitors, surveyors, accountants and architects as well as general insurance matters, particularly policy and coverage disputes. He is also experienced in advising on general liability matters such as property and construction risks.
Career: Qualified 1980. Solicitor *Trump & Partners*, Bristol 1981. Joined *Wansbroughs Willey Hargrave*, Bristol 1981. Relocated to *Wansbroughs Willey Hargrave* (now *Beachcroft Wansbroughs*), Birmingham 1985.

NICHOLAS, Paul D.
Reynolds Porter Chamberlain, London (020) 7242 2877
Partner in Insurance and Professional Indemnity department.
Specialisation: Insurance and professional indemnity.
Career: Qualified in 1970, having joined *Reynolds Porter* in 1968. Became a Partner in 1972.
Personal: Born 24th April 1946. Educated at Mill Hill School 1959-63 and Emmanuel College, Cambridge (BA 1967, LLB 1968). Governor of Lockers Park School and Trustee of S.W. Hertfordshire Hospice Charitable Trust.

PATON, Andrew J.
Pinsent Curtis, Birmingham (0121) 200 1050
andrew.j.paton@pinsents.com
See under Alternative Dispute Resolution, p.83

REGAN, Michael
Rowe & Maw, London (020) 7248 4282
See under Construction, p.205

RIDGWELL, Robert
Browne Jacobson, Nottingham (0115) 976 6000
rridgwell@brownej.co.uk
Specialisation: Defendant Professional Indemnity work, particularly on behalf of surveyors, financial/insurance intermediates and solicitors. Has particular expertise in advising Underwriters on coverage issues coupled with policy drafting.
Prof. Memberships: MCI Arb.
Career: Educated at Lincoln School and Queens College, Cambridge. Joined *Browne Jacobson* 1980. Specialising in defendant Professional Indemnity work since 1986. Partner since 1984.
Personal: Married, with teenage family.

ROXBURGH, James A.R.
Biggart Baillie, Glasgow (0141) 228 8000
jroxburgh@biggartbaillie.co.uk
See under Personal Injury, p.647

SALOMONSEN, V. Erik
Bond Pearce, Exeter (01392) 211 185
xves@bondpearce.com
Partner and Head of the Insurance Group.
Specialisation: Defends claims against a wide range of professionals, including medical professionals. Work also includes employers' and public liability claims including work in the farming industry and for local authority and health trusts. Panel solicitor for Composites, Lloyd's underwriters and mutual funds. An accredited mediator.
Prof. Memberships: Member of the International Bar Association.
Career: Qualified in 1975. Joined *Bond Pearce* in 1975, becoming a partner 1979.

SCHOFIELD, Belinda
CMS Cameron McKenna, London (020) 7367 3000
Partner in insurance and reinsurance group.
Specialisation: Principal areas of practice are handling professional indemnity claims against accountants, actuaries, financial institutions, insurance brokers and directors' and officers' liability. Acting for insurers and insureds. Growing and significant area of practice is in the field of regulation and risk management acting for professionals and insurers in risk control and avoidance projects, due diligence exercises and advising on the impact of regulatory controls, including representing individuals in regulatory proceedings and monitoring such proceedings for insurers. Work also includes general insurance and reinsurance advice and drafting and construction of policy wordings. Experienced in handling large commercial disputes. Speaks at numerous market seminars.

SEYMOUR, Michael J.
Lovells, London (020) 7296 2000
michael.seymour@lovells.com
Specialisation: Main areas of practice: professional negligence, commercial litigation and arbitration often involving an international dimension, particularly in the area of trade and business. Has acted for foreign governments in cases involving state immunity and for banks, insurers and other companies in contract fraud and property related cases.
Prof. Memberships: Law Society, Chartered Insti-

tute of Arbitrators, member (President: 1994-96) of London Solicitors Litigation Association, member of the joint working party of the Bar and the Law Society on the Civil Courts.
Career: Articled at *Lovells*; Qualified 1974; Partner 1982.

SMITH, Antony
Beale and Company, London (020) 7240 3474

SUMMERFIELD, Neil
Lightfoots, Thame (01844) 212305 or 212574/5
Specialisation: Professional Negligence work with particular emphasis on claims against solicitors and surveyors on behalf of lending institutions and private clients.
Career: Qualified 1985. *Lightfoots*, Solicitors, 1983 to date. Became Litigation Partner 1989.
Personal: Born 18th February 1959. University of East Anglia. LL.B (Hons).

TAYLOR, Elisabeth
James Chapman & Co, Manchester (0161) 828 8000
Specialisation: Professional Indemnity cases on behalf of Insurers and Indemnifiers.
Prof. Memberships: The Law Society and The Manchester Law Society.
Career: Educated University of Bristol (LLB) 1971. Admitted–April 1974. Joined *James Chapman & Co*–1976, Partner–1979.

TESTER, Stephen
CMS Cameron McKenna, London (020) 7367 2894
skt@cmck.com
Specialisation: Practises in construction and surveyors' PI, D & O and Contractors All Risk Insurance (both litigation and policy interpretation and drafting). Clients include insurance companies, Lloyd's syndicates, insurance brokers and construction companies.
Prof. Memberships: Society of Construction Law.
Career: KCS Wimbledon and St. John's College Cambridge. Qualified 1981. Partner since 1988.
Personal: Interests include family and friends, golf and squash.

THOMAS, Nicholas
Kennedys, London (020) 7638 3688
Senior Partner. Also Partner in associated Northern Ireland and Hong Kong practices.
Specialisation: Principal area of expertise is professional indemnity, particularly in the construction field and CAR ALOP and property claims, particularly overseas (Middle East, India, Far East and the Americas). Also covers insurance work generally, including disputes as to whether insurers should respond and which insurers should respond. Acted in 'BBL v. John D. Wood and others', and 'National Trust v Hayden Young; Heathrow Express Terminal collapse and Terminal 1 fire. Author of 'Professional Indemnity Claims (An Architect's Guide)', published by Architect's Press in 1981. Regularly addresses conferences and seminars, particularly for insurers.
Prof. Memberships: Member of the Law Society, Fellow of the Chartered Institute of Arbitrators. Also qualified as a solicitor in Hong Kong, Northern Ireland and the Republic of Ireland.
Career: Joined *Kennedys* in 1977 and qualified in 1980. Became a Partner in 1981. Became Senior Partner in 1997.
Personal: Born 16th October 1954. Attended Bristol University 1973-76. School Governor. Leisure pursuits include all sports, travel and the arts. Lives near Berkhamsted, Herts.

TROTTER, John G.
Lovells, London (020) 7296 2000
john.trotter@lovells.com
Specialisation: Main area of practice is litigation and other dispute resolution involving insurance and re-insurance, including professional indemnity and product liability. Has been involved in numerous actions and arbitrations in these areas, including the defence of major claims against lawyers. Has written and spoken widely about issues affecting the insurance industry such as the Civil Procedure Rules and coverage for millennium IT claims.
Prof. Memberships: Vice-chairman of the Insurance Committee of the International Bar Association. Member of the London Solicitors Litigation Association and the City of London Law Society. Member British Insurance Law Association, co-author of 'Liability of Lawyers and indemnity insurance' (Kluerer/IBA).
Career: Qualified in 1977 with *Lovells*; based in New York office 1980-82; Partner in 1983.

TURTLE, W. Brian W.
Carson & McDowell, Belfast (028) 9024 4951
See under Litigation (Commercial), p.569

WARD, John J.
Beale and Company, London (020) 7240 3474

WAREING, Diana M.
Shakespeares, Birmingham (0121) 632 4199
Specialisation: Defendant Professional Indemnity work, particularly on behalf of accountants, surveyors and insurance brokers/intermediaries.
Prof. Memberships: BILA and FOIL.
Career: Includes: Assistant Solicitor at *Linklaters & Paines* from 1975 to 1979. Partner at *Duggan Lea & Co.* (now *Shakespeares*) from 1980 to date. Has dealt with Defendant Professional Indemnity work since 1979.

WELSH, John
Morison Bishop, Glasgow (0141) 248 4672
See under Construction, p.208

WHITE, Stuart
Hextall Erskine, London (020) 7488 1424
stuartwhite@hextalls.com
Partner in Commercial Dispute Resolution Department.
Specialisation: A significant area of practice is professional indemnity, principally construction related, for architects and engineers. Also handles general insurance work, covering insurance disputes, policy wordings and general liability and property litigation. Extensive experience of mediation. Acted in 'Investors in Industry v. South Bedfordshire D.C.', 'Crown v. Mowlem' (re final certificates), 'Citibank v. Excess' (re costs liability of insurers), and was also involved in the personal accident insurance claim following the death of Robert Maxwell. Major clients include insurance companies, mutual insurance associations and Lloyd's syndicates. Has given seminars on a range of topics including architects' liability, product liability, liability for pollution, drafting of policy wordings, 'Chapman v. Christopher', the impact of the Woolf reforms on insurers, and 'True Professionalism'. Has addressed the Fire Loss Association, the Chartered Institute of Loss Adjusters and the British Insurance Brokers Association. Regularly contributes to various insurance publications. Co author with partner Adrian Bingham of the Professional Indemnity section of LLP publication 'Insurance Disputes'.
Prof. Memberships: Society of Construction Law, British Insurance Law Association, CEDR, Fire Loss Association, Chartered Insurance Institute.
Career: Qualified in 1984. Joined *Hextall Erskine* in 1980, becoming a Partner in 1987.
Personal: Born 1957. Attended The Queen's College Oxford, MA (Hons) 1975-78.

WILLIAMSON, David
Brodies WS, Edinburgh (0131) 228 3777
dswilliamson@brodies.co.uk
See under Litigation (Commercial), p.569

WILSON, Michael G.
Barlow Lyde & Gilbert, London (020) 7247 2277
mgwilson@blg.co.uk
Specialisation: Professional Indemnity litigation, in particular, claims against domestic and international banks. Direct involvement in many of the leading cases against merchant banks arising as a result of the takeover activity of the late 80s.
Prof. Memberships: Member of the Law Society; City of London Solicitors Company; Asia Pacific Lawyers Association; International Bar Association; Southwestern Legal Foundation; Inter-Pacific Bar Association; Freeman of the City of London; Fellow of the Royal Society of Art.
Career: Articled with *Slaughter and May*; qualified in 1975; Assistant Solicitor 1977-1979; Partner *Berwin Leighton* 1979 to 1999; Partner *Barlow Lyde & Gilbert* 1999 to date.
Personal: Golf, tennis, squash, swimming, travel, reading, music.

WYLDE, Peter R.
Irwin Mitchell, London (020) 7250 1884
wyldep@irwinmitchell.co.uk
Specialisation: Leads *Irwin Mitchell's* Professional Negligence Unit which, uniquely, acts primarily for Claimants in claims against professionals, in particular, solicitors, accountants and financial advisers. Specialises in claims arising from commercial transactions, mergers and acquisitions and commercial litigation. A strong proponent of mediation, Peter sits on the Mediation Committee of the Central London County Court and initiated the Wilkinson case which established that legal aid is available for mediation. Contributed to the development of the pre-acion protocol for claims against solicitors. Currently advising on potential claims arising from the Versailles Group insolvency; handling several claims against pension and other trustees; advising in relation to the insolvency of the Football League Managers Pension Scheme.
Prof. Memberships: ADR Group; Association of Northern Mediators; ADR London Regional Forum; Central London County Court Mediation Committee; London Litigation Solicitors Association; Law Society.
Career: Qualified 1983. *Irwin Mitchell* Partner 1985. Educated at Royal Grammar School, Newcastle Upon Tyne and Sheffield University. Head of *Irwin Mitchell* Commercial Dispute Resolution Department. Member *Irwin Mitchell* Management Board 1996-99. Managing Partner, *Irwin Mitchell* London office since 1998. Head of Professional Negligence Unit.
Personal: Leisure: sport, music, cinema/theatre.

PROJECTS / PFI

OVERVIEW: "PFI is and always has been a subset of Project Finance." In this edition we attempt to reflect the cross-over in the principles of the government backed Private Finance Initiative and the increasingly international sphere of project finance by merging our tables of leading London firms. The PFI/PPP revolution is an important aspect of the domestic market and an area in which the regional firms are making headway, particularly considering their dominance of the public sector procurement authorities. However it is the city firms with their international resources who are at the front of exporting PFI principles.

Clients continue to stress the need for extensive teams of well rounded individuals to get the deals done. Strength in depth and a sector-based track record are deciding factors in their choice. The US firms continue to snag major international projects, with infrastructure, energy and telecoms as their most dominant areas. However, the market perceives that the London offices of US firms do not have the established presence to threaten the leaders and take comparatively little interest in the domestic market, despite recent high profile recruitment. It is the firms with a strong UK projects practice and US tie-ups that perform well across the board, and are capturing the increasingly profitable Asian markets.

RESEARCH APPROVED BY BMRB: *For this edition,* Chambers' *researchers conducted 6083 interviews – 4408 with law firms, 598 with barristers and 1077 with clients.*

The validity of the research was scrutinised by BMRB International, who audited both the methodology and the results at our offices in July 2000. They interviewed Chambers' *researchers and cross-checked sample interviews. Details of the audit appear on page 7.*

LONDON

PROJECTS/PFI • London	Ptnrs	Assts
❶ Allen & Overy	27	50
❷ Clifford Chance	20	55
Linklaters	36	90
❸ Freshfields Bruckhaus Deringer	25	50
Norton Rose	12	52
❹ CMS Cameron McKenna	22	50
Denton Wilde Sapte	27	12
Herbert Smith	30	50
❺ Ashurst Morris Crisp	8	17
Lovells	12	15
Milbank, Tweed, Hadley & McCloy	6	4
Shearman & Sterling	⚐	⚐
Slaughter and May	28	-
White & Case	4	18
❻ Baker & McKenzie	8	15
Berwin Leighton	7	16
Bird & Bird	8	22
DLA	10	30
Masons	4	11
Rowe & Maw	4	6
Simmons & Simmons	22	18
SJ Berwin & Co	6	7
Trowers & Hamlins	2	14
Weil, Gotshal & Manges	2	6

Within each band, firms are listed alphabetically.
⚐ *Figures unavailable at time of going to press.*

Allen & Overy • **Projects**: A *"stunningly brilliant"* projects team packed with *"big personalities,"* it is seen to be pulling away from the chasing pack with a successful leverage of banking expertise and recent moves into the sponsor market. The firm advises on all industry sectors with particular strengths in power, energy and transport and has a truly international penetration. **Graham Vinter** is universally recognised as *"a star"* and the mainstay of the projects team along side the seasoned **Jonathan Horsfall Turner** (*"a get it done lawyer"*) and **David Sedgley** (*"technically strong,"*) who also is seen as active in the PFI sphere. Experienced players **Anthony Humphrey** (*"a good head for complex documentation"*) and **Brian Harrison** who is *"sensitive without being soft,"* are joined by new names to our lists, **Stephen Gillespie**, receiving praise for his *"excellent finance mind,"* and **Mark O'Neill** for his real estate work. Advised Japan Bank for International Co-operation on its involvement in the US$1.6 billion limited recourse financing of oil and gas reserves in Brazil.

• **PFI**: A star player in the PFI market, **Anne Baldock** is *"extremely bright, personable and practical,"* leading the PFI/PPP side of this practice which has a good mix of clients, notably the firm's traditional bias towards lenders, but also sponsors and concession granting authorities. Growth areas are health, defence, accommodation and transport. Acted for lenders on resurrected Treasury Building projects including refurbishment and subsequent facilities management, and acted for a joint sponsor of St George's Hospital Project who contributed both equity and debt to the project. Recent PFI/PPP instructions have come from Germany, South Africa and Portugal. **Clients:** The Japan Bank for International Co-operation, Barclays Bank, Premier Prison Services.

Clifford Chance • **Projects**: *"Impressive"* practice praised for its *"flexibility and cohesion,"* which has an enviable reputation acting mainly for sponsors and banks. London Projects Group head, **Peter Blake**, is recognised for his expertise in the energy field, and his enthusiasm has played a leading role in successful projects such as Sidi Krir Power Project in Egypt (for sponsors) and Ujpest CHP Power Project in Hungary (for lenders). He is ably supported by a balanced team including **Tim Soutar**, who has long overseas experience. **David Bickerton**, *"commercially astute and pragmatic,"* is praised for his construction work, and the *"excellent"* **Margaret Gossling** is a strong force in the banking aspects of project finance. **Chris Wyman** has spent the bulk of the year increasing the practice's presence in India, resulting in advice on 27 IPPs, but a diminished profile in the domestic market. Acted as local counsel for lenders in the US$575 million Flag Atlantic telecoms deal in the US and as foreign sponsor counsel for Phillips Petroleum on the US$1 billion Q Chem petrochemical project in Qatar.

• **PFI**: Perceived by the market as a balanced practice in terms of UK domestic PFI and International projects, the practice has been involved in high profile deals such as advising the consortium (Rotch Property Group

LEADING INDIVIDUALS • Project Finance	
❶ **BARRATT Jeffery** Norton Rose	**BLACK Alan** Linklaters
SALT Stuart Linklaters	**VINTER Graham** Allen & Overy
❷ **BLAKE Peter** Clifford Chance	**HORSFALL TURNER Jonathan** Allen & Overy
MACRITCHIE Kenneth Shearman & Sterling	**SEDGLEY David** Allen & Overy
TAYLOR Michael Norton Rose	
❸ **BELLHOUSE John** White & Case	**BUCKWORTH Nicholas** Shearman & Sterling
COLE Margaret White & Case	**ELSEY Mark** Ashurst Morris Crisp
FINLAY Peter White & Case	**FLETCHER Phillip** Milbank, Tweed
FOX Jason Herbert Smith	**GILLESPIE Stephen** Allen & Overy
GOSSLING Margaret Clifford Chance	**HARRISON Brian** Allen & Overy
HUMPHREY Anthony Allen & Overy	**RANSOME Clive** Linklaters
ROWEY Kent Freshfields Bruckhaus	**WEBER David** Linklaters
WYMAN Chris Clifford Chance	
❹ **BICKERTON David** Clifford Chance	**CRANE David** Norton Rose
HALL Peter Norton Rose	**LEVINE Marshall** Linklaters
MCCORMICK Roger Freshfields Bruckhaus	**MCQUATER Gavin** Lovells
PHILLIPS Robert CMS Cameron McKenna	**PREECE Andrew** Herbert Smith
SOUTAR Tim Clifford Chance	**TEMPLETON - KNIGHT Jane** Milbank, Tweed
UP AND COMING	
ARMITAGE Richard Simmons & Simmons	**O'NEILL Mark** Allen & Overy
ONES TO WATCH	
EDWARDS Stephen Slaughter and May	**MORRISON Neil** Rowe & Maw

LEADING INDIVIDUALS • PFI	
✪ **BALDOCK Anne** Allen & Overy	**BLISS Nick** Freshfields Bruckhaus
WHITE Bruce Linklaters	
❶ **MATHEOU Mike** Lovells	**NOBLE Perry** Freshfields Bruckhaus
STEADMAN Tim Clifford Chance	**TOTT Nicholas** Herbert Smith
❷ **COULTER David** Norton Rose	**DUFFICY Frank** CMS Cameron McKenna
ELSEY Mark Ashurst Morris Crisp	**FOX Jason** Herbert Smith
JOHNSTON Bruce Weil, Gotshal & Manges	
❸ **FRANCIS Barry** Buchanan Ingersoll	**GNIADKOWSKI Stan** Denton Wilde Sapte
IVISON Andrew CMS Cameron McKenna	**MARLOW Ed** Denton Wilde Sapte
McCORMACK Carol Berwin Leighton	**PREECE Andrew** Herbert Smith
SEDGLEY David Allen & Overy	
❹ **ALLAN Simon** Berwin Leighton	**BALLINGALL James** Theodore Goddard
GATES Ellen Denton Wilde Sapte	**ROLFE Andrew** Clifford Chance
SANDERS Jan Ashurst Morris Crisp	
UP AND COMING	
SPACIE Dominic Mayer, Brown & Platt	

See *Profiles* on page 695

Ltd and J. Henry Schroder & Co Ltd) on the Chichester NHS Trust project which involved a £1 billion bond monoline wrapped programme for public sector-related projects. Prominence across the board including defence (MoD Tornado Simulator Project), accommodation (advice to bidding consortium on transfer of Inland Revenue and Customs & Excise property portfolio STEPS) and transport (A13 Thames Gateway). The integrated team includes **Andrew Rolfe**, bringing his renowned expertise in property to the table, and *"first class"* **Tim Steadman**, a strong-minded player who is recognised for his construction work. The latter is also seen as the force pushing international PFI deals which include the Beira Interior road project in Portugal (advising project company) and Nedco N4 Platinum Toll Highway in South Africa (advising lenders.) **Clients:** Abbey National Treasury Services, Banque Paribas, Babcock & Brown, Hyder Investments.

Linklaters • **Projects**: Recommended for *"consistent"* quality of work and a smooth operating process, this practice is headed by **Alan Black** *("sharp mind, impressive style")* who has a strong reputation in the energy markets. The *"marvellous"* **Stuart Salt** is seen as a commercially minded and pragmatic deal-doer who occupies the top spot in our rankings. *"Old hand"* **David Weber** is highly rated for his work on the Chad-Cameroon pipeline, **Clive Ransome** maintains his reputation for international work, while a new name, prominent for his construction work is *"always on the ball"* **Marshall Levine**. With a well balanced client base, this practice has strengths in power generation and distribution, transport, water telecoms and infrastructure work. Acted for sponsors on US$2.5 billion Dabhol Power projects in India which closed Phase II in 1999 and included the financing for the LNG and Shipping Infrastructure. Also advised the Greek Government on US$2.5 billion project financing of ring-road around Athens.

• **PFI**: Regarded as having a good focus on the domestic PFI market but perhaps overshadowed by the success within international project finance. The integrated team benefits from the presence of **Bruce White**, universally recommended as *"a star"* for his leadership skills, huge personality and following in the banking sector. Growth areas for the practice this year include defence (MoD Skynet 5 projects) and education (Glasgow Schools.) Acted for the sponsors of the £340 million London CityLink radio transmission project, for the lenders in the refinancing of Fazakerley prison and for the sponsors on the £60 million IT PFI project for HM Customs & Excise. **Clients:** National Power, ABN Amro, Deutsche Bank, Carillion.

Freshfields Bruckhaus Deringer • **Projects**: A significant practice in project finance, although it is perceived by the market to be dwarfed by the firm's PFI activity. The team is said to be *"slicker than most,"* with a strong international presence acting on both the sponsor and lender side. The market was fulsome in its praise of the team's *"financial acumen."* Head of global project finance practice, **Kent Rowey** is *"a highly skilled, personable chap,"* and is joined in the rankings by the *"diligent"* **Roger McCormick**. Strengths include transport (advised Derech Eretz Highways on the US$1.35 billion financing of the Cross-Israel Toll Road project, the largest in Israel) and energy. The department advised OPIC on the financing of US$600 million Cuiaba Integrated Power project, one of first combined pipeline and power station projects to be financed on a limited recourse basis.

• **PFI**: With major clients in all sectors of the market and a firm grip on the domestic scene, this side of the practice is seen as particularly impressive. **Nick Bliss** remains the leading light and is recommended as *"commercial, aggressively bright and a value for money lawyer."* The team is further strengthened by **Perry Noble**, who is admired for his London Transport work and is praised as *"experienced, trustworthy and intelligent."* Advised Warburg Dillon Read on the financing of Section 2 of the Channel Tunnel Rail Link and over the last three years has advised London Underground on the Connect (digital communication) project. The firm was also recognised for its work with Financial Security Assurance in advising on the Eurobond issuance programme of up to £1 billion for the financing of PPP and public sector-related projects. **Clients:** Warburg Dillon Read, Financial Security Assurance, London Transport, Conoco.

Norton Rose • **Projects**: *"Delightful"* projects team praised across the board for its international presence and pre-eminence in the energy and infrastructure market, with a balanced client base acting for financiers, multi-laterals and developers. The seasoned team is led by **Jeffery Barratt** *("traditional, excellent in attitude and skill")* and benefits greatly from the experience of **Michael Taylor** *"an outstanding, creative performer"* who is seen as hugely active in the electricity, oil and gas fields. They are joined by new names to the rankings. **Peter Hall** is recommended for his skilled construction work and **David Crane** is felt to bring specialist contractual strengths to power deals *("he handles complex issues with ease, distilling points clearly and accurately.")* However, the firm is perceived to suffer from a lack of US capacity and a weakness in capital markets which sets it apart from the three market leaders. Acted for AES Corporation and achieved financial close of the acquisition of Drax power station from National Power plc (£1.875 billion.) Also advised Paribas in connection with the TotalFina SA/Tractabel SA consortium bid for Taweelah A1 independent power and water project. Advising the project company in the Athens Ring Road project (US$3 billion.)

• **PFI**:Perceived by the market as a minor focus for the projects finance team, PFI activity has nevertheless included a number of high profile clients. *"Charismatic"* **David Coulter** is praised for his focus on this area and his reputation with the financial sector. Acted for Bank of America, RBS, Toronto-Dominion and Bayerische Landesbank in the funding of the London Underground Project Connect. Advised the consortium of Taylor Woodrow and London & Regional Properties on the £130 million Sheffield, Heart of the City regeneration project. **Clients:** Paribas, RBS, Charterhouse Bank, Norsk Hydro (UK) Ltd.

CMS Cameron McKenna • **Projects**: Recommended as a *"professional"* team with a niche strength in electricity, the practice is finding it hard to shake off the Public Sector tag which has historically generated the most work. The *"excellent"* **Robert Phillips** is perceived to be making the push into international project finance and is praised for his strong leadership style. The firm has a niche strength in electricity, both in the domestic and international market and has advised Budapest Eromu (a joint venture between Fortnum of Finland and Tomen Corporation of Japan) on Hungary's second independent power project.

• **PFI**: With a background in construction, **Frank Dufficy** is praised as *"a commercial, capable lawyer, a deal maker"* and is ably supported by **Andrew Ivison** who is recommended as *"highly practical."* Advised the Government on the restructuring of Channel Tunnel Rail Link (including raising £2.65 billion of new financing) and advised private sector sponsors on concession agreements, finance agreements and other project documents for the first local authority DBFO (A130) road project (£80 million.) **Clients:** Department of Transport, Cinergy Global Power.

Denton Wilde Sapte • **Projects**: Market perception of the February 2000 merger is *"a natural fit with obvious synergies,"* the team benefiting from the traditional Wilde Sapte banking strengths and the Denton Hall energy market domination. However, the jury is still out on the strategy needed to lift the team out of the chasing pack, with the firm's smaller international offices not considered sufficient to compete evenly with the market leaders. The projects team has a focus on the areas of energy/power, telecoms and infrastructure. Active overseas, it has recently advised ECGD on prospective financing to the US$1.4 billion Visakhapatnam Power project in India and advised Oman LNG and Abu Dhabi Gas Liquefaction Co on supply arrangements for Enron's Dabhol power project Phase II.

• **PFI**: This year the firm's leading players are recommended for their PFI work: **Stan Gniadkowski** is "impressive, a strong player," the *"skilled"* **Ed Marlow** is *"easy to work with"* and recommended for his MoD work and **Ellen Gates** remains in our ranking, recognised for her work on the A130 road scheme (acted for Essex County Council.) Continued as advisers on MoD's nationwide water and waste water project and acted for a Carillion-led consortium on healthcare projects, including a major acute hospital project for Swindon and Marlborough NHS Trust. **Clients:** MoD, Laing Hyder, Total Oil UK, Virgin Rail, Standard Chartered Bank.

Herbert Smith • **Projects**: Perceived to be a leading figure in the domestic market, but lacking the banking strengths and overseas presence necessary to threaten the leaders. The team is felt to have a more balanced client base than most, acting for its traditional base of public sector outfits as well as a growing number of funders and sponsors. Leading figures ranked in the tables for both. Projects and PFI are **Jason Fox**, recommended as *"a delight to work with,"* and *"old hand"* **Andrew Preece**, who advised London and Continental Railways Ltd on its reorganisation and the joint venture with Railtrack on the £5 billion bond and loan financing of the Channel Tunnel Rail Link construction. The practice also acted as international counsel for ICICI, the lead arranger in relation to the Samayanallur power project in Tamil Nadu, India and advised Chase Manhattan Bank on the limited recourse financing arrangement for an oil and gas field in Burma.

• **PFI**: Renowned for its big ticket work for the Public Sector, the firm has advised bidding consortia (Bechtel, GKN/McDonnell Douglas) and banks (Bank of Tokyo Mitsubishi Ltd, Bank of America, Deutsche Bank, Barclays.) **Nick Tott** is praised as *"a professional, clever person with good ideas"* and *"handles complex documentation with a clear head."* The team as a whole receives mixed reviews, with commendations for a *"pleasant"* office, *"working to a common purpose,"* being countered by fears over a lack of quality support at assistant level. Advised Bank of Tokyo Mitsubishi Ltd on its debt financing of the IT infrastructure transaction for HM Customs & Excise and advised Bombardier Group on the £150 million PFI project providing aircraft and services to the RAF's Light Aircraft Flying Task. **Clients:** Bank of Tokyo Mitsubishi Ltd, GCHQ, Highways Agency, Bechtel.

Ashurst Morris Crisp • **Projects**: Recognised as a sponsor-led practice active in energy, transport and the niche sector of mining, it also benefits from international exposure with Europe, Africa and India being particularly strong areas for work. Department head **Mark Elsey** is recommended both in project finance and PFI work but is perceived to receive *"variable"* support. Acted for the winning bidder, N3TC for the N3 toll road project in South Africa and acted for Marubeni (sponsors) and EPC (contractor) on the $300 million PPN power project in Tamil Nadu, India.

• **PFI**: A number of big-name construction clients have driven this area of the practice which is also active in exporting PFI principles to Portugal (acting for Aenor consortium on North Toll road project) and Japan (representing Vivendi/Marubeni consortium on water and waste treatment projects.) **Jan Sanders** has a good reputation. The team acted on the £150 million Treasury Building project (GOGGS) for Exchequer Partnership consortium (Bovis, Stanhope and Chesterton). Also acted for the Carillion, Group 4, BT consortium, the preferred bidder on the GCHQ New Accommodation project. **Clients:** National Power, Marubeni, Barclays Bank, Amey, Sir Robert McAlpine Ltd.

Lovells • **Projects**: Perceived by the market to be most active in PFI, the team has yet to achieve similar recognition for its international project finance work. It may, however, benefit from the merger with Boesebeck Droste and a greater access to European-based clients. Group head **Gavin McQuater** is well respected *("good finance brain")* but is thought to spread himself over a wide spectrum of work. On the international front, acted for Nissho Iwai Corporation (sponsor and senior lender) on the US$344 million combined cycle power plant in Playas de Rosicrito, Mexico. Domestically, acted for Sport England (Lottery funder and original promoter) on the £480 million Wembly National Stadium project.

• **PFI**: Good reputation for both its Public Sector and private client capacity. **Mike Matheou**, *"strong in corporate documentation and commercially pragmatic"* has recently advised the Government on the standardisation of PFI documentation. Acted for the Inland Revenue and Customs & Excise on the STEPS project, and acted for National Air Traffic Services Ltd on its high profile planned PPP. **Clients:** Inland Revenue, Nissho Iwai Corporation, Sport England.

Milbank, Tweed, Hadley & McCloy A force to be reckoned with on the global market and perceived to be the one US firm active in the domestic energy market, advising NatWest in relation to the £200 million Shoreham power project. A strong base within the banking sector and pre-eminence in the energy market has given the team the depth to develop niche sectors such as the financing of wind farms and satellite projects. Led by **Phillip Fletcher** *("a strong personality,")* the team is thought easily able to weather the defection of Jane Templeton-Knight to Hunton & Williams. Advised CSFB on the $160 million financing for construction and delivery of Nigeria LNG's expansion project to transport gas to Europe. The practice continues to be strong in India ($1 billion North Chennai power project, for the lenders,) the Middle East (Taweelah A1 power and desalination facility in Abu Shabi for the consortium of Total and Tractebel) and continues to dominate the Italian power market. **Clients:** CSFB, NatWest.

Shearman & Sterling Renowned for banking strength and global presence, the *"well-established"* London team is highly regarded in the oil, gas and telecoms fields and is perceived to be a team of *"international stars"* rather than competitors on the domestic scene. Highly regarded department head **Kenneth MacRitchie** is *"a great lawyer with a top level intellect"* and is supported by the increasingly high-profile **Nick Buckworth**, praised for his *"sensible"* work in Eastern Europe. Advised Barclays Capital on the Taweelah A2 Power and Desalination project and the arranging banks (including ABN-Amro, Citibank, Credit Lyonnaise and West LB) on the US$450 million San Lorenzo Gas-Fired Power Project. **Clients:** ABN-Amro, Barclays Capital, BG plc, P&O Ports.

Slaughter and May • **Projects**: The *"blue-blooded"* team draws on the talents of partners and associates from across the whole firm. A lack of international leverage has been cited as a hindrance to the firm in this area of practice. Despite this, the firm is seen acting on big-ticket projects and PFIs, thanks to a *"stunning"* client base. The practice is particularly recommended for its strength in tax and complex financial documentation. Advised RBS and Bankers Trustees Company Ltd on the Virgin Trains project, providing new rolling stock for West Coast Main Line. Internationally prominent deals include acting for Eastern Power & Electricity Trading Ltd on funding for a hydro-electric power project in Svartisen, Norway.
• **PFI**: High-profile work in this arena has included advising Department of the Environment, Transport and the Regions on the PPP for National Air Traffic Services, and acted for the arranging banks for the preferred bidders on the MoD redevelopment of offices in Whitehall. **Clients:** NATS, RBS, Eastern Power & Electricity Trading Ltd.

White & Case *"Serious projects people,"* praised for their *"versatility, the quality of work and balanced client base."* Market perception remains that while they are a powerful force on the global scene, domestic project/PFI work is a lesser focus. Department head **Peter Finlay** has the *"exposure to major international clients"* and is recognised for establishing the London office. He is supported by the *"seasoned"* **John Bellhouse**, recommended for his construction expertise, and by **Margaret Cole** who is *"active, bright and impressive."* Domestically, the team has advised the National Grid Company plc on the first project financing for the 40 MW electrical interconnector, linking the Isle of Man to the electricity pool of England. International deals include representing state-owned Cross-Israel Highway Authority on the US$1.3 billion road toll project (Israel's first BOT project) and representing senior lenders (IFC, Asian Development Bank and CDC) on the US$240 million financing of a container terminal in the Colombo, Sri Lanka. **Clients:** IFC, Asian Development Bank, National Grid plc.

Baker & McKenzie Mainly recognised for its international project finance work, a strong corporate practice and a global network of sixty offices means that this team picks up interesting work. Has yet to make a similar impact on the UK market, as the London office is said to be *"patchy."* Roads, power (particularly oil and gas) and telecoms are strengths, with a balance in acting for the lender and sponsor market. Advised Sanwa Bank and Paribas on the first independent power project in Tunisia (Rades) and is acting for Petrobas on its US$3 billion Barracuda and Caratinga offshore oil projects. Continues to dominate the Eastern Europe infrastructure market, representing Austostrada Wielkoplska SA (project company) on the A2 toll motorway in Poland. **Clients:** Sanwa Bank, Paribas, Petrobas, Nortel.

Berwin Leighton Perceived to have an established PFI practice, the team of *"good individuals doing a credible job"* are in the stages of developing projects presence with a niche in the rail market. The firm however is thought to lack the capacity for large project finance deals. In the PFI market, the team benefits from the presence of **Carol McCormack**, a strong construction lawyer. Team head **Simon Allan** is recommended for steering big-ticket Public Sector work, including work in the health care sector (also involves NHS PFU documentation standardisation) and for the MoD. Acted for the Treasury in the Government Offices at Great George Street (GOGGS) PFI accommodation project which also resulted in the Treasury Taskforce Guidance documents. In healthcare, the team has acted for the winning consortium on the King's College hospital and for the NHS Trust on the New General Hospital at Barnet. **Clients:** Jarvis Projects Ltd, Norwest Holst, MoD.

Bird & Bird It is no surprise to see this *"strong"* team establishing and developing Government policy on IT PFIs. Well respected for its domination of the public sector in this area, the firm have advised on third party debt-funded IT PFI projects, but is thought to lack the banking clout to challenge the main players. Advised HM Customs & Excise on the first central government ITPFI project to be financed on a limited recourse basis by third party banks. Also advised the Vehicle Inspectorate on the MOT computerisation project. On an international scale, the team is advising the Foreign and Commonwealth Office on the Global Telecoms project to establish a global voice and data network under PFI concepts. **Clients:** HM Prison Services, Vehicles Inspectorate, HM Customs & Excise.

DLA With a national spread of offices, this firm is receiving recommendations for its PFI work offering *"efficient, sound, practical and knowledgeable advice."* Traditionally seen acting for local authorities and the consortia rather than financial institutions, the fields of health, defence and education continue to grow, and the team has been instructed on five of the six second wave hospital PFI projects. In education, acted for Tower Hamlets on both a bundled and single school projects and for bidders Tibury Douglas, Alfred McAlpine and Molem on regional school bundles. Recognised for its work in defence, the team is acting for the MoD on the £350 million Colchester Garrison project and for CAE on the Hawk Tornado and E3D projects. **Clients:** MoD, Alfred McAlpine, Charterhouse Bank.

Masons Overwhelmingly recognised for construction and engineering expertise. This base has given the firm an entrée into the PFI market, where they are considered *"strong contenders,"* having recovered from last year's defections to US firm Mayer, Brown & Platt. The practice has an even balance between public sector advisory work and private sector consortia but is not seen to have a meaningful banking presence. Successful in exporting the principles of PFI, the team has acted on two prison projects in South Africa, and is working with the project company on a port development in India. Acted for John Molem & Co plc on the South Tees Acute Services NHS Trust and advising Adtranz Consortium on the £150 million Nottingham Light Rail project (includes construction, O&M, property, planning and funding.) **Clients:** John Molem & Co plc, MoD, Metropolitan Police Service, Carillion plc.

Rowe & Maw Recognised as active in PFI, this team has a traditional base in local authority work and a niche strength in rail and transport, including fleet renewal projects for Virgin Rail Group Ltd. Successfully entered the international market, advising on hospital projects in India. A team praised for its juniors said to display leadership skills and deal management. Acting for the Road Management Consortium on the A13 Thames Gateway DBFO project and for Alfred McAlpine Construction Ltd in a consortium bidding for the Newport Southern Distributor road project (a pathfinder local authority DBFO project.) **Clients:** Virgin Rail Group Ltd, Serco Healthcare, DTI.

Simmons & Simmons • **Projects**: *"Trustworthy and competent,"* the firm is particularly seen in the defence and transport sectors, and has a significant international presence. Acted for UAE Offsets on Project Dolphin, the international gas pipeline linking countries in the Middle East.
• **PFI**: Prominent in exporting the principles of PFI and PPP, the team has acted for the European Investment Bank on the Beira Interior toll road project in Portugal (constructed on a DBFO basis.) The team has received particular praise for its work for the MoD and in defence, with **Richard Armitage** seen as *"extremely focused, a quality player."* Advised the MoD on the future Strategic Tanker Aircraft project (total value £2.5 billion.) Recognised as the *"flagship firm"* for Railtrack, acted in its negotiations with London Underground Ltd and Department for the Environment, Transport and the Region on a proposed PPP. Advised on the PPP with the Tyne and

Wear Passenger Transport Executive to create the Sunderland Metro extension. **Clients:** Railtrack plc, MoD, European Investment Bank, UAE Offsets.

S J Berwin & Co A *"commercial"* team, thought to lack the substantial banking practice needed to leverage itself against the leading firms. It is recognised for drawing in clients based on the strength of its property reputation and is active in public sector-oriented PFI projects. The firm has undergone a re-focus away from volume PFI projects to an emphasis on big-ticket deals and clients. Has acted for Babcock & Brown on the Norfolk Police Authority project, the Strathclyde Police Training Centre and on the Metropolitan police stations. Continue to represent Bouygues on the Barnet and West Middlesex hospital PFIs. **Clients:** Babcock & Brown, Bouygues (UK) Ltd, Innisfree.

Trowers & Hamlins • **Projects**: A small international practice with five offices in the Middle East and *"pockets of notable local activity,"* this team is well received for its limited work in the energy market. Advised CMS Energy (developer) on the Taweelah A2 Independent Power and Water Project in Abu Dhabi designed on a BOO basis.

• **PFI**: Active in the domestic market covering a wide set of industry sectors, the team is seen to have particular strength in healthcare and housing. Pre-eminent as a firm in social housing, the team has acted for Lovell Partnerships Ltd on their bid for Castle Vale Housing Action Trust PFI scheme and acted for Ryhurst Ltd the Oxleas and Black Country mental health projects. **Clients:** United Power Co (SAOG Oman), Borealis, Ryhurst Ltd.

Weil, Gotshal & Manges Increasing its profile in the London market with a focus on international project finance, including the emerging markets, this firm is regarded as a *"credible"* competitor. *"Impressive"* **Bruce Johnston** (formerly of Wilde Sapte) is *"a diligent, highly -rated operator."* With a global network of offices and extensive involvement in power, telecoms and infrastructure deals across Europe, this small team has acted on a number of significant transactions. Domestically, advised MBIA and Royal Bank of Canada on the Sterling Water project, and in Europe is advising the EIB on the Athens ring-road project and Saur and Gelsenwasser on Poland's first major water project. **Clients:** EIB, West LB, NatWest.

Top Ten UK Completed Project Finance/PFI Deals (Jan to June 2000)

	Project Name	Project Value	Sponsors	Underwriters	Lawyers to the Project Owners	Lawyers to the Sponsors	Lawyers to the Underwriters
1	**Property** MoD Main Building	£551m	• Hyder Investments • MacQuarie Infrastructure • Amey • Innisfree	Dresdner KB	Herbert Smith	Clifford Chance	Slaughter and May
2	**Power** Acquisition of 650MW Killinghome Power Project	£390m	• NRG	Bank of America	Linklaters	Ashurst Morris Crisp	Shearman & Sterling
3	**Oil & Gas** Project Finance of 8% Stake in Elgin North Sea Development	£260m (debt value)	• British Borneo	ABN Amro Barclays Capital	N/A	In-House Herbert Smith	Linklaters
4	**Transport** Nottingham Light Rail Scheme	£241m	• Carillion • Adtranz • Innisfree • Nottingham City Transport • Transdev	ABN AMRO Dresdner KB Bankgesellschaft Berlin	Eversheds	Consortium: Masons Nabarro Nathanson Nottingham City Transport: Garretts	Linklaters
5	**Transport** A13 DBFO Toll Road	£224m	• Road Management Group	Arranger: Greenwich NatWest Guarantor: AMBAC MBIA	N/A	Rowe & Maw	Arranger and Guarantor: Clifford Chance
6	**Property** Treasury Building PFI	£140.8m	• Bovis • Stanhope • Chesterton	Warburg Dillon Read	Allen & Overy	Consortium: Ashurst Morris Crisp Chesterton: Osborne Clark Stanhope: Herbert Smith	Allen & Overy
7	**Property** Army Foundation College	£84m	• Jarvis • Halifax	Halifax	Masons	Jarvis: Walker Morris Halifax: Theodore Goddard	Halifax: Theodore Goddard
8	**Property** Birmingham Group Schools Project	£80m	• Galliford • Innisfree	Lloyds TSB	In-House	Galliford: Martineau Johnson Innisfree: Clifford Chance	CMS Cameron McKenna
9	**Power** Heartlands Power	£65m	• Rolls Royce Power Ventures	ABN Amro	Skadden, Arps Slate, Meagher & Flom LLP Theodore Goddard Milbank, Tweed, Hadley & McCloy	Freshfields Bruckhaus Deringer	Allen & Overy
10	**Property** St. Georges Hospital	£65m	• Edison Capital • Canmore Partnership • Noble Fund	Lloyds TSB	Masons	Allen & Overy	Dundas & Wilson

Source: Project Finance International/Thomson Financial Securities Data Project Finance Database; *Source: Law Firms – Chambers & Partners*

Other Notable Practitioners Head of Theodore Goddard's projects team, **James Ballingall** has a strong reputation not yet matched by the firm overall. He is praised for his high profile public sector PFI work for clients such as the MoD and the National Audit Office. Although Buchanan Ingersoll has yet to establish itself, the reputation of **Barry Francis** (formerly Beachcroft Wansbroughs) remains strong *"A skilled player,"* he is praised for his *"aggressive drive and focus"* in PFI. US firm Mayer, Brown & Platt has yet to make a significant impact on the UK projects market. However associate, **Dominic Spacie** (formerly at Masons) is building a solid reputation for his project finance work. **Jane Templeton-Knight** has moved to Hunton & Williams from Milbank Tweed, and has a reputation for *"understanding complex transactions."*

THE SOUTH & WALES

PROJECTS/PFI • The South & Wales	Ptnrs	Assts
❶ **Bevan Ashford** Bristol	7	7
Masons Bristol	4	4
❷ **Burges Salmon** Bristol	2	7
Eversheds Cardiff	2	3
Morgan Cole Cardiff	4	7

LEADING INDIVIDUALS	
❶ **FAIRBAIRN Iain** Masons	**HUGHES Stephen** Bevan Ashford
HUTTON David Bevan Ashford	
UP AND COMING	
MANSON Stephen Eversheds	

Within each band, firms are listed alphabetically. See **Profiles** on page 695

Bevan Ashford *"Customer-focused and practical,"* the team is recognised primarily for its public sector PFI work, with a traditional niche in healthcare, although it benefits from a growing private client base across all sectors. Department head **Stephen Hughes** *("approachable")* is seen to be active in pushing forward new markets and is ably supported by the *"outstanding"* **David Hutton**, recommended for his negotiation and deal management skills. In defence, the team is advising Rolls Royce plc on the Future Strategic Tanker Aircraft project (£9 billion expenditure) and in education, representing Canterbury College and Newbury college on their Pathfinder PFI schemes. **Clients:** Rolls Royce plc, Bro Morganng NHS Trust, Parkwood Holdings.

Masons A strong office in the national network, the Bristol team led by **Iain Fairbairn** is active in a cross-section of major PFI industry sectors. PFI work driven out of this office includes advising Amey Business Services on the refurbishment of the MoD and (as preferred bidder) on the reprovision of the Glasgow schools bundle. Also acted as principal advisors to the St George's Healthcare NHS Trust on the £48 million development of services. **Clients:** Amey Business Services, HBG Construction Ltd.

Burges Salmon With defence a recognised stronghold of the firm, the team has acted for the MoD from the earliest days of PFI, including the Skyn et V satellite communication system and DECS project, standardising electronic trading for suppliers. The team is praised for its *"efficiency and commerciality"* and also covers predominantly public sector local government PFIs. Advising @Bristol (formerly Bristol 2000) on the £95m development of Bristol's Harbourside project. **Clients:** MoD, London Fire & Civil Defence.

Eversheds A *"practical and experienced"* projects team seen to tap into its public sector expertise in acting for local authorities and private sector bidders. *"Outstanding"* **Stephen Manson** is praised as *"helpful and easy to work with."* Has acted for Ceredigion County Council on Wales' first PFI school (a £12 million Pathfinder project) and acted for private sector contractor Impregilo Medical Technologies on the £7 million equipment PFI for Central Middlesex Hospital. **Clients:** Impregilo UK Ltd, Macob Holdings Ltd, Ceredigion County Council.

Morgan Cole A solid, balanced practice spreading work across the Cardiff and Oxford offices acting on predominantly PFI/PPP projects, with a growing reputation in the construction and facilities management sphere. Its base is the lower end of the projects market, the bulk of its deals falling between £5-50 million. However, a recent highlight saw the practice act for Cardiff Bay Development Corporation on the £120 million Bute Avenue PPP/PFI scheme involving infrastructure and urban regneration. Also acted for Gwent Police Authority on the DBFOM Home Office Pathfinder Scheme to provide a custody unit and section station at Ystrad Mynach. **Clients:** Gwent Police Authority, University Hospital of Wales NHS Trust.

MIDLANDS & EAST ANGLIA

PROJECTS/PFI • Midlands & East Anglia	Ptnrs	Assts
❶ **DLA** Birmingham	2	2
Eversheds Nottingham	2	11
Pinsent Curtis Birmingham	3	3
❷ **Mills & Reeve** Cambridge	3	6
❸ **Wragge & Co** Birmingham	2	12

LEADING INDIVIDUALS	
❶ **RANDLE Anthony** DLA	**WOODROW Cameron** Pinsent Curtis
❷ **MATTHEW Stephen** Eversheds	**PICKUP Raith** Mills & Reeve
❸ **AISBETT Alan** Pinsent Curtis	**KENNY Stephen** Wragge & Co
TWIST Patrick Pinsent Curtis	

Within each band, firms are listed alphabetically. See **Profiles** on page 695

DLA Drawing on the strength of a national practice, the firm is able to service a national client base with the Birmingham office well regarded for its expertise in education. The team has a specialism in public procurement and this is helping to drive the cross-section of PFI clients, including construction companies and bidding consortia, local authority bodies and national government departments. Team head **Tony Randle** is a *"skilled practitioner"* and particularly recommended for his education PFI work. Advised Tilbury Douglas plc on the Sheffield schools bundle providing new and refurbished buildings (£240 million.) Other work from the Birmingham office includes advising South Gloucestershire Council on its integrated waste project (£300 million) and North Wales Police on its accommodation project. **Clients:** Department of Education, Tilbury Douglas, London Borough of Tower Hamlets.

Eversheds Starting from a base of the *"strongest credibility"* in public sector work, the team is increasingly active in the private bidders market (for major contractors.) The team is led by the highly regarded **Stephen Matthew** *("it's good to see him on other side")* and is notable for its advice on education PFI projects. Acts for Stoke City Council on the £125 million, Pathfinder pilot schools project, and act for Lincolnshire County Council on its £170 million local authority outsourcing project (including IT and Telecoms.) **Clients:** Nottinghamshire County Council, Ryder, Jarvis, Dorset Police Authority.

Pinsent Curtis Like most regional firms, this team of *"serious players"* is traditionally strong in the public sector, and is now growing an enviable reputation for private sector clients, including financial institutions, facilities managers and service providers. **Cameron Woodrow** *("a true PFI man")* leads the team which also includes **Patrick Twist**, who has a strong banking background and **Alan Aisbett** who is recognised for the 4P Treasury Task Taskforce work, providing PFI document standardisation. Acted on three projects for ISS Mediclean, and for Vivendi Group on its bids for waste disposal projects. Also acting for Nationwide Building Society on school project bids. **Clients:** Nationwide Building Society, ISS UK Ltd, Waltham Forest LBC.

Mills & Reeve A niche practice in healthcare, the firm is yet to command a national presence to rival the leading firms. **Raith Pickup** is highly rated at a department where healthcare trusts continue to dominate the client base. Education and accommodation are growing markets. Acted for University of Luton on a residential accommodation project and for the University of Hertfordshire on an £80-100 million Pathfinder project. Also acted for Northern Birmingham mental health NHS Trust on a £16 million development project. **Clients:** Essex Rivers Healthcare NHS Trust, UEA, Imperial College.

Wragge & Co Strong links to the MoD, including a place on its panel and a recent advisory secondment, yet the practice is felt to lack the volume of transactions needed to compete on a national scale. Department Head **Stephen Kenny** is a *"strong player"* in defence, advising the Defence Procurement Agency on funding issues for PFI projects in this area. Other areas of work include a growing number of magistrate court projects and schools PFIs where the firm has a good balance between local authority bodies and private clients (mainly contractors.) Advising MJ Gleeson on the St George's Hospital NHS Trust PFI projects. Work for the MoD includes advising on the £100 million RAF Light Training Aircraft PFI project. **Clients:** MoD, MEPC, MJ Gleeson, East London Waste Authority.

THE NORTH

PROJECTS/PFI • The North	Ptnrs	Assts
❶ **Addleshaw Booth & Co** Leeds, Manchester	23	19
Pinsent Curtis Leeds	4	11
❷ **Eversheds** Manchester	8	15
❸ **Dickinson Dees** Newcastle upon Tyne	6	9
❹ **Nabarro Nathanson** Sheffield	3	8
Walker Morris Leeds	1	1

LEADING INDIVIDUALS	
❶ **CIRELL Stephen** Eversheds	**LOVITT Arthur** Pinsent Curtis
❷ **COCKRAM Richard** Addleshaw Booth & Co	**FELLOWS Alison** Dickinson Dees
O'CONNOR Mike Addleshaw Booth & Co	
❸ **SUTTIE Frank** Addleshaw Booth & Co	
ONE TO WATCH	
BENNETT John Eversheds	

Within each band, firms are listed alphabetically. *See **Profiles** on page 695*

Addleshaw Booth & Co Seen to be attracting very good clients in this field, this *"impressive firm"* has carved a stronghold in the North and has a national spread of clients. Group head **Mike O'Connor** is *"practical"* and has a strong team beneath him including the *"effective"* **Richard Cockram** who is praised for his schools PFI work (with particular strengths in construction law) and **Frank Suttie** (formerly of Garretts) with his strong Public Sector healthcare reputation. The team covers a broad range of PFI/PPP projects with strengths in education, health, transport and defence (on MoD panel for PFI projects.) Has a growing number of instructions from financial institutions, and acted for Lloyds Bank and the Bank of Scotland on the Newbury College pathfinder scheme. A balanced client base has seen the team acting for local authority clients such as Tameside Council on its 3 Schools PFI and for contractors, acted for Nord Anglia plc on the MoD's army foundation college at Harrogate. **Clients:** MoD, AMEC Developments Ltd, Jarvis Group plc.

Pinsent Curtis The Leeds office of this integrated group is seen by City firms to be picking up *"meaty deals."* The *"experienced, trustworthy"* **Arthur Lovitt** is the dominant force in the group. With over 25 NHS Trusts advised by the practice, traditional strength in healthcare continues. Other public sector body clients include central government, advising the MoD, DETR, and DfEE. Also represents banks, contractors and service providers. Acted on the £30 million IT scheme for Dudley Council, linking 105 schools in the closed scheme forming part of the government's flagship National Grid for Learning. Advising the RBS on the Leeds Community Heath PFI scheme and DfEE on template documents for student accommodation. **Clients:** RBS, Clugston Ltd, Defence Housing Executive, North Durham Acute Hospitals NHS Trust.

Eversheds A *"superb local authority practice,"* reputed nationally for its dominance in the public sector. *"Leading light"* **Stephen Cirell** is praised for his intelligence and is said to *"run an excellent team."* The team is at the forefront of PPP and is well-known for its activities in education and waste management. Instructed by Haringey LBC on the DBFO solution for the provision of new and rebuilt schools with a capital spend of £100 million. Acting for East Sussex County Council and Brighton & Hove County Council on its integrated waste management PFI. **Clients:** Haringey LBC, Liverpool City Council, Kier Group.

Dickinson Dees A *"capable and sensible"* team, recognised as active in the healthcare PFI sector, acting for both local authorities and private consortia. The firm's profile has been raised by the secondment of the *"highly rated"* **Alison Fellows** to the PFU of the NHS Executive in Leeds, advising on leading PFI projects and the standard NHS PFI contracts. Growth areas include social housing and the transport sector. Acted for Newcastle Hospital NHS Trust on redevelopment of two hospitals and for Bovis on schools projects in Liverpool and Cornwall. **Clients:** North British Housing Association, Newcastle Hospitals NHS Trust, Bovis.

Nabarro Nathanson *"Active on the smaller projects,"* this practice has seen a growth in its PFI and PPP projects, acting for both the public sector and private clients. In the public sector, the team has acted for Derbyshire Police Authority on the Pathfinder projects for division headquarters and City section police station in Derby. Forming part of the firm's private client base, acted for Norwich Union PPP Fund on numerous projects including healthcare (Dudley NHS Trust Pathfinder scheme) and education (Temple School, Manchester Pathfinder project.) **Clients:** Norwich Union PPP Fund, Liverpool City Council, Wates Construction.

Walker Morris Reputed to have the beginnings of a fine practice, building on a traditional reputation in the public sector. The practice also acts for private clients including contractors and service providers. With a national client base, growth is seen in the areas of accommodation, waste management and healthcare. Has advised Jarvis as sole contractor to the MoD flagship training college at Beckwithshaw (value £350 million,) and is advising RBS on due diligence concerns over the construction of the Rotherham NHS EMI Unit. **Clients:** Jarvis Plc, Sheffield City Council, RBS.

SCOTLAND

PROJECTS/PFI • Scotland	Ptnrs	Assts
❶ **Dundas & Wilson CS** Edinburgh, Glasgow	5	11
MacRoberts Edinburgh, Glasgow	7	12
❷ **McGrigor Donald** Edinburgh, Glasgow	2	3
❸ **Maclay Murray & Spens** Glasgow	3	6
McClure Naismith Edinburgh, Glasgow	1	3
Shepherd & Wedderburn WS Edinburgh	4	4
❹ **Burness** Edinburgh	3	6
Henderson Boyd Jackson WS Edinburgh	4	2
Masons Glasgow	1	2
Tods Murray WS Edinburgh, Glasgow	2	5

LEADING INDIVIDUALS	
❶ **HENDERSON David** MacRoberts	**McAULEY Michael** Dundas & Wilson CS
MURPHY Michael MacRoberts	
❷ **BROWN Steven** McClure Naismith	**NASH David** Shepherd & Wedderburn WS
❸ **CAMPBELL Alan** Dundas & Wilson CS	**GRAHAM Drysdale** McGrigor Donald
McEWAN Alastair Maclay Murray & Spens	
READ Anthony Burness	
SIMMONS William Tods Murray WS	

Within each band, firms are listed alphabetically. See **Profiles** on page 695

Dundas & Wilson CS Associated with its foothold in the funders' market, this *"clever"* team is regarded as *"on top of the pile,"* and is active in both projects and PFI. Infrastructure group head, the *"experienced"* **Alan Campbell** is able to draw on a strong banking and construction practice. The *"commercial"* **Michael McAuley** is recommended for his attitude *("listens and always plays fair")* and his industrial background. Acting for Glasgow City Council and Edinburgh City Council in the re-development and on-going management of its bundled schools project, and advised Lloyds TSB Bank on the St George's Hospital redevelopment in London. **Clients:** Glasgow City Council, Bank of Scotland, West of Scotland Water Authority.

MacRoberts *"A punchy outfit with skilled practitioners,"* envied for the firm's strong construction base and its work with both banks and private sector clients. *"Aggressive"* **Michael Murphy** is recommended for his grasp of complex documentation and leads a team which includes the *"smooth"* **David Henderson**, praised for his *"formidable intellect."* Traditionally strong in the education sector, the team acted for the preferred bidder on the £250 million Glasgow schools project (largest in the UK.) Active areas include accommodation, healthcare and waste water management. Acted for Bank of Ireland on the MoD Defence Housing Executive project and for the preferred bidder on the Tay Wastewater project (value £100 million.) **Clients:** Royal Bank of Scotland plc, Bank of Scotland, Miller Construction.

McGrigor Donald Renowned for its work in the two water PFI projects currently in progress in Scotland and for a strong base in the consortium market. The team is led by the *"sensible"* **Drysdale Graham** and is seen to have widened its net, acting on projects across education, accommodation and healthcare. The team is also building a base in its London office. Acted for Stirling Water consortium on the £100 million Almond Valley and Seafield water and sewerage project, and for Kinnoull House, a joint venture between Morrison Construction and RBS to provide accommodation for local authority staff in Perth. **Clients:** Stirling Water, Morrison Construction Ltd, City of Edinburgh Council.

Maclay Murray & Spens A growing profile in this field due in part to an increasingly national client base. The team is recommended for *"super work"* on the St George's Hospital PFI project (for the preferred bidder) in London. The respected **Alastair McEwan** has strong construction connections and a profile with the banks. Traditionally proficient at waste water management, the team acted for North of Scotland Water Authority on the Aberdeen Wastewater project (c£100 million) and the Moray Coast Wastewater project (c£80 million.) **Clients:** North of Scotland Water Authority, Bank of Scotland, Lloyds TSB Bank plc, Canmore Partnership Ltd.

McClure Naismith *"Always a name to consider,"* this practice is seen acting for NHS Trusts (a traditional stronghold) and for the bidders, particularly construction and engineering companies. **Steven Brown** is said to have a *"big personality"* and is respected for his healthcare work. The team is currently advising three NHS Trusts and acting for bidders in education, health and local government projects. Achieved financial closure on Derby police headquarters project and East Ayrshire Community Hospital. **Clients:** HBG Construction, Robertson Group, Melville Dundas.

Shepherd & Wedderburn WS Seen to be building strong relationships with prominent clients, particularly among public sector authorities. The team is currently acting for the MoD on five major Pathfinder PFI projects. Department head, **David Nash**, is praised for his commercial attitude. Growth areas include IT (Edinburgh City Council's ICT Services PFI) and water management (acted for Miller Northumbrian Consortium on the Aberdeen Wastewater project.) The firm is also advising four out of the eight local authorities involved in schools PFI/PPP projects. **Clients:** Scottish Power plc, Angus Council, East Renfrewshire Council, MoD.

Burness *"The boys for the Bank of Scotland,"* the firm is seen to have a strong balance between acting for the funders and bidding consortia. **Anthony Read** is *"efficient,"* although the team overall is felt to lack depth. Public sector commissions this year include Fife Council and Lothian Primary Care NHS Trust. Acted for Bank of Scotland on the James Watt College and West Lothian College, and advised Ballast Wiltshier on the Falkirk Council PFI schools project (value £70 million.) **Clients:** Bank of Scotland, Strathclyde Police, Jarvis Construction plc.

Henderson Boyd Jackson WS *"A small outfit doing small projects well."* Despite the high profile loss of team members (to McGrigor Donald), this practice continues to act for a well-regarded client base which leans towards the bidders market (particularly contractors.) Most active in the fields of education and housing, the team advised Jarvis on the Balfron schools projects (in Stirling) and acted for Miller Group on the West Lothian Housing Initiative. **Clients:** Jarvis Construction plc, Miller Group.

Masons *"A good little team"* seen to benefit from its regional offices, and notably active in the private sector. A fine reputation in construction and engineering nationally gives the team a solid client base of leading contractors. Acted on the West Lothian College (for the contractor) and advised SPV on the MoD's Defence Housing Executive project. **Clients:** John Molem & Co plc, AMEC plc.

Tods Murray WS *"Succinct and intellectual"* **William Simmons** is the most prominent player in this *"active"* team. The team was involved in all three Scottish Pathfinder hospital projects and is recognised for its work in waste water management. It also has a presence in English PFI projects (including the Stoke-on-Trent schools project.) Advising the preferred bidder on the Aberdeen Wastewater treatment project. Also advised North of Scotland Environmental Services and East of Scotland Environmental Services on bids for the Almond Valley and Seafield, Levenmouth, Tay and Aberdeen and Moray Coast Wastewater projects. **Clients:** Balfour Beatty Capital Projects, Scottish Environmental Services, Consort Healthcare.

LEADERS IN PROJECTS / PFI

AISBETT, Alan
Pinsent Curtis, Birmingham (0121) 200 1050
alan.aisbett@pinsents.com
Partner in Major Projects.
Specialisation: Major projects, PFI and PPP. Acts for both public and private sectors. Major transactions have included £100m concession based financing of London Luton Airport, an £18m schools PFI Project for Londonn Borough of Waltham Forest, £20m schools PFI project financing for Nationwide Building Society, a £30m schools PFI project for Newham LBC, a £50m housing PFI project for Islington LBC, and a £12m schools PFI project for Brighton BC and a £30m outsourcing of Barnsley MBC's leisure facilities. Appointed by DETR/4Ps/TTF to prepare standardisation guidance for local authority housing PFI projects and a contributor to the local authority PFI contract produced by 4Ps in commercial, finance, housing and public law.
Prof. Memberships: Law Society.
Career: LLB University of Hull. LLM University of Exter. Qualified 1983. South Bucks District Council 1980-1982. Waltham Forest LBC 1982-1988. *SJ Berwin & Co* 1988-1993. *Winckworth & Pemberton* 1993-1994. *Price Evans* 1994-1998. *Prinsent Curtis* to date.
Publications: General Editor of Local Government Precedents and Procedures: Sweet & Maxwell Editorial Board of PFI Focus: Jutastat.
Personal: Married with two children and interests in travel and football.

ALLAN, Simon L.
Berwin Leighton, London (020) 7760 1000
simon.allan@berwinleighton.com
Specialisation: Head of Finance Department and specialist in major developments and infrastructure-related projects. Major projects include the disposal of the Millennium Dome for Government, Elephant and Castle project, Longbenton PFI project for the project vehicle, Kings College/UMDS PFI project again for the project vehicle, construction of the new Parliamentary Building over Westminster tube station and the White City retail development for European Land.
Career: Qualified in 1979, assistant solicitor with *Kenneth Turner Brown* (1979-81) and *Ashurst Morris Crisp* (1981-88). Partner with *Berwin Leighton* since 1988.
Personal: Family of four children. Hobbies include reading, music and wine.

ARMITAGE, Richard
Simmons & Simmons, London (020) 7628 2020
Specialisation: Partner in the Major Projects Group, specialising in PFI/PPP projects and privatisations. Has particular experience of the defence sector, including the contractorisations of the Royal Dockyards and the Atomic Weapons Establishment, the privatisation of Devonport Royal Dockyard and PFI projects, such as the pathfinder Medium Support Helicopter Training Facility Project. He is advising the MoD on PPP options for the Defence Evaluation and Research Agency and on the Future Strategic Tanker Aircraft Project, the largest defence PFI project. He has also advised on projects in the telecommunications and energy sectors and a wide range of commercial transactions.
Prof. Memberships: Law Society, International Bar Association, Union Internationale des Avocats
Career: Articled Simmons & Simmons, qualified 1982, partner since 1987
Publications: Author of the defence section of the Butterworth's PFI Manual
Personal: Educated at King's School, Ely and Sussex University. Married with one son and two daughters. Leisure interests include sport (cricket, tennis, football, skiing, sailing and windsurfing), opera, cinema and theatre

BALDOCK, Anne
Allen & Overy, London (020) 7330 3000
Specialisation: Head of the PFI team and experienced in all aspects of major projects and PFI work in the UK and abroad including acting for banks, sponsors and multi-laterals. Has worked in all major PFI sectors including road, rail, prison, MoD, property and local authority.
Career: Articled at *Allen & Overy*; qualified 1984; partner 1990. Secondment with major US bank 1986-88.
Personal: Born 1959. Graduate of LSE.

BALLINGALL, James G.M.
Theodore Goddard, London (020) 7606 8855
Head of PFI and Asset Finance Teams
Specialisation: Has lead the teams on numerous hospital, schools, further education, colleges, prison, police and railway projects. Has also advised the National Audit Office on their review of seven PFI projects to date, and advises the Business Services Association on PFI matters. Acts for both banks and consortia. Background in asset finance and banking. Other project finance work includes Euro Tunnel, BSB, Lakeside Thurrock Shopping Centre, and a major cementation project. Specialises in structured finance and lease work, particularly in the transportation field, having set up *Theodore Goddard's* railways group.
Prof. Memberships: Law Society, FRGS.
Career: Born 1958. Educated: Eastbourne College, Cambridge (Emanuel). Qualified 1984.
Personal: Interests: hiking, cycling, squash, piano, writing (wrote 'A Taste of China', published John Murrays 1984), carpentry.

BARRATT, Jeffery
Norton Rose, London (020) 7283 6000
barrattjvc@nortonrose.com
Partner, Head of Global Projects Group.
Specialisation: All areas of banking, financing and capital markets debt instruments, in particular project related financings. Involved in many complex infrastructure and other project financings in the UK and worldwide, acting for banks, sponsors, project companies, export credit agencies and multilateral agencies. On The Editorial Board of Butterworths Financial Law and Practice.
Career: Qualified 1973, joined *Norton Rose* 1976, Partner 1979. Established and ran Bahrain office 1979-82. Training Partner 1987-91. Headed South East Asian Project Finance Group, based in Hong Kong 1993-95. Chairman Partnership Committee 1997.

BELLHOUSE, John
White & Case, London (020) 7600 7300
jbellhouse@whitecase.com
Specialisation: Valued advisor to the international construction industry with particular expertise in project finance and arbitration.
Prof. Memberships: Law Society of England & Wales.
Career: Partner, *White & Case*, London.

BICKERTON, David
Clifford Chance, London (020) 7600 1000
David.Bickerton@cliffordchance.com
Specialisation: Structured finance including: project bonds, acquisition finance and PFI/PPP. Recent highlights include: MoD Main Building Refurbishment, Owengate Keele Bonds, Kings Hospital Bonds, A13 Road Bonds, Bond Refinancings.
Career: *Clifford Chance* 1987 to date. Seconded to Citibank (1992) and Bankers Trust (1993). Partner 1997.
Personal: Education: Downing College, Cambridge - MA. Family Details: three daughters.

BLACK, Alan
Linklaters (A member firm of Linklaters & Alliance), London (020) 7456 5948
alan.black@linklaters.com
Partner 1983. Head of Global Projects.
Specialisation: Main area of practice has been international projects. Extensive experience of acting for governments, sponsors and lenders on major projects for transport, airports and aviation, oil, gas, and derivative products, and projects involving concessions granted by governments to private developers in both civil law and common law countries.
Career: Qualified 1976. Attended Kings College, London.
Personal: Born 1952.

BLAKE, Peter M.W.
Clifford Chance, London (020) 7600 1000
peter.blake@cliffordchance.com
See under Energy & Natural Resources, p.356

BLISS, Nick
Freshfields Bruckhaus Deringer, London (020) 7936 4000
nbliss@freshfields.com
Specialisation: Project finance and PFI. He led the *Freshfields* teams which acted for Road Management Group in the (March 1996) A1(M) and A419/A417 DBFO Road Projects: the first UK monoline insured eurobond infrastructure financing and, subsequently, the M6 DBFO Road monoline insured eurobond infrastructure financing, acting for FSA the monoline insurer. Has now completed a number of monoline enhanced project financings (Tyseley, Criterion, Endeavour SCH, Baglon Moor.) In June 1999 completed the first eurobond financing of a multi-project Programme (Investors Finance). He has been heavily involved in projects in a number of other areas of PFI (prisons, health and MOD projects). Other recent projects of note were acting for the leading institutions to the N4 South African Maputo Corridor Toll Road Project (February 1998) (the first infrastructure project financing in South Africa), the Istrian Highway Toll Road and the lenders to the US$1.1 billion Portuguese North Toll Road.
Prof. Memberships: Law Society.
Career: Barnard Castle School, Corpus Christi College, Cambridge.
Personal: Rowing, cycling, back surgery, childcare and other strenuous pursuits.

BROWN, Steven
McClure Naismith, Edinburgh (0131) 220 1002
Specialisation: Project finance and PFI. Advises public sector, private sector consortia and banks. Practice covers many PFI sectors and holds overseas appointments on BOO/BOT schemes in power generation, water and sewerage. Represented Grampian Health Board at Stonehaven hospital, Bank of Scotland at Stirling College, the NHS Trust at Hairmyres district general hospital and participated in the consortium advisory team on South Bucks hospital, all amongst the first PFI projects to reach financial closing. Recently achieved financial closing on East Ayrshire community hospital, Derby Police headquarters, Larkfield hospital, Craig Phadrig hospital and West Lothian College. Currently advising on a range of projects in health, education, local authority and transport.
Prof. Memberships: Society of Writers to HM Signet, Law Society of Scotland.
Career: Qualified in 1980. Partner in *McClure Naismith since 1986, now Head of Projects Group.*
Personal: Born 20 November 1956. Educated at Irvine Royal Academy 1969-74, University of Edinburgh 1974-78. Lives near Edinburgh. Leisure pursuits include family, computers, music, golf. Past Chairman of a charity for adults with learning difficulties.

BUCKWORTH, Nicholas
Shearman & Sterling, London (020) 7655 5000
NBuckworth@shearman.com
Partner in Project Finance Department.
Specialisation: Advising project developers and financial institutions on all aspects of the structuring, negotiation, development and financing of major infrastructure projects particularly in the power and transportation sectors. Nicholas has particular experience of advising developers and lenders in the Middle East and North Africa. He is currently advising the InterGen-Enka consortium on the deveolopment and financing of three Build Operate natural gas fired power projects in Turkey, the first to be developed under this regime. He also led the team which advised the Lenders on the Taweelah A2 Power Generation and Water Desalination Project, named 'Energy/Project Finance Team of the Year 1999' by Legal Business. He is currently working on projects in Abu Dhabi, Oman, Qatar and elsewhere in the Middle East, as well as in the United Kingdom and mainland Europe.
Career: Qualified in 1986. With *Clifford Chance* 1984-94. Partner *Milbank, Tweed, Hadley & McCloy* 1994- November 1996. Partner, *Shearman & Sterling* November 1996.
Personal: Born 2nd February 1961. Educated at Dundee University (LL.B Hons, 1983). Leisure activities include skiing, squash, golf, music and cinema.

CAMPBELL, Alan
Dundas & Wilson CS, Edinburgh (0131) 228 8000

CIRELL, Stephen
Eversheds, Leeds (0113) 243 0391
stephencirell@eversheds.com
See under Local Government, p.586

COCKRAM, Richard
Addleshaw Booth & Co, Leeds (0113) 209 2000
rac@addleshaw-booth.co.uk
See under Construction, p.198

COLE, Margaret B.
White & Case, London (020) 7600 7300
mbcole@whitecase.com
Specialisation: One of the country's leading advisors in the field of international project finance.
Prof. Memberships: Law Society of England & Wales, New York State Bar, New South Wales Supreme Court, Australian Capital Territory and Supreme Court of Queensland.
Career: Partner, *White & Case*, London. Executive partner of *White & Case's* London office.

COULTER, David
Norton Rose, London (020) 7283 6000
coulterdx@nortonrose.com
Specialisation: PFI, Project Finance, Asset Finance, Public Sector Finance and Banking - PFI Projects in last year have included Scottish Water Project at Dalmuir; Hereford and Worcester Magistrates Courts; Oldham Schools; Islington and Newham HRA Housing PFI; Eden Project; National Physical Laboratory.
Prof. Memberships: Law Society, Law Society of Scotland, City of London Solicitors Company.
Career: Mainholm Academy, Ayr to 1979; Edinburgh University LLB (1984), DIPLP (1985); Admitted Scotland (1986), Notary Public (Scotland) (1986); Admitted England & Wales (1989).
Personal: Sailing, hillwalking and travel. Married (Catriona Rose) - one daughter, Fiona, one son, Alasdair.

CRANE, David
Norton Rose, London (020) 7283 6000
Specialisation: Partner in the projects group, specialising in project finance and asset finance. He also handles general commercial work. He has advised on numerous major plant leasing transactions, on sales of leasing companies as well as other company acquisitions and joint ventures. He also has considerable experience of public sector financing, particularly relating to local authorities.
Prof. Memberships: Law Society.
Career: Articled at *Norton Rose*. Qualified 1975. Partner since 1985.

DUFFICY, Frank
CMS Cameron McKenna, London (020) 7367 2904
fd@cmck.com
Specialisation: Project Finance and PFI/PPP in a range of sectors including health, education, defence (both accommodation and fleets), courts and other DETR facilities, advising sponsors, funders and bond wrappers in the full range of PFI/PPP sectors. Typically selected by clients to lead teams and manage the legal process between the principle parties to PFI/PPP transactions. In the last year, led the team appointed by the Innisfree/Galliford Consortium in conjunction with Lloyds Bank to advise the Bank as senior funder and manage the whole legal process as between the Bank, the Sponsors and the Local Authority for the Birmingham Schools transaction being the first English Schools Cluster.
Prof. Memberships: The Law Society.
Career:1981 - 1983 - Articled Clerk - *Linklaters & Paines.* 1983-1989; Solicitor - *Linklaters & Paines.* 1990- to date; Partner, *CMS Cameron McKenna.*
Personal: Education: St Michael's Prep School. St Michael's College. North Carolina State University; BA Political Science. City University; Diploma in Laws. College of Law; Law Society Finals. Leisure Interests: Diving (Olympic competitor - Munich 1972, British Team 1969/1975 (inclusive). Sailing, Ski-ing, Fell Walking, Shooting, Tennis. Family Details: Married to Alison with three children, Georgia, Jack and Thomas.

ELSEY, Mark
Ashurst Morris Crisp, London (020) 7638 1111
mark.elsey@ashursts.com
Specialisation: Acting for governments, sponsors, contractors and lenders in relation to UK and international infrastructure and energy projects, including PFI/PPP projects. Head of the firm's Projects Group.

FAIRBAIRN, Iain
Masons, Bristol (0117) 924 5678
ian.fairbairn@masons.com
Head of Projects and PFI team in Bristol office.
Specialisation: Advising both sides of Public Private Partnerships and including facilities management contracts and procurement and vires issues, covering all fields of PFI but with an emphasis on healthcare schemes.
Prof. Memberships: Law Society.
Career: 1977-1982 *Slaughter and May* Assistant Solicitor. 1982-1996 *Bevan Hancock/Bevan Ashford.* 1996-1998 *Bevan Ashford* Head of Commercial Department. October 1998, Partner *Masons.*
Personal: Sailing, Skiing, Hill Walking.

FELLOWS, Alison
Dickinson Dees, Newcastle upon Tyne (0191) 279 9289
Specialisation: PFI projects. Lead partner acting for Carlisle Hospital NHS Trust on PFI project for the redevelopment of the Cumberland Infirmary, followed by 6 months secondment to Private Finance Unit of NHS Executive to assist with ongoing projects. Now acting on several further major NHS projects.
Career: Cambridge University 1980-83. *Field Fisher Waterhouse* 1985-88. *Dickinson Dees* 1988 to date. Married to Tim Care, also a partner at Dickinson Dees, 2 children.

FINLAY, Peter
White & Case, London (020) 7600 7300
pfinlay@whitecase.com
Specialisation: Has a unique range of international project finance and M&A law expertise.
Prof. Memberships: Law Society of England & Wales, Irish Bar, New York State Bar and the Paris Bar.
Career: Partner, *White & Case*, London. Member of the firm's world-wide management board and head of the firm's practices in the Middle East and Africa.

FLETCHER, Phillip
Milbank, Tweed, Hadley & McCloy, London (020) 7448 3000
PFletcher@milbank.com
Partner (Project Finance Group).
Specialisation: Specialising in the development and financing of major infrastructure projects, including power plants, pipelines, roads and satellites. Has represented parties in relation to projects in Europe, the US and Asia, including: the Orion and Arianespace Satellite financings; Yanpet Petrochemicals Project, Saudi Arabia; the Birecik and Marmara Ereglisi power projects, Turkey; the Taweelah Power Project, Abu Dhabi; the Tapada Power Plant, Portugal; the Med-

way, Shoreham and Drax Power Projects, UK; and the Teverola, Ferrara, Serene, Lomellina and Rosen Power Plants, Italy.
Career: Has been with *Milbank, Tweed* since 1983 and was resident in the firm's Hong Kong office in 1987 and 1988.
Personal: Born 16th September 1957. Educated at Georgetown University School of Foreign Service (B.S. 1979), Fletcher School of Law & Diplomacy (MA, 1983) and the University of California, Berkeley (JD, 1983).

FOX, Jason
Herbert Smith, London (020) 7374 8000
Partner, Projects Group.
Specialisation: Advising the public sector, corporates and banks on all aspects of the structuring, development and financing of projects in a variety of sectors including oil and gas, power, water, property and public infrastructure. Main areas of practice are advising on PFI projects and oil and gas projects. Regular participant in industry conferences on the PFI.
Career: Qualified in 1987 with *Herbert Smith* and became a partner in 1994. Seconded to the Private Finance Panel Executive February to September 1994. Author (jointly with Nicholas Tott) of 'The Private Finance Initiative Handbook' (Jordans, December 1998).

FRANCIS, Barry
Buchanan Ingersoll, London (020) 7920 3800
francisb@buchananingersoll.com
Specialisation: Public/private interface transactions including PPP, PFI, major outsourcing projects and other commercial transactions including public sector/private sector joint ventures, facilities management contracts and procurement and administrative law advice. Current projects include major hospital building and services projects (PFI). Managing Partner *Buchanan Ingersoll*. Regular speaker at conferences and seminars. Contributor to a range of specialist publications including Butterworth's PFI Manual. A member of the Editorial Board of 'The PFI Report'.
Prof. Memberships: Law Society
Career: Admitted 1977, at *Beachcroft Hyman Isaacs* (now *Beachcroft Wansbroughs*) Associate 1979-80, Partner 1980-1999, Managing Partner *Buchanan Ingersoll* 2000
Personal: Born 14th March 1953. Educated at Enfield Grammar School and University of Bristol. Interests include travel, history and food. Lives in North London.

GATES, Ellen
Denton Wilde Sapte, London (020) 7242 1212

GILLESPIE, Stephen
Allen & Overy, London (020) 7330 3000
Specialisation: Partner at Allen & Overy in 1995. He has extensive experience in all types of international financing, including acquisition financing, structured financing, project financing, and a number of multi-source financings. He led/is leading the teams advising the underwriters/arrangers/lenders on the leveraged acquisitions of Bosch Telecom, Giraudy, IPC Magazines, Panta Electronics and Newmond Holdings. He also advised the arrangers/underwriters on the api Energia IGCC financing (and refinancing) in Italy, the £1.5 billion Bouygues Telecom third mobile telecommunications financing in France and the Euro595 million financing for KPN Orange Belgium N.V., the third Belgian mobile telecommunications operator. He is currently leading the team advising the arrangers/underwriters of the Euro2.43 billion financing for WIND Telecommunicazioni, the third Italian mobile operator. He recently led the team advising Chase, Deutsche and IBJ as lead arrangers of the £1.725 billion financing for the acquisition of the Drax Power Station by AES from National Power. In the rail sector, he led the team advising Virgin Rail Group in connection with the financing of its rolling stock procurement programme for the UK's West Coast and Cross-Country Passenger rail franchises (the largest single rolling stock procurement ever undertaken in the UK). He also has extensive expertise in PFI transactions: he advised the sponsors/project company in connection with the Law Hospital PFI financing and is currently leading the teams advising the sponsors/project company in connection with the King's College hospital, St George's Hospital and Dumfries and Galloway Hospital PFI financings. He is also leading the team advising the financiers on the Scottish/Northern Irish electricity interconnector project.
Prof. Memberships: Law Society. City of London Solicitors Company.
Career: Articled *Stephenson Harwood* 1985-87, Solicitor *Freshfields* 1987-91, Solicitor *Allen & Overy* 1991-95, Partner 1995.
Personal: Born 1962. Educated at Foyle and Londonderry College and Trinity College, Oxford (MA (Hons) Jurisprudence 1984). Interests include family, reading, outdoor pursuits and music. Lives in St. Albans.

GNIADKOWSKI, Stan
Denton Wilde Sapte, London (020) 7242 1212
Specialisation: Specialises in property and project development work. As a necessary adjunct to that practice also advises on non-contentious construction law matters. Usually acts for the project company. Stan has advised Laing Hyder on the police stations and firearms training facility projects for the Metropolitan Police where Laing Hyder is preferred bidder and also in relation to the Newham hospital project where Laing Hyder is also preferred bidder. Stan has led the team advising Octagon Healthcare in connection with a 144 bed extension to the Norfolk & Norwich hospital project which is currently in the course of construction. Advising on two grouped schools projects where Laing Hyder have been shortlisted to the BAFO stage.
Prof. Memberships: British Council for Offices, Investment Property Forum.
Career: After Articles in local government followed by a year with a development corporation, joined the legal department of *John Laing PLC* with whom he worked from 1984 to 1987. Joining City solicitors, *D J Freeman*, in 1987 he became a partner the following year and played a significant part in the development of *D J Freeman's* property practice. In January 1997, left *D J Freeman* to become a senior equity partner at *Wilde Sapte* where continues to advise on major property and project development matters.
Personal: Single. Interests include photography, motor racing (watching not participating) and the cinema.

GOSSLING, Margaret
Clifford Chance, London (020) 7600 1000
margaret.gossling@cliffordchance.com

GRAHAM, L. Drysdale
McGrigor Donald, Edinburgh (0131) 226 7777
www.mcgrigors.com
Partner in Projects Unit.
Specialisation: Specialises in capital projects/PFI work, although has broad experience of corporate finance and general corporate work. Recent projects experience includes advising the Stirling Water Seafield Consortium (Thames Water International Services Limited, MJ Gleeson Group plc and Montgomery Watson Enterprises Inc) in respect of the award-winning £100m Almond Valley and Seafield waste water and sewerage project and the £29m Esk Valley waste water and sewage project led by East of Scotland Water Authority and the advice to the New Schools consortium (Innisfree and W S Atkins Investments) with Wates Construction on the £14m Leyton Schools projects. Currently working on various projects at the preferred bidder stage in the water, schools, social housing and e-commerce sectors.
Prof. Memberships: Law Society of Scotland; Law Society of England and Wales; the Society of Writers to Her Majesty's Signet; Notary Public.
Career: Trained *Biggart Baillie*; qualified Scotland 1982; qualified England and Wales 1990; corporate department *Dundas & Wilson* 1982-84; company department *McGrigor Donald* 1984-87; manager corporate department *Freshfields*, London 1987-91; rejoined *McGrigor Donald*, London office for 18 months; returned to Scotland to become a partner in Edinburgh office 1992.
Personal: Born 1958; resides Edinburgh. Leisure interests include theatre, music, golf, gardening.

HALL, Peter M.
Norton Rose, London (020) 7283 6000
hallpm@nortonrose.com
Specialisation: A Partner in the Construction and Engineering Group with considerable experience of the construction and engineering aspects of infrastructure projects around the world, including project finance and PFI deals. Recently acted for the commerical lenders on the Connect project, for the developers on a number of recent independent power projects and on a series of road and rail projects. Contentious work encompasses High Court and international arbitration claims.
Career: Member of the Technology and Construction Court Solicitors Association, an accredited adjudicator and an associate of the Chartered Institute of Arbitrators.

HARRISON, Brian
Allen & Overy, London (020) 7330 3000
Specialisation: One of the senior partners in *Allen & Overy's* highly regarded international projects practice. He has a broad client base advising banks, sponsors and multi-laterals on major international telecoms, power and infrastructure projects. Recently he has been involved in projects and telecoms fundings based in Europe and Eastern Europe, the Middle East and the United Kingdom. He also has wide international banking and commercial transaction experience including shipping and aircraft financing, acquisition financing, structured financings, property reconstructions and work-out.

Career: Auckland University (1975, LLB), qualified New Zealand 1976, England 1985; assistant solicitor, *Johnson Stokes & Master*, Hong Kong 1980-1983; assistant solicitor *Allen & Overy*, London and Dubai 1983-1985; Partner New York and London 1987.
Personal: Born 1953. Interests include yachting and motorcycling.

HENDERSON, David
MacRoberts, Glasgow (0141) 332 9988
djh@macroberts.co.uk
Partner in Construction and Capital Projects Groups.
Specialisation: Main area of practice is construction and engineering law with emphasis on PFI and other infrastructure projects. Currently involved in a variety of PFI projects in the healthcare, railway and waste-water sectors. Led legal team for successful consortium at Highland sewerage project and acted for the Trust in the largest healthcare PFI project in Scotland to date. Advised on Scots law aspects of 1998 edition of GC Works Contracts. Co-author of 'MacRoberts on Scottish Building Contracts' and contributor to Butterworths 'PFI Manual'.
Prof. Memberships: Associate of Chartered Institute of Arbitrators (ACIArb).
Career: Qualified in 1979, having joined *MacRoberts* in 1977. Became Partner in 1983.
Personal: Born 18th July 1955. Educated at Kilmarnock Academy and Edinburgh University.

HORSFALL TURNER, Jonathan
Allen & Overy, London (020) 7330 3000
Specialisation: Partner dealing with syndications, securitisations, project finance, capital markets, privatisations, debt restructurings, bank and financial institution acquisitions and disposals and general banking.
Career: Articled *Allen & Overy*, qualified 1970, Partner 1973.
Personal: Cambridge University (1968 MA). Born 1945.

HUGHES, Stephen
Bevan Ashford, Bristol (0117) 923 0111
Specialisation: Head of projects and PFI team. Practice covers private and public sector specialising in healthcare.
Prof. Memberships: Faculty of Building, Society of Construction Law.
Career: *Bevan Ashford* (partner 1993).

HUMPHREY, Anthony R.
Allen & Overy, London (020) 7330 3000
anthony.humphrey@allenovery.com
Specialisation: Partner specialising in structured finance with substantial experience in a wide range of corporate and financing transactions. Has extensive experience in all aspects of financing, particularly tiered or structured debt/equity financings including international project financings, acquisition financings and other complex multi-sourced financings. He has advised on transactions worldwide including the North Sea, North America, the Gulf, the Far East and Australia. He has given numerous public lectures on various aspects of financing, including project financing and has delivered papers on 'The Bankability of Project Agreements', 'Project Finance - The Security Package', 'Sponsor Support' and 'Comparative Off-take Arrangements'.
Prof. Memberships: Member, Section on Energy and Natural Resources Law of the International Bar Association.
Career: Articled *Allen & Overy*, qualified 1975, Partner 1981.
Personal: Durham University (1972 BA). Born 1951.

HUTTON, David
Bevan Ashford, Bristol (0117) 923 0111
Specialisation: Partner in PFI and Projects team. Practice covers most PFI sectors and private and public sector clients. Involved in schemes in health, defence, local government (including pathfinder leisure schemes) and specialising in education where acting on the leading FE College schemes at Newbury and Canterbury schools and higher education developments.
Prof. Memberships: Law Society.
Career: *Baker & Mckenzie* (1990-1995) - Qualified 1992. *Linklaters* (1995-1997). *Bevan Ashford* (1997 -). Partner 1999
Personal: Married with two sons. Leisure includes golf, football and art.

IVISON, Andrew S.
CMS Cameron McKenna, London
(020) 7367 3410
asi@cmck.com
Specialisation: Project finance and banking partner, advising on the financing of major infracture and capital projects in the United Kingdom and overseas. Recent examples of major project include the London Underground PPP, the restructuring of the Channel Tunnel Rail Link and a grouped schools project in Birmingham.
Career: Partner at *CMS Cameron McKenna* since 1987. Admitted as a solicitor in 1980.

JOHNSTON, Bruce
Weil, Gotshal & Manges, London (020) 7903 1000
bruce.johntson@weil.com
Specialisation: Head of the project finance practice in London. His project finance experience covers a range of sectors including infrastructure, electricity, oil and gas, telecoms, transportation and waste and water. Recent projects include: Athens Ringroad in Greece, Stirling Water in Scotland, Poznan Water in Poland, Belchatow II in Poland and VSZ in Slovakia. Frequent speaker at conferences and author of articles.

KENNY, Stephen
Wragge & Co, Birmingham (0121) 685 2728
stephen_kenny@wragge.com
Specialisation: Private Finance Initiative and project work particularly defence sector, IT PFI and serviced accommodation. Advising government, local authorities and private sector bidders on public private partnerships. Recently seconded as a banking adviser to Private Finance Group at Defence Procurement Agency, Ministry of Defence. Acted for Cap Gemini on Defence E-Commerce Service Project. Acting on four magistrates' court PFI projects. Advised M.J. Gleeson on St Georges Hospital PFI and MEPC on Bute Avenue PFI Scheme, Cardiff.
Prof. Memberships: Law Society, British Italian Law Association.
Career: Trained at *Bettinsons*, Birmingham. Joined *Wragge & Co* 1987. Partner 1998.
Personal: Educated at Leicester University (1980-83). Interested in walking, music, second-hand books and Italy. Lives in Bromsgrove, Worcestershire.

LEVINE, Marshall
Linklaters (A member firm of Linklaters & Alliance), London (020) 7456 3580
marshall.levine@linklaters.com
Specialisation: Partner and Head of the Construction and Engineering Group. Involved in a wide range of construction and engineering matters, including advice in relation to many construction and engineering projects and major real estate joint ventures, property developments and construction financing. Highly experienced in drafting construction contracts, and in advising on dispute resolution over a wide variety of projects including process plants, civil engineering, substantial headquarter office redevelopment, relocations and refurbishments as well as PFI transactions in the health, property, transportation and waste water sectors. Was involved in the BR privatisaton. Publications include 'Construction Insurance' (Lloyds); 'Commercial Development Property Precedents' (Longman); Construction and Engineering Precedents and and Consultant Editor on Butterworth's PFI Manual.

LOVITT, Arthur
Pinsent Curtis, Leeds (0113) 244 5000
arthur.lovitt@pinsents.com
Partner in Property Department. Head of Major Projects/ PFI, Leeds.
Specialisation: Involved in significant property developments including a major business park in Rochdale for Wilson Bowden. PFI and Public Sector Partnership work includes: representing, as lead partner, North Durham Acute Hospitals NHS Trust on their PFI scheme (the fifth major NHS scheme in the country to achieve financial close); Royal Bank of Scotland plc on the funding of an MOD accommodation scheme with Riverside Housing Association which closed in April 1999; Royal Bank of Scotland plc on £47m major pathfinder community health PFI scheme in Leeds (the largest to date) which closed in February 2000. He is currently advising the MOD on their Wattishham Housing Scheme.
Prof. Memberships: Round Table (former Chairman of Leeds Round Table), Institute of Directors.
Career: Bradford Grammar School and Nottingham University (LLB 2:1). Qualified with *Daynes Hill & Perks* (now *Eversheds*) in Norwich. Three years in Commercial Property Department of *Linklaters & Paines*. Joined *Simpson Curtis* in 1990. Partner in 1994.

MACRITCHIE, Kenneth
Shearman & Sterling, London (020) 7448 3000
KMacRitchie@shearman.com
Specialisation: Co-Head of Project Finance Group. Advising clients on major infrastructure projects. Recent transactions comprise advising on transport infrastructure including Channel Tunnel Rail Link power projects including Sidi Krir in Egypt and Edison Nission's acquisition of Fidler's Ferry and Ferrybridge in the UK; telecom including Dutchtone in Holland and Finner Telecom's acquisition of Orange; mining including Anglogold's acquisition of Ninorco's gold assets and oil and gas financings. Clients include international banks and project developers.
Prof. Memberships: Law Society, Law Society of Scotland.
Career: Qualified in 1976. Partner, *Clifford Chance 1991-94. Milbank, Tweed, Hadley & McCloy* in 1994 - 1996. *Shearman & Sterling* partner, since1996.

MANSON, Stephen
Eversheds, Cardiff (02920) 471147
Specialisation: Partner specialising in town and country planning, Private Finance Initiative/Public Private Partnership work together with general public sector work.. Former member of Government's Private Finance Panel Executive. Advises a number of local minerals developers on such matters as the current minerals review procedures. Currently advising United News and Media on planning appeal for alternative use of studio site in Cardiff. Acts for both public and private sectors on PFI schemes in a variety of areas such as education (currently advising Wiltshire County Council on its three schools deal - £30m), health (advised health trust on local hospital scheme in Cardiff - £15m) and transport (advising Newport County Borough Council on its Southern Distributor Road - £40m).
Career: Bristol University (LLB Hons). Bristol Polytechnic (LSF First Class Hons).
Personal: Recreations include windsurfing and badminton.

MARLOW, Ed
Denton Wilde Sapte, London (020) 7242 1212

MATHEOU, Michael S.
Lovells, London (020) 7296 2000
mike.matheou@lovells.com
Specialisation: Working in the firm's Project Finance Unit advising on privatisation, financiers and public sector on PPP/Private Finance Initiative projects (all sectors) and international limited recourse financial projects. Heavily involved in PFI/PPP work across a range of sectors including transport (London Underground PPP/DBFO Roads and light rail), Healthcare (New Royal Infirmary of Edinburgh; South Buckinghamshire NHS Trust), Government Accommodation (DSS PRIME; STEPS project). Also worked on a range of infrastructure projects internationally including BOT Waste Water Project in Oman, Bauxite mine and harbour development in Guyana and Oil refinery and petro-chemicals project in India.
Prof. Memberships: Law Society.
Career: *Lovells*, London and Hong Kong since 1980, Partner 1989. LLB (Hons) Nottingham University.

MATTHEW, Stephen
Eversheds, Nottingham (0115) 950 7000
Specialisation: Joined *Eversheds* in 1995 as Partner, having previously worked for fifteen years within local government where he was County Secretary and Solicitor of Shropshire County Council.
Career: Educated at Farnham Grammar School, University of Sheffield and the College of Law, London. Specialises in local authority and project work and is a member of the Association of Council Secretaries and Solicitors. Began his career with South Yorkshire County Council, moved to Derbyshire County Council and joined Shropshire County Council in 1998.
Personal: Married with three children and lives on the outskirts of Nottingham.

MCAULEY, Michael
Dundas & Wilson CS, Glasgow (0141) 221 8586

MCCORMACK, Carol
Berwin Leighton, London (020) 7760 1000
carol.mccormack@berwinleighton.com
Partner in projects and public sector department.
Specialisation: Principal area of work is advising government departments, health bodies, educational establishments, local authorities, private sector consortia and service providers on major commercial transactions such as those undertaken through the Private Finance Initiative, Public Private Partnerships and other joint venture arrangements including town centre redevelopments and refurbishment agreements.
Career: Articled with *Berwin Leighton* 1983-85 and became a partner in 1989.
Personal: Born in Middlesbrough 22nd February 1961, attended Selwyn College, Cambridge.

MCCORMICK, Roger
Freshfields Bruckhaus Deringer, London
(020) 7832 7036
rmccormick@freshfields.com
Specialisation: Project Finance (all sectors, all countries) and other financial/commercial transactions.
Prof. Memberships: International Bar Association.
Career: Partner of *Freshfields* since 1981. Head of Project Finance 1991-97.
Personal: Born 1951, Educated M.G.S. and Oxford.

MCEWAN, Alastair J.A.
Maclay Murray & Spens, Edinburgh
(0131) 226 5196
ajm@maclaymurrayspens.co.uk
Specialisation: Partner specialising in capital projects and PFI transactions. Completed deals last year included St.Georges Hospital PFI project, Dumfries and Galloway Acute Maternity PFI project, Edinburgh Inland Revenue and Glasgow Inland Revenue Accommodation Projects and the Cairngorm Funicular Railway project. Currently advising in connection with Midlothian Community PFI project, Findley House Care Centre PFI project, Aberdeenshire Schools PFI project, Highland Schools PFI project and Copeland Borough Council PFI project.
Career: George Watson's College; Edinburgh University (LLB 1979) Scottish School of Business Studies (MBA 1980); Queen's University, Canada (LLM 1982). Articled *Brodies*, 1986-88; assistant solicitor, *Maclay Murray & Spens*, 1988-90, associate 1990-91; partner 1991.
Personal: Born 1958; resides Edinburgh. Enjoys cross country skiing, hill walking.

MCQUATER, Gavin J.
Lovells, London (020) 7296 2000
gavin.mcquater@lovells.com
Specialisation: Project finance. Handles UK (including a number of public/private partnership) projects and international limited recourse transactions, across a range of industries including transport, water and general infrastructure, dealing with sponsors, financial institutions and contracting authorities. Advises on transaction structuring, such as bankable risk allocation and the tender process. Experience of a wide spread of joint ventures, business set ups, corporate reorganisations and M&A transactions. International work includes Europe, Asia and Middle Eastern transactions.
Prof. Memberships: Law Society.
Career: Qualified with *Lovell White & King* in 1979; partner since 1985; 1990-1994 in Hong Kong office; now head of firm's project finance unit.

MURPHY, Michael G.
MacRoberts, Glasgow (0141) 332 9988
mgm@macroberts.co.uk
Specialisation: Head of MacRoberts' Capital Projects Group, specialising in project finance. Acted for Bank of Scotland in Workington Police Station new-build; Acted for Bank of Ireland in DHE Central Scotland Housing Project; Acting for SPV in the Dumfries & Galloway Royal Infirmary PFI Project.
Prof. Memberships: Law Society of Scotland.

NASH, David
Shepherd & Wedderburn WS, Edinburgh
(0131) 228 9900
david.nash@shepwedd.co.uk
Specialisation: PFI/PPP Procurement and Commercial Contracts. Current projects: A92 DBFO, Glasgow Southern Orbital DBFO, Aberdeenshire Schools PFI; Midlothian Schools PFI; MoD Heavy Equipment Transport, MoD construction vehicles PFI. Past projects: Greater Glasgow Sewage Treatment PFI, East Renfrewshire Schools PFI, Scottish Children's Reporters Administration IT PFI, M8 DBFO: M6 DBFO: New Scottish Office, Victoria Quay: Skye Bridge.
Prof. Memberships: Law Society of Scotland.
Career: School: George Watson University College, Edinburgh. Edinburgh University - Hons MA, LLB (1969-1976). 1983-98 - Scottish Office Legal Department.
Personal: Music, travel, skiing.

NOBLE, Perry
Freshfields Bruckhaus Deringer, London
(020) 7936 4000
pnoble@freshfields.com
Specialisation: Project finance and banking. PFI, transportation and telecommunications projects. Acted for London Underground on Power and Prestige PFI projects. Acts for Abbey National, Babcock & Brown and London Underground on full range of PFI projects. Currently acting for Chase on telecoms financings, Hutchison Whampoa on UMTS financings and First Mark Communications on broadband projects throughout Europe.
Prof. Memberships: Law Society.
Career: Letchworth Grammar School, North East London Polytechnic, Bristol University (LL.M Commercial Law).
Personal: Married, two sons. All sport, particularly cricket. Dog walking and cinema.

O'CONNOR, Mike G.
Addleshaw Booth & Co, Manchester
(0161) 934 6000
mgo@addleshaw-booth.co.uk
Head of PFI/ Projects unit.
Specialisation: Specialises in PFI, public private partnerships and project finance also in mainstream corporate banking; public/ private finance, structured finance; finance transactions involving public bodies of all types. Contributing editor to Butterworths 2 volume PFI Handbook. Contributes to CIPFA Handbook on PFI.
Prof. Memberships: Law Society. British South Africa Lawyers Association. Institute of Fiscal Studies.
Career: Qualified 1989. Partner 1996.
Personal: Leisure interests include horse-racing, electric guitar, travel, piano. Governor of Appleton Thorn County Primary School.

O'NEILL, Mark
Allen & Overy, London (020) 7330 3000
Specialisation: Partner in the Finance department specialising in banking and commercial transactions with particular emphasis on property finance, project finance, acquisition finance, syndicated finance and reconstructions.
Career: Victoria University, Wellington, NZ. Trained Bubble Findlay, Wellington, NZ; qualified 1985, associate. Assistant solicitor, *Allen & Overy* 1991, partner *Allen & Overy*, 1995.
Personal: Born 1961.

PHILLIPS, Robert
CMS Cameron McKenna, London (020) 7367 2500
rjp@cmck.com
Partner in Projects Group.
Specialisation: Principal area of practice is advising on transactions involving private/ public sector participation with particular emphasis on major infrastructure and capital projects. Work covers specialist contract drafting, development with other consultants of a risk profile, and negotiating terms of project documents required for limited recourse financed infrastructure schemes. Major projects include independent power projects in Sub Saharan Africa, Portugal, Ireland and India; road, rail and intended transport schemes in the UK, Poland, and Portugal, India and, in particular, advising the Department of Transport on the High Speed Channel Rail Link and the Dutch Government on HSL South. Regular speaker at international conferences and has been retained by the World Bank to assist in development courses for the introduction of competition for public/private sector partnerships.
Prof. Memberships: Major Projects Association.
Career: Partner at *McKenna & Co.* since 1979, including period as Senior Resident Partner in Hong Kong 1983-88. Admitted as a Solicitor, England and Wales 1971, Hong Kong, 1983 and as a Barrister and Solicitor, State of Victoria, Australia, 1986.
Personal: Born 15th May 1947. Lives in Walton-on-Thames, Surrey.

PICKUP, Raith
Mills & Reeve, Cambridge (01223) 222 283
raith.pickup@mills-reeve.com
Specialisation: Has considerable experiance of advising both the public and private sectors on large projects such as energy plants, power stations, new hospitals and university campuses. Currently (July 2000) leading team on PFI projects in the health, education, local authority and defence sectors.

PREECE, Andrew
Herbert Smith, London (020) 7374 8000
Partner and Head of International Projects Group.
Specialisation: Has considerable experience in major projects work including project finance, lease finance and general commercial work, with particular expertise in oil and gas and infrastructure matters, both domestic (including numerous transactions effected under the Private Finance Initiative) and international, and in complex project, lease and property financings.
Prof. Memberships: Law Society, International Bar Association, Major Projects Association, UK Energy Lawyers Group, Finance & Leasing Association.
Career: Qualified in 1970. Became a Partner at *Herbert Smith* in 1977.
Personal: Educated at Selwyn College, Cambridge.

RANDLE, Anthony R.
DLA, Birmingham (08700) 111 111
tony.randle@dla.com
Partner in corporate group.
Specialisation: Practice is exclusively local government and commercial work between the public and private sectors. Heads *DLA's* public/private partnerships group which includes the firm's PFI and local government practices. Has acted for numerous local authorities (Midland and national) on joint ventures, privatisations and externalisations. Led the *DLA* team advising Coventry City Council on the privatisation of Coventry Airport. Advised South Gloucestershire Council on its integrated waste management PFI project.
Prof. Memberships: Law Society.
Career: Qualified 1987. Partner 1993.
Personal: Born 1962. Exeter University (LLB).

RANSOME, Clive
Linklaters (A member firm of Linklaters & Alliance), London (020) 7456 5904
clive.ransome@linklaters.com
Partner in the Project & Asset Finance Group, London. Hong Kong based 1993-98.
Specialisation: Has worked on a number of major projects, project financings and structured financings in the UK, Europe and Asia. These include the Channel Tunnel (acting for the arranging banks), Northern Ireland's power privatisation (for NIGEN), the Pego power project in Portugal (acting for National Power, EdF and Endesa), the TelecomAsia telecommunications project in Bangkok (acting for KFW and other lenders), power, telecommunications projects and road projects in the PRC, Thailand and Indonesia, Southern's US$2.7 billion acquisition of CEPA (acting for Southern) representing IFC and the offshore banks on the Star refinery project in Thailand, advising Shell Brasil and Petrobras on an LNG import and gas sales joint venture in north-eastern Brazil and advising the project sponsors on the Renor refinery in Brazil.

READ, Anthony J.M.
Burness, Edinburgh (0131) 473 6000
ajmr@burness.co.uk
Specialisation: Advising the public sector, bidders and banks on all aspects of the structuring, development and financing of projects. Main area of practice is advising on PFI projects in local authority, education, accommodation and health sectors. Current PFI projects include acting for Fife Council on schools PPP and private sector bidders on West Lothian and Edinburgh Schools projects. Acted for Strathclyde Police on new training and recruitment centre and Dundee Healthcare Services Ltd on Tayside Primary Care Acute Psychiatric Unit project. Acted for Class 98 in award winning Falkirk Schools project, advised Perth & Kinross Council on office accommodation and car park project and Bank of Scotland on James Watt College, North Ayrshire Campus project. Regular speaker at conferences.

ROLFE, Andrew
Clifford Chance, London (020) 79560071
andrew.rolfe@cliffordchance.com
Specialisation: Specialises in major infrastructure project and property development work, with particular involvement in the Private Finance Initiative (since its introduction), where he has acted for sponsors and for financiers on schemes in the defence, education, health, local authority and transport sectors. He recently led the *Clifford Chance* team which advised the sponsor group on the £1.6 billion MoD Main Building Redevelopment project which reached financial close in May 2000.
Career: Qualified in 1982. Partner in *Clifford Chance* since 1988.
Personal: Born 1956. Attended Nottingham University - LL.B (Hons) 1977.

ROWEY, Kent
Freshfields Bruckhaus Deringer, London (020) 7936 4000
Specialisation: Head of *Freshfields'* international project finance group, with over fourteen years experience representing lenders, sponsors and suppliers in independent power projects and other project financing throughout Europe, Asia and the Americas. Currently involved in projects in Israel, Croatia, Australia, Russia and the Indian Sub-continent.
Prof. Memberships: State Bar of California, American Bar Association, International Bar Association.
Career: B.A. Philosphy, University of California, Los Angeles, (Magna cum laude) J.D. New York University. Partner, *Perkins Coie*, London. Associate *Milbank, Tweed, Hadley & McCloy*, Los Angeles, London.
Personal: Lives in Oxfordshire with wife Rosalie and two children, Allison and Austin. Avid (but average) golfer.

SALT, Stuart
Linklaters (A member firm of Linklaters & Alliance), London (020) 7456 5912
stuart.salt@linklaters.com
Partner in the Project & Asset Finance Group.
Specialisation: Main area of practice has been international projects. Extensive experience of acting for governments, sponsors and lenders on major projects in the power, energy and transport sectors.

SANDERS, Jan
Ashurst Morris Crisp, London (020) 7638 1111
jan.sanders@ashursts.com
Specialisation: Projects and general corporate. Acted for Summit, preferred bidder for Dudley Hospital; Barclays Private Equity Limited as equity provider on various hospital and university accommodation projects and as joint sponsor with Jonson Controls bidding for Tower Hamlets Schools; Consort Healthcare (Durham) Limited, sponsor of New DGH Durham.
Career: University College London, articled *Withers* Partner *Ashurst Morris Crisp* 1994.
Personal: Married with two children.

SEDGLEY, David
Allen & Overy, London (020) 7330 3000
Specialisation: Project Finance and PFI. Partner with wide experience of projects and structured financing including infrastructure, power and energy. He has particular experience in PFI transactions.
Career: Articled *Allen & Overy*, qualified 1989. Partner 1995.
Personal: Born 1964.

SIMMONS, William G.
Tods Murray WS, Edinburgh (0131) 226 4771
william.simmons@todsmurray.co.uk
Specialisation: Work includes infrastructure projects and PFI, corporate finance, mergers and acquisitions, banking and general commercial work including joint ventures.
Prof. Memberships: Law Society of Scotland.
Career: Qualified 1981 *Bishop & Co.* Joined *Dorman*

Jeffrey & Co 1983 (Partner 1984). Joined *Tods Murray* as a Partner in 1986.
Personal: Born 1958. Attended Hutchesons Boys Grammar School 1967-1975 and Glasgow University 1975-79 (LL.B Hons). Leisure: hill walking and skiing.

SOUTAR, Tim
Clifford Chance, London (020) 7600 1000
tim.soutar@cliffordchance.com
Specialisation: Partner in London office specialising in project finance, banking and energy, oil, gas, and natural resources. Project finance experience includes power, refinery, petrochemical and transport infrastructure projects: Shajiao B, Shajiao C, Pagbilao and Sual Power Projects - Hopewell/CEPA Group, Zhuhai Power Project - HSBC/CDFC, Star Refinery Project, Thailand - Caltex and PTT, NODCO Refinery Expansion - NODCO/QGPC, Luton Airport Expansion - AGI Consortium, Chad - Cameroon Oil Transportation Project - senior lenders.
Prof. Memberships: Power Sector Working Group.
Career: Bradford Grammar School; St Catherine's College, Oxford (BA Jurisprudence 1977); University of East Asia, Macau (Diploma in Chinese Law 1987). Articled *Coward Chance*; qualified 1980, Hong Kong 1983; assistant solicitor banking practice *Coward Chance* 1980-82; *Clifford Chance* Hong Kong 1982-88; partner Hong Kong 1988.
Personal: Distance running, golf. Born 1955, resides Kent.

SPACIE, Dominic
Mayer, Brown & Platt, London (020) 7246 6200
DSpacie@mayerbrown.com
Specialisation: Project Finance, PFI/PPP, Secured Lending
Career: 1988-93 *Linklaters & Paines*, 1993-6 *Freshfields*, 1994/5 Secondment to *EBRD*, 1996-9 *Masons*, 1999 + *Mayer Brown and Platt.*
Personal: Harrow School, Cambridge University, Guildford College of Law

STEADMAN, Tim
Clifford Chance, London (020) 7600 1000
tim.steadman@cliffordchance.com
Specialisation: Partner and Head of Construction Group. Member of PFI/PPP Group, specialising in concession and construction aspects of projects arising from the Private Finance Initiative in the UK and PFI/PPP schemes elsewhere.
Prof. Memberships: European Construction Institute; IBA committee "T"; CBI Procurement Committee.
Career: Hertford College; Oxford University. Trainee and assistant *Lovell White & King* 1976-1982; associate *Baker & McKenzie* 1982-1985; partner *Baker & McKenzie* 1985-1997; partner *Clifford Chance* since March 1997.
Personal: Born 1955; resides London.

SUTTIE, Frank
Addleshaw Booth & Co, Leeds (0113) 209 2000
fzs@addleshaw-booth.co.uk
Specialisation: Private Finance Initiative and other project finance/ privatisation work. Advised in three of the Government's prioritised health PFI projects and currently advises in similar projects in health, education, transport and for Government Departments. Specialises in procurement strategies, commercial contract negotiation, bid evaluations, client approval procedures and funding issues. He is a contributor to various PFI publications and a regular conference speaker on PFI subjects.
Prof. Memberships: Law Society. Admitted as a Solicitor 1985.
Career: Kirkcaldy High School. University of Stirling. University of London.

TAYLOR, Michael
Norton Rose, London (020) 7283 6000
taylormpg@nortonrose.com
Partner, *Norton Rose.*
Specialisation: Project finance and energy and natural resources. Has specialised in the development and financing of projects in the energy and natural resources fields since joining *Norton Rose* in 1974; became a partner 1979. Head of the firm's energy group. Member of the editorial board of 'International Energy'. Co-author of a book on oil and gas joint ventures.

TEMPLETON - KNIGHT, Jane
Hunton & Williams, London (020) 7427 7850

TOTT, Nicholas P.
Herbert Smith, London (020) 7374 8000
nicholas.tott@herbertsmith.com
Specialisation: Principal areas of work include all forms of financing and banking work with particular emphasis on asset finance, leasing, project financing and Private Finance Initiative (PFI) Projects. Seconded to the Private Finance Panel Executive for fifteen months with responsibility for PFI Projects in Scotland, Northern Ireland and the Ministry of Defence. Publications include a chapter 'Public Finance in the U.K.' in Leasing Finance (Euromoney 1997, 3rd Edition.) Co-author of 'The PFI Handbook' (Jordans, March 1999).
Prof. Memberships: Law Society; City of London Solicitors' Company.
Career: Qualified Scotland (1985), England and Wales (1991). Partner 1992.
Personal: Born 8th May 1960. Educated at Edinburgh University. Leisure pursuits include Golf and Skiing.

TWIST, G. Patrick A.S.
Pinsent Curtis, Birmingham (0121) 200 1050
patrick.twist@pinsents.com
Partner and head of project finance.
Specialisation: Specialises in the development and financing of major projects. Work includes railway infrastructure, energy from waste plants, oil and gas facilities, hospitals and schools. Also experienced in acquisition finance and banking generally.
Prof. Memberships: Chairman, Law Society Banking Law Committee.
Career: Finance and Leasing Association. Ford Credit Europe, Bank of Scotland. Joined *Pinsent & Co* (now *Pinsent Curtis*) 1987. Partner in 1988.
Personal: Born 1952. Educated Downside School and Keele University.

VINTER, Graham D.
Allen & Overy, London (020) 7330 3000
Specialisation: Partner specialising in all aspects of project finance. Involved in numerous projects acting for sponsors and lenders in the oil, gas, mining, electricity, waste, energy and infrastructure sectors worldwide. He has extensive experience of ECA and multilateral financings.
Career: Articled *Allen & Overy*, qualified 1982, Partner 1988. Author of "Project Finance: a Legal Guide" (2nd.ed., 1998).
Personal: Oxford University (BA 1979). Ludwig-Maximilians University, Munich (1977-78). Born 1956.

WEBER, David
Linklaters (A member firm of Linklaters & Alliance), London (020) 7456 5870
david.weber@linklaters.com
Partner, project and project finance department.
Specialisation: Co-founder of *Linklaters'* projects department. Specialist in the development and financing of major international projects, including infrastructure, power generation and oil and gas projects, acting for project sponsors, borrowers and lenders.
Career: Qualified *Linklaters* 1978; Partner since 1984. Born 1953.

WHITE, Bruce
Linklaters (A member firm of Linklaters & Alliance), London (020) 7456 5988
bruce.white@linklaters.com
Partner, project finance group.
Specialisation: Specialist in project finance concentrating particularly on its infrastructure projects under the UK government's private finance initiative as well as advising on major international infrastructure projects.
Personal: Attended University of Dundee, LL B, DIP LP 1984. Qualified 1986. Became a Partner in 1995.

WOODROW, Cameron
Pinsent Curtis, Birmingham (0121) 200 1050
cameron.woodrow@pinsents.com
Specialisation: Major projects; public-private partnerships (including PFI); privatisations; corporate restructuring; joint ventures; acquisitions and disposals; project management. Major transactions have included the pre-franchising reorganisation of the Central Trains Operating Unit of British Rail; the £150 million restructuring and refinancing of Birmingham International Airport; a US$150 million joint venture for LucasVarity; the £100 million concession based financing of London Luton Airport; and the acquisition by GEC Alsthom/Tarmac of the Central Infrastructure Maintenance Unit of British Rail. Significant experience in advising both public bodies (including local authorities) and major private sector clients in the transport, automotive and engineering sectors. Expertise in commercial, company, contract and public law.
Prof. Memberships: Law Society.
Career: BA (Jurisprudence), Brasenose College, Oxford. *Freshfields* 1983-93 (qualified 1986). Partner *Pinsent Curtis* 1993 to date. Birmingham head and national practice co-ordinator for major projects. Awarded "PFI Team of the Year" by Legal Business for Birmingham Airport restructuring.
Personal: Common Purpose graduate.

WYMAN, Chris
Clifford Chance, London (020) 7600 1000
chris.wyman@cliffordchance.com
Specialisation: Partner specialising in project acquisition and general finance in the energy, communications and infrastructure sectors.
Career: Epsom College; Cambridge University. Articled *Coward Chance/ Clifford Chance*; qualified 1981; partner *Clifford Chance* since 1986.

PROPERTY (COMMERCIAL)

London: 702; South: 707; Thames Valley: 708; South West: 709; Wales: 711; Midlands: 712; E. Anglia: 714; North West: 715; Yorkshire: 717 ; North East: 718; Scotland: 719; N. Ireland: 721; *Profiles*: 722

OVERVIEW: As the UK property boom continues, solicitors and clients in the market report a trend towards increasingly sophisticated property deals. Firms looking for big-ticket work need to be able to call not only upon planning and environmental experience but also property finance and tax expertise in order to complete substantial securitisations, sale and leaseback deals, and complex limited partnership transactions. The buoyant UK market is particularly attractive to foreign investors, giving those firms with international connections an edge in the emerging pan-European property market. Other hot issues of the moment include the impact of e-commerce on high street retailers, the corporate consolidation and privatisation of large property companies such as MEPC in response to a poor market performance against the companies' net asset values, the outsourcing and privatisation of government property as in the STEPS transaction, and the need to find tax-transparent vehicles to counteract the effects of stamp duty hikes.

Most major clients tend to divide their commercial property work amongst a panel of solicitors firms, so firms of all sizes are benefiting from this dispersal of work. The London tables have been reorganised this year into over and under 100 (total) fee-earner categories, placing such distinguished smaller firms as Gouldens and Olswangs in among the giants. In the under 100 fee-earner category, Forsters and Maxwell Batley were deemed pre-eminent. Mishcon de Reya is the only new name to enter the leading firm tables.

RESEARCH APPROVED BY BMRB: *For this edition,* Chambers' *researchers conducted 6083 interviews – 4408 with law firms, 598 with barristers and 1077 with clients.*

The validity of the research was scrutinised by BMRB International, who audited both the methodology and the results at our offices in July 2000. They interviewed Chambers' *researchers and cross-checked sample interviews. Details of the audit appear on page 7.*

LEADING IN-HOUSE LAWYERS

Michael ASHLEY-BROWN, Group Legal Counsel, *Canary Wharf*

Sarah CORBETT, General Counsel, *Burberry*

Mark KINGSTON, European General Counsel, *Tishman Speyer*

Angeline SWIFT, Legal Manager, *BG Property Holdings Ltd*

Jayne WALTERS, Commercial Director, *Akeler*

Michael Ashley-Brown of Canary Wharf knows his business and is *"very commercial."* **Sarah Corbett** at Burberry has come from an intellectual property background and has *"grasped the property law area very quickly."* **Mark Kingston** at Tishman Speyer is *"a very good lawyer."* **Angeline Swift** at British Gas is *"incredibly efficient and knows a lot about the law."* **Jayne Walters** at Akeler is *"exceptionally good."*

In-House lawyers profiles: page 1177

'CLIENT ONLY' NATIONAL SURVEY

This table differs from the other tables in this section in two respects. It is derived from the results of a *written* survey of buyers of property legal services in FTSE All Share companies. The survey also asked respondents to rank firms and individuals on a *national* basis.

The table below is based on 102 returned questionnaires and lists the fourteen firms with most recommendations in descending order.

1=) **Eversheds** (3=)
1=) **Nabarro Nathanson** (1)
3=) **Clifford Chance** (3=)
3=) **Linklaters** (2)
5) **Berwin Leighton** (5)
6) **Herbert Smith** (6)
7) **Addleshaw Booth & Co** (-)
8) **Ashurst Morris Crisp** (10)
9=) **CMS Cameron McKenna** (7=)
9=) **SJ Berwin & Co** (-)
11=) **DLA** (12)
11=) **Freshfields Bruckhaus Deringer** (11)
11=) **Lovells** (7=)
11=) **Pinsent Curtis** (-)

(Numbers in brackets denote 1999 positions)

LONDON

FIRMS WITH 100+ FEE EARNERS

Linklaters What keeps Linklaters ahead of the pack for commercial property? *"Why is a Rolls Royce better than other cars?"* Most interviewees see *"clear blue water"* between Linklaters and its nearest competitors, citing as reasons an incomparable *"quality and consistency at all levels"* of the department, the firm's *"international coverage,"* and *"a client list to die for." "You never come across a bad lawyer at Linklaters"* – its team members are known for their *"responsiveness"* and ability to *"come up with radical solutions."* Although *"ferocious"* **Robert Finch**'s time has been almost entirely absorbed by his role as Sheriff, he remains *"unquestionably pre-eminent"* and it is expected that his return to full time practice in September 2000 will add further strength to an already formidable team. **Jeffrey Bailey** is a *"lawyer's lawyer"* with tax expertise. *"Relaxed"* **Martin Elliott** *"built a name for himself"* acting for Lend Lease in the Bluewater letting. **Patrick Plant** *"belongs to the younger generation of property lawyers."* His reputation for *"client-oriented service"* brings him into the tables this year. The group has a particular niche in corporate headquarters and rent review work and is seen to be increasingly active on property finance. Cross-border capabilities were demonstrated by work establishing the € 1.2 billion ProLogis European Properties Fund, a Luxembourg FCP targeting distribution facilities. **Clients:** MEPC; Development Securities; Lend Lease.

Berwin Leighton The firm's noted commitment to property as a core area of practice gives it the reputation of having *"the most eggs in the property basket."* This is a *"classic property industry firm with a strong local authority practice,"* considered *"brilliant"* for *"large projects and innovative tax and planning schemes."* By comparison with other City property firms, Berwin Leighton is seen as more UK-based and some voiced concern that the nature of the practice might lead them towards more and more commoditised property work. Nevertheless, they are recognised as *"unbeatable*

PROPERTY (COMMERCIAL): 100+ FEE-EARNERS • London	Ptnrs	Assts
❶ Linklaters	13	45
❷ Berwin Leighton	15	58
Clifford Chance	16	75
❸ Herbert Smith	12	44
Lovells	11	43
Nabarro Nathanson	33	76
❹ CMS Cameron McKenna	18	45
Freshfields Bruckhaus Deringer	10	45
SJ Berwin & Co	12	34
❺ Ashurst Morris Crisp	11	41
Dechert	13	26
Denton Wilde Sapte	20	43
D J Freeman	13	26
Macfarlanes	13	26
Norton Rose	8	35
❻ Allen & Overy	10	40
DLA	8	18
Eversheds	10	22
Gouldens	9	16
Lawrence Graham	26	47
Olswang	6	20
Simmons & Simmons	12	27
Slaughter and May	7	26

LEADING INDIVIDUALS

❶ **BRETHERTON Philip** Berwin Leighton
FINCH Robert Linklaters
FOGEL Steven Dechert
HELLER Laurie Berwin Leighton
KIDBY Robert Lovells
LANDER Geoffrey Nabarro Nathanson
LE PARD Geoffrey Freshfields Bruckhaus Deringer
MacGREGOR Robert Clifford Chance
MORPETH Iain Clifford Chance
TAYLOR David Berwin Leighton

❷ **BAILEY Jeffrey** Linklaters
BARNES James Herbert Smith
BRIAM Tony Clifford Chance
ELLIOTT Martin Linklaters
HAMILTON Sophie Forsters
HARRISON Christopher Herbert Smith
LUST Graham Nabarro Nathanson
PLANT Patrick Linklaters
RUDOLF Peter Berwin Leighton
RYLAND David SJ Berwin & Co
SAMSON John Nabarro Nathanson
STANCOMBE Michael Lovells
WHITE Graham Slaughter and May
WRIGHT David Nabarro Nathanson

❸ **ALBERT David** Ashurst Morris Crisp
BROWN Nicholas CMS Cameron McKenna
BUTLER Alan Simmons & Simmons
CLARK Paul D J Freeman
FIELD Christopher Macfarlanes
GNIADKOWSKI Stan Denton Wilde Sapte
KUSTOW David Olswang
LAKE Tim Stepien Lake Gilbert & Paling
MORRIS Christopher Freshfields Bruckhaus Deringer
NISSE Ian Ashurst Morris Crisp
ODY Jonathan Norton Rose
ROBINSON Patrick Herbert Smith
SOLOMON Jonathan Norton Rose
TAVENER Chris Herbert Smith
VIVIAN Jon CMS Cameron McKenna
WATSON Gary Hammond Suddards Edge

UP AND COMING

GEORGE James Freshfields Bruckhaus Deringer
RICE Dermot Slaughter and May
WESTHEAD Tim Olswang

Within each band, firms are listed alphabetically.

See ***Profiles*** *on page 722*

for sheer hitting power in the retail shopping area" and public sector work. The *"unflappable"* department head, **David Taylor** is *"spot on"* and has made strides at *"expanding the practice and getting clients."* Although no longer running the department, *"academic"* **Laurie Heller** still devotes *"tremendous energy"* to commercial property work. *"The longer he's there the longer Berwin Leighton remains strong." "Clever"* **Philip Bretherton** *"simply devours"* tax-led property transactions and PFI projects. *"Hard-working"* **Peter Rudolf** specialises in joint venture and complex development work. He recently led the team acting for Legal & General in the redevelopment, letting and disposal of 59-67 Gresham Street, London EC2 to CGI's open-ended fund HausInvest, for circa £210 million. **Clients:** Legal & General; Tesco; Prudential.

Clifford Chance *"Geared for mega-transactions"* Clifford Chance are seen as having *"pound for pound more resources devoted to property than anyone else."* They are in a *"superb position for picking up work that spins off the corporate side"* and the *"sheer manpower"* at their disposal ensures their place as leaders in the commercial property field. As one interviewee noted, he is *"not sure there is another firm who could have handled the Canary Wharf transactions."* The team has considerable expertise in real estate finance, as illustrated by its work on the Citigroup flotation at Canary Wharf. Recent mergers with firms Pünder, Volhard, Weber & Axster and Rogers & Wells promise to give the team an increasing share of the international market. Despite the retirement of senior practitioner Teddy Bourne, the team retains a number of heavy hitters. To some, **Robert MacGregor** *"IS Clifford Chance"* – his expertise in superstore developments and *"flexible approach"* make him *"one of the stars"* of the field. *"Confident"* **Iain Morpeth** was rated for his work *"pioneering property funds"* and *"relaxed"* **Tony Briam** was recommended as a *"sensible negotiator."* The only criticism levelled at the team was that it was sometimes *"patchy"* – *"there are some who get bogged down in detail."* **Clients:** Burford Holdings plc; Canary Wharf plc; Tishman Speyer & Travelers Real Estate Venture LP.

Herbert Smith Although better known in the market for PFI and litigation work, the firm maintains a solid reputation for pure property work, built largely on work for institutional clients such as Standard Life and Greycoat. Recent reorganisation of the firm's management committee has fed the perception that the firm's commitment to property is weakening under the pressures exerted by the corporate department. The group nevertheless receives strong recommendations from peers and clients alike for *"quality service"* and an *"eye for detail,"* and has recognised strengths in planning and public sector development projects. This group of *"hugely talented people"* is led by **Christopher Harrison**, a *"charming"* lawyer with the *"gravitas to assuage both clients and the other side."* **James Barnes** *"makes deals easy"* through his ability to *"get his head around corporate issues."* A *"scarily bright guy,"* **Patrick Robinson** has a commanding knowledge of the planning and environmental aspects of property law while **Chris Tavener** was rated as *"well organised,"* and able to *"sort things out."* Advised Moorfield Group on the formation of a joint venture with Ellerman Investments Ltd and the acquisition of a £390 million portfolio from Royal & Sun Alliance, with subsequent disposals of approximately £250 million. **Clients:** Hermes; Moorfield Group; Carisbrooke Investments.

Lovells Seen to be *"making a play for corporate PFI work"* the firm is also expanding into the European market following its merger with Boesebeck Droste. An *"active"* and *"well-organised"* property group that *"clearly has a quality system in place."* The group is recommended for a *"spread and depth across a number of related specialisms"* including property finance and private partnering. Recently achieved a major coup when instructed by the Inland Revenue/Customs and Excise in connection with the STEPS transaction, with a total value of £4 billion. **Robert Kidby** *("good at keeping up the department profile and holding down demanding clients,") "runs a first-class department."* Team also includes the *"eminently fair and sensible"* **Michael Stancombe** and is further strengthened by the recruitment of two new partners from Nabarro Nathanson and DJ Freeman. **Clients:** Prudential; Argent; Granada

Nabarro Nathanson A *"property-led firm"* with an enormous team dedicated to property work for investors and developers across a range of sectors, and widely-acknowledged expertise in property finance. The department receives mixed reviews from the market. Often described as *"aggressive,"* and having *"quality control"* problems at more junior levels, the group nevertheless *"clearly handles a great volume of complex transactions,"* including a £183 million securitisation of 800 public houses for Alchemy Partners Ltd and a joint venture agreement for BAA McArthur-Glen concerning outlets in Swindon and Bridgend. The team also has a reputation for local authority work and recently acted for Land Securities plc on the creation of the Birmingham Alliance £800 million city centre regeneration project. There are a number of stars at partner level. *"The elder statesman of property"* **Geoffrey Lander** has taken on the firm's international business development role, but remains *"in the swing of things property-wise,"* while *"phenomenally quick"* **David Wright** steps up as department head. **Graham Lust** was noted for his securities work and **John Samson** for his ability to *"distil a problem in documentation."* **Clients:** Land Securities plc; Slough Estates; GE Capital Corporation (Estates) Ltd; Scudder Threadneedle Property Investments Ltd.

CMS Cameron McKenna This *"impressive"* team, accomplished at *"managing large transactions,"* rises steadily in market opinion following its involvement in a number of *"high-profile"* deals. Interviewees point to its ability to *"integrate well with other groups within the firm to bring in other skills to transactions"* as an asset which gives the team a *"commercial edge"* on the field. Acting for UK and international investors, the group is known for *"finance work of the highest order"* involving complex tax structures, offshore vehicles, and fund work. Most notably acted for J. Sainsbury in a £335 million sale and leaseback securitisation of 16 supermarkets. *"Courteous"* **Nick Brown** *"understands what his clients want,"* while **Jon Vivian**, a new entry to the tables, has the necessary *"personal skills to deal with a wide range of people."* **Clients:** J Sainsbury plc; Brixton Estate.

Freshfields Bruckhaus Deringer Due to the firm's *"massive strength on the corporate side"* the group is sometimes perceived as more of a *"corporate support department"* despite a large property-led client base of institutions, investment banks and tenant developers. The team is best known for its work for Scottish Widows, whom it advised on the £700 million purchase of the nine properties in the Guardian Portfolio. The August 2000 merger with Bruckhaus Westrick Heller Löber will reinforce the firm's international client base, consisting largely of German banks. *"Firm of choice for Canary Wharf tenants,"* the group recently acted for Citibank and Credit Suisse First Boston on the letting of 850,000 square feet at Canary Wharf. Now that *"civilised"* **Geoffrey Le Pard** has stepped down as department head, many expect him to become more *"visible"* in the field. New department head **Chris Morris** is described as *"technically skilled and commercial – can see his way through transactions."* **James George**, *"first on the list for big-ticket deals"* remains rated as up and coming. **Clients:** Scottish Widows; P&O; Trillium.

S J Berwin & Co British Land remains the group's dominant client, bringing them such big-ticket work as the £1.17 billion acquisition of the Meadowhall Shopping Centre and property work on a multi-tranche securities bond offering of £1.546 billion. The firm has managed to expand its client base to include increasing numbers of investment banks and institutional clients. Although sometimes described as *"confrontational,"* the group's *"seamless multi-disciplinary approach"* serves them well in their work for major retailers and hoteliers. *"Intellectual"* **David Ryland** draws upon tax expertise in work involving offshore unit trusts and limited partnerships. **Clients:** British Land Company; Barclays Property; Schroder Property.

Ashurst Morris Crisp Seen to suffer from a *"steady leak of property lawyers."* No strong leader has yet been found to pick up the mantle following Laurence Rutman's retirement over a year ago. *"Exceptional"* **Ian Nisse** remains rated as an *"innovative practitioner"* but, due to his time-consuming role as managing partner, is only able to devote a small percentage of his time to a select group of clients. *"Efficient and self-deprecating"* **David Albert** remains the only fully active partner well known in the market. By most accounts, the team is both *"commercial and proactive"* and has been involved in a number of *"juicy deals"* including the £392 million disposal of a portfolio of 75 properties for Royal & Sun Alliance Group Properties to Moorfields Capital Partners. Also acting for the Exchequer Partnership in connection with the flagship PFI transaction at the Government Treasury Building. **Clients:** British Telecommunications plc; Tesco; Chelsfield; Canary Wharf.

Dechert Although occupiers now compose only 30 percent of the group's client base, the team retains its reputation as *"retail kings."* Has particular expertise in shopping centres, hypermarkets, and factory outlets but also acts frequently for property companies, investors, and government councils. A *"well-organised"* department commended for its *"quality documents"* and *"reliability"* in restructuring leases. Managing partner **Steven Fogel** is *"big in academic circles"* and takes a *"constructive"* approach to landlord/tenant issues. Advised Nike on property and construction issues for the redevelopment of the London Niketown store and associated lease agreements. **Clients:** Dixons; Chelsfield; Helical Retail

Denton Wilde Sapte Some describe the merger combining the general commercial property expertise of Denton Hall and property finance strengths of Wilde Sapte as a case of *"2 + 2 = 4.5."* The team handles a concentration of property work for retail occupiers and property funds with a niche in hotel and leisure work. *"Workaholic"* **Stan Gniadkowski** is reckoned a *"star"* on PFI deals. Acted for a joint venture between Taylor Woodrow Capital Developments Ltd and Hutchison Whampoa Properties Ltd in the purchase of Lots Road Power Station from London Underground Ltd. **Clients:** Equitable Life Assurance co; J Sainsbury Group; City & West End Developments.

D J Freeman A multi-disciplinary group with particular strengths in property finance and building contracts. Involved in a number of unusual limited partnerships such as the £90 million THI Leisure Fund limited partnership, an investment fund targeting the leisure industry. The group's property finance team has also handled the refinancing of Ashford International Passenger Station for John Laing. **Paul Clark** heads a *"steady and straightforward"* team and was noted for his *"pragmatic"* style and skills in *"explaining a deal clearly"* to partnerships. **Clients:** Land Securities; Regus; AXA Equity & Law

Macfarlanes Interviewees *"take their hats off"* to this *"good firm with an eye on maintaining quality."* Acts for a large number of investors ranging from large institutions such as Abbey Life to private client investors. A *"tightly run"* department recommended for offshore spvs and deals with taxation implications. Also maintains a niche in Enterprize Zone urban regeneration work. **Chris Field** is a *"shrewd operator,"* seen to be *"driving the property department forward."* Acted for London Bridge Holdings Ltd in the development and letting of the GLA building, the new home for the Mayor of London. **Clients:** Abbey Life; CIT Group; P&O Developments Ltd.

Norton Rose A *"class act" "focusing on high value work for blue-chip corporates."* Best known for working for developers, especially in forward funded or pre-let development projects. *"A leading player in property,"* **Jonathan Solomon** *"works well under pressure."* However, he will be leaving to join Clifford Chance in October 2000. The *"gentlemanly"* **Jonathan Ody** is a new addition to our tables. Team recently acted for the AES Corporation on the acquisition of Drax power station from National Power plc for £1.875 billion and the £1.3 billion secured financing arranged by Chase Manhattan plc, Deutsche Bank AG London and the Industrial Bank of Japan Ltd. **Clients:** Helical Bar plc; Workspace Group plc; Benchmark Group plc; CGI.

Allen & Overy Less active on pure property matters, the group's strength lies in property finance and property banking and is felt to benefit from the market trend towards more complex transactions. Some report that it is already a *"victim of its own success"* in that it may not have the necessary manpower to deal with all the work generated after *"cornering the market on German banks."* Recommended for *"seamless"* forward funding of developments, structured financing, and securitisation deals. Advising Leconport Estates, a joint venture between GE Capital Real Estate and pension fund manager Hermes, on its recommended cash offer for MEPC plc. **Clients:** J. Henry Schroder & Co; Schroder Exempt Property Unit Trust; HypoVereinsbank; DePfa-Bank.

DLA Refers property work between six offices with complex work concentrated in the London and Liverpool branches. An *"efficient"* team with a *"tremendous turnover."* Acts for a mixed base of institutions, developers, occupiers and property companies. Advised MEPC on the creation of a joint venture with GE Capital Real Estate involving an MEPC property portfolio of £200 million. **Clients:** MEPC plc; Sun Life Assurance Society plc; Granada Group plc.

Eversheds Seen to *"operate as a franchise"* with a network of offices extending across the UK. Client base includes a number of pension funds, retailers, and leisure developers. Has a strength in regeneration projects and recently acted for the South West of England Regional Development Agency in the redevelopment of the £25 million Falmouth Maritime Site. **Clients:** ESN; Marconi Property; Stanhope Pension Trust.

Gouldens A *"quality act,"* the department *"operates at the highest level"* in both commercial property and property finance transactions and is said to be comparable with those of much larger firms. Experienced in out of town retail park developments and secured lending schemes. This *"down to earth"* team *"doesn't make a drama out of transactions."* Acted for Pillar Property plc in a limited partnership joint venture with Equitable Life Assurance for 12 UK retail parks valued at £245 million. **Clients:** Pillar Property plc; Arlington Securities plc; Ashtenne plc.

Lawrence Graham A well respected group that has *"done well at pitching for new work"* since the 1998 absorption of Forsyte Saunders Kerman. Described by clients as *"enthusiastic"* and *"attentive,"* the team has expertise in rent review, shopping centres and mixed-use development. Advised London & Regional Property Group on £225 million worth of acquisitions including the TBI plc property portfolio and Green Park Hotel. **Clients:** Legal & General Group; J Sainsbury Developments; Universities Superannuation Scheme.

Olswang The field's most recent *"success story,"* the firm has rapidly built up a reputation for *"major"* property work. *"Charming"* **David Kustow** has been instrumental in raising the team's profile. The group draws upon the firm's telecommunications and hi-tech experience in advising retailers on the impact of e-commerce issues. Made a *"considerable splash"* by leading the purchase of the P&O property portfolio of over 130 properties by the Whitehall Green Partnership for £400 million. New department head **Tim Westhead** was rated as up and coming for his role in the transaction and talent at *"maximising returns."* **Clients:** Capital and Regional Properties; Green Property UK Ltd; Minerva plc

Simmons & Simmons Seen to be *"struggling somewhat to rebuild a quality practice"* following the loss of two property partners. A broad client base of institutional investors, property companies, and occupiers with niche strengths in transportation and private client work. **Alan Butler**'s *"formidable intellect shines through in transactions,"* particularly in regard to German funds work. Acted for Railtrack in connection with its £350 million joint venture with British Land for the redevelopment of a new phase of Broadgate EC2. **Clients:** Abu Dhabi Investment Authority; Despa; Railtrack plc.

Slaughter and May Although perceived largely as a *"corporate support department,"* the group receives kudos for its *"first-rate"* work on the property aspects of corporate acquisitions. The group's small amounts of stand-alone property work are focused on *"sophisticated transactions"* involving large portfolios or structured finance. Acted for Punch Taverns in a disposal of 550 pubs to Bass implemented by way of an asset transfer. *"Impressive"* **Graham White** receives special praise for his ability to *"see both detail and the big picture"* and his efforts to *"build up a property group against the odds in a corporate oriented environment."* An up and coming name, **Dermot Rice** *"looks through the mire and sees where a deal is to be made."* **Clients:** Derwent Valley Holdings plc; Abbey National plc; Whitbread plc.

Other Notable Practitioners Although the London branch of Hammond Suddards Edge does not have a high enough profile in commercial property to enter our leaders' tables, practitioner **Gary Watson** was individually ranked as an *"outstanding lawyer," "head and shoulders above the rest of his team."*

FIRMS WITH FEWER THAN 100 FEE EARNERS

Forsters A *"West End boutique property firm"* said to be *"going from strength to strength."* Seen to be *"rising"* in the field with a client list that includes large institutional funds, listed and unlisted property companies, and leisure, restaurant, and retail occupiers. Also acts for Hong Kong and Singaporean residential property developers and investors and advises three major London estates. A definite *"presence"* in the market, **Sophie Hamilton**'s *"strong personality"* inspires a *"loyal client following."* The group was involved in the disposal by Guardian Assurance of its portfolio of properties to Scottish Widows in relation to 23 properties with an aggregate value of £200 million. **Clients:** Crown Dilmun; PRICOA (Northern Retail Properties); McDonalds Restaurants Ltd; Clerical Medical Investment Group.

Maxwell Batley A *"sensible"* group of *"well-connected lawyers"* with a *"fantastic client base"* of pension funds, property development companies, and institutional investors. Has particular expertise in development funding and setting up corporate vehicles for the joint ownership of properties. Practitioners are recommended for providing *"tailor made documents"* that allow clients to settle right away. The group maintains a high profile in the field, primarily through its work for Hermes Property Asset Management Ltd, for whom the team recently acted in a joint venture with GE Capital in connection with the purchase of MEPC plc. **Clients:** BT Pension Scheme; Post Office Pension Scheme; National Mutual Life Assurance; Hermes Property Asset Management Ltd.

Boodle Hatfield An *"effective"* team of lawyers who *"see their way to the end of a deal."* Best known for acting for the Grosvenor Estate whom the team advised on the £300 million funding of the Basingstoke Festival Palace retail and leisure development. The group also has niche strengths in petrol filling stations and healthcare centres. **Clients:** Grosvenor Estate Holdings; Primary Health Care Centres Ltd; Magram plc.

Manches A *"classic"* West End firm with a *"name"* for retail property transactions. Also handles a substantial amount of development work and support work from construction, planning, and environmental departments. Acted for Green Property on the purchase of a £400 million property portfolio from P&O. **Clients:** Burford Group plc; Green Property plc; WH Smith.

Stepien Lake Gilbert & Paling A niche property firm with a high proportion of unquoted property company, individual and overseas investor clients. Team includes *"straightforward"* **Tim Lake** who is skilled at *"putting complex legal issues into layman's terms."* Experienced in mixed-use and res-

PROPERTY (COMMERCIAL): UNDER 100 FEE-EARNERS • London	Ptnrs	Assts
❶ Forsters	6	18
Maxwell Batley	7	4
❷ Boodle Hatfield	11	9
Manches	8	15
Stepien Lake Gilbert & Paling	4	1
❸ Finers Stephens Innocent	12	13
Fladgate Fielder	14	9
Speechly Bircham	7	10
Trowers & Hamlins	5	6
❹ Coudert Brothers	4	5
❺ Hamlins	7	5
Julian Holy	5	3
McGuinness Finch	7	3
Mishcon de Reya	10	16
Park Nelson	7	-
Teacher Stern Selby	7	5
Thomas Eggar Church Adams	3	3

Within each band, firms are listed alphabetically.

idential developments, and acted on the St. George's Wharf development. **Clients:** Overseas investors; developers.

Finers Stephens Innocent Finers' merger with Stephens Innocent, with its internet company client base, has increased the firm's capacities to advise clients on the impact of e-commerce on the property sector, but has not diluted its *"aggressive"* image. Has a dedicated retail property group, handling instructions from High Street retailers and restaurant chains. Acted for Marylebone Warwick Balfour Group plc in the £35 million forward sale of Development of West India Quay. **Clients:** Marylebone Warwick Balfour plc; DHL (UK) Ltd; Pizza Hut (UK) Ltd.

Fladgate Fielder A *"resourceful"* team handling both property development work and 'spin off' property matters relating to corporate takeovers. A *"switched-on outfit"* with strengths in secured lending and retail/leisure parks. Represented Morgan Guaranty Trust Company of New York in relation to two facilities totalling £366 million made to Whitehall Green Trading Ltd and the Whitehall Green Partnership to fund the acquisition of the P&O Main Portfolio. **Clients:** Capital and Regional Properties plc; Regal Hotel Group plc; Woolwich Building Society plc.

Speechly Bircham There is a *"lot of experience locked up"* in this growing team of property specialists. Draws on tax expertise in working for a number of offshore companies. Acted for Thai investor Kian Gwan Land Ltd in the acquisition of a 500,000 square foot site for a mixed-use development in Islington. Better known for acting for investors but receives an increasing amount of development work. **Clients:** Sun Life Assurance Company of Canada; Scottish Life Assurance Company; P&O Properties Ltd.

Trowers & Hamlins Although the firm's pure property practice is sometimes overshadowed by its outstanding reputation for housing association work, the group has had a banner year after being chosen by Guardian Assurance to lead the sale of a property portfolio of 70+ retail parks, shopping centres, and industrial parks. The sites were sold on the back of certificates of title on individual properties. The team *"won't get sidetracked by details"* and has recognised strengths in handling property matters for US retailers and healthcare clients. **Clients:** Guardian Assurance plc; Palmer & Harvey; Castlemore Securities.

Coudert Brothers Despite the retirement of a senior practitioner and the perception that the firm is increasingly concentrating on corporate matters, the practice retains its reputation as a leader, particularly in regard to shopping centre work in which the team employs expertise in turnover rents. Also handles Housing Association work and property matters for telecommunications companies. Acted for Hilstone Corporation in the acquisition of a portfolio of 15 properties valued at £50 million. **Clients:** Capital Shopping Centres; Hilstone Corporation Ltd; MCI Worldcom.

Hamlins A *"realistic"* group who take a *"commercial approach"* to work for occupiers, property investors and developers, lenders and tenants. Particularly recommended for property-related debt recovery and an ability to *"pick up issues quickly."* Involved in the sale of Dwyer Estate plc to Warner Estate Holdings plc for the sum of £50 million. **Clients:** National Car Parks; London & Regional Properties; Greycoat.

Julian Holy A niche practice with a loyal entrepreneurial client base of individual overseas investors. This small but *"active"* group is said to *"work 25.5 hours a day"* and has a reputation for *"challenging and demanding wheeler-dealer type work."* The practice is weighted towards landlords and *"pops up"* in shopping centre, company acquisitions, and securitisation work. **Clients:** Landlords; investors.

McGuinness Finch A West End specialist property and planning firm in a period of transition following the resignation of two founding partners and the loss of the Leeds property team. The practice is largely partner-led and was recommended for its client care. Seen primarily on development transactions. Acted in the Norwich Riverside joint development between Railtrack plc and Gazeley Developments Ltd involving a mixed retail and leisure scheme of 425,000 square feet. **Clients:** Invensys plc; Gazeley Properties Ltd; Welbeck Land Ltd.

Mishcon de Reya A new entry to the tables, the department contains a number of widely respected personalities, although there is sometime seen to be a *"lack of glue"* between them. Client base includes a number of entrepreneurial clients and public/private partnerships. The group has specialisms in retail, leisure, and residential property work. Acted for Frogmore Estates plc in connection with the acquisition of a 13.6 acre site in Maidenhead for a £29 million office development and pre-let of 52,000 square feet to Business Objects (UK) Ltd. **Clients:** Frogmore Estates plc; Helical Bar plc; Topland Group plc.

Park Nelson A *"solid"* firm with a reputation for quality retail and landlord/tenant work. Acts for a number of tenants in Ireland and Northern Ireland and has particular experience in out of town retail parks. **Clients:** Tenants.

Teacher Stern Selby Accomplished in shopping centre management, multi-let buildings, and pub portfolio acquisitions. The group is commended for its ability to *"find solutions while protecting the client's interests."* Act for a number of overseas investors, particularly from the Middle East. **Clients:** Britannia Building Society; Fordgate; Baggage Centre.

Thomas Eggar Church Adams Bulk of the firm's property work carried out for a small number of clients, most within the railway sector, but extending also to housing trusts and pension funds. A dedicated rail team *"knows the wrinkles"* of railway legislation and commercial conveyancing issues specific to the industry. Also act in standard commercial landlord/tenant matters including a number of corporate headquarter leases. **Clients:** Railtrack plc; Woolwich plc; Sun Life.

THE SOUTH

PROPERTY (COMMERCIAL) • The South	Ptnrs	Assts
❶ **Blake Lapthorn** Fareham	4	13
❷ **Bond Pearce** Southampton	7	10
Stevens & Bolton Guildford	3	6
❸ **Clyde & Co** Guildford	3	6
Cripps Harries Hall Tunbridge Wells, Kent	8	7
DMH Brighton	5	2
Lester Aldridge Bournemouth	7	3
Paris Smith & Randall Southampton	3	8
Sherwin Oliver Solicitors Portsmouth	4	5
Thomas Eggar Church Adams Chichester, Horsham, Worthing, Reigate	9	9
Thomson Snell & Passmore Tunbridge Wells	6	1
❹ **Brachers** Maidstone	5	3
Coffin Mew & Clover Fordham, Portsmouth, Southampton	6	3
GCL Solicitors Guildford	4	7
Laytons Hampton Court	5	3
Moore & Blatch Southampton	3	6
Penningtons Basingstoke, Godalming, Newbury	7	5
Rawlison & Butler Crawley	3	6
Shoosmiths Solent	2	6
Steele Raymond Bournemouth	4	5

LEADING INDIVIDUALS

❶ **BAILEY Michael** Argles Stoneham Burstows

BAILY Tim Bond Pearce

BENNETT Graham Shoosmiths

BLAKE Carey Blake Lapthorn

PUGH Nigel Bond Pearce

UP AND COMING

HOWARTH Mark Paris Smith & Randall

Within each band, firms are listed alphabetically. *See **Profiles** on page 722*

Blake Lapthorn The *"undoubted kings of the Solent,"* this Fareham and Southampton practice is now seen to dominate commercial property in the South. Praised for its *"uniformity of standards"* and strength in depth (*"even the juniors are switched on,"*) the team is highly rated for its retail and development work for leading regional and national clients. Localised strengths include secured lending and waterfront development. Team head **Carey Blake** is well known in the market and enters the rankings this year. Handled land acquisitions in excess of £30 million for Bellway Homes. **Clients:** Bellway Homes; Premier Marinas.

Bond Pearce Known in the market for its close relationship with retail giants B&Q and Comet, the firm's geographical reach across the South and South West allows the practice to maintain a broad spread of work, and a strong regional presence. Clients include investors, educational institutions, PFI funders/developers and media organisations. **Nigel Pugh** remains respected for his development work, while **Tim Baily** *"maintains his sense of humour in difficult situations"* and has niche expertise in offshore cable laying for the Crown Estate Marine. The team is particularly active in out of town retail developments, and recently acted in the acquisition of a retail park for £38 million. **Clients:** B&Q plc; Associated British Ports; Taylor Woodrow.

Stevens & Bolton Small but *"quality"* property team of *"good pedigree"* and *"high intellect,"* which acts for a number of substantial retail and logistics organisations. Its noted expertise in corporate support is exemplified by a recent due diligence exercise on a £51 million company acquisition by the Hays Group. Other core strengths include secured lending, development and acquisitions for overseas investors. Handles property work for three NHS trusts and advised Hammersmith Hospital NHS Trust on a multi-million pound redevelopment of part of the Hammersmith Hospital and the related construction of the new Queen Charlotte's and Chelsea Hospitals. **Clients:** BOC Group plc; Hays plc; Addecco Alfred Marks.

Clyde & Co Though seen by many as a decentralised City practice, this recent arrival to the Guildford market is beginning to build a profile in the region. Skilled in substantial national development and investment work for institutions and overseas investors, recent lateral hires have boosted the practice's presence in the retail sector. Involvement in the town centre redevelopment of Walton-on-Thames and related occupational lettings highlight the team's ability to take on large-scale development work. Also have expertise in funding and property finance arrangements. Acted on the acquisition through a limited partnership of 15 office blocks with a value in excess of £100 million. **Clients:** Frogmore Estates plc; Carphone Warehouse; Wincanton.

Cripps Harries Hall *"Professional"* and *"commercial"* outfit, whose acknowledged reputation in the house-building sector may be bolstered by the recent recruitment of an in-house development lawyer. Also maintains a significant public sector practice, with clients including government departments and local authorities. Portfolio management for landowners and corporate support are other areas of expertise. Appointed as one of the property firms to undertake a due diligence exercise for a large collection of properties in England and Wales. **Clients:** HM Customs and Excise; Berkeley Homes (Eastern); Union Railways Property.

DMH Remains a respected practice despite the departure of Michael Bailey to Argles Stoneham Burstows. This was highlighted by its recent appointment to BG's panel on the Transco Project. Maintains particular strengths in leisure and licensing, development and property work for public organisations and charities. Counts a number of hi-tech businesses amongst its clients, and acted in relation to the development of a high specification simulation centre in West London. Recently handled a large number of acquisitions, upgrades, lease renewals and disposals of convenience stores for Forbuoys Ltd. **Clients:** CSMA; TM Retail; University of Sussex.

Lester Aldridge *"Sound"* team which is increasing its profile in the sector, both within and outside the region. Acts for a range of national property developers, companies and institutional investors, with niche experience in marina and waterside developments. Handled the acquisition of a large industrial site for Orb Estates plc from the MOD, with related environmental issues. **Clients:** Orb Estates plc; Newday Group; Meggitt Group plc.

Paris Smith & Randall Headed up by **Mark Howarth**, who enters the table after several recommendations from the market, this is a *"solid team"* with a broad range of work and *"its feet on the ground."* Specific expertise includes retail, portfolio work for investors and traders, marina work and secured lending. Handles a variety of property work for a public authority, including a regeneration project and redevelopment of two leisure facilities. Acted on the property aspects of the sale of Southampton Football Club's ground at the Dell and acquisition of a new site. **Clients:** Alldays.

Sherwin Oliver *"Spanking outfit"* with an *"entrepreneurial"* edge, which specialises in substantial commercial development and landlord and tenant work. Other matters handled include investment work for wealthy individuals, waste management, landfill and mineral extraction work. **Clients:** Xyratex; Inchcape Family Investments (on English matters).

Thomas Eggar Church Adams Large *"well-run"* team with an emphasis on operational work for plcs and local authorities, and portfolio sales and acquisitions for institutional clients. Work for Railtrack ranges from retail work to large-scale development. Well-versed in negotiating option agreements for house-builders or landowners' consortia. **Clients:** Railtrack plc; MJ Gleeson Group; Glanmore Property Trust.

Thomson Snell & Passmore Low-key, partner-heavy practice best known for its substantial residential development work. Manages property portfolios for private individuals and pension funds. Also handles property work for plcs, and advised a trading plc on the acquisition of a multi-million pound site for the extension of its business. **Clients:** Antler Homes Kent Ltd; Marley plc Pension Fund; Colas.

Brachers Notable for its healthcare and agriculture niches, the team looks after the property portfolios of six NHS Trusts in Kent and Sussex and a large farming clientele. Additional work includes investment management, corporate support and operational work for end users such as manufacturers and hauliers. Acted in the disposal of a factory for £13 million. **Clients:** National hauliers; manufacturers; farmers.

Coffin Mew & Clover Solid commercial property practice with a name in the market for urban regeneration work. Handles residential and commercial development, portfolio management and acquisition/disposal for a range of clients including entrepreneurial investors and business space occupiers. Sector strengths include medical surgery development, leisure projects and development of ex-MoD stock. **Clients:** University of Portsmouth; Gieves & Hawkes plc; Southampton University Hospitals NHS Trust.

GCL Solicitors Niche residential development practice that is *"unusual in having made the grade almost entirely in that sector,"* and is new to the rankings this year. Counts a number of national house-builders amongst its clients. Acted in a major land acquisition for over £30 million. **Clients:** Barclay Group

Laytons *"Efficient, co-operative"* practice which retains a strong reputation in residential development work, an enviable client portfolio of *"serious players"* and particular experience in development of brown field sites and environmentally sensitive developments. Supplementary expertise includes corporate support and waste disposal, minerals and aggregates. Act as project lawyers for the consortium of McAlpine, Bovis and Bryant in building a substantial new village development at Cambourne. **Clients:** Cambourne Development Project; Barratt Homes Ltd; St James Homes Ltd.

Moore & Blatch Residential development specialists seen as *"active in the local market."* Ongoing work includes site acquisitions, highway agreements, options and joint ventures, local authority work and commercial development. Also skilled in waterfront development, the team have recently handled two multi-million pound marina developments, including residential and leisure development. Acted in the £5 million acquisition of a Premier League football ground for a national house-builder. **Clients:** Linden Homes (Southern) Ltd; Banner Homes Ltd; Barratt Homes Ltd.

Penningtons Based across three offices, this low profile practice covers the full range of commercial property work, from portfolio management to commercial sales and purchases, landlord and tenant, corporate support and secured lending. Niche strengths include agricultural land and environmental expertise. Has an acknowledged reputation in development work, with a recent example being the acquisition and pre-let of a development site for a 60,000 square foot retail warehouse estate. **Clients:** Audley Developments; Berkeley Homes Hampshire; Sun Life of Canada (UK.)

Rawlison & Butler Despite recent setbacks, the team maintains a respected mixed development and general commercial property practice. On the residential side, the team acts for national developers, while other property work includes commercial development, landlord and tenant, property investment and finance. Clients range from retail and industrial concerns to leisure facilities, petrol stations, hotels and pubs. Acted in the acquisition of a site for a major new hotel development and on the disposal for development of the UK headquarters building of an international company. **Clients:** Nicholson Estates Ltd; Charles Church Developments Ltd; JT Davies & Sons Ltd

Shoosmiths Less visible than in recent years, but retaining a broad property practice, with particular strengths in portfolio management and commercial development. Additionally undertakes property finance work for a range of banks and some residential development. Industry sector specialisms include hotels, airports, power and petroleum. Team head **Graham Bennett** remains a known player. **Clients:** HJ Heinz; Esso Petroleum; Central Board of Finance of the Church of England.

Steele Raymond Highly rated in the Bournemouth area, with a strong emphasis on retail and commercial development work. Major clients range from educational institutions to national furniture and garden centre businesses. Ongoing work includes corporate support and the sale of a substantial greenfield site for mixed-use development. **Clients:** Transport facilities; educational institutions; national retailers.

Other Notable Practitioners *"Thorough professional"* **Michael Bailey** has now left DMH for newly-merged firm Argles Stoneham Burstows, the wider impact of which remains to be seen.

THAMES VALLEY

PROPERTY (COMMERCIAL) • Thames Valley	Ptnrs	Assts
❶ **Denton Wilde Sapte** Milton Keynes	2	12
Morgan Cole Oxford, Reading	7	9
Pitmans Reading	5	15
❷ **BrookStreet Des Roches** Witney	4	7
Clarks Reading	4	8
❸ **Iliffes Booth Bennett** Uxbridge	6	5
❹ **BP Collins** Gerrards Cross	2	3
Harold Benjamin Littlejohn Harrow	4	1
Linnells Oxford	5	3
❺ **Colemans** Maidenhead	2	-
Fennemores Milton Keynes	2	2
Matthew Arnold & Baldwin Watford	3	2
Pictons St. Albans	6	1

LEADING INDIVIDUALS	
❶ **BILLINGS Martin** Morgan Cole	**BURGESS James** Pitmans
❷ **DAVIES Andrew** Pitmans	**SILVA David** Iliffes Booth Bennett

Within each band, firms are listed alphabetically. *See **Profiles** on page 722*

Denton Wilde Sapte Though operating in different markets to most firms in the region, its *"quality work and quality assistants"* makes it *"difficult not to rate them."* The team is largely concentrated in two areas, large scale retail and leisure portfolio management, and development advice in relation to English Partnerships' property. Much of the retail work is sourced from the firm's London office, and the team manages two-thirds of Barclays Bank's entire branch portfolio. Work for English Partnerships is locally and nationally based, and includes current major development projects in central Milton Keynes and many disposals of residential and commercial sites in the area. Local authority work has been a growing area of recent instruction. **Clients:** English Partnerships; Bradford & Bingley; Barclays Bank plc.

Morgan Cole Now firmly entrenched in both the Reading and Oxford hubs, the team rises in the rankings this year to reflect its position as a serious regional outfit. Skilled in all aspects of property work, with key strengths in commercial development, insolvency, property finance and portfolio management for clients including energy multinationals and hi-tech businesses. According to clients, *"nothing is too much trouble"* for team head **Martin Billings**, who enters the rankings after repeated recommendation from the market. Acted for Tech Data Corporation on the Supershed project, a national distribution centre financed through forward funding at a value of £50 million. **Clients:** MEPC; Xerox Ltd; Integralis.

Pitmans *"Busy"* practice with a heavy presence in the residential and commercial development sectors, which leads it to rise to the major league this year. Praised in the market for its *"broad-brush strategic approach"* the team is *"good at thinking laterally and getting things done."* Department head **James Burgess** has a *"depth of experience"* in the field, while *"bright"* **Andrew Davies** was praised for his *"get up and go attitude."* Development expertise includes long term option agreements and complex funding arrangements. Commercial landlord and tenant advice and portfolio management are other areas of work. Recent substantial developments include a new campus for a computer company and a £100 million business park. **Clients:** MEPC; Veritas; Barratts Thames Valley.

BrookStreet Des Roches Small and commercial outfit with an impressive client list of national retail businesses, charities, development companies and restaurants. Praised in the market for its ability to *"get to the heart of the issue,"* the team covers the full range of commercial property, from acquisitions and development to leasehold work and secured lending. Work for Oxford colleges includes buying and selling industrial estates and redeveloping investment property in the city centre. Acted for National Grid in the acquisition and development of its northern headquarters in Leeds. **Clients:** Blockbuster Entertainment; Oxford, Swindon and Gloucester Cooperative Society; Booker.

Clarks Long established firm with a *"thorough grasp"* of commercial property work, particularly *"at the detailed end."* Undertakes all aspects of property work for prominent IT, distribution and motor vehicle manufacturing companies and public sector organisations including charities, NHS organisations and further education institutions. House-building and estate management for private investors and investment companies are other significant areas of practice. Recent examples of work include multi-million pound sales and leasebacks of corporate headquarters, re-financing of funding for new university halls of residence and the purchase of a site for 800 houses and related planning agreements. **Clients:** David Wilson Homes; NHS organisations; Bunzl plc.

Iliffes Booth Bennett Steadily building a reputation in commercial development work, with a *"substantial portfolio"* of national clients. **David Silva** *"holds his own against the London firms,"* and makes his debut in the rankings. Specialist experience in complex funding arrangements, construction and pre-letting. Residential development, investment and operational work are other important areas of practice, with recent instructions including substantial office lettings in the South East and London. Acted on a forward funded industrial/warehouse development at Riverside Park, Northampton with an estimated end value of £25 million. **Clients:** CGU International Insurance; Frontier Estates Ltd; Lands Improvement Holdings

BP Collins *"Good on commercial lease and acquisition work,"* for clients ranging from local private companies to some multi-nationals. General market perception is that the practice has lost some profile over the last year. The team also handles residential development. **Clients:** JD Wetherspoon; Michael Shanly Investments; Amazon.com.

Harold Benjamin Littlejohn Highly regarded, partner-heavy team with an array of impressive plc clients. The practice is anchored on the twin specialisms of residential development and commercial landlord and tenant. Acts for a range of national house-builders, investment developer clients and chartered surveyors in acquisition of development land and strategic land management. A separate team handles all aspects of leasehold work, including the sale and acquisition of freeholds subject to occupational leases for investment. Acted for Bellway Homes in the redevelopment of Carson's chocolate factory site in Bristol. **Clients:** Bellway Homes; Michael Shanly Investments Ltd; Ladbrokes Ltd.

Linnells Known as an *"established Oxford practice"* with a reputation for technical expertise. Has particular experience in VAT planning and mining/gravel extraction. Work for the retail sector includes portfolio management of Oxfam's charity shops and Blackwell Retail's store chain. Other clients include large developer plcs, Oxford colleges and institutional investors. Handled the sale of Ixion Motor Group, including all garage premises, in a £15 million transaction. **Clients:** B.H. Blackwell Ltd; Coventry Building Society; Berkeley Homes (Oxford) Ltd.

Colemans Maintains its noted profile in local residential development work, and acts for two national house-builders. Also active in portfolio management and commercial landlord and tenant, with a number of hi-tech clients. Acted for Cincom Systems (UK) Ltd on the lease of their new headquarters building in Maidenhead. **Clients:** Persimmon Homes (Thames Valley) Ltd.

Fennemores Enters the rankings this year after praise from the market as a *"specialist"* and *"technically sound"* practice with a *"broad range of work."* Commercial and residential development and related strategic land acquisition are major practice areas, with ongoing work including retail, office, multi-storey car park and leisure schemes in the region. **Clients:** Abbeygate Developments.

Matthew Arnold & Baldwin New to the rankings, the team focuses on commercial landlord and tenant, portfolio management work and house-building. Clients include commercial tenants, property companies, restaurants, pubs and hotels. Has particular expertise in acting for banks and LPA receivers in the sales of properties in receivership. **Clients:** Nationcrest plc; Allied Irish Bank plc; Cerplex Ltd.

Pictons *"The most geared up firm"* in its area, with a range of residential and commercial developer clients, and long-standing experience in leasehold work and secured lending. Also handles portfolio management for individual property investors and private pension funds. Transactions over the past year have ranged in value from £250,000 to £5 million. **Clients:** Pilling Volvo; City Lights.

SOUTH WEST

Burges Salmon Large and *"robust"* team which remains *"as grindingly competent as ever."* The practice is particularly known in the market for its substantial portfolio management and restructuring work, and is seen to be beefing up its development practice. Acts for blue-chip clients in a variety of sectors including power, bank finance, agriculture and manufacturing. Its particular experience in the transport and logistics sectors is exemplified by recent advice to a logistics operator on the acquisition, expansion and lease restructuring of two regional distribution depots. Rated players include **Robert Smyth**, who is now doing more environmental work, but retains a strong reputation in property, **Robin Battersby** *("good on development land")* and **John Dunn**. It remains to be seen how the departure of personality lawyer Stuart King for Veale Wasbrough will affect the practice. **David Gidney** is seen as a *"man on a mission"* to win new development clients, and enters the rankings as an up and coming name this year. Acted for Orange in the procurement of four new call centres in Plymouth, Darlington and Newcastle. **Clients:** Orange plc; Canadian & Portland Estates plc; British Waterways.

Osborne Clarke OWA While seen by some to concentrate on corporate support, others in the market have noted a *"clear decision to put more resources in the area"* which confirms the team as a *"major player"* in the region. Respondents also noted a strengthening of complementary areas of planning and construction and an increase in client referrals from the London office. Retail, strategic land and investment work remain the core areas of strength, and the team acted jointly for British Airways Pension Fund and Henderson Investors on the funding and acquisition of a 75 percent interest in the Printworks Leisure Scheme in Manchester. **Charles Gait** is new to

PROPERTY (COMMERCIAL) • SOUTH WEST

PROPERTY (COMMERCIAL) • South West	Ptnrs	Assts
❶ **Burges Salmon** Bristol	8	28
Osborne Clarke OWA Bristol	7	21
❷ **Beachcroft Wansbroughs** Bristol	7	18
Bevan Ashford Bristol, Exeter	5	10
Bond Pearce Bristol, Exeter, Plymouth	8	15
Clarke Willmott & Clarke Bristol, Taunton	9	-
Michelmores Exeter	5	12
Veale Wasbrough Bristol	4	5
❸ **Davies and partners** Gloucester	11	17
TLT Solicitors Bristol	5	15
❹ **Bretherton Price Elgoods** Cheltenham	5	3
Cartwrights Bristol	2	4
Charles Russell Cheltenham	3	4
Foot Anstey Sargent Exeter, Plymouth	3	5
Lyons Davidson Bristol	2	3
Rickerby Watterson Cheltenham	8	4
Stephens & Scown Exeter, St Austell, Truro, Liskard	9	6
Townsends Swindon	5	2

LEADING INDIVIDUALS	
❶ **BOTHAMLEY Michael** Beachcroft Wansbroughs	
DAVIES JONES Martin Beachcroft Wansbroughs	
GUNN David Bond Pearce	**MAYNARD Andrew** Michelmores
SMYTH Robert Burges Salmon	
❷ **BATTERSBY Robin** Burges Salmon	**DAVIDSON Timothy** Lyons Davidson
DUNN John Burges Salmon	**KING Stuart** Veale Wasbrough
LOWLESS Peter Michelmores	**PRITCHARD Nicholas** TLT Solicitors
SCOTT Peter Bevan Ashford	**SMITHERS Tim** Veale Wasbrough
UP AND COMING	
GAIT Charles Osborne Clarke OWA	**GIDNEY David** Burges Salmon

Within each band, firms are listed alphabetically. *See **Profiles** on page 722*
Figures unavailable at time of going to press.

the rankings this year after widespread praise for his *"substantial client base"* and growing reputation in the development field. Acted for Benchmark Group plc on a 100,000 sq ft office and residential development at Carlton Garden, London SW1, including joint venture arrangements with the Crown Estate. **Clients:** Imperial Tobacco Pension Trustees Ltd; Somerfield; Lucent Technologies.

Beachcroft Wansbroughs Rises in the rankings this year after taking on the rated Crawford Owen team (including the *"highly experienced"* **Martin Davies Jones**) and consolidating its position as one of the most visible in the Bristol market. Though public sector work remains important, the practice is seen to be pushing more healthcare-related work to its London office and focusing strongly on commercial development, investment, secured lending and portfolio management. *"Good client man"* **Michael Bothamley** heads up the team. Acted for Bristol and West in the acquisition and development of their new headquarters. **Clients:** C & J Clark; Bristol & West plc; The Unite Group plc.

Bevan Ashford Continues to be notable for its expertise on the public sector and PFI side, with work for NHS Trusts, local authorities and educational institutions making up a substantial part of the practice. Team head **Peter Scott** is particularly respected in this sphere, and has a reputation for *"making things happen."* Also skilled in investment, development, property finance and retail, the team's clients range from pension funds (including acting for Allied Domecq Pension Fund on the lettings of South Quay in London Docklands), brewers and house-builders. Acted for Invicta Leisure Ltd in the sale of three golf clubs at £12 million. **Clients:** Invicta Leisure; Allied Domecq; BS Group.

Bond Pearce Large practice which maintains a leading reputation in Plymouth and Exeter, where **David Gunn** *"has a strong name,"* while the recently opened Bristol office has yet to have an impact on the market. The team's client base takes in national retailers, leisure facilities, developers, major companies and marine clients. A recent lateral hire bolsters the public sector practice, where it continues to act for the Highways Agency, and has won several further substantial clients. Advised on the property aspects of the £150 million merger of Roach Foods with Dalehead Foods. **Clients:** NatWest; Midas Group; Stovax.

Clarke Willmott & Clarke The acquisition of Alsters' property team, and relinquishing of local offices to concentrate on Taunton and Bristol, signal that the practice is *"having a real go"* at challenging the big regional players. Backed up by a vigorous planning practice, which is a prolific client-winner, the team is particularly rated in residential development work, with national house-builder clients and an increasing flow of strategic and forward planning property schemes and urban regeneration projects. Taunton remains the team's centre of gravity, while the Bristol office additionally handles specialist work such as secured lending and work for universities. Also experienced in licensed premises work, the practice acts as sole South West regional solicitor for the Unique Pub Company Ltd. Acted for Beazer Homes in a large urban regeneration scheme in Gloucester involving the site assembly and redevelopment of 280 new units split between private and housing association work. **Clients:** Beaufort Western Ltd (part of Berkeley Group plc); Prowting Homes; Nationwide Business Finance.

Michelmores *"Sound, commercial outfit"* which is seen to lead the field in Exeter and makes up a significant part of the firm's turnover. In addition to expertise in development, investment, corporate support and property work for educational and religious institutions, the team has an expanding public sector/PFI group which acts for three local authorities and at least six government departments and agencies. Lead players remain the *"assiduous"* team head **Peter Lowless** (*"he won't let you get away with anything"*) and *"classic senior partner figure"* **Andrew Maynard**, who has a *"loyal client base."* Acted in the pre-let and forward sale of a town centre shopping centre valued at £16.5 million. **Clients:** MOD Defence Estates; The Court Service.

Veale Wasbrough Despite continued mutterings about the firm's past defections, there is no doubt that this is a *"genuine property practice"* with substantial clients. The recruitment of **Stuart King** (*"committed to the local marketplace"*) from Burges Salmon has been seen as a *"smart move,"* and the *"raw materials are now in place"* for a return to form. Existing rated practitioners are **Tim Smithers** and *"pre-eminent development lawyer"* Nigel Somerville, who is now a consultant. Key strengths include development and portfolio management, with strong niche expertise in central and local government property work. Continues to act for Bristol City Council in the regeneration of Bristol Harbourside, and for the joint landowners in the negotiation of the development agreements for the disposal of the remainder of the site. **Clients:** Crest Nicholson Property; PACE; BANES.

Davies and partners Continued recommendation from firms in the region and beyond leads this practice to rise in the rankings this year. Specifically rated in residential development, of which the team *"does a huge amount."* Their *"sharp"* and *"sensible approach"* received high market praise. The group also handles retail work and investment property management. **Clients:** Westbury Homes; Crest Nicholson plc.

TLT Solicitors Known particularly for its strong retail and property finance practices, the team also handles investment and asset management, including several office and industrial schemes in Bristol, the West Country and the Midlands. Development and minerals work are other areas of expertise. **Nick Pritchard** *"likes to find solutions"* and remains a rated individual. Acted for Hanson plc on the disposal for development of its ten-acre site beside the Millennium Dome and the acquisition of Victoria Deep Water

Terminal at Greenwich. **Clients:** Beaufort Homes; Sun Life Investment Management; C & J Clark International.

Bretherton Price Elgoods Solid practice with noted development expertise and additional strengths in property investment and commercial landlord and tenant work. Recent client gains have included a retail coffee house chain and a major national clothing manufacturer. Advised on the property aspects of the setting up of the Cheltenham Family Healthcare Centre, involving freehold purchase by a single asset company of doctors' practices and related occupation arrangements. **Clients:** Wolseley; Stirling House Estates Ltd; Britannia Group plc.

Cartwrights Notable for its licensing and transport work, this small team acts for breweries, pub companies, transport companies and local authorities. Work includes development, Compulsory Purchase Orders, auction work, free trade loan work and block acquisitions. Acted in the acquisition of a major development site, including a distribution depot, at a value in excess of £10 million. **Clients:** British Railways Board; Ambishbus Pub co plc; Morrells of Oxford Ltd.

Charles Russell Respected team, with a particular emphasis on secured lending and investment work, as highlighted by its management of large portfolios of residential property for high street institutions and investment purchases for Irish investors to a value of £30 million. Mortgage lending is another area of expertise, and the team acts for Eagle Star on its entire commercial loan book, including restructures, sales and advances. On the development side, handles disposal of consented land for farmers and option work for house-builders. Also skilled in tax, compliance and competition issues relating to bulk acquisitions. **Clients:** JSS Pinnacle Management Ltd; Lambert Fenchurch Group plc; Fairbridge Estates.

Foot Anstey Sargent Newly merged practice seen as *"ambitious"* and *"good at gauging the underlying motives of the client."* Acts for a range of owner-managed businesses, house-builders and property developers. Ongoing work includes sale of development land, sales and purchases of holiday parks, hotels and pubs and development agreements. Recently concluded a long disagreement with householders on the amount of an average payment due. **Clients:** M Baker (Property Services) Ltd.

Lyons Davidson Maintains a lower profile than in previous years, with recent departures of planning/environmental lawyers highlighting *"a general malaise."* However retains a solid property practice, with sector strengths in health-care, funding/investment arrangements, development, volume estate conveyancing and mortgage schemes. Also acts for a variety of institutional clients including universities, colleges and NHS Trusts in transactions ranging from acquisitions and development to sale and leaseback projects. The *"sensible and commercial"* **Tim Davidson** remains recommended by the market. **Clients:** Lloyds TSB; University of the West of England; Appleby Westward plc.

Rickerby Watterson Well-known for its long-standing work for Whitbread, which includes disposals and acquisitions of 1,000 properties in the South of England, this is a *"reliable"* team, with a *"well-established local clientele."* Additional niche strengths include property work for charities and schools, insolvency-related work, rural estates and advising substantial land owners on disposals of land for development. Acted in the purchase of a landmark city centre office block and retail units, with planning permission for hotel use being granted at £3.9 million. **Clients:** Whitbread plc; Group 4; Hambro Countrywide.

Stephens & Scown *"Sizeable"* and *"switched on"* team which has noted expertise in minerals and landfill work and enters the rankings this year after repeated recommendation in the market as well-known players in Devon and Cornwall. Other core areas of practice are institutionally funded development and house-building. Recent highlights include the sale of 200 acres of land for town centre development and the development of an Innovation Centre at Exeter University **Clients:** Aggregate Industries plc; IMERYS plc; Wainhomes Ltd.

Townsends Remains *"the obvious choice in Swindon."* Handles the full range of property work from strategic land management and commercial and residential development to landlord and tenant and commercial sales and purchases. Recent work for National Power has included the sale of a disused power station at West Ham and the acquisition of a headquarters building for a subsidiary. Currently acting for a consortium of developers in relation to the next stage of town development in Swindon. **Clients:** Trench; Farrow & Partners; National Power.

WALES

PROPERTY (COMMERCIAL) • Wales	Ptnrs	Assts
❶ **Eversheds** Cardiff	10	13
❷ **Berry Smith** Cardiff	3	2
Edwards Geldard Cardiff	4	9
Morgan Cole	11	18
❸ **Palser Grossman** Cardiff Bay	2	3
❹ **Hugh James Ford Simey** Cardiff	5	1
❺ **Robertsons** Cardiff	2	2

LEADING INDIVIDUALS	
❶ **BERRY Roger** Berry Smith	**DAVIES Rowland** Edwards Geldard
MEREDITH Alan Eversheds	
❷ **IVIN Alison** Palser Grossman	**JAMES Robert** Morgan Cole
ROBERTS David Lloyd Hugh James Ford Simey	
WILLIAMS Martell Robertsons	
❸ **EVANS Eric** Eversheds	**GATES Kathryn** Edwards Geldard
JONES Chris Berry Smith	**MORGAN Rosemary** Morgan Cole
UP AND COMING	
JONES Nefydd Eversheds	

Within each band, firms are listed alphabetically.

*See **Profiles** on page 722*

Eversheds Still *"dominate the scene"* in terms of size and clientele, with public sector and institutional work seen as the core areas of strength. Particular experience in private/public property joint ventures, PPP/PFI development work and secured lending for banks and a building society. Also handle operational and corporate support work for the firm's blue-chip clients. **Alan Meredith** and **Eric Evans** *"lead from the top,"* while *"young colt"* **Nefydd Jones** is seen to handle a lot of the substantial work and makes his debut in the rankings as up and coming. Acted for Guardian Property Holdings Ltd in the £15 million refurbishment and new lettings programme at Capitol Centre, Cardiff. **Clients:** Welsh Development Agency; Annington Property Ltd; National Assembly for Wales.

Berry Smith Niche property team which moves up a notch on the recommendation of fellow practitioners and surveyors. Notable for its client base of local property developers, private companies and wealthy individuals, the practice also handles banking, investment, licensed property and general commercial property work. Recently boosted by a strong lateral hire from Bevan Ashford. Team head **Roger Berry** *"never loses the commercial sense of a deal,"* while **Chris Jones** *"is worth keeping an eye on."* Acted in the acquisition of a redistribution centre for Lidl. **Clients:** Lidl; TBI plc; wealthy property investors.

Edwards Geldard Remains *"strong across the board."* Ongoing work includes land acquisitions for housing schemes, investment acquisitions and disposals, corporate support, commercial development and secured lending. The team has specific expertise in public/private sector relationships, and negotiated the transfer of assets and liabilities of Cardiff Bay Development Corporation to the Welsh Development Agency. Known players remain the *"high-profile"* department head **Rowland Davies** and the *"thorough and efficient"* **Kathryn Gates**. Acted for Sydney and London Properties Ltd on the purchasing and subsequent refinancing of Blackwood Shopping Centre. **Clients:** Cardiff Bay Development Corporation; Sydney & London Properties Ltd; Welsh Development Agency.

Morgan Cole Large team with specific public sector, health trust and institutional expertise. Undertakes substantial estate management and disposals and acquisitions for local authorities, NHS trusts, retailers and plcs including BP Amoco and Whitbread plc. Public/private sector partnership and joint venture expertise is highlighted by its role in advising the Welsh Development Agency in its joint venture with the public and private sectors in the development of an international rail terminal in Wentloog, Cardiff. **Robert James** remains a noted big hitter. The Swansea office has drawn particular praise this year, and its team head **Rosemary Morgan** *("cracking lawyer – very sharp")* joins the rankings after repeated recommendation. **Clients:** Associated British Ports plc; Cardiff City Council; Welsh Development Agency.

Palser Grossman Despite a general market perception that the practice relies too heavily on the *"splendid"* **Alison Ivin**, it remains an *"up and coming"* team with a strong presence in the local development market. Continues to act for Grosvenor Estates and other developers in Cardiff Bay development projects. Also handles property finance work and an increasing retail practice. Acted in the sale of a site to the first Welsh Morrisons superstore and in the large-scale office letting of Caspian Point. **Clients:** Bellway Homes; Clerical Medical; Oneida.

Hugh James Ford Simey Though its wider property reputation remains in the housing association field, the team is building a noted client base of local and national house-builders and private developers. Ongoing work includes site acquisition, option agreements and conditional contracts, with commercial lending, pension fund investment and corporate support being additional core areas. The *"technical"* and *"firm negotiator"* **David Roberts** remains highly respected by his peers. **Clients:** Barratt Homes; Limeridge Properties Ltd; Welsh Rugby Union.

Robertsons Small, niche team which picks up a lot of local development work, largely due to the efforts and reputation of *"excellent front man"* **Martell Williams** *("a hearty fellow")*. **Clients:** Developers.

MIDLANDS

PROPERTY (COMMERCIAL) • Midlands	Ptnrs	Assts
❶ **Eversheds** Birmingham, Nottingham	11	51
Wragge & Co Birmingham	18	55
❷ **Hammond Suddards Edge** Birmingham	11	24
Pinsent Curtis Birmingham	10	22
❸ **DLA** Birmingham	4	7
Lee Crowder Birmingham	3	9
❹ **Freethcartwright** Leicester, Nottingham	13	13
Knight & Sons Newcastle-under-Lyme	8	4
Martineau Johnson Birmingham	6	7
Shoosmiths Northampton, Nottingham	12	10
❺ **Browne Jacobson** Nottingham	7	13
Harvey Ingram Owston Leicester	7	7
Higgs & Sons Brierley Hill	2	0
Manby & Steward Wolverhampton	2	1
Wright Hassall Leamington Spa	4	4

LEADING INDIVIDUALS	
❶ **BRICE Barry** Pinsent Curtis	**CADDICK Robert** Wragge & Co
DAKEYNE Mark Wragge & Co	**WATSON Adrian** DLA
❷ **ASKIN David** Wragge & Co	**KORDAN Joel** Lee Crowder
WEBB Tim Eversheds	
❸ **HEPPEL Meg** Eversheds	
NEWCOMBE Mark Hammond Suddards Edge	
O'MEARA Anne Hammond Suddards Edge	
THORNE Peter Wragge & Co	
UP AND COMING	
SINGH Parmjit Eversheds	**YATES Andrew** Pinsent Curtis

Within each band, firms are listed alphabetically. *See **Profiles** on page 722*

Eversheds Remains a regional giant in property work, with a *"long pedigree"* and a *"solid squad,"* and is seen nationally as the strongest link in the Eversheds chain. The large Birmingham team is envied by rivals for its involvement in large local schemes such as the Birmingham Mailbox project, while continuing to do a huge amount of work for national house-builders. Other clients include a wide spread of blue-chip plc, retail and investment concerns. Complex funding and property finance arrangements have been flagged up by several in the market as an area of significant recent activity. New entry **Tim Webb** is seen as a prolific marketeer, but is clearly the face of the property department to most clients and other firms, while **Parmjit Singh** also joins the rankings as a young pretender active at the coalface. Though spending much of her time in a managerial role, managing partner **Meg Heppel** continues to act in substantial transactions, and remains highly rated in the market. The firm's Nottingham office, which has built up an impressive reputation in the East Midlands, is particularly rated for its inward investment and development work. Acted on the £800 million redevelopment of the Birmingham Bull Ring. **Clients:** Birmingham Mailbox Ltd; Hammerson; Grosvenor Estate Holdings.

Wragge & Co A stream of recommendations from leading regional and London practitioners highlights the practice's continued presence in the top rank, and in the national market as a whole. *"At the top for consistency,"* the team is seen to have *"kept it together despite being so big"* and to maintain a highly *"technical and commercial approach."* Offers across the board skill to a range of clients *"of the highest quality,"* with the last year seeing sustained growth in residential development. The team is currently acting for a consortium of major builders in developing a potential 2,500 home settlement in the South East of England. Leading partners remain **Mark Dakeyne**, lauded for his *"innovative"* style *("he can see a problem from all angles")* and **Robert Caddick** *("a serious player, and nobody's fool.")* **David Askin** is seen less than in past years but *"is firm in his client's interests and easy to deal with,"* while *"straightforward, no frills"* **Peter Thorne** has a strong reputation in development and investment work and enters the rankings this year. Acted for Norwich Union in a swap with Royal & Sun Alliance involving three industrial estates at a total value of £66 million. **Clients:** MEPC; ProLogis; Castlemore Securities.

Hammond Suddards Edge Despite internal difficulties running up to the merger, the team is viewed as a *"pure property practice"* which has retained substantial clients and quality individuals. Chief amongst these are national head of property, the *"up-front"* and *"in your face"* **Mark Newcombe** and the *"decisive"* **Anne O'Meara**, who is best known in the field of urban regeneration. Development and retail property remain the key areas of strength, with increasing activity in property finance including a £31 million funding package for Prologis Kingspark from the Bank of Scotland.

The closure of the Leicester office should not affect the team's wider profile, but it will be a blow to the local market, where it retained a respected presence. Continue to advise the Millennium Point in Birmingham on a £113 million funded project. **Clients:** ProLogis Kingspark; Wilson Bowden Ltd.

Pinsent Curtis Though seen to languish *"in the shadow of the corporate department"* this is a strong practice which is seen to *"concentrate on well-defined areas,"* notably institutional investment and corporate support. A recent lateral hire from Martineau Johnson may signal a real intention to develop a stand-alone practice. Maintains recognised niche expertise in PFI work, local authority town centre development schemes and retail parks. Rated practitioners at different ends of the age spectrum are the *"bombastic"* **Barry Brice**, who is *"still doing the business,"* and *"young Turk"* **Andrew Yates** *("good, if a little pedantic.")* Handled the property aspects of Lex's £80 million disposal of its franchised car dealerships to Pendragon plc. **Clients:** Lex Service plc; Wilson Bowden plc; Castlemore Securities.

DLA *"Entrepreneurial"* outfit which is *"beginning to make an impact"* in the Birmingham market and moves up the rankings this year. Particular inroads are being made in the banking and commercial development sectors, including out of town, office and industrial schemes. Also handles corporate support, occupational work and portfolio management, with a noted emphasis on retail clients. The team acted for Selfridges in its acquisition of a £40 million department store in the Bull Ring. *"Technically gifted"* **Adrian Watson** is *"liked by clients"* and remains the driving force behind the practice. Acted for Stoford Developments Ltd in the development of 35,000 sq ft of offices for Norwich Union. **Clients:** Claire's Accessories; Stoford Developments; Halfords.

Lee Crowder Though seen by many in the market as a *"middle tier"* firm with a concentration on 'old money' investors and charitable trust property, the well-known and *"affable"* **Joel Kordan** continues to build up an impressive portfolio of corporate clients. The team handles large-scale development and operational work. Has specific expertise in the logistics sector, with recent trends of practice including growing residential development and housing association work. **Clients:** Excel; Bombardier Transportation; c-Plex.

Freethcartwright Split across its Nottingham and Leicester offices, this *"acknowledged regional property presence"* has *"decent clients and decent people"* and rises in the rankings this year. A noted player in residential development and urban regeneration schemes, the team also handles secured lending, investment for local authorities and retail work. Recently appointed as one of the two firms in England to act for the Millennium Commission, which has provided a wide variety of property work, including the creation of national forest land on former colliery sites. Acted for the developer in the £10 million relocation of Gunn and Moore to new factory premises in Collick. **Clients:** Bellway Homes; David Wilson Homes Ltd; The Outdoor Group.

Knight & Sons Less mainstream, but highly *"commercial"* team, with a high profile in mines and minerals work, *"an excellent reputation in the brewing field"* and several substantial clients. Also skilled in investment portfolio work and commercial development, including joint ventures and funding arrangements. Retail clients include a number of pottery companies, such as Josiah Wedgwood and Sons Ltd. **Clients:** Hanson; Morrison Developments Ltd; Trillium Group of Companies.

Martineau Johnson Now concentrating more on property work for its substantial educational institution, public sector and charity clients, the team has been seen less in the wider market over the last year. The firm handles investment work, estate management and development. Acted in a number of warehousing and industrial transactions for a charity with a total value in excess of £12.5 million. **Clients:** USF Nominees Ltd; SLC Asset Management Ltd; CNC Property Management Ltd.

Shoosmiths Large team which moves up the rankings after sustained praise for the quality of its regional retail, leisure and national house-builder clients. Also noted for its *"ambitious"* approach to marketing. The Nottingham office is handling an increasing amount of asset acquisition and management work for London finance houses. Acted for Crosby Homes Ltd in their acquisition of the residential element of the Birmingham Mailbox development. **Clients:** Boots Company plc; Gala Leisure Ltd; Crosby Homes Ltd.

Browne Jacobson New to the rankings this year to reflect its growing presence in the East Midlands market, while a prominent development lawyer has been recruited from Martineau Johnson to head up its new Birmingham practice. Retail work is an important focus, with clients ranging from national chain stores to high value London fashion shops. Public sector property work, secured lending, corporate support and regional development are additional areas of strength. Acted for Wilkinson Hardware Stores in the acquisition of a site for a distribution centre, a £50 million project. **Clients:** Mayne Nickless Express; Fii Group plc; Wilkinson Hardware Stores.

Harvey Ingram Owston Maintains a strong reputation in Leicester, with a *"broad based practice"* which *"knows the local market."* Retail remains the core strength, and the team acts for several national retail groups such as Vision Express. Has further sector expertise in housing associations, licensing, residential development and pension fund portfolio management. **Clients:** Alliance & Leicester; Coral Racing; Everards Brewery.

Higgs & Sons Seen to *"maintain their position in the Black Country,"* this small but *"technically sound"* team is well known for its commercial lease work, in which it acts mainly for landlords. Also handles development work for small building concerns. **Clients:** London & Cambridge Properties.

Manby & Steward Though seen to excel on small-ticket deals, this is a *"solid"* team which remains a *"known name in the field"* and acts for a broad range of clients including medium-sized companies, a national building society, educational and public sector institutions. **Clients:** Public sector clients; building society.

Wright Hassall *"Good clients and good contacts"* ensure the practice's continued profile in the market. Act for household name residential developers and retail clients, and have established expertise in licensing, commercial development and public sector work. Acted for British Waterways Board in an £80 million mixed commercial development in West London. **Clients:** Lunn Poly; British Waterways Board; Laing Homes.

EAST ANGLIA

PROPERTY (COMMERCIAL) • East Anglia	Ptnrs	Assts
❶ **Eversheds** Cambridge, Ipswich, Norwich	15	24
Mills & Reeve Cambridge, Norwich	10	25
❷ **Birketts** Ipswich	5	2
Hewitson Becke + Shaw Cambridge	13	13
❸ **Taylor Vinters** Cambridge	4	8
❹ **Ashton Graham** Bury St Edmunds, Ipswich	2	2
Wollastons Chelmsford	2	5
❺ **Ellison & Co** Colchester	5	-
H. Montlake & Co Ilford	2	-
Kenneth Elliott & Rowe Romford	5	3
Prettys Ipswich	2	3
Tolhurst Fisher Chelmsford, Southend-on-Sea	2	4

LEADING INDIVIDUALS	
❶ **COWPER Tony** Mills & Reeve	
❷ **BRISTOL Jeremy** Birketts	**GIBBS Robert** Eversheds
GILLERY Bryan Eversheds	**HAMILTON Keith** Eversheds
ROBINSON Herbert Mills & Reeve	
❸ **BEACH Steven** Taylor Vinters	**BRETT Alan** Hewitson Becke + Shaw
HUBBARD Penny Mills & Reeve	**HUTTON Robert** Mills & Reeve
JONES Elizabeth Hewitson Becke + Shaw	**MEDVEI Cornelius** Eversheds
UP AND COMING	
HENSON Michaela Taylor Vinters	

Within each band, firms are listed alphabetically. *See* ***Profiles*** *on page 722*

Eversheds Already pre-eminent in the east of the region, this dynamic team is *"emerging"* in Cambridge and attracting considerable praise for their *"commercially minded, progressive"* attitude. Within a team that is *"constantly looking for new approaches to legal work,"* **Robert Gibbs** is *"good on development issues"* while **Keith Hamilton** is a *"competent technical solicitor"* and *"dedicated"* **Bryan Gillery** is *"respected on residential development." "Prominent"* **Cornelius Medvei** still conducts major transactions despite his managerial role. With particular expertise in commercial and residential development, last year the team acted for 24Seven, the joint venture company established by TXU Europe Group plc and London Electricity to operate and maintain their entire network distribution systems. **Clients:** Wilcon Homes Ltd; NHP plc; 24Seven.

Mills & Reeve Probably the leading firm in Cambridge, a strong health and university client base remains the core of this practice, but it is increasingly active working for developers and hi-tech occupiers. *"Fine lawyer"* **Tony Cowper** retains his reputation as the leading practitioner in the region, supported by *"outstanding"* **Penny Hubbard** and *"reliable pair of hands"* **Herbert Robinson**. In the Norwich office, **Robert Hutton** *"knows what he's doing and gets on with it well."* Advised last year on a £12 million project finance lease transaction for a major millennium project. **Clients:** Chiroscience Group plc; SCA Group; Alcatel; over half of all Cambridge Colleges.

Birketts *"Solid Ipswich firm"* with *"good property people,"* of whom *"first class"* **Jeremy Bristol** is the *"outstanding property lawyer."* The team is known for leasing and transactional work for regional ports, but is also developing a particular expertise in the leisure and licensing sectors. Acted last year in a number of public house acquisitions for a local brewer. **Clients:** Willis Group Ltd; Port of Ipswich; Port of Felixstowe.

Hewitson Becke + Shaw This innovative practice is extremely strong in the West of the region, and recently consolidated their position in Cambridge by acquiring the University's Estates Management and Building Service as clients. Acting increasingly for hi-tech companies and educational institutions, they have strength in funding and development work and represented a developer this year in a major Cambridge leisure scheme. *"Excellent"* **Elizabeth Jones** is *"extremely competent"* while **Alan Brett** is considered *"a name to be reckoned with."* **Clients:** Travis Perkins plc; Scottish and Newcastle Retail; Linnco Ltd.

Taylor Vinters *"Certainly one of the best firms in the region,"* they have been through some upheavals recently but are perceived as *"back on track."* Head of department **Steven Beach** *"knows his stuff"* while **Michaela Henson** was highly praised for her competence and efficiency. Working for a broad range of clients, the group has particular expertise in institutional investment, development and joint venture work. Last year completed the sale of the Martlesham Heath Industrial Estate for £26 million on behalf of the Bradford Property Trust. **Clients:** Bradford Property Trust plc; Lafarge Redland Aggregates Ltd; Granta Park Ltd.

Ashton Graham Market opinion considers that a *"sensible merger"* has given this firm *"a lot of strength within Suffolk."* Acting for a range of clients including developers, institutional investors and a leading player in the privatised gas transportation market, the firm has recently been working for developers in the acquisition of sites in central London and of retail sites throughout the country. Also act for health sector clients and manage the property portfolios for several religious charities. **Clients:** The Gas Transportation Company Ltd.

Wollastons *"Switched on and forward-looking"* this *"serious modern firm"* is a *"slick operation."* With niche expertise in the further education and motor trade sectors, the team acts for a number of owner-managed companies, but also conducts transactional and leasing work across the country for larger companies. Involved last year in a major Essex town centre sale. **Clients:** Anglia Polytechnic University.

Ellison & Co *"The premier firm in Colchester,"* this practice acts for NHS trusts and housing associations, but is regarded as particularly *"strong on development."* Growth areas include site acquisition and assembly for house builders. **Clients:** Essex Wildlife Trust; DFDS plc; Colne Housing Association.

H. Montlake & Co Highly regarded for a commercial approach and *"able to do anything you throw at them,"* this firm acts for entrepreneurs and developers and *"has some fine clients"* on the investment side. Acted last year in several substantial central London transactions. **Clients:** Major property companies; developers; a merchant bank.

Kenneth Elliott & Rowe Experienced, partner-led firm admired for *"accessibility, flexibility and professionalism."* The team is said to *"do high quality work,"* in particular for developers and local authorities, and capped a good year by winning the London Borough of Newham as clients. **Clients:** London Borough of Barking & Dagenham; Hallmark Developments Ltd; Thorneycroft Asset Management Ltd.

Prettys Working for lenders, commercial and industrial developers and offshore companies on large disposals, the firm is developing an interesting niche expertise on French commercial property. Involved last year on especially complex funding and leasing arrangements surrounding the development of the Mid-Suffolk business park. **Clients:** Major regional developers; secured lenders; offshore investors.

Tolhurst Fisher Developments form the bulk of the work for this *"successful"* department. Highly rated for technical ability, if *"somewhat low profile,"* the team was recently involved in the purchase of ninety acres of development land for £6 million, and the sale of a redundant quarry to a national house-builder for £10.75 million. **Clients:** Developers.

NORTH WEST

PROPERTY (COMMERCIAL) • North West	Ptnrs	Assts
❶ **Addleshaw Booth & Co** Manchester	9	30
Cobbetts Manchester	16	34
DLA Liverpool, Manchester	9	17
Eversheds Manchester	7	17
Halliwell Landau Manchester	11	20
❷ **Bullivant Jones** Liverpool	6	13
Hammond Suddards Edge Manchester	2	8
❸ **Beachcroft Wansbroughs** Manchester	5	11
Davies Wallis Foyster Liverpool	7	10
Field Cunningham & Co Manchester	4	2
❹ **Jones Maidment Wilson** Altrincham, Manchester	3	3
Mace & Jones Liverpool, Manchester	7	13
Pannone & Partners Manchester	5	6
❺ **Aaron & Partners** Chester	2	2
Berrymans Lace Mawer Liverpool	5	5
Brabner Holden Banks Wilson Liverpool	6	12
Cuff Roberts Liverpool	6	3
Gorna & Co Manchester	4	4
Hill Dickinson Chester, Liverpool	12	13
Kuit Steinart Levy Manchester	3	5
❻ **Bermans** Liverpool	*	*
Chaffe Street Manchester	2	3
Wacks Caller Manchester	4	4
Walker Smith & Way Chester	4	4
Weightmans Liverpool, Manchester	3	4

LEADING INDIVIDUALS

❶ **BECKETT Roy** DLA
GOODMAN Stephen Halliwell Landau
JONES Pamela Bullivant Jones
MARKS Geoffrey Halliwell Landau
SORRELL Stephen Eversheds

❷ **ASHWORTH Peter** Field Cunningham & Co
BUCKLEY Liam Hammond Suddards Edge
MOODY John Eversheds

❸ **BENSON Stephen John** Cobbetts
CRAVEN Diana Addleshaw Booth & Co
FITZMAURICE Anthony Cobbetts
LEONARD Tessa Eversheds
PATTISON Mark Beachcroft Wansbroughs
ROONEY Philip DLA
STRATTON David Field Cunningham & Co
WEIGHTMAN Anita DLA

UP AND COMING
JACKSON Karl Mace & Jones
KERSHAW Peter Addleshaw Booth & Co
WORRALL Simon Cobbetts

ONE TO WATCH
CONROY Paul Halliwell Landau
WALLER Corin Addleshaw Booth & Co

Within each band, firms are listed alphabetically.
See **Profiles** *on page 722*
** See editorial entries for explanations of team sizes.*

Addleshaw Booth & Co Considered by some *"the leading firm in Manchester,"* the team has consolidated its position in the top band with the addition of people from the superb Leeds office. *"Expert property lawyer"* **Diana Craven** retains a presence, while **Peter Kershaw** *"will make a mark in the future."* Working for developers, blue-chip investors, plcs and regional development agencies, the team has particular expertise in town centre redevelopment schemes. Advised on the acquisition by Green Property plc of the P&O property portfolio for a reported price of £450 million. **Clients:** Green Property plc; AMEC Developments Ltd; Standard Life Investments Ltd.

Cobbetts *"Authoritative"* **Stephen Benson** heads a highly respected team. *"Charming"* and *"pragmatic"* **Tony Fitzmaurice** also stands out, while *"extremely efficient"* **Simon Worrall** is considered a rising talent. National reputation in the licensed and unlicensed food and drink retail sector, but strength exists across the board, especially in retail and residential development, property investment and portfolio management. Acted last year on behalf of Bruntwood Estates Ltd in the purchase of 1 Portland St, Manchester, a 52,000 sq ft office building, and in the development of Highland House, a 145,000 sq ft, 23-story mixed use commercial and residential building. **Clients:** Morrison Developments Ltd; Whitbread plc; Premier Hotels plc; Burger King.

DLA Acting for commercial, industrial and retail developers and occupiers, institutional investors and lenders, they are considered a *"good outfit"* with a *"national presence"* and are the strongest of the top five firms in Liverpool. *"Commercial, friendly"* and *"good to deal with,"* **Roy Beckett**, *"efficient and organised"* **Philip Rooney** and *"good operator"* **Anita Weightman** are the major players here. Acted last year on the acquisition of 201 Deansgate for Ropemaker Properties Ltd and the sale of the Tees Barrage on behalf of English Partnerships. **Clients:** English Partnerships; Abbey National plc; MEPC plc; JJB Sports.

Eversheds With property deals transacted last year totalling £1.75 billion, the Manchester team has kept its reputation as a market leader. *"High profile"* **Stephen Sorrell** has *"built up a good practice."* **John Moody** is *"a fine lawyer"* and remains active despite his managerial responsibilities, while **Tessa Leonard** is building up an enviable reputation. Conducting the full range of property work for developers, investors, large companies and institutions, the team is *"especially strong on public developments and large regeneration schemes."* Acted for Manchester City Council in the £50 million leisure, retail and residential re-development of Piccadilly Gardens. **Clients:** Manchester City Council; AMEC Developments Ltd; United Norwest Co-operatives Ltd.

Halliwell Landau *"Positive and proactive,"* the team is led by the *"charismatic and colourful"* **Stephen Goodman**, a *"great rainmaker." "First-rate"* **Geoffrey Marks** is *"expert"* on development work, institutional funding and investments. With expertise in joint ventures, funding and enterprise zone transactions, the team is strongly development-oriented. Acted last year on the acquisition, development, letting and pre-sale for over £20 million of the Havelock Mills offices in Manchester, and also the acquisition of the BG Northern Development portfolio by Miller Group Ltd. **Clients:** Tritax; Taylor Woodrow Developments Ltd; Kwik-Fit Holdings Ltd.

Bullivant Jones *"Extremely strong on property"* and considered by some *"as strong as anybody outside London,"* the description *"leading firm in Liverpool"* is perhaps fairer. *"They're efficient and quick and there's no point scoring." "Excellent property lawyer"* **Pamela Jones** is the leading property lawyer in Liverpool. Clients are roughly divided between developers, retailers and investors, and the team acted this year on a £70 million investment by MEPC in the industrial estate adjoining Ford Jaguar at Speke. **Clients:** Iceland Frozen Foods; Somerfield Stores; Morbaine Ltd; MEPC plc.

Hammond Suddards Edge *"Extremely sharp and hard working"* **Liam Buckley** is *"one of the brighter sparks"* in a department that includes a recommended team of associates. Ultra-commercial, the firm is best-known for acting on the property aspects of large transactions, but it also works for commercial and industrial occupiers and for banks on development finance. Have a niche in the energy and power sector, and particular expertise in commercial and leisure developments, where the team recently acted for Pubmaster Ltd in the acquisition and subsequent securitisation of over

600 licensed properties from Swallow Hotels. **Clients:** Allied London Properties plc; British Energy plc; Morrison Developments plc.

Beachcroft Wansbroughs Acting this year in the sales by MEPC of the Orchard Square Shopping Centre in Sheffield and Urmston Shopping Centre in Manchester, the firm's investment and development expertise is supplemented by experience in working for major occupiers and landlords, and Government agencies. *"Helpful and to the point,"* the team is considered *"commercial and competent."* **Mark Pattison** has a stand-out name here. **Clients:** MEPC plc; Inland Revenue; Going Places Leisure Travel Ltd; TDG plc; Pirelli Group.

Davies Wallis Foyster This large team is considered *"good local providers."* Has a broad range of expertise, working for companies with property requirements and developers, especially on the retail and residential sides. Acted last year in the £37 million redevelopment of the former Northern Airport in Liverpool including the conversion of the terminal into a 122 bed Swallow Marriott hotel, and one of the hangars into a seven acre David Lloyd leisure complex. **Clients:** Liverpool John Moores University; Manchester Airport plc; Neptune Developments Ltd; St. Modwen Group.

Field Cunningham & Co A niche property practice with a strong reputation for housing development work, it also acts for commercial, retail and leisure developers and is enjoying substantial growth on secured lending matters. **David Stratton** is considered an *"expert property lawyer"* while *"hard and commercial"* **Peter Ashworth** *"knows the development world inside out."* Represented Thornfield Developments Ltd in their Parrs Wood retail and leisure development. **Clients:** Barratt Developments plc; The Royal Bank of Scotland plc; AMEC Group plc; Sterling Capitol Properties plc.

Jones Maidment Wilson A *"quietly impressive practice"* which tends to be development-oriented, with large investment clients and a few major tenants. Particular expertise exists in brownfield regeneration developments and joint ventures with local authorities. Acted recently on a number of schemes for Brookhouse, including the B&Q at Oldham, the Prescot retail park near Liverpool and a substantial acquisition of residential units in London's docklands. **Clients:** ASDA plc; Brookhouse Group; Dransfield Properties.

Mace & Jones *"A cracking firm,"* the team is considered *"really on the up."* Part of the success is due to **Karl Jackson**, *"a very affable guy and a good lawyer."* The majority of the work is for investors or developers, though the group also provides advice on secured lending and landlord and tenant work. Acted last year for Artisan Holdings in the £10 million regeneration of Regency House in Manchester. **Clients:** Artisan Holdings Ltd; Peel Holdings Ltd; Pochins plc; CWS.

Pannone & Partners A *"proper commercial property firm"* with a good profile, the firm works for developers on industrial, residential and urban regeneration schemes and manages the portfolios of large companies and institutions. This year has seen the team expand and take on new clients including Humberside Airport and a portfolio of filling stations. **Clients:** Texaco; Urban Splash; Highways Agency.

Aaron & Partners *"A tidy small practice"* with a strong property profile. Niche expertise includes transactional work for the manufacturing, chemical and haulage industries, and buying and selling land for waste disposal or mineral extraction. Acted in the sale of a calcite quarry and the acquisition of a large abattoir. **Clients:** Crown Estate in Wales; Water Hall Group plc; Welsh Water; William Wild & Sons Ltd.

Berrymans Lace Mawer *"An excellent firm to deal with"* with *"a good presence in Liverpool,"* the team has particular strength in retail and is handling an increasing amount of development work, including urban regeneration. Acted this year for one of the parties to a joint venture in the creation of the £10 million Corner Project office and retail development in Liverpool. **Clients:** JD Wetherspoon plc; Edinburgh Woollen Mill Ltd; TJ Hughes plc; TM Retail.

Brabner Holden Banks Wilson A balanced practice which is said to produce work of a *"really professional standard."* With strength in the brewery and local authority sectors, the firm acts for a number of owner-managed businesses and was recently involved in the assembly and disposal of a major industrial development for Knowsley Metropolitan Borough Council. **Clients:** Scottish & Newcastle Retail; Country Larder Ltd; Inenco Group.

Cuff Roberts A balanced practice highly regarded for its work in the retail and leisure sector, it is active on the full range of property work. An enviable client base includes numerous household names. **Clients:** Everton Football Club Ltd; Littlewoods Pools; Famous Army Stores Ltd; Global Video plc.

Gorna & Co *"Do property properly"* according to one source, and has a solid client base, including tenants, private investors and a range of developers. Known for working for friendly societies and housing associations, the team handled the property move for a major plc, including the disposal and subsequent lease of a new site near London. **Clients:** National Car Parks; North British Housing Ltd; UPS Ltd.

Hill Dickinson Better known on the insurance side, it is perhaps surprising that such a large and expanding department does not have a higher market profile. Known for doing *"a lot of work for house-builders"* the group also acts for a range of developers, large lenders, NHS trusts, tenants, institutional investors and universities. Responsible this year for the acquisition of over a hundred shops nation-wide for a major retailer and a £40 million hotel disposal and associated funding agreements. **Clients:** The Merchant Navy Pension Funds; Wainhomes Ltd; Bank of Scotland; North West Water.

Kuit Steinart Levy Small but *"efficient"* team, which has been occupied this year handling site acquisitions and disposals, including numerous portfolio transactions. Also works for landlords and major industrial, retail and leisure occupiers. Acted for Manchester City in the acquisition and development of a new stadium. **Clients:** Large property companies; Developers; retail, industrial and leisure tenants.

Bermans (3 ptnrs and 2 assts 40-60%) Firm whose commercial property tends to spin off from brewery finance and commercial work. Also advises on leasing work for commercial and industrial landlords. **Clients:** Hampton Trust plc.

Chaffe Street Better known for a high-quality corporate department, a proportion of the property work is corporate support, although the team does also have a stand-alone practice. Advised Bank of Scotland plc on property finance aspects of Caledonian Motor Group plc. **Clients:** Co-operative Bank plc; Boss Group Ltd; NM Rothschild & Sons; Danzas UK Ltd.

Wacks Caller *"On an upward curve,"* this firm is *"beginning to become a force in the city."* With particular expertise in acting for developers, the team has been involved in a number of town centre redevelopments and also work for lenders, investors and tenants. **Clients:** Modus Properties Ltd; Lemonpark Developments Ltd; Beva Investments Ltd.

Walker Smith & Way Large firm with a *"big market position in Chester,"* which has a particular specialism in easement work for gas pipelines and well sites. **Clients:** Developers, investors, landlords and tenants.

Weightmans Better known for insurance work, although a strong retail and leisure presence ensures a steady stream of property work. Increasingly active in secured lending work for brewers, the team advised on transferring the property portfolios of Whitbread and Punch Retail into the First Quench joint venture company. **Clients:** First Quench Retailing; Carlsburg/Tetley Brewing Ltd; Neptune Developments Ltd.

YORKSHIRE

PROPERTY (COMMERCIAL) • Yorkshire	Ptnrs	Assts
❶ **Addleshaw Booth & Co** Leeds	10	31
❷ **Walker Morris** Leeds	11	15
❸ **DLA** Leeds, Sheffield	4	17
Eversheds Leeds	6	23
Hammond Suddards Edge Leeds	7	16
Pinsent Curtis Leeds	10	16
❹ **Andrew M. Jackson & Co** Hull	9	9
Irwin Mitchell Sheffield	4	6
Nabarro Nathanson Sheffield	5	20
Read Hind Stewart Leeds	7	6
❺ **Gordons Cranswick Solicitors** Bradford, Leeds	7	6
Gosschalks Hull	9	3
❻ **Denison Till** York	3	1
Frith Partnership Leeds	4	-
Keeble Hawson Sheffield	5	2
Rollit Farrell & Bladon Hull	8	3
Wake Smith Sheffield	1	4

LEADING INDIVIDUALS	
❶ **McCLEA Nigel** Pinsent Curtis	**McLEAN Neil** DLA
PIKE John Addleshaw Booth & Co	
❷ **FLOUNDERS Andrew** Read Hind Stewart	
GRABINER Martin Nabarro Nathanson	**INNES Richard** Walker Morris
❸ **COPLEY Dean** Addleshaw Booth & Co	**DILLON Paula** Addleshaw Booth & Co
FOSTER John Eversheds	
MARKS Christopher Hammond Suddards Edge	
REEVEY Michael Addleshaw Booth & Co	**STONE David** Andrew M. Jackson & Co

Within each band, firms are listed alphabetically. See **Profiles** on page 722

Addleshaw Booth & Co Whether it's because of the *"breadth and depth"* of expertise, the *"quality of clients,"* the *"step up in terms of work quality"* or simply because it is *"undoubtedly the biggest,"* everyone accepts that it is *"just that bit ahead of the crowd." "Good and solid"* **John Pike** remains *"a premier property lawyer in the region"* and *"notable player"* **Paula Dillon** is *"well-liked by clients."* Newly rated **Dean Copley** is considered *"amongst the best,"* while **Michael Reevey** has attracted a lot of attention for his work on one of the UK's largest ever property transactions, the disposal by Stadium Group of the equity shareholding in Meadowhall for £1.17 billion. The team has been retained by British Land for the ongoing management work. **Clients:** Halifax plc; Stadium Group; J. Sainsbury plc; Commercial Developments Projects Ltd.

Walker Morris *"The country's leading retail lawyers"* according to one source, the team is felt this year to have broken away from the pack chasing Addleshaws. Good leadership plays a part in the success, with *"well-organised"* and *"effective"* management having *"built a fine, cultured practice."* The strength of this team is felt to lie in excellence across the board, rather than a few big names, although *"important player"* **Richard Innes** is building a strong reputation on the retail side. Alongside retail excellence, the team has a *"strong orientation towards the residential sector"* and also has a reputation for banking and property finance. Dealt with the English property work on the £1.3 billion purchase of Zeneca's speciality chemical business. **Clients:** Forte (UK) Ltd; Barratt Homes Ltd; Debenhams Retail plc.

DLA *"Quality act"* **Neil McLean**, *"a good manager as well as a good lawyer"* stands out here. Still *"the market leaders in Sheffield,"* across the region as a whole the team's profile has decreased. Particular strengths exist in development and in conducting freehold and leasehold transactions for retail occupiers. Currently acting for Teelsand Group plc in the Doncaster Interchange, a 300,000 sq ft mixed retail regeneration scheme in Doncaster town centre, and acted for Boots in their major disposal of the Prince Bishops' Shopping Centre in Durham. **Clients:** Sterling Capitol plc; Boots Properties plc; Town Centre Securities plc; Department of Education and Employment.

Eversheds With an impressive client list including major developers, retailers, industrial and commercial businesses and financial institutions, it is nonetheless the strong public sector practice that stands out. **John Foster** is known as a *"good, sensible, thorough, commercial operator"* but the team has been hit by recent defections. Acted in a number of national schemes for Hammerson, including the sale of the Wolsey Palace Shopping Centre, Woking, for £46 million and the purchase of an interest in the Liberty Shopping Centre, Romford, from Standard Life for over £50 million. **Clients:** Asda Group plc; Hammerson; Miller Group; Barclays Bank Property Holdings.

Hammond Suddards Edge Under the leadership of *"good operator"* **Christopher Marks**, the team is felt to have reversed a recent drop in profile, with the acquisition of a team from Eversheds considered a particular coup. Acting for a wide range of clients across the public and private sectors, including developers, investors, retailers and utility companies. Represented English Partnerships on the funding of the Vinopolis Museum of Wine, and Sheffield City Council on its £35 million Norfolk Park regeneration scheme. **Clients:** Beezer plc; Sheffield City Council; Allied London Properties plc; Scottish Power plc; Yorkshire Forward.

Pinsent Curtis Widely felt to have had a good year, this *"quality practice"* has increased turnover, gained clients and appears to be *"a firm that's moving forward again."* Leeds based national property head **Nigel McClea**, *"a tremendous guy,"* stands out but there is *"an air of professionalism"* surrounding the whole team. Property developers still represent the core of the practice, but the team is increasingly acting for investment companies and pension funds, and has niche expertise in mines and minerals and acquisitions in enterprise zones. Acted this year on the £16.85 million acquisition, funding and ongoing management of Orchard Square, a major Sheffield city centre retail site, on behalf of London & Associated Properties. **Clients:** Ministry of Agriculture Fisheries and Food; Concert BV; Crest Homes (Northern) Ltd; London & Associated Properties plc.

Andrew M. Jackson & Co *"The market leaders in Hull"* have a traditional retail base and a growing national reputation for development work. *"Technically first class,"* the firm *"acts for some major clients,"* with **David Stone** considered the person to highlight from a strong team. Increasingly active in all property aspects of the leisure industry, such as the mixed-use retail and leisure redevelopment of Scunthorpe town centre, the team recently acted for MFI on the £110 million sale to MEPC and leaseback of ten retail parks totalling 614,000 sq ft. **Clients:** MFI Properties Ltd; Carpetright plc; Associated British Ports; Cannons Health & Fitness Ltd.

Irwin Mitchell Strong in Sheffield, the new Leeds office is just beginning to bear fruit and the firm is enjoying a growth in retail development. This remains the strength, although the team also works for multiple retailers, commercial and industrial clients and on leisure and industrial developments. Recently acted for Peveril Securities on the site assembly and development of a new football stadium for Mansfield Town Football Club, incorporating a 150,000 sq ft mixed leisure and retail space. **Clients:** Peveril Securities Ltd; Henry Boot Development Ltd; Minit UK.

Nabarro Nathanson *"Fabulous property firm"* who is *"making inroads"* across the region. Coal Authority work remains important, but a strong client base now includes developers, investors and industrial companies, and it is *"particularly good on local authority work." "Lawyer's lawyer"* **Martin Grabiner** is *"a strong force for good"* at the firm. Acted last year for

British Waterways in connection with the complex redevelopment of the Leeds Waterfront adjoining the Royal Armouries Museum. **Clients:** Coal Authority; British Waterways; Capital Shopping Centres; Harrogate Borough Council.

Read Hind Stewart The relatively small size of this firm belies its property strength. **Andrew Flounders** *"doesn't lose track of his clients' interests."* Those clients include breweries, for whom the team conducts secured lending as well as acquisitions, retail landlords and, increasingly, local developers. Acted in the Bradford city centre regeneration scheme for Forster Square Developments. **Clients:** Helios Properties plc; Caddick Group; Stainsby Grange Ltd.

Gordons Cranswick Solicitors The April 2000 merger between Cranswick Watson and Gordons Wright & Wright was widely heralded as *"a good move for both of them."* Strength in Leeds and Bradford now makes the firm *"more of a viable force in commercial property."* With particular strength in retail and licensed premises, acted for Morrisons on a number of site acquisitions and on national secured lending for Bass Brewers. **Clients:** Wm Morrison Supermarkets plc; Bass Brewers Ltd; Ponden Mill.

Gosschalks *"Highly professional"* department that *"gets around a bit through its licensing experience"* but also acts for developers and on property management for plcs. Responsible last year for the £41 million disposal of a large pub portfolio and the disposal of three sites for a plc with an aggregate value of £30 million. **Clients:** Leisure operators; developers; plcs.

Denison Till Currently completing the final phase of an 80,000 sq ft retail park in Oldham, the team works mainly for small developers and investors. Considered *"a good firm who know what they're doing."* **Clients:** Consolidated Property Group; Townson plc.

Frith Partnership Formerly the Leeds offices of McGuinness Finch, this heavily partner-led firm has been independent since December 1999. Strong in retail and distribution, the firm is primarily focused on development, although it also acts for occupiers. **Clients:** Asda; Gazeley Properties Ltd; Redrow Commercial Developments Ltd; Abstract Securities Ltd.

Keeble Hawson This has been a year of consolidation for the firm, with the acquisition of niche Leeds practice James Kendall counterbalanced by the loss of the head of department. Acted last year in the purchase of commercial, retail, residential and leisure development sites across the country, and has a particular niche in NHS and nursing-home work. **Clients:** Scotfield Ltd; Hepworth plc; Weaver Group; Qualmark Ltd.

Rollit Farrell & Bladon Better known for its agricultural and social housing expertise, this firm also has a thriving commercial property practice. Acting for developers, especially on the residential side, and companies on corporate support, the firm also works for nursing homes. Conducted a series of large land acquisitions for Persimmon Homes and the property due diligence for a telecommunications flotation. **Clients:** Fenner plc; Heron Frozen Foods Ltd; Associated British Ports; Sanctuary Housing Association.

Wake Smith Small but established property department acting for manufacturers, NHS trusts and residential care homes on transactional work. The developer base is growing and the team has a particular niche in student housing developments. Acted in the acquisition of a large retail unit in The Moor, Sheffield and the subsequent letting to J Sainsbury plc for £4.5 million. **Clients:** Campus Living Ltd; TWIL Ltd; Shop Moor Ltd; Capitec Ltd.

NORTH EAST

PROPERTY (COMMERCIAL) • North East	Ptnrs	Assts
❶ **Dickinson Dees** Newcastle upon Tyne	12	21
❷ **Eversheds** Newcastle upon Tyne	10	18
❸ **Robert Muckle** Newcastle upon Tyne	2	5
Ward Hadaway Newcastle upon Tyne	8	6
Watson Burton Newcastle upon Tyne	5	4
❹ **Archers** Stockton-on-Tees	2	2
Jacksons Stockton-on-Tees	2	-

LEADING INDIVIDUALS	
❶ **BRAITHWAITE Neil** Dickinson Dees	**MORGAN Claire** Eversheds
WARD Ian Dickinson Dees	

Within each band, firms are listed alphabetically.

See **Profiles** on page 722

Dickinson Dees *"Prompt and efficient,"* this practice is the clear leader in the North East. **Neil Braithwaite** has moved his focus to the management side, but continues to conduct major property projects, while *"prominent"* and *"successful"* **Ian Ward** also stands out, although *"the people are good across the board."* Working for developers, banks, retail and leisure clients, and investors, the team is also involved in volume conveyancing for builders and lenders. With particular expertise in urban regeneration projects for local authorities and developers, the team has advised on a number of major schemes across the country for Bellway. **Clients:** Bellway plc; Northern Rock plc; Miller Homes.

Eversheds With considerable experience in urban redevelopment, enterprise zone development funding and the health and education sectors, this firm has a particularly high profile within the public sector. This should not obscure, however, the expertise in commercial and residential development and portfolio management. **Claire Morgan** is highly regarded for her technical ability. Acted last year in the purchase of the Regents Plaza Maida Vale for £36 million on behalf of Swallow Group plc. **Clients:** Scottish & Newcastle plc; Bellway Homes Ltd; One North East.

Robert Muckle *"Efficient"* regional practice with strength in all areas of private sector development, it also acts for investors and banks. Involved last year in nine separate industrial developments with an aggregate area of 520,000 sq ft. **Clients:** City and Northern Projects Ltd; Dysart Developments Ltd; Miller Homes; Cecil M Yuill.

Ward Hadaway Well respected department with a *"strong name for residential development."* The team works for a range of clients including retail outlets, banks, large companies, local authorities and charitable institutions. Bolstered by the merger with Gateshead firm Keenlyside & Forster, the team acted last year on the multi-million pound disposal of a retail park. **Clients:** Barratt Developments plc; Northern Rock plc; Hunting plc.

Watson Burton Acting last year in the sale of the 150,000 sq ft Benton Hypermarket for CWS, this firm is nimble enough to have completed the tax-driven sale of an office block at Silverlink Business Park in three working days. Highly regarded, with *"sensible and practical"* staff, the team acts for retailers, educational institutions and banks on secured lending, but the focus remains on development work. **Clients:** Co-operative Wholesale Society Ltd; Northern Electric plc; Collingwood Properties Ltd; Silverlink Property Development plc.

Archers Respected for good clients and property expertise, the team works on purchases, sales, leases and associated fundings for clients from the industrial, office, leisure, hotel and investment sectors, including a chain of betting shops. **Clients:** Cameron Hall Developments Ltd; Industrial Estates (Scotland) Ltd; John Joyce Ltd.

Jacksons Local firm providing the full range of property services to large and small businesses, regional developers and local authorities. Typical work includes acquisitions and disposals, leasing, options and securities. **Clients:** Northern Electric; THPA; Middlesborough BC.

SCOTLAND

PROPERTY (COMMERCIAL) • Scotland	Ptnrs	Assts
❶ **Dundas & Wilson CS** Edinburgh, Glasgow	16	59
McGrigor Donald Edinburgh, Glasgow	11	28
❷ **Burness** Edinburgh, Glasgow	11	15
Maclay Murray & Spens Edinburgh, Glasgow	15	34
Semple Fraser WS Glasgow	6	18
Shepherd & Wedderburn WS Edinburgh, Glasgow	9	23
❸ **Brodies WS** Edinburgh	8	12
Steedman Ramage WS Edinburgh	10	13
Tods Murray WS Edinburgh	11	18
❹ **Archibald Campbell & Harley WS** Edinburgh	7	6
DLA Edinburgh, Glasgow	7	9
Fyfe Ireland WS Edinburgh	7	7
MacRoberts Edinburgh, Glasgow	7	14
Paull & Williamsons Aberdeen	9	7
❺ **Biggart Baillie** Glasgow	7	16
Davidson Chalmers WS Edinburgh	3	3
Ledingham Chalmers Aberdeen	10	12
Miller Samuel & Co Glasgow	4	1
Morison Bishop Edinburgh, Glasgow	6	7
Thorntons WS Dundee	3	7
❻ **Boyds** Glasgow	5	5
Dickson Minto WS Edinburgh	1	5
Harper Macleod Glasgow	7	4
Henderson Boyd Jackson WS Edinburgh	4	6
Leslie Wolfson & Co Glasgow	5	-
McClure Naismith Edinburgh, Glasgow	6	13
Mitchells Roberton Glasgow	2	2
Morton Fraser, Solicitors Edinburgh	4	6
Wright, Johnston & Mackenzie Edinburgh, Glasgow	5	6

Within each band, firms are listed alphabetically.

LEADING INDIVIDUALS

❶ **ANDERSON Thomas** McGrigor Donald
BANKIER David McGrigor Donald
DORAN Iain Dundas & Wilson CS
GARRETT Robin Maclay Murray & Spens
HANIFORD Paul Semple Fraser WS
JOHNSON Jennifer Maclay Murray & Spens
REID Sandy Steedman Ramage WS
RYDEN Nicholas Shepherd & Wedderburn WS
SMITH David Shepherd & Wedderburn WS
STEEL David Dundas & Wilson CS

❷ **BRYMER Stewart** Thorntons WS
COCKBURN David Archibald Campbell & Harley WS
DALGARNO Leslie Paull & Williamsons
HODGE James (Hamish) Dundas & Wilson CS
MacNIVEN Iain Maclay Murray & Spens
MOST Lionel Burness
QUIGLEY Ian Maclay Murray & Spens
REID David Burness
SHAW Donald Dundas & Wilson CS
STRACHAN Dale Brodies WS
WALLACE Andrew Archibald Campbell & Harley WS
WATTIE Ian Burness

❸ **CURRAN John** Ledingham Chalmers
DEWAR Mark Harper Macleod
DOBIE James Shepherd & Wedderburn WS
GRIFFITHS Keith Brodies WS
MOFFAT Douglas Tods Murray WS
NEWTON Alison McGrigor Donald
ROSCOE James Fyfe Ireland WS
ROSS Kenneth Burness
WILSON Alistair Fyfe Ireland WS

UP AND COMING
KINNIBURGH Linda Brodies WS

See *Profiles* on page 722

Dundas & Wilson CS Almost universally acknowledged to be the one of the two outstanding commercial property firms in Scotland. Size and a blue-chip client base continue to keep the team in the top band. Head of Department **Donald Shaw** has now *"gone to superstar level,"* but is spending a substantial proportion of his time outside Scotland. **Hamish Hodge** has suffered a drop in profile with his move from partner to consultant, though he is the key partner for some important clients and something of a legend: *"He has a way of getting what he wants without you knowing it!"* A strong department also includes **David Steel**, *"a delight to deal with,"* and **Iain Doran** who *"knows his stuff and knows how to work with people."* The tie-up with Arthur Andersen, *"hasn't done them any harm,"* and the team is increasingly involved in international transactions, such as the recent sale of 400 retail properties world-wide for Erlikhon Buerhle and subsequent work, with the consent of the vendors, for the buyers, Texas Pacific Group. **Clients:** Lend Lease; Land Securities; Scottish Widows; London and Regional Properties.

McGrigor Donald *"Practical and proactive,"* a sizeable number of people thought that this firm was also pulling away from the chasing pack, but unlike Dundas & Wilson, the team *"has gone the independent route and done it very well."* An excellent department, well supported by specialists in other areas, includes **Thomas Anderson** who is *"pragmatic, commercial and doesn't miss any good points,"* and **David Bankier** who is *"good technically and has a commercial edge as well."* **Alison Newton** is *"an able lawyer"* but primarily *"a rainmaker, she gets a lot of clients."* With particular experience in development, institutional investment and property finance, the team acts for a number of retail and leisure clients and is involved in an increasing amount of work relating to call centres. Acted this year for a consortium of private investors in relation to the purchase of SFG Properties Ltd, with a portfolio of 51 properties throughout Scotland, for over £75 million. **Clients:** Bank of Scotland; Morrison Developments Ltd; The Scottish Metropolitan Property plc; British Broadcasting Corporation.

Burness Perceived to be improving, this vigorous practice has *"grown a lot in the last year"* and *"seems to be pressing ahead."* **Ian Wattie** heads a strong department including **Lionel Most** who is *"well respected"* on the retail side. **David Reid**, now something of an elder statesman, is often consulted by solicitors outside the practice because of his *"technical knowledge,"* while **Ken Ross** returns to full-time fee earning after a period as managing partner. Recently reorganised, the department continues to concentrate on its key areas of development, retail/leisure, investment and property finance. Acted last year for the Royal Bank of Scotland on its purchase and proposed redevelopment of St James House, the largest single office building in Edinburgh. **Clients:** Royal Bank of Scotland plc; Inland Revenue/Customs and Excise; First Choice Holidays plc; Sun Life.

Maclay Murray & Spens Head of Department **Jennifer Johnson** received considerable praise for having *"built up an extremely good practice."* The team also includes *"commercially aware"* **Robin Garrett**, *"sound and well respected"* **Ian Quigley** and **Iain MacNiven** who *"has a good name acting for landlords."* Acted this year on behalf of Friends First UK Commercial Property Ltd on the acquisition of 80 properties throughout England and Scotland for £92.5 million. The firm's client base includes institutional investors, retailers and pure property companies. **Clients:** Scottish Enterprise; Abbey Life; Scottish Amicable; Wilson Bowden.

Semple Fraser WS *"Market opinion suggests they're on the way up."* *"Switched on and commercial"* **Paul Haniford** is *"good at getting business."* The team works for a large number of developers and investment funds, with pure or mixed-use leisure development remaining a growth area.

Acted in the sale of SFG Properties Ltd for over £75 million and recently obtained a new lease for the Halifax on their Internet Bank at South Gyle, Edinburgh, for an annual rent of £1 million. **Clients:** Tesco Stores Ltd; Royal & Sun Alliance Property Investments Ltd; MWB Group; Bass Developments Ltd.

Shepherd & Wedderburn WS Market opinion suggests that the team, although unable to repeat last year's annus mirabilis, is still a leading name. *"Clear and thorough"* **David Smith** has an *"extremely good name,"* while **Nicholas Ryden** is an *"aggressive"* lawyer but *"clients patently love him."* **James Dobie** is also well regarded. A genuine full-service firm with experience in all areas of commercial property, the team has particular expertise in city centre office development, letting and financing, business park development and retail investment and development. Acted for New Tollcross Ltd in its disposal to the Crown Estate Commissioners of a 1.88 acre Edinburgh City Centre site and its development to create Princes Exchange. **Clients:** Pillar Property plc; New Edinburgh Ltd; Horizon Properties Ltd.

Brodies WS *"They're good lawyers and they do decent work." "Sensible"* **Dale Strachan** has a *"good style"* and is ranked alongside **Keith Griffiths** and **Linda Kinniburgh**, the latter for the first time. Strong on retail and all aspects of development, the team is acting for Corus in the ongoing mixed-use redevelopment of over 1,100 acres of former industrial land at Ravenscraig, Motherwell. **Clients:** Corus plc; Sydney & London Properties plc; Asda Group plc; John Menzies plc.

Steedman Ramage WS *"Traditionally a retailer's firm,"* the team still has *"a brilliant client base"* in that sector, together with *"one or two successes on the investment side"* and strength in development and leisure. *"Outstanding"* **Sandy Reid** is a *"good technician"* but the team as a whole has been hit recently by the loss of partners. Acted this year in the sale of the Gyle Shopping Centre on behalf of Marks & Spencer, and for tenants taking leases of over half the total floor space at the Braehead Shopping Centre. **Clients:** Marks & Spencer plc; Next plc; J. Sainsbury plc.

Tods Murray WS In what is widely seen as a firm on the up, newly ranked **Douglas Moffat** stands out from a team of *"top flight property lawyers."* The firm services its clientele notably on investment and pension fund matters. The team advises on a large amount of secured lending work and acts for developers on commercial, leisure and residential schemes. Last year conducted the acquisition by Kenmore Caledonian Ltd of the Caledonian Exchange, Edinburgh, and the subsequent leasing and onward sale to an overseas investor for £19.8 million. **Clients:** Kenmore Investments Ltd; Thus plc; Hermes; Co-operative Insurance Society Ltd.

Archibald Campbell & Harley WS A strong property team includes *"well known"* **David Cockburn**, a *"good tenant's lawyer,"* and *"very helpful"* **Andrew Wallace**. *"Strong on retail,"* the team also works for a wide range of property clients including developers and investors. Acted in the acquisition of a large site in New Street, Edinburgh, for £12 million which is set to become a 350-400,000 sq ft mixed use commercial, residential and leisure development. **Clients:** Dixons plc; Boots the Chemists Ltd; Safeway Stores plc.

DLA The merger with the former Bird Semple has generated some adverse comment, but it was accepted that the strength of the brand makes it a name to watch in the Scottish market. With a cross-border capacity, the team has an impressive client list including some major institutional investors and a wide spread of developers. Acted for Capital Shopping Centres in the acquisition, development and letting of the Braehead Shopping Centre. **Clients:** Capital Shopping Centres plc; Clerical Medical Investment Group; Friends Provident; Bank of Scotland.

Fyfe Ireland WS A sound, reliable firm with intelligent lawyers: *"what they do is good quality stuff." "Extremely able and pleasant"* **Alistair Wilson** *"looks after the client and gets the job done,"* while **James Roscoe** received a flood of positive comment. With a client base weighted towards investment and retail, the team acted recently for Whitehall Green Partnership on the Scottish due diligence aspects of a 6,000,000 sq ft property portfolio purchase. **Clients:** Kingfisher Group; Green Property plc; Kier Homes Ltd.

MacRoberts A sound firm with particular strength in PFI and construction, seen by some as *"more involved in the property market now."* Major property focus is on retail, leisure, and development work, though there are interesting niches in the energy and mining sectors and working for Railtrack. Acted for Pathfinder (Scotland) Ltd in the site assembly for its Merchant Village development in Glasgow, intended to comprise 500,000 sq ft of mixed retail, leisure and housing. **Clients:** Railtrack plc; Pathfinder Properties plc; HBG Properties plc; Odeon Ltd; AMEC plc.

Paull & Williamsons A perception exists that the firm *"has got the Aberdeen market sewn up."* Increasingly obvious across Scotland, *"deal maker"* **Leslie Dalgarno** is *"well-known and well regarded."* Acting this year in two major new office developments in Aberdeen City Centre, respectively for the eventual tenant and the developer. **Clients:** Jawlaw Ltd/Westhill Development co Ltd; Crown Park/European Development co Ltd; Inverness Retail Parks Ltd/Jaymarke.

Biggart Baillie With a *"good property base"* and a large department, this solid general firm has kept a generally low profile. Acting for the full range of clients the team has a particularly strong following amongst developers, utility companies and financial institutions, and niche expertise in cross country projects and railway industry work. Advised Westminster Healthcare Ltd on all Scots Law aspects of a complex £195 million securitisation. **Clients:** Scottish Power plc; Thus plc; Wilcon Homes plc; ScotRail Railways Ltd.

Davidson Chalmers WS A *"decent small practice,"* this *"solid performer continues to grow."* With a strong following amongst developers and private investors, the team was recently involved in the development of a contaminated and undermined 100 acre site for use as a distribution park, and a 7.5 acre leisure scheme in West Edinburgh. **Clients:** Developers and investors.

Ledingham Chalmers Although it has Edinburgh and Inverness offices, this *"excellent"* firm is still primarily associated with Aberdeen, where it is seen to be *"challenging hard."* Highly regarded rainmaker **John Curran** *"fronts a lot of deals."* Last year these included acting for Talisman Energy (UK) Ltd on their pre-letting from the developer of a 95,000 sq ft office site for a new Aberdeen Headquarters. The team acts regularly for builders, developers and landlords, and is doing increasing amounts of institutional lending work. **Clients:** Cala Ltd; Talisman Energy (UK) Ltd; HIE (Highlands & Islands Enterprise); Scottish Capital Group.

Miller Samuel & Co *"A good small practice"* with some sound lawyers who *"do a reasonable amount of work."* Particularly active on the retail front where they *"act for an awful lot of tenants,"* they also have thriving development and investment interests. **Clients:** Developers; investors; tenants.

Morison Bishop The team is felt to have become *"a sizeable player."* Doubts remain about whether the firm will be affected by the loss of a senior partner. Seen mainly as a residential developers' firm, the team also acts for secured lenders on fundings and major institutions and plcs, for whom they *"can pick anything up."* **Clients:** Beazer Homes; BT plc.

Thorntons WS *"Strong in Dundee"* and the surrounding area, the firm also has something of a national reputation, acting inter alia for E&J Glasgow Ltd in a £15 million Glasgow city centre leisure scheme. The team also receives major referrals from London firms, such as the £25 million new-build development of a research laboratory and offices for a major American technology company. **Stewart Brymer** is the stand-out name here. **Clients:** Grantchester Group plc; Bett Brothers plc.

Boyds Works for a broad range of clients including developers, investors, banks and companies as both landlords and tenants. Recently acted on a £23 million acquisition in Edinburgh by an overseas investor. **Clients:** Safeway Stores plc; Shanks Waste Services; I Philp Holdings Ltd; Premier Hotels Ltd.

Dickson Minto WS The firm's small commercial property department is essentially viewed as a corporate service arm, although it does also perform stand-alone work for banks, retailers, developers and investment companies. Responsible for the sale of forty stores for Somerfield at over £300 million. **Clients:** Highcross Group; Shanks & McEwan plc; Somerfield plc.

Harper Macleod Opinion is divided about this firm, but a substantial section of it regards **Mark Dewar** as the man who has *"increased the firm's profile in the market."* Acting for property investors, developers and, increasingly, tenants, the firm was instructed in the £22 million acquisition by Clerical Medical/Britel of The Guild Hall, Queen Street, Glasgow. **Clients:** Clerical Medical Investment Group/Britel Fund Trustees Ltd; Arlington Securities plc; Imperial Chemical Industries plc; Pfizer Ltd.

Henderson Boyd Jackson WS Currently focusing on the investment, development and funding side of the practice, the team has experienced a growth in volume conveyancing for lenders. An excellent client base includes a number of large investors and banks, and the team also acts on behalf of nursing homes. Acted last year on behalf of NTL in acquiring communication sites throughout Scotland. **Clients:** British Land; Arrowcroft; Standard Life; Royal Bank of Scotland.

Leslie Wolfson & Co Small partner-led firm with a good reputation and *"some jolly good clients."* Acts for a wide range of property interests including investors, retailers and banks. **Clients:** Woolwich plc; Aldi Stores Ltd; Electronics Boutique plc; Carphone Warehouse Ltd.

McClure Naismith A reliable firm of *"good, sound conveyancers,"* which acts for a broad range of clients including banks, retail tenants, NHS trusts, major national house-builders and big names in the leisure industry. Experienced in security work, the team recently acted in the acquisition and securitisation of over 30 nursing homes for NHP Group plc. **Clients:** Coal Pension Properties Ltd; NHP Group plc; Lloyds TSB Group.

Mitchells Roberton This small, long established firm *"has had a cracking year"* with the purchase of the Gyle Shopping Centre for the Universities Superannuation Scheme. The team is said to have *"one or two jolly good clients,"* especially among banks and institutional investors. **Clients:** Universities Superannuation Scheme Ltd.

Morton Fraser, Solicitors Considered *"good, sound people,"* they work for small and medium-sized developers on residential, commercial and leisure schemes and service the portfolio management needs of blue-chip companies. Acted recently in the sale of a large portfolio by Scottish Newcastle and three sizeable cross-border disposals. **Clients:** Scottish Newcastle; Diageo; Halifax plc; Bank of Scotland.

Wright, Johnston & Mackenzie Well known for licensed property work, where the firm's name is linked with the likes of Bass. Also involved in the property aspects of alternative energy transactions. **Clients:** Vodafone; Bass Brewers; Tennent Caledonian Breweries.

NORTHERN IRELAND

PROPERTY (COMMERCIAL) • Northern Ireland	Ptnrs	Assts
❶ L'Estrange & Brett Belfast	5	6
❷ Carson & McDowell Belfast	2	5
Elliott Duffy Garrett Belfast	5	4
Tughan & Co Belfast	4	5
❸ Cleaver Fulton Rankin Belfast	2	3
Johns Elliot Belfast	5	2
McKinty & Wright Belfast	2	3
Mills Selig Belfast	4	3
❹ Arthur Cox Belfast	1	1
C & H Jefferson Belfast	2	5
Hewitt & Gilpin Belfast	2	2
Johnsons Belfast	2	3
Kearney Sefton Belfast	3	-

LEADING INDIVIDUALS	
❶ AGNEW Phyllis Tughan & Co	HEWITT Alan L'Estrange & Brett
MAHOOD Laurence Elliott Duffy Garrett	REILLY Alan Carson & McDowell
❷ HENDERSON Brian L'Estrange & Brett	
❸ FARIS Neil Cleaver Fulton Rankin	HAMILTON Christine Elliott Duffy Garrett
LEITCH David Johns Elliot	
UP AND COMING	
PIERCE Graham L'Estrange & Brett	TINMAN Mark C & H Jefferson

Within each band, firms are listed alphabetically. *See **Profiles** on page 722*

L'Estrange & Brett *"Expanding rapidly"* and *"increasing its client base,"* the team is now seen to have broken away from its nearest competition to become the *"clear leader"* in property work in the province. Particularly noted for its busy development practice, which is involved in many of the large developments currently underway in Belfast and around the country. Also handles retail work for substantial national clients and major public sector/PFI schemes. Leading individuals remain team head **Alan Hewitt**, secured lending and funding expert **Brian Henderson**, whose *"practical and friendly approach"* won plaudits in the market, and up and coming **Graham Pierce**. Acted for Cusp in the development of Halifax plc's call centre at Cromack Wood. **Clients:** J Sainsbury plc; Laganside Corporation; Morrison Homes.

Carson & McDowell *"Substantial property practice"* best known for acting for Belfast Harbour Commissioners, the landlord in a rash of major current development schemes. Particularly active in the retail sector. Some in the market feel that the team relies too heavily on **Alan Reilly**, who *"knows all the angles"* and *"does a good job for his clients."* **Clients:** Belfast Harbour Commissioners.

Elliott Duffy Garrett Despite a somewhat lower profile than recent years, this remains an *"up to date"* practice with a *"good cross section of clients"* and a strong reputation. Acts for large national property companies, shopping centres and tenants, with expertise in major development work and investment sales and purchases. Rated practitioners are the *"organised"* **Laurence Mahood** who is a *"good negotiator"* and *"knows his law"* and the *"bright"* **Christine Hamilton**. Acted for BG plc in the development of their purpose built facility for Phoenix Natural Gas. **Clients:** Land Securities; British Land; BG plc.

Tughan & Co With particular expertise in development work, this large department also acts for a lot of institutional investors. With a *"good spread of work"* and some *"serious, heavyweight clients,"* the firm *"always appears in big deals."* An example is the acquisition by the Railway Pension Nominees of a retail park from MEPC, the Northern Irish aspect of a £176 million pound deal. *"Focused"* **Phyllis Agnew** is *"extremely thorough and meticulous."* **Clients:** Tesco; Prudential; Marks and Spencer.

Cleaver Fulton Rankin The first Northern Irish firm to have created a fully dedicated property team along English lines, it retains a healthy and diverse practice. Handles big-ticket development, acquisition and operational work for national retail chains, corporates, telecommunications organisations and property investors. Notable recent trends include an increasing amount of public sector work, instructions from US investors and involvement in the acquisition of call centres for clients such as BT, NIE and Prudential. Though now seen more in his role as environmental law consultant, **Neil Faris** retains his *"first-class"* reputation in property work. Acted for The Post Office in the development of the Belfast Mail Centre, which was funded on a sale and leaseback basis. **Clients:** The Post Office; BT plc; Cellnet.

Johns Elliot Notable for its *"active"* development practice, in which field new entrant **David Leitch** *("an analytical mind")* is well known. Also acts for substantial commercial landlords and investor clients. Completed the sale of a retail park in Newry for MEPC plc. **Clients:** MEPC plc; Dunloe Ewart plc; Belfast International Airports Ltd.

McKinty & Wright Though perhaps better known as a litigation practice, this *"solid, dependable firm"* also has a respected commercial property department. With *"quite a few established clients"* across the sector, the team has particular strength in retail and retail development. **Clients:** Morrison Developments Ltd; Next plc; Littlewoods plc.

Mills Selig Seen generally as an *"ambitious"* firm which is *"on the up"* and *"picking up a lot of work,"* particularly from local developers. Market perception is that it is too early to push the team up, but this is *"one to keep an eye on."* Other strengths include commercial landlord and tenant and banking work. Acted for McAleare and Rush in the development of a £16 million hotel complex in Belfast City Centre, with linked apartments, leisure and retail units. **Clients:** McAleare & Rush; the Herbert Group of Companies; Piller Properties plc.

Arthur Cox Although only four years old, the Belfast offshoot of this premier Dublin firm is considered *"well established and going well in the local market place."* With a reputation for secured lending and work for retail tenants, the team has expertise in cross-border work and increasingly attracts direct instructions from high-quality clients and referrals from British firms. Acted alongside major names in the acquisition of a retail chain by Scottish Midlands Co-operative and the sale of the Belfast Telegraph newspaper titles by the Trinity Mirror Group. **Clients:** Bank of Ireland; First Active plc; Eircom plc; Fitness First plc.

C & H Jefferson *"Trying to develop its commercial property department."* Leading the charge is the high profile *"young upstart"* **Mark Tinman** who is *"grabbing a lot of retail clients with gusto"* and enters the rankings this year. **Clients:** Retail concerns.

Hewitt & Gilpin Well established, traditional practice considered to be *"a good business."* With particular experience in retail lettings the team also *"acts for some good developer clients."* Currently experiencing a growth in retail development and the property aspects of corporate acquisitions. **Clients:** Developers.

Johnsons *"Low key"* outfit which maintains an *"excellent"* reputation in smaller scale property work, and some *"very good clients."* **Clients:** Local corporates.

Kearney Sefton Well known on the development side, the firm *"acts for some substantial local developers"* and is considered by some to have *"strength in depth."* Acted in the purchase of the Yorkgate retail and leisure park. **Clients:** Deramore Property Group; Belfast Office Properties Ltd; Finbrook Investments Ltd.

LEADERS IN PROPERTY (COMMERCIAL)

AGNEW, B.E. Phyllis M.
Tughan & Co, Belfast (028) 9055 3300
Partner and Head - Commercial Property Department.
Specialisation: Main area of practice is commercial property development including property finance, bank and institutional funding, institutional investment, joint venture arrangements and PFI projects.
Prof. Memberships: Law Society of Northern Ireland, IBA, SIP and European Lawyers Group.
Career: Qualified 1981. Assistant Solicitor at Tughan & Co. 1981 - 1988. Partner since 1988.
Personal: Two daughters, aged 16 and 18. Leisure interests include golf, duplicate bridge and skiing.

ALBERT, David E. P.
Ashurst Morris Crisp, London (020) 7638 1111
david.albert@ashursts.com
Partner in Commercial Property Department.
Specialisation: All aspects of Commercial Property, with particular emphasis on joint ventures, development and investment work. Acts for funds, developers, property companies, public authorities and occupiers.
Prof. Memberships: City of London Law Society Land Law Sub-Committee.
Career: Qualified in 1969. Joined *Ashursts* 1976; became partner in 1978.

ANDERSON, Thomas D.
McGrigor Donald, Glasgow (0141) 248 6677
www.mcgrigors.com
Partner in Property Unit.
Specialisation: Joint Ventures; Property Finance.
Prof. Memberships: Law Society of Scotland.
Career: 1971-75 Edinburgh University (LLB Hons); 1980-89 *Biggart Baillie & Gifford*, Partner (Commercial Property/ Corporate); 1989 to date *McGrigor Donald*, Partner (Commercial Property).

ASHWORTH, P.H.
Field Cunningham & Co, Manchester (0161) 834 4734
Senior Partner.
Specialisation: Acts for major developers and housebuilders throughout the North. Responsible for the acquisition of land for approximately 1400 houses annually. Involved with large retail and leisure developments throughout the United Kingdom including superstores, cinemas, bingo clubs and bowling alleys. Deals with numerous joint ventures with other developers and financiers for residential and commercial developments. Handles the funding of major commercial developments. Non-executive Director of Barratt Developments plc.
Career: Qualified March 1961. Articled at *Field Cunningham & Co.* and became a Partner in 1962.
Personal: Born 23rd January 1938. Educated at Arnold School Blackpool. Lives in Hale, Cheshire.

ASKIN, David J.
Wragge & Co, Birmingham (0121) 214 1014
david_askin@wragge.com
Specialisation: All types of commercial property development, letting, funding, sales, especially town centre redevelopments, offices, retail/business parks and private/public sector joint ventures. Acts for developers, local authorities and investor-purchasers. Heavyweight experience on complex schemes.
Career: Educated Bilston Grammar School; St Catharine's College, Cambridge (1967 MA Law); (1968 LLM). Articled *Wragge & Co*; qualified 1970; partner 1973; Director Worfield Golf Club plc.
Personal: Born 1946. Lives Newport, Shropshire. Interests include cricket, golf and fishing.

BAILEY, Jeffrey
Linklaters (A member firm of Linklaters & Alliance), London (020) 7456 4756
jeffrey.bailey@linklaters.com
Partner 1980, Real Estate Department. Joint Head of European Real Estate Practice Group, Linklaters & Alliance.
Specialisation: Property Law specialist. Significant involvement for overseas clients on inward investment into UK real estate.
Prof. Memberships: Attended Neath Grammar School, attained LLB (Hons) from University of Wales 1971. Qualified in 1974.
Personal: Born 1949

BAILEY, Michael D.
Argles Stoneham Burstows, Croydon (020) 8628 2589/Brighton(01273) 828 000
michael.bailey@asb-law.com
Partner in Property Department.
Specialisation: Specialises in commercial property. Work includes handling the development of new sites, construction work, joint ventures, landlord and tenant, sales and purchases of businesses and land transactions for charities. Provides solicitor expert reports on conveyancing practice. CAB Tutor 1974-84, University of Sussex and Brighton College of Technology part-time lecturer 1967-80.
Prof. Memberships: Law Society, Associate of School of Urban and Regional Studies, University of Sussex.
Career: Qualified in 1965. Assistant and partner at *Gates & Co* in Brighton 1966-71. Partner in *Whitley Hughes & Luscombe/Donne Mileham & Haddock*, Crawley and Brighton from 1973- 1998.
Personal: Educated at Varndean Grammar School, Brighton and College of Law. Positions held include

President Sussex Law Society 1995, Treasurer/Trustee of the Webb Memorial Trust (an educational charity), member of Legal Aid Area Committee from 1975, Chairman 1990-91. Member Know How Housing team to Eastern Europe.

BAILY, Tim G.
Bond Pearce, Southampton (023) 8063 2211
xtgb@bondpearce.com
Specialisation: Associate in the Commercial Property Group. Wide experience of all aspects of commercial property work especially development and commercial landlord and tenant. Has been closely involved in a number of the firm's niche areas of work such as wind farms and waste and minerals. Current emphasis is on retail development and port and marine related work.
Career: Qualified 1987, becoming Associate 1997.

BANKIER, David A.
McGrigor Donald, Glasgow (0141) 248 6677
davidban@mcgrigors.com
Senior Property Partner and Chairman of Belfast Office.
Specialisation: Main area of practice is property development and investment within tax efficient structures, joint ventures and public/private sector initiatives in commercial property. Acted for BAA-McArthur/Glen in the development of their first designer outlet centre in Scotland and for Resolution Property plc in their first major retail development in Scotland, a 50% interest in the £80m The Forge shopping centre, Glasgow. Advised Downing Corporate Finance as sponsor of collective investment in two major EZ developments in Gourock and in Sunderland. Advised Akeler Developments and Royal Bank on "golden contracts" at Greenock prior to the expiry of the Renfrewshire Enterprise Zone and subsequently the letting by Akeler and investment sale of a new call centre building for Mercury Communications. Advised Glasgow Zoo on the development plan and funding package for its 90 acre site at Calderpark, Glasgow to create a new bio diverse Discovery Centre. Gave strategic advice to a private property company which resulted in a tax effective demerger. Presently advising North Lanarkshire Council on Cumbernauld Town Centre redevelopment, and the developer in the third phase of the Broomielaw, Glasgow's premier office development site, including the funding of a new 100,000 sq. feet headquarters building for Scottish Enterprise.
Career: Qualified in 1972, having joined *McGrigor Donald* in 1970. Became a partner in 1978.
Personal: Born 24th March 1949. Educated at Edinburgh University (LLB 1970). Leisure interests include travel, art history, Scottish contemporary paintings, sailing and skiing. Lives in Glasgow.

BARNES, James C.
Herbert Smith, London (020) 7374 8000
Partner in Property Department.
Specialisation: He has a broad range of experience in commercial property and property related matters with a particular emphasis on development projects, property joint ventures, property finance and security and, latterly, on schemes promoted under the UK Government's Private Finance Initiative. Recent projects include Broadgate; Tate Gallery of Modern Art, Bankside; Millbank Tower.
Career: Queen's University, Belfast (LLB); qualified 1980; partner *Herbert Smith* 1989.
Personal: Sport - skiing, sailing, motoring.

BATTERSBY, Robin
Burges Salmon, Bristol (0117) 939 2279
robin.battersby@burges-salmon.com
Specialisation: Commercial property development, acting on development projects for landowners, developers and for consortia of landowners/developers, including the tax aspects of property transactions. Recent projects include acting for consortium of commercial and residential developers in mixed development project in the Midlands, including planning aspects and joint venture documentation.
Prof. Memberships: Law Society.
Career: Joined *Burges Salmon* in 1968 and became a partner in 1972.

BEACH, Steven
Taylor Vinters, Cambridge (01223) 423444
sb@taylorvinters.com
Specialisation: All types of commercial property transactions specialising in Institutional Investment, development, joint ventures, property insolvency and securities work; dilapidations.
Prof. Memberships: Law Society Member
Career: Graduated in law at Oxford University and joined *Taylor Vinters* in 1983. Qualified in 1985. Became a partner in 1989 and head of the commercial property department in 1994.
Personal: Amateur dramatics, sport.

BECKETT, Roy G.
DLA, Manchester (08700) 111111
roy.beckett@dla.com
Specialisation: Property development and investment and structured finance for institutions and property companies.
Prof. Memberships: Law Society and Interact.
Career: Qualified 1983. Joined *Alsop Wilkinson* 1987 becoming partner in 1989. Head of Manchester Property Department in 1992 (*Dibb Lupton Alsop* 1996). Regional Managing Partner Manchester Office 1998.
Personal: Born 1958. Lives Bowdon, Cheshire. Leisure interests include skiing, squash, tennis and overseas travel.

BENNETT, Graham
Shoosmiths, Solent (01489) 881010
graham.bennett@shoosmiths.co.uk
Specialisation: Commercial Property - all aspects including privatisations (Chatham Docks and Southend Airport), insolvency, funding (1 Cockspur St, Trafalgar Square) and charities (Central Board of Finance of Church of England). Joint author 'Housing Act 1988 - A Practical Guide'. Recent transactions include completing finance leasing and property aspects of the Heinz NDC project; advising Aeromatic Fielder on the property and VAT aspects of its acquisition of Galley Systems Limited in Birmingham; acquisition by East Hampshire Housing Association of its new development site in Portsmouth; Simpson Lawrence's disposal of its warehouse at Sopwith Park, Segensworth; acted for Zoffany Hotels in the purchase of the former Post House Hotel, Bournemouth; acted for Esso Petroleum in the disposal of its former depot at Tynemouth.
Prof. Memberships: Law Society; Society of Practitioners of Insolvency; Charity Law Association.
Career: Articled *Ashurst Morris Crisp*, assistant *Clifford-Turner*, Partner *Wilde Sapte*, 1994 Partner *Shoosmiths*.
Personal: Golf, cricket and riding.

BENSON, Stephen John
Cobbetts, Manchester (0161) 833 3333
stephen.benson@cobbetts.co.uk
Specialisation: Commercial Property Division Manager. Commercial property in the Retail and Leisure sector. Acts for household name retailers and licensed premises operators in the pub, restaurant and hotel sector.
Prof. Memberships: Law Society. Associate member of American Bar Association.
Career: Educated at Manchester University and Chester College of Law. Qualified 1980.
Personal: Born 1955. Married with 3 children. Lives in Knutsford. Leisure interests, exercise, motor cars and Vice-chairman of Patrons of Manchester City Art Galleries.

BERRY, Roger John
Berry Smith, Cardiff Cardiff (029) 2034 5511
Specialisation: Full range of commercial property work including investment and development with particular emphasis on landlord and tenant. Also joint ventures and banking.
Career: Qualified 1978. Articled *Broomheads & Neals* (Sheffield). At *Simpson Curtis* (Leeds)1978-1981 and *Phillips & Buck* now *Eversheds*, Cardiff 1981-1986. Established Berry Smith 1986.
Personal: Born 19 March 1952, Colne, Lancashire. Educated at Sedbergh School and Emmanuel College, Cambridge (MA). Interests: football and cycling.

BILLINGS, Martin J.
Morgan Cole, Oxford (0118) 955 3000
martin.billings@morgan-cole.com
Specialisation: Commercial property with wide ranging experiance of property financing, development and portfolio management. Recent transactions include development projects for MEPC and TechData and significant projects for British Alcan.
Prof. Memberships: The Law Society
Career: Qualified 1988. *Cole & Cole/Morgan cole* 1988-Date. Partner: 1994.

BLAKE, Carey
Blake Lapthorn, Fareham (01489) 579990
csblake@blakelapthorn.co.uk
Specialisation: Main area of practice is development work relating to out of town sites. Also has a special reponsibility for agricultural law. Head of the firm's Commercial Property Department, comprising 25 lawyers on the South Coast and in London.
Prof. Memberships: Law Society; Notaries Society
Career: Articled at *Theodore Goddard*, London and qualified in 1968. Joined *Blake Lapthorn* on qualification and became a partner in 1971. Admitted as a Notary Public in 1976.
Personal: Born 11th May 1943. Attended Sidney Sussex, Cambridge 1962-65. Chairman of Fareham Hockey Club. Other leisure interests include theatre. Married and lives in Curdridge.

BOTHAMLEY, H.L. Michael
Beachcroft Wansbroughs, Bristol (0117) 918 2000
mbothamley@bwlaw.co.uk
Specialisation: Acts for a range of national and regional developers, retailers and institutions. Has particular expertise in development work where current projects include a number of office, retail and leisure schemes. Also acts for several major residential portfolio investment companies.
Career: Durham University. 1980 joined *Wansbroughs Willey Hargrave*. Partner with *Wansbroughs*

Willey Hargrave 1986. 1999- Partner in *Beachcroft Wansbroughs.*

BRAITHWAITE, Neil
Dickinson Dees, Newcastle upon Tyne (0191) 279 9233
Managing Partner
Specialisation: Handles Urban Regeneration, Development Agreements and property joint ventures, minerals and waste disposal work, Building Preservation Trusts, historic house rescues. Recent projects include: Development agreements for Building Preservation Trusts for major listed buildings in Gosport, Plymouth and South Wales Coalfields. Sunderland City Centre redevelopment for Arriva plc. Durham City development for Northern Electric plc. Agreement for Wind Farm development in Cumbria. Waste Disposal site acquisition and joint venture in Cheshire. Development and part disposal of Urban Village in East London for Bellway plc.
Career: Trinity College, Cambridge M.A. Law Society Finals. *Joynson Hicks* 1976-78. *Coward Chance* 1978-80. *Dickinson Dees* 1980 to date. (Partner 1981 onwards - Head of Property from 1990-98). Managing Partner from 1998.

BRETHERTON, Philip.J.
Berwin Leighton, London (020) 7760 1000
philip.bretherton@berwinleighton.com
Partner in the Commercial Property Department
Specialisation: Specialises in commercial property with particular emphasis on development and tax led work and, more recently, in projects promoted under the Private Finance Initiative. In the past year, he acted for Government Offices for London on the contract for the new London Parliament building; for the Ministry of Defence in the disposal of the Duke of York Headquarters; and for the Secretary of State for the Environment, Transport and the regions in the disposal of Bletchley Park to the Bletchley Park Trust. He represented Norwest Holst and MEPC, the promoters of the Bute Avenue scheme in Cardiff and for Norwest Holst in relation to the new Dorset Police Headquarters, both schemes being promoted under the PFI.
Prof. Memberships: Member of the Law Society.
Career: Articled *Slaughter and May*; qualified 1974; Assistant Solicitor 1974-78; Assistant *Solicitor Simmons & Simmons* 1978-79; Property Partner *Simmons & Simmons* 1979-94; Partner *Berwin Leighton* 1994.
Personal: Born 1950, educated at Oxford University (MA). Leisure interests include opera, collecting 78s, tennis and reading. Lives in Maidenhead.

BRETT, Alan K.
Hewitson Becke + Shaw, Cambridge (01223) 461155

BRIAM, Tony
Clifford Chance, London (020) 7600 1000
tony.briam@cliffordchance.com
Specialisation: Partner dealing with all aspects of commercial property work with particular emphasis on advising local authorities and developers in relation to city centre office and retail developments.
Career: Stratton School, Biggleswade; Clare College, Cambridge (MA). Articled *Boodle, Hatfield & Co*; qualified 1974; partner *Clifford Turner/ Clifford Chance* since 1981.
Personal: Born 1950.

BRICE, Barry
Pinsent Curtis, Birmingham (0121) 200 1050
barry.brice@pinsents.com
Partner
Specialisation: Specialises in property development and investment. Major projects in last 12 months include: development of site in Kidderminster as a retail park and its sale by way of forward funding; development and letting of business park at Stratford-upon-Avon; town centre retail development scheme at Stoke-on-Trent.
Career: St John's College, Oxford. Qualified in 1975 at *Pinsent Curtis* (then *Pinsent & Co*). Partner 1980. National head of property 1995.

BRISTOL, Jeremy
Birketts, Ipswich (01473) 232300

BROWN, Nicholas A.
CMS Cameron McKenna, London (020) 7367 3000
Partner and Manager of Property Group.
Specialisation: Handles property development and investment work for national and international property companies, institutions and retailers. Work includes acquisition and disposal of investment properties, acquisition funding and disposal of office and retail properties and development sites, and leases of all types of commercial property, both completed and in course of construction, and subsequent management of investments. Examples of matters handled are the development of Bristol Harbourside; development of supermarkets; the acquisition of a business park site for a 500,000 square foot head office development for an international company and the property aspects of the Channel Tunnel Rail Link.
Prof. Memberships: City of London Law Society, Land Law Committee/Investment Property Forum.
Career: Qualified in 1974. Became a Partner of *McKenna & Co* in 1980 and Head of the Property Group in 1991, Solicitor to the Leathersellers' Company.
Personal: Born 21st November 1949. Educated at Bristol University 1968-71.

BRYMER, Stewart
Thorntons WS, Dundee (01382) 229111

BUCKLEY, Liam
Hammond Suddards Edge, Manchester (0161) 830 5000
liam.buckley@hammondsuddardsedge.com
Partner - Commercial Property
Specialisation: Specialises in Commercial Property Finance and Development, Property Investment and Joint Ventures. Member of the firms Energy / Utilities Grouping dealing particularly with power station development. Recent transactions include the sale of Manchester Arndale Centre, acting for P & O Properties Limited.
Career: Articled *Last Suddards*; Qualified 1987. Partner *Hammond Suddards* 1994.
Personal: Born 1961. Resides Skipton. Enjoys golf and skiing. Member of Northcliffe Golf Club.

BURGESS, James C.A.
Pitmans, Reading (0118) 9580224
Specialisation: Considerable experience in commercial property matters, including acquisitions, sales, joint venture agreements, funding, investment and developments. He also has significant knowledge pertaining to residential development, land assembly and acquisition.
Prof. Memberships: Law Society.
Career: He qualified in 1982 and joined *Pitmans* in 1989.
Personal: Born 1957. Educated Radley College. Leisure interests: Tennis, skiing and fishing.

BUTLER, Alan J.
Simmons & Simmons, London (020) 7628 2020
Partner 1977. Property Department.
Specialisation: Broad-based commercial property practice with emphasis on bank and institutional funding, institutional investment and development financing transactions. Acts for banks, institutions and property companies in connection with property transactions. Clients past and present include NatWest Investment Bank, Security Pacific, Chase Manhattan, BNP, Swiss Bank Corporation, Banque Paribas, Mitsubishi Estate Company, DESPA, the Abu Dhabi Investment Authority, Land Securities, MEPC, Railtrack and some of the UK's largest property companies.
Prof. Memberships: Law Society.
Career: Qualified in 1973 while at *Simmons & Simmons* and became a Partner in 1977.
Personal: Born 26th April 1947. Attended St. Edmund Hall, Oxford 1966-69 Lives in Oxshott, Surrey.

CADDICK, Robert J.
Wragge & Co, Birmingham (0121) 214 1030
robert_caddick@wragge.com
Specialisation: Robert Caddick is one of the senior commercial property partners at Wragge & Co and has over 20 years' experience dealing in all kinds of commercial property development and investment. Robert's work for property developers and investors such as MEPC, Scudder Threadneedle Property Investments Limited, Castlemore Securities Limited and Norwich Union has involved him in some major schemes in the office and retail sectors. Robert specialises in property joint ventures and major development projects including partnerships between public and private sectors. He has particular experience of structuring joint ventures including the use of limited partnerships in property transactions. Recently examples include The Hampshire Centre, Bournemouth and The Clarendon Centre, Oxford.
Career: Articled *Wragge & Co*. Qualified 1975. Partner at *Wragge & Co* from 1981.
Personal: Born 1951.

CLARK, Paul E.
D J Freeman, London (020) 7583 4055
pec@djfreeman.co.uk
Partner, Senior Property Partner
Specialisation: Commercial property - especially landlord and tenant, shopping centres, development projects, limited partnerships. An advocate of plain English. Author of the leasebook - a new concept in leasing multi-let property. Lectures and writes, principally on landlord and tenant issues.
Prof. Memberships: Law Society, City of London Solicitors Company (member land law sub-committee), British Council of Shopping Centres, Anglo American Real Property Institute, committee member of Clarity.
Career: Qualified in 1970. *Rubinstein Nash & Co* 1968-72 *Linklaters & Paines* 1972-83. *DJ Freeman* 1984, Partner 1985, Head of Property 1990, Senior Property Partner 2000. UK member of European Board of DePfa-Bank. Commercial property adviser to the Oxford Institute of Legal Practice.

Personal: Born 18th March 1946. Educated at Bemrose Grammar School, Derby 1957-64. Manchester University 1964-67 (LLB Hons). Leisure pursuits include music, reading and the church. Lives in Hitchin.

COCKBURN, David
Archibald Campbell & Harley WS, Edinburgh (0131) 220 3000
Partner in Commercial Property Department.
Specialisation: Handles a full range of commercial property matters, including purchases, development, sales, leasing (for both landlords and tenants), funding and security work. Also advises on planning matters. Contributes book reviews and articles to Law Journal of Law Society of Scotland and Scottish Planning and Environmental Law. Regularly contributes by way of lectures to Law Society Update, Scottish Young Lawyers' Association, Surveyors' bodies and Edinburgh University.
Prof. Memberships: Society of Writers to HM Signet. Member of Law Society panel awarding accreditation.
Career: Qualified in 1966. Worked with Glasgow Corporation 1966-67, then *Breeze, Paterson & Chapman* 1967-70. Joined *Archibald Campbell & Harley WS* in 1970, becoming a Partner in 1971.
Personal: Born 4th February 1943. Attended Edinburgh University 1961-1964. Leisure pursuits include sport and reading.

COPLEY, Dean T.
Addleshaw Booth & Co, Leeds (0113) 209 2000
dnc@addleshaw-booth.co.uk
Specialisation: Adviser on all aspects of commercial property development including large office, retail and industrial schemes and urban regeneration projects. Acts for developers, funders and end users. Recent deals include; acting for developer on the major development for retail of a former gas works site in Humberside; acting for developer on 2 Objective One regeneration projects in South Yorkshire; acting for a leading Northern financial institution on the development of its members call centre.
Career: 1986-1988: Articles with *Wright & Wright*, Keighley; 1988-1994: Associate with *Simpson Curtis*, Leeds; 1994-1999: Partner with *Garretts*, Leeds; 1999 to date: Partner with *Addleshaw Booth & Co*, Leeds.
Personal: Plays drums and piano, married with 3 children, interests include snowboarding, photography and wine.

COWPER, Tony
Mills & Reeve, Cambridge (01223) 222 231
tony.cowper@mills-reeve.com
Specialisation: Partner with responsibility for commercial property and development and redevelopment issues.
Prof. Memberships: Law Society Member
Career: Director of a former residential property BES company. Acted in setting up one of the Cambridge Colleges. Client partner to some of the largest property owning educational institutions in the country. Responsible for setting up Cambridge Science Park and all subsequent legal work associated with it. Currently acting in connection with one further Science/ Business Park (including site set-up, subsequent lettings and sales), having recently sold another Park in its entirety. Recently acted as lead partner on the acquisition of 42 ground lease estates containing some 298 properties. Also acted in connection with what is believed to be the first forward funded PFI job in England.
Personal: Golf.

CRAVEN, Diana
Addleshaw Booth & Co, Manchester (0161) 934 6000
dmc@addleshaw-booth.co.uk
Partner in the Commercial Property Group.
Specialisation: Wide ranging commercial property interests but specifically including development schemes, land reclamation, property partnerships and joint ventures and funding agreements. Clients include Government agencies, plc developers, banks and companies with substantial property portfolios.
Prof. Memberships: Law Society, Association of Women Solicitors, Network.
Career: Joined firm in 1977 and became a Partner in 1981.
Personal: Interests include professional and managerial level womens groups, gardening and antiques.

CURRAN, John W.
Ledingham Chalmers, Aberdeen (01224) 408 563
john.curran@ledinghamchalmers.com
Senior Commercial Property Partner.
Specialisation: Advises listed and unlisted property companies on land acquisition, planning procedures and financing for residential and commercial property development. Accredited by The Law Society of Scotland as a specialist in Planning Law.
Career: Qualified 1975. With *Edmonds & Ledingham* 1972-1990 (Partner from 1977) and with merged firm *Ledingham Chalmers* since 1991.
Personal: Born 15th February 1951. Educated at Aberdeen Grammar School and Aberdeen University. Interests include football, squash, golf and reading.

DAKEYNE, Mark L.
Wragge & Co, Birmingham (0121) 214 1053
mark_dakeyne@wragge.com
Partner.
Specialisation: Commercial property development, particularly large retail/leisure schemes and, recently, telecoms switch centres.
Career: Articled in London and spent four years after qualification in 1983 with *Herbert Smith*. Joined *Wragge & Co* in 1987 and became a Partner in 1990. Head of Property Group and Property Development Group from 1993-2000.
Personal: Born 1958.

DALGARNO, Leslie S.
Paull & Williamsons, Aberdeen (01224) 621621
lsdalgarno@paull-williamsons.co.uk
Specialisation: Head of Commercial Property Department, advising private and public property companies and financial institutions on all aspects of property acquisition, development funding and disposal throughout the whole of Scotland. Acted on all aspects of the acquisition and planning and financial matters in relation to No.1 George Square, Glasgow, a major retail, leisure and lifestyle development in the city centre of Glasgow.
Prof. Memberships: Law Society of Scotland and member of Investment Property Forum.
Career: Graduated from Aberdeen University in 1971, LL.B. with Distinction. Joined Messrs. *Paull & Williamsons* as Trainee in 1971, becoming a Partner in the Commercial Property Department in 1977. Head of Department since 1986. Notary Public.
Personal: Born 19th March 1950. Educated at Robert Gordon's College and Aberdeen University. Leisure pursuits include golf and football. Lives in Aberdeen.

DAVIDSON, Timothy J.
Lyons Davidson, Bristol (0117) 904 6000
Partner in Property Department.
Specialisation: Principal area of practice is property development and investment work. Types of development include offices, retail, shopping centres, business and industrial parks and residential estates. Also handles general commercial conveyancing for a range of business clients and landlord and tenant work. Clients include developers, several local authorities, NHS Trusts and Further Education Colleges.
Prof. Memberships: Law Society, Bristol Law Society.
Career: Qualified in 1971. Partner at *Lyons Davidson* since 1972. Under-Sheriff of Bristol.
Personal: Born 27th June 1948. Educated at Downside School (to 1966). Lives in Bristol.

DAVIES, Andrew
Pitmans, Reading (0118) 9580224
Specialisation: Specialises in all aspects of commercial property, but in particular residential development; site acquisition by conditional contracts options; joint ventures with other residential developers. Clients include a number of publicly quoted residential developers.
Prof. Memberships: Law Society.
Career: Articles *Lovell White Durrant* and joined *Pitmans* in 1995.
Personal: Born in 1962. Educated Birkenhead School and Robinson College, Cambridge. Interests: cricket, rugby and golf. Married with 3 children.

DAVIES, Rowland
Edwards Geldard, Cardiff (029) 2023 8239
rowland.davies@geldard.co.uk
Partner in Commercial Property Department.
Specialisation: Work includes development work, urban regeneration, investment and acquisitions and disposals. Acted for the Cardiff Bay Barrage Scheme and undertook the land assembly and project development for the Millennium Stadium, Cardiff. Is a Consultant to Cardiff University Legal Practice Course.
Prof. Memberships: Law Society and Cardiff and District Law Society.
Career: Qualified in 1978. Joined *Edwards Geldard*, becoming a Partner 1981.
Personal: Born 27th August 1953. Attended Cardiff High School 1964-71 and Downing College, Cambridge 1972-5. Leisure interests include art, music, literature, cinema, theatre and gardening. Is a founder member of the Academy for Design in Wales and a Trustee of Ty Hafen Children's Hospice. Lives in Cardiff.

DAVIES JONES, Martin
Beachcroft Wansbroughs, Bristol (0117) 918 2000
modj@bwlaw.co.uk
Property
Specialisation: Specialist in property development work.
Career: Assistant solicitor *Herbert Smith* 1966-1968. Partner *Osborne Clarke* 1969-1988. Senior Partner *Crawford Owen* 1988-2000. Partner *Beachcroft Wansbroughs* 2000.

DEWAR, Mark A. M.
Harper Macleod, Glasgow (0141) 221 8888
mark.dewar@harpermacleod.co.uk
Specialisation: Commercial leasing, property investment and property development. Acted in purchase, redevelopment and ongoing letting of Princes Square Speciality Shopping Centre, Buchanan Street, Glasgow, development and letting of Stirling Thistle Marches Shopping Centre, Stirling, site acquisition and development of Glasgow Business Park; letting of major office development at 191 West George Street, Glasgow and acquisition and funding of redevelopment for retail purposes of former George Hotel site, Buchanan Street, Glasgow.
Prof. Memberships: Law Society of Scotland accredited Specialist in Commercial Leasing.
Career: Trained at *McGrigor Donald*, Glasgow; Associate *McGrigor Donald* 1989; Partner *Harper Macleod* 1996.
Personal: Born 1959. Educated at Marr College, Troon and University of Glasgow. Married; two children. Interests include golf, football and hillwalking. Lives in Troon.

DILLON, Paula
Addleshaw Booth & Co, Leeds (0113) 209 2000
pmd@addleshaw-booth.co.uk
Specialisation: Specialises in commercial property. Particularly well regarded for development and development finance, acting for developers, lenders, tenants and PFI participants. Recognised as a lawyer who will make deals happen. Skilled negotiator with ability to reconcile potentially conflicting interests.
Prof. Memberships: Law Society
Career: University of Manchester. Qualified 1986. Joined firm as partner in 1999.
Personal: Walking, cycling, skiing.

DOBIE, James A.
Shepherd & Wedderburn WS, Edinburgh (0131) 228 9900
james.dobie@shepwedd.co.uk
Specialisation: Property Development and institutional investment with particular emphasis on retail developments. Acted for Freeport Leisure plc in development of first factory outlet centre in Scotland, and for Pillar Property plc in retail park developments. Acted for New Edinburgh Limited on a number of lettings and onward sales at Edinburgh Park and for the University of Edinburgh in major land sales. Also involved in specialist telecommunication property acquisitions for Orange plc.
Prof. Memberships: Law Society of Scotland. Writer to the Signet.
Career: Educated at Edinburgh University. Joined *Shepherd & Wedderburn WS* 1988 as trainee, became partner in 1995.
Personal: Born 14/08/64. Leisure interests: football, literature, wine and East African culture.

DORAN, Iain A.
Dundas & Wilson CS, Glasgow (0141) 222 2200

DUNN, John
Burges Salmon, Bristol (0117) 939 2256
john.dunn@burges-salmon.com
Specialisation: Widely experienced in complex commercial property transactions including portfolio management, development and funding.
Prof. Memberships: Law Society.
Career: Joined *Burges Salmon* in 1988 becoming a Partner in 1989.

ELLIOTT, Martin
Linklaters (A member firm of Linklaters & Alliance), London (020) 7456 4722
Martin.elliott@linklaters.com
Specialisation: Partner and specialist with over 20 years' experience in all aspects of commercial property work with particular emphasis on development, investment and financing work. Transactions involving retail and leisure developments, offices, shops, warehouses and industrial premises, acting for property companies, funds and end-users on sales, purchases, lettings, developments, rent reviews and joint ventures.

EVANS, Eric
Eversheds, Cardiff (02920) 471147
Partner in commercial property department and head of both the planning and PFI units.
Specialisation: Specialises in all aspects of property law including complex planning obligations, major town centre regeneration/shopping schemes, site assembly, agreements for the construction of major highways associated with developments, public/private sector joint ventures, planning gain, valuations, urban development/regeneration grants and land reclamation. 30 years public sector experience, dealing with all areas of local government. Extensive experience of PFI and led one of the first PFI/PPP deals in Wales, at University Hospital of Wales NHS Trust. Has since advised on numerous deals including Newport Southern Distributor Road, Chepstow Community Hospital, Wiltshire's grouped schools scheme and "Waste to Energy" scheme at Neath.
Prof. Memberships: Member of Law Society's Planning Panel.
Career: Qualified in 1980. Town Clerk, Borough of Blaenau Gwent (1981-89). Deputy Chief Executive and Legal Adviser, Land Authority for Wales (1989-92). Partner *Eversheds* 1992.
Personal: Director of Silent Valley Waste Services. Lives in Abertillery.

FARIS, Neil C.
Cleaver Fulton Rankin, Belfast (028) 9024 3141
n.faris@cfrlawonline.com
Specialisation: A major area of practice is advisory and transactional work for local authorities and a wide range of public bodies.
Prof. Memberships: Council Member of UKELA, Council Member for Irish Centre for European Law. Member Competition Working Party.
Career: Qualified in 1977 and Managing Partner and Head of Consultancy Department.
Personal: Born 1950, educated in Belfast and at Trinity College Dublin and University of Cambridge.

FIELD, Christopher M.
Macfarlanes, London (020) 7831 9222
cmf@macfarlanes.com
Specialisation: Specialises in property law, with particular emphasis on property development and property financing. Practice includes: property investment for domestic and international investors; retail development both in and out of town centres; business park developments; construction projects; development and financing of property in Enterprise Zones; joint ventures. Recent significant work: acting for London Bridge Holdings in the development and letting of the GLA building at London Bridge, and Legal and General's Investment Property Fund in the purchase of a portfolio of industrial estates forming part of P&O's recent portfolio sale to Green Property.
Prof. Memberships: City of London Law Society.
Career: Graduated with a law degree from Magdalen College, Oxford in 1974 and joined Macfarlanes in 1975. Became a partner in 1981. In 1995 became head of the firm's property department.
Personal: Golf.

FINCH, Robert
Linklaters (A member firm of Linklaters & Alliance), London (020) 7456 4722
robert.finch@linklaters.com
Specialisation: Partner of real estate department; experienced in all aspects of commercial property transactions, including acquisition, development, funding, leasing and disposal of City, Regional and International properties. Also involved in development sector and/or investment property transactions in the USA, Middle East and Europe.
Career: Assistant solicitor *Linklaters* 1969-73; partner 1974 - present
Personal: Educated Felsted School Essex. Born 1944.

FITZMAURICE, Anthony
Cobbetts, Manchester (0161) 833 3333
tony.fitzmaurice@cobbetts.co.uk
Specialisation: Specialist in property (commercial, landlord and tenant, development/investment construction (non-contentious).
Career: Articled *Sydney Mitchell & Co* Birmingham; *Bromley Hyde & Robinson*, Ashton-Under-Lyne; qualified 1984. Education - De La Salle College; Birmingham University (LLB Hons); Trent Polytechnic.
Personal: Born 1958; resides Prestwich. Leisure - children, golf, skiing, tennis.

FLOUNDERS, Andrew J.
Read Hind Stewart, Leeds (0113) 246 8123
Specialisation: Head of Commercial Property Department. Extensive experience in major out of town industrial retail and leisure schemes including financing and joint venture arrangements. Acts primarily for developers. Emphasis on Constructive Commercial approach.
Prof. Memberships: Law Society.
Career: Educated - Benton Park Grammer School and Manchester University.Qualified - *Read Hind Stewart*1983 and Partner since 1984.
Personal: Born 1958. Resides Bramhope. Keen sports spectator and plays 5-a-side football. Leisure interests include family, cinema, theatre and Round Table.

FOGEL, Steven
Dechert, London (020) 7583 5353
advice@dechertEU.com
London Managing Partner and member of the Property Department. Leader of the firm's Property Industry Group.
Specialisation: Advises UK and non-UK organisations on all property, and landlord and tenant matters, especially advising on the structure of property transactions and, in particular, preparing complex funding and rent review provisions. Active mainly in the private sector for owner and occupiers but also in the public sector.
Prof. Memberships: Director Investment Property Forum, member British Council of Shopping Centres; Anglo-American Real Property Institute; Lambda Alpha International; associate member of Chartered Institute of Arbitrators, member of Board of Advisers, the Centre of Property Law, University of

Reading (1997), Fellow of Institute of Continuing Professional Development
Career: *Cohen & Meyohas*, Paris 1973-74; Qualified 1976; articled *Titmuss Sainer & Webb (now Dechert)* 1974-76; partner 1980; Head of Property Department 1990-98; Senior Partner (1998), London Managing Partner (2000), Blundell law lecturer, 1985 and 1996; member of Law Commission Working Party on PACT (Property Arbitration on Court Terms) Landlord and Tenant-LCWP 95 HMSO, 1985-86; member Joint Working Party of Law Society and RICS on commercial leases; legal adviser to Property Committee of British Retail Consortium and acted for them in the passage through parliament of the Landlord & Tenant (Covenants) Act 1995; member of RICS Commercial Property Panel; member British Property Federation Customer Focus Working Party; director of Spiro Institute (1992-); trustee "Motivation" wheelchair charity (1992-). Treasurer and now non-voting governor of Anglo American Real Property Institute. Co-author several books on Landlord & Tenant.
Personal: Born 1951. Educated at Carmel College and King's College London; LLB (Hons) Hickling prize 1972; LLM 1973; ACI Arb 1991; Leisure activities - Jazz, cycling, skiing, cinema and creative writing. Married to Joan, they have three children, Frances, George and Jonathan. Lives in London.

FOSTER, John
Eversheds, Leeds (0113) 243 0391
johnfoster@eversheds.com
Head of Property in Leeds. Leader of Development Team.
Specialisation: Property Development of all types to include site assembly, construction, pre-letting, funding and investment sales and participation or profit sharing arrangments. Enterprise Zones work, public and private sector partnerships, grants and PFI.
Prof. Memberships: Law Society.
Career: MA Oxford. Articles with *Macfarlanes*. 1983 joined *Eversheds* becoming a partner in 1985.
Personal: Interests - Munros.

GAIT, Charles
Osborne Clarke OWA, Bristol (0117) 917 3366
charles.gait@osborneclarke.com
Specialisation: Partner specialising in commercial property development and development finance and acts for a range of public and private property companies, developers, pension funds and other institutions with substantial experience of office, retail, leisure, industrial and distribution schemes. Recent work includes: acting jointly for British Airways Pension Fund and Henderson Investors on their funding and acquisition of the 350,000 sq. ft. Printworks Leisure Scheme in Manchester; acting for Wilson Bowden Developments Limited on the sale of the newly developed White Lion Retail Park in Dunstable to F`rs‰kringsbolaget SPP, ˆmsesidigt (known as SPP), and its investment managers Celexa REIM for £25.5 million.
Career: Articled *Cameron McKenna* (formerly McKenna & Co); qualified 1980; solicitor 1980-1985; partner 1985-1999; partner *Osborne Clarke* 1999; lecturer, speaker and trainer in property law.

GARRETT, Robin J.
Maclay Murray & Spens, Glasgow
(0141) 248 5011
rjg@maclaymurrayspens.co.uk
Partner in Commercial Property Department.
Specialisation: Main area of practice is development work for developers and occupiers, including site assembly, planning, letting and disposals. Also handles general acquisitions, including freehold purchases and assignations of leases. Has lectured and led groups at various seminars.
Prof. Memberships: Writer to the Signet.
Career: Qualified in 1983. Previously partner with *Steedman Ramage*. Joined *Maclay Murray & Spens* 1997.
Personal: Born 2nd April 1959.

GATES, Kathryn
Edwards Geldard, Cardiff (029) 2023 8239
kathryn.gates@geldards.co.uk
Specialisation: Partner in Commercial Property Department. Work includes, broad range of Commercial development and leisure, investment portfolio and housing land acqusitions on behalf of public and private sectors.
Prof. Memberships: Law Society and Cardiff and District Law Society. Women in Property. Cardiff Business Forum.
Career: Qualified in 1987. Joined *Edwards Geldard* in 1995 and became a Partner in 1999.
Personal: Interests include travelling, walking and rugby. Property advisor to Prince's Youth Business Trust.

GEORGE, James P.
Freshfields Bruckhaus Deringer, London (020) 7936 4000
Specialisation: Handles all aspects of commercial property, with special emphasis on commercial property in a corporate context and large-scale property finance transactions. Recent highlights: acting for Pelham Partners/ Apollo Fund/ Portfolio Holdings in connection with various transactions, including the acquisition of the Oldham Estate portfolio for MEPC, acting for PowerGen UK plc on various matters, including power station disposals and for Goldman Sachs' Whitehall Street Real Estate Fund, and its investment vehicles such as Trillium, on various matters e.g. Project PRIME and Project STEPS.
Prof. Memberships: Bucks, Berks and Oxon Law Society and City of London Law Society.
Career: Worked as surveyor from 1973 to 1980. Qualified as solicitor 1984. Joined Freshfields in 1988, becoming a partner in 1991.
Personal: Born 4 April 1952. Educated at Whitgift 1962-1970. Reading University (Faculty of Urban and Regional Studies) 1970-1973 (B.Sc. in Estate Management), CPE at Chancery Lane College of Law 1980-1981 and law finals at Guildford College of Law 1981-1982. Leisure activities: music, motoring/motor racing and photography. Married to Lill since 1977, with two boys, Flemming and Christian. Live in Beaconsfield.

GIBBS, Robert
Eversheds, Ipswich (01473) 284428
robertgibbs@eversheds.com
Specialisation: Property development (residential and commercial), investment and portfolio management. Acts for Stock Exchange quoted and non-quoted businesses. Considerable care home sector experience.
Prof. Memberships: Law Society.
Career: Trained in London before moving to East Anglia.
Personal: Upper Second Llb Honours Degree (Leeds). Plays tennis, golf and squash. Married with two children.

GIDNEY, David
Burges Salmon, Bristol (0117) 902 2750
david.gidney@burges-salmon.com
Specialisation: Head of Property Department Unit acting for developers, public sector bodies and landowners. Also specialises in Property Investment. Recent or current transactions include:- Acting for Honda on new headquarter offices near Heathrow. Acting for Dutch fund PVF on sale of West End Offices for c£35M. Acting for Shearer Property Group and Deutsche Asset Management on retail scheme in Chelmsford. Acting for Rugby Estates plc on retail warehouse scheme in Salisbury.
Prof. Memberships: Member of British Property Federation and Investment Property Forum. On Committee of South West and Wales Chapter of British Council for Offices.
Career: Where trained: *Rowe & Maw*. Year Qualified: 1977. Year made partner at *Burges Salmon*: 1998.
Personal: First Class Honours in Literae Humaniores, Oxford. Born 1952. Resides Bristol. Married with 4 children. Enjoys tennis, theatre.

GILLERY, Bryan
Eversheds, Norwich (01603) 272727
Specialisation: Site acquisitions, funding, property and development work.
Prof. Memberships: Law Society, Cambridgeshire Forum for the construction industry.
Career: Admitted April 1976. Joined *Eversheds* 1976. Became a partner in 1979.

GNIADKOWSKI, Stan
Denton Wilde Sapte, London (020) 7242 1212
Specialisation: Specialises in property and project development work. As a necessary adjunct to that practice, also advises on non-contentious construction law matters. Usually acting for developers, land owners or institutions, his practice covers all development related matters including rights of light, adjoining owners' issues and pre-let agreements. Stan leads the team that advises City & West End, a company which since March 1998 has established a £500m portfolio in Central London. Highlights include the structured acquisition in collaboration with Citibank of Milton Gate in the City, the disposal of Cleveland House St James's Square and the letting of the whole of City & West End's new development at South Street in Mayfair within a month of practical completion. Advised Asticus on the acquisition of a long leasehold interest and development agreement relating to 29 Gresham Street London EC2 for a new 120,000 square foot office development. Advising quoted property company, Grainger Trust, on a number of development related acquisitions.
Prof. Memberships: British Council for Offices, Investment Property Forum.
Career: After Articles in local government followed by a year with a development corporation, joined the legal department of *John Laing PLC* with whom he worked from 1984 to 1987. Joining City solicitors, *D J Freeman*, in 1987 he became a partner the following year and played a significant part in the development of *D J Freeman*'s property practice. In January 1997, left *D J Freeman* to become a senior equity partner at

Wilde Sapte where he continues to advise on major property and project development matters.
Personal: Single. Interests include photography, motor racing (watching not participating) and the cinema.

GOODMAN, Stephen L.
Halliwell Landau, Manchester (0161) 835 3003
Specialisation: Head of Property Department. Stephen is particularly active in development transactions and advises on the structure of property transactions, including land assembly, development agreements, funding arrangements, joint ventures and statutory agreements.
Career: Articled *Bennett & Co*; qualified 1985; Assistant *Nabarro Nathanson* 1986 - 1989; Partner *Gorna & Co*; Partner *Halliwell Landau* 1993.
Personal: Born 1961. Resides Cheshire. Keen golfer and Evertonian.

GRABINER, Martin
Nabarro Nathanson, Sheffield (0114) 279 4261
m.grabiner@nabarro.com
Specialisation: All types of commercial property work with emphasis on development and joint venture arrangements involving both the private and public sector. Retail portfolio acquisition and disposal and financing arrangements. Also commercial property and commercial work in relation to infrastructure and transport (in particular canals and railways).
Prof. Memberships: Director of The Wakefield Metropolitan Festival Co Ltd.
Career: 1984-86 First In-house Solicitor for the Wickes Group of Companies, London. 1986-88 Partner - *Boodle Hatfield*, London. 1989-98 Partner - *Dibb Lupton Broomhead* and *Dibb Lupton Alsop*, Leeds. 1998-date Partner *Nabarro Nathanson*, Sheffield. Education: St Paul's School, London; Trinity College, Cambridge (MA).
Personal: Born 1953; resides North Yorkshire. Married with five children. Leisure: Member of the Leeds Library.

GRIFFITHS, Keith M.
Brodies WS, Edinburgh (0131) 228 3777
kmgriffithiths@brodies.co.uk
Specialisation: Commercial Property partner with particular emphasis on advising national multiple retailers on their Scottish property portfolios.
Career: Qualified 1979. Employed at *W & J Burness* 1977-1982; joined *Steedman Ramage* in 1982, Partner 1984-1996; joined *Brodies* as a Partner in 1996.
Personal: Born 1956. Interests include hillwalking, hockey, golf and theatre.

GUNN, David J.
Bond Pearce, Exeter (01392) 211185
xdjg@bondpearce.com
Partner and head of the Commercial Property Group.
Specialisation: Has specialised in Commercial Property work since qualifying dealing with development, investment and funding including joint ventures and major project management. Has a particular interest in waste management, acting for a number of waste disposal companies in connnection with site acquisition/disposal and management issues including gas extraction and electricity generation. As a french speaker has worked on property and other commercial transactions involving french companies and organisations.
Prof. Memberships: Member of the Law Society, Association Des Juristes Franco-Britanniques.
Career: Qualified in 1982. Joined *Bond Pearce* in 1980, becoming partner in 1987.

HAMILTON, Christine A.
Elliott Duffy Garrett, Belfast (028) 9024 5034

HAMILTON, Keith
Eversheds, Norwich (01603) 272727
Specialisation: Landlord and tenant, investment acquisitions and development work.
Prof. Memberships: Law Society.
Career: Admitted June 1978. Read Jurisprudence at Oxford. Spent several years with *Slaughter and May* in London before joining *Eversheds* in 1982. Became a partner in 1985.

HAMILTON, Sophie C.
Forsters, London (020) 7863 8333
Specialisation: Broad based commercial property practice including acquisition and funding (clients include Clerical Medical); acting for occupiers on major relocations (this year including Elsevier Science to Theobalds Court); leisure (including Multiplex cinemas for Warner Village); shopping centres (Delancey Estates plc and Clerical Medical); institutional work (solicitor to the Goldsmith's Company); private trusts and residential developers.
Career: Educated St Mary's School, Calne; Marlborough College; Clare College, Cambridge. Qualified 1979; partner 1985; head of property dept 1991-1994 (all at *Frere Cholmeley Bischoff*); founding partner of *Forsters* 1998.
Personal: Married, lives in London, enjoys theatre, cinema, reading and cooking.

HANIFORD, Paul S.
Semple Fraser WS, Glasgow (0141) 221 3771
psh@semplefraser.co.uk
Fax: (0141) 221 3776/3859
Specialisation: Property investment and development; also landlord and tenant work customarily offering advice to a non-Scottish client base.
Prof. Memberships: Society of Writers to HM Signet, Law Society of Scotland.
Career: Articled *Fyfe Ireland & Co WS* 1978-1980; legal assistant *Moncrieff Warren Paterson* 1980-81; legal assistant *Bird Semple* 1981-83; partner 1983-90; founding partner *Semple Fraser* 1990. Member: President's Committee, Glasgow & Renrewshire Branch of British Red Cross.
Personal: Born 26 November 1955. Educated at Glasgow Academy and Glasgow University (MA-LL.B). Interests include skiing, squash, tennis and travel. Lives in Glasgow.

HARRISON, Christopher H.
Herbert Smith, London (020) 7374 8000
Specialisation: Institutional property investment. The sale of the Ministry of Defence Married Quarters Estate. The redevelopment of the Brent Cross Shopping Centre. The proposed re-development of Kings Cross on behalf of London & Continental Railways. The Ministry of Defence Main Building Redevelopment (PFI). Former member of the Law Society Land Law Committee (led the Law Society's response to the DETR Commercial Lease Best Practice guide).
Career: Harrow School. Articled *Halliley & Morrison*. Joined *Herbert Smith* 1969.
Personal: Cricket, walking (preferably with dog), being with family, Philippa, Oliver and Claudia.

HELLER, Laurie
Berwin Leighton, London (020) 7760 1000
Partner in Commercial Property Department.
Specialisation: Main area of practice is general commercial property with special emphasis on property development, forward funding and joint venture arrangements. Also handles general commercial law. Recent matters have included the acquisition, development and letting of the Royal Bank of Canada Centre, Queen Victoria Street EC4; the acquisition and other aspects of the refurbishment of 99 City Road, London EC1 for Inmarsat, acting for Development Securities PLC on the development of Shire House and Milton House, Silk Street, London EC2 and acting for Legal & General Assurance on its acquisition of Breakspear Park, Hemel Hempstead and its investment in the Arlington Securities Group. Clients include PDFM Ltd, St. Martins Property Corporation Ltd, Prudential Assurance Co. Ltd, Legal & General Assurance and the Royal Bank of Canada. Editor of and contributor to Sweet & Maxwell's 'Practical Commercial Precedents' and 'Commercial Property Development Precedents'. Frequent contributor to *The Estates Gazette* and other property based journals. Regular contributor to BBC Select/ Legal Network Television. Charge-out rate is £260.00 per hour.
Prof. Memberships: City of London Law Society Property Sub-Committee.
Career: Qualified in 1959. At *Titmuss Sainer & Webb* 1959-63 (Partner from 1962. Partner at *Leighton & Co* 1963-70. Founder and Senior Partner of *Berwin Leighton* from 1980.
Personal: Born 14th April 1934. Educated at Battersea Grammar School 1945-52 and Sidney Sussex College, Cambridge 1953-56 (Legal Tripos, 1st Class Hons). Leisure activities include reading, writing and pontificating as well as skiing and gardening. Lives in London.

HENDERSON, Brian L.
L'Estrange & Brett, Belfast (028) 9023 0426
See under Banking, p.118

HENSON, Michaela
Taylor Vinters, Cambridge (01223) 423444
mjh@taylorvinters.com
Specialisation: Commercial acquisitions, sales and lettings. Property development and investments. Corporate support work. Clients include property developers, educational establishments, high-technology businesses and a major airline. Current projects include development of a new Cambridge Technology Park.
Prof. Memberships: Law Society
Career: Qualified in 1995 with London firm *Baileys Shaw & Gillett*. Joined *Taylor Vinters* in 1997. Currently a senior solicitor with *Taylor Vinters*. Specialist diploma in planning and environmental Law in 1998.
Personal: Born 1970. Educated at Hinchingbrook School, Huntingdon and New Hall College, Cambridge. Interests include sports and horses.

HEPPEL, Meg E.M.
Eversheds, Birmingham (0121) 232 1000
Specialisation: Retail investment for clients including Grosvenor Investments and Hammerson and portfolio management for occupiers including Bass, Focus Do It All, Ryland, Partco Group and Jessops. Lead partner for the Birmingham Alliance's New Bull Ring and Martineau Galleries Scheme in Birmingham.

Career: Joined *Eversheds* in 1979. Partner 1989. Head of Property Department 1997. Managing Partner 2000.
Personal: Born 1957

HEWITT, V. Alan
L'Estrange & Brett, Belfast (028) 9023 0426
Senior Partner and Head of Commercial Property Department.
Specialisation: Main areas of work: Commercial Property and Trusts.
Prof. Memberships: Law Society of Northern Ireland. (Council Member 1991-; Chairman, Professional Indemnity Insurance Committee 1995-97; Chairman, Professional Conduct Committee, 1997- 99); Chairman, Financial Services Committee 1999-2000. Law Reform Advisory Committee for Northern Ireland. International Bar Association.
Career: Qualified 1967. Partner in *L'Estrange & Brett* since 1969. Senior Partner since 1994.
Personal: Born 1941. Education: Queen's University, Belfast (L.L.B.), University of Michigan (L.L.M.).

HODGE, James (Hamish) S.
Dundas & Wilson CS, Edinburgh (0131) 228 8000

HOWARTH, Mark H.
Paris Smith & Randall, Southampton (023) 8048 2482
Specialisation: All aspects of commercial property work. Including portfolio management for large investors, landlord and tenant work, site acquisition and disposal, sales and lease backs, creation and implementation of lease schemes in respect of development sites and subsequent management thereof, Statutory Agreements, development work. Work includes transactions relating to golf course and other leisure related activities.Clients include public authorities, large commercial organisations, friendly societies, retailers, substantial investors (both corporate and private).
Prof. Memberships: Law Society.
Career: Joined Paris Smith & Randall in 1979, qualifying in 1981. Became a Partner in 1985 and has been Head of the Commercial Property Department since 1993.
Personal: Attended Southampton University. In his free time enjoys sport, reading and spending time with his family.

HUBBARD, Penny
Mills & Reeve, Cambridge (01223) 222462
penny.hubbard@mills-reeve.com
Specialisation: Has a wide general property experience with particular expertise on the negotiation and agreement of documentation for development schemes. Recent work includes acting for Amresco Inc in relation to the scale of its £102m loan portfolio, acting for the developer in the joint venture documentation for the development of a 44 acre business park and dealing with the loan documentation and security required by institutions and banks lending on property development.
Publications: Author of 'Securitisation and Unitisation of Real Estate Worldwide' published by Legal Studies and Service Limited 1988.
Career: 1984-1994, Solicitor and then Partner, *Macfarlans* London. 1995 to date, Solicitor, *Mills & Reeve.*

HUTTON, Robert D.
Mills & Reeve, Norwich (01603) 693218
robert.hutton@mills-reeve.com
Specialisation: Commercial Property.
Prof. Memberships: Law Society
Career: Articled *Clifford Chance*. Qualified 1977. Joined *Mills & Reeve* 1981. Partner *Mills & Reeve* 1985.
Personal: Educated St Dunstan's College, London; Magdalen College, Oxford. Married, 2 children.

INNES, Richard
Walker Morris, Leeds (0113) 283 2500
rhi@walkermorris.co.uk
Specialisation: Retail property with emphasis on acting for anchor tenants and supermarkets.
Career: Qualified 1984. Partner *Walker Morris* since 1987.
Personal: Music and awaiting the day that both children will sleep through the night.

IVIN, Alison
Palser Grossman, Cardiff Bay (029) 2045 2770
Specialisation: All aspects of commercial property with particular experience in development, option agreements, property joint ventures, landlord and tenant including premier office leases and portfolio acquisitions and disposals including acting for Grosvenor Waterside (the development arm of Associated British Ports) in the Lease to W M Morrison Supermarkets plc of the first Morrison store in Wales and acting for various consortia of house builders in collaboration agreements to promote strategic land to include a new settlement.
Prof. Memberships: Law Society.
Career: Joined *Palser Grossman* 1996; became a partner in 1997. Land Authority for Wales 1988-96. Deputy Legal Adviser from 1993. Legal Officer Gwent County Council 1982-88.
Personal: Travel, art, countryside.

JACKSON, Karl
Mace & Jones, Manchester (0161) 236 2244
Specialisation: Broad range of commercial property work with increasing emphasis on commercial property development and in particular urban regeneration projects in Manchester and Liverpool. Established Land Resources Alliance to advise on redevelopment of contaminated land. Lectured widely.
Prof. Memberships: Law Society.
Career: Qualified in 1989 with *Vaudrey Osborne & Mellor*. Joined *Mace & Jones* in 1997. Partner since 1998.
Publications: Various published articles.
Personal: Born 1964. Married: 1 daughter. Lives in Hale, Cheshire. Leisure pursuits: cinema and visual arts, running, sport and theatre. Trustee of Cornerhouse Arts Centre.

JAMES, Robert W.
Morgan Cole, Cardiff (029) 2038 5385
robert.james@morgan-cole.com
Specialisation: Principle area of practice is large scale public and private development work. Advising on joint ventures, disposals for administrative receivers, secured lending, licensed trade (brewing) leases and construction contracts.
Prof. Memberships: One of the first accredited mediators under the Law Society/ RICS PACE scheme for the renewal of business leases.
Career: Qualified 1978.
Personal: Born 8th August, 1953. Educated Wrekin College Wellington and Jesus College Oxford. Spare time pursuits include: Rugby, Cricket and Theatre. *Morgan Cole* liaison partner for the Association of European Lawyers.

JOHNSON, Jennifer D.
Maclay Murray & Spens, Edinburgh (0131) 226 5196
jdj@maclaymurrayspens.co.uk
Specialisation: Head of commercial property department. Practice covers all areas of commercial property including property development, funding and investment security work and leasing. Has particular experience in cross border property portfolios and the acquisition, letting and sale of shopping centres.
Prof. Memberships: Writer to the Signet and Notary Public.
Career: Edinburgh University. Qualified 1979. Partner in *Maclay Murray & Spens* in 1988.

JONES, Chris
Berry Smith, Cardiff (029) 2034 5511
Specialisation: Full range of commercial property work; investment, commercial and residential development; landlord and tenant and secured lending.
Prof. Memberships: Law Society.
Career: Qualified in 1992. Articled in *Eversheds*, Cardiff. Joined *Berry Smith* in 1994 and became a partner in 1996. Welsh speaker, born 30.12.66. Educated at University College Wales, Aberystwyth and Guildford College of Law.
Personal: Rugby and travel.

JONES, Elizabeth J.
Hewitson Becke + Shaw, Cambridge (01223) 461155

JONES, Nefydd
Eversheds, Cardiff (02920) 471147
nefyddjones@eversheds.com
Specialisation: Deals with all aspects of commercial property investment, development and funding inculding landlord and tenant work. Significant recent experiance includes a major office and leisure refurbishment scheme, a retail development involving a joint venture, a shopping centre redevelopment and disposal, a rail-related development transaction and several significant joint ventures involving public bodies.
Prof. Memberships: The Law Society.
Career: Qualified in 1985. *Berwin Leighton* 1988-1995. Partner *Eversheds* 1999.
Personal: Born 1961. Married with 2 daughters. Reluctant gardener; keen reader; motor racing fan; social golfer.

JONES, Pamela
Bullivant Jones, Liverpool (0151) 227 5671
Senior Partner in Commercial Property Department.
Specialisation: Deals in all aspects of Commercial Property especially in development schemes and agreements, retail property for occupiers and as investment and Landlord & Tenant.
Prof. Memberships: Law Society.
Career: Qualified in 1977. Joined *Bullivant Jones* in 1973, becoming a Partner in 1978 and Senior Partner in 1994.
Personal: Born 7th January 1951. Attended Holyhead Comprehensive 1962-68. Leisure interests include reading, gardening and walking her dogs. Lives near Tarporley, Cheshire.

KERSHAW, Peter J.
Addleshaw Booth & Co, Manchester (0161) 934 6000
pjk@addleshaw-booth.co.uk
Partner in Commercial Property.

Specialisation: Specialising in mainstream commercial property with emphasis on development work.
Prof. Memberships: Law Society.
Career: Qualified 1989. Partner 1996. External Examiner for the Law Society.
Personal: Leisure: Family time and mountain biking.

KIDBY, Robert J.
Lovells, London (020) 7296 2000
robert.kidby@lovells.com
Specialisation: Property related financing, PFI, secured lending, institutional sales/ purchases/ management, property joint ventures and development projects including shopping centres, offices, airports and hotels. Has lectured extensively on property development and property investment to audiences in England, Europe and Japan.
Career: Qualified as a solicitor in 1977 and has specialised in commercial property work ever since. Partner 1985 at *Lovells*. Head of Property since 1995.

KING, Stuart
Veale Wasbrough, Bristol (0117) 939 2274
Specialisation: Commercial property. Has extensive experience in a broad range of commercial property transactions including property investment, development and insolvency.
Prof. Memberships: Member of the Investment Property Forum and International Real Estate Association.
Career: Qualified in 1984, joined *Burges Salmon* in 1986 and became a partner in 1989. Moved to *Veale Wasbrough* as a partner in 2000.

KINNIBURGH, Linda M.
Brodies WS, Edinburgh (0131) 228 3777
lmkinniburgh@brodies.co.uk
Commercial Property Department Partner
Specialisation: Linda Kinniburgh was educated at Trinity Academy, Edinburgh and the University of Edinburgh. She qualified as a solicitor in 1982 and has been a partner in *Brodies* since 1985. She is involved in property investment and banking work, and has particular experience in cross border corporate finance deals. She also deals with property aspects of insolvency and coal and mineral exploitation law and has recently acted in the large scale disposals of public sector housing.
Personal: She is married with 2 young children and spends such spare time as she has going to the theatre and the opera. She would like to find more time to pursue her recent interest in micro-liting.

KORDAN, Joel
Lee Crowder, Birmingham (0121) 236 4477
joel.kordan@leecrowder.co.uk
Specialisation: All areas of commercial property development including lettings, sales, funding and joint venture agreements, with particular emphasis on largescale industrial distribution/warehouse/factory schemes. Also, large residential property development practice. Clients include developers, contractors and end users, including many multinational companies.
Career: Articled *Wragge & Co.* Qualified 1990. Joined *Lee Crowder* as a partner in 1997.
Personal: Born 1961, USA. Attended King Edward VI Five Ways Grammer School, Birmingham and LSE (B.Sc. (Econ)).

KUSTOW, David
Olswang, London (020) 7208 8888
Specialisation: All aspects of commercial property law - investment, development retail centre and funding transactions. Acts for a variety of quoted and unquoted property companies, including large private investment vehicles and property based funds. Also serves the property requirements of various companies in the advertising and media sectors, particularly those involved in film, satellite and cable. Notable transactions recently undertaken include a single investment property disposal for a consideration of £105 million, the property aspects of a re-organisation of assets with values exceeding £200 million, the property aspects of a flotatation and the acquistition of a number of investment/ development properties for a single client, over a 12 month period, for an aggregate consideration exceeding £150 million.
Prof. Memberships: A member of the International Real Estate Federation (FIABCI); a Governor of the British Film Institute and chair of their Property Committee.
Career: Admitted 1973; 1970-91 - *Brecher &Co* (Partner since 1975); 1991-2000 - *Olswang* (Partner Property Group).
Personal: Married with two children. Principal leisure interests include reading (particularly modern history), travel, films and music.

LAKE, Tim
Stepien Lake Gilbert & Paling, London (020) 7655 0000
Partner.
Specialisation: Large scale development work (commercial and residential) including joint venture and consortia arrangements with all attendant property finance issues. Acts for listed and unlisted developers and equity investors.
Career: Qualified December 1980. Set up own practice in 1985 and subsequently merged his practice with *Birkbeck Montagu's.* A founding partner of *Stepien Lake Gilbert & Paling* in 1991.
Personal: Born December 1955. Educated Radley and Exeter University. Interests include shooting, tennis, golf and skiing. Lives in Oxfordshire.

LANDER, Geoffrey
Nabarro Nathanson, London (020) 7524 6254
g.lander@nabarro.com
Partner
Specialisation: Acts for corporate occupiers (Chase Manhattan Bank, JP Morgan and HSBC), investors (Hanover Property Unit Trust and BBC Pension Trust Limited) and property companies (Capital & Counties plc). Conference speaker. Published a number of articles. Chargeout rate £415 per hour.
Prof. Memberships: Past President of the British Council for Offices. Chairman of the European Advisory Board Board of NACORE and member of the Board of the UK Chapter. Board Member of the American Chamber of Commerce.

LE PARD, Geoffrey
Freshfields Bruckhaus Deringer, London (020) 7936 4000
Specialisation: Handles all aspects of commercial property including landlord and tenant, investment, development, planning and finance.
Career: Qualified in 1981. Joined *Freshfields* in 1981, becoming a partner in 1987. Head of property department from 1993 to 2000.

Personal: Born 30th November 1956. Attended Purley Grammar School 1968-70, Brockenhurst Grammar School 1970-75, Bristol University 1975-78 and Guildford College of Law 1978-79. Lives In Dulwich.

LEITCH, David A.
Johns Elliot, Belfast (028) 9032 6881

LEONARD, Tessa
Eversheds, Manchester (0161) 832 6666
tessaleonard@eversheds.com
Specialisation: Commercial development in particular business parks and leisure schemes handling both development and disposal. Also specialises in development agreements and joint ventures between the public and private sector. Recent public sector projects include: acting for English Partnerships in providing funding to revitalise Manchester City Centre after the 1996 IRA bomb and for the North West Development Agency inrelation to a proposed strategic business park in Rochdale. Recent/current private sector projects include: acting for AMEC Developments in relation to investment sales and lettings at Cheadle Royal business park and major leisure schemes in Durham and Ahton under Lyne.
Career: Manchester High School for Girls; Birmingham University; articled *Halliwell Landau*, achieving Partnership; joined *Eversheds (Alexander Tatham)* 1990, Partner 1993.
Personal: Resides Wilmslow, married with one son. Leisure: DIY, theatre, wine, books.

LOWLESS, Peter
Michelmores, Exeter (01392) 436244

LUST, Graham
Nabarro Nathanson, London (020) 7524 6000
g.lust@nabarro.com
Property Finance specialist.
Specialisation: Extensive experience in commercial property investment and development transactions for major property institutions, public property companies and public sector organisations including Central Government Departments. Currently instructed on substantial office developments in Central London. Has developed innovative forms of property financing documentation for inward investors including tax based property financings for multinational clients.
Prof. Memberships: Law Society.
Career: Qualified in New Zealand in 1974, and in England in 1979. Became a Commercial Property Partner in 1980. Member of Property Finance Group.
Personal: Born 1950.

MACGREGOR, Robert
Clifford Chance, London (020) 7600 1000
robert.macgregor@cliffordchance.com
Specialisation: Partner specialising in property development, financing and leasing of office and retail schemes, also hotels and marina developments.
Prof. Memberships: BCO, Anglo American Real Property Institute.
Career: Berkhamsted School; Nottingham University (LLB Hons). Articled *Titmuss Sainer & Webb*; qualified 1985; partner *Clifford Chance* since 1992.
Personal: Sailing and classic cars. Born 1960; resides London.

MACNIVEN, Iain G.
Maclay Murray & Spens, Glasgow (0141) 248 5011
igm@maclaymurrayspens.co.uk
Specialisation: Commercial property partner with extensive experience of all aspects of commercial property work, including investment deals, development work and leasing. Clients include Scottish Amicable Life Assurance Society, ASDA Plc and British Waterways Board. Particular areas of interest include joint venture development work, and specialist rent review advice as well as the education sector. Member of the Investment Property Forum and the British Council of Shopping Centres.
Career: Glasgow University (MA 1975, LL.B 1977). Been with *Maclay Murray & Spens* throughout his professional career. Past examiner for the Law Society of Scotland.
Personal: Born 1953. Resides Glasgow and West Highlands. Leisure interests include travel, food and drink and crosswords.

MAHOOD, Laurence
Elliott Duffy Garrett, Belfast (028) 9024 5034
laurence.mahood@edgsolicitors.co.uk
Specialisation: Commercial property development, letting and investment, acquisitions and disposals. Current projects include major retail, office and leisure developments and has recently acted in a number of high value investment acquisitions and disposals.
Prof. Memberships: Law Society of N.Ireland. Representative on joint Law Society/RICS Forum.
Career: LLB Queens University, Belfast 1976. Admitted solicitor 1978. Law Society Silver Medal awarded. Partner since 1982.
Personal: Contributing author to Butterworth's 'Property in Europe - Law and Practice'.

MARKS, Christopher
Hammond Suddards Edge, Leeds (0113) 284 7000
christopher.marks@hammondsuddardsedge.com
Specialisation: All aspects of property development and investment, urban regeneration, public sector, grant and funding agreements, joint ventures and dealing with the property aspects of inward investment projects and major infrastructure projects. Landlord and tenant advice, acquisitions and disposals, secured lending on properties. Acts for public and government authorities, major corporates and utilities including advising on pipeline leases and gas exploration and development.
Career: Education; (BA (Hons) Law 1979), LLM 1980. Career history: 1980-1982 *Waltons & Morse*; 1983-1988 *Edge & Ellison* - solicitor associate; 1988 joined Hammond Suddards; Partner 1989.

MARKS, Geoffrey
Halliwell Landau, Manchester (0161) 835 3003
Specialisation: Former Head of Property Department. Deals with full range of property work including development and investment work and all property aspects of property secured lending.
Prof. Memberships: Member of the Royal Chartered Institute of Arbitrators.
Career: Articled *AH Howarth & Co*; qualified 1963; partner *AH Howarth & Co* (now *Howarth Goodman & Co*) 1965-74; partner *Maurice Rubin & Co* 1974-84; partner *Halliwell Landau* 1984.
Personal: Born 1941; resides Prestwich. Educated at Arnold School, Blackpool. Recreations include theatre and opera.

MAYNARD, Andrew E.
Michelmores, Exeter (01392) 436244

MCCLEA, Nigel
Pinsent Curtis, Leeds (0113) 244 5000
nigel.mcClea@pinsents.com
National Head of Property.
Specialisation: Specialises in large scale commercial property projects, in public and private sectors (with particular focus on leisure, education and health). Major projects: Royal Armouries Museum, Leeds; Relocation of Sunderland Football Club; Redevelopment of Odsal Stadium, Bradford; Disposal of Epsom cluster of redundant hospital sites for Secretary of State; New residential settlement at Lichfield.
Career: Qualified 1975. Partner in *Simpson Curtis* (now *Pinsent Curtis*) 1978. Fellow of the Royal Society of Arts, Manufactures and Commerce. Friend of Historic Houses Association.
Personal: Born 1951. Educated at Ashville College, Harrogate and Queen's College, Cambridge.

MCLEAN, Neil M.
DLA, Leeds (08700) 111111
neil.mclean@dla.com
Specialisation: Regional Managing Partner, Head of Property Group in Leeds. Commercial Property. Principal areas of specialisation are property development, Funding, PFI and retail work. Acts for a wide range of national clients in all aspects of development, portfolio management and acquisitions and disposals.
Career: Qualified 1977, Partner 1981.

MEDVEI, Cornelius
Eversheds, Norwich (01603) 272727
corneliusmedvei@eversheds.com
Specialisation: Property finance, property development - £194m securitisation of nursing homes acting for the issuer. *Eversheds* Head of Property responsible for UK and European Property team.
Prof. Memberships: Law Society; British Property Federation; City Property Association.
Career: Admitted 1978; Assistant *Markbys/Cameron Markby (now Cameron McKenna)*; *Mills & Reeve*; Partner *Eversheds* 1988 to date.

MEREDITH, Alan
Eversheds, Cardiff (02920) 471147
alanmeredith@eversheds.com
Senior partner. Head of Commercial Property Department.
Specialisation: Work includes property joint ventures between private and public sector and general commercial conveyancing. Also handles urban regeneration in the public sector, acting for both public and private sector bodies. Has given seminars on contaminated land for the Chartered Surveyors Study Group and has co-authored with his environmental partner, Martin Warren, a book entitled 'Contaminated Land - Managing Liabilities'.
Prof. Memberships: Law Society, Country Landowners Association.
Career: Qualified in 1976. Joined *Phillips & Buck* (now *Eversheds*)as a Partner in 1982. Currently Head of Commercial Property Department.
Personal: Born 8th January 1952. Attended University of Wales, Aberystwyth. Member of Management Committee of Swansea Cricket and Football Club. Trustee of Dragons Rugby Trust. Leisure interests include golf, rugby and reading. Lives in Cowbridge near Cardiff.

MOFFAT, Douglas W.J.
Tods Murray WS, Glasgow (0141) 275 4771
douglas.moffat@todsmurray.co.uk
Specialisation: Commercial property. Phases 3 and 4 South Gyle Park, Edinburgh (development and letting on behalf of Britel Fund Trustees), sale of Atlantic Quay, Glasgow (£67.5m on behalf of Commerz Grunbesitz-Investmentgesellschaft), purchase of Centre Point Retail Park, Aberdeen (£14.6m on behalf of Railway Pension Nominees).
Prof. Memberships: Law Society, WS Society, British Council of Shopping Centres (Scottish Secretary), British Council of Offices, Investment Property Forum.
Career: Edinburgh University - LLB, apprenticeship and then assistant - *Shepherd & Wedderburn WS* 1968-73, *Tods Murray WS* 1993 to date (partner 1974, Head of Property 1980-98).
Personal: Golf, hill walking, cricket (SCH committee), squash. One daughter and one son.

MOODY, John
Eversheds, Manchester (0161) 832 6666
johnmoody@eversheds.com
Partner in Commercial Property Department.
Specialisation: Work covers all aspects of commercial property with a particular emphasis on investment and management work. Involved in several high profile residential and commercial developments and advises several FTSE 100 companies on their strategic property requirements. Contributes articles to professional journals and local press.
Prof. Memberships: Law Society.
Career: Articled 1973-75 at *Ingham Clegg & Crowther* in Preston and became a Partner in 1980. Joined *Yates Barnes* in 1989, then moved to *Eversheds Alexander Tatham* in 1990. Became Head of Commercial Property Department in 1990 and Managing Partner in 1993. Following the merger of *Eversheds* offices in Leeds and Manchester became Deputy Managing Partner of these offices.
Personal: Born 19th February 1950. Attended Nottingham High School 1961-69, then Jesus College, Cambridge 1969-72. Leisure pursuits include golf (Cambridge Blue 1970-71 and 71-72 and County Golfer), theatre, overseas travel, mowing the lawn and terrorising the cat. Lives in Bowdon, Cheshire.

MORGAN, Claire
Eversheds, Newcastle upon Tyne (0191) 261 1661
Partner in Commercial Property Department.
Specialisation: All aspects of urban regeneration and development including site assembly, infrastructure agreements, joint ventures, public/private sector partnerships/PFI, particularly in the Health sector, public sector grant funding agreements, portfolio acquisitions and disposals. Recent projects include property joint ventures and acting for the seller in the sale of a portfolio of eleven let industrial estates and for English Partnerships and One Northeast in relation to the redevelopment of the former coalery sites inherited from Brtish Coal.
Prof. Memberships: Law Society; Newcastle upon Tyne Law Society.
Career: University of Nottingham; qualified 1975; Partner 1979 onwards.
Personal: Married, 3 children, lives in Newcastle. Walking, reading, built environment.

MORGAN, Rosemary
Morgan Cole, Swansea (01792) 634634
rosemary.morgan@morgan-cole.com
Specialisation: Public/private sector joint venture property development in the leisure, retail & commercial sectors. Gaming and liquor licensing. Major matters are: (1) The Waterfront Destination, Swansea; (2) Chester Business Park; (3) Re-development of a 400 acre redundant BP terminal.
Prof. Memberships: The Law Society.
Career: LLB, Birmingham University, Birmingham. 1969-71 Assistant Solicitor with *Douglas Jones & Mercer*. 1971-present: Partner with *Morgan Cole.*
Personal: Travelling, wildlife conservation (especially endangered species), and vintage cars.

MORPETH, Iain
Clifford Chance, London (020) 7600 1000
iain.morpeth@cliffordchance.com
Specialisation: Partner specialising in Real Estate transactions (domestic and international). Transaction Types include project development, single asset and portfolio acquisitions; leasing projects; real estate private equity projects; real estate and FM backed PFI and corporate outsourcing; and joint ventures. Clients include investment banks, such as Nomura, Lehman, CSFB, Schroders and Citibank; international investors such as Witkoff Group,Europa Fund and Dallah Albaraka Group; and domestic developers and investors such as Thornfield Properties, Universities Superannuation Scheme Limited and HSBC Pension Trust. Recent Transactions include the Shell Mex House transaction for Witkoff Group, project STEPS for Nomura; the Thornfield/National Car Parks multi site joint venture; acquisition of Redditch Shopping Centre for a number of equity investors; and a variety of investment acquisition, development and joint venture projects.
Prof. Memberships: Law Society; City of London Solicitors Company; Investment Property Forum; British Property Federation.
Career: Partner *Clifford Chance* 1988.
Publications: Contributing author: 'Joint Ventures in Property; Structures and Precedents' published by Sweet and Maxwell; contributor of various articles; regular speaker at Real Estate conferences.
Personal: Born: December 1953; Educated: Fettes College, Edinburgh; Bristol University (LLB) (Hons). Admitted Solicitor 1978.

MORRIS, Christopher A.
Freshfields Bruckhaus Deringer, London
(020) 7936 4000
cmorris@freshfields.com
Specialisation: Commercial property, development, property finance and insolvency law.
Career: Qualified in 1984 and became a partner in 1991. Head of real estate department since May 2000.
Personal: Born 1960. Eastbourne Grammar School 1973-1978. Lincoln College Oxford 1978 to 1981. Lives in Bromley. Interests include family, sport, music and Italy.

MOST, Lionel D.
Burness, Glasgow (0141) 248 4933
Specialisation: Main area of practice is commercial leasing, and all aspects of property and development work where the main issue is leasing. Law Society of Scotland Accredited Specialist in Commercial Leasing. Occasional Arbiter and Expert Witness in Commercial Leasing Disputes. Part time lecturer in conveyancing for LL.B degree and for Commercial leasing in LLM in Commercial Law, both at the University of Glasgow. Periodic lecturer for CPD seminars.
Prof. Memberships: Law Society of Scotland (Member of Conveyancing Committee).
Career: Joined *Alexander Stone & Co* in 1977 as apprentice, qualified in 1979, becoming a partner in 1983. Merged with *Burness* and became partner with the firm in 1998.

NEWCOMBE, Mark
Hammond Suddards Edge, Birmingham
(0121) 200 2001
mark.newcombe@hammondsuddardsedge.com
Specialisation: Partner in the firm's Commercial Property Department, Mark specialises in the acquisistion of all types of greenfield sites, letting of new build offices, retail schemes, warehouses and factories as well as investment sales and forward funding.
Prof. Memberships: Law Society and British Urban Regeneration Association (BURA). Chairman of the East Midlands Property Forum, co-sponsored by East Midlands Development Agency which is now in its ninth year.
Career: Partner at *Edge Ellison* since 1989.
Personal: Born 1957, Graduate of Manchester University LL.B (Hons) and College of Law, Chester. Interests include skiing and motorcycling. Lives in Leicestershire.

NEWTON, Alison
McGrigor Donald, Glasgow (0141) 248 6677
www.mcgrigors.com
Partner, Edinburgh office.
Specialisation: Recent transactions have included: the sale and leaseback of numerous residential/nursing homes for various Diawa, MEPC and UBK healthcare funds; the development, construction and management contract for a new Glasgow city centre hotel; acquisition work for Tom Cobleigh plc and Yates Brothers plc; the development and lease for a major new call centre at Cardonald for Thomson Holidays; the co-ordination and lettings of the £20m redevelopment of St Enoch Centre, Glasgow for Despa; the construction and property deals for Dawn Developments to provide a new HQfacility for Fullarton Computer Industries in Irvine.
Prof. Memberships: Law Society of Scotland. Member of Committee of Scottish Branch of British Council of Shopping Centres.
Career: 1980-84 Dundee University (LLB, DIP.LP); 1984-86 Trainee, 1986-90 Assistant; 1990-94 Associate; 1994-99 Partner; January 1999 to July 2000 Managing Partner, Glasgow office; July 2000 to date Partner in Edinburgh office, charged with development.
Personal: Riding, skiing, reading and now running.

NISSE, Ian
Ashurst Morris Crisp, London (020) 7638 1111
Partner in Commercial Property Department and currently *Ashursts'* Managing Partner.
Specialisation: Commercial Property matters with an emphasis on development projects, investment transactions and joint ventures. Clients for whom he is the lead partner include British Telecom, Chelsfield, Church Commissioners for England, Hemingway Pearson and Stanhope.
Career: Became a partner at *Ashursts* in 1987.

O'MEARA, Anne M.
Hammond Suddards Edge, Birmingham (0121) 200 2001
Specialisation: Partner in the firm's commercial property department, Anne specialises in property development, property-related regeneration work and in particular acting as a legal project manager for regeneration projects involving public/private sector. Over the past year Anne has acted as lead partner and legal project manager for £113 million Millenium point in Birmingham, the National Space Science Centre in Leicester and is currently acting for Advantage West Midlands in connection with the regeneration of the Fort Dunlop building.
Prof. Memberships: Law Society, Birmingham Law Society and British Urban Regeneration Association (BURA).
Career: Joined *Edge Ellison* in 1978, qualified in 1980 and became a partner in 1984.
Personal: Graduate of Birmingham University LL.B (Hons) and College of Law, Chester.

ODY, Jonathan
Norton Rose, London (020) 7283 6000
odyjw@nortonrose.com
Specialisation: Partner in the Property planning and Environmental Department. Has extensive experience of property development and investment work and related banking and finance documentation. Also has long involvement with central and local government financing (including PFI and PPP) transactions, tax-based leasing work, and inward investment structures for non-residents.
Prof. Memberships: Anglo American Real Property Institute, British Council for Offices, City of London Law Society, City Architecture Forum.
Career: Articled *Romney Fraser & Ody*, (Malvern, Worcestershire); Qualified 1965; Assistant Solicitor 1964-1967; Partner 1967-1968 *Pattinson & Brewer*; Assistant Solicitor *Freshfields*, 1969-1972; Partner [IT+Norton Rose 1972 - date.

PATTISON, Mark
Beachcroft Wansbroughs, Manchester
(0161) 934 3000
mpattison@bwlaw.co.uk
Specialisation: Property development, strategic and tactical advice, Landlord & Tenant new letting and Management, investment acquisitions and disposals cases. Deals include an agreement for the construction and lease of office buildings for Inland Revenue; the redevelopment, extension and letting of a shopping centre; and the development of a new urban village at Warrington.
Career: Articled *Vaudreys*; qualified 1982. Remained at *Vaudreys* untill it merged with *Beachcroft Wansbroughs*. Directorships: Disley Properties Limited; Winters Nominees.
Personal: Born 1958, educated at Stockport Grammar School, Manchester University and College of Law Chester. Married with two daughters. Leisure interests include clay pigeon shooting, swimming, running, walking and fishing.

PIERCE, Graham L.
L'Estrange & Brett, Belfast (028) 9023 0426
graham.pierce@lestrangeandbrett.com
Specialisation: Commercial property development and institutional investment. Also acts for a number of retail multiples. Recent work has included joint ventures for residential property developments and

sale of retail park investments. Has also advised on Northern Irish aspects of UK-wide PFI accommodation schemes.
Career: Qualified 1988. Assistant solicitor at *L'Estrange & Brett* 1988-93. Partner since 1993.
Personal: Born 1965.

PIKE, John D.
Addleshaw Booth & Co, Leeds 0113 209 2000
jdp@@addleshaw-booth.co.uk
Head of Commercial Property Group (includes Commercial Property, Environmental, Construction, Planning, Licensing and Property Litigation).
Specialisation: Main area of practice is commercial property work, in particular development, banking, investment and private sectors. A particular specialism is land pollution and he frequently advises on land contamination and remediation, waste and lender risk.
Career: Qualified 1972. Partner 1976.
Personal: Jesus College Cambridge (MA: Hons). De Montfort University (MA: Environmental Law). Governor Moorlands School, Leeds and Governor of St Peters School, York. Director of Urban Mines Limited and heavily involved in the Brownfields project as a member of the Advisory Group. Interests include sports and family.

PLANT, Patrick
Linklaters (A member firm of Linklaters & Alliance), London (020) 7456 4718
patrick.plant@linklaters.com
See under Travel, p.808

PRITCHARD, Nicholas D.M.
TLT Solicitors, Bristol (0117) 917 7777
npritchard@TLTsolicitors.com
Specialisation: Has specialised in commercial property since 1972. Undertakes a wide range of commercial conveyancing transactions with particular emphasis on leisure and office development both town centre and out of town. Widespread experience of site assembly, acquisition development funding and disposals of business parks and leisure developments. Now concentrates on 'problem' properties which are suited to his entrepreneurial approach.
Career: Qualified 1970, moved to Bristol and *Trumps (now TLT Solicitors*, the merged firm of *Trumps* and *Lawrence Tucketts*) in 1972, became partner in 1974.
Personal: Tennis, sailing and generally enjoying life.

PUGH, Nigel
Bond Pearce, Southampton (023) 8063 2211
nmp@bondpearce.com
Partner in the Commercial Property Group.
Specialisation: All types of commercial property transactions. Specialises in institutional funding, commercial leases, site acquisition, retail development in town, out of town and edge of town, multiple town centre purchases, construction work, joint ventures, landlord and tenant, statutory agreements, retail parks, student accommodation schemes. Clients include public quoted companies, banks, receivers, a large number of southern based (including London) developers, further education colleges.
Prof. Memberships: Member of the southampton University Court, Society of Notaries Public, and Solicitors European Group.
Career: Qualified in 1970. Articles in the City. Joined *Hepherd Winstanley & Pugh* in 1973 as a Partner and *Bond Pearce* in 1998 on merger.

QUIGLEY, Ian S.
Maclay Murray & Spens, Edinburgh
(0131) 226 5196
isq@maclaymurrayspens.co.uk
Specialisation: Partner dealing in all aspects of commercial property work, including development and leasing pre-funding and development finance.
Prof. Memberships: Writer to the Signet and Notary Public.
Career: Glasgow University (LL.B (Hons) 1969).
Personal: Born 1946.

REEVEY, Michael A.
Addleshaw Booth & Co, Leeds (0113) 209 2000
mar@addleshaw-booth.co.uk
Partner in Commercial Property Group.
Specialisation: Substantial development projects; the financing of property assets and representing both landlords and tenants of retail property.
Career: Oxford University 1976-1979; joined the firm in 1980; admitted as a solicitor 1982 and made a partner in 1988.

REID, David R.
Burness, Edinburgh (0131) 473 6000
drr@burness.co.uk
Specialisation: Deals primarily with large commercial and institutional clients, advising on property developments, high street retailing and commercial leases. He is involved very heavily with major joint ventures and pre-funded developments. Also frequently consulted for opinions on property disputes. Major clients include Grosvenor Developments Ltd, Sun Life Assurance Society plc, St Andrews University and Johnson Group Cleaners plc. Spent some time as a conveyancing tutor at Edinburgh University.

REID, Sandy
Steedman Ramage WS, Edinburgh
(0131) 260 6600
alexander.reid@steedmanramage.co.uk
Specialisation: Development, letting, purchase/sale, investment and joint ventures. Experience includes acquisition, development and letting of major shopping centres; mixed use developments both in and out of town; large portfolio transactions. Accredited as a Planning Specialist by the Law Society of Scotland. Recent transactions include acting for Marks and Spencer in the £186m sale of Gyle Shopping Centre, Edinburgh; J Sainsbury Developments in the acquisition, development, letting and sale of a major mixed use development at St Andrew Square, Edinburgh; Helical Retail in acquisition, pre-letting and funding of development of George/Commercial Hotels complex in Glasgow; and advising EDI Group on planning for Princes Street Galleries, Edinburgh.
Prof. Memberships: Law Society of Scotland. Society of Writers to H.M.Signet.
Career: Educated Robert Gordon's College, Aberdeen 1966-1972; Aberdeen University 1972-1975. Joined *Steedman Ramage* 1975, qualified 1977; Partner 1980; Chairman 1993.
Personal: Born 15th September 1954. Married, two sons. Leisure activities include music and sport.

REILLY, Alan J.
Carson & McDowell, Belfast (028) 9024 4951
Alan.Reilly@carson-mcdowell.com
Specialisation: Acquisition and disposal of commercial property and all types of interests therein. Development of commercial property. Traditional specialisation in retail property originally for tenants latterly more particularly for landlords including from site acquisition through development to initial letting and ultimately disposal. More recently diversification into commercial property services in higher education, leisure, culture and arts sectors. This year acting for landlords relocating existing tenants and introducing new tenants in five shopping centres in consequence of alteration or extension. Acquiring four public houses for new entrant to the Northern Ireland market. Advising in relation to property adjustment in the changing proposals for privatisation of Port of Belfast.
Career: M.A. (CANTAB). Whole career with *Carson & McDowell* (qualified 1976), partner 1978.
Personal: Married with two daughters.

RICE, Dermot
Slaughter and May, London (020) 7600 1200
Specialisation: Specialises in all types of commercial property work including development, investment, securitisation and structured finance. Recent significant transactions include: acting for Abbey National plc in connection with its £2 billion+ mastertrust mortgage securitisation; acting for Grosvenor Estate Holdings in connection with the establishment of the £170 million GMETRO Limited Partnership, and in its role as preferred development partner of Preston Council in relation to the proposed redevelopment of Preston town centre; acting for HRO International in connection with the proposed redevelopment of Victoria Plaza; and acting for Whitecliff Properties (the Blue Circle Industries/Landlease joint venture) in relation to its interests in Ebbsfleet and the Thames corridor.
Career: Articled *Gamlens*; qualified 1984; partner *Slaughter and May* 1991.
Personal: Married, 3 children. Resides: London.

ROBERTS, David Lloyd
Hugh James Ford Simey, Cardiff (029) 2022 4871
Partner and Head of Commercial Property Department.
Specialisation: Work includes site assembly and acquisition, including option work, agreement and grant of lease and forward sale agreements in relation to office, retail and industrial developments. Undertakes large scale land acquisition for a large volume house builder, as well as loan documentation. Specialises in Housing Association stock transfers and other social housing initiatives. Acted in the transfer of Glyn Taff Estate from Taff Ely BC to Newydd Housing Association (the first and only Pt. IV Housing Act 1988 transfer in Wales).
Prof. Memberships: Legal Advisor to Sports Council of Wales Drugs Abuse Advisory Committee.
Career: Qualified in 1974. Joined *Hugh James* in 1972, becoming a Partner in 1975. Member of British Athletics Team 1974-78. Competed at European and Commonwealth Championships. Member of Hawks Club and Achilles Club.
Personal: Born 5th June 1949. Attended Grove Park Grammar School, Wrexham 1960-68; Selwyn College, Cambridge 1968-72 (MA, LLB) and Guildford College of Law. Leisure interests include sport, particularly golf. Lives in Cardiff.

ROBINSON, E. Patrick G.
Herbert Smith, London (020) 7374 8000
patrick.robinson@herbertsmith.com
Specialisation: Commercial property development and planning work including all aspects of planning (see entry under Planning section). Established track

record in all aspects of property work, with an emphasis on corporate relocations, site assembly and development cases.
Prof. Memberships: Law Society's Specialist Planning Panel.
Career: Articled at *Herbert Smith* (1978-80). Partner 1986. Joint Editor of Blundell & Dobry's Planning, Applications, Appeals and Proceedings (5th Ed) 1996.
Personal: Born April 1956. Educated at University of Nottingham (LLB 1977). Leisure pursuits include jazz, the CÈvennes and family. Lives in London.

ROBINSON, Herbert
Mills & Reeve, Norwich (01223) 222 233
herbert.robinson@mills-reeve.com
Specialisation: Partner specialising in property development advice and transactional work; option agreements; joint venture arrangements; 25 years' experience in the field of commercial property including: major project work for Cambridge HEIs; setting up Granta Park, Abington, Cambridge and Papworth development near Cambridge.
Career: Trained *Kenneth Brown Baker*, qualified 1969; Assistant Solicitor *Taylors*, Newmarket 1970-72; Partner 1972-87; Partner *Taylor Vintors*, Cambridge 1988-99; Chairman 1990-99; Partner *Mills & Reeve* since 1999.
Personal: Resides near Newmarket. Sailing, walking, military history.

ROONEY, P.J.
DLA, Liverpool (08700) 111111
philip.rooney@dla.com
Specialisation: Commercial property; advises a wide range of investors, funders, developers and occupiers on all manner of property related projects; acts for local authorities, urban regeneration bodies and other public and quasi public sector organisations on the exploitation of their public property assets.
Prof. Memberships: Law Society.
Career: After graduating from Oxford University, joined the firm in 1978, partner in 1984. Head of Liverpool property department 1992-1998; appointed national head of Real Estate Group 1998.
Personal: Married; three children. Enjoys classical music, sport, theatre.

ROSCOE, James
Fyfe Ireland WS, Edinburgh (0131) 343 2500
jroscoe@fyfeireland.com
Specialisation: Qualified in both Scotland and England, with extensive experience of cross-border transactions. Main specialisms are property investment and property finance. Largely for English based, American and German investors and lenders including Teachers Insurance, Helaba and CCF Charterhouse.
Prof. Memberships: WS, NP, admitted as a solicitor in England and Wales.
Career: Qualified 1988. Partner with *Bird Semple Fyfe Ireland* and thereafter *Fyfe Ireland* since 1992. Head of Commercial Property Department.
Personal: Born 22nd December 1960. Educated Dundee High School and Oxford and Edinburgh Universities. Interests include cycling and gardening.

ROSS, Kenneth A.
Burness, Edinburgh (0131) 473 6000
kar@burness.co.uk
Specialisation: Partner in Commercial Property and Projects teams. Deals primarily with work on the sectors of PPP, PFI, commercial and finance leasing, and inward investment. Contributes to conferences on planning law, environmental law, VAT and commercial leases.

RUDOLF, Peter.D.
Berwin Leighton, London (020) 7760 1000
peter.rudolf@berwinleighton.com
Specialisation: Property development, particularly retail and office, and investment. Recent transactions include the acquisition and development of The Mall, Cribbs Causeway (Prudential Assurance); redevelopment, letting and forward sale of 59 Gresham Street, London EC4 (Legal & General); acquisition and development of Serpentine Green regional shopping centre, Peterborough (Tesco); acquisition, development and forward sale of Midsummer Place, Milton Keynes (London and Amsterdam Properties); redevelopment of Albert Dock, Liverpool (Arrowcroft); acquisition, development and forward sale of New Bond Street, Weymouth (Shearer Property Group).
Prof. Memberships: Law Society.
Career: Bedford School; St Johns, Cambridge - MA 1st Class Honours.
Personal: Participation in sports especially squash and triathalons.

RYDEN, Nicholas
Shepherd & Wedderburn WS, Edinburgh (0131) 228 9900
nick.ryden@shepwedd.co.uk
Specialisation: All aspects of Commercial Property and Property Development.
Prof. Memberships: Member, Governor and Chairman of Anglo-American Real Property Institute; occasional lecturer Law Society of Scotland post-qualifying legal education, RICS and Heriot-Watt University; member of Investment Property Forum; member of Investment Property Forum Securitisation Working Party; member of BPF Scottish working party.
Career: Articled *Shepherd & Wedderburn WS*; qualified 1976; assistant solicitor 1976-78; partner 1978.
Personal: Born 1953; resides Edinburgh. Leisure intrests: Travel, hill walking and photography. Education: Fettes College; Aberdeen University (LLB;WS)

RYLAND, David S.
SJ Berwin & Co, London (020) 7533 2222
david.ryland@sjberwin.com
See under Travel, p.808

SAMSON, John
Nabarro Nathanson, London (020) 7524 6000
j.samson@nabarro.com
Specialisation: Adding value to clients' property interests through development, funding, joint ventures and restructuring schemes. Financing, acquisitions, sales and collective investments; Landlord and tenant and drafting innovations. Consultancy advice and provision of second opinions.
Prof. Memberships: Law Society, British Property Federation commonhold committee.
Career: Partner at *Nabarro Nathanson* since 1972. Editor of Property Law Bulletin since 1985. Blundell Memorial lecturer (1992). Regular conference lecturer.

SCOTT, Peter .J.
Bevan Ashford, Bristol (0117) 923 0111
Head of Commercial Property Department.
Specialisation: Covers a wide range of property work including commercial development work (particularly in the leisure field), PFI contractual work in the education and health sectors, and regeneration schemes.
Prof. Memberships: Law Society.
Career: *Norton Rose* 1969-72; *Boodle Hatfield* 1972-75. Joined *Bevan Ashford* 1975; Partner 1977.

SHAW, Donald G.B.
Dundas & Wilson CS, Edinburgh (0131) 228 8000

SILVA, David
Iliffes Booth Bennett, Uxbridge 01895 207801
david.silva@ibblaw.co.uk
Specialisation: Head of property development team which has recently completed a number of transactions with an estimated end value in excess of £100 Million. Acts for a number of significant developer and investor clients. Specialises in office industrial retail and leisure developments, development funding including joint venture agreements and investment sales and acquisitions. Recent highlights include acting on behalf of Frontier Estates Limited in connection with two of the largest speculatively funded industrial developments in the south east estimated end value in excess of £45 Million.
Prof. Memberships: Law Society.
Career: Articled at *Frere Cholmeley Bischoff* and joined the commercial property department upon qualification in September 1990. Joined *Iliffes Booth Bennett* in September 1996 and made a partner in May 1998.
Personal: Born December 1962. Leisure interests include football, tennis and swimming. Lives in Chalfont St. Peter and is married with two children.

SINGH, Parmjit
Eversheds, Birmingham (0121) 232 1000
Specialisation: Development: clients include Birmingham Mailbox, Severn Trent Property, Stoford Developments and Urban Box. Major projects in the last 12 months include the redevelopment of The Mailbox (biggest single building mixed use scheme in the UK- 1m plus sq ft). Urban regeneration: acts for Advantage West Midlands on various strategic schemes including its major inward investment sites at Ansty, Coventry and Hilton, Staffordshire. Investment: clients include The Birmingham Alliance (Hammerson, Henderson and Land Securities) on the redevelopment of The New Bull Ring, Birmingham.
Prof. Memberships: Investment Property Forum.
Career: Trained *Eversheds*, qualified 1989, partner 1997.
Personal: Born 1965. Warwick University, LLB (Hons). College of Law, Chester. Enjoy watching and playing football. Married, 2 children.

SMITH, David A.
Shepherd & Wedderburn WS, Edinburgh (0131) 228 9900
david.smith@shepwedd.co.uk
Partner in Commercial Property Department and Joint Chairman of Firm.
Specialisation: Main areas of practice are development projects, leases and opinion work. Regular speaker at conferences and seminars.
Prof. Memberships: Law Society of Scotland, Soci-

ety of Writers to the Signet.
Career: Joined *Shepherd & Wedderburn* in 1969. Partner in 1974.
Personal: Born 17th November 1947. Edinburgh University 1966-69. Leisure pursuits include veterans' hockey, golf, hill walking, gardening and enjoying good food and wine in good company. Lives in Edinburgh.

SMITHERS, Tim M.D.
Veale Wasbrough, Bristol (0117) 925 2020
tsmithers@vwl.co.uk
Partner in property services department.
Specialisation: Main areas of practice are development, energy and environmental law with specialisms in wastes management, contaminated land and Pipelines Act work. An editor of Butterworths' 'Property Law Service'. Regular contributor to professional publications and speaker at seminars.
Prof. Memberships: Pipeline Industries Guild, Institute of Wastes Management, Environmental Services Association.
Career: Qualified 1982. Joined *Veale Wasbrough* in 1986, becoming a partner in 1988.
Personal: Born 1958. Attended University of Wales LLB(Hons) 1979.

SMYTH, Robert
Burges Salmon, Bristol (0117) 939 2224
bob.smyth@burges-salmon.com
Specialisation: Environmental law and property. Provides legal and strategic management advice to large corporate occupiers of property and to government bodies (Scottish & Southern Energy plc, NAAFI, MoD). World Bank accredited consultant (Eastern Europe) specialising in land reform and property markets.
Prof. Memberships: Fellow of the Society for Advanced Legal Studies; Law Society.
Career: Trained at *DJ Freeman & Co*; short-term placement Bristol City Council; joined *Burges Salmon* 1983, Partner 1987. Established Planning Unit (1989) and Environmental Law Unit. *Burges Salmon* marketing partner 1988-99, business development partner 1999 to date, Deputy Managing Partner.
Personal: Born Scotland. Degree in Economics, UCW 1975. Married; keen cyclist ('End to End' 1998); Director of Bristol Circus School (Circomedia) and Cycle West; business representative in Bristol's LA21 strategic process.

SOLOMON, Jonathan
Norton Rose, London (020) 7283 6000
solomonjd@nortonrose.com
Specialisation: Jonathan is a partner in the Commercial Property Department and specialises in major development, funding and investment transactions acting for developer, tenants, investors and lenders. He has extensive experience of Central London office developments and lettings, as well as retail leisure and other development projects, and led the team that won the Legal Business Property Team of the Year Award in 1998 for the proposed 700,000 square foot LIFFE development at Spitalfields Market, London EC1.Jonathan also has considerable experience of acting on investment acquisitions both for overseas and UK clients and in acting on different, and sometimes novel, property financing arrangements. Recent examples of work include acting for Helical Bar plc on the acquisition, letting to *Slaughter & May* and funding of a 265,000 square foot office development at Chiswell Street, London EC2 and on the adjoining 100,000 square foot office building, and acting for Spitalfield Developments Limited and the City Corporation on all aspects of the redevelopment of Spitalfields Market, London EC1 to provide over 1 million square feet of offices.
Career: Articled *Norton Rose*; qualified 1986; Partner 1995. King Alfred School; Warwick University (1993 LLB Hons); College of Law Guildford.

SORRELL, Stephen
Eversheds, Manchester (0161) 832 6666
stephensorrell@eversheds.com
Partner and Head of Department: Commercial Property - Eversheds - Leeds and Manchester.
Specialisation: Commercial property development (industrial, office, leisure, residential and retail) and urban regeneration. Acts as strategic legal adviser to English Partnerships (the Government's Urban Regeneration Agency) and the North West Development Agency. He advises private sector developers such as AMEC Developments Limited (Cheadle Royal, the 80 acre business park in South Manchester, Ashton Moss in East Manchester and 'The Circus' leisure development in city centre, Manchester) and several local authorities (including Manchester, Preston and Burnley) with regard to town centre regeneration and with regard to public and private sector joint venture arrangements to procure urban development.
Prof. Memberships: Law Society, International Bar Association and Government Urban Task Force.
Career: Training, *Abson Hall* (Manchester and Stockport) Solicitor and Partner, *Abson Hall*, Partner in *Eversheds* from 1989 to present.
Personal: Born 5th October 1959. Educated Marple Hall Grammar School, Manchester University and Chester College of Law. Leisure interests include cinema, music and a passion for Manchester City FC. Lives in South Manchester and is married with 2 children.

STANCOMBE, Michael F.
Lovells, London (020) 7296 2000
michael.stancombe@lovells.com
Specialisation: Investment, financing and development (acting for both institutions and developers). Investment structures and indirect investment vehicles. Management of major portfolios. Also acts for a major retail group on new developments.
Prof. Memberships: Member of the British Council for Offices, the Investment Property Forum and Urban Land Institute. Representative Member of the British Property Federation, City Property Owners Association, Global Real Estate Investors and Westminster Property Owners Association.
Career: Articled at *Durrant Piesse* (now *Lovells*); qualified 1979; Partner 1982.

STEEL, David A.
Dundas & Wilson CS, Glasgow (0141) 222 2200

STONE, David J.
Andrew M. Jackson & Co, Hull (01482) 325242
Specialisation: Wide range of experience in commercial property development schemes (retail, leisure, and industrial) for developers, funders, owners and tenants. Recent experience includes acquisition, letting and funding of several retail/leisure schemes, joint venture agreements (including joint venture for redevelopment of a regional town centre). Acts for major leisure operator on schemes nationwide.
Prof. Memberships: Law Society
Career: King Henry VIII School, Coventry and Cambridge University
Personal: Married, two children. Golf.

STRACHAN, Dale
Brodies WS, Edinburgh (0131) 228 3777
dstrachan@brodies.co.uk
Specialisation: Commercial Property Partner dealing with Development, Construction Law and Practice, Tenant Representation and Property PFI.
Prof. Memberships: Society of Writers to Her Majesty's Signet. International Bar Association.
Career: George Heriot's School. University of Aberdeen (1977 LLB). Qualified 1979. Assistant Solicitor *Brodies* 1979-83; Partner since 1983.
Personal: Fishing, skiing, motorcycling, flying.

STRATTON, D.
Field Cunningham & Co, Manchester (0161) 834 4734
Partner.
Specialisation: Undertakes a wide range of commercial conveyancing transactions. Has specialised in major developments of all types, with particular emphasis on retail and office development, both town centre and out of town. Widespread experience of joint venture, institutional funding and secured lending work, as well as acquisition and disposal of major investment portfolios. Increasingly acting for banks in connection with property secured lending, particularly with a development bias.
Prof. Memberships: Law Society.
Career: Articled with Warrington Borough Council. Qualified in 1971. Worked for Christian Salvesen Properties as Group Legal Adviser. Joined *Halliwell Landau* in 1979 and became Deputy Senior Partner. Joined *Field Cunningham & Co.* in 1996.
Personal: Born 16th May 1947. Educated at Altrincham Grammar School for Boys and Colwyn Bay Grammar School, then Leeds University 1965-68. Lives in Bowdon, Cheshire.

TAVENER, Chris D.
Herbert Smith, London (020) 7374 8000
Partner in property department.
Specialisation: Deals with a full range of commercial property work for developer and institutional clients. Particular expertise in landlord and tenant work.
Career: Became a Partner of the firm in 1982.
Personal: Born in 1948. Educated at RGS, Guildford and Christ Church, Oxford. Leisure time devoted to golf, skiing, music and family. Lives in Islington and (whenever possible) North Norfolk.

TAYLOR, David
Berwin Leighton, London (020) 7760 1000
david.taylor@berwinleighton.com
Head of Property Department.
Specialisation: Main areas of practice are commercial property development and investment. Broad commercial practice including acquisition development and joint ventures with specialist involvement for local authority and public sector clients. Recent transactions include significant purchases for the Prudential, Development Projects for AMEC, British Land and Kingspark. In addition, clients include BG Plc, CLS Holdings, Godfrey Bradman and Akeler.
Career: With *Lovell White & King* from 1974 to 1979. Joined *Berwin Leighton* in 1980 and became a Senior Associate in 1987. Became Head of Property Depart-

ment 1996. Member Contributory Board PLJ. Member of 'PROP's' committee of variety club. Pro Bono Adviser to museum in Docklands.
Personal: Born 5th August 1956. Educated at Shooters Hill Grammar School. Leisure interests include classic cars. Lives in London.

THORNE, Peter D.
Wragge & Co, Birmingham (0121) 214 1048
peter_thorne@wragge.com
Specialisation: Commercial property development and investment.
Prof. Memberships: Investment Property Forum.
Career: A partner at *Wragge's* 1990.

TINMAN, Mark
C & H Jefferson, Belfast (028) 9032 9545
Specialisation: Acquisition development and disposal of Commercial Property. Acting for a number of retail multiples, developers and banks.
Prof. Memberships: Law Society of Northern Ireland
Career: Whole career with *C & H Jefferson*. Qualified 1987. Partner since 1994.
Personal: Born 1962: Education: Queens University Belfast (LL.B) 1985. Institute of Professional Legal Studies, Belfast 1986.

VIVIAN, Jon
CMS Cameron McKenna, London (020) 7367 2116
jmv@cmck.com
Specialisation: All aspects of property work including development and acquisitions and disposals. Sits on the firm's Retail Group. Major transactions in the past year include: Acting on behalf of Prestbury in connection with £188m portfolio acquisition. Acting for Brixton Estate on the establishment of a limited partnership with Henderson Investors and subsequent acquisitions of Premier Park, Park Royal. Acting for ProLogis Kingspark on the acquisition, development and forward sale of the Post Office site, Greenford.
Prof. Memberships: Law Society, City of London Law Society.
Career: Partner *McKenna & Co*, now *CMS Cameron McKenna*, since 1989.
Publications: Regular column in 'Property Week'.
Personal: Sport, Theatre.

WALLACE, Andrew
Archibald Campbell & Harley WS, Edinburgh (0131) 220 3000
Specialisation: Partner specialising in commercial property, leasing, investment and development acquisition with particular emphasis on investment and industrial property. Known as a hard-nosed deal maker, he excels in concluding deals and identifying where value can be realised. Clients include Ashtenne Holdings plc, Frogmore Developments & Quintiles Transnational Corporation.
Career: Strathclyde University (LLB Hons), qualified in 1985, joined *Archibald Campbell & Harley WS* same year. Appointed Partner in 1988. He has been a regular lecturer to surveyors and the WS Society on leasing and related subjects.

WARD, Ian
Dickinson Dees, Newcastle upon Tyne (0191) 279 9000
Specialisation: Urban Regeneration, including public/private sector Joint Ventures, mixed use commercial/residential developments, business parks and town centre developments. Acts for developers, national housebuilders and public authorities such as urban development corporations and local authorities. Also actively engaged in PFI, especially in the NHS. Recent work includes extension of Ipswich Town Centre, advising on Millennium Commission projects and large scale PFI schemes for Leeds Teaching Hospitals and Belfast city Hospitals Regional Cancer Centre for Northern Ireland.
Prof. Memberships: Law Society.
Career: Articled at *Eversheds* (Newcastle). Qualified 1983, Partner 1989-1997. Became a partner at *Dickinson Dees* 1997 - Head of Property.
Personal: Durham University B.A. Hons Law 1980. Swimming and family holidays.

WATSON, A.K.
DLA, Birmingham (08700) 111111
adrian.watson@dla.com
Specialisation: Development of all types of commercial property, including industrial, office and retail and also property finance and secured lending. Act for Stoford Developments Limited, John Folkes properties Limited, Chesterhouse Properties Limited, Peter Maddox & Associates, Stockdale Properties Limited. Banks include Dunbar Bank and Bank of Ireland. Acted for Stoford Barberry Limited in the development of 35, 000 square feet of office space on speculative basis for Norwich Union, Chesterhouse Properties development of 80,000 square feet of out of town retail for PC World and Dixons at Apex Retail Park, Stockdale Properties in the development of 29,000 square feet of retail space let to Designer Rooms and Shoe City at Trident Retail Park and John Folkes Properties in a speculative development of 115,000 square feet of manufacturing and distribution units at Wellingborough.
Career: Articled at *Rigbeys* in Birmingham, subsequently a partner at *Pinsent & Co*, *Anthony Collins* and *Garretts*.
Personal: Born 1952 in Birmingham and loves modern music, skiing and golf. Married with one son and lives near Kidderminster.

WATSON, Gary
Hammond Suddards Edge, London (020) 7655 1000
gary.watson@hammondsuddards.co.uk
Specialisation: All aspects of property law with particular emphasis on institutional investment and funding, property development, leasing and relocation work. Has acted in numerous large relocations including for a number of UK and overseas law firms as well as many tenants at Canary Wharf. Also has particular expertise in advising overseas investors.
Prof. Memberships: Investment Property Forum, Council Member of the International Council of the Urban Land Institute of America, British Propety Federation, Law Society.
Career: Qualified as a solicitor in 1979 and specialised in property law ever since. Assistant Solicitor at *Clifford Turner* 1979 to 1982; Assistant Solicitor and then Partner at *Lovell White & King* (subsequently *Lovell White Durrant*) 1982-1995; Partner at *Hammond Suddards* 1995 to date, head of London office 1997-open.
Personal: Born August 1955. Educated at Oxford University (BA 1976). Leisure pursuits include travel, eating out, cinema and reading.

WATTIE, J.Ian
Burness, Edinburgh (0131) 473 6000
jiw@burness.co.uk
Specialisation: Commercial Property Law, principally development, property investment and finance. Institutional client portfolio includes The Miller Group Limited, The Royal Bank of Scotland plc and Trillium. In 1999/2000 has advised The Royal Bank of Scotland plc on acquisition of 600 licensed properties from Scottish + Newcastle plc (value £200+m). Currently leading *Burness* team in advising Inland Revenue/customs + Excise on Scottish aspects of Project STEPS.

WEBB, Tim
Eversheds, Birmingham (0121) 232 1000
timwebb@eversheds.com
Specialisation: Development: developers include Chase Midland plc, Folkes Group plc, John Mowlem & Co plc, Lingfield Securities plc, Highbridge Properties plc, Bryant Homes plc, St Modwen Properties plc. Deals include leading on 1,100 acre development of Newcastle Great Park for Bryant Northern/Beazer Homes and circa £25m Enterprise Zone purchase and forward sales for Highbridge Properties. Portfolio: clients include Headlon Group plc, Hampson Industries plc, Hagermeyer (UK) Limited, Carlsberg Tetley, Volvo, Rover Group, Mesyrs Plc, Mertmore Abbey plc. Deals include £150m merger of Mertmore Abbey with Birkby plc and Phoenix Consortium purchase of Rover Group. Urban Regeneration: Advantage West Midlands.
Prof. Memberships: Investment Property Forum. Director of Birmingham Contemporary Music Group (one of the leading orchestras of its type in the world)
Career: Qualified *Eversheds* Sept 1989. Associate May 1993, senior associate May 1995, partner May 1997.
Personal: Married, two children. Jazz, cooking, live music, film and motor sports.

WEIGHTMAN, Anita
DLA, Manchester (08700) 111111
anita.weightman@dla.com
Specialisation: Development finance and secured lending. Portfolio acquisitions and disposals. Capital raising (sale and leaseback). Leisure development (A3, D2 Users). Acts for a major international cinema operator involved in both in town and out of town new-build leisure schemes.
Prof. Memberships: Law Society. Manchester Law Society.
Career: Westholme School, Blackburn. University of Newcastle Upon Tyne. College of Law, Chester.

WESTHEAD, Tim
Olswang, London (020) 7208 8888
tew@olswang.com
Specialisation: Commercial Property for listed property companies and institutional investors with a specialisation in the acquisition and management of shopping centres. Major transactions include the acquisition of a portfolio of five shopping centres for Capital & Regional plc for £147m, the sale of a portfolio of 44 properties for MEPC for £100m, the acquisition of The Pallasades Shopping Centre, Birmingham and The Ashley Centre, Epsom for £94m and £70m respectively, the acquisition and subsequent development of a series of office sites around the M25 for Green Property plc. Highlights of the last year include the acquisition of 151 Buckingham Palace Road, London SW1 for £101m on behalf of Delancey

Estates plc and the acquisition on behalf of Green Property plc of the P&O property portfolio for £430m.
Career: *Stafford Clarke & Co* - 1980-1985. *Stones Porter* - 1985-1996 (Partner1986). *Olswang* - Partner - 1996 to date - Head of Property 1999 to date.
Personal: Education: Loughborough Grammar, University of Newcastle upon Tyne (LL.B Hons). Leisure Interests: Triathlon, mountain biking, marathon running and watching rugby. Married with three children. Resides - Godalming.

WHITE, Graham
Slaughter and May, London (020) 7600 1200
Specialisation: Experienced in all aspects of commercial property work, including landlord and tenant matters, structured and tax-based finance, commercial property investment, secured lending and development work. Extensive landlord and tenant practice, frequently acting for tenants. *Slaughter and May's* extensive corporate client list means the Commercial Property Department is frequently involved in major private company sales and purchases and he has been responsible for the property aspects of a large number of such deals. He recently advised Whitbread plc on the disposal of its brewing business. Regular contributor to Property Week. Member of the committee which has produced the Standard Commercial Property Conditions.
Prof. Memberships: City of London Law Society Land Law Sub-Committee; The Law Society.
Career: Qualified in 1980 after articles at *Slaughter and May*. Became a Partner in 1987.
Personal: Born 1955. Educated at Haberdashers' Aske's, Elstree and St. Catherine's College, Oxford.

WILLIAMS, Martell
Robertsons, Cardiff (029) 20237777

WILSON, Alistair J.
Fyfe Ireland WS, Edinburgh (0131) 343 2500
awilson@fyfeireland.com
Specialisation: Senior partner in firm. Acts extensively for investors, retailers, finance providers and developers, with considerable experience of providing strategic commercial advice in substantial property transactions and in negotiating the necessary documentation. Has particular experience of cross-border property transactions involving conflict of laws.
Prof. Memberships: WS, NP.
Career: Qualified 1968. Partner with *Fyfe Ireland WS* since 1971.
Personal: Born 19th July, 1945. Educated Peebles High School and Edinburgh University. Interests include fishing, hill-walking and motorcycling.

WORRALL, Simon
Cobbetts, Manchester (0161) 833 3333
simon.worrall@cobbetts.co.uk
Specialisation: Landlord and Tenant, Development and Investment Property, and Licensed Premises Acquisitions.
Prof. Memberships: Law Society
Career: Articled to *Cobbett Leak Almond* 1987; Qualified 1989; Partner *Cobbetts* 1999.
Personal: Married with two children. Hulme Grammar School Oldham; Sheffield University (LLB (Hons)). Chester College of Law. Interests: Golf, theatre.

WRIGHT, David
Nabarro Nathanson, London (020) 7524 6000
d.wright@nabarro.com
Head of Property
Specialisation: Dealing exclusively with commercial property with emphasis on development projects and institutional investment; extensive experience of leading teams in acquisition, disposal and leasing of major property portfolios.
Career: Qualified 1971.
Personal: Born 1946. Bishop Vesey's Grammar School, Sutton Coldfield then Bristol University 1965-68. Member of Deveplopment Board of Investment Property Forum. Director of Direct Wines Limited. Leisure: golf, gardening.

YATES, Andrew
Pinsent Curtis, Birmingham (0121) 200 1050
andrew.yates@pinsents.com
Specialisation: Property development, joint ventures and leading other major property projects. Over the last two years he has become particularly focused upon town centre development projects.
Career: 1986-1990 *Slaughter and May* 1990-1994 *Ashurst Morris Crisp* 1994-2000 *Pinsent Curtis*
Publications: Joint editor of the chapters of Sweet and Maxwells 'Local Government Precedents and Procedures' dealing with Local Authority Partnership Arrangements and Joint Ventures (D29-D41).
Personal: Interests: Martial arts and playing band guitar in the Pinsent Curtis band.

SHIPPING

London: 738; The South & South West: 741; East Anglia: 742; The North: 742; Scotland: 743; *Profiles*: 743

RESEARCH APPROVED BY BMRB: *For this edition,* Chambers' *researchers conducted 6083 interviews – 4408 with law firms, 598 with barristers and 1077 with clients.*

The validity of the research was scrutinised by BMRB International, who audited both the methodology and the results at our offices in July 2000. They interviewed Chambers' *researchers and cross-checked sample interviews. Details of the audit appear on page 7.*

LONDON

SHIPPING • DRY • London	Ptnrs	Assts
❶ Holman Fenwick & Willan	27	33
Ince & Co	39	46
❷ Clyde & Co	47*	69*
❸ Hill Taylor Dickinson	8	14
Richards Butler	14	21
❹ Norton Rose	12	34
Sinclair Roche & Temperley	14	16
Stephenson Harwood	5	3
❺ Bentleys, Stokes & Lowless	10	8
Clifford Chance	3	11
Constant & Constant	5	3
Holmes Hardingham	8	7
Jackson Parton	12	6
More Fisher Brown	10	6
Thomas Cooper & Stibbard	10	10
Watson, Farley & Williams	11	23
❻ Barlow Lyde & Gilbert	4	7
Curtis Davis Garrard	4	8
Fishers	⚐	⚐
Lawrence Graham	4	8
Middleton Potts	10	6
Shaw and Croft	7	6

SHIPPING • WET • London	Ptnrs	Assts
❶ Holman Fenwick & Willan	9	11
Ince & Co	10	10
❷ Clyde & Co	47*	69*
❸ Hill Taylor Dickinson	6	3
❹ Clifford Chance	2	3
Holmes Hardingham	2	2
Norton Rose	7	7
Richards Butler	3	3
Sinclair Roche & Temperley	2	-
❺ Bentleys, Stokes & Lowless	1	2
Constant & Constant	5	2
Shaw and Croft	7	6
Stephenson Harwood	2	5
Thomas Cooper & Stibbard	10	10
Waltons & Morse	5	6

Within each band, firms are listed alphabetically.

*See **Profiles** on page 743*

⚐ *Figures unavailable at time of going to press.*

* *See editorial entries for explanations of team sizes.*

Holman Fenwick & Willan Seen as a *"supremely confident"* outfit, the firm's individual litigators are perceived to *"get to the merits of a dispute quickly."* While the firm's worldwide reputation for salvage work is felt to be *"beyond compare,"* the team move up in our dry table, largely due to their involvement in heavyweight foreign litigation. The firm's continuing global expansion (particularly the recent opening of the Shanghai office) has noticeably lifted its profile in this area. For wet work, salvage expert **Archie Bishop**, while less involved in day to day work, is still thought to be the figurehead. He is the principal architect of the well publicised SCOPIC clause. Fellow wet lawyer **James Gosling** *("an absolute gent")* receives high praise from the London market. His ability to *"turn his hand to anything"* is much admired. The firm is known to be well connected within the German, Far East and Greek owner markets. For dry work, **Hugh Livingstone** *("the rainmaker")*, **Robert Wilson** *("committed to his clients")*, **Richard Crump** *("outstanding – a good fighter")*, **Marcus Bowman** and **Michael Donithorn** were singled out for mention. The team has strong ties with the Scandinavian club market. **Clients:** Owners; clubs; charterers.

Ince & Co Ubiquitous shipping practice *("they seem to be everywhere at the moment")* who have a *"big reputation and some loyal clients."* The market views the firm's ability to secure both *"volume and quality"* from a diverse client-base as the main driving force behind its success. The practice is seen by many to be *"more rounded"* than the immediate competition. Particularly respected for marine casualty work, the team has acted on a host of pollution incidents. Amongst a whole host of recommended *"stars,"* **Richard Williams** *("my God, he's good")* is perceived as *"extremely knowledgeable"* and *"tactically astute,"* and is especially revered by the market for his marine insurance expertise. **Richard Sayer** has a reputation as *"one of the eminences grises,"* **Bob Deering** *("goes the extra mile")* is felt to have had a particularly good year and **Paul Herring** *("straightforward and excellent to deal with")* is highly recommended for charterparty work. **James Wilson** and **Colin de la Rue** are seen as *"true heavyweights"* for their admiralty work, while **Jonathan Lux** and **Malcolm Strong** also maintain their reputations. An acknowledged ability in dry work is highlighted by the firm's huge caseload on behalf of container operators. The team has advised clients inter alia on the termination of charters by reason of the operation of war clauses. **Clients:** Container operators; P&I clubs; insurers; underwriters.

Clyde & Co (Figures in tables are totals for wet and dry teams.) An extremely diverse practice *("the firm is clearly not embedded in any one house")* which, although historically aligned with cargo interests, has a substantial owner and banking client base. However, while the firm is clearly a major shipping force *("you ignore them at your peril,")* its sustained push into corporate work has led to market opinion that it lacks the punch of the leading pair for pure shipping instructions. The quality of the individual partners, particularly towards the top end of the notepaper, is beyond doubt. Of those recommended, **Clive Thorp** *("enthusiastic")*, cargo claims expert **Derek Hodgson** *("a true problem-solver")*, **Benjamin Browne, Tony Thomas** and **Simon Fletcher** *("the archetypal cargo man")* all receive strong market feedback. The team has seen increased work on behalf of owners, P&I clubs, charterers and salvors, and advised on collisions such as Bukhta

LEADING INDIVIDUALS: WET & DRY	
✪ **BISHOP Archie** Holman Fenwick & Willan	**SAYER Richard** Ince & Co
VLASTO Tony Clifford Chance	**WILLIAMS Richard** Ince & Co
❶ **CRUMP Richard** Holman Fenwick & Willan	**DEERING Bob** Ince & Co
GOSLING James Holman Fenwick & Willan	**HERRING Paul** Ince & Co
HODGSON Derek Clyde & Co	**ROOTH Anthony** Watson, Farley & Williams
TAYLOR Andrew Richards Butler	**TAYLOR Tim** Hill Taylor Dickinson
WALLIS Robert Hill Taylor Dickinson	**WILSON James** Ince & Co
WILSON Robert Holman Fenwick & Willan	
❷ **BARDOT Andrew** Bentleys, Stokes & Lowless	**BUSH Philip** Jackson Parton
CROFT Roger Shaw and Croft	**DONOGHUE Andrew** Middleton Potts
EAST Lindsay Richards Butler	**EVANS John** Hill Taylor Dickinson
FISHER Nicholas Fishers	**FLETCHER Simon** Clyde & Co
GHIRARDANI Paolo Stephenson Harwood	**HARVEY Richard** Richards Butler
HEBDEN David Thomas Cooper & Stibbard	**HOBBS Christopher** Norton Rose
JOHNSON Andrew Hill Taylor Dickinson	**LIVINGSTONE Hugh** Holman Fenwick & Willan
LUX Jonathan Ince & Co	**PARTON Nicholas** Jackson Parton
STRONG Malcolm Ince & Co	**THOMAS Tony** Clyde & Co
THORP Clive Clyde & Co	**WINTER Glenn** Holmes Hardingham
❸ **ASPINALL Mark** Shaw and Croft	**ATKINSON Joe** Sinclair Roche & Temperley
BATESON Douglas Thomas Cooper & Stibbard	**BOWMAN Marcus** Holman Fenwick & Willan
BROWN Anthony More Fisher Brown	**BROWNE Benjamin** Clyde & Co
CRANE Graham Constant & Constant	**CURTIS Simon** Curtis Davis Garrard
DE LA RUE Colin Ince & Co	**DONITHORN Michael** Holman Fenwick & Willan
GINSBERG Roy Waltons & Morse	**GRAY Edward** More Fisher Brown
HARRIS Graham Richards Butler	**LAX Michael** Lawrence Graham
LOWE Steven Stephenson Harwood	**MEAD Ray** Barlow Lyde & Gilbert
MILLER Anthony Constant & Constant	**RIDLEY Russell** Middleton Potts
SCOTT Kenneth Holmes Hardingham	**SEWELL Vernon** Bentleys, Stokes & Lowless
UP AND COMING	
BLANCH Juliet Norton Rose	

Within each band, firms are listed alphabetically. *See **Profiles** on page 743*
** See editorial entries for explanations of team sizes.*

Uliss/Olympic Frost and casualty instructions from such clients as the owners of the Giovanna. A successful litigation practice and a number of leading salvage cases (the firm is counsel to Lloyd's and IUA on all Salvage and General Average matters) round out a high-profile portfolio. **Clients:** Lloyd's; IUA; salvors; P&I clubs; charterers; oil companies; banks.

Hill Taylor Dickinson This *"ambitious"* firm is accorded respect from the London market, not least because of the *"absolute quality"* of its individual litigators. **Andrew Johnson** *("the thinking man's lawyer")* is an *"impressive"* character who, despite his sea-faring background, focuses predominantly on dry work – marine insurance and coverage disputes are particular areas of expertise. Fears that the team's strong Lloyd's connections may be detracting from its pure shipping profile have been allayed, although there is no doubt that the departure of Kevin Sach will hurt the practice in the short term. A traditional focus on salvage and hull market work has been bolstered by a strong owner presence in both wet and dry instructions – the team is known to be well-connected in continental Europe, Japan and Scandinavia. The firm's wet practice is particularly well respected, although its ability to compete for the headline casualty work is thought to be hampered by a paucity of foreign offices. Nonetheless, **Tim Taylor**, **Robert Wallis** and **John Evans** *("very bright – rarely gets it wrong")* are much admired by their competitors. The group has acted on a number of charterparty disputes, including unsafe port claims, and has been instructed in several recent salvage and insurance claims cases. **Clients:** P&I clubs; owners; insurers.

Richards Butler Felt to be *"in the ascendancy,"* the shipping group has recovered its strong reputation within the London market. Although known historically as a dry practice, the team are making a play for a greater share of wet work, with ex-seafarer **Richard Harvey** *("gets straight down to business")* newly recommended by his peers. The team has been involved in major collision and salvage work, including the Sea-land Mariner and Maersk Tokyo cases. On the dry side, the team are respected for *"making a point properly and not being unduly aggressive."* **Lindsay East** *("great clients, liked by the clubs")*; **Andrew Taylor** *("sensible, knows what he's talking about")* and **Graham Harris** *("facilitates the deal – doesn't posture unnecessarily")* all come highly recommended. Strong owner and club connections are especially notable in Italy, and the team gets a lot of spin-off litigation work from the firm's established ship financing arm. Acting for the liquidators, the team has handled all the disposals, selling and arresting relating to the liquidation of the Romanian state shipping fleet Navron. **Clients:** Louis Dreyfus; Steamship Mutual; Thomas R Millers.

Norton Rose Although historically considered a bolt-on to the firm's superior asset financing arm, the firm's litigation team is now being taken seriously in its own right. Known for the strength of its dry and commodities practices, the firm is acknowledged to be building up wet side strength, making a number of lateral hires. Overseas offices in Piraeus and Singapore have also been key elements in raising the firm's all-round profile. **Chris Hobbs** *("smooth and good with clients")* is the club man, (particularly within the Italian market) although he is also known for his oil and gas commodities work. **Juliet Blanch**, meanwhile, straddles both wet and dry, and is particularly prominent in the US and Mediterranean cruise and passenger ship markets. On the ship financing side, the firm's profile is on the up, with both **John Shelton** (debt restructuring) and **Jeremy Gibb** (leasing) considered practitioners of unusual merit. **Simon Hartley** *("well organised and calm")* is ranked for the first time this year. The team acts for a range of owners, managers, clubs and underwriters and acted for ANZ Investment Bank in documenting a large syndicated loan facility in connection with the construction of the first LNG carrier for transportation from the Middle East to the Dabhol power plant in India. The firm has also acted on the Ya Mawlaya collision action. **Clients:** Columbia Ship Management; North of England P&I, A. Bilbrough & Co Ltd; Stena Group, P&O Group.

Sinclair Roche & Temperley After some much publicised personnel departures in recent years, the firm continues to surprise the market with the speed with which it has turned things around. Although still viewed as lacking a sprinkling of 'big hitters', the firm moves up in wet and receives good market feedback for its impressive financing arm. Indeed, it is for ship financing work that the firm is best known, due mainly to its impressive international banking clients. Bolstered by the recent addition of two specialists from Constant & Constant, the team is particularly strong in the German and Scandinavian markets where it has long-standing connections. The team notably represented Kreditanstalt fur Wiederaufbau in a complex structured UK tax lease transaction for a £250 million containerships contract. Also active in the cruise ship and ferry markets. On the wet side, **Joe Atkinson** is ranked for the first time and is viewed to be *"quietly yet competently"* increasing the firm's market presence. The practice is widely perceived to get a high volume of litigation (wet and dry) referrals from its banking clients. Well connected within the German, South East Asian and Korean owner markets, the team also acts for a range of owners and charterers. **Clients:** Kreditanstalt fur Wiederaufbau; Commerzbank; Daewoo; Den Norske Bank; owners/charterers/tankers.

Stephenson Harwood The firm attracts mixed views from the market this year, possessing undoubted *"pockets of excellence"* although appearing to lack identity as a group. The firm's reputation in this area continues to lie with its ship financiers whose competitive fee structures and volume output afford the team excellent market coverage. Lead partner **Mark Russell** *("an intelligent practitioner")* is known to act predominantly for interna-

SHIPPING: FINANCE • London	Ptnrs	Assts
❶ Norton Rose	8	20
❷ Watson, Farley & Williams	27	54
❸ Allen & Overy	18	25
Stephenson Harwood	3	-
❹ Clifford Chance	4	12
Sinclair Roche & Temperley	6	7

LEADING INDIVIDUALS	
❶ **SHELTON John** Norton Rose	**WATSON Martin** Watson, Farley & Williams
❷ **FARLEY Alastair** Watson, Farley & Williams	**SMITH David** Allen & Overy
❸ **GIBB Jeremy** Norton Rose	**RUSSELL Mark** Stephenson Harwood
WARDER David Watson, Farley & Williams	
❹ **TURNER Paul** Clifford Chance	
UP AND COMING	
HARTLEY Simon Norton Rose	

Within each band, firms are listed alphabetically. *See **Profiles** on page 743*

tional shipyards and owners – the firm is particularly well-connected in Piraeus and Singapore where they have established offices. The finance department provides the dry litigators with a substantial amount of court-approved sales and mortgage enforcement work. The litigation team is known for its involvement in complex foreign litigation, with **Paolo Ghirardani** *("forever on your back but does an unbelievable job for his clients")* considered a star performer for his asset tracing work. **Steven Lowe** is also mentioned for his shipping and re-insurance practice. The team acted for a P&I club to assist in negotiations leading to the release of a crew held hostage on the Dubai Valour for two years in an inland Nigerian port. **Clients:** Greek owners; banks; owners; clubs; insurers.

Bentleys, Stokes & Lowless A good review overall for this diverse, (predominantly) dry and related insurance practice. **Andrew Bardot** *("smart, civilised and astute")* has strong connections with the Italian hull and owners insurance market. The firm's international client base is reflected in its strong ties with the Scandinavian (particularly Denmark) and North African owners markets. **Vernon Sewell** *("cerebral – one for complicated points")* makes his debut in the ratings and is considered to have a strong and diverse following. **Clients:** International owners.

Clifford Chance Perceived as a *"mega-case"* firm which, whilst lacking market profile for day to day shipping work, is known to be largely synonymous with the bigger-ticket deals. On the litigation side, the team's reputation rests on the shoulders of charismatic partner **Tony Vlasto** *("a superstar in the City")* who receives overwhelming praise from the London market. Known historically for the quality of his wet practice, his caseload now straddles most aspects of contentious shipping including some mortgage enforcement work. The team continues to advise NYK on a significant dispute with the shipyard CIBC, involving three new buildings. On the ship financing side the team is active in the highly remunerative cruise and ferry markets. Notable examples of work include cruise industry projects for Star Cruises, Norwegian Cruise Line and Residensea. **Paul Turner** enters our tables for the first time and is known to be well connected within the Korean owners market. **Clients:** Owners; clubs, insurers, charterers.

Constant & Constant The firm is working more closely with its Paris office, particularly on non-contentious matters. This has, in turn, increased the team's European dry presence as work spins off from the financing arm. However, while its share of French work is increasing, the London market considers the firm to be marking time. **Tony Miller**'s retirement from head of wet to become a consultant will affect the firm's profile in this area and the team currently lacks a big hitter. On the wet side the team retains solid links with Japanese and Chilean owners, while the dry team is well-connected within the Italian, French and Icelandic markets. Dry litigator, **Graham Crane**, *("a considered guy")* is involved in international arbitration work for P&I Clubs. He was involved in a substantial $600 million arbitration in Italy relating to a partnership dispute over ownership of a shipbuilding company. **Clients:** Clubs; Total (French Operator); owners.

Holmes Hardingham The team has been commended by many elements of the London market this year. Dry litigator **Glenn Winter** is considered a *"charterparty specialist,"* although he is also involved, to a lesser extent, in some large cargo claims for owners and clubs. He is known to have links with the Scandinavian club market. On the wet side, **Ken Scott** makes a *"long overdue"* entry into our tables for his impressive UK salvage and international collision practice. The team is perceived to have a *"fairly small yet extremely loyal clientele."* **Clients:** Skuld; Stolt Nielson(US owner); BP for lubricant and bunker work.

Jackson Parton Described by some as *"bullish"* and others as *"aggressive,"* the firm is thought to have *"charismatic and well-organised"* individual lawyers. Largely a dry practice, the team is reliant on club work, and has long-standing connections with the Greek and Dutch markets. Name partner **Nick Parton** is considered a *"star"* and has particular experience in Francophone jurisdictions. **Philip Bush** *("a one-off")* is admired by most for his firm litigation style. The team are also involved in a significant amount of Japanese work, where they have language capability. **Clients:** P&I Clubs; shipowners and operators; charterers; trading houses.

More Fisher Brown Perceived as a *"firm on the up,"* with particularly strong P&I club ties. **Tony Brown** stands out. A sound firm with a staunch client base, it acts most notably for the clubs. Dry litigator **Eddie Gray**, *"frighteningly clever, yet incredibly good to do business with,"* is a new addition to the rankings. The team handles a variety of litigation, including class actions and casualties. **Clients:** P&I clubs; charterers.

Thomas Cooper & Stibbard Perceived to have turned the corner after a difficult last decade. Nevertheless, the firm's international coverage (Athens and Singapore) is thought to have bolstered its profile in London. **David Hebden** is universally considered a major player, and it is mainly due to his high profile that the firm has re-entered our wet table. The team were involved in the 'Aconcagua', 'Lancer' and 'Tyne' salvage cases. On the dry side, **Douglas Bateson** is an *"extremely clever"* lawyer, known to be particularly active in the Spanish and South American markets. An increasing amount of this work has been cargo-related, although many in the market regard him as being more involved in commodities work, particularly oil and gas. Notable examples of work include the 'Metro', 'Maersk Tokyo' and 'Contship Harmony' international trade cases. **Clients:** Exxon; owners; insurers.

Watson, Farley & Williams Considered an *"immense force"* in international financings although, for the more complex structured deals, it is thought to lack the substantial capital markets expertise of its nearest competitor. Nonetheless, the firm's strength in New York and Paris cannot be underestimated and gives the London team its edge. Led by **Martin Watson** *("a phenomenon")* and ex-senior partner **Alistair Farley** *("now back at the coalface")*, the team acts for both banks and owners and has particularly strong connections within the French and Scandinavian markets. **David Warder** *("intellect, tenacity and ability")* enters our tables for the first time this year. On the dry litigation side, **Tony Rooth** *("brilliant")* appears to have steadied the ship and is building an impressive practice. Known to have strong long-standing Turkish owner connections, the team is kept busy by the firm's overall blue chip client base, and a smaller amount of P&I Club work. **Clients:** Owners; clubs.

Barlow Lyde & Gilbert A respected practice viewed as quietly but consistently performing for an *"extremely loyal client base."* Although historically viewed as an insurance practice, the firm has an increasingly diverse clientele, including a larger cargo and financing presence. The inherent quality of the team's dry practice hinges upon the excellent market reputation of **Ray Mead**. His *"focused and effective"* style is much admired. The firm has gained a growing number of referrals from Greek practitioners, cultivated by a dual qualified UK/Greek lawyer. Advised the Greek liquidator on a US$400 million claim against Metro Trading International. On the (less well-known) wet side, the team have advised the insurers and owners in respect to a stern failure to the ship 'Kraka' off South Africa. **Clients:** Owners; cargo interests; insurers.

Curtis Davis Garrard A *"turbulent year"* for this Heathrow-based firm which has made a number of partner hires, as well as suffering well-publicised defections. However, ship-building expert **Simon Curtis** *("he wrote the book – quite literally")* garners high praise as a *"hard but effective opponent."* Known particularly for the quality of its off-shore shipping and commodities practice, the team have been involved in big-ticket projects and disputes. **Clients:** Louis Dreyfus Armateurs.

Fishers. Nick Fisher receives high praise from his London competitors although his *"lack of support"* was constantly mentioned. He has a significant client base in container reefer and tanker operations. **Clients:** Container owners.

Lawrence Graham The firm has not had an easy time this year, their fortunes being strongly allied with the former Soviet Union market. High praise continues to be heaped on **Michael Lax**, who is consistently viewed as an *"aggressive yet effective"* litigator. The market feeling that *"it's Michael or no-one,"* however, is seen as a weakness for the firm. **Clients:** Owners; charterers; P&I Clubs.

Middleton Potts Although viewed primarily as a niche commodities practice, the team retain a respected dry presence within the London market. Much of this reputation hinges upon the high profile of **Andrew Donoghue** *("one of the best dry lawyers in London")* who is well respected by clubs and commodity houses alike. The team have a strong Scandinavian club practice and are known to be active within the Italian hull insurance market. Whilst oil and energy work appears to be a major growth area, the team have an acknowledged expertise on liquid bulk cargoes. **Russell Ridley** *("a strong understanding of client's needs")* is particularly well respected in this area. The team have advised on some high profile cases this year: the 'Berge Sisar' – alleged contamination of cargo; the 'Baltic Flame' – interpretation of the Carriage of Goods by Sea Act and the 'Maersk Blazer' – alleged termination of the charterparty of anchor handler and rig support. **Clients:** P&I clubs; International commodity houses; Skuld; Swedish Club; Southern Seas.

Shaw and Croft Perceived as *"a firm you can do business with,"* its individual lawyers are seen as both *"intelligent and commercial."* **Roger Croft** *("runs a tight ship")* is well known by the London market for his wet expertise, although he has been kept particularly busy this year by an international fraud case. Newly made up partner, **Mark Aspinall,** has a solid reputation for his tanker trade practice. The firm is increasing the amount of work undertaken in Eastern Europe and Italy, where they have language capability. This work is usually dry litigation. The team's diverse practice is illustrated by its super yacht and fishing vessel transactional work. **Clients:** Salvage companies; owners; The Mediterranean Yacht Brokers Association.

Waltons & Morse *"Personable"* specialist shipping and transit practice known predominantly for representing cargo underwriters in salvage and collision work. **Roy Ginsberg** *("a very sensible pair of hands")*, very much the figurehead of the group, is known to be well-connected within the London market. Involved in some headline casualty work including the well publicised 'Ever Decent'/'Norwegian Dream' collision. The firm's relatively small dry presence hinges predominantly on container operator work for the German Defence Club and a long-standing connection with one major Japanese operator. **Clients:** Cargo underwriters; hull underwriters; owners.

Allen & Overy A relative newcomer to the ship financing world, the firm are being carefully watched by the more established market players *("you never underestimate A&O")*. Although its current penetration is thought to be relatively small, the team is establishing a reputation for undertaking some extremely *"sexy"* (i.e. complex and highly remunerative) transactional work. The firm's superior capital markets and banking expertise is an obvious advantage. The focal point of the team is (ex-Wilde Sapte partner) **David Smith** *("aggressive when required")* who is considered an expert on structured leasing deals. The team acts predominantly for banks, although two ship owners have been added to the client base this year. Advised on the headline US$262m financing for the construction of 'ultra-luxury' apartments at sea. **Clients:** Banks, owners.

THE SOUTH & SOUTH WEST

SHIPPING • The South & South West	Ptnrs	Assts
❶ Davies, Johnson & Co Plymouth	4	3
DMH Brighton	-	2
Foot Anstey Sargent Plymouth	2	3
Grant & Horton Marine Solicitors Plymouth	⚐	⚐

LEADING INDIVIDUALS	
❶ HORTON Nicholas Grant & Horton Marine Solicitors	
JOHNSON Jonathan Davies, Johnson & Co	
❷ HAYES Barry Hayes	KELLY Russell Shoosmiths

Within each band, firms are listed alphabetically. See **Profiles** on page 743

⚐ *Figures unavailable at time of going to press.*

Davies, Johnson & Co A respected niche practice consisting of ex-City lawyers. Known to have strong Greek, Dutch and Norwegian connections, the firm are involved in dry shipping and related commodities work. Strong Scandinavian P&I connections drive the dry practice which is active in charterparty disputes. Name partner **Jonny Johnson** (ex-Richards Butler) is known to be *"great with clients"* and is well known both within and outside the London market. **Clients:** Major P&I clubs; oil and commodity traders; European owners.

DMH Retain an impressive reputation in the market despite the loss of the respected Michael Bloomfield to a niche City practice. Yachting work dominates the team's advice in this area, although its commercial shipping work is aided by the firm's personal injury and finance capability. On the yacht side, the team is involved in all aspects of both wet and dry work, including buying and selling, salvage and marine personal injury. The commercial practice is predominantly P&I Club based yet also contains an international element – the team's client base includes Greek, Sudanese and Romanian owners. Involved in prolonged limitation of liability proceedings in the Court of Appeal, arising from a collision between two privately owned vessels. **Clients:** Owners; insurers; port authorities.

Foot Anstey Sargent The firm receives mixed (and frequently strong) views from the market. Known predominantly for acting for plaintiffs in commercial wet disputes, the firm is involved regularly in some high value shipbuilding contracts. On behalf of Devonport Management Limited, for example, the team have been involved in assisting, drafting and finalising in excess of £80 million worth of contracts this year. Despite the department's *"aggressive"* litigation style, it has continued its involvement in some substantial 'total loss' and 'limitation of liability' proceedings. Notable cases include the MV 'Rema', acting for the owners, and the MFV 'Margaretha Maria' acting for the crew claimants. The team have expanded its client base into Germany, Finland and the US. **Clients:** Georg Duncker; Riverside Fabrications Limited; Nordrey Shipping Limited; P&I Clubs; marine insurers; hull and machinery insurers (Fishing Industry.)

Grant & Horton Marine Solicitors A Plymouth based practice whose expansion into Southampton is indicative of a sustained push on the commercial shipping side. Perceived to be *"out on their own"* for yachting advice, the team also carry out some local salvage work. Name partner **Nick Horton** is considered by most to be pre-eminent for yachting advice on the south coast and a *"sensible head on comparatively young shoulders."* **Clients:** Salvors.

Other Notable Practitioners Sole practitioner **Barry Hayes** *("sensible and dedicated to his clients")* enjoys a solid personal reputation within UK shipping circles. His marine insurance niche is viewed as an essentially dry practice with a small amount of salvage work, and he has a particular reputation for acting for insurers on the cargo side. **Russell Kelly** has recently joined Shoosmiths (Solent) from Bond Pearce. He is widely respected and is known to have a substantial client following.

EAST ANGLIA

SHIPPING • East Anglia	Ptnrs	Assts
❶ **Dale & Co Solicitors** Felixstowe	1	2
Eversheds Ipswich	-	2
John Weston & Co Felixstowe	1	-

LEADING INDIVIDUALS	
❶ **DALE Michael** Dale & Co Solicitors	**KEMP Jonathan** Eversheds
WESTON John John Weston & Co	
❷ **WHITE-THOMSON John** Birketts	

Within each band, firms are listed alphabetically. *See* **Profiles** *on page 743*

Dale & Co Solicitors Experienced shipping lawyer **Michael Dale** drives this diverse Felixstowe niche practice. Active in local, national and international markets, the team have a substantial P&I Club bent, but also represent local freight forwarders and Swiss oil traders. Close links with the German shipping market have provided some owner work. **Clients:** International P&I Clubs; freight forwarders; Swiss oil traders.

Eversheds A small team which works closely with its more developed Newcastle office. Former mariner (and ex-Sinclair Roche & Temperley lawyer) **Jonathan Kemp** is thought to have a *"good pedigree"* for both wet and dry work. The majority of the firm's work is P&I club (including defence FF&D work) and owner-related, although international commodities work (mainly grain) and marine personal injury advice are also key features of the practice. Internationally, the team represented a Turkish owner on a collision in Middle Eastern waters while locally, the firm acted in connection with the development of a major coastal port. **Clients:** International P&I clubs; shipowners.

John Weston & Co The practice is well known within the local market and is held in high esteem by local lawyers for both its wet and dry capability. Known to have solid P&I club ties, **John Weston** *("plays with a straight bat")* is well respected within shipping circles. In fact, his *"no-nonsense, distinctive"* style led one interviewee to term him the *"Geoffrey Boycott of shipping."* **Clients:** Oil traders; international P&I Clubs; freight forwarders.

Other Notable Practitioners **John White-Thomson** is the respected head of Birketts' shipping practice, and has gained a reputation as a *"reliable all-rounder."*

THE NORTH

SHIPPING: DRY • The North	Ptnrs	Assts
❶ **Hill Dickinson** Liverpool	5*	7*
Mills & Co Newcastle-upon-Tyne	5	4
Rayfield Mills Newcastle-upon-Tyne	7	4
❷ **Andrew M. Jackson & Co** Hull	1	1
DLA Liverpool, Manchester	3	3
Eversheds Newcastle upon Tyne	4	5

SHIPPING: WET • The North	Ptnrs	Assts
❶ **Andrew M. Jackson & Co** Hull	1	2
Hill Dickinson Liverpool	5	7
Rayfield Mills Newcastle-upon-Tyne	3	1
❷ **DLA** Liverpool, Manchester	1	1
Eversheds Newcastle upon Tyne	4	5

LEADING INDIVIDUALS: WET & DRY	
❶ **HILL Martin** DLA	**HILTON Chris** Eversheds
MAWDSLEY David DLA	**MAXWELL John** Hill Dickinson
MILLS Stephen Rayfield Mills	**PENROSE Robert** Andrew M. Jackson & Co
RAYFIELD Richard Rayfield Mills	**TAYLOR Silas** Andrew M. Jackson & Co
WAREING David Hill Dickinson	
❷ **BROWN Alistdair** Mills & Co	**MACKIN Stephen** Eversheds
JACKSON Peter Hill Dickinson	**MILLS Geoffrey** Mills & Co
MILLS Guy Mills & Co	**PHILLIPS Raymond** DLA
UP AND COMING	
JEANES Nicola Rayfield Mills	

Within each band, firms are listed alphabetically. *See* **Profiles** *on page 743*
** See editorial entries for explanations of team sizes.*

Hill Dickinson (Figures in tables are totals for wet and dry teams.) The team consists of several very highly rated individuals split between Manchester (Cargo) and Liverpool (Owners.) Perceived to have superb P&I club relationships, the team are considered *"top tier"* for both wet and dry work. **John Maxwell** *("the big case man")* has a stellar reputation acting for shipowners on casualty work and in response to pollution claims. Fellow wet lawyer **David Wareing** meanwhile, has made his name advising owners in cases of crew negligence and with regard to stevedore claims. His profile has dipped slightly this year, however, owing to a more managerial role within the firm. **Peter Jackson** *("commercial and takes realistic positions")* is very well known by the market for both wet and dry work and duly moves up in the tables this year. The team acts for many of the major composite insurers in the UK. **Clients:** Mersey Docks & Harbour Board; Lloyds underwriters; Royal & Sun Alliance; CGU.

Mills & Co A diverse practice known for having *"outstanding individual quality."* Although the practice has its roots in shipbuilding advice, its reputation for classic P&I club dry work has continued. Founding partner **Geoffrey Mills**, while involved to a lesser extent these days, is considered *"an absolute authority"* on shipbuilding contracts and continues to represent British Shipbuilders in 'The Derbyshire' enquiry. His reputation for this type of work was viewed as *"beyond compare."* **Alistdair Brown** operates in a similar vein, although his focus is on heavy engineering off-shore shipping work for European shipbuilders and ship repair yards. **Guy Mills**, (son of Geoffrey) is seen to be increasingly well connected with the P&I Clubs, where the team has built a leading position. **Clients:** British shipbuilders; P&I clubs; ship repair yards.

Rayfield Mills An essentially dry practice specialising in marine insurance work, policy disputes and commodity trading. Have a serious P&I club presence which has led to market perception of a narrowness of focus. Both name partners **Stephen Mills** *("sensible and extremely thorough")* and **Richard Rayfield** are considered by the market to be excellent dry litigators whilst up and coming **Nicola Jeanes** is considered responsible for the expansion in the firm's ship finance work over the past twelve months. The team represented Exxon Mobil in connection with the collapse of a major bunker supplier in the Middle East. **Clients:** Exxon Mobil; Swiss Commodity Traders; European and North American ship Management Companies; P&I Clubs.

Andrew M. Jackson & Co The team is well-known by the London market for both wet and dry work and its associated Falklands office has increased its number of South American instructions, particularly from Chile. On the wet side, **Silas Taylor** is considered a *"sensible operator"* with superb P&I Club connections. He has developed a particularly strong reputation for maritime personal injury defence work. Making his debut in our tables this year is **Rob Penrose** who, according to clients, is *"indispensable"* when it comes to specialist fishing vessel transactional work. His long-standing connections with MAAF and *"fantastic response times"* are considered second to none. His global practice has seen him spend much of the past year advising on innovative international joint ventures between European Union and Argentine ship owners. The team are thought to be pushing hard on the cargo side with the addition of a new lawyer this year. **Clients:** International P&I; insurers; trailer owners/bunker; suppliers/chandlers.

DLA An expanding practice which appears to be slowly closing the gap on its great rival Hill Dickinson in the North West. The team undertake the gamut of shipping work, with an impressive triumvirate of lead partners in Liverpool. *"Jack of all trades"* **David Mawdsley** is liked by the market for his *"tenacious yet commercial"* approach. His practice encompasses salvage/collision, cargo (wet or dry) and non-contentious contract work. **Martin Hill** *("a singular guy, gives 110%")* is viewed as the main driving force behind the team's development and is involved mainly in coverage work for the major locally-based and London marine composite insurers. **Raymond Phillips**, meanwhile, is less well known for classic shipping work, although his commodities and ship building profile remains intact. The team have particularly good connections with ferry companies using the Irish Sea and strong individual ties with some P&I Clubs. The relatively small team in Manchester handle recoveries and liability work for the local market. **Clients:** P&I clubs; insurers; ferry companies.

Eversheds (Figures in tables are totals for wet and dry teams.) Seen to be on the rise this year, not least because of the unanimous high praise accorded to the *"master analyst"* **Chris Hilton**. Perceived to be active in the market (despite his role as senior partner), he is known to be well-connected internationally (particularly in Russia and Scandinavia) and to be an *"outstanding shipping lawyer, wet or dry."* The team have had a busy year, notably representing tanker companies in response to oil contamination claim and pumping warranties. **Steve Mackin** *("clients take to him")*, who steps up into the main individuals list, is particularly well known in this regard and is equally adept at handling wet or dry work. The team's good market profile for marine personal injury work has been consolidated. **Clients:** Sovcomflot/UK Club West of England P&I.

SCOTLAND

SHIPPING • Scotland	Ptnrs	Assts
❶ **Henderson Boyd Jackson WS** Edinburgh	2	3
Mackinnons Aberdeen	5	3
Maclay Murray & Spens Glasgow	4	3

LEADING INDIVIDUALS
❶ **LOWE James** Henderson Boyd Jackson WS
MACLEAN Duncan Henderson Boyd Jackson WS
MACRAE Keith Mackinnons
SCOTT Charles Mackinnons

Within each band, firms are listed alphabetically. *See **Profiles** on page 743*

Henderson Boyd Jackson WS Held in high esteem by clients and competitors alike, this broad shipping practice is adept at handling both the contentious and financing aspects of shipping work. Viewed as specialists on oil pollution claims, the team advised Clydeport on the implementation of its national pollution response plan. Department Head, **James Lowe** *("affable and experienced – a practical guy")* covers the gamut of litigious and non-contentious work. He advised BUE Marine with regard to its purchase of a large fleet of ships from US company Tidewater. Litigator **Duncan Maclean,** meanwhile, is considered *"energetic and efficient"* and is rated by the market for *"giving opinions swiftly"*. The pair are viewed in Scotland as an *"extremely cohesive"* partnership. **Clients:** Steamship Mutual (insurer); BUE Marine; MacBrayne (ferry company); J&A Gardner (coastal shipping firm.)

Mackinnons Pre-eminent in the North East of Scotland, the firm's fishing industry expertise is viewed by the market as *"unsurpassed."* Involved in virtually all the major fishing vessel casualties of the past few years, the team are strong in both wet, dry and non-contentious work, including sale and purchase of shipping and fishing vessels, fishing vessel licences and quota advice and, increasingly, personal injury claims. Litigator **Keith Macrae** has the unanimous respect of his peers and is considered *"persistent and committed to the job in hand."* His impressive CV includes both the 'Green Lily' and 'Silvery Sea' casualties. **Charles Scott**, *("considered, doesn't waste time")* meanwhile, is a commercial specialist with particular expertise with regard to shipbuilding contracts. **Clients:** Aberdeen Harbour Authority; International P&I Clubs; Peterhead Bay Authority; International oil companies.

Maclay Murray & Spens Scotland's premier ship financing practice, particularly on the banking side. The team advises on loans and other leasing transactions, as well as undertaking major litigation matters. Acted for BP and their insurers on a multi-million pound claim relating to damage to an oil tanker arising from a collision at Sullom Voe. **Clients:** Skuld; P&I clubs.

LEADERS IN SHIPPING

ASPINALL, Mark
Shaw and Croft, London (020) 7645 9000
mark.aspinall@shawandcroft.com
Specialisation: Main areas of practice are split between shipping litigation of all types but predominantly in tanker operations, including collisions, charterparty disputes, cargo claims and shipbuilding contracts and oil trading disputes involving independent oil traders in connection with contracts for sale of crude and products and associated problems concerning letters of credit and trade finance. Also involved in shipping fraud, asset tracing and joint venture agreements (predominantly in the oil markets).
Prof. Memberships: Baltic Exchange, Institute of Petroleum.
Career: Articled *Shaw & Croft*. Qualified 1994. Partner 1998.
Personal: Born 1962. Lives in London. Leisure interests: golf, tennis, travel and occasional surfing.

ATKINSON, Joe
Sinclair Roche & Temperley, London
(020) 7452 4000
joe.atkinson@srtlaw.com
Partner.
Specialisation: Litigation, arbitration and public enquiry work arising from the full spectrum of marine casualties - collisions with fixed and floating objects, salvage, groundings, wreck removal, actual and constructive total loss, fire and explosion, oil pollution and emergency response.
Prof. Memberships: Association of Average Adjusters.
Career: Joined *Sinclair Roche & Temperley* 13 years ago and from the outset was involved in high-profile casualties such as the Khark V Kowloon Bridge and 'Herald of Free Enterprise'. Became a partner in 1995 and head of the admiralty department in 1996. Has been involved in a number of major casualties all for significant cases over the past decade including 'Nassia', 'Mighty Servant II'/North Nember Project, 'DG

Harmony', 'ABT Summer', 'Patraikos II'.
Publications: Has written a number of articles for the Trade Press on a variety of "wet" topics . Is also a regular speaker at seminars, both in the UK and overseas.
Personal: Born 30 November 1962. Graduated from Aberystwyth University with an honours degree in law and economics.

BARDOT, Andrew
Bentleys, Stokes & Lowless, London
(020) 7782 0990
Specialisation: Qualified 1980. Partner 1982. Principal areas of practice: all aspects of "dry" shipping and insurance related litigation and arbitration and non contentious matters, including sale and purchase and M.O.A. matters. French speaker.
Prof. Memberships: London Maritime Arbitration Association supporting member. Baltic Exchange member.

BATESON, Douglas W.
Thomas Cooper & Stibbard, London
(020) 7481 8851
douglas.bateson@tcssol.com
Specialisation: Specialises in all aspects of international marine law, including charterparties, bills of lading, collisions, salvage and banking; fluent French and Spanish speaker.
Prof. Memberships: Law Society, London Maritime Arbitrators' Association (supporting member). Fellow of the Royal Geographical Society.
Career: Qualified 1985. Partner 1989.

BISHOP, Archie
Holman Fenwick & Willan, London
(020) 7488 2300
Archie.Bishop@hfw.co.uk
Senior Partner.
Specialisation: Main area of practice is Admiralty law, with an emphasis on collision, salvage, oil pollution and marine insurance. Legal advisor to International Salvage Union. Contributes a variety of articles to specialised marine publications. Regular speaker at conferences and seminars. Visiting Lecturer to International Maritime Law Institute of Malta.
Prof. Memberships: Law Society; British Maritime Law Association; City of London Solicitors Company; Royal Institute of Navigation; Average Adjustors Association; Secretary, Admiralty Solicitors Group.
Career: Deck officer with P&O Line 1954-60. Joined *Holman Fenwick & Willan* 1960, became a Partner in 1971 and Senior Partner in 1989. Appointed Examiner in Admiralty 1996.
Personal: Born 21st July 1937. Thames Nautical Training College HMS Worcester 1952-54. British First Mates Foreign Going Certificate 1959, Solicitor 1971. Leisure pursuits horse riding, golf, art and music. Lives in Farnham.

BLANCH, Juliet
Norton Rose, London (020) 7283 6000
blanchjs@nortonrose.com
Specialisation: Partner in the shipping litigation group, commercial litigation department and head of both the marine insurance and the international arbitration groups; specialises in passenger/cruise ships, disaster litigation, marine insurance, all types of charterparty and bill of lading disputes; has major casualty experience in connection with lost passenger vessels, together with all related insurance aspects; also experienced in oil and commodity disputes; ship building and ship repair disputes; and banking and international trade disputes; regular speaker at international conferences on shipping law; and editor of the *Norton Rose* Disputes Resolution Newsletter. Recent cases include: representing owners and their P & I Clubs in relation to the losses of the 'Pegasus', 'Oceanos' and 'Katerina SG' and representing hull and machinery underwriters of the 'Achille Lauro'; representing cruise indemnity underwriters in relation to the 'Saga Rose', 'Starship Oceanic' and 'Odysseus'; representing steel traders Transworld on multi-jurisdictional dispute; representing diamond producers Archangel Diamond Corporation in exploration and production dispute - Clients include all the major P & I Clubs; CoeClerici; Fortum Oil and Gas Oy; Royal Olympic Cruises; Varnima, Archangel Diamond Corporation and the Transworld Group.
Prof. Memberships: London Maritime Arbitrators Association; London Court of International Arbitration; The Baltic Exchange.
Career: Articled *Norton Rose* 1986-88; Qualified 1988; Partner 1997.
Personal: Married with three children.

BOWMAN, Marcus
Holman Fenwick & Willan, London
(020) 7488 2300
Marcus.Bowman@hfw.co.uk
Specialisation: Partner in shipping litigation department. Specialising in maritime litigation with emphasis on charterparty and bill of lading disputes; P & I claims handler for seven years.
Career: Oceanus P & I club, 1980-83; Britannia P & I club, 1983-87; articled *Holman Fenwick & Willan*; qualified 1990; partner 1993; solicitor of the Supreme Court of England and Wales. University of Cape Town (BA); University of London (LLM).
Personal: Born 1954. Resides London.

BROWN, Alistdair B.
Mills & Co, Newcastle-upon-Tyne
(0191) 233 2222

BROWN, Anthony
More Fisher Brown, London (020) 7247 0438
abrown@m-f-b.co.uk
Specialisation: Commercial shipping litigation, with particular involvement in container transport, stowage collapses (containers and general cargoes), fire and total loss cases. Currently acting in 'Nedlloyd Recife' (grounded off Sao Francisco do Sul, March 1996) and 'Albion Two' (total loss, February 1997). Fluent German speaker, hence significant client base in Hamburg, Bremen and Lubeck. Also has close contacts in the Korean and Croatian markets. Frequent speaker on shipping topics both in the UK and overseas.
Prof. Memberships: Law Society, LMAA.
Career: Exeter School and Trinity Hall, University of Cambridge. Admitted as a soliciter May 1981 while with *Richards Butler*. Founder partner of *More Fisher Brown* June 1988.

BROWNE, Benjamin
Clyde & Co, Guildford (01483) 555 555
Partner in Marine Casualty Department.
Specialisation: Specialises in all aspects of marine casualties, in particular salvage, collision, oil pollution, general average, transhipments and disputes arising from contracts of carriage of goods by sea. Advises marine cargo, hull and P&I insurers, shipowners, charterers and oil companies on shipping problems. Advisor to the International Underwriting Association of London and Lloyd's Underwriters' Association on salvage matters. Member of Lloyd's Open Form (Salvage) Working Party, Salvage Liaison Group, three man SCOPIC Drafting Committee and British Maritime Law Association General Average Sub-committee. Co-ordinated the Ocean Marine Mutual Members Action Group following the Provisional Liquidation of that P & I Club. Has contributed many articles, chapters and papers on salvage, collision, general average and oil pollution. Has a special interest in the Middle East where he helped establish the firm's Middle East Regional Office in Dubai.
Prof. Memberships: Fellow of the Institute of Advanced Legal Studies, Member of Comite Maritime International, Subscriber to Average Adjusters' Association, Middle East Association, Indian Maritime Association.
Career: Qualified in 1978 while at *Lovell White & King*. *Morrell Peel & Gamlen*, Oxford 1979-81. Joined *Clyde & Co* in 1981 and became a Partner in 1985.
Personal: Born 18th May 1953. Educated Eton College and Trinity College, Cambridge.

BUSH, Philip
Jackson Parton, London (020) 7702 0085
Specialisation: Formerly an equity partner with *Richards Butler*, Philip Bush has been influential in the rapid rise of *Jackson Parton*'s reputation and profile in London's shipping law sector. Primarily renowned as a litigator specialising in sale and purchase, charterparty and bill of lading matters, he also acts regularly in Bank/Borrower workout situations and advises a number of owners, charterers, operators and traders in non-contentious commercial and strategic issues. His promotion of commercially sensible swift dispute resolution has resulted in several appointments as mediator.

CRANE, Graham
Constant & Constant, London (020) 7261 0006
Partner in shipping department.
Specialisation: Dry shipping litigation and arbitration, including carriage of goods by sea, charterparties, cargo claims and bill of lading disputes. Acts primarily for P&I Clubs, Defence Associations, shipowners and charterers. London partner responsible for French offices; fluent French speaker.
Prof. Memberships: Law Society, supporting member London Maritime Arbitrators Association and Association Française Du Droit Maritime.
Career: Joined *Constant & Constant* 1973, qualified 1975. Partner 1978.

CROFT, Roger
Shaw and Croft, London (020) 7645 9000
roger.croft@shawandcroft.com
Senior partner specialising in admiralty law and insurance law.
Specialisation: Principal area of practice is admiralty and insurance law. Work includes collision, salvage, pollution, environmental damage and total loss. Other main area of practice is fraud and money laundering. Acted in the Goring (House of Lords), the Mare (Court of Appeal) cases and KOTC v. Al Bader & Others (Court of Appeal). Clients include major shipowners, salvors, insurers and P&I clubs.
Prof. Memberships: Law Society, City of London Solicitors Company, London Maritime Arbitrators Association, Royal Institute of Navigation, Average

Adjusters Association, Admiralty Solicitors Group, International Bunker Industry Association, Worshipful Company of Shipwrights.
Career: Joined the Royal Navy in 1962. Electronic Engineer from 1967. Qualified in 1978. Senior partner at *Shaw and Croft* from 1992.
Personal: Born 19th May 1946. Educated at Wallington County Grammar School and London University. Interests include golf, cricket, music, gardening and reading.

CRUMP, Richard
Holman Fenwick & Willan, London
(020) 7488 2300
Richard.Crump@hfw.co.uk
Partner in Commercial Litigation Department.
Specialisation: Practice encompasses all areas of shipping litigation, including charterparty disputes, cargo claims, ship sale disputes, joint venture and pool agreement disputes and related commercial litigation. Has spoken at seminars in Athens and Bombay. Accredited CEDR Mediator.
Prof. Memberships: Law Society Member.
Career: Qualified in 1981 having joined *Holman Fenwick & Willan* in 1979. Became a Partner in 1987.
Personal: Born 6th September 1957. Educated at St. Paul's School, London 1970-74, Oriel College, Oxford 1975-78 and College of Law, Guildford 1979. Lives in London.

CURTIS, Simon R.
Curtis Davis Garrard, Heathrow Airport
(020) 8400 2400
simon.curtis@cdg.co.uk
Partner in shipping group.
Specialisation: Main area of practice is shipping and offshore (oil and gas) work. Covers range of maritime litigation matters and non-contentious project work principally relating to shipbuilding, conversion and repair. Author of 'The Law of Shipbuilding Contracts', Lloyd's of London Press (2nd edition). Contributor to 'Force Majeure and Frustration of Contracts' (2nd Edition), Lloyds of London Press. Regular speaker at conferences on maritime law.
Prof. Memberships: London Maritime Arbitrators Association (Supporting Member). Fellow of the Chartered Institute of Arbitrators.
Career: Joined *Ince & Co.* in 1979. Qualified 1982. Left to join *Watson Farley & Williams* in 1984. Partner 1986 in Litigation Department. Left in 1996 to establish *Curtis Davis Garrard*, a specialist shipping, offshore and energy law practice based at London's Heathrow Airport.
Personal: Born 10th November 1955. Attended Jesus College, Oxford BA (Hons) (1st Class) (Davies Prize 1977) and Bachelor of Civil Law. Leisure pursuits include scuba diving, skiing and fishing. Lives in Berkshire.

DALE, Michael
Dale & Co Solicitors, Felixstowe 07074 794708

DE LA RUE, Colin
Ince & Co, London (020) 7623 2011
Specialisation: With others in the firm he has acted in most major oil pollution incidents worldwide in the last 15 years and on a day-to-day basis advises shipowners, oil companies, P & I Clubs, marine underwriters and others. Extensive experience of claims under compensation conventions and on the commercial ramifications of the subject. Has spoken on marine pollution and disaster response at seminars and conferences in many countries around the world.
Prof. Memberships: British Maritime Law Association Pollution Sub-Committee; elected titulary member of the ComitÈ Maritime International for work in drafting the Guidelines on Oil Pollution Damage adopted by the CMI Conference in 1994.
Career: Bar Finals 1977; admitted as solicitor 1980; partner *Ince & Co* 1986; head of firm's pollution group; General Editor of 'Liability for Damage to the Marine Environment' and co-author of 'Shipping and the Environment' (LLP, 1998), the main textbook on the subject; Visiting Lecturer in Shipping Law at the City University Business School in London 1986-96.
Personal: Born 11th October 1953. Education: Elizabeth College, Guernsey and Pembroke College, Cambridge (modern languages and law). Married with three children. Lives in Woodbridge, Suffolk. Spare time activities include golf, tennis, natural history and music.

DEERING, Bob
Ince & Co, London (020) 7623 2011
Specialisation: Joined *Ince & Co* in 1976; Partner in 1985. Over the years has become involved in all aspects of the firm's shipping practice such that now represents a number of substantial ship owners and P&I Clubs both in their own capacity and on behalf of their shipowner members. Also acts for Underwriters in the investigation of hull claims and, as a result, has experience of casualties from all sides of the fence.
Prof. Memberships: Law Society.
Career: Pembroke College, Cambridge. Joined *Ince & Co* 1976. Qualified 1978. Partner 1985.
Personal: Married, 3 children. Sport - both watching and playing.

DONITHORN, Michael
Holman Fenwick & Willan, London
(020) 7488 2300
Michael.Donithorn@hfw.co.uk
Partner in Commercial Litigation Department.
Specialisation: Principal area of practice is marine litigation. Specialises in commercial disputes arising from casualties. Particular experience of bulk and liner trades, P&I insurance and liability insurance generally. Other areas of practice are marine insurance and international sale of goods. Clients include major P&I clubs, liner operators, time charter operators, bulk vessel owners, gas carrier owners and market underwriters. CEDR Accredited Mediator.
Prof. Memberships: Law Society, BMLA, LMAA (supporting member), Member of Baltic Exchange.
Career: Called to the Bar 1974. Practiced at the Bar 1974-76. Lawyer for West of England P&I Club 1976-78. Joined *Coward Chance* 1978. Admitted Solicitor 1980. Partner at *Coward Chance* (subsequently *Clifford Chance*) 1984-94. Joined *Holman Fenwick & Willan* as a Partner in 1994.
Personal: Born 27th January 1951. Educated at Cannock Grammar School 1962-69, Balliol College, Oxford 1969-72 (BA Hons, Modern History 1972, MA 1979) and the College of Law, Chancery Lane 1972-74. Leisure pursuits include farming. Lives in Surrey.

DONOGHUE, Andrew
Middleton Potts, London (020) 7600 2333
Partner in shipping litigation department.
Specialisation: Main areas of practice are charterparty, bill of lading and ship sale & purchase disputes together with problems arising under contracts for the international sale of goods. Acts primarily for P&I Clubs, Defence Associations and individual shipowners, charterers and commodity houses.
Prof. Memberships: Supporting Member LMAA.
Career: M.A. Degree in Jurisprudence, Lincoln College, Oxford 1973; articled clerk and assistant solicitor *Richards Butler & Co* 1974-80. With *Middleton Potts* since 1980.
Personal: Born 15th November 1951. Leisure interests: mountaineering, naval and ancient history.

EAST, Lindsay
Richards Butler, London (020) 7247 6555
Partner. Head of Shipping and Insurance Group.
Specialisation: Main area of practice is shipping and insurance. Acts for owners and charterers direct or through their insurers (P&I and defence clubs) in all contractual disputes, charterparty, bill of lading, MOA, and building contracts. Particular expertise in drafting and advising on club rules and shipbuilding disputes. Also handles general marine and non-marine insurance, acting for cargo insurers and reinsurers and war-risk underwriters. Cases have included 'Antaios', 'Antares', 'Antonis P. Lemos', Standard Steamship v. Gann, 'Aditya Vaibhav', 'Aegean Maritime v. Flender Werft' and 'Sagheera'. Speaker at and chairman of various seminars.
Prof. Memberships: Baltic Exchange.
Career: Qualified in 1973, having joined *Richards Butler* in 1971. Became a Partner in 1977.
Personal: Born 24th March 1949. Attended Skinners School to 1966, then Worcester College, Oxford 1967-70 (MA Jurisprudence). Leisure interests include cricket, golf, opera and travel. Lives in Rickmansworth, Herts.

EVANS, John
Hill Taylor Dickinson, London (020) 7283 9033
john.evans@htd-london.com
Specialisation: Shipping and insurance litigation. A partner for 20 years, who has practised shipping and marine insurance litigation/arbitration throughout his career. Wide experience of resolution of disputes and pursuit of claims arising from major maritime casualties including actual and constructive total losses of vessels. Group leader of one of the firm's maritime and insurance litigation groups, leading a team of professional staff, including two solicitors who were formerly Master Mariners. Cases of interest include Ventouris v. Mountain (Italia Express); Choko Star; Royal Volker Stevin v. Mountain; Dutch Dredgers; Star Sea; Apostolis and Tjaskemolen. He is the partner in London responsible for the firm's Piraeus office.
Prof. Memberships: A supporting Member of LMAA, and inter alia a Member of the British Italian Lawyers' Association, of the BMLA and the IBA.
Career: Llandovery College; University College of Wales, Aberystwyth (1972 LLB).
Personal: Resides Stebbing.

FARLEY, Alastair
Watson, Farley & Williams, London
(020) 7814 8000

FISHER, Nicholas
Fishers, London (020) 7709 7203
info@fishcity.co.uk
Partner specialising in commercial shipping litigation, insurance and reinsurance litigation.
Specialisation: Handles commercial shipping litiga-

tion, including significant client base in container, reefer and tanker operations. Also insurance and reinsurance litigation involving brokers' PI claims.
Prof. Memberships: London Maritime Arbitrators Association (Supporting Member), Baltic Exchange, The City of London Solicitors' Company.
Career: Qualified in 1979. Partner at *Richards Butler* 1984-88. Founding Partner of *More Fisher Brown* 1988-93. Founded *Fishers* in May 1993.
Personal: Educated at Glyn Grammar School, Epsom, then Clare College, Cambridge (MA).

FLETCHER, Simon
Clyde & Co, Guildford (01483) 555 555
Senior partner in marine casualty department.
Specialisation: On the 'wet' side: salvage, collision, transhipment, general average for cargo, ship, salvor and banking clients including cargo, hull, P&I and MII insurance matters - recent cases: collision between EVER DECENT and NORWEGIAN DREAM and the sinking of the MIGHTY SERVANT 2. On the energy litigation side: acting for insurers, oil companies and contractors, mainly in respect of insurance, construction and operating problems including PIPER ALPHA and SLEIPNER A. Seconded to an oil company for 18 months regarding an FPSO construction dispute and now involved in disputes concerning flexible risers, process skid construction and single point mooring for an FSU.
Prof. Memberships: The Law Society, Chairman of the BMLA Sub-committee for Offshore Structures.
Career: LLB (Hons) Manchester 1968. Qualified and joined *Clyde & Co.* in 1971. Became a partner 1975.

GHIRARDANI, Paolo
Stephenson Harwood, London (020) 7809 2612
paolo.ghirardani@shlegal.com
Partner, Head of the Dry Litigation Group.
Specialisation: Handles all areas of dry shipping litigation. However he has developed a highly successful niche practice area - shipping fraud - with a particular emphasis on Africa. Regularly represents the interests of leading shipowners, P&I Clubs and underwriters. Investigates fraudulent cargo shortage claims - in bulk and containerised cargoes. Has made over 30 investigative trips to West Africa, including sailing on client vessels to conduct "undercover" investigations. Most of the cases involve complex evidence, the threat of prolonged arrests of clients' vessels in foreign jurisdictions and innovative legal tactics, especially on jurisdictional issues. Has gained a reputation as a tough, determined and well-respected lawyer. Has lectured at various seminars in the UK and abroad on fraud investigation and prevention in containerised and bulk cargoes. Reported cases include: A/S D/S Svendborg & Another v Mohamed Wansa (t/a 'Melbourne Enterprises') [1996] 2 Lloyd's Law Rep. 559- Clarke J; A/S D/S Svendborg & Another v Mohamed Wansa (t/a 'Melbourne Enterprises') [1997] 2 Lloyd's Law Rep. 193- Court of Appeal.
Career: Qualified in November 1985 at *Holman Fenwick & Willan.* Joined *Stephenson Harwood* in 1989 and became partner in 1992.
Personal: Born 11 October 1959. Educated at St George's College, Weybridge, Surrey; University College Cardiff BA (Hons) Law and Spanish 1978-82. Married. Interests include wine making (from real grapes). Languages: fluent Spanish, a little French and Italian.

GIBB, Jeremy S.P.
Norton Rose, London (020) 7283 6000
Partner in banking department.
Specialisation: Principal area of practice is asset finance, especially for ships and aircraft. In particular has considerable expertise in domestic and cross-border leasing structures. In the shipping field has over 15 years experience in the City of London, acting for financiers and owners of all types of vessels, including cruise ships and offshore vessels, and has been involved in numerous FPSO financings. Also deals with acquisition finance, especially acquisition and disposal of leasing companies.
Prof. Memberships: Law Society, Connecticut Maritime Association.

GINSBERG, Roy
Waltons & Morse, London (020) 7623 4255

GOSLING, James
Holman Fenwick & Willan, London
(020) 7488 2300
James.Gosling@hfw.co.uk
Partner in admiralty department.
Specialisation: Principal areas of practice are salvage, collision, total loss and wreck removal, acting mainly for salvors, shipowners, hull underwriters and P & I Clubs. Also handles marine insurance, general shipping and commercial law MOA disputes, charterparty disputes and cargo claims. Important cases have included 'Scandanavian Star', 'Europa' collision with 'Inchon Glory', 'Happy Fellow' collision with 'Darfur', 'Estrella Pampeana' collision with 'Sea Parana' and 'Smit Tak B.V. v Selco Salvage'. Clients include several leading salvage companies, ship owners, hull underwriters, ship managers, insurance brokers and one southern hemisphere tycoon. Is on the editorial board of the *International Maritime Law.* Has lectured on Admiralty Law in Mexico and Venezuela in Spanish, and in London and Piraeus.
Prof. Memberships: Member of the Instituto Ibero-Americano De Derecho Maritimo.
Career: Qualified in 1980. Became a Partner in 1988.
Personal: Born 28th June 1955. Educated at Ampleforth College, York and at St.Catherine's College Cambridge. Leisure interests include rugby, skiing, tennis, sailing, rowing, motor cycling, antiques and crosswords. Speaks French and Spanish. Lives near Saffron Walden.

GRAY, Edward
More Fisher Brown, London (020) 7247 0438
egray @m-f-b.co.uk
Specialisation: Principal area of practice is dispute resolution advice to ship owners and operators, and their insurers. Specialises in contractual and tortious disputes arising out of the carriage of goods by sea, and second-hand and newbuilding sale and purchase contracts. Particular experience with tankers, container vessels and offshore vessels. Also advises in contentious and non-contentious matters in the shipping area in connection with EU competition and regulatory matters, sales and acquisitions of businesses, and debt refinancing.
Career: *Richards Butler*, London 1979-1983 *Richards Butler*, Hong Kong 1983-1991, *More Fisher Brown* since 1992.
Personal: St Edmund Hall, Oxford - BA Jurisprudence, First Class Hons.

HARRIS, Graham D.
Richards Butler, London (020) 7247 6555
gdh@richardsbutler.com
Specialisation: Wide experience of dispute resolution, commercial negotiation and e-commerce in the shipping and transportation industries including shipbuilding, sale and purchase, charterparties, bills of lading, through transport documentation and insurance.
Career: Qualified October 1981 *Norton, Rose* then *Richards Butler.* Partner at *Richards Butler* 1988.
Personal: Born 28th September 1956. Educated at King's School, Canterbury and Oriel College Oxford (MA Jurisprudence, First Class Hons). Lives in London.

HARTLEY, Simon
Norton Rose, London (020) 7283 6000
hartleys@nortonrose.com
Specialisation: Specialising in shipping finance representing shipping companies, banks, export credit agencies and other financial institutions in connection with all types of ship lending and leasing, capital raising, sale and purchase of second-hand ships, ship registration, shipbuilding contracts, bareboat chartering, management agreements and related financial arrangements. The shipping finance group is one of the leading shipping finance practices in London, working closely with other *Norton Rose* lawyers experienced in advising shipping industry clients on competition and regulatory matters, taxation, litigation, insurance, mergers and acquisitions and corporate finance for the shipping industry.
Prof. Memberships: Member of the Law Society and Baltic Exchange.
Career: Trained *Norton Rose*; qualified 1988; partner 1997.
Publications: Has been a regular contributor to the 'Economy Shipping Finance Annual' over the last three years.
Personal: Married with one child. Leisure interests are sport and hill walking.

HARVEY, Richard
Richards Butler, London 020 7247 6555
rhjph@richardsbutler.com
Specialisation: Heads the firm's casualty response team of mainly legally qualified ex-seafarers, which handles all types of casualty including fires and explosions, groundings, salvage, collisions, wreck removal, reef damage and pollution, and their associated insurance and general average issues. Acts for Clubs, Hull underwriters, shipowners and major salvors. Has handled for owners such cases as the Europa/Inchon Glory, MSC Samia /Carina, Lula 1/Graceous, Polydefkis P/Anna Spiritou collisions and the Sea-Land Mariner fire and explosion. Acted for salvors in the European Gateway and for owners in the salvage of the MSC Rosa M as well as in the Maersk Tokyo, Erika and World Discoverer.
Prof. Memberships: Law Society; British Maritime Law Association; BMLA Arrest Convention sub-committee., City of London Admiralty Solicitors Group.
Career: Served as an officer in the British Merchant Navy before qualifying as a solicitor in 1980. Became a partner in *Richards Butler* in 1983.
Personal: Educated at Christ Church, Oxford (M.A.); Southampton College of Technology. Interests include sailing, gardening, music, photography and engineering.

HAYES, Barry
Hayes, Exeter (01392) 202 742

HEBDEN, David
Thomas Cooper & Stibbard, London (020) 7481 8851
Senior Partner.
Specialisation: Main area of practice is admiralty and marine insurance law. Work includes shipping and maritime law, collision, salvage, shipping safety, rules and regulations, and emergency response team management. Also management adviser to shipping and marine insurance industries. Handles day to day shipping problems, including criminal offences at sea, discipline and passenger ship operations. Edited and prepared Laws of Oleron. Author of numerous articles on shipping matters and safety at sea. Has addressed a variety of conferences and seminars.
Prof. Memberships: Law Society, British Maritime Law Association, Admiralty Solicitors Group, Honourable Company of Master Mariners.
Career: Qualified 1971, having joined *Thomas Cooper & Stibbard* in 1964. Became a Partner in 1973 and Senior Partner in 1992. FG Master's Certificate of Competency 1962; BMLA Committee on Salvage 1992.
Personal: Born 2nd March 1937. Attended Barnard Castle School 1948-52; HMS 'Worcester' 1952-54; School of Navigation, Southampton University 1962-64. ISM Lead Auditor 1997.

HERRING, Paul
Ince & Co, London (020) 7623 2011
Specialisation: Specialises in carriage of goods by sea, charterparty, bills of lading, sale and purchase and new building disputes. Regular lecturer on sale and purchase and charterparty issues.
Career: First Class Honours Degree in Law from Leicester University. Articled at *Ince & Co* in 1979 and became a partner in 1987.
Personal: Golf.

HILL, Martin
DLA, Liverpool (08700) 111 111
martin.hill@dla.com
Specialisation: Insurance coverage disputes subrogation and defence of liability claims. Acts for a number of major insurers and Lloyds Syndicates both in the UK and overseas.
Prof. Memberships: Committee member of Liverpool Underwriters Association and associate member of Manchester Marine Insurance Association.
Career: Qualified 1977. Partner with *Hill Dickinson & Co* and then *Hill Dickinson Davies Campbell* until 1993. Practice of *Alsop Wilkinson* from 1993.
Personal: Born 12.5.1953. Sixth generation solicitor. Personal interests include rebuilding and racing vintage and classic cars and working on the bench.

HILTON, Chris
Eversheds, Newcastle upon Tyne (0191) 261 1661
hiltonc@eversheds.com
Head of shipping department.
Specialisation: Shipping and maritime law. Has over 25 years experience in London and Newcastle, including 15 years managing a mutual FD & D association. Experienced in all aspects of maritime law ('wet' and 'dry') and is an arbitrator. Also handles insurance work. On various drafting committees of BIMCO.
Prof. Memberships: Chartered Institute of Arbitrators (Fellow).
Career: Qualified 1975. Member of the BMLA Committee on Carriage of Goods by Sea.
Personal: Cambridge University 1968-71, Adelaide University in 1972.

HOBBS, Christopher
Norton Rose, London (020) 7283 6000
hobbsc@nortonrose.com
Specialisation: Partner in the Shipping Litigation Group. Handles a wide range of shipping and shipping-related international commercial disputes ranging from major casualties (including related insurance aspects) to oil, gas and other commodity trading, all aspects of carriage of goods by sea and charterparty disputes. Has particular experience in relation to off-shore and other specialist vessels and frequently advises in relation to shipbuilding and ship repair disputes on behalf of both owners and shipyards in the Far East and Japan. Often asked to advise in relation to the drafting of contracts for the sale and purchase of commodities, charterparties, contracts of affreightmant and shipbuilding agreements. Also has wide experience in court and arbitration both in England and internationally. Major cases include representing owners and P&I clubs in relation to losses of 'OCEANOS' and 'KYRIAKI', representing cargo interests in relation to the 'SEA EMPRESS' grounding, acting for owners in major follow lead underwriter action, the 'DAYLEM' representing owners in a leading loss of oil major approvals case, the 'SEAFLOWER', advising Enron in the complex litigation arising out of the CATS pipeline in the North Sea.
Prof. Memberships: Member of the Law Society, the UK Energy Lawyers Group, the British Maritime Law Association Baltic Exchange, and has passed the necessary exams for fellowship of the Institute of Risk Management.
Career: 1980-1983, Lieutenant, 3rd Royal Tank Regiment; 1984, Articled Clerk, *Norton Rose*; Qualified 1986; Partner 1995.
Publications: Numerous articles published in Lloyd's List on a wide variety of topics including risk management, bunker contamination, the new Gencon 94 form of charterparty, NYPE 93, the Arbitration Act 1996, delivery of cargo against forged bills of lading, signing bills of lading, Classification Societies, tender of notice of readiness under a voyage charterparty and appeals from arbitrators' awards in respect of their own jurisdiction. Has written an article for Waterfront concerning the prosecution of Milford Haven Port Authority under the Water Resources Act 1996 and has had an article published in BIMCO Review concerning the decision in Charter Re v Fagan.
Personal: Married with two children.

HODGSON, Derek
Clyde & Co, London (020) 7623 1244
Partner in Marine Department.
Specialisation: Shipping/marine/insurance. Experienced in representing Shipowners/P&I Clubs/Hull underwriters, Charterers and Trading Companies in High Court actions and Arbitrations. Particular speciality in Thailand, Greece, South America and Africa.

HORTON, Nicholas
Grant & Horton Marine Solicitors, Plymouth (01752) 265265
Partner specialising in marine work.
Specialisation: Full legal service to insurance and marine industries with particular specialism in yachts - in the UK and internationally; litigation and commercial contract work; marine insurance; sale and purchase; build and refit contracts; international litigation.
Prof. Memberships: British Marine Industries Federation, Royal Ocean Racing Club, Royal Western Yacht Club.
Career: Qualified 1986. *Ingledew Brown Bennison & Garrett* 1984-88. Partner *Davies Grant & Horton* 1990-97; Co-founder of *Grant & Horton*, Marine Solicitors, May 1997.
Personal: Born August 1960, Merton College, Oxford 1979-82. Leisure: Sailing and family. Lives Plymouth.

JACKSON, Peter
Hill Dickinson, Manchester (0161) 2788800
Jacko@HillDicks.com
Partner in Marine Department and Head of *Hill Dickinson's* Manchester office and Cargo and Transport group.
Specialisation: Main areas of practice are marine, goods in transit and insurance litigation. Work includes cargo claims, for both cargo and liability insurers, particularly international road haulage claims; ship related cargo claims for cargo interests; salvage and monitoring foreign litigation. Also handles marine insurance work, particularly marine insurance policy interpretation for underwriters. Acted in ICI plc v MAT Transport, ITT v Birkart, the Breydon Merchant F & W Freight, the Los Angeles, Microfine v Transferry Shipping and Inco Europe.
Prof. Memberships: Liverpool Underwriters Association, Manchester Marine Insurance Association, London Maritime Arbitrators Association.
Career: Qualified in 1985, having joined *Hill Dickinson Davis Campbell* in 1983. Became a Partner in 1989.
Personal: Born 3rd April 1961. Attended St Edward's College, Liverpool 1972-79, then Exeter College, Oxford 1979-82. Leisure interests include football, season ticket holder at Anfield. Former Chairman of Football Supporters Association. Cricket and squash. Lives in Liverpool.

JEANES, Nicola
Rayfield Mills, Newcastle-upon-Tyne (0191) 261 2333

JOHNSON, Andrew
Hill Taylor Dickinson, London (020) 7283 9033
andrew.johnson@htd-london.com
Partner in Shipping and Maritime Law Department.
Specialisation: Main area of practice is shipping litigation, covering charter parties, bills of lading, collision and salvage. Co-author of 'A Guide to the Hamburg Rules'; contributor to 'Marine Claims'.
Prof. Memberships: Law Society.
Career: Qualified in 1984, having joined *Hill Dickinson* in 1980. Became a Partner in 1987.
Personal: Born 5th February 1955. Lives in London.

JOHNSON, Jonathan
Davies, Johnson & Co, Plymouth (01752) 226020
Partner specialising in Shipping and Maritime Law.
Specialisation: Shipping and maritime law since 1976, also handles commercial litigation work.
Prof. Memberships: LMAA (Supporting), BMIA
Career: Qualified in 1976. Worked at *Richards Butler* London and Hong Kong 1976-92, became Partner in 1980. Joined *Davies Grant & Horton* in 1992 as Partner. Founded *Davies, Johnson & Co* May 1997.

Personal: Born 31st March 1951. Attended Nottingham University, taking LLB in 1972. Lives in Plymouth.

KELLY, Russell
Shoosmiths, Solent (01489) 881010
russell.kelly@shoosmiths.co.uk
Shipping and Marine Department
Specialisation: Specialises in Shipping and Maritime issues; particularly charterparties and contracts for the carriage of goods, defending MCA prosecutions, investigating and defending passenger and crew injury claims, bunker suppliers' claims and claims by repairers and suppliers of goods and services to vessels. Instructed frequently on behalf of a number of the leading P&I Associations. Regularly engaged in both Commercial and Admiralty Court litigation and arbitration. Supporting member London Maritime Arbitrators Association.
Career: Qualified 1986 with *Thomas Cooper & Stibbard*, London, becoming a partner in 1990. Joined *Bond Pearce* 1997. Joined *Shoosmiths* 2000.

KEMP, Jonathan
Eversheds, Ipswich (01473) 284428
Specialisation: Shipping and maritime law. Handles all types of admiralty claims and commercial shipping dispute resolution. Also deals with port and harbour law and maritime insurance disputes. Acted as arbitrator in two collision claims.
Prof. Memberships: Nautical Institute. Law Society.
Career: Royal Navy (navigating officer) 1976-86. Qualified 1990. Joined *Sinclair Roche & Temperley* in 1988 for articles and practised in Singapore and London. Joined *Eversheds*, Ipswich, 1998.
Personal: Born 1958. Educated at Norwich School and King's College, London. Lives near Felixstowe. Sports: sailing and skiing.

LAX, Michael
Lawrence Graham, London (020) 7379 0000
mike.lax@lawgram.com
Partner in Shipping Department.
Specialisation: Deals with a range of shipping and maritime law matters. Work includes international trade litigation and arbitration, charter party disputes, cargo claims, marine insurance disputes, oil pollution claims, ship finance, sale and purchase, and shipbuilding contracts.
Career: Qualified in 1977. B.A. (Dunedin).
Personal: Born 22nd December 1952. Member of Cannons Sports Club. Lives in Wallington.

LIVINGSTONE, Hugh
Holman Fenwick & Willan, London
(020) 7488 2300
Hugh.Livingstone@hfw.co.uk
Specialisation: Partner in commercial litigation department. Specialising in all types of marine litigation on behalf of shipowners, charterers and insurers (P & I and market), as well as sellers and buyers of ships.
Career: Educated University of Cape Town (BA LLB) and University College London (LL M). Admitted 1976 (South Africa), 1985 (England and Wales) and 1986 (Hong Kong). Partner in *Holman Fenwick & Willan* 1986. Resident Partner in Hong Kong office 1986-88 and subsequently at London office.

LOWE, James A.G.
Henderson Boyd Jackson WS, Edinburgh
(0131) 226 6881
Principal maritime partner.
Specialisation: Handles sale and purchase agreements, ship building and financing, ship registration as well as admiralty work, such as collisions, salvage, marine pollution, ship building and repair contract disputes. Author of 'Maritime Securities' in the Stair Memorial Encyclopaedia and various articles for the legal, marine and fishing industry press. Has presented papers at Law Society Maritime Law courses and to marine insurers on aspects of the Marine Insurance Act 1906.
Prof. Memberships: Law Society of Scotland, Honourable Company of Master Mariners, Writer to the Signet, British Maritime Law Association, Nautical Institute.
Career: Ship's Officer 1966-1980. Gained Master Mariners Certificate in 1976. Joined *Boyd Jameson WS* and qualified as a solicitor in 1985. Became a partner in 1986. Joined *Henderson Boyd Jackson* 1993 upon the merger of *Boyd Jameson* and *Henderson & Jackson* in 1993.
Personal: Born 14th April 1949. Educated at Edinburgh University 1980-84. Enjoys sailing. Lives in East Lothian.

LOWE, Steven
Stephenson Harwood, London (020) 7809 2325
steven.lowe@shlegal.com
Partner, Marine/Insurance and Reinsurance.
Specialisation: Commercial shipping and insurance litigation and arbitration, both domestic and international (US, several European countries, ICC arbitration etc), including new building/sale and purchase disputes (frequently involving complex issues of naval architecture or marine engineering), charterparty, ship management, banking and oil trading disputes, insurance coverage issues (especially P&I, marine hull and reinsurance), advising on policy wordings and drafting policy/Club Rule changes.
Prof. Memberships: BMLA
Career: Qualified November 1972. *Holman Fenwick & Willan* 1972 and became partner in 1976. Joined *Stephenson Harwood* as partner in 1989.
Personal: Born 1946. Educated at Cambridge University, BA (Classics and Law) 1966-69. Married with one son. Interests include music, books and golf (intermittently).

LUX, Jonathan
Ince & Co, London (020) 7623 2011
Partner from 1983 onwards.
Specialisation: Work includes shipping, international trade and insurance advice and litigation. Has acted in many cases and transactions in these fields. Co- author of 'The Law of Tug, Tow and Pilotage' and 'The Law and Practice of Marine Insurance and Average' and 'Bunkers'. Editor of 'Classification Societies'. Author of various other publications in the fields of maritime law and international trade. Regular speaker at conferences and seminars on shipping, international trade and insurance subjects.
Prof. Memberships: Law Society, London Maritime Arbitrators Association, Chartered Institute of Arbitrators, CEDR, ADR Net, British Academy of Experts, International Bunker Industry Association, International Bar Association.
Career: Qualified and joined *Ince & Co.* in 1975. Became a Partner in 1983.
Personal: Holds LLB (Hons) (Exhib), 1973, and DES from the University of Aix-Marseilles, 1974. Freeman of the City of London, Liveryman of the Worshipful Company of Solicitors, former Chairman of the International Bar Association's Committee on Maritime and Transport Law; Chairman of the Committee 2 (Trial Observations and Interventions) of the International Bar Association's Human Rights Institute, Fellow of the Chartered Institute of Arbitrators and former Council Member of the International Bunker Industry Association Ltd. Member of the Steering Committee of London Law. Leisure interests include opera, theatre, golf, sailing and single-seater motor racing (holder of a national licence). Participated in the Peking to Paris Car Rally (1997) finishing First in Class and awarded gold medal. Lives in London.

MACKIN, Stephen
Eversheds, Newcastle upon Tyne (0191) 261 1661
mackins@eversheds.com
Specialisation: Charterparty and Bill of Lading disputes, particularly "oil tanker" related disputes: oil shortage, cargo contamination, off-hire, unsafe port/berth disputes and market loss claims. Liepaya/Lloyd; Rep [1999], caustic soda/vegetable oil contamination and early re-delivery dispute.
Prof. Memberships: Member of the Nautical Institute.
Career: Qualified 1994. Previously Navigating Officer - Shell Tankers (UK) Ltd (experience of: VLCCs, product tankers, LNG and OBOs).
Personal: Married with two children. Golf.

MACLEAN, A. Duncan
Henderson Boyd Jackson WS, Edinburgh
(0131) 226 6881
Partner, maritime department.
Specialisation: All aspects of contentious shipping work in both the Court of Session and local Sheriff Courts including arrests, cargo claims (sea and land), collisions, marine pollution, personal injury claims in the merchant, offshore and fishing fleets, salvage, insurance disputes, ship building and repair disputes, and general commercial disputes. Acts for P&I clubs and other marine underwriters and also on behalf of owners, repairers, banks and various interests in the fishing industry. Has presented papers to marine underwriters, the Nautical Institute and fellow solicitors on various topics relating to maritime law and insurance, and court procedure.
Prof. Memberships: Law Society of Scotland, British Maritime Law Associaton, Writer to the 'Signet'.
Career: Qualified 1988. Senior solicitor *Brodies WS* until 1994. Joined *Henderson Boyd Jackson* in 1994. Became a partner in 1996.
Personal: Born: 1966. Lives in Edinburgh. Married with two daughters. Educated: Edinburgh University 1983-1987. Interests: Sports, the outdoors.

MACRAE, Keith G.
Mackinnons, Aberdeen (01224) 632464
Partner in maritime and litigation department.
Specialisation: Acts for marine insurers, covering hull and machinery and P&I. Has particular experience in fishing vessel insurance and claims. Practice split between hull/ admiralty work (collisions, salvage, total loss and casualty investigation) and P&I claims (in particular personal accident/ employers liability claims from accidents on oil rigs and ships). Also handles oil pollution cases. Work includes on-

site investigation on- and off-shore. Has a substantial case load in the Sheriff Court and Court of Session, acting for Defenders in personal injury claims and for Pursuers in ship repair and ship builders negligence claims and contractual disputes. Gave a paper to Law Society of Scotland's Second Maritime Law Seminar. Presents seminars on Marine Insurance to clients.
Career: Qualified in 1982. Joined *Mackinnons* in 1980, becoming a partner in 1983.
Personal: Born 23rd May 1953. Attended Aberdeen University 1971-76 (MA(Hons)) and 1977-80 (LLB). Honorary Norwegian Consul in Aberdeen; Honorary Danish Vice-Consul in Aberdeen. Leisure interests include football, rock and jazz music and travelling. Lives in Catterline.

MAWDSLEY, David H.
DLA, Liverpool (08700) 111 111
david.mawdsley@dla.com
(0114) 272 0202 (International)
Partner in marine department.
Specialisation: All aspects of shipping and insurance law, including collision, salvage, general average, bill of lading and charterparty disputes, carriage of passengers and goods by sea, conditions of carriage, shipbuilding and ship finance documentation, charter and ship management agreements, port user agreements and marine insurance.
Prof. Memberships: Liverpool Underwriters' Association, Manchester Marine Insurance Association, London Maritime Arbitrators' Association, Association of Average Adjusters.
Career: Qualified in 1969. Partner with *Dibb Lupton Alsop* (and predecessor firms) since 1973.
Personal: Educated at Liverpool Institute High School and Liverpool University. Interests include fell walking, classical music, and all aspects of transport.

MAXWELL, M. John
Hill Dickinson, Liverpool (0151) 236 5400
Partner in Mercantile Department.
Specialisation: Specialises in shipping and commercial litigation, in particular on behalf of Shipowners, P&I Associations and Port Authorities. Marine accidents and casualty investigations for UK and foreign clients including collision, salvage, cargo claims, environmental and personal injury investigations. Charterparty and commercal disputes and Arbitrations.
Prof. Memberships: London Maritime Arbitrators Association.
Career: Qualified 1969. Partner in Mercantile Department of *Hill Dickinson* since 1976. Notary Public.
Personal: Education: Sedbergh School. Liverpool University.

MEAD, Ray
Barlow Lyde & Gilbert, London (020) 7247 2277
Specialisation: Main area of practice is shipping and international trade; also handles general commercial litigation and arbitrations - national and international. Author of numerous articles and occasional lecturer.
Prof. Memberships: London Maritime Association, London Maritime Arbitration Association.
Career: Qualified in 1975. Joined *Barlow Lyde & Gilbert* in 1990 as a Partner.
Personal: Born 1st February 1951. Attended Latymer Upper School 1962-70, then Birmingham University 1971-74. Leisure interests include sport, arts and family. Lives in Hurtspierpoint West Sussex.

MILLER, RD*, Anthony
Constant & Constant, London (020) 7261 0006
Admiralty consultant in shipping and maritime law.
Specialisation: Has handled salvage, collision, pollution, damage to offshore structures and wreck removal cases since 1966. Also handles charterparty, marine insurance, P&I and ports work. Acted in the 'Amoco Cadiz' case. Lt Cdr, (Retired) Royal Naval Reserve. Has command experience in Mine Counter Measure vessels. Qualified as a naval diver. Lectured at ABA, LLP seminars, and International Tug and Salvage Conventions.
Prof. Memberships: Law Society, Nautical Institute.
Career: Qualified 1965, joined *Constant & Constant* 1966. Admiralty consultant.
Personal: Born January 1942. Governor of Haberdashers Askes' Schools, Elstree.

MILLS, Geoffrey G.
Mills & Co, Newcastle-upon-Tyne
(0191) 233 2222

MILLS, Guy B.
Mills & Co, Newcastle-upon-Tyne
(0191) 233 2222

MILLS, Stephen
Rayfield Mills, Newcastle-upon-Tyne
(0191) 261 2333

PARTON, Nicholas
Jackson Parton, London (020) 7702 0085
One of the founding partners.
Specialisation: Cargo claims, charterparty disputes, collision and salvage, general average, casualty investigations and international trade. Particularly experienced in Francophone Jurisdictions.

PENROSE, Robert
Andrew M. Jackson & Co, Hull (01482) 325242
Specialisation: EU fishery law, defence of fishery prosecutions; fishing vessel quota, licence, sale purchase and leasing; international joint ventures and enterprises; commercial ship build, second hand sale and purchase, and finance documentation. Representation in Merchant Shipping Act proceedings. Clients include major UK and European fishing vessel owners, Fish Producers Organisations, P&I clubs, banks and owners in relation to finance. Recent cases include advising on prosecutions in the Southern Oceans; j.v. in South America; Fishery Protection Vessel contracts in the Indian Ocean; ship build contracts in China.
Prof. Memberships: Law Society.
Career: Nottingham University. Joined *Andrew M. Jackson & Co*. Partner 1985.
Personal: Born 1955, resides near Louth, Lincolnshire. Interests include food, wine and TVR cars.

PHILLIPS, Raymond J.
DLA, Liverpool (08700) 111 111
raymond.phillips@dla.com
Partner in Litigation Department.
Specialisation: Specific areas of practice include carriage of passengers and goods by sea and road, fire, toxic tort, crisis and disaster management, shipbuilding and repair.
Prof. Memberships: Liverpool Underwriters' Association, Manchester Marine Insurance Association.
Career: Qualified 1970. Partner with *Dibb Lupton Alsop* (and predecessor firms) from 1973.
Personal: Educated Liverpool Institute High School and Birmingham University. Interests include sailing, skiing, fell walking, chess and bridge.

RAYFIELD, Richard
Rayfield Mills, Newcastle-upon-Tyne
(0191) 261 2333

RIDLEY, Russell
Middleton Potts, London (020) 7600 2333
Partner in shipping litigation department.
Specialisation: Has a sound technical background, particularly in the oil, gas and chemical industry from offshore oilfield practice and all aspects of upstream E&P through to tanker shipments of hydrocarbons, hydrocarbon products, petrochems and all bulk liquids. Considerable experience and market knowledge of marine and energy insurance actions on behalf of insurers, reinsurers and captive underwriters in claims and recoveries under policies for H&M, P&I and Cargo, FD&D, IV, LOH, CAR, BI and Energy Packages. General commercial maritime law experience includes carriage of goods and charterparty disputes, commodity disputes involving international contracts of sale, ship S&P, newbuilding and offshore unit construction. Is a regular speaker at international conferences and organises the Middleton Potts annual lectures - Shipping & Commodities in October and Offshore Energy in May.
Prof. Memberships: Supporting member LMAA, Annual Subscriber: Association of Average Adjusters.
Career: Originally qualified as a barrister, and then as a solicitor, with a Masters Degree (LL.M.) in Maritime Law. Over 18 years' experience in maritime and energy claims.
Personal: Born 18th March 1951. Lives in Buckinghamshire. Married with two children. Interests: Gardening.

ROOTH, Anthony
Watson, Farley & Williams, London
(020) 7814 8000

RUSSELL, Mark A.
Stephenson Harwood, London (020) 7809 2600
mark.russell@shlegal.com
Partner, Head of Shipping Department, Head of Ship Finance Group.
Specialisation: All aspects of non-contentious shipping law, acting for lenders and shipowners. He specialises in project finance and in the energy, oil and gas and natural resources fields. He was the lead partner in connection with the first oilfield development in the West of Shetland area. He has strong experience in acting for banks and other lending institutions in a wide variety of cross border ship finance transactions. Major banking clients include Mees Pierson N.V, The Chase Manhattan Bank N.A and Christiana Bank. Lectures on syndicated loans, loan transferes, loan participations and work-outs.
Career: Qualified October 1983. *Simmons & Simmons* as Assistant Solicitor 1983-84. *Sinclair Roche & Temperley* in 1984 and became partner in 1989. Joined *Stephenson Harwood* in 1995 as partner. Head of Shipping Department in 1996.
Personal: Born 7 October 1958. Educated at Bradfield College; Bristol University, LLB 2:1 1980. Married with two children. Interests include theatre. Resides Harpenden.

SAYER, Richard
Ince & Co, London (020) 7623 2011
richard.sayer@ince.co.uk
Partner covering maritime law.
Specialisation: Main areas of practice are admiralty (collision, salvage and other casualties), charter party disputes, sale and purchase litigation and maritime fraud. Acted for owners of numerous headline casualties including 'The Braer' following the Shetland disaster in 1993. Also a member of the four-man FERIT (Far East Regional Investigation Team) established by all the major Far East insurance associations to investigate the incidence of maritime fraud in the South China Sea in the 1970s.
Prof. Memberships: Chairman (since 1991) of the City of London Admiralty Solicitors Group (Secretary 1972-91), Chairman of the BMLA Salvage Sub-Committee, member of the Baltic Exchange, supporting member of the Association of Average Adjusters, and of the London Maritime Arbitrators Association, member of the Admiralty Court Committee since 1986, and member of the Lloyd's Form Working Party. Assistant to the Court of the Worshipful Company of Shipwrights. Appointed Examiner in Admiralty by Lord Taylor C.J. 1996.
Career: Qualified in 1966, having joined *Ince & Co.* in 1962. Became a Partner in 1970. Was admitted in Hong Kong in 1979 and spent five months there opening the firm's Hong Kong office. Became Senior Partner in 1995, and stepped down in May 2000 after a 5 year stint.
Personal: Born 7th May 1943. Attended Framlingham College 1956-61. Leisure interests include golf, cricket and jazz. Lives in London.

SCOTT, Charles M.
Mackinnons, Aberdeen (01224) 632464
Specialisation: Acts for vessel owners, vessel managers and major harbour authorities. Current specialisation and wide experience in harbour law, negotiating shipbuilding contracts and advising on commercial issues arising form them, purchase and sale of vessels, financing documentation, agreements concerning fishing licences and quota rights, fishing vessel partnership and company structures for fishing enterprises.
Career: Educated at Robert Gordon's College, Aberdeen and University of Aberdeen (LLB with distinction 1973). Qualified in 1975. Joined *Mackinnons* in 1978 and became a partner in 1979. Currently managing partner. Part-time lecturer at University of Aberdeen from 1976 until 1995.
Personal: Born 13th January 1953. Married with daughter and son. Lives in Aberdeen. Leisure interests include hill-walking, golf and music.

SCOTT, Kenneth
Holmes Hardingham, London (020) 7283 0222
Ken.Scott@HHLaw.co.uk
Specialisation: Admiralty law, collision and salvage, marine insurance and total loss. Represents salvors on a national and international level; also acts for Owners and P & I Clubs in charterparty and bill of landing disputes.
Prof. Memberships: Member of the Baltic Exchange; British Maritime Law Association; and Admiralty Solicitors' Group.
Career: Deck officer on tankers, general cargo and bulk carriers; navigating officer on icebreakers in the Canadian Coastguard. Qualified 1980, partner at *Horrocks & Co* 1981-1990; partner at *Holmes Hardingham* 1990 to date.

SEWELL, Vernon
Bentleys, Stokes & Lowless, London
(020) 7782 0990
law@Bentleys.co.uk
Specialisation: Specialises in all aspects of "dry" shipping and insurance related litigation and arbitration.
Career: Qualified in 1982. Partner in 1986.
Prof. Memberships: The Law Society, supporting member of London Maritime Arbitrators' Association.
Personal: Born 1956. Married with two children.

SHELTON, John H.
Norton Rose, London (020) 7283 6000
Specialisation: Shipping finance, acting for owners, lenders, lessors, builders, and others.
Prof. Memberships: The Law Society, The Baltic Exchange.
Career: Articled at *Pinsent & Co*, Birmingham, joined *Norton Rose* on qualifying in 1981. Became partner 1987.
Personal: Married, four children. Principal interests: fatherhood.

SMITH, David
Allen & Overy, London (020) 7330 3000
Partner Asset Finance and Leasing, Shipping and Maritime Law.
Specialisation: Partner specialising in banking and asset finance, primarily relating to ships, aircraft and railways representing financiers, operators and manufacturers in domestic and cross-border structured transactions, both leasing and debt-based. Transaction structures have included export credit backed government-guaranteed debt facilities, tax-based lease structures (including UK tax leases, Japanese leveraged leases and US leases), off-balance sheet structures and non tax-based leases including operating leases both with and without residual value support. A significant part of his experience has involved combining these structures. Also regularly involved in sale and purchase, construction and registration matters relating to ships and aircraft.
Career: BA Jurisprudence, Brasenose College, Oxford, 1981; Admitted as a Solicitor, 1984; Solicitor *Richards Butler*, 1984; Partner *Richards Butler*, 1989; Partner *Wilde Sapte*, 1991; Partner *Allen & Overy*, 1999.
Personal: Born 1960, married with two children, enjoys family, motor cars, golf, cricket, eating out and theatre.

STRONG, Malcolm
Ince & Co, London (020) 7623 2011
Specialisation: Sale and purchase and finance of ships including related corporate, insurance, charterparty and other aspects. Was partner in the 'Niobe' (House of Lords case on sale of ships in 1995).
Prof. Memberships: Law Society. Supporting member London Maritime Arbitrators' Assocation.
Career: Cambridge University (Sidney Sussex College) MA., LL.M. Partner in *Ince & Co.* since 1970.
Personal: Married with one daughter. Interests: music, cinema, theatre, rugby and cricket.

TAYLOR, Andrew
Richards Butler, London (020) 7247 6555
Partner in shipping unit.
Specialisation: Specialises in marine casualty response, charter disputes, cargo liabilities, pollution, marine insurance, P&I clubs, Club and Rules and sale and purchase. Speaker at conferences. Co-author of 'Voyage Charters' - Lloyds of London Press.
Career: Qualified in 1980. Partner at *Richards Butler* since 1983.
Personal: Born 1952. Educated at Magdalen College School and Lincoln College, Oxford (MA).

TAYLOR, Silas W.
Andrew M. Jackson & Co, Hull (01482) 325242
Partner and head of admiralty and shipping department.
Specialisation: Main area of practice is marine casualty work. Acts on behalf of all main P&I clubs in collisions, salvage and major personal injury cases. Particular expertise in legal matters relating to the fishing industry. Also deals with disputes in respect of towage, pilotage, shipbuild and repair, etc, and claims under hull and machinery insurance. Has spoken on maritime law at conferences arranged by the Nautical Institute. Has contributed articles to 'Lloyd's Maritime and Commercial Law Quarterly', and the Nautical Institute's 'Seaways'.
Career: Qualified and joined *Andrew M. Jackson* in 1975. Became a partner in 1980.
Personal: Born 3rd February 1953. Educated at Bedford Modern School 1964-71 and Hull University 1971-74. Leisure pursuits include fishing, badminton and bowling.

TAYLOR, Tim
Hill Taylor Dickinson, London (020) 7283 9033
tim.taylor@htd-london.com
Partner in Shipping and Insurance Department.
Specialisation: Principal area of practice is insurance and shipping litigation. Cases of interest include the 'Stena Nautica' (1982) 'Piper Alpha' (1989), the 'Bowbelle' (1990) and the 'Wondrous' (1992).
Prof. Memberships: Chairman Marine Insurance Standing Committee, British Maritime Law Association; British Insurance Law Association; Association of Average Adjusters; London Maritime Arbitrators' Association; International Bar Association.
Career: Qualified in 1978 while with *Hill Dickinson & Co.* and became a Partner in 1982. CEDR Accredited Mediator.
Personal: Born 22nd June 1954. Attended Clifton College. Member of the MCC. Leisure pursuits include golf. Lives in Walton-on-the-Hill.

THOMAS, Tony
Clyde & Co, Guildford (01483) 31161
Partner in Shipping and Litigation Department.
Specialisation: Main area of practice is shipping litigation. Has considerable experience in litigation in the Commercial Court in London, London Arbitration and proceedings overseas. Handles shipping and cargo claims and marine insurance disputes. Author of numerous articles. Has spoken at a number of lectures around the world.
Prof. Memberships: Law Society.
Career: Qualified in 1976, joining *Clyde & Co.* the same year. Partner 1981.
Personal: Born 27th May 1952. Attended Leamington College 1963-70, then Manchester University 1970-73. Leisure interests include sport, art and architecture. Lives in Grayshott, Surrey.

THORP, Clive
Clyde & Co, London (020) 7623 1244
Partner in Marine Department.
Specialisation: Main areas of practice are charterparties, commodities, oil, Mareva injunctions, Anton Piller sequestration, payment of judgment debts, sovereign immunity and demurrage arbitrations. Also

handles enforcement of judgments. Acted in 'Sonangol v. Lundquist', privilege against self-incrimination; and 'Griparion' on indemnity costs. Lectures on Mareva injunctions, demurrage and shipbroker commissions.
Prof. Memberships: Baltic Exchange.
Career: Qualified 1976. Worked at *Holman Fenwick and Willan* 1976-79, joining *Clyde & Co.* in 1979. Became Partner in 1982. Member of Law Society Committee on Arbitration.
Personal: Born 28th August 1950. Attended Malvern College 1963-68, Hull University 1969-72 and College of Law. Common Councillor. City of London Committee Member London Court of International Arbitration. Chairman, Association for Research into Stammering in Childhood. Married, 2 children.

TURNER, Paul Alan
Clifford Chance, London (020) 7600 1000
Specialisation: Main area of practice is commercial shipping covering the negotiation of ship sale contracts, shipbuilding contracts, joint venture and management agreements, finance agreements, and maritime securities.
Career: Educated at Peterhouse, Cambridge (MA). Joined *Clifford Chance* in 1982. Worked in Hong Kong between 1985 and 1988. Now working in London.
Publications: Part author and general editor of 'Ship Sale and Purchase'.

VLASTO, Tony
Clifford Chance, London (020) 7600 1000
tony.vlasto@cliffordchance.com
Specialisation: Partner in international maritime, trade and insurance group. Head of Shipping and Admiralty practice group, specialising in particular in all aspects of casualty work, covering also a wide range of general maritime work including charterparty and bill of lading disputes, marine insurance litigation/arbitration and sale and purchase disputes.
Prof. Memberships: Baltic Exchange; BMLA, City of London Admiralty Solicitors Group; supporting member of the London Maritime Arbitrators Association and the Association of Average Adjusters; Steering Committee member of the London Shipping Law Centre; Liveryman Worshipful Company of Shipwrights.
Career: LLB 1972. Qualified 1975; partner 1981.

WALLIS, Robert
Hill Taylor Dickinson, London (020) 7283 9033
robert.wallis@htd-london.com
Specialisation: Admiralty law, particularly Collision, Salvage, Wreck Removal, Total Loss, Pollution Claims, Limitation of Liability and Marine Insurance Litigation.
Prof. Memberships: Law Society and Solicitors' European Group, British Maritime Law Association, CMI Sub-Committee on LoF 95, International Bar Association, Asia-Pacific Lawyers' Association.
Career: Leicester University LLB 1972, qualified 1975, Partner with Elborne Mitchell 1976-1988, joined *Hill Taylor Dickinson* as Partner 1988. Elected Chairman of Partnership 1999. CEDR accredited mediator.
Personal: Born 1950, married with two children. Interests include golf, tennis and rugby.

WARDER, David
Watson, Farley & Williams, London
(020) 7814 8000

WAREING, W. David
Hill Dickinson, Liverpool (0151) 236 5400
Partner.
Specialisation: Representing shipowners and their insurers, hull and machinery underwriters and P & I Associations. Particular involvement with crew and stevedore accidents and occupational disease claims. Also acting on behalf of liability underwriters in relation to pleasure craft accidents.
Prof. Memberships: Liverpool Underwriters Association, Manchester Marine Insurance Association.
Career: Qualified 1978 with *Hill Dickinson & Co.* Partner from 1982.

WATSON, Martin A.
Watson, Farley & Williams, London
(020) 7814 8000

WESTON, John
John Weston & Co, Felixstowe (01394) 282527

WHITE-THOMSON, John
Birketts, Ipswich (01473) 232300

WILLIAMS, Richard
Ince & Co, London (020) 7623 2011
Partner handling chartering, carriage of goods by sea, commodities and insurance.
Specialisation: Acts regularly for shipowners, charterers, cargo interests, P& I and other underwriters. Major cases include 'Nanfri', 'Scaptrade', 'Galatia', 'Atlantic Emperor', 'Lefthero', 'Gregos' and 'Houda'. Drafted documents for a UN Agency. Co-author of Limitation of Liability of Maritime Claims (3rd Ed. 1998) and numerous articles on shipping topics. Regular speaker at conferences worldwide and long-standing member of Lloyd's of London Speakers Panel and Maritime Training Programme.
Prof. Memberships: Law Society, Average Adjusters' Association, Supporting Member of London Maritime Arbitrators Association.
Career: Articled with *Ince & Co*, qualified in 1973 and became a Partner in 1978.
Personal: Born 13th June 1948. Gained LLB at UCW Aberystwyth 1966-69, then LLM at University College, London 1971. Leisure pursuits include travel, suffering Welsh rugby, archaeology and learning to play the guitar. Lives in Surrey.

WILSON, James
Ince & Co, London (020) 7623 2011
Specialisation: James initially worked mainly on the charterparty and cargo claims side of the firm's business. In recent years however, he has concentrated on the 'wet' side of the practice and has been increasingly involved in marine casualties, including the 'Braer' and 'Sea Empress', where the breadth of his admiralty experience has been of great value. His client base is drawn from across the maritime industry and includes owners, Clubs and marine underwriters.
Career: James graduated from Cambridge with an Honours Degree in Law. He joined*Ince* in 1983 and on the completion of his Articles he joined *Ince & Co's* Hong Kong office for 3 years. He became a partner in 1991.
Personal: Out of the office James is a keen sportsman and enjoys golf, squash and shooting.

WILSON, Robert
Holman Fenwick & Willan, London
(020) 7488 2300
Robert.Wilson@hfw.co.uk
Partner in commercial litigation department and senior partner of the firm (from 1st November 2000).
Specialisation: Principal area of practice is shipping and maritime law. Work covers commercial legal advice, handling and resolving disputes, negotiations, conducting litigation and arbitration: including newbuildings, conversion and repair (ship/offshore), MOA, pools, charters, bills of lading, P&I and Defence Club work, marine insurance (including total losses), international trade, especially tankers and the oil trade. Also deals with insurance, commercial and banking law where related to shipping and trading interests. House of Lords and Court of Appeal cases include 'Delfini' (title to sue), 'Kyzikos' (laytime), 'Evpo Agnic' (arrest), 'Arta' (shipbrokers negligence), 'Apj Priti' (safe berth) and 'Padre Island' (P&I club/third party claims), 'Factortame' (European law) and 'Haji-Ioannou v Frangos' (European Convention and ship arrests).
Prof. Memberships: Law Society, London Maritime Arbitrators Association (supporting member).
Career: Qualified in 1977, having joined *Holman Fenwick & Willan* in 1975. Became a partner in 1982.
Personal: Born 8th February 1952. Educated at Watford Grammar School 1962-69 and Corpus Christi College, Cambridge 1970-74 (MA Maths, History; Law). Interests include family, golf and travel. Lives in Hadley Wood, Herts.

WINTER, Glenn
Holmes Hardingham, London (020) 7283 0222
Glenn.Winter@HHLaw.co.uk
Specialisation: Main areas of specialisation are charterparty disputes and bulk liquid cargo claims. Major cases handled include 'The Mito' (1987), ' The Stena Pacifica' (1990), 'The Holstencruiser' (1992) and 'The Stolt Sydness' (1996), 'The Sun Sapphire' (1999) and 'The Erika' (2000).
Career: Attended Keble College, Oxford and the University of Illinois. Qualified in 1982. Founding Partner of *Holmes Hardingham.*
Personal: Born 7th May 1956. Married with two children.

SOCIAL HOUSING

London: 752; The South: 754; Thames Valley: 754; South West: 754; Wales: 755; Midlands: 755; North West: 756; North East: 756; Scotland: 757; *Profiles*: 758

OVERVIEW: Most social housing practitioners confidently expect a large increase of activity in this sector following the recent Green Paper 'Quality and Choice: A Decent Home For All.' Housing Associations are becoming increasingly sophisticated purchasers of legal services and almost invariably put out new work to tender. An interesting trend in the profession is the move by some firms to become 'full service' providers, while others concentrate on developing a smaller portfolio of specialities. With most Housing Associations instructing a mixed panel of firms and deals increasing in complexity, it will be interesting to see whether the smaller firms' investment in full service provision proves to be worthwhile. An increasing move to mixed funding and multi-faceted projects, together with tax-led restructuring have contributed to a general increase in most firms' activities in the social housing sector.

RESEARCH APPROVED BY BMRB: *For this edition,* Chambers' *researchers conducted 6083 interviews – 4408 with law firms, 598 with barristers and 1077 with clients.*

The validity of the research was scrutinised by BMRB International, who audited both the methodology and the results at our offices in July 2000. They interviewed Chambers' *researchers and cross-checked sample interviews. Details of the audit appear on page 7.*

LONDON

SOCIAL HOUSING • London	Ptnrs	Assts
❶ Trowers & Hamlins	10	37
❷ Devonshires	15	16
❸ Jenkins & Hand	2	-
Lewis Silkin	2	6
Winckworth Sherwood	3	8
❹ Lawrence Graham	8	14
Prince Evans	4	14
❺ Coudert Brothers	3	4
Maclays	1	3
Marsons Solicitors	1	3
Sharratts	2	2
❻ Dawson & Co	2	2
Evans Butler Wade	4	3
G.L. Hockfield & Co	2	2
Hodge Jones & Allen	1	1

LEADING INDIVIDUALS	
❶ **ADLINGTON Jonathan** Trowers & Hamlins	**BASTOW Gillian** Lewis Silkin
COWAN Andrew Devonshires	**DOOLITTLE Ian** Trowers & Hamlins
GRAHAM Ian Trowers & Hamlins	**HAND Catherine** Jenkins & Hand
HAYES Sarah Trowers & Hamlins	**JENKINS Keith** Jenkins & Hand
MURRAY Andrew Winckworth Sherwood	**ROBERT Louis** Prince Evans
❷ **HART Rosemary** Trowers & Hamlins	**MORLEY Trevor** Prince Evans
PANTELIA Despina Clifford Chance	**RANDALL Simon** Lawrence Graham
❸ **CARTER Adrian** Trowers & Hamlins	**EVANS Chris** Evans Butler Wade
FITTON Roger Winckworth Sherwood	**GUBBINS Jennie** Trowers & Hamlins
HAWKINS James Trowers & Hamlins	**HUDSON Allan James** Devonshires
JENNINGS Robert Prince Evans	**SMITH Chris** Maclays, Murray & Spens
TURNER Nicholas Lawrence Graham	
UP AND COMING	
BROWN Duncan Devonshires	**GOODE Naomi** Winckworth Sherwood
HALL Gareth Devonshires	

Within each band, firms are listed alphabetically. *See* ***Profiles*** *on page 758*

Trowers & Hamlins *"Top dogs, no-one gets near them!"* The scale of the department, quality of lawyers and extensive client list (they act for over 250 RSLs) lift this firm well above the rest. Sometimes victims of their own success, *"overstretched"* is the only criticism occasionally levelled at them. Acting primarily for borrowers they are viewed favourably by lenders as they are *"a pleasure to deal with."* The *"smooth"* **Jonathan Adlington** is perceived as *"grander than ever."* **Sarah Hayes** is *"intellectually fantastic,"* while **Adrian Carter** moves up the rankings following numerous positive recommendations. Team head **Ian Graham**, **Ian Doolittle**, **Rosemary Hart** and the *"polished, impressive"* **James Hawkins** all continue to enjoy exalted status among peers. **Jennie Gubbins**, although best known for her corporate finance work, still maintains a reputation in this area. The group acts on increasingly complex projects, including urban regeneration, PFI and PPP projects such as the provision of student accommodation for the London Institute by the Shaftesbury Housing Society. **Clients:** Harvest Housing Group; Dexia Municipal Bank; North British Housing Association; Western Challenge Housing Group.

Devonshires *"Coming along fast."* This team continues to grow and is seen to be chasing Trowers hard at the head of the rankings. Acting now for over 200 RSLs, the team is respected for advice on management, development and governance issues. The group's reputation is less widely established for funding advice, however. Senior partner Julian Roberts, the 'soul' of Devonshires, has retired, and it is **Andrew Cowan**'s *"drive"* which is now felt to be largely responsible for the team's growth. He is regarded as *"enthusiastic to a fault"* in defence of his client's corner. *"Sensible"* **Allan James Hudson** is joined in our tables by **Gareth Hall**, who *"gets things done,"* and *"reliable"* **Duncan Brown**, who has made NHS accommodation projects a speciality. This year, the team has acted on five local authority transfers and on the landmark House of Lords decision in Bruton v London & Quadrant Housing Trust. **Clients:** East Thames HA; London & Quadrant HT; Circle 33.

Jenkins & Hand Strong niche practice, achieving a high ranking for sheer level of expertise. The team is seen on complex projects and is known for its *"creative solutions"* to problems. **Keith Jenkins** is still considered to be *"the guv'nor,"* while the *"tenacious"* **Catherine Hand**, the *"social housing lawyer's lawyer"* is admired for her client care. Have been involved in a borough transfer and large scale urban regeneration matters in the past year. **Clients:** Southern Housing group; William Sutton Trust; Boston Mayflower Ltd.

Lewis Silkin Having been historically regarded as an under-resourced team in this area, the group has made a determined recruitment drive this year.

Gillian Bastow leads a team that is *"efficient without being aggressive"* and is a *"frequent recommendation."* The firm acts for over 65 varied housing associations, ranging from one of the largest LSVT associations to single scheme co-operatives. Recent work includes s106 planning agreements, purchases of brownfield sites, regeneration schemes, financing and some interesting possession cases. **Clients:** Peabody Trust; Wandle HA; Community HA.

Winckworth Sherwood Felt to have established a *"comfortable niche"* in this area of practice, the group is felt to provide *"excellent"* service to clients. **Andrew Murray** remains *"relaxed"* and *"easy to deal with,"* **Roger Fitton** is a rated practitioner, and the *"attentive"* **Naomi Goode** joins him in our tables. Corporate restructurings, a student accommodation project for Pavilion HA and an increased amount of work for lenders have kept the firm busy. **Clients:** Southern HG; Hanover HA; Paddington Churches HA.

Lawrence Graham LSVT specialists who have acted on 40 transfers to date, involving 120,000 units. **Simon Randall** fronts all the work on the housing associations side, while the *"impressive"* **Nick Turner** is the lead partner on finance. The highlight of the past year was the £292 million restructuring of the Flagship Housing Group, a combined bank-debt and capital markets facility. **Clients:** Flagship Housing Group; Peabody Trust; 1066 HA.

Prince Evans Seen mainly on inter-association transfers at present, the firm is not felt to have quite the breadth of practice of the top players. However, **Louis Robert** remains *"one of the best"* in the sector, particularly on complex deals. **Trevor Morley** is good at *"negotiating the deal,"* while **Robert Jennings** moves up the table on peer recommendation. Currently active in the extensive Trowbridge regeneration scheme. **Clients:** Notting Hill Housing Group; Circle HA; London & Quadrant.

Coudert Brothers The Debenham & Co team continues to thrive at this US firm. Although the firm primarily acts on development work, it has seen an increase in planning gain agreements, joint ventures with commercial developers and PFI bids. Stand-out work over the past year includes a £15 million funding exercise for a housing association. **Clients:** Notting Hill Housing Trust; Soho HA.

Maclays Chris Smith has assembled an enviable client base at a firm which acts on regeneration and PFI projects together with site acquisition and employment matters. The team is making use of cross-departmental practitioners, including banking, construction and capital projects specialists. **Clients:** Guinness Trust; Oxford Citizens HA.

Marsons Solicitors The firm has undergone a turbulent year, with the loss of partner Kevin Lee and a senior assistant. Both replacements have a background in housing legal aid. The firm is still recognised for its strength in nuisance litigation. **Clients:** Hyde HA; Circle 33; Medway HA.

Sharratts Gaining an increasing reputation. Their *"team-based approach"* draws praise as does their efficiency. The practice concentrates on property work and acts on development, securitisations and management for clients. **Clients:** Peabody Trust; other RSLs in the South and London.

Dawson & Co. An established, traditional firm coming at the work from a background in charities. Refinancing, property acquisitions and disposals and development form the bulk of its work. **Clients:** Family HA; Landmark HA; United Reformed Church.

Evans Butler Wade Chris Evans has an established name at a firm where around three-quarters of the work revolves around social housing, primarily management and property aspects. Clients tend to be small to medium-sized housing associations. The team also gives employment advice and continues to act on high-volume shared ownership leases. **Clients:** 60 HA clients.

G.L. Hockfield & Co The team is developing a niche in training for HAs to enable them to do their own possession work. In addition, the group continues its bread and butter litigation and management advice. **Clients:** Paddington Churches HA; Southern Housing Group; St Marylebone HA.

Hodge Jones & Allen A property, employment and corporate HA practice. This year's highlight was advising on the restructuring of Bridge HA, now a subsidiary of Novas Overtures Group. The firm also provides litigation support. **Active Clients:** Bridge HA; housing co-operatives in the South-East.

FIRMS ADVISING LENDERS UK-WIDE

SOCIAL HOUSING: ADVISING LENDERS (UK WIDE) • London	Ptnrs	Assts
❶ **Clifford Chance** London	8	-
❷ **Addleshaw Booth & Co** Leeds	5	12
Allen & Overy London	3	13
Denton Wilde Sapte London	5	9
Trowers & Hamlins London	*	*
❸ **Devonshires** London	*	*

Within each band, firms are listed alphabetically.
** Practitioners are drawn from the required specialist areas within the firm*

Clifford Chance *"It doesn't feel as if you're dealing with the largest firm in the world."* Client care and excellent service are felt to have made Clifford Chance *"definitely number one"* in this area of practice. The team has handled the majority of the government's transfer programme. Receive accolades for their *"innovative"* approach in pioneering funding products involving on-lending and pooled borrowing mechanisms. Described as *"a Mercedes among lawyers,"* **Despina Pantelia**'s qualities have been rewarded with partnership this year. **Clients:** Nationwide BS; Halifax PLC; Natwest Bank.

Addleshaw Booth & Co Fielding a *"very strong"* team, this practice has a national reach and appears to be *"transformed,"* increasingly shedding its former reputation for a draconian approach. The firm seems to be finding the balance of toughness and flexibility and received *"utmost praise"* from those on the other side of deals. Clients are particularly satisfied and the firm is seen as the only regional challenger to the City giants. Acted for Nationwide in a £250 million loan portfolio acquisition and major LSVTs worth over £150 million for Bradford & Bingley. **Clients:** Nationwide BS; Bradford & Bingley BS; Britannia BS.

Allen & Overy Not felt to be as balanced a practice as Clifford Chance, the team's profile this year has not been as high in the bank-debt market. The capital markets team however is seen as the leaders on bonds, having acted on over 30 issues in the last year. Although the group is felt to have *"some of the smartest"* people, it is not yet considered to have a big hitter to replace Heather McCallum, following her move to Frankfurt. Acted for Natwest on the innovative group structure and £300 million capital markets issue for Flagship HA, combining bank-debt and capital markets structures. **Clients:** Abbey National PLC; Halifax PLC; Nationwide BS.

Denton Wilde Sapte *"As good as the best"* say clients of this merged firm, now combining Denton Hall's strong property practice with Wilde Sapte's experienced banking team. Relatively new to the LSVT market, it acted on three out of four of the first transfers of the season. Has also acted on bilateral and syndicated transactions worth some £500 million, and is becoming involved in the PFI Pathfinder projects. **Clients:** Natwest Bank; AIB Group PLC; Bank of Scotland.

Trowers & Hamlins – see under previous section.

Devonshires – see under previous section.

THE SOUTH

SOCIAL HOUSING • The South	Ptnrs	Assts
❶ **Coffin Mew & Clover** Portsmouth	4	7
❷ **Cripps Harries Hall** Tunbridge Wells, Kent	2	3
❸ **Penningtons** Newbury	2	2
❹ **DMH** Brighton	2	5

LEADING INDIVIDUALS
❶ **BENNETT Jennifer** Coffin Mew & Clover

Within each band, firms are listed alphabetically. *See **Profiles** on page 758*

Coffin Mew & Clover Leaders in the South, the team is led by **Jennifer Bennett**, who has over 20 years' experience in the sector. The group advises around 40 HAs on complex development, litigation – particularly vis-à-vis antisocial tenants – and group structures and funding. Last year acted for Eastleigh HA in their partnership with a national house builder on a major mixed-tenure redevelopment. **Clients:** Parchment Housing Group; Downland HA; Eastleigh HA.

Cripps Harries Hall Completed the merger of two housing associations last year. Advising more on governance issues at present, the firm offers a range of services including refinancing, litigation, purchases and leases and model agreements drafting. **Clients:** High Weald HA; New Downland Housing Group.

Penningtons Provides routine management and development services such as right-to-buy, possessions and ESPs. **Clients:** Oakfern HA; Sovereign HA.

DMH Now primarily seen as a litigation practice, the team handles enforcement work for housing associations. With over ten years' experience in the sector, the group provides conveyancing, employment and commercial services. **Clients:** Sanctuary HA; Guinness Trust; Brighton HT.

THAMES VALLEY

SOCIAL HOUSING • Thames Valley	Ptnrs	Assts
❶ **Owen White** Slough	4	6
❷ **Manches** Oxford	1	1
❸ **Sherrards** St. Albans	1	3

Within each band, firms are listed alphabetically. *See **Profiles** on page 758*

Owen White *"Major players"* in the Thames Valley, the firm combines a specialist nuisance possession practice with a spread of management and development work including urban regeneration, site purchases and property-user conversions. Acts for around 25 RSLs. **Clients:** Paradigm Housing Group; Windsor & District HA; Maidenhead & District HA.

Manches The firm has been increasingly seen on PPP and PFI matters, where clients have been particularly warm in their recommendations. However, the retirement of the much-admired Richard Frost and the loss of a senior assistant has raised market concerns about the firm's strength in depth. **Clients:** Swan HA; Anchor Trust; Christian Action HA.

Sherrards A niche landlord litigation practice specialising in anti-social tenant cases, this firm acts for some 11 RSLs, and counts a solicitor-advocate among the team. **Clients:** Aldwyck HA; East Hertfordshire Dc; North British HA.

SOUTH WEST

SOCIAL HOUSING • South West	Ptnrs	Assts
❶ **Trowers & Hamlins** Exeter	2	5
❷ **Bevan Ashford** Bristol	4	6
Burges Salmon Bristol	4	4
❸ **Stones** Exeter	1	1

LEADING INDIVIDUALS	
❶ **KEULS Peter** Trowers & Hamlins	**McNULTY Stephen** Burges Salmon
❷ **ACTON Joseph** Trowers & Hamlins	**DYER Nick** Stones
❸ **MORTIMER Ken** Bevan Ashford	

Within each band, firms are listed alphabetically. *See **Profiles** on page 758*

Trowers & Hamlins Increasingly complex deals handled with *"typical Trowers expertise"* have ensured that the firm is recognised as number one in the region. **Peter Keuls** likes to *"get things done – quickly!"* **Joseph Acton** is *"meticulous and thorough."* Diversity has been a watchword over the past year with clients providing more non-housing products such as doctors' surgeries and office accommodation as ancillaries. **Clients:** Devon & Cornwall HA; Restormel HT; North Devon Homes Ltd.

Bevan Ashford This strong public sector firm is perceived to be using an aggressive pricing policy as as it looks to expand its housing work. The team, led by the *"extremely able"* **Ken Mortimer**, has handled tax-led transfers, large scale urban regeneration and an acquisition of married quarters from the MOD for a client in the Swindon Partnership. A niche speciality exists in advising on ecologically-friendly housing. **Clients:** Westlea HA; Sarsen HA; Knightstone HA.

Burges Salmon Profile for housing work has diminished in recent years as the firm concentrates on more commercial work. *"Highly rated by clients,"* **Stephen McNulty** heads this practice which is said to *"anticipate the potential problems."* Acted for Bristol Churches in the groundbreaking merger with North British. Advise on development, regulation, funding, management and employment. **Clients:** Bristol Churches HA; Redland HA; Jephson HA.

Stones **Nick Dyer** and one full-time assistant act for South Hams Housing on high-volume RTBs, provide management for a client with over 10,000 units and act for mortgage lenders on title certification. **Clients:** Western Challenge; Sanctuary HA; South Hams Housing.

WALES

SOCIAL HOUSING • Wales	Ptnrs	Assts
❶ **Eversheds** Cardiff	2	5
Hugh James Ford Simey Cardiff	4	-
❷ **Edwards Geldard** Cardiff	3	4
Morgan Cole Cardiff	9	10

Within each band, firms are listed alphabetically.

Eversheds Base of the national social housing operation. The brand name and some serious investment in the sector are paying off for Eversheds, seen to provide the *"most noticeable change"* in the market. Its commercial approach, *"personable"* staff and *"quick and efficient"* service makes the firm *"worth the money."* Acts now for 26 clients in the sector on financing, where it is one of the few firms rated outside London. Also handle landlord/tenant nuisance possessions and general property advice. **Clients:** Wales & West HA; Eastern Valley HA; Gwalia HA.

Hugh James Ford Simey With a long record in social housing this firm is the other leader in Wales. Focusing more on development work where they are *"getting stronger."* Advising on regeneration and redevelopment schemes, and transfers and agreements for the new Cardiff Capital Homes Ltd. **Clients:** Charter HA; Hafod HA; Glamorgan & Gwent HA.

Edwards Geldard *"Definitely players"* in Wales, and a new addition to this section. Clients have taken a notably favourable view of the practice. Advise on refinancing and loan restructuring, debt recovery, property development and litigation. **Clients:** United Welsh HA; Wales & West HA.

Morgan Cole Mixed reviews this year. An overall market perception is that of less energy in the last couple of years by comparison with leading competitors. In the past year, the team has acted on a £10 million funding facility, a £5 million revolving finance facility and two major inner-city regeneration schemes. **Clients:** Over 15 registered housing associations in Wales.

MIDLANDS

SOCIAL HOUSING • Midlands	Ptnrs	Assts
❶ **Anthony Collins Solicitors** Birmingham	7	18
❷ **Browne Jacobson** Nottingham	2	3
Irwin Mitchell Birmingham	8	10
Lee Crowder Birmingham	2	8
❸ **Freethcartwright** Nottingham	2	3
Harvey Ingram Owston Leicester	2	2
Needham & James Stratford upon Avon	3	4
Wright Hassall Leamington Spa	3	7

LEADING INDIVIDUALS	
❶ **KNOX Martin** Anthony Collins Solicitors	**STEPHENS Hugo** Irwin Mitchell
❷ **HUDDLESTON David** Browne Jacobson	
❸ **BALLARD Andy** Lee Crowder	**DUDLEY Andrew** Needham & James
MATTHEWS Carol Wright Hassall	

Within each band, firms are listed alphabetically. See **Profiles** on page 758

Anthony Collins Solicitors **Martin Knox** is a *"top man"* although some concerns were voiced over the strength of the team behind him. Over the past year, the firm has acted for a number of LSVT associations, advised on regeneration schemes and New Deal schemes, a merger and a reorganisation. Acts for over 50 RSLs. **Clients:** Lichfield district HA; Hanover HA.

Browne Jacobson **David Huddleston**, a *"professional with a tinge of humour,"* heads this long-established department. Concentrating on funding and planning where they are said to be *"excellent."* The practice also advises on acquisitions and development and is said to have a *"good working knowledge"* of the field. Clients include over 20 RSLs. **Clients:** North British HA; East Midlands HA; Leicester HA.

Irwin Mitchell With the loss of its entire housing team to Lee Crowder, Irwin Mitchell has had to reinvent the department and now concentrates on corporate constitutional finance in the public sector. Stock transfers are the main area of work in the social housing sector. **Hugo Stephens** is felt to be shouldering much of the burden himself, and *"overstretched"* is a word frequently mentioned by the market. However clients feel *"safe in his hands"* and praise his client-oriented approach. **Clients:** Huntingdon DC; Burnley BC; West Wiltshire DC.

Lee Crowder Going up the tables on the strength of the move from Irwin Mitchell of **Andy Ballard**, who has a *"deserved reputation"* in housing litigation, and his team. The firm now advises some 30 RSL clients on all aspects of management, development and human resources in social housing. **Clients:** Focus HA; Midland Area HA; Accord HA.

Freethcartwright A busy year in acquisitions and over £20 million worth of refinancing for a number of associations. Redevelopment of brownfield sites, urban regeneration schemes and care in the community projects have also featured. **Clients:** Nottingham Community HA; Derwent HA; Guinness Trust.

Harvey Ingram Owston Would *"knock the spots off"* most people on development matters, although it does not possess the same strength in financing. The firm acts for a *"loyal clientele"* across the east Midlands. **Clients:** Wolds HA.

Needham & James A year of consolidation following last year's very busy period. **Andrew Dudley**, who *"mucks in there and gets involved,"* is considered to be a *"good all-rounder."* The firm acted for Accord HA in the transfer of care homes from Telford & Wrekin Council, and continues to advise on management and litigation. **Clients:** Accord HA.

Wright Hassall & Co The *"engaging"* **Carol Matthews** has had *"a very good year."* She comes highly recommended for her *"professional"* work on two major stock transfers, development, constitutional and litigation work. **Clients:** East Lindsey Partnership; Wyre Forest DC; Barnsley Urban Metropolitan Council.

NORTH WEST

SOCIAL HOUSING • North West	Ptnrs	Assts
❶ **Brabner Holden Banks Wilson** Liverpool	6	2
Cobbetts Manchester	6	3
Howarth Goodman Manchester	5	4
Trowers & Hamlins Manchester	6	1
❷ **Croftons** Manchester	2	-
Eversheds Manchester	1	1
❸ **A. Halsall & Co** Birkenhead	1	2
Gorna & Co Manchester	1	1
❹ **Bremner Sons & Corlett** Liverpool	3	1
❺ **Bell Lamb & Joynson** Liverpool	-	1

LEADING INDIVIDUALS
❶ **HOLDEN Lawrence** Brabner Holden Banks Wilson
TURNER Graham Trowers & Hamlins
❷ **BODE Adrian** Trowers & Hamlins
GASKELL Mike Cobbetts
❸ **RHATIGAN Michael** Eversheds

Within each band, firms are listed alphabetically. *See **Profiles** on page 758*

Brabner Holden Banks Wilson A well-known, solid practice. *"Deep thinker"* **Lawrence Holden** remains involved in this firm, which fields a large regeneration team. Group structures and tax-led reorganisations have occupied the firm over the last year. **Clients:** Liverpool HA; CDS HA; Cosmopolitan HA.

Cobbetts Often mentioned among the leading firms in the region, Cobbetts have been instructed by Blackburn LA to advise on the 10,000 unit LSVT for Darwen BC. **Mike Gaskell** *"knows his stuff."* The team is seen to be especially active in funding work. **Clients:** North British HA; Progress Housing Group; Wyre HA.

Howarth Goodman Doing *"an awful lot"* of *"mainstream"* work in property and housing management, this *"development-driven"* firm is particularly rated for complex funding and larger-scale projects. **Clients:** Guinness Trust; Northern Counties HA.

Trowers & Hamlins Although undoubtedly *"thorough and credible,"* the firm is unanimously seen as the option for larger rather than smaller clients. **Graham Turner** who *"seeks solutions, not problems"* is recommended for his years of experience. **Adrian Bode** is *"straightforward"* and *"knows HA work backwards."* The firm acted on all three stock transfers for the Manchester City Council overspill estates as well as an £8 million transfer of 900 units for Impact HA. **Clients:** Impact HA; Bromford HG; Irwell Valley HA.

Croftons Small but respected firm acting for a variety of local housing associations, with particular expertise on financing aspects of the sector. Said to be a *"good high-volume player."* **Clients:** Numerous HAs.

Eversheds Michael Rhatigan has a *"fair background"* in housing, and is seen as the top Eversheds man in the North. The consensus is that this *"impressive"* practice is *"doing more"* at a *"higher level"* and so moves up the tables. Known to be especially strong in refinancing matters. **Clients:** Half a dozen RSLs in the Manchester and Leeds area.

A. Halsall & Co Maintain a presence in the regional market, with recent activity in co-ownership sales, right to buy sales and financing. **Clients:** Harewood Housing Society.

Gorna & Co *"Respected"* team which acts primarily for local housing associations, generally approaching the sector from a refinancing angle. **Clients:** N. British HA.

Bremner Sons & Corlett Now felt to be an emerging force in Liverpool, the team's experience has led to an increased work-load and heightened profile this year. Act most notably on funding issues for a solid local client base. **Clients:** Regional RSLs.

Bell Lamb & Joynson Diminished profile in the market this year, although still acknowledged to be a presence in the Merseyside area.

NORTH EAST

SOCIAL HOUSING • North East	Ptnrs	Assts
❶ **Dickinson Dees** Newcastle upon Tyne	4	8
Rollit Farrell & Bladon Hull	3	2
Walker Charlesworth & Foster Leeds	3	3
❷ **Eversheds** Newcastle upon Tyne	1	3
Gordons Cranswick Solicitors Bradford	3	2
Savage Crangle Skipton	2	2

LEADING INDIVIDUALS
❶ **BROWN Mitch** Dickinson Dees
❷ **BIRTWISTLE Colin** Walker Charlesworth & Foster
HURST Andrew Savage Crangle

Within each band, firms are listed alphabetically. *See **Profiles** on page 758*

Dickinson Dees One of the outstanding firms in the North East, with a *"massively strong"* reputation. The firm brings an *"informed commercial"* approach to its development-oriented practice which clients *"swear by,"* although a minority feel that the team can adopt an *"unnecessarily hard line."* **Mitch Brown** really *"gets things moving."* The firm has recently advised on a Pathfinder PFI project, numerous group structures and two urban village partnerships. **Clients:** Home Housing Group; Tees Valley HA; Nomad Housing Group.

Rollit Farrell & Bladon Solid endorsements from practitioners and clients, who confirmed the firm as a major player in the region. The team advises on standard housing corporation schemes, grant funded projects and developments and PFI transactions. Acting in innovative schemes such as a continuing care community development for the Joseph Rowntree Foundation. **Clients:** Joseph Rowntree Foundation; Peabody Trust.

Walker Charlesworth & Foster Clients were *"particularly satisfied"* with this team, which *"certainly delivers!"* **Colin Birtwistle** is both *"helpful and loyal"* to his clients. His team does a substantial quantity of social housing work, advising on regeneration, development, transfers and funding. **Clients:** North British HA; Yorkshire Community Housing; Leeds Federated Housing.

Eversheds A new entry this year, the practice covers litigation, securitisation and general property development work, and is especially recommended by clients. **Clients:** The Home Group; Three Rivers HA; Enterprise Five.

Gordons Cranswick A new entry this year with good reviews for *"excellent service"* and a *"proactive"* attitude. Acts on nuisance litigation and employment issues in addition to mainstream development, funding and constitutional practice. **Clients:** Anchor Trust; Housing 21; Jephson HA.

Savage Crangle The *"approachable"* **Andrew Hurst** has recently completed a £47 million structuring deal for Leeds Community Mental Health Trust. **Clients:** Accord plc.

SCOTLAND

SOCIAL HOUSING • Scotland	Ptnrs	Assts
❶ **Harper Macleod** Glasgow	6	5
❷ **Brechin Tindal Oatts** Glasgow	5	7
Henderson Boyd Jackson WS Edinburgh	4	5
❸ **Shepherd & Wedderburn WS** Edinburgh	-	2
Skene Edwards WS Edinburgh	3	1
TC Young & Son Glasgow	3	2
❹ **Burness** Edinburgh	6	5
Dundas & Wilson CS Edinburgh	3	5
Golds Glasgow	1	3
McGrigor Donald Glasgow	1	1
❺ **Anderson Strathern WS** Edinburgh	3	3
Ledingham Chalmers Aberdeen, Edinburgh	2	1
Macleod & MacCallum Inverness	1	1
❻ **Baird & Company** Kirkcaldy	3	1

LEADING INDIVIDUALS	
❶ **FREEDMAN Leonard** Harper Macleod	
❷ **COWAN Andrew** TC Young & Son	**DEWAR Kate** Henderson Boyd Jackson WS
EWING Mark TC Young & Son	**JACKSON Fraser** Henderson Boyd Jackson WS
MacGREGOR Stephen Brechin Tindal Oatts	**PIA Paul** Burness
ROBERTSON Andrew TC Young & Son	
❸ **HOGG Derek** Skene Edwards WS	**MILNE Charles** Baird & Company
THOMPSON Alison Shepherd & Wedderburn WS	

Within each band, firms are listed alphabetically. See ***Profiles*** on page 758

Harper MacLeod The team is said to be *"unmatched"* for quality, depth of advice and the specialist departments that it can bring onto deals. **Len Freedman** is *"very active"* in the housing movement and *"a safe pair of hands."* The firm has been involved in a substantial amount of transfers, lender work and a variety of other complex issues over the past year. Also involved in option studies for projected local authority transfers. **Clients:** Aberdeen City Council; Nationwide BS; Irvine HA.

Brechin Tindal Oatts *"Highly effective"* **Stephen MacGregor** heads this practice which is praised for its work on stock transfers, an area where its expertise is beyond question. Advising on a wide range of large and complicated transactions, the firm acted on the £40 million Abbey Club deal recently. **Clients:** Queens Cross HA; Shettleston HA; Cube HA and 47 RSL clients.

Henderson Boyd Jackson WS Not quite at the pinnacle, but in many views *"as good as you can get."* **Fraser Jackson**, a *"most complete lawyer,"* has taken a less prominent role this year, although **Kate Dewar** is a frequently-seen, *"tenacious"* practitioner. The firm has recently been active in large-scale development, site acquisitions, complex multi-party arrangements and funding work. A recent development has been the firm's instruction by the City of Edinburgh Council in a number of NHP related transactions. **Clients:** Homes for Life Housing Management; Waverley Housing Management; City of Edinburgh Council.

Shepherd & Wedderburn WS The social housing unit is a niche part of the commercial property practice and interviewees praised **Alison Thompson** as a *"bright"* young practitioner. Acted for the Bank of Scotland in a £13 million pathfinder project last year and handle stock transfer funding, site acquisitions and development funding. **Clients:** Hanover (Scotland) Housing; Castle Rock Housing; Edinvar HA.

Skene Edwards WS This *"cuddly and cosy"* firm hides a *"wealth of experience"* under its *"understated exterior."* Relatively new to the market, they have impressed Scotland's more established players. **Derek Hogg** is a new entry to our tables on recommendations of peers who *"like working with him."* Acted on a large new stock transfer for Fyfe Special recently. **Clients:** Fyfe Special HA; Melville HA; Cunningham HA.

T C Young & Son Punching well above its weight, this small firm is *"steeped"* in social housing and advises on LSVTs, funding and partnership development. *"Well-connected"* **Andrew Robertson** *"appreciates the nuances of the sector."* **Andrew Cowan** knows tenancy law *"better than most"* and the *"pragmatic"* **Mark Ewing** is a *"quiet star."* **Clients:** Home in Scotland; Thenew HA.

Burness The firm has particular expertise on constitutional issues, such as group structures and cross-sector joint ventures, where **Paul Pia** is described as a *"doyen."* The firm also acts on stock transfers, funding and development. **Clients:** Scottish Federation of Housing Associations; Link HA; Margaret Blackwood HA.

Dundas & Wilson CS Unique in this table in that it primarily advises lenders. The firm acted for Abbey National on its £30 million 'club' funding of eight HAs and for Lloyds TSB on the pathfinder funding of Aberdeenshire Housing Partnership. **Clients:** Abbey National plc; Halifax plc; Lloyds TSB.

Golds Known for their love of IT development, members of this *"hugely systems-oriented"* team are *"impressive"* and *"not pompous."* Rated for their work in securitisation and advising lenders. **Clients:** Bank of Scotland; Britannia BS.

McGrigor Donald A new entry, the firm has recently brought its commercial expertise in tailoring bespoke solutions to bear in social housing, and received wide commendation for the results. Acted on setting up the first new housing partnership in Scotland – the Aberdeenshire Housing Partnership – worth some £20 million and involving around 600 units. The firm developed the model with the council, incorporated it and did all the project work. **Clients:** Aberdeenshire Housing Partnership.

Anderson Strathern WS Act for HA clients on acquisitions, disposals and lending work. The firm has also acted for Dunfermline Building Society in negotiating funding and loan agreements. **Clients:** East Lothian HA; Wester Hailes HA; Dunfermline BS.

Ledingham Chalmers Seen to be *"coming up,"* the practice continues to build up its social housing practice and is involved with the development of rental units for West Lothian Housing Partnership, an ongoing project. Advises the Dunfermline Building Society in its housing association lending. **Clients:** West Lothian Housing Partnership; Cumbernauld Housing Partnership; Dunfermline Building Society.

MacLeod & MacCallum Advising mainly on development work for Highland associations, this practice also acts on some financing and stock transfer deals. **Clients:** Albyn HS; Pentland HA; Muirneag HA.

Baird & Co **Charles Milne** heads the team that acts for RSL clients on acquisitions, debt recovery and litigation matters. **Clients:** Three RSLs.

LEADERS IN SOCIAL HOUSING

ACTON, Joseph
Trowers & Hamlins, Exeter (01392) 217466
jacton@trowers.com
Specialisation: Advises upon all areas of Housing Association law and practice including acquisition and development, building contracts, partnering and construction issues, PFI matters, homelessness initiatives, funding and major consortium agreements and joint ventures. Speaks regularly at client seminars on matters of current interest.
Prof. Memberships: Member of the Law Society.
Career: Torquay Grammar School (1977-84); Magdalen College Oxford (1984-87); *Trowers & Hamlins* (1989-date). Partner from 1995.

ADLINGTON, Jonathan
Trowers & Hamlins, London (020) 7423 8000
jadlington@trowers.com
Partner. Head of property department, senior partner.
Specialisation: Vast experience of housing law and the housing association movement having built a specialist practice over more than 25 years. Deals with all aspects of commercial and residential property, from purchases, sales and mortgages to development agreements, structures and funding. Instrumental in the development of private finance for social housing. Acts for Housing Associations, Local Authorities and lenders. Regular speaker at housing events and for funding bodies.

BALLARD, Andy
Lee Crowder, Birmingham (0121) 236 4477
Specialisation: Heads the Housing Group at *Lee Crowder* which is one of the largest within the region advising in excess of 50 Registered Social Landlords. Lectures and trains nationally and locally on a full range of Housing Management and Human Resource Issues.
Prof. Memberships: Law Society.
Career: Qualified in 1981 before joining the Birmingham practice of *Rigbeys* in 1983. Became a partner in *Rigbeys* in 1996 which in due course merged with *Irwin Mitchell.* Became a partner in *Lee Crowder* when transferring his team in 1999.

BASTOW, Gillian
Lewis Silkin, London (020) 7227 8000
bastowg@lewissilkin.com
Partner and head of social housing group.
Specialisation: All aspects of housing association activity including land acquisition and development, regeneration schemes, partnerships involving RSLs, local authorities/health authorities, private and public finance, care in the community schemes, landlord and tenant issues, constitutional/corporate matters and specialist work with housing co-operatives.
Prof. Memberships: Law Society, NHF Lawyers Sub-Group, Housing Association Committee Member.
Career: Qualified 1981 with *Lewis Silkin*. Partner 1984.
Personal: Born October 1953. Attended Somerville College Oxford (MA) and Leicester University (LLM). Lives in London.

BENNETT, Jennifer
Coffin Mew & Clover, Fareham (01329) 825617
cmcfareham@compuserve.com
Partner. Head of social housing department.
Specialisation: Over 20 years experience in Housing Association Law, with particular interest in new housing initiatives and low cost home ownership schemes, but with a very broad expertise in this sector. Heads a team of dedicated professionals who provide comprehensive services to a large number of local and regional RSLs.
Prof. Memberships: Member of Chartered Institute of Housing.
Personal: Born 1955. Educated University College, London. Admitted 1979. Non-executive Director of Portsmouth Hospitals NHS Trust.

BIRTWISTLE, Colin
Walker Charlesworth & Foster, Leeds
(0113) 245 3594
colinbirtwistle@walkercharlesworth.co.uk
Specialisation: Housing Association Law and Practice particularly in the field of constitutional matters for Housing Associations e.g. dealing with several rule changes and mergers. Also heavily involved from 1989 with Leeds Partnership Homes which dealt with the transfer of £33m of City Council land largely for Housing Association development but also for outright sale. Now involved with the Single Regeneration Budget Agreement for Leeds and related sales. Also involved with Health Service Reprovision Agreements for two charities.
Prof. Memberships: The Law Society, and Solicitor Benevolent Fund Member.
Career: LLB Birmingham Class 2(i). Senior partner in the Leeds office of *Walker Charlesworth & Foster* which has two other branches.
Personal: Family: married with three children aged 21, 19 and 15. Outside interests - sport, fell walking and charity work.

BODE, Adrian F.
Trowers & Hamlins, Manchester (0161) 211 0000
abode@trowers.com
Specialisation: A partner since 1983 and has acquired wide ranging experience. Particular specialisations are large scale acquisitions and disposals, joint venture work and private finance.
Career: University of Nottingham. Qualified 1978. *Trowers & Hamlins* (1978 to date). Partner 1983.

BROWN, Duncan
Devonshires, London (020) 7628 7576
duncan.brown@devonshires.co.uk
Specialisation: Partner, head of projects and public partnership group at *Devonshires*, acts for RSLs, NHS Trusts and Local Authorities in relation to Public Private Partnership Projects and has acted recently on a number of NHS Trust Accommodation Projects with RSLs, Leisure PFIs and Education PFIs. Also provides advice to RSLs on special needs projects and VAT and property.
Prof. Memberships: Society of Construction Law.
Career: Admitted as a solicitor 1974, Maurice Nordon Prize for contract law, joined *Devonshires* 1990. Partner 1991.
Personal: BSC (Econ) Hons 2.1. Resides Surrey, leisure interests gardening, swimming, fine art antiques.

BROWN, Mitch
Dickinson Dees, Newcastle upon Tyne
(0191) 279 9291
Specialisation: Partner in the commercial property department and head of the social housing group. Handles all aspects of housing association work in the fields of development, governance and finance. Has in the past year dealt with social housing lending facilities on behalf of RSL's and lenders, housing association/housebuilder partnerships, and the establishment of RSL Group structures. Currently dealing with the second housing association merger transaction of this year.
Prof. Memberships: Law Society.
Career: Born 1962. Educated Royal Grammar School, Newcastle upon Tyne. University of Newcastle upon Tyne 1984 (LLB). Qualified 1987, became a partner in 1995.
Personal: Leisure interests include sport, music, art and reading. Married with three daughters.

CARTER, Adrian
Trowers & Hamlins, London (020) 7423 8000
acarter@trowers.com
Partner, Housing Finance Group.
Specialisation: Specialist in housing finance, acting for borrowers and lenders. Experience includes innovative work on group borrowing arrangements, hedging arrangements, stock and bond issues, as well as bilateral and syndicated lending and borrowing. Regular speaker.
Career: University of Exeter. *Trowers & Hamlins* 1987-date. Qualified 1989, Partner 1994.
Personal: Married, four children.

COWAN, Andrew
Devonshires, London (020) 7628 7576
andrew.cowan@devonshires.co.uk
Specialisation: Partner and head of finance. The RSL finance unit has negotiated over £2 billion of housing association funding and group structures since 1988 from the capital markets, banks, building societies and new initiatives; Andrew acts for ten banks, building societies and over 165 RSL based all over England and Wales and a group association borrowing vehicle. Andrew and his team act for over 50 RSLs on their group structures, including in relation to mergers, PFI, and new initiatives. Lectures widely on finance, ERCF/SRB bids and RSL strategies.
Career: Articled *Hobson Audley*; qualified 1989; *Trowers & Hamlins*1990-1991; *Devonshires* 1991; Partner 1993; regular speaker; committee member of a London based housing association and credit committee member of an international charity.
Personal: Educated University of East Anglia. Born 1964: resides London. Leisure: backpacking, football, swimming, Latin America.

COWAN, Andrew
TC Young & Son, Glasgow (0141) 221 5562
Specialisation: Housing Association tenancies and housing management issues. Representation in all areas of litigation and employment related disputes. He has an extensive knowledge of the regulatory regime for secured and assured tenancies and regularly contributes to training conferences and seminars. Has a developing caseload dealing with construction related disputes. Currently extensively involved in a number of transfer of engagements between housing associations.
Prof. Memberships: Law Society of Scotland and Chartered Institute of Arbitrators.
Career: Dundee University LL.B 1984; *T.C. Young & Son* trainee 1985-87; *McArthur Stanton* partner 1986-95; *T.C. Young & Son* partner 1995.

DEWAR, Kate M.
Henderson Boyd Jackson WS, Edinburgh (0131) 226 6881
Specialisation: With a background in commercial law has worked extensively in the last six years on multi variety transactions for and involving Housing Associations, Housing Management companies, Local Housing companies and similar bodies. Has been involved in all aspects of Large Scale Voluntary Transfers from Scottish Homes and the New Town Corporations. Involved in the legal formation of Housing Associations, local Housing Companies and Housing Partnerships. Has been involved in new build and housing development projects with both the public and private sector and was one of the lead solicitors involved in two of the first new housing partnership deals in Scotland. Advises on tenancy and compliance issue for Housing Associations. Has also acted extensively for a variety of funders on housing projects.
Prof. Memberships: Law Society of Scotland. Writer to the Signet, Notary Public.
Career: Qualified as a Solicitor in 1982 and after initially working in the field of litigation joined *Henderson Boyd Jackson* and has worked in the areas of domestic followed by commercial conveyancing for the past 12 years. Since working full time has been partner in the firm's commercial department specialising in housing and public sector work.
Personal: Obtained Law Degree (Honours) from Edinburgh University; married to an advocate at the Scottish Bar and has three children. Lives in Edinburgh. Interests include swimming and travelling.

DOOLITTLE, Ian
Trowers & Hamlins, London (020) 7423 8000 idoolittle@trowers.com
Partner, public sector, Head of public sector.
Specialisation: Team leader on many housing stock transfers, first LSVT and more recently urban estate-based transfers. Now a specialist adviser on complex metropolitan transfers. Is an authority on public/private sector partnerships. Also specialist in environmental law.

DUDLEY, Andrew P.
Needham & James, Stratford upon Avon (01789) 414 444 adudley@neejam.co.uk
Specialisation: Acted for Housing Associations since 1982. Specialises in site acquisition and disposal, nomination rights, planning and planning agreements, infrastructure agreements and environmental issues. Lead solicitor advising Orbit Bexley Housing Association Limited in the acquisition of the housing stock of the London Borough of Bexley and lead advisor to Telford & Wrekin Council in its sale of housing stock to the Wrekin Housing Trust Limited. Has also acted for a number of diverse bodies acquiring care homes for the elderly and homes for persons with learning disabilities.
Prof. Memberships: Law Society.
Career: Kings Norton Grammar School Birmingham. LLB (Hons) Wales (Cardiff). Qualified 1981.
Personal: Married. Enjoys cricket, soccer, motor racing, theatre and travel. Past president Old Nortonians Association. Member of Housing Today Readers Panel.

DYER, Nick J.
Stones, Exeter (01392) 666 777
Specialisation: Specialised in social housing work for nearly 20 years. Experience of site acquisition and development funding, management agreements with Health Trusts and Local Authorities, Shared Ownership and a wide variety of LSE schemes and other issues involving Registered Social Landlords.
Career: Law graduate (Trinity Hall, Cambridge). Formerly partner (latterly managing Partner) in *Cann & Hallett* and now partner in *Stones* in charge of social housing work.
Personal: Married with young daughter. Interests include foreign travel, skiing, trying (and largely failing) to keep fit.

EVANS, Chris
Evans Butler Wade, London (020) 8858 8926 cclevans@netcom.co.uk
Specialisation: Advises social landlords on a wide range of matters including acquisition and development, loans and finance, partnerships and constitutional, student accommodation. Also handles employment contracts, claims and discrimination cases.
Prof. Memberships: Employment Lawyers Association. Member of London Committee of N.B.H.A.–now Places for People Group.
Career: Admitted 1980. Partner in *Stitt & Co.* 1980. Founded own firm in 1985 with Gill Butler.
Personal: Born March 1952. Queens College Cambridge. Lives in London. The renaissance of Welsh Rugby, Hymns and arias. Vespine interests.

EWING, Mark E.
TC Young & Son, Glasgow (0141) 221 5562
Specialisation: Represents a large number of social housing providers with extensive experience in all aspects of stock transfers from local authorities, Scottish Homes, NHS and the Ministry of Defence. Has acted in numerous transfers of engagements between Housing Associations. Regularly provides advice on corporate structures and governance issues and has developed group structures for Scottish and UK organisations. Also experienced in preparing multi-agency and private sector development agreements. Currently instructed in relation to a number of New Housing Partnership stock transfers from local authorities throughout Scotland.
Prof. Memberships: Law Society of Scotland.
Career: Qualified in 1983; *T.C. Young & Son* partner (1987). Co-ordinating housing association work.

FITTON, Roger
Winckworth Sherwood, London (020) 7593 5000 drfitton@winckworths.co.uk
Specialisation: Housing law with emphasis on public and private schemes brownfield urban regeneration projects, externalisations in social services, staff, student and NHS projects and a wide range of charitable and constitutional work.
Prof. Memberships: Law Society.
Career: Oulder Hill Community School, Rochdale 1974-1979; Exeter College, Oxford, Law 1980-1983; Trained, *Boodle Hatfield* 1984-1986; Assistant Solicitor, *Denton Hall* 1986-1989; Assistant, then partner, *Winckworth Sherwood* 1989-1998.

FREEDMAN, Leonard
Harper Macleod, Glasgow (0141) 221 8888 leonard.freedman@harpermacleod.co.uk
Head of corporate department.
Specialisation: Has led the firm's social housing team in some thirty deals with a value in excess of £200 million since 1995. Also Scottish advisor in relation to the only bond issue which has taken place in the Scottish social housing market. Has particular interest in public/private partnerships and over the past twelve months has been advising some of Scotland's largest Local Authorities on legal implications of options available to them with regard to their housing stock. Also advises funders and developers on a wide range of social housing issues.
Prof. Memberships: Regular and well known speaker on public/private partnerships, funding and group structure issues relating to profit and not-for-profit organisations. For some years tutor in company law and formation at University of Glasgow.

GASKELL, Mike
Cobbetts, Manchester (0161) 833 3333 michael.gaskell@cobbetts.co.uk
Specialisation: Advising Housing Associations–group structures and constitutional issues, joint ventures, stock transfer, acquisition and development, landlord and tenant. Currently advising on a number of group structures and stock transfers.
Prof. Memberships: Law Society.
Career: LLB Liverpool. Advising Housing Associations for seventeen years.
Personal: Married. Three children. Trustee of school charity and voluntary board member of Manchester Care and Repair.

GOODE, Naomi
Winckworth Sherwood, London (020) 7593 5000 ngoode@winckworths.co.uk
Specialisation: Partner in a housing and local government department. Has wide ranging social housing practice including private finance (acting for borrowers and lenders); stock transfers (including from NHS Trusts); constitutional matters; shared ownership; tenancy and leashold management. Frequently advised on legal aspects of RSLS' housing management policies. Enjoys acting for tenant groups, frequently acting as legal advisor to tenant bodies on stock transfers.
Prof. Memberships: Law Society.
Career: Qualified in 1990; Courtauld Institute of Art 1991; *Norton Rose* 1991-1994, joined *Winckworth Sherwood* 1994, partner 1998. Committee member of Threshold Tennant Trust; chair Threshold Key Homes; member National Housing Federation Regulation Panel; member Housing Corporation Advisory Panel on Resident Controlled Housing.
Publications: Wrote National Housing Federation's 'Right to Acquire Lease'.

GRAHAM, Ian
Trowers & Hamlins, London (020) 7423 8000 igraham@trowers.com
Partner, housing.
Specialisation: Work for Associations includes advising on PFI projects, group structures, powers, management contracts with local authorities, stock transfer, local housing companies, education, joint ventures, assured and secure tenancies and partnership projects in health, care and urban regeneration. A prolific author and public speaker.

GUBBINS, Jennifer
Trowers & Hamlins, London (020) 7423 8000 jgubbins@trowers.com
Partner, Company & Commercial. Head of Corporate Group.
Specialisation: A corporate finance specialist and leading practitioner in funding for the housing movement. Experience includes innovative work on

securitisation as well as stock/bond issues, loans and the acquisitions/transfers of public sector companies and undertakings. Experience covers PFI, Charity law, Local Housing Companies and Health. Member of The National Blood Authority and on editorial board of Charity Law & Practice Review.

HALL, Gareth
Devonshires, London (020) 7628 7576
gareth.hall@devonshires.co.uk
Specialisation: A broad finance and company/commercial practice, advising housing associations and general corporate clients. Advice includes banking and capital market finance (recently completed a PFI financing acting for lead bank); corporate/constitutional including housing group structures (just completed structure for a leading UK association); mergers, acquisitions and joint ventures; information technology. He has negotiated over 40 IT supply and support contracts over 2 years, ranging from standard packages to bespoke projects.
Career: Trainee at *Lovell White & King* 1982-1984; assistant (corporate) solicitor, *Simmons & Simmons* 1984-1994; joined *Devonshires* 1994, partner since 1995.
Personal: Born 1959. Educated Manchester Grammar School and Merton College, Oxford. Lives in Beckenham. Leisure interests include playing and listening to music of all eras, cycling and the National Trust.

HAND, Catherine
Jenkins & Hand, London (020) 7222 5002
See under Local Government, p.587

HART, Rosemary
Trowers & Hamlins, London (020) 7423 8000
rhart@trowers.com
Partner, Housing.
Specialisation: Works primarily for housing associations, voluntary and public sector bodies. Experience includes: property acquisition and development including projects in the Private Finance Initiative relating to staff and student accommodation, nursing and care homes, joint ventures and security work; nomination agreements, leases, tenancies, constitutional advice, care in the community and management schemes. Regular author and speaker.

HAWKINS, James
Trowers & Hamlins, London (020) 7423 8000
jhawkins@trowers.com
Partner public sector department.
Specialisation: Specialist in public/ private sector partnerships. Is an authority on housing stock transfers and, in particular, urban transfers, local housing companies and regeneration schemes. Also specialises in group structure and residential care home transfers.
Career: University of Birmingham; Qualified 1989. *Trowers & Hamlins* 1991 to date. Partner 1996.

HAYES, Sarah
Trowers & Hamlins, London (020) 7423 8000
shayes@trowers.com
Partner, Head of Housing Finance/Corporate Finance.
Specialisation: General expertise in property finance, secured and unsecured. Particular specialism in housing finance, acting for borrowers and lenders. Experience covers hedging arrangements, bond issues (domestic and Eurobond, rated and insured, own name and group issues), syndicated lending, bonds and securities, group structures, general commercial and charitable issues. Writes regularly for housing and charitable press. Experienced speaker at housing, charitable and funding events.

HOGG, Derek W.
Skene Edwards WS, Edinburgh (0131) 225 6665
Specialisation: All aspects of social housing work, specialising in stock transfers, corporate structures, funding and advisory work. Heads the firm's social housing team, responsible for all contractual and financial aspects of transactions. Acted for Fife Special Housing Association in largest Scottish LSVT to date. Major clients include Bridgewater, Cunninghame, Fife Special and Melville HAs.
Prof. Memberships: Committee Member of Kirk Care and Old Town Housing Associations.
Career: Trained with local authority. Joined *Skene Edwards* in 1988 and became partner in 1994.

HOLDEN, Lawrence
Brabner Holden Banks Wilson, Liverpool (0151) 236 5821
lawrence.holden@bhbw.co.uk
Senior Partner.
Specialisation: Principal area of practice involves advising a number of major housing associations and charities. Also deals with general property and private client work. Advised in relation to many charitable incorporations and group structures. Author of a number of articles on computers and the law and law practice management and legal education. Was a Panel Member of NFHA Independent Inquiry into Governance of Housing Associations 1994-5. Article on "Charities and Governance" in Charity Law and Practice Review Vol. 4 Issue 4.
Prof. Memberships: Law Society, Charity Law Society, National Federation of Housing Association Solicitors' Group, Society for Computers and Law.
Career: Qualified in 1965 while with *Brabner Holden*, became a Partner in 1966 and now Senior Partner. Past President Liverpool Law Society, Pro Chancellor and former President of Council Liverpool University. Deputy Lieutenant of Merseyside.
Personal: Born 19th September 1940. Attended Liverpool College 1951-59, then Liverpool University 1959-62. Leisure pursuits include fell walking, gardening and wood sculpture. Lives in Birkenhead.

HUDDLESTON, David
Browne Jacobson, Nottingham (0115) 976 6000
dhuddleston@brownej.co.uk
Specialisation: Partner in Property Department. Advising both local and national Housing Associations on acquisitions of sites for residential developments including a consortium of a number of Associations. Advising Housing Associations on private financing and security agreements. Continues to receive instructions in connection with large value security work for Housing Associations and from banks lending to the sector. Clients include North British Housing Limited, Metropolitan Housing Trust Limited, East Midlands Housing Association Limited, Leicester Housing Association Limited, South Oxfordshire Housing Association Limited. With the recent opening of the Birmingham office instructions are being received from Associations in the West Midlands and the firm now acts for 25 Associations. Other work includes advising on acquisition of development sites for residential, office and industrial developments. Advising on development agreements associated with acquisition of sites and subsequent sales and leases. Acting for developers on the development of sites including financing and subsequent sales by either grant of leases (including industrial, retail and offices) or to investors of whole developments. Advising major retailers on leases on retail parks.

HUDSON, Allan James
Devonshires, London (020) 7628 7576
Partner in property department.
Specialisation: Principal area is complex consortium developments of sites, PFI type projects and provision of private finance. Also patient hotels. Practice also covers commercial property work, including acquisition, disposal and management of investment property. Has done pioneering work on patient hotels in Glasgow, Liverpool and Nottingham.
Career: Qualified in 1978. At *Penningtons* 1978-81, *Nabarro Nathanson* 1981-82 and *Knapp Fishers* 1982-84. Joined *Devonshires* in 1984 and became a partner in 1985.
Personal: Born 7th July 1954. Educated at Poole Grammar School and Durham University (BA 1st Class Hons). Leisure interests include theatre, cinema and gardening. Lives in Godalming, Surrey.

HURST, Andrew L.T.
Savage Crangle, Skipton (01756) 794611
Partner, specialising in Housing Association and PFI work.
Specialisation: Work includes acquisition, development funding and general advice on governance Housing Association Law. Has advised a number of Housing Associations on refunding Housing Corporation debt and use of long tern SWAP agreements. Instructed on eight substantial PFI Projects in Health and Education Sectors.
Career: Articled–*Walker Morris & Coles*. Qualified 1978. Appointed Partner 1981. *Walker Morris* 1981-98. 1998 joined *Savage Crangle.*
Personal: Loughborough and Selby Grammar Schools. Manchester Polytechnic. Married, 3 children, lives in Bingley. Leisure interests – tennis, motorcycling, history.

JACKSON, Fraser S.
Henderson Boyd Jackson WS, Edinburgh (0131) 226 6881
Specialisation: Worked extensively in last four years in large scale voluntary transfers from Scottish Homes and new town corporations to housing associations and similar bodies. Currently extensively involved in advising on public/ private housing partnerships, local housing companies and related structures.
Prof. Memberships: Law Society of Scotland, Writer to the Signet, Notary Public.
Career: Qualified solicitor since 1977. Worked in local government and with Shell Expro before joining *Henderson Boyd Jackson* in 1982. Partner in firm's capital projects group.
Personal: Educated at George Watsons College and Edinburgh University. Married with four children. Lives in Edinburgh. Interests include soccer, ski-ing, canoeing and golf.

JENKINS, Keith
Jenkins & Hand, London (020) 7222 5002
Specialisation: Closely involved with the Housing Association movement for over twenty years, spe-

cialises in Housing, Co-ops and local authorities. Has made a significant contribution to the growth and development of social housing. Is regarded as one of the most imaginative achievers in this sector.
Career: Qualified in 1974. Joined *Winckworth & Pemberton* in 1972, becoming a partner in 1977. Set up *Jenkins & Hand* 1996.
Personal: Born 10th May 1949. Read law at Lincoln College, Oxford. Leisure interests include reading & rock music. Lives in London. Board member Poplar HARCH and BCHT.

JENNINGS, Robert
Prince Evans, London (020) 8567 3477
Specialisation: Finance partner and head of the litigation department; strong reputation for conducting all types of commercial disputes before the County/High Court and in arbitration; considerable experience in the conduct of complicated contentious property work including judicial review; head of the largest dedicated landlord and tenant litigation function in London; expertise in all types of contentious and non-contentious construction work, with particular specialism in JCT Forms of Build Contracts; advises on all aspects of employment law, including the transfer of undertakings and the conduct of employer/employee matters before the Employment Tribunal; Recent cases include: Tower Housing Association Ltd v Technical and General Guarantee Company Ltd–lead construction case re: interpretation of performance bonds; Greenwich Healthcare National Health Service Trust v London & Quadrant Housing Trust and others–lead property case re: construction of restrictive covenants and compulsory purchase powers.
Career: Articled *Prince Evans*; qualified 1987; partner 1988.
Personal: Born 1963; Newcastle University (LLB Hons); Resides Ealing.

KEULS, Peter
Trowers & Hamlins, Exeter (01392) 217466
pkeuls@trowers.com
Specialisation: Housing associations, local housing companies, large scale voluntary transfers of housing stock: East Dorset, West Dorset, Penwith, North Dorset, Basingstoke & Deane, Kennet, Kerrier, West Somerset, West Devon, South Hams, Bath and North-East Somerset, Restormel, North Devon and Weymouth and Portland; PFI and PPP projects with educational bodies and local authorities.
Career: Worth School, Sussex; College of Law, Guildford; Qualified 1977, *Trowers & Hamlins* (1972-date), Partner 1982.

KNOX, Martin
Anthony Collins Solicitors, Birmingham (0121) 200 3242
Specialisation: Provides specialist legal services on housing and local government law to a significant number of Local Authorites and Registered Social Landlords and numerous community associations, charities and businesses. Pioneered significant iniatives for community regeneration and increased investment in the provision and management of social housing. Particular experience of mayor urban regeneration and transfer work including SRB, particularly local housing companies and recently NDCs.
Career: Qualified 1980. Worked as legal adviser to Sheffield and Birmingham City Councils' Housing Committees. Since joining *Anthony Collins Solicitors* in 1989, has been closely involved in creating innovative solutions to housing and regeneration in urban local authorities. Has developed the community association model in a number of locations throughout the country both for provision of new stock and improvement of existing council housing.

MACGREGOR, Stephen
Brechin Tindal Oatts, Glasgow (0141) 221 8012
asm@bto.co.uk
Head of firm's corporate department.
Specialisation: Leads the firm's established Social Housing Unit. Has acted on behalf of Housing Associations and Housing Cooperatives throughout his career and specialises in large scale voluntary transfers and funding. Extensive experience in funding issues also means regular instruction by Scottish Clearing Banks and other UK and European lenders. Advises on constitutional issues and corporate structures. He was appointed by Scottish Homes to head a statutory inquiry into the affairs of Bridgeton and Dalmarnock Housing Association in 1999. Currently advises 47 RSLs. Acted for syndicate of borrowers in the recent Abbey National Club deal.
Prof. Memberships: Law Society of Scotland.
Career: Qualified in 1993. Partner *Brechin Robb* (now *Brechin Tindal Oatts*) 1986.

MATTHEWS, Carol A.
Wright Hassall, Leamington Spa (01926) 886688
carolm@wrighthassall.co.uk
Specialisation: Solicitor in constitutional issues and structures for registered social landlords and Housing Groups. Solicitor in LSVTs in acting for both Housing Associations and Councils and with property work. Purchase of development sites and advising on housing management issues. Giving seminars and lectures on all aspects of housing law.
Career: Qualified in 1980. Subsequently with *Winckworth & Pemberton* in Westminster before joining *Wright Hassall & Co.* in June 1995 heading the housing & local government department.
Personal: Born 7th December 1954. Educated at Grammar school in Hertfordshire and Warwick University. Married with two daughters. Interests include literature and theatre. Lives in Stratford-upon-Avon.

MCNULTY, Stephen
Burges Salmon, Bristol (0117) 939 2250
stephen.mcnulty@burges-salmon.com
Specialisation: Head of commercial property and social housing. Although much of his work is concerned with property development by housing associations, has wide experience of commercial property issues which arise when working with large corporate clients in particular those in the transport sector. Recent projects have included: major estate regeneration projects, several foyer schemes, redevelopment of former NHS hospital premises to provide housing for rent and shared ownership units and stock transfer arrangements, and major call centre projects for a blue chip client.
Prof. Memberships: Law Society, British Italian Law Association.
Career: Joined *Burges Salmon* in 1984 becoming a partner in 1988.

MILNE, Charles M.
Baird & Company, Cupar (01334) 656644
cmilne@Bairdco.co.uk
Partner in Cupar office.
Specialisation: Principal areas of practice are housing law, housing association work, conveyancing and commercial leasing. Has practiced in cases relating to damages for injuries caused by dampness in dwellings and also handles employment law. Has co-ordinated major Housing Association refinancing projects and has been active recently in advising on a Housing Association group structure and implementation of model rules.
Personal: Labour Party candidate in North East Fife at General Election 1997 and 1999 Scottish General Election. Born 23.7.1954.

MORLEY, Trevor
Prince Evans, London (020) 8567 3477
Specialisation: Managing partner and head of housing finance and low cost home ownership departments; considerable experience in advising both lenders and borrowers of housing and public sector finance; acting on behalf of numerous borrowers in a range of transactions from bilateral and syndicated loans to group borrowing arrangements and capital market issues; expertise in advising on all aspects of banking law; including treasury management and related issues; head of largest low cost home ownership unit in the UK responsible for land acquisition and low cost home ownership development schemes including mixed use/tenure regeneration projects primarily on behalf of registered social landlords; acts for the majority of London based low cost home ownership registered social landlord providers; recent projects include: conduct of the sale of shared ownership portfolios; acting for the consortium of developer and housing association in the Trowbridge Regeneration project in the London Borough of Hackney.
Career: Articled Cambridgeshire; qualified 1979; partner *Prince Evans* 1982.
Personal: Born 1953. Resides Cobham, Surrey.

MORTIMER, Ken .A.
Bevan Ashford, Bristol (0117) 923 0111
Specialisation: Qualified with *Bevan Hancock & Co* in 1975 and returned to *Bevan Ashford* in 1984 having worked in the mean time with *Laurence & Co.* A Senior Associate specialising in commercial property with particular emphasis on public sector clients including RSLs; including development acquisition and disposals; planning and statutory agreements; nomination agreements; management agreements and other agreements with local and similar authorities.
Personal: Married with three children and formerly in the Territorial Army for 28 years; hobby – canal narrow boating.

MURRAY, Andrew J.
Winckworth Sherwood, London (020) 7593 5000
ajmurray@winckworths.co.uk
Partner in Housing and Local Government.
Specialisation: Main area of practice is housing law, with particular expertise in finance and development projects. Addresses various seminars organised by professional bodies and clients.
Prof. Memberships: Law Society.
Career: Qualified in 1987. Joined *Winckworth Sherwood* in 1988, becoming a Partner in 1989.
Personal: Attended Manchester University 1978-81 (English Language and Literature). Lives in Richmond, Surrey.

PANTELIA, Despina
Clifford Chance, London (020) 7600 1000
despina.pantelia@cliffordchance.com
Specialisation: Housing association finance.
Career: Admitted 1987; *Clifford Chance* 1987-95;

Allen & Overy 1996-97; *Clifford Chance* 1997–head of housing finance. Partner since 2000.

PIA, Paul D.
Burness, Edinburgh (0131) 473 6000
Specialisation: A corporate lawyer specialising in corporate governance issues, business and company formations and reorganisations and corporate contracts across the private, public and not-for-profit sectors. He also sets up joint venture and partnering arrangements between different bodies and companies across the sectors. He has extensive knowledge of social housing issues and of the regulatory regimes which impinge upon the activities of housing associations; Scottish Homes registration; Charity Law and the requirements of the Registrar of Friendly Societies. Also provides legal advice to funders of social housing projects and prepares security documentation. Lead legal advisor to the Scottish Federation of Housing Associations; the Institute of Housing in Scotland and a large number of housing associations. Co-author of 'Care, Diligence and Skill', a hand book for directors of not-for-profit companies.

RANDALL, Simon
Lawrence Graham, London (020) 7379 0000
simon.randall@lawgram.com
Partner, Head of Local Government Services.
Specialisation: Principal area of practice is public sector work advising local authorities on externalisation, charitable trusts, urban regeneration and public procurement, PFI, housing and competitive tendering. Involved in large scale voluntary transfers of housing stock to housing associations and local housing companies. Author of many articles and pamphlets on local government and social issues ranging from the private rented sector, large scale voluntary sector of housing stock, local authority companies, community care and housing finance. Organises many seminars on health service, housing and local government related matters.
Prof. Memberships: Law Society.
Career: Articled with *Lawrence Graham* and became a Partner in 1970. Member, London Borough of Bromley 1968–1994. Chairman London Borough of Bromley Housing Committee 1971-76 and Leader of the Council 1976-81. Member Greater London Council 1981-86. Chairman, London Boroughs Association Housing and Social Services Committee 1978–1994. Non-executive Director Bethlem Royal and Maudsley Special Health Authority 1971-94.
Personal: Born 1944. Attended Westminster School. Appointed CBE in June 1991 for housing work in London. Chairman Kelsey Housing Association Ltd and member of Management Committee of Broomleigh Housing Association Ltd. Member National Housing Federation Council and director H.O.M.E.S. Limited.

RHATIGAN, Michael
Eversheds, Manchester (0161) 832 6666
michaelrhatigan@eversheds.com
Partner in commercial property department.
Specialisation: All property aspects for Housing Association law including acquisition development and letting of properties and funding.
Career: Partner *Maurice Rubin Clare* 1979-90; partner *Davies Arnold Cooper* 1990-95; partner *Eversheds* 1995.
Personal: Born 1952. Leisure interests include Bolton Wanderers and opera.

ROBERT, Louis
Prince Evans, London (020) 8567 3477
Specialisation: Senior partner of *Prince Evans*: specialises in innovative projects for the acquisition and development of land on behalf of registered social landlords; recent and current projects involve stock transfers of run down estates using ERCF funding, HAT succession projects, path-finder PET projects with Social Services Authorities, Health Authority reprovision schemes involving PFI, residential care home transfers with VAT and capital finance efficiency, regeneration and on estate planning schemes, foyer schemes, flexible tenure projects and joint venture company/off-balance sheet transactions using special purchase vehicles; at the forefront of next generation PFI and quasi PFI schemes involving Housing Revenue Account assets and multi-commissioner healthcare schemes; over twenty years experience in the housing sector; author of report to Audit Commission/CMHD on legal and financial framework of NHS bodies and social services authority 1995.
Career: Articled *Butcher & Barlow*; qualified 1968, partner *Prince Evans* 1972.
Personal: Manchester University (1965 LLB). Resides Kew, Surrey. Born 1943.

ROBERTSON O.B.E., Andrew O.
TC Young & Son, Glasgow (0141) 221 5562
Senior partner.
Specialisation: Works for community based charitable and generalist Housing Associations as well as fully mutual and non-fully mutual Co-ops. He acts on behalf of Housing Associations across the whole field of their activity. He was instrumental in the forming of the first Employers Federation for Housing Association Committees (now EVH) and provided full administrative and advisory support during its early years.
Prof. Memberships: Law Society of Scotland.
Career: LLB Edinburgh 1964. Trainee *Maclay Murray & Spens* 1964-67. Partner, *T.C. Young & Son* 1968.
Personal: Chairman of the Scottish Housing Associations Charitable Trust from 1992 to date. Trustee of HACT from 1991 to 1997.

SMITH, Chris
Maclay Murray & Spens, London (0171) 606 6130
cps@maclaymurrayspens.co.uk
Partner in housing association department.
Specialisation: Principal area of practice covers all aspects of social housing work with particular expertise in employment law, constitutional work, urban regeneration and Care in the Community. Other main area of practice is development work including consortium arrangements. Currently engaged in a major south coast reprovision project involving two hundred and fifty properties and associated amenities.
Career: Qualified in 1978. Became a Partner with *Asshetons* in 1980 and in the merged firm of *Manches & Co*, then joined *Stones Porter* as a partner in 1993, and *Maclays* (associated with *Maclay Murray & Spens*) in 1998.
Personal: Born 22 October 1953. Attended University College, Cardiff 1972-75. Leisure pursuits include golf and squash. Lives in Godalming.

STEPHENS, Hugo
Irwin Mitchell, Birmingham (0121) 212 1828
stephensh@irwinmitchell.co.uk
Specialisation: A leader in local authority housing stock transfers with expertise in all forms of corporate, constitutional and finance work for registered social landlords. Has advised on all forms of housing stock transfer, local housing companies, group structures, transfers of engagements and charities; particular expertise in housing finance acting for borrowers and lenders; wrote the National Housing Federation's guide to Understanding Loan Documentation and the loan and security documentation sections for their new revised Private Finance Manual.
Prof. Memberships: Law Society.
Career: Qualified in 1989 with *Trowers & Hamlins*; 1989-94, Assistant Solicitor *Trowers & Hamlins*; 1994-97, Senior Assistant Solicitor *Prince Evans*; 1997, Partner *Irwin Mitchell*; 1999 head of Housing and Public Sector Department.
Personal: Born 20th March 1956. Member of the Magic Circle.

THOMPSON, Alison
Shepherd & Wedderburn WS, Edinburgh (0131) 228 9900
alison.thompson@shepwedd.co.uk
Specialisation: Handles all aspects of housing association law including stock transfers, public/private housing partnerships, commercial contracts funding, policy, corporate structures, tenancies, tenures, shared ownership developments, site acquisition and development.
Prof. Memberships: Law Society (Scotland), Notary Public.
Career: Qualified 1988; Associate *Shepherd & Wedderburn WS* 1995.

TURNER, Graham F.
Trowers & Hamlins, Manchester (0161) 211 0000
gturner@trowers.com
Partner, Head of Manchester Office.
Specialisation: Has specialised in housing association law for 25 years, heading a team of eight Manchester lawyers (six Partners) who provide a comprehensive housing law service on a regional and national basis. Experience ranges from stock transfer major development and partnership projects, urban renewal and regeneration to private finance and group structures. Constitutional Vires and PFI issues. All legal issues relating to the housing movement are covered by the Manchester office, including litigation, construction and environmental matters.

TURNER, Nicholas
Lawrence Graham, London (020) 7379 0000
nicholas.turner@lawgram.com
Specialisation: Partner in *Lawrence Graham*'s banking team and specialises in advising housing associations and local housing companies on all aspects of financing. Particular specialisation in the funding aspects of large scale voluntary transfers, syndicated and bilateral lending arrangements, restructuring and refinancing of facilities, capital markets facilities and bond issues, funding issues relating to group structures, security documentation and issues relevant to all of the above. Experience also includes development facilities, derivatives, PFI and ERCF. General experience in most aspects of banking and finance (and in particular property finance) and capital markets.
Career: Prior to joining *Lawrence Graham* spent one year as a money/derivatives broker with EXCO Plc. Qualified at *Lawrence Graham* in 1989 and became a partner in 1997.
Personal: Educated at University of East Anglia (LLB (Hons)). Lives in North London. Married with two children.

SPORT

London: 763; South West: 766; Midlands: 766; The North: 766; Scotland: 767; *Profiles*: 768

OVERVIEW: The sector is now attracting heavyweight attention from commercial leaders across the UK. Competition law has become a major issue in this area of practice, and it is in this field that newly-ranked practitioners such as Alisdair Bell excel.

It is thought that as the rise of sport as a big-money industry gains momentum, work will increasingly shift to leading City firms with serious corporate and anti-trust practices. However, for now, the role of the specialist small firm is safe, and names such as McCormicks, James Chapman & Co and Grower Freeman & Goldberg continue to flourish.

RESEARCH: *Administrative and public law covers advice to public bodies and challenges to decisions of public bodies by means of judicial review (JR) or statutory appeals. It is a process rather than a subject. While it has been accepted that JR is not as creative and generative of new legal principles as it once was, the general opinion has been that this will change when the Human Rights Act comes into effect in late 2000.*

LEADING IN-HOUSE LAWYERS

Darren BERMAN, Company Solicitor, *Football Association*

Nic COWARD, Company Secretary, *Football Association*

Robert DATNOW, Lawyer, *British Olympic Association*

Andy GRAY, Head of Legal Affairs, *Amateur Swimming Association*

Jonathon HALL, Secretary and Legal Officer, *Rugby Football Union*

Bruce MELLSTROM, Lawyer, *Lawn Tennis Association*

Sascha WOODWARD-HILL, Lawyer, *Formula One*

Nic Coward at the Football Association *"really stands out in the industry"* as an excellent lawyer and manager who *"knows his organisation backwards."* Also at the Football Association is the *"very commercial"* **Darren Berman**. "New kid on the block" **Robert Datnow** has *"acclimatised quickly"* and is doing a great job modernising the ways of the British Olympic Association. Another up and comer is the "very capable" **Jonathan Hall** at the Rugby Football Union. He is admired for his problem-solving skills and for *"always questioning the fundamentals."* **Andy Gray** of the Amateur Swimming Association is *"very sharp"* and has *"a very broad range of experience."* **Bruce Mellstrom** at the Lawn Tennis Association is *"quite exceptional"* owing to his real depth of experience together with his ability to *"get things done in a political environment."* **Sascha Woodward-Hill** knows the Formula One industry *"better than anyone"* and is known for her *"tough negotiation skills."*

In-House lawyers profiles: page 1177

LONDON

Denton Wilde Sapte Considered *"a great sports brand"* by the market, the team's *"deep industry knowledge"* sets it apart from its full-service competitors. The firm has the requisite corporate, competition and litigation strength to *"handle anything."* Its successful defence of The FA Premier League Limited in the Restrictive Practices Court was a headline case last year. Front man **Adrian Barr-Smith** *("top of the tree – pragmatic and a good thinker")* handles non-contentious work and led the team in drafting all commercial and organisational agreements for Cricket World Cup 1999. Ex-Herbert Smith litigator **Mark Gay**, *("has presence – you take him seriously")* made his name in drugs cases for the IAAF. His reputation has clearly strengthened the team's reputation for governing body and regulatory advice, although he is regarded as a technical, rather than a commercial practitioner. He advised on both the Linford Christie and Doug Walker doping inquiries. **Clients:** England and Wales Cricket Board; IAAF; The FA Premier League Limited.

Townleys The only firm in the country with an exclusive sports focus, its lawyers are considered *"young, entrepreneurial and dedicated."* Although some queried the firm's ability to take on the bigger-ticket competition and corporate work, the sheer breadth of their involvement in sport is considered to be *"beyond compare."* The *"straight-talking"* **Stephen Townley** has *"an unbelievable track record,"* and is the firm's figurehead. His work for the 'Super 12' UK racecourses has been characterised as *"ground-breaking."* The *"impressive"* **Darren Bailey** is well-known for his anti-doping and disciplinary work. On behalf of Rugby World Cup Limited he led the team in drafting and implementing a doping control programme for the event. **Nick Couchman** *("commercially aware")* and new media specialist **Jonathan Higton** are also recommended. **Clients:** Formula One; Rugby World Cup Limited; Sport England.

Bird & Bird A large sports group, whose combination of *"technical brilliance"* and *"commercial savvy"* is admired by the market. Work covers the spectrum of industry-related matters on behalf of corporate entities, governing bodies, sports rights agencies and high net worth individuals. The firm's entrenched reputation for IP, IT and e-commerce advice has aided the sports group's growth in these areas. A highlight was the team's advice to Europe@web on its $50 million lead investment in Sportal, the European Internet company. Department Head **Justin Walkey** *("big name, big reputation")* is known particularly for his rights protection work and advises on both contentious and non-contentious matters. **Felicity Reeve** *("superbly resourceful")* is largely active on digital broadcasting and internet issues, but also led the team advising SEGA Europe Limited on the sponsorships of Arsenal, St. Etienne and Sampdoria Football Clubs. **Clients:** The Football Association; SEMA Group plc; Sega Europe plc.

Nicholson Graham & Jones The firm is felt to possess both the depth to handle big-ticket corporate and competition advice, and the *"industry nous"* required to advise rights owners on new media deals. The team advised Leeds Sporting plc on its strategic media alliance with, and equity subscription by, British Sky Broadcasting plc. The *"ubiquitous"* **Warren Phelops** is perceived to be *"an effective operator who understands the industry."* His practice centres on finance and structuring work, as well as rights packaging, exploitation and acquisitions. The firm's wide-ranging client base includes rights owners such as governing bodies and event owners. The team acted for Rugby Hospitality 99 Limited on the official hospitality arrangements for Rugby World Cup. **Clients:** Sports Network; Leeds Sporting plc; Rugby Hospitality 99 Limited.

Farrer & Co Regarded as the firm for constitutional advice, its client roster includes significant governing bodies, sports institutions and charities. Market perception is of a team with *"extremely thorough"* individuals. However, the firm's profile is more than ever considered to be *"old school,"* and it is rarely encountered by competitors outside its traditional areas of excellence. The firm accordingly drops a notch in the ratings. **Karena Vleck** *("forceful when required")* heads the team and is known predominantly for her constitutional work for UK Athletics. The team comprises lawyers drawn from litigation, commercial, property and IP departments, but is still felt to function as a *"cohesive unit."* Commercial advice is a continued strength, the firm representing UK Athletics in its sponsorship contract with CGU – the largest ever such deal in athletics history. **Clients:** UK Athletics Limited; British Olympic Association; British Paralympic Association.

SPORT • London	Ptnrs	Assts
❶ Denton Wilde Sapte	6	11
Townleys	4	17
❷ Bird & Bird	8	12
Nicholson Graham & Jones	2	2
❸ Farrer & Co	8	2
Max Bitel, Greene	1	1
SJ Berwin & Co	14	11
❹ Collyer-Bristow	1	1
Harbottle & Lewis	2	2
Herbert Smith	6	12
❺ Charles Russell	4	2
Clintons	2	3
Freshfields Bruckhaus Deringer	9	10
Grower Freeman & Goldberg	1	3
Memery Crystal	2	2
Mishcon de Reya	3	-
Olswang	6	5
Russell Jones & Walker	1	5
❻ Ashurst Morris Crisp	6	12
Field Fisher Waterhouse	2	3
Moorhead James	6	-
Simmons & Simmons	5	10
The Simkins Partnership	*	*
Theodore Goddard	3	4

LEADING INDIVIDUALS	
✪ **BARR-SMITH Adrian** Denton Wilde Sapte	**BITEL Nicholas** Max Bitel, Greene
TOWNLEY Stephen Townleys	
❶ **GAY Mark** Denton Wilde Sapte	**GOLDBERG Mel** Grower Freeman & Goldberg
PHELOPS Warren Nicholson Graham & Jones	**REEVE Felicity** Bird & Bird
VLECK Karena Farrer & Co	**WALKEY Justin** Bird & Bird
❷ **RUSSELL Patrick** Charles Russell	**STINSON Philip** Clintons
❸ **BAILEY Darren** Townleys	**BELL Alasdair** White & Case
BURDON-COOPER Alan Collyer-Bristow	**COUCHMAN Nicholas** Townleys
CRYSTAL Peter Memery Crystal	**GREGORY Lesley** Memery Crystal
HIGTON Jonathan Townleys	**McINERNEY Peter** SJ Berwin & Co
METLISS Jonathan SJ Berwin & Co	**PARKER Raj** Freshfields Bruckhaus Deringer
VEROW Richard Osborne Clarke OWA	
UP AND COMING	
BROWN Jacqueline Clintons	**REID Fraser** Theodore Goddard

Within each band, firms are listed alphabetically. See **Profiles** on page 768

* *See editorial entries for explanations of team sizes.*

Max Bitel, Greene Nick Bitel *("sharp and business-like")* dominates this varied sports practice, his reputation heightened by his continued role as Chief Executive of the London Marathon. The team is associated with high profile work and advised athlete Doug Walker on his fight against drug-taking allegations. Internet work has been a recent growth area, and the team has regularly advised on buying and restructuring rights on the internet. The market's sole caveat here concerns the size of the team, which is far smaller than its principal competitors. **Clients:** Ryder Cup; Wembley National Stadium; Worldsport.com.

S J Berwin & Co Said to have made an *"all-out assault"* in this field, the firm rises sharply in the rankings this year. Essentially corporate driven (the team recently floated Sports Internet Group on AIM), the group also draws on the firm's other areas of expertise, notably media, IP, competition, litigation and employment. Two names stand out as market leaders: **Peter McInerney** *("personable and well respected – you can do business with this guy")* who concentrates on IP and commercial matters, and the *"confrontational"* corporate lawyer **Jonathan Metliss**. The latter, while *"something of an acquired taste,"* is widely accepted as the driving force behind the group's success. The firm represented ENIC against UEFA in the Court of Arbitration for Sport in Switzerland, and advised ONdigital in its negotiations with ITV to cover the UEFA Champions League. **Clients:** Sports Internet Group; ENIC plc; Arsenal FC.

Collyer-Bristow Built its reputation on the back of a strong commercial practice (sports marketing, commercial rights and television), but this year, the firm has been notable for its involvement in large-scale litigation. A significant example was Hogan and Others v London Irish, a case which resulted in a landmark decision for professional rugby players. Department Head **Alan Burdon-Cooper** is particularly known in the market for his competition expertise, although the loss of Richard Verow to Osborne Clarke OWA must be considered a setback. The team carried out substantial brand management work for the RFU. **Clients:** RFU; Octagon; Bass plc.

Harbottle & Lewis Well known media/entertainment firm developing a solid sports niche on the back of its sponsorship and IP expertise. Growth areas include high-profile player representation – the team advised Lawrence Dallaglio on his appearance before a RFU disciplinary inquiry. Dot.com work, particularly for on-line publishers, is another area of specific proficiency. A broad client base includes governing bodies, companies, clubs and individual sportsmen. **Clients:** Loftus Road plc; Ryder Cup Limited; Lawrence Dallaglio.

Herbert Smith City firm which gravitates towards big-ticket corporate work, litigation and competition. Top-class London and Brussels competition expertise is a particular forte, and the firm successfully advised BSkyB on the Premier League Restrictive Practices Court Proceedings. In addition, the group is commended for an enviable client base covering a wide range of sports. However, the team is not considered to have replaced Mark Gay (who joined Denton Wilde Sapte last year) adequately, and still has no recognised leader. **Clients:** BSkyB; FOA/FIA; Tottenham Hotspur.

Charles Russell Patrick Russell *("old school and utterly dependable")* is a respected focal point for the team and his in-depth knowledge of the horse racing sector is considered *"beyond any doubt"*. However, the practice is viewed as narrow and relies predominantly upon one major client (The Jockey Club.) As a result, the group's ranking has suffered by comparison with other, more rounded rivals. **Clients:** The Jockey Club.

Clintons Entertainment firm known predominantly for the strength of its sports marketing and sponsorship practice. **Philip Stinson** acts for numerous agency clients on clearance work and rights exploitation. IP work in sports-related dot.coms is a growth area. Litigator **Jacqueline Brown** is making her mark this year and is known for high profile player representation. **Clients:** Sports marketing agencies; high net worth individuals; manufacturers.

Freshfields Bruckhaus Deringer Associated almost exclusively with high-value corporate related sports issues, the firm has received a mixed press in this area of practice. Criticism has focused on the degree of the firm's focus on sports law. Linchpin **Raj Parker** is well known within the market, but has been kept busy this year by large scale insurance litigation. Historically known for its work on behalf of the FA, the team represented Manchester United during the abortive bid by BSkyB. Overall, the market speaks highly of the firm's ability to apply itself to sport *"when a sufficiently large instruction arrives."* **Clients:** The Football Association.

Grower Freeman & Goldberg Mel Goldberg *("without question, one of the top names")* is well known in the market for his representation of high net worth individual sporting personalities. Viewed as a *"one stop shop for sports stars,"* he is primarily known for his connections with football and boxing. He has also advised international tennis players on contractual matters. The firm itself is considered to stand firmly in his shadow. **Clients:** Chris Eubank; Dennis Wise; FIFA; contract agents.

Memery Crystal Acknowledged to have an *"interesting client base,"* the firm has not been seen with its usual frequency this year. However, in **Peter Crystal** and **Lesley Gregory** the team boasts two practitioners of sound repute. A broadened case-load has featured increased advice on corporate and sponsorship matters in sports as varied as football, boxing and tennis. Recent work has included advice on a joint venture in the field of digital radio. **Clients:** Wembley; David Lloyd Leisure.

Mishcon de Reya A team with an improved profile, traditionally strong in constitutional and governing body disputes. Niche strengths include representing individuals in drugs-related cases. The firm acts for Diane Modahl in her ongoing claim against the British Athletics Federation, and successfully defended Spencer Smith, Britain's double World Champion triathelete in his case before the BTA and ITU. On the commercial side, the team act for Arrows Formula One following its acquisition last year. **Clients:** UK Sports Council; Diane Modahl; West Indies Cricket Board.

Olswang A new entrant to our tables this year, the firm's top-flight media and IT expertise has helped to build a much-hailed client base. Act for a wide range of media platforms, including dot.com start-ups, television and radio stations and rights agencies. The team advised Granada Media Group on its ground-breaking strategic partnership with Liverpool Football Club, giving Granada a 9.9% stake in the club, as well as the right to exploit its media rights. The sports department includes corporate, competition and IP lawyers and is commended for *"its increasingly serious focus."* **Clients:** Sportal; Media Partners; Talk Radio (Talk Sport).

Russell Jones & Walker Sports practice with a varied client roster. The team represents both individuals and companies, particularly sports marketing organisations, player associations and governing bodies. However, the departure of rising star Fraser Reid must be regarded as a severe set-back to the team's profile. The team advised Capitalize (sponsorship consultancy) on the advertising and sponsorship campaign of Carlsberg Tetley through Tetley Bitter, the official sponsors of the England Rugby Team during the 1999 World Cup. **Clients:** Squash Rackets Association; Professional Sports Partnerships; English Hockey Association.

Ashurst Morris Crisp Not a name readily associated by the market with sports work, although the firm is acknowledged for its corporate transactional acumen in the sports arena as elsewhere. The team acted for Morgan Grenfell Private Equity on its acquisition of a 50% interest in Formula One Holdings, a deal which brought together leading corporate and competition lawyers. Acting for Wizja TV on its purchase of TV rights to sports events in Poland. **Clients:** European Rugby Cup; Canal Plus; Professional Cricketers Association.

Field Fisher Waterhouse Respected for the quality of its sports sponsorship work. On commercial matters, the team advised Premier Waters, the producers of Evian and Volvic mineral waters, on its appointment as the official supplier of mineral water to the Stella Artois Grass Court Championships in 1999. The team's litigators acted for the Australian Rugby Union in a case against Cotton traders over the unlicensed sale of Wallaby rugby jerseys. **Clients:** Amsport; Whitbread; Premier Waters Limited.

Moorhead James Partner-driven, comparatively low-profile young sports team which deals with licensing, trade mark disputes and new media cases. The group has additional experience in doping cases, and has acted for a variety of institutional clients. **Clients:** Sports Council, UK Sport.

Simmons & Simmons Sizeable sports practice which, despite an impressive client list (MCC and ICC are long-standing clients), has an extremely low market profile. Insolvency-related sports matters are a niche speciality, and

High Profile Sports Cases

Parties	Lawyers	Significance
English National Investment Co v UEFA	• UEFA – White & Case; Alistair Bell; Swiss Lawyers • ENIC – S J Berwin; Michael Beloff QC; Tim Kerr	ENIC unsuccessfully challenged the UEFA rule that prevents football club owners from controlling more than one team in the UEFA cup. Heard before the Court of Arbitration for Sport.
Doug Walker v UK Athletics & IAAF	• Douglas Walker – Max, Bitel Greene; Charles Flint QC; Andrew Hunter • IAAF – Denton Wilde Sapte; Mark Gay; Robert Howe • UKA – Farrers; David Pannick QC ; Adam Lewis	Sprinter's action against UK Athletics and IAAF to overturn a suspension based on Nandrolone steroid tests. Early case hearings involved Gary Cadogan and Linford Christie. Ensuing dispute between the IAAF regarding substances similar to Nandrolone that had not been banned at the time of Walker's dismissal.
Justice for Women v Home Secretary	• Justice for Women – Fisher Meredith; Nicholas Blake QC; Lawrie Fransman QC; Stephanie Harrison • Home Secretary – Treasury Solicitors; Robin Tam	Judicial Review of Home Secretary's decision to admit Mike Tyson to Britain to fight against Julius Francis in Manchester.
RFU v Lawrence Dallaglio	• RFU – Edwin Coe; Richard Lissack QC • Mr Dallaglio – Harbottle & Lewis; George Carman QC	Former England rugby captain Lawrence Dallaglio fined £15,000 by the RFU after admitting bringing the game into disrepute. Also ordered to pay £10,000 costs. Followed allegations of drugs use.
RFU v Celtic Unions (Five Nations Valuation)	• RFU – Denton Wilde Sapte; Michael Brindle QC • Celtic Unions – Townleys; Nicholas Green QC; Simon Salzedo	Hearing before a valuer over the value of Five Nations TV rights. The case concerned the valuation of England's part in the Five Nations Championship, with a maximum figure believed to be up to £ 65m, following Englands £87.5m deal with Sky.
Office of Fair Trading v FA Premier League, BBC, BSkyB	• OFT– Geoffrey Vos QC; Ken Parker QC; Jon Turner; Daniel Beard • FAPL – Denton Wilde Sapte; Charles Aldous QC; Richard Fowler QC; Catherine Otton–Goulder QC • BBC – Richards Butler; Christopher Carr QC; Rhodri Thompson; Jennifer Skillbeck; • BSkyB – Herbert Smith; Jonathan Sumption QC; Nicholas Green QC	Competition law case concerning the sale of Premier League TV rights. The Office of Fair Trading brought proceedings against the Football Association Premier League claiming it was acting as an unlawful cartel by negotiating exclusive television licensing agreements for matches. It also claimed that this restricted competition and was detrimental to the public. The Restrictive Practices Court rejected these claims. The value of the agreements was £743m.
Michael Watson v British Boxing Board of Control	• Mr Watson – Myers Fletcher & Gordon ; Colin Mackay QC; Neil Block • BBBC – Lawrence Graham; Ronald Walker QC; Stephen Worthington	Boxer Michael Watson suffered brain damage due to delay in obtaining adequate medical assistance. The High Court held that a regulatory body owes a duty of care to boxers to provide appropriate medical assistance and damages of over £1m were awarded.

the team advised Buchler Phillips on the administration of Richmond Rugby Club. The firm advised on similar matters in respect of the proposed administrations of Oxford United FC and Portsmouth FC. Elsewhere, the group has acted for the MCC, ICC and individual sports stars on rights protection. **Clients:** TWR; MCC; World in Motion Limited.

The Simkins Partnership Well-known media and entertainment practice whose two sports specialists are assisted by employment, corporate, litigation and IP practitioners. Eclectic body of work, although not often seen by peers. The team acted for English First Division Rugby over the reduction of the size of Allied Dunbar Division 1. This reduction was challenged in the High Court by Division 2 clubs and successfully defended by the firm. The firm's strength in broadcasting was underlined by its advice on behalf of Test Match grounds on their agreement with the ECB on the broadcasting of Test cricket. **Clients:** English First Division Rugby; Test Match Grounds Consortium.

Theodore Goddard The arrival of the fast-rising **Fraser Reid** from Russell Jones & Walker should provide the practice with a much-needed shot in the arm. Well-known for his work on athletics doping cases, he is said to be able to *"create something out of nothing."* The team has been active on advertising and sponsorship matters for football clubs as well as having niche expertise in horse-racing. **Clients:** British Horseracing Board Ltd.

Other Notable Practitioners For non-contentious work, **Richard Verow** *("relatively new to the game but really impressive")* is highly praised by clients for his sponsorship, merchandising and general IP expertise. His move to Osborne Clarke OWA from Collyer-Bristow should be a real fillip for his new firm. **Alasdair Bell** of White & Case, formerly at the firm's Brussels office, comes highly recommended, and is considered by many to be *"the first point of call for sports-related competition advice."* Active clients include UEFA and ENIC.

SOUTH WEST

SPORT • South West	Ptnrs	Assts
❶ Clarke Willmott & Clarke Bristol	1	1
Osborne Clarke OWA Bristol	4	4
❷ Stones Exeter	3	3

LEADING INDIVIDUALS
❶ POWELL David Clarke Willmott & Clarke
❷ BRAITHWAITE Andrew Osborne Clarke OWA; COURTENAY-STAMP Bronwen Stones
JEACOCK David David Jeacock

Within each band, firms are listed alphabetically *See **Profiles** on page 768*

Clarke Willmott & Clarke Number one in the region, having acquired a ready-made sports practice from Alsters last year. The team is especially noted for its advice on behalf of individual players. **David Powell** is known as a rugby specialist, although he has also advised a number of footballers and cricketers. The team successfully defended Jeremy Guscott against well publicised assault charges in 1999. **Clients:** Jeremy Guscott; England Rugby Squad; Marcus Stewart.

Osborne Clarke OWA Lauded for its client base, the team undertakes a variety of work for institutions, clubs and individuals. Sponsorship deals, player's contracts, and wide-ranging litigation matters have constituted the group's recent case-load. **Andrew Braithwaite** has a recognised name for his expertise in IP-related sports matters. The team advised the Professional Event Riders' Association on the formation and launch of sponsorship deals with MasterCard, Credit Suisse and Husky. **Clients:** Professional Golfers Association; Professional Cricketers Association; Bolton Wanderers Football Club.

Stones Team which is almost exclusively known for its contentious work in skiing, acting largely for claimants after accidents. **Bronwen Courtenay-Stamp**'s expertise in this field is not in doubt. **Clients:** Fogg Travel, EuropAssist.

Other Notable Practitioners Sole practitioner **David Jeacock** has a national reputation for his constitutional and governing body work. His focus is on athletics and disabled sport.

MIDLANDS

SPORT • Midlands	Ptnrs	Assts
❶ Hammond Suddards Edge Birmingham	1	1

LEADING INDIVIDUALS
❶ ALDERSON Richard Hammond Suddards Edge

Within each band, firms are listed alphabetically *See **Profiles** on page 768*

Hammond Suddards Edge The only serious player in the region, the firm has a national reputation for the quality of its regulatory and constitutional advice. **Richard Alderson** *("personable and dedicated")* is long-established in the field. He led the team advising the British Athletics Federation (In Administration) on the successful defence of claims made by Diane Modahl in the House of Lords. New media, internet and e-commerce advice have also continued to flourish. **Clients:** The Football League; Professional Cricketers Association; The Amateur Boxing Association.

THE NORTH

James Chapman & Co Viewed historically as a one client firm (its work on behalf of Manchester United is legendary) it has been commended for a much greater depth this year *("they understand commercial reality")*. Led by the ubiquitous **Maurice Watkins** *("quietly but effectively goes about his business – you never underestimate him")*, the team has been bolstered by the arrival of **Jason Smith** *("a superb acquisition")* from ISL, Switzerland. A specialist in sports rights, he advises governing bodies, sports marketing companies and sporting clubs in all areas of rights protection and exploitation. The team was appointed sole adviser to a leading multi-national company on its staging of a proposed round the world challenge, and advised Manchester United on its ground-breaking £30 million sponsorship deal with Vodafone. **Clients:** Manchester United plc; Swansea City AFC.

McCormicks An eclectic sports practice, which has received strong client recommendations this year. The team is led by **Peter McCormick**, *("bright, engaging, knows his subject")* who, assisted by *"sensible operator"* **Clive Lawrence**, is well known for his pivotal role in advising the FA Premier League. Mr McCormick will be part of the Premier League team negotiating the new television contracts which are up for renewal in 2001/2002. **Richard Cramer** has solid rugby league connections, advising the Board of Castleford Tigers on the funding and running of the club. His profile was further raised as a result of acting for boxer Richie Woodhall in his successfully mediated dispute with Frank Warren. **Clients:** Leeds FC; Keighley Cougars RLFC Ltd; FA Premier League.

SPORT • The North	Ptnrs	Assts
❶ James Chapman & Co Manchester	2	-
McCormicks Leeds	5	-
❷ George Davies Manchester	3	4
Walker Morris Leeds	2	3
❸ Addleshaw Booth & Co Manchester	4	1
Gorna & Co Manchester	1	1
❸ Zermansky & Partners Leeds	4	-

LEADING INDIVIDUALS	
✪ McCORMICK Peter McCormicks	WATKINS Maurice James Chapman & Co
❶ CAISLEY Christopher Walker Morris	
❷ CRAMER Richard McCormicks	HEWISON John George Davies
MORRISON Michael Gorna & Co	
❸ HOVELL Mark George Davies	LAWRENCE Clive McCormicks
LINDLEY Richard Zermansky & Partners	
UP AND COMING	
SMITH Jason James Chapman & Co	

Within each band, firms are listed alphabetically See **Profiles** on page 768

George Davies Known primarily for the quality of its rugby practice, although has one major footballing client, the PFA. The *"worthy"* **John Hewison** is the group's stand-out name, although **Mark Hovell** also retains a share of market support. The firm's client base includes managers, individuals and associations. **Clients:** PFA.

Walker Morris Renowned for the quality of its rugby league advice, although the team is also active in football and cricket. **Chris Caisley** (*"excellent – understands the commercial point of a deal"*) has a national reputation for sports work and led the team negotiating and settling overseas television rights deals and radio broadcast contracts for the Rugby Super League. He moves up in the tables this year. The team also advise a number of well-known sporting personalities, including Peter Reid and Courtney Walsh. **Clients:** Bradford Bulls; Professional Cricketers' Players Association; Professional Rugby Players Association.

Addleshaw Booth & Co A respected IP and sponsorship-led practice which is steadily increasing its profile within the sector, and consequently rises in the tables this year. Football and rugby are the focus, although motor-sport is a growth area for the team, which advises Ferrari on unlicensed merchandising and World Superbike Champion, Carl Fogarty, on trade-mark matters. A highlight this year is the team's continuing representation of Manchester 2002 Limited and Manchester City Council on the Host Broadcasting Agreement with the BBC for the 2002 Commonwealth Games. **Clients:** Adidas UK Ltd; Manchester 2002 Limited Commonwealth Games; Manchester Sale Rugby Club.

Gorna & Co Football is the focus of this group, with particular expertise in employment matters. **Michael Morrison** has carved a respectable niche representing significant individuals (players and managers) in football, as well as commercial employees of large clubs. Sports covered to a lesser extent include tennis, golf and rugby. **Clients:** High net worth individuals.

Zermansky & Partners Partner-driven niche firm where **Richard Lindley** continues to enjoy a polished reputation for his litigation prowess. Rugby is the core sport of expertise here, although the firm continues to advise a number of sporting institutions in other areas. **Clients:** Governing bodies and institutions.

SCOTLAND

SPORT • Scotland	Ptnrs	Assts
❶ Anderson Strathern WS Edinburgh	2	3
Harper Macleod Glasgow	3	4
❷ Burness Glasgow	3	3
Dundas & Wilson CS Edinburgh	5	4
Henderson Boyd Jackson WS Edinburgh	1	1
Morison Bishop Edinburgh	1	2

LEADING INDIVIDUALS	
❶ DUFF Alistair Henderson Boyd Jackson WS	GROSSET Alan Morison Bishop
KERR John Anderson Strathern WS	
❷ McKENZIE Rod Harper Macleod	MILLER Stephen Harper Macleod
SLEIGH Andrew Burness	

Within each band, firms are listed alphabetically. See **Profiles** on page 768

Anderson Strathern WS **John Kerr** (*"a good chap"*) leads a firm which continues to be rated in the front rank for sports law. The group has been involved in sponsorship, employment issues, drugs disciplinary cases and competition matters within the field. Known primarily for advising governing bodies, the team advised the Scottish Rugby Union on a variety of endorsement agreements in connection with the European Rugby Cup. **Clients:** SRU; Scottish Games Association.

Harper Macleod High profile team with a specific name for work in the contentious sphere, including player registrations and disciplinary proceedings. The newly-ranked **Rod McKenzie** and **Stephen Miller** both have leading names in Scotland for their litigation work. Client base largely comprises governing bodies and clubs. The team advised on the work registration of Jorge Cadete. **Clients:** Celtic plc; Scottish Premier League; Scottish Rugby Union.

Burness **Andrew Sleigh** is the focus of a group which is mainly known for its role as advisor to the Scottish Football Association on both contentious and non-contentious matters. The firm's significant media/entertainment presence is aiding the growth of its sport practice – it acted for Radio First on its joint venture with Celtic FC. **Clients:** St Andrews Sporting Club; Scottish Football Association; Clansmen Sporting Club (Sports promoters).

Dundas and Wilson CS Although not possessing the stand-out names of some of its competitors, the team is considered *"as good as anyone"* for corporate-related sports cases. A substantial client base also accounts for the team's new ranking this year. Acted for Queens Park FC/The National Stadium plc on the redevelopment of Hampden Park stadium and the associated debenture issue. **Clients:** The Rangers FC plc; Carnegie Sports Management.

Henderson Boyd Jackson WS Contentious lawyer **Alistair Duff** (*"he doesn't waste words"*) fronts this small sports group known in the market almost exclusively for its player representation. However, while many household name football and rugby players are clients of the firm, it has also acted on a number of major sponsorship deals in Scotland. The team advised NTL on its sponsorship of Celtic and Rangers football clubs. **Clients:** Hearts FC; Hibernian FC.

Morison Bishop Elder statesman **Alan Grosset** is the pre-eminent figure at a department which acts for a variety of institutions and clubs in Scotland. The team acts on both contentious and non-contentious matters. **Clients:** Dundee Utd FC; Scottish Premier Rugby Ltd.

LEADERS IN SPORT

ALDERSON, Richard A.
Hammond Suddards Edge, Birmingham (0121) 200 2001
Partner and Head of Sports Unit.
Specialisation: Since 1987, sole area of practice is sport administration and associated commercial activities, advising governing bodies on television, new media and internet rights, sponsorship, discipline and constitutional matters. Also works for industry, covering sport and event sponsorship and broadcast sponsorship. Acts for The Football League and other sports governing bodies.
Prof. Memberships: British Association for Sport and the Law.
Career: Qualified in 1976 with *Edge Ellison*, becoming a Partner in 1981.
Personal: Born 17th July 1951. Attended Bristol University 1970-73. Trustee of St Giles' Hospice (Special interest: charity shops). Leisure interests include tennis and Aston Villa. Lives in Birmingham.

BAILEY, Darren
Townleys, London (020) 7713 7000
Partner.
Specialisation: Representation of domestic and international sports governing bodies, major sporting events, sports leagues and football clubs on a wide range of sport specific issues including doping, general and player disciplinary matters, constitutional, league and event structures, sports equipment, youth development programmes, liability/insurance issues and the application of risk management programmes. Also advises governing bodies and professional sports clubs on commercial issues in sport, including sponsorship and television, eligibility/registration matters, freedom of movement and competition issues (domestic and European) and defamation in sport. Editor Sports Law Administration and Practice.
Prof. Memberships: Officer of the British Association for Sport and the Law, The Law Society.
Career: Stoneham School: Windsor and Maidenhead College, University of Birmingham, Partner in 1998. (F.A. Coach 1992).
Personal: Former footballer turned Coach with a keen interest in all sports.

BARR-SMITH, Adrian
Denton Wilde Sapte, London (020) 7320 6501

BELL, Alasdair
White & Case, London (020) 7600 7300
Specialisation: EU and competition: acting for UEFA in connection with rules on common ownership of clubs, central marketing of TV rights and proposed salary cap structures.
Prof. Memberships: Law Society of Scotland.
Career: Partner, *White & Case*, London.

BITEL, Nicholas
Max Bitel, Greene, London (020) 7354 2767

BRAITHWAITE, Andrew
Osborne Clarke OWA, Bristol (0117) 917 4178
andrew.braithwaite@osborneclark.com
See under Intellectual Property, p.509

BROWN, Jacqueline
Clintons, London (020) 7379 6080
Specialisation: Advises on contentious matters including intellectual property rights and contract law with reference to the music industry, sport and entertainment generally. Clients include celebrated sports people and entertainers, managers, sports agents and marketing consultants and multinational entertainment groups (especially recording and publishing companies). Has been involved in the following landmark cases: for U2/Polygram against the Performing Rights Society (including before the Monopolies and Mergers Commission), for the Stone Roses against Zomba and for Sony against George Michael. Recent cases include representing various Premiership footballers in FA hearings and Gina G in proceedings against FX Music. Particular knowledge and experience of restraint of trade issues in sports and entertainment.
Prof. Memberships: Member of the British Association for Sport and Law.
Career: Educated in Scotland and at Birmingham University (LLB 19.) Articled at *Clintons* in 1990. Partner from 1996.
Personal: Born 12th January 1966. Owns and competes two showjumpers, member of the British Showjumping Association and occasional stunt rider.

BURDON-COOPER, Alan R.
Collyer-Bristow, London (020) 7242 7363
Specialisation: Sponsorship in sports, arts and television; licensing and merchandising. Recent highlights include advice to Esprit Marketing Limited in relation to the London Triathlon; sponsorship of the Rugby World Cup; advice relating to the sponsorship of the Millennium Stadium in Cardiff; advising West Indian Players Association in their dispute with West Indies Cricket Board regarding their South African tour; advising on CGU sponsorship of UK Athletics and on appointment of Fast Track as event organisers and marketing agents for UK athletics; Co-author 'Vol 39, Sports and Sponsorship: Encyclopaedia of Forms and Precendents' (Butterworths).
Prof. Memberships: Member of the Executive Committee of the Institute of Sports Sponsorship.
Career: Articled at *Collyer-Bristow*, qualified 1968, partner 1969.
Personal: Born 1942. Educated at Oundle School (1955-1961), Emmanuel College, Cambridge (1964 MA LLB). Governor of the Rose Bruford College of Speech and Drama. Liveryman of the Worshipful Company of Dyers. Leisure pursuits include music, sport and gardening. Lives near Hemel Hempstead.

CAISLEY, Christopher
Walker Morris, Leeds (0113) 283 2500
Chairman of the firm and Head of Commercial Litigation Department and Sports Division.
Specialisation: Main area of practice is sports law. Work includes sports broadcasting rights, contract negotiations and disputes, personality merchandising, licensing agreements, publishing contracts and acting for sports personalities, clubs and associations. Other area of practice is commercial litigation. Cases have involved acting for the RFL in defence of High Court proceedings brought for relief against an alleged unfair restraint of trade by an international rugby player, bringing into question the entire system for the transfer of players between countries; the prosecution of actions by football league managers against their former clubs subsequent to dismissal; and applications for declaratory relief by Football League players for release from their contracts. Chairman of Bradford Bulls RLFC and of The Super League and a director of the Rugby Football League, creating regular contact with the media.
Prof. Memberships: The Rugby Football League, The British Association for Sport and the Law.
Career: Qualified in 1978, becoming a Partner in 1979. Member of the *Walker Morris* International Committee; also Practice Development Partner.
Personal: Born 2nd June 1951. Attended Grange Boys Grammar School, Bradford. Vice-Consul for the Netherlands Yorkshire and Derbyshire. Leisure interests include running, reading and an interest in most sports. Lives in Lancashire.

COUCHMAN, Nicholas
Townleys, London (020) 7713 7000
Partner and head of IP/rights management group.
Specialisation: Contract and intellectual property aspects of sports marketing in over 20 sports (particularly football and rugby union and Formula 1), including sponsorship contracts, character licensing, personality endorsement agreements, the development and protection of sports brands, sports rights management and digital sports exploitation and intellectual property on the internet. Has advised on many groundbeaking sponsorship and licencing transactions, including Nationwide's football sponsorships and Worldpop.com's sponsorship of the UK Top 40 singles and albums charts. Particular specialism in sports rights piracy and 'ambush marketing' (prevention and litigation), and advising on protection and licensing of sports brands and intellectual propert rights internationally. Clients include/ have included major sports events rights owners (e.g. Formula One Administration, Rugby World Cup 1999, Six Nations Championship, European Rugby Cup, Royal Ascot), corporate sponsors (Carlsberg/ Tetley, Times Newspapers, Nationwide Building Society, Worldpop), sports organisations (the International Olympic Committee, England and Wales Cricket Board, Sports England, UK Sport, the FIA), clubs (Fulham FC, Spartak Moscow, Saracens RFC) and several licensing/ sponsorship agencies. Consultant Editor of 'Sports & Character Licensing' magazine. Author 'Ambush/ Parasitic Marketing and Sport' and numerous trade press articles. Regular lecturer at sports media law conferences.

COURTENAY-STAMP, Bronwen
Stones, Exeter (01392) 666 777
Specialisation: Heads the personal injury, travel and insurance team. Concentrates on travel and tourism litigation and sports law in connection with skiing. Provides an on-call 24 hour service for several client companies who may require immediate specialist advice. Organises attendance at the scene of ski accidents of a serious nature where that proves necessary. Gives lectures and writes articles for both the travel industry and lawyers.
Prof. Memberships: A Member of the Law Society Personal Injury Panel and of the Association of Personal Injury Lawyers.
Career: Educated in the North East of England. Law

Degree at Exeter University, First Class Honours in Law Society Finals. Articled at *Stones* spending the majority of her qualified career dealing with personal injury, travel, tourism and skiing law.
Personal: Married with two children. Enjoys foreign travel and watersports. A very keen snow skier.

CRAMER, Richard G.
McCormicks, Leeds (0113) 246 0622
Partner.
Specialisation: Substantial experience in sports law and in particular Rugby League, Rugby Union and Football, dealing with both contentious and non-contentious aspects. Acts for Keighley Cougars RLFC, Wakefield Trinity RLFC, Dewsbury Rams RLFC, Oldham Bears RLFC, Workington Town RLFC, Barrow Braves RLFC, Castleford Tigers RLFC, and a number of top rugby league players and coaches. Represented Ellery Hanley with regard to disciplinary proceedings brought by his club, St Helens, and subsequent wrongful dismissal claim; represented Malcolm Reilley, the former Great Britain Coach, in a claim for compensation following the merger of Huddersfield and Sheffield RLFC; continues to represent the interests of the Australian Rugby League in the UK; represents the Rugby League Players' Association. Successfully conducted the first personal injury claim for a Rugby League Player arising from the field of play and continues to deal with a number of sporting injury cases. Represented the Super-Middleweight World boxing Champion, Richie Woodhall, in his dispute with the promoter Frank Warren which was the first case of its type dealt with by Mediation; represented the Scunthorpe United Director, Des Comerford, in his litigation with the club, again resolved by Mediation; represented the Newcastle United "Save Our Seats" Campaign in proceedings against Newcastle United FC.

CRYSTAL, Peter
Memery Crystal, London (020) 7242 5905
pmcrystal@memerycrystal.com
Senior partner in corporate/ commercial department.
Specialisation: Corporate finance and sports law. Advises management and companies on take-overs, purchase and sale of large private companies and raising money on AIM, OFEX and the official list, other capital raising, MBO, MBI, and commercial sports law, including transaction structures and corporate aspects. Acts, inter alia, for Wembley plc, Will Carling and Lennox Lewis. Examiner with the Law Society in Company Law and Partnership 1974-1978.
Prof. Memberships: Law Society, Sports Lawyers Association.
Career: Qualified in 1972. Articled at *Simpson Curtis*: with *Clifford Turner* 1973-1978; Founded *Memery Crystal* in 1978.
Personal: Born 1948. Attended Leeds Grammar School; St Edmund Hall Oxford (MA Hons PPE); College of Law; McGill University, Montreal (LLM). Played rugby and boxed for Oxford, captained Otley RUFC. Leisure interests include all sports, reading and travel. Lives in London.

DUFF, Alistair M.
Henderson Boyd Jackson WS, Edinburgh (0131) 346 3617
a.duff@hbj.co.uk
Litigation/Sports Partner.
Specialisation: Handles all types of sports work including damages actions between players, team contracts with players, commercial agreements regarding sponsorship/merchandising and other related matters. Has published 34 articles for journals on sporting matters, is regularly quoted in the national press and lectures on sporting matters.
Prof. Memberships: Law Society of Scotland, Writer to the Signet, Committee Member and on the Advisory Board for the British Association for Sport and the Law. One of the Scottish Arbiters for 'The Sports Dispute Resolution Panel Ltd'.
Career: Qualified Solicitor since January 1982 and Litigation Partner since 1987. Joined *Henderson Boyd Jackson* as a Litigation Partner in 1992 and has specialised in Sports Law since 1994.
Personal: Personal: Born 2 November 1956. Educated at George Watsons College, Edinburgh, Hamilton College, New York USA (Scholarship) and Aberdeen University 1976-1979. Has completed 13 marathons including New York, Boston and Mount Everest and has taken part in 3 climbing trips to the Himalayas. Ambition – to climb K2. Married to a doctor, has 2 young children and lives in Edinburgh. Company secretary of Medical Expeditions Ltd & regularly lectures on medical legal aspects of high altitude mountaineering.

GAY, Mark
Denton Wilde Sapte, London (020) 7242 1212
meg@dentonwildesapte.com
Partner in Media and Technology Department.
Specialisation: Has substantial experience in both the contentious and non-contentious aspects of sports law and advises various sporting bodies on constitutional media rights issues, disciplinary and contractual issues.
Career: Qualified in 1988. Became a Partner at *Herbert Smith* in 1995. Joined *Denton Hall* 1 January 1999.
Personal: Educated at Lady Margaret Hall, Oxford.

GOLDBERG, Mel
Grower Freeman & Goldberg, London (020) 7723 3040
Specialisation: A partner and head of the sports division at *Grower Freeman & Goldberg* in London. He has represented numerous international football players and clubs, olympic gold medallists and several world champions in boxing, squash, tennis and athletics. He has arranged the transfers of several million pound football players from one club to another. He was the legal advisor of the International Squash Players Association (ISPA) and was Vice-Chairman of the British Olympic Travel Association to the Moscow Olympic Games in 1980. He has written several articles for leading sports magazines both in the USA and the UK, and has appeared on several television programmes both in the UK and in the USA. He recently represented Hans Segers in the successful defence of that footballer in the match fixing trial which was billed as the football trial of the century.
Prof. Memberships: Committee member of the British Association for Sport & Law. Professional member of the Sport Dispute Resolution Panel and an associate mediator of the Sports Dispute Resolution Panel of Mediators.
Career: Founded own firm under the style of *Douglas Goldberg & Co.*
Publications: He is co-author of the book entitled 'The Final Score' published by Robson Books.
Personal: Educated at St. John's College, Cambridge.

GREGORY, Lesley
Memery Crystal, London (020) 7242 5905
lgregory@memerycrystal.com
See under Corporate Finance, p.252

GROSSET, Alan G.
Morison Bishop, Edinburgh (0131) 226 6541
Specialisation: Sports Law. Legal advisor to the Scottish Sports Association and numerous other sports governing bodies, representative bodies and charities. Has advised on constitutional issues for governing bodies and sports clubs as well as disciplinary procedures, doping control issues and sponsorship agreements. Centrally involved in the campaign for rate relief for amateur sports clubs in Scotland and led the successful valuation appeal 'Lasswade RFC and Others v. Lothian Regional Assessor'. Has participated in the SSC/SSA Financial and Legal Advisory Panel on the constitutional review of 30 governing bodies in Scotland. Written and spoken at several conferences on sports law topics including the 1992 Barcelona Sport and the Law Conference on "Nations without Countries and Sport". In 1998/99 has acted in governing body, Premier Division rugby and other sports club incorporations.
Prof. Memberships: Law Society of Scotland (Member of E-Commerce Committee); Society of Writers to Her Majesty's Signet (Council Member); British Association for Sport and the Law. Founder member of the Financial and Legal Advisory Panel of the SCC/SSA.
Career: Educated Royal High School and Edinburgh University. Joined *Alex Morison & Co* (now known as *Morison Bishop*) in 1965, qualified 1967, became a partner in 1970.
Personal: Born 18 January 1942. Leisure interests include tennis and golf, past Chairman Scottish Sports Association; past President Scottish Lawn Tennis Association; past Captain Duddingston Golf Club Limited; currently Vice-Chairman of the Scottish Sports Council, Scottish Director of the Sports Dispute Resolution Panel Ltd. and Vice Chairman, Confederation of British Sport.

HEWISON, John
George Davies, Manchester (0161) 236 8992
Partner in commercial department and managing partner.
Specialisation: Principal area of practice is sports law, representing sportsmen (mainly professional footballers) in relation to employment, management agreements, taxation disputes and sponsorship. Also handles general commercial and EC law. Director of PFA Financial Management Limited. Clients include the Professional Footballers Association and numerous professional footballers. Also advises the Basketball Players Association. Defended Alan Shearer against FA charge for alleged kicking. Sits on FA working party drafting new standard football contract. Conference speaker on trades unions in sport.
Prof. Memberships: Law Society, British Association for Sport and the Law.
Career: Qualified in 1973. Assistant and then partner (1978) with *George Davies* since qualification.
Personal: Born 16th November 1948. Educated at Manchester Grammar School 1960-1968 and Nottingham University 1968-1971 (LL.B). Plays golf and follows most sports. Lives in Lymm, Cheshire.

HIGTON, Jonathan
Townleys, London (020) 7713 7000
Partner.
Specialisation: All television and new media sports matters, in particular sports rights acquisition, representation and distribution agreements throughout the World.
Career: Called to the Bar 1984. Joined *ITV Sport* in 1987 with responsibility for all the ITV Network's sports agreements, including the first exclusive Football League television agreement. Joined *Townleys* 1991. Responsible for all television and related issues both domestically and internationally for sports clients and specialist sports television distributors/agents. Has advised on projects including Rugby World Cup, Davis Cup, Fed Cup, 6 Nations Rugby, European Rugby Cup, IRB World Sevens Series, Table Tennis World Championships, International Cricket and worldwide distribution and other exploitation of both domestic and international football and other domestic and international sports rights, programming and content.
Personal: Born 1958. Attended Wycliffe College, Reading University and the University of Westminster.

HOVELL, Mark
George Davies, Manchester (0161) 236 8992
Specialisation: Partner in the commercial department specialising in sports law. Acts for various professional footballers, rugby players, basketball players and other sportspeople on contractual, employment, taxation and insolvency related matters. Advises the Professional Footballers Association and the Basketball Players Association on commercial and trade union related matters. Recently appointed the head of David Seaman's Testimonial Committee.
Prof. Memberships: British Association for Sport and Law. Licensed insolvency practitioner.
Personal: Lives in Manchester.

JEACOCK, David
David Jeacock, Swindon (01793) 854111
jeacock@lineone.net
Sole principal specialising in sports law.
Specialisation: Main area of practice is sports law, concentrating on constitutional and drug related issues, but including intellectual property issues arising out of sport. Also handles company and commercial matters. Major clients include sports governing bodies. Formerly Secretary to British Athletics Federation Drug Advisory Committee. Currently General Secretary of and Legal Adviser to British Athletics League and Legal Adviser to the Sportshall Athletic Federation. Vice chairman British Wheelchair Sport Foundation.
Prof. Memberships: Law Society, British Association for Sport & Law.
Career: Qualified in 1970. Deputy Legal Adviser to Burmah Castrol 1973-1981. Group Solicitor to Fisons PLC 1981-1983. Established own practice in 1984.
Personal: Born in 1946. Educated at Exeter College, Oxford 1964-1967. Member Swindon Harriers. Lives in Wootton Bassett.

KERR, John N.
Anderson Strathern WS, Edinburgh
(0131) 220 2345
john.kerr@andersonstrathern.co.uk
Specialisation: Handles general corporate and commercial work, including acquisitions and disposals, corporate finance, banking law, general contract work, agency, distribution and EU law. Specialises in sports law. Acts as lead partner for Scottish Rugby Union as well as other governing bodies and clubs; involved with constitutional issues, sport sponsorship and product endorsement, discipline and drug related issues as well as the provision of new facilities.
Prof. Memberships: Founder member of Financial and Legal Advisory Panel of the Sportscotland; member of British Association of Sport and Law; Professional Member of Sports Dispute Resolution Panel; member of Napier University Sports Law Forum.
Career: LL.B (Hons) Edinburgh 1978; Qualified 1980, partner in *Strathern & Blair* in 1984 and became partner in merged *Anderson Strathern* in 1992.
Personal: Born 1956. Lives in Edinburgh. Enjoys sport at all levels.

LAWRENCE, Clive S.
McCormicks, Leeds (0113) 246 0622
Specialisation: Main area of practice is company/commercial including intellectual property, mergers/acquisitions, contractual advice and drafting, broadcasting, sponsorship, media/entertainment and sporting issues. Extensive sports law portfolio including work with Peter McCormick (see entry in Leaders section) for the F.A.Premier League on broadcasting, commercial and corporate and sponsorship matters; substantial workload for Leeds Sporting Plc and Leeds United FC on all commercial work including the Stadium acquisition and redevelopment of Elland Road including the proposals for the Leeds Arena and allied commercial development with a total project value in excess of £50 million; advised on the proposed investment in Leeds Sporting plc by Granada plc and subsequent investment and media contract with BSkyB; advised on the multi million pound sponsorship deals with Bulmers and Nike; handles commercial issues for one of the leading motor racing teams including sponsorship, drivers agreements and engine supply contracts. Advises two leading rugby league clubs in particular on re-financing and re-structuring. Advises a number of sporting agents. Handled a contentious dispute in the High Court for a jockey, Barrie Wright, against The Jockey Club. Co-author of 'Sport, Business and The Law' with Peter McCormick; addressed the 1999 International Trade Mark Association Annual Conference and the International Sports Law Conference in Cardiff preceding the Rugby Union World Cup.
Prof. Memberships: Law Society.
Career: Downing College, Cambridge 1987-1990 M.A.Law. Served articles with Peter McCormick 1991-1993; associate with *McCormicks* 1993-1996; partner since 1st April 1996.

LINDLEY, Richard C.
Zermansky & Partners, Leeds (0113) 245 9766
richard@zermansky.demon.co.uk
Specialisation: All areas of civil litigation/dispute resolution; sports law: represented Rugby Football League in major dispute with the Australian Rugby Football League.
Prof. Memberships: Leeds Law Society.
Career: BA (First Class Honours) from Oxford in Philosophy. Politics and Economics D. Phil from Oxford. Academic philosopher from 1975-89, then switched to law. Maxwell Law Prize, Leeds Polytechnic 1989. Qualified as solicitor 1992, having trained at *Zermansky & Partners*. Head of litigation/dispute resolution department. Interest in alternative dispute resolution in sports cases and other commercial disputes, including professional negligence.
Personal: Walking, theatre, cinema, opera, sport (now as a spectator) especially rugby league and football. Married with three children.

McCORMICK, Peter D.G.
McCormicks, Leeds (0113) 246 0622
Senior partner.
Specialisation: Substantial area of practice is Sports Law (allied to portfolio of media and entertainment) with considerable experience in both contentious and non-contentious aspects. Acts for Leeds United Football Club and is Associate Director and Legal Counsel. Dealt with the multi-million pound sale of the Club to Leeds Sporting plc and continues to advise the Club and its associated/subsidiary companies and Leeds Sporting Plc. Acts for a number of other sports clubs and bodies and professional sportsmen. Also has expertise in horse-racing, particularly disciplinary hearings and appeals; the only British lawyer to have appeared before the Jockey Club of Germany. Also handles matters relating to Rugby (Union and League), athletics, cricket, boxing, shooting (advises renowned Yorkshire Shoot) and motor racing. Other clients include The F.A. Premier League, The Football Association, Jenny Pitman, Freddie Trueman, Howard Wilkinson, Gordon Strachan, Gary Speed, Harry Kewell, Gary McAllister, David Batty, Castleford RLFC, Wakefield Trinity RLFC, Keighley Cougars RLFC, Otley RUFC and a number of other personalities and the Football Supporters Association. Negotiates contracts for personal benefits, corporate sponsorship and ancillary matters including broadcasting and deals with a substantial workload of intellectual property matters (registration, protection and enforcement). Advised on IP enforcement in Euro '96 tournament for UEFA and World Cup 1998. Deals with litigation cases including defamation and complaints relating to broadcasting and the Press. Acted in the Leeds United/Stuttgart UEFA Disciplinary Hearing in Zurich. Also has twenty years experience of tax investigation and enquiry work, both Revenue and VAT and serious fraud cases. Handles increasing amount of commercial work acting for DFS Furniture Company plc, Iceland Frozen Foods plc, Polypipe plc, The Duke of Edinburgh's Award, Hays plc and others. Columnist with the Yorkshire Post. Writes for a number of publications. Author of 'Sport, Business and the Law', published by Jordans. Lectures widely. Awarded the Higher Courts (Criminal Proceedings) Qualification in 1994. Resident legal expert on Radio Leeds, Yorkshire Television and the Yorkshire Post.
Personal: Vice President of the Outward Bound Trust. Chairman of the Yorkshire Young Achiever Awards. Member of the Advisory Board, Sports Law Centre, Anglia University; Solicitor to The Duke of Edinburgh's Award. Patron, Harrogate Junior Chamber of Commerce; Trustee, Friends of War Memorials.

MCINERNEY, Peter B.G.
SJ Berwin & Co, London (020) 7533 2521
peter.mcinerney@sjberwin.com
Specialisation: Partner in the Media, Communications and Sports Groups. Specialist in entertainment and sport industries including television and film production, distribution and finance, merchandising, sponsorship, advertising and publishing.

Career: Royal National Theatre (1981-1983). Thames Television (1983-1989). *S J Berwin & Co* (1989 to date)

MCKENZIE, Rod
Harper Macleod, Glasgow (0141) 221 8888
Specialisation: Lead partner in the Litigation Department specialising in employment law and sport. Undertakes work for major public companies and sporting bodies, local authorities, Trades Unions, and the Equal Opportunities Commission. Law Society of Scotland accredited specialist in employment law. Regularly lectures and writes on the subject. Also specialises in planning and environmental law, construction law and mining and mineral law. Chairman of Scottish Rugby Union Disputing Appeals Committee and International Rugby Football Board Diciplinary Appeals Panel.
Prof. Memberships: Law Society of Scotland; Industrial Law Group.
Career: Qualified 1982. Assistant solicitor, *Harper Macleod* 1982-84. Partner since 1984.
Personal: Educated at High School of Stirling 1970-1976, Strathclyde University 1976-1979, and Stirling University 1979-1980. Leisure pursuits include golf and gardening. Born 1st July 1958. Lives in Uddingston, Lanarkshire.

METLISS, Jonathan A.
SJ Berwin & Co, London (020) 7533 2222
Specialisation: Head of the sports business group at SJ Berwin & Co. Is a senior partner in the corporate finance department and a founder member of the firm. Has established and developed a sports business group dealing in all aspects of the business of sport, which is now recognised as one of the leading dedicated sports practices in the UK. Has recently been described as one of the top football lawyers in the country. Has been involved in sports and soccer related businesses for a number of years. Has acted in numerous sports related transactions such as the take over of the Tottenham Hotspur Football Club in the early 1980's, the acquisition by Pentland Group of the Speedo business and the investment by ENIC plc, of which he is a non-executive director, in Glasgow Rangers Football Club (the single largest investment in a UK football club), the acquisition by ENIC of interests in Vicenza Calcio, AEK Athens, Slavia Prague and FC Basel, the flotation and subsequent fund raisings by Birmingham City Football Club and the flotation of Sports Internet Group. Has been involved in English Premier League clubs such as Arsenal, Chelsea, Derby County, Leeds, Manchester United, Watford and West Ham and for nationwide football league clubs such as Birmingham City and Swindon Town. Has advised companies in the sports and leisure area, such as Blacks Leisure, Claremont Garments, ENIC plc and Pentland. Is advising the England and Wales Cricket Board on the issue of central contracts and other related matters. Is actively involved in South African sport, in particular the United Cricket Board of South Africa. Jonathan is a commercial adviser to the Football Taskforce and a member of the British Association of Sport and Law. His opinion is often sought on sporting issues and is widely quoted in the sports press and regularly speaks at sports related conferences and seminars.
Prof. Memberships: The executive committee of the Weizmann Institute Foundation; joint secretary and member of the executive of the Inter-Parliamentary Council against Anti-Semitism; vice-president of the Commonwealth Jewish Council; member of the board of the British Israel Public Affairs Centre (BIPAC); member of the Executive of the British-Israel Chamber of Commerce and chairman of the British-Israel Chamber of Commerce Professional Services Committee; member of the board of governors of Haifa University and chairman of the British Friends of Haifa University; member of UJIA (United Jewish Israel Appeal) Sports Committee, member of The Jewish Care Sports Club, member of the Committee on South African Trade (COSAT), which provides commercial advice to the Department of Trade and Industry on Britain's trade promotion activities in South Africa; Law Society; Holborn Law Society; member IoD; Lord's Taverner's; Royal Horticultural Society.
Career: Articled *Nabarro Nathanson*, qualified 1973; assistant solicitor *Nabarro Nathanson* 1973-1976; merchant banker, Capel Court Merchant Bank, Sydney 1976-1978; assistant solicitor, *Berwin Leighton* 1978-1982; senior corporate finance partner and founder member, *S J Berwin & Co* 1982; director of ENIC plc, Lindow Investment Company Ltd, Pownall Investment Company Limited, Interlaw Limited, The Weizman Institute Foundation, the Southern Africa Business Association, and the Parkes Centre Development Board (University of Southampton).
Publications: Articles for 'Sport Business;' 'Travel Trade Gazette;' 'Commercial Lawyer;' 'Law Society Gazette'.
Personal: Born 1949, resides London and Sussex. Education: Haberdashers' Aske's, Elstree; Southampton University (LLB Hons). Leisure: Squash, cricket, rugby, football, travel, Israel and South Africa; clubs: Arundel CC, Middx CCC, Sussex CCC; RAC; Saracens RFC; Alcester RFC; MCC, Surrey CC, Rugby Club, Cricketers' Club; Middlesex County Rugby Football Union, Broadgate Club.

MILLER, Stephen C.
Harper Macleod, Glasgow (0141) 221 8888
stephen.milller@harpermacleod.co.uk
See under Employment, p.341

MORRISON, Michael
Gorna & Co, Manchester (0161) 832 3651
Specialisation: Vast experience in wide range of Sport related business including Employment Law (contentious and non-contentious), Endorsement and Sponsorship Agreements, exploitation and protection of Intellectual Property Rights, Media Law including Publishing and Defamation, and Administrative Law. Involved mainly in Professional Football, has acted for clubs, Players and Agents dealing with a variety of work including Contracts, Claims, Commercial Agreements, Arbitrations and Disciplinary Tribunals. Has acted for the majority of Managers of Premier League and Football League Clubs for more than 25 years in the negotiation and documentation of Contracts, in the pursuit and settlement of Unfair and Wrongful Dismissal Claims and in Disciplinary proceedings. Other sports include Rugby (both codes), swimming, golf and tennis.
Prof. Memberships: Law Society, British Association for Sport and Law, Manchester Law Society, Employment Lawyers Association.
Career: Educated at Cardinal Langley School at St Ambrose College, joined *Gorna & Co* in July 1967. Admitted 1974. Partner 1976.
Personal: Married 1971 with 2 sons. Enthusiastic but incompetent golfer, passionate Manchester United supporter, member of the Variety Club of Great Britain.

PARKER, Raj D.
Freshfields Bruckhaus Deringer, London
(020) 7936 4000
See under Litigation (Commercial), p.566

PHELOPS, Warren
Nicholson Graham & Jones, London
(020) 7648 9000
warren.phelops@ngj.co.uk
Specialisation: Business issues relating to sport: in particular, corporate finance (including flotations, takeovers, mergers and acquisitions), corporate structuring and strategy, company, commercial and media (including television, sponsorship and merchandising).
Prof. Memberships: Director of Institute of Sports Sponsorship, City of London Solicitors Company, ESCA, British Association of Sport and the Law.
Career: *Slaughter and May*: trainee solicitor, March 1990-1992; Assistant Solicitor, March 1992-June 1993. *Nicholson, Graham and Jones*: Assistant Solicitor, June 1993 to Jan 1996. Partner and Head of Sports Group, January 1996 to date.
Personal: Fanatical sports player (rugby, football, cricket (for any teams that will have him), squash and tennis) and watcher, especially rugby (Wasps), football (Arsenal) and cricket (Middlesex).

POWELL, David
Clarke Willmott & Clarke, Bristol (0117) 941 6664
dpowell@cw-c.co.uk
Specialisation: Partner. Developed a nationally renowned sports department which concentrates on representing individuals. Advises footballers, rugby players, athletes, golfers and cricketers as well as acting on behalf of a number of golf clubs. The department lists among its clients the current Bath Rugby squad and represented the England squad and Anglo-Irish members of the Irish squad in negotiating their World Cup contracts with their respective unions. Specialist advice in all relevant fields of law from commercial contracts, employment to litigation and personal injury.
Prof. Memberships: British Association for Sport and Law; Executive Committee of the players' union, the Professional Rugby Players Association (PRA) with Brian Moore, Martin Bayfield and Damien Hopley.
Career: Qualified in 1981, articled at *Herbert Alpass & Co* in Bristol, set up own practice in 1984, took over Bristol offices of *Alsters* in 1989 with two other partners. Joined *Clarke Wilmott & Clarke* in October 1999.
Personal: Leisure interests include: scratch golfer – representing Gloucester since 1978; rugby – played for Bristol in 1970's. Educated at St. Brendan's College Bristol and University of the West of England.

REEVE, Felicity
Bird & Bird, London (020) 7415 6000
Partner in Sports Group.
Specialisation: Advises governing bodies, broadcasters, sports marketing agencies, sponsors and individuals on the creation, acquisition and exploitation of sports related rights. Advises on new digital forms of rights distribution and delivery including the acquisition of content for exploitation via the Internet and via on demand services. Advises on the application of traditional legal principles to the Inter-

net including terms and conditions of sale, on-line gambling and jurisdiction and rights clearance issues. Author of a number of articles on sports related issues in the national, legal and sports industry press. Clients include The Football Association, Wembley National Stadium, Octagon.

Prof. Memberships: Law Society, British Association for Sport and Law.
Career: Qualified 1993. Joined *Bird & Bird* from *Macfarlanes* in 1994. Became a partner in 1998.
Personal: Educated at School of St Helen and St Katherine and Lady Magaret Hall, Oxford.

REID, Fraser
Theodore Goddard, London (020) 7606 8855
Specialisation: Sports Law, Entertainment/Media Law, Commercial Law, Disciplinary Proceedings. Specialising from 1997 in sports related work. Clients include: individuals in sports and entertainment fields, players associations, sports governing bodies and sports marketing companies. Advised on a broad range of issues including sponsorship, broadcasting, commercial rights and players contracts. Niche specialisation in disciplinary issues, particularly doping. Successfully represented the weightlifter Paul Supple in doping case before the BAWLA in March 1999.
Prof. Memberships: Committee member of the British Association for Sport and Law. Member of the Law Society and the International Bar Association – Sports and Gaming Law Group.
Career: Qualified 1992 with *Beale & Co.* Joined *Russell Jones & Walker* (Head of Sports Law) in February 1998 from Advantage International.
Personal: Football, golf, rugby, squash, diving. Member of Lancashire Cricket Club and Blackburn Rovers supporter.

RUSSELL, Patrick
Charles Russell, London (020) 7203 5018
patrickr@cr-law.co.uk
Partner in Litigation Department.
Specialisation: Acts for sporting regulatory authorities and clubs in the regulatory and disciplinary field. Experienced in public law, judicial review and restraint of trade. Also handles building and construction disputes and is head of *Charles Russell's* Trust and Fidiciary Disputes Group. Acted in judicial review decisions for the Jockey Club and The Law Society, and in ex parte H.H, Aga Khan, and Swindon Town FC.
Prof. Memberships: Law Society, British Association for Sport and Law.
Career: Joined *Charles Russell* in 1976 and qualified in 1979. Became a Partner in 1980. Director of the Solicitors Indemnity Mutual Insurance Association Ltd. Contributing Editor, 'Cordery on Solicitors'.
Personal: Born 11th May 1952. Educated at Ampleforth College 1965-1970 and University College, Oxford 1971-1974. Recreations include golf, sailing, tennis and motorcycling. Lives near Towcester, Northants.

SLEIGH, Andrew F.
Burness, Glasgow (0141) 248 4933
afs@burness.co.uk
See under Corporate Finance, p.264 and Insolvency/Corporate Recovery, p.484

SMITH, Jason
James Chapman & Co, Manchester
(0161) 828 8000
jason.smith@james-chapman.co.uk
Specialisation: Specialises in the protection and exploitation of rights in the areas of event organisation, sponsorship, licenced merchandise, broadcasting and digital media for governing bodies, sports marketing companies, clubs and leading individuals. Has advised on contracts relating to the FIFA World Cups 2002 and 2006, FIFA Club World Championship 2000, UEFA's EURO 2000, African Cup of Nations, Chinese Football Association, US Championship Auto Racing Teams, Inc. series, FINA World Swimming Championships 2000 and 2003, and the IAAF World Championships 1999. Advises Manchester United on rights protection, sponsorship, licencing and the Internet. Recent work includes agreements with Vodafone (sponsorship and mobile telephone and wireless internet services) and Eurobet (sponsorship and internet betting services), and international licence for the Republic of South Africa. Also advises leading footballers, Rugby League players, swimmers and cyclists. Guest Lecturer, MA (Sport and Law), Manchester Metropolitan University.
Prof. Memberships: British Association for Sport and Law. The Law Society.
Career: Qualified *Denton Hall* 1995. Solicitor, *Cobbetts* 1995-1998. Legal Counsel ISL Marketing AG, Switzerland 1998-1999. Senior assistant solicitor, *James Chapman & Co.*
Personal: Born 1970. Brasenose College, Oxford 1988-1991 (Blues Soccer Player, Vincent's Club Member). Leisure interests include skiing and golf.

STINSON, Philip
Clintons, London (020) 7379 6080
Partner in Entertainment Department.
Specialisation: The law as it applies to marketing, advertising and broadcasting with particular reference to the business of sport. Clients include sponsorship, advertising and other marketing consultants and agencies, internet entrepreneurs, international sportsmen and women, television production companies, sponsoring and sponsored organisations, governing bodies and organisers of major charitable and other events. Often advises in-house legal departments of sponsoring organisations. Author of articles in British Association for Sport and Law Journal and in numerous trade journals. Author of section on Sport in Practical Commercial Precedents.
Prof. Memberships: Member of Advisory Board and Officer of the British Association for Sport and Law.
Career: Articled and qualified with *Richards Butler* 1988-1991. Joined *Collyer-Bristow* in 1991, Partner 1995. Joined *Clintons* as a partner in 1996.
Personal: Born 16th May 1962. Educated at Marlborough College and Worcester College, Oxford. Enjoys real tennis, football and the arts. Lives in London.

TOWNLEY, Stephen
Townleys, London (020) 7713 7000
Partner and founder.
Specialisation: Main area of practice covers sports marketing. Assists and advises on the creation, management and exploitation of sports marketing rights, including sponsorship, television, new media and merchandising. Has been involved in this capacity with the Rugby World Cup, Olympic Games, Soccer World Cup, Tour de France, Davis Cup, the Consortium of UK Racecourses (the "super 12") and many others. Co-author of 'Sponsorship Sport Art and Leisure' and various other publications. 1995 *Townleys* appointed official legal rights consultants to GAISF (General Association of International Sports Federations). General Counsel to the International Tennis Federation.
Prof. Memberships: IBA (former Chairman of Sports Committee), International Committee SLA, ANZSLA, Sponsorship Association (Founder), European Sponsorship Consultants Association (Co-founder). Arbitrator – Court of Arbitration for Sport, Switzerland. Fellow of the Chartered Institute of Arbitrators.
Career: Qualified in 1978, having articled at *Ingledew Brown Bennison & Garrett*. Company Secretary and legal adviser for Hawker Siddley Diesels 1978-1979, then in-house counsel to the Société Monégasque de Promotion Internationale West Nally SA 1979-1983. Founded *Townleys* in 1983.
Personal: Born 15th December 1952. Took an LLM in 1975. Leisure interests include basketball, tennis and game fishing. Lives in London and Grosmont.

VEROW, Richard A.
Osborne Clarke OWA, London (020) 78091346
richard.verow@osborneclarke.com
Specialisation: Commercial lawyer specialising in sports and entertainment. Clients include governing bodies, television companies, event organisers, sports marketing agencies, managers and individuals. Work includes advice on television, broadcasting and sports marketing agreements, internet and WAP agreements, player pool arrangements, player contracts and disputes including Hogan v London Irish. Co-author 'Media and Entertainment Law', 'Sport Business and the Law' (Jordans), and 'Volume 39: Sports and Sponsorship: Encyclopaedia of Forms and Precedents' (Butterworths).
Prof. Memberships: Board member European Sponsorship Consultants Association; British Association of Sport and the Law.
Career: Articled *Rubenstein Callingham*, qualified 1992. *Collyer-Bristow* 1997-2000. *Osborne Clarke OWA* May 2000 to date.

VLECK, Karena
Farrer & Co, London (020) 7242 2022
Partner in the commercial team.
Specialisation: Principal area of practice is sports law providing specialist advice for sports governing and representative bodies, individual sports people, sports charities and sponsors. Areas of practice include sponsorship agreements, broadcasting agreements, disciplinary procedures and rules, sports doping cases, formations and advice on constitutions both corporate and unincorporated, merchandising and representation agreements. Other areas of practice are intellectual property generally, charity law and company and commercial law. Appointed Director of UK Athletics 98, the interim governing body for athletics in the UK and appointed a member of the Non-Executive Council of UK Athletics, the new governing body for athletics in the UK. Acted for the British Athletic Federation in relation to Diane Modahl. Acting for UK Athletics in relation to Doug Walker, Linford Christie, Mark Richardson and Paul Edwards. Other clients include the Central Council of Physical Recreation, the Football Association, the

British Paralympic Association and the All England Netball Association.
Prof. Memberships: Committee Member of British Association for Sport and Law.
Career: Qualified in 1992 after articles at *Farrer & Co.* Partner 1998.
Personal: Born 10th March 1967. Educated at Millfield School, Street, Somerset 1983-1985 and St John's College, Cambridge 1986-1989. Lives in London.

WALKEY, Justin
Bird & Bird, London (020) 7415 6000
Partner in company department and head of sports group.
Specialisation: In-depth knowledge covers the media, sports and entertainment industries. Particular expertise includes sports marketing (creation, protection and exploitation of events; sale and purchase of events; constitutional and disciplinary matters; TV, video, film and publishing rights deals; sponsorship; licensing and merchandising) and individual representation (general business management, tax planning, endorsement and appearance contracts). Founder of Sportslink Worldwide. Other area of practice is general corporate and commercial law, both nationally and internationally, primarily in the areas of media and communications to include digital media, telecommunications, broadcasting, advertising, publishing and promotion. Recent high profile work in football for The F.A. in relation to the New National Stadium prefect and The F.A.'s broadcast arrangements for England internationals and F.A. Cup matches.
Prof. Memberships: Law Society, Licensing Executives Society.
Career: Qualified in 1984. Joined *Bird & Bird* the same year and became a partner in 1987.
Personal: Born 1957. Attended Sherborne School, then the University of Westminster. Lives in London.

WATKINS, Maurice
James Chapman & Co, Manchester (0161) 828 8000
Partner in commercial department.
Specialisation: Sports law specialist. Solicitor for Manchester United Football Club since 1976 and, since flotation, Manchester United PLC. Also an adviser to the Football Association Premier League and other Premier and Football League clubs on various matters. Member of the Premier League Legal Working Party. Premier League representative on Association of European Union Premier Football Leagues. Also solicitor to a number of first-class sportsmen and administrators. Director of Manchester United Football Club plc and Manchester United PLC. Has handled numerous high-value soccer transfers at home and abroad. Represents clubs and players before UEFA and FA Disciplinary bodies and International and League Compensation Tribunals and negotiates TV, sponsorship, licensing and advertising contracts. Former lecturer in law at Manchester University. Extensive media experience on football related matters.
Prof. Memberships: Chairman of the British Association for Sport and the Law.
Career: Qualified in 1966. Solicitor for the Co-operative Insurance Society 1966-1968. Joined *James Chapman & Co* as a partner in 1968. Senior partner with effect from May 1999.
Personal: Educated at Manchester Grammar School 1952-1960 and University College, London (LLB and LLM). Secretary of Manchester Homeopathic Clinic and trustee of The Football League Limited Players Retirement Income Scheme. Interests include cricket, soccer and tennis. Lives in Cheshire.

TAX (CORPORATE)

London: 774; The South & South West: 778; Midlands: & East Anglia: 779; The North: 779; Scotland: 780; *Profiles*: 781

OVERVIEW: Tax lawyers have never been busier. All have reported an increase in both the support work that they do and in own-account work. Corporate, finance and property transactions are increasingly tax-driven, with the lawyers involved from the beginning. Own-account work, principally financial product tax work and contentious (investigation and litigation) work have also considerably increased.

The tightening of domestic tax leasing regimes has meant that increasingly sophisticated and innovative products are being developed. The continuing increase in stamp duty is providing much work for property tax specialists. Other areas such as e-commerce, share schemes, contentious and international are major growth sectors for tax work.

The big five accountants have not made an impact on the high profile transactional work. In day-to-day direct and indirect tax work they maintain the upper hand. In the regions, the accountants are seen by the few specialised tax departments at law firms to be their most direct competitors. Only qualified lawyers from the Big 5 are mentioned in this year's addition, but players such as Peter Jenkins at Ernst & Young for VAT work in London and Jeremy Brittain of KPMG for corporate and international tax work in Birmingham ought not be neglected.

RESEARCH APPROVED BY BMRB: *For this edition,* Chambers' *researchers conducted 6083 interviews – 4408 with law firms, 598 with barristers and 1077 with clients.*

The validity of the research was scrutinised by BMRB International, who audited both the methodology and the results at our offices in July 2000. They interviewed Chambers' *researchers and cross-checked sample interviews. Details of the audit appear on page 7.*

LONDON

TAX (CORPORATE) • London	Ptnrs	Assts
❶ Freshfields Bruckhaus Deringer	13	31
Slaughter and May	8	25
❷ Clifford Chance	17	36
Linklaters	11	24
❸ Allen & Overy	7	30
❹ Ashurst Morris Crisp	5	20
Herbert Smith	4	16
Lovells	9	10
Macfarlanes	3	4
Norton Rose	6	11
SJ Berwin & Co	6	10
❺ Berwin Leighton	3	5
CMS Cameron McKenna	4	6
Denton Wilde Sapte	8	10
Nabarro Nathanson	3	5
Olswang	3	3
Simmons & Simmons	6	9
Theodore Goddard	3	7
❻ Clyde & Co	1	3
DLA	5	13
Field Fisher Waterhouse	3	–
Hammond Suddards Edge	2	1
McDermott, Will & Emery	2	4
Travers Smith Braithwaite	4	8
Watson, Farley & Williams	6	9

Within each band, firms are listed alphabetically.

Freshfields Bruckhaus Deringer Most solicitors clearly regard the practice as London's number one, due to the *"sheer number of quality people." "They have the full range, talent is widespread and there are no weak links in the chain."* Most acknowledged that this was the first team to spring to mind for cross-border work, a position reinforced by the Bruckhaus link-up. The growing London practice, headed by all-rounder **Richard Ballard** (a *"bright, knowledgeable and common sense"* practitioner) is involved on the majority of high-profile UK and cross-border M&A and specialist financing transactions. It also has strong reputations in insurance and energy as well as in general corporate advisory, traditional litigation and investigation work. The internationalisation of the practice continues apace, with cross-referrals from Continental offices on the increase. Around half the practice's work is self-generated, consisting mainly of pure corporate consultancy work and advisory work for investment banks on financial products.

The asset finance and securitisation practices of the firm are market leaders and as these are tax-heavy areas, it is no surprise that the firm is considered to have a leading finance tax team. Head of the tax finance practice is the *"super"* **David Taylor**, a leasing and structured finance expert who *"can turn his hand to anything"* and who is appreciated for his drafting skills and *"commercial and non-combatitive approach."* **Sue Porter** is a *"technical and sensible"* capital markets and securitisation expert who *"takes a focused approach."* The *"easy to get on with"* **Ben Staveley** is considered *"real quality."* His work is primarily in banking and derivatives, though he was praised for securitisation and other structured finance work. **Colin Hargreaves** (leasing and project financing) and **Murray Clayson** (international financing) are also held in high esteem.

Head of the corporate finance practice is **Timothy Ling**, a highly rated lawyer who is perceived to have *"eschewed the limelight."* The popular **Francis Sandison**, is well regarded on VAT matters, but is principally known for his M&A corporate tax work. He is appreciated for his *"clear-thinking and his sense of humour."* All in the market find **Sarah Falk** *"impressive,"* and she is *"bright, pleasant and on top of things."* Maintaining their reputations in more specialist areas are **Stephen Hoyle**, who spends around half his time on insurance tax issues, and **Michael Thompson**, an energy specialist. High profile merger work this year includes the RBS bid for NatWest (£26.5 billion), the AirTouch merger with Vodafone (£37.5 billion), the EMI music business merger with Time Warner (£12 billion) and reorganisations of AstraZeneca and ICI. **Clients:** Goldman Sachs, Deutsche, ING, Chase Manhattan, HSBC, Warburg Pincus, General Motors, Ford, L'Oreal, ICI, Monsanto, Nestlé, RJR Nabisco, IBM, Olivetti, Matra Marconi, MCI Worldcom, Nokia, Reuters, Siemens, Lloyd's of Lon-

LEADING INDIVIDUALS • TAX	
✪ **EDGE Steve** Slaughter and May	
❶ **BALLARD Richard** Freshfields Bruckhaus	**FRENCH Douglas** Clifford Chance
LEWIS David Allen & Overy	**MARTIN David** Herbert Smith
MEARS Patrick Allen & Overy	**NORFOLK Chris** Norton Rose
NOWLAN Howard Slaughter and May	**STAVELEY Ben** Freshfields Bruckhaus
TAYLOR David Freshfields Bruckhaus	
❷ **AIRS Graham** Slaughter and May	**ELMAN Jonathan** Clifford Chance
FALK Sarah Freshfields Bruckhaus	**FRASER Ross** Herbert Smith
NOBLE Nicholas Field Fisher Waterhouse	**PORTER Sue** Freshfields Bruckhaus
RUPAL Yash Linklaters	**SANDISON Francis** Freshfields Bruckhaus
THOMPSON Michael Freshfields Bruckhaus	**WALTON Miles** Allen & Overy
WATSON John Ashurst Morris Crisp	
❸ **BALDWIN Mark** Macfarlanes	**BALL Susan** Clyde & Co
BEARE Tony Slaughter and May	**BRANNAN Guy** Linklaters
BUTLER Kay Olswang	**CRAWFORD Susan** Ashurst Morris Crisp
DORAN Nigel Macfarlanes	**ELLIOTT Peter** Clifford Chance
GREENBANK Ashley Macfarlanes	**HARDWICK Michael** Linklaters
JOHNSON Ian Ashurst Morris Crisp	**LING Timothy** Freshfields Bruckhaus
MEHTA Nikhil Linklaters	**NIAS Peter** McDermott, Will & Emery
OVERS John Berwin Leighton	**ROSS Howard** Clifford Chance
SCOTT Tom Linklaters	**TROUP Edward** Simmons & Simmons
❹ **BLAKE Jonathan** SJ Berwin & Co	**BRAILSFORD Mark** Allen & Overy
CHALLONER John Norton Rose	**CLAYSON Murray** Freshfields Bruckhaus
COLEMAN Brenda Allen & Overy	**DOUGLAS Alasdair** Travers Smith Braithwaite
EHRLICH Michael Clifford Chance	**FERGUSON Fiona** Slaughter and May
HARGREAVES Colin Freshfields Bruckhaus	**HARKNESS David** Clifford Chance
HIGGINBOTTOM Louise Norton Rose	**HOYLE Stephen** Freshfields Bruckhaus
HURLEY Conor Linklaters	**JACOBS Russell** Cadwalader, Wickersham
KELLY Don Lovells	**LYNCHEHAN Martin** Linklaters
McGOWAN Michael Allen & Overy	**PRESTON Christopher** Watson, Farley & Williams
SANDERS Tim McDermott, Will & Emery	**SMITH Isla** Norton Rose
TRASK Michael SJ Berwin & Co	**WHITTY Oonagh** Watson, Farley & Williams
UP AND COMING	
DUGDALE Pat Olswang	**McILWEE Richard** Clifford Chance
NORWOOD Andrew Weil, Gotshal & Manges	

LEADING INDIVIDUALS • VAT	
✪ **SINFIELD Greg** Lovells	
❶ **CANT Michael** Nabarro Nathanson	
CROKER Richard CMS Cameron McKenna	
HUMPHREY Ann Ann L. Humphrey	
PRESTON Christopher Watson, Farley & Williams	
WONG Etienne Clifford Chance	
❷ **AVERY JONES John** Speechly Bircham	**BALDWIN Mark** Macfarlanes
CLARK Simon Linklaters	
GARCIA Dario Ernst & Young	**GOWTAGE Jill** Allen & Overy
HALE Paul Simmons & Simmons	**LYNCHEHAN Martin** Linklaters
MAINPRICE Hugh Hutchinson Mainprice	**ROSE Simon** SJ Berwin & Co
SANDISON Francis Freshfields Bruckhaus	
STAPLETON Mark Dechert	**WARRINER Neil** Herbert Smith
ONES TO WATCH	
BIRTWELL Jan Linklaters	**IFERENTA Richard** KLegal
THOMPSON David Herbert Smith	

See *Profiles* on page 781

don, Marsh & McLennan, AMP, SwissRe, RJB Mining, Enron, Gazprom, Airbus, Virgin Atlantic, Associated Newspapers, Bank of England, EMI Group, Sotheby's, Tesco.

Slaughter and May As well as M&A-related tax, where *"they are top,"* the practice is highly regarded for structured finance work, particularly asset finance and financial product development work. What really keeps the practice at the top and differentiates it from the competition is its *"confident and robust"* attitude towards tax advice, summed up by one US investment banker: *"If they think it'll work they'll say so and they'll believe what they say."*

The doyen of tax lawyers remains **Steve Edge** who *"stands alone."* He is a *"seriously able practitioner"* who some say is *"a victim of his own success as it is hard to pin him down."* He works on a mix of M&A and structured finance, with more of a bias towards financial work and consultancy for US clients. While his *"creativity and experience"* alone entitle him to respect, it is his *"appreciation of commercial imperatives and how markets work"* as well as his *"helpfulness"* which are really appreciated by clients and peers alike. He has *"seen and done everything"* – *"a client would say fine to the most creative and innovative idea, but would want to get Steve's blessing."*

One of the *"understated tax heroes of the City"* is **Howard Nowlan**, traditionally an M&A tax expert. He is *"one of a dying breed,"* an all-round adviser who *"balances common sense, charm, a sense of humour and technical expertise."* He is said to have *"a clear understanding of the objectives he's working to, he is not distracted by irrelevant detail and he gets things done."* **Tony Beare** is an all-rounder, especially appreciated by financial clients, while **Graham Airs** is regarded as a *"creative international tax man."* **Fiona Ferguson** maintains her *"sound"* reputation.

This is a broad practice which, as well as providing advice for the firm's well-known UK clients, also advises US and other international corporates and financials. A high proportion of the team's work is pure tax consultancy, and the department includes an ex-Inland Revenue investigation team for investigatory and litigation work. High profile M&A transactions this year include the Reckitt & Colman/Benckiser, Astra/Zeneca, BAT/Rothmans and Carlton/United News & Media link-ups. Other corporate transactions include the disposals involving Allied/Punch, Guardian Royal Exchange/Aegon and Huntsman/ICI and the demutualisations of Old Mutual and Canada Life. The team also advised on asset finance transactions for groups such as RBS (Virgin Rail West Coast Financing) and British Airways. **Clients:** Royal Bank of Scotland, British Airways, Punch, Reckitt & Colman, Carlton, Guardian Royal Exchange, Old Mutual.

Clifford Chance The team offers a *"technically proficient and never less than reasonable service."* While some view the practice as *"a bit of a sleeping giant,"* clients and solicitors alike comment on the *"range of expertise at partner level."* This is especially seen on the finance side, where the team is seen as *"the first choice."* In particular, the practice is felt to have *"a huge share of the securitisation market."* Advice here is generally regarded as *"sound and cautious rather than aggressive."*

Head of the practice is the popular and *"commercial"* **Douglas French**, known primarily for his M&A work. He *"makes sure you have an answer. He always knows who knows and quite often he knows himself."* **Jonathan Elman** is a leader for structured finance work. He is *"extremely perceptive"* and *"highly creative; nothing is too difficult for him."* Although *"he can be abrasive,"* no-one doubts his commitment. He is admired for *"going the extra mile, he really cares."* Although retired as an equity partner, **Howard Ross** continues to run the tax litigation practice, and is admired for his *"experience and wide knowledge."* All-rounder **Peter Elliott**, M&A, securitisation and insurance player **David Harkness** and securitisation expert **Michael Ehrlich** maintain their reputations. New to the rankings is **Richard McIlwee**, who is felt to be a reliable sounding-board for new ideas and the *"imaginative"* **Michael Wistow**.

Financial highlights this year were the Barclays Credit Card and Formula One securitisations. M&A work includes the attempted Air Products/Air Liquide joint bid for BOC Plc and mergers in areas such as telecoms and insurance. The tri-partite international merger has encouraged an increasing number of instructions across the network, such as advising on the Merrill Lynch and HSBC joint venture in internet private banking. The *"dedicated"* **Etienne Wong**'s *"aggressive"* work on VAT matters continues to win him market plaudits. The international VAT practice was involved on the Barclays Credit Card securitisation and has been active in the property and financial (including credit card) sectors. **Clients:** ABN-Amro, Barclays, Candover, Chase Manhattan, Coca Cola, Deutsche, Dresdner, GE Capital, Goldman Sachs, KKR, Merrill Lynch, Morgan Stanley, Nomura Securities, Morgan Stanley Dean Witter, VW/Audi, Whitbread, Societe Generale, Paribas, CVC Capital Partners, Carlton.

Linklaters Whilst involved on the major corporate deals of the year, the practice is generally viewed by the market to have *"lost a bit of punch."* Tony Angel's move to managing partner last year is considered to have *"damaged the practice's flair"* in the medium to long term. Of the younger generation, **Yash Rupal** *("a clever financial products person")* is seen as one of the team's torch-bearers, and his secondment to Merrill Lynch's M&A department is perceived to have deprived the practice of a leading light on the finance side, though the long-term benefits may be greater. The firm is perceived to have a practice skewed heavily towards M&A as opposed to structured finance, especially when compared to leading rivals.

However, the tax team is still considered to be *"strong and steady,"* and *"still appears on the top deals."* Internationally, clients praise the *"ideas and ability to implement them"* at the firm, as well as the consistent quality of the drafting. Corporate tax all-rounder **Guy Brannan** is *"good to deal with."* Other rated M&A-connected practitioners include **Michael Hardwick**, **Tom Scott** and **Conor Hurley**. The *"tough"* Scott also works on financial issues and Hurley, who enters the lists this year, has been singled out for his advice on public M&A and cross-border transactions. **Nikhil Mehta** is respected for international work, works on financial issues and is also head of the practice's contentious group. **Simon Clark** is a property tax specialist, rated for his VAT work. Among others in the highly-rated VAT team is the versatile **Martin Lynchehan**. He is a *"creative and incredibly user-friendly"* practitioner who is also known for structured finance where he does *"more than just dabble."*

Corporate work includes the Vodafone/Airtouch/Mannesmann and Reckitt & Colman/Benckiser NV link-ups, NatWest's bid defence, BP Amoco's acquisitions and Lloyds TSB's acquisition of Scottish Widows. Major reorganisations were those of Allied Domecq, Cable & Wireless Communications, BAe and Tarmac. Advised Halifax on the first issue by a UK bank of tax-deductible Tier 1 Capital. **Clients:** Allied Domecq, Bass, British Airways, BG, BP, BT, Elf, Enron, Rio Tinto, Unigate, AstraZeneca, Sedgwick, Scottish & Newcastle, National Power, Jardines, Halifax, CitiGroup, CSFB, DLJ, Goldman Sachs, Merrill Lynch.

Allen & Overy Seen to have *"gone for it in a big way,"* the tax practice has *"beefed up and considerably raised its profile."* It is especially well regarded for finance work (although corporate work makes up nearly half the practice's workload), but is not yet considered to possess the profile of its most direct competitor in tax finance work, Clifford Chance. The team has a reputation for *"professional, technically good and conservative advice."* All-rounder **Patrick Mears** *("a careful lateral thinker")* is recognised as the driving force behind the growth of the practice, which includes talent at all levels. **Michael McGowan** and **Miles Walton** both have excellent reputations in the financial world. Another finance expert is the *"creative"* **Mark Brailsford** who enters the rankings this year following strong recommendation for his *"intelligent, straightforward and politically aware advice."* On corporate matters, the *"meticulous and streetwise"* **David Lewis** is *"a joy to work with."* **Brenda Coleman** also maintains her reputation in this area.

The team advised on the Punch Taverns saga and on disposals for Cable & Wireless. Work includes advising on the Drax power station acquisition and the Vodafone/Airtouch/Mannesman deal, advising on the Broadgate and London City airport securitisations and on British Aerospace exchangeables into Orange. Tax investigation and litigation advice are other fortes, while **Jill Gowtage** *("urbane and bright")* has a strong market following for her VAT work. **Clients:** Hill Samuel Asset Management, ING Barings, Misys, NatWest, Citibank, Chase Manhattan, Deutsche Bank, IBJ, Bass, Cable & Wireless, Morgan Stanley, WDR, Lehman Brothers, Goldman Sachs, Barclays, Bank of America, British Aerospace, Flemings, TI Group plc, Rexam plc, News International.

Ashurst Morris Crisp A growing corporate and financial practice held in high regard for its venture capital expertise. Commentators have immense respect for the *"unique"* **John Watson** who heads the department. The *"impressive"* **Sue Crawford** has *"real energy, she puts a lot into it."* **Ian Johnson** is *"nobody's fool"* on the financial side, and clients find him *"great for brainstorming."*

Outside traditional tax work (corporate, property and financial advisory), the practice advises on a range of issues, including litigation and VAT matters. Work this year includes advising venture capital houses Cinven and CVC on their joint £825 million acquisition of William Hill, acting for Nabisco Holdings on its £1.5 billion recommended offer for United Biscuits in conjunction with Hicks Muse and advising NRG Energy in its $640 million power station acquisition. Expanding areas include e-commerce, property (enterprise zones) and private company work. **Clients:** Deutsche Telekom, ABN-Amro, Electra Fleming, Imperial Tobacco, Virgin, Yahoo, IBM, Royal & Sun Alliance, Imetal, Finmaccanica, Invesco, AMVESCAP, Candover, Cinven, Barclay Private Equity.

Herbert Smith The team is especially recommended for property, energy, insurance, projects, VAT and M&A. The team also gained recognition for its work on collective investments. Regarded to have the *"slight edge in M&A"* over its immediate competitors, clients praised the team for its *"technical ability"* and for *"understanding our corporate culture."*

Ross Fraser is an all-rounder, especially well regarded for insurance work, while **David Martin**'s primary reputation is in the corporate arena. **Neil Warriner** is respected for his VAT work *("he is creative and understands the commercial aspects",)* although he also advises on PFI and energy work.

The practice continues to be strong for contentious work and is increasing its e-commerce and internet workload. Work includes advising Merrill Lynch in connection with its role as lead manager of £1.2 billion of bonds issued by Edison First Power to finance power station acquisitions, advising Securicor Plc on tax aspects of the £3.15 billion disposal of its share in Cellnet to BT, and advising CSFB and Cazenove on the Freeserve IPO. **Clients:** Pearson, Highland Distillers, Hammerson, Automobile Association, Lazards, Goldman Sachs, Bombardier Group, Moorfield Estates, BAT, Merrill Lynch.

Lovells A *"creative and pragmatic"* team, rated for its *"technical expertise."* A broad practice, particularly well regarded for property and VAT work. **Don Kelly** maintains his reputation. A range of talented individuals are making their mark in a practice with *"genuine depth."* Work includes advising Racal on the £1 billion disposal of Racal Telecoms to Global Crossings, Granada on a joint venture with Nomura, Wyndham International on the disposal of a hotel chain and Texaco on the sale and leaseback of its UK corporate headquarters at Canary Wharf. *"Technically adept"* **Greg Sinfield** is a high-profile VAT litigator, with the leading name for indirect tax advice. Although primarily known for his tribunals work, he also advises on non-contentious indirect tax matters. The VAT team were involved on the Barclays Bank Plc v Customs and Excise case in front of the VAT and Duties Tribunal and has been involved in VAT investigations and challenges to a higher rate insurance premium tax. **Clients:** Racal, Wyndham International, Texaco, Granada Group.

Macfarlanes A small, concentrated team, generally regarded to be doing cutting-edge work on public and private corporate matters. *"They have done well, especially in M&A, and the individual partners are bloody good."* The *"superb"* **Mark Baldwin** *"does everything,"* and is known for investment funds and property work. He is also considered a *"bright guy and good bloke"* on VAT matters. **Nigel Doran** and **Ashley Greenbank** maintain their reputations in corporate, funds and private (entrepreneurial) client work. Private equity and property fund work are growth areas. Advised on Vivendi's acquisition of Medi Media, Virgin's sale of a stake in Virgin Atlantic to Singapore Airlines and Hawkpoint on the buy-out of the company from NatWest. **Clients:** Cordiant Communications plc, Abbey Life, Deutsche Morgan Grenfell, Legal & General, Alchemy, 3i, Scottish Life, Vivendi.

Norton Rose An *"intelligent"* team, *"capable of acting on major city work"* and rated as one of the best for asset finance-related work. Also received praise from solicitors and clients for other structured finance work. The senior player of the team is the *"clever, experienced and sensible"* **Chris Norfolk**. *"The complexity of the deal is why we went to him,"* commented one client after a recent major acquisition in the financial sector. He has an *"unbelievable work capacity"* and is *"great for uncovering technical problems."* **Isla Smith** has a solid reputation for a range of financial work. All-rounders **Louise Higginbottom** and **John Challoner** maintain their reputations. Corporate work accounts for around half the practice's workload. Growing areas include collective investment scheme advice. **Clients:** AES, Mannesmann, Finalrealm, AIG, Anheuser-Bush Group, Carlsberg International, Deutsche Morgan Grenfell, HSBC, KLM, Lloyds Leasing, Mitsubishi Trust & Banking Corporation, Siemens, P&O, Stena AB Group.

SJ Berwin & Co This *"transactional"* practice is regarded as being *"at the forefront of venture capital and collective investment scheme work."* Commentators mentioned the difficulty of picking out individuals from a team regarded as *"top from the technical point of view."* However, for private equity work, **Michael Trask** is singled out. Although more of a corporate lawyer, **Jonathan Blake** was also mentioned for his tax work on fund matters. The team works on private equity, public M&A, restructuring, property, film financing, share schemes and partnership disposals/mergers. Advised on Candover's acquisition of the night club and bars operations of First Leisure and on Future Publishing's admission to the LSE and its acquisition of Imagine Media Inc. On the propertry side, the team acted for Chelsfield on its acquisition of the City Gate Complex and British Land on its acquisition of Sheffield's Meadowhall shopping centre. **Simon Rose** maintains his quality reputation for VAT work. The team acted for British Land in relation to a new headquarters for Abbey National at Regents Place and advised Milners Estates on the establishment of a partnership with Norwich Union. **Clients:** The British Land Company plc, Abbey National plc, Candover, Apax partners, Electra Fleming, Delancey Group, Deutsche Bank, Schroder Ventures, Paribas Principal Investments, Dresdner Kleinwort Benson, J Sainsbury plc.

Berwin Leighton Primarily known for its depth of property expertise, market comment on the practice was very positive and the firm rises in the tables this year. The practice is headed by all-rounder **John Overs**. A broad practice has been active on property, asset finance, e-commerce, PFI and litigation. The VAT team handles property, asset finance and cross-border indirect tax issues. Advised on the redevelopment and letting of Barrington House in the City for Robert Fleming, and handled the tax aspects of the acquisition of the RAC group by Lex Service plc. **Clients:** Prudential Portfolio Managers, Legal & General, Tesco, Lex Service plc, AMEC Developments Ltd, Fluor Corporation, GAP, Monsoon plc, Godfrey Bradman.

CMS Cameron McKenna A *"transactional"* practice which gained plaudits from the market for its work in the energy and projects sectors. Work this year includes the development of new JV tax efficient structures for Brixton Estate plc, a £200m acquisition for the Prestbury group in the property sector and advice to Deutsche AMP on property acquisitions. A growing VAT practice is headed by the *"excellent"* **Richard Croker**, especially noted for his property-related work. This year the team has advised BAA on the VAT aspects of development programmes, Enterprise Taverns on pub acquisitions and has been active on property issues for a range of clients. **Clients:** National Australia Bank, Lloyd's Leasing, Black & Decker, BAA Plc, BAe plc, Investec, Kredietbank NV, General Motors/Vauxhall Motors, J Sainsbury, Angel Train Contracts, Legal and General Ventures, National Grid Group plc.

Denton Wilde Sapte A practice combining strengths in asset financing, media, telecoms, energy, property and projects. The firm has also been active on film financing matters. Advised Boxman AB on its merger with iMVS to create Boxman.com, and Allied Leisure on its acquisition of European Leisure plc and the consequent restructuring of its business. On the finance side, the team acted for three lessors in connection with the financing of Jersey European Airways Ltd's new fleet of Dash 8Q series turboprop aircraft valued at US$116m. **Clients:** National Westminster Bank, Lombard North Central, J Sainsbury plc, Discovery Communications Inc, Halifax, Airtours, Barclays Mercantile, Equitable Life Assurance Society, Enelpower SpA, London Electricity plc, TotalFina SA, Shell, Energis, Libert Media, Bertelsmann AG, Pearson, Brambles, Electricite de France.

Nabarro Nathanson A traditionally strong reputation, particularly for mainstream corporate and property work. Following strong market recommendation this year for its all-round skills, the practice moves up in the tables. A solid corporate and property diet is complemented by work on PFI, e-commerce, securitisation and share scheme matters. The *"bright and balanced"* **Michael Cant** is renowned for advice on indirect taxes. Work this year includes acting for Land Securities plc on the creation of the Birmingham Alliance (a city centre re-generation project), advising Alehouse Group Ltd on a £183m pub securitisation arranged by Morgan Stanley and acting on the demerger of Saga. **Clients:** Dana, Mayflower, Granada, Baring Houston Saunders, Land Securities. Azlan, Heron, Alchemy, Pearl.

Olswang An *"always impressive"* tax team which is valued for its *"interactive advice."* Its primary reputation is for media issues. **Kay Butler** retains a strong following among clients. With a lot of her work in the joint venture area, her advantage is that *"she's capable of dealing with the corporate as well as the tax,"* and she is considered *"particularly strong on strategic issues."* **Pat Dugdale** enters the tables this year following strong market recommendation, with much of her work on investment funds. The team has advised on joint ventures and other activities for Delancey Estates Plc and advised both sides on the structuring of the Quantum Realty Fund and its relocation to the UK. The team has worked on matters pertaining to new media funds, on a variety of e-commerce transactions, on share incentive schemes, on film leasing work and retains a leading reputation for property work. **Clients:** BBC Worldwide Ltd, Bain & Co, Bloomberg LP, Body Shop International plc, Delancey Estates, Carphone Warehouse plc, Freeserve plc, Granada, Motorola Inc, Thus plc, Warner Bros/Warner Music, eDreams.

Simmons & Simmons Maintains its reputation for a mix of M&A and structured finance capabilities. The best-known figure at the practice is the head of tax strategy **Edward Troup**. Commentators have a *"lot of time for his ability to intellectualise things,"* and although he is regarded as more interested in policy and strategy, he is also active on transactional work. **Paul Hale** maintains his reputation for VAT and other indirect tax work, and also advises on collective investment schemes.

Corporate work this year includes advising on Wal-Mart's £6.8 billion bid for Asda plc, Carlson's merger with Thomas Cook, Booker plc's disposal programme, the EDF & Man demerger and the UK aspects of the HFC/Beneficial Bank merger ($8.6 billion.) A well-regarded capital markets and securitisation practice keeps the firm at the cutting edge of financial work. In this area, it advised on the Broadgate securitisation. On the VAT side the practice advised Morgan Stanley on VAT aspects of launching the Discover card. Telecoms and e-commerce are growing areas. **Clients:** Railtrack, HFC, Booker plc, Wal-Mart Stores Inc, Citibank NA.

Theodore Goddard Although the loss of Tim Sanders to McDermott, Will & Emery was regarded as a blow to the practice, it is still a highly regarded outfit. Clients admire the team for its *"responsiveness, and ability to pull a deal together."* With a well-known media, IT and telecoms practice, the tax team is especially active in the new media areas. The practice has a large base of overseas clients, including US banks. Advised on brand disposal by Diageo and the reorganisations of Universal Pictures and Signet Group. **Clients:** Universal Pictures, Signet Group plc, Lehman Brothers, Anglia Railways, Blagden plc.

Clyde & Co Known for litigation, shipping and insurance, the tax practice also acts across a broad spectrum of corporate and private client matters. **Susan Ball** is *"fun to deal with"* and has a strong following. Work this year includes advising on Microgen's acquisition of the Kaisha Group, on Brockbank's disposal of Admiral Insurance and on WS Atkin's acquisition of Ventron Technology. Alternative Risk Transfer work is a growing area for the tax practice. **Clients:** Lloyd's vehicles, Credit Suisse, Swiss Re, Pacific Dunlop, Dell, Hewlett-Packard, Microgen.

DLA A broad practice, which is especially noted for its work on PFI matters. Growth areas are e-commerce and contentious issues. Share scheme work is on the increase, with the team working in conjuction with the human resources team of DLA Consulting. Acted for Xyratex on disposals, for Barlow on acquisitions and for Genus on a take-over of VDC plc. **Clients:** Euramax International Inc, Kleinwort Benson Deveopment Capital, Barclays Ventures, Clementine Investments, Granada plc, MEPC plc, UBS AG, Barlow plc, Genus plc, Axa Sun Life.

Field Fisher Waterhouse In a firm not especially known for financial work **Nicholas Noble** has an established reputation as a leading tax player. Half the practice's work is self-generated, of which the majority is financial work, advising leading City institutions such as Robert Fleming, Salomon Smith Barney and Deutsche Bank on financial instruments and financial services. Aside from financial work, the practice also covers mainstream corporate (M&A and restructuring) and property work.

Advised GMG-Endemol Entertainment Plc and Level 3 Communications on corporate acquisitions. Other work includes employee incentive scheme advice, asset financing, securitisation and venture capital transactions. **Clients:** BB Securities Ltd, BG plc, Save & Prosper Group Ltd, SG Asset Management, Belland Vision Ltd, Gentia Software plc, Hippo Pizza, London Regional Transport, RSL Communications, Arab Bank plc, General Medical Council, ICI plc, One2One, Shell Pensions Trust Ltd, Whitbread plc.

Hammond Suddards Edge Known for straight corporate, property, PFI and private equity work. Acted for the shareholders on the disposal of part of the Cork Industries Group, advised Perma Industries on the acquisition of companies within the Arlen plc group and Fort JamesCorp on the restructuring of ownership of intellectual property rights outside the US. **Clients:** GLE Development Capital Limited, General Guarantee Finance Limited, Fort James.

McDermott Will & Emery *"One to watch, they're really putting energy into it."* The arrival of **Tim Sanders** from Theodore Goddard added a boost to an already growing practice which has made its mark in London. Head of the practice is the well-regarded **Peter Nias**. He has a leading name in the area of transfer pricing. The team advises on a range of corporate and financial transactions, including international restructurings and asset finance. Advised on a £2 billion plus cross-border structured finance transaction. **Clients:** US and European multi-nationals.

Travers Smith Braithwaite The bulk of the transactional practice's work is in M&A, together with structured finance work, property, share schemes and e-commerce. Tax investigation work is also an area of growth. **Alasdair Douglas** remains the stand-out name for tax work at a practice which attracts *"high-quality work."* Work this year includes advising on ntl. Inc's acquisition of Cable & Wireless Communications Consumer Co (£9.8 billion), and VAI's acquisition of the metals equipment division of Kvaerner. On the private equity side, transactions include advising the management team on the tax aspects of the £220 million MBO of Thompson Directories, advising Candover and Newco on the £180 million acquisition of Earl's Court to Olympia from P&O and the public to private £135 million acquisition of Hall Engineering. **Clients:** ntl.Inc, Candover, Clearwater Estates and Properties, Card Clear plc.

Watson, Farley & Williams Primarily known for its asset finance (shipping and aircraft leasing) rather than straight corporate or property work. A broad practice covering direct and indirect taxes. **Oonagh Whitty** maintains her reputation as an *"able mind"* in the sector. Advised Vivendi on the indirect acquisition of shares in BSkyB, and acted for P&O Nedlloyd on leasing arrangements. In the VAT sector, the firm's Chairman **Chris Preston** is considered to be an *"all-rounder with knowledge and brains."* In this area, the practice has been advising in the sports sector and continues its advice to Inmarsat on VAT and customs issues arising from its quasi-privatisation. **Clients:** Credit Lyonnais, Daiwa, Inmarsat, Petroleum Geo-Services ASA, Robert Fleming & Co Ltd, Vivendi, Dresdner Kleinwort Benson.

Other Notable Practitioners **Russell Jacobs** at Cadwalader Wickersham & Taft is considered to *"really know his stuff."* **Andrew Norwood** of Weil Gotshal & Manges is popular with financial clients who admire his *"creative"* approach. **Ann Humphrey** is considered an *"extremely bright and capable"* sole practitioner who *"knows her onions"* on VAT matters. She edits a bulletin for the VAT Practitioners Group. **Hugh Mainprice** at Hutchinson Mainprice has been *"practising longer than everyone else."* He has a reputation for litigation, where he is seen to have an *"aggressive and unorthodox"* style. **John Avery Jones** of Speechly Bircham is a *"bright and experienced"* all-round practitioner, well regarded for indirect tax work. **Mark Stapleton** at Dechert has a strong reputation for non-contentious VAT work, principally in the property sector. Also in VAT, **Dario Garcia** of Ernst & Young is a lawyer who *"sticks out for litigation,"* with some considering him the *"number one litigator of the Big Five firms."*

THE SOUTH & SOUTH WEST

TAX (CORPORATE) • South & South West	Ptnrs	Assts
❶ Burges Salmon Bristol	1	1
Osborne Clarke OWA Bristol	2	1
❷ Blake Lapthorn Fareham	1	1
Wiggin & Co Cheltenham	[figures unavailable]	[figures unavailable]

LEADING INDIVIDUALS	
❶ MOSS Philip Osborne Clarke	MURPHY Niall Blake Lapthorn
POPPLEWELL Nigel Burges Salmon	

Within each band, firms are listed alphabetically. *See Profiles on page 781*

Figures unavailable at time of going to press.

Burges Salmon Advises a wide range of listed and international corporates, private companies, private equity groups, entrepreneurs and property consortia. The practice is headed by the *"bright and able"* **Nigel Popplewell.** The team plays a strong hand in asset finance and syndicated loans. Other non-mainstream areas of activity include litigation, investigations, human rights and indirect tax work. Advised on a £750 million syndicated debt instrument. **Clients:** First Group plc, Denmans plc, National Mobility.

Osborne Clarke OWA **Philip Moss** leads the team which *"has experience and knows what it's talking about."* The team's main work is in supporting the corporate practice, and it has further strengths in property and asset finance. The firm has increasingly been advising on venture capital fund raising issues and on e-commerce issues. Advised Quester Venture Capital trust on investments in emerging IT companies and on the establishment of a venture capital limited partnership for the Universities of Bristol and Bath. **Clients:** Scottish & Newcastle, 3i Group, Arjo Wiggins, Bank of Scotland, British Airways Pension Fund, Newcourt Credit, Beeson Gregory.

Blake Lapthorn With a background as an accountant and barrister, **Niall Murphy** has a reputation as a *"sensible"* all-round tax advisor. Advises a range of clients, from plcs to private individuals, and is perceived as the leader in the area for expert tax advice. Main areas of work include corporate support, tax-driven corporate work (eg reorganisations) and property-related work. **Clients:** GTB, Alcatel.

Wiggin & Co Not seen as regularly in the local market, as an international focus characterises this practice. Its main reputation is for advising on the worldwide structuring of affairs for internationally-based clients. Traditionally well regarded for its private client tax work, it is perceived to be growing on the IP/IT side. **Clients:** IT service providers.

MIDLANDS & EAST ANGLIA

TAX (CORPORATE) • Midlands & East Anglia	Ptnrs	Assts
❶ **Pinsent Curtis** Birmingham	3	3
Wragge & Co Birmingham	2	6
❷ **DLA** Birmingham	1	2
Eversheds Norwich, Nottingham	3	14
❸ **Mills & Reeve** Cambridge	2	2

LEADING INDIVIDUALS
❶ **COLECLOUGH Stephen** PricewaterhouseCoopers
HARRISON Philip Eversheds
HYDE Ian Pinsent Curtis
LOWE Kevin Wragge & Co
MORRIS Gregory DLA
SOMERSET Louise PricewaterhouseCoopers
TAILBY Christopher PricewaterhouseCoopers

Within each band, firms are listed alphabetically.

*See **Profiles** on page 781*

Pinsent Curtis A respected team providing a range of direct and indirect corporate tax advice, as well as share scheme advice, for clients ranging from corporates to entrepreneurs. Boasts a sizeable consultancy practice, with around half of the team's work being independently generated. The team has a specialism in property, an area where **Ian Hyde** is highly regarded, and has been appointed to the panel advising on the tax and VAT aspects of the construction of the £475 million new Wembley Stadium. Advised on buyouts, international construction projects and tax structures for investments by venture capital groups. **Clients:** Onyx Environmental Group, Bristol Street Holdings, IMI plc, Alstom UK, TRW Inc, Glanbia plc, Murray Johnstone.

Wragge & Co A range of high quality corporate transaction work characterises this team. **Kevin Lowe** is the most recommended partner here. Aside from mainstream corporate, the team also advises on inward investment, employee incentives, indirect tax and litigation. Advised the purchaser on the Adams Childrenswear MBO, MEPC on structuring a retail portfolio acquisition and Heinz on its acquisition of the chilled foods business of United Biscuits. **Clients:** AT&T, BI Group, MEPC, HJ Heinz Europe, Phoenix Pharmahandel, PowerGen.

DLA A well-regarded tax team headed by **Greg Morris**. Areas of growth have been in advising e-commerce businesses and on employee incentive structures. Advised on the disposal of Midland Laundry Group and on public to privates, including JBA, Concentric and the Henry Cooke Group. **Clients:** Cammell Laird, Centrica Group plc, Intelek plc, JJB Sports plc, Lonrho Africa plc, Pressac plc, Symbian Ltd, Night Freight plc.

Eversheds National head of the tax practice, **Philip Harrison** has a good reputation. The firm is rated across the Midlands and has a solid reputation in East Anglia. Property and VAT are considered to be particular areas of strength. Share scheme advice is a growing area. Advised NHP on the securitisation of a portfolio of nursing homes, acted on the MBO of Computer Answers International Ltd and acted for Romeike Group Holdings Ltd on the disposal of its issued share capital. **Clients:** Bryant Group, Britax International, Matrix Securities Ltd, TXU Europe Group, Plant Bioscience, Worldwide Travel.

Mills & Reeve A specialist and broad-based team. The year has seen the team advise on restructurings, litigation, property developments and employee share scheme work. Clients range from the hi-tech sector to universities. **Clients:** Local and national corporates and institutions.

Other Notable Practitioners At PricewaterhouseCoopers in Birmingham, three lawyers were rated for their tax skills. Ex-Simmons & Simmons **Stephen Coleclough** is regarded as a leader for stamp duty work. He works on a range of indirect taxes, principally in the property sector. Barrister **Chris Tailby** is well regarded for his contentious VAT work. **Louise Somerset** has a reputation as an *"innovative"* lawyer on tax planning for owner-managed businesses.

THE NORTH

TAX (CORPORATE) • The North	Ptnrs	Assts
❶ **Addleshaw Booth & Co** Leeds, Manchester	4	6
Pinsent Curtis Leeds	3	4
❷ **Hammond Suddards Edge** Leeds, Manchester	3	4
❸ **Eversheds** Leeds, Manchester	2	4
❹ **Dickinson Dees** Newcastle upon Tyne	1	3
Walker Morris Leeds	1	3

LEADING INDIVIDUALS	
❶ **CHRISTIAN John** Pinsent Curtis	**GREAVES Judith** Pinsent Curtis
JENKINS Edmund Addleshaw Booth & Co	
SIMPSON Mark Hammond Suddards Edge	
❷ **CONCANNON Simon** Walker Morris	**HAYES Richard** Addleshaw Booth & Co
HENNESSY Tony Dickinson Dees	**JERVIS David** Eversheds
TOON John Addleshaw Booth & Co	

Within each band, firms are listed alphabetically.

*See **Profiles** on page 781*

Addleshaw Booth & Co *"They are at the top, you'd expect nothing less."* Strong in Leeds and Manchester, the growing practice is well regarded for advice on mainstream corporate and financial work as well as property, employee benefits and venture capital issues. All rounder **Ed Jenkins** is regarded as *"the leading light in the Manchester market,"* and is admired for his *"proactive"* approach, having masterminded *"a number of innovative schemes."* **Richard Hayes** maintains his reputation as a generalist. The *"quiet and technically able"* **John Toon** has a niche in property-related matters. Advised on the acquisition of Crompton & Knowles' speciality dyes business by the Yorkshire Group, and NatWest Private Equity on the acquisition of Pennine Computer Services. **Clients:** Yorkshire Group, Halifax plc, Scapa Group plc, GEHE UK plc, Skillsgroup plc, 3i Group, Airtours plc, Kelda Group plc, J Sainsbury plc.

Pinsent Curtis A high profile corporate tax team with a cutting-edge profile in employee share schemes work. Has a national reputation for tax work. Advises corporates and wealthy individuals and entrepreneurs. **Judith Greaves** retains a high profile for share-scheme work as well as mainstream corporate advice. **John Christian** is a corporate tax all-rounder *"who really knows his stuff."* International work, property and projects are strengths of the team. Work this year includes advising on the £192 million disposal of AM Paper Group to SCA of Sweden and advising Polypipe plc on the corporate tax and employee share scheme aspects of the £337 million offer from IMI plc. **Clients:** BPT plc, Cytec Industries Inc, HSBC Private Equity.

Hammond Suddards Edge UK and US practices based in London rate the team highly for its strength across the Pennines. The *"constructive"* **Mark Simpson** has *"high technical ability,"* and the team is considered to have had a successful year. In the North, the general corporate tax practice has been growing on all fronts. Advised BASF, ITW, Sports Internet and Pubmaster Inns on acquisitions, JSB Software Technologies on its EASDAQ float and Umbro on the disposal of its European businesses and subsidiaries. The team has also advised Vibroplant and Kelda Group on the establishment of share schemes. On VAT matters, the practice has been busy on advisory and contentious work, and has been advising the Goldsmith Foundation for European Affairs on its appeal to the VAT and Duties Tribunal. **Clients:** Lorien plc, BASF plc, Pubmaster Inns Ltd, Torotrak plc, Sports Internet plc, ITW, Fine Art Developments plc, MBNA, Caravan Brill.

Eversheds Forming part of the corporate department, the tax team advises private clients, large plcs, property developers and institutional investors on a wide range of corporate tax issues. A trans-Pennine practice also covering Tyneside and Teesside with skills in both direct and indirect taxes. Practice leader **David Jervis** has a reputation as a *"reasonable and commercial"* practitioner. Growing areas for the group include advice to e-commerce, telecoms and biotechnology companies. Advised on Datagroup's acquisition of Thesaurus Computers Ltd and on Ferranti Technologies' IBO. The practice also advised on employee share schemes for clients such as Stanley Leisure Group and Armstrong Laing **Clients:** Du Pont, AEA Technology, Stanley Leisure, Armstrong Laing, Martin Dawes, Chapelthorpe, Peterhouse Group, BF Goodrich, ANI Aurora, Dutton Forshaw Group.

Dickinson Dees The *"pre-eminent team for tax advice in Newcastle"* works on a mix of corporate and finance advisory and contentious-related issues. Head of practice **Tony Hennessy** has a national reputation. Advises a range of clients from blue-chips to owner-managed businesses. Growth areas over the past 12 months include share schemes work, corporate disposals and structured finance. Advised Arriva plc on the sale of its vehicle finance/leasing function and advising Grainger Trust on the bid for Park Estates Plc. **Clients:** The Go-Ahead Group, Arriva plc, Northern Rock plc.

Walker Morris Areas of activity over the past 12 months have been in property, corporate reorganisations, tax investigations, share scheme work, PFI projects and venture capital matters. Practice leader is **Simon Concannon**, a *"good operator"* who has *"all the expertise you need."* Advised Finaref SA (the largest provider of consumer credit in France) on the establishment of its UK operations, advising on a £125 million Eurobond issue for Cattles plc and acted for Swallow Group on a succesful stamp duty case in the High Court. **Clients:** Bradford City FC, Kalon Group plc, Tay Homes plc, Empire Stores plc, Royal Bank of Scotland, Rosebys, Debenhams Retail.

SCOTLAND

TAX (CORPORATE) • Scotland	Ptnrs	Assts
❶ McGrigor Donald Glasgow	2	–
❷ Maclay Murray & Spens Glasgow	1	2
MacRoberts Glasgow	1	1
❸ Brodies WS Edinburgh	–	1
Burness Edinburgh	–	3

LEADING INDIVIDUALS	
❶ D'INVERNO Isobel MacRoberts	GORDON Ian McGrigor Donald
JONES Martyn Maclay Murray & Spens	
❷ BARR Alan Brodies WS	HOYLE Susan McGrigor Donald
NELSON Victoria Burness	
UP AND COMING	
TOSH Nial Dickson Minto WS	WHITE Andy McGrigor Donald
ONES TO WATCH	
CAIRNS Roger McGrigor Donald	

Within each band, firms are listed alphabetically. *See **Profiles** on page 781*

McGrigor Donald An *"excellent and commercial"* tax team. Head of the tax group **Ian Gordon** has an all-round reputation, with a perceived strength in benefits planning. **Susan Hoyle** in Glasgow is a highly regarded corporate tax all-rounder. Assistant **Andy White** was praised for his VAT work. As well as mainstream corporate work, the tax team has been busy in the last 12 months advising on property, finance leasing, pensions and share scheme transactions. Advised on the MBO of CALA plc, on the acquisition by Stakis plc of Hilton Group plc and the public to private of Avonside Group plc. **Clients:** The Scottish Metropolitan Property plc, Forth Ports plc, Royal Bank of Scotland plc, CALA Ltd.

Maclay Murray & Spens Headed by the popular **Martyn Jones**, a *"fun"* practitioner with *"experience across the board"* and a *"good grasp of technicalities."* A transactional corporate tax group advising on a range of corporate direct tax issues as well as indirect tax and contentious matters. Work this year includes advising on the £600m acquisition of Highland Distillers Co plc by 1887 plc and advising on the sale of Phillips to the LVMH Group on behalf of 3i and the management shareholders. **Clients:** Vericore Holdings, national plcs and private corporates.

MacRoberts Qualified chartered accountant **Isobel d'Inverno** heads the tax group. PFI, M&A, employee schemes and property transactions have been the staple diet of the practice over the past twelve months. Among a number of M&A transactions this year, the team advised on the sales of B&S Visual to Photobition Group, Datavault to Pierce Leahy and Feathers Brooksbank to Aegis plc. The practice also acted for Railtrack plc on developments and advised other groups on the tax aspects of various PFI projects. **Clients:** Bank of Scotland, British Energy, Campbell Distillers Ltd, Clydesdale Bank, Ford Motor Company, Skandiaverken AB, 3i plc.

Brodies WS Works on a range of corporate and property matters, both direct and indirect. Whilst the majority of the work is in a support function, the practice also has some stand-alone planning and investigatory work. Although not full time with the firm, consultant **Alan Barr** is the main tax practitioner within the group. Mixing the academic and the practical, he is well regarded for personal and corporate work. **Clients:** Corporates, developers and financials.

Burness A team which has established itself over the past 18 months, mainly through the efforts of **Victoria Nelson**, a practitioner *"experienced in all sorts of deals."* Provides a full range of corporate and indirect tax advice. Work this year includes advising the Royal Bank of Scotland on acquisitions, VAT planning and joint venture issues and advising Insider Publications on its sale to Scottish Daily Record & Sunday Mail. **Clients:** Royal Bank of Scotland, Ritchie & Co, GE Capital Bank, Bank of Scotland.

Other Notable Practitioners At Dickson Minto WS, all rounder **Nial Tosh**'s main specialism is in tax transactions, where he is recognised in the market as an able practitioner. His work is composed of direct tax work on mainstream corporate (including buy-outs) and share scheme matters.

LEADERS IN TAX (CORPORATE)

AIRS, Graham
Slaughter and May, London (020) 7600 1200
Specialisation: Principal area of practice is corporate tax. Particular experience of privatisations, securitisations, mergers and acquisitions. Author of chapter on EC Direct Tax Measures in Tolley's Tax Planning.
Prof. Memberships: Member of The Law Society's Revenue Law Committee, The Law Society, European American Taxation Institute.
Career: Qualified in 1978 after articles at *Slaugher and May* and stayed at firm until 1980. Partner in *Airs Dickinson* 1980-1984. Returned to *Slaughter and May* 1984 and became a Partner in 1987.
Personal: Born 8 August 1953. Married Stephanie 1981. Educated Newport Grammar, Emmanuel College, Cambridge.

AVERY JONES C.B.E., John
Speechly Bircham, London (020) 7427 6400
john.averyjones@speechlys.co.uk
See under Trusts & Personal Tax, p.818

BALDWIN, Mark
Macfarlanes, London (020) 7831 9222
mark.baldwin@macfarlanes.com
Partner in corporate tax group.
Specialisation: (For Tax (Corporate)) Handles a broad spectrum of corporate tax work, including private equity transactions and cross-border investment. Has particular expertise in indirect tax (particularly VAT), property investment, development and finance and the structuring of collective investment vehicles (particularly domestic and pan-European private equity funds and property funds) and associated carried interest and co-investment structures. Regular conference speaker and writer.
Specialisation: (For VAT) Handles all areas of indirect tax work, principally VAT, but also excise duties and customs duty. As well as general planning advice, conducts litigation and has represented clients in the VAT and Duties Tribunal. Also practises in other business tax fields, principally property finance, development and investment and collective investment schemes. Regular conference speaker and writer, and a contributor to 'De Voil's Indirect Tax Intelligence'. Reporter on UK taxes for the 1999 & 2000 IBA Conferences.
Prof. Memberships: Member of the Law Society's VAT and Duties Sub-Committee, VAT Practitioners Group, IBA.
Career: Qualified in 1987. Assistant Solicitor at *Freshfields* between 1987 and 1995, when he returned to *Macfarlanes*, becoming a partner in May 1997.
Publications: A contributor to 'De Voil's Indirect Tax Intelligence'.
Personal: Born 24 January 1963. German speaker.

BALL, Susan
Clyde & Co, London (020) 7623 1244
Partner and Head of Tax Department.
Specialisation: Main area of practice is corporate tax. Work covers tax aspects (including Stamp Duty) of corporate reorganisations, mergers, acquisitions and corporate disposals. Also handles taxation aspects of inward and outward investment for the UK and of new issues and flotations. Other area of practice is taxation of employees, including share schemes, ESOPs and employee benefits. Conducts occasional external and internal lecturing. Member of the Law Society Revenue Law Committee 1982-89 and Corporation Tax sub-committee 1995-. Co-Author of 'Gammie and Ball-Tax on Company Reorganisations.' Has written frequently on taxation topics.
Prof. Memberships: Law Society, City of London Solicitors Company, Law Society of New South Wales.
Career: Qualified in 1973. Worked at *Linklaters & Paines* 1971-89 (Partner 1981-89). Assistant Solicitor at *Blake Dawson Waldron* in Sydney 1989-91; admitted in New South Wales in 1989. Joined *Clyde & Co.* as Deputy Head of Tax Department in 1993.
Personal: Born 3rd November 1948. Holds an MA (Oxon) from St Hugh's College, Oxford 1967-70.

BALLARD, Richard M.
Freshfields Bruckhaus Deringer, London (020) 7936 4000
Partner
Specialisation: Specialises in corporate finance (including mergers, demergers, reconstructions and cross border transactions); tax-based and structured financing of all types, including cross border transactions; capital markets work including structured bond issues, hybrid instruments, repackaging and securitisation; derivatives transactions of all types; experience in Inland Revenue enquiries and in Commissioners and court litigation. Contributor to 'Tolley's Tax Planning' and 'Tolley's Company Law' and frequent contributor to tax journals and to various *Freshfields* publications.
Career: Qualified 1978. Became a Partner at *Freshfields* in 1984.
Personal: Born 1953. Attended Queens' College, Cambridge.

BARR, Alan
Brodies WS, Edinburgh (0131) 228 3777
abarr@brodies.co.uk
Specialisation: One of Scotland's leading authorities in the field of Tax Law. Has carried out substantial research on the subject and his papers and books have been published widely. Is a prominent member of the Law Society of Scotland's Tax Committee and Convenor of the VAT Sub-Committee. Frequent speaker at professional seminars. Admitted as a solicitor in Scotland in 1984, has spent much of his career as a Senior Lecturer specialising in all aspects of Taxation, and is currently Director of Edinburgh University's Legal Practice Unit. (The 'Diploma' Course.) Joined *Brodies* as the firms Corporate Tax and VAT Consultant by agreement with Edinburgh University. Consolidates *Brodies'* position as a leading legal firm in the field of Taxation generally, and the aspect of tax on property in particular. When added to the specialist areas of environmental and planning law, His expertise ensures full coverage in all disciplines relevant to Property Development and Acquisition.
Personal: Married and despite the fact that he lives in Edinburgh, keeps an optimistic eye on the progress of St. Mirren Football Club. He enjoys watching rugby and cricket and collecting Marvel Comics.

BEARE, Tony
Slaughter and May, London (020) 7600 1200
Specialisation: Corporate Tax. Qualified 1987. Partner 1994. Main area of practice is corporate tax and, in particular, structured finance, corporate finance and capital markets.
Prof. Memberships: The Law Society.
Personal: Born 30 November 1959. Educated at Durban High School, Haberdashers' Aske's, Elstree, St. Catharine's College, Cambridge and St Edmund Hall, Oxford.

BLAKE, Jonathan E.
SJ Berwin & Co, London (020) 7533 2222
jonathan.blake@sjberwin.com
See under Investment Funds, p.522

BRAILSFORD, Mark R.
Allen & Overy, London (020) 7330 3000
Specialisation: Corporate tax, with major focus on structural finance and Securitisations.
Career: Joined *Allen & Overy* 1987. Qualified 1989. Partner 1996.
Personal: Married with one daughter. Keen tennis and football enthusiast. Member of the AFA Council.

BRANNAN, Guy C.H.
Linklaters (A member firm of Linklaters & Alliance), London (020) 7456 5690
guy.brannan@linklaters.com
Partner and Head of Tax Department.
Specialisation: Specialises in corporate tax matters. Main areas of practice include mergers and acquisitions, reorganisations, reconstructions, cross-border transactions, capital markets and finance transactions, EC tax law and tax litigation. Member of the permanent Tax Commission on the Union Internationale des Avocats. Member of the American Bar Association (Taxation Section). Co-editor of Taxation of Companies and Company Reconstructions (2nd and 3rd editions).
Career: Qualified 1981, Partner 1987, Resident tax partner New York office 1989-93.

BUTLER, Kay
Olswang, London (020) 7208 8888
Partner, Head of Tax Unit
Specialisation: Spans the spectrum of tax work including corporate tax strategy, international group structuring, joint ventures (particularly in the property and media sectors) both domestic and cross border, limited partnerships, sale and lease backs, film investment, employee incentives and VAT and other tax disputes. She has lobbied the EC Commission, the Inland Revenue and HM Customs and Excise for changes in the law. She was also the only legal representative on the British Screen Advisory Counsel's committee which negotiated the statement of practice concerning the new relief for investment in film with the Inland Revenue.
Prof. Memberships: Law Society; VAT Practitioners Group.
Career: Qualified 1987 at *Oppenheimers*; Assistant Solicitor *Richards Butler* 1988-90; *S.J. Berwin & Co* 1990-95, becoming a partner in 1993. Joined *Olswang* in 1995 as Head of Tax.
Personal: Interests include perfecting my golf swing and entertaining my young daughter.

CANT, Michael
Nabarro Nathanson, London (020) 7524 6000
m.cant@nabarro.com
Partner in Corporate Tax Department.
Specialisation: Specialises in Corporate Tax, particularly VAT and Stamp Duties.

Prof. Memberships: Law Society, VAT Practitioners Group.
Career: Qualified in 1984. Joined *Turner Kenneth Brown* as an Assistant in 1988.
Personal: Born 19th September 1958. Attended Leeds Polytechnic 1976-79, then Guildford Law School 1980. Leisure interests include golf. Lives in Haslemere, Surrey.

CHALLONER, John
Norton Rose, London (020) 7283 6000
challonerj@nortonrose.com
Partner in Commercial Tax Department.
Specialisation: Principal area of practice is corporate taxation. Extensive experience in relation to the taxation of company acquisitions, property developments, UK corporate restructurings, collective investment schemes and dealing with the complex VAT and other tax issues relating to international ventures. Author of Sale and Leaseback chapter in Longman's Tax Planning and Precedents. Frequent speaker at conferences and seminars.
Prof. Memberships: International Fiscal Association.
Career: Qualified 1977 while with *Nelson & Steele* in Stoke-on-Trent. H.M. Inspector of Taxes 1979-84. Joined *Norton Rose* in 1984 and became a Partner in 1988.
Personal: Born 9th August 1952. Attended Wilmslow School and Exeter University. Lives in Saffron Walden.

CHRISTIAN, John M.S.
Pinsent Curtis, Leeds (0113) 244 5000
john.christian@pinsents.com
Partner in Corporate Tax Department.
Specialisation: Corporate and property tax, including corporate finance, reconstructions and demergers, asset finance, treasury and financing, property taxation, employee incentives, VAT, collective investment schemes and public bodies.
Prof. Memberships: VAT Practitioners Group. Member of the Corporation Tax Sub-Committee of Law Society Revenue Law Committee. Fellow of the Chartered Institute of Taxation.
Career: Qualified 1985. *Freshfields* 1983-89. Joined *Simpson Curtis* in 1990 (now *Pinsent Curtis*), becoming a Partner in 1991.

CLARK, Simon
Linklaters (A member firm of Linklaters & Alliance), London (020) 7456 4902
simon.clark@linklaters.com
Specialisation: Head of Real Estate Department; specialist in the UK taxation of real estate transactions and investment structuring, advising UK and non-UK institutions, property companies, developers and occupiers. Has long been involved in the UK property markets efforts to create listed tax-transparent real estate vehicles in the UK.
Career: Articled at *Linklaters* and qualified in 1981, Solicitor in Tax Department 1981-83, Solicitor in Commercial Property Department 1983-88. Made Partner in 1988. Head of Real Estate Department since 1999.

CLAYSON, Murray J.
Freshfields Bruckhaus Deringer, London
(020) 7936 4000
Specialisation: International tax, corporate structuring especially cross-border, financing, banking, securities, capital markets, derivatives, structured finance.
Prof. Memberships: Chartered Institute of Taxation (FTII). Member of International Tax Sub-Committee. International Fiscal Association: Vice-Chairman of British Branch and Chairman of the Technical Sub-Committee.
Career: Sidney Sussex College, Cambridge (MA, LL.M). Partner 1993.

COLECLOUGH, Stephen
PricewaterhouseCoopers, Birmingham
(0121) 265 5000

COLEMAN, Brenda
Allen & Overy, London (020) 7330 3000
Specialisation: Tax Corporate. Partner in the Tax department advising on all aspects of corporate tax but has a particular interest in mergers and acquisitions, corporate reorganisations, joint ventures, investment vehicles, tax litigation, financial instruments and tax (and property clawback) advice on, privatisations and PFI projects. She is a member of *Allen & Overy's* Tax Investigations Unit and Investment Funds Group.
Career: Qualified 1984, Partner *Herbert Smith* 1991-98. Partner *Allen & Overy* since 1998.
Personal: Born 1959. King's College London 1979-81, LL.B Hons, AKC.

CONCANNON, Simon
Walker Morris, Leeds (0113) 283 2500
stc@walkermorris.co.uk
Partner in Corporate Department, Head of Tax Unit.
Specialisation: Principal area of practice is corporate and property tax. Work includes restructuring, leasing, structured bank financing, MBOs, venture capital funding, employee remuneration schemes and VAT planning. Also handles tax disputes including dealing with the Inland Revenue Special Compliance Office and the Special Investigation Section. Major clients include Empire Stores, Yorkshire Water, Greenwoods Menswear, Persimmon, Bank of Scotland, Royal Bank of Scotland, Roseby's, Selfridges, Tay Homes, Capital for Companies VCT, Murray Johnstone, Bradford City Football Club, Jarvis and IMS Group.
Career: Qualified in 1990. With *Clifford Chance* 1990-94. Joined *Walker Morris* in 1994 and became a Partner in 1996.
Personal: Born 1966. Educated at Hertford College, Oxford 1984-87 and the College of Law, Chester 1987-88. Lives in Ilkley.

CRAWFORD, Susan
Ashurst Morris Crisp, London (020) 7638 1111
Partner in Tax Department.
Specialisation: Principal area of practice is corporate tax with particular emphasis on corporate reorganisatons, mergers, de-mergers, and acquisitions including cross-border transactions. Also specialises in oil and gas tax; property taxation and taxation of financial institutions/transactions (including tax based structured financing), extending to securitisation, leasing and enterprise zones.
Career: Articled *Coward Chance (Clifford Chance)*; qualified 1984. Partner *Ashurst Morris Crisp* since 1994.
Personal: Educated at Wycombe Abbey School; Girton College Cambridge University.

CROKER, Richard
CMS Cameron McKenna, London
(020) 7367 2149
radc@cmck.com
Specialisation: All aspects of corporate tax with particular emphasis on VAT and other indirect taxes, tax planning for property transactions, PFI, mergers/acquisitions and joint ventures. Acted for J Sainsbury plc on Project Redwing, an innovative securitisation of property rentals launched in March 2000.
Prof. Memberships: Technical Secretary of City Chapter of VAT Practitioners Group; Member of VAT and Duties Sub-Committee of Law Society's Revenue Law Committee.
Career: Qualified 1989. Partner *CMS Cameron McKenna* 1997.
Publications: Regular contributor to tax and property press.
Personal: Married with 3 sons. Lives Winchester.

D'INVERNO, Isobel
MacRoberts, Edinburgh (0131) 226 2552
isobeld@macroberts.co.uk
Director – Corporate Tax.
Specialisation: Main area of practice is corporate taxation work. Includes corporate acquisitions, disposals, re-organisations, EIS and Reinvestment Relief issues, PFI's and VAT on commercial property and corporate transactions. Has addressed seminars on PFI tax, VAT and Stamp Duty and company re-organisations, as well as lecturing on VAT and corporate work. VAT examiner for Chartered Institute of Taxation.
Prof. Memberships: Institute of Chartered Accountants (England & Wales), Chartered Institute of Taxation, VAT Practitioners Group, Member of Tax Law Committee of Law Society of Scotland.
Career: Trained as Chartered Accountant with *Ernst & Whinney* in London. Practised with *Ernst & Young* from 1980 and *Arthur Young* from 1985 as Tax Specialist. Joined *Brodies WS* as VAT and Corporate Tax Specialist in June 1991. Joined *MacRoberts* in August 1997.
Personal: Educated at St Andrew's University (MA Russian Language and Literature 1979). Gained ACA 1983, then ATII 1984. Non-executive member of the National Board for Nursing, Midwifery and Health Visiting for Scotland.

DORAN, Nigel J.L.
Macfarlanes, London (020) 7831 9222
Partner in Corporate Tax Group.
Specialisation: Corporate tax specialist. Work includes mergers and acquisitions, joint ventures, MBO's, MBI's, corporate finance, international, employment, investment funds, banking and property. Important transactions include the demerger of Saatchi & Saatchi, sale by Allders plc of Allders International, sale by Lonrho plc of London Metropole, sale of J O Hambro Magan to NatWest Markets and acting for management on the sale of William Hill. Regular speaker at tax conferences, author of 'Taxation of Corporate Joint Ventures' (Butterworths) and joint author of "Collective Investment Schemes: the Law and Practice" (FT Law and Tax).
Prof. Memberships: City of London Law Society (Revenue Law Subcommittee), Chartered Institute of Taxation, Association of Certified Accountants, Chartered Institute of Bankers.
Career: Qualified in 1984 having joined *Macfarlanes*

in 1982. Became a Partner in 1988.
Personal: Born 11th March 1950. Educated at Trinity College, Glenalmond 1963-69 and St. Edmund Hall, Oxford 1969-73. Leisure interests include golf and modern languages. Lives in Twickenham.

DOUGLAS, Alasdair F.
Travers Smith Braithwaite, London (020) 7295 3000
Alasdair.Douglas@Traverssmith.com
Specialisation: Head of corporate tax department and managing partner of firm. Main areas of work are corporate finance, mergers, acquisitions, reconstructions and investigation work.
Career: Qualified 1977. Partner 1985. Managing partner 1995.

DUGDALE, Pat
Olswang, London (020) 7208 8888
apd@olswang.com
Specialisation: General, corporate, property and international tax, including tax planning for international groups and corporate reconstructions, acquisitions and disposals. Particular areas of specialist expertise include UK and overseas investment funds, EIS, corporate venturing and private equity transactions and e-commerce. Recent transactions include the establishment of a number of incubator and other new media investment funds.
Prof. Memberships: British German Jurists Association. International Fiscal Association.
Career: Qualified 1985. Corporate and commercial assistant at *Kennedys* 1986 to 1989 and *S.J. Berwin* 1989 to 1992; Tax assistant at *Norton Rose* 1992 to 1998, Tax Partner *Olswang* May 1998.
Publications: Editor of Taxation chapter of Sweet & Maxwell's Encyclopaedia of International Technology Law. Articles on international tax and incorporation of partnerships. Regular conference speaker on taxation of e-commerce and general corporate taxation.
Personal: University College Cardiff and Heidelberg University 1978-82. BA Law and German (First Class Hons). LLM Taxation: Kings College London 1992. Married with two energetic small boys.

EDGE, Steve
Slaughter and May, London (020) 7600 1200
Partner in Corporate Tax Department.
Specialisation: Principal area of practice is corporate taxation with a particular emphasis on corporate finance and structured asset finance. Expertise in investment funds, financial instruments, cross border financial transactions, securitisations and other capital markets work. Advises many UK and non-UK multinationals and banks on a wide range of tax matters. Contributes to a number of publications on corporate tax.
Career: Qualified in 1975 while with *Slaughter and May* and became a Partner in 1982.
Personal: Born 29 November 1950. Attended Canon Slade Grammar School, Bolton 1962-69, then Exeter University 1969-72. Lives in London.

EHRLICH, Michael
Clifford Chance, London (020) 7600 1000
michael.ehrlich@cliffordchance.com
Specialisation: Partner specialising in tax on financing transactionsand real estate (including VAT).
Career: Bedales School; Southampton University; Warwick University (BSc Mathematics, MSc). Articled *Dawson & Co*; qualified 1977; partner *Clifford Chance* since 1986.
Personal: Born 1948.

ELLIOTT, Peter
Clifford Chance, London (020) 7600 1000
peter.elliott@cliffordchance.com

ELMAN, Jonathan
Clifford Chance, London (020) 7600 1000
jonathan.elman@cliffordchance.com

FALK, Sarah
Freshfields Bruckhaus Deringer, London (020) 7936 4000
Partner in Tax Department.
Specialisation: Main area of practice is corporate tax. Work covers corporate tax planning and corporate finance.
Prof. Memberships: Law Society.
Career: Qualified 1986, having joined *Freshfields* in 1984. Became a Partner in 1994.
Personal: Born 1962. Attended Sidney Sussex College, Cambridge, 1980-83.

FERGUSON, Fiona
Slaughter and May, London (020) 7600 1200
Specialisation: Banking, Structured Finance, M&A, Conversion of Building Societies.
Career: MA Cambridge.
Personal: Flying, sailing, playing piano.

FRASER, R.D.A.
Herbert Smith, London (020) 7374 8000
Specialisation: Main practice areas include insurance company mergers and acquisitions (highlights of the last year include acting on the acquisition of United Assurance group by Royal London); and various structured finance transactions. On the non-insurance side, recent transactions include the acquisition by Ireland Group of Booker.
Career: London School of Economics (LLM 1970); qualified 1973; partner *Herbert Smith* 1982.

FRENCH, Douglas
Clifford Chance, London (020) 7600 1000
douglas.french@cliffordchance.com
Specialisation: Partner specialising in tax, particularly tax related to corporate and commercial transactions.
Career: Walbottle High School, Newcastle; Oxford (MA Law) ATII. Articled *Freshfields*; qualified 1981; partner *Clifford Chance* since 1988.
Personal: Born 1956; married, three children.

GARCIA, Dario
Ernst & Young, London (020) 7951 2000

GORDON, Ian
McGrigor Donald, Glasgow (0141) 248 6677
Partner in Corporate Unit.
Specialisation: Principal area of practice is employee benefits, including share incentive schemes, option schemes, and employee share ownership arrangements for listed, AIM and Ofex companies. Also advises on corporate acquisitions, reconstructions and tax driven financing arrangements. Frequent lecturer on taxation issues.
Prof. Memberships: Association of Pension Lawyers.
Career: Joined *McGrigor Donald* as a trainee in 1979. Qualified in July 1979. One year secondment to *Thomson McLintock CA* in 1983. Became a Partner at *McGrigor Donald* in the same year.
Personal: Educated at Edinburgh University 1975-79. Born 15th August 1957. Lives in Glasgow.

GOWTAGE, Jill
Allen & Overy, London (020) 7330 3000

GREAVES, Judith
Pinsent Curtis, Leeds (0113) 244 5000
judith.greaves@pinsents.com
See under Employee Share Schemes, p.314

GREENBANK, Ashley
Macfarlanes, London (020) 7831 9222
ashley.greenbank@macfarlanes.com
Specialisation: Partner in the Corporate Tax Group specialising in UK and cross-border tax aspects of corporate finance transactions, mergers and acquisitions and venture capital work.
Prof. Memberships: Law Society (Member of Corporation Tax Sub-Committee of the Revenue Law Committee); BVCA (Tax Committee).
Career: King Edwards School Birmingham, Selwyn College Cambridge MA (1985), Lincoln College Oxford BCL (1989). Qualified 1988. Articles at *Freshfields* (1986-1988) Assistant solicitor *Freshfields* Tax Department (1989-1994). Assistant solicitor *Macfarlanes* Company Commercial and Banking Department (1994-1997). Partner 1997.

HALE, Paul D.
Simmons & Simmons, London (020) 7628 2020
Partner in Corporate and Indirect Taxes Group.
Specialisation: Main area of practice is corporate tax and value added tax. Work includes mergers and acquisitions, stock exchange listings, project finance, structured finance and property transactions. Also handles taxation of collective investment schemes, including unit trusts, investment trusts and offshore funds. Author of various articles.
Prof. Memberships: Law Society, City of London Solicitors' Company (Member of Revenue Law sub-Committee), VAT Practitioners Group, International Bar Association.
Career: Qualified 1985, having joined *Simmons & Simmons* in 1983. Became a Partner in 1990.
Personal: Born 1st August 1959. Attended Winchester College 1973-77, then Worcester College Oxford 1977-81. Leisure interests include family life, gardening, tennis and bridge. Lives in Amersham.

HARDWICK, Michael
Linklaters (A member firm of Linklaters & Alliance), London (020) 7456 5658
michael.hardwick@linklaters.com
Partner in Tax Department., since 1991
Specialisation: Specialises in tax aspects of mergers and acquisitions, takeovers, joint ventures, flotations, privatisations and PFI transactions.
Career: Joint author of 'Taxation of Companies and Company Reconstructions (7th edition)'. Qualified in 1984, having joined *Linklaters* in 1982. Became a Partner in 1991.
Personal: Born 1958.

HARGREAVES, Colin
Freshfields Bruckhaus Deringer, London (020) 7832 7352
chargreaves@freshfields.com
Specialisation: Corporate tax.
Prof. Memberships: Law Society. City of London Law Society (member, CLLS Revenue Law Sub-Committee).
Career: Uppingham School; Leeds University; Qualified 1988; Partner *Freshfields* 1996.
Personal: Sailing (member, Burnham Overy Staithe Sailing Club).

HARKNESS, David
Clifford Chance, London (020) 7600 1000
david.harkness@cliffordchance.com
Specialisation: Partner specialising in corporate tax including mergers and acquisitions, corporate restructurings, joint ventures, international tax planning, financing transactions and securitisations.
Career: Colchester Royal Grammar School; Sheffield University (LLB Law 1985). Articled *Clifford Chance*; qualified 1989; partner 1996.
Personal: Football, golf, juggling with fire, pig breeding. Born 1963; resides London.

HARRISON, Philip J.
Eversheds, Nottingham (0115) 950 7000
Head of Tax-East & West Midlands. Head of firm-wide Business Tax Group.
Specialisation: Work includes tax aspects of corporate and property transactions, tax disputes, employee taxation and personal tax planning for business clients (especially planning for the sale of unquoted companies). Acts for a sponsor of enterprise zone trusts, also handles employee share incentives, including revenue approved and unapproved schemes and ESOPs (both onshore and offshore). Acted for the taxpayer in Mairs v Haughey (arising from the H&W privatisation) up to his victory in the House of Lords in 1993. Divides time between Birmingham and East Midlands practices.
Prof. Memberships: Law Society, Society of Trust and Estate Practitioners.
Career: Qualified in 1986. Articled with *Evershed & Tomkinson* 1984-86. Associate with *Evershed Wells & Hind* 1989, Partner 1991.
Personal: Born 22nd November 1960. Attended King Edward VI School, Lichfield 1972-79; Emmanuel College, Cambridge 1979-82 (BA 1982, MA 1986) and 1983-84 (LLM); College of Law, Chester 1982-83. Leisure interests include family, reading, walking and old cars. Resides in Nottingham.

HAYES, Richard
Addleshaw Booth & Co, Manchester
(0161) 934 6000
See under Employee Share Schemes, p.314

HENNESSY, Tony
Dickinson Dees, Newcastle upon Tyne
(0191) 279 9207
Specialisation: A broad range of corporate tax work, including all tax aspects of mergers, acquisitions, corporate reorganisations and flotations together with employee share scheme and remuneration planning work, asset financing and leasing and VAT planning.
Career: Called to the Bar 1979. Practised corporate tax in both a City of London practice and in a major provincial firm before being appointed as head of the corporate tax group at *Dickinson Dees* in 1992.
Personal: Educated St. Mary's College Crosby and University College Oxford (MA). Leisure interests include rugby, hill walking and 18th century music.

HIGGINBOTTOM, Louise
Norton Rose, London (020) 7283 6000
Partner in Tax Department.
Specialisation: Corporate and asset finance.
Prof. Memberships: Law Society, Associate of Institute of Tax, Member of Corporation Tax Sub-committee of Revenue Law Committee of Law Society, IBA, ABA.
Career: Joined *Norton Rose* 1981. Qualified 1983. Partner 1991.
Personal: Born 17th August 1958. Attended Southampton University 1977-80.

HOYLE, Stephen L.
Freshfields Bruckhaus Deringer, London
(020) 7936 4000
Partner 1988. Tax department.
Specialisation: Main area of practice is the taxation of insurance business, financings and general corporate.
Personal: Born 17.9.1955. Attended St Catherine's College Oxford 1973-76, Gonville & Caius College Cambridge, 1976-77, and Northwestern Law School, Chicago, 1977-78.

HOYLE, Susan
McGrigor Donald, Glasgow (0141) 248 6677
Partner in Corporate Unit.
Specialisation: Main area of practice is corporate tax law, dealing with acquisitions and disposals, group reorganisations and MBO's. Also deals with employee share schemes.
Prof. Memberships: The Chartered Institute of Taxation.
Career: Qualified in October 1986. Worked for Ernst & Young and Coopers & Lybrand. Joined *McGrigor Donald* in 1995.
Personal: Educated Glasgow University.

HUMPHREY, Ann
Ann L. Humphrey, London (020) 7378 9370
annlhumphrey@dial.pipex.com
Fax: 0171 378 9360
Specialisation: Wide-ranging tax experience during fifteen years in the City, particular emphasis on VAT. Tax litigation experience at all levels, from VAT Tribunal or Special Commissioners up to the Court of Appeal.
Prof. Memberships: Member of the Law Society's Revenue Law Committee and its VAT and Duties Sub-Committee and of Custom's VAT Land and Property Liaison Group, and the VAT Practitioners Group.
Career: Admitted as a solicitor in 1977. Master's degree in Law. Master of Business Administration. Until May 1993 corporate tax partner in City firm, *Richards Butler*. In July 1993 set up her own practice, concentrating on VAT and corporate tax. The firm's work is around 40% corporate tax, and 60% VAT. The firm expanded in 1997 and moved to new custom-built offices at Tower Bridge.
Personal: French and Japanese speaker. Deputy Social Security Commissioner.

HURLEY, Conor
Linklaters (A member firm of Linklaters & Alliance), London (020) 7456 5662
conor.hurley@linklaters.com
Specialisation: Partner – Corporate Taxation, Head of Investment Funds Tax Practice, Specialist – Mergers and Acquisitions, Domestic and International Corporate Tax Issues, Banking, Capital Markets, Structured Finance and Financial Products, Investment Funds Taxation and Flotations. Recent transactions include: Vodafone/Mannesmann takeover, Vodafone/Air Touch merger, BP/Amoco Merger, BP Amoco/ARCO acquisition, Reckitt & Coleman/Benckiser merger and NatWest Bank defence of hostile bids from Royal Bank of Scotland and Bank of Scotland.

HYDE, Ian R.
Pinsent Curtis, Birmingham (0121) 200 1050
ian.hyde@pinsents.com
Specialisation: Corporate and property taxation including tax efficient structures for joint ventures, demergers, reconstructions and property development. Ian also advises on VAT planning, stamp duty, taxation of intellectual property and tax based investment structures.
Prof. Memberships: VAT Practitioners Group. Consulting Editor to Butterworths Encyclopaedia of Forms and Precedents on VAT and Stamp Duty.
Career: BA Oxford University (1987). *Rowe & Maw* (1988 – 1992). *Pinsent Curtis* (1992 – date).

JACOBS, Russell
Cadwalader, Wickersham & Taft, London
(020) 7456 8500
rjacobs@cwt-uk.com
Specialisation: Has significant expertise in the financial services sector, focusing on the development and implementation of new financial cross-border products. Has wide experience in both the structuring of international consortia and joint ventures in mergers, acquisitions and corporate reconstructions.
Prof. Memberships: The Law Society of England & Wales. European – American Tax Institute.
Career: Trained *Slaughter & May*; qualified 1985; partner, tax department, *Wilde Sapte* 1992-97, partner, *Cadwalader Wickersham & Taft* 1997.
Publications: Written articles for: Butterworths 'Finance Bill Handbook,' 'Tax Journal,' 'Financial Instrument Tax and Accounting Review.'

JENKINS, Edmund
Addleshaw Booth & Co, Manchester
(0161) 934 6000
egj@addleshaw-booth.co.uk
Partner in Commercial Tax Department, Commercial Group.
Specialisation: Practice covers all areas of business and property tax and includes advising upon the tax aspects of mergers and acquisitions, reorganisations and restructurings, exiting strategies for persons selling their business and MBOs and other venture capital transactions. Acts for a mixture of quoted and private companies, individuals and venture capital houses.
Career: Called to the bar 1985. Re-qualified as a Solicitor 1991. Joined the firm as a Partner in 1996.
Personal: Educated at Princethorpe College and Liverpool University. Interests include playing squash, golf and Italian wines. Married with two daughters and a son. Lives in Hale, Cheshire.

JERVIS, David M.
Eversheds, Leeds (0113) 243 0391
davidjervis@eversheds.com
Partner in the Corporate Tax and Employee Share Scheme Unit.
Specialisation: Experience of a broad range of corporate transactions specialising in corporate acquisitions and disposals, all aspects of property taxation and employee share schemes and has set up both Inland Revenue approved schemes and long term incentive plans for both private and listed companies. Advised clients in the education and local authority sectors on stamp duty planning and tax efficient structures for their commercial operations.
Prof. Memberships: Member of the Institute of Taxation.
Career: Paralegal with *Minter Ellis Morris Fletcher* in

Brisbane. Qualified 1992 with *McKenna & Co.* Joined *Eversheds* 1994.
Personal: Born 21st September 1966. Garforth Comprehensive School in Leeds and University of Kent at Canterbury. Lives in Leeds. Interests include scuba diving and most sports.

JOHNSON, Ian L.
Ashurst Morris Crisp, London (020) 7638 1111
Partner in Tax Department.
Specialisation: Involved in advising on the taxation implications of a wide range of corporate transactions advising both overseas and UK clients.
Prof. Memberships: Associate of the Chartered Institute of Taxation.
Career: Graduated in law from Edinburgh University. Co-author of Butterworth's Taxation of Loan Relationships, Financial Instruments and Foreign Exchange.

JONES, Martyn
Maclay Murray & Spens, Glasgow
(0141) 248 5011
mhj@maclaymurrayspens.co.uk
Specialisation: Partner, head of tax department and formerly senior tax lecturer at Glasgow University. Advises on VAT and property, company taxation, capital allowances and capital gains. Co-author of 'Revenue Law in Scotland'. Much respected for his analysis, writings and lectures on the taxation implications of the Scottish Parliament.
Prof. Memberships: Member of the Tax Law Committee of the Law Society of Scotland and its income tax and VAT sub-committees, and CBI Scotland's Economics and Taxation Committee.
Career: Glasgow University (LL.B 74).
Personal: Born 1952.

KELLY, Don C.
Lovells, London (020) 7296 2000
don.kelly@lovells.com
Specialisation: Corporate tax partner specialising in all aspects of business tax including taxation implications of mergers, acquisitions and joint ventures (particularly cross-border), UK equipment leasing and property transactions and North Sea oil tax.
Prof. Memberships: Law Society, City of London Solicitors' Company.
Career: Articled *Lovells*; qualified 1980; partner 1986; specialised in UK corporate tax since qualification.

LEWIS, David E.
Allen & Overy, London (020) 7330 3000
Specialisation: Partner dealing with all aspects of UK international corporate tax work. His experience is primarily in the fields of corporate acquisitions, disposals, mergers, reconstructions and joint ventures and their structuring on a tax efficient basis. He also has wide experience of a range of banking and bond transactions and tax-based structured financing.
Prof. Memberships: Member Law Society Revenue Committee, Chairman of the Stamp Duty Sub-Committee of the Law Society Revenue Law Committee; Member Corporation Tax Sub-Committee of The Law Society Revenue Law Committee.
Career: Articled *Allen & Overy*, qualified 1976, Partner 1982.
Personal: Exeter University 1973. Born 1952.

LING, Timothy A.
Freshfields Bruckhaus Deringer, London
(020) 7936 4000
Partner in Tax Department.
Specialisation: All aspects of corporate tax, and particularly UK and cross-border mergers and acquisitions, reconstructions, joint ventures, demergers, private company acquisitions and disposals, new issues.
Prof. Memberships: Law Society and City of London Law Society.
Career: Qualified in 1973. Became partner in *Freshfields* 1977. Head of Tax Department 1985-91. Member of Law Society Revenue Law Committee 1981-91.
Personal: Born 17th September 1948. Educated The King's School, Canterbury and The Queen's College, Oxford (MA). Leisure interests include sailing and music. Member of Royal Harwich Yacht Club.

LOWE, Kevin
Wragge & Co, Birmingham (0121) 685 2779
kevin_lowe@wragge.com
Specialisation: Pre-sale tax planning for vendors and purchasers; extracting value from owner-managed and family companies and businesses; corporate tax planning generally. Heads *Wragge & Co's* Corporate Tax Transaction Team.
Prof. Memberships: Law Society, Chartered Institute of Taxation (Chairman of West Midlands Branch).
Career: Sheffield University 1986-89; *Eversheds* 1990-97 (Associate 1996); *Wragge & Co.* 1998 (Associate); Partner 1999.
Personal: A 'social' sportsman.

LYNCHEHAN, Martin
Linklaters (A member firm of Linklaters & Alliance), London (020) 7456 5716
martin.lynchehan@linklaters.com
Specialisation: Tax Partner with considerable experience of the taxation issues arising in corporate and corporate finance transactions including public and private company disposals and acquisitions and securities offerings as well as extensive experience of structured finance transactions. Proven track record in building successful transactional working relationships with other tax professionals both from in-house tax departments and external accounting firms.
Career: Trained *Oppenheimers/Richards Butler*; Qualified 1989; joined *Linklaters* 1993; partner 1998; secretary to VAT Land and Property Consultative Committee (1993-95); VAT Practitioners' Group Technical Committee member (1994-97); co-author 'Fiscal Frontiers – tax changes for the international market'.
Personal: Educated at St Ignatius, Enfield; University of Nottingham (1986 BA Hons Law); Queen Mary College, London (LLM); Fellow Chartered Institute of Tax (FTI.) Born 1963.

MAINPRICE, Hugh
Hutchinson Mainprice, London (020) 7730 8705
info@hhmainprice.co.uk
Specialisation: Value Added Tax and Insurance Premium Tax. Has appeared in more VAT tribunal cases for appellants than any one else in the UK commencing with the case of Rentokil v C & E Commrs 1973 VATTR 31 heard on the 4th April 1973 and since then has been involved in over 50 cases in the Higher Courts including the House of Lords.
Prof. Memberships: Law Society, Chartered Institute of Taxation; Ordem dos Advogados, Portugal, Royal Geographical Society.
Career: Called to the Bar, Gray's Inn in 1961, became a Solicitor in 1978. Employed in the Colonial Legal Service from 1950 to 1964. Joined the Solicitors Office *HM Customs & Excise* in 1965 and, as a Senior Legal Assistant participated in the drafting of the original VAT legislation. Resigned from the *Customs* in March 1972 to set up his own legal/consultancy practice on VAT. Was the first person to be awarded a fellowship of the Chartered Institute of Taxation for a thesis on VAT. Author of 'Concise Guide VAT' (1972); 'Mainprice & Willson on VAT' (1973); 'Mainprice on VAT' (Butterworths) (1978); 'Practical VAT Planning' (Tolleys) (1983); 'VAT Disputes' (CCH) (1986). Wrote and edited the original CCH 'British VAT Reporter' (1984). Original editor of the News letters 'VAT Intelligence' (Gee & Co) and 'Practical VAT' (Legal Studies & Services). Author of numerous articles in Accountancy Age, British Tax Review, Taxation and Tax Practitioner. Has made frequent broadcasts on Television and Radio.
Personal: Born 24 April 1928. Educated at Sherborne and London University. Interests include music, photography and travel.

MARTIN, David
Herbert Smith, London (020) 7374 8000
Specialisation: Partner heading the firm's tax department advising on all kinds of business-related tax matters and has played a significant role in many high-profile transactions including company reorganisations, demergers, disposals and acquisitions of companies and businesses; has also been involved in many finance leasing transactions and other financing methods as well as advising on several substantial tax litigation matters.
Career: Qualified 1979; partner *Herbert Smith* 1986.
Personal: Educated at St John's College, Cambridge.

MCGOWAN, Michael T.
Allen & Overy, London (020) 7330 3000
michael.mcgowan@allenovery.com
Specialisation: Experienced in most areas of UK taxation, but, in particular, tax-driven structured finance transactions, including securitisations. He advised on the UK tax aspects of the acquisition and financing of the MoD Married Quarters Estate, on the takeover bids for Northern Electricity and Yorkshire Electricity, on the 1997 Canary Wharf securitisation and 1999 floatation, as well as the 1999 securitisation of the Broadgate Estate. More recently he has acted on the securitisation of the Trafford Centre in Manchester, and the takeover bid for MEPC plc.
Career: Articled and qualified as a solicitor at *Clifford Chance*: 1987-90. Assistant solicitor, *Linklaters & Paines* 1990-95 (including two years in New York 1993-94, part of which was spent on secondment at *Sullivan & Cromwell*). Assistant solicitor *Allen & Overy* 1995-97. Partner *Allen & Overy* 1997.
Personal: Born 1963. Educated Newcastle-under-Lyme High School and Magdalen College, Oxford (MA BCL). Married with two daughters. Interests: reading, listening to music, walking, being a parent, drinking wine and playing golf badly.

MCILWEE, Richard
Clifford Chance, London (020) 7600 1000
richard.mcIlwee@cliffordchance.com
Specialisation: Specialisies in corporation tax and in particular taxation. Considerations of UK and non

UK collective investment schemes and structuring cross border tranactions.
Prof. Memberships: Associate of Institute of Taxation
Career: Qualified 1989, partner since 1990.
Personal: Fluent French spoken

MEARS, Patrick M.
Allen & Overy, London (020) 7330 3000
Specialisation: Advises on the corporate tax aspects of transactions in a wide range of areas. Experience covers, in particular, the giving of UK tax advice in the fields of domestic and cross-border acquisitions, corporate reorganisations, IPO's, transfer pricing and tax investigations, domestic and international banking, asset and tax structured financing, capital markets issues and securities trading and lending. Head of the *Allen & Overy* tax department.
Prof. Memberships: Member of the City of London Law Society's Revenue Law Sub-committee.
Career: Articled *Allen & Overy*; qualified 1982; partner 1988.
Personal: Born 1958. London School of Economics 1979.

MEHTA, Nikhil
Linklaters (A member firm of Linklaters & Alliance), London (020) 7456 5686
nikhil.mehta@linklaters.com
Partner. Tax Department
Specialisation: Specialises in corporate taxation with particular emphasis on international and structured finance, contentious tax, derivatives, mergers and acquisitions, cross-border structures and joint ventures. Head of the India Business Group. Practised tax law in Bombay, India from 1977-80, Legal Assistant in Inland Revenue Solicitor's Office 1981-83. Joined *Linklaters* in 1983, becoming a Partner in 1989.

MORRIS, Gregory
DLA, Birmingham (08700) 111111
greg.morris@dla.com
Specialisation: Main areas of practice are corporate tax, business tax, capital gains tax, employee share based incentive schemes and VAT. Provides tax planning advice to companies and individuals.
Prof. Memberships: Institute of Chartered Accountants.
Career: Qualified 1984. *Arthur Young* (tax department) 1984-86, *TI Group Plc* (tax department) 1986-87, *Wolsely Plc*: Group Financial Accountant 1987-89, *Edge & Ellison* 1989-97, *Dibb Lupton Alsop* 1997 to present.
Personal: Born 1955. Educated St. Philip's Birmingham, Oscott College, Birmingham and, eventually, University of Birmingham. Lives in Sutton Coldfield.

MOSS, Philip G.S.
Osborne Clarke OWA, Bristol (0117) 917 4264
philip.moss@osborneclarke.com
Specialisation: Responsible for the co-ordination of Osborne Clarke's tax practice for company and business and is often involved additionally with related personal tax planning issues for the shareholders/owners/managers of those businesses. Specialises in all areas of direct tax (except for inheritance tax, trusts and estate tax planning) and Value Added Tax. Recent cases and deals include business and company sales; mergers; management buyouts; stock exchange issues; lease financing; financial instruments; VAT schemes (property and other); international tax planning.
Career: Qualified 1983 and joined *Osborne Clarke* in 1990 and was promoted to partner in 1991.

MURPHY, Niall
Blake Lapthorn, Fareham (01489) 579990
nkdmurphy@blakelapthorn.co.uk
Specialisation: Taxation aspects of corporate, reorganisations and reconstructions; mergers and acquisitions, joint ventures and international tax planning; taxation issues in property development and investment, the design and drafting of employee share schemes.
Prof. Memberships: ICAEW, ATII, Solicitor.
Career: Accountant with Binder Hamlyn (1980-1986), Solicitor *Nabarro Nathanson* (1987-1991), Senior Solicitor *Wilde Sapte* (1991-1992); sole practice (1992-1995); Solicitor *Blake Lapthorn* (1996), Partner (1998).

NELSON, Victoria
Burness, Edinburgh (0131) 473 6000
vjn@burness.co.uk
Specialisation: Heads up the tax unit at *Burness* and advises an all areas of corporate tax, VAT and stamp duty. Deals regularly with the tax aspects of corporate and property transactions. Has presented seminars on VAT and property, stamp duty and business taxation.
Prof. Memberships: Law Society of Scotland (including membership of the Tax Law Committee); Law Society of England + Wales; Chartered Institute of Taxation; Secretary if local chapter of VAT Practioners Group.
Career: Trained as solicitor with *Dickson Minto*; assistant at *Simmons + Simmons* in London1994 – 1998; joined *Burness* as an Associate in 1998.
Publications: Won the Victor Durcakz Essay Competition in 2000 for entry entitled 'Proposal for a US Federal VAT System'; co-wrote the chapter on tax clearances in PLC Tax manual.
Personal: LLB (Hons) at Glasgow University; Diploma in legal practise at Edinburgh University. Gained ATII in 1996. Intrests include all types of theatre, especially ballet and other dance.

NIAS, Peter
McDermott, Will & Emery, London (0171) 577 6920
pnias@europe.mwe.com
Specialisation: Main areas of practice are corporate, commercial and international taxation. Work includes cross border transactions (in particular, mergers, acquisitions, reorganisations), transfer pricing and thin capitalisation, finance leasing and structured finance transactions. Author of the PLC Tax Manual – 'Tax Clearances' chapter; frequent speaker at conferences and seminars and regular contributor of articles on EU and international tax issues.
Prof. Memberships: Law Society. Member of Law Society International Tax Sub-committee, the Chartered Institute of Taxation International Tax Sub-committee and ICC UK Tax Committee, International Fiscal Association, International Tax Planning Association, European-American Tax Institute.
Career: Qualified in 1979. Joined *Simmons & Simmons* in 1976, becoming a partner in 1982 and Head of Tax Department in 1992. Joined *McDermott, Will & Emery*, November 1998 as Head of Tax to set up full-service London office.
Personal: Born 24th November 1953. Attended Manchester University 1973-76. LLB. Leisure interests include family and outdoor life, clay and game shooting, music and skiing. Lives in Great Horkesley.

NOBLE, Nicholas R.
Field Fisher Waterhouse, London (020) 7861 4000
Partner and Head of Tax Department.
Specialisation: Practice covers the taxation of UK and international transactions, and in particular companies and company reorganisations, securities and transactions in securities. Co-author of 'Butterworths Company Reorganisations: Tax and Tax Planning' and 'Butterworths International Taxation of Financial Instruments and Transactions' and joint editor of and contributor to 'Butterworths Tax Planning Service'.
Prof. Memberships: ATII.
Career: Qualified in 1979 having joined *Field Fisher Waterhouse* in 1977. Became a partner in 1984.
Personal: Born 1st October 1953. Educated at Winchester College and Durham University. Recreations include fencing, walking and reading.

NORFOLK, Edward Christopher Dominic
Norton Rose, London (020) 7283 6000
Partner in Commercial Tax Department.
Specialisation: Principal area of work involves advising on tax aspects of mergers and acquisitions, corporate structuring (domestic and international), banking and oil and gas. Author of 'Taxation Treatment of Interest and Loan Relationships' (Butterworths, 3rd Ed. 1997). Member of Editorial Committee 'Practical Law for Companies'. Frequent speaker at conferences and seminars.
Prof. Memberships: Law Society (Member, Revenue Law Committee; Chairman, International Tax Sub-Committee); Chartered Institute of Taxation (FTII), International Bar Association, International Fiscal Association, American Bar Association (Chairman, Foreign Lawyers Forum of the Section of Taxation).
Career: Articled at *Longmores* in Hertford, then joined *Gabb & Co.* in Abergavenny. Joined *Norton Rose* in 1975 and became a Partner in 1979.
Personal: Born 8th August 1948. Attended St. John's School, Leatherhead 1962-66, then Southampton University (LL.B) 1966-69. Leisure pursuits include skiing and fishing. Lives in Wimbledon.

NORWOOD, Andrew
Weil, Gotshal & Manges, London (020) 7903 1000
andrew.norwood@weil.com
Specialisation: Financial taxation partner. Has wide experience of all financial taxation matters and has been involved in advising both issuers and investors in respect of numerous capital markets and international equity offerings and in advising on all aspects of the taxation of derivative products. Specialises in advising on various UK and international innovative securitisation transactions involving a wide variety of asset types and has advised on numerous repackaging projects, and on receivables financings.
Career: Qualified in 1986. *Allen & Overy* 1986-1996. *Weil, Gotshal & Manges* 1996, partner 1999.
Personal: Born 1961. Educated at William Ellis School and Gonville & Caius College, Cambridge (BA, MA). Interests include skiing and gardening.

NOWLAN, Howard
Slaughter and May, London (020) 7600 1200
Specialisation: Corporate tax – general, restructurings, demutualisations, transfer pricing.
Career: MA Oxon.

OVERS, John H.
Berwin Leighton, London (020) 7760 1000
Partner in Tax Department.
Specialisation: Principal area of practice covers corporate taxation and VAT.
Prof. Memberships: Law Society.
Career: Qualified in 1978 while at *Berwin Leighton*. Became a Partner in 1981.
Personal: Born 15th August 1953. Attended Kilburn Grammar 1964-69, then St. Peter's College, Oxford 1972-75. Leisure pursuits include music, photography and tennis. Lives in London.

POPPLEWELL, Nigel
Burges Salmon, Bristol (0117) 902 2782
nigel.popplewell@burges-salmon.com
Specialisation: Head of corporate tax unit, specialising in all aspects of corporate, commercial and property taxation (both direct and indirect), including cross border transactions, restructuring, inward investment and financing arrangements. Considerable experience in representing clients before the general and special commissioners and VAT tribunals. Further extensive experience in advising clients in investigations ranging from small scale enquiries to full-blown SCO investigations and subsequent criminal proceedings.
Prof. Memberships: Fellow, Chartered Institute of Taxation, Law Society.
Career: Natural sciences degree at Cambridge, then seven years playing professional cricket for Somerset, teaching biology and chemistry during the winters. In 1985 retrained as a lawyer, joined *Clarke Wilmott & Clarke* in 1987, partner 1993; joined *Burges Salmon* in 1999 as a partner.

PORTER, Sue
Freshfields Bruckhaus Deringer, London (020) 7936 4000
Specialisation: Specialises in corporate taxation and corporate tax planning, particularly in the finance/capital markets area, including structured finance, securitisation, derivatives, banking and bond issues and general corporate tax advice. Acts for banks, building societies, consumer finance, media and corporates. Contributor, Tolley's Tax Planning.
Career: Qualified 1984. Partner 1992 in tax department.

PRESTON, Christopher A.L.
Watson, Farley & Williams, London (020) 7814 8000
cpreston@wfw.com
Partner in International Tax Group.
Specialisation: Main area of practice covers leasing and asset finance/ structured finance, company taxation and international tax planning. Leasing work typically involves large sophisticated transactions. Also specialises in VAT and customs duties, including both contentious and non-contentious matters and appearing before the VAT tribunal.
Prof. Memberships: Law Society (Member of Revenue Law Committee and VAT & Duties Sub-Committee), Institute of Tax, VAT Practitioners Group (Founder Member). Fellow of the Institute of Taxation. Lectures extensively on leasing topics.
Career: Admitted 1975. Joined *Watson, Farley & Williams* as a partner in 1982. Chairman 1999-.
Personal: Born 9th October 1950.

ROSE, Simon
SJ Berwin & Co, London (020) 7533 2222
simon.rose@sjberwin.com
Specialisation: VAT and indirect taxes in property and commercial transactions, private equity and offshore funds, including venture capital trusts and investment trusts; VAT litigation in the UK and the European Community.
Prof. Memberships: Law Society, Institute of Indirect Taxation, VAT Practitioners Group, Law Society Revenue Law Committee, Law Society VAT and Duties Sub Committee.
Career: Articled *Lovell White Durrant* 1990-92; Qualified 1992; Joined *S J Berwin & Co* 1994.
Personal: Born 1968: Exeter University 1986-89 LLB (Law), London University 1996-98 LLM (Taxation).

ROSS, Howard
Clifford Chance, London (020) 7600 1000
howard.ross@cliffordchance.com
Specialisation: Partner specialising in corporate and commercial tax, international corporate tax planning, transfer pricing, oil and gas taxation and tax disputes.
Career: LLB (first class) LSE 1966. Qualified 1971; partner 1981.
Personal: Tennis. Married with three children.

RUPAL, Yash
Linklaters (A member firm of Linklaters & Alliance), London (020) 7456 5646
yash.rupal@linklaters.com
Partner, Tax Department.
Specialisation: Specialises in general corporate tax with particular emphasis on structured finance/product development, derivatives and other financial instruments. Currently on long term client secondment with *Merrill Lynch* (Investment Banking Division) working on cross-border mergers and acquisitions and other corporate finance transactions.

SANDERS, Tim
McDermott, Will & Emery, London (020) 7577 6900
TSanders@europe.com
Specialisation: All corporate and banking related tax matters including cross-border financial structuring. Co-author of Butterworths Tax Indemnities and Warranties. Contributor to Tolleys Company Law.
Prof. Memberships: Law Society; Fellow of the Chartered Institute of Taxation.
Career: Llandovery College (Thomas Phillips Scholar), Thames Valley G.S., London University (LLB). Joined *McDermott, Will & Emery*, (MWE) in May 2000, as a Partner in the Corporate Tax Department. Head of the Corporate Tax Department at *Theodore Goddard* prior to joining *MWE*
Personal: Born 1959. Qualified 1984. Married with 2 children. Interests (pre-children) included rowing, golf, cinema, theatre and gardening. Current (post children) interests include televised sport and watching rented videos. Lives in Epsom.

SANDISON, Francis G.
Freshfields Bruckhaus Deringer, London (020) 7936 4000
Partner in tax department.
Specialisation: Main area of practice is corporate tax and VAT. Cases have included Collard v Mining and Industrial Holdings (H.L. 1989), R v HM Treasury, ex parte Daily Mail and General Trust (ECJ 1988). Worked on SmithKline Beckman's merger with Beecham, Varity's merger with Lucas, Amoco's merger with BP and Compass's merger with Granada. Co-author of 'Whiteman on Income Tax' (3rd edition, 1988). Member, Tax Law Review Committee.
Prof. Memberships: Law Society (Member, Revenue Law Committee,) City of London Law Society (Distinguished Service Award 1997), Addington Society, VAT Practitioners' Group.
Career: Qualified in 1974. Assistant Solicitor at *Freshfields* 1974-80, Partner in *Freshfields'* Tax Department from 1980.
Personal: Born 1949. Educated Charterhouse and Magdalen College Oxford. Leisure interests include fishing, wine and reading. Lives in Surrey.

SCOTT, Tom
Linklaters (A member firm of Linklaters & Alliance), London (020) 7456 5692
tom.scott@linklaters.com
Partner in Tax Department.
Specialisation: Specialist in the corporate taxation aspects of domestic and cross-border mergers, acquisitions and capital restructurings with almost 20 years experience in this area. Attended Magdalen College, Oxford University (MA Hons). Lecturer in Law, Lincoln College, Oxford in 1980. Qualified in 1983 at *Linklaters*, becoming a Partner in 1989. Publications include 'Tolley's Tax Planning' and 'Tolley's Company Acquisitions Handbook'.

SIMPSON, Mark C.
Hammond Suddards Edge, Leeds (0113) 284 7000
Partner and Head of Tax Unit.
Specialisation: Deals with the tax aspects of all types of business transaction, including corporate and asset finance and banking matters, employment tax including share schemes and ESOP's, and VAT with particular reference to property transactions. Also undertakes tax planning for business proprietors (tax mitigation on investment and disposals including venture capital). Regular contributor at conferences and seminars; author of chapter in PLC Tax Manual.
Prof. Memberships: Law Society, VAT Practitioners Group.
Career: Qualified 1985. With *Freshfields* until joining *Hammond Suddards* in 1991.
Personal: Downing College, Cambridge 1978-82 (MA, LL.B). Lives in North Yorkshire.

SINFIELD, Greg J.
Lovells, London (020) 7296 2000
greg.sinfield@lovells.com
Specialisation: VAT and other indirect taxes (customs/excise duty, insurance premium tax) relating to commercial, financial services and property sectors. Investigation and litigation regarding indirect tax including judicial review, condemnation proceedings and appeals to the VAT and Duties Tribunal and the higher courts. Represents clients in VAT Tribunals and has appeared in the High Court and Court of Appeal as a solicitor advocate. Writes articles on VAT matters and lectures in the UK and Europe on the above.
Prof. Memberships: Law Society, VAT Practitioners' Group.
Career: Called to the Bar 1981. Customs & Excise Solicitor's Office 1983-1988. *Durrant Piesse* 1988. Qualified as a Solicitor 1989. Partner *Lovells* 1993. Solicitor advocate 1994.

SMITH, Isla M.
Norton Rose, London (020) 7283 6000
Partner in Taxation Department.
Specialisation: Principal area of practice is the tax aspects of financing transactions, including leasing and asset finance, banking, structured finance and securitisation, project finance and international corporate tax structuring. Other main areas of practice are tax issues relevant to the insurance sector, corporate restructuring and company acquisitions and disposals. Has dealt with a substantial number of tax based aircraft, ship, rolling-stock and project financings and cross border asset finance transactions. Clients include banks, bank leasing companies, airlines, shipping companies, rolling stock companies, multinational groups of companies, financial intermediaries and arrangers. Author of chapters in the ICAEW 'Taxation Service' and Longman's 'Practical Tax Planning'. Speaker at a number of conferences.
Prof. Memberships: Law Society, City of London Law Society, Chartered Institute of Taxation, International Fiscal Association, International Bar Association, Finance and Leasing Association.
Career: Admitted as an Attorney of the Supreme Court of S.Africa in 1974. Qualified as a solicitor in England & Wales in 1980. Became a Partner at *Norton Rose* in 1985.
Personal: Born 17th February 1952. Educated at Westville Girls' High School, Natal, S.A. 1960-68, the University of Pretoria and the University of Natal, Durban 1969-72. Leisure pursuits include keeping up with two children, aerobics, music, tennis and skiing. Lives in Wimbledon.

SOMERSET, Louise
PricewaterhouseCoopers, Birmingham (0121) 265 5000

STAPLETON, Mark
Dechert, London (020) 7583 5353
advice@dechertEU.com
Partner, Tax and Private Client Department
Specialisation: Advises on UK and international direct and indirect taxation issues, in particular VAT. Specialises in property sector work such as commercial property developments, joint ventures and overseas aspects. Also, taxation of corporate mergers and acquisitions works and onshore and offshore investment funds.
Prof. Memberships: Associate of the Institute of Taxation (1989-), National Secretary of the VAT Practitioners Group.
Career: Articled at *Turner Kenneth Brown*. Qualified in 1988. Solicitor at *Turner Kenneth Brown* until 1993. Joined *Titmuss Sainer Webb* (now *Dechert*) 1993. Appointed partner at *Dechert* 1996-. Has written articles for the Tax Journal and has appeared on videos for both Television Education Network and Legal Network television. Conference speaker for Henry Stewart Conferences.
Personal: Born 1964. Educated at King Edward VI Grammar School, Chelmsford. Graduated from Nottingham University (LLB). Resides in London. Interests include tennis, football, cinema and theatre.

STAVELEY, Ben W.
Freshfields Bruckhaus Deringer, London (020) 7936 4000
Specialisation: Specialisations include the tax treatment of capital markets, derivatives and securities transactions and the tax position of banks and other financial institutions.
Career: Education – Magdalene College, Cambridge. Became partner 1987.

TAILBY, Christopher
PricewaterhouseCoopers, Birmingham (0121) 265 5000

TAYLOR, David
Freshfields Bruckhaus Deringer, London (020) 7936 4000
Partner in tax department.
Specialisation: Main area of work is corporate tax including banking, asset and structured finance, and some corporate finance.
Prof. Memberships: Law Society, City of London Solicitors' Company.
Career: Qualified in 1984.
Personal: Born 26th July 1959. Attended Cambridge University 1977-80 and 1981-82. Lives in Hampshire.

THOMPSON, Michael
Freshfields Bruckhaus Deringer, London (020) 7936 4000
Partner in tax department.
Specialisation: Advises on most UK tax aspects of corporate transactions. Has a particular specialisation in oil and gas taxation and a second specialisation in structuring the financing of all types of receivable through securitisation techniques. Acts for a number of oil and gas companies and banks. Chairs the Law Society's sub-committee on oil taxation and was the first lawyer representative for professional firms on the Steering Group of the UK Oil Industry Taxation Committee.
Prof. Memberships: Law Society. UK Oil Industry Taxation Committee.
Career: Became a partner at *Freshfields* in 1985.
Personal: Educated at Bradford Grammar School and Trinity College, Cambridge.

TOON, John
Addleshaw Booth & Co, Leeds (0113) 209 2000
jtt@addleshaw-booth.co.uk
Specialisation: To a significant degree, John's practice focuses on the tax advice for property transactions and capital projects for a mix of retail, developer, institutional and public sector clients. John is also heavily involved in the tax aspects of a broad range of corporate and commercial transactions.
Prof. Memberships: Law Society, Chartered Institute of Taxation, VAT Practitioners Group.
Career: Qualified as a solicitor in 1991; Joined firm in January 1995.
Personal: Married with two children. Enjoys golf, theatre and gardening.

TOSH, A Nial R
Dickson Minto WS, Edinburgh (0131) 225 4455
nial.tosh@dmws.com
Specialisation: Experienced in a wide range of corporate tax matters, with a particular focus on M&A work, MBOs and employee share schemes and benefits.
Prof. Memberships: Law Society of Scotland.

Career: Joined *Dickson Minto WS* in 1994. Based in the Edinburgh and London Offices.
Personal: Educated at Edinburgh University.

TRASK, Michael A.
SJ Berwin & Co, London (020) 7533 2222
Specialisation: Structuring private equity funds including the Schroder Ventures European fund, the Dresdner Kleinwortbenson Italian fund, Amphion European equity fund and Granville fund.
Career: Called to the Bar 1971; *Slaughter & May* 1982-1985; *S J Berwin* 1985 – present (partner 1986).
Publications: '*S J Berwin* Guide to Going Offshore'.
Personal: Dulwich College 1958-1967; Christ Church, Oxford 1967 -1970. Classical music, wine, Rugby Union.

TROUP, Edward
Simmons & Simmons, London (020) 7628 2020
Specialisation: He was head of the corporate tax group at *Simmons & Simmons* until 1995 when he was appointed Special Adviser on tax at the Treasury. He returned to the firm in 1997 since when he has advised on a wide range of corporate and financial transactions, and at the same time has remained active in tax policy, advising and commenting on numerous legislative changes, both in the UK and the EU. Corporate tax, including financing and corporate transactions. Advises on tax policy and strategic tax planning.
Prof. Memberships: Law Society (Chairman, Revenue Law Committee), Chartered Institute of Taxation, Institute for Fiscal Studies, International Fiscal Association, Chairman of British Branch.
Career: MA, MSc (Oxon).
Personal: Cinema, cycling, opera, Anglo-Saxon history, sleep.

WALTON, Miles
Allen & Overy, London (020) 7330 3000
Partner in Corporate Tax Department.
Specialisation: Deals with all aspects of corporate tax but has particular experience of bank taxation and tax-related financing transactions, including domestic and cross-border asset finance, project finance, structured finance, securitisation and capital markets. Co-author of 'Taxation and Banking' (Sweet & Maxwell). Has written various articles for legal journals and is a regular speaker at conferences on tax-based asset finance techniques and other tax subjects.
Prof. Memberships: Law Society, Institute of Taxation (Associate).
Career: Qualified in 1980. Partner *Wilde Sapte* in 1984-97. Partner *Allen & Overy* in 1997.
Personal: Born 1955. Brasenose College, Oxford (MA). Leisure interests include saxophone, wine, scuba diving and clocks.

WARRINER, Neil
Herbert Smith, London (020) 7374 8000
Specialisation: Partner dealing with corporate tax matters generally with particular expertise in indirect taxes (VAT, stamp duty), PFI projects and the tax aspects of transactions in the energy and property industries. Recent major transactions include the redevelopment of the Bull Ring, Birmingham, the opening of the electricity supply market to greater competition the outsourcing PSI project for the Department of National Savings and the recommended offer by Leconport Estates for MEPC.
Prof. Memberships: The Law Society; The City of London Solicitor's Company; UKOITC.
Career: St Peter's College, Oxford 1981-84; qualified 1987; partner *Herbert Smith* 1994.
Personal: Keen golfer.

WATSON, John G.
Ashurst Morris Crisp, London (020) 7638 1111
Partner in Tax Department.
Specialisation: Fund work, enterprise zones, private equity, international tax, general corporate tax, tax litigation and leasing. Legal adviser to the EZPUTA. Leads IFMA Steering Committee on UK aspects of PFPVs. Contributor to Tolleys Tax Planning and other textbooks.
Career: Barrister 1975-1978; *Neville Russell* 1978-1983. Joined *Ashurst Morris Crisp* in 1983. Partner in 1989.
Personal: Born 23 April 1951. Christs College Cambridge (1970-1973). Exhibition and MA in mathematics.

WHITE, Andy
McGrigor Donald, Glasgow (0141) 248 6677
Specialisation: VAT - Specialist in land and property transactions. Project planning and all compliance issues.
Prof. Memberships: Institute of Indirect Taxation.

WHITTY, Oonagh A.
Watson, Farley & Williams, London
(020) 7814 8000
owhitty@wfw.com
Partner in International Tax group.
Specialisation: Specialises in tax aspects of asset/structured finance and international tax.
Career: Qualified 1981; Partner *Watson, Farley & Williams* 1987.
Personal: Born 1954; resides London; attended Imperial College, London University (BSc).

WISTOW, Michael John
Clifford Chance, London (020) 7600 1000
michael.wistow@cliffordchance.com
Specialisation: Tax Partner specialising in finance transactions including securitisation, leasing, and tax-based structured and property financings.
Career: Manchester University; Trained *Clifford Chance*; Partner 1997.

WONG, Etienne
Clifford Chance, London (020) 7956 0206
etienne.wong@cliffordchance.com
Specialisation: Partner specialising in VAT and other indirect taxes (such as stamp duty and IPT), e-commerce, online services and the Internet, financing transactions (including securitisations) and property transactions.
Prof. Memberships: Institute of Indirect Taxation (associate); VAT Practitioners Group (City Chapter).
Career: Uppingham School; University of Bristol. Trained at *Clifford Chance*.
Personal: Writing, film, computer graphics, music.

TELECOMMUNICATIONS

London: 790; The Regions: 792; Profiles: 792

RESEARCH APPROVED BY BMRB: *For this edition,* Chambers' *researchers conducted 6083 interviews – 4408 with law firms, 598 with barristers and 1077 with clients.*

The validity of the research was scrutinised by BMRB International, who audited both the methodology and the results at our offices in July 2000. They interviewed Chambers' *researchers and cross-checked sample interviews. Details of the audit appear on page 7.*

LONDON

TELECOMMUNICATIONS • London	Ptnrs	Assts
❶ Bird & Bird	25	35
Clifford Chance	11	-
❷ Allen & Overy	8	30
❸ Baker & McKenzie	9	9
Denton Wilde Sapte	8	12
Freshfields Bruckhaus Deringer	18	57
Linklaters	8	36
Olswang	10	17
Simmons & Simmons	9	11
❹ Ashurst Morris Crisp	7	20
Field Fisher Waterhouse	3	12
Taylor Joynson Garrett	7	6
❺ Charles Russell	7	8
Rakisons	1	7
Rowe & Maw	12	11

LEADING INDIVIDUALS	
❶ **HIESTER Elizabeth** Clifford Chance	**KERR David** Bird & Bird
LONG Colin Olswang	
❷ **LISTON Stephanie** McDermott, Will & Emery	
MERCER Edward Taylor Joynson Garrett	**SCHWARZ Tim** Clifford Chance
STRIVENS Peter Baker & McKenzie	**WATSON Chris** Allen & Overy
WHEADON Tom Simmons & Simmons	**WRIGHT Claire** Allen & Overy
❸ **BALLARD Tony** Field Fisher Waterhouse	**DICKINSON Peter** Rowe & Maw
DURIE Robyn Linklaters	**EDWARDS John** Taylor Joynson Garrett
FERGUSON Ian Allen & Overy	**HIGHAM Nicholas** Denton Wilde Sapte
MONCREIFFE Mark Charles Russell	**NICHOLSON Kim** Olswang
WILLIAMS Rhys Simmons & Simmons	

Within each band, firms are listed alphabetically. *See* **Profiles** *on page 792*

Bird & Bird *"The firm is very clever in its strategy."* Highly rated for domestic work, the team is acknowledged as the top infrastructure player: *"They are very much the tops – an IBM choice."* **David Kerr**, leader of the group, firm chairman and *"tough negotiator,"* is one of the giants of the field. His profile somewhat overshadows the excellent support he receives from the team, enhanced last year by the addition of an OFTEL lawyer. The scope of industry involvement of the practice is impressive, although the market perceives that the team does not always get the corporate support it needs. Known for being *"BT's lawyers"*, the team has acted for BT on its international ventures (such as the AT&T/BT concert j/v). Advising Telefónica in its 3G mobile spectrum licence auction efforts and acting for Racal Telecommunications in its reorganisation to facilitate its £1 billion sale to Global Crossing. In fibre swaps, the group acted for Worldwide Fibre Networks on its deal with Telia. On commercial matters the team advised Viatel on UK matters on the establishment of their European network, and acted for Eurotunnel on a series of dark fibre leases through the Channel Tunnel. Litigation and arbitration round out a *"well-balanced"* portfolio. **Clients:** British Telecommunications plc; Video Networks Ltd; Viatel Inc.

LEADING IN-HOUSE LAWYERS

Robert BRATBY, Head of Telecommunications, *Colt Telecommunications*

Natasha HOBDAY, European Regulatory Counsel, *First Telecom*

Victoria HULL, Company Secretary, *TeleWest*

Anna MCKIBBIN, Legal Counsel, *WorldCom Ltd*

Phil REYNOLDS, UK Director of Regulatory Affairs, *WorldCom Ltd*

Robin SAPHRA, Public Policy Director, *One2One*

Chris SMEDLEY, Legal Director, *Colt Telecommunications*

Alan WHITFIELD, Group General Counsel, *BT*

Natasha Hobday at First Telecom has effectively combined a civil service background with commercial savvy and is *"very impressive."* **Victoria Hull** is an *"absolute star,"* her determination and pragmatism bringing *"tremendous personal qualities to the Board of TeleWest."* Admired for his active role in lobbying, the commercially focused **Phil Reynolds** is *"imaginative, creative and good at looking at problems from all angles."* Also from the well-respected team at WorldCom is the *"intelligent and impressive"* **Anna McKibbin**. One2One's **Robin Saphra** really stands out as *"very bright"* and *"switched on in the regulatory environment."* At Colt, **Chris Smedley** is an *"outstanding manager"* with the more high-profile **Robert Bratby** being described as *"a bright and effective lawyer."* At BT, **Alan Whitfield** is particularly respected for his leadership abilities.

In-House lawyers profiles: page 1177

Clifford Chance *"Superb in most respects,"* the team is led by the *"intimidatingly sharp"* **Liz Hiester**, who receives admirable support from **Tim Schwarz**, *"technically first-rate and doesn't take cheap points."* Benefiting from the world-wide brand name, and *"always a feature"* on the big cross-border corporate transactions, the firm's London office is a full-service affair, with expertise in regulatory, competition, infrastructure and privatisations. The team acts for a range of international governments, operators and private companies, advising on proposed investments in global satellites, and representing overseas states on the creation of a new legal and regulatory framework for their telecoms sectors. As well as acting on numerous overseas privatisations, notably in Africa and the Middle East, the firm has advised a leading international player on a range of commercial agreements relating to submarine and terrestrial cable networks. **Clients:** financial institutions; operators; multi-nationals.

Allen & Overy *"A very professional outfit – they give the impression of being committed to the area."* A&O's telecoms team is making waves for two reasons. The first is their respected work for the Government on the 3G mobile spectrum licence auction. *"Easy to work with,"* **Claire Wright** earned praise for her 3G work and moves up the rankings this year. Secondly, the recruitment of **Chris Watson** from Simmons & Simmons has gained unanimous approval (*"a really valuable acquisition for them"*). Respected for his regulatory and technical skills, Watson's arrival is evidence of further commitment to the sector. Regulatory work includes advising the Government of Pakistan on creation of a telecoms regulatory framework. **Ian Ferguson** (*"a real professional"*) is known for his privatisation work. However, the firm's major track record this year has been in its corporate and financing deals. This year the team acted for KPN Telecom on its joint venture with BellSouth to acquire the German cellular operator, E-Plus. It also helped Global Crossing acquire Racal Telecom and represented C&W plc on the sale of One2One to Deutsche Telekom. In financing the group advised the eleven-bank syndicate footing the facility for Vodafone AirTouch's offer for Mannesmann, said to be the largest ever. Equipment financing and high yield issues are also part of the firm's repertoire. **Clients:** Cable & Wireless plc; Radio Communications Agency; KPN Telecom.

Baker & McKenzie Well respected worldwide, the team combines its telecoms nous with IT expertise. The market still mentions Stephanie Liston's departure from the telecoms team and the consequent loss of profile. However, **Peter Strivens** leads the group in a *"laid back, pragmatic"* style and elicited praise from peers as *"someone you can work towards a common objective with"*. Known as a regulatory and commercial practice, the team represented AOL Europe in its 'Stop the Clock' campaign to end BT's current practice of charging by the minute for internet access. Another highlight was marshalling its network to act for Pangea on the negotiation, construction and related financing of a US$436 million fibre optic network to connect eight European countries. **Clients:** AOL Europe; Cisco Systems Inc; Pangea.

Denton Wilde Sapte The telecommunications practice has clearly gained from February's combination of Wilde Sapte's telecoms financing expertise with Denton Hall's *"far-flung"* regulatory and privatisation practice. For new client Energis, the team handled four acquisitions (including the $600m acquisition of EnerTel). The team has been involved in numerous international matters, including representing Fibernet plc on its European roll-out, advising the Telecoms Regulatory Authority on creating a new legal and regulatory framework for Egypt, and advising on the sale of MediaOne's interest in TITUS and Singapore CableVision. In privatisation work **Nick Higham** *"pops up quite a bit."* Although the team can handle telecoms dispute work, it is better known for its financing of industry initiatives. Acted for ABN AMRO on financing for Tele 2 Europe SA incorporating guaranteed long-form notes issued by Tele 2, and for Nokia in relation to vendor financing £215m worth of equipment to the Dolphin Group. **Clients:** Nokia; SG; MediaOne.

Freshfields Bruckhaus Deringer A firm famed for its corporate finance and competition work for telecoms players and the media/dotcom world is said to have *"a good grasp of convergence."* Advised Airtouch and Mannesmann in response to Vodafone's advances, and acted for TeleWest Communications on its £10.5 billion merger with Flextech. They were also seen acting for the global co-ordinators of Telefónica's Yellow Pages subsidiary, and raised their profile by acting for on the IPO of Thus. *"You know you're in good hands"* say clients. The team acted for CSFB and Chase as Esat's financial advisers in respect of bids by Telenor and BT, as well as being instructed by London Transport in the PFI outsourcing of the LUL's transmission network and radio system. On a more regulatory basis, the group advised a bidder in the 3G mobile telephony licence auction. The practice represented numerous clients on interconnection proceedings before the Regulatory Authority for Telecommunications and Post, and advised, amongst others, GEC and ICO on telecoms equipment financings. Brussels capability is integral to the practice and well respected, but the team lacks a high-profile individual in London. **Clients:** Modern Times Group; TeleWest Communications plc; MCI WorldCom Inc.

Linklaters *"A successful regulatory practice"* but one that falls in the shadow of the firm's high profile corporate and financing work for the telecoms industry. The firm has a strong relationship with Vodafone, acting in a high profile flurry of telecoms mergers, including with AirTouch Communications and more recently with Mannesmann. It also acted for Vodafone in the 3G mobile telephony licence auction. Kingston Communications was advised on numerous regulatory issues, while Linklaters acted for Robert Fleming and Deutsche Bank on Kingston's well received 1999 IPO. In addition to supply contract and outsourcing work, the firm has also undertaken a variety of telecoms privatisations, including those of Turk Telecom and Kenya Telecom. Acted for the global co-ordinators of the Telecom Eireann IPO, while continuing to advise the newly listed company on regulatory issues. **Robyn Durie** is the firm's best known regulatory telecoms lawyer. A mighty presence in telecoms financing matters, the firm helped Vodafone AirTouch with a syndicated facility for its Mannesmann bid. **Clients:** Vodafone AirTouch plc; Freeserve plc; Bell Canada International Inc.

Olswang Said to be building into a force on the regulatory and commercial side, this telecoms practice is known for its good domestic work and for convergent matters. In **Colin Long**, *"the guru of private telecoms law,"* the practice has a heavyweight practitioner who is *"without doubt the most experienced telecoms lawyer in the market."* Newly-ranked **Kim Nicholson** is a highly-regarded player in a number of convergence spheres. On the regulatory side, the team acted for MCI WorldCom on its 3G mobile telephony licence auction efforts, and working with One2One and TeleWest on regulatory initiatives and developments, such as internet access pricing and unbundling of the local loop. Strong on the e-commerce side, the telecoms team is known for the role it plays advising ISP's such as Demon Internet and Freeserve plc. Acted for Thus plc in its £2.2 billion LSE/Nasdaq float and was involved in the reorganisation of Virata and in advising Esat Telecom in its defence of the Telenor bid. **Clients:** UUNet; Esat Telecom; Thus plc.

Simmons & Simmons *"Focused on getting and keeping clients and giving them what they want."* Although *"unlikely to benefit from Chris Watson's departure,"* the team has recruited four new senior members to bolster the team. Highlights of the year included advising Telespazio (a subsidiary of Telecom Italia) on its investment and involvement in one of the largest satellite deals of late, the global broadband wireless business of Astrolink LLC. Also advised TeleWest on its purchase of an intelligent network platform from Alcatel Telecom, and Global TeleSystems in its acquisition of Esprit Telecom. The London office worked with Hong Kong in representing Century Pacific CyberWorks on its US$38 billion acquisition of C&W HKT. On financing matters, the team acted for First Telecom and Geneva Technology in their venture capital raisings. One2One was represented on its bid in the 3G mobile telephony licence auction and in judicial review applications. Respected for his *"outstanding"* commerciality **Tom Whead-on** is *"a real deal-maker."* Senior assistant **Rhys Williams** is said to be *"concise and knowledgeable."* Advising on numerous regulatory issues in convergent communications, the team acted for AIG on the establishment of a central world marketplace to trade telecoms band widths on the internet. **Clients:** FLAG Atlantic UK Ltd; LDInet; First Telecom plc.

Ashurst Morris Crisp A *"corporate telecoms practice"* which, while it has no high profile individual, is nevertheless at the sharp end of M&A and acquisition financing in the telecoms industry. The team advised Deutsche Telekom on its £8.4 billion acquisition of One2One, and its further £450 million acquisition of the French company, SIRI S.A.S. Also acted for Kingston Communications on its £750 million LSE listing, and represented Virgin in its joint venture with One2One to set up Virgin Mobile. On regulatory issues, the group represented BT in the 3G mobile telephony licence auctions and advising OTE, Chase Capital Partners and BellSouth on regulatory matters. With considerable strength in satellite financing, procurement and insurance, the group has advised Thuraya Satellite Telecommunications on its satellite system refinancing. **Clients:** Deutsche Telekom; Atlantic Telecom Communications plc; DirectNet Telecommunications (UK) Ltd.

Field Fisher Waterhouse A small team seen to have done well over the past year, having *"put effort into bringing people into key areas."* Leading the commercial and regulatory drive is **Tony Ballard**, who is recommended as *"capable of making regulations work in practice."* In mobile telephony, the team was selected by Orange to advise on regulatory matters, including its 3G auction bid and judicial review proceedings. Also advised long-standing client One2One, amongst others, on issues concerning the development of the Wireless Application Protocol (WAP), and COLT on the purchase of new network technology for its inter-city network and on tele-housing issues. **Clients:** Eurobell (Holdings) plc; Kingston Communications (Hull) plc; NextCall UK plc.

Taylor Joynson Garrett *"We know them and respect them,"* say peers. This is a successful, albeit low profile, commercial and regulatory telecoms practice which forms a third of the IP department. **Ted Mercer**'s efforts over the last 12 months to build up the practice have garnered praise and the imminent arrival of the *"experienced"* **John Edwards**, recently of Sidley & Austin, should make for *"an interesting combination."* The team represented Symphony Telecom Ltd in the £10.5 million sale of its plc to 365 Corp. **Clients:** IDT; iaxis Ltd; Convergence Group.

Charles Russell A low profile, broadly based telecoms practice which handles not only M&A and regulatory work but also litigation and property matters. **Mark Moncreiffe**'s reputation reflects the traditional media weighting to the practice, accentuating the convergence aspects of telecoms. Recent deals include acting for Cable & Wireless plc in the acquisition of Network Services, and representing a consortium member in its 3G mobile telephony licence bid. Also acted for Scoot.com in its £200m joint venture with Vivendi and for other industry players in financing matters. One of the partners specialises in dispute resolution within the telecoms industry and has handled contentious work under the Telecoms Act and in relation to restrictive trade practices. **Clients:** NTL Group; Tellit Communications Ltd; Inter Digital Networks Ltd.

Rakisons *"Popular with new entrant types,"* this small, *"pure telecoms"* practice has a reputation for *"meeting the needs of the customer,"* from flexible fee arrangements to timely advice. Although recent departures will *"put a dent"* in the practice, the team has still acted on high-profile matters, such as advising on telecoms issues relating to the completion of the US$600m disposal of WorldPort's European subsidiaries to Energis. The team of multi-jurisdictional lawyers is best known, however, for advising telecoms operators on all aspects of pan-European roll-out, both regulatory and commercial. There is also niche strength advising foreign governments (Tanzania, Gabon) on telecoms regulatory policy. **Clients:** Frontier Corporation; Band-X Ltd; Easynet plc.

Rowe & Maw An evolving practice, with telecoms work occupying some 35% of the corporate group's time. Already known for its communications industry M&A work, over the last year this *"responsive, effective"* telecoms team has picked up a series of heavyweight regulatory and commercial deals. These include advising two members of the SpectrumCo consortium (Nextel Communications and EMI Group) on their bids in the 3G mobile telephony licence auction. Also advised long-standing client CWC on the sale of its mobile services division to Vodafone and the renegotiation of CWC's outsourcing agreement. **Peter Dickinson** is recommended as an *"excellent"* lawyer who will give clients the answers they need to a tight time-frame. The team acted for Swedish PTT Telia AB, advising on its US$110m trans-Atlantic dark fibre and collocation space swap with Worldwide Fibre, the first pan-European, pan-US fibre swap. **Clients:** Cable & Wireless Communications plc; Reuters Group plc; Global TeleSystems (Europe) Ltd.

Other Notable Practitioner **Stephanie Liston** of McDermott Will & Emery retains an excellent reputation for regulatory telecoms expertise. Although most in the market believe that it is too early to rate the firm, it is acknowledged that this should ultimately be a foregone conclusion.

THE REGIONS

TELECOMMUNICATIONS • The Regions	Ptnrs	Assts
❶ **Eversheds** Leeds	2	4

LEADING INDIVIDUALS
❶ **BROWN Neil** Eversheds

Within each band, firms are listed alphabetically. *See **Profiles** on page 792*

Eversheds *"By far"* the leading regional telecoms force, the firm's Leeds office, headed by the respected **Neil Brown**, undertakes a variety of commercial and regulatory work, and is particularly noted for its infrastructure expertise. The team services a clientele from both fixed and mobile telephony, including service providers, manufacturers and major users. Also undertakes a range of overseas projects. Acted for Kingston-upon-Hull Council on the £750 million flotation of Kingston Communications (Hull) plc, and subsequent work establishing the Kingston/Torch virtual mobile network. **Clients:** Telia UK Ltd; Torch Communications Ltd; Spectra Site Communications Ltd.

LEADERS IN TELECOMMUNICATIONS

BALLARD, Tony
Field Fisher Waterhouse, London (020) 7861 4000
jab@ffwlaw.com
Partner
Specialisation: Main area of practice is communications with a recent focus on network platforms at the leading edge of recent developments in this field; including telecommunications, broadcasting and IT; advising both established operators and new entrants on the new technologies. Other areas of practice include television network and service providers in both public and private sectors, including established broadcasters and new entrants in the satellite, cable, multimedia and general major feature film production and distribution, competition, copyright and administrative law. Arbitrator on International Arbitration panel of American Film Marketing Association and trained mediator for alternative dispute resolution. Frequent speaker at conferences.
Prof. Memberships: International Bar Association, Communication Lawyers Association, Royal Television Society and Chairman of UK branch of European Centre for Space Law.
Career: Qualified in 1974, having joined *Allison & Humphreys* in 1971. Became a Partner in 1975. Merged with *Field Fisher Waterhouse* in 1998.
Personal: Born 21st August 1945. MA (Cantab) 1964-68. Fellow of Royal Anthropological Institute. Leisure interests include astrophysics and painting. Lives in London and Suffolk.

BROWN, Neil
Eversheds, Leeds (0113) 243 0391
neilbrown@eversheds.com
Partner. Head of *Eversheds* Telecoms Group.
Specialisation: Heads team of eight full time specialist telecom lawyers. The team has a leading reputation in regulatory advice, industry specific commercial work, network infrastructure development and increasingly in corporate and international projects. Clients include Kingston Communications, Spectrasite, Project Telecom, Torch, Martin Dawes, Telia, Orange, PSI Net, Eskom Telecommunications (South Africa) and DST (Brunei).
Prof. Memberships: International Bar Association (Communications Utilities Committee).
Career: Joined *Breeze & Wyles*, Hertford 1981. Qualified 1983 and left to join *Watson Burton*, Newcastle. Moved to *Eversheds* in 1986. Partner 1988.
Personal: Born 17th January 1957. Attended Richard Hale, Hertford 1969-77, then Warwick University 1977-80. Leisure pursuits include supporting Newcastle United F.C., performing magic; the theatre. Speaks Spanish and French. Lives near Ilkley.

DICKINSON, Peter
Rowe & Maw, London (020) 7248 4282
Partner, corporate department. Head of communications group.
Specialisation: Main area of practice is corporate

and commercial work involving transactions in the telecommunications and related converging industries, including mergers and acquisitions, disposals, joint ventures, network infrastructure projects and outsourcing.
Prof. Memberships: Law Society.
Career: Articled clerk *Clifford Turner* 1986-88; assistant solicitor 1988-93; assistant solicitor *Lovell White Durrant* 1993-94; senior legal adviser Mercury Communications Limited 1994-95; *Rowe & Maw* 1995 to present.
Personal: Born 24th March 1962. Educated at Wells Cathedral School and Southampton University (LLB Hons). Leisure activities include sailing, cycling and skiing. Married to Sarah, they have two children, Ben and Ellen. Lives in London.

DURIE, Robyn
Linklaters (A member firm of Linklaters & Alliance), London (020) 7456 3256
robyn.durie@linklaters.com
Partner, Corporate Department, Information Technology, Communications Group.
Specialisation: Wide experience in broadcasting, telecommunications, both commercial and regulatory, and intellectual property, e-commerce and information technology work over the past 15 years. Qualified 1977 – Australia, 1987 – England & Wales. Became a Partner, 1990. Publications include telecommunications section of Outsourcing Manual. Co-author of 'Broadcasting Law & Practice' and 'Whale on Copyright' (Fourth Edition). Editorial Board of the 'Telecommunications & Computer Law Journal'.

EDWARDS, John
Taylor Joynson Garrett, London (020) 7300 7000
jedwards@tjg.co.uk
Partner in IT/telecommunications group.
Specialisation: Telecommunications, broadcasting and information technology law including corporate and commercial transactions in the sector as well as regulatory advice including UK and EC competition law aspects.
Prof. Memberships: Law Society. City of London Solicitors' Company.
Career: 1970 to 1994 *Clifford Turner/Clifford Chance*. 1994 to 2000 *Sidley & Austin*; managing partner of London office. 2000 to date; partner *Taylor Joynson Garrett.*

FERGUSON, Ian
Allen & Overy, London (020) 7330 3000
Specialisation: Partner specialising in telecommunications, advising on all aspects in the UK and internationally, including regulation, strategic investments, privatisations, mergers and acquisitions, joint ventures and on contracts for the supply of telecommunications systems, equipment and services; he has substantial experience of telecoms privatisations, acting for both governments and investors, having advised on privatisations in Austria, the Czech Republic, Belgium, South Africa, Turkey, Estonia, and Pakistan; he has also been involved in mobile telecommunications investments and ventures in Argentina, Republic of Ireland, Poland, India and Malaysia; he has also advised on the network infrastructure and services projects; heads the telecommunications group at *Allen & Overy's* communications, media and technology group which services clients in the telecommunications, satellite, broadcasting and technology sectors.
Prof. Memberships: IBA.
Career: Articled *Allen & Overy*, qualified 1985, Partner 1992.
Personal: Educated at Southampton University 1982 (LLB).

HIESTER, Elizabeth
Clifford Chance, London (020) 7600 1000
elizabeth.hiester@cliffordchance.com
Specialisation: Partner in corporate practice area with primary responsibility for telecommunications, computer, IT and media industry practice group, focusing on international and domestic projects, commercial contracts, joint ventures, regulatory advice and antitrust and intellectual property law issues pertinent to those sectors.
Prof. Memberships: Member of Law Society of England and Wales; International Bar Association Communication Sub-Committee; America Bar Association; International Telecommunications Committee; Telecommunications Industry Association; Royal Television Society; INTUG; International Institute of Communications.
Career: Manchester (LLB 1st class Hons 1973); Amsterdam (Diplomá in European Integration 1974). Articled *Clifford Chance* 1980-1982; qualified 1982; lecturer in law University of Kent 1974-1980; solicitor *Clifford Chance* 1982-1988; partner since 1988; author of 'Telecommunications' in 'UK and EC Competition Law Encyclopaedia' (Butterworth).
Personal: Music. Born 1952; resides Canterbury.

HIGHAM, Nicholas
Denton Wilde Sapte, London (020) 7242 1212
nach@dentonwildesapte.com
Partner in Media and Technology Group.
Specialisation: Main areas of practice are telecommunications, internet and digital media. Work includes telecoms regulation (19 countries), privatisations (five countries), market entry and acquisitions, network services and interconnection, internet start-ups, content and netcasting, data protection, systems development and outsourcing. Regular lecturer on telecommunications and internet.

KERR, David
Bird & Bird, London (020) 7415 6000
Partner in Company Department.
Specialisation: Main area of practice is corporate and commercial work involving deals in the telecommunications, e-commerce, media and information technology sectors. Has extensive experience of major transactions in these areas, including acquisitions, joint ventures, project finance, privatisation and outsourcing agreements. Frequent speaker at conferences on the global issues relating to telecommunications, e-commerce and information technology.
Prof. Memberships: Communications Lawyers Association, IBA, Law Society.
Career: Qualified in 1985. Joined *Bird & Bird* in 1985, becoming a partner in 1987.
Personal: Born 1960. Attended Jesus College, Cambridge (MA Hons, 1982). Lives in London.

LISTON, Stephanie
McDermott, Will & Emery, London (020) 7577 6900
Partner, Corporate Department, leads the firm's European Communications and Technology Practice.
Specialisation: Communications work includes advising upon, drafting and negotiating communications related contracts and commercial transactions and providing EC and UK regulatory advice in connection with telecommunications and broadcasting activities. Regular guest speaker.
Career: Qualified in England (1994); District of Columbia (1988) and Texas (1985). Associate with *Fulbright & Jaworski*, in London, Houston, Texas, and Washington, D.C. 1984-89. Senior attorney with MCI 1990-92. *Freshfields'* Company Department 1992-95. *Baker & McKenzie*, London 1995-1999. Joined *McDermott, Will & Emery* in 1999.
Personal: Born 15th March 1958. Attended The Colorado College (BA in History/Political Science 1980), University of San Diego Law School 1980-82 and University of Notre Dame London Law Centre 1982-83 (Juris Doctor 1983). Attended Trinity Hall, Cambridge University (LL.M. in English Law – 1st Class – 1984). Lives in Hampstead.

LONG, Colin
Olswang, London (020) 7208 8888
cdl@olswang.com
Partner and Joint Head of Telecommunications Unit.
Specialisation: Main area of practice is the corporate, commercial and regulatory aspects of communications in UK and around the world. Also advises on competition law. Has advised on a number of leading telecom and internet deals and projects, such as; Merger of WorldCom/MCI (Regulatory/Merger Control); EC Studies on Multimedia, Interconnection (Regulatory/Competition Rules); Successful litigation against the Director General of Telecommunications; Study for a Global Mobile Satellite Services Operator (Regulatory); Third Generation Mobile Auction. Author of Global Telecommunications Law & Practice (Sweet & Maxwell Third Edition 2000); author of numerous articles, and a regular speaker.
Prof. Memberships: Law Society, International Bar Association, (former Joint Chairman Communications Law Committee), Society for Computers and Law.
Career: Qualified in 1970 at *Clifford Turner*. Partner *Bird & Bird* 1978-90. Partner *Coudert Brothers* 1990-98. Joined *Olswang* in 1998 as a Partner.
Personal: Born 4th June 1946. Attended Epsom College 1959-64, then Bristol University 1964-67. Leisure interests include swimming, skiing, golf and tennis. Lives in London.

MERCER, Edward
Taylor Joynson Garrett, London (020) 7300 7000
tmercer@tjg.co.uk
Head of IT/telecommunications group.
Specialisation: Main area of work covers the regulatory competition and commercial aspects of running telecommunications systems worldwide. Particular expertise in the regulatory field, interconnect, procurement agreements and in relation to the cable industry. Has worked extensively in the fields of submarine cable and high bandwidth pan-European networks. Does much work in development of 'telehouses' and IP protocol broadband wireless systems. Has particular knowledge of the regulation of conditional access and access control. Acted in a number of private placements and involved in regulatory aspects of flotation work associated with cable companies in the UK. Acts for cable and telecoms trade associations and operators' groups. Contributor to the Law Society Gazette, Annual Media Law Review and trade magazines. Frequent lecturer at seminars on cable and telecommunication issues in the UK and Europe.
Prof. Memberships: Law Society, Association of

Council Secretaries and solicitors.
Career: Qualified 1980. Head of Legal Section Adur District Council 1980-83, then Borough Solicitor, Rossendale Borough Council 1983-85. Secretary to Cable Authority 1985-89. Joined *Allison & Humphreys* in 1989, becoming a partner in 1990. Partner *Taylor Joynson Garrett* 1996.
Personal: Born 1st February 1956. Attended King Edward's Five-Ways School 1967-74, then Trinity College, Cambridge 1974-77. Leisure pursuits include clay pigeon shooting, acting and badminton. Lives in Lewes.

MONCREIFFE, Mark
Charles Russell, London (020) 7203 5113
markm@cr-aw.co.uk
Partner in company/commercial department, Head of media and communications group.
Specialisation: Main area of specialisation is the corporate commercial and regulatory aspects of telecommunications, both in the UK and internationally. He heads *Charles Russell's* Telecommunications Unit which promotes industry focused advice to clients in the telecommunications field. He speaks at conferences and contributes specialist articles to journals.
Prof. Memberships: Law Society.
Career: Qualified in 1978. Joined *Charles Russell* in 1984 and became a partner in 1985.
Personal: Born 23rd March 1953. Attended Uppingham School 1966-70, Queens' College, Cambridge, 1971-4, and Université Libre de Bruxelles 1974-5, (licence en droit européen). Leisure interests include varied outdoor sports

NICHOLSON, Kim
Olswang, London (020) 7208 8731
kan@olswang.com
Partner and Head of IT and Telecommunications Unit.
Specialisation: Practice covers on the corporate side: corporate finance, venture capital, syndicated equity funding, mergers and acquisitions, IPOs, takeovers, all within the online, communications and technology industries; on the commercial side: contracts for exploitation of products, licensing, content deals, distribution exploitation and carriage deals in or related to the online and communications industry for clients ranging from multi-national plcs through to internet start ups, for example Thus plc, NetStore plc, Sportal International, Peoplesound.com, UUNet Technologies Inc and Motorola Inc.
Career: Qualified 1985. Joined *Olswang* as a Partner in 1993.
Personal: Born 30.11.60. Educated at Birmingham University and College of Law, London. Interests include opera, music, hill walking, art and antiques.

SCHWARZ, Tim
Clifford Chance, London (020) 7600 1000
tim.schwarz@cliffordchance.com
Specialisation: Partner focusing on international telecoms, internet posts and IT.
Career: Oxford University (BA Jurisprudence); Oxford University (BCL); Université de Bruxelles (Premiére et deuxiéme licences en droit européen); trainee lawyer *Clifford Chance* 1987-89; seconded to OFTEL's Legal Department 1989-90; associate *Clifford Chance* 1989-95; main telecoms lawyer World Bank legal department 1995-97; partner *Clifford Chance* 1997.

STRIVENS, Peter
Baker & McKenzie, London (020) 7919 1000
Specialisation: Partner and the head of the Telecommunications Practice Group. Work includes advice on licensing and regulatory issues in the UK and other jurisdictions, investments and joint ventures in the telecommunications industry and advising on a wide range of industry issues, including contractual negotiations and disputes. Has extensive experience of cross-border transactions and telecoms privatisations. Gives frequent conference presentations on telecommunications issues and has written the UK and International Chapters of 'Baker & McKenzie – Telecommunications Laws in Europe', Butterworths 1998. Qualified in 1984 with *Baker & McKenzie* and became a Partner in 1990.
Career: Educated at St Johns College, Johannesburg, University of Witwatersrand (1971-75) and Balliol College, Oxford (1979-81).
Personal: Born 15 December 1954. Leisure activities include painting, tennis and looking after a growing family. Lives in London.

WATSON, Chris
Allen & Overy, London (020) 7330 3000
Telecommunications Partner
Specialisation: Telecoms; Competition; European Union and Trade Law. Recent major cases/ matters: Prohibition of BT/ BSkyB joint marketing campaign by Oftel; Prohibition of BT Reconnect Offer by Oftel; Issue of International facilities licences by Oftel – advice to 35 of 46 applicants, principally in relation to community and competition law; Advice to CCA on Fair Trading Condition and drafting submissions to Oftel; Advice to CCA on Reform of Competition Law and drafting submissions to DTI; Advice to Rapture TV Limited on carriage terms and start up arrangements; member of the panel of experts advising the National Audit Office on its review of Oftel's use of its competition regulation powers; Advice to Viatel Inc on all European aspects (including licensing, construction, etc) of its US$ 1 billion debt and equity issue for a project in eight jurisdictions; Advice to ACC Corporation in relation to its European subsidiaries in its merger with Teleport Communications Group, Inc; numerous international projects for the World Bank. Speaking Engagements: Speaker in Londson (CLT Training Course) on the Interconnection 21 i 98; Speaker in London (Presentation for One2One) on Interconnection 18 & 19 ii 98; Speaker in London at (Euroforum Conference) on Regulating Digital Broadcasting in London 20 ii 98. Speaker in Lisbon (Lisbon 2000) – March 1999; speaker in Madrid (University of Madrid) on the experience of telecommunications by cable in the United Kingdom – 15 April 1999; speaker in Madrid (International Conference on the Status and Challenges of information technology practice in Europe and worldwide) – 10/11 June 1999. Chaired Competition Law & Regulation in telecoms, in London 28th February 2000, chaired Global IP Carriers in London, 15th March 2000.
Prof. Memberships: Solicitor, England and Wales. Avocat à la Cour (Member of Paris Bar).
Career: Education: Marlborough College 1970-74, New College Oxford 1976-79; MA (Modern Languages); College of Law, Guildford 1980 (CPE) and 1981 Law Society Finals. Career History: admitted as a solicitor in 1983; partner *Simmons & Simmons* 1988; admitted as an Avocat à la cour Paris 1993; partner, communications, Media and Tecnology Group, *Allen & Overy*, 2000. Languages: French, German, Italian (all spoken), Spanish, Portuguese, Russian (reading only).
Personal: Leisure interests: Chablis growing; fly fishing; bird watching; hockey (Honourable Artillery Company); cricket; music and books.

WHEADON, Tom
Simmons & Simmons, London (020) 7628 2020
Specialisation: Specialisation is in the law, regulation and policy of telecommunications.
Prof. Memberships: Law Society and International Bar Association.
Career: Southampton University, Guildford Law School, admitted as a solicitor in England and Wales in 1989. 1987-1989: Trainee Solicitor, *Ashurst Morris Crisp*. 1989-1995: Solicitor, *Ashurst Morris Crisp*. 1995-1996: Corporate and Regulatory Affairs Solicitor, Videotron Corporation Ltd. 1996 to date: Partner, Communications Practice at *Simmons & Simmons*.
Personal: Married to Kate with three sons, Fred, Henry and George.

WILLIAMS, Rhys
Simmons & Simmons, London (020) 7628 2020
rhys.williams@simmons-simmons.com
Specialisation: Main area of practice is in commercial and regulatory aspects of communications law, in particular in respect of licensing, interconnection, and construction/infrastructure issues. Contributor to "Telecommunications: The EU Law" (Palladian Law Publishing, 1999).
Prof. Memberships: Law Society.
Career: Educated at Emmanuel College, Cambridge; Manchester University and University of North Carolina, Chapel Hill.
Personal: Born 29 October 1965. Married. Interests include playing and listening to blues, American literature; Welsh rugby.

WRIGHT, Claire M.
Allen & Overy, London (020) 7330 3000
Specialisation: Main area of specialisation is telecommunications, advising on telecommunications-related projects both in the UK and internationally including telecommunications and satellite regulation, strategic investments, joint ventures and privatisations. Seconded to the Network Competition Department of Oftel in 1994. Recently has advised the Radiocommunications Agency on the auction of third generation mobiles, KPN and KPN Quest on a number of infrastructure projects and bank consortia on two major satellite financings. Has also advised on telecommunications privatisations in the Czech Republic, South Africa, Belgium, Turkey, Moldova, Lithuania, Jordan, Bulgaria, Estonia and Pakistan. Principal clients include Swisscomm, Cable & Wireless, KPN, KPN Quest and France Telecom.
Prof. Memberships: TMA, City of London Solicitors Company.
Career: Articled *Allen & Overy*, qualified 1988, seconded to Oftel in 1994, Partner 1996.
Personal: Born, 6th December, 1962. Attended University College London. Leisure interests include golf and tennis.

TRANSPORT

OVERVIEW: Carriage and Commercial: This is a sector in transition. Requirements are changing as fewer cases go to court and mediation becomes more important. In addition, while firms used to work for either carriers or owners, they now tend to do both. The amalgamation of last year's three regional sections reflects the national nature of a sector within which firms sometimes operate out of several offices.

Regulatory: Disciplinary and licensing work makes up the bulk of this sector, although advisory work is becoming more common. Most firms serve both goods and passenger operators, with a large proportion of haulage work being awarded by the RHA and FTA. The top dogs are mainly to be found in the north, as 60-70% of all haulage companies operate north of Birmingham. The past year has seen a substantial increase in disciplinary work, largely because of a more aggressive attitude by the Department of Transport.

This year's section has seen a major overhaul. As the larger firms increasingly operate on a nation-wide basis, it was felt appropriate to compile a national section. As a result, several firms have disappeared from the section altogether.

Rail: Buoyancy is returning to the rail sector for the first time since privatisation, as the industry gears up for the re-franchising process. In addition, several bids are being made for the operational contracts for the proposed part-privatisation of London Underground. The in-house teams of the TOCs and other rail bodies tend to be lean, so rail practices attract a substantial amount of work. Commercial contracts, leasing agreements for rolling stock and regulated access agreements all continue to generate work. With the development of more local tram and metro systems, there is also more work for the regional players.

RESEARCH APPROVED BY BMRB: *For this edition,* Chambers' *researchers conducted 6083 interviews – 4408 with law firms, 598 with barristers and 1077 with clients.*

The validity of the research was scrutinised by BMRB International, who audited both the methodology and the results at our offices in July 2000. They interviewed Chambers' *researchers and cross-checked sample interviews. Details of the audit appear on page 7.*

ROAD: CARRIAGE/COMMERCIAL - NATIONAL

ROAD: CARRIAGE/COMMERCIAL • National	Ptnrs	Assts
❶ **Hill Dickinson** London, Manchester, Liverpool	2	1
Holmes Hardingham London	4	5
❷ **Clyde & Co** London, Guildford	1	2
Waltons & Morse London	2	4
❸ **Berrymans Lace Mawer** London	1	2
Davies Lavery Maidstone	1	-
DLA London, Manchester, Liverpool	6	9
John Weston & Co Felixstowe	2	1
❹ **Andrew M. Jackson & Co** Hull	1	1
Davies Arnold Cooper London	1	1
Eversheds Leeds	2	2
Prettys Ipswich	2	2.

LEADING INDIVIDUALS	
❶ **HARDINGHAM Adrian** Holmes Hardingham	**KNIGHT Tim** Holmes Hardingham
MARSHALL Julia Hill Dickinson	**MESSENT Andrew** Holmes Hardingham
❷ **DUNN Chris** Waltons & Morse	**PYSDEN Kay** Davies Lavery
JACKSON Peter Hill Dickinson	
❸ **HILL Martin** DLA	**HOBBS Jane** Holmes Hardingham
SHARP Roland Prettys	**SILK Ken** Davies Arnold Cooper
WESTON John John Weston & Co	
❹ **ARMSTRONG Stuart** Berrymans Lace Mawer	
HENNING Caroline DLA	**MELBOURNE William** Clyde & Co
REYNOLDS Justin Hill Dickinson	**THOMAS Tony** Clyde & Co
WARD Dominic Andrew M. Jackson & Co	

Within each band, firms are listed alphabetically

See ***Profiles*** *on page 799*

Hill Dickinson A strong presence in the field, the firm is consistently mentioned as one of the top players. Noted by the market for its transit work, it is considered to have a leading intermodal practice. Spread over three offices, the team boasts several impressive individuals. **Julia Marshall** has a good reputation, particularly on non-contentious matters and is considered a weighty opponent who *"is difficult to catch out."* **Peter Jackson** *"knows the subject well"* and is *"easy to deal with."* **Justin Reynolds** is steadily *"making progress"* and moves up in this year's tables. However, the loss of Kay Pysden to Davies Lavery is clearly a setback to the firm.

Holmes Hardingham With a host of impressive individuals and an excellent reputation in the field, the firm maintains its position in the top band. Handling most aspects of intermodal disputes, its workload includes domestic road haulage work, carriage-related insurance work, and some warehousing and freight forwarding. Acts for underwriters and is recognised by peers as a top practice with *"an impressive pedigree."* **Adrian Hardingham** is possibly *"the most notable figure in the field."* He is *"a cracking guy"* who *"doesn't mess around."* The academically-inclined **Andrew Messent** is *"experienced and bright." "Personable"* **Tim Knight** and the *"thoughtful"* **Jane Hobbs** complete an impressive group of practitioners.

Clyde & Co Remains a major player although the departure of star man David Hall is perceived to have left a void. Although the firm is no longer considered to be the *"establishment firm,"* its shipping practice continues to attract a substantial amount of work. Elsewhere, the team has a strong international reputation and has dealt with a number of cargo claims involving thefts in transit in Russia and the Baltic States. Better known for its work on the claimant side, the team includes *"substantial player"* **William Melbourne** and **Anthony Thomas**, *"a safe pair of hands."*

Waltons & Morse A solid practice *"with a good following,"* its position has stabilised in the rankings. The firm's core shipping practice overlaps into transit work. Noted for its terms and conditions work within carriage of goods by road, the team has been involved in a number of disputes, representing both subrogated cargo insurers and hauliers' liability insurers. *"Business-like"* **Chris Dunn** is *"particularly accomplished"* and is commended for his commercial nous.

Berrymans Lace Mawer A claimant practice which approaches the field from a marine perspective and is especially noted for recovery work for goods in transit on behalf of insurance companies. The practice is driven by **Stuart Armstrong**, who is *"sound"* but is felt to *"lack significant back-up."* An eclectic client base includes recovery agents, cargo and hauliers' liability underwriters as well as road hauliers and a variety of trading houses.

Davies Lavery A firm who are known for their contacts with, and referrals from, leading London firms. Recognised by the market as a serious presence with a sizeable clientele, the newly recruited **Kay Pysden** ("certainly not a pushover") provides the firm with a recognised big hitter.

DLA Making progress, particularly in the North-West, the firm is considered to *"know what it's about."* Acts primarily on behalf of insurers, specialising in coverage and arranges logistical agreements between owners and hauliers. *"Idiosyncratic"* **Martin Hill** is noted both for his in-depth knowledge of the sector and his *"different and refreshing approach."* **Caroline Henning** is also recommended.

John Weston and Co A new entry this year, the firm *"features more and more these days"* and is widely perceived to be a growing force. The practice handles work on behalf of both cargo underwriters and carriers by road and sea. **John Weston** himself is described as *"a good operator"* who inspires loyalty in his clients.

Andrew M. Jackson & Co A niche practice, most of the firm's work in the sector is allied to its shipping and freight work. Acts for domestic and foreign forwarders, trailer operators and hauliers. Also known for its lien work. The firm's leading light is the *"pleasant and able"* **Dominic Ward.**

Davies Arnold Cooper Known as a small but solid practice, but is generally considered to be *"doing less high-profile stuff."* Acts for insurers of hauliers, freight forwarders and consolidators, and has attracted more coverage work over the past year. **Ken Silk** is *"pragmatic, commercial and easy to get on with,"* but is considered to be playing a lone hand.

Eversheds Not boasting a specialist practice, the firm has nevertheless attracted some notable clients. Concentrating on contracting and road logistics, the firm advises major retail names such as Marks and Spencers and Reebok on distribution.

Prettys Deals with debt collections, freight disputes and corporate work for haulage firms. The firm is also known for its logistics and liens work. Acts for four out of the five hauliers in and around Felixstowe. The firm enjoys a consistently high profile, partly prompted by *"maverick"* **Roland Sharp.** He is considered *"efficient and effective,"* and is an established name in the sector.

ROAD: REGULATORY – NATIONAL

ROAD: REGULATORY • National	Ptnrs	Assts
❶ **Ford & Warren** Leeds	3	2
❷ **Backhouse Jones** Blackburn	3	1
❸ **Wake Dyne Lawton** Chester	1	1
Wedlake Saint London	2	1
❹ **Barker Gotelee** Ipswich	1	2
Carless Davies & Co Halesowen	1	1
Cartwrights Bristol	1	2
Jeffrey Aitken Solicitors Glasgow	1	-
Jeremy Fear & Co Enfield	1	1
Rothera Dowson Nottingham	3	-
❺ **Arthur Cox** Belfast	1	-
Bannister Preston Sale	1	-
Michael S. Allen Aberdeen	1	-
Over Taylor Biggs Exeter	2	1

LEADING INDIVIDUALS	
✪ **KIRKBRIGHT Stephen** Ford & Warren	
❶ **BACKHOUSE James** Backhouse Jones	**LAWTON Jonathan** Wake Dyne Lawton
ROTHERA Ian Rothera Dowson	
❷ **GOTELEE Michael** Barker Gotelee	**HODGSON Gary** Ford & Warren
WHITEFORD Michael Jeffrey Aitken Solicitors	
❸ **CARLESS Michael** Carless Davies & Co	**FEAR Jeremy** Jeremy Fear & Co
JONES Geoffrey Cartwrights	**KNOTT Alice** Wedlake Saint
OVER Christopher Over Taylor Biggs	**PRIOR Barry** Wedlake Saint
❹ **HEATON John Graham** Bannister Preston	**WOOLFALL Andrew** Wake Dyne Lawton
UP AND COMING	
ALLEN Michael Michael S. Allen	**WYLIE Amanda** Arthur Cox

Within each band, firms are listed alphabetically

*See **Profiles** on page 799*

Ford & Warren Consistently rated the number one firm, *"they have the size and they have the talent."* The team covers all areas of road regulatory law, working for national haulage and passenger transport concerns. Handles transport employment work, advises on flagging out, and is noted for the quality of its pre-litigation advice. Perceived to be *"publicity-conscious,"* the team is composed of *"the best HGV lawyers in the business."* **Stephen Kirkbright** is *"an absolute star."* He has *"immense knowledge"* of the field, is good with people and is commended for his advocacy. Although sometimes overshadowed, **Gary Hodgson** is also highly respected by the market, which finds him *"impressive in his advocacy."*

Backhouse Jones Rated *"keen and first-rate,"* the firm has established itself as a national force. The team has an impressive client base and has grown substantially. Works for national passenger transport groups, and is known for its transport enquiry work. Also does some defendant work, mostly in PI. *"Enthusiastic"* **James Backhouse** is establishing himself as a major player. He *"lives, eats and sleeps transport law."*

Wake Dyne Lawton A major player in the field, the firm is best known for its work in magistrates courts, public enquiries and industrial tribunals. It has an HGV and PSV clientele ranging from owner drivers to international hauliers. **Jonathan Lawton** is noted as *"humorous, witty, bombastic and great fun."* He *"takes appeals where angels fear to tread,"* and although his aggressive style is not to everyone's taste, *"clients love him for it."* He is enthusiastically supported by **Andrew Woolfall**, who *"is making a name for himself."*

Wedlake Saint The premier outfit in the south of England, the firm is best known for its passenger transport work. The team is known for dealing with operators' licensing and prosecutions, as well as its commercial and PI work. Seen by some as *"academic lawyers,"* the team has a national reputation. The firm's two transport partners are considered to form *"a fine team, who have a good rapport with clients."* **Barry Prior** *"has tons of experience"* in the bus and coach industry, while **Alice Knott** is noted for being *"good on details."*

Barker Gotelee Handles the whole regulatory gamut, from magistrates court prosecutions and public enquiries to employment and health and safety disputes. The firm's clientele includes major national hauliers, and a large proportion of its workload stems from Felixstowe. *"Calm"* **Michael Gotelee** is regarded as *"highly trustworthy," "a really nice chap"* and is held in high regard by his clients. Market opinion has also noted some emerging talent among the firm's assistants.

Carless Davies & Co Working for road haulage contractors, the firm handles Vehicle Inspectorate prosecutions. With a high media profile and long-standing reputation, it is a major regional player. **Michael Carless** *"has a nice way about him"* and *"knows his onions."*

Cartwrights Broad-ranging practice which handles public enquiries, criminal procedures and traffic regulation orders, although it is not seen as frequently as some of its national competitors. Its haulage clientele is mainly based in the South-West, although its bus clients are generally located outside the region. **Geoffrey Jones** is considered to be *"a sound and knowledgeable practitioner."*

Jeffrey Aitken Solicitors The leading road transport practice in Scotland, the firm defends cases for the major haulage companies, and appears at the operator licence public enquiries for haulage and freight companies. It is on the FTA panel and does some work for the RHA. **Michael Whiteford** is *"top dog in Scotland."* He is *"knowledgeable and effective"* and widely praised by clients and peers alike.

Jeremy Fear & Co As an HGV niche firm, the practice is widely famed for its work on the London Lorry Ban. It also handles more general regulation work, including overloading, tachograph and employment issues. Clients include a major legal expenses insurer and large hauliers. **Jeremy Fear** is a noted expert in road regulation; he *"gets massive amounts of work"* in his areas of expertise.

Rothera Dowson The firm specialises in haulage work, although it also handles a little bus and coach work. A strong regional player, it works on operator licensing public enquiries and has expertise in transport knowledge. **Ian Rothera** (*"extremely sound on the law,"*) is said to *"put himself out for his clients"* and is considered to be one of the national leaders for road regulatory matters.

Arthur Cox Considered to be the road regulation outfit in Northern Ireland, it acts for the defence in magistrates courts and deals with the construction in use regulations, including overloading, maintenance, tachographs and vehicle excise. Represents UK and cross-border insurers and hauliers. **Amanda Wylie** is *"relatively inexperienced"* but is *"getting better as the months go by"* and is steadily making a name for herself.

Bannister Preston A new entry for this year, **John Heaton**'s growing profile has brought the firm to the market's attention. He takes on both prosecution and defence roles, representing the Vehicle Inspectorate, and dealing with drivers' hours, tachograph and construction work. Acts on appeals to the Traffic Commissioners.

Michael S. Allen Working mainly in the north and east of Scotland, **Michael Allen** specialises in road haulage. Since setting up his own firm three years ago, he has steadily built up his clientele and is gaining the respect of his peers. His clients include several international and long distance hauliers, and his remit includes drivers' hours and public enquiries.

Over Taylor Biggs Specialising in haulage work, the firm handles overloading and operator licence work. It has been commended for its tachograph prosecutions and PI work. The firm has a solid reputation with its clients, who range from owner drivers up to large haulage outfits. **Chris Over** is *"a very good advocate,"* and is noted as *"an extrovert who is good on the minutiae."*

RAIL – NATIONAL

RAIL • National	Ptnrs	Assts
❶ Freshfields Bruckhaus Deringer London	15	40
❷ Linklaters London	15	17
Simmons & Simmons London	10	30
❸ Clifford Chance London	3	4
Denton Wilde Sapte London	7	15
DLA London	8	16
Eversheds London , Birmingham, Leeds	9	19
Hollingworth Bissell London	2	-
❹ Field Fisher Waterhouse London	4	5
Herbert Smith London	9	10
Norton Rose London	8	10
Rowe & Maw London	2	2
Slaughter and May London	*	*
❺ Burges Salmon Bristol	6	14
Edwards Geldard Derby	2	3
Osborne Clarke Bristol	3	7
❻ Allen & Overy London	8	15
Dickinson Dees Newcastle upon Tyne	4	4
Nabarro Nathanson London	2	2
Pinsent Curtis London	5	7
Wragge & Co Birmingham	3	6

Within each band, firms are listed alphabetically.
** See editorial entries for explanations of team sizes.*

*See **Profiles** on page 799*

Freshfields Bruckhaus Deringer Possessing *"a wide rail portfolio,"* the firm is generally perceived to be the leading rail practice because of the range and quality of its client base. Peers recommend them for their work with freight companies, particularly for EWS on freight issues. Corporate specialist **Richard Phillips** maintains his position at the top of our rankings, and is generally recognised as outstanding on major deals. **Bob Charlton**'s move to the firm has added to an already impressive team. He is highly respected by colleagues, exhibits *"amazing energy"* and is a noted procurement lawyer. Handled the securitisation for the purchase of Angel Trains by Virgin and worked for the DETR, London Underground and the SSRA on the proposed restructuring of the tube system. **Clients:** English Welsh and Scottish Railways.

Linklaters The firm moves up a band after being appointed principal legal advisors to the SSRA for the renegotiation of the passenger rail franchises. This may restrict its room for manoeuvre on other deals, but is undoubtedly a major coup. In addition, it is noted for its work on leasing agreements for OPRAF. *"Scholarly"* **John Ellard** is *"highly respected"* for his *"strategic mind."* **Simon Gwynne** received several mentions as *"a capable, up and coming lawyer."* The team has expertise in advising on the restructuring of a number of European rail networks, and acted for one of the consortia bidding for the task of constructing a new high speed rail line in the Low Countries. **Clients:** Stagecoach; SSRA.

Simmons & Simmons The firm maintains its position near the top of the tree largely thanks to the big-ticket work it attracts from Railtrack. Although this relationship clearly brings a number of conflicts in its wake, the accompanying work is high-quality and substantial. During the past year it has advised on the upgrade of the West Coast main line, the London Underground PPPs and the refranchising of the national passenger services. The loss of Gareth Davies to KLegal was a blow which currently leaves the practice without a recognised big hitter. **Clients:** Railtrack.

Clifford Chance As sole advisors to the DETR on the proposed transport bill, the firm is obviously a respected rail practice. It is also acting for Railtrack on the redevelopment of London stations, and is noted for its work on rolling stock negotiations. The firm has a wide clientele, ranging from financiers and export credit agencies to major industry bodies. However, the departure of Bob Charlton to Freshfields constitutes a grave set-back. No major figure has emerged to fill the breach, although the quality of work is still considered sufficient for the practice to maintain high rank. **Clients:** ROSCOs; TOCs; TOC manufacturers.

LEADING INDIVIDUALS	
❶ **CHARLTON Bob** Freshfields Bruckhaus Deringer	
ELLARD John Linklaters	
McGEE-OSBORNE Christopher Denton Wilde Sapte	
PHILLIPS Richard Freshfields Bruckhaus Deringer	
❷ **THOMPSELL Nicholas** Field Fisher Waterhouse	
❸ **BONAR Mary** Nabarro Nathanson	**COPPEN Simon** Burges Salmon
DAVIES Gareth KLegal	**HARRIS Anne** Eversheds
HOLLINGWORTH Sara Hollingworth Bissell	**HORTON Naomi** Rowe & Maw
PHILLIPS Simon Slaughter and May	**WHITEHOUSE Michael** Wragge & Co
UP AND COMING	
GWYNNE Simon Linklaters	

See *Profiles* on page 799

Denton Wilde Sapte Historically a major rail practice, the team is acknowledged to be *"good on regulatory and project finance"* and *"still a force to be reckoned with."* Acts for all twenty-five train operators to varying degrees, and is negotiating with the regulator and the SSRA on behalf of the Train Operating Companies. Currently working on track access and upgrade of the West Coast line. **Chris McGee-Osborne** is *"a top operations lawyer"* and *"is endeavouring to take up the reins from Tom Winsor."* **Clients:** Virgin Trains; The Association of Train Operating Companies; GB Railways.

DLA Known for its work with Connex, the firm handles franchising in London and the North. It is advising Connex on the bidding and negotiation of franchise extensions with the Strategic Rail Authority. The practice is acting for South Yorkshire PTE on Sheffield Supertram sale, leasing and disputes with Railtrack, and is also noted for its engineering infrastructure work. **Clients:** Connex South East; Stagecoach; MTL.

Eversheds The firm has rail clients at several of its offices, but it is Birmingham, London and Leeds which win the majority of market approval. Eversheds' Birmingham office advises the SSRA on franchise management for the renegotiation of passenger rail franchises. The London group tend to be more project based, while Leeds does mainly freight work, including some for EWS. The firm is also noted for its leasing and commercial contract work. **Anne Harris** (*"commercial, practical and efficient"*) is the linchpin of the firm's rail practice, and has established herself as a major player on regulatory issues. **Clients:** SSRA; CATALIS Rail; Port of Tyne.

Hollingworth Bissell Niche firm set up by two ex-BR lawyers, who *"have the knowledge that others don't have"* and are rapidly making a name for themselves. The team is particularly esteemed for its *"understanding of the industry."* Respected by clients for its high-volume station and property work, the firm also does some regulatory work. **Sara Hollingworth** *"is moving mountains"* in putting the practice on the map. She advised Gibb Rail in connection with the privatisation of the Estonian railway system. **Clients:** Chiltern Railways; Virgin Trains.

Field Fisher Waterhouse Known mostly for doing *"an awful lot"* of corporate work for London Underground, the firm has its fingers in a number of pies. The team handles day to day affairs for South West Trains and has advised Northern Spirit on the £120 million leasing transactions regarding the replacement of its fleet of trains. **Nicholas Thompsell** is *"worth his salt"* and *"was there at an early stage in the birth of the industry."* He is *"good at sums and accountants love him."* **Clients:** South West Trains; Northern Spirit.

Herbert Smith Known for team rather than individual strength, the firm is noted for its work for Stagecoach. Handles work from M&A and project financing, to construction and property. Considered to have gained rail expertise from their involvement in the Channel Tunnel Rail Link. Advised London & Continental Railways on the redevelopment of London St Pancras, and the issue of two tranches of bonds. Also act for Zuid Rail Group in its attempt to be appointed Infrastructure Provider of the new High Speed Rail Link in the Netherlands. **Clients:** Eurotunnel; Zuid Rail Group; London & Continental.

Norton Rose The firm is known almost exclusively for its work with ROSCOs. Having *"cornered this area of the market,"* it is acting for all three ROSCOs on the introduction of the PPWS. Known for its strength in asset financing, the team is currently representing HSBC Rail and Angel Trains on leasing of new rolling stock. **Clients:** HSBC Rail; Angel Trains.

Rowe & Maw Known almost exclusively for its work for Virgin. Acted as the main advisors for Virgin Rail on the renewal of their fleet for the West Coast Line and completed the sale of the Virgin depot business. Also has experience in light rail and in rail internet sales. **Naomi Horton** is *"strong on procurement"* and *"gained a lot of knowledge on the Virgin deal."* Peers view her as *"a delight to deal with."* **Clients:** Virgin Rail.

Slaughter and May Known for its advisory work for the Rail Regulator, particularly on access matters, as well as its M&A work in the rail sector, the firm draws on partners and assistants as required. Also acted for the Royal Bank of Scotland on Virgin's purchase of tilting trains. Represented the London Infrastructure Company on its PPP bid to run a number of London Underground lines. **Simon Phillips** *"knows regulatory work"* and is viewed as a knowledgeable player. **Clients:** Rail Regulator; Rail Industry Dispute Committee.

Burges Salmon One of the major regional practices, the firm works for TOCs and specialist rail insurers. Acts for four operators most of the time and for five others on an ad hoc basis. Noted for its train access and regulatory work, as well as project finance and procurement. Acted for ATOC in relation to the Ladbroke Grove disaster and the Cullen Enquiry. **Simon Coppen** is known for his work for FirstGroup and his peers *"have a lot of time for him."* **Clients:** TOCs; rail insurers.

Edwards Geldard A new entry this year, the firm's historic links with National Express have brought some rail work. Is felt to have genuine rail expertise and generally attracts high volume work. Rated by peers as a regional force. **Clients:** National Express.

Osborne Clarke OWA A strong regional practice best known for its work for Prism and its associated franchises. Represented LTS Rail on a major procurement of rolling stock while the construction department is also working with LTS on the refurbishment of stations. Acted for a freight company on contracts for the transport of cars by rail. **Clients:** LTS Rail; Prism.

Allen & Overy Specialising in rail financing, the firm does capital markets, securitization, commercial and regulatory work. Advised Virgin on leasing agreements in one of the biggest transactions of the past year. **Clients:** Virgin.

Dickinson Dees A new entry, the firm has a rising profile thanks to several notable deals over the past year. Acted for the Tyne and Wear PTE on the £98 million public private partnership deal to extend the Tyneside Metro into Sunderland. Its historic link with Go-Ahead have also brought work on the Go-Via Thameslink franchise. Is acting for Thames Trains on the Paddington rail crash. The practice also handles a range of documentation and access agreements. **Clients:** Thames Trains; Go-Ahead.

Nabarro Nathanson **Mary Bonar** is a noted figure in the field, and heads a firm which handles passenger operator, re-franchising and access work. She is viewed as *"quite a character,"* and has been considered the practice's greatest asset. **Clients:** Major passenger operators.

Pinsent Curtis Viewed by the market as more of a regional player than a competitor for London work. Known for its regulatory and franchise work for Connex, the firm also works for Arriva. The Leeds office does commercial and trade mark work, Birmingham does property, while London handles corporate and commercial. Also handles commercial contract, litigation and property work. **Clients:** Connex; Arriva.

Wragge & Co A strong local player, the firm advised Rover Group on the procurement of a £40 million rail link and acts for Travel West Midland on the construction of the Midlands Metro. Also carries out health and safety work. Known for its work for Cummins Engines on the purchase of Bombardier trains by Virgin. **Michael Whitehouse** is *"very keen"* and is known for his highly detailed knowledge. **Clients:** Daimler-Chrysler Rail Systems; Travel West Midland; Cummins.

Other Notable Practitioners The experienced **Gareth Davies'** move to KLegal from Simmons & Simmons raised a number of eyebrows. He provides a weighty focus to the firm's caseload in the industry.

LEADERS IN TRANSPORT

ALLEN, Michael
Michael S. Allen, Aberdeen (01224) 480 890

ARMSTRONG, Stuart
Berrymans Lace Mawer, London (020) 7865 8543
stuart.armstrong@blm-law.com
Specialisation: Main areas of practice are cargo and goods in transit claims (charterparties, bills of lading, CMR and domestic road haulage, Warsaw Convention) and related cargo and G.I.T. liability insurance disputes. Acts for cargo underwriters, recovery agents, hauliers' liability underwriters, freight forwarders and hauliers.
Prof. Memberships: London Maritime Arbitrators' Association (supporting member). Association of Average Adjusters (annual subscriber).
Career: Articled with *Ingledew Brown*, qualified in 1983 and became a partner in 1985. Joined *Berrymans* in December 1996.
Personal: Born 1958. Educated at The King's School, Canterbury 1971-76 and Southampton University 1976-79 (LLB Hons). Leisure interests include golf and chess.

BACKHOUSE, James
Backhouse Jones, Blackburn (01254) 677311
Specialisation: Commercial transport law including: Defending prosecutions brought by the Vehicle Inspectorate, Police and Trading Standards, Environment Agency, Health & Safety Executive; Operators and Vocational Licensing including Inquiries, Environmental, Maintenance and Financial; Employment all issues; Health & Safety all issues. Recent cases include the successful defence in 'Nuttall v. Wing' in the House of Lords dealing with tachograph issues and 'R v. Hennessey' (Court of Appeal) an appeal against conviction of causing death by dangerous driving. Successfully dealt with eight cases of causing death by dangerous driving in the past four years, arising out of the passenger and goods transport industry. Has lectured on Article 177 references to the European Courts of Justice and involvement in two such references to the ECJ. Experience in rebated diesel cases, including Vat & Duties Tribunal. Currently involved in defending alleged illegal transportation of arms to Nigeria prosecution.

BONAR, Mary
Nabarro Nathanson, London (020) 7524 6000
m.bonar@nabarro.com
Partner in Energy and Transport Group and Head of Rail Sector Group.
Specialisation: Main areas of practice are rail law, project finance and asset finance. Experience commercialisation of rail industry, financing of rail infrastructure (including using Public Private Partnerships) and rolling stock; in domestic market. Specialises in track access, regulation and franchising. Clients include public sector, major banks, lessors, ECAs, governments, franchise groups and other corporates. Lectures and writes on rail industry and project finance.
Prof. Memberships: Liveryman, Worshipful Company of Carmen and City of London Solicitors Company; Women Solicitors Association. Member of Chartered Institute of Transport.
Career: LLB. London. Admitted in 1971. Partner *Wilde Sapte* Banking Department 1989 to 1999.

CARLESS, Michael
Carless Davies & Co, Halesowen (0121) 550 2181

CHARLTON, Bob
Freshfields Bruckhaus Deringer, London (020) 7936 4000
See under Asset Finance & Leasing, p.96

COPPEN, Simon
Burges Salmon, Bristol (0117) 939 2291
simon.coppen@burges-salmon.com
Specialisation: Has had extensive involvement in rail issues since 1994, with an emphasis on track access matters for both passenger and freight, track access performance issues and passenger franchise agreements. Work has included new train procurement, joint venture train services and both arrangements for, and claims for compensation in connection with, capital projects.
Prof. Memberships: Law Society.
Career: 1985-89, *Allen & Overy*; 1989 to date, *Burges Salmon*; 1993, Partner. Head of commercial unit.
Personal: Brasenose College, Oxford 1981-84.

DAVIES, Gareth
KLegal, London (020) 7694 2500
Specialisation: Specialises in commercial law in particular relating to railways. Played a leading role in advising on the legal steps to be taken to restructure British Rail and in creating the framework to handle safety, environment, competition, liability and operational matters as well as facilitating future renewal of and investment in Britain's rail network. Led and managed the team of lawyers acting for Railtrack Plc in creating the matrix of contracts to give effect to this new regime. Advised on the legal arrangements for the financing and implementation of a number of major new rail projects including ThamesLink 2000, West Coast Mainline and the Channel Tunnel Rail Link and has been closely involved with drafting and negotiating the contracts for these projects. Advises on crossborder rail transactions for example relating to "Freight Super Highways" in the EU. Also handles PFI and other projects work. Clients include Railtrack Plc. Contributor (re sale of goods and joint ventures) to Butterworth's 'Encyclopaedia of Forms and Precedents'.
Prof. Memberships: Law Society, Food Law Group (Committee Member).
Career: Qualified in December 1979 (England & Wales) and May 1981 (Hong Kong). Partner at *Simmons & Simmmons* from1989 until earlier this year.
Personal: Born 5th July 1955. Educated at the University of Sheffield 1973-76 (LL.B Hons) and the City of London Polytechnic 1978-81 (MA, Business Law). Leisure interests include sailing, cookery, board games and history. Lives in Burnham-on-Crouch.

DUNN, Chris
Waltons & Morse, London (020) 7623 4255

ELLARD, John
Linklaters (A member firm of Linklaters & Alliance), London (020) 7456 3324
john.ellard@linklaters.com
Specialisation: Partner in the corporate department with extensive experience of tax and corporate finance, particularly in the field of privatisations and international equity offers.

FEAR, Jeremy
Jeremy Fear & Co, Enfield (020) 8367 4466

GOTELEE, Michael
Barker Gotelee, Ipswich (01473) 611211
Specialisation: Road haulage and public service vehicle licensing, vehicle operation, prosecutions, disciplinary and environmental public inquiries, accidents, drivers' hours, CMR and employment. The firm covers other commercial aspects for businesses, tax, land, planning, pollution and waste.
Career: Qualified 1963. Since 1966 has acted for a wide range of operators and RHA and FTA members.
Personal: Born 1938. Interests are old vehicles, sailing and walking.

GWYNNE, Simon
Linklaters (A member firm of Linklaters & Alliance), London (020) 7456 5994
simon.gwynne@linklaters.com
Specialisation: Associate in the asset finance group, with extensive experience in a broad range of structured financings involving aircraft, cable and telecommunications equipment, rolling stock and other big ticket assets.
Career: 1993-1995, articles, *Linklaters.* 1995 to date, solicitor, *Linklaters.*

HARDINGHAM, Adrian
Holmes Hardingham, London (020) 7283 0222
Adrian.Hardingham@HHLaw.co.uk
Senior partner
Specialisation: Principal areas of practice are transport and shipping law, encompassing international and domestic carriage of goods by road, sea and air. Other main areas of work are marine insurance, particularly cargo risks, and general commercial insurance. Major cases handled include Buchanan v. Babco (H.L.) (1978), Silber v. Islander Trucking (1985), ITT v Birkart (1988), the 'Rewia' (1991), and Spectra v Hayesoak (1997). Major clients include UK and overseas underwriters, traders, freight forwarders, hauliers and insurance recovery agents. Contributor of various articles on the CMR Convention in Lloyd's Maritime & Commercial Law Quarterly.
Career: Qualified 1978. Founding partner of *Holmes Hardingham.*
Personal: Attended University College, Oxford. Holds private pilot's licence.

HARRIS, Anne
Eversheds, Birmingham (0121) 232 1000
anneharris@eversheds.com
Specialisation: Specialises in commercial law and project work, in particular relating to railways. Having advised on railway facility access agreements, infrastructure developments, rolling stock and regulatory issues. Worked on the privatisation (pre-franchising) of West Coast Trains, and since 1997 for OPRAF/SSRA.
Prof. Memberships: Law Society. Railway Study Association
Career: Qualified 1987 with *Eversheds*, partner 1994. Head of Rail Group.
Personal: BA English and American Literature. Married (to Simon). Has a keen interest in sport particularly Aston Villa FC. Friend of Barber Institute of Fine Arts.

HEATON, John Graham
Bannister Preston, Sale (0161) 973 2434
info@bannisterpreston.co.uk
Specialisation: Road Transport Law (prosecuting and defending). Acted for the Crown in Bird v. Vehicle Inspectorate, Case C235/94[1996]ECJ165 – Re: scope of road safety exemption under Act 12 EEC 3820/85; Birkett & Naylor v. VO (1998) RTA 264: and Mahmood v. Veh Inspectorate (1998) 18 WRTLB – first binding authority on what constitutes payment for purposes of driving instruction under S123 RTA 1988. Particular interest in jurisdiction issues and procedures.
Career: 1967-75 William Hulme Grammar School, Manchester; LLB (Hons) Liverpool University 1978; Qualified 1981; Partner, *Bannister Preston & Ormerod* 1985.
Publications: Articles in legal journals on road transport law.
Personal: Married, two sons. Interests include travel, choral singing, transport generally, family life.

HENNING, Caroline A.
DLA, Liverpool Mobile: 0589 484 001
caroline.henning@dla.com
Specialisation: Main areas of practice including marine, goods in transit and insurance advice and litigation. Particularly cargo claims for both cargo and liability insurers, national and international freight forwarding, warehousing and road haulage claims. Bill of lading and charterparty disputes, and air carriage claims. Also advises on and drafts terms and conditions of business.
Prof. Memberships: Honourable Society of Middle Temple, BMIA.
Career: Called to bar 1993. *Hill Dickinson Davies Campbell* 1993 to 1999. Joined *Dibb Lupton Alsop* in 1999 operating from Liverpool, Manchester and London.
Personal: Wadham College, Oxford. Inns of Court School of Law. Leisure pursuits include food, wine and films. Lives in Liverpool but supports Newcastle United. Leisure pursuits include sleeping and gardening.

HILL, Martin
DLA, Liverpool (08700) 111 111
martin.hill@dla.com
Specialisation: Insurance coverage disputes subrogation and defence of liability claims. Acts for a number of major insurers and Lloyds Syndicates both in the UK and overseas.
Prof. Memberships: Committee member of Liverpool Underwriters Association and associate member of Manchester Marine Insurance Association.
Career: Qualified 1977. Partner with *Hill Dickinson & Co* and then *Hill Dickinson Davies Campbell* until 1993. Practice of *Alsop Wilkinson* from 1993.
Personal: Born 12.5.1953. Sixth generation solicitor. Personal interests include rebuilding and racing vintage and classic cars and working on the bench.

HOBBS, Jane
Holmes Hardingham, London (020) 7283 0222
Jane.Hobbs@HHLaw.co.uk
Transport: Road-carriage/commercial
Specialisation: Main areas of practice are carriage of goods by road and sea and related insurance issues. Handles a wide range of cases involving domestic road haulage and CMR, including freight forwarding and warehousing. Insurance work includes advising on policy disputes and handling subrogated claims on behalf of underwriters. Experienced in pursuing and defending bill of lading and charterparty cargo claims.
Career: Attended Merton College, Oxford 1985 – 1988. Qualified 1991. Joined *Holmes Hardingham* in 1992 and became a partner in 1997. Contributor to 'Multimodal Transport' and 'Insurance Disputes'.

HODGSON, Gary
Ford & Warren, Leeds (0113) 243 6601
Specialisation: Partner in Commercial Law Department. Main area of expertise – LGV transport. Particularly experienced on operators licensing and regulatory matters. Extensive defence experience before magistrates courts and crown courts throughout England and Wales on full range of road traffic and Transport related Health and Safety prosecutions. Particular specialisation in drivers' hours and records offences and European regulations. Extensive appearances throughout England and Wales on prosecutions arising from 'lost wheels' mystery. Recommended solicitor for the Road Haulage Association and Freight Transport Association. Specialisation in consultancy advice to transport companies on internal systems for monitoring safety and general operation. Consultancy work for businesses in the Haulage industry seeking BS5750 and ISO9000 accreditation. Regularly lectures to trade associations on road transport matters. Co-author of Commercial Motor Legal Bulletin. Regular contributor to the Trade Press.
Career: Qualified 1977. Joined *Ford & Warren* in 1978. Became Partner in 1985.

HOLLINGWORTH, Sara
Hollingworth Bissell, London (020) 7233 3300
Specialisation: Provides a wide range of legal services to the railway industry, dealing with the negotiation and drafting of many types of commercial contracts; advises on foreign railway privatisations; joint ventures, station trading, sales promotion and advertising copy, in partnership with Helen Bissell who provides complementary advice on franchise matters, access and the implications of the Railways Act for rail businesses.
Career: Born and educated in Derbyshire and at Durham University. Trained at *Cameron Markby* and since 1985 has worked in the railway industry, initially as a lawyer with the British Railways Board (Head of Commercial within legal department 1993-96) and latterly as a partner in *Hollingworth Bissell.*
Personal: Married with two sons and lives in rural Kent. Interests include tennis, cookery, antique furniture and the theatre. Member of the English-Speaking Union.

HORTON, Naomi
Rowe & Maw, London (020) 7248 4282
nhorton@roweandmaw.co.uk
Specialisation: Specialises in infrastructure projects and PFI projects, including heavy and light rail and general rail related commercial advice. Advised Virgin Rail Group on the procurement of new rolling stock for each of the West Coast and CrossCountry passenger rail franchises, the largest train procurements in the UK.
Prof. Memberships: Law Society.
Career: Educated at Sheffield High School, Merton College Oxford and Chester Law School. Articled at *Clifford Chance*, admitted 1992, joined *Rowe & Maw* in 1997 and became a partner in 1998. Now head of Rail Group at *Rowe & Maw* within the banking and projects group. Published (as co-author) a Special Report on the Private Finance Initiative (Pearson Professional) and articles for IFLR and PFI journals.
Personal: Born 1967. Rowed at Women's Henley Regatta and UK National Rowing Championships. Associate of the London College of Music.

JACKSON, Peter
Hill Dickinson, Manchester (0161) 2788800
Jacko@HillDicks.com
Partner in Marine Department and Head of *Hill Dickinson's* Manchester office and Cargo and Transport group.
Specialisation: Main areas of practice are marine, goods in transit and insurance litigation. Work includes cargo claims, for both cargo and liability insurers, particularly international road haulage claims; ship related cargo claims for cargo interests; salvage and monitoring foreign litigation. Also handles marine insurance work, particularly marine insurance policy interpretation for underwriters. Acted in ICI plc v MAT Transport, ITT v Birkart, the Breydon Merchant F & W Freight, the Los Angeles, Microfine v Transferry Shipping and Inco Europe.
Prof. Memberships: Liverpool Underwriters Association, Manchester Marine Insurance Association, London Maritime Arbitrators Association.
Career: Qualified in 1985, having joined *Hill Dickinson Davis Campbell* in 1983. Became a Partner in 1989.
Personal: Born 3rd April 1961. Attended St Edward's College, Liverpool 1972-79, then Exeter College, Oxford 1979-82. Leisure interests include football, season ticket holder at Anfield. Former Chairman of Football Supporters Association. Cricket and squash. Lives in Liverpool.

JONES, Geoffrey
Cartwrights, Bristol (0117) 929 3601
gnjones@cartwrights.com
Specialisation: Senior partner practising transport law with over 25 years experience in relation to all aspects of bus and lorry licensing and related public inquiries, road use public inquiries and judicial review challenges to local authorities. Also specialises in employment and industrial relations law with experience of all aspects of employment and industrial relations matters in contracts, service agreements and disciplinary procedures; multi-applicant employment tribunals; TUPE; commercial transactions and advice and legal action in relation to industrial action.
Personal: Educated at Bristol University, 1956-1959. Former lecturer at the College of Law. Trustee, Southmead Hospital Research Foundation. Lives in Bristol.

KIRKBRIGHT, Stephen
Ford & Warren, Leeds (0113) 243 6601
Partner in Business Law Department.
Specialisation: Main area of practice is transport. Experienced since 1970 in all aspects of road transport law. Particular specialisation in LGV and PCV, nationally and internationally, regularly appears before traffic commissioners on Public Inquiries and Transport Tribunals on appeals. Extensive experience in all aspects of criminal defence work particularly drivers hours and records. Particular experience in cases of utmost severity including HSE prosecutions, manslaughter and corporate manslaughter. Acted in connection with |Sowerby |Bridge and M2. Supervises department dealing with civil claims throughout Europe, CMR and GIT. Acts as legal advisor to the Road Haulage Association, recommended solicitor to the Freight Transport Association, the Irish Road Haulage Association and Transport Logistik Netherlands. Acted in 500 plus claims against the French Government following the French lorry drivers strike on behalf of Irish, UK, Dutch and Spanish Hauliers. Co-ordinated the 'RHA flagging out' scheme following the 1999 budget to assist hauliers to re-locate to other EU member states. Involved in leading authorities before Transport Tribunal on finance, for HGV and PCV operators, particularly Rosswood, RHA v John Dee Limited, and JJ Adam Limited. Handled the leading cases on 'causing and permitting' (Kelly v Shulman and Redhead Freight v Shulman); and on 'using' (Travel-gas Midlands Ltd v Reynolds and others). Acts throughout the UK for PCV operators at Public Inquiries and Transport Tribunal appeals in relation to PSV operators licence and registration of local bus services. Acted in leading authority before Transport Tribunal (Midland Bluebird) in relation to fuel duty rebate and for operators in the Manchester and Merseyside inquiries. Regular contributor to trade press.
Prof. Memberships: Fellow of the Chartered Institute of Transport.
Career: Qualified in 1968. Joined *Ford & Warren* in 1966 becoming a Partner in 1970. Currently Head of Business Law and member of Managing Board of *Ford & Warren*. Born 18 October 1941. Attended Sheffield University 1961-64 and College of Law 1965-66.
Personal: Leisure interests include music (plays guitar and piano) and painting. Lives in Wakefield.

KNIGHT, Tim
Holmes Hardingham, London (020) 7283 0222
Tim.Knight@HHLaw.co.uk
Partner in cargo claims department.
Specialisation: Main area of practice is carriage of goods by road, covering national and international carriage by road, warehousekeeping, related insurance matters and terms and conditions of business. Also experienced in carriage by sea work, including bill of lading claims, and carriage by air and rail.
Career: Joined *Ingledew Brown* in 1986, qualifying in 1988. Joined *Holmes Hardingham* in 1989. Became partner in 1993.
Personal: Born 17th March 1964. Attended University of Kent 1983-85. Leisure pursuits include golf and squash. Lives in Enfield.

KNOTT, Alice
Wedlake Saint, London (020) 7405 9446
Specialisation: A Partner in the firm's transport law department. Main areas of practice include goods vehicle and PSV operating licencing matters. Conducting public inquiries before the Traffic Commissioner; The defence of Road Traffic Act prosecutions; Personal injury actions both road traffic accidents and employer's liability matters. Major cases have involved multi-defendant prosecutions in respect of EEC and domestic drivers hours/records matters and civil litigation arising as a result of major motorway accidents.
Prof. Memberships: Memberships include The Law Society, The Road Operations Committee of the Confederation of Passenger Transport, The Freight Transport Association, The Chartered Institute of Transport. Institute of Logistics and Transport.
Career: Born 30.12.63. Attended Benenden School 1976-1981. Exeter University 1982-85.
Personal: Horse riding, swimming and tennis.

LAWTON, Jonathan
Wake Dyne Lawton, Chester (01829) 773106
jsl@wdl.co.uk
Specialisation: Road traffic law specialist since 1972, with particular emphasis on commercial operations. Also handles employment law matters, health and safety, and some environmental work. Regular contributor to a number of trade publications, including Croners. Joint honorary legal adviser to the UK Warehousing Association. Freeman of the City of London. Gives frequent lectures and seminars on road haulage law, health and safety and employment.
Prof. Memberships: Heavy Transport Association.
Career: Qualified in 1962. Solicitor-Advocate (Higher Courts Criminal) 1997.
Personal: Born 18th February 1935. Cambridge University 1956-59.

MARSHALL, Julia
Hill Dickinson, London (020) 7695 1000
Partner in Marine & Cargo and Transit Department (London).
Specialisation: Advice and litigation in the field of insurance (marine and non-marine) and goods in transit inter-modally. Has a particular interest in the emerging rail freight industry. Drafts and advises Underwriters on policy wordings and advises merchants and carriers on conditions of trading. Has been involved in a number of leading decisions relating to CMR, e.g. Cicatiello and others v Anglo European Shipping Services Ltd and others, which successfully argued the first armed hijack defence under CMR Article 17.2. Founder of ELLSA (European Lawyers for Land, Sea and Air), a specialist European group ensuring expedient international assistance in shipping, transit, insurance, company and commercial areas. Represents the European Intermodal Association on a United Nations Group advising on a global intermodal convention.
Prof. Memberships: LL.B 1974 : F.C.I.Arb 1995. Supporting Member of the London Maritime Arbitrators Association. Member of the Rail Freight Group. Freeman of the City of London Solicitors Company.
Career: Admitted 1977 after first training and working in the medical field. Proprietor of own firm 1981. May 1994 merged with and became a partner in the current firm of *Hill Dickinson*.

MCGEE-OSBORNE, Christopher
Denton Wilde Sapte, London (020) 7242 1212

MELBOURNE, William
Clyde & Co, Guildford (01483) 555 555
Specialisation: In addition to road carriage, including GIT and removers block/warehousing related disputes, domestic and international road haulage and heavy haulage; also specialises in marine insurance (including rejection risks) and dry shipping/cargo claims, with particular experience of reefer cargoes (especially bananas and frozen meat), bulk ore, refractories (magnesite) and groundnuts (especially inherent vice-related issues). Also has experience of international sale of goods (especially steel), including ICC Arbitration.
Prof. Memberships: Solicitor (admitted 1985)
Career: BA (Hons) (C.N.A.A.) 1981; LLM (Lond) 1986

MESSENT, Andrew
Holmes Hardingham, London (020) 7283 0222
Adrian.Messent@HHLaw.co.uk
Partner in cargo claims department.
Specialisation: Main area of practice is claims arising from the carriage of goods by sea, road and air, and related insurance issues. Co-author of 'CMR: Contracts for the International Carriage of Goods by Road' (2nd edition 1995; 3rd edition scheduled for 2000). Contributor to 'International Carriage of Goods by Road (CMR)' (1987).
Career: Qualified 1975. Worked with *Ingledew Brown* until 1976, then took up a lecturing post until 1985. Returned to IBBG, becoming a partner in 1987, and moved to *Holmes Hardingham* as one of the founding partners in 1989.
Personal: Born 1951. Attended Wimbledon College, then Gonville & Caius College, Cambridge.

OVER, Christopher
Over Taylor Biggs, Exeter (01392) 823811

PHILLIPS, Richard
Freshfields Bruckhaus Deringer, London (020) 7936 4000
Specialisation: Work includes asset and project finance, commercial and corporate law, mergers and acquisitions, joint ventures, disposals and privatisations. Specialist industry focus of railways,wide experience of high profile corporate, project and finance work within this industry.
Prof. Memberships: Law Society, Chartered Institute of Transport, City Solicitors' Company.
Career: Qualified in 1981. (1985 joined *Freshfields*, 1989 became partner).
Personal: Born 1955, lives in London.

PHILLIPS, Simon
Slaughter and May, London (020) 7600 1200
Specialisation: Corporate finance, M&A, general corporate.
Career: Educated Winchester College and Queens' College, Cambridge. Joined *Slaughter and May* 1982. Partner since 1991.

PRIOR, Barry
Wedlake Saint, London (020) 7405 9446 and Redbourn (01582) 790 900
barryp@wsch.co.uk
Partner and Head of firm's Transport Law team of 5 fee-earners and para-legals.
Specialisation: Main area of practice is road transport law for goods and passenger vehicles; work covers operators licensing, defence of prosecutions, personal injury (road traffic and employers' liability), contract drafting, and commercial litigation associated with the

industry. Also handles carriage of goods and passengers claims, including CMR/ Domestic contracts and local authority tendering bus contracts. Cases have included litigation arising from many major motorway multi-vehicle accidents, public inquiries into operators licenses and major driver's hours/records prosecutions. Contributor to 'Coach and Bus Week'.
Prof. Memberships: Law Society, Chartered Institute of Transport, Institute of Logistics and Transport, Freight Transport Association, Confederation of Passenger Transport, Law Society Personal Injury Panel.
Career: Qualified in 1969. Joined *Wedlake Saint* as a Partner in 1985.
Personal: Born 24th October 1943. Attended Lawrence Sheriff School, Rugby, then Sheffield University. Fellow of the Chartered Institute of Transport; and of Institute of Logistics and Transport. Affiliate Member Institute of Road Transport Engineers; Council Member of CPT UK. Lives in Marlow, Bucks.

PYSDEN, Kay
Davies Lavery, Maidstone (020) 7780 6868
mark.lane@davies-lavery.co.uk
Specialisation: Advice, Litigation and Arbitration in the fields of uni and multi modal transport including disputes of jurisdiction and law and ship arrest. Advising on appropriate terms and conditions of freight operators and insurers on policy wording. Has been involved in a number of leading decisions e.g. the KOMNINOS S, where the issue of conflict of laws arose; Spectra v Hayesoak on bailment and construction of limitation provisions under RHA 1991; Texas Instruments and Ors v Nason Europe & Ors, being one of the first High Court actions where the carriers right to limit liability was disallowed due to a finding of wilful default under article 29.1, CMR and Rhone Poulenc Rorer Ltd v TGA Ltd + Ors (CA) where due incorporation of terms was considered.
Prof. Memberships: Supporting member of the London Maritime Arbitrators Association, Panel Member of the Conciliation Panel of the London Maritime Arbitrators Association, Member of the Advisory Body of Legal Matters of FIATA and FIATA's representative on the CMI working party for uniformity of the law of the Carriage of Goods by Sea and rapporteur on matters of multi modal transport to FIATAS ABLM..
Career: Admitted 1987 having been educated at Tormead School, Guildford and gaining an LLB Hons Degree at University College London. Partner in 2 previous firms, having joined *Hill Dickinson Davis Campbell* in 1997 as a Partner. Currently Partner *Hill Dickinson.*

REYNOLDS, Justin
Hill Dickinson, London (020) 7695 1000
Specialisation: Carriage of goods nationally and internationally and all related insurance and trade matters.
Prof. Memberships: London Solicitors Litigation Association. Law Society.
Career: Qualified with *Hill Dickinson* in 1995, becoming a partner in the firm in 2000.
Personal: Cinema and martial arts.

ROTHERA, Ian
Rothera Dowson, Nottingham (0115) 9100 600
Head of Transport Department.
Specialisation: Since qualifying in 1973, has specialised in all aspects of road transport and traffic law. Acts for National and International HGV and PCV operators and drivers. Defence of prosecutions in Magistrates and Crown Courts throughout the UK, including Construction & Use offences and drivers' hours and tachograph cases. Handles Operator's Licence applications, disciplinary and environmental public inquiries before the Traffic Commissioners and appeals to the Transport Tribunal. Panel solicitor for the RHA and the FTA. Member of Nottinghamshire Chamber of Commerce Transport Committee. Deputy Coroner for Nottinghamshire.

SHARP, Roland
Prettys, Ipswich (01473) 232121
rhs@prettys.co.uk
Specialisation: Significant part of practice is carriage of goods by road – national and CMR. Acts for insurers as well as carriers and associated businesses on business terms, distribution, warehousing and logistics aspects and related transport matters.

SILK, Ken
Davies Arnold Cooper, London (020) 7936 2222
Specialisation: Senior Associate, Property, Construction and Insurance.

THOMAS, Tony
Clyde & Co, Guildford (01483) 31161
Partner in Marine & Transport Department.
Specialisation: In addition to road carriage, including GIT and removers block/warehousing related disputes, domestic and international road haulage and heavy haulage, also specialises in marine insurance and dry shipping/cargo claims.
Prof. Memberships: Law Society.
Career: Qualified in 1976, joining *Clyde & Co.* the same year. Partner 1981.
Personal: Born 27th May 1952. Attended Leamington College 1963-70, then Manchester University 1970-73. Leisure interests include sport, art and architecture. Lives in Grayshott, Surrey.

THOMPSELL, Nicholas P.
Field Fisher Waterhouse, London (020) 7861 4000
Specialisation: Corporate/commercial lawyer. Particular interests include transport /travel (especially rail) and privatisation / PFI. Acts for South West Trains in relation to commercial /regulatory aspects of its rail operations. Advised Northern Spirit on rolling stock leasing. Acted for British Railways in relation to numerous disposals. Acted for The Thomas Cook Group Limited in various transactions. Acted for an airline in relation to BA Franchise. Advised London Underground on its police accommodation PPP scheme and has advised on various other PFI schemes. Advised on the privatisation of HMSO and the Paymaster Agency.
Prof. Memberships: Law Society. City of London Law Society, Rail Study Association, Association of Partnership Practitioners.
Career: School: Bablake School, Coventry. University: King's College, London (LLB, AKC). Law School: College of Law, Chester. Articled *Slaughter and May*. Assistant Solicitor *Slaughter and May* 1987 – 92. Assistant Solicitor *Field Fisher Waterhouse* 1992, becoming a partner in 1993.
Personal: Trying to keep up with daughters' interests in music and computers. Trustee London Suzuki Group.

WARD, Dominic
Andrew M. Jackson & Co, Hull (01482) 325242
Partner in 1992.
Specialisation: Disputes involving carriage of goods by sea and road including advising transport intermediaries. International trade disputes, other contractual disputes involving marine or transport related matters.
Career: Qualified 1987.
Prof. Memberships: AIJA, SEG.
Personal: Born 30.3.63 in London. Education to age 14 in Germany. Speaks German. Interests include rugby, golf, badminton, cinema, books and travel.

WESTON, John
John Weston & Co, Felixstowe (01394) 282527

WHITEFORD, Michael G.
Jeffrey Aitken Solicitors, Glasgow (0141) 221 5983
m.whiteford@jeffrey-aitken.co.uk
Specialisation: Road transport law. Practice covers representation at operator licence public inquiries before the Traffic Commissioner and appeals to the Transport Tribunal,employment tribunals and defending in prosecutions in the Scottish courts. Acts for many leading haulage and bus operators.
Prof. Memberships: Law Society of Scotland. Panel Solicitor for the Freight Transport Association. The Royal Faculty of Procurators in Glasgow.
Career: Qualified 1971. Joined *Jeffrey Aitken* and has been a partner since 1972.
Personal: Born 15th December 1946. Educated Glasgow University.

WHITEHOUSE, Michael
Wragge & Co, Birmingham (0121) 214 1040
michael_whitehouse@wragge.com
Specialisation: Head of transport and infrastructure group: privatisations, acquisitions and mergers, joint ventures, railports, light rail, performance related outsourcing, maintenance, franchising, infrastructure, new railways, accident enquiries and international projects.
Prof. Memberships: Non executive Director of Rail Freight Group and Member of Chamber of Commerce Rail Forum.
Career: Malvern College, University of Liverpool. Articled *Slaughter and May*. Qualified 1977. Partner at *Wragge & Co* from 1987. Head of transport and infrastructure projects 1998.
Personal: Railways, photography and travel.

WOOLFALL, Andrew
Wake Dyne Lawton, Chester (01829) 773106
aaw@wdl.co.uk
Specialisation: Road transport law, covering goods and passenger vehicles. Representing clients in Magistrates and Crown Courts as well as at Public Inquiries. Also been involved in cases before High Court and House of Lords. Appears at courts and tribunals throughout England and Wales. Provides consultancy advice to companies on internal systems for compliance with road transport law and operators' licensing requirements. Acted for companies and individuals in relation to drugs/smuggling seizures on the continent.
Prof. Memberships: The Law Society. Member of the Institute of Transport Administrators. Practice membership of HTA and RHA.
Career: Lancaster University. Early career in general practice before moving on to specialise in transport.

WYLIE, Amanda
Arthur Cox – Northern Ireland, Belfast
(028) 9023 0007

TRAVEL

OVERVIEW: The Package Travel Regulations of 1993, the continual increase in travel and the growing preparedness of customers to seek redress, have led the travel industry to demand lawyers who have in-depth knowledge of this sector.

The growing amount of claimant work has given birth to claimant specialists, several of whom have been ranked for the first time this year.

Growing opportunities have prompted the establishment of a number of new travel units, although not all have prospered. There is a lot of turnover in the industry but not much profit – partly because a handful of travel companies dominate the market. Within the travel sector, vertical integration and competition are the major issues.

LEADING IN-HOUSE LAWYERS

Travel & Tourism

Richard ASTON, *Thomsons Travel Group Ltd*

Andrew COOPER, Company Secretary and Head of Legal Services, *Airtours plc*

Rebecca STARLING, Group Company Secretary, *First Choice Holidays plc*

Richard Aston is praised as a *"very good lawyer"* who *"balances the law with the business world."* He is noted as a *"good manager."* **Andrew Cooper** is *"the only guy who stands out"* and he *"knows the industry backwards."* He is recommended for being *"pre-eminent"* in both *"commercial and managerial roles."* Also highly regarded is **Rebecca Starling** who is noted as a *"good professional."*

In-House lawyers profiles: page 1177

RESEARCH APPROVED BY BMRB: *For this edition,* Chambers' *researchers conducted 6083 interviews – 4408 with law firms, 598 with barristers and 1077 with clients.*

The validity of the research was scrutinised by BMRB International, who audited both the methodology and the results at our offices in July 2000. They interviewed Chambers' *researchers and cross-checked sample interviews. Details of the audit appear on page 7.*

TRAVEL

LONDON

TRAVEL • London	Ptnrs	Assts
❶ Field Fisher Waterhouse	2	3
❷ Nicholson Graham & Jones	3	4
❸ Barlow Lyde & Gilbert	3	6
Lane & Partners	2	2
Norton Rose	3	8
❹ Berrymans Lace Mawer	2	4
Herbert Smith	7	10
Kingsford Stacey Blackwell	3	3
Piper Smith & Basham	3	1

LEADING INDIVIDUALS
❶ **BARBOR Cynthia** Nicholson Graham & Jones
STEWART Peter Field Fisher Waterhouse
❷ **CHAMBERLAIN Simon** Field Fisher Waterhouse
FARRELL Patrick Norton Rose
GIMBLETT Richard Barlow Lyde & Gilbert
ROBINSON Tim Nicholson Graham & Jones
VENABLES Richard Lane & Partners
❸ **MULLIGAN Claire** Berrymans Lace Mawer
SEARS Trevor Kingsford Stacey Blackwell
SKUSE Ian Piper Smith & Basham

Within each band, firms are listed alphabetically. *See* ***Profiles*** *on page 806*

Field Fisher Waterhouse The *"excellent"* team maintains its position just ahead of the pack. With a dedicated travel group, they *"do it all,"* and are noted for the quality and quantity of a client base which includes a number of the country's leading travel organisations. Universally praised for corporate, commercial and disaster work, the team includes **Peter Stewart**, *"the top academic authority in the field."* He is widely complimented for being a top-notch litigator. **Simon Chamberlain** has a reputation for handling *"tricky"* regulatory work and is said to have steadily *"grown into the role"* as a travel specialist. **Clients:** Thomas Cook Holdings Ltd; ITT; AITO.

Nicholson Graham & Jones Considered to have *"an extremely good understanding of the industry,"* the firm is described as *"user friendly"* and *"on the ball".* With a rounded practice, it handles everything from corporate to claims work. **Cynthia Barbor** advises the Federation of Tour Operators and is noted for her *"sound commercial judgement."* Several industry commentators rate her *"the outstanding lawyer in travel law."* She handles most of the contentious work, while **Tim Robinson** is rated for his non-contentious ability. The team acted for Crystal Holidays in connection with an Austrian white-water rafting accident. **Clients:** Thomsons; Crystal Holidays; Federation of Tour Operators.

Barlow Lyde & Gilbert Perceived to be a major regulatory practice, the firm deals with IATA and also handles EU regulatory work. During the past year, they have advised the FTO on the EU review of the Package Travel Directive, and also dealt with the Kuoni-First Choice case on aviation regulatory requirements. They continue to advise the CAA on tour operator failure. **Richard Gimblett** is considered to be a *"hard-working technician."* **Clients:** Federation of Tour Operators (FTO); International Federation of Tour Operators; Air 2000.

Lane & Partners. Another regulatory practice, the firm is noted for its work in insurance and air-related matters. Much of its workload consists of assisting tour operators to obtain and keep CAA licences. **Richard Venables** is a respected individual within the sector. He is described as *"a good scrapper"* and *"a good man for lost causes."* **Clients:** Travel Club of Upminster; medium sized tour operators.

Norton Rose The firm concentrates on competition work for major tour operators. During the past year they have worked on acquiring a string of smaller travel agents for Lunn Poly and Thomsons. **Patrick Farrell** is the head of the Travel and Leisure Group and has a particular reputation for handling claims. **Clients:** Thomson Holidays; TV Travel Shop; easy-group.

Berrymans Lace Mawer Mostly noted for PI travel work. **Claire Mulligan**, an assistant, is the principal name here, although a partner also works in the sector. She specialises on the defence side of travel litigation. The firm also handles insurance work, often handling class actions. It successfully defended a number of ski-lift accidents and worked on a number of coach crashes in Turkey and Spain. **Clients:** Thomson Holidays; Thomson Travel Group; First Choice.

Herbert Smith Mainly does commercial work, specialising in competition and regulation. Although not specialists in the field, they are considered a formidable acquisitions unit. Worked for First Choice on the proposed merger with Kuoni, then on the hostile Airtours bid, and subsequently on the acquisition of Sunsail International and Meon Holdings. Also worked on the MMC enquiry into travel in the UK. **Clients:** First Choice.

Kingsford Stacey Blackwell Well-known for its expertise in the niche area of travel insolvency. **Trevor Sears** is the stand-out practitioner. He is local counsel for the International Airline Transport Association (IATA), and represented them during the Debonair and AB airline insolvencies. **Clients:** IATA.

Piper Smith & Basham A long-term name in the sector, the firm handles M&A and insolvency work for liquidators. Clients include major travel retailers, destination specialists and recent breakthroughs have been made in the growing business travel sector. **Ian Skuse** has an established reputation. Major deals this year have included the purchase of another tour operator for Kuoni, and work on regulatory problems between the CAA and charity tours. **Clients:** Lunn Poly; Omega World Travel; Kuoni.

THE REGIONS

TRAVEL • The Regions	Ptnrs	Assts
❶ **Mason Bond** Leeds	1	5
❷ **Eversheds** Middlesbrough, Newcastle upon Tyne	1	5
Stones Exeter	3	3
❸ **Andrea & Co** Guildford	1	3
Clairmonts Glasgow	1	4
Irwin Mitchell Sheffield	2	6
❹ **Shakespeares** Birmingham	2	3
Tozers Exeter	2	1

LEADING INDIVIDUALS	
❶ **MASON Stephen** Mason Bond	
❷ **GARNER Clive** Irwin Mitchell	**INGLEBY Claire** Mason Bond
PEARS Melanie Eversheds	
❸ **ANDREA Costas** Andrea & Co	
COURTENAY-STAMP Bronwen Stones	

Within each band, firms are listed alphabetically. See **Profiles** on page 806

Mason Bond *"One of the top three in the UK."* The firm acts for the industry and does everything but top-level corporate work. Travel industry work makes up the lion's share of the caseload, with a clientele including over 100 travel agents. **Stephen Mason** is regarded as *"one of the pioneers of the industry."* An experienced litigator, his work includes warding off contract legislation aimed at booking conditions. A strong team also boasts **Claire Ingleby**, who works on terms and conditions. Opponents have said that *"she gives you a good run for your money."* **Clients:** Thomson Holidays; JMC Holidays; Cosmos.

Eversheds Specialising in commercial work, the firm also works on customer complaints and e-commerce issues. The range of clients includes major plcs, niche operators and new business start-ups. **Melaine Pears** is *"switched on and determined"* and handled the UK end of the sale of routes and ships from Colorline to Fjordline. **Clients:** S&N (Center Parcs); EuroDisney; Fjordline.

Stones A niche firm which does claimant and some defendant work on skiing, coach and other accidents, largely for travel insurers. **Bronwen Courtenay-Stamp** has a particular profile in skiing claims. **Clients:** Fogg Travel; Europ Assist; T&C Adjusters.

Andrea & Co The firm is exclusively concerned with overseas travel litigation, mainly on behalf of claimants, although it also litigates against hotels on behalf of tour operators on an ad hoc basis. Currently working on claims in over 50 countries. **Costas Andrea** moved from Penningtons to set up on his own in May 1997, and has recently taken on two new assistants. He is *"easy to get on with"* and *"know his stuff."* **Clients:** First Assist; numerous individuals and groups.

Clairmonts The main lawyers in Scotland for the top UK tour operators and travel agents. Carry out contractual litigation, conveyancing, contract and trading standards cases. This year they have attracted a large amount of property work. **Clients:** Major UK tour operators and agents.

Irwin Mitchell The leading claimant firm, it specialises in illness and accident claims. *"They are the bane of our lives"* is the overwhelming industry view, following some very substantial claims against tour operators. **Clive Garner** *"causes frothing at the mouth of his opponents,"* though his fiercest critics admit that *"he knows his onions."* He represented the claimant in Brown v Thomson Holidays – the first and so far only successful personal injury case under the Package Travel Regulations. The firm attracts a lot of work from legal expenses insurers and from Holiday Travel Watch, a respected industry pressure group. **Clients:** The Law Society, Eastgate; First Assist; Countrywide.

Shakespeares This 'niche within a niche' practice looks after the Parliamentary side of waterways law. The team includes a consultant who has worked in the sector for over 30 years. **Clients:** Inland Waterways Association and subsidiaries; individuals.

Tozers Small niche practice with specific expertise in the caravan industry. Advises on corporate transactions in the caravan industry for a mixed client base. **Clients:** Caravan park owners and developers.

HOTELS & LEISURE

OVERVIEW: The hotels and leisure sector is a composite of other specialisms and the number of true experts is necessarily circumscribed. The main aspects of the hotel sector are property, M&A and management agreements, while leisure projects can involve a multitude of legal specialisms, including management agreement work.

TRAVEL: HOTELS & LEISURE • London	Ptnrs	Assts
❶ Clifford Chance	7	-
SJ Berwin & Co	2	6
❷ Richards Butler	*	*
❸ Denton Wilde Sapte	5	5
Field Fisher Waterhouse	3	9
Linklaters	2	1
Lovells	6	7
Norton Rose	*	*
Paisner & Co	5	8
❹ Douglas Wignall & Co	1	-
Garretts	-	3
❺ Allen & Overy	8	15
Stephenson Harwood	2	5
Taylor Joynson Garrett	3	6

LEADING INDIVIDUALS	
❶ **CARNEGIE Andrew** Clifford Chance	**LITTLE Andrew** Garretts
PICKUP Bryan SJ Berwin & Co	**RYLAND David** SJ Berwin & Co
❷ **NICOLL Richard** Richards Butler	
PLANT Patrick Linklaters	
WIGNALL Douglas Douglas Wignall & Co	
❸ **LEVY David** Paisner & Co	

Within each band, firms are listed alphabetically. *See Profiles on page 806*
** See editorial entries for explanations of team sizes.*

Clifford Chance Massive *"professional"* team which deals with the acquisition and disposal of large hotels for a vast corporate client base, as well as advising on the establishment of management contracts. **Andrew Carnegie** *"personifies efficiency"* and is *"good on the complex matters."* Notable deals of the past year have included advising Jarvis Hotels on the purchase of the Regents Park Hilton. **Clients:** Sol Melia Hotels; Millennium and Copthorne Hotels; Jarvis Hotels plc.

S J Berwin & Co Recognised by its peers as a serious player, the firm specialises in acquisition and disposal, and also handles management contract work. **David Ryland** is described as a *"workaholic"* and is particularly rated for his property expertise within the hotel industry. **Bryan Pickup** also has a long-term name in the sector. During the past year, the team set up their third leisure fund for MWB for £270 million and acted for Hilton on the disposition of hotels worth £160 million. **Clients:** Hilton Hotels; MWB.

Richards Butler (15 partners and 30 assistants available from various departments as required) Handling property, franchising, and management agreements, the firm has a dedicated unit, is considered to know the industry well and does *"a hell of a lot of work"* for good clients. The sale of Rank's nightclubs, bars and bowling centres for £150 million was one of the highlights for the firm's large entertainment department. **Richard Nicoll** *"knows his stuff"* on property and is *"a man you can rely on."* **Clients:** Mecca Bingo; Thistle Hotels; Grosvenor Casinos; Odeon Cinemas.

Denton Wilde Sapte Known as a reliable, experienced leisure property outfit, the firm acts for developers, and concentrates its efforts within the cinema and health and fitness sectors. The team acted for Virgin Active in the acquisition of seven of its new leisure concept centres, and also advised Virgin on the disposal of its cinemas to UGC. **Clients:** UGC Ltd (Virgin Cinemas); Virgin Active Ltd; Chelsea F.C.

Field Fisher Waterhouse The dedicated Hotel and Leisure Property unit handles IP franchising and property work. However, the perceived absence of an individual big-hitter and a comparatively low-profile corporate capacity mean that the firm is felt to have lost ground on its leading rivals. The team acquired several city centre sites for Travel Inn, and advised Luminar on the £35 million acquisition of a chain of bars and restaurants from Allied Leisure. **Clients:** Marriott Hotels; Travel Inn; David Lloyd Leisure; Whitbread.

Linklaters The firm's client base derives largely from its top-flight real estate expertise. Considered to be one of the few firms to do serious work on both corporate and contract matters, it acted for Lehman Brothers on the disposal of the former Thistle Hotels portfolio. **Patrick Plant** is a widely recommended expert in the field. **Clients:** S&N; Lehman Brothers; Bass; Mandarin Hotels.

Lovells Property and corporate specialists who specialise in hotel M&A work, and have some knowledge of management contracts. The firm has a low volume, big-ticket caseload. The most notable deal of the year was advising Stakis on its £1.46 billion take-over by Ladbrokes. **Clients:** Granada; Cliveden; Wyndham International.

Norton Rose (11 partners and 20 assistants available from various departments as required) Although not seen as frequently this year, the firm's standing in the sector is unquestioned following its advice on all construction and contract work for the Millennium Dome Company. The team also advised Hanover International PLC on its acquisition of the training centre business of Birchin International for £17 million. **Clients:** Millennium Dome Company; Landmark Hotel Group; Hanover International plc.

Paisner & Co Handles substantial M&A deals, as well as management agreements, IP, media and copyright arrangements. The team acted for First Leisure Corporation on the sale of its Family Entertainment Division for £111 million, and its nightclubs and bars division for £212 million. **David Levy** is well-known for his work on behalf of leading operators, and is commended for his *"business-like approach."* **Clients:** Wellcome Break; First Leisure Corporation; Chorion.

Douglas Wignall & Co. A major player within his niche of management contracts and franchise deals, **Douglas Wignall** *"knows his way around the hotel world"* having previously worked in-house at a leading hotel group. He has handled management agreements for Sheridan Group in Northern Ireland. **Clients:** Starwood Hotels and Resorts (Sheraton); Sheridan Group; Morrissons International Development Ltd.

Garretts Possessing a respected property capacity, the firm deals with significant commercial outsourcing agreements and also does contract and commercial property work. However, the team's reputation rests primarily with **Andrew Little**, formerly in-house at Holiday Inn, who is rated one of the leading names in the field. **Clients:** Marylebone Balfour Group plc; Capricorn International.

Allen & Overy Expertise in banking, property and corporate matters provides the basis for a number of high-profile deals in this area. The team has acted for a number of travel agents on their acquisitions and disposals. **Clients:** Leading corporates and travel operators.

Stephenson Harwood Handles a range of hotel work, including property acquisition and financing. Advised Accor on the redevelopment of a Crown Estate Building on Pall Mall into a hotel. **Clients:** Accord Group; Intercontinental (Bass) MacDonald Hotels.

Taylor Joynson Garrett Noted for a *"sharp"* litigation ability, the team has been catapulted into the limelight by acting for Stoll Moss on the property aspects of its sale to Really Useful. It has also worked on the MBO at Daiwa Europe. **Clients:** Stoll Moss; Virgin; Granada; Avebury.

TIMESHARE

TRAVEL: TIMESHARE • London	Ptnrs	Assts
❶ Rowe & Maw	1	3
Tods Murray WS Edinburgh	3	2
❷ Stones Exeter	3	4
❸ Volks Hedley	1	1

LEADING INDIVIDUALS	
❶ ANDERSON David Tods Murray WS	BOURNE Tim Stones
❷ JENKINS Colin Volks Hedley	

Within each band, firms are listed alphabetically. *See Profiles on page 806*

Rowe & Maw Handles the biggest client base, coming at the sector from a corporate perspective, and does not act for individuals. Despite some loss of personnel, the firm continues to *"maintain its market share."* Works in the regulatory and commercial field for timeshare developers, exchange organisations and financiers. Advised RCI Europe on day-to-day commercial timeshare transactions and the I.C.E. Gallery on its entrance into the UK timeshare market. **Clients:** RCI; Sunterra Corporation; Hilton.

Tods Murray WS Deals with the full range: commercial property, tax, corporate and IP. The firm's hotels and leisure team handled Britain's first timeshare deal in 1975, and it continues to act for the industry. Several commentators describe the firm as *"right at the top."* **David Anderson** is one of the most recognisable names in the field. **Clients:** OTE; RCI; Barrett International Resorts.

Stones The firm works on litigation, financing and corporate deals. The team does act for resort owners, although consumer representation forms the principal work-load. **Tim Bourne** is the stand-out practitioner here. During the past year, the firm completed its work on the Odessa Wharf development. **Clients:** Owners associations; timeshare developers; timeshare funders.

Volks Hedley The firm acts for smaller operators and does some developer work. **Colin Jenkins** remains a practitioner of *"remarkable energy,"* who has *"a wealth of knowledge on the industry."* **Clients:** Developers.

LEADERS IN TRAVEL

ANDERSON, David S.
Tods Murray WS, Edinburgh (0131) 226 4771
david.anderson@todsmurray.co.uk
Specialisation: All aspects of timeshare and leisure related work throughout the UK and Europe; 1975 devised legal structure for first UK timeshare project; advises developers, banks, management companies, trade bodies and other suppliers of services to timeshare industry; legal advisor and secretary to Timeshare Council; author of numerous articles.
Prof. Memberships: Law Society of Scotland.
Career: Qualified *Tods Murray* 1972; partner 1974.
Personal: Born 1948. Attended Perth Academy and Edinburgh University (1970 LLB). Leisure – golf.

ANDREA, Costas
Andrea & Co, Guildford (01483) 889 880
ca.andreaco@btinternet.com
Specialisation: Principal of the firm of *Andrea & Co.* Deals exclusively with travel and tourism law predominantly acting for claimants injured abroad. Currently pursuing personal injury claims in over 50 countries, as well as against UK defendants, primarily tour operators. Acted on higher profile claims such as Estonia ferry disaster and the Ethiopian airline hijacking.
Prof. Memberships: The Law Society Personal Injury Panel; Travel and Tourism Lawyers Association; Pan European Organisation of Personal Injury Lawyers. Founder member of the International Personal Injury Lawyers Association, being a network of personal injury lawyers throughout the world.
Career: Qualified in 1990 and set up the firm of *Andrea & Co* in 1997, which has trebled in size in its first three years.
Publications: The author of numerous articles and a consultant to the BBC and 'Holiday Which' magazine.
Personal: Born 28 December 1962. Travelled extensively prior to obtaining an LLB in 1987 before coaching the Guildford College of Law Volleyball Club. Lives in Guildford, Surrey.

BARBOR, Cynthia M.
Nicholson Graham & Jones, London (020) 7648 9000
cynthia.barbor@ngj.co.uk
Partner in litigation department and joint head travel and leisure law unit.
Specialisation: Main area of practice is travel and leisure law. Has over fifteen years experience in acting for major UK and international tour operators, travel agents, ground handlers, insurers, hotels, airlines, car hire companies and trade associations, advising on substantial litigation, commercial agreements and regulatory issues. Also handles general commercial litigation, including insurance and personal injury actions. Writes regularly for Travel Trade Gazette and other travel publications. Speaks frequently on travel law at UK and international conferences.
Prof. Memberships: Institute of Travel and Tourism, Incentive Travel and Meetings Association. Law Society.

BOURNE, Tim
Stones, Exeter (01392) 666 777
Partner
Specialisation: All aspects of timeshare law. Acts for and has advised banks, developers, hotel groups, Owners Associations, the main timeshare exchange organisations and national timeshare organisations. Author of articles for the Law Society and 'Estates Gazette', 'International Banking and Financial Law Journal', 'New Law Journal' and travel magazines. Lectures on timeshare law to the Institute of Bankers and several universities.
Prof. Memberships: The Law Society, Institute of Management.
Career: Qualified 1981. Partner *Stones* 1983.
Personal: Born 22nd March 1945. Educated Clifton College and HM Royal Marines. Lives in Exeter.

CARNEGIE, Andrew
Clifford Chance, London (020) 7600 1000
andrew.carnegie@cliffordchance.com
Specialisation: Partner with real estate background but specialising in property finance and hotel related work, particularly large, complex transactions. Advises hotel owners and financiers on acquisitions, sales, development projects, financings (including securitisations), management contracts and joint venture agreements.
Career: Dollar Academy, Scotland; University of Newcastle-upon-Tyne. Articled *Cartmell Shepherd*, Carlisle; solicitor *Cameron Markby* 1986-88; partner *Clifford Chance* 1996.
Personal: Fishing, shooting, skiing, hill walking. Born 1962.

CHAMBERLAIN, Simon
Field Fisher Waterhouse, London (020) 7861 4000
Specialisation: Partner in the Aviation & Travel Department specialising in commercial, corporate and regulatory work within the aviation and travel industries.
Career: Qualified in 1977. *Richards Butler & Co.* 1973-81. British Airways Plc 1981-1990. *Rowe & Maw* 1990-1994. Partner at *Field Fisher Waterhouse* since 1994.
Personal: Educated at Downside School. Born 8th August 1953. Lives in East Sussex.

COURTENAY-STAMP, Bronwen
Stones, Exeter (01392) 666 777
Specialisation: Heads the personal injury, travel and insurance team. Concentrates on travel and tourism litigation and sports law in connection with skiing. Provides an on-call 24 hour service for several client companies who may require immediate specialist advice. Organises attendance at the scene of ski accidents of a serious nature where that proves necessary. Gives lectures and writes articles for both the travel industry and lawyers.
Prof. Memberships: A Member of the Law Society

Personal Injury Panel and of the Association of Personal Injury Lawyers.
Career: Educated in the North East of England. Law Degree at Exeter University, First Class Honours in Law Society Finals. Articled at *Stones* spending the majority of her qualified career dealing with personal injury, travel, tourism and skiing law.
Personal: Married with two children. Enjoys foreign travel and watersports. A very keen snow skier.

FARRELL, Patrick
Norton Rose, London (020) 7283 6000
Partner in commercial litigation department
Specialisation: Advises tour operators, travel agents and airlines on claims handling, contractual disputes of all descriptions, brochure terms and conditions, bonding arrangements and regulatory matters. Also acts for airlines (including start ups) and financiers advising on domestic and European regulatory matters. Acts regularly in aircraft finance litigation.
Prof. Memberships: MRAeS, Chairman of the Royal Aeronautical Society Air Law Group, Chairman of the UK ICC Commission on Air Transport, Member of Institute of Travel and Tourism, IBA, LSLA, CLLS (Chairman of the CLLS Aeronautical Law Sub-Committee).

GARNER, Clive
Irwin Mitchell, Birmingham (0121) 212 1828
Garnerc@irwinmitchell.co.uk
Specialisation: Partner heading *Irwin Mitchell's* expanding International Travel Litigation Group. Acts for Claimants in accident and illness claims arising abroad. Successfully acted in many high value head and spinal injury claims and co-ordinated a large number of multi-party claims against English tour operators arising from illness outbreaks, coach, aviation and maritime accidents. Acted in several reported and precedent setting cases, recovering many millions of pounds in damages for clients injured abroad. Lectured nationally and internationally on personal injury, foreign claims and multi-party issues.
Prof. Memberships: Lord Chancellor's Department Holiday Claims Protocol Working Party; Law Society Personal Injury Panel; Association of Personal Injury Lawyers, American Trial Lawyers Association; Australian Plaintiff Lawyers Association; Pan European Organisation of Personal Injury Lawyers; Travel and Tourism Lawyers Association; Society for Advanced Legal Studies.
Career: Education: LLB (1988), MA (1989), LLM (1997). Articled at *Irwin Mitchell*. Qualified in 1992; Partner 1997.
Publications: Author of several published articles in various journals. Regular commentator on television, radio and in the press on travel and personal injury related issues.
Personal: Born 3 April 1966. Lives in Sheffield.

GIMBLETT, Richard
Barlow Lyde & Gilbert, London (020) 7247 2277
See under Aviation, p.103

INGLEBY, Claire
Mason Bond, Leeds (0113) 242 4444
Partner in Travel Law Department.
Specialisation: Specialises in drafting and advising on contractual and other documentation of all descriptions for tour operators. Has drafted booking conditions for many major operators and prepares, amongst others, supplier's contracts, agency agreements, promotional agreements and conditions and brochure wording. Presently particularly involved in advising on "unfair terms" in booking conditions. Also advises on regulatory matters. Conducts in-house seminars for tour operators on a number of subjects, including the Disability Discrimination Act. Provides advice on all areas of law affecting tour operators. Firm acts on behalf of more than 100 tour operators of varying sizes. Also represents travel agents, newspapers and a trade association. Author of a number of articles for the 'Travel Law Journal' and one for 'The Legal Executive'. Has lectured for the University of Northumbria and addressed the annual conference of ABTOF in 1994, 1995 and 1996.
Prof. Memberships: Law Society.
Career: Joined *Mason Bond* on qualification in 1990. Became a Partner in 1994.
Personal: Born 5th December 1965. Exeter University 1984-87. Leisure activities include hill walking. Lives near Skipton, North Yorkshire.

JENKINS, Colin
Volks Hedley, London (020) 7584 6733

LEVY, David N.
Paisner & Co, London (020) 7353 0299
Specialisation: Partner in property department specialising in all types of commercial property work including planning. Acts in particular for the leading companies in the hotel and leisure fields and over 20 years has dealt with the acquisition and disposal of many hundreds of hotels, restaurants and leisure properties of all types. Also has specialist involvement with motorway service areas.
Prof. Memberships: Law Society. Business In Sport & Leisure. British Israel Law Association.
Career: Educated at Wanstead County High School and Hertford College Oxford. Qualified in 1972. Became a partner at *Paisner & Co* in 1976.
Personal: Born 1948. Resides Finchley, London. Married with two children.

LITTLE, Andrew
Garretts, London (020) 7438 5174
Partner specialising in hotels and leisure industry related work.
Specialisation: Main area of practice involves advising clients in the hotel industry. Work includes purchases and sales of hotel and leisure businesses, negotiating hotel management agreements and operating leases, advising on financing of hotels and leisure projects, negotiating joint venture and development agreements and advising on franchising and time-sharing arrangements. Also advises on restructuring schemes for hotels, and in negotiating loan and security documents. An adviser to the British Hospitality Association. Frequently lectures at seminars and conferences for the hotel industry.
Prof. Memberships: Law Society, International Bar Association, Hotel Catering & International Management Association, British Association of Hotel Accountants.
Career: Qualified in 1973. With *Lawrence Graham* 1971-76, then at *Fox & Gibbons*, Dubai and London 1976-84. Vice President and General Counsel, Holiday Inns International 1985-89. Partner at *Field Fisher Waterhouse* 1990-1997. Joined *Garretts* 1997.
Personal: Born 25th November 1948. Educated at Uppingham School, Exeter University and Guildford College of Law. Leisure pursuits include sailing, golf, theatre, and travel. Lives in London W11. RAC, Hurlingham Club, St. Mawes Sailing Club.

MASON, Stephen M.
Mason Bond, Leeds (0113) 242 4444
Partner in Travel Law Department.
Specialisation: Advises tour operators and travel agents. Work includes defending claims brought by consumers, advocacy, dealing with trading standards departments, conducting seminars. Also handles commercial aspects of travel law, including commercial disputes and litigation, copyright, trademarks and passing off. Acted in Bowerman and Wallace v ABTA 1995 CA, Thomson Holidays v Birch 1999 DC and in many first instance travel law cases reported in Current Law. Joint Editor of the 'Travel Law Journal'. Has addressed numerous seminars on travel law topics advertised by the University of Northumbria, held at the Institute of Advanced Legal Studies, London; and also teaches Civil Advocacy. Higher Courts (Civil Proceedings) Qualification 1994. Used these Rights of Audience to defend a major tour operator successfully against a large claim in the High Court, January 1997 and to appear in the Divisional Court in Dudley v Inspirations East Ltd 1997. Joint Author 'Holiday Law' Sweet & Maxwell (2nd ed.) 1998; Member of the Law Society Civil Litigation Committee since 1997.
Prof. Memberships: Law Society, International Federation of Travel and Tourism Advocates.
Career: Qualified 1974. Senior Partner since 1986.
Personal: Married, 3 children. Attended Bradford Grammar School to 1967, and Cambridge University to 1971. Leisure interests include travel, acting and supporting Leeds United FC. Lives in Ilkley, West Yorkshire.

MULLIGAN, Claire
Badhams Thompson, London (020) 7242 4154
claire.mulligan@blm-law.com
Specialisation: Senior solicitor/team leader in travel litigation unit. Advises tour operators, insurers, travel agents, hotels. Handles a variety of claims including class actions involving resort outbreaks, and substantial litigation. Usually acts for tour operators as opposed to individuals. Regularly contributes to insurance press and many recent successes are reported in law reports. Provides in-house seminars to tour operators.
Prof. Memberships: Travel and Tourism Lawyers Association. Law Society.
Career: Qualified in 1995, joined *BLM* in 1996.

NICOLL, Richard C.
Richards Butler, London (020) 7247 6555
Partner and Head of Property
Specialisation: All aspects of commercial property investment and development and acts for a broad range of investors, developers and end users of commercial and residential properties in the UK and internationally. Advises extensively on the acquisition and development of a number of new high-profile leisure projects for major clients including Odeon Cinemas, Rank Entertainment, Warner Holidays, Oasis Villages, British Gas Pension Fund, Battersea Power Station and Prestbury Group.
Prof. Memberships: Law Society.
Career: Qualified 1974, joined *Richards Butler* in 1972.
Personal: Born 1950. Leisure interests include fishing, rugby and sports generally. Member of MCC.

PEARS, Melanie
Eversheds, Middlesbrough (01642) 247456
Partner.
Specialisation: Acts as adviser to many household name travel sector clients. Work involves client compliance audits, drafting of terms and conditions, consumer complaint handling, intellectual property disputes and general commercial matters. Has written for the Travel Law Journal and has presented papers at many recent IBA conferences.
Career: Qualified in 1994. Originally trained as a barrister, after which worked in industry for Shell and then in publishing, before joining *Eversheds* 1989.
Personal: Born 10th February 1965.

PICKUP, Bryan J.
SJ Berwin & Co, London (020) 7533 2468
bryan.pickup@sjberwin.com
Partner in Property Department.
Specialisation: Main area of practice is leisure. Handles the sale, purchase and funding of leisure businesses such as golf clubs, hotels, bingo clubs, cinemas, arenas and sports facilities. Has acted on the funding and acquisition and disposal of leisure parks, the flotation of Holmes Place plc, the acquisition of the nightclubs and bars businesses of First Leisure and a number of their restaurant transactions.
Prof. Memberships: Business in Sport & Leisure. British Property Federation.
Career: Qualified in 1981. Joined *S J Berwin & Co.* in 1988 as a Partner.
Personal: Born 15th April 1953. Attended Whitgift School Croydon 1961-69 and Fitzwilliam College, Cambridge 1970-74. Leisure interests include golf and hockey. Lives in Wimbledon.

PLANT, Patrick
Linklaters (A member firm of Linklaters & Alliance), London (020) 7456 4718
patrick.plant@linklaters.com
Specialisation: Partner specialising in commercial property, hotel and leisure. Advises investors, developers, lenders and tenants on all aspects of commercial property in the UK and has particular expertise in joint ventures, management and franchise agreements for hotel and leisure projects.
Career: Educated at St. Joseph's College, Blackpool and Manchester University. Articled *Wilsons*, Salisbury, qualified 1986, with *Linklaters* since qualification (save for 1989-90 when with *Mallesons Stephen Jaques*, Sydney Australia). Partner *Linklaters* since 1994.
Personal: Born 1962.

ROBINSON, Tim S.H.
Nicholson Graham & Jones, London (020) 7648 9000
tim.robinson@ngj.co.uk
Partner in Litigation Department, joint Head Travel and Leisure Law Unit.
Specialisation: Travel, Tourism and Leisure law. Acts for tour operators, travel agents, hotel groups, insurers, airlines and trade associations. Also handles general commercial litigation, libel and media acting for newspaper and magazine publishers. Writes for Travel Trade Gazette and major travel and tourism publications, the national press, TV and radio. Speaks at travel industry conferences in the UK and worldwide.
Prof. Memberships: Institute of Travel and Tourism, Media Society, Incentive Travel and Meeting Association, Board Director of Pacific Asia Travel Association (UK and worldwide), European Tour Operators Association, International Hotel and Restaurant Association.
Career: Qualified 1977. Joined *Nicholson Graham & Jones* 1979. Partner 1982.
Personal: Born in 1953. Attended St Edmund Hall, Oxford 1971-73. Leisure interests include music, reading, riding and classic cars.

RYLAND, David S.
SJ Berwin & Co, London (020) 7533 2222
david.ryland@sjberwin.com
Specialisation: Hotel & leisure sales and purchases, structured finance transactions, management contracts, joint ventures and the establishment of collective investment schemes. Transactions dealt with in the last year relating to the hotel and leisure industry include the establishment of the MWB Leisure Fund IIB, negotiation of forward funding agreements relating to substantial leisure parks including West India Leisure Scheme, Leisure Park Enfield, Eureka Leisure Park Ashford and Fiveways Birmingham, the purchase of the Caledonian Hotel, the negotiation of new Hilton hotels in Manchester and Newcastle, the sale of Regents Park Hilton and a portfolio of seven hotels for Hilton and the redevelopment of the Great Western Hotel. He has also been involved in the establishment of a wide range of tax efficient collective investment vehicles for property investment for an aggregate value of £2.5 billion.
Career: *Clifford Chance* 1981-88; *S J Berwin & Co* 1988-date. Dulwich College: 1965-72; Exeter College Oxford University: 1973-77 (double first in Mods and Greats). Frequent lecturer and writer of articles on property investment related matters.
Personal: Married. Interests include sport, music and cinema.

SEARS, Trevor P.R.
Kingsford Stacey Blackwell, London (020) 7447 1200
tsears@kingsfords.co.uk
Specialisation: Local counsel to the International Air Transport Association (IATA) and consultant to airlines with particular regard to their relationship with travel agents. Licensed Insolvency Practitioner and speaker at airline and travel seminars, radio and T.V. Acting for several airlines in connection with current IATA Trust cases.
Prof. Memberships: FABRP
Career: Qualified 1972. Joined *Booth and Blackwell.* Partner 1974. Senior partner 1990.
Personal: Born 1948. Educated at Epsom College. Lives in Surrey. Interests include travel, music, hockey and people.

SKUSE, Ian G.
Piper Smith & Basham, London (020) 7828 8685

STEWART, Peter J.
Field Fisher Waterhouse, London (020) 7861 4000
Partner and Head of Aviation Travel and Tourism Department.
Specialisation: Practice covers commercial areas (contentious and non-contentious) concerning the travel industry. Non-contentious work includes contractual arrangements between travel companies and their suppliers, compliance with regulatory requirements, joint ventures and business sales/purchases Contentious work includes disputes with suppliers, other travel companies and customers. Author of 'A Practical Guide to Package Holiday Law and Contracts' (third edition 1993) and regular articles for ITT journal and other trade papers. Regularly lectures for IBC and ITT at travel industry conferences.
Prof. Memberships: IFTTA, ITT.
Career: Qualified 1982, having joined *Field Fisher Waterhouse* in 1980. Became a Partner in 1985.
Personal: Born 3rd February 1956. Attended Campbell College in Belfast 1969-73, then Pembroke College Cambridge 1974-77. Leisure interests include golf, tennis and music. Lives near Sevenoaks, Kent.

VENABLES, Richard
Lane & Partners, London (020) 7242 2626
venables@lane.co.uk
See under Aviation, p.104

WIGNALL, Douglas
Douglas Wignall & Co, London (020) 7583 1362
Principal.
Specialisation: Main area of practice is hotels and leisure. Special area of expertise is drafting and negotiating international hotel management contracts and related agreements involved in hotel developments such as joint venture/shareholder agreements. Work also includes negotiating hotel franchise agreements, acquisitions and disposal of hotels in the United Kingdom and advising on all aspects of hotel operational matters. Has been involved in hotel and/or resort projects primarily in the United Kingdom and Europe and also in Africa, Middle East, Russia and former CIS countries. Major clients include Starwood Hotels and Resorts Inc, Morrison International Developments Ltd, Blakes Hotel Ltd and The Sheridan Group. Has lectured and written articles on hotel management contracts. Individual charge out rate is £210.00 per hour.
Prof. Memberships: Law Society, International Bar Association, International Society of Hospitality Consultants, Member of British Middle East Law Council, Member of the Company of Scriveners.
Career: Qualified in 1974. Worked in industry for approximately 10 years including Legal Counsel with Sheraton Management Corporation between 1981-84. Set up *Douglas Wignall & Co* in 1984.
Personal: Born 15th April 1950. Attended Brentwood School 1957-68, Leeds University 1968-71, and Guildford Law College 1971-72. Leisure interests include squash and music; member of Hurlingham Club. Lives in London SW6.

TRUSTS & PERSONAL TAX

London: 809; South: 811; Thames Valley: 812; South West: 813; Wales: 814; Midlands: 814; East Anglia: 815; North West: 816; North East: 816; Scotland: 817; N. Ireland: 818; *Profiles*: 818

RESEARCH APPROVED BY BMRB: *For this edition,* Chambers' *researchers conducted 6083 interviews – 4408 with law firms, 598 with barristers and 1077 with clients.*

The validity of the research was scrutinised by BMRB International, who audited both the methodology and the results at our offices in July 2000. They interviewed Chambers' *researchers and cross-checked sample interviews. Details of the audit appear on page 7.*

LONDON

TRUSTS & PERSONAL TAX • London	Ptnrs	Assts
❶ Macfarlanes	7	13
❷ Allen & Overy	4	18
Lawrence Graham	9	10
Withers	19	17
❸ Boodle Hatfield	6	5
Charles Russell	10	5
Currey & Co	7	4
Farrer & Co	12	9
❹ Bircham & Co	8	8
Forsters	4	5
Nicholson Graham & Jones	3	3
Payne Hicks Beach	5	3
Speechly Bircham	7	12
Taylor Joynson Garrett	7	4
❺ Hunters	7	2
Lee & Pembertons	5	7
Paisner & Co	6	3
Simmons & Simmons	3	8
Wedlake Bell	6	4
❻ Dawson & Co	6	4
Dechert	1	3
Fladgate Fielder	1	2
Gouldens	1	2
Linklaters	1	3
Maxwell Batley	1	3
May, May & Merrimans	6	5
Park Nelson	2	1
Radcliffes	7	5
Rooks Rider	6	6
Trowers & Hamlins	4	2
Witham Weld	1	3

Within each band, firms are listed alphabetically.

Macfarlanes Seen by many as the *"golden practice"* with an *"outstanding combination of intellect and clients,"* it edges to the top of the rankings this year. The team is respected for its commercial approach and quality across the board, with work ranging from UK and offshore tax and trust advice to heritage property, corporate support, the Lloyd's insurance market and trust litigation. Its major clients include landed individuals, entrepreneurs (including Richard Branson and Sir Paul Getty) and institutions and the practice is particularly rated for the strength of its international private client base. **John Rhodes** is seen as a *"first rate player"* and heads up a large team which also includes the *"brilliant"* **Michael Hayes.** One highlight of the last year was acting for an offshore trust company on the sale of its 90% shareholding in a private company to a UK plc, which involved supplementary tax, bankruptcy and insolvency issues.

Allen & Overy Retains its reputation as a *"strong, high value private client practice."* Its big hitters include **Richard Turnor**, an *"intelligent and serious player"* particularly known in the market for his expertise in emigration issues and asset tracing, and the *"sound"* **Clare Maurice.** The team advises UK and foreign-domiciled individuals and families on all aspects of trust and tax planning and is increasingly known for its corporate support role. The group advised on the creation of a discretionary trust as part of the securitisation of a large portfolio of trading assets. Noted by the market for its international capability and offshore work, the firm's renowned trust litigation group acted for off-shore trustees on claims brought in 'Grupo Torras v Sheikh Fahad Al Sabah'.

Lawrence Graham Respected practice whose broad UK, offshore and commercial expertise is supplemented by an investment management unit. The *"hugely experienced"* senior partner **Martyn Gowar** remains highly rated by his peers and *"has succeeded in building up a large department"* which counts leading private banks, trust companies and UK and foreign-domiciled families amongst its clients. The full range of non-contentious and contentious tax, trusts and probate work is handled, with particular strengths in offshore and institutional private client work. Highlights of the last year include continuing administration of the estate of the late Diana, Princess of Wales, and advising the Protector of a $500 million Bermuda trust on the defence of the structure's integrity against several cross-jurisdictional challenges.

Withers The largest private client practice in the country, its *"vast client base and accumulation of collective knowledge"* ensures its continuing position in the top league. The practice acts for around 15% of individuals in The Times Rich List in addition to trust companies and private banks, while its international client base has continued to expand, particularly in the Middle East, the USA and Europe. On top of the strength of its trusts and tax, commercial, international and probate groups, the group is seen to be at the forefront of trust litigation, and has acted in several multi-jurisdictional trust disputes. Leading players in the team remain **Anthony Thompson, Stephen Cooke** (who is noted for his *"presence"* and *"strong legal knowledge"*), **John Riches** and **Robin Paul.** Recent highlights include the structuring of a privately owned business empire in the Lebanon worth approximately £100 million.

Boodle Hatfield *"High profile"* practice which is particularly known for its landed estate clients. Senior Partner **Richard Moyse** is seen as *"quite excellent," "constructive"* and *"good on the esoteric sphere"* and joins the top tier of individuals, while **Kate Howe** is also respected in the field. Core strengths include domestic trust and estate planning, off-shore trust structuring and complex probates, while recent trends include Family Office and contentious trust and probate work. An example of the latter was involvement in litigation surrounding the estate of Francis Bacon. The team maintains strong links with other departments in the firm, particularly in the areas of corporate and property tax.

Charles Russell Respected *"academic"* **Catriona Syed** continues to be a practitioner of repute here, while colleague **David Long** rises in the rankings to reflect his reputation as a *"sound all-round practitioner"* with noted skills in contentious work and negotiation. Advice to its client portfolio of wealthy UK and international families, private banks and trust companies, includes domestic and international tax planning, advice to trustees on

LEADING INDIVIDUALS • London	
❶ **AVERY JONES John** Speechly Bircham	**GOWAR Martyn** Lawrence Graham
HAYES Michael Macfarlanes	**MOYSE Richard** Boodle Hatfield
RHODES John Macfarlanes	
❷ **BOYD-CARPENTER Henry** Farrer & Co	**BRIDGES Mark** Farrer & Co
BROWN Graham Payne Hicks Beach	**COOKE Stephen** Withers
GARNHAM Caroline Simmons & Simmons	
JARMAN Chris Payne Hicks Beach	**KENNEDY John** Hunters
LONG David Charles Russell	**MAURICE Clare** Allen & Overy
MELLOR Eliza Nicholson Graham & Jones	**POWELL Nicholas** Currey & Co
THOMPSON Anthony Withers	**TURNOR Richard** Allen & Overy
WILLIS David Forsters	
❸ **DOLMAN Robert** Wedlake Bell	**GOODWIN Peter** Bircham & Co.
HOWE Kate Boodle Hatfield	**JACOBS Michael** Nicholson Graham & Jones
KIRBY Richard Speechly Bircham	**PAUL Robin** Withers
REID Nigel Linklaters	**RICHARDSON Joseph Charles** Dawson & Co
RICHES John Withers	**ROBINSON David** Forsters
STANFORD-TUCK Michael Taylor Joynson Garrett	
SYED Catriona Charles Russell	

See Profiles on page 818

corporate matters, probate and supplementary property issues. One highlight of the year was a court endorsement of the team's advice to the trustees of the Baily Thomas Trust, leading to the sale of a 48% stake in Mansfield Brewery.

Currey & Co *"Quintessential niche practice,"* known for its concentration on landed estate *"rolling acres and mansion houses"* clients and its deliberately low-key profile. While steering clear of international and contentious work, the team handles all aspects of traditional tax and trusts work *"to a very high standard."* **Nicholas Powell** is respected throughout the market as a *"superb practitioner"* and a *"first-class mind – he sees the issues and explains them with enormous clarity."*

Farrer & Co While still seen as a *"wonderful practice,"* the team sometimes stands accused of *"lacking dynamism."* However, several recent lateral hires from City firms highlight the practice's continued expansion, particularly in the entrepreneurial sphere. As part of a wider private client group, the tax and trusts team advises some of the most prominent royal and landed individuals and families in the country (including the Queen and the Duchy of Lancaster). In addition, the group is continuing to build up its new money and international practices. Work handled ranges from UK and offshore financial planning advice to succession issues, advising trustees and beneficiaries on their powers and duties and trust litigation. The leading players at the firm remain **Henry Boyd-Carpenter**, who is *"incredibly intelligent"* and has recently been appointed senior partner, and **Mark Bridges** who is known for his *"strong offshore practice."* Significant work of the last year has included acting in a number of large international succession disputes involving holding structures set up around the world.

Bircham & Co Maintains its reputation as an *"honourable and safe"* team with a *"strong trust practice"* and a client base made up of landed estates, wealthy UK and foreign-domiciled families and individuals and both UK and offshore trustees. The respected **Peter Goodwin** heads up the team, which has particular expertise in contentious probate and family disputes, international succession/conflict of law cases, trust management and tax trust compliance. The department also has a specialist Anglo-French practice and a discrete investment management team. Recent highlights include acting on the administration of the estate of the late Jill Dando, and advising on the partial distribution of a large US trust involving several complex UK and US trust and tax issues.

Forsters Rises in the rankings as a reflection of its growing reputation for quality and profitability *("everyone is talking about them")* which was further strengthened by the arrival of the private client department of Masons in May 2000. Work handled includes the full range of UK and offshore tax and trust advice, wills and probate, trusts litigation and conflict of laws. The team has specialist expertise in safeguarding heritage property and is currently preparing, in tandem with several other firms, a test case which will challenge the Inland Revenue's new rules on access to conditionally exempt heritage property. **David Willis** and **David Robinson** received approval from peers.

Nicholson Graham & Jones Small department which retains its position in the rankings largely owing to the eminent reputation of two partners, the *"technically capable"* and *"impressive"* **Eliza Mellor** (who several believe to be the *"powerhouse"* of the department and who is noted for her international practice) and the *"intelligent"* **Michael Jacobs.** Tax-driven advice is the fulcrum of the practice's work, and the group has a particular reputation for acting on cases with a foreign element.

Payne Hicks Beach *"Traditional firm"* seen to have *"kept up with its peers"* with *"some good new money and offshore work,"* although it is not felt to have the corporate strength of some of its competitors. **Graham Brown** and **Chris Jarman** remain highly rated, and the team caters to a broad and growing range of clients, from landed money to new entrepreneurs (including some dot.com millionaires). Internationally, the practice administers a number of trusts through its own offshore trust corporation. European-domiciled individuals and cross-border work continue to make up a significant proportion of the practice.

Speechly Bircham The practice's profile has risen over the last year due to its pioneering of packaged tax-saving products which have brought in a substantial amount of new business, notably the Speechly Bircham Loan Plan. The team is felt to rely heavily on the *"simply brilliant"* **John Avery Jones**, who has *"the most encyclopaedic knowledge of tax"* and is a member of the Steering Committee on the rewriting of UK tax law. The full range of tax and trust advice is handled for 50% offshore (offshore trust corporations and non-UK domiciled individuals) and 50% onshore clients (landed estates, entrepreneurs and packaged product clients), while the team has niche expertise in heritage property. Advised a Southern Hemisphere sovereign state on the establishment of a major international financial and offshore trust centre. **Richard Kirby** is also a recommended practitioner.

Taylor Joynson Garrett City firm which *"has some substantial private clients whom it looks after very well."* The team received praise in the market for its offshore capability, which ranges from international tax planning for entrepreneurs (with an increasing number of e-commerce clients) to advising leading offshore private banks. **Michael Stanford-Tuck** heads the team, which is part of an integrated private client department and cross-refers heavily with its corporate and IP practices. The last year has seen the practice become increasingly involved in investment work.

Hunters Traditional Lincoln's Inn practice with a reputation for a *"nice and civilised"* approach and an impressive client base. In addition to trust, tax and probate advice, the firm has noted strengths in the fields of heritage property and charitable trusts. **John Kennedy** is the team's leading player.

Lee & Pembertons Retains its name as a *"good, solid practice"* which handles the gamut of trust work and tax planning for a largely domestic client base, including agricultural and residential London estates and wealthy individuals. Overseas, the team acts for a number of offshore trusts and corporations and advises on issues of domicile and tax residence.

Paisner & Co Particularly known in the wider market for its involvement in the area of trusts litigation (one partner is the founding member of the Association of Contentious Trust and Probate Specialists), the team's key strengths lie in its corporate support role and in tax and estate planning for 'new money' clients. In addition to advising prominent international banks and trust companies on tax and trust issues, the group provides its UK and overseas entrepreneur clients with associated personal tax and trust planning advice affecting family businesses, flotations, corporate sales and acquisitions. Highlights of the last year have included reviewing changes in the capital tax regime, particularly with regard to 'flip flop' schemes, and the purchase of trust losses.

Simmons & Simmons Retains its position in the rankings largely due to the strong reputation of the *"increasingly good"* tax and trusts specialist **Caroline Garnham** who is seen by many in the market as a *"one-woman band."* The practice has emphasised integrated private capital work for individuals, family offices and private banks. Clients include private banks, two prominent Middle Eastern Royal families, wealthy European families, leading UK entrepreneurs and businessmen. The practice has recently won a tender to review all standard wills and trust documentation for JR Rothschild's South of England clients.

Wedlake Bell **Robert Dolman** remains the leading player at this respected practice which offers tax, trust and probate work across the board. The group maintains an office in Guernsey to administer offshore companies and handle offshore tax and trust issues, asset protection and tax efficient structures. Particular strengths include trust litigation, advising traditional Lloyds names and owner/managers of small and medium-sized companies. Niche specialisms include advice on exemptions for certain works of art. Recently advised on a trust reorganisation worth £60 million.

Dawson & Co Particularly notable for its numbers of landed estate clients and its expertise in capital tax planning for heritage property, reinvestment relief and enterprise investment. All aspects of onshore and offshore tax and trust work are handled, and team head **Joseph Richardson** is rated by the market.

Dechert Continues to be rated for its growing trust litigation practice. The firm's US and European connections give the practice added strength in offshore and cross-border tax and estate planning. Dealing with the administration of the £59 million estate of the late Christina Batty.

Fladgate Fielder Small team which combines a traditional private client practice with tax planning for the firm's business clients. Handles the full range of tax, trust and probate work, with particular expertise in the structuring of property investments, offshore tax work and implementing share schemes. Acted as court appointed receiver in the estate of a murdered East European politician.

Gouldens Known in the market for its *"lucrative offshore trust practice"* and for private client work brought in on the the back of its overseas investor clients and corporate referrals. In addition to UK and overseas individuals, clients include a number of trust companies and private banks. The team have recently acted for the executors of Matthew Harding in winding up the estate and providing supplementary legal advice.

Linklaters The *"first-class"* **Nigel Reid** is the trusts expert at this Magic Circle heavyweight, and is new to the rankings this year. Provides tax and trust advice for individual clients and support to other departments where trusts or trustees are involved. Particular strengths include international trust and asset protection structures and issues arising from the ownership of shares in private and public companies. Acts for a number of insurance companies in relation to trusts of life policies.

Maxwell Batley Noted in the market for its substantial overseas investor clients. Additional niche strengths include acting for private banks and trust corporations, UK and cross-border probate administration and contentious trust and probate work.

May, May & Merrimans Niche private client practice renowned for its substantial landed estate client base. Handles all aspects of tax and financial planning, with particular expertise in heritage property work.

Park Nelson Long established firm which continues to have a reputation in the area, and a strong international clientele.

Radcliffes Remains a recommended, broad-based team despite the recent departure of its head of department. Specialisms include Court of Protection/elderly care advice and international trust work, boosted by an associated independent trustee company in Switzerland. Advised on the tax implications for a major family-related investment through a collective investment vehicle.

Rooks Rider Notable for its fashion industry and Far Eastern clients, the team maintains a strong offshore practice with an emphasis on inward investment and relevant property tax planning and structuring of corporate holdings. Tax planning for e-commerce and offshore clients has been a growth area over the last year.

Trowers & Hamlins Maintains across-the-board trust and personal tax capability within a wider private client department. Clients include City professionals, entrepreneurs, landowners and non-residents.

Witham Weld Has an acknowledged presence in trusts, probate and charities work, with a large number of Roman Catholic individual and institutional clients.

THE SOUTH

Cripps Harries Hall *"An extremely well run set-up"* which received praise across the market and retains its leading position. The *"experienced"* and *"technically capable"* **Simon Leney** heads the department, while tax specialist **Gary Rogerson** is seen as *"good on the rocket science stuff"* and enters the rankings this year. The practice has a strong reputation for its integrated investment management service, and on the tax side offers particular expertise in capital tax planning, US/UK tax disputes and inheritance disputes. Additionally the team handles all aspects of trust creation and management, wills and estate administration and professional trusteeship. Recently took over a multi-million pound trust with an international element after one of the previous trustees was charged with fraud.

Thomas Eggar Church Adams Highly rated trusts and tax practice seen to have grown on the back of its investment management arm *("a serious rival to stockbrokers in the region")*. The Chichester office remains the hub of the private client group, which handles the full range of domestic and offshore tax planning, trust and tax administration work. Clients include retired business figures, entrepreneurs, farmers and private trusts, of which the team administers over 500. Recommended individuals are the *"technical and thoughtful"* **Richard Thornely** and the *"impressive"* **Amanda King-Jones**. The team regularly acts as trustees of occupational pensions schemes.

Adams & Remers Still felt to be one of the leading private client firms in the south, this determinedly low-profile outfit is recognised to have an outstanding niche in advising on inheritance tax for substantial landed estate clients. Recently involved in the sale of major football memorabilia, which contained an offshore element.

Thomas Snell & Passmore **James Krafft** remains the leading light of a team whose core areas of practice include probate, tax planning, trusts and estate planning, with niche strengths in international wills, estate planning and offshore trusts work. The last year has seen an expansion in the receivership and Court of Protection practice as a result of increasing referrals from the Personal Injury and Clinical Negligence departments. Administers trusts worth £75 million and recently advised on a dispute over a complex £12 million estate.

Blake Lapthorn Now concentrated in its Portsmouth office, the practice continues to flourish in conjunction with its investment management work. The team handles all aspects of wills and probate, personal taxation and trusts relating to family inheritance and disposal of assets. A broad

TRUSTS & PERSONAL TAX • The South	Ptnrs	Assts
❶ **Cripps Harries Hall** Tunbridge Wells, Kent	6	3
Thomas Eggar Church Adams Chichester	6	1
❷ **Adams & Remers** Lewes	2	2
Thomson Snell & Passmore Tunbridge Wells	5	9
❸ **Blake Lapthorn** Portsmouth	2	5
Moore & Blatch Lymington	1	5
Paris Smith & Randall Southampton	1	2
Stevens & Bolton Guildford	2	1
❹ **Brachers** Maidstone	1	2
DMH Brighton	1	1
Lester Aldridge Bournemouth	2	2
Mundays Esher	2	-
Penningtons Godalming	3	3
White & Bowker Winchester	3	1
❺ **Barlows** Guildford	2	3
Buss Murton Tunbridge Wells	⚑	⚑
Staffurth & Bray Bognor Regis	2	4
❻ **Charles Russell** Guildford	1	4
George Ide, Phillips Chichester	2	2
Griffith Smith Brighton	⚑	⚑
Whitehead Monckton Maidstone	2	2

LEADING INDIVIDUALS	
❶ **KING-JONES Amanda** Thomas Eggar Church Adams	
LENEY Simon Cripps Harries Hall	
THORNELY Richard Thomas Eggar Church Adams	
❷ **GLAZIER Barry** Lester Aldridge	**KRAFFT James** Thomson Snell & Passmore
ROGERSON Gary Cripps Harries Hall	**THURSTON Martyn** White & Bowker

Within each band, firms are listed alphabetically.

See Profiles on page 818

⚑ *Figures unavailable at time of going to press.*

spread of clients include business people and farmers, and the team has niche expertise in large estates and farm advice.

Moore & Blatch Respected private client department, which handles work across the spectrum of trusts and personal tax. Well-known for its fund management advice, the team also includes two in-house members of the Securities Institute. Clients include leading charities and local landed estates.

Paris Smith & Randall Maintains its strong reputation for tax planning (including tax saving trusts) and estate work. The team also offers financial services provision and has recently entered into a joint venture to assist a large Jersey firm with its trusts work. Clients include lottery winners, 'old' and 'new' money and an increasing number of sports personalities.

Stevens & Bolton A strong and growing reputation in the market as *"progressive," "switched on"* and *"ambitious"* leads the practice to rise in the rankings. Notable for its substantial amount of offshore work, including tax planning for foreign-domiciled shareholders, establishing offshore employee benefit trusts and 'flip-flop' schemes. The team's domestic clients include professionals, entrepreneurs and individuals of established wealth. Advised on and implemented an "Ingram" lease carve out scheme for a £2 million stately home.

Brachers Notable for its large farming clientele, the team remains rated in the market for its tax and trust work and is retained by a number of landed estate and entrepreneurs. Typical work areas include restructuring farming business prior to sale, family tax planning in the context of divorce and capital gain tax mitigation through the use of retirement relief for company shareholders. Recently provided tax planning advice to a non-domiciliary worth over $1 million.

DMH Handles capital and inheritance tax planning and trust provision for high value clients including large estates and business people. A separate Asset Management Department provides integrated investment advice.

Lester Aldridge Headed by the *"effective"* **Barry Glazier**, the practice provides all aspects of tax, investment and estate planning to clients including family owned companies, entrepreneurs and offshore clients. On the probate side the team provides a will writing service for a major assurance company and maintains an international probate unit with clients in South Africa, Zimbabwe and Spain. Contentious trust and probate is another specialism and one partner was one of the first lawyers out of London to become a full member of the Association of Contentious Trust and Probate Practitioners. Recent work has included capital tax schemes prior to sales of family companies to plcs.

Mundays Well-regarded team which enters the rankings this year after repeated recommendation from the market. Provides specialist tax, trust and wills advice to company-owner clients, and receives referrals from other solicitors in the area. Recently dealt with tax planning for the owner of an £11 million group of companies, including trust creation, re-arrangement of the exisiting trust and associated corporate restructuring.

Penningtons New to the rankings this year, the practice is known for its *"technical expertise."* Handles onshore and offshore trust and tax work for a range of clients including family trusts, business owners and directors, farming partnerships and wealthy individuals. Niche expertise in business succession and restructuring in the agricultural sector. Acted in 'Farmer and Giles v Inland Revenue Commissioners' which established that diversified farming assets could qualify for 100% relief from Inheritance Tax.

White & Bowker Known in the market for its substantial landed and agricultural estate practice, the team is building up its 'new money' clientele which includes owner/managers and conflict referrals from both London and regional firms. **Martyn Thurston** enters the rankings this year following strong recommendation from his peers.

Other Notable Firms **Barlows, Buss Murton** and **Staffurth & Bray** remain recommended as experienced and broad ranging practices. **Charles Russell, George Ide Phillips, Griffith Smith** and **Whitehead Monckton** are all considered to have solid trusts teams.

THAMES VALLEY

Boodle Hatfield Remains the top practice in the region with accountants recommending it for *"the more complex tax and trusts work,"* which includes reorganising UK and offshore trusts, complex probates and trust and probate litigation. Strong links with the London office ensure a healthy national and international client base including landed estates, entrepreneurs, expatriates and members of the Oxford arts and academic community. **Sue Laing** heads the team and is widely known as a trusts specialist.

Blandy & Blandy Long established practice which *"has a big presence in the area"* and is known to act for several landed estates. The team is similarly well-versed in trust and tax planning for owner/managers, directors of plcs and an increasing number of London clients. Other areas of advice include high volume probate, wills, EPAs and related Court of Protection work. Recently received instructions to act on the administration of a £22 million estate.

Henmans Rises in the rankings to reflect the team's growing profile in the region and its strong client portfolio. The latter includes individuals (including several well-known television personalities) and substantial landed estates. Probate is another mainstay of the practice, which regularly administers estates between £1 million and £5 million. Other core ser-

TRUSTS & PERSONAL TAX • Thames Valley	Ptnrs	Assts
❶ **Boodle Hatfield** Oxford	3	2
❷ **Blandy & Blandy** Reading	2	3
Henmans Oxford	2	2
❸ **Iliffes Booth Bennett** Uxbridge	2	3
❹ **BP Collins** Gerrards Cross	2	1
Clarks Reading	1	1
Matthew Arnold & Baldwin Watford	1	3
Pictons Hemel Hempstead	1	-
Stanley Tee & Company Bishop's Stortford	1	2
❺ **Boyes Turner & Burrows** Reading	1	2

LEADING INDIVIDUALS
❶ **LAING Sue** Boodle Hatfield

Within each band, firms are listed alphabetically.

See Profiles on page 818

vices include capital tax advice, onshore and offshore trust administration and Court of Protection work.

Iliffes Booth Bennett Notable for its probate practice, which has established links with the Alzheimers Society and last year handled probates worth £5 million and estates of £1 million. In financial planning matters, the team provides tax and trust work for an established clientele of high net worth individuals and a growing number of family businesses. Provision for the elderly and disabled by means of discretionary trusts and enduring powers of attorney are increasing areas of practice.

Other Notable Firms **BP Collins** and **Clarks** remain recommended for their tax and trust work and high net worth clients, while **Matthew Arnold & Baldwin** are particularly strong on corporate support work (such as trust work for pension funds, retirement relief trusts and employee benefit trusts) and estate planning for commercial clients. **Pictons** retains its reputation in the sector, and is experienced in issues concerning the provision of care for the elderly, disabled and terminally ill. **Stanley Tee & Co** continue to have a presence in the market, while **Boyes Turner Burrows** is new to the rankings this year on the recommendation of solicitors and accountants in the region, and is particularly rated for capital tax planning.

SOUTH WEST

TRUSTS & PERSONAL TAX • South West	Ptnrs	Assts
❶ **Burges Salmon** Bristol	3	7
Osborne Clarke OWA, Bristol	2	9
Wiggin & Co Cheltenham	5	2
Wilsons Salisbury	5	2
❷ **Bond Pearce** Plymouth	2	1
Charles Russell Cheltenham	2	1
Foot Anstey Sargent Exeter	3	2
❸ **Clarke Willmott & Clarke** Taunton	4	6
TLT Solicitors Bristol	1	6
❹ **Coodes** St. Austell	⚐	⚐
Hooper & Wollen Torquay	3	2
Meade-King Bristol	⚐	⚐
Michelmores Exeter	3	8
Rickerby Watterson Cheltenham	2	5
Veale Wasbrough Bristol	1	1
❺ **Stephens & Scown** Liskeard, Exeter, Truro	4	-
Stones Exeter	2	3
Woollcombe Beer Watts Newton Abbot	⚐	⚐

LEADING INDIVIDUALS •
❶ **EMMERSON John** Wilsons
FITZGERALD Peter Wilsons
MILLER Adrian Foot Anstey Sargent
NICHOLSON Jonathan Bond Pearce
WOLLEN Nigel Hooper & Wollen
❷ **BROWN Sandra** Osborne Clarke
ELPHINSTON Alexander Foot Anstey Sargent
EVANS Michael Burges Salmon
FULLERLOVE Michael Wiggin & Co
MITCHELL Martin Burges Salmon
WYLD Charles Burges Salmon
❸ **NELLIST Peter** Clarke Willmott & Clarke
VOREMBERG Rhoderick Wilsons

Within each band, firms are listed alphabetically.

See Profiles on page 818

⚐ *Figures unavailable at time of going to press.*

Burges Salmon *"A class team"* seen to *"have the market sewn up for old money,"* it retains its position in the leading band. In addition to its expertise in acting for the landed and farming sectors (in which it continues to pick up new estate clients), the team acts for an increasing number of non-domiciliaries, business owners, directors and shareholders, often on referral from the firm's corporate department. The well regarded **Charles Wyld** heads a team which includes **Martin Mitchell** *("a good reputation amongst his business clients")* and **Michael Evans** *("particularly good on tax – and has the knack of explaining it well.")* Advised on the formation of 40 offshore trusts for wealthy clients of a US bank.

Osborne Clarke OWA Large team with *"a number of good individuals"* and *"serious clients,"* often referred from the firm's commercial operations. Core areas of work include advising owner/managers on business start-ups or exits, international work, such as multi-jurisdictional tax planning, and traditional estate planning for landed estates. The team also gives tax and trust advice to a number of leading institutional clients. Team head **Sandra Brown** is seen as a *"tough cookie"* and remains highly rated in the market.

Wiggin & Co Nationally rated for its niche specialism in providing offshore tax and investment structuring for wealthy overseas families, the department maintains an office in Los Angeles for its large US client base. The practice also handles traditional tax and trust work for a substantial domestic client portfolio of landed estates, and regularly advises on heritage property matters. **Michael Fullerlove** is recommended for his offshore expertise.

Wilsons Retains its leading reputation, with a *"super client list"* and several recommended individuals.The respected **John Emmerson** has a *"fantastic offshore practice,"* particularly from South East Asia, while **Peter Fitzgerald** is known for the quality of his landed estate clients. **Rhoderick Voremburg**'s abilities are also acknowledged.

Bond Pearce The mainstay of the practice is tax planning for business owners and entrepreneurs on the back of the firm's commercial practice, alongside work for 'old money' and institutional clients. Niche specialisms include probates for non-domiciled families referred from foreign banks and corporate support trust work. **Jonathan Nicholson** retains his reputation as a *"real technician."*

Charles Russell Maintains its *"big Cheltenham presence"* with a strong emphasis on landed estate clientele. Handles all aspects of tax, trusts and probate work and administers 300 trusts. Recently restructured the ownership of three large estates.

Foot Anstey Sargent **Adrian Miller** and **Alex Elphinstone** retain respected reputations in the local market at the head of a team which handles fund management, Court of Protection cases and estate and tax planning. Clients include bank trustees, charities and offshore trusts.

Clarke Willmott & Clarke Known in the market for its integrated asset management work, the team handles the full range of wills, tax and trusts work for a broad client base of business people, landed wealth and farmers. **Peter Nellist** is highly rated for his estate planning and investment expertise and makes his debut in the rankings this year. One highlight of last year was providing a client with an IHT saving through the use of a succession of Deeds of Variation.

TLT Solicitors Respected team which provides wills, tax and trusts advice for a mixture of 'new money' and 'old money' clients in addition to some offshore work and corporate support. Has particular expertise in Court of Protection work. Recently acted in a £180 million company share sale which involved setting up a tax planning scheme for the individuals involved, advising on the share scheme and preparing wills.

Other Notable Firms **Coodes** and **Hooper & Wollen** are highly rated in the 'deep south' and **Nigel Wollen**, at the latter firm, is seen as *"knowledgable, experienced and practical."* **Meade-King** retains its long-standing reputation in the field, as do **Michelmores**. **Rickerby Watterson** enters the rankings this year, and is known for its *"broad based practice"* which includes a dedicated trust litigation specialist. **Veale Wasbrough** maintains its reputation in the market, and is particularly strong on wills work and deeds of variation. **Stephens & Scown** (new to the rankings this year,) **Stones** and **Woollcombe Beer Watts** are also recommended.

WALES

TRUSTS & PERSONAL TAX • Wales	Ptnrs	Assts
❶ **Edwards Geldard** Cardiff	1	2
❷ **Hugh James Ford Simey** Cardiff	1	3
❸ **Bevan Ashford** Cardiff	-	1
Eversheds Cardiff	⚐	⚐
Margraves Llandrindod Wells	1	3

LEADING INDIVIDUALS •
❶ **MORTIMER Fay** Edwards Geldard
WRIGHT Cherry Hugh James Ford Simey

Within each band, firms are listed alphabetically. *See Profiles on page 818*

⚐ *Figures unavailable at time of going to press.*

Edwards Geldard *"The leading private client practice"* in the region with a substantial client base including lottery winners and business people referred from other departments in the firm, banks and financial advisers. The team also handles trust work for its corporate clients (such as putting shares into a trust to reduce the IHT due) and tax work for private banks and accountancy firms. **Fay Mortimer** remains rated for her *"pragmatic and commercial approach."*

Hugh James Ford Simey Enters the rankings this year after widespread recommendation, as does the *"technically able"* **Cherry Wright**. Acts for a broad client base, with work ranging from tax planning to setting up Special Needs trusts and discretionary trusts for personal injury damages. The practice is also well-versed in handling trust and probate litigation matters.

Other Notable Firms **Bevan Ashford** is a respected broad-based practice with niche expertise in NHS trusts, while the part-time team at **Eversheds** concentrates on tax planning for owner/managers in addition to private client work for elderly clients. Niche practice **Margraves** is new to the rankings this year and is recommended as *"the firm to go to in mid-Wales."*

MIDLANDS

TRUSTS & PERSONAL TAX • Midlands	Ptnrs	Assts
❶ **Martineau Johnson** Birmingham	4	3
❷ **Browne Jacobson** Nottingham	3	1
Hewitson Becke + Shaw Northampton	2	2
Lee Crowder Birmingham	2	3
Wragge & Co Birmingham	2	3
❸ **Freethcartwright** Nottingham	3	1
Higgs & Sons Brierley Hill	4	3
Lodders Stratford-upon-Avon	2	6
Pinsent Curtis Birmingham	3	6
Shakespeares Birmingham	2	3
❹ **Gateley Wareing** Birmingham	⚐	⚐
The Wilkes Partnership Birmingham	1	2
Willcox Lane Clutterbuck Birmingham	3	4

LEADING INDIVIDUALS •
❶ **CARSLAKE Hugh** Martineau Johnson
JENKINS Paul Browne Jacobson
WOODHEAD Louise Wragge & Co
❷ **GREEN Martin** Lodders

Within each band, firms are listed alphabetically. *See Profiles on page 818*

⚐ *Figures unavailable at time of going to press.*

Martineau Johnson Retains its leading position after unanimous praise in the market, and the *"charming and self-effacing"* **Hugh Carslake** maintains his strong reputation. The team is particularly known for its 'old money' clients and supplementary heritage property work (it acts for nineteen landed estates), and is increasingly instructed by entrepreneurs, owner/managers and accountants in the West Midlands and London. Handles the full range of tax and estate planning, wills and trusts work and administers private trusts worth in excess of £210 million.

Browne Jacobson Well known tax and trusts team known for its offshore capability, which is new to the rankings this year. The *"brilliant"* **Paul Jenkins** is seen as *"the top man in the East Midlands"* and enters the individuals' rankings. The team provides tax, trusts and wills advice for a client base, comprising proprietors of family businesses. Other areas of expertise include trust litigation and business restructuring. A separate team works in conjunction with the corporate department to advise on the tax implications of deals for shareholders and trustees. Includes a barrister who has niche expertise in acting for French-domiciled individuals.

Hewitson Becke + Shaw Well-regarded practice with *"breadth of experience"* which specialises in tax and trust advice for landed and investor clients, often with international connections. Also handles administration of deceased estates and family trusts, with 300 trusts currently under administration. Fund management and pensions consultancy is available from a separate Investment Services Unit. Administered a substantial estate where the deceased was domiciled in a Far Eastern country and had assets in the UK and several other jurisdictions.

Lee Crowder Long established private client practice seen by the market as *"keen to expand,"* with a large team and growing client list, particularly amongst entrepreneurs and 'new money.' Handles all aspects of trusts, wills, estate planning and investment advice.

Wragge & Co The highly-rated **Louise Woodhead** heads this recommended team, which maintains its steady growth in the sector. The group advises business owners on sales and trustees involved in corporate transactions. Has particular expertise in UK/US estate planning and large probates (including international wills.)

Freethcartwright Maintains its strong reputation for domestic tax planning and probate work, including contentious probate/IFPDA claims and Wills advice, particularly in relation to second marriages. Its investment team specialises in trust investment for a range of trust portfolios, including personal injury trusts and medical negligence settlements. Recently devised an IHT scheme for an estate worth in excess of £6 million.

Higgs & Sons Highly regarded team which is receiving an increasing amount of referral work from accountants and financial advisers. In addition to core estate planning and trust administration for company owners and directors, onshore/offshore trustees and wealthy individuals and families, the team handles Court of Protection /EPA work and asset protection for older clients. Set up a number of trusts to take advantage of CGT Retirement Relief.

Lodders New to the rankings this year, the team is perceived to *"have built up a substantial private client practice"* with a *"strong South Warwickshire client base."* Though particularly known for its farming and landowner clientele, the team's onshore and offshore tax expertise has led to an increasing number of referrals from regional commercial firms, and clients extend to members of the Stratford acting community. The team has niche specialism in community care and nursing home funding issues, for which it receives recommendations from around the country. The *"excellent"* **Martin Green** also makes his debut in the rankings.

Pinsent Curtis The practice is distinct in that it operates from within the corporate tax department, providing personal tax and trust advice as part of an all-round tax service to businesses, their owners/directors and shareholders. Clients include e-commerce entrepreneurs and private investors, international entrepreneurs and some land-owners. Niche expertise includes personal tax advice on sales of private companies and offshore trust work. Recently restructured high value offshore trusts for several major entrepreneur families.

Shakespeares The private client department acts for a variety of wealthy individuals, including entrepreneurs and landed gentry. Work handled includes offshore taxation matters, trust taxation and accountancy and tax planning.

Other Notable Firms **Gateley Wareing** is new to the rankings this year while **The Wilkes Partnership** and **Willcox Lane Clutterbuck** remain recommended for their private client base.

EAST ANGLIA

TRUSTS & PERSONAL TAX • East Anglia	Ptnrs	Assts
❶ Hewitson Becke + Shaw Cambridge	2	4
Mills & Reeve Norwich	6	8
❷ Eversheds Norwich	3	3
❸ Cozens-Hardy & Jewson Norwich	1	3
Howes Percival Norwich	1	1
Taylor Vinters Cambridge	3	1
❹ Ashton Graham Bury St Edmunds	2	3
Greene & Greene Bury St. Edmunds	1	-
Hood Vores & Allwood Dereham	2	-
Prettys Ipswich	2	-
Roythorne & Co Spalding	2	3
Ward Gethin King's Lynn	3	3
Willcox & Lewis Norwich	2	2

LEADING INDIVIDUALS •
❶ BARCLAY Jonathan Mills & Reeve
BRADLEY David Hewitson Becke + Shaw
EWART Peter Hewitson Becke + Shaw
RIPMAN Justin Mills & Reeve
❷ HEAL Jeremy Howes Percival

Within each band, firms are listed alphabetically.

See Profiles on page 818

Hewitson Becke + Shaw An *"extremely responsive and extremely professional"* outfit, which retains its top-flight reputation. Strong recommendations came from the market for the *"effective"* **Peter Ewart** and **David Bradley**, who enters the rankings this year. The team handles all aspects of tax and trust work for a substantial client base including landed estates, farmers, local businessmen and an increasing number of wealthy London clients. Advised racing commentator Peter O'Sullevan on the creation of a charitable trust for the benefit of injured jockeys and animal welfare.

Mills & Reeve *"Excellent"* practice whose *"sheer size and quality of people"* leads it to *"stand head and shoulders above the rest"* in Norwich. **Justin Ripman** heads the team and is highly rated for his *"broad based practice"* and offshore expertise while **Jonathan Barclay** has also received widespread commendation. Handles onshore and offshore tax planning, trusts, wills, probate and heritage property work for landowners and businessmen.

Eversheds The leading office of the national firm's comparatively low-profile private client practice, the team is known in the market for its *"considerable experience."* The group provides a broad range of succession planning, wills, probate, estates and trust administration, trust litigation and supplementary investment advice to private clients including owner/managers, individuals and traditional landed families. Receives a number of referrals from other Eversheds offices, including multi-jurisdictional matters referred from the Brussels and Monaco offices. Currently advising on the structuring and tax, trust and financial issues of a multi-million pound company sale.

Cozens-Hardy & Jewson Rises in the rankings after repeated recommendation in the market. Known for its *"solid mixed client base"* of landed wealth and business people.

Howes Percival Enters the rankings largely on the reputation of the *"bright"* **Jeremy Heal** who is seen as an *"extremely good technician, both on trusts law and taxation aspects."* Handles estate planning largely for wealthy landowning and farming families with assets worth £1 million to £50 million. Recent growth areas include discretionary trusts formed with the proceeds of sales of substantial development land, and Nil Rate Band discretionary will trusts. In addition the practice has set up a separate unit to ensure integrated accountancy, investment and legal advice.

Taylor Vinters *"Thorough"* and *"constructive"* team which handles trusts, tax and probate work for estates and farming clients in addition to a growing number of high-tech entrepreneurs. Has specialist expertise in trust work and financial planning for successful personal injury litigants.

Other Notable Firms **Ashton Graham**, **Greene & Greene** and **Hood Vores & Allwood** remain recommended as *"respectable"*, *"traditional"* practices with long-established farming and landowning client bases. **Ward Gethin** retains a *"substantial private client practice"* which is rated in the market while **Prettys** also maintains its reputation. **Willcox & Lewis** have a very different profile and act largely for entrepreneurs and offshore clients. Lincolnshire firm **Roythorne & Co** has an established reputation for private client work.

NORTH WEST

TRUSTS & PERSONAL TAX • North West	Ptnrs	Assts
❶ **Brabner Holden Banks Wilson** Liverpool	3	10
Halliwell Landau Manchester	2	2
❷ **Addleshaw Booth & Co** Manchester	2	-
Birch Cullimore Chester	2	-
Cobbetts Manchester	2	2
❸ **Cuff Roberts** Liverpool	1	1
Davies Wallis Foyster Liverpool	1	3
Pannone & Partners Manchester	3	-

LEADING INDIVIDUALS •
❶ **SHINDLER Geoffrey** Halliwell Landau
❷ **BISHOP David** David Bishop & Co
FEENY Mark Brabner Holden Banks Wilson
STURROCK Alan Addleshaw Booth & Co
❸ **TAYLOR Philip** Bullivant Jones

Within each band, firms are listed alphabetically. *See Profiles on page 818*

Brabner Holden Banks Wilson *"A tight practice"* which retains its leading position and is rated across the market for its *"good assistants"* and *"strength in depth."* Head of the team **Mark Feeny** is a well-regarded practitioner. Handles all aspects of tax planning, wills and probate work for an established client base of 'old' and 'new' money and receives a steady flow of referrals from accountants. In addition the team is increasing its corporate support role, notably on tax planning for owners and shareholders on acquisitions and disposals of companies.

Halliwell Landau *"A strong team"* which provides wills and probate work, estate planning and trust creation and administration for a broad client base which includes wealthy private families and Barclays Bank Trust Corporation (for whom the practice carries out all non-litigious legal work.) A recent lateral hire has strengthened the offshore practice. Team head **Geoffrey Shindler**, who has a *"wealth of experience"* and edits two leading trusts journals, is seen as *"the senior player in the region."* Recently awarded national contract to advise the partners of J Rothschild Assurance plc on tax planning.

Addleshaw Booth & Co Following several lateral hires, the team is seen to have successfully *"beefed up"* its trusts and tax practice. Notable among the new recruits is **Alan Sturrock**, formerly of Cobbetts, who enters the rankings and is respected in the market as a *"forceful character"* who *"knows his stuff."* The team handles the full range of onshore and offshore tax planning for landed estates and owner/managers. Recently advised on pre and post sale tax planning involving multi-million pound trusts and offshore structures for the shareholders of a major commercial enterprise.

Birch Cullimore *"Highly competent, old practice"* noted for its *"solid land-owning Cheshire client base."*

Cobbetts Despite the loss of Alan Sturrock, the team maintains its *"huge bank of work"* and has recruited to fill the gap. The firm is acting for an increasing number of owner/managers referred from professionals in the area, and from the recently expanded corporate department.

Other Notable Firms **Cuff Roberts**, **Davies Wallis Foyster** and **Pannone & Partners** are new to the table on the recommendation of several in the market. **David Bishop** of **David Bishop & Co** has an established name for private client work. **Philip Taylor** at **Bullivant Jones & Co** also enters the rankings after repeated recommendations *("very good indeed",)* and services the individual tax planning needs of the firm's commercial clients.

NORTH EAST

TRUSTS & PERSONAL TAX • North East	Ptnrs	Assts
❶ **Dickinson Dees** Newcastle upon Tyne	7	5
Wrigleys Leeds	7	8
❷ **Addleshaw Booth & Co** Leeds	1	10
❸ **Andrew M. Jackson & Co** Hull	1	2
Pinsent Curtis Leeds	2	5
❹ **Brooke North** Leeds	1	2
Gordons Cranswick Solicitors Bradford, Leeds	2	2
Grays York	⚐	⚐
Irwin Mitchell Sheffield	2	1
Lupton Fawcett Leeds	⚐	⚐
Rollit Farrell & Bladon Hull	4	2
Ward Hadaway Newcastle upon Tyne	3	2
❺ **Armitage Sykes Hall Norton** Huddersfield	1	-
Askews Redcar	2-	-
Walker Morris Leeds	1	2

LEADING INDIVIDUALS •	
❶ **BINKS Nigel** Pinsent Curtis	**CHADWICK Peter** Wrigleys
DICKINSON Alexander Dickinson Dees	**EATON John** Lupton Fawcett
GIFFORD Adrian Dickinson Dees	**HOWELL Paul** Addleshaw Booth & Co
LYALL George Dickinson Dees	**WEBSTER Kevin** Andrew M Jackson & Co
WRIGLEY Matthew Wrigleys	

Within each band, firms are listed alphabetically. *See Profiles on page 818*
⚐ *Figures unavailable at time of going to press.*

Dickinson Dees Large team which *"has been around a long time"* and is highly rated throughout the region for its expertise and *"large and diverse client base,"* which includes many of the major private land-owning families in the North. Recommended individuals are team head **George Lyall**, **Alexander Dickinson** and **Adrian Gifford.** In addition to the full range of offshore and onshore tax and trust work, wills and probate, the team is well-versed in landed estate administration, pension scheme administration, trust litigation and contentious probate. Has recently taken on a senior financial planning team from Arthur Andersen which will boost its investment, pensions and shareholder tax services. One recent highlight was advising shareholders including individuals and trust companies on a scheme to minimise tax liability on the £125 million sale of a company.

Wrigleys Strongly recommended private client practice which rises this year to share top billing in the rankings. Seen as a *"premier division team,"* the team is especially lauded for *"the calibre of the people – from the senior partner to the trust managers, all are extremely able."* The addition of **Peter Chadwick** *("a good technical reputation",)* his team and substantial landed client base from Eversheds, further strengthens the practice, which offers across the board advice on estate planning and administration, wills and probate. While known particularly for its landed estate clientele, the team also act for a number of commercial individuals (and some well-known entertainment personalities) and are increasingly instructed by non-domiciliaries. **Matthew Wrigley** heads the team and is respected for *"his ability to build up strong relationships with staff and clients."*

Addleshaw Booth & Co Assistant-heavy practice seen across the market to be committed to the area and *"punching above its weight."* Sole partner and head of department **Paul Howell** *"has taken the private client department* *by the throat and made it go places"* and received strong recommendations. Handles all aspects of on and offshore tax planning and succession advice for clients including private company shareholders, owner/managers, banks, insurance companies, landowners and internationallly based individuals. Particularly skilled in corporate support issues such as pre-sale tax planning for shareholders. Recently advised family trustees on the sale of property assets valued at over £1 billion.

Andrew M Jackson & Co Well regarded Hull practice estate planning, trust administration and trust restructuring work, which is receiving an increasing amount of referrals from accountants. Has niche expertise in drafting of wills and settlements, advicing elderly clients and trust administration. The *"able"* **Kevin Webster** remains rated by the market. Recently completed an estate planning exercise for a client worth £30 million which included the preparation of settlements and a complex will.

Pinsent Curtis *"Quality practice,"* whose team ethos has been especially commended. Full-time consultant **Nigel Binks** is particularly recommended, and *"thinks on a completely different level to most mere mortals."* Acting for a range of clients, including family trusts, landed estates, private banks and offshore trust companies, the team specialises in tax planning for entrepreneurs and MBO/MBI teams, particularly on start-up and exit. Recently advised an individual worth approximately £50 million on emigration planning, which included all aspects of his UK shareholding interests and restructuring existing offshore trust interests.

Other Notable Firms **Brooke North** and **Gordons Cranswick** retain a strong presence in the market, while **Grays** is new to the rankings this year and has *"longstanding experience"* in acting for landed estates and farmers. **Irwin Mitchell** remains respected for its estate planning work, and has niche expertise in trust and probate litigation, personal injury and special needs trusts and Court of Protection work. It has recently set up a dedicated will writing section which receives substantial instructions from major financial institutions. **Lupton Fawcett** is particularly notable for its *"prominence on the investment business side,"* in which field **John Eaton** is highly regarded, as well as for tax and trust expertise. **Rollit Farrell & Bladon** *("a long established practice with good clients")* is continuing to build its profile in the sector and receives an increasing number of referrals from leading accountants and solicititors. **Ward Hadaway** remains a *"respected competitor"* in its region while **Armitage Sykes Hall Norton**, **Askews** and **Walker Morris** maintain solid practices.

SCOTLAND

TRUSTS & PERSONAL TAX • Scotland	Ptnrs	Assts
❶ **Turcan Connell WS** Edinburgh	7	20
❷ **Brodies WS** Edinburgh	2	4
Maclay Murray & Spens Glasgow	2	3
Tods Murray WS Edinburgh	4	3
❸ **Anderson Strathern WS** Edinburgh	4	2
Balfour & Manson Edinburgh	2	1
Ledingham Chalmers Aberdeen	3	5
MacRoberts Glasgow	2	3
Morton Fraser, Solicitors Edinburgh	3	2
Murray Beith Murray WS Edinburgh	3	3
❹ **Pagan Osborne** Cupar	3	1
Thorntons WS Dundee	⚐	⚐
Wright, Johnston & Mackenzie Glasgow	⚐	⚐

LEADING INDIVIDUALS •	
❶ **BIGGAR John** Tods Murray WS	**CONNELL Douglas** Turcan Connell WS
DALGLEISH Andrew Brodies WS	**FULTON Robin** Turcan Connell WS
MACKINTOSH Simon Turcan Connell	**MacROBERT David** MacRoberts
RAE Scott Morton Fraser, Solicitors	**ROSS Hubert** Turcan Connell WS
STUBBS Ian Maclay Murray & Spens	
UP & COMING	
HENDERSON Colin Anderson Strathern WS	

Within each band, firms are listed alphabetically. *See Profiles on page 818*
⚐ *Figures unavailable at time of going to press.*

Turcan Connell WS Having consolidated its recent growth, this firm is now seen as the leading private client practice in Scotland *("it's difficult to go past them")* with *"a remarkable collection of good people."* **Simon Mackintosh** is seen by many as *"the strongest technician"* and enters the rankings this year, while **Robin Fulton**, **Hubert Ross** and **Douglas Connell** remain highly rated by their peers. Known for its large number of landed estate clients and related heritage property expertise, the team is building its 'new money practice' and receives entrepreneur referrals from leading Scottish commercial firms (eg for individual tax planning on MBOs and company sales). Also maintain an asset management and actuarial team, while an office in Guernsey assists with the firm's offshore work. Currently administers over 2000 trusts and acts as legal adviser to over 150 historic houses.

Brodies WS Continues to receive strong recommendations for its *"leading landed estate practice."* Traditional family trusts, heritage property and estate planning are the mainstay of the team's work in addition to business spin-off trusts. Internationally, the team acts for a number of offshore companies buying property in the UK. The *"sound"* **Andrew Dalgliesh** remains highly rated across the market for his technical ability.

Maclay Murray & Spens *"The leading firm in the West"* for trusts and tax work. Boast the *"experienced"* and *"practical"* **Ian Stubbs**, who is recommended for his estate planning and partnership expertise. However, the *"formidable"* Ronald Graham, who *"has been a key player for many years,"* has now retired, thus leaving a hole at the top of the practice. Handles all aspects of tax planning, wills and succession for a range of clients including individuals, estates and development companies. Recent developments include the establishment of an investment unit and a notable increase in the use of family and charitable trusts.

Tods Murray WS Remains respected in the market for its *"organic growth"* and *"some good people"* with particular praise directed at the *"client-orientated"* **John Biggar**, who has *"excellent tax knowledge"* and enters the rankings this year. Asset and estate protection makes up the bulk of the work, in addition to wills and trust administration. Significant recent work includes tax efficient disposal of heritage property (especially works of art) and generational skipping schemes in relation to landed estates and interests in companies.

Anderson Strathern WS Well regarded team whose client base includes 'old' and 'new' money individuals and families. The firm has experience in all aspects of CGT and IHT schemes, trust reorganisations and owner/managed company restructuring. Also maintains a large probate section and specialist investment unit. **Colin Henderson** is rated for his tax expertise and enters the rankings as an up and coming practitioner this year.

Balfour & Manson *"A completely different type of practice, but very sound,"* it specialises in legal advice for the elderly and adults with disabilities. In addition, the team advises individuals, charities and trustees on fund management, tax and insurance matters.

Ledingham Chalmers Maintains its strong reputation for private client work in the North-East. Work includes the preparation of wills and related tax planning advice, the administration of estates and trusts and advice to the elderly. The team is also able to provide its broad client base with financial planning services.

MacRoberts Reputation largely derives from team head **David MacRobert**, who continues to garner unanimous praise in the market. Particularly skilled in corporate support work, including creating trusts for directors and shareholders as part of overall tax planning arrangements on commercial deals. Receives an increasing number of referrals from other solicitor firms.

Morton Fraser, Solicitors **Scott Rae** continues to warrant his *"strong reputation"* and heads a team which acts for a variety of landed estate and entrepreneurial clients. Areas of niche expertise include cross-border probate work, setting up trusts in damages cases and specialist trust advice to institutions including IFAs, banks and insurance companies. Recently completed the unravelling of a large multi-jurisdictional trust, with confirmation of related tax breaks.

Murray Beith Murray WS Retaining *"substantial expertise,"* the practice largely advises on setting up and administering trusts for established families, as well as wills and probate. Particularly known in the market for its separate asset management unit.

Other Notable Firms **Pagan Osborne** and **Thorntons** enter the rankings this year after extensive recommendation as specialist regional tax and trust practices with substantial farming and landowner clienteles. **Wright Johnston & Mackenzie** also has a solid team in the field.

NORTHERN IRELAND

TRUSTS & PERSONAL TAX • Northern Ireland	Ptnrs	Assts
❶ **Cleaver Fulton Rankin** Belfast	3	2
L'Estrange & Brett Belfast	1	1
❷ **C & J Black** Belfast	1	-
Johns Elliot Belfast	-	1

LEADING INDIVIDUALS •
❶ **HEWITT Alan** L'Estrange & Brett
RANKIN Alastair Cleaver Fulton Rankin
❷ **McCAW Elma** C & J Black

Within each band, firms are listed alphabetically. *See Profiles on page 818*

Cleaver Fulton & Rankin Well regarded team which handles all aspects of wills and probate, tax and trusts and heritage property, with niche specialisms in work for elderly clients, charities and clients with a disability. The *"excellent"* **Alastair Rankin** is *"a specialist in the field."*

L'Estrange & Brett **Alan Hewitt** is known for his *"integrity"* and *"depth of experience"* and heads the practice, which is particularly rated for its estate planning, including substantial family settlements and trust work arising from company sales.

C & J Black *"A steady practice"* with long established clients and a strong reputation in probate and trusts work. **Elma McCaw** is highly regarded in the market.

Johns Elliot New to the rankings this year, the firm has a growing reputation for its private client work.

LEADERS IN TRUSTS & PERSONAL TAX

AVERY JONES C.B.E., John
Speechly Bircham, London (020) 7427 6400
john.averyjones@speechlys.co.uk
Specialisation: Taxation of all kinds.
Prof. Memberships: Member of Treasury appointed Tax Law Rewrite Steering Committee, Law Society (Member and past Chairman of Revenue Law Committee), Chartered Institute of Taxation (Past President), International Fiscal Association, Institute for Fiscal Studies, International Academy of Estate & Trust Law, International Bar Association.
Career: Partner in *Speechly Bircham* since 1970, Senior Partner since 1985, Deputy Special Commissioner of Income Tax and part-time Chairman of VAT and Duties Tribunals, Consulting Editor of British Tax Review, Member of the Editorial Board of Simon's Taxes, Chairman of the Board of Trustees of the International Bureau of Fiscal Documentation.
Personal: Born 1940, educated at Rugby School and Trinity College, Cambridge.

BARCLAY, Jonathan R.
Mills & Reeve, Norwich (01603) 693211
jonathan.barclay@mills-reeve.com
Specialisation: Specialises in tax and estate planning with particular emphasis on trust and tax issues affecting landed estates.
Career: Articled *Whithers*; qualified 1971; partner *Mills & Reeve* 1976; managing partner 1987-90; chairman *Norton Rose* M5 Group 1990-94; senior partner 1995 to date; director *Jarrold & Sons Ltd*; East of England Investment Agency Ltd; chairman Norwich Area Development Agency Ltd; Theatre Royal (Norwich) Trust Ltd.
Personal: Born 1947; resides Norfolk.

BIGGAR, John M.H.
Tods Murray WS, Edinburgh (0131) 226 4771
maildesk@todsmurray.co.uk
Specialisation: Wills; tax and asset protection planning; trusts, formation and administration; probate; personal financial planning.
Prof. Memberships: Society of Trust and Estate Practitioners; Society for Computers and Law; Law Management Section; WS Society.
Career: Articled *Murray Beith & Murray* 1973-1975; admitted solicitor 1975; assistant solicitor *Murray Beith & Murray* 1975-1977; admitted WS 1976; partner *Murray Beith & Murray* 1977-1991; partner *Tods Murray* 1991-
Publications: Co-author-'Drafting Wills in Scotland' (Butterworths 1994); occassional professional magazine contributions.
Personal: Oundle School; University of Edinburgh. Family; golf; music; married; four sons.

BINKS, Nigel
Pinsent Curtis, Leeds (0113) 244 5000
nigel.binks@pinsents.com
Specialisation: Wide experience of tax and trust work with particular expertise in capital gains tax and inheritance tax planning for entrepreneurs and owner-managed businesses and estate planning, trusts and off-shore structures.
Prof. Memberships: STEP.
Career: Born 1951. Educated at Repton School and Trinity College, Cambridge. Qualified in 1976. Partner in *Simpson Curtis* (now *Pinsent Curtis*) in 1978. Consultant with *Pinsent Curtis* from 1995.
Personal: Leisure interests include golf and skiing.

BISHOP, David C.
David Bishop & Co, Liverpool 01704 878 421
David_Bishop@compuserve.com
Specialisation: Main areas of specialisation are trusts and tax planning for individuals and private companies including offshore arrangements; all aspects of occupational pensions and charities. Notary Public.
Prof. Memberships: Law Society, Chairman, Liverpool Branch Society of Trust and Estate Practitioners 1991-99, International Tax Planning Association, ass. Association of Pension Lawyers.
Career: Qualified 1972 partner *Laces & Co* (now *Berrymans Lace Mawer*) 1974. Head of private client department 1995-2000. 2000 Principal, *David Bishop & Co.*
Personal: Born 6th April 1947. Educated Sedbergh School 1960-65, Caius College, Cambridge 1966-69. Lives in Formby.

BOYD-CARPENTER C.V.O., Henry
Farrer & Co, London (020) 7242 2022
Senior Partner and Partner in Private Client and Financial Services Team.
Specialisation: Main areas of practice are general private client work, wills, settlements, probate, settled land, landed estates and charities.
Prof. Memberships: Law Society, Holborn Law Society.
Career: Joined *Farrer & Co* in 1962. Qualified in 1966, became a partner in 1968. Private Solicitor to the Queen since 1995, Solicitor to the Duchy of Cornwall 1976-1994.
Personal: Born 11th October 1939. Educated at Charterhouse 1953-58 and Balliol College, Oxford

1959-62. School governor and Charity Trustee. Member of the Board of the British Library since 1999 and Chairman of the Board of Governors of Charterhouse. Enjoys reading, music, hill walking and gardening. Lives in Ascot, Berkshire.

BRADLEY, David G.
Hewitson Becke + Shaw, Cambridge (01223) 461155

BRIDGES, Mark T.
Farrer & Co, London (020) 7242 2022
mtb@farrer.co.uk
Partner, head of international private client team.
Specialisation: Handles tax and trust matters, particularly for non-domiciled and non-resident individuals.
Prof. Memberships: Law Society, Member of STAR Group,Trust Law Committee, IBA and ITPA.
Career: Joined *Farrer & Co* in 1978. Qualified in 1980, became a partner in 1985. Solicitor to the Duchy of Lancaster 1998.
Personal: Born 25th July 1954. Educated at Cambridge University 1973-77. Special Trustee of Middlesex Hospital and of University College Hospital, Treasurer of Bach Choir 1992-97, Council Member of Royal School of Church Music 1989-97. Recreations include sailing and music. Lives in London and Suffolk.

BROWN, Graham S.
Payne Hicks Beach, London (020) 7465 4300
Senior Partner, and Head of Tax and Trust Department.
Specialisation: Areas of practice include legal and fiscal advice to shareholders and boards of family and other private companies; landed estates and heritage property; international trusts, probates and family property; charities and educational institutions; French property and succession. Delivered papers on charities and non-profit organisations, trusts and estates at international conferences in London, Paris, Amsterdam, Munich and Taipei.
Prof. Memberships: Associate of Institute of Taxation in Ireland; sometime member of Law Society's Revenue Law Committee Capital Taxes Sub-Committee and of Law Society's Working Party on the Financial Services Act, Committee of Holborn Law Society; member: International Fiscal Association, Franco-British Lawyers' Association.
Personal: Born 1944. Educated at Bristol University (LL.B, 1966), Catholic University of Louvain (Diploma, 1970), and King's College, London (LL.M, 1975). Leisure interests include arts, heritage and music. Fellow of the Royal Society of Arts; Liveryman Clockmakers' Company. Lives in Bath.

BROWN, Sandra
Osborne Clarke OWA, Bristol (0117) 917 3000
sandra.brown@osborneclark.com
Specialisation: Head of tax and trust department. Leads a team of lawyers who specialise in the provision of trusts and tax advice to a variety of clients: specialising in complex tax planning and wealth management, including advising on offshore structures, provides consultancy advice to clients and corporate support function on transactions carried out within the firm.
Career: Trained: *Burges Salmon*; qualified 1983; joined *Osborne Clarke*; became partner 1989. Notary Public.

CARSLAKE, Hugh
Martineau Johnson, Birmingham (0121) 678 1486
hugh.carslake@martjohn.com
Partner in Private Client Department.
Specialisation: Main area of practice covers tax planning, trusts and estate planning and ecclesiastical law. Acts for the owners of landed estates and private individuals in their personal and trustee capacities. Registrar for and legal adviser to the Diocese of Birmingham.
Prof. Memberships: Law Society, STEP. Ecclesiastical Law Association (ELA).
Career: Qualified in 1973, having joined *Martineau Johnson* in 1972. Became a Partner in 1974, Notary Public in 1981, Head of Private Client Department in 1991 and Diocesan Registrar in 1992.
Personal: Born 15th November 1946. Attended Rugby School, 1960-65, then Trinity College, Dublin, 1966-70. Chairman of the Barber Institute of Fine Arts (University of Birmingham); Member of the Council of the University of Birmingham; Trustee of the Worcester Cathedral Appeal Trust. Council Member of the Notaries society. Leisure interests include family, music and gardening. Lives in Warwickshire.

CHADWICK, Peter
Wrigleys, Leeds (0113) 244 6100
peterchadwick@eversheds.com
Specialisation: Over 20 years specialising in trusts and estate planning, probate and wills, landed estates and charity law.
Prof. Memberships: Law Society, CLA, Charity Law Assocation.
Career: Qualified 1975. Partner with *Eversheds* (formerly *Hepworth & Chadwick*) since 1978. Non-executive director Next plc 1980-86.
Personal: Born 1951. Educated Oundle School and Newcastle-upon-Tyne University. Trustee various charities.

CONNELL, Douglas A.
Turcan Connell WS, Edinburgh (0131) 228 8111
dac@turcanconnell.com
Specialisation: Joint Senior Partner. Specialist in trusts, tax planning, asset protection, charities and heritage property; acts as principal adviser to many chairmen and chief executives regarding their personal business and to the trustees of a number of major national charities, as well as private charitable foundations.
Prof. Memberships: President Scottish Young Lawyers Association 1975-76; member of Revenue Committee the Law Society of Scotland 1979-92; chairman Edinburgh Book Festival 1991-95; member Scottish Arts Council and chairman Lottery Committee, Scottish Arts Council 1994-97.
Career: Attended University of Edinburgh (LLB). Articled *Dundas & Wilson CS*; qualified 1976; Partner 1979-97.
Personal: Born 1954. Resides Edinburgh. Leisure interests include books, travel and good food.

COOKE, Stephen
Withers, London (020) 7936 1000
Partner in private client department.
Specialisation: Main area of practice is tax and asset management planning for the private client, both in the UK and offshore. Speaker at seminars on a wide range of trust, tax and related issues. Contributor to 'Tax Cases Analysis' and co-author of 'Inheritance Tax on Lifetime Gifts' (1987).
Prof. Memberships: City of London Law Society, International Fiscal Association, Society of Trust and Estate Practitioners.
Career: Qualified in 1971, having articled with *Clay Allison & Clark*, Nottinghamshire. Awarded the Law Society SH Clay prize. Joined *Withers* in 1971; partner in 1973.
Personal: Born 30th July 1946. Attended Stamford School 1956-64 and Leicester School of Architecture. Chairman of the London Handel Society Ltd. Leisure interests include art, music, cricket, gardening and tennis. Lives in Well, Basingstoke.

DALGLEISH, Andrew M.C.
Brodies WS, Edinburgh (0131) 228 3777
amcdalgleish@brodies.co.uk
Specialisation: Main areas of practice are capital tax planning, trusts (private client, commercial and public), wills and executries. Co-author Barr Biggar Dalgleish and Stevens,'Drafting Wills in Scotland'; contributor to Withers, 'International Trust Precedents'; Lawrence, 'International Personal Tax Planning Encyclopaedia'; Norrie & Scobbie, 'Trusts'; and George, 'International Charitable Giving'.
Prof. Memberships: Law Society of Scotland, Society of Trust and Estate Practitioners, Association of Pension Lawyers (associate).
Career: Qualified 1975. Partner *Brodies* 1978.
Personal: Born 1951, resides Edinburgh.

DICKINSON, Alexander
Dickinson Dees, Newcastle upon Tyne (0191) 279 9615
Specialisation: Partner in private client department advising wealthy individuals and their families. Particular emphasis on capital taxation, heritage property, maintenance funds, trusts, wills and probates. Acts mainly for individuals with significant property interests (landed estates, commercial and residential portfolios) and entrepreneurs.
Prof. Memberships: Law Society, STEP.
Career: Qualified 1989. Joined *Dickinson Dees* in 1993 and appointed partner in 1997.
Personal: Born 1964 and lives in Northumberland. Keen sportsman and follower of Leeds United. School Governor and Charity Trustee. Travels extensively when time permits.

DOLMAN, Robert A.
Wedlake Bell, London (020) 7395 3000
Specialisation: Specialises principally in private client tax and trusts both in UK and offshore.
Prof. Memberships: Law Society: STAR group.
Career: Qualified in 1971; Partner with *Baileys, Shaw and Gillett* until 1985; Partner with *Wedlake Bell* 1986 to date (Senior Partner from 1994).
Personal: Born 15 October 1945: Educated at Felsted and Oxford University. Chairman of Family Assurance Society. Chairman of the Jesters Club. Lives in West Sussex; interests are court games and theatre.

EATON, John C.J.
Lupton Fawcett, Leeds (0113) 280 2000

ELPHINSTON, Alexander
Foot Anstey Sargent, Exeter (01392) 411221
Specialisation: Partner in private client department. Tax planning for individuals through wills and trusts: particular involvement in attorneyship and court of protection work as well as living wills. Also Trustee of and advisor to various Charities.

Prof. Memberships: Member of the Law Society: Secretary of STEP (West of England).
Career: Qualified with *Waterhouse* in London, before moving to Devon, joining *Anstey Sargent & Probert* in 1987.
Personal: Born 6th June 1955. Repton School and Durham University. Married with four young children: interests include theatre, cricket, jazz and jigsaw puzzles. Trustee and governor of local school.

EMMERSON, John C.
Wilsons, Salisbury (01722) 412412
Consultant in Trust and Tax Department.
Specialisation: Main area of practice is tax planning (UK and international), trust law and charitable trusts. Cases handled have included Ampthill Peerage Claim(1976), 'Raikes v. Lygon' (1988) and 'Hatton v. IRC' (1992). Author of articles in British Tax Review and other publications.
Prof. Memberships: Law Society, International Tax Planning Association, Society of Tax and Estate Practitioners. Admitted to practice in Hong Kong.
Career: Qualified 1967. Former Head of Private Client Department at *McKenna & Co.* in London.
Personal: Born 1937. Attended Merchant Taylor's School, then Magdalen College Oxford 1958-61. Part – time immigration adjudicator. Leisure interests include fly-fishing. Lives in Wylye, near Salisbury, Wiltshire and in London.

EVANS, Michael
Burges Salmon, Bristol (0117) 939 2249
michael.evans@burges-salmon.com
Specialisation: Head of International Tax & Trust Unit, focusing on international work for both UK and non-UK based clients. Recent work includes: drafting trusts for the Mexican clients of one of the largest US banks; reviewing standard trust documentation for the same bank for use by their customers world-wide; tax and estate planning for substantial international families; advice on Double Tax Treaty schemes; analysis of existing and new offshore structures in light of the newly in force Transfer Pricing legislation; Capital Gains Tax planning for owner managers on company sales, including offshore trust schemes and non-residence.
Prof. Memberships: Law Society, STEP (member of International Committee).
Career: Joined *Burges Salmon* as a trainee in 1990 and became a partner in Tax and Trusts in 1999.
Personal: University of Bristol 1986-89. Enjoys golf and cricket.

EWART, Peter W.
Hewitson Becke + Shaw, Cambridge (01223) 461155

FEENY, Mark R.
Brabner Holden Banks Wilson, Liverpool (0151) 236 5821
Head of Probate and Trust Department.
Specialisation: Deals with trusts, estate and tax planning and contentious probate and related matters.
Prof. Memberships: Law Society. Liverpool Law Society. Society of Trust and Estate Practitioners.
Career: Qualified in 1981. Partner 1983.
Personal: Chairman Merseyside branch STEP, Treasurer of Liverpool Law Society. Deputy Sheriff for Counties of Merseyside, Lancashire and Greater Manchester. Chairman Merseyside Housing Association. Born 16.10.55.

FITZGERALD, Peter R.
Wilsons, Salisbury (01722) 412412
Partner in Farms and Estates Department.
Specialisation: Specialises in agricultural estates including stately homes, chattels, heritage law, agricultural law and tax. Firm represents some 280,000 acres of agricultural land. Author of occasional articles on heritage and taxation matters and occasional speaker at conferences and seminars.
Prof. Memberships: CLA, HHA.
Career: Qualified in 1969. Partner at *Fladgate Fielder* 1975-95. Joined *Wilsons* as a Partner in 1995.
Personal: Educated at Canford School and Trinity College, Oxford (MA). Lives near Wincanton, Somerset.

FULLERLOVE, Michael Reame
Wiggin & Co, Cheltenham (01242) 224 114
Specialisation: Private client work for high net worth individuals, both in the UK and elsewhere. A large part of his practice involves international asset and tax structuring on work inbound and outbound to and from the USA.
Prof. Memberships: The Law Society; International Tax Planning Association; STEP.
Career: University of Birmingham: LLB. Magdalen College, Oxford: BCL. Articles and Assistant Solicitor: *Freshfields*, City of London.
Personal: Born 1948. Gardening and genealogy.

FULTON, Robin D.
Turcan Connell WS, Edinburgh (0131) 228 8111
rdf@turcanconnell.com
Partner.
Specialisation: Specialist areas taxation, trusts and estates, partnerships and charity law.
Prof. Memberships: Qualified Solicitor Scotland 1979. Law Society of Scotland and Society of Writers to H.M. Signet.
Career: *Shepherd & Wedderburn*; qualified 1979; Assistant Solicitor 1979-82, Partner 1982-99; Partner *Turcan Connell* WS 1999. Scottish Editor 'Sergeant & Sims on Stamp Duties' and 'Foster's Inheritance Tax'; senior tutor in wills, trusts and executries, Edinburgh University Diploma in Legal Education.
Personal: Born 1956; resides Edinburgh. Interests: sport generally but particularly squash, tennis, golf, skiing and food and wine.

GARNHAM, Caroline
Simmons & Simmons, London (020) 7628 2020
Specialisation: Capital Gains Tax and Inheritance Tax, succession and estate planning, cross border tax and estate conflict resolution, offshore trust dispute resolution, creation and reorganisation for individuals, family offices, trusts and the institutions which advise them.
Prof. Memberships: Fellow of the Chartered Institute of Tax – committee member of Capital Taxes Sub Committee. Member of Society of Trusts and Estates Practitioners – member of Technic Committee and International Committee. Member of the editorial boards of Butterworths 'Offshore Cases and Materials' and STEPS publication of Wills and Trusts Law Report. Regular international speaker.
Career: BSc Exeter University. Solicitor, qualified 1981. Head of Private Capital Group and Partner *Simmons & Simmons*. Fellow of the Chartered Institute of Tax. F.T.I.I.
Personal: Hunting, tennis, singing. Married with two children, homes in London and Gloucestershire.

GIFFORD, Adrian C.
Dickinson Dees, Newcastle upon Tyne (0191) 279 9622
Specialisation: Advises major landowners and businessmen on their personal affairs.
Prof. Memberships: STEP.
Career: Qualified in 1977. Became partner at *Dickinson Dees* in 1979.
Personal: Born 1946. Educated at Merchant Taylors School and St Andrew's University. Lives in Northumberland.

GLAZIER, Barry
Lester Aldridge, Bournemouth (01202) 786161
Partner in private client department.
Specialisation: Corporate and personal tax, particularly for family-owned businesses, as well as landed estates, onshore and offshore trusts, and charities. Appointed Managing Partner in 1994.
Career: Articled *Penningtons*, London; qualified 1966; Solicitor *Clifford Turner* 1966-1971; Partner *Lester Aldridge* since 1972; President of Dorset Chamber of Commerce and Industry 1992-1993, President Bournemouth & District Law Society 1991-1992; Director and Company Secretary, Dorset Training and Enterprise Council; chairman of Eurolegal 1991-1995; Chairman of Hurstpierpoint Lawyers' Society.
Personal: Born 1941; resides Wimborne Minster. Educated at Hurstpierpoint College (1950-1960); St Peter's College, Oxford (1960-1963 BA, 1968 MA Oxon); Notary Public. Recreations include concerts and opera, piano playing, walking, ornithology, gardening.

GOODWIN, Peter
Bircham & Co., London (020) 7222 8044
Specialisation: Estate planning for UK families and non-UK domiciliaries; advice on UK and non-UK trusts.
Prof. Memberships: Law Society; Westminster Law Society; STAR Group; STEP.
Career: Qualified as solicitor (1968). Partner: *Freshfields* (1974-1990). Partner: *Bircham & Co.* (1990 to date).
Personal: Born October 1943. Shrewsbury School (1957-62). Worcester College, Oxford (1962-65). Member of Committee of 1930 Fund for District Nurses.

GOWAR, Martyn
Lawrence Graham, London (020) 7379 0000
martyn.gowar@lawgram.com
Senior Partner and Partner in Tax Department.
Specialisation: Specialises principally in Private Client Tax, acting for large landed estates, trustees (particularly offshore trusts), and private clients with business interests. Also inter-generational transfers of family businesses and general tax work, income tax, capital gains tax and inheritance tax advice generally, including income tax on structured settlements and tax on insurance policies. Editor of Butterworths Encyclopaedia of Forms and Precedents (Vol. 30 on Partnership) and contributor to Simon's Taxes on the tax and trust treatment of demerger shares issues and enhanced scrip dividends. Has lectured widely over the last 20 years.
Prof. Memberships: Law Society; Chartered Institute of Taxation (Associate 1976, Fellow 1981); Secretary of International Academy of Estate and Trust Law. Member Addington Society.
Career: Joined *Lawrence Graham* in 1967, qualifying in 1970 and becoming Partner in 1973 and Senior

Partner in 1997. Member of numerous revenue law committees including the Tax Committee of the Association of Corporate Trustees (1987 to 1996) and the Capital Taxes Committee of the Chartered Institute of Taxation. Also Clerk to the Governors of Wellington College and Clerk to the Trustees of the Hamlyn Trust. A trustee of the Laura Ashley Foundation and the Council of St. Paul's Cathedral Choir School. Fellow of the Royal Society of Arts.
Personal: Born 11th July 1946. Educated at King's College School, Wimbledon and Magdalen College, Oxford 1964-67. Lives in Elstead, Surrey and enjoys golf, cricket and gardening.

GREEN, Martin
Lodders, Stratford-upon-Avon (01789) 293259
martin.green@lodders.co.uk
Specialisation: Trusts and tax planning with a special interest in all personal financial planning issues. In the last 12 months in addition to the usual tax planning matters, has been involved in repatriating a number of offshore trusts to the UK and also in advising the elderly in connection with funding of care costs.
Prof. Memberships: Law Society Capital Taxes Sub-Commitee (former chair of Birmingham Revenue Law Commitee Birmingham Law Society) STEP. Associate member Securities Institute. Current member of the Prudential Source Book Standing Group.
Career: Articled: *Pinsent & Co* (later *Pinsent Curtis*) September 1978 – September 1980. Partner private client department *Pinsent & Co* April 1984 – December 1985. Partner in charge private client department *Lodders* January 1986 to present day.
Publications: In the past contributed to CTT 'News and Reports' and articles in the 'Law Society Gazette'.
Personal: Married with four children. Interested in tennis, table tennis, golf and the countryside. Educated Cheltenham College and Birmingham University.

HAYES, Michael
Macfarlanes, London (020) 7831 9222
Partner and head of tax and financial planning department from 1991 to 1999.
Specialisation: Specialises in private client tax planning.Work includes tax and estate planning, both national and international, for high net worth individuals, their trusts and closely held companies. Also wills and probate. Other area of practice is charities, including formation of charitable trusts and companies; establishing subsidiary trading vehicles; and negotiations with Charity Commission and Inland Revenue. Contributor to Tolley's 'Administration of Estates' and to Tolley's 'Administration of Trusts'. Has spoken at numerous national and international conferences.
Prof. Memberships: Law Society, City of London Law Society, Society of Trusts and Estates Practitioners, Committee Member of the Law Society Wills and Equity Committee, Association of Pension Lawyers, Association of Contentious Trust and Probate Specialists. Member of Camelot Winners Advisory Panel.
Career: Qualified in 1968 while with *Macfarlanes*. Became a Partner in 1974. Head of Tax and Financial Planning since 1991.

HEAL, Jeremy P W
Howes Percival, Norwich (01603) 762103
jpwh@howes-percival.co.uk
See under Agriculture, p.75

HENDERSON, Colin B.
Anderson Strathern WS, Edinburgh
(0131) 220 2345
colin.henderson@andersonstrathern.co.uk
Specialisation: Capital taxes planning for high net worth individuals and trusts, landowners, family businesses, non-domiciliaries.
Prof. Memberships: Society of Trust and Estate Practioners. Chartered Institute of Taxation.
Career: Qualified 1990 after army service; 1990-1996 *Coopers & Lybrand CA*; partner *Anderson Strathern WS* 1997. Member of Law Society of Scotland Tax Law Committee. Member of Chartered Institute of Taxation (Scotland Branch) Committee.
Publications: Articles on taxation subjects in trade press. Conference speaker.
Personal: Born 1960; resides Edinburgh. Interests: fishing, walking, military history and national heritage.

HEWITT, V. Alan
L'Estrange & Brett, Belfast (028) 9023 0426
See under Property (Commercial), p.729

HOWE, Kate
Boodle Hatfield, London (020) 7629 7411
khowe@boodlehatfield.co.uk
Specialisation: Private client taxation, including planning for the landed estate and international tax planning for UK and non-UK residents and domiciliaries; UK and offshore trust advice; heritage property; commercial property taxation, particularly VAT.
Prof. Memberships: Law Society. STEP (Society of Trust & Estate Practitioners)
Career: Articled at *Boodle Hatfield*; qualified in 1982 and became a partner in 1987. Has lectured widely on tax planning and contributed to 'Legal Network Television'.
Personal: Attended the London School of Economics (LLB). Lives in London.

HOWELL, Paul J.
Addleshaw Booth & Co, Leeds (0113) 209 2000
Specialisation: Head of the firm's private client group. Main areas of expertise are in UK and offshore personal tax planning and trusts, and charities.
Prof. Memberships: Society of Estate and Trust Practitioners. Country Land Owners Assocation. Law Society.
Career: Liverpool University 1974; admitted in 1977; joined the firm in 1990 as a partner.
Personal: Tennis, skiing, sailing, windsurfing and bridge.

JACOBS, Michael
Nicholson Graham & Jones, London
(020) 7648 9000
michael.jacobs@ngj.co.uk
Head of Private Client Department.
Specialisation: Tax; employee share schemes; international tax, trusts, charities, and public sector bodies. Author of 'Tax on Take-overs' (7 editions) and 'Rewarding Leadership' (published by CISCO, February 1998); contributor to 'Tolley's Tax Planning' and 'Tolley's VAT Planning'. Consultant editor of Tolley's Trust Law International.
Prof. Memberships: Trust Law Committee (Founder Member and (1994-97) Secretary); Share Scheme Lawyers Group (Founder Member and Vice-Chairman); Employee Share Schemes Committee (Chairman) Quoted Companies Alliance; STEP; IFA; IFS; Charity Law Association; FRSA; Academician of the Academy for the Social Sciences.
Career: Articled at *Nicholson Graham & Jones* 1970; Partner 1976. Head of Private Client Department 1981.

JARMAN, Chris
Payne Hicks Beach, London (020) 7465 4300
Partner in Tax, Trust & Probate Department.
Specialisation: Deals with a wide range of domestic and international trust, estate and tax planning for both old and new money clients, whether based in the U.K. or abroad; advice to "private" and institutional charities; property-related VAT advice for charity, commercial and land-owning clients; and commercial property advice to landowners seeking to realise potential development value. Member of Law Society's Revenue Law Committee and Capital Taxes Sub-Committee. Member of two-man Law Society team which procured significant changes to the Trusts of Land and Appointment of Trustees Act 1996 as it went through the House of Lords.
Prof. Memberships: Law Society; Holborn Law Society; STEP; Charity Law Association; Charities Property Association.
Career: Called to the Bar in 1976, qualified as solicitor 1980. Member of *Freshfields* Private Client Department 1978-84, joined *Payne Hicks Beach* in 1984 (Partner in 1986).
Personal: Born 1954, educated at Sherborne School and Magdalene College, Cambridge. Leisure interests include singing and music generally, and "social" cricket and golf; cycles approx. 2,800 miles per year commuting from South London.

JENKINS, Paul H.
Browne Jacobson, Nottingham (0115) 976 6000
pjenkins@brownej.co.uk
Specialisation: Has over thirty years experiance in the field of personal tax planning and trusts. Acts for clients of very substantial means, including entrepreneurs and landowners and their respective families. He deals with the creation, settlement, variation and termination of both domestic and offshore trusts. The aggregate value of trusts with which he is concerned exceeds £1bn.

KENNEDY, John
Hunters, London (020) 7412 0050
jmsk@hunter-solicitors.co.uk
Specialisation: Private client work including landed estates, national heritage property, inheritance tax planning, trusts and probate.
Prof. Memberships: Law Society, STEP.
Career: Sherborne School. Emmanuel College, Cambridge. Articled at *Hunters*, qualified in 1967 and became a partner in 1970.
Personal: Cricket, skiing, gardening.

KING-JONES, Amanda
Thomas Eggar Church Adams, Chichester
(01243) 786 111
amanda.king-jones@teca.co.uk
Partner.
Specialisation: Main areas of practice are personal tax and financial planning probate and trusts. Also deals with the affairs of the elderly.
Prof. Memberships: Law Society and Society of Trust and Estate Practitioners.
Career: Joined *T.E.C.A.*in 1981. Qualified 1983. Partner 1987. Co-Author of 'Probate Practice Manual' (Sweet & Maxwell).

Personal: Educated at Roedean School 1969-77. Exeter University (LLB) 1978-1981.

KIRBY, Richard C.
Speechly Bircham, London (020) 7427 6400
richard.kirby@speechlys.co.uk
Partner 1973.
Specialisation: Main area of practice is private client work, handling estate and tax planning for UK and non-UK domiciliaries and trusts. Has written numerous articles for national newspapers and specialist taxation periodicals.
Prof. Memberships: Law Society.
Career: Head Private Client and Charity Team 1980. Solicitor Worshipful Company of Pewterers 1981 (Hon. Freeman 1991, Liveryman 2000).
Personal: Born 18th September 1946. Educated Sevenoaks School 1960-65 and Jesus College, Oxford 1965-68 MA. Member Council Mental After Care Association 1982 (Hon. Treasurer 1987-). Member Carlton Club. Enjoys reading, theatre and cycling. Lives in Dulwich.

KRAFFT, James A.
Thomson Snell & Passmore, Tunbridge Wells (01892) 510000
jkrafft@ts-p.co.uk
Partner and head of private client department.
Specialisation: Main areas of practice are general private client work, personal financial planning, tax planning, Wills, settlements, powers of attorney and probate.
Prof. Memberships: Law Society and Society of Trust and Estate Practitioners.
Career: Qualified in 1971, Articled and practised in London before joining *Thomson Snell & Passmore* in 1976.
Personal: Born 1st May 1944. Educated at Downside School and St.Catherine's College, Oxford. Leisure interests include golf, tennis, bridge, reading and psychology. Lives in Langton Green, Kent.

LAING, Sue
Boodle Hatfield, Oxford (01865) 790744
slaing@boodlehatfield.co.uk
Specialisation: Handles UK capital, income and corporation tax planning for landed estates, individuals, trusts, partnerships and private companies; the creation, running and termination of UK and overseas trusts; the interaction of UK and foreign taxes via double tax treaties or UK unilateral relief; the taxation of land transactions within the UK or involving UK entities; UK and overseas taxation of complex trust/corporate structures; and long-term planning for individuals, particularly with a foreign element.
Prof. Memberships: STEP.
Career: Qualified 1978; partner in *Boodle Hatfield* 1981; established Oxford office as first resident partner, 1994. Regular contributor to various tax publications and 'Legal Network Television'.
Personal: Born 1954. MA (Oxon) 1978. Lives near Oxford.

LENEY, Simon
Cripps Harries Hall, Tunbridge Wells, Kent (01892) 515121
sdl@crippslaw.com
Head of Private Client Department and member of firm's Private Office group.
Specialisation: Handles creation/ use of settlements and will trusts; trusteeships and executorships; wills and administration of estates; powers of attorney and attorneyships; inheritance tax and estate planning; charity law; Inheritance (Provision for Family and Dependants) Act claims and other trust or inheritance disputes or claims; appointed to represent large estate in high profile professional trustee and fraud case.
Prof. Memberships: Member of Securities Institute, Director of Solicitors Benevolent Association, member of Society of Trust and Estate Practitioners (STEP), Notary Public.
Career: Educated at Sherborne School, Dorset. Articled at *Donne Mileham and Haddock*; Qualified1977; Salaried partner 1979; Equity partner 1982; Head of Private Client Department 1989; joined *Cripps Harries Hall* 1994; Head of Private Client Department 1996 to date.
Personal: Married with two children. Interests include rugby, vintage and classic cars, home and garden.

LONG, David
Charles Russell, London (020) 7203 5096
Partner in private client department.
Specialisation: Handles a wide range of trusts, wills, probate, estate planning and charity law. Especially interested in international succession problems and contentious probate and trust litigation. Has broadcast on radio and television on wills and lectured on Powers of Attorney.
Prof. Memberships: Law Society, Holborn Law Society (President 1992-93, Chairman Trust Section), Charity Law Association, STEP. Member of joint committee of The Law Society with the Court of Protection 1993-7.
Career: Joined *Charles Russell* in 1972 and became a partner in 1974. Hon. Solicitor Royal Philharmonic Society. Hon. Auditor the Law Society, 1994-98.
Personal: Born 3rd March 1946. Educated at King Edward's School, Birmingham and Balliol College, Oxford 1964-67.

LYALL, George
Dickinson Dees, Newcastle upon Tyne (0191) 279 9643
Specialisation: Personal tax partner and private/charitable trust specialist. Provides advice on domicile and related issues to UK expatriates in Northern Europe, including appeals of EC rulings and international estate planning.
Prof. Memberships: English and Scottish Solicitor, CA, NP and TEP.
Career: 1976-1982 Edinburgh University – B.Com, LLB and Dip.LP. 1982-1985 Scottish Court Solicitor and Notary Public. 1985-1994 chartered accountant and senior tax manager at Arthur/Ernst & Young. March 1994 Joined *Dickinson Dees*.
Personal: Married to Roz with three sons.

MACKINTOSH, Simon A.
Turcan Connell WS, Edinburgh (0131) 228 8111
sam@turcanconnell.com
Specialisation: Main areas of practice are tax, trusts and charities. Work includes tax planning, heritage property, charity law and practice; and trust establishment, variation and practice. Lead partner for a number of the firm's major charity clients. Joint head of the firm's Charity Unit. Co-author of 'Revenue Law in Scotland', 1987. Convener of the Law Society of Scotland Tax Law Committee.
Prof. Memberships: Society of Trust and Estate Practitioners, International Academy of Estate and Trust Law.
Career: Partner *Turcan Connell* 1997; Partner *W & J Burness WS* 1985-1997; Non-executive Director of Macphie of Glenbervie Ltd and Director of the Edinburgh Book Festival. Member of the Scottish Executive Commission on reform of charity law.

MACROBERT, David J.C.
MacRoberts, Glasgow (0141) 332 9988
cjcm@macroberts.co.uk
Partner and head of trust department.
Specialisation: Specialist areas include wills, trusts, inheritance tax, capital gains tax, income tax, executries, power of attorney, charities and investments.
Career: Glenalmond College; Dundee University (1975 LLB). Trainee *Brechin Robb*; qualified 1977; assistant solicitor *MacRoberts* 1977-19801; partner 1980; former senior tutor Glasgow University; former external examiner in finance tax and investment Edinburgh University, Diploma in Legal Practice; member Revenue Committee Law Society of Scotland; Capital Taxes Sub Committee of Chartered Accountants of Scotland. Trustee of Scottish Civic Trust.
Personal: Born 1953; resides Paisley. Leisure: skiing, sailing, shooting, fishing, gardening; member: Royal Gourock Yacht Club, Royal Western Yacht Club, Western Club, Western Club, RSAC.

MAURICE, Clare M.
Allen & Overy, London (020) 7330 3000
Specialisation: Partner specialising in advising UK and non-UK domiciled individuals and families on how to structure their assets both on shore and internationally. She has special experience advising on the UK taxation of offshore structures and Inland Revenue investigations into such activities. She also acts for grant-making and operational charitable organisations advising on all aspects of their activities.
Career: Articled *Allen & Overy*; qualified 1978, partner 1985, Chairman of the Special Trustees for St Bartholomew's Hospital, Director English Touring Opera Limited.
Personal: Educated Sherborne School for Girls. Birmingham University (1975 LL.B). Born 1954. Resides London.

MCCAW, Elma
C & J Black, Belfast (028) 90550060
Specialisation: Probate, Inheritance Tax Planning, Discretionary Trusts, Wills, Deeds of Family Arrangement.
Prof. Memberships: Member of the Incorporated Law Society of Northern Ireland, Belfast Solicitors' Association.
Career: LL.B. (Second Class Honours first Division), Queens University, Belfast. Qualified as a Solicitor in 1976. Partner in *C & J Black*, Solicitors since 1982.

MELLOR, Eliza
Nicholson Graham & Jones, London (020) 7648 9000
eliza.mellor@ngj.co.uk
Partner in Private Client Department.
Specialisation: Has over 25 years experience advising UK and overseas-based clients on UK and international estate planning and trust matters including trust litigation as well as on UK domestic tax issues, domicile and residence.
Prof. Memberships: Law Society; Technical Committee of STEP; International Academy of Estate & Trust Lawyers.

Career: Qualified in 1974. Became a Partner of *Nicholson Graham & Jones* in 1985.
Personal: Educated at City of Worcester Grammar School for Girls and Cambridge University. Lives in London.

MILLER, Adrian W.M.
Foot Anstey Sargent, Exeter (01392) 411221
adrian.miller@foot-ansteys.co.uk
Exeter based Senior Partner.
Specialisation: Family and financial planning for individuals, families, entrepreneurs, and landed estates; tax, trusts and attorneyship, equity and offshore, advance directives, charities and friendly society work.
Prof. Memberships: Law Society Probate Section Executive Committee, Vice Chairman STEP (West of England).
Career: Joined *Anstey Sargent & Probert* in 1974 from *Gregory Rowcliffe & Co.*
Personal: Born 7th November 1947. Radley College and Corpus Christi College, Oxford: Jurisprudence. Chief personal interest is his family and their home and grounds in mid-Devon where he is church warden. His family Scottish estate and French holiday property absorb the rest of his leisure time.

MITCHELL, A.W. Martin
Burges Salmon, Bristol (0117) 902 2792
martin.mitchell@burges-salmon.com
Specialisation: Tax and trusts. He advises on all aspects of UK and offshore trusts and probate, and on capital taxation and charity law. Clients are private individuals with commercial, agricultural and non-resident interests.
Prof. Memberships: Law Society, STEP.
Career: Joined *Burges Salmon* from *Macfarlanes* in 1981 and became a partner in 1983.

MORTIMER, Fay
Edwards Geldard, Cardiff (029) 2023 8239
fay.mortimer@geldards.co.uk
Specialisation: Deals with both old and new money clients of substantial means. All areas of estate planning covered including advising entrepreneurs both prior to acquisition or start up of businesses and all disposal. Considerable expertise in advising elderly clients. Works closely with clinical negligence team regarding Court of Protection applications and the subsequent investment and management of settlement monies.
Prof. Memberships: Local Branch Secretary of STEP; Law Society Probate Section; The Notaries Society.
Career: Cardiff University (LLB); Articles with large Liverpool firm with substantial private client department. Associate and later Senior Associate with *Edwards Geldard* since 1988. Notary Public 1995.
Personal: 3 young children, juggling home and career a speciality. Tennis, skiing, cooking and theatre.

MOYSE, Richard M.
Boodle Hatfield, London (020) 7629 7411
rmoyse@boodlehatfield.co.uk
Senior partner and partner in charge of private client/tax and financial planning department.
Specialisation: Main areas of practice are tax, trusts and financial planning (with an international emphasis), post-mortem tax planning and probate. Specialist fields are capital taxation, trusts, succession, heritage property, contentious trusts and probates. Experienced in the use of trusts in different jurisdictions for estate planning, asset protection and avoidance of forced heirship situations. Has experience in handling large international trusts with conflicts of law, family disputes and succession problems. Has made numerous contributions to professional and in-house publications. Extensive lecturing experience, especially on capital taxation and international tax planning in the UK and abroad, to audiences such as the International Academy of Estate and Trust Law. He is regularly called as an expert witness.
Prof. Memberships: Law Society, International Academy of Estate and Trust Law, International Tax Planning Association, International Bar Association, STAR Group.
Career: With *Lawrence Graham* from 1969-73. Qualified in 1970. Joined *Boodle Hatfield* in 1973 and became a partner in 1974. Elected senior partner in 1999. Member of the Revenue Law Committee of the Law Society and Chairman of Capital Taxes Sub-Committee. President Elect of the International Academy of Estate and Trust Law. Member of the 1994 Principal Private Residence Relief Working Party and 1997 Transfer of Assets Abroad Working Party.
Personal: Born 29th September 1943. Educated at Plymouth College 1948-62, then St. John's College, Oxford 1962-65. Married with four children. Leisure pursuits include travel, cricket, music, genealogy, fly fishing and painting. Lives in London.

NELLIST, Peter
Clarke Willmott & Clarke, Taunton (01823) 329 842
pnellist@cw-c.co.uk
Specialisation: Trust, probate and inheritance tax planning, general financial advice. The winner of the 1999/2000 Money Management's 'Investment Planner' section of its IFA of the Year competition. Runner up 'Investment and Investment Planning' section of Planned Savings 2000 IFA of the Year competition. In January 1999 took and passed the Chartered Insurance Institute's Advanced Financial Planning G60 pension exam. Believed to be the only practicing solicitor holding (by virtue of examination passes) all three Law Society financial qualifications – retail branded packaged products, securities and portfolio management and corporate pensions. A member of and lectures for the Society of Financial Advisers.
Prof. Memberships: Society of Trusts and Estates Practitioners (STEP); chairman of the Bristol Law Society Tax Trust and Probate Committee for 2000; clerk to the Somerton Tax Commissioners; a director of the Association of Solicitor Investment Managers (ASIM).
Career: Articled with *Theodore Goddard*. Qualified in 1973; associate partner from 1977; joined *Clarke Willmott & Clarke* in July 1978; made partner in 1980.
Publications: Has had investment based articles published recently in the Law Society's Gazette Corporate Solutions and Trust and Estates Law Journal 'Investment advice – hidden agendas'.
Personal: Born 1948. Guildford College of Law; Bristol University (LLB). Leisure activities include art and antiques, upholstery, surfing, travel, gardening – hedge laying – chain sawing. Married with two children currently at university.

NICHOLSON, Jonathan B.
Bond Pearce, Plymouth (01752) 266633
xjbn@bondpearce.com
Partner in the Private Client Group.
Specialisation: Almost forty years experience in wills, trusts and personal tax. Specialist in charity law and solicitor to several major charities.
Prof. Memberships: Member of the Society of Trust and Estate Practitioners (Chairman of West of England branch) and the Association of Charity Lawyers.
Career: Graduate of Trinity College, Dublin, qualified in 1968 and joined the University of Zambia as lecturer in law, returning to the UK in 1971. Joined *Meade King* in Bristol and was solicitor to the Bristol Municipal Charities. Moved to *Bond Pearce* in 1983, becoming partner in 1985.

PAUL, Robin
Withers, London (020) 7936 1000
Partner in private client department.
Specialisation: Main area of practice is probate and succession. Head of probate group, advising executors and beneficiaries on all aspects of probate and post death tax planning, often with an international element. Also deals with trusts, tax and estate planning and heritage property. Co-author of 'The Lawyers Factbook' (Aministration of Estates section), 'Practical Will Precedents' and Tolley's 'Administration of Estates' '(Chapter on Business and Agricultural Property). Contributor to various legal journals and to Sweet & Maxwell's `Practical Tax Planning with Precedents' and the Succession Section of 'Practical Commercial Law'. Has lectured at various conferences on wills and succession, with particular emphasis on international aspects.
Prof. Memberships: STEP, Law Society, Westminster Law Society.
Career: Qualified in 1977, having joined *Withers* in 1975. Became a partner in 1982.
Personal: Born 19th December 1952. Educated at Malvern College, then Brasenose College, Oxford 1971-74. Lives in London.

POWELL, Nicholas R.D.
Currey & Co, London (020) 7828 4091

RAE, Scott A.
Morton Fraser, Solicitors, Edinburgh (0131) 247 1000
sar@morton-fraser.com
Specialisation: Tax, Trusts, Estate Planning, Charities.
Prof. Memberships: Solicitor, WS, NP, TEP.
Career: LL.B. (Hons 1st) Edinburgh University – 1966. Partner with *Morton Fraser* since 1970. Appointments:- Member and past Convener Law Society of Scotland Tax Law Committee; Convener Law Society's Trust Law Committee; Member and Past Secretary, The International Academy of Estate and Trust Law; Collector, W.S. Society; Member VAT and Duties Tribunal (Scotland); former National Coordinator, Wills Trust Course of Diploma in Legal Studies.
Personal: Born 17.12.44.

RANKIN, Alastair J.
Cleaver Fulton Rankin, Belfast (028) 9024 3141
Specialisation: Chancery and Equity, Probate, Taxation, Trusts and Estates, Wills.
Prof. Memberships: Member of Council The Law Society of Northern Ireland since 1985: Treasurer 1991-1995; Junior Vice-President 1995-96; President 1996-97. Senior Vice-President 1997-98.
Career: Qualified as Solicitor 1977 (Northern Ireland 1977) (Republic of Ireland 1997). Partner 1980. Part-time Lecturer on Wills, Revenue and Administration

of Estates since 1988 at the Institute of Professional Legal Studies, Queens University of Belfast. General Commissioner of Income Tax. Part-time Chairman Pensions Appeal Tribunals for Northern Ireland.
Personal: Born 5 September 1951. Educated Trinity College Dublin (BA Dublin University). Member, Society of Trust and Estate Practitioners.

REID, Nigel W.
Linklaters (A member firm of Linklaters & Alliance), London (020) 7456 5702
nigel.reid@linklaters.com
Specialisation: Partner. Head of trust department. Specialist in trusts and trust taxation in both commercial and family contexts; commercial and family trusteeships; tax and estate planning for individuals; charities; chancery litigation.
Career: 1994 – to date: head of trust department. 1987 – to date: Partner *Linklaters.* 1980-1987 Solicitor *Linklaters.* 1978-1980 Articles *Linklaters.*
Publications: Editor and co-author – Tolley's 'Estate Planning' (1st-4th Editions).

RHODES, John
Macfarlanes, London (020) 7831 9222
Partner and head of tax and financial planning department.
Specialisation: Particular areas of interest include UK Inheritance and Capital Gains Tax. UK and offshore trusts, the law of domicile and international trust and estate planning.
Prof. Memberships: Law Society, Society of Trust and Estate Practitioners.
Career: Qualified in 1970 while with *Macfarlanes.* Became a partner in 1975.

RICHARDSON, Joseph Charles
Dawson & Co, London (020) 7421 4800
J.Richardson@Dawson-and-co.co.uk
Partner in private client department.
Specialisation: Main area of specialisation is taxation. Covers all areas, particularly capital taxation planning (CGT and IHT) and all aspects of settlements (offshore, variation, etc) and heritage property. Also deals with a range of general private client work for high net worth individuals and families (both old and new money) and some charity work. Acts for a number of major landed estates and offshore clients. Has lectured on IHT and agricultural tenancies, and has specialised recently in various aspects of CGT planning, particularly reinvestment and EIS deferral reliefs.
Prof. Memberships: Law Society, Society of Trusts and Estates Practitioners and the Heritage Group.
Career: Qualified in 1974. Partner in *Dawson & Co* since 1976.
Personal: Born 21st October 1949. Educated at St Olave's and St Peter's Schools, York 1959-68, then Durham University 1968-71 (BA in Law). Ex-squash international and former Chairman of Selectors, Squash Racket Association. Leisure interests include reading, walking, cricket, golf and squash. Married with three children and lives near Basingstoke, Hants.

RICHES, John
Withers, London (020) 7936 1000
Specialisation: Partner in private client department leading commercial group. Main practice areas are estate and capital tax planning for U.K. and non U.K. domiciled individuals. Clients include entrepreneurs, private banks and offshore trustees. Has lectured at major conferences in U.K. and overseas and contributes to professional journals and professional training videos.
Prof. Memberships: Council Member of STEP serving on the Technical and Education Committees.
Career: Qualified in 1985. Worked with two major regional firms before joining *Simpson Curtis* in 1990. Partner *Simpson Curtis/ Pinsent Curtis* 1992-96, partner of *Withers* since May 1996.
Personal: Born 1961. Squash, theatre, walking. Active member of local church.

RIPMAN, Justin
Mills & Reeve, Norwich (01603) 693 256
justin.ripman@mills-reeve.com
Specialisation: Partner specialising in tax and estate planning with particular emphasis on trust and tax issues affecting landed estates and offshore trusts.
Prof. Memberships: Member of CLA Tax Committee and STEP Technical Committee. Contributor to Tolley's 'Administration of Trusts'.

ROBINSON, David J.R.
Forsters, London (020) 7863 8333
djrrobinson@forsters.co.uk
Partner.
Specialisation: Private client specialist, with particular expertise in estate planning, capital taxation and heritage property.
Prof. Memberships: Holborn Law Society and City of London Law Society.
Career: Qualified in 1981. With *Glover & Co* 1982-85. Joined *Frere Cholmeley* in 1985 and became a partner in 1989. Founding partner of *Forsters* August 1998.
Personal: Born in 1955. Educated at Westminster School and Pembroke College, Cambridge. Leisure interests include collecting books, music, art and travel.

ROGERSON, Gary
Cripps Harries Hall, Tunbridge Wells, Kent (01892) 515121
gr@crippslaw.com
Specialisation: Tax planning, trusts and probate; some international estate planning, epecially involving US citizens; closely involved in the firm's Private Office which co-ordinates the legal and financial affairs of individuals with substantial assets and complex affairs.
Prof. Memberships: Society of Trust and Estate Practitoners.
Career: Articled *Cripps Harries Hall*; qualified 1984; partner *Cripps Harries Hall* since 1989.
Personal: Brinkburn Grammar School, Hartlepool; Christ Church, Oxford (BA Jurisprudence). Bridge, sport, gardening. Born 1960; married, three children.

ROSS, Hubert J.
Turcan Connell WS, Edinburgh (0131) 228 8111
hjr@turcanconnell.com
Specialisation: Specialises in advising family companies and businesses, entrepreneurs and high net worth individuals on all aspects of personal and corporate taxation. Having worked for seven years as a merchant banker, he brings an understanding of finance as well as taxation to bear. He liaises with Firm's Guernsey office when acting for non-residents, non-domiciliaries and offshore groups of companies.
Prof. Memberships: Law Society of Scotland; Society of Writers to H.M. Signet; Securities Institute; Society of Trust and Estate Practitioners.
Career: Partner *Turcan Connell* 1997; partner *W&J Burness WS* 1984; Parliamentary Draftsman, Lord Advocate's Department; Group Company Secretary, Leopold Joseph (Holdings) plc 1977; Parliamentary Draftsman, Lord Advocates Department 1976.

SHINDLER, Geoffrey A.
Halliwell Landau, Manchester (0161) 835 3003
Head of trust and estate planning department.
Specialisation: Specialises in trusts, personal taxation with specific reference to inheritance tax and capital gains, and wills and probate. Consulting Editor of Trusts and Estates Law Journal. Trusts and Estates Tax Journal and Member Editorial Board Wills and Trusts Law Reports. Regular conference speaker.
Prof. Memberships: Chairman Society of Trust and Estate Practitioners (STEP) 1994-98, now Vice-President; International Bar Association; American Bar Association Real Property, Probate and Trust Law Section; Institute for Fiscal Studies; Securities Institute; Trust Law Committee; Academician International Academy of Estate and Trust Law; Member Editorial Board Tolley's Trust Law International.
Career: Qualified in 1969. Articled at *March Pearson.* Joined *Halliwell Landau* as a partner in 1986. Honorary Associate of Centre for Law and Business, Manchester University; Director of various local companies.
Personal: Born 1942. Attended Bury Grammar School and Cambridge University (MA LLM Cantab). Leisure interests include Marylebone Cricket Club, Lancashire CCC, Manchester United FC, Manchester Literary and Philosophical Society and Portico Library; Chairman Development Committee Royal Exchange Theatre, Manchester. Lives in Prestwich, Manchester.

STANFORD-TUCK, Michael
Taylor Joynson Garrett, London (020) 7300 7000
mstanford-tuck@tjg.co.uk
Partner in and head of tax and personal planning department.
Specialisation: Principal area of practice is international trust and tax planning, acting for high net worth individuals, mainly those who are non-UK domiciled. Work includes protection of assets, structuring cross-border investments, asset enhancement, diversification and protection. Also deals with domestic private client work, encompassing UK based estate and tax planning, landed estates, heritage property, contentious and non-contentious probate and chancery litigation. Has administered a major multinational estate, principally in Japan involving detailed assessment of Japanese estate tax and capital gains tax law. He also undertakes trust restructuring for high net worth families relocating to or investing in the UK and has handled high profile contentious and non-contentious chancery proceedings under the Settled Land Act 1925. Experienced lecturer and author of various articles.
Prof. Memberships: Law Society, City of London Solicitors Company, Freeman of the City of London, Society of Trust and Estate Practitioners, Bermuda Society (Committee Member), Star Group.
Career: Qualified in 1972. With *Lovell White & King* 1972-75. partner with *Appleby Spurling & Kempe* (Bermuda) 1975-84. Admitted Barrister and Attorney Supreme Court of Bermuda 1978. Joined *Taylor Joynson Garrett* as a partner in 1985.
Personal: Born 3rd November 1946. Educated at

Radley College 1960-65 and Southampton University 1965-68. Leisure activities include golf, gardening, skiing and country sports. Lives in Newbury, Berks.

STUBBS, Ian M.
Maclay Murray & Spens, Glasgow
(0141) 248 5011
ims@maclaymurrayspens.co.uk
Specialisation: Private client partner specialising in personal tax planning, trusts, partnership law, agricultural property and forestry investment. Also a qualified chartered accountant.
Prof. Memberships: Member of Institute of Chartered Accountants of Scotland. Fellow of the Chartered Institute of Taxation. Sits on the Council of the Law Society of Scotland and a member of the Tax Law Committee. Member of the Society of Trust and Estate Practitioners.
Career: Glasgow University (LL.B 1965), CA 1968, FTII 1991.
Personal: Born 1943.

STURROCK, Alan
Addleshaw Booth & Co, Manchester
(0161) 934 6459
aas@addleshaw-booth.co.uk
Specialisation: Trust creation and administration, wills and estate related matters. Wealth tax planning both onshore and offshore. Contentious trust and estate work.
Prof. Memberships: National Council Member STEP (Society of Trust and Estate Practitioners).
Career: Liverpool University (LLB) 1971-1974; *Cobbetts* 1974-1999; *Addleshaw Booth & Co.* 1999-present.
Personal: Married (2 children); Hobbies: sailing, outdoor rural pursuits.

SYED, M. Catriona
Charles Russell, London (020) 7203 5000
catrions@cr-law.co.uk
Specialisation: International and domestic private client work, including tax and estate planning for UK and non-UK domiciliaries; trusts; charity law and practice; trust aspects of commercial transactions.
Prof. Memberships: STEP Technical Committee member; Charity Law Association; City of London Solicitors Company; Law Society; Fellow of the Society of Advanced Legal Studies.
Career: Practised at the Chancery Bar 1983-1986. *Norton Rose* 1986-97. Joined *Charles Russell* (partner 1997).
Personal: Leisure interests include family, opera, fine wine, walking, travel and reading.

TAYLOR, Philip G.
Bullivant Jones, Liverpool (0151) 227 5671
Specialisation: Main area of practice in probate, wills and trusts.
Prof. Memberships: Law Society, STEP Membership.
Career: Qualified in 1973. Joined *Bullivant Jones* in 1986. Partner in 1994.
Personal: Golf, cricket and gardening.

THOMPSON, Anthony J.
Withers, London (020) 7936 1000
Partner in private client department.
Specialisation: Main areas of practice are tax planning, asset structuring, trusts and probate. Acted in Hambro & Others v Marlborough & Others (application under the Settled Land Act for an order to resettle the Blenheim Parliamentary Estates). Clients include proprietors of landed estates, proprietors of businesses (particularly in the property industry) and offshore trustees. Editor of Trusts Section of Private Client Business.
Prof. Memberships: Law Society, Society of Trust and Estate Practitioners. Member of Advisory Committee of FTSE International Private Client Indices.
Career: Qualified in 1968. Partner of *Withers* since 1970. Head of Private Client Department 1980-87. Managing Partner 1987-93.
Personal: Born 29th May 1943. Educated at Haberdashers Aske's School 1956-60 and Trinity College, Cambridge 1961-65. Chairman of Governors Glenesk School. President of Horsley & Sand Cricket Club. Recreations include golf and amateur dramatics. Lives near Guildford.

THORNELY, Richard
Thomas Eggar Church Adams, Horsham
(01403) 214500
richard.thornely@teca.co.uk
Partner and head of private client department.
Specialisation: Main areas of practice are personal tax planning, wills, probate and trusts, charities and the affairs of the elderly.
Prof. Memberships: Law Society, S.T.E.P.
Career: Qualified in 1981. After training at *Slaughter & May,*joined current firm in 1992 and became a partner in 1993.
Personal: Born 20th January 1957. Educated at Rugby School 1969-74 and Trinity Hall, Cambridge 1975-78. Governor of Queen Alexandra Hospital Home, Worthing and honorary solicitor to various charities. Married with three sons. Recreations include mountaineering, skiing and music, particularly playing the piano. Lives in Horsham.

THURSTON, Martyn
White & Bowker, Winchester (01962) 844440
martyn.thurston@wandb.co.uk
Partner and head of private client.
Specialisation: Main areas of practice are tax planning for individuals and trusts, both UK and offshore, wills and succession planning.
Prof. Memberships: STEP, International Tax Planning Association.
Career: Partner *Woodham Smith* 1976-1990; partner *Radcliffes* 1990-1997; partner *White & Bowker* 1998 to present.
Personal: Born 1946. Interests include climbing and music. Lives in London.

TURNOR, Richard
Allen & Overy, London (020) 7330 3000
Specialisation: Partner who advises wealthy private individuals, their families and trustees in connection with all aspects of tax and estate planning, especially where there is an international aspect. Also advises private banks and professional trustees about the related services provided by them to private clients and about trust litigation and banks and corporates in connection with any transaction working a trust structure. Also advises museums and other institutions on heritage and cultural property matters.
Prof. Memberships: Member Society of Trust and Estate practitioners; Trustee of International Bar Association Educational Trust; member Law Society Regulatory Review Working Party.
Career: Articled *Allen & Overy*, qualified 1980, Partner 1985.
Personal: Oxford University 1977. Born 1956.

VOREMBERG, Rhoderick P.G.
Wilsons, Salisbury (01722) 412412
Specialisation: Partner specialising in general private client work and charity law; advises many substantial landowners and family trusts; also leads the firm's charity team (members of which include commercial, litigation, insolvency and property lawyers, all experienced in advising charities) providing advice on a wide range of legal issues affecting charities. He advises on most aspects of charity law, including the establishment and registration of new charities, the revision of their constitutions, restructuring mergers (particularly private schools and other educational charities), trustee powers and responsibilities, Charity Commission inquiries, trading by charities, commercial loans, property development and fund-raising. He advises both charities and private clients on trust law, taxation and heritage property matters. He is himself a trustee of several substantial charities and clients include many others such as the Royal Commonwealth Society, the National Rifle Association, the Salisbury Diocesan Board of Finance, the Stanley Picker Trust and the National Motor Museum Trust. He advised the National Rifle Association on the Charity Commission's review of the register of charities and successfully defended its retention of charitable status.
Prof. Memberships: Member of STEP, Charity Law Association, Charities Property Association and Land Trusts Association.
Career: Qualified 1980; joined *Wilsons* 1982; partner from 1985. Head of Private Client services.
Personal: Married with 3 children (12-17). Amateur silversmith. Captain of the English Eight (Match Rifle) since 1993 and has represented England and Great Britain in match rifle competitions on numerous occasions since 1979.

WEBSTER, Kevin S.
Andrew M. Jackson & Co, Hull (01482) 325242
Head of tax & trust department.
Specialisation: Specialises in estate planning, creation and administration of trusts, complex wills and probate and charity law.
Prof. Memberships: Associate member of Chartered Institute of Taxation and member of Society of Trust and Estate Practitioners.
Career: Admitted 1986.
Personal: Interests include supporting York City.

WILLIS, David. C.
Forsters, London (020) 7863 8333
dcwillis@forsters.co.uk
Senior partner of *Forsters*.
Specialisation: Trusts (UK and Offshore), estates and personal taxation together with some family law work.
Prof. Memberships: Society of Trusts and Estate Practitioners; Country Landowners Association; Solicitor's Family Law Association.
Career: Oxford University (MA). Qualified initially as a barrister before becoming a solicitor. Partner in *Frere Cholmeley Bischoff* 1978-1998. Founding partner of *Forsters* August 1998.

WOLLEN, Nigel J.
Hooper & Wollen, Torquay (01803) 213251
Partner in Probate, Tax and Trust Department.
Specialisation: Qualified 1969. Partner 1971. Specialises in wills, trust probate, personal family and financial planning (including landed estates and non-

residents), and charities. Heads a specialist department of five fee earners.
Prof. Memberships: Law Society, STEP.
Career: Qualified in 1969, having joined *Hooper & Wollen* in 1965. Assistant Solicitor at *Herbert Smith* 1970-71; Partner at *Hooper & Wollen* from 1971.
Personal: Born 16th August 1945. Attended Marlborough College 1959-64. Vice Admiral of Royal Torbay Yacht Club. Leisure interests include sailing and skiing. Lives in Torquay.

WOODHEAD, Louise S.
Wragge & Co, Birmingham (0121) 214 1002
louise_woodhead@wragge.com
Specialisation: Main areas of practice include trusts, estate planning and tax planning, with emphasis on exit planning for owners of businesses.
Prof. Memberships: Charity Law Association, STEP, Law Society.
Career: Qualified in 1983. Became a partner in 1994. Head of private client team.

WRIGHT, Cherry E.
Hugh James Ford Simey, Cardiff (029) 2022 4871
cherryw@hjfs.co.uk
Partner and head of wills, probate and trusts department
Specialisation: Handles all aspects of wills, probate, trusts, tax (especially capital tax) and Court of Protection receiverships, but in particular tax planning trusts for private clients, company directors and shareholders, special needs trusts for accident victims and those with learning difficulties; charitable trusts for both large and fledgling institutions and the constitutional aspects of registered social landlords with charitable rules.
Prof. Memberships: Law Society, STEP
Career: Qualified in 1969. Became a partner in *Shaen, Roscoe and Bracewell* (London) in 1972. Lecturer UCL 1974-6. Lecturer University of Wales, Cardiff 1976 – 1988. Consultant at *Hugh James* 1980 – 1988. Became partner in *Hugh James* 1988.
Publications: 'Succession – Cases and Materials' (Butterworths 1986); Editor Butterworths 'Wills Probate and Administration Service' (loose-leaf).
Personal: Educated at Wolverhampton Girls High School and then at UCL. Graduated UCL LLB first class honours 1966. Obtained honours in Solicitors Finals. Leisure interests include tennis, opera, fell walking and reading. Lives in Vale of Glamorgan, one child.

WRIGLEY, W.Matthew
Wrigleys, Leeds (0113) 244 6100
Partner.
Specialisation: Private client and charities, particularly agricultural, and heritage property; educational, religious and conservation charities.
Career: Qualified 1972. Partner *Biddle & Co* 1975. Partner *Dibb Lupton Broomhead* 1978. Partner *Wrigleys* 1996.
Personal: Born 1947. Educated Westminster School (Queen's Scholar), King's College, Cambridge (Scholar).

WYLD, Charles
Burges Salmon, Bristol (0117) 902 2773
charles-wyld@burges-salmon.com
Specialisation: Head of tax and trusts department where his practice encompasses tax and estate planning for UK and overseas clients, including financial planning; advising on formation and ongoing legal requirements of charities, whether trusts or companies.
Prof. Memberships: Law Society, Capital Taxes Sub-committee of the Revenue Law Committee of the Law Society, International Tax Planning Association, Charity Law Association, STEP and Institute of Financial Planning.
Career: Trained, qualified and practised at *Frere Cholmeley*, joining *Burges Salmon* in 1986, becoming a partner in 1989. Qualified as financial planner in 1996.
Personal: New College, Oxford 1975-79.

SOLICITORS
A-Z OF LAW FIRMS

AARON & PARTNERS

Grosvenor Court, Foregate St, Chester, CH1 1HG **Tel:** (01244) 405555 **Fax:** (01244) 405566 **DX:** 19990 **Email:** aarons@dial.pipex.com **Website:** www.aaronandpartners.com **Ptnrs:** 10 **Asst solrs:** 13 **Notaries public:** 2 **Other fee-earners:** 6 **Contact:** Simon Carter • Commercial law practice covering property, litigation and company commercial. Niche specialisms include: planning; environment; minerals and waste; transport and warehousing; employment; insolvency; construction; agriculture.

AREAS OF PRACTICE

Corporate & Commercial	30%
Commercial Litigation	25%
Property	15%
Minerals & Waste	10%
Planning & Environmental	10%
Transport	5%
Insolvency	3%
Private Client	2%

ACTONS

2 King Street, Nottingham, NG1 2AX
Tel: (0115) 910 0200 **Fax:** (0115) 910 0290 **DX:** 1001 Nottingham 1
Email: enquiries@actons.co.uk **Website:** www.actons.co.uk

Managing partner:	John Britten
Senior partner:	Richard Leman
Number of partners:	10
Assistant solicitors:	12
Other fee-earners:	12

CONTACTS

Area	Contact
Commercial Litigation	Giles Gunstone
	Kendal Litherland
Commercial Property	Susan Lawson
Company/Commercial	Adrian Forster
Corporate Prosecutions	John Britten
Insolvency	Richard Leman
	Nicky Calthrop-Owen
Matrimonial	Diane Dobney
	Michael Spencer
Personal Injury	Peter Seymour
	Gary Chadwick
Private Client	Mandy Kelly

THE FIRM: Actons has developed an enviable reputation and prides itself on a partner-led service, and on finding practical solutions to difficult legal problems. The partners have the breadth and depth of expertise to deal with such matters seamlessly and effectively.

PRINCIPLE AREAS OF WORK:

Insolvency: Actons is widely regarded as the niche insolvency firm in the East Midlands and acts for the majority of insolvency practitioners in the area.
Commercial Litigation: Most litigation is handled including employment, property, contract disputes and professional negligence.
Commercial Property: Surveyors and clients welcome its pragmatic approach and ability to meet tight deadlines.
Company Commercial: Servicing a significant number of predominantly owner managed businesses.
Personal Injury: The department is retained by the RAC and represents a number of insurers and local authorities.
Private Client: Covering all aspects of private client services involving estate planning, wills, trusts and probate services for high net worth clients.

A

ADAMS & REMERS

Trinity House, School Hill, Lewes, BN7 2NN **Tel:** (01273) 480616 **Fax:** (01273) 480618 **DX:** 3100 Lewes 1 **Email:** post@adams-remers.co.uk **Website:** adams-remers.co.uk **Ptnrs:** 7 **Asst solrs:** 7 **Other fee-earners:** 18

ADAMS WHYTE

24 Palmerston Place, Edinburgh, EH12 5AL **Tel:** (0131) 225 8813 **Fax:** (0131) 226 7623 **DX:** ED212 **Email:** hotline@adamswhyte.com **Website:** www.adamswhyte.com

ADDLESHAW BOOTH & CO

Sovereign House, PO Box 8, Sovereign Street, Leeds, LS1 1HQ
Tel: (0113) 209 2000 **Fax:** (0113) 209 2060 **DX:** 12004 Leeds
Email: info@addleshaw-booth.co.uk **Website:** www.addleshaw-booth.co.uk

60 Cannon Street, London, EC4N 6NP
Tel: 020 7982 5000 **Fax:** 020 7982 5060 **DX:** 98948 Cheapside 2
Email: info@addleshaw-booth.co.uk

100 Barbirolli Square, Manchester, M2 3AB
Tel: (0161) 934 6000 **Fax:** (0161) 934 6060 **DX:** 14301 Manchester
Email: info@addleshaw-booth.co.uk

Managing Partner:	Mark Jones
Senior Partner:	Paul Lee
Number of partners:	112
Assistant solicitors:	285
Total staff:	1079

AREAS OF PRACTICE

Commercial Property	25%
Corporate Finance	18%
Housing	16%
Commercial Services	15%
Banking & Finance	14%
Litigation & Dispute Resolution	7%
Private Client	5%

CONTACTS

Area	Contact
Banking & Finance	Mark Chidley
Commercial Property	John Pike
Commercial Services	Malcolm Pike
Corporate Finance	Jonathon Shorrock
Housing	Anthony Ruane
Litigation and Dispute Resolution	John Gosling
Private Client	Paul Howell

THE FIRM: Addleshaw Booth & Co is a leading independent law firm with an international capability offering a full range of commercial legal services. A business which works for business, the firm has developed quickly its national markets to provide commercial solutions to a wide range of clients in the corporate, financial, public and private sectors. With offices in Leeds, Manchester and London, the firm combines top level expertise and experience with strength in depth to provide clients with a range of legal services that their businesses need. Clients have a dedicated contact partner who creates a tailor-made team, drawing on the skills of the firm's many nationally recognised specialists. The wide range of clients from the corporate, financial, public and private sectors includes, amongst others, 3i plc, Airtours plc, British Vita, BT plc, Trinity Mirror plc and GEHE (UK) plc, as well as 135 UK based financial institutions. In the past year Addleshaw Booth & Co has further developed its capabilities and now has 112 partners, a further 458 lawyers and 173 other fee earners firmwide. It has bid for more than 140 proposals across all sectors and industries in the past year.

Continued overleaf

PRINCIPAL AREAS OF WORK:

Corporate Finance: Addleshaw Booth & Co's corporate finance practice is one of the most significant in the UK. The practice has a tradition of deal-making, not just providing outstanding technical advice but also in making deals happen through extensive business and professional networks and by strategic input to deals at every stage. The group had its most successful year in 1999, advising on deals with a total value of £5 billion.

Banking: During 1999, the firm's banking & finance practice acted on significant transactions involving total funding/facilities in excess of £5.5 billion, an 80% increase on the previous year's total funding figure.

Commercial Property: In commercial property, the firm is recognised as one of the leading practices in volume and diversity of market sectors. It has a national reputation for work in retail and leisure.

Commercial Services: Commercial services' expertise is provided in intellectual property, European and competition law, commercial contracts, employment law, pensions, share schemes and tax issues.

Litigation/Dispute Resolution: The firm's litigation and dispute resolution group has widely respected practices in international litigation and arbitration, recognition and enforcement of foreign judgements and regularly provides corporate support advice on international and UK transactions on choice of law, jurisdiction and dispute resolution agreements.

Private Client: The private client practice is regarded as a leading practice across the UK with an increasing number of national appointments and a strong national reputation in family law.

Housing: Addleshaw Booth & Co's housing practice was relaunched in April 2000, under the brand name enact. The service incorporates remortgaging and transactional conveyancing.

Other: In addition the firm has a number of cross-disciplinary units, including pharmaceuticals, sport and entertainment and PFI, which bring together experts in a variety of legal disciplines.

A

CLIENTELE: The firm's clients include: 3i Group plc; Abbey National plc; Airtours plc; ASDA Group Ltd; British Aerospace plc; BT plc; GEHE UK plc; Halifax plc; HSBC Bank plc; J Sainsbury plc; Manchester 2002: Commonwealth Games; Ministry of Defence; Nationwide Building Society; Scapa Group plcStadium Group; Trinity Mirror plc; Yorkshire Bank; Yorkshire Electricity Group plc.

RECRUITMENT & TRAINING: In addition, the firm has invested 4% of revenue towards state-of-the-art hardware, software, training and support across all offices. The firm continues to win significant new appointments through competitive tenders and client recommendations, and through an ever-growing recognition of the firm as a 'City calibre' player able to deliver real value to transactions of all sizes. For further information please visit Addleshaw Booth & Co's website at www.addleshaw-booth.co.uk or contact Lucy Cluskey, External Communications Manager, 0113 209 2510.

AGNEW, ANDRESS, HIGGINS

92 High Street, Belfast, BT1 2DG **Tel:** (028) 90320035 **Fax:** (028) 90249380 **Ptnrs:** 3 **Asst solrs:** 2 **Other fee-earners:** 1

AITKEN NAIRN WS

7 Abercromby Place, Edinburgh, EH3 6LA
Tel: (0131) 556 6644 **Fax:** (0131) 556 6509 **DX:** 18 Edinburgh
Email: reception@aitkennairn.co.uk **Website:** www.aitkennairn.co.uk

Managing partner:	Kenneth Stanley
Number of partners:	4
Assistant solicitors:	3
Other fee-earners:	3

AREAS OF PRACTICE

Residential Property	30%
Litigation	25%
Private Client	25%
Commercial Property	20%

CONTACTS

Commercial Property	Kenneth Stanley
Litigation	Paul Harper
Private Client	Morag Yellowlees
Residential Property	Kenneth Stanley

THE FIRM: Aitken Nairn WS is a long established Scottish practice located in Edinburgh's New Town. It has two distinct areas of expertise for both of which it enjoys a strong reputation. Four partners and their staff deal with estate agency, property management, domestic and commercial conveyancing, domestic and commercial leasing, executries, trusts and private client advice. The emphasis is on a quality service at the top end of the market. Two partners and their litigation team handle personal injury, family law, commercial litigation, housing law, bankruptcies, judicial review and Industrial Tribunals. They will resolve disputes at whatever end of the market.

LANGUAGES: Spanish.

AKIN, GUMP, STRAUSS, HAUER & FELD

One Angel Court, London, EC2R 7HJ
Tel: (020) 7726 9600 **Fax:** (020) 7726 9610
Website: www.akingump.com

Managing Partner:	J. Stephen Hatfield
UK:	
Number of partners:	2
Senior advisors,	1
Senior counsel,	2
Associates,	1
Resident lawyers:	6
Total lawyers (Worldwide):	950

CONTACTS

Insurance ....Patrick G. Devine
International/Capital Markets
....J. Stephen Hatfield
....John Edwards
Project Finance ....J. Stephen Hatfield

THE FIRM: Akin Gump is a fully integrated, major, multinational law firm, headquartered in the United States with offices in eight US cities and three of Europe's leading centres of commerce, finance, and government. The London office is staffed to deliver first class US and UK qualified legal services in strategically important practice disciplines, including corporate finance, capital markets, project finance, mergers and acquisitions and insurance. Founded in 1945, this leading international law firm numbers 950 lawyers in 11 offices across the United States and Europe.

PRINCIPAL AREAS OF WORK: The firm has a diversified practice and represents regional, national and international clients in a wide range of areas, including antitrust; banking and financial institutions; bankruptcy, reorganisation and creditors' rights; capital markets; communications; corporate and securities; employee benefits; energy; entertainment; environmental; estate planning and probate; food and drug; government contracts; health; insurance and reinsurance; intellectual property; international trade; investment management; labour and employment; litigation; mergers and acquisitions; privatisation; project finance; structured finance; public law and policy; real estate and finance; taxation and technology.

London Office: Akin Gump's London office numbers six lawyers (three UK qualified, three US qualified) and adds one of the world's most important financial and commercial centres to Akin Gump's international practice. Akin Gump's global practice has been built on a solid reputation for making large international transactions happen successfully. In today's business environment, Akin Gump believes that success often hinges on a law firm's ability to field a closely integrated, multinational team that best matches the requirements of the assignment. The London office is one of the firm's central hubs in such a network, offering dual law capability (UK and US) principally in the areas of corporate finance, capital markets, project finance, private placements, mergers and acquisitions, privatisations and insurance. In addition to the local law capabilities in the firm's Brussels and Moscow offices, the firm also maintains a network of relationships and resources which enable it to arrange for local law capabilities in many European jurisdictions, South Africa and the Kingdom of Saudi Arabia.

Corporate Finance: Lawyers from the London office have been involved in a wide range of corporate finance transactions. For example, the firm has represented both underwriters and issuers in a number of notable and innovative capital markets transactions, including the first major global offering by Russian oil giant LUKOIL. It has also represented a group of underwriters in structuring a multibillion dollar global offering of convertible bonds and Eurobonds by another major Russian issuer. The London office has also represented the underwriters in a US$150 million bond offering by a Belgian commercial bank; a large UK independent oil company in connection with debt and equity financing for a US$264 million property acquisition; and a major US life insurance company in a 144A placement by an offshore Asian fund. On the project finance front, the London office is engaged in transactions ranging from the development of power projects in India to regional airports across Europe. Recent major merger and acquisition activity includes the representation of Swedish company in a US$400 million acquisition of an oil refinery in Morocco, major US clients in the acquisition of a retail coffee chain in the UK, and one of the largest US life insurance companies in ventures such as entry into the newly privatised life insurance industry in India. London office lawyers also played pivotal roles in the organisation of LUKOIL's historic US$5 billion joint venture with ARCO, and have served as counsel to a consortium of major Western European and Russian energy companies in connection with a tender for an oil company in a Russian privatisation programme. The London office also was involved in the representation of a major Russian financial group in the purchase and successful launch of a communications satellite.

Insurance: With clients drawn from the insurance, banking and investment communities, specialist insurance lawyers with extensive experience of the Lloyd's, UK company and international insurance and reinsurance markets advise on a wide range of insurance and related issues including insurance regulation and compliance, the development and documentation of alternative risk transfer products, policy and treaty wordings, drafting and interpretation, dispute resolution, insurance and reinsurance insolvency, claims, run-off and commutations. Often working with insurance and reinsurance specialists in other Akin Gump offices in the US and Europe and in conjunction with overseas correspondent law firms, the international reach of the practice is extensive. In the past 12 months, the London office has advised on insurance matters in the UK, the US, Latin America, Russia, the Middle East, the Indian sub-continent, Asia and a number of offshore insurance centres including Bermuda. For many of Akin Gump's clients, London is an important gateway to business opportunities in Europe, Africa, Russia and the former Soviet Union and the Middle East, and a key commercial centre for access to global markets. Akin Gump's proven ability to staff projects from multiple offices allows its London office lawyers to efficiently and effectively serve as the focal point for handling all sizes of transactions centred in multiple geographic regions.

INTERNATIONAL CONNECTIONS: The firm has offices in Austin, Brussels, Dallas, Houston, Los Angeles, Moscow, New York, Philadelphia, San Antonio, Washington DC, and Riyadh (affiliation).

A

ALEXANDER HARRIS

Ashley House, Ashley Road, Altrincham, WA14 2DW
Tel: (0161) 925 5555 **Fax:** (0161) 925 5500 **DX:** 19866 Altrincham 1
Email: info@alexharris.co.uk **Website:** www.alexharris.co.uk

1 Dyers Buildings, London, EC1N 2JT
Tel: (020) 7430 5555 **Fax:** (020) 7430 5500 **DX:** 460 London Chancery Lane
Email: info@alexharris.co.uk

Managing Partner:	Ann Alexander
Senior Partner:	David Harris
Number of partners:	6
Assistant solicitors:	11
Associates:	6
Other fee-earners:	21

AREAS OF PRACTICE

Claimant Clinical Negligence	60%
Claimant Personal Injury	20%
Pharmaceutical Product Liability/ Medical Devices/Disasters & Multi-Party Actions	20%

CONTACTS

Clinical Negligence	Ann Alexander
	Grainne Barton
	Lesley Herbertson
Personal Injury	David Harris
	Richard Barr
Pharmaceutical Product Liability & Multi-Party Actions	David Harris
	Richard Barr

THE FIRM: Specialists in health-related work in the UK and USA, including clinical and dental negligence, pharmaceutical product liability and personal injury. Founded in 1989 by Ann Alexander and David Harris, the firm has offices in London and Altrincham (Cheshire).The firm's fee-earners include a US-qualified lawyer, and close links have been developed with practices in North America and Canada.

PRINCIPAL AREAS OF WORK:
Clinical Negligence: The department deals with all aspects of medico-legal matters, with emphasis on brain injury, anaesthesia, general surgery, misdiagnoses claims, radiation damage, and all aspects of dental negligence. The department are supported by a team of medico-legal assistants, all of whom are qualified nurses.
Pharmaceutical Product & Multi-Party Actions: The department deals with adverse drug reactions and faulty medical devices, including Myodil, Persona, LSD, MMR vaccine, Septrin, radiotherapy and pacemakers. It has expertise in multi-party claims, and is on the Law Society's multi-party action panel. It has represented victims of the Hillsborough disaster and the serial murderer, Beverly Allit.
Serious Personal Injury: The department includes two members of the Law Society personal injury panel and specialises in serious personal injury cases, particularly those involving catastrophic head and spinal injuries in the UK and abroad. The department also includes a specialist unit handling transatlantic compensation claims.

CLIENTELE: Clients include UK citizens injured during visits to the US and Canada, and claimants against US-based manufacturers. The firm receives an increasing volume of referrals from non-specialist solicitors.

ALEXANDER PAUL
32 Bampton Street, Tiverton, EX16 6AH **Tel:** (01884) 252361 **Fax:** (01884) 253461 **Email:** peterbucchal@alexanderpaul.com
Website: www.alexanderpaul.com

ALEXANDERS

203 Temple Chambers, Temple Avenue, London, EC4Y 0DB
Tel: (020) 7353 6221 **Fax:** (020) 7583 0662 **DX:** LDE 264 Chancery Lane
Email: info@alexanders-solicitors.co.uk **Website:** www.alexanders-solicitors.co.uk

Senior Partner:	Graham Ogilvie
Number of partners:	5
Assistant solicitors:	4
Other fee-earners:	3

AREAS OF PRACTICE

Litigation	45%
Tax & Trust	35%
Property	20%

THE FIRM: The firm is a specialist private client practice.

PRINCIPAL AREAS OF WORK: Probate, Tax & Trust: Contact Graham D Ogilvie; Property & Agricultural: Contact Elisabeth A Jupp; Family & Matrimonial: Contact Martyn J Daldorph; Personal Injury & Medical Negligence: Contact Richard D O'Halloran.

ALISTAIR MELDRUM & CO

8-9 Genotin Terrace, Enfield, Middlesex, Enfield, EN1 2AF
Tel: (020) 8367 0064 **Fax:** (020) 8366 8578 **DX:** 90609 Enfield

Managing Partner:	Richard Pugh
Senior Partner:	Alistair Meldrum
Number of partners:	3
Assistant solicitors:	2
Other fee-earners:	4

AREAS OF PRACTICE

Crime	85%
Family/Matrimonial	15%

CONTACTS

Criminal	Alistair Meldrum
Family	Mark Bowman

THE FIRM: Founded 10 years ago, Alistair Meldrum & Co has always specialised in criminal defence work and has become one of the foremost criminal firms in North London.

PRINCIPAL AREA OF WORK:
Criminal: All aspects of criminal defence work undertaken. The firm has extensive experience in all areas of criminal law.
Family: Family, matrimonial and childcare law undertaken.
Agency Work: Advocacy in local Magistrates' Courts.
Legal Aid: Legally aided work undertaken for both criminal and family law. The firm has been franchised in both these categories since 1995.

CLIENTELE: Both privately paying and legally aided clients.

ALLAN JANES

21-23 Easton Street, High Wycombe, HP11 1NU **Tel:** (01494) 521301 **Fax:** (01494) 442315 **DX:** 4402 High Wycombe **Email:** enquiries@allanjanes.com **Website:** www.allanjanes.com **Ptnrs:** 7 **Asst solrs:** 4 **Other fee-earners:** 4

ALLEN & FRASER

78 Dean St, London, W1V 6BE **Tel:** (020) 7437 4001 **Fax:** (020) 7439 0650 **DX:** 44714 Soho Square **Ptnrs:** 2 **Asst solrs:** 2 **Other fee-earners:** 1 **Contact:** Mr R.M.B. Walter • Known for its licensing law expertise and for its conveyancing (commercial and domestic), litigation and trust and probate departments.

AREAS OF PRACTICE

Liquor & Entertainment Licensing	60%
Domestic & Commercial Conveyancing	30%
Other Private Client Work	10%

ALLEN & OVERY

One New Change, London, EC4M 9QQ
Tel: (020) 7330 3000 **Fax:** (020) 7330 9999 **DX:** 73
Email: information@allenovery.com **Website:** www.allenovery.com

THE FIRM: Allen & Overy is a premier international law firm. Founded in 1930, it has over 300 partners and some 3,200 staff working in 23 major centres on three continents serving businesses, financial institutions, governments and private individuals where there is a need for decisive legal advice on complex matters.

PRINCIPAL AREAS OF WORK:

Corporate: The firm's corporate department provides a comprehensive legal service to clients covering all aspects of company, corporate finance and commercial law. Lawyers in the department advise on public takeovers, international and cross border mergers and acquisitions, Stock Exchange flotations, international equity offerings, private equity, joint ventures and strategic alliances, corporate restructuring, management buyouts and public private partnership. In addition, the corporate department is actively involved in the work of specialist cross-departmental practice groups including those that deal with the energy sector, environmental law, insurance, media and communications (including telecommunications, new digital media, broadcasting and satellite), healthcare, financial services and compliance, international projects, construction, mining and metals, European anti-trust, intellectual property and information technology.

Banking: The firm advises financial institutions and borrowers on all types of financing transactions in the UK and overseas including acquisition finance, project finance, property finance, trade finance, restructurings including debt for equity swaps and all forms of structured finance, asset finance (including aviation and shipping), securitisations, risk reduction techniques and derivatives and all forms of international finance. The practice acted for more than 800 international banks in deals involving over 100 jurisdictions.

International Capital Markets: The firm advises in relation to capital markets transactions by issuers from all over the world (including developing countries as well as those with developed economies). These include eurobond issues, euro-equity offerings, equity linked issues, securitisations and derivatives. The firm also has a highly regarded US law practice which now numbers 28 partners and over 100 US qualified lawyers. The practice advises on a wide range of transactions with a significant or dominant US element. For example, A&O was the first non-US firm to advise the underwriters on a public securitisation deal in the US.

Litigation: The firm's litigation and dispute resolution practice deals with all forms of commercial dispute including banking and finance, commercial fraud and crime, construction, defamation, DTI enquiries, employment, environmental law, EU & competition, information technology, intellectual property, product liability, professional negligence, property, shipping and trade sanctions.

Private Client: The firm's large practice provides comprehensive advice to wealthy individuals, entrepreneurs and senior directors, trustees, families, museums, universities and charities worldwide.

Project Finance: The firm has one of the leading project finance practices advising all parties in major projects in the UK, Europe (including Central and Eastern Europe), the Middle East, South East Asia and China, and elsewhere, acting for lenders, project owners and sponsors, governments, public authorities, contractors, developers and investors.

Property: The firm provides a full commercial property service to landowners, institutions, property companies, developers, contractors, investors and banks on areas including building contracts, commercial leases and underlettings, development agreements, housing association law, joint ventures, planning procedures and appeals, redevelopments, short and long term funding and site acquisition.

Taxation: The firm provides a comprehensive corporate tax service including advice on employee benefits and share schemes, and VAT and other indirect taxation.

INTERATIONAL CONNECTIONS: The firm has offices in Amsterdam, Bangkok, Beijing, Bratislava, Brussels, Budapest, Dubai, Frankfurt, Hong Kong, Luxembourg, Madrid, Milan, Moscow, New York, Paris, Prague, Rome, Singapore, Tirana, Tokyo, Turin and Warsaw.

LANGUAGES: Afrikaans, Arabic, Bengali, Bulgarian, Cantonese, Czech, Danish, Dutch, Finnish, French, German, Greek, Gujarati, Hebrew, Hindi, Hungarian, Italian, Japanese, Korean, Malay, Mandarin, Persian, Polish, Russian, Spanish, Tamil and Urdu.

Managing Partner:	John Rink
Senior Partner:	Guy Beringer
UK:	
Number of partners:	159
Assistant solicitors:	532
Other fee-earners:	202
International:	
Number of partners:	147
Assistant solicitors:	410
Other fee-earners:	207

CONTACTS

Banking	David Morley
Building Societies	Peter Holland
Business Reconst & Insolvency	Gordon Stewart
Communications/ Media & Technology	Ian Ferguson
Construction	John Scriven
Corporate/Commercial	Richard Cranfield
Derivative Products	Jeff Golden
European Anti-Trust	Mark Friend
Employment, Pensions & Incentives	Derek Sloan
Energy	Roger Davies
Environmental	Owen Lomas
Financial Services	Paul Phillips
Housing Association Finance	Andrew Joyce
Insurance	Ian Stanley
Intellectual Property	Colleen Keck
International Capital Markets	Boyan Wells
Litigation	Andrew Clark
MBOs	Alan Paul
Mergers/Acquisitions/Takeovers	Alan Paul
Pharmaceutical & Med. Prods.	Colleen Keck
Private Clients	Richard Turnor
Public Private Partnerships	Anne Baldock
Privatisation	Peter Holland
Projects & Project Finance	Graham Vinter
Property (Commercial)	Gideon Hudson
Securitisation	David Krischer
Tax (Corporate)	Patrick Mears
VAT & Indirect Tax	Linda Adelson

ALLEN & OVERY

ALLINGTON HUGHES
10 Grosvenor Rd, Wrexham, LL11 1SD **Tel:** (01978) 291000 **Fax:** (01978) 290493 **DX:** 26651 **Email:** AllingtonW@aol.com **Ptnrs:** 11
Asst solrs: 5 **Other fee-earners:** 8

AMBROSE APPELBE

7 New Square, Lincoln's Inn, London, WC2A 3RA
Tel: (020) 7242 7000 **Fax:** (020) 7242 0268 **DX:** LDE 467
Email: mailbox@ambrose.appelbe.co.uk **Website:** www.ambrose.appelbe.co.uk

Managing Partner:	Lisa Bolgar Smith
Senior Partner:	Felix Appelbe
Number of partners:	5
Number of assistants:	1
Other fee-earners:	4

CONTACTS

Litigation	Martin Chater
Matrimonial & Family	Lisa Bolgar Smith
Probate	Phillipa Seaton
Property	Felix Appelbe

THE FIRM: The firm was founded in 1935 by Ambrose Appelbe in partnership with the first ever woman solicitor, Carrie Morrison and has remained in Lincoln's Inn since that time. A radical thinker, Ambrose was one of the four founders of the National Marriage Guidance Council now known as Relate. He continued to practice until 1990 and sadly died in early 1999.

PRINCIPAL AREAS OF WORK:
Matrimonial & Family: A strong niche matrimonial practice specialising in national and often international high net worth Divorce and Ancillary relief, co-habitees disputes, pre-nuptial agreements and all children's matter. All members of the family department are members of the SFLA.
Property: Residential and commercial conveyancing.
Probate: Drafting wills, tax advice, probate and estate administration.
Litigation: Plaintiff personal injury litigation, employment disputes, solicitor's professional negligence.

CLIENTELE: The firm acts for a large number of successful, professional husbands and wives as well as partners and co-habitees. These range from investment bankers to academics, consultants, musicians, international businessmen and women, journalists and actors. They also act for businesses, charities and local authorities.

AMERY-PARKES

Law Courts Chambers, 33 Chancery Lane, London, WC2A 1EN
Tel: (020) 7404 7100 **Fax:** (020) 7404 6588 **DX:** 162 Lon Chancery Lane WC2
Email: lond@ameryparkes.co.uk **Website:** www.ameryparkes.co.uk

Senior Partner:	Damian Knowles
Number of partners:	23
Assistant solicitors:	16
Other fee-earners:	42

AREAS OF PRACTICE

Accident Claims Recovery/Personal Injury	60%
Conveyancing, Commercial & Domestic	15%
Commercial & General Litigation	10%
Corporate	10%
Probate Trust & Tax	5%

CONTACTS

Commercial Litigation	Darryl Greer
Common Law	Nigel Mears
Conveyancing	Peter Black
	Derrick Dudley
Corporate	William Davis
Fleet and Insurance	David Faithful
Personal Injury	Celia Sohpal
Probate, Trust & Tax	Anne Lewis

THE FIRM: Founded in 1892 the firm now has offices in five major centres. Whilst principally known for its personal injury and accident litigation work (both for claimants and defendants), the firm also has a large private client practice in all locations. In Basingstoke, there is a large conveyancing practice, both residential and commercial as well as a substantial PI department. There is also a developing defendant PI section.The Birmingham office also has a substantial PI department, dealing with both claimant and defendant work. In addition, there is a common law department dealing with all aspects of matrimonial, criminal and child care work, as well as Mental Health Act tribunals. Bristol office again has a substantial PI department, as well as a conveyancing department, dealing with residential and commercial matters. In London there are significant departments dealing with company commercial, commercial litigation, employment law and probate, trust and tax.
Agency work is handled in all offices.

INTERNATIONAL CONNECTIONS: In London the firm has French and Spanish speakers and international work is undertaken. The firm has an associated office in Paris.

AMHURST BROWN COLOMBOTTI

2 Duke Street, St. James's, London, SW1Y 6BJ
Tel: (020) 7930 2366 **Fax:** (020) 7930 2250 **DX:** 412
Email: amlaw@abc-solicitors.com **Website:** www.abc-solicitors.com

Managing Partner:	Chris Langford
Senior Partner:	Peter Smithson
Number of partners:	17
Assistant solicitors:	13
Other fee-earners:	8

AREAS OF PRACTICE

Commercial Property	30%
Company Commercial	30%
Litigation	30%
Private Clients	10%

THE FIRM: Amhurst Brown Colombotti is a highly progressive international practice. Recognised as one of the leading central London firms for providing high quality commercial services, the firm attributes its success to a dynamic and entrepreneurial approach by its use of multi-talented lawyers combining legal, commercial and language skills. The firm is a well-established international practice respected for its commercial acumen. It has a high quality reputation in its chosen specialisations including: property, leisure, employment, international commercial litigation and hi-tech/internet. The firm has particular expertise in handling cross-border matters spanning Italy, Spain, Poland and Middle East. Amhurst Brown Colombotti provides a committed and reliable service to its clients. It recognises the importance of delivering clients' business objectives by means of practical, creative and cost effective expertise.

PRINCIPAL AREAS OF WORK: Amhurst Brown Colombotti is divided into four core groups: corporate, property, litigation and private client. However the firm also works through other specialist teams which combine lawyers from each of these disciplines. These include employment, leisure and insolvency.

CONTACTS

Corporate .... Tom Mackay
Employment .... Nigel Forsyth
Internet Hi-tech .... Tom Mackay
Leisure .... Eric Gummers
Litigation & ADR .... Steven Morris
Private Client .... Peter Smithson
Property .... Paul Amandini

ANDERSON FYFE

90 St. Vincent Street, Glasgow, G2 5UB
Tel: (0141) 248 4381 **Fax:** (0141) 204 1418 **DX:** GW 138
Email: mail@andersonfyfe.co.uk **Website:** www.andersonfyfe.co.uk

Managing Partner:	David H. Chaplin
Number of partners:	6
Assistant solicitors:	8
Other fee-earners:	19

THE FIRM: Anderson Fyfe provides services in business, company and employment law, while its private client division provides a comprehensive portfolio of services to individuals. The practice is responsive and flexible to the changing needs of its clients.

PRINCIPAL AREAS OF WORK:

Business Law: The firm's corporate division provides a range of services including company formation, finance, acquisitions and sales. The firm also advises on commercial contracts, intellectual property and trade protection, and has an expanding employment law division.
Private Client: The private practice division looks after individual clients' investments, trusts, tax, wills and executry matters as well as residential conveyancing.
Commercial Property: Services include land acquisition and development, house building developments, leasing, retail leasing, quarrying, security work, planning appeals and Housing Association work.
Litigation: The firm has an extensive commercial and public sector litigation and recoveries department and has been instructed in a number of leading Scottish cases in the Court of Session and House of Lords. Roddy McIlvride is a solicitor advocate with rights of audience in the Court of Session and the House of Lords.
Public Sector: The firm carries out work for public sector bodies in education, enterprise and housing.

AREAS OF PRACTICE

Property 32%
Litigation and Recovery 29%
Corporate/Business Law/Insolvency 26%
Private Client/Trust/Executry 13%

CONTACTS

Business Law .... David Chaplin
Commercial Property .... Kenneth Meldrum
Employment Law .... Tom McEntegart
Litigation .... Roddy McIlvride
Private Client Services .... Christopher Wilkin
Public Sector .... David Chaplin
.... Kenneth Meldrum
Residential Property .... Lesley Forrest

Anderson Fyfe *Solicitors*

ANDERSON MACARTHUR & CO

Old Bank of Scotland Buildings, Stornoway, HS1 2BG **Tel:** (01851) 703356 **Fax:** (01851) 702766 **Email:** simon@anderson-macarthur.com **Ptnrs:** 3 **Other fee-earners:** 3 **Contact:** Simon Fraser • Established early this century the firm has three partners operating two offices in Stornoway, Isle of Lewis and Portree on the Isle of Skye. Deal with general work and specialise in crofting. The firm has developed a specialism in the new area of community ownership.

ANDERSON PARTNERSHIP

125 West Regent Street, Glasgow, G2 2SA
Tel: 0141 248 6688 **Fax:** (0141) 248 9697 **DX:** 512403 Glasgow - Bath St
Email: mailbox@anderson-partnership.co.uk

1 St Colme Street, Edinburgh, EH3 6AA
Tel: 0131 220 8242 **Fax:** 0131 220 8342 **DX:** 551112 Edinburgh 7
Email: edinburgh@anderson-partnership.co.uk

Senior Partner:	Gilbert M. Anderson
Number of partners:	8
Assistant solicitors:	6
Other fee-earners:	10

THE FIRM: Established in 1994 under Gilbert Anderson & Partners, the practice has since doubled in size. At the end of 1999, the firm opened its Edinburgh office.

PRINCIPAL AREAS OF WORK:

Insurance Law/Insurance Litigation & Claims: Including advice on coverage, conduct of litigation in the Court of Session and in Sheriff Courts throughout Scotland, and representation at Fatal Accident Inquiries. They provide advice on all aspects of road traffic claims/public/employers' liability, product liability and undertake all related investigative work for insurers throughout Scotland. They have two members of FOIL.
Commercial/Commercial Property: Including commercial leasing; security; business acquisition; disposal and start-ups for sole traders, partnerships and companies; contractual advice; employment law; commercial dispute resolution; asset recovery.
Private Client: Including residential conveyancing tax planning; wills and executries, financial services; matrimonial dispute resolution.

AREAS OF PRACTICE

Insurance/Insurance Litigation and Recoveries 75%
Company/Commercial Property 20%
Private Client 5%

CONTACTS

Administrative Law .... Frank Hughes
Co/Comm Property .... Alan Paton
Commercial Litigation .... Andrew R. Ireland
Employment Law .... James G. Herd
Ins/Ins Lit & Recoveries .... Gilbert M. Anderson
.... John P. Maillie
.... Alan S. Taylor
Private Client .... Morag Gibb

ANDERSON STRATHERN WS

48 Castle Street, Edinburgh, EH2 3LX
Tel: (0131) 220 2345 **Fax:** (0131) 226 7788 **DX:** 3 Edinburgh
Email: forename.surname@andersonstrathern.co.uk
Website: www.andersonstrathern.co.uk

Managing Partner:	Robin M. Stimpson
Chairman:	Alan S. Menzies
Number of partners:	25
Assistant solicitors:	27
Other fee-earners:	39

CONTACTS

Charities	George Russell
Commercial Property	Alan Menzies
	David Hunter
	Andrew Morris
Construction	Micheal Essery
	Neil Smith
Corporate	Jonathan MacQueen
Corporate/Sports	John Kerr
Employment	Alun Thomas
Family Law	Mac Rigg
Intellectual Property/Information Technology	Simon Brown
Litigation	Robert Carr
	Robert Fife
	Ruari
	MacNeill
	Fiona Stephen
Private client	John Blair
	Colin Henderson,
	Robin Watt
	Lynda Pennel
	George Russell
Property	Bob Williams
Residential Property	Jean Broadwood
Rural Property	Robin Stimpson
	Alasdair Fox
	Fiona Gibb,
	James Drysdale

THE FIRM: This prominent Edinburgh practice offers services to business and private clients throughout Scotland and beyond. Anderson Strathern is a highly competitive, full service firm servicing major national and international companies, local authorities, financial institutions, property investors and developers, insurance companies and a number of substantial landowning interests. As a member of The Association of European Lawyers, the firm is strongly placed to provide advice on any matters which require cross border expertise and makes full use of an advanced communications and management system. The partnership combines legal expertise, commercial awareness, strength in depth and value for money.

PRINCIPAL AREAS OF WORK:

Corporate: The corporate department undertakes mergers and acquisitions, MBOs and MBIs, business start-ups and institutional finance, joint ventures and insolvency. It also has considerable experience of advising on intellectual property matters, commercial contracts (including computer contracts), competition matters and European law. The firm has specialist experience in media and entertainment, publishing, sports and leisure and education.

Commercial Property: Anderson Strathern covers all aspects of commercial property work including planning, construction law and environmental law. The firm has particular expertise in Housing Association lending and acquisition work, landlord and tenant law, property acquisition and financing and development work with two partners accredited specialists in commercial leasing law.

Litigation: The litigation department is renowned for its liability insurance work and health service law with one partner an accredited specialist in employment law and another in medical negligence. Three are solicitor advocates with rights of audience in the highest Scottish civil courts.

Agriculture & Private Client: The firm maintains, and intends to develop, its position as one of the foremost practices in rural/agricultural and private client work. The rural department provides a full service on all agricultural and heritage matters, with two partners accredited specialists in agricultural law. Private client work covers trusts, tax planning, insurance, financial planning and investments, residential conveyancing and mortgage advice.

Other Information: In addition to its commitment to existing areas of practice, the firm is developing a series of firm-wide units which focus on particular client requirements. These draw on a wide range of expertise to build the optimum team for every client requirement. Areas covered include Liability Insurance, the Financial Sector, Employment and Land Ventures, which offers advice on commercial diversification projects to land owners, and intellectual property. The use of new technology is central to the efficiency of a modern law firm. Anderson Strathern has consistently kept abreast of the latest developments in legal software with the belief that an investment in technology and in training pays dividends in the provision of an effective service. The firm also recognises the importance of investing in its people, having recently been awarded the IIP standard, and runs a detailed in-house training programme, covering both legal and management issues.

CLIENTELE: Clients include The Royal College of Nursing, Napier University, the National Trust for Scotland, the Scottish Rugby Union and the Coal Authority.

ANDREA & CO

Triatha House, Millbrook, Guildford, GU1 3XJ **Tel:** (01483) 889 880 **Fax:** (01483) 889 881 **DX:** 83156 Guildford 2
Email: ca.andreaco@btinternet.com **Website:** www.andreaco.com

ANDREW BRYCE & CO

7 Queen St, Coggeshall, CO6 1UF **Tel:** (01376) 563123 **Fax:** (01376) 563336 **Email:** 113147.733@compuserve.com **Ptnrs:** 1

ANDREW M. JACKSON & CO

Essex House, Manor Street, Hull, HU1 1XH
Tel: (01482) 325242 **Fax:** (01482) 212974 **DX:** 11920
Email: lawyers@amj.co.uk **Website:** www.amj.co.uk

Managing Partner:	John Hammersley
Senior Partners	Martin Whitehead and Silas Tylo
Number of partners:	22
Assistant solicitors:	31
Other fee-earners:	20

THE FIRM: 125 years old last year, the firm's services are founded on committed and well-motivated lawyers delivering top quality advice and value for money.

PRINCIPAL AREAS OF WORK:

Company/Commercial: M&A, corporate finance, partnership, franchise and agency agreements and joint ventures.

A

Shipping & Fishing: Ship sale, purchase and finance, collision, salvage, charterparty, and Bills of Lading disputes.
Commercial Property: Landlord and tenant, property development and planning.
Commercial Litigation: Landlord and tenant, property development and planning.
Private Client: Tax, trusts and tax planning.
Agency Work: Undertaken in all local civil courts.
Legal Aid: Family law and family mediation. Franchise holder.

CLIENTELE: Local and national companies both public and private including MFI, Carpetright, Northern Foods, Express Dairies, Associated British Ports and P&O North Sea Ferries.

AREAS OF PRACTICE

Commercial Property	30%
Litigation	20%
Private Client	20%
Shipping	20%
Company	10%

CONTACTS

Area	Contact
Commercial Property	Bill Fisher
Company	Martin Whitehead
Litigation	Hugh Smith
Private Client	Kevin Webster
Shipping	Silas Taylor

ANDREW KEENAN & CO

Nickleby House, Charles Dickens Terrace, Maple Road, London, SE20 8RE **Tel:** (020) 8659 0332 **Fax:** (020) 8659 3689 **DX:** 34860 Penge
Ptnrs: 1 **Asst solrs:** 1 **Other fee-earners:** 4

ANNE HALL DICK & CO.

157 Kilmarnock Road, Shawlands, Glasgow, G41 3JE **Tel:** (0141) 636 0003 **Fax:** (0141) 636 0303 **DX:** 501146 Shawlands
Email: ahdco@globalnet.uk **Ptnrs:** 2 **Asst solrs:** 2

A

ANN L. HUMPHREY

The Boathouse Office, 57a Gainsford Street, London, SE1 2NB **Tel:** (020) 7378 9370 **Fax:** (020) 7378 9360 **Email:** annlhumphrey@dial.pipex.com **Website:** under construction **Ptnrs:** 1 **Other fee-earners:** 1 **Contact:** Ann L. Humphrey • Niche tax practice with substantial experience in VAT and corporate tax planning which operates from purpose-built offices at Tower Bridge.

AREAS OF PRACTICE

VAT	60%
Corporate Tax	40%

ANTHONY COLLINS SOLICITORS

St Philip's Gate, 5 Waterloo Street, Birmingham, B2 5PG **Tel:** (0121) 200 3242 **Fax:** (0121) 212 7442 **DX:** 13055 Birmingham 1 **Email:** acs@acollins-sol.co.uk **Ptnrs:** 15 **Asst solrs:** 30 **Consultants**5 **Other fee-earners:** 24 **Contact:** Deborah Evans • A proactive niche market practice providing services primarily to the voluntary sector, the business sector, the housing sector, local government and the individual.

AREAS OF PRACTICE

Housing & Local Government	33%
Commercial Property	18%
Business Law/Licensing	16%
Litigation/PI/Medical Negligence	16%
Private Client (Family)	12%
Charities/Church Law	5%

ANTHONY GOLD, LERMAN & MUIRHEAD

New London Bridge House, 25 London Bridge Street, London, SE1 9TW
Tel: (020) 7940 4000 **Fax:** (020) 7378 8025 **DX:** 39915 London Bridge South
Email: mail@anthonygold.co.uk **Website:** www.anthonygold.co.uk

43 Streatham Hill, London, SW2 4TP
Tel: (020) 8678 5500 **Fax:** (020) 8674 8004 **DX:** 58604 Streatham
Email: mail@anthonygold.co.uk

Managing Partner:	David Marshall
Number of partners:	10
Assistant solicitors:	12
Other fee-earners:	11

CONTACTS

Area	Contact
Admin/Public/Property Litigation	Andrew Brookes
Commercial Litigation	Sarah Ahmed
Commercial Property	Howard Lerman
Corporate & Commercial	David Marshall
Family Law/Mediation	Kim Beatson
	Caroline Bowden
Medical Negligence	David Marshall
	Jon Nicholson
Personal Injury	David Marshall
	Jon Nicholson
Professional Negligence	Sarah Ahmed
Trusts & Estates Planning	Mark Politz

THE FIRM: Anthony Gold, Lerman & Muirhead was founded in 1963. The firm is a progressive and expanding practice with specialist departments who represent both business and individual clients. Based at London Bridge, and also with offices in SW2, the firm excels at meeting the needs of both individual and business clients. The firm's highly regarded litigation practice is largely claimant-focused and aims to work in a way which matches clients' ability to pay its fees. In particular, it has been instrumental in the development of conditional fee agreements. David Marshall is co-author of *Conditional Fees: Law and Practice* (Sweet and Maxwell, 1999).

PRINCIPAL AREAS OF WORK:
Company & Commercial: The acquisition and disposal of companies and unincorporated businesses, all general commercial agreements including joint ventures, agency and distribution and IT and intellectual property matters.
Commercial Dispute Resolution: General commercial contracts of both a national and international content with particular expertise in computer, engineering and construction disputes.
Employment: Advising businesses and individuals on contracts of employment, redundancy, dismissal, European law, HR/employment policies at work and discrimination claims.
Family & Divorce: Financial cases, maintenance and property, children's cases (including abductions), mediation and Inheritance Act cases. Kim Beatson is on the National Committee of the Solicitors' Family Law Association. Both Kim Beatson and Partner, Caroline Bowden are accredited family mediators.
Landlord & Tenant/Property: Landlord and tenant claims (for either party), disrepair, dilapidations, possession, forfeiture and lease renewals.

Continued overleaf

Clinical Negligence: All categories of clinical negligence with particular expertise in cerebral palsy and other brain injuries, obstetrics and gynaecology, infectious diseases, neurosurgery, orthopaedics, anaesthetics, accident and emergency medicine and general practice. Jon Nicholson and David Marshall are members of the Law Society's Clinical Negligence Panel.
Personal Injury: A wide spectrum of personal injury claims for claimants, ranging from catastrophic brain and spinal injuries to road traffic accidents, accidents at work and tripping cases. All personal injury solicitors are members of APIL and those with more than three years post-qualification experience are on the Law Society's personal injury panel.
Professional Negligence: Acting for businesses and individuals in claims against solicitors, accountants, surveyors and financial advisors. Sarah Ahmed is a member of the Office for the Supervision of Solicitors' negligence panel.
Public law: Judicial reviews of the decisions of local and public authorities in particular the housing, community care and education sectors. Andrew Brookes is Chair of the Housing Law Practitioners' Association.
Property: Acquisitions, development and financial work for retailers, investors, landlords and homebuyers.
Trusts & Estates: Specialising in tax planning, wills and the administration of estates and trusts. Mark Politz is a Chartered Tax Adviser.

ARCHERS

Barton House, 24-26 Yarm Road, Stockton-on-Tees, TS18 3NB **Tel:** (01642) 673431 **Fax:** (01642) 613602
Email: admindept@archerssolicitors.co.uk **Website:** www.archerssolicitors.co.uk **Ptnrs:** 9 **Asst solrs:** 8 **Other fee-earners:** 12

ARCHIBALD CAMPBELL & HARLEY WS

37 Queen Street, Edinburgh, EH2 1JX **Tel:** (0131) 220 3000 **Fax:** (0131) 220 2288 **DX:** 181 Edinburgh **Email:** admin@achws.co.uk **Website:** www.achws.co.uk **Ptnrs:** 13 **Asst solrs:** 12 **Other fee-earners:** 16
Contact: Andrew Wallace • Known for innovative work in commercial property, corporate, planning, environment, debt recovery/insolvency, litigation and housing. Reputation for quality service, commercial flair and relevant, expert, practical advice.

AREAS OF PRACTICE	
Commercial Property	43%
Private Clients	31%
Litigation	12%
Corporate/Commercial	9%
Planning/Environmental	5%

ARGLES STONEHAM BURSTOWS

8 Ifield Road, Crawley, RH11 7YY
Tel: (01293) 603603 **Fax:** (01293) 603666 **DX:** 57100 CRAWLEY 1
Email: crawley.office@asb-law.com **Website:** www.asb-law.com

Managing Partner:	Russell Bell
Number of partners:	42
Assistant solicitors:	65
Other fee-earners:	33

THE FIRM: Argles Stoneham Burstows is one of the strongest law firms in the South East and is unrivalled in its coverage throughout Kent, Surrey, Sussex and South London. It provides a range of specialist legal services to both business and private clients. The firm is committed to providing an innovative, partner-led service focusing on approachability, friendliness and accessibility. Its prime aim is to deliver specialist advice to its clients in an efficient manner while providing true value for money. Argles Stoneham Burstows was formed as a result of the merger in November 1999 of the highly respected Maidstone practice, Argles & Court, the leading Sussex practice, Burstows and Croydon's successful commercial practice, Stonehams.

PRINCIPAL AREAS OF WORK: The firm has two divisions; the commercial division headed by Caroline Armitage and the private client division headed by Colin Trelfer. Within these divisions are specialist work groups:-
Corporate & Commercial: Easily one of the largest in the South East region outside London. Corporate work includes private company mergers, acquisitions and disposals, management buy-outs supported by either private or venture capital funding, acting for investors on capital injections and corporate tax restructuring. Commercial work includes considerable growth of activity in IP, IT, telecommunications and E-Commerce as well as Public Sector work, CCT contracts and franchising. The firm is an associate member of the BFA.
Commercial Property: Includes acquisitions, leasing, disposal of commercial property, agricultural interests, hotels and licensed premises, offices and shops, estate development, building contracts, housing association law and secured lending. Development and funding of commercial and residential schemes including leasehold enfranchisement are also areas of substantial expertise.
Employment Law: The largest in the region with an impressive and prestigious client base, and has an active relationship with the Institute of Personnel and Development. They offer their own unique employment advice and insurance package, "Praesidium Employment Law Protection". The group deal with the full range of contentious and non-contentious employment work.
Aviation Law & Travel: Includes advice to governments and commercial organisations both in Eastern Europe and Africa and work with national and international airlines. A busy 'holiday claims' department works for a range of travel companies.
Insolvency: A licensed insolvency practitioner heads a group of 5 solicitors acknowledged as the leading insolvency team in the South East. The firm also acts for the DTI in bringing directors' disqualification proceedings.

AREAS OF PRACTICE	
Corporate and Commercial including Employment	35%
Private Client	29%
Commercial Property including Planning	15%
Personal Injury	14%
Insolvency	7%

CONTACTS	
Aviation	Michael Butler
	Lee Hills
Commercial Litigation & Debt Recovery	Andrew Pawlik
	Andrew Clinton
Commercial Property	Carol Fletcher
	Marcel Bradbury
Corporate & Commercial	Don Burstow
	Alina Nosek
Employment	Jonathan Maude
	Jonathan Simmons
Family	Ursula Danagher
	John Innes
Franchising	Don Burstow
	Nigel Spells
General Civil Litigation	
Insolvency	Albert Passmore
	Andrew Taylor
	Anne Kane
IP	Karen Lord
IT Contracts	Alina Nosek
	Margaret Craton
Licensing	Stephen Thomas
Personal Injury	Mike Cutler
	Francis Lacy Scott

Commercial Litigation: Considerable expertise in corporate and commercial disputes, professional negligence, construction, property and debt collection. A wide range of liquor licensing and gaming matters are dealt with as well as substantial High Court litigation for both UK and overseas clients.
Planning & Environmental: Specialises in all aspects of planning law and acts for a number of local authorities and large property developers.
Personal Injury & Medical Negligence: This team continues to expand dramatically, particularly in relation to defendant work for insurance companies and plaintiff medical negligence and personal injury work. It also specialises in handling personal injury claims for holiday companies and airlines and is one of the leading specialists in the country.
Other: ASB continue to be a broadly based practice with full ISO 9001 accreditation and provides a full range of private client services including residential property, family and wills, trusts and probate.

CLIELNTELE: The client base includes airlines and travel companies, universities and colleges, blue-chip companies, local authorities, insurance companies, breweries, construction companies and accountants. The firm also acts for a wide range of substantial listed and privately owned companies with turnovers ranging from £500,000 to £100m.

CONTACTS CONTINUED

Property Litigation........................Rex Cowell
Residential Property................Tim Rodemark
....Robert Moyle
Town & Country Planning..........Roger Curtis
....Sarah Cox
Trusts, Personal Tax & Probate ....John Catterick
....Clare Jeffries

ARMITAGE SYKES

72 New North Rd, Huddersfield, HD1 5NW **Tel:** (01484) 538121 **Fax:** (01484) 518968 **DX:** 711270 Huddersfield 9 **Ptnrs:** 7 **Asst solrs:** 4 **Other fee-earners:** 10

A

ARNOLD & PORTER

Level 30, Tower 42, 25 Old Broad Street, London, EC2N 1HQ
Tel: (020) 7786 6100 **Fax:** (020) 7786 6299
Website: www.arnoldporter.com

Managing partner:	James Sandman
Chairman	Michael N Sohn
UK: Number of partners:	7
Assistant solicitors:	16
US Associates:	2
Other fee-earners:	23
International: Number of partners:	203
Associates:	259
Of Counsel:	13
Special Counsel:	21

CONTACTS

Antitrust & Trade Regulation............Bill Baer
Bankruptcy ....Daniel Lewis
Benefits & Employment Law ..Peter Schmidt
Corporate & Securities ....Steven Kaplan
Environmental ....Thomas Milch
Financial Institutions..................Patrick Doyle
Food, Drug & Medical Devices William Vodra
Government Contracts ....Joseph West
Health Care ....Grant Bagley
Intellectual Property & Technology ....Charles Ossola
International....................Lawrence Schneider
Legislative/Public Policy ....Jeffrey Smith
Life Sciences ....Richard Johnson
Litigation ....Peter Grossi
Product Liability ....Peter Grossi
Project Finance..................Whitney Debevoise
Real Estate ....George Covucci
Tax ....Richard Hubbard
Telecommunications ....Norman Sinel

THE FIRM: Arnold & Porter, founded in 1946, is one of the largest law firms headquartered in Washington, D.C. With over 525 lawyers organised into over 25 practice areas, it maintains an international practice spanning a broad spectrum of legal practice. Its core specialties focus on litigation, transactional matters, and regulatory issues. Arnold & Porter has worked hard to maintain a reputation for effectiveness, integrity, and access, as well as a high level of respect for the quality of its work.
London Office: In recent years, the integration of the world economy and the regulatory systems to which businesses are subject has accelerated at an unprecedented pace. Governments, companies and the legal profession are all evolving their practices in response to these developments. To augment their international practice, Arnold & Porter established the London Office to provide their clients in the London market – European, International and American – with the same quality of service and approach to legal representation that they have provided in the United States. The firm intends to focus in London on select legal areas where it can capitalise on the combined experience of its lawyers in London and its other offices and can provide sophisticated representation of the highest calibre. The firm has a deserved reputation of providing high quality and efficient legal services. Central to the historic practice of the firm has been a focus upon the intersection of law, business and public policy and an understanding of the industries in which its clients operate. Lawyers have frequently been retained by clients confronted with the most complex legal and business problems, often with a regulatory or governmental component, requiring innovative and practical solutions. The practice has evolved to include the representation of multinational corporations and financial institutions, governments, international organisations and others in a broad range of regulatory, litigation and transactional matters.

PRINCIPAL AREAS OF WORK: The firm's principal areas of work include antitrust & trade regulation, bankruptcy, benefits & employment law, corporate & securities, environmental, financial institutions, food, drug & medical devices, government contracts, health care, intellectual property & technology, international, legislative/public policy, life sciences, litigation, product liability, project finance, public policy, real estate, tax, and telecommunications.
Antitrust & Trade Regulation: In connection with Computer Associates' $4 billion acquisition of Sterling Software, Arnold & Porter's London Competition team successfully coordinated and executed the filing of premerger notifications in nine jurisdictions (Austria, Brazil, Finland, Germany, Netherlands, Poland, Portugal, South Africa and Turkey) in roughly two weeks. A voluntary filing in the UK was also completed. The transaction did not involve an EU Community-wide filing, so Arnold & Porter lawyers had to determine where filings would be required, arrange for local counsel, coordinate information collection, and ensure consistency in the substance of the filings in coordination with a parallel US filing.
Product Liability/Litigation: Managing some of the largest and most complex product liability matters in the United States, Arnold & Porter acts both as national counsel and as trial counsel in many individual cases. For example, the firm serves as the national coordinating counsel and trial counsel for American Home Products in its phen-fen diet drug litigation, which involves a wide range of issues, including compliance with Food and Drug Administration (FDA) new drug and adverse event reporting regulations; the development and evaluation of epidemiological and clinical data; and novel class action issues in both the litigation and settle-

Continued overleaf

ment contexts. The firm is defending approximately 15,000 cases in 49 states, as well as the 1,000 federal cases that have been consolidated in Philadelphia. The firm's lawyers have drafted most of the class action briefs and argued those motions. Arnold & Porter is also responsible for working with approximately 500 scientific and regulatory experts who have appeared in one or more of the cases. Most recently, the attorneys were the principal architects of a $4.75 billion settlement that should resolve much of that litigation. Arnold & Porter served as national defense counsel for a large volunteer blood collector in cases concerning individuals who allegedly contracted the AIDS virus from blood transfusions. The firm obtained numerous rulings granting summary judgment on negligence, strict liability and breach of warranty claims and won favorable verdicts in four cases that have been tried before juries.

Litigation: The firm represented a former Counsel to the President of the United States in extended Congressional hearings on the Whitewater matter; the case involved testimony before both the House and Senate Whitewater Committees and presentations to the majority and minority members of the Committees. They coordinated with the White House lawyers and defended the position of the client in television interviews.

Intellectual Property: The United States Court of Appeals for the Federal Circuit recently affirmed a judgment that Arnold & Porter had won for Xerox Corp. in 1997 ñ the culmination of 8 years of litigation defending Xerox's policies on the sale of replacement parts and the licensing of diagnostic software to its competitors who service Xerox copiers and printers. The unanimous decision upheld Xerox's refusal to sell patented parts or license the software against an antitrust challenge. In so doing, the Federal Circuit expressly rejected Ninth Circuit authority to the contrary.

Telecommunications: In providing legal counsel to the City of New York on the relationship between the city and its telecommunications providers, lawyers were responsible for the regulatory aspects of the largest telecommunications mergers to date: the merger of SBC and PacTel. Arnold & Porter handled the legal aspects of a worldwide placement of common shares in each of two formerly government-owned telephone companies. The two transactions netted the country's treasury in excess of $2 billion.

Corporate: Arnold & Porter is regularly listed among the top 25 US law firms for the amount of merger & acquisition deals completed in any given year. Representative transactions include: the acquisition of Sterling Software, Inc. by Arnold & Porter's client Computer Associates International, Inc. for an estimated value of $4 billion; the acquisition of Sterling Commerce, Inc. by Arnold & Porter's client, SBC Communications, Inc. for an estimated value of $3 billion; and the acquisition of Network Solutions, Inc., Arnold & Porter client, by Verisign, Inc. for an estimated value of $21 billion.

Pro Bono Work: Arnold & Porter's distinguished 55 year tradition of pro bono service has established an exceptional reputation among the public interest bar and in the community as a whole. The firm has special ties with many important public interest organizations in the community that provide critical legal services to the disadvantaged. Their pro bono work is characterised by diversity - the issues taken on are as wide-ranging as the interests of their attorneys and staff. The firm has a long-standing tradition of groundbreaking representation in matters involving the arts, capital murder, civil rights, due process, education, employment discrimination, environmental matters, free speech, international human rights, prisoner's rights, reproductive rights and criminal matters. The firm has grown and changed dramatically since the early pro bono days of the firm's defense of government employees accused of disloyalty during the McCarthy era, the representation of Clarence Gideon in Gideon v Wainwright, which established the rights of criminal defendants to legal representation, and the precedent setting litigation that was undertaken on behalf of 600 victims of the Buffalo Creek disaster, but Arnold & Porter's commitment to reaching out to the larger community in which it prospers remains constant.

INTERNATIONAL CONNECTIONS: The firm's headquarters is located at: 555 Twelfth Street NW, Washington DC, 20004. Additional offices are located in New York, Los Angeles, Century City and Denver.

CLIENTELE: Arnold & Porter's clients range from Fortune 500 corporations to high tech start-up companies. With such a broad spectrum of legal specialties and experience, their approach to service is multidimensional.

RECRUITMENT & TRAINING: The firm's hiring standards are rigorous. They seek candidates who have demonstrated academic excellence. Outstanding law school performance is a major factor in hiring decisions, although other professionally related activities and experience, personal references, and participation in law review or clinical legal work also are weighed. Most new associates are recent law school graduates, many of whom have just completed judicial clerkships or other government service. Arnold & Porter is committed to equal employment opportunity and to a program of affirmative action to fulfill that policy. They value diversity and affirmatively solicit applications from all qualified applicants, including women, minorities, and individuals with disabilities. The firm also considers associate training a high priority. Excellent training begins by working closely with experienced attorneys who have varying styles and approaches to the practice of law, providing associates with an opportunity to learn a broad range of skills. The firm's commitment to excellence ensures rigorous instruction in legal research and writing. In addition, the firm presents a series of programs, seminars, and discussions for new associates to introduce them to the firm's operations and to strengthen basic skills such as research, oral advocacy, deposition practice, contract drafting, and negotiations. Seminars concerning particular areas of practice are also conducted by partners specialising in these areas. The firm maintains a current video and print library of continuing legal education materials and electronic research services.

ARNOLD THOMSON

205 Watling Street West, Towcester, NN12 6BX **Tel:** (01327) 350266 **Fax:** (01327) 353567 **DX:** 16932 Towcester **Email:** enquiries@arnoldthomson.com **Website:** www.arnoldthomson.com **Ptnrs:** 1 **Asst solrs:** 6 **Other fee-earners:** 1 **Contact:** Mr M.A. Thomson. • Mike Thomson heads a team which includes several very senior lawyers with extensive experience in areas of work handled across England and Wales. The firm regularly deals with agricultural tenancy work for other solicitors.

AREAS OF PRACTICE

Sales, Purchases & Development Work	35%
Trusts/Tax and Probate	25%
Agricultural Tenancies	15%
Civil Litigation	10%
Partnerships	10%
Quotas	5%

ARTHUR COX - NORTHERN IRELAND

Stokes House, 17-25 College Square East, Belfast, BT1 6HD
Tel: (028) 9023 0007 **Fax:** (028) 9026 2650 **DX:** 2012 NR Belfast 2
Email: bt@arthurcox.ie **Website:** www.arthurcox.ie

THE FIRM: Arthur Cox – Northern Ireland was established in 1996, following the merger of the Belfast office of Arthur Cox, one of the largest practices in the Republic of Ireland, with the long established law firm of Norman Wilson & Co which has particular strengths in the areas of corporate banking, commercial, property and employment law. The firm merged in December 1997 with Martin & Brownlie to give added strength to its employment and litigation departments. The firm is in a unique position to provide a range of cross-border services from its Belfast and Dublin Offices.

PRINCIPAL AREAS OF WORK:
Banking/Financial Services: The firm is established as one of the leading practices in all aspects of banking and secured lending.
Company/Commercial: Includes all types of company/commercial law matters, mergers and acquisitions, joint ventures, agency and distribution agreements with particular emphasis on cross-border transactions.
Competition/European: Competition and EU regulatory advice with particular reference to cross-border transactions.
Commercial Property: Covers a significant range of property and commercial property related transactions including commercial development for private and public companies and financial institutions.
Litigation/Employment: A wide range of litigation services with particular reference to employment and commercial litigation.

INTERNATIONAL CONNECTIONS: The firm has offices in Dublin and New York.

Contact Partner:	Angus Creed
UK:	
Number of partners:	6
Assistant solicitors:	7
Other fee-earners:	5
International:	
Number of partners:	42
Assistant solicitors:	57
Other fee-earners:	31

AREAS OF PRACTICE

Litigation (including Employment)	30%
Property	30%
Banking/Financial Services	20%
Company/Commercial Law	20%

CONTACTS

Banking/Financial Services	Angus Creed, Peter Stafford
Civil Litigation	Peter Martin, Angela Maguire, Amanda Wylie, Anna Beagan
Commercial Property	Rowan White, Anne Donnelly, Patricia Lyons
Company/Commercial	Kerry Canavan, Peter Stafford, Judith Keogh
Competition/European	John Meade

ASHTON GRAHAM

Electric House, Lloyds Avenue, Ipswich, IP1 3HZ **Tel:** (01473) 232425 **Fax:** (01473) 230505 **DX:** 3221 IPSWICH
Email: lawyers@ashtongraham.co.uk **Website:** www.ashtongraham.co.uk

ASHURST MORRIS CRISP

Broadwalk House, 5 Appold St, London, EC2A 2HA
Tel: (020) 7638 1111 **Fax:** (020) 7972 7990 **DX:** 639 London
Email: enquiries@ashursts.com **Website:** www.ashursts.com

THE FIRM: Ashurst Morris Crisp is a major international law firm with headquarters in London and offices in Europe, Asia and America. Ashursts provides a high quality integrated legal service across all its offices, focused on all major aspects of business and financial law, with specialist sector knowledge and highly developed transaction management skills, supported by major investment in training and know-how infrastructure.

PRINCIPAL AREAS OF WORK: Ashursts operates in all principal areas of commercial law including:
Company & Commercial: Advising clients on cross-border mergers and acquisitions, joint ventures, private equity transactions, corporate finance, EU and competition law, reconstruction and insolvency, IP, IT, insurance and employment.
Banking & Capital Markets: Advising lenders, issuers, borrowers and advisers in the fields of corporate debt derivatives, bond issues, acquisitions and project finance, leveraged finance transactions and trade finance.
Commercial Property/Real Estate: Working with landlords, developers, tenants and public authorities, offering general property, planning, environmental law and litigation advice.
Commercial Litigation: Advising on construction and development issues, international arbitration and dispute resolution, EU and competition law, product liability, insolvency and professional negligence and property litigation.
Tax: All aspects of cross-border work including international buy-outs, collective investment schemes, demergers, securitisations and debt trading.
Employment: Advising on employment and employee benefits including pensions and employee share schemes.

Continued overleaf

Senior Partner:	Geoffrey Green
Managing Partner:	Ian Nisse
UK:	
Number of partners:	83
Assistant solicitors:	274
Other fee-earners:	151

AREAS OF PRACTICE

Company & Commercial	49%
Commercial Litigation	17%
Commercial Property	16%
Banking & Capital Markets	13%
Tax	5%

CONTACTS

Banking & Capital Markets	Justin Spendlove
Buy-Outs/Private Equity	Charlie Geffen
Commercial Contracts	Jeremy Hill
Commercial Litigation	Edward Sparrow
Commercial Property	Simon Cookson
Construction/Engineering	Christopher Vigrass
Corporate	David Macfarlane
E-Commerce	Mark Lubbock
Employment & Benefits	Caroline Carter
Energy & Natural Resources	Michael Johns
EU/Competition	Nigel Parr, Julian Ellison
Financial Services	James Perry
Information Technology	Mark Lubbock
Insurance & Reinsurance	Jeremy Hill

INTERNATIONAL CONNECTIONS: In addition to London, the firm has offices at: Avenue Louise 375, 1050 Brussels, Belgium; Oberlindau 76-78, 60323 Frankfurt am Main, Germany; Via C. Finocchiaro Aprile, 14, 20124 Milano, Italy; 712 Fifth Avenue, 21st floor, New York, NY 10019, USA; 22 rue de Marignan, 75008 Paris, France; 6 Battery Road, #15-08, Singapore 049909; Kioicho Building, 8th floor, 3-12 Kioicho, Chiyoda-Ku, Tokyo 102-0094, Japan; and a liaison office at 6 Aurangzeb Road, D-1, New Delhi 110011, India.

LANGUAGES: All business and commercial languages spoken.

RECRUITMENT & TRAINING: The firm recruits both qualified and trainee solicitors into all areas of its practice. Applicants need not only to have achieved high academic standards, but also to possess individuality and commercial awareness that can be applied to issues, ensuring the most appropriate solution for the client. For more information, please visit our website, www.ashursts.com, or contact Isabelle Sorgo, graduate recruitment manager.

CONTACTS

Intellectual Property	Ian Starr
International ADR	Ronnie King
Investment Banking	Chris Ashworth
Investment Funds	Roger Walsom
Life Sciences	Mark Lubbock
Media & Film	Tony Ghee
Planning	Michael Cunliffe
Product Liability	John Evans
Projects	Mark Elsey
Property Litigation & Licensing	Michael Maddon
Public Sector	Anthony Curnow
Reconstruction & Insolvency	Nick Angel
Tax	John Watson
Telecommunications	Tony Ghee, Chris Ashworth
World Trade	Mark Clough QC

B

ASKEWS

4-6 West Terrace, Redcar, TS10 3BX **Tel:** (01642) 475252 **Fax:** (01642) 482793 **DX:** 60020 Redcar **Email:** info@askews.com **Website:** www.askews.com **Ptnrs:** 3 **Asst solrs:** 6 **Other fee-earners:** 2 **Contact:** P. Medd • General practice known for child care and matrimonial, personal injury, probate and trusts.

AREAS OF PRACTICE

Property & Probate	35%
Family Law	30%
Litigation	30%
Business	5%

A S LAW

Myrtle Parade, Liverpool, L7 7EL **Tel:** (0151) 707 1212 **Fax:** (0151) 707 2458 **DX:** 28953 Liverpool 2 **Email:** aslaw@dircon.co.uk **Ptnrs:** 3 **Asst solrs:** 3 **Other fee-earners:** 8

B. M. NYMAN & CO

181 Creighton Avenue, London, N2 9BN **Tel:** (020) 8365 3060 **Fax:** (020) 8883 5151 **Email:** bernie.nyman@iname.com

BABBINGTON BRAY AND KRAIS SOLICITORS LIMITED

70-71 New Bond Street, London, W1Y 9DE **Tel:** (020) 7493 8840 **Fax:** (020) 7493 8841 **Email:** bbandk@bbandk.com **Ptnrs:** 3 **Asst solrs:** 2 **Other fee-earners:** 1

BABINGTON & CROASDAILE

9 Limavady Road, Waterside, Londonderry, BT47 1JV **Tel:** (02871) 349531 **Fax:** (02871) 345785 **DX:** 3060 Nr Londonderry 1 **Email:** bab.cro@lineone.net **Ptnrs:** 7 **Asst solrs:** 4 **Other fee-earners:** 3

BACKHOUSE JONES

23 Wellington St (St. John's), Blackburn, BB1 8DE **Tel:** (01254) 677311 **Fax:** (01254) 676075 **DX:** 17976 Blackburn **Email:** enquiries@backhouses.co.uk **Website:** www.backhouses.co.uk **Ptnrs:** 3 **Asst solrs:** 2 **Contact:** Mr James A Backhouse • Expertise in law relating to the transport industry, both HGV and coach/passenger travel.

AREAS OF PRACTICE

Road Transport Law (bus/coach/haulage offences)	50%
Transport Licensing (driver/vehicle/operator)	25%
Personal Injury Litigation	20%
Other	5%

BADHAMS THOMPSON

95 Aldwych, London, WC2B 4JF **Tel:** (020) 7242 4154 **Fax:** (020) 7404 0009 **DX:** 14 Ch.Ln. **Ptnrs:** 8 **Asst solrs:** 10 **Other fee-earners:** 4

BAIRD & COMPANY

2 Park Place, Kirkcaldy, KY1 1XL **Tel:** (01592) 268608 **Fax:** (01592) 203369 **DX:** 10 Kirkcaldy **Ptnrs:** 11 **Asst solrs:** 4 **Other fee-earners:** 2

BAKER BOTTS

45 Ludgate Hill, London, EC4M 7JU
Tel: (020) 7778 1400 **Fax:** (020) 7778 1450
Email: jay.kolb@bakerbotts.com **Website:** www.bakerbotts.com

THE FIRM: Founded in 1840, Baker Botts is one of the oldest and largest law firms in the United States. Its business has been for many years global in scope and influence. The firm has leading reputation in energy law, acting for established leaders in the oil, gas, power and petrochemical sectors. It focuses also on the groundbreaking entrepreneurs in the dynamic industries of today's business world.

PRINCIPAL AREAS OF WORK: Baker Botts established its London office in 1998 and has expanded by hiring UK partners and associates. The objective is to offer advice on all aspects of energy work in the UK and internationally. Tony Higginson, former head of energy practice at Lovells, and Samantha Hampshire, formerly with Slaughter and May and Arnheim Tite & Lewis, joined to complement existing resources. The firm has plans for significant further expansion in the near term.

International	
Managing Partner:	Richard C. Johnson
Number of partners:	204
Number of associates:	297
Number of other fee-earners:	328
London Office	
Managing Partner:	Jay T. Kolb
Number of partners:	6
Number of associates:	4
Number of other fee-earners:	2

BAKER BOTTS

BAKER & MCKENZIE

100 New Bridge Street, London, EC4V 6JA
Tel: (020) 7919 1000 **Fax:** (020) 7919 1999 **DX:** 233
Email: london.info@bakernet.com **Website:** www.bakernet.com

Managing partner:	Russell Lewin
UKNumber of partners:	70
Assistant solicitors:	164
Other fee earners:	70
InternationalNumber of partners:	582
Assistant solicitors:	1471
Other fee earners:	924

AREAS OF PRACTICE

Corporate/Finance/EC/Tax/Commercial 48%
Litigation/Construction 20%
Employment/Pensions/Immigration 17%
Intellectual Property 10%
Commercial Property 5%

THE FIRM: Baker & McKenzie is a leading global law firm. Baker & McKenzie was founded in 1949. The firm has grown by anticipating trade and capital flows around the world. Today Baker & McKenzie has 60 offices in 35 jurisdictions. Its strategy is to provide for its clients the best combination of local legal and commercial knowledge and international expertise and resources. Baker & McKenzie aims, above all, to provide commercially orientated advice of the highest quality which adds value to the client's business. The firm looks at the best method of service delivery in each case.The firm is sensitive to the need to provide not only legal excellence but also a user friendly service which is efficient, transparent and value for money. To this end the firm implements a variety of client care and quality management programmes. Baker & McKenzie is uniquely well placed to blend advice on the law and practice of a number of jurisdictions to help the client achieve its objectives: their lawyers work in national, European and international practice groups in their areas of expertise. Many lawyers have the benefit of work experience in the firm's overseas offices.
London Office: The London office is an established City firm with a strong domestic and foreign client base. The London office has more than 300 lawyers, the vast majority of whom are UK qualified, together with resident US admitted banking and securities specialists. Many lawyers have worked in other offices of the firm, enabling them to bring a fresh perspective even to purely domestic assignments. It provides a full range of legal services to corporations, financial institutions, governments and entrepreneurs. The office offers 'hot line' arrangements and secondments of its lawyers to major clients. As an integral part of its service, the firm offers to its clients regular seminars and workshops, newsletters and bulletins on legal developments, magazines and publications. The firm also offers access to its library services and to a number of commercial and legal databases and rapid internal and external communications through its proprietary BakerNet email network and other networks.

PRINCIPAL AREAS OF WORK:
International and domestic banking and finance; swaps and derivatives; financial services; privatisations; domestic and cross-border corporate and commercial transactions; the structuring of multinational groups; domestic and international equity and debt offerings; corporate finance & flotations; venture capital; privately financed projects; international tax; VAT and import/export questions; litigation, arbitration and ADR; civil & commercial fraud; insolvency; European Union and competition law; trade law (WTO); energy; environmental; intellectual property; patents & trademarks; biotechnology; pharmaceuticals & healthcare; information technology; on-line services and e-commerce; telecommunications, entertainment and media; employment and pension matters; insurance & reinsurance; construction and engineering; commercial property; tax and trust planning and the legal aspects of lobbying.

INTERNATIONAL CONNECTIONS: The firm has offices in Almaty, Amsterdam, Bahrain, Baku, Bangkok, Barcelona, Beijing, Berlin, Bogotá, Brasilia, Brussels, Budapest, Buenos Aires, Cairo, Caracas, Chicago, Dallas, Dusseldorf, Frankfurt, Geneva, Hanoi, Ho Chi Minh City, Hong Kong, Houston, Hsinchu, Juarez, Kyiv, Madrid, Manila, Melbourne, Mexico City, Miami, Milan, Monterrey, Moscow, Munich, New York, Palo Alto, Paris, Prague, Rio de Janeiro, Riyadh, Rome, St Petersburg, San Diego, San Francisco, São Paulo, Santiago, Singapore, Stockholm, Sydney, Taipei, Tijuana, Tokyo, Toronto, Valencia, Warsaw, Washington DC, Zurich.

LANGUAGES: The firm conduct business in: Afrikaans, Bulgarian, Cantonese, Czech, French, German, Greek, Hebrew, Hindi, Hungarian, Italian, Indonesian, Japanese, Kiswahili, Malay, Marathi, Polish, Portuguese, Punjabi, Russian, Spanish, Taiwanese.

RECRUITMANT & TRAINING: For graduate recruitment opportunities, please contact Jo Darby on tel: 020 7919 1000 or email her at jo.darby@bakernet.com

CONTACTS

Banking and Finance ....Chris Hogan
Central & Eastern Europe ....Peter Magyar
Civil and Commercial Fraud ......Nick Pearson
Commercial ....Michael Herington
Construction ....Jeremy Winter
Corporate Finance ......Gabriel Fisher, Tim Gee
Dispute Resolution ....Andrew Keltie
....Nick Pearson
E-commerce ....Robbie Downing
Employee Benefits ....Michael Ingle
Employment ....Christine O'Brien
Energy ....Hugh Stewart
Environment..................................Alison Flood
EU, Competition & Trade..Lynda Martin Alegi
Financial Services ....Marwan Al-Turki
Information Technology ....Michael Hart
....Harry Small
Insolvency.............................Jeremy Goldring
..............................Peter Knight, Nick Pearson
Insurance.....................................David Fraser
....Michael Herington
....Peter Schwartz
Intellectual Property ....Michael Hart
....Paul Rawlinson
Latin American Centre ....
..................................Beatriz Pessoa de Araujo
Patents and Trademarks..........Stephen Jones
Pensions ....Robert West
Pharmaceuticals and Healthcare ....
..................................Beatriz Pessoa de Araujo
Privatisations ....Tim Gee
Projects.....................................Mike Webster
Securities ....Michael Caro, Tim Gee
Structured and Project Finance..Peter Gaines
Swaps and Derivatives ....Iona Levine
Tax ....Geoffrey Kay
....James MacLachlan
Trade Law (WTO)........................Ross Denton
VAT, Customs and Excise ....Andrew Hart,
....Geoffrey Kay
Venture Capital ....Charles Whitefoord

B

BALFOUR & MANSON

54-66 Frederick Street, Edinburgh, EH2 1LS
Tel: (0131) 200 1200 **Fax:** (0131) 200 1300 **DX:** 4 Edinburgh
Email: enquiry@balfour-manson.co.uk

Chairman:	Andrew Gibb
Number of partners:	18
Assistant solicitors:	14
Associates:	8
Other fee-earners:	23

AREAS OF PRACTICE

Litigation	50%
Private Client	20%
Property	20%
Commercial/Commercial Property	10%

CONTACTS

Commercial Property	J. Hodge
Corporate	A. Keatinge
Domestic Property	K. Robertson
	A. Pacey
Employment	M. Neilson
Family	A. Gibb
Financial Services & Tax	M. Burns
Litigation	I. Leach
	S. Kennedy
	F. Tyler
Private Client	B. Rennie

THE FIRM: One of the leading Scottish litigation practices, Balfour & Manson also has substantial commercial, private client and property client bases. The practice provides a comprehensive range of legal, financial and general advice, from a wide variety of departments with in-depth expertise, for Scottish, English and foreign clients and solicitors. The principal departments are litigation, commercial/corporate, private client and property.

PRINCIPAL AREAS OF WORK:
Litigation: Headed by Fred Tyler, the firm has a strong litigation department which handles all aspects of litigation. It has particular expertise in acting in personal injury; professional negligence and contractual claims; multi-party actions; and family law, with considerable experience in international child abduction. Additionally, this department handles commercial work, including insurance; intellectual property disputes; tribunal work; planning and building contracts.
Commercial/Commercial Property: Led by John Hodge, this department handles purchase, lease, sale and security work for clients of all types and sizes and provides corporate services for medium-sized private companies.
Private Client: Headed by Brenda Rennie, the department advises clients from within and without Scotland, providing wills, trusts and executries; tax work; finance and investment advice; and insurance services. This department offers unique support for elderly and infirm clients and their families.
Property: led by Kenneth Robertson, services include estate agency; house purchase and sale; residential lease and repossession work.

INTERNATIONAL CONNECTIONS: Scottish Member of the PARLEX Group of European Lawyers.

LANGUAGES: French and German

B

BAND HATTON

1 Copthall House, Station Square, Coventry, CV1 2FY
Tel: (024) 7663 2121 **Fax:** (024) 7622 9038 **DX:** 11207
Email: bandhatton@compuserve.com

Contact Partner:	Philip Costigan
Number of partners:	5
Assistant solicitors:	4
Other fee-earners:	7

CONTACTS

Commercial Property	Philip Costigan
Other Commercial/Corporate	Haydn Jones
Private Client Litigation	Paul Wright
Private Client Non-contentious	Simon Rock

THE FIRM: A well-established practice, Band Hatton offers a high quality legal service to both business and private clients, utilising up-to-date working methods, while maintaining traditional values and a commitment to a personal and approachable service. The firm combines a thorough and accurate technical approach, with a commitment to providing a very personal service, which offers good value for money. The firm enjoys a strong reputation in the commercial field, in particular for its commercial property work. The litigation practice is expanding rapidly in the areas of commercial, employment and family law. Band Hatton is a member of LawNet, the Federation of Independent Law Firms, and LawNet Europe, and has attained accreditation under ISO 9002, as well as holding a Legal Aid Franchise.

BANNATYNE, KIRKWOOD, FRANCE & CO

Exchange House, 16 Royal Exchange Square, Glasgow, G1 3AG **Tel:** (0141) 221 6020 **Fax:** (0141) 221 5120 **Email:** martin@b-k-f.demon.co.uk **Website:** www.bfk.co.uk **Ptnrs:** 4 **Asst solrs:** 2 **Other fee-earners:** 1 • **Contact:** Mr Martin Smith Established in 1785, the firm specialises in media law and defamation, representing several national newspaper companies. Other areas of expertise include employment law, reparation and trusts.

BANNERS JONES MIDDLETON

Marsden Chambers, 2 Marsden Street, Saltergate, Chesterfield, S40 1JY **Tel:** (01246) 560560 **Fax:** (01246) 231188 **DX:** 12370 Chesterfield 1 **Email:** info@bjm-soicitors.co.uk **Website:** www.bjm-solicitors.co.uk **Ptnrs:** 14 **Asst solrs:** 4 **Other fee-earners:** 8

BANNISTER PRESTON

30 Washway Road, Sale, M33 7QY **Tel:** (0161) 973 2434 **Fax:** (0161) 962 9562

BARBARA CARTER

117 Vicarage Road, King's Heath, Birmingham, B14 7QG **Tel:** (0121) 441 3238 **Fax:** (0121) 441 2191 **Ptnrs:** 1 **Other fee-earners:** 1

BARCAN WOODWARD

King William House, 13 Queen Square, Bristol, BS1 4NT **Tel:** (0117) 925 8080 **Fax:** (0117) 925 8081 **DX:** 7854 (Bristol) **Ptnrs:** 5 **Asst solrs:** 4 **Other fee-earners:** 6

BARKER GOTELEE

41 Barrack Square, Martlesham Heath, Ipswich, IP5 3RF **Tel:** (01473) 611211 **Fax:** (01473) 610560 **DX:** 124722 MARTLESHAM HEATH **Email:** bg@barkergotelee.co.uk **Ptnrs:** 3

BARLOW LYDE & GILBERT

Beaufort House, 15 St Botolph Street, London, EC3A 7NJ
Tel: (020) 7247 2277 **Fax:** (020) 7643 8500 **DX:** 155 London CDE
Website: www.blg.co.uk

Lloyd's, Lime Street, London, EC3M 7DQ
Tel: (020) 7643 8051 **Fax:** (020) 7643 8053

Managing Partner:	Kennan Michel
Senior Partner:	Ian Jenkins
Number of partners:	76
Assistant solicitors:	143
Other fee-earners:	65

CONTACTS

- **Aviation** .... Ian Awford
- **Banking** .... Graham Wedlake
- **Commercial Litigation** .... Richard Dedman
- **Commercial Property** .... Malcolm Rogerson
- **Competition and EU** .... David Strang
- **Construction** .... Richard Dedman
- **Corporate & Finance** .... John Longdon
- **Corporate Insurance** .... Verner Southey
- **Employment** .... Gary Freer
- **Environment** .... Valerie Fogleman
- **Information Technology/E-Commerce** .... David Strang
- **Insolvency** .... Douglas Howie
- **Insurance Litigation** .... John Hanson
- **Medical Negligence** .... Kevin Bitmead
- **Personal Injury** .... Graham Dickinson
- **Professional Indemnity** .... David Arthur

Barlow Lyde & Gilbert

THE FIRM: Barlow Lyde & Gilbert, with over 70 partners, advises corporate organisations, government bodies, financial and other institutions in all spheres of business activity. The firm's reputation is founded on its pre-eminence in commercial litigation and insurance, and it has unrivalled expertise in reinsurance and professional indemnity. The traditional range of M&A, banking and corporate finance services is also provided by a specialist team. The firm is consistently highly placed in legal league tables and rankings in its core areas.

PRINCIPAL AREAS OF WORK:

Litigation: Barlow Lyde & Gilbert has an outstanding reputation for its expertise in litigation and other forms of dispute resolution. The practice is distinguished from competitors by the breadth and depth of its specialisms. Of particular note are the reinsurance and international risk, insurance, professional indemnity and aerospace teams who are all recognised as market leaders. Other areas of expertise include banking and financial institutions, construction, defamation, employment, information technology, intellectual property, property and shipping. Our lawyers are geared to obtain the best possible result for the clients – alternative dispute resolution methods are used whenever appropriate and several partners are CEDR accredited mediators.

Corporate: In recent years, Barlow Lyde & Gilbert has developed an increasingly significant corporate and finance practice. The firm handles the full range of corporate work to include buy-outs, joint ventures, flotations, reconstructions, corporate finance, corporate capital, banking, regulatory investigations, taxation, insolvency, commercial property and EU and competition. By combining the practice's growing corporate and finance skills with the pre-eminence in both reinsurance and insurance work, the firm is uniquely placed to undertake corporate and corporate finance transactions for the insurance sector and to remain at the forefront of alternative risk transfer and innovative bancassurance products.

RECRUITMENT & TRAINING: The firm is committed to education and training. An extensive range of in-house publications covering insurance, liability, employment, environment, construction, banking and commercial law and regular seminars and conferences on topical areas of law are provided for clients. Dedicated training programmes ensure that the firm's solicitors are completely up to date with all legal and practice developments. The firm offers 15 training contracts each year. Prospective trainees should contact Caroline Walsh (cwalsh@blg.co.uk) for details of the recruitment programme. Further information on Barlow Lyde & Gilbert is available at the firm's offices or can be viewed on the website at www.blg.co.uk

BARLOWS

55 Quarry Street, Guildford, GU1 3UE
Tel: (01483) 562901 **Fax:** (01483) 573325 **DX:** 2407 Guildford
Email: enquiries@barlows.co.uk **Website:** www.barlows-legal.co.uk

Managing Partner:	David Knox
Number of partners:	12
Assistant solicitors:	22
Other fee-earners:	6

AREAS OF PRACTICE

- **Probate, Trusts & Tax** 24%
- **Litigation (general/commercial)** 23%
- **General Commercial** 16%
- **Private Client Property** 15%
- **Commercial Property** 14%
- **Litigation (family)** 8%
- **Reinsurance** .... Colin Croly
- **Shipping** .... Ray Mead
- **Tax** .... Gary Richards
- **Travel & Tourism** .... Richard Gimblett

THE FIRM: Founded in 1816, Barlows has grown by expansion and acquisition. Growing specialisation and concentration on commercial and corporate work has lead to an increased division between private client and business departments.

PRINCIPAL AREAS OF WORK:

Commercial: Activities include property development work, business formation, shareholders' agreements, sales, M&A, company reorganisation, partnership affairs, insolvency, commercial and trading agreements, licensing applications and appeals, service agreements, and all aspects of employment law. A company secretarial service is also offered. The firm handles commercial agreements involving other EU countries, and has developed links with firms abroad.

Other Areas: Personal Injury litigation, ADR, debt recovery and private client work. Agency work is undertaken in Guildford County Court, Guildford District Registry and Staines County Court.

BARNETT ALEXANDER CHART

60 Grays Inn Road, London, WC1X 8LT **Tel:** (020) 7242 4422 **Fax:** (020) 7242 1102 **DX:** 42 LDE **Email:** mail@bac-solicitors.co.uk **Website:** www.bac-solicitors.co.uk **Ptnrs:** 15 **Asst solrs:** 15 **Other fee-earners:** 4 **Contact:** Mr Peter Moody • BAC is a central London commercial law firm with strengths in corporate, intellectual property, employment, dispute resolution, insolvency and property. The firm acts for national and international clients.

BARNETT SAMPSON

High Holborn House, 52-54 High Holborn, London, WC1V 6RL **Tel:** (020) 7831 7181 **Fax:** (020) 7269 5141 **DX:** 254 LDE **Email:** lawyers@barnett-sampson.co.uk **Ptnrs:** 4 **Asst solrs:** 3 **Other fee-earners:** 1 **Contact:** Richard Barnett • An effective approach to commercial law, family law, litigation, including substantial group actions, particularly in the financial services field, and property.

AREAS OF PRACTICE

Family	45%
Company/Commercial	25%
Financial Services/Commercial Litigation/Administrative law	20%
Commercial Property	6%
Private Client	4%

B

BARRATT GOFF & TOMLINSON

The Old Dairy, 67a Melton Road, West Bridgford, Nottingham, NG2 5GR **Tel:** (0115) 981 5115 **Fax:** (0115) 981 9409 **DX:** 719903 West Bridgford **Ptnrs:** 5 **Asst solrs:** 2

BARRIE WARD & JULIAN GRIFFITHS

5 Clarendon Street, Nottingham, NG1 5HS **Tel:** (0115) 941 2622 **Fax:** (0115) 924 0485 **DX:** 711344 NOTTM 16 **Ptnrs:** 2 **Asst solrs:** 3 **Other fee-earners:** 4

BARRY SHAW

13 Blackheath Village, London, SE3 9LA **Tel:** (020) 8297 8899 **Fax:** (020) 8297 2122 **Ptnrs:** 1

BARTRAM & CO

1st Floor, 302 Bath Road, Hounslow, TW4 7DN **Tel:** (020) 8814 1414 **Fax:** (020) 8814 1515 **Ptnrs:** 1 **Asst solrs:** 1 **Other fee-earners:** 3

BATES, WELLS & BRAITHWAITE

Cheapside House, 138 Cheapside, London, EC2V 6BB
Tel: (020) 7551 7777 **Fax:** (020) 7551 7800 **DX:** 42609 (Cheapside 1)
Email: mail@bateswells.co.uk **Website:** www.bateswells.co.uk

Senior Partner:	Hugh Craig
Number of partners:	34
Assistant solicitors:	13
Other fee-earners:	19

THE FIRM: Located in the City, Bates, Wells & Braithwaite is a unique firm combining a strong commercial and charity practice with a highly regarded family department and a general emphasis on public interest work and the Arts. The firm is renowned for its expertise in advising charities, businesses and individuals according to their particular needs. Bates, Wells & Braithwaite was founded more than 100 years ago. The main office in London was opened in 1970. Originally handling the needs of smaller business clients, the firm has developed a strong reputation for administrative law, family and matrimonial work, employment and immigration law, as well as a pre-eminence in charity law. The firm is particularly notable for the large proportion of individuals who actively participate in the sectors on which they advise inboth a legal and non-legal capacity. Bates, Wells & Braithwaite has significant involvement in international legal developments, being a co-founder of the Parlex Group of European Lawyers which consists of a network of firms throughout Western Europe.

PRINCIPAL AREAS OF WORK:

Charity Law: The charity department has one of the largest charity law practices in the country and acts for many household names and international charities. It has particular expertise in obtaining charitable status for new groups and for initiatives within the charity sector. The firm provides a national advisory service to solicitors on charity matters and has been responsible through the years for many books, articles, and other publications.

Company & Commercial: The company/commercial department undertakes work for a wide range of businesses and has developed considerable expertise. The work undertaken includes take-overs, joint ventures, management buy-outs, commercial contracts and tax advice.

Litigation: The thriving litigation department is broad-based with particular specialisations in commercial litigation, property litigation, administrative law, civil liberty law, social work law and defamation.

Family Law: The family department is acknowledged to be one of London's leading departments and the only such department within the City. There is a strong emphasis on work with financial complexity and international aspects. All solicitors within the department are members of the SFLA.

Property: The property department handles all types of commercial property work and related financing and development work. There is particular expertise in advising charities.

AREAS OF PRACTICE

Charity	20%
Family	20%
Litigation	15%
Company/Commercial	10%
Employment	10%
Property	10%
Immigration	5%
Media	5%
Private Client	5%

CONTACTS

Charity	Lord Phillips of Sudbury
	Stephen Lloyd
	Fiona Middleton
Company/Commercial	Hugh Craig
	David Robinson
Employment	William Garnett
Family	Frances Hughes
	Pauline Fowler
Immigration	Philip Trott
	Peter Moss
Litigation	John Trotter
	Martin Bunch
Media	Sean Egan
Private Client	Con Alexander
Property	Tony Cartmell
	Nick Ivey
Property Litigation	Eve Smith

Immigration & Nationality: The well-respected immigration department handles all aspects of immigration and nationality law including work permits, citizenship, residency and asylum work, and human rights.
Employment: The employment department advises on all aspects of employment law, including restrictive covenants, employee rights, discrimination, service agreements, dismissals and redundancies.
Media & Entertainment: The recently expanded media department advises on all aspects of the theatre, film and television industries dealing with theatrical production in the West end and throughout the UK, feature film production, all types of television production and internet and multimedia issues.
Private Client: The firm now has a private client department which handles a wide range of tax and trust work.

BATTENS (WITH POOLE & CO)

Church House, Yeovil, BA20 1HB
Tel: (01935) 423685 **Fax:** (01935) 706054 **DX:** 100503

17 Market Street, Crewkerne, TA18 7JU
Tel: (01460) 74401 **Fax:** (01460) 73988 **DX:** 43401

Savernake House, 42 High West Street, Dorchester, DT1 1UU
Tel: (01305) 250560 **Fax:** (01305) 260876 **DX:** 8705

The Bank House, Long Street, Sherborne, DT9 3BU
Tel: (01935) 814811 **Fax:** (01935) 816436 **DX:** 49151

26 St Thomas Street, Weymouth, DT4 8EJ
Tel: (01305) 774666 **Fax:** (01305) 760423 **DX:** 8753

Chairman:	Graham Hughes
Chief Executive:	Andy Marshall
Number of partners:	22
Assistant solicitors:	18
Other fee-earners:	26

AREAS OF PRACTICE

Property	33%
Litigation	31%
Private Client	29%
Commercial	7%

CONTACTS

CHC Ltd	Mervyn Ellis
CHI Ltd	Graham Hughes
Civil Litigation	Roger Paul
Commercial	Melanie Shuldham
Commercial Property	Rupert Vaughan
Dryfield Trust plc	David Batten
Family	Julian Hayes
Personal Injury	Peter Bayliss
Private Client	Jeanie Bogaardt
Residential Property	Chris May

THE FIRM: Battens has 22 partners and five offices in Somerset and Dorset. During 1999, Battens restructured its business to form the group of businesses outlined below.

PRINCIPAL AREAS OF WORK:
Battens Legal Practice: Handles private client, property (commercial and residential), litigation, (family, civil and personal injury) and commercial.
Church House Investments Ltd (CHI Ltd): A newly formed company, wholly owned by the partners and regulated by IMRO, which handles the firm's investment management business.
Church House Consultants Ltd (CHC Ltd): A newly formed company which offers financial planning and tax advisory and compliance services to private clients.
Dryfield Trust plc: A private bank, established 20 years ago and authorised under the Banking Act, which offers banking products and services to private clients.These form a group of businesses unique in the UK offering, in addition to the traditional range of legal services for commercial and other clients, a competitive and complimentary range of quality products and services to attract and retain private clients. A Joint Venture Board, with members from each of the above, has been formed to co-ordinate their development and activities.

BEACHCROFT WANSBROUGHS

100 Fetter Lane, London, EC4A 1BN
Tel: (020) 7242 1011 **Fax:** (020) 7831 6630 **DX:** 45 London, Chancery Lane
Email: rheslett@bwlaw.co.uk **Website:** www.bwlaw.co.uk

30-40 Eastcheap, London, EC3M 1HD
Tel: (020) 7208 6800 **Fax:** (020) 7208 6801 **DX:** 753 London City EC3

10-22 Victoria Street, Bristol, BS99 7UD
Tel: (0117) 918 2000 **Fax:** (0117) 918 2100 **DX:** 7846 BRISTOL 1

Nine Brindleyplace, Oozells Square, Birmingham, B1 2HE
Tel: (0121) 698 5200 **Fax:** (0121) 698 5290 **DX:** 13057 BIRMINGHAM 1

7 Park Square East, Leeds, LS1 2LW
Tel: (0113) 251 4700 **Fax:** (0113) 251 4900 **DX:** 14099 LEEDS PARK SQUARE

13 Police Street, Manchester, M2 7WA
Tel: (0161) 934 3000 **Fax:** (0161) 934 3288 **DX:** 14341 MANCHESTER 1

241 Glossop Road, Sheffield, S10 2GZ
Tel: (0114) 209 5000 **Fax:** (0114) 209 5010 **DX:** 719530 SHEFFIELD 32

St Swithun's House, 1a St Cross Road, Winchester, SO23 9WP
Tel: (01962) 705500 **Fax:** (01962) 705510 **DX:** 2540 WINCHESTER 1

Managing partner:	Robert Heslett
Senior partner:	The Rt Hon the Lord Hunt of Wirral MBE
Number of partners:	130
Assistant solicitors:	301
Other fee-earners:	199

AREAS OF PRACTICE

Insurance	48%
Commercial	30%
Health	22%

Continued overleaf

THE FIRM: Beachcroft Wansbroughs is a dynamic and progressive national partnership providing a strong regional office network with major offices in the City of London. The firm's services are structured around client market sectors, primarily in the commercial, health and insurance arenas, supported by multi-disciplinary partner-led teams focused on serving client needs. Beachcroft Wansbroughs was formed from the merger of three of the UK's most respected legal practices - Beachcroft Stanleys, Wansbroughs Willey Hargrave and Vaudreys. Beachcroft Wansbroughs is able to provide an integrated and consistent national service capability across its strong regional office network and its major offices in the City of London. With a particular reputation in litigation, Beachcroft Wansbroughs provides a comprehensive legal service to the health and insurance sectors, supported by in-depth capability for the commercial, financial and public and private sectors. The new firm has implemented an operational structure to reflect its commitment to assisting clients in meeting their business and commercial objectives nationwide. The firm is constantly evaluating and implementing improved mechanisms for service delivery and feedback, including case management systems, client assistance, contract management, and client access to data. As well as being an integral member of European wide legal networks, Beachcroft Wansbroughs has a fully integrated Brussels office which provides advice on competition law and all European issues. Feedback from long-standing clients acknowledges both the depth of expertise and the approachable nature of the firm.

PRINCIPAL AREAS OF WORK: The firm is structured into three market-focused divisions and five functional departments. The three divisions are commercial, heath and insurance. The five departments comprise - corporate services, property, employment, projects and litigation.

Insurance Division: The firm's insurance practice has taken full account of the radical changes that the insurance industry continues to undergo. With corporate mergers and acquisitions leading to the rationalisation and increased concentration within the sector, Beachcroft Wansbroughs has responded effectively to help the sector to meet cost effectiveness and productivity challenges, through IT initiatives and the use of specialist services. The firm provides a comprehensive range of services to cover all aspect of the insurance industry's activities including claims management, contentious and non-contentious work, investment, strategy and operations. The firm works closely with insurers and brokers to develop existing and new products and is regularly instructed by the leading general insurers, re-insurers, Lloyd's syndicates, underwriting agencies, governing bodies and companies which self-insure. Beachcroft Wansbroughs handles a wide range of professional indemnity, employers' product and public liability, personal injury and motor claims, policy coverage disputes and has specialist knowledge and expertise of major international product liability claims.

The firm's London Market Services team specialises in the efficient handling of large insurance disputes, together with professional negligence and property claims. It is supported by specialist lawyers, all of whom are fully conversant with the market's particular practices and procedures. In Europe, Beachcroft Wansbroughs provides general claims advice and cross-border litigation via Insurolaw, a formal alliance (founded by Beachcroft Wansbroughs), comprising specialist insurance law firms extending across sixteen countries in Europe.

Health Division: Beachcroft Wansbroughs' Health Division carries out a vast range of work for both public and private healthcare providers. The firm acts for over 200 NHS bodies and is a panel member of the NHSLA. In addition to a comprehensive litigation capability, work covered includes a wide range of employment, property, PFI, IP/IT, procurement, construction and commercial matters. The firm's specialist PFI capability has, for example, been involved in handling five of the 14 Phase 1 PFI schemes and has been advising on four of the Phase II schemes with capital spends of up to £470m. The firm's tried and trusted approach ensures a speedy resolution of contentious cases. Furthermore, Beachcroft Wansbroughs offers a wealth of knowledge in the rapidly evolving arena of health provision services.

Commercial Division: Beachcroft Wansbroughs looks after the needs and requirements of industry, financial and public and private sector clients across a wide range of disciplines. Solutions are delivered through skills based teams from across the departmental spectrum.

Corporate Services Department: A high profile City presence and expansive nationwide coverage guarantees clients a seamless service. The department includes commercial litigation and corporate finance capabilities. The department handles the full range of commercial disputes in the courts, arbitration tribunals and mediation. It advises on a comprehensive set of issues from intellectual property and product liability to insolvency. It also has a strong capability in M&A, disposals, listings, new issues, capital restructuring and joint ventures for a variety of UK and international clients. This is supplemented by additional specialist expertise in the advertising and media, construction, education, European Union law, information technology, retail, sports and water sectors. Working closely with the corporate services practice, the dedicated Education Law team advise a range of leading institutions in the sector on funding and related issues. Beachcroft Wansbroughs' European law team is supported by the firm's office in Brussels. The profile of the Brussels office has risen in the last year. Having a solicitor at the centre of European Government law ensure that the team respond quickly to any changes that occur and have an excellent understanding of the EU law making process and how it can be influenced.

Litigation Department: The department handles a range of medical/clinical negligence and employer's liability/public liability cases and a variety of advisory work on patient care issues, corporate governance, public sector law and the management of ad hoc incidents and crises.

CONTACTS

Advertising & Marketing	Simon Hodson
Alternative Dispute Resolution	Richard Evans
Charity	Julian Korn
Chemical & Pharmaceutical	Anthony Cherry
Commercial	Simon Hodson
Construction	John Vassey
Corporate Services	Laurence Markham
Education	Julian Gizzi
Employment	Elizabeth Adams
European Community	Julie Nazerali
Fraud	Glenn Miller
Health & Safety	Iain Moore
Health/Public Sector	Trevor Blythe
Housing Association	Anne Quirk
Information Technology	Alan Wood
Insolvency	Peter Rees
Insurance	Trevor Chamberlain
Intellectual Property	Jonathan Radcliffe
Litigation	Paul Murray
Personal Injury	Tania Sless
Product Liability	Chris Wilkes
Professional Indemnity	Paul Murray
Projects	Malcolm Austwick
Property	John Phelps
Public Law	Julian Gizzi
Retail	Lawrence Markham
Tax & Trust	Paul Solon

Employment Department: Beachcroft Wansbroughs works with a diverse range of businesses, providing up-to-the-minute know how on the legal implications of human resource management. The department undertakes employment work for both the public and private sectors and acts for health service providers, local authorities, educational establishments and employers covering the full range of contentious and non-contentious matters, including High Court and tribunal actions and all forms of discrimination and industrial relations matters.
Property: With a team of more than 60 property lawyers the Property Department is one of the largest practices in the country specialising in non-contentious work, complemented by a strong contentious capability. The team provides a full range of services in property management, property investment and finance, dispute resolution and property litigation, planning and environment, construction, lease negotiation and total facility management.
Projects: The projects team has a market leading reputation and a track record to match with clients existing across the public and private sectors. The team's lawyers are experienced in structuring complex, large-scale, high value transactions, working with clients in construction, IT, facilities management and the provision of major services. In particular, it has played a pivotal role in developing PFI projects in the health sector; the team's knowledge and expertise in the health industry has been instrumental to its appointment on a significant number of the principal PFI health projects during the last few years

INTERNATIONAL CONNECTIONS: The firm has an overseas office at 85 rue du Prince Royal, 1050 Brussels, Belgium. Tel: +32 2 511 9126, Fax: +32 2 511 9525.

BEALE AND COMPANY

Garrick Hse, 27-32 King St, Covent Garden, London, WC2E 8JD
Tel: (020) 7240 3474 **Fax:** (020) 7240 9111 **DX:** 51632 Covent Garden
Email: reception@beale-law.com **Website:** www.beale-law.com

Managing Partner:	John Ward
Senior Partner:	John Ward
Number of partners:	9
Assistant solicitors:	9
Other fee-earners:	9

AREAS OF PRACTICE

Construction	30%
Insurance	30%
Company and Commercial/IT	25%
Other Commercial Litigation	10%
Private Client	5%

CONTACTS

Company and Commercial	Michael Archer
Construction	John Ward
Engineers	Rachel Barnes
Insurance	Christopher Cullen
Litigation	Anthony Smith
Private Client	Rachel Barnes

THE FIRM: Beale and Company is a long established firm (founded in 1837) which provides a comprehensive range of services to commercial clients. The main areas of the firm's practice are construction, insurance and IT. The firm has a strong international practice. The firm provides high quality legal advice combined with a practical and commercial approach.

PRINCIPAL AREAS OF WORK:
Construction: The firm provides legal advice and, where necessary, representation, in relation to projects in the UK and throughout the world, to employers, contractors and professionals, on all aspects of civil and structural engineering contracts, related insurance and bond provisions and collateral warranties, and on joint ventures, corporate structures, partnerships, DBFO forms of contract and other forms of contract, on disputes and dispute resolution, and on and in negotiations, litigation, arbitration and other alternative forms of dispute resolution.
Engineers: This is a special section of the firm's construction practice. The firm are the solicitors for the Association of Consulting Engineers and have acted for more than thirty of the top fifty firms of consulting engineers in the UK. The firm acts for engineers and others prosecuted under Health and Safety legislation.
Insurance: The firm acts for insurers and their insureds in handling professional indemnity and public liability claims and on risk management and other ways of reducing or preventing claims. The firm advises insurers on policy wording, coverage issues and disputes between insurer and insured.
Litigation: The firm handles a wide range of other commercial litigation, including disputes in the fields of banking, IT, intellectual property, supply of goods and services and employment. The firm handles a large amount of international litigation and are Privy Council Agents.
Company & Commercial: The firm advises on all aspects of company commercial transactions, including acquisitions and disposals of businesses, setting up joint ventures, corporate finance arrangements, restructuring of companies and partnerships and establishing commercial contractual relationships such as distribution, agency and licensing networks and on intellectual property, directors' duties and liabilities, employment problems and claims, partnership disputes and corporate compliance. There is a strong emphasis on acting for clients in the IT and digital media industries. These range from dot com businesses (the firm having represented some of the first dot com enterprises in selling their bussinesses and raising finance) to national and multinational companies including a number of technology companies quoted on Nasdaq.
Private Client: The firm advises private clients, domiciled and non-domiciled, on tax planning, formation of trusts, wills and probates.

INTERNATIONAL CONNECTIONS: The firm is a member of a European network of correspondent law firms. The firm also has correspondent law firms in Bombay, Calcutta, Dhaka, Kampala, Karachi, Mombasa, Nairobi and Port Louis. One of the firm's consultants works in Bangladesh.

RECRUITMENT & TRAINING: The firm recruits on average three graduate trainees each year. Currently there are five graduate trainees in the firm.

BEAUMONT AND SON

Lloyds Chambers, 1 Portsoken St, London, E1 8AW **Tel:** (020) 7481 3100 **Fax:** (020) 7481 3353 **DX:** 551 **Ptnrs:** 19 **Asst solrs:** 23 **Other fee-earners:** 17

BECKFORD & CO

35A Prince of Wales Road, Norwich, NR1 1BG **Tel:** (01603) 660 000 **Fax:** (01603) 660 010

BEDELL CRISTIN

PO Box 75, 26 New Street, St Helier, Jersey, JE4 8PP
Tel: (01534) 814814 **Fax:** (01534) 814815
Email: enquiries@bedellcristin.com **Website:** www.bedellcristin.com

Managing Partner:	Michael Richardson
Senior Partner:	Anthony Dessain
Number of partners:	12
Assistant solicitors:	22
Other fee-earners:	47

CONTACTS

Banking & Legal Opinions ....Peter Byrne
..........Anthony Dessain
Capital Markets & Structured Finance
..........Richard Gerwat
Insolvency & Liquidations ....Anthony Dessain
Investment Funds & Pension Schemes
..........Simon Howard
Litigation..........Anthony Robinson
..........Anthony Dessain
..........Mark Taylor
..........Simon Young
Local Business Clients ....Guy Le Sueur,
..........Simon Young
Partnerships ....Simon Howard
Private Client ....Guy Le Sueur
..........Anita Regal
Tax ....Richard Gerwat
..........Michael Richardson
Trust & Corporate Law..........Alan Dart
..........Edward Bennett

THE FIRM: Established more than 60 years ago, the firm has been at the forefront of providing legal advice to the offshore banking and finance industry in Jersey for over 30 years. Consistently ranked one of the top three firms in Jersey and highly rated for the professionalism and technical expertise of its partners and associates, Bedell Cristin aims to provide a fast service tailored to the commercial needs of clients and intermediaries from all over the world. The firm has been responsible for the establishment of a significant proportion of the banks, mutual funds and, more recently, structured finance vehicles carrying on business from Jersey. The firm was ranked amongst the top three by number and value of investment fund clients in Jersey in a 1999 survey of the Jersey Fund Management Industry and the leading firm of lawyers and administrators for securitisations. Bedell Cristin has established a professional association with Guernsey law firm, Babbé Le Poidevin Allez, the principal purpose of which is to allow the provision of 'one stop' advice in matters of Jersey and Guernsey law to clients of both firms and to emphasise the unitary nature of the Channel Islands for financial services purposes.

PRINCIPAL AREAS OF WORK:

Capital Markets & Structured Finance: The capital markets and structured finance practice area has considerable experience in asset backed financing having acted as Jersey counsel in some of the most innovative securitisation transactions in the market, and is rated as a market leader in securitisation. The dedicated structured finance practice area is organised to provide the highest level of service. Together with Bedell Cristin Trust and Bedell SPV Management (Jersey) Limited (a joint venture SPV administration specialist jointly owned by Bedell Cristin Trust and SPV Management Limited) the practice area provides a 'one stop shop' for establishing special purpose vehicles in Jersey.

Investment Funds & Pensions: The investment funds and pension schemes practice area focuses on the establishment and legal servicing of pooled investment structures qualifying as public collective investment funds or non-public collective investment schemes and defined contribution pension schemes. Sponsorship and listing services in connection with the Channel Islands Stock Exchange are available through Bedell Channel Islands Limited which is a category 1 sponsorship member of the Exchange.

Banking: Bedell Cristin's banking practice area provides banking and lending advice to a very high proportion of the 60 plus banks having a branch or subsidiary in Jersey. Advice and legal opinions on matters of Jersey law are also provided to banks from all over the world whose customers may have assets in Jersey. In such cases, advice on corporate and trust law, and/or the taking of a security interest over Jersey assets is often sought through other professional firms in leading finance centres around the world.

Litigation: The litigation group is best known for its involvement in trust and asset tracing litigation, acting both for trustees and beneficiaries and for liquidators/receivers seeking to recover property in Jersey. Anthony Robinson is the head of the group and Anthony Dessain is well known in insolvency practitioner circles having acted in many of the leading cases in Jersey as well as being the co-author of the book *Insolvency Law in Practice*. Mark Taylor, another partner in the group, is the first lawyer in Jersey to have gained an LLM in advanced litigation practice.

Private Client: The private client and local business group is headed by Guy Le Sueur and advises on a wide range of Jersey property matters as well as running a private client practice including matrimonial matters and estate planning and probate. Local business clients are also advised within this group with the additional assistance of Simon Young who advises on IT and telecoms matters for Jersey Telecoms and with other IT industry clients.

Bedell
Cristin

BEECHAM PEACOCK

7 Collingwood Street, Newcastle upon Tyne, NE1 1JE **Tel:** (0191) 232 3048 **Fax:** (0191) 261 7255 **DX:** 61041 Newcastle upon Tyne **Email:** genenquiry@beechampeacock.co.uk **Website:** www.beechampeacock.co.uk **Ptnrs:** 5 **Asst solrs:** 4 **Other fee-earners:** 7

BELL & BUXTON

Telegraph House, High Street, Sheffield, S1 2GA **Tel:** (0114) 249 5969 **Fax:** (0114) 249 3804 **DX:** 10529 SHEFFIELD **Email:** legals@bellbuxton.co.uk **Website:** www.bellbuxton.co.uk

BELL LAX LITIGATION

New Bank House, 21 Maney Corner, Sutton Coldfield, Birmingham, B72 1QL **Tel:** (0121) 355 0011 **Fax:** (0121) 355 0099 **DX:** 15736 Sutton Coldfield **Email:** mail@litigation.demon.co.uk **Ptnrs:** 2 **Asst solrs:** 6 **Associate** 1 **Other fee-earners:** 4

BELL LAMB & JOYNSON

39 Walton Vale, Liverpool, L9 **Tel:** (0151) 474 8463 **Fax:** (0151) 474 8468 **DX:** 24703 WALTON VALE **Ptnrs:** 14 **Asst solrs:** 4 **Other fee-earners:** 13

BELL & SCOTT WS

16 Hill Street, Edinburgh, EH2 3LD **Tel:** (0131) 226 6703 **Fax:** (0131) 226 7602 **DX:** 114 Edinburgh 1 **Email:** maildesk@bellscott.co.uk **Website:** www.bellscott.co.uk **Ptnrs:** 7 **Asst solrs:** 7 **Other fee-earners:** 10

BELMORES

Goodchild House, 27 Castle Meadow, Norwich, NR1 3DS **Tel:** (01603) 617947 **Fax:** (01603) 630086

BELTRAMI & CO

93 West Nile Street, Glasgow, G1 2FH **Tel:** (0141) 221 0981 **Fax:** (0141) 332 9892 **DX:** GW8 **Ptnrs:** 2 **Asst solrs:** 4 **Other fee-earners:** 1 **Contact:** Mr Murray Macara • Long-established and prominent criminal defence practice with substantial reputation in many high profile cases, specialising in all aspects of criminal defence work throughout Scotland.

AREAS OF PRACTICE

Criminal Litigation	95%
Other	5%

B

BENSON MAZURE & CO

22 Bentinck St, London, W1U 2AB **Tel:** (020) 7486 8091 **Fax:** (020) 7935 8825 **DX:** 9007 London West End **Email:** info@bensonmazure.co.uk **Ptnrs:** 2 **Asst solrs:** 1 • Commercial and residential conveyancing; landlord and tenant; commercial litigation and company commercial; personal injuries, matrimonial and general litigation; probate and trusts.

AREAS OF PRACTICE

Conveyancing/Landlord & Tenant	50%
Litigation (incl. commercial)	20%
Company Commercial	17%
Probate & Trusts	13%

BENTLEYS, STOKES & LOWLESS

International House, 1 St. Katharine's Way, London, E1 9YL
Tel: (020) 7782 0990 **Fax:** (020) 7782 0991 **DX:** 1074
Email: law@bentleys.co.uk

Senior Partner:	Andrew Bardot
Number of partners:	11
Assistant solicitors:	7
Other fee-earners:	3

THE FIRM: Bentleys, Stokes & Lowless is traditionally associated with the maritime and insurance sectors.

PRINCIPAL AREAS OF WORK:

Admiralty: Specialist advice and representation is offered in relation to: salvage, pollution, total loss, groundings, unsafe port claims, damage claims, collisions and public, official and casualty inquiries and investigations.
Shipping, Insurance & Litigation: The department advises on a wide range of marine and insurance related matters, including charterparty/bill of lading contracts, marine, cargo and aviation insurance, cargo claims, road transport, commodity contracts, commercial contracts, ship sale and purchase, construction, building and general litigation.

LANGUAGES: French, Italian and Spanish.

AREAS OF PRACTICE

Shipping, Marine & Non-Marine Insurance	100%

CONTACTS

Admiralty	J. Quain
Charterparty/Marine Insurance	A.D. Bardot
	W.J. Chetwood

BENUSSI & CO

5th Floor, 20 Waterloo Street, Birmingham, B2 5TB **Tel:** (0121) 248 4001 **Fax:** (0121) 248 3990

BERG & CO

Scottish Mutual House, 35 Peter Street, Manchester, M2 5BG
Tel: (0161) 833 9211 **Fax:** (0161) 834 5566 **DX:** MDX 14379
Email: help@berg.co.uk **Website:** www.berg.co.uk

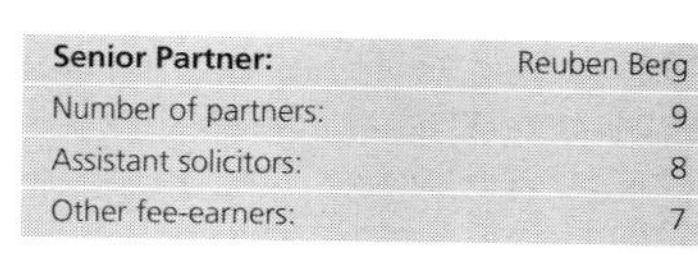

Senior Partner:	Reuben Berg
Number of partners:	9
Assistant solicitors:	8
Other fee-earners:	7

THE FIRM: Occupying modern offices at the heart of Manchester's commercial district, Berg & Co is a leading Manchester-based law firm, with a reputation for innovative and effective commercial problem-solving. The firm provides decisive, commercial advice to businesses of all sizes.

PRINCIPAL AREAS OF WORK:

Corporate & Commercial: Including choice of business structure, mergers and acquisitions, joint ventures and shareholders' agreements, directors' duties and responsibilities, banking and finance, stock exchange and

Continued overleaf

other regulatory issues, insolvency procedures, commercial contracts, standard terms and conditions, internet law, agency and distribution agreements, intellectual property and information technology, EC law and competition law.
Litigation: Including contractual claims, shareholders' actions, boardroom disputes and corporate fraud, professional negligence, insolvency, intellectual property, emergency applications, debt collection and matrimonial finance.
Commercial Property: Including sales and purchases, leases, development work, multi-let units and secured lending.
Human Resources: Including employment contracts, contested dismissals and severance issues, business transfers, redundancy, discrimination, sickness and maternity, legislative changes and audit of employment practices.

INTERNATIONAL CONNECTIONS: The firm has an extensive range of contacts in Europe, the USA and the Far East which enable it to progress its clients' affairs beyond UK boundaries.

LANGUAGES: French and German.

CLIENTELE: Clients include public (including listed) and private companies, education institutions, financial institutions, partnerships, innovative entrepreneurs seeking an innovative and practical approach to legal services.

CONTACTS

Commercial Litigation	Charles Khan
	Sydney Fulda
Commercial Property	Stephanie Klass
	Gabriel Rechnitzer
Corporate & Commercial	Reuben Ber
	Stephen Foster
Human Resources	Alison Loveday
	Stephanie Klass
Matrimonial Finance & Professional Negligence	Peter Woolf

BERMANS

Pioneer Buildings, 65-67 Dale St, Liverpool, L2 2NS **Tel:** (0151) 227 3351 **Fax:** (0151) 236 2107 **DX:** 14116 **Email:** info@bermans.co.uk **Website:** www.bermans.co.uk **Ptnrs:** 10 **Asst solrs:** 7 **Other fee-earners:** 41

BERRY & BERRY

11 Church Road, Tunbridge Wells, Kent, TN1 1JA
Tel: (01892) 526344 **Fax:** (01892) 511223 **DX:** 3908 Tunbridge Wells
Email: mail@the-solicitors.co.uk

3 Tonbridge Road, Maidstone, ME16 8R
Tel: (01622) 690777 **Fax:** (01622) 662555 **DX:** 400307 Maidstone West
Email: mail@the-solicitors.co.uk

185 High Street, Tonbridge, Tonbridge, TN9 1BX
Tel: (01732) 355911 **Fax:** (01732) 355191 **DX:** 5500 Tonbridge
Email: mail@the-solicitors.co.uk

Senior Partner:	Anthony Herman
Number of partners:	8
Assistant solicitors:	13
Other fee-earners:	7

AREAS OF PRACTICE

Civil Litigation	30%
Matrimonial & Family	20%
Property/Commercial	20%
Criminal Litigation	15%
Probate	15%

CONTACTS

Civil Litigation	Ian Tysh
Commercial	Anthony Herman
Criminal Litigation & Mental Health	Iain Reed
Matrimonial & Family	Yashin Masoliver
Probate/Finance	Nigel Stratton
Property	Zai Koder

THE FIRM: Established over 260 years. The Tunbridge Wells and Maidstone offices are very close to the courts.

PRINCIPAL AREAS OF WORK:
Litigation: Employment, personal injury, landlord and tenant, housing, commercial disputes.
Crime: Magistrates and Crown Court Scheme.
Mental Health: Tribunals and general advice.
Family: Divorce, ancillary relief, public and private, child cases, cohabitee disputes, domestic violence.
Property & Commercial: all types of conveyancing and general commercial work.
Probate: Wills, probate tax, trusts, enduring power of attorney, elderly client care.
Agency Work: Available for Magistrates County and Crown Courts covering a wide area of the South East.
Legal Aid: Franchised in family, crime and personal injury. Member of Law Net.

LANGUAGES: Spanish, French, Dutch, German, Punjabi, Hindi and Welsh spoken.

BERRYMAN SHACKLOCK

Park House, Friar Lane, Nottingham, NG1 6DN **Tel:** (0115) 941 7574 **Fax:** (0115) 947 3930 **DX:** 10004 Nottingham 1 **Email:** legal@berryman.co.uk **Website:** www.berryman.co.uk **Ptnrs:** 23 **Asst solrs:** 24 **Other fee-earners:** 20 **Contact:** Ms Lynne Morgan.

AREAS OF PRACTICE

Corporate/Commercial	32%
Private Client	24%
Property	20%
Insurance Litigation	18%

BERRYMANS LACE MAWER

Salisbury House, London Wall, London, EC2M 5QN
Tel: (020) 7638 2811 **Fax:** (020) 7920 0361 **DX:** 33861 Finsbury Sq.
Email: postbox@blm-law.com **Website:** www.blm-law.com

Castle Chambers, 43 Castle Street, Liverpool, L2 9SU
Tel: (0151) 236 2002 **Fax:** (0151) 236 2585 **DX:** 14159 Liverpool 1
Email: postbox@blm-law.com

King's House, 42 King Street West, Manchester, M3 2NU
Tel: (0161) 236 2002 **Fax:** (0161) 832 7956 **DX:** 14302 Manchester 1
Email: postbox@blm-law.com

National Senior Partner:	Paul Taylor
Number of partners:	85
fee-earners:	359
Total staff:	758

AREAS OF PRACTICE

Insurance Liability Group	60%
Special Risks Group	20%
Commercial Group	15%
Private Client Group	5%

CONTACTS

Birmingham	Chris Wiggin
Dubai	Jason Blick
Leeds	Jonathan Clay
Liverpool	David Evans
London EC2	Paul Taylor
London EC3	David Wilkinson
Manchester	Nigel Roden
Southampton	Martin Bruffell

THE FIRM: Berrymans Lace Mawer is the leading insurance law firm in the UK, and includes the UK's largest personal injury practice. With offices in Birmingham, Leeds, Liverpool, London EC2 and EC3, Manchester, Southampton and Dubai, they provide a comprehensive legal service to all their clients. BLM has grown significantly in the last three years. Increased instructions and innovative solutions have enabled the firm to consolidate and expand the practice to provide a standardised, high level of service. Every BLM office has ISO9001 accreditation. The firm employs high-calibre lawyers and recruits 19 trainees a year. It has established national professional and training standards to ensure clients at all offices receive the same high standards of service. BLM have recently developed a revolutionary computerised case management system, XClaim, which provides clients with the ability to check the status of individual claims at any time and receive detailed management information reports. XClaim sets new standards for computerised case management systems and is set to revolutionise standards of service and efficiency within insurance claims handling.

PRINCIPAL AREAS OF WORK: The firm is divided into four groups all represented in each of the firms branches.
Insurance Liability Group: Advice and assistance with general liability, personal injury claims and agency work.
Specialist Group: Advice and assistance with construction, defamation, environment, clinical negligence, insurance & reinsurance, marine, product liability, professional indemnity & recovery.
Commercial Group: Advice and assistance with company commercial, commercial litigation, commercial property, employment & EU/competition.
Private Client Group: Advice and assistance with private client work, family law and domestic conveyancing. For more information, please contact the marketing department on 020 7638 2811, or consult the firm's website.

INTERNATIONAL CONNECTIONS: The firm has an overseas office in Dubai. In addition, through the BLM Europe EIG and the Association of European Lawyers, the firm works closely with associate and correspondent firms in 28 other European jurisdictions. It also has an associate firm in Singapore.

CLIENTELE: Berrymans Lace Mawer act for many large insurance companies, Lloyds syndicates, professional firms, government bodies, utility companies, major policy holders, commercial organisations and private clients in the UK and overseas. BLM are committed to the provision of an efficient, proactive, cost-effective and pragmatic legal service. They aim to provide that service at levels tailored to clients' specific requirements, in partnership with them, and in a way which delivers a consistent quality of service. BLM's success is reflected by the increasing number of clients who are attracted to the firm.

BERRY SMITH

Brackla House, Brackla Street, Bridgend, CF31 1BZ **Tel:** (01656) 645525 **Fax:** (01656) 645174 **DX:** 38004 Bridgend
Email: Bridgend@Berrysmith>co.uk **Ptnrs:** 7 **Asst solrs:** 6 **Other fee-earners:** 9

BERWIN LEIGHTON

Adelaide House, London Bridge, London, EC4R 9HA
Tel: (020) 7760 1000 **Fax:** (020) 7760 1111 **DX:** 92 London Chancery Lane WC2
Email: info@berwinleighton.com **Website:** www.berwinleighton.com

Managing Partner:	Neville Eisenberg
UK:	
Number of partners:	66
Assistant solicitors:	147
Consultants:	10
Other fee-earners:	41
International:	
Number of partners:	1
Other fee-earners:	4

THE FIRM: Berwin Leighton is a top 20 City firm, highly regarded for its property, corporate, finance and litigation expertise. It is a modern, growing practice with a clear client service focus and an expanding blue-chip client base. Its strategy is to build on the firm's high quality reputation in its chosen specialisms. Berwin Leighton puts a premium on commercial, as well as technical advice, client relations and quality transactional care. The firm is entrepreneurial, tenacious and innovative.

Continued overleaf

PRINCIPAL AREAS OF WORK:

Property: Berwin Leighton's property department is one of the country's leading commercial property practices. It represents institutions, investors, developers, retailers, banks and government bodies in the full range of commercial property activity. The planning group is a clear market leader and the construction and environment groups enjoy similar reputations.

Corporate: The corporate department acts for investors, companies and advisers operating in the mid-market or entering into mid-market deals, particularly in the private equity and growth/emerging company sectors, such as the ICT (information, communications and technology) sector. It acts for large corporates for mid-market and specialist advisory work, e.g. e-commerce. The department also acts on regenerations and insolvencies for under-performing businesses, or those undergoing significant change, and their advisers. Specialist groups provide media, IT, IP, commercial and competition, employment and employee benefits advice.

Finance: The finance department brings together Berwin Leighton's experience in banking, debt financing, equipment leasing and property financing and also includes the firm's highly regarded tax group. The department advises lenders and borrowers on major financing projects in the UK and overseas. A unique combination of the firm's project finance and public sector experience has been the driving force behind the firm's emergence as a market leader in Private Finance Initiative work on behalf of project vehicles, funders and sponsors.

Litigation & ADR: The litigation and dispute resolution department has extensive expertise in international and domestic litigation, arbitration and ADR, applying innovative and cost-effective risk management techniques throughout. It is proactive and commercial in the solutions it provides. Specialist work groups operate in the property, banking, insolvency, corporate and construction sectors. It has expertise in IT, intellectual property, judicial review, professional negligence and defamation disputes. The firm is regularly involved with investigations and enquiries for and by regulatory authorities.

INTERNATIONAL CONNECTIONS: Berwin Leighton's Brussels office is the base of the firm's EC law practice which provides specialist advice to its public and private sector clients in the areas of competition and public procurement, employment, environment, transport and telecommunications and IT. For further information please contact Velia Leone at: 13b avenue de Tervuren, 1040 Brussels, Belgium, tel: +32 2 732 3144, fax: +32 2 732 3979. The firm maintains strong relationships with firms in the US and Europe and has a number of major clients in Israel and South Africa.

RECRUITMENT & TRAINING: Berwin Leighton is committed to the retention and development of its staff which it views as its key asset. The firm has a comprehensive programme for trainee solicitors and recruits up to 25 trainees each year. Further details, including a copy of the firm's recruitment literature, are available on request.

AREAS OF PRACTICE	
Property and Planning	40%
Company/Commercial (including Corporate Finance)	25%
Finance (including tax)	20%
Litigation	15%

CONTACTS	
Banking	Jennifer Mackerras
Commercial Property	David Taylor
Construction	Terry Fleet
Construction Litigation	Michael Blackburne
Contentious Property	Roger Cohen
Corporate	John Bennett
EC and Competition	Peter Stone or Velia Leone
Employee Benefits	David Dennison
Employment	Robert Eldridge
Environment	Andrew Waite
Finance	Simon Allan
Information Technology & Telecommunications	Quentin Solt
Intellectual Property	Peter Stone
IT/IP Litigation	Ian Lowe
Litigation	Michael Goldmeier
Media	Peter Stone
Planning	Ian Trehearne or Tim Pugh
Private Equity	Peter Martin
Private Finance Initiative	Simon Allan
Property Finance	Mark Waghorn
Public Sector	Simon Allan or Velia Leone
Reconstruction & Insolvency	Keith Bordell
Tax	John Overs

BERWIN LEIGHTON

SJ BERWIN & CO

222 Gray's Inn Road, London, WC1X 8HB
Tel: (020) 7533 2222 **Fax:** (020) 7533 2000 **DX:** 255 London Chancery Lane WC2
Email: info@sjberwin.com **Website:** www.sjberwin.com

THE FIRM: Founded in 1982, S J Berwin & Co's rapid growth and success is best explained by its ability to handle complex corporate and commercial transactions, coupled with a creative approach to clients' problems, a speedy response and close involvement in their strategic decision making. S J Berwin & Co acts for clients ranging from major multi-national business corporations and financial institutions to internet entrepreneurs and to high net worth individuals. The firm is especially favoured by entrepreneurial business clients who find the firm particularly well attuned to their outlook and needs. Increasingly, the firm is focusing on industry sectors including e-commerce, pharmaceuticals and biotechnology, media, communications and information technology, sport and leisure.

PRINCIPAL AREAS OF WORK:

Corporate: The firm is well known for its corporate work and offers a full range of corporate finance services including mergers and acquisitions, capital markets, private equity, management buy-outs and securities regulation, coupled with an active international banking practice, including business reconstruction and insolvency.

Commercial Property: Winner of 'The Lawyer Awards 2000' Property Team of the Year. All aspects of commercial property work are handled for a wide range of clients, including property companies, developers, institutions, retailers and hoteliers. Specialist groups advise on public and private funding programmes for major infrastructure projects, construction and local government finance issues. A highly regarded planning and environment team is an integral part of this growing and expanded practice. The property finance team is an established market leader in the development of innovative fund structures.

EU and Competition: The firm has a strong European dimension. Its EU, competition and trade law practice is conducted principally through the London and Brussels offices (the latter opened in 1990) and advises on domestic and EU mergers and acquisitions, competition, anti-trust and anti-dumping, regulatory work

UK:	
Number of partners:	80
Assistant solicitors:	184
Other fee earners:	56
International	
Number of partners:	15
Assistant solicitors:	22
Other fee earners:	30
Total Staff (UK & International):	641

AREAS OF PRACTICE	
Company/Commercial	49%
Commercial Property	21%
Litigation	16%
EU/Competition	8%
Tax	6%

and judicial review proceedings. The firm is a recent winner of 'The Competition Team of the Year' award in the annual Legal Business Awards. In 1999 the practice published a comprehensive loose-leaf guide to the UK Competition Act 1998, in force from March 2000.

Litigation: The firm's litigation practice handles a broad range of substantial international and domestic commercial litigation as well as mediation and arbitration which is undertaken by the specialist ADR Services Unit. In addition, the practice includes a specialist property litigation group and an advocacy group.

Reconstruction and Insolvency: An active insolvency group handles the whole spectrum of insolvency work, from corporate insolvency and bankruptcy to reconstructions.

Intellectual Property: International trade mark, copyright and patent litigation, international trade mark registration and the identification, exploitation and protection of intellectual property rights are undertaken by a specialist intellectual property group.

Tax: National and international taxation advice, including the structuring of international transactions and property development, is provided by the tax group. Estate planning and asset protection advice is given to private clients in the UK and overseas.

Other Areas: E-commerce work is handled across the firm, with particular strengths in the venture capital, flotations, commercial, financial services and competition practices. Other leading areas of commercial work include film financing and animation production and also communications, as well as commercial contracts, frequently with an international dimension, including franchising, agency distributorship, joint venture and trading agreements, and information technology. The charities group advises on all aspects of charity law, including advice on large fund-raising and lottery-assisted projects. The firm also handles Pro Bono work.

INTERNATIONAL CONNECTIONS: Internationally, the firm operates through its own network of overseas law firms and is also the English member of Interlaw.

Brussels: Square de Mee's 19, Bte 3, 1050 Brussels, tel +32 (0)2 511 5340, fax +32 (0)2 511 5917, brussels Directly connected and working closely with the EU & Competition Department in London, the office comprises UK qualified solicitors, Spanish 'abogados', French and Belgian 'avocats' and trainee solicitors. The office extends a multi-lingual environment to clients with fluency in several European languages. Key experience and strength lies in matters involving Article 81 (ex Article 85) and Article 82 (ex Article 86) of the EC Treaty and the EC merger control regulation and lobbying contact with various European institutions. Specific areas of practice include biotech regulation, tax law, environment, telecommunications and fishery law.

Madrid: S J Berwin Pazos Gallardo y Asociados, Serrano 38-5°, 28001 Madrid, tel +34 (91) 426 0050, fax +34 (91) 426 0066, madrid The firm provides corporate legal services with a strong focus on private equity and M&A work. Clients include major corporations acquiring top local companies entering into joint-venture agreements with local partners in the IT business. Specialisation covers advising investment services companies in matters related to setting up local branches launching venture capital funds and co-operating in pan-European Investment funds.

Frankfurt, S J Berwin Knopf Tulloch: Poseidon-Haus, Hamburger Allee 1, 60486 Frankfurt am Main, tel: + 49(0)69 50 50 32500, fax: + 49 (0) 69 50 50 32499, e-mail: info

RECRUITMENT & TRAINING: In order to maintain its commitment to organic growth and development, S J Berwin & Co will recruit up to 40 ambitious, commercially-minded individuals to begin training in September 2002. All trainees will be required to undertake two corporate seats. Apply to Charlotte Bishop, Recruitment Manager.

CONTACTS

ADR	David I Shapiro
Advocacy	Richard Slowe
Banking	Gillian Smith
Charities	Moira Protani
Commercial Litigation	Tim Taylor
Construction	Ian Insley
Corporate Finance	Jonathan Blake
	Robert Burrow
Defamation	Hilton Mervis
E-commerce	Martin Bowen
	Simon Holmes
Employment	Nicola Kerr
Environment	Mark Brumwell
EU/Competition	Ralph Cohen
	Stephen Kon
Financial Services	Charles Abrams
	Tamasin Little
Hotels	David Ryland
Immigration	Andrew Osborne
Intellectual Property	Jeremy Schrire
	Ray Black
Investment Funds	Josyane Gold
Leisure	Bryan Pickup
Media & Communications	Nigel Palmer
Parliamentary Lobbying	Simon Holmes
Pensions	Wyn Derbyshire
Pharmaceuticals & Biotechnology	Jeremy Schrire
Planning	Patricia Thomas
Projects/PFI	Simon McLeod
Property	Stephen Willson
Property Finance	David Ryland
Property Litigation	Michael Metliss
Reconstruction & Insolvency	Stephen Maffey
Sport	Jonathan Metliss
	Peter McInerney
Tax	Heather Corben
Trademark Litigation	Ray Black

BETESH FOX & CO

17 Ralli Courts, West Riverside, Manchester, M3 5FT
Tel: (0161) 832 6131 **Fax:** (0161) 832 8172 **DX:** 14359 Manchester 1
Email: chambers@beteshfox.co.uk **Website:** www.beteshfox.co.uk

Managing Partner:	Martin Coyne
Senior Partner:	Stephen Fox
Number of partners:	6
Assistant solicitors:	13
Other fee-earners:	15

THE FIRM: Operating nationally and internationally from Manchester city centre, Betesh Fox & Co combines the traditional high standards expected of the legal profession with a progressive outlook.

PRINCIPAL AREAS OF WORK:
Personal injury, company/commercial & property; commercial litigation; regulatory offences & commercial fraud; serious crime.

AREAS OF PRACTICE

Personal Injury	45%
Commercial Litigation	20%
Company/Commercial & Property	20%
Commercial Crime	15%

BEVAN ASHFORD

35 Colston Avenue, Bristol, BS1 4TT
Tel: (0117) 923 0111 **Fax:** (0117) 929 1865 **DX:** 7828 Bristol 1
Email: njk@bevanashford.co.uk **Website:** www.bevanashford.co.uk

Waterloo House, Fitzalan Court, Newport Road, Cardiff, CF24 0BA
Tel: (029) 2046 2562 **Fax:** (029) 2046 1388 **DX:** 33011 Cardiff
Email: c.metherell@bevanashford.co.uk **Website:** www.bevanashford.co.uk

Curzon House, Southernhay West, Exeter, EX1 3LY
Tel: (01392) 411111 **Fax:** (01392) 250764 **DX:** 8301 Exeter
Email: s.rous@bevan-ashford.co.uk **Website:** www.bevan-ashford.co.uk

1 Chancery Lane, London, WC2A 1LF
Tel: (020) 7421 4400 **Fax:** (020) 7421 4422 **DX:** 1058 Chancery Lane
Email: d.widdowson@bevanashford.co.uk **Website:** www.bevanashford.co.uk

Mutley House, 23 Princess Street, Plymouth, PL1 2EX
Tel: (01752) 256888 **Fax:** (01752) 256012/250508 **DX:** 8273 Plymouth 2
Email: a.wilkinson@bevan-ashford.co.uk **Website:** www.bevan-ashford.co.uk

41 St James Street, Taunton, TA1 1JR
Tel: (01823) 284444 **Fax:** (01823) 270869 **DX:** 32115 Taunton
Email: i.daniells@bevan-ashford.co.uk **Website:** www.bevan-ashford.co.uk

Gotham House, Tiverton, EX16 6LT
Tel: (01884) 242111 **Fax:** (01884) 259303 **DX:** 49002 Tiverton
Email: c.palmer@bevan-ashford.co.uk **Website:** www.bevan-ashford.co.uk

Management Board Chairman:	Nick Jarrett-Kerr
Number of partners:	71
Assistant solicitors:	127
Other fee-earners:	101

AREAS OF PRACTICE

Company/Commercial/Projects	28%
Health	25%
Property	25%
Litigation	16%
Private Client	6%

CONTACTS

Bristol	Nick Jarrett-Kerr
Cardiff	Charles Metherell
Exeter	Simon Rous
London	David Widdowson
Plymouth	George Wilkinson
Taunton	Ian Daniells
Tiverton	Christopher Palmer

▪BEVAN▪
ASHFORD
SOLICITORS

THE FIRM: Bevan Ashford is one of the largest regional law firms in the UK with 68 partners, over 570 staff and a network of seven offices. The firm prides itself on the quality and client focus of its services and is constantly seeking new ways to add value by providing innovative yet practical solutions for business clients. It has developed specific IT systems in response to specialist client requirements and is developing a knowledge management system designed to enable it to respond as quickly and cost-effectively as possible to clients' needs. Bevan Ashford believes that the quality of its staff and their ongoing development through training and support are fundamental to the continuous improvement of client services. It was one of the first law firms in the South West to achieve Investors in People accreditation. A number of its lawyers are dual qualified, including engineers, doctors and barristers. Others are qualified arbitrators, mediators and insolvency practitioners. Many of its partners and staff are nationally recognised as leaders in their fields. They regularly contribute to journals, hold seminars and chair conferences. Bevan Ashford is committed to using its exceptional range of commercial expertise to provide added value business solutions to meet each client's needs efficiently and cost effectively.

PRINCIPAL AREAS OF WORK: The focus of the firm is specialist commercial work. In addition to core corporate services the firm offers a range of leading specialist cross department teams e.g. IT/IP, employment, construction, insolvency, insurance and reinsurance, commercial fraud and international litigation, media, planning, energy and waste, local government and education, pensions, German law unit.
PFI: The firm has a growing national reputation for PFI and PPP projects. A fast expanding team is working on numerous complex private sector as well as public sector schemes.
Healthcare: The firm is nationally renowned for its expertise in healthcare. A new cross departmental health and social care group has been formed across the Bristol, Cardiff and London offices to advise the firm's numerous NHS Trust and local government clients on challenging issues facing them in today's changing environment, such as mental heath, clinical governance, judicial review and commercial contracts. The team regularly attracts work in particularly unusual, complex and sensitive or high profile matters in place of panel firms covering routine work.
Clinical Negligence: The firm has a substantial clinical negligence defence practice and is an NHSLA panel firm. It also has a similar insurance claims handling service.

LANGUAGES: French, German, Italian, Punjabi, Russian, Spanish, Urdu and Welsh are spoken fluently by solicitors within the firm.

BEVISS & BECKINGSALE

Law Chambers, Holyrood Street, Chard, TA20 2AJ **Tel:** (01460) 61494 **Fax:** (01460) 63821 **DX:** 43701 Chard **Email:** enquiries@bevissandbeckingsale.co.uk **Website:** www.bevissandbeckingsale.co.uk **Ptnrs:** 7 **Asst solrs:** 8 **Other fee-earners:** 12 **Contact:** Mrs Charlotte Jackson • Substantial agricultural and general practice in South Somerset, West Dorset and East Devon.

BHATT MURPHY

23 Pitfield Street, London, N1 6HB **Tel:** (020) 7253 7744 **Fax:** (020) 7253 7766 **Email:** mail@bhattmurphy.demon.co.uk

BIDDLE

1 Gresham St, London, EC2V 7BU
Tel: (020) 7606 9301 **Fax:** (020) 7606 3305 **DX:** 1008 London Chancery Lane
Email: marketing@biddle.co.uk **Website:** www.biddle.co.uk

Managing Partner:	Martin Lane
Senior Partner:	Martin Winter
Number of partners:	32
Assistant solicitors:	26
Other fee-earners:	14

AREAS OF PRACTICE

Corporate/Commercial	35%
Litigation	20%
Media & Publishing	16%
Pensions	14%
Property	8%
Employment	7%

CONTACTS

Construction	David Lancaster
Corporate Finance	Martin Lane
E- Business	Susan Biddle
Employment	Geoff Tyler
Food Law	Julian Harris
Fraud & Insolvency Litigation	Bill Dixon
Gaming	Julian Harris
Litigation	David Lancaster
M&A	Jonathan Reardon
Media	David Hooper
Pensions	Chris Mullen
Pensions Litigation	Bill Dixon
Private Equity	Roger Fink
Private Finance & Estates	David Biddle
Professional Indemnity	David Lancaster
Property	Peter Watson
Taxation	Mark Cawthron

THE FIRM: Biddle is a highly progressive City business law practice with a strong reputation in the corporate finance, private equity, pensions, employment, publishing, media, e-business and litigation fields.

PRINCIPAL AREAS OF WORK:

Corporate: The corporate department has had another extremely successful year. Private equity work has been very strong and includes acting for ABN Amro Mezzanne in the £45M public to private of Epwin Group plc; Bridgepoint Capital on the £23M public to private of Salehurst plc and in fund raising for the Carluccio deli-café concept. The firm advised Dawson Holdings plc on the £30M sale of its global information systems group; CarrAmerica Realty Corporation on the US$1billion merger of HQ Global Workplaces with Frontline, and successfully defended Lopex plc from a hostile bid before its £67M takeover by Llavas Advertising. Listings include acting for Hawkpoint and Charterhouse on the AIM flotation of OneClick.HR and for Albert E Sharpe on the placing of InternetDirect on the Official List.

IT/Telecomms: E-business work has included advising on many new web site services, mobile phone based information services, content licensing and direct sale of goods. In particular the firm acted in the sale of MetaDesign, the web branding and strategy consultancy, to Icon Medialab International AB, the listed Swedish company.

Media: Well-known for its work for TV news organisations, newspapers, publishers and international news agencies and advising on internet and electronic commerce issues, its major clients include ITN. Biddle advises the main book publishing companies in London on libel, copyright and contractual matters arising out of mainstream publishing as well as new media. Recently the firm acted for Michael Ashcroft in his libel action with Times Newspapers, for ITN in respect of the Bloody Sunday Enquiry, for rugby player Jonah Lomu in respect of advertising issues and for 'celebrity chefs' Gary Rhodes and Jamie Oliver on trademarks and merchandising.

Litigation: The litigation department remains heavily involved in major cases concerning the most complex issues both in the UK and worldwide. There has been a particular emphasis on pensions, construction, gaming and professional negligence with trusts, insolvency, asset tracing and fraud. ADR techniques have been widely used.

Pensions: The pensions group has a substantial presence comprising 15 lawyers with an outstanding reputation for depth of expertise and quality of advice and is renowned for the practical nature of its advice, whether on mainstream pensions issues for trustees or employers, pensions litigation or in connection with corporate transactions. The firm is a member of the OPRA panel of legal advisers.

Gaming & Leisure: Biddle has the City's only specialist group dedicated to gaming and leisure, advising the industry on all aspects of its business, and was one of the first firms to advise on internet gaming.

Employment: The employment department handles all aspects of UK and European employment law and HR practices and is frequently involved in high profile cases relating to senior executives' compensation on wrongful dismissal and TUPE. The department has particular expertise in search and seize orders and injunctive relief to recover and prevent the wrongful use of confidential information and in the enforcement of restrictive covenants as well as fraud and misconduct investigations.

INTERNATIONAL CONNECTIONS: Membership of an independent European group of law firms (LOGOS) is used to support international transactions. The firm has a strong US and Middle East involvement.

CLIENTELE: The firm's hallmark is the ability to advise on and implement precise, imaginative legal solutions to clients' business objectives in a user friendly manner. Instructions come from an exceptionally wide client base, reflecting the firm's reputation for all round excellence as well as in its specialist areas. They include institutions, major pension funds, banks, listed companies, internet start-ups, TV companies, newspapers, insurers, publishers and major casinos.

Biddle

BIGGART BAILLIE

Dalmore House, 310 St. Vincent Street, Glasgow, G2 5QR
Tel: (0141) 228 8000 **Fax:** (0141) 228 8310 **DX:** GW9
Email: info@biggartbaillie.co.uk **Website:** www.biggartbaillie.co.uk

7 Castle Street, Edinburgh, EH2 3AP
Tel: (0131) 226 5541 **Fax:** (0131) 226 2278 **DX:** ED15
Email: info@biggartbaillie.co.uk

Managing partner:	Campbell Smith
Senior partner:	James Roxburgh
Number of partners:	24
Assistant solicitors:	36
Other fee-earners:	23

AREAS OF PRACTICE

Commercial Property	30%
Litigation	30%
Corporate	29%
Private Client	11%

CONTACTS

Banking	Derek Ellery
Construction/Planning	Murray Shaw
Corporate Finance	David Allan
Employment	Paul Brown
Energy & Utilities/PFI	David Ross
Insurance Litigation	David Stevenson
IT/IP	Colin Miller
Property/Projects	Peter Cruickshank

THE FIRM: One of Scotland's leading commercial law practices with a balance of quality work across the main practice areas of litigation, corporate and property. The firm has strength and depth of expertise in a number of specialist areas and a good reputation amongst the Scottish business community. Training and development of all its staff is regarded by the firm as vital to its future and the continuing provision of service which exceeds clients' expectations.

PRINCIPAL AREAS OF WORK: Specialisms are in the areas of corporate finance, banking, PFI, IT/IP, mergers and aquisitions, pensions, construction and planning, employment, energy and utilities, property, defender reparation (especially professional negligence and industrial disease cases), ADR and insolvency.

CLIENTELE: Acts for major industrial, financial and commercial enterprises across Scotland and with its membership of the Euro-American Lawyers Group, of which partner David Ross is chairman, the firm has access to legal representation in many of the world's most important centres of commerce.

B

BIGGER & STRAHAN

Sinclair House, 89 Royal Avenue, Belfast, BT1 1EX **Tel:** (028) 9032 5229 **Fax:** (028) 9024 4086 **DX:** 412
Ptnrs: 3 **Asst solrs:** 6

BINDMAN & PARTNERS

275 Gray's Inn Rd, London, WC1X 8QF
Tel: (020) 7833 4433 **Fax:** (020) 7837 9792 **DX:** 37904 King's Cross

Senior Partner:	Geoffrey Bindman
Number of partners:	15
Assistant solicitors:	15
Other fee-earners:	10

CONTACTS

Administrative Law	Stephen Grosz
Children	Katherine Gieve
Civil Litigation	Clive Romain
Criminal Law & Prisoners	Neil O'May
Defamation/Media	Geoffrey Bindman
	Nick Braithwaite
Employment/Discrimination	Robin Lewis
	Camilla Palmer
Family Law	Felicity Crowther
Housing	Stephen Brown
	Barbara Wyatt
Immigration	Alison Stanley
Medical Negligence	Claire Fazan
Mental Health	Saimo Chahal
Personal Injury	Terry Donovan

THE FIRM: Founded in 1974, Bindman & Partners are specialists in civil liberties and human rights issues. The firm has the resources to handle major litigation of all types, and considerable specific experience and expertise in the following areas. A large amount of legal aid work is handled.

PRINCIPAL AREAS OF WORK:
Defamation & Media Law: Wide experience in representing individuals, newspapers, TV companies and other media organisations in defamation, copyright, confidentiality and contract claims cases.
Administrative Law: Work includes judicial review, human rights, environmental protection, discrimination and police powers.
Civil Litigation: General litigation including actions against the police.
Employment: In addition to its large employment practice, the firm acts for many employers, notably from the not for profit sector, including colleges and public authorities, voluntary groups, charities and pressure groups, in a wide range of casework. It has particular experience and expertise in discrimination issues.
Crime: Work ranges from major fraud cases and serious crimes to minor offences.
Housing: The firm deals with a wide range of landlord and tenant law, especially for tenants.
Family: An extensive matrimonial and family practice includes legally-aided clients.
Children: Work includes wardship, adoption, care proceedings, child abduction, residence and contact disputes.
Medical Negligence & Personal Injury: The firm has an established expertise in medical negligence and other personal injury cases.
Mental Health: This covers advising patients on their rights when detained, on false imprisonment and consent to treatment.
Immigration & Nationality: An established practice in all areas of immigration and nationality law, including business and EU-related applications, personal immigration and asylum.
Prisoners: Acting for prisoners against prison authorities.

BINGHAM DANA LLP

8-10 Mansion House Place, London, EC4N 8LB **Tel:** (020) 7375 9770 **Fax:** (020) 7220 7431 **Ptnrs:** 3 **Asst solrs:** 3

BIRCHALL BLACKBURN

Crystal House, Birley Street, Preston, PR1 2AQ
Tel: (01772) 561663 **Fax:** (01772) 202438 **DX:** 713290
Email: ixjones@birchallblackburn.co.uk

Senior Partner:	W. Denison Robbins
Contact Partner:	W. Denison Robbins
Number of partners:	11
Assistant solicitors:	18
Other fee-earners:	18

THE FIRM: Birchall Blackburn has two main offices in Preston and Manchester, supported by a network of satellite offices in Central and East Lancashire, allowing clients ready access to a comprehensive range of legal services. Founded in 1950 to provide a full range of legal service for corporate, institutional and private clients, Birchall Blackburn is one of the most progressive firms in the North West with a growing reputation within the commercial field. The firm has specialist departments which include commercial and company law, commercial property, commercial and civil litigation, licensing and the leisure sector, family law, corporate and personal insolvency and debt recovery and private client work. Close partner contact is central within the service which combines commercial awareness and experience with a pragmatic down to earth approach. Legal aid work is also undertaken and the firm are holders of the Legal Aid Franchise.

B

BIRCHAM & CO.

1 Dean Farrar St, Westminster, London, SW1H 0DY
Tel: (020) 7222 8044 **Fax:** (020) 7222 3480 **DX:** 2317 VICTORIA SW1
Email: reception@bircham.co.uk **Website:** www.bircham.co.uk

Senior Partner:	Ian McCulloch
Executive Committee Chairman:	Nicholas Brown
Number of partners:	32
Assistant solicitors:	38
Other fee-earners:	37

AREAS OF PRACTICE

Private Client/Charities	31%
Litigation	20%
Parliamentary/Public Affairs	19%
Property	17%
Company/Commercial	11%
Investment Management	2%

CONTACTS

Charities	Simon Weil
Company/Commercial	John Turnbull
Employment	Ian Adamson
Investment Management	Christopher Jones-Warner
Litigation	George Josselyn
Parliamentary/Public Affairs	Robert Owen
Private Client	Sarah Stowell
Property	John Stephenson

BIRCHAM & CO.
SOLICITORS
INCORPORATING DYSON BELL MARTIN, PARLIAMENTARY AND PUBLIC AFFAIRS

THE FIRM: Established for many years in London SW1, this firm combines a balanced private client and commercial practice. The firm has a leading parliamentary and public affairs practice. Over the last year, the firm has expanded considerably, including taking on most of the Bower Cotton partners and practice. This trend is continuing. By attracting partners and senior lawyers from other firms, and maintaining the high percentage of internal partner promotions, the firm has grown to be the largest in Westminster. Recent developments have included a significant expansion in the volume of corporate finance work undertaken. In addition, the private client department, one of the largest of any central London firm, is closely linked to a growing investment management division. The firm's work in leasehold reform has grown strongly as has the civil litigation practice. The work of the charities group has grown substantially since the arrival of a former Charity Commissioner and other senior practitioners. Because the firm places strong emphasis on maintaining a close working relationship between partners and clients, it is noted for the quality of the service it is able to provide.

PRINCIPAL AREAS OF WORK:

Private Client: Private client services include all aspects of financial planning for the individual including wills, trusts and tax compliance for individuals and trustees. In the area of tax planning, the firm acts increasingly for foreign nationals both within the UK and internationally.
Charities: Charity clients range from major national charities to family charitable trusts, the firm advising on all aspects, including formation, administration and promotion. All 'commercial' aspects of charities' activities are covered.
Investment Management: Bircham Investment Management (BIM) offers private clients a comprehensive investment management service.
Property Activities: Property activities for private clients include all aspects of landed estates, both urban and rural, such as estate management, agricultural and other tenancies and town and country planning.
Company & Commercial: Company and commercial services include corporate finance (in particular flotations on the Official List, AIM and OFEX), company acquisitions and disposals, partnerships and joint ventures and all types of commercial agreements. A full range of employment law services is provided.
Commercial Property: Commercial property expertise covers all the main areas, in particular investment, retail, landlord and tenant, development schemes, project management, funding and securing loan arrangements and site acquisitions and disposals. The recent arrivals from Bower Cotton add substantial experience in banking and offshore petroleum activities.
Litigation: All aspects of commercial litigation are handled, including building litigation, property disputes and insurance litigation as well as matrimonial work.
Parliamentary & Public Affairs: Bircham & Co's parliamentary and public affairs department advises on all aspects of the law-making process, whether at a European, national or local level. This includes advice on influencing government policy and resulting legislation, advice on transport infrastructure and other major public works, public enquiries and promoting and opposing private and local legislation.

INTERNATIONAL CONNECTIONS: A member of Lexwork International, an association of independent law firms.

BIRCH CULLIMORE

Friars, White Friars, Chester, CH1 1XS **Tel:** (01244) 321066 **Fax:** (01244) 312582 **DX:** 19985 Chester **Ptnrs:** 8 **Asst solrs:** 2 **Other fee-earners:** 7

BIRD & BIRD

90 Fetter Lane, London, EC4A 1JP
Tel: (020) 7415 6000 **Fax:** (020) 7415 6111 **DX:** 119 London
Email: info@twobirds.com **Website:** www.twobirds.com

Executive Chairman:	David Kerr
Number of partners:	60
Number of assistants:	150
Other fee-earners:	35

AREAS OF PRACTICE

Company	55%
Intellectual Property	22%
Litigation	14%
Property	8%
Private Client	1%

CONTACTS

Banking	Trystan Tether
Brands & Trade Marks	Morag Macdonald
Communications	David Kerr
Corporate/Commercial	Justin Walkey
	Chris Barrett
E-commerce	Graham Defries
Employment	Ian Hunter
Environment	Robert Scott
EU & Competition	Simon Topping
	Jean-Paul
	Hordies
Information Technology	Hamish Sandison
	Christopher Rees
Intellectual Property	Trevor Cook
	Morag Macdonald
Litigation	Trevor Asserson
	Duncan Quinan
PFI	Roger Bickerstaff
Pharmaceuticals	Trevor Cook
Property	Robert Scott
Sport	Justin Walkey
Tax	Richard Ward

THE FIRM: Working with some of the world's most innovative and technologically advanced companies, Bird & Bird has established a formidable reputation for advice at the cutting edge of law. Yet the firm's approach is strongly commercial too, enabling its clients to capitalise on business opportunities and manage change effectively. Combining entrepreneurial ethos and hi-tech know-how in this way brings the firm's clients significant benefits. Sectoral focus has been pivotal to Bird & Bird's success, borne out by the fact that they are amongst the market leaders in the sectors in which they are active. As convergence issues increasingly affect every business, their unrivalled expertise in e-commerce, communications, information technology, intellectual property, media, pharmaceuticals and biotechnology gives them a unique perspective. Across each of these sectors, they offer a fully comprehensive service. With offices in London, Brussels, Paris and Hong Kong, Bird & Bird's lawyers are strategically placed to offer local expertise within a global context. That's how they've been successful in realising their clients' business goals, both domestically and internationally.

B

PRINCIPAL AREAS OF WORK: By providing a full range of legal services within its principal industry sectors, Bird & Bird offers both breadth and depth of expertise, in the following areas:
Banking: Working with leading banks and financial institutions, the firm advises on a full range of banking issues including e-banking, project finance, PFI, secured and syndicated lending, insolvency, corporate reconstruction and banking litigation.
Commercial Litigation: The department offers specialist dispute resolution advice, both in the UK and internationally, focusing, in particular, on the communications, IT and sports sectors.
Commercial Property: Advising telecoms providers, Government departments and financial institutions, the firm's expertise ranges from PFI structures and commercial agreements to pan-European regulatory issues.
Communications: The firm advises both telecoms users and suppliers on a variety of domestic and international issues including major infrastructure projects; regulatory issues; joint ventures and strategic alliances; M&A; interconnection agreements, outsourcing arrangements and 3G licences.
Corporate: Offering a comprehensive range of corporate services, including tax, the firm's corporate lawyers undertake a wide variety of transactional work spanning M&A, joint ventures, strategic alliances, investments, equity financing, venture capital and public offerings.
E-commerce: One of Europe's leading practices in e-commerce, expertise spans all the firm's principal departments and encompasses every aspect of e-commerce including: VC and Incubators funds; 'dot-com' start-ups; funding and IPO's; established businesses developing an Internet presence and e-banking.
Employment: Working with companies and individuals, the firm advises on both non-contentious and litigious issues, ranging from employee contracts and termination agreements to changes in employment regulation.
EU: With substantial offices in both Brussels and Paris, the firm has a significant EU and competition capability, concentrating on antitrust enforcement and legislative developments.
IP: One the largest IP practices in Europe, the firm offers comprehensive expertise across all areas. Lawyers advise on brands and trademark strategy, advertising, media and Internet domain name issues. They have established a strong reputation for conducting successful patent actions as well as providing transactional and litigation advice.
IT: With considerable experience gained in-house within the IT industry and specialist technical backgrounds, the firm's lawyers advise both IT users and suppliers from the public, private and utilities sectors on a variety of major projects.
Media: The firm's expertise spans all areas of media including music, film, TV, publishing and computer games, with a particular focus on negotiating and drafting finance and distribution agreements, publishing deals and issues of digital convergence.
Pharmaceuticals & Biotechnology: The firm offers wide-ranging advice on IP, corporate and commercial issues, to diverse UK and multi-national companies within these sectors.
Sport: The firm's sports lawyers have extensive experience of advising governing bodies, rights purchasers, broadcasters, sponsors and leading sportsmen and women.

INTERNATIONAL CONNECTIONS: The firm has offices in:
Brussels at 15, rue de la Loi, 1040 Brussels, Belgium, Tel: (322) 282 6000, Fax: (332) 282 6011;
Paris at Centre d'Affaires Edouard VII, 3 Square Edouard VII, 75009 Paris, France, Tel: (33 1) 42 68 60 00, Fax: (33 1) 42 68 60 11;
Hong Kong at Suites 602-4, 6/F Asia Pacific Finance Tower, Citibank Plaza, 3 Garden Road, Central, Hong Kong, Tel: (852) 2248 6000, Fax: (852) 2248 6011.

BIRKETT LONG

Essex House, 42 Crouch St, Colchester, CO3 3HH **Tel:** (01206) 217300 **Fax:** (01206) 572393 **DX:** 3603 Colchester **Email:** mail@birkettlong.co.uk **Website:** www.birkettlong.co.uk **Ptnrs:** 18 **Asst solrs:** 6 **Other fee-earners:** 20 **Contact:** Philip George • Birkett Long's team of specialist lawyers offer expertise, professionalism and cost effective solutions to both business and private clients.

AREAS OF PRACTICE

Litigation - Commercial	30%
Litigation - PI and Private	20%
Private Client	20%
Property	20%
Company and Business	10%

BIRKETTS

24-26 Museum St, Ipswich, IP1 1HZ **Tel:** (01473) 232300 **Fax:** (01473) 230524 **DX:** 3206 Ipswich **Ptnrs:** 20 **Asst solrs:** 9 **Other fee-earners:** 38

BIRNBERG PEIRCE & PARTNERS

14 Inverness Street, Camden Town, London, NW1 7HJ **Tel:** (020) 7911 0166 **Fax:** (020) 7911 0170 **DX:** 57059 Camden Town **Email:** [name]@birnberg.demon.co.uk **Ptnrs:** 2 **Asst solrs:** 11 **Other fee-earners:** 8

BISHOP & SEWELL

90 Great Russell Street, London, WC1B 3RJ
Tel: (020) 7631 4141 **Fax:** (020) 7636 5369 **DX:** 278 Chancery Lane
Email: mail@bishopandsewell.co.uk

Senior Partner:	Stephen Bishop
Number of partners:	5
Assistant solicitors:	5
Other fee-earners:	5

CONTACTS

Commercial Litigation	T. Tribius
Company/Commercial	J Sewel
	R. Williams
Conveyancing	S Bishop
Family/Private Client	M. Gillman

THE FIRM: Established in 1979 to provide the range and expertise of services of a larger city practice with an emphasis on establishing a personal partner/client relationship. Clients include international banks, public and private companies,trusts, charities and high net-worth private clients.

PRINCIPAL AREAS OF WORK: The firm is a general practice and its case-load includes the following work: banking; insolvency; company/commercial (including franchising, mergers and acquisitions and management buy-outs); commercial and residential conveyancing; litigation (commercial, construction and general civil work); employment; trusts; family law; wills and probate; and agency work.

BLACKADDER REID JOHNSTON & CARLTONS

30 & 34 Reform Street, Dundee, DD1 1RJ **Tel:** (01382) 229222 **Fax:** (01382) 201132 **DX:** DD2 Dundee **Ptnrs:** 13 **Asst solrs:** 9 **Other fee-earners:** 16

BLACKLOCK THORLEY

2 Commercial Street, Leith, Edinburgh, EH6 6JA **Tel:** (0131) 555 3399 **Fax:** (0131) 555 3388

BLAIR ALLISON & CO

Fountain Court, Steelhouse Lane, Birmingham, B4 6EE **Tel:** (0121) 233 2904 **Fax:** (0121) 236 8913 **DX:** 23534 **Ptnrs:** 3 **Asst solrs:** 4 **Other fee-earners:** 2 **Contact:** Mrs M Meisel • Concentrates on family law. Nine fee-earners all highly specialist and experienced in family law. Three also specialising in mediation, and three in care work. High level work, national reputation.

AREAS OF PRACTICE

Family Law (including care and mediation)	90%
Conveyancing	4%
Civil Litigation including agency	3%
Probate	3%

BLAIR & BRYDEN

27 Union Street, Greenock, PA16 8DD **Tel:** (01475) 888777 **Fax:** (01475) 781836 **DX:** GR2 Greenock-1 **Ptnrs:** 15 **Asst solrs:** 12 **Other fee-earners:** 12

BLAKE DAWSON WALDRON

5th Floor, 66 Gresham Street, London, EC2V 7PL **Tel:** (020) 7600 3030 **Fax:** (020) 7600 3392 **Email:** legal.info@bdw.co.uk **Website:** www.bdw.com.au **Ptnrs:** 2 **Asst solrs:** 2 **Other fee-earners:** 2 **Contact:** Mr Geoffrey W. Hone • Australian lawyers. M&A, stock exchange listings/rules, capital markets, banking and finance, taxation and stamp duty, insolvency, joint ventures, foreign investment, IP, IT, communications, anti-trust law and general commercial law.

AREAS OF PRACTICE

Company/Commercial	30%
Tax	30%
Banking & Finance	20%
Intellectual Property	10%
Insolvency	5%
Litigation	5%

BLAKE LAPTHORN

Harbour Court, Compass Road, North Harbour, Portsmouth, PO6 4ST
Tel: (023) 9222 1122 **Fax:** (023) 9222 1123 **DX:** 124490 Portsmouth 9
Email: post@blakelapthorn.co.uk **Website:** www.blakelapthorn.co.uk

New Court, 1 Barnes Wallis Road, Segensworth, Fareham, PO15 5UA
Tel: (01489) 579990 **Fax:** (01489) 579126 **DX:** 132290 Fareham 5
Email: post@blakelapthorn.co.uk

Holbrook House, 14 Great Queen Street, London, WC2B 5DG
Tel: (020) 7430 1709 **Fax:** (020) 7831 4441 **DX:** 37957 Kingsway
Email: post@blakelapthorn.co.uk

Kings Court, 21 Brunswick Place, Southampton, SO15 2AQ
Tel: (023) 8063 1823 **Fax:** (023) 8022 6294 **DX:** 38538 Southampton
Email: post@blakelapthorn.co.uk

Managing Partner:	Caroline Williams
Senior Partner:	David W. Russell
Number of partners:	47
Number of fee-earners:	190
Total staff:	432

AREAS OF PRACTICE

Property	28%
Corporate/Commercial	27%
Litigation	24%
Private Client and Personal Injury	21%

CONTACTS

Banking	Kathryn Shimmin
Charity Law	Elizabeth Davis
Clinical Negligence	Alison McClure
Company/Commercial	Mark Shepherd
Company/Property	Carey Blake
Construction	Peter Barber
Debt Collection	Nicholas Poole
Education	Sarah Palmer
Employment	Max Craft
Environment	David Rayner
Financial Planning	Simon Brooks
Information Technology	Chris McClure
Insolvency & Business Rescue	Nicholas Keitley
Intellectual Property	Chris McClure
Licensing Law	John Mitchell
Litigation	Stephen Murfitt
Pensions	Maria Riccio
Personal Injury	Alison McClure
Planning	Tim Driver
Private Client	David Russell
Professional Indemnity	David Higham
Regulatory and Criminal Law	Bradley Albuery
Residential Property	Michael Profit
Tax	Niall Murphy

Blake Lapthorn
solicitors

B

THE FIRM: Blake Lapthorn, based in the South East and London, is one of the UK's largest law firms. Founded in 1869, Blake Lapthorn now has 47 partners and over 430 staff. While Blake Lapthorn's immediate centre of activity is the South East and London, the firm undertakes national work for clients who operate throughout the UK and for overseas clients wishing to operate in the UK and in Europe. The firm has seen considerable expansion over the last decade having opened two purpose built out of town centre offices in Fareham and Portsmouth, formed an association with a specialist European law firm based in Brussels and merged with niche commercial property firm Abbott King & Troen in London. In February 2000, the firm opened a new Southampton office, Kings Court, which will effectively double the size of the teams based in Southampton.

PRINCIPAL AREAS OF WORK: The firm is organised into four departments listed below.
Company/Commercial: This department has developed a high reputation for its work in MBO's, MBI's, acquisitions, disposals and mergers as well as general advice to public and private companies. Within the department there are specialist lawyers dealing with employment, pensions, intellectual property, IT, insolvency and corporate re-organisations, corporate finance, banking, mergers and acquisitions and tax, each of whose skills may be drawn on during the course of a transaction. In addition the Department has one of the country's leading licensing practices and a regulatory unit which handles all aspects of regulatory law for commercial clients.
Commercial Property: The department has benefited significantly from the merger with London-based Abbott King & Troen. It acts for a number of household names in connection with their property portfolios and undertakes a wide variety of property work including major office, retail and leisure developments. The Department is supported by expanding environmental and planning teams which are growing strongly. Blake Lapthorn also has a large conveyancing department servicing private clients, banks and building societies.
Litigation: This department covers work a wide spectrum. It views itself as the resolver of disputes, be it by way of litigation, arbitration, mediation or negotiation. Specialist areas covered by the Department include all aspects of construction, engineering and property disputes, general contractual disputes, information technology and computer law, environmental law, foreign export insurance, professional negligence, and professional disciplinary tribunals. The department has been involved in the Risk Assessment in Litigation project, a national project funded by the European Social Fund which has been launched to help small and medium sized legal firms in the process of risk assessment in litigation cases. The firm also has a large and successful personal injury and medical negligence team, and a high-volume debt recovery team.
Private Client: The department, based primarily in the Portsmouth office, offers the advice for individuals and trusts ranging from tax and financial planning, wills and probate, matrimonial and family to criminal defence work.

BLANDY & BLANDY

1 Friar St, Reading, RG1 1DA
Tel: (0118) 958 7111 **Fax:** (0118) 958 3032 **DX:** 4008 Reading
Email: law@blandy.co.uk **Website:** www.blandy.co.uk

Senior Partner:	R.G. Griffiths
Number of partners:	11
Assistant solicitors:	10
Other fee-earners:	11

AREAS OF PRACTICE

Corporate & Commercial	23%
Family	19%
Private Client	19%
Residential Property	16%
Litigation	14%
Commercial Property	9%

THE FIRM: Founded in 1733, Blandy & Blandy is the oldest established legal practice in Reading. Despite its longevity, the firm is modern and progressive in outlook, whilst remaining friendly and approachable. The firm's work is organised into specialist departments providing a full range of legal services to both business and individual clients.

PRINCIPAL AREAS OF WORK:
Commercial: The firm's commercial services are organised under the umbrella of the Commercial Group. Emphasis is placed on providing a practical and pro-active service and clients can expect a high degree of partner involvement.

Corporate & Commercial: The department deals with a wide range of corporate and other non-contentious commercial work and has particular expertise in the area of mergers and acquisitions and other corporate transactional work, as well as in IT and intellectual property law.
Employment: All aspects of employment law, both contentious and non-contentious are dealt with. One of the partners sits as a part-time chairman of employment tribunals and the firm is accordingly well placed to advise on industrial disputes and TUPE issues.
Litigation: The firm has built a particularly strong reputation for litigation. Particular specialisms have been developed in relation to insurance litigation and betting, gaming and liquor licensing and the department is regularly involved in heavy licensing work. A computerised debt collection service is offered and agency work is undertaken.
Commercial Property: All aspects of commercial conveyancing work are handled including landlord and tenant, development and planning.
Private Client: The firm has an enviable reputation for its private client work and its clients range from individuals to large landed estates.
Trusts, Probate & Tax Planning: The department specialises in all aspects of trusts and tax planning work, including the preparation of wills and has a substantial probate practice. The firm has particular expertise in handling the administration of large (including landed) estates.
Conveyancing: The department's workload includes estate development, planning matters, work for housing associations as well as routine residential conveyancing.
Family: The firm has an extensive and highly regarded matrimonial and family law practice. The firm is able to offer the services of trained mediators and has expertise in child-care and child support work. The firm's StepAhead initiative offers a 'one-stop' legal advice, mediation and counselling service.
Civil Litigation: A full range of civil litigation work is dealt with including personal injury claims, probate litigation and bankruptcy. The firm holds a legal aid franchise and legal aid or conditional fee arrangements are available in appropriate cases.

RECRUITMENT & TRAINING: The firm attaches great importance to recruitment and training. Applications in writing, with CV, to Philip Tranter. Further information on the firm can be found on its website: http://www.blandy.co.uk

CONTACTS

Child Care	Brenda Long
Commercial Property	Kate Taylor
Corporate & Commercial	Philip Tranter
Employment	Richard Griffiths
Family	Andrew Don
Intellectual Property	Philip Tranter
Licensing	Sue Dowling
Litigation	Philip D'Arcy
Personal Injury	Julie Simmons
Pharmaceutical & Healthcare	Kathy Minter
Private Client	Graham Benwell

B

BLICK & CO

6 Artillery Passage, Bishopsgate, London, E1 **Tel:** (020) 7247 9696 **Fax:** (020) 7247 9740 **Email:** blickco@btinternet.com **Website:** www.blickco.com **Ptnrs:** 7 **Asst solrs:** 2 **Other fee-earners:** 1 **Contact:** Mr Robert Blick • Highly-regarded commercial practice with international bias comprising only senior lawyers with specialist experience. Specialists in maritime and property law offer services to commercial clients. Particular expertise in all aspects of family law.

AREAS OF PRACTICE

Family law	40%
Shipping	40%
Commercial and Property Litigation etc	20%

BLYTHE LIGGINS

Edmund House, Rugby Road, Leamington Spa, CV32 6EL **Tel:** (01926) 831231 **Fax:** (01926) 831331 **DX:** 11872 **Email:** blytheliggins.co.uk **Website:** www.blytheliggins.co.uk **Ptnrs:** 9 **Asst solrs:** 4 **Other fee-earners:** 12 **Contact:** Mr Donald Hunter • The firm serves both commercial and private clients specialising in commercial property, commercial litigation, IT and family (legal aid franchise).

AREAS OF PRACTICE

Litigation	40%
Property	30%
Company & commercial	20%
Private client	10%

BOBBETTS MACKAN

17 Berkeley Square, Clifton, Bristol, BS8 1HB
Tel: (0117) 929 9001 **Fax:** (0117) 922 5697 **DX:** 37011 Clifton (Bristol)

THE FIRM: Committed to providing quality, independent, efficient and cost-effective legal services. Provides a contemporary service based upon an established reputation. Organised in specialist teams, it aims to ensure that the service offered meets the clients' needs, be they 'lay clients' or referral and agency work for the profession. Advocacy services, including higher courts, are available. Member of LawGroup UK, an independent grouping of quality law firms subject to an annual and external quality audit. The firm undertakes franchised and contracted legal aid work.

PRINCIPAL AREAS OF WORK: Civil litigation, including personal injury, employment, medical and professional negligence with expertise in judicial review and public law. Education and social welfare law, family and childcare including divorce, complex financial matters and children. Criminal defence including motoring matters, fraud and courts martial. Real property including conveyancing.
Agency Work: Civil litigation; criminal defence; family and childcare.

Managing Partner:	Anthony Miles
Senior Partner:	Anthony Grove
Number of partners:	6
Assistant solicitors:	15
Other fee-earners:	19

AREAS OF PRACTICE

Civil Litigation	35%
Criminal Defence	35%
Matrimonial/Care/Children	20%
Non-contentious	10%

CONTACTS

Criminal Defence	Anthony Miles
Employment	Kevin Wood
Family & Childcare	Sally Mitchell
Non-contentious	Anthony Grove
Personal Injury	John Peake

BOGUE AND MCNULTY

3 Carlisle Gardens, Belfast, BT14 6AT **Tel:** (028) 9035 1502 **Fax:** (028) 9074 2185

BOLT BURDON

16 Theberton Street, Islington, London, N1 0QX **Tel:** (020) 7288 4700 **Fax:** (020) 7288 4701 **DX:** 122237 Upper Islington
Email: www.boltburdon.co.uk **Ptnrs:** 8 **Asst solrs:** 20 **Other fee-earners:** 20

BONAR MACKENZIE WS

9 Hill Street, Edinburgh, EH2 3JT
Tel: (0131) 225 8371 **Fax:** (0131) 225 2048/240 0749 **DX:** 7 Edinburgh
Email: law@bonarmac.co.uk **Website:** www.bonarmac.co.uk

Senior Partner:	David Flint
Number of partners:	9
Associates:	1
Other fee-earners:	11

CONTACTS

Commercial Conveyancing ....David Jennings
Debt Recovery & General Litigation ....David Flint
Estate Agency & Residential Conveyancing ....Stephen Murray
Matrimonial & Family ....Lisa Girdwood
Wills & Trust ....Alistair Bowman

THE FIRM: One of Scotland's longest established firms providing a full range of legal services with an emphasis on personal attention and a high level of direct partner involvement. The firm has an impressive client base, acting for various well known financial institutions, High Street retailers and other PLCs. The firm is committed to providing a high quality professional service at competitive fee levels and is always pleased to meet prospective clients to discuss their requirements and terms of engagement.The firm is highly regarded for its expertise and efficiency in debt recovery and repossessions having gained considerable experience acting for various banks and building societies for many years.

B

BOND PEARCE

Ballard House, West Hoe Road, Plymouth, PL1 3AE
Tel: (01752) 266633 **Fax:** (01752) 225350 **DX:** 8251 Plymouth
Email: xnat@bondpearce.com **Website:** www.bondpearce.com

Bristol Bridge House, Redcliff Street, Bristol, BS1 6BJ
Tel: (0117) 929 9197 **Fax:** (0117) 929 9198 **DX:** 200561 Bristol Temple Meads
Email: xvst@bondpearce.com

Darwin House, Southernhay Gardens, Exeter, EX1 1LA
Tel: (01392) 211 185 **Fax:** (01392) 435 543 **DX:** 8321 Exeter
Email: xdjg@bondpearce.com

Town Quay House, 7 Town Quay, Southampton, SO14 2PT
Tel: (023) 8063 2211 **Fax:** (023) 8022 2480 **DX:** 2005 Southampton
Email: aja@bondpearce.com

1 City Square, Leeds, LS1 2ES
Tel: (0113) 300 2026 **Fax:** (0117) 929 9298
Email: xim@bondpearce.com

10 Fenchurch Avenue, London, EC3M 5BN
Tel: (020) 7663 5607 **Fax:** (020) 7663 5978
Email: xnmt@bondpearce.com

Managing Partner:	Simon Richardson
Senior Partner:	Nigel Theyer
Number of partners:	51
Assistant solicitors:	108
Other fee-earners:	79

AREAS OF PRACTICE

Insurance & Commercial Litigation 42%
Property 26%
Commercial/Banking/Insolvency 18%
Private Client & Personal Injury 14%

CONTACTS

Banking & Insolvency ....Victor Tettmar
Construction ....Christine Hanley
Corporate Finance/ Commercial/Tax ....Roger Acock
....Simon Hawes
Employment ....Simon Richardson
....Nikki Duncan
Insurance/Professional Indemnity ....Erik Salomonsen
Intellectual Property Commerce ....Tom Phipps
....Julian Hamblin
International ....Nick Page
Litigation ....Tony Askham
Mediation & ADR ....Andrew Tobey
Personal Injury ....Mark Thompson
Private Client ....Jonathan Nicholson
Property, Planning & Environment ....David Gunn
Regulatory Services & Pensions ....Geoffrey Clarkson

THE FIRM: Regarded as one of the country's top ten regional law firms, Bond Pearce is a major commercial player with a national client base. Commercially aware, progressive and innovative, the firm's culture places strong emphasis on delivering creative legal solutions to individual client requirements. Bond Pearce is amongst the largest law firms nationally to have met the stringent demands of ISO9001, and is committed to achieving Investors in People accreditation. Equally important is Bond Pearce's investment in the development of new specialisations, practice areas and skills for all staff and not least communications – its services are provided within the framework of the very latest in office facilities and modern technology.

PRINCIPAL AREAS OF WORK:

Litigation: Litigation remains an important part of the practice, and Bond Pearce is particularly well known for its work in the fields of professional indemnity, insurance, personal injury, corporate recovery, construction, employment, insolvency, intellectual property and e-commerce. One key strength is a litigation team that acts for national and local retailers, advising in areas such as customer complaints, consumer credit, security issues, employment matters, food law, licensing, trading standards and Sunday trading. This team has acted in a number of cross border matters and actions in the European Court of Justice. Bond Pearce accepts all types of agency work and is at the forefront of Alternative Dispute Resolution with trained mediators. A major provider of ADR experience to others, Bond Pearce acts regularly at mediations on behalf of clients.

Commercial Property: The commercial property group encompasses a variety of property work, especially retail, commercial and industrial park development, dealing with a wide range of investment, development, management and construction issues. The firm has a significant profile in the public sector working on regional and national projects and its strong planning and environmental unit remains at the forefront of work relating to renewable energy and waste management.

Corporate: The corporate group has built its reputation acting for management teams, lending institutions

and investors across southern England in MBOs, MBIs, IBIs, acquisitions, disposals and mergers. Commercial work is handled by a specialist team advising on the full spectrum of commercial agreements, often with an international element. Work includes advice on intellectual property rights, research and development agreements, licensing, joint ventures and competition law. Bond Pearce recognises that commercial clients need much more than just legal advice – the firm works closely with clients, providing a level of service, commitment and practical understanding one would expect from an in-house legal team.

Corporate Recovery & Banking: The team, including two licensed insolvency practitioners, has established a national reputation acting for financial institutions and insolvency practitioners.

Private Client: The team handles the personal legal affairs of the firm's clients including wills, trusts, tax advice, powers of attorney, conveyancing, family and matrimonial law.

CLIENTELE: Bond Pearce acts on behalf of commercial and institutional clients throughout the UK. A national client base enhanced through the firm's commitment to providing a specialist service across a wide range of sectors including: agriculture, aviation, construction, education, regulatory services, insolvency, insurance, lenders and venture capitalists, retail, shipping, waste, energy and the public sector.

BOODLE HATFIELD

61 Brook Street, London, W1Y 2BL
Tel: (020) 7629 7411 **Fax:** (020) 7629 2621 **DX:** 53 CHANCERY LANE
Email: law@boodlehatfield.co.uk

6 Worcester Street, Oxford, OX1 2BX
Tel: (01865) 790744 **Fax:** (01865) 798764 **DX:** 4329 OXFORD 1
Email: law@boodlehatfield.co.uk

Senior Partner:	Richard Moyse
Number of partners:	35
Assistant solicitors:	25
Other fee-earners:	16

AREAS OF PRACTICE

Property	45%
Tax and financial planning	23%
Corporate and employment	20%
Litigation	12%

CONTACTS

Anglo-German Service	Chris Putt
Banking	Nigel Stone
Charities	Andrew Farley (London)
	Nigel Roots (Oxford)
Commercial	Andrew Drake
Commercial Litigation	Simon Fitzpatrick
Commercial Property	Tim Manning
	Richard Maughan (London)
	Lucy Slate (Oxford)
Contentious Trust and Probate	Alison Meek
Corporate and Property Tax	Sara Maccallum
Corporate Finance/M&A	Jonathan Brooks
Employment	Russell Brimelow
Environment	Edward Sutherland
	Hugh Devas
Estate conveyancing/Leasehold enfranchisement	Peter Scoble
	Laura Blackwell
Family	Michael Tulloch
	Vivien Gifford (London)
	Barbara Simpson (Oxford)
IT/E-Commerce	Andrew Drake
	Jonathan Brooks
Partnership	Andrew Drake
Personal tax	David Way (London)
	Alan Ciechan (Oxford)
Private Client, Trusts	Richard Moyse (London)
	Sue Laing (Oxford)
Private Equity	Chris Putt
	Nigel Stone
Property Litigation	Michael Tulloch
Residential property	Jane Littlejohn (London)
	Richard Bell (Oxford)
Town & Country Planning	Lucy Slater
	Deborah Ceadel (Oxford)

THE FIRM: Founded in 1722, Boodle Hatfield is a leading central London practice, with a fast-growing second office in Oxford. Known originally for representing wealthy individuals and landed estates, and still outstanding in those fields, it now acts for a wide, international corporate, commercial and private client base. The firm aims to combine technical excellence with genuinely personal service and to provide practical, cost-effective advice.Services are tailored to the needs and methods of each client, who can rely upon the close, continuing involvement of partners with broad experience as well as specialist knowledge. Clients have commended the firm's high standard of advice, efficiency, commitment and ability to 'think outside the box'. The partnership has grown rapidly in recent years as the firm has invested in its core business and developed complementary skills. Several cross-departmental groups have been created. The private capital group, for example, assists high net worth individuals and entrepreneurs to complete their transactions in tax-efficient ways. Other groups specialise in agrochemicals, Anglo-German services, employment law, IT and e-commerce and inward investment.

PRINCIPAL AREAS OF WORK:

Property: The highly-rated property department is involved in major town centre and out-of-town office, retail and leisure developments and in large urban estate transactions with associated landlord and tenant matters, including leasehold reform issues. It acts for developers, owners, occupiers, funders and UK-based and international corporate and private investors. Skills include property finance and secured lending, property taxes, town and country planning, construction and environmental law and, especially in Oxford, agricultural, university and college property. Sector specialisations include golf clubs, petrol filling stations and primary health care centres.

Tax & Financial Planning: The department is a leader in its field, domestically and internationally, and handles tax planning for large complex estates, private companies, high net worth individuals and families, trustees, executors and charities. It advises on inheritance, capital gains and income tax planning, wills and probate, domicile and residence issues, VAT, property and corporate taxes, the establishment of UK and overseas trusts, and on trust and probate disputes.

Corporate: The expanding corporate department acts for entrepreneurs, private and public companies, partnerships and overseas businesses investing in the UK, with many clients in IT-related sectors. It advises on mergers and acquisitions, MBOs and private equity transactions, joint ventures, banking transactions (especially property-related), listings and the issue of securities, and commercial agreements. The employment group has a growing reputation and acts both for major multinationals and high-profile individuals.

Litigation: The department is active in a broad range of commercial disputes and has substantial, well-regarded expertise in property litigation, acting for major organisations; in construction; employment; and agrochemicals. Its established and growing matrimonial and family law practice has notable international experience, including child abduction cases.

INTERNATIONAL CONNECTIONS: Much of the firm's work is international, arising in particular from the USA, Germany, France, the Middle East and the Far East.

RECRUITMENT & TRAINING: The firm has openings for assistant solicitors in each department. Four or five trainees are recruited each year; some spend six months on secondment to ICI or Shell International. Application forms are available from the Recruitment Administrator.

BOODLE
HATFIELD

THE BOWER COTTON PARTNERSHIP
36 Whitefriars Street, London, EC4Y 8BQ **Tel:** (020) 7353 1313 **Fax:** (020) 7353 3535 **DX:** 94 London **Email:** paulsimms@aol.com
Website: www.bcptnr.com **Ptnrs:** 3 **Asst solrs:** 2 **Other fee-earners:** 3 **Contact:** Guy Vincent

BOYDS

Thistle House, 146 West Regent Street, Glasgow, G2 2RZ
Tel: (0141) 221 8251 **Fax:** (0141) 226 4799 **DX:** 120 Glasgow
Email: mail@boydslaw.com **Website:** www.boydslaw.com

Managing Partner:	Robert Gall
Senior Partner:	David Boyce
Number of partners:	14
Assistant solicitors:	13
Other fee-earners:	7

AREAS OF PRACTICE

Commercial Property Development/Funding	42%
Litigation	22%
Corporate/Commercial	21%
Insolvency	10%
Private Client	5%

CONTACTS

Commercial Property	David Boyce
Corporate	John McMuldroch
Insolvency	Calum Jones
IT & IP Law	John McMuldroch
Litigation	Denise Loney
Private Client	Robert Weir

THE FIRM: Boyds is a medium-sized Glasgow-based firm which has always been at the centre of the commercial scene in Scotland. They also handle UK work, having lawyers qualified in both England and Scotland. Also, through their Law Exchange International connections, they regularly deal with international work, which is managed from Glasgow. They pride themselves on being a dynamic and progressive business. Boyds is one of only a small number of legal firms in Scotland to be accredited as Investors in People. The firm is the first, and, currently remains the only, legal firm authorised by Scotland the Brand to use the Country of Origin Device as part of their planned program for development and recognition of quality Scottish Products and Services. The firm's commitment to training and development permits it to constantly improve its skills and thereby to retain its competitive edge. Clients benefit from a quality service across the board and a united, motivated staff. The firm's IT system is top of the range, allowing it to assist clients efficiently, as well as to be efficient internally.

PRINCIPAL AREAS OF WORK:
Commercial Property: Commercial leases; purchases and sales; development and management work; and security work.
Corporate: Mergers and acquisitions; buy-outs; buy-ins; corporate finance; commercial contracts; insolvency advice; competition law advice; and websites.
Litigation: Employment; construction disputes; landlord and tenant disputes; repossession work; general contractual disputes; debt recovery; and matrimonial.
IT Law and IP Law: Contractual issues; copyright; design disputes; and advice on the internet.
Private Client: House purchase and sales, with relevant mortgage and policy advice.

CLIENTELE: Boyds client base extends from entrepreneurs and those in fast growing sectors through to established medium-sized companies as well as substantial companies which are household names and plcs. The firm are committed to getting close to their clients, to being in tune with them, and to understanding what is and is not important to them so that they can give them tailored focused advice.

RECRUITMENT & TRAINING: The practice is growing and is looking to recruit lawyers who are client-focused and personable.

BOYES TURNER & BURROWS

10 Duke St, Reading, RG1 4RX
Tel: (0118) 959 7711 **Fax:** (0118) 957 3257 **DX:** 54741 Reading 2
Email: mail@b-t-b.co.uk **Website:** www.btb-solicitors.co.uk

Senior Partner:	Peter Daniel
Chief Executive:	Andrew Chalkley
Number of partners:	16
Assistant solicitors:	16
Other fee-earners:	16

AREAS OF PRACTICE

Corporate/Commercial (including Insolvency)	25%
Commercial Property and Planning	20%
Litigation (including Employment)	20%
Medical Negligence/Personal Injury	20%
Private Client	10%
Family	5%

THE FIRM: Over the last five years, Boyes Turner & Burrows has undergone major expansion making it one of the fastest growing legal practices in the Thames Valley. It is one of Reading's major law firms specialising in commercial and private client services. With some 100 staff, including 40 lawyers, the firm is committed to providing clients with in-depth, high quality expertise while still remaining accessible and approachable. Boyes Turner & Burrows was one of the first firms to achieve a Legal Aid franchise. Recently, it became one of a small number of firms to be awarded the new clinical negligence franchise.

PRINCIPAL AREAS OF WORK:
Banking & Insolvency: Headed by an LIP, the firm acts for all the major insolvency practices as well as for clearing banks and other financial institutions in both corporate and personal insolvency and securities work.
Corporate: Business formations, acquisitions and disposals, partnerships and joint ventures, inward investment, and corporate restructuring.
Commercial: The firm acts for many substantial businesses including UK subsidiaries of multi-nationals. Advice includes general business law, commercial and trading agreements, including distribution and licensing, competition law, EU issues and company secretarial work.
Debt Collection: A fully computerised system providing competitive rates and handling bulk recoveries for major trading companies and financial institutions.
Employment: Preparation of employment contracts, advice on disciplinary issues, industrial tribunal representation, restraint of trade, wrongful dismissal, and sex and race discrimination.

Family: Divorce and separation, financial provision, children, emergency procedures, education (members of SFLA).
Intellectual Property: Ownership and exploitation of IPR, licensing, disputes, computer contracts (software and hardware), product liability. Clients include engineering, electronics and computer companies as well as internet and software houses.
Litigation: Contract disputes, shareholder and partnership disputes, negligence claims, property disputes, mortgage repossessions, landlord and tenant. Agency work undertaken.
Clinical Negligence: A specialist team acts exclusively for the victims of medical accidents (AVMA and Law Society referral solicitors, members of APIL)
Personal Injury: RTAs; work related injuries, CICB/A, Personal Injury Panel; SIA referral panel and Headway, maximum severity claims. (Members of APIL and Accident Line).
Private Client: Wills, trusts, probate, personal tax planning and residential conveyancing.
Property: Sales and leases of commercial property, commercial and residential development projects, commercial lending, landlord and tenant.
Planning: Planning advice for property development projects as well as for appeals and planning enforcement.

CLIENTELE: The firm acts for a number of organisations across a broad spectrum of activity, with many clients in the hi-tech, electronics and engineering sectors. Key clients include a national house builder and several household names in the IT and electronics sectors. It also acts for banks, public authorities as well as for start-ups and newly established subsidiaries of foreign parents.

RECRUITMENT & TRAINING: The firm restricts the number of trainee solicitors recruited to ensure that the best possible training is given. The firm takes its personal development responsibilities seriously, for both trainees and assistant solicitors, and operates an in-house training programme.

CONTACTS

Banking and Insolvency	Chris Branson
Clinical Negligence	Adrian Desmond
	Susan Brown
Commercial	Bill Gornall-King
Corporate	Roy Butler
Debt Collection	Elaine Price
Employment	Michael Farrier
Family	Tony Roe
Human Resources	Helen Barnett
Intellectual Property/IT	Bill Gornall-King
Litigation	Mike Robinson
	Gary Parkinson
Partnership Secretary	John Brunnen
Personal Injury	Kim Milan
Private Client	Ashley Wilkin
Property	Peter Daniel
	Mark Appleton
Town and Country Planning	Anthony Cooley

B

B P COLLINS

Collins House, 32-38 Station Road, Gerrards Cross, SL9 8EL
Tel: (01753) 889995 **Fax:** (01753) 889851 **DX:** 40256 Gerrards Cross **Email:** enquiries@bpcollins.co.uk
Website: www.bpcollins.co.uk **Ptnrs:** 16 **Asst solrs:** 14 **Other fee-earners:** 14

BRABNER HOLDEN BANKS WILSON

1 Dale St, Liverpool, L2 2ET
Tel: (0151) 236 5821 **Fax:** (0151) 227 3185 **DX:** 14118 Liverpool
Email: tony.harper@bhbw.co.uk **Website:** www.rudex2.com/brabner-holden.html

6-8 Chapel Street, Preston, PR1 8AN
Tel: (01772) 823921 **Fax:** (01772) 201918 **DX:** 17118 Preston
Email: ross.shine@bhbw1.co.uk

Managing Partner:	Michael Brabner
Senior Partner:	Lawrence Holden
Number of partners:	17
Assistant solicitors:	26
Other fee-earners:	22

AREAS OF PRACTICE

Corporate	26%
Commercial Litigation	25%
Probate & Trust/Tax Planning	22%
Commercial Property	19%
Private Client Property & Litigation	8%

CONTACTS

Commercial Litigation	Mark Manley
	Amanda Webster
Commercial Property	Keith Housley
	Ross Shine
Corporate	Denise Walker
	Mike Livesey
Employment	Andy Cross
Housing Assocs & Charities	Lawrence Holden
Intellectual Property	Nik White
Media & Defamation	Mark Manley
Private Client	Mark Feeny
	George Erdozain

THE FIRM: Brabner Holden Banks Wilson is a leading corporate and commercial law firm serving the North-west. This dynamic, expanding practice was formed in 1990 by the merger of Brabner Holden in Liverpool and Banks Wilson in Preston, bringing together the experience, talent and prestige gained by the two firms over their 200+ year histories. Brabner Holden Banks Wilson is committed to a client-focused approach. Every retained client - from large plcs to private individuals - is assigned a Client Relationship Manager responsible for delivering services of the highest technical skill, provided swiftly and efficiently. The firm acts for public and private companies across the UK, local and national institutions, local authorities, housing associations, brewers and an increasing number of media clients.

PRINCIPAL AREAS OF WORK:
Corporate: The firm is highly regarded for all corporate work, advising on acquisitions, disposals, buy-outs, buy-ins, demergers, venture capital, joint ventures, corporate finance, private finance for housing associations, distributorships, agencies and franchising. The firm has developed a growing list of clients from the multi-media sector.
Commercial & Agricultural Property: The department has expertise in handling acquisitions, leases, development and sales. Recognised as the North's leading firm for Housing Association work, Brabner Holden Banks Wilson also acts for local authorities and a number of breweries both locally and nationally.
Litigation: The litigation team are renowned for their expertise in employment law, media and defamation work, as well as contractual disputes, construction litigation, intellectual property actions, landlord and tenant and competition law. The department also has a national specialism in environmental protester legislation, and operates a computerised debt collection service.
Private Client: Brabner Holden Banks Wilson provides tax-planning, trust administration, probate and conveyancing advice to an impressive base of high net-worth clients. The firm also has an enviable reputation in the area of charity law.

Continued overleaf

INTERNATIONAL CONNECTIONS: Through the firm's active involvement in Eurolegal, an association of European lawyers, it offers its commercial clients speedy access to foreign legal advice as and when required.

RECRUITMENT & TRAINING: Recruiting four trainee solicitors annually, the firm is committed to a comprehensive personal development programme for all staff. Prospects for recruits are good – nine of the current partners trained with the firm. Constantly driving for quality, Brabner Holden Banks Wilson was the first legal practice on Merseyside and one of the first in Britain to achieve the prestigious Investor in People standard.

BRABY & WALLER (debt recovery division of Irwin Mitchell Solicitors)

48-50 St. John St, London, EC1M 4DP
Tel: (020) 7250 1884 **Fax:** (020) 7250 1749 **DX:** 87 Ch.Ln.
Email: braby&waller@irwinmitchell.co.uk **Website:** www.imonline.co.uk

Managing Partner:	Peter Wylde
Senior Partner:	Michael Napier
Number of partners:	5
Assistant solicitors:	10
Other fee-earners:	11

THE FIRM: Braby & Waller was founded in the 19th century and developed as a City of London commercial practice with particularly close connections to the building materials, manufacturing, finance and supply industries. The firm merged with Irwin Mitchell (see separate entry) in May 1998. The well known Braby & Waller name has been retained for the merged recovery and credit control services.

PRINCIPAL AREAS OF WORK: Debt recovery, nationally and internationally; credit control and insolvency. There is a particular emphasis on trade, commercial and professional debt recovery.
Debt Recovery: Braby & Waller has historically been one of the best known and highly regarded firms in London and the South East for commercial debt recovery and credit control services. The merger with Irwin Mitchell has enhanced the delivery of these servcies through added resource and the firm's national presence. The senior managers in the debt recovery department have over 150 years combined experience in the field. The services provided include advice and training in pre-legal credit control, trading terms and credit management. The department is fully integrated with Irwin Mitchell's insolvency practice. The firm acts for major national and international manufacturers, suppliers, distributors, communication providers, lenders and professional firms.

BRACHERS

Somerfield House, 59 London Road, Maidstone, ME16 8JH
Tel: (01622) 690691 **Fax:** (01622) 681430 **DX:** 4806 Maidstone 1
Email: name@brachers.co.uk **Website:** www.brachers.co.uk

Managing Partner:	Geoffrey G. Dearing
Number of partners:	19
Assistant solicitors:	26
Other fee-earners:	41

CONTACTS

Company/Commercial	Stuart Butler-Gallie
Debt Collection and Insolvency	John Craig
Litigation	John Sheath
Private Client	Simon Palmer
Property	Geoffrey Burr

THE FIRM: Brachers is a major regional firm with an established city office at 12 New Fetter Lane, London, EC4.

PRINCIPAL AREAS OF WORK: With 85% of its turnover from commercial work, the firm has developed a growing corporate finance and commercial practice, recruiting city specialists to its team. It has also developed a substantial practice in the health care sector, reflected in its NHSLA panel appointment and 14 NHS trusts and authorities. It has also developed strong employment teams, together with defendant and plaintiff insurance work. The debt collection team, supported by its insolvency services practice, is the largest in the south east. The firm also operates a subsidiary multi-lingual credit management operation. The firm retains close links with Kent's agricultural community and is the sole NFU legal panel member of the southeast region. As befits a firm more than 100 years old, Brachers has a well-established private client department which is focused on tax planning and trust work. The firm recently incorporated its successful investment management operation in a project with Wilsons Solicitors, headed by ASIM Chairman, John Morton.

RECRUITMENT & TRAINING: The firm is continuing with a policy of strong organic growth and now recruits six trainee solicitors a year.

BRECHIN TINDAL OATTS

48 St. Vincent Street, Glasgow, G2 5HS
Tel: (0141) 221 8012 **Fax:** (0141) 221 7803 **DX:** 96 Glasgow
Email: lawyers@bto.co.uk

Managing Partner:	W.S. Young
Number of partners:	13
Assistant solicitors:	20
Other fee-earners:	22

CONTACTS

Commercial Property	Alan Borthwick
Corporate	Stephen MacGregor
Litigation	Dorothy Hatfield
Private Client	Susan Lang

THE FIRM: Brechin Tindal Oatts advises on a wide range of commercial and corporate matters. The firm has notable expertise in insurance litigation (membership of Insurolaw – European Insurance Lawyers Group – allows access to international know-how) and in employment law, with an accredited specialist in this field, which led to the establishment of the Employment Law Consultancy. The Consultancy provides a specialist employment law service to the legal and other professions. In addition, Brechin Tindal Oatts has a specialised Social Housing Unit, which acts for housing associations and co-operatives, together with Scottish clearing banks and other UK and European lenders involved with Social Housing bodies. Niche specialisms are being developed in charity law, timeshare and other areas.

PRINCIPAL AREAS OF WORK:
Corporate: Brechin Tindal Oatts advises on all aspects of corporate law including company formations, acquisitions, re-structuring and disposal, business start up/buy out, banking and finance, commercial contracts, partnerships, franchising, service contracts and intellectual property.
Commercial Property: A range of commercial property work is undertaken including property development, property investment, leasing (landlord and tenant), acquisitions and disposals, social housing, farms and estates, hotels and leisure, timeshare, commercial renting, securities and planning.
Litigation: The firm carries out a wide range of civil and commercial litigation and has an Edinburgh office primarily servicing Court of Session work. Brechin Tindal Oatts advises many leading insurers, and has a particular strength in professional indemnity insurance. The litigation department also deals with contractual disputes, product liability actions, licensing, debt recovery, insolvency and corporate recovery work. In addition, the firm has a solicitor-mediator accredited by the Law Society to offer Alternative Dispute Resolution services.
Private Client: A comprehensive service is provided for private clients including residential conveyancing, employee relocation, personal investments, tax and financial advice, wills, trust and executry work. Brechin Tindal Oatts also deals with family law matters and offers a mediation service in this area.

INTERNATIONAL CONNECTIONS: Through membership of Insurolaw, the firm has associations with law firms in most European jurisdictions.

LANGUAGES: French, German and Spanish.

BREMNER SONS & CORLETT
1 Crosshall Street, Liverpool, L1 6DH **Tel:** (0151) 227 1301 **Fax:** (0151) 227 1300 **DX:** 14119 Liverpool 1 **Email:** bremcor@aol.com **Ptnrs:** 10 **Asst solrs:** 2 **Other fee-earners:** 7

BRENDAN KEARNEY KELLY & CO
4 Clarendon Street, Derry, BT48 7EX **Tel:** (028) 71266935 **Fax:** (028) 7137 1845 **Ptnrs:** 5 **Asst solrs:** 1 **Other fee-earners:** 1

BRETHERTON PRICE ELGOODS

St James's House, St James' Square, Cheltenham, GL50 3PR
Tel: (01242) 224433 **Fax:** (01242) 574285 **DX:** 141660 Cheltenham 11
Email: bpe@bpe.co.uk **Website:** www.bpe.co.uk

Managing Partner:	Malcolm Price
Senior Partner:	David Oldham
Number of partners:	16
Assistant solicitors:	15
Other fee-earners:	31

AREAS OF PRACTICE

Business Services:
Commercial Property 33%
Corporate 29%
Personal Injury 24%
Commercial Litigation 14%
Residential Services:
Remortgage & Reposession Sales 74%
Sales & Purchases 26%

CONTACTS

Commercial Litigation ....Philip Radford
Commercial Property ....Richard Handley
Construction ....John Beevor
Corporate/Corporate finance ....John Workman
....Richard Bretherton
Employment ....Matthew Jenkin
Personal Injury ....Mark Ovington
Remortgage & Repossession sales ....David Oldham
Residential Sales & Purchases Natalie Claridge

BRETHERTON
PRICE
ELGOODS
Solicitors
Total solutions in Law

THE FIRM: Bretherton Price Elgoods was formed in 1989 by the merger of two strong commercial practices. The firm serves a wide range of business, corporate and institutional clients, locally and nationally, through its two divisions: Business Services and Volume Residential Property. Operating from offices in Cheltenham and London, BPE is rapidly growing and commercially driven. Over the past few years, the firm has more than doubled in turnover and staff. The focus for the firm is, simply, to understand each client's business and then to provide precisely the service that the client requests.

PRINCIPAL AREAS OF WORK:
BUSINESS SERVICES
Corporate: BPE has a strong and proactive corporate department, advising on a wide-range of corporate and company/commercial matters, particularly mergers and acquisitions, AIM flotations, venture capital and banking transactions (on behalf of clearing banks and clients). The department also operates in a number of commercial niches including substantial building and civil engineering contracts and IT matters. Within the department, a dedicated employment team deals with both contentious and non-contentious matters, including share option schemes. The team also specialises in planning and implementation of preventative procedures and its lead partner sits as a Tribunal Chairman in London.
Commercial Property: The large commercial property team acts for a number of public companies including a substantial retail multiple chain. The department has special niche strengths in portfolio management and innovative property investment and development.
Commercial Litigation: This department has a reputation for its 'no nonsense' forensic approach to its business-to-business litigation. The team has particular expertise in complex commercial disputes and intellectual property work. Other specialisms include construction and property litigation and arbitration.
Personal Injury: This department handles defendant work for a number of major insurance companies and a high volume of plaintiff cases for union members and private clients. The department also advises on claimant fraud, policy interpretation and other contractual insurance elements.
RESIDENTIAL PROPERTY DIVISION
Remortgages & Repossession Sales: This team-based division undertakes substantial work for major insti-

Continued overleaf

tutional lenders working to demanding service standards. The division, which represents 42% of total turnover, has dealt with over 20,000 remortgages in the past four years.
Residential Conveyancing: The firm provides a customer focused high volume residential conveyancing service to clients introduced by institutions and substantial estate agency chains.

BRETHERTONS
16 Church St, Rugby, CV21 3PW **Tel:** (01788) 579579 **Fax:** (01788) 570949 **DX:** 11672 Rugby **Email:** clientcare@brethertons.co.uk **Website:** www.brethertons.co.uk **Ptnrs:** 8 **Asst solrs:** 8 **Other fee-earners:** 17

BREWER HARDING & ROWE
1 The Square, Barnstaple, EX32 8LX **Tel:** (01271) 342271 **Fax:** (01271) 377685 **DX:** 34957 Barnstaple **Email:** bhr.solrs@virgin.net **Website:** www.brewerhardingrowe.co.uk **Ptnrs:** 9 **Asst solrs:** 5 **Other fee-earners:** 7 **Contact:** Mr John Gibbs • General practice, with four offices. Principal area of work is property based, with a growing civil and criminal litigation department.

BRIAN KOFFMAN & CO
Queen's Chambers, 5 John Dalton St, Manchester, M2 6ET **Tel:** (0161) 832 3852 **Fax:** (0161) 833 2547 **Ptnrs:** 2 **Asst solrs:** 4 **Other fee-earners:** 9

B

BRIFFA
Business Design Centre, Upper St, Islington Green, London, N1 0QH
Tel: (020) 7288 6003 **Fax:** (020) 7288 6004
Email: name.surname@briffa.com **Website:** www.briffa.com

Number of partners:	1
Assistant solicitors:	5
Other fee-earners:	1

AREAS OF PRACTICE

Intellectual Property Protection Exploitation and Enforcement	100%

CONTACTS

Intellectual Property	Margaret Briffa
	Alexander Chapman
	Clare Griffiths
	Oliver Maland
	Ralph Wehrle

THE FIRM: A leading and award winning intellectual property practice. Briffa's underlying principle is to offer the expertise of a big firm coupled with a personal service from a focused, committed and creative team of lawyers. The firm has broken down barriers between lawyers and clients and works well as a bolt on to new media and other companies.

PRINCIPAL AREAS OF WORK: A wide range of intellectual property work including protection and enforcement of patents, copyrights, designs, trade marks and trade secrets. Briffa has a significant IT and e-commerce practice.

CLIENTELE: Briffa has a diverse client base representing many of the industry sectors. The firm acts for new media and internet companies. Budgets are calculated on the basis of anticipated time required to achieve desired result and are fixed. The upper limit of budgets is never exceeded and client can be charged less when work is completed in less time than anticipated.

BRISTOWS
3 Lincoln's Inn Fields, London, WC2A 3AA
Tel: (020) 7400 8000 **Fax:** (020) 7400 8050 **DX:** 269 London/Chancery Lane
Email: info@bristows.com **Website:** www.bristows.com

Senior partner:	Ian Judge
Managing partners	John Lace and Sally Field
Number of Partners:	26
Number of Assistant Solicitors:	49
Other Fee-earners:	31
Total Staff:	170

AREAS OF PRACTICE

Intellectual Property	54%
IT	16%
Company/Commercial	15%
Litigation (inc. Employment)	10%
Property (inc. Environmental)	5%

CONTACTS

Charities	John Lace
Commercial & Partnership	John Lace
Commercial Litigation	David Brown
	Kevin Appleton
Commercial Property	Michael Rowles
	Alexandra Lethbridge
Company	Paul Cooke, John Lace
Competition & Anti-trust	Pat Treacy
Computer Games	Paul Cooke
Corporate Finance	Paul Cooke, Mark Hawes
E-Business	Philip Westmacott, David Wilkinson
Employment	Linda Farrell

THE FIRM: Bristows is a law firm dedicated to serving businesses with interests in technology or intellectual property, ranging from pharmaceuticals, electronics, IT, and telecommunications to brands, media and e-business. The firm is a market leader in this area and acts for many major corporations. With over 150 years of experience in this field, Bristows has earned an enviable international reputation and has developed one of the largest intellectual property practices in Europe; yet it remains a friendly niche firm compatible with the needs of new and growing companies. Bristows is a young partnership in a long established firm committed to excellence in its chosen fields. With the continuing recruitment of lawyers and scientists of the highest quality, Bristows aims to stay at the forefront of specialist firms advising businesses with a strong technology or intellectual property base.

PRINCIPAL AREAS OF WORK: The firm has a substantial number of lawyers who first trained as scientists and who are readily able to understand sophisticated technology. This factor sets it apart from its competitors and has generated unparalleled expertise in litigation and corporate and commercial transactions in which intellectual property or an understanding of technology plays a significant part. The firm's litigation expertise also extends to commercial disputes of all kinds, including product liability and employment matters.
Bristows is able to field teams of lawyers to handle litigation and transactions demanding multidisciplinary skills, often with an international or cross-border flavour. This is an increasingly important aspect of its business, particularly in the light of European integration and its effect on the development of intellectual property and competition law.

Bristows has lawyers who are experienced in corporate and commercial law and in all forms of transaction from take-overs and mergers to joint ventures and technology spin-offs from universities. The firm also has significant complementary practices in real property, tax, competition, charity, employment and environmental law.

RECRUITMENT & TRAINING: Bristows recruits outstanding trainee solicitors each year. The long-term prospects are excellent; many of the firm's present partners trained with the firm. Although a scientific background is useful for intellectual property, applicants with other subjects are encouraged to apply. In-house training is comprehensive and many trainees spend time on secondment at multinational companies including IBM, Gillette and UDV.

CONTACTS CONTINUED

Environmental	Richard Burnett-Hall
IP: Biotechnology & Pharmaceuticals	Tim Powell, Penny Gilbert
IP: Brands/Trademk	Sally Field, Paul Walsh
IP: Commercial/Comp	Laura Anderson, Matthew Warren
IP: General	Edward Nodder, Alan Johnson
IP: Patents	Ian Judge, David Brown
IP: Regulatory	Christine Hore
IT	Philip Westmacott, John Allcock
Media	Paul Walsh, David Wilkinson
Tax	Miranda Cass

BROBECK HALE AND DORR

Alder Castle, 10 Noble Street, London, EC2V 7EE
Tel: (020) 7638 6688 **Fax:** (020) 7638 5888
Email: info@bhd.com **Website:** www.bhd.com

25 Milton Park, Abingdon, Oxford OX14
Tel: (01235) 834447 **Fax:** (01235) 823399

Managing Partner:	Thomas W. Kellerman
Number of partners:	6
Assistant solicitors:	8
Associates:	8
Other fee-earners:	1

THE FIRM: Brobeck Hale & Dorr is a multinational partnership founded in 1990 by the independent law firms of Brobeck, Phleger & Harrison LLP and Hale Dorr LLP. BHD is a leading international law firm dedicated to advising clients in the global technology industry. BHD's clients include a a wide range of companies in the internet, information technology, computer software/hardware, biotechnology and life sciences industries, as well as the investment banks, venture capitalists and other financial intemediaries that serve technology companies.

PRINCIPAL AREAS OF WORK: High technology, biotechnology, securities, mergers & acquisitions, intellectual property, information technology, labour/employment and tax.

INTERNATIONAL CONNECTIONS: Hale and Dorr LLP has offices in Boston, New York, Reston, Washington DC and Wellesley. Brobeck, Phleger & Harrison LLP has offices in San Francisco, Los Angeles, Palo Alto, San Diego, Irvine, Austin, Dallas, Denver, New York, Washington DC.

CONTACTS

Biotechnology	Pierre-André Dubois
Brands & Trade Marks	Pierre-André Dubois
Capital Markets	David M Ayres
Company Commercial	Julia H Bracewell
Corporate Finance/ Governance	Thomas W Kellerman
Digital Media	Pierre-André Dubois
Employment	Henry Clinton-Davies
Intellectual Property	Pierre-André Dubois
IT/Internet	Christopher A Grew
M&A	Richard C Eaton
Telecommunications	Christopher A Grew
Venture Capital	Thomas A Kellerman

B

BRODIES WS

15 Atholl Crescent, Edinburgh, EH3 8HA
Tel: (0131) 228 3777 **Fax:** (0131) 228 3878 **DX:** ED10 Edinburgh
Email: mailbox@brodies.co.uk **Website:** www.brodies.co.uk

Managing Partner:	William Drummond
Senior Partner:	J. Ronald Gardiner
Number of partners:	30
Assistant solicitors:	52
Other fee-earners:	30

THE FIRM: Brodies is one of Scotland's leading law firms, with more than 100 fee earners. An independent, full-service firm, Brodies' client base covers both public and private sector businesses, as well as private individuals in the UK and overseas. For decades, the firm has provided expert legal advice in the core areas of corporate and commercial, litigation, property and trust and tax.Brodies has always been driven by market requirements and has, from the very beginning, been at the forefront of the development of such specialist areas as employment, planning, environment, corporate tax and VAT, PFI, construction law and IP/IT law. The firm is increasingly involved in legal matters relating to the Scotland Act and new Scottish Parliament. Brodies has undertaken substantial market research and economic analysis to ensure that the correct framework and services are in place for clients' future requirements. This has resulted in a restructuring of their client service groups to provide an increasingly proactive and market-facing range of units utilising the depth of expertise within the firm to apply the necessary legal input towards achieving solutions for business and private clients alike. The units are: business affairs, corporate, foreign direct investment, ip/it, public affairs, retail property, commercial, property industry, banking, employment, planning & environmental, town & country, land & property, further & higher educational, family law and trust & tax. Brodies aims to combine knowledge, skill and experience with commercial realism to provide a practical problem-solving service for clients.The firm is delighted to carry out the Scottish aspects of transactions led from south of the border, and for this reason has taken a strategic decision not to compete in England for work in its core service areas.

PRINCIPAL AREAS OF WORK:

Corporate: The firm is able to advise on all areas of corporate and commercial law. It has an excellent reputation for PFI work, mergers, acquisitions, corporate finance, banking and franchising, as well as VAT and corporate tax.

Commercial Property: Provides a full service on the acquisition, development and disposal of commercial land and buildings for institutional investors, developers and landlords, and the leasing of all space requirements, including retail and licensed property matters. In-house expertise on construction, tax, environment and planning is available. Property advice is also provided in agricultural and forestry matters, and as a consultancy service to local government and other public authority bodies.

Continued overleaf

AREAS OF PRACTICE

Property	45%
Commercial Litigation	25%
Corporate	15%
Trust & Tax	15%

CONTACTS

Administrative Law	William Holligan
Banking	Linda Kinniburgh
Construction	Moira Clark
Corporate	Alistair Campbell
Corporate Tax	Alan Barr
Devolution	William Holligan
Employment	Susan Craig
Environment	Charles Smith
Family	Karen Bruce Lockhart
Financial Planning	Hew Dalrymple
Franchising	Julian Voge
Intellectual Property	Grant Campbell
Inward Investment	Alistair Campbell
Litigation	William Holligan
Local Authority	Charles Smith
Minerals	Hew Dalrymple
PFI	Charles Smith
Planning	Neil Collar
Property (Agricultural & Estates)	David Houldsworth
Property (Commercial)	Dale Strachan
Property (Residential)	Jim Clark
Property Marketing	Mark Atkinson
Trust & Tax	Andrew Dalgleish
Wills & Executries	Hugh Stevens

Corporate Tax & VAT: Our tax expert advises both directly to clients and in support of the firm's other practice groups. The planning and environmental unit operates in the same way and works particularly closely with the firm's property and litigation services.
Civil & Commercial Litigation: Brodies' expertise is in banking, employment, intellectual property, corporate, insurance, reparation and property work, including building contracts. Professional negligence, partnership, shipping and licensing litigation services are also provided. The firm has an excellent reputation in personal injury litigation and family law. A substantial debt recovery service is provided. The firm has five solicitor-advocates with extended rights of audience in the Court of Session, House of Lords and Judicial Committee of the Privy Council and three Law Society Accredited Specialists in Employment Law and a part-time Chairman of Employment Tribunals.
Private Client: Brodies is well known for its expertise in personal financial planning, inheritance tax advice and trust work, as well as agricultural law, sporting estates and forestry. The firm also offers a comprehensive residential and rural property service, incorporating both the conveyancing and estate agency aspects. The firm's surveyors are particularly experienced in landed estate, farming and town house properties. Full details of the firm's services can be found on their website. Newsletters and brochures are available on request from Stuart Gristwood.

B

BROOKE NORTH

Crown House, Great George Street, Leeds, LS1 3BR
Tel: (0113) 283 2100 **Fax:** (0113) 283 3999 **DX:** 713100 Leeds, Park Square
Email: address@brookenorth.co.uk **Website:** www.brookenorth.co.uk

Managing Partner:	Gordon Watson
Number of partners:	17
Assistant solicitors:	9
Other fee-earners:	8

AREAS OF PRACTICE

Commercial Property	28%
Company/Commercial	20%
Commercial Litigation	19%
Insolvency	17%
Tax and Trusts	11%
Employment Law	5%

THE FIRM: An ISO 9001 approved practice, with a long-standing reputation for handling the affairs of a wide range of commercial concerns. There is an emphasis on UK and international company and commercial work, commercial litigation, insolvency, commercial property and property management, employment, offshore trusts and strategic tax planning, rights of way and environmental law. Commercial acumen and quality of service are the watchwords of the practice. Agency work undertaken. Recent developments include: Steven Thomas, Commercial Litigation partner, recently represented the liquidator in a landmark case involving the protection of pensions against liquidators; partner Jerry Pearlman, who played an active role in the drafting of the Right to Roam Bill, successfully represented the ramblers association in a bitterly contested, high profile case against a major southern landowner.

CLIENTELE: Major clients include: Evans of Leeds, Illingworth Morris Ltd, Oakgate Group plc, Sirdar plc, Hyundai Heavy Industries Europe NV, Travelworld Group Ltd, Ramblers Association, Yorkshire Dales Millenium Trust, Open Spaces Society, Best Western Hotels, Aram Resources plc, Headway plc, Airtours plc.

INTERNATIONAL CONNECTIONS: Carter Jones McDonald, Isle of Man and Ray Pilley, Gibraltar.

BROOKSTREET DES ROCHES

1 Des Roches Square, Witan Way, Witney, OX8 6BE
Tel: (01993) 771616 **Fax:** (01993) 779030 **DX:** 40205 Witney
Email: bsdr@bsdr.com **Website:** www.bsdr.com

Managing partner:	Nigel J. Street
Senior partner:	Nigel J. Street
Number of partners:	8
Assistant solicitors:	7
Other fee-earners:	2

AREAS OF PRACTICE

Commercial Property	45%
Commercial Litigation	25%
Company	25%
Other	5%

THE FIRM: BSDR was eastablished in 1994. It is committed to delivering a responsive high quality and cost effective legal service in a relaxed astmosphere. The firm's primary objective is to provide pragmatic advice and solutions.

PRINCIPAL AREAS OF WORK: BSDR is one of the leading law firms in the South East with particular expertise in commercial property and commercial litigation.
Property: The group handles retail, warehouse, factory and office acquisitions advising on property finance and landlord & tenant matters.
Litigation: The team scored notable success in the Court of Appeal in 1999 for National Grid plc and Nurdin & Peacock plc.
Corporate/Commercial: The team advises on a range of business matters, particularly in the high-tech and bioscience sectors. The technology group is very familiar with the OFEX trading facility.

R.M. BROUDIE & CO

1-3 Sir Thomas St, Liverpool, L1 8BW **Tel:** (0151) 227 1429 **Fax:** (0151) 236 5161 **DX:** 14248 **Ptnrs:** 2 **Asst solrs:** 5 **Other fee-earners:** 12

BROUGH SKERRETT

99 Charterhouse Street, London, EC1M 6NQ **Tel:** (020) 7253 5505 **Fax:** (020) 7253 5525 **Email:** law@broughskerrett.co.uk
Website: www.broughskerrett.co.uk **Ptnrs:** 4 **Asst solrs:** 7 **Other fee-earners:** 3

BROWELL SMITH & CO.

Pearl Assurance House, 7 New Bridge Street, Newcastle-upon-Tyne, NE1 8AQ
Tel: (0191) 221 1611 **Fax:** (0191) 241 8200 **DX:** 61084 Newcastle
Email: advice@browells.co.uk **Website:** www.browells.co.uk

Number of partners:	4
Assistant solicitors:	14
Other fee-earners:	39

AREAS OF PRACTICE

Personal Injury	70%
Private Client	30%

THE FIRM: Browell Smith & Co specialises in personal injury and industrial disease cases on behalf on Trade Union clients and their members, as well as for the general public. In particular, the firm undertakes work for the National Union of Mineworkers, GMB, Transport & General Workers Union, NUM (COSA) and NACODS. The firm continues to grow and develop in the plaintiff personal injury and industrial disease where expertise covers industrial deafness, chronic bronchitis and emphysema, vibration white finger, asbestos related diseases, industrial cancers, work related upper limb disorders and stress cases. Product liability cases are handled and the firm also deals with a variety of employment law cases on behalf of complainants only.
At its satellite offices, family law, probate, wills and trusts, domestic conveyancing and crime are undertaken on behalf of private clients of the firm.

BROWN COOPER

7 Southampton Place, London, WC1A 2DR
Tel: (020) 7404 0422 **Fax:** (020) 7831 9856 **DX:** 35731 Bloomsbury
Email: clientcare@browncooper.com **Website:** www.browncooper.com

Senior Partner:	Robin Cooper
Number of partners:	5
Assistant solicitors:	1
Other fee-earners:	3

THE FIRM: Brown Cooper provides a distinctive, high quality but cost-effective service for commercial clients. Matters are invariably supervised by an experienced partner. As well as bringing to bear extensive experience in the fields of corporate commercial (Contact: Nigel Urwin), property transactions (Contact: Michael Coyne) and litigation, the firm has in depth knowledge of industries including film and television, upstream oil and gas, publishing and printing, fashion, hotel and restaurant, and travel. The impressive litigation team (Contact: Robin Cooper) has particular expertise in VAT litigation, insurance, medical negligence, employment, crossborder debt recovery, libel and media litigation as well as domestic and international arbitration.

LANGUAGES: Italian, French, German.

BROWNE JACOBSON

44 Castle Gate, Nottingham, NG1 7BJ
Tel: (0115) 976 6000 **Fax:** (0115) 947 5246 **DX:** 718130 Nottingham 27
Email: info@brownej.co.uk **Website:** www.brownej.co.uk

81 Aldwych, Aldwich House, London, WC2A 4HN
Tel: (020) 7404 1546 **Fax:** (020) 7836 3882 **DX:** 37960 Kingsway
Email: lon@brownej.co.uk

102 Colmore Row, Birmingham, B3 3BL
Tel: (0121) 237 3900 **Fax:** (0121) 236 1291 **DX:** 13009 Birmingham 1
Email: info@brownej.co.uk

Managing partner:	Derek Bambury
Senior partner:	David Hibbert
Head of Commercial Group	Rob Metcalfe
Head of Insurance Group	Nick Parsons
Number of Partners:	46
Number of Associates:	21
Assistant Solicitors:	56
Other fee-earners:	60

AREAS OF PRACTICE

Insurance & Personal Injury Litigation	35%
Corporate/Commercial	34%
Professional Indemnity	12%
Commercial & other Litigation	11%
Taxation/Trusts	7%
Other	1%

CONTACTS

Biosciences	Sharon Jones
Commercial Litigation	Peter Ellis
Commercial Property	Brian Smith
Company/Commercial	Peter Hands
Corporate Finance	Rob Metcalfe
Employment	Edward Benson
Environmental & Planning	Brian Smith
Freight/Logistics	Caroline Green
Health Law	Paul Southby
Information Technology/ E-commerce	Mark Snelgrove
Intellectual Property	Peter Ellis
Medical Negligence	Carole Ayre
Pensions	Richard Davis
Personal Injury	Nick Parsons
Professional Indemnity	Robert Ridgwell
Public & Administrative	Richard Barlow
Retail	Candida Thomson
Sport	David Hibbert
Taxation/Trusts	Maryvonne Hands

THE FIRM: Browne Jacobson is a substantial commercial and institutional law firm which has a practical approach providing first class client service. Already acknowledged as a leading regional practice offering a comprehensive range of services the firm has continued to develop a nationwide reputation for quality and has a growing international presence. It operates from Nottingham, London and Birmingham. The International development is driven primarily through London and Paris where the firm has an associated office and through key relationships with selected US law firms. The firm's planned expansion continued through 1999 with a total staff increase of 20% and new partners in pensions, banking and insolvency, corporate and medical negligence appointed during the year. Browne Jacobson has experienced and enthusiastic teams which adopt an integrated and problem solving approach for all their clients. This is coupled with a firm-wide philosophy of being dedicated to providing value for money without compromising quality.

PRINCIPAL AREAS OF WORK: Services to clients are focused through the firm's commercial and insurance operating groups.

COMMERCIAL GROUP Led by Rob Metcalfe, the corporate and commercial teams provide a broad spectrum of expertise including; corporate commercial, commercial property, commercial litigation and tax.

Corporate: The corporate team acts on flotations and new issues, fund raising, M&A, MBO/MBI/IBO and private equity transactions (in 1999 to an aggregate value in excess of £650m). Sector focus groups (convergent technologies (including e-commerce), retail, freight/logistics, bio-sciences and sport) provide a tailored service to targeted industry sectors.

Continued overleaf

Commercial: The commercial team advises on all commercial contracts or arrangements (including joint ventures, agency, distribution, franchising and competition matters) and regulatory matters.
Corporate Tax: The firm is also noted for high level corporate tax and personal financial planning expertise (being concerned with individuals and settlements with an aggregate net worth in excess of £1.5 billion) and expert advice on pensions, employee benefits and general employment.
Commercial Property: Clients include investors, developers, local authorities, housing associations and major retailers. The market facing team advises on all planning and environmental issues construction law and landlord and tenant matters.
Commercial Litigation: Employment disputes, contentious intellectual property matters, licensing, debt collection and trading standards matters are all within the scope of the commercial litigation team. The firm is founder member of the Centre for Dispute Resolution and actively seeks alternative solutions to disputes.
INSURANCE GROUP Led by Nick Parsons, the insurance division is divided into four specialist areas of public authority, professional indemnity, medical negligence and technical insurance. Each has a team of experts with a breadth of knowledge and experience covering every aspect of this evolving industry.
Medical Negligence: The team includes legal experts with a background in public bodies and medicine including registered medical practitioners. It represents clients throughout the public sector, including mental health trusts, community health trusts, ambulance trusts and acute hospitals. The firm is appointed to the National Health Service Litigation Authority Panel.
Personal Injury: The Technical Insurance group acts for major insurers on a national basis handling personal injury, employers' liability, motor liability, accidents at work, industrial disease, public liability, property claims and product liability. The team also advises on risk management strategies.
Professional Indemnity The team includes a CEDR accredited mediator and works for a broad range of clients including solicitors, accountants, construction professionals; architects, engineers, quantity surveyors, financial professionals, surveyors and valuers, insurance professionals; brokers and loss adjusters and I.T. professionals.
Public Authority: The public authority department acts for more than 100 Local Authorities in England and Wales and includes five senior lawyers with direct experience of working in Local Government. It handles public, employers and property liability claims as well as offering environmental, administrative and public law advice.

LANGUAGES: The firm includes fluent French, Welsh, Spanish and Italian speakers.

B

BROWN & WOOD, A MULTINATIONAL PARTNERSHIP

Princes Court, 7 Princes Street, London, EC2R 8AQ
Tel: (020) 7778 1800 **Fax:** (020) 7796 1807
Website: www.brownwoodlaw.com

Senior Partner:	Christopher B. Mead
Number of partners:	9
Assistant solicitors:	16
Other fee-earners:	6

CONTACTS

English Securities & Corporate Law ....Michael Doran, ...Mark Walsh
Investment Funds ....William Morrison
Securitisation ....Michael Durrer ....Margaret Boswell
Structured Finance ....John Russell
Tax ....R.J. Ruble
US Securities & Corporate Law ....Christopher Mead ....Mark Walsh ....Scott Cameron

THE FIRM: Founded in 1914, Brown & Wood has developed a major global securitisation practice and provides legal services to major participants in the world's capital markets.

PRINCIPAL AREAS OF WORK:
US Securities & Corporate Law: Including advising on all aspects of US securities laws, including 144A issues, SEC registrations, exempt transactions, stock exchange listings, depositary receipt programmes, Investment Company Act matters and other regulatory considerations.
English Securities & Corporate Law: Mainstream, as well as emerging markets, transactions, including equity and debt financings and debt restructurings.
Securitisation: Securitisation of a wide variety of assets, including mortgages, credit card receivables, future flows, lease receivables, trade receivables etc; collateratised loan obligations.
Structured Finance: Assisting with English law structured finance transactions and products, including repackagings, credit linked notes, preferred debt and other forms of secured lending.
Investment Funds: Offshore investment funds, including umbrella and single fund structures. Advice on hedged, structured and guarenteed products for sale to institutional and retail investors in the US, Europe and Far East, including Japan.
Tax: Cross-border financing transactions and unique expertise in the complex interaction of the US tax system with the UK and other European systems.

INTERNATIONAL CONNECTIONS: The firm's offices outside of the UK are: Brown & Wood LLP, One World Trade Center, New York, NY 10048-0557, Tel: 001 212 839 5300, Fax: 001 212 839 5599; 10877 Wilshire Boulevard, Suite 1402, Los Angeles, CA 90024-4341, Tel: +1 310 443 0200, Fax: +1 310 208 5740; 555 California Street, Suite 5000, San Francisco, CA 94104-1715, Tel: +1 415 772 1200, Fax: +1 415 397 4621; 1666 K Street, NW, Washington, DC 20006-1208, Tel: +1 202 533 1300, Fax: +1 202 533 1399; China World Tower, Suite 3527, 1 Jian Guo Men Wai Avenue, Beijing 100004, China, Tel: +8610 6505 5359, Fax: +8610 6505 5360; Bank of China Tower, One Garden Road, Central, Hong Kong, Tel: +852 2509 7888, Fax: +852 2509 3110; Tokyo Representative Office, Kioicho Building, 6th Floor, 3-28 Kioicho, Chiyoda-Ku, Tokyo 102, Japan, Tel: +813 5276 0045, Fax: +813 5276 0049.

BRUNTON MILLER

Herbert House, 22 Herbert Street, Glasgow, G20 6NB **Tel:** (0141) 337 1199 **Fax:** (0141) 337 3300 **DX:** GW21 **Email:** bruntonmil@aol.com **Ptnrs:** 7 **Asst solrs:** 4 **Other fee-earners:** 5 **Contact:** Mr Archie MacIver • The firm is well-known for its licensing expertise, and also advises on criminal matters, debt collection, family/matrimonial law, and commercial and domestic conveyancing.

AREAS OF PRACTICE

Licensing	42%
Conveyancing	24%
Court (legal aid and non-legal aid)	20%
Commercial	14%

BRUTTON & CO

West End House, 288 West Street, Fareham, PO16 0AJ **Tel:** (01329) 236171 **Fax:** (01329) 289915 **DX:** 40809 **Email:** mail@brutton.co.uk **Ptnrs:** 7 **Asst solrs:** 4 **Other fee-earners:** 8

BRYAN CAVE

33 Cannon Street, London, EC4M 5TE **Tel:** (020) 7246 5800 **Fax:** (020) 7246 5858 **Website:** www.bryancave.com **Ptnrs:** 8 **Asst solrs:** 11 **Other fee-earners:** 3 **Contact:** Harold G. Blatt • UK, US and international business ventures, onshore and offshore investment funds, contentious and non-contentious employment. US private client, international tax, estate planning advice.

AREAS OF PRACTICE

Commercial	50%
Private Client	50%

BUCHANAN INGERSOLL

Tower 42, International Financial Centre, Old Broad Street, London, EC2N 1HQ
Tel: (020) 7920 3700 **Fax:** (020) 7374 8884 **DX:** 671 London City
Email: info@buchananingersoll.com **Website:** www.buchananingersoll.com

Managing partner (UK):	Barry Francis
UK	
Number of partners:	9
Assistant solicitors:	11
Worldwide	
Number of partners:	194
Assistant solicitors:	240

CONTACTS

Administrative & Procurement .... Diane Wilson
Banking & Finance .... Michael Park
Commercial .... Peter Brazel
Construction .... Laurence Bruce
.... David Hartley
Corporate Finance .... Jonathan Griffiths
Project Work & PFI .... Barry Francis
Property .... Rupert Jones

THE FIRM: Buchanan Ingersoll opened in January 2000 with 18 lawyers. It is the London office of Buchanan Ingersoll Professional Corporation, one of the 100 largest firms in the United States, with more than 440 lawyers. It was founded in Pittsburgh in 1850 and is one of the two oldest large commercial law firms in continous practice in Pennsylvania. The firm's offices in the City of London have been fitted out to achieve a modern relaxed yet efficient environment. The firm's lawyers strive to provide prompt high quality commercial and legal advice and the firm intends to replicate in London its US strategy. Lawyers based in London are committed to understanding and delivering clients' requirements. The firm works with its clients and their other advisors in identifying and developing opportunities, assessing risks, overcoming obstacles and achieving commercially realistic solutions.

PRINCIPAL AREAS OF WORK: The firm's level of business has quadrupled in the past decade demonstrating dramatic long-term growth. The firm's lawyers in London have learned their deal making skills in a range of sectors and transactions: corporate finance, public/private partnerships, joint ventures, private placements, share issues, corporate reconstructions, construction, intellectual property, lending, securitisation: the whole range of transaction types in the healthcare, banking, commercial property, technology, security, transport and property development sectors, as well as information technology, media and advertising, local government, manufacturing and hotel and leisure sectors. The new London office is part of the firm's strategic growth. It is concentrating initially on major projects, public/private partnerships, technology and corporate finance and is developing a major UK and international transactions practice. Lawyers in the London office are also experienced in projects, construction, public and administrative law, property, financial institutions, corporate finance, technology, commercial and European law. As a result the firm is well placed to advise on a wide spectrum of commercial issues. A particular specialism is advising inward investors, particularly from the US, on doing business in the UK. Buchanan Ingersoll is a transatlantic leader in counseling dot.coms on a variety of legal issues. Firm wide, Buchanan Ingersoll represents more than 600 technology and entrepreneurial growth companies, investment banks, venture capital firms and technology investors.

INTERNATIONAL CONNECTIONS: In the US the firm's revenues have increased seventeen fold in the last 20 years and the number of lawyers increased from 78 to over 440. During the past four years the firm has advised in the US on transactions with a value in excess of £90 billion. The last year has seen the US firm open a new office in New York, focusing on venture capital and technology companies, and expanding its Washington DC office through a merger with Silverstein & Mullens, a major international tax practice known for its editorial role in the *Tax Management* publication series.

CLIENTELE: Buchanan Ingersoll's clients in the US range from individuals and start up companies to private and publicly held institutions and multinational conglomerates, including more than 50 of the Fortune 500 corporations.

BUCKLE MELLOWS

35/51 Priestgate, Peterborough, PE1 1LB **Tel:** (01733) 568175 **Fax:** (01733) 562064 **DX:** 12312 P'Boro 1 **Email:** bucklemellows.co.uk **Website:** www.bucklemellows.co.uk **Ptnrs:** 14 **Asst solrs:** 10 **Other fee-earners:** 20

BULLER JEFFRIES

36 Bennetts Hill, Birmingham, B2 5SN **Tel:** (0121) 212 2620 **Fax:** (0121) 212 2210 **DX:** 13051 Birmingham 1 **Email:** buller-jeffries@link.org **Website:** www.bullerjeffries.co.uk **Ptnrs:** 8 **Asst solrs:** 9 **Other fee-earners:** 7

BULLIVANT JONES

State House, 22 Dale St, Liverpool, L2 4UR
Tel: (0151) 227 5671 **Fax:** (0151) 227 5632 **DX:** 14120 Liverpool
Email: mail@bullivantjones.co.uk

Senior Partner:	Pamela Jones
Number of partners:	10
Assistant solicitors:	20
Other fee-earners:	6

AREAS OF PRACTICE

Commercial Property	70%
Litigation & Employment law	20%
Company/Commercial	5%
Probate/Trust/ Residential Conveyancing	5%

Bullivant Jones

THE FIRM: Bullivant Jones was founded in 1970 by Peter Bullivant. Since the late 1970's, when Pamela Jones (the present senior partner) became a partner, it has focused on carrying out high-quality commercial conveyancing and related matters for a small client base, with a strong emphasis on the retail sector. It acts in particular for two large food retailing businesses. The firm's partners have the knowledge and experience to advise where appropriate on the commercial aspects of a client's business, as well as offering high-calibre legal expertise. They aim to be innovative and forward-looking in their approach to transactions. The firm has expanded steadily over the years and now has ten partners and six associates, with another 19 fee-earners. The firm continues to take every opportunity to strengthen its existing team of solicitors in all its practice areas. Bullivant Jones has an award as an Investor in People and in 1999, gained the Law Society's Lexcel accreditation.

PRINCIPAL AREAS OF WORK: The firm concentrates largely on commercial conveyancing. It also has departments in general commercial work, litigation, employment, probate, trusts and residential conveyancing.
Commercial Conveyancing: This department generates the largest portion of work carried out by the firm. Work includes sales, purchases and leases of offices, businesses and shops, new developments such as out-of-town retail parks as well as high street premises. Clients include developers, retailers and investors.
Planning: Work includes obtaining planning permission and handling planning appeals.
Litigation: The litigation department deals with a considerable volume of property-based matters, including building contract disputes. In addition it handles cases concerning food safety and health and safety litigation and liquor licensing.
Employment: The firm's expanded resource in employment law deals with all aspects of employment law, including redundancy, unfair and wrongful dismissal, discrimination claims and Industrial Tribunal and Employment Appeal Tribunal cases.
Private Client: The firm has expanded its private client department which already had considerable experience in wills, settlements, probate and trust work, as well as residential conveyancing.

BUNKERS

7 The Drive, Hove, BN3 3JS **Tel:** (01273) 329797 **Fax:** (01273) 324082 **DX:** 59257 Hove **Ptnrs:** 8 **Asst solrs:** 1 **Other fee-earners:** 13

BURGES SALMON

Narrow Quay House, Narrow Quay, Bristol, BS1 4AH
Tel: (0117) 939 2000 **Fax:** (0117) 902 4400 **DX:** 7829
Email: email@burges-salmon.com **Website:** www.burges-salmon.com

Managing and senior Partner:	David Marsh
Number of partners:	44
Assistant solicitors:	124
Other fee-earners:	42

CONTACTS

Agribusiness	Roger Hawes
Agriculture	William Neville
Arbitration	Adrian Llewelyn Evans
Asset Finance	Sandra Forbes
Charities	Charles Wyld
Construction	Marcus Harling
Corporate Banking	Sandra Forbes
Corporate Finance	Christopher Godfrey
Corporate Rescue	Guy Stobart
Corporate Tax	Nigel Popplewell
Dispute Resolution	Adrian Llewelyn Evans
Employment	Christopher Seaton
Environment	Ian Salter
EU/Competition	Laura Claydon
Financial Services	Christopher Godfrey
Housing Associations	Stephen McNulty
Information Technology	Simon Coppen
Insurance	Christopher Jackson
Intellectual Property	Simon Coppen
Land Use	Ian Salter
Mergers & Acquisitions	Alan Barr

THE FIRM: Burges Salmon is a major regional commercial law firm - and one of the top ten single office practices in the UK. The firm's simple and effective strategy of focusing strength in one office has enabled it to develop characteristics which attract and motivate high quality lawyers to practice from one of the UK's leading professional service locations, and to deliver a high quality service from that base. From a single office, the firm delivers better job management and achieves greater cohesion between its lawyers, rather than fragmenting its considerable resources. Burges Salmon stresses to its clients its emphasis on professional independence, leading to a paramount commitment to the clients' interests. The firm scores very highly in terms of client satisfaction and in the longevity of client relationships. This virtuous circle has reaped abnormally high and sustainable growth. The rate of growth is also reflected in the acquisition of new clients and in the secure relationships forged with them. The majority of clients are UK-based organisations, although a very substantial part of the firm's business is for those whose activities extend overseas. Burges Salmon is currently handling projects in over 40 jurisdictions.

PRINCIPAL AREAS OF WORK:
Corporate: The firm works on a full range of company and corporate finance transactions and advises on a growing number of flotations and stock exchange work. The international practice of this group extends to inward investment, UK offshore and international tax planning and asset protection. The group has a national reputation for unit trust and financial services work and a significant presence in the fields of employment, pensions and agribusiness.

Commercial Property: The full range of property transactions are covered, including all aspects of planning, development, environment, funding, building procurement, management, lettings and construction, engineering and other disputes. The firm deals with portfolio acquisitions and disposals for property investors in addition to its flourishing corporate support work.
Finance: The firm covers all aspects of banking, securities, investment work and asset finance.
Commercial Litigation: A full service is available with particular expertise in IP, professional negligence, employment, insolvency, white collar crime, insurance and partnership disputes. The team includes experts on ADR and arbitration. The agricultural practice of this group covers the complete range of UK and EU agricultural law, both contentious and non-contentious and extends to the provision of high quality advocacy services.
Private Client: Wide range of trust and tax issues including estate and tax planning, financial planning, heritage preservation, UK and offshore trusts, immigration and emigration, family and matrimonial breakdown, charities, high value residential conveyancing and staff relocation. In addition the following areas have specialist units:
Competition: The thriving regulatory and competition law practice has conducted many merger cases and competition investigations before the OFT, acting particularly for clients in the transport, food, sports and media and oil and gas industries.
Land Use: A unique regulation practice, which has recently expanded into nuclear licensing.
Corporate Tax: Changes to national and international tax regimes has meant an explosion of work in all areas.
E-commerce: The firm acts for e-commerce clients on funding from venture capitalists, trademark registrations and software licensing. Its involvement in the hi-tech sector is growing considerably through litigation, international domain name disputes, and corporate finance.
PFI: The firm has an extraordinarily high capability in this area handling major capital projects.
Food: The firm's nationally dominant agri-business practice has expanded successfully out of mainly primary production through the supply chain to include processing and storage and distribution.

RECRUITMENT & TRAINING: The firm recruits law, non-law and mature graduates and offers both in-house training and residential courses. Vacation experience is also available. Apply two years in advance: Contact Lisa Head, lisa.head@burges-salmon.com

CONTACTS CONTINUED

Pensions	Tim Illston
PFI & Partnering	Richard Wynn-Jones
Planning	Patrick Robinson
Private Client	Martin Mitchell
Product Liability	Adrian Llewelyn Evans
Professional Indemnity	Paul Haggett
Property	Bob Smyth
Property Development	David Gidney
Property Finance	Paul Browne
Property Litigation	Neil Ham
Rail	Nick Olley
Trade & Industry	Richard Wynn-Jones
Transport & Distribution	Philip Davey
Unit Trusts	Christopher Godfrey
Venture Capital	Richard Spink

B

BURNESS

50 Lothian Road, Festival Square, Edinburgh, EH3 9WJ
Tel: (0131) 473 6000 **Fax:** (0131) 473 6006 **DX:** ED73 Edinburgh
Email: edinburgh@burness.co.uk **Website:** www.burness.co.uk

242 West George Street, Glasgow, G2 4QY
Tel: (0141) 248 4933 **Fax:** (0141) 204 1601 **DX:** GW154 Glasgow
Email: glasgow@burness.co.uk

Chairman:	John Rafferty
Number of partners:	30
Assistant solicitors:	35
Other fee-earners:	19

AREAS OF PRACTICE

Corporate	35%
Commercial Property	33%
Capital Projects	16%
Dispute Resolution	14%
Other	2%

CONTACTS

Banking & Finance	Scott Wilson
	Alan Soppitt
Capital Projects/PFI	Ken Ross
Commercial Litigation	Philip Rodney
	Marsali Murray
Commercial Property	Ian Wattie
	David Gibson
Company/Commercial	John Rafferty
	Andrew Sleigh
Construction/Engineering/ PFI	Anthony Read
	Chris Mackay
Dispute Resolution	Philip Rodney
E-commerce	Brent Haywood
Employment	Shona MacLean
Product Liability	Marsali Murray

THE FIRM: Burness is one of Scotland's premier commercial law firms with a strong UK and overseas client base. Last year the firm was shortlisted as 'most enterprising UK law firm' in the prestigious Legal Business Awards. The firm's business is sharply focused on commercial work and services clients from three core groups: corporate, property and dispute resolution. Offices are located in Glasgow and Edinburgh.

PRINCIPAL AREAS OF WORK:
Property: Burness has one of the largest and strongest property teams in Scotland and adds value to its property clients through an integrated team of planning, environmental and construction experts. The award winning capital projects team has an outstanding reputation and last year closed an impressive 11 projects. The firm has specialist groups in retail and leisure, property development, investment and property finance. Clients include Argos, Burger King, Pizza Express, Grosvenor, Miller Developments, NFU, Sun Life, Bank of Scotland and The Royal Bank of Scotland. The property group has added three new partners in the last year - retail & leisure and property investment specialists, Richard Rennie and Nicholas Jones, and PFI and facilities management expert, Christa Reekie.
Banking & Finance: The firm has a dedicated banking and finance group. Its range and quality of instructions are impressive, ranging from substantial PFI and other capital projects work to property, mezzanine and acquisition finance. The firm has been at the forefront of development where lenders are showing an increased willingness to take an 'equity' stake in a business by way of mezzanine finance, share options or other profit participation mechanisms.
Corporate: E-commerce, venture capital and consumer finance are strong features of the corporate group. In the last year the firm has completed an important string of MBOs. The firm has won increasing private equity work particularly in e-commerce related companies and PFI projects. Clients include Royal Bank of Scotland, Charterhouse, Scottish Equity Partnership and Bank of Scotland. The firm is developing a strong e-commerce related practice on the back of significant experience in acting on behalf of investors in e-commerce businesses and carrying out due diligence for proposed equity investments in e-commerce projects. The firm

Continued overleaf

regularly advises clients on issues of domain name protection, defamation on the internet, data protection requirements and copyright issues. Other distinguishing features of the corporate practice include a unique experience in relation to motor finance, to which the corporate tax group makes a significant contribution, and a significant inward and outward investment practice.

Dispute Resolution: The firm has launched a progressive new commercial dispute resolution service. The new service focuses on constructive resolution - pre-empting and diffusing disputes and where appropriate proposing business strategies rather than destructive, drawn out and expensive battles in court. Significant new dispute resolution clients include Scottish Equitable and BBC Scotland. The firm's commercial litigation team also has specialist and highly regarded groups in employment, product liability, e-commerce and corporate and commercial disputes.

BURNETT & REID
15 Golden Square, Aberdeen, AB10 1WF **Tel:** (01224) 644333 **Fax:** (01224) 632173 **DX:** 19 Aberdeen **Email:** mail@burnett-reid.co.uk **Ptnrs:** 9 **Asst solrs:** 5 **Other fee-earners:** 9

BURNETTS
6 Victoria Place, Carlisle, CA1 1ES **Tel:** (01228) 552222 **Fax:** (01228) 522399 **DX:** 63005 Carlisle **Email:** info@burnetts.co.uk **Website:** www.burnettssolicitors.com **Ptnrs:** 13 **Asst solrs:** 9 **Other fee-earners:** 19

B

BURNSIDE KEMP FRASER

48 Queens Road, Aberdeen, AB15 4YE **Tel:** (01224) 327500 **Fax:** (01224) 327501 **DX:** 78 Aberdeen **Email:** law@burnside-kemp-fraser.co.uk **Website:** www.scoot.co.uk/burnside_kemp_fraser/ **Ptnrs:** 3 **Asst solrs:** 3 **Other fee-earners:** 1 **Contact:** Mr David M. Burnside • A specialist practice with emphasis on employment and personal injury with two accredited specialists in those fields. Also offers family law and conveyancing services.

AREAS OF PRACTICE	
Employment	40%
Personal Injury	25%
Matrimonial	20%
Other	15%

BURT BRILL & CARDENS

30 Old Steyne, Brighton, BN1 1FL
Tel: (01273) 604123 **Fax:** (01273) 570837 **DX:** 2709 Brighton 1
Email: help@bbc-law.co.uk **Website:** www.bbc-law.co.uk

Senior Partner:	J.R. Summers
Number of partners:	6
Assistant solicitors:	3
Other fee-earners:	7

AREAS OF PRACTICE	
Private Client	45%
Litigation	35%
Corporate/Commercial	20%

CONTACTS	
Commercial	A. Zeal
Litigation	K.G. Smyth
Private Client	D.J. Edwards

THE FIRM: Burt Brill & Cardens was established in 1897. Offices in Brighton and Worthing serve both businesses and private clients. Whenever consulted, the firm's policy is to remain independent and objective, and to identify the best results desirable in each case. Members of the firm are approachable, understanding and courteous and provide a service that is both practical and reliable. Clients are regularly kept informed about the progress of their cases and about costs.

PRINCIPAL AREAS OF WORK: Company and commercial law, personal injury, medical negligence, family, employment, commercial disputes, conveyancing, wills, trusts, probate and tax planning.

CLIENTELE: The firm acts for a wide range of clients including the University of Brighton, a plc, businesses, charities, churches, trusts, schools, as well as numerous private clients.

BURTON COPELAND

51 Lincoln's Inn Fields, London, WC2A 3LX
Tel: (020) 7430 2277 **Fax:** (020) 7430 1101 **DX:** 37981 Kingsway
Email: law@burtoncopeland.co.uk **Website:** www.burtoncopeland.co.uk

Royal London House, 196 Deansgate, Manchester, M3 3NE
Tel: (0161) 834 7374 **Fax:** (0161) 832 2619 **DX:** 14362 Manchester 1
Email: crime@burton-copeland.co.uk

7-9 Bexley Square, Salford, M3 6DB
Tel: (0161) 833 9298 **Fax:** (0161) 833 9975 **DX:** 14362 Manchester 1
Email: crime@burton-copeland.co.uk

Senior Partner:	Ian R. Burton
Number of partners:	23
Assistant solicitors:	12
Other fee-earners:	30

AREAS OF PRACTICE	
Commercial Fraud/ Regulation/Investigation	50%
Crime	50%

CONTACTS	
Commercial Fraud/ Regulation/Investigation	I.R. Burton
	H.A. Travers
	(London)
	M.J. Kenyon
	(Manchester)
General Crime	M. Haslam
	(London)
	M.P. Macheu
	(London)

THE FIRM: Burton Copeland is widely regarded as one of the most prominent firms nationally in the areas of serious crime, commercial fraud, international financial regulation and investigation by the tax authorities. Its clients range from large international corporations to individuals. It assists those who are the subject of investigation, potential witnesses in investigations, and those whose rights and assets have been affected by fraud. It specialises in the protection of the rights and liberties of its clients in accordance with the European Convention on Human Rights and other international treaties.

PRINCIPAL AREAS OF WORK:

Commercial Fraud: Burton Copeland has one of the largest commercial fraud departments in the country, with 13 partners practising full-time in this area and 12 full-time solicitors/fee earners. Its expertise developed in major prosecutions brought by the SFO and DTI such as Barlow Clowes, Maxwell, BCCI, and various UN sanctions cases, has given it particular speciality in accountancy, banking, and international investment matters. This expertise and experience is carried over into the related areas of international judicial assistance, confiscation, restraint, money laundering and extradition. It is amember of the Serious Fraud Panel formed by the Legal Services Commission.

Regulatory & Disciplinary: The firm advises companies and individuals in respect of investigations and proceedings brought by the FSA, Lloyd's, the Law Society, the Bar Council and other regulatory and investigatory bodies. Its work ranges from protecting individuals in an area where procedural safeguards are ill-defined, to conducting internal investigations on behalf of companies concerned with potential regulatory breaches.

Inland Revenue & Customs & Excise Investigations: An area of particular speciality where the client's best interests often lie in a negotiated settlement, Burton Copeland specialises in the protection of its clients' interests in the face of the exceptional powers of investigation which the Inland Revenue and Customs and Excise possess. It has substantial experience in securing negotiated financial settlements with the tax authorities as an alternative to prosecution.

Environmental & Health & Safety Matters: The firm acts for individuals and companies facing prosecutions for breaches of environmental protection and health and safety legislation, and/or orders for the compulsory provision of information to the Environment Agency.

Criminal Law: The firm has an established reputation as market leader in criminal law, and offers specialist advice across the whole spectrum from road traffic to homicide. It has substantial experience in areas such as serial serious crime, major drug trafficking cases and confiscation proceedings.

Civil Litigation: The firm acts in a range of civil proceedings ancillary to its core specialisms of commercial fraud and serious crime.

C

BURY & WALKERS

4 Butts Court, Leeds, LS1 5JS **Tel:** (0113) 244 4227 **Fax:** (0113) 246 5965 **DX:** 12048 Leeds 1 **Email:** leeds@burywalkers.com **Ptnrs:** 11 **Asst solrs:** 8 **Other fee-earners:** 9 **Contact:** Mr Michael P Burke (Leeds office) • Well respected commercial property department. Involved with corporate and charity work. Acts for a number of local authorities, plc's and private companies. Commercial litigation expanding.

AREAS OF PRACTICE	
Litigation	40%
Commercial Property	28%
Commercial	12%
Private Client	20%

BUSS MURTON

The Priory, Tunbridge Wells, TN1 1JJ **Tel:** (01892) 510222 **Fax:** (01892) 522500 **DX:** 3913 Tunbridge Wells **Email:** info@bussmurton.co.uk **Ptnrs:** 21 **Asst solrs:** 8 **Other fee-earners:** 32

CADWALADER, WICKERSHAM & TAFT

55 Gracechurch Street, London, EC3V 0EE
Tel: (020) 7456 8500 **Fax:** (020) 7456 8600 **DX:** 98944 Cheapside 2
Email: cwtinfo@cwt.com **Website:** www.cadwalader.com

Managing Partner:	Robert O. Link Jr.
Co-ordinating Partner:	Paul Griffin
UK:	
Number of partners:	7
Assistant solicitors:	16
Other fee-earners:	5
International:	
Number of partners:	87
Assistant solicitors:	231
Other fee-earners:	125

CONTACTS	
Capital Markets	Jim Croke
Financial Restructuring/ Corporate	Andrew Wilkinson
	James Roome
Real Estate	Alan Lawrence
Tax/Private Client	Russell Jacobs

THE FIRM: Cadwalader was founded in New York in 1792, and is one of the leading international law practices. In 1997, the firm opened the London office with the goal of building on its pre-eminent US financial services practice and expanding such services to UK, European and Asian clients. The firm's practice group management ensures that colleagues collaborate closely and provide seamless global client representation. 1999 has been the year of innovative deals and transactions and further development of a broad and high quality client base. In London, they now have just under 30 lawyers, the great majority of whom are UK-qualified. They are continuing to grow with lateral partner recruitment and the hiring young and dynamic lawyers. The development and growth of the firm in London is set to continue, driven bu the nature of their practice areas and the quality of the individuals they have and those they are recruiting.

PRINCIPAL AREAS OF WORK:

Capital Markets: All forms of debt, equity and hybrid financing, including derivatives, securitisation, structured finance and re-financing.

Financial Restructuring: Contentious and non-contentious insolvency and workouts, with a particular specialisation in the insurance, re-insurance and distressed debt sectors and all forms of corporate structuring and reconstructions.

Corporate: All forms of corporate and corporate finance activities, with a particular regard to international mergers and acquisitions, joint ventures and corporate reconstructions.

Tax & Private Client: All forms of domestic and international corporate taxation, with a focus on cross-border structured financing arbitrage, and planning opportunities for corporate and high net worth individuals.

Real Estate: Complete spectrum of real estate transactions from financings, acquisitions, sales and exchanges to development, construction, joint ventures, management and leasing.

Banking & Finance: All aspects of banking and finance activities, including commercial lending, special bank regulatory needs, mortgage banking, energy and project finance and equipment finance and domestic and cross-border leasing.

RECRUITMENT & TRAINING: Cadwalader is keen to consider high quality lawyers to practise in the aforementioned areas. The London office also runs a programme yearly for trainee solicitors and a summer placement scheme.

CAMPBELL HOOPER

35 Old Queen St, London, SW1H 9JD
Tel: (020) 7222 9070 **Fax:** (020) 7222 5591 **DX:** 2365 Victoria
Email: ch@campbell-hooper.co.uk **Website:** www.campbell-hooper.co.uk

Managing Partner:	Martin Wright
Number of partners:	15
Assistant solicitors:	17
Other fee-earners:	17

AREAS OF PRACTICE

Commercial Litigation (including Construction & Employment)	27%
Company	23%
Commercial Property	22%
Private Client	16%
Media/Entertainment	12%

CONTACTS

Company	M.J. Wright
Construction	D.A. Salmon
Domestic Conveyancing	A. Gill
Employment	W.D. Granger
Family	A. Jackson
Immigration	C.S. Jennings
Litigation	J.W. Whitehead
Media	C.S. Jennings
Property	J.S. Siddall
Trust and Estate Planning	A.G. Cuppage

THE FIRM: Campbell Hooper is a medium-sized commercial firm with an established base of commercial and individual clients. The firm is a member of Proteus, a European network of independent law firms committed to providing an integrated service.

PRINCIPAL AREAS OF WORK:
Company/Commercial: Multi-disciplinary teams provide a comprehensive service to domestic and overseas business clients. From start-ups and venture capital to mergers, acquisitions and company restructuring. Particular expertise in telecommunications; IT contracts; banking; finance; financial services, and business immigration.
Commercial Property: Extensive experience in commercial and residential development, as well as funding work including office, retail, leisure and town centre developments with specialist construction advice. Expertise extends to investment; landlord and tenant; planning; social housing, and environmental law.
Employment: The firm advises and trains employers and senior management on contracts, policies, acquisition and removal of personnel, together with the full range of tribunal disputes.
Media: Extensive experience in film; TV; theatre; broadcasting; recording and music publishing and collecting societies; video; cable and satellite TV; character and other merchandising and publishing; trademarks and intellectual property. Clients include writers, performers, and creative personnel – many of them leaders in their field.
Litigation: A strong team handles a variety of work including intellectual property; construction disputes; contracts; landlord and tenant; insolvency, contractual disputes, defamation and libel.
Private Client: Handles conveyancing; estate planning; establishment and administration of charities; wills; trusts; settlements; probate, and personal taxation.
Family & Matrimonial: Solicitors Family Law Association members. The firm promotes a constructive and conciliatory approach to resolving all issues relating to divorce, separation, finance and children.

CAMPBELL SMITH WS
21 York Place, Edinburgh, EH1 3EN **Tel:** (0131) 556 3737 **Fax:** (0131) 473 7700 **DX:** 51 Edinburgh **Email:** mailbox@camsmith.co.uk **Ptnrs:** 5 **Asst solrs:** 4 **Other fee-earners:** 3

CANTER LEVIN & BERG

46-48 Stanley St, Liverpool, L1 6AL
Tel: (0151) 474 5757 **Fax:** (0151) 474 5763 **DX:** 14122
Website: www.canter-law.com

Managing Partner:	Lee Heaven
Senior Partner:	Lee Heaven
Number of partners:	14
Assistant solicitors:	17
Other fee-earners:	31

THE FIRM: Whilst continuing to develop and expand its traditional base of private client work, particularly RTA and personal injury work, the firm has experienced strong growth recently in commercial areas, particularly employment, housing management and commercial property. The commercial department at The Corn Exchange in Liverpool is staffed primarily by solicitors with a background in industry, as well as in private practice. The other city and town centre offices cater for the full range of private client work, not only for the regional population but increasingly for clientele drawn from all parts of the country.

CAPSTICKS

77-83 Upper Richmond Road, London, SW15 2TT
Tel: (020) 8780 2211 **Fax:** (020) 8780 1141 **DX:** 59461 Putney
Email: info@capsticks.co.uk **Website:** www.capsticks.com

Senior Partner:	Brian Capstick
Number of partners:	23
Assistant solicitors:	34
Other fee-earners:	22

AREAS OF PRACTICE

Clinical Law	54%
Employment	18%
Property	15%
Disputes Resolution	7%
Commercial	6%

CONTACTS

Administrative Law	James Reynolds
Clinical Law	Janice Smith
Commercial	Christopher Brophy
Commercial Litigation & Regulatory	John Witt
Commercial Property	Hilary Blackwell
Employment	Peter Edwards
Private Finance Initiative	Colin Lynch

THE FIRM: CAPSTICKS is one of the leading legal advisers to the National Health Service. It handles litigation, advisory, commercial and property work for over 100 NHS Trusts and Health Authorities and regulatory bodies, as well as other health-related public and voluntary sector organisations. Founded in the 1970s to act on behalf of the NHS, CAPSTICKS has developed an outstanding level of expertise through a modern infrastructure of research, training and data management. The firm operates modern quality controls and has held the ISO 9001 standard of quality assurance for professional firms since 1994. It was also in the first wave of firms to be awarded the Law Society's quality standard, LEXCEL, in 1998. CAPSTICKS' innovative approach and standards of excellence have helped the firm to attract an exceptionally able team of lawyers. CAPSTICKS has won a number of accolades for excellence, including the *Lawyer*/HIFAL award 'Law firm of the year (best medium-sized firm)' in 1997 and the TSB Business of Law award in 1994. Its website includes 'NHS Online', an innovative healthcare legal advice area which draws on the firm's 20 years of experience at the forefront of NHS law and provides online answers to questions on issues such as the Woolf reforms, Primary Care Groups and the Human Rights Act. Supporting all of this work is an expert system which provides on-line access to CAPSTICKS' database of previous advice, articles and precedents derived from more than 25,000 NHS cases. The firm maintains its own information technology company (which also looks after about 30 other legal practices) and has one of the most advanced IT applications in private practice. CAPSTICKS sees its future in further expansion in the health service and the public sector, through development of all its areas of expertise and innovative services.

PRINCIPAL AREAS OF WORK: The firm's work is divided between the clinical law, commercial, disputes resolution, employment and property departments.
Clinical Law: This department deals with a large volume of cases, ranging from small clinical negligence claims to disasters arising from obstetric accidents, which comprise some of the largest PI claims in this country. Part of CAPSTICKS' research has been into how such accidents may be avoided and this work forms a large part of the firm's pro bono programme. This department also deals with Mental Health Act issues and emergency treatment cases.
Commercial: This department advises on the contractual aspects of major PFI and other projects. This work is carried out in multidisciplinary teams with members of the property and employment departments. The department has already completed several major PFI schemes including the first specialist mental health facility and the country's first dedicated ambulatory care and diagnostic centre. The commercial department has particular expertise in the procurement of computer and facilitates management services to the NHS, including the European Union Rules.
Disputes Resolution: This department guides clients through some of the most sensitive decisions taken by the NHS, such as decisions to close major hospitals or departments, from which judicial reviews may well follow. The department also has a growing reputation in the field of healthcare regulatory advice. The department's commercial litigators continue to recover substantial sums of money lost through fraud on the NHS.
Employment: This department provides employment law advice and representation to the NHS, which takes account of the ever growing volume of regulations and guidance which applies to Europe's largest employer.
Property: This department carries out major property development work for the NHS, one of the largest land owners in the country, including PFI. Innovative work is also being carried out in conjunction with other departments including development of new state of the primary care facilities and joint ventures between health authorities and local authorities.

CARLESS DAVIES & CO

140 Stourbridge Road, Halesowen, B63 3UL **Tel:** (0121) 550 2181 **Fax:** (0121) 550 9954 **DX:** 14506 Halesowen **Ptnrs:** 2 **Asst solrs:** 1
Other fee-earners: 2

CARNSON MORROW GRAHAM

80 Main Street, Bangor, BT20 5AE **Tel:** (028) 9145 7911 **Fax:** (028) 9145 0679 **DX:** 2501 NR BANGOR 1
Email: mail@cmgbangorlaw.demon.co.uk

C

CARRICK CARR & WRIGHT

Norwich House, Savile Street, Kingston-upon-Hull, HU1 3ES
Tel: (01482) 325385/590000 **Fax:** (01482) 327584 **DX:** 11935 Hull
Email: info@carricks.solicitors.co.uk **Website:** www.carricks-solicitors.co.uk

Appleton House, 3a Wednesday Market, Beverley, HU17 0DG
Tel: (01482) 869342 **Fax:** (01482) 867796 **DX:** 28321 Beverley
Email: info@carricks.solicitors.co.uk

106 Micklegate, York, YO1 1XZ
Tel: (01904) 686631 **Fax:** (01904) 686621 **DX:** 61511 York 1
Email: info@carricks.solicitors.co.uk

Senior Partner:	John Wright
Number of partners:	6
Assistant solicitors:	5
Other fee-earners:	28

PRINCIPAL AREAS OF WORK: Best known for its debt recovery, accident claims, commercial litigation and company/commercial work. Also handles commercial property; conveyancing; family and private client matters; medical negligence.

CARRICK READ INSOLVENCY

Trafalgar House, 29 Park Place, Leeds, LS1 2SP
Tel: (0113) 243 2911 **Fax:** (0113) 244 2863 **DX:** 14085 Leeds

Norwich House, Saville Street, Hull, HU1 3ES
Tel: (01482) 211160 **Fax:** (01482) 585798 **DX:** 119935 Hull

Managing Partner:	Christopher Garwood
Number of partners:	3
Assistant solicitors:	11
Other fee-earners:	16

AREAS OF PRACTICE

Insolvency	100%

THE FIRM: Carrick Read Insolvency is the merged insolvency departments of Read Hind Stewart and Garwood Devine forming a specialist insolvency practice operating from offices in Hull, Leeds and London. The firm is backed by the combined resources of three offices and more than 140 staff. The partners are all licensed insolvency practitioners and the practice acts on behalf of liquidators, receivers, administrators, trustees and those on both sides of the insolvency procedure..

CARSON & MCDOWELL

Murray House, Murray Street, Belfast, BT1 6DN
Tel: (028) 9024 4951 **Fax:** (028) 9024 5768 **DX:** 403 NR Belfast
Email: law@carson-mcdowell.com **Website:** www.carson-mcdowell.com

Senior Partner:	W.B.W. Turtle
Number of partners:	9
Assistant solicitors:	13
Other fee-earners:	10

AREAS OF PRACTICE

Civil Litigation	35%
Commercial Property	30%
Company/Commercial	30%
Private Client	5%

CONTACTS

Civil Litigation	Brian Turtle
Commercial Lit./Arbitration	Peter Davison
Commercial Property	Alan Reilly
Commercial Security	Roger Nixon
Company/Commercial	Michael Johnston
Employment	Brian Turtle
PFI	Michael Johnston
Professional Negligence	Ken Gouk

THE FIRM: Founded in 1852, the firm has considerable reputation in Northern Ireland and beyond for its experience in all aspects of corporate and commercial practice, PFI, commercial property, corporate finance, insolvency, employment, commercial contracts, civil litigation and arbitration. We also have a particular reputation in professional negligence defence, both medical and legal. Outside the province, we have strong relationships with leading firms in Dublin, London and the regional centres, often operating as the NI link in projects for inward investment.

PRINCIPAL AREAS OF WORK:
Company & Commercial: The department offers a complete service, covering all areas of practice and involving close co-operation with other professionals. It has established links with a number of firms in the City of London through working in concert with them on many transactions. It has acted in the privatisation of Northern Ireland Public Utilities and in PFI projects.
Commercial Property: The department deals with the purchase, development, management and sale of business property, from the single shop unit to the city centre office building and provides a complete package, including site assembly, project management, developments by way of lease, mortgage and onward investment sale. It is equally experienced in residential development.
Commercial Security & Banking: An established finance department which has built sound relationships with financial institutions in the province and beyond, it has extensive experience with the various forms of security which are available and will also deal with investigation of property title, land searches and enquiries, companies office file searches, property insurance cover and appropriate legal registrations and statutory notices.

Litigation: An experienced team, not only in the traditional court system but also in equal opportunity, employment and lands tribunal, planning applications and building arbitrations. The firm also acts in more specialised fields of law such as professional negligence, marine law, defamation, carriage of goods and environment and in areas of the law which are unique to Northern Ireland such as The Criminal Damage Legislation, Fair Employment Law, and the licensing of the sale of intoxicating liquor and bookmakers' premises. In the business field it handles all types of commercial litigation, from simple debt collection (our debt collection system has its own dedicated computer base) through normal contractual claims, intellectual property and employment problems to the major commercial dispute which may involve domestic and European law. In addition, the firm will deal with all aspects of corporate insolvency, both contentious and non-contentious.

CARTER HODGE

18 Hoghton St, Southport, PR9 0PB
Tel: (01704) 531991 **Fax:** (01704) 537475 **DX:** 20102
Email: information@carterhodge.co.uk **Website:** www.carterhodge.co.uk

Managing Partner:	Stephen Holmes
Number of partners:	7
Assistant solicitors:	6
Other fee-earners:	8

CONTACTS

Commercial Conveyancing	Stephen Holmes
Criminal	Nick Archer
Financial Services	Stephen Holmes
General Litigation	Mark Robinson
Matrimonial	Philip Porter
Personal Injury	Mark Robinson
Probate & Trust	David Byard
Residential Conveyancing	Stephen Holmes

THE FIRM: Carter Hodge is a general practice offering a wide range of services to business and private clients. Tracing its origins from 1889, the firm has a modern and progressive outlook from its involvement with Legal Aid Franchising, Investors in People and Practice Management Standards, to the award-winning Financial Services Department. The firm is regulated by The Law Society in the conduct of investment business.

PRINCIPAL AREAS OF WORK: Litigation (High Court work, commercial litigation, PI and professional negligence); family; company/commercial; property; private client; criminal and employment.
The firm has other offices in Ainsdale, Birkdale, and Heswall.

CARTER LEMON CAMERONS

11 Breams Building, London, EC4A 1DW
Tel: (020) 7405 7554 **Fax:** (020) 7242 3926 **DX:** 25 London Chancery Lane
Email: [name]@CarterCamerons.co.uk

Senior Partner:	John Newth
Number of partners:	15
Assistant solicitors:	5
Other fee-earners:	11

CONTACTS

Banking Law	Charles Douglas
Charity Law	Michael Stewart
Church Law	John Beaumont
	Duncan Tuft
Commercial Litigation	Seamus Smyth
Commercial Property	Gaynor Lloyd
	Martin Standen
Corporate	Charles Douglas
	Philip Ross-Smith
Divorce	John Newth
Employment/Intellectual Property	Philip Ross-Smith
Health	Justin Cumberlege
Partnership	John Newth
Property Litigation	Lisa Ginesi
Residential Property	Rufus Ballaster
Wills/Trusts (including off-shore)/Probate/Tax	Margaret Lang

THE FIRM: Carter Lemon Camerons was formed on 3rd April 2000, when the London partners of Camerons joined Carter Lemon. Carter Lemon Camerons brings together a specialist reputation in property law, commercial law and commercial litigation with the skills of one of the leading firms on charity and church law. The strength of the firm is in its ethos: complete integrity in all its dealings with dedication to best advice. The firm values its close and long-standing relationship with clients, enabling its highly experienced lawyers quickly and cost effectively to deal with those clients' transactions and disputes.

PRINCIPAL AREAS OF WORK:
Commercial Property: All aspects of acquisitions and disposals, portfolio management, Landlord and Tenant (with a particular specialisation in default work and dilapidations.
Commercial Litigation: A wide range of work for small and large clients, both national and international.
Charity Law & Church Law: Acting for many leading national and local charities including medical Royal Colleges, professional bodies, foundations, schools and colleges. Advisers to the Baptist Union and hundreds of individual churches.
Corporate & Banking: Mergers, acquisitions, joint ventures, funding arrangements and partnership structures; intellectual property and employment law.
Health: Acting for NHS bodies and general practitioners. Partnerships disputes.
Private Client: Residential property, wills, trusts (including off-shore), tax planning, probate, family matters and (where necessary) divorce as a core and valued part of the business.

CARTMELL SHEPHERD

Viaduct House, Carlisle, CA3 8EZ **Tel:** (01228) 516666 **Fax:** (01228) 401490 **DX:** 63006 **Ptnrs:** 14 **Asst solrs:** 15 **Other fee-earners:** 12

CARTWRIGHT KING

Norwich Union House, South Parade, Old Market Square, Nottingham, NG1 2LJ **Tel:** (0115) 958 7444 **Fax:** (0115) 958 8666 **DX:** 10032 Nottingham **Email:** ck@cartwrightking.co.uk

CARTWRIGHT & LEWIS

100 Hagley Road, Edgbaston, Birmingham, B16 8LT **Tel:** (0121) 246 3000 **Fax:** (0121) 246 3050 **DX:** 707293 Edgbaston **Email:** legal@cartwrightlewis.co.uk **Website:** www.cartwrightlewis.co.uk **Ptnrs:** 10 **Asst solrs:** 8 **Other fee-earners:** 8 **Contact:** Mr Anthony Rich • Known for commercial litigation. Has one of the largest personal injury departments in the West Midlands.

AREAS OF PRACTICE

Personal Injury	40%
Private Client	20%
Property	18%
Commercial Litigation	11%
Company/Commercial	11%

CARTWRIGHTS

Marsh House, 11 Marsh Street, Bristol, BS99 7BB
Tel: (0117) 929 3601 **Fax:** (0117) 926 2403 **DX:** 7851 Bristol
Email: info@cartwrights.com **Website:** www.cartwrights.com

Regus House, Malthouse Avenue, Cardiff Gate Business Park, Cardiff, CF23 8RU
Tel: (029) 2026 3627 **Fax:** (029) 2026 3733
Email: info@cartwrights.com

Managing Partner:	Christopher Eskell
Senior Partner:	Geoffrey Jones
Number of partners:	16
Assistant solicitors:	22
Other fee-earners:	27

AREAS OF PRACTICE

Insurance Claims Resolution/Litigation ..30%
Licensing and Leisure 26%
Company Commercial 21%
Commercial Property 12%
Employment 11%

CONTACTS

Commercial Litigation ......Nigel Puddicombe
Commercial Property ......Ian Dunn
Compulsory Purchase/Planning & Local Government ......Emrys Parry
Construction ......Jan Grimshaw
Corporate ......Chris Mitchell
Employment ......Jane Oakland
......Glynis John
Food Safety/Consumer Protection ......Michael Parrott
Health & Safety ......Christopher Eskell
Insurance Claims Resolution/ Personal Injury ......David Vernalls
Licensing & Leisure/Gaming ......Tim Davies
Technology Law ......Nigel H. Williams
Transport ......Geoffrey Jones
......Peter Woodhouse

THE FIRM: Cartwrights is recognised as a leading national firm in the fields of transport, leisure and licensing and has one of the largest insurance departments in the South West and South Wales. The firm is also known for its expertise in employment, property and company commercial work. Lawyers increasingly work together in market sector groups to meet the needs of a wide range of businesses, from start-ups to quoted plcs. The firm places significant emphasis on IT-based legal services for clients.

PRINCIPAL AREAS OF WORK:
Commercial: The department regularly handles large scale commercial transactions. It comprises specialist units dealing with company/commercial; commercial property; construction; compulsory purchase and planning; commercial litigation; employment; technology law; and transport. The firm's employment unit offers a complete service to employers, combining legal, human resource and industrial relations skills in a seamless package, supplemented by practical training services.
Leisure & Licensing: This department offers a complete nationwide and EU-wide service to clients operating in the food and drink retailing, licensed trade, bingo, casino, cinema and leisure sectors, including many high street names. It has designed, tested and implemented a computerised case management system for licensing applications. A section of the department specialises in food hygiene, packaging and labelling matters.
Insurance: Work includes investigating and handling insurance litigation claims, criminal prosecutions under health and safety and road traffic legislation, inquests and public inquiries. The department is organised into client teams and is appropriately structured to undertake high and low value work. Each team is supported by specialists in health and safety; occupational diseases; motor; employers' liability; public liability; property risks; and product liability. The department is a leading player in a consortium of UK insurance litigation law firms, who operate standardised case management systems, enabling the provision of on-line management information and related services for the insurance industry.

CARTWRIGHTS
SOLICITORS

INTERNATIONAL CONNECTIONS: Cartwrights has established contacts with law firms in Europe, the USA, the Far East and Australia. The firm is a member of Euro-Link for Lawyers and acts as its administration office.

LANGUAGES: French, German and Welsh.

CLIENTELE: Over 15 FTSE 100 companies including major UK leisure and brewery companies, supermarket chains and insurance companies. Other clients are local authorities, including regional airports and port authorities; construction companies; computer companies; entrepreneurs; local businesses of all sizes; loss adjusters; self-insuring plcs, and private individuals.

RECRUITMENT & TRAINING: Recruitment of professional staff is dealt with by Christopher Eskell. Applications for a training contract should be made two years in advance. A brochure and application form are available on request or visit their website.

CARTWRIGHTS ADAMS & BLACK

36 West Bute Street, Cardiff, CF10 5UA **Tel:** (029) 2046 5959 **Fax:** (029) 2048 0006 **DX:** 200751 Cardiff Bay **Ptnrs:** 5 **Asst solrs:** 5 **Other fee-earners:** 1

CAWDERY KAYE FIREMAN & TAYLOR

25-26 Hampstead High Street, London, NW3 1QA
Tel: (020) 7431 7262 **Fax:** (020) 7431 7261 **DX:** 57567 Hampstead
Email: law@ckft.com

Number of partners:	8
Assistant solicitors:	7
Total Number of staff:	34
Other fee-earners:	4

CONTACTS

Commercial Litigation ......Simon Taylor
Commercial Property ......Daniel Fireman
......Graham Kaye
Company Commercial ......Adam Blain
Employment ......Lanny Silverstone
Family/Matrimonial ......Pamela Collis
Insolvency ......Adam Taylor
Personal Injury ......Joel Leigh

THE FIRM: Cawdery Kaye Fireman & Taylor was established in January 1992 and provides a wide range of legal services for both commercial and private clients from its well located offices in the heart of Hampstead. The firm has a modern and pro-active approach to providing legal solutions for private and commercial clients including companies, financial institutions and high net worth individuals. Due to its location, the firm is able to offer its excellent service at competitive rates. State of the art computer and database facilities complement this progressive firm and its established reputation.

PRINCIPAL AREAS OF WORK: Commercial litigation; commercial property; family and matrimonial; company/commercial; private client (including conveyancing, trusts, wills and probate); personal injury; employment; and insolvency.

CEDR

Princes House, 95 Gresham Street, London, EC2V 7NA **Tel:** (020) 7600 0500 **Fax:** (020) 7600 0501

CHADBOURNE & PARKE

Regis House, 45 King William Street, London, EC4R 9AN
Tel: (020) 7337 8000 **Fax:** (020) 7337 8001

Managing Partner:	William Greason
Number of partners:	7
Assistant solicitors:	6
Other fee-earners:	4

CONTACTS

Corporate Finance .... William Greason
Litigation .... Anna McConnell
Privatisation/Energy .... Lynne Gedanken
Project Finance .... Paul Weber

CHADBOURNE & PARKE

THE FIRM: Chadbourne & Parke, is a multi-national partnership including registered foreign lawyers and solicitors. The London partnership offers a range of legal services under both English and New York law and in particular, focuses on project finance, privatisation, energy, capital markets, banking, structured finance, corporate finance, litigation and product liability. It acts as the London operation of Chadbourne & Parke LLP, a leading international firm with its main office in New York City and additional offices in Washington, Los Angeles, Moscow and Hong Kong. Founded in 1902, Chadbourne & Parke LLP has an established, integrated network of offices in important financial and political centres. The London operation, which began in 1994, is now a multi-national partnership employing both English-qualified solicitor and US lawyers and works closely with other offices to provide seamless service to its international clients. The development of London into a regional hub for the firm has continued with plans to increase the size of the London operation to meet the increasing demands of the practice.

PRINCIPAL AREAS OF WORK:

Project Finance: The project finance lawyers in London form an integral part of the global project finance practice which has over 60 lawyers who work full time on project finance and privatisation matters. Since the early 1980's, the project finance practice has been a worldwide leader in the energy sector, and now represents project developers, commercial lenders, bilateral and multilateral agencies, governments and government-owned entities, investors and offtakers in a wide variety of privatisation and infrastrcture projects in more than 47 countries. During the past two years, the group has participated in the development and/or financing of over US$30 billion in projects and in the last year alone worked on the negotiation, solicitation, financing or construction of more than 70 significant projects around the globe.

Corporate: The corporate practice represents purchasers and sellers as well as commercial and investment banks in connection with mergers, acquisitions and divestitures. It represents issuers, underwriters and selling stockholders in connection with public and private securities offerings, including offerings relying on Rule 144A and Regulation S. It also advises clients in connection with corporate and SEC compliance issues, investment funds, joint ventures, lending and structured financings.

Litigation: Whether through mediation, negotiated settlement, arbitration or trial, the litigation group delivers effective and commercial strategies for avoiding and resolving disputes. The litigation practice covers a wide range of matters including securities, product liability, intellectual property, antitrust and trade regulation, bankruptcy, lender liability, employment, environmental, insurance and reinsurance, tax, government contracts and general commercial litigation. The litigation group represents clients in disputes in the US, the UK, Ireland, Russia and elsewhere.

CLIENTELE: Clients in London include international financial institutions, multinational companies, independent power companies and governments. The London operation is currently involved with transactions in the Middle East, Africa, Europe, Latin America and Asia.

INTERNATIONAL CONNECTIONS: The firm's overseas offices are: Chadbourne & Parke LLP, 30 Rockefeller Plaza, New York, NY 10112-0127, tel: +1 212 408 5100, fax: +1 212 541 5369, contact Chaim Wachsberger; 1200 New Hampshire Avenue, NW, Washington, DC 20036, tel: +1 202 974 5600, fax: +1 202 974 5602 contact Keith Martin; 601 South Figueroa Street, Los Angeles, CA 90017-5704, tel: +1 213 892 1000, fax: +1 213 622 9865 contact Jay Henneberry; 38 Kosmodamianskaya Nabezezhnaya, Moscow, Russian Federation 113035, tel: +7 095 974 2424, fax: +7 095 974 2425 contact Laura Brank; 1701A The Hong Kong Club Building, 3-A Carter Road, Central Hong Kong, tel: +852 2842 5400, fax: +852 2521 7527, contact N. Theodore Zink.

CHAFFE STREET

Brook House, 77 Fountain Street, Manchester, M2 2EE
Tel: (0161) 236 5800 **Fax:** (0161) 228 6862 **DX:** 14431 Manchester
Email: lawyer@chaffestreet.co.uk

Senior Partner:	R.H. Street
Number of partners:	16
Assistant solicitors:	8
Other fee-earners:	7

AREAS OF PRACTICE

Company/Commercial/ Corporate Recovery 65%
Commercial Property 25%
Commercial Litigation 10%

FIRM: The firm provides a full range of specialist commercial legal services, namely company/commmercial work, commercial propery, corporate recovery and commercial orientated litigation.

PRINCIPAL AREAS OF WORK: The services available include flotations, acqusitions and disposals, mergers, management buy-outs, banking law, venture and investment capital, project and asset financing, corporate finance, insolvency, intellectual property, competition law, employment law, pensions, aircraft, commercial property and environmental law.

CHALLINORS LYON CLARK

Guardian House, Cronehills Linkway, West Bromwich, B70 8SW **Tel:** (0121) 553 3211 **Fax:** (0121) 553 2079 **DX:** 713650 West Bromwich 6
Email: jr@challinors.co.uk **Website:** www.challinors.co.uk **Ptnrs:** 20 **Asst solrs:** 25 **Other fee-earners:** 19

CHAMBERS & CO

Jonathan Scott Hall, Thorpe Road, Norwich, NR1 1UH **Tel:** (01603) 616 155 **Fax:** (01603) 616 156

CHAPMAN EVERATT

8 Temple Street, Birmingham, B2 5BT
Tel: (0121) 633 7440 **Fax:** (0121) 633 7262 **DX:** 13025 Birmingham 1
Email: richardchapman@chapmaneveratt.demon.co.uk

Senior Partner:	Richard Chapman
Number of partners:	5
Assistant solicitors:	2
Other fee-earners:	3

AREAS OF PRACTICE

Defendant Personal Injury 100%

CONTACTS

Litigation ....Richard Chapman
..........................Graeme Middleton

THE FIRM: Chapman Everatt, founded in 1992, has developed a niche insurance based practice, acting for insurance companies, loss adjusters, local authorities, claims assessors and handlers, and brokers specialising in employers' and public liability and RTA claims.

PRINCIPAL AREAS OF WORK: Include employers/public liability claims; Road Traffic Act claims; fraud and other insurance work.

C

CHARLES LUCAS & MARSHALL

28 Bartholomew St, Newbury, RG14 5EU
Tel: (01635) 521212 **Fax:** (01635) 37784 **DX:** 30802
Email: info@clmsolicitors.co.uk **Website:** www.clmsolicitors.co.uk

Senior Partner:	S.M. Burnell
Practice Manager:	R.E. Talbot FCA
Number of partners:	17
Assistant solicitors:	8
Other fee-earners:	20

CONTACTS

Agricultural ....D Thomas
Charity Law ....M Overend
Company/Commercial ....S McMinn
Litigation ....P Trincas
Property ....M Poynter
Taxation ....R Mead
Wills and Probate ....R Mead

THE FIRM: Charles Lucas & Marshall was established over 100 years ago. It is now a substantial commercial practice with offices covering a wide area throughout Central Southern England. The firm has offices in Wantage, Hungerford and Swindon.

PRINCIPAL AREAS OF WORK:
Company & Commercial: Includes general company law; advice to small businesses; finance and corporate lending; commercial agreements covering computers; franchises; product liability and intellectual property; EU law and employment law. Also trademarks and patents and the firm has a Trademark Agent.
Property: Includes commercial conveyancing; town and country planning; property development and domestic conveyancing.
Litigation: Includes civil litigation; divorce; commercial disputes; property disputes; debt collection; licensing and criminal cases.
Taxation: Includes financial planning; commercial and corporate tax; agricultural tax planning and trusts.
Agricultural: Includes sale and purchase of farms; leases; agricultural holdings; partnerships; tied cottages.
Wills & Probate: Includes preparation of wills, grants of probate and advice on Inheritance Tax.
Charity Law: Includes registration, formation, disputes. Members of the Charity Lawyers Association.

RECRUITMENT & TRAINING: Applications by letter and CV to Lance Parker.

CHARLES RUSSELL

8-10 New Fetter Lane, London, EC4A 1RS
Tel: (020) 7203 5000 **Fax:** (020) 7203 0200 **DX:** 19 London/Chancery Lane
Email: enquiry@cr-law.co.uk **Website:** www.charlesrussell.co.uk

Killowen House, Bayshill Road, Cheltenham, GL50 3AW
Tel: (01242) 221122 **Fax:** (01242) 584700 **DX:** 7442 Cheltenham 1
Email: enquiry@cr-law.co.uk

Buryfields House, Bury Fields, Guildford, GU2 4AZ
Tel: (01483) 252525 **Fax:** (01483) 252550 **DX:** 2436 Guildford 1
Email: guildford@cr-law.co.uk

36-38 Leadenhall Street, London, EC3A 1AT
Tel: (020) 7203 5000 **Fax:** (020) 7480 6640 **DX:** 19 London/Chancery Lane
Email: enquiry@cr-law.co.uk

Managing Partner:	Grant Howell
Senior Partner:	Laurie Watt
Number of partners:	76
Assistant solicitors:	79
Other fee-earners:	51

AREAS OF PRACTICE

Private Capital/Family 26%
Commercial Property 18%
Litigation (Commercial) 15%
Media & Communications 15%
Other Corporate & Commercial/Employment 12%
Charities 9%
Insurance/Reinsurance 5%

THE FIRM: Charles Russell has been building its brand for over 200 years and has achieved its present status through diligent service to succeeding generations of clients. The firm has all the positive values that its traditional private client business brings, namely: its longevity, heritage, and experience – qualities which have won it the respect of clients, staff and peers. Charles Russell has successfully combined these qualities with those required of a thriving commercial practice, namely: dynamism, innovation and modernity. The complexities of communicating these diverse elements are challenging but through the commitment and quality of its staff, the firm is getting the balance right. Charles Russell has undergone a period of considerable development and growth in recent years and staff and fee income have doubled. Over seventy percent of the firm's fee income is derived from its commercial client base. However, at a time when many firms are divesting their private client practice the firm is committed to providing legal services to both the commercial and private client market. After all, where there is commerce, there are people.

PRINCIPAL AREAS OF WORK: The firm's core markets are media and communications (telecommunications, entertainment, IT, IP and sport), insurance and reinsurance, charities, commercial property and private clients. Industry groups are supported by a number of specialist teams which include employment and employee benefits, corporate finance, tax, EU/competition, intellectual property, computer law and planning.

Commercial/Corporate: Includes stock market flotations; mergers and acquisitions; venture capital financing; banking; institutional funding arrangements; management buy-outs and buy-ins; business start-ups and corporate rescues. Advice is also given on commercial contracts of all kinds, agency and distribution agreements, partnership matters and all aspects of corporate tax.

Litigation: The litigation team deals with a full range of matters, both in the UK and overseas, with a special emphasis on commercial disputes, contentious IP, sports regulation, judicial review, pharmacy law and medical and professional negligence.

Commercial Property: Charles Russell's commercial property group advises investors, developers and occupiers. In addition to handling the acquisition/disposal of industrial, commercial and retail property, the team devises and negotiates financing agreements. It also handles landlord and tenant arrangements and all aspects of management for commercial property.

Media & Communications: The group provides an integrated service to the converging industries which include telecommunications, information technology, multimedia, film, music, entertainment and sport.

Insurance: From its specialist insurance office, the firm advises international insurance/reinsurance companies and consultants, Lloyd's syndicates, mutuals, brokers, underwriting agents and run-off managers on both contentious and non-contentious matters.

Charities: The firm has a long established, varied and expanding charities practice comprising a team of specialists who provide a full range of legal services.

Private Capital: Charles Russell is home to one of the UK's leading private client and family practices. The family team deals with issues relating to marriage, its breakdown, separation, divorce, residence, contact and child abduction, often involving legal and financial disputes in differing international jurisdictions. Furthermore, the firm advises wealthy individuals, successful entrepreneurs, professionals and institutions, both in the UK and internationally, on tax, trust, estate restructuring, probate, including contentious probate, trust administration, agriculture and property transactions and management. Literature and briefing notes are available on request.

CONTACTS

Charities	Michael Scott
Commercial Property	Amanda Crowe
Computer Law	David Berry
Corporate & Commercial	James Holder
Employment	David Green
Family	David Davidson
Insurance/Reinsurance	Stephen Carter
Intellectual Property	Robin Bynoe
Litigation	Richard Vallance
Media & Communications	Mark Moncreiffe
Pensions & Employee Benefits	George Duncan
Planning	Geoffrey Jordan
Private Capital	W. Paul Harriman
Private Property	Hugh Jackson
Sport	Patrick Russell
Tax	George Duncan

Charles Russell
SOLICITORS

C

CHARSLEY HARRISON

Madeira House, Madeira Walk, Windsor, SL4 1EU
Tel: (01753) 851591 **Fax:** (01753) 832550 **DX:** 3800 Windsor
Email: mail@charsleyharrison.com **Website:** www.charsleyharrison.co.uk

THE FIRM: Formed by the merger in 1973 of two long established and well respected Thames Valley practices, Charsley Harrison is a modern, forward-thinking firm geared to meet the needs of both commercial and private clients. The practice has developed rapidly in recent years to represent a wide range of business clients throughout the UK, the EC, the USA and the Pacific Basin and has established links with commercial lawyers in the major cities of the USA, Australia and throughout Europe. Two offices of the practice have recently joined forces in Windsor which will enable a high degree of partner involvement in the day-to-day matters of clients, together with a prompt, efficient and professional service. Other offices are located in Ascot and Slough.

PRINCIPAL AREAS OF WORK:

Company /Commercial: A comprehensive service both domestically and internationally encompassing corporate finance; competition; acquisitions and disposals; mergers; MBOs and joint ventures; distribution and agency agreements; intellectual property rights; taxation; insolvency and employment law matters.

Litigation: All aspects of litigation for both corporate and private clients in the UK and abroad before a wide range of courts and tribunals. Work includes general contractual and commercial disputes; misrepresentation; employment matters; insolvency and banking-related litigation; personal injury; professional negligence and defamation.

Property: Extensive experience of property transactions including purchase; sale; leasing and mortgaging of commercial and retail property; estate development; planning and environmental advice; licensing; site assembly; joint ventures and agricultural property.

Continued overleaf

Notaries Public:	Phillip Jones (01753) 851591 Giles Shedden (01753) 851591 Peter Beech (01753) 517 600
Number of partners:	5
Assistant solicitors:	5
Other fee-earners:	6

AREAS OF PRACTICE

Property	40%
Company/Commercial	35%
Litigation/Family Law	20%
Probate/Trust	5%

CONTACTS

Company/Commercial/Property	Phillip Jones
Litigation/Family Law	Kate McCulloch
Probate/Trust	Giles Shedden

Private Client: The firm has a long tradition in providing a friendly and efficient service to individuals in all aspects of their private legal affairs. Work includes wills; tax and estate planning; personal and family finance; investment management; pensions; saving schemes and school fees planning; charity law and Court of Protection work. A full service is also provided in relation to matrimonial and family law including childcare and adoption.

INTERNATIONAL CONNECTIONS: The firm works with an associate firm in the Netherlands.

CHATTERTONS
28 Wide Bargate, Boston, PE21 6RT **Tel:** (01205) 351114 **Fax:** (01205) 356018 **DX:** 26803 **Email:** e-mail@chattertons.demon.co.uk
Website: www.chattertons.co.uk **Ptnrs:** 10 **Asst solrs:** 13 **Other fee-earners:** 16

CHRISTIAN FISHER

42 Museum Street, Bloomsbury, London, WC1A 1LY
Tel: (020) 7831 1750 **Fax:** (020) 7831 1726 **DX:** 35737 Bloomsbury
Email: info@christianf.co.uk **Website:** www.christianf.co.uk

Number of partners:	3
Assistant solicitors:	13
Other fee-earners:	9

Christian Fisher
Solicitors
(Incorporating Inyama & Co Solicitors)

THE FIRM: Christian Fisher was set up in 1985 and specialises in civil liberties and human rights work. The firm has a long standing reputation for undertaking high profile test cases in these areas and a commitment to delivering high quality legal aid work. It has a franchises in personal injury, crime, housing, employment and immigration, cases against the police, mental health, clinical negligence, education, community care and public law.

PRINCIPAL AREAS OF WORK:
Human Rights Cases: The firm expects to bring many test cases on the new Human Rights Act. Past cases have included the lead Court of Appeal case on damages against the police (Hsu). Cases on suing the police for negligence (Osman in the ECHR and Reeves in the House of Lords), racial attacks and murders (Ricky Reel), deaths in custody (Wayne Douglas) many judicial reviews of government and miscarriage of justice cases.
Personal Injury: The firm has a particular profile in the areas of construction, environmental and transport safety and a substantial case load in these areas. It has acted in the Lockerbie and Marchioness disasters and is the lead firm in the Steering Committees representing the victims of the Paddington and Southall train crashes.
Medical Negligence: Wrongful birth and obstetric cases; accident and emergency cases; GMC prosecutions.
Crime: Major criminal trials including fraud, political crime and miscarriages of justice.
Employment: Particularly race and sex discrimination and trades union cases.
Housing: For tenants – disrepair and homelessness
Immigration: A track record in acting for asylum seekers.
Public Law: Inquests and judicial reviews.

C & J BLACK
Linenhall House, 13 Linenhall Street, Belfast, BT2 8AA **Tel:** (028) 90550060 **Fax:** (028) 90234125 **DX:** 431 NR Belfast 1 **Ptnrs:** 3 **Asst solrs:** 1
Other fee-earners: 1

CLAIRMONTS
9 Clairmont Gardens, Glasgow, G3 7LW **Tel:** (0141) 331 4000 **Fax:** (0141) 221 0123 **DX:** 512212 Glasgow **Email:** info@clairmonts.co.uk

CLAREMONT SMITH

125 High Holborn, London, WC1V 6QF
Tel: (020) 7405 8811 **Fax:** (020) 7831 0973 **DX:** 372 London Chancery Lane
Email: rds@claremontsmith.demon.co.uk

Managing Partner:	Howard Richards
Senior Partner:	Roger D. Smith
Number of partners:	10
Assistant solicitors:	3

THE FIRM: The origins of Claremont Smith can be traced back in Central London to February 1814. It is best known for its work in the fields of pensions and commercial property acting as it does in relation to all legal affairs of one of the UK's larger pension funds.

PRINCIPAL AREAS OF WORK: Pensions; commercial property; telecommunications law; European and competition law; commercial litigation; trade associations; employment law.

CLARICOAT PHILLIPS
140 Barnsbury Road, London, N1 0ER **Tel:** (020) 7226 7000 **Fax:** (020) 7833 4408 **Email:** Philcoat@aol.com **Ptnrs:** 2

CLARKE WILLMOTT & CLARKE

St James Court, St James Parade, Bristol BS1 3LH
Tel: (0117) 941 6600 **Fax:** (0117) 941 6622 **DX:** 78247 Bristol 1
Website: www.cw-c.co.uk

Blackbrook Gate, Blackbrook Park Avenue, Taunton, Blackbrook, TA1 2PG
Tel: (01823) 442266 **Fax:** (01823) 443300 **DX:** 97175 Taunton Blackbrook

6 Hammet Street, Taunton, TA1 1RG
Tel: (01823) 329800 **Fax:** (01823) 259643 **DX:** 32100 Taunton

Executive Chairman:	
Number of partners:	40
Assistant solicitors:	51
Directors:	4
Other fee-earners:	94

AREAS OF PRACTICE

Litigation Services	32%
Property & Planning Services	31%
Private Client Services	19%
Commercial Services	18%

CONTACTS

Agriculture & Estates	Tim Russ
Asset Management	Peter Nellist
Banking & Lender Services - Non-contentious	David Emanuel
Banking & Lender Services - Contentious	Robert Morfee
Clinical Negligence	Andrew Hannam
Commercial Litigation	Chris Taylor (Blackbrook)
Commercial Property	Roger Seaton (Blackbrook)
Corporate	David Emanuel (Bristol)
Employment	Kevin Jones
Environmental	Tim Hayden
Family	Felicity Shakespear
Heath & Safety	Martin Pettingell
Insolvency and Debt Collection	Stephen Allinson LIP
IT/IP	Matthew Bernstein
Licensing	Tim Hayden
Local Authority Claims Unit	David Sedgwick
Mediation/ADR/CEDR	David Sedgwick
Personal Injury	Peter Livingstone
PFI	Stephen Rosser
Planning	Nick Engert
Private Client	Stuart Thorne (Taunton)
Probate & Trusts	Peter Nellist
Professional Indemnity	Tim Russ
Sports Law	David Powell
Volume (residential) Conveyancing	Angela Thompson

THE FIRM: Clarke Willmott & Clarke is one of the leading regional South West firms, with a reputation and client base that extends far outside the region. The firm's reputation has been built on the strengths of both their litigation and property teams, but with complementary skills in commercial services and private client work. Increasingly, clients require skills taken from several discipline areas and this has led to the growing importance of the firm's market sector teams, which include agriculture and food services, lender services, land developers, and legal expenses insurers (personal injury). CW&C's client research shows that they are consistently regarded for their practical, results-oriented, commercial solutions with an emphasis on cost-effective delivery. In recognition of this, CW&C has been awarded the Law Society's Lexcel accreditation. The firm is equally recognised for its ability to grow and maintain long-term client relationships using multi-disciplinary teams. Technology plays an increasingly vital role in maintaining internal communications, reducing client costs, providing management data and enhancing client relationships. The firm recently took the bold and innovative decision to outsource its entire IT function which has greatly enhanced the role and prominence of IT within the firm.

PRINCIPAL AREAS OF WORK:

Litigation: This remains a key part of the practice and CW&C is particularly regarded for its work in the areas of professional negligence, claimant personal injury, clinical negligence, corporate recovery and insolvency, employment disputes, landlord and tenant, international contract disputes and specialist prosecution services, such as health and safety, environmental pollution offences, food safety, and fraud. Through the merger with Alsters, the firm now has a nationally regarded sports law practice, which handles both contentious and non-contentious work in this sector.

Property: The property team continues to develop its three key areas of expertise: land development, planning and environmental, and commercial property. Strategic lateral hires in the last 12 months have grown their client base in all three areas, but particularly in land development and planning and environmental work. The firm is now able to offer land developers a full range of services including strategic land advice, land acquisition and plot sales. CW&C work on behalf of an expanding list of land developers throughout the South and Midlands. The firm's planning and environmental team has unrivalled expertise regionally and is particularly recognised for its advice regarding town and country planning, 'brown land' issues, Section 106 agreements and public enquiry representation. The environmental team offers a full range of contentious and non-contentious advice, particularly in the areas of contaminated land, minerals and waste disposal. The commercial property team specialises in secured lending, licensed premises, project management of complex sites and commercial developments, including PFI contracts.

Commercial/Corporate: The commercial/corporate team continue to support these teams by providing transactional advice on take-overs, MBOs, MBIs, joint ventures, share holder agreements, management restructures, acquisitions and sales, intellectual property and competition law.

Private Client: Private client and asset management also play a key role in complementing the two main practice strengths and is recognised as the South West's leading private client team. Their asset management expertise was acknowledged this year when the head of the asset management team was named Investment Planner of the Year 1999 by 'Money Management' magazine. Private client services include personal tax planning, asset management, wills, trusts and probate, and family and matrimonial.

Other: Market sector teams are growing in importance with the biggest growth this year in the areas of agriculture and food services and lender services. The firm provides a comprehensive range of contentious and non-contentious services to lenders, including a volume conveyancing service.

RECRUITMENT & TRAINING: Training and personal development continue to be given high prominence and the firm has been awarded the 'Investor in People' accreditation in recognition of this. The firm has a commitment to fast-tracking talented individuals.

CLARK HOLT

1 Sanford Street, Swindon, SN1 1HJ **Tel:** (01793) 617444 **Fax:** (01793) 617436 **DX:** 38606 Swindon (2) **Email:** richardc@clarkholt.co.uk **Website:** www.clarkholt.co.uk **Ptnrs:** 4 **Asst solrs:** 3 **Other fee-earners:** 1 **Contact:** Richard Clark • Specialises exclusively in commercial law in the area of corporate, commercial and computer law, and commercial property.

AREAS OF PRACTICE

Corporate	40%
Commercial Property	36%
Commmercial/Computer	24%

CLARK RICKETTS

Kingsway House, 103 Kingsway, London, WC2B 6QX **Tel:** (020) 7404 1551 **Fax:** (020) 7404 2662 **Email:** aviationlaw@clarkricketts.com

Ptnrs: 2 **Asst solrs:** 1 **Other fee-earners:** 1

CLARKS

Great Western House, Station Rd, Reading, RG1 1SX
Tel: (0118) 958 5321 **Fax:** (0118) 960 4611 **DX:** 54700 Reading 2
Email: inmail@clarks-solicitors.co.uk **Website:** www.clarks-solicitors.co.uk

Managing Partner:	Michael Sippitt
Number of partners:	16
Assistant solicitors:	33
Other fee-earners:	19

CONTACTS

Advertising	Jane Gunnell
Banking & Finance	David Few
Commercial/European	Peter James
Commercial Property	Tom Howell
Company/Corporate Finance	Richard Lee
Construction	David Rintoul
Corporate Recovery	David Few
Dispute Resolution/Litigation	Antony Morris
Employment Services	Helen Beech
Environment	Derek Ching
Health & Medical Services	Tom Howell
Information Technology	Peter James
Intellectual Property	Peter James
Pensions	David Clark
Planning	Simon Dimmick
Public Sector	Simon Dimmick
Residential Property	Mary Robertson
Wills/Trusts/Tax Planning	Peter Clark

THE FIRM: Clarks is a commercial law firm with a proven track record across the UK and overseas. Its clients range from small and medium sized enterprises to multi-nationals. Clarks is particularly recognised for the number of international and FTSE 250 clients who have chosen to use the firm. Clarks is committed to a strategy based on forging proactive relationships. Clarks' lawyers are supported by the latest technologies and the best of in-house resources. This provides maximum opportunity for efficiency and innovation. The end result is that whatever clients' legal needs, a specialist team at Clarks can be depended upon to work in partnership with the client to meet its objectives. Clarks is determined to stay one step ahead in the evolving market place by listening carefully to its clients and responding quickly to their needs. In over 85 years Clarks has built the practice its clients want. Clarks' lawyers take pride in providing high standards of skill and service. They share a common objective which is to provide clear and constructive commercial advice. The firm enjoys a straightforward business relationship with its clients and offers a variety of approaches to pricing. Clarks creates training programmes geared to individual clients and industry sectors. These are specifically designed to equip managers to identify and avoid potential legal problems. Clarks is part of TAGLaw, an international network of law firms providing clients with professional services in numerous locations around the world. It operates on the principles of transparency of business terms, close client relationships, consistent quality and the provision of timely and cost-effective service.

PRINCIPAL OF WORK:
Corporate: Clarks has a long established and highly regarded corporate practice. It manages substantial and specialist transactions. It has a growing reputation for its work in finance related fields, particularly consumer finance and advertising and insolvency. This combines with general commercial work to offer a highly resourced general corporate/commercial service.
Commercial Property: A large commercial property team acts for owners, developers, investors and funders, providing a comprehensive service. A highly skilled planning and development consultancy handles planning applications and appeals. COMBAT (Clarks owner managed business advisory team) is a new service launched recently which combines cross-departmental skills to offer a tailored team to meet the particular needs of owner managed businesses.
Employment: The employment services unit is one of the fastest growing areas and enjoys an enviable national reputation. It also carries out extensive training and is particularly proactive in developing new employment related services including workshops, in-house seminars and human resources support.
IT & IP: The firm's growing IT and Intellectual Property unit handles a varied portfolio of contentious and non-contentious work. Services include copyright, E-commerce, internet domain name issues, trademark, passing off, patents, licensing & infringement issues, computer system supply and software licence terms and IT outsourcing.
Private Client: The firm also has busy private client and residential conveyancing teams, offering private client services to corporate quality standards.
Other Areas of Work: Clarks remains the principal regional commercial litigation practice offering specialist expertise, including hands-on experience of successful ADR and a highly successful debt recovery service. The construction law service handles both contentious and non-contentious work.

CLIENTELE: Clients include listed companies, public sector bodies and not-for-profit organisations especially health, education and local government. Clarks assigns a partner to each client providing a consistent personal point of contact. The firm actively encourage the development of relationships with other specialists from different disciplines, providing clients with a known and trusted team of lawyers to help with more complex projects.The firm strongly believes in working in partnership with clients and has developed Case Plans and Client Protocols to facilitate this. Case Plans provide a client with a project snapshot detailing timings, key events and estimated costs. Client Protocols clearly define the basis of an ongoing relationship and the manner in which services are provided. Clarks' lawyers also devise and deliver highly successful client training workshops, enhancing management performance through greater knowledge of the relevant law and procedures.

RECRUITMENT & TRAINING: The firm continues to seek individuals who can contribute to its success. Current growth provides opportunities for qualified solicitors across a range of specialisms.

Clarks
Solicitors

CLARKSON WRIGHT & JAKES

Valiant House, 12 Knoll Rise, Orpington, BR6 0PG
Tel: (01689) 887887 **Fax:** (01689) 887888 **DX:** 31603 Orpington
Email: cwj@cwj.co.uk **Website:** www.cwj.co.uk

Managing Partner:	Andrew C. Wright
Senior Partner:	Leslie Seldon
Number of partners:	10
Assistant solicitors:	4
Other fee-earners:	18

AREAS OF PRACTICE

Private Client	25%
Personal Injury Litigation	20%
Commercial Litigation	15%
Commercial Property	15%
Company/Commercial (including Notarial)	15%
Employment	10%

CONTACTS

Commercial	Michael North
Commercial Litigation	Leslie Seldon
Personal Injury	David Greenhalgh
Private Client	Peter Giblin
	Amanda Custis

THE FIRM: Established in 1875, Clarkson Wright & Jakes is a substantial commercial practice whose aim is to offer a personal service tailored to clients' specific needs. The firm, a member of LawNet, undertakes a wide range of legal work, and offers notarial services and the expertise of units specialising in employment, partnership and doctors' matters. The firm advises French commercial clients and UK clients with interests in France. It has been recognized as an Investor in People and has achieved ISO 9002 accreditation.

PRINCIPAL AREAS OF WORK:

Company & Commercial: Company and business acquisitions and sales; MBOs and MBIs; franchise; agency; distribution and other commercial agreements; conditions of sale; terms of business; partnership especially for doctors; business start-ups.

Employment: Contracts of employment and other employment documentation; claims in the Industrial Tribunals and civil courts for dismissal, discrimination and breach of contract.

Commercial Property: Acquisition; mortgage and disposal of freehold and leasehold shops; factories and other properties; landlord and tenant matters (including lease renewals and surrenders).

Commercial Litigation: Company; commercial and partnership disputes; construction disputes; arbitration; landlord and tenant matters; defamation; professional negligence; passing off actions and contractual disputes; licensing; debt collection; and mortgage repossessions.

Personal Injury Litigation: Motor; employers' and public liability claims; industrial disease and professional indemnity claims; and medical negligence.

Private Client: Residential property; wills and trusts; tax planning; enduring powers of attorney; winding-up of estates and executorships; Court of Protection; and matrimonial.

LANGUAGES: French, German and Spanish.

C

CLAUDE HORNBY & COX

35-36 Great Marlborough Street, London, W1V 2JA
Tel: (020) 7437 8873 **Fax:** (020) 7494 3070 **DX:** 37211 Piccadilly
Email: law@claudehornbycox.fsnet.co.uk

Senior Partner:	Richard Hallam
Number of partners:	2
Assistant solicitors:	6
Other fee-earners:	5

CONTACTS

Civil Litigation/ Conveyancing	Mohammed Mir
Criminal Litigation/ Disciplinary Proceedings	Richard Hallam
	Michael Butler
	Christopher Green

THE FIRM: A leading specialist criminal practice for over 70 years, providing all its clients, whether privately-paying or legally-aided, with high quality but reasonably priced advice and representation on any criminal matter.

PRINCIPAL AREAS OF WORK:

Crime: The firm defends clients in cases ranging from murder, terrorism, firearms and drug-related offences, and corporate fraud on a multi-million pound scale, to driving offences and shoplifting. The fraud work includes acting in major SFO, HM Customs and Excise, and Inland Revenue Investigations. The practice also prosecutes for individuals and corporate clients. The partners regularly represent defendants in Court Martial cases tried in the UK and abroad.

Other Areas: General civil litigation, personal injury, and both commercial and residential conveyancing. The firm provides representation before Professional Disciplinary Tribunals.

RECRUITMENT & TRAINING: Two trainee solicitors are recruited each year. Applications to the training partner, Michael Butler.

CLAYTONS

PO Box 38, 22 Rothesay Rd, Luton, LU1 1PT **Tel:** (01582) 724501 **Fax:** (01582) 405815 **DX:** 5909 Luton **Ptnrs:** 4 **Asst solrs:** 4
Other fee-earners: 5

CLEARY, GOTTLIEB, STEEN & HAMILTON

City Place House, 55 Basinghall Street, London, EC2V 5EH
Tel: (020) 7614 2200 **Fax:** (020) 7600 1698
Website: www.cleary.com

Number of Partners:	9
Assistant solicitors:	31
Other fee-earners:	12

AREAS OF PRACTICE

Corporate	100%

THE FIRM: A leading US and international law firm with offices in New York, Washington DC, Paris, Brussels, London, Frankfurt, Rome, Tokyo and Hong Kong. The firm is well known for its expertise in finance, mergers and aquisitions, and for its tax, regulatory and litigation practice. The London office advises on all areas of international financial transactions, practising both English and US law.

CLEAVER FULTON RANKIN

50 Bedford Street, Belfast, BT2 7FW
Tel: (028) 9024 3141 **Fax:** (028) 9024 9096 **DX:** 421 NR Belfast
Email: cfr@cfrlaw.co.uk **Website:** www.cfrlawonline.com

Contact Partner:	Neil C Faris
Number of partners:	10
Assistant solicitors:	16
Other fee-earners:	14

AREAS OF PRACTICE

Commercial Property	25%
Company/Commercial	25%
Litigation	25%
Private Client	15%
Employment	10%

CONTACTS

Commercial Property	James Houston
	Kathryn Collie
Company/Commercial	Jennifer Ebbage
	Stephen Cross
Consultancy	Neil C. Faris
	Karen L. Blair
Employment	Rosalie Prytherch
	Alyn Hicks
Litigation	Brendan Fox
	William Cross
Private Client	Joy Scott
	Alastair Rankin

THE FIRM: Cleaver Fulton Rankin's aim is world class law in Northern Ireland: in particular to provide clients with a thorough understanding of the legal context of their matters and to offer them sound and practical legal advice and assistance. They specialise in working with lawyers from other jurisdictions.

PRINCIPAL AREAS OF WORK:

Commercial Property: All aspects of acquisition, development and investment. The practice's property lawyers assist clients in all aspects of business start-ups, development agreements and in lease negotiations, renewal and rent review. The practice also specialises in advisory and litigation services relating to property.

Company Commercial: The firm provides a comprehensive service which includes: mergers and acquisitions; management buy-outs; joint ventures; corporate finance; banking; securities; commercial contracts and business start-ups. The company and commercial lawyers aim to provide a speedy and effective service and specialise particularly in working with lawyers from other jurisdictions.

Litigation: The department aims to provide clients and lawyers from other jurisdictions with an experienced and able assistance in litigation matters including the specialist areas of: commercial litigation; employment law; defamation; product liability; licensing; intellectual property; and construction law.

Private Client: An extensive service to private clients entails giving advice on a variety of legal matters and maintaining close working relationships with other professionals including accountants, stockbrokers and estate agents. Some aspects of matrimonial law and children's law are also covered.

Consultancy: The firm has established a team to service the specialised needs of clients in legal consultancy and legal advisory work in Northern Ireland, including public law and judicial review. Training seminars are organised for clients and their employees on the impact of new legislation.

Employment & Labour: The firm handles all aspects of employment, including tribunals, TUPE and Northern Ireland's special discrimination legislation.

Agency Work: The firm specialises in providing agency services to lawyers in other jurisdictions. Contact the partner or associate in the relevant area.

Pro Bono Work: The firm is a member of the Environmental Law Foundation and the Professional Firms Group of Business in the Community (NI).

RECRUITMENT & TRAINING: The firm currently take four trainee solicitors per year. Applications to commence in September of each year should be made, in writing, early in the year, to Patrick Cross.

CLIFFORD CHANCE

200 Aldersgate Street, London, EC1A 4JJ
Tel: (020) 7600 1000 **Fax:** (020) 7600 5555 **DX:** 606 London
Email: info@cliffordchance.com **Website:** www.cliffordchance.com

Managing Partner:	Peter Charlton
Chairman:	Keith Clark
UK:	
Number of partners:	197
Assistant solicitors:	727
Other fee-earners:	242
Total staff:	1,166
International:	
Number of partners:	587
Assistant solicitors:	1913
Other fee-earners:	240
Total staff:	2740

THE FIRM: The tripartite merger between Clifford Chance, Rogers & Wells and Pünder, Volhard, Weber & Axster created the first integrated law firm to cover the world's major financial centres. The new firm is in a unique position to deliver fully integrated advice to multi-national clients, assembling multi-disciplinary and multi-jurisdictional teams from a global pool of over 2700 legal advisors. Fee earners advise on both common and civil law providing high quality advice delivered quickly and seamlessly. The firm advises many of the world's leading financial institutions and corporations, as well as governments and multilateral agencies. Integrated services are provided to clients in many different industries, combining lawyers' specialist skills with multiple language, commercial and legal abilities.

PRINCIPAL AREAS OF WORK: The firm provides a comprehensive range of legal services in the areas of finance, capital markets, corporate, litigation and dispute resolution, real estate, taxation, pensions and employment.

Finance: The firm has the world's largest international finance practice with over 185 partners and some 700 fee earners located in major financial and commercial centres worldwide. The practice provides advice across the full spectrum of financial products including banking, asset finance, derivative products, project finance, securitisation and structured finance. It is the first firm to bring together lawyers in Europe, the United States and Asia to advise on national and international regulatory issues and the relationship between regulatory systems.

Capital Markets: This practice is founded on a full-service US and UK securities law capability - the law of choice for the majority of international transactions - complemented by local securities law expertise in each of the key financial centres. The firm acts on the whole range of securities offerings whether public or private where the proceeds may be used to finance mergers or acquisitions or for general capital. Its clients include issuers, guarantors, arrangers, managers, investors, trustees and regulatory bodies such as banks and financial institutions, specialised lenders, corporate originators, security and share trustees, rating agencies, monoline insurers and swap counterparties.

Corporate: The corporate practice handles some of the world's largest and most complex M&A transactions. Apart from mainstream M&A work, the firm also encompasses leading specialist practices in private equity; funds; financial institutions; insurance; media, computers and telecommunications; financial services; commercial contracts and competition and antitrust. The firm focuses on providing practical, commercial legal advice and its clients include investment banks and financial institutions, multi-nationals and other public and private corporations, private equity providers and management teams, asset management clients, international partnerships and governments.

Litigation and Dispute Resolution: The firm has a team of more than 550 litigators internationally, the world's largest and most comprehensive practice of its kind. Lawyers work with clients to resolve disputes efficiently and effectively - whether through arbitration, litigation or other techniques, in a manner that promotes their business objectives. They also work with clients to develop compliance programs and other techniques to minimise future litigation risks. The firm is representing clients in some of the largest and most significant current actions, particularly in the areas of antitrust and competition law, white collar and regulatory, intellectual property, insurance and banking and securities.

Real Estate: The international real estate practice is at the forefront of the increasingly sophisticated and fast changing real estate market, providing innovative, commercial advice to the full range of market participants. The firm has a wide client base including banks, property companies, hoteliers, institutions, local and public authorities and REITs as well as open and closed real estate funds. The group advises them in their roles as investors, developers, landowners, occupiers, borrowers, funders or lenders.

Tax: The firm has the largest international tax group of any single law firm internationally, providing advice on international and domestic taxation and covering a wide range of financing, investment, corporate and commercial issues, together with advice on tax litigation, disputes and transfer pricing.

Pensions: The firm advises companies and pensions on an ongoing basis as well as on specific transactions, including all aspects of the establishment, merging and winding-up of pension schemes (both tax approved and unapproved); pensions aspects of corporate takeovers, mergers, MBOs and flotations; pensions litigation, and advice to pension providers and fund managers covering the design and implementation of pension products.

Employment: The employment practice advises clients on all key employment issues from appointment and severance of senior executives to immigration, health and safety, discrimination, equal opportunities, outsourcing of services, aspects of executive and employee share schemes and other employee benefits, including international employee incentive programmes.

INTERNATIONAL CONNECTIONS:

Europe: Amsterdam, Barcelona, Berlin, Brussels, Budapest, Düsseldorf, Frankfurt, Leipzig, London, Luxembourg, Madrid, Milan, Moscow, Munich, Padua, Paris, Prague, Rome, Warsaw.
North America: New York, Washington D.C.
South America: São Paulo.
Asia: Bangkok, Beijing, Hong Kong, Singapore, Shanghai, Tokyo.
Middle East: Dubai.

LANGUAGES: All known business and commercial languages.

RECRUITMENT & TRAINING: The firm is aiming to recruit up to 130 trainee lawyers to join the firm in September 2002/March 2003. Clifford Chance believes its trainees are the future of the firm and works hard to provide first class training for them. Trainees may come from law or other disciplines. The firm looks for individuals who will be excellent technical lawyers but who are also effective and persuasive communicators, able to put advice in a commercial context whom clients will seek out for their legal and all-round abilities. The firm keeps in touch while they are studying and helps them find places on CPE/LPC courses as well as paying their fees and maintenance. In particular, the firm wants the LPC to be a stimulating and relevant course, balancing legal and practical training. This is why Clifford Chance (with a consortium of other city firms) are working with Nottingham, Oxford and BPP law schools to create a City LPC designed to extend trainees training, not limit it. When trainees begin their training contract, they are given an introduction to the firm and each practice area runs a focused induction course for the trainees at the start of each "seat" as they rotate around the firm. Clifford Chance aims to give the trainees a mix of experience, both general and specialist, so as to maximise the chances of each trainee finding a qualification "home" which fits his or her skills and aptitude. Many trainees want to spend time internationally - approximately 75 % do so. Clifford Chance also offers excellent career opportunities for lawyers joining post-qualification. Just as for trainees, the firm looks for a blend of top quality legal skills and an astute commerciality in its qualified hires. If you are interested in joining as a qualified lawyer, the extent of the technical knowledge you will bring will depend on your degree of seniority and specialisation. At the more junior level there may be scope for you to cross over between commercial disciplines or retarget your skills within one of the broad product groups. The firm provides industry-leading training and development programmes and opportunities to support lawyers at all stages in their careers. The firm helps lawyers develop their legal knowledge and business skills through both formal training programmes and on-the-job experience. Recruitment enquiries for trainee positions can be addressed to Anna Mortimer at anna.mortimer@cliffordchance.com and enquiries for qualified lawyers can be addressed to Miles Pulver at careers@cliffordchance.com

CONTACTS

Asset Finance	Geoffrey White
Banking	Mark Campbell
	Stuart Popham
Collective Investments	James Barlow
	Tim Herrington
	Stephen Ross
Commercial	Michael Howell
Commercial Litigation	John Potts
Commodities	Ed Patton
	Tim Plews
Company	Peter Charlton
	David Childs
	Graham Smith
Construction & Engineering	John Beechey
	Tim Steadman
Corporate Finance	David Childs
Corporate Immigration	Chris Goodwill
Derivatives	Habib Motani
	Tim Plews
Employee Benefits	Robin Tremaine
	Kevin Thompson
Employment	Chris Osman
Energy & Natural Resources	Tony Bankes-Jones
Environment	Robin Griffith
	Brian Hall
EU & Competition	Chris Bright
Financial Services	Chris Bates
	Tim Herrington
Hotels	Andrew Carnegie
Housing Association Finance	Robert Smith
	Despina Pantelia
Insolvency	Mark Hyde
	David Steinberg
Insurance & Reinsurance	Katherine Coates
Intellectual Property	David Perkins
International Capital Markets	David Dunnigan
	Robert MacVicar
	John Connolly
International Financial Markets	Tim Plews
Marketing and Advertising	Richard Thomas
MBOs	James Baird
Media, Computer & Communications	Elizabeth Hiester
	Christopher Millard
	Tim Schwarz
Pensions	Helen Cox
Pharmaceuticals	David Perkins
Planning	Brian Hall
Project Finance	Peter Blake
Property	Robert MacGregor
	Tony Briam
	Cliff McAuley
Property Litigation	John Pickston
Public Policy	Richard Thomas
Public Sector	Richard Thomas
Retail	Michael Edwards
Securitisation	Kevin Ingram
	Chris Oakley
	John Woodhall
Shipping	Tony Vlasto
	Mark Morrison
Sovereign Debt Rescheduling	Cliff Godfrey
	Andrew Yianni
Tax	Douglas French
Telecommunications	Elizabeth Hiester
	Tim Schwarz
VAT	Etienne Wong

C L I F F O R D
C H A N C E

CLINTONS

55 Drury Lane, London, WC2B 5SQ
Tel: (020) 7379 6080 **Fax:** (020) 7240 9310 **DX:** 40021 Covent Gdn. 1
Email: info@clintons.co.uk **Website:** www.clintons.co.uk

Senior Partner:	John Cohen
Number of partners:	17
Assistant solicitors:	10
Other fee-earners:	12

THE FIRM: Clintons is widely recognised as one of the foremost firms in the world of media and entertainment. The firm also has an extensive general commercial practice and has acknowledged strengths in intellectual property, new media, family and property.

PRINCIPAL AREAS OF WORK:
Media & Entertainment: The firm acts for a wide range of clients, from high profile individuals to major corporations. Specialist advice is provided in the businesses of music, theatre, television, e-commerce, advertising and marketing, merchandising and sport, film and publishing and generally in the protection and exploitation of intellectual property rights.
Litigation: Clintons is recognised for the strength of its practice in this area and for its ability to deal with heavyweight and high profile litigation. The firm advises on a wide range of contentious work in its core practice areas, as well as in banking, employment and personal injury.
Corporate & Commercial: The firm provides advice in all aspects of the commercial world including new ventures, corporate restructuring, e-ventures, international taxation, employment, liquidation and receivership.
Family: Clintons has a significant and highly regarded practice in family law and divorce, offering advice in all aspects, often for clients in the public eye. The family team is noted for its expertise in the detailed financial arrangements surrounding marriage breakdown and in advising on complex issues concerning children.
Property: Clintons handles all types of property transaction, from commercial developments to residential conveyancing. The firm has special expertise in secured lending and includes banking and other lending institutions as its clients.
Private Client: Clintons advises on all aspects of arrangements for private individuals, including offshore settlements, tax, wills, probate, trusts and matrimonial finance. The work undertaken includes advice relating to the links between the business and personal assets of private individuals. The firm works closely with other professional advisers in the establishment of tax-efficient and practical arrangements for the benefit of its clients.

INTERNATIONAL CONNECTIONS: Clintons has considerable overseas connections, particularly in the USA, continental Europe, Ireland, Israel, the Channel Islands, Cayman and the Bahamas.

CONTACTS

Advertising & Marketing	Philip Stinson
Corporate/Commercial & Employment	John Seigal
E-commerce	James Jones
Family	Maggie Rae
	Tim Bienias
	Elizabeth Vernon
Film & Television	David Landsman
Litigation	David Davis
	Tim Bienias
	Jacqueline Brown
	Andrew Sharland
Music	David Landsman
	Peter Button
	Andrew Myers
Property	Lawrence Middleweek
	Michael Goldman
Publishing	Sally Hamwee
Sport	Philip Stinson
	Jacqueline Brown
Tax/Trusts & Private Client	Sally Hamwee
Theatre	John Cohen

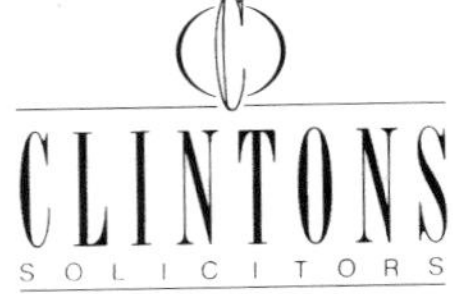

CLYDE & CO

51 Eastcheap, London, EC3M 1JP
Tel: (020) 7623 1244 **Fax:** (020) 7623 5427 **DX:** 1071
Email: joan.radley@clyde.co.uk **Website:** www.clydeco.com

Senior Partner:	Michael Payton
Practice Partner:	John Whittaker
UK:	
Number of partners:	78
Assistant solicitors:	112
Other fee earners:	79
International:	
Number of partners:	19
Assistant solicitors:	22
Other fee earners:	30
Associate Office:	
Number of partners:	1

THE FIRM: Clyde & Co is a major international commercial law firm with an outstanding reputation in insurance and reinsurance work in both the contentious and corporate fields. It continues to be a dominant force in the shipping, transport, trade and energy sectors. The firm has over 270 lawyers, who are qualified in 17 jurisdictions. Clients are served by offices in Europe (London, Guildford, Cardiff, Paris, St Petersburg and Piraeus), Asia (Hong Kong and Singapore), the Gulf (Dubai) and South America (Caracas). The firm's litigation practice is one of the largest in the United Kingdom.

PRINCIPAL AREAS OF WORK:
Insurance/Reinsurance:
Contentious: The firm advises on disputes in a wide range of areas including aviation; general liability; insolvency and recovery; marine and energy; medical negligence; personal injury; political and credit risks; professional indemnity; property and construction.
Non-Contentious: Clyde & Co was one of the first City firms to establish a distinct corporate insurance group. The group specialises in insurance-related corporate transactions and regulatory matters of all kinds including: mergers and acquisitions and alternative risk transfer projects in the life and non-life sectors; the establishment of insurance and reinsurance companies; captives (including Lloyd's captive syndicates) and Lloyd's underwriting vehicles; Lloyd's capacity offers; and the provision of all kinds of insurance regulatory advice.
Marine & Transport: The firm's practice in the shipping and transport sector continues to thrive. The firm is expert in handling all areas of work in the shipping field including disputes arising from salvage and collision; carriage of goods; charterparties; marine insurance policies; general average; pollution and ship repairs. On the non-contentious side, the firm advises all sectors of the maritime industry on an international basis on all aspects of ship sale and purchase; new building contracts; the management and operation of ships and ship finance transactions. Expertise extends to all litigious aspects of aviation work. Acting for aircraft manufacturers, airlines and lessors on the non-contentious side, the firm has developed a particular specialisation in cross-border financing. The firm is also involved in disputes arising out of the carriage of goods by road and rail.

AREAS OF PRACTICE

Insurance/Reinsurance	26%
Banking/Corporate/Commercial & Tax	25%
Marine & Transport	24%
Commercial Litigation	10%
Energy & Natural Resources	7%
Property	5%
Employment	3%

CONTACTS

Alternative Dispute Resolution	Jane Andrewartha
Arbitration	John Whittaker
Asset Finance & Leasing	Simon Poland
	Austen Hall
Aviation	Jane Andrewartha
	Richard Hames
Banking	David Page
Commercial Litigation	Jonathan Wood
	Stuart Macdonald

Corporate & Commercial: The firm's corporate and commercial department handles a wide range of corporate and commercial transactions including flotations; mergers and acquisitions; MBOs; MBIs; joint ventures and inward investments.The corporate and commercial department also advises on intellectual property rights, data protection issues and on all types of commercial contracts, including distribution and agency arrangements. It acts for suppliers and users of IT equipment and services and can advise on a broad range of issues relating to the IT and telecommunications industries. Specialists advise on the UK and European regulatory and competition implications of corporate transactions, financing arrangements and commercial contracts, including sports law.The banking group advises on a broad range of international and domestic financing arrangements, including asset and project finance.
Commercial Litigation: The breadth of the practice in this field is extensive. It encapsulates many of the work areas identified separately. The firm is involved in litigation and arbitration before courts and tribunals in the UK and worldwide through its overseas business and correspondent lawyers. Its particular areas of expertise also embrace commodity and trade disputes apart from the other specific work areas mentioned. Resolution of all types of commercial disputes including through mediation is a major strength of the practice.
Energy & Natural Resources: The firm advises on the commercial, regulatory and environmental aspects of petroleum exploration and production worldwide; on oil refining; product distribution and transportation and petrochemical investment. Advice is given on power projects throughout the world from large scale combustion plants to combined heat and power plants designed for industrial purposes. The firm advises on the financing aspects of energy projects and regulatory issues affecting the energy sector. A comprehensive range of legal services is provided for international mining and minerals transactions. This includes advice on acquiring mineral rights, mineral exploration, mine finance, processing, tolling, smelting and distribution. All aspects of trading commodities in the energy and natural resources sectors, and on energy derivatives and the regulatory implications of trading activity are covered. The firm has been involved in advising on the aftermath of major casualties, including Exxon Valdez, Piper Alpha and the Braer. The firm's energy group clients include governments, state oil companies, recognised regulatory bodies, privatised utilities, banks, independent companies, some of the world's largest commodities traders and mining exploration and production companies. A number of the energy group's lawyers were previously in-house lawyers with energy companies and so have particular insight into the sector's requirements.
Property: The firm represents UK and international developers, contractors, consultants, funders and investors in relation to property transactions. It has been involved in a number of high profile property transactions during the year, including the PFI transaction leading to the creation of the Richmond Community Hospital. Advice is also given on all litigious aspects of the construction industry.
Employment: The firm's expertise in employment law extends to preparing service and consultancy agreements; terms and conditions of employment; staff handbooks; health and safety policies; equal opportunities policies; restrictive covenants; unfair dismissal disputes; discrimination cases; redundancy programmmes and directors' duties and liabilities. Immigration is another area in which the firm has considerable expertise.
Taxation: Highly-regarded tax specialists advise all of the practice and deal with all aspects of corporate and personal taxation, including company reorganisations; financings; employee remuneration packages; equity incentive schemes; estate planning and settlements.

RECRUITMENT & TRAINING: A number of assistant solicitors will be required due to expansion in 2001. All enquiries should be made to the recruitment officer. For details of our trainee solicitor recruitment programme, call 020 7648 1580.

INTERNATIONAL CONNECTIONS: The firm has overseas offices in Caracas, Dubai, Hong Kong, Paris, Piraeus and Singapore, as well as an associate office in St Petersburg.

CONTACTS CONTINUED

Commodities (Derivatives) ...... Clare Hatcher
Commodities (Physical) ...... Paul Turner, Andrew Wells
Construction ...... John Morris
Corporate & Commercial ...... David Page
...... David Salt, Andrew Holderness
Corporate Finance ...... Gary Thorpe
...... Tim Matthews
Corporate Insurance - General ...... Daivd Salt, James O'Shea
Corporate Insurance - Lloyd's
...... Andrew Holderness, Diane Rickard
Corporate Litigation ...... Conrad Walker
EC & Competition Law ...... Stuart Macdonald
Employment ...... Chris Duffy
Energy & Natural Resources - Electricity ...... Clare Hatcher
Energy & Natural Resources - Mining ...... Martin Byatt
Energy & Natural Resources: Oil and Gas
...... Martin Byatt, Andrew Wells
...... Peter Felter
Immigration ...... Paul Newdick
Insolvency ...... Jonathan Wood
...... Paul Newdick
Insurance (Contentious) - Non-Marine/General ...... Michael Payton
...... Rod Smith
Insurance - Marine ...... Nigel Chapman
...... John Dunt
Intellectual Property ...... David Page
...... Tim Matthews
International Trade ...... John Whittaker
...... David Best
IT & Telecommunications ...... Philip Hooley
...... Tim Matthews
Life Assurance ...... James O'Shea
Medical Negligence ...... John Mitchell
Product Liability ...... Christ Harris
...... John Blacker
Professional Indemnity ...... Peter Farthing
...... Chris Harris
Property ...... Ross Johnstone, Paul Berry
Reinsurance ...... Nigel Brook
...... Paul Bidgen
Ship Finance ...... Simon Poland
Shipping ...... Anthony Thomas
...... Derek Hodgson, Benjamin Browne
Sport ...... Michael Breen
Tax ...... Susan Ball
Transport ...... Anthony Thomas, David Hall

CMS CAMERON MCKENNA

Mitre House, 160 Aldersgate Street, London, EC1A 4DD
Tel: (020) 7367 3000 **Fax:** (020) 7367 2000 **DX:** 135316 BARBICAN 2
Email: info@cmck.com **Website:** www.cmck.com

THE FIRM: Experience, resource, focus and enterprise – the hallmark of CMS Cameron McKenna. CMS Cameron McKenna has a wealth of experience and the depth of resource to handle the largest assignments. More than that, the firm's focus on industry expertise marks it out as a world class leader in many areas and, being as enterprising as its clients, CMS Cameron McKenna is determined to make things happen, giving a business lead, not just a legal opinion. Clear communication is the key – the firm speaks with authority and gets straight to the point. It is open about fees, who is responsible for the client's overall relationship with the firm and who is on the team on any particular transaction. CMS Cameron McKenna has joined forces with other major European law firms to create CMS, the transnational legal services organisation. CMS has 31 offices in 20 jurisdictions in Europe, the CIS, Asia-Pacific and North America and is committed to providing clients with integrated, seamless services. The firm has two additional UK offices located in Aberdeen and Bristol.

Continued overleaf

Managing Partner:	Dick Tyler
Senior Partner:	Bill Shelford
Chief Executive:	Robert Derry-Evans
UK:	
Number of partners:	154
Assistant solicitors:	344
Other fee-earners:	138
International:	
Number of partners:	57
Assistant solicitors:	158

CONTACTS

Aviation ...... Tim Brymer
Banking & International Finance
...... Duncan Aldred

C

PRINCIPAL AREAS OF WORK: CMS Cameron McKenna is a major full service City and international commercial law firm, with particular strengths in the banking and finance, corporate, construction, infrastructure projects, energy, healthcare and bioscience, insurance and property sectors. It advises businesses and governments throughout the world.

Finance: CMS Cameron McKenna has a broad and balanced corporate finance practice for both public and private companies, as well as M&A, MBO and MBI work, financial restructurings, privatisations and corporate tax. The firm acts for some 90 UK and international banks and, with its experience in the financing of infrastructure projects, is regarded as one of the pre-eminent firms in banking and asset and project finance, including PFI/PPP work. Its outstanding insurance and reinsurance practice is founded on a close involvement with the insurance market over the last 60 years.

Property: Its property practice is one of the strongest, with high-profile clients in the institutional, development and retail areas; it is ranked as a leader in environmental law, financial services regulation, health & safety at work, immigration, pensions, planning and product liability; and has strong specialist expertise in such topics as advertising and marketing, anti-trust and competition law, EU law, employment, fraud, information technology, immigration, multimedia and telecommunications, intellectual property, press disputes and securitisation.

Litigation: CMS Cameron McKenna has significant firm-wide litigation resources covering the whole practice with experience in dispute management, arbitration and mediation allied to specific industry expertise.

Other Areas: Industry expertise is a factor which marks out CMS Cameron McKenna. The firm is a leader in advising clients in a range of industries including construction, energy (oil & gas, electricity, power generation and water), financial services, life sciences (particularly pharmaceuticals and biotechnology), transport (aviation, railways, roads and ports) and waste management. More information is available from either the Senior or the Managing Partner, or from any of the contact partners listed.

INTERNATIONAL CONNECTIONS: The firm has offices in Almaty, Brussels, Beijing, Budapest, Bucharest, Hong Kong, Moscow, Prague, Tashkent and Warsaw. Associated offices are located in Amsterdam, Arnhem, Berlin, Chemnitz, Dresden, Dusseldorf, Frankfurt, Hamburg, Hilversum, Leipzig, Munich, Stuttgart, Toronto, Utrecht, Vienna, Washington DC and Zurich.

CONTACTS CONTINUED

- **Charities** ....Andrew Crawford
- **CIS** ....Elena Kirillova
- **Construction** ....Ann Minogue, John Uwins
- **Corporate Finance** ..Sean Watson, Arfon Jones
- **Corporate Tax** ....Mark Nichols
- **Defamation/Trade Libel/Media Complaints** ....Tim Hardy
- **EC Law/Competition/Anti-trust** ....Richard Taylor, Nick Paul
- **Employment** Simon Jeffreys, Anthony Fincham
- **Energy** ....Fiona Woolf, Penelope Warne
- **Environment** ....Paul Sheridan
- **Financial Services Regulation** ..Simon Morris
- **Health & Safety** ....Mark Tyler
- **Immigration** ....Julia Onslow-Cole
- **Infrastructure Projects/PFI** ....Robert Phillips
- **Insolvency** ....John White
- **Insurance & Reinsurance** ..Anthony Hobkinson
- **IP/Advertising & Marketing** ....Stephen Whybrow, Guilherme Brafman
- **IT/Telecoms** ....John Armstrong
- **Life Sciences** ....Ian Dodds-Smith
- **Litigaton/Arbititration & Dispute Management** ....Tim Hardy
- **M&A** ....Richard Price, Mike Rich
- **Pensions** ....Nigel Moore
- **Planning** ....Tony Kitson
- **Product Liability & Integrity** ....Chris Hodges, Anthony Hobkinson
- **Project Finance** ....Andrew Ivison
- **Property** ....Charles Romney, Nick Brown
- **Transport** ....Richard Price, Trevor Butcher
- **Venture Capital** ....Andrew Sheach
- **Water** ....Richard Temple

COBBETTS

Ship Canal House, King Street, Manchester, M2 4WB
Tel: (0161) 833 3333 **Fax:** (0161) 833 3030 **DX:** 14374 Manchester 1
Email: lawyers@cobbetts.co.uk **Website:** www.cobbetts.co.uk

Managing Partner:	Michael Shaw
Senior Partner:	Stephen White
Number of partners:	41
Assistant solicitors:	46
Other fee-earners:	42

THE FIRM: Cobbetts, with its long history in the city and strong independent stance, continues to impress its clients with the virtues of using a purely 'Manchester' firm. Although Cobbetts has always represented quality of work and high service standards, it has, in recent years, undergone a programme of radical internal changes under the direction of Managing Partner Michael Shaw which are now being reflected in changing external perceptions about the firm. Its overall image continues to be one of quiet conservatism, but this underlying drive for structured progression now places it at the forefront of successful long-term relationship building. For example, the firm's sustained IT investment and ambitious programme of implementation now places it amongst the most technologically sophisticated of any legal firm. It remains committed to further development of intranet technology and the application of e-commerce in order to better service client needs. Over the past four years the firm has achieved an enviable record of controlled, sustained growth of around 20% pa through good management of the business as a whole and an emphasis on identifying and meeting the needs and expectations of clients, intermediaries and the firm's own personnel. However, unlike many of its competitors, the general ethos of the firm is not geared solely towards financial reward, and strong and continuing emphasis is placed on relationships, quality of environment and job satisfaction for all. This commitment was formally recognised in January 2000 when the firm became the first in the North West to simultaneously receive accreditation in both Investors in People and Lexcel (the Law Society's Quality Award).

PRINCIPAL AREAS OF WORK: Cobbetts operates through a number of flexible service teams based on work type and managed within two divisions.

Property: The Property Division is the largest under one roof in the North West and incorporates the resources and expertise capable of handling commercial property work of any type and size from greenfield acquisitions through development, letting and general property management. The division has particular expertise in the retail and licensed trade sectors with the licensing and planning team in particular enjoying a national reputation. There is also a flourishing housing association client base.

Corporate: The Corporate Division has the resources and expertise to handle all M&A-related work, corporate finance transactions and banking work. Within this division dedicated teams include lawyers specialising in contentious and non-contentious industrial relations and employment law, IT and computer contracts, agency and distribution agreements and intellectual property work, and an expertise in co-operative law which is unrivalled outside London. The firms' strong OMB client base is supplemented with numerous multi-national plc's and public sector organisations. The firm's private client team is the largest within a major Manchester commercial

AREAS OF PRACTICE

- **Commercial Property** 38%
- **Company/Commercial** 28%
- **Litigation** 27%
- **Private Client** 7%

CONTACTS

- **Banking** ....Paul Brown
- **Commercial/IP** ....Robert Roper
- **Commercial Litigation** ....Mark Whittell
- **Commercial Property** ....Stephen Benson
- **Construction** ....Peter Taylor
- **Corporate Finance** ....Robert Turnbull
- **Debt Recovery** ....Richard Webb
- **Defamation** ....Peter Stone
- **Education** ....Kevin Jaquiss
- **Employment** ....Judith Watson
- **Environmental** ....Simon Jones
- **Housing Associations** ....Mike Gaskell
- **Insolvency** ....Mark Whittell
- **IT** ....Susan Hall
- **Licensing** ....Hamish Lawson
- **Media** ....Peter Stone
- **Planning** ....Peter Oldham
- **Private Client** ....David Pickering
- **Sport** ....Jeremy Orrell

firm and in the past year has been supplemented by the recruitment of an independent financial adviser, enabling Cobbetts to offer OMB clients in particular, a true 'one stop shop' for legal and financial advice.

INTERNATIONAL CONNECTIONS: Cobbetts are members of the European legal network Eurolegal and have an associated office in Brussels, Renouf & Co. They are also members of the American State Law Group. These affiliations, together with other close relationships around the world ensure that the firm can meet clients' needs for international legal services and enables it to offer proactive advice to clients in respect of international commerce and trade.

COFFIN MEW & CLOVER

17 Hampshire Terrace, Portsmouth, PO1 2PU **Tel:** (023) 9281 2511 **Fax:** (023) 9229 1847 **DX:** 2207 Portsmouth 1
Email: cmcportsmouth@compuserve.com **Website:** www.coffinmew.co.uk **Ptnrs:** 23 **Asst solrs:** 18 **Other fee-earners:** 29

COKER VIS PARTNERSHIP

49 Broad Lane, Tottenham, London, N15 4DJ **Tel:** (020) 8885 1415 **Fax:** (020) 8885 2882 **DX:** 55604 Sth Tottenham
Email: broadlane@cokervis.com **Ptnrs:** 2 **Asst solrs:** 1 **Other fee-earners:** 3

COLE & CO

St Andrew House, 141 West Nile Street, Glasgow, G1 2RN **Tel:** (0141) 353 0007 **Fax:** (0141) 353 1110
DX: GW15 Glasgow 1 **Email:** rlc@coleandco.co.uk **Ptnrs:** 1 **Associates** 3 **Contact:** Ron Cole
Commercial property practice established in 1996 by experienced former property partner of a large national firm.

AREAS OF PRACTICE

Commercial Property	95%
Residential Property	5%

COLE & CO

23 Tombland, Norwich, NR3 1RF **Tel:** (01603) 617018 **Fax:** (01603) 630050 **DX:** 5220 Norwich **Ptnrs:** 5 **Associates:** 3
Contact: Richard Temple

COLEMANS SOLICITORS

Elisabeth House, 16 St. Peter's Square, Manchester, M2 3DF
Tel: (0161) 236 5623 **Fax:** (0161) 228 7509 **DX:** 14380
Email: info@colemans-sols.co.uk **Website:** www.colemans-sols.co.uk

Managing Partner:	Roger Coleman
Senior Partner:	Roger Coleman
Number of partners:	4
Assistant solicitors:	9
Other fee-earners:	37

CONTACTS

Commercial Litigation	Roger Coleman
Debt Recovery	Sue Paterson
Insurance	Roger Coleman
Personal Injury	Sarah Barr
	John Hesketh
	David Stevenson
Private Client	Karen Hartley
Uninsured Loss Recovery/PI	John Hesketh
	Sarah Barr
	(Manchester)
Uninsured Loss Recovery/PI	
	David Stevenson
	(Walsall)

THE FIRM: Established in the early 1980s, Colemans is a forward-thinking niche law firm, practising from offices in Manchester and Walsall. It now concentrates on its core strengths of personal injury work, commercial litigation and private client work.

PRINCIPAL AREAS OF WORK:

Commercial Litigation: A wide range of civil disputes is handled for both claimants and defendants, including commercial contract disputes, property litigation, employment matters and landlord and tenant disputes. The firm has particular expertise in franchising litigation.

Debt Recovery: The firm operates a fully computerised debt recovery service and advises clients on all aspects of their credit control.

Insurance Litigation: The department has continued to grow in the past year, with particular emphasis on high value personal injury claims and professional negligence claims.

Personal Injury: The firm has a specialist uninsured loss recovery department which is one of the largest in its field, acting for motor fleets and legal expenses schemes nationwide. The practice has access to a nationwide panel of associated experts to enable it to handle claims anywhere in the country. John Hesketh, David Stevenson and David Erwin are members of the Law Society's Personal Injury Panel. The department is experienced in handling claims for medical negligence and fatal accidents including representation at inquests.

Private Client: The department handles residential conveyancing, building estate work, probate, Court of Protection and wills.

COLEMANS

27 Marlow Road, Maidenhead, SL6 7AE **Tel:** (01628) 631051 **Fax:** (01628) 622106 **DX:** 6405 Maidenhead
Email: info@colemans.co.uk **Ptnrs:** 4 **Other fee-earners:** 1

COLE'S

5 Rigbys Court, St Giles Street, Norwich, NR2 1NT **Tel:** (01603) 441 111 **Fax:** (01603) 442 222

COLLYER-BRISTOW

4 Bedford Row, London, WC1R 4DF
Tel: (020) 7242 7363 **Fax:** (020) 7405 0555 **DX:** 163 Ch.Ln.
Email: firstname.lastname@collyer-bristow.co.uk **Website:** www.collyer-bristow.co.uk

Senior Partner:	Roger Woolfe
Number of partners:	20
Assistant solicitors:	12
Other fee-earners:	15

AREAS OF PRACTICE

Litigation	25%
Matrimonial & Family	20%
Property (Commercial)	20%
Private Client	18%
Commercial	12%
Sport Entertainment and Marketing	5%

CONTACTS

Agency	Mathew Marsh
Banking	Stephen Rosen
Commercial Property	Janet Armstrong-Fox
Company/Commercial	John Bailey
Construction	Joanna Kennedy
Defamation	Joanna Kennedy
Employment	Keith Corkan
Entertainment/Music	Howard Ricklow
Family	Michael Drake
Immigration	Joe Cohen
Intellectual Property	Joe Cohen
Litigation	Joanna Kennedy
Personal Injury/ Clinical Negligence	Sean Barratt
Residential Property	Janet Armstong-Fox
Sport & Sponsorship	Alan Burdon-Cooper
Tax Planning & Trusts	Paul Clark
Wills & Probate	John Saner

THE FIRM: Collyer-Bristow is an imaginative and innovative firm based in Bedford Row. It was established in 1760 but its environment and approach is progressive and friendly. The firm acts for a wide range of institutional clients; public and private companies; charities; businesses; professional partnerships; and private clients. An association with a group of European practices provides valuable continental links. The bright modernised offices now contain a professionally run art gallery where regular and varied exhibitions are held.

PRINCIPAL AREAS OF WORK: The firm has a strong commercial property practice and an expanding corporate and commercial department. The litigation and family law departments have excellent reputations within the profession. The sport, entertainment and marketing practice is developing, and the firm remains committed to providing a comprehensive personal service for its private clients, both in the UK and offshore.
Company/Commercial: The department's work includes company formations; mergers; acquisitions; sales; buy-outs; reorganisations and all the related range of contractual and commercial advice, including an expertise in advice to company directors.
Commercial Property: Freehold and leasehold sales and disposals, residential and office development schemes, major shopping centre developments, agricultural matters, planning and other related work. Residential and domestic transactions are also handled, including leasehold enfranchisement advice.
Litigation: This strong team has experience in property-related and construction litigation and arbitration; judicial review work; commercial and contractual disputes; professional negligence; defamation; personal injury and clinical negligence; and in representation before professional tribunals.
Intellectual Property: The firm has a strong reputation for handling contentious trademark and patent disputes; and in the licensing of rights, publishing, franchising and technology transfer.
Private Client: Unlike most central London firms, Collyer-Bristow has maintained and expanded its private client practice, for whom it handles tax planning; trusts; financial and investment advice within the UK and offshore; wills; and the administration of estates and charities.
Family: This is one of the leading matrimonial practices in the country. Its reputation extends across the entire range of family work, including: divorce; custody; financial disputes; wardship; cohabitation; international forum-shopping; child abduction; and the recognition of decrees. It is one of the appointed firms on the Lord Chancellor's child abduction panel.
Employment: The team handles a wide range of employment and boardroom disputes, industrial tribunal applications, executive service contract advice, and the preparation of employment terms and conditions and advice on business-related immigration.
Sport, Entertainment & Marketing: The firm acts for sponsorship, promotions and merchandising consultancies; advertising and marketing agencies; governing bodies; sponsors; sports photographers and publishers; film and video producers; and distributors. In the music industry, the firm acts for artists, managers, record labels and publishers.
Agency Work: The agency litigation department provides a service for more than 100 firms outside the capital and overseas.

RECRUITMENT & TRAINING: For those candidates who do not believe that biggest necessarily means best, the firm offers a refreshing alternative; trainee solicitors work closely with partners on a wide variety of work in a friendly atmosphere – opportunities that only a smaller firm can provide. Applicants should have a good academic background, an assured and lively personality, a positive approach and preferably some computer literacy and linguistic ability. CV and references to John Saner.

COMERTON & HILL

Murray House, 4 Murray Street, Belfast, BT1 6DN **Tel:** (028) 90234629 **Fax:** (028) 90233908 **DX:** 415 NR BELFAST 1
Email: solicitors@comerton.co.uk **Ptnrs:** 4 **Asst solrs:** 1 **Other fee-earners:** 3

CONDIES

2 Tay Street, Perth, PH1 5LJ **Tel:** (01738) 440088 **Fax:** (01738) 441131 **DX:** 25 Perth
Email: enquiry@condies.co.uk **Ptnrs:** 5 **Asst solrs:** 7 **Other fee-earners:** 4 **Contact:** Mr Richard Blake • Well established general practice handling a wide range of property work, including landed estate and agricultural law; trusts and executries; criminal and civil litigation.

CONINGSBYS

87-89 High Street, Croydon, CR9 1XE **Tel:** (020) 8680 5575 **Fax:** (020) 8681 3941 **DX:** 2611 Croydon 1
Email: reception@coningsbys.co.uk **Website:** www.coningsbys.co.uk **Ptnrs:** 3 **Other fee-earners:** 8
Contact: Paul Conrathe

AREAS OF PRACTICE

Conveyancing	30%
Education	30%
Matrimonial	10%
Personal Injury	10%
Probate	10%

CONSTANT & CONSTANT

Sea Containers House, 20 Upper Ground, Blackfriars Bridge, London, SE1 9QT
Tel: (020) 7261 0006 **Fax:** (020) 7401 2161 **DX:** 1067 London City
Email: twoconstants@dial.pipex.com **Website:** www.constantlaw.com

Senior Partner:	Jonathan Ecclestone
UK:	
Number of partners:	22
Assistant solicitors:	12
Other fee-earners:	9
International:	
Number of partners:	4
Assistant solicitors:	5
Other fee-earners:	0

CONTACTS

Banking & Finance	Jonathan Ecclestone
Company/Commercial	André Harries
	Ian Taylorson
Construction	Tim Reynolds
Employment	John Dickinson
Maritime	John Rudd
	Graham Crane
Media	Ian Taylorson
Property/Private Client	Richard Wilson
	Denis Dowling
Taxation	Andrew Terry

THE FIRM: Established in 1911 to provide legal services to the shipping industry, the firm remains one of the leading specialists in the maritime area. In addition, the practice has expanded over the years, and now also provides a broad range of other commercial law services. As a medium-sized firm with an international reputation, Constant & Constant combines personal service with technical expertise. The firm's success in this respect is reflected in its broad client base, ranging from private individuals to government agencies. The firm also act for many insurers, financial institutions and public and private companies world-wide.

PRINCIPAL AREAS OF WORK:
Maritime: The most established area of the practice, with an international reputation as specialists advising in matters ranging from cargo claims to marine casualties, from ship finance to competition law.
Taxation: Legal services in both corporate and personal taxation, advising on all areas of direct and indirect tax, but with a particular emphasis on cross-border issues.
Company & Commercial: UK and international corporate affairs, from business structuring to a wide range of commercial contract issues.
Private Client: Services in connection with such matters as wills, trusts, probate, financial planning, nationality and immigration, and family law.
Media: The department's all-round commercial perspective, together with an excellent working knowledge of the industry, enables a quality service on media and related issues, such as contracts, intellectual property, regulatory matters and corporate affairs.
Banking & Finance: Areas of expertise include asset financing, project and corporate finance, property acquisition and development finance, documentary credits and derivatives.
Property: The department deals with all aspects of residential sale and purchase, landlord and tenant and property investment. It also manages property investment portfolios.
Employment: The firm advises on all aspects of employment law, acting for both employers and employees.
Construction: International and domestic advice, contract drafting and litigation/arbitration in all aspects of construction and civil engineering matters.

INTERNATIONAL CONNECTIONS: The firm has other offices in Paris and Le Havre.

COODES

8 Market Street, St. Austell, PL25 4BB **Tel:** (01726) 75021 **Fax:** (01726) 69103 **DX:** 81250 **Email:** coodes@link.org **Ptnrs:** 13 **Asst solrs:** 5
Other fee-earners: 17

COOLE & HADDOCK

5 The Steyne, Worthing, BN11 3DT
Tel: (01903) 213511 **Fax:** (01903) 237053 **DX:** 3717 Worthing

14 Carfax, Horsham, RH12 1DZ
Tel: (01403) 210200 **Fax:** (01403) 241275 **DX:** 57600 Horsham

Managing Partner:	W.Paul Burke
Senior Partner:	F.N.F. Haddock
Number of partners:	10
Assistant solicitors:	6
Other fee-earners:	3

CONTACTS

Commercial & Civil Litigation/ Employment	Stephen Loosemore
Company Commercial/ Commercial Property	Iain Swalwell
Matrimonial/Childcare	Penny Barker
Probate & Trusts	Jennifer Murphy
Residential Conveyancing	Paul Burke
	Peter Graves

THE FIRM: Established in Horsham in 1873 and Worthing in 1960, Coole & Haddock built its reputation initially on an extensive private client base mainly in Sussex. This is now complemented by expanding commercial and litigation departments which offer a comprehensive service to businesses over a wider area.

PRINCIPAL AREAS OF WORK: Company; commercial/commercial property; town & country planning; commercial and civil litigation/personal injury; property litigation; residential conveyancing; probate and trust; wills and estate planning; matrimonial/child care; debt recovery and crime.

COPLEYS

Red House, 10 Market Hill, St. Ives, PE17 4AW **Tel:** (01480) 464515 **Fax:** (01480) 467171 **DX:** 46402 **Ptnrs:** 5 **Asst solrs:** 4 **Other fee-earners:** 6

CORBETT & CO

Churcham House, 1 Bridgeman Road, Teddington, TW11 9AJ **Tel:** (020) 8943 9885 **Fax:** (020) 8977 3122 **Email:** mail@corbett.co.uk **Website:** www.corbett.co.uk **Ptnrs:** 1 **Asst solrs:** 3 **Other fee-earners:** 1 **Contact:** Edward Corbett • The firm has a growing reputation as a specialist in international and UK construction projects and disputes. Established in 1993, when Edward Corbett left the partnership of Masons, the firm has advised on a wide range of projects in the UK and all over the world. Dispute work includes TCC litigation, ICC arbitration and ADR including adjudication.

AREAS OF PRACTICE

International Construction Projects/Disputes	60%
UK Construction Projects/Disputes	40%

SJ CORNISH

Twyford House, Kennedy Way, Tiverton, EX16 6RZ **Tel:** (01884) 243377 **Fax:** (01884) 243388 **Email:** Solicitors@SJCornish.co.uk **Website:** www.SJCornish.co.uk **Ptnrs:** 3 **Asst solrs:** 2 **Other fee-earners:** 1 **Contact:** Sarah Cornish • Specialist West Country niche litigation practice established in 1991. Defendants' professional indemnity claims; defendants' personal injury and liability claims; also commercial litigation and debt collection.

AREAS OF PRACTICE

Professional Indemnity	70%
Personal Injury	25%
Commercial Litigation/ debt collection	5%

C

COUDERT BROTHERS

60 Cannon Street, London, EC4N 6JP
Tel: (020) 7248 3000 **Fax:** (020) 7248 3001 **DX:** LDE 49
Email: info@london.coudert.com **Website:** www.coudert.com

Managing partner:	Phillip Burroughs
Senior partner:	Steven Beharrell
Number of partners:	14
Assistant solicitors:	16
Other fee-earners:	10

THE FIRM: Coudert Brothers in London is a multi-national partnership of registered foreign lawyers and solicitors. It is part of a worldwide network of offices established in 29 cities in 16 countries around the world. Coudert Brothers is one global partnership and the London office provides the facilities of a full service London law firm as well as access to the international network of Coudert Brothers. The London office has 14 partners, 12 of whom are solicitors and two of whom are US attorneys. The London office specialises in international investment, trade and finance with particular expertise in corporate finance, mergers and acquisitions and joint ventures; capital markets, banking and project finance, international tax and trust planning; telecommunications and IT law; energy privatisation and infrastructure projects; real estate; and arbitration and litigation.

INTERNATIONAL CONNECTIONS: Coudert Brothers has offices in the major financial centres in Europe, Central Asia, North America and the Asia Pacific region. In Europe, the firm has offices in London, Paris, Brussels, Antwerp, Ghent, Berlin, Frankfurt, Bonn, Munich, Milan, Moscow, St. Petersburg and Almaty. The North American offices are established in New York, Washington, Los Angeles, San Francisco, San Jose, Palo Alto, Denver and Montreal and the Asia Pacific offices in Bangkok, Beijing, Hanoi, Hong Kong, Jakarta, Singapore, Sydney and Tokyo. Coudert Brothers has associated offices in Budapest, Prague and Mexico City. The firm's Moscow office was the first established by a foreign law firm (1988) and is now one of the largest in Moscow servicing all the states of the former Soviet Union. Coudert Brothers opened an office in Kazakhstan in 1998.

AREAS OF PRACTICE

Corporate Finance	30%
Banking/ Project/ Structured Finance	15%
Litigation/ Arbitration	15%
Capital Markets/ Funds	10%
Energy/ Telecoms/ Multimedia	10%
Real Property	10%
Other	10%

CONTACTS

Banking/Finance	Alexander Janes
Competition/Telecoms	Alastair Gorrie
Corporate Finance	Steven Beharrell
Energy	Steven Beharrell
Funds	Alasdair Gordon
Litigation/Arbitration	Bridget Wheeler
Project Finance	Peter O'Driscoll
Real property	Philip Burroughs

COUDERT BROTHERS
INTERNATIONAL LAWYERS

COURTS & CO

15 Wimpole St, London, W1M 8AP
Tel: (020) 7637 1651 **Fax:** (020) 7637 0205 **DX:** 42722 Oxford Circus North
Email: law@courtsandco.com **Website:** www.courtsandco.com

Senior Partner:	Bill Holmes
Number of partners:	6
Assistant solicitors:	4
Other fee-earners:	2

THE FIRM: Courts & Co is a niche firm, specialising in company and commercial work. The firm provides an in-depth, personal service to companies and their directors, working closely with their business advisers, particularly their accountants. The firm's policy is to combine the highest level of technical expertise with a close understanding of the client's business and commercial requirements.

PRINCIPAL AREAS OF WORK: A large part of the firm's work consists of advising on the purchase and sale of businesses, corporate mergers and reorganisations, as well as a full range of business and commercial matters, including taxation and intellectual property work. The firm handles commercial conveyancing; heavy commercial litigation (including environmental and town and country planning matters); employment work (both litigious and non-litigious) mainly (but not exclusively) for employers; and estate planning, trusts and probate work.

CLIENTELE: Clients include private and public companies, professional partnerships and individual entrepreneurs in all areas of business; charities and trusts. Much of the firm's work is for overseas clients.

AREAS OF PRACTICE

Company/Commercial/Tax	40%
Commercial Litigation	30%
Conveyancing/Trusts/Wills & Probate	30%

CONTACTS

Company/Commercial	Ian Paterson
	Patrick Gilmour
Conveyancing/Probate & Trusts	Bill Holmes
Employment	Frank Ryan
Intellectual Property	Micheal Krantz
Litigation	Michael Krantz
	Frank Ryan

COVINGTON & BURLING

Leconfield House, Curzon Street, London, W1Y 8AS
Tel: (020) 7495 5655 **Fax:** (020) 7495 3101
Website: www.cov.com

Managing Partner:	Richard Kingham
Senior Partner:	Charles E. Lister
Number of partners:	8
Assistant solicitors:	17
Other fee-earners:	7

AREAS OF PRACTICE

Intellectual Property	30%
Corporate & Commercial	20%
Medicines & Consumer Product Regulation	20%
International Taxation	15%
General litigation & Arbitration	10%
Other	5%

THE FIRM: Covington & Burling was founded in Washington DC in 1919 and now has approximately 440 lawyers in the Washington DC, New York and San Francisco offices, and 40 lawyers and solicitors in the London and Brussels offices, as well as a correspondent office in Paris. The London office was established in 1988 and founded a multi-national partnership in 1993. It has 13 UK qualified staff, in addition to US and German lawyers. The office maintains extensive collections of EU and national legal resources and is a focal point for multi-national issues for Covington & Burling and clients worldwide. The London office has particular expertise in coordinating, on behalf of multi-national clients, legal matters involving a number of jurisdictions and the firm has an informal network of international local counsel contacts in over 30 countries throughout Western and Eastern Europe, Australasia, Africa and the Americas. In particular, the firm has developed an ability to advise clients on policy issues and to lobby policy makers, particulary in connection with the IT and pharmaceutical industries.

PRINCIPAL AREAS OF WORK: Major practice areas in London include intellectual property; communications and technology issues; regulation of food, drugs and other consumer products; corporate and securities law; international taxation; litigation and arbitration; competition and trade. The firm acts as principle legal advisor for a wide range of companies that depend on and provide advanced technology, both in the IT industries and the life sciences industries.

LANGUAGES: English, French, German, Italian, Portuguese and Spanish.

C

COZENS-HARDY & JEWSON
Castle Chambers, Opie St, Norwich, NR1 3DP **Tel:** (01603) 625231 **Fax:** (01603) 627160 **DX:** 5214 **Email:** lawyers@cozens-hardy.com
Website: www.cozens-hardy.com **Ptnrs:** 8 **Asst solrs:** 8 **Other fee-earners:** 13

CRIPPS HARRIES HALL

Seymour House, 11-13 Mount Ephraim Road, Tunbridge Wells, Kent, TN1 1EN
Tel: (01892) 515121 **Fax:** (01892) 544878 **DX:** 3954 Tunbridge Wells
Email: reception@crippslaw.com **Website:** www.e-cripps.co.uk

14 Buckingham Street, London, WC2N 6DF
Tel: (020) 7930 0004 **Fax:** (020) 7839 9224
Email: reception@london.crippslaw.com

Croham House, Croham Road, Crowborough, TN6 2RL
Tel: (01892) 662233 **Fax:** (01892) 601010 **DX:** 36852 Crowborough
Email: reception@crippslaw.com

Managing Partner:	Jonathan Denny
Senior Partner:	Andrew Fermor
Number of partners:	31
Assistant solicitors:	40
Other fee-earners:	59

AREAS OF PRACTICE

Commercial Litigation	25%
Corporate & Commercial Property	23%
Finance & Investment Services	23%
Private Client	14%
Residential & Agricultural Conveyancing	9%
General Litigation	6%

CONTACTS

Agriculture and Bloodstock	John Mulcare
Alternative Dispute Resolution	Charles Broadie
Arbitration	John Mulcare
Charities	Peter Scott
Commercial Contracts	Caroline Farrant
Commercial Litigation	Peter Ashford
Commercial Property	Michael Stevens
Construction Litigation	Peter Ashford
Corporate Finance	Trevor Carney
Debt Collection	Russell Simpson
Employment	Roger Byard
Environment	Jason Towell
Estate Planning	Peter Scott
Family/Matrimonial	Michael Rowlands
Information Technology	Christopher Langridge
Insolvency	Julian Dobson
Insurance Litigation	Charles Broadie
Intellectual Property	Joanna Case
Investment Management	David Lough
PFI Projects	Lawrence Leporte
Planning	Jason Towell
Professional Negligence	Gavin Tyler
Property Litigation	Carol Wakeford

THE FIRM: Cripps Harries Hall is regarded by many businesses and institutions in the South East as the natural first choice among the region's commercial law firms. A large part of the reason for this success is to be found in the firm's claim to provide 'London style skills at out-of-London prices'. The high calibre of its legal advisers is evidenced by the high proportion of the commercial partners and solicitors who have either joined from or trained at London firms, including several of the 'top ten' City firms.With headquarters out of London, yet within easy reach of the City, the firm's low overheads are reflected in charges to clients which, typically, are at least one third less than those of comparable London firms. In addition to competitive hourly charging rates, the firm is happy to agree to a wide range of other methods of remuneration if these are preferred by the client.The desire to deliver standards of service associated with the best London firms led Cripps Harries Hall to become the first 'top 100' law firm to achieve accreditation to the Law Society's quality assurance standard for solicitors' firms known as 'Lexcel'. This involves the practice being subjected to rigorous assessments by the British Standards Institution for compliance with the exacting standards set by the Law Society designed to encourage excellence in law firms.Cripps Harries Hall is committed to integrating the provision of legal advice with the effective use of IT; during the last 12 months alone the firm has spent over £1 million on new systems.In summary, Cripps Harries Hall has grown to become a leading commercial law firm in the South East. The firm is committed to providing clients with a combination of a high quality of service, commercial awareness, responsiveness, good value and the close involvement of the partners. Cripps Harries Hall believes it is on course to become one of the top regional law firms in the country.

PRINCIPAL AREAS OF WORK: The broad spectrum of commercial and institutional clients is drawn from an increasingly wide area with many new clients being based in London and outside of the South East, including several national clients. All clients have ready access to a very wide range of services. The firm has developed

Continued overleaf

a particularly strong practice in a number of markets, as follows. A significant part of the firm's client base is mid-sized corporates, particularly within the high technology sector. Many of these clients came to the firm initially for corporate finance work such as venture capital agreements, MBOs, mergers or different Stock Exchange work. Others are attracted by the firm's responsive and flexible approach. The firm is also respected for its employment, insolvency and corporate recovery work. Among the firm's institutional property clients are Government departments, utility companies, insurance companies, asset management companies, national pension funds, property portfolio companies and housing associations. The services provided cover planning and environmental law, as well as the full spectrum of commercial property work, PFI projects and property disputes. Also, the firm has a reputation for providing a cost-effective resource for major property projects, such as the Channel Tunnel High Speed Rail Link.

Property: A particular niche for the firm is property developers and house builders. The firm's clients include several household name companies in this sector. The practice was enhanced in 2000 when the head of the in-house legal department at Wates Group Ltd and a respected figure in the industry, joined Cripps Harries Hall as a partner.

Insurance: The specialist team defending professional liability insurance claims at Cripps Harries Hall is well established and is known for providing a combination of forceful defence of claims and a high quality of service. Between them, the members of this team have acted on behalf of insurers for solicitors, surveyors, accountants, architects, valuers and management consultants.

Commercial Litigation: The commercial litigation practice of the firm is broad and includes mediation and other forms of dispute resolution which enable clients to avoid costly and protracted litigation. Two partners of the firm are accredited mediators and one partner is a member of the Chartered Institute of Arbitrators.

Private Client: In private client work, the firm has extensive experience and has developed a reputation in managing the affairs of wealthy private clients to rival the top London firms in this field. The firm is believed to have the most comprehensive integrated legal and financial services operation of any solicitors' firm in the country. The total of clients' funds under management is over £325 million.

INTERNATIONAL CONNECTIONS: A network of independent law firms in 18 European countries.

CONTACTS CONTINUED

Residential Conveyancing	Peter Lintott
Residential Property Development	Michael Ellis
Social Housing	Mike Vos
Trusts & Personal Tax	Gary Rogerson
Wills & Probate	Simon Leney

CRIPPS HARRIES HALL

C

CROCKERS OSWALD HICKSON

10 Gough Square, London, EC4A 3NJ
Tel: (020) 7353 0311 **Fax:** (020) 7583 1417 **DX:** 52 CHANCERY LANE
Email: lawyers@c-o-h.co.uk **Website:** www.c-o-h.co.uk

Joint Senior Partners:	Simon Kingston
	Rupert Grey
Number of partners:	9
Assistant solicitors:	19
Other fee-earners:	11

AREAS OF PRACTICE

Defamation & Media	44%
Personal Injury & Non-Media Litigation	33%
Property	10%
Company & Commercial	9%
Private Client	4%

CONTACTS

Company/Commercial	Katy Jones
Defamation/Media	Rupert Grey
	Richard Shillito
Personal Injury/ Non-Media Litigation	Peter Norman
Private Client	Alan Macfadyen
Property	Simon Kingston
	Diana Cornforth

THE FIRM: A long-established City reputation built in the field of insurance forms the core of the corporate and commercial work of the firm. With an international reputation for libel, slander and copyright work, the firm has a substantial practice in defamation and intellectual property. The firm's links with insurers also provide significant work in the areas of personal injury claims and general litigation. In addition, the firm provides a wide range of legal services in property and company and commercial law. Private clients are welcomed and there is a busy private client department.

PRINCIPAL AREAS OF WORK:

Media: The department offers advice on libel, slander, copyright, passing-off, contempt of court, reporting restrictions, PACE applications, pre-publication and pre-broadcasting advice and breach of confidence, as well as on libel insurance and publishing and licensing agreements.

Company/Commercial: The department handles a broad range of commercial work, including private company sales and acquisitions, joint ventures and employment law, predominantly for clients in the insurance industry.

Litigation: The department deals with all non-media litigation and the principal areas of activity are professional indemnity, employers' liability, personal injury and motoring claims and general commercial litigation.

Property: The department handles all types of commercial property work including development and landlord and tenant as well as domestic conveyancing.

Private Client: The department deals with trusts, wills, probate, personal tax and related areas of work. The estates of both UK and foreign Lloyd's Names are handled by the department.

Clientele: The firm acts for international, national and provincial newspaper groups as well as some of the larger magazine and book publishers, television companies, syndication agencies and picture libraries. It also acts for a major property development company and, reflecting its historical connection with the insurance industry, it also numbers amongst its clients several insurance companies, as well as numerous Lloyd's Brokers and Underwriting Agents. The partnership sees itself as an effective and competitive commercial firm, prominent in publishing and insurance law, providing a personal service second to none.

RECRUITMENT & TRAINING: The firm is always happy to hear from high-calibre assistant solicitors and usually recruits two trainee solicitors each year.

CROFTONS

Television House, Mount Street, Manchester, M2 5FA **Tel:** (0161) 834 4391 **Fax:** (0161) 839 1743 **DX:** 18572 Manchester 7
Email: croftons@memail.com **Ptnrs:** 5 **Asst solrs:** 3 **Other fee-earners:** 7

CROMBIE WILKINSON

Clifford House, 19 Clifford Street, York, YO1 9RJ **Tel:** (01904) 624185 **Fax:** (01904) 623078 **DX:** 61501
Email: york@crombiewilkinson.feeserve.co.uk **Website:** www.crombie-wilkinson.co.uk **Ptnrs:** 8 **Asst solrs:** 8
Other fee-earners: 8

CROSSE & CROSSE

14 Southernhay West, Exeter, EX1 1PL **Tel:** (01392) 258451 **Fax:** (01392) 278938 **DX:** 8313 EXETER **Ptnrs:** 10 **Asst solrs:** 8 **Other fee-earners:** 11

CRUTES

7 Osborne Terrace, Newcastle-upon-Tyne, NE2 1RQ
Tel: (0191) 281 5811 **Fax:** (0191) 281 3608 **DX:** 62553 Jesmond
Email: advice@crutes.co.uk **Website:** www.crutes.co.uk

28 Portland Square, Carlisle, CA1 1PE
Tel: (01228) 25446 **Fax:** (01228) 511517 **DX:** 63000 Carlisle
Email: advice@crutes.co.uk

93 Borough Road, Middlesbrough, TS1 3YS
Tel: (01642) 230103 **Fax:** (01642) 231549 **DX:** 60502 Middlesborough
Email: advice|@crutes.co.uk

37-38 West Sunniside, Sunderland, SR1 1BY
Tel: (0191) 565 8271 **Fax:** (0191) 5145247 **DX:** 60701 Sunderland
Email: advice@crutes.co.uk

Senior Partner:	Tim Wallis
Managing Partner	Stephen Crute
Number of partners:	17
Assistant solicitors:	25
Other fee-earners:	22

AREAS OF PRACTICE

Insurance/Personal Injury	59%
Insurance/Professional Indemnity	16%
Commercial	8%
Private Client	8%
Health Related Work	6%
Employment	3%

CONTACTS

ADR/Mediation	Tim Wallis
	Helen Ager
Commercial	Stuart Palmer
Employment	Tim Smith
Health Related Work	Tim Wallis
	Peter Henry
	Dagmar Leonard
Insurance/Personal Injury	David Drewe
	Stephen Crute
Insurance/Professional Indemnity	John Parker
	Helen Ager
Private Client	Brian Mackenow

THE FIRM: Crutes services clients' litigation and commercial needs from the Scottish Border down to North Yorkshire. The firm is particularly committed to resolving disputes more efficiently and cost effectively. To achieve those ends they make use of ADR, invest heavily in IT and are looking closely at innovative fee arrangements with clients, eg task based billing. The firm is approaching its centenery.

PRINCIPAL AREAS OF WORK:

Insurance: Insurance work is a particular strength of Crutes and the firm acts for a large number of the major insurance companies. The firm has maintained a strong presence on a number of insurance panels following a number of re-tendering exericisies - including Broker Direct, CGU and Zurich Municipal. Much of the insurance work is personal injury including the whole range of claims and some specialisms in more unusual areas, eg physical and sexual abuse claims by children, stress claims, disease and structured settlements.

Public Sector Services: Across all its four offices, Crutes acts for virtually all of the local authorities in the North in the areas of insurance litigation, employment, property and commercial. The firm also acts for the police, ambulance services and the fire brigade in their insurance litigation claims.

Professional Indemnity: Crutes have had a professional indemnity practice for many years. Crutes continue on the SIF panel and have an expanding professional negligence team which also acts for other professionals such as accountants and surveyors.

Health: Crutes has acted for the NHS since its inception and now act for many of the NHS Trusts in the North for litigation, employment, property and commercial matters. The firm has strengthened its Health Unit by the recent appointment of new partner Dagmar Leonard. Ms Leonard has a background of both private practice as well as many years with a Northern Health Authoity. The firm is also appointed to the NHS Litigation Authority panel.Employment, Commercial Property & Commercial Litigation: The employment, commercial property and commercial litigation departments are all expanding. The commercial department has recently been strengthened by the addition of new partner Stuart Palmer who joins the firm from a career in Local Government and practice. Mr Palmer has substantial expertise in many areas of commercial law and is an expert in housing association Law.

Dispute Resolution: Crutes is committed to ADR and has been one of the firms leading the development of ADR since 1992. The firm has been delighted to see ADR achieving official recognition given its heavy involvement and investment in this area. All Crutes' litigators are trained in ADR and the firm has been involved in a substantial number of mediations (whether as a party, mediator or trainee mediator). The firm has recently been awarded first place in the Training and Education category of the Tees Valley Business Awards for its innovative training scheme, 'The Woolf Diploma'. The firm has ISO 9001 accreditation and was awarded the Investors in People Standard earlier this year.

CUFF ROBERTS

100 Old Hall Street, Liverpool, L3 9TD
Tel: (0151) 237 7777 **Fax:** (0151) 237 7676 **DX:** 14126 Liverpool 1
Email: email@cuffroberts.co.uk **Website:** www.cuffroberts.co.uk

Executive Board David Rawlinson, Sue Russell and Ian Black
Practice Director John Rimington

AREAS OF PRACTICE

Commercial Property	30%
Private Client	27%
Commercial Litigation	21%
Insolvency & Debt Recovery	13%
Company Commercial	9%

CONTACTS

Commercial Litigation	Anne Heseltine
Commercial Property	Roger Calvert
Company Commercial	Sue Russell
Insolvency & Debt Recovery	Paul Spence
	Jonathan Hogg
Private Client	Carol Mason

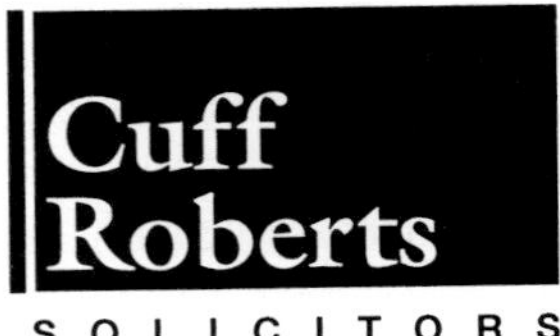

THE FIRM: Cuff Roberts was established in 1861. In 1982, Cuff Roberts merged with North Kirk and, in 1987, the combined firm merged again with Banks Kendall. Well-known and respected for its expertise in commercial property, the mergers of the 1980s strengthened and developed the company commercial and litigation departments. The firm now carries on a commercial practice in the company commercial, commercial property, commercial litigation and insolvency and debt recovery fields. It has maintained its commitment to the provision of private client services to enable the owners, directors and senior management of its corporate clientele to be provided for fully.

PRINCIPAL AREAS OF WORK:
Company Commercial: Work includes charity law; commercial lending; corporate finance; partnership; drafting and reviewing commercial contracts; sale and purchases of companies and businesses; sports and music law.
Commercial Property: Work includes all aspects of commercial property with particular emphasis on retail properties including acquisitions; disposals; leasing; property development and estate conveyancing.
Commercial Litigation: Work includes contract and negligence, contentious and non-contentious construction work, including arbitration and mediation; defamation, defence of specialist prosecutions (e.g. Environmental Protection Act, Health and Safety at Work Act, Food Act); employment; environment; licensing; planning; professional negligence; property litigation; sports law.
Insolvency & Debt Recovery: Work includes advising insolvency practitioners, institutions and banking clients on all aspects of insolvency, including liquidation, receivership, personal bankruptcy and business rescues and all aspects of debt recovery with particular expertise in consumer credit, agricultural and insolvency debts. Fully computerised system allows rapid and efficient processing of large and small batches of cases at highly competitive rates. Fixed charges are offered for all common debt recovery steps. Full litigation support is provided.
Private Client: Work includes wills and probate, trusts and tax planning, matrimonial and family, residential conveyancing.

INTERNATIONAL CONNECTIONS: The firm has established contacts with law firms in a large number of countries both in Europe and worldwide.

RECRUITMENT & TRAINING: The firm usually requires candidates with a good law degree, preferably with computer and keyboard skills, but CPE qualifiers are considered on merit.

CULBERT AND MARTIN
7 Donegall Square West, Belfast, BT1 6JB **Tel:** (028) 9032 5508 **Fax:** (028) 90438669 **DX:** 498 NR Belfast 1

CUMBERLAND ELLIS PEIRS INCORPORATING BARTH & PARTNERS

Columbia Hse, 69 Aldwych, London, WC2B 4RW
Tel: (020) 7242 0422 **Fax:** (020) 7831 9081 **DX:** 250 Ch.Ln.
Email: cep@cep-law.co.uk **Website:** www.cep-law.co.uk

Managing Partner:	Lionel Judd
Senior Partner:	Roger Hollinshead
Number of partners:	12
Assistant solicitors:	10
Other fee-earners:	9

CONTACTS

Commercial Property	Rod Forsyth
Company/Commercial	Suzanne Eva
Financial Services	Lionel Judd
	Rosa Gunston
Litigation	Neil Turner
Private Client	Roger Hollinshead
Residential Conveyancing	Robert Maclean

THE FIRM: A merger of two long-established central London practices, the firm has attracted considerable company/commercial and commercial property work and has a substantial litigation department; it also continues to provide the full range of private client services. The firm's philosophy is to combine high quality advice with a positive, personal service, at reasonable cost.

PRINCIPAL AREAS OF WORK:
Company/Commercial: A wide variety of work is handled, including takeovers; buy-outs; flotations; intellectual property; and employment law for businesses of all sizes.
Litigation: The firm is active in High Court and County Court work (both commercial and private), including personal injury, landlord and tenant, and debt recovery. It is particularly strong in employment and family law.
Property: The department acts for institutions and companies in a wide variety of commercial property work. A separate section deals with residential conveyancing.
Private Client: The department handles all aspects of a client's personal affairs, including probate; wills; trusts; tax planning and landed estates. It also has expertise in charity law.

Financial Services: All aspects of independent financial advice, including tax-efficient investments; pension and pre-retirement planning; life assurance; school fees; mortgages and health and income protection.

CLIENTELE: The firm acts for public and private companies; institutions; charities (particularly City Livery companies); NGOs; sports associations; and a large number of private individuals.

CUNNINGHAM JOHN

Fairstead House, 7 Bury Road, Thetford, IP24 3PL
Tel: (01842) 752401 **Fax:** (01842) 753555 **DX:** 124810 Thetford 2
Email: postmaster@cunningham-john.co.uk **Website:** www.cunningham-john.co.uk

Manchester House, 113 Northgate Street, Bury St. Edmunds, IP33 1HT
Tel: (01284) 761233 **Fax:** (01284) 702225 **DX:** 130760 BSE4

1 Norwich Road, Watton, IP25 6DA
Tel: (01953) 881994 **Fax:** (01953) 883746 **DX:** 31550 Watton

Managing & senior partners:	David Cunningham, Simon John
Number of partners:	10
Assistant solicitors:	13
Other fee-earners:	24

CONTACTS

Commercial/Corporate ....Michael Spencer
Company ....David Cunningham
Family ....Amita Terry
General Litigation ....Donal Sheahan
PI/CN...Simon John
....Tom Cook
....Sandra Patton
....Graemem Peart (DJ)
....William Jackson (DJ)
....(Bury)
Private Client ....Robert Chalmers

THE FIRM: Cunningham John's rapid and successful growth can be best explained by their extensive expertise and ability to handle high profile personal injury/clinical negligence actions as well as corporate and commercial transactions.

PRINCIPAL AREAS OF WORK:
Company/Commercial: Clients include leading plc and property companies; recent transaction of £500m major waste merger illustrates expertise in complex dealings. Clients nationwide, a London presence and a reputation as problem solvers - focused on clients interests and needs.
Personal Injury/Clinical Negligence: Nationwide reputation for high awards and settlements - see 'Leaders in Field (CN), Simon John.
Other Areas: General & commercial litigation, full private client service, family, child care & residential work.

CUNNINGHAMS

Second Floor, Bridge Street Chambers, 72 Bridge Street, Manchester, M3 2RJ
Tel: (0161) 833 1600 **Fax:** (0161) 833 1060

Senior Partner:	Martin Cunningham
Number of partners:	3
Assistant solicitors:	3
Other fee-earners:	11

AREAS OF PRACTICE

Crime 100%

CONTACTS

Private Client and Business Crime ....Martin S. Cunningham
Crime - Legal Aid ....David Caplin

THE FIRM: The firm operates from offices in central Manchester and practices exclusively in criminal law.

PRINCIPAL AREAS OF WORK: The practice represents both private and legally aided clients in all aspects of criminal law from road traffic offences to homicide cases. The senior partner, Martin Cunningham, specialises in white collar crime including Customs and Excise cases and business fraud. The practice also has Punjabi and Urdu speaking lawyers.Philip Lythgoe joined the practice as a partner in July 1998 having previously been a partner in Maidments since the inception of that practice. He has brought with him a substantial case load and former Maidments clients continue to seek him out.

CURREY & CO
21 Buckingham Gate, London, SW1E 6LS **Tel:** (020) 7828 4091 **Fax:** (020) 7828 5049 **DX:** 2300 Victoria **Ptnrs:** 7 **Asst solrs:** 4
Other fee-earners: 2

CURTIS DAVIS GARRARD

Bedfont Cross, Stanwell Road, Heathrow Airport, Feltham, TW14 8NY
Tel: (020) 8400 2400 **Fax:** (020) 8400 2420/1
Email: cdg@cdg.co.uk **Website:** www.cdg.co.uk

Senior Partner:	Simon Curtis
Partner:	Ian Garrard
Number of partners:	6
Assistant solicitors:	8
Other fee-earners:	1

AREAS OF PRACTICE

Shipping & Offshore 60%
Energy 20%
General Commercial Litigation 20%

THE FIRM: Curtis Davis Garrard is an international firm with an outstanding reputation in providing comprehensive advice on project and contentious matters to the shipping, offshore and energy sectors. Services range from contract preparation and negotiation to commercial litigation, arbitration and mediation. The firm is a market leader in shipbuilding and offshore construction law. The firm's rapid growth and success since its establishment in 1996 is based on its business philosophy which is to provide clients with the highest quality commercially led legal advice at a sensible and transparent cost. The firm's unique location at London Heathrow makes it one of the most accessible firms in England for international clients.

PRINCIPAL AREAS OF WORK: The firm covers the full spectrum of work, ranging from projects relating to the construction and financing of new tonnage to the settlement of disputes arising from the employment of vessels and offshore equipment, applying in each case the commercial approach that current market conditions

Continued overleaf

C

dictate including shipbuilding and construction; conversion and repair contracts; acquisition, financing, and disposal of second-hand vessels and offshore equipment, including demolition contracts; time, voyage and bareboat charterparties for the tanker (including LNG and LPG) and dry trades; contracts of affreightment; production, storage and supply contracts; collision and salvage and General Average.

CLIENTELE: Within the shipping, offshore and energy communities, the firm's clients range from shipowners, offshore contractors, oil and gas companies, charterers, ship managers, shipyards and marine equipment suppliers, to the financiers and insurers operating in those sectors.

RECRUITMENT & TRAINING: The firm seeks high quality City trained lawyers who want top quality work and flexible working practices in a progressive culture with good partnership prospects.

M.B. CUTTLE & CO

Bridge Street Chambers, 72 Bridge St, Manchester, M3 2RJ **Tel:** (0161) 835 2050 **Fax:** (0161) 831 7986 **Email:** cuttles_mcr@lineone.net **Ptnrs:** 4 **Asst solrs:** 2 **Other fee-earners:** 14 **Contact:** Mr. R.G. Williamson • One of the largest and most experienced criminal firms in Manchester. The firm also handles personal injury, civil litigation, commercial and domestic conveyancing.

AREAS OF PRACTICE

Crime	60%
Accident	15%
Children/Family	15%
Contract	5%
Employment	5%

D

DALE & CO SOLICITORS

10 Victoria Street, Felixstowe, IP11 7ER **Tel:** (0)70 74 79 47 08 **Fax:** (0)70 74 79 47 09 **Email:** law@daleandco.com **Ptnrs:** 1 **Asst solrs:** 1 **Other fee-earners:** 1 **Contact:** Mr Michael Dale • Specialists in maritime, transport, commercial and insurance law, undertaking contentious and non-contentious work for a wide range of UK and international clients.

DARBYS MALLAM LEWIS

Sun Alliance House, 52 New Inn Hall Street, Oxford, OX1 2QA **Tel:** (01865) 811700 **Fax:** (01865) 811777 **DX:** 4304 Oxford **Email:** info@darbys-mallam-lewis.co.uk **Website:** www.darbys-mallam-lewis.co.uk **Contact:** Mr. M.J. Clifton. • An expanding practice established in the 1920s. Handles a comprehensive range of work including conveyancing, litigation, company and commercial, probate, matrimonial work, child-care and criminal.

M C DARLINGTON

Diocesan Registry, Church House, 90 Deansgate, Manchester, M3 2QH **Tel:** (0161) 834 7545 **Fax:** (0161) 839 0093

DARLINGTON & PARKINSON

78 Pitshanger Lane, Ealing, London, W5 1QX **Tel:** 0181 998 4343 **Fax:** (020) 8566 8285 **DX:** 99631 Acton 2 **Ptnrs:** 5 **Asst solrs:** 6 **Other fee-earners:** 5

DAVENPORT LYONS

1 Old Burlington Street, London, W1X 2NL
Tel: (020) 7468 2600 **Fax:** (020) 7437 8216 **DX:** 37233 Piccadilly 1
Email: dl@davenportlyons.com **Website:** www.davenportlyons.com

Senior Partner:	Leon R. Morgan
Number of partners:	23
Assistant solicitors:	28
Other fee-earners:	17

AREAS OF PRACTICE

Company Commercial	25%
Litigation	23%
Entertainment/ Media	22%
Commercial Property	20%
Private Client	10%

THE FIRM: Davenport Lyons is a long-established firm in the West End of London. The firm is a leading media and entertainment practice and also has an excellent reputation in company and commercial work providing a service normally associated with larger city firms. The firm has wide experience in providing comprehensive legal services to corporate and commercial clients across a broad spectrum of market sectors. Those markets include media in all its forms (film, television, radio, music, theatre, publishing and the newspaper industry); information technology, e-commerce and new media; the retail sector; advertising; the restaurant, hotel, sport and leisure industries; property investment and development. The firm prides itself on an unusual blend of high quality legal expertise and commercial sensitivity to clients' needs. This service is provided with speed and efficiency and at a competitive price. The firm's continuing expansion has broadened its experience and expertise but it still recognises the importance to clients of partner attention. The firm also enjoys close involvement with many US and EU businesses and lawyers and the practice has a significant international dimension. Two of the firm's partners are admitted in New York and California respectively.

PRINCIPAL AREAS OF WORK: The firm provides legal services to a wide range of corporate and individual clients and has expertise in a number of particular specialised fields:
Company & Commercial: Advice on formations, reorganisations, acquisitions, venture capital, business start-ups, joint ventures, competition issues, corporate tax planning, employment matters and banking and finance. The firm is particularly well known for its work for growing companies up to and including stock exchange quotations.

Media: The firm's wide experience in the fields of intellectual property, media, IT, technology, e-commerce, new media and entertainment law is reflected in its client list which includes substantial film and television companies, national newspapers, magazines, book and music publishers, record companies and advertising and media agencies. The firm covers every aspect of the entertainment market and is the principal legal adviser to several banks and other financial institutions lending to the film and television sector.
Music, Entertainment & Theatre: The firm has a strong reputation in the UK and US, and acts for many leading music publishing corporations and individual musicians advising on recording contracts, copyright and the problems of performers and artists. The firm covers every aspect of the entertainment market and advises on the impact of EU legislation.
Property: A strong commercial property department acts for major developers, property investors, lending institutions and is particularly active in the retail sector in a broad range of substantial property and property related matters. The department is supported by a strong property litigation team. The firm also provides a first class specialist residential property service.
Liquor Licensing: The firm has developed its liquor and entertainment licensing work for its large numbers of clients in restaurant and nightclub businesses. The leading liqour and entertainment licensing lawyer, David Lavender, has joined the firm further enhancing its client base.
Defamation: A leader in this field, the firm's clients include a large number of national newspapers, book and magazine publishers as well as Private Eye magazine. The firm represents both plaintiffs and defendants.
Litigation: Commercial litigation is a long-established, substantial and successful element of the practice servicing not only the firm's corporate, property, media and entertainment clients, but also businesses in a wide range of sectors.
Employment: The firm provides specialist and comprehensive advice in all areas of employment law and represents and defends cases in the Employment Tribunal, the County Court and the High Court.
Private Client: This department provides a full service to private clients, both domestic and overseas, including matrimonial matters, wills, the administration of estates, personal tax, trusts and residential property work. The Tax and Trust Group advises on tax planning, compliance and appeals trust charities and pensions; wills and administration of estates and Court of Protection practice.
Sport: The firm has a well-established practice advising promoters of sporting events and individual sportsmen in connection with protecting and enhancing their interests.

INTERNATIONAL CONNECTIONS: Davenport Lyons has wide and long-standing contacts in the international sphere particularly with US and EU businesses and lawyers.

CONTACTS

Company/Commercial......Michael Hatchwell, ...Alon Domb ......Rebecca Ferguson
Competition ......David Marchese
Copyright & Trademark Litigation ......David Gore ......Stuart Lockyear
Defamation ......Kevin Bays ......Philip Conway, ...Robin Shaw
Employment ......Kathryn Pavey, ...Michael Hatchwell ......Alon Domb
Entertainment & Liquor Licensing ......Philip Conway ......David Lavender ......Kathryn Pavey
Intellectual Property & New Media ......Stephen Digby ......David Marchese
International Coordinator Michael Hatchwell
IT/Technology/E-commerce ..David Marchese ......Michael Hatchwell, ...Stephen Digby
Litigation (general) ......Kevin Bays, ...David Gore ......Robin Shaw
Litigation (Property) ......Jonathan Aubrey
Media/Film/TV ......Leon Morgan ......Richard Moxon, ...Melanie Haddad
Music/Entertainment/ Theatre ......James WareJay Quatrini
Private Client (Tax & Trusts) ......Judith Spells
Private Client (Matrimonial)......John Burrell
Property ......Graham Atkins ......John Downing, ...Richard Kelsey ......Paul McCombie
Publishing ......Leon Morgan ......James Ware
Sport ......Kevin Bays

DAVID BIGMORE & CO

Thornton Grange, Chester Road, Gresford, LL12 8NU **Tel:** (01978) 855058 **Fax:** (01978) 854623 **Email:** davidbigmore@hotmail.com **Website:** Under construction **Ptnrs:** 1 **Asst solrs:** 1 **Other fee-earners:** 1 **Contact:** David Bigmore • Niche practice specialising in both British and international franchising. Also advises on a broad range of corporate and commercial matters (with particular emphasis on mergers and acquisitions), and commercial litigation and commercial property work. Additional offices in London.

AREAS OF PRACTICE

Franchising (and Related work)............75%
Other Corporate and Commercial 25%

DAVID BISHOP & CO

14 Chapel Lane, Formby, Liverpool, L37 4DY **Tel:** 01704 878 421 **Fax:** 01704 878 959 **Email:** David_Bishop@compuserve.com

E. DAVID BRAIN & CO

8 Church Street, St. Austell, PL25 4AT **Tel:** (01726) 68111 **Fax:** (01726) 61433 **DX:** 81252 St. Austell **Email:** info@david-brain.co.uk **Website:** www.david-brain.co.uk **Ptnrs:** 2 **Other fee-earners:** 4

DAVID CHARNLEY & CO

Phoenix House, 102-106 South Street, Romford, RM1 1RX **Tel:** (01708) 766155 **Fax:** (01708) 730743 **DX:** 4614 Romford **Ptnrs:** 1 **Asst solrs:** 14 **Other fee-earners:** 16 • **Contact:** Mr Ben Thomas. The largest specialist franchised criminal practice in Essex, with legal aid and private client base. Fraud and other serious cases a particular strength, amongst general practice. Higher Court advocacy undertaken.

AREAS OF PRACTICE

Crime 100%

DAVID DU PRÉ & CO

90-92 Parkway, Regents Park, London, NW1 7AN
Tel: (020) 7284 3040 **Fax:** (020) 7485 1145 **DX:** 57070

Senior Partner:	David du Pré
Number of partners:	1
Assistant solicitors:	1
Other fee-earners:	0

AREAS OF PRACTICE

Family/Matrimonial/Divorce 100%

CONTACTS

Family/Matrimonial/Divorce ....David du Pré

THE FIRM: Established by David du Pré, a former matrimonial barrister, who later qualified as a solicitor in 1980 and held senior positions in leading City family departments before setting up his own specialist matrimonial practice in 1991. He is a member of the Solicitors Family Law Association, the International Society of Family Law, the Family Mediators Association, and the UK College of Family Mediators.

PRINCIPAL AREAS OF WORK: Matrimonial, family and co-habitation law including: separation and parental responsibility agreements; divorce petitions; financial applications, including complex and emergency applications, cases involving substantial assets/income or where there is an international dimension. Although both big and small cases are welcomed, a legal aid service is not available.

D

DAVID GIST & CO

21/23 Clare Street, Bristol, BS1 1TZ **Tel:** (0117) 927 9111 **Fax:** (0117) 927 9101 **DX:** 7880 Bristol
Email: info@davidgist.co.uk **Ptnrs:** 4 **Asst solrs:** 8 **Associates:** 2 **Contact:** Ms Susan Brewster
David Gist & Co deals mainly with claimant personal injury claims, predominantly those arising from motor accidents, and also an increasing number of clinical negligence and industrial accident claims.

DAVID GRAY & COMPANY

Old County Court, 56 Westgate Road, Newcastle upon Tyne, NE1 5XU **Tel:** (0191) 232 9547 **Fax:** (0191) 230 4149
DX: 61036 Newcastle upon Tyne **Email:** lawyers@davidgray.co.uk **Website:** davidgray.co.uk **Ptnrs:** 5 **Asst solrs:** 13 **Other fee-earners:** 12

DAVID JEACOCK

16 Church St, Wootton Bassett, Swindon, SN4 7BQ
Tel: (01793) 854111 **Fax:** (01793) 853600
Email: jeacock@lineone.net

Principal:	David Jeacock
Number of partners:	1

AREAS OF PRACTICE

Company/Commercial............................50%
Sports Law..30%
Private and General 20%

THE FIRM: After 10 years personal experience as an in-house lawyer, David Jeacock established the practice in 1984 to provide practical commercial advice to business clients. Because of his involvement and experience in sports administration and doping control, the practice soon provided practical advice in those areas as well and is now well established in this field. Clients include three national governing bodies of sports.This is a small personal practice that clearly enjoys working with all its clients, to solve their problems.

DAVID LEVENE & CO

Ashley House, 235-239 High Road, Wood Green, London, N22 8HF
Tel: (020) 8881 7777 **Fax:** (020) 8889 6395 **DX:** 135576 Wood Green 4
Email: info@davidlevene.co.uk **Website:** www.davidlevene.co.uk

The McLaren Building, 35 Dale End, Birmingham, B4 7LN
Tel: (0121) 212 0000 **Fax:** (0121) 233 1878 **DX:** 23502 Birmingham 3
Email: enquiries@davidlevene.co.uk

South Gate House, Wood Street, Cardiff, CF10 1EW
Tel: (029) 2039 0777 **Fax:** (029) 2023 0777 **DX:** 122790 CARDIFF 13
Email: contact@davidlevene.co.uk

Number of Partners:	11
Assistant solicitors:	39
Other fee-earners:	33

AREAS OF PRACTICE

Personal Injury..55%
Employment 15%
Crime 10%
Education, Disability & Human Rights..10%
Family & Other Legal Aid 5%
Property 5%

CONTACTS

Crime ....David Nicolls
Education/Disability & Human Rights ....David Ruebain
Employment ....Audrey Onwukwe
Family...Katy Rensten
Personal Injury ....David Levene
Property..Sue Pond

THE FIRM: David Levene & Co is a socially aware firm providing a national service to both individual and commercial clients. The 200 staff are grouped in specialist teams at five locations across England and Wales (Birmingham, Cardiff and three offices in London). The firm has a particularly strong reputation for personal injury and employment. The innovative work undertaken by the education and disability department is nationally recognised and has an expanding human rights dimension.

PRINCIPAL AREAS OF WORK:
Personal Injury: A leading team of 40 lawyers handling all types of personal injury claim including spinal and head injury cases with several successful appeal decisions in the past twelve months.
Employment: An expert team specialising in employment litigation for both employers and employees with particular expertise in race, sex and disability discrimination.

Education, Disability & Human Rights Law: A specialist department offering a unique service in the areas of special educational needs, school and college matters, care assessments, and disability discrimination. The department is already one of the key advisers on human rights.
Property: A team dedicated to the needs of individual and corporate clients involved in residential and commercial property transactions.
Family: All types of family work, including the full range of children's cases, as well as property and financial matters following separation or divorce.
Legal Aid: Includes family, crime, housing and welfare benefits.

DAVID PRICE & CO

5 Great James Street, London, WC1N 3DA **Tel:** (020) 7916 9911 **Fax:** (020) 7916 9910 **Email:** davidp@davidpricesolicitors.com
Website: www.davidpricesolicitors.com **Ptnrs:** 1 **Asst solrs:** 1 **Other fee-earners:** 3

DAVIDSON CHALMERS WS

10 Castle Terrace, Edinburgh, EH1 2DP **Tel:** (0131) 228 9191 **Fax:** (0131) 228 9003 **DX:** 408 Edinburgh **Email:** mailbox@dcws.co.uk
Website: www.dcws.co.uk **Ptnrs:** 4 **Asst solrs:** 8 **Other fee-earners:** 3

DAVIES AND PARTNERS

Rowan House, Barnett Way, Barnwood, Gloucester, GL4 3RT
Tel: (01452) 612345 **Fax:** (01452) 611922 **DX:** 55253

5 Highlands Court, Cranmore Avenue, Solihull, Birmingham, B90 4LE
Tel: (0121) 711 7107 **Fax:** (0121) 711 4851 **DX:** 715358 Solihull 19

135 Aztec West, Almondsbury, Bristol, BS32 4AW
Tel: (01454) 619 619 **Fax:** (01454) 619696 **DX:** 35007 Almondsbury

Senior Partner:	D.B. Davies
Number of partners:	18
Assistant solicitors:	29
Other fee-earners:	24

CONTACTS

Commercial Litigation	Geoffrey Hand
Commercial Property	Peter Mitchell
Company/Commercial	Tom Brennan
Land Development	Barrie Davies
Personal Injury & Medical Negligence	Ewan Lockhart
Private Client	Richard Maisey

THE FIRM: Davies and Partners is forward-thinking and objective in approach. The firm handles a large amount of commercial property, estate conveyancing, company and commercial, commercial litigation, and secured lending work and has also developed a strong personal injury and medical negligence practice.

PRINCIPAL AREAS OF WORK:
Land Development: The firm handles all aspects of development land, from initial site acquisition to individual unit transfers and ancillary documentation, planning applications and appeals, building contracts and freehold and leasehold matters.
Company/Commercial: The firm has extensive experience in the whole range of company and commercial work, including corporate finance; mergers, acquisitions and restructuring; MBOs; publicly-quoted companies; company and partnership formation; joint ventures; shareholders' agreements; banking; financial services and franchising; intellectual property, including international, EU and UK competition implications.
Commercial Property: The firm handles all aspects of commercial property including industrial, office and retail premises for both landlords and tenants and all associated funding, development and property management issues.
Commercial Litigation: Work includes building contracts; judicial review; landlord and tenant; employment; insurance; professional negligence; public liability; economic torts; corporate insolvency; unlawful trading; licensing; debt collection and banking litigation.
Personal Injury & Medical Negligence: The firm handles extensively both plaintiff and defendant personal injury work. Medical negligence work is plaintiff-orientated. Two fee earners are members of the Law Society Personal Injury Panel.
Other Areas: All aspects of corporate and personal tax and financial planning, agricultural law (including land acquisition and disposal, agricultural holdings, grazing agreements, share farming agreements, EU implications and business tenancies) and private client work (including residential conveyancing, re-mortgaging, wills, trusts and estate management, and distribution and winding-up of estates.)

DAVIES ARNOLD COOPER

6-8 Bouverie Street, London, EC4Y 8DD
Tel: (020) 7936 2222 **Fax:** (020) 7936 2020 **DX:** 172 London Chancery Lane WC2
Email: daclon@dac.co.uk **Website:** www.dac.co.uk

85 Gracechurch Street, London, EC3V 0AA
Tel: (020) 7936 2222 **Fax:** (020) 7410 7998 **DX:** 172 London Chancery Lane WC2
Email: daclon@dac.co.uk

60 Fountain Street, Manchester, M2 2FE
Tel: (0161) 839 8396 **Fax:** (0161) 839 8309 **DX:** 14363 Manchester
Email: dacman@dac.co.uk

Milburn House, Dean Street, Newcastle-upon-Tyne, NE1 1LE
Tel: (0191) 230 5115 **Fax:** (0191) 230 0296 **DX:** 715139 Newcastle upon Tyne 19
Email: dacnew@dac.co.uk

Senior Partner:	David McIntosh
Executive Partner:	Daniel Gowan
Operations Partner:	David Hertzell
UK:	
Number of partners:	39
Assistant solicitors:	88
Other fee-earners:	57
International:	
Number of partners:	2
Assistant solicitors:	7
Other fee-earners:	1

CONTACTS

ADR	Nick Sinfield
Banking	John Nelmes
Banking Disputes	Allan Reason
Commercial Litigation	David McIntosh
	Pippa Ellis
Commercial Property	Robert Lee
Construction & Engineering	Daniel Gowan
Construction & Property Insurance	Nick Young
Corporate & Employment	David Smellie
E-risk	Nick Sinfield
Energy	Akbar Ali
Fraud	Nick Young
Health & Safety	Richard Tovell
Healthcare	Simon Pearl
Insolvency	Bryan Green
Insurance Litigation	Nick Sinfield
International Transport/European Competition	Marjorie Holmes
Marine/Shipping	Marjorie Holmes
Medical Negligence - Defendants	Simon Pearl
Occupational Health	Geoff Meyer
Personal Injury - EL/PL	Allison Dias, Phil Jepson
Personal Injury - Motor	Phil Jepson Alan Jones
Product Liability	Anne Ware
Professional Indemnity/D&O	Nick Sinfield
	Kenneth McKenzie
Reinsurance	Michael Dobias

THE FIRM: At DAC, the focus is on the firm's core strengths. They are a leading practice in dispute resolution (including all forms of litigation, arbitration and alternative dispute resolution), corporate risk and commercial property services. Their commercial and pragmatic approach demonstrates a genuine market commitment to the clients they serve in the industry sectors of insurance, financial services, construction, commercial property, pharmaceutical, healthcare, manufacturing and retailing. The firm has collaborative relationships with its clients and focuses its resources towards developing products and service delivery which add value to their businesses. A passion for their clients' markets has led to the firm championing issues affecting their clients' business. DAC looks towards the issues of the future and has recently been at the forefront of such issues as transnational litigation, rehabilitation, human rights, e-risks, occupational health and employee issues, reputation management, corporate accountability and health and safety. They have taken a lead in the firm-wide usage of ADR and technological advances such as paperless litigation. The firm remains the number one choice for multi-party actions arising in the UK and internationally relating to product liability or physical disasters and accidents. Examples of high profile litigation include actions arising out of the collapse of the Maxwell empire, Barings, Polly Peck, Banesto, Piper Alpha, haemophilia and the Heathrow Tunnel collapse. In high profile and high value disputes, DAC is the preferred choice. They also undertake high volume work and are seen to be the nation's number one personal injury defence firm. DAC works for major British and international public and private companies, most of the large UK and international insurance and reinsurance companies, Lloyd's and many quoted and non-quoted property companies. The firm also acts for numerous banks, financial institutions, and professional partnerships of all disciplines. Davies Arnold Cooper was established in 1927. It has offices in London, the London Market, Manchester, Newcastle and Madrid, as well as strong contacts with leading foreign law firms throughout the world.

INTERNATIONAL CONNECTIONS: The firm has an overseas office at Paseo de la Castellana, 41, 1a Planta, 28046 Madrid, Spain, Tel: +34 91 391 3200, Fax: +34 91 319 7532, Email: dacmadrid@dacspain.com (Contact: Pablo Wesolowski.)

DAVIES, JOHNSON & CO

The Old Harbour Office, Guy's Quay, Sutton Harbour, Plymouth, PL4 0ES **Tel:** (01752) 226020 **Fax:** (01752) 225882 **DX:** 8254 Plymouth 2 **Email:** admin@djco.co.uk **Website:** www.djco.co.uk **Ptnrs:** 4 **Asst solrs:** 2 **Other fee-earners:** 1 **Contact:** Jonathan Johnson • A niche practice providing a complete range of services to the commercial shipping industry and the international trading community. An extensive website provides full details.

DAVIES LAVERY

Victoria Court, 17 - 21 Ashford Road, Maidstone, ME14 5FA
Tel: (01622) 625625 **Fax:** (01622) 625600 **DX:** 51971 Maidstone 2
Email: victoriacourt@davieslavery.co.uk **Website:** www.davies-lavery.co.uk

King Edward House, 135A New Street, Birmingham, B2 4QQ
Tel: (0121) 689 8900 **Fax:** (0121) 689 8901 **DX:** 13043 Birmingham
Email: newstreet@davieslavery.co.uk

64-66 Mark Lane, London, EC3R 7HN
Tel: (020) 7780 6868 **Fax:** (020) 7780 6800 **DX:** 623 London/City EC3
Email: marklane@davieslavery.co.uk

Managing Partners:	Kathy Dwyer (Maidstone), Claire McKinney (Birmingham), Philip West (London)
Number of partners:	15
Other fee-earners:	32

AREAS OF PRACTICE

Personal Injury/Insurance	78%
Commercial Property	7%
Commercial Litigation	5%
Company/Commercial	5%
Property Litigation	5%

THE FIRM: Davies Lavery provides the insurance and commercial sectors with a proactive, professional and expert service at a competitive rate. The firm is forward looking and innovative and its lawyers combine considerable experience and expertise with a progressive approach to work. With over 40 fee-earners, Davies Lavery is able to deal with a wide range of insurance disputes in terms of complexity and quantum. For further information, visit the firm's website.

PRINCIPAL AREAS OF WORK: Specialists in insurance-related work, Davies Lavery is particularly experienced in such areas as: personal injury; policy disputes; property damage; professional negligence; property liability; transit matters; company and commercial law; commercial property.

DAVIES LAVERY
SOLICITORS

DAVIES WALLIS FOYSTER

5 Castle Street, Liverpool, L2 4XE
Tel: (0151) 236 6226 **Fax:** (0151) 236 3088 **DX:** 14128 Liverpool
Email: enquiries@dwf-law.com **Website:** www.dwf.law.co.uk

Harvester House, 37 Peter Street, Manchester, M2 5GB
Tel: (0161) 228 3702 **Fax:** (0161) 835 2407 **DX:** 14313 Manchester
Email: enquiries@dwf-law.com

Senior partner:	Jim Davies
Number of partners:	43
Assistant solicitors:	48
Other fee-earners:	44

AREAS OF PRACTICE

Corporate and Commercial	70%
Insurance	30%

CONTACTS

Asset Finance	Andrew Maskill
Banking	James Szerdy
Business Agreements	Mark O'Connor
Competition	Laurence Pritchard
Construction	Ross Wellman
Corporate Transactions	Mark O'Connor
Debt Recovery	Sharon Williamson
Dispute Resolution	Graham Sidlow
Employment	Tim Scott
Health Safety & Environment	Ian Slater
Insolvency	Andrew Gregory
Insurance	Paul Berry
Intellectual Property	Laurence Pritchard
Internet & Technology	Laurence Pritchard
Licensing	Carl Bruder
Music & Media	Laurence Pritchard
Pensions	Gerald Power
Planning	Simon Richardson
Property	Guy Wallis
Public Company Work	Mark O'Connor
Training Services	Nigel Wallis
Wealth Protection	Paul Liddle

THE FIRM: Davies Wallis Foyster is one of the leading law firms in the North West, providing a full range of services for corporate and commercial clients and insurance clients. The firm acts for a substantial number of successful and growing businesses in most market sectors and has a proven track record of helping businesses to grow and compete. It has a reputation for the quality, style and energy of its people and its willingness to provide client references. Over the years, the firm has recruited market leaders in all its service areas and has built substantial, multi-skilled teams around them. It is therefore capable of providing clients with a menu of world-class services to help clients achieve their business objectives.

PRINCIPAL AREAS OF WORK:
Services for Corporate & Commercial Clients: Include asset finance, banking, business agreements, competition, construction, corporate transactions & advice, debt recovery, dispute resolution, employment, health/safety & environment, insolvency, insurance, intellectual property, internet & technology, licensing, music & media, pensions, planning, property, public company work, training services and wealth protection.
Services for Insurance Clients: Include accident & injury claims, commercial claims, policy documentation, recovery services and training services.

INTERNATIONAL CONNECTIONS: DWF is a member of EU LEX International Practice Group, a well integrated and respected network of international law firms, and handles a large amount of cross-border work.

RECRUITMENT & TRAINING: DWF wants trainee solicitors to play a part in building on its success. The firm is looking for trainees who enjoy working as part of a busy team, who respond positively to a challenge and have what it takes to deliver results for clients. The firm is looking for its partners of the future and in 1999 all of its qualifying trainees were offered jobs.

DAVIES WALLIS FOYSTER
SOLICITORS

DAVIS BLANK FURNISS

90 Deansgate, Manchester, M3 2QJ **Tel:** (0161) 832 3304 **Fax:** (0161) 834 3568 **DX:** 14311 Manchester **Email:** dbf-solicitors@tvc.org.uk
Ptnrs: 14 **Asst solrs:** 8 **Other fee-earners:** 9

DAWSON & CO

2 New Square, Lincoln's Inn, London, WC2A 3RZ
Tel: (020) 7421 4800 **Fax:** (020) 7421 4848 **DX:** 38 LDE
Email: legal@dawson-and-co.co.uk

Senior Partner:	Kenneth Wood
Number of partners:	22
Assistant solicitors:	12
Other fee-earners:	13

AREAS OF PRACTICE

Property	25%
Litigation	19%
Probate/Trusts	18%
Tax	18%
Family	13%
Company	7%

THE FIRM: A medium-sized firm which handles a substantial volume of all types of litigation, employment, property and property development, town and country planning, and tax planning work. Other areas of work include probate, matrimonial and company and commercial, minerals and waste, and international asset management.The firm has grown by attracting and keeping very good lawyers who want high quality and varied work but also a better quality of life than they might experience in the City. Please apply to the Practice Director.

CLIENTELE: Include major companies and institutions, old money and new, property developers, charities, waste operators, surveyors' firms and other professionals, colleges and housing associations.

DAWSON CORNWELL

16 Red Lion Square, Howborn, London, WC1R 4QT
Tel: (020) 7242 2556 **Fax:** (020) 7831 0478 **DX:** 35725 Bloomsbury
Email: mail@dawsoncornwell.co.uk

Senior Ppartner:	John Cornwell
Number of partners:	9
Assistant solicitors:	2
Other fee-earners:	3

THE FIRM: Dawson Cornwell is a specialist family law firm. All areas of matrimonial and family law are covered including divorces, separations, pre-marriage agreements, emergency procedures and all issues relating to children. Many cases involve the resolution of complex financial issues. Others involve child abduction and international custody disputes. The firm runs a well established mediation service.The senior partner founded the Solicitors Family Law Association in 1982 and, in accordance with the principles of the SFLA, the firm aims to resolve family disputes in a constructive and cost effective manner.Other areas of practice include property, probate, tax and family financial planning.

AREAS OF PRACTICE

Family and Matrimonial	73%
Conveyancing	12%
Wills, Trusts and probate	10%
Litigation and Miscellaneous	4%

CONTACTS

Children's Issues	Anne-Marie Hutchinson
Family Law (general)	Henry Rumbold

D

DEAN WILSON LAING

96 Church Street, Brighton, BN1 1UJ
Tel: (01273) 327241 **Fax:** (01273) 770913 **DX:** 2706 Brighton
Email: thelawyers@deanwilson.co.uk

Number of Partners:	9
Assistant solicitors:	4
Other fee-earners:	7

THE FIRM: Offers high quality service to its clients over a comprehensive range. It covers commercial and private clients and has the benefit of a Legal Aid franchise. It offers particular expertise in relation to property development, landlord and tenant, employment, family and licensing matters. The partners include a Recorder, a former local authority planning committee Chairman, a former Chairman of industrial tribunals, the holder of a High Courts Advocates Certificate, members of the Personal Injuries Panel (2), Family Law Panel and the Childrens Panel, an accredited family law Mediator together with a member of the Society of Trust & Estate Practitioners.

PRINCIPAL AREAS OF WORK:

Corporate & Commercial: The firm can advise on all aspects of corporate, commercial and financial matters, including company and partnership formation; restructuring; acquisitions and disposals; and insolvency. Expertise is offered in employment law and licensing law relating to pubs, clubs, restaurants and gaming. A full range of commercial property work is undertaken including estate development, planning work, commercial leasing and commercial conveyancing.

Landlord & Tenant: The firm specialises in all aspects of landlord and tenant law, both residential and commercial. A substantial amount of litigation of this type is dealt with. The firm are honorary solicitors to the Association of Residential Letting Agents and also to the Southern Private Landlords Association. Leasehold enfranchisement is fully covered.

Employment: The firm covers all areas of this work, acting for both employers and employees.

Family Law: The family law department covers all aspects of family law, including mediation and has particular experience of substantial settlements.

Personal Injury: With two panel members certificates, this firm has wide experience acting for both claimants and defendants.

Sports Law: The firm has experience acting for a number of this country's international sports persons before their sports disciplinary tribunals and also dealing with complex constitutional issues.

Litigation: A range of civil and criminal litigation is undertaken including civil engineering and construction disputes, marine disputes, professional negligence actions, disputes including applications for restraint of trade and non-competition injunctions, licensing matters and debt recovery. Agency work for mortgage lenders and others.

Private Client: Private client service includes wills, probate, administration of estates, trusts and tax planning, residential conveyancing and leases, charity law, and criminal and immigration law.

Information Technology: This firm was one of the first to install a network and has consequently a depth of experience in this area.

Financial Services: The firm is authorised to carry out discrete investment business.

AREAS OF PRACTICE

Domestic Conveyancing/Probate	20%
General Litigation, including Personal Injury	14%
Landlord & Tenant	14%
Commercial Property	12%
Employment	12%
Matrimonial	12%
Company Commercial	8%
Miscellaneous	3%
Planning	3%
Sport	2%

CONTACTS

Children	L. Wall
Commercial/Commercial Property/ Landlord & Tenant (Non-contentious)	David Barling
Employment	Ian Wilson
Financial Services	John Atkinson
Landlord & Tenant Litigation	Claire Whiteman
Licensing	Nick Perkins
Matrimonial	David Laing
Personal Injury	Ian Wilson
Planning	David Barling
Probate & Trusts	Georgina James
Residential/Long Leasehold	Joanna Ward
Sport	David Laing

DEAS MALLEN

Eldon Chambers, 23 The Quayside, Newcastle upon Tyne, NE1 3DE **Tel:** (0191) 221 0898 **Fax:** (0191) 232 0930 **DX:** 61085
Email: advice@deas-mallen.co.uk **Ptnrs:** 7 **Asst solrs:** 2 **Other fee-earners:** 1

DEBEVOISE & PLIMPTON

Tower 42, International Finance Centre, Old Bond Street, London, EC2N 1HQ
Tel: (020) 7786 9000 **Fax:** (020) 7588 4180
Website: www.debevoise.com

Managing partner:	James Kiernan
UK:	
Number of partners:	4
Assistant solicitors:	21
Worldwide:	
Number of partners:	92
Assistant solicitors:	302

CONTACTS

M&A .... James Kiernan
.... Colin Bogie
Corporate Finance .... Robert Bruce
.... Katherine Ashton
Dispute Resolution .... Arthur Marriott QC

THE FIRM: Debevoise & Plimpton is a leading international firm practising in the areas of corporate law, litigation, tax, real estate and trusts and estates.

PRINCIPAL AREAS OF WORK: The London office, which advises on matters of US and English law, represents US, UK and other clients in connection with mergers, acquisitions and joint ventures; global offerings and other securities transactions; telecommunications including privatisations; acquisitions and other financings; private investment funds, tax planning; international commercial arbitration and dispute resolution. The office works closely with the firm's head office in New York and branch offices in Paris, Moscow, Hong Kong and Washington DC.

LANGUAGES: French, German, Hungarian, Italian, Potuguese, Russian and Spanish.

DEBORAH MILLS ASSOCIATES

Tamsin House, 4 Chapel Street, Marlow, SL7 1DD **Tel:** (01628) 487 711 **Fax:** (01628) 481 678 **Email:** info@dm-a.com

D

DECHERT

2 Serjeants' Inn, London, EC4Y 1LT
Tel: (020) 7583 5353 **Fax:** (020) 7353 3683 **DX:** 30 London
Email: advice@dechertEU.com **Website:** www.dechert.com

Senior partner:	Steven Fogel
Chief executive:	Peter Duffell
UK:	
Number of partners:	46
Assistant solicitors:	90
Other fee-earners:	45
International:	
Number of partners:	168
Assistant solicitors:	276
Other fee-earners:	155

AREAS OF PRACTICE

Property	34%
Corporate	23%
Litigation	18%
Financial Services	13%
Commercial (including Trademarks)	5%
Employment	4%
Tax & Private Client	3%

CONTACTS

Banking/Finance & Securitisation ....
.... Trevor Beadle
Commercial .... Peter Crockford
Commercial Litigation/ Investigations ....
.... David Byrne
Construction .... Charles Brown
Corporate .... David Vogel
Corporate Recovery .... Sally Unwin
Corporate Tax .... Mark Stapleton
Customs & Excise/VAT ....
.... Malachy Cornwell-Kelly
Employment .... Charles Wynn-Evans
EU & Competition .... Eddie Kling
Financial Services .... Peter Astleford
Insurance/Reinsurance .... Michael Smith
IP/Defamation .... Andrew Hearn
IT/E-commerce .... Renzo Marchini
Planning .... Justin True
Property .... Chris Edwards
Property Litigation .... Jeremy Grose
Retail .... Paul Harding
Tax & Private Client .... Ian Marsh
Trade Marks .... Paul Kavanagh

THE FIRM: On 1 July 2000, City of London law firm, Titmuss Sainer Dechert, merged with US law firm, Dechert Price & Rhoads, to form an international legal practice called Dechert. The merger followed a successful six-year alliance between the two firms. Dechert has 780 lawyers in ten offices located in the US and Europe serving clients operating in markets around the globe.

PRINCIPAL AREAS OF WORK: The London office of Dechert offers:
Corporate Services: Core services include flotations, capital issues, transborder and domestic mergers, acquisitions and disposals and corporate reorganisations and recoveries. Specialist teams handle banking, securitisation and insolvency work.
Property: A comprehensive range of property services including commercial, industrial and retail development, investment, planning, environment, property litigation and construction. Clients include investment funds, major retailers, property developers, large corporations and public authorities.
Financial Services: Legal, regulatory and tax advice to financial service firms and advice on the legal aspects of operating an investment management business in Europe, North America and other markets around the globe.
Insurance: Serves Lloyd's and non-Lloyd's insurance and reinsurance clients and deals with mergers and acquisitions in the insurance market, insurance litigation and arbitration.
Investigations: All civil and criminal aspects of corporate fraud, DTI inquiries, SFO investigations, Inland Revenue and Customs & Excise investigations, disciplinary proceedings, insider dealing, investigations by the SROs, money laundering and compliance.
Litigation: A broad range of national and international commercial disputes in most areas of civil law with particular expertise in antitrust, take-over, fraud-related cross-border tracing, intellectual property and defamation. Also provide ADR services.
Commercial: Intellectual property, UK and EU competition law, computer law, product liability, overseas joint ventures and general commercial contracts. The trade mark practice offers a unified approach to the selection, requisition, exploitation and enforcement of intellectual property rights. Dechert also has specialist practices in employment, tax and private client, customs and excise and international trade.

CLIENTELE: The firm's clients include substantial UK and international listed and private companies from a wide cross-section of industry and commerce.

RECRUITMENT & TRAINING: In London, the firm recruits up to 15 trainees annually. Contact: Lynn Muncey for a trainee solicitor recruitment brochure.

DEIGHTON GUEDALLA

Top Floor, 30-31 Islington Green, London, N1 8DU **Tel:** (020) 7359 5700 **Fax:** (020) 7359 9909 **DX:** 58251 Islington **Ptnrs:** 2 **Asst solrs:** 3
Other fee-earners: 1

DENISON TILL

Goodbard House, Infirmary Street, Leeds, LS1 2JS
Tel: (0113) 246 7161 **Fax:** (0113) 246 7518 **DX:** 26426 LEEDS
Email: mail@denisontill.com **Website:** www.denisontill.com

Stamford House, Piccadilly, York, YO1 9PP
Tel: (01904) 611411 **Fax:** (01904) 646972 **DX:** 65206 YORK6
Email: mail@denisontill.com

Managing partner:	Christopher Barton
Senior partner:	Anthony P. Ridge
Number of partners:	14
Assistant solicitors:	10
Other fee-earners:	16

AREAS OF PRACTICE

Commercial Property	22%
Company/Commercial	20%
Dispute Resolution	20%
Construction	18%
Private Litigation	10%
Tax, trusts and wills	6%
Residential Property	4%

CONTACTS

Agriculture & Estates	David Grice
Banking	Andrew Lindsay
Commercial Property	Bill Marshall-Smith
Company/Commercial	Anthony Ridge
Construction	Gareth Hevey
Debt Recovery	Jonathan Cripwell
Dispute Resolution	Anthony Glaister
Employment	Brian Harrington
Family	Mark Hepworth
Insolvency	Duncan Graham
Pensions	Alistair Duncan
Planning	Lionel Lennox
Tax, Trusts & Wills	John Goodrich

THE FIRM: Denison Till is generally recognised as the leading commercial practice in York, and has an expanding office in Leeds. Denison Till has expanded through developing various specialisations, including construction law, dispute resolution, personal injury litigation, insolvency, company law, employment, pensions, commercial property, agriculture and ecclesiastical law.
The firm has grown strongly over the last few years and has been able to attract experienced high calibre staff from a number of the leading national law firms. Denison Till plans to grow steadily in its existing locations, especially in Leeds. More expertise in niche areas is being and will be established.

PRINCIPAL AREAS OF WORK: The firm comprises eight principal departments with a strong commercial bias: company/commercial; insolvency; employment and pensions; dispute resolution; construction; commercial property; ecclesiastical; private client.

INTERNATIONAL CONNECTIONS: Denison Till has established overseas contacts and clients and is a member of Lawspan International, an international grouping of commercial lawyers. Partners are proficient in a number of European languages.

CLIENTELE: Clients include prominent construction, property and industrial companies many of which are plc's. The firm also acts for public institutions and a wide range of private companies, partnerships and individuals.
Denison Till is the largest commercial and private practice in York, and has an expanding commercial office in Leeds. Denison Till has expanded through developing various specialisations, including construction law, dispute resolution, personal injury litigation, insolvency, company law, employment, pensions, commercial property, agriculture and ecclesiastical law.

DENTON WILDE SAPTE

Five Chancery Lane, Clifford's Inn, London, EC4A 1BU
Tel: (020) 7242 1212 **Fax:** (020) 7404 0087 **DX:** 242
Email: info@dentonwildesapte.com **Website:** www.dentonwildesapte.com

One Fleet Place, London, EC4M 7WS
Tel: (020) 7242 1212 **Fax:** (020) 7246 7777 **DX:** 145 London City EC4

Bankside House, 107-112 Leadenhall Street, London, EC3A 4AA
Tel: (020) 7242 1212 **Fax:** (020) 7246 7722

Regency Court, 206/208 Upper Fifth Street, Milton Keynes, MK9 2HR
Tel: (01908) 690260 **Fax:** (01908) 668535 **DX:** 31431

Chairmanr:	James Dallas
Deputy Chairman:	Mark Andrews
Managing Partner, Strategic Initiative:	Steve Blakely
Managing Partner:	Victoria Glastonburt (UK)
International Managing Partner:	David Moroney
UK:	
No of partners:	157
Assistant solicitors:	318
Other fee earners:	141
International:	
No of partners:	39
Assistant solicitors:	102
Other fee earners:	49

CONTACTS

Alternative Risk Transfer	George Sandars
Aviation	Hugh O'Donovan
Banking & Finance	Adrian Miles
Construction	Julian Pope
Corporate & Commercial	Steve Goodman
Employment	Stephanie Dale
Energy & Natural Resources	Michael Doble
Environmental	Jacqui O'Keeffe
EU & Competition	David Aitman
Financial Markets	Robert Finney
Reconstruction & Insolvency	Mark Andrews
Insurance & Reinsurance	Adrian Mecz
Insolvency	Mark Andrews
Intellectual Property	Clive Thorne
International	David Moroney
International Projects	Neil Cuthbert

THE FIRM: Denton Wilde Sapte is a leading international law firm based in the City of London. Formed by the merger of Denton Hall and Wilde Sapte on 1 February 2000, this truly international organisation offers a comprehensive range of the highest quality and affordable commercial legal advice. The combination of Denton Hall and Wilde Sapte has created a premier law firm that is heralded for its innovative and commercial approach. The firm's business is focused on a number of key sectors which ensures that its lawyers provide clients with a real understanding of the market as well as a comprehensive command of the law. Denton Wilde Sapte has 16 offices across Europe, the Middle East and Asia - a network that is further strengthened by Denton International, a group of leading law firms that brings the overall total to 35 offices in 23 jurisdictions around the world.

PRINCIPAL AREAS OF WORK: Denton Wilde Sapte provides a wealth of contentious and non-contentious commercial legal advice and its extensive knowledge and experience spans many jurisdictions and different business sectors, both public and private.
Banking & Finance: The Banking and Finance department acts for banks and finance houses on both routine and complex ground-breaking transactions. It covers a wide range of work from corporate lending, project finance, PFI and acquisition finance through to general asset finance (including shipping and aviation), trade finance, structured finance, financial markets and regulation and insolvency and workouts.
International Projects: Boasting an extensive international projects practice, the firm works in a wide range of sectors including electricity, oil and gas, water, mining and minerals, telecommunications infrastructure, transportation and environmental issues. The firm acts for banks, sponsors, governments and contractors.

Media & Technology: Denton Wilde Sapte is a leader in media and technology. Its highly experienced department has worked extensively in broadcasting, publishing, IT, film, TV, telecommunications, sport, digital media and music.
Energy & Infrastructure: This leading practice & infrastructure brings together extensive international experience across a wide range of energy industries including oil and gas, electricity, water, mining and minerals and construction.
Property: The property department advises on all aspects of commercial property and combines development, retail, institional investment, property, finance, planning and public sector.
Corporate & Commercial: Handling all aspects of corporate finance law, the department acts for many major public listed companies, advising on M&As, joint ventures/POs, employment law, regulatory and competition matters, EU law and corporate tax.
Litigation: The firm deals with all forms of commercial dispute including administrative law, arbitration, aviation law, banking, finance and financial services regulation, fraud, construction disputes, environmental law, business reconstruction, intellectual property, judicial review, M&A, professional negligence, shipping and tax.
Other: In addition to these key areas, the firm has built up considerable expertise in a large proportion of specialist e sectors such as insurance, aviation, rail, shipping and retail.

INTERNATIONAL CONNECTIONS: The firm has offices in Almaty, contact Marla Valdez, +7 3272 917 422; Beijing, contact David Ben Kay, +8610 6505 4891; Brussels, contact Blanche Sas, +32 2 223 0621; Cairo, contact Bridget McKinney, +202 340 1563; Dubai, contact Martin Kitchen, +971 4 331 0220; Gibraltar, contact Nicholas Keeling, +350 77750; Hong Kong, contact Raymond Kwok, +852 2820 6272; Istanbul, contact Ece Güner-Ünlü, +90 212 282 4385; Moscow, contact Pat Seferovich, +7095 255 7900; Paris, contact Jaques Salès, +33 05 16 00; Singapore, contact Oliver Wright, +65 538 1551; Tokyo, contact Philip Quirk, +81 3 5641 8455. Associated Offices: Abu Dhabi, Barcelona, Berlin, Budapest, Chemnitz, Cologne, Copenhagen, Dresden, Dar Es Salaam, Düsseldorf, Frankfurt, Gothenburg, Hamburg, Madrid, Malmö, Munich, Muscat, Oslo, Stockholm, Vienna.

CONTACTS CONTINUED

IT & E-commerce	John Worthy
Leasing	Adrian Miles
Litigation	Mark Gill
	Liz Tout
Media & Technology	Tony Grant
Pensions	Alan Jarvis
PFI	Ed Marlow
Project Finance	Howard Barrie
Property	Stephen Ashworth
Rail	Christopher McGee-Osborne
Sports	Adrian Barr-Smith
Tax	Andy Collins
Telecommunications	Nicholas Higham
Trade	John Miles
Trade Finance	Geoffrey Wynne

DEVONSHIRES

Salisbury House, London Wall, London, EC2M 5QY
Tel: (020) 7628 7576 **Fax:** (020) 7256 7318 **DX:** 33856 Finsbury Square
Email: info@devonshires.co.uk **Website:** www.devonshires.com

Managing Partner:	Julie Bradley
Senior Partner:	Nigel Hardy
Number of partners:	18
Assistant solicitors:	19
Other fee-earners:	21

THE FIRM: City based, Devonshires provides an extensive range of high-quality legal services for public and private sector clients including housing associations, general commercial organisations, local authorities, banks, building societies, other commercial investors, charities, government and entrepreneurs. Devonshires has seen considerable growth over recent years both in size and expertise, having attracted and retained clients from all business disciplines. With it, their reputation for providing expert, cost-effective advice has grown and helped draw in 'up and coming' solicitors and trainees from prominent legal practices and other backgrounds. The firm has strength in depth, allowing the team of partners and fee earners to work together enabling them to gain a clear picture of client needs' and how best to achieve them with legal solutions. Clients feel secure in the knowledge that they receive a one-stop service from Devonshires. The property, litigation, finance, PFI and corporate departments all demonstrate complete flexibility no matter what size or complexity of project. Work is provided in a variety of charging structures including: fixed fee, competitive tendering, hourly rate and conditional fee.

PRINCIPAL AREAS OF WORK: A recognised leader in the social housing market Devonshires currently advises over 200 registered social landlords; financial institutions and stock exchange listed debt issuers; charities; corporations; government (domestic and international); insolvency practitioners; local authorities, NHS trusts; private clients; professional service providers; property developers and investors (including financial institutions). In addition, the expanding litigation department, which handles complex civil and criminal proceedings on behalf of many high profile corporate and private clients, is rapidly gaining recognition for a consistent number of prominent successes. Devonshires undertakes a broad range of commercial services and all work required by registered social lenders; assisting businesses in all aspects including: major project work; property acquisition, development and transfer; construction finance and securitisation; PFI; corporate acquisitions, services and structures; commercial contracts (e.g. employment, commercial and IT) and all areas of litigation.

AREAS OF PRACTICE

Property	35%
Litigation	30%
Banking & Corporate	20%
Construction	10%
Religious & Charities	5%

CONTACTS

Commercial Property	Allan Hudson
Company/Commercial	Gareth Hall
Construction	Nigel Hardy
Development	David Brittain
Employment	Amanda Harvey
Finance/Corporate Structures	Andrew Cowan
Housing Management	Nick Billingham
	Jane Mogollon
Litigation/Dispute Resolution	Philip Barden
Low Cost Home Ownership	Jane Nunnerley
PFI	Mark Johnson
Property Securitisation/Local Authorities	Julie Bradley
Public Private Partnerships/Special Projects	Duncan Brown
Religious/Charities	Daniel Clifford

DEWAR HOGAN

15 New Bridge St, London, EC4V 6AU
Tel: (020) 7822 7400 **Fax:** (020) 7822 7401 **DX:** 98939 Cheapside 2
Email: info@dewarhogan.co.uk

Managing partner:	R.D. Hogan
Senior partner:	R.D. Hogan
Number of partners:	2
Assistant solicitors:	3
Other fee-earners:	2

AREAS OF PRACTICE

Property Litigation 100%

CONTACTS

Property Litigation ..Ronald Hogan, John Cox

THE FIRM: Dewar Hogan specialises exclusively in contentious property matters and property litigation in relation to commercial and residential property. The firm's clients include property companies, property funds, retailers, public authorities, banks and private investors. All of its solicitors were formerly with leading London firms.

PRINCIPAL AREAS OF WORK: Contractual disputes, solicitors' negligence and landlord and tenant.

DEWEY BALLANTINE

1 Undershaft, London, EC3A 8LP
Tel: (020) 7456 6000 **Fax:** (020) 7456 6001
Email: firstname.surname@deweyballantine.com **Website:** www.deweyballantine.com

Managing Partner:	Frederick R. Gander
Senior Partner:	Stuart I. Odell
Number of partners:	10
Total resident staff:	65
Other fee-earners:	27

AREAS OF PRACTICE

Capital Markets 20%
Project Finance.......................................20%
Energy 15%
Structured Finance 15%
Corporate Finance 10%
Leasing 10%
Tax 10%

CONTACTS

Capital Markets ....Camille Abousleiman
....Drew Salvest
Central Europe ....Stephen Jones
Energy......................................Mark Saunders
Mergers & Acquisitions ....Mark Saunders
....Stephen Jones
Project Finance ....James D. Simpson.
Tax, Leasing...................................Stuart Odell
Tax, Structured Finance ....Fred Gander

THE FIRM: Dewey Ballantine is one of the major US-based law firms. It has had a significant international practice for some years, particularly in Central Europe, Latin America and Asia. The international presence was further developed in 1996, when the firm substantially expanded its London office which, with the addition of English qualified partners and assistants, now offers English as well as New York law advice, with a particular emphasis on capital markets, project financing in emerging markets, structured finance and cross border leasing, energy, mergers and acquisitions. Having its origins in New York in 1909, where the firm is based, the firm also has substantial offices in Washington DC and Los Angeles. Internationally, in addition to its London office, the firm has Central European offices in Warsaw, Prague and Budapest and an office in Hong Kong. The firm is also active in the Middle East.

PRINCIPAL AREAS OF WORK: Dewey Ballantine has a highly diversified practice, the breadth of which is reflected in the London office activity, which combines a significant capital markets practice focusing on emerging markets (involving both debt and equity issues) with project finance, structured finance (including securitisation), tax related cross-border leasing and financial products (two of the London partners being tax specialists) and privatisation, mergers and acquisitions and other transactional work, particularly in Central and Eastern Europe (including Russia).

CLIENTELE: The firm's regular clients include multinational companies, commercial and investment banks, governmental organisations, energy companies, telecommunications service providers and insurance companies.

S.J. DIAMOND & SON
Corry House, 7-19 Royal Avenue, Belfast, BT1 1FB **Tel:** (028) 90243726 **Fax:** (028) 90230651 **Ptnrs:** 4 **Asst solrs:** 3 **Other fee-earners:** 2

DICKINSON DEES

St. Ann's Wharf, 112 Quayside, Newcastle-upon-Tyne, NE99 1SB
Tel: (0191) 279 9000 **Fax:** (0191) 279 9100 **DX:** 61191
Email: law@dickinson-dees.co.uk **Website:** www.dickinson-dees.com

Senior Partner:	Graham Wright
UK:	
Number of partners:	50
Assistant solicitors:	70
Other fee-earners:	70
International:	
Number of partners:	1
Assistant solicitors:	2
Other fee-earners:	3

CONTACTS

Commercial Property ....Ian Ward
Company & Commercial................Nigel Bellis
Litigation ....Glenn Calvert
Private Client ....George Lyall

THE FIRM: Dickinson Dees is the largest firm of solicitors in the North East region, with a total staff of over 380.

PRINCIPAL AREAS OF WORK: The practice offers both commercial and private client services. Specialist services include development and construction; banking and commercial lending; corporate tax; pensions; employee incentives; public procurement; commercial and EU law (based locally and in Brussels); health sector; environmental and planning; local authority and public sector work; employment; information technology; social housing and agriculture. The firm has an associated office in Brussels.For further information contact John Flynn, Business Development Partner or Graham Wright, Senior Partner.

DICKINSON MANSER

5 Parkstone Rd, Poole, BH15 2NL **Tel:** (01202) 673071 **Fax:** (01202) 680470 **DX:** 07602 **Email:** dmgen@lds.co.uk **Ptnrs:** 6 **Asst solrs:** 7 **Other fee-earners:** 8 **Contact:** Lewis H. Parkyn • General practice. Clients include small businesses, private individuals and PLCs. Legal Aid Franchise. Members of LawGroup UK. Investors in People. Agency work undertaken.

AREAS OF PRACTICE

Litigation	33%
Probate & Trusts	33%
Property/Commercial	33%

DICKSON MINTO WS

Royal London House, 22-25 Finsbury Square, London, EC2A 1DX
Tel: (020) 7628 4455 **Fax:** (020) 7628 0027

11 Walker Street, Edinburgh, EH3 7NE
Tel: (0131) 225 4455 **Fax:** (0131) 225 2712

Senior Partner:	Alastair R. Dickson
Managing Partner	Bruce W. Minto
Number of partners:	13

AREAS OF PRACTICE

Company/Commercial/ Corporate finance	85%
Banking	15%

CONTACTS

Banking	Michael J. Barron
Company/Commercial/ Corporate Finance	Alastair R. Dickson

THE FIRM: Established in 1985, the firm, through its offices in London, Edinburgh and Glasgow, has grown substantially and handles a full range of corporate transactions. As a result of the concentration of numbers of specialist lawyers in each of its offices, the firm has the resources to deal with transactions of all sizes and complexity for its wide range of clients, including private companies, listed companies and financial institutions. Dickson Minto has advised on some of the largest MBOs and MBIs in Europe, frequently involving numerous other jurisdictions in the USA, South America, Australasia and the Far East. The firm was lead adviser on the largest LBOs in Europe in each of the 1980s and 1990s.

PRINCIPAL AREAS OF WORK: Although best known for its private equity work for financial institutions, the firm has specialist resources in the areas of banking, financial services, EU and competition law, pensions law, information technology, intellectual property and taxation which enable it to provide the best service to clients on a full range of corporate transactions. The firm has wide experience in dealing with and co-ordinating transactions involving other advisers, such as accountants, actuaries and environmental specialists and through its well established contacts with foreign lawyers in international transactions. The firm instructed lawyers in over fifty jurisdictions during 1999 on behalf of its clients. Dickson Minto continues to expand and, through its emphasis on the recruitment and intensive training of high-quality staff, it has been able to maintain and continues to provide a flexible service, responsive and dedicated to the needs of all corporate clients, whether large, medium or small, private or public.

DIGBY BROWN

The Savoy Tower, 77 Renfrew Street, Glasgow, G2 3BZ
Tel: (0141) 566 9494 **Fax:** (0141) 566 9500 **DX:** GW17
Email: maildesk@digbybrown.co.uk **Website:** www.digbybrown.co.uk

7 Albyn Place, Edinburgh, EH2 4NG
Tel: (0131) 225 8505 **Fax:** (0131) 240 0949 **DX:** ED 182
Email: maildesk@digbybrown.co.uk

Royal Exchange, Panmure Street, Dundee, DD1 1DU
Tel: (01382) 322197 **Fax:** (01382) 205915 **DX:** DD 26
Email: maildesk@digbybrown.co.uk

Compensate, 2/3 Teviot Place, Edinburgh, EH1 2QZ
Tel: (0131) 240 8800 **Fax:** (0131) 240 8801 **DX:** ED 42
Email: maildesk@digbybrown.co.uk

Managing Partner:	Robert Swanney
Number of partners:	11
Assistant solicitors:	6
Other fee-earners:	12

AREAS OF PRACTICE

Pursuer Litigation	80%
Insurance	14%
Conveyancing/Executry	6%

THE FIRM: Established in 1906, the firm of Digby Brown has grown into one of the leading firms involved in personal injury litigation. The firm originally made its name in the trades union sector, but now also acts for a number of road traffic legal expenses insurers. More recently, the firm has developed connections with several claims handlers who use them as their main Scottish representative. The firm is now perceived as being the leading firm in litigation involving head and spinal injuries, with Robert Swanney, an expert in the field. Other areas of work include adoption, employment law and industrial tribunals.The firm also trades under the name 'Compensate', an innovative approach to personal injury litigation. This division operates as a shop, and has proved very successful. Although staffed by qualified solicitors, the concept of a walk-in service is aimed at demystifying the complex and sometimes intimidating procedures of litigation for the general public. For further information, see our website, or contact Robert Swanney, partner, or Jim Wright, partnership secretary.

D

DIXON, COLES & GILL

Bank House, Burton Street, Wakefield, WF1 2DA **Tel:** (01924) 373467 **Fax:** (01924) 366234 **DX:** 15030 **Email:** box@dixon-coles-gill.co.uk **Website:** www.dixon-coles-gill.co.uk **Ptnrs:** 2 **Asst solrs:** 1 **Other fee-earners:** 1 **Contact:** Linda M. Box • The partners of the firm have been the Registrars to the Diocese of Wakefield since 1988.

D J FREEMAN

43 Fetter Lane, London, EC4A 1JU
Tel: (020) 7583 4055 **Fax:** (020) 7353 7377 **DX:** 103 London Chancery Lane WC2
Email: marketing@djfreeman.co.uk **Website:** www.djfreeman.co.uk

Senior Partner:	Colin Joseph
Chief Executive:	Jonathan Lewis
Number of partners:	58
Assistant solicitors:	56
Other fee-earners:	35

AREAS OF PRACTICE

Property Services	42%
Insurance Services	26%
Commercial Litigation	20%
Media & Communications	12%

CONTACTS

Commercial litigation	Sally Hine
Construction	David Johnson
Employment	Jane Moorman
Insolvency	Christine Derrett
Insurance/Corporate/ Regulatory	Richard Spiller
Insurance Insolvency	Vivien Tyrell
Insurance Litigation	David Kendall
IP and Branding	Alexander Carter-Silk
IT and e-commerce	Clive Davies
Media & Communications - Corporate	Tony Leifer
Planning	Richard Max
Property	Susan Hall
Property/Corporate/ Joint Ventures	Alan Magnus
Property Finance	John Clark
Property Litigation	Vivien King
Public International Law	Tim Daniel
Public Sector	Ted Totman
Retail Property	Monica Blake
Taxation	Chris Comyn

THE FIRM: Shortlisted by *Chambers* in their 'Law Firm of the Year 1999' awards, DJ Freeman continues to expand and excel in its four chosen areas of business: commercial litigation, insurance, media and communications and property. In each market sector, multi-disciplinary teams of lawyers combine legal services of the highest standard with a commercial approach and deep understanding of their clients' business. This strategy means the lawyers become wholly familiar with the issues, opportunities, competitive advantages and pressures of their clients – a highly effective out-of-house resource for in-house lawyers. The firm is acknowledged as a leader and innovator in its use of technology in all areas of business and has a reputation as a promoter of the use of plain English in legal documents. The firm's regular newsletters are read by thousands of professionals within these industries. They complement the many workshops, seminars and conferences arranged by the firm on a range of topical issues.

PRINCIPAL AREAS OF WORK:
Insurance & Reinsurance: One of the leading insurance practices, this 40-strong team specialises in coverage disputes, reinsurance, commercial, corporate finance, and insolvency. Clients include major insurance companies, Lloyd's syndicates, reinsurers, brokers, underwriting agents, P&I clubs, and finance providers. Insurance litigators handle market and coverage disputes, third party and product liability claims, and shipping contracts. A specialist team handles all aspects of insurance company insolvency. Insurance corporate finance and commercial lawyers handle flotations, rights issues, the formation and authorization of insurance and reinsurance companies, mergers and acquisitions, restructurings, and joint ventures including consortium and pool arrangements. D J Freeman is one of the leading firms advising on Lloyd's corporate capital with a particular expertise in insurance derivatives and other innovative risk financing products.
Media & Communications: The rapidly expanding 25-strong media and communications team has clients who include three of the five leading terrestrial television broadcasters, satellite channels, international publishing houses, and telecommunications and computer companies and a growing number of e-commerce and dot.com clients. Media litigators handle high profile libel, copyright and contempt issues as well as contract and other disputes. Corporate and commercial lawyers handle corporate finance transactions, give regulatory advice to broadcasters, deal with programme acquisitions and advise on computer contracts and joint ventures. The department also has a highly regarded specialist IP and branding team.
Property: The 60-strong property services team includes construction law specialists and property litigators who handle landlord and tenant disputes, rent reviews and arbitration. Corporate finance and tax lawyers are involved in some of the largest limited partnerships, joint ventures, corporate acquisitions and restructuring work in the property sector. A specialist property finance team advises banks, lending institutions and borrowers on all types of property finance and finance leasing transactions. Property lawyers deal with leasing, disposals and property development in relation to some of the most important schemes in the UK. Planning lawyers handle town planning appeals and local plan inquiries and frequently undertake advocacy work.
Commercial Litigation: The 30-strong commercial litigation team acts for major corporates in relation to a wide range of disputes. They focus on the special requirements of in-house lawyers and work to achieve results that put the client first. They handle some of the largest and most complex contractual disputes in the High Court as well as employment, insolvency and regulatory matters, including judicial review. The department's public international law team is regarded as one of the top five in the UK.

DJ WEBB & CO

61 Old Street, London, EC1V 9HW **Tel:** (020) 7253 2400 **Fax:** (020) 7253 2800 **Email:** djwebb@webbimmigration.com **Website:** www.webbimmigration.com **Ptnrs:** 1 **Asst solrs:** 2 **Other fee-earners:** 0 **Contact:** Mr David J. Webb • Specialist City practice devoted exclusively to UK immigration and nationality law. The Principal is recognised as a leading practitioner in his field.

AREAS OF PRACTICE

Immigration & Nationality	100%

DLA

3 Noble Street, London, EC2V 7EE
Tel: (08700) 111111 **Fax:** (020) 7796 6666 **DX:** 33866 London Finsbury Square
Email: paul.nicholls@dla.com **Website:** www.dla.com

Victoria Square House, Victoria Square, Birmingham, B2 4DL
Tel: (08700) 111111 **Fax:** (0121) 262 5794 **DX:** 13022 Birmingham 1
Email: chris.rawstron@dla.com

Arndale House, Charles Street, Bradford, BD1 1UN
Tel: (08700) 111111 **Fax:** (01274) 513718 **DX:** 712510 Bradford 10
Email: andrew.bennett@dla.com

Napier House, 27 Thistle Street, Edinburgh, EH2 1BS
Tel: (08700) 111111 **Fax:** (0131) 459 5600 **DX:** ED 271 Edinburgh 1
Email: fenella.mason@dla.com

249 West George Street, Glasgow, G2 4RB
Tel: (08700) 111111 **Fax:** (0141) 204 1902 **DX:** GW10 Glasgow 1
Email: gordon.hollerin@dla.com

Princes Exchange, 2 Princes Square, Leeds, LS1 4QY
Tel: (08700) 111111 **Fax:** (0113) 245 2632 **DX:** 12017 Leeds 1
Email: neil.mclean@dla.com

India Buildings, Water Street, Liverpool, L2 0NH
Tel: (08700) 111111 **Fax:** (0151) 236 9208 **DX:** 14103 Liverpool 1
Email: michael.prince@dla.com

101 Barbirolli Square, Manchester, M2 3DL
Tel: (08700) 111111 **Fax:** (0161) 235 4111 **DX:** 14304 Manchester 1
Email: roy.beckett@dla.com

Fountain Precinct, Balm Green, Sheffield, S1 1RZ
Tel: (08700) 111111 **Fax:** (0114) 270 0568 **DX:** 708580 Sheffield 10
Email: paul.firth@dla.com

Managing partner:	Nigel Knowles
Senior partner:	Roger Lane-Smith
UK:	
Number of partners:	240
Number of other solicitors:	435
Other fee-earners:	368
International	
Number of partners:	10
Number of other solicitors:	10
Other fee-earners:	9

AREAS OF PRACTICE

Corporate	26%
Real Estate	17%
Litigation	16%
Human Resources	8%
Insurance	8%
Banking	6%
BS&R	6%
Business Services	6%
MARS	6%
Law Training	1%

CONTACTS

Banking	Michael Collins
Business Services	Mary Barlow
Business Support & Restructuring	Peter Cranston
Corporate	Bruce Westbrook
Human Resources	David Bradley
Insurance	Mike Tinker
Law Training	Paul Nicholls
Litigation	David Gray
Marine/Aviation/ Reinsurance	Michael Clarke
Real Estate	Philip Rooney

THE FIRM: DLA is an innovative international law firm with over 2,000 staff and a turnover in excess of £130m. The firm has established itself as the UK's only truly integrated national legal practice following its merger with Scottish practice Bird Semple. In addition to its new Glasgow and Edinburgh offices the firm has a significant presence in the City of London and has major offices in the UK's main regional legal centres of Birmingham, Bradford, Leeds, Liverpool, Manchester and Sheffield. The culture of DLA is reflected in its corporate values and robust determination to deliver the highest quality service to match and then exceed the expectations of its clients. The firm believes that the provision of excellent service is fundamental to its continuing success, and views itself as business advisers just as much as lawyers. An example of this approach is the launch of 'DLA Consulting', which provides HR professionals with a complete solution to their legal and business issues, believed to be a first amongst UK law firms. In addition, the launch of 'DLA Upstream', the firm's newly created UK and European public affairs practice, is further evidence of DLA's client focused approach. The firm has also spent a great deal of time developing its E-Business capability. Apart from the highly regarded website – www.dla.com – the firm has also established a dedicated E-commerce website – www.dla.net – which offers clients complete advice about taking their ventures forward.

INTERNATIONAL CONNECTIONS: Apart from DLA's growth in the domestic market, the past twelve months have seen the practice grow its existing international presence in Brussels and Hong Kong, through a series of joint ventures and strategic alliances. The formation of DLA & Partners during 1999 built further upon the firm's vision to establish a leading European legal capability, and included a joint venture with Price and Partners, a major Brussels legal practice, which trebled the size of the firm's existing office in the EU capital. This was later supplemented by exclusive association agreements with Ginestié, Paley-Vincent & Associés in Paris and Brugueras, Garcia-Bragado, Molinero and Asociados in Barcelona. In addition 1999 witnessed the merger of DLA's commercial practice in Hong Kong with that of the high profile legal firm Lui & Carey. This merger followed the strategic alliance which DLA formed with Charltons, a leading firm of Corporate Finance lawyers in Hong Kong in December 1998. The firm has overseas offices at: 59th Floor, Bank of China Building, 1 Garden Road, Central Hong Kong. tel: +852 2 524 2003, fax: +852 2 810 1345, email: stewart.crowther +32 2 629 6969, fax: +32 2 629 6970, email: david.church@dla.com

CLIENTELE: DLA's approach to commercial legal services is driven by the desire to understand its clients' needs, objectives, preferences, priorities and concerns. It is only by being aware of these key issues that it is able to deliver demonstrable value. To this end the firm has successfully introduced a Client Relationship Manage-

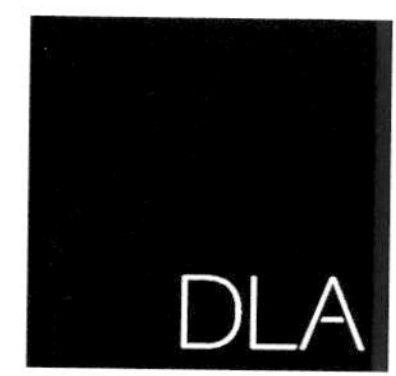

Continued overleaf

ment (CRM) programme. CRM allows the firm to talk to its clients, and the feedback obtained has resulted in improved quality of service and distinguishes DLA from its competitors.

RECRUITMENT & TRAINING: DLA's priority is to add value to its clients businesses by delivering the highest quality professional advice and expertise. Its policy is to retain and recruit highly motivated and skilled professionals who are essential to achieving these high standards. Operating a team approach, the firm believes that meticulous project management, combined with solid partnership with clients, is the key to an efficient and cost-effective provision of legal services.

DMH

100 Queens Road, Brighton, BN1 3YB
Tel: (01273) 329 833 **Fax:** (01273) 747 500 **DX:** 2701 Brighton 1
Email: tim.aspinall@dmh.co.uk **Website:** www.dmh.co.uk

Managing partner:	Tim Aspinall
Chairman	Derek Sparrow
Number of partners:	28
Assistant solicitors:	24
Other fee-earners:	52

CONTACTS

Asset Management	Rod Gentry
Commercial	Mike Long
Commercial Litigation	Tim Aspinall
Commercial Property	Marion Wilcock
Corporate	Dennis Edmonds
Dot.org	Rustom Tata
E-Commerce	Justin Ellis
Employment	Simon Bellm
Innovation & Media	Tim Ashdown
Israeli Desk	Penina Shepherd
Planning & Environment	Tony Allen
Private Client	Richard Pollins
Property Litigation	Martin Allen
Shipping / Marine	Alistair Rustemeyer

D

THE FIRM: DMH launched a new corporate image in 2000 to more accurately reflect its approach to clients and staff. The new identity includes a modern logo and embodies the firm's forward-looking culture, values and strategy. Large multi-disciplinary teams have been established to meet the needs of commercial and private clients, particularly those in the innovation and media and dot.org (not-for- profit, education, local authorities, housing associations and charities) sectors. Such a structure ensures that clients receive a seamless service delivered by specialists operating from Crawley, Brighton and Worthing.The introduction of a new case management system and customer care training have also had a positive impact on service delivery. Clients with international interests benefit from the firm's membership of Law Europe and it's associated offices in the USA. Many find this association particularly useful in the context of the Internet. To assist those with a business interest in Israel DMH has an Israeli Desk. Due to considerable growth in the last couple of years, the firm is expanding its office in Crawley to enable its large employment team, innovation and media specialists, commercial property and planning experts to join dedicated corporate lawyers. Like the Brighton office, Crawley is to create a contemporary art gallery to showcase work by local artist.

PRINCIPAL AREA OF WORK:
Corporate/Commercial: An experienced team handles a comprehensive range of high value projects on a regular basis including company/ partnership formations, takeovers, mergers and acquisitions, MBOs, Stock Exchange flotations, franchises, intellectual property work, e-commerce and commercial contracts. The firm acts on behalf of fast growth businesses, high profile national and international clients.
Employment: The firm has extensive experience in acting for employers, employees and TUs on such matters as service contracts, redundancies and unfair dismissal, disciplinary and grievance procedures, discrimination, pensions and incentive schemes.
Litigation: The firm is well -known for its litigation expertise and is skilled in handling large and complicated cases. The firm's litigators are particularly experienced in property and construction cases; trademark, domain name and IT disputes; major commercial cases; professional negligence; shipping and foreign litigation matters.
Commercial Property: Leading specialists in commercial conveyancing, planning and property and construction litigation act for land developers and investors, as well as a full range of businesses and institutions. All forms of freehold and leasehold transactions are handled, with particular expertise in site assembly and development, development funding and joint ventures, planning and environmental law, institutional secured funding and property litigation.
Other Areas: The firm provides a wide range of private client services to address personal injury, residential conveyancing, and asset management, wills, trust and probate and family matters.

DOBERMAN HORSMAN

College Chambers, 92-94 Borough Road, Middlesbrough, TS1 2HL **Tel:** (01642) 230130
Fax: (01642) 230133 **DX:** 60508 **Email:** Doberman.Horsman@onyxnet.co.uk
Website: www.doberman.horsman.co.uk **Ptnrs:** 3 **Asst solrs:** 3 **Other fee-earners:** 5
Contact: Ms R Matharu • A general practice specialising in civil litigation and commercial work.

AREAS OF PRACTICE

Personal Injury & Medical Negligence	50%
Commercial Litigation	20%
Commercial Work & Commercial Property	20%
Others	10%

DOLMANS

17-20 Windsor Place, Cardiff, CF10 3DS
Tel: (029) 2034 5531 **Fax:** (029) 2039 8206 **DX:** 33005 Cardiff

18A Merthyr Road, Whitchurch, Cardiff, CF4 1DG
Tel: (029) 20692979 **Fax:** (029) 20624415

Managing Partner:	Adrian Oliver
Senior Partner:	Jeffery MacWilkinson
Number of partners:	11
Assistant solicitors:	15
Other fee-earners:	16

THE FIRM: With roots going back over 180 years and a presence in South Wales since 1893, Dolmans is a large Cardiff firm providing commercial legal services to corporate, public sector and individual clients. The partnership was restructured in 1970, with the Cardiff practice retaining and continuing under the name of Dolmans and has, since then, expanded to meet client needs. It considers the supervision of assistant solicitors by the partners to be of primary importance in ensuring a thorough quality service to its clients.

PRINCIPAL AREAS OF WORK:
Litigation: The firm is well known for its experience and expertise in the field of litigation, becoming the dominant firm in the region for insurance and public sector defendant work, with the majority of instructions coming from local authorities and constabularies, either direct or through insurers or others. Its workload covers employers' and public liability, personal injury and landlord and tenant work and includes private sector work. Dolmans is well respected also in the field of plaintiff litigation and a specialist team was established five years ago to deal with motor claims. It is now the leading firm in the region for plaintiff motor claims litigation. Its insurance workload has increasingly become national.
Property, Commercial & Private Client: Dolmans has a strong reputation for property, commercial and private client work. This includes commercial and domestic conveyancing; property development; landlord & tenant and institutional mortgages; business start-ups; company formation; partnership agreements; takeovers; insolvency; finance; employment and contract. It also deals with matrimonial and family law, trusts, wills, probate and taxation.

CONTACTS

Agency	David Boobier
Company & Commercial	John Wilkins
Employment	John Wilkins
Insolvency	John Wilkins
Institutional Defendant Litigation	Jeffrey MacWilkinson
Landlord & Tenant	Roger Morgan
Licensing	John Wilkins
Matrimonial	Randolph Jones
Motor Claims Plaintiff Litigation	Philip Bradley
Private & Commercial Litigation	David Boobier
Private Client & Small Company	Roger Morgan
Property	Moy Lewis
Wills/Trusts /Probate	Roger Morgan

D

DONALD RENNIE WS

7 Blinkbonny Cresent, Edinburgh, EH4 3NB **Tel:** (0131) 476 7007 **Fax:** (0131) 476 7008 **DX:** 539943 Edinburgh 19
Email: donald.rennie@cableinet.co.uk

DONNS SOLICITORS

PO Box 41, 201 Deansgate, Manchester, M60 1DZ **Tel:** (0161) 834 3311 **Fax:** (0161) 834 2317 **DX:** 14312 **Email:** lawyers@donnlaw.co.uk
Website: www.donnslaw.co.uk **Ptnrs:** 11

DONNELLY & WALL

Callender House, 58/60 Upper Arthur Street, Belfast, BT1 4GP **Tel:** (028) 9023 3157 **Fax:** (028) 9032 9743
Email: mail@donnelly-wall.freeserve.co.uk **Website:** http://go.to/ni-law **Ptnrs:** 4 **Asst solrs:** 3 **Other fee-earners:** 3

DORSEY & WHITNEY

Veritas House, 125 Finsbury Pavement, London, EC2A 1NQ **Tel:** (020) 7588 0800 **Fax:** (020) 7588 0555 **Ptnrs:** 4 **Asst solrs:** 9 **Other fee-earners:** 2 **Contact:** Peter E. Kohl • Corporate finance (equity and debt securities offerings, capital market transactions), mergers and acquisitions, venture capital financings, joint ventures, contract negotiation and tax and energy law. (English and US law.)

AREAS OF PRACTICE

Mergers & Acquisitions	40%
Securities Offerings	40%
General Corporate	20%

DOUGLAS-JONES MERCER

147 St. Helens Rd, Swansea, SA1 4DB **Tel:** (01792) 650000 **Fax:** (01792) 458212 **DX:** 39556 **Email:** post@djm.law.co.uk **Ptnrs:** 12 **Asst solrs:** 13 **Other fee-earners:** 12 **Contact:** Mr Jeremy Wolfe • A high street practice with specialist departments in commercial, defendant and plaintiff personal injury, family, crime, conveyancing and probate law. The firm's commercial department is currently undergoing a period of growth.

AREAS OF PRACTICE

Commercial	20%
Conveyancing & Probate	20%
Crime	20%
Defendant & Plaintiff PI	20%
Family	20%

DOUGLAS & PARTNERS

116 Grosvenor Road, St. Pauls, Bristol, BS2 8YA **Tel:** (0117) 955 2663 **Fax:** (0117) 954 0527 **Ptnrs:** 4 **Asst solrs:** 5 **Other fee-earners:** 8

DOUGLAS WIGNALL & CO

44 Essex Street, Strand, London, WC2R 3JF **Tel:** (020) 7583 1362 **Fax:** (020) 7583 0532 **DX:** 48 London/Chancery Lane **Email:** doug@easynet.co.uk **Ptnrs:** 1 **Asst solrs:** 0 **Other fee-earners:** 0 **Contact:** Douglas Wignall • This practice specialises in hotels and leisure, and in particular international hotel management agreements. Work also includes acquisitions and disposals of hotels; hotel franchise agreements; advising on hotel operational matters; commercial and residential conveyancing and commercial law.

AREAS OF PRACTICE

Hotels & Leisure	75%
Commercial & Residential Conveyancing	15%
Other Company/Commercial	10%

DOWNS

156 High Street, Dorking, Surrey, RH4 1BQ
Tel: (01306) 880110 **Fax:** (01306) 876266 **DX:** 57300 Dorking
Email: Downs.commercial@downslaw.co.uk **Website:** www.downslaw.co.uk

Senior Partner:	David Rea
Number of partners:	10
Assistant solicitors:	12
Other fee-earners:	7

THE FIRM: Founded in 1835, Downs is a leading regional firm, offering a pro-active and effective approach.

PRINCIPAL AREAS OF WORK:
For the Business Client: Centered around corporate and commercial, commercial property and litigation sections, specialist teams also focus on employment law, IP/IT and planning/local government law. Clients range from multinationals to single entrepreneurs, and around 10% of work has an international element. The firm has particular expertise in mergers and acquisitions, corporate finance, industrial/office developments, nursing homes, agricultural property, cross border litigation and arbitrations.
For the Private Client: Core sections are residential property, trusts, tax planning, wills and probate, matrimonial and personal injury.

INTERNATIONAL CONNECTIONS: A well-developed network of contacts exists throughout Europe, USA and the Middle East.

AREAS OF PRACTICE

Commercial Property	20%
Company/Commercial	20%
Litigation	20%
Trusts/Probate	20%
Conveyancing	10%
Matrimonial	10%

CONTACTS

Area	Contact
Commercial Property	Iain MacLeod
Company Commercial	Christopher Shipley
Conveyancing	Celia Perry
Litigation	Christopher Millar
Matrimonial	Andrew Christmas
Trusts/Probate	Tim Hughes, Rosanne Baker

D

DRAYCOTT GIBBON MORE & WRIGHT

Peel Court, 45 Hardman Street, Manchester, M3 3PL **Tel:** (0161) 833 1333 **Fax:** (0161) 833 1444

DRUCES & ATTLEE

Salisbury House, London Wall, London, EC2M 5PS
Tel: (020) 7638 9271 **Fax:** (020) 7628 7525 **DX:** 33862 Finsbury Square
Email: info@druces.com **Website:** www.druces.com

Senior partner:	David Goodwin
No of partners:	14
Assistant solicitors:	10
Other fee earners:	8
Total no of fee-earners:	32
Total no of staff:	66

THE FIRM: A City firm since 1767 with a strong commercial base, providing a wide range of legal services to the property and corporate sectors, and high net worth individuals. Strong traditional values of client care based on integrity, knowledge and reliability, are underpinned by a modern and dynamic approach to providing legal solutions. The firm specialises in advising investors in commercial property, and those in the financial services and hotel, pub & leisure trades. It is well established in advising high net worth individuals on the deployment and protection of assets. Druces & Attlee is a founder member of Druces International, linking law firms in 11 countries in Europe.

PRINCIPAL AREAS OF WORK: Commercial property investment; finance & investments; hotel pub & leisure; insolvency; private capital.

RECRUITMENT & TRAINING: The firm aims to expand its core practice areas through recruitment at all levels. A trainee is taken on every six months, for four six-month placements (private capital, litigation, property and company commercial). Additional trainee places may be available for strong applicants interested in the firm's core practice areas. All applications should be forwarded to Richard Monkcom, Staff Partner.

AREAS OF PRACTICE

Commercial Property	40%
Company/Commercial	30%
Private Client	15%
Commercial & Property Litigation	10%
Insolvency	5%

CONTACTS

Area	Contact
Commercial Property	Chris Hamer
Commercial/Litigation	Richard Sherrin
Company/Commercial	Richard Monkcom
Employment	Toby Stroh
Financial Services	Philip Mitchell
Property Litigation	Jon Redding
Insolvency	Simeon Gilchrist
Private Capital	Roy Campbell

DRUMMOND MILLER WS

32 Moray Place, Edinburgh, EH3 6BZ **Tel:** (0131) 226 5151 **Fax:** (0131) 225 2608 **DX:** 104 Edinburgh **Email:** mail@drumil.demon.co.uk **Website:** www.drummond-miller.co.uk **Ptnrs:** 20 **Asst solrs:** 14 **Other fee-earners:** 18 **Contact:** Grant McCulloch • Litigation department handles a large volume of Court of Session actions on behalf of correspondent solicitors. The firm also has a private client department and a large conveyancing department handling commercial and residential work

AREAS OF PRACTICE

Residential Conveyancing	24%
Sheriff Court (Civil)	23%
Court of Session (Reparation & Commercial Litigation)	22%
Trust/Executry	12%
Other	19%

DUNDAS & WILSON CS

Saltire Court, 20 Castle Terrace, Edinburgh, EH1 2EN
Tel: (0131) 228 8000 **Fax:** (0131) 228 8888 **DX:** 553001 Edinburgh 18

180 Strand, London, WC2R 2NN
Tel: (020) 7256 9191 **Fax:** (020) 7256 6464 **DX:** 137 London Chancery Lane

191 West George Street, Glasgow, G2 2LB
Tel: (0141) 222 2200 **Fax:** (0141) 222 2201 **DX:** 561475 GLASGOW 16

Managing Partner:	Chris Campbell
Chairman:	Neil Cochran
Number of partners:	53
Assistant solicitors:	144
Other fee-earners:	49

AREAS OF PRACTICE

Corporate/Commercial	37%
Real Estate	36%
Banking	17%
Litigation	10%

THE FIRM: Dundas & Wilson is a leading corporate and commercial law firm with a spread and depth of specialist skills largely unmatched in Scotland. The firm differentiates itself from its competitors in its industry-focused approach and international reach. Dundas & Wilson is one of the largest commercial law firms in

Scotland, with 246 lawyers, including 53 partners. The firm uses a client-orientated approach to business. The operational structure is industry-focused using teams of lawyers with different technical skills. Each team works closely together to service the needs of industry sectors such as banking, construction and engineering, corporate finance, government services, technology, real estate and infrastructure. Dundas & Wilson services a wide range of blue-chip companies, including commercial companies, insurance companies and public sector organisations, both at home and abroad. The firm is a leading FTSE 350 client representative in Scotland. Dundas & Wilson is a member firm of Andersen Legal and is associated with Garretts in England. Together with Garretts, it ranks in the UK's top 20 law firms by size and fee income. Andersen Legal is a global legal services network associated with Andersen Worldwide SC. The network operates as integrated practices by sharing knowledge, resources and technology, and offers a broad range of legal services to business clients around the world. Through its association with Andersen Worldwide SC, Andersen Legal has unique access to the professional services of Arthur Andersen and therefore an unmatched ability to provide integrated legal and business solutions to clients when required. For example, client teams can be tailored to provide all the skills and resources to meet the legal, financial, accounting, tax and consulting requirements of major projects, whilst offering a single point of contact to provide strategic advice and facilitate project management. The Andersen Legal network, including its member law firms as well as several correspondent firms and practices, is represented by more than 2,700 lawyers working in 92 offices in 35 countries throughout Europe, Asia Pacific and Latin America.

PRINCIPAL AREAS OF WORK: Dundas & Wilson has an exclusively corporate and commercial practice, providing the legal services as shown in the work contacts box.

CONTACTS

Banking	Philip Mackay
	Michael Stoneham
Commercial Litigation	Lorna Sibbald
Construction & Engineering	Alistair McLean
Corporate & Commercial	Robert Pirrie
Corporate Finance	David Hardie
Corporate Recovery/ Insolvency	Ian Cuthbertson
Education	Brian Leggat
Employment,/Pensions/ Incentives	Eilidh Cameron
Government Services	Christian Hook
Infrastructure	Alan Campbell
Insurance Litigation	Colin Macleod
Private Equity	Robert Pirrie
Real Estate	Donald Shaw
Technology	Laurence Ward

D

DUNDONS

261 Lavender Hill, London, SW11 1JD **Tel:** (020) 7228 2277 **Fax:** (020) 7924 2759 **DX:** 58556 **Ptnrs:** 1 **Asst solrs:** 5 **Other fee-earners:** 1

DUTHIE HART & DUTHIE

517-519 Barking Rd, Greengate, Plaistow, London, E13 8PT **Tel:** (020) 8472 0138 **Fax:** (020) 8470 7628 **DX:** 52407 Canning Town **Email:** enquiries@dhd.co.uk **Website:** www.dhd.co.uk **Ptnrs:** 5 **Asst solrs:** 16 **Other fee-earners:** 17 **Contact:** Mr. S. Murphy • Established general practice with reputation for particular expertise in criminal law. Franchised by the Legal Aid Board.

AREAS OF PRACTICE

Criminal Litigation	60%
Matrimonial	12%
Personal Injury and General Common Law	10%
Conveyancing	8%
Mental Health	5%
Probate	5%

EAMONN MCEVOY & CO

22 Church Place, Lurgan, BT66 6EY **Tel:** (028) 3832 7734 **Fax:** (028) 3832 1760 **Ptnrs:** 3 **Asst solrs:** 6

Principally recognised for personal injury work, the practice has a strong reputation in all areas of litigation. They offer a professional, personal and efficient service.

EATONS

22 Blades Court, Deodar Rd, Putney, London, SW15 2NU
Tel: (020) 8877 9727 **Fax:** (020) 8877 9940 **DX:** 59483 Putney
Email: eatonslaw.com

Managing partner:	Martin Dacre
Senior partner:	Michael Eaton
Number of partners:	6
Assistant solicitors:	5
Other fee-earners:	1

THE FIRM: Eatons specialise in all aspects of media and entertainment work with particular emphasis on legal and commercial advice in connection with music and all related areas such as recording, publishing, video, management, merchandising, internet and television arrangements for a full range of emerging and established artists as well as independent and major companies. The firm also has a fast growing corporate entertainment practice covering acquisitions, joint ventures and specialist due diligence investigations. The combined qualifications of the partners encompass many years of industry and private practice experience.

PRINCIPAL AREAS OF WORK: Company Commercial; Litigation; Media & Entertainment; Property.

CONTACTS

Company Commercial	Michael Eaton
Litigation	Jeremy Wakefield
Media & Entertainment	David Glick
	Martin Dacre
Property	Jeremy Wakefield

EDDOWES WALDRON

12 St. Peter's Churchyard, Derby, DE1 1TZ **Tel:** (01332) 48484 **Fax:** (01332) 291312 **DX:** 17501 **Email:** advice@ewlaw.co.uk **Website:** www.ewlaw.co.uk **Ptnrs:** 7 **Asst solrs:** 3 **Other fee-earners:** 13

EDGE ELLISON (see Hammond Suddards Edge)

EDMONDS BOWEN

4 Old Park Lane, London, W1Y 3LJ **Tel:** (020) 7629 8000 **Fax:** (020) 7221 9334/495 6382 **DX:** 37217 Piccadilly **Ptnrs:** 4 **Asst solrs:** 3 **Other fee-earners:** 3 • Provides client-orientated advice including corporate; employment; property; media/entertainment; sport; litigation and dispute resolution; and matrimonial.

AREAS OF PRACTICE

Company/Commercial	30%
Litigation/Dispute Resolution	30%
Media/Entertainment	30%
Property/Private Client	10%

EDMONDSON HALL

25 Exeter Rd, Newmarket, Newmarket, CB8 8AR **Tel:** (01638) 560556 **Fax:** (01638) 561656 **DX:** 50521 Newmarket **Email:** solicitors@edmondson-hall.co.uk **Ptnrs:** 2 **Asst solrs:** 2 **Other fee-earners:** 5 **Contact:** Mark Edmondson • Niche bloodstock practice. Five solicitors. Acts for many of leading owners, trainers, jockeys, stud farmers etc, both in UK and overseas. Modern , forward-thinking practice.

AREAS OF PRACTICE

Commercial & Bloodstock Litigation	45%
Property (Commercial & Domestic)	35%
Family	10%
Company Commercial & Charities	5%
Employment	5%

EDWARD FAIL BRADSHAW & WATERSON

402 Commercial Road, Stepney, London, E1 0LG
Tel: (020) 7790 4032 **Fax:** (020) 7790 2739 **DX:** 300701 Tower Hamlets

Managing partner:	John Lafferty
Senior partner:	Edward Preston
Number of partners:	5
Assistant solicitors:	4
Other fee-earners:	10

CONTACTS

Civil Litigation	John Lafferty
Criminal	Edward Preston
Family	Maeve O'Higgins

THE FIRM: One of the oldest established firms in East London, Edward Fail have had a reputation as specialists in criminal law since the 1920s. A merger in 1961 with the general practice of Bradshaw & Waterson (founded in 1887) brought a wide range of legal services to the firm, and the merged practices have over a century of experience of dealing with the family and business problems of the area.

PRINCIPAL AREAS OF WORK: The firm has a particularly strong reputation in the area of criminal law and deals with the whole spectrum of criminal offences, including serious crime, petty crime and white collar fraud. The firm also has thriving departments in family law and litigation.

EDWARD HARRIS & SON

Heathfield House, 91 Heathfield, Swansea, SA1 6EL **Tel:** (01792) 652007 **Fax:** (01792) 641533 **DX:** 39597 Swansea 1
Email: EdwardHarrisSon@cs.comAssistant Solicitor :1Consultant Solicitor: 1Associate Solicitor: 1 Other fee earners: 4

EDWARDS & CO

28 Hill Street, Belfast, BT1 2LA **Tel:** (028) 90321863 **Fax:** (028) 90332723 **DX:** 410 NR Belfast **Email:** edwards.itm@tibus.com **Ptnrs:** 3

EDWARDS GELDARD

Dumfries House, Dumfries Place, Cardiff, CF10 3ZF
Tel: (029) 2023 8239 **Fax:** (029) 2023 7268 **DX:** 33001
Email: info@geldards.co.uk **Website:** www.geldards.com

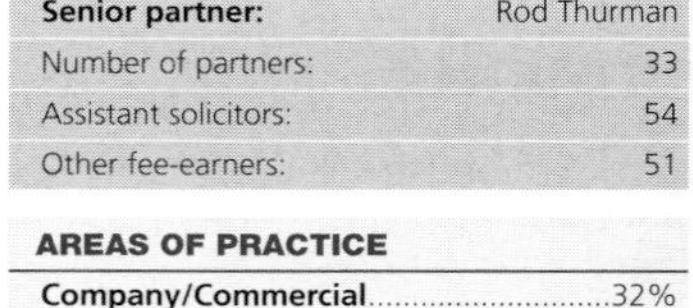

Senior partner:	Rod Thurman
Number of partners:	33
Assistant solicitors:	54
Other fee-earners:	51

AREAS OF PRACTICE

Company/Commercial	32%
Property	30%
Litigation	26%
Other	12%

Aled House, Lakeside Business Village, St Davids Park, Deeside, CH5 3XL
Tel: (01244) 538191 **Fax:** (01244) 538190 **DX:** 708574
Email: info@geldards.co.uk

St Michaels Court, St Michaels Lane, Derby, DE1 3HQ
Tel: (01332) 331631 **Fax:** (01332) 294295 **DX:** 11509
Email: info@geldards.co.uk

72 St James's Street, Nottingham, NG1 6FJ
Tel: (0115) 924 0631 **Fax:** (0115) 924 0431 **DX:** 10185
Email: info@geldards.co.uk

THE FIRM: Edwards Geldard is one of the leading regional law firms. The firm's offices are located in Cardiff, Deeside, Derby and Nottingham. Whilst continuing to expand the traditional areas of work in the company and commercial, commercial property, litigation and private client departments, the firm has acquired particular expertise in a variety of niche areas of legal work. These include mergers and acquisitions, corporate finance and banking, intellectual property, public law, planning and environmental law, energy law, rail and transport law, construction contracts and building arbitration, employment law, insolvency, trusts and tax, secured lending, property litigation and clinical negligence. The firm's growth in recent years has been characterised by an expansion of its work for major Stock Exchange listed clients and for City of London based organisations and by the growing reputation of its work for public sector bodies.

PRINCIPAL AREAS OF WORK: The following services are offered from each office (initial enquiries can be directed to the most convenient office): Company/corporate; intellectual property; EU law; environmental law; secured lending; construction & engineering; banking & insolvency; tax, trusts & estate administration;

commercial contracts/utilities; employment; commercial property; property & development; planning & public law; commercial dispute resolution & clinical negligence; personal injury; and private client.

LANGUAGES: French, German, Italian, Polish, Spanish, Ukrainian & Welsh.

E. EDWARDS SON & NOICE

9-15 York Road, Ilford, IG1 3AD **Tel:** (020) 8514 9000 **Fax:** (020) 8514 9009 **DX:** 200850 Ilford 4 **Email:** eesn@solicitors.uk.com **Website:** www.solicitors.uk.com **Ptnrs:** 10 **Asst solrs:** 31 **Other fee-earners:** 25

EDWIN COE

2 Stone Buildings, Lincoln's Inn, London, WC2A 3TH
Tel: (020) 7691 4000 **Fax:** (020) 7691 4111 **DX:** 191 London Chancery Lane WC2
Email: mail@edwincoe.com **Website:** www.edwincoe.com

Senior partner:	John Tomlins
Number of partners:	22
Assistant solicitors:	10
Other fee-earners:	13

AREAS OF PRACTICE

Litigation	30%
Corporate	27%
Property	21%
Private Client	14%
Insolvency	8%

CONTACTS

Corporate	Russel Shear
Employment	Rachel Harrap
Insolvency	Christopher Berry
Litigation	David Greene
Private Client	John Shelford
Property	John Tomlins

Edwin Coe

SOLICITORS

THE FIRM: The emphasis of this thriving London firm is providing high quality advice on commercial and business issues to a worldwide client base. The firm is committed to providing a partner led service which is responsive to clients needs and achieves their objectives quickly and cost effectively.

PRINCIPAL AREAS OF WORK:

Corporate: The firm's corporate group acts in all areas of business law and corporate activity including mergers, acquisitions, joint ventures and investments. The group has a growing reputation in offshore and international transactions, banking work and raising capital for hi-tech and internet start-ups.

Litigation: The litigation group offers a complete dispute resolution service including arbitration, asset protection and recovery, banking, commercial litigation, factoring, fraud, insurance claims, intellectual property, landlord and tenant protection, professional and disciplinary tribunals and professional negligence claims. Edwin Coe provides general litigation support including a debt collection service, and accepts High Court litigation agency work from other solicitors.

Employment: The employment team has a growing reputation advising on service contracts, remuneration, relocation, wrongful dismissal, discrimination and redundancy, including representation at Employment Tribunals.

Property: The property group advises investors and developers, insurance companies, banks and retailers and undertakes all aspects of banking security work, property development, landlord and tenant, licensing, mortgages and debentures, planning, investment acquisitions, property portfolios and rent review advice.

Private Client: The private client group specialises in the commercial development and management of the affairs of high-net-worth individuals and the creation and management of domestic and foreign trusts, charities, estate planning and administration, tax planning and wills.

Insolvency: The firm's insolvency team is headed by a licensed practitioner and has strong connections with banks and accountants. It advises corporate and individual clients on all aspects of administration, liquidation and receivership.

CLIENTELE: Edwin Coe's client focus ensures that it understands the business of its clients and offers clear, practical advice. Clients include public and private companies, institutions, sovereign states, charities, unincorporated associations and private individuals. The firm receives instructions from larger law firms and undertakes agency work. The firm has a seminar and briefing programme for clients and contacts, and partners have written standard works on several areas of law including insolvency and the responsibility of directors.

LANGUAGES: Cantonese, French, German, Italian, Mandarin, Polish and Russian.

EKING MANNING

44 The Ropewalk, Nottingham, NG1 5EL **Tel:** (0115) 840 4499 **Fax:** (0115) 840 4500 **DX:** 10010 **Email:** info@ekings.co.uk **Website:** www.ekings.co.uk **Ptnrs:** 9 **Asst solrs:** 7 **Other fee-earners:** 6

ELAINE MAXWELL & CO

26 Sun Street, Lancaster, LA1 1EW
Tel: (01524) 840810 **Fax:** (01524) 840811
Email: elaine.maxwell@virgin.net

Managing partner:	Elaine Maxwell
Number of partners:	1
Other fee-earners:	2

AREAS OF PRACTICE

Special Educational Needs	70%
Student Work	20%
Other Education & Community Care	10%

CONTACTS

All areas	Elaine Maxwell

The Firm: A niche firm, dealing solely with education law and community care, acting for clients nation-wide. Elaine Maxwell has worked in the field since 1990, acting for schools, universities, parents and students, offering expert legal advice in this highly specialised area. She has now been joined by Beth Coxon who was previously an advisor based in a university students' union. The firm works closely with charities involved in education to provide a full service for all clients. The firm has a full legal aid franchise and contract in education law.

ELBORNE MITCHELL

One America Square, Crosswall, London, EC3N 2PR **Tel:** (020) 7320 9000 **Fax:** (020) 7320 9111 **DX:** 1063 **Email:** lawyers@elbornes.com **Website:** www.elbornes.com **Ptnrs:** 14 **Asst solrs:** 9 **Other fee-earners:** 4

ANSELM ELDERGILL

Solicitors Chambers, 169 Malden Road, London, NW5 4HT
Tel: (020) 7284 1006 **Fax:** (020) 7916 2553 Tel: (0797) 119 8742
Email: medicolegal@hotmail.com

Number of partners:	1

AREAS OF PRACTICE

Health	75%
Social Services	25%

THE FIRM: Anselm Eldergill specialises in mental health law, health service law, and inquiries. He is the author of a 1400-page textbook on mental health law, a Mental Health Act Commissioner, an assessor for the Law Society's Mental Health Panel, and an Alexander Maxwell Scholar. Further information about his practice appears in the editorial section of this directory. Highlights of 1998-1999 include: Chairmanship of five NHS homicide inquiries; invitation to lecture at the Sorbonne; chairmanship of the Mental Health Act Commission's Legal & Ethics Committee; advising foreign states on the revision of their mental health legislation; articles in legal, medical and health management journals; keynote speaker, 1st National Conference on Risk Management in Mental Health; chairman, IBC Conference, Mental Health Law, Regents Park.

PRINCIPAL AREAS OF WORK: Inquiries; all aspects of mental health law; consultancy, drafting and training services for Health Authorities, NHS trusts, and social services authorities.

E

ELIZABETH CAIRNS

Knowle Hill Farm, Ulcombe, Maidstone, ME17 1ES **Tel:** (01622) 858191 **Fax:** (01622) 858004 **Email:** Elizabeth.Cairns@btinternet.com **Ptnrs:** 1

ELLIOT MATHER

The Courtyard, 49 Low Pavement, Chesterfield, S40 1PB **Tel:** (01246) 231288 **Fax:** (01246) 204081 **DX:** 12362 Chesterfield **Email:** admin@elliotmather.co.uk **Ptnrs:** 13 **Asst solrs:** 6 **Other fee-earners:** 16

ELLIOTT DUFFY GARRETT

2nd Floor, Royston House, 34 Upper Queen Street, Belfast, BT1 6FD
Tel: (028) 9024 5034 **Fax:** (028) 9024 1337 **DX:** 400 NR Belfast
Email: edg@edgsolicitors.co.uk **Website:** www.edgsolicitors.co.uk

Managing partner:	Michael P. Lynch
Senior partner:	Harry Coll
Number of partners:	11
Assistant solicitors:	9
Other fee-earners:	5

AREAS OF PRACTICE

Commercial Property	25%
Company/Commercial	25%
Commercial Litigation	20%
Labour/Employment	20%
Insolvency	5%
Private Client	5%

CONTACTS

Area	Contact
Commercial Property	W. Laurence Mahood
Company/Commercial	Michael Wilson
Employment Law	Harry Coll
Insolvency	Michael Wilson
Litigation	Michael P. Lynch
Private Client	Barry E. Thompson

THE FIRM: Established in1973, Elliott Duffy Garrett is well regarded for its role in serving the business community in Northern Ireland, and for its links with international clients. A wide range of commercial legal services is offered with particular emphasis on company law, commercial property and planning, litigation and insolvency. Member of IBA, AIJA, INSOL and Business in the Community (Professional Firms Group).

PRINCIPAL AREAS OF WORK:

Company Law: A full service is provided with particular emphasis on corporate finance; mergers and acquisitions; joint ventures; management buy-outs; secured lending and related banking work; inward investment and venture capital services.

Commercial Property and Planning: Work includes commercial property development; letting and investment acquisitions and disposals; planning and environmental law.

Employment Law: Specialist advice provided in relation to all aspects of employment and anti-discrimination law and practice.

Litigation: Advice and representation covering product liability; construction law; professional negligence; insurance; insolvency and general litigation.

INTERNATIONAL CONNECTIONS: The firm has a formal association with A & L Goodbody, one of Dublin's principal law firms, through the A & L Goodbody (NI) Association.

LANGUAGES: French, German and Italian.

ELLIOTTS

Centurion House, Deansgate, Manchester, M3 3WT
Tel: (0161) 834 9933 **Fax:** (0161) 832 3693 **DX:** 14346
Email: mail@elliott-law.co.uk

Senior partner:	Katharine Mellor
Number of partners:	13
Assistant solicitors:	16
Other fee-earners:	8

CONTACTS

Aviation Law .... Katharine Mellor
Commercial Litigation .... Fiona Miller
Commercial Property .... David Walton
Company Commercial .... Katharine Mellor
Construction .... Mike Woolley
Employment Law .... Fiona Miller
Insurance Litigation .... John Groome
.... Graham Hughes
Intellectual Property .... Robert Jones
Licensing .... Barry Holland
Motor Litigation .... Clare Edwards
Personal Injury .... Julian Holt
.... Neal Samarji
Private Client .... Tim Chapman
Professional Negligence .... John Groome

THE FIRM: A well-established independent firm, founded in Manchester in 1968, Elliotts offers a comprehensive and commercially-aware service to its client base, both in the UK and overseas.

PRINCIPAL AREAS OF WORK:

Litigation: The firm specialises in contentious work, and has particular experience in insurance law, handling work ranging from professional indemnity, employer and public liability cases to fire and disaster claims and international claims. A wide variety of commercial litigation is undertaken, including construction disputes, product liability, insolvency work, debt recovery, personal injury claims, and consumer problems.
Company/ Commercial: A full range of commercial services is available. Work includes: corporate finance matters, mergers and acquisitions, franchising, computer law, aviation law, intellectual property work, and employment law.
Licensing: The specialist licensing department has handled the licensing of the Trafford Centre in Manchester.
Property: Work includes commercial and residential conveyancing and agricultural law. The firm has significant experience in retail property and in the fields of planning and environmental law.
Food Safety: Barry Holland is currently chairman of the Law Society's food law group.

INTERNATIONAL CONNECTIONS: The firm is a founder member of the Euro-American Lawyers Group, which provides instant access to expert advice throughout Europe and America.

E

ELLIS WOOD

Langdales, New Garden House, 78 Hatton Garden, London, EC1N 8LD **Tel:** (020) 7242 1194 **Fax:** (020) 7831 9480 **DX:** 248 Ch.Ln.
Email: enquiries@elliswood.co.uk **Ptnrs:** 3 **Asst solrs:** 2 **Other fee-earners:** 1

ELLISON & CO

Headgate Court, Head Street, Colchester, CO1 1NP **Tel:** (01206) 764477 **Fax:** (01206) 764455 **DX:** 3601 Colchester
Email: mail@ellison-and-co.com **Ptnrs:** 15 **Asst solrs:** 6 **Other fee-earners:** 22

ENSOR BYFIELD

Equity Court, 73-75 Millbrook Road East, Southampton, SO15 1RJ
Tel: (023) 8048 3200 **Fax:** (023) 8021 2127 / 8033 1376 **DX:** 49665 Southampton 2
Email: law@ensorbyfield.com **Website:** www.ensorbyfield.com

Fifth Floor, Broad Quay House, Prince Street, Bristol, BS1 4DJ
Tel: (0117) 905 8725 **Fax:** (0117) 905 8790 **DX:** 7848 Bristol
Email: mg@ensorbyfield.com

63-66 Hatton Garden, London, EC1N 8LE
Tel: (020) 7242 7444 **Fax:** (020) 7242 7445
Email: law@ensorbyfield.com

Joint Senior Partners:	John Byfield, Rod Evans
Number of partners:	7
Assistant solicitors:	9
Other fee-earners:	23

AREAS OF PRACTICE

Insurance Litigation 50%
Commercial 32%
Commercial Property 10%
Commercial Litigation 7%
Private Client 1%

CONTACTS

Commercial .... J. Byfield
Commercial Litigation .... M. Wilson
Commercial Property .... T. Southorn
Defendant Insurance Litigation .... M. Guy (Bristol)
Defendant Insurance Litigation .... R Evans (Southampton)
Intellectual Property .... C. Jay
Private Client .... L. Borrett-Lynch

THE FIRM: Ensor Byfield is a regional business-focused law firm based in Southampton, Bristol and London, committed to supporting local, national and international companies in all aspects of their business activities, from start-up to the realisation of their objectives. A brochure is available on request and more information is available via our website.

PRINCIPAL AREAS OF WORK: The firm falls broadly into two departments, commercial and insurance litigation.
Commercial: The department provides a wide range of commercial, contractual and intellectual property advice to both companies and individuals. Particular strengths are in the following sectors: sports, information technology, healthcare, biotechnology and leisure. Within the department there are experts dealing with all aspects of employment law, both contentious and non-contentious, and commercial property. The firm also has a small private client department.
Insurance Litigation: The department is the largest and longest established defendant insurance litigation department in the southern region and provides advice to insurance companies nationwide. Divided into specialist teams with particular areas of expertise, the department handles a wide spectrum of cases including industrial disease, major disasters, catastrophic personal injury, employers' liability and motor claims.

ERIC ROBINSON & CO

359 Bitterne Road, Bitterne, Southampton, SO18 1DN **Tel:** (02380) 425000 **Fax:** (02380) 446594 **DX:** 52750 Bitterne **Ptnrs:** 10 **Asst solrs:** 14 **Other fee-earners:** 20

ERNST & YOUNG

Becket House, 1 Lambeth Palace Road, London, SE1 7EU **Tel:** (020) 7951 2000 **Fax:** (020) 7951 1345

ERSKINE MACASKILL & CO

4 Gayfield Square, Edinburgh, EH1 3NW **Tel:** (0131) 557 1520 **Fax:** (0131) 557 5970 **DX:** 191 Edinburgh, Ptnrs: 3, Associates: 2, Asst Solrs: 1 **Contact:** Sarah Erskine • Specialist matrimonial and child law practice. Also undertakes conveyancing and criminal defence work.

AREAS OF PRACTICE	
Matrimonial/Child Law	53%
Criminal Defence Work	22%
Conveyancing	20%
Others	5%

EVANS BUTLER WADE

165 Greenwich High Road, London, SE10 8JA **Tel:** (020) 8858 8926 **Fax:** (020) 8858 8131 **Email:** info@evansbutlerwade.co.uk **Website:** www.evansbutlerwade.co.uk **Ptnrs:** 4 **Asst solrs:** 4 **Other fee-earners:** 2 **Contact:** Mr C. Evans • Specialists in housing association developments and management work, employment work, and family work, especially in relation to same-sex relationships.

AREAS OF PRACTICE	
Social Housing (Management)	30%
Social Housing (Property)	30%
Domestic Conveyancing	10%
Employment	10%
Family	10%
Commercial Conveyancing	5%
Other	5%

E

EVANS DODD

5 Balfour Place, Mount Street, London, W1K 2AU
Tel: (020) 7491 4729 **Fax:** (020) 7499 2297 **DX:** 44644 Mayfair
Email: mail@evansdodd.co.uk

Managing partner:	Geoffrey Dodd
Senior partner:	Geoffrey Dodd
Number of partners:	6
Assistant solicitors:	1
Other fee-earners:	2

THE FIRM: Established in 1975 as a commercial practice with a strong international bias.

PRINCIPAL AREAS OF WORK:
Company and Commercial: All aspects of company and commercial work including public and private corporate law; acquisitions; new issues; joint ventures; banking and finance; aircraft acquisitions; financing and tax planning.
Commercial Property: Commercial property acquisitions, sales, leases and financing. Domestic property work also undertaken.
Litigation: All types of claims, including commercial litigation, contractual disputes, employment and matrimonial matters, debt recovery and professional negligence.

AREAS OF PRACTICE	
Company/Commercial	50%
Litigation	25%
Property	15%
Taxation	10%

CONTACTS	
Company & Commercial	Geoffrey Dodd
Commercial Property	Joseph Hyde
Litigation	Jeremy Hershkorn

EVERATT & COMPANY

104 High Street, Evesham, WR11 4EU
Tel: (01386) 47191 **Fax:** (01386) 48515 **DX:** 16167 EVESHAM
Email: post@everatt.co.uk

Senior partner:	Catherine Arkell
Number of partners:	4
Assistant solicitors:	2
Other fee-earners:	3

AREAS OF PRACTICE	
Defendant Personal Injury	90%
Other	10%

THE FIRM: Specialists in defendant personal injury litigation since its foundation in 1970, Everatt & Company has earned a reputation within its field that is the envy of many a large legal firm. Its size and independence has played a significant part in this success, ensuring levels of flexibility, internal communication and access to partners that clients rarely see elsewhere. Its central location, too, has been a factor, placing the majority of UK courts within serviceable reach.

PRINCIPAL AREAS OF WORK:
Defendant Personal Injury Litigation: Including employers' liability; motor accident claims; industrial deafness; work-related upper limb disorders; asbestos-related claims; other respiratory claims; hand/arm vibration syndrome/VWF; catastrophic injury; and work-related stress claims.

CLIENTELE: The firm acts for insurance companies, both large and small and various liability adjusters.

RECRUITMENT & TRAINING: The firm is a strong believer in internal training. The firm has recruited individuals and trained them through to qualification.

EVERSHEDS

Senator House, 85 Queen Victoria Street, London, EC4V 4JL
Tel: (020) 7919 4500 **Fax:** (020) 7919 4919 **DX:** 83 Chancery Lane WC2
Website: www.eversheds.com

115 Colmore Row, Birmingham, B3 3AL
Tel: (0121) 232 1000 **Fax:** (0121) 236 1900 **DX:** 13004

11-12 Queen Square, Bristol, BS1 4NT
Tel: (0117) 929 9555 **Fax:** (0117) 929 2766 **DX:** 78212

Daedalus House, Station Road, Cambridge, CB1 2RE
Tel: (01223) 355 933 **Fax:** (01223) 460 266 **DX:** 5807

Fitzalan House, Fitzalan Road, Cardiff, CF24 OEE
Tel: (02920) 471147 **Fax:** (02920) 464347 **DX:** 33016

11 St James Court, Friar Gate, Derby, DE1 1BT
Tel: (01332) 360992 **Fax:** (01332) 371469 **DX:** 11535

Franciscan House, 51 Princes Street, Ipswich, IP1 1UR
Tel: (01473) 284428 **Fax:** (01473) 233666 **DX:** 3249

Cloth Hall Court, Infirmary Street, Leeds, LS1 2JB
Tel: (0113) 243 0391 **Fax:** (0113) 245 6188 **DX:** 12027 Leeds-27

London Scottish House, 24 Mount Street, Manchester, M2 3DB
Tel: (0161) 832 6666 **Fax:** (0161) 832 5337 **DX:** 14344

Permanent House, 91 Albert Road, Middlesbrough, TS1 2PA
Tel: (01642) 247456 **Fax:** (01642) 240446 **DX:** 60550

Sun Alliance House, 35 Mosley Street, Newcastle upon Tyne, NE1 1XX
Tel: (0191) 261 1661 **Fax:** (0191) 261 8267 **DX:** 61166

Holland Court, The Close, Norwich, NR1 4DX
Tel: (01603) 272727 **Fax:** (01603) 610535 **DX:** 5206

1 Royal Standard Place, Nottingham, NG1 6FZ
Tel: (0115) 950 7000 **Fax:** (0115) 950 7111 **DX:** 10031
Email: nottingham@eversheds.com

Chairman:	Keith James
UK:	
Number of partners:	350
Assistant solicitors:	660
Other fee-earners:	536
International Number of partners:	44
Assistant solicitors:	98
Other fee earners:	75

AREAS OF PRACTICE

Corporate/commercial	35%
Property	25%
Litigation/Dispute Management	25%
Employment	9%
Other	6%

THE FIRM: A European law firm, Eversheds has 1,750 legal and business advisers based in 19 locations. Each office provides a wide range of services to the business and financial community and to the public sector. Their distinctive approach gives clients access to a large team of lawyers who combine local market knowledge with an international perspective. Most commercial law firms offer clients the same core services, and Eversheds is no exception. Their difference, and their competitive advantage, lies in their strength and depth. They have vast resources and an unparalleled breadth of expertise and industry know-how.

PRINCIPAL AREAS OF WORK: Alongside the five core areas of corporate, commercial, litigation and dispute management, commercial property and employment, each Eversheds office provides expertise in a range of specialist legal services and market sectors. Specialist services: business risk services; computer/IT; corporate tax; environment/health and safety; EU/competition; franchising; insolvency; intellectual property; international public law; licensing; PFI; planning; pensions; private capital/tax and venture capital. Market sectors: banking; bioscience; chemicals; construction; education; energy; engineering; financial services; insurance and reinsurance; media and communications; public sector and retail/leisure.

INTERNATIONAL CONNECTIONS: The firm has overseas offices at 75 Avenue de Cortenberg, 1000 Brussels, Belgium, tel: +32 2 737 9340, fax: +32 2 737 9345; Est-Ouest, 24 Boulevard Princesse Charlotte, Monte Carlo, 98000 Monaco, tel: +3 77 93 105510, fax: +3 77 93 105511; 42 Avenue du Président Wilson, 75116 Paris, France, tel: +33 1 4434 7100, fax: +33 1 4434 7111; Associated offices are located at Boekel De Nerée, Atriumbuilding, 2nd Floor, Strawinskylaan 3037, 1077 2X Amsterdam, Tel: + 31 20 431 3131, Fax: +31 20 431 3143; Østergade 27, DK-1100 Copenhagen, Denmark, tel: +45 33 75 05 05, fax: +45 33 75 05 00; Georgiev, Todorov & Co, 58-V Tzar Assen Street, 1463 Sofia, PO Box 15, Bulgaria, tel: +359 2 951 5665, fax: +359 2 518 616.

EVERY & PHILLIPS

The Laurels, 46 New Street, Honiton, EX14 8BZ **Tel:** (01404) 43431 **Fax:** (01404) 45493 **DX:** 48800 Honiton **Ptnrs:** 10 **Asst solrs:** 5
Other fee-earners: 13

EVILL AND COLEMAN

113 Upper Richmond Road, Putney, London, SW15 2TL **Tel:** (020) 8789 9221 **Fax:** (020) 8789 7978 **DX:** 59451 Putney **Email:** evill@globalnet.co.uk **Ptnrs:** 3 **Asst solrs:** 4 **Other fee-earners:** 5 **Contact:** Stewart Graham • Leading reputation in personal injury and clinical/medical negligence claims. Clinical negligence and Legal Aid franchise. Conducted many ground breaking cases in these fields.

AREAS OF PRACTICE	
Personal Injury/Medical Negligence	100%

FAEGRE BENSON HOBSON AUDLEY

7 Pilgrim Street, London, EC4V 6LB
Tel: (020) 7450 4510 **Fax:** (020) 7450 4544 **DX:** 401 London
Email: lawyers@faegre.com **Website:** www.faegre.com

Joint Managing Partners:	Gale Mellum, Gerald Hobson
Number of partners:	6

AREAS OF PRACTICE	
Company/Commercial/ Financial Services	25%
Corporate Finance/ M&A	20%
Dispute Resolution	20%
Property	15%
Employment	10%
Innovation & Technology	10%

THE FIRM: Faegre Benson Hobson Audley is a multinational partnership of English and American lawyers in London, formed between Faegre & Benson LLP and Hobson Audley to provide English business law services to US clients and American business law services to English clients. Faegre &Benson LLP is a firm of more than 325 lawyers with offices in Minneapolis, Minnesota; Denver, Colorado; Des Moines, Iowa; and Frankfurt, Germany. Hobson Audley is a firm of more than 35 solicitors in London. In the London Office, English business law services are provided in corporate and commercial finance; intellectual property; innovation and technology; employment, dispute solution and real estate matters. American business law advice is provided in London and through the US offices of Faegre & Benson LLP, both on US corporate law and on commercial transactions, including acquisitions; incorporations; joint ventures; distribution agreements; product liability and immigration.

LANGUAGES: French, German, Italian, Portuguese and Spanish.

FAIRMAYS

10 Babmaes St, London, SW1Y 6HD
Tel: (020) 7959 0202 **Fax:** (020) 7959 0234 **DX:** 37219 Piccadilly
Email: advice@fairmays.com **Website:** www.fairmays.com

Managing partner:	A Langford
Senior partner:	A Cowen
Number of partners:	10
Assistant solicitors:	11
Other fee-earners:	18

AREAS OF PRACTICE	
Company/Commercial	42%
Property	29%
Litigation	24%
Private Client	5%

CONTACTS	
Company/Commercial	Robert Brooks
Employment	Alistair Langford
IP/IT	Rosanna Cooper
Litigation	Anthony Cowen
Private Client	Andrew Miller
Property	Nicholas Plaut

THE FIRM: Fairmays is a progressive international commercial practice specialising in company/commercial, litigation, property and private client work. The firm's international clientele includes a significant proportion of high net worth individuals and SMEs as a consequence, it has developed the skills necessary to meet the demands of that particular market sector and handles a significant amount of new start up, corporate finance and flotation work coupled with specialist advice in the fields of IP/IT, employment and immigration (both individual and corporate). It's private client department offers a sophisticated tax planning service and works closely with the company/commercial department to provide strategic planning advice to the firm's client both on an individual and on a corporate level. Fairmays has established an infrastructure in its new offices in St James' to augment the service which it provides to its clients both on and off-line, including the availability of video conferencing facilities. The firm has considerable experience of doing business in both India and the Middle East having a branch office in Bahrain. Fairmays strives to offer a competitively priced yet high quality personal service to its clients, working in tandem with them to produce innovative solutions to their business problems.

PRINCIPAL AREAS OF WORK:
Company/Commercial: The cornerstone of the practice adapting to the needs of new media clients. A dedicated IP/IT unit has been formed. Services offered include acquisitions and disposals, flotations, restructuring corporate finance, joint ventures, partnerships, communications law, sports law, taxation, distribution and agency and international and domestic commercial agreements of all kinds.
Litigation: All aspects of commercial litigation, insolvency, insurance/fraud, negligence and personal injury, matrimonial, defamation and building disputes.
Property: The full range of commercial property matters, planning, construction law. Particular strengths include secured lending, portfolio, leisure and retail work.
Employment: Both contentious and non contentious work mainly on behalf of employers or senior executives. Wide experience of employment disputes, representing clients at the ET, County Court or High Court involving matters such as wrongful dismissal, unfair dismissal and discrimination cases, and other statutory claims.
Private Client: The work of this department includes estate planning and administration, immigration, wills, trusts, probate and personal taxation. A significant amount of offshore work is undertaken.

INTERNATIONAL CONNECTIONS: The firm has considerable experience of doing business in India and the Middle East, having a branch office in Bahrain.

RECRUITMENT & TRAINING: Two trainees are recruited annually and it is planned that they spend six months in each of the company/commercial, private client, property and litigation departments. The firm looks for an engaging personality with both a creative and sensible approach to work. CVs to Andrew Miller. A brochure about Fairmays is available on request. Further details can be found on their website, www.fairmays.com.

THE FAMILY LAW CONSORTIUM

2 Henrietta Street, London, WC2E 8PS
Tel: (020) 7420 5000 **Fax:** (020) 7420 5005 **DX:** 40012 Covent Garden
Email: flc@tflc.co.uk **Website:** www.tflc.co.uk

Number of partners:	6
Assistant solicitors:	3
Total Mediators:	9
Other fee-earners:	3

THE FIRM: The firm has five (=10%) of London's family/ matrimonial leaders (*Chambers 99/2000*) and two of the capital's most respected non-lawyer mediators. As a result the firm has expertise in law, mediation and counselling, which they can offer alone or in combination to provide ground-breaking services for all stages of the relationship, from its formation, through difficulties, to its end and the development of post-separation arrangements. The firm helps clients reach their own agreements or offers effective action through lawyer-led settlements or the courts. Detailed information available on their website. Emergency out of hours contact, James Pirrie, 01727 811 478.

FARLEYS

22-27 Richmond Terrace, Blackburn, BB1 7AQ
Tel: (01254) 606000 **Fax:** (01254) 583526 **DX:** 13604 Blackburn 3
Email: info@farleys.com **Website:** www.farleys.com

Senior partner:	M.G. Corrigan
Number of partners:	9
Assistant solicitors:	28
Other fee-earners:	21

AREAS OF PRACTICE

Civil Litigation	30%
Criminal	25%
Family	25%
Commercial & Property	15%
Probate/Private Client	5%

CONTACTS

Company/Commercial	Chris Porter
	Ian Liddle
Crime/Environment	Paul Schofield
	Andrew Church-Taylor
	Bernard Horne
	Kevin Preston
Family/Matrimonial	Kathryn Hughes
	Ann Bamford
	Tony Rebello
Personal Injury/Litigation	Mike Corrigan
	Steve McNeill
	Kieran O'Connor
	Desmond Draper
	Jonathan Bridge
Property/Private Client	Ian Liddle

THE FIRM: Established in 1957, Farleys is a broad-based practice encompassing a number of specialised departments in its offices in Blackburn, Accrington and Burnley. The firm has built up a reputation in the North West of England for providing a high level of service both to private clients and to an increasing number of well-known commercial clients. Farleys has Legal Aid franchises for family, criminal, welfare benefits and mental health.

PRINCIPAL AREAS OF WORK:

Commercial: A very successful and growing department covering all aspects of company and commercial work, with a growing expertise in entrepreneurial and manager-owned businesses.
Personal Injury/General Litigation: The firm handles personal injury, both medical and professional negligence, employment matters and environmental disputes. Members of the Personal Injury Panel and the Mental Health Review Tribunal Panel.
Family/Matrimonial: One of the largest family law departments in the North West dealing with all aspects of family law, especially care proceedings and substantial ancillary relief matters.
Criminal: One of East Lancashire's busiest and most effective criminal practices, dealing with all matters. The department has a serious crime unit dealing with serious fraud/crime.
Property: All aspects of private client property transactions.
Private Client: An extensive range of services offered in the area of wills, probate, trustee and executorship.

FARRER & CO

66 Lincoln's Inn Fields, London, WC2A 3LH
Tel: (020) 7242 2022 **Fax:** (020) 7831 9748 **DX:** 32 London Chancery Lane WC2
Email: enquiries@farrer.co.uk **Website:** www.farrer.co.uk

Senior partner:	Henry Boyd-Carpenter
Chief executive:	Andrew Mills-Baker
Management board:	Robert Clinton, James Furber, Judith Hill
Number of partners:	41
Assistant solicitors:	50
Other fee-earners:	24

CONTACTS

Agriculture	Simon Pring
Banking and FSA	Jonathan Bayliss
Charities	Judith Hill
Commercial Property	Raymond Cooper
Company/Commercial	James Thorne
E-commerce	Peter Wienand
Employment & Pensions	Geoffrey Richards
	Elizabeth Potter
Estates and Private Property	James Furber
Family	Fiona Shackleton
	Richard Parry
Heritage Property	Judith Hill
	Michael Chantler
Intellectual Property	Peter Wienand
International Private Client	Mark Bridges
Litigation	Adrian Parkhouse
Media	Robert Clinton

THE FIRM: Farrer & Co is one of the UK's leading law practices. It provides a range of specialist advice to private, institutional and corporate clients. The firm has long been recognised for the quality of its service, both technical and personal. This has been achieved by consistently recruiting team players possessing flair and intellect coupled with a desire to exceed clients' expectations. Their client base is worldwide and clients are frequently leaders in their fields.To meet the increasingly specialised demands of clients, the firm is divided into flexible, client-focused teams. Its breadth of expertise is reflected in the fact that it has an outstanding reputation in fields as diverse as family law, offshore tax planning, employment, heritage work, charity law and defamation.

PRINCIPAL AREAS OF WORK:

Private Client: The firm is recognised as an established leader in the services it provides to its private clients. Core work includes tax planning, heritage property, wills and the administration of estates, probate and trusts. Agricultural estates and private property specialists advise on property matters, while clients also benefit from the firm's strong reputation in management and employment practices. The family team is highly regarded and advises on family disputes arising from marriage breakdown or inheritance claims, family provision and child-related issues.
Charities, Heritage and Sport: Work for institutions is focused on a highly successful and expanding charities team. In addition to charity law, teams advise these clients on taxation, employment, sponsorship and

Continued overleaf

intellectual property issues. The firm has long had a reputation for advising sports industry clients and for its work for museums, galleries and educational organisations.

Commercial: A full range of work is undertaken for commercial clients, with notable expertise in the media industry. Specialisations include employment and pensions, mergers and acquisitions, intellectual property, corporate tax, banking and FSA. The commercial property team manages all types of work for clients, while the litigation team has advised on almost every type of business dispute: contract, fraud, insolvency, construction, asset recovery, libel, government inspections and prosecutions.

Recruitment & Training: Six trainee solicitors are recruited annually; a 2(1) degree is preferred, not necessarily in law. Applications to the Graduate Recruitment Manager.

LANGUAGES: French and German.

CONTACTS CONTINUED

Private Client ....Anthony Edwards
........Richard Powles
Probate and Trust Administration
........Catherine McAleavey
Sport ....Karena Vleck
........Charles Woodhouse

FENNEMORES

200 Silbury Boulevard, Central Milton Keynes, Milton Keynes, MK9 1LL **Tel:** (01908) 678241 **Fax:** (01908) 665985 **DX:** 84757 Milton Keynes - 3
Email: info@fennemores.co.uk **Website:** www.fennemores.co.uk **Ptnrs:** 11 **Asst solrs:** 8 **Other fee-earners:** 40

F

FENNERS

15 New Bridge Street, London, EC4V 6AU
Tel: (020) 7936 8000 **Fax:** (020) 7936 8111 **DX:** Chancery Lane LDE 256
Email: info@fenners.co.uk **Website:** www.fenners.co.uk

Managing partner:	Robert Fenner
Senior partner:	John Fenner
Number of partners:	3
Assistant solicitors:	5
Other fee-earners:	3

AREAS OF PRACTICE

Commercial Property 50%
Corporate/Commercial 50%

CONTACTS

Commercial ....David Wisbey
Commercial Property ....John Fenner
........Caroline Frampton
Corporate/Commercial ....Robert Fenner
Development ....Caroline Frampton
Planning ....John Fenner
Property Finance ....John Fenner

THE FIRM: Fenners is a City-based firm specialising in company/commercial law, commercial property, town planning and residential property development and offers a leading capability in urban regeneration. The firm has a broad client base including public and private companies, financial advisers, banks and other institutions.

PRINCIPAL AREAS OF WORK:

Commercial Property: Investment acquisitions and disposals; site assembly and development (retail, office and industrial); regional and city centre schemes involving both the public and private sectors; institutional funding and forward sale agreements; commercial lettings for landlords and tenants; building agreements; secured lending for borrowers and lenders.

Corporate: New issues on the Official List and the Alternative Investment Market; corporate finance, corporate reorganisations; management buy-outs; venture capital investments; mergers and acquisitions.

Commercial: Joint ventures; intellectual property; licensing arrangements; franchising; employment law; employee share option schemes and competition law.

Planning: Redevelopment schemes, urban regeneration schemes; planning agreements for infrastructure work; planning gain and use restrictions; planning appeals and inquiries.

Development: Site assembly and acquisition, management schemes; sales; town planning matters; road; sewer and other similar.

Property Finance: Portfolio reconstructions, development finance and property joint venture schemes.

LANGUAGES: French, German, Italian and Portuguese.

FENWICK ELLIOTT

353 Strand, London, WC2R 0HS
Tel: (020) 7956 9354 **Fax:** (020) 7956 9355 **DX:** 178 LDE
Email: reception@fenwickelliott.co.uk **Website:** www.fenwickelliott.co.uk

Senior partner:	Robert Fenwick Elliott
Number of partners:	7
Assistant solicitors:	8
Other fee-earners:	2

AREAS OF PRACTICE

Contentious Construction (including ADR and Arbitration) 60%
Non-Contentious Construction 30%
Other Related Work 10%

THE FIRM: Fenwick Elliott is a commercial law firm which specialises exclusively in building, engineering and energy law. The firm provides a cost-effective service, drawing on a wealth of expertise to provide commercially aware and practical advice. Robert Fenwick Elliott and Tony Francis are joint editors of the Construction Industry Law Letter, and Robert Fenwick Elliott is the author of Building Contract Litigation and Building Contract Disputes: Practice and Precedents. Julian Critchlow is author of Making Partnering Work in the Construction Industry, joint arbitration editor of Amicus Curiae and former editor of Construction Law Newsletter. Various of the partners are members of the Technology and Construction Solicitors Association TeCSA and accredited adjudicators and CEDR accredited mediators, and regularly lecture in the firm's specialist area. Simon Tolson has a monthly column in Building Magazine. The firm's practice is both domestic and international.

PRINCIPAL AREAS OF WORK:

Contentious: The firm handles large volumes of litigation and arbitration from routine loss and expense claims to the unique. The firm has particular expertise in Alternative Dispute Resolution (ADR) and adjudication procedures, and in the preparation of claims and delay analysis.

Fenwick Elliott
SOLICITORS

Non-Contentious: The firm handles contract drafting and advice from major complex developments to standard form sub-contracts, including substantial experience of PFI and BOT type schemes.

CLIENTELE: The firm acts nationally and internationally for developers, institutional investors, local authorities, utilities, main contractors, specialist subcontractors, architects, engineers, surveyors, PFI consortia and private clients. Further, the firm acts for various foreign government corporations. Most of the firm's clients are well known in the construction industry.

LANGUAGES: French.

FIELD CUNNINGHAM & CO

St. John's Court, 70 Quay St, Manchester, M3 3EJ
Tel: (0161) 834 4734 **Fax:** (0161) 834 1772 **DX:** 728855 Manchester 4

Senior partner:	Peter Ashworth
Number of partners:	4
Assistant solicitors:	3
Other fee-earners:	10

AREAS OF PRACTICE

Commercial Property	78%
Commercial Litigation	15%
Company Commercial	5%
Private Client	2%

THE FIRM: Established in 1867, Field Cunningham & Co is a successful niche commercial property practice specialising in development work and associated commercial and property litigation. It places much importance on providing a high level of personal service and commitment within a commercial environment.

PRINCIPAL AREAS OF WORK:
Commercial Property: The firm deals with all aspects of commercial property, with particular emphasis on development work in the retail, residential, office, leisure and commercial sectors, development funding, and joint ventures. Activities include work in associated planning, environmental and Lands Tribunal matters. An increasing volume of property secured lending work is being undertaken on behalf of banks. In addition to its commercial development and re-development work, the firm acts for national and local house-builders – the volume of new house sales undertaken is approximately 1 per cent annually of all UK private housing starts.
Commercial Litigation: Especially in property and construction-related and environmental matters. Also intellectual property; employment and general commercial disputes.
Company/commercial: Private company sales and purchases; joint ventures; MBOs; business start-ups; partnerships; intellectual property and employment.

RECRUITMENT & TRAINING: The firm normally takes one law graduate (2:1 required) annually. Applications by covering letter and CV. (See: Leading Firms Property (Commercial) – North West).

FIELD FISHER WATERHOUSE

35 Vine Street, London, EC3N 2AA
Tel: (020) 7861 4000 **Fax:** (020) 7488 0084 **DX:** 823 London City EC3
Email: info@ffwlaw.com **Website:** www.ffwlaw.com

Managing partner:	John Price
Senior partner:	John Wilson
Number of partners:	65
Assistant solicitors:	91
Other fee-earners:	61

CONTACTS

Advertising & Marketing	Hayley Stallard
Anglo-French Trade	Marie-Caroline Frochot
Anglo-German/Austrian Trade	Robert Wieder
Aviation	Simon Chamberlain
Banking & Finance	Jon FifeJohn Wilson
Capital Markets	Jon FifeGuy Usher
Charity	Catherine Newcombe
Commercial Property	Howard CoffellJohn Pedder
Competition	Charles Whiddington
Construction	Colin McArthur
Corporate	Tim Davies
Derivatives	Guy UsherJon Fife
E-commerce	Michael Chissick
Employee Benefits	Graeme Nuttall
Employment	Steven Lorber
Energy & Pipelines	Howard Coffell
Financial Services Regulation	Christopher Bond
Franchising & Licensing	Mark Abell
Hotels & Leisure	Paul Houston
Immigration	Heather Prescott
Intellectual Property	Mark Abell
International Trade & Projects	John Wilson
Investment Funds & Products	Kirstene Baillie
IT	Michael Chissick
Licensing	Peter Glazebrook
Litigation (Commercial)	Mark Lowe

THE FIRM: Field Fisher Waterhouse is a City-based firm with a substantial corporate and commercial practice. It has a reputation for providing an excellent all-round service to an impressive list of UK and international clients. In particular, it is well known for advising clients who are at the forefront of technological developments. The firm is expanding rapidly, both through organic growth and lateral hires. Five new partners were made up in 1999 in the following areas: corporate; IT & e-commerce; advertising & marketing; commercial litigation; and professional regulation. In addition, Anthony Brockbank and Teruo Kato (reputedly the only Japanese national who is a partner at a City firm) joined the firm's corporate/finance teams, and Marie-Caroline Frochot (dual qualified in England and France) joined to head up the firm's Anglo-French Desk. A distinctive feature of the firm is the number of close and long-standing relationships which it has developed with its clients, achieved by ensuring a high quality service and maintaining a high level of partner involvement in clients' affairs. The firm is well known for its commercial and practical approach, and for its ability to create innovative solutions to legal problems.

PRINCIPAL AREAS OF WORK: The firm's core practice areas are banking & finance; corporate finance; intellectual property; IT and e-commerce; and commercial property. The firm is also well known for its expertise in a number of industry sectors including: advertising; aviation; communications and media; energy; financial services; franchising; hotels and leisure; the internet; and travel and tourism. It also has expertise in the health, rail, shipbuilding and ship finance, and sport sectors. Other areas in which the firm has a leading reputation are: corporate tax; employment; employee share schemes; pensions; investment funds and products; commercial litigation; partnership; personal injury and medical negligence.

INTERNATIONAL CONNECTIONS: The firm also acts for a substantial number of overseas clients and has particularly strong connections with China, France, Germany, Italy, Japan, Korea, Scandinavia and the US. The firm works closely with firms in these and other countries and its partners include French, German, American and Japanese lawyers.

Continued overleaf

LANGUAGES: The firm's lawyers speak a wide range of European languages, as well as Japanese, Korean and Mandarin.

CLIENTELE: The firm has a wide-ranging client base. It includes: commercial and industrial companies; banks and other financial institutions; governments; trade associations; regulatory bodies and professional partnerships.

RECRUITMENT & TRAINING: At least ten trainees are recruited annually. There is a structured training programme for both trainees and assistant solicitors. Literature about the firm and its specialist services is available from the marketing department or from the firm's web site (at http://www.ffwlaw.com). The firm also has several specialist websites at: www.AD-visers.com (advertising and marketing) www.ecomlex.com (European e-commerce lawyers' association) www.ecommerceincubator.net (internet start-ups) www.european-franchising.com (franchising) www.e-ploymentlaw.com (employment) www.globalrewardplangroup.com (international network of specialists in employee benefits) www.sponsorshiplaw.com (sponsorship).

CONTACTS CONTINUED

Litigation (IP/IT)	Nick Rose
Media	Ellen Fleming
Medical Litigation	Paul McNeil
Partnership	Colin McArthur
Pensions	Belinda Benney
Personal Injury	Rodney Nelson-Jones
Planning & Environmental	Richard Webber
Private Client	Penny Wotton
Professional Regulation	Robert Wills
Rail	Nicholas Thompsell
Shipbuilding	John Wilson
Tax (Corporate)	Nicholas Noble
Telecommunications	Tony Ballard
Trade Marks	John Olsen
Travel & Tourism	Peter Stewart

FIELDINGS PORTER

Silverwell House, Silverwell Street, Bolton, BL1 1PT **Tel:** (01204) 387742 **Fax:** (01204) 362129 **DX:** 24144 **Email:** info@fpsols.co.uk **Website:** http\\home.clara.net\fpsols **Ptnrs:** 10 **Asst solrs:** 14 **Other fee-earners:** 10

F

FIELD SEYMOUR PARKES

The Old Coroner's Court, 1 London Street, PO Box 174, Reading, RG1 4QW **Tel:** (01189) 391011 **Fax:** (01189) 502704 **DX:** 4001 Reading **Email:** enquiry@fieldseymour.co.uk **Website:** www.fsp-law.com **Ptnrs:** 7 **Asst solrs:** 14 **Other fee-earners:** 18 **Contact:** Mr Ian Wood-Smith • A general practice handling all areas of company/commercial, litigation, licensing, residential and commercial property, planning, employment, probate, wills and trusts.

AREAS OF PRACTICE

Civil Litigation	22%
Company/Commercial	21%
Commercial Conveyancing	15%
Domestic Conveyancing	14%
Probate, Wills and Trusts	14%
Debt Collection	5%
Matrimonial	5%

FINERS STEPHENS INNOCENT

179 Great Portland St, London, W1N 6LS
Tel: (020) 7323 4000 **Fax:** (020) 7580 7069 **DX:** 42739 Oxford Circus North
Email: mralli@fsilaw.co.uk **Website:** www.fsilaw.com

Managing partner:	Anthony Barling
Number of partners:	41
Assistant solicitors:	36
Other fee-earners:	17

THE FIRM: Finers Stephens Innocent, a 41 partner firm, is the result of the December 1999 merger between Finers, a fast growing mid-sized property and corporate law firm, and high profile niche media practice Stephens Innocent. The firm now employs approximately 180 staff involved in providing a focused range of services to meet the requirements of clients. Partner involvement, for which the firm is recognised, ensures that the firm's reputation for understanding clients' business as well as it understands its own is maintained. The latest acquisition of a team of partners and assistants from Edward Lewis strengthens the firm across the board. The firm has a finely targeted marketplace for each of its departments and ensures that each is fully supported by cross-discipline and industry-led groups. The ability to provide an all-round commercial service ensures that many clients are serviced across departments according to their specific needs. The success of this strategy is evidenced by the number of new services that are now being provided to clients in such areas as intellectual property and construction. The firm is focused on its target markets, providing a high degree of care and skill to its clients. It has tailored its service to match the current and anticipated requirements of its client base. The firm has grown by identifying new markets and implementing a strategy to secure a position in these markets. The firm brings a proactive, commercial approach to its work embracing the changes of a constantly developing environment and has continued to undertake high quality work across a broad base of skills. In particular the firm has acted for a series of port side developments amounting to tens of millions of pounds for Grosvenor Waterside, a subsidiary of Associated British Ports, and the sale of a multi-million pound office development on behalf of Deutsche Bank Asset Management. In property development the firm has acted for Marylebone Warwick Balfour Group PLC in the £50m landmark hotel development in Pall Mall as well as various construction projects for the same clients. The hotel theme continues with a number of major transactions for Radisson SAS Hotels Worldwide including the sale and grant back of a management contract of the London Portman Hotel. A particular highlight has been acting for the sale of Aroma to McDonalds in 1999 and the subsequent involvement in Aroma's roll out programme. Significant lateral hires this year commenced with the recruitment of employment partner Howard Goulden from Pritchard Englefield to strengthen the employment group. The merger with Stephens Innocent resulted in the arrival at Great Portland Street of well known media lawyer Mark Stephens, publishing expert Nicola Solomon and commercial litigator Peter Woods. The year ended with five lateral hires to provide across the board strengthening from Edward Lewis; Peter Carter - corporate and commercial, Alan Kaufman - family law, Michael Kutner - property development, Michael Lewis - private client, Howard Zetter - litigation. In addition, the number of solicitors has increased to provide a more structured growth to the firm.

AREAS OF PRACTICE

Litigation	36%
Property	34%
Corporate/Commercial	23%
Private Client	7%

CONTACTS

Commercial	Anthony Barling
Commercial Litigation	Philip Rubens
Construction Law	James Harvey
Corporate	Peter Jay
Corporate Finance	Paul Millett
Defamation	Mark Stephens
Employment	Howard Goulden
Hotels	Richard Gerstein
Information Technology	Anthony Barling
Insolvency	Johnathan Lewis
Intellectual Property	Mark Stephens
International	Mark Stephens
Leasehold Enfranchisement	John Hewitt
Litigation	Richard Gerstein
Matrimonial	David Taylor
Media	Mark Stephens
Medical Negligence	Daniel Marks
Offshore Tax	Michael Lewis
Partnership	Michael Simmons
Personal Injury	Leon Marks
Planning	Nichola Armstrong
Professional Negligence	Richard Gerstein
Property	David Battiscombe
Property Development	Michael Kutner
Property Investment	Melvyn Orton
Property Litigation	John Hewitt
Property Retail	Katherine Miller
Property Trading	Sam Charkham
Publishing	Nicola Solomon
Sports Law	Daniel Marks
Trusts & Charities	Robert Craig

Finers Stephens Innocent

PRINCIPAL AREAS OF WORK: Finers Stephens Innocent is primarily involved in five key areas of the law: property, corporate & commercial, litigation, media and private client work which each have their own departments. Traditional strengths lie in property (both commercial property and property litigation) where the firm is considered to be one of the key players amongst mid sized firms and media. It has developed a growing reputation in corporate finance, especially in the internet/e-commerce field. The firm is also recognised as having expertise in the fields of defamation, partnership law, insolvency, family law and private client.

Property: Property expertise is provided in a wide range of matters including investment, development, construction, retail, hotels, trading, finance and landlord and tenant issues.

Company and Commercial: This work includes special expertise in OFEX and AIM markets and other corporate finance expertise as well as commercial work, employment, intellectual property, media, insolvency, partnership law and sports law expertise. 1999 was a particularly active year for the rapidly expanding corporate finance team who have handled in excess of £300m with a particular strength in internet related start-up ventures which require fund raising exercises.

Litigation: Litigation services include commercial matters, insolvency, property, personal injury and matrimonial cases as well as construction and professional negligence. The commercial litigation team have continued to act on high profile cases such as the Canadian Dollar fraud claim in action commenced by Chrysler.

Media: The merger with Stephens Innocent has led to a substantially increased portfolio of media work in IP, IT, film and media as well as publishing and defamation. A highlight is the trademark work for Jonathan Ross as well as international copyright and trademarks in counterfeiting involving US, Japan, Netherlands, Germany, France, Korea, Philippines.

Private Client: These services include offshore tax planning for a number of offshore financial institutions and high profile individuals in the music sector as well as the preparation of wills, probate and trusts.

INTERNATIONAL CONNECTIONS: In the international arena the firm continues to service the needs of its clients on both sides of the Atlantic via the Network of Leading Law Firms and in Europe through membership of Lawrope an EEIG.

CLIENTELE: The firm's expertise has developed through the combined strengths introduced through recent mergers and as a result the client base has both expanded and diversified. The firm's client list includes a number of FTSE 250 listed companies and high profile names across a variety of industries.

F

FINN, GLEDHILL

1-4 Harrison Rd, Halifax, HX1 2AG **Tel:** (01422) 330000 **Fax:** (01422) 342604 **DX:** 16022 Halifax **Email:** marc.gledhill@finngledhill.co.uk **Website:** www.finngledhill.co.uk **Ptnrs:** 8 **Asst solrs:** 2 **Other fee-earners:** 5 **Contact:** Michael Gledhill • An all-round practice with an emphasis on commercial work.

AREAS OF PRACTICE	
Commercial	35%
Civil Litigation (Commercial and other)	18%
Conveyancing	12%
Crime	10%
Divorce & Matrimonial	10%
Probate & Trust	9%

FISHBURN MORGAN COLE

60 Strand, London, WC2N 5LR **Tel:** (020) 7925 2884 **Fax:** (020) 7486 3256 **DX:** 8 Ch.Ln. **Email:** info@fishburn-morgan-cole.co.uk **Ptnrs:** 12 **Asst solrs:** 18 **Other fee-earners:** 10

FISHER MEREDITH

2 Binfield Road, Stockwell, London, SW4 6TA
Tel: (020) 7622 4468 **Fax:** (020) 7498 0415 **DX:** 37050
Out of Hours Emergency No: 078 36 780 109
Email: central@fismer.co.uk **Website:** www.fismer.co.uk

Managing partner:	Stephen Hewitt
Senior partner:	Eileen Pembridge
Number of partners:	11
Assistant solicitors:	27
Other fee-earners:	17

AREAS OF PRACTICE	
Civil	36%
Crime	34%
Family (including Children)	22%
Conveyancing	5%
Other	3%

THE FIRM: Founded by Eileen Meredith Pembridge and another in 1975, Fisher Meredith now consists of eleven partners and 84 other staff. The firm remains firmly committed to personal litigation and legal aid work. It is departmentalised for increased efficiency and to meet specialisation needs. Fisher Meredith has departments specialising in: family work of all types including a children's team dealing with children's advocacy and civil domestic violence; all aspects of criminal law; civil actions against the Police; prison law; mental health work; conveyancing; community care and education; immigration; welfare benefits; housing law and employment law.

Eileen Pembridge is the Law Society Council member for London South, and a former Chair of the Law Society's Family Law Committee. The firm has legal aid franchises in family, crime, housing, immigration, welfare benefits, mental health, civil actions against the police, employment, community care and education, and prison law.

Continued overleaf

PRINCIPAL AREAS OF WORK:
Crime: A large thriving department well known for expertise in acting for defendants across a range of offences including difficult human right and civil liberties issues and complex appellate cases. Offer a breadth of expertise including high calibre business crime specialists.
Police and Prison Law: Cutting edge civil liberties service.
Community Care and Education: High level specialist service.
Immigration: Covering all aspects from asylum to judicial review.
Residential and Commercial Conveyancing: A friendly personalised service from experienced solicitors.
Mental Health Law: A caring specialist service which includes Court of Protection work.
Housing Law: A specialist service for tenants and residential occupiers.
Welfare Benefits: All aspects of social security law including judicial review.
Employment Law: A specialist service for employers and employees with specialism in discrimination claims.
Agency Work: Fisher Meredith accept instructions in its areas of expertise.
Charges: For legal aid work, the charges are as fixed by the LCD. For private clients, the firm charges £100-180 per hour.

CONTACTS

Children	Tanya Zabihi
Community Care/Education	Patricia Wilkins
Conveyancing	Joy Bailey
Crime	Stephen Hewitt
Debt/Welfare benefits	Stefano Ruis
Employment	David Tyme
Family	Eileen Pembridge
Housing	David Foster
Immigration	Douglas Noble
Mental Health	Rebecca Ellison
Police Actions/Prison Law	David Tyme

F

FISHERS

9-13 Fenchurch Buildings, London, EC3M 5HR
Tel: (020) 7709 7203 **Fax:** (020) 7709 7204 TELEX: 922792FISHING
Email: info@fishcity.co.uk

Number of partners:	3
Assistant solicitors:	3

AREAS OF PRACTICE

Commercial Shipping and International Trade Litigation	70%
Professional Indemnity and Insurance Litigation	25%
Drafting Shipping and Insurance Documentation	5%

CONTACTS

Contacts	Nicholas Fishe
	Graeme Lloyd
	Jamie Lyons

THE FIRM: Founded in 1993. Small, independently minded, City firm specialising in commercial shipping and international trade litigation, also with signficant practice in insurance and re-insurance disputes.

PRINCIPAL AREAS OF WORK:
Shipping: Commercial litigation work predominantly for shipowners and charterers. Strong following of container and liner operators, tanker and gas carriers and reefer operators. The firm has close links with a number of P&I Clubs and Defence Associations. Experienced also in drafting charterparties and bills of lading.
International Trade: Advises on disputes relating to buying and selling of hard and soft commodities and petroleum products, and on drafting sale contracts.
Insurance and Reinsurance: Litigation principally on behalf of Lloyd's brokers. Advises on compliance and Lloyd's proceedings.

FLADGATE FIELDER

25 North Row, London, W1R 1DJ
Tel: (020) 7323 4747 **Fax:** (020) 7629 4414 **DX:** 9057 West End
Email: fladgate@fladgate.com **Website:** www.fladgate.com

Chairman:	Paul Leese
Number of partners:	28
Assistant solicitors:	30
Other fee-earners:	19

AREAS OF PRACTICE

Property	39%
Corporate/Commercial	32%
Litigation	23%
Tax	6%

CONTACTS

Anglo-American	Nicolas Greenstone
Anglo-French	Nicolas Greenstone
Anglo-Germanic	Andrew Kaufman
Anglo-Israeli	Avram Kelman
Commercial Contracts	Charles Boundy
Corporate	Nicolas Greenstone
Employment	Jessica Learmond-Criqui
Immigration	Jessica Learmond-Criqui
Libel	Simon Ekins
Litigation	Paul Leese
Property	Allen Cohen
Tax	Andrew McKenzie
Town Planning	Daniel Drukarz

THE FIRM: Fladgate Fielder is one of the leading business law practices in the West End of London, providing legal advice of the highest quality for a diverse portfolio of clients. Pivotal to the firm's success are the following factors; namely its standard of excellence in client service, the calibre of its expertise, its innovative and commercial approach to the solution of problems and the combination of efficiency and cost-effectiveness to reach the optimum result.

PRINCIPAL AREAS OF WORK:
Corporate: Corporate; listings and flotations; AIM, EASDAQ and OFEX quotations; mergers and acquisitions; venture capital; MBOs; UK and cross-border corporate and commercial transactions; employment; immigration; computer and intellectual property law; banking; partnership law and company secretarial work.
Property: Acquisition and disposal; funding; construction and development; investment; secured lending; landlord and tenant; housing associations; joint ventures; portfolio management; residential estate conveyancing; town and country planning; environmental issues; and enterprise zone development.
Litigation: General commercial litigation; professional negligence; asset recovery; corporate recovery; landlord and tenant; intellectual property; libel; matrimonial; construction disputes; building and product liability; and insurance litigation.
Tax: All aspects of taxation including corporate and business taxes as well as off-shore and international aspects; personal tax planning; wills; probate; charities and land estate matters.

INTERNATIONAL CONNECTIONS: Fladgate Fielder has an expanding international dimension based on multilingual lawyers working in London. The firm has Anglo-American, Germanic, Israeli and French Desks.

LANGUAGES: The firm is able to conduct business in French, German, Hebrew, Italian and Spanish.

CLIENTELE: The firm's client base has a strong commercial focus, comprising leading public and private companies, financial institutions and entrepreneurs in the UK and overseas.

FLETCHERS

111 Carrington Street, Nottingham, NG1 7FE **Tel:** (0115) 959 9550 **Fax:** (0115) 959 9597

FLYNN & MCGETTRICK

24-26 Arthur Street, Belfast, BT1 3EF **Tel:** (028) 90244212 **Fax:** (028) 90236490 **Ptnrs:** 3 **Asst solrs:** 3

FOLLETT STOCK

Malpas Road, Truro, TR1 1QH **Tel:** (01872) 241700 **Fax:** (01872) 225052 **DX:** 81225 Truro **Email:** martin@follettstock.co.uk **Website:** www.follettstock.demon.co.uk **Ptnrs:** 3 **Asst solrs:** 3 **Other fee-earners:** 3

FOOT ANSTEY SARGENT

4-6 Barnfield Crescent, Exeter, EX1 1RF
Tel: (01392) 411221 **Fax:** (01392) 218554 **DX:** 8308 Exeter
Email: richard.coombs@foot-ansteys.co.uk **Website:** www.foot-ansteys.co.uk

Foot & Bowden Building, 21 Derry's Cross, Plymouth, PL1 2SW
Tel: (01752) 675000 **Fax:** (01752) 671802 **DX:** 118102 Plymouth 2
Email: mark.lewis@foot-ansteys.co.uk

Managing partner:	Jane Lister
Senior partners	William Jones
	Adrian Miller
Number of partners:	35
Assistant solicitors:	35
Other fee-earners:	36

CONTACTS

- **Advocacy** ... Tony Daniel
- **Banking** ... Robin Brown
- **Commercial Litigation** ... Angus McNicol
- **Commercial Property** ... Simon Gregory, Cindy Rai
- **Company & Commercial** ... Mark Lewis, Richard Coombs
- **Employment** ... Jon Loney
- **Family & Childcare** ... Margaret Bonner, Vanessa Priddis
- **Information Technology** ... Edmund Probert
- **Insolvency** ... Stephen Lawson, Gillian Smith
- **Investment Management** ... John Crowley
- **Marine** ... Charles Hattersley
- **Media** ... Tony Jaffa
- **Planning & Land Use** ... Isabel Diver, Sebastian Head
- **Private Client/Tax Planning** .. Alex Elphinston, Adrian Miller
- **Property Litigation** ... John Westwell

THE FIRM: Foot Anstey Sargent is a major regional practice with a growing national and international client base. The recent merger of Foot & Bowden and Anstey Sargent & Probert has meant greater strength and depth in a range of specialist areas. The firm prides itself on providing efficient, practical advice at a competitive price. Many of the firm's solicitors trained in large City firms and have proven expertise in their field. Investment in the latest technology ensures the best possible service. The firm provides a complete service for clients. Cross-departmental teams can handle large and complex corporate transactions, with specialists in commercial property, planning, employment law and commercial litigation. Private clients benefit from expertise in the most complex areas of trust and estate planning, and there is a growing portfolio management team. Other offices are situated in Exeter and Budleigh Salterton.

PRINCIPAL AREAS OF WORK: The firm combines strong commercial and private client teams. Particular specialisms include corporate finance, e-commerce and IT law, commercial property, planning and land use, insolvency, investment management, marine and media law.

CLIENTELE: Includes Northcliffe Newspapers, Wrigley's, Exeter Friendly Society, University of Plymouth, UKRD, Beer Seller, South West Highways, Arbuthnot Latham, Bank of Scotland.

FORBES

Rutherford House (Commercial department), 4 Wellington Street, (St. Johns), Blackburn, BB1 8DD
Tel: (01254) 54374 **Fax:** (01254) 52347 **DX:** 17952 Blackburn-1
Email: forbes@f-p.co.uk **Website:** www.forbessolicitors.co.uk

Marsden House (Insurance/Litigation department), 28 Wellington Street, (St Johns), Blackburn, BB1 8DA
Tel: (01254) 662831 **Fax:** (01254) 681104 **DX:** 17969 Blackburn-1
Email: forbes@f-p.co.uk

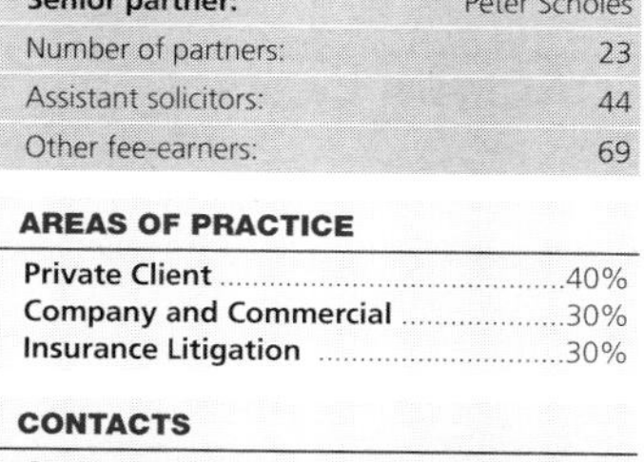

Senior partner:	Peter Scholes
Number of partners:	23
Assistant solicitors:	44
Other fee-earners:	69

AREAS OF PRACTICE

- **Private Client** ... 40%
- **Company and Commercial** ... 30%
- **Insurance Litigation** ... 30%

CONTACTS

- **Company and Commercial** ... John Barker
- **Insurance Litigation** ... Martin Crabtree
- **Private Client** ... David Forbes

THE FIRM: This prominent Lancashire practice provides a range of company & commercial services, particularly in insurance matters and commercial property. Forbes was established more than 100 years ago and has expanded both organically and through a series of amalgamations.The practice has a progressive approach to commercial matters and believes that its policy of attracting high-calibre lawyers and a commitment to training enables it to offer expertise and ability in key areas. At the same time, it offers a fee structure that is highly competitive.Each business client's case is handled by a large, dedicated team of specialists led by a partner. The team aims to acquire a thorough understanding of clients' business objectives and to handle cases with both speed and efficiency. The firm has other offices in Accrington, Blackburn, Chorley, Clitheroe and Preston.

PRINCIPAL AREAS OF WORK:

Commercial: Activities carried out by the commercial department include all types of property transaction, such as sales, acquisitions, leasing and development. All types of commercial agreement are dealt with by the department, including joint ventures and acquisitions.

Employment: A specialist employment team deals with all key areas including contracts and service agreements, redundancy, Industrial Tribunals, race relations, sex discrimination and contracting out services.

Continued overleaf

Commercial Litigation: Experience is offered in a range of commercial litigation matters including contract disputes, employers' and public liability, health and safety at work and construction law.
Insurance Litigation: Insurance litigation on behalf of defendants is a notable specialism of the firm. A close working relationship has been forged with a number of major composite insurer clients to achieve a pro-active and cost-effective approach to the resolution of cases. This department offers specialism in key areas, including severe brain injury cases, industrial disease and occupational stress.

CLIENTELE: The firm's client base includes large local and national companies, including a number of Plcs, as well as smaller businesses. Instructions are also received from a number of international companies.

FORD & WARREN

Westgate Point, Westgate, Leeds, LS1 2AX
Tel: (0113) 243 6601 **Fax:** (0113) 242 0905 **DX:** 706968 Leeds
Email: clientmail@forwarn.com **Website:** www.forwarn.com

Managing partner:	Keith Hearn
Number of partners:	14
Assistant solicitors:	33
Other fee-earners:	42

FORD & WARREN
Solicitors

F

THE FIRM: Ford & Warren is a major commercial firm in the North of England. The size and strength of the firm enables expert teams of lawyers to be put together helping clients achieve their business objectives.

PRINCIPAL AREAS OF WORK:
Employment and Corporate: The business law department provides a full range of management advice to employers. The Managing Partner, Keith Hearn, is in this department as head of employment law along with Peter Reeve, head of corporate. The employment team deal with issues right across the board from tribunal claims, fraudulent directors, trade union disputes and injunctions. Corporate law encompasses mergers, acquisitions, MBOs, MBIs and commercial contracts along with intellectual property issues. Gary Gillman, of the Ontario and Quebec Bars and based in Toronto, is our North America Consultant.
Commercial: The commercial law department provides a full range of contentious and non-contentious services. From property litigation, planning and environment through to transport public inquiries. This department handles major commercial litigation in close liaison with the business law department. Head of department, Stephen Kirkbright, and partner, Gary Hodgson, have enormous expertise in the transport industry. Jeremy Rowland deals with insolvency issues and Joanne McKenzie heads the debt recovery department. Ted Brown heads up the commercial property department and Chris Charlesworth deals with commercial litigation and professional negligence.
Claims: In the claims department, Blaise Smith and Nick Collins run strong teams acting for major insurance companies throughout the country. Litigation includes employers liability, road traffic, fire and insurance fraud claims. As well as the defendant claims team, the department has a plaintiff team who have unrivalled expertise in high profile multi-plaintiff claims, including Bradford stadium fire, Zeebrugge ferry sinking and the Hillsborough stadium disaster. The firm's medical negligence team goes from strength to strength.
Private Client: This department caters for all the needs of the private client from matrimonial law to employee relocation. John Robson deals with residential conveyancing and relocation and Jo McConville handles matrimonial issues.

FOREMAN LAWS

25 Bancroft, Hitchin, SG5 1JW **Tel:** (01462) 458711 **Fax:** (01462) 459242 **DX:** 7102 Hitchin **Email:** lawyers@foremanlaws.co.uk **Ptnrs:** 10 **Asst solrs:** 3 **Other fee-earners:** 6 **Contact:** Martin Foreman • Strong commercial, property development and construction base, alongside full range of private client services. Well-developed use of IT.

AREAS OF PRACTICE	
Company	30%
Commercial Property	25%
Civil Litigation	15%
Family	10%
Probate & Trusts	10%
Residential	10%

FORSTERS

67 Grosvenor Street, London, W1X 9DB
Tel: (020) 7863 8333 **Fax:** (020) 7863 8444 **DX:** 82 988 Mayfair
Email: mail@forsters.co.uk **Website:** www.forsters.co.uk

Managing partner:	Paul Roberts
Senior partner:	David Willis
Number of partners:	17
Assistant solicitors:	33
Other fee-earners:	12

THE FIRM: Forsters is a new commercial law firm with a particularly strong reputation for its property and private client work. It also has thriving commercial and litigation practices. Forsters opened in 1998, a new firm with a long history. Eleven of the 12 founding partners were previously partners of Frere Cholmeley Bischoff. Forsters was formed with the objective of offering clients a highly professional, personal service which is not always available in larger firms. It is recognised as a leading firm in the areas of property and private client, the latter group having been enhanced by the addition of the private client team from Masons. Forsters is a new and dynamic firm with a commitment to providing legal services of the highest quality.

AREAS OF PRACTICE	
Property	55%
Private Client	20%
Corporate	12%
Commercial Litigation	8%
Property Litigation	5%

PRINCIPAL AREAS OF WORK:

Property: The firm has a strong reputation for all aspects of commercial property work. Principal strengths are: investment work (both institutional and private investment clients), development (mainly UK development companies) and leisure and retail. The group handles investment and funding; development; planning; construction; landlord and tenant; secured lending; receivership; property taxation; property litigation; residential investment and development. Forsters is one of the few leading London firms with a specialist residential property group acting for both landlords and tenants and for developers, investors and individual purchasers. It has a strong reputation at the upper end of the London residential property market, offering speed, efficiency, and a genuinely personal service. Areas of special expertise include: leasehold reform, including leasehold enfranchisement schemes; the acquisition, development and sale of major residential schemes in London; advising residential management companies.

Private Client: The firm is recognised as one of the leading proponents of private client work in London, with a client base comprising a broad range of individuals and trusts in the UK and elsewhere including landed estates, entrepreneurs, rock stars, well-known charities, private banks and corporate trustees. The private client group advises on tax and estate planning for UK and non-UK clients; wills, trusts and probate; charity law; family law; and heritage property. The firm offers the full range of legal advice in family matters advising on divorce and separation, children, and financial planning issues.

Company/Commercial/Tax/Media: Forsters' commercial practice specialises in acquisitions and financing for technology, communications and media companies. The firm handles work for both quoted and unquoted property companies including financing.

Litigation: The firm's litigation group conducts commercial litigation and arbitration and advises on a broad spectrum of matters including professional negligence disputes, intellectual property disputes, fraud recovery and insolvency and administration. It has particular expertise in arbitration and dedicated teams in property and construction (the latter undertaking both contentious and non-contentious work).

CLIENTELE: Forsters' clients range from wealthy private individuals, both UK and foreign domiciled, to major multinational companies. The client base is predominantly corporate, although there are a significant number of individual clients for whom the firm acts, either in relation to their personal or business affairs.

RECRUITMENT & TRAINING: Forsters recruits between three and five trainees per year and has positions for paralegals on a full and part-time basis. The firm places a high emphasis on training both through the provision of internal and external courses.

CONTACTS

Commercial Property	Tony Patterson
Litigation	Caroline Bassett
Private Client	David Robinson
Residential Property	Paul Neville

F

FOSTER BAXTER COOKSEY

6-10 George Street, Snow Hill, Wolverhampton, WV2 4DN
Tel: (01902) 311711 **Fax:** (01902) 311102 **DX:** 702433 Wolverhampton 5
Email: solicitors@fbc-sol.co.uk

Managing partner:	Graham Sower
Senior partner:	Peter Lawley
Number of partners:	15
Assistant solicitors:	8
Other fee-earners:	25

THE FIRM: Formed by the merger of four well-established Midlands firms, Foster Baxter Cooksey now has over 100 staff and serves a broad spectrum of private and business clients. The firm has particular expertise in corporate work, commercial property, intellectual property, civil litigation, matrimonial and family. Other Offices: Telford and Willenhall.

PRINCIPAL AREAS OF WORK: Commercial; property; corporate finance; building societies; civil litigation; family and trusts.

RECRUITMENT & TRAINING: The firm recruits two trainee solicitors (with at least a 2.1 degree) each year. Applicants should write to Kim Carr, Training Partner, with a full CV.

CONTACTS

Commercial Property	Simon Bowdler
Corporate Services	James Hayes
Employment	Graham Sower
Insolvency	Guy Birkett
Legal Audits	James Hayes
Litigation	Richard Dalton
Private client	Ian Fallon

FOSTERS

William House, 19 Bank Plain, Norwich, NR2 4FS **Tel:** (01603) 620508 **Fax:** (01603) 624090 **DX:** 5225 Norwich-1 **Ptnrs:** 9 **Asst solrs:** 11 **Other fee-earners:** 13 **Contact:** Andrew Saul • 1999 The Lawyer Awards: UK Law Firm of the Year (best medium size). Leaders in mediation, professional negligence, personal injury and family work. Growing reputation for commercial litigation and commercial property. Commitment to first class and cost effective service.

AREAS OF PRACTICE

P.I./medical & Professional Negligence	32%
Family	18%
Commercial Litigation	16%
Crime and Mental Health	16%
Private Client/Residential Property	12%
Commercial Property	6%

FOX WILLIAMS

City Gate House, 39-45 Finsbury Square, London, EC2A 1UU
Tel: (020) 7628 2000 **Fax:** (020) 7628 2100 **DX:** 33873 Finsbury Sq.
Email: mail@foxwilliams.co.uk **Website:** www.foxwilliams.co.uk

Senior partner:	Ronnie Fox
Number of partners:	14
Assistant solicitors:	27
Other fee-earners:	6

AREAS OF PRACTICE

Employment	34%
Corporate	31%
Commercial	14%
Litigation	14%
Property	7%

CONTACTS

Commercial Agreements	Stephen Sidkin
Commercial Property	Bryan Emden
Corporate Finance	Paul Osborne
Corporate Rescue & Insolvency	Robin Tutty
Corporate Tax	Vishvas Kanji
Corporate/Financial Services	Tina Williams
Discrimination & Business Immigration	Jane Mann
E-commerce & Internet Law	Nigel Miller
E-commerce & IT Law	Robin Baron
Employment (Executive Termination & International)	Clare Murray
Employment (UK and Corporate)	Mark Watson
Litigation (Commercial and Financial Services)	Lindsay Hill
M&A	Mark Tasker
Partnership	Ronnie Fox

THE FIRM: Fox Williams is a City firm handling a wide variety of company and commercial matters, with particular skills in corporate and employment matters. Fox Williams adopts a particular approach to its work, involving a special effort to understand the business needs of its clients, a high degree of partner involvement in work done by the firm, a close relationship between clients and members of the Fox Williams team and, a fast, responsive service. The firm pays meticulous attention to detail and to quality assurance, and strives to create a happy and efficient working environment for members of the firm.

PRINCIPAL AREAS OF WORK: The firm is organised into departments focussed on corporate law, commercial law, employment, commercial litigation and commercial property. Cross-departmental groups advise on partnership and Internet law.
Commercial: Commercial work includes distribution and agency arrangements, joint ventures, franchising, licensing of technology, data protection legislation, UK and EC competition law, and intellectual property. Fox Williams has considerable experience in advising on legal issues arising from on-line commerce and the use of the Internet.
Corporate: Corporate work includes international and domestic takeovers and mergers, company acquisitions and disposals, share issues, management buy-ins and by-outs, private placings, flotations, film financing and venture capital projects. General corporate matters such as business start-ups, restructurings and shareholder agreements are also handled.
Employment: The firm is well known for its employment law expertise which includes service agreements, employee rights and restrictive covenants, share incentive and option schemes, golden handshakes, dismissals and redundancies. Employment litigation is handled by employment lawyers in the employment department.
Litigation: A broad range of substantial UK and international litigation and arbitration is undertaken by the litigation department. It has specialist expertise in regulatory financial services work. It also resolves disputes relating to intellectual property, trading, shareholder and joint venture arrangements. The litigation department also presents cases for mediation.
Property: Commercial property work is concerned with a wide range of matters including land acquisitions and disposals, secured lending, business leases, and landlord and tenant issues.
Other: Fox Williams has an outstanding reputation for partnership work.

CLIENTELE: The firm's clients range from multinational corporations and major public companies to family businesses and individual entrepreneurs. They include banks, other financial institutions, regulatory authorities, accountants and other professionals (including overseas lawyers). Firms of solicitors often refer work to Fox Williams when City expertise is required.

FOY & CO

PO Box 111, 63 Hallgate, Doncaster, DN1 3DQ
Tel: (01302) 327136 **Fax:** (01302) 367656 **DX:** 12563 Doncaster
Email: info@foyandco.co.uk **Website:** www.foyandco.co.uk

Church Steps, All Saints Square, Rotherham, S60 1QD
Tel: (01709) 375561 **Fax:** (01709) 828479 **DX:** 12601 Rotherham
Email: info@foyandco.co.uk

15 Peaks Mount, Crystal Peaks, Sheffield, S20 7HZ
Tel: (0114) 251 1702 **Fax:** (0114) 251 1750 **DX:** 717230 Sheffield 28
Email: info@foyandco.co.uk

102 Bridge Street, Worksop, S80 1HZ
Tel: (01909) 473560 **Fax:** (01909) 482760 **DX:** 12207 Worksop
Email: info@foyandco.co.uk

Managing partner:	Paul Evans
Senior partner:	Stephen J. Paramore
Number of partners:	8
Assistant solicitors:	11
Other fee-earners:	12

THE FIRM: Established legal practice offering a wide range of domestic and commercial services including conveyancing, litigation, matrimonial and family, criminal and motoring, wills and probate, all commercial matters.

FRANCIS HANNA & CO
Central Chambers, 75-77 May Street, Belfast, BT1 3JL **Tel:** (028) 90243901 **Fax:** (028) 90244215 **DX:** 473NR Belfast **Email:** info@fhanna.co.uk
Website: www.fhanna.co.uk **Ptnrs:** 3 **Asst solrs:** 4 **Other fee-earners:** 6

FRANCIS J IRVINE & CO

86 Great Victoria Street, Belfast, BT2 7BD
Tel: (028) 9024 6451 **Fax:** (028) 9033 1735 **DX:** 437NR Belfast **Ptnrs:** 2 **Asst solrs:** 2
Contact: Christopher G Walls LLB. The firm has acted for several Insurance companies in the defence of personal injury litigation for over 25 years and has wide experience in commercial and professional negligence litigaion.They have acted in an action which went to the House of Lords.

FREEMAN & CO
Rodesia House, 52 Princess Street, Manchester, M1 6JX **Tel:** 0161 236 7007 **Fax:** 0161 236 0440

FREEMANS SOLICITORS
Stuart House, Lower Chepstow, NP16 5HH **Tel:** (01291) 623 225 **Fax:** (01291) 628 162

FREEMANS
7 St Mary's Place, Newcastle-upon-Tyne, NE1 7PG **Tel:** (0191) 222 1030 **Fax:** (0191) 222 1819 **DX:** 61100 Newcastle-upon-Tyne
Email: freemans@btinternet.com

FREETHCARTWRIGHT

Willoughby House, 20 Low Pavement, Nottingham, NG1 7EA
Tel: (0115) 936 9369 **Fax:** (0115) 936 9358 **DX:** 10039 Nottingham
Email: postmaster@freethcartwright.co.uk **Website:** www.freethcartwright.co.uk

Imperial House, 108-110 New Walk, Leicester, LE1 7EA
Tel: (0116) 201 4000 **Fax:** (0116) 201 4001 **DX:** 715612 Leicester 2
Email: postmaster@freethcartwright.co.uk

Norman House, Friargate, Derby, DE1 1NU
Tel: (01332) 361000 **Fax:** (01332) 207177 **DX:** 11502 Derby 1
Email: postmaster@freethcartwright.co.uk

Senior partner:	Ian Payne
Chairman:	Colin Flanagan
Chief executive:	Peter Smith
Number of partners:	47
Assistant solicitors:	53
Other fee-earners:	54

AREAS OF PRACTICE

Dispute Resolution	31%
Commercial Property	28%
Private Client	21%
Corporate and Commercial Services	20%

CONTACTS

Administrative/Public Law	Richard Beverley
Banking	Paul Thorogood
Charities	Nigel Cullen
Company/Commercial	Ian Worthington
Competition	Philip Raven
Construction	Guy Berwick
Corporate Finance	Karl Jansen
Employment	David Potter
Family/Childcare	Beth Henderson
Housing Associations	Gary Reynolds
Immigration	Sue Miles
Information Technology	Andrew Margiotta-Hills
Insolvency	Graham Greenfield
Intellectual Propety	Helen Driscoll
Internet	Andrew Margiotta-Mills
Licensing	Malcolm Radcliffe
Litigation (Commercial)	Philippa Dempster
Litigation (Property)	Martin Lee
Pensions	John Heaphy
Personal Injury	Jane Goulding
Planning	Ian Tempest
Private Client	Nigel Cullen
Product Liability	Paul Balen
Professional Negligence	Richard Beverley
Property (Commercial)	George Taylor
Risk Management	Philippa Dempster
Sports	Simon Taylor

THE FIRM: Freethcartwright is a major Midlands practice offering services to both commercial and private clients across the entire legal spectrum. Although based in Nottingham, Derby and Leicester, the firm has a wide range of clients throughout the UK and many of its clients have strong international connections.freeth-cartwright has grown rapidly in recent years and now ranks as one of the leading East Midlands' firms offering comprehensive legal services in the public and private sectors.Whilst aiming to provide the very best service possible in all areas, the firm also prides itself on its wish and ability to understand the businesses of its clients and to demonstrate to them that with a properly developed relationship it can significantly add value. It believes that major legal practices should be in 'partnership' with their clients, not merely reacting to clients' specific instructions and dealing with problems after they have arisen. The firm aims to combine first-class legal expertise with a thorough knowledge of our clients' business. Its lawyers are encouraged and trained to be both practical and commercial in their approach to the provision of legal services.

PRINCIPAL AREAS OF WORK:

Commercial: The firm's commercial practice covers a broad spectrum of corporate, commercial and financial work from small day-to-day transactions to significant mergers and acquisitions, some with an international content.

Corporate and Commercial: The corporate and commercial team provides the full range of services specialising in MBOs, MBIs, the re-organisation and financing of businesses, mergers, acquisitions and joint ventures. The firm also has a significant capability in specialist areas including pensions, competition, EU law, corporate tax and sport and entertainment law. It has a specialist intellectual property unit dealing with both contentious and non-contentious work including a comprehensive international trademark registration service and significant work in the telecommunications, internet and IT sectors.

Commercial Property: With one of the largest commercial property departments in the Midlands, the firm acts for developers of industrial, residential and commercial property; institutional lenders and investors; privatised utilities; housing associations; and commercial landlords and tenants. The firm has dedicated units covering planning, environment issues and construction.

Dispute Resolution: The emphasis in dispute resolution is on risk management and risk avoidance. The firm has specialist groups in employment, landlord and tenant, construction litigation, professional negligence and insurance. The firm also undertakes significant insolvency, recovery and litigation work for major banks and accountants. The firm acts for Lloyds underwriters, insurers and indemnity institutions. The firm has particular expertise in medical negligence and product liability under the leadership of Paul Balen who enjoys an

freethcartwright

Continued overleaf

established national reputation in the field. The group has significant experience in co-ordinating high profile group actions, both in the UK and overseas.
Private Client: Emphasising the firm's range of services, the private client units provide expertise in family and childcare matters, housing litigation, immigration, personal injury, residential conveyancing and wills and probate.The firm plans to continue growth through organic development, by pursuing pro-active strategic and marketing policies and by investing in high calibre people, from trainee solicitors to partners.

FRESHFIELDS BRUCKHAUS DERINGER

65 Fleet Street, London, EC4Y 1HS
Tel: (020) 7936 4000 **Fax:** (020) 7832 7001 **DX:** 23
Email: email@freshfields.com **Website:** www.freshfields.com

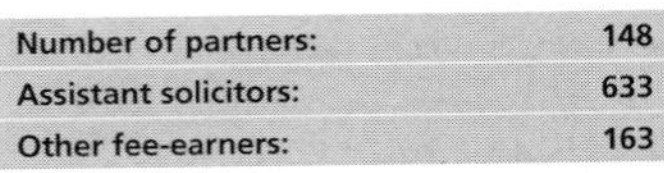

Number of partners:	148
Assistant solicitors:	633
Other fee-earners:	163

CONTACTS

Arbitration	Nigel Rawding
Asset Finance	Tim Lintott
Banking	Edward Evans
Communications & Media	Rachel Brandenburger
Construction & Engineering	Sally Roe
Corporate/M&A	Barry O'Brien
Dispute Resolution	Josanne Rickard
Employment	Peter Jeffcote
Energy	Jon Rees
Environment	Paul Bowden
EU/Competition	Nick Spearing
Finance	Simon Hall
Financial Services	Guy Morton
Insolvency	Peter Bloxham
Insurance	Philip Richards
Intellectual Property	Avril Martindale
International Tax	Roger Berner
Investment Funds	Anthony McWhirter
Project Finance	Kent Rowey
Real Estate	Chris Morris
Securities	Tom Joyce
	Tim Jones
Structured Finance	Ian Falconer
Tax	David Taylor

THE FIRM: Freshfields Bruckhaus Deringer is a leading international law firm with a network of 30 offices in Europe, Asia and the US providing a full range of business legal services and a wealth of experience in the world's major economies.

PRINCIPAL AREAS OF WORK: Freshfields Bruckhaus Deringer has advised on many of the world's largest or most complex deals and the firm is widely recognized as a world leader in fields ranging from arbitration and environmental law to privatizations and aircraft finance.

INTERNATIONAL CONNECTIONS: Freshfields merged with the leading German law firm Bruckhaus Westrick Heller Löber on 1 August 2000, building on the success of its earlier merger with Deringer Tessin Herrmann & Sedemund. The firm's international approach is founded on strong local capabilities and experience. This is backed up by the quality and experience of its lawyers, the consistency of its service delivery and a common client focused culture.
Europe: Freshfields Bruckhaus Deringer now has a powerful platform throughout Europe for assisting clients with EU interests, especially those engaged in cross-border activities.
The Americas: The US is another key part of the firm's legal services to clients around the world especially in areas such as securities and projects. Freshfields Bruckhaus Deringer has over 120 US qualified lawyers throughout its network. Much of the project work out of New York and Washington involves Latin America where the firm is able to offer advice across a broad range of areas.
Asia: Freshfields Bruckhaus Deringer is also a leading international law firm in Asia and through its eight Asian offices practices international law and where permitted local law. Its lawyers also undertake work in countries where it does not have offices such as India, Korea, Malaysia, the Philippines and Indonesia.
International Contacts: Amsterdam, Ian Hewitt, +31 20 488 0900; Bangkok, James Lawden, +662 344 9200; Barcelona, Toni Valverde, +34 93 363 7400; Beijing, Doug Markel, +8610 6410 6338; Berlin, Helmut Bergmann, +49 30 20 17 440; Bratislava, Paul Luiki, +421 754 131 121; Brussels, John Davies, +32 2 504 7000; Budapest, Klára Oppenheim, +36 13 563 458; Cologne, Ludwig Leyendecker, +49 22 120 5070; Düsseldorf, Thomas Kreifels, +49 21 149 790; Frankfurt, Karsten Muller-Eising, +49 69 170 990 and Wolfgang Hauser, +49 692 73 080; Hamburg, Hans Jochen Waitz, +49 40 369 060; Hanoi, Tony Foster, +84 48 247 422; Ho Chi Minh City, Mark Fraser +84 88 226 680; Hong Kong, Ruth Markland, +852 2846 3400; Leipzig, Nikolaus Reinhuber, +49 341 127 230; Madrid, John Byrne, +34 91 319 1024; Milan, Giovanni Lega, Laurie McFadden, +39 02 625 301; Moscow, Jacky Baudon, +7 095 785 0085; Munich, Bernhard Heiss +49 892 42 18 222; New York, Stephen Revell, +1 212 277 4000; Paris, James Vaudoyer +33 1 44 56 44 56; Prague, Josef Vejmelka and Petr W‚nsch, +420 222 253 050; Rome, Neil Falconer, +3906 695 331; Shanghai*, Christian Bunsen, +86 21 6445 1799; Singapore, Roger Dyer, +65 535 6211; Tokyo, Charles Stevens, +81 3 3584 8500; Vienna, Georg Bahn, +43 15 15 150; Washington, Thomas Hechl, +1 202 969 4500.
* Associated office

FRIED, FRANK, HARRIS, SHRIVER & JACOBSON

4 Chiswell Street, London, EC1Y 4UP **Tel:** (020) 7972 9600 **Fax:** (020) 7972 9602 **Email:** info@ffhsj.com **Website:** www.ffhsj.com **Ptnrs:** 3 **Associates:** 8 **Other fee-earners:** 1 **Contact:** Robert P. Mollen • US and international lawyers. Wall Street type practice focusing on mergers and acquisitions, private equity, global capital markets, acquisition finance, general securities and corporate matters.

AREAS OF PRACTICE

Global Capital Markets	40%
M & A/Private Equity	30%
Acquisition Finance	20%
Securities/General Corporate	10%

THE FRITH PARTNERSHIP

53 The Calls, Leeds, LS2 7EY **Tel:** (0113) 242 6633 **Fax:** (0113) 242 6620 **DX:** 22124 Leeds 1 **Email:** robertkelly@thefrithpartnership.co.uk

FURLEY PAGE FIELDING & BARTON

39 St. Margaret's Street, Canterbury, CT1 2TX
Tel: (01227) 763939 **Fax:** (01227) 762829 **DX:** 5301 Canterbury
Email: postmaster@furleypage.co.uk **Website:** www.furleypage.co.uk

52-54 High St, Whitstable, CT5 1BG
Tel: (01227) 274241 **Fax:** (01227) 275704 **DX:** 32352 Whitstable
Email: postmaster@furleypage.co.uk

Managing partner:	P.W. Hawkes
Senior partner:	V.E. Barton
Number of partners:	18
Assistant solicitors:	7
Other fee-earners:	20

AREAS OF PRACTICE

Litigation	32%
Commercial Services	30%
Trust & Estates	25%
Residential	13%

CONTACTS

Company/Commercial	Christropher Wacher
Employment	Jonathan Gauton
Litigation	Peter Hawkes
Private Client	Harvey Barrett

THE FIRM: One of the largest practices in Kent. Lawyers are organised in specialist groups and offer a level of service that competes both regionally and nationally. The firm has associations with commercial practices in many countries to handle an increasing volume of overseas work.

PRINCIPAL AREAS OF WORK:

Commercial Services: Clients include national and international plcs, insurers and a wide range of private companies. Work includes company commercial, commercial property, intellectual property, competition, planning and environmental. There is a specialist e-business group.

Education and Charities: The firm acts for charities, higher education institutions, colleges and schools.

Agriculture: A long standing and significant area of practice for the firm.

Litigation: Groups specialise in personal injury and clinical negligence, commercial and building, landlord and tenant and matrimonial. Agency work is regularly undertaken.

Employment: A team of lawyers and specialist consultants advises nationally and internationally on employment, human resources, health & safety and commercial immigration.

Debt Recovery: A specialist computer supported service operating debt recovery at fixed rates.

Private Client: Comprehensive Tax Planning, domestic conveyancing, probate, court of protection and wills.

Financial Services: Investment, life assurance, pensions and other financial advice.

FYFE IRELAND WS

Orchard Brae House, 30 Queensferry Road, Edinburgh, EH4 2HG
Tel: (0131) 343 2500 **Fax:** (0131) 343 3166 **DX:** ED 23
Email: mail@fyfeireland.com **Website:** www.fyfeireland.com

99 Charterhouse Street, London, EC1M 6NQ
Tel: (020) 7253 5202 **Fax:** (020) 7253 5525 **DX:** 53346 Clerkenwell

Senior partner:	Alistair Wilson
Number of partners:	15
Assistant solicitors:	19
Other fee-earners:	22

AREAS OF PRACTICE

Commercial Property	36%
Private Client & Lender Services	25%
Corporate	24%
Litigation	15%

CONTACTS

Commercial Property	James Roscoe
Corporate	David Lindgren
Litigation	Drew Taylor
Private Client & Lender Services	Greig Honeyman

THE FIRM: Fyfe Ireland is a dynamic law firm providing a comprehensive range of legal services to commercial and private clients. It is particularly well regarded in the commercial property field but with solid corporate, private client and litigation practices.

PRINCIPAL AREAS OF WORK:

Commercial Property: All aspects of work are undertaken on behalf of tenants, landlords, institutions and lenders. There is particular experience of cross border security transactions and an expanding construction practice.

Private Client and Lender Services: The usual range of private client services (including conveyancing) is undertaken with particular strength in capital taxes planning, trusts and owner- managed businesses. There is specialist expertise in the provision of quality lender services to institutions including reposessions, remortgages and related advice work.

Corporate: The team has considerable experience of all aspects of public and private company work. This broad base underpins strong capabilities in PFI and PPP, employment, IP, higher education and banking. Work is undertaken throughout the UK.

Litigation: A wide range of litigation in both the Court of Session and Sheriff Courts. There is particular expertise in construction law with considerable experience in other areas including planning, employment, media law, IP and judicial review.

RECRUITMENT & TRAINING: The firm is always keen to consider quality candidates. Any application with an appropriate CV should be sent to Steve Kerr.

FYNN & PARTNERS

70 Richmond Hill, Bournemouth, BH2 6JA
Tel: (01202) 551991 **Fax:** (01202) 295403 **DX:** DX 7608 Bournemouth
Email: enquiries@fynnpartners.co.uk **Website:** www.fynnpartners.co.uk

Managing partner:	Alan Arnold
Number of partners:	6
Assistant solicitors:	4
Other fee-earners:	9

THE FIRM: Fynn & Partner's national reputation in environmental, licensing and planning law is enhanced by its in-house planning consultancy and advocate teams and supported by a commercial property department with extensive expertise in leisure/licensed and foreign property matters. All aspects of company and commercial (including e-commerce and immigration), employment and private client law work are undertaken.

GABB & CO

32 Monk St, Abergavenny, NP7 5NW **Tel:** (01873) 852432 **Fax:** (01873) 857589 **DX:** 43752 Abergavenny **Email:** abergavenny@gabb.co.uk **Website:** www.gab.co.uk **Ptnrs:** 16 **Asst solrs:** 9 **Other fee-earners:** 6 **Contact:** Mr. D.J. Vaughan • A long established and high quality practice best known for company/commercial, employment, residential and commercial conveyancing, wills and tax planning.

AREAS OF PRACTICE

Property & Agriculture	35%
Litigation	30%
Private client & tax & probate	25%
Commercial	10%

GADSBY WICKS

91-99 New London Road, Chelmsford, CM2 OPP
Tel: (01245) 494929 **Fax:** (01245) 495347 **DX:** 89707 Chelmsford 2
Email: mail@gadsbywicks.co.uk

Managing partner:	Gillian Gadsby
Senior partner:	Roger Wicks
Number of partners:	3
Assistant solicitors:	3
Other fee-earners:	2

AREAS OF PRACTICE

Medical Negligence	75%
Medical Products Liability	15%
Commercial Litigation	5%
Personal Injury	5%

CONTACTS

Clinical Negligence	Gillian Gadsby
Commercial Litigation	Roger Wicks
Medical Products Liability	Roger Wicks
Personal Injury	Alison Clarke

THE FIRM: Gadsby Wicks was founded in 1993 as a specialist practice dealing with clinical negligence and medical products liability litigation on behalf of claimants. The firm now comprises eight lawyers, an in-house medical adviser and a dedicated team of support staff.The firm holds a clinical negligence legal aid frachise, is a member of the Legal Aid Board Multi Action Panel and has members of both the Law Society Clinical Negligence and AVMA Referral Panels.Gadsby Wicks has been at the leading edge of innovation in finding alternative methods of funding litigation and is able to offer affordable litigation to all clients with viable cases.

PRINCIPAL AREAS OF WORK:

Clinical Negligence: The firm is well known for its clinical negligence work obtaining several million pounds in compensation for its clients every year.

Medical Products Liability: The firm has considerable experience and expertise in litigating successful claims on behalf of clients who have been injured by pharmaceutical or other medical products.

G

GALLEN & CO

40 Carlton Place, 142 Queen Street, Glasgow, G5 9TW **Tel:** (0141) 420 1441 **Fax:** (0141) 420 8258 **DX:** GW204 **Ptnrs:** 4 **Asst solrs:** 1 **Other fee-earners:** 1

GAMLINS

31-37 Russell Road, Rhyl, LL18 3DB **Tel:** (01745) 343500 **Fax:** (01745) 343616 **DX:** 17352 RHYL **Email:** Gamlins@gamlins.co.uk **Ptnrs:** 11 **Asst solrs:** 16 **Other fee-earners:** 12

GAMON ARDEN & CO

Church House, 1 Hanover Street, Liverpool, L1 3DW **Tel:** (0151) 709 2222 **Fax:** (0151) 709 3095 **Ptnrs:** 2 **Other fee-earners:** 2

GARRETTS

180 Strand, London, WC2R 2NN
Tel: (020) 7344 0344 **Fax:** (020) 7438 2518 **DX:** 127 LDE
Website: www.glegal.com

1 Victoria Square, Birmingham, B1 1BD
Tel: (0121) 698 9000 **Fax:** (0121) 698 9050 **DX:** 13017 Birmingham 1

Betjeman House, 104 Hills Road, Cambridge, CB2 1LH
Tel: (01223) 355977 **Fax:** (01223) 535327 **DX:** 88010 Cambridge

1 City Square, Leeds, LS1 2AL
Tel: (0113) 207 9000 **Fax:** (0113) 207 9001 **DX:** 26444 Leeds Park Square

Bank House, 9 Charlotte Street, Manchester, M1 4EU
Tel: (0161) 228 0707 **Fax:** (0161) 228 1926 **DX:** 14349 Manchester 1

Abbots House, Abbey Street, Reading, RG1 3BD
Tel: (0118) 949 0000 **Fax:** (0118) 949 0049 **DX:** 54711 Reading 2

Senior partner:	Tony Williams
Managing Director	Peter Ridley (London)
Number of partners:	48
Assistant solicitors:	125
Other fee-earners:	52

AREAS OF PRACTICE

Corporate	48%
Human Capital Services	18%
Property/Construction	16%
Intellectual Property/Information Technology	10%
Litigation	8%

CONTACTS

Banking	Douglas Colliver
Collective Investments	Simon Atiyah
Construction	Siobhan Mc Closkey-Oudahar
Corporate/M&A	David Roberts
	Paul Finlan
E-business	Jeff McGeachie
EC & Competition	Phil McDonnell
Employment & Benefits	Paul McCarthy
Information Technology	Mark Crichard
	Alison Harrington
Insurance	James Greig
Intellectual Property	Angus Phang
Litigation	Raymond Joyce
	Fiona Walkinshaw
Pensions	Duncan Buchanan

THE FIRM: Garretts was founded in 1993 and is a growing, entrepreneurial law firm, which provides commercial advice in the major business and financial centres around the country to UK and foreign companies. It is associated in Scotland with Dundas & Wilson. Together, the firms currently rank in the UK's top 25 law firms by size and fee income. Garretts provides a full range of high quality legal services to business and private clients. Multi-jurisdictional transactions are facilitated through their membership of Andersen Legal, the global legal services network associated with Andersen Worldwide SC. The network now has over 2700 lawyers operating in 35 countries around the world. In addition, close links with Arthur Andersen enable Garretts to offer clients integrated business solutions, should they be required. Garretts attracts first class lawyers and continues to invest in a high quality recruitment programme at all levels. They pride themselves on their commitment to training and to their people. They operate overseas and client secondment programmes for trainees and newly qualified solicitors, and have developed an in-house programme of training on legal and business skills for Garretts' lawyers. They also participate in Arthur Andersen's management training, including its sponsored MBA programme. The firm will continue to grow by investing in people, technology and information and by strengthening links with Andersen Legal member firms.

PRINCIPAL AREAS OF WORK: Legal services include: banking; capital markets; collective investments; commercial litigation and dispute resolution; construction; corporate and commercial; EC and competition; employment; employee share schemes; environmental law; financial services; hospitality and leisure; immigration; intellectual property; mergers and acquisitions; new media and IT; pensions; pharmaceuticals and biotechnology; planning; projects; private client and real estate.

CONTACTS CONTINUED

Planning	Stephen McNaught
Private Client	Judith Powell
Property	Keith Barnett
Public Sector/Projects	Nick Painter
	Hamid Yunis

GARSTANGS

115A Chancery Lane, London, WC2A 1PP
Tel: (020) 7242 4324 **Fax:** (020) 7242 4329 **DX:** 496 LDE Chancery Lane
Email: rcornthwaite@garstangs.co.uk **Website:** www.garstangs.co.uk

THE FIRM: A leading radical specialist practice in the fields of white-collar crime, extradition, restraint proceedings and ancillary civil and public litigation. The firm was established in 1989 and specialises in criminal law. The London office was opened in 1990.

PRINCIPAL AREAS OF WORK:
Criminal Litigation: White-collar crime, including major SFO, HM Customs and Excise and Inland Revenue prosecutions; money laundering, restraint proceedings and asset tracing investigations. The firm also handles general crime from both offices.
Other Areas: The Greater Manchester office is more broadly based with specialist property/commercial acquisitions and family departments.

LANGUAGES: French, German, Greek and Italian.

Senior partners:	Richard Cornthwaite (London)
	Nick Horsfall (Bolton)
Number of partners:	4
Assistant solicitors:	7
Other fee-earners:	9

AREAS OF PRACTICE

Criminal/Civil Litigation	60%
Criminal General	30%
Company/Commercial	10%

CONTACTS

Company/Commercial	N. Horsfall
Conveyancing	N. Horsfall
Family	R. Jackson
Fraud Litigation	R. Cornthwaite
General Crime	M. Garstang
Probate/Private Client	M. Ryan

GATELEY WAREING

Windsor House, 3 Temple Row, Birmingham, B2 5JR
Tel: (0121) 234 0000 **Fax:** (0121) 234 0001 **DX:** 13033 B'ham 1
Email: gw@gateleywareing.co.uk

Knightsbridge House, Lower Brown Street, Leicester, LE1 5NL
Tel: (0116) 285 9000 **Fax:** (0116) 285 9001 **DX:** 10829 Leicester 1
Email: gw@gateleywareing.co.uk

THE FIRM: With offices in Birmingham and Leicester, Gateley Wareing is a leading independent firm of solicitors specialising in owner-led businesses. The firm is keen to remain a medium sized practice in order to offer its extensive client base partner-led commercial advice on the legal issues that face businesses today. With a strong reputation for an innovative and practical approach, the firm has an impressive client list from sole traders, partnerships and family ventures to corporate groups, fully quoted public companies and financial institutions. Although much of the client base is located in the Midlands, increasingly Gateley Wareing is gaining a reputation for working with national and international companies.

PRINCIPAL AREAS OF WORK: Although the company does undertake family and private client work, its main areas of expertise are in:
Corporate Services: Gateley Wareing has developed a particular reputation for its MBO work, whether acting for management, vendors, equity or senior debt providers.
Banking and Recoveries: This department has an emphasis on realisations for financial institutions of all kinds.
Commercial Property: This growing department acts for a number of property developers across the UK and has an expertise in housing association law.
Construction: The firm has one of the most highly regarded construction departments in the country.
Dispute Resolution: The firm acts for a wide range of organisations engaged in contentious and non contentious work.
Private Client: Gateley Wareing is one of the few commercial firms operating in the Midlands to provide a comprehensive service to its private clients.

Senior partner:	Brendan McGeever
Number of partners:	14
Assistant solicitors:	35
Other fee-earners:	18

AREAS OF PRACTICE

Corporate Services	35%
Banking and Recoveries	23%
Commercial Property/ Housing Associations	14%
Construction	12%
Private Client	8%
Dispute Resolution	7%

CONTACTS

Banking and Recoveries	Andrew Madden
	Brendan McGeever
Commercial	Andrew Evans
Commercial Property	John Beckett
	Craig Mitchell
Construction	Peter Davies
Corporate Services	Michael Ward
Dispute Resolution	Stephen Goodrham
Employment	Ruth Armstrong
Family	Michael Vale
Housing Associations	Neil Handel
Private Client	Mark Reid
Recoveries	Brendan McGeever

GCL SOLICITORS

Connaught House, Alexandra Terrace, Guildford, GU1 3DA **Tel:** (01483) 577091 **Fax:** (01483) 579252 **DX:** 141450 Guildford 12
Email: partners@gcl-solicitors.co.uk **Website:** www.gcl-solicitors.co.uk

GENTLE JAYES

26 Grosvenor Street, London, W1X 0BD **Tel:** (020) 7629 3304 **Fax:** (020) 7493 0246 **DX:** 44618 MAYFAIR **Ptnrs:** 3 **Asst solrs:** 2
Other fee-earners: 2

GEOFFREY WILLIAMS & CHRISTOPHER GREEN (SOLICITOR ADVOCATES)

2a Churchill Way, Cardiff, CF1 4DW **Tel:** (029) 2034 3377 **Fax:** (029) 2034 3388 **Ptnrs:** 2 **Other fee-earners:** 1 **Contact:** Geoffrey Williams • This is a niche practice of higher court advocates specialising in the representation of professional bodies, professional clients in conduct difficulties and the transport industry.

AREAS OF PRACTICE	
Professional Conduct	75%
Transport	25%

G

GEORGE DAVIES

Fountain Court, 68 Fountain Street, Manchester, M2 2FB
Tel: (0161) 236 8992 **Fax:** (0161) 228 0030 **DX:** 14316 Manchester 1
Email: mail@georgedavies.co.uk **Website:** www.georgedavies.co.uk

Managing partner:	John Hewison
Senior partner:	John Hewison
Number of partners:	13
Assistant solicitors:	16
Other fee-earners:	8

THE FIRM: Historically a general practice, the firm has in recent years developed noted specialisms in healthcare, sports and insolvency law. It acts for NHS trusts and health authorities throughout the region and is on the NHSLA panel. In the field of sports law, it has acted for the Professional Footballers' Association for over 40 years. The firm's growing insolvency department is headed by a qualified insolvency practitioner. A member of LawNet, it was the first large law firm in Manchester to become an Investor in People, and has gained ISO 9002 reflecting its commitment to quality standards.

CONTACTS	
Healthcare	Claire Batchelor
Insolvency	Mark Hovell
Sports	John Hewison

GEORGE GREEN & CO

195 High St, Cradley Heath, Cradley Heath, B64 5HW
Tel: (01384) 410410 **Fax:** (01384) 634237 **DX:** 20752
Email: gg@georgegreen.co.uk **Website:** www.georgegreen.co.uk

Halesowen,
Tel: 01384 410 410 **Fax:** 0121 585 5455 **DX:** 14523 Halesowen
Email: ss@georgegreen.co.uk

Senior partner:	R.M. Cliff
Number of partners:	11
Assistant solicitors:	8
Other fee-earners:	10

CONTACTS	
Commercial Litigation	Neil Cutler
Company/Commercial	Richard Cliff
	Rob Parry
Private Client	Neill Robb
Property Development/Planning	
	Cheryl Leyser
	Ceri Mort

THE FIRM: Established in 1897 and based in the heart of the Black Country, George Green is acknowledged to provide the business community with a real cost effective alternative to City firms, whilst retaining its commitment to the provision of legal advice to its private clientele. Its strong reputation has attracted work from well beyond its Black Country base.

PRINCIPAL AREAS OF WORK:
Company/Commercial: Work includes start-ups, acquisition and mergers, reconstructions, corporate finance, MBOs, flotations, partnerships, commercial agreements, joint ventures and taxation.
Commercial Litigation: Work includes contract disputes, debt collection, employment intellectual property, building disputes, landlord and tenant, planning disputes, insolvency, defamation, European law and emergency injunctions and claims litigation. The work involves both High Court and County Court actions, in addition to arbitrations and industrial tribunal hearings.
Property Development/Planning: The department undertakes and advises on acquisitions and disposals of land and buildings, leasing, building and development contracts, taxation, property finance, commercial/residential estate development and planning.
Private Client: Work includes wills, probate, estate planning, trusts charities, pensions, matrimonial law, residential conveyancing and personal taxation.

GEORGE IDE, PHILLIPS

Lion House, 79 St Pancras, Chichester, PO19 4NL
Tel: (01243) 786668 **Fax:** (01243) 831300 **DX:** 30306 Chichester
Email: maildesk@georgeide.chi.co.uk **Website:** www.georgeide.co.uk

52 North Street, Chichester, PO19 1NQ
Tel: (01243) 786668 **Fax:** (01243) 813000 **DX:** 30306 Chichester
Email: maildesk@georgeide.chi.co.uk

Belmont Lodge, Belmont Street, Bognor Regis, PO21 1LE
Tel: (01243) 829231 **Fax:** (01243) 825553 **DX:** 31204 Bognor Regis
Email: maildesk@georgeide.bognor.co.uk

Senior partner:	Jeffrey Hopkins
Number of partners:	10
Assistant solicitors:	11
Other fee-earners:	20

AREAS OF PRACTICE

Personal Injury/Medical Negligence 50%
Non Contentious 30%
Other Litigation 20%

CONTACTS

Clinical Negligence ....Julian Bobak
....Philip Lea
Commercial Property ....Jeffrey Hopkins
Commercial/Company ....Robert Enticolt
Crime ....Ian Mellor
Employment ....Dorlee Monschau
Family/Children ....Fraser Poole
Mediation ....Renella Squires
Mental Health ....Ian Oliver
Personal Injury ....Tony Goff
Trust & Probate ....Ursula Watt

THE FIRM: Operating from computer linked offices and founded in 1966, George Ide, Phillips has become one of the leading firms in this part of the South East. With its niche areas of practice and broader specialities, the firm is well placed to serve both its business and private clientele.

PRINCIPAL AREAS OF WORK:

Litigation: Strongly biased towards personal injury and high value clinical negligence claims. In addition, the firm undertakes other forms of litigation including mental health, crime, building disputes, professional negligence, employment and civil actions against the police. The firm also carries out work on a conditional fee basis with no win/no fee agreements. Landlord and tenant litigation is a speciality.

Personal Injury: This department, headed by Tony Goff, who is a senior fellow of the College of personal Injury Lawyers (CPIL), concentrates on claimant work and represents many of the major legal costs insurers. The firm was a founder member of MASS (Motor Accident Solicitors Society) and is still heavily involved with that organisation. Much of the personal injury work is of a high value, and the firm has been involved in a number of recent high profile trials, including the Westmoquette v Dean litigation (£1.75 million after appeal) and in the reported case of Hughes v Makosz, which is believed to be the highest ever award for a person over the age of 60 years. The firm is an active participant on Accident Line and is a participating member of the Headway Personal Injury Solicitors' List, as well as having a number of lawyers who are on the Law Society's Personal Injury Panel and who are also members of the Association of Personal Injury Lawyers.

Clinical Negligence: Julian Bobak leads the team in this field. Philip Lea is a member of Scope and specialises in cerebral palsy cases. The team attend inquests. The firm has acted for the claimant in reported cases including Waghorn v Lewisham and North Southwark Health Authority, Ritchie v Chichester Health Authority and Sandell v Worthing Health Authority; in a £1.7 million self-structured settlement; in the case of Joshua Barry v Isle of Wight Health Authority where the child claimant was not a patient; and in Kneller v Portsmouth and Southeast Hants Health Authority in a £1.5 million cerebral palsy case. Julian Bobak is a member of the Law Society Medical Negligence Panel and the AVMA Referral Panel.Both the PI and clinical negligence departments have expanded rapidly in recent years following significant increases in workload and referrals.

Commercial Property: The firm has a substantial commercial property department with an established reputation. Besides acting for major property companies in connection with their portfolio, the department has expertise in retail, office, industrial and other types of property as well as in the related areas of planning, licensing and landlord and tenant problems. Acquisitions, options and development are dealt with in this strong and experienced department.

Company/Commercial: A wide variety of work is handled including company formations, acquisitions and disposals, start-ups, partnership, commercial contracts and the associated disciplines of insolvency, employment law and franchising.

Employment: The firm is continuing to expand in this area, through its wide involvement in commercial activities. Employment specialists act for major employers including dealing with TUPE transfers, most redundancies and dismissal/discrimination cases and particularly the Disability Discrimination Act 1996. This department also supports the commercial department.

Family/Children: A strong team with members of SFLA and Law Society Family and Children Panels.

Private Client, Probate and Trusts: The firm has a strong private client department with an acknowledged expertise in this field where clients are advised on trusts, personal tax and estate planning, probate, wills and estate administration, and residential property. The firm shortly hopes to be offering in-house specialist investment advice through a partner and it is expected that this aspect of the private client department will also support the personal injury and clinical negligence departments in advising successful claimants on investment strategies.

Mediation: The firm are leaders in the region in the provision of mediation services. The service is headed by a mediator who is a member of BALM (British Association of Lawyer Mediators), the UK College of Mediators, and who has been approved by the Legal Aid Board to mediate. The department deals with a range of family issues and particularly specialise in children's matters, domestic violence and divorce, and ancillary issues.As well as having a Legal Aid franchise in all categories (except welfare benefit and debt), the firm has members of the personal injury, clinical negligence, children and mental health review panels and is qualified for the Lexcel Award.

GEORGE, JONAS & CO

Citadel, 190 Corporation Street, Birmingham, B4 6QD
Tel: (0121) 212 4111 **Fax:** (0121) 212 1770 **DX:** 13013
Email: info@georgejonas.co.uk **Website:** www.georgejonas.co.uk

Senior partner:	S.M. Jonas
Number of partners:	2
Assistant solicitors:	3
Other fee-earners:	8

AREAS OF PRACTICE

Crime	75%
Personal Injury	25%

THE FIRM: The firm specialises in crime, libel, personal injury law, including medical negligence and civil actions against the police. Its longstanding reputation of dealing with the most serious criminal trials has been extended in recent years into white collar crime and fraud trials, particularly being instructed by professionals. Agency commissions undertaken.

GEORGE MATHERS & CO

23 Adelphi, Aberdeen, AB1 2BL **Tel:** (01224) 588599 **Fax:** (01224) 584147 **Ptnrs:** 3 **Asst solrs:** 12 **Other fee-earners:** 2

GEPP & SONS

58 New London Rd, Chelmsford, CM2 0PA **Tel:** (01245) 493939 **Fax:** (01245) 493940 **DX:** 3306 Chelmsford **Email:** mail@gepp.co.uk **Ptnrs:** 11 **Asst solrs:** 8 **Other fee-earners:** 16 **Contact:** Jonathan Douglas-Hughes • General practice, handling agriculture, commercial, criminal, insurance, litigation, matrimonial, personal injury, probate and trust, commercial and residential property and shrievalty.

AREAS OF PRACTICE

Litigation	31%
Criminal Law	21%
Matrimonial	13%
Trust & Probate	10%
Domestic Conveyancing	9%
Property	8%
Other	5%
Commercial	3%

G

GERMAN & SOAR

Fenchurch House, 12 King St, Nottingham, NG1 2AZ **Tel:** (0115) 916 5200 **Fax:** (0115) 910 1290 **DX:** 10040 **Ptnrs:** 7 **Asst solrs:** 4 **Other fee-earners:** 6 **Contact:** Mr J. Gardiner • Known for child care, matrimonial, crime, personal injury, conveyancing, probate. Also experienced in sports law, defamation, commercial litigation.

GHERSON & CO

1 Great Cumberland Place, London, W1H 7AL
Tel: (020) 7724 4488 **Fax:** (020) 7724 4888
Email: gherson@macline.co.uk **Website:** www.gherson.com

Senior partner:	Roger Gherson
Number of partners:	1
Assistant solicitors:	2
Other fee-earners:	2

AREAS OF PRACTICE

UK immigration/ nationality law/ EU freedom of movement	98%

CONTACTS

Immigration and nationality	Roger Gherson

THE FIRM: Established in 1988, now in its eleventh year, this is one of the few specialist practices providing in-depth advice on UK immigration law, British nationality law, and European Union freedom of movement of persons. Roger Gherson is a well-known solicitor with many years' experience in the field of immigration law. He is complemented at the firm by Anne Morris, Judith Hinds and Kate Sutherland. The firm is committed to solving the most challenging problems.

PRINCIPAL AREAS OF WORK: Particular expertise in employment and work permits for a wide range of employers, banks, financial institutions, software houses, year 2000 problem companies, film production companies and other business related immigration (including executive relocation, and the admission of entrepreneurs, investors, sole representatives, writers, artists and composers). In addition to a strong corporate caseload, the firm also deals with: EU Associate nationals, EU related immigration issues, an increasing number of cases under the same sex concession; the acquisition of settlement and citizenship; complex nationality issues; family reunion; students and other temporary categories; appeals to Adjudicators and the Immigration Tribunal against the refusal of entry clearance, further leave to remain, threatened deportation, etc; judicial review to the High Court.

CLIENTELE: Wide corporate and private client base including other firms of solicitors.

INTERNATIONAL CONNECTIONS: Extensive links overseas particularly in China (including Hong Kong), FSU, South Africa and the USA. Associate Office: 2303-7 Dominion Centre, 43-59 Queens Road East, Wan Chai, Hong Kong, tel: 00 852 280 23210, fax: 00 852 282 42051.

GILFEDDER & MCINNES

34 Leith Walk, Edinburgh, EH6 5AA **Tel:** (0131) 553 4333 **Fax:** (0131) 555 3712 **Ptnrs:** 6 **Asst solrs:** 5 **Other fee-earners:** 2

GILL AKASTER

25 Lockyer Street, Plymouth, PL1 2QW **Tel:** (01752) 203500 **Fax:** (01752) 203503 **DX:** 8284 Plymouth 2 **Email:** rhm@gillakaster.co.uk **Ptnrs:** 12 **Asst solrs:** 5 **Other fee-earners:** 11 **Contact:** Malcolm Pillar • Particular knowledge of commercial and property, employment and members of the Children and Mental Health Panel with an SLFA Mediator. Also offices at Scott Lodge, Milehouse, Plymouth.

AREAS OF PRACTICE

Commercial & Property	27%
Residential Property	25%
Matrimonial & Family	20%
Civil Litigation	15%
Probate/Trusts/Tax	13%

GILL & CO

37 Grays Inn Road, London, WC1X 8PP **Tel:** 020 7242 0404 **Fax:** 020 7831 8537 **DX:** 35747 BLOOMSBURY 1 **Email:** gillandco@easynet.co.uk

GILLESPIE MACANDREW WS

31 Melville Street, Edinburgh, EH3 7JQ
Tel: (0131) 225 1677 **Fax:** (0131) 225 4519 **DX:** ED 113 Edinburgh-1
Email: mail@gillespiemacandrew.co.uk **Website:** www.gillespiemacandrew.co.uk

Managing partner:	Ian Turnbull
Senior office manager:	David Macfarlane
Number of partners:	8
Assistant solicitors:	12
Other fee-earners:	18

AREAS OF PRACTICE

Private Client, Trust, Tax and Investment	46%
Corporate Client	33%
Agriculture/Estate/Residential	21%

CONTACTS

Area	Contact
Agriculture/Estates	Michael Gascoigne
Charities	Tom Murray
Commercial Property	Neil Wilson
Corporate/Commercial	Derek McCulloch
Corporate/Small Business	Christopher Smith
Employment	Ian Turnbull
Energy-Electricity	Derek McCulloch
Executry/Probate	John McArthur
Investment/Fund Management	Charles Fotheringham
Litigation	Ian Turnbull
Residential Property	Michael Grey
Tax & Trust	Simon Leslie

THE FIRM: Gillespie Macandrew, with roots established for more than 300 years, has developed leading specialist disciplines for private and business clients and emphasis on high level partner/associate contact. Gillespie Macandrew's private client department is a leader in offering a fully integrated investment management, tax and financial planning service. The commercial department represents Scottish and European interests of both multinational companies and investors abroad. The firm's activities now also focus on charities, professional partnerships, farmers, and the developing SME business sectors of Scotland.

PRINCIPAL AREAS OF WORK:

Agriculture and Farming: This core specialist practice advises on partnerships, contract farming, crofting, landlord/tenant relations, quotas, mineral rights, fish farming and sporting estates. The firm is provider of NFU Scotland legal Helpline.

Charities: Charities are a specialist focus of management and advice from the combined corporate, tax and investment teams. Clients include leading animal, disability, ex-service, arts and rural/environmental charities.

Corporate Client: Company formation, acquisition and business support services include specific areas in technology, agribusiness, employment, and equity finance. Partners are experienced in providing general counsel to companies and assisting with negotiations. The firm supports Edinburgh Business Development with free consultancy for start up and developing businesses and also Edinburgh International Trade.

Commercial Property/Lending Finance: The firm is experienced in investment, leasing and development of property including leisure, brownfield, agribusiness, licensed property, construction, and planning and environmental law.

Energy and Electricity: Energy and electricity is an area of specialist expertise and Gillespie Macandrew advises generators, industrial users and hydro/windpower SRO and NFFO projects.

Litigation & Employment Law: Contentious and non-contentious cases are handled with specialist expertise in construction, employment, commercial and rural property, trust and family law disputes. The firm operates a debt recovery service.

Private Client/Tax Trust and Financial Planning: This team of over 20 fee-earners combines tax, trust and financial planning advice with discretionary and advisory fund management and an execution-only dealing service.

Investment: The investment department has six professionals from a wide range of investment disciplines with average experience of over 20 years each; and is an active participant in the Law Society of Scotland, ASIM and SIFA.

Residential Property: The department maintains a full range of estate agency, conveyancing, relocation and letting services.

INTERNATIONAL CONNECTIONS: The firm is the Scottish member of Lexwork International in Europe and maintains additional USA, Asian and other international contacts for both corporate and private client transactions.

GILLS

Equity Chambers, 5 Hortus Road, Southall, UB2 4AJ **Tel:** (020) 8893 6869 **Fax:** (020) 8893 6396 **DX:** 52256 Southall 2 **Email:** jgill@lawfirm99.fsnet.co.uk **Website:** www.gills-solicitors.co.uk **Ptnrs:** 2 **Asst solrs:** 2 **Other fee-earners:** 2 **Contact:** Mr Jaswinder Gill • Specialises in education law.

AREAS OF PRACTICE

Education	65%
General Civil Litigation	35%

GIRLINGS

3-6 Dane John, Canterbury, CT1 2UG
Tel: (01227) 768374 **Fax:** (01227) 450498 **DX:** 5303 Canterbury
Email: ChrisByrne@Girlings-Solicitors.co.uk **Website:** www.girlings.com

Managing partner:	Andrew Watson
Number of partners:	22
Assistant solicitors:	3
Other fee-earners:	26

INVESTOR IN PEOPLE

THE FIRM: With seven offices, Girlings is the largest firm in East Kent, and provides a complete legal service to commercial and private clients. Commercial work includes company, commercial, partnerships, employment, litigation, property and planning, injury claims, road transport (RHA panel solicitor), licensing, health and safety, environment law and debt collection. The firm has additional offices in Ashford, Herne Bay, Margate, Ramsgate, Broadstairs and Birchington.

GLAISYERS

10 Rowchester Court, Printing House St, Birmingham, B4 6DZ
Tel: (0121) 233 2971 **Fax:** (0121) 236 1534 **DX:** 24933 Birmingham 4
Email: advice@glaisyers.co.uk **Website:** www.glaisyers.co.uk

Managing partner:	Charles P. Royle
Senior partner:	Charles P. Royle
Number of partners:	11
Assistant solicitors:	11
Other fee-earners:	17

A QUALITY SERVICE
Approved by The Legal Aid Board

G

THE FIRM: The firm specialises in criminal, family law, child care and personal injury (no win, no fee). In addition, it also handles consumer law, debt recovery, general contract, landlord and tenant, conveyancing, trust and probate, estate planning, licensing, mental health, housing law and welfare benefits. Close to all courts. All types of agency work undertaken.

GLAZER DELMAR
223-229 Rye Lane, Peckham, London, SE15 4TZ **Tel:** (020) 7639 8801 **Fax:** (020) 7358 0581 **DX:** 34258 Peckham **Ptnrs:** 4 **Asst solrs:** 7 **Other fee-earners:** 5

GLENISTERS

Television House, 269 Field End Road, Eastcote, Ruislip, HA4 9LS
Tel: (020) 8868 4343 **Fax:** (020) 8429 3606 **DX:** 35150 Eastcote
Email: sols@glenisters.com **Website:** www.glenisters.com

Managing partner:	Robert Moseley
Senior partner:	Michael O'Brien
Number of partners:	3
Assistant solicitors:	4
Other fee-earners:	11

AREAS OF PRACTICE

Litigation & Family	30%
Property	30%
Banking & Finance	25%
Private Client	15%

CONTACTS

Banking & Finance	Doreen Jones
Litigation & Family Law	Mark Faith
Private Client	Michael O'Brien
Property	Robert Moseley

THE FIRM: Established in 1906, Glenisters aims to provide innovative solutions to many of the problems which face its commercial, corporate, institutional and individual clients.

PRINCIPAL AREAS OF WORK:
Banking and finance: A dedicated banking and finance unit responds quickly to the needs of the firm's lending clients in the areas of professional indemnity, mortgage arrears recovery and repossessions, sales and lettings and loan administration.
Corporate Services: Work includes commercial litigation, company and partnership, and advice on all employment matters.
Family Law: Advice on divorce and separations, financial ancillary matters and mediation.
Personal Injury: A committed claimant personal injury unit.
Property: Commercial and residential conveyancing, advice on planning matters and landlord and tenant.
Private Client: Work includes wills and probate, administration of estates, trusts and settlements, tax and financial services.

GLOVERS

115 Park Street, London, W1Y 4DY
Tel: (020) 7629 5121 **Fax:** (020) 7491 0930 **DX:** 44438 Marble Arch
Email: central@glovers.co.uk **Website:** www.glovers.co.uk

Senior partner:	Jeremy Simmonds
Number of partners:	10
Assistant solicitors:	9
Other fee-earners:	6

CONTACTS

Banking	Catherine Cava
Commercial Litigation	Tony Bourne
Commercial Property	John Barber
Company/Commercial	Stephen Clow
Construction	David Miles
Employment	Peter Pitt
Professional Negligence	Edward Vaughan

PRINCIPAL AREAS OF WORK: Glovers is an established firm which specialises in the following principal areas:
Commercial Property: The firm has an acknowledged reputation in commercial property, development and in commercial landlord and tenant matters. Work includes development agreements, acting for major retailers, developers, maufacturers and investors, planning negotiations, selling and leasing of commercial developments, rent reviews and all other aspects of landlord and tenant law.
Company/Commercial: Work includes company formations, MBOs, purchases and sales, corporate finance work and joint ventures, marketing agreements and the drafting of conditions of sale.

Banking & Finance: The firm acts for a number of UK and overseas banks on a wide variety of banking matters, including secured lending and the restructuring of loans and charges.
Commercial Litigation: The department is proactive in its approach to litigation, but does not ignore the value of forceful and structured negotiations in the litigation process. Work includes landlord and tenant matters, commercial disputes, banking cases, insolvency and professional negligence. Glovers in one of the four original firms reponsible for implementation of ADR practices in this country and has its own ADR unit.
Construction: The firm acts for one of the UK's leading construction companies and has wide experience in advising on construction contracts, collateral warranties and complex building disputes.
Employment: The firm covers all areas of employment law, both contentious and non-contentious, discrimination, transfer of undertakings and compromise agreements.
Professional Negligence: Litigation arising out of property and banking disputes, white collar fraud and claims against solicitors and surveyors.

GOLDKORN MATHIAS

6 Coptic Street, Bloomsbury, London, WC1A 1NW
Tel: (020) 7631 1811 **Fax:** (020) 7631 0431 **DX:** 35705 Bloomsbury
Email: gdmlaw@compuserve.com

Managing partner:	Roy Mathias
Number of partners:	4
Other fee-earners:	5

AREAS OF PRACTICE

Criminal Work	30%
Litigation	30%
Conveyancing	15%
Probate	15%
Commercial	10%

CONTACTS

Commercial	Roy Mathias
Crime	Philip Smith
Litigation	Geoffrey Goldkorn
Probate/Conveyancing	David Barchan

THE FIRM: Established in 1979 and reconstituted in its present form in March 2000. The Bloomsbury office is a niche practice specialising in civil litigation, commercial work and probate. The associated office at Camberwell practising under the name Goldkorns is an exclusively criminal practice.

PRINCIPAL AREAS OF WORK:
Civil Litigation: The partners are very experienced litigators, including a Deputy District Judge and solicitor with rights of audience in the High Court. The firm offers a comprehensive litigation service including in-house advocacy in the County Court, the High Court and the Court ofAppeal. The firm has an acknowledged reputation for handling complex legal disputes and for assimilating cases involving large volumes of documents. The firm has particular experience in a variety of commercial disputes, breach of trust, copyright, designright and passing off disputes, litigious probate, professional negligence (lawyers and accountants) and civil actions against the police. Agency work is regularly undertaken.
Crime: The Camberwell office is a well run very substantial criminal practice with a legal aid franchise in crime and is one of the firms on the Inner London contracting pilot scheme. The workload dealt with each year is very high - in excess of 1,000 individual cases.
Property: Work includes commercial and residential conveyancing; landlord and tenant cases.
Probate: Departmental work involves drafting wills and estate planning as well as winding-up estates.
Commercial: Work includes employment contracts, partnerships, sports agreements.

GOLDS

8 Newton Terrace, Glasgow, G3 7PJ **Tel:** (0141) 300 4300 **Fax:** (0141) 300 4350 **DX:** GW40 **Email:** golds@golds.co.uk
Website: www.golds.co.uk **Ptnrs:** 7 **Asst solrs:** 13 **Other fee-earners:** 22

GOLDSMITH WILLIAMS

42-44 Stanley Street, Liverpool, L1 6AL **Tel:** (0151) 231 1292 **Fax:** (0151) 231 1369 **DX:** 14186 Liverpool **Ptnrs:** 3 **Asst solrs:** 2
Other fee-earners: 48

GOODMAN DERRICK

90 Fetter Lane, London, EC4A 1PT
Tel: (020) 7404 0606 **Fax:** (020) 7831 6407 **DX:** 122
Email: law@goodmanderrick.co.uk **Website:** www.goodmanderrick.co.uk

Managing partner:	Patrick Swaffer
Senior partner:	John Roberts
Number of partners:	20
Assistant solicitors:	9
Other fee-earners:	5

AREAS OF PRACTICE

Corporate	26%
Media	25%
Commercial Litigation	22%
Property	17%
Charities/Private Client	5%
Employment	5%

THE FIRM: Goodman Derrick is a medium-sized City practice, founded in 1954 by Lord Goodman. It has a broad commercial practice focusing on commercial and corporate finance, property and litigation work with an excellent reputation for media work in television, publishing and related industries.

PRINCIPAL AREAS OF WORK: The main groups for Goodman Derrick are media, corporate, property, litigation, tax, employment, private client and charities.
Media/Media Litigation: This department advises both corporate and individual clients on the whole range of contentious and non-contentious matters in the fields of broadcasting, television, film, publishing, theatre and newspapers, as well as other areas of the media and arts. These include film and television production and financing, cable, satellite, distribution, digital, broadcasting, book and magazine publishing, sponsorship and licensing agreements. Notable experience has been developed in defamation and in other advice relating to broadcast material, newspaper and magazine articles and book manuscripts. The department also deal with

such areas as contempt, protection of journalists' sources, privacy, official secrets and copyright.
Property: Work includes all aspects of commercial property transactions, especially work for retail companies, investors, property development, funding, leases, planning and agricultural holdings. In addition, the firm handles some high-quality residential work.
Commercial Litigation: Work includes a broad range of commercial disputes, professional negligence, insolvency, insurance, employment, fraud, intellectual property, property litigation and debt recovery.
Corporate: Work includes mergers and acquisitions, flotations, banking and finance, joint ventures, business start-ups, shareholders' agreements, management buy-outs rights issues, share offers, mergers and reorganisations, commercial agreements, European law, intellectual property and IT law.
Private Clients/Charities: Work includes establishment and drafting, tax and financial planning, wills and estates, probate, and trusts.
Employment: This department offers the whole range of contentious and non-contentious advice and specialist advice to the recruitment industry.

CLIENTELE: Goodman Derrick has an impressive client list acting for many public figures, public and private companies, charities, large retail chains, property companies and developers, television companies, broadcasters and independent producers, publishers and newspapers, and trade associations.

RECRUITMENT & TRAINING: Applications by letter and CV to Mr. Nicholas Armstrong, Recruitment Partner.

CONTACTS

Charities/Private Client	Diana Rawstron
Commercial Litigation	Tim Langton
	Annabel Crumley
Company Commercial	David Edwards
Construction	Susan White
Corporate	John Roberts
Defamation	Patrick Swaffer
	Jeffery Maunsell
Employment	Noel Deans
Film	Keith Northrop
Insurance	Tim Langton
Media	Patrick Swaffer
	Paul Herbert
Property	Michael Collins
	Greg Hamlen
Publishing	Jeffery Maunsell
	Nicholas Armstrong
Tax	Ian Montrose

GOODMANDERRICK

G

GOODMAN RAY

450 Kingsland Road, Dalston, London, E8 4AE **Tel:** (020) 7254 8855 **Fax:** (020) 7923 4345 **DX:** 46807 Dalston **Ptnrs:** 4 **Asst solrs:** 3 **Other fee-earners:** 1 **Contact:** Peggy Ray • Specialist family law with criminal law department. Strong reputation for child-related work. All partners are members of the Law Society Children Panel. Legal Aid franchise. Employed barrister: 1.

AREAS OF PRACTICE

Family	95%
Criminal	5%

GORDON & SMYTH

420 Sauchiehall Street, Glasgow, G2 3JS **Tel:** (0141) 332 5705 **Fax:** (0141) 332 6036 **DX:** GW33

GORDON DADDS

80 Brook Street, Mayfair, London, W1Y 2DD
Tel: (020) 7493 6151 **Fax:** (020) 7491 1065 **DX:** 131

Managing partner:	Roger Peters
Senior partner:	Douglas Alexiou
Number of partners:	14
Assistant solicitors:	6
Other fee-earners:	7

THE FIRM: Founded in 1921, Gordon Dadds offers specialist areas of expertise to clients. Although best known for its family and private client work, Gordon Dadds also provides to the commercial client a comprehensive service from a co-ordinated team drawn from the departments in the firm.

PRINCIPAL AREAS OF WORK:
Family: The department doubled in size last year with the arrival of three new family law partners, making it one of the largest in London. Combining determination with sensitivity, the firm handles complex financial cases, frequently with international aspects, contact to children, wardship and adoption, and divorce and separation agreements. Emergency procedures, such as dealing with child abduction are also handled as are injunction proceedings and problems arising from cohabitation.
Company/Commercial: The department offers a personal and efficient service which provides effective and practical solutions for clients. Areas of expertise include project finance, venture capital and joint ventures, asset finance and leasing, share and business sales and purchases, mergers and reorganisations, hotel acquisitions and management and commercial agreements.
Litigation: The litigation department handles all forms of commercial litigation as well as company directors' disqualification, defamation, employment, inheritance, personal injury, professional negligence, property (including landlord and tenant) matters and road traffic cases (civil and criminal).
Private Client: Advice is given in the fields of tax and estate planning and administration, with particular regard to overall personal considerations as well as to strictly legal matters. Assignments include administration of estates and post death tax planning, advice on tax returns, drawing up and executing wills and financial management. The firm has built up a range of expertise in acting for charities.
Property: The property department has extensive experience in dealing with a wide range of commercial activities including development, acquisitions, capital enhancement, offices, leasing, building contracts, retail, trading estates, hotels, complexes, joint ventures and mortgages and lending.

LANGUAGES: French and Greek.

RECRUITMENT & TRAINING: The firm recruits two high-calibre graduates a year as trainee solicitors. Applications should be received by July, two years before articles commence. Please address applications to Miss Sue Bland.

AREAS OF PRACTICE

Family law	50%
Company/Commercial	15%
Private Client	15%
Litigation	10%
Property	10%

CONTACTS

Company/Commercial	Michael Jepson
Family	Douglas Alexiou
Litigation	Hugh Elder
Private Client	Roger Peters
Property	David Goff

GORDONS CRANSWICK SOLICITORS

14 Piccadilly, Bradford, BD1 3LX **Tel:** (01274) 202202 **Fax:** (01274) 202100 **DX:** 11716 Bradford **Email:** mail@gordonscranswick.co.uk
Website: www.gordonscranwick.co.uk **Ptnrs:** 31 **Asst solrs:** 18 **Other fee-earners:** 21

GORNA & CO

Virginia House, Cheapside, King St, Manchester, M2 4NB
Tel: (0161) 832 3651 **Fax:** (0161) 834 8572 **DX:** 14339

Managing partner:	Peter Doyle
Senior partner:	Michael Morrison
Number of partners:	9
Assistant solicitors:	8
Other fee-earners:	2

CONTACTS

Commercial Litigation ....Helen Hoath
Commercial Property ......Stephen Hindmarsh
Company and Commercial ....Tony Lomax
Trusts and Probate ....Tony Hall

THE FIRM: Essentially a commercial firm, Gorna & Co has a national reputation for its work in commercial property development. The practice has a nationwide clientele and provides its corporate and commercial clients with the full range of commercial advice.

PRINCIPAL AREAS OF WORK: In addition to commercial property, development and disposal work, the practice handles a broad spectrum of corporate and commercial matters, including corporate finance work, mergers, acquisitions and disposals and franchising. A variety of contentious work is undertaken, including commercial litigation, commercial property litigation, intellectual property protection, employment law and debt recovery.
Other Areas of Work: In addition, extensive private client services are available, ranging from wills, trusts and probate to tax planning. There is particular expertise in inheritance tax work. The firm has a reputation in sports law, notably professional football, and a growing practice in media and entertainment work.

CLIENTELE: The firm represents the interests of a number of well-known medium-sized and large companies, including property companies, as well as Friendly Societies, Housing Associations and Health Authorities and Trusts throughout the country.

G

GORVIN SMITH FORT

6-14 Millgate, Stockport, SK1 2NN
Tel: (0161) 930 5151 **Fax:** (0161) 930 5252 **DX:** 719421 Stockport 7
Email: enquiries@gorvin.co.uk **Website:** www.gorvin.co.uk

Managing partner:	Andrew Callaghan
Senior partner:	Peter Gorvin
Number of partners:	9
Assistant solicitors:	18
Other fee-earners:	7

AREAS OF PRACTICE

Company/Commercial...........................29%
Commercial Property 18%
Commercial Litigation..........................15%
Accident/Personal Injury......................12%
Residential Conveyancing & Estate Planning 12%
Employment 4%
Family/Matrimonial................................4%
Personal Litigation 3%
Professional Negligence 3%

CONTACTS

Accident/Personal Injury ....Duncan Manners
Commercial Property Ian FletcherNeil Sutcliffe
Company/Commercial ....Tim Dennis
Employment.............................Nigel Crebbin
Estate Planning.................Andrew Cusworth
Family/Matrimonial ....Matthew Lord
Litigation ....Iain CampbellPaul Humphreys
Professional Negligence ......George Marriott
Residential Conveyancing Andrew Callaghan

THE FIRM: Based in Stockport the practice was created in December 1998 by the merger of Stockport's two leading legal firms: Gorvin Kenyon, founded in 1971 and Smith Forts, established in 1865. Gorvin Smith Fort is thus a dominant player in its area of expertise, building on the complementary range of activities carried out by its predecessor firms. The Firm's range of legal services has recently been enhanced by the establishment of dedicated employment and professional negligence departments. Major investment has been made in information technology in order to enhance communication and efficiency. The firm has a strong commitment to recruiting high-calibre lawyers and other staff, as well as providing appropriate training for those already at the firm.

PRINCIPAL AREAS OF WORK:
Company and Commercial: Expertise in all aspects of business sales, purchases and reconstructions; IT and other intellectual property protection; consultancy agreements, EU restrictive trade practices, commercial contracts, health and safety; agency distribution and franchise agreements; partnerships; pensions, share options, shareholder agreements; venture capital funding, and media and sports contracts.
Commercial Property: Area of expertise comprises commercial and industrial retail property, building construction contracts; joint venture agreements, finance, funding and security documentation; landlord and tenant issues.
Commercial Litigation: All aspects including contractual and commercial disputes, minority shareholder protection, partnership disputes, and dissolutions, landlord and tenant litigation, emergency order applications, licencing, unfair competition, debt collection, and insolvency advice. Professional Negligence issues are dealt with by the newly established dedicated department.
Employment Division: The employment division undertakes work on behalf of employers and employees, dealing with issues relating to contracts of employment, recruitment and dismissal issues, business transfers, tribunal and court work, discrimination, and health and safety issues.
Private Client Division: This division handles personal litigation; domestic property sales and purchases; wills, probate and inheritance advice; matrimonial and family issues.

GOSSCHALKS

Queens Gardens, Hull, HU1 3DZ **Tel:** (01482) 324 252 **Fax:** (01482) 590 290 **DX:** 11902 Hull 1 **Email:** info@gosschalks.co.uk
Website: www.gosschalks.co.uk **Ptnrs:** 26 **Asst solrs:** 20 **Other fee-earners:** 24

GOTELEE & GOLDSMITH

31-41 Elm St, Ipswich, IP1 2AY **Tel:** (01473) 211121 **Fax:** (01473) 230387 **DX:** 3220 Ipswich **Email:** mail@gotelee.co.uk **Website:** www.gotelee.co.uk **Ptnrs:** 13 **Asst solrs:** 8 **Other fee-earners:** 14

GOULDENS

10 Old Bailey, London, EC4M 7NG
Tel: (020) 7583 7777 **Fax:** (020) 7583 6777 **DX:** 67
Email: info@gouldens.com **Website:** www.gouldens.com

Managing partner:	Charters Macdonald-Brown
Senior partner:	Patrick Burgess
Number of Partners:	37
Assistant Solicitors:	102
Other fee-earners:	27

AREAS OF PRACTICE

Company/Commercial (including Corporate Tax)	42%
Property (including Planning)	25%
Litigation (including IP)	20%
Banking/Capital Markets	12%
Personal/International Tax Planning	1%

CONTACTS

Banking & Insolvency	Tom Budd
	Barry Donnelly
CIS/Central Europe	James Campbell
Commercial litigation	Charters Macdonald-Brown
Commercial Property	Clare Deanesly
Communications, Media & IT	Simon Chalkley
Company/Commercial	Max Thorneycroft
Construction	Craig Shuttleworth
Corporate Finance	Russell Carmedy
Corporate Tax	Patrick Harrison
Defamation	Barton Taylor
Employment	Martin Piers
Environment	Clare Deanesly
EU and International	Charters Macdonald-Brown
Far East/Japan	Max Thorneycroft
Fraud/White Collar Crime	David Cooper
Insurance/Reinsurance	Ian Lupson
Intellectual Property	Charters Macdonald-Brown
Pensions/Employee Benefits	John Papadakis
Personal/Int'l Tax Planning	Jennet Davies
Project Finance/PFI	Russell Carmedy
Regulatory	Barry Donnelly

THE FIRM: Based in the City of London, Gouldens' leading corporate practice provides a range of legal services to major UK and international commercial clients. Gouldens has grown steadily over the past decade and established a first class reputation in the corporate field. The firm consistently appears in the league tables of the Top 30 (and most consulted) UK legal advisers (viz: ranked 25th in Corporate Money's Year End League Table of the Top 30 Law Firms (by deal value) on deals announced in 1999; and ranked in KPMG's New Issue Statistics (summary of flotations between 1 January 1994 and 30 December 1998) equal 8th (by solicitor to the company) and 9th (by solicitor to the issue).The firm's corporate clients operate in many different areas including banking, capital markets, corporate finance, insurance, healthcare, retailing, mining, waste management, telecommunications, information technology, property development and construction. Gouldens assists clients to achieve their business objectives effectively and cost-efficiently, whilst maintaining the highest levels of technical legal excellence.

PRINCIPAL AREAS OF WORK: Gouldens divides its work into the main practice areas described below. There are also a number of specialist areas staffed by multi-skilled teams such as construction, environment, insurance and reinsurance, communications, media and information technology, intellectual property, employment, employee benefits and pensions, regulatory matters, fraud and white collar crime.
Company/Commercial: The firm's company and commercial department has a strong reputation in the City and advises, amongst others, major public companies and institutions on all aspects of commercial activity including corporate finance, public company takeovers and flotations, mergers and acquisitions, joint ventures, venture capital, management buy-outs, international agreements and franchise and distribution networks and agreements, as well as providing specialist support in areas such as EU and competition law, intellectual property and pensions and employee benefits.
Banking and Insolvency: The banking and insolvency department advises borrowers, lenders, issuers, lead managers and trustees on corporate debt, syndicated lending, capital market issues and structures, asset and project finance, and insolvency practitioners and lenders on corporate recovery and insolvency.
Property and Planning: The firm's property and planning departments advise developers, institutional investors, surveyors, and other professionals on the financing, planning implications, tax structuring, and implementation of major developments.
Litigation, Insurance and Reinsurance: The firm handles a wide variety of domestic and international commercial disputes relating to construction, defamation, employment, financial and corporate matters, insurance and reinsurance and intellectual property and has a strong reputation in the field of patent and trade mark disputes. The insurance and reinsurance practice is broadly based, advising Lloyds and other London market insurers on many classes of risk including professional indemnity and directors' and officers' liability, increasingly with an international bias.

INTERNATIONAL CONNECTIONS: As well as dealing with high profile EU legal and trade issues, the firm has developed a significant international practice, particularly in the CIS and Central Europe, advising major companies and institutions on infrastructure projects, privatisations and joint ventures as well as governments on a number of issues including the development of new banking, securities, and foreign investment-related legislation.

LANGUAGES: Czech, Dutch, German, Greek, Hebrew, Italian, Romanian, Russian, Spanish and Welsh.

RECRUITMENT & TRAINING: The firm seeks to recruit (and retain) solicitors and trainees who wish to accept the challenge of responsibility in an atmosphere where not only technical expertise but flair, originality and enthusiasm are highly regarded and rewarded. Its system of training is unique and up to 20 trainees are recruited each year.

GRAEME CARMICHAEL

9 Paget Road, Ipswich, IP1 3RP **Tel:** (01473) 252159 **Fax:** (01473) 214778 **Ptnrs:** 1 • Specialist family lawyer. Membership of Law Society Children Panel and Family Law Panel. See under family law section.

AREAS OF PRACTICE

Public Law (Children)	60%
Private Law (Children)	20%
Divorce/Ancillaries	20%

GRAHAME STOWE, BATESON

5-7 Portland St, Leeds, LS1 3DR **Tel:** (0113) 246 8163 **Fax:** (0113) 260 1749 **DX:** 12022 **Email:** janet@grahamestowebateson.freeserve.co.uk **Ptnrs:** 10 **Asst solrs:** 10 **Other fee-earners:** 11

GRAHAM EVANS & PARTNERS

Moorgate House, 6 Christina Street, Swansea, SA1 4EP **Tel:** (01792) 655822 **Fax:** (01792) 645387 **DX:** 39573 Swansea **Ptnrs:** 9 **Asst solrs:** 4 **Other fee-earners:** 10

GRANT DEWAR

180 West Regent Street, Glasgow, G2 4RW
Tel: (0141) 572 1900 **Fax:** (0141) 572 1909 **DX:** GW 32, Glasgow
Email: maildesk@grantdewar.co.uk

48 West Regent Street, Glasgow, G2 2QT
Tel: (0141) 332 7314 **Fax:** (0141) 332 6786 **DX:** 32 Glasgow

Number of partners:	4
Assistant solicitors:	4
Other fee-earners:	8

CONTACTS

Commercial	Andrew F. Dewar
	Ronald W. Brown
Litigation	Hugh J. Grant
Personal Injury	Norman Lindsay
Private Client	Ronald Brown
	Andrew F. Dewar

THE FIRM: Grant Dewar is a recent amalgamation of the firms of Grant & Company and Downie Aiton, with a strong commercial/private client base. The firm is a substantial litigation practice with a particular specialisation in contract disputes, personal injury claims, debt recovery, judgement enforcements and professional negligence claims.

PRINCIPAL AREAS OF WORK:

Commercial: An experienced department both in company law, partnerships, commercial property, commercial and employment contracts and computerised debt recovery.

Litigation: A broadly based department which undertakes contract disputes, industrial tribunals, professional negligence, family law and all other types of court related work.

Personal Injury: Grant Dewar acts on behalf of a number of corporate organisations which provide a litigation service for customers in the recovery of loss as a result of road traffic accidents and personal injury. A specialised team/department is dedicated to this area of the law.

Private client: Property law, creation of trusts, wills, executries, financial services, tax planning and life insurance.

Property: Domestic house purchase and sales.

GRANT & HORTON MARINE SOLICITORS

Lynher Building, Queen Anne's Battery, Plymouth, PL4 0LP **Tel:** (01752) 265265 **Fax:** (01752) 265260 **DX:** 8262 Plymouth 2 **Email:** grant&horton@marine-law.co.uk **Website:** www.marine-law.co.uk **Ptnrs:** 2 **Asst solrs:** 3 **Other fee-earners:** 2 **Contact:** Mr Nicholas Horton • Specialists in commercial shipping, marine and insurance law. The firm is noted for its expertise in the yacht/superyacht industry. Offices in Plymouth and Southampton.

AREAS OF PRACTICE

Commercial	30%
Insurance	30%
Admiralty	25%
Personal Injury	15%

GRANVILLE-WEST

23 Commercial Street, Pontypool, Torfaen, NP4 6XT **Tel:** (01495) 751111 **Fax:** (01495) 753858 **DX:** 44250 Pontypool **Email:** pontypool@g-west.co.uk **Ptnrs:** 9 **Asst solrs:** 2 **Other fee-earners:** 6

GRAYS

Duncombe Place, York, YO1 7DY **Tel:** (01904) 634771 **Fax:** (01904) 610711 **DX:** 61505 **Email:** grays@dial.pipex.com **Website:** Under construction **Ptnrs:** 7 **Asst solrs:** 1 **Other fee-earners:** 3 **Contact:** Mr. F.A. Lawton. • Best known for trusts and taxation, charities (Tony Lawton), agriculture, and property work. Also increasing specialism in employment and high value matrimonial financial disputes.

AREAS OF PRACTICE

Private Client and Charity	50%
Agricultural, Commercial and Residential Property	32%
Litigation	9%
Other	7%
Family	2%

GREEN & CO

Alberton House, St. Mary's Passage, Manchester, M3 2WJ **Tel:** (0161) 834 8980 **Fax:** (0161) 834 8981 **Ptnrs:** 1 **Asst solrs:** 5 **Other fee-earners:** 1

GREENE & GREENE

80 Guildhall Street, Bury St. Edmunds, IP33 1QB **Tel:** (01284) 762211 **Fax:** (01284) 705739 **DX:** 57205 **Ptnrs:** 9 **Asst solrs:** 2 **Consultant:** 1 **Other fee-earners:** 9

GREENLAND HOUCHEN

38 Prince of Wales Rd, Norwich, NR1 1HZ
Tel: (01603) 660744 **Fax:** (01603) 610700 **DX:** 5217 Norwich
Email: mail@ghlaw.co.uk **Website:** www.greenland-houchen.co.uk

Managing partner:	Anita C. Piper
Senior partner:	Robert Plumbley
Number of partners:	9
Assistant solicitors:	3
Other fee-earners:	6

THE FIRM: A long established general practice which seeks to offer at its three offices a full range of legal services. The partners include in their clientele builders and developers, housing associations, members of the local farming community and other commercial and corporate enterprises, as well as the private client. All aspects of litigation are undertaken with a significant legal aid element.

GREENWOODS
20 Bedford Square, London, WC1B 3HL **Tel:** (020) 7323 4632 **Fax:** (020) 7631 3142 **DX:** 35706 BLOOMSBURY
Email: greenwoodslaw@compuserve.com **Ptnrs:** 7 **Asst solrs:** 12 **Other fee-earners:** 6

G

GREENWOODS

Monkstone House, City Road, Peterborough, PE1 1JE
Tel: (01733) 887700 **Fax:** (01733) 424900 **DX:** 12599 Peterborough 4
Email: showard@greenwoods.co.uk **Website:** www.greenwoods.co.uk

Managing partner:	Shelagh Smith
Senior partner:	David Weekes
Number of partners:	15
Assistant solicitors:	16
Other fee-earners:	20

AREAS OF PRACTICE

Commercial Services	40%
Property	27%
Construction	13%
Insurance	13%
Private Client	7%

CONTACTS

Agricultural	Nick Plumb
CDR	James Maxey
Commercial Property/Planning	Stephen Illingworth
Company/Commercial	Michael Evans
Construction	Martin Wood
Employment	Robert Dillarstone
Family	Jane Proctor
Housing Law	Michael Taylor
Information Technology	Nigel Moore
Insolvency	James Maxey
Insurance Litigation	David Weekes
Intellectual Property	Philip Sloan
Probate	Nick Monsell

THE FIRM: Greenwoods is one of East Anglia's leading commercial law firms providing a comprehensive range of legal services to corporate clients, together with private client services tailored to meet specific clients' needs.The Greenwoods approach is to provide clients with strong, responsible, partner-led teams who take a practical approach, within the legal framework, to enable clients to achieve their objectives. The firm's teams look for innovative solutions and actively seek opportunities to provide an added-value service. Looking to the future, the firm is growing by recognising its strengths and developing them. The firm continues to invest in its employees and in information technology and telecommunications to ensure that it is at the leading edge of service delivery.

PRINCIPAL AREAS OF WORK: The firm's legal services include: construction; commercial property and planning; commercial litigation; company and commercial; EU and competition law; corporate recovery and insolvency; employment and employee benefits; housing law; information technology; intellectual property; mediation; personal injury; clinical negligence and private client advice.

INTERNATIONAL CONNECTIONS: The firm has an association with Crivello Carlson Mentkowski Steeves S.C. in Milwaukee.

CLIENTELE: Greenwoods' client base includes local, regional, national and international companies and organisations. They service their clients in their operations nationally, throughout Europe and in some cases worldwide.

RECRUITMENT & TRAINING: Greenwoods generally recruits up to four trainees annually. Financial support may be provided in some circumstances. A minimum 2:1 degree is required, not necessarily in law. Apply by handwritten letter (plus typed CV) to Rosemary Gearing.

GREGG GALBRAITH QUINN
6 Queen Square, Bristol, BS1 4JE **Tel:** (0117) 925 8123 **Fax:** (0117) 925 5567 **DX:** 7845 Bristol **Ptnrs:** 3 **Asst solrs:** 5

GREGORY, ROWCLIFFE & MILNERS WITH SIMMONDS CHURCH SMILES

1 Bedford Row, London, WC1R 4BZ
Tel: (020) 7242 0631 **Fax:** (020) 7242 6652 **DX:** 95
Email: law@grm.co.uk **Website:** www.grm.co.uk

Managing partner:	John Anderson
Number of partners:	18
Assistant solicitors:	2
Other fee-earners:	16

AREAS OF PRACTICE

Litigation	31%
Company/Commercial	30%
Property	27%
Private Client	12%

THE FIRM: Gregory, Rowcliffe & Milners is a progressive firm with an established reputation in quality private client advice, litigation services, corporate and business law. The firm has its roots going back to 1784. It consists of a well-established private client, company/commercial and litigation practice with strongly developed Anglo-German connections, (with fluent German-speakers at all levels throughout the firm); and long standing links with a number of organisations concerned with Anglo-German trade.

PRINCIPAL AREAS OF WORK:
Company/Commercial: The department has excellent international links with Europe, especially Germany, the USA and the Far East, and represents national and multi-national concerns, providing practical legal and taxation solutions to business problems and objectives over a broad spectrum of commerce and industry.

Litigation: The firm provides a full range of litigation services to institutional, business and private clients in respect of administrative law (especially judicial review applications against public bodies); commercial, employment and property disputes; family law, including matrimonial disputes with legal aid where appropriate; personal injury, clinical negligence and claims relating to trusts and wills. The firm is noted for the international (especially German) aspect of its commercial and family litigation. It also has an extensive and well regarded London agency practice.
Employment: A strong employment group specialising on employment contracts, negotiations on termination of senior executives, unfair dismissals and discrimination claims.
Private Client: The firm has expertise in inheritance and tax planning, including the preservation of listed buildings and works of art, the creation of charitable trusts, and the administration of estates, often with an international dimension.
Property: All aspects of commercial, industrial, agricultural, residential and investment conveyancing including estate management, planning and tax planning.

CONTACTS

Anglo German	Lesley Pendlebury Cox
Company/Commercial	Adrian Mezzetti
	Paul Holloway
Employment	Jane Laidler
	Ingrid McKeown
Family/Matrimonial	Fenella Pringle
Litigation	Christopher Harper
	Jack Sadleir
Personal Injury/ Clinical Negligence	Anthony Benbow
Private Client	Michael Parnell-King
Property	David King
	William Bennett
Tax	Michael Parnell-King

GRIFFITH SMITH

47 Old Steyne, Brighton, BN1 1NW **Tel:** (01273) 324041 **Fax:** (01273) 384000 **DX:** 2701 Brighton-1 **Email:** brighton@griffithsmith.co.uk **Website:** www.griffithsmith.co.uk **Ptnrs:** 11 **Asst solrs:** 5 **Other fee-earners:** 17 **Contact:** Mr Tim Smith • Company/commercial, civil litigation, and private client with specialist skills including planning and environmental law and charity services.

G

GRIGOR & YOUNG

1 North Street, Elgin, IV30 1UA **Tel:** (01343) 544077 **Fax:** (01343) 548523 **DX:** 520656 **Ptnrs:** 6 **Asst solrs:** 4 **Other fee-earners:** 4

GRINDEYS

Glebe Court, Stoke on Trent, ST4 1ET **Tel:** (01782) 846441 **Fax:** (01782) 416220 **DX:** 21053 **Email:** grindeys@aol.com **Website:** www.grindeys.co.uk **Ptnrs:** 14 **Asst solrs:** 7 **Other fee-earners:** 31 **Contact:** Paul Godfrey • Grindeys is a long-established firm. Strengths in company/commercial work, commercial litigation, commercial property and personal injury litigation. ISO 9001 accredited.

AREAS OF PRACTICE

Company/Commercial	35%
Insurance/Commercial Litigation	20%
Commercial Property	18%
Private Client	15%
Criminal	8%
Employment	4%

GROSS & CO.

84 Guildhall Street, Bury St. Edmunds, IP33 1PR
Tel: (01284) 763333 **Fax:** (01284) 762207 **DX:** 57203
Email: gdk@gross.co.uk

23 Bentinck Street, London, W1M 6AB
Tel: (020) 7935 5541 **Fax:** (020) 7935 6638
Email: gdk@gross.co.uk

Senior partner:	G.D. Kirk
Number of partners:	4
Assistant solicitors:	4
Other fee-earners:	4

AREAS OF PRACTICE

Immigration & Nationality Law	20%
Company/Commercial	15%
Wills & Probate	15%
Civil Litigation	12%
Commercial Property & Agriculture	10%
Matrimonial	10%
Residential Conveyancing	10%
Employment	8%

CONTACTS

Civil Litigation	S. Kerr
Commercial Property & Agriculture	J. Cobbold
Company/Commercial	G. Kirk
Employment	N. Amor
Immigration/Nationality Law	G. Kirk
Matrimonial	K. Vipas
Residential Conveyancing	A. Gordon-Stables
Wills & Probate	A. Day

THE FIRM: Established in W. Suffolk for over 150 years, this progressive firm offers a specialist immigration service and has a fast-expanding commercial practice as well as a traditional general practice. The firm has an unusually international clientele, as well as sizeable private companies, small businesses and private clients. It is a member of the NIS Group of Independent Solicitors. The firm has an office in London W1 to service its London and international clients.

PRINCIPAL AREAS OF WORK:
Immigration and Nationality: The majority of work is in the field of business immigration. Assistance is also given in US and Canadian immigration law, and a consultancy service is offered to other solicitors through the ImmLaw service (brochure available).
Company/ Commercial: Expertise in most areas of commercial practice, including commercial property, for a wide range of business clients. Act for many doctors and dentists.
Litigation: All types of litigation including commercial, civil, matrimonial and legal aid. Agency work undertaken.
Private Client: Conveyancing, wills/ estate planning.

INTERNATIONAL CONNECTIONS: The firm has overseas associate offices in USA, Canada, South Africa, India, Spain, Russia and Hong Kong.

LANGUAGES: French, German and Russian.

GROWER FREEMAN & GOLDBERG

Suite Two, Fourth Floor, One Great Cumberland Place, London, W1H 8DQ **Tel:** (020) 7723 3040 **Fax:** (020) 7723 9015 **DX:** 44433 Marble Arch **Email:** sportslaw@gfg-law.co.uk **Website:** www.gfg-law.co.uk **Ptnrs:** 3 **Asst solrs:** 4 **Associates:** 2 **Other fee-earners:** 2 • The partnership has specialists in insurance & sports law; white collar crime; commercial litigation; and private client work.

AREAS OF PRACTICE

Litigation	40%
Conveyancing	25%
Criminal	15%
Sport & Commercial	20%

GSC SOLICITORS

31-32 Ely Place, London, EC1N 6TD
Tel: (020) 7822 2222 **Fax:** (020) 7822 2211 **DX:** 462 London/Chancery Lane
Email: info@gsc-solicitors.co.uk **Website:** www.gsc-solicitors.co.uk

Senior partner:	Douglas J. Green
Managing partner:	Saleem R. Sheikh
Number of partners:	6
Other fee-earners:	17

THE FIRM: This City firm undertakes a broad range of services for business and private clients. It is known for its expertise in media and intellectual property, commercial property and corporate work. GSC Solicitors, previously Green David Conway & Co, was founded in 1972 by the current senior partner and over the years has established a reputation for excellence in its chosen fields. Clients range from small businesses and family-owned companies to multinational plc's and industry bodies, as well as individuals. Recent developments in the firm include the setting up of a corporate department with a dedicated partner and an increase in the international side of its work which includes connections in Asia, Africa and the Middle East. The firm is located in purpose designed air conditioned offices with a full range of technological equipment.

CONTACTS

Commercial Litigation	D.J. Green
Commercial Property	H.D. Posener
	P.L. Belcher
Corporate Commercial/Tax/Trusts/ IT/Employment	S.R. Sheikh
	C.J. Halperin
Media/Intellectual Property	D.J. Green
	P.J. Leathem
	S.R. Sheikh
Private Client	S.R. Sheikh

G

GULBENKIAN HARRIS ANDONIAN

181 Kensington High Street, London, W8 6SH
Tel: (020) 7937 1542 **Fax:** (020) 7938 2059 **DX:** 47204 Kensington
Email: gulbenk@nildram.co.uk

Senior partner:	Paul Gulbenkian
Number of partners:	9
Assistant solicitors:	5
Other fee-earners:	3

THE FIRM: Whilst the firm engages in a wide range of commercial work (including litigation), it is best known for its expertise in immigration and nationality law which is undertaken for both commercial and private clients.The highlight of 1998/9 was a successful House of Lords Appeal in the case of 'Shah and Islam' reported in The Times on the 26 March 1999 under the heading *Pakistan's Failure to Protect Women.*

PRINCIPAL AREAS OF WORK:

Immigration and Nationality Law: Work includes nationality applications, all aspects of UK immigration and advice (business and private), refugee and asylum work and obtaining work permits. The firm has experience in US immigration, Hong Kong, Eastern Europe (including Russia), Middle East, Sri Lanka and South Africa. The firm is a founder member of the European Immigration Lawyers Group of which Paul Gulbenkian is the President. Paul Gulbenkian and Bernard Andonian are both part-time Immigration Adjudicators.

Matrimonial and Family Law: Comprehensive services are provided including advice on separation, divorce, wardship, custody, adoption and all related financial, property and taxation matters. The senior partner is one of the founder members of the Solicitors Family Law Association.

OTHER AREAS: In addition, the firm handles commercial litigation, commercial and domestic property transactions, defamation, intellectual property and probate and trust.

CLIENTELE: A largely international client base including multinationals as well as small to medium sized companies and private individuals.

LANGUAGES: Armenian, Arabic, Chinese, Danish, Farsi, French, Spanish and Swedish.

AREAS OF PRACTICE

Immigration	70%
Matrimonial	20%
General	10%

CONTACTS

General	Paul Gulbenkian
Immigration	Peter Wyatt
	Bernard Andonian
Matrimonial	Paul Gulbenkian
	Bernard Andonian

GWYNNES

Edgbaston House, Walker Street, PO Box 23 Wellington, Telford, Wellington, TF1 1HF **Tel:** (01952) 641651 **Fax:** (01952) 247441 **DX:** 23107 **Email:** info@gwynnes.com **Website:** www.gwynnes.com **Ptnrs:** 7 **Asst solrs:** 9 **Other fee-earners:** 10

H2O (HENRY HEPWORTH ORGANISATION)

5 John Street, London, WC1N 2HH
Tel: (020) 7539 7200 **Fax:** (020) 7539 7201
Email: h2o@h2o-law.com **Website:** www.h2o-law.com

THE FIRM: H2O (Henry Hepworth Organisation), based close to Grays Inn, is a specialist law firm offering a full media, intellectual property and information technology legal service to domestic and international clients. H2O is dedicated to working with the following industry sectors: entertainment; it/technology; leisure; media; retail. H2O is a single solution for the above industry sectors, dedicated to advise on commercial, transactional and litigation issues. H2O is a friendly firm with a knowledge-led culture whose objectives are to provide a top quality commercial service to its clients from a secure and happy environment. H2O understands its clients business (and their commercial objectives) and works closely with its clients, in-house lawyers and agents to deliver effective commercial advice. The firm is active in the following fields of activity (recognised by *Chambers Guide to the Legal Profession*): advertising/marketing; broadcasting; defamation; digital media; education, fashion, films, intellectual property; music; publishing; sports; theatre. H2O is a highly organised, successful firm. It has invested heavily in technology and has implemented its radical 'New Ways to Work' programme, including developing a paperless law office and allowing lawyers to work flexibly from home, one day a week. The firm has devised and implemented an active social re-investment policy (which contributes towards projects in the developing world and towards the encouragement of education and the arts).

PRINCIPAL AREAS OF WORK: Entertainment; intellectual property; IT/technology; leisure; media; retail.

INTERNATIONAL CONNECTIONS: H2O have established working relationships worldwide with specialist media/intellectual property lawyers. Partners are also qualified in the Republic of Ireland and Hong Kong. The firm has a reputation for multi-jurisdictional actions and overseeing European actions for clients (including insurance companies).

LANGUAGES: Members of the firm are fluent in French, Spanish, and German.

CLIENTELE: Clients include: Arena Leisure plc, Carlton UK Television Limited, Tottenham Hotspur plc, European Asian Satellite Television Limited, Express Newspapers plc, Hay and Robertson plc, IPC Magazines Limited, Littlewoods plc, London & Quadrant Community Cable Television Project, News International plc, NBC News Inc, Time Warner Inc, University for Industry, Young and Rubicam plc, Tesco Stores Limited, Times Newspapers Limited, Entuity Ltd, Best People Limited.

RECRUITMENT & TRAINING: The Firm has an active recruitment and training progamme at all levels. Those interested in joining the H2O team should contact www.h20-law.com.

AREAS OF PRACTICE

Media, Intellectual Property, IT	100%

CONTACTS

Corporate/Commercial/IT	Michael Henry
	Elizabeth Croker
IP Litigation/IT	Catrin Turner
	Eddie Powell
Media/Media Litigation (Defamation)	Jason McCue
	Paul Fox

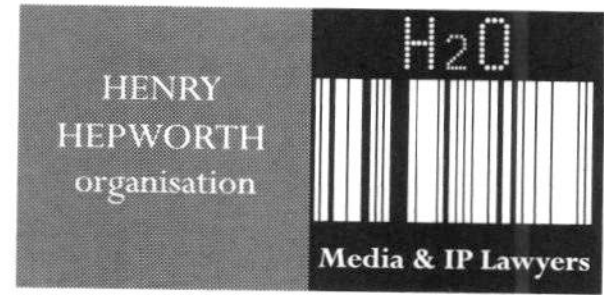

HACKING ASHTON

Berkeley Court, Borough Road, Newcastle-under-Lyme, ST5 1TT **Tel:** (01782) 715555 **Fax:** (01782) 715566 **DX:** 20954 **Email:** hackingashton@dial.pipex.com **Ptnrs:** 6 **Asst solrs:** 7 **Other fee-earners:** 5 **Contact:** R F Ashton • A commercial practice covering a broad spectrum of litigation, property and company commercial work with specialisms in construction and development work, alternative dispute resolution, employment law and agricultural matters. The firm has wide-ranging foreign connections.

AREAS OF PRACTICE

Commercial Property	35%
Commercial Litigation	30%
Company/Commercial	20%
Private Client	10%
Agricultural	5%

HADENS (FORMERLY HADEN STRETTON SLATER MILLER)

Leicester Buildings, Bridge Street, Walsall, WS1 1EL **Tel:** (01922) 720000 **Fax:** (01922) 720023 **DX:** 12122 Walsall **Email:** walsall@hadens.co.uk **Website:** www.hadens.co.uk **Ptnrs:** 15 **Asst solrs:** 13 **Other fee-earners:** 18

HALL & HAUGHEY

Ground Floor, 63 Carlton Place, Glasgow, G5 9TW **Tel:** (0141) 418 0505 **Fax:** (0141) 429 3131 **DX:** GW 395 **Email:** hh@hallhaughey.fsnet.co.uk

HALLETT & CO

11 Bank St, Ashford, TN23 1DA **Tel:** (01233) 625711 **Fax:** (01233) 643841 **DX:** 30202 Ashford **Email:** info@hallettandco.co.uk **Ptnrs:** 8 **Asst solrs:** 4 **Other fee-earners:** 8 **Contact:** Mr C.A. McDonald • One of the largest firms in Ashford, with renowned expertise in agricultural and employment law. Expanding commercial practice.

HALLINAN, BLACKBURN, GITTINGS & NOTT

Suite 22, Westminster Palace Gardens, Artillery Row, London, SW1P 1RR **Tel:** (020) 7233 3999 **Fax:** (020) 7233 3888 **Ptnrs:** 1 **Asst solrs:** 3 **Other fee-earners:** 2 **Contact:** Valerie Walsh • Specialise in crime, extradition, fraud, infanticide and road traffic offences. Legal Aid Franchise/private client. Experienced, well respected in the defence of a broad spectrum of clients.

HALLIWELL LANDAU

St. James's Court, Brown St, Manchester, M2 2JF
Tel: (0161) 835 3003 **Fax:** (0161) 835 2994 **DX:** 14317
Email: info@halliwells.com **Website:** www.halliwells.co.uk

Senior partner:	Roger Lancaster
Number of partners:	53
Assistant solicitors:	83
Other fee-earners:	60

AREAS OF PRACTICE

Corporate & Banking	24%
Commercial Litigation	20%
Commercial Property	17%
Insolvency	12%
Insurance Litigation	12%
Intellectual Property	4%
Planning & Environmental Law	4%
Trust & Estate Planning	4%
Employment	3%

CONTACTS

Commercial Litigation	Paul Thomas
Commercial Property	Stephen Goodman
Corporate	Alec Craig
Corporate Tax	Adam Pappworth
Employment	Stephen Hills
Insolvency	Andrew Buchanan
Insurance Litigation	Chris Phillips
Intellectual Property	Jonathan Moakes
Planning & Environmental Law	Roger Lancaster
Trusts & Estate Planning	Geoffrey Shindler

halliwell landau

THE FIRM: Halliwell Landau is a leading independent UK law firm. The firm has an impressive client list and provides a comprehensive range of commercial legal advice to support their business activities. The partnership has a reputation for combining experience, commercial awareness and a willingness to consider new approaches and ideas. The firm's philosophy of entrepreneurial awareness with close attention to detail and dedication to high professional standards has become the hallmark of its work.

PRINCIPAL AREAS OF WORK:

Corporate: This is one of the largest departments in the region, advising on mergers, acquisitions, disposals, MBOs/MBIs, banking law and corporate finance.
Commercial Property: One of the leading commercial property advisers in the North West advising on a range of commercial property issues including the acquisition and disposal of properties, site assembly and negotiation of leases.
Commercial Litigation: Advises on all aspects of commercial litigation including property litigation, banking and recovery work, professional negligence.
Planning and Environmental: Widely acknowledged as one of the most respected planning appeal practices in the country, advising some of the region's top companies and local and national developers.
Construction and Bonds: Advises on all facets of construction law including bonds and guarantees, which play a crucial role in construction agreements.
Employment: Advises clients on both contentious and non-contentious aspects of legislation.
Trusts and Estate Planning: Acknowledged as one of the leaders in the field in the north west advising senior business executives and individuals of high net worth on income and estate planning, the creation of trusts and administration of investments. Also advises trustees and charities.
Intellectual Property: This department advises on traditional categories of patents, copyright, trademarks and registered designs as well as advice on any form of intangible rights.Insolvency and Corporate Recovery: Principally directed at supporting banks and insolvency practitioners on specialised insolvency matters. Also advises companies and directors on the legal aspects of restructuring, reorganising and refining.
Insurance Litigation: The department advises on general insurance issues, policy disputes, indemnity and warranty issues. All types of defendant personal injury work.

A. HALSALL & CO
47-48 Hamilton Square, Birkenhead, CH41 5BD **Tel:** (0151) 647 6323 **Fax:** (0151) 647 9818 **DX:** 17853 **Email:** info@halsalls **Ptnrs:** 6 **Asst solrs:** 2 **Solicitor/Consultant** 1 **Other fee-earners:** 2

HAMERS
9-11 Scale Lane, Hull, HUI 1PH **Tel:** (01482) 326666 **Fax:** (01482) 324432 **DX:** 11933 Hull **Email:** info@hamers.com **Ptnrs:** 6 **Asst solrs:** 28 **Other fee-earners:** 18

HAMLINS

Roxburghe House, 273-287 Regent St, London, W1A 4SQ
Tel: (020) 7355 6000 **Fax:** (020) 7518 9100 **DX:** 53803 Oxford Circus North
Email: admin@hamlins.co.uk **Website:** www.hamlins.co.uk

Managing partner:	B.M. Casey
Number of partners:	18
Assistant solicitors:	9
Other fee-earners:	25

AREAS OF PRACTICE

Property Services	35%
Company and Commerical	19%
Entertainment/Intellectual Property	18%
Litigation Services	16%
Secured Lending	12%

CONTACTS

Property services	Brian Casey
Litigation including Entertainment, Media and Intellectual Property	Laurence Gilmore
Company and commercial	Gordon Oliver
Secured lending	Keith Roffey

THE FIRM: This medium sized London practice, formerly known as Hamlin Slowe, is property-orientated with a substantial commercial client base. Founded in 1906, the firm undertakes a wide variety of work, but has particular expertise in commercial property, commercial, secured lending, intellectual property, entertainment and media matters. The firm's clients include several public companies and many large and well-known private companies.

PRINCIPAL AREAS OF WORK:

Property: The department has a long and established reputation in financing, acquisition, letting and disposal of shop, office and industrial property as well as handling development, town and country planning, compulsory purchase and landlord and tenant matters.
Secured Lending: The department acts for lenders in professional negligence, possession, mortgage documentation, arrears, sales, insolvency, consumer credit and unsecured loss recovery matters. The department has developed on-line computer systems for mortgage and arrears recovery.

Litigation: The firm is known for the strength of its litigation department which supports the non-litigious departments, handles heavy commercial litigation, matrimonial and personal injury matters and includes the entertainment, media and intellectual property department which has an outstanding reputation in the entertainment sector, particularly in the areas of copyright infringement. It handles all aspects of entertainment law for clients who include copyright societies, music publishers, record companies, record producers, composers, authors, recording artists, and film and video production companies. The department also advises on matters of defamation, libel, information technology, multi-media, trade marks, passing off and design right.
Company and Commercial: The department deals with mergers, acquisitions, disposals, franchising, employment and partnership matters. The department also advises on share and rights issues, public flotations, corporate reorganisations, liquidations and joint ventures. This department encompasses a division which specialises in advising the leisure industry and has an asset planning division which handles personal taxation, inheritance tax planning, pensions, trusts, wills and probates. Hamlins has a strong client base of both large and small clients.
The firm's brochure describing the services that the firm has to offer is available upon request.

HAMLINS

HAMMOND SUDDARDS EDGE

7 Devonshire Square, Cutlers Gardens, London, EC2M 4YH
Tel: (020) 7655 1000 **Fax:** (020) 7655 1001 **DX:** 33885 Finsbury Square
Email: enquiries@hammondsuddardsedge.co.uk **Website:** www.hammondsuddardsedge.com

Suite 688 Lloyd's, One Lime Street, London (Lloyd's), EC3M 7HA
Tel: (020) 7327 3388/3399 **Fax:** (020) 7621 1217 **DX:** 807 London City EC3
Email: enquiries@hammondsuddardsedge.co.uk

2 Park Lane, Leeds, LS3 1ES
Tel: (0113) 284 7000 **Fax:** (0113) 284 7001 **DX:** 26441 Leeds-1
Email: enquiries@hammondsuddardsedge.co.uk

Trinity Court, 16 John Dalton Street, Manchester, M60 8HS
Tel: (0161) 830 5000 **Fax:** (0161) 830 5001 **DX:** 14347 Manchester-1
Email: enquiries@hammondsuddardsedge.co.uk

Rutland House, 148 Edmund St, Birmingham, B3 2JR
Tel: (0121) 200 2001 **Fax:** (0121) 200 1991 **DX:** 708611 Birmingham-17
Email: enquiries@hammondsuddardsedge.co.uk

Pennine House, 39-45 Well Street, Bradford, BD1 5NU
Tel: (01274) 764400 **Fax:** (01274) 730484 **DX:** 11796
Email: enquiries@hammondsuddardsedge.co.uk

Managing partners	Chris Jones, Gil Hayward
Senior partner	John Heller
Number of Partners:	185
Other Lawyers:	900
Total staff:	2000

CONTACTS

Advocacy	Patrick Walker
Asset Finance	Angela Davies
	Gwenyth Maynard
Banking	Gwendoline Griffiths
Charities	Neil Pearson
Commercial Dispute Resolution	Peter Crossley
Computer Law & E-commerce	Mike Henley
Construction & Engineering	David Jones
Corporate Finance	Richard Burns
Corporate Tax	Mark Simpson
EC & Competition	Konstantinos Adamantopoulos
Employment	Sue Nickson
Environmental	Paul BrattGwyn Williams
Financial Services	Bruce Gardner
HammondsDirect	Lucci Dammone
Insolvency & Corporate Recovery	Paul Rhodes
Insurance	Michael Robin
Intellectual Property	Marija Danilunas
Licensing	Andrew Potts
	Stephanie Perraton
Media & Entertainment	David Hull
Pensions	Jane Marshall
PFI	Jonathan Hosie
Property & Planning	Chris Marks
Retail	Simon Boss
Sports Law	Richard Alderson

THE FIRM: The merger of Hammond Suddards and edge ellison on 1 August 2000, created one of the UK's largest legal practices. The firm has a formidable London corporate practice and top-flight status in all the major financial and industrial centres of England: Birmingham, Manchester, Leeds and Bradford. Hammond Suddards Edge has 185 partners, 900 lawyers and a total staff of 2,000, operating as an integrated national practice using the best IT networking systems available to deliver a seamless service to clients, irrespective of location.

PRINCIPAL AREAS OF WORK:
Corporate Finance: The corporate finance unit has an outstanding record in mergers & acquisitions both domestically and overseas. The unit is respected for its considerable expertise and experience in flotations, disposals, reorganisations, joint ventures, MBOs, funding operations and the full range of corporate and commercial services. The majority of the work is for listed companies; indeed, the firm acts for more than 80 UK Stock Market listed companies and 16 US Fortune 500 companies. Other corporate clients include private companies, UK subsidiaries of overseas companies and various financial institutions, including six of the top 10 UK building societies.
Banking: The banking unit undertakes all types of banking work for financial institutions including UK and overseas banks, building societies and borrowers on a broad range of secured and unsecured transactions and restructerings. A dedicated financial law team draws together specialists from disciplines including banking, treasury products, factoring & discounting, asset-based lending, capital markets, compliance, insolvency, composite recovery, banking litigation and bespoke debt recovery systems.
Financial Services and Corporate Tax: The financial services and corporate tax units provide advice on tax planning at all levels, employee share option schemes and offshore tax. Unusually, this unit incorporates derivatives expertise including a derivatives documentation team which provides a cost-effective execution service for a variety of market standard derivatives agreements.
Commercial Dispute Resolution: The commercial dispute resolution unit encompasses all aspects of commercial claims and disputes for the firm's corporate clients. The firm has particular expertise in alternative

Continued overleaf

dispute resolution (ADR) and arbitration, which was recognised in 1998 when the firm won the CEDR (Centre for Dispute Resolution) award for excellence in ADR. The unit also handles regulatory work, directors' and officers' liabilities and other aspects of criminal law which present risks for businesses. In addition there is a safety, health and environmental team carrying out all litigious and non-litigious environmental work.

Insolvency and Corporate Recovery: The insolvency and corporate recovery unit provides advice to insolvency practitioners and banks on all aspects of their work as receivers, liquidators, trustees, administrators and supervisors. The unit also advises companies and partnerships experiencing serious financial difficulties. Much of the work has an international focus.

Property and Planning: The property unit advises major national developers, institutions and end-users on all aspects of commercial property, particularly major City centre schemes and out of town developments. The planning team continues to go from strength to strength with largescale involvement in major national planning enquiries for UK and international companies and utilities. A dedicated retail team advised a wide range of retailers from high street names to breweries and charities.

Intellectual Property: The intellectual property unit has established itself as a market leader in both litigious and non-litigious IP matters for a broad spectrum of multinationals and UK companies. The unit has specific teams dedicated to telecommunications, media and film, pharmaceuticals, IT and e-commerce. In addition, a dedicated enterprise & technology team has expertise in advertising and brand clearance, character merchandising, computer contracts for hardware and software, domain name recovery, e-commerce, media contracts, rights agreements for sports governing bodies, companies, clubs and sales promotions.

H

Insurance: The commercial insurance unit, one of the largest based at Lloyd's of London, is recognised for its expertise in professional indemnity for accountants, solicitors, surveyors, architects, engineers, computer consultants and financial institutions. The unit also advises on policy coverage disputes, product liability matters and non-contentious insurance work.

Construction and Engineering: The construction and engineering unit is one of the largest bespoke practices in the UK. The unit acts for employers and contractors both in the UK and overseas on all aspects of contentious and non-contentious construction law from building projects (including operation and facilities management contracts) to civil, process and chemical engineering projects.

Employment: Hammond Suddards Edge has one of the UK's largest employment practices with a large team of dedicated employment lawyers across all locations. Work encompasses all aspects of contentious and non-contentious employment advice.

Pensions: The pensions unit is widely recognised as one of the UK's largest and most experienced pensions advisers. The unit advises employers and trustees on all aspects of pensions arrangements from large occupational schemes to product development work for providers and unapproved top-up schemes.

Lender Services: HammondsDirect is the UK's leading high volume legal support service for lenders and financial institutions. Through sophisticated IT solutions, HammondsDirect offers the ability to handle effectively and efficiently large volumes of litigation cases, conveyancing transactions and mortgage arrears management services.

EU Law: An increasing part of the firm's work is of an international flavour. The Brussels office is now among the largest of those operated by a UK firm in the EU capital and provides specialist expertise in EU, commercial and environmental law. Many of the firm's clients have international interests and/or are making overseas acquisitions, particularly in Europe, the US, Canada and Australia. The firm accepts EU work in Brussels from other solicitors and overseas law firms.

INTERNATIONAL CONNECTIONS: The firm's Belgium office is located at: avenue Louise 250, B-1050 Brussels, tel: +32 2 627 7676, fax: +32 2 627 7686, email: enquiries@hammondsuddardsedge.co.uk

CLIENTELE: With an impressive range of major national and international companies and institutions on its client list, Hammond Suddards Edge advises more than 80 UK Stock Market listed companies, including 18 of the FTSE 100 companies, and 16 US Fortune 500 companies. The firm is recognised and respected for its entrepreneurial and innovative approach and is constantly looking for new ways to enhance client service.

RECRUITMENT & TRAINING: Hammond Suddards Edge continues to recruit qualified staff for most areas of the practice across all offices. Enquiries should be addressed to Rebecca Ellis, based in the Manchester office. Around 40 trainees are recruited each year, who carry out six four-month seats during their training contract. All trainees are encouraged to move around the offices during their training and subsidised accommodation is provided in all locations to facilitate this process. Applications (in the form of a CV and covering letter) should be send to Alison Archer at the London office.

HANCOCK CAFFIN

Princes House, Princes Street, Truro, TR1 2EY **Tel:** (01872) 272333 **Fax:** (01872) 242458 **DX:** 81200 Truro **Email:** hc@hancockcaffin.co.uk **Website:** www.hancockcaffin.co.uk **Ptnrs:** 15 **Asst solrs:** 4 **Other fee-earners:** 5 **Contact:** Mr Bruce Holt • Product of the merger between the long-established and respected firms of Hancock & Lawrence and Frank & Caffin. Particular strengths: commercial property; agriculture; landlord and tenant; defendant insurance; professional indemnity; family.

AREAS OF PRACTICE	
Litigation	38%
Property	30%
Family	13%
Trust & Probate	13%
Miscellaneous	6%

HARBOTTLE & LEWIS

Hanover House, 14 Hanover Square, London, W1R 0BE
Tel: (020) 7667 5000 **Fax:** (020) 7667 5100 **DX:** 44617 Mayfair
Website: www.harbottle.com

Managing partner:	Colin Howes
Number of partners:	18
Assistant solicitors:	50
Other fee-earners:	15

CONTACTS

Advertising, Marketing & Sponsorship	Alice Rayman
Aviation	Dermot Scully
Brand Management & Protection; IP Rights	Mark Owen
Broadcasting	Medwyn Jones
Charities	Robert Porter
Company & Commercial	Colin Howes
Corporate Finance	Mark Bertram
Corporate Recovery & Insolvency	Samantha Phillips
Employment	Lisa Bennett
Film & TV Production	Robert Storer
Immigration	Susan May
Interactive Entertainment	Sebastian Belcher
IT & Telecommunications	Mark Owen
Leisure	Justin Dunlop
Litigation	Gerrard Tyrrell
Music	Ann Harrison
New Media, E-Commerce & On-Line	Mark Phillips
Property Development & Investment	Alan Patten
Publishing	Rachel Atkins
Sport	Bob Mitchell
Theatre & Performing Arts	Alice Rayman

THE FIRM: Media and entertainment work has formed the core of Harbottle & Lewis' work since the firm was established some 40 years ago and the firm remains unique in having expertise right across these industries. Its reputation for handling high profile work in these sectors is unrivalled. Increasingly the firm specialises in new media and e-commerce work, which has evolved from its traditional strengths acting for entrepreneurial clients in the creative industries. An impressive number of partners and senior associates at the firm are recognised as leaders in their field by various independent sources.

PRINCIPAL AREAS OF WORK: Harbottle & Lewis prides itself on its extensive knowledge of and contacts in the sectors making up the various media and entertainment industries. The range of cross-departmental groups and other initiatives within the practice ensures that lawyers within the firm are constantly exchanging information and ideas in relation to the latest developments both in the law and the industries in which they act.

Film/Television/Publishing: Radio and television broadcasters, cable and satellite operators work closely both with the film and television broadcasting group and with the IT group on convergence issues. The team acts on film and television production, financing, digital streaming, merchandising, book and magazine publishing.

Music/Theatre: The firm acts for many of the world's musical leading players. Work includes recording contracts, music publishing agreements, on-line and internet issues, merchandising and sponsorship agreements, licensing, and tour and distribution agreements. In theatre, the firm advises leading talent, subsidised theatres, theatre owners, commercial producers and industry bodies on all relevant issues from rights agreements to funding and capital projects.

New Media: The firm advises on a wide range of e-commerce arrangements including investment, content acquisition, technology and hosting issues, site development and user relationships. The interactive entertainment practice leads the field in this specialist area and they act for both hardware and software publishers, advising on a range of interactive and internet issues.

Intellectual Property: The firm has been involved in pioneering work in establishing and protecting brands based around both products and personality as well as being at the forefront of cutting edge issues surrounding web branding issues. The IP group was recently voted 'Trade Mark Team of the Year' by the leading industry journal *Managing Intellectual Property*.

Litigation: The litigation group specialises in the media, intellectual property, defamation and other aspects of media management. The group acts for numerous leading personalities in the UK and the USA.

Aviation/Commercial: The firm's aviation experts deal with airline regulation and competition, aircraft acquisition and all other legal aspects of the aviation business. In more general commercial matters the firm is involved in mergers, takeovers, capital markets work, financing, joint ventures and management buyouts and advise extensively on employment, competition and antitrust law.

Commercial Property: The firm acts for a wide-ranging portfolio of clients in the property, investment and development sectors.

Sport: The sports group represents governing bodies, clubs, promoters and sports persons and handles matters ranging from sponsorship to player contracts. This combines with the work of the advertising group in dealing with all aspects of advertising, promotion and general sponsorship.

HARDING EVANS

Queen Chambers, 2 North Street, Newport, NP9 1TE **Tel:** (01633) 244233 **Fax:** (01633) 246453 **DX:** 33202 **Ptnrs:** 8 **Asst solrs:** 5
Other fee-earners: 2

HARDWICK STALLARDS

Centurion House, 37 Jewry Street, London, EC3N 2ER
Tel: (020) 7423 1000 **Fax:** (020) 7481 3002 **DX:** 822 London/City
Email: mail@hardwick.co.uk **Website:** www.hardwick.co.uk

Managing partner:	Simon J. Hardwick
Senior partner:	Keith M. Robinson
Number of partners:	13
Assistant solicitors:	8
Other fee-earners:	4

CONTACTS

Commercial Property	Michael Pearson
Company and Commercial	Alan Williams
Corporate Finance	Keith Robinson
Employment	Tola Ogundimu
Litigation	Rhodri James
Transportation	Paul Bugden

PRINCIPAL AREAS OF WORK:

Company & Commercial: A broad range of corporate and commercial work, including intellectual property, partnerships, acquisitions and disposals, joint ventures, commercial contracts, share option arrangements and general commercial advice.

Corporate Finance: Stock Exchange work, AIM and OFEX flotations, debt/equity issues, venture capital investment, institutional funding and secured lending, MBOs and MBIs, and corporate reconstructions.

Commercial Property: Commercial development and investment work for private and public companies,

Continued overleaf

overseas investors, financial institutions and individual entrepreneurs, together with all aspects of landlord and tenant work, estate management and work for local authorities.
Litigation: Dealing with most kinds of commercial disputes, particular experience in the areas of landlord and tenant, construction contracts, factoring and banking, together with personal injury work.
Employment: Contentious and non-contentious work.
Transportation: Contentious and non-contentious shipping matters, multi-modal transport, containerisation, and trade finance and insurance.

CLIENTELE: Clientele consists principally of entrepreneur-managed businesses and a number of listed companies. The partner-led approach provides an in-house style of service with an emphasis on business experience.

HAROLD BENJAMIN LITTLEJOHN

Hill House, 67-71 Lowlands Road, Harrow, HA1 3EQ
Tel: (020) 8422 5678 **Fax:** (020) 8864 7530 **DX:** 4243 Harrow
Email: hbl@hben.co.uk **Website:** www.hben.co.uk

Senior partner:	Roger Lane
Number of partners:	15
Assistant solicitors:	2
Other fee-earners:	10

AREAS OF PRACTICE

Commercial Property	60%
Corporate	15%
Litigation	15%
Private Client, Family and Probate	10%

CONTACTS

Commercial Leases	Sarah Paul
	Lindsay Wilner
Company/Commercial	David Korman
	Roger Duncan
Development	Chris Batty
	John Cawthorn
Family	Keith Flavell
General Litigation	Keith Boddy
Private Client	Jonathan Dorman
Property Litigation	Richard Crowe

H

THE FIRM: Known as Harold Benjamin & Collins until April 2000, the firm has undergone rapid growth in the past 5 years investing in key people and information technology. Widely known for development and commercial conveyancing and property litigation, the firm is ideally located in central Harrow, which is increasingly convenient for a rapidly expanding base of property and other commercial clients, at regional and national levels. The increase in volume and quality of work has seen a series of expansions led by the property department but teams from all departments are fielded for multi-disciplinary and high value transactions. The company/commercial and litigation departments have doubled in size in the past 12 months and continue to attract new clients through recommendation.

PRINCIPAL AREAS OF WORK:
Property: Development, commercial and residential conveyancing, including the acquisition and legal management of sites for residential and mixed commercial, leisure and residential development; town planning and environmental law; commercial leasehold premises work acting for both landlords and tenants, including the grant and renewal of leases of commercial property and the sale and purchase of tenanted commercial property for investment; retail premises; commercial mortgage work for institutional lenders.
Litigation: Building and property litigation with particular emphasis on the Landlord and Tenant Act 1954; personal injury and clinical negligence; employment law; general litigation; housing association tenant management.
Corporate/Commercial: Wide range of corporate clients with broad spread of work including acquisitions, joint ventures, intellectual property, partnership, general commercial contracts, agency distribution, finance and competition law.
Private Client: A full service of family law; wills and probate; residential conveyancing, especially substantial properties.
Family: Recent expansion has led to the strengthening of the Family Department to include members of the Solicitors Family Law Association, Family Law Panel and qualified mediators enabling the firm to offer a broad range of services in Family Law but particularly in high value ancillary relief work.

CLIENTELE: The firm acts for a wide range of clients on a national basis including plcs, national house builders and private property developers engaged in both residential and commercial property development. The company commercial and litigation departments have national and local clients. The firm acts for a company with an excess of 1,500 retail units spread throughout the country. High value residential transactions are carried out for international clients, and the firm continues to value its associations with private clients, many of whom are local and have been with the firm for many years.

HARPER MACLEOD

The Ca'd'oro, 45 Gordon Street, Glasgow, G1 3PE
Tel: (0141) 221 8888 **Fax:** (0141) 226 4198 **DX:** GW86
Email: maildesk@harpermacleod.co.uk **Website:** www.harpermacleod.co.uk

Managing partner:	Lorne D Crerar
Senior partner:	J Ross Harper CBE
Number of partners:	15
Assistant solicitors:	15
Other fee-earners:	9

CONTACTS

Banking	Prof Lorne Crerar
Commercial Litigation	Rod McKenzie
Commercial Property	Mark Dewar
Construction	Michael Conroy
Corporate	Len Freedman

THE FIRM: Harpers, specialising in commercial law, commenced trading in 1984 and changed to Harper Macleod on the acquisition of the niche commercial law practice of Macleods in 1991. As a young technology driven firm, Harper Macleod is dedicated to an innovative and progressive approach to the delivery of legal services. Harper Macleod is also known for the ability of its key personnel to respond to market needs and its focus on the development of fee earners and staff. The firm is committed to helping clients achieve their commercial goals. In the past year, Harper Macloed has continued to expand and the practice group structure continues to encourage the development of flexible and tailored legal services to meet the individual needs of clients.

PRINCIPAL AREAS OF WORK: In addition to the five principal departments, corporate; commercial; commercial property; litigation; private client and recoveries, the firm operates 15 multi-disciplinary practice groups covering the key areas of specialism. These are banking, commercial property, commercial litigation, construction, corporate, employment, IP & T, licensing, medical, planning and environmental, private client, public sector and housing, recoveries, reparation and sport.

CONTACTS

Employment ....Stephen Miller
IP & Technology ....Tom Thomas
Licensing ....Graeme Nisbet
Medical ....Claire McManus
Planning & Environmental ....Peter Ferguson
Private Client ....Gordon Stoddart
Public Sector and Housing ......Len Freedman
Recoveries ....Dawn McKenzie
Reparation ....Richard Henderson
Sport ....Stephen Miller

HARRIS & CARTWRIGHT

Windsor Crown House, 7 Windsor Rd, Slough, SL1 2DX
Tel: (01753) 810710 **Fax:** (01753) 810720 **DX:** 42268 Slough (West)
Email: enquiries@harrcart.co.uk **Website:** www.harrcart.co.uk

Senior partner:	Paul Norris
Number of partners:	8
Assistant solicitors:	19
Other fee-earners:	18

THE FIRM: Established in 1922, Harris & Cartwright is a progressive and enlightened firm, building on its accumulated knowledge and experience to provide a high quality, responsive and cost-effective service to all its clients. With two offices in Slough (one dedicated to company/commercial work) and others in nearby Langley and Burnham the firm is one of the largest in the Thames Valley. In February 2000, the firm established a partnership with Lawrence Cartier & Co of Lincolns Inn Fields, London. This partnership, known as Harris & Cartwright, Cartier operates out of premises at 1 New Square, Lincolns Inn (telephone 020 8400 7082) and provides a wide range of corporate and commercial services.

PRINCIPAL AREAS OF WORK:
Company & Commercial: A rapidly expanding department, now accounting for approximately one third of total fee income, assists business clients across the full spectrum of problems faced from start-up to flotation and beyond. Services include commercial conveyancing, business sales, takeovers, mergers and acquisitions, partnership formations and agreements, commercial negotiations, company secretarial and administrative matters, commercial litigation, insolvency and receivership, employment, terms and conditions of sale, service contracts and similar agreements.
Personal Injury and Clinical Negligence: All members of the department specialise in the work they undertake and are, variously, members of: the Law Society's Personal Injury and Clinical Negligence Panels, the AVMA Referral Panel, APIL Clinical Negligence Special Interest Group, MASS, PEOPIL, ATLA, The Spinal Injuries Association and Headway. The practice has considerable experience in dealing with catastrophic injury cases, having achieved the highest and second highest awards of damages for personal injury cases in English courts (£19.3m and £5.1m).
Family: All qualified staff are members of the Solicitors Family Law Association and are specialists in this field. They are also, variously, members of the Law Society's Family and Children Panels. Matters dealt with include high profile ancillary relief, divorce, children and injunction proceedings.
Financial Services: Headed by an independent financial adviser with 30 years industry experience, the department provides advice on investment, insurance and pensions to both individuals and organisations.
Residential Conveyancing: Operating from offices in Slough, Burnham and Langley, this department offers a full conveyancing service together with advice on development, planning and finance for residential properties.
Probate and Trusts: Working closely with the financial services department, a full range of wills, probate, trusts and estate administration, tax and inheritance tax planning is provided.

LANGUAGES: French, German and Punjabi.

AREAS OF PRACTICE

Company/Commercial 32%
Civil Litigation 25%
Conveyancing 20%
Family 14%
Wills, Probate, Trusts 5%
Crime 4%

CONTACTS

Clinical Negligence ..Christopher Gooderidge
Commercial Litigation ....Andrew Grant
Commercial Property ....Paul Norris
Company/Commercial ....Stephen Fuller
............Raj Dhokia
Crime ....Mark Moorcraft
Debt Collection ....Andrew Grant
Employment ....Raj Dhokia
Family ....Punam Denley
Financial Services ....David McIntosh
Landlord & Tenant ....Andrew Grant
Personal Injury ....Kent Pattinson
Residential Conveyancing ......Richard Palmer
Wills, Probate, Trusts ....Ron Kerslake

H

HARRIS & HARRIS

14 Market Place, Wells, BA5 2RE **Tel:** (01749) 674747 **Fax:** (01749) 676585 **DX:** 44900 Wells **Email:** enquiries@harris-harris.co.uk **Website:** www.harris-harris.co.uk **Ptnrs:** 8 **Asst solrs:** 3 **Other fee-earners:** 6 **Contact:** Mr. T.F. Berry. • Firm with specialists in commercial, family law, construction, ecclesiastical, insolvency and mental health. Also, office in Frome and Consultant in France.

HARRISON BUNDEY & CO.

219-221 Chapeltown Road, Leeds, LS7 3DX **Tel:** (0113) 200 7400 **Fax:** (0113) 237 4685 **DX:** 713106 Leeds Park Square **Website:** www.harrisonbundey.co.uk **Ptnrs:** 13 **Asst solrs:** 6 **Other fee-earners:** 9 **Contact:** Ruth Bundey • A legal aid franchised inner city high street practice specialising in crime, civil liberties, immigration and family, childcare, inquests and personal injury.

HARRISON CURTIS

40 Great Portland Street, London, W1N 5AH **Tel:** (020) 7637 3333 **Fax:** (020) 7637 3334 **Email:** mail@harrisoncurtis.co.uk **Ptnrs:** 2 **Asst solrs:** 1 **Associates** 1 **Other fee-earners:** 0 **Contact:** Lawrence Harrison or Tim Curtis • A small firm offering high quality advice to a broad range of media and entertainment clients. Expertise in music, film, television, theatre, advertising, design and marketing, new media and sports law.

AREAS OF PRACTICE	
Media and Entertainment	80%
Company Commercial	10%
Sport	10%

HARRISON, LEITCH & LOGAN

Victoria House, 54 - 58 Chichester Street, Belfast, BT1 4HN **Tel:** (028) 9032 3843 **Fax:** (028) 9033 0187 **DX:** 401 NR Belfast **Email:** HarrisonLL@compuserve.com **Ptnrs:** 5 **Asst solrs:** 7 **Other fee-earners:** 3 **Contact:** Jonathan Hool • Personal injury and commercial litigation, company, commercial property, banking, insolvency and private client.

AREAS OF PRACTICE	
Litigation	45%
Commercial Property	20%
Company/Commercial	20%
Private Client/Probate/Employment	15%

HARTNELL & CO

20 Cathedral Yard, Exeter, EX1 1HB **Tel:** (01392) 421777 **Fax:** (01392) 421237 **DX:** 8388 Exeter **Ptnrs:** 2 **Asst solrs:** 4

H

HARVEY INGRAM OWSTON

20 New Walk, Leicester, LE1 6TX
Tel: (0116) 254 5454 **Fax:** (0116) 255 4559 **DX:** 17014 Leicester 2
Email: hio@hio.co.uk **Website:** www.hio.co.uk

22 The Parade, Oadby, Leicester, LE2 5BF
Tel: (0116) 271 4129 **Fax:** (0116) 271 5669

44 Long Street, Wigston, Leicester, LE18 2AH
Tel: (0116) 288 0841 **Fax:** (0116) 288 1418 **DX:** 29841 Wigston

Managing partner:	Stephen Woolfe
Senior partner:	Roger Bowder
Number of partners:	26
Assistant solicitors:	26
Other fee-earners:	41

AREAS OF PRACTICE	
Litigation	33%
Commercial Property	26%
Company/Commercial	18%
Residential Property	15%
Probate & Trusts	8%

THE FIRM: Based in Leicestershire, this prominent practice acts for commercial and other clients not only in the East Midlands but also nationally. The firm makes client service a priority and has been accredited to ISO9001 since 1995. It is dedicated to further improvements to quality of service within a total quality programme.

PRINCIPAL AREAS OF WORK: The firm has five departments: company commercial; commercial property; residential property; litigation; and trusts.

Company/Commercial: For the company commercial department, under the leadership of Martin Smith, there have been a number of major corporate deals involving comprehensive commercial expertise including bank and development capital financing, MBOs and MBIs, business purchases and sales, commercial contracts, insolvencies, partnerships, pension funds, terms and conditions of trading and competition law. The emergence of e-commerce and its growing importance to business has led to the expansion of work undertaken in this area, not only on the basis of legal skills, but also in relation to the level of service offered to clients. The firm has advised a number of Internet start-ups on all issues relating to the emergence of e-commerce as well as updating clients on all forthcoming legislative changes in the electronic world.

Commercial Property: This department covers all aspects of commercial dealings, including freehold and leasehold transactions, site acquisition matters, landlord and tenant law, rent control, agricultural and environmental law. Retail property is a particular strength and there has been significant growth in the area of planning and development.

Residential Property: Apart from private conveyancing this department specialises in housing association work and repossession sales for major institutions.

Litigation: Expertise includes commercial matters such as intellectual property, insolvency and building disputes, all aspects of employment law and licensing and professional negligence. A range of general litigation is also handled including personal injury and debt collection. The firm's growing family law group also works within the litigation department.

Trusts: Expertise includes estate planning, the drafting of trusts and wills, trust and estate administration as well as charity and Court of Protection work.

CLIENTELE: A prominent provider of legal services to national and regional companies, as well as looking after the needs of smaller businesses. Clients include Alliance & Leicester plc, Everards Brewery Limited, The BSS Group plc, De Montfort Housing Association, Leicester Housing Association, National Car Rental Limited, Stead & Simpson Limited, WR Group Holdings Limited, Benson Shoe Limited, Vision Express (UK) Limited, and Samworth Brothers Limited. A network of overseas contacts enables the firm to advise on foreign matters, particularly in Europe and the United States.

Harvey Ingram Owston
solicitors

HASTIES

51 South Bridge, Edinburgh, EH1 1PP **Tel:** (0131) 556 7951 **Fax:** (0131) 558 1596 **DX:** 16 Edinburgh **Email:** edin.hastie@ukonline.co.uk **Ptnrs:** 2 **Asst solrs:** 4

HATCH BRENNER

4 Theatre Street, Norwich, NR2 1QY **Tel:** (01603) 660811 **Fax:** (01603) 619473 **DX:** 5237 Norwich **Ptnrs:** 9 **Asst solrs:** 4 **Other fee-earners:** 10 **Contact:** Alan Dobbins. • Property, commercial, civil litigation (including employment and personal injury), family and crime. Legal Aid Franchise, Personal Injury and Children Panels.

HAWLEY & RODGERS

19-23 Granby St, Loughborough, LE11 3DY **Tel:** (01509) 230333 **Fax:** (01509) 239390 **DX:** 19602 **Ptnrs:** 12 **Asst solrs:** 8 **Other fee-earners:** 8

HAYES

63-64 Magdalen Street, Exeter, EX2 4HN **Tel:** (01392) 202 742 **Fax:** (01392) 202 743

HAY & KILNER

Merchant House, 30 Cloth Market, Newcastle-upon-Tyne, NE1 1EE
Tel: (0191) 232 8345 **Fax:** (0191) 221 0514 **DX:** 61019 Newcastle upon Tyne
Email: Lawyers@hay-kilner.co.uk **Website:** www.hay-kilner.co.uk

Senior partner:	John Kilner
Number of partners:	23
Assistant solicitors:	9
Other fee-earners:	9

AREAS OF PRACTICE

Company & Commercial (inc Litigation)	42%
Personal Injury/Clinical Negligence/Insurance Litigation	37%
Private Client	21%

CONTACTS

Clinical Negligence	David Bradshaw
Commercial Litigation	Martin Soloman
Commercial Property	Paul Taylor
Company/Commercial	Nick James
Construction	Graham Sutton, Martin Soloman
Debt Recovery	Kevan Stronach
Employment	Rod Jones, Neil Dwyer
Insolvency	Neil Harrold
Insurance	Peter Pescod, Ros Sparrow
Personal Injury	Alun Williams
Private Client	Keith Hately
Professional Indemnity	Ros Sparrow

THE FIRM: Established in 1946, Hay & Kilner is one of the North East's major legal practices, dealing with a full range of work on behalf of commercial organisations, institutions and private clients. The firm is a member of LawNet and Eurojuris and has French-speaking solicitors. It has been appointed to the Legal Aid Board's clinical negligence panel and multi-party action panel. The firm also holds a Legal Aid franchise for employment, personal injury, crime, family and matrimonial. The firm has additional offices in Wallsend and Gosforth.

PRINCIPAL AREAS OF WORK:

Commercial: Company, commercial, takeovers and mergers, management buyouts, investments and securities, banking, building societies, employment, computer contracts, intellectual property, partnership law, licensing and leisure, insolvency, commercial property, leasing, tax, planning and construction.Litigation: Personal injury, insurance, clinical negligence, commercial litigation, employment disputes, landlord and tenant, product liability, professional negligence, construction disputes, debt collection, defamation, criminal law, alternative dispute resolution.

Private Client: Domestic conveyancing, family and matrimonial, inheritance tax, wills, probate and trust.

HBM SAYERS

13 Bath Street, Glasgow, G2 1HY **Tel:** (0141) 353 2121 **Fax:** (0141) 353 2181 **DX:** 47 Glasgow **Email:** mail@hmbsayers.com **Ptnrs:** 13 **Asst solrs:** 14 **Other fee-earners:** 7

HEGARTY & CO

48 Broadway, Peterborough, PE1 1YW **Tel:** (01733) 346333 **Fax:** (01733) 562338 **DX:** 16850 Peterborough **Email:** mail@hegarty.co.uk **Website:** www.hegarty.co.uk **Ptnrs:** 6 **Asst solrs:** 12 **Other fee-earners:** 24

HEMPSONS

33 Henrietta Street, Covent Garden, London, WC2E 8NH
Tel: (020) 7836 0011 **Fax:** (020) 7836 2783 **DX:** 40008 Covent Garden
Email: London@hempsons.co.uk **Website:** www.hempsons.co.uk

Clarendon House, 9 Victoria Avenue, Harrogate, HG1 1DY
Tel: (01423) 522331 **Fax:** (01423) 500733 **DX:** 11965 Harrogate 1
Email: Harrogate@hempsons.co.uk

Portland Tower, Portland Street, Manchester, M1 3LF
Tel: (0161) 228 0011 **Fax:** (0161) 236 6734 **DX:** 14482 Manchester 2
Email: Manchester@hempsons.co.uk

Managing partner:	Janice Barber
Senior partner:	Bertie Leigh
Number of partners:	27
Assistant solicitors:	80
Other fee-earners:	27

CONTACTS

Charity	Ian Hempseed (London)
Commercial	Ian Hempseed (London)
	Barry Blakemore (Harrogate)
Commercial Litigation	Hilary King (London)
Commercial Property	Graham Lea (London)
	Louise Holroyd (Harrogate)
	Alan Burns (Manchester)
Defamation	Mark Shaw (London)
Employment	Janice Barber (London)
	Kerry Devlin (Harrogate)
	Sean Reynolds (Manchester)
Healthcare	Bertie Leigh (London)
	John Lovel (Harrogate)
	Ann Meadowcroft (Manchester)
Medical Litigation	Bertie Leigh (London)
	Kathleen Wilson (Harrogate)
	Frances Harrison (Manchester)
Partnership	Lynne Abbess (London)

HEMPSONS SOLICITORS

THE FIRM: Hempsons is well known for its particular expertise in the field of medical and healthcare law, partnership work and charity law. The firm has long provided a comprehensive range of services to the NHS, the professions and charities. Clients include health authorities, NHS trusts, healthcare organisations, professional bodies, Royal Colleges and individual professionals.

PRINCIPAL AREAS OF WORK:

Clinical Litigation: The firm has long been renowned for its expertise in this field and handles matters relating to medical and dental negligence (all areas of hospital and general practice.) Also covered are class actions, disciplinary cases for NHS trusts, professional organisations and individual practitioners, codes of professional practice and medical crime. Hempsons is one of the national firms on the NHS Litigation Authority's restricted panel of healthcare solicitors to act in defence of clinical negligence claims.

Healthcare: The firm advises a range of healthcare organisations on all aspects of law and ethics, mental health and community care law, administrative law, NHS regulatory law and the constitution and formation of PCGs and PCTs.

Partnership: Advice to doctors and other professionals on the formation of partnerships and partnership agreements, the accession and retirement of partners, the dissolution of partnerships and partnership disputes.

Commercial Litigation/Defamation: Advice in relation to all forms of UK commercial disputes, including litigation in respect of employment, insurance, arbitration and ADR work. Defamation work is principally carried out for local authorities.

Commercial Property: The department handles commercial, institutional and professional property, including acquisitions and developments, grant, renewal and termination of leases, rent reviews and the Cost Rent Scheme for general practitioners, including funding proposed surgery developments. Recent deals have included the sale of a 250,000-sq. ft. factory retail outlet centre with a developed value of £60 million, the acquisition of substantial new office space for Lehman Bros. Ltd. and the funding and leasing of the London Zoo site.

Charity Law: A complete service to charities, large and small and currently numbering in excess of 100. This includes: formation and restructuring of charities; advice to trustees and management on legal duties and powers; updating constitutions; employment issues; dealings with the Charity Commission and the Inland Revenue; financial and commercial activities; trading subsidiaries; fundraising and appeals; disputed legacies. The firm has been active in running seminars on topics of concern to charities and other 'not for profit' organisations, including a new series of seminars on employment law.

Commercial Work: This team specialises in the commercial problems of NHS Trusts and Health Authorities, charities and professional clients.

Employment: The firm has a lively and proactive team of employment lawyers providing solutions to HR problems in the NHS, for employers and professionals, and those of our charity clients. Hempsons has particular experience in all types of discrimination work and all the relevant NHS circulars.

HENDERSON BOYD JACKSON WS

19 Ainslie Place, Edinburgh, EH3 6AU **Tel:** (0131) 226 6881 **Fax:** (0131) 225 1103
DX: ED27 EDINBURGH Video 0131 220 0523
Email: hbj@hbj.co.uk **Website:** www.hbj.co.uk

Managing partner:	Philip Dacker
Number of partners:	21
Assistant solicitors:	41
Other fee-earners:	31

AREAS OF PRACTICE

Corporate	32%
Commercial Property (incl. Housing)	31%
Litigation (incl. Sports Law)	20%
Maritime	12%
Private Client	5%

THE FIRM: The essence of Henderson Boyd Jackson is embodied in the partners and staff of the firm. Their entrepreneurial approach and adaptability have enabled the firm to maintain its growth rate at 25% during the past year. As the firm has grown, so too has the size of transactions in which it is involved. In 1999 the commercial property and corporate departments were involved in deals with a value in excess of £500m; many of which featured cross border expertise. While growth in traditional sectors has been consistent, the firm has also been keen to embrace emerging sectors of work and introduce new systems and technology to allow such instructions to be managed effectively for clients who include Standard Life Bank, Direct Line and Scottish Widows. Consequently, HBJ's on-line mortgage, uninsured loss and debt recovery teams have doubled in the last year. Capitalising on this experience, the firm is now planning systems that will handle volume litigation on a level not surpassed in Scotland. Further, through its maritime department HBJ were the first firm of solicitors to introduce lap top technology to a Court of Session case. By these means, HBJ were able to present in the Braer disaster, relevant evidence to all parties "on screen" thus negating the need for multiple reams of paper. Henderson Boyd Jackson were one of the first Scottish firms of solicitors to launch a web site in 1995. The firm has now embarked on a major reconstruction of the site and it is scheduled for re-launch in the summer of 2000. In accordance with the firm's general approach to technological developments, much of the latest available technology will be utilised to provide clients with access to the most current information available. Further, in response to market demands, the site will feature extranet capabilities for those clients who require such a facility and truly transactional options which can only serve to improve the service provided by the firm. 1999 also witnessed the launch of a new HBJ subsidiary – HBJ Consulting Limited. Billed as the electronic business strategist, HBJC was established to provide truly independent e-business consultancy. The new company works with clients to develop ways in which their businesses may be optimised utilising electronic means.

CONTACTS

Commercial Property .... Stephen Webster
Corporate .... Hugh Macmaster
Litigation .... Maggie Keith
Maritime .... James Lowe
Private Client .... Ross Mackay

PRINCIPAL AREAS OF WORK:

Corporate: The corporate partners continue to be involved in the full spectrum of transactions including MBOs, MBIs, joint ventures, start ups, acquisitions and disposals. With increasing M&A activity together with public company work, the department is clearly a growth area for the firm. The demand for expertise in the law of intellectual property is accelerating and HBJ's corporate department has ample resource to manage the needs of clients in this field. The corporate department's clients include a number of Scotland's leading public and private companies.

Commercial Property: The commercial property department has grown by almost 50% in the last three years while turnover has virtually doubled. The department continues to be involved in all aspects of commercial property transactions and incorporates the acclaimed housing law team. Clients include development, trading and investment companies, as well as a number of internationally recognised tenants.

Litigation: The litigation department was further augmented during 1999 with a view to significant development in 2000. The appointment of a number of solicitors will enable the firm to expand its service provision which currently comprises debt recovery, building arbitration, personal injury and increasingly insolvency instructions; plus Scotland's leading sports law team.

Maritime: The firm's maritime department is the recognised leader in its sector. The department continues to provide expertise in all aspects of maritime law from the drafting of ship building contracts and ship sale and purchase agreements to collisions, salvage, pollution, personal injury and port and harbour operations.

Private Client: The private client department has grown significantly in recent years as a result of increasing investment in this area. The department provides a full range of services including estate agency, trusts and executry advice and financial planning with its subsidiary organisation – HBJ Futurity Limited.

HENMANS

116 St. Aldates, Oxford, OX1 1HA
Tel: (01865) 722181 **Fax:** (01865) 792376 **DX:** 4311 Oxford 1
Email: welcome@henmans.co.uk **Website:** www.henmans.co.uk

Managing partner:	Sam Eeley
Senior partner:	Anthony Henman
Number of partners:	15
Assistant solicitors:	27
Other fee-earners:	14

AREAS OF PRACTICE

Professional Negligence and Commercial Litigation 29%
Personal Injury 26%
Property 17%
Private Client (including Family)/Charities/Trusts 16%
Corporate/Employment 12%

THE FIRM: Henmans' philosophy is to be extremely client focused to deliver exceptional levels of service. They achieve this through an emphasis on teamwork to ensure clients always have access to a specific partner with specialist support, and through an ongoing program of training to guarantee clients optimum advice and guidance. The firm's policy of bespoke services and controlled costs ensures that both corporate and private clients benefit from City level litigation standards at competitive regional prices.

PRINCIPAL AREAS OF WORK: The past five years have seen considerable growth in litigation and commercial work, and the firm has a growing reputation for employment law.

Litigation: The firm has a substantial insurance company client list. Personal injury and medical negligence litigation is strong, and there are a number of AVMA and personal injury panellists. The firm holds a Legal Aid Franchise.

Professional Negligence: Henmans has greatly expanded its specialist professional indemnity work on behalf of solicitors and other professionals, and has assembled a large team of lawyers (including a Higher Courts Solicitor-Advocate) with expertise in professional negligence litigation. The firm also undertakes an increasing volume of insurance and commercial litigation and provides specialist teams appropriate to each case and full litigation support, and has the capacity to handle marine insurance disputes.

Corporate: Henmans offers wide-ranging corporate work for both listed and private compnaies, including venture capital, sales and acquisitions. The corporate team is experienced in copyright, publishing and computer law, and the firm acts for several leading trade organisations. There is a strong commitment to the enterprise movement and to emergent businesses.

Commercial Property: Specialist advice focuses on planning and development, option deals, management

Continued overleaf

techniques, sales, purchases, landlord and tenant and employee relocation. Henmans' agricultural and land practice has developed to meet client needs both locally and nationally. The firm represents a number of substantial estates over a wide area of the country as well as Oxford colleges and national charities.
Employment: Employer and employee based work in employment tribunals and the courts is undertaken, as well as strategic employment work for major national companies.
Private Client: There is a strong private client department providing tax planning for high net worth individuals and all types of trust and probate work including contentious probate actions. Three members of the team belong to the society of Trust and Estate Practitioners. Matrimonial and family work is undertaken including a substantial amount of high quality financial work and a Legal Aid Franchise is now held for this type of work. Domestic property work is also offered in the full range of services for private individuals.
Charities: The firm's reputation for charity law is increasing with a specialist department concentrating on legacy recovery work, as well as charity start-ups, commercial ventures for charities, property matters and all types of advice to charity trustees. The firm's lawyers are effective, hard negotiators, respected by competitors for their integrity, expertise and enthusiasm to obtain the best possible results for their clients.

HENRY HYAMS & CO

7 South Parade, Leeds, LS1 5QX **Tel:** (0113) 243 2288 **Fax:** (0113) 242 9714 **DX:** 12028 **Ptnrs:** 8 **Asst solrs:** 5 **Other fee-earners:** 10

HENRY MILNER & CO

County House, 14 Hatton Garden, London, EC1N 8AT
Tel: (020) 7831 9944 **Fax:** (020) 7831 9941 **DX:** 53305 Clerkenwell

Managing partner:	Henry F. Milner
Senior partner:	Henry F. Milner
Number of partners:	1
Other fee-earners:	1

THE FIRM: Henry Milner has specialised exclusively in criminal defence work for 25 years. His practice offers a personal and experienced service, handling serious and complicated criminal cases of all types.

PRINCIPAL AREAS OF WORK: Work handled by the firm consists mainly of: all types of fraud cases including the defence of Customs and Excise prosecutions for diversion and VAT frauds; drugs importation and restraint order work; all other serious charges including murder, robbery and money laundering. Mr Milner also specialises in difficult High Court bail applications. The firm was involved in defending in all the 'Brink's Mat' trials and many other high profile cases of the 1980s and 1990s.

HEPTONSTALLS

7-15 Gladstone Terrace, Goole, DN14 5AH
Tel: (01405) 765661 **Fax:** (01405) 764201 **DX:** 28831 Goole
Email: legal@heponstalls.co.uk

1 Vicar Lane, Howden, DN14 7BP
Tel: (01430) 430209 **Fax:** (01430) 432101 **DX:** 700844 Howden
Email: legal@heponstalls.co.uk

9-11 Ropergate End, Pontefract, WF8 1JU
Tel: (01977) 602804 **Fax:** (01977) 602805 **DX:** 22255 Pontefract
Email: legal@heponstalls.co.uk

72 Mary Street, Scunthorpe, DN15 6LA
Tel: (01724) 289959 **Fax:** (01724) 289965 **DX:** 14732 Scunthorpe
Email: legal@heponstalls.co.uk

Senior partner:	Roger Beattie
Number of partners:	7
Assistant solicitors:	12
Other fee-earners:	14

AREAS OF PRACTICE

PI/Clinical Negligence	48%
Property/Common Law/Civil	22%
Matrimonial	13%
Criminal	9%
Trusts & Probate & Tax	8%

CONTACTS

Agriculture	M.G. Walker
Commercial/Property	R. Beattie
Criminal	A.S. Pinchbeck
Employment	A.S. Pinchbeck
Medical Negligence	J. Burman
Personal Injury	J. Burman
Tax/Probate and Trust	M.G. Walker
Welfare and Family	C. Luckett

THE FIRM: Heptonstalls, with its Goole and Pontefract offices and recently opened Scunthorpe office, is a major provider of legal services in Yorkshire and North Lincolnshire. The firm aims to ensure that clients receive an efficient personal and friendly service whatever their legal needs.

PRINCIPAL AREAS OF WORK:
Personal Injury and Clinical Negligence: This department has a leading regional reputation for claimnant work arising from medical treatment, road traffic accidents, industrial accidents and disease, defective products and related matters. Special interests include obstetrics and gynaecology, head and spinal injuries, and traumatic brain injury. John Burman is one of two members of the AVMA panel and both the Law Society Medical Negligence and Personal Injury Panels. The department has both clinical negligence and personal injury franchises in Goole and Pontefract.
Commercial/Agriculture: Advice on a wide range of business and commercial law including employment and commercial litigation. The firm has extensive experience in advising agricultural businesses on such areas as land law, conservation, agricultural tenancies and other aspects of land management.
Private Client: The firm advises on property, tax and family finance, wills, probate and trusts, landlord and tenant disputes, family and matrimonial law, and welfare benefits.

HERBERT SMITH

Exchange House, Primrose Street, London, EC2A 2HS
Tel: (020) 7374 8000 **Fax:** (020) 7374 0888 **DX:** 28
Email: enquiries@herbertsmith.com **Website:** www.herbertsmith.com

Senior partner:	Richard Bond
Worldwide figures:	
Number of Partners:	167
Number of Assistants:	453
Other Fee-earners:	247

CONTACTS

Administrative & Public Law Andrew Lidbetter
Commercial Arbitration ....Julian Lew
Commercial Litigation ....Harry Anderson
Competition and Regulation..Jonathan Scott
Construction and Engineering Michael Davis
Corporate Recovery ....Stephen Gale
Debt Capital Markets.................Dina Albagli
Employee Incentives ....Colin Chamberlain
Employment ....John Farr
Energy and Natural Resources Ted GreenoAlan Jowett
Equity Capital Markets........Caroline Goodall
Finance and Banking ....Clive Barnard
Fraud and Asset Tracing ......Sonya Leydecker
Insurance ....David HigginsMarian Pell
Intellectual Property ....Bill Moodie
Investment Funds..........................Nigel Farr
IT and E-commerce ....Nick Gardner
Life Sciences ....Andrew RichTim Steadman
Media ....Charles PlantStephen Wilkinson
Mergers & Acquisitions..........Michael Walter
Pensions...Ian Gault
Planning and Environment..Patrick Robinson
Private and Public International Law Campbell McLachlan
Projects/PFI/PPP ....Andrew Preece
Real Estate.....................Christopher Harrison
Tax ....David Martin
Telecoms ....Tim Bellis
Trusts & Charities.........................John Wood
WTO/World Trade Law...........Craig Pouncey

HERBERT SMITH

THE FIRM: Founded in 1882, Herbert Smith is an international law firm with offices throughout Europe and Asia. With 167 partners, 700 other lawyers, and a total staff of more than 1,600, it provides clients worldwide with industry-tailored advice. The firm is committed to providing high quality and innovative legal services to major corporations, governments, financial institutions and all types of commercial organisations. Herbert Smith offers an unrivalled balance of corporate, commercial and dispute resolution advice to its clients worldwide. Each of the firm's offices has access to the firm's global expertise, resources and capabilities.

PRINCIPAL AREAS OF WORK:

Corporate and Commercial: Herbert Smith provides a comprehensive range of legal services across all areas of corporate and commercial life. The firm is consistently highly placed in legal league tables and rankings. Frequently, its role puts it at the centre of industries which are reshaping, and the firm is well known for its innovative work in ground-breaking deals and restructurings. The firm has a long-standing reputation for advice on mergers, acquisitions and takeovers and is highly regarded for its expertise in corporate finance. In recent years, Herbert Smith has developed an increasingly significant role in the area of international finance and banking, particularly in the specialised field of international capital markets. Herbert Smith is widely acknowledged as a leading adviser on international energy law, and the firm is regularly involved in restructurings, privatisations and complex transactions around the world. Many such deals reflect Herbert Smith's strength in international projects and project finance where the firm's expertise also extends to developments and infrastructure projects of many kinds and on which it advises clients throughout the world. Other areas of corporate expertise include: competition law; corporate recovery; employment; European law; insurance; investment funds; media; telecommunications; pensions and share schemes; and trusts and charities.

Litigation and Arbitration: Herbert Smith enjoys a formidable reputation for its expertise in both domestic and international litigation and arbitration - a pre-eminent position it has held for several decades. The firm has consistently been ranked as the leading UK and Asian firm for commercial litigation. In this area the breadth of the firm's practice distinguishes Herbert Smith from its competitors. Areas of specialism include: administrative and public law; banking; civil fraud; construction; defamation; employment; energy; environment; information technology; insurance and reinsurance; intellectual property; public and private international law; professional indemnity; regulatory and compliance cases; and sport. The firm also has one of the most distinguished and broad-based international arbitration practices amongst the world's major law firms. Herbert Smith has experience before every type of court and tribunal, and conducts arbitrations in all parts of the world. It is the firm's consistent aim to add value to our client's business as a whole, and not to concentrate alone on the narrow issues in dispute. It uses alternative dispute resolution procedures in appropriate cases and several of our partners are accredited mediators.

Planning and Development: The firm's planning and development expertise is well recognised, following its involvement in a number of high-profile projects in recent years. Herbert Smith is also highly regarded in the field of institutional investment - buying, selling and managing national portfolios on behalf of some of the UK's leading property investors.

HEWITSON BECKE + SHAW

Shakespeare House, 42 Newmarket Road, Cambridge, CB5 8EP
Tel: (01223) 461155 **Fax:** (01223) 316511 **DX:** 133155 Cambridge 8
Email: mail@hewitsons.com (for all offices) **Website:** www.hbslaw.co.uk (for all offices)

7 Spencer Parade, Northampton, NN1 5AB
Tel: (01604) 233233 **Fax:** (01604) 627941 **DX:** 12401 Northampton

53 High Street, Saffron Walden, CB10 1AR
Tel: (01799) 522471 **Fax:** (01799) 524742 **DX:** 200300 Saffron Walden

Managing partner:	Alan Brett
Senior partner:	Ian Barnett
Number of partners:	51
Assistant solicitors:	40
Other fee-earners:	53

AREAS OF PRACTICE

Corporate...33%
Property 30%
Private 19%
Technology..18%

THE FIRM: Hewitson Becke + Shaw is one of the UK's leading corporate and commercial firms. It also has a substantial private client practice. With origins in 1865 and established in its current form in 1989, the firm continues to show substantial growth year on year through a policy of high investment in senior personnel and commitment to a dynamic corporate management structure and quality care systems providing flexibility and responsiveness to client needs. HB+S has a total of 110 lawyers, including 51 partners, meeting growing demand for its services regionally, nationally and internationally. The firm has established a leading reputation in many specific areas of law, including company/commercial, intellectual property, information technology, commercial litigation, commercial property, construction, employment, competition law, planning and pensions. Its private client section is one of the largest outside London. HB+S has been closely asso-

Continued overleaf

ciated over many years with the development of Cambridge and the 'Silicon Fen' region as a world-leading centre for hi-tech and IT-based business. The firm's legal expertise and professional approach matches that of major City of London firms, but HB+S' strategic locations in East Anglia and the East Midlands add the benefits of cost-effectiveness and extensive local knowledge. The firm provides a valuable international dimension to its client services through LawExchange International, a dynamic and growing network of like-minded firms in Europe, North America and the Pacific Rim which HB+S co-founded in 1994.

CONTACTS

Agriculture	Ian Barnett
Biotechnology	Simon Portman
Commercial Property	Alan Brett
Company/ Commercial	John Dix
Construction	Tim Richards
Debt Services	Clare Bangor-Jones
Employment	Nick Sayer
Investment Services	Andrew Lowin
IT & IP	Ian Craig
Litigation	Dominic Hopkins
Pensions	Clare Colacicchi
Planning & Environmental	Peter Brady
Private Client	Peter Ewart
Property Funding	Alan Brett
Residential Property	David Sabberton

Hewitson Becke+Shaw
SOLICITORS

PRINCIPAL AREAS OF WORK:

Commercial Property: The firm handles a large volume of commercial property work, from the construction of major commercial residential developments and science parks to small retail and industrial units. The firm is increasingly used by major concerns abroad, including Hong Kong. Work includes the acquisition, development and letting of all manner of commercial sites. The firm has particular expertise in complex funding mechanisms and joint ventures.

Company/Commercial: Work includes mergers and acquisitions, company structuring and restructuring, venture and development capital investment, management buy-outs/buy-ins, rights issues, Stock Exchange flotations, European Union and International law, merger control, OFT/Commission investigations, joint ventures, pensions, employee share option and incentive schemes, partnerships and insolvency. The firm acts for a significant number of public limited companies as well as owner-managed businesses and is doing an increasing amount of UK-related work from an expanded US client base.

Intellectual Property: The firm advises on all aspects of obtaining, exploiting and enforcing intellectual property rights, with particular expertise in computer hardware and software, biotechnology, pharmaceutical, film, music and book publishing industries.

Information Technology: HB+S acts for users and suppliers including major IT companies, software houses and ISPs. The firm handles licensing, distribution, development, support and other procurement issues, as well as disputes, data protection and e-commerce.

Private Client: Work includes administration of estates, trusts, tax, wills, enduring powers of attorney, pensions, charities, residential property advice, landed estates, court of protection and matrimonial.

Litigation: The services are provided through eight groups each consisting of staff dedicated to one of the following areas of specialisation: banking, intellectual property, personal injury, crime and family. The firm acts nationally for several major clearing banks.

Employment: Work includes injunctions, service contracts, pensions, dismissal, redundancy, compensation for unfair dismissal, profit sharing and share option schemes and general employee benefits. The firm is a member of the Employment Lawyers Association and six members of the firm are individual members of the Association.

Agriculture: Work includes the granting of development options by landowners, joint venture and share farming agreements, farm partnerships, taxation and environmental matters, sales and tenancies and mineral exploitation. The firm has a significant number of landed estates and farming clients.

Bloodstock: The firm advises on all aspects of bloodstock law with particular emphasis on property transactions and general litigation.

Planning & Environmental: Work includes planning appeals and local plan inquiries, advising developers, investors, local authorities, conservation and amenity groups, and individuals. The firm has two members of the Law Society's Specialist Planning Panel.

Residential Property: Work includes sales, purchases and mortgages of freehold/leasehold houses/flats for private clients and institutions as well as builders and developers.

Investment Services: Work includes a comprehensive range of services for individuals, company executives, private trustees, pension fund trustees and charities.

Debt Services: Work includes consultancy, outsourced credit control, pre-legal service, debt recovery.

HEWITT & GILPIN

Thomas House, 14-16 James Street South, Belfast, BT2 7GA
Tel: (028) 9057 3573 **Fax:** (028) 9057 3574 **DX:** 2000 NR Belfast 2
Email: law@hewittandgilpin.co.uk **Website:** www.hewittandgilpin.co.uk

Managing partner:	Gavin Pantridge
Senior partner:	David Hewitt
Number of partners:	7
Assistant solicitors:	2

THE FIRM: Formed in 1930, Hewitt and Gilpin is a general legal practice providing a comprehensive range of services to corporate, business and private clients throughout Northern Ireland, Great Britain, the Republic of Ireland and the European Union.

PRINCIPAL AREAS OF WORK: The range of services includes all aspects of domestic and commercial conveyancing; company and commercial law (including intellectual property, computer contracts and European law); employment matters; civil litigation (ranging from construction disputes to public health and consumer law cases); charities (including church matters) and debt recovery. Services for the private client include wills, trusts and probate; family matters (including wardship, adoption and child care and the welfare of the elderly and disabled) and general financial advice.

HEXTALL ERSKINE

28 Leman Street, London, E1 8ER
Tel: (020) 7488 1424 **Fax:** (020) 7481 0232 **DX:** 562 CITY
Email: info@hextalls.com **Website:** www.hextalls.com

Senior partner:	John Bundy
Number of partners:	21
Assistant solicitors:	15
Other fee-earners:	20

AREAS OF PRACTICE

Insurance Related	80%
Other Commercial Dispute Resolution	10%
Corporate Services	5%
Private Client Services	5%

CONTACTS

ADR	Anna Dalglish
Commercial Litigation	David Hadfield
Commercial Property	Tony Millson
Company/Commercial	Tony Millson
Construction & Engineering	Jill Heaton
Employers' & Public Liability	Charles Martin
Employment	Anne Lumsden
Family	Anne Lumsden
Insurance Litigation	Bill Jarvis
Policy Wordings	Bill Jarvis
Product Liability	Bill Jarvis
Professional Indemnity	Stuart White
Property Risks	Jill Heaton
Reinsurance	Robert Wilson
Sports	Andrew Deans
Travel, Tourism & Leisure	Andrew Deans
Wills, Probate & Tax Planning	Tony Millson

THE FIRM: Hextall Erskine is a leading provider of specialist legal services primarily to the insurance industry. The firm was founded in 1949 and over the years has steadily expanded its activities into most areas of claims and advisory work within the London market but also nationally and internationally. Clients include major UK and international insurance companies, Lloyd's syndicates, private corporations and local authorities. The firm also handles non-contentious work for corporate and private clients. Hextall Erskine is a founder member of a national consortium of insurance claims specialists developing compatible case management systems to provide the insurance industry with on-line claims information. The firm is also a founder member of the Centre for Dispute Resolution (CEDR) and a corporate member of the Forum of Insurance Lawyers (FOIL).

PRINCIPAL AREAS OF WORK:
Insurance: Hextall Erskine deals with all aspects of insurance litigation/dispute resolution. Specialisms include insurance and reinsurance disputes, product liability, professional indemnity, employers' and public liability, industrial diseases, health and safety, property risks, sport, leisure and travel, policy wordings and advice, legal expenses, ADR.
Commercial Dispute Resolution: The firm handles commercial litigation/dispute resolution in a range of sectors including automotive, chemicals, engineering and construction.
Corporate Services: Specialisms include company commercial, commercial property and employment law.
Private Client Services: Main areas of expertise include family law, wills, trusts, probate, tax planning and conveyancing.

INTERNATIONAL CONNECTIONS: Hextall Erskine has ready access to foreign lawyers and has established a network of contacts in most key jurisdictions. In 1999 the firm set up a formal multi-national partnership - Clausen Miller Europe - with law firms in the US (Clausen Miller) and Europe (La Giraudière Larroze et Associés) to ensure synergy of legal service on a multi-jurisdictional level.

RECRUITMENT & TRAINING: Hextall Erskine is committed to training and development of all staff and this year achieved 'Investors in People'. This commitment extends to clients and the firm provides added value benefits such as briefings, in-house training, and seminars on relevant areas of law to help clients keep abreast of developments affecting their business. The firm recruits four trainees a year. Applications by letter and CV to Davina Haydon.

HICKMAN & ROSE

144 Liverpool Road, London, N1 OLA **Tel:** (020) 7700 2211 **Fax:** (020) 7609 6044
DX: 122234 Upper Islington emergencies: 01459 138106
Email: mail@hickmanandrose.co.uk

Number of partners:	5
Assistant solicitors:	15
Other fee-earners:	8

AREAS OF PRACTICE

Crime	50%
Serious Fraud	15%
Police Actions	10%
Prisoners Rights	10%
Discrimination	5%
Mental Health	5%
Public Law	5%

CONTACTS

Crime	Liz Sargeant
Discrimination Law	Sarah Ricca
Mental Health	Matthew Evans
Police Actions	Hope Liebersohn
Prisoners Rights	Liz Sutcliffe
Public Law	Daniel Machover
Serious Fraud	Ben Rose

THE FIRM: Hickman & Rose is a leading criminal law and human rights firm. It delivers a consistently high quality of work across the full spectrum of criminal justice issues. The firm has an excellent reputation in serious crime and commercial fraud and is renowned for its work on behalf of prisoners.

PRINCIPAL AREAS OF WORK:
Crime: A substantial criminal caseload is run with total commitment to qualify and client care. A small group of highly experienced lawyers specialises in larger matters.
Serious Fraud: Serious and international fraud work is backed by the commitment to hold prosecution authorities to the letter and the spirit of the law.
Police Actions: This team has fought and won many cases involving police wrongdoing.
Prisoners Rights: A tough and combative prison rights practice has succeeded on securing improvements in conditions for many prisoners.
Public Law/ECHR: Specialist litigation in the UK and Strasbourg challenging human rights abuses across the criminal justice system.
Mental Health: A growing team works for those detained under the Mental Health Act or affected by Community Care legislation.
Discrimination: A newly established team specialises in sex, race and disability discrimination within the criminal justice and mental health systems.

HIGGS & SONS

Blythe House, 134 High Street, Brierley Hill, DY5 3BG **Tel:** (01384) 342100 **Fax:** (01384) 342000 **DX:** 22751 Brierley Hill **Email:** law@higgs-and-sons.co.uk **Ptnrs:** 23 **Asst solrs:** 15 **Other fee-earners:** 11 **Contact:** Mr David Morgan • Established 1875. Legal Aid Franchise. ISO 9002. Company/commercial; insolvency; commercial/residential/agricultural property; planning; environment; employment/sex discrimination; personal injury/medical negligence; motor accidents; commercial & consumer litigation; crime; family/matrimonial/children; education; charities; trusts/probate/estate and tax planning.

AREAS OF PRACTICE

Common Law	48%
Domestic conveyancing	16%
Probate, Wills & Trusts	13%
Company/Commercial	12%
Commercial Conveyancing	11%

R. & J.M. HILL BROWN & CO

3 Newton Place, Glasgow, G3 7PU **Tel:** (0141) 332 3265/333 0636 **Fax:** (0141) 332 2613 / 332 0414 **DX:** 512207 Glasgow-Sandyford Place **Email:** info@hillbrown.co.uk **Ptnrs:** 6 **Asst solrs:** 1 **Other fee-earners:** 1 **Contact:** Mr Jack Cummins or Mr Peter Lawson • General practice specialising in licensing work for licensed trade and the entertainment industry.

AREAS OF PRACTICE

Licensing	35%
Domestic/Commercial Conveyancing	25%
Trusts and Securities	21%
General Court	19%

H

HILL DICKINSON

Pearl Assurance House, 2 Derby Square, Liverpool, L2 9XL
Tel: (0151) 236 5400 **Fax:** (0151) 236 2175 **DX:** 14129 Liverpool 1
24 Hour Emergency Number: (01426) 179 605
Email: Law@HillDicks.com **Website:** www.hilldickinson.com

34 Cuppin Street, Chester, CH1 2BN
Tel: (01244) 896600 **Fax:** (01244) 896601 **DX:** 19991 Chester
24 Hour Emergency Number: (01426) 179 605

50 Fountain Street, Manchester, M2 2AS
Tel: (0161) 278 8800 **Fax:** (0161) 278 8801 **DX:** 14487 Manchester 2
24 Hour Emergency Number: (01426) 179 605

Sun Court, 66/67 Cornhill, London, EC3V 3NB
Tel: (020) 7695 1000 **Fax:** (020) 7695 1001 **DX:** 98940 Cheapside 2
24 Hour Emergency Number: (01426) 179 605

Managing partner:	David Wareing
Senior partner:	Paul Walton
Number of Partners:	76
Assistant solicitors:	63
Other fee-earners:	70

AREAS OF PRACTICE

Litigation (inc Insurance/Construction/Professional Negligence)	50%
Commercial Property/Planning & Environmental	15%
Shipping	15%
Company/Commercial/Pensions/ Tax/Intellectual Property/PFI	10%
Health/Medical Negligence	10%

CONTACTS

Area	Contact
Commercial	Elizabeth Mackay
Corporate	Andrew Smithson
Health	Allan Mowat
Insurance	Mike McKenna
	Simon Parrington
Marine & Cargo	John Hulmes
	Julia Marshall
Private Client	Mike Quinn
Property/Construction	David Swaffield
	David Chinn

THE FIRM: Founded in 1810, Hill Dickinson is now one of the largest commercial law firms in the North West, providing a portfolio of specialist legal advice to both the domestic and international market. It is fundamental to the Hill Dickinson philosophy to care for clients, whilst delivering a highly professional, cost effective service. ISO 9001 accreditation reflects a demonstrated and on-going commitment to client care. The practice has a strong and marked reputation in the insurance, litigation, company commercial, commercial property, marine and transport domain, and provides specialists to deal with an increasingly wide range of legal requirements. The firm has a total of 400 staff, including more than 70 partners. Operations have been substantially extended over recent years with offices now in Liverpool, Manchester, Chester and the City of London. All offices have full conference facilities, on-line communication links, an extensive reference library and access to a number of electronic legal data sources. Literature, outlining in detail, all aspects of the firm's activities, is available on request, and members of the firm are pleased to have a preliminary discussion on any specific requirement.

PRINCIPAL AREAS OF WORK: With a wealth of specialist advisers, the firm undertakes a wide range of legal work in the commercial and private domain and is structured into specialist groups.
Insurance: One of the largest departments of its kind in the country, Hill Dickinson acts for most major insurers and, through them, a large proportion of their corporate and individual policy holders. The department has the capacity and resources to deal with a wide range of litigation issues, including the most complex of 'test' or multi-party actions, and to react quickly to incidents or claims requiring immediate legal assistance.
Health: The firm has one of the UK's largest medico-legal practices, acting on behalf of health authorities, NHS trusts and other health service bodies. The firm is a member of the panel of solicitors maintained by the National Health Service Litigation Authority and was the first in the country licensed to provide health/medical negligence elements within training contracts.
Property & Construction: The Hill Dickinson property and construction team provides legal advice across the full range of property matters, including construction and engineering projects. They act for retailers, manufacturers, service providers, developers, investors, contractors and public sector clients. They have experience in retail, office, industrial, leisure and residential projects and provide specialist advice in relation to environmental and planning issues.
Commercial: The commercial group advises on a broad range of matters as diverse as intellectual property, European law, franchising, employment, pensions and PFI. They are one of the leading commercial litigation firms in the North West and where litigation is inevitable the commercial litigation team provides full support.

Corporate: Lawyers in the corporate group provide advice on all aspects of corporate law including company formation, mergers, acquisitions, management buy-outs and buy-ins, venture capital, flotation and insolvency.

Marine & Cargo: Recognised as one of the leading specialist shipping solicitors in the UK, Hill Dickinson has provided advice to both national and international clients since 1810. The department also has well-established experts handling cargo and transit matters, and consequently has the resources to offer a truly comprehensive service.

Private Client: The firm retains a strong private client base, providing specialist advice on for example, tax and estate planning, wills, trusts, probate and financial planning matters.

HILL TAYLOR DICKINSON

Irongate House, Duke's Place, London, EC3A 7HX
Tel: (020) 7283 9033 **Fax:** (020) 7283 1144 **DX:** 550
Email: enquiry@htd-london.com **Website:** www.htd.co.uk

Managing partner:	Rhys Clift
Chairman:	Robert Wallis
UK	
Number of Partners:	19
Assistants/Associates:	24
Other fee-earners:	10
International	
Number of Partners:	5
Assistants/Associates:	6

AREAS OF PRACTICE

Shipping & Commodities 56%
Insurance 18%
Commercial Transactional 17%
Personal Injury 8%
Others 1%

CONTACTS

Commercial Property ......Richard Taylor
Commodities ......Jeff Isaacs
Company/Commercial ......Malcolm Entwistle
Insurance ......Tim Taylor
Personal Injury ......Maria Pittordis
Shipping ......John Evans
......Stephen Cropper
Shipping ......Robert Wallis
......Andrew Johnson

Hill
Taylor
Dickinson
solicitors

THE FIRM: Hill Taylor Dickinson is a commercial firm servicing the business and financial community in the United Kingdom and internationally. The firm is based in the City of London, and also has offices in Dubai and Greece. The firm has expanded considerably through the 1990s. The overseas offices have been established and new areas of business have been developed. This growth has been achieved by organic growth within the firm complemented by external recruitment (including at partner level). Clients range from major international corporations to owner managed businesses. Critical to the success of the firm's relationship with all of them is close partner involvement and understanding of their operations and markets. Hill Taylor Dickinson is a progressive and dynamic firm seeking to provide an effective personal service to both national and international clients and a commercial approach to legal problems and their resolution.

PRINCIPAL AREAS OF WORK: Hill Taylor Dickinson's practice is entirely commercial.

Company/Commercial and Finance: The firm's transactional work includes company/commercial and financing, including venture capital, leasing and asset finance, ship building and finance, corporate buy-outs and buy-ins, as well as commercial property. Its clients include banks and other financial institutions, both City-based and overseas, insurers, employers' organisations and a wide variety of corporate clients, notably in the leisure, manufacturing and publishing sectors.

Personal Injury, ITF and Employment: This department acts mainly for employers, insurers, owners and P&I clubs in shipping and transport and a wide variety of industries. It deals with mass and individual claims. The department's work includes preventative and practical advice, including the drafting of accident reporting documents and procedures, drafting contractual clauses and employment contracts, safety policies and a whole spectrum of employment and personal injury claims.

Shipping: Hill Taylor Dickinson's expertise in shipping, an area in which it acts for shipowners, P&I clubs, insurers, as well as major oil companies, makes it one of the foremost practices in this field. The shipping department handles the full range of commercial problems arising out of international trade and transport, including major maritime casualties, disaster litigation, pollution claims, charterparty disputes and cargo claims.

Commodities: The firm has also significantly increased its practice in commodities disputes in recent years. Its clientele in this area includes trading houses and a number of trade associations.

Insurance and Reinsurance: This division acts for underwriters, insurance companies, brokers and assureds. London – both Lloyd's and the companies market – is a major source of the division's work, but the firm derives its clients from all over the world. Hill Taylor Dickinson's reputation in marine insurance is well established.

HOBSON AUDLEY

7 Pilgrim Street, London, EC4V 6LB
Tel: (020) 7450 4500 **Fax:** (020) 7450 4545 **DX:** 401 London
Email: lawyers@hobsonaudley.co.uk **Website:** www.hobsonaudley.co.uk

Managing partner:	Gerald Hobson
Number of partners:	13
Assistant solicitors:	20
Other fee-earners:	5

AREAS OF PRACTICE

Corporate Finance/Company Commercial 36%
Dispute Solution 22%
Property 21%
Innovation and Technology 15%
Employment 6%

THE FIRM: A City firm specialising in business law, with a broad range of international and UK corporate clients, and ranking highly in the league table for new issues. Hobson Audley combines strength in corporate law, litigation and commercial property with specialist areas such as employment, intellectual property, innovation and technolgy, multimedia and electronic commerce. The firm's commercial property group offers specialist advice in the areas of development, finance, institutional investment and urban regeneration. The firm's broad range of legal skills is coupled with an international perspective and an awareness of business needs.

Continued overleaf

PRINCIPAL AREAS OF WORK:

Company: The firm provides a full range of corporate law services to public and private companies, investors and buy-out teams. Transactional work includes mergers and acquisitions, MBOs, Stock Exchange work, venture capital finance, banking and debt financing.
Commercial: The firm advises on joint ventures, distribution and agency, franchising, UK and EU competition law, international trade, terms of business, general contract law.
Litigation and Dispute Solution: The firm enjoys a strong reputation for litigation and handles substantial actions, arbitrations and appeals up to the House of Lords. It also has practical experience in ADR and mediation.
Commercial Property: The commercial property group has a depth of experience in the private and public sectors, with a strong bias towards development, finance, property joint ventures and institutional investments.
Intellectual Property: Copyrights, design rights and registered designs, patents, trademark and service mark infringement actions, passing off, trade libel and comparative advertising, protection and misuse of confidential information, franchising, know-how and show-how, technology transfer agreements, disputes and arbitration.
Information Technology: The firm acts for a well-established client base ranging from multi-nationals to small businesses in the high technology, computing, multimedia, publishing, telecommunications and biotech fields, and advises on IT contract negotiation, telecommunications, electronic commerce, multimedia and interactive software contracts.
Employment: Employment contracts, disciplinary matters, maternity rights, discrimination, health and safety issues, redundancy, employment legislation relating to transfer of businesses, contentious employment matters including termination arrangements, unfair and wrongful dismissal claims and industrial action.
Insolvency Services: Contentious and non-contentious aspects of corporate insolvency law and practice in areas such as receiverships, company voluntary arrangements, liquidations, administrations, cross-border insolvencies and directors' responsibilities.

INTERNATIONAL CONNECTIONS: In August 1997, the firm formed a multinational partnership with Faegre & Benson LLP of Minneapolis under the name of Faegre Benson Hobson Audley. Association with Faegre & Benson LLP has enhanced the firm's international contacts with the introduction of a number of substantial US corporations whose UK interests are now represented by Faegre Benson Hobson Audley.

LANGUAGES: French, German, Italian, Spanish and Portuguese.

CLIENTELE: The firm's client base is drawn principally from the UK, continental Europe and North America. Clients are involved in manufacturing, high technology, computing, telecommunications, publishing, marketing services, healthcare, oil and gas, oil field services, banking, the financial services and securities industries, building societies and property investment and development.

CONTACTS

Commercial Property	Simon Smith
	Godfrey Bruce-Radcliffe
	Malcolm Headley
Corporate Finance/Company Commercial	Max Audley
	Tony Gordon
	Nick Mallet
	Paul Taylor
Dispute Solution	Roger Hopkins
	Gerald Hobson
Employment	Caroline Whiteley
Innovation & Technology (including IP)	Robert Bond
	Claire Poll
	Edward Hoare

H

G.L. HOCKFIELD & CO

41 Reedworth Street, Kennington Rd, London, SE11 4PQ **Tel:** (020) 7735 0489 **Fax:** (020) 7820 1707 **DX:** 33252 **Ptnrs:** 4 **Asst solrs:** 4 **Contact:** James Garvey • Principal areas of work are housing litigation, claimant personal injury and professional negligence work.

AREAS OF PRACTICE

Housing	48%
Personal Injury	37%
Professional Negligence	12%
Miscellaneous Areas	3%

HODGE JONES & ALLEN

Twyman House, 31-39 Camden Road, London, NW1 9LR
Tel: (020) 7482 1974 **Fax:** (020) 7267 3476 **DX:** 57050 Camden Town
Email: hja@hodge-jones-allen.co.uk **Website:** www.hodge-jones-allen.co.uk

Senior partner:	Patrick Allen
Number of partners:	21
Assistant solicitors:	23
Other fee-earners:	19

AREAS OF PRACTICE

Crime	28%
Personal Injury & Clinical Negligence	36%
Family	20%
Housing & Landlord & Tenant Litigation	7%
Employment & Discrimination	7%
Property/Corporate	2%

THE FIRM: Hodge Jones & Allen was established in 1977 and has expanded rapidly, especially since moving to new premises in September 1997. The firm has a particular reputation for legal aid work. It has been involved in a number of high profile and leading cases, notably cases involving racial discrimination and personal injury cases arising from the King's Cross fire and the Marchioness disaster. The firm is handling three major group claims including Gulf War Syndrome.

PRINCIPAL AREAS OF WORK:

Criminal: The criminal team deals with the full range of magistrates and crown court work. Specialist fields include fraud, extradition, homicide, drug related offences, youth work and mentally disordered offenders. Solicitors can be contacted outside of office hours by the emergency phone number (01459) 111192.
Employment: The employment team deals with all types of employment and discrimination claims. All members of the team do their own advocacy. The team also provides non-contentious advice predominantly to voluntary and statutory sector employers.
Family: The family team covers all aspects of family work including property disputes following separation or divorce, conflicts over children, care proceedings and applications for emergency injunctions. Five mem-

bers of the team are on the child care panel and two on the Lord Chancellor's Department's Child Abduction Panel. All solicitors belong to the Solicitor's Family Law Association. Mediation is now offered by accredited family mediators

Housing: The housing team deals with disrepair, homelessness claims including applications for judicial review, possession cases and all aspects of landlord and tenant work, principally on behalf of tenants. The team is led by Wendy Backhouse who was Chair of the Housing Law Practitioner's Group for four years.

Personal Injury: The team acts for claimants, particularly those who have been injured in road accidents, tripping cases, accidents at work or as a result of medical negligence and claims against the police. The team has four solicitors on the Personal Injury Panel and two on the Clinical Negligence Panel. The multi-party unit is handling three group actions - Gulf War Illness, Kerrin Point and Organophosphate/sheep dip. In each action the firm holds a generic contract with the Legal Aid Board. It also acts for large numbers of children with MMR claims.The police claims unit led by Tina Salvidge deals with unlawful arrest, assault, malicious prosecution and false imprisonment. It is handling compensation claims for the Bridgewater Four. The personal injury team is led by Patrick Allen who is a member of the Executive Committee of the Association of Personal Injury Lawyers.

Property: This teams handles residential and commercial property work for private individuals, local businesses and charities.

Other: Other significant areas of work include corporate and contractual advice; representation at mental health tribunals; public law; wills and probate.

RECRUITMENT & TRAINING: The firm runs a structures and popular training scheme for trainee solicitors. The annual intake is presently five. Interviews take place in October for training places the following September.

CONTACTS

Civil Claims against the Police	Tina Salvidge
Clinical Negligence	Nicola Mooney
Crime	Nigel Richardson
Employment/Discrimination	James Lynas
Family and Children	Lynn Roberts
Housing Litigation	Wendy Backhouse
Mental Health Tribunals	Louise Coubrough
Multi-party (PI/Med Neg/Product Liability)	Patrick Allen
Personal Injury	Louise Whitfield
Property/Corporate	Charles Pigott

H

HOLLINGWORTH BISSELL

10 Storey's Gate, London, SW1P 3AY **Tel:** (020) 7233 3300
Fax: (020) 7233 3336

Number of partners:	2

AREAS OF PRACTICE

Contracts	75%
Commercial Property	15%
Sales Promotions	10%

THE FIRM: Hollingworth Bissell is a two partner firm providing legal services (both general and specialist rail related) to the railway industry.

PRINCIPAL AREAS OF WORK:

Commercial - General: Sales and acquisitions of companies and businesses, joint ventures, shareholders' agreements, reorganisations, procurement contracts, advice on foreign railway privatisations, intellectual property rights, computer contracts, agency contracts, conditions of trading and advice on the legal aspects of advertising, including the running of sales promotions.

Commercial - Rail Specific: Advice on refranchising, licence conditions, station redevelopments, agreements for access to rail facilities, connection agreements, agreements for railway services, traffic agreements.

Property: Station trading and general commercial property advice.

HOLMAN FENWICK & WILLAN

Marlow House, Lloyds Avenue, London, EC3N 3AL
Tel: (020) 7488 2300 **Fax:** (020) 7481 0316 **DX:** 1069 London City EC3
Email: holmans@hfw.co.uk **Website:** www.holmanfenwick.com

Senior partner:	Archie Bishop
UK	
Number of partners:	52
Assistant solicitors:	62
Trainee solicitors:	12
Other fee-earners:	23
International	
Number of partners:	26
Assistant solicitors:	18
Other fee-earners:	10

AREAS OF PRACTICE

Shipping (Admiralty and Marine Litigation)	50%
Commercial Litigation/ International Trade	20%
Corporate/Marine Finance and related non-contentious work	15%
Reinsurance	15%

HOLMAN FENWICK & WILLAN

THE FIRM: Holman Fenwick & Willan is an international law firm and one of the world's leading specialists in maritime transportation, insurance, reinsurance and trade. The firm is a leader in the field of commercial litigation and arbitration and offers comprehensive commercial and financial advice. Founded in 1883, the firm today is one of the largest operating in its chosen fields with an extensive team of lawyers world-wide, and a reputation for excellence and innovation.

PRINCIPLE AREAS OF WORK:

Marine: Holman Fenwick & Willan has one of the world's largest admiralty and marine litigation practices with a wealth of experience in the field. Areas of expertise include charter parties, bills of landing, other carriage contracts and related disputes.

Admiralty and Crisis Management: The firm has a pre-eminent reputation as a leader in this field and operates a 24-hour emergency service geared to providing an immediate response to maritime casualties worldwide. Specialists deal predominantly with collisions, fire and explosions; salvage, towage, wreck removal and recovery; personal injury; damage to oil terminals, rigs and offshore structures; pollution, environmental damage and clean up.

Insurance and Reinsurance: The firm advises on coverage issues, policy interpretation, captive insurance/reinsurance, errors and omissions coverage, insolvency and schemes of arrangement, contract drafting and regulatory advice.

Continued overleaf

Commercial Litigation and Arbitration: The firm also deals with commercial litigation, arbitration and disputes in the areas of banking and financial disputes, engineering and construction claims, coal, oil and gas, environmental claims, professional negligence, corporate fraud, insolvency and schemes of arrangement, and sovereign debt and asset recovery.
International Trade and Commodities: Holman Fenwick & Willan's international trade and commodity practice provides a service to meet the needs of the international trading and financial community. This includes advising on sale, purchase and futures contracts, quality claims, damage and shortfall disputes, swaps and barter trade, trade finance, EU competition law, and transportation agreements.
Corporate and Financial: The firm's corporate and financial lawyers provide a wide ranging service in company formations, corporate finance and acquisitions, project and asset finance, joint ventures, agency and distribution agreements, EC and competition law, intellectual property and information technology, and commercial property.
Air, Road and Rail: Holman Fenwick & Willan also has extensive experience of air and land based carriage, advising operators, financiers and underwriters on transactions, litigation and regulatory issues.
Energy: The firm's energy team is well equipped to advise on exploration, development and production issues, refining, transport and sales.

INTERNATIONAL CONNECTIONS: The firm has a network of offices throughout the world, in London, Paris, Rouen, Nantes, Pireaus, Hong Kong, Shanghai and Singapore. Its network of offices enables the firm to assist its clients at a local and regional level and the firm has considerable experience in guiding litigation in numerous jurisdictions. The firm's unique style ensures proper partner involvement in its client's affair, and an emphasis on understanding clients' business and commercial requirements in order to maintain a close commitment to their needs.

CONTACTS

Admiralty & Crisis Management .... Archie Bishop
.... James Gosling
Air, Rail and Road .... Glenn Moore
.... Patricia Martin
Commercial Litigation .... Peter Bennett
.... Simon Congdon
Corporate & Financial .... Nick Hutton
.... Jay Tooker
Energy .... Roderic O'Sullivan
.... Keith Michel
EU & Competition Law .... Philip Wareham
Insolvency .... Noel Campbell
Insurance and Reinsurance .... Ian McKenna
.... John Duff
International Trade and Commodities .... Patricia Martin
.... Simon Blows
Marine Litigation .... Robert Wilson
.... Hugh Livingstone
Personal Injury .... Alan Walls
Property .... Nick Barr
Ship & Asset Finance .... Stephen Drury
.... Dan Tindall

H

HOLME ROBERTS & OWEN

Heathcoat House, 20 Savile Row, London, W1X 1AE
Tel: (020) 7494 5600 **Fax:** (020) 7287 9344
Email: kohlerb@hro.com **Website:** www.hro.com

Managing partner:	Bruce R. Kohler
Number of partners:	4
Assistant solicitors:	10
Other fee-earners:	2

CONTACTS

Corporate Finance .... Paul G. Thompson
Finance .... Martha Collins Rolle

THE FIRM: Holme Roberts & Owen LLP is a leading Colorado law firm with offices in Denver and elsewhere in the state and in Salt Lake City, Utah. The London office, which was established nine years ago, operates as a multi-national partnership under the name Holme Roberts & Owen (HRO). Partners and assistants include US and English qualified lawyers with extensive experience of multi-jurisdictional transactions throughout Europe. HRO's clients represent a variety of industries including cable television, telecommunications and other high technology sectors.

PRINCIPAL AREAS OF WORK: HRO's practice focuses on market entry strategies, joint ventures and acquisitions, corporate and project finance, public and private securities offerings and other complex multi-jurisdictional commercial transactions.

HOLMES HARDINGHAM

22-23 Great Tower Street, London, EC3R 5HE
Tel: (020) 7283 0222 **Fax:** (020) 7283 0768 **DX:** 636
Email: firstname.surname@HHLaw.co.uk

Managing partner:	David Johnston
Senior partner:	Adrian Hardingham
Number of partners:	11
Assistant solicitors:	11
Other fee-earners:	8

THE FIRM: Holmes Hardingham is a commercial and maritime law firm with an international practice, concentrating on litigation and arbitration related to shipping and transportation.

PRINCIPAL AREAS OF WORK: The firm was founded 11 years ago and has more than doubled in size in that time. Further expansion is expected in response to a growing work-load. All 11 partners and 19 other fee earners handle a variety of shipping and transport related matters including: carriage of goods by sea, road and air; commercial and admiralty litigation and arbitration; marine and goods in transit insurance; collision and salvage; commodity sale disputes; ship sale, purchase and finance; oil and gas exploration; and yachts and pleasure craft.

HOLMES MACKILLOP

109 Douglas Street, Glasgow, G2 4HB **Tel:** (0141) 226 4942 **Fax:** (0141) 204 0136 **DX:** GW50
Email: general@homack.co.uk **Website:** www.holmesmackillop.co.uk **Ptnrs:** 8 **Asst solrs:** 4
Other fee-earners: 3 **Contact:** KDB McLew • All areas of commercial practice. Specialities include agricultural law, corporate and charity law, property development and leasing, commercial litigation and family law.

AREAS OF PRACTICE

Commercial Property 40%
Corporate 20%
Litigation 20%
Private Client 20%

HOOD VORES & ALLWOOD

The Priory, Church St, Dereham, NR19 1DW **Tel:** (01362) 692424 **Fax:** (01362) 698858 **DX:** 45050 **Ptnrs:** 6 **Asst solrs:** 1 **Other fee-earners:** 6

HOOPER & WOLLEN

Carlton House, 30 The Terrace, Torquay, TQ1 1BS **Tel:** (01803) 213251 **Fax:** (01803) 296871 **DX:** 59204 Torquay (2) **Email:** lawyers@hooperwollen.co.uk **Website:** www.hooperwollen.co.uk **Ptnrs:** 10 **Asst solrs:** 5 **Other fee-earners:** 9 **Contact:** Mrs P. C. Bear • Specialising in conveyancing, family, child care, litigation, employment, PI, probate, trust, commercial, company, private client. Agency instructions accepted.

HORWICH FARRELLY

National House, 36 St Ann Street, Manchester, M60 8HF
Tel: (0161) 834 3585 **Fax:** (0161) 834 3630 **DX:** 14322 Manchester 1
Email: info@horwichfarrelly.co.uk **Website:** www.horwichfarrelly.co.uk

Managing partner:	Nigel Yates
Senior partner:	Stephen Boylan
Number of partners:	10
Assistant solicitors:	9
Other fee-earners:	47
Total staff:	121

THE FIRM: Since its formation in 1969, Horwich Farrelly has grown to become one of the North West's leading niche practices. The firm specialises in insurance litigation, commercial litigation, property and employment law whilst also carrying out a wide variety of private client work. Sound legal and commercial advice, excellent service and an intuitive understanding of their clients' needs, forms the basis of the firm's success.Investment in people and the recruitment process has given Horwich Farrelly a significant advantage. It has ensured that prospective, as well as current clients, benefit from an array of legal skills, delivered by people who are easy to talk to. Horwich Farrelly has achieved the Investor in People standard, and it is committed to providing the highest quality of service to all clients. A commitment to on-going investment in case management technology has enabled the firm to expand and compete with the largest firms. However the firm's success is also based on never losing site of the importance of providing a personal friendly service.

HOUGHTON & CO

Penn House, 10 Broad Street, Hereford, HR4 9AP **Tel:** (01432) 352202 **Fax:** (01432) 355513 **DX:** 17237 Hereford 1 **Email:** houghton@lawyersonline.co.uk **Ptnrs:** 1 **Asst solrs:** 1 **Other fee-earners:** 4 **Contact:** Mrs R. Houghton • The firm's reputation stems from Rosalie Houghton's Oral Contraceptive Pill Group Litigation and a substantial medical negligence case load. Founding director of Lawyers on Line, a dedicated internet service provider for lawyers. Members of APIL & SCL.

AREAS OF PRACTICE

Medical Negligence	85%
PI	15%

HOWARD & HOWARD

42 Wimpole Street, London, W1M 7AF
Tel: (020) 7486 6610 **Fax:** (020) 7486 6620 **DX:** 83308 West End 2
Email: wimpole@compuserve.com **Website:** www.wimpole.com

Managing partner:	Barry Howard
Number of partners:	1
Other fee-earners:	3

AREAS OF PRACTICE

Employmant	50%
Licensing and Commercial Conveyancing	50%

THE FIRM: Howard & Howard is a niche practice founded in 1992, offering a personal and efficient service. The firm handles major commercial property transactions and acts for both multinational corporations as well as individuals in the field of employment law. Discrimination and unfair dismissal are particular specialities.

PRINCIPAL AREAS OF WORK: The firm specialises in employment law; occupational health and occupational medicine; health and safety; licensing; commercial conveyancing and other commercial matters relating to the leisure industry. One member of the firm has considerable expertise in drafting employment contracts and all employment documents. She also specialises in occupational medicine.

LANGUAGES: Spanish, French, Italian, Dutch and Afrikaans.

CLIENTELE: Multinationals, major corporations, small firms, professional practices and other individuals.

HOWARD KENNEDY

19 Cavendish Square, London, W1A 2AW
Tel: (020) 7636 1616 **Fax:** (020) 7499 6871 **DX:** 42748 Oxford Circus North
Email: webmaster@hk.law.co.uk **Website:** www.hk.law.co.uk

Senior partner:	Trevor J. Newey
Number of partners:	40
Assistant solicitors:	32
Other fee-earners:	27

AREAS OF PRACTICE

Property	47%
Corporate/Commercial	30%
Litigation	20%
Trust and Estate Planning	3%

CONTACTS

Company/Commercial	Alan Banes
Construction	Irvinder Bakshi
Intellectual Property and Information Technology	John Fleming
International	Anthony Slingsby
Litigation	Craig Emden
Project Finance	Philip Leacock
Property	Paul Springall
Trust and Estate Planning	Roger Seaton

THE FIRM: Established in the mid-1930s, Howard Kennedy is a well-regarded firm. Primarily a commercial practice, the firm offers a wide range of services for its clients, which include public companies, public authorities, entrepreneurial businesses and private individuals. The firm provides an international service to clients and professional advisers. All the major European languages are spoken. Howard Kennedy is a registered Sponsor of the London Stock Exchange.

PRINCIPAL AREAS OF WORK:

Corporate/Commercial: The department deals with a high calibre of corporate and corporate finance work which includes stock exchange flotations, public share offerings on the London Stock Exchange and the Alternative Investment Market including those under the Enterprise Investment Scheme, Venture Capital Trusts, mergers and acquisitions, reconstructions and amalgamations, Stock Exchange Yellow Book, The City Code on Take-Overs and Mergers, venture capital and private equity. The department also advises on shareholder disputes in conjunction with the litigation department. The department combines a high degree of technical know-how and personal partner-led service, and frequently deals with the large city firms. Commercial services include commercial contracts, employment law, agency, distribution and franchising agreements, share option and incentive schemes, consumer protection legislation, corporate taxation and EU law.

Intellectual Property (IP) and Information Technology (IT): The department's work covers a wide range of IP, IT and technology matters, including: patents, copyright, design rights and trade marks; computer hardware, software and networking issues; internet and multimedia; drafting and negotiating agreements relating to technology.

Litigation: A broad range of disputes is handled, for both commercial and private clients, domestic and international. Work includes commercial arbitration, mediation, ADR, and disputes relating to company and partnership matters, shareholders, commercial contracts, education, negligence, insolvency, property, including landlord and tenant actions, professional negligence, employment, banking, insurance related matters, intellectual property and debt recovery. Private litigation including matrimonial problems, family law, personal injury claims, defamation, inheritance trust-related disputes, and immigration.

Commercial Property: A strong and experienced department includes a number of partners who handle large-scale commercial and residential developments and investments. Besides acting for banks, property developers and investors, this department acts for several major retail, leisure, restaurant and hotel chains. The department has considerable expertise in office, industrial and all other types of property, as well as in the related specialities of secured lending, planning, licensing, compulsory purchase, compensation, housing law and tenancy problems. Expertise extends to VAT and other tax-related aspects of property transactions.

Construction: All aspects of contentious and non-contentious work covered. Non-contentious advice on developments, appointments, contracts, bonds, warranties and guarantees on projects in the UK and abroad. Full litigation, arbitration and ADR service in respect of disputes arising both in the UK and internationally. Clients range from state governments, local authorities and institutions to developers, contractors, sub-contractors and individual entrepreneurs.

Trust and Estate Planning: The department's work includes estate planning, wills, trusts (including offshore arrangements), probate and personal taxation.

HOWARTH GOODMAN

8 King Street, Manchester, M60 8HG **Tel:** (0161) 832 5068 **Fax:** (0161) 833 2917 **DX:** 14308 Manchester 1
Email: sb-kmm@howathgoodmn.u-net.com **Ptnrs:** 4 **Asst solrs:** 4 **Other fee-earners:** 10
Contact: Steve Baddiel (Manchester) or Peter Brogan (Preston) • Specialist firm in Housing Association Law.

HOWELL & CO

1341 Stratford Road, Hall Green, Birmingham, B28 9HW
Tel: (0121) 778 5031 **Fax:** (0121) 777 3967 **DX:** 714513 Hall Green 2
Email: mail@howell-solicitors.co.uk **Website:** www.howell-solicitors.co.uk

Number of partners:	2
Assistant solicitors:	5
Other fee-earners:	5

AREAS OF PRACTICE

Crime	70%
Litigation	15%
Conveyancing	10%
Other	5%

THE FIRM: Established in 1979, Howell & Co provides a comprehensive legal service to both commercial and private clients. The firm deals with property law dealing both with residential and commercial conveyancing and litigation specialising in white collar crime, large scale frauds including Inland Revenue, Customs and Excise and Serious Fraud Office cases and Police Commercial Fraud Departments. The firm is a member of the Legal Services Commission's Fraud and High Cost Panel.

PRINCIPAL AREAS OF WORK:

Inland Revenue Hansard Cases, White Collar Crime: Defence work in relation to Inland Revenue, Customs and Excise and Serious Fraud Offence prosecutions. Also defence work in relation to commercial frauds prosecuted by the police commercial fraud departments. The firm acts for solicitors, accountants, surveyors, other professional people and non professional people.

Crime (non white collar): Magistrates' Court and Crown Court work. The firm has acted in numerous rape, armed robbery and murder cases and recently acted for a professional person accused of gross negligence manslaughter. The firm also defends prosecutions relating to importation and supplying of drugs.

Litigation: The work includes litigation in the County Court, High Court and other Tribunals for both private clients and commercial clients and a practice in regulatory work especially Trading Standards.

Family: Divorce, ancillary relief, cohabitee disputes and Children Acts matters.

Private Clients: Work includes drafting of wills, probate and administration of estates.

Property and Conveyancing: Work includes residential and commercial conveyancing for both private and commercial clients including major national developers and housing associations dealing with both the conveyance of plots and the purchase of development land.

HOWELLS

427-431 London Road, Sheffield, S2 4HJ
Tel: (0114) 249 6666 **Fax:** (0114) 250 0656 **DX:** 10584

The Avery Buildings, 15-17 Bridge Street, Sheffield, S3 8NL
Tel: (0114) 249 6666 **Fax:** (0114) 249 1455 **DX:** 10584

42 Spital Hill, Sheffield, S4 7LG
Tel: (0114) 249 6666 **Fax:** (0114) 249 6700 **DX:** 10584

Managing partner:	Jonathon Whybrow
Number of partners:	12
Assistant solicitors:	15
Other fee-earners:	20

AREAS OF PRACTICE

Civil & Community	33%
Crime	33%
Family	33%

CONTACTS

Civil & Community	Guy Baddeley
Crime	Danny Simpson
Family	Alyson Siddall

THE FIRM: Established in 1979 to specialise in protecting the rights of individuals, the firm has grown to be one of the country's largest legal aid practices with legal aid quality franchises in all available areas of work.

PRINCIPAL AREAS OF WORK:

Crime: The criminal department is now one of the largest in the country having four partners and a further seven fee earners. Work includes all criminal matters with particular expertise in public order offences, serious fraud, juveniles and youth, cases involving mentally disordered defendants and road traffic law. Increasing caseload in civil liberties work including miscarriages of justice, prisoners rights and judicial reviews.

Family Law: The family department is the largest in Sheffield and one of the largest in the country. The department is divided into two teams covering children and matrimonial law. The children team consists of eight fee earners (including three partners) of whom five are members of the Law Society's Children's Panel. The team covers all areas of child law, including private and public law children cases, adoption and education advice and representation covering special educational needs, school admissions and exclusions appeals, grant disputes and higher and further education proceedings. Jonathan Whybrow (Head of the Children Team) is a co-author of Emergency Remedies in Family Courts and contributory editor to Children Law and Practice. A former civil servant, he worked on the Children Act 1989 as it was divised and enacted.The matrimonial team consists of seven fee earners (including two partners) of whom four are members of The Law Society's Family Law Panel. The team deals with all aspects of matrimonial law with particular expertise in domestic violence and financial relief of matrimonial breakdown. The family department also offers a family mediation service and has two qualified mediators.

Civil and Community: The department provides a wide range of legal services for individuals through its litigation and community law teams.

Litigation: Services include accident claims, industrial disease claims, clinical negligence and actions against the police. A strong team consists of three partners supported by a further six fee earners. The team has three Law Society personal injury panellists and one clinical negligence panellist.

Community Law: The team provides specialist advice and representation in housing, employment and equal opportunities law, immigration, mental health and welfare benefits. The firm has one of the few specialist housing law teams in South Yorkshire and is a member of the South Yorkshire Housing Practitioners Group and deals with possession proceedings, disrepair, harassment by landlords etc. The employment team specialises in advising employees in the full range of employment problems and are members of The Discrimination Law Association, Equal Opportunities Commission Equality Exchange, Stonewall and Lawyers for Liberty. The immigration team has been the leading firm of immigration lawyers in the region for 20 years and deals with the full range of immigration cases. The team is led by John Donkersley who has over 10 years immigration law experience and is South Yorkshire's leading immigration lawyer. The mental health team are members of The Law Society Mental Health Review Tribunal Panel and specialise in representing patients before tribunals and provide general mental health law advice and help. An experienced welfare benefits team is able to provide an in-depth service advising clients on all benefits administered by the Government or the Local Authority together with judicial reveiws, advocacy and representation.

HOWES PERCIVAL

Oxford House, Cliftonville, Northampton, NN1 5PN
Tel: (01604) 230400 **Fax:** (01604) 620956 **DX:** 12413 Northampton
Email: law@howes-percival.co.uk **Website:** www.howes-percival.co.uk

Senior partner:	Michael Percival
Number of partners:	27
Assistant solicitors:	27
Other fee-earners:	35

AREAS OF PRACTICE

Company Commercial	30%
Commercial Property	25%
Commercial Litigation	20%
Employment	10%
Insolvency	10%
Private Client	5%

CONTACTS

Commercial Litigation	Ashwin Mody
Commercial Property	Roger Burnell
Company Commercial	Brandon Ransley
Employment	Nick Jew
Insolvency	Gerald Couldrake
Private Client	Michael Percival

THE FIRM: Howes Percival is a 27 partner commercial law firm with offices in Leicester, Milton Keynes, Northampton and Norwich. It is the firm's aim to be the leading provider of commercial legal services in each of the locations that it has a presence. The vast proportion of new instructions received by Howes Percival are from referrals or recommendations by banks, accountants, financial institutions and existing clients. It is not uncommon for Howes Percival to be instructed by clients who they have previously acted against in corporate or commercial transactions. Seminars and weekend workshops are regularly given for clients and prospective clients. Specialist in-house seminars are also given to particular clients as well as to fee-earners on new areas of law. Clients are kept up-dated by regular newsletters and an employment extranet will soon be available. Howes Percival is willing to act as an agent for other solicitors in High Court and County Court cases.

PRINCIPAL AREAS OF WORK:
Company Commercial: Howes Percival provides wide-ranging company and commercial services, with notable experience in corporate finance, acquisitions and disposals, MBO's and MBI's. A variety of outsourcing agreements are also handled. All aspects of banking law are dealt with and insolvency is a particular specialism.
Commercial Litigation: A variety of commercial litigation services are provided, including specialised work handling directors' disqualifications for the insolvency service of the DTI. A debt recovery service is also provided. The firm has two partners who have been accredited by the Centre for Dispute Resolution as mediators.
Licensing: The firm is recognised as an expert in liquor and entertainment licensing and provides a range of bespoke training courses, including the National Licensee Certificate, to leisure industry clients.
Employment: Employment law matters are undertaken and advice is given on taxation issues. Employee relocation services are also offered. The firm's private client work has seen substantial growth, particularly in trusts, probates and independent financial services. White collar crime is another area of expertise
Commercial Property: Commercial property expertise is strengthened by a specialism in environmental law.

CLIENTELE: The top quality work that is carried out by the firm places them in a market whereby they are able to attract instructions from major companies such as DaimlerChrysler (UK) Ltd, Scania (Great Britain) Ltd, Shanks Group plc and Start-Rite Shoes Ltd. City standards of work are provided to our clients at prices lower than those of the city. Howes Percival acts for both private and public companies of varying sizes throughout the UK and abroad. It also has informal links with law firms around the world. Clients include major UK financial institutions, manufacturers, retailers, drinks companies, transport companies, businesses in the leisure industry as well as private clients with substantial assets.

RECRUITMENT & TRAINING: Howes Percival aims to develop all four of its offices with a recruitment drive at all levels, in order to further improve its position as a forward-thinking, high quality provider of legal services.

HUGH JAMES FORD SIMEY

Arlbee House, Greyfriars Rd, Cardiff, CF10 3QB
Tel: (029) 2022 4871 **Fax:** (029) 2038 8222 **DX:** 33300 Cardiff
Email: cardiff@hjfs.co.uk **Website:** www.hjfs.co.uk

Managing partner:	Matthew Tossell (Wales)
Senior partner:	Russell Jenkins (Wales)
Number of partners:	59
Assistant solicitors:	55
Other fee-earners:	90

AREAS OF PRACTICE

Claimant Personal Injury	30%
Commercial & Insurance Litigation	25%
Commercial Property	12%
Commercial Services	15%
Private Client	10%
Construction & Professional Indemnity	10%

CONTACTS

Agency	Alun Jones
Claimant Personal Injury	Andrew Harding
Commercial Litigation	Gareth Williams
Commercial Property	David Roberts
Commercial Services	William Snowdon
Construction & Professional Indemnity	Michael Jefferies
Employment	Alison Love
Insolvency	Catrin Thomas
Private Client	Cherry Wright

THE FIRM: Hugh James Ford Simey is one of the largest regional practices in the UK. Formed in May 1999 as a result of the merger between Hugh James, one of the 'big four' Welsh firms, and Ford Simey Daw Roberts, the firm provides a comprehensive service for the whole of South Wales and the West country. It offers its clients expertise in over 30 court locations. The firm has a national reputation for its commercial and insurance litigation practice. It also has a strong reputation for its commercial property and insolvency work and has a rapidly growing commercial practice. The firm is proud of its commitment to private client work and the Community Legal Services Scheme and continues to be involved in high profile litigation. Hugh James Ford Simey is a dynamic firm which has an enthusiastic and forward thinking approach to its work and the way in which its services are provided, without sacrificing traditional qualities. It has and will continue to recruit experts in a range of legal disciplines to meet the needs of national and local commercial clients.
Highlights of 1999/2000: In Wales 1999 was the year of the Millennium Stadium and the Rugby World Cup. The Building and Construction Group, headed by partner Mike Jefferies, was responsible for handling more than 200 commercial contracts for Millennium Stadium plc and the Welsh Rugby Union. This included the contract to build the Stadium itself and the contract that secured Graham Henry as the Welsh Rugby Union Coach until 2003. The group has been joined by one of the UK's top construction experts, barrister Paul Newman. Several new teams have been formed within the firm in line with the continuing expansion and development of the Commercial Services Group which is headed by Bill Snowdon in Cardiff and Geoff Adams in Methyr Tydfil.

PRINCIPAL AREAS OF WORK:

Sports: A dedicated Sports Law Unit has been launched in response to the increasing demand for commercial advice from professional sportsmen and women and the clubs and other organisations that employ them.
E-Business: A specialist e-business team has been formed which offers clients an e-Business Support Package. The team has already acted for a number of major e-business start-ups including Web2u Corporation and tvresource.it.limited and is instructed by national and international IT companies. The firm is itself moving into the area of e-business and is working in partnership with HSBC to provide legal services on a national basis via an interactive web-site.
Employment: The firm's Employment Services Package was launched by the specialist employment team, headed by partner Alison Love. Following a full assessment of their needs, a tailor-made package of legal services is agreed with clients at a fixed cost.
Secured Lending: A new division dealing with secured lending has been created within the Commercial Property Group in response to the needs of numerous lenders such as Halifax plc who instruct the firm on a national basis.
Insurance: The expansion of the firm's Insurance Division has continued with three new members joining the team. David Groves and Maureen Harvey have both joined as partners and were formerly at Veale Wasborough. Glynn Hannaford has also joined as an assistant solicitor. Following the firm's successful prosecution of the claims for lead plaintiffs in the miners' respiratory litigation, the year saw the successful conclusion of the negotiation with the DTI resulting in the signing of the handling agreement which will see compensation paid to tens of thousands former mineworkers.
Personal Injury: The firm's reputation in the field of claimant personal injury work has this year resulted in an increase in union clients. The firm has been appointed by the Royal College of Nursing as its panel solicitors for Wales and the South West. The firm continues to be instructed in areas of high profile litigation with teams advising the Gerona Aircrash Action Group, handling the cervical smear claims against an NHS Trust and advising groups of claimants following explosions and disasters.Highlighting the firm's commitment to providing a complete service to those who have suffered catastrophic injury, particularly head injury, and it's holisitic approach to such work is the appointment of a qualified social worker who specialises in working with the disabled.

HUGH POTTER & COMPANY, SERIOUS INJURY SOLICITORS

14-32 Hewitt, Manchester, M15 49B **Tel:** (0161) 237 5888 **Fax:** (0161) 237 5999

HUMPHREYS & CO

14 King St, Bristol, BS1 4EF **Tel:** (0117) 929 2662 **Fax:** (0117) 929 2722 **DX:** 78239
Email: lawyers@humphreys.co.uk **Website:** www.humphreys.co.uk **Ptnrs:** 5 **Asst solrs:** 5
Other fee-earners: 2 **Contact:** Mr R.A. Humphreys • Principal areas of work are company/commercial, litigation, employment, intellectual property, reinsurance, property, insurance, personal injury, entertainment, professional (including clinical) negligence, competition and insolvency.

HUMPHRIES KIRK

Glebe House, North Street, Wareham, BH20 4AN
Tel: (01929) 552141 **Fax:** (01929) 556701 **DX:** 49700 Wareham
Email: wareham@humphrieskirk.co.uk **Website:** www.humphrieskirk.co.uk

Senior partner:	M.J. Greenleaves
Number of partners:	9
Assistant solicitors:	8
Other fee-earners:	10

AREAS OF PRACTICE

Trusts & Probate	30%
Conveyancing	29%
Commercial	15%
Litigation	10%
Matrimonial	9%
Personal Injury	6%
Criminal	1%

THE FIRM: Humphries Kirk is one of the most innovative firms in the South, which manages to retain a successful balance between catering for substantial commercial clients and the traditional private client. Humphries Kirk was one of the first firms to qualify for ISO 9001 in this region. Other offices located in Swanage, Dorchester, Bournemouth and London (Consulting rooms).

PRINCIPAL AREAS OF WORK:

Company/Commercial: Intellectual property (the firm acts for the Design Business Association), mergers and acquisitions (including international).
Commercial Litigation: All work from industrial tribunal work up to High Court, international litigation and arbitrations.
Banking and Financial Law: The firm acts for a number of substantial German financial institutions and also for several German savings banks.
Other Areas: Full range of private client services, including an in house nominee company, trustee company and off-shore client account. The firm has on staff trained mediators, family mediators and arbitrators.

INTERNATIONAL CONNECTIONS: The firm has associated offices in Versailles, France and Cologne, Germany. It maintains a network of relationship lawyers worldwide.

LANGUAGES: French, German, Italian, Spanish.

HUNT & COOMBS
35 Thorpe Rd, Peterborough, PE3 6AG **Tel:** (01733) 565312 **Fax:** (01733) 552748 **DX:** 12302 **Email:** reception@hunt-and-coombs.co.uk
Website: www.hunt-and-coombs.co.uk **Ptnrs:** 10 **Asst solrs:** 14 **Other fee-earners:** 8

HUNTERS

9 New Square, Lincoln's Inn, London, WC2A 3QN
Tel: (020) 7412 0050 **Fax:** (020) 7412 0049 **DX:** 61
Email: email:@hunters-solicitors.co.uk **Website:** www.hunters-solicitors.co.uk

Senior partner:	H.A. Woodeson
Number of partners:	10
Assistant solicitors:	4
Other fee-earners:	10

THE FIRM: Although founded in the early 18th century, the firm is a thriving modern partnership, serving a broadly-based private and institutional clientele.

PRINCIPAL AREAS OF WORK: The firm has a long-established reputation in private client, charity, banking security, and matrimonial work; and an increasing emphasis on commercial property, company/commercial law, employment and litigation.
Private Client: Work includes trusts, tax planning, tax returns, heritage and agricultural property, wills, probate and conveyancing.
Charities: Work includes acting for major charities; registrations, schemes, trading arrangements, and housing associations.
Banking Security Work: Work includes security work for banks.
Matrimonial: Work includes all aspects, but particularly cases with a substantial financial element.
Commercial Property: Work includes acquiring and selling property investments, and business tenancies.
Company/Commercial Law and Employment: Work includes private companies, partnerships, commercial contracts, acquisitions and disposals, employment, contracts and staff handbooks, unfair and wrongful dismissal, redundancy, service occupancies, equal opportunity and race discrimination.
Litigation: Work includes wide range of High Court/County Court work; breach of contract; landlord and tenant disputes, and enforcement of security.

INTERNATIONAL CONNECTIONS: Close relationship with firms in Australia.

RECRUITMENT & TRAINING: One trainee solicitor with a good degree is recruited annually. Fortnightly seminars. Wide spread of work and direct client contact.

HUNTON & WILLIAMS
61/63 St. John Street, London, EC1M 4AN **Tel:** (020) 7427 7850 **Fax:** (020) 7427 7872

HUTCHINSON MAINPRICE

80 Ebury Street, London, SW1W 9QD
Tel: (020) 7730 8705 **Fax:** (020) 7730 8706
Email: reception@hutchinson-mainprice.co.uk
Website: www.hutchinson-mainprice.co.uk

Number of partners:	3
Assistant solicitors:	2
Other fee-earners:	3

THE FIRM: Hutchinson Mainprice was established on 1 May 1999, when Hugh Mainprice joined Alastair Hutchinson & Co, a leading firm of property law specialists in Belgravia. With the increasing complexity of VAT in relation to property, the new firm will be in a unique position to offer an unrivalled service in the property field. Alastair Hutchinson has had over 20 years experience in property law, while Hugh Mainprice, who assisted in the drafting of the original VAT legislation in 1972, has acted for more clients in the VAT Tribunals, the High Court, the Court of Appeal, the House of Lords, and the European Court of Justice than any other solicitor in the UK. These have included a large number of cases involving property which resulted in a change in the law or Customs' practice.

INTERNATIONAL CONNECTIONS: The firm has an associated office in Quinta do Lago.

LANGUAGES: Japanese, French, German, Punjabi, Swahili.

HUTTONS

16-18 St Andrews Crescent, Cardiff, CF1 3DD
Tel: (029) 2037 8621 **Fax:** (029) 2038 8450 **DX:** 33065 CARDIFF
Email: email@huttons-solicitors.co.uk

Senior partner:	Stuart Hutton
Finance partner:	Clare Strowbridge
Number of partners:	4
Associates:	3
Assistant solicitors:	4
Other fee-earners:	4

THE FIRM: A leading litigation practice in Wales, noted for plaintiff personal injury and medical negligence law; family and childcare law and criminal defence advocacy. 'Leaders in their Field' (Chambers) in medical negligence and criminal law. Awarded membership of several Law Society Panels, AVMA and Spinal Injuries Association. Franchised by the Legal Aid Board. Expanding commercial division.

PRINCIPAL AREAS OF WORK: The firm provides specialist litigation services.
Personal Injury and Medical Negligence: RTA cases (including CFAs) to brain injury in children and multi-party actions.
Litigation: Emphasis on miscarriages of justice including police actions and judicial review; employment disputes, housing disrepair, landlord and tenant and general contractual disputes. Family and Child Care: Divorce, children matters, high value ancillary relief applications and Court of Appeal work.
Criminal Advocacy: High profile murder cases including the Lynette White murder trial and the Tooze murder and appeal case.
Commercial: Business formation, acquisitions and sales, partnership disputes, property matters, insolvency, employment, probate and wills.

AREAS OF PRACTICE

Criminal Advocacy	35%
Family/Childcare	20%
Litigation	20%
PI/Medical Negligence	15%
Commercial	10%

CONTACTS

Commercial	Clare Stowbridge
Criminal Advocacy	Stuart Hutton
Family/Childcare	Gerard Griffiths
Litigation	David Evans
PI/Medical Negligence	Tim Musgrave

IAIN SMITH & COMPANY

18-20 Queen's Road, Aberdeen, AB15 4ZT **Tel:** (01224) 645454 **Fax:** (01224) 646671 **DX:** AB4 Aberdeen **Email:** info@iainsmith.com **Website:** www.iainsmith.com **Ptnrs:** 5 **Asst solrs:** 9 **Other fee-earners:** 8 **Contact:** Peter A. Macari (Managing Partner) • An investor in people. Specialist expertise in corporate, insolvency, employment law, commercial law, commercial litigation and debt recovery.

AREAS OF PRACTICE

Corporate/Commercial	30%
Litigation/Family Law	25%
Conveyancing - Commercial	15%
Conveyancing - Domestic	15%
Wills & Executives	10%
Insolvency	5%

I

IAN DOWNING FAMILY LAW PRACTICE

8 The Crescent, Plymouth, PL1 3AB **Tel:** (01752) 226224 **Fax:** (01752) 226213 **Email:** ian.downing@virgin.net **Ptnrs:** 1 **Asst solrs:** 1 **Contact:** Ian Downing • The practice deals exclusively in family law matters, particularly higher asset divorce and separation issues and cohabitation, child and Inheritance Act cases.

ILIFFES BOOTH BENNETT

Lovell House, 271 High Street, Uxbridge, UB8 1LQ
Tel: (01895) 230941 **Fax:** (01895) 811926 **DX:** 45105 Uxbridge
Email: Reception.lh@ibblaw.co.uk **Website:** www.ibblaw.co.uk

Managing Partner:	Steven Booth
Number of partners:	20
Assistant solicitors:	29
Other fee-earners:	39

THE FIRM: With offices in Middlesex, Berkshire, Buckinghamshire and Essex, this firm is one of the largest practices in the South East outside central London. Its principal aim is to deliver efficient and effective legal services to an extensive business and private client community. It has particular strengths in commercial property and litigation including employment, private client work, personal injury litigation, family and criminal law.

PRINCIPAL AREAS OF WORK:
Commercial Property: All aspects of commercial property work including purchase and sale of retail, office and industrial property, lease negotiations and renewals, portfolio acquisitions and disposals, major construction and development work. Agricultural property dealing. Secured lending work for banks and financial institutions.
Company and Commercial: A broad range of corporate work, mainly sales and acquisitions, restructuring and mergers, start-ups, commercial contracts, company formations, franchise and distribution agreements.
Litigation: An extensive litigation practice acting for both business and private clients. For business clients, the work includes company and partnership disputes, commercial property and construction matters, negligence claims, insolvency, landlord and tenant actions and substantial debt recovery. Private client litigation includes divorce and financial relief, and all matters relating to children, personal injury work and criminal defence cases including white collar crime.
Private Client: Wills, probate, estate administration, taxation advice, trusts. Residential conveyancing and independent financial advice.
Employment: Service contracts, unfair and wrongful dismissal, redundancy, discrimination at work, contracts of employment and pensions, compromise agreements.

LANGUAGES: French, Gujerati, Hindi, Punjabi, Urdu.

CLIENTELE: Business clients range from major public companies to family business and individual entrepreneurs. High net worth private clients form a significant part of the client base although the firm remains committed to the availability of legal aid services where appropriate.

RECRUITMENT & TRAINING: IBB has a full training programme for all professional and support staff, being fully aware of the need to maintain an appropriately skilled and motivated workforce. Trainee solicitors are offered a structured period of training with extensive professional supervision and maximum client contact. Member of Lawnet - a federation of independent law firms and ISO 9002 accredited.

AREAS OF PRACTICE

Commercial and Agricultural Property	25%
Family/Matrimonial	18%
Crime	17%
Company/Commercial and Commercial Litigation	13%
Personal Injury	9%
Residential Conveyancing	9%
Wills, Probate, Tax, etc.	9%

CONTACTS

Commercial Litigation	Rosemary Jeffries (01494) 790045
Commercial Property	Susan Mawson (01895) 207803
Commercial Property Litigation	Andrew Olins (01895) 207800
Company/Commercial	David Jackson (01895) 207804
Crime	Tom Brownlow (01895) 207844
Family	Shon Roberts (01895) 207863
Personal Injury Litigation	Tony Wiseman (01895) 2207858
Residential Conveyancing	Gillian Outram (01494) 790013
Wills, Probate, Tax and Trusts	Gillian Murray (01494) 790024

INCE & CO

Knollys House, 11 Byward Street, London, EC3R 5EN
Tel: (020) 7623 2011 **Fax:** (020) 7623 3225 **DX:** 1070 London City EC3
Email: firstname.surname@ince.co.uk **Website:** www.ince.co.uk

Administration Partner:	Allan Hepworth
Senior Partner:	Peter Rogan
Number of partners:	53
Assistant solicitors:	70
Other fee-earners:	45

AREAS OF PRACTICE

Shipping/Aviation	39%
Insurance/Reinsurance/ Professional Indemnity	28%
Energy/Construction/Environment/ Pollution/Personal Injury	16%
Corporate/Private Client/Property	6%
International Trade/Commodities	6%
Sale & Purchase	5%

CONTACTS

Admiralty	James Wilson, Richard Sayer, Chris Beesley
ADR	Jonathan Lux, Gillie Belsham
Arbitration	Richard Williams
Aviation	Anthony Fitzsimmons, Mike Pollen
Construction	David Sheehan, Chris Jefferis
Corporate	Nick Gould
Dry Shipping	Richard Williams, Paul Herring, Bob Deering, Chris Moore
Energy	David Steward, Chris Sprague
Environment and Pollution	Colin de le Rue, Ian Chetwood
EU law	Denys Hickey, Anthony Fitzsimmons
Insurance & Reinsurance	Peter Rogan, Julian Hill
International Trade & Commodities	Stuart Shepherd, Clare Calnan
Litigation, Commercial	Richard Sayer, Peter Rogan
Personal Injury	Chris Sprague, Gillie Belsham, Charlotte Davies
Professional Indemnity	David Rutherford, Andrew Ottley, Charlotte Davies
Property and Private Client	Albert Levy
Ship Finance	Malcolm Strong, Tony Suchy
Shipbuilding	Mike Pollen, David Steward

THE FIRM: Ince & Co has an unparalleled worldwide reputation in maritime and insurance law and handles, on a global basis, cases covering all aspects of international trade and energy. Ince & Co is based in the City of London with offices in Hong Kong, Shanghai and Singapore serving Asia and the Pacific Rim, and in Piraeus serving the Greek shipping community and the eastern Mediterranean. Close links with a network of leading international lawyers complements the firm's service to clients around the world. A feature of the firm's service is that clients deal with the same partner from initial advice to trial. Appropriate efforts are made to avoid the expense of litigation, including the use of alternative dispute resolution (ADR). Ince & Co has a reputation for clear legal analysis and tenacious imaginative litigation, arbitration and ADR. Crucially underpinning the legal expertise is a firm-wide belief in the need for its fee-earners to understand clients' industries and particular commercial interests.

PRINCIPAL AREAS OF WORK: Ince & Co specialises in litigation relating to all aspects of international trade, shipping, insurance and energy.
International Insurance: The firm covers all aspects of UK and international insurance including marine, aviation, non-marine and reinsurance. The partners include some of the most notable City lawyers in this field, who have advised on many of the issues, both litigious and non-contentious, confronting all sectors of the world's insurance industry. Over the past two decades the firm has participated in the majority of the leading insurance cases which have been instrumental in determining many points of principle, often instructing in drafting and regulatory matters. The firm also specialises in professional indemnity litigation and personal injury.
Maritime: Since before the Torrey Canyon in 1967, Ince & Co has been involved in the aftermath of many of the major international maritime casualties including significant pollution incidents worldwide: the Exxon Valdez, Haven, Aegean Sea, Braer, Sea Empress and New Carissa oil spills. The firm also acted for the owners on the Piper Alpha oil rig disaster, advising on technical and insurance problems as well as personal injury and loss of life; and in respect of loss of life and injury aspects of the Herald of Free Enterprise and the Marchioness and Bowbelle collision. Ince also advised the owners and hull and P&I insurers of the vessel 'Ever Decent' when she was involved in the headline collision with the 'Norwegian Dream'. The firm operates a 24-hour emergency response service 365 days a year in respect of maritime, aviation or energy-related casualties. This service includes unrivalled experience of partners who are trained in the management of the media, and is complemented by several experienced ex-mariners.
Energy: Energy work, both litigious and non-contentious, continues to expand, and the extensive industry knowledge of partners in this specialised area provides clients with informed solutions to their business problems.
Other Specialisms: Ince & Co also specialises in construction work, e-commerce, EU law and commercial conveyancing. Ince & Co's developing corporate practice covers the full range of company matters and the firm has a growing involvement in the FSU and Eastern Europe.

RECRUITMENT & TRAINING: Ince & Co recruits between eight and ten trainee solicitors annually. Early responsibility is encouraged under close supervision by partners. The majority of trainee solicitors stay on after qualification.

INNES MACKAY SOLICITORS
2 Downs Hill, Beckenham, BR3 5HB **Tel:** (020) 8249 2600 **Fax:** (020) 8249 2616 **Email:** innesmackay@yahoo.co.uk

INTERNATIONAL FAMILY LAW CHAMBERS

218 Strand, London, WC2R 1AP
Tel: (020) 7583 5040 **Fax:** (020) 7583 5151 **DX:** 252 London/Chancery Lane
Email: mail@internationalfamilylaw.com **Website:** www.internationalfamilylaw.com

Head of Chambers:	David Truex
Number of principals:	4
Other fee-earners:	3

AREAS OF PRACTICE

English & international Family Law (including consultancy and agency)	100%

THE FIRM: Chambers specialising in international family law with principal members qualified in England and Wales, Australia, Germany and USA. Head of Chambers David Truex, also qualified as an Australian barrister and solicitor, is an SFLA accredited specialist family lawyer. He is Chairman of the SFLA International Committee and the UK Host Committee for the 2001 World Congress on Family Law and the Rights of Children and Youth. Members of the Chambers have expertise in dealing with multi-jurisdictional disputes in England and overseas.

PRINCIPAL AREAS OF WORK: Most litigation is conducted in the English courts, generally involving international issues. Particular expertise is claimed in forum disputes, international enforcement, analysis of foreign laws, international treaties and complex financial matters where off-shore assets are in issue. International consultancy and agency work for other lawyers is a substantial part of the practice. Most clients are referred by law societies, embassies and other lawyers.

CONTACTS

Family Law ..... David Truex
..... Henry Brookman
..... Kerstin Beyer
..... Madeleine M. Dimitroff

IRWIN MITCHELL

St. Peter's House, Hartshead, Sheffield, S1 2EL
Tel: (0114) 276 7777 **Fax:** (0114) 275 3306 **DX:** 10513
Email: enquiries@irwinmitchell.co.uk **Website:** www.IMonline.co.uk

Managing Partner:	Howard Culley
Senior Partner:	Michael Napier
Number of partners:	77
Assistant solicitors:	134
Other fee-earners:	633

AREAS OF PRACTICE

Corporate Services 33%
Insurance Litigation Services 32%
Plaintiff Personal Injury Litigation 25%
Private Client 10%

CONTACTS

Business Crime ..... Kevin Robinson
Commercial Litigation ..... Peter Bellamy
Commercial Property ..... Kevin Docherty
Company/Commercial ..... Kevin Cunningham
Competition ..... Michael Jelly
Corporate Services ..... Kevin Cunningham
Employment ..... Simon Coates
Family and Matrimonial ..... Martin Loxley
Insurance ..... Joe Simpson
Intellectual Property ..... James Love
Personal Injury ..... John Pickering
Police Prosecution ..... Mike Whitworth
Residential Conveyancing ..... Steve Martin
Wills and Trusts ..... Paul Hirst

THE FIRM: Now firmly established as one of the top national firms in the UK, Irwin Mitchell offers a distinctive approach to its clients' needs. Whether acting for national or international companies, family businesses or private clients, the firm provides the highest levels of service delivery and customer care. The practice is accredited to ISO 9001.

PRINCIPAL AREAS OF WORK:

CORPORATE SERVICES

Company/Commercial/EU: Services offered include mergers, buy-outs and acquisitions; formation of companies and partnerships; education and charities; commercial contracts; joint ventures; banking; corporate finance and taxation; sports law; computers & IT and pensions. The EU unit offers guidance on European and International law.

Commercial Property: This department covers all areas of property transactions including joint venture agreements, development projects, development funding, construction, building contracts and planning. The department has specialist retail, development and commerical units within it.

Commercial Litigation: Work includes commercial and financial disputes, intellectual property, insolvency, employment, professional negligence, insurance, sale of goods, product liability, building contracts and property disputes.

Business Crime: The firm is well-known in this field for handling the Matrix-Churchill 'arms to Iraq' affair, and also provides advice on criminal law generally.

Insolvency/Debt Recovery: In 1998 Irwin Mitchell merged with Braby & Waller enabling the merged practice to provide an enhanced specialist national debt recovery service. With over 100 years experience, Braby & Waller prides itself in providing a cost effective, specialist service. Services offered include: pre-litigation collection of debts; litigation; enforcement; insolvency.

INSURANCE LITIGATION SERVICES The firm handles both contentious and non-contentious insurance work in the form of advising on policy conditions and insurance litigation, acting for insurers in defending claims particularly in the fields of employers' liability, product liability and public liability. The firm also operates a large legal expenses unit.

PERSONAL INJURY LITIGATION Mainly acting for claimants, the firm has a national and international reputation for personal injury litigation.

Disaster Law: The firm offers a specialist service covering defective products, adverse drug reactions, large-scale and multiple accidents and international disasters. Major involvement in claims arising from disasters include: Manchester Air Crash, sinking of 'Herald of Free Enterprise', 'Marchioness' disaster, King's Cross Fire, 'Piper Alpha' explosion, and Land's End tragedy.

PRIVATE CLIENT SERVICES

Family Law: The full range of matrimonial and family services are offered.

Conveyancing: Acting on behalf of private individuals, clearing banks and others, the firm operates a fully computerised conveyancing service with close partner involvement.

Trust & Probate: The trust and probate team deals with wills, personal taxation, trusts and probate on behalf of private individuals and business clients requiring personal advice for their directors or employees. In addition the firm handles police prosecutions.

INTERNATIONAL CONNECTIONS: Well established links with lawyers in the USA and most other foreign jurisdictions. Particular expertise in transatlantic and Far Eastern work.

CLIENTELE: Clients range from the private individual and the family business to public companies and institutions on a national and international scale.

ISADORE GOLDMAN

125 High Holborn, London, WC1V 6QF **Tel:** (020) 7242 3000 **Fax:** (020) 7242 9160 **DX:** 124 **Ptnrs:** 10 **Asst solrs:** 3 **Other fee-earners:** 2

ISON HARRISON & CO

Duke House, 54 Wellington Street, Leeds, LS1 2EE **Tel:** (0113) 284 5000 **Fax:** (0113) 284 5020/40/50 **DX:** 713106 Leeds Park Square **Ptnrs:** 13 **Asst solrs:** 21 **Other fee-earners:** 42 **Contact:** Stephen C. Harrison • Expanding general practice with strong civil litigation.

AREAS OF PRACTICE

Personal Injury	30%
Civil Litigation & Family	30%
Conveyancing & Other	25%
Crime	15%

JACKSON & CANTER

32 Princes Road, Liverpool, L8 1TH **Tel:** (0151) 282 1700 **Fax:** (0151) 282 1735 **DX:** 14156 **Email:** aholroyd@jacksoncanter.co.uk **Website:** www.jacksoncanter.co.uk **Ptnrs:** 2 **Asst solrs:** 11 **Other fee-earners:** 10 **Contact:** Andrew Holroyd • A franchised Legal Aid practice with IIP and Lexcel accreditation and one of only 18 firms in England and Wales to be awarded a multi-party franchise by the Legal Aid Board.

AREAS OF PRACTICE

Litigation	30%
Crime	18%
Family	15%
Immigration	10%
Welfare	10%

JACKSON PARTON

J

18 Mansell Street, London, E1 8AA
Tel: (020) 7702 0085 **Fax:** (020) 7702 0858

THE FIRM: Jackson Parton is a medium-sized niche City practice specialising in shipping, commodity, insurance and related commercial litigation and arbitration. The firm was founded in 1992 and has flourished ever since.

PRINCIPAL AREAS OF WORK: The firm offers expertise in the full range of P&I and FD&D work, including charter disputes, cargo claims, pollution and general average. Other work includes sale and purchase, shipbuilding, mortgage enforcement disputes, marine insurance matters, commodity disputes, grounding, collision and salvage cases.

LANGUAGES: Arabic, Dutch, French, German, Greek, Italian, Japanese, Norwegian, Persian (Farsi) and Spanish.

Managing Partner:	Graham Jackson
Senior Partner:	Graham Jackson
Number of partners:	1
Assistant solicitors:	4
Other fee-earners:	2

AREAS OF PRACTICE

Commercial Shipping: Owners/Charterers/ Cargo Owners & Insurers	70%
Admiralty: Collision and Salvage	30%

CONTACTS

Admiralty	Brian Roberts
Commercial Shipping	Nicholas Parton

JACKSONS

Innovation House, Yarm Road, Stockton-on-Tees, TS18 3TN
Tel: (01642) 643643 **Fax:** (01642) 873737 **DX:** 715796 Stockton
Email: genquiry@jacksons.law.co.uk **Website:** www.jacksons.law.co.uk

Queens House, Wellington Street, Leeds, LS1 2DE
Tel: (0113) 244 1666 **Fax:** (0113) 386 0600 **DX:** 706967 Leeds Park Square

Mayflower House, Fifth Avenue Business Park, Team Valley, Gateshead, NE11 0HF
Tel: (0191) 497 7300 **Fax:** (0191) 497 7301 **DX:** 60407 Whickham
Email: genquiry@jacksons.law.co.uk

PRINCIPAL AREAS OF WORK:

Insurance Litigation: The firm's insurance litigation department offers expertise in disease work for defendants as well as traumatic injury, property damage and road traffic accidents. The client list includes eight out of the UK's top ten insurers.

Employment: The firm has a national reputation for its experience in employment law and offers specialist representation at employment tribunals throughout the UK, as well as in the Employment Appeal Tribunal.

Company/Commercial: The firm covers the full range of services for the corporate client, including company formations, share issues, joint ventures and corporate insolvency. The commercial property team specialises in commercial leasing and conveyancing for builders and major developers. The commercial litigation team offers expertise in insolvency, professional negligence, contract disputes, corporate debt collecting and insurance recovery work.

Mediation: Jacksons have also been at the forefront of alternative dispute resolution and have pioneered mediation techniques as founder members of ADR Net Limited.

Managing partner:	Richard Clarke
Senior partner:	Kevin Fletcher
Number of Partners:	19
Assistant Solicitors:	11
Other Fee-earners:	18
Total Staff:	140

AREAS OF PRACTICE

Insurance Litigation	60%
Company/Commercial & Commercial Property	20%
Commercial Litigation	14%
Employment Law	6%

CONTACTS

Commercial Litigation	Nigel Kidwell
Commercial Property	Geoff Skeoch
Company/Commercial	Tony Wentworth
Employment	Kevin Fletcher
Insolvency	Stephen Wiles
Insurance Litigation	Richard Clarke

JAMES & CO

99 Manningham Lane, Bradford, BD1 3BN **Tel:** (01274) 729900 **Fax:** (01274) 721100 **DX:** 712442 Bradford 8 **Email:** Jamesco@ukimmigration.co.uk **Website:** www.ukimmigration.co.uk **Ptnrs:** 1 **Other fee-earners:** 4 **Contact:** Charles James • Specialist immigration firm. Charles James started in immigration in 1981. Marriage, business, dependent relatives, political asylum.

AREAS OF PRACTICE

Immigration	95%

JAMES CHAPMAN & CO

76 King Street, Manchester, M2 4NH
Tel: (0161) 828 8000 **Fax:** (0161) 828 8018 **DX:** 14492 Manchester 2
Email: generalenquiries@james-chapman.co.uk

Managing Partner:	Elisabeth Taylor
Senior Partner:	Maurice Watkins
Number of partners:	25
Assistant solicitors:	30
Other fee-earners:	19

AREAS OF PRACTICE

Defendant Insurance/Indemnity 80%
Company work 10%
Conveyancing Residential/ Commercial & Probate 5%
Plaintiff Personal Injury 5%

CONTACTS

Comp/Commercial & Sports Law ....Maurice Watkins
Personal Injury ....Kevin Finnigan
Professional Indemnity ....Elisabeth Taylor
Property/Private Client..........Peter Marsden

THE FIRM: James Chapman & Co was established over 100 years ago and from its earliest days concentrated on insurance and indemnity work. It has maintained this specialisation and also handles corporate and commercial work, commercial and residential conveyancing and private client work. The firm also has a recognised specialisation in sports and media law. Clients of the firm include many major insurance companies and substantial corporate entities. The firm is one of the leading practices in the insurance and indemnity field in the North West. With 67 dedicated fee earners, the firm can handle an individual claim or a series of claims, of any size and complexity. James Chapman & Co intends to sustain the high quality provision of insurance and indemnity services that has been its hallmark since the firm was founded, as well as developing its expertise in other areas. In recent years, the practice has expanded steadily and has invested heavily in its office infrastructure and IT systems. It believes it will maintain this growth. The firm's policy is to increase the number of qualified staff, not only to meet the increase in demand for its services, but also to ensure that all clients receive a cost-efficient service.

PRINCIPAL AREAS OF WORK: The firm consists of four departments: personal injury work on behalf of defendants and insurers, insurance and professional indemnity work on behalf of defendants, company/commercial work, including sports law and media and entertainment law, and property and private client work.
Personal Injury: The department has dedicated specialists for cases of catastrophic injury, involving brain and spine injuries. The firm has been appointed as a member of restricted panels to several major insurers to deal with cases of the utmost severity and has a team of lawyers exclusively handling these cases. James Chapman & Co has pioneered a pro-active consensual approach to the settlement of significant personal injury cases and the encouragement of negotiations between solicitors. The firm has handled an increasing number of stress and other occupational disease claims.
Professional Indemnity: The department undertakes a wide range of high quality, complex claims on behalf of solicitors, surveyors, architects, barristers, valuers, insurance brokers, accountants and other professional groups. The firm has wide experience in general litigation and handles a variety of actions in product liability, building and construction risks, policy disputes, subrogation recoveries, motor claims, fire damage and employers' and public liability claims.
Company/Commercial: The department provides services to a variety of clients from listed public companies to smaller owner-run businesses. The services include advice on general company law, including acquisition and sales of companies, commercial contracts, intellectual property law, employment law, commercial litigation and debt recovery, with a growing media and IT practice. James Chapman & Co's sports law team is led by partner Maurice Watkins, who is also a director of Manchester United PLC and Manchester United Football Club. This field of work includes sponsorship, advertising and merchandising. It has been at the forefront in advising world-leaders in this sector for many years, and this year advised Manchester United on its record-breaking £30m sponsorship deal with Vodafone. James Chapman & Co acts for sporting bodies, event organisers, clubs and managers, as well as for individual sportsmen and women.
Commercial Property & Private Client: The firm advises commercial property clients on property development, commercial leases, planning applications, estate management, landlord and tenant matters and secured lending. Private clients are advised on all aspects of financial planning, including personal tax advice, inheritance tax and estate planning, probates and trusts including wills, estate administration and preparing and administering settlements, and residential conveyancing.

RECRUITMENT & TRAINING: The firm recruits four trainees a year, as well as additional assistant solicitors.

JAMES KENDALL

Saint Martins House, 210-212 Chapeltown Road, Leeds, LS7 4HZ **Tel:** (0113) 294 5059 **Fax:** (0113) 294 5001 **Email:** Enqs@JamesKendall.co.uk **Website:** www.JamesKendall.co.uk **Ptnrs:** 2 **Other fee-earners:** 2 • A niche practice specialising in corporate finance, venture capital transactions, financial services, private company acquisitions and disposals and related company and commercial work.

JAMESON & HILL

72-74 Fore Street, Hertford, SG14 1BY **Tel:** (01992) 554881 **Fax:** (01992) 551885 **DX:** 57908 Hertford **Email:** jail@nildram.co.uk **Ptnrs:** 5 **Asst solrs:** 6 **Other fee-earners:** 6

J.B. WHEATLEY & CO

119 Camberwell Road, London, SE5 OHB **Tel:** (020) 7701 2983 **Fax:** (020) 7703 1621 **DX:** 34901 WALWORTH
Email: enquiries@jbwheatley.co.uk

C & H JEFFERSON

Norwich Union House, 7 Fountain Street, Belfast, BT1 5EA
Tel: (028) 9032 9545 **Fax:** (028) 9024 4644 **DX:** 439 NR Belfast
Email: infor@jefferson.u-net.com **Website:** www.jefferson.u-net.com

Managing Partner:	H.L.I. Jefferson
Number of partners:	8
Assistant solicitors:	13
Other fee-earners:	4

AREAS OF PRACTICE

Litigation	65%
Commercial	20%
Employment	10%
Private Client	5%

CONTACTS

Commercial	Kenneth Rutherford
Employment	Mark Tinman
Litigation	Gareth Jones
Private Client	David Lennon

THE FIRM: Established in 1898, C & H Jefferson is one of the leading practices in Northern Ireland with an excellent reputation for its comprehensive legal and agency services.

PRINCIPAL AREAS OF WORK:

Litigation: The firm is one of the largest litigation practices in Northern Ireland, specialising in all areas of defence and commercial litigation and has corporate membership of FOIL.

Commercial: The firm has a strong commercial department embracing commercial property transactions; banking and securities, company formations, sales, acquisitions and reconstructions; partnerships; insolvency; debt recovery; agency work for leading firms in Great Britain and elsewhere, maritime law and defamation.

Employment: The firm has a vibrant employment law practice with a dedicated team, particularly acting for employers, with extensive expertise in discrimination law (sex, religion and disability), and advising on contracts of employment.

Private Client: We provide a full range of services commensurate with a long-established practice including conveyancing; wills and administration of estates; tax planning and trusts and family law.

LANGUAGES: French, Italian and Spanish.

J

JEFFREY AITKEN SOLICITORS

Fortune House, 74 Waterloo Street, Glasgow, G2 7DA **Tel:** (0141) 221 5983 **Fax:** (0141) 225 5750 **DX:** GW2
Email: maildesk@jeffrey-aitken.co.uk **Ptnrs:** 4 **Asst solrs:** 1

JEFFREY GREEN RUSSELL

Apollo House, 56 New Bond Street, London, W1Y OSX
Tel: (020) 7339 7000 **Fax:** (020) 7339 7001 **DX:** 44627 Mayfair
Email: jgr@jgrlaw.co.uk **Website:** www.jgrweb.com

Managing Partner:	C. Whitfield-Jones
Senior Partner:	C. Whitfield-Jones
Number of partners:	23
Assistant solicitors:	21
Other fee-earners:	16

CONTACTS

Company/Commercial	Anthony Coles
Insurance Litigation	Bryan Lincoln
Leisure & Licensing	Julian Skeens
Litigation	Phillip Cohen
Private Client	Phillip Harris
Property	Clive Whitfield-Jones

THE FIRM: Jeffrey Green Russell is a medium-sized commercial law firm based in Bond Street, London W1. The firm is committed to technology and human resources development, both of which have made a significant contribution to its success. The firm has a local area network running Novell Netware. Staff at all levels have PCs running Windows for Workgroups as the desktop GUI and lawyers have Gateway 2000 Pentium PCs. All PCs are capable of internal and external e-mail via the Internet; scheduling and diary (Novell Groupwise); word processing (WordPerfect 8.0); document management and know-how retrieval (iManage); desktop fax; spreadsheets (Microsoft Excel 97); Internet research; the CMS Open Practice Management system and other specialised programs. The firm uses Solcase for large scale insurance claims litigation and some litigation matters.

PRINCIPAL AREAS OF WORK:

Company/Commercial: A broad spectrum of services focus on commercial and financial activity. Corporate work includes formations, mergers, acquisitions, MBOs, joint ventures, reorganisations and share issues. Other areas of expertise are commercial work (including computer contracts and the Internet), banking and finance, intellectual property and franchising, and corporate taxation.

Litigation: Quick, positive, effective action is the hallmark of this department in general commercial litigation, insurance disputes, including professional negligence and product liability, personal injury and legal expenses insurance, property litigation, employment matters, debt collection and insolvency, mortgage re-possession and commercial fraud including computer and technology-related offences.

Property: The department offers a full range of services including planning, development work, property finance, investment, dealing (including portfolio break-ups and auction work) and landlord and tenant law.

Licensing & Leisure: A strong department caters for the special demands of the leisure industry, offering a comprehensive service representing clients in courts throughout the country. The firm deals with bingo, nightclubs and discos, pubs, off licences, restaurants and catering, hotels, cinemas, amusement arcades and gaming.

Personal Finance: The department provides a specialist service dedicated to the protection and enhancement of clients' personal wealth. The range of services includes wills and probate, estate and financial planning, trusts and settlements, administration of estates and overseas tax arrangements.

INTERNATIONAL CONNECTIONS: The firm is a member of ACL International, an association of commercial lawyers worldwide. For further information contact Tony Coles.

CLIENTELE: Clients cover a spectrum of commerce, finance and industry, ranging from small businesses to multi-national corporations. Activities include banking, finance, mortgage lenders, the Internet, technology, leisure, restaurants, the licensed trade, brewers, insurance, airlines and property development.

JENKINS & HAND

Clutha House, 10 Storey's Gate, London, SW1P 3AY **Tel:** (020) 7222 5002 **Fax:** (020) 7222 5004 **DX:** 99924 Victoria **Ptnrs:** 2 **Contact:** Ms Catherine Hand • Specialising in work for social landlords, local authorities and public sector bodies, including stock transfers, urban regeneration projects, governance of housing associations and local authority powers.

AREAS OF PRACTICE

Housing Association	70%
Local Authority	30%

JEREMY FEAR & CO

5a St. Onge Parade, Southbury Road, Enfield, EN1 1YU **Tel:** (020) 8367 4466 **Fax:** (020) 8367 3481 **Asst solrs:** 1

J.J. RICE

Law Society House, 94 Victoria House, Belfast, **Tel:** (028) 9028 8688 **Fax:** (028) 9028 8588 **Email:** j_rice_llm@compuserve.com

JOELSON WILSON & CO

70 New Cavendish Street, London, W1M 8AT
Tel: (020) 7580 5721 **Fax:** (020) 7580 2251
Email: info@joelson-wilson.co.uk **Website:** www.joelson-wilson.co.uk

Managing Partner:	Paul Baglee
Senior Partner:	Paul Wilson
Number of partners:	7
Assistant solicitors:	4
Other fee-earners:	5

THE FIRM: Established in 1957, Joelson Wilson & Co provides a personal and individual approach and a highly commercial service to its clients. Traditionally known for its strong company/commercial, commercial litigation and commercial property practice, the firm has an established reputation for its work in the leisure industry in the UK and overseas. Solicitors in its specialised licensing department appear in Licensing Courts throughout the entire country. The firm's employment law unit has a growing reputation. There is a strong international element to the firm's practice. It is the UK member of European Lawyers Network (EEIG) working closely with the other member firms in Amsterdam, Brussels, Frankfurt, Paris and Stockholm and the US associated member firms in Pittsburgh, PA and Sacremento, CA.

AREAS OF PRACTICE

Company/Commercial	34%
Licensing Lliquor/Gaming/Betting/ Entertainment	34%
Commercial Litigation & Employment	20%
Property	12%

JOHN BATTERS & CO

Craigie Hall, 6 Rowan Road, Glasgow, G41 5BS **Tel:** (0141) 427 6884 **Fax:** (0141) 427 7909 **Ptnrs:** 1

JOHN BOYLE AND CO

The Square, 5 West End, Redruth, TR15 2SB **Tel:** (01209) 213507 **Fax:** (01209) 219470 **DX:** 81758 Redruth **Ptnrs:** 3 **Asst solrs:** 3 **Other fee-earners:** 4

JOHN COLLINS & PARTNERS

Copper Court, Phoenix Way, Enterprise Park, Swansea, SA7 9EH **Tel:** (01792) 773773 **Fax:** (01792) 774775 **DX:** 82804 SWANSEA 2 **Email:** law@johncollins.co.uk **Website:** www.johncollins.co.uk **Ptnrs:** 9 **Asst solrs:** 31 **Other fee-earners:** 5

JOHN FORD MORRISON

Third Floor, Sun Court House, 18-26 Essex Road, London, N1 8LN **Tel:** (020) 7288 1066 **Fax:** (020) 7288 1099 **Email:** admin@johnfordmorisson.co.uk

JOHN GAUNT & PARTNERS

Omega Court, 372 Cemetery Road, Sheffield, S11 8FT **Tel:** (0114) 266 8664 **Fax:** (0114) 266 0101 **DX:** 717212 Sheffield 27 **Email:** post@john-gaunt.co.uk **Website:** www.john-gaunt.co.uk **Ptnrs:** 4 **Asst solrs:** 1 **Other fee-earners:** 3 **Contact:** John R.T. Gaunt. • Specialist commercial practice, particularly for the licensed and leisure industries, handling over 3000 licence applications each year

AREAS OF PRACTICE

Liquor licensing	60%
Commercial Property	20%
CommercialLitigation	10%
Landlord & Tenant (contentious/non-contentious)	10%

JOHN HODGE & CO

27/31 Boulevard, Weston-super-Mare, BS23 1NY **Tel:** (01934) 623511 **Fax:** (01934) 418210 **DX:** 8403 **Ptnrs:** 10 **Asst solrs:** 3 **Other fee-earners:** 10

JOHN KENDALL

The Manor House, St. David's Street, Presteigne, LD8 2BP **Tel:** (01544) 260019 **Fax:** (01544) 260717 **Email:** jkendall@btinternet.com

JOHN MCKEE & SON

55 Royal Avenue, Belfast, BT1 1FD
Tel: (028) 9023 2303 **Fax:** (028) 9023 0081 **DX:** 470 NR Belfast
Email: info@jmckee.co.uk **Website:** www.jmckee.co.uk

Senior partner:	Lex Ross
Number of partners:	5
Assistant solicitors:	6
Other fee-earners:	2

AREAS OF PRACTICE

Commercial	42%
Litigation	41%
Private client	14%
Other	3%

CONTACTS

Corporate/Commercial	Lex Ross
	Avril McCammon
Litigation	Leonard Edgar
	Melanie Jones
Property	Albert Jordan

THE FIRM: John McKee & Son is a major Belfast law firm, highly regarded for its corporate and litigation expertise. Founded in 1887, the firm is a progressive law firm which continues to enjoy rapid growth. The firm's lawyers have extensive experience in their fields, enabling them to serve the needs of both local and national clients.

PRINCIPAL AREAS OF WORK:
Corporate/ Commercial: (Contact partners: Lex Ross and Avril McCammon) The firm advises business clients on all aspects of corporate and commercial law. Work includes advice on company acquisitions and disposals, corporate insolvency and personal insolvency acting in the main for insolvency practitioners, and banking and secured lending together with private finance initiative work, acting on behalf of the lending institutions.
Litigation: (Contact partners: Leonard Edgar and Melanie Jones) The firm has an excellent reputation in insurance litigation, commercial and insolvency litigation, employment tribunals and debt recovery.
Property: (Contact partner: Albert Jordan) All aspects of commercial property transactions are undertaken together with building society repossession work.Other Areas: The firm also provides a full range of private client advice, including wills, tax planning, residential conveyancing and matrimonial matters.

J

JOHN MORSE SOLICITORS

St Helen's House, 156 St Helen's Road, Swansea, SA1 5DG **Tel:** (01792) 648 111 **Fax:** (01792) 648 028 **Email:** mail@johnmorse.co.uk

JOHN PICKERING & PARTNERS

9 Church Lane, Oldham, OL1 3AN
Tel: (0161) 633 6667 **Fax:** (0161) 626 1671 **DX:** 23616
Website: www.johnpickering.co.uk

6 St Ann's Passage, 29/31 King Street, Manchester, M2 6BE
Tel: (0161) 834 1251 **Fax:** (0161) 834 1505 **DX:** 718161
Email: law@jpicks.u-net.com

19 Castle Street, Liverpool, L2 4FX
Tel: (0151) 227 1214 **Fax:** (0151) 258 1262 **DX:** 14222

11 Clare Road, Halifax, HX1 2HX
Tel: (01422) 345 535 **Fax:** (01422) 438 500 **DX:** 16023 Halifax

Number of partners:	6
Assistant solicitors:	6
Other fee-earners:	1

AREAS OF PRACTICE

Personal Injury	95%
Clinical Negligence	5%

THE FIRM: Established in 1979, John Pickering & Partners is a personal injury firm, acting only for plaintiffs.

PRINCIPAL AREAS OF WORK: The firm has a special interest and expertise in acting for people disabled by industrial diseases, and they are specialists in asbestos disease claims, having referrals from doctors, trade unions, specialist advice agencies. The firm has pioneered asbestos factory neighbourhood injury litigation in the UK and in 1995 won the first case of environmental injury to be tried in England.
In addition to personal injury, industrial accidents and disease claims, the firm also takes on medical negligence claims. In April 1998, John Pickering & Partners won a landmark group action against British Gas for victims of vibration white finger. In April 1999, John Pickering & Partners settled a product liability claim against T&N shortly before trial. This was a major breakthrough in asbestos litigation.

CLIENTELE: The firm has clients throughout England and Wales and also in Ireland, Australia, Canada, USA, New Zealand and South Africa.

JOHNS ELLIOT

40 Linenhall Street, Belfast BT2 8BA (from mid October 2000)
Tel: (028) 9032 6881 **Fax:** (028) 9024 8236 **DX:** 419 NR Belfast
Email: info@johnselliot.com **Website:** www.johnselliot.com

Managing Partner:	Maurice Butler
Senior Partner:	Maurice Butler
Number of partners:	8
Assistant solicitors:	3
Other fee-earners:	7

THE FIRM: Johns Elliot is a leading City firm offering a wide range of legal services, with particular emphasis on commercial and corporate matters. The firm was established in 1837. Each client has contact with a single partner who bears responsibility for the conduct of that client's business, although individual aspects will be dealt with by specialist lawyers.

PRINCIPAL AREAS OF WORK:

Company/Commercial Property: Work includes company formations, reconstructions and acquisitions, and all aspects of commercial property, from initial planning applications to satisfying the requirements of the developers' financiers.

Employment: An increasingly problematic area for commercial clients, legal advice is given at an early stage to assess the potential impact of legislation, evolve efficient working practices and ensure good industrial relations are established and maintained.

Litigation: A major part of the firm's practice, this department deals with commercial litigation, building contract arbitrations, medical negligence, personal injury claims and debt collection, and is also involved in defamation actions for newspapers and local broadcasting networks.

AREAS OF PRACTICE

Company/Commercial	45%
Litigation & Employment	25%
Other	15%
Probate and Tax	15%

CONTACTS

Company/Commercial	Maurice Butler
Litigation	Ronald Robinson
Private Client	David Leitch

THE JOHNSON PARTNERSHIP

Cannon Courtyard, Long Row, Nottingham, NG1 6JE **Tel:** (0115) 941 9141 **Fax:** (0115) 947 0178 **DX:** 10082 **Ptnrs:** 8 **Asst solrs:** 5 **Other fee-earners:** 13

JOHNSONS

Johnson House, 50-56 Wellington Place, Belfast, BT1 6GF
Tel: (028) 9024 0183 **Fax:** (028) 9024 9239/9031 3300 **DX:** 405 NR Belfast 1
Email: pt@johnsonslaw.co.uk

Senior partner:	M McCracken
Number of partners:	6
Assistant solicitors:	3
Other fee-earners:	5

THE FIRM: Johnsons offers partner-driven, pragmatic and cost-effective services to commercial and private clients. It has an extensive insurance litigation practice representing many international insurance companies. The firm has an established reputation in defamation/media and entertainment law representing high profile clients and newspapers.

PRINCIPAL AREAS OF WORK: Johnsons handles a high volume of commercial and private property transactions and provides a full range of corporate legal services including mergers and acquisitions and joint ventures. The firm also has particular expertise in banking law, acting for the largest financial institution in Northern Ireland.

AREAS OF PRACTICE

Litigation	50%
Defamation/Media and Entertainment Law	25%
Company/Commrcial/Employment	20%
Private Client	5%

JOHNSTON & HERRON

George Johnston House, Bank Street, Lochgelly, KY5 9QN **Tel:** (01592) 780421 **Fax:** (01592) 782726 **Email:** mail@johnston-herron.co.uk **Ptnrs:** 4 **Asst solrs:** 4 **Other fee-earners:** 1 **Contact:** Tom Johnston • Full range of legal services. Specialists in licensing, personal injuries and criminal defence.

JOHN WESTON & CO

10 Victoria Street, Felixstowe, IP11 7ER **Tel:** (01394) 282527 **Fax:** (01394) 276097 **DX:** 31467 Felixstowe **Email:** info@johnweston.co.uk **Website:** www.johnweston.co.uk **Ptnrs:** 1 **Other fee-earners:** 2

JOHN WINKWORTH-SMITH

Churchdale Farm, Ashford-in-the-Water, Bakewell, DE45 1NX **Tel:** (01629) 640269 **Fax:** (01629) 640608

JONATHAN STEPHENS & CO

Ty Cornel, 11 Castle Parade, Usk, NP15 1AA **Tel:** (01291) 673344 **Fax:** (01291) 673575 **DX:** 32552 Usk **Email:** js.agrilaw@oyeznet.co.uk **Ptnrs:** 2 **Other fee-earners:** 1 **Contact:** Jonathan Stephens Specialises in agricultural work, mainly acting for family farms and farming partnerships throughout South Wales and the West. Work includes quotas, boundaries, tenancies, partnership matters, rural and agricultural property etc. Also handles probate and conveyancing.

AREAS OF PRACTICE

Agricultural Law	60%
General Practice (mainly non-contentious)	40%

JONES & WARNER

60 Lombard Street, London, EC3V 9EA
Tel: (020) 7464 8454 **Fax:** (020) 7464 8747
Email: jw@jwlaw.co.uk

Number of partners:	3
Other fee-earners:	3

THE FIRM: Jones & Warner was launched in March 1999 and provides top quality advisory services in employment-related matters, with particular emphasis on strategic issues, asset protection, problem avoidance and negotiated resolution. The firm combines the expertise of barristers and solicitors in one practice and uses HR professionals in the delivery of these services. Its clients are drawn from City and FTSE 250 companies.

Continued overleaf

AREAS OF PRACTICE

Employment	100%

PRINCIPAL AREAS OF WORK: Employment specialists with focus on strategic issues, statutory and regulatory aspects,employment tribunals, litigation and arbitration. Also non-contentious aspects, senior executives, employee benefits, pensions and tax.

CLIENTELE: Listed and emerging corporates in the following sectors: advertising; business process outsourcing; e-commerce; professional services; retail; senior executives.

CONTACTS

Non-contentious Aspects/Senior Executives/Employee Benefits/ Pensions & Tax ....David Warner
Strategic Issues/Statutory & Regulatory Aspects/Employment Tribunals/Litigation & Arbitration ....Jennie Wade, Michael Jones

---

JONES & CASSIDY
220 Ormeau Road, Belfast, BT7 2FY **Tel:** (028) 9064 2290 **Fax:** (028) 9064 2297 **Ptnrs:** 2 **Asst solrs:** 1 **Other fee-earners:** 3

JONES, DAY, REAVIS & POGUE

Bucklersbury House, 3 Queen Victoria Street, London, EC4N 8NA
Tel: (020) 7236 3939 **Fax:** (020) 7236 1113 **DX:** 98949 Cheapside 2
Email: Query_JDRP_London@jonesday.com **Website:** www.jonesday.com

Senior Partner:	Robert L Thomson
Number of partners:	7
Assistant solicitors:	29
Other fee-earners:	6

J

THE FIRM: Founded in the United States, Jones Day's international practice has developed in response to the globalisation of capital, trade, and technology, as well as to the changing needs of the firm's clients. Today, Jones Day employs more than 1,300 lawyers resident in 24 worldwide locations, and ranks among the world's largest and most geographically diverse law firms. The firm is notable for the breadth of its representation of major international corporations, providing significant legal services to over half of the Fortune 500 companies. Established over 20 years ago, Jones Day London now has 42 lawyers and fee-earners and one of the largest presences in London among US-based firms. Almost all of its partners and fee-earners are UK qualified; the remainder are US or dual qualified. The London office provides a full range of business legal services to UK and overseas clients, focusing principally on UK and cross-border mergers and acquisitions, corporate finance and private equity/venture capital transactions; corporate tax planning and tax-based structured finance; litigation and arbitration; commercial property and environmental law; share schemes and employment and pension matters. As part of the single, integrated Jones Day worldwide partnership, the London office has direct and immediate access to the wide range of foreign law expertise and support services provided by the firm's offices in the US, mainland Europe, Asia and Australia.

PRINCIPAL AREAS OF WORK:
Corporate/Corporate Finance/Commercial: The London office advises UK, US and other overseas companies and organisations on domestic and cross-border mergers and acquisitions, take-over bids, securities issues and financings, leveraged and management buy-outs/buy-ins and other private equity/venture capital transactions, joint ventures, commercial and licensing agreements, financial services and regulatory compliance (including corporate governance) and other corporate and commercial issues.
Taxation: The London office tax group, which is the largest tax practice of any non-English firm in London, advises UK, US and other overseas enterprises on the tax aspects of international transactions and investments. It provides both UK and US tax expertise, with particular emphasis on the tax dimensions of cross-border mergers, acquisitions, post-acquisition restructurings, and other internal reorganisations and associated tax planning. The London office is a recognised leader in tax-based structured finance transactions.
Finance: The London office handles a variety of financing and banking transactions, including leveraged acquisition financing, high-yield debt issues and other forms of capital market issues, tax-based structured finance, securitisations, and other secured and unsecured financial transactions.
Litigation and Arbitration: The London office represents clients in English High Court litigation, English and other European arbitration proceedings, and alternative dispute resolutions in a broad range of substantive areas of law. The litigation group also frequently advises on the many complex issues that arise in cross-border litigation and arbitration, including questions of jurisdiction, conflicts of law, pre-trial investigations, discovery, and enforcement of judgements. Jones Day's London-based lawyers have significant experience in matters that include fraud and white-collar crime, disputes arising out of international trade, commodities, shipping, energy, insurance, employment, product liability, tax, and other general contractual and tortious actions.
Property & Environmental Matters: The London office team advise on a full range of commercial property transactions for both UK and overseas clients with a particular focus on maximising the value of the corporate real estate asset for clients. The team is also a key part of all corporate transactions providing advice on the liabilities relating to property and environmental issues, and in particular the negotiation of environmental indemnities.
Employment/Pensions/Share Schemes: The London office has a team of employment and pensions lawyers who advise on transactional and ongoing employee and pensions matters. They play a key role in the M&A practice and advise on all aspects of contentious and non-contentious employment and pensions issues. In addition, they work closely with members of the tax group in advising on and designing employment benefit schemes, such as profit sharing schemes and phantom share plans.

INTERNATIONAL CONNECTIONS: The firm has other offices in Atlanta, Brussels, Chicago, Cleveland, Columbus, Dallas, Frankfurt, Geneva, Hong Kong, Irvine, Los Angeles, Madrid, New York, Paris, Pittsburgh, Riyadh, Shanghai, Sydney, Taipei, Tokyo, Washington DC, New Delhi (associate office) & Bombay (associate office.)

LANGUAGES: Cantonese, German, French, Hindi, Italian and Turkish.

JONES MAIDMENT WILSON INCORPORATING HATTON SCATES HORTON

5 Byrom Street, Manchester, M3 4PF **Tel:** (0161) 832 8087 **Fax:** (0161) 835 3123 **DX:** 14372 Manchester 1 **Email:** manager@jmw.co.uk **Website:** www.jmw.co.uk **Ptnrs:** 13 **Asst solrs:** 18 **Other fee-earners:** 4

JONES MYERS GORDON

Pearl Chambers, 22 East Parade, Leeds, LS1 5BZ **Tel:** (0113) 246 0055 **Fax:** (0113) 246 7446 **DX:** 14080 Leeds Park Square **Email:** info@jmg.co.uk **Website:** www.jmg.co.uk **Ptnrs:** 4 **Asst solrs:** 2 **Other fee-earners:** 2 **Contact:** Mr P.G. Jones • A specialist family and child care practice.

AREAS OF PRACTICE	
Matrimonial/Childcare	95%
Conveyancing	5%

JOY MERRIAM & CO

67 Burdett Road, London, E3 4TN **Tel:** (020) 8980 7171 **Fax:** (020) 8981 7981 **DX:** 55652 Bow **Email:** solicitors@joymerriman.co.uk **Ptnrs:** 3 **Asst solrs:** 5 **Other fee-earners:** 2 **Contact:** Joy Merriam • Legal Aid practice specialising in crime and childcare. The criminal team comprises a number of senior solicitors. The childcare team includes three panel members.

AREAS OF PRACTICE	
Crime	55%
Family	37%
Conveyancing	8%

K

J.R. JONES

56A The Mall, Ealing, W5 3TA **Tel:** (020) 8566 2595 **Fax:** (020) 8579 4288 **DX:** 5134 Ealing **Email:** Solicitors@jrjones.co.uk **Ptnrs:** 3 **Asst solrs:** 11 **Other fee-earners:** 7 **Contact:** T Raza Expanding practice with legal aid franchises in eight areas and increasing emphasis in civil liberty/human rights cases.

JULIAN HOLY

31 Brechin Place, London, SW7 4QD **Tel:** (020) 7370 5443 **Fax:** (020) 7244 7371 **DX:** 35765 South Ken. **Email:** law@julianholy.co.uk **Ptnrs:** 7 **Asst solrs:** 1 **Other fee-earners:** 3 **Contact:** Simon J. Edwards • Languages: Polish, Russian. An innovative niche practice specialising in both commercial property and litigation, renowned for its rapid reaction time. The firm provides clear and incisive advice coupled with a high standard of service, personal attention and a determined approach to achieving each client's specific needs.

AREAS OF PRACTICE	
Commercial Property	60%
Commercial Litigation	25%
Company/Commercial	15%

KANAAR & CO

1/7 Shand Street, London Bridge, London, SE1 2ES
Tel: (020) 7403 9200 **Fax:** (020) 7403 9204 **DX:** 39908 London Bridge South
Email: kan-do-law@msn.com **Website:** www.kan-do-law.com

Managing Partner:	Nicholas Kanaar
Senior Partner:	Nicholas Kanaar
Number of partners:	2
Assistant solicitors:	1
Other fee-earners:	2

AREAS OF PRACTICE	
Litigation	40%
General (incl. prop., copyright, empl., matrim., private client)	35%
Contract	25%

CONTACTS	
Contract	N. Kanaar
Conveyancing	B. Martelli
Copyright	N. Kanaar
Litigation	N. Kanaar
	John Simmons

THE FIRM: Kanaar & Co is a general practice firm specialising in all aspects of media and entertainment law. The bulk of its clients are from the entertainment industry. Traditionally, the firm's focus has been music and copyright matters but is becoming increasingly involved in TV, film, publishing and the visual arts. The senior partner, Nicholas Kanaar, has over 30 years experience of acting for clients in the media and entertainment industry.

PRINCIPAL AREAS OF WORK:

Litigation: Considerable experience in all types of litigation, in particular intellectual property disputes and entertainment related fields such as defamation. Nicholas Kanaar's experience includes acting in the landmark case of Schroeder v McCaulay (1974) and the recent notable cases of Godfey v Lees & Others (1995) and ZYX Music GmbH v King & Others (1995).

Contract: The firm undertakes all forms of company/commercial work, specialising in the exploitation of intellectual property in all formats.

General: The firm also handles residential and commercial conveyancing, personal injury, employment, matrimonial and private client matters.

KEARNEY SEFTON

Franklin House, 12 Brunswick Street, Belfast, BT2 7GE **Tel:** (028) 9023 2940 **Fax:** (028) 90332865 **Email:** email@kearseft.net.co.uk **Website:** www.kearneysefton.co.uk

KEEBLE HAWSON

Old Cathedral Vicarage, St. James' Row, Sheffield, S1 1XA **Tel:** (0114) 272 2061 **Fax:** (0114) 270 0813 **Email:** postroom@keeblehawson.co.uk **Website:** www.keeblehawson.co.uk **Ptnrs:** 24 **Asst solrs:** 22 **Other fee-earners:** 28

KEELY BEEDHAM

28 Dam Street, Lichfield, WS13 6AA
Tel: (01543) 420000 **Fax:** (01543) 416551 (comm/property) **DX:** 19005
(01543) 258469 (litigation/matrimonial) **Website:** www.keelybeedham.co.uk

3 The Courtyard, 707 Warwick Road, Solihull, B91 3DA
Tel: (0121) 705 6363 **Fax:** (0121) 705 5885 **DX:** MDX 14036 Solihull 2 (01543) 258469 (litigation/matrimonial)

Managing partner:	Andrew Beedham
Senior partner:	John E Smith
Number of partners:	8
Assistant solicitors:	9
Other fee-earners:	5

AREAS OF PRACTICE

Company/Commercial	43%
Commercial Property	20%
Domestic Property	15%
Litigation	15%
Matrimonial	7%

CONTACTS

Commercial Property	John Parkes
Company/Commercial	John Primmer
Domestic Property	John Smith
Employment	Danny Keane
Litigation (Commercial)	Michael Phillips
Matrimonial	Marc Saunderson
Probate/Trusts/Tax Planning	Melissa Merry

THE FIRM: A commercial law practice specialising in the provision of a wide range of legal services to national and multinational businesses. The firm offers a level of expertise and service comparable with many large city firms. A major strength of the firm lies in the fact that it has depth and ability to deal with complex and specialised commercial work and yet remains sufficiently small and flexible to offer a highly personal and focused partner-lead service. The firm's work reflects a diverse range of business activities ranging from heavy manufacturing and engineering to hi-tech and service businesses with a strong international bias. The firm is continuing to evolve and has plans to expand it's office base.

PRINCIPAL AREAS OF WORK: The firm has built a reputation for mergers, acquisitions and buy outs, as well as general corporate finance work. It has a strong conveyancing department for both commercial and domestic property and is also developing its commercial litigation team. In addition the firm provides a full range of private client legal services including family law, probate, trusts and tax planning.

K

KEMP & CO

Saddlers House, Gutter Lane, London, EC2V 6BR **Tel:** (020) 7600 8080 **Fax:** (020) 7600 7878 **Email:** info@comlegal.com **Website:** www.comlegal.com **Ptnrs:** 5 **Asst solrs:** 5 **Other fee-earners:** 2 **Contact:** Mr Richard Kemp • 'A law firm for the .com world' servicing corporate, employment and commercial work for computer, information and communications industry clients.

AREAS OF PRACTICE

Corporate	30%
Commercial	25%
Competition	20%
Intellectual Property	15%
Employment	10%

E. & L. KENNEDY

72 High Street, Belfast, BT1 2BE **Tel:** (028) 9023 2352 **Fax:** (028) 9023 3118 **Ptnrs:** 3

KENNEDYS

Longbow House, 14-20 Chiswell Street, London, EC1Y 4TW
Tel: (020) 7638 3688 **Fax:** (020) 7638 2212 **DX:** 46628 Barbican
Email: mailbox@kennedys-law.com **Website:** www.kennedys-law.com

50 Mark Lane, London, EC3R 7QT
Tel: (020) 7638 3688 **Fax:** (020) 7702 9757 **DX:** 514 London/City

Ewing House, 130 Kings Road, Brentwood, CM14 4EA
Tel: (01277) 233636 **Fax:** (01277) 219175 **DX:** 5020 Brentwood

64-66 Upper Church Lane, Belfast, BT1 4QL
Tel: (028) 9024 0067 **Fax:** (028) 9031 5557 **DX:** 490 NR Belfast 1

Senior Partner:	Nick Thomas
Chairman:	Stephen Cantle
Number of partners:	50
Assistant solicitors:	61
Other fee-earners:	40

AREAS OF PRACTICE

Insurance litigation	83%
Company/Commercial	6%
Employment	6%
Construction (non-contentious)	3%
Commercial Property	2%

CONTACTS

Banking	Eric Sumner
Clinical Negligence	Janet Sayers
Commercial Property	Jeremy Palmer
Company/Commercial	James Shaw
Construction (contentious)	Nick Thomas
Construction (non-contentious)	James Shaw
Defamation/Media	Philip Hartley
Digital Risk	Gary Wadsworth
Employment	Marc Meryon
Financial Institutions/ Crime/Insurance	Chris Sharrock
Insolvency	John Harvey
Insurance	Steve Cantle
Motor	John Yates
Personal Injury	Tim Wilson
Pharmaceutical/ Prod. Liability	Shane Sayers (Mark Lane)
Professional Indemnity	Nick Thomas
Railway Litigation	Andrew Gilbert
Reinsurance	Nick Williams

THE FIRM: Kennedys is one of the leading commercial litigation firms within the UK, known primarily for its insurance driven practice. The firm is also recognised for its skills in the non-contentious commercial field, particularly in the insurance, construction and transport industries. In early 1999 the firm expanded with the addition of seven partners and their teams from major insurance legal practices. These teams added to Kennedys' insurance litigation expertise as well as adding extra personnel to the Commercial Unit. Kennedys also acquired an office in Hong Kong in December 1999. This year, Kennedys has taken on three partners and 15 lawyers from Edward Lewis, together with a substantial part of that firm's insurance litigation business. Kennedys continues to expand globally. Following on from last year's association with a law firm in Beirut and the recruitment of a native Russian speaking, English trained litigation executive, Kennedys is now strengthening its relationships with its existing associated office in Paris and a new connection in Madrid via joint ventures. These additions together with its associated offices in New York, San Francisco, Dublin, Beirut, New Delhi and Karachi and its French, German, Italian and Spanish lawyers based in-house in London ensure that Kennedys can advise its clients on all of their commercial problems within most jurisdictions. Kennedys' strategic business developments have enabled the firm to build on its strengths and increase its profile in recent years in various market sectors, most significantly in the areas of employment law, product liability, clinical negligence and insolvency.

PRINCIPAL AREAS OF WORK: This is a City practice acting for a wide range of clients both nationally and internationally.

Kennedys
Legal advice in black and white

Litigation: The firm is one of the leading defendant insurance litigation firms in the country with expertise built up over a considerable number of years. The practice is structured to allow specialised litigation teams to handle the whole spectrum of insurance work, including personal injury, professional indemnity, reinsurance, clinical negligence, banking and finance, product liability, directors' and officers' liability and employers' and public liability.
Construction: The firm's work within the construction sector is renowned. The team handles both contentious and non-contentious mainstream construction matters as well as dealing with professional indemnity issues within the industry.
Commercial: The streamlined commercial unit, comprising the insolvency, company, commercial property, employment and partnership law teams, provides a wide range of commercial services for several industry sectors. The employment team's work is a mix of litigation, advisory and transactional matters for the railway, healthcare, insurance and financial sectors. The insolvency team acts for insurers, accountants, banks and commercial concerns, nationally and internationally. Work for banks is predominantly debt recovery, security reviews and enforcement of security.
Transport: Considerable expertise has been built up in transport work and Kennedys has a large, experienced team handling railway litigation matters including employment law, disaster response, health and safety, corporate manslaughter and personal injury issues. The Healthcare Department acts for the NHSLA and hospitals and their insurers, advising on clinical negligence, employment and commercial matters.
Other: Developing areas of work within the firm are defamation law and e-commerce. Teams in both the Brentwood and City offices specialise in defendant personal injury work for insurers, including disaster and fatal accidents, industrial disease and motor-claims work. The expanding Belfast and Mark Lane offices provide the same wide-ranging legal work as the main Chiswell Street office. The focus of the Hong Kong office is dispute resolution, arising from insurance, construction and banking.

INTERNATIONAL CONNECTIONS: The firm has an overseas office at: Suite 1304, The Hong Kong Club Building, 3A Chater Road, Hong Kong, tel. +852 2848 6300, fax. +852 2848 6333

RECRUITMENT & TRAINING: Due to sustained expansion, the firm is always keen to consider applications from qualified lawyers who are competent, confident and commercially driven. Fluency in a European language is a positive asset, as is experience in insurance related-law. Trainee solicitor places are available from September 2002. All enquiries should be sent to the personnel department.

KENNETH BUSH
Evershed House, 23/25 King Street, King's Lynn, PE30 1DU **Tel:** (01553) 692737 **Fax:** (01553) 691729 **DX:** 57802 King's Lynn
Email: kenbush@aol.com **Ptnrs:** 14 **Asst solrs:** 3 **Other fee-earners:** 7

KENNETH CURTIS & CO
88 Aldridge Road, Perry Barr, Birmingham, B42 2TP **Tel:** (0121) 356 1161 **Fax:** (0121) 356 2973 **DX:** 21502 **Ptnrs:** 3 **Asst solrs:** 3
Other fee-earners: 1

KENNETH ELLIOTT & ROWE

162-166 South Street, Romford, RM1 1SX
Tel: (01708) 757575 **Fax:** (01708) 766674 **DX:** 4602 Romford
Email: law@ker.co.uk **Website:** www.ker.co.uk

109 Baker Street, London, W1M 1FE
Tel: (020) 7224 0522 **Fax:** (020) 7224 0546 **DX:** Marylebone 2

Managing Partner:	C. Dixon
Number of partners:	13
Assistant solicitors:	9
Other fee-earners:	20

AREAS OF PRACTICE

Commercial Property	30%
Common Law	30%
Employment	10%
Insolvency	10%
Licensing/Transport	10%
Private Client	10%

CONTACTS

Commercial Property	Chris Dixon
Employment	Martin Phillips
Film Production	Mark Sadler
Financial Services	David Rogers
Insolvency	Mark Dixon
Licensing	Beverley Hamblin
Litigation	Neville Filar
Matrimonial	Rebecca Gardiner
Private Client	David Farr
Transport	Adam Carr

THE FIRM: Whilst the firm's foundations were laid in the 1930s, its largely organic growth has taken place over the last 15 years, as the firm has evolved from its high street roots to one with offices in London's West End and Essex, serving an increasingly commercial and cosmopolitan client base with a substantial foreign element. The firm's administrative base remains in Essex, where it is known as a major player in the metropolitan Essex region, acting for local authorities, as well as major manufacturers, shipping companies and many others in addition to a burgeoning personal injury practice.

PRINCIPAL AREAS OF WORK:
Commercial Property: The firm's best known expertise is in the field of commercial property and the firm has now added specialist property litigation to its range of services.
Insolvency: The firm has its own licensed insolvency practitioner.
Film & Finance: The firm acts for low budget production and investors.
Company/Commercial: The firm regularly acts on acquisitions, disposals, MBOs and MBIs of varying descriptions.
Employment: The firm has been joined by specialist employment lawyer, Martin Phillips, who is also a director of Lawrite and publisher of an interactive CD Rom employment advice package.

Continued overleaf

Licensing: The firm acts as agents for the legal departments of large brewers and their independent law firms, as well as local licensing committees and businesses.
Transport: Specialists in road haulage, transport and carriage of goods. Jim Duckworth, an acknowledged expert in this field and author of Road Transport Law, is a consultant to the practice.

INTERNATIONAL CONNECTIONS: The firm is a founder member of LaWorld, an international law firm network and has independent links with clients in China, India and the Far and Middle East.

LANGUAGES: Arabic, Bengali, French, German, Greek, Gujerati, Hindi, Punjabi, Russian, Spanish, Turkish and Urdu.

RECRUITMENT & TRAINING: The firm takes three trainees a year and currently employs seven. They look for plenty of brains and a sense of humour. Trainees may be sent on overseas work experience with other firms within the LaWorld network.

KENT JONES AND DONE

K

Churchill House, Regent Road, Stoke-on-Trent, ST1 3RQ
Tel: (01782) 202020 **Fax:** (01782) 202040 **DX:** 20727 Hanley
Email: mail@kjd.co.uk

Managing Partner:	Adrian Ross
Senior Partner:	A.A. Reeves
Number of partners:	16
Assistant solicitors:	13
Other fee-earners:	13

CONTACTS

Banking/Security	Peter Ellis
Commercial	Adam Kelly
Commercial Property	Philip Medford
Construction	Graham Neyt
Corporate Finance	Peter Ellis
Development	Philip Medford
Dispute Resolution	Graham Neyt
Employment	Peter Gavin
EU/Competition	Adam Kelly
Insolvency	Peter Ellis, Adrian Ross
Intellectual Property	Michael Servian
Pensions	Roderick Ramage
Planning/Environmental	Grant Anderson
Private Client/Personal	Michael Gee
Subsidence	Adrian Ross
Taxation/Charities	Jim Moore

THE FIRM: The dominant corporate practice in the region outside Birmingham providing a wide range of specialist and general commercial advice. Corporate finance, commercial dispute resolution, commercial property, planning and environmental, and employment are among its particular strengths. The firm received Investor in People accreditation during the year.Prominent matters in which the firm has recently been involved include acting for venture capitalists, Alchemy Partners, in the £22m successful take private of Avonside plc; a category A action against the Coal Authority; the disposal of over 30 acres of residential development land, having prepared the site for sale by obtaining planning consents and advising on various planning and infrastructure agreements, advising a mineral operator in respect of enforcement proceedings in a six day public inquiry and advising on the competition law aspects of an EC investigation. The firm is recognised nationally for its specialist knowledge of the ceramics industry and mines/minerals including coal mining and other subsidence claims.

CLIENTELE: The client base is broad, ranging from small to medium-sized private companies to public companies and subsidiaries of multinationals. Their activities range from manufacturing, distribution and retailing to the financial sector, media/ entertainment and include several household names. The firm also acts on behalf of several housing associations and some private individuals.

KEOGHS

Gould House, 59 Chorley New Road, Bolton, BL1 4QP
Tel: (01204) 532611 **Fax:** (01204) 362944 **DX:** 25851 Bolton 2
Email: mod@keoghs.co.uk **Website:** www.keoghs.co.uk

1 Eastwood Business Village, Harry Weston Road, Binley, Coventry, CV3 2UB
Tel: (024) 7665 8200 **Fax:** (024) 7665 8262 **DX:** 700127 Coventry 4
Email: mod@keoghs.co.uk

4 Saxon Gate, Back of the Walls, Southampton, SO14 2HA
Tel: (023) 8023 5642 **Fax:** (023) 8023 0765 **DX:** 2014 Southampton 1
Email: mod@keoghs.co.uk

Senior Partner:	Barry Taziker
Insurance Managing Partner:	David Tyson
Commercial Managing Partner:	Alan Robins
Number of partners:	23
Assistant solicitors:	61
Other fee-earners:	58

AREAS OF PRACTICE

Insurance Litigation	85%
Company/Commercial	15%

CONTACTS

Commercial Litigation	Jonathan Lowe
Commercial Property	David Johnson
Company/Commercial	Alan Robins
Employment	Alan Lewis
Fraud	Howard Young
Insurance Litigation	David Tyson
Professional Indemnity	Nicola McLoughlin

THE FIRM: Sustained growth over recent years has seen Keoghs develop into one of the country's leading commercial law firms, specialising in insurance litigation and commercial business advice. The practice's success is based upon a combination of its no-nonsense, commercial outlook, the depth and variety of the legal services it provides, the approachability of its staff and, above all, its commitment to both high quality service delivery and competitive charges. Keoghs has full ISO quality accreditation and its clients range from national 'blue chip' organisations to small, growing businesses.

PRINCIPAL AREAS OF WORK:
Defendant Litigation: Keoghs is one of the country's leading advisers to the insurance industry, currently acting for more than thirty insurance organisations including the majority of the UK's top ten composite insurers and many Lloyds syndicates. Working closely with clients to avoid costly, protracted disputes, Keoghs has the capacity and experience to handle not only large volume defendant personal injury litigation including RTA cases but also high-profile, specialist cases including catastrophic injury and disease and deafness. The firm has also developed a wide base of expertise in other insurance related areas ranging from employer's

and public liability, product liability and negligence to insurance property work, subsidence claims and good-in-transit cases.

Fraud: Over recent years and to anticipate insurer clients' needs for specialist assistance Keoghs has established specific units to deal with both motor fraud and general fraud. The motor fraud unit now operates in tandem with many insurers' claims departments to identify fraud cases at an early stage and deal with them rapidly and effectively. The results have demonstrated substantial cost savings for clients.

Commercial Litigation: Keoghs commercial litigation team acts for both insurer and commercial business clients dealing with professional negligence claims, building and contractual disputes, injunctions, financial disputes and the recovery of outstanding debts. The team actively employs ADR methods wherever possible, saving clients both time and money.

Company/Commercial: The company and commercial team provides advice to a wide variety of clients from national organisations to privately owned and managed businesses. It offers down-to-earth advisory services including corporate finance, company formation, disposals and acquisitions, contract drafting, buy-outs and shareholders' agreements. In addition we offer a full range of commercial property advice and assistance. The commercial team specialises in providing assistance to small and medium sized business.

Employment: Keoghs employment team has abandoned the traditional methods of dealing with employment related disputes in favour of a new preventative approach. This approach, embodied in the firm's 'PeoplePack' product, not only ensures that employers receive the right advice and take the correct steps before problems arise, but also provides insurance to cover any legal fees that may be incurred where disputes are unavoidable.

Private Client: The firm has a dedicated team dealing with trusts and estate planning and wills and domestic conveyancing for clients who require these specialist services.

K

KERSHAW ABBOTT

Queen's Chambers, 5 John Dalton Street, Manchester, M2 6FT
Tel: (0161) 839 0998 **Fax:** (0161) 839 1019 **DX:** 14348 Manchester 1
Email: mail@kershaw-abbott.co.uk **Website:** www.kershaw-abbott.co.uk

Contact Partners:	Anne Kershaw
	Christopher Abbott
Number of partners:	4
Assistant solicitors:	3
Other fee-earners:	2

THE FIRM: Based in the centre of the Manchester business community, Kershaw Abbott is a modern and progressive practice serving commercial and insurance clients. Work of quality is handled in an effective and individual manner by partner-led teams, conscious always to provide a cost-effective service.

PRINCIPAL AREAS OF WORK: The firm is best known for its work in the fields of construction, professional partnership disputes, commercial and insurance litigation and employment. Expertise is offered in alternative forms of dispute resolution including mediation, adjudication and arbitration. The firm undertakes agency work in the specialist courts of the North West.

KIDSTONS & CO

1 Royal Bank Place, Buchanan Street, Glasgow, G1 3AA
Tel: (0141) 221 6551 **Fax:** (0141) 204 0507 **DX:** 56 Glasgow
Email: mail@kidstons.co.uk **Website:** www.kidstons.co.uk

3rd Floor, Conference House, The Exchange, 152 Morrison Street, Edinburgh, EH3 8EB
Tel: (0131) 200 6272 **Fax:** (0131) 200 6200

Managing partner:	Iain Atack
Senior partner:	Iain Atack
Number of partners:	8
Assistant solicitors:	5
Other fee-earners:	9

AREAS OF PRACTICE

Trusts and Probate	22%
Employment Law	20%
Business Law/Corporate	18%
Civil Litigation	15%
Commercial Property	15%
Residential Property	10%

CONTACTS

Civil Litigation	Iain AtackAlexander Reid
Commercial Property	Kenneth Gerber
Corporate/Business Law	Kenneth Gerber
Employment	Iain Atack
Insolvency	Alexander Reid
Residential Property	Alison Atack
Trusts	Douglas G McKerrell

THE FIRM Established in Glasgow over 150 years ago, Kidstons & Co. has grown to provide expertise in employment law, commercial property, civil litigation, trusts, corporate and business law, insolvency law and residential property. The firm has two partners who are accredited by the Law Society of Scotland: Iain Atack, specialist in employment law and Kenneth Gerber, specialist in commercial leasing. The firm has eight partners and four associates with full support from assistant solicitors; the firm has numerous contacts in Hong Kong, the Middle East and the Republic of Ireland. A significant part of the client base is from outwith Scotland.

CLIENTELE: The firm has a varied client base of UK manufacturing and retail plcs, commercial private companies, medical and other partnerships, trusts and family owned property investment and other businesses, many of whom are based in England and Europe. The firm's philosophy is that transactions should be very much partner led with the emphasis on pro-active and commercially orientated advice being given so as to enable clients to achieve their goals effectively.

KIERAN & CO
20 The Cross, Worcester, WR1 3PZ **Tel:** (01905) 28635 **Fax:** (01905) 21803 **DX:** 16265 **Ptnrs:** 1

KIMBELL & CO

352 Silbury Court, Silbury Boulevard, Milton Keynes, MK9 2HJ
Tel: (01908) 668555 **Fax:** (01908) 674344 **DX:** 31408
Email: recep@kimbell-mk.co.uk **Website:** www.kimbell.co.uk

Senior Partner:	Stephen Kimbell
Number of partners:	6
Assistant solicitors:	11
Other fee-earners:	6

AREAS OF PRACTICE

Corporate	30%
Litigation	27%
Commercial property	22%
Securities	21%

CONTACTS

Brewing/Services	Peter Holden
Commercial Litigation	Richard Brown
Commercial Property	Timothy Clark
Corporate	Stephen Kimbell, Jonathan Hambleton
Employment	Amanda Smith
IT	Robert Cain

THE FIRM: Established in 1986 by former City solicitors, Kimbell & Co aims to offer corporate clients practical, commercial advice. The firm has particularly strong links with the brewing, distribution and high-tech industries and also with the financial services sector.

PRINCIPAL AREAS OF WORK:

Corporate: The firm has built a reputation for buy-outs and mergers and acquisitions.

Banking: Services include acquisition finance, securities and associated loan documentation.

Commercial Litigation: Specific experience is offered in property-related matters, insolvency, recovery and EU competition law.

Commercial Property: Expertise covers large commercial developments, acquisitions and disposals, and landlord and tenant with particular experience in the retail sector.

Employment: Advice is offered on a wide range of contentious and non-contentious issues.

Information Technology: All aspects of IT law are covered, including e-commerce, internet and data protection.

Services to the Brewing/Licensed Trade Sector: A specialist knowledge of relevant issues has been developed through working for major national and regional brewers and pub companies.

INTERNATIONAL CONNECTIONS: Contacts have been developed with European law firms in order to provide a full range of services to clients with interests outside the UK.

K

KINGSFORD STACEY BLACKWELL

14 Old Square, Lincoln's Inn, London, WC2A 3UB
Tel: (020) 7447 1200 **Fax:** (020) 7831 2915 **DX:** 141 Chancery Lane
Email: ksb@kingsfords.co.uk **Website:** www.kingsfords.co.uk

Lincoln House, 34 High Street, Harpenden, AL5 2SX
Tel: (01582) 766866 **Fax:** (01582) 712424 **DX:** 80454 Harpenden

Managing partner:	Charles Rankmore
Senior partner:	Jonathan Wood
Number of partners:	25
Assistant solicitors:	16
Other fee-earners:	60

AREAS OF PRACTICE

Litigation	44%
Property (Residential & Commercial)	26%
Company/Commercial	16%
Private Client	6%
Licensing	4%
Personal Injury	4%

CONTACTS

Agency	Diana Oxford
Commercial Litigation	Niki Olympitis
Company/International	Robert Neville
Employment	Marie van der Zyl
Family	Andrew Hamilton
Licensing	Robert Edney
Personal Injury	Simon Pinner
Private Client	Susan Floyd
Property	Robert Sweet
Property Litigation	David White
Travel & Insolvency	Trevor Sears

THE FIRM: Kingsford Stacey Blackwell is a progressive, commercial law firm, based in Lincoln's Inn. The firm prides itself on its approachable partner-led range of services. Technical expertise is matched by practical, commercial advice and competitive fees.

PRINCIPAL AREAS OF WORK: Commercial litigation; airline and travel; insolvency; commercial property; company/commercial; licensing; defamation; employment; private client; factoring; landlord and tenant; family; residential property; and personal injury. Areas of recent growth include the property and company/commercial departments, as well as commercial litigation and family law. The firm also offers a specialist London Agency Service. Kingsford Stacey Blackwell has experienced rapid expansion since 1997, particularly with the setting up in the last year of a fully-staffed personal injury department in which it has installed a case management system and a claims handling process to ensure high client care standards.

INTERNATIONAL CONNECTIONS: The firm is the English member of Consulegis, a closely co-ordinated network of over 100 independent English speaking law firms in Europe, USA, Latin-American and the Far East. Kingsford Stacey Blackwell is a founder member of the network and as a result is able to offer its clients access to like minded English speaking lawyers throughout the world.

RECRUITMENT & TRAINING: Kingsford Stacey Blackwell is committed to continued expansion in its key departments. Lawyers with expertise and a following in these areas and who are considering a move are invited to contact the firm's practice manager with details. For further information about the firm, visit the website.

KINGSLEY NAPLEY

Knights Quarter, 14 St John's Lane, London, EC1M 4AJ
Tel: (020) 7814 1200 **Fax:** (020) 7490 2288 **DX:** 22 Ch.Ln.
Email: mail@kingsleynapley.co.uk **Website:** www.kingsleynapley.co.uk

Managing Partner:	Paul Terzeon
Senior Partner:	David Speker
Number of partners:	33
Assistant solicitors:	25
Other fee-earners:	17
Total staff:	150

THE FIRM: Kingsley Napley is an internationally recognised commercial law firm based in the City of London. The firm has expertise in corporate and commercial work, criminal and commercial litigation, commercial property, employment, immigration, clinical negligence and family law. Kingsley Napley specializes in dealing with matters of particular complexity and difficulty in all branches of the law. The client base is wide and varied, ranging from large public companies to 'owner-managed' businesses and individuals.

PRINCIPAL AREAS OF WORK:
Litigation: Work encompasses commercial and civil litigation and dispute resolution, professional negligence, construction disputes, landlord and tenant, and defamation. There is particular experience in asset tracing investigations. The firm's employment law unit handles contentious and non-contentious employment law issues.
Criminal Litigation: Work covers a broad spectrum including corporate and City fraud, SFO, DTI and Inland Revenue investigations, money-laundering, asset tracing enquiries and mutual assistance.The department is internationally recognised for advising on extradition matters and crime. Members of the department appear regularly before various regulatory and professional bodies, both prosecuting and defending. Two of the partners also undertake licensing work.
Family: All aspects of family and matrimonial work are undertaken, including issues concerning childcare such as child abduction, through to cohabitation and complex financial matters on divorce.
Corporate & Commercial: Advice on a wide range of business issues including joint ventures, corporate finance, taxation, flotations, rights issues, takeovers, insolvency and liquidation and partnerships.
Property: All aspects of conveyancing of commercial freehold and leasehold property undertaken, together with a small amount of residential property work.
Clinical Negligence: All types of clinical negligence work are undertaken with an emphasis on cases involving injuries of maximum severity, in particular, cerebral palsy. Also handles surrogacy and adoption personal injury work.
Business Immigration: A highly personalised specialist business immigration service is provided to both corporate clients and individuals, advising on all aspects of UK and EU immigration and nationality issues.

LANGUAGES: French, German and Spanish are spoken.

AREAS OF PRACTICE

Criminal Litigation	21%
Commercial Property	18%
Litigation	17%
Corporate and Commercial	14%
Business Immigration	10%
Clinical Negligence	10%
Family	10%

CONTACTS

Clinical Negligence	Julia Cahill
Commercial Property	Francis Weaver
Construction	Michael Janney
Corporate and Commercial	David Walsh
Criminal Litigation	Christopher Murray
Employment	Richard Fox
Family	Jane Keir
Immigration	Hilary Belchak
Licensing	Michael Caplan
Litigation	Paul Terzeon
Partnership	Tony Sacker

K

KIRBYS
32 Victoria Avenue, Harrogate, HG1 5PR **Tel:** (01423) 542 000 **Fax:** (01423) 542 001 **DX:** 11956 HARROGATE 1
Email: mail@kirbyssolicitors.demon.co.uk

KIRK JACKSON
97 Chorley Rd, Swinton, Manchester, M27 2AB **Tel:** (0161) 794 0431 **Fax:** (0161) 794 4957 **DX:** 28201 **Email:** law@kirk-jackson.com
Ptnrs: 9 **Asst solrs:** 2 **Other fee-earners:** 2

KIRKLAND & ELLIS
Tower 42, 25 Old Broad Street, London, EC2N 1HQ **Tel:** (020) 7816 8700 **Fax:** (020) 7816 8800 **Email:** samuel_haubold@uk.kirkland.com **Website:** www.kirkland.com **Ptnrs:** 7 **Asst solrs:** 17 **Other fee-earners:** 3 **Contact:** Mr Samuel Haubold • An international firm advising on arbitration, litigation, intellectual property, e-commerce, mergers and acquisitions, private equity, corporate finance and commercial matters.

AREAS OF PRACTICE

Private Equity	30%
Mergers & Acquisitions	20%
Antitrust/Competition	10%
Arbitration/Litigation	10%
Corporate/Commercial	10%
E-commerce	10%
Intellectual Property	10%

KLEGAL
Ludgate House, 107-111 Fleet Street, London, EC4A 2AB
Tel: (020) 7694 2500 **Fax:** (020) 7694 2501 **DX:** 38050 BLACKFRIARS
Email: firstname.lastname@kpmg.co.uk **Website:** www.klegal.com

Managing Partner:	Nick Holt
Number of partners:	11
Assistant solicitors:	35
Other fee-earners:	3

THE FIRM: KLegal was established on 1 July 1999 by six founding partners James Hodgson, Alastair Holmes, Tim Johnson, Patrick Martin, Timothy Parsons and Philip Rogers in association with KPMG. The initial focus has been to develop practice areas which complement those services offered by KPMG. These include Banking and Finance, Corporate, Commercial, E-Commerce, Employment, Financial Services, Intellectual Property, IT/Telecoms, Projects/PFI, Property, Tax Litigation and Trade & Customs. The firm provides legal advice & assistance to clients both on a stand-alone basis and as part of a multi-disciplinary offering in conjunction with other KPMG professionals in consulting, tax, audit and corporate finance/transaction services.

PRINCIPAL AREAS OF WORK: KLegal provides legal advice and assistance (often working in conjunction with KPMG) in relation to a wide variety of corporate and commercial transactions, in particular, acquisitions and disposals, MBO's and joint ventures. It has also advised in relation to a diverse range of banking and finance related matters (including structured and acquisition finance transactions, treasury products and financial services issues), employment and HR issues, intellectual property matters (both contentious and non-contentious), IT & telecoms work (including major outsourcing projects), property, tax litigation and trade & customs. Increasingly, much of the work has an e-commerce angle, especially where the firm is advising alongside other professionals from KPMG.

INTERNATIONAL CONNECTIONS: KLegal is a founder member of the KLegal International network of correspondent law firms of KPMG which has over 1,700 lawyers in 50 jurisdictions including Australia, Belgium,

Continued overleaf

AREAS OF PRACTICE

Banking & Financial Services	20%
Corporate & Commercial	20%
IT/Telecoms	15%
E-commerce	10%
Employment	10%
IP/Litigation	10%
Tax Litigation/Trade & Customs	10%
Property	5%

Finland, France, Germany, Greece, Italy, Netherlands, New Zealand, Norway, Poland, Portugal, Romania, Russia, Slovakia, Spain and Switzerland. The firm is able to offer and/or co-ordinate legal advice & assistance across all major disciplines in most leading jurisdictions, which capability will be significantly enhanced during the next two to three years. Opportunities exist for secondments to member firms.

CLIENTELE: The firm's client base is drawn from a diverse range of industry sectors including finance; infrastructure and government; information, communications and entertainment; consumer and industrial markets and owner managed businesses. Clients range from national and multi-national corporations, government bodies and banks through to internet start ups and entrepreneurs. They have been introduced to the firm from a variety of sources including referrals from KPMG (both UK and overseas) and member firms of KLegal International, as well as by lawyers who have joined the firm from elsewhere.

RECRUITMENT & TRAINING: The firm has grown rapidly since its formation in July 1999 having recruited name partners in a number of practice areas including e-commerce (Mark Haftke- Bird & Bird), Employment (Stephen Levinson - Paisner & Co), Projects/PFI (Gareth Davies - Simmons & Simmons) and IT/Telecoms (Chris Hoyle - Rakisons). It has also recruited Nick Holt, co-founder and former managing partner of Weil Gotshal & Manges' London office, as managing partner of the firm. Further rapid growth is planned over the next 12 months and the firm expects to pass the 100 lawyer mark in early 2001. Applications are invited from ambitious and energetic lawyers with leading City and regional law firms, or with first rate experience in-house, who are attracted by the prospect of working in a dynamic, multi-disciplinary and international environment (contact : Tim Johnson), and from law students with good academics who are looking for training contracts in 2001 and 2002 (contact : Patrick Martin).

CONTACTS

Banking	Timothy Parsons
	Michael Dickie
Commercial	Arun Singh OBE
Corporate	Patrick Martin
	Philip Rogers
E-commerce	Mark Haftke
Employment	Tim Johnson
	Stephen Levinson
Financial Regulation	Alastair Holmes
Intellectual Property & Litigation	James Hodgson
IT/Telecoms	Chris Hoyle
	Anthony Lee
Project Finance/PFI	Gareth Davies
Property	Bruce Dear
	Stephen Sumpton
Tax Litigation	James Bullock
Trade & Customs	Jeremy White

K

KNIGHTS

Regency House, 25 High Street, Tunbridge Wells, TN1 1UT **Tel:** (01892) 537311 **Fax:** (01892) 526141 **DX:** 3919 Tunbridge Wells **Email:** knights@atlas.co.uk **Website:** www.knights-solicitors.co.uk **Ptnrs:** 2 **Asst solrs:** 1 **Other fee-earners:** 4 **Contact:** Mr M. D. M. Knight • Litigation practice, specialising in country sports and countryside law, defamation, trespass, judicial review, crime, personal injury, employment, contract and rights of way disputes.

AREAS OF PRACTICE

Civil Litigation	80%
Criminal Litigation	20%

KNIGHT & SONS

The Brampton, Newcastle-under-Lyme, ST5 0QW
Tel: (01782) 619225 **Fax:** (01782) 717260 **DX:** 711120 Newcastle under Lyme 7
Email: commercial@knightandsons.co.uk

75 Mosley Street, Manchester, M2 3HR
Tel: (0161) 281 4000 **Fax:** (0161) 281 4010 **DX:** 14376 Manchester 1
Email: man@knightandsons.co.uk

Managing Partner:	Robert Hayle
Senior Partner:	Anthony Peter Bell
Number of partners:	16
Assistant solicitors:	7
Other fee-earners:	11
Associates:	6
Consultants:	6
Trainees:	7

THE FIRM: Knight & Sons took the opportunity during 1999 to overhaul the firm and gear up for the millennium. After several years of sustained above average growth the partners took a decision to review the management structure devolving more control to the heads of the fee earning departments to enable the firm to be more focused on those areas where it already excels and to develop new niche areas.

PRINCIPAL AREAS OF WORK: The prospects for developing and enhancing the firm's reputation in a number of areas is viewed by the partners with considerable excitement.
Agriculture: Of particular note is the firm's expertise and reputation in agricultural work where it is clearly the pre-eminent firm in the West Midlands. In 1999 the firm's expanding agricultural unit was awarded the contract for the NFU for the whole of Cheshire, Staffordshire, Derbyshire, Shropshire and North Wales.
Commercial Property: The commercial property department continues to go from strength to strength. Within this department is based the mines and minerals unit which has gained itself a national reputation and continues to attract new major clients.
Corporate: Corporate work grew with 11 deals over £1m and the department embarking upon the firm's first PFI/securitisation project.
Employment: Under the new focused approach the employment unit has achieved remarkable growth in a short space of time forging links for the benefit of clients with an international firm of business consultants.
Personal Injury: The personal injury department has been successful in being appointed to the Solicitors Panel of a local legal expenses insurance company, at a time when the numbers of firms on panels are being reduced. New work is being received at an unprecedented rate and recruitment is a priority.
Tax Trust/Private Client: The tax trust and private client department is now the envy of many firms in Birmingham and Manchester. A team of specifically recruited lawyers and accountants has increased the revenue of this department from some 10% of the firm's fee income to approaching 20% in just a few years. The expertise within this department has ensured that it will continue to expand and flourish. Given the breadth and quality of the firm's client base prospects for the future look extremely encouraging.

AREAS OF PRACTICE

Commercial Property	40%
Commercial Litigation	22%
Corporate & Commercial	20%
Private Client	18%

CONTACTS

Agriculture	Robert Hoyle
Charities	Charles Jones
Commercial Property	Ian White
Commercial/Competition	Derek Miller
Construction	Richard Lashmore
Corporate Finance	Derek Miller
Development	Richard Lashmore
Employment	Christine Dyson
Insolvency	Derek Miller
Licensing	Richard Jones
Litigation	Andrew Davidson
Mines and Minerals	Paul Calladine
Planning and Environment	Andrea Bruce
Taxation	Henry Davenport

Other: The firm's Manchester office continues its focused approach from the new premises acquired in Mosley Street at the end of 1997 and is proving to be well equipped to meet the challenges presented by the competitive Manchester environment. The firm is ambitious and optimistic of developing further in the Manchester area and has been highly encouraged by the reception so far received from Manchester based clients and professionals.

KUIT STEINART LEVY

3 St. Mary's Parsonage, Manchester, M3 2RD **Tel:** (0161) 832 3434 **Fax:** (0161) 832 6650 **DX:** 14325 **Email:** ksllaw@aol.com **Website:** www.kuits.com **Ptnrs:** 12 **Asst solrs:** 12 **Other fee-earners:** 11 **Contact:** Mr Robert Levy • This Manchester firm is a prominent provider of legal services to business clients ranging from plcs to SMEs in the North-West and nationally.

AREAS OF PRACTICE	
Company/Commercial	35%
Litigation	25%
Property	25%
Tax & Trusts	15%

LAMPORT BASSITT

46 The Avenue, Southampton, SO17 1AX
Tel: (023) 8083 7777 **Fax:** (023) 8083 7788 **DX:** 38529 Southampton 3 Video Conferencing: (023) 8083 7760 **Email:** e-mail@lamportbassitt.co.uk **Website:** www.lamportbassitt.co.uk

Senior Partner:	A.J. Lightfoot
Number of partners:	11
Assistant solicitors:	17
Other fee-earners:	12

AREAS OF PRACTICE	
Litigation	70%
Company/Commercial	21%
Private Client	9%

CONTACTS	
Commercial	S.P. Kelly
Litigation	R.G.B. Solomon
Private Client	J.E. Excell

LAMPORT BASSITT
solicitors

THE FIRM: The firm operates an expanding and predominantly commercial practice, and places particular emphasis on technical ability and specialisation. The firm is a niche practice aiming to provide high quality services within specialist areas. The firm makes full use of modern technology. Most senior fee-earners are highly experienced in their chosen fields. The firm is ISO 9001 registered.

PRINCIPAL AREAS OF WORK:
Commercial: A wide range of corporate, employment, insolvency, planning, property, and liquor, betting and gaming licensing work.
Litigation: The firm is involved in the full range of litigation work including building disputes, commercial contracts, debt collection, employment disputes, intellectual property matters, maritime law, property disputes, professional negligence, and has a large personal injury department. Agency work undertaken.
Private Client: Residential property, personal tax, probate, trusts, wills and matrimonial.

CLIENTELE: Clients include substantial UK and overseas-based listed and private companies from a wide area of industry and commerce, insurance companies, trade unions and trade associations.

RECRUITMENT & TRAINING: A minimum of two trainee solicitors are recruited each year. Enquiries to Mr John Newton, partner.

LANDWELL

St Andrew's House, 20 St Andrew Street, London, EC4A 3TL
Tel: (020) 7212 1616 **Fax:** (020) 7212 1570 **DX:** 218 Chancery Lane, London WC2
Email: firstname.lastname@uk.pwcglobal.com **Website:** www.landwell.co.uk

Senior Partner:	Chris Arnheim
Number of partners:	11
Assistant solicitors:	45
Other fee-earners:	9
Total	117

THE FIRM: Landwell, (previously known as Arnheim Tite & Lewis) is a City-based firm of solicitors practising international business law. Drawn from top UK firms, its lawyers provide local expertise in a global environment. The firm is backed by the Landwell network of 1500 business lawyers in over 40 countries which means that it is part of one of the world's largest legal practices. Landwell is the correspondent legal practice of PricewaterhouseCoopers, the world's largest professional services organisation. Landwell represents a new model for the delivery of legal advice that responds to the needs of today's changing global economy. The practice offers the unique ability to provide legal advice as part of integrated professional consulting service teams to address complex client business needs. In this way, Landwell lawyers act as deal architects and project managers to provide complete solutions to a client's needs. Landwell delivers legal solutions of the highest technical quality, through an international network of strong local law practices and in-depth expertise across the spectrum of legal disciplines relevant to business. These resources provide clients with a rapid speed of response to the highest international and local standards.

LANE & PARTNERS

15 Bloomsbury Square, London, WC1A 2LP
Tel: (020) 7242 2626 **Fax:** (020) 7242 0387 **DX:** 134442 Bloomsbury
Email: info@lane.co.uk **Website:** www.lane.co.uk

Senior Partner:	Terence Lane
Contact Partner:	William Morton
Number of partners:	12
Assistant solicitors:	8
Other fee-earners:	6

THE FIRM: Lane & Partners concentrates on providing a partner-led service at competitive rates to commercial clients, covering all the main areas of law of relevance to them. It is well known for its work in the areas of international arbitration, construction, aviation and travel law.

PRINCIPAL AREAS OF WORK:

Company & Commercial: The firm advises clients on all aspects of company and commercial law, including mergers and acquisitions, joint ventures, listing requirements, financial services, insolvency and employment law and UK and EU competition law.

Intellectual Property: The firm advises in respect of patent, trade mark and copyright matters, including licensing, franchising, merchandising, all aspects of infringement and on IT and e-commerce issues.

Litigation: The firm is active in all aspects of commercial litigation with particular emphasis on actions in the Commercial Court.

Arbitration: The firm has an active international arbitration practice, with particular emphasis on major construction disputes.

Commercial Property: The firm is involved on behalf of commercial clients in all aspects of property work including the acquisition of freehold and leasehold properties for occupation, investment or development, the sale and management of properties, planning law and appeals and environmental law.

Construction: The firm advises on all aspects of construction law, including the negotiation and preparation of construction contracts, the interpretation of the standard forms used by the industry and the preparation and handling of claims.

Aviation & Travel: The firm advises UK and foreign airlines and tour operators and travel agents. Advice is also given on aviation insurance and liability cases and on aircraft acquisition and leasing transactions.

INTERNATIONAL CONNECTIONS: The firm has links with firms in New York, Washington DC, Los Angeles, Tokyo, Düsseldorf, Stockholm, Lahore, Toronto, Mexico City, Seoul, Geneva and Singapore.

LANGUAGES: French and Italian.

CLIENTELE: As well as acting for UK companies, the firm has a considerable number of foreign clients, particularly Swedish, American and Japanese companies. In size, they range from well-known multinationals to small private companies. Their businesses are equally diverse, stretching from international construction and heavy engineering to cosmetics, computers and tour operating.

RECRUITMENT & TRAINING: One/two trainees are taken on per annum.

AREAS OF PRACTICE	
Litigation	30%
Company/Commercial	20%
Property (Commercial)	17%
Aviation and Travel	13%
Construction/Arbitration	12%
Intellectual Property/Marketing	8%

CONTACTS	
Aviation/Travel	Richard Venables
Company/ Commercial	Keith Gallon
	William Morton
Construction/Arbitration	Terence Lane
	Colin Hall
Intellectual Property/ Marketing	Michael Varvill
Litigation	Ludovic de Walden
	Piers Lane
Property	Richard Hardman
	Mark Barber

L

LANGLEY & CO

66-67 Cornhill, London, EC3V 3NB
Tel: (020) 7397 9650 **Fax:** (020) 7929 6316 **DX:** 706 London/City

Number of partners:	3
Assistant solicitors:	4
Other fee-earners:	4

THE FIRM: Langley & Co was established in 1993 and specialises exclusively in employment law. Its principals are Jill Andrew and Nick Ralph who between them have over 30 years' experience, and all of whom were previously with major City firms.

PRINCIPAL AREAS OF WORK: The firm deals with all aspects of employment law for corporate clients including contentious and non-contentious matters and also acts for individuals in employment disputes. It aims to provide a highly personalised and responsive service geared to the needs of clients. It is pleased to offer competitive fee quotations and also has a range of fixed price services including the conduct of and representation at Employment Tribunals. Other services which the firm currently provides include bespoke employment law training courses for clients and the legal profession.

AREAS OF PRACTICE	
Employment	90%
General Commercial Advice	10%

LANYON BOWDLER

23 Swan Hill, Shrewsbury, SY1 1NN **Tel:** (01743) 236400 **Fax:** (01743) 354994 **DX:** 19721 Shrewsbury **Ptnrs:** 14 **Other fee-earners:** 33

LARBY WILLIAMS

53 Mount Stuart Square, Cardiff, CF10 5LR **Tel:** (029) 2047 2100 **Fax:** (029) 2047 2011 **DX:** 200750 Cardiff Bay **Ptnrs:** 2 **Asst solrs:** 2

LARCOMES

168 London Rd, North End, Portsmouth, PO2 9DN **Tel:** (023) 9266 1531 **Fax:** (023) 9267 1043 **DX:** 42401 **Ptnrs:** 6 **Asst solrs:** 5 **Other fee-earners:** 10

LAST CAWTHRA FEATHER SOLICITORS

Airedale House, 128 Sunbridge Road, Bradford, BD1 2AT **Tel:** (01274) 848800 **Fax:** (01274) 370552 **DX:** 11723 Bradford 1 **Email:** mail@lcf.co.uk **Website:** www.lcf.co.uk **Ptnrs:** 12 **Asst solrs:** 11 **Other fee-earners:** 12 **Contact:** Mr Simon R.B. Stell • A commercial practice with three offices and a total of 87 staff, undertaking a variety of work for businesses and private individuals.

AREAS OF PRACTICE	
Litigation (including liquor licensing)	25%
Property	25%
Company/Commercial	15%
Family	15%
Employment	10%
Wills/Probate/Trusts	10%

LATHAM & WATKINS

99 Bishopsgate, London, EC2M 3XF
Tel: (020) 7710 1000 **Fax:** (020) 7374 4460
Email: webmaster2@lw.com **Website:** www.lw.com

Managing Partner (office):	Joe Blum
Managing Partner (firm):	Robert Dell
Number of partners:	9
Assistant solicitors:	32
Other fee-earners:	2

AREAS OF PRACTICE

Company/Commercial	30%
Corporate Finance	30%
Project Finance	30%
Telecomms/Media	10%

THE FIRM: Latham & Watkins is a multi-national partnership with nine US and five international offices. The lawyers in the London office practice English and US law and represent a cross-section of the firm's transactional and regulatory expertise. As client needs dictate, London-based lawyers can also call upon the collective expertise of over 1000 Latham & Watkins lawyers practising worldwide in disciplines encompassing virtually every aspect of business-related law.

London Office: The work undertaken by the London office is primarily in project finance, corporate finance and company/commercial and also covers telecommunications and media.

Other Offices: Los Angeles, New York, Chicago, San Diego, Orange County, New Jersey, Washington DC, San Francisco, Silicon Valley, Hong Kong, Moscow, Singapore and Tokyo.

LANGUAGES: French, German, Italian, Spanish, Japanese and Urdu.

L

LATIMER HINKS

5-8 Priestgate, Darlington, DL1 1NL **Tel:** (01325) 341500 **Fax:** (01325) 381072 **DX:** 69282 Darlington 6 **Email:** lh@latimerhinks.co.uk **Ptnrs:** 8 **Asst solrs:** 7 **Other fee-earners:** 15

LAWFORD KIDD

12 Hill Street, Edinburgh, EH2 3LB **Tel:** (0131) 225 5214 **Fax:** (0131) 226 2069 **DX:** ED 159 **Email:** law@lawfordkidd.co.uk **Ptnrs:** 3 **Asst solrs:** 4 **Other fee-earners:** 2 **Contact:** Mr David Sandison • Specialise in personal injury litigation for trade union clients; medical negligence, Court of Session litigation; relocation conveyancing. Associate office, Lawfords, Watchmaker Court, 65 St. John Street, London, EC1M 4NG.

AREAS OF PRACTICE

Personal Injury	60%
Conveyqncing/Estate Agency/General Business	25%
Litigation (general)/Employment	10%
Wills and Executries	5%

LAWFORDS

Watchmaker Court, 65 St John Street, London, EC1M 4NG
Tel: (020) 7353 5099 **Fax:** (020) 7353 5355 **DX:** 53311 Clerkenwell
Email: enquiries@lawford.co.uk **Website:** www.lawford.co.uk

Senior Partner:	Graham Humby
Management Partner:	Linda Fletcher
Number of partners:	16
Assistant solicitors:	14
Other fee-earners:	16

AREAS OF PRACTICE

Personal Injury	75%
Education/Civil Litigation/Commercial Property/Company Commercial	13%
Employment	12%

CONTACTS

Education	Clive Robertson
Employment	Stephen Blunt
Personal Injury	Graham Humby
Property	Laraine Phillips
	Clive Robertson

LAWFORDS
SOLICITORS

THE FIRM: Established in 1952 Lawfords is a medium-sized practice with offices in the City and the principal regions, and is well known for its expertise in PI (Claimant) litigation. The firm offers clients the personal attention of a smaller firm as well as the breadth of legal knowledge offered by a large nationwide practice. The firm has other offices in Richmond, Manchester and Nottingham and an associated office in Lawford Kidd, Edinburgh.

PRINCIPAL AREAS OF WORK:

Personal Injury: The personal injury department receives instructions from a wide range of trade unions, professional associations, institutional clients and legal expenses insurers. The firm has particular expertise in representing claimants following accidents at work and has dealt with some of the largest UK financial awards and settlements in recent years. The firm employs 31 case-handlers in England and Wales and has an associate office with Lawford Kidd in Scotland to provide national coverage.

Employment: The firm has a large and thriving employment department representing predominantly trade union members and private clients. The department currently consists of two partners, one consultant and three assistant solicitors and has specialists in all aspects of employment law.

Education: The firm acts for a number of institutions in further and higher education advising and acting in matters such as property acquisition and financing, commercial contracts and company formation, student and staff issues.

Property: The firm acts on behalf of commercial and institutional clients and deals with all aspects of property work. This includes the acquisition and disposal of substantial freehold and leasehold properties for investment, development, occupation or management.

CLIENTELE: Clients include trade unions and employee associations, universities, higher education institutions, legal expenses insurers and private clients.

THE LAW OFFICES OF MARCUS J. O'LEARY

Centennial Court, Easthampstead Road, Bracknell, RG12 1YQ
Tel: (01344) 303044 **Fax:** (01344) 300808
Email: moleary@mjol.co.uk **Website:** www.mjol.co.uk

Number of partners:	5
Assistant solicitors:	2
Other fee-earners:	1

AREAS OF PRACTICE

IT/IP/Internet/Multimedia	75%
Company/Commercial	10%
Advertising/Media/Entertainment	5%
Employment	5%
Litigation	5%

CONTACTS

Advert./Media/Entertainment	Marcus O'Leary
	Celia Nortcliff
Company/Commercial	Rupert Wright
Employment	Andrew Fishleigh
IT/IP/Internet/Multimedia	Marcus O'Leary
	Paul Milton
	Celia Nortcliff
Litigation	Andrew Fishleigh

THE FIRM: A well-known and innovative niche practice specialising in information technology, intellectual property and related commercial matters. Comprising established practitioners in these fields, the practice is modern, progressive and provides an excellent cost effective service to all of its clients.

PRINCIPAL AREAS OF WORK:
Information Technology: Experienced practitioners with in-house experience offer a full range of advice to high technology companies and other companies using high technology products.
Intellectual Property: All copyright, design, patent, biotechnology, trade mark, passing off and confidential information issues handled quickly and efficiently with regard to the client's best interest.
Internet/Multimedia: The firm acts for well-known international companies active in this specialist area. Good quality leading edge advice is assured.
Music, Media & Entertainment: Advice and contracts for musicians and composers.
Advertising: The firm has extensive experience in dealing with advertisements and promotions in different media formats both nationally, internationally and on the internet.
Competition Law: Advice on UK and EU Competition law is available in relation to all matters dealt with by the firm.
Company/Commercial: The firm provides a full range of legal services including mergers and acquisitions, joint ventures, MBOs and MBIs restructuring, flotations, particularly in connection with high technology companies.
Employment: Advice on all aspects of employment law is available, tempered with down-to-earth practical advice relevant to the situation.
Litigation: Can be undertaken by the firm in connection with any of the matters listed above.

LANGUAGES: French, German, Hindi, Spanish and embryonic Japanese.

CLIENTELE: Mainly well known international high technology companies.

RECRUITMENT & TRAINING: A small number of very highly qualified and experienced assistant solicitors are needed each year.

LAWRENCE GRAHAM

190 Strand, London, WC2R 1JN
Tel: (020) 7379 0000 **Fax:** (020) 7379 6854 **DX:** 39 Chancery Lane WC2
Email: info@lawgram.com **Website:** www.lawgram.com

61 St Mary Axe, London, EC3A 8JN
Tel: (020) 7379 0000 **Fax:** (020) 7480 5156 **DX:** 1072 London City LDE
Email: info@lawgram.com

Senior partner:	Martyn Gower
Number of partners:	79
Assistant solicitors:	92
Other fee-earners:	67

AREAS OF PRACTICE

Property	36%
Corporate & Commercial	29%
Litigation	23%
Tax & Financial Management	12%

THE FIRM: Lawrence Graham is a London based firm acting principally for UK and international public and private companies, pension funds, financial institutions, public authorities, shipping companies, small businesses and private individuals. The firm's business is divided into four principal practice areas; company and commercial, commercial property, litigation and tax and financial management. Each of these areas is organised into specialist teams according to clients' requirements or the services being provided. The firm has associations with many law firms throughout the world including North America, Europe, the Middle and Far East. It also has an office in the Ukraine, serving clients since the 1920s primarily, but not exclusively, involved in shipping. The firm works in partnership with clients to achieve their objectives in the most cost effective and practical way. The aim is to add value to client's businesses.

PRINCIPAL AREAS OF WORK:
Company/Commercial: The department advises on a wide range of transactions including public company takeovers, mergers and acquisitions (both domestic and international) bank and other financings, new media/internet and EU/Competition related issues. It is organised into three main focus groups; corporate, finance and commerce/technology, with four other specialist teams supplying advice on employment/employee benefits, insolvency, energy and pensions/insurance. The firm's highly regarded public authority/housing association practice is also located in the company and commercial department.
Commercial Porperty: The department acts for major institutions, corporate occupiers, pension funds, banks, developers and investors (both plc and private companies), retailers, local authorities and many other public bodies. The range of work undertaken is comprehensive. It includes acquisitions, disposals and financings,

joint ventures, securitisation and telecommunications code powers. Construction, planning and property litigation teams are all located in this department.

Litigation: The department is organised into teams advising on disputes relating to insurance, reinsurance, shipping and more general business disputes including, in particular, those arising out of banking and insolvency, financial services, intellectual property issues and employment rights. A feature of our litigation practice is that much of our work has an international dimension to it. In addition to its extensive High Court practice, the department is actively engaged in arbitrations and other forms of dispute resolution. The tax and financial management department provides various specialist services. They include input as part of larger teams working on corporate and property transactions, fiduciary risk management for both UK and international corporate trustees and a wide range of advice to private individuals. The latter includes tax, trust and estate planning work much of which has an international element to it. In addition, the firm has an established investment management business for its private clients.

LAWSON COPPOCK & HART

18 Tib Lane, Cross St, Manchester, M2 4JA **Tel:** (0161) 832 5944 **Fax:** (0161) 834 4409 **DX:** 14370 **Email:** info@lawsons-uk.com
Website: www.lawsons-uk.com **Ptnrs:** 8 **Asst solrs:** 1 **Other fee-earners:** 1

LAW SOUTH

66 Guildford Street, Chertsey, KT16 9BB
Tel: (01932) 560902 **Fax:** (01932) 571250 **DX:** 48259 Chertsey
Email: office@lawsouth.demon.co.uk

Director of Administration:	Christina Myers
Number of partners:	234
Assistant solicitors:	203
Other fee-earners:	268

THE GROUP: Law South is a group of ten independent law firms in major centres throughout the South East of England. Formed in 1988, the Group's major objective is the establishment of inter-firm networks to provide collective resources for training, marketing and pooled legal expertise, thus ensuring a consistently high standard of service throughout the region. Quality projects leading to ISO9001, Legal Aid Franchising and Investors in People are implemented, and all member firms have one or more external accreditation.

MEMBER FIRMS: Barlows: (Guildford and Surrey)Blake Lapthorn: (Portsmouth, London and Hampshire)Brachers: (Maidstone & London)Donne Mileham & Haddock: (Brighton and East Sussex)Girlings: (Canterbury, Ashford and East Kent)Leigh Williams: (Bromley and North Kent)Thomas Eggar Church Adams: (London, Chichester, Worthing, Horsham and Reigate)Thomson Snell & Passmore: (Tunbridge Wells and Mid-Kent)White & Bowker: (Winchester and Hampshire)Wilsons: (Salisbury, and Wiltshire/Dorset)

LAYTONS

Carmelite, 50 Victoria Embankment, Blackfriars, London, EC4Y 0LS
Tel: (020) 7842 8000 **Fax:** (020) 7842 8080 **DX:** 253 Chancery Lane
Email: london@laytons.com **Website:** www.laytons.com

Saint Batholomews, Lewins Head, Bristol, BS1 2NH
Tel: (0117) 930 9500 **Fax:** (0117) 929 3369 **DX:** 7895 Bristol-1
Email: bristol@laytons.com

76 Bridge Road, Hampton Court, Surrey, KT8 9HF
Tel: (020) 8481 7000 **Fax:** (020) 8481 7070 **DX:** 80052 East Molesey
Email: surrey@laytons.com

22 St John St, Manchester, M3 4EB
Tel: (0161) 834 2100 **Fax:** (0161) 834 6862 **DX:** 14382 Manchester-1
Email: manchester@laytons.com

Chief Executive Partner:	Richard Kennett
Number of partners:	29
Assistant solicitors:	39
Other fee-earners:	25

AREAS OF PRACTICE

Company/Commercial	45%
Commercial Property/Land Development	19%
General Litigation	15%
Employment	10%
Building Litigation	5%
Insolvency	3%
Other including Private Client/Trusts	3%

THE FIRM: Laytons is a commercial law firm whose primary focus is corporate/commercial and property/land development/construction. The firm's commitment is service to its clients. To provide advice which combines technical excellence, practical effectiveness and timely service, Laytons assigns a core legal team to each client who knows its business and can advise directly or by deploying the specialist skills of colleagues. The approach to legal issues is practical, creative and energetic, providing high quality advice founded on a range of complementary specialist skills relevant to the firm's primary fields of focus. The firm is a single national team operating through its four offices, each of which draws on the strengths of the whole with the benefit of excellent IT and communications. Internally, the firm shares and supports, in an environment in which each can learn and contribute; Laytons pools its knowledge to the benefit of all.

PRINCIPAL AREAS OF WORK:

Corporate/Commercial: Comprises corporate finance (domestic and cross-border mergers, acquisitions and joint ventures, stock exchange work, regulatory compliance, venture capital, management buy-outs, recon-

Continued overleaf

structions, bank lending); commercial (commercial contracts, e-commerce, competition, product safety, international trade); intellectual property and technology (acquisition, protection, licensing and enforcement; internet, advertising law); human resources (employment contracts, share-related and other incentives, pensions, termination of employment, redundancy programmes, TUPE, health & safety); insolvency and turnaround.

Property, Land Development & Construction Services: Combines a range of skills serving those industries and the commercial property interests of clients generally; land development - Laytons are project solicitors for a number of land development consortia (site acquisition, land warehousing, housebuilding, joint ventures, planning advice, hearings and infrastructure agreements); environmental services (contaminated land projects, environmental claims, waste management, mineral extraction, contracts/tenders for environmental services); construction law (adjudication, arbitration, contract preparation, collateral warranty advice); portfolio management. Both fields of focus draw on the skills of each other and also on specialist teams dealing across both fields: corporate tax (corporation tax, employment taxation, capital taxation, value added tax, property taxation, customs duties); regulatory compliance (environmental, transport, licensing petroleum and other licensing, property misdescriptions); liquor and entertainment licensing. Strong dispute resolution skills are an integral part of the service provided across the range of the firm's services, with specialist skills in particular fields of work, including UK and international mediation, litigation and arbitration; property disputes; insurance and professional negligence; product safety; land and environment; debt recovery; intellectual property; employment-related issues.

Private Client: An essential element of the firm's approach and service to clients. A strong family law team is complemented by a comprehensive and specialist service concentrating on the traditional areas of private client work. The firm provides practical advice focusing on the modern day needs and demands of its client base of high net worth individuals and trustees, covering tax and estate planning for UK resident and non-resident individuals and all aspects of charity law, including tax, fundraising and trading issues.

INTERNATIONAL CONNECTIONS: International advice is a natural part of the commercial capability and is provided partly from the UK offices and partly through associated overseas law firms.

L

LEA & COMPANY

Bank Chambers, Market Place, Stockport, SK1 1UN **Tel:** (0161) 480 6691 **Fax:** (0161) 480 0904 **DX:** 19651 STOCKPORT 1
Email: mail@lealaw.com **Ptnrs:** 2 **Other fee-earners:** 2

LEATHES PRIOR

74 The Close, Norwich, NR1 4DR **Tel:** (01603) 610911 **Fax:** (01603) 610088 **DX:** 5205 Norwich **Email:** info@leathesprior.co.uk
Website: www.leathesprior.co.uk **Ptnrs:** 13 **Asst solrs:** 5 **Other fee-earners:** 15

LEBOEUF, LAMB, GREENE & MACRAE

No 1, Minster Court, Mincing Lane, London, EC3R 7AA
Tel: (020) 7459 5000 **Fax:** (020) 7459 5099 **DX:** 520 London/City
Website: www.llgm.com

THE FIRM: LeBoeuf, Lamb, Greene & MacRae is a multinational partnership affiliated with LeBoeuf, Lamb, Greene & MacRae LLP, a United States law firm with over 750 lawyers in 14 US and 8 other international offices. The lawyers in the London office include English solicitors and US lawyers, as well as lawyers from other jurisdictions and represent a cross-section of the firm's clientele in corporate, finance, litigation and regulatory matters. Close co-ordination is maintained between the lawyers in the London office and those in other LeBoeuf offices so that the full resource of the firm may be called upon to assist clients in virtually every aspect of the law.

PRINCIPAL AREAS OF WORK: The London office principally serves clients in the insurance/reinsurance, banking, asset finance, energy, aviation and marine industries. A full range of legal services including civil litigation, US, UK and EU insurance regulations, corporate/commercial, property, energy/utilities/project finance, insolvency, aircraft and ship finance, tax and banking regulation are provided.

Insurance & Reinsurance: US, UK and EU corporate regulation and litigation matters of all types.

Civil/Commercial Litigation: Litigation, arbitration and alternative dispute resolution of all types, including transnational and in particular US/UK disputes.

Energy/Utilities: Electricity, oil and gas transactional and advisory matters; regulatory advice and privatisations.

Project Finance: Major international project work in numerous industry sectors including oil/gas, power and telecommunications.

Corporate/Commercial: Corporate mergers and acquisitions, joint ventures and general corporate finance/commercial advice.

Banking & Finance: All kinds of secured and unsecured lending and lease finance and litigation with specialist knowledge in the aviation and shipping industries.

Insolvency: All matters involving insolvencies in the US, UK and EU including, in particular, insurance insolvency.

Commercial Property: All aspects of commercial property investment and transactions.

Managing Partners:	Alan Jones, Garry Pegg
Number of partners:	9
Assistant solicitors:	41
Other fee-earners:	7

CONTACTS

Asset Finance	Robert Dibble
	Paul Flood
Aviation	Robert Dibble
	Mitri Najjar
Banking	Robert Dibble
	Paul Flood
Civil/Commercial Litigation	Peter J. Sharp
	Nicholas Rochez
Commercial Property	Nick Shepherd
Corporate Finance	
	Charles Ashton
	Anthony Richmond
Corporate/Commercial	Alan Jones
	Garry Pegg
E-commerce & Telecommunications	Anthony Richmond
	Alan Jones
Energy/Utilities	Alan Jones
	Garry Pegg
Insolvency	Paul Flood
	Peter J. Sharp
Insurance/Reinsurance	James F. Johnson
	4th Peter J. Sharp
	Nicholas Rochez
Project/Finance	Alan Jones
	Garry Pegg
Shipping & Marine	Robert Dibble
Tax	Anthony Concanon

INTERNATIONAL CONNECTIONS: LeBoeuf, Lamb, Greene & MacRae LLP has offices in the United States in New York, Washington DC, San Francisco, Albany, Boston, Denver, Harrisburg, Hartford, Houston, Jacksonville, Los Angeles, Newark, Pittsburgh, Salt Lake City, and elsewhere in Brussels, Paris, Riyadh, Beijing, Moscow, Almaty, Tashkent and Bishkek, together with working arrangements with local lawyers in numerous other jurisdictions.

LE BRASSEUR J TICKLE

Drury House, 34-43 Russell Street, London, WC2B 5HA
Tel: (020) 7836 0099 **Fax:** (020) 7831 2215 **DX:** 37985 Kingsway WC2
Email: enquiries@lbjt.co.uk **Website:** www.lbjt.co.uk

6-7 Park Place, Leeds, LS1 2RU
Tel: (0113) 234 1220 **Fax:** (0113) 234 1573 **DX:** 14086 Leeds Park Square
Email: enquiries@lbjt.co.uk

Senior Partner:	Robert Sumerling
Number of partners:	24
Assistant solicitors:	36
Other fee-earners:	9

AREAS OF PRACTICE

Healthcare	35%
Commercial Property	20%
Commercial Law	15%
General & Commercial Litigation	15%
Employment	10%
Personal Injury	5%

CONTACTS

Commercial Law	Michael Canlan (London)
	Stephen Everett (Leeds)
Corporate Law	Jonathan North (London)
Employment	Alex Leslie
	Simon Dinnick (London)
	Kate Williams (Leeds)
Environmental	Geoffrey Sparks (London)
Healthcare - Commercial Law	Geoffrey Sparks (London)
Healthcare - Contentious & Regulatory	Stephen Janisch
	Ralph Shipway (London)
	Nick Rawson (Leeds)
Insurance	Michael Scanlan (London)
Litigation	Simon Dinnick
	Michael Scanlan (London)
Personal Injury	Rena Field (London)
	Kate Williams (Leeds)
PFI	Geoffrey Sparks (London)
Property	Simon Wakefield (London)
	Michael Thorniley-Walker (Leeds)

THE FIRM: Le Brasseur J Tickle have continued to expand with the opening of their Cardiff office and further individual appointments. Further expansion in the corporate commercial, employment and IT sectors are planned for this year.

PRINCIPAL AREAS OF WORK:

Healthcare: The firm is a market leader in its provision of legal services to the healthcare sector. It acts for NHS Trusts, Health Authorities, medical mutuals and defence organisations, private sector hospitals and their insurers, insurance companies, medical partnerships and associated professional regulatory bodies.
A) Contentious and Regulatory: Clinical and dental negligence, class actions and steering group committee members, risk management, criminal, disciplinary and regulatory law and professional ethics, mental health and community care law, administrative and child care law.
B) Commercial Law and PFI: EU public procurement and PFI projects, development and construction contracts, energy and utilities supply agreements and outsourcing arrangements, facilities management, information systems and maintenance agreements, environmental and clinical waste disposal arrangements and insurance coverage loss, joint ventures, corporate governance and partnership law.
C) Property: Transfers from the Secretary of State to Trusts, acquisitions and disposal of Trust property and assets, acquisition of health centres and other primary care units, leasing and landlord and tenant matters.
Corporate Law: The firm handles a wide range of corporate matters, including the acquisition and disposal of companies and businesses, corporate restructuring, stock exchange listings and transactions, e-commerce, venture capital and management buyouts/ins, secured lending and debt restructuring.
Commercial: The commercial group advise on and structure and negotiate a wide range of commercial agreements and joint ventures, both domestic and international, including telecommunications (satellite broadcasting), computer contracts and online contracts, distribution and agency agreements, franchise agreements, e-commerce, EU law, environmental law and construction and intellectual property matters. The firm's international practice, primarily in the USA has also continued to expand.
Property: The property group handles all aspects of commercial property work on behalf of property companies and developers, ranging from prime retail development sites to light industrial, manufacturing and business premises, with a particular expertise in the development of medical practitioners/primary care premises.
Litigation: The firm handles a wide range of domestic and international disputes including insurance, corporate disputes, product liability, construction and engineering disputes, partnerships, professional negligence, defamation claims and emergency injunctions and proceedings before the European Court and the Privy Council.
Employment: The firm has a strong employment team who advise on all aspects of the field and the firm has acted in several landmark cases both before the domestic courts and tribunals and the European Court. Whilst primarily acting as advisers to institutional clients the firm also regularly represents individuals typically in Executive roles. The firm has particular experience in acting for the Health Sector in this field and advises on issues arising out of the Whitley Council regulations.
Insurance: In addition to the firm's professional indemnity practice and the provision of insurance services to the UK health sector, the Insurance Group provides legal services to a wide range of UK and International corporate policy holders, particularly from the US, advising on regulation, law and practice of Lloyd's of London and the London Insurance Market and represents policyholders in UK coverage litigation and international and domestic arbitrations.
Personal Injury: The firm has much experience in this area with several partners having extensive experience in a wide range of personal injury claims and product liability class actions, including the benzodiazepine and hepatitis blood bank litigation.

RECRUITMENT & TRAINING:

London Office: The London office has continued to strengthen its complement with the recent recruitment of three new assistant solicitors and also a Human Resources Manager.

LEDINGHAM CHALMERS

5 Melville Crescent, Edinburgh, EH3 7JA
Tel: (0131) 200 1000 **Fax:** (0131) 200 1080 **DX:** ED275 Edinburgh
Email: mail@ledinghamchalmers.com **Website:** www.ledinghamchalmers.com

1 Golden Square, Aberdeen, AB10 1HA
Tel: (01224) 408408 **Fax:** (01224) 408402 **DX:** AB15 Aberdeen

Kintail House, Beechwood Business Park, Inverness, IV2 3BW
Tel: (01463) 667400 **Fax:** (01463) 713755 **DX:** 521009 Inverness-3

Senior Partner:	David Laing
Number of partners:	27
Assistant solicitors:	35
Other fee-earners:	25
International:	
Assistant solicitors:	8
Other fee-earners:	1

AREAS OF PRACTICE

Company/Commercial	35%
Commercial Property	26%
Residential Property	16%
Litigation	15%
Private Client	8%

CONTACTS

Agriculture	Allan Collie (Aberdeen)
Commercial Property	John Curran (Aberdeen)
Company/Commercial	Malcom Laing (Aberdeen)
Construction	Jennifer Howitt (Aberdeen)
Corporate Finance	David Laing (Edinburgh)
Employment	Peter Sharp (Aberdeen)
International	Gavin Farquhar (Edinburgh)
IP/IT	Roger Connon (Aberdeen)
Litigation	Marysia Lewis (Aberdeen)
Oil and Gas	Robert Ruddiman (Aberdeen)
Private Client	Daniel Stewart (Aberdeen)

LEDINGHAM CHALMERS

THE FIRM: Ledingham Chalmers provides a full range of business law services from a unique network of offices in three Scottish locations – Edinburgh, Aberdeen and Inverness – and in three overseas locations – Baku (Azerbaijan), Istanbul (Turkey) and Stanley (Falkland Islands). The firm has developed a reputation for its entrepreneurial, 'can do' approach, giving clients the benefit of its own business experience. The development of an international practice adds an important dimension which is further evidenced by the firm's membership of the Trans European Law Firms Alliance.

L

PRINCIPAL AREAS OF WORK: The domestic practice in Scotland is structured in divisions – corporate, commercial property, dispute resolution, oil and gas and private client. The firm encourages individual excellence within teams without suffering the extremes of rigid specialisation, with the aim of developing rounded business lawyers who can provide pragmatic solutions. There is also a focus on exportable skills which, while developed at home, can be applied to work overseas in both developed and developing jurisdictions. The firm has developed a particularly strong reputation within the oil and gas and oil services sectors and the land, leisure and construction sectors. Within the Scottish offices, the main services are corporate/commercial, corporate and project finance, commercial property (including planning and environmental), construction, employment, energy law and practice, intellectual property, information technology, insolvency, litigation and dispute resolution, agriculture and estates and private client (which in Scotland includes residential property).

INTERNATIONAL CONNECTIONS: The overseas offices have a special focus on oil and gas, transportation, infrastructure projects, banking and project finance in their respective regions and are supported by the projects team based in the firm's Edinburgh office. The firm regularly works alongside lawyers in other jurisdictions sometimes as instructing counsel for UK clients or as part of a larger professional team.

LEE BOLTON & LEE

1 The Sanctuary, Westminster, London, SW1P 3JT
Tel: (020) 7222 5381 **Fax:** (020) 7222 7502 **DX:** 2301 Victoria
Email: enquiries@1thesanctuary.com **Website:** www.leeboltonlee.com

Senior Partner:	PFB Beesley
Number of partners:	14
Assistant solicitors:	7
Other fee-earners:	13

CONTACTS

Charities	P.F. Beesley
	A.C. James
Commercial Property	G.J. Fountain
Company/Commercial	A.O.E. Davies
Ecclesiastical/Education	P.F. Beesley
	N.J. Richens
Litigation	J.P. Sergeant
Parliamentary	J.A. Durkin
Private Client	M.J.G. Fletcher
Public Law	P.R. Lane
	M.A.R. Peto
Railway Property	J. Taplin
	K.E. Wallace
	P. Robinson

THE FIRM: Established at 1 The Sanctuary in 1855, Lee Bolton & Lee is a well-established Westminster practice, incorporating both commercial, charity, education and private client work. The firm offers extensive experience and advice across a wide spectrum of activities, and is associated with a firm of solicitors and parliamentary agents, Rees and Freres, to provide a specialist service in parliamentary, public and administrative law.

PRINCIPAL AREAS OF WORK:
Private Client: The firm provides expert advice on a full range of private client matters including domestic property, personal taxation and individual financial planning, wills, trusts, probate and the administration of estates. In addition, a separate department handles all aspects of family and matrimonial law.
Ecclesiastical, Education & Charities: As well as general advice on ecclesiastical matters and disciplinary proceedings, the firm advises three diocesan bishops as Registrars. Advice is provided to independent schools on all matters from establishing a new school or hiving-off a school from a larger charity to day-to-day operational and employment issues. In the maintained sector the firm has considerable knowledge of the Education Acts and advises a number of diocese and many individual schools and trustees on education law and the law relating to school sites. The firm's charity practice is linked, but not confined to, its educational and ecclesiastical work and covers all aspects of charity creation, registration and administration including trusts, tax and charitable property.
Corporate Services: Advice is provided for clients ranging from established organisations to emerging businesses and entrepreneurs on every aspect of commercial life including company formations, reconstructions, mergers, MBOs, joint ventures, Stock Exchange work, employment law and pensions, banking and financial services. Funding, planning and development work is handled for banks, institutional clients, investors and developers.
Litigation: A thriving litigation department handles a range of matters including general commercial contracts, employment disputes, professional and medical negligence, property building and landlord and tenant

disputes, defamation, insurance and personal injury claims. The firm has long standing relations with numerous public bodies and has developed a considerable expertise in the area of judicial review proceedings.
Commercial Property: This department acts for a wide variety of clients from small businesses to major companies, banks, institutional clients, housing associations , investors and developers. All types of commercial property transactions are undertaken including aquisitions and diposals, leasing of commercial property whether acting for Landlord or Tenant, renewal or termination of business lettings, Development Agreements and Joint Venture Agreements. The department draws on expertise elsewhere in the firm; for example where litigation or tax aspects arise. In addition, Rees & Freres have a large commercial property department currently handling work from the major rail transport providers and operators.

LEE CROWDER

39 Newhall Street, Birmingham, B3 3DY
Tel: (0121) 236 4477 **Fax:** (0121) 236 4710 **DX:** 13034
Email: info@leecrowder.co.uk

Senior partner:	Stephen Gilmore
Number of partners:	22
Assistant Solicitors:	29
Consultants:	1
Other fee earners:	26

AREAS OF PRACTICE

Corporate Services	28%
Litigation	24%
Property	24%
Construction	14%
Private Client	10%

CONTACTS

Construction & Engineering	Jeffrey Brown
Corporate Services	Graham Muth
	Stephen Gilmore
Litigation	Bernard Singleton
	Andy Ballard
Private Client	Drummond Kerr
Property	Kevin Nagle
	Joel Kordan
	Simon Denslow

LEE CROWDER
Solicitors

THE FIRM: Lee Crowder is one of the oldest firms in the country (and certainly the oldest firm in Birmingham) and is one of the most dynamic and rapidly expanding medium-sized firms in the region. The firm has grown by leaps and bounds over the last few years and there is no sign of a slowdown in the rate of expansion. It is the firm's intention to continue its growth by recruiting only the highest quality fee earners at all levels. The firm is committed to providing an excellent service to its clients at a competitive rate, with an emphasis on partner involvement and to maintain and enhance its reputation, both regionally and nationally.

PRINCIPAL AREAS OF WORK:
Corporate Services: The department acts for a broad range of clients, both large and small, including publicly quoted companies and deals with specialist corporate and commercial work as well as acting in corporate finance transactions. Principal activities involve acquisitions, mergers and disposals, AIM flotation's, joint ventures and shareholder agreements, non-contentious insolvency, venture capital and commercial agreements. It is also recognised as a leading firm in e-commerce on a regional and national basis. The recent appointment of a specialist media partner has now placed the firm as a leader in media and entertainment, providing services in music, film, television, the arts and computer law.
Commercial Property: The department now has an extremely high profile and acts for commercial and residential property developers, institutions, retailers and landed estates. Clients range from individual and owner/managed businesses to publicly quoted companies.
Commercial Litigation: The department handles a broad range of litigation with particular specialisation in insolvency/director's disqualification, property litigation and employment.
Private Client: The firm is now a major player in the regional market dealing with all aspects of estate and tax planning, charity advice and has particular expertise in financial services.
Housing: With over 30 years experience as Housing Corporation Panel Solicitors, the firm currently acts for over 50 housing associations nationwide and assists several local authorities.
Construction and Engineering: In April 2000 the firm established a construction and engineering department. The department deals with the drafting of bespoke contracts and approval of special amendments produced in relation to standard forms. It advises funding institution employees, both public and commercial, main contractors and major sub-contractors.

LEEDS DAY
6 Bedford Road, Sandy, SG19 1EN **Tel:** (01767) 680251 **Fax:** (01767) 691775 **DX:** 47801 Sandy **Ptnrs:** 11 **Asst solrs:** 8 **Other fee-earners:** 22

LEE & PEMBERTONS

45 Pont St, London, SW1X 0BX
Tel: (020) 7589 1114 **Fax:** (020) 7589 0807 **DX:** 38166 Knightsbridge
Email: law@leepem.co.uk **Website:** www.leepem.co.uk

Managing Ppartner:	Giles Pemberton
Senior Partner:	Richard Roney
Number of partners:	20
Assistant solicitors:	15
Other fee-earners:	12

AREAS OF PRACTICE

Property	40%
Private Client	35%
Litigation	15%
Commercial	10%

THE FIRM: Established in the late 18th century, Lee and Pembertons is a successful Knightsbridge firm, noted for its substantial property and private client work. In recent years the firm has expanded its practice to offer the full range of corporate and commercial legal services. It has established a reputation for providing a partner-led personal service to clients, and there is a commitment to client care and quality management at all levels.

PRINCIPAL AREAS OF WORK:
Property: Work includes acquisitions and disposals of commercial, residential and agricultural properties, agricultural tenancies and farming partnerships, landlord and tenant and Rent Act law, property development, construction law, town and country planning and leasehold enfranchisement.
Private Client: Work includes creation, administration and termination of all types of trusts (in particular

Continued overleaf

charitable trusts), wills, probate and the administration of estates, financial services and tax planning, pensions and life insurance, charity administration.
Commercial: Work includes company formations, acquisitions, sales, mergers and liquidations, purchases and financing of businesses and partnerships, oil and gas projects, service agreements, banking, insurance, gaming and clubs, environmental law, EU law and regulations affecting businesses.
Dispute Resolution: Work includes commercial, landlord and tenant, company, building and intellectual property disputes, planning appeals, insolvency, defamation, professional negligence, personal injury, matrimonial and family law; immigration and nationality matters; mediation.

LANGUAGES: Cantonese, French, German, Italian, Spanish and Swedish.

RECRUITMENT & TRAINING: Two trainee solicitors are recruited annually. Applications with CV to Diana Graves.

CONTACTS

Commercial	Richard Roney
Litigation	John Roney
Private Client	Andrew Stebbings
Property	Damian Greenish

LEE & PEMBERTONS

LEE & PRIESTLEY

12 Park Square, Leeds, LS1 2LF
Tel: (0113) 243 3751 **Fax:** (0113) 246 7357 **DX:** 14074 Leeds Park Square
Email: firstname.surname@lee-priestley.co.uk

Managing Partner:	John Priestley
Senior Partner:	John Priestley
Number of partners:	14
Assistant solicitors:	15
Other fee-earners:	25

THE FIRM: With offices in Leeds and Bradford, this practice provides the full range of corporate and commercial services. Lee & Priestley is now seeing tangible benefits and growth resulting from a programme of heavy investment in people able to bring skills to the firm.The range and quality of services offered has seen a significant increase and the firm aims to move further up the league table of regional firms in the coming years. The firm is achieving considerable growth in Leeds, whilst maintaining its position as one of the leading firms in Bradford.

PRINCIPAL AREAS OF WORK: The corporate team is handling an increasing volume of acquisitions and disposals and has particular expertise in management buy-outs and buy-ins. Commercial matters covered include agency, distribution, franchise and supply agreements. The firm has particular expertise in acting for funding institutions in transactional work.
Other Areas: The firm has a strong and rapidly expanding employment and commercial litigation practice and also handles all aspects of commercial property and insolvency work.The firm is well know for the quality of its personal injury and civil litigation work, family and childcare law.Lee & Priestley also has expertise on a wide range of private client matters, including wills, tax and trusts and acts for a number of charities.

CLIENTELE: The commercial clients of the firm include a number of PLCs and a large range of small to medium size enterprises. In addition, it serves a large number of private clients in the Yorkshire area. Lee & Priestley sees its dedication to client relationships as the reason for its success.

CONTACTS

Childcare & Education Law	Charles Prest
Commercial Litigation and Employment	Iain Jenkins
Commercial Property	Bruce Copsey, James Dale, Robert Hall
Conveyancing	James Priestley
Corporate & Commercial	Jonathan Oxley, Morgan Williams
Family Law	Charles Prest, Andrea Dyer
Insolvency	Nigel Whitfield
Personal Injury & Clinical Negligence	Brian Walker, Sonia Hume-Dawson
Professional Negligence	Michael Rakusen
Trust & Probate	Henry Beckwith

LEES LLOYD WHITLEY

Castle Chambers, 43 Castle Street, Liverpool, L2 9TJ **Tel:** (0151) 227 3541 **Fax:** (0151) 227 2460 **DX:** 14164 Liverpool **Ptnrs:** 11 **Asst solrs:** 8 **Other fee-earners:** 43

LEE & THOMPSON

Green Garden House, 15-22 St. Christopher's Place, London, W1M 5HD **Tel:** (020) 7935 4665 **Fax:** (020) 7486 2391
Email: leeth@globalnet.co.uk **Website:** www.leeandthompson.com **Ptnrs:** 7 **Asst solrs:** 4

LEIGH, DAY & CO

Priory House, 25 St John's Lane, London, EC1M 4LB
Tel: (020) 7650 1200 **Fax:** (020) 7253 4433 **DX:** 53326 Clerkenwell
Email: postbox@leighday.co.uk **Website:** www.leighday.co.uk

International House, 82-86 Deansgate, Manchester, M3 2ER
Tel: (0161) 832 7722 **Fax:** (0161) 839 2329 **DX:** 718178 Manchester 3

Senior Partner:	Martyn Day
Number of partners:	15
Assistant solicitors:	14
Other fee-earners:	10

THE FIRM: A leading firm specialising in all aspects of complex personal injury work and multi-party actions. Winner of the Lawyer/HIFAL Law firm of the Year Award 1996.

PRINCIPAL AREAS OF WORK:
Environmental: Specialising in claims as a result of exposure to pollution (radiation, chemicals, pesticides, sewage in the sea) together with industrial disease and nuisance claims.
Clinical Negligence: Concentrates on cases involving serious disabilities or death. Also specialises in medical devices such as artifical heart valves, pacemakers and silicone breast implants.

CONTACTS

Accident	Jenny Kennedy (London) Geraldine McCool (Manchester)
Administrative Law	Richard Stein
Clinical Negligence	Sarah Leigh
Environmental	Martyn Day

Accident Litigation: This department deals with a full range of personal injury claims including road traffic accidents, accidents at work and product liability claims. There is a special expertise in horse riding accidents, actions against the MOD and aviation disasters.
Administrative Law: The department's clients include local authorities and objectors concerning plan making, development control, enforcement and appeals. It undertakes a large number of judicial reviews.

LEMON & CO

Chelsea House, 1 Little London Court, Albert Street, Swindon, SN1 3HY
Tel: (01793) 496341 **Fax:** (01793) 511639 **DX:** 400912 Swindon 6
Email: lemonco@star.co.uk

34 Regent Circus, Swindon, SN1 1PY
Tel: (01793) 527141 **Fax:** (01793) 614168 **DX:** 400912 Swindon 6
Email: enquiries@lemon-co.co.uk

Senior Partner:	Richard Fry
Number of partners:	9
Assistant solicitors:	5
Other fee-earners:	5

AREAS OF PRACTICE

Conveyancing	35%
Litigation	30%
Company/Commercial	20%
Trusts & Probate	15%

CONTACTS

Commercial Litigation	Clive Bell
Commercial Property	Martin Evans
Company/Commercial	Nial Ledingham
Employment	Clive Bell
Family	Stephen Moss
Personal Injury	Tim Dixon
Private Client	Deirdre Moss
Residential Property	David Halfhead

THE FIRM: Founded in 1914, Lemon & Co is are one of the largest and longest established firms in Swindon, providing an extensive range of services for businesses and private clients and is dedicated to client care. It is one of the few Swindon firms specialising in commercial law and has participated in several complex property and corporate transactions in recent years.

PRINCIPAL AREAS OF WORK:
Company/Commercial: Company formations, acquisitions and disposals, MBO/MBI, employment contracts and conditions, shareholders and partnership agreements, jv agreements, intellectual property, franchise, agency and distribution agreements, commercial property and all aspects of landlord and tenant law.
Litigation: All matters. Specialists in commercial litigation, employment, personal injury, family, and childcare.
Private Client: Estate planning, wills, charity law, management of trusts and settlements, probate work, administration of estates and financial and tax advisory services. The firm's specialist residential conveyancing department is also widely acknowledged for providing a quality service.

LEO ABSE & COHEN

40 Churchill Way, Cardiff, CF10 2SS
Tel: (029) 2038 3252 **Fax:** (029) 2034 5572 **DX:** 33002
Email: law@leoabse.co.uk

Managing partner:	Ian Hopkins
Senior partner:	John Sherratt
Number of partners:	11
Assistant solicitors:	40
Other fee-earners:	20

AREAS OF PRACTICE

Plaintiff Personal Injury	49%
Commercial	23%
Insurance Litigation	18%
Legal Aid	10%

THE FIRM: Leo Abse & Cohen has an outstanding reputation in Litigation with specialist services in personal injury, insurance litigation, medical negligence, commercial and general litigation, employment, family and serious crime. In addition, the firm has a strong property section and deals with an increasing amount of company commercial matters. Leo Abse & Cohen has enjoyed considerable growth in recent years, continuously recruiting high calibre solicitors from all over England and Wales. The firm is the first in Wales to achieve Lexcel status and only the third firm nationally to achieve both Lexcel and ISO9001.

LEONARD GRAY

72-74 Duke St, Chelmsford, CM1 1JY **Tel:** (01245) 251411 **Fax:** (01245) 490728 **DX:** 3309 Chelmsford 1
Ptnrs: 5 **Asst solrs:** 2 **Other fee-earners:** 7 **Contact:** Mr Richard Randall • Committed to providing quality, independent legal services with specialist departments. All aspects of family law with an emphasis on middle and higher income financial cases. Childcare, mediation and adoption.

LÉONIE COWEN & ASSOCIATES

3A Loveridge Mews, London, NW6 2DP
Tel: (020) 7604 5870 **Fax:** (020) 7604 5871
Email: leonie.cowen@lcowen.co.uk **Website:** www.lcowen.co.uk

Managing Partner:	Leonie Cowen
Number of partners:	1
Other fee-earners:	1

AREAS OF PRACTICE

Local Government Law	80%
Charities	10%
Commercial Property	5%
Corporate	5%

THE FIRM: Founded in 1989, the firm specialises in local government and administrative law. LÈonie Cowen spent years at senior level in local government.

PRINCIPAL AREAS OF WORK:
Powers & Functions of Local Authorities
Public Private Partnerships/Joint Ventures/Trading: Including sport and leisure, arts, culture and libraries service transfers to new not-for-profit bodies, management buy-outs, municipal and cross-border trading.
Local Authority Companies: The Part V framework and its impact, company structures.

Continued overleaf

PFI/Project Funding/Local Authority Finance: The capital finance regime, audit issues and relationships with external auditors.
Social Services (esp. Community Care): Transfer of residential homes for older people/adults, and capital funding for development and refurbishment.
Best Value VCT/Procurement: Implementation of quality systems and public procurement.
Employment: TUPE, local authority terms and conditions (including sensitive senior level cases), superannuation schemes and pensions.
Education: Services to education authorities and governing bodies.
Charities: Setting-up and management of charities and other non-profit bodies.
Corporate: Business transfers, joint ventures, shareholders agreements.
Commercial Property: Acquisition, funding, management and disposal of property for public authorities, housing associations, businesses and investors.

CONTACTS

Charities.....Léonie Cowen
.....Andrew Riddell
Commercial Property.....Andrew Riddell
Corporate.....Léonie Cowen
.....Andrew Riddell
Local Government Law.....Léonie Cowen

LESLIE WOLFSON & CO
19 Waterloo Street, Glasgow, G2 6BQ **Tel:** (0141) 226 4499 **Fax:** (0141) 221 6070 **DX:** 106 Glasgow **Email:** enquiries@lwolfson.co.uk **Ptnrs:** 5 **Asst solrs:** 4 **Other fee-earners:** 1

L

LESTER ALDRIDGE

Russell House, Oxford Road, Bournemouth, BH8 8EX
Tel: (01202) 786161 **Fax:** (01202) 786110 **DX:** 7623 Bournemouth 1
Email: sales&marketing@lester-aldridge.co.uk **Website:** www.lester-aldridge.co.uk

Managing Partner:	Barry Glazier
Chairman:	Colin Patrick
Number of partners:	31
Assistant solicitors:	24
Other fee-earners:	39

AREAS OF PRACTICE

Private Client Legal Services.....31%
Commercial Litigation.....25%
Commercial Property.....14%
Banking and Asset Finance.....13%
Corporate/Corporate Finance.....10%
Investment Services.....7%

CONTACTS

Banking & Asset Finance.....
.....Yasmin Dossabhoy
Business Property.....Bob Robertson
Commercial Litigation.....Jeremy Allin
Corporate.....David Ashplant
Employment.....Susan Evans
Family Law.....Stephen Foster
Investment Services.....Steve Dean
LA Fast Track (Debt Services)..Andrew Corke
Personal Injury.....Karen Thompson
Property Development.....Roger Woolley
Residential Property.....Rachel Lapworth
Trusts & Tax.....Barry Glazier
Wills & Estates.....David Parkhouse

THE FIRM: Lester Aldridge is progressive and innovative in its approach to both management and marketing. Lawyers provide legal solutions to business problems and the firm employs non-solicitors eg accountants to develop certain areas of the business. LA's legal and associated services are delivered via teams (shown opposite). Within the team structure, specialist units focus on areas such as care homes, construction, contentious trust and probate, corporate recovery and insolvency, environmental, health and safety, insurance litigation, intellectual property, IT and e-commerce, landlord and tenant, marina and leisure development, medical practices, pension schemes, and planning. Unusually for a law firm, Lester Aldridge offers a one stop corporate finance service for buying and selling companies. LA Corporate Finance is led by the former chief executive of a quoted plc. The firm also markets an innovative product, LA Gain, which uses the law to find business opportunities.

Pro Bono Work: The firm undertakes a substantial amount of pro bono work.

INTERNATIONAL CONNECTIONS: Lester Aldridge is a member of Eurolegal. The firm's existing european links with major law firms in the EU are under-pinned by a number of lawyers fluent in French, Spanish, German, Dutch and Afrikaans. The firm is in the process of developing international services following the success of its international probate service. Lester Aldridge has a Southern African desk which services clients wishing to trade with Southern Africa or vice versa.

RECRUITMENT & TRAINING: The firm recruits at least four trainee solicitors every year. Apply by letter and CV to Robert Camping, Director of Personnel and Administration. Alternatively, visit the firm's website for further information.

L'ESTRANGE & BRETT

Arnott House, 12-16 Bridge Street, Belfast, BT1 1LS
Tel: (028) 9023 0426 **Fax:** (028) 9024 6396 **DX:** 424 NR Belfast 1
Email: law@lestrangeandbrett.com **Website:** www.lestrangeandbrett.com

Senior Partner:	V. Alan Hewitt
Number of partners:	10
Assistant solicitors:	19
Other fee-earners:	6

AREAS OF PRACTICE

Corporate & Commercial Law.....39%
Commercial Property.....38%
Litigation (including Employment Law).....
.....18%
Private Client.....5%

CONTACTS

Banking & Financial Services/
Insolvency.....Brian Henderson
Commercial Law.....Richard Gray
Commercial Property.....Alan Hewitt
Corporate Law.....John Irvine
Employment.....Adam Brett
Litigation.....Sam Beckett
Private Client.....Ian Huddleston

THE FIRM: L'Estrange & Brett is one of the leading commercial firms in Northern Ireland and one of the oldest practices in Ireland, having been in existence since 1796. Today, it is a modern practice geared to the demands of a fast moving business environment and committed to giving clients the best professional advice and support available in the market. The firm has strong links with many City of London, national and regional firms in Great Britain. It also works on international transactions with firms in many parts of the world. Along with leading Dublin practice McCann FitzGerald, L'Estrange & Brett formed the North South Legal Alliance in 1999. The two firms retain their independence, but work together to provide clients with an integrated service in matters involving elements in both Northern Ireland and the Republic of Ireland.

PRINCIPAL AREAS OF WORK:

Corporate Law: The firm provides fast and effective legal advice across all types of work in the corporate sector, ranging from acquisitions, disposals and mergers to management buy-outs, buy-ins, joint ventures and new inward investment projects.
Commercial Law: As commercial law becomes increasingly complex, the firm's services are designed to help clients run their businesses more smoothly. The firm advises in diverse areas ranging from sales/distribution and competition law to intellectual property information, technology and e-commerce.

Commercial Property: L'Estrange & Brett has extensive experience across a full range of property related matters with an emphasis on commercial property. The firm's skills cover site acquisition and development, planning, building contracts and arbitration, landlord and tenant, housing developments and environmental law.
Litigation: The litigation department is focused on the requirements of commercial clients. Its work covers commercial actions, building contracts, litigation, professional negligence, administrative law and judicial review, as well as personal injury claims.
Banking & Financial Services/Insolvency: The firm acts for all types of borrowers and for leading lenders in the banking and financial services sector. Its cross-disciplinary unit advises on all aspects of borrowing, lending and corporate finance, including asset and project finance, corporate reconstructions and reorganisations. Its insolvency practice has wide experience of corporate rescue and recovery involving receivership, administration and liquidation.
Projects/PFI: The firm has unrivalled experience of project finance and PFI transactions in Northern Ireland, acting for both public and private sector clients.
Employment: The firm provides a comprehensive service for employers and employees advising on all aspects of litigious and non-litigious employment work.
Private Client: The firm provides legal services to private clients across a wide range of matters, including domestic conveyancing, wills and trusts, probate and tax planning.

LEVI & CO
33 St Pauls Street, Leeds, LS1 2JJ **Tel:** (0113) 244 9931 **Fax:** (0113) 244 6789 **DX:** 12033 Leeds **Ptnrs:** 8 **Asst solrs:** 4 **Other fee-earners:** 9

LEVISON MELTZER PIGOTT
9-13 St Andrew Street, London, EC4A 3AE
Tel: (020) 7556 2400 **Fax:** (020) 7556 2401 **DX:** 200 London Chancery Lane
Email: lmp@lmplaw.co.uk

Number of partners:	3
Assistant solicitors:	2

AREAS OF PRACTICE

Family/Matrimonial/Finance	60%
Children	30%
Co-habitation	10%

THE FIRM: Levison Meltzer Pigott is a specialist divorce and family law firm formed on 1 June 1998. The three partners have, however, worked together for almost 15 years. The firm deals with all areas of divorce and family law, including advising on pensions, the rights of unmarried couples, and all the changes that have been or will be made under the Family Law Act 1996.Jeremy Levison is a founder member of the International Academy of Matrimonial Lawyers and currently vice-president of its European section. His contacts with family lawyers worldwide assists in the significant proportion of cases that have an international dimension. Claire Meltzer regularly broadcasts on television and radio, particularly on the subject of pensions and divorce, and has written numerous articles and papers on matters of divorce and family law. Simon Pigott has lectured for the College of Law, was one of the first family law mediators trained by the Family Mediators Association, was its Chair between 1995 and 1997, and was Vice-Chair of the United Kingdom College of Family Mediators between 1996 and 1998.Each of the partners is an Associate of the American Bar Association (Family Section) and all the firm's solicitors are members of the Solicitors Family Law Association.

LEVY & MCRAE
266 St Vincent Street, Glasgow, G2 5RL **Tel:** (0141) 307 2311 **Fax:** (0141) 307 6857/8 **DX:** GW149 Glasgow **Email:** peterwatson@lemac.co.uk **Website:** www.lemac.co.uk **Ptnrs:** 4 **Asst solrs:** 6 **Other fee-earners:** 9 **Contact:** Peter Watson • Specialist areas include media, aviation, international claims and litigation, personal injury, accident inquiries, civil/criminal litigation, Inland Revenue, Customs and Excise, employment, partnership & company law, defamation and libel.

LEWIS SILKIN
Windsor House, 50 Victoria Street, London, SW1H 0NW
Tel: (020) 7227 8000 **Fax:** (020) 7222 4633 **DX:** 2321 Victoria
Email: info@lewissilkin.com **Website:** www.lewissilkin.com

Managing Partner:	Trevor Watkins
Senior Partner:	Roger Alexander
Number of partners:	29
Assistant solicitors:	30
Other fee-earners:	20

AREAS OF PRACTICE

Corporate Finance/Commercial	26%
Property/Project Finance/Construction/Social Housing	24%
Advertising/Media/Defamation/IP/IT	18%
Litigation & Dispute Resolution	17%
Employment	15%

THE FIRM: Lewis Silkin has a reputation for excellence and expertise. The firm's forward looking and commercial approach is respected by clients and competitors. It is well suited to the fast changing world of e-commerce and emerging technologies. Entrepreneurs, plc's, private companies and government agencies are amongst the clients who benefit from the firm's emphasis on personal service, teamwork and quality advice. This distinctive commercial law firm has a successful profile in eight key areas: corporate services; litigation and dispute resolution; property; housing and project finance; construction; employment; marketing services; technology and communications.

Continued overleaf

PRINCIPAL AREAS OF WORK:

Corporate Services: Lewis Silkin has a highly successful corporate finance team which undertakes an impressive range of work including M&A flotations, MBOs, employee benefits, shareholders agreements and regulatory advice, acting on behalf of company clients, venture capitalists and sponsors. Alongside this, the commercial work includes project finance, joint ventures, franchising, outsourcing and a range of other commercial agreements.

Litigation & Dispute Resolution: The group is known for its success in winning and resolving disputes as a result of a string of high profile victories. Recent successes have involved contractual disputes, defamation, intellectual property, property disputes and arbitration.

Property: The group provides a quality service on acquisitions and disposals, development, property financing and landlord and tenant issues.

Housing & Project Finance: The firm is a recognised leader in this field with a strong record of innovative and challenging work in the social housing sector and in the financing of grant aided projects.

Construction: A highly-regarded team provides a comprehensive service to the construction, engineering and property development industries providing non-contentious advice for all stages of project procurement and dispute management and resolution.

Employment: The team is now one of the most highly regarded in London, with a reputation for providing straightforward, practical advice when a sensitive and commercial approach is needed. It has a good record of acting both for employers and employees.

Marketing Services: Lewis Silkin is an acknowledged leader in providing a comprehensive service to the advertising and marketing services industry with an increasing emphasis on new media. It also advises advertisers on promoting their products and services within today's complex legal and regulatory framework.

Technology & Communications: The group acts on behalf of IT and new media companies, as well as other commercial clients. It advises on all aspects of IT, licensing, sales, development, procurement and outsourcing, intellectual property, regulatory issues and commercial contracts.

CLIENTELE: Clients range from large corporations and plc's to entrepreneurs. They are in sectors as diverse as advertising, e-commerce, dot.coms, marketing services, publishing, newspapers, IT, restaurants, retail, government agencies, utilities, social housing and property development.

INTERNATIONAL CONNECTIONS: The firm has links throughout the world, including in the US, and is the UK representative of the Global Advertising Lawyers' Alliance (GALA), which incorporates the European Advertising Lawyers' Association (EALA).

CONTACTS

Advertising & Marketing Services	Roger Alexander
	Brinsley Dresden
Company Commercial	Trevor Watkins
Construction	Helen Garthwaite
Corporate Finance	Clare Grayston
Defamation	Roderick Dadak
Employment	Michael Burd
	James Davies
Information Technology	Gillian Cordall
Intellectual Property	Ian Jeffery
Litigation & Dispute Resolution	Tom Coates
	Clive Greenwood
Project Finance	Lynne Murray
Property & Planning	Len Goodrich
Social Housing	Gillian Bastow

lewissilkin

LIDDELL ZURBRUGG

15-17 Jockey's Fields, London, WC1R 4BW
Tel: (020) 7404 5641 **Fax:** (020) 7831 8460 **DX:** 0061 London/Chancery Lane
Email: info@liddell-zurbrugg.co.uk **Website:** www.liddell-zurbrugg.co.uk

Managing Partner:	Michael Zurbrugg
Senior Partner:	Michael Zurbrugg
Number of partners:	3
Assistant solicitors:	2
Other fee-earners:	10

THE FIRM: Liddell Zurbrugg specialises in insurance and personal injury litigation, both on behalf of insurers and private clients within the UK and other European countries. The firm also specialises in serious injury work particularly head injury. Clients include a number of Lloyd's syndicates and insurance companies, both UK and foreign including legal expense insurers. Several languages are spoken fluently and the firm has established connections in most European countries with particular emphasis on France, Spain, Portugal, Belgium, Switzerland and Germany. The firm includes a Spanish lawyer whose main area of work consists of personal injury claims in Spain and giving evidence before English Courts in relation to Spanish law. In addition, he deals with general litigation, property transactions, child abduction and custody cases.

LIGHTFOOTS

The Old Red Lion, 1-3 High Street, Thame, OX9 2BX
Tel: (01844) 212305 or 212574/5 **Fax:** (01844) 214984 **DX:** 80550 Thame
Website: www.lightfoots.co.uk

Senior Partner:	Martin Hector
Number of partners:	5
Assistant solicitors:	5
Other fee-earners:	15

THE FIRM: This progressive firm, the first nationally to gain and be re-awarded the 'Investors in People' award, provides sound advice on most aspects of English corporate and private client law. It also holds a legal aid franchise.

PRINCIPAL AREAS OF WORK:

Commercial: Services include company/commercial, commercial property, employment, tax, property litigation and specialist debt collection, mortgage repossession and asset management, professional negligence and pharmaceutical consulting departments.

Private Client: Work includes wills, probate, trusts, residential conveyancing, other general civil litigation and a specialist family law and mediation department.The firm also has a thriving Estate Agency and a property letting and management business, trading under the name of Vernons.

LANGUAGES: French and Hungarian.

AREAS OF PRACTICE

Commercial Litigation	30%
Commercial	15%
Domestic Conveyancing	15%
Family	15%
Pharmaceutical	8%
Trusts & Probate	7%
Commercial Conveyancing	5%
Employment	5%

LINDER MYERS

Phoenix House, 45 Cross Street, Manchester, M2 4JF **Tel:** (0161) 832 6972 **Fax:** (0161) 834 0718
DX: 14360 **Email:** law@lindermyers.co.uk **Ptnrs:** 12 **Asst solrs:** 19 **Other fee-earners:** 18
Contact: Mr Bernard F. Seymour • Commercial and litigation practice.

AREAS OF PRACTICE

Company/Commercial	25%
Personal Injury	25%
General Litigation	15%
Medical Negligence	13%
Matrimonial	12%
Private Client	10%

LINDSAYS WS

11 Atholl Crescent, Edinburgh, EH3 8HE
Tel: (0131) 229 1212 **Fax:** (0131) 229 5611 **DX:** 25 Edinburgh
Email: mail@lindsays.co.uk **Website:** www.lindsays.co.uk

77 Main Street, Davidsons Mains, Edinburgh, EH4 5AD
Tel: (0131) 312 7276 **Fax:** (0131) 312 6029 **DX:** ED 115
Email: cmc@lindseys.co.uk

201-203 Bruntsfield Place, Edinburgh, EH10 4DH
Tel: (0131) 228 6993 **Fax:** (0131) 228 5584 **DX:** 25 Edinburgh
Email: mt@lindsays.co.uk

Barlas & Sharpe WS, 33a Westgate, North Berwick, EH39 4AG
Tel: (01620) 893481 **Fax:** (01620) 894442 **DX:** ED 1245
Email: rfm@lindsays.co.uk

Senior Partner:	R.J. Elliot, D.K.S.
Number of partners:	16
Assistant solicitors:	9
Other fee-earners:	39

AREAS OF PRACTICE

Private Client	34%
Commercial	27%
Residential Conveyancing	21%
Litigation	18%

CONTACTS

Asset Finance	Alasdair Cummings
Banking	Alasdair Cummings
Building Arbitration	Alan MacKay
Charitable Companies	David Reith
Commercial Contracts	Nora Kellock
Commercial Property	David Reith
Corporate	Alasdair Cummings
Crofting/Agriculture	Roy Shearer
Education	Roy Shearer
Employment	Douglas Tullis
Executry & Wills	Callum Kennedy
Intellectual Property	Nora Kellock
Investments	Rodger Urquhart
Liquor Licensing	Nora Kellock
Litigation	Alistair Mackie
Personal Financial Planning	John Elliot
Residential Property	Bob Arbuthnott
Trusts & Tax Planning	Brian Robertson

THE FIRM: Lindsays provides a partner-led personal service with an emphasis on quality. The Firm has a substantial private client base as well as a strong commercial and litigation practice. To complement these legal services, Lindsays has developed a significant presence in the residential property market through its estate agency service. Lindsays was one of the first legal practices in Scotland to recognise the benefit to its clients of adopting written quality procedures, and has gained approval under the quality standard ISO 9001.

PRINCIPAL AREAS OF WORK:

Company/Commercial: All aspects of commercial property work are covered: purchases, sales, leasing and secured lending. Asset finance, asset recovery and building contracts particularly in relation to disputes. Other more specialised areas of expertise are education, intellectual property, especially licensing agreements, road haulage, liquor licensing, including the purchase and sale of licensed premises. The department deals with company formations and secretarial services, take-overs and acquisitions and the formation and management of charitable trusts and companies.

Litigation: A comprehensive debt-recovery service is offered as is advice on employment law, contractual disputes, damages claims, arbitration and matters falling within the jurisdiction of the Scottish land courts. The members of the department are also experienced in dealing with personal litigation and can offer advice in connection with divorce and other family disputes and motoring offences.

Residential Conveyancing: The department assists with all aspects of buying and selling residential property and is authorised to arrange mortgages and insurance.

Private Client: In addition to traditional private client work involving the preparation of wills, acting for and as executors in winding up estates, setting up and administering trusts, this department now offers an in-house Investment Management service which has some £100,000,000 under management. Complementary income tax, tax planning and other independent financial advice is also available.

CLIENTELE: Lindsays has a wide range of clients including plc's, large and small companies, building societies, financial and educational institutions, charities, farmers and a broad spectrum of private individuals.

LINKLATERS (A MEMBER FIRM OF LINKLATERS & ALLIANCE)

One Silk Street, London, EC2Y 8HQ
Tel: (020) 7456 2000 **Fax:** (020) 7456 2222 **DX:** 10 London City EC3
Website: www.linklaters-alliance.com

Managing Partner:	Tony Angel
Senior Partner:	Charles Allen-Jones
Linklaters & Alliance Number of partners	
Worldwide:	over 500
Number of Lawyers	over 2,500

THE FIRM: Linklaters is one of the world's premium global law firms operating from the UK and major financial centres around the world. It is a member firm of Linklaters & Alliance, which comprises six European law firms: De Bandt, van Hecke, Lagae & Loesch (Belgium and Luxembourg); De Brauw Blackstone Westbroek (Netherlands); Gianni, Origoni & Partners (Italy); Lagerl^f & Leman (Sweden); Linklaters; and Oppenhoff & R%odler (Germany). Linklaters & Alliance currently has over 2,500 lawyers plus other professionals operating from 36 offices, covering the world's major financial and business centres. Since its formation over 150 years ago, Linklaters has had offices in the City of London. With the growth in financial markets, cross-border transactions and project finance, and in response to the commercial needs of its clients, the firm has developed globally with offices throughout the world. Linklaters & Alliance was formed in 1998.

Brussels • Frankfurt • Hong Kong
Moscow • New York • Paris • São Paulo
Singapore • Tokyo • Washington

Continued overleaf

PRINCIPAL AREAS OF WORK:

Corporate: Finance and commercial transactions and advice on company matters including share offerings, take-overs and mergers, company reconstructions and privatisations. Specialist groups also advise on UK and offshore investment funds, regulatory compliance, insurance, competition and EU law, project and asset finance and employee benefits.

Project/Asset finance: Project and asset financings primarily concerned with power, infrastructure, oil and gas, petrochemicals, telecoms and industrial projects throughout the world. International capital markets work and bank lending, including international securities issues, international offerings of debt and equity, structured and derivative products, project bonds and securitisations as well as acquisitions finance, PFI, property finance, trade finance, telecoms and tax structured products.

Real Estate: All types of real estate transactions from sales and purchases to lettings and development. Specialists handle planning (zoning) and environmental work, construction and engineering projects, tax and structuring advice as well as real estate management and litigation.

Litigation & Arbitration: Most types of contentious business arising in a financial, commercial or industrial context. Court and tribunal work, investigations, document handling and debt recovery. International arbitration focused on London, Paris and Hong Kong; extensive experience of ad hoc arbitrations and main arbitral institutions in Europe and Asia, of which many of our partners are members. Particular expertise in disputes concerning financial products and major infrastructure and power products.

Tax: Tax aspects of international transactions including domestic and cross-border mergers and acquisitions, capital market transactions, lease and project financing, real estate transactions (investment, development and financing), investment funds, structured finance, including litigation and international tax planning.

Other Services: The firm has specialist departments in intellectual property, technology and communications, pensions, employee incentives, environment and trusts serving clients around the world.

LANGUAGES: All commercial languages and local language of countries in which Linklaters & Alliance has offices.

CLIENTELE: The firm advises major corporations, banks, financial institutions and governments worldwide.

CONTACTS

Banking	John Tucker
Competition/EU	Bill Allan
Construction & Engineering	Marshall Levine
Corporate	David Cheyne
E-commerce Business	Chris Kelly
	Charlie Jacobs
Employment	Raymond Jeffers
Environment	Ray Jackson
Financial Markets	Paul Nelson
International Finance & Capital Markets	Stephen Edlmann
Investment Funds	Paul Harris
Litigation & Arbitration	Christopher Style
Project and Asset Finance	Alan Black
Real Estate	Simon Clark
Restructuring & Insolvency	Robert Elliott
Securities	Michael Canby
Tax Planning	Guy Brannan

L

LINNELLS

Greyfriars Court, Paradise Square, Oxford, OX1 1BB
Tel: (01865) 248607 **Fax:** (01865) 728445 **DX:** 82261 Oxford 2
Email: law@linnells.co.uk **Website:** www.linnells.co.uk

Senior Partner:	Jonathan Lloyd-Jones
Number of partners:	19
Assistant solicitors:	15
Other fee-earners:	27

THE FIRM: Linnells, a leading firm in the South East, provides services of outstanding quality and value to a well-established local client base as well as clients located in major centres. Linnells has a strong commercial and property bias and is becoming increasingly well-known for its specialist expertise in publishing, construction and charity law. The firm has an additional office in Bicester.

PRINCIPAL AREAS OF WORK:

Property: With one of the largest teams in the South East, Linnells handles all aspects of property work: residential and commercial development; relocation; landlord and tenant; agricultural tenancies; freehold and leasehold; taxation of land transactions, planning and environmental matters. A new partner addition has brought further expertise and strength to this area.

Corporate/Commercial: Acting for major corporations, institutions and SMEs, Linnells handles a broad mix of corporate work, from formations and restructurings through to M&A. The team advises on share options and shareholder agreements, MBOs, MBIs and specialist finance work, including the sourcing of funds and sale documentation. Other specialist areas include IP and IT with strong expertise in electronic publishing, technology and education.

Commercial Litigation/Dispute Resolution: This area continues to expand with specialist construction, asset finance and employment work on the increase. The firm is a leader in ADR with a number of trained mediators and is also a founder member of ADR Net.

Charities: This specialist unit has established a national reputation for contract work and now acts for three of the country's top ten aid agencies.

Litigation: This department has refocused its services, specialising in clinical negligence work, accident claims, family and property disputes, and now acts in a support role to the firm's core areas. The Human Rights team undertakes immigration and some criminal work.

CLIENTELE: Well-known companies including property developers, construction companies, national charities, high tech companies, publishers and Oxford University Colleges. Major clients include: Dun & Bradstreet; Oxfam; World Vision; The Artificial Heart Fund; Coventry Building Society; Blackwell Retail; Oxford University Press; Blackwell Science; Berkeley Homes (Oxford); Leadbitter Construction; British Potato Council; Institute of Education; Digitext; British Institute for Radiology; Wyeth Laboratories; Renault Retail Group.

AREAS OF PRACTICE

Development/Residential Property	30%
Corporate	20%
Private Client Litigation	16%
Commercial Property	13%
Commercial Litigation	12%
Private Client	9%

CONTACTS

Aviation & Tourism	Glenvil Smith
Charities	Joss Saunders
Clinical Negligence	Jeremy Irwin-Singer
Commercial Litigation	Jonathan Lloyd-Jones
Commercial Property	John Deech
Company/Commercial	Edward Lee
Construction	Jonathan Lloyd-Jones
Corporate Finance	Edward Lee
Employment	James Whiter
Family	Christine Plews
Human Rights/Crime	Warwick Clarke
Immigration	Philip Turpin
Intellectual Property	Joss Saunders

LINSKILLS SOLICITORS

6-8 Castle Street, Liverpool, L2 0NA **Tel:** (0151) 236 2224 **Fax:** (0151) 236 0151 (Criminal) **DX:** 14215 **Ptnrs:** 1 **Asst solrs:** 8 **Other fee-earners:** 20 **Contact:** Mr M.B.Heller (Practice Manager) • Legal aid franchise in crime, family, welfare, police actions and personal injury. Branch office (welfare advice & civil litigation) 195 Kensington, Liverpool L7 2RF Tel: (0151) 260 1001 Fax: (0151) 261 1936. Legal Aid Franchise in welfare, family and housing.

AREAS OF PRACTICE

Criminal	58%
Road Traffic Accident	10%
Welfare	8%
Conveyancing	7%
Personal Injury	7%
Matrimonial	6%
Civil Litigation	4%

LIVINGSTONE BROWNE

84 Carlton Place, Glasgow, G5 9TD **Tel:** (0141) 429 8166 **Fax:** (0141) 429 1337 **DX:** 60 Glasgow

LLEWELYN ZIETMAN

Temple Bar House, 23-28 Fleet Street, London, EC4Y 1AA
Tel: (020) 7842 5400 **Fax:** (020) 7842 5444 **DX:** 209 Chancery Lane London WC2
Email: post@llz.co.uk **Website:** www.llz.co.uk

Managing Partner:	Ian Macdonald
Senior Partner:	Clive Zietman
Number of partners:	13
Number of fee-earners:	31
Total staff:	53

AREAS OF PRACTICE

Commercial Litigation	50%
Intellectual Property	50%

CONTACTS

Banking Litigation	Duncan McNair
	Geoffrey Gauci
Brand Protection	Belinda Isaac
	Andrew Shaw
Commercial & Fraud Litigation	
	Clive Zietman
	John Bramhall
Commercial Law	Ian MacDonald
E-Commerce	Lorna Robertson
	Belinda Isaac
Financial Services Regulation	Clive Zietman
Insolvency Litigation	Charles Pugh
International Commercial Arbitration	Geoffrey Gauci
Patents/Designs & Copyright	James Irvine
	Conrad Arnander
	Gerard Cronin
Trademarks (Registration & Enforcement)	Belinda Isaac
	Andrew Shaw

THE FIRM: Llewelyn Zietman is a young commercial law practice specialising in the resolution of commercial disputes, and in the protection, exploitation and enforcement of intellectual property rights. The specialist services of the commercial litigation department have an emphasis on fraud and financial services, and the intellectual property department is extensively experienced in all aspects of contentious and non-contentious matters. Llewelyn Zietman was founded in 1994 as a specialist niche practice focusing on commercial litigation and intellectual property, and has since greatly expanded its strengths in its chosen areas of expertise. The firm focuses on bringing a pro-active and partner driven approach to the resolution of commercial disputes, and to its intellectual property practice. It seeks to provide services with the highest of standards, but at competitive prices.

PRINCIPAL AREAS OF WORK:

Commercial: Commercial disputes of all kinds are dealt with. Expertise includes banking, including the enforcement of securities, actions based on guarantees and performance bonds, letters of credit and negligence, as well as a wide range of financial services matters. There is significant expertise within the firm in the fields of tracing and the recovery of assets, both within the UK and abroad. In that connection the firm has extensive practical experience in the application of the Brussels and Lugano Conventions and the conduct of multi-jurisdictional proceedings.

Fraud: The firm advises on all aspects of fraud, including prevention and investigation, as well as assisting in the recovery of monies. It has considerable experience in dealing with Serious Fraud Office, DTI and LIFFE investigations, and Clive Zietman - who has written extensively about fraud – is an acknowledged expert in the field.

Intellectual Property: Intellectual property expertise includes all aspects of patents, trademarks and service marks, copyright, registered and unregistered design and breach of confidence, together with all types of litigation and intellectual property aspects of corporate transactions.

Patents & Trademarks: Llewelyn Zietman has special expertise in three areas: European patent litigation including obtaining provisional and protective remedies; chemical, pharmaceutical and software patents; and brand protection, from advice on new product development with a view to gaining maximum legal protection; clearance searches in respect of new brand names; registration of trade marks and designs (in the UK and elsewhere) and enforcement of rights.

LANGUAGES: The firm has French, German and Italian speaking solicitors, and because of the nature of the work carried out, the firm has a strong international focus, and is conversant with the languages, laws and procedures of a number of foreign jurisdictions.

CLIENTELE: The firm's client base ranges from individuals to major multinationals, with about 75 per cent of the work being of an international nature.

LOCHNERS TECHNOLOGY SOLICITORS

Craven House, Station Road, Godalming, GU7 1EX **Tel:** (01483) 414588 **Fax:** (01483) 416065 **DX:** 58370 Godalming 2 **Email:** lochners@lochners.co.uk **Website:** www.lochners.co.uk **Ptnrs:** 3 **Asst solrs:** 1 **Para legal** 1 **Other fee-earners:** 1 • Specialists in technology-related law and associated areas of the law including patents, trade marks, copyright, design, confidential information and information technology.

AREAS OF PRACTICE

Intellectual Property	75%
Information Technology	25%

LODDERS

7 Warwick Road, Stratford-upon-Avon, CV37 6YL **Tel:** (01789) 293259 **Fax:** (01789) 268093 **Email:** lawyers@lodders.co.uk **Website:** www.lodders.co.uk

LOOSEMORES

Alliance House, 18-19 High St, Cardiff, CF10 1BP **Tel:** (029) 2022 4433 **Fax:** (029) 2037 3275 **DX:** 33008 CARDIFF 1 **Email:** post@loosemores.co.uk **Ptnrs:** 11 **Asst solrs:** 13 **Other fee-earners:** 30

LOUDONS WS

29 St Patrick Square, Edinburgh, EH8 9EY **Tel:** (0131) 662 4193 **Fax:** (0131) 662 1910 **DX:** ED 294 Edinburgh 1 **Email:** loudons@btconnect.com **Website:** www.loudons.co.uk **Ptnrs:** 3 **Asst solrs:** 1 **Consultants/Associates**2 **Other fee-earners:** 2 **Contact:** Mr Alasdair Loudon • Specialist practice with very strong reputation for its family law expertise, particularly financial claims and settlements.

AREAS OF PRACTICE	
Family Law (incl Child Law)	100%

LOVELLS

L

65 Holborn Viaduct, London, EC1A 2DY
Tel: (020) 7296 2000 **Fax:** (020) 7296 2001 **DX:** Box 57
Email: information@lovells.com **Website:** www.lovells.com

Managing partner:	Lesley MacDonagh
Senior partner:	Andrew Walker
Deputy managing partner	Oliver Felsenstein
Deputy senior partner	Walter Klosterfelde
Number of Partners Worldwide:	247
Assistant Solicitors Worldwide:	554
Other Fee Earners Worldwide:	320
Total Staff Worldwide:	2,128

THE FIRM: Lovells is one of the leading international law firms, with more than 1,100 lawyers across 24 offices in 17 countries. Lovells combines the expertise of two leading practices - Lovell White Durrant and Boesebeck Droste. Building upon strong and broadly-based domestic practices, they provide co-ordinated, multi-jurisdictional services from their offices around the world.

INTERNATIONAL CONNECTIONS: The practice of each of the firm's international offices reflects the requirements of clients and the nature of local and regional markets. London is the largest office and offers the full range of the firm's specialist services. The firm's German practice mirrors the decentralised structure of Germany in the heart of the 'Euro-zone', with offices in Frankfurt, Dusseldorf, Hamburg, Munich, Berlin and Dresden from which they provide legal services in all business matters whether domestic or international. Elsewhere in Continental Europe, the Brussels, Budapest, Moscow, Paris, Prague, Warsaw, Vienna and Zagreb offices offer a combination of local and cross-border legal services covering the areas of banking, corporate finance, private equity, project finance, capital markets, tax, IP, competition and trade regulation, financial services and property. The firm's office in Alicante specialises in trademark matters with the European Trademark Office. The Asia practice of Lovells is managed from the Hong Kong office and focuses on regional banking, project finance, capital markets, corporate transactions, insolvency, construction, IP, litigation and property. The North America offices in New York, Chicago and Washington DC concentrate particularly on UK and EU advice on corporate transactions, US securities law advice, insurance and reinsurance litigation, insurance insolvency, consumer financial services including regulatory advice and product liability. Lovells places great emphasis on helping clients to achieve their business objectives by providing legal advice that is both imaginative and commercially aware. It is also known for nurturing its working relationships with clients both large and small and consistently achieves very high ratings for client satisfaction in independent research. The size and international strengths of the firm enable it to put together expert teams of lawyers with direct experience of advising on some of the largest and most complex transactions and cases of recent years, both in the UK and elsewhere in the world. Lovells' services are tailored to the needs of individual clients, drawing on the collective knowledge of the firm. Size, experience and international strengths enable the firm to assemble expert teams of lawyers to advise on transactions or issues that concern its clients. Lovells aims to add value at all stages of a project, from its initiation, through its planning to its execution. Lawyers at Lovells are members of broad practice areas which work together closely. These practice areas operate internationally and are structured to facilitate the sharing of technical know-how and the development of a consistently high standard of legal advice across the firm.

RECRUITMENT & TRAINING: Prospective trainee solicitors should contact Clare Walton for details of the recruitment programme. Further information is available from any Lovells office or via the firm's internet website at www.lovells.com. A comprehensive selection of brochures, client notes and newsletters is available from Jan Frangs in the London office.

CONTACTS	
Advertising/Consumer Law	Andrew Skipper
Arbitration/ADR	Andrew Foyle
	Patrick Sherrington
Asset Finance	Robin Hallam
Banking	Matthew Cottis, Andrew Gamble
Broadcasting	Jennifer McDermott
	Michael Golding
Business Restructuring	Nicholas Frome
Capital Markets	David Hudd
Commodities	David Moss
Computers/IT	Quentin Archer
Construction/Engineering	Nicholas Gould,
	Philip Capper
Corporate Finance/M&A	Hugh Nineham
Defamation	Jennifer McDermott
Employee Benefits	Louise Whitewright
Employment	Andrew Williamson, David Harper
Energy	David Moss, Michael Stanger
Environmental	Louise Moore
EU/Competition	Simon Polito
Financial Services	Richard Stones
Fraud/Asset Recovery	Keith Gaines
Insurance/Reinsurance	John Young
	John Powell
Intellectual Property	Robert Anderson
Litigation	Russell Sleigh
Media Law	Jennifer McDermott
Pensions	Jane Samsworth
Planning	Michael Gallimore
Private Equity	Allan Murray-Jones
Product Liability	John Meltzer
Professional Indemnity	John Trotter
Project Finance	Gavin McQuater
Property	Robert Kidby
Property Litigation	Nicholas Cheffings
Public Policy	Gordon Innes
Shipping/International Trade	David Moss
Tax	Daniel Friel
Telecommmunications	Heather Rowe
VAT	Greg Sinfield

LOXLEYS

Bishopsgate House, 5-7 Folgate Street, London, E1 6BX **Tel:** (020) 7377 1066 **Fax:** (020) 7377 5004 **DX:** 131418 Bishopsgate **Email:** mail@loxleys.demon.co.uk **Website:** www.loxleys.com **Ptnrs:** 7 **Asst solrs:** 3 **Other fee-earners:** 6 **Contact:** Graeme Harris • A general property, commercial, employment law, probate and trust practice, liquor, gaming, entertainment licensing and overseas work a speciality. Associate firms worldwide. Main European and Indian languages spoken.

LUCAS & WYLLYS

5 South Quay, Great Yarmouth, NR30 2QJ **Tel:** (01493) 855555 **Fax:** (01493) 330055 **DX:** 41100 **Ptnrs:** 8 **Asst solrs:** 3 **Other fee-earners:** 11

LUMB & MACGILL

Prudential Buildings, 11 Ivegate, Bradford, BD1 1SQ **Tel:** (01274) 730666 **Fax:** (01274) 723453 **DX:** 11714 **Ptnrs:** 4 **Asst solrs:** 2 **Other fee-earners:** 6 **Contact:** Paul Milner • Franchised specialists in criminal, care, mental health and legal aid.

AREAS OF PRACTICE

Crime	85%
Child Care	10%
Mental Health	5%

LUPTON FAWCETT

Yorkshire Hse, Greek St, Leeds, LS1 5SX **Tel:** (0113) 280 2000 **Fax:** (0113) 245 6782 **DX:** 12035 Leeds **Website:** www.lupton-fawcett.co.uk **Ptnrs:** 20 **Asst solrs:** 30 **Other fee-earners:** 47

LUQMANI THOMPSON

77-79 High Road, Wood Green, London, N22 6BB **Tel:** (020) 8365 7800 **Fax:** (020) 8826 0169 **DX:** 34715 WOOD GREEN 2 **Email:** luqthom@btinternet.com **Website:** www.luqhom.com

LYONS DAVIDSON

Victoria House, 51 Victoria Street, Bristol, BS1 6AD **Tel:** (0117) 904 6000 **Fax:** (0117) 904 6001 **DX:** 7834 **Website:** www.lyonsdavidson.co.uk **Ptnrs:** 16 **Asst solrs:** 42 **Other fee-earners:** 101 **Contact:** Mr Bernard Rowe • By concentrating on satisfying it's clients needs, the firm continues to enjoy year on year growth in insurance, company, commercial property and family services.

AREAS OF PRACTICE

Litigation	59%
Company/Commercial	17%
Property	15%
Family	9%

M

MACDONALDS

1 Claremont Terrace, Glasgow, G3 7UQ **Tel:** (0141) 248 6221 **Fax:** (0141) 333 0318 **DX:** 142 Glasgow **Email:** enquiries@macdonalds-uk.com **Website:** www.macdonalds-uk.com **Ptnrs:** 11 **Asst solrs:** 8 **Other fee-earners:** 5

MACE & JONES

Drury House, 19 Water Street, Liverpool, L2 0RP
Tel: (0151) 236 8989 **Fax:** (0151) 227 5010 **DX:** 14166 Liverpool
Email: law@maceandjones.co.uk **Website:** www.maceandjones.co.ukl

30 Sherborne Square, Huyton, L36 9UR
Tel: (0151) 480 7000 **Fax:** (0151) 449 1953 **DX:** 15453 Huyton
Email: law@maceandjones.co.uk

98 King Street, Knutsford, WA16 6EP
Tel: (01565) 634234 **Fax:** (01565) 652711 **DX:** 22959 Knutsford
Email: law@maceandjones.co.uk

14 Oxford Court, Bishopsgate, Manchester, M2 3WQ
Tel: (0161) 236 2244 **Fax:** (0161) 228 7285 **DX:** 18564 Manchester 7
Email: law@maceandjones.co.uk

THE FIRM: A leading regional practice in the North West, Mace & Jones remains a full service firm, while enjoying a national reputation for its commercial expertise, especially in employment, litigation/insolvency, corporate and property, with the firm being voted Property Law of the Year by *Insider North-West* magazine. The firm's clients range from national and multi-national companies and public sector bodies to owner-managed businesses and private individuals, reflecting the broad nature of the work undertaken. Sound practical advice is given always on a value-for-money basis. Today, nearly 100 lawyers deliver a service which is founded on an intimate understanding of the needs and objectives of their clients. Low staff turnover leads to a continuity of service which is rarely found in firms of this size. This in turn ensures an understanding of the client, whether in the business or private sector, which enables probelms to be anticipated and a pro-active approach adopted.

Managing Partner:	Lawrence Downey
Senior Partner:	Graeme Jump
Number of partners:	27
Assistant solicitors:	42
Other fee-earners:	22

AREAS OF PRACTICE

Commercial Litigation/Insolvency	20%
Commercial Property	20%
Company/Commercial	20%
Employment	20%
PI/Private Client/Family	20%

CONTACTS

Commercial Litigation	Craig Blakemore
Commercial Property	Tim Williams
Company/Commercial	Alan Thompson
Employment	Martin Edwards
Insolvency	Graeme Jump
Personal injury	Stewart McCulloch

MACFARLANES

10 Norwich Street, London, EC4A 1BD
Tel: (020) 7831 9222 **Fax:** (020) 7831 9607 **DX:** 138
Email: cpp@macfarlanes.com **Website:** www.macfarlanes.com

THE FIRM: The firm's distinctive market position as a City law firm is founded on a reputation for quality which rivals that of the largest firms in the City. This, and an emphasis on excellence of client service and investment in training, have helped the firm to recruit the best lawyers who thrive in an environment which the larger City firms cannot offer. They serve a broad range of clients from multi-national companies to private individuals. Unusually, amongst City firms, Macfarlanes combines top quality corporate work with real strengths across their other practice areas of property, litigation and tax and financial planning. People are chosen for their intellectual rigour and drive. A reputation for excellence for UK work is matched world-wide by their policy of forming close friendships with the best firms in other jurisdictions to give Macfarlanes effective global coverage.

Continued overleaf

Number of partners:	52
Assistant solicitors:	114
Other fee-earners:	61

AREAS OF PRACTICE

Company/Commercial/Banking	49%
Property	22%
Litigation	16%
Tax & Financial Planning	13%

PRINCIPAL AREAS OF WORK:

Corporate: Macfarlanes is particularly highly regarded for its work in the areas of corporate finance and M&A, including private equity and take-overs. The firm's related specialist areas, such as intellectual property, corporate tax, banking and employee benefits, mean that Macfarlanes can provide its broad range of commercial clients with high quality legal services, both in relation to corporate transactional work and at the clients' operational level. The firm has earned a strong reputation for advertising and marketing work as well as investment funds and financial services.

Property: Work for the property sector covers all transactions involving ownership, development, investment in and financing of land. Commercial property investment and development transactions are at the core of the work of the Property Department whose reputation and profile continues to rise as the quality of its work and of the transactions in which it is involved are more widely recognised.

Litigation: Macfarlanes' wide range of litigation and other dispute resolution work includes: leading employment law cases; acting for insured and insurer, especially in advertising and surveying cases; IP cases and disputes over computer hardware and software; financial services regulatory issues and enquiries; Lloyd's-related work; sovereign debt, securities and other banking disputes; judicial review, breach of contract and professional negligence claims. Recent work includes working on major EU and competition disputes including the Davidoff parallel imports case; major shipping and construction arbitration and advising on a number of jurisdictional disputes and EU juridsdiction questions.

Private Client: Macfarlanes is one of the leading UK firms in advising private clients and their family trusts, both domestically and internationally. Tax planning, including the creation and administration of trusts, the preparation of wills and the administration of estates are central to this work. The firm forms and advises many charitable companies and trusts. The international element is very important both for UK-based families and for overseas taxpayers seeking advice on tax and trust law. The firm is frequently instructed at the request of many of the largest US firms and private banks for this work.

INTERNATIONAL CONNECTIONS: The firm has an office in Brussels.

CONTACTS

Acquisitions & Disposals	Robert Sutton
Advertising	Jeremy Courtenay-Stamp
Agricultural	John Hornby
Banking	Mark Furman
Corporate Finance	Tim Lewis
Corporate Property	Chris Field
Employee Benefits	Douglas Shugar
Employment	Tony Thompson
Enterprise Zones	Chris Field
Financial Services	Bridget Barker
General Commercial and I.P.	Jeremy Courtenay-Stamp
Health Care	John Moore
Investment Funds	Bridget Barker
Lending	Tony Evans
Litigation	Willie Manners
MBOs/MBIs, Financial Purchases	Kevin Tuffnell
Pensions	Hugh Arthur
PFI	John Skelton
Planning & Environmental Work	Andrew Jackson
Private Client	John Rhodes
Property Development	Chris Field
Property Investment	Chris Field
Residential Property	John Hornby
Retail Property	Richard Reuben
Unit Trusts	Tim Cornick

M

MACKAY SIMON

58 Queen Street, Edinburgh, EH2 3NS
Tel: (0131) 240 1400 **Fax:** (0131) 240 1401 **DX:** ED 243
Email: law@mckay-simon.co.uk

Managing Partner:	Malcolm R. Mackay
Number of partners:	7
Assistant solicitors:	2
Other fee-earners:	7

AREAS OF PRACTICE

Employment	100%

CONTACTS

Employment	Malcolm R. Mackay

THE FIRM: The firm was established in 1988 by Malcolm Mackay with the sole aim of providing a specialised employment law service and Shona Simon was assumed as a partner in 1993. Since then the firm has expanded significantly and in the last year a further 5 partners have been assumed. In addition, offices have recently been opened in Glasgow and London. However, the firm continues to provide advice only in relation to employment law matters. All at Mackay Simon recognise that employment law is a complex subject but that it must be applied in a sensible and realistic way. The firm's general approach is to achieve a practical resolution to disputes if possible. However when litigation is necessary, representation is almost always provided in-house.

PRINCIPAL AREAS OF WORK: Malcolm Mackay is primarily involved in collective matters such as business transfers and reorganisations, while Shona Simon specialises in discrimination and equal pay. One of the recently assumed partners, David Leckie has particular expertise in health and safety and human rights issues. All other partners and fee earners cover areas of expertise from working time and industrial relations to unfair dismissal and drafting of contracts. The firm also has an expanding programme of training for clients covering all aspects of employment law. Many of the partners lecture regularly at academic institutions, conferences and seminars on their various areas of expertise. Malcolm Mackay and Shona Simon have co-written *Green's Concise Guide to Employment Law* and also edit *Green's Employment Law Bulletin*. David Leckie contributes to *Tolley's Health and Safety at Work* and has co-authored a guide to the Human Rights Act 1998. The firm also has two academic consultants and places a great emphasis on achieving the correct balance between the academic and practical aspects of employment law.

CLIENTELE: Mackay Simon has a wide client base from small to large commercial organisations, trade unions and private clients. The firm is also regularly instructed by the Equal Opportunities Commission in Scotland. As many of the firm's clients have operations throughout the UK, solicitors appear regularly in Employment Tribunals and the Employment Appeal Tribunal in Scotland and England. The firm regularly instructs counsel in employment matters in the higher courts in Scotland and England including two cases in the House of Lords.

Mackay Simon ws

MACKINNONS

21 Albert Street, Aberdeen, AB25 1XX
Tel: (01224) 632464 **Fax:** (01224) 632184 **DX:** AB 34
Email: admin@mackinnons.com **Website:** www.mackinnons.com

379 North Deeside Road, Cults, Aberdeen, AB15 9SX
Tel: (01244) 868687 **Fax:** (01224) 861012 **DX:** AB34
Email: admin@mackinnons.com

Managing Partner:	Charles M. Scott
Senior Partner:	Denis N. Yule
Number of partners:	6
Assistant solicitors:	4
Other fee-earners:	5

CONTACTS

Commercial ....Charles M. Scott
..........Graham Jones
Marine & Litigation ..........D.N. Yule
..........K. MacRae
..........B. Craig
Private Client & Property ....Mrs P.J. Gray

THE FIRM: Progressive six-partner practice specialising in shipping and commercial law with substantial private client department providing a full range of legal services. The firm is very experienced in all aspects of marine and admiralty law including marine insurance, collisions, salvage, litigation and personal injury as well as acting in the defence of prosecutions under the full range of merchant shipping, pollution and fisheries legislation. The firm acts for numerous P&I clubs and fishing mutuals providing a hands-on service aboard ships, fishing boats and oil rigs. Mackinnons has a substantial marine and commercial practice dealing with purchase, sale, finance and chartering of fishing boats, offshore oil supply and stand-by vessels, and other vessels.

M

MACKINTOSH DUNCAN

103 Borough High Street, London, SE1 1NN **Tel:** (020) 7357 6464 **Fax:** (020) 7357 8448 **DX:** 39921 London Bridge South
Email: admin@mackdunc.co.uk

MACLAY MURRAY & SPENS

151 St Vincent Street, Glasgow, G2 5NJ
Tel: (0141) 248 5011 **Fax:** (0141) 248 5819 **DX:** GW 67
Email: lawyer@maclaymurrayspens.co.uk **Website:** www.maclaymurrayspens.co.uk

3 Glenfinlas Street, Edinburgh, EH3 6AQ
Tel: (0131) 226 5196 **Fax:** (0131) 226 3174 **DX:** ED137

10 Foster Lane, London, EC2V 6HR
Tel: (020) 7606 6130 **Fax:** (020) 7600 0992 **DX:** 42616

Managing Partner:	Michael J. Walker
Senior Partner:	Bruce Patrick
Number of partners:	50
Associate solicitors:	29
Assistant solicitors:	62
Other fee-earners:	49

AREAS OF PRACTICE

Company/Commercial 40%
Commercial Property 28%
Litigation 17%
Private Client 15%

CONTACTS

Banking ....Robert Laing
Commercial Property ....Jennifer Johnson
Company/Commercial ....Magnus Swanson
Construction ....Mark Macaulay
Employee Benefits ....Maureen Burnside
Employment ....Mark Hamilton
Environmental ....Chris Smylie
EU ....Michael Dean
Fraud and Financial Services ....Richard Clark
Intellectual Property ....Fiona Nicolson
Litigation ....Ewan Easton
Pensions ....Gary Cullen
Private Client ....Andrew Biggart
Tax ....Martyn Jones

THE FIRM: Maclay Murray & Spens is a leading commercial law firm, committed to offering all of its clients the highest quality – commercial advice at competitive prices. The firm has a significant English, European and international client base, which can be serviced from any or all of the firm's four offices in Edinburgh, Glasgow, London and Brussels. These are linked by an integrated computer, video-conferencing and telephone network ensuring a fast, efficient service, and expert advice are delivered. The London office which offers a full English Law service, provides an ideal platform both for Scottish clients doing business in the City and for London-based clients looking for a premier law firm without City overheads. The development and growth of the Brussels office reflects the firm's commitment to meet client needs.

PRINCIPAL AREAS OF WORK: Understanding clients and their business is the focus of the firm's approach. Maclay Murray & Spens has developed well-organised expert departments in fields such as employment, pensions and benefits, intellectual property, taxation, banking, fraud, construction, EU and competition, and capital projects. These specialist units augment the four more traditional areas of company, commercial property, litigation and private client. The litigation department which has always been known for its advice in commercial litigation in general - and shipping, aircraft and intellectual property litigation in particular - has developed specialisations in property litigation, employment and planning. The department also has a growing reputation in Solicitor Advocacy, with four partners now able to offer this service to clients. The firm recognises that many transactions require hand-picked teams made up of lawyers with differing skills from differing departments if the specific needs of the client and the transaction are to be fully met. To this end, the firm ensures that all departments and units are closely linked to give the client the best possible service. The firm continues to move into new areas, most recently the formation of its Scottish Parliamentary group which provides clients with a monitoring service of Scottish legislation, presented the First Business Petition to the new Parliament.

INTERNATIONAL CONNECTIONS: The firm has an overseas office at Scotland House, Rond-Point Schuman 6, B-1040 Brussels, Belgium, tel: +32 2 282 8415, fax: +32 2 282 8418.

Maclay Murray  Spens

SOLICITORS

LANGUAGES: French, German, Italian, Norwegian

MACLEOD & MACCALLUM

P.O. Box No.4, 28 Queensgate, Inverness, IV1 1YN **Tel:** (01463) 239393 **Fax:** (01463) 222879 **DX:** 12 Inverness **Email:** mail@macardmac.co.uk
Website: www.macardmac.co.uk **Ptnrs:** 10 **Asst solrs:** 3 **Other fee-earners:** 13

MACPHEE & PARTNERS

St Mary's House, Gordon Square, Fort William, PH33 6DY **Tel:** (01397) 701000 **Fax:** (01397) 701777 **DX:** FW 531408 **Email:** law@macphee.co.uk **Website:** www.macphee.co.uk **Ptnrs:** 3 **Asst solrs:** 5 **Other fee-earners:** 4 **Contact:** Duncan MacPhee • Largest practice in area. Winner 1997 TSB Law Society of Scotland Business of Law Awards (small firms) and 1998 Highlands and Islands Business Awards – Best Newcomer. Investors in people 1999. Crofting law specialism.

MACROBERTS

152 Bath Street, Glasgow, G2 4TB
Tel: (0141) 332 9988 **Fax:** (0141) 332 8886 **DX:** GW70
Email: maildesk@macroberts.co.uk **Website:** www.macroberts.co.uk

27 Melville Street, Edinburgh, EH3 7JF
Tel: (0131) 226 2552 **Fax:** (0131) 226 2501 **DX:** ED207
Email: maildesk@macroberts.co.uk

Managing Partner:	John Macmillan
Senior Partner:	Raymond Williamson
Number of partners:	31
Assistant solicitors:	71
Other fee-earners:	12

CONTACTS

Banking	Norman Martin
Charities	David MacRobert
Commercial Property	Laurence Fraser
	Allan Mackenzie
Construction	Lindy Patterson
Corporate	Ian Dickson
	Norman Martin
Corporate Tax & VAT	Isobel d'Inverno
Employment	John Macmillan
	Raymond Williamson
Energy Law	Ian Dickson
Environmental & Planning	Jamie Grant
EU & Competition	David Flint
Intellectual Property/IT	David Flint
Litigation & Arbitration	Richard Barrie
	Lindy Patterson
Pensions & Employee Benefits	Peter Trotter
PFI & Capital Projects	Michael Murphy
	David Henderson
Private Client	David MacRobert

M

THE FIRM: MacRoberts is a leading commercial law firm offering a comprehensive range of legal services to corporate, commercial, public sector and private clients. Established almost 150 years ago, MacRoberts, through its offices in Edinburgh and Glasgow, provides quality legal services in a prompt, efficient and friendly manner. The firm is committed to delivering the highest standards of professional advice and expertise.

PRINCIPAL AREAS OF WORK:

Corporate: All aspects of corporate and commercial law including: incorporations, reorganisations, takeovers and mergers, management buy-outs and joint ventures (UK and international); loan debenture and equity finance, syndications, consumer credit; banking flotations, Stock Exchange requirements, new issues, placings and other issues, employee share schemes and pension schemes; receivership, administration, liquidation and bankruptcy; partnership agreements; EU law; commercial contracts, including agency distribution and finance agreements; entertainment law; privatisations.

Commercial Property: Corporate clients are advised on all aspects of property matters including: acquisition, sale and leasing of commercial and industrial property; commercial, industrial and housing development, investment and finance; commercial secured loans; environmental law; agricultural law, including forestry; company relocation schemes; timeshare and leisure developments; planning law; licensing and gaming law.

Construction: Advice in connection with drafting of construction contracts, professional appointments, collateral warranties; building and engineering disputes and arbitration.

Corporate Tax & VAT: Including tax & VAT aspects of corporate acquisitions, disposals and reorganisations, commercial property transactions and PFI/PPP projects.

Employment: Employment and service contracts, disciplinary and grievance procedures, other procedural rules, employment policies including health & safety, sex and race discrimination, equal pay and trade union disputes.

Intellectual Property & IT: Franchising, patents and patent licensing, copyright, trademarks and know-how agreements; data protection; computer contracts.

Litigation and Arbitration: The group acts for and advises on all aspects of: civil litigation in both Sheriff Courts and the Court of Session; building and engineering disputes and arbitration; insurance and other commercial litigation; rating and valuation; planning; professional negligence; liquidation, administration, receivership and bankruptcy; product liability; debt recovery; reparation claims; intellectual property disputes; licensing.

PFI/PPP & Capital Projects: One of the largest practices in Scotland, clients include NHS Trusts, local authorities, bidding consortia and banks in a wide range of sectors including healthcare, education, roads, wastewater and office accommodation.

Private Client: Specialist advice to individuals, trustees and executors in relation to tax planning and mitigation; preparation of tax returns; investment advice; establishment and administration of trusts; wills; administration of estates; preparation of Powers of Attorney; financial services; acquisition, sale and leasing of estate and domestic property; setting up and administration of curatories.

INTERNATIONAL CONNECTIONS: Member of ADVOC, an international network of independent lawyers, providing access to legal services throughout Europe and Asia.

LANGUAGES: Dutch, French, German, Greek, Italian and Norwegian.

MADDEN & FINUCANE

88 Castle Street, Belfast, BT1 1HE **Tel:** (028) 9023 8007 **Fax:** (028) 9043 9276 **DX:** 434 NR Belfast **Email:** Enquiries@Madden-Finucane.com **Website:** Madden-Finucane.co **Ptnrs:** 5 **Asst solrs:** 8 **Other fee-earners:** 30

MADGE LLOYD & GIBSON

34 Brunswick Road, Gloucester, GL1 1JW **Tel:** (01452) 520 224 **Fax:** (01452) 306 866

MAGRATH & CO

52-54 Maddox Street, London, W1R 9PA
Tel: (020) 7495 3003 **Fax:** (020) 7409 1745 **DX:** 9009 West End
Email: magrath@magrath.co.uk **Website:** www.magrath.co.uk

Managing Partner:	Rosalind Morris
Senior Partner:	Chris Magrath
Number of partners:	6
Assistant solicitors:	17
Other fee-earners:	9

AREAS OF PRACTICE

Immigration/Employment	56%
Crime	15%
Civil Litigation	14%
Entertainment	9%
Commercial	4%
Property	2%

CONTACTS

Civil Litigation	Nick Goldstone
Commercial	David Ashton
Corporate Fraud/Crime (General)	Gary Summers
Employment	Chris Magrath
Entertainment	Alexis Grower
Immigration	Chris Magrath
Property	David Ashton

THE FIRM: Founded in 1990, Magrath & Co has niche expertise in corporate immigration/employment, fraud and entertainment law, as well as providing general commercial and litigation services. The firm's lawyers have extensive experience in their fields, and are dedicated to providing prompt, expert advice which meets and anticipates their clients' requirements.

PRINCIPAL AREAS OF WORK:

Immigration: The firm's dedicated immigration department covers the full range of immigration issues but advises primarily on commercial immigration including global expatriation planning, work permits, applications and appeals. The firm has particular experience in US-UK immigration matters and produces a regular bulletin each quarter to provide legal updates on immigration and employment law.

Employment Law: The firm's employment department deals with all aspects of employment law including contentious employment disputes, mass redundancies, consultation and industrial action, contract drafting and discrimination issues.

Corporate Fraud: The firm is experienced in a wide variety of 'white collar' crime, and can also advise in cases of investigation by agencies such as the Serious Fraud Office, DTI, Inland Revenue and Customs & Excise. Additionally the firm handles a wide range of criminal allegations of a more general nature.

Civil Litigation: The firm is instructed by a wide range of clients on a variety of commercial and entertainment related issues. Although increasingly geared towards the corporate sector, the firm welcomes private clients on both a fee paying and legally aided basis.

Entertainment Law: Advice on music and literature publishing, recording, production and management agreements; financing, production, distribution and marketing of TV, film, theatre and commercials. Also: merchandising and sponsorship agreements; sports-related advice; and gaming and betting law.

Other Areas: All aspects of company and commercial law and commercial property.

INTERNATIONAL CONNECTIONS: The practice is affiliated to New York-based Gibney Anthony & Flaherty, and to Munich-based David Hole and has links with other legal and professional services firms throughout the rest of the world's major commercial centres. Chris Magrath is also a qualified US Attorney, admitted to the New York State Bar.

CLIENTELE: The firm acts for a large number of major multinationals, together with other public companies, owner-managed businesses and private individuals throughout Britain, the US and Europe.

MAIDMENTS

St Johns Court, 74 Gartside Street, Manchester, M3 3EL **Tel:** (0161) 834 0008 **Fax:** (0161) 832 4140 **DX:** 14307 Manchester 1 **Email:** law@maidments.com **Website:** www.maidments.com **Ptnrs:** 8 **Asst solrs:** 9 **Other fee-earners:** 44 **Contact:** Allan Maidment • National criminal lawyers specialising in serious crime and commercial fraud. Manchester, Liverpool (0151 236 8100), Birmingham (0121 200 2221), London (020 7353 5788), Bristol (0117 900 8234), Leeds (0113 209 5772), Bolton (01204 455 455), Sale (0161 969 8111).

AREAS OF PRACTICE

Commercial Fraud	40%
Criminal	30%
Serious Crime	30%

MAITLAND WALKER

22 The Parks, Minehead, TA24 8BT
Tel: (01643) 707777 **Fax:** (01643) 700020 **DX:** 117408 Minehead
Email: office@maitwalk.co.uk

Managing Partner:	J.H. Maitland Walker
Number of partners:	1
Assistant solicitors:	2
Other fee-earners:	4

AREAS OF PRACTICE

Competition/IP Law	40%
Commercial Litigation	20%
EC/Trade Law	20%
General Commercial	10%
Private Client	10%

THE FIRM: Established in 1996 by Julian Maitland-Walker, the firm has expanded rapidly to become one of the leading niche EU and competition law practices. The firm acts for a wide range of commercial clients, individual traders, companies and trade associations. In addition, a consultancy service is offered as a facility to other law firms in both the UK and abroad in specialist EU and competition law matters. Recently, the firm has amalgamated with Makin & Co to offer an enhanced private client service. The firm has another office, in association with Campbell Hooper, in London (tel: 020 7222 9070).

PRINCIPAL AREAS OF WORK:

EU/Trade Law: Including free movement of goods, persons and freedom of establishment, national and international trade, operational logistics, anti-dumping investigations, state aids and public procurement.

Continued overleaf

Competition/IP Law: Advising EC and UK competition law, representing clients before the EU Commission and the UK Competition Authorities in anti-trust investigations. Advising on all aspects of intellectual property rights, registration, enforcement and licensing.
Commercial Litigation: Group actions involving breach of EU Competition law in the brewery and petrol retailing sectors together with a range of other commercial disputes. Employment law, work permits and immigration.
General Commercial: Advice on mergers and acquisitions, joint ventures, banking and insurance law, commercial agreements and commercial property.
Private Client: Residential property, matrimonial, wills, taxation and probate.
Consultancy Services: The firm offers a unique consultancy service to other law firms both in the UK and abroad providing specialist advice on competition and trade law and other areas of EU law. Julian Maitland Walker is currently a consultant with (inter alia) the following firms: Gouldens, Campbell Hooper (London), Brabner Holden Banks Wilson (Liverpool), Veale Wasbrough (Bristol) and Clark Holt (Swindon).

LANGUAGES: French, German and Italian.

MALCOLM LYNCH

19 High Court Lane, The Calls, Leeds, LS2 7EU
Tel: (0113) 242 9600 **Fax:** (0113) 234 2080 **DX:** 12100 Leeds 1
Email: law@malcolmlynch.com **Website:** www.malcolmlynch.com

Managing Partner:	Malcolm Lynch
Senior Partner:	Malcolm Lynch
Number of partners:	2
Assistant solicitors:	2
Other fee-earners:	1

THE FIRM: The firm is a niche practice with significant experience in commercial legal work and commercial property. The firm has a strong reputation in charity law and a significant proportion of its clients are drawn from national and local charities and registered social landlords. It has advised energy service companies and clients in the renewable energy industry for several years.Its corporate finance work encompasses public share issues and bank security documentation for financial institutions, and there is a strong focus on social and ethical investment.

AREAS OF PRACTICE

Charity Law	30%
Commercial Property	25%
Company/Commercial	25%
Employee Share Schemes & ESOP's	5%
Employment Law	5%
Energy	10%

MALLESONS STEPHEN JAQUES

2nd Floor, Aldermary House, 15 Queen Street, London, EC4N 1TX **Tel:** (020) 7982 0982 **Fax:** (020) 7982 9820 **Email:** lon@msj.com.au **Website:** www.msj.com.au **Ptnrs:** 1 **Asst solrs:** 5 **Contact:** Tim Blue • Mergers and acquisitions, foreign investment in Australia, banking and capital markets, international and domestic securities offerings, telecommunications law, general corporate/commercial, stamp duty and taxation, energy and resources law.

AREAS OF PRACTICE

Mergers & Acquisitions	30%
Securities Law	30%
Capital Markets	20%
Foreign Investment	10%
General Commercial Work	10%

MANBY & STEWARD

Mander House, Mander Centre, Wolverhampton, WV1 3NE
Tel: (01902) 578000 **Fax:** (01902) 424321/713564 **DX:** 10403
Email: manbys.manderhouse@dial.pipex.com

George House, St John's Square, Wolverhampton, WV2 4BZ
Tel: (01902) 578000 **Fax:** (01902) 311886 **DX:** 702431
Email: manbys.georgehouse@dial.pipex.com

Managing Partner:	Clive H.G. Williams
Senior Partner:	John Thorneycroft
Number of partners:	14
Assistant solicitors:	12
Other fee-earners:	26

THE FIRM: Established in Wolverhampton for more than 175 years and with offices in Telford and Bridgnorth, Manby & Steward provides an extensive range of services for the business and private client. The firm has a structure of specialist groups, which are partner led. It has invested extensively in information technology to ensure its efficient and competitive operation. Manby & Steward ensures that it is aware of what clients think and require from them. It aims to provide practical, responsive advice in accordance with its clients' requirements.

PRINCIPAL AREAS OF WORK: All aspects of commercial property; company & commercial; commercial litigation; town and country planning; employment; agricultural; private client; family & child care; residential conveyancing.

INTERNATIONAL CONNECTIONS: The firm is a founder member of LAWNET and is a member of Eurojuris.

AREAS OF PRACTICE

Litigation incl Planning	31%
Commercial Property	24%
Residential Property	20%
Company Commercial	15%
Private Client	10%

CONTACTS

Agricultural	Steve Corfield
Commercial Litigation	Peter Taylor
Commercial Property	Kevin Styles
Company Commercial	Gavin Southall
Ecclesiastical	John Thorneycroft
Employment	Sue Massey
Planning	Niall Blackie

MANCHES

Aldwych House, 81 Aldwych, London, WC2B 4RP
Tel: (020) 7404 4433 **Fax:** (020) 7430 1133 **DX:** 76
Email: manches@manches.co.uk **Website:** www.manches.com

3 Worcester Street, Oxford, OX1 2PZ
Tel: (01865) 722106 **Fax:** 01865 201012 **DX:** 4322
Email: manches@manches.co.uk

Senior Partner:	A.J. Simpson
Chief Executive:	Alun Lamerton
Number of partners:	49
Assistant solicitors:	61
Other fee-earners:	25

AREAS OF PRACTICE

Commercial Property	20%
Corporate	20%
Commercial Litigation	16%
Family Law	12%
Construction	10%
Employment	8%
Intellectual Property	8%
Banking and Insolvency	6%

CONTACTS

Commercial Property	Louis Manches
Commercial Tax	Stephen Goldstraw
Commercial/IT	Peter Stevens
Construction	James Foster
Corporate	Melvin Pedro
Employment	Alasdair Simpson
Environment/Planning	George Gandy
	Richard Smith
Family Law	Jane Simpson
Insolvency	Ashley Booker
Insurance	Peter Angel
	Charles Gordon
Intellectual Property	John Rubinstein
Litigation	James Foster
Personal Estate Planning	Alan Poulter
Publishing	Peter Stevens
	John Rubinstein
Social Housing	Richard Frost

THE FIRM: Manches is an innovative commercial firm at the forefront in a number of specialist legal practice areas and industrial sectors. Manches has arrived at its current position among London's leading firms through organic growth and strategic merger. This has enabled it to consolidate its expertise in corporate and commercial, property, litigation and to expand in specialist areas such as employment, intellectual property, biotechnology, information technology, insurance, construction and family law. Manches recognises that the legal market is client driven, and aims to offer clients premium service and niche expertise at competitive prices. To this end, the firm emphasises a plain-speaking, straightforward, value-for-money approach and is run along corporate lines, with all non-legal functions handled by the Chief Executive.

PRINCIPAL AREAS OF WORK:

Company & Commercial: Work includes M&A, venture capital, corporate reorganisations, AIM flotations, joint ventures and partnerships, Enterprise Investment Schemes, Private Finance Initiatives, service agreements, share options and other executive incentive schemes, competition law, franchising, commercial tax and employment.

Property: Work includes all aspects of commercial property, including investment and development work for institutions and property companies, social housing, secured lending and joint ventures, retail property and construction.

Litigation: Work includes commercial dispute resolution with particular expertise in construction and property, banking, insolvency, insurance, product liability, breach of contract and intellectual property. Cross-department groups focus on employment, publishing tax, computers and environmental law.

Intellectual Property: Work includes advertising, sales promotions, marketing and trade description law, biotechnology, computer law, copyrights, film, television and entertainment products and services, multimedia exploitation, passing off, publishing, defamation and UK and EU Competition.

Family: Work includes divorce, children, financial provision, separation agreements, adoption, guardianship, affiliation proceedings, and jurisdiction crossing.

Employment: Work includes executive remuneration and benefits, termination package, staff manual, discrimination policies, unfair and wrongful dismissal claims in the Industrial Tribunal, County and High Court.

Tax: Work includes mergers and acquisitions, joint ventures, flotation planning, profit extraction, leasing, management buy-outs, employee benefits, property tax, VAT planning, stamp duty planning, partnership tax, off-shore trading arrangements, insurance and tax, company pension schemes and tax appeals.

Personal Estate Planning: Work includes estate planning, preparation of wills, establishment of trusts, administration of estates and charities.

RECRUITMENT & TRAINING: There are currently 20 trainee solicitors. The firm's Director of Education and Training has responsibility for directing and monitoring each individual's training. Application forms can be obtained by telephoning the recruitment line (020 7872 8690) or by e-mailing sheona.clark@manches.co.uk

M AND A SOLICITORS

Kenneth Pollard House, 5-19 Cowbridge Road East, Cardiff, CF11 9AQ
Tel: (029) 2066 5793 **Fax:** (029) 2066 57989
Email: enquiries@manda.uk.com

Number of partners:	2
Assistant solicitors:	2

THE FIRM: The firm was stablished in 1999 as a niche practice offering a specialist corporate and commercial service. The firm is satisfying a growing trend among clients to instruct specialist advisors so as to receive the best possibble quality advice on a particular matter. The prospectof having an alternative to the large, multi-disciplinary practices is proving attractive to the firm's rapidly expanding client base. Due to the focused nature of the firm's area of practice, the firm is able to offer clients a cost effectient and commercial service. M and A Solicitors provides more thatn just a legal documentation service and has a research facility to help clients identufy and exploit business opportunities.

PRINCIPAL AREAS OF WORK:

Corporate Finance: The firm advises on the whole range of corporate finance transactions including, mergers, acquisitions, disposals, MBOs, MBIs, development capital and listings.

Commercial Services: The firm advises on commercial contracts, projects, and joint ventures and has supporting expertise in areas such as intellectual property, competition, property and employment.

MAPLES TEESDALE

21 Lincoln's Inn Fields, London, WC2A 3DU
Tel: (020) 7831 6501 **Fax:** (020) 7405 3867 **DX:** 192 London
Email: enq@maplesteesdale.co.uk **Website:** www.maplesteesdale.co.uk

Senior Partner:	Richard Read
Number of partners:	10
Assistant solicitors:	7
Other fee-earners:	10

CONTACTS

Commercial	Richard Read
Commercial property	Mark Bryan
Litigation	Paul Matcham
Private client	Sally Wilkins
Residential property	Edward Bliss

THE FIRM: Maples Teesdale aims to provide a first class service to business and private clients and value for money in its areas of practice.

PRINCIPAL AREAS OF WORK:

Commercial Property: The department deals with all aspects of commercial property work including large scale developments, acquisitions and disposals, landlord and tenant matters, secured lending, funding agreements, joint ventures and auctions.

Litigation: The department handles a broad spectrum of commercial litigation ranging from simple debt collection to complex contractual, company and partnership disputes and insolvency matters. It also handles all aspects of property-related litigation and disputes including landlord and tenant matters, management problems, reconstruction/redevelopment, eviction actions, forfeiture work, rent collection, rent reviews, lease renewals, service charge disputes, dilapidations claims, disputed options to break, planning enquiries, secured loan realisations and restructurings and professional negligence arising from the provision of property-related services. In addition, it deals with all aspects of building contracts and consultants' appointments.

Commercial: The department advises on all aspects of corporate and commercial work including corporate finance, flotations, mergers and acquisitions, sales, buy-outs, venture capital, capital structures, national and international joint ventures and banking. Expertise is also available in relation to employment law and most types of commercial contracts, including computer and internet contracts.

Private Client: The department advises on all aspects of family affairs, including the preparation of wills, financial and tax planning, the formation and administration of trusts, the administration of estates, matrimonial matters and the formation of and advice to charities.

Residential Property: A full range of residential property services is provided to private clients and the department also undertakes the purchase, sale and lettings of agricultural land and estates.

CLIENTELE: The firm's clients range from a government department and blue chip household name companies to smaller companies and private individuals.

MARGARET BENNETT

Charlton House, 5A Bloomsbury Square, London, WC1A 2LX
Tel: (020) 7404 6465 **Fax:** (020) 7240 5492 **DX:** 35740 Bloomsbury 1
Email: exclusive@divorce.uk.com

Senior and Managing Partner:	Margaret H. Bennett
Number of partners:	1
Assistant solicitors:	3
Other fee-earners:	1

AREAS OF PRACTICE

Family Law	100%

CONTACTS

Family Law	Margaret H. Bennett

THE FIRM: Established in 1990, as the first law firm practising exclusively in family law (uniquely with in-house divorce counselling, as well), Margaret Bennett Solicitors provides outstanding experience in this specialist field. The Principal, Margaret Bennett, is a former Chairman of the Family Law Committee of the International Bar Association and now Chairman of its Hague Child Abduction Task Force; a founder member and former Vice-President of the International Academy of Matrimonial Lawyers; founder of the Inter-country Adoption Lawyers' Association; a Deputy District Judge, Principal Registry of the Family Division, High Court, London; and a member of the Lord Chancellor's Panel of Solicitors on International Child Abduction, the firm having sound expertise in cases under The Hague and European Conventions on Child Abduction. The consultant, John D Bieber, is the author of If Divorce is the Only Way, published by Penguin Books. The consultant counsellor is Lady Patricia Harris, co-founder (1980) of the Divorce Conciliation and Advisory Service. All solicitors within the firm are members of the SFLA.

PRINCIPAL AREA OF WORK:

Family: Practising exclusively in family law, the firm offers an in-house counselling service to help clients with the emotional burden of marital breakdown creating better awareness of client needs and how their problems may best be resolved. Selective with its clientele, Margaret Bennett Solicitors can devote the time and attention to each matter that it deserves. In complex international cases, the firm's work is facilitated by a close connection with family law specialists around the world and in cases involving trusts companies and other specialist areas, the firm works closely with the client's other professional advisers.

LANGUAGES: French, German and Italian.

MARGETTS & RITCHIE
Coleridge Chambers, 177 Corporation Street, Birmingham, B4 6RL **Tel:** 0121 236 5517 **Fax:** 0121 236 5520

MARGRAVES
Old Court Chambers, Llandrindod Wells, LD1 5EY **Tel:** (01597) 825565 **Fax:** (01597) 825220 **DX:** 200154 Llandrindod
Email: law@margraves.co.uk **Website:** www.margraves.co.uk **Ptnrs:** 1 **Asst solrs:** 3 **Other fee-earners:** 1

MARRIOTT HARRISON

12 Great James Street, London, WC1N 3DR
Tel: (020) 7209 2000 **Fax:** (020) 7209 2001 **DX:** 0001 London Chancery Lane
Email: email@marriottharrison.co.uk **Website:** www.marriottharrison.com

Managing Partner:	Tony Morris
Number of partners:	9
Assistant solicitors:	2
Other fee-earners:	7

AREAS OF PRACTICE

Company/Commercial	50%
Media	35%
Litigation	10%
Property	5%

CONTACTS

Commercial	Mark Halama
Company	Jon Sweet
Litigation	Peter Curnock
New Media/Music	Tony Morris
Property	Vivienne Elson

THE FIRM: This central London firm provides a range of commercial and corporate services, with particular emphasis on media law. Most of the partners have been partners in major London firms, which they had left with a commitment to provide a high-quality personalised service to clients. The majority of the founding partners specialised in the media industry. With its rapidly increasing corporate and corporate finance practice, the firm has repositioned itself as a specialist corporate/media niche player.

PRINCIPAL AREAS OF WORK:

Media: The commercial media group deals with all aspects of production of software in its widest sense (films, television, music and sound recordings, CD-ROM, computer games, computer programs and the like) through to their delivery to the consumer. This involves in-depth knowledge of intellectual property rights and copyright as well as regulatory matters relating to broadcasting, cable and satellite operations. Clients include multinational media corporations, cable channels and operators, banks, film distributors, film and television production companies and creative talent, record companies and music publishers, web-site designers and producers, internet service providers, leading computer games publishers and developers and producers of commercial computer software.

Company & Commercial: Company and commercial expertise is provided in such areas as mergers, acquisitions and disposals, AIM and OFEX listings, management buy-outs and venture capital, restructuring, banking and financial services. The department also advises on a wide variety of commercial agreements and arrangements. The group is particularly strong in venture capital and corporate acquisitions both within and without the firm's media industry clients which it increasingly supports in a broad range of complex commercial transactions, including television and radio licence applications.The media and corporate teams increasingly co-operate in relation to projects involving the acquisition, disposal or financing of companies and businesses operating across the entire spectrum of the media and new media industries.Projects undertaken by the cross-departmental teams in 1999 included the merger of on-line CD sales companies IMVS and Boxman, the sale of a controlling interest in leading UK independent record company Eagle Rock Entertainment plc and various transactions involving Formula One Motor Racing.

Litigation: The litigation group is widely experienced in commercial litigation with particular expertise in media-related cases and general intellectual property matters. Considerable work is undertaken in co-operation with US lawyers in international litigation involving intellectual property rights. There is a substantial proportion of interlocutory work seeking injunctive relief.

MARRONS

58 Jesmond Road West, Newcastle upon Tyne, NE2 4PQ **Tel:** (0191) 281 1304 **Fax:** (0191) 212 0080 **DX:** 62555 Jesmond **Ptnrs:** 2 **Asst solrs:** 6 **Other fee-earners:** 3

MARRONS

1 Meridan South, Meridan Business Park, Leicester, LE3 2WY
Tel: (0116) 289 2200 **Fax:** (0116) 289 3733 **DX:** 710910 Leicester Meridian
Email: enquiries@marrons.co.uk **Website:** www.marrons.net

Senior Partner:	Peter Marron
Number of partners:	7
Assistant solicitors:	5
Other fee-earners:	4

CONTACTS

Company Commercial	Kevin Sumner
Environmental & Public Law	Mike Jones
Planning	John Edmond
Property	Nick Robinson

THE FIRM: The practice has an established reputation in the areas of planning, property development, environmental and public law and is deliberately located on junction 21 of the M1 motorway to allow national accessibility.The RTPI publication Planning recently published a league table showing three of the partners as being amongst the highest rated individual planning solicitors as chosen by leading solicitors and planners. Marrons acts on behalf of most of the major national house builders, a large number of developers and local authorities. Marrons also has a thriving company commercial department based on a small number of high value transactions and also provides commercial litigation support for its commercial clients.

MARSHALL ROSS & PREVEZER

4 Frederick's Place, London, EC2R 8AB
Tel: (020) 7367 9000 **Fax:** (020) 7367 9001 **DX:** 133107 CHEAPSIDE 2
Email: mail@mrp-law.co.uk

Senior Partner	Mark Prevezer
Managing Partner	Richard Marshall
No. of Partners:	7
Assistant Solicitors:	3
Consultants:	2
Other Fee-earners:	6

THE FIRM: Established since the early 1980s, Marshall Ross & Prevezer is a well-regarded City firm, which has attracted a strong property, corporate, commercial and private client base. The firm is best known for commercial property, company/ commercial, commercial litigation (including insolvency and large debt recoveries), computer law, white collar crime, franchise and trade finance. The firm also has strong overseas

Continued overleaf

connections in India, China, Hong Kong, Africa, the United States, as well as most European countries. Acting for a number of household names Marshall Ross & Prevezer has grown on its reputation of being one of the youngest firms in the City, and for being able, as a result of its size, to give a personal and individual service to its clients at partner level.

MARSONS SOLICITORS

Amadeus House, 33-39 Elmfield Road, Bromley, BR1 1LT **Tel:** (020) 8313 1300 **Fax:** (020) 8466 7920 **DX:** 121100 Bromley 9 **Email:** bromley@marsons.co.uk **Ptnrs:** 5 **Asst solrs:** 11 **Other fee-earners:** 106

MARTINEAU JOHNSON

St Philips House, St Philips Place, Birmingham, B3 2PP
Tel: (0121) 200 3300 **Fax:** (0121) 200 3330 **DX:** 721090 Birmingham 550
Email: marketing@martjohn.com **Website:** www.martineau-johnson.co.uk

Managing Partner:	David Gwyther
Senior Partner:	Michael Shepherd
Number of partners:	34
Assistant solicitors:	60
Other fee-earners:	32

AREAS OF PRACTICE

Litigation	20%
Corporate	18%
Private Client	15%
Property	16%
Trade & Utilities	10%
Banking & Insolvency	7%
Education	5%
Employment	5%
Intellectual Property	5%

CONTACTS

ADR	Andrew Spooner
Automotive	Geraldine Tickle
Banking & Insolvency	Ian Baker
Charities	Keith Dudley
Corporate/Commercial	Roger Blears
Commercial Litigation	Andrew Spooner
Commercial Property	Simon Arrowsmith
Computer/IT	Geraldine Tickle
Construction	Paul Mountain
Debt Recovery	Andrew Adams
Education	Nicola Hart
Employment	Ian Marshall
Energy/Utilities	Andrew Whitehead
EU & Competition	Geraldine Tickle
Intellectual Property	William Barker
Licensing	Andrew Spooner
Pensions	Simon Laight
PFI	Andrew Whitehead
Professional Indemnity	David Gwyther
Tax (Corporate)	Roger Blears
Wills, Tax & Trusts	Hugh Carslake

M

THE FIRM: As a full service commercial law firm, Martineau Johnson is located in the centre of Birmingham and its practice dates back to the early 19th century, but is now divided into teams operating in specialist focused areas of law. The firm's approach to business encourages continuity and the development of long-term relationships. This has formed the basis of the firm's expansion into new areas of activity. It is one of the largest single office firms in the country; but not preoccupied with growth for the sake of it. Yet large enough to offer the specialist skills that clients demand and small enough to maintain partner contact at every level. It looks to introduce the lawyer into the bloodstream of the client's organisation, to become part of the decision-making process at the earliest stage. It has invested substantially in information technology and systems to ensure efficiency and more accessibility. It has recruited carefully to assemble teams which are expert not only in the law, but in the business and activities of the clients they represent. It has responded both to the needs of its clients and anticipated them. It does not pay lip service to the fashionable concept of partnership with clients. It puts it into practice day-by-day, discreetly and without fuss, in the worlds of business and finance for public and private clients alike. They are business professionals who understand the importance of being part of their clients' team. What all their clients have in common is a need for solutions which address the key issues directly and solve their problems. It delivers! Its service is based on people. They are team players and clients respond to this personal involvement; they know who they are dealing with. It is committed to working long-term with all clients. Whatever the nature of the case, it explores every angle in order to achieve the best possible result for clients. It has combined modern expertise with personal service and maintained the continuing contact for clients with the individual partner.

INTERNATIONAL CONNECTIONS: The firm is a founder member of MultiLaw, an international association of independent law firms, which has more than 48 members worldwide and enables it to deliver legal services internationally.

RECRUITMENT & TRAINING: The firm has adopted a policy of recruiting the best trainees and firmly believes in a training partnership with them. The majority of trainees stay on after qualification. The firm has a unique system of seat rotation together with quality supervision and a mentor for each trainee. The firm recruits 10 trainee solicitors annually and details about open days and recruitment procedures are available from the firm's Human Resources Director, Diane Price on (0121) 678 1416.

MARTYN PROWEL SOLICITORS

Hallinans House, 22 Newport Road, Cardiff, CF24 0TD **Tel:** (029) 2047 0909 **Fax:** (029) 2049 8566 **DX:** Cardiff 33037 **Email:** mped@globalnet.co.uk **Ptnrs:** 6 **Asst solrs:** 3 **Other fee-earners:** 6 **Contact:** Martyn Prowel • Established in 1996 by three partners of the demerged Hallinans. Remaining at the same location, the new practice undertakes criminal, civil litigation, employment, family and conveyancing work.

AREAS OF PRACTICE

Civil Litigation	30%
Crime	30%
Conveyancing	15%
Family	15%
Other	10%

MASON BOND

King Charles House, King Charles Croft, Leeds, LS1 6LA **Tel:** (0113) 242 4444 **Fax:** (0113) 246 7542 **DX:** 26409 Leeds 1 **Email:** stephen@masonbond.co.uk **Website:** www.masonbond.co.uk **Ptnrs:** 5 **Asst solrs:** 3 **Other fee-earners:** 4 **Contact:** Mr Stephen Mason • Specialise in advising tour operators, travel, holiday and leisure companies. Also handles childcare and family law.

AREAS OF PRACTICE

Travel Industry	80%
Child Care Work	10%

MASON & MOORE DUTTON

Kirkton House, 4 Hunter St, Chester, CH1 2AS **Tel:** (01244) 348881 **Fax:** (01244) 351513 **DX:** 22151 **Email:** users@mmd.u-net.com **Website:** www.mmd.u-net.com **Ptnrs:** 7 **Asst solrs:** 1

MASONS

30 Aylesbury Street, London, EC1R 0ER
Tel: (020) 7490 4000 **Fax:** (020) 7490 2545 **DX:** 53313 Clerkenwell
Email: info@masons.com **Website:** www.masons.com

1-4 Portland Square, Bristol, BS2 8RR
Tel: (0117) 924 5678 **Fax:** (0117) 924 6699 **DX:** 78154 BRISTOL

9/10 St Andrew Square, Edinburgh, EH2 2AF
Tel: (0131) 718 6006 **Fax:** (0131) 718 6100

(Regulated by the Law Society of Scotland), 33 Bothwell Street, Glasgow, G2 6NL
Tel: (0141) 248 4858 **Fax:** (0141) 248 6655 **DX:** GW74 Glasgow

Springfield House, 76 Wellington Street, Leeds, LS1 2AY
Tel: (0113) 233 8905 **Fax:** (0113) 245 4285 **DX:** 706955 Leeds Park Square

100 Barbirolli Square, Manchester, M2 3SS
Tel: (0161) 234 8234 **Fax:** (0161) 234 8235 **DX:** 14490 Manchester 2

Worldwide Managing Partner:	Anthony Bunch
UK Managing Partner:	Peter Wood
Senior Partner:	John Bishop
Worldwide Number of Partners:	92
Assistant Solicitors:	256
Other fee-earners:	66
Total Staff:	790

CONTACTS

Construction & Engineering	John Bishop
	Martin Roberts
Energy	Anthony Bunch
	Peter Cassidy
Infrastructure	Martin Harman
	Ron Nobbs
IT	Rob McCallough
	Clive Seddon
	Andrew Smith
Commercial Dispute Resolution	Raymond Werbicki
Corporate & Commercial	Russell Booker
Data Protection	Shelagh Gaskill
E-commerce & New Media	Jon Fell
	John Salman
Employment & Pensions	Michael Ryley
	Patrick Kennedy
Insolvency	Richard Williams
Intellectual Property	Paul Sanderson
Projects & Finance	Chris Brown
	Steven Bond
Property/Planning/Environment	Guy Jordan

MASONS
M
Solicitors
& Privy Council Agents

THE FIRM: Masons is an international law firm with a distinctive reputation for its services to the information technology, construction & engineering, energy and infrastructure industries. It also provides a range of specialist skills both to clients working within these sectors and to an independent client base. Founded in the 1940's, Masons has over 90 partners and over 750 staff working in offices in five different regions in the UK as well as in Europe and Asia Pacific. The last year has been one of increasing activity resulting in a growth in group turnover of 20%. A similarly high level of recruitment activity has particularly enhanced the firm's expertise in the areas of project finance, e-commerce, data protection, intellectual property, commercial property, corporate tax and pensions. Masons operates on a 'one firm' approach. Each office is viewed as equally important, and each offers a national service range based on the same focus areas, a consistent standard of service, the transfer of resources and effective communications. Resources can be provided from any office as necessary and clients have immediate access to the widest possible range of knowledge available within the firm.International matters are handled by our offices in Brussels, Dublin, Hong Kong, Guangzhou (PRC) and Singapore, as well as by the firm's UK based lawyers who work regularly in continental and central Europe, Scandinavia, the Middle East, the Pacific Rim, Africa and the Indian subcontinent.Masons' main priorities are client service, value for money and a strong imperative to achieve our clients' objectives. The firm also seeks a quality of work which combines professional satisfaction with pleasure from working relationships with clients and colleagues. Clients speak highly of the commitment of the firm to their cases, and the calibre of work undertaken ensures that the firm is ranked highly in directories and league tables.

PRINCIPAL AREAS OF WORK: Masons' aim is to be widely recognised as the pre-eminent advisers to the IT, construction & engineering, energy and infrastructure industry sectors. In addition to providing the composite range of non-contentious services, the firm is also highly regarded for its national and international dispute avoidance and resolution expertise. In addition, Masons operates a number of specialist skill groups which provide the following range of services: corporate & commercial, commercial dispute resolution, data protection, employment, environmental, insolvency, intellectual property, pensions, planning, property, project finance and taxation.

MATTHEW ARNOLD & BALDWIN

PO Box No. 101, 20 Station Rd, Watford, WD1 1HT
Tel: (01923) 202020 **Fax:** (01923) 215050 **DX:** 4508 Watford
Email: info@mablaw.co.uk **Website:** www.mablaw.co.uk

Senior partner:	John M. Baldwin
Number of partners:	16
Assistant solicitors:	16
Other fee-earners:	25

AREAS OF PRACTICE

Company Commercial	22%
Commercial Litigation/Banking/Debt Recovery	18%
Commercial Property/Agricultural	17%
Residential Conveyancing	11%
Insolvency	9%
Tax, Trusts & Probate	9%
Intellectual Property & Information Technology	6%
Family & Childcare	4%
Personal Injury	4%

THE FIRM: Based in Watford since its foundation in 1900, its client base is now national and international. Recognised as the major firm in the region, Matthew Arnold & Baldwin has established a considerable reputation for its commercial services. It also has a strong reputation for its private client work. As a member of both LawNet, the federation of independent UK law firms, and Eurojuris International, the firm has developed strong links throughout Europe and in particular Scandinavia. The commitment to quality and continuous improvement have been recognised by the award of the LawNet Standard, (presently being accredited for ISO 9002) and a legal aid franchise for family work. The firm prides itself on forming strong relationships with its clients.

PRINCIPAL AREAS OF WORK:

Commercial: The commercial team is one of the largest in the region. The size and background of the team gives them the strength and depth to handle multiple, complex, commercial transactions. Some of the team have worked "in house" and are widely respected for their commercial awareness. Specialist units dealing with employment, competition, IP, IT, company formation and secretarial, support them.

Continued overleaf

Information Technology: Building on its long experience of the computer industry, the IT team has developed a reputation for its support of the e-commerce sector.
Commercial Litigation/Banking/Debt Recovery: The commercial litigation, banking and debt recovery team is particularly well known for its recovery work for Barclays Bank plc and other financial institutions. This large team has the depth and experience to handle all types of major commercial dispute, especially pre-emptive remedies.
Insolvency & Corporate Recovery: The insolvency and corporate recovery unit is lead by Licensed Insolvency Practitioner Gavin Jones. As well as servicing the firm's banking and financial sector clients, the team is well regarded by corporate recovery specialists.
Commercial Property: The commercial property team services all aspects of the acquisition, financing and disposal of freehold and leasehold property, from shops to large residential and industrial developments.
Intellectual Property: The intellectual property unit has created an enviable and much reported reputation for their contentious IP work. They advise both listed and small businesses in all areas of IP and IT law. Clients include those in the media, healthcare and e-commerce sectors.
Employment & Employee Benefits: Using the expertise of human resources professionals and an Industrial Tribunal Chairman the team have a track record of providing innovative services. The unit specialises in supporting the needs of personnel departments, and is noted for its work on restraints, on TUPE and in Tribunals. Services for senior executives also feature in its workload, as does the creation of share and other employee benefit plans.
Private Client: A full range of private client services is offered including residential conveyancing, family, personal injury and advice on personal tax, trusts and related financial planning.

CONTACTS

Commercial Litigation, Banking & Debt Collection	Steven Mills
Commercial Property	Richard Hanney
Corporate & Commercial	Chris Green
Employment	James Simpson
Family	Juliet Wilson
Information Technology	Chris Green
Insolvency & Corporate Reconstruction	Gavin Jones
Intellectual Property	Clare Stothard
Licensing	Alan Piper
Personal Injury	Anna Bailey
Residential Conveyancing & Estate Development	David Marsden
Tax, Trusts & Probate	Iain Donaldson

M

MAURICE COHEN & CO

309 Kentish Town Road, London, NW5 2TJ
Tel: (020) 7267 2967 **Fax:** (020) 7267 0839 **DX:** 46475 Kentish Town

Managing Partner:	M. Cohen
Senior Partner:	M. Cohen
Number of partners:	1
Assistant solicitors:	1
Other fee-earners:	2

THE FIRM: Maurice Cohen & Co is well established in the niche area of immigration law and has rapidly gained repute particularly in the field of political asylum. Notably in the last year it has appealed to the Court of Appeal in relation to an Iranian asylum seeker claiming political asylum on the basis of his sexual orientation and is currently acting in many similar cases. The firm additionally has substantial expertise in all areas of business immigration and handles all types of immigration work. The firm prides itself on the efficient, professional and personal attention given to all clients.

AREAS OF PRACTICE

Immigration	95%
Litigation	5%

MAX BARFORD & CO

16 Mount Pleasant Road, Tunbridge Wells, TN1 1QU **Tel:** (01892) 539379 **Fax:** (01892) 521874
DX: 3918 **Email:** alert@mbarford-u-net.com
Ptnrs: 4 **Asst solrs:** 5 **Other fee-earners:** 5 **Contact:** Mr M Barford

MAX BITEL, GREENE

1 Canonbury Place, London, N1 2NG **Tel:** (020) 7354 2767 **Fax:** (020) 7226 1210 **DX:** 51852 Highbury **Email:** office@MBG.co.uk **Ptnrs:** 2
Asst solrs: 1 **Other fee-earners:** 6

THE MAX GOLD PARTNERSHIP

Suffolk House, 21 Silver Street, Hull, HU1 1JJ **Tel:** (01482) 224900 **Fax:** (01482) 216068 **DX:** 11939 Hull **Email:** law@maxgold.demon.co.uk
Ptnrs: 3 **Asst solrs:** 11 **Other fee-earners:** 12

MAXWELL BATLEY

27 Chancery Lane, London, WC2A 1PA
Tel: (020) 7440 4400 **Fax:** (020) 7440 4444 **DX:** 190 London Chancery Lane WC2
Email: mailroom@maxwellbatley.com **Website:** www:maxwellbatley.com

Senior Partner:	Michael Cassidy
Number of partners:	16
Assistant solicitors:	7
Other fee-earners:	11

THE FIRM: Maxwell Batley is a multi-disciplinary City law firm with highly regarded commercial property expertise and a strong reputation in corporate, banking, litigation and private client work. The firm is known for working in partnership with clients and for providing a partner-led service, using the latest technology. Maxwell Batley takes a business-like approach to the law, by offering practical, innovative advice, good value for money and prompt service.

AREAS OF PRACTICE

Property & Construction	40%
Company/Commercial	20%
Litigation & Employment	20%
Banking	12%
Private Client/Matrimonial	8%

PRINCIPAL AREAS OF WORK:
Property & Construction: The firm's largest discipline is recognised as a real alternative to the large international firms. Advice is based on the assessment of risk in a competitive and commercial context - not merely

legal analysis. The group has substantial experience in acquisitions and sales, property finance and development, joint ventures, landlord and tenant matters and portfolio management. A key expertise is construction work, greatly developed in recent years. Clients include leading pension funds, institutional investors, and blue chip property companies, developers and occupiers of all types of property. A wide range of innovative transactions is handled, including development finance transactions and setting up of creative structures to deal with the joint ownership of property. The group advises on the use of various types of corporate and non-corporate vehicles, ensuring that the right balance between risk, control and taxation is achieved in the structure adopted. The group also acts extensively for smaller investors and occupiers.

Banking & Finance: The group works extensively with both UK and international banks and financial institutions, as well as their clients in all types of banking and financial transactions. It provides an expert, cost-effective service, enabling clients to achieve their commercial objectives with their interests being fully protected. Transactions handled include secured and unsecured lending, project finance, structured finance, acquisition finance, portfolio acquisitions and securitisations.

Company & Commercial: The group adopts a practical approach, working closely with its clients to achieve their commercial aims. It advises on mergers and acquisitions, venture capital, loan capital, management buy-outs, PFI, local authority and competitive tendering, distribution and marketing agreements, information technology and insolvency. The corporate finance team advises companies and their financial advisors on flotations, take-overs, placings and rights issues. The group also advises on joint ventures, shareholder agreements and the resolution of corporate disputes.

Litigation & Dispute Resolution: The aim is to prevent contentious situations arising. Where they do arise, expert representation in tribunal or court applications is provided. The group acts for institutional, corporate and private clients and particularly strong on property-related litigation, including construction disputes. It also handles banking, commercial disputes, insolvency, partnership disputes, professional negligence and general insurance work (including employers and product liability claims).

Employment: The employment group provides comprehensive, pragmatic advice to business and private clients on the whole range of employment related law. It advises on service and consultancy agreements, recruitment and all areas of remuneration, including changes in terms of conditions. The group's expertise extends to intellectual property matters, restrictive covenants, maternity and discrimination issues.

Private Client and Family Law: The group provides a comprehensive service for private capital and family affairs. It deals with estate planning, trusts, probate and wills, both UK and offshore, and capital tax planning; charities; residential conveyancing for offshore buyers, sellers and lenders as well as UK based private and corporate clients. The family law section provides a full service for divorce, financial and property settlements, pre-marital arrangements, co-habitation, children's care and residence and cross-border family issues.

CONTACTS

Banking	Fraser McColl
Commercial Property	Nigel Wilson
Company/Commercial	Ian McIntyre
Contruction & Property Development	Raymond Levine
Employment	Philip Wood
Litigation	Philip Knights
Matrimonial	David Sterrett
Private Client	Frank O'Shea

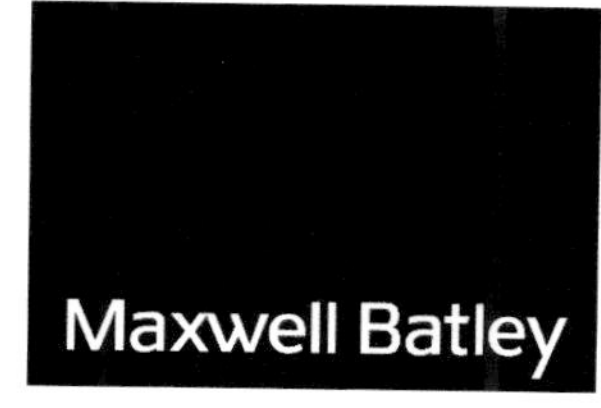

M

MAXWELL MACLAURIN

100 West Regent Street, Glasgow, G2 2QB **Tel:** (0141) 332 5666 **Fax:** (0141) 332 6757 **DX:** 95 Glasgow
Email: mailbox@maxwellmaclaurin.co.uk **Website:** www.maxwellmaclaurin.co.uk **Ptnrs:** 8 **Asst solrs:** 3 **Other fee-earners:** 1

MAYER, BROWN & PLATT

Bucklersbury House, 3 Queen Victoria Street, London, EC4N 8EL
Tel: (020) 7246 6200 **Fax:** (020) 7329 4465
Email: rherbert@mayerbrown.com **Website:** www.mayerbrown.com

Senior Partner:	Ian R. Coles
Resident lawyers:	31
Total lawyers:	990

AREAS OF PRACTICE

CIS	33%
Corporate	33%
Finance	33%

CONTACTS

UK Partners	N. Wright
	N Weiss
	M. Uhrynuk
	M. Nicolaides
	D. Levin
	N. Khodadad
	S. Janes
	K. Hawkes
	I. Coles
	R. Cole

THE FIRM: Mayer, Brown & Platt is a large, long-established commercial practice encompassing the full range of general corporate and financial matters. Founded in 1881, Mayer, Brown & Platt is one of the oldest and largest law firms in the United States. The London office was opened in 1974. In 1996 the London office became a multi-national partnership and now practises English law. The London office undertakes all types of sophisticated corporate, commercial and financing work. Its clients consist of major UK, US and foreign public companies and financial institutions. In recent years, the activity of the London office has increased substantially as its involvement in international mergers, acquisitions and structured finance transactions has increased. In the US, the firm is probably best known for its representation of major commercial banks (in particular in connection with complex financing transactions and innovative financial products), and its appellate litigation practice (particularly in the US Supreme Court). The work of the London office includes domestic and international financings, banking, capital markets and derivatives, trade finance, project finance (including PFI/PPP), work-outs and restructuring, leasing and asset finance, joint ventures, international securities transactions, corporate reorganisations and mergers and acquisitions. The firm has an extensive practice in the former Soviet Union, with various representative offices and is involved in major joint venture and financing transactions in a variety of industry sectors in the region including mining and natural resources.

PRINCIPAL AREAS OF WORK: The principal areas of the firm's practice may be categorised as follows: corporate and securities; finance and banking; derivatives; litigation; taxation; real estate; bankruptcy and reorganisation; anti-trust and trade regulation; franchising; ERISA; employee benefits and executive compensation; emerging markets (Russia, Central Asia, Latin America, Africa); environmental law; white-collar crime; insur-

Mayer, Brown & Platt

Continued overleaf

ance and reinsurance; international trade; investment and finance; international joint ventures; government relations; natural resources; public law and finance; regulated industries; trusts; estates and foundations; labour; ecclesiastical; healthcare and pro bono work. Lawyers within the firm have experience in every context of legal problem-solving, negotiation, arbitration, trial and appellate litigation, legislation and regulation.

INTERNATIONAL CONNECTIONS: The firm also has offices in Berlin, Charlotte, Chicago, Cologne, Houston, Los Angeles, New York, Santa Fe and Washington DC. They also have representative offices in Ashgabat, Bishkek, Tashkent.
Correspondent Offices: Paris (Lambert & Lee), Mexico City (Jauregui, Navarrete, Nader y Rojas SC).

MAY, MAY & MERRIMANS

12 South Square, Gray's Inn, London, WC1R 5HH
Tel: (020) 7405 8932 **Fax:** (020) 7831 0011 **DX:** 225 London
Email: mmm@link.org

Senior Partner:	Christopher Walsh
Number of partners:	11
Assistant solicitors:	7
Other fee-earners:	1

AREAS OF PRACTICE

Private Client (Tax/Trust/Probate) 50%
Property (Domestic/Agricultural/Comm.) 30%
Litigation/Matrimonial 15%
Company/Commercial 5%

CONTACTS

Civil Litigation ....Sarah Gillette
Company/Commercial ....Alexandra Sarkis
Family/Matrimonial ....Susan Black
Private Client ....Giles Gostwick
Property ....Sandy Schofield

THE FIRM: Founded in 1786, May, May & Merrimans is best known for its private client work, offering a high-quality personal service to individuals and families, some of whom are the owners of substantial residential and agricultural estates , including heritage property. The firm brings the same quality of service to its corporate clients and undertakes a broad range of company and commercial business.

PRINCIPAL AREAS OF WORK:
Private Client: Specialist advice includes estate planning, will drafting, the creation and variation of all types of settlements including offshore and charitable trusts, and personal and estate taxation. A considerable volume of probate work is handled, often involving large estates which may include overseas property.
Property: A full range of property work is undertaken, ranging from new town sites to mineral excavations, office and shop leases, agricultural tenancies, estate sales and substantial domestic conveyancing transactions.
Litigation: The litigation element of the practice deals with most types of contentious civil law, including landlord and tenant issues, negligence claims, employment, defamation and general commercial disputes.
Matrimonial: This department handles all aspects of family law, including marriage breakdown and related financial issues, disputes involving children and Inheritance Act claims.
Company & Commercial: The firm can assist in the formation of companies and partnerships, in the sale and acquisition of existing enterprises and in all matters which arise in the course of running a business or private company, including share issues, the drafting of contracts and employment questions.

MCCANN & GREYSTON

38 Church Lane, Canston House, Belfast, BT1 4KH **Tel:** (028) 9024 6098 **Fax:** (028) 9033 0795

MCCLENAHAN CROSSEY & CO

41 New Row, Coleraine, BT52 1AE **Tel:** (028) 7034 3491 **Fax:** (028) 7034 2377 **Email:** info@colerainesolicitors.co.uk

MCCLOSKEYS

Fountain House, 19 Donegall Place, Belfast, BT1 5AB
Tel: (028) 9024 0310 **Fax:** (028) 9024 0312 **DX:** 495 NR Belfast 1
Email: mccloskeys@mccloskeys.co.uk

Senior Partner:	Joseph McGuigan
Number of partners:	2
Assistant solicitors:	2

AREAS OF PRACTICE

Other Defence Negligence 40%
Professional Negligence 40%
General 20%

CONTACTS

Other Defence Litigation ....H. McGrattan
Professional Negligence ....J. McGuigan

THE FIRM: McCloskeys is a long-established and predominantly defendants litigation practice. Litigation clients include UK insurers, Lloyds syndicates and government bodies.

PRINCIPAL AREA OF WORK: The firm is one of Northern Ireland's leading insurance litigation practices. It has expertise in professional negligence, public liability, employers' liability, product liability, road traffic claims, and all other areas of insurance litigation. It has developed a particular expertise in dealing with the defence of fraudulent fire claims.

MCCLURE NAISMITH

292 St Vincent Street, Glasgow, G2 5TQ
Tel: (0141) 204 2700 **Fax:** (0141) 248 3998 **DX:** 64 Glasgow
Email: Glasgow@McClureNaismith.com **Website:** www.McClureNaismith.com

49 Queen Street, Edinburgh, EH2 3NH
Tel: (0131) 220 1002 **Fax:** (0131) 220 1003 **DX:** 135 Edinburgh
Email: Edinburgh@McClureNaismith.com

Pountney Hill House, 6 Laurence Pountney Hill, London, EC4R 0BL
Tel: (020) 7623 9155 **Fax:** (020) 7623 9154 **DX:** 764 CDE London
Email: London@McClureNaismith.com

Senior Partner:	Kenneth Chrystie
Number of partners:	23
Assistant solicitors:	41
Other fee-earners:	19

AREAS OF PRACTICE

Commercial Property	25%
Corporate/Commercial	25%
Litigation	25%
Banking/Finance	10%
Private Client	10%
Intellectual Property	5%

CONTACTS

Banking/Asset Finance	John Blackwood
Commercial Property	Wilson Aitken
Consumer Credit/Debt	Frank Johnstone
Corporate/Commercial	Kenneth Chrystie
Employment	Alan Thomson
Intellectual Property	Kenneth Chrystie
Litigation	William Walker
Private Client	Gordon Shearer
Project Finance/PFI	Steven Brown

THE FIRM: McClure Naismith is a commercially focused Law firm dedicated to providing the highest quality legal services to its clients in Scotland, England and overseas. Through its membership of the World Law Group the firm enjoys access through similar commercial firms to all major jurisdictions in the Americas, Europe and the Far East. McClure Naismith has continued to develop its range of specialist commercial services and its reputation for a determined approach to achieving results for clients. All of its offices have grown substantially in the last three years and it is one of the few Scottish firms with a London office providing a full range of English Law advice in the fields of corporate, banking, commercial property and commercial litigation.

PRINCIPAL AREAS OF WORK:

Corporate/Commercial: The firm advises on all aspects of corporate and commercial law. It has a particularly strong reputation for handling complex commercial negotiations and commercial contracts. Specialist advice is offered on corporate finance, MBO's/MBI's, mergers, acquisitions and joint ventures; shareholder disputes; agency distribution and licensing contracts; insolvency; competition law; and oil and gas developments. Industrial expertise embraces the mining, transport, pharmaceuticals, distilling and electronic sectors.

Project Finance & PFI: The firm provides project finance advice to companies promoting infrastructure projects principally in the energy and water industries in the UK and overseas, as well as a range of public sector organisations, construction consortia and banks in PFI projects, mainly in the health, water and education sectors.

Commercial Property: The firm handles property development work for institutional, corporate and private clients including site acquisition, sale and leasing; secured lending and funding; factory, shop and office developments; private sector rented housing contracts; housing associations and joint venture agreements. The firm advises landlords and tenants on commercial, agricultural and residential leasing and also advises on environmental law.

Litigation: Litigation work of all types is undertaken in all courts, tribunals and inquiries throughout Scotland and in the High Court and County Courts in England. The firm is well regarded for its personal injury/reparation practice acting for many leading defence insurers. It also covers property planning and construction litigation; intellectual property disputes; and matrimonial and family litigation.

Consumer Credit/Debt Recovery: This department's clients include many of the country's leading finance houses, leasing companies and banks and advises the Consumer Credit Trade Association. The firm is a member of the Finance and Leasing Association. It gives advice on drafting credit documentation and increasingly on data protection issues as well as providing a volume debt and asset recovery service to a wide range of commercial and financial companies.

Banking & Asset Finance: The Firm acts for many UK and overseas banks including all of the Scottish clearing banks on secured lending, corporate lending and asset finance as well as in relation to PFI projects. Contentious banking/recovery work is carried out for leading banks and building societies in addition.

Employment: In this growing area of practice the firm advises principally employers on all aspects of employment law, contentious and non-contentious, including drafting terms and conditions of employment, advice on individual employment rights, and claims for unfair and wrongful dismissal and common law claims before employment tribunals and courts throughout the UK.

Intellectual Property: The firm has considerable expertise in negotiating licence agreements for client companies worldwide and for its handling of IP disputes including patent infringement, breach of copyright or trademark and passing off. The firm has a growing practice in computer contracts and e-commerce.

Private Client: The firm offers advice on estate planning, wills, trusts and executries, insurance, pensions, investments, and the purchase sale and leasing of residential property.

MCCORMACKS

122 Mile End Road, London, E1 4UN **Tel:** (020) 7790 4339 **Fax:** (020) 7790 5846 **DX:** 300704 Tower Hamlets **Email:** city@mccormacks.co.uk
Website: www.mccormacks.co.uk **Ptnrs:** 2 **Asst solrs:** 15 **Other fee-earners:** 1

MCCORMICKS

Britannia Chambers, 4 Oxford Place, Leeds, LS1 3AX
Tel: (0113) 246 0622 **Fax:** (0113) 246 7488 **DX:** 26427 Leeds Park Square
Email: McCormicks@btinternet.com

Wharfedale House, 37 East Parade, Harrogate, HG1 5LQ
Tel: (01423) 530630 **Fax:** (01423) 530709 **DX:** 11974 Harrogate 1

Managing Partner:	Peter D.G. McCormick O.B.E.
Senior Partner:	Peter D.G. McCormick O.B.E.
Number of partners:	8
Assistant solicitors:	11
Other fee-earners:	15

AREAS OF PRACTICE

Company/Commercial & Litigation	70%
Criminal	15%
Matrimonial, Private Client & Conveyancing	15%

CONTACTS

Commercial Litigation	Roger Hutton, Richard Cramer
Company/Commercial	Clive Lawrence, Richard Moran
Debt Collection	Richard Cramer, Mark Burns
Defamation	Peter McCormick, Clive Lawrence
Employment	Neil Goodrum, Richard Cramer
European Law	Richard Moran
Family/Matrimonial	Mark Burns, Geoff Rogers
Insolvency	Richard Cramer, Roger Hutton
Intellectual Property	Clive Lawrence, Richard Moran
Media and Entertainment Law	Peter McCormick, Clive Lawrence
Personal Injury	Neil Goodrum
Serious Fraud	Peter McCormick, Geoff Rogers
Sports Law	Peter McCormick, Richard Cramer

THE FIRM: McCormicks is a high profile, progressive and highly regarded firm, which has expanded by planned organic growth to attain a reputation for expertise in a number of fields. It has offices in Leeds and Harrogate and associated offices throughout Europe. It offers a comprehensive range of legal services, both to its national and international corporate clients as well as to many notable private clients. It has been described in a survey of the law firms in Yorkshire and Humberside by the Yorkshire Post as 'A law firm in the top rank' and by Yorkshire Television as 'one of the region's top law firms'. The firm is admired for its continued ability to operate successfully in the company and commercial field, whilst at the same time maintaining its commitment to the private client. The average age of the partners is 35, and the firm has a reputation for a vibrant and dynamic atmosphere.Currently, company/commercial and litigation account for 70% of the fee income, criminal (serious fraud, tax cases and complex criminal matters) 15% and matrimonial, private client and conveyancing 15%. Partners hold the Higher Courts Qualification, memberships of the Law Society's Personal Injury, Family and Child Care Panels and Fellowship of the Chartered Institute of Arbitrators; partners are also trained and experienced in Mediation and Alternative Dispute Resolution. The firm is a member of the Law Society's Accident Line scheme. Both the Leeds and Harrogate practices were the first in the region to be awarded Legal Aid Franchises and membership of the Law Society's Family Law Scheme. The firm has strengthened it's corporate recovery department dealing with all aspects of insolvency work with personnel having worked on the Maxwell and BCCI cases.

PRINCIPAL AREAS OF WORK: Commercial litigation, company and commercial, corporate and white collar crime including VAT and Inland Revenue investigation work and tribunals, debt collection and mortgage repossesion, employment, European law, family law, intellectual property, media and entertainment, sports law (one of the premier practices in the country), insolvency, personal injury, general crime (especially road traffic), private client, defamation, charity law. Agency instructions welcomed.

INTERNATIONAL CONNECTIONS: Associated offices in France, Germany, The Netherlands, Belgium, Eire, Spain, Italy, Portugal and Gibraltar.

LANGUAGES: Fluent French, German, Italian and Spanish spoken.

McCormicks
SOLICITORS

MCCOURTS
53 George IV Bridge, Edinburgh, EH1 1EJ **Tel:** (0131) 225 6555 **Fax:** (0131) 225 5054 **Ptnrs:** 3 **Asst solrs:** 4 **Other fee-earners:** 2

MCDERMOTT, WILL & EMERY
7 Bishopsgate, London, EC2N 3AQ **Tel:** (020) 7577 6900 **Fax:** (020) 7577 6950 **Email:** (initial)(surname)@europe.new.com
Website: www.nwe.com

MCGRATH & CO
4th Floor, King Edward House, 135a New Street, Birmingham, B2 4QJ **Tel:** (0121) 643 4121 **Fax:** (0121) 624 1060 **Ptnrs:** 7 **Asst solrs:** 14
Other fee-earners: 57

MCGRIGOR DONALD

Pacific House, 70 Wellington Street, Glasgow, G2 6SB
Tel: (0141) 248 6677 **Fax:** (0141) 204 1351 **DX:** GW 135
Email: market@mcgrigors.com **Website:** www.mcgrigors.com

Senior Partner:	Robert Glennie
UK Managing Partner:	Kirk Murdoch
Number of partners:	57
Assistant solicitors:	98
Other fee-earners:	44

AREAS OF PRACTICE

Property	32%
Corporate	23%
Litigation	10%
Projects	9%
Construction	8%
Employment	5%
Private Capital	5%
Banking	4%
Technology	4%

THE FIRM: McGrigor Donald is a business and commercial law practice with offices in London, Edinburgh, Glasgow, Belfast and Brussels. The firm has developed specialist teams offering advice to clients across all three UK jurisdictions. The firm's ability to provide a truly UK-wide service is increasingly attractive to both national and international clients operating throughout Britain. The firm aims to be a constructive and effective force in achieving the commercial objectives of clients. Its handling of legal work is widely recognised as direct and forthright. With over 220 lawyers across five offices, the firm prides itself on its commitment to providing expert, seamless advice guided by the needs of the client and the individual project. During the course of 1999 the firm received a number of accolades. Morag McNeill won Corporate Dealmaker of the Year (Business Insider Deals & Dealmakers Awards) and Professional Adviser of the Year (Corporate Elite Awards) for her role as a key adviser in the MBO of CALA plc. The firm's projects, planning and corporate units were each shortlisted for the 1999 Legal Business Awards. Recent lateral appointments have included Stuart Nash from Freshfields and planning specialist Ann Krieger from SJ Berwin. Catriona Macritchie joined the firm in August 1999 as its first London-based technology partner. The London appointments of David Mandell from SJ Berwin and Anthony Edwards from DJ Freeman will further strengthen the firm's corporate and construction units respectively. Internally, Robert Glennie of the firm's London office succeeded Fred Shedden as senior partner on his retirement in April 2000.

PRINCIPAL AREAS OF WORK: Working in partnership with each client, experienced teams of accomplished advisers are drawn from across the firm's nine principal business units. The success of this strategy is supported by a number of practical examples of work handled by McGrigor Donald during 1999.

Corporate: The firm's London corporate team, in conjunction with its property unit, acted for the entrepreneurs Richard Emanuel and John Whyte in the corporate reconstruction and subsequent sale of the retail wing of DX Communications to BT Cellnet. A technology and corporate team carried out successful fundraising work for a number of the key players in the technology/biosciences sector, whilst a combined banking and corporate team acted for a major UK bank in the funding of the £600m offer for Highland Distillers plc.

Property: Scotland's largest property transaction of 1999 was handled by a team drawn from the firm's property and corporate units.

Banking/Projects: The firm's banking and projects units continue to provide creative solutions for both funders and bidders across the spectrum of PFI/PPP transactions.

Public Policy: 1999 saw the launch of the firm's Public Policy Unit. Headed up by Adam Bruce and Craig Harrow, the unit provides an independent monitoring service in connection with the Scottish Parliament and advises a varied client base on their government relations programmes.

Litigation: The firm is committed to solicitor advocacy and partner Craig Connal appears regularly in the Court of Session - the Scottish equivalent of the High Court. Other lawyers frequently provide an advocacy service at planning inquiries, arbitrations and other hearings.

CONTACTS

Banking	Colin McKay
Commercial Property	Tom Perrie
Construction Law	Brandon Nolan
Corporate Finance	Morag McNeill
Corporate Services	Colin Gray
Employment Law	Jim Young
Entreprenerial Services	Robert Glennie
Environmental Law	Michael Spence
Financial Services	Frank Doran
Inward Investment	Colin Gray
IP/Technology	Shonaig Macpherson
Joint Ventures	Tom Anderson
Litigation	Niall Scott
Pensions & Employee Benefits	Ian Gordon
Planning	Craig Connal
Private Client	Allan Nicolson
Property Development	David Bankier
Property Investment	Ian Lyall
Public Affairs	Adam Bruce
Public Sector	Alan Boyd

M

MCGUINNESS FINCH

9 Stratford Place, London, W1N 9AE **Tel:** (020) 7493 9593 **Fax:** (020) 7629 2839 **DX:** 9076 West End **Ptnrs:** 12 **Asst solrs:** 4 **Other fee-earners:** 1

MCKAY & NORWELL WS

5 & 7 Rutland Square, Edinburgh, EH1 2AS **Tel:** (0131) 229 2212 **Fax:** (0131) 228 4538 **DX:** 138 Edinburgh **Ptnrs:** 7 **Asst solrs:** 11 **Other fee-earners:** 11

MCKENZIE BELL

19 John St, Sunderland, SR1 1JG
Tel: (0191) 567 4857 **Fax:** (0191) 510 9347 **DX:** 60719
Email: mckbell@dial.pipex.com

Managing Partner:	Paul R. Heron
Senior Partner:	William B. Temperley
Number of partners:	8
Assistant solicitors:	2
Other fee-earners:	3

THE FIRM: Mckenzie Bell has been established in Sunderland for well over 100 years, providing legal services throughout the North East. Operating from two local offices, the firm is able to offer a wide range of client services. Other Offices: Washington.

PRINCIPAL AREAS OF WORK:

Company/Commercial: Work undertaken by the department includes commercial leases, partnerships, limited companies, business transfers and contracts.

Property: A full range of residential property services are offered, including conveyancing, re-mortgages and further alterations to finance and title.

Litigation: The firm provides a litigation service which includes personal injury cases and criminal defence work. Legal Aid work is undertaken. The firm has a legal aid franchise.

Private Client: Advice includes matters relating to family/ matrimonial law, child care, landlord and tenant, employment, wills, trusts and probate.

Licensing: The firm undertakes work regarding all aspects of the application for, or opposition to, liquor, betting and public entertainment licences.

MCKINTY & WRIGHT

Eagle Star House, 5-7 Upper Queen Street, Belfast, BT1 6FS
Tel: (028) 9024 6751 **Fax:** (028) 9023 1432 **DX:** 510 NR Belfast 1
Email: post@mckinty-wright.co.uk

Senior Partner:	John Cross
Number of partners:	13
Assistant solicitors:	9
Other fee-earners:	2

THE FIRM: McKinty & Wright is a Belfast-based firm with a client-oriented, commercial and litigation practice. Although the firm offers specialist expertise on matters peculiar to Northern Ireland, it has a wide client base outside the province, including international and multi-national companies. It is also pleased to include amongst its clients many leading insurance companies, Lloyds syndicates and insurance intermediaries. McKinty and Wright strives to provide an efficient and cost-effective service to all its clients and to maintain a close working relationship.

Continued overleaf

CONTACTS

Commercial Property	Ivan Frazer
Company/Commercial	Eric Boyd
Litigation	Paul Johnston

PRINCIPAL AREAS OF WORK: McKinty & Wright offers a wide range of services to the commercial and insurance client, from routine advice to insolvency, property, insurance matters and litigation. The firm's litigation department has extensive experience in all aspects of commercial litigation with specialised expertise in personal injury, construction, professional negligence, defamation, insurance and general commercial litigation. The firm also has departments handling employment, licensing, corporate finance, property and general commercial advice.

MCLEAN & STEWART
51/53 High Street, Dunblane, FK15 0EG **Tel:** (01786) 823217 **Fax:** (01786) 822575 **DX:** 631 Dunblane **Ptnrs:** 4 **Asst solrs:** 1

MCLELLANS

Old Cross House, Old Cross, Hertford, SG14 1RB
Tel: (01992) 300800 **Fax:** (01992) 300844 **DX:** 57921 Hertford
Email: slocke@mclellans1.co.uk

Senior Partner:	Nigel Mahoney
Number of partners:	6
Assistant solicitors:	3

AREAS OF PRACTICE

Commercial Property	45%
Licensing	25%
Employment	15%
Property Litigation	10%
Matrimonial	5%

CONTACTS

Commercial Property	S. Locke
Employment	N. Mahoney
Licensing	C. Eames
Property Litigation	S. Heath

THE FIRM: McLellans is a niche commercial practice specialising in commercial property, licensing and employment law and is one of the leading leisure practices in the northern Home Counties. Four fee earners are experienced advocates (including two former barristers).

PRINCIPAL AREAS OF WORK:
Commercial Property: The firm provides a comprehensive commercial property service, including planning, development work and complex property acquisitions and the specialist aspects of licensed premises.
Licensing: The firm has a dedicated liquor licensing department which handles advocacy from within its own ranks throughout England and Wales.
Employment: The firm advises on all aspects of employment and disciplinary matters and handles advocacy in the Employment Tribunal and Employment Appeal Tribunal, particularly in relation to licensed trade employment matters.

CLIENTELE: Clients include a national pub chain, a regional brewer, a national airline and other leisure, travel and manufacturing companies.

MCMANUS & KEARNEY
Law Society House, 106 Victoria Street, Belfast, BT 1 3JZ **Tel:** (028) 90243658 **Fax:** (028) 90332151 **Email:** law@mcmanus-kearney.co.uk

MCNEIVE SOLICITORS

26 Cowper Street, London, EC2A 4AP
Tel: (020) 7253 0535 **Fax:** (020) 7253 0537
Email: law@mcneive.com **Website:** www.mcneive.com

Senior partner:	Liam McNeive
Number of partners:	1
Assistant solicitors:	1

AREAS OF PRACTICE

New media, e-commerce and communications	100%

CONTACTS

All areas	Liam McNeive
	Natasha Doman

THE FIRM: A specialist practice, focusing on the new media, e-commerce and communications industries. The firm acts for some of the world's most progressive businesses in these sectors. They provide a highly personal, commercial and informal service in a way that facilitates their clients' fast rate of growth and high ambitions.

PRINCIPAL AREAS OF WORK: All aspects of online and web-based commerce including copyright and content-related law; web-based contracting and sales; domain name recovery; telecommunications, broadcast and convergence; to data protection and privacy.

CLIENTELE: Europe's leading online auction house; the world's largest internet/online service provider; an international provider of online advertising technology/representation; the UK's premier vendor of downloadable music; a Europe-wide provider of webcasting services; and two of the UK's leading web design/production businesses.

MEADE-KING
24 Orchard Street, Bristol, BS1 5DF **Tel:** (0117) 926 4121 **Fax:** (0117) 929 7578 **DX:** 7812 **Email:** gen@meadeking.co.uk **Ptnrs:** 8
Other fee-earners: 4

MEMERY CRYSTAL

31 Southampton Row, London, WC1B 5HT
Tel: (020) 7242 5905 **Fax:** (020) 7242 2058 **DX:** 156 Chancery Lane
Email: info@memerycrystal.com **Website:** www.memerycrystal.com

Managing Partner:	Jonathan P. Davies
Senior Partner:	Peter M. Crystal
Number of partners:	12
Assistant solicitors:	14
Other fee-earners:	7

AREAS OF PRACTICE

Corporate Finance 35%
Litigation 35%
Property Litigation 20%
Property 10%

CONTACTS

Corporate Finance .... Lesley Gregory
Litigation & Employment .... Harvey Rands
Property .... Douglas Robertson
Property Litigation .... Andrew Darwin

THE FIRM: The emphasis in this thriving London firm is on commercial business and corporate issues. The firm focuses on providing its clients with practical and commercially viable advice with an entrepreneurial flair and a strong sense of commitment. The partners all have backgrounds in large City practices and have come together with the same belief that only through direct partner involvement can the best possible legal service be given, based on skills and experience built up over many years. Memery Crystal operates in corporate finance, commercial litigation and property. Within these areas, specialist groups deal with company/commercial matters, intellectual property, sports law, tax, insolvency, construction, insurance, corporate crime and regulatory law, employment and property litigation. Memery Crystal is a progressive and growing firm, able to deal with all the requirements of small to medium sized companies and specialist requirements of larger companies. The firm is committed to establishing long term relationships with its clients, providing a cost effective, personal, partner-led service.

MERCY MESSENGER - SOLE PRACTITIONER

1683B High Street, Knoll, Solihull, B93 0LL **Tel:** (01564) 779 427 **Fax:** (01564) 778 732

M

MERRICKS

Fountain House, 130 Fenchurch Street, London, EC3M 5DJ
Tel: (020) 7256 3500 **Fax:** (020) 7256 3501 **DX:** 522 London/City
Email: london@merricks.co.uk **Website:** www.merricks.co.uk

Lancaster House, 67 Newhall Street, Birmingham, B3 1LX
Tel: (0121) 233 0062 **Fax:** (0121) 233 9880 **DX:** 13145 Birmingham 1
Email: birmingham@merricks.co.uk

207-208 Moulsham Street, Chelmsford, CM2 0LG
Tel: (01245) 491414 **Fax:** (01245) 263829 **DX:** 89702 Chelmsford 2
Email: chelmsford@merricks.co.uk

8 Lion Street, Ipswich, IP1 1DQ
Tel: (01473) 231331 **Fax:** (01473) 230041 **DX:** 3264 Ipswich
Email: ipswich@merricks.co.uk

Managing Partner:	Andrew Hunn
Senior Partner:	Anthony Sheppard
Number of partners:	19
Assistant solicitors:	23
Other fee-earners:	16

AREAS OF PRACTICE

Construction 20%
Defendant Personal Injury 20%
Other Insurance Litigation (eg recoveries, liability, fraud) 20%
Professional Indemnity 20%
Commercial Property 8%
Marine & Transit 6%
Other 6%

CONTACTS

Commercial Property .... Mike Alexander
Construction/Engineering .... Philip Harris
Employment .... Sean Stanton-Dunne
Insurance .... Andrew Hunn
Marine & Transit .... Mariel Monk
Professional Indemnity .... Anthony Sheppard

THE FIRM: Merricks is predominantly a litigation practice with particular expertise in construction and insurance matters, servicing clients throughout the country from its London and regional offices. It also handles marine and transit, commercial property and employment work.

PRINCIPAL AREAS OF WORK:

Insurance: Merricks has a long and close relationship with clients in the insurance markets. Work includes a substantial volume of personal injury and industrial disease work, property damage, Contractors' All Risks, fraudulent claims and policy disputes.

Professional Indemnity: Acting for leading players including accountants, solicitors and construction related professionals.

Construction/Engineering: An expert team handles dispute resolution and non-contentious work, contractual claims, payment of certificates, liability disputes, contract drafting and interpretation, duty of care warranties, joint venture agreements and insurance claims.

Marine & Transit: Areas handled include cargo and charterparty disputes, cargo claims and recoveries, marine insurance, collision and salvage, international trade, CMR and domestic road haulage, freight forwarding, warehouse keeping, Road Traffic Act defences and vehicle operators licences.

Commercial Property: Investment property work of all description undertaken including property management, commercial development, commercial conveyancing and landlord and tenant.

Employment: All aspects of employment law in both the contentious and non-contentious fields covered.

MERRIMAN WHITE

3 King's Bench Walk, Inner Temple, London, EC4Y 7DJ
Tel: (020) 7936 2050 **Fax:** (020) 7583 1783 **DX:** 1015 London Chancery Lane
Email: info@merrimanwhite.com **Website:** www.merrimanwhite.com

Merlaw House, 12 The Mount, Guildford, GU2 4HN
Tel: (01483) 574466 **Fax:** (01483) 506910 **DX:** 2457 GUILDFORD
Email: j.wolff@merrimanwhite.co.uk

61 Fleet Street, London, EC4Y 1JU
Tel: (020) 7936 2050 **Fax:** (020) 7583 1783 **DX:** 1015 London Chancery Lane
Email: info@merrimanwhite.com

Managing Partner:	Jeremy Wolff
Senior Partner:	Raymond St. J. Murphy
Number of partners:	2
Assistant solicitors:	12
Other fee-earners:	22

AREAS OF PRACTICE

Litigation	60%
Property	20%
Commercial	10%
Private Client	10%

THE FIRM: A long-established compact City firm with offices in Fleet Street, King's Bench Walk and Guildford.

PRINCIPAL AREAS OF WORK: Litigation, property and commercial work for business clients of all sizes including major companies in house building, contracting, insurance and publishing. It does arbitration work in both the construction and commodities fields. Its clientele is both UK and internationally-based and it carries out a wide spectrum of property, tax estate, and matrimonial services for private clients, as well as specialising in insurance and personal injury work.

M

LANGUAGES: The firm benefits from staff who are fluent in a variety of languages including French, Spanish, Italian, Hungarian and Farsi.

METCALFE COPEMAN & PETTEFAR

8 York Row, Wisbech, PE13 1EF
Tel: (01945) 464331 **Fax:** (01945) 476695 **DX:** 41350 Wisbech
Email: info@mcp-law.co.uk

25 Priestgate, Peterborough, PE1 1JL
Tel: (01733) 349151 **Fax:** (01733) 312728 **DX:** 12319 Peterborough
Email: info@mcp-law.co.uk

Cage Lane, Thetford, IP24 2DT
Tel: (01842) 764141 **Fax:** (01842) 752818 **DX:** 100902 Thetford
Email: info@mcp-law.co.uk

28-32 King Street, King's Lynn, PE30 1HQ
Tel: (01553) 765231 **Fax:** (01553) 766807 **DX:** 57811 King's Lynn
Email: info@mcp-law.co.uk

Senior Partner:	Richard Carlson
Number of partners:	12
Assistant solicitors:	10
Other fee-earners:	10

AREAS OF PRACTICE

Commercial/Property/Retail Law	26%
Residential Property	24%
Family	17%
Personal Injury/Litigation	17%
Crime	10%
Probate/Trusts/Tax Planning	6%

CONTACTS

Commercial property	Jonathan Burton (Peterborough)
Company/Commercial	Tim Stevenson (Thetford)
Crime	Alison Muir (King's Lynn)
Employment	Paul Garner (Wisbech)
Family	Steve Welcomme (Wisbech)
Litigation/Dispute Resolution	David Rutter (Wisbech)
Personal Injury	David Rutter (Wisbech)
Probate/Trusts	Simon Scott (King's Lynn)
Residential Poperty	Andrew Davies (Thetford)
Retail	Richard Carlson (Wisbech)

THE FIRM: Metcalfe Copeman & Pettefar provides services to three distinct markets. It is a commercial practice with a national reputation, particularly amongst retail clients. The firm is rated for the quality of its service to commercial clients which is characterised by partner-level attention, accessibility and responsiveness. There is a well established sector team providing specialist services to retailers. The firm is one of the leading claimant personal injury practices in East Anglia, serving claimants both from the local area and nationally. It is also a high street general practice providing community legal services to both private and legally-aided clients.

PRINCIPAL AREAS OF WORK:

Company commercial: The firm acts for a range of clients from national plcs to owner-managed businesses, property developers, retailers and local agricultural companies. Work includes the full range of company and commercial legal services including refinancing and restructuring, business acquisition and disposal and demergers. Specialist groups advise on retail law and employment matters.

Retail: Metcalfe Copeman & Pettefar is a significant national retail sector player. Clients are invariably plcs from across the UK and include a number of leading high street names. As well as offering specialist advice on non-contentious matters, employment issues and debt recovery the firm is also particularly strong in health & safety, trading standards, food law and product liability.

Employment: A fast-growing practice which is seeing increased demand from commercial clients and from individuals. The firm advises on contentious and non-contentious employment issues and acts for a range of clients including national retailers, East Anglian employers and employees.

Commercial Property: Work includes organising, structuring and acquiring development sites in UK and abroad for property development companies, establishing and servicing property investment portfolios for overseas investors and the acquisition, disposal and leasing of retail properties. Recent work includes acquiring dental practices for a national chain of surgeries, the lease of a 30,000 sq ft department store for a department store chain and acquiring a residential development site in the USA for a UK

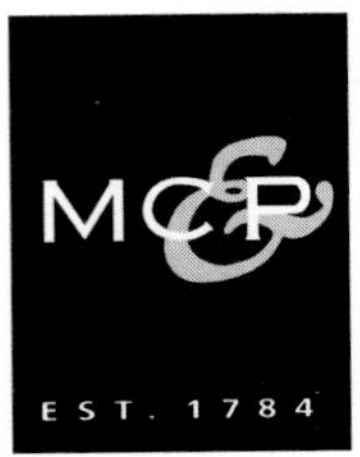

property development company. The firm also deals with agricultural property.
Civil Litigation: The firm handles a range of commercial litigation, debt collection, professional negligence, product liability and employment law matters. The department advises on health & safety, consumer protection and trade descriptions.
Personal Injury: The personal injury group has a leading reputation for claimant PI work in East Anglia including road traffic accidents, accidents at work and public liability claims.
Private Client: The firm offers a full range of services to private clients including residential conveyancing and other property matters, family law, probate, wills, trusts and tax planning.

MICHAEL HUTCHINGS

Sandhayes, Corsley, Warminster, BA12 7QQ **Tel:** (0468) 105777 **Fax:** (01373) 832785 **Email:** mbh@dircon.co.uk **Ptnrs:** 1 • Michael Hutchings specialises in EU law and advises on competition cases before the Office of Fair Trading, Competition Commission, European Commission and European Court.

MICHAEL S. ALLEN

Unit 5, Tillydrone Shopping Centre, Hayton Road, Aberdeen, AB24 2UY **Tel:** (01224) 480890 **Fax:** (01224) 480980

M

MICHELMORES

18 Cathedral Yard, Exeter, EX1 1HE
Tel: (01392) 436244 **Fax:** (01392) 215579 **DX:** 8304
Email: mail@michelmores.co.uk **Website:** www.michelmores.com

Managing partner:	Andrew Maynard
Senior partner:	Andrew Maynard
Number of partners:	16
Assistant solicitors:	17
Other fee-earners:	16

CONTACTS

ADR	Tim Richards
Charities	Richard Wheeler
Commercial Property	Peter Lowless
Company/Commercial	Malcolm Dickinson
Corporate Finance	Rupert Cattell
Employment	Nick Benson
Family	Simon Thomas
Intellectual Property	Stephen Morse
Internet /E-commerce	David Gebbie
Litigation	Trevor Coleman
Medical Negligence	Lawrence Vick
Private Client	Will Michelmore

THE FIRM: Michelmores is a dynamic law practice which takes a practical approach to providing a first class service to a wide range of clients. The firm has an entrepreneurial management team and the last year has seen the firm handle some of the largest and most complex transactions in the south of England and attract London based internet clients keen to use the firm's expertise and competitive cost base. Michelmores combines state of the art technology with a progressive management style which promotes the highest possible professional standards yet respects the individual. The firm believes in the maxim that a happy firm is a successful firm. Its modern practices, youthful atmosphere and attractive location make it an unrivalled place in which to work which means it attracts top lawyers who want a better career and a better life. Michelmores is a regionally based alternative for national and international commercial clients who are looking for service, intellectual quality and value for money. Many of the firm's partners trained in the City of London and are experienced in acting for large commercial clients which range from multinational and local businesses to institutions, government departments and high net worth entrepreneurs. Unusually, it has a dedicated corporate finance division working full time on deal origination and finance raising and the firm prides itself on its ability to make transactions happen ensuring a deal flow which has seen the Commercial Services Department alone complete 20 transactions in 1999. In addition, the firm has recently formed a medical negligence department acting for the families of the Bristol Royal Infirmary inquiry. The firm has doubled in size in the last three years through organic growth and lateral hires from City based practices. Its Commercial Property Department, already one of the largest and most prominent in the Southwest, has this year achieved critical mass of 21 lawyers through a bolt on of a further 8 lawyers specialising in public sector property work. The firm has recently entered into a joint venture management consultancy advising internet companies on finance raising, intellectual property law, joint venture partnerships and strategic alliances. The firm is a founding member of the internet based network karatkrunch.com.

MIDDLETON POTTS

3 Cloth Street, Barbican, London, EC1A 7NP
Tel: (020) 7600 2333 **Fax:** (020) 7600 0108 **DX:** 46621
Email: mail@middletonpotts.co.uk

Senior Partner:	Christopher Potts
Number of partners:	19
Assistant solicitors:	9
Other fee-earners:	9

THE FIRM: Middleton Potts was founded in 1976 by six partners, all of whom had previously been with a well-established City practice, and has grown steadily over the past two decades. The firm acts for shipping, commodity, financial, commercial and industrial clients from all over the world. It has four principal areas of work, as described below, and where a matter requires the involvement of lawyers from more than one discipline the client partner will ensure close co-ordination between the disciplines and provide continuity and a regular point of contact between the client and the firm.

PRINCIPAL AREAS OF WORK:
Shipping/Commodities Litigation: The firm's commodities practice has long been one of the most respected in the City, and the department contains several of the best known names in this field. Cases involving all types of commodities are handled, the main clients being international trading houses. The shipping practice

Continued overleaf

also has a long-established and solid reputation. The cases handled are primarily charterparty and bill of lading disputes, though salvage, wreck removal and pollution cases are also undertaken. The main clients are P&I and defence clubs, shipowners, charterers and their insurers, and companies in the off-shore energy field.

Corporate/Commercial/Banking/Insurance: This department has also achieved considerable success, enjoys work of the highest calibre and often acts in transactions where the largest City firms are on the other side. The department handles international and domestic banking and financial matters of all kinds (including ship and project finance transactions), insurance and reinsurance work, the establishment by foreign entities of branches and subsidiaries in the UK, regulatory, compliance and administrative work, the preparation of standard documentation, acquisitions and disposals of shares and assets, corporate reorganisations, joint ventures, ship sales and purchases, international construction contracts and other major industrial, commercial and infrastructure projects (including schemes under the Private Finance Initiative), tax matters and a very broad spectrum of corporate and general commercial matters (including employment law, pensions law, insolvency and intellectual property work).

Commercial Litigation: This expanding group handles commercial disputes of all kinds and conducts both High Court litigation and domestic and international arbitration proceedings. The main areas of work are: insurance and reinsurance, construction and technical disputes, banking and financial services litigation; insolvency; commercial fraud; tracing actions and cross-border litigation and disputes in relation to real property, intellectual property, employment and corporate matters.

Property: The areas handled by this department include the acquisition, funding, development and disposal of freehold and leasehold office and residential premises, industrial sites and other commercial property units and portfolios, planning matters, the general management of property interests, and general commercial transactions related to property.

INTERNATIONAL CONNECTIONS: With a very strong international focus to the practice, Middleton Potts has developed close contacts with clients, lawyers and other professionals from different jurisdictions throughout the world.

LANGUAGES: Many of the firm's lawyers speak at least one, and some speak several, of the following languages: Arabic, Bengali, French, German, Italian, Portuguese, Spanish and Turkish.

CLIENTELE: The client base covers a very broad spectrum and includes: commodity trading houses; shipowners and charterers; P&I clubs; oil majors and traders; major international banks, insurance companies and other financial institutions; freight forwarders and transportation companies; airlines; multi-national manufacturing and trading corporations; property companies; international construction companies and project joint ventures; foreign state enterprises.

RECRUITMENT & TRAINING: The firm places a high priority on recruitment, education and development of trainees and young assistant solicitors, whom it considers to be the most important source of potential future partners. In order to attract the highest calibre of candidates, the firm offers remuneration competitive with the best on offer in the City of London. Applications should be made by letter, accompanied by a full CV, to Patrick Hann.

CONTACTS

Shipping/Commodities Litigation	Christopher Potts
	David Lucas
	Andrew Donoghue
	Russell Ridley
	Robert Parson
Corporate/Commercial/ Banking/Insurance	David Godfrey
	David Rabagliati
	Stephen Morrall
Commercial Litigation	Derek West
	Patrick Hann
Property	Richard Schmidt
	Howard Lupton

MILBANK, TWEED, HADLEY & MCCLOY

Dashwood House, 69 Old Broad Street, London, EC2M 1QS
Tel: (020) 7448 3000 **Fax:** (020) 7448 3029
Website: www.milbank.com

Managing partner:	Phillip Fletcher
Number of partners:	7
Assistant solicitors:	22
Other fee-earners:	3

THE FIRM: Offers a full range of legal services to many of the world's leading financial, industrial and commercial enterprises, as well as to government and multilateral institutions. The London MNP offers a range of services in international finance under English and New York law with particular skills in infrastructure finance, project finance (in which the firm is a global leader), banking and structured finance, leasing, capital markets (including securitisation and high yield) and corporate finance (including M&A and private equity).

CLIENTELE: Clients of the London office include UK clearing banks and major US, European and Asian financial institutions as well as prominent multinational and international utilities.

AREAS OF PRACTICE

Project Finance	40%
Banking and Structured Finance	30%
M&A, Corporate and Acquisition Finance	20%
Aviation Finance	5%
Other	5%

MILES PRESTON & CO

10 Bolt Court, London, EC4A 3DQ
Tel: (020) 7583 0583 **Fax:** (020) 7583 0128
Email: milespreston@aol.com

Managing Partner:	Miles Preston
Senior Partner:	Miles Preston
Number of partners:	4
Assistant solicitors:	2

THE FIRM: Miles Preston & Co is a specialist matrimonial and family law practice formed in May 1994, the three founding partners having previously worked together for over 10 years in a large central London general practice.

PRINCIPAL AREAS OF WORK:

Family: The firm deals with all aspects of matrimonial and family law including divorce and separation, cohabitation and pre-marriage agreements, all issues relating to children and the full range of emergency procedures. Many of the cases involve the resolution of complex financial issues usually concerning substantial assets, some with an international dimension. The practice aims to adopt a firm, effective and fair approach to the conduct of its cases and to offer a high quality and cost efficient service to its clients. All its solicitors are members of the Solicitors' Family Law Association.

INTERNATIONAL CONNECTIONS: The practice has close contacts with a number of other family lawyers worldwide. In addition Miles Preston has been President of the International Academy of Matrimonial Lawyers which has as its members 280 prominent international family lawyers practising in various countries around the world.

CLIENTELE: The firm acts for UK and foreign individuals from a wide variety of backgrounds including business people, professionals and those in the entertainment world and the media.

AREAS OF PRACTICE

Family & Matrimonial	90%
Cohabitation/Paternity Disputes	10%

CONTACTS

Cohabitation/Paternity	Julia Stancyzk
Family & Matrimonial	Siobhan Readhead

MILLAR SHEARER & BLACK

40 Molesworth Street, Cookstown, BT80 8PH **Tel:** (028) 8676 2346 **Fax:** (028) 8676 6761 **DX:** 3272 Nr Cookstown **Ptnrs:** 5 **Asst solrs:** 4 **Other fee-earners:** 14

MILLER HENDRY

10 Blackfriars Street, Perth, PH1 5NS **Tel:** (01738) 637311 **Fax:** (01738) 638685 **DX:** 21 Perth **Email:** info@miller-hendry.co.uk **Ptnrs:** 19 **Asst solrs:** 9 **Other fee-earners:** 11

MILLER SAMUEL & CO

RWF House, 5 Renfield Street, Glasgow, G2 5EZ
Tel: (0141) 221 7934 **Fax:** (0141) 221 5376 **DX:** 161 Glasgow
Email: email@milsam.demon.co.uk

Managing Partner:	P. Michael Samuel
Senior Partner:	P. Michael Samuel
Number of partners:	12
Assistant solicitors:	5
Other fee-earners:	12

THE FIRM: Founded in 1973, Miller Samuel is a well-established city centre firm, which provides a comprehensive legal service to commercial clients, with particular expertise in property development and leasing. The firm has developed a thriving litigation practice which complements the commercial work, including landlord and tenant litigation and employment law. It also handles a substantial amount of debt recovery, personal injury and matrimonial work. Its range of services include all private client fields.

PRINCIPAL AREAS OF WORK:

Commercial Property/Corporate: Corporate property development; commercial leasing; investment; funding; construction etc, service with specialist rent review arbitration/expert services. Private company work and general commercial contracts also handled.

Litigation: Contract disputes; employment; debt collection; recovery of possession of heritable property; finance leasing; consumer credit; arbitration; industrial injury claims; road traffic accident claims; matrimonial; and food law.

Private Client: A comprehensive service is provided, offering clients advice on the administration of estates, tax planning, charities and wills. This department also deals with the purchase and sale of residential property.

AREAS OF PRACTICE

Commercial Litigation, Employment and Reparation	50%
Commercial Property/Corporate	40%
Personal (including Residential, Conveyancing, Wills, Trusts)	10%

CONTACTS

Commercial Litigation	Marie McDonald
Commercial Property/Corporate	J. Cowan, D.C. Lamb, K.T. Gibson, John McQuillan
Employment Law	Robert P. Kerr
Matrimonial	Laura M. Doherty
Motor Claims	Diane Cairney
Reparation	Robert P. Kerr
Residential Conveyancing/ Wills and Trusts	P.M. Samuel, E.L. Laverty

MILLER SANDS

75-79 Regent St, Cambridge, CB2 1BE **Tel:** (01223) 366741 **Fax:** (01223) 227300 **DX:** 5816 Cambridge **Email:** miller.sands@dial.pipex.com **Ptnrs:** 6 **Asst solrs:** 3 **Other fee-earners:** 5

MILLS & CO

Milburn House, Dean Street, Newcastle-upon-Tyne, NE1 1LE **Tel:** (0191) 233 2222 **Fax:** (0191) 233 2220 **Email:** law@mills-co.com **Website:** www.mills-co.com **Ptnrs:** 5 **Asst solrs:** 5

MILLS & REEVE

Francis House, 112 Hills Road, Cambridge, CB2 1PH
Tel: (01223) 364422 **Fax:** (01223) 355848 **DX:** 122891 Cambridge 4
Email: dmo@mills-reeve.com **Website:** www.mills-reeve.com

Bankside House, 107/112 Leadenhall Street, London, EC3A 4AH
Tel: (020) 7891 2670 **Fax:** (020) 7891 2671
Email: dmo@mills-reeve.com

Midland House, 132 Hagley Road, Edgbaston, Birmingham, B16 9NN
Tel: (0121) 454 4000 **Fax:** (0121) 456 3631 **DX:** 707290 Edgbaston 3
Email: dmo@mills-reeve.com

Francis House, 3-7 Redwell Street, Norwich, NR2 4TJ
Tel: (01603) 660155 **Fax:** (01603) 633027 **DX:** 5210 Norwich
Email: dmo@mills-reeve.com

Senior Partner:	Jonathan Barclay
Managing Partner:	Duncan Ogilvy
Number of partners:	59
Assistant solicitors:	130
Other fee-earners:	83

AREAS OF PRACTICE

Health	25%
Corporate	20%
Education	10%
Insurance	10%
Land & Agriculture	10%
Private Client	10%
Property	10%
Local Authorities	5%

CONTACTS

Corporate	Mark Jeffries
Education	Glynne Stanfield
Health	Sheila Waddington
Insurance	Guy Hodgson
Land & Agriculture	William Barr
Local Authorities	Nick Hancox
Private Client	Matthew Arrowsmith-Brown
Property	Beverley Firth

M

THE FIRM: Mills & Reeve is one of the UK's largest regional law firms with 59 partners, more than 200 other lawyers and a total strength of over 500. It operates throughout England and Wales from offices in Birmingham, Cambridge, London and Norwich. The firm has a national reputation for the quality of its advice and service, in particular: to businesses in the East of England especially in the hi-tech and bio-tech sectors; in corporate finance for deals in the East of England; in all aspects of property legal services; to the main suppliers of professional indemnity insurance; to the NHS; to higher and further education institutions and to large landowners and entrepreneurs. For all its clients, the firm's aim is to provide creative solutions to their problems, be innovative in developing new products and services to meet their needs, and to consistently meet the high standards of delivery and quality of service they expect.

PRINCIPAL AREAS OF WORK:

Corporate & Property: The corporate and property teams handle matters as diverse as the businesses they advise. As well as substantial corporate, commercial, property and the dispute resolution teams, the firm has specialist teams in intellectual property, tax, employment, pensions, insolvency, building and engineering, PFI, planning and environmental matters and licensing. The firm is developing a particular specialism in advising hi-tech and bio-tech businesses with the highest concentration in Europe of such businesses now located in the East of England. They provide clients with a complete service including advocacy in-house at all levels of the civil and criminal courts and the use of alternative dispute resolution (ADR).

Healthcare: NHS Trust and Health Authority work continues to expand over a wide geographical basis throughout the UK. In November 1998 the firm merged with The Lewington Partnership to form one of the top three healthcare law practices in the country with over 90 healthcare lawyers. The firm acts for over 150 NHS bodies and is currently advising on over 20 PFIs within the healthcare sector.

Education: Significant growth continues to be achieved in work for higher education institutions where the firm has acted for over 60 universities and colleges. A full range of work is undertaken including PFI schemes and tax-efficient funding schemes. The firm also has a growing reputation acting for further education institutions.

Local Government: Alongside its commitment to healthcare and educational institutions in the public sector, the firm also has a growing practice advising local authorities. In the past year the team advised over 25 local government institutions.

Agriculture & Bloodstock: The firm enjoys a well-established national reputation in farming and food, expanding its range of advice to clients at all points on the food chain.

Private Client: Mills & Reeve has one of the largest landed estate and private client practices outside London advising a wide range of landowners, entrepreneurs and business people both in the UK and offshore.

Insurance: The insurance team embraces all liability risks and now has specialist professional indemnity teams in each office.

Alternative Dispute Resolution: The team promotes the use of ADR and a number of lawyers have extensive experience in ADR techniques.

MILLS SELIG

21 Arthur Street, Belfast, BT1 4GA
Tel: (028) 9024 3878 **Fax:** (028) 9023 1956 **DX:** 459 NR BELFAST
Email: info@nilaw.com **Website:** www.millsselig.com

Managing Partner:	Richard Fulton
Senior Partner:	Brian E Ham
Number of partners:	7
Associate partners:	1
Assistant solicitors:	5
Consultants:	2
Other fee-earners:	4

THE FIRM: Founded in 1959, Mills Selig has since developed to become a major force both in Northern Ireland and beyond, providing a comprehensive range of services to its predominantly corporate clientele. The firm's traditional strengths are in commercial property and corporate/corporate finance work but it has also developed a strong presence in litigation, particularly defamation, commercial litigation, product liability and employment law. Placing a strong emphasis on high quality service and developing close working relationships with clients, each client has an assigned partner to act as a contact point with overall knowledge of the client's affairs. To accomodate growth and improve service to clients, the firm moved to new offices in July 1999.

PRINCIPAL AREAS OF WORK:

Commercial Property: Acting for developers of retail, industrial, commercial and residential property, institutional lenders and investors and commercial landlords and tenants.

Company & Commercial: Complete range of company and commercial services with particular expertise in merger and acquisition of companies and businesses, joint ventures both locally and internationally, corporate finance, distribution and agency agreements. Specialist knowledge of retail, pharmaceuticals, energy, textiles, food industries, agrichemicals and franchising.

Litigation: Full range of civil litigation and tribunal services, with particular expertise in commercial litigation (including particular expertise in injunction work), defamation, product liability, professional indemnity, employment, construction, criminal damage and property litigation.

Private Client: Residential conveyancing, wills, trusts, estate planning and probate.

AREAS OF PRACTICE

Commercial Property	40%
Company and Commercial	30%
Litigation	25%
Other	5%

CONTACTS

Commercial Litigation	Paul Spring, Brian Ham, Adam Curry
Commercial Property	Stratton Mills, Brian Ham
Company/Commercial	Richard Fulton, Bill McCann, Ivan Selig
Corporate Finance	Richard Fulton
Defamation	Paul Spring
Employment	Bill McCann, Adam Curry
Environment & Planning	Michael Burns
Insolvency	John Kearns
Private Client	Jeremy Mills
Product Liability	Paul Spring

MINCOFFS

Kensington House, 4-6 Osborne Road, Newcastle-upon-Tyne, NE2 2AA **Tel:** (0191) 281 6151 **Fax:** (0191) 281 8069 **DX:** 62550
Email: mail@mincoffs.u-net.com **Ptnrs:** 6 **Asst solrs:** 7 **Other fee-earners:** 11

MINTER ELLISON

20 Lincoln's Inn Fields, London, WC2A 3ED **Tel:** (020) 7831 7871 **Fax:** (020) 7404 6722
Website: www.minters.com.au Number of partners (London): 2Number of partners (worldwide): 200Fee-earners (London): 5Fee-earners (worldwide): 600 **Contact:** Mr Michael Whalley • Minter Ellison is a leading Australian law firm with offices in most Australian states and internationally in London, New York, Hong Kong and New Zealand.

MISHCON DE REYA

21 Southampton Row, London, WC1B 5HS
Tel: (020) 7440 7000 **Fax:** (020) 7404 5982 **DX:** 37954 Kingsway
Email: feedback@mishcon.co.uk **Website:** www.mishcon.co.uk

Chairman:	John Jackson
Joint Managing Partners:	Kevin Gold, Philip Freedman
Number of partners:	31
Assistant solicitors:	31
Other fee-earners:	19
Trainees:	19

THE FIRM: Established in 1929, Mishcon de Reya is not just any law firm. It is an unconventional commercial law firm with a substantial reputation. Its operational philosophy distinguishes it from other solicitors. The tenets of this philosophy include its belief that its partnership with clients extends beyond office walls. It is run by lawyers who understand business; innovation not replication is key, as is the belief that the biggest risk lies in never taking one. The firm is committed to developing individuals and sees its main role as a provider of access to intelligent and creative legal advice. The practice is run by young partners, with an open culture. The firm is chaired by John Jackson, a senior business figure and chairman of Hilton Group plc.

PRINCIPAL AREAS OF WORK: Traditionally organised departmentally into litigation, corporate and commercial, property and family, the firm also anticipated the value of reflecting client environments. It has developed specialist client sector-focused groups composed of lawyers from various departments.

Litigation: The commercial litigation department covers a vast range of work which includes corporate disputes, employment law, fraud and all contentious media. The department also acts for high profile individuals, and institutions. Other specialist practices include art, design and sport. All litigators are mediation trained and consideration is always given to alternative dispute resolution.

Property: The property team acts for a broad spread of clients. Among them are publicly quoted companies, developers, pension funds, banks, house builders as well as private investors and occupiers. It has a growing reputation in the retail and leisure sector and urban regeneration. Work ranges from major site assemblies, sale and purchase of investment portfolios, joint venture structuring, secured lending, planning and environment, construction, pre-lets and plot sales. Their lawyers are also active in associations that are influential in relation to both the property industry and property law.

Corporate & Commercial: The corporate group has a developing niche in new start-ups and technology, e-commerce and communications. It advises on mergers, acquisitions and disposals, MBOs, flotations, joint ventures, venture capital as well as providing general corporate advice including contract negotiation, strategic alliances and distribution agreements. Other areas of work include competition and EU law, non-contentious employment, media and IP advice. The financial services and banking group specialises in US and European regulation of financial institutions with expertise in derivatives, managed funds, secured lending, cross-border transactions and structured products. The immigration group provides strategic advice from minimising clients' overseas tax liability to helping establish new business in the UK.

Continued overleaf

AREAS OF PRACTICE

Litigation	37%
Property	27%
Corporate	26%
Family	10%

CONTACTS

Banking & Finance	Richard Tyler, Eric Bettelheim
Competition Law	Michael Cover
Corporate & Commercial	Larry Nathan
Employment	James Libson
Family	Sandra Davis
Fraud	Gary Miller, Kasra Nouroozi
Immigration	Philip Barth, Kamal Rahman
Intellectual Property	Michael Cover
Litigation	Tony Morton-Hooper
Media & Communications	Andrew Millett
Media (Contentious) incl Defamation	Karen Sanig
Planning & Environmental	Gordon Campell
Property	Nick Doffman
Retail & Leisure	Nick Doffman
Sport	Tony Morton-Hooper, Grant Gordon
Technology & E-commerce	Grant Gordon

Family: One of the leading practices in this field, the well respected team advises comprehensively on children, complex money and tax issues emanating from both domestic and international divorce and separation. Other areas covered are co-habitation disputes, property, pre-nuptial contracts and child abduction. The firm has established a particular expertise in acting for high net worth and high profile individuals who have the additional pressure of dealing with personal and emotional issues whilst under the media spotlight.

CLIENTELE: The firm provides legal services to a wide range of corporate, entrepreneurial and individual clients and has a continuing commitment to a range of pro bono causes. Further details of the firm's services are available from its main website www.mishcon.co.uk

MITCHELLS ROBERTON

George House, 36 North Hanover Street, Glasgow, G1 2AD **Tel:** (0141) 552 3422 **Fax:** (0141) 552 2935 **DX:** Glasgow 77 **Email:** info@mitchells-roberton.co.uk **Ptnrs:** 11 **Asst solrs:** 4 **Other fee-earners:** 9 **Contact:** Craig Dunbar • Established for over 250 years, with a strong private client base, and vibrant company/commercial, property and litigation departments.

AREAS OF PRACTICE	
Private Client	30%
Company/Commercial	25%
Property	25%
Litigation	20%

M

MONIER-WILLIAMS & BOXALLS

71 Lincoln's Inn Fields, London, WC2A 3JF
Tel: (020) 7405 6195 **Fax:** (020) 7405 1453 **DX:** 37975 Kingsway
Email: mwb@71lif.com

Number of partners:	7
Other fee-earners:	5

CONTACTS	
Charity law	Michael Dunn
Company/Commercial and Partnership	John Randel
Employment	Pamela Davies
Litigation	Gerald Neylan
Property	Christopher Hughes
Surrogacy	Gerald Neylan
Wine Trade Matters	David Sills

THE FIRM: Monier-Williams & Boxalls originated in 1790, and has developed a comprehensive range of services for business clients and for private individuals. The firm has been well known since the last century for its expertise in the wine trade and has a unique reputation in related intellectual property law. It has also acquired and developed particular expertise in employment law, professional partnerships, charity and surrogacy law.

INTERNATIONAL CONNECTIONS: Include acting for agencies of the French, Spanish and Mexican governments.

LANGUAGES: French, Gujarati and Spanish.

CLIENTELE: The firm's clients include major public companies, banks, multiple retailers, insurance companies, educational establishments and well known charities. The approach is one of providing a personal service, with close involvement of partners, both in its specialised areas of work and in its wider general practice.

H. MONTLAKE & CO

197 High Rd, Ilford, IG1 1LX
Tel: (020) 8553 1311 **Fax:** (020) 8553 3066 **DX:** 124842 Ilford 7
Email: montlake@link.org

Senior Partner:	Henry Montlake
Number of partners:	5
Assistant solicitors:	1

CONTACTS	
Commercial Property	Michael Bonehill
Company & Commercial	Andrew Montlake
Litigation	Daniel Hockman
Probate & Trusts	Jeremy Davies
Residential Conveyancing	Jacqueline Josephs

THE FIRM: H Montlake & Co has been established since 1953 and has always specialised in carrying out property, company & commercial work and litigation for business clients of all sizes. A wide spectrum of property, tax, estate and matrimonial services is also available to private clients. The practice also has substantial experience in the sporting field where its clients include two premier league football clubs. Michael Bonehill, the managing partner, also has extensive experience in relation to theatrical work and charitable work and is the chairman of the National Youth Theatre of Great Britain and a Life Governor of the Imperial Cancer Research Fund. The practice has formed and acted for a large number of charities including theatrical, musical and medical charities.

MOORE & BLATCH

11 The Avenue, Southampton, SO17 1XF
Tel: (023) 8071 8000 **Fax:** (023) 8033 2205 **DX:** 38507 Southampton 3
Email: marketing@m-b.co.uk **Website:** www.mooreandblatch.co.uk

Managing Partner:	Michael Caton
Senior Partner:	Robert Miles
Number of partners:	15
Assistant solicitors:	27
Other fee-earners:	40

AREAS OF PRACTICE	
Commercial	35%
Insurance/Personal Injury	34%
Private Client	31%

THE FIRM: Moore & Blatch is one of the major law firms in central Southern England, with separate commercial and insurance offices in Southampton and a private client office in Lymington. The firm is expanding and 15 new fee earners joined in the last year. Moore & Blatch prides itself on producing high-quality work and developing the services it provides to clients. Particular areas of strength are company, personal injury, commercial property, private client and wealth administration. The firm's fund management operation has in 1997 and 1998 won awards in the Lawyer Hifal awards for best financial services firm.

PRINCIPAL AREAS OF WORK:

Company: This department specialises in corporate transactions, including share and business acquisitions, MBOs and public offers and has been involved in bringing companies to AIM. Advice on company law, directors' responsibilities, insolvency, competition and EU law, partnership, employment and commercial matters.
Personal Injury & Insurance: This department handles all aspects of personal injury work, including industrial disease, medical negligence and road traffic injuries for both plaintiffs and defendants. Within the department is a specialist serious injury team. The department also advises insurers on all aspects of insurance law.
Litigation: The department provides a range of litigation services including employment law, health and safety legislation, insolvency work, banking litigation, substantial trade and construction disputes, professional negligence and debt collection. In addition the firm undertakes admiralty work.
Property: The department handles the acquisition, disposal and management of commercial property, joint ventures, loan work and social housing schemes. The department also handles volume residential conveyancing schemes, landlord and tenant work and residential and commercial land development and planning.
Planning & Development: Work includes planning agreements, planning appeals and inquiries and judicial reviews on behalf of developers, landowners and local authorities.
Private Client: The department provides a complete wealth administration service for private client families and work includes tax and estate planning, investments, wills, trusts, charitable trusts, probate and retirement finance, family law, general civil litigation and property. The department includes MSI. (Dip), ATII. and ACIB. qualified specialists and has four members of STEP. The firm is a full member of the Association of Solicitor Investment Managers.
Intellectual Property: The firm handles all matters relating to intellectual property rights and undertakes trade mark registrations. Work includes transfer of intellectual property rights, licensing, infringement actions, related contracts, including computer software, franchising, agency and distribution.
Housing Associations: A broad range of services is provided by the firm ranging from finance and development to the recovery of rent arrears and the provision of conveyancing services.
Lender Services: The firm provides a wide range of legal services to both residential and commercial lenders including both secured and unsecured lending. Work includes drafting lending documentation, asset recovery, repossession litigation, professional negligence litigation and conveyancing services to mortgage lenders.
Transport Law: The firm acts for and advises shipping companies, ferry operators and road haulage companies and has considerable expertise of representing these companies at public and transport enquiries. In addition the firm advises on related environmental issues.

CLIENTELE: The firm acts for public and private companies, insurance companies, financial institutions, partnerships and individuals. The firm is committed to providing clients with advice which is tailored to meet their specific needs.

CONTACTS

Commercial Property	Steve Ingram
Company	Roger Bailey
Insolvency	Peter Jeffery
Insurance	David Thompson
Intellectual Property	Mike Brown
Litigation	Dinshaw Printer
Private Client	David Rule
Residential Property	Melanie Cordice
Town Planning	John Barrington

MOORHEAD JAMES

21 New Fetter Lane, London, EC4A 1AW
Tel: (020) 7831 8888 **Fax:** (020) 7936 3635
Email: moorheadjames@compuserve.com

Senior Partner:	Ben Moorhead
Number of partners:	6
Assistant solicitors:	2
Other fee-earners:	1

THE FIRM: Moorhead James is a commercial practice offering a comprehensive range of services to clients ranging from private individuals to multinational businesses.

PRINCIPAL AREAS OF WORK:

Corporate & Commercial: Work includes formations, flotations, corporate restructuring, franchising and licensing, sports and leisure, banking, corporate finance, education, EU law and aviation.
Property: The department advises on all aspects of commercial and residential conveyancing, environmental law, construction and development and oil and gas, landlord and tenant.
Litigation: This includes High Court and County Court Actions, landlord and tenant and other property disputes, employment matters, debt collection, professional negligence and insolvency.
Matrimonial: All aspects of divorce, financial settlements, cohabitation.
Private Client: Work includes tax planning, charities, wills and probate.

INTERNATIONAL CONNECTIONS: Offices in Frankfurt, Rome, Milan, Paris, Hong Kong, Beijing, Prague, Budapest.

LANGUAGES: Cantonese, French, German.

AREAS OF PRACTICE

Company/commercial/ international	40%
Property & Secured Lending	35%
Litigation/Matrimonial/Landlord & Tenant/Employment & Immigration	25%

CONTACTS

Company/Commercial	Ben Moorhead
Company/Commercial	David James
Corporate Finance	Ben Moorhead
Corporate Finance	David James
Employment	Christine Bowyer-Jones
Litigation	Christine Bowyer-Jones
	Wayne de Nicolo
Matrimonial/Family	Susan Leon
Offshore Tax Planning	R. Moorhead
Oil and Gas	Julian Bishop
Property	Julian Bishop, Susan Leon
Sports and Leisure	Ben Moorhead

MORE & CO

19 Dublin Street, Edinburgh, EH1 3PG **Tel:** (0131) 557 1110 **Fax:** (0131) 557 8882 **Ptnrs:** 3 **Asst solrs:** 15 **Other fee-earners:** 3

MORECROFT URQUHART
8 Dale Street, Liverpool, L2 4TQ **Tel:** (0151) 236 8871 **Fax:** (0151) 236 8109 **DX:** 14142 **Email:** mail@morecroft.co.uk
Website: www.morecroft.co.uk **Ptnrs:** 12 **Asst solrs:** 5 **Other fee-earners:** 22

MORE FISHER BROWN
1 Norton Folgate, London, E1 6DA **Tel:** (020) 7247 0438 **Fax:** (020) 7247 0649 **Email:** mail@m-f-b.co.uk **Ptnrs:** 10 **Asst solrs:** 7
Other fee-earners: 1

MORGAN COLE

Bradley Court, Park Place, Cardiff, CF10 3DP
Tel: (029) 2038 5385 **Fax:** (029) 2038 5300 **DX:** 33014 Cardiff
Email: info@morgan-cole.com **Website:** www.morgan-cole.com

167 Fleet Street, London, EC4A 2JB
Tel: (020) 7822 8000 **Fax:** (020) 7822 8222 **DX:** 261 London
Email: info@morgan-cole.com

Buxton Court, 3 West Way, Oxford, OX2 0SZ
Tel: (01865) 262600 **Fax:** (01865) 721367 **DX:** 96200 Oxford West
Email: info@morgan-cole.com

Apex Plaza, Forbury Road, Reading, RG1 1AX
Tel: (0118) 955 3000 **Fax:** (0118) 939 3210 **DX:** 117878 Reading Apex Plaza
Email: info@morgan-cole.com

Chief Executive:	David Main
Chairman:	John Cole
Number of partners:	98
Assistant solicitors:	142
Other fee-earners:	110

AREAS OF PRACTICE

Insurance Litigation	31%
Business Services	26%
Commercial Litigation	21%
Property	17%
Private Client	5%

CONTACTS

Commercial Litigation	Allan Wilson
Commercial Property	Martin Billings
	Neil Logan Green
Company/Commercial	Graeme Guthrie
	Bruce Potter
Construction	Jeremy Williams
Corporate Finance	Joe Pillman
Dispute Resolution	Phillip Howell-Richardson
Employment	Sue Ashtiany
Energy	Paul Dillon
Health	Philip Jardine
Insurance	Iain Tenquist
IT & Intellectual Property	
	Alison Sarsfield-Hall
Landlord & tenant	Jonathan Cantor
Public law & PFI/Projects	Alun Cole

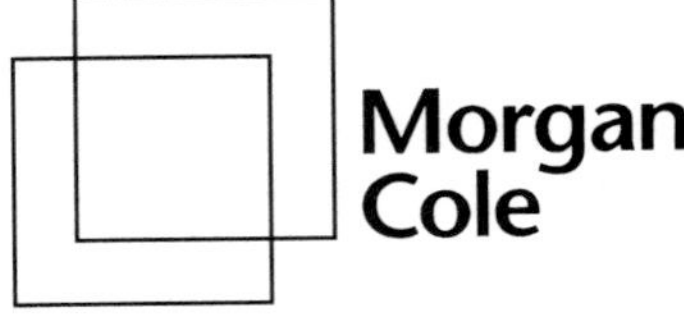

THE FIRM: Morgan Cole is a major law firm holding an unrivalled position across the southern half of the UK. With eight offices in London, Thames Valley and South Wales the firm provides a comprehensive service to commercial clients throughout the UK. Morgan Cole is a forward-looking firm committed to providing its clients with legal services to the highest possible standards. The firm enjoys a reputation for being both commercially aware and progressive and for giving strong and practical advice. Its aim is to be one of the UK's leading business law firms providing services to clients in the UK, Europe and beyond. It is committed to investment in clients, staff, IT and training, and to innovation and the continual pursuit of excellence. Partnership is key to the firm's approach and the reason for its committment to gaining a real understanding of clients' businesses and building relationships. Lawyers work cross-office providing clients with access to greater resources and skills from all offices. The firm is working towards ISO 9001 accreditation with some offices already having achieved this. It has set up a number of industry-focused groups within the firm to ensure that specialised knowledge is always the basis on which advice is given. These groups include agriculture, banking, construction, education, energy, health, housing, IT, leisure, and media.

PRINCIPAL AREAS OF WORK: The firm services a wide range of organisations in a variety of sectors. Main areas of work include ADR; agriculture; banking; charities; commercial litigation; construction; corporate and commercial; debt recovery; EU and competition law; employment; energy; health; insolvency; insurance litigation; intellectual property; information technology; landlord and tenant; leisure and licensing; PFI and projects; professional negligence; property, planning and environmental; public law.
ADR: At the forefront of alternative dispute resolution for many years the firm has 27 trained mediators who have experience in mediating a wide range of cases.
Insurance: The firm has a specialist insurance division, Fishburn Morgan Cole, which is listed separately.

INTERNATIONAL CONNECTIONS: Enjoying strong international links Morgan Cole is a founder member of the Association of European Lawyers and has established connections with law firms in North America and the Far East.

MORGAN JONES & PETT
95 St Georges Road, Great Yarmouth, NR30 2NR **Tel:** (01493) 334700 **Fax:** (01493) 334710 **DX:** 41102 **Email:** yarmouth@m-j-p.co.uk
Website: www.m-j-p.co.uk **Ptnrs:** 3 **Other fee-earners:** 6

MORGAN, LEWIS & BOCKIUS

2 Gresham Street, London, EC2V 7PE
Tel: (020) 7710 5500 **Fax:** (020) 7710 5600 **DX:** 42603 Cheapside 1
Website: www.mlb.com

UK:	
Number of partners:	7
Assistant solicitors:	13
Other fee-earners:	5
International:	
Number of partners:	330
Assistant solicitors:	683
Other fee-earners:	240

THE FIRM: Founded in Philadelphia in 1873, Morgan Lewis & Bockius LLP is one of the oldest and largest law firms in the US with over 300 partners and 900 lawyers. As one of the first major US law firms to develop a multi-city practice, Morgan Lewis & Bockius LLP is a leading international law firm able to draw on a wide diversity of capabilities and substantive experience. As a multi-national partnership, the firm has a commitment to utilise technology in order to provide a superior service to clients. E-mail, voice messaging and state-of-the-art data communications enable lawyers throughout the firm to work together, pooling resources and talents on single projects despite geographical separation. Many of the firm's lawyers have attained positions of recognition in their respective fields of expertise.

London Office: Established in 1981 and based in the city since 1998, the London office specialises in international and cross-border mergers and acquisitions, corporate financings and tax planning for corporations and individuals and acts as a focal point for many of the international and cross-border business transactions which are handled by the firm in Europe and the Middle East. Such financing work includes broad expertise in loan, equity and guarantee financings from national and multilateral financing institutions. In addition, this includes the full range of English company/ commercial; commercial litigation; property; tax; trusts; food and drug regulatory work and other ancillary practice areas. In January 1994 the London office became a multi-national practice of Registered Foreign Lawyers and Solicitors recognised by The Law Society.

PRINCIPAL AREAS OF WORK: Worldwide, the firm handles a vast diversity of legal work including antitrust; arbitration and ADR; banking and financial services; bankruptcy and reorganisation law; business and corporate law; construction; customs law; energy; environmental law; executive compensation and employee benefits; food, drug and cosmetics law; foreign direct investment in the US; Government contract and regulation; immigration; insurance law; intellectual property and technology; international financings and trade; litigation; mergers and acquisitions; personal and private client law; product liability; securities law; trademark and copyright law and transport law.

INTERNATIONAL CONNECTIONS: Other offices in Philadelphia, Washington, New York, Los Angeles, Miami, Harrisburg, Pittsburgh, Princeton, Brussels, Frankfurt, Tokyo.

AREAS OF PRACTICE

Corporate/Commercial	39%
Litigation	33%
Trusts and Tax	17%
Pharmaceutical	5%
Employment	4%
Other	2%

CONTACTS

Area	Contact
Corporate/Commercial	Tom Benz
	Zôe Ashcroft
Employment	Malcolm Mason
Litigation	Bob Goldspink
Pharmaceutical	Anthony Warnock-Smith
Trusts & Tax	Charles Lubar
	Michael Cashman

M

MORISON BISHOP

2 Blythswood Square, Glasgow, G2 4AD
Tel: (0141) 248 4672 **Fax:** (0141) 221 9270 **DX:** GW 11
Email: mail@morisonbishop.co.uk **Website:** www.morisonbishop.co.uk

Erskine House, 68 Queen Street, Edinburgh, EH2 4NN
Tel: (0131) 226 6541 **Fax:** (0131) 226 3156 **DX:** ED38
Email: mail@morisonbishop.co.uk

51 Frederick Street, Edinburgh, EH2 1LH
Tel: (0131) 226 6000 **Fax:** (0131) 226 2540 **DX:** ED 38
Email: mail@morisonbishop.co.uk

Managing Partner:	Ewen Dyce (Edinburgh)
Chairman:	John Welsh (Glasgow)
Number of partners:	30
Assistant solicitors:	35
Other fee-earners:	39

CONTACTS

Area	Contact
Asset Recovery	Roddy McIntyre (Edinburgh)
Commercial Property	Kenneth Ross (Glasgow)
Corporate	James Millar (Glasgow)
Litigation	David Whyte (Glasgow)
Private Client	Helen Stirling (Glasgow)
Residential Property	Ross Hadden (Edinburgh)

THE FIRM: Morison Bishop was created on 16 August 1999 as a result of successful merger talks between Bishop and Robertson Chalmers and Alex Morison & Co. Morison Bishop has strengths and abilities in corporate law, commercial property and litigation and has dedicated units for asset recovery, reparation, insolvency, employment, debt recovery and housebuilders. The firm also has an enviable reputation in the fields of pensions, construction and environmental law. The firm is one of the biggest legal practices in Scotland with offices in Glasgow and Edinburgh. Comprising 30 Partners and over 100 fee-earners Morison Bishop has the depth and breadth of experience to be able to assist clients across the full spectrum of legal services.

PRINCIPAL AREAS OF WORK:

Corporate: Specialist areas of work within this division include; corporate finance, pensions, constitutional, competition & EU law, intellectual property & IT, general corporate, insolvency and media & sports law.

Commercial Property: Specialist advice includes purchase and sale, leasing, property investment, shopping and retail centres, environmental law, licensing and franchising. This division also includes a housebuilders unit which deals with land acquisition and disposals, leasing and redevelopment.

Litigation: Specialist areas of work within this division include: reparation; family law; employment law; debt recovery; alternative dispute resolution; construction; professional negligence; health and safety; general civil litigation.

Asset Recovery: Specialist services within this division include: repossessions; recovery of mortgage arrears; property management; valuers' and solicitors' negligence claims.

Residential Conveyancing: Specialist areas of work within this division include: purchase and sale of property; letting; property management; estate agency service; financial advice.

Private Client: Specialist areas of work within this division include: wills; tax; trusts and executries; financial and investment advice; elderly client advice.

INTERNATIONAL CONNECTIONS: UAB Morison Bishop, Vytauto, str. 8/7, 2004 Vilnius Lithuania, tel: +370 261 4875 Fax: +370 262 4147, email: office@bishops.it

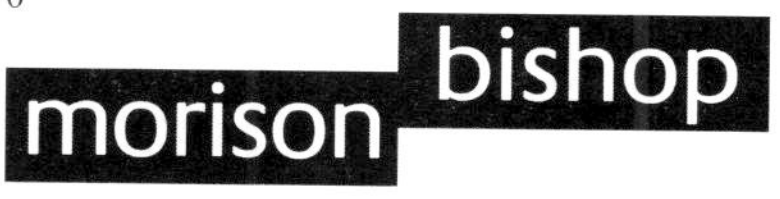

MORTON FISHER

Carlton House, Worcester St, Kidderminster, DY10 1BA
Tel: (01562) 820181 **Fax:** (01562) 820066 **DX:** 16301/16302

Managing partner:	M. Burton
Senior partner:	J.S Quinn
Number of partners:	19
Assistant solicitors:	24
Other fee-earners:	24

AREAS OF PRACTICE

Civil litigation	30%
Family	25%
Commercial	15%
Probate/Trusts	15%
Residential conveyancing	15%

CONTACTS

Agricultural	JSC Quinn
Charity	DC Bishop
Commercial Litigation & Planning	TML Jones
Debts	N Robertson Smith
Family	K Reynolds, G Trenchard
Health	JSC Quinn
Medical Negligence	BA Cairns, CGA Stanley
Personal Injury	MV Burton
	N Robertson Smith, CGA Stanley

THE FIRM: Morton Fisher has six offices covering a wide geographical area throughout Worcestershire. The firm serves the needs of the local community, specialising in company/ commercial work for business, agricultural law, and private client work. The firm handles a substantial amount of litigation, including matrimonial work, commercial litigation, planning, property and estate administration. Members of the firm are on the Law Society's Children Panel, the Personal Injury Panel and the Family Law Panel. It holds the Legal Aid Franchise. Other offices are in Stourport-on-Severn, Bromsgrove, Bewdley, Worcester and Cleobury Mortimer.

PRINCIPAL AREAS OF WORK:

Financial Services: Morton Fisher are one of the first firms to start a financial services department, employing two IFAs and support staff.

E-commerce: The firm has an e-commerce department which is headed by by Bruce Cairns, who is himself an IT expert. The firm has its own website which is constantly being updated. Further details of any matters are available at www.mortonfisher.co.uk

Additional Areas: Agricultural, charity, childcare, commercial litigation and planning, debts, health, matrimonial, medical negligence and personal injury.

M

MORTON FRASER, SOLICITORS

30-31 Queen Street, Edinburgh, EH2 1JX **Tel:** (0131) 247 1000 **Fax:** (0131) 247 1007 **DX:** ED119 **Email:** infodesk@morton-fraser.com **Website:** www.morton-fraser.com **Ptnrs:** 20 **Asst solrs:** 28 **Other fee-earners:** 77 **Contact:** Ms Kirsty Tod

AREAS OF PRACTICE

Commercial	47%
Litigation	22%
Private Clients	17%
Residential Property	14%

MOURANT DU FEU & JEUNE

PO Box 87, 22 Grenville Street, St Helier, JE4 8PX
Tel: (01534) 609000 **Fax:** (01534) 609333
Email: enquiry@mourant.com **Website:** www.mourant.com

4th Floor, 35 New Bridge Street, Blackfriars, London, EC4V 6BW
Tel: (020) 7332 6161 **Fax:** (020) 7332 6199
Email: jonathan.walker@mourant.com

Managing Partner:	Richard Jeune
Senior Partner:	Peter Mourant
Jersey Number of partners:	18
Assistant solicitors:	24
Other fee-earners:	18

AREAS OF PRACTICE

International Finance	38%
Employee Benefits	25%
Private Wealth Management	14%
Commercial Corporate	10%
Commercial Litigation	8%
Property	5%

CONTACTS

Commercial Litigation	Beverley Lacey
Corporate Structures	Nicola Davies
Employee Benefits	James Crill
International Finance	Jacqueline Richomme

THE FIRM: A world leader in offshore legal services, Mourant du Feu & Jeune has expanded rapidly through the last five years, in keeping with the increasing growth and strength of the financial sector in Jersey. Established in 1947, the firm now has eighteen partners heading a staff of 350 making it the largest law firm in the Channel Islands. Mourant du Feu & Jeune prides itself on having some of the finest lawyers in Jersey, many of whom gained experience in major City firms before practising Jersey law. It is a true innovator and has led the way in many aspects of the development of Jersey's world-renowned financial services industry. In 1999 Mourant du Feu & Jeune and Mourant & Co acted for 70% of the FTSE100 companies and 22% of the top 100 companies in *Business Week 1998 Global 1000*. Recognising the importance of its City client base, the firm opened a London branch office in April 2000, the first Channel Islands law firm to do so.

PRINCIPAL AREAS OF WORK:

International Finance: The international finance team advises global financial institutions in the Jersey legal aspects of securitisation, capital markets transactions, structured and corporate finance and banking. This has been an area of particular growth for the firm in recent years and is a field in which it has established a particularly strong reputation, having advised in many innovative and high profile transactions. The latest research by financial data publishers, *Fitzrovia*, shows Mourant du Feu & Jeune as market leader in Jersey-domiciled securitisations with almost 50% of the market by asset value. Private equity and venture capital funds are also an area of particular expertise, with the *Fitzrovia Jersey Fund Encylopdedia 1999-2000* showing the firm as clear market leader.

Commercial: The commercial team specialises in advising businesses on matters of Jersey commercial and corporate law. Its particular areas of expertise include trust and company law, collective investments, regulation of financial services, mergers and acquisitions and employment law.

Commercial Litigation: The firm has a strong commercial litigation team which, with the benefit of the firm's considerable expertise in commercial matters, is able to deal with a wide range of commercial litigation with particular emphasis on banking and trust litigation, asset tracing and fraud.

Corporate Structures: The firm's trust and company administration organisation, Mourant & Co, specialises in providing a full range of administration services for onshore and offshore structures for a range of commercial applications. Areas of particular growth in recent years include structures for employee benefits plans,

Mourant du Feu & Jeune

capital markets transactions, collective investment funds assets and structures for international property and ownership.

Private Wealth Management: Mourant & Co's highly-regarded private wealth management group is trusted by many high-profile individuals to manage their financial and legal affairs in a discreet, innovative and competent fashion.

MOWAT DEAN & CO WS

45 Queen Charlotte Street, Leith, Edinburgh, EH6 7HD **Tel:** (0131) 555 0616 **Fax:** (0131) 553 1523 **Email:** mailroom@mowatdean.demon.co.uk
Ptnrs: 3 **Asst solrs:** 3 **Other fee-earners:** 4

MULLIS & PEAKE

Marshalls Chambers, 80A South Street, Romford, RM1 1QS **Tel:** (01708) 784000 **Fax:** (01708) 784099 **DX:** 138126 Romford 4 **Email:** office@mplaw.co.uk **Website:** www.mplaw.co.uk **Ptnrs:** 11 **Asst solrs:** 4 **Other fee-earners:** 6 **Contact:** Mr P.D. Connell • Well known locally for commercial development conveyancing, commercial and probate work. The firm also specialises in both gaming and liquor licensing.

AREAS OF PRACTICE

Private Client	60%
Commercial	25%
Probate	15%

MUNDAYS

Crown House, Church Road, Claygate, Esher, KT10 0LP
Tel: (01372) 809000 **Fax:** (01372) 463782 **DX:** 36300 Esher
Email: hub@mundays.co.uk **Website:** www.mundays.co.uk

Hamilton House, 1 Temple Avenue, London, EC4Y 0HA
Tel: (020) 7437 8080 **Fax:** (020) 7437 8180
Email: hub@mundays.co.uk

Oak House, 39-41 The Parade, Claygate, Esher, KT10 0PZ
Tel: (01372) 809000 **Fax:** (01372) 460661

Senior Partner:	Peter Munday
Chief Executive:	Roger Formby
Number of partners:	16
Assistant solicitors:	10
Other fee-earners:	7

AREAS OF PRACTICE

Corporate/Commercial	36%
Commercial Property	22%
Dispute Resolution/Litigation	17%
Family/Matrimonial	11%
Private Client	7%
Residential Conveyancing	7%

CONTACTS

Aviation Law	David Irving
Commercial Property	Simon Withers
Corporate/Commercial	David Irving
	Peter Munday
Family	Karen Barhamlan Connell
Franchising	Manzoor Ishani
Intellectual Property/IT	Valerie Toon
Litigation	Fiona McAllister
Pharmacy	Simon Withers
Residential Property	Sue Poulton
Wills, Probate & Tax	Ray Walley
	Mehboob Dharamsi

THE FIRM: Mundays is a comprehensive legal practice that is particularly strong in the commercial field, with notable franchising, mergers and acquisitions, corporate finance, retail pharmacy, intellectual property and European/competition law practices. Based in Esher in Surrey, the firm has widespread connections. Established in 1960, Mundays has acquired a diverse client base that includes major international and national companies as well as smaller local businesses and individuals. As part of the firm's commitment to providing quality services, each client is encouraged to look upon a particular partner as its principal contact in the firm. Each specialised department has a department head who is responsible for overseeing case management. Departments work with each other flexibly in cases where more than one is involved. At the outset of every new matter, clients are advised on Mundays' terms of business and the basis upon which fees are to be charged.

PRINCIPAL AREAS OF WORK:

Corporate: The corporate department handles a range of high quality transactions and contracts including acquisitions and disposals of companies, buy-outs, joint ventures, flotations and general company work. The department also has experience in capital markets as well as in specialised areas such as employee share schemes. In the past year it has handled over 80 major transactions with values exceeding £200m.

Commercial: The commercial department has a specialist financial services unit that gives advice to banks and other lenders as well as to borrowers. Its expertise covers equity and venture capital, secured lending transactions and matters arising from the Financial Services Act. The department also deals with distribution, employment law, general commercial law and dispute resolution.

Intellectual Property: The intellectual property department handles copyright, trademarks and know-how and patent licensing, IT and media law.

Property: The complete range of property transactions is handled by the commercial property department, including commercial leasehold transactions for both landlords and tenants, sale and purchase of unincorporated businesses as going concerns and town and country planning matters.

Franchising: As one of the leading franchising practices in the UK, Mundays handles a variety of work concerning franchise agreements, franchise disputes, international franchising and specialised aspects of property transactions in franchises. The firm was instrumental in establishing The Franchise Lawyers European Group, whose members have offices in many countries both inside and outside the European Union. Manzoor Ishani is the author of a number of books on franchising matters and a regular contributor to *Business Franchise Magazine, Franchise World, Business Money* and numerous other journals. He is also an active lecturer in Britain and abroad.

Private Client: Mundays also has a significant private client team. Seven partners, three assistant solicitors and four FILEX/clerks comprise the team. Trust and estate accounts are handled in-house by a chartered accountant.

INTERNATIONAL CONNECTIONS: Mundays also has wide experience in European Union and other foreign legislation. Manzoor Ishani is available as an arbitrator, a member of the Association of Swiss Arbitrators.

MURRAY BEITH MURRAY W.S.

39 Castle Street, Edinburgh, EH2 3BH
Tel: (0131) 225 1200 **Fax:** (0131) 225 4412 **DX:** ED40 Edinburgh
Email: maildesk@murraybeith.co.uk

Managing Partner:	F. Adam J. More
Chairman:	William Berry
Number of partners:	8
Assistant solicitors:	14
Other fee-earners:	21

AREAS OF PRACTICE

Private Client	44%
Asset Management	32%
Commercial	24%

CONTACTS

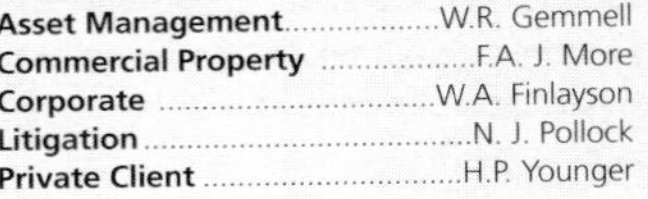

Asset Management	W.R. Gemmell
Commercial Property	F.A. J. More
Corporate	W.A. Finlayson
Litigation	N. J. Pollock
Private Client	H.P. Younger

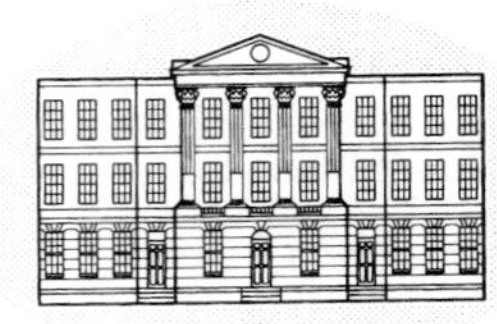

THE FIRM: This progressive Edinburgh-based practice offers an extensive range of services to private and business clients, with specialities including asset management and tax planning, agricultural law and land purchase, and advising high growth young companies. Established in 1849, Murray Beith Murray actively seeks to combine its traditional strength of a dedicated client service with modern management and innovative use of technology.The firm's services are provided through three separate divisions, namely private client, asset management and commercial.

PRINCIPAL AREAS OF WORK:
Private Client: Murray Beith Murray's core business is private client work and the firm is regarded as one of the leading private client legal firms in Scotland. This division provides a comprehensive range of legal, financial and administrative services, including wills and estate planning, trusts, taxation and executries. In the area of property law it offers a full service on agricultural law and rural property matters alongside a residential estate agency and conveyancing service.
Asset Management: The asset management division offers a full financial planning service including a comprehensive, independent overview of a client's investment and financial needs. Advice is given on a wide range of financial planning issues, including protection of the family, school fees planning, insurance, pensions advice for retirement planning and investment.
Investment: Measured by funds under management, Murray Beith Murray is one of the largest solicitor investment managers in the United Kingdom. It provides a full range of investment management and administration services on both a discretionary and advisory basis.
Commercial: The commercial division offers an extensive range of legal services to assist companies from start-up, through the early years to flotation and beyond. An efficient, competitive and personal service is combined with excellent financial contacts, deal-making skills and information-technology systems.
Commercial Property: Services include the acquisition, development and realisation of commercial property of all kinds, together with advice on regulatory planning and environmental issues. These are supported by a litigation service, which includes amongst its specialities, work in the areas of professional negligence claims, property and commercial disputes.

CLIENTELE: Murray Beith Murray's client base includes national and international companies, property investors and developers, financial institutions and private investors and a significant number of land owning interests. The firm's aim is to create, enhance and protect the wealth of its clients.

MYER WOLFF & MANLEY

15/16 Bowlalley Lane, Hull, HU1 1YE **Tel:** (01482) 223693 **Fax:** (01482) 225089 **DX:** 11904 **Email:** info@myer-wolff.co.uk **Ptnrs:** 5 **Asst solrs:** 6 **Other fee-earners:** 11 **Contact:** Timothy F. Durkin • A Legal Aid and private client practice specialising in criminal law, child care, matrimonial and mental health Tribunal work.

AREAS OF PRACTICE

Crime	47%
Family (including Child Care and Mental Health)	21%
Personal Injury/Claims	13%
Matrimonial	10%
Conveyancing/Probate	9%

NABARRO NATHANSON

Lacon House, Theobald's Road, London, WC1X 8RW
Tel: (020) 7524 6000 **Fax:** (020) 7524 6524 **DX:** 77 London/Chancery
Website: www.nabarro.com **Email:** info@nabarro.com

The Anchorage, 34 Bridge Street, Reading, RG1 2LU
Tel: (0118) 950 4700 **Fax:** (0118) 950 5640 **DX:** 4068 Reading
Email: info@nabarro.com

1 South Quay, Victoria Quays, Wharf Street, Sheffield, S2 5SY
Tel: (0114) 279 4000 **Fax:** (0114) 278 6123 **DX:** 712550 Sheffield 20
Email: info@nabarro.com

Senior Partner:	David Bramson
Managing Partner:	Nicole Paradise
Number of partners:	105
Assistant solicitors:	208
Other fee-earners:	136

CONTACTS

Banking	Andrew McLean
Charities	Jonathan Burchfield
Construction	Justin Ede
Corporate/Commercial	Rhidian Jones
	Clive Lightburn
Electricity	Robert Tudway
Employment	Valmai Adams
	Keith Pugh
Environment	Mike Renger
EU/Competition	Cyrus Mehta
Health	David Anderson
Health & Safety	Gareth Watkins
Information Technology	Tony Bailes
Insolvency	Patricia Godfrey

THE FIRM: Nabarro Nathanson is one of the country's leading commercial practices, providing the full range of legal services to national and international clients. The firm is a focused commercial practice, with more than 100 partners and some 300 fee-earners. The firm has recently undergone a period of growth that has seen major infrastructure changes, significant increases in fee earning and a new emphasis on client relationships. The firm is recognised as a leading player in many areas of the law including the corporate sector, property, IT, pensions, public sector, planning, property litigation and PFI. More than 25 per cent of the firm's work is with clients based overseas.In 1999 the firm moved its London office to new premises between the City and the West End, where it can optimise investments in IT and other support systems. There is also a new focus on training and development from which all members of Nabarro Nathanson now benefit. The breadth of work undertaken is matched by the qualtiy of servce provided – Nabarro Nathanson prides itself in being a highly commercial and forward-thinking practice with friendly, high quality professional staff.

PRINCIPAL AREAS OF WORK: Nabarro Nathanson's strength and diversity is a reflection of its varied, and growing, client base. Clients' needs are addressed through a range of industry sector groupings that run alongside traditional legal departments. These groupings comprise commercial property, energy, computers, communications and electronic publishing, pensions, insurance and financial services, public and private projects, corporate finance and a National Centre for Law in Industry which services the needs of the manufacturing sector.

Corporate: The corporate department covers mergers and acquisitions, flotations, venture capital and management buyouts, EU law, intellectual property, tax, energy and insurance. The firm is also a leader in banking transactions for domestic and international banks and other major financial institutions.

Property: Nabarro Nathanson has long been one of Britain's leading property law firms specialising in development, portfolio management, property finance, large scale acquisitions and investments and overseas property. Separate departments deal with property litigation, construction law work, and public sector matters (including planning, PFI and CPO).

Other areas: Other areas where the firm has significant strengths are IT (based in Reading), tax, health and community care, personal injury, charities and pensions. Nabarro Nathanson also has a high reputation for its general litigation and corporate insolvency work.

INTERNATIONAL CONNECTIONS: Nabarro Nathanson has an office at 209a Avenue Louise, 1050 Brussels. Tel: (+32) 2 626 0740, Fax: (+32) 2 626 0749. It is also in association with Cabinet Lipworth at 130 Rue de Faubourg, St Honoré, 75008 Paris. Tel: (+33) 1 53 75 41 41, Fax: (+33) 1 53 75 14 12. In addition, the firm has associated offices in Dubai and Hong Kong.

RECRUITMENT & TRAINING: The firm is always looking for individuals who can make a contribution to its success. Recent growth provides opportunities for qualified solicitors across a range of specialisms. There are also vacancies for trainee solicitors – mostly in London but also in the firm's Reading and Sheffield offices. Candidates must have an upper second degree, although not necessarily in law. Long-term prospects are excellent. Contact Jane Drew for application information.

CONTACTS CONTINUED

Intellectual Property	Guy Heath
	Jim Kinnier-Wilson
International Tax	Huw Witty
Litigation/Dispute Resolution	Peter Sigler
	Gareth Watkins
	Peter Sheppard
National Centre for Law in Industry	Gareth Watkins
Oil and Gas	Gareth Jones
Pensions	John Quarrell
Personal Injury	Steve Daykin
PFI	Malcolm Iley
	Tim Shaw
Planning	David Hawkins
	Norna Hughes
Property	Martin Grabiner
	David Wright
	Amanda Howard
Property Litigation	Iain Travers
Public Sector	Malcolm Iley
Sports	Michael Hales
Tax	Huw Witty
Trusts/Private Client	Jim Edmondson
Venture Capital	Rhidian Jones

N

NAPIER & SONS

1/9 Castle Arcade, Belfast, BT1 5DF **Tel:** (028) 9024 4602 **Fax:** (028) 9033 0330 **Email:** jgg@napiers.com **Website:** www.napiers.com **Ptnrs:** 4 **Asst solrs:** 6 **Other fee-earners:** 2

NAPTHEN HOUGHTON CRAVEN

7 Winckley Square, Preston, PR1 3JD
Tel: (01772) 883883 **Fax:** (01772) 257805 **DX:** 714572 Preston 14
Email: napthen.houghton.craven@nhc-sol.co.uk

Senior Partner:	Peter J. Hosker
Number of partners:	13
Assistant solicitors:	7
Other fee-earners:	12

THE FIRM: Created on the merger in 1990 of two of Preston's leading firms, Houghton Craven & Dicksons and Napthens. Since the merger, the firm has continued to expand, concentrating on the development of specialist departments, partner-managed and led, and designed to provide a speedy response for all clients, with particular emphasis on commercial work. Whilst the practice is based in the North West, the firm's clients are spread throughout the country and include offshore companies and trusts. Much of the firm's work is carried out on a national level.

PRINCIPAL AREAS OF WORK:

Commercial: Provides a wide range of legal services for commerce, industry, and investor clients. Best known for its commercial property (including planning and compensation) and corporate work, the firm has developed a thriving department specialising in employment law, and also specialises in commercial litigation. The firm has been appointed as sole panel solicitors for the North West region by the National Farmers Union and deals with agricultural legal work of all kinds.

Private Client: Handles property, probate and trust work, and family matters. A specialist department handles personal injury work with particular emphasis on road traffic accidents.

NATHAN, SILMAN

Osprey House, 78 Wigmore St, London, W1H 9DQ
Tel: (020) 7935 0898 **Fax:** (020) 7486 4803 **DX:** 9019 WE
Email: info@nathansilman.co.uk

Number of partners:	4
Assistant solicitors:	3
Other fee-earners:	2

CONTACTS

Commercial Property	M. Nathan
	S Lewis
	N. Kravitz
Company/Commercial	M. Nathan
Retail	G. Silman
	S. Lewis
Secured Lending	N. Kravitz

THE FIRM: A commercial practice serving the needs of the established corporate client, the entrepreneur and the individual. The practice style is based on personal, partner-led service, with prompt and accurate advice being enhanced by sound commercial judgement. Best known for its niche retail specialisation, the firm's client base includes market leaders in that sector as well as in the property development and investment and construction industries, as well as banking.

PRINCIPAL AREAS OF WORK: The firm is recognised as having developed a particular expertise in retail property and related work and acts for a number of 'household name' retailers, with specialist seminars on topical issues being held regularly for clients and others. The firm is also known for its commercial property expertise (with a particular emphasis on development and joint-ventures), company/commercial, banking and commercial and property litigation.

N

NEEDHAM & JAMES

25 Meer Street, Stratford upon Avon, CV37 6QB **Tel:** (01789) 414 444 **Fax:** (01789) 296 608 **DX:** 16202 Stratford upon Avon
Email: info@neejam.co.uk **Website:** www.needham-james.co.uk **Ptnrs:** 13 **Asst solrs:** 12 **Other fee-earners:** 9

NEIL MYERSON SOLICITORS

The Cottages, Regent Road, Altrincham, WA14 1RX **Tel:** (0161) 941 4000 **Fax:** (0161) 941 4411 **Email:** lawyers@neil-myerson.co.uk **Website:** www.neil-myerson.co.uk **Ptnrs:** 6 **Asst solrs:** 16 **Other fee-earners:** 9 **Contact:** Mr Neil Myerson • Established in 1982, Neil Myerson Solicitors is a company/commercial law firm offering specialist expertise in IT and internet, and motor law. For further information see the firm's website at www.neil-myerson.co.uk and www.internetlawnet.co.uk

AREAS OF PRACTICE

Company Commercial	70%
Personal Injury/Housing	25%
Private Client	5%

NELSON & CO

St Andrew's House, St Andrew's Street, Leeds, LS3 1LF
Tel: (0113) 227 0100 **Fax:** (0113) 227 0113 **DX:** 713103 Leeds
Email: enquiries@nelson-and.co.uk

Managing Partner:	Mark Overend
Number of partners:	11
Assistant solicitors:	12
Other fee-earners:	34

AREAS OF PRACTICE

Insurance Litigation	35%
Company Commercial	30%
Commercial Property	20%
Private Client	15%

CONTACTS

Commercial Property	Ian R. Shuttleworth
Company Commercial	Andrew R. Jordan
Litigation	Keith M. Nightingale
Private Client	Andrew J.R. Linden

THE FIRM: Established in 1946, the firm initially specialised in insurance litigation. In recent years the partnership has grown considerably, dramatically increasing its work in company/commercial matters and sports law. By providing a flexible, highly responsive, client-driven service, the firm offers clients all the advantages of a large firm's expertise, within a highly personal environment.

PRINCIPAL AREAS OF WORK: Company/commercial services including employment; commercial property; insurance litigation; sports law; and private client.

CLIENTELE: Clients range from national companies to small businesses. Individuals instructing the firm include nationally prominent sportsmen.

NELSONS

Pennine House, 8 Stanford Street, Nottingham, NG1 7BQ
Tel: (0115) 958 6262 **Fax:** (0115) 958 4702 **DX:** 179462 Nottingham 35
Email: mailbox@nelsons-solicitors.co.uk **Website:** www.nelsons.solicitors.co.uk

Managing partner:	Tim Hastings
Senior partner:	Richard Nelson
UKNumber of partners: 60Assistant solicitors:	
77Other fee earners: 85	

CONTACTS

Advocacy & Higher Court	Simon Chaplin
Business Defence	Richard Nelson
Corporate	Duncan Taylor
Family	Hilary Freeman
Immigration	David Smith
Litigation	Chris Adams
PI	Bruce Williams
Private Client	Richard Grosberg
Property	Anthony Holt

THE FIRM: With headquarters in Nottingham and other offices in Derby, Leicester and Grantham, Nelsons is a prominent broad-based practice for commercial, private and legal clients. Nelsons is one of the new firms in the region to offer strength and depth in all areas. Highlights of 1999/2000 include a four-way merger in May 2000 with Leicester based practices Ironsides, Tollers and Greene Deavin, and the recruitment of three former partners of Shacklocks: David Lucas, Richard Staniland and Karen Medhurst.

PRINCIPAL AREAS OF WORK: The firm has a national reputation in business defence work and has recently been appointed to The Serious Fraud Panel. Company and commercial expertise includes corporate finance, venture capital work and all forms of agreements. All aspects of litigation are handled, including cross-border cases. Liqour, gaming and bingo licensing is also dealt with. Construction and employment are both rapidly expanding specialisms. The firm offers an insurance-backed employment package. The personal injury department has particular expertise in asbestos-related cases and group actions. The firm has been accepted onto the Multi Party Action panel. Family law, crime, immigration and mental health are also areas of strength. Recent mergers have significantly enhanced the commercial property and private client departments.

NESS GALLAGHER

95 Stewarton Street, Wishew, ML2 8AG **Tel:** (01698) 355525 **Fax:** (01698) 262012 **DX:** 571075 WISHAW
Email: post@nessgallagher.pretsel.co.uk

NEWSOME VAUGHAN

Greyfriars House, Greyfriars Lane, Coventry, CV1 2GW
Tel: (024) 7663 3433 **Fax:** (024) 7625 6496 **DX:** 18854 Coventry 2
Email: pauls@n-v.co.uk **Website:** www.n-v.co.uk

Senior partner:	Rupert M.B. Griffiths
Number of partners:	4
Assistant solicitors:	7
Associates:	6
Other fee-earners:	13

AREAS OF PRACTICE

Litigation	55%
Private Clients	25%
Commercial/Business	20%

THE FIRM: Newsome Vaughan is a leading practice in Coventry and Warwickshire, enjoying a strong reputation in civil litigation. The firm continues to attract high quality instructions in corporate and commercial property work, and has recently been appointed as solicitor for a large Midlands housing association. The firm has attained the ISO9001 Quality Standard.

PRINCIPAL AREAS OF WORK: The firm specialises in civil litigation and plaintiff and personal injury litigation; clinical negligence litigation; commercial property; company & commercial; employment law; housing associations law; private client work; mortgage reposessions and mortgage lending law; and professional negligence.

NJ GOODMAN & CO

14 Market Street, Altrincham, WA14 1QB **Tel:** (0161) 928 0990 **Fax:** (0161) 941 6254

NICHOLAS PRYOR - SOLE PRACTITIONER

19 Sotheby Rd, Highbury, London, N5 2UP **Tel:** (020) 7359 2819 **Fax:** (020) 7359 4984

NICHOLSON GRAHAM & JONES

110 Cannon Street, London, EC4N 6AR
Tel: (020) 7648 9000 **Fax:** (020) 7648 9001 **DX:** 58 London Chancery Lane
Email: info@ngj.co.uk **Website:** www.ngj.co.uk

Managing Partner:	Michael Johns
Number of partners:	56
Assistant solicitors:	46
Other fee-earners:	25

CONTACTS

Banking	Richard Talbot
Charities	Michael Jacobs
Competition	Peter Bond
Construction/Engineering	David Race
Corporate and Commercial	Richard Talbot
Corporate and Property Tax	Richard Woolich
Corporate Finance	Richard Herbert
Election Law	Piers Coleman
Employee Share Schemes	Michael Jacobs
Employment	Jane Liddington
Insolvency	Shashi Rajani
	Paul Oughton
IP	Sarah Kirk
	Peter McBride
New technolgies	Michael Webster
Litigation	Antony Walker
Planning and Environment	John Garbutt
Private Client & Tax	Michael Jacobs
	Eliza Mellor
Property	Richard Smith
Property Finance	Paul Salsbury
Property Litigation	Richard Franklin
Sport & Sponsorship	Warren Phelops
Travel & Leisure	Tim Robinson
	Cynthia Barbor

THE FIRM: Nicholson Graham & Jones is a broad-based commercial practice in the heart of the City of London. During the 1990s the firm has doubled in size and has expanded its specialist capabilities. The construction and insolvency teams which joined Nicholson Graham & Jones a couple of years ago have been integrated outstandingly successfully into the firm. The firm is continuing to extend its specialist legal expertise including in particular the formation of a separate intellectual property & new technologies department. Nicholson Graham & Jones aims to provide, through the creation of close, integrated professional relationships amongst all partners and staff, a better partnership for, and with, clients. This partnership provides a cost-effective, responsive and commercial legal service driven by the needs of its clients, as well as giving its lawyers satisfying, stimulating careers and staff an enjoyable working environment. The firm has enjoyed a healthy increase in turnover over the past year.

PRINCIPAL AREAS OF WORK: There are six departments: corporate commercial, litigation, property, construction & engineering, intellectual property & new technologies and private client & tax.. The development of the firm is increasingly based on cross-departmental groups focused on particular industry and business sectors. This allows for specialist legal expertise to be enhanced by a profound understanding of the particular industry.

Corporate/Commercial: The firm is particularly well known for its corporate work, including flotations, mergers and acquisitions, corporate finance, joint venture structures and all UK, EU and international business transactions. Banking, insolvency, venture capital, UK and EC competition, intellectual property, sport and sponsorship law are areas of specialist expertise within the corporate department.

Litigation: The litigation department has extensive experience in commercial dispute resolution, both domestic and internationally, through ADR, arbitration and the courts. Specialist areas include financial services and banking, insolvency, employment, travel and leisure in addition to a wide range of general commercial, corporate and property litigation.

Property: The property department has one of the leading and most experienced teams in the property, property investment, property finance, planning and environmental law sectors. It has provided advice and innovative solutions to some of the largest and most complex property projects of recent times.

Continued overleaf

N

Construction & Engineering: The construction & engineering department is one of the largest and strongest in the country advising on contentious and non-contentious construction matters. A unique range of services is offered covering project/contract work through to litigation, arbitration and alternative dispute resolution including adjudication, mediation and conciliation.

Intellectual Property & New Technologies: The IP & IT department is continuing to expand rapidly. The department deals with the exploitation of IP rights, particularly in the media, Internet and on-line sectors. We are proactively involved in online and internet aspects of our clients businesses including many at the cutting edge of technology.

Private Client & Tax: The private client department advises on all aspects of estate and individual tax planning, frequently with an international element, specialising in international trust and tax advice, probate and acting for charities.

INTERNATIONAL CONNECTIONS: Through the foundling membership of GlobaLex, an international alliance of independent law firms represented in 23 cities worldwide, the firm has access to a global network of over 950 lawyers. Their Brussels office has quick and effective access to the EU.

CLIENTELE: Nicholson Graham & Jones acts for a wide range of clients, many of whom have international interests including listed and privately owned companies, institutions, the public sector and entreprenuers.

RECRUITMENT & TRAINING: The firm is always keen to consider applications from qualified lawyers who are confident and commecially driven. The firm recruits up to ten trainee solicitors each year. Our website has details of our trainee recruitment programme. Apply to Gail Harcus with CV and names of referees.

N

NICHOLSONS

23 Alexandra Rd, Lowestoft, NR32 1PP **Tel:** (01502) 532300 **Fax:** (01502) 568814 **DX:** 41204 **Email:** tbaker@nicholsons-uk.com **Website:** www.nicholsons-uk.com **Ptnrs:** 4 **Asst solrs:** 1 **Other fee-earners:** 5 **Contact:** Mrs Tonia Baker • Long-established firm known for company/commercial, debt recovery, insolvency, litigation and conveyancing.

AREAS OF PRACTICE

Company/Commercial/Partnership	28%
Civil Litigation & Agency	23%
Domestic Property	23%
Liquidation/Bankruptcy/VAT	14%
Probate/Trust and Wills	12%

NICOL, DENVIR & PURNELL

798 Newport Road, Rumney, Cardiff, CF5 8DH **Tel:** (029) 20796311 **Fax:** (029) 20779261 **DX:** 118475 Rumney Cardiff **Ptnrs:** 4 **Asst solrs:** 4 **Other fee-earners:** 2

NOLAN MACLEOD

39 Donaldson Street, Kirkintilloch, Glasgow, G66 1XE **Tel:** (0141) 777 6366 **Fax:** (0141) 777 8639 **Email:** nolmac@dial.pipex.com

NORTON ROSE

Kempson House, Camomile Street, London, EC3A 7AN
Tel: (020) 7283 6000 **Fax:** (020) 7283 6500 **DX:** 85 London/1064 City
Website: www.nortonrose.com

Managing Partner:	Roger Birkby
Senior Partner:	David Lewis
UK:	
Number of partners:	120
Assistant solicitors:	304
Other fee-earners:	165
International:	
Number of partners:	29
Assistant solicitors:	71
Other fee-earners:	14

AREAS OF PRACTICE

Banking & Asset Finance	27%
Corporate Finance	27%
Litigation	24%
Misc	13%
Property, Planning & Environmental	9%

THE FIRM: Norton Rose continues to excel as the finance and business firm uppermost in its chosen markets – corporate finance, asset finance, project finance, acquisition finance, development finance and financial litigation. The firm's offices are in London, Paris, Brussels, Moscow, Bahrain, and Singapore with associated offices in Athens, Piraeus, Prague, Bangkok and Jakarta. In addition Norton Rose has significant experience in advising clients in Scandinavia, Central, Eastern and Southern Europe and throughout the Middle East, East Asia and Sub-Saharan Africa. Norton Rose provides expert services to a select number of international industry and market sectors. The firm is clearly established as an acknowledged leading professional adviser in banking, insurance, shipping, aviation, railways, construction, energy, media and telecoms. Clients rely upon Norton Rose's in-depth understanding of industry issues, commitment to industrial expansion and ability to develop new techniques to accelerate commercial advantage. For each sector, Norton Rose provides banking and corporate clients with asset finance, equity and structured financial advice, development, acquisition, consolidation and restructuring services, contractual, tax and employee relations advice, regulatory and competition advice, real and intellectual property services, and, where necessary, risk management, arbitration, litigation, workouts and insolvency advice. Their specialist teams in corporate finance, capital markets, project finance and commercial litigation build long term relations with clients both internationally and in their various domestic markets. In April, the London office was awarded the Queen's award for Export Achievement given in recognition of the significant growth in the firm's export earnings over the last three years, and for its success in entering new markets. The firm was also awarded 'Law firm of the Year' in an independent survey carried out by *Chambers and Partners Guide to the Legal Profession 1999-2000.*

PRINCIPAL AREAS OF WORK:

Corporate Finance: The firm's corporate finance teams advise on public and private company mergers and acquisitions, privatisations, international joint ventures, inward investments, collective investment media, venture capital and general commercial work.

Capital Markets: The capital markets teams advise banks and other financial institutions on international and domestic equity issues, securities trading, bonds, convertibles, derivatives, swaps, options, and asset, property and development finance securitisations. Norton Rose also offers its clients fully integrated UK/US securities law advice. This adds an important dimension to an already thriving capital markets practice and enables the firm to advise on a full range of US securities matters.

Project Finance: The firm's project finance teams act for banks, contractors, sponsors, ECAs and mezzanine finance interests. They advise on all financial issues, inter-creditor agreements, risk management, receivables and trading issues, securitisation and restructuring, land, environmental, property and construction matters. Projects include energy, oil and gas, water, telecoms, infrastructure and transportation.

Commercial Litigation: The commercial litigation teams undertake a high proportion of multi-jurisdictional and international disputes. Clients are advised on risk management, arbitration and alternative dispute resolution, litigation, regulatory disputes, work outs and insolvency.

Other Areas: Other specialist teams cover intellectual property; competition and EC law, state aid, public procurement and international trade and utilities regulation; employment law, employee benefits, pension and employment-related immigration matters; international, corporate and commercial taxation; property development, investment and management, planning and the environment. During the past year, Norton Rose has advised on significant matters for, amongst others, AES, AIG, Ashanti, AXA, BMW, BNP Paribas, Chase Manhattan, Citigroup, EBRD, France Telecom, HSBC, Lehman Brothers, Mannesmann, Merrill Lynch, P&O, Royal Bank of Scotland, United Airlines.

INTERNATIONAL CONNECTIONS: Other offices are in Paris, Brussels, Moscow, Bahrain and Singapore, with associated offices in Athens, Piraeus, Prague, Bangkok and Jakarta.The firm expanded internationally in March, by establishing a joint venture office in Prague, with leading Czech law firm, Balcar, Polanský & Spol. The joint venture, focusing primarily on international corporate finance and banking work will also provide the opportunity to develop the scope of services to the Czech market.

CLIENTELE: The firm's clients are international banks, financial institutions and funds, multi-national corporate businesses, major public and private companies in the firm's various domestic markets, government departments and agencies, statutory undertakings and sovereign states.

RECRUITMENT & TRAINING: The firm's team structure enables partners and assistants to work closely together on related types of work. This provides a more in-depth and pro-active level of service to clients, improves know-how and quality of training, and gives better support and career development for trainee solicitors and junior assistants. As the firm expands it creates excellent career prospects, including opportunities to work overseas both before and after qualification. Norton Rose recruits 70 trainee solicitors every year. It encourages high quality graduates of any discipline to apply: intellectual ability, personality, determination, and the ability to get on with others are more highly prized than degree subject matter. The firm has always been a pioneer of training and personal development. It has a training programme dedicated specifically to trainee solicitors. Highly competitive salaries are offered, as well as other benefits including sports club, regular social events, and a staff restaurant. Recruitment brochures and application forms are available from Brendan Monaghan, Graduate Recruitment Manager. Norton Rose remains one of the most genuinely pleasant places to work. There is a cohesiveness and camaraderie in the firm that is hard to find elsewhere. This provides real benefits for the firm's clients. The ability to field teams of lawyers who work effectively together and who enjoy the development and achievement of long-term relationships with their clients is clearly welcomed.

CONTACTS

Aviation	Jeremy Edwards
Banking	Stephen Parish
Capital Markets	Gilles Thieffry
Commercial Litigation & Arbitration	Peter Rees
Construction	Peter Hall
Corporate Finance	Barbara Stephenson
	Robin Brooks
Energy	Michael Taylor
EU & Competition	Martin Coleman
Human Resources	Tim Russell
Insurance	Francis Mackie
Intellectual Property	Richard Barratt
Media & Telecommunications	Martin Coleman
Project Finance	Jeff Barratt
Property Planning & Environmental	Robin Mitchell
Railways	Gordon Hall
Shipping	Jeremy Gibb
Taxation	John Challoner
	Isla Smith

N

J.G. O'HARE AND CO

37-41 High Street, Belfast, BT1 2AB **Tel:** (028) 9023 4800 **Fax:** (028) 9024 3391 **Email:** mail@jgohare.com

Ptnrs: 5 **Asst solrs:** 4 • Founded in 1982; now one of the busiest medium size firms in N. Ireland, specialising in personal injury litigation, (defence and plaintiff).

OFFENBACH & CO

60 Great Marlborough Street, London, W1V 2BA
Tel: (020) 7434 9891 **Fax:** (020) 7734 2575 **DX:** 89260 Soho Square
Email:(user)@offenbachs.co.uk

Managing partner:	Bernard Carnell
Senior partner:	David Offenbach
Number of partners:	5
Assistant solicitors:	6
Other fee-earners:	3

AREAS OF PRACTICE

Criminal Defence	85%
Commercial & Civil	15%

CONTACTS

Company Commercial	David Offenbach
Criminal Defence	Bernard Carnell
	Anthony Harris
	Ray Giltrow
	Richard Shearman
	Brian Rose-Smith
Property/Other	David Offenbach

THE FIRM: Offenbach & Co has been involved in the area of serious and complex criminal defence work for over a quarter of a century. It has built up an enviable reputation and continues to expand. It has an excellent network of connections with other disciplines. It's legal aid practice will continue to be a principal part of its service.

PRINCIPAL AREAS OF WORK: The firm has a high reputation for criminal defence work, especially commercial fraud, drug-related matters, computer crime and obscene publications (both legally aided and privately paid).

OTHER AREAS: Company commercial; property; all aspects of licensed premises.

O

OGIER & LE MASURIER

Whiteley Chambers, Don Street, St. Helier, JE4 9WG
Tel: (01534) 504000 **Fax:** (01534) 735328
Email: legal@ogier.com **Website:** www.ogier.com

Coutts House, Le Truchot, St Peter Port, Guernsey, GY1 1WD
Tel: (01481) 721672 **Fax:** (01481) 721575
Email: legal@ogier.com

Managing partner:	Sarah Fitz
Chairman:	Jonathan White
Number of partners:	17
Assistant solicitors:	20
Other fee-earners:	0

AREAS OF PRACTICE

Banking	20%
Litigation	20%
Structured Finance	20%
Investment Funds	15%
Trust	15%
Property	10%

CONTACTS

Banking	Chris Byrne
	(Jersey)
	Roger Le Tissier
	(Guernsey)
Employment Benefits	Clive Chaplin
	(Jersey)
	Marcus Leese
	(Guernsey)
Investment Funds	Nick Kershaw
	(Jersey)
	Gavin Farrell
	(Guernsey)
Litigation	Matthew Thompson
	Timothy Le Cocq
	(Jersey)
Securitisation & Capital Markets	Michael Lombardi
	Marc Yates
	(Jersey)
	Roger Le Tissier
	(Guernsey)
Trusts	Steve Meiklejohn
	Jonathan White
	(Jersey)
	Marcus Leese
	Gavin Farrell
	(Guernsey)

THE FIRM: Ogier & Le Masurier is one of the largest legal practices in the Channel Islands and is unique in having the first presence in both jurisdictions of Jersey and Guernsey, through associated offices. Ogier & Le Masurier is able to trace its roots back to 1867 and has grown in parallel with the development of the Channel Islands as an international finance centre. The firm now has more than 50 lawyers and over 175 professional and support staff across both Islands. The firm provides a specialised range of legal services to financial institutions and business clients with banking and finance work, securitisations, investment funds and commercial litigation forming the core of the practice. All the work done by the firm is undertaken by teams of specialists, led by a partner, selected to achieve the commercial objectives of the client. A large proportion of qualified lawyers have worked in major financial centres outside Jersey and bring to the firm the international experience and commercial awareness sought by today's clients. The firm places a great importance on the referral of work to them by professional advisers in other jurisdictions, and seeks to work closely with those advisers not only to meet client requirements but to exceed their expectations.

PRINCIPAL AREAS OF WORK:

Banking: Ogier & Le Masurier is widely regarded as the premier firm for banking and international finance work in Jersey. The banking team specialises in advising on all areas of banking, security, banking regulation and on the establishment of banks.

Securitisation: Securitisation of assets is a particular expertise of the firm. The firm acted during 1999 on securitisation and capital market issues exceeding US$100 billion in aggregate principal amount and has significant strength in their area. With particular expertise in asset-backed securities, collateralised bond offerings and structured debt instruments, the firm is able to add value to the structuring process.

Investment Funds: In the field of invesment funds, the firm advises on the establishment and structuring of funds, as well as on regulatory and compliance aspects. The firm also advises on listings on the Channel Islands Stock Exchange.

Trusts: Trust work is undertaken for private clients as well as corporate and institutional clients. Trusts are of increasing importance in the commercial field, particularly in structured financing and the employee benefits sphere.

Litigation: The firm's litigation group is regarded as the strongest in the Island for commercial litigation. Its specialisations include trust disputes, shareholder remedies and asset tracing and freezing.

LANGUAGES: English, French, German, Portuguese and Spanish

CLIENTELE: Clients for whom the firm acts on a regular basis include Abbey National, ANZ, Bank of America, Bank of Scotland, Barclays Private Bank, BNP, Cazenove, Chase Manhattan, Citibank, Deutsche Bank, Dresdner, Flemings, SG Hambros, Hill Samuel, HSBC, ING, Lloyds/TSB, Lazards, Merrill Lynch, Morgan Guaranty, Royal Bank of Canada, Schroders, UBS and Zurich Financial Services. The firm's client list also includes many private clients worldwide who use Jersey structures to preserve and manage their wealth as well as trust companies providing trustee services.

OGIER & Le MASURIER

OGLETHORPE STURTON & GILLIBRAND

16 Castle Park, Lancaster, LA1 1YG **Tel:** (01524) 67171 **Fax:** (01524) 382247 **DX:** 63500 Lancaster **Email:** osg@provider.co.uk **Ptnrs:** 7 **Asst solrs:** 6 **Other fee-earners:** 5 **Contact:** Andrew Penny. Well established family firm, specialising in agricultural property and private client work, together with an associated commercial and litigation practice.

AREAS OF PRACTICE

Private Client	35%
Litigation	28%
Commercial	12%
Commercial Property	12%
Agriculture	10%

OLSWANG

90 Long Acre, London, WC2E 9TT
Tel: (020) 7208 8888 **Fax:** (020) 7208 8800 **DX:** 37972 London Kingsway
Email: olsmail@olswang.com **Website:** www.olswang.com

THE FIRM: Olswang does things differently. Established in 1981, Olswang is a specialist law firm providing a broad range of legal and business advice to clients in the media, communications and technology sectors. The firm's impressive growth record has been fuelled by strong client demand, an insistence on excellence, a deep understanding of their core markets and their application of modern management practices. In January 2000 the firm had a total staff of more than 350 and high growth is anticipated through the year.

PRINCIPAL AREAS OF WORK: Olswang offers the full range of services for the areas below. Visit their website for more detailed information at www.olswang.com

Advertising: Corporate structure; brand protection; agency services; regulation; employment; sponsorship; taxation and clearance; defamation.

Banking: All aspects of corporate debt financing and insolvency.

Commercial Litigation: Contractual claims for breach of warranty, and other breaches of contract; shareholder and boardroom disputes; negligence claims; film and production disputes; claims involving fraud

Corporate and Commercial: Flotations; private fundraisings; MBOs; MBIs; start-ups; secured lending; acquisitions and disposals; share option schemes

Defamation: Libel and content related litigation for media defendants; pre-publication/ broadcast advice; challenging reporting restrictions by Courts and internet libel and content.

E commerce: ISP terms and conditions; finance raising; start-ups; www advice online trading.

Employment: Employee packages; incentive schemes and disciplinary issues; unfair dismissal; redundancy programmes; discrimination; restrictive covenants; employment disputes; High Court and employment tribunal work; industrial relations; legal and tactical issues relating to team moves.

EU and Competition: Merger control; clearances; commercial agreements; special rules for businesses with market power; handling investigations; dealing with Government bodies; protecting/improving clients' competitive position.

Film and TV (finance/production): Production finance and services; talent agreements; accessing UK benefits; international co-productions; international sales and distribution; dispute resolution and risk avoidance; corporate finance.

Information Technology: Hardware/software procurement and maintenance; systems integration; outsourcing agreements; development; implementation and maintenance of e-commerce systems and website development.

Intellectual Property: IP protection; acquisition strategy; IP rights; trade secrets; copyright; cross border IP litigation including multi-jurisdictional internet/e-commerce patent issues and trade mark problems; trademark design and patent filings.

Music: M&A; competition law; IP; e-commerce; digital distribution; copyright enforcement; anti piracy; artist disputes.

Private Equity/Venture Capital: MBO's; MBI's; develpoment capital; start ups; corporate reconstructions; debt and mezzanine financing.

Property: Investment with specialisation in shopping centres; development funding; planning; construction; property litigation.

Publishing: Prepublication; negotiating commercial contracts; contractual and IP disputes.

Sport: Broadcasting rights; sports finance; EU and competition law regulation; intellectual property rights; sponsorship; on-line business; dispute resolution; risk avoidance.

Tax: Acquisitions and disposals; corporate reorganisations; partnerships; joint ventures; structured finance arrangements; property transactions; employee incentives; designing new financial products; VAT.

Telecommunications: Pan-European and global telecom projects investments in network infrastructure; terrestrial (both fixed and mobile) and satellite services; ISPs; M&A; financings; commercial contracts; regulation; competition issues; litigation.

TV/Broadcasting: Technical elements involved in compression, encryption and transmission to the commercial aspects of producing original programming. Launches and day to day operations of channels in UK, Europe, Middle East, Africa and Asia.

Senior partner:	Mark Devereux
Chairman:	Simon Olswang
Chief executive:	Jonathan Goldstein
UK:	
Number of partners:	45
Assistant solicitors:	96
Other fee-earners:	31
International:	
Number of partners:	1
Assistant solicitors:	2

CONTACTS

Advertising	Jonathan Goldstein
	Jane Moore
Banking	Graeme Levy
	Moni Mannings
Commercial Litigation	David Stewart
	Martin Davies
Corporate	Adrian Bott
	Heather Wilby
	Simon Morgan
	Stephen Hermer
Defamation	Geraldine Proudler
	Julia Palca
	Debbie Ashenhurst
E-commerce	Kim Nicholson
	Victor Timon
	John Enser
	Matthew Cowan
Employment	Catherine Taylor
	Julia Palca
	Sarah Keeble
EU and Competition	Howard Cartlidge
	Dirk Van Liedekerke
Film & TV Finance	Mark Devereux
	Lisbeth Savill
	Charles Moore
	Jane Moore
Film & TV Production	Mark Devereux
	Lisbeth Savill
	Charles Moore
Information Technology	Kim Nicholson
	Victor Timon
Insolvency	Graeme Levy
Intellectual Property	Andrew Inglis
	Paul Stevens
	Gill Smaggasgale
Music	John Enser
	Stephen Hermer
Planning	Geoffrey Searle
Private Equity/Venture Capital	
	Fabrizio Carpanini
	Tina Cowen, Chris Mackie
Property	Tim Westhead, Martyn Needham
Property Litigation	Marcus Barclay
Publishing	Selina Potter
	Geraldine Proudler
Sport	Michael Brader
Tax	Kay Butler
	Mark Joscelyne
Telecommunications	Kim Nicholson
	Colin Long
TV/Broadcasting	David Zeffman
	Selina Potter

O'MELVENY & MYERS

3 Finsbury Square, London, EC2 1LA **Tel:** (020) 7256 8451 **Fax:** (020) 7638 8205 **Website:** www.omm.com **Ptnrs:** 3 **Asst solrs:** 5 **Other fee-earners:** 1 **Contact:** Christopher Hall/Adrian Harris/Christopher Kandel • Acquisition and leveraged financing facilities, high yield and other securities transactions, corporate recovery, insolvency and restructuring work, project finance, securitisation, venture capital, private equity, mergers and acquisitions, and general banking matters.

ORCHARD

99 Bishopsgate, London, EC2M 3YU
Tel: (020) 7392 0200 **Fax:** (020) 7392 0201 **DX:** 690 LONDON CITY
Email: info@orchardlaw.com **Website:** www.orchardlaw.com

Managing partner:	David Orchard
Number of partners:	9
Assistant solicitors:	8
Other fee-earners:	7

AREAS OF PRACTICE

Corporate/ Corporate Finance	45%
Litigation & Dispute Resolution	29%
Property	14%
Employment & Employee Benefits	6%
IT/IP	6%

CONTACTS

Banking/Financial Services & Markets	David Orchard
Commercial Contracts	Paul Taylor
Commercial Litigation/Dispute Resolution	David Orchard
Commercial Property	Roger Coral
Corporate Finance	Susan Breen
Corporate Insolvency	David Orchard
Employment/Employee Benefits	Simon Malcolm
IT/IP	Paul Taylor
Mergers & Acquisitions	Nick Davis
New Media	Nick Davis

THE FIRM: Formed in 1995, Orchard remains one of the newest law firms in the City of London. The timing of its creation coincided with, arguably, one of the most buoyant, exciting and evolutionary periods in commercial history, both domestically and internationally. The firm therefore did not have to adapt to change, but could rather embrace it from the outset. Thus, Orchard's outlook, composition and personality reflect that set of circumstances, blending the best of traditional values, such as quality of service and attention to detail, with the flexibility, fast response and rapid focus demanded by today's challenging business environment.

Orchard has set out to be a different type of law firm, one that has not sought growth for its sake, but has rather recognised and planned for change, both current and anticipated. Its domestic base has been rapidly expanded and developed largely by attracting experienced partners from other leading law firms who bring complementary skills and sector expertise, but who are also like-minded and share a common view of the future. Similarly, the international reach of Orchard has been extended outside the UK, specifically in North America and Europe, either by establishing Orchard offices, as in New York, or by forging alliances with established law firms, such as CMC SociÈtÈ d'Avocats in Paris. Orchard's energetic and progressive approach has been rewarded by a healthy inflow of clients, ranging from ambitious newcomers in the corporate sector, to established blue-chip companies and financial services institutions to individual entrepreneurs. Corporate finance activity, including flotations, mergers and acquisitions, continues to flourish, whilst litigation and dispute resolution services are provided on a wide variety of matters. The firm's new media group now operates under the name of orchard. Orchard has also made heavy investment in technology, concentrating on rapid information exchange systems and video conferencing facilities in order to keep pace with change and to ensure access and rapid response capability. In all aspects Orchard sees itself as the modern face of law today.

PRINCIPAL AREAS OF WORK: Commercial litigation and dispute resolution; corporate/corporate finance; mergers and acquisitions; financial services and markets; commercial contracts; commercial property; employment and employee benefits; IT/IP; corporate insolvency and insurance litigation.

O'REILLY STEWART

O'Reilly Stewart House, 114-116 Royal Avenue, Belfast, BT1 1DL
Tel: (028) 9032 1000 **Fax:** (028) 9032 3003 **DX:** 3700 NR Belfast
Email: oreillystewart@dnet.co.uk **Website:** www.oreilly-stewart.co.uk

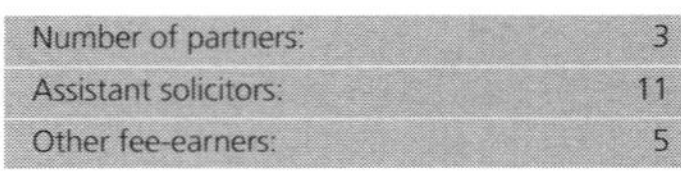

Number of partners:	3
Assistant solicitors:	11
Other fee-earners:	5

AREAS OF PRACTICE

Litigation	45%
Company/Commercial	20%
Conveyancing	15%
Building Society Work	5%
Criminal	5%
Family	5%
Licensing & Gaming	5%

CONTACTS

Commercial	Linus Murray
Conveyancing	Janet McMillan
Litigation	Joe Moore

THE FIRM: OReilly Stewart can trace its roots back to 1920 and combines a wealth of experience with a steadily increasing number of young highly qualified solicitors familiar with all the latest developments in law, business and technology.

PRINCIPAL AREAS OF WORK:

Litigation: Senior Partner Brian Stewart has practised in the province since 1980 and now deals primarily with defence work. He is a member of the International Association of Defence Counsel and Chairman of the Legal Aid Committee. He leads a team of six solicitors with emphasis on insurance defence work, multi jurisdictional class actions, product liability, plaintiff personal injury, medical negligence and a strong emphasis in commercial litigation.

Commercial/Licensing: Senior partner Garrett OReilly has a long established reputation in relation to licensing and commercial property work. He leads a team of five solicitors with emphasis on all aspects of commercial conveyancing and property work including acquisition of freehold and leasehold properties for investment or development, planning law and appeals, multi-national property transactions, agency work for English firms, Building Society panel work, mortgage portfolio acquisitions and all aspects of liquor licensing, gaming and entertainment law.

General: Within the firm there are also individual solicitors who practice in employment law, criminal law, domestic conveyancing, matrimonial and probate law.

CLIENTELE: Direct Line Insurance, Hastings Hotels, Bradford & Bingley Building Society, Irish Permanent.

OSBORNE CLARKE

50 Queen Charlotte Street, Bristol, BS1 4HE
Tel: (0117) 917 3000 **Fax:** (0117) 917 3005 **DX:** 7818 Bristol – 1
Email: info@osborneclarke.com **Website:** www.osborneclarke.com

Hillgate House, 26 Old Bailey, London, EC4M 7HW
Tel: (020) 7809 1000 **Fax:** (020) 7809 1005 **DX:** 466 London Chancery Lane WC2
Email: info@osborneclarke.com

Apex Plaza, Forbury Road, Reading, RG1 1AX
Tel: (0118) 925 2000 **Fax:** (0118) 925 0038 **DX:** 117882 – Reading, Apex Plaza
Email: info@osborneclarke.com

Managing partner:	Leslie Perrin
Senior partner:	Chris Curling
Number of partners:	60
Assistant solicitors:	128
Other fee-earners:	50
Total Staff:	505

THE FIRM: For one of the UK's most progressive commercial law firms, Osborne Clarke has two surprisingly simple business objectives: to serve its clients and to provide its people with interesting and rewarding careers. In London, Bristol and the Thames Valley, Osborne Clarke competes with the largest City and national firms in its chosen international practice areas: corporate finance, private equity, IT telecoms and media, and employment. Increasingly international in focus, the firm also advises a growing number of clients from Europe and the US.

In the past year, the firm's international expansion has been significant. Osborne Clarke clients now have access to over 400 lawyers in 16 European cities, and to a range of cross-border specialisms. In London, the addition of the market-leading Anglo-Danish practice made it an international law firm and the number one player in the Anglo-Danish field.

In the UK, the firm is particularly well-endowed with prominent sector specialists and has an enviable reputation in advertising and marketing, litigation, commercial property, construction, corporate banking, competition, tax, environmental and pensions law. In London and across the South of England, the firm's corporate finance and private equity teams have been exceptionally active. In 1998, it advised on £2 billion worth of corporate deals which included 68 venture capital deals, 55 disposals and 46 acquisitions. Its IT and telecoms team advises some of the sector's most recognisable names (and many who have the potential to be); and the employment team has grown in stature and in size to become one of the UK's largest and best regarded teams of employment advisors.

PRINCIPAL AREAS OF WORK: Osborne Clarke services a wide range of sectors. Currently, it advises companies in: advertising and marketing, biosciences, commercial property, corporate banking, corporate finance, distribution, facilities management, financial services, interactive digital media, IT, leisure, manufacturing, outsourcing, packaging, the public sector, professional services, transport, retailing, telecoms and waste management.

INTERNATIONAL CONNECTIONS: Barcelona, Brussels, Cologne, Copenhagen, Frankfurt, Hamburg, Milan, Paris and Rotterdam.

AREAS OF PRACTICE

Corporate	33%
Litigation	18%
Commercial Property	15%
Employment	15%
IT, Telecoms and Media	15%
Tax and Trust	5%

CONTACTS

- **Advertising & Marketing** ....Tim Birt (London), Stephen Groom (London)
- **Anglo-Danish Matters** ....Roy Lambert (London), Per Troen (London)
- **Anglo-German Matters** ....Adrian Taylor (Frankfurt), Claire Wagner (Bristol), Kieran O'Connor (London)
- **Commercial Property** ....Simon Speirs (Bristol), Jane Lougher (London)
- **Corporate Banking** ....Margaret Childs (Bristol)
- **Corporate Finance** ....Simon Beswick (Bristol), Andrew Saul (London), Andrew Gowans (Thames Valley), Adrian Taylor (Frankfurt)
- **Corporate Tax** ....Philip Moss (Bristol)
- **Employment** ....Nicholas Moore (Bristol), Chris Southam (London), Danielle Kingdon (Thames Valley)
- **Insolvency** ....Patrick Cook (Bristol), Richard Baines (London)
- **IT, Telecoms and Media** ....Simon Rendell (London), Andrew Braithwaite (Bristol), Russell Bowyer (Thames Valley)
- **Litigation** ....Clare Robinson (Bristol), Adrian Lifely (London)
- **Tax and Trusts** ....Sandra Brown (Bristol)

O

OSBORNE MORRIS & MORGAN

Danbury House, West Street, Leighton Buzzard, LU7 7DD **Tel:** (01525) 378177 **Fax:** (01525) 851006 **DX:** 90804 Leighton Buzzard **Ptnrs:** 6 **Asst solrs:** 4 **Other fee-earners:** 4

OSBORNES

68 Parkway, London, NW1 7AH **Tel:** (020) 7485 8811 **Fax:** (020) 7485 5660 **DX:** 57053 Camden Town. **Email:** law@osbornes.demon.cd.uk **Website:** www.osbornes.net **Ptnrs:** 7 **Asst solrs:** 8 **Other fee-earners:** 10 **Contact:** Angus Andrew. • Well-established high street firm delivering quality legal services in specialist fields. Holds Legal Aid Franchise and BSI Certification.

AREAS OF PRACTICE

Matrimonial & Family:	25%
Personal Injury Litigation:	25%
Landlord & Tenant:	20%
Residential & Commercial Property	15%
Wills & Probate	10%
Mediation	5%

OSWALD GOODIER & CO

10 Chapel St, Preston, PR1 8AY
Tel: (01772) 253841 **Fax:** (01772) 201713 **DX:** 714571 Preston 14
Email: oswgoodier@aol.com

Senior partner:	Mark Belderbos
Number of partners:	3
Other fee-earners:	1

AREAS OF PRACTICE

Charity, Trust & Probate	30%
Residential Property & Landlord & Tenant	30%
Commercial Property/Company	18%
Personal Injury & Other Litigation	11%
Matrimonial & Family	7%
Other	4%

THE FIRM: Established in 1897, in central Preston, the firm has a substantial charity, trust, property and private client practice in the North West and further afield. For very many years, Oswald Goodier & Co have represented numerous charities, both religious and secular, involving much work in the fields of trusts, property, educational and ecclesiastical law. Highlights include regular substantial property transactions, and continuous involvement in charity law matters. The firm is highly regarded as experienced in all aspects of private client work, as well as being much involved in civil litigation, licensing, employment and elderly client work.

CLIENTELE: Substantial connections in private client work and several religious, diocesan and secular charities, schools and colleges and long-established trust and estate clients.

OURY CLARK SOLICITORS

5 Arlington Street, London, SW1A 1RA **Tel:** (020) 7629 8844 **Fax:** (020) 7629 8855 **DX:** 140543 Piccadilly **Email:** oury.clark@btconnect.com **Website:** www.ouryclark.com **Ptnrs:** 3 **Asst solrs:** 2 **Other fee-earners:** 4 **Contact:** Aileen Colhoun or James Oury • Specialists in criminal defence work (particularly white-collar crime) adopting a multi-disciplinary legal/accountancy approach.

OVERBURY STEWARD EATON & WOOLSEY

3 Upper King St, Norwich, NR3 1RL **Tel:** (01603) 610481 **Fax:** (01603) 632460 **DX:** 5208 Norwich **Email:** info@overburys.co.uk **Website:** www.overburys.co.uk **Ptnrs:** 12 **Asst solrs:** 6 **Other fee-earners:** 15

OVER TAYLOR BIGGS

1 Oak Tree Place, Manaton Close, Matford Business Park, Exeter, EX2 8WA **Tel:** (01392) 823811 **Fax:** (01392) 823812 **DX:** 300350 Exeter 5 **Email:** law@o-t-b.co.uk **Ptnrs:** 3 **Asst solrs:** 3 **Other fee-earners:** 3 **Contact:** Mr Christopher Over • New firm formed to offer partner-only service from business park on outskirts of Exeter. Company commercial, property and litigation work.

AREAS OF PRACTICE

Commercial Pproperty	25%
Company/Corporate	25%
Medical Negligence/Personal Injury	20%
Transport	20%
Construction Litigation	10%

OWEN WHITE

Senate House, 62-70 Bath Road, Slough, SL2 3SR
Tel: (01753) 876800 **Fax:** (01753) 876876 **DX:** 3409
Email: law@owenwhite.com **Website:** www.owenwhite.com

Managing partner:	Richard Keen
Number of partners:	8
Assistant solicitors:	6

AREAS OF PRACTICE

Housing	30%
Litigation (inc. Employment)	30%
Company/Commercial	20%
Commercial Property Development	10%
Franchising	10%

CONTACTS

Commercial Litigation	Richard Keen
	Russell Ford
Company & Commercial	Jane Masih
	Andrew Hayward
Dispute Resolution	Richard Keen
Franchising	Anton Bates
Property	Phil Lawrence
Social Housing – Housing Management	Caroline Cowley
Social Housing – Property	Nick Barnard

THE FIRM: Commercial practice providing a wide range of legal disciplines with a strong reputation in the fields of social housing, franchising and commercial mediation.

PRINCIPAL AREAS OF WORK:

Social Housing: Acts for many RSL's undertaking both property work and housing management work.
Franchising: Acts as legal advisor to the British Franchise Association and the practice regularly represents many well known franchises.
Dispute Resolution: Three partners are trained mediators and have successfully mediated many complex, multi-party disputes.
Company/Commercial: Provides wide ranging advice from acquisitions to disposals with employment law as an important specialisation.
Property: Acts for nationally known property developers.
Commercial Litigation: Provides a full range of litigation services for the firm's commercial clients.

OXLEY & COWARD

34/46 Moorgate St, Rotherham, S60 2HB **Tel:** (01709) 510999 **Fax:** (01709) 512999 **DX:** 12600 Rotherham **Email:** mailbox@oxcow.co.uk **Website:** oxcow.co.uk **Ptnrs:** 7 **Asst solrs:** 6 **Other fee-earners:** 13

PAGAN OSBORNE

12 St. Catherine Street, Cupar, KY15 4HN **Tel:** (01334) 653777 **Fax:** (01334) 655063 **DX:** 560543 **Email:** enquiries@pagan.co.uk
Website: www.pegan.co.uk **Ptnrs:** 12 **Asst solrs:** 7 **Other fee-earners:** 9

PAISNER & CO

Bouverie House, 154 Fleet St, London, EC4A 2JD
Tel: (020) 7353 0299 **Fax:** (020) 7583 8621 **DX:** 198
Email: info@paisner.co.uk **Website:** www.paisner.co.uk

Managing partner:	Stephen Rosefield
Senior partner:	Harold Paisner
Number of partners:	53
Assistant solicitors:	58
Other fee-earners:	39

AREAS OF PRACTICE

Company/Commercial (including e-commerce, IP & Media)	37%
Property	20%
Litigation (including insurance & reinsurance)	19%
Trusts & Estate Planning	10%
Employment	8%
Construction & Engineering	6%

CONTACTS

Asset & Consumer Finance	Dennis Rosenthal
Banking/Insolvency	Stephen Marshall
	Stephen Nelson
Charities	Anne-Marie Piper
Company/Commercial	Jonathan Kropman
Computer/Media & IP	Linda Fazzani
Construction	Hugh Nicholls
	Terry de Souza
Corporate Finance	David Collins
	Keith Stella
Corporate Tax	Amanda Rowland
Employment	Alexandra Davidson
EU/UK Competition Law	Adrian Magnus
Food Law/Health & Safety	Craig Baylis
Liquor Licensing	Craig Baylis
Litigation & Dispute Resolution	David Parkin
Pensions	Norman Russell
Property	Kate Fisher
Property Litigation	David Cox
	Gerry Aylott
Reinsurance/Insurance	Jonathan Sacher
Trademarks	Debrett Lyons
Trusts and Estate Planning	Martin Paisner

THE FIRM: Paisner & Co is an expanding City law firm offering a full range of legal services to commercial clients both national and international. The firm operates a free on-line briefing service via its website, which alerts subscribers to developments in a range of disciplines.

PRINCIPAL AREAS OF WORK:

Corporate/Corporate Finance and Commercial: A broad range of corporate work is handled including corporate finance, venture capital, banking and insolvency and on the commercial side, asset/consumer finance, retail banking, data protection, franchising and all other kinds of commercial agreements. All aspects of EU/UK competition law are also handled.

Property: A full commercial property service is provided to some of the UK's largest property portfolio owners/managers as well as developers. In addition a well respected property litigation group acts for both landlords and tenants.

Litigation and Dispute Resolution: Commercial disputes of all kinds (whether arising in the UK or abroad) leading to court, tribunal or arbitration are handled by the firm's litigation and dispute resolution practice. In addition, a high profile regulatory law group, comprising four advocates, is dedicated to food law, licensing and business protection issues. Associated areas of expertise include health and safety and trading standards.

Computer, Media and Intellectual Property: Has expanded considerably into a specialist practice area. The firm's computer, media and intellectual property team is particularly well known for its work in the IT, publishing, digital media and e-commerce fields. It also has a dedicated trade mark unit.

Employment and Pensions: The firm advises employers and employees on all contentious and non-contentious aspects of employment law and on all aspects of occupational pension schemes.

Insurance/Reinsurance: The firm deals with international and UK reinsurance and insurance dispute resolution, arbitration and litigation; the formation, acquisition and disposal of insurance companies, brokers, agents and captives; corporate reorganisations and regulatory and compliance work.

Tax: A comprehensive advisory service is offered by the firm's tax department on the UK and international tax aspects of all areas of its practice.

Construction: The construction and engineering group handles contentious and non-contentious matters and has experience in dispute resolution, both nationally and internationally through ADR, arbitration and the courts.

Trusts and Estate Planning: The well known trusts and estate planning department advises individuals and trustees on estate and tax planning, trusts and off-shore arrangements. The department is also recognised for its expertise in contentious probate and charity work.

INTERNATIONAL CONNECTIONS: Internationally, the firm has formed an EEIG with Uettwiller Grelon, Gout, Canat & Associes (UGGC), a French legal practice with a branch in Brussels. Additionally, Paisner & Co has established close working relationships with other overseas law firms particularly in Europe and North America.

CLIENTELE: Clients include UK and international listed and smaller companies from a wide range of industry sectors, in particular, hotels and leisure, media and new media/e-commerce, telecommunications, information technology, manufacturing, healthcare, food and drink, insurance and financial services.

RECRUITMENT & TRAINING: Paisner & Co recruits around ten trainee solicitors each year. A brochure and application details are available from the firm or via its website.

PALSER GROSSMAN

Discovery House, Scott Harbour, Cardiff Bay, CF10 4HA
Tel: (029) 2045 2770 **Fax:** (029) 2045 2328 **DX:** 33064 Cardiff 1
Email: law@palser-grossman.co.uk

120 Edmund Street, Birmingham, B3 2ER
Tel: (0121) 212 0029 **Fax:** (0121) 236 1132 **DX:** 13029 Birmingham 1

One Bridewell Street, Bristol, BS1 2AA
Tel: (0117) 927 9889 **Fax:** (0117) 927 9411 **DX:** 78186 Bristol 1

Waterside House, Town Quay, Southampton, SO14 2EJ
Tel: (023) 8033 9934 **Fax:** (023) 8063 4700 **DX:** 96886 Southampton 10

Clipper House, Quay West, Quay Parade, Swansea, SA1 8AB
Tel: (01792) 653336 **Fax:** (01792) 649004 **DX:** 92062 Swansea 3

Managing and senior partner	Howard Palser
Number of partners:	21
Assistant solicitors:	22
Other fee-earners:	25

AREAS OF PRACTICE

Personal Injury Litigation	60%
Commercial Property	15%
Company & Commercial	15%
Commercial Litigation	10%

CONTACTS

Commercial Litigation	Christopher Nott
Commercial Property	Alison Ivin
Company Commercial	Laurence James
PI Birmingham	Peter Fletcher
PI Bristol	Julian Lewis
PI Cardiff	Richard Crane
PI Southampton	James Morris
PI Swansea	Jane Garland-Thomas

P

THE FIRM: The firm was founded in 1992 as a niche litigation practice with five fee earners and five support staff. Since then, in response to client demand, the firm has expanded geographically and numerically, and now has a total staff of 120 including 68 fee earners, with offices in five cities in England and Wales. The core business is the handling of defendant personal injury cases for major insurers and, in addition, the firm undertakes contentious and non-contentious corporate and commercial work, with a deserved reputation in employment and commercial property.

PRINCIPAL AREAS OF WORK:

Defendant Personal Injury: Following the substantial reduction in the number of solicitors on the panels of leading insurers, the firm has emerged as a major player, having been confirmed on the panels of Zurich (personal, commercial and international), AXA, CGU amd Admiral Insurance amongst others. The firm's specialist teams operate from offices in Cardiff, Swansea, Bristol, Birmingham and Southampton.

Commercial Litigation/Employment: This department handles the complete spectrum of commercial, employment, environmental, property, and construction litigation. Headed by Christopher Nott (see leader profile), the employment department is strong in employment matters, acting principally for employers.

Company and Commercial: The practice covers the full range of corporate activity. The team is headed by corporate finance partner, Laurence James.

Commercial Property: Led by partner Alison Ivin (see leader profile), the department handles large value complex commercial transactions. The team acted for Grosvenor Waterside, the property arm of Associated British Ports in the sale of land and buildings for the Welsh Assembly, the sale of land to the First National Bank of Chicago for its European Headquarters, and in a major PFI relating to the road link between Cardiff Bay and the city centre.

INTERNATIONAL CONNECTIONS: The firm is a member of CONSULEGIS, an international association of lawyers. Howard Palser is vice-chairman of the organisation.

LANGUAGES: French, German, Italian and Welsh.

PANNONE & PARTNERS

123 Deansgate, Manchester, M3 2BU
Tel: (0161) 909 3000 **Fax:** (0161) 909 4444 **DX:** 14314 Manchester 1
Website: www.pannone.com

Managing partner:	Joy Kingsley
Senior partner:	Rodger Pannone President of the Law Society, 1993-94
Number of partners:	57
Assistant solicitors:	36
Other fee-earners:	62

AREAS OF PRACTICE

Commercial Litigation	25%
Personal Injury	24%
Corporate	12%
Clinical Negligence	9%
Family	9%
Private Client	9%
Commercial Property	7%
Employment	5%

THE FIRM: Pannone & Partners is one of the largest practices in the North West. It has strengths not shared by firms of a similar size in the ability to service all types of work for both personal and commercial clients with the firm's strength and size being split evenly between the two. Pannones were the first law firm to achieve BS5750 accreditation, now ISO9001, and also hold several Legal Aid Franchise certificates. Pannone's ethos is to pride itself on its ability to work in partnership with its clients and to offer practical and cost effective solutions, meeting clients' needs.

PRINCIPAL AREAS OF WORK:

Corporate & Commercial: A comprehensive range of corporate services are available including all aspects of business start up and formation, banking and finance, commercial contracts, company law and competition law. This department also contains specialists offering expertise in public sector, intellectual property and advertising & marketing.

Commercial Property: This department undertakes the full range of commercial property transactions including purchases, sales, mortgages, planning, development, leases, joint ventures and portfolio management.

Commercial Litigation: This progressive and successful department is acknowledged by its competitors to be tough, knowledgeable and effective. Experienced in litigating in all courts and tribunals, their watchword is commerciality. It also houses the Debt Collection Unit.

Employment: This team handles its own tribunal advocacy and provides quality advice nationally and locally, predominantly for employers, but also for employees dealing with all aspects of the employment relationship.
Business Crime: An experienced, highly-regarded team advising on white collar, serious and complex criminal/regulatory cases and investigations.
Construction: A dedicated team of construction specialists who carry out work of both a contentious and non-contentious nature.
Insolvency: This team aims to give prompt considered practical advice from which clients can derive financial and commercial benefit.
Licensing: Headed by Nick Dickinson, recently recruited from Davies Wallis Foyster, where he was head of licensing. Nick is one of a handful of English lawyers with expertise in Scottish licensing.
Personal Injury: This department is consistently accredited as the strongest PI team in the North West, with a demonstrable national and international reputation for the quality of its work, the size of settlements obtained and expertise in handling multi-party and complex claims. The department also handles many hundreds of claims each year arising out of less serious accidents. As with clinical negligence, a significant amount of work is referred from non-specialist solicitors.
Clinical Negligence: This dedicated team of medical negligence specialists act for clients throughout the country seeking redress for sometimes catastrophic injuries received during medical treatment. Members of this department do not undertake any other form of PI work thereby guaranteeing a high degree of specialism.
Family: This is one of the foremost family law departments in the country, handling divorce and all that goes with it. Its specialities include substantial and complex financial cases acting for high net worth individuals and contested adoption.
Private Client: A large department dealing with residential conveyancing, tax planning, wills and estates and Court of Protection work. The staff provide a caring and efficient service when undertaking their clients' most personal transactions.

INTERNATIONAL CONNECTIONS: The firm is a founder member of the Pannone Law Group, Europe's first integrated international law group taking the form of a European Economic Interest Grouping. Its lawyers recognised the need to offer creative, imaginative and practical advice on a Pan-European basis. PLG maintains offices in: Andorra, Belgium, Brazil, Canada, France, Germany, Italy, Luxembourg, Netherlands, Portugal, Spain, Sweden, Switzerland and the UK.

LANGUAGES: The firm recognises the importance of communication between different cultures and often transacts business in French, German, Swedish and Danish.

RECRUITMENT & TRAINING: The firm offers eight training contracts each year with a programme of in-house lectures and seminars. The firm encourages trainees to stay on qualification. Application forms are available from Julia Hearn.

CONTACTS

Corporate & Commercial	Søren Tattam
Commercial Property	Andrew Simpkin
Commercial Litigation	Vincent O'Farrell
Employment	Christine Bradley
Construction	Gareth Jessop
Business Crime	Paul Taylor
Insolvency	Paul Johnson
Intellectual Property	Laurie Heizler
Public Sector	Steven Grant
Licensing	Nick Dickinson
Debt Collection	Simon McCrum
Private Client	Hugh Jones
Personal Injury	Carol Jackson
Clinical Negligence	John Kitchingman
Family	Catherine Jones
Financial Services	Tony Ashton
French Property	Lindsay Kinnealy

SOLICITORS

P

PARDOES

6-9 King Square, Bridgwater, TA6 3YB **Tel:** (01278) 457891 **Fax:** (01278) 429249 **DX:** 80602 **Website:** www.pardoes.co.uk **Ptnrs:** 13
Asst solrs: 10 **Other fee-earners:** 17

PARIS SMITH & RANDALL

Number 1 London Road, Southampton, SO15 2AE
Tel: (023) 8048 2482 **Fax:** (023) 8063 1835 **DX:** 38534 Southampton 3
Email: info@parissmith.co.uk **Website:** www.parissmith.co.uk

Number of partners:	12
Assistant s°olicitors:	24
Other fee-earners:	20

THE FIRM: Paris Smith & Randall are totally dedicated to providing exceptional service to their clients. This means they spend the majority of the time listening to their clients. From this they learn each day how to serve them better. Their greatest satisfaction is sharing in their client's hopes, aspirations and ambitions. The firm is accredited as an Investor in People and with Lexcel, the Law Society's practice management standard.

PRINCIPAL AREAS OF WORK: As Southampton's premier solicitors and a leading firm in the South, the firm prides itself in serving both commercial clients and private clients. Commercial clients have access to a complete range of services including legal advice on company and commercial, IT, intellectual property, employment and commercial property advice. Private clients can take advantage of a full range of services: family, child protection, personal injury, wills, personal taxation, estate planning, financial and pension advice.

RECRUITMENT & TRAINING: CV's are always welcome from applicants for training contracts, qualified staff and secretarial and administrative staff. These should be sent to David Cooksley, Practice Manager. The firm is committed to providing all its staff with interesting and fulfilling careers, provided they are prepared to become actively involved in learning more about their clients and their businesses and always have a thirst for knowledge and acquiring new skills.

AREAS OF PRACTICE

Company & Commercial	21%
Commercial Property	20%
Family	14%
Tax & Estate Planning	14%
Litigation	13%
Residential Property	13%
Employment	5%

CONTACTS

Child Care	Justin Belcher
Company & Commercial	Andrew Heathcock
Employment	Malcolm Ross
Family & Mediation	Neil Davies
Insolvency	Malcolm Le Bas
Litigation	Clive Thomson
Probate/Tax/Trusts	Crispin Jameson
Property (Commercial)	Mark Howarth
Property (Residential)	Peter Gammie

PARKER BULLEN

45 Castle Street, Salisbury, SP1 3SS
Tel: (01722) 412000 **Fax:** (01722) 411822 **DX:** Salisbury 58001
Email: law@parkerbullen.com **Website:** www.parkerbullen.co.uk

8 Newbury Street, Andover, SP10 1DW
Tel: (01264) 400500 **Fax:** (01264) 355957 **DX:** Andover 90304
Email: law@parkerbullen.com

Managing partner:	Chris Nichols
Senior partner:	Robert Sykes
Number of partners:	11
Assistant solicitors:	12
Other fee-earners:	9

CONTACTS

Commercial Property ....Tim Crarer
....Chris Nichols
Company/Commercial ....Mark Lello
Education/Employment/Licensing ....
....Richard Le Masurier
General & Commercial Litigation ....
....James Welsh
Licensed Property ....Tim Crarer
Matrimonial & Family ....Richard Le Masurier
Private Client ....Robert Sykes

THE FIRM: The firm's turnover, profits and plc list have grown substantially in each of the last five years. Further increases are planned as implementation of the partners' strategy of organic growth continues.

PRINCIPAL AREAS OF WORK: Particular expertise in commercial and general litigation; insolvency; personal injury; matrimonial & family; licensing; employment; landlord & tenant; debt recovery; education; charities & trusts; commercial & residential property; licensed property; and full company & commercial services including MBOs, franchising, employment and intellectual property.

CLIENTELE: Include Lloyds/TSB Group, Enterprise Inns plc, Norcros plc, Icon Clinical Research (UK) Ltd, The Hop Back Brewery, Bryanston School, Clayesmore School, RNIB, Dean & Chapter of Salisbury, Civil Service Pensioners Alliance, Civil Service Benevolent Fund and JJ Fox International Ltd.

P

PARKER & GREGO

18-19 Freeman Street, Birmingham, B5 5H2 **Tel:** (0121) 633 3031 **Fax:** 0121 633 3029

PARK NELSON

1 Bell Yard, London, WC2A 2JP
Tel: (020) 7539 2000 **Fax:** (020) 7405 4266 **DX:** 186 Chancery Lane WC2
Email: law@parknelson.co.uk **Website:** www.parknelson.co.uk

Managing partner:	Timothy Ford
Senior partner:	Eugene O'Keeffe
Number of partners:	19
Assistant solicitors:	11
Other fee-earners:	7

AREAS OF PRACTICE

Commercial Property	46%
Litigation/Dispute Resolution/Construction/Insurance	31%
Private Client Services	12%
Corporate	11%

CONTACTS

Commercial Property ....Eugene O'Keeffe
Corporate ....Tim Ford
Litigation/Construction ....John Kings
Private Client Services ....Richard Fairbairn

THE FIRM: Park Nelson is one of the oldest firms of solicitors having celebrated its 200th birthday in 1996. It is now continuing its independent development with the most advanced technology pursuing controlled growth through strong management and a determination that services will be partner-led. Clients always have immediate access to partners who supervise the provision of services day to day and control the work of the firm to ensure constant excellence of standards. The four-partner specialist insurance law firm, Rayfields, joined Park Nelson's litigation and dispute resolution department on 25 January 1999.

PRINCIPAL AREAS OF WORK:

Commercial Property: The firm believes that its considerable strengths in commercial property are equal to those of much larger practices. It is particularly well known for its expertise in handling developments, funding agreements and commercial leases in the retail and other fields. Special areas of property expertise include negotiating and advising on retail licensing and franchising agreements, as well as advice on all aspects of town and country planning, compulsory purchase negotiations, and public inquiries and appeals.

Litigation, Dispute Resolution and Insurance: The firm is prominent in construction litigation and dispute resolution, and also in non-contentious construction law as well as contract matters. The litigation department handles specialist professional indemnity work for leading underwriters and professional firms, personal injury and medical negligence cases, landlord and tenant disputes, commercial and contractual matters and employment issues, intellectual property litigation and judicial review proceedings.

Corporate and Business Services: Includes acquisitions and disposals of companies and their businesses, advice on drafting and negotiating commercial agreements, handling joint venture and marketing agreements and preparing financing, banking and loan, funding agreements and insolvency. The firm has specialist and extensive skills in employment law matters, as it does for consumer and consumer credit matters. With its strong international connections, UK and Irish business operations for overseas companies is an important feature and there is a rapidly growing expertise and client base in e-commerce ventures.

Private Client Services: The work of the private client department involves trust management, probate, estate and tax planning, tax returns and the preparation of wills, with particular expertise in French, South African and Italian cases.

International Connections: The firm has strong international connections and conducts work throughout the world, in the United States, southern Africa, the Far East and Australia. These connections include eastern Europe, but are particularly strong in the European Union member states and neighbouring territories, especially France and Ireland. Three of the partners are also admitted as solicitors in the Republic of Ireland. The firm has associated offices in Dublin, Paris, Rome and Milan.

CLIENTELE: The firm's clients include substantial UK companies, as well as private, professional, institutional and commercial firms in Europe and internationally. A number of French, Belgian and Dutch governmental, cultural and educational institutions in London are also clients. Many of the firm's lawyers are fluent in foreign languages.

PARLETT KENT

Signet House, 49 – 51 Farringdon Rd, London, EC1M 3JB
Tel: (020) 7430 0712 **Fax:** (020) 7430 1796 **DX:** 53308 Clerkenwell
Email: enquiries@parlettkent.co.uk

Portland House, Longbrook Street, Exeter, EX4 6AB
Tel: (01392) 494455 **Fax:** (01392) 491199 **DX:** 134052 – Exeter 15
Email: enquiries@exeter.partlettkent.co.uk

Senior partner:	Caroline Jenkins
Number of partners:	6
Assistant solicitors:	3
Other fee-earners:	5

AREAS OF PRACTICE

Clinical Negligence 70%
Conveyancing & General (non-contentious) 10%
Personal injury 10%
Matrimonial 5%
Professional negligence 5%

CONTACTS

Clinical Negligence ....Caroline Jenkins ....(London)
....Maji Young ....(Exeter)
Family ....Elizabeth Batten
Personal Injury ....Julie Say
Private Client ....Maggie Leiper

THE FIRM: Established in the 1950's Parlett Kent is a firm noted in particular for its expertise in a wide range of complex, clinical negligence and personal injury litigation. The firm has in house para-medical support and is committed to applying its expertise to cases of merit regardless of venue or quantum of case. The firm has legal aid franchises for personal injury and clinical negligence litigation and undertakes private work including Conditional Fee Agreement cases. Four partners are members of the Law Society's Medical Negligence Panel, the Association of Personal Injury Lawyers, the AVMA referral Panel and Magi Young and Julie Say are members of the Law Society's Personal Injury Panel. Caroline Jenkins and Magi Young are members of the Association of Trial Lawyers of America. The firm has an office in Exeter where they specialise in clinical negligence and personal injury litigation.

PRINCIPAL AREAS OF WORK:
Clinical Negligence: This department deals with cases of the utmost severity (accidents at birth, brain injuries and spinal injuries) as well as a wide range of both High Court and County Court claims. The firm has particular expertise in cases of obstetric and psychiatric negligence as well as cases arising out of failures to diagnose and treat cancer. It also specialises in claims against the legal profession arising out of mishandling of clinical negligence claims. Members of the practice regularly lecture lawyers, doctors, nurses, Health Service managers and social workers on medical negligence and risk management.
Personal Injury: This department deals with a full range of personal injury claims, including road traffic accidents and accidents at work, for both claimants and defendants. Two of the partners are members of the Personal Injury Panel.
Other Areas: Conveyancing, wills, trusts, probate, taxation and family.

LANGUAGES: French, Punjabi, Urdu.

RECRUITMENT & TRAINING: At least one trainee solicitor is recruited annually. The firm has an equal opportunities policy and all posts are advertised.

O.H. PARSONS & PARTNERS

Sovereign Hse, 212-224 Shaftesbury Avenue, London, WC2H 8PR **Tel:** (020) 7379 7277 **Fax:** (020) 7240 1577 **Ptnrs:** 6 **Asst solrs:** 4 **Other fee-earners:** 4 **Contact:** Barry Sullivan • Best known for Trade Union work, personal injury litigation and employment law. Founded 1949.

AREAS OF PRACTICE

Personal Injury 80%
Employment 15%
Crime/Consumer Entertainment Law & Defamation 5%

PATTINSON & BREWER

30 Great James Street, London, WC1N 3HA
Tel: (020) 7400 5100 **Fax:** (020) 7400 5101 **DX:** 394
Email: enquiries@pattinsonbrewer.co.uk **Website:** www.pattinsonbrewer.co.uk

Managing partner:	John Davies
Number of partners:	14
Assistant solicitors:	13
Other fee-earners:	32

AREAS OF PRACTICE

Personal Injury 59%
Employment/Labour Law 18%
Medical Negligence 10%
General Litigation 6%
Conveyancing/Commercial 5%
Criminal 2%

THE FIRM: The firm of Pattinson and Brewer was founded in about 1892. It has long been a leading trade union practice, having connections going back to the Taff Vale case in 1901 and the formation of the TGWU in 1921. It has a proud commitment to claimant personal injury and disease work, and a well-established reputation in the fields of equal opportunities, and clinical and professional negligence. It has developed a leading profile in the field of employment law and acts frequently for directors and senior executives on their personal employment issues. It has a strong team of general litigators and a very experienced property department. The firm also has offices in Chatham, Bristol, York and the City.

RECRUITMENT & TRAINING: The firm presently recruits one or two trainee solicitors each year, and looks for an interest in claimant-orientated work.

PAUL DAVIDSON TAYLOR
Chancery Court, Queen Street, Horsham, RH13 5AD **Tel:** (01403) 262 333 **Fax:** (01403) 262 444 **DX:** 57617 Horsham **Email:** law@pdt.co.uk
Website: www.pdt.co.uk

PAULL & WILLIAMSONS

Investment House, 6 Union Row, Aberdeen, AB10 1DQ
Tel: (01224) 621621 **Fax:** (01224) 640446 **DX:** 35 Aberdeen
Email: info@paull-williamsons.co.uk **Website:** www.paull-williamsons.co.uk

New Investment House, 214 Union Street, Aberdeen, AB10 8QY
Tel: (01224) 621621 **Fax:** (01224) 627437 **DX:** 82 Aberdeen
Email: info@paull-williamsons.co.uk

13 North Bank Street, Edinburgh, EH1 2LP
Tel: (0131) 226 6180 **Fax:** (0131) 226 6797 **DX:** ED 261 Edinburgh
Email: info@paull-williamsons.co.uk

Senior partner:	Bruce Smith
Number of partners:	31
Assistant solicitors:	46
Other fee-earners:	8

CONTACTS

Commercial Property	Leslie S. Dalgarno
Corporate	Sidney Barrie
Litigation	James K. Tierney
Private Client	George Alpine
	David O.M. Geddie

PAULL & WILLIAMSONS
SOLICITORS

THE FIRM: One of the largest firms in Aberdeen, Paull & Williamsons have enhanced their legal services to meet the increased pace of economic activity in the North East of Scotland in recent years. Moreover the client benefits from an efficient internal cross-referral system which provides immediate access to other departments on other areas of the law. The firm also conducts seminars for clients on matters of concern to them, including employment, industrial relations and the effects of new legislation.

P

PRINCIPAL AREAS OF WORK:
Corporate Services: The firm has a long reputation for serving commercial clients in the North East and has close links with the local financial community. The department handles all types of corporate and commercial transactions including business start-ups, partnerships and incorporation; company administration; takeovers and acquisitions; disposals; management buy-outs; insolvency, receivership, liquidation and administration; commercial contracts, licensing and intellectual property; shipping and vessel finance; venture capital financing and investment.
Commercial Property Services: The department has recently expanded its operations and now has considerable experience in commercial property developments throughout Scotland. Valuable connections are maintained with other professionals in the commercial property field, such as surveyors, architects and project managers. The firm offers a comprehensive service covering the acquisition and development, leasing and funding of both office and industrial developments. In addition proven experience has been demonstrated in the fields of retail development, major residential development, licensed premises, agricultural and sporting estates, and woodland and aquacultural development. Planning applications, whether at first instance or at appeal stage, are also handled by the firm.
Private Client Services: The first practice in Aberdeen to open a separate estate agency office, the department now operates from large premises in the heart of the city. The service includes advice on valuation, marketing strategy, mortgages, insurance, contracts of sale and purchase and the handling of enquiries prior to sale. The firm also attends to the client's personal financial requirements in tax planning, succession, trusts, insurance and personal financial management. This expertise extends to cover agricultural partnerships and estate work.
Litigation: The firm has the experience to deal with all areas of contentious work either prior to formal litigation or arbitration or through representation in the courts and tribunals. The department's work ranges from matters which might face the commercial client, including commercial contracts, employment matters, credit control, health and safety at work, and insolvency to matters of personal concern, such as matrimonial disputes and employment problems. Having developed expertise in the negotiation, pursuit and defence of personal injury claims, the firm has also recently achieved a significant reputation in advising clients and their insurers following major disasters and representing them at subsequent public inquiries.

THE PAUL ROONEY PARTNERSHIP

19-23 Stanley Street, Liverpool, L1 6AA **Tel:** (0151) 227 2851 **Fax:** (0151) 255 0455 **DX:** 14183 **Ptnrs:** 6 **Asst solrs:** 7 **Other fee-earners:** 36 **Contact:** Mr Paul Rooney • Established in 1977, a specialist civil and criminal litigation firm dealing mainly with personal injury claims including factory accidents, industrial diseases, medical and professional negligence, sports injuries and road traffic accidents.

AREAS OF PRACTICE

Road Traffic Accidents/Personal Injury	85%
Crime	10%

PAYNE HICKS BEACH

10 New Square, Lincoln's Inn, London, WC2A 3QG
Tel: (020) 7465 4300 **Fax:** (020) 7465 4400 **DX:** 40 Ch.Ln.
Email: [contact]@payne-hicks-beach.co.uk

Senior partner:	Graham Brown
Managing Partner	Guy Green
Number of partners:	19
Assistant solicitors:	10
Other fee-earners:	17

THE FIRM: Well-known and respected Inns of Court firm, established in the early eighteenth century. Although the firm draws strength from its long traditions, the character of the firm is an entirely modern one which has been created by the present partners' own chosen specialisations, several of which have been the object of favourable comment in journals in the last few years.

PRINCIPAL AREAS OF WORK: The firm is organised into five departments.

Tax, Trust and Probate: These are areas of specialisation for which the firm has a reputation as one of the best in London. The range of work undertaken is wider than traditionally associated with private client work, and extends from heritage and agricultural work and property development taxation, to advising entrepreneurs and senior directors, charities, and to off-shore and continental transactions.

Corporate/Commercial: This department deals with the full range of corporate and business law acting for public and private companies and a range of individual entrepreneurs. The international section deals with many clients and correspondents abroad, and has strong connections both within the European Community and elsewhere, including North America and Japan. Work includes: acquisitions and mergers, banking, competition law, employment law, EC law, intellectual property including computers and franchising, management buy-outs, marketing and sale of goods law, new issues and partnership agreements.

Commercial Litigation: The firm has a strong commercial litigation department handling a broad range of work including commercial disputes requiring urgent injunctive relief, arbitration, intellectual property, commercial, landlord and tenant and town and country planning. There is also particular experience in representing clients before regulatory enquiries. Specialised areas of work include advising clients in yacht racing and design and construction, building contract work, partnership disputes and all other aspects of insolvency for both corporate and individual clients.

Family Law: This department is well known for its specialisation in all aspects of family law including divorce and separation, adoption, custody and wardship, and financial claims. Personal injury actions are also handled.

Commercial Property: This section deals with all aspects of property transactions, leases, secured lending, management of investment property, development work including joint ventures and planning agreements.

Residential and Agricultural Conveyancing: This section deals with residential conveyancing, farm and forestry transactions, agricultural property and staff loan schemes.

INTERNATIONAL CONNECTIONS: The firm has associates in Paris with a network of other correspondents internationally. Several of the partners conduct legal work in French, German or Danish.

RECRUITMENT & TRAINING: There are usually two or three vacancies for trainee solicitors every year. The minimum educational requirement is a good degree, but emphasis is placed on personality as well as academic achievements. Applications should be made by letter (with CV and references) to the recruitment partner. The firm is also always interested to receive appplications from high quality solicitors seeking to move from the City.

AREAS OF PRACTICE	
Private Client	33%
Commercial Litigation	13%
Commercial Property	12%
Corporate/Commercial	10%
Matrimonial & Family Law/Litigation	10%
Residential/Agricultural Property	10%
Tax (Business & Corporate)	10%
General/Miscellaneous	2%

CONTACTS	
Commercial Litigation	Richard Butcher
Commercial Property	David FitzGerald
Corporate/Commercial	Guy Green
	Max Hudson
Employment/Sports	Richard Butcher
Family/Matrimonial	David Leverton
	Ian Airey
General Conveyancing	Andrew Crawford
	David Fitzgerald
Intellectual Property	Richard Butcher
Probate	Alastair Murdie
Tax/Trust	Graham Brown

P

PAYNE MARSH STILLWELL

6 Carlton Crescent, Southampton, SO15 2EY **Tel:** (023) 8022 3957 **Fax:** (023) 8022 5261 **DX:** 38514 Southampton 3 **Ptnrs:** 6 **Asst solrs:** 1 **Other fee-earners:** 4

PEDEN & REID

22 Callender Street, Belfast, BT1 5BU
Tel: (028) 9032 5617 **Fax:** (028) 9024 7343 **DX:** 389 NR Belfast
Email: peden-reid@dna.co.uk

Senior partner:	George A Palmer
Number of partners:	5
Assistant solicitors:	2
Other fee-earners:	1

THE FIRM: Founded in 1895, the firm acts in a general advisory capacity for a number of large public and private companies, public sector and statutory bodies, agricultural and marketing organisations, lending institutions, insurers and property developers.

PRINCIPAL AREAS OF WORK:

Company and Commercial Property: Formation and structuring of companies and inter-shareholder arrangements; preparation of vending and purchase agreements; partnerships and joint venture agreements relating to business acquisitions and disposals; capital and other finance sourcing; commercial mortgages and secured lending.

Employment: Advising on drafting of complex service agreements and in disputes arising out of employment contracts including fair employment, discrimination and Industrial Tribunal cases.

Family: Marriage breakdown and divorce. The firm has a large and successful family law practice often involving complex and substantial financial settlements.

Litigation: Wide experience in prosecuting and defending all types of civil actions including personal injuries, professional negligence, employer's and public liability, repossession proceedings, breach of contract, defamation, disputes relating to property rights and product liability including representation of insurers and the interests of other parties.

CONTACTS	
Commercial Property	Richard J.R. Palmer
Company/Employment	Niall K. Browne
Family	George A. Palmer
Litigation	Nicholas G. Harvey

PENNINGTONS

Bucklersbury House, 83 Cannon Street, London, EC4N 8PE
Tel: (020) 7457 3000 **Fax:** (020) 7457 3240 **DX:** 98946 Cheapside 2
Email: info@penningtons.co.uk **Website:** www.penningtons.co.uk

Clifton House, Bunnian Place, Basingstoke, RG21 7QY
Tel: (01256) 406300 **Fax:** (01256) 479425 **DX:** 122362 Basingstoke 8
Email: info@penningtons.co.uk

Phoenix House, 9 London Road, Newbury, RG14 1DH
Tel: (01635) 571000 **Fax:** (01635) 523444 **DX:** 30801 Newbury
Email: info@penningtons.co.uk

Highfield, Brighton Road, Godalming, GU7 1NS
Tel: (01483) 791800 **Fax:** (01483) 424177 **DX:** 58300 Godalming 1
Email: info@penningtons.co.uk

P

THE FIRM: Penningtons is a commercial law firm which provides legal services tailored to individual requirements. Specialist teams address the specific objectives of each client and provide a partner led service with an emphasis on team working. Their aims are always to match clients' expectations in the areas of quality, time of delivery and cost of service and to add value. The firm's principal office is in the City of London. There are further UK offices in Basingstoke, Godalming and Newbury and an office in Paris. In addition, Penningtons has close links with law firms in jurisdictions throughout the world. They are therefore able to offer flexibility in the scope of the specialist commercial and private client services they deliver to a wide range of clients with differing requirements.

PRINCIPAL AREAS OF WORK: The main areas of legal services provided are property, litigation (including shipping), corporate and commercial (including intellectual property), and private client (including immigration, family and matrimonial). The firm also has several specialist teams providing focused and co-ordinated services to specific industry sectors often on a cross departmental basis.

Corporate and Commercial: The department offers a full range of legal skills and experience in corporate finance, management buy-outs and buy-ins, mergers and acquisitions and joint ventures. Multi-disciplinary and cross-border transactions are regularly undertaken. Advice is also given on most aspects of commercial law, including intellectual property (where there is a particular expertise in information technology, especially e-commerce and computer law) publishing, trade marks and technology transfer, distribution, agency and supply, competition law, inward investment and establishment in the UK, banking, pensions and employees' benefits schemes. The department can provide taxation support in relation to all aspects of its corporate and commercial work.

Litigation: The department handles a broad range of work, national and international, including banking, construction disputes, employment matters, insolvency work, insurance, partnership disputes, personal injury and clinical negligence claims (for which legal aid franchises are held in the firm's Godalming and Basingstoke offices), professional indemnity claims, secured lending recoveries, share sale and purchase disputes, trade arbitrations and including all aspects of commercial property and landlord and tenant matters. Agency work is also carried out. Members of the department are familiar with ADR techniques in addition to litigation and arbitration. The shipping group provides a world wide international commercial and corporate shipping and arbitration service from the firm's London and Paris offices. The group has extensive experience of major marine casualties and total losses. The professional regulation group acts for a number of professional bodies, not only investigating and presenting cases for hearing by their disciplinary committees, but also advising on rules, procedures and codes of conduct and conducting appeals and applications for judicial review.

Property: The department has wide experience in dealing with a range of property related transactions including investment sales and purchases, funding agreements, development schemes, landlord and tenant matters, portfolio management, agricultural investments, as well as general commercial property work and high value residential sales and purchases. Specialist town and country planning, environmental and construction law advice is also available.

Private Client: A wide range of services is provided, including, in particular, all aspects of personal tax planning (including offshore), wills, trusts, charities and the administration of estates. All aspects of immigration and nationality law are covered, including investors, work permits, business applications and sole representatives of overseas companies.

Family: The group deals with all areas of family law including property disputes between partners, separation, divorce, the welfare of children, child abduction and adoption. Members of the group are members of the Solicitors Family Law Association and the Family Mediators Association.

INTERNATIONAL CONNECTIONS: A full international service is provided by Penningtons in association with the member firms of MULTILAW and the European Law Group (ELG). The firm, through its merger with Walker Martineau, is a founder member of MULTILAW, a multinational association of over 50 law firms in more than 40 countries, and is also a founder member of ELG, an association of business law firms in the EU,

Managing partner:	Lesley Lintott
UK:	
Number of partners:	47
Assistant solicitors:	74
Other fee-earners:	35
International:	
Number of partners:	1
Assistant solicitors:	1

AREAS OF PRACTICE

Property	34%
Litigation (including Shipping)	31%
Corporate	19%
Private Client (including Family)	16%

CONTACTS

ADR	Henry Brown, Sue Dixon
Agricultural	Michael Fellingham
	Julian Chadwick
Banking	Richard Tyson
Clinical Negligence	David Raine
	Chris Mather
Commercial Property	Catriona Smith
	Anthony Bussy
	Tom Rossiter
	Tim Rafter
Construction	Roger Loveland
	Sue Dixon
Corporate/Commercial	Ron Allsopp
	Charles Brooks
	Robin Peile
	David Wilson
Corporate Recovery/ Insolvency	Noel McMichael
	Sue Dixon
Employment	Paul Hadow
Environmental	John Mathé
Family	Jeremy Abraham
Immigration	Henry Brown, Gülay Mehmet
Intellectual Property	Geoffrey Walkley
Litigation	Paul Hadow
	Jonathan Rouse
	Michael Felce
	Julian Calnan
Personal Injury	David Raine
	Chris Mather
Planning	Roger Bullworthy
Private Client	Lesley Lintott
	Richard Underwood
	Michael Fellingham
	Julian Chadwick
Professional Negligence	Chris Mather
	Michael Felce
Professional Regulation	Katrina Wingfield
	Geoffrey Hudson
Relocation/Housing Ass'ns	
	Andrew Templeman
	Jonathan Rouse
Residential Property	Paul Collard
	Anthony Bussy
	Tim Rafter
	Richard Hornsby
Shipping	Peter Allan
	Greg O'Neill

Norway and Switzerland. It is also a member of the Law Society Solicitors European Group. Penningtons has in-house lawyers qualified in several overseas jurisdictions. Overseas activity includes specialist knowledge of and experience in many different jurisdictions, particularly France, Hong Kong and the Far East, India, Italy, South Africa and the USA.

LANGUAGES: Chinese, French, German, Gujerati, Italian, Spanish and Turkish are spoken.

RECRUITMENT & TRAINING: For training placements and recruitment enquiries contact Lesley Lintott. Penningtons is always interested to hear from first class individuals who wish to advance their careers within an outward looking and entrepreneurial firm.

PETER CARTER-RUCK AND PARTNERS

International Press Centre, 76 Shoe Lane, London, EC4A 3JB
Tel: (020) 7353 5005 **Fax:** (020) 7353 5553 **DX:** 333 Ch.Ln.
Email: lawyers@carter-ruck.com **Website:** www.carter-ruck.com

Senior partner:	Andrew Stephenson
Number of partners:	9
Assistant solicitors:	6
Other fee-earners:	5

CONTACTS

Employment	Nigel Tait
Intellectual Property	Guy Martin
	Lee Penhaligan
	Sarah Coe
Literary Property Trusts	Lee Penhaligan
Media Litigation	Andrew Stephenson
	Alasdair Pepper
	Nigel Tait
	Charlotte Watson
	Ruth Collard
	Cameron Doley

P

THE FIRM: Peter-Carter Ruck and Partners sees itself as a young and progressive partnership with an average partner age of 37. It is committed to retaining, and indeed expanding upon, its undoubted predominance in the field of defamation, whilst at the same time building upon its name and client base to develop a higher profile and presence on the part of its intellectual property and entertainment media practice. The firm also runs a Conditional Fee Agreement ('no win no fee') scheme for actions involving defamation, intellectual property and other media related matters. This has proved to be highly successful with, to date, not a single loss in a CFA case.

PRINCIPAL AREAS OF WORK: The firm handles both contentious and non contentious media work, undertaken by two main groups, the media litigation group and the intellectual property and media group.
Media Litigation Group: The firm's media litigation group, offers both pre and post publication advice on libel, slander, contempt, breach of confidence, privacy and advertising law and regulatory and Official Secrets Act issues. The firm probably has more than twice the number of full time specialist defamation practitioners of any other firm. Moreover, year in and year out, the firm has more leading individuals in the field identified by *Chambers* than any of its competitors. The group's partners are frequent contributors both to the national press and to specialist and legal publications and are asked regularly to present seminars and lectures to the legal profession and to the publishing and media industries.
Intellectual Property and Media Group: The firm has always had a strong presence in the fields of intellectual property and publishing, acting as it does for a wide range of broadcasters, publishers and literary trusts. The intellectual property and media group advises both in relation to contentious matters, including infringement of copyright, passing off and trade mark disputes, and non contentious matters, including licensing, commercial and Internet content agreements.The group advises on the development of Internet projects and specialises in pre-on line and pre-publication advice. The group also offers trade mark registration and portfolio management services and advises high profile individuals in the sports and media areas. Its workload and client base have continued to grow over the past 12 months.

INTERNATIONAL CONNECTIONS: The firm has appointed agents in over 50 countries which enables it, for example, to provide definitive copyright advice in cases involving international publications.

CLIENTELE: The firm's clients are drawn equally from the media and from those seeking advice on dealing with the media. It has an enviable client base in the media and publishing industries, with clients including United Broadcasting and Entertainment (the owner of Meridian and Anglia television companies), Penguin Books, Express Newspapers and the National Magazine Company (the publisher of Cosmopolitan, Good Housekeeping, Esquire, Company, Harpers and Queen etc). Claimant clients include high profile individuals from the worlds of business and politics, well known celebrities, leading sportsmen and women and companies of every size up to multinational corporations.

PETER EDWARDS & CO

Ventura, 8 Market Street, Hoylake, Hoylake, Wirral, CH47 2AE **Tel:** (0151) 632 6699 **Fax:** (0151) 632 0090 **Email:** Peter@imhl.com **Website:** www.Peteredwardslaw.com **Ptnrs:** 2 **Asst solrs:** 1 **Other fee-earners:** 5

PETERKINS

100 Union Street, Aberdeen, AB10 1QR **Tel:** (01224) 428000 **Fax:** (01224) 626123 **DX:** AB3 **Email:** nch@peterkins.com **Website:** www.peterkins.com **Ptnrs:** 18 **Asst solrs:** 8 **Other fee-earners:** 14 **Contact:** Neil Hunter • Corporate/commercial, especially oil and gas, sea fishing industry and commercial property, and general practice with Glasgow office and associated European offices, including Brussels.

AREAS OF PRACTICE

Residential Property	35%
Corporate/Commercial	21%
Litigation	16%
Private Client	16%
Commercial Property	12%

PETER MAIR & CO

10 Hamlet Green, Dallington Park, Northampton, NN5 7AR **Tel:** (01604) 755110 **Fax:** (01604) 755108 **Email:** Legal@petermair.co.uk **Website:** www.petermair.co.uk • Expertise in law relating to the transport industry including LGV and bus/coach travel. Considerable experience and expertise with health and safety/environmental work.

AREAS OF PRACTICE	
Road Transportation	45%
Transport Licensing	25%
Health and Safety Law	20%
Road Traffic Law	10%

PETER MAUGHAN & CO

15A Walker Terrace, Gateshead, NE8 1EB **Tel:** (0191) 477 9779 **Fax:** (0191) 477 7997 **DX:** 60323 Gateshead
Email: mailroom@gatlaw.demon.co.uk **Ptnrs:** 2 **Other fee-earners:** 2

PETER RICKSON AND PARTNERS

6 Winckley Square, Preston, PR1 3JJ
Tel: (01772) 556677 **Fax:** (01772) 562030 **DX:** 714570 Preston 14
Email: info@ricksons.co.uk

The Stock Exchange Building, 4 Norfolk Street, Manchester, M2 1DW
Tel: (0161) 833 3355 **Fax:** (0161) 833 1042 **DX:** 14318 Manchester 1
Email: mcr@ricksons.co.uk

Union Chambers, 63 Temple Row, Birmingham, B2 5LS
Tel: (0121) 631 3304 **Fax:** (0121) 643 0787 **DX:** 13026 Birmingham 1
Email: birm@ricksons.co.uk

43 Park Place, Leeds, LS1 2RY
Tel: (0113) 2431576 **Fax:** 0113 2431888 **DX:** 12054 Leeds 1
Email: leeds@ricksons.co.uk

Managing partner:	Fraser Haddleton
Senior partner:	Peter Rickson
Number of Partners:	21
Assistant Solicitors:	13
Consultants:	2
Other fee-earners:	28

AREAS OF PRACTICE	
Insurance Litigation	69%
Commercial Property & Private Client	11%
Commercial Litigation	10%
Corporate Services	10%

CONTACTS	
Commercial Litigation	Steve Hackett (Preston)
	Paul Williams
	Peter Moore (Manchester)
	Jean Hindmoor (Birmingham)
	Richard Parker (Leeds)
Commercial Property and Private Client	Terry McMahon (Preston)
Corporate Services	Paul Lockett (Manchester)

THE FIRM: The practice is one of the best-known in the North of England and West Midlands dealing with insurance litigation. There are also substantial commercial property, private client, commercial litigation and corporate services departments.

PRINCIPAL AREAS OF WORK:

Insurance Litigation: The firm acts for most of the major insurance companies and is one of the North's leading specialist practices. The insurance litigation department handles employers' liability, public and product liability and road traffic claims. There is a specialist team dealing with disease claims. In addition, the department advises extensively on policy interpretation.

Commercial Property & Private Client: Freehold acquisitions and disposals, leases of commercial, industrial and retail sites. For house builders, a comprehensive service in relation to land acquisitions and development and residential plot sales. The private client services include wills, probate and domestic conveyancing.

Commercial Litigation: All types of business and contractual disputes, partnership litigation, intellectual property, construction and arbitration, landlord and tenant actions and debt collection.

Corporate Services: Acquisitions, disposals, mergers, joint ventures, capital restructuring, flotations, commercial agreements, employment law and intellectual property and a full company secretarial service including in-house incorporation.

PETERS & PETERS

2 Harewood Place, Hanover Square, London, W1R 9HB
Tel: (020) 7629 7991 **Fax:** (020) 7499 6792 **DX:** 44625 Mayfair
Email: law@petersandpeters.co.uk **Website:** www.petersandpeters.co.uk

Managing partner:	Julia Balfour-Lynn
Senior partner:	Monty Raphael

AREAS OF PRACTICE	
Financial Regulation/Business Crime	65%
Commercial Litigation	30%
Commercial Conveyancing	5%

THE FIRM: This specialist practice is best known as a leading firm in the areas of financial regulation, business crime and commercial litigation. It additionally offers high quality services in employment law and in providing anti-money laundering and prevention of corruption advice. Peters & Peters concentrates not only on the quality of the service it provides, but also on its technical expertise and practical know-how. It aims to be innovative and to provide solutions to problems that cut across the traditional boundaries of legal disciplines. The firm believes it was one of the first practices to develop such a multi-disciplinary approach; consequently both partners and staff have built up a very considerable level of expertise. Much of the practice's work is high profile and is frequently international in scope. The firm has built up close working relationships with law firms overseas. As a result it regularly receives instructions by way of referral and invitations to speak at international conferences and seminars as well as to contribute to business and legal journals throughout the world. Members of the firm have received requests to serve on government committees and to advise foreign regulators and international organisations.

PRINCIPAL AREAS OF WORK: Areas in which the firm's practice has expanded rapidly include commercial litigation and financial regulation.

Commercial Litigation: Heavy and intricate commercial litigation is now recognised as one of Peters & Peters' core strengths. Expertise covers the whole range of contentious work including civil fraud, contractual disputes, employment law and defamation, as well as personal and corporate bankruptcy and related insolvency matters. The firm has a wealth of experience in the application of emergency procedures both outside and within the jurisdiction of the UK. Because of the firm's particular mix of specialisms, it is often asked to deal with civil litigation matters where criminal proceedings are also contemplated, with all the complications of parallel litigation. Often such cases include the further complexities of private or public international law. The practice's longstanding experience in business crime is universally recognised. This has been built up over a huge variety of cases in which it has acted for large organisations in both an investigative and preventive role, as well as for many private clients. Case loads encompass all forms of corporate fraud, cross border issues including extradition and mutual assistance, as well as forensic tax and revenue work. Expertise includes VAT and customs infractions, insolvency crime, securities offences and all examples of business delinquency. Money laundering has become of universal concern and the firm is pre-eminent in giving advice, not only to financial institutions, but also to the professions.

Financial Regulation: The firm has been instructed in most of the high profile cases involving alleged financial mismanagement in the last two decades. As a result, it has built up a group of fee earners with an in-depth knowledge of the domestic and international regulation of the markets. Their work has contributed significantly to legal development in this area.

Other: The firm also provides a service to corporate and private clients in commercial conveyancing and conducts agency work in all its specialist areas.

CONTACTS	
Business Crime	Monty Raphael
	Louise Delahunty
	Keith E. Oliver
	Jo Rickards
	David Corker
	Peter Binning
	Claire Lipworth
Commercial Conveyancing	Geoffrey Herman
Commercial Litigation	Keith E. Oliver
	Kathryn Garbett
	Sarah Hannam
Customs & Excise	Monty Raphael
	Louise Delahunty
	Jo Rickards
	David Corker
Financial Regulation	Monty Raphael
	Keith E . Oliver
	Jo Rickards
	David Corke
	Peter Binning
Tax	Monty Raphael
	Louise Delahunty
	Sarah Hannam

P

PETTMAN SMITH

79 Knightsbridge, London, SW1X 7RB
Tel: (020) 7235 1288 **Fax:** (020) 7235 2683 **DX:** 38168 Knightsbridge
Email: ps@pslaw.co.uk

Managing partner:	Ann Glaves-Smith
Senior partner:	Michael Pettman
Number of partners:	8
Assistant solicitors:	2
Other fee-earners:	2

THE FIRM: A modern commercial practice, established in 1982, which has since grown considerably. The firm seeks to provide practical and commercially viable solutions to legal and business problems in a friendly, professional manner. The practice is particularly noted for its work in intellectual property.

PRINCIPAL AREAS OF WORK:

Commercial Litigation: A comprehensive service includes commercial fraud, employment disputes and property and building contract litigation.

Commercial Property: The firm handles development work from acquisition to sale, mortgage and other bank security work.

Intellectual Property: Both contentious and non-contentious work is handled. Actions include copyright and designs, patents, trademarks, passing-off and confidential information. The firm has particular experience in interlocutory proceedings. Non-contentious work includes software licensing and character merchandising.

Company/Commercial: Company acquisitions and mergers, joint ventures and shareholders' agreements. Venture capital funding and technology-related work. Company reorganisations and restructuring. Business acquisitions and disposals. Management buy-outs and investments. Financial services work including disciplinary and regulatory work. Shareholder and partnership disputes. Insolvency advice, personal and corporate. Company formation and administration. Commercial agreements in particular intellectual property licensing agreements. Software licencing and development and hardware contracts. Service and consultancy agreements. Other commercial advice.

Taxation: International tax planning is a particular strength, and immigration and nationality questions are also handled.

CLIENTELE: Clients include major public companies, small businesses and entrepreneurs. There is a substantial client base in America and the Middle East.

AREAS OF PRACTICE	
Company and Commercial	33%
Litigation	33%
Property	33%

CONTACTS	
Commercial Litigation	Jonathan Sachs
Commercial Property	Ann Glaves-Smith
	Marie-Garrard Newton
Company and Commercial	Michael Pettman
Intellectual Property	Peter Jennings

PHILIP CONN & CO

Parsonage Court, 1 North Parade, Parsonage Gardens, Manchester, M3 2HN
Tel: (0161) 833 9494 **Fax:** (0161) 834 4540
Email: philipconnco@btinternet.com **Website:** www.philip-conn.co.uk

Managing partner:	A.I. Morris
Number of partners:	4
Assistant solicitors:	3
Other fee-earners:	4

THE FIRM: Philip Conn & Co was founded in 1975 solely as a commercial practice. It has now established a reputation for having one of the strongest intellectual law practices outside of London with an equal emphasis on contentious and non-contentious work. A multi-disciplinary approach is taken, and scientists are

Continued overleaf

recruited to meet the needs of intellectual property. Clients ranges from multi-national public companies to medium-sized and owner- managed companies. In the last year the volume of corporate work has continued to grow with a variety of multi-million pound transactions for both publicly quoted and private companies taking place. A number had an intellectual property element. A large number of licensing deals were concluded including in the biotechnology sector. Commercial property work has expanded with the appointment of Nicky Greene who becomes a partner.

INTERNATIONAL CONNECTIONS: The firm has strong links with lawyers, patent attorneys and firms in the EU, USA and Australasia in particular, and extensive experience in the conduct of both litigation and intellectual property licensing overseas.

AREAS OF PRACTICE

Corporate/Commercial	35%
Intellectual Property (contentious and non-contentious)	35%
Commercial Conveyancing	15%
Commercial Litigation	15%

CONTACTS

Conveyancing	N. Greene
Corporate	T.J. Osborn
Intellectual Property	A.I. Morris
IP Litigation & Employment	A.P. Gibson

PICKWORTHS

55 Marlowes, Hemel Hempstead, HP1 1LE **Tel:** (01442) 261731 **Fax:** (01442) 230356 **DX:** 8809 Hemel Hempstead **Ptnrs:** 5 **Asst solrs:** 6 **Other fee-earners:** 4

PICTONS

Keystone, 60 London Rd, St. Albans, AL1 1NG
Tel: (01727) 798000 **Fax:** (01727) 798002 **DX:** 122730 St. Albans 10
Email: comm@pictons.co.uk **Website:** www.pictons.co.uk

30-32 Bromham Road, Bedford, MK40 2QD
Tel: (01234) 273273 **Fax:** (01234) 353110 **DX:** 5614

1 The Waterhouse, Waterhouse Street, Hemel Hempstead, HP1 1ES
Tel: (01442) 242441/250111 **Fax:** (01442) 248569 **DX:** 8800

Carlton Court, 66 Alma Street, Luton, LU1 2PL
Tel: (01582) 410114 **Fax:** (01582) 402736 **DX:** 130465 Luton 10

Ashton House, 409 Silbury Boulevard, Central Milton Keynes, MK9 2LJ
Tel: (01908) 663511 **Fax:** (01908) 661800 **DX:** 31411

13 Town Square, Stevenage, SG1 1BP
Tel: (01438) 342400 **Fax:** (01438) 359255 **DX:** 6006

24 The Avenue, Watford, WD1 3NS
Tel: (01923) 237631 **Fax:** (01923) 226135 **DX:** 4505

Managing partner:	Gerard Sampson
Chairman:	Christopher Brown
Number of partners:	34
Assistant solicitors:	35
Other fee-earners:	50

AREAS OF PRACTICE

Commercial	25%
Crime	22%
Litigation/PI	18%
Family	17%
Domestic Conveyancing	15%
Probate/Trusts and Wills	3%

CONTACTS

Civil Litigation/PI/ Medical Negligence	Sue Jarvis (Milton Keynes)
Commercial Dispute Resolution	Sarah Staines (St Albans)
Corporate Finance	Roger Talbot (St Albans)
Crime	David Healey (Luton)
Domestic Conveyancing	Chris Tate (Luton)
Employment	David Fagan (St Albans)
Family	Drenne Dunphy (Hemel Hempstead)
Insolvency	Antony Sampson (St Albans)
Probate, Trusts and Wills	Elizabeth Harrold (Hemel Hempstead)
Sport	Peter Baines (St Albans)

THE FIRM: Offering a comprehensive range of legal services to both commercial and private clients, Pictons Solicitors, established in 1967, remains a dominant legal force across Herts, Beds, and Bucks. The Firm provides practical solutions, actionable advice and support in a friendly, helpful and accessible environment. Within each department of the firm there are specific areas of specialisation, to provide a significant depth of expertise and client service.

PRINCIPAL AREAS OF WORK:

COMMERCIAL DEPARTMENT:

Corporate Finance: The team provides expertise and advice on any corporate transaction, with particular emphasis in the areas of: mergers and acquisitions, buy ins and buy outs, share and asset sales/purchases and venture capital.

Employment: Advising the employer or the employee on all aspects of employment law including sex discrimination, race relation and disability discrimination.

Commercial Property: Dealing with everything from major property development on behalf of large PLC's to individual business leases. Within this broad portfolio the team also address such associated issues as planning, housing associations, environmental matters, and security work for lending institutions.

Insolvency: The team primarily advises and acts for IPs although some work is carried out for companies and privately owned business.

Dispute Resolution: With two qualified mediators and an arbitrator in their number, the team is well equipped to provide practical solutions to any dispute arising from business transactions including those in the areas of Information technology and e-commerce.

Intellectual Property: Handling both contentious and non-contentious matters; with its main body of work stemming from both the music and information technology industry.

OTHER DEPARTMENT:

Crime: One of the leading criminal departments in the area, undertaking a wide spectrum of criminal matters including those which are more serious and complex such as, drug offences, rape and murder and white collar fraud. All police stations within the firms branch network are covered on a 24 hours a day basis throughout the year.

Domestic Conveyancing: The team's increasing focus is on bulk conveyancing and relocation. To private client the team offers a service, which aims to takes the stress and strain out of completing a conveyance, by providing an efficient IT lead service.
Personal Injury and Clinical Negligence: A substantial area of the firm's practice, for which it has an excellent reputation especially in cases involving head injuries and multi party actions. The firm was one of the first in the country to gain the Legal Aid Franchise for clinical negligence in all of its branches.
Probate, Trust and Taxes Wills: The team offers expert guidance in will drafting, an imaginative approach to tax planning tailored to meet individual needs and the sympathetic approach to the administration of estates.
Family: Specialisms include in the areas of divorce, pension, ancillary relief and children law. Pictons Children law team consists of five Children's Panel members who deal with a wide spectrum of children law matters including abuse and abduction.

PINSENT CURTIS

3 Colmore Circus, Birmingham, B4 6BH
Tel: (0121) 200 1050 **Fax:** (0121) 626 1040 **DX:** 703167 Birmingham 12
Email: john.pratt@pinsents.com **Website:** www.pinsents.com

1 Park Row, Leeds, LS1 5AB
Tel: (0113) 244 5000 **Fax:** (0113) 244 8000 **DX:** 26440 Leeds 28
Email: nigel.kissack@pinsents.com

Dashwood House, 69 Old Broad Street, London, EC2M 1NR
Tel: (020) 7418 7000 **Fax:** (020) 7418 7050 **DX:** 119516 Finsbury Square
Email: alan.greenough@pinsents.com

Senior partner:	Julian Tonks
Number of partners:	129
Assistant solicitors:	199
Other fee-earners:	105

AREAS OF PRACTICE

Litigation & Professional Indemnity	38%
Corporate/Commercial	34%
Property	19%
Tax	9%

CONTACTS

Commercial	Stephen Chandler
Corporate	Alan Greenough
Employment	John McMullen
Litigation	Nigel Kissack
Property	Nigel McClea
Tax	David Pett

THE FIRM: Leading UK law firm, large publicly-listed client base. Consistently ranked in the Hemscott Guide top group of legal advisers to listed companies, in addition to high-ranking as adviser to techMARK and AIM listed companies. Growing international focus and sole UK membership of US/European network of legal firms. Pinsent Curtis adopts a highly focused approach to its business concentrating on a number of key market sectors which reflect its depth of experience and expertise in those fields. Its strong commitment to client service has set it apart. It was first to appoint lawyers as dedicated client service partners working full time on ensuring the consistent delivery of quality services. It puts the client firmly at the heart of its business.

PRINCIPAL AREAS OF WORK: Six main practice areas: commerce, trade & technology; corporate; employment; litigation; property; and tax & pensions. A number of specialist sector groups including technology, financial institutions, insurance, private equity, manufacturing, automotive, retail & leisure and PFI /major projects.
Corporate: Large national corporate finance department, regularly ranked among leading advisers in independent surveys. Three specialist operating groups – stock exchange; private equity and banking and finance.
Commerce, Trade & Technology: Multi-disciplinary specialist department advising on commercial contracts, complex IP and IT issues, e-commerce, franchising, EU & UK competition notably EC Merger Regulation notification.
Employment: Among the largest of UK employment practices. Independently recognised as the leading UK adviser on TUPE and discrimination law. At the forefront of interpreting UK and EU employment legislation. Runs bespoke training for blue chip clients.
Litigation: With 120 lawyers, this is one of the largest national litigation teams with considerable specialist City expertise and international experience. Specialises in commercial contract disputes, corporate recovery, libel and defamation, financial services issues, product liability disputes and shareholder and director disputes. A pioneer in Alternative Dispute Resolution with several trained mediators. Sizeable professional indemnity and insurance/reinsurance practice. Has taken a lead on pensions misselling and professional negligence in financial services selling.
Property: 7th largest commercial property department of any UK firm advising clients with property interests throughout the UK. Specialises in portfolio management, property development and investment, planning and environment, secured lending, mines and minerals, property litigation and construction.
Tax & Pensions: Dedicated tax team ranking in size and quality alongside leading City practices with a number of nationally-recognised experts in corporate tax and employee share schemes. UK and international clients advised on all areas of corporate tax, restructuring, offshore trusts, VAT, personal tax planning and charities. Leading edge pensions practice advising schemes, trustees and companies.

INTERNATIONAL CONNECTIONS: Brussels presence.

LANGUAGES: Chinese (Cantonese), Dutch, French, German, Greek, Hebrew, Hindi, Italian, Japanese, Shona, Spanish, Swedish, Ukrainian, Urdu, Welsh.

RECRUITMENT & TRAINING: Extensive in-house national training scheme for lawyers and managers at all levels interwoven with a programme of targeted external seminars and residential courses.

PIPER SMITH & BASHAM

31 Warwick Square, London, SW1V 2AF
Tel: (020) 7828 8685 **Fax:** (020) 7630 6976 **DX:** 110 Ch.Ln.
Email: postmaster@pipersmith.co.uk **Website:** www.pipersmith.co.uk

Managing partner:	Mark D. Spash
Senior partner:	R. Berns
Number of partners:	6
Assistant solicitors:	4
Other fee-earners:	3

CONTACTS

Commercial and Other Real Property .... Richard Berns
Private Client .... Mark Spash
Tour Operating and Travel .... Ian Skuse

THE FIRM: A long established firm based in Westminster since 1875. The firm still retains its Pimlico roots, but has developed into a number of areas of property, commercial, travel and tour operating work, charities, immigration and white collar crime.

PRINCIPAL AREAS OF WORK:
Tour Operating and Travel: The firm acts for many companies in this industry both large and small.
Commercial and Other Real Property: Development and investment property, landlord and tenant, housing association and local authority work together with residential conveyancing.

Other Areas: Private client, corporate,and general litigation, company, immigration and charity law.

P

PITMANS

47 Castle Street, Reading, RG1 7SR
Tel: (0118) 958 0224 **Fax:** (0118) 958 5097 **DX:** 40102 Reading (Castle Street)
Email: cavery@pitmans.com **Website:** www.pitmans.com

Managing partner:	Christopher Avery
Senior partner:	Tony Jones
Number of partners:	14
Assistant solicitors:	25
Other fee-earners:	42

AREAS OF PRACTICE

Property (Commercial)	24%
Company/Commercial	23%
Commercial Litigation	21%
Residential Development	12%
Employment	6%
Planning & Environmental	6%
Intellectual Property	4%
Corporate Recovery	3%
Private Client	1%

CONTACTS

Commercial Property .... Christopher Avery
Company Commercial .... John Hutchinson
Corporate Recovery .... David Archer
Employment .... Mark Symons
Environmental .... Richard Valentine
Intellectual Property .... Philip Weaver
Litigation .... Sue O'Brien
Planning .... Richard Valentine
Private Client .... Tony Jones

THE FIRM: Pitmans is one of Thames Valley's leading commercial practices, offering a comprehensive legal service to local, national and international businesses. In recent years the partnership has grown and with it, the breadth of skills and specialisations offered. Pitmans' membership of InterAct Europe 1993 EEIG has proved to be invaluable to the success and growth of the practice.

PRINCIPAL AREAS OF WORK:
Company/Commercial: The company/commercial department is one of the largest in the South East, outside London. It handles a wide variety of work including company formations, mergers and acquisitions, management buy-outs, institutional investment agreements, trading agreements, employment issues, share option schemes and financial services. It advises overseas clients on questions of location and handles work overseas for British clients. The department also offers specialist reports tailored to the needs of individual clients on developing European law affecting them, and is able to review legal frameworks in other countries.
Corporate Security and Insolvency: A specialist department is dedicated to corporate security and insolvency work.
Intellectual Property: The intellectual property department has gone from strength to strength and acts for a large number of the international computer and software companies both in the Thames Valley and overseas. The department offers a wide range of services both of a contentious and non-contentious nature in the patent, copyright, trademark, know-how and entertainment sectors.
Commercial Property: A significant percentage of Pitmans' work is in the commercial property sector. The firm is renowned for its work in land acquisitions, joint venture arrangements and particularly for its expertise in planning and public enquiries. The department's clients include some of the largest housebuilders in the country, a number of substantial plcs, and local authorities. It also has a department specialising in the sale of new homes for residential developers.
Environmental Law: The environmental law department integrates well with the existing commercial property, general commercial and planning work. This department offers a wide range of services within this complex area of law with particular emphasis on the new laws developing in the European Union.
Litigation: The litigation department has wide experience in all areas of commercial litigation, especially in the hi-technology, construction and finance industries and in international trade. It regularly works with other departments to provide a team approach for larger litigation matters. A debt collection service is available to clients. Criminal and matrimonial litigation is not undertaken.
Planning: Nearly all the commercial property partners have specialist knowledge of planning law, and a broad range of expertise covers: development strategy, agreements with highway and planning authorities, major planning appeals and judicial reviews of planning decisions.

Other Areas: Pitmans undertakes a substantial amount of other non-contentious business, such as residential conveyancing, trust and probate work, wills, family settlements and personal tax planning.

CLIENTELE: Clients include both public and private companies, banks and local authorities throughout the UK, as well as an increasing number of organisations in Europe and the US.

INTERNATIONAL CONNECTIONS: Pitmans is a founder member of an EEIG, with associated law firms in Amsterdam, Berlin, Copenhagen, Hamburg, Leipzig, Lisbon, London, Madrid, Malmo, Moscow, Munich, New York, Oslo and Paris.

POOLE & CO

Plaza 1, Telford Plaza, Ironmasters Way, Telford, TF3 4NT
Tel: (01952) 236000 **Fax:** (01952) 236001 **DX:** 720920 Telford 9
Email: enquiries@poole-solicitors.com **Website:** www.poole-solicitors.com

Managing and senior partner:	Colin Poole
Number of partners:	1
Assistant solicitors:	13
Other fee-earners:	48

THE FIRM: A young, dynamic and rapidly expanding firm. Established in 1996, the firm now has a total staff compliment of around 100. Originally formed to specialise in claimant personal injury work, the firm has now developed the following successful practice areas: domestic and commercial conveyancing (Northampton); company/commercial (Telford); commercial litigation (Telford); employment (Northampton); wills & probate/private client (Northampton).

RECRUITMENT & TRAINING: The key to the firm's rapid expansion has been the recruitment of high calibre lawyers at all levels of experience. For details of current vacancies, please contact Vincenza Perkins at the Northampton office.

P

POPPLESTON ALLEN

37 Stoney Street, The Lace Market, Nottingham, NG1 1LS
Tel: (0115) 953 8500 **Fax:** (0115) 953 8501 **DX:** 10100 Nottingham
Email: mail@popall.co.uk **Website:** www.popall.co.uk

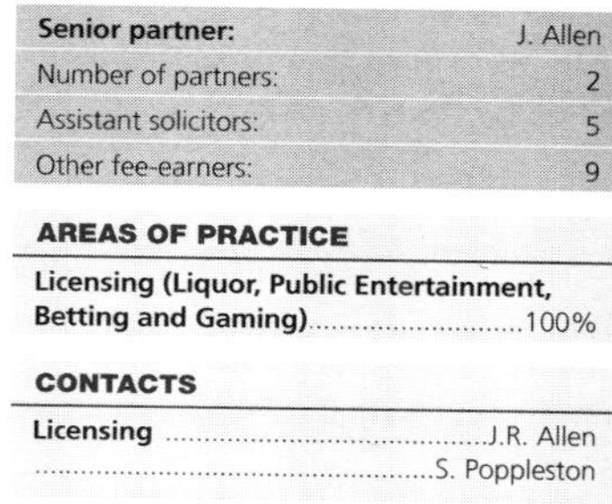

Senior partner:	J. Allen
Number of partners:	2
Assistant solicitors:	5
Other fee-earners:	9

AREAS OF PRACTICE

Licensing (Liquor, Public Entertainment, Betting and Gaming)..........100%

CONTACTS

Licensing ..........J.R. Allen
..........S. Poppleston

THE FIRM: Winners of the Best Small Law Firm of the year 1999 – The Lawyer Annual Awards – for its focus on client care, staff training and information technology. Established in May 1994 by two nationally-renowned solicitors, Jeremy Allen and Susanna Poppleston. Poppleston Allen is a niche practice specialising exclusively in licensing matters.

PRINCIPAL AREAS OF WORK:

Licensing: Poppleston Allen deals with liquor, public entertainment, and betting and gaming licensing. First class legal expertise is provided from the conception stages of a project through acquisition, regular renewal, upgrading and transfer of licences, to dealing with particular problems at licensed premises. In addition, the firm has appointed a Head of Planning, Jonathan Phillips, to ensure a co-ordinated approach to planning and licensing.

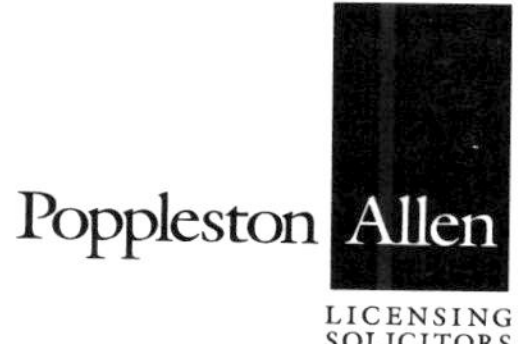

CLIENTELE: The firm's client base is wide and not restricted to its immediate area, and its consequent experience of the policies and quirks of licensing authorities covers every county in England and Wales. It offers unrivalled expertise in the niche area of discotheques and clubs, as well as dealing with pubs, bars and off-licences.Poppleston Allen currently acts for Allied Leisure, Bass Leisure Entertainment, Belgo, Chorion plc, Luminar Leisure, Pizza Express, Scottish & Newcastle, Wolverhampton & Dudley Breweries and XS Leisure. Poppleston Allen acts for more student unions than any other solicitor and also has developed particular expertise in dealing with developers. It is also able to market the specialist practice to other law firms who themselves lack a dedicated licensing department.

PORTER DODSON

Central House, Church Street, Yeovil, BA20 1HH **Tel:** (01935) 424581 **Fax:** (01935) 706063 **DX:** 100501 Yeovil
Email: porterdodson@porterdodson.co.uk **Ptnrs:** 25 **Asst solrs:** 13 **Other staff:** 160 **Other fee-earners:** 72

PORTRAIT SOLICITORS IN ASSOCIATION WITH DENTON WILDE SAPTE

1 Chancery Lane, London, WC2A 1LF **Tel:** (020) 7320 3888 **Fax:** (020) 7430 1242 **DX:** 69
Email: dbf@dentonwildesapte.com **Ptnrs:** 2 **Asst solrs:** 3 **Associates:** 1 **Other fee-earners:** 1
Contact: Miss Judith Portrait or Mr Dominic Flynn • Specialist private client and charity practice.

POTHECARY & BARRATT

Talbot Hse, Talbot Court, Gracechurch St, London, EC3V 0BS **Tel:** (020) 7623 7520 **Fax:** (020) 7623 9815 **DX:** 590 City
Email: advice@pothecary.co.uk **Ptnrs:** 7 **Asst solrs:** 5 **Other fee-earners:** 3

POWELL & CO

77 Woolwich New Road, Woolwich, London, SE18 6ED **Tel:** (020) 8854 9131 **Fax:** (020) 8855 4174 **Ptnrs:** 2 **Asst solrs:** 1 **Other fee-earners:** 5

POWELL SPENCER & PARTNERS

290 Kilburn High Rd, London, NW6 2DD
Tel: (020) 7624 8888 **Fax:** (020) 7328 1221 **DX:** 123862 Kilburn 2

Managing partner:	G. Powell
Senior partner:	G. Powell
Number of partners:	7
Assistant solicitors:	14
Other fee-earners:	15

AREAS OF PRACTICE

Criminal Defence	60%
Civil Family	18%
Personal Injury	18%
Welfare Benefits	4%

THE FIRM: Powell Spencer & Partners is one of London's foremost legal aid practices, with a strong reputation for its work in the areas of criminal, family, matrimonial, personal injury, clinical negligence, political asylum and human rights litigation. The firm offers a community-based service and has adapted its offices to meet the requirements of clients with disabilities and undertakes home visits.

PRINCIPAL AREAS OF WORK:
Litigation: A specialist range of litigation is undertaken, namely criminal defence, personal injury and medical negligence, child care, family and matrimonial work; welfare benefits advice. Contact: Greg Powell for criminal; Mike Tait for childcare; Toby Hales for matrimonial and family; John Gillman for personal injury and clinical negligence; Sue Davies for welfare benefits advice.

PRAXIS PARTNERS

Manchester, **Tel:** (0161) 976 4827 **Fax:** (0161) 976 4827

PRESTON GOLDBURN

The Old Brewery Yard, High Street, Falmouth, TR11 2BY **Tel:** (01326) 318900 **Fax:** (01326) 311275 **DX:** 81169
Email: mail@prestongoldburn.co.uk **Website:** prestongoldburn.co.uk **Ptnrs:** 3 **Asst solrs:** 1 **Other fee-earners:** 1

PRETTYS

Elm House, 25 Elm Street, Ipswich, IP1 2AD
Tel: (01473) 232121 **Fax:** (01473) 230002 **DX:** 3218
Email: mail@prettys.co.uk **Website:** www.prettys.co.uk

Managing partner:	Jonathan Gorst
Senior partner:	Clive Brynley-Jones
Number of partners:	16
Assistant solicitors:	20
Other fee-earners:	29

CONTACTS

Agriculture	Toby Pound
Commercial Litigation	Peter Blake
Commercial Property	David Clark
Company/Commercial	Ian Waine
Employment	Richard Stace
Insurance	Clive Brynley-Jones
Personal Law	Carol Lockett
Shipping	Paul Dickie
Transport	Roland Sharp

THE FIRM: Prettys is one of the largest practices in East Anglia, with an established private client base and a comprehensive commercial law service. The majority of its commercial clients are small to medium sized companies key to the regional economy. The firm's insurance clients are large composite insurers for whom it operates internationally.

PRINCIPAL AREAS OF WORK: Company, commercial property, litigation, alternative dispute resolution, construction, employment, insolvency, credit management, intellectual property, health and safety, estates, financial services, family, French property, personal injury, clinical negligence, transport, shipping, agriculture and insurance. Further information at the firm's web site: www.prettys.co.uk.

RECRUITMENT & TRAINING: Four to five high calibre graduates gain training contracts each year. Brochure available.

PRINCE EVANS

77 Uxbridge Rd, Ealing, London, W5 5ST
Tel: (020) 8567 3477 **Fax:** (020) 8840 7757 **DX:** 5100 Ealing
Email: rjennings@prince-evans.co.uk

Managing partner:	Trevor Morley
Senior partner:	Louis Robert
Number of partners:	7
Assistant solicitors:	24
Other fee-earners:	13

AREAS OF PRACTICE

Housing and Public Sector including Banking & Finance	50%
Litigation	25%
Personal Injury	10%
Private Client including Company/Commercial	10%
Crime including Childcare	5%

CONTACTS

Banking and Finance	Trevor Morley
Company/Commercial	Tom Lemon
Crime/Childcare	Philip Eldin-Taylor
Housing & Public Sector	Louis Robert
Litigation	Robert Jennings
Personal injury	Bryan Neill
Private Client	Tom Lemon

THE FIRM: Prince Evans is a broad-based West London firm which has an enviable reputation in housing and public sector work, but also has built strong specialisms in banking and finance, litigation, company/commercial, personal injury and private client work. Prince Evans was founded in 1978 from a merger of three established firms. The firm has one of the largest dedicated housing and public sector departments in the UK, acting for over 100 registered social landlords and numerous local authorities. Prince Evans prides itself on its innovative and energetic approach to work with the highest commitment to client care. The partners and staff of the firm hold regular seminars for clients and have forged a significant client base of public and private limited companies together with residential/commercial landlords.

PRINCIPAL AREAS OF WORK:
Housing and Public Sector: This is the largest area of the firm's practice, for which it has developed a reputation for innovation. It involves: constitutional development of registered social landlords; acquisition and development of land for individuals/consortium registered social landlords; stock transfers of rundown estates using ERCF funding; HAT Succession projects; Pathfinder PFI projects with Social Services Authorities; Health Authority re-provision schemes involving PFI; residential care home transfers with VAT and capital finance efficiency; regeneration and on-estate planning gain schemes; Foyer schemes; mixed tenure, multi-tenure, and

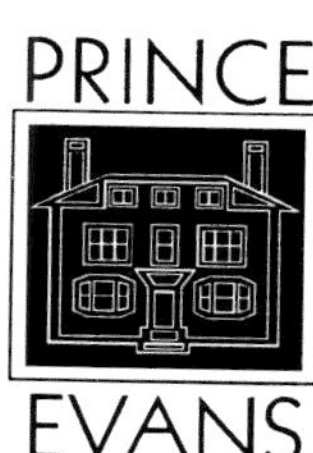

flexible tenure projects; joint venture company/off-balance sheet transactions using special purpose vehicles. The department is at the forefront of next generation PFI and quasi-PFI schemes involving housing revenue account assets and multi-commissioner healthcare schemes, and has the largest low-cost home ownership unit in the UK, responsible for land acquisition, development and regeneration for developer and registered social landlord partnerships as well as more traditional mainstream development and refurbishment on behalf of registered social landlords, together with volume street property acquisition.

Banking and Finance: This department continues to be an expanding area of the firm, acting for both lenders and borrowers of housing and public sector finance. It advises on a range of transactions from bilateral and syndicated loans to group borrowing arrangements and capital market issues, and undertakes large scale security based transactions and related work. The firm advises clients on all aspects of banking law, including treasury management and related issues.

Litigation: The firm has a strong reputation for the conduct of all types of commercial disputes before the Courts and/or in arbitration. The department has developed one of the largest dedicated landlord and tenant functions in London, providing a variety of housing management advice. Recognition has been received for its growth in expertise in both contentious and non-contentious construction work together with employment advice, including the transfer of undertakings and matters before the Employment Tribunal.

Company/Commercial: This department has considerable expertise in company/commercial transactions, including company formations, acquisitions, mergers and takeovers together with partnership matters; drafting service and commercial agreements; lettings and disposals both for occupation and, in particular, for investment companies.

Personal Injury and Medical Negligence: The firm handles all aspects of personal injury and medical negligence. In particular, it specialises in severe spinal injury (tetraplegia and paraplegia) and head injury claims, and has a national reputation as a pioneer in cases involving major catastrophic injury/disability, having obtained record UK damages on several occasions.

Private Client: A wide range of private client work is also undertaken, including planning, residential/commercial conveyancing, UK tax and financial/estate planning, trusts, wills and probate, and matrimonial/family law.

Crime/Childcare: The department has considerable experience in the conduct of all criminal matters and has a strong reputation in childcare.

PRITCHARD ENGLEFIELD

14 New St, London, EC2M 4HE
Tel: (020) 7972 9720 **Fax:** (020) 7972 9722 **DX:** 88 London
Email: po@pritchardenglefield.co.uk **Website:** www.pritchardenglefield.co.uk

Managing partner:	Stuart McInnes
Senior partner:	Michael Cohn
Number of partners:	26
Assistant solicitors:	14
Other fee-earners:	20

CONTACTS

Banking	Anthony Harris
Clinical Negligence	Jane Lynch
	Brenda Gilligan
Company/ Commercial	David Glass
Employment	Belinda Avery
Family	Marian Joseph
Litigation	Michael Cohn
Personal Injury	Ros Ashby
Private Client	David King-Farlow
Property	David Levene

PRITCHARD ENGLEFIELD
SOLICITORS

THE FIRM: Pritchard Englefield, which can trace its origins to 1848, is a well-known City of London law firm practising primarily in general commercial law. The firm is committed to working in and with Europe and is one of the leading law firms in the areas of Anglo-German and Anglo-French trade. Approximately half the firm's fee earners are fluent in a second European language, and the practice was given the Silver award for Best European Law Firm in The Lawyer HIFAL Awards.Particular emphasis is placed on mergers and acquisitions, property, corporate and tax advice including offshore structures and trusts, commercial and civil litigation, banking law, employment law and all aspects of commercial law.The firm has a broad client base including substantial foreign and UK-based corporations, investors, banks and private individuals.

PRINCIPAL AREAS OF WORK: Company/commercial, banking, litigation, property, clinical negligence, personal injury, employment, private client, family.

INTERNATIONAL CONNECTIONS: The firm has other offices in Frankfurt and Hong Kong and is a member of Pannone Law Group EEIG and International Lawyers' Group.

LANGUAGES: French, German, Spanish.

RECRUITMENT & TRAINING: Accepting only trainees fluent in German or French.

PRYCE COLLARD CHAMBERLAIN

6 East Saint Helen Street, Abingdon, OX14 5EW **Tel:** (01235) 523411 **Fax:** (01235) 533283
DX: 35853 Abingdon **Email:** pryce.ab@virgin.net **Ptnrs:** 3 **Asst solrs:** 4 **Other fee-earners:** 1
Contact: Mr. S.P.B. Capel • Established 1820s. General practice with particular experience in agriculture, company, property and personal injury work. Also at 1 Church Street, Wantage, Oxon.

AREAS OF PRACTICE

Probate/Wills/Trusts	24%
Agriculture	22%
Personal Injury	14%

PUBLIC INTEREST LAWYERS

Centre Court, 50-54 St Paul's Square, Birmingham, B3 1QS **Tel:** (0121) 702 2110 **Fax:** (0121) 702 2206
Email: phil_shiner@publicinterestlawyers.co.uk

PULLIG & CO

Bridewell House, 9 Bridewell Place, London, EC4V 6AZ **Tel:** (020) 7353 0505 **Fax:** (020) 7936 2548 **DX:** 123 Chancery Lane **Ptnrs:** 4 **Asst solrs:** 6 **Other fee-earners:** 9 **Contact:** John Pullig • Specialist areas include immigration, liquor and entertainment licensing, insolvency and debt recovery. All aspects of civil litigation, property and private client work handled.

PURCELL PARKER

204-206 Corporation Street, Birmingham, B4 6QB **Tel:** (0121) 236 9781 **Fax:** (0121) 236 8218

QUINN MARTIN & LANGAN

87 Carlton Place, Glasgow, G5 9TD **Tel:** (0141) 429 4354 **Fax:** (0141) 429 6826

RD BLACK & CO.

31 Old Jewry, London, EC2R 8DQ **Tel:** (020) 7600 8282 **Fax:** (020) 7600 8228 **Ptnrs:** 1 **Asst solrs:** 2 **Other fee-earners:** 0 • Established in 1996 by Richard Black, formerly of Middleton Potts this niche practice is renowned for its expertise in handling commodity, shipping and commercial disputes.

AREAS OF PRACTICE

Commodities	40%
Shipping	40%
Commercial Litigation	20%

R

RADCLIFFES

5 Great College Street, Westminster, London, SW1P 3SJ
Tel: (020) 7222 7040 **Fax:** (020) 7222 6208 **DX:** 113 London Chancery Lane WC2
Email: radcliffes@radcliffes.co.uk **Website:** www.radcliffes.co.uk

Managing partner:	Richard Price
Senior partner:	Robert Vallings
Number of partners:	32
Assistant solicitors:	28
Other fee-earners:	24

THE FIRM: A distinctive, highly accomplished law firm, Radcliffes combines traditional values like integrity and prompt response with a client-focussed approach to everything it does. From its offices in the heart of Westminster, the firm handles commercial matters and private client work with equal skill, empathy and understanding of clients' individual needs.

PRINCIPAL AREAS OF WORK: The firm is organised into five departments: company commercial, litigation and dispute resolution, commercial property, tax and private client, and family law. Experts within these departments integrate their knowledge in the firm's specialist groups:
Growing Businesses: The firm has an outstanding reputation as a principal adviser to growing businesses, notably hi-tech companies. They provide advice and guidance to businesses not only on legal issues, but also on commercial issues.
Corporate: Joint ventures, limited partnerships, co-operation agreements for on-going businesses, venture capital, project finance and equity offerings, due diligence reviews, acquisitions and disposals, management buy-outs and buy-ins and listings on AIM and the Stock Exchange.
Business Issues: IP, marketing, distribution and agency agreements, standard terms, outsourcing, competition law in the UK and EU and industry specific legislation.
Employment & Human Resources: Advice on all aspects of contentious and non-contentious employment and HR matters including pensions advice.
Technology: E-commerce, internet trading, software and hardware supply and procurement, IP, data protection and licensing.
Dispute Resolution: Negotiation, arbitration, mediation and litigation of business disputes in both domestic and overseas markets including those relating to general contract and tort, shareholder and partnership disputes, contractual claims, negligence and the sale of goods and services.
Property Investment & Development: Clients are provided with proactive, commercial advice to aid their business. Acting for property investors, developers and occupiers, including institutions, livery companies and landed estates, our specialist property group handles mainstream property work in addition to advising on property dispute resolution, planning (including consultancy and advocacy) environmental law, property VAT and secured lending.
Private Client: The firm is committed to serving the needs of the private client and advises business owners, senior executives, professionals, individuals, executors and trustees on a wide range of matters. The work covers both UK and international tax considerations and includes tax and estate planning, tax compliance and investigation, uses and variation of trusts, wills, estate and trust administration, receivership, elderly care, family law and residential property.
Charity: Radcliffes is a recognised name in the field of charity law providing services to national and international charities, not-for profit organisations, schools and colleges. The firm is ranked in the top 10 of charity legal advisers according to *Top 3000 Charities Guide to UK Charities 2000* and currently acts for more than 170 charities and not-for-profit organisations, with a particular strength in advising health, mental health and welfare charities.

CONTACTS

Charities	Robert Bieber
	Guy Greenhous
Company Commercial	Roland Gillott
Corporate Finance	Rupert Lescher
Employment	Mike Thomas
European law	Rupert Lescher
Family	Roger Cobden-Ramsay
Growing Businesses	Roland Gillott
	Michael Elks
Health	Andrew Parsons
Immigration	Tim Newsome
International – Italy	Michael Nathanson
International – Other	Philip Peacock
International – South Africa	Tim Newsome
International – USA/Canada	Paul Clements
IT	Douglas Preece
Litigation & Dispute Resolution (commercial)	Michael Elks
Litigation & Dispute Resolution (property)	Robert Highmore
Property Investment & Development	Charles Farrer
	Michael Higginson
Residential Property	Karen Mayne
Tax & Private Client	Robert Vallings

Health: Radcliffes has been acting for the health sector for over 30 years, providing high quality, commercial advice and assistance to health authorities, NHS Trusts, GPs, Primary Care Groups, insurers, the Royal Colleges, nursing homes and the private sector healthcare providers. The health group has particular expertise in the field of mental health and acts for some of the largest Mental Health NHS Trusts. They are frequently called upon to advise on the operation of the Mental Health Act, the impact of government reforms and on all aspects relating to the treatment and detention of the mentally ill and people with learning disabilities.

RECRUITMENT & TRAINING: Four trainees are required each year. A recruitment brochure is available on request and application is by CV or employers application form with covering letter, to the Administration Secretary of the Recruitment Partner.

RAEBURN CHRISTIE & CO

16 Albyn Place, Aberdeen, AB9 1PS
Tel: (01224) 640101 **Fax:** (01224) 638434 **DX:** 2 Aberdeen
Email: info@raeburns.co.uk **Website:** www.raeburns.co.uk

Managing partner:	Lawrence Tough
Senior partner:	Reg Christie
Number of partners:	18
Assistant solicitors:	15
Other fee-earners:	14

AREAS OF PRACTICE

Privare Client (Including Estate Agency)	44%
Corporate & Commercial Property	34%
Litigation & Employmenty	22%

CONTACTS

Corporate	Keith Napier
EC & Competition Law	David McEwing
Employment/Commercial Litigation	Reg Christie
Estate Agency	Keith Allan
Family/Matrimonial	Verity Jenner
Housing Development	Valerie Macdougall
Licencing	Mike Taylor
Litigation, Agency debts & General	Peter Littlejohn
Private Client	Kate Crosby
Social Housing	Calum Macdonald

THE FIRM: Modern in outlook and approach the firm has expanded to service especially the businesses and individuals in the oil community. Growth has particularly focused on commercial work, quality litigation and licensing. Clients include major oil companies, developers, financial institutions, insurers and professional partnerships. The firm aims to add value from local knowledge and genuine specialisation. The firm has branches in Banchory, Ellon, Inverurie and Stonehaven.

PRINCIPAL AREAS OF WORK:

Litigation and Employment: Workload particularly includes oil-related matters, fatal accident inquiries and Health and Safety prosecutions. Personal injury cases (mainly defendant) but also plaintiffs are also undertaken. Agency litigation throughout Scotland. Frequently engaged by solicitors and other professional partnerships in respect of their own partnership matters both contentious and non contentious. A substantial volume of employment law is dealt with, including Industrial Tribunal work, preparation of contracts of employment, preparing staff handbooks and advising on employee termination and compromise agreements. A large amount of matrimonial and family law work is also carried out.

Corporate: This rapidly expanding department generally acts for small and medium sized companies. Matters handled include: management buy-outs; management buy-ins acquisitions and sales; company formations and related issues contracts; EC and competition law. Oil & gas and intellectual property expertise is also offered. Some of the firm's lawyers have previously worked in industry; helping the firm to achieve a sound understanding of its clients' businesses and requirements.

Commercial Property: The firm acts for major house developers and is also involved in social housing. The firm also has wide experience in commercial leasing, of office, retail and industrial premises, acquisitions and disposals. In several cases it has acted for oil companies moving into new premises. The firm also specialises in licensing work throughout Northern Scotland.

Private Client and Estate Agency: The firm also offers a full private client service, including estate agency conveyancing, including relocation conveyancing, wills and trusts and and financial services.

RAKISONS

Clements House, 14/18 Gresham Street, London, EC2V 7JE
Tel: (020) 7367 8000 **Fax:** (020) 7367 8001 **DX:** 206 London
Email: rakisons@rakisons.co.uk **Website:** www.rakisons.co.uk

Senior partner:	Tony Wollenberg
No of partners:	16
Assistants/Associates:	28
Other fee-earners:	5
Consultants:	1
Total staff:	83

AREAS OF PRACTICE

Corporate/Commercial	27%
Telecommunications/IT	26%
Litigation	24%
Commercial Property/Environment	11%
Employment	7%
Financial Rescue	5%

THE FIRM: In the past 20 years, Rakisons has developed a powerful reputation for providing cutting edge, cost effective and commercially pro-active legal services. Based in the heart of the City, Rakisons has developed a formidable practice, concentrating on English and international commercial law on behalf of a broad range of clients, both from the UK and abroad. It is the 'small City firm with the right attitude'. Rakisons was founded in 1979 to provide large City firm expertise in a smaller environment. The firm has a strong international emphasis. It provides a comprehensive range of legal services to market leading businesses throughout the UK, EU, Eastern Europe, USA and the Middle and Far East. Clients range in size from the largest international conglomerates to owner-managed businesses. Rakisons moulds its legal services to meet each client's particular needs so that their commercial objectives are met. This means developing close working relationships with clients and gaining an in-depth understanding of their business so that complex matters are handled with speed and creativity. The firm is widely acknowledged as a world leader in providing comprehensive legal services to clients in the telecommunications and information technology sectors, particularly e-businesses and outsourcing. It continues to gain strengths in the more traditional areas of corporate/commercial, banking and commercial litigation, and in their dedicated employment and financial rescue departments.

PRINCIPAL AREAS OF WORK:

Corporate/Commercial: Corporate includes takeovers and mergers, joint ventures (UK and cross-border), shareholders agreements and venture capital finance, internet start-ups, establishing businesses in the UK for overseas clients and handling international agreements, EU law, international banking and international corporate structures. Commercial includes agency, distribution, franchising, and intellectual property. Specialist gaming and licensing services are also offered.

Litigation: Includes all commercial, contractual, corporate and partnership disputes, banking, defamation, insurance, professional negligence, cross-border tracing of assets and fraud.

Employment: Includes employee/employer relations, employment documentation, redundancy, termination packages, maternity, discrimination, TUPE, collective disputes and advocacy at tribunals.

Financial Rescue: Includes reconstructions, recoveries and documentary credits.

Commercial Property: Deals with industrial and residential development, investment, acquisitions and disposals, property finance, portfolio management, planning and environmental law.

Telecommunications and IT: Includes obtaining UK and pan-European telecoms licences, interconnection, strategic sales, e-business, regulatory advice, software and hardware licensing, outsourcing, distribution agreements and turnkey advice to non-EU operators entering the EU telecoms market.

INTERNATIONAL CONNECTIONS: Through its vast international connections, Rakisons is able to provide a seamless flow of legal advice regardless of the location of the client or the nature of the work involved.

LANGUAGES: Several of its partners and staff are fluent in foreign languages and legal services can be provided in Dutch, French, German, Hebrew, Italian, Persian, Portuguese, Russian and Spanish. Rakisons' partners are frequently invited to lecture worldwide on cross-border, technical and commercial issues.

CONTACTS

Commercial Litigation	Tony Wollenberg
	Jane Jales
	Mark Parkhouse
	Adam Greaves
Commercial Property	Brendan Patterson
	Martin Gordon-Russell
	Lance Conway
Corporate/Commercial	Simon Vivian
	Jonathan Polin
	Michael Thompson
Employment	David von Hagen
Financial Rescue	Mark Parkhouse
Telecommunications Information Technology	David Judah
	Danny Preiskel
	Paul Hosford

RALPH HUME GARRY

Swan House, 37-39 High Holborn, London, WC1V 6AA
Tel: (020) 7831 3737 **Fax:** (020) 7831 5757 **DX:** 174 London Chancery Lane
Email: email@ralphhumegarry.com **Website:** www.ralphhumegarry.com

Managing partner:	Peter Garry
Senior partner:	Stephen Ralph
Number of partners:	6
Assistant solicitors:	7

AREAS OF PRACTICE

Commercial Litigation including Arbitration & ADR	100%

THE FIRM: The practice, placed in the centre of the legal world between the High Court and the Old Bailey, specialises exclusively in litigation and dispute resolution. Partnership law, fraud and regulatory, insolvency, insurance, employment and e-commerce are notable areas of expertise.The partners have come together from other law firms where they were all senior litigation specialists with many years of experience in all forms of dispute resolution. The firm has been established to serve the needs of existing clients and contacts and to provide for changes to the system of litigation and arbitration in England and Wales. The firm attaches particular importance to achieving an early resolution of disputes which is both commercial and cost effective in cases where such an approach is appropriate. It concentrates on detailed analysis of the dispute by identifying the issues, the evidence and the merits of the parties' respective positions before advising on appropriate strategies. Stephen Ralph, the senior partner, is a licensed insolvency practitioner. He also sits as an arbitrator in relation to partnership matters. John Hume is a Solicitor Advocate. Peter Garry and David Grant are accredited mediators. Berry Holding-Parsons is the editor of an e-commerce newsletter for the insurance industry, *e-insurance*.

PRINCIPAL AREAS OF WORK: The firm acts across a broad spectrum of commercial litigation and dispute resolution, including arbitrations. The partners have conducted a number of high profile white collar fraud trials and regulatory investigations, DTI inquiries and SFO prosecutions relating to allegations of fraud, insider dealing and multiple share applications. The partners also represent company directors facing disqualification and assist clients appearing before professional disciplinary tribunals and other self-regulating bodies.

CLIENTELE: The firm acts for banks, insolvency practitioners and borrowers on matters including enforcement of securities, tracing of assets, actions on preferences and avoidance of prior transactions, recovery of assets and examination of directors under the Insolvency Act 1986. The firm also acts for professional firms, groups of partners or individuals on problems relating to dissolution, expulsion, internal disputes and restructuring of partnerships. It has also assisted client partnerships and their bankers in financial reviews, often involving negotiations with landlords and other creditors and re-financing, and negotiations concerning the interests of individual partners.It acts in boardroom, shareholder and other corporate disputes. The firm also deals with employment and pension disputes, acting for employers, employees, beneficiaries, pension fund trustees and their advisers. The firm acts for insurers and brokers on a wide variety of matters including professional negligence, D&O, bankers' blanket bond and legal expenses. It specialises in the effects on the insurance market of IT and e-commerce. The firm acts in all types IT matters, especially claims resulting from failure of software. It also advises generally on all aspects of e-commerce. The firm also advises a wide range of clients on contentious intellectual property matters, including patents, trademarks, passing-off and copyright and media and entertainment matters, particularly in relation to the music industry. The firm has extensive experience of injunction applications and having obtained, executed and supervised search orders, it is able to provide supervising solicitors in relation to such orders.

INTERNATIONAL CONNECTIONS: The firm has close ties with law firms in Europe (notably in France, Switzerland, Germany and Liechtenstein), North America, Australasia and the Pacific rim.

LANGUAGES: Instructions can be taken in French and German.

CONTACTS

Alternative Dispute Resolution	Peter Garry
	David Grant
Arbitration	Stephen Ralph
Commercial Litigation	Any Partner
Company Boardroom/Shareholder Disputes/Take-over Litigation	John Hume
E-commerce/IT	Berry Holding-Parsons
Employment	Roberta Sacaloff
Inland Revenue & Customs & Excise Prosecutions	John Hume
	David Grant
Insolvency	Stephen Ralph
	David Grant
Insurance	Berry Holding-Parsons
Intellectual Property/Media & Entertainment	Peter Garry
Partnership	Stephen Ralph
	Peter Garry
Pensions	Peter Garry
White Collar Fraud/Regulatory	John Hume
	David Grant

RAMSBOTTOM & CO

25-29 Victoria St, Blackburn, BB1 6DN **Tel:** (01254) 672222 **Fax:** (01254) 681723 **DX:** 15251 **Ptnrs:** 6 **Asst solrs:** 5 **Other fee-earners:** 5

RAWLISON & BUTLER

Griffin House, 135 High Street, Crawley, RH10 1DQ
Tel: (01293) 527744 **Fax:** (01293) 520202 **DX:** 120750 Crawley 8
Email: info@rawlis.co.uk **Website:** www.rawlisonbutler.com

15 Carfax, Horsham, RH12 1DY
Tel: (01403) 252492 **Fax:** (01403) 241545 **DX:** 57602 HORSHAM

Managing partner:	James Chatfield
Number of partners:	9
Assistant solicitors:	11
Other fee-earners:	10

AREAS OF PRACTICE

Commercial property	30%
Company commercial	25%
Commercial litigation	24%
Private client	21%

CONTACTS

Commercial	Mark O'Shea (Crawley)
Commercial Litigation	Clive Lee (Crawley)
Commercial Property	Clive Prior (Crawley)
Corporate Finance	Tim Sadka (Crawley)
Employment	Louise Dabbs (Crawley)
Family	Robert Worthing (Horsham)
Insolvency	Richard Homewood (Crawley)
Private client	Digby Armstrong (Horsham)

THE FIRM: A leading regional practice, Rawlison & Butler is an ambitious and growing firm serving clients predominantly in the south-east of England offering a comprehensive service from its office close to London-Gatwick. Rawlison & Butler's success reflects its reputation as a responsive and creative organisation providing legal advice focused on the needs and ambitions of its clients. The firm offers a comprehensive range of legal services. There is an international dimension to the firm's practice with an emphasis towards the EU, North America and Asia Pacific. Clients range from owner-managed businesses to listed companies, multinational corporations and local government authorities. The firm is organised on a departmental basis with partners responsible for practice groups that draw on the experience of lawyers from across the firm's formal departmental structure. Rawlison & Butler strives to achieve the highest standards by a commitment to investing in its people and organisation. This is reflected in the firm embracing the latest technology and the continued development of its know-how resources. Private client services are provided from the Horsham office.

PRINCIPAL AREAS OF WORK: Particular areas of expertise include: corporate transactions; purchase and sale of businesses; corporate finance; commercial property; planning and residential development; commercial contracts; employment law; intellectual property; commercial litigation; probate, and tax planning. Brochures outlining the services offered by Rawlison & Butler are available on request.

RECRUITMENT & TRAINING: Rawlison & Butler is keen to recruit driven high calibre qualified lawyers with a proven record of high academic achievement and professional success.

R

RAYFIELD MILLS

3 Collingwood Street, Newcastle-upon-Tyne, NE1 1JE **Tel:** (0191) 261 2333 **Fax:** (0191) 261 2444 **Email:** law@rayfield-mills.co.uk **Ptnrs:** 8 **Asst solrs:** 5

RAYNER DE WOLFE

31 Southampton Row, London, WC1B 5HJ
Tel: (020) 7405 1212 **Fax:** (020) 7405 1191 **DX:** 143 London Chancery Lane WC2
Email: rdw@raynerdewolfe.co.uk **Website:** www.raynerdewolfe.co.uk

Managing partner:	Alan Finlay
Senior partner:	Stephen Rayner
Partners:	7
Assistant solicitors:	5
Other fee earners:	2

AREAS OF PRACTICE

Corporate/commercial	32%
Litigation and Dispute Resolution	30%
Property	21%
Family Law and Mediation	12%
Employment	4%
Wills, Probates and Trusts	1%

THE FIRM: Rayner De Wolfe traces its origins to 1938 and is an expanding central London based firm acting for commercial clients (e.g. banks, airlines, publishers) and high net worth individuals. As a founding member of INTERLEGES the firm's international practice is increasingly active in all departments. While large enough to meet the needs of major corporations the firm also provides a highly personal and cost-effective service to smaller commercial and private clients.

PRINCIPAL AREAS OF WORK: Mergers and acquisitions, intellectual property and IT; domestic and international dispute resolution and arbitration; family law and mediation; employment law; investment property and development; international tax planning; private client, wills and probate.

READ HIND STEWART

Trafalgar House, 29 Park Place, Leeds, LS1 2SP
Tel: (0113) 246 8123 **Fax:** (0113) 244 2863 **DX:** 14085
Email: rhslaw@rhs-law.co.uk **Website:** www.rhs_law.co.uk

Managing partner:	David Hymas
Number of partners:	15
Assistant solicitors:	11
Other fee-earners:	28

AREAS OF PRACTICE

Commercial Property	35%
Company/Commercial	25%
Commercial Litigation	23%
Employment	9%
Debt Recovery	8%

THE FIRM: Read Hind Stewart was established in 1987, and has now developed into a major practice in the commercial centre of Leeds.

PRINCIPAL AREAS OF WORK: The practice undertakes commercial work and has particularly strong corporate, commercial property, commercial litigation and employment departments. European law is a specialisation, specifically German law-related matters.

RECRUITMENT & TRAINING: As a developing practice, Read Hind Stewart is continually looking for outstanding candidates. Please contact David Hymas, Managing Partner.

REES & FRERES

1 The Sanctuary, Westminster, London, SW1P 3JT **Tel:** (020) 7222 5381 **Fax:** (020) 7222 4646 **DX:** 2301 Victoria **Email:** enquiries@1thesanctuary.com **Website:** www.rees&freres.com **Ptnrs:** 14 **Asst solrs:** 8 **Other fee-earners:** 13 **Contact:** Susie Hust • Specialise in commercial property, public, parliamentary and local government law, transport infrastructure projects, planning, compulsory acquisition and commercial litigation.

REES PAGE

30-36 Lichfield Street, Wolverhampton, WV1 1DN **Tel:** (01902) 577777 **Fax:** (01902) 577735 **DX:** 10405 Wolverhampton **Ptnrs:** 15 **Asst solrs:** 8 **Other fee-earners:** 8

REID MINTY

R

14 Grosvenor Street, Mayfair, London, W1X OAQ
Tel: (020) 7318 4444 **Fax:** (020) 7318 4445 **DX:** 44615 Mayfair
Email: lawyers@reidminty.co.uk **Website:** www.reidminty.co.uk

Managing partner:	Stephen Moss
Senior partner:	Andrew Reid
Number of Partners:	10
Number of Fee-earners:	40
Total Staff:	130

AREAS OF PRACTICE

Commercial Litigation	50%
Personal Injury	20%
Commercial Property	10%
Company/Commercial	10%
Healthcare	10%

CONTACTS

Commercial Litigation	Stephen Moss
Commercial Property	Martin Gunson
Company/Commercial/Sports	Jonathan Ebsworth
Container Leasing	Stephen Moss
Costs Consultancy	Andrew Reid
Defamation	Nick Neocleous
Employment/Health Authority	Ashley Irons
Horseracing	Andrew Reid
Insolvency	Simon Goldhill
Insurance	Simon Edwards
Personal Injury	Sue Brown

THE FIRM: Founded in 1980, the firm continues to build on its ability to successfully handle substantial commercial litigation matters, and has now gained an excellent reputation in the niche areas of insurance, general commercial, healthcare/health authority, sports law and commercial property matters. The firm handles City work, but with a lower cost base, and no difference in quality.

PRINCIPAL AREAS OF WORK:

Litigation: Handle major domestic and international commercial disputes, insolvency, insurance, defamation, employment, minority shareholders actions, and partnership problems. The firm is recognised one of the leading European lawyers in the container leasing industry.

Corporate: Advice on all aspects of commercial activity including corporate finance, mergers and acquisitions, joint ventures, venture capital, and management buy-outs.

Sport: The sports department is known for its activity in European competition law, player contracts, horseracing and bloodstock work.

Healthcare: This department advises specialist hospitals on sensitive decisions concerning secure unit prisoners (e.g. Ian Brady v Ashworth Hospital; R v Broadmoor SHA ex parte S). Expert advice is given on nursing home transactions, local authority healthcare regulations, and on a wide range of specialist employment matters of particular interest to large healthcare institutions.

Personal Injury: The firm has built a reputation in the personal injury field for handling volume work, as well as carrying out risk assessment and other related services for a number of Europe's largest defendant insurance companies.

Commercial Property: The commercial property department advises on funding, acquisitions, construction and disposals, planning enquiries, and claims following planning and/or property related negligence. A full service is available to developers and commercial property clients as well as for residential purchases and sales.

CLIENTELE: Prominent clients include domestic and international banks, financial institutions, international insurers, Plc's, substantial multi-national corporations, health authorities, investment trusts, international transport and container leasing companies, private companies and individuals.

RECRUITMENT & TRAINING: Reid Minty has a comprehensive programme for trainee solicitors, and recruits five to six trainees per year, as well as taking on a number of paralegals.

REYNOLDS PORTER CHAMBERLAIN

Chichester House, 278-282 High Holborn, London, WC1V 7HA
Tel: (020) 7242 2877 **Fax:** (020) 7242 1431 **DX:** 81 Chancery Lane
Email: rpc@rpc.co.uk **Website:** www.rpc.co.uk

Senior partner:	Alan Toulson
Number of partners:	50
Assistant solicitors:	68
Other fee-earners:	50

AREAS OF PRACTICE

Insurance/Reinsurance	25%
Professional Indemnity	25%
Commercial Litigation	10%
Construction	10%
Corporate	10%
Property	10%
Media & Technology	5%
Private Client/Family	5%

THE FIRM: Reynolds Porter Chamberlain is a substantial commercial firm and one of the country's leading insurance and litigation practices. The firm also has a thriving corporate and commercial practice providing a wide range of legal services to both UK and international businesses, institutions and private individuals. It has strong overseas connections and is a founder member of TerraLex, an international association of law firms across over 100 jurisdictions.

PRINCIPAL AREAS OF WORK:

Insurance/Reinsurance: The department meets the needs of insurance and reinsurance companies and Lloyd's underwriters. It handles general insurance and reinsurance market litigation and is also particularly noted for its professional indemnity work, acting for the insurers of accountants, architects, barristers, brokers, engineers, financial advisers, solicitors and other professionals. It also has a substantial practice acting for the insurers of Directors and Officers, banks and financial institutions. Its office in Leadenhall Street provides easy access for the surrounding insurance market.

Corporate: The corporate department acts for publicly quoted companies, multinational corporations, private companies, trade associations and partnerships. Work includes mergers and acquisitions, corporate finance, banking, Yellow Book work, insolvency, franchise and distribution, tax, competition law and financial services regulations.

Media and Technology: The firm's expertise in this area covers publishing, IT and internet law, defamation, media-related litigation and commercial agreements. Media clients include national newspapers, broadcasters and IT companies. This group specialises in both contentious and non-contentious media and IT related work.

Commercial Litigation: Covering disputes relating to contracts, product liability, shareholder agreements, agency and franchising, insolvency, personal injury, partnership and property.

Intellectual Property: Patents, trademarks, designs, copyright and licensing are handled for industries ranging from pharmaceutical companies to computing, publishing and entertainment companies.

Employment: The firm deals with contracts, restrictive covenants, misuse of confidential information and trade secrets, employee benefits, pensions and industrial tribunal hearings.

Education: The firm acts for teachers' professional associations, universities, colleges and schools and advises on all aspects of education law including the further and higher education sectors.

Commercial Property: The department acts for publicly quoted property companies and investment funds as well as general trading companies. Areas of work include property investment, site acquisitions, joint ventures, development, town and country planning and landlord and tenant law.

Construction: The firm gives advice on building contracts and related documentation and a substantial amount of arbitration and litigation.

Private Client: The department offers a considerable range of services to private clients, including financial services, personal taxation, wills, trusts and probate.

Family: This department handles all aspects of matrimonial and family law and is especially noted for high profile child abduction work as well as wardship cases on behalf of local authorities and the Lord Chancellor's department.

CLIENTELE: Clients include multinational corporations, publicly quoted companies, private companies, publishers and broadcasters, property developers, professional and trade associations, insurance and reinsurance companies, underwriters, mutuals, private individuals and partnerships.

RECRUITMENT & TRAINING: The firm recruits six trainee solicitors a year. Bursaries are available. There is also a summer vacation scheme for prospective trainees. Application forms are available from Sally Andrews, Head of Personnel.

CONTACTS

Commercial Litigation	Stephen Mayer
Commercial Property	Edward Meerloo
	David Haywood
Company/Commercial	Alan Toulson
Construction	Charles Gardner
Corporate Finance	Jonathan Watmough
Defamation	Liz Hartley
Education	Geraldine Elliott
Employment	Geraldine Elliott
Family	Jeffrey Freeman
Insolvency	Justin Westhead
Insurance/Reinsurance	Simon Greenley
Intellectual Property	Andrew Hobson
Media & Technology	Tim Anderson
Personal Injury	Duncan Harman-Wilson
Private Client	Colin Russell
Professional Indemnity	Paul Nicholas
Tax & Pensions	Charles Suchett-Kaye

R

RICHARD BUXTON

40 Clarendon Street, Cambridge, CB1 1JX **Tel:** (01223) 328933 **Fax:** (01223) 301308 **Email:** law@richardbuxton.co.uk **Website:** www.richardbuxton.co.uk **Ptnrs:** 1 **Associates** 1

RICHARD MONTEITH

34 Portmore Street, Portadown, BT62 3NG **Tel:** (028) 3833 0780 **Fax:** (028) 3835 0271 **Ptnrs:** 3 **Asst solrs:** 2 **Contact:** Mr Richard Monteith
Specialisation in criminal law in addition to general practice of conveyancing, wills and probate, matrimonial and civil litigation.

RICHARDS BUTLER

Beaufort House, 15 St. Botolph Street, London, EC3A 7EE
Tel: (020) 7247 6555 **Fax:** (020) 7247 5091 **DX:** 1066 City/18 London
Email: law@richardsbutler.com **Website:** www.richardsbutler.com

THE FIRM: Richards Butler's international law practice now has a presence in 10 countries around the world, and continues to grow within both developed and emerging markets. Richards Butler experienced another year of significant growth in revenues in 1999/00 and has grown in strength becoming a firm of over 100 partners for the first time. The firm is City-based and services the needs of its large international clients which are concentrated in the market sectors of banking and financial services; insurance; media; entertainment; leisure and sports; information technology and telecommunications; shipping; international trade and commodities; property. Two thirds of the firms' work has an international dimension.

PRINCIPAL AREAS OF WORK: Richards Butler advises in all major areas of commercial law.

Corporate and Commercial: Advising clients on domestic and international mergers and acquisitions, joint ventures and inward investment; e-commerce; EU and competition law; intellectual property and information technology; insurance company regulatory requirements; tax issues in the UK and other jurisdictions; all

Continued overleaf

Chairman	Andrew Taylor
Chief executive	Chris Schulten
UK:	
Number of partners:	72
Assistant solicitors:	88
Other fee-earners:	61
International:	
Number of partners:	30
Assistant solicitors:	85
Other fee-earners:	29

AREAS OF PRACTICE

Corporate/Commercial/Banking/Finance	31%
Dispute Resolution/Litigation	29%
Shipping/Commodities/Insurance	24%
Property (Commercial)	16%

aspects of international finance and banking including financial services and other regulatory requirements; project finance including asset-based financing and cross-border leasing; media and entertainment law, both regulatory and transactional; anti-piracy and copyright protection; corporate recovery and insolvency including cross-border matters; employment and industrial relations; pensions and unit trust issues; advice on contracts in all areas of energy law.
Property: Advising on all aspects of property, environmental and planning law including investment and financing of land and commercial property; VAT; planning requirements for local authorities; construction and contract negotiation; financing and claim preparation; and advice on licensing of hotels and leisure premises including liquor licensing, betting, gaming, late-night licensing and multi-leisure site licensing.
Dispute Resolution: Advising on all matters requiring dispute resolution skills including litigation at all Court levels. As one of the largest litigation practices in the UK, the group has expertise in all major litigation areas including financial services/regulatory and banking: all aspects of media and information technology; anti-piracy prosecutions; insurance; employment; and general corporate litigation. The group has substantial experience in arbitration and mediation techniques. The group has acted, and is acting, in many of the major commercial disputes in the City.
Shipping: Advising on all aspects of shipping, including charterparty disputes, bill of lading claims; ship sale and purchase; drafting of, and disputes concerning, shipbuilding contracts; marine insurance and reinsurance; the drafting of, and litigation concerning, all aspects of mutual insurance (such as P&I and Defence Clubs); salvage, collision and major casualties (the firm has a 24-hour casualty response line) all aspects of ship finance acting for both banks and borrowers; trade and commodities, including the buying and selling of hard and soft commodities; and trade finance.

INTERNATIONAL CONNECTIONS: The firm has other offices in Abu Dhabi, Beijing, Brussels, Hong Kong, Paris, Piraeus, São Paulo and Warsaw and also associated offices in Doha and Muscat.

CONTACTS

Admiralty	Richard Harvey
ADR	John Hull
Aviation and Aircraft Finance	Adam Morgan
Banking	Gordon Stewart
Commercial and EC	Stephen Sayer
Commercial Disputes	Roger Parker
Competition Law	Katherine Holmes
Construction and Engineering	Roger Parker
Corporate	David Boutcher
Employment	Tim Archer
Energy	Stephen Sayer
Environmental Law	John Aylwin
Financial Services	Lista Cannon
Information Technology	Stella Holt
Insolvency	Jon Yorke
Insurance and Reinsurance	Mark Connoley
Intellectual Property	Graham Simkin
Licensing	Elizabeth Southorn
Local Government	John Austin
Media and Entertainment	Stephen Edwards
Pensions and Unit Trusts	Andrew Fleming
Property	John Pike
Ship Finance	Adam Morgan
Shipping	Lindsay East
Tax	Leslie Powell
Trade and Commodities	David Pullen

RICHARD WHISH – SOLE PRACTITIONER

School of Law, King's College, The Strand, London, WC2R 2LS **Tel:** (020) 7848 2237 **Fax:** (020) 7848 2211 **Email:** richard.whish@kcl.ac.uk

RICKERBY WATTERSON

Ellenborough House, Wellington Street, Cheltenham, GL50 1YD
Tel: (01242) 224422 **Fax:** (01242) 518428 **DX:** 7415 Cheltenham
Email: rw@rickerby.co.uk **Website:** www.rickerby.co.uk

Managing partner:	Mark Fabian
Senior partner:	John Clarke
Number of partners:	17
Assistant solicitors:	15
Other fee-earners:	20

THE FIRM: Rickerby Watterson is a leading Gloucestershire firm with an established commercial law practice and a strong private client base.

PRINCIPAL AREAS OF WORK:
Corporate: The sale and purchase of businesses, re-structuring and re-financings, shareholder agreements, and raising finance and venture capital.
Commercial: Partnership and joint venture agreements, agency and distribution agreements, UK and EU competition law, e-commerce and intellectual property. All aspects of employment law for both employer and employee.
Insolvency: A specialist group advises office holders, creditors and business proprietors on all aspects of insolvency and debt recovery.
Property: Commercial property experts advise clients on acquisitions, funding, development and disposal, environmental and planning work, landlord and tenant matters, and licensing. The firm also has an active residential property team. Bulk remortgage, security and banking work is also undertaken.
Private Client: The firm has a substantial private client practice offering asset management and advice in such areas as capital tax planning, trusts, investments, mental incapacity and care for the elderly.
There is close co-operation between the various groups to ensure that specialist skills throughout the firm are delivered to clients in a co-ordinated and structured manner.

CLIENTELE: The firm mainly acts for plcs and owner-managed companies, local subsidiaries of national and multi-national plcs, companies in commercial property, leisure companies and operators allied to the licensed trade, educational establishments, and high net worth individuals.

AREAS OF PRACTICE

Property	40%
Private Client/Asset Management	21%
Company Commercial	19%
Company Litigation	9%
Employment	4%
Insolvency	4%
Family	3%

CONTACTS

Agriculture	Robin Beckley
Asset Management	Mark Hartley
Commercial Property	Robin Beckley
Company Commercial	Richard Knight
Corporate Litigation	Derek Jones
EC & Competition Law	Anne Compton
Education	John Clarke
Employment	John Clarke
Family Law	Carolyn Green
Insolvency & Realisation	Derek Jones
Licensed Trade	Robin Beckley
Private Client	Mark Hartley
Residential Property	Henry Marshall

RIDLEY HALL DRABBLE & CO

Permanent House, 1 Dundas Street, Huddersfield, HD1 1LE **Tel:** (01484) 538421 **Fax:** (01484) 533076 **DX:** 710083 Huddersfield 8 **Email:** ridley_hall@compuserve.com **Ptnrs:** 5 **Asst solrs:** 3 **Other fee-earners:** 3 • Specialists in education, disability and community care. Strong in licensing and issues involving the elderly as well as property, private client, personal injury and matrimonial.

ROBERTA MCDONALD – SOLE PRACTITIONER

12 Wake Green Road, Moseley, Birmingham, B13 9EZ **Tel:** (0121) 449 6821 **Fax:** (0121) 449 5160

ROBERT LIZAR

159 Princess Road, Moss Side, Manchester, M14 4RE **Tel:** (0161) 226 2319 **Fax:** (0161) 226 7985 **Email:** 106475.3436@compuserve.com
Ptnrs: 3 **Asst solrs:** 3 **Other fee-earners:** 2

ROBERT MUCKLE

Norham House, 12 New Bridge Street West, Newcastle-upon-Tyne, NE1 8AS
Tel: (0191) 232 4402 **Fax:** (0191) 261 6954 **DX:** 61011
Email: enquiries@robertmuckle.co.uk **Website:** www.robertmuckle.co.uk

Managing partner:	Ian Gilthorpe
Senior partner:	Hugh Welch
Number of partners:	11
Assistant solicitors:	22
Other fee-earners:	18

AREAS OF PRACTICE

Commercial	38%
Commercial Property	33%
Commercial Litigation	29%

CONTACTS

Commercial	Hugh Welch
Employment	Tony McPhillips
Litigation	Roddy Gordon
Property	Jonathan Combe

THE FIRM: Robert Muckle is one of the leading commercial law firms in the North East of England. It primarily works with corporate clients based in the northern region who are competing in both local and worldwide markets.

PRINCIPAL AREAS OF WORK: 95% of the firm's business is commercial, and the firm is well known for mergers, acquisitions, disposals and management buy-outs, intellectual property, employment, property development, construction and planning, banking law, loan finance, insolvency and commercial litigation.

CLIENTELE: The firm has a particularly strong following amongst the manufacturing, engineering and electronic sectors. Robert Muckle is now the leading firm in the North East in the significant owner-managed business market. These clients have been attracted to the firm by its blend of service quality, enthusiasm and value for money.

RECRUITMENT & TRAINING: Excellent career prospects for talented and enthusiastic lawyers. Great emphasis is placed on training all staff to exceed clients' expectations. Regular in-house training covers legal, IT, management and marketing courses. Training contracts: Three per year – apply to Paul Johnstone. Work experience – apply to Stewart Irvine.

R

ROBERTSON & CO, TECHNOLOGY LAW PRACTICE

18 Broomhouse Road, London, SW6 3QX **Tel:** (020) 7731 4626 **Fax:** (020) 7731 4598
Email: drcr@techlaw.co.uk **Ptnrs:** 1 **Contact:** Mr Ranald Robertson • Specialist legal support to users and suppliers on computing, software and internet issues. Benefits include speedy access to senior IT/computer law experience at a reasonable and affordable cost.

ROBERTSONS

6 Park Place, Cardiff, CF1 3DP **Tel:** (029) 20237777 **Fax:** (029) 2034 0219 **DX:** 33039 Cardiff **Email:** law@robsols.co.uk **Ptnrs:** 10
Asst solrs: 3 **Other fee-earners:** 4

ROBSON MCLEAN WS

28 Abercromby Place, Edinburgh, EH3 6QF
Tel: (0131) 556 0556 **Fax:** (0131) 556 9939 **DX:** ED162 Edinburgh
Email: info@robson-mclean.co.uk **Website:** www.robson-mclean.co.uk

Managing partner:	Duncan L. Murray
Senior partner:	William F. MacTaggart
Number of partners:	8
Assistant solicitors:	17
Other fee-earners:	9

AREAS OF PRACTICE

Litigation	38%
Private Client	33%
Commercial/Corporate	29%

CONTACTS

Commercial Litigation	Robin Macpherson
Commercial Property	Nick Atkins
Corporate	Walter Thomson
Private Client	Neil Paterson

THE FIRM: This leading Scottish firm, operating from Edinburgh's city centre, continues to see growth in its commercial litigation and commercial/ corporate departments. It has a strong client focus offering value-for-money services tailored to individual client needs. The firm is approved to ISO 9001 and is the only Scottish member of LawGroup UK.

PRINCIPAL AREAS OF WORK: Specialisms include commercial litigation, corporate, employment, environmental/ planning, IP/ technology, personal injury, PFI, property and trusts & tax.

CLIENTELE: Major clients include government bodies, local authorities, leading insurers and financial institutions, property companies, charities and special interest groups, trade unions and associations.

RODGERS & BURTON

15-17 Church Rd, Barnes, London, SW13 9HG
Tel: (020) 8939 6300 **Fax:** (020) 8876 8228 **DX:** 59702 Barnes
Email: mw@randb.law.co.uk

Senior partner:	David Moore
Number of partners:	5
Assistant solicitors:	1
Other fee-earners:	3

AREAS OF PRACTICE

Private & Commercial Conveyancing	52%
Civil Litigation	33%
Matrimonial	10%
Wills & Probate	5%

CONTACTS

Conveyancing/Wills & probate	Kathryn Kinnear
Landlord and tenant	David Moore
Matrimonial	Gillian Tyndall
Personal Injury/Employment/ Debt Recovery	Mark Woloshak

THE FIRM: The firm was founded in 1835, and has had a presence in Barnes since 1952. The firm occupies offices overlooking Barnes Common and incorporated another local firm, Messrs Ashbys, in 1998.

PRINCIPAL AREAS OF WORK: Whilst being a general High Street practice, Rodgers & Burton offers certain specialist advice in servicing landlords and Housing Associations. In particular, they offer experience in landlord and tenant litigation, housing association law and finance, disposals and acquisitions of property, lease back financing of acquisitions, shared ownership schemes, construction contracts and disputes.

OTHER AREAS: Rodgers & Burton also have fee earners with experience in employment law, personal injury, debt recovery , contractual disputes, commercial litigation and a busy matrimonial department. Contingency fee arrangements are available if appropriate. The firm will draft wills, where no tax planning or will trust advice is required, for a fixed fee. The firm has obtained a franchise for community legal service specialist help in family. The firm offers an Agency Service in Wandsworth, West London and Brentford County Courts. Rodgers & Burton have a well respected residential conveyancing department, and following the incorporation of Messrs Ashbys have considerable expertise in commercial conveyancing as well.

R

RODGERS HORSLEY WHITEMANS

Castle House, Castle Street, Guildford, GU1 3UL **Tel:** (01483) 302000 **Fax:** (01483) 301242 **DX:** 2445 Guildford 1
Email: martyn.whiteman@rhw.co.uk **Website:** www.rhw.co.uk **Ptnrs:** 3 **Asst solrs:** 6

ROEBUCKS

12 Richmond Terrace, Blackburn, BB1 7BG **Tel:** (01254) 668855 **Fax:** (01254) 680838 **DX:** 15254 Blackburn 2 **Ptnrs:** 6 **Asst solrs:** 3
Other fee-earners: 4

ROITER ZUCKER

5-7 Broadhurst Gardens, Swiss Cottage, London, NW6 3RZ
Tel: (020) 7328 9111 **Fax:** (020) 7644 8900 **DX:** 38850 Swiss Cottage
Email: mail@roiterzucker.co.uk **Website:** www.roiterzucker.co.uk

Number of partners:	7
Assistant solicitors:	7
Other fee-earners:	6

AREAS OF PRACTICE

Litigation (incl. Contentious IP Work)	45%
Commercial Law (incl. IP/Pharmaceutical Work & Competition Law)	35%
Company/Property	20%

CONTACTS

General Contact	Anna McKay

THE FIRM: Roiter Zucker carries out all types of commercial work, and is particularly well-known for its intellectual property work. The firm has an excellent reputation for IP litigation, having acted in many leading cases, including the Terfenadine and Paclitaxel patent cases and the Glaxo/Dowelhurst case concerning parallel imports and the extent of free movement of goods. As well as its high profile litigation, RZ does a full range of non-contentious IP work for clients in various fields: pharmaceutical (from start-up biotech companies to multinational companies); media and an increasing amount of brand work. RZ is small, but highly skilled. It is used to working in the international arena, and can draw on expert advice worldwide.

ROLLIT FARRELL & BLADON

Wilberforce Court, High Street, Hull, HU1 1YJ
Tel: (01482) 323239 **Fax:** (01482) 326239 **DX:** 715756 Hull 15
Email: info@rollits.co.uk **Website:** www.rollits.co.uk

Rowntree Wharf, Navigation Road, York, YO1 9WE
Tel: (01904) 625790 **Fax:** (01904) 625807 **DX:** 61534 York
Email: info@rollits.co.uk

26 & 28 Lairgate, Beverley, HU17 8ER
Tel: (01482) 882278 **Fax:** (01482) 871901 **DX:** 28307 Beverley
Email: info@rollits.co.uk

4 Bondgate, Helmsley, YO62 5BS
Tel: (01439) 770207 **Fax:** (01439) 771650 **DX:** 63752 Helmsley
Email: info@rollits.co.uk

Managing partner:	Stephen J. Trynka
Senior partner:	James Brennand
Number of partners:	33
Assistant solicitors:	14
Other fee-earners:	25

AREAS OF PRACTICE

Company & Commercial	34%
Property	24%
Litigation	18%
Private Client	12%
Planning & Development	7%
Employment	5%

THE FIRM: One of the principal firms in the Yorkshire region offering a comprehensive legal service. Highly regarded as a commercial practice. Expertise in corporate and commercial law is unrivalled in East Yorkshire.

PRINCIPAL AREAS OF WORK:
Company: Acquisitions and disposals, flotations, share issues, fund raising, joint ventures, MBOs, finance and credit agreements, corporate recovery.
Commercial: Equipment leasing and financing agreements, intellectual property, trading law, franchising, competition law, employment law, educational law and EU law.
Commercial and Residential Property: Commercial conveyancing, planning and development, environmental law, landlord and tenant, housing association work and agriculture.
Litigation: Commercial litigation, insurance litigation, intellectual property disputes, licensing, building and construction, mediation debt recovery, professional indemnity and matrimonial.
Private Client: Tax planning, settlements, wills, estate administration, enduring powers of attorney, domestic conveyancing and Court of Protection work.

CONTACTS

Commercial	Keith Benton
Commercial Litigation	George Coyle
Company	Richard Field
Employment	Pauline Molyneux
Environmental	Steve Hawkins
Planning	John Downing
Private Client	John Lane
Property	Martyn Justice

ROOKS RIDER

Challoner House, 19 Clerkenwell Close, London, EC1R 0RR
Tel: (020) 7689 7000 **Fax:** (020) 7689 7001 **DX:** 53324 Clerkenwell
Email: jwhiteson@rooksrider.co.uk **Website:** www.rooksrider.co.uk

Managing partner:	Clare Foinette
Senior partner:	Christopher Cooke
Number of partners:	12
Assistant solicitors:	15
Other fee-earners:	14

AREAS OF PRACTICE

Company/Commercial	40%
Litigation	22%
Private client	20%
Property	18%

CONTACTS

Banking	Clare Foinette
	Jeremy Whiteson
Commercial Litigation	Richard Walker
	Paul Whitaker
Company/Commercial	Christopher Cooke
	Nicholas Jacob
	Keir Gordon
	Jeremy Whiteson
Employment	Paul Whitaker
Insolvency	Jeremy Whiteson
Intellectual Property	Richard Walker
	Keir Gordon
International Tax	Christopher Cooke
	Nicholas Jacob
	Gerald Chappel,
	Karen Methold
Matrimonial	Janet Tresman
Private client	Christopher Wright
	Nicola Jenkins
Property	Clare Foinette

THE FIRM: Established in 1761 (making Rooks Rider one of the oldest law firms in the country) it has a tradition of offering a high quality service to individuals and businesses. Building from this foundation, the partnership is continually expanding the breadth of its expertise to respond to the needs of its clients and the changing business environment. It has a friendly and informal atmosphere and prides itself on finding creative and practical solutions to its clients needs. The firm is committed to the continued development of both the private client and commercial sides of its practice. It achieved Investors in People accreditation in 1999. In addition to offering a comprehensive, high quality service to businesses and individuals Rooks Rider has developed an international reputation for its tax planning skills both in the UK and offshore. It has particular expertise in serving growing businesses (from startup to major listed company). It is a leading firm in the private client field.

PRINCIPAL AREAS OF WORK: The firm has growing practices in a broad spread of commercial and private client areas.
Commercial: Rooks Rider commercial clients range from substantial listed companies to family businesses and in a diverse array of market sectors. The firm offers clients a full service in handling transactions, managing disputes and providing advice on commercial issues. The firm's commercial practice is dovetailed with its international tax practice, and within the commercial practice, solicitors are encouraged to develop a broad legal knowledge. This structure has allowed the firm to provide balanced, practical advice to entrepreneurs and entrepreneurial business in a seamless manner and to create a stimulating working environment. The approach has worked particularly well for inward investment into the UK, business start ups and company sales.
E-Commerce: Existing strengths in advising start ups, intellectual property and corporate sales have been applied to good effect to the growing group of e-commerce clients.
International Tax: The international tax practice has particular strengths in the fields of offshore trusts and international corporate structures for companies and individuals. It is instructed by professional trustees, banks and individuals around the world and partners visit virtually all of the major low tax jurisdictions each year. Team members regularly contribute to conferences and journals in this area and are invited to lecture as far afield as Hong Kong and New Zealand.
Private Client: Its traditional private client base has expanded considerably, advising in relation to landed estates, wills, trusts, probate, and tax planning. This enables the firm to provide an extensive service to wealthy individuals be they UK residents, foreign nationals or expatriates. It works closely with the matrimonial practice which has dedicated specialists dealing with family law issues including complex financial cases.
Property: The property team handles all types of commercial and residential property transactions, and landlord and tenant matters. It has developed a particular expertise on leasehold reform and is a founder member of the Leasehold Advisory Group. It counts developers and investment funds amongst its regular clients and has built a major specialisation in designing tax efficient structures for property purchases in the UK by foreign nationals and residents.Litigation: Commercial disputes are dealt with by the litigation department which has particular focuses upon, patent litigation, contentious employment matters, family disputes, property litigation and professional negligence.
Other: Cross departmental teams deal with employment, intellectual property, banking and insolvency.
Recruitment & Training: The firm is always seeking to recruit high calibre qualified staff and recruits at least two trainee solicitors each year. All areas of the practice are expanding. Enquiries should be sent to the staff partner

ROOKS RIDER
SOLICITORS

ROSLING KING

2-3 Hind Court, Fleet St, London, EC4A 3DL
Tel: (020) 7353 2353 **Fax:** (020) 7583 2035 **DX:** 154
Email: roslingking.co.uk **Website:** www.roslingking.co.uk

Senior partner:	Owen Rafferty
Number of partners:	11
Assistant solicitors:	26
Other fee-earners:	21
Total staff:	90

AREAS OF PRACTICE

Litigation/Insurance 40%
Company/Commercial/Banking/Sports/ Employment 30%
Property/Construction/Environmental 30%

CONTACTS

Banking/Finance ....Owen Rafferty
Company/Commercial ....Ruth Neil
....John Pearson
Construction ....John Beagley
Employment ....Jessica Knight
Environmental ....Paul Lowe
Insurance & Reinsurance ....Georgina Squire
....Ruth Neil
Litigation ....Georgina Squire
Property ....Owen Rafferty
Sports ....John Beagley

THE FIRM: Rosling King is a young, dynamic commercial firm based in the City of London. The firm's main office is on Fleet Street. They also have a London insurance market office in Leadenhall Street, EC1. The firm offers an imaginative and practical approach to working with clients to achieve their objectives. Rosling King values its clients and is constantly looking for ways to improve its relationships with them. With this in mind it has developed a unique client care programme.

PRINCIPAL AREAS OF WORK: This niche firm provides advice in the following areas:
Banking/Finance: Banking advice for both secured and unsecured lending, including loan and other standard form documentation, debt enforcement, insolvency, refinancing, securitisation and risk sharing, structuring of lending and underwriting.
Commercial Property: Including development from conception to completion, funding, landlord & tenant, leasehold enfranchisement, planning, portfolio acquisition and management and property investment and taxation.
Company and Commercial: Including intellectual property, joint ventures, mergers and acquisitions, new business ventures and investments and taxation planning.
Construction: Including all forms of construction documentation for contractors, sub-contractors and professionals, collateral warranties and advice on regulatory matters.
Litigation: All forms of litigation and dispute resolution, including professional indemnity, civil fraud, IT, defamation, sale of goods and general commercial claims as well as disputes in all the firm's listed areas of expertise.
Employment: Including contracts, impact of legislation on the workplace, business restructuring, redundancy and other forms of disputes.
Environment: Including appointment documentation for advisors and contractors, environmental liabilities for business and the impact of EU legislation.
Health & Safety: Including CDM regulations, developments in EU law, risk assessments, HSE matters and all forms of dispute.
Insurance & Reinsurance: Including claims handling coverage and market disputes, policy and treaty drafting and interpretation, investigations and commutations of problem portfolios, ART, regulatory work, risk assessment advice and dealing with run-offs, all of which advice is for domestic and international clients.
Sport: Including contractual advice, global representation of overseas interests, branding, IP & sponsorship negotiation, merchandising and promotions.

INTERNATIONAL CONNECTIONS: The firm has developed a large international network of associated firms in over 150 cities worldwide to assist its clients' internationally based work requirements. Associated offices can be found in Berlin, Brussels, Düsseldorf, Edinburgh, Hong Kong, Madrid, Milan, New York, Paris, Singapore, Stockholm and Zurich. The firm also offers international surgeries for clients in the UK.

CLIENTELE: The firm's clientele has developed significantly over the last 10 years. It is an almost exclusively commercial firm and its client base reflects its established areas of expertise. They include a significant number of banks, lenders, building societies, major financial institutions, insurance and reinsurance companies, Lloyd's Syndicates and other insurance professionals, property companies, developers and investors.

ROSS & CONNEL
10 Viewfield Terrace, Dunfermline, KY12 7JH **Tel:** (01383) 721156 **Fax:** (01383) 721150 **DX:** DF 11 **Ptnrs:** 6 **Asst solrs:** 1
Other fee-earners: 1

ROSS & CRAIG

12A Upper Berkeley Street, London, W1H 7PE
Tel: (020) 7262 3077 **Fax:** (020) 7724 6427 **DX:** 44416 Marble Arch
Email: reception@rosscraig.com

Managing partner:	David Leadercramer
Senior partner:	Leonard Ross
Number of partners:	9
Assistant solicitors:	8
Other fee-earners:	5

THE FIRM: Established in the 1950's with an emphasis on commercial client work, acting for public and private companies, businesses and individual entrepreneurs but with strong teams in respect of private client matters, family, personal injury, trusts, financial planning and bankruptcy.

PRINCIPAL AREAS OF WORK:
Commercial Property: Development projects, acquisitions, portfolio break-ups, structuring joint venture schemes of varying complexity with associated planning and funding requirements conducted through tax

efficient procedures. Clients number major developers retailers and hotel operators. Particular niche in banking security.

Company/Commercial: Includes a full range of corporate and commercial transactions, with ancillary employment, shareholder and director agreements, floatation, institutional and other funding schemes. Some of our specialist areas include intellectual property, computer contracts, media, entertainment, film and TV funding and production documents.

Litigation: Commercial disputes, landlord and tenant litigation and property disputes, employment law, intellectual property, complex personal injury work, professional negligence, insolvency and liquidations.

Environmental Law: The specialist land regeneration unit enjoys high level connections with relevant professionals and government departments. It provides services in a consultancy capacity and as a principal adviser on legal and risk management recognised as "leaders in the field".

Family Law: As well as usual areas of advice, this team has special expertise in dealing with cohabiting partners and in advising on the financial issues in a practical way.

Employment: Advice to clients in respect of both contentious and non-contentious work.

INTERNATIONAL CONNECTIONS: The firm has close links with lawyers in Europe, America, Middle East, Far East and much off-shore and EU compliancy work.

CLIENTELE: Clients range from internationally known companies to small businesses and individuals.

AREAS OF PRACTICE

Property	50%
Company/Commercial	20%
Litigation	12%
Family	10%
Employment	6%
Private Client	2%

CONTACTS

Company/commercial	Ian Bloom
Employment	Karen Fernandes
Environmental	Martin Polden
Family/private client	Simone E. Katzenberg
Litigation	David Leadercramer
Property	Daniel Polden

R

ROSS HARPER & MURPHY WS

163 Ingram Street, Glasgow, G1 1DW **Tel:** (0141) 552 6343 **Fax:** (0141) 552 8150 **DX:** 190 Glasgow **Email:** ingramstreet@rossharper.com **Website:** www.rossharper.com **Ptnrs:** 16 **Asst solrs:** 27 **Other fee-earners:** 21

ROTHERA DOWSON

2 Kayes Walk, Stoney Street, The Lace Market, Nottingham, NG1 1PZ
Tel: (0115) 9100 600 **Fax:** (0115) 9100 800 **DX:** 10028 Nottingham
Email: enquiries@rotheradowson.co.uk **Website:** www.rotheradowson.co.uk

Managing partner:	Jane George
Senior partner:	Chris Hodson
Number of partners:	14
Assistant solicitors:	6
Other fee-earners:	11

THE FIRM: Rothera Dowson was established following the merger of Rotheras and Dowsons with effect from 1 January 1999. The merger represented a growth in the depth and variety of services offered, including financial services.

PRINCIPAL AREAS OF WORK:

Corporate and Commercial: Small company formations, share issues, acquisitions, commercial agreements, employment contracts, intellectual property, commercial property including landlord and tenant, compulsory purchase, leases, Town and Country Planning.

Litigation: Civil litigation of all kinds, including a significant personal injury department with PI Panel members, crime, contentious intellectual property matters, employment disputes, contractual disputes, including construction. This department also includes specialist road transport lawyers advising clients in connection with operator licensing, traffic prosecutions, insurance-related work, carriage of goods.

Private client: All aspects of personal taxation, trusts, wills, probate and administration. Family and matrimonial solicitors covering all kinds of family work including advice on mediation and advocacy for mental health cases.

Independent Financial Advice: In-house independent adviser for all kinds of investment advice.

Agency work undertaken.

General civil contract for family and mental health.

AREAS OF PRACTICE

General Litigation (inc PI/ Transport/Commercial Litigation)	25%
Probate/Trusts and Tax	20%
Property	20%
Company Commercial and Employment	15%
Family (inc. Childcare)	15%
Other	5%

CONTACTS

Commercial Litigation	R, Hammond
Company, Commercial & Planning	C.C. Hodson
Crime	A.G. Priest
Ecclesiastical/Education	C.C. Hodson
Employment	M. Butler
Family and Matrimonial	C. Bianchina
Financial Advice	B. Morgan
Personal Injury	A. Balkitis
Property	A.J. Redgate
Transport	P.I. Rothera
Wills, Trusts, Probate and Tax	J.D. Allen

ROWBERRY MORRIS & CO.

17 Castle Street, Reading, RG1 7SB **Tel:** (0118) 958 5611 **Fax:** (0118) 959 9662 **DX:** 40125 Reading **Ptnrs:** 5 **Asst solrs:** 4 **Other fee-earners:** 4

ROWE & COHEN

Quay House, Quay Street, Manchester, M3 3JE **Tel:** 0161 830 4600 **Fax:** 0161 831 7436

ROWE & MAW

20 Black Friars Lane, London, EC4V 6HD
Tel: (020) 7248 4282 **Fax:** (020) 7248 2009 **DX:** 93
Email: roweandmaw@roweandmaw.co.uk **Website:** www.roweandmaw.co.uk

Suite 892-894, Lloyds, One Lime Street, London (Lloyd's), EC3M 7QD
Tel: (020) 7327 4144 **Fax:** (020) 7623 7965

Canada House, 3 Chepstow Street, Manchester, M1 5FW
Tel: (0161) 236 1612 **Fax:** (0161) 236 9712

Senior partner:	Stuart James
UK:	
Number of Partners:	80
Assistant solicitors:	125
Other fee-earners:	70
Brussels Office:	
Number of Partners:	1
Assistant solicitors:	2
Other fee-earners:	6

AREAS OF PRACTICE

Corporate	33%
Litigation	23%
Property	10%
Intellectual property	8%
Pensions	8%
Banking & Projects	7%
Construction	7%
Employment	4%

CONTACTS

Aviation & Transport	P. Maher
Banking & Projects	N. Morrison
Commercial Property	J. Clay
Construction Litigation	M. Regan
Corporate Finance	S. Bottomley
Employment	J. Roskill
Environment	A. Copley
EU/Competition Law	K. Desai
Insolvency	D. Allen
Insurance	S. Connolly
Intellectual Property	S. Gare
Litigation & Dispute Resolution	A. McDougall
Mergers and Acquisitions	P. Maher
Partnership	R. Linsell
Pensions	S. James
Public and Administrative	T. Child
Tax	P. Steiner

THE FIRM: Rowe & Maw is one of the country's leading commercial law firms, based in the City of London. Founded over 100 years ago, the firm's reputation is based upon delivering pragmatic commercial advice, and is praised for its professionalism. With over 80 partners and almost 300 lawyers in total, the firm offers its clients a broad range of legal services, both in the UK and internationally. In the past five years the firm has grown rapidly, adding to its traditional strengths in corporate, litigation, pensions and construction with innovative new teams in public law, projects and PFI international regulatory law. Although the firm is classified as a medium-sized firm, its position in the legal market derives from its 'top ten' client base. Industry experience is one factor which differentiates Rowe & Maw. Many of the firm's lawyers have spent time working in industry and, therefore have a better understanding of the commercial needs of its client.

PRINCIPAL AREAS OF WORK: The firm's main strength has always been in advising companies and businesses, both in day to day matters and on special projects. The firm is divided into a number of practice groups, the principal ones of which are listed opposite. The firm also has a number of specialist industry groups, the most notable of which are chemicals and communications (including telecoms, cable TV, broadcasting and satellite).

Corporate: The firm's corporate group is recognised as one of the leading groups in the country. It acts for a number of FTSE 250 companies, as well as a wide range of private and public companies, partnerships, financial institutions and intermediaries. The group advises on all aspects of corporate and commercial law, both in the UK and overseas. Under the corporate umbrella, tax, environment, professions, aviation & transport and EU & competition law have established high profile practices in their own right.

Litigation and Dispute Resolution: The group has grown significantly in recent years and, in addition to general commercial litigation and arbitration, has developed a number of specialist litigation based market sectors, most notably in insurance and reinsurance, public law, property, insolvency, international regulatory and competition work, all of which are considered to be leaders in their respective fields.

Construction, Pensions and Employment: These groups have long been identified as leaders in their fields. Over the last two years, they have been joined by more recently established groups such as the professions and projects and banking groups.

Commercial Property: The group has taken advantage of the resurgent property market and had a highly successful year.

Intellectual Property: The firm's IP group has trebled in size over the last eighteen months and has seen a corresponding growth in the volume of work, particularly from the IT sector.

INTERNATIONAL CONNECTIONS: Rowe and Maw advise clients internationally, either through its EU and competition law office in Brussels or through a well established network of contacts, particularly in Europe, North America and South East Asia.

ROWLANDS

3 York Street, Manchester, M2 2RW
Tel: (0161) 835 2020 **Fax:** (0161) 835 2525 **DX:** 14475 Manchester 2
Email: manchester@rowlands-solicitors.co.uk **Website:** www.rowlands-solicitors.co.uk

Managing partner:	Ron Taylor
Senior partner:	Philip Bellamy
Number of partners:	17
Number of fee-earners:	45
Total number of staff:	130

CONTACTS

Children	Anthony Broadley
Civil Litigation	William O'Neill
Commercial	Philip Bellamy
Criminal Law	Aidan Carr
Employment	Ron Taylor
Family & Matrimonial	Sidney Oxley
	Peter Dignan
Personal Injury	Malcolm Horner
	Jon Andrews
Private Client	Simon Hughes

THE FIRM: The roots of the present law firm can be traced back to 1885. Rowlands is a general practice providing a full range of legal services to both private and corporate clients on a specialist department basis, having 7 branches in the Greater Manchester area and its head office at the heart of the professional and commercial sectors of the city of Manchester.

PRINCIPAL AREAS OF WORK:

Personal Injury Litigation: The practice handles a substantial amount of claimant personal injury work. Six members of the firm have been appointed to the Law Society Specialist Personal Injury Panel. The firm undertakes a large volume of CFA's.

Civil Litigation: All aspects of commercial litigation, property and partnership disputes, debt recovery and insolvency problems, housing, community care and education.

Commercial: Acting for the company, partnership or sole trader, the firm is able to advise on a wide range of transactions including the acquisition, disposal of shares or assets, joint ventures and trading contracts, and all aspects of commercial property for both trader and investor.
Private Client: Work includes wills, trusts, the administration of estates, inheritance tax planning and financial services. In addition, all offices handle a large volume of residential property sales and purchases.
Family & Matrimonial: Divorce and breakdown in relationships outside marriage and all financial issues. Supportive, quality advice from specialist family practitioners at all offices. Several members of the firm have been appointed to the Law Society Family Panel and the Children Panel.
Children: All aspects of public and private law relating to children including care proceedings, adoption and contact. The firm regularly acts for all parties in such proceedings including parents, children and Guardians ad Litem.
Employment Law: The firm has in-depth experience in the preparation and negotiation of employment contracts at all levels from the shop floor assistant to the plc board member with corresponding expertise in appearing before industrial tribunals and the civil courts on matters of unfair and wrongful dismissal, redundancy and discrimination.
Criminal Law: The practice undertakes a wide range of criminal work including motoring, commercial fraud and serious crime. The firm also undertakes defence work relating to health and safety, environmental prosecutions and prosecutions brought by other regulatory authorities.

ROWLEY ASHWORTH

247 The Broadway, Wimbledon, London, SW19 1SE
Tel: (020) 8543 2277 **Fax:** (020) 8543 0143 **DX:** 300003 Wimbledon South
Email: ra@rowley-ashworth.co.uk

Managing partner:	David Prain
Number of partners:	21
Assistant solicitors:	26
Other fee-earners:	26

CONTACTS

Employment & Labour Law ....Michael Short
Personal Injury (Midlands & North)............ ....David Feenan
Personal Injury (South) ....John Moore

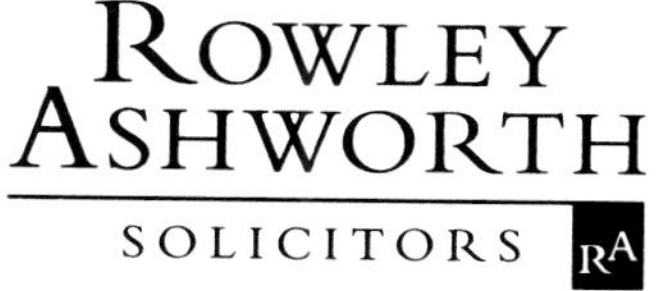

THE FIRM: Rowley Ashworth is a prominent specialist personal injury and employment law practice, acting for trade unions and their members from six offices in London, Birmingham, Exeter, Leeds, Liverpool and Wolverhampton. The practice was founded in 1829 and has been acting for the country's leading trade unions for more than a century. In 1986, partners committed to working for trade union members and other accident and disease victims decided to focus all their efforts on this area. Since then, it has been the firm's policy not to act for defendants in personal injury cases, or for employers in employment law matters (except where the employer is a trade union client). This policy has been extremely successful, enabling the firm to open offices in Wolverhampton in 1988, Leeds in 1992 and Liverpool in 1995. All have since moved to larger premises to cope with their expanding workload.In the year ending April 1999, the firm recovered more than £30 million in personal injury damages for accident victims. Every lawyer in the firm is a specialist in his or her particular field, thus ensuring the highest level of expertise. The firm provides substantial in-house education and training for all members of staff and is accredited by the Law Society to provide its own training under the Compulsory Practice Development System. In the past two years, substantial sums have been invested in information technology, including the total replacement of practice management and case management systems.

PRINCIPAL AREAS OF WORK:
Personal Injury: All types of accidents and industrial disease are handled, from high profile, high value complex claims to relatively minor claims. Rowley Ashworth has vast experience of asbestos related conditions (including asbestosis, mesothelioma and lung cancer) and serious head and spinal injuries.
Employment Law: A comprehensive employment law service is provided to trade unions on the full range of legal issues affecting unions and their members. These include rule drafting and interpretation, amalgamations, industrial action and legal relationships with other bodies as well as all aspects of individual employment and discrimination law.

CLIENTELE: Clients include many of the UK's best-known trade unions such as TGWU, AEEU, GMB, MSF and USDAW. In addition, the firm acts for many individuals who have suffered personal injury, including those introduced by major charities in the sector.

ROWLEY DICKSON

65 Church Street, Birmingham, B3 2DP **Tel:** (0121) 233 2298 **Fax:** (0121) 236 9155 **DX:** 13018 Birmingham
Email: info@rowleydickinson co.uk **Website:** www.rossharper.com **Ptnrs:** 8 **Asst solrs:** 8 **Other fee-earners:** 10

ROYDS TREADWELL

2 Crane Court, Fleet Street, London, EC4A 2BL
Tel: (020) 7583 2222 **Fax:** (020) 7583 2034 **DX:** 102 Chancery Lane
Email: info@royds.com **Website:** www.royds.com

18 Crown Lane, Morden, SM4 5BS
Tel: (020) 8542 1067 **Fax:** (020) 8544 0246

Number of partners:	15
Assistant solicitors:	7
Other fee-earners:	8

AREAS OF PRACTICE

Litigation & Employment	40%
Company	20%
Private Client & Tax	20%
Property	20%

CONTACTS

Company/Commercial	Peter Wootton
Employment	Richard Woodman
Family	Patrick Hart
Litigation	Stewart Wilkinson
Personal Injury	James Millar Craig
Private Client	Christopher Wright
Privy Council	Richard Woodman
Property	Robert Lloyd Davies
Tax	Arthur Alexander

PRINCIPAL AREAS OF WORK:

Company/Commercial: The department deals in company formations, disposals, acquisitions, shareholders agreements, joint ventures, MBOs and has particular expertise in intellectual property, insolvency, banking, construction, agency and e-commerce.

Property: The department deals with all aspects of commercial property together with landlord & tenant, and other property related matters. The department also has a wide practice in residential conveyancing.

Litigation: The department deals with the full range of litigation matters. It has experience of all types of litigation for both individuals and corporate clients with expertise in agency, company and partnership disputes, insurance related matters, insolvency, banking, intellectual property construction, and trust and probate disputes. The firm has fully embraced the use of ADR and will do conditional fee work.

Personal Injury: The department has a substantial personal injury unit headed by a member of the personal injury panel, also dealing with fatal accidents and accidents at work as well as specialising in cycle and motorbike accidents.

Family: The department deals with all types of divorce, children and financial provision disputes.

Privy Council: Royds Treadwell is proud to be retained to act for the government of Mauritius in connection with appeals to the Privy Council.

Employment: We have a substantial and well regarded employment law practice which is retained by large employers and membership organisations as well as acting for senior executives and employees in a full range of boardroom and workplace disputes.

Private Client and Tax: The firm has a significant private client department acting for substantial high net-worth individuals and trusts. The work of this department includes wills, trusts, probate, pensions, specialist financial services investment advice, estate planning and offshore trusts and tax planning or advice.

INTERNATIONAL CONNECTIONS: The firm has strong links in France, the Channel Islands, the Far East, Mauritius, Sri Lanka and the USA.

LANGUAGES: French, German.

R

ROYTHORNE & CO

10 Pinchbeck Rd, Spalding, PE11 1PZ **Tel:** (01775) 724141 **Fax:** (01775) 725736 **DX:** 26701 Spalding **Ptnrs:** 15 **Asst solrs:** 12 **Other fee-earners:** 28

RUDLINGS & WAKELAM

1 Woolhall Street, Bury St Edmunds, IP33 1LA **Tel:** (01842) 754151 **Fax:** (01284) 762436 **DX:** 57202 Bury St Edmunds **Email:** rudlings-wakelam.co.uk **Ptnrs:** 6 **Asst solrs:** 5 **Other fee-earners:** 7 **Contact:** Julia Wakelam • Specialists in childcare/family and matrimonial, personal injury and employment (particularly discrimination) law. Also handles agricultural, company/commercial, civil litigation, probate and conveyancing (both commercial and domestic).

RUPERT BEAR MURRAY DAVIES

Union Chambers, 11 Weekday Cross, Nottingham, NG1 2GB
Tel: (0115) 924 3333 **Fax:** (0115) 924 2255 **DX:** 10015 Nottingham
Email: rbmdlaw@aol.com

Senior partner:	Murray Davies
Number of partners:	3
Assistant solicitors:	6

AREAS OF PRACTICE

Matrimonial/Public Child Law	90%
Conveyancing	5%
Mental Health Tribunal	5%

CONTACTS

Matrimonial	Murray Davies
	Sarah Heathcote
	Isobel England
Mediation	Sarah Heathcote
	Catherine Stevens

THE FIRM: A specialist family law practice founded in 1992, by Rupert Bear, an established Nottingham family solicitor. The firm encompassed the family law practice of Eversheds, Nottingham and in 1996, was supplemented by the arrival of Murray Davies as partner, bringing with him in excess of 16 years experience in the field. Sarah Heathcote became a partner in the same year, having been with the firm since its inception. Upon Rupert Bear's retirement in 1999, Isobel England, with some 20 years experience, joined the firm, bringing a particular interest in the law relating to children, adoption and matrimonial finance.The firm has established contacts with accountants, pensions advisers, insurance brokers and other professionals, to assist in resolving financial matters resulting from the breakdown of relationships. A Legal Aid franchise for family work is also held by the firm.

PRINCIPAL AREAS OF WORK: Work includes separation and divorce and the financial agreements relating to all aspects of family relationships, the resolution of disputes involving children, their legal status, and adoption. The firm has considerable experience in co-habitation issues, pre-marriage arrangements and Mental Health Tribunal work. Mediation work, conveyancing, wills and the legal requirements of the elderly are also catered for.

CONTACTS CONTINUED

Mental Health Tribunal	David Burdett
Public Child Law	Isobel England
	Russell Tolley

RUSSELL & CRESWICK

2 Bells Square, Off Trippet Lane, Sheffield, S1 1JN **Tel:** (0114) 276 7481 **Fax:** (0114) 273 1289 **Email:** law@russell-creswick.co.uk
Website: www.russell-creswick.co.uk

RUSSELL-COOKE, POTTER & CHAPMAN

8 Bedford Row, London, WC1 4BU
Tel: (020) 7405 6566 **Fax:** (020) 7831 2565 **DX:** 112 London
Email: recepbr@russell-cooke.co.uk

2 Putney Hill, Putney, London, SW15 6AB
Tel: (020) 8789 9111 **Fax:** (020) 8785 4286 **DX:** 59456 Putney
Email: advice@russell-cooke.co.uk

Bishop's Palace House, Kingston Bridge, Kingston-upon-Thames, KT1 1QN
Tel: (020) 8546 6111 **Fax:** (020) 8541 4404 **DX:** 31546 Kingston
Email: recepking@russell-cooke.co.uk

Managing partner:	John Gould
Senior partner:	Michael Maskey
Number of partners:	24
Assistant solicitors:	29
Other fee-earners:	23

AREAS OF PRACTICE

Property	30%
Family/Child Care/PI Litigation/other	25%
Probate Wills & Trusts	15%
Commercial Litigation	10%
Company/Commercial	10%
Criminal Law	10%

CONTACTS

Abduction	Fiona Read
Administrative Law/Solicitors	John Gould
Capital Taxes	John Milverton
Child Care	John Hackett
Commercial & Construction Litigation/ADR	Francesca Kaye
Commercial Property	Peter Dawson
Company/Commercial	Jonathan Thornton
Conveyancing	Nigel Coates
Criminal Matters & Disciplinary Tribunals	Peter Cadman, Ian Ryan
Employment	Anthony Sakrouge
Family Law	Camilla Thornton
Family Mediation	Therese Nicholls
French Property	Dawn Alderson
Medical Negligence & Personal Injury	Janice Gardner
Probate and Wills	Richard Frimston
Property Litigation	Jason Hunter
Trusts	Michael Best

THE FIRM: Russell-Cooke Potter & Chapman is an energetic, professionally managed firm which has developed a reputation for specialist expertise in a number of areas without sacrificing its collective breadth of experience. The partial merger with solicitors Evill and Coleman in February 2000 has greatly enhanced the commercial property, employment and private client departments. The firm has offices in Bedford Row and Kingston but with the majority of staff based at the Putney office, it manages to keep overheads lower than competing firms based solely in central London and make substantial reinvestment in technology, facilities and human resources. Russell-Cooke's distinctive culture has produced cohesive and committed legal teams which are encouraged to develop and maintain long-term relationships with clients.

PRINCIPAL AREAS OF WORK: The areas covered include: commercial property; commercial litigation; company commercial; private client; trusts; wills and probate; family; medical negligence and personal injury; crime; child care; and conveyancing including French property.Within these areas the firm encourages specialisation. The firm has an unusually large client base (in excess of 10,000 clients instructing within the last three years). The requirements of these clients, who tend to have an ongoing relationship with the firm, mean that the range of services provided by the firm is unusually broad. The firm continues to be successful because its cost base is appropriate, it has young partners and staff and it has for many years sub-specialised to match the best competing expertise in the areas in which it operates.

RUSSELL JONES & WALKER

Swinton House, 324 Gray's Inn Road, London, WC1X 8DH
Tel: (020) 7837 2808 **Fax:** (020) 7837 2941 **DX:** 202 London Chancery Lane
Email: enquiries@rjw.co.uk **Website:** www.rjw.co.uk

Senior partner:	John M. Webber
Chief Executive:	Mark Feeney
Number of partners:	42
Assistant solicitors:	82
Other fee-earners:	71

AREAS OF PRACTICE

Personal Injury	64%
Crime and Fraud	9%
Defamation	8%
Employment	8%
Clinical Negligence	5%
Professional Negligence/Commercial Litigation, General Litigation	4%
Property/Family and Probate	2%
Business Services	Simone Kilka
Clinical Negligence	Gillian Solly, Rosamund Rhodes-Kemp
Crime, Business Investigations and Fraud	Rod Fletcher, Scott Ingram
Defamation	Jeremy Clarke-Williams, Sarah Webb
Employment	Edward Cooper

THE FIRM: Russell Jones & Walker, founded in London in the 1920s has grown rapidly in the last 10 years expanding from 100 to over 500 staff and partners, establishing regional offices in Newcastle, Sheffield, Leeds, Manchester, Birmingham, Bristol, Cardiff and Northampton. The emphasis on people has enabled the firm to develop an impressive range of specialist services of particular value to individuals and those who represent them. A Northampton-based call centre has recently been opened, providing additional legal and financial services to clients. The services include 24 hour legal helplines, a range of financial and insurance products, and a wills and conveyancing service. All are available to clients as part of membership benefit packages alongside existing legal services.

PRINCIPAL AREAS OF WORK:

Personal Injury: The firm is one of the leading claimant personal injury practices. A total of over 90 lawyers deal with a wide range of claimant personal injury work including compensation for industrial injury, disasters, chemical poisoning and environmental pollution, road traffic accidents, disease and disablement and criminal assault.

Employment: The firm has a large specialist employment department with a highly respected reputation within the industry, dealing with all aspects of individual and collective claimant employment law, both litigious and non litigious and including contracts, discrimination, dismissal issues, transfers and pensions.

Continued overleaf

R

Criminal Law and Investigations: The firm has a reputation as one of the leading criminal law practices within the UK advising and representing clients on all aspects of criminal law with a particular focus on white collar crime and commercial fraud.
Litigation: The commercial litigation department advises on all aspects of commercial litigation including professional negligence, defamation, intellectual property and insolvency. Specialist groups focus on copyright and sports law but the department is particularly regarded for its libel expertise having successfully acted against all national daily and Sunday newspapers and most radio and TV companies.
Clinical Negligence: The firm has a first class reputation for resolving clinical negligence cases. The department is a rapidly expanding area of the practice. The department has an exceptional success rate. All types of claimant clinical negligence work is undertaken with particular expertise in claims involving young children, representation at inquests and alternative dispute resolution in litigation including mediation.
Other Areas: In addition to the specialist areas of work listed above the firm has expertise in the following areas: commercial and residential conveyancing, landlord and tenant contracts, public and administrative law, public inquiries, family matrimonial law and other private client services including wills, probate and trusts and financial services.

CONTACTS CONTINUED

Family, Wills, Probate and Trusts .... Oliver Gravell
Financial Services .... Keith Halford
Personal Injury .. Ian Walker, Fraser Whitehead
Professional Negligence, Commercial Litigation and General Commercial .... Jeremy Clarke-Williams, Sarah Webb
Property .... Peter Klim
Sport .... Fraser Reid

S

RUSSELL & RUSSELL
Churchill House, Wood Street, Bolton, BL1 1EE **Tel:** (01204) 399299 **Fax:** (01204) 389223 **DX:** 24146 Bolton 1 **Ptnrs:** 17 **Asst solrs:** 11 **Other fee-earners:** 23

RUSSELLS

Regency House, 1-4 Warwick St, London, W1R 6LJ
Tel: (020) 7439 8692 **Fax:** (020) 7494 3582 **DX:** 37249 Piccadilly 1
Email: media@russells.co.uk

Managing partner:	R.A.W. Page
Senior partner:	A.D. Russell
Number of partners:	11
Assistant solicitors:	2
Other fee-earners:	2

THE FIRM: Founded by its present senior partner in 1974, Russells is best known for its experience and reputation in the entertainment industry.

PRINCIPAL AREAS OF WORK: Although recognised as one of the leading firms in the entertainment industry, with seven commercial partners, the firm also advises on general commercial matters. Three litigation partners also handle all types of litigation including breach of copyright, defamation, property disputes and divorce. It is also active in commercial and residential property, wills and probate.

RUSSELLS GIBSON MCCAFFREY
13 Bath Street, Glasgow, G2 1HY **Tel:** (0141) 332 4176 **Fax:** (0141) 332 7908 **Ptnrs:** 5 **Asst solrs:** 3 **Other fee-earners:** 1

RUSTONS & LLOYD
Beaufort House, 136 High Street, Newmarket, CB8 8NN **Tel:** (01638) 661221 **Fax:** (01638) 661732 **DX:** 50501 **Email:** rustons@netcomuk.co.uk **Ptnrs:** 7 **Asst solrs:** 2 **Other fee-earners:** 14

SACKER & PARTNERS

29 Ludgate Hill, London, EC4M 7NX
Tel: (020) 7329 6699 **Fax:** (020) 7248 0552 **DX:** 63 Ch.Ln.
Email: enquiries@sacker-partners.co.uk

Senior partner:	Jonathan Seres
Number of partners:	17
Assistant solicitors:	16
Other fee-earners:	1

AREAS OF PRACTICE

Pensions 100%

CONTACTS

Pensions .... Ian Pittaway, Peter Lester, Chris Close, Mark Greenlees

THE FIRM: Sacker & Partners was established in 1966 and is the largest specialist pensions law practice in the UK.

PRINCIPAL AREAS OF WORK:

Pensions and Employment Law: All the fee earners practise exclusively in pensions law and related areas of employment law. The full range of pensions work is undertaken, including pensions litigation, international aspects of pensions provision, and merger and acquisition work. Clients are employers (including leading public companies), trustees (including professional trustees) and trade unions. Referral work from other law firms (for example pensions advice on transactions) is an important part of the practice. The practice also has expertise in independent trusteeship through its company Independent Trustee Limited.

SALANS HERTZFELD & HEILBRONN HRK

Clements House, 14-18 Gresham Street, London, EC2V 7NN
Tel: (020) 7509 6000 **Fax:** (020) 7726 6191 **DX:** 196
Email: london@salans.com **Website:** www.salans.com

THE FIRM: Salans Hertzfeld & Heilbronn (SHH) is an international law firm with substantial offices in London, Paris, New York, Moscow, St Petersburg, Warsaw, Kyiv, Almaty and Baku. The firm currently has approximately 375 fee earners, including about 100 partners. The firm's London office is situated in the City and provides a full range of services to both domestic and international clients. It is particularly well known for its work in the banking/finance sector and the motor vehicle industry. Its employment department enjoys a strong reputation. Founded just over 20 years ago as a general law practice, the firm's growth has been continuous and rapid. On 1 January 1998, SHH merged with London-based Harris Rosenblatt & Kramer and now has a London presence of 65 fee earners, including 16 partners. On 1 January 1999, SHH merged with New York-based Christy & Viener, in the first transatlantic law firm merger. The merged firm is a multinational partnership which includes lawyers of more than a dozen nationalities. The diverse skills, professional qualifications, national backgrounds and linguistic abilities of its lawyers enable the firm to handle matters requiring local expertise as well as skill in cross-border transactions.

PRINCIPAL AREAS OF WORK: The London office acts for a wide range of domestic and international businesses, including UK and foreign banks, finance houses, building societies, international financial institutions and investment funds.

Banking: The firm has a well-deserved reputation for its work both in UK and overseas financing (including the emerging markets of Eastern Europe and the former Soviet Union). Its services include advising upon a wide variety of loans (including syndicated loans), lease and security documentation, and terms and conditions for trade, asset-based and project financings and arrangements for development capital and investment funds in the UK and overseas. The department has specialist knowledge of motor vehicle stocking finance, lease and hire purchase arrangements, consumer credit-related documentation, portfolio securitisations and insolvency-related issues.

Litigation: The firm has extensive expertise in banking and recoveries litigation and professional negligence claims, acting for clearing banks and major institutional lenders. In addition the firm is experienced in all aspects of general commercial litigation including contractual disputes, insolvency, fraud, asset tracing and breach of trust claims. The firm's work encompasses landlord and tenant disputes, consumer credit claims, LPA receiverships and an expanding domestic and international arbitration practice. Their litigators have experience in mediation and ADR.

Corporate: The firm offers a full domestic and international corporate and commercial service and advice on corporate structuring and privatisation in emerging markets. This includes structuring, documenting and negotiating domestic and cross-border mergers and acquisitions, licensing agreements, agency, distribution and franchise arrangements, joint venture agreements and IT and IP contracts.

Property: The firm acts for developers, contractors, financiers, operators and investors on projects in the UK and abroad. The work embraces all aspects of acquisitions, disposals, development and financing of commercial properties.

Employment: The firm is widely recognised as a leader in its practice area. It is headed by Barry Mordsley, who sits as a part-time chairman of Employment Tribunals, is a member of the Employment Lawyers' Association and was on the Law Society Employment Law Committee. The department deals with both contentious and non-contentious work, providing advice on such matters as restrictive covenants, employee benefits, unfair dismissals, redundancies and discrimination cases. A dedicated out-of-town office deals with volume recoveries and title perfection for leading banks, finance houses and building societies.

INTERNATIONAL CONNECTIONS: The firm has other offices in Paris, New York, Warsaw, Moscow, St Petersburg, Kyiv, Almaty and Baku.

Senior partner:	Lionel Rosenblatt (London)
UK:	
Number of partners:	17
Assistants:	25
Number of other fee-earners:	10
International:	
Number of partners:	101
Number of other fee-earners:	285

AREAS OF PRACTICE

Banking & Finance/Corporate	35%
Company & Commercial	25%
Litigation	20%
Commercial Property	10%
Employment	10%

CONTACTS

Banking and Finance	Stephen Finch
	Howard Cohen
Banking Recoveries	Caroline Havers
Commercial Arbitration	Lionel Rosenblatt
Commercial Property	Roger Abrahams
Corporate and Commercial	Philip Enoch
	Kevin Alexander
	Richard Thomas
Emerging Markets	Robert Starr
	Philipp Windemuth
	Joel MacDonald
	Timothy Stubbs
Employment	Barry Mordsley
	Michael Bronstein
General Commercial Litigation	Jeffrey Elton
Insolvency	Alison Gaines
International Banking and Finance	George Macdonald
	Philip Prowse
Professional Negligence	Lionel Rosenblatt

SHH
SALANS HERTZFELD & HEILBRONN HRK

SAMUEL PHILLIPS & CO

Gibb Chambers, 52 Westgate Road, Newcastle upon Tyne, NE1 5XU
Tel: (0191) 232 8451 **Fax:** (0191) 232 7664 **DX:** 61028
Email: admin@samuelphillips.co.uk **Website:** www.samuelphillips.co.uk

THE FIRM: A long-established firm offering a comprehensive range of legal services to private and business clients. In particular, the firm has many years' experience in medico-legal matters, and acts for a number of NHS Trusts. Members of Law Society Panels: Clinical Negligence, Personal Injury, Children, Family. Legal Aid Franchise including clinical negligence, crime, family, employment, personal injury, immigration.

PRINCIPAL AREAS OF WORK:

Litigation: Work dealt with includes clinical negligence, employment, commercial disputes, building contract disputes, debt collection, tribunal representation, crime, immigration and personal injury matters.

Continued overleaf

Managing partner:	Barry N. Speker
Senior partner:	Barry N. Speker
Number of partners:	4
Assistant solicitors:	9
Other fee-earners:	6

AREAS OF PRACTICE

Clinical Negligence and Related Medico-Legal Work	30%
Crime	20%
Family and Childcare	20%
Property	15%
Civil Litigation	10%
Employment	5%

Company and Commercial: Work includes partnerships and joint ventures, acquisitions, formations, reconstructions, commercial contracts, intellectual property, advising on funding, tax and insurance requirements, licensing and services to overseas companies.
Property: The work covers all aspects of commercial and residential property including investment, funding, planning and residential building estates.
Other Areas: The firm also deals with all family and matrimonial matters, particularly in relation to child care and adoption, as well as wills, probate and tax planning, and has a large criminal department. Specialists in Chinese businesses.

CONTACTS

Childcare	Barry Speker, Robert Gibson
Clinical Negligence	Barry Speker
Company/Commercial	Stephen Doberman
Crime	Stuart Grant
Employment	Robert Gibson, Barry Speker
Family Law	Jenny Goldstein
Immigration	Barry Speker
Personal Injury	Robert Gibson
Property	Stephen Doberman

SAUNDERS & CO

71 Kingsway, London, WC2B 6ST **Tel:** (020) 7404 2828 **Fax:** (020) 7404 2929 **DX:** 37995 Kingsway **Email:** rcp@saunders.co.uk **Website:** www.saunders.co.uk **Ptnrs:** 4 **Asst solrs:** 9 **Other fee-earners:** 12 **Contact:** James Saunders • Specialists in all types of criminal litigation, particularly fraud, heavy traditional crime asset forfeiture and Privy Council. Also civil litigation generally and non contentious.

AREAS OF PRACTICE

Civil Litigation	30%
Crime (general)	30%
Fraud	30%
Non Contentious	10%

S

SAVAGE CRANGLE

15 High Street, Skipton, BD23 1AJ **Tel:** (01756) 794611 **Fax:** (01756) 791395 **DX:** 21751 **Email:** mail@savagecrangle.co.uk **Website:** www.savagecrangle.co.uk **Ptnrs:** 5 **Other fee-earners:** 5 **Contact:** Peter Crangle • General practice known for private client, agricultural, housing, PI and commercial work.

AREAS OF PRACTICE

Private Client/Agricultural	50%
Commercial	20%
Housing	20%
Personal Injury	10%

SCHILLING & LOM AND PARTNERS

Royalty House, 72-74 Dean St, London, W1V 6AE
Tel: (020) 7453 2500 **Fax:** (020) 7453 2600 **DX:** 89265 (Soho Square 1)
Email: legal@schillinglom.co.uk **Website:** www.schillinglom.co.uk

Senior partner:	Keith Schilling
Number of partners:	6
Assistant solicitors:	5
Other fee-earners:	5

THE FIRM: Established niche practice with expertise in all areas of media entertainment, sport, internet and related industries. This includes media management, interactive and multi-media, digital, cable and satellite, as well as the more traditional film and TV. The firm continues to excel in its core market areas and has proven industry knowledge with an acute understanding of its clients business. It is fast developing its specialised internet and electronic business department advising clients on both commercial and litigation aspects. Schilling & Lom and Partners achieves the best results for clients in a cost effective way by combining practical commercial attitude with knowledge of their clients business sector.

PRINCIPAL AREAS OF WORK: The firms work is driven by the need to protect reputation and brand image, contractual and statutory rights. It is structured into the key areas listed below.
Litigation and Dispute Resolution: Swift and effective solutions are obtained by a combination of industry expertise and tenacity, often without Court proceedings being neccessary. Work undertaken includes privacy, media management, defamation, intellectual property, breach of confidence and all contract disputes. Our clients range from major corporations and brand owners, small and medium sized enterprises to sports stars, entertainers and other high profile celebrity individuals.
Commercial: The team combine their individual strengths and skills to provide a first class service specialising in commercial negotiation such as finance, licensing, options and merchandising, company documentation and employment contracts. Advice is given to major film studios, distributors of audio visual products, independent producers and artists as well as computer game companies, manufacturers and businesses trading on the internet.
Industry Specialities: The firm provides expert services to the media industry and has an enviable reputation for robust but practical litigation. Its in-depth knowledge and experience of the various media industries provides it with a better understanding of the needs of its clients and also a distinct advantage in legal disputes. In its entertainment work, the firm is innovative and commercial with an intimate knowledge of the industry. Recently, the firm has developed particular expertise in advising all those involved in the developing, publishing and exploitation of computer and video games and other forms of digital technology.

AREAS OF PRACTICE

Media and Commercial Litigation	35%
Intellectual Property and Multi-media	25%
Film and Television Advice	20%
Company Commercial	10%
Sport	10%

CONTACTS

Film & Television Advice	Nicholas Lom
Intellectual PropertyEmploymentSports Disputes	Eddie Parladorio
International Media Disputes & Crime	Simon Smith
Media Advice & Company/Commercial	Mark Wenborn
Media Libel & Commercial Disputes	Mark Thomson
Media Management & Multimedia Publication Advice	Jonathan Coad
Multimedia Interactive Games & Sports Law Advice	Pam Dalton

SCOTT-MONCRIEFF, HARBOUR & SINCLAIR

19 Greenwood Place, London, NW5 1LB **Tel:** (020) 7485 5588 **Fax:** (020) 7485 5577 **DX:** 46465 Kentish Town
Email: scomo@scomo.demon.co.uk **Website:** www.scomo.demon.co.uk **Ptnrs:** 2 **Other fee-earners:** 9

SCRIVENGER SEABROOK

26 New Street, St. Neots, PE19 1XB **Tel:** (01480) 214900 **Fax:** (01480) 474833 **DX:** 100315 St Neots **Email:** email@sslaw.co.uk **Ptnrs:** 5 **Asst solrs:** 1 **Contact:** Vicki Seabrook • The firm deals exclusively in defendants, clinical negligence and general healthcare work, with a small percentage of personal injury.

AREAS OF PRACTICE

Medical Negligence	95%
Personal Injury	5%

SEARLES

The Chapel, 26A Munster Road, London, SW6 4EN **Tel:** (020) 7371 0555 **Fax:** (020) 7371 7722 **Email:** searles@searles-solicitors.co.uk **Ptnrs:** 2 **Asst solrs:** 2 **Other fee-earners:** 1 **Contact:** Helen Searle, Tim Northrop, Christy McNaughtan or Martin Deller • Specialising in intellectual property with particular emphasis on entertainment law. Specialist in the music, multimedia and design industries (contentious and non-contentious), merchandising, and literary publishing. Sponsorship advice is also given.

AREAS OF PRACTICE

Music industry (both classical and popular)	70%
Film and Television	20%
Sponsorship/Merchandising and Advertising	10%

SEARS TOOTH

50 Upper Brook Street, London, W1Y 1PG
Tel: (020) 7499 5599 **Fax:** (020) 7495 2970 **DX:** 44643 Mayfair

Senior partner:	R.C. Tooth
Number of partners:	5
Assistant solicitors:	3
Other fee-earners:	3

THE FIRM: Sears Tooth is a specialist matrimonial and family law niche practice, with a commercial and residential property department. The firm is headed by Raymond Tooth, and is supported by three other partners specialising in matrimonial law, namely Elaine Williams, David Lister and Ann Ison. The firm handles all aspects of matrimonial and family law, predominantly dealing with financial issues arising on separation or breakdown of marriage, but also some private child work. The financial issues handled by the firm are usually complex, involving significant assets and frequently have an international aspect. The firm has a reputation for a forthright approach, and the often difficult nature of the cases it routinely tackles is reflected in the quantity of citations the firm enjoys in Family Law Reports, notwithstanding the relatively small size of the practice. Most of the members of the firm are members of the Solicitors Family Law Association. Raymond Tooth is a member of the International Academy of Matrimonial Lawyers.

AREAS OF PRACTICE

Divorce & Matrimonial	95%
Conveyancing (commercial and residential)	5%

CONTACTS

Conveyancing	J.F.W. Wilson
Matrimonial	R.C. Tooth

SEDDONS

5 Portman Square, London, W1H 0NT
Tel: (020) 7725 8000 **Fax:** (020) 7935 5049 **DX:** 9061 West End
Email: Postmaster@seddons.co.uk
Website: www.seddons.co.uk (London) / www.seddons.cz (Prague)

Managing partner:	Harvey P Ingram
Number of Partners:	15
Assistant Solicitors:	8
Associates:	3
Other fee-earners:	4

THE FIRM: Seddons is an international commercial law firm with offices in the West End and Prague (Czech Republic).

PRINCIPAL AREAS OF WORK:

Litigation: Has a strong international focus and a reputation for quality cross-border litigation work. Specialist Commercial and Physical Commodity Partners.

Property: Deals with commercial and residential property matters for a broad client base including investors; funding institutions and overseas investors.

Company and Commercial: Advises on corporate and commercial instructions, including mergers and acquisitions; bank trade facilities; Partnership; Licensing and franchising; agency and distribution; company structuring (UK and off-shore); and Corporate funding.

Media and Entertainment: Advises on a wide range of different talent, from large corporate clients to established and newly emerging artists in the entertainment industry.

Employment: Provides an employment service to corporate and private clients and all aspects of contentious and non-contentious employment law.

Prague: Provides advice on an extensive range of legal issues ranging from straight-forward commercial transactions to complex joint ventures with particular focus on inward and outward investments.

Other areas: The firm also has expertise in Far Eastern commercial property matters, Tax and Private client issues and has recently acquired 3 PI lawyers.

CLIENTELE: Client range includes overseas companies, banks, record and publishing companies, institutions; publicly quoted companies and owner managed businesses. Also advise the British Embassy in Prague and the Czech Embassy in London.

AREAS OF PRACTICE

Property	50%
Litigation	30%
Company and Commercial (including Employment, and Entertainment)	20%

CONTACTS

Company Commercial	Harvey Ingram
Employment	Julian Cohen
Entertainment/Media	David Kent
Litigation	Robin Austin
Personal Injury	Marvin Simons
Prague	Anthony Seddon
Private Client/Tax	Richard Burbury
Property	Simon Ross

S

SEDGWICK, DETERT, MORAN & ARNOLD

120 Cannon Street, London, EC4N 6LR
Tel: (020) 7929 1829 **Fax:** (020) 7929 1808
Email: sdmauk@msn.com **Website:** www.sdma.com

Managing partner:	A. C. Barker
Number of partners:	4
Assistant solicitors:	1
Other fee-earners:	3

AREAS OF PRACTICE

Insurance Litigation	40%
Arbitration	20%
Commercial Litigation	20%
Non-contentious Insurance	20%

THE FIRM: Sedgwick, Detert, Moran & Arnold is America's third largest firm specialising in commercial litigation, including insurance and product liability law. Founded in 1933, the firm has a total of 270 attorneys with offices in San Francisco, Los Angeles, Orange County, Chicago, New York and Zurich.

The London office was opened in 1985, and became one of the first multinational partnerships in 1992. Most of the practitioners are dual qualified (US/UK) and one holds a third qualification (Bermuda). With an emphasis on insurance and reinsurance litigation including directors' and officers' liability, fidelity, employment, professional indemnity, entertainment and property claims, as well as international arbitrations, the office acts for a number of major international corporations, insurers and reinsurers and is frequently involved with multijurisdictional disputes.

S

SEMPLE FRASER WS

130 St Vincent Street, Glasgow, G2 5HF
Tel: (0141) 221 3771 **Fax:** (0141) 221 3776/3859 **DX:** GW 337
Email: info@semplefraser.co.uk **Website:** semplefraser.co.uk

10 Melville Crescent, Edinburgh, EH3 7LU
Tel: (0131) 273 3771 **Fax:** (0131) 273 3776 **DX:** ED 447
Email: info@semplefraser.co.uk

Managing partner:	Alister Fraser
Chairman:	David Semple
Number of Partners:	14
Associate Partners:	6
Assistant solicitors:	25
Consultants:	2

AREAS OF PRACTICE

Commercial Property	35%
Company/Commercial	20%
Litigation	15%
Banking	10%
Construction	10%
Planning	10%

CONTACTS

Banking	Angus MacRae
Commercial Property	Angus MacRae
	Alister Fraser
Company/Commercial	Kathleen Stewart
	Stuart Russell
Construction	Ewan Thomson
Construction Litigation	Kenneth Carruthers
	Stuart Mcfarlane
Employment	Alison Gow
Enviromental	Margaret McLean
Insolvency	David Ogilvy
IP/IT	Stuart Russell
Landlord and Tenant	Paul Haniford
Leisure	Dolina Caie
Litigation	Alison Gow
PFI	Alister Fraser
Planning	June Gilles
	Kenneth Carruthers
Property Tax	Heather Nisbet
Venture Capital	David Deane

SEMPLE FRASER W.S.
THE BUSINESS LAW PARTNERSHIP

THE FIRM: Established in 1990, Semple Fraser is a specialist commercial law practice with a very strong reputation built on commercialism, innovation and cohesion. A focused practice, the firm believes in doing what it does extremely well, so as to maximise the clients' benefit. With one of the largest commercial property teams in Scotland the firm has developed highly regarded experts in areas such as construction, planning, property tax and property litigation. The firm is also well recognised for its expertise in corporate transactions including MBOs, MBIs, mergers & acquisitions. Semple Fraser's approach is to develop close relationships with clients so as to have a full understanding and appreciation of their individual circumstances and business objectives. The firm is organised on the basis of special sector groups made up of lawyers who share expertise in different and complementary areas of law and industry. These groups keep abreast of business and legal developments in their sector in order to develop optimum and innovative responses to complex commercial transactions. The firm continues to invest heavily in IT, and is committed to maintaining business advantages derived from that investment and enabling the client to receive better value from a faster and better service. The firm believes strongly in the continuous training and development of all its staff. The team spirit at Semple Fraser is the result of this investment and the benefit is recognised by its clients.

PRINCIPAL AREAS OF WORK:

Company and Commercial: Business start-up, acquisition and disposal, take-overs, M&A, corporate finance, MBOs & MBIs, institutional investment, banking, insolvency and reconstruction, taxation, interactive media law, IP, PFI, leisure and recreation matters.

Commercial Property: All matters relating, including property development and investment, leasing, retail, offices, industrial, leisure and recreation and property finance.

Commercial Litigation: A wide range of commercial litigation in both the Court of Session and Sheriff Court with particular strength on property litigation, employment, construction and alternative dispute resolution.

Planning and Environmental law: Pre-application negotiations, drafting S 75 agreements and planning conditions, representations at planning appeals and other inquiries, statutory challenges in the Court of Session and judicial review.

Construction: Representing a broad cross-section of employers, funders, contractors and design team members; drafting and negotiating building and engineering contracts, professional appointments and warranties; construction related litigation including disputes in the commercial court; arbitration, adjudication and insurance claims.

SENIOR CALVELEY & HARDY

8 Hastings Place, Lytham St. Annes, FY8 5NA **Tel:** (01253) 733333 **Fax:** (01253) 794430 **Email:** lawyers@seniors.lawyersonline.co.uk **Ptnrs:** 4 **Asst solrs:** 2 **Other fee-earners:** 1 **Contact:** Mr R.N. Hardy • Best known for private client work, particularly trust, tax and charity law work. Provides a comprehensive service to elderly clients and deals with commercial, development and agricultural matters.

AREAS OF PRACTICE

Private Client	65%
Commercial	20%
Litigation	15%

SHADBOLT & CO

Chatham Court, Lesbourne Road, Reigate, RH2 7LD
Tel: (01737) 226277 **Fax:** (01737) 226165 **DX:** 30402 Reigate 1
Email: mail@shadboltlaw.co.uk **Website:** www.shadboltlaw.co.uk

Managing partner:	Richard Shadbolt
Senior partner:	Richard Shadbolt
Number of partners:	19
Assistant solicitors:	14
Other fee-earners:	10

AREAS OF PRACTICE

Disputes	60%
Construction and Engineering (Non-Contentious/Major Projects)	20%
Corporate/Other	20%

CONTACTS

Aviation	Tim Unmack
Construction and Engineering	Simon H. Delves
Corporate	Andrew J. Trotter
Disputes Resolution/Litigation	Peter L. Sheridan
Employment	Helen J. Boddy
IT/E-Commerce	John Warchus
Projects	George Rosenberg
	Joe Bellhouse
Property	Sean Ryan

THE FIRM: Shadbolt & Co is a specialist commercial law practice providing a high quality service to business clients in the United Kingdom and internationally. As well as its office in Reigate, it has other offices in the City of London, Hong Kong and an associated office in Paris. The firm originally acquired its outstanding reputation advising clients in the field of major projects and in the construction and engineering industries. It now works in a wide range of practice areas including corporate, property, employment and aviation. The firm offers a cost-effective and imaginative commercial service backed by an unusual degree of experience.

PRINCIPAL AREAS OF WORK:

Construction and Engineering: The firm handles a wide range of contentious and non-contentious work relating to the construction, engineering and facilities management industries in the UK and internationally. Recent disputes have been handled in Uganda, China, Hong Kong, Egypt, Ethiopia and Tanzania.

Projects: The firm advises a variety of clients on the commercial and legal aspects of PFI, concession and BOT schemes and other major projects including reviewing and drafting contract documentation. The firm is used to working in collaboration with financial and other advisers on major projects both in the United Kingdom and elsewhere in the world.

Corporate: The firm has particular expertise in company sales and purchases, corporate finance, reorganisations and joint ventures. The firm also undertakes a wide variety of other high quality commercial work, including IT, intellectual property, franchising, European law, competition law and advice on general commercial agreements of all kinds.

Commercial Dispute Resolution: The firm's work includes litigation, arbitration and other forms of dispute resolution in relation to international and domestic business disputes. The firm is experienced in ADR techniques.

Commercial Property: The firm's commercial property practice is able to provide specialist advice on development and commercial property matters of all kinds, particularly in the fields of sales and purchases, property financing and landlord and tenant law.

Employment: The firm acts for many substantial employers as well as for employees. The firm represents clients in the Courts and employment tribunals and deals with employment and related matters such as health and safety. Clients are kept up to date with developments under both European and UK law.

Aviation: The firm's work covers all aspects of international aviation operations including liabilities, insurance, airport planning, air traffic control and environmental and regulatory questions.

CLIENTELE: Clients range from multi-national quoted companies to entrepreneurial family businesses. The firm's clientele has a strong international bias.

RECRUITMENT & TRAINING: The firm has an on-going recruitment programme for trainee solicitors and for qualified candidates with particular experience and expertise in the construction and engineering industry. Considerable importance is attached to in-house training and the continuing education programme for its solicitors.

SHAKESPEARES

10 Bennetts Hill, Birmingham, B2 5RS
Tel: (0121) 632 4199 **Fax:** (0121) 643 2257 **DX:** 13015
Email: info@shakespeares.co.uk **Website:** www.shakespeares.co.uk

Managing partner:	Andrew Argyle
Senior partner:	Anthony Jones
Number of partners:	24
Assistant solicitors:	26
Other fee-earners:	22

AREAS OF PRACTICE

Business Services	47%
Insurance Litigation	18%
Private Client	14%
Banking Litigation	11%
Other	10%

THE FIRM: As one of Birmingham's larger and broader based firms of solicitors, Shakespeares provides comprehensive legal advice to a wide range of clients including plcs, banks, owner-managed businesses, private individuals, universities, schools and colleges, insurance companies and charities.

The firm is recognised for its commitment to the quality of its service, having ISO 9001 accreditation and the Investors in People standard. As one of Birmingham's larger leading law firms, Shakespeares continues to strengthen its position as a key regional player reflected in a number of key long-term strategic decisions. The firm has made some considerable changes in personnel. It has injected young blood into the partnership, through promotions from within the firm and external recruitment of high quality specialists. The firm continues to remain a partner-oriented practice, ensuring access to senior expertise as and when required, and still aims to offer a flexible and personal approach.

PRINCIPAL AREAS OF WORK:

Business Services: Business services offers wide ranging legal services with the aim of providing clients with one pro-active department that can meet all their needs. It includes company & commercial, corporate finance,

Continued overleaf

commercial property, business litigation, employment law, charities and debt recovery work. Business services' client base is varied ranging from large plcs to owner-managed businesses and includes many inward investor organisations from countries such as Germany, USA, Italy, Denmark and the Netherlands.

Company and Commercial: Shakespeares' company and commercial advice extends to a broad range of areas including company structure, corporate finance, general contractual work and other commercial activities, such as licensing and franchising, distribution and agency agreements and insolvency. The firm also has a considerable specialism in employment law acting for both employers and employees. The firm also offers business litigation including alternative dispute resolution. There are three CEDR accredited mediators in business services. The firm also has a large computerised debt recovery department and also handles matters such as intellectual property and construction cases.

Property: A comprehensive range of property services are provided for financial institutions, property developers and housing associations, as well as private individuals. Leasing and financing of commercial property are handled as well as joint ventures and taxation matters for a broad range of businesses from owner-managed businesses to Plcs.

Charities: Shakespeares has a specialist charity team handling all matters relating to charity law and associated areas such as property, employment and general commercial advice. The charity team is led by Gary De'Ath who is one of the leading specialists in the area. The firm acts for over 100 charities which include several national ones.

Insurance, Banking and Institutional Litigation, Medical Negligence and Crime: Shakespeares has a substantial litigation department covering a broad range of legal services. The thrust of the work in the department is for business insurance companies, institutional clients, local authorities and banks.Shakespeares also handles litigation matters for individuals including medical negligence, crime particularly white collar fraud and professional indemnity claims.

Private Client: The firm offers a broad range of private client services including wills, probate, trusts, enduring power of attorney and tax planning advice. Additionally, Shakespeares has a dedicated investment management department – currently with £60 million under investment. Shakespeares has a specialist family law unit dealing with divorce and ancillary matters, cohabitee disputes, Children's Act matters and childcare provision.

CONTACTS

Banking Litigation	Stephen Jones
Business Litigation	Mark Beesley
Charities	Gary De'Ath
Company and Commercial	Jill Kennedy
Corporate Finance	Richard Baizley
Crime	Stephen Daly
Debt Collection	Rohit Deepak
Education	Anthony Jones
Employment	Mike Hibbs
Family Law	Nicola Walker
Insurance Litigation	John Buckingham
Investment Management	Graham Englefield
Medical Negligence	Gary Christianson
Private Client	Clare Laird
Professional Indemnity	Diana Wareing
Property	Paul Reading

S

SHARPE PRITCHARD

Elizabeth House, Fulwood Place, London, WC1V 6HG
Tel: (020) 7405 4600 **Fax:** (020) 7242 2210 **DX:** 353
Email: planning@sharpepritchard.co.uk **Website:** www.sharpepritchard.co.uk

Senior partner:	Ashley Badcock
Number of partners:	11
Assistant solicitors:	11
Other fee-earners:	14

THE FIRM: A well established practice in the fields of litigation and commercial work mainly for the public sector; with conveyancing, trusts, tax and some company and commercial. Also well known parliamentary agents.

PRINCIPAL AREAS OF WORK:

General Description: A general practice with a strong emphasis on litigation for a wide variety of clients; particularly public and local authorities and professional clients. Undertakes joint ventures, development agreements and PFIs for the public authorities. Expanding town and country planning practice.

Litigation: All areas covered particularly construction, environmental and property related litigation, personal injury including medical negligence; local and public authority related litigation – judicial review; commercial and defamation; employment; insolvency and debt collection; Chancery, child care and family.

Parliamentary: A substantial practice for public and local authorities, promotion and opposition of bills for a variety of clients.

Property and Commercial: A wide variety of property-related work, conveyancing and some company/commercial.

Contracts: The firm undertakes drafting and negotiation of contracts for works, services and supplies and advises on EU and UK public procurement, and joint ventures and private finance transactions.

Planning: All aspects of town and country planning, mainly for local authorities.

Private Client: Will drafting, probate, tax advice and all types of trust work.

Agency Work: Substantial agency practice in all areas; urgent work. Charges on application.

CLIENTELE: Public and local authorities, professional, private and small corporate, housing trusts, charities etc.

LANGUAGES: Italian and French spoken.

RECRUITMENT & TRAINING: Three trainee solicitors a year are taken on. They should have good academic qualifications and the ability to work as part of a well-knit team. Applications with a CV should be made in September of each year to Ashley Badcock.

AREAS OF PRACTICE

Civil Litigation	42%
Contracts	24%
Property Trusts/Tax	16%
Parliamentary	8%
Planning	8%
Private Client	2%

CONTACTS

Civil Litigation	A. Badcock
Contracts	S. Millen
Parliamentary	A. Lewis
Planning	J. Sharland
Private Client	C Belcher
Property	S. O'Donovan

SHARRATTS

12 Oxford Street, Whitstable, CT5 1DE **Tel:** (01227) 770888 **Fax:** (01227) 265507 **DX:** 32350 Whitstable **Ptnrs:** 4

SHAW AND CROFT

115 Houndsditch, London, EC3A 7BR
Tel: (020) 7645 9000 **Fax:** (020) 7645 9001 **DX:** 824
Email: ShawandCroft@btinternet.com **Website:** shawandcroft.com

Senior partner:	Roger Croft
Number of partners:	9
Assistant solicitors:	8
Other fee-earners:	13

THE FIRM: Established in 1980 as a specialist shipping and commercial law practice, the firm has grown steadily in these fields, while developing expertise in related areas.

PRINCIPAL AREAS OF WORK:
Shipping and Maritime Law: The firm handles every aspect of contentious shipping work, including collisions, salvage, charter parties, bills of lading, cargo damage, pollution, and shipbuilding disputes.
Ship Finance and Corporate: Sale and purchase, finance and registration of ships, yachts and fishing vessels, company acquisitions and disposals, joint ventures, agency and employment law.
Commercial Fraud and Asset Tracing.
Commodities: Work handled includes international sale of goods (particularly oil, grain and other commodities) together with other international commercial transactions.
Insurance: Litigation and advice on all aspects of the insurance markets in London and abroad, particularly marine insurance, P&I, Brokers E and O, reinsurance.
Property: Acquisition and disposal of commercial and residential property, landlord and tenant, probate.

INTERNATIONAL CONNECTIONS: The firm has an office in Greece as well as connections with France, Eastern Europe, North Africa and the Middle East. A worldwide network of correspondent lawyers in all major shipping and commercial centres is actively maintained.

LANGUAGES: French, German, Greek, Italian and Spanish.

CLIENTELE: Shipowners, charterers, P and I clubs and insurers, salvage companies, banks, commodity traders, oil companies, ship managers, shipbuilders, insolvency practitioners, property developers and investors.

AREAS OF PRACTICE

Commercial Litigation (and Fraud)	30%
Admiralty	20%
Shipping Litigation	20%
Ship Finance, Corporate & Other Non-contentious	16%
Insurance (Marine and Non-Marine)	9%
Commodities	5%

CONTACTS

Admiralty	Roger Croft
	Hamish Edgar
Commercial litigation	Nicholas Taylor
Commodities	Bob McCunn
Fraud	Roger Croft
	Bob McCunn
Insurance	Jonathan Kenyon
Personal Injury	Hamish Edgar
Property	Roger Colton
Ship Finance/Corporate	Richard Coles
Shipping litigation	Roland Jackson
	Mark Aspinall

S

SHAW PITTMAN

Tower 42, Level 23, 25 Old Broad Street, London, EC2N 1HQ **Tel:** (020) 7847 9500 **Fax:** (020) 7847 9501 **Website:** www.shawpittman.com **Ptnrs:** 4 **Asst solrs:** 9 **Other fee-earners:** 1 • Shaw Pittman is a world leader in complex technology transactions. The London office specialises in advice on the complete range of technology, e-commerce and outsourcing projects in the UK and internationally.

AREAS OF PRACTICE

Technology Law	100%

SHEAN DICKSON MERRICK

14/16 High Street, Belfast, BT1 2BS
Tel: (028) 9032 6878 **Fax:** (028) 9032 3473 **DX:** 460 Nr Belfast
Email: sdmlegals@dnet.co.uk

Senior partner:	David Moffett
Number of partners:	4
Assistant solicitors:	2
Other fee-earners:	2

THE FIRM: A long established firm providing a full range of services to corporate commercial and private clients. The firm is renowned for its constructive and pragmatic approach to servicing its clients' needs.

PRINCIPAL AREAS OF WORK:
Commercial: All aspects of commercial work are undertaken. The firm has an expanding practice in the area of mergers and acquisitions and has earned an excellent reputation in that field.
Licensing: The firm is highly regarded for its expertise in licensing and acts for major players in the drinks industry in Northern Ireland.

CONTACTS

Commercial/Corporate	David Moffett
Liquor licensing	Maura McKay

SHEARMAN & STERLING

Broadgate West, 9 Appold Street, London, EC2A 2AP
Tel: (020) 7655 5000 **Fax:** (020) 7655 5500
Website: www.shearman.com

Managing partner:	Pamela Gibson
Number of partners:	19

THE FIRM: Shearman & Sterling is one of the world's leading global law firms with expertise in virtually every major area of commercial activity. The London office advises on all areas of international financial transactions, providing both US and English law expertise, and is a recognised market leader in corporate finance and capital markets, mergers and acquisitions, project, banking and leverage finance and international arbitration and litigation. Founded in 1873, Shearman & Sterling has more than 850 lawyers at 14 offices in major financial centres worldwide. Its international expansion has been carefully planned to ensure consistency, depth and quality across borders and in local markets. The London office was established in 1972 and with

Continued overleaf

over 120 lawyers forms a major part of the firm's substantial European practice. Today, nearly 300 lawyers in Europe serve clients from the firm's London, Paris, Dusseldorf, and Frankfurt offices in the major practice areas of the firm, corporate finance/capital markets; mergers and acquisitions; project finance; structured and leverage finance, banking, securitisation and restructuring, tax; EU competition law and international trade; and international arbitration and litigation. About half of Shearman and Sterling's lawyers in Europe are admitted to practice locally in France, Germany and the United Kingdom, with the balance qualified in the United States. The London office work closely with these and other Shearman & Sterling offices around the globe depending on client needs. Since 1996, when the London office began offering dual US/English law capability, growth has been spectacular; the number of legal staff has increased fivefold in that time. January 2000 saw a relocation of the office to substantial new premises incorporating space for further growth. The practice groups are leaders in their areas of operation. The project finance group was selected as Project Finance/Energy Team of 1999 by Legal Business magazine, and globally ranked equal first on deals with a value of over $500 million. Leadership in the growing European high yield debt market was maintained with the office working on thirteen new issues, while the European equity capital markets practice was ranked first for equity offerings by European issuers for the third consecutive year. The European leverage finance team worked fourteen of Europe's fifteen largest LBO's and signed up ten. The combined US/English M&A team was ranked number one among US law firms for the number of European and UK deals. The office's securitisation practice was boosted by admission to partnership of Marke Raines, a market leader in this area. The clear strategy of the office is to be the market leader in London in the provision of US/UK legal services while leveraging off the strength of its other European offices. Building on the expansion of its English law practice, Shearman & Sterling will continue to enhance its comprehensive corporate service in all its fields of expertise, combining global coverage with local expertise to its clients.

PRINCIPAL AREAS OF WORK:

Equity Capital Markets: The London office has one of the largest equity capital markets practices in London for US offerings. It specialises in US-registered public offerings, in Rule 144A offerings and private placements of equity, in establishing ADR facilities, and in obtaining US listings. The office has participated in most of the privatisations in the UK with US tranches, as well as those in Italy, Spain, Greece, the Nordic countries and Eastern Europe. Together with the firm's French and German offices, Shearman & Sterling has the leading market share for international equity offerings for European issuers.

Debt Capital Markets: The London office has a dedicated team of US and English lawyers specialising in the structuring and execution of high-yield and investment grade debt financing, either US registered or privately placed under Rule 144A in the US and internationally. Shearman & Sterling pioneered the non-US dollar denominated high-yield debt structure, and has a leading market share for high yield debt offerings for European issuers.Project Finance: The office has one of the leading project development and finance practices with in-depth expertise advising projects developers and financial institutions on all aspects of structuring, negotiation, development and financing of major projects, particularly in the sectors of power, oil and gas, telecommunications, mining and transport infrastructure.

M&A: Another main strength of the London office is its cross-border mergers and acquisitions and joint ventures practice. The office handles public and private, intra-European and Europe/US cross-border acquisitions, divestitures, mergers and LBO's. It has the ability to structure and execute M&A transactions under both English and US law, in addition to its strong local M&A practices in France and Germany.

Banking and Leverage Finance: The London office is also a focal point of the firm's European banking, leverage finance and securitisation practices, providing structured senior and subordinated debt, bridge facilities, debt trading and restructuring capability.

International Arbitration and Litigation: The London office has a dedicated team handling a broad range of international arbitration matters. The firm's international arbitration group is headed by Emmanuel Gaillard in Paris. Worldwide, the group comprises 20 lawyers of different nationalities and backgrounds, many of whom work in both the English and French languages. Shearman & Sterling's international arbitration practice group is one of the few specialist teams operating in this field on a global basis.

CLIENTELE: Clients represented by the London office include UK and Continental European companies, investment and merchant banks, commercial banks, and European governments. Among them are BG, BT, The BOC Group, Barclays, Corus, Cinven, Citigroup, Deutche Bank, Edison Mission Energy, LM Ericsson, Goldman Sachs, InterGen, Investcorp, Merrill Lynch, Morgan Stanley, Nokia, Novartis, Orange, PowerGen, The Rank Group and Volvo.

SHEPHERD & WEDDERBURN WS

Saltire Court, 20 Castle Terrace, Edinburgh, EH1 2ET
Tel: (0131) 228 9900 **Fax:** (0131) 228 1222 **DX:** 553049 Edinburgh 18
Email: mail.desk@shepwedd.co.uk **Website:** www.shepwedd.co.uk

155 St Vincent Street, Glasgow, G2 5NR
Tel: (0141) 566 9900 **Fax:** (0141) 565 1222 **DX:** GW 409, Glasgow-1
Email: mail.desk@shepwedd.co.uk

75 Cannon Street, London, EC4N 5BN
Tel: (020) 7556 7028 **Fax:**
Email: mail.desk@shepwedd.co.uk

THE FIRM: Shepherd & Wedderburn pride themselves on being one of the largest Scottish based commercial legal firms with a strong brand image of delivering excellent quality of service, an in-depth knowledge of clients' affairs and areas of business, and practical, innovative solutions to its clients' business problems. The firm acts on behalf of clients throughout the United Kingdom but focuses outwith Scotland in the sectors of competition and regulation, corporate finance, employment, energy, funds & financial services, pensions, PFI, technology and IP. The firm operates primarily from offices in the heart of the business districts of both Glasgow and Edinburgh, from where it provides the best possible service supported by excellent resources in terms of training, technology, administration and communications. All the firm's lawyers understand that delivering an excellent legal service in today's environment demands not only high quality legal advice but a thorough understanding of the client's business and of the client's commercial objectives. Through its office facility in the City of London, the firm acts on behalf of, and conducts business for, clients in England and in the City in the focused areas referred to above. Within Scotland, in addition to the firm's strengths on a UK basis, the firm is an acknowledged leader in the commercial property market and a leading adviser to a range of local authorities, governmental or quasi governmental agencies. In working with such agencies, the firm brings to the partnership the same commitment to clients' objectives and flexibility in response to requirements as it does when acting on behalf of the private sector, tempered with an appreciation of the political context within which clients require to operate. The business experience at Shepherd & Wedderburn, acquired through acting for the private sector, is also a relevant asset which the firm brings to its actings on behalf of the public sector. In line with the firm's presence in the Scottish technology market, it acts on behalf of start up and growth companies, owner managed and small to medium enterprises operating within the Scottish economy. The firm has particular strengths in delivering services cost-effectively to this sector. In addition, its private client department delivers personal tax planning to the owners and proprietors of such businesses. For further information on Shepherd & Wedderburn and the various services provided, please contact the Chief Executive, Paul Hally. Alternatively, if you would wish to speak to a member of staff with regard to a specific area of law, please contact the relevant person named in the right hand column.

Chief executive	Paul Hally
Number of partners:	32
Number of fee-earners:	112
Total staff:	313

CONTACTS

Banking	Shona Sanders
Charities	Andrew Holehouse
Commercial	James Saunders
Commercial Litigation	David Anderson
Competiton and Regulation	Gordon Downie
Construction	Kevin Taylor
Corporate Finance	James Will
Corporate Recovery	Gillian Carty
Debt Recovery	Gillian Carty
Employment	Sheila Gunn
Energy	James Saunders
Funds and Financial Services	Malcolm Gillies
Hotels & Leisure	Hugh Smith
Housing Associations	Alison Thompson
Medical Negligence	Hugh Donald
Pensions	Andrew Holehouse
Personal Injury	Hugh Donald
PFI	David Nash
Planning & Environment	Colin Innes
Property	Nick Ryden
Public Sector	Ian MacLeod
Tax	Malcolm Rust
Technology and IP	Liz McRobb

SHEPHERD & WEDDERBURN WS

SHERIDANS

14 Red Lion Square, London, WC1R 4QL
Tel: (020) 7404 0444 **Fax:** (020) 7831 1982 **DX:** 270
Email: general@sheridans.co.uk

THE FIRM: Sheridans has a substantial international practice, is particularly noted for its work in all branches of the entertainment, media and communications industries, and offers a wide range of litigation services. The firm also has a growing reputation for its work in company/commercial and property law.

PRINCIPAL AREAS OF WORK:

Entertainment & Media: Work includes legal services relating to recording artistes, publishing and record companies, intellectual property, theatre, TV, copyright, merchandising, books, video, the press and related areas.
Litigation: The department has considerable experience in litigation involving commercial, entertainment, media, computer and public law work; matrimonial and immigration law and some criminal work. It also specialises in defamation and employment cases, banking litigation, and obtaining emergency orders.
Company/Commercial: Work includes the raising of finance, setting up of companies, negotiation of joint ventures, management buy-outs, demergers, acquisitions and disposals, reorganisations, insolvency and employment, intellectual property law, trademarks, copyright, and general commercial work.
Property and Planning: Work in the commercial sphere includes secured lending, property development, building schemes, property financing, investments and planning. The department also handles residential conveyancing, licensing, wills and probate.

INTERNATIONAL CONNECTIONS: The work undertaken in the entertainment, media and communications field, and the commercial field generally, requires extensive overseas contact, with the result that the firm is well-versed in dealing with foreign lawyers and professional advisers.

Continued overleaf

Managing partner:	Cyril Glasser
Number of partners:	16
Assistant solicitors:	6
Other fee-earners:	8

AREAS OF PRACTICE

Entertainment & Media	40%
Commercial & Other Litigation	35%
Property & Planning	15%
Company/Commercial	10%

CONTACTS

Commercial Litigation	Stephen Taylor
Company/Commercial	Murray Wells
Computers & IT	Michael Thomas
Entertainment & Media	Howard Jones
Matrimonial & Immigration	Richard Gifford
Property/Planning/Probate	Jay Soneji

CLIENTELE: The clientele includes major recording artistes and companies, television production companies, classical music composers and publishers. The firm has a substantial private client base as well as corporate clients.

RECRUITMENT & TRAINING: The firm recruits three trainee solicitors every year. Applications should be made with a CV and an accompanying letter to Cyril Glasser during August 2000 (for September 2002).

SHERRARDS

35 Market Place, St. Albans, AL3 5DN
Tel: (01727) 840271 **Fax:** (01727) 836775 **DX:** 6100 St. Albans
Email: law@sherrards.com **Website:** www.sherrards.co.uk

3rd Floor, 45 Grosvenor Road, St. Albans, AL1 3AW
Tel: (01727) 832830 **Fax:** (01727) 832833 **DX:** 6100 St. Albans
Email: law@sherrards.co.uk

Managing partner:	Alasdair McMillin
Number of partners:	6
Assistant solicitors:	13
Other fee-earners:	5

AREAS OF PRACTICE

Residential Conveyancing and Development	23%
Commercial Property	20%
Commercial Litigation (including Employment)	16%
Company Commercial	16%
Other Litigation	14%
Private Client	11%

CONTACTS

Commercial Litigation	Simon Braun
Commercial Property	Mark Peters
Company/Commercial	Mark Peters
Conveyancing	Andrew Moore

THE FIRM: Sherrards is one of the major providers of corporate and commercial advice in the area (a position strengthened through a recent merger with a niche commercial firm) and one of the few firms to specialise in antisocial tenant issues with housing associations and local authorities. It is also renowned for its expertise in employment law. A dedicated office at Grosvenor Road serves their ever-increasing commercial client base. Private client departments include an expert team of Personal Injury Panel specialists.

PRINCIPAL AREAS OF WORK: Commercial litigation (including employment); commercial property; corporate/commercial; conveyancing; matrimonial; personal injury; private client; wills, trusts, estate planning; crime.

SHERWIN OLIVER SOLICITORS

New Hampshire Court, St Pauls Road, Portsmouth, PO5 4JT
Tel: (023) 9283 2200 **Fax:** (023) 9286 5884 **DX:** DX 2268 Portsmouth
Email: mail@sherwinoliver.com **Website:** www.sherwinoliver.com

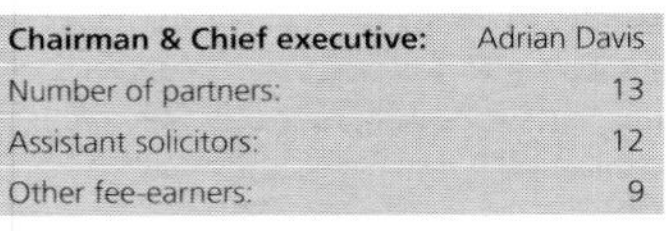

Chairman & Chief executive:	Adrian Davis
Number of partners:	13
Assistant solicitors:	12
Other fee-earners:	9

AREAS OF PRACTICE

Company Commercial & IP	30%
Commercial Litigation	25%
Commercial Property	25%
Corporate Recovery/Insolvency	10%
Employment	5%
General	5%

CONTACTS

Commercial Litigation	Christopher Brockman
Commercial Property	Andy Peck
Company/Commercial	Nigel Craig
Computers/IT	Nigel Craig
Corporate Recovery/Insolvency	David Oliver
Employment Law	Philip Broom
IP/Franchising	Geoffrey Sturgess
Tax, Trusts & Probate	Clive Saunders

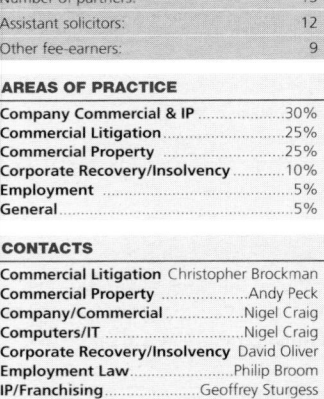

THE FIRM: Sherwin Oliver Solicitors is one of the leading commercial law practices in South Hampshire, providing a wide range of legal services to the business community. The firm is a member of LawNet.

PRINCIPAL AREAS OF WORK:

Company Commercial: The firm advises on acquisitions, mergers, expansion and restructuring of businesses, contracts, conditions of sale and purchase, licensing and all aspects of commercial law.

Commercial Property: This department handles a wide range of property transactions, with a particular speciality in waste management, environmental law and planning, commercial landlord and tenant matters and development.

Corporate Recovery: One of the largest specialist corporate recovery and insolvency departments on the South Coast specialises in all aspects of corporate and personal insolvency, realisation of assets and LPA receiverships and directors disqualification proceedings.

Commercial Litigation: All forms of commercial litigation are handled by this department, including contract disputes, landlord and tenant, construction disputes, insurance claims and debt recovery. The department has acted for two national business organisations in bringing claims against the government in the European Court of Human Rights.

Employment Law: This specialist department advises national and local businesses on all aspects of the law, including trade union negotiations and industrial relations. It also acts for senior employees and members regularly appear in industrial tribunals nationwide.

Intellectual Property: The firm has one of the few specialist IP departments in the region. It deals with IP licensing, litigation, trademarks and franchising. The firm is an affiliate member of the British Franchising Association.

Tax, Trusts & Probate: This department deals with all aspects of wills and probate. It also establishes and administers trusts, and advises upon tax planning.

INTERNATIONAL CONNECTIONS: Sherwin Oliver Solicitors is a member of LawNet Europe and Eurojuris which provide access to a network of 650 associated firms in 19 countries.

LANGUAGES: French, German, Russian and Swedish.

SHERWIN OLIVER
Solicitors

SHOOSMITHS

The Lakes, Bedford Road, Northampton, NN4 7SH
Tel: (01604) 543000 **Fax:** (01604) 543543 **DX:** 712280 Northampton-12
Email: northampton@shoosmiths.co.uk **Website:** www.shoosmiths.co.uk

Quantum House, Basing View, Basingstoke,
Tel: (01256) 696200 **Fax:** (01256) 696201 **DX:** 98574 BASINGSTOKE
Email: basingstoke@shoosmiths.co.uk

Exchange House, 482 Midsummer Boulevard, Milton Keynes, MK9 2SH
Tel: (01908) 488300 **Fax:** (01908) 488488 **DX:** 3140 Central Milton Keynes
Email: milton.keynes@shoosmiths.co.uk

Property Direct, Rushmills, Northampton, NN4 7PD
Tel: (01604) 543000 **Fax:** (01604) 542245 **DX:** 712280 Northampton-12
Email: northampton@shoosmiths.co.uk

Lock House, Castle Meadow Road, Nottingham, NG2 1AG
Tel: (0115) 906 5000 **Fax:** (0115) 906 5001 **DX:** 10104 Nottingham
Email: nottingham@shoosmiths.co.uk

Regents Gate, Crown Street, Reading, RG1 2PQ
Tel: (0118) 965 8765 **Fax:** (0118) 965 8700 **DX:** 4009 Reading
Email: reading@shoosmiths.co.uk

Russell House, 1550 Parkway, Solent Business Park, Whiteley, Fareham, Solent, PO15 7AG
Tel: (01489) 881010 **Fax:** (01489) 881000 **DX:** 124693 Whiteley
Email: solent@shoosmiths.co.uk

52-54 The Green, Banbury, OX16 9AB
Tel: (01295) 267971 **Fax:** (01295) 265620 **DX:** 24204 Banbury
Email: banbury@shoosmiths.co.uk

Managing partner:	Graham New
Number of partners:	78
Assistant solicitors:	107
Other fee-earners:	328

AREAS OF PRACTICE

Commercial	49%
Claims Compensation	30%
Financial Institutions	21%

CONTACTS

Claims Compensation	John Spencer
Commercial Property	Nigel Haynes
Construction	Chris Whittington
Corporate/Commercial	Nigel Thorne
Dispute Resolution	Claire Rowe
E-Commerce	Nicki Martienssen
Employment	Peter Ellis
Environment	Grania Thompson
Financial Institutions/ Property Direct	Andrew Tubbs
Food	Ron Reid
Insolvency	Andrew Pickin
Intellectual Property	John Hill
Marine & Shipping	Jonathan Hadley-Piggin
Occupational Safety	Ron Reid
Planning	Iain Gilbey
Private Capital	Trevor George
Retail	Gary Assim
Technology	Nicki Martienssen

THE FIRM: Shoosmiths is widely regarded as one of the most progressive, innovative and technology-driven national law firms. The firm has an outstanding reputation in the commercial, financial institutions and insurance worlds. Clients include a wide range of internationally known blue chip companies, financial institutions, large private companies, public sector organisations, SMEs and partnerships. Shoosmiths also serves the private needs of directors, executives and staff of client organisations, and other high net worth individuals, through its thriving private capital practice. Shoosmiths' gross fee income in 1999/00 exceeded £41m, representing yet another year of successful growth. Throughout the whole of Shoosmiths, clients can access substantial local resources backed by additional national strength and expertise when required. The firm's offices across the country are integrally linked through wide area computer and telecommunications networks and video conferencing, providing clients with access to the resources of the whole firm comprising some 1200 personnel. Shoosmiths actively encourages and assists clients to instigate service agreements which clearly set out the service standards demanded of their lawyers and the agreed charging basis including, where possible, an estimate or fixed fee quotation. The firm is accredited to ISO9001 and is recognised by Investors in People.

PRINCIPAL AREAS OF WORK: The business is organised into three divisions – commercial, financial institutions and claims compensation. Each has its own management structure designed to enable a flexible and responsive approach to the markets which they serve. The Commercial Division caters for the legal and other related requirements of companies and organisations and comprises six specialist units ñ company/commercial, employment, commercial property, dispute resolution, private capital and personal injury. Importantly, a number of multi-disciplinary industry sector teams exist which enable us to draw together the various legal disciplines in the context of in-depth industry-specific experience. These sector teams include technology, retail, food, construction, marine, education and property development.

Financial Institutions: The Financial Institutions Division acts for many of the UK's top lending institutions. It has a national reputation for its recoveries arm and is leading the revolution in direct conveyancing with its Property Direct operation.

Personal Injury: The Claims Compensation Division represents one of the largest personal injury practices in the country and deals with claimant personal injury work in a mould-breaking way. Claims Compensation's target market comprises major Legal Expenses Insurers and other institutional work providers.

S

SHORT RICHARDSON & FORTH

4 Mosley St, Newcastle upon Tyne, NE1 1SR
Tel: (0191) 232 0283 **Fax:** (0191) 261 6956 **DX:** 61037
Email: lawyers@short-richardson-forth.co.uk

Managing partner:	Michael Short
Number of partners:	5
Assistant solicitors:	5
Other fee-earners:	0

AREAS OF PRACTICE

Employment Law	42%
Commercial Property	20%
Civil Litigation	18%
Company Commercial	15%
Private Client	5%

CONTACTS

Civil Litigation	David Forth
Commercial Property	David Richardson
Company & Commercial	John Harrison
Employment Law	Michael Short
Tax/Trusts & Probate	Vanessa Harrison

THE FIRM: Short Richardson & Forth is a well established commercial firm acting for a wide range of clients, ranging from large plcs to local firms. It is particularly well known for its employment law expertise, but every department provides specialist advice coupled with a very personal service to all clients. All work in the firm is carried out by solicitors; no unqualified executive staff are employed.

PRINCIPAL AREAS OF WORK:

Employment Law: The firm has vast experience covering the full range of employment law matters. All department members are experienced advocates who are able to conduct their own cases before employment tribunals.

Commercial Property: This department handles a wide range of property transactions, but with a particular emphasis on property development, investment purchase and commercial leases.

Commercial Litigation: A full litigation service is provided, including commercial contracts, professional negligence, building disputes, landlord and tenant, arbitrations and common law duty of care.

Company Commercial: Advice is given on a wide range of corporate and commercial matters including mergers, acquisitions, formations, joint ventures, manufacturing and other commercial agreements, as well as advice to directors and shareholders.

S

SIBLEY & CO

6th Floor, 1 Heathcock Court, 415 The Strand, London, WC2R 0N8 **Tel:** (020) 7395 9790 **Fax:** (020) 7379 3371

SIDLEY & AUSTIN

1 Threadneedle Street, London, EC2R 8AW
Tel: (020) 7360 3600 **Fax:** (020) 7626 7937 **DX:** 580 London City
Email: lfelming@sidley.com **Website:** www.sidley.com

Managing partner:	Drew Scott
Number of partners:	16
Assistant solicitors:	30
Other fee-earners:	15

CONTACTS

Banking Regulation	Graham Penn
	Sarah Smith
	Andew Marsh
Banking, Trade & Project Finance, Derivatives	Howard Waterman
	Graham Penn
	Elizabeth Uwaifo
Capital Markets	Jane Borrows
	Howard Waterman
Commercial	Gill Andrews
	Chris Jeffery
Corporate	Mark Pinder
	Robert Asher
	Struan Oliver
Information Industries	Gill Andrews
	Chris Jeffery
Intellectual Property/ Technology	Gill Andrews
	Nick Lockett
Property	Julian Goodman
Structured Finance	Jane Borrows
	Graham Penn
	Robert Plehn
	(US Matters)
	Sarah Smith
	Jenifer Williams
Tax	Drew Scott
	Graeme Harrower
US matters	Robert Plehn
	Robert Asher
	Tom Thesing

THE FIRM: This leading international law firm gives advice in all major areas of commercial activity. Its London practice comprises principally English solicitors with particular expertise in banking, structured finance, information industries and technology, taxation, corporate finance, property and corporate law.

Sidley & Austin was founded in Chicago in 1866 and established in London in 1974 where it operates as a multinational partnership. Clients include many of the world's leading institutions, banks and businesses.

The London practice aims to maintain the firm's tradition of furnishing high quality, cost-effective advice in a collegiate environment. It has adopted a strategy of matching its clients' requirements with customised advice, emphasising long-term client relationships.

Lawyers in the London office have extensive European practice experience and can assist clients with matters within the European Union and elsewhere. Teams of lawyers are quickly mobilised, and carefully managed, to assist clients wherever their needs arise. The English qualified lawyers are supported by US-qualified lawyers resident in London and in the other offices of the firm and by relationships with leading independent law practices around the world.

PRINCIPAL AREAS OF WORK:

Banking & Structured Finance: Expertise in banking and structured finance covers such areas as banking regulation, domestic and international lending, single bank and syndicated facilities, project finance, trade finance, structured derivatives and capital markets. Asset securitisation is a particular strength and work in this field is carried out for originators, underwriters, credit enhancers, liquidity banks and credit rating agencies. The London office works closely with lawyers in the firm's US offices in adapting US financing techniques to European and other non-US assets and markets.

Information Industries and Technolgy: Sidley & Austin's London information industries group consists of lawyers who focus on those sectors of industry and commerce which revolve around the creation, exchange, exploitation and protection of information, communications and technology. With a focus on e-commerce, the group advises on the converging commercial and internet areas and the emerging technology sector with one of the leading European practices in the market.

Taxation: Taxation advice is provided by the London office regarding both domestic and international transactions, including mergers and acquisitions, joint ventures, corporate finance, banking and structured finance, commercial property, oil and gas, and asset finance. The tax group also undertakes tax litigation.

Corporate & Commercial: Advice on corporate and commercial matters includes mergers, acquisitions and takeovers, joint ventures, flotations, inward investment, company formations and employment law. The group provides expert advice across a broad range of transactions and industries, including a special emphasis on the growing e-commerce and internet markets.

Property: Property and property finance expertise includes debt and equity based financing, development arrangements, acquisitions and disposals and institutional investment work.

SILKS

Barclays Bank Chambers, 27 Birmingham St, Oldbury, B69 4EZ **Tel:** (0121) 511 2233 **Fax:** (0121) 552 6322 **DX:** 20876 Oldbury 2 **Email:** info@silks-solicitors.co.uk **Website:** www.silks-solicitors.co.uk **Ptnrs:** 8 **Asst solrs:** 4 **Other fee-earners:** 12 **Contact:** Mr.J.B. Burn • A wide range of services available. The firm has three offices.

SILVERBECK RYMER

Heywoods Building, 5 Brunswick Street, Liverpool, L2 0UU
Tel: (0151) 236 9594 **Fax:** (0151) 227 1035 **DX:** 14189 Liverpool
Email: law@silverbeck-rymer.co.uk

County House, County Square, 100 New London Road, Chelmsford, CM2 0RG
Tel: (01245) 293910 **Fax:** (01245) 351661 **DX:** 139166 Chelmsford 11
Email: law@silverbeck-rymer.co.uk

21 Newton Street, Manchester, M1 1HH
Tel: (0161) 236 8394 **Fax:** (0161) 236 0640 **DX:** 14413 Manchester
Email: lawgw@silverbeck-rymer.co.uk

Managing partner:	Patricia Ewen
Senior partner:	James Rymer
Number of partners:	9
Assistant solicitors:	40
Other fee-earners:	60

CONTACTS

Catastrophic Personal Injury ....James Rymer
............Keith Popperwell
Claimant (RTA) ....John Mooney
Claimant Personal Injury (non RTA) ....Joseph Skinner
Commercial Litigation and Employment ....Joseph Skinner
Defendant Insurance/ Insurance Fraud ....Andrea Lally
............James Pinder

THE FIRM: Silverbeck Rymer was founded in 1946 and is a niche firm focusing on civil litigation. Primarily, it services the insurance industry. For over a decade, Silverbeck Rymer's litigation work has increased year on year. This has given rise to increased staffing levels, mainly through organic growth, larger Liverpool premises, and in 1997, the opening of a second office in south east England. This strong strategy for growth has provided a steadily increasing annual financial turnover. The firm has a strong business focused partnership which sustains its competitive advantage by accurate and thorough research providing a comprehensive understanding of client needs and delivering services accordingly. Silverbeck Rymer has retained a strong and prestigious client base over many years, and is constantly increasing its market share of business. In June 2000 Silverbeck Rymer opened their Manchester office and recruited the defendant litigation team from Geoffrey Warhurst & Company including Keith Popperwell Warhurst's former senior partner together with two other partners.

PRINCIPAL AREAS OF WORK:

Litigation: Silverbeck Rymer is a leading specialist firm in the field of litigation, and over a number of years, it has developed particularly close links with the insurance industry. Its range of services is constantly being developed to meet changing client needs. In particular, extensive research of post Woolf requirements and subsequent implementation of re-designed services have addressed current and future needs. Dedicated departments and continuous training are in operation to retain focus and enhance the specialism of skills.

Insurance: Silverbeck Rymer are panel members for the UK's largest major insurance companies, including both main line and legal expense insurers. The defendant insurance department offers a wide range of services to main line insurers including defended liability claims and insurance fraud investigation. The latter being a particular area of growth.

Claimant Litigation: Silverbeck Rymer's large claimant litigation department has expertise in all liability areas with specialist units dealing with either motor or non-motor claims, contractual disputes, debt recovery and actions in tort. The non-motor claims department services in particular, the industrial sector and undertakes a wide range of industrial diseases claims including asbestos-linked conditions, chronic bronchitis and emphysema, industrial deafness and vibration white finger.

Personal Injury: Silverbeck Rymer has a thriving technical personal injury department which handles multi track cases on quantum levels in excess of £50m. This is one of the fastest growing departments within the firm and exists to answer clients requirements for expertise in catastrophic and serious personal injury claims. The firm has a panel of prestigious evidential experts and has strong connections with the Senior Bar.

Other Information: Silverbeck Rymer prides itself on thorough file management and case planning across all departments of the firm to keep cases on track. This is particularly relevant in the technical personal injury litigation department. Matters are handled with skill, efficiency and cost effectiveness within parameters and protocols agreed with clients. Silverbeck Rymer practises from prestigious, listed buildings in the heart of Liverpool's business community, in Chelmsford, Essex and in Manchester. It has projected forecasts and strategy for future considerable growth.

SILVER FITZGERALD

15-17 Castle Street, Cambridge, CB3 0AH
Tel: (01223) 562001 **Fax:** (01223) 518310 **DX:** 88009 Cambridge 1

Sen & Manag partner:	Raphael Silver
Number of partners:	2
Assistant solicitors:	9
Other fee-earners:	3

CONTACTS

Childcare ....Raphael Silver
Civil ....Victoria Davey
Crime ....Jason Coulter
Matrimonial ....Dawn Casterton

THE FIRM: This successful firm offers a specialist range of legal services and is widely recognised as a leading advocacy practice. The firm was one of the first in Cambridge to obtain a Legal Aid Franchise. The firm is a niche litigation practice specialising in family law & childcare, crime, civil litigation and immigration. The family department is the largest in Cambridge, being the only firm with three solicitors on the Children Panel, two solicitors on the Family Law Panel, and a trained mediator. The firm is situated close to both the County Court and Magistrates Court and so is ideally located to undertake agency instructions.

THE SIMKINS PARTNERSHIP

45-51 Whitfield St, London, W1P 6AA
Tel: (020) 7907 3000 **Fax:** (020) 7907 3111 **DX:** 7 Ch.Ln
Email: info@simkins.com **Website:** www.simkins.com

Senior partner:	Michael Simkins
Number of partners:	20
Assistant solicitors:	5
Other fee-earners:	5

AREAS OF PRACTICE

Media, Entertainment & Sport	70%
Other	30%

CONTACTS

Advertising	Charlie Swan
Commodities	Dominic Free
Competition	Stephen Hornsby
Corporate	Jonathon Sellors
Digital Media	Jonathon Sellors
Employment	Roger Billins
Family	Howard Stacey
Film	Nigel Bennett
Immigration & Work Permits	Vanessa Hall-Smith
Litigation: General	Roger Billins
Litigation: Media	Dominic Free
Music	Julian Turton
Photography	Charlie Swan
Private Client	Bob Rutteman
Property	Cyrus Fatemi
Publishing	Julian Turton
Sport	Nigel Bennett
Television & Video	Antony Gostyn
Theatre	David Franks
Travel	Nicola-Jane Taylor

THE FIRM: One of the largest and most broadly-based dedicated media law firms in Europe. A leading adviser in related areas including film, theatre, television, advertising and marketing, sport, publishing, digital media and photography. Long term relationships characterise and reflect the success of the firm's approach to its clients. Simkins lawyers are involved in their clients' businesses in a direct way – as business advisors, not just lawyers. This highly personal client/solicitor relationship reflects a culture closely focussed on the specific needs of different client industries. While divided into sector groups, music and film lawyers as well as publishing and marketing lawyers frequently work together. This reflects the trend towards convergence. With distinct specialisms, the firm is delivering more collaborative advice, as clients' needs develop with digital technology-driven opportunities. A feature of the past year has been the increase in the firm's corporate media clients, including two major banks. The firm is generally known as a media firm. The firm is the sole UK member of Advertising Law International. As well as its core areas, the firm advises on competition law, employment and immigration law (including artist/performer work permits), commercial litigation, private client and family law.

PRINCIPAL AREAS OF WORK: Media, entertainment and sport.

CLIENTELE: The firm advises the top four advertising agencies as well as the largest UK below-the-line agency. Unusually, the firm represents both talent and corporates. Music clients include Sony Europe, BMG and EMI International. Artists include Leftfield, James, Underworld, former Spice Girl Geri Halliwell and Sir Cliff Richard. Theatre companies include The Really Useful Group. Film and television clients include Film Four Matrix Securities and Channel Four and over 40 production companies. Publishing clients include The Publishing Team, two of the largest photo libraries and Everyman as well as individual writers such as Sebastian Faulks and a number of well-known photographers. This year, the firm launched "Virtual Advertising Lawyer" – a constantly evolving, interactive on-line database for the advertising industry. Created by partner and leading advertising lawyer, Charlie Swan, it draws on 15 years' experience in advising top advertising agencies. VAL works in conjunction with the firm's on-line 'early warnings' – email bulletins which flag up topical issues in the media sector.

RECRUITMENT & TRAINING: The firm takes on two trainees a year, and welcomes applications from people with particular experience in the world of media.

THE SIMKINS PARTNERSHIP
SOLICITORS

SKADDEN, ARPS, SLATE, MEAGHER & FLOM LLP

1 Canada Square, Canary Wharf, London, E14 5DS **Tel:** (020) 7519 7000 **Fax:** (020) 7519 7070 **Website:** www.sasmf.com **Ptnrs:** 9
Asst solrs: 34 **Other fee-earners:** 8

SIMMONS & SIMMONS

21 Wilson Street, London, EC2M 2TX
Tel: (020) 7628 2020 **Fax:** (020) 7628 2070 **DX:** 12
Email: enquiries@simmons-simmons.com **Website:** www.simmons-simmons.com

Managing partner:	David Dickinson
Senior partner:	Bill Knight
UK:	
Number of Partners:	107
Assistant Solicitors:	271
Other Fee-earners:	153
International:	
Number of Partners:	39
Assistant Solicitors:	154
Other Fee-earners:	59

AREAS OF PRACTICE

Corporate/Corporate Finance/M&A	41%
Commercial/Intellectual Property/EU	14%
Property	13%
Litigation	12%
Banking & Capital Markets	10%
Tax	6%
Employment	3%
Environmental	1%

CONTACTS

Aviation/Asset Finance	Kim Walkling
Banking	Harvey Chalmers
Capital Markets	Tony Smith
Commercial	Edwin Godfrey, Jeremy Sivyer
Communications	Tom Wheadon

THE FIRM: Simmons & Simmons is a leading international law firm providing advice worldwide to governments, listed companies, public and international bodies, and private individuals, through its network of offices and other associations and alliances. The firm was founded over 100 years ago in 1896. Since that time the firm's growth has been continuous. The firm has 146 partners, with 39 partners overseas and a total staff worldwide of over 1,400. It provides a comprehensive range of legal services with strength and depth and consistently to the highest possible standards. The firm aims to help its clients achieve their objectives by identifying opportunities and by providing practical and effective solutions. Quality of service delivery is recognised to be at the heart of good legal practice. The firm has developed its own unique project management system which ensures legal advice is delivered as efficiently and effectively as possible within budget. It has also invested heavily in technology. It is the first City firm to have linked its offices using a data communication link, enabling common access to and transfer of complex information above and beyond basic word processing and e-mail information. Simmons & Simmons also recently became the first law firm to launch as a free internet service provider. elexica.com brings together the best sources of legal knowledge on the internet and provides the first open online community for lawyers by an international law firm.

PRINCIPAL AREAS OF WORK: As a leading international law firm, Simmons & Simmons has particular expertise in mergers & acquisitions, privatisations, venture capital, international securities, corporate finance, major projects, PFI and PPP, financial services, capital markets products, repackagings, securitisations, corporate treasury and bank lending. It is also able to provide a strength and depth of quality advice in commercial law, EU and competition, intellectual property, communications and media law, development and construction work, property and planning, environmental law, energy, biotechnology, railways, all forms of dispute resolution, employment and pensions advice, and taxation. Other areas of expertise include corporate recovery, structured finance, unit trusts, insurance, commodities, asset finance and aviation, sports, shipping and advice on private capital to individuals.

INTERNATIONAL CONNECTIONS: Since the early 1960s, Simmons & Simmons has been committed to developing an international practice. Offices were opened in 1962 in Brussels, in 1979 in Hong Kong, in 1988 in Paris, in 1990 in New York, in 1992 in Lisbon, in 1993 in Milan, in 1994 in Abu Dhabi, in 1995 in Shanghai, in 1997 in Rome and in 1999 in Madrid. The firm also has strong international practices serviced from its overseas offices and through its alliances advising clients in, for example, Japan, Australia, India, Thailand, Korea, Taiwan, Sweden, Germany, Spain, Poland and Brazil.

LANGUAGES: Languages spoken in the firm include English, French, German, Spanish, Italian, Swedish, Portuguese, Dutch, Greek, Mandarin, Japanese, Russian, Czech, Slovakian, Polish, Cantonese, Afrikaans, Hungarian, Latvian, Hindi, Arabic and Vietnamese.

CONTACTS CONTINUED

Construction	Robert Bryan
Corporate Finance	Stuart Evans
Corporate Recovery	John Houghton
Corporate/M&A	Jerry Walter, Ken Woffenden
Dispute Resolution	Simon Morgan
Employment	William Dawson, Janet Gaymer
Energy	Jerry Walter
Environmental	Kathryn Mylrea
EU/Competition Law	Peter Freeman
Financial Services	Iain Cullen, Richard Slater
Insurance	Jerry Walter
IP	Kevin Mooney, Helen Newman
Pensions	Michael Wyman
Pharmaceuticals/Biotech	Gerry Kamstra
Private Client	Caroline Garnham
Project Finance/PFI	Edwin Godfrey
Property (commercial)	Alan Butler
Securitisation	James Bresslaw
Tax (corporate)	Paul Hale
Transport	Charles Mayo
Venture Capital	Alan Karter, Chris Wilkinson

S

SIMON BENNETT

35 High Street, Marlow, SL7 4XD **Tel:** (01628) 478088 **Fax:** (01628) 474441 • Niche matrimonial practice

SIMONS MUIRHEAD & BURTON

50 Broadwick Street, Soho, London, W1V 1FF
Tel: (020) 7734 4499 **Fax:** (020) 7734 3263 **DX:** 44738 Soho Sq
Email: rec@smab.co.uk **Website:** www.smab.co.uk

1 Garrett Lane, London, SW18 2PT
Tel: (020) 8874 7433 **Fax:** (020) 8870 4770 **DX:** 59062 Wandsworth North
Email: smabcrim@dircon.co.uk

Senior partner:	Anthony Burton
Managing partner	David Kirk
Number of partners:	11
Assistant solicitors:	3
Other fee-earners:	9

THE FIRM: Simons Muirhead & Burton, founded in Covent Garden in 1972 as a human rights, music and criminal practice, is now established in Soho to service the expanding media side of its practice. The firm, which aims to provide a partner led quality service at competitive rates, undertakes work for commercial and private clients, and operates the Legal Aid scheme in criminal cases and has the benefit of Legal Aid Franchise.

PRINCIPAL AREAS OF WORK:
Media and Entertainment: Independent film and television production companies, theatre (including Royal Court and Soho Theatre Company) and publishing.
Civil Litigation: Defamation, intellectual property and media work for newspapers and magazines, as well as employment and general litigation.
Commercial Fraud: All fraud investigations, including SFO prosecutions, DTI enquiries, insider dealing, corruption, money laundering and Regulatory proceedings. The firm also has extensive experience of conducting investigations for corporate clients.
Company/Commercial: All aspects of company commercial work, with a particular emphasis on media related companies.
General Crime: All types of criminal allegations are handled both in the firm's Soho and Wandsworth offices.
Privy Council: Civil and criminal cases (private).
Civil Liberties and Human Rights: The firm has won awards for its commitment to death row cases in the Caribbean, and has a long tradition of general work in this area.
Property: Commercial property; development projects; funding; Building Contracts; residential conveyancing; licencing.
Agency Work: The location of the firm enables it to service cases in the High Court and all central London courts and tribunal. The firm also acts as Privy Council agents.

AREAS OF PRACTICE

Criminal litigation	40%
Civil litigation	20%
Media law	20%
Company and commercial law	10%
Conveyancing	10%

CONTACTS

Civil Liberties	A.C. Burton
Civil litigation	R. Mireskandari
Commercial fraud	D.N. Kirk
	A C Burton
Company and commercial	M. Smith
Employment	M. Smith
General Crime	A.C. Burton
	SD Bird
Investigations	D.N. Kirk
Media/entertainment	S.M. Goldberg
Privy Council	R. Mireskandari
Property	D.G. Michaels

simons muirhead & burton

SIMPSON & CO

65 Church Street, Birmingham, B3 2DP
Tel: (0121) 233 2298 **Fax:** (0121) 236 9155 **DX:** 13018 Birmingham
Email: law@simpsonsol.com

Managing partner:	Kirk Simpson
Senior partner:	Kirk Simpson
Number of partners:	3
Assistant solicitors:	5
Other fee-earners:	3

THE FIRM: A new firm established in April 2000. It was formerly the Birmingham office of Rowley Dickinson. Partner, Chris Ball is Deputy Coroner in Birmingham.

Continued overleaf

PRINCIPAL AREAS OF WORK: Personal injury, claimant and defendant insurance; employment law; commercial litigation; commercial and domestic property.

LANGUAGES: English and French.

CLIENTELE: Insurance companies, local authorities, police and fire authorities, power utilities and small companies.

AREAS OF PRACTICE	
Defendant Insurance	80%
Claimant Personal Injury	10%
Commercial & Domestic Property	5%
Employment & Commercial Litigation	5%

SIMPSON & MARWICK WS

18 Heriot Row, Edinburgh, EH3 6HS
Tel: (0131) 557 1545 **Fax:** (0131) 557 4409 **DX:** 161 Edinburgh
Email: email@simpmar.co.uk **Website:** www.simpmar.co.uk

1 Carden Place, Aberdeen, AB10 1UT
Tel: (01224) 624924 **Fax:** (01224) 626590 **DX:** AB6
Email: email@simpmar.co.uk

15 South Tay Street, Dundee, DD1 1NU
Tel: (01382) 200373 **Fax:** (01382) 200370 **DX:** DD52
Email: email@simpmar.co.uk

93 West George Street, Glasgow, G2 1PB
Tel: (0141) 248 2666 **Fax:** (0141) 248 9590 **DX:** GW377
Email: email@simpmar.co.uk

THE FIRM: Simpson & Marwick is a specialist civil litigation practice with particular expertise in defender reparation work. From offices in Edinburgh, Glasgow, Aberdeen and Dundee, the firm represents clients in courts throughout Scotland. The firm's team of litigators is one of the largest and most experienced in the country.

PRINCIPAL AREAS OF WORK: Personal injury, professional and medical negligence, major accident actions, commercial litigation, public/employers' liability, health and safety, healthcare law, employment law and property.

Senior partner:	John Miller
Chairman:	Gordon Keyden
Number of partners:	14
Assistant solicitors:	27
Other fee-earners:	13

AREAS OF PRACTICE	
Personal Injury	40%
Professional Negligence/ Clinical Negligence	35%
Commercial Litigation	15%
Property/Private Client	10%

CONTACTS	
Commercial Litigation	Peter Anderson, Charles McGregor
Family	John Thomson
Health & Safety	Robert Leith, Gordon Keyden
Insurance	Gordon Keyden, Douglas Russell
Local Government	Michael Wood, Kate Shaw
Oil Industry	Douglas Russell, Robert Leith
Personal Injury	Gordon Keyden, Michael Wood
Private Client	John Miller
Professional & Clinical Negligence	Dr Pamela Abernethy, Peter Anderson
Property	Richard Loudon

SINCLAIR ABSON SMITH

30 Greek Street, Stockport, SK3 8AD **Tel:** (0161) 480 1221 **Fax:** (0161) 480 4246 **DX:** 22603 Stockport **Email:** help@saslawyers.co.uk
Website: www.saslawyers.co.uk **Ptnrs:** 9 **Asst solrs:** 5 **Other fee-earners:** 7

SINCLAIR ROCHE & TEMPERLEY

Royex House, 5 Aldermanbury Square, London, EC2V 7LE
Tel: (020) 7452 4000 **Fax:** (020) 7452 4001
Email: info@srtlaw.com **Website:** www.srtlaw.com

THE FIRM: Sinclair Roche & Temperley is a major international law firm specialising in international trade and transportation. The firm was founded in the City of London in 1934 and provides high quality, specialised legal advice to the international business community, with particular focus on shipping, aviation, trade and energy.

PRINCIPAL AREAS OF WORK: In London, the firm's principal practice areas are shipping and commercial litigation; arbitration and alternative dispute resolution; ship, asset and project finance; marine casualty and insurance; commodities; energy; aviation; corporate finance; company/commercial; commercial property; insolvency; employment; tax and European Union law. The firm has developed an active practice in China in shipping, energy, corporate banking and is a leading international maritime law firm in Shanghai. In Hong Kong, the firm's practice comprises primarily shipping and commercial litigation; arbitration and alternative dispute resolution; ship, asset and project finance; marine casualty and insurance commodities; energy; insolvency and corporate finance. In Romania and elsewhere in Europe, the firm is extensively involved in corporate and project finance, particularly energy and water projects, privatisation, investment and property work, with clients ranging from multi-national corporations and international financial institutions to local banks and businesses.

INTERNATIONAL CONNECTIONS: The firm has offices in London, Hong Kong, Shanghai and Bucharest, with associated offices in Singapore, Jakarta and Bangkok, in alliance with the law firm Colin Ng & Partners.

RECRUITMENT & TRAINING: The firm recruits up to eight trainees a year. Candidates should apply by letter and CV to the Director of Human Resources.

Managing partner:	Jeff Morgan
UK:	
Number of partners:	25
Assistant solicitors:	29
Other fee-earners:	27
International:	
Number of partners:	9
Assistant solicitors:	15
Other fee-earners:	11

CONTACTS	
Aviation	David Relf
Commercial Litigation/Insolvency	Rod Cowper
Commercial Property	Martin Whitworth
Commodities	Sian Fellows
Company/Commercial	Kevin Dean
Employment	Alan Bercow
Energy	Gary Campbell
European Union Law	Alfred Merckx
Maritime Casualty and Insurance	Joe Atkinson
Privatisation/Project Finance	Kevin Dean
Ship and Asset Finance	George Hodgkinson
Shipping Litigation	Ben Leach
Sport	James Felt
Tax	David Relf

SINCLAIRS

Windsor Chambers, Stanwell Road, Penarth, CF64 2AA **Tel:** (029) 2070 6444 **Fax:** (029) 2071 1199 **DX:** 52361
Email: sinclairs.solicitors@bt.internet.com

SINCLAIR TAYLOR & MARTIN

9 Thorpe Close, Portobello Road, London, W10 5XL **Tel:** 0208 969 3667 **Fax:** 0208 969 7044 **DX:** 47601 Ladbroke Grove
Email: enquiries@sinclairtaylor.co.uk **Ptnrs:** 6 **Asst solrs:** 5

SINGLETONS

The Ridge, South View Road, Pinner, London, HA5 3YD
Tel: (020) 8866 1934 **Fax:** (020) 8429 9212
Email: susan@singlelaw.com **Website:** www.singlelaw.com

THE FIRM: Founded in 1994 by well known competition/intellectual property solicitor, Susan Singleton, Singletons provides highly specialised advice on EU/ UK competition law, intellectual property, computer/IT and commercial and EU law to over 250 well known public companies and others at £150 per hour. The firm also advises other solicitors' firms and provides in-house training to clients and solicitors. Both contentious and non-contentious work is undertaken. Full use is made of new technology. Susan Singleton is author of 20 books including: *Commercial Agency*; *Competition Act 1998*; *Data Protection*; *Business, the Internet & the Law* and edits *IT Law Today* and *Comparative Law of Monopolies*.

Managing partner:	E. Susan Singleton
Number of partners:	1

AREAS OF PRACTICE

Commercial	30%
Competition	30%
Intellectual Property	25%
Computer/Internet	15%

CONTACTS

All Categories	Susan Singleton

S

SINTON & CO

5 Osborne Terrace, Newcastle upon Tyne, NE2 1SQ **Tel:** (0191) 212 7800 **Fax:** (0191) 281 3675 **DX:** 62551 Jesmond **Email:** law@sinton.co.uk **Website:** www.scoot.co.uk/sinton-solicitors **Ptnrs:** 9 **Asst solrs:** 7 **Other fee-earners:** 12 **Contact:** Mr J. R. Cawood • General practice with substantial personal injury, litigation department and expertise in company, conveyancing and matrimonial work.

AREAS OF PRACTICE

Personal Injury and Insurance Litigation	56%
Conveyancing/Family/ Wills and Probate	32%
Company and Commercial	18%

SKENE EDWARDS WS

5 Albyn Place, Edinburgh, EH2 4NJ **Tel:** (0131) 225 6665 **Fax:** (0131) 220 1015 **DX:** 59 Edinburgh **Ptnrs:** 10 **Asst solrs:** 7 **Other fee-earners:** 4

SLAUGHTER AND MAY

35 Basinghall Street, London, EC2V 5DB
Tel: (020) 7600 1200 **Fax:** (020) 7600 0289 **DX:** LDE and CDE Box No. 11
Email: mail@slaughterandmay.com **Website:** www.slaughterandmay.com

THE FIRM: Slaughter and May is one of the pre-eminent law firms in the world. It has a diverse and extensive international practice dealing with a wide range of corporate, commercial and financial work for UK, overseas and international clients. Slaughter and May aims to provide a professional service of the highest quality. The firm has a distinctive approach to the practice of law and encourages all its lawyers to gain a wide experience in commercial and financial matters so that they offer not only a depth of legal expertise but also versatility and a breadth of commercial experience. Slaughter and May is noted for its positive approach combining technical excellence, commercial awareness and an ability to provide practical, constructive solutions.

PRINCIPAL AREAS OF WORK: Slaughter and May's practice covers a broad spectrum of corporate, commercial and financial work. Clients include industrial and commercial companies from all business sectors, banks, financial institutions and professional firms as well as governments, public bodies and other organisations. The principal areas of practice comprise:

Corporate and Corporate Finance: Securities issues, flotations, mergers and acquisitions and corporate and commercial transactions generally, including privatisation-related work.

Banking and Capital Markets: International debt and equities issues and derivatives; international and domestic lending, structured finance and project and asset finance; and insolvency and asset-tracing work.

Financial Regulation: The regulatory aspects of corporate finance, fund management, securities and derivatives as well as supervision and regulation of banks, building societies and friendly societies, insurance companies and Lloyd's.

Litigation and Arbitration: A wide range of commercial proceedings and disputes including hearings before the High Court, the House of Lords and the Privy Council, domestic and international arbitrations, formal enquiries, investigations and inter-jurisdictional disputes.

Intellectual Property: All aspects of the creation and ownership of intellectual property rights including the acquisition, development and licensing of computer systems and programs.

Property: All types of commercial property transactions as well as advice on construction and engineering projects in the UK and overseas.

Continued overleaf

AREAS OF PRACTICE

Corporate & Financial	67%
Commercial Litigation	10%
Property (Commercial)	6%
Tax (Corporate)	6%
EC & Competition	4%
Pensions & Employment	4%
Intellectual Property	3%

CONTACTS

Asset Finance	Tom Kinnersley
Banking	Richard Slater
Building Societies	Tim Clark
Capital Markets	David Frank
Corporate Finance	Michael Pescod
EC & Competition	Malcolm Nicholson
Environment	Dermot Rice
Financial Regulation	Ruth Fox
General Corporate & Commercial	Nigel Boardman
Information Technology	Nigel Swycher
Insolvency & Restructuring	Jonathan Rushworth
Insurance	Glen James
Intellectual Property	Chris Hickson
Investment Funds	James Cripps
Litigation & Arbitration	Richard Grandison
Pensions & Employment	Eddie Codrington
Project Finance, Energy & Natural Resources	Martin Roberts
Property	Graham White
Taxation	Steve Edge

SLAUGHTER AND MAY

Environment: Specialist advice on a broad spectrum of environmental issues.
Tax: The tax aspects of corporate transactions and activities, including the development of tax-efficient structures and instruments.
EC and Competition: Advice from London and Brussels on UK and EC competition law, particularly in relation to acquisitions and mergers and joint ventures.
Pensions and Employment: Employee share benefit schemes, industrial conflicts, sex discrimination and equal pay problems and pensions and employment aspects of company acquisitions, disposals and takeovers.

INTERNATIONAL CONNECTIONS: International work is fundamental to the firm's practice both in London and in its overseas offices and Slaughter and May's lawyers travel widely. The firm has close working relations with the leading independent law firms in all major jurisdictions so that the best local advice and service is available to each client wherever this is required.

RECRUITMENT & TRAINING: Approximately 75 trainee solicitors are recruited every year. Financial assistance is available for the CPE and LPC in the form of a maintenance grant plus tuition and examination fees. For further information on recruitment, please write to Neil Morgan, head of personnel.

S

SLEE BLACKWELL

10 Cross Street, Barnstaple, EX31 1BA **Tel:** (01271) 372128 **Fax:** (01271) 344885/22505 **DX:** 34952 Barnstaple **Email:** info@sleeblackwell.co.uk **Website:** www.sblaw.co.uk **Ptnrs:** 8 **Asst solrs:** 9 **Other fee-earners:** 13 **Contact:** Mr Lee Dawkins • Devon based practice with recently opened offices in Exeter. Substantial commercial following with growing reputation in civil litigation, most notably employment law and personal injury.

AREAS OF PRACTICE	
Civil Litigation	25%
Commercial	20%
Matrimonial	20%
Property	20%
Probate/Taxation	10%
Criminal	5%

AE SMITH & SON

Frome House, London Road, Stroud, GL5 2AF
Tel: (01453) 757444 **Fax:** (01453) 757586 **DX:** 58801 Stroud
Email: AE.Smith.Stroud@cwcom.net

Stokescroft, Cossack Square, Nailsworth, GL6 0DZ
Tel: (01453) 832566 **Fax:** (01453) 835441 **DX:** 123329 Nailsworth
Email: AE.Smith.And.Son@farmline.com

Number of partners:	4
Assistant solicitors:	5
Other fee-earners:	2

CONTACTS	
Nailsworth Office	Caroline James
Stroud Office	John Bridges

THE FIRM: Founded about 1835 the firm operates from offices in Stroud and Nailsworth. As well as dealing with a very wide range of commercial and private client work, the firm has particular experience in the fields of agricultural law, trusts and probate, property and estate development, advocacy, mental health and education (particularly special educational needs). The firm has a Legal Aid Franchise in matrimonial & family, mental health, crime and personal injury. The firm also has connections with European lawyers.

SMITH LLEWELYN PARTNERSHIP

18 Princess Way, Swansea, SA1 3LW **Tel:** (01792) 464444 **Fax:** (01792) 464726 **DX:** 92051 Swansea 3. **Email:** slp@easynet.co.uk **Ptnrs:** 7 **Asst solrs:** 8 **Other fee-earners:** 9 **Contact:** Mark Harvey • Undertakes all work but is also one of the largest plaintiff, personal injury and clinical negligence practices in South Wales.

AREAS OF PRACTICE	
Clinical Negligence	25%
Personal Injury	25%
Other	18%
Matrimonial	15%
Conveyancing	10%
Social Welfare	7%

THE SMITH PARTNERSHIP

Derby, **Tel:** (01332) 346084 **Fax:** (01332) 292 183 **DX:** 11539 DERBY **Email:** commercial@smithpartnership.co.uk **Website:** www.smithpartnership.co.uk **Ptnrs:** 21 **Asst solrs:** 26 **Other fee-earners:** 53

SPEECHLY BIRCHAM

6 St Andrew Street, London, EC4A 3LX
Tel: (020) 7427 6400 **Fax:** (020) 7427 6600 **DX:** 54 Chancery Lane
Email: speechlys@speechlys.co.uk **Website:** www.speechlybircham.co.uk

Managing partner:	Michael Lingens
Senior partner:	John Avery Jones CBE
Number of partners:	37
Assistant solicitors:	44
Total:	106
Other fee-earners:	25

THE FIRM: Speechly Bircham is an independent mid-sized City law firm with an excellent client base including a number of well known corporate and institutional clients. Speechly Bircham's strong commercial focus is complemented by a highly regarded private capital practice. The firm handles major transactions and commercial disputes and provides a number of specialist advisory services, notably, tax. The firm has several discrete practice groups in many of which the firm has an acknowledged reputation and where its performance is competitive with that of larger firms. The structure of the firm and its ability to provide the partner time and attention make it a good alternative to large City firms for many clients. The legal affairs of each client are managed by a single partner, responsible for ensuring that the service is delivered quickly and cost-effectively. Much of the firm's work has an international dimension acting for UK clients doing business overseas, as well as advising non-UK clients on legal issues and transactions in this country. The firm has long-standing referral and working relationships with major independent law firms in most jurisdictions.

PRINCIPAL AREAS OF WORK:

Corporate: M&A work includes corporate acquisitions and divestments, cross-border acquisitions, buy-outs, joint ventures and the sale of family companies. A specialist team advises on banking and finance transactions. There is a particular focus on the financial services and technology sectors. The firm carries out an extensive range of transactional and advisory work in the financial services and insurance sectors, and has a well established reputation for advising on investment funds. The firm also has a growing reputation in advising communication, technology and internet businesses. The corporate tax practice is headed by the senior partner, John Avery Jones CBE, who has an international reputation for tax work and has served on many tax review bodies. Much of the tax work has an international dimension.

Private Capital: The private capital practice is recognised as a leading firm for advising individuals and families on wealth management issues. The group has considerable expertise in planning and implementing tax strategies, including setting up offshore investment vehicles and other structures to protect assets in the UK and abroad. It also includes a reputed charity practice.

Employment: The employment practice works closely with the firm's corporate, tax and pensions lawyers on contentious and non-contentious matters, helping businesses cope with change and develop employment strategies to resolve problems. Other areas of specialisation include share and incentive plans and termination agreements.

Commercial Dispute Resolution: For clients seeking a cost-effective and commercially satisfactory outcome, the firm advises on UK and international dispute resolution methods, including litigation, arbitration, mediation and other forms of Alternative Dispute Resolution (ADR).

Commercial Property: The commercial property practice has an established reputation in advising major life companies, property companies, urban estate owners, developers and local authorities on all aspects of commercial and industrial property. The practice includes a strong property litigation team who advise on management issues, such as possession orders, dilapidation claims, renewals, rent reviews and recovery of arrears.

Construction & Engineering: The construction practice works with investors, developers and contractors to assist them with their construction and engineering projects, both on contentious and non-contentious aspects.

Other Areas: In addition these practice groups are supported by specialists in IT, e-commerce, pensions, planning, environment and other ancillary areas.

CONTACTS

Commercial Dispute Resolution .... Stephen Dobson
Commercial Property .... Charles Palmer
Construction & Engineering .... Tim Raper
Corporate .... Michael Lingens
Corporate Tax .... John Avery Jones
Employment .... Alan Julyan
Private Capital .... Richard Kirby
Property Litigation .... Graham Ling

SPEECHLY BIRCHAM

S

SPIRO GRECH & CO

Clifton House, 8 Four Elms Road, Roath, Cardiff, CF2 1LE **Tel:** (029) 20222255 **Fax:** (029) 20450162 **Ptnrs:** 2 **Asst solrs:** 3 **Other fee-earners:** 4

SPRAGGON STENNETT BRABYN

225 Kensington High Street, London, W8 6SA **Tel:** (020) 7938 2223 **Fax:** (020) 7938 2224 **Email:** legal@ssb.co.uk **Ptnrs:** 3 **Asst solrs:** 2

SPRECHER GRIER HALBERSTAM

Lincoln House, 300 High Holborn, London, WC1V 7JH
Tel: (020) 7544 5555 **Fax:** (020) 7544 5565 **DX:** 0041 www.weblaw.co.uk
Email: info@sprgr.co.uk **Website:** www.sprgr.co.uk

Senior partners: David Sprecher and Ian Grier	
Number of partners:	11
Assistant solicitors:	4
Other fee-earners:	5

THE FIRM: Sprecher Grier Halberstam is a highly-motivated commercial law firm founded on the philosophy of providing pro-active, practical and results-orientated advice over a broad range of commercial legal work. The firm has particular expertise in banking, corporate recovery, professional negligence and insolvency work for a client base which includes financial institutions, professional practices and major companies and has established an excellent reputation since its formation in 1984. With the arrival of Simon Halberstam, as head of the IT, Year 2000 and e-commerce department, the firm has added another highly regarded lawyer to the partnership and further enhanced its range of services. This year has seen a further expansion with the launch of the firm's Employment Law Group.

PRINCIPAL AREAS OF WORK:

Company/Commercial: The department has a strong reputation for handling all forms of acquisitions disposals and joint ventures including complex reconstructions. Work includes mergers and acquisitions, MBOs, computer software agreements, shareholder & partnership agreements, banking and security documents and advice on a wide range of commercial matters.

CONTACTS

Commercial Litigation .... Ian Grier
.... Peter Loosley
Commercial Property .... Lesley Goring
.... Angela Robinson
Company/Commercial .... David Sprecher
.... Emma Shipp
Employment .... Bronwen Jenkins
Insolvency & Debt Recovery .... Ian Grier
.... Edward Judge
.... Daniel Sejas
IT/E-commerce .... Simon Halberstam
Litigation for Lenders .... David Bailey

Continued overleaf

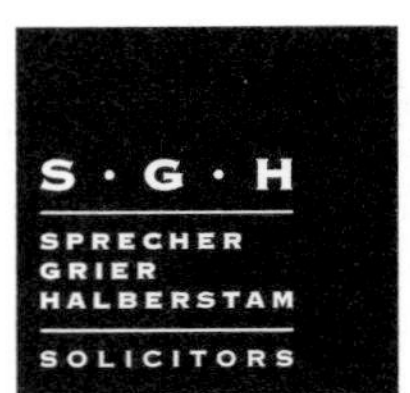

Insolvency and Debt Recovery: The firm is widely recognised as one of the UK's leading specialists in this area, and operates by combining effective legal advice with practical business action. Work involves advising insolvency practitioners on the technicalities of the law, assisting with liquidations, receiverships or petitions for administration orders and voluntary arrangements. Corporate rescue and restructuring is also an area of expertise. The debt recovery team offers speed and efficiency to obtain the best possible solution for clients.
IT, Y2K and e-commerce: The firm advises on all aspects of IT and e-commerce including contracting on the web, setting up and running an internet business and all related issues including copyright, trade registrations and data protection.The department has a large number of software house clients for which it performs a full range of contractual services. The firm has developed a methodology based on that of the IT world, namely fixed price standard products which are customised for each client. The firm also represents a variety of clients, including ISPs, Domain Name Registrants and webdesigners. It has developed a fixed-price contractual package for webdesigners comprising specification, design and maintenance agreements.
Litigation: The firm has been active in the lending market for over 10 years and has developed expertise in mortgage possession and related work. It offers a complete cost-effective service fully supported by a sophisticated third party case management system, which has been developed internally to provide a high level of functionality for mortgage possession, unsecured loss recovery and debt recovery cases. The department also has a dedicated professional indemnity team, which acts for lenders against solicitors, valuers and brokers.The firm favours direct IT links with its lender clients to ensure efficient exchange of up to the minute information. All undefended cases can be dealt with on a fixed fee basis.
Commercial Litigation: A wide range of contentious business is handled, focusing on the need to achieve a fast and cost-effective result for clients. Work includes banking litigation, building and construction disputes, intellectual property matters (especially design and copyright), service contracts, disputes involving employment agencies and recruitment consultants, and property related actions.
Commercial Property: A focus on broad business issues underlies advice on the acquisition and disposal of business premises, commercial landlord and tenant and property transactions on behalf of a wide range of commercial clients including financial institutions and insolvency practitioners.
Employment Law: A briefing service together with advice and tribunal representation in all areas of employment law is offered, including drafting of contracts and peronnel policies, employee share option agreements, wrongful dismissal claims, restrictive covenants, professional disciplinary cases, transfers of undertakings, unfair dismissal and sex and race and disability discrimination claims, working time, parental leave, European directives, and advising on the impact of The Human Rights Act.

SQUIRE & CO

49-50 St. Johns Square, London, EC1V 4JL **Tel:** (020) 7490 3444 **Fax:** (020) 7250 4087/4115 **DX:** 46617 Barbican **Email:** squires@squires.co.uk **Ptnrs:** 7 **Asst solrs:** 7 **Asst Solrs/Barr:** 12 **Contact:** Nicholas Squire, Alan Brown or Quentin Fox • The firm's main areas of work are: professional indemnity, and all classes of liability business; insurance investigations; insurance and reinsurance disputes; construction; civil fraud; alternative dispute resolution; commercial litigation and arbitrations.

SQUIRE SANDERS & DEMPSEY LLP

Royex House, Aldermanbury Square, London, EC2V 7HR
Tel: (020) 7776 5200 **Fax:** (020) 7776 5233
Website: www.ssd.com

UK	
Number of Partners:	7
Assistant Solicitors:	14
Other Fee-earners:	1
Worldwide	
Number of Partners:	195
Assistant Solicitors:	326
Other Fee-earners:	61

AREAS OF PRACTICE

Corporate/Company/Commercial	45%
Information Technology & E-Commerce	30%
Telecommunications	15%
Dispute Resolution	4%
Employment	3%
Property	3%

CONTACTS

Corporate/Commercial/Company ....
.........Cathy B Horton
.........James A Nimmo
.........Richard Sterling Surrey
.........Michael J Sussman
.........Carol M Welu
Dispute Resolution ....Carol M Welu

THE FIRM: International, full service law firm with over 675 lawyers. Twenty-five offices throughout the US, Europe and Asia, including a 'Renaissance' network of 18 law firms in China.

PRINCIPAL AREAS OF WORK: Corporate/company/commercial; information technology and e-commerce; telecommunications; dispute resolution; property; employment.

INTERNATIONAL CONNECTIONS: Offices abroad: Asia: Almaty, Beijing, Hong Kong, Taipei; Europe: Bratislava, Brussels, Budapest, Kyiv, Madrid, Moscow, Prague; US: Cincinnati, Cleveland, Columbus, Houston, Jacksonville, New York, Los Angeles, Miami, Palo Alto, Phoenix, San Francisco, Tokyo, Washington.

LANGUAGES: Cantonese, French, German, Mandarin, Russian, Spanish, Thai, Yoruba.

CLIENTELE:
Corporate/Company/Commercial: Global multi-nationals (including those in the technology, toys, plastics, brewing, automotive business, heavy equipment manufacturing, petroleum exploration, development and refining, steel mills, petrochemicals, market research and publishing, advertising and media, food and food processing and energy sectors), corporates, investment banks, international financial institutions, merchant banks, venture capital and private equity funds, financial leasing companies, power generation and transmission companies, privatised companies, utilities conglomerate, broadband network and cable providers, energy/telecom sector privatisations.

Employment: Media, manufacturing, electronic, information technology, engineering and hotel/catering.
Telecommunications: (sectors) wireline; wireless; broadcast; satellite; voice; data; Internet; computing; communications; consumer electronics equipment. (Governments) privatisations; regulatory restructuring.
Dispute Resolution: international brewers; shipping container manufacturers; clothing manufacturer; construction companies; telecommunications providers.
Property: International financial institutions; European institutional investors; venture capitalists; manufacturing companies and retail and industrial clients.
Information Technology: Sophisticated global vendors and purchases of hardware, software, systems integration services, network configuration and management, outsourcing and other IT services; web bespoke development and hosting transactions, e-business and general technology business transactions, including cross-border mergers and acquisitions, joint ventures and seed, secondary and public company financings.

CONTACTS CONTINUED

Employment	Fiona McLaren
Information Technology/ E-Commerce	Cathy B Horton
Property	Peter A Lloyd
Telecommunications	Joseph P Markoski
	Richard Sterling Surrey
	James A Nimmo

STAFFORD YOUNG JONES

The Old Rectory, 29 Martin Lane, London, EC4R 0AU
Tel: (020) 7623 9490 **Fax:** (020) 7929 5704 **DX:** 176 London

Managing partner:	Helen Wenham
Senior partner:	P.B. Adams
Number of partners:	11
Assistant solicitors:	3
Other fee-earners:	6

THE FIRM: Stafford Young Jones is a long established City of London practice serving the needs of both corporate and individual clients to a high professional standard, using modern methods and technology where appropriate whilst maintaining a friendly and personal service.

PRINCIPAL AREAS OF WORK:
Family Law: Paul Adams is a member of the SFLA and the firm is a member of the Relate Quality Partnership Scheme. Advice on all aspects of family law, including: separation and divorce; arrangements for children's residence and education; arrangements for contact with children; separation agreements and financial settlements.
Housing Association Work: The firm acts for a considerable number of registered social landlords in the area of housing and landlord and tenant litigation.
Employment Law: Advice given to both employer and employee on a full range of employment issues.
General Litigation: Experienced in all claims, including contractual and consumer disputes and personal injury litigation, acting for both plaintiffs and defendants; commercial litigation, particularly property litigation. Computerised and cost effective debt recovery for individual and corporate clients.
Wills and Probate: Preparation of wills and living wills; enduring powers of attorney; inheritance tax planning; administration of estates; advice to executors and beneficiaries on probate and succession law; variation of estates and the obtaining of grants of representation in England to the estates of foreign nationals.
Trusts & Personal Tax Planning: Formation, management and administration of trusts; asset management and financial planning; Court of Protection work. The firm offers a Nominee Company service which is a sponsored member of CREST. The firm is authorised by the Law Society to conduct Investment Business.
Residential Property: A fast and efficient service in the purchase and sale of freehold and leasehold property, short term letting and remortgages with specialist advice in the area of insolvency.
Commercial Property: A comprehensive service acting for corporate and individual clients advising buyers and sellers, landlords and tenants and borrowers and lenders in the acquisition, disposal and management of commercial property with specialist advice in the area of insolvency.
Company and Commercial: Advice on the formation, acquisition and disposal of commercial ventures and associated matters. Acting for financial institutions in the areas of lending and borrowing.

RECRUITMENT & TRAINING: The firm has a maximum number of two trainee solicitors. Prospective trainees should write to Paul Adams enclosing a CV.

LANGUAGES: French, German and Portuguese.

CONTACTS

Company/Commercial	Terry Chandler
Employment	Paul Adams
Family	Paul Adams
Housing Associations	Pamela Yelland
Litigation (general)	Andrew Strong
Property (commercial)	Martin Gaston
Property (residential)	Francis Backman
Tax & Personal Planning	Neil Fulton
Wills & Probate	Christopher Munday

STAFFURTH & BRAY

York Road Chambers, Bognor Regis, PO21 1LT **Tel:** (01243) 864001 **Fax:** (01243) 860708 **DX:** 31212 **Email:** staffurth_bray@compuserve.com
Website: www.staffurth.co.uk **Ptnrs:** 5 **Asst solrs:** 2 **Other fee-earners:** 10

STAMP JACKSON AND PROCTER

5 Parliament Street, Hull, HU1 2AZ **Tel:** (01482) 324591 **Fax:** (01482) 224048 **DX:** 11927 HULL 1 **Email:** aje@sjp.demon.co.uk **Ptnrs:** 9
Asst solrs: 10 **Other fee-earners:** 15

STANLEY TEE & COMPANY

High Street, Bishop's Stortford, CM23 2LU
Tel: (01279) 755200 **Fax:** (01279) 758400 **DX:** 50404 Bishop's Stortford
Email: law@stanleytee.co.uk **Website:** www.stanleytee.co.uk

42 High Street, Great Dunmow, CM6 1AH
Tel: (01371) 872166 **Fax:** (01371) 875747 **DX:** 89803 Great Dunmow
Email: law@stanleytee.co.uk

Star House, 38 Rayne Road, Braintree, CM7 2QP
Tel: (01376) 552277 **Fax:** (01376) 551919 **DX:** 56203 Braintree
Email: law@stanleytee.co.uk

Senior partner:	Rodney Stock
Number of partners:	13
Assistant solicitors:	10
Other fee-earners:	13

AREAS OF PRACTICE

- **Litigation (incl Family Law)** 40%
- **Private Client** 20%
- **Residential Property** 17%
- **Commercial Property** 12%
- **Company Commercial** 7%
- **Crime & Regulatory** 4%

CONTACTS

- **Civil & Insurance Litigation** .... John Donovan, David Redfern
- **Commercial & Environmental Litigation** .... Caroline Metcalf
- **Commercial Property** .... Jeremy Gillham
- **Company Commercial** .... Govan Bramley
- **Crime & Regulatory** .... Simon Becker
- **Employment** .... Helena Myska
- **Family** .... David Redfern
- **Private & Agricultural Property** .. Robert Elms
- **Residential Property** .... Allan Wright
- **Trust/Probate/Tax & Financial** ...... Richard Tee

THE FIRM: Stanley Tee supplies comprehensive services to private and commercial clients, including agricultural concerns, insurance companies and plcs. The practice has a strong and highly regarded expertise in defendant personal injury and commercial insurance claims and important niche areas in commercial and agricultural work. The private client department has a burgeoning client base supported by a high level of personal service with specialist tax and trust advice. With a long tradition of quality service Stanley Tee & Company is a progressive firm continuing expansion in its regional and national influence, and in the range of services it offers. Its approach is responsive and proactive and its high level investment in, and practical use of technology have enabled delivery of a friendly and efficient legal service tailored to clients' individual requirements. The summer of 2000 brings the commissioning of additional new office expansion at Bishop's Stortford, a centre closely linked with the growing Stansted airport as well as swift connections to London, the M25, Midlands and East Anglia. Constant investment in information technology and communication systems is matched by the growing number of high quality solicitors joining from the city and the regions.

S

STATHAM GILL DAVIES

55 New Cavendish Street, London, W1M 7RE **Tel:** (020) 7487 5565 **Fax:** (020) 7487 4409 **DX:** 83310 West End 2 **Email:** sgd@stathamgilldavies.com **Website:** www.stathamgilldavies.com **Ptnrs:** 9 **Asst solrs:** 2 **Other fee-earners:** 1 **Contact:** Philip Loveday • Provide legal advice for clients in the entertainment and media related industries. Work includes entertainment/media, advertising/sponsorship, company/commercial (including employment), sport and litigation.

STEEDMAN RAMAGE WS

6 Alva Street, Edinburgh, EH2 4QQ
Tel: (0131) 260 6600 **Fax:** (0131) 260 6610 **DX:** ED 95
Email: info@steedmanramage.co.uk

Afton House, 26 West Nile Street, Glasgow, G1 2PF
Tel: (0141) 242 6600 **Fax:** (0141) 242 6610 **DX:** GW14
Email: info@steedmanramage.co.uk

Managing partner:	Iain MacKinnon
Chairman:	Sandy Reid
Number of partners:	16
Assistant solicitors:	17
Other fee-earners:	3

AREAS OF PRACTICE

- **Commercial Property** 74%
- **Corporate** 14%
- **Litigation** 12%

CONTACTS

- **Banking and Finance** .... Iain MacKinnon, Alex Innes
- **Commercial Litigation** .... Kenneth Cumming, Victoria Craig
- **Commercial Property** .... Sandy Reid, Iain McHardy
- **Construction** .... Euan McLeod
- **Corporate/Commercial** .. Scott Kerr, Alex Innes
- **Employment** .... Scott Kerr, Victoria Craig
- **Environment** Kenneth Cumming, David Ratter
- **EU and Competition** .... Scott Kerr
- **Housing Associations** .... Gregor Mair
- **Insolvency** .... Gregor Mair, Rachel Grant
- **IP and IT** .... Scott Kerr
- **Licensing** .... Victoria Craig
- **Media and Entertainment** .... Scott Kerr
- **Planning** .... Sandy Reid, Kenneth Cumming
- **Retail** .... Iain McHardy, Iain McLean

THE FIRM: Steedman Ramage is a commercial law firm with offices in Edinburgh and Glasgow specialising in providing tactical and technical advice on matters involving Scottish law. The firm offers a range of corporate/commercial legal services and maintains a recognised expertise in all aspects of commercial property work allied to the provision of specialist corporate advice.

With a reputation as a positive, progressive and proactive law firm, Steedman Ramage attracts like-minded clients who appreciate the way the firm works for them. Equally important in a very competitive market, the firm is very successful in retaining established clients and is continuing to win more business from them in the context of their work.

The firm aims at supplying legal services in an effective and profitable manner. The now well-established management team provides the back up to compete at the highest level. The Steedman Ramage 'can do' approach is appreciated and respected. The service is always delivered to the expected level from a team of experienced, trained and enthusiastic lawyers.

PRINCIPAL AREAS OF WORK:

Commercial Property: Including development and site assembly, investment and funding, commercial leasing, portfolio management, rent review, joint ventures and property related aspects of corporate transactions, property finance and secured lending, planning and environmental law, relocation schemes and housing association work.

Corporate: Including business and company sales and purchases, joint ventures, loan facilities, intellectual property/IT, commercial contracts, pensions and employee benefits, competition law.

Litigation: Covers all aspects of general commercial litigation including property litigation, planning, environment, licensing, insolvency and employment work, judical review, arbitration and mediation, interdict and reparation.

Construction: Including advice on contracts and ancillary documentation for construction and engineering projects, construction aspects of property-related and corporate transactions, resolution of construction related disputes.

STEELE & CO

2 Norwich Business Park, Whiting Rd, Norwich, NR4 6DJ
Tel: (01603) 627107 **Fax:** (01603) 625890 **DX:** 5218 Norwich
Email: ca@steele.co.uk **Website:** www.steele.co.uk

10 Park Place, Lawn Lane, London, SW8 1UD
Tel: (020) 7735 9006 **Fax:** (020) 7735 7875 **DX:** 33265 Kennington London
Email: lbc@steele.co.uk

Managing partner:	Philip Hyde
Number of partners:	14
Assistant solicitors:	21
Other fee-earners:	58

AREAS OF PRACTICE

Commercial Property	25%
Commercial Disputes and Debt Recovery	15%
Corporate & Commercial	15%
Local Authority/Planning	13%
Employment	9%
Private Client/Tax/Trusts & Probate	8%
Medical Negligence & Personal Injury (Plaintiff)	6%
Domestic Conveyancing	5%
Other	4%

THE FIRM: Steele & Co is one of the larger independent commercial law firms. The firm has an increasingly national client base, and is recognised in particular for the strength of its commercial practitioners and for the range and quality of its services to local authorities and the public sector.

The firm offers a full range of corporate, commercial, property, litigation and public sector services. The firm is dedicated to delivering high quality value for money services to its clients regardless of location. It was one of the first firms in the country to have fully voice and data networked offices. It was also one of the first and largest firms in the country to be accredited to both ISO 9001 and Investor in People standards. It was recently re-accredited to both standards and was praised by the Assessors.

The firm prides itself on its innovative team-based structure. This provides clients with assistance to their legal problems at all levels and ensures appropriate expertise and continuity of service. The firm has been recognised as being truly innovative in the way it has developed its products and services and their delivery to clients. The firm has other offices in Diss and Thetford.

STEELE RAYMOND

Richmond Point, 43 Richmond Hill, Bournemouth, BH2 6LR
Tel: (01202) 294566 **Fax:** (01202) 552285 **DX:** 7643 Bournemouth 1
Email: mail@steeleraymond.co.uk **Website:** steeleraymond.co.uk

31 West Street, Wimborne, BH21 1JT
Tel: (01202) 885211 **Fax:** (01202) 887746 **DX:** 45303 Wimborne
Email: mail@steeleraymond.co.uk

Managing partner:	John Raymond
Chairman:	David Steele
Number of partners:	13
Assistant solicitors:	7
Other fee-earners:	7

AREAS OF PRACTICE

Litigation	30%
Company and commercial	27%
Commercial property	26%
Private client	10%
Education	7%

CONTACTS

Aviation/medical negligence	John Andrews
Commercial litigation	Simon Outten
Commercial property	John Daniels
	Bill Oliver
Company & commercial	Paul Longland
	David Steele
Education	Bill Oliver
Employment	Simon Outten
	Peter Rolph
Insolvency, landlord & tenant	Julian Fenn
Partnership	John Raymond
Personal injury	John Andrews
Private client	Paul Causton
Residential developments	Sue Middleton
Taxation	Paul Causton

THE FIRM: Steele Raymond was formed in 1979 and has expanded rapidly since that date, building up a wide range of business clients both in this country and abroad. The firm advises on all areas of company, commercial and business law, with a niche speciality in education law. It also has a substantial private client practice. Steele Raymond has achieved ISO 9001 accreditation for the complete range of its services and is thought to be the only major commercial law firm in Bournemouth to have done so. The Wimborne office undertakes all areas of work other than criminal matters. The main contact there is Mr John Andrews.

PRINCIPAL AREAS OF WORK: Company and business sales and purchases, company formations and reorganisations, partnership matters, intellectual property, EC law, competition law, commercial contracts (including computer contracts), aviation, commercial property matters, town and country planning, environmental law, insolvency and commercial litigation, personal injury, professional and medical negligence, education law and high level tax planning and advice. Unusually, the firm has a partner with a particular interest in canine law.

Agency Work: The firm undertakes work, other than criminal work, on an agency basis. Contact: Simon Outten or John Andrews.

INTERNATIONAL CONNECTIONS: Increasingly the firm's work involves an overseas element, and it works with legal firms in Europe and the USA.

CLIENTELE: The firm advises a wide range of clients including individuals, partnerships, housing associations, higher, further and other educational bodies, insolvency practitioners, private and public companies and insurance companies.

RECRUITMENT & TRAINING: The firm aims to take on one or two trainee solicitors per year and normally has opportunities for specialist staff in various parts of its practice. Strong emphasis is placed on training at all levels.

S

STEPHENSON HARWOOD

One, St Paul's Churchyard, London, EC4M 8SH
Tel: (020) 7329 4422 **Fax:** (020) 7606 0822 **DX:** 64 Chancery Lane WC2
Email: info@stephensonharwood.com

Senior partner:	Tony Scales
Chief executive:	John Pike
UK:	
Number of partners:	60
Assistant solicitors:	101
Other fee-earners:	54
International:	
Number of partners:	14
Assistant solicitors:	37
Other fee-earners:	31

THE FIRM: Stephenson Harwood is a major City firm with a considerable reputation for contentious and non-contentious expertise in the corporate/commercial, banking and financial services, shipping, property and private client fields. Putting a premium on technical excellence, responsiveness and commercial pragmatism, the firm delivers top quality results on time. Clients are served through an international network of offices and associations. Stephenson Harwood has a 170-year-old tradition of delivering a personal service to clients, which include multinational corporates, public and private companies, large financial institutions, institutional investors, government and public bodies, insurance companies, professional partnerships and individuals. With an international capability, the firm's size and flexibility enable it to provide a closely-tailored response to clients' needs. It combines transactional flair, clear-cut advice and decisive action with a working atmosphere that clients appreciate. In sectors where industry knowledge is the key, the firm's understanding of clients' businesses and markets means that it can provide even sharper and more precisely targeted advice. The firm focuses on finding innovative legal solutions and structures that meet clients' business objectives in a cost-effective way. It believes in looking after clients rather than simply processing their work, which includes ensuring that they are advised by the individual lawyers they have come to know and rely on. In all that it does, Stephenson Harwood is a client-centered practice.

PRINCIPAL AREAS OF WORK:

Corporate/Commercial: Advising on a broad spectrum of corporate/commercial transactions, Stephenson Harwood has a well-established expertise in corporate finance. Specialised groups also offer extensive experience of fund management and the launching of funds; the regulatory aspects of the financial services market; intellectual property and IT; infrastructure projects; EU/competition matters; and employment and pensions issues. A dedicated group advises on all related tax questions.

Litigation and Arbitration: Stephenson Harwood has a very high profile litigation and arbitration practice. Handling an extensive range of substantial commercial disputes, the firm is widely recognised for its expertise in complex fraud, asset tracing, money laundering, professional indemnity and insurance cases. It has established a pre-eminent reputation for its handling of regulation and corporate investigation work. It is also highly experienced in the successful deployment of ADR techniques.

Banking: The firm's established banking practice covers commercial lending and syndications, as well as more specialised areas such as trade and project finance, bringing an innovative and versatile approach to the wide range of transactions and issues on which it advises. The firm also has a considerable reputation for its insolvency work.

Property: In the property field, Stephenson Harwood covers all aspects of commercial property (including tax issues), with a particular expertise in property investment; planning; property finance; office and retail development; management; urban regeneration; and PFI transactions.

Shipping: The international shipping group is a full-service practice advising on finance, marine accidents (including collision and salvage) and commercial issues (such as P&I and marine insurance, and international trade). It also acts for clients in disputes.

Private Clients: Stephenson Harwood remains one of the few leading City law firms to undertake private client, family and matrimonial work. It has particular experience helping non-domiciled/non-resident clients.

INTERNATIONAL CONNECTIONS: The firm has overseas offices in Brussels, Guangzhou, Hong Kong, Madrid, Piraeus and Singapore. It is also associated with Zuric i Partneri, Croatia; Barbe Carpentier Thibault Groener, France; Elias Sp. Paraskevas Attorneys at Law 1933, Greece; De Berti Jacchia Perno & Associati, Italy; Al Sarraf & Al Ruwayeh, Kuwait; and Routledge-Modise, South Africa.

CONTACTS

Banking and Capital Markets	Tony Stockwell
Charities	Ann Phillips
Commercial Litigation	John Fordham
Commercial Property	Richard Light
Company/Commercial	Judith Shepherd
Construction	Steven Wait
Corporate Finance	Judith Shepherd
Corporate Investigations/Asset-Tracing	John Fordham
Corporate Tax	Hugo Jenney
Employment	Kate Brearley, Tom Flanagan
Environment	David Cuckson
EU and Competition	Antony Mair
Family and Matrimonial	Jonathan Walsh
Fraud and Regulation/Business Crime	Tony Woodcock
Funds and Financial Services	Andrew Sutch
Information Technology	John Enstone
Insolvency	Paul Gordon-Saker
Insurance Insolvency	Peter Fidler
Insurance/Reinsurance	James Crabtree
Intellectual Property and Patent Agency	Tibor Gold
International Arbitration	Robin Neill
International Projects & Privatisation	Colin Fergusson
Pensions and Benefits	Michael Cowley
Private Client	Mark Baily
Private Finance Initiative	Peter Walters
	David Cuckson
Professional Indemnity	Roland Foord
Project Finance	Tony Stockwell
Property Development	Marcel Haniff
Property Finance	Richard Light
Property Litigation	Ken Duncan
Shipping Admiralty	Robin Slade
Shipping Dry Litigation	Paolo Ghirardani
	Andrew Keates
Shipping Finance	Mark Russell
Town and Country Planning	Barry Jeeps
Trade and Project Finance	Tony Stockwell

STEPHENSONS

26 Union St, Leigh, WN7 1AT
Tel: (01942) 777777 **Fax:** (01942) 679778 **DX:** 22504

Senior partner:	Chris Stephenson
Number of partners:	22
Assistant solicitors:	26
Other fee-earners:	54

THE FIRM: A leading practice with roots going back to 1831. A progressive law firm which continues to enjoy rapid growth. A member of the firm has been recommended as 'Leaders in his Field' (*Chambers*) in family/matrimonial law.

PRINCIPAL AREAS OF WORK:

Family & Child Care: Work handled includes divorce, children matters, adoption, ancillary relief and Court of Appeal work. The firm employs five specialist solicitors on children matters who are members of the Law Society's Children Panel. Michael Devlin is recognised as a leader in the field of children's issues and has been involved in numerous high profile cases, many of which have been reported.

AREAS OF PRACTICE

General	34%
Personal Injury	25%
Crime	21%
Family	20%

Criminal Advocacy: All aspects of criminal law are handled including high profile cases. This specialist department deals with serious crime appeals and miscarriages of justice. It is led by Campbell Malone who represented, interalia, Stefan Kiszco, Kevin Callan.
Commercial: Work handled includes business formations, acquisitions and sales, partnership disputes and property matters.
Litigation: The firm undertakes all types of litigation in all courts. Specialist departments deal with personal injury and clinical negligence cases.
Private Client: Work includes wills, probate, conveyancing, employment and welfare rights.

CLIENTELE: The firm's clients range from high net worth individuals to legally aided clients.

CONTACTS

Commercial	Nick Yates
Conveyancing	Nicola Emo
Crime	Tom Bridge
	Campbell Malone, Mark Carr
Family	Liz Tait, Michael Devlin
Litigation	Ann Harrison, Andrew Leakey
Probate/Wills	Olwen Williams

STEPHENS & SCOWN

25-28 Southernhay East, Exeter, EX1 1RS
Tel: (01392) 210700 **Fax:** (01392) 274010 **DX:** 8305 Exeter
Email: solicitors@stephens-scown.co.uk **Website:** www.stephens-scown.co.uk

17 Dean Street, Liskeard, PL14 4AB
Tel: (01579) 342745 **Fax:** (01579) 346771 **DX:** 81654 Liskeard
Email: solicitors@stephens-scown.co.uk

3 Elizabeth Court, Whimple Street, Plymouth, PL1 2DH
Tel: (01752) 213 850 **Fax:** (01752) 213 854 **DX:** 8217 Plymouth
Email: solicitors@stephens-scown.co.uk

3 Cross Lane, St Austell, PL25 4AX
Tel: (01726) 74433 **Fax:** (01726) 68623 **DX:** 81251 St. Austell
Email: solicitors@stephens-scown.co.uk

Richmond Villa, 37 Edward Street, Truro, TR1 3AR
Tel: (01872) 265100 **Fax:** (01872) 279137 **DX:** 81203 Truro
Email: solicitors@stephens-scown.co.uk

Senior partner:	Roger Keast
Chief executive:	Richard Hoskin FCA
Number of partners:	32
Assistant solicitors:	27
Other fee-earners:	38

AREAS OF PRACTICE

Family	20%
Property	17%
Litigation	16%
Financial/Probate	15%
Personal Injury	14%
Commerce	13%
Magistrates Court/Crown Court	5%

CONTACTS

Agriculture	Martin Clayden
	Richard Jones
Commerce	Guy Curry
Debt Collection	Phillip Gregory
	Mark Stubbs
Employment	Nigel Moore
	Ian Pawley
Family	Peter Payne
	Michael Lowry
Financial/Probate	Ian Pawley
	Alan Williamson
Insolvency	Matthew Wald
Litigation	Chris Harper
	Mark Stubbs
Magistrates/Crown Court	Stephen Nunn
Personal Injury	Simon Middleton
Planning/Environment	Richard Hull,
	Ian Lamond
Property	Michael Beadel
	Jonathan Hoggett

THE FIRM: Stephens & Scown is one of the largest firms in the South West, with its head office in Exeter, a recently opened office in Plymouth and three other offices in Cornwall. It is a well established commercial and private client practice, with a large number of national and international clients. Stephens & Scown currently holds franchises in nine Legal Aid categories, and also has Lexcel accreditation by the Law Society. Three solicitors at the Exeter office have rights of audience in the higher courts. The firm has three solicitors who are members of the Law Society's Planning Panel, three on the Personal Injury Panel, six on the Children Panel, five on the Family Law Panel and one is a member of the Spinal Injuries Association Panel of specialist lawyers. Two partners and a legal executive are trained Mediators for family work.

PRINCIPAL AREAS OF WORK: The firm is divided into seven main departments: commerce, litigation, personal injury, Magistrates Court & Crown Court, family law, property and private client. Within these main departments are groups concentrating on more specialist areas of legal practice, including banking, corporate finance, employment, debt, agriculture, planning and environmental, waste disposal, minerals, domestic conveyancing and land development. All departments are organised on a practice-wide basis.
Commerce: The firm handles all aspects of company and commercial work. Specialisms include sales and acquisitions, business start-ups and planning, joint ventures, company formations and reorganisation. Services include "Businesslink", an advice service for small and starter businesses. The firm is experienced in European matters.
Litigation: Activities include a substantial amount of banking work, particularly insolvency and repossessions with a high-turnover, low-cost debt collection system as well as dealing with building and construction disputes. There is also a specialist employment law unit providing employment law advice and handling industrial tribunal cases.
Personal Injury: The personal injury and medical negligence department deals with a substantial workload of institutional and private work for both plaintiffs and defendants.
Magistrates Court and Crown Court: The firm has the largest criminal practice in Exeter and Devon, including a large youth court practice, and has a significant presence in Cornwall.
Family: This department is one of the largest in the country, handling all aspects of family law ranging from large financial disputes to heavyweight public law/child care cases and more recently mediation.
Property: This includes the general sale and purchase of commercial property, property development and tenancy agreements. Stephens & Scown is one of the leading agricultural practices in the west country with work including tenancy law, milk quota regulations, tax planning and pollution claims. The firm is well-known for its expertise in the law relating to mineral extraction and waste disposal work, and other environmental issues. There is an important Land Development Unit.

Continued overleaf

Private Client: Three partners handle wills and probate and the firm also administers trusts and provides other financial advice as well as residential conveyancing.
Agency Work: All types of work undertaken.
Charges: Fees are normally charged on an hourly basis. Quotations are given for residential conveyancing but fixed fees can be agreed in advance for certain types of work including debt recovery.

CLIENTELE: The firm has a wide client base ranging from major plcs and a full range of general commercial clients and institutions to smaller firms and individuals.

LANGUAGES: French, German and Spanish.

RECRUITMENT & TRAINING: The firm recruits two to three trainee solicitors each year. There are annual vacancies for assistant solicitors and executives.

STEPIEN LAKE GILBERT & PALING

4 John Street, London, WC1N 2EH
Tel: (020) 7655 0000 **Fax:** (020) 7655 0055 **DX:** 9 Chancery Lane

Senior partner:	K.J. Stepien
Number of partners:	4
Other fee-earners:	5

CONTACTS

Banking/Funding	K.J. Stepien
Development	T.M.D. Lake, M.W.Thomas
Investment	K.J. Stepien, S.P. Paling
Retail/Offices	S.P. Paling

THE FIRM: The firm was founded in April 1991. The firm's major activities are in the commercial property field, and this covers all aspects of commercial and residential development, banking, secured lending, investment, property finance and joint ventures.

CLIENTELE: The firm acts for a number of banks, major commercial and residential developers, and a number of UK and overseas investors. The firm also acts for a number of UK property investment funds and high net worth individuals.

RECRUITMENT & TRAINING: The recruitment partner is MW Thomas.

STEVENS & BOLTON

The Billings, Walnut Tree Close, Guildford, GU1 4YD
Tel: (01483) 302264 **Fax:** (01483) 302254 **DX:** 2423 Guildford 1
Email: mail@stevens-bolton.co.uk **Website:** www.stevens-bolton.co.uk

5 Castle Street, Farnham, GU9 7HT
Tel: (01252) 725040 **Fax:** (01252) 723501 **DX:** 32800 Farnham
Email: mail@stevens-bolton.co.uk

Managing partner:	Michael Laver
Senior partner:	Michael Hunter
Number of partners:	19
Assistant solicitors:	25
Other fee-earners:	4

AREAS OF PRACTICE

Company/Commercial	29%
Litigation	23%
Commercial Property	19%
Tax/Trust/Will & Probate	14%
Other Property	6%
Employment	5%
Family/Matrimonial	4%

CONTACTS

Commercial	Tudor Alexander
Commercial Litigation	Richard King
Commercial Property	James Mitchell
Commercial Recovery Service	Michael Frisby
Competition	Rebecca Holmes-Siedle
Corporate	Richard Baxter
E-Commerce, IT & IP	Nick Fieldhouse
Employment	Paul Lambdin
Family/Matrimonial	Caroline Gordon-Smith
Insolvency	Paul Lambdin
Personal Injury	Janet Waine
Personal Tax & Trusts	Nicholas Acomb
Planning & Environment	Catherine Davey
Residential Property	Andrew Bussy
Sales & Marketing	Beverley Whittaker
Wills & Probate	Michael Hunter

THE FIRM: Stevens & Bolton is one of Surrey's largest firms, and is well known for its extensive commercial practice in Guildford. It has experienced litigation and commercial property departments, an established reputation in the field of company law, and is able to combine specialist taxation advice with its other areas of practice. The firm also has a strong private client office in Farnham, which has been particularly successful at attracting business away from City firms.

PRINCIPAL AREAS OF WORK:
Company/Commercial: The department is experienced in corporate finance and transactional work, including acquisitions and disposals of companies and businesses, management buy-outs, company restructurings, venture & development capital and other business finance. A broad spectrum of other commercial matters is dealt with, including computer law, intellectual property, outsourcing, franchising, competition law and trading agreements.
Commercial Property and Planning: This department is equipped to handle a wide range of freehold and leasehold transactions, including funding and security issues, rent reviews, planning, taxation and environmental matters. The firm also provides a comprehensive service for developers, agricultural clients and residential property matters.
Litigation: Work is predominantly UK/international contract disputes, including complex litigation in the IT and finance and leasing sectors. Specialist expertise is available on professional negligence claims, intellectual property disputes (primarily trademark and copyright infringement), insurance matters, construction and civil engineering disputes, shareholder and partnership disputes and property-related litigation (including landlord and tenant). Insolvency matters and debt recovery are undertaken by separate units. A dedicated employment team handles contentious and non-contentious employment work. As part of the private client services, based at the Farnham office, separate departments handle personal injury and family law matters, especially complex matrimonial cases with an international element.
Private Client: The firm has a strong reputation in this area, advice ranging from wills and probate to personal tax planning including UK and offshore trusts. The firm also handles more complex institutional trust work, often for overseas clients. Charity work is also handled by this department.

CLIENTELE: UK and overseas clients include listed public companies, large private companies, partnerships and individuals.

STEWARTS

63 Lincoln's Inn Fields, London, WC2A 3LW
Tel: (020) 7242 6462 **Fax:** (020) 7831 6843 **DX:** 369 London
Email: info@stewarts-solicitors.co.uk **Website:** www.stewarts-solicitors.co.uk

Managing partner:	John Cahill
Number of partners:	12
Assistant solicitors:	8
Other fee-earners:	8

AREAS OF PRACTICE

Personal Injury & Clinical Negligence	70%
Commercial Litigation	20%
Commercial & Property	5%
Company & Charity	5%

CONTACTS

Commercial & Property	Chris Horspool
Commercial Litigation	Jack Leonard
Company& Charity	Graham Fisher
Personal Injury & Clinical Negligence	John Cahill

THE FIRM: This medium sized London based firm was founded in 1989. Whilst being well known for its litigation practice (personal injury, clinical negligence, commercial litigation and professional negligence), it is also active in non-contentious matters for a wide range of clients. The firm's philosophy has been to develop focused teams in specialist areas. It provides the quality of service commonly associated with much larger firms at a cost which is highly competitive. All client matters are handled or supervised by a partner with the relevant expertise. The partners seek pragmatic and cost effective solutions to their clients problems. It is a forward thinking, expanding firm with international contacts delivering a high quality of service to clients.

PRINCIPAL AREAS OF WORK:

Personal Injury/Clinical Negligence: In the past twelve months there has been significant growth in the personal injury and clinical negligence departments both of which have legal aid franchises and are acknowledged leaders in their field. The focus is on claims of the utmost severity (particularly brain and spinal injuries) although further niche areas are developing, including abuse litigation, US travel claims and multi-party work following the award of a multi-party franchise on 1st March 2000.

Commercial Litigation: The commercial litigation department has strengthened connections with Lloyds with two partners now acting for Lloyds Syndicates with an emphasis on professional negligence and product liability claims. In the broader context, the commercial litigation department continues to service its clients wide-ranging requirements.

Non-Contentious: The firm maintains a significant non-contentious client following acting for individuals, private companies, charities, banks and other financial institutions.

Alternative Dispute Resolution: Stewarts are committed to alternative dispute resolution procedures and two partners are now active mediators.

INTERNATIONAL CONNECTIONS: The firm is a founder member of a worldwide network of lawyers, Legalink, and receives regular instructions from foreign lawyers.

STIBBE SIMONT MONAHAN DUHOT

66 Gresham Street, London, EC2V 7PP
Tel: (020) 7600 4400 **Fax:** (020) 7600 4411
Email: ssmd@stibbe.co.uk **Website:** www.stibbe.nl

Senior partner:	Jeroen Fleming

AREAS OF PRACTICE

Banking, finance, securities	50%
Mergers and acquisitions	45%
Miscellaneous	5%

CONTACTS

All areas	Jeroen Fleming

THE FIRM: The firm operates as a truly multinational partnership of Dutch, Belgian and French lawyers. The history of the constituent parts of the firm goes back to the beginning of the century. The firm has well over 100 partners and 450 fee earners. It is one of the leading law firms in each of its three home jurisdictions.

PRINCIPAL AREAS OF WORK: The firm is a full service law firm with an internationally-oriented general commercial practice, and special emphasis on mergers and acquisitions, banking, securities, corporate and structured finance, project finance, real estate, telecommunications, intellectual and industrial property, environmental law, administrative law, insolvency, litigation and arbitration. The firm distinguishes itself from many other large law firms in Continental Europe because of its specialised tax practice.

INTERNATIONAL CONNECTIONS: The firm has its principal offices in Amsterdam, Brussels and Paris with a branch office in New York.

THE STOKES PARTNERSHIP

Kingfisher House, Market Square, Crewkerne, TA18 7LH **Tel:** (01460) 279279 **Fax:** (01460) 279289 **DX:** Crewkerne 43400 **Email:** info@law-solutions.co.uk **Website:** www.law-solutions.co.uk **Ptnrs:** 4 **Asst solrs:** 3 **Other fee-earners:** 20 • Established on 1 May 1998. The firm's principal areas of work are business law, commercial litigation, family, personal injury, residential & commercial property, wills & estate administration, and tax planning.

AREAS OF PRACTICE

Family	25%
Litigation	25%
Commercial Property	20%
Residential Conveyancing	15%
Trust & Estate Administration	15%

S

STONE KING

13 Queen Square, Bath, BA1 2HJ
Tel: (01225) 337599 **Fax:** (01225) 335437 **DX:** 8001 Bath
Email: admin@stoneking.co.uk

39 Cloth Fair, London, EC1A 7JQ
Tel: (020) 7796 1007 **Fax:** (020) 7796 1017

Senior partner:	Michael King
Number of partners:	9
Assistant solicitors:	9
Other fee-earners:	12

AREAS OF PRACTICE

Commercial and Charities	40%
Private Client Litigation	33%
Private Client	27%

THE FIRM: Established in 1785, Stone King has a substantial commercial and private client practice in the West Country, where its particular strengths are in the fields of commercial property, employment and commercial litigation, family and matrimonial, crime and trusts. It is known nationally for its charity and education expertise, and has a London office to service clients in those sectors.

CLIENTELE: The firm's work is divided between private clients and, in the commercial sphere, medium-sized businesses, schools, colleges, other large charities, and landed estates.

S

STONES

6 Northernhay Place, Exeter, EX4 3QQ
Tel: (01392) 666 777 **Fax:** (01392) 666 770 **DX:** 8306 Exeter
Email: mail@stones-solicitors.co.uk

Trinity Court, Southernhay East, Exeter, EX1 1PG
Tel: (01392) 666777 **Fax:** (01392) 666770 **DX:** 8306 Exeter
Email: mail@stones-solicitors.co.uk

21 Fore Street, Okehampton, EX20 1AJ
Tel: (01837) 52416 **Fax:** (01837) 54540 **DX:** 82500 Okehampton
Email: mail@stones-solicitors.co.uk

14 South Street, Torrington, EX38 8AF
Tel: (01805) 623725 **Fax:** (01805) 624040
Email: mail@stones-solicitors.co.uk

Senior partner:	W.H Winterbotham
Managing partner:	Bronwen Courtenay-Stamp
Number of partners:	18
Associates:	3
Assistant solicitors:	14
Other fee-earners:	19
Total staff:	115

AREAS OF PRACTICE

Property	25%
Family (inc. Crime)	19%
PI	18%
Trusts & Probate	16%
Commercial	13%
Commercial Litigation	9%

CONTACTS

Agriculture	Paul Tucker
Charity Law	Helen Honeyball
Childcare	David Howell-Richardson
Commercial Litigation	Paul Keeling
Commercial Property	Christopher Rundle
Company/Commercial	Tony Lloyd
Construction/Civil Engineering	Peter Buechel
Crime	Peter Seigne
Defence Insurers	Robin Challans
Employment	Kate Gardner
Family	Robin Challans
General Litigation (Okehampton & Torrington offices)	John Dobie
Housing Association	Nick Dyer
Insolvency	Paul Keeling
Leisure/Timeshare	Tim Bourne
Plaintiff Personal Injury	James Browne
Planning & Development	Hugh Winterbotham
Property Landlord/Tenant (Okehampton & Torrington offices)	Philip Bailey
Residential Property	Hugh Winterbotham
Skiing & Travel Personal Injury	Bronwen Courtenay-Stamp
Wills/Trusts/Probate/Tax	Helen Honeyball
	Mike Harris

THE FIRM: Stones is one of the largest practices in Exeter with a strong presence in Okehampton and a smaller office in Torrington, offering a range of services to both private and corporate clients. The firm was established early in the century, and has a progressive outlook with all offices linked by modern communications systems. It has a Legal Aid Franchise and has recently been awarded the Law Society's Family Lawyers scheme.In the past two years, the firm merged with Cann & Hallett and then Burd Pearse, extending their geographical spread and commitment to providing top quality legal services throughout Devon and not just concentrating on Exeter.Stones were the first law practice to open the region's legal retail outlet, in September 1997, known as The Law Shop. In September 1999, Stones re-launched this as The Family Law Shop concentrating on family work. The Family Law Shop opens on Saturdays and offers legal advice at convenient times and in relatively informal surroundings.

PRINCIPAL AREAS OF WORK: The firm has a particularly strong private client and commercial base in the West Country covering private client property, commercial, commercial litigation, personal injury, employment law, family, trust & probate and criminal. It is known regionally and nationally for its timeshare, housing association, construction and personal injury claims with a speciality in international ski law and holiday claims. The firm's niche areas are:

Housing Associations: Expertise in site acquisition throughout the south and south west; shared ownership schemes; HAMA and Care in the Community schemes with local authorities and health trusts; funding of housing schemes; and repossession work.

Personal Injury: With four members on the Personal Injury Panel and Robin Challans also a member of FOIL (The Forum of Insurance Lawyers), the department has longstanding experience of this type of work with particular specialisation in international skiing law and holiday claims and defence litigation for major insurers.

Timeshare: This department acts for some of the leading timeshare development companies, Owners' Committees, funders and advising other countries on compliance with international regulations.

Construction: This expanding department has an established reputation acting for employers, funds, professionals and their insurers, contractors and sub-contractors at all levels in relation to both non-contentious matters and disputes. Experienced in Arbitration and Court proceedings as well as other dispute resolution techniques.

Family: A strong growing family team with representation on the Children Panel and as a member of the Relate Quality Partnership. Partner David Howell-Richardson specialises in childcare and the firm recently achieved membership of the new Law Society's Family Lawyers scheme.

Development & Planning: This department acts for a number of developers dealing with site acquisition, planning, service agreements and site sales. Hugh Winterbothom acts on a regular basis for landowners looking to co-operate in promoting their land for development. This involves option agreements with development companies, joint venture agreements between the land owners and the schemes involved in both residential and retail development.

INTERNATIONAL CONNECTIONS: The firm has been a member of a European Law Association for some ten years and has connections with Legal Netlink, an American group of independent law firms with affiliates in Japan and Korea. Stones are also members of OTE, Tim Bourne being a committee member.

LANGUAGES: French, German, Maltese, Spanish and Tagalog (Philippines).

STRINGER SAUL

17 Hanover Square, London, W1R 9AJ
Tel: (020) 7917 8500 **Fax:** (020) 7917 8555 **DX:** 82984 Mayfair
Email: law@stringersaul.co.uk **Website:** www.stringersaul.co.uk

Executive partner:	Diana Sternfeld
Number of partners:	14
Assistant solicitors:	11
Other fee-earners:	1

AREAS OF PRACTICE

Company/Commercial	35%
Intellectual Property (Contentious & Non-Contentious)	24%
General Commercial Litigation	17%
Property	14%
Employment	6%
Tax	4%

CONTACTS

Commercial Property & Planning	Bill Harrup
Company/Commercial	Norman Ziman
	David Smith
E-commerce	Allistair Booth
Employment	Ruth Hickling
General Commercial Litigation	Martin Russell
Intellectual Property & Information Technology	Gary Howes
Mergers & Acquisitions	David Smith
	Nigel Gordon
Pharmaceuticals & Biotechnology	Diana Sternfeld
	Gary Howes
Property	Bill Harrup
Publishing	Norman Ziman
Reconstruction & Recovery	David Smith
Secured Lending	Martin Ackland
Taxation	Paul Yerbury

THE FIRM: Stringer Saul is a general commercial law firm with a number of specialisms. A major focus is advising 'knowledge-based' businesses. As such it acts for many clients involved in intellectual property, for example in the pharma/biotech, publishing and IT sectors.Work conducted for these organisations however, is much broader than IP advice alone; one third of the firm's business is company/commercial work, nearly 20% litigation and 15% property.

PRINCIPAL AREAS OF WORK: The main areas of work are commercial property and planning; corporate advice including insolvency, reconstruction and recovery; corporate finance; mergers and acquisitions; employment; general commercial litigation; e-commerce; intellectual property and information technology (contentious and non-contentious; pharmaceuticals and biotechnology; publishing; secured lending; taxation.

INTERNATIONAL CONNECTIONS: Stringer Saul regularly acts for clients overseas and has long standing relationships with a number of European and US lawyers and accountants with whom the partners work on a regular basis.

LANGUAGES: Italian.

CLIENTELE: The firm's clients range from multinational public companies to small owner managed businesses, including companies in the pharmaceutical and biotechnology sectors, e-commerce, finance, leisure, publishing, the media, property and mining. It currently acts for around 20 plc's across a range of business sectors, including: Celltech Medeva, e-capital investments, The eVestment Company, Nycomed-Amersham, Probus Estates, SmithKline Beecham, SkyePharma and Wolters Kluwer. The firm typically has very long-standing relationships with clients – many reaching back to its very beginnings. Because the firm is committed to its focus on knowledge-based businesses, there is true value to clients in the advice they receive across the full range of commercial legal disciplines – from corporate finance to patent litigation.

STRONACHS

34 Albyn Place, Aberdeen, AB10 1FW
Tel: (01224) 845845 **Fax:** (01224) 845800 **DX:** AB 41
Email: info@stronachs.co.uk **Website:** www.stronachs.co.uk

Number of partners:	20
Assistant solicitors:	17
Other fee-earners:	15

AREAS OF PRACTICE

Corporate	43%
Private Client	29%
Litigation	16%
Commercial Property	12%

CONTACTS

Banking	Ewan Neilson
Corporate Finance	Stephen Park
Employment	James Hendry
Environmental	David Rennie
Insolvency	James Merson
Intellectual Property	Ewan Neilson
Oil and Gas	David Sheach

THE FIRM: Stronachs can trace its roots back to the 1850s in Aberdeen but its main corporate division was formed almost a decade ago and has now grown to include 10 partners, (6 of which do company commercial work) and 23 fee earners. Stronachs has a strong presence in acting for management teams. They are currently processing or have processed several deals worth between £6m and £111m together with a number of smaller deals. The largest deal was the acquisition by Halliburton Company of PES (International) Limited in which Stronachs acted for PES. Many of these deals are not often publicised. Due to the nature of the oil and gas industry which, they heavily represent, a lot of the firm's deals tend to have an international element. They have recently acted for clients in North and South Africa, Trinidad and Tobago, Texas, Russia, Europe and Vietnam.For the past few years the firm has held and hosted external annual conferences on current business and legal topics. The firm also have a large private client department which specialises in executories, trust work and an element of personal tax planning as well as a residential division which specialises in sale and purchase of properties and financial services. The commercial property department is also a growth area for the firm. They are involved in construction projects, licensing, planning and acting for both landlords and tenants in terms of commercial leases.

PRINCIPAL AREAS OF WORK: The main areas of the practice are in corporate commercial work, including corporate finance, commercial, oil and gas, intellectual property and employment and they also have an estab-

Continued overleaf

lished and growing Commercial Property Unit and Commercial Court Unit. In addition, they have a strong private client department with a wide range of skills as well as residential property department. Stronachs' business is particularly geared to the oil and gas industry, where they act for not only service sector companies but also upstream companies, and the food industry which includes fish processors, agricultural merchants and other food processing businesses. The firm act for many new start hi-tec engineering and computer companies through their very active Intellectual Property Unit. Stronachs have Scots, English and Australian qualified lawyers in their team as well as multi-disciplinary personnel including accountants, insurance brokers and financial consultants.

LANGUAGES: French, German and Japanese

RECRUITMENT & TRAINING: The firm has an ongoing policy of actively growing their business and recruiting both at a trainee and assistant level. They currently offer 3-4 traineeships a year.

STUART MILLER
247 High Road, Wood Green, London, N22 4HF **Tel:** (020) 8881 7440 **Fax:** (020) 8889 5871 **Ptnrs:** 1 **Asst solrs:** 4 **Other fee-earners:** 5

S

STUDIO LEGALE SUTTI

19 Princes St, London, W1R 7RE
Tel: (020) 7409 1384 **Fax:** (020) 7409 1384
Email: maildesk@sutti.com **Website:** www.sutti.com

Managing partner:	Stefano Sutti
Office concact:	Livia Oglio
Worldwide:	
Number of Partners:	8
Other fee-earners:	32

AREAS OF PRACTICE	
Commercial/Company	45%
Intellectual Property/Competition	35%
Employment	20%

THE FIRM: Studio Legale Sutti was established in Milan in 1952 and its activity is organised across three main departments: commercial and company law, intellectual property and competition, and employment law.
London Office: The aim of Studio Legale Sutti's presence in London is that of offering a full range of prompt and efficient on-site legal services regarding Italian law and jurisdiction. In this respect, the SLS operation in the UK would like to be viewed as a barrister-like practice – fully backed by the combined resources and know-how of its Italian offices to which it is connected through a high-speed encrypted link – with the purpose of serving British law firms, patent and trademarks agents and corporate counsel for their clients' and employers' needs related to Italy.

PRINCIPAL AREAS OF WORK: The firm covers the following areas of specialisation: company law; commercial contracts; international contracts; international tax law; M&A; joint ventures; foreign investments; agency and franchise arrangements; EU law; competition law; financial and banking law; debt collection; insolvency; environmental law; construction law; product liability; IT and TLC law; entertainment law; maritime law; commercial litigation and arbitration; white collar crime; administrative law; intellectual property advice and litigation; industrial models and design; licence negotiation; technology transfer; advertising law; pharmaceuticals; patent and trade mark agency service; labour law; employment law; employer's liability; industrial relations and pensions law.

INTERNATIONAL CONNECTIONS: The firm's main office is situated at Via Montenapoleone 8, 20121 Milan, Italy, tel: + 39 02 762041, fax: + 39 02 76204.805. Other offices are located in Rome and Genoa.

STURTIVANT & CO

17 Bulstrode St, London, W1M 5FQ
Tel: (020) 7486 9524 **Fax:** (020) 7224 3164
Email: visas@sturtivant.co.uk

Number of partners:	1
Assistant solicitors:	1

AREAS OF PRACTICE	
UK Immigration & Nationality Law & Work Permits	100%

viSa & CO

THE FIRM: Established in 1985, and well-known as a specialist practice which is devoted exclusively to UK immigration law. The principal, Karen Sturtivant, is an active member of various professional associations concerned with immigration law and she regularly lectures and gives seminars on this subject.

PRINCIPAL AREAS OF WORK: All types of immigration work undertaken; primarily client representation for work permits, business residence, investor status and other residence categories. Also settlement; extension of stay; visitors, students and temporary stay. Appeals to Adjudicators and Tribunals; Judicial Review and deportation and removal cases.
Additional Areas: Nationality and citizenship problems.

CLIENTELE: Wide corporate and private client base.

INTERNATIONAL CONNECTIONS: Contacts with immigration lawyers in many other jurisdictions.

SUGARÉ & CO
36 Park Square, Leeds, LS1 2NY **Tel:** (0113) 244 6978 **Fax:** (0113) 245 5708 **Ptnrs:** 3 **Asst solrs:** 2 **Other fee-earners:** 5

SWEPSTONE WALSH

9 Lincoln's Inn Fields, London, WC2A 3BP **Tel:** (020) 7404 1499 **Fax:** (020) 7404 1493 **DX:** 142 **Ptnrs:** 4 **Asst solrs:** 4 **Other fee-earners:** 3

TARLO LYONS

Watchmaker Court, 33 St. John's Lane, London, EC1M 4DB
Tel: (020) 7405 2000 **Fax:** (020) 7814 9421 **DX:** 53323 Clerkenwell
Email: info@tarlo-lyons.com **Website:** www.tarlo-lyons.com

Managing partner:	Nigel McEwen
Number of partners:	26
Assistant solicitors:	17
Other fee-earners:	14

AREAS OF PRACTICE

Commercial	25%
Litigation	24%
Property	21%
Information technology	20%
Entertainment	10%

CONTACTS

Commercial	K. Barrow
Entertainment	D. Michael Rose
Information technology	Lawrence Phillips
Litigation	Nick Arnold
Property	P. Diamond

Tarlo Lyons Solicitors

THE FIRM: Tarlo Lyons is recognised as one of the leading law firms in the country for its expertise in information technology and related areas. The development of Scaffold IT, the firm's automated intelligent document generation system, demonstrates its ability to innovate and to embrace change in the legal marketplace. Over the past five years, Tarlo Lyons has transformed itself from a general commercial practice by pursuing a strategy of developing niche areas of expertise and specialist knowledge of particular business sectors. The firm now has one of the largest teams of dedicated non-contentious IT lawyers in England. With its focus on IT, nearly 40% of the firm's turnover now derives from IT and internet-related clients, including e-commerce. The firm's profits have grown by over 100% in the past three years and turnover has similarly doubled. Tarlo Lyons has continued to recruit lawyers in all areas of its practice over the past 12 months and, in particular, has attracted senior lawyers from big City firms.

PRINCIPAL AREAS OF WORK:

Technology: The IT, telecommunications and digital technology practice now numbers more that 25 lawyers including six partners. Areas of expertise include internet and e-commerce; global IT procurement and supply arrangements; outsourcing; software and data licensing; intellectual property including designs and trademarks; electronic data interchange and data protection.

Media: Entertainment and media is another strength of the firm, which has among its client list arguably the world's leading theatre producer and a leading film financier. Advice on all aspects of the film, theatre and television industries is provided by a dedicated team of lawyers. Digital technology is taking the entertainment industry into new distribution channels and the firm is well-placed to advise clients by combining expertise in entertainment and media with its leading reputation in IT.

Company/Commercial: The firm's company and commercial lawyers are experienced in advising on corporate finance, mergers and acquisitions, business start-ups, company re-organisations and all kinds of commercial agreements. The team has particular expertise in capital-raising and flotations of internet and IT-related businesses and has an 'equity for fees' scheme for promising high tech start-up companies. Advice is also available on EU and UK competition law, intellectual property licensing and for companies in financial difficulties and receivership. Outsourcing of internal functions such as IT or HR, and advising recruitment companies, are expanding areas of work.

Commercial Property: The firm's expertise in commercial property encompasses specialised areas including theatres; hotels; retail and business parks; shopping centres; betting and gaming establishments; and other leisure premises. Work undertaken includes investment, acquisitions and disposals, landlord and tenant, portfolio acquisitions and sales, finance and funding, site assembly, development and planning, environmental issues and property-related disputes.

ADR: The firm's dispute resolution practice includes a number of specialist areas of expertise in addition to dealing with general commercial disputes. These are: IT/intellectual property, gaming and licensing, tax investigations (mainly defendant), fraud – including confiscation of assets on behalf of the authorities, insolvencies and corporate recovery.

Employment: Advice on all kinds of employment matters, including disputes, is available and ranges from contracts, service agreements, EU and UK employment law, and collective agreements, to all types of discrimination, unfair or constructive dismissals, and tribunals.

CLIENTELE: The firm has a broad and balanced spread of clients, from banks and insurance companies to internet companies, film financiers and one of the world's largest theatrical producers. Whatever the nature and size of clients' businesses, the firm believes in developing a thorough understanding of clients' commercial priorities in order to provide the right advice. Tarlo Lyons is the co-ordinating member and UK representative of Euro IT Counsel, a quality circle of European lawyers which advises on legal issues affecting IT and telecommunications clients in Europe.

TAYLOR & EMMET

Norfolk Row, Sheffield, S1 1SL **Tel:** (0114) 290 2200 **Fax:** (0114) 290 2290 **DX:** 10549 **Email:** solicitors@tayloremmet.co.uk **Website:** www.tayloremmet.co.uk **Ptnrs:** 13 **Asst solrs:** 10 **Other fee-earners:** 7 **Contact:** Mr AP Long (Practice Manager) • Handles both private client and company/commercial work. Housing association matters are a speciality.

AREAS OF PRACTICE

Company/Commercial	35%
Residential Conveyancing	35%
Private Client Litigation	12%
Family	10%
Wills & Probate	8%

TAYLOR JOYNSON GARRETT

Carmelite, 50 Victoria Embankment, Blackfriars, London, EC4Y 0DX
Tel: (020) 7300 7000 **Fax:** (020) 7300 7100 **DX:** 41 London
Email: enquiries@tjg.co.uk **Website:** www.tjg.co.uk

Managing partner:	Declan Tarpey
Senior partner:	Richard Marsh
Number of partners:	87
Assistant solicitors:	116
Other fee-earners:	62

AREAS OF PRACTICE

Corporate & Banking	33%
Intellectual Property	19%
Litigation	19%
Commercial Property	14%
Tax & Personal Planning	8%
Employment	7%

CONTACTS

Banking	Rodney Dukes
Central/Eastern Europe	Simon Dayes
Commercial Litigation	David Greig
Commercial Property	John Whitfield
Construction	Neil White
	Peter Shaw
Corporate Finance	Gordon Jackson
Corporate Tax	Peter Jackson
Corporate/Commercial	Tim Eyles
Employment	Andrew Granger
Entertainment/Multimedia	Paul Mitchell
Environment & Planning	Alison Askwith
European Union/Competition	Martin Baker
Information Technology/ E-commerce/Internet	Glyn Morgan
Insolvency	Michael Frawley
Insurance/Reinsurance	Peter Kempe
Intellectual Property	Charles Lloyd
Inward Investment	David Kent
Life Sciences	Simon Cohen
	David Kent
London Stock Exchange	Paul Manser
Pharmaceutical	Mark Hodgson
Projects and PFI	Declan Tarpey
Rail	Jane McKee
Shipping	James Sleightholme
Tax and Personal Planning	
	Philippa Blake-Roberts
	Michael Stanford-Tuck
Telecommunications/Broadcast	
	John Edwards
	Ted Mercer

THE FIRM: Taylor Joynson Garrett is a major City and international law firm. It has an impressive UK and international client base, with strength and depth across the range of commercial disciplines enabling it to offer a full service to its corporate clients. Recognising that clients need advisers with specific industry knowledge, Taylor Joynson Garrett has developed various industry focus groups. The most notable of these groups is the technology and life sciences group which draws on its recognised expertise and reputation in corporate, intellectual property, IT and telecoms.

PRINCIPAL AREAS OF WORK:
Corporate: The firm has a highly-regarded corporate department dealing with international and domestic work. It has particular expertise in corporate and project finance, tax, mergers & acquisitions, inward investment, energy PFI and European Union law issues. It acts for a varied client base including public companies, banks and other financial institutions, management teams, private companies and venture capitalists.
Intellectual Property: The firm's intellectual property department is one of the largest in Europe and recognised as a leader in the field. It deals with contentious and non-contentious work in all aspects of intellectual property, including patent litigation, trade marks, industrial design, passing-off and trade libel. An experienced and respected sector-focused group, forged from the IP and corporate departments, deals with the advances in digital media, e-commerce, internet, IT and telecoms, advising and protecting inventors, manufacturers, suppliers and users.
Banking: The banking department advises on all aspects of banking and finance for a number of clearing, merchant and foreign banks (including Eastern European banks) and borrowers in relation to a broad range of industry sectors, with particular emphasis on transactional work, projects, PFI and securitisation. This department encompasses specialist teams dealing with corporate recoveries and building societies.
Commercial Property: In the field of commercial property, the firm offers a range of services incorporating specialist planning, property management and environmental teams. It is able to meet the differing needs of trading companies, developers, finance institutions and national and international investors.The firm's dedicated rail practice group adopts a multi-disciplinary approach to meet the needs of businesses active in the rail industry, including development companies.
Litigation: Taylor Joynson Garrett's litigation department handles a wide variety of commercial litigation and arbitration matters and has particular strengths in construction, banking, property, and insurance.
Construction and Engineering: The specialised construction and engineering group assists clients to achieve their commercial objectives through drafting of documents to protect their interests, support and assistance in maintaining the smooth running of projects, and if necessary the pursuit or defence of claims in court or arbitration.
Employment: The firm's specialist employment department handles a wide variety of employment related matters including pensions and employee benefits together with increasingly complex legal relationships both domestically and internationally.
Private Client: The firm also remains one of the few leading City firms with a well respected private client department, providing advice on taxation, wills and settlements (including trusts & estates), matrimonial law and residential property.

INTERNATIONAL CONNECTIONS: Taylor Joynson Garrett has a long established and well-respected international practice, with offices in Brussels and Bucharest. TJG has built an extensive network of developed relationships with lawyers in all the world's leading financial centres to deliver the high quality, practical advice which clients expect. This international perspective has helped TJG become one of the leaders in advising US and other non-UK based clients on protecting their interests or making investments in the UK.

TAYLOR NICHOL
3 Station Place, London, N4 2DH **Tel:** (020) 7272 8336 **Fax:** (020) 7281 9148 **DX:** 57453 Finsbury Park. **Ptnrs:** 2 **Asst solrs:** 3
Other fee-earners: 2

TAYLORS
Rawlings House, Exchange Street, Blackburn, BB1 7JN **Tel:** (01254) 563333 **Fax:** (01254) 682146 **DX:** 15252 Blackburn
Email: taylors@taylaw.co.uk **Website:** www.taylaw.co.uk **Ptnrs:** 4 **Asst solrs:** 7 **Other fee-earners:** 2

TAYLOR VINTERS

Merlin Place, Milton Rd, Cambridge, CB4 0DP
Tel: (01223) 423444 **Fax:** (01223) 423486 **DX:** 122892 Cambridge 4
Email: info@taylorvinters.com **Website:** www.taylorvinters.com

Managing partner:	Christine Berry
Number of partners:	23
Assistant solicitors:	32
Other fee-earners:	18

CONTACTS

Bloodstock	Rachel Flynn
Commercial Litigation	Edward Perrott
Commercial Property	Steven Beach
Company and Commercial	John Short
Corporate Finance	Steve Sharratt
Personal Injury	Paul Tapner
Planning, Development and Construction	Philip Kratz
Private Client	Jocelyn Fox
Rural Services	Adrian Horwood-Smart

THE FIRM: As one of the largest law firms in East Anglia, Taylor Vinters has a reputation for quality legal services to the commercial sector. The University of Cambridge is just one of a number of substantial institutional clients. Taylor Vinters' main strength lies in the firm's extensive experience with high-technology industries.

PRINCIPAL AREAS OF WORK:

Corporate and Commercial: Acquisitions; disposals; MBOs; joint ventures; venture capital funding; construction; employment; insolvency; intellectual property; and commercial litigation.

Commercial Property: Investment sales and purchases; landlord and tenant; large scale sales and purchases; development planning; agricultural and environmental law.

Rural Business Services: Encompasses the wide range of rural-based business activity undertaken for food processors, farmers, estates, institutions and related organisations. The firm has a national reputation for bloodstock and equestrian work.

Other specialisms: Claimant personal injury, charities and private client.

T

TAYLOR WALTON

28-44 Alma Street, Luton, LU1 2PL
Tel: (01582) 731161 **Fax:** (01582) 457900 **DX:** 130460 Luton 10
Email: luton@taylorwalton.co.uk **Website:** www.taylorwalton.co.uk

Harpenden,
Tel: (01582) 765111 **Fax:** (01582) 769089 **DX:** 80450 Harpenden
Email: harpenden@taylorwalton.co.uk

Hemel Hempstead,
Tel: (01442) 251411 **Fax:** (01442) 254634 **DX:** 8803 Hemel Hempstead
Email: hemel@taylorwalton.co.uk

St Albans,
Tel: (01727) 845245 **Fax:** (01727) 864970 **DX:** 133335 St Albans 14
Email: stalbans@taylorwalton.co.uk

Managing partner:	David Fryer
Senior partner:	John Hobson
Number of partners:	20
Assistant solicitors:	34
Other fee-earners:	40

AREAS OF PRACTICE

Commercial/Private Litigation	22%
Commercial Property	21%
Residential Property	20%
Company Commercial	13%
Direct/Relocation Property	10%
Private Client	9%
Employment	5%

CONTACTS

Commercial Litigation	A.R. Knight
Commercial Property	M.P. Kelly
Company & Commercial	C.O. Borthwick
Employment	J.D. Hobson
Family/Child Care	A.P. Hartnett
Financial Services	D.M. Fryer
Personal Injury	J.F.J. Carter
Private Client	J.C. Stevens
Property	T.M. Shillabeer
Residential/Direct & Relocation	T.M. Shillabeer

THE FIRM: Taylor Walton has continued to develop and expand over the last year. The firm has continued its policy of recruiting staff from city or equivalent firms.

PRINCIPAL AREAS OF WORK:

Corporate & Business Services: As an integral part of the firm's specialist commercial business unit the company/commercial team offers in-depth specialist assistance with prompt service and efficient use of IT a priority. Mergers and acquisitions work and advice on corporate finance matters comprise a significant proportion of matters handled.

Commercial Property Services: The commercial property teams list of significant clients includes national retailers and service providers who benefit from provincial fee rates and substantial expert support. Development and site planning, risk assessment, environmental and planning advice are provided along with property portfolio management.

Commercial Litigation: The department's stated policy of advising proactively on settlement opportunities has enabled the department to further develop its links with clients who appreciate a commercial approach to litigious matters from an early stage. Main areas of work include contract disputes, shareholder and partner disputes, negligence claims, property disputes and contentious probate.

Direct and Relocation Property: The firm has expanded its direct conveyancing services to employees of major companies and institutions. Increased use of IT and interactive internet instruction points have been developed and high service levels have drawn further corporate referrals. Employee benefit packages have been successfully implemented with over 15 major national plc's the majority ranked within the FTSE top 250.

Employment: The employment unit has been expanded to facilitate the handling of referred work by a national insurance company. The unit provides representation on contentious matters in the employment tribunal, restraint of trade, sex, race and disability discrimination and wrongful dismissal claims.

Personal Injury: The firm is a member of MASS with personal injury panel members advising claimants and defendants in respect of work related, road traffic accident and other personal injuries.

Value Added Services: The firm runs a proactive seminar programme to provide at least one seminar each month. Bespoke newsletters and advice sheets are also distributed without charge to clients and contacts. Networking forums form part of the firm's strong base of business contacts. Expert back up in the form of IT support, training in IT usage, library resources, document assembly and control ensure that the firm's lawyers work efficiently and time spent working on clients' matters is entirely productive.

TEACHER STERN SELBY

37-41 Bedford Row, London, WC1R 4JH
Tel: (020) 7242 3191 **Fax:** (020) 7242 1156 **DX:** 177 Ch.Ln.
Email: tss@tsslaw.co.uk **Website:** www.tsslaw.co.uk

Managing partner:	Graham Shear
Number of partners:	16
Assistant solicitors:	18
Other fee-earners:	6

AREAS OF PRACTICE

Commercial Property	37%
Commercial Litigation	36%
Company & Commercial	13%
Secured Lending	8%
Personal Injury/Education/ Judicial Review	3%
Residential Conveyancing/Probate	3%

CONTACTS

Commercial Litigation	Jack Rabinowicz
Commercial Property	Stuart Stern
	Russell Raphael
Computer Law	David Teacher
Education	Jack Rabinowicz
Entertainment	Graham Shear
General Commercial	David Salisbury
	David Teacher
IT/IP Litigation	Colin Richman
Media Companies	David Teacher
Media Litigation	Graham Shear
Medical Negligence	Jack Rabinowicz
Secured Lending	Phil Berry

THE FIRM: A Central London based general commercial firm, with clientele and case load normally attributed to larger firms. It has a wide range of contacts overseas.

PRINCIPAL AREAS OF WORK:
Commercial Property: Work includes acquisitions and disposals for developers, investors, landlords and tenants. Secured lending and the drafting of security documentation (acting for banks and building societies) are also handled, as is every aspect of landlord and tenant work.
Company/Commercial: The department is active in the corporate sector, handling takeovers, mergers, joint ventures, MBOs and disposals, demergers, reconstructions and asset sales. The firm also deals with employment law, intellectual property licences and confidentiality agreements. The firm has particular experience in computer hardware and software contracts, oil exploration agreements and financing, entertainment law (music, film,TV, cable and multimedia), and in the pharmaceutical industry.
Litigation: Primarily in the commercial field, particularly banking, insolvency and finance house matters, together with commercial property litigation. The firm also specialises in medical negligence and personal injury cases, and has a national reputation in the field of education law. The firm has considerable experience in media and entertainment litigation, headed by Graham Shear.
Other Areas: The firm gives specialist tax planning advice and has substantial experience in the formation and use of foreign trusts and offshore corporate entities to produce the most efficient tax structure to suit individual circumstances. A full range of private client services from residential conveyancing to wills, trusts, probate and estate administration is also provided.

CLIENTELE: Primarily from the finance, commercial property, corporate and entertainment fields, and also corporate and business clients from Canada, Israel and Eastern Europe. The firm also has excellent links with accountants, banks, financial institutions, surveyors and has wide-ranging legal contacts overseas.

LANGUAGES: Afrikaans, Arabic, Chinese(Mandarin), French, German, Hebrew, Italian, Russian, Serbo-Croat and Spanish.

THANKI NOVY TAUBE

The Mews, 1A Birkenhead Street, London, WC1H 8NB
Tel: (020) 7833 5800 **Fax:** (020) 7833 5805 **DX:** 37900 Kings Cross
Email: info@tntsolicitors.com **Website:** www.tntsolicitors.com

Number of partners:	3
Assistant solicitors:	7
Other fee-earners:	5

CONTACTS

Extraditions/Prison Law/Human Rights	Girish Thanki
General Crime & Appellate	Rod Novy
White Collar Crime	Martin Taube

THE FIRM: The firm specialises in the criminal litigation field and the civil liberties area with considerable experience of handling complex and weighty cases, often with a forensic element. In 1999 the firm dealt with the following: a large number of murder cases (including slow-burn provocation cases) extraditions to the USA, Sweden, Italy; serious frauds; armed robberies; serious assault cases. The firm acts for Manjit Kaur Basuta (the British nanny in California) baby battering case. Martin Taube appears regularly on the Jimmy Young show on Radio 2 to advise on legal matters. Girish Thanki is a member of the Law Society's Task Force on implementation of Human Rights Act 1998. The firm has a strong commitment to excellence and a quality-driven approach. A networked computer system is used for file management, costing and diary systems. The firm provides high quality training to all its staff. It organises conferences in a number of subject areas. Legal Aid rates apply. For private clients charges vary from £150 per hour upwards depending on degree of expertise required.

PRINCIPAL AREAS OF WORK: Work includes criminal litigation; civil liberties; criminal work (comprising white collar crime, murder, child abuse, armed robbery); Customs & Excise cases; general first division crime. It also has specialist knowledge of extradition law. It has substantial experience of appellate work. It deals routinely with judicial reviews and has specialisation in prison law. It has a specialist department dealing with civil actions against the police and the Home Office. It deals with a large number of inquests. The firm has particular expertise in police station representation and offers 24 hours, 7 days service to a detained person. It accepts instructions for advocacy in central London Magistrates' Courts.

CLIENTELE: This is mostly legal aid but with a growing private client base.

THE BERKSON GLOBE PARTNERSHIP
27 Dale Street, 4th Floor, Dale House, Liverpool, L2 2HD **Tel:** (0151) 236 1234 **Fax:** (0151) 236 5678

THEODORE GODDARD

150 Aldersgate Street, London, EC1A 4EJ
Tel: (020) 7606 8855 **Fax:** (020) 7606 4390 **DX:** 47 London Chancery Lane WC2
Email: info@theodoregoddard.co.uk **Website:** www.theodoregoddard.com

Managing partner:	Peter Cooke
Senior partner:	Paddy Grafton Green
Number of partners:	59
Assistant solicitors:	120
Other fee-earners:	36
Total staff:	366

AREAS OF PRACTICE

Corporate/Corporate Finance	32%
Property	20%
Media/IP	18%
Banking & Finance	10%
Litigation	8%
Corporate Tax	6%
Employment	6%

CONTACTS

Advertising	Rupert Earle
Arbitration & ADR	Peter Fitzpatrick
Asset Finance	James Ballingall
Aviation	Rory MacCarthy
Banking & Finance	Nigel West
Collective Investment Schemes	Simon Goodworth
Commercial Litigation	John Kelleher
Commercial Property	Mark Gilbert
Construction	Clive Lovatt
Corporate	Graham Stedman
Corporate Tax	Peter Sayer
E-commerce	Paul Renney
EC/Competition	Guy Leigh
Employment	Peter Cooke
Entertainment	Paddy Grafton Green
Environment	Claire Sheppard
Film/TV	Peter Armstrong
Insolvency	Julian Maples
Insurance	Jennifer Donohue
Intellectual property	Hamish Porter
IT	Arnold Segal
Media litigation	Martin Kramer
Music	Paddy Grafton Green
Pensions	Mark Catchpole
PFI	James Ballingall
Planning	Douglas Evans
Private Client	Jo Goldby
Property Finance	Jayesh Patel
Railways	William James
Telecommunications	Edward Pitt
Trade	Dan Horovitz

THE FIRM: Theodore Goddard is a major City law firm serving the business and financial communities, with particular emphasis on the banking and finance and the media and communications sectors. Theodore Goddard's aim is to provide clients with innovative, high quality, practical and speedy advice. Although London-based, Theodore Goddard operates worldwide through an office in Brussels and a network of international associates, including Klein-Goddard in Paris and Theodore Goddard Jersey.

PRINCIPAL AREAS OF WORK:

Banking & Finance: The firm advises on the full range of corporate and finance work, including mergers and acquisitions, management buy-outs and demergers, investment capital and new issues, including Stock Exchange flotations. It has an expanding practice in the field of collective investments, insurance and financial services regulation. The firm acts for a wide range of banks, borrowers, lessors and lessees, arrangers and airlines on general banking and asset finance transactions as well as on more specialist PFI, property, structured and tax driven financings. The firm has a strong record in insolvency and restructuring work. It also has a recognised practice in securities and corporate trust work. Its banking and finance team is led by a banker.
Tax: The firm deals with all tax issues connected with corporate finance work, including the development of tax-related financial instruments and asset finance packages; international tax planning; the tax aspects of takeovers, corporate reconstructions and demergers, management buy-outs and buy-ins; employee share schemes and other employee benefits; personal tax planning including, together with the associated firm in Jersey, the formation and administration of off-shore trusts and companies.
Media and Communications: The firm has a leading practice in the media and communications sector, concentrating on music, film, television, theatre, and, centred on its expertise in defamation law, newspapers, advertising and publishing; it also advises extensively on the issues relating to new media and information technology including e-commerce, computer games and on-line publishing. The convergence of businesses and technologies in these industries results in the continuous creation of new and complex legal problems, particularly in relation to the creation and exploitation of intellectual property rights and competition and regulatory issues.
Commercial Litigation: The firm has considerable expertise in commercial litigation, particularly in relation to the banking and securities sector; fraud and asset recovery; major contractual disputes; insurance and re-insurance; product liability, especially in the healthcare industry; and in arbitration and ADR.
Property: In the property field, the emphasis is on commercial and industrial sectors. Specialist groups handle public authority work, environmental law, planning and rating, construction and development, funding and investment, secured lending, property and construction litigation, and retail and leisure transactions.
Other Areas: Other groups have excellent reputations in the fields of EC, competition and trade law, employment (both contentious and non-contentious) and pensions. The firm has an established practice in transport law, particularly in relation to aviation and railways.

INTERNATIONAL CONNECTIONS: The firm has offices at: 118 Avenue de Cortenberg/Kortenberglaan, B-1000 Brussels, Belgium, tel: +32 2 732 2700, fax: +32 2 735 2352. Associated offices are: Theodore Goddard Jersey, tel: (01534) 512 512, fax: (01534) 512 513; Klein Goddard, Paris, tel: +33 1 44 95 20 00, fax: +33 1 49 53 03 97.

LANGUAGES: Cantonese, French, German, Hebrew, Italian, Japanese and Spanish.

RECRUITMENT & TRAINING: The firm recruits around 20 trainee solicitors a year. A good degree (2:1 plus), which may or may not be in law, is necessary. The firm is looking for trainees with confidence, commitment and sound commercial sense. There is an extensive award-winning training and development programme covering all fee earners, from trainees to partners and including personal skills development, commercial management and business development training alongside legal training. The firm recruits with a view to retaining trainees who after qualification will go on to become partners with the firm. Tuition fees and a maintenance allowance are paid by the firm for both CPE and LPC. The firm runs a summer placement and open day programme. Details of these, along with the firm's brochure for training contracts and application forms, are available from the personnel department. Applications should be made to Penny Alison (Miss), Personnel Director.

THEODORE GODDARD

THE LAW OFFICES OF RICHARD HEMMINGS LLM SOLICITOR

Sandy Lane, Barham, Ipswich, IP6 0PB **Tel:** 01473 833 844 **Fax:** 01473 833 230 **Email:** hemminga@dial.pipex.com **Website:** hemmings.co.uk

THOMAS A. HIGGINS & CO

Capital Buildings, 10 Seaview Road, Wallasey, L45 4LA **Tel:** (0151) 691 1211 **Fax:** (0151) 630 8007 **DX:** 20063 **Ptnrs:** 1 **Asst solrs:** 1

THOMAS COOPER & STIBBARD

Ibex House, 42-47 Minories, London, EC3N 1HA
Tel: (020) 7481 8851 **Fax:** (020) 7480 6097 **DX:** 548
Email: tcs@tcssol.com **Website:** www.tcssol.com

Managing partner:	T.J.R. Goode
Senior partner:	D.G. Hebden
Number of partners:	16
Assistant solicitors:	10
Other fee-earners:	13

AREAS OF PRACTICE

Shipping (Admiralty, Maritime & Carriage)	60%
Business Finance & Insurance	20%
Commercial Litigation & International Arbitration	10%
Personal Injury	10%

CONTACTS

Banking	Grant Eldred
Commercial Litigation	Nick Green
Company Law	Stephen Swabey
Construction	Tim Goode
Environment	Paul Barfield
Insurance	Tim Goode
Personal Injury	John Strange
Property	Kate Harrison
Shipping and Maritime Law	David Hebden
	Tim Kelleher

THOMAS COOPER & STIBBARD

THE FIRM: Thomas Cooper & Stibbard is a well established City of London firm, specialising in commercial law, with a particular emphasis towards shipping and international trade. The firm offers advice to industrial, commercial and financial clients worldwide. Thomas Cooper & Stibbard has built strong, long lasting relationships with clients, through a thorough understanding of the demands and developments of their different market places. The firm's client base is broadly international, with many of its multi-lingual lawyers travelling widely on client business. The firm has a branch office in Singapore which covers both admiralty and shipping work. It has seen a great expansion in the Spanish and South American markets, with increasing instructions from shipowners, underwriters and oil companies; the firm also has a strong presence in Greece, where it opened a branch office (Athens) undertaking non-contentious work for clients.

PRINCIPAL AREAS OF WORK:

Admiralty: The firm's admiralty specialists handle collisions at sea, salvage and towage, pollution and wreck removal and marine insurance. The firm has been instructed in connection with many of the major casualties of recent years and David Hebden is particularly well known for his work on crisis management.

Shipping: Shipping litigation expertise includes charterparty disputes, bills of lading, carriage of goods, cargo damage, storage or contamination, shipbuilding and repair contracts, management disputes and multi-modal carriage. The firm is a leading practitioner in electronic shipping and trade documentation. Apart from the mainstream shipping areas, the firm has an unusual specialisation. Stephen Swabey acts for the plaintiffs in the Factortame litigation.

Personal Injury: The firm is well known for marine personal injury work, acting in the main for P & I clubs and shipowners.

Company/Commercial: The firm's company and commercial department advises all types of UK and international businesses including public and private companies, partnerships and individuals. Particular areas of expertise include banking, corporate finance including mergers and acquisitions, Stock Exchange listings, venture capital commercial contracts, employment law, financial services, insolvency, property and commercial litigation.

CLIENTELE: The client base is strongly international and covers a broad spectrum including shipowners, charterers, banks, insurance companies, foreign governments and ministries, major oil companies, commodity traders and manufacturers.

LANGUAGES: Many of the firm's lawyers are fluent in several languages, including Arabic, Bahasa, French, German, Greek, Italian, Mandarin and Spanish.

THOMAS EGGAR CHURCH ADAMS

5 East Pallant, Chichester, PO19 1TS
Tel: (01243) 786111 **Fax:** (01243) 775640 **DX:** 30300 Chichester
Email: info@teca.co.uk **Website:** www.teca.co.uk

Managing partner:	John Stapleton
Chairman:	Neil Hart
Number of Partners:	50
Associates:	17
Assistant solicitors:	41
Other fee-earners:	78

CONTACTS

Banking & Finance	Stephen Clifford
Commercial Property	Chris Bell
Company & Commercial	Tony Edwards
Construction	Tina Webster
Debt Recovery	Paula Jones
E-Commerce	Philip Krauss
Employment	Peter Stevens
Financial Services	Anthony Wands
Franchising	Michael Crooks
Insolvency	Martin Cross
Intellectual Property	Michael Camps
Litigation	Tom McKeown
Mediation/Family	Jill Goldman
Personal Injury	Stephen Richards
Private Client	Richard Thornley

THE FIRM: Thomas Eggar Church Adams has now passed the second anniversary of its highly successful merger between two leading law firms in the South East. They combined complementary practices in commercial and private client with histories that reach back two centuries. The firm is a fully diversified legal and financial services group and is one of the largest firms of solicitors across the region. The firm has offices in Chichester (2), Horsham, London (2), Reigate and Worthing. Clients are at the heart of Thomas Eggar Church Adams' business. The firm has a strong regional reputation for its private client services and it also supports some of the largest corporations in the country with London-based specialist litigation, commercial property, banking and e-commerce expertise. It has particular experience in acting for mortgage lenders and the railway and franchising industries. Private client services focus mainly on tax and trusts. The firm established an investment management company, Thesis (now Thesis Asset Management plc) in 1984 which is now one of the largest such businesses to be incorporated by a law firm, as well as being a past winner of the Lawyer-HIFAL national award for the best financial services department of a law firm. It has in excess of £400 million of client funds under advisory and discretionary management. Thomas Eggar Church Adams has offices spanning Surrey and Sussex, in Chichester, Horsham, Reigate and Worthing, plus a London office. Growth has continued through 1998/99 and the firm has built on its specialisations in its private client division and its commercial division, which services national and international corporations.

PRINCIPAL AREAS OF WORK: Thomas Eggar Church Adams has invested heavily in its commercial and private client service, as a conscious response to the changing needs of its clients and building on its position in its traditional heartland and expanding its expertise nationally. The firm handles property, commercial and litigation matters for banks, building societies and other financial institutions, railway and track operators and others. It also has a specialist focus on franchising. It is a leading adviser to the Church of England and various charities. Private client services focus on taxation and trusts and more than 500 trusts are now administered.

Corporate Finance: Thesis Corporate Finance Limited offers corporate finance advice to a range of companies.
Commercial: In the past year commercial matters handled by the firm have included several property portfolio deals and development transactions involving considerations of up to £40 million, as well as the pooling of shares in a UK medical marketing company into a listed US-based multinational pharmaceuticals company. The firm acts for dot.com companies and internet retailers. As well as providing general business and e-commerce advice it also advises in the raising of substantial capital.
Private Client: Whether for straight forward wills or complicated trust and domestic or transnational tax advice, the leading skills and resources of TECA continue to attract increasing work from private individuals. Within the major professional disciplines specialist groups handle the fast changing areas of law such as e-commerce and intellectual property, employment discrimination, human rights, tax and pensions.

CLIENTELE: Main industry sectors are banks and building societies, life companies, franchise businesses, utilities, house builders and other property developers, manufacturers and suppliers. Major clients include the British Railways Board in property matters, Railtrack Plc in property and litigation, Link Interchange Network, Alliance and Leicester Group Union Staff, the Glanmore Property Fund, Alliance Unichem Plc, Hamptons Estates Ltd and Marshall-Tufflex Ltd.

THOMAS EGGAR
CHURCH ADAMS
SOLICITORS

THOMPSONS

39 Frances Street, Newtownards, BT23 7DW **Tel:** (028) 9181 1652 **Fax:** (028) 9181 9645 **Ptnrs:** 1 **Asst solrs:** 3 **Other fee-earners:** 1

THOMPSONS MCCLURE

Congress House, Great Russell Street, London, WC1B 3LW **Tel:** (020) 7637 9761 **Fax:** (020) 7637 0000 **DX:** 35722 Bloomsbury 1
Website: www.thompsons.law.co.uk **Ptnrs:** 80 **Asst solrs:** 84 **Other fee-earners:** 92

THOMPSON SMITH & PUXON

4-5 North Hill, Colchester, CO1 1EB **Tel:** (01206) 574431 **Fax:** (01206) 563174 **DX:** 3617 Colchester
Email: info@tsplegal.com **Website:** www.tsplegal.com **Ptnrs:** 14 **Asst solrs:** 5 **Other fee-earners:** 11 **Contact:** Lindsay Brydson, Practice Manager • General practice with three offices. Members of child-care panel, medical negligence panel and Law Society family panel; Legal Aid franchise holders.

THOMPSONS

Congress House, Great Russell Street, London, WC1B 3LW **Tel:** (020) 7637 9761 **Fax:** (020) 7637 0000 **DX:** 35722 Bloomsbury 1
Website: www.thompsons.law.co.uk **Ptnrs:** 68 **Asst solrs:** 103 **Other fee-earners:** 147

THOMSON SNELL & PASSMORE

3 Lonsdale Gardens, Tunbridge Wells, TN1 1NX
Tel: (01892) 510000 **Fax:** (01892) 549884 **DX:** 3914 Tunbridge Wells 1
Email: solicitors@ts-p.co.uk **Website:** www.ts-p.co.uk

Stafford House, 16 East Street, Tonbridge, TN9 1HG
Tel: (01732) 771411 **Fax:** (01732) 770445

Senior partner:	Trevor May
Number of partners:	34
Assistant solicitors:	21
Other fee-earners:	16

AREAS OF PRACTICE

Commercial Litigation	25%
Private Client	21%
Corporate & Commercial Property	17%
PI/Clinical Negligence	15%
Residential Property	14%
Family	8%

THE FIRM: This large leading South East law firm, founded in 1570, is renowned for providing a high quality service, focusing on approachability and friendliness. Thomson Snell & Passmore, an organisation of talented, energetic and efficient lawyers, is a founder member of The Law South Group and holds the highly regarded 'Lexcel' award, the Law Society's quality assurance standard.
During the last two years, the firm has grown in all areas and has a long standing reputation for its expertise in company/commercial, commercial property, commercial litigation, professional negligence, clinical negligence, personal injury and private client work.
Thomson Snell & Passmore are committed to new technology and are regarded as truly modern solicitors who pride themselves on giving excellent value for money.

PRINCIPAL AREAS OF WORK:
Company/Commercial: Work handled includes acquisitions and disposals, corporate finance, venture capital, MBOs and MBIs, mergers and joint ventures, partnerships, commercial contracts, insolvency, employment law, intellectual property, franchising, EU and general competition law.
Commercial Property: The department advises landlords, tenants, investors and institutions on all aspects of commercial property including funding and tax implications. It provides a full service to residential and

Continued overleaf

commercial developers, including land acquisition and options, joint ventures, funding agreements, planning and environmental issues, unit sales/leases and estate management. The firm also advises farmers and estates on all aspects of land ownership, agricultural holdings, tax, inheritance, development, environmental legislation and EU regulations.
Litigation: Work includes commercial disputes, insolvency, employment claims, intellectual property disputes and property related claims including landlord and tenant, building contracts and possession actions.
Private Client: The department handles wills, probate, trust formation and management, investment management, tax and financial planning, pensions, charities, inheritance tax, capital gains tax, income tax and tax returns.
Other: The personal injury, clinical negligence and professional negligence departments are recognised as leaders in the region handling high volumes of work. The family department advises on all areas of matrimonial and other family problems. There is also a large residential property department and an immigration section which deals with private and business clients.

INTERNATIONAL CONNECTIONS: The firm is a founder member of INTERLEGAL with associate offices throughout Europe, the USA and Canada.

CONTACTS

Agriculture	Gilbert Green
Clinical Negligence	Andrew Watson
Commercial Litigation	Peter Radula-Scott
Commercial Property	David White
Company/Commercial	James Partridge
Matrimonial/Family	Barbara Wright
Personal Injury	Julie Reynolds
Probate and Trusts	James Krafft
Professional Negligence	Trevor May
Property Development	Gilbert Green
Property Litigation	Raymond Beard
Residential Property	Michael Sugden
Tax Planning	Jeremy Passmore
Trust Management and Tax Returns	Kathy Larter

T

THOMSON WEBB CORFIELD

94 Regent Street, Cambridge, CB2 1DP **Tel:** (01223) 578070 **Fax:** (01223) 578330 **DX:** 5840 CAMBRIDGE

THORNHILL INCE

Suite 3, Third Floor, Grampian House, 144 Deansgate, Manchester, M3 3ED **Tel:** (0161) 839 2550 **Fax:** (0161) 819 5005

THORNTONS WS

50 Castle Street Dundee, DD! 3RU **Tel:** (01382) 229111 **Fax:** (01382) 202288 **DX:** DD 28 **Ptnrs: 23** **Asst solrs:** 19 **Other fee-earners:** 26
Email: enquiries@thorntonsws.co.uk **Website:** www.thorntonsws.co.uk

THRINGS & LONG

Midland Bridge, Bath, BA1 2HQ
Tel: (01225) 340000 **Fax:** (01225) 319735 **DX:** 8002 Bath
Email: info@thrings.co.uk **Website:** www.thrings.co.uk

2 North Parade, Frome, BA11 1AT
Tel: (01373) 465431 **Fax:** (01373) 473992 **DX:** 43803 Frome
Email: info@thrings.co.uk

Unit 9, The Agricultural Centre, Standerwick, Frome, BA11 1AT
Tel: (01373) 831036 **Fax:** (01373) 831036
Email: info@thrings.co.uk

Senior partner:	Jeremy Thring
Chief executive:	Nigel Cobb
Number of partners:	17
Assistant solicitors:	10
Other fee-earners:	40

AREAS OF PRACTICE

Agriculture/Probate/Trusts and tax	29%
Litigation	26%
Company/Commercial and Charities	25%
Conveyancing	20%

CONTACTS

Agriculture	Jonathan Cheal
	Neil Barbour
Charity	Quentin Elston
Commercial Property	David Holt
	Thomas Sheppard
Company & Commercial	Jonathan Wyld
	Paul Hardman
Debt Recovery/Credit Control	
	Amanda Noyce
Employment Law	Stephen Roberts
	Simon Holdsworth
Family Law	Meg Moss
Financial Services	William Power
Investment Management	Adrian Cantwell
Litigation	Stephen Roberts
Probate & Trusts	Helen Starkie
	Jeremy Thring
Residential Property	William Power
Sports Law	Stephen Roberts
	Thomas Sheppard
Tax	Michael Young
Traded Endowment	William Power

THE FIRM: The firm has established itself as the principal private client firm based in the SouthWest which also acts for clients nationally and internationally. An expanding area has been agriculture where the firm has been recognised by the National Farmers Union (NFU) as the premier practice for central and southern England. A niche market in traded endowments has increased substantially over the past year. Employment and sports law continue to grow along with family, clinical negligence and personal injury. The firm has continued to be innovative by launching investment management to compliment the complete range of services offered. Overall, the firm has, through expansion and recruitment, developed strong specialist areas for clients throughout the UK. The firm remains highly committed to meeting the challenge of changing requirements.

PRINCIPAL AREAS OF WORK:

Agriculture: Widely recognised and respected as a specialist department providing advice to farmers and landowners throughout central and southern England. One of only nine firms chosen by the NFU to provide legal services to their members throughout the UK. The recognition of Jonathan Cheal as the premier agriculture lawyer in the region and the recruitment of a land surveyor have established the firm's overall reputation.
Company/Commercial: Wide experience of company sales and acquisitions, business start up's, reorganisations and partnerships, intellectual property, IT, Insolvency, trading terms and conditions. Developing area with dot.com company start up's and high profile recruitment.
Commercial Property: Sales and acquisitions, developments and joint ventures, leases, planning and environmental law, specialists in mine, mineral and quarrying.
Residential Property: Volume sales, purchase and remortgage for plc lenders, conveyancing case management service, relocation, repossession, french property and traded endowment specialists.
Litigation: A highly regarded employment law department, particularly in the education and agriculture sections with Stephen Roberts being renowned for his expertise. Commercial litigation, personal injury, clinical negligence, sports law, computerised debt collection, administrative law and judicial review.

Family: Two members on the Law Society Family Law Panel, three members on the Children Panel and a qualified mediator. Recognised for high net worth divorce and ancillary relief cases, child abduction and mediation throughout the UK.

Private Client: Experts in tax and trust works, wills and probate with an accountant and ex tax inspector employed. Recently launched an investment management department to compliment the services available to the private client.

Charity: Niche firm in medical and operational charities, schools and churches, almshouses and grant making. Expert advise on all aspects of charity law and practice.

TINSDILLS

Chichester House, Broad Street, Hanley, Stoke-on-Trent, ST1 4EU **Tel:** (01782) 262031 **Fax:** (01782) 287571 **DX:** 20710
Email: lawyers@tinsdills.co.uk **Ptnrs:** 16 **Asst solrs:** 15 **Other fee-earners:** 12

TITMUSS SAINER DECHERT (see Dechert)

TLT SOLICITORS

One Redcliff St, Bristol, BS99 7JZ
Tel: (0117) 929 5252 **Fax:** (0117) 929 8313 **DX:** 7830 Bristol
Email: connect@lawrence-tucketts.co.uk

Managing partner:	Robert Bourns
Senior partner:	Tim Pyper
Number of partners:	27
Assistant solicitors:	51
Other fee-earners:	47

AREAS OF PRACTICE

Dispute resolution...38%
Commercial and corporate...35%
Commercial property and planning...27%

CONTACTS

Banking...Judith Brown
Commercial...Nick Moss
Commercial Dispute Resolution...Philip May
Corporate...David Pester
Employment...Alana Weeks
Family...David Woodward
Insolvency...Philip May
Planning/Development/ Environmental...Edward Cooke
Professional Conduct...Sarah Mumford
Property Dispute Resolution...Julia Lucas
Property Investment...Andrew Glynn
Retail...Roger Clothier
Tax & Estate Planning...David Bird

THE FIRM: On the 1st May 2000 Trumps and Lawrence Tucketts merged to form TLT, the third largest firm in Bristol and one of the top 100 in the country. The combined firm has over 100 lawyers and a total complement of over 250 people. This provides a substantial base of skills and experience from which to service a complementary client base which includes Barclays, Lloyds TSB, Woolwich PLC, Avon Rubber PLC, Alfred McAlpine, Hanson, Brandon Hire PLC, Topps Tiles PLC, C&J Clark (Clarks Shoes) and Bakers Dolphin. Both firms have grown impressively in the past two years and the merger advances the aim of the firms to strengthen UK and other European services in their key specialist areas of corporate work, property and dispute resolution. A larger firm gives greater scope for maximising investment in people, know-how and rapidly changing technology. The joint corporate expertise of the merged firm will be matched by few regional competitors and the consolidation of the two banking teams will create one of the strongest regional banking groups. The firm works extensively in the following sectors, banking and lender services, corporate finance, property management and development, minerals, retail and IT. Its geographical location provides the firm with a competitive cost base from which to service clients wherever they are based. TLT is a modern, outward looking firm that delivers creative legal solutions by looking at clients' business from the inside out.

PRINCIPAL AREAS OF WORK:

Corporate: An extensive range of corporate work is handled by one of the largest dedicated corporate teams in the region, including corporate finance, acquisitions, disposals, JVs, stock exchange AIM and OFEX work. A separate commercial team handles IP and other commercial contracts and includes dedicated partnership and franchising units, both with national reputations. A specialist employment team also provides HR consultancy services and management training.

Banking: Banking and services to lenders team has an impressive client base including Birmingham Midshires, Barclays, Bristol and West, Lloyds TSB, Woolwich PLC and Triodos Bank.

Property/Planning: Property and planning expertise is well recognised with particular strengths in retail and development work, minerals and landfill, ĈPOs, property finance and recovery for financial institutions, building and constructions claims.

Environmental: The firm advises on all aspects on environmental law, including environmental policies, waste management agreements, waste control and advising lenders on difficult sites.

Litigation/ADR: TLT has one of the leading commercial litigation practices in the South West handling a wide range of disputes including extra jurisdictional litigation, misrepresentation/fraud claims, IP disputes, claims involving companies and their directors and sale/supply of goods/services. The team has substantial ADR experience, particularly mediation and arbitration.

Family: The renowned family team is led by David Woodward, who is considered the leading family lawyer in the South West.

Other: Property and Tax services are provided to high net worth individuals.

TODS MURRAY WS

66 Queen Street, Edinburgh, EH2 4NE
Tel: (0131) 226 4771 **Fax:** (0131) 225 3676 **DX:** ED58
Email: maildesk@todsmurray.co.uk

33 Bothwell Street, Glasgow, G2 6NL
Tel: (0141) 275 4771 **Fax:** (0141) 275 4781 **DX:** 512815 Glasgow Central
Email: maildesk@todsmurray.co.uk

Managing partner:	John Biggar
Chairman:	Charles Abram
Number of partners:	36
Assistant solicitors:	46
Other fee-earners:	21

AREAS OF PRACTICE

Corporate	37%
Commercial Property	32%
Private Client	24%
Litigation	7%

CONTACTS

Agriculture, Landed Estates & Forestry	John Fulton
Banking	Hamish Patrick
Capital Projects/PFI/PPP	Ian McPake
	William Simmons
Charities	Peter Ryden
Commercial Property	Douglas Moffat
	Sandy McEwen
Construction	Ross Campbell
Corporate & Commercial	David Dunsire
Corporate Finance	Granger Brash
Corporate Financial Services	Chris Athanas
	Martin Thurston Smith
Employment Law	Robert Dobie
Entertainment & Media	Richard Findlay
Hotels & Leisure	Angus McIntyre
Information Technology	Lynn Beaumont
Insolvency	Robert Dobie
Intellectual Property	Lynn Beaumont
Investment Funds	Chris Athanas
Litigation	Michael Simpson
Pensions	Martin Thurston Smith
Planning & Environment	Ian McPake
Residential Property	Gordon Cunningham
Securitisation	Graham Burnside
Timeshare	David Anderson
Wills, Tax & Trusts	John Biggar

THE FIRM: Tods Murray is recognised as a leading Scottish firm offering a wide range of services with an emphasis on corporate and commercial work. Tods Murray's strategy for development is focusing particularly on three areas of its commercial practice – commercial property including construction, environmental and planning law; banking and securitisation; capital projects and PFI/PPP. These focus areas are of high quality in which the firm is seen to be very competitive. The firm's other areas of expertise including corporate and commercial law, litigation and employment law, private client services, investment funds and corporate financial services, entertainment and media, intellectual property, travel and leisure law including timeshare are also thriving and continuing to grow. As part of this strategy, Tods Murray opened an office in Glasgow in June 1999 which has specialists in the fields of commercial property, banking and commercial and corporate law. At Tods Murray the focus is client-orientated, offering teams with a range of technical skills to meet clients' needs. The firm has a wide-ranging client base including listed companies, institutional investors, landowners and farmers, small businesses and private individuals. Tods Murray has developed good working relationships with various English law firms, for whom it conducts the Scottish aspects of cross-border transactions, and has a significant clientele based outwith Scotland. On an international level, membership of Multilaw provides Tods Murray with a network of associated law firms located in the world's major commercial centres.

PRINCIPAL AREAS OF WORK:

Banking: The banking team has extensive experience in corporate and public sector lending, project finance, property finance and securitisation.
Capital Projects: The capital projects team deals with all capital and infrastructure projects including PFI/PPP with particular expertise in healthcare, water, waste to energy, social housing and local authority projects.
Commercial Property: The commercial property team, which specialises in major developments and funding agreements, acts for a number of insurers, pension funds and property companies in relation to their property portfolios. The team also offers advice on planning, construction and environmental projects.
Corporate: The corporate team is recognised for its' experience in corporate finance including public issues, acquisitions, placings, and buy-outs. The team also has significant information technology, intellectual property, entertainment and media, leisure and travel expertise including timeshare. In addition, the investment funds and corporate financial services team is recognised as having a leading reputation in these specialist areas.
Litigation: The litigation team handles all types of commercial and civil litigation across the firm for both commercial and private clients.
Private Client: The private client team, with a renowned reputation, provides services to landowners and farmers, undertaking all the legal work associated with landed estates and farms. The team deals with wills, trusts and executries, charities, tax and estate planning, financial management (on behalf of both individuals and trusts) and the purchase and sale of residential property.

TOLHURST FISHER

Trafalgar Hse, 8 Nelson Street, Southend-on-Sea, SS1 1EF **Tel:** (01702) 352511 **Fax:** (01702) 348900 **DX:** 2811 **Email:** info@tolhurstfisher.com
Website: www.tolhurstfisher.com **Ptnrs:** 8 **Asst solrs:** 4 **Other fee-earners:** 5

TOLLER HALES & COLLCUTT

Castilian Chambers, 2 Castilian Street, Northampton, NN1 1JX
Tel: (01604) 258558 **Fax:** (01604) 258500 **DX:** 12422
Email: info@tollers.co.uk **Website:** www.tollers.co.uk

Managing partner:	David Fowler
Senior partner:	Anthony Noone
Number of partners:	21
Assistant solicitors:	16
Other fee-earners:	28

AREAS OF PRACTICE

Litigation	36%
Private Client	28%
Family	24%
Commercial	12%

THE FIRM: Established in 1877, Toller Hales & Collcutt is a broadly based provincial practice with four offices in Northamptonshire. It offers a full range of legal services to both commercial and private clients. Legal Aid Franchise awarded during 1995 covering crime, personal injury, family, debt, employment and consumer issues. The firm has other offices in Corby, Kettering and Wellingborough.

PRINCIPAL AREAS OF WORK:

Corporate/Commercial: The department undertakes all aspects of company formation, acquisition and disposal, MBOs and MBIs, joint ventures, reconstruction, franchise, agency and distribution agreements, taxation, intellectual property, EC law and insolvency.

Commercial Property: The firm offers a wide-ranging property service covering industrial, retail and offices premises, and acquisition, disposal, leasing, landlord and tenant law, building contracts, joint ventures, property taxation (VAT), investment and development work. A specialist Planning Unit deals with all planning issues. Liquor licensing is also included in this department.
Litigation: The litigation team handles all aspects of commercial and private client litigation. Specialist areas of practice include employment disputes (contracts, redundancy, wrongful dismissal and discrimination), personal injury (seven PI Panel Solicitors), medical negligence, professional negligence, construction and insurance.
Family/Childcare: The firm has a specialist unit dealing with all aspects of family disputes which is the largest in the County.
Private Client: The firm offers a comprehensive service to the private client, including all types of property transfers, wills, trusts, probate and a dedicated financial planning department.

CLIENTELE: Clients range from insurance companies and Plcs to businesses of all sizes. The firm has a strong private client base and is a member of the Conquest Network.

RECRUITMENT & TRAINING: The firm expects to take on two trainee solicitors every year and applications should be made on the firm's own application form to Mr David Fowler.

TOWNLEYS

Dalby House, 396-398 City Road, London, EC1V 2QA
Tel: (020) 7713 7000 **Fax:** (020) 7713 2999 **DX:** 400214 FINSBURY 2
Email: townleys@townleys.co.uk **Website:** www.townleys.com

Managing partner:	Darren Bailey
Senior partner:	Stephen Townley
Number of partners:	4
Assistant solicitors:	14
Other fee-earners:	5
Total Staff:	40

AREAS OF PRACTICE

Sport/Media.........95%

CONTACTS

Event Management ....Mark Whitehead
Litigation/ADR..........Jonathan Taylor
Sports Broadcasting ....Jonathan Higton
Sports Digital..........Dan Harrington
Sports Governance ....Darren Bailey
Sports IP/Rights Management ....Nicholas Couchman
Sports Sponsorship ....Andy Korman
Trainee Applications ....Andrea Lambie-Shaw

THE FIRM: Established in 1983, Townleys is widely regarded as being the pre-eminent specialist sports law firm in Europe. As the only dedicated sports law practice operating in this rapidly developing market, Townleys remains at the cutting edge of new legal developments relating to the sports industry both at home and internationally. With specialist fee-earners organised into practice groups, Townleys is large and experienced enough to bring multi-disciplinary skills to bear in relation to any sports property or transaction, whatever the size, yet flexible and entrepreneurial enough to bring a personalised and innovative approach to all its clients' needs.

PRINCIPAL AREAS OF WORK:
Sports Broadcasting: Advising sports and their advisers on domestic broadcasting arrangements and on international exploitation and distribution.
Event Management: Providing wide-ranging legal advice in areas such as joint ventures, employment, share structures, shareholder agreements, option schemes, the raising and maintenance of capital, financial services and company/commercial matters relating to the sports industry.
Sports Digital: Providing the full range of legal services relating to interactive digital media including advising upon web site and multimedia products, developing interactive rights licensing, revenue-collection and E-commerce models, domain name registration and dispute resolution services, and advising upon and implementing programmes for protecting and developing sports rights in digital media.
Litigation/ADR: Advising on challenges to the enforceability (under competition law or otherwise) of rules and regulations governing particular sports; advising on the disciplinary and other decisions of governing bodies pursuant to those rules and regulations; acting in a broad range of contractual and non-contractual disputes, generally in the area of sports rights exploitation and particularly in the areas of broadcasting, sponsorship and merchandising; and managing the contentious aspects of world-wide sports brand management/protection programmes.
Sports Governance: Providing advice to governing bodies and other sports organisations on disciplinary regimes, doping programmes, the movement of players, player discipline and participation/eligibility issues, general liability issues and general regulatory frameworks, including manuals of good practice and codes of ethics.
Sports Intellectual Property/Rights Management: Advising sports on their intellectual property portfolios and development strategies and related areas; managing and implementing global trademark protection, brand management and enforcement programmes for sports events and properties, utilising its extensive international network of specialist agents; drafting and advising on licensing, merchandising and other sports intellectual property agreements and IP issues in major sports marketing contracts; and undertaking litigation and enforcement actions to protect clients' IP rights.
Sports Sponsorship: Advising sports rights owners and major sponsors on the structuring and negotiation of substantial sponsorship and sports marketing ventures.

CLIENTELE: Clients include many major international and domestic governing bodies (e.g. International Rugby Board, International Tennis Federation), event organisers (e.g. Rugby World Cup, Five/Six Nations, Asian PGA, Davis Cup, Fed Cup), corporate sponsors (e.g. Bacardi-Martini, Nike, Nationwide, Carlsberg-Tetley), sponsorship consultancies, sports television distribution agencies and broadcasters, and communications agencies.A great deal of the firm's practice concerns the legal structuring and commercial exploitation of all types of sporting and cultural events and properties. These have included (in 1999/2000 alone): the "Super 12" UK racecourses'

Continued overleaf

groundbreaking deal with Channel 4, NTL, the BBC and the Racing Post; Rugby World Cup '99; RWC Sevens 2001; European Rugby Cup, including the Heineken Cup sponsorship deal; Five/Six Nations broadcasting rights; the Laureus Sports Awards; Davis Cup and Fed Cup; Royal Ascot; Formula One motor-racing and many more.

LANGUAGES: Fluent French, German, Spanish, Polish, Mandarin, Cantonese, and Afrikaans are spoken by members of the firm.

TOWNSENDS

42 Cricklade Street, Swindon, SN1 3HD
Tel: (01793) 410800 **Fax:** (01793) 616294 **DX:** 6204 Swindon 1
Email: solicitors@townsends.co.uk **Website:** www.townsends.co.uk

18 London Road, Newbury, RG14 1JX
Tel: (01635) 31720 **Fax:** (01635) 32877 **DX:** 30810 Newbury
Email: solicitors@townsends.co.uk

Senior partner:	Julian George
Number of partners:	19
Assistant solicitors:	19
Total staff:	126
Other fee-earners:	27

AREAS OF PRACTICE

Personal Client	37%
Business Services	36%
Litigation	27%

CONTACTS

Agriculture	Chris Goldingham
Building & Construction	David Patterson
Commercial Property	Brian Jacomb
Company/Commercial	Nick Smith
Employment	Mike Nield
Family	Richard Sharp
Industrial Diseases	Brigitte Chandler
IT & IP	Mike Sefton
Litigation	Nigel Musgrove
Pensions Related Property Work	Rosalind Sopel
Personal Injury	Melanie Richens
Private Client	Sir John Sykes
Property Development	Alan Goulding

T

THE FIRM: Townsends is a leading firm serving the M4 corridor from its offices in Swindon and Newbury. It is renowned as an approachable, progressive firm providing a focused range of specialist commercial and private client services. Quality and client care are given top priority at Townsends. It is the first law firm in Wiltshire to receive IIP accreditation and the firm's Legal Aid franchise continues into its fourth year.

PRINCIPAL AREAS OF WORK:
Corporate & Commercial/Commercial Property: Services to business are comprehensive from cross-border acquisition work to business start-ups. The employment team is very active in advising on the contentious and non-contentious aspects of employment law. The property teams cover all landlord and tenant work as well as specialist options, development and pension fund work.
Litigation: Work of the litigation division includes commercial and construction disputes, licensing, debt recovery, defamation, employment law, insurance claims, landlord and tenant, product liability and professional negligence.
Personal Injury: The firm's reputation for personal injury litigation is outstanding, and Townsends has a national reputation in asbestosis, deafness, spinal injuries and serious head injury cases for claimants.
Private Client: The personal client division provides expertise in tax and trusts, administration of estates, wills and advice for the elderly.
Family: The family team is one of the largest in the South West and the team offer a specialist divorce finance unit and mediation service.

RECRUITMENT & TRAINING: The firm makes considerable investment in both the skills and welfare of its staff and four trainee solicitors are recruited annually.

TOZERS

Broadwalk House, Southernhay West, Exeter, EX1 1UA
Tel: (01392) 207020 **Fax:** (01392) 207019/ 207018 **DX:** 8322
Email: mail@tozers.co.uk **Website:** www.tozers.co.uk

Strand Chambers, Dawlish, EX7 9EZ **DX:** 82051 Dawlish
Tel: (01626) 862323 **Fax:** (01626) 866 851
Email: mail@tozers.co.uk **Website:** www.tozers.co.uk

2-3 Orchard Gardens, Teignmouth, TQ14 8DR **DX:** Teignmouth
Tel: (01626) 772376 **Fax:** (01626) 770317
Email: mail@tozers.co.uk **Website:** www.tozers.co.uk

8 Paul's Road, Newton Abbot, TQ12 4PR **DX:** 59102 Newton Abbot
Tel: (01626) 207020 **Fax:** (01626) 207019
Email: mail@tozers.co.uk **Website:** www.tozers.co.uk

73 Abbey Road, Torquay, TQ2 5NN **DX:** Torquay
Tel: (01803) 407020 **Fax:** (01803) 407021
Email: mail@tozers.co.uk **Website:** www.tozers.co.uk

8 The Crescent, Plymouth, **DX:** Torquay 118106 Plymouth
Tel: (01752) 206460 **Fax:**
Email: mail@tozers.co.uk **Website:** www.tozers.co.uk

Managing partner:	PW Edwards
Chairman	GGN Bond
Number of partners:	16
Assistant solicitors:	15
Other fee-earners:	22

AREAS OF PRACTICE

Litigation	32%
Commercial	30%
Property	21%
Probate	17%

CONTACTS

Charities and Schools	Richard King
Family & Childcare	Philip Kidd
Clinical Negligence	Paul Haynes
Commercial Lending & Property	Tim Fogarty
Litigation	Jill Headford
Leisure Planning & Mobile Home Law	Tony Beard
Probate	Vernon Clarke

THE FIRM: Tozers was established in 1785 and is one of the largest law firms in Devon. The firm offers a successful blend of experience and traditional values on the one hand, and a progressive outlook and a high degree of commercial awareness on the other. Specialist teams have been developed to ensure expertise in niche areas.

PRINCIPAL AREAS OF WORK: Planning and environmental law including caravan parks and mobile home law; charities and schools, the specialist team advises religious, educational and other charities as well as schools both in the private and state sectors; commercial lending and recovery; commercial and residential property; litigation, including employment, property disputes, debt recovery, criminal law and general tribunal and court work; family and childcare; clinical negligence and personal injury; professional negligence including pensions mis-selling; wills, probate, tax and trusts, including tax planning and investment management for trusts and individuals; agency work including all aspects of civil and criminal litigation, licensing and personal searches.

Members of Law Society Panels for Children, Family Law, Clinical Negligence, Personal Injury and Planning.

TRAVERS SMITH BRAITHWAITE

10 Snow Hill, London, EC1A 2AL
Tel: (020) 7295 3000 **Fax:** (020) 7295 3500 **DX:** 79
Email: Travers.Smith@TraversSmith.com **Website:** www.traverssmith.com

Managing partner:	Alasdair F. Douglas
Senior partner:	Christopher Bell
UK:	
Number of partners:	43
Assistant solicitors:	85
Other fee-earners:	42
International:	
Number of partners:	1
Assistant solicitors:	1

AREAS OF PRACTICE

Corporate	38%
Litigation	15%
Property	15%
Finance	14%
Tax	8%
Employment	5%
Pensions	5%

CONTACTS

Banking	Neil Murray
Commercial	Margaret Moore
Competition & EU law	Margaret Moore
Construction	Alistair Graham
Corporate	Oliver Barnes
Employment	Dorothy Henderson
Environment	Alison Lea
Financial Services	Margaret Chamberlain
Insolvency	Jeremy Walsh
Insurance/Reinsurance	Stephen Paget-Brown
Litigation	John Kingston
Pensions	Paul Stannard
Planning	Alison Lea
Property	Robert Harman
Tax	Alasdair Douglas
Venture Capital	Christopher Hale

THE FIRM: Travers Smith Braithwaite is a leading corporate, financial and commercial law firm with the expertise and capability to advise on a wide range of business activities. Today's clients include regulatory, financial, trade and industrial organisations throughout the UK and from all over the world. Travers Smith Braithwaite prides itself on not being so large as to have an impersonal atmosphere yet enjoys a quality of work and a range of clients normally associated with larger firms. By resisting rapid growth, the firm has been able to maintain the high standards of service it provides to clients. Closely-knit and consistent teams of lawyers will provide advice to a client year in year out, ensuring a clear understanding of the client's business and an effective working relationship. Central to the firm's approach is the philosophy that partners should be closely involved in most of the matters undertaken and that delegation should not be automatic but considered in every case in the light of both effectiveness and cost.

PRINCIPAL AREAS OF WORK: The firm's business comprises eight main areas:
Corporate Law: Takeovers, mergers and acquisitions, new issues, company law, financial services and regulatory law, capital markets, private equity and venture capital.
Commercial Law: Business agreements, EU and competition law, intellectual property, information technology, environment, multi-media, privatisations and broadcasting.
Banking/Insolvency: Secured and unsecured lending, finance leasing, acquisition finance, trade and project finance, property finance, banking regulations, rescheduling and insolvency.
Employment: Executive service agreements, restrictive covenants, health and safety, works councils and employee consultation, industrial disputes and employment litigation, employment aspects of mergers, acquisitions and reorganisations (including transfers of undertakings).
Litigation: Domestic and international, commercial litigation, arbitration and ADR.
Property: Acquisition, disposal and development of industrial, retail and office property, planning and construction law.
Pensions: Establishment, administration and winding up of pension funds and pension litigation.
Tax: Domestic and international corporate tax planning, acquisition and structured finance, employee share (and other) incentive schemes, private client tax planning.

INTERNATIONAL CONNECTIONS: The firm enjoys a close working relationship with foreign law firms in the main legal jurisdictions and is a member of a network of European law firms. The firm believes that its clients' best interests are served by the firm having access to, and the ability to select, established overseas firms which have the necessary expertise and experience. This approach also allows the firm the flexibility to work with a client's existing advisers in different jurisdictions or to select alternative advisers where conflicts of interest arise. Travers Smith Braithwaite opened a Paris liaison office in April 1999. The office sources and manages the provision of French legal services to the firm and its UK and overseas clients. In addition, the office acts as a liaison between French clients (including French law firms) and the London office. The Paris office partner is David Patient (David.Patient@TraversSmith.com), based at 21 Place de la Madeleine, 75008 Paris, France. Tel: +33 (0)1 43 12 53 00 Fax: +33 (0)1 43 12 53 09 Website: www.TraversSmith.com

LANGUAGES: French, German, Italian, Spanish.

RECRUITMENT & TRAINING: Travers Smith Braithwaite continues to develop and is always looking to recruit, at both assistant and trainee level, people of academic excellence and sound judgement who are able to take their careers, but not themselves, seriously. The firm's training philosophy is that skill and expertise are best acquired through practical experience complemented by carefully targeted formal instruction. Great emphasis is placed on ensuring that trainees are actively involved in a broad range of work. Applications for traineeships should be made in writing to Christopher Carroll enclosing a full CV together with the names and addresses of academic and personal referees.

TRAVERS SMITH BRAITHWAITE

TRETHOWANS

College Chambers, New Street, Salisbury, SP1 2LY
Tel: (01722) 412512 **Fax:** (01722) 411300 **DX:** 58004 SALISBURY
Email: Info@treth.co.uk

The Director General's House, Rockstone Place, Southampton, SO15 2EP
Tel: (023) 8032 1000 **Fax:** (023) 8032 1001 **DX:** 49678 SOUTHAMPTON 2
Email: Info@treth.co.uk

Managing partner:	Miles Brown
Number of partners:	17
Assistant solicitors:	14
Other fee-earners:	24

AREAS OF PRACTICE

Litigation	25%
Property	25%
Company/Commercial	20%
Private Client	20%
Licensing	10%

CONTACTS

Commercial Litigation	Phil Banks-Welsh
Company/Commercial	Catherine MacRae
Licensing	Michael Messent
Litigation Services	Neil Elliott
Private Client	Michael Ricketts
Property	John Fletcher

TRETHOWANS
SOLICITORS

THE FIRM: One of the largest and strongest general law firms in the South of England, this expanding firm provides a complete range of legal services for both commercial and private clients. Genuine expertise and increasing reputations in key areas are a feature of the firm.Trethowans has four offices across Wiltshire and Hampshire. Its commercial client expertise is increasingly focused on the Southampton office. The private client expertise is spread across the firm but with the Salisbury office at its core. Teams of specialists work as client needs dictate, either individually or, particularly on corporate work and larger litigation cases, in team groups. The firm places an unusually high emphasis in 'knowing its clients' and their objectives. The firm regards its commercial services as providing large London law firm expertise but with more competitive costs structures, and with close direct partner involvement in the work in hand.

PRINCIPAL AREAS OF WORK:

Commercial Client Work

Licensing Services: The firm has an unrivalled reputation in betting, gaming and liquor licensing. Work is undertaken nationwide for Ladbrokes, Pizza Hut, Bacardi Martini and other household names.

Commercial Property Services: A strong client base involving all types of commercial property and significant project work, including insolvency. Again, the firm acts for major national companies in this area.

Commercial & Business Services: An experienced team dealing with major clients shared with other groups within the firm, as well as its own client base. A wide range of corporate work including acquisitions, disposals, management-led transactions, commercial contracts of various kinds including sports/sponsorship, insolvency, intellectual property and IT.

Commercial Litigation Services: This includes advisory as well as straightforward representational work in all areas including credit management, general claims and liability cases, and employment. Recent work includes a House of Lords case on directors' personal liabilities in corporate matters.

Private Client Work

Litigation Services: This group has a strong reputation for its personal injury and medical negligence work. The firm acts for both claimants and defendants.

Family Services: A wide range of matrimonial and childcare cases are undertaken for both legally aided and privately funded clients.

Property Services, Tax Trusts and Agricultural/Estates Services: These areas remain an important part of the practice. The firm has an established and strong client base requiring these services.

CLIENTELE: The firm's clients range from major quoted public companies to start-up businesses, and from private individuals to large landed estates.

TREVOR ROBINSON & CO

Howard House, 70 Baker Street, Weybridge, KT13 8AL **Tel:** (01932) 859655 **Fax:** (01932) 847469 **DX:** 30910 Weybridge
Email: lawyers@trlaw.co.uk **Ptnrs:** 2 **Asst solrs:** 3 **Other fee-earners:** 1

TREVOR SMYTH & CO

13 Chichester Street, Belfast, BT1 4JB **Tel:** (028) 90320360 **Fax:** (028) 90325636 **Ptnrs:** 9 **Asst solrs:** 9 **Other fee-earners:** 11

TROBRIDGES

1 Ford Park Road, Mutley Plain, Plymouth, PL4 6LY **Tel:** (01752) 664022 **Fax:** (01752) 223761 **DX:** 120154 Mutley Plain **Ptnrs:** 3 **Asst solrs:** 4 **Other fee-earners:** 3 **Contact:** Mr C. Matthews • General practice with a litigation bias.

AREAS OF PRACTICE

Personal Injury Litigation/ Civil Litigation	55%
Conveyancing/Commercial work	20%
Probate	13%
Family	12%

TROWERS & HAMLINS

Sceptre Court, 40 Tower Hill, London, EC3N 4DX
Tel: (020) 7423 8000 **Fax:** (020) 7423 8001 **DX:** CDE 774 Lon/City
Email: marketing@trowers.com **Website:** www.trowers.com

Portland House, Longbrook Street, Exeter, EX4 6AB
Tel: (01392) 217466 **Fax:** (01392) 221047 **DX:** 134051 Exeter 15
Email: marketing@trowers.com

Heron House, Albert Square, Manchester, M2 5HD
Tel: (0161) 211 0000 **Fax:** (0161) 211 0001 **DX:** 14323 Manchester 1
Email: marketing@trowers.com

Managing partner:	David Biggerstaff
Senior partner:	John Clark
UK:	
Number of partners:	58
Assistant solicitors :	64
Other fee-earners :	38
International:	
Number of partners:	7
Assistant solicitors:	8
Other fee-earners:	7

AREAS OF PRACTICE

Property (Housing, Public Sector, Commercial Property)	34%
Litigation	32%
Company/Commercial & Construction	26%
Private Client	8%

CONTACTS

Banking	Ralph Picken
Charities	Jean Dollimore
Commercial Property	Elizabeth McKibbin
Company/Commercial	Jennie Gubbins
Construction	David Mosey
Corporate Finance	Jennie Gubbins
Employment	Emma Burrows
Environmental	Ian Doolittle
Health	Joanne Easterbrook
Housing (General)	Jonathan Adlington
	Ian Graham
Housing Finance	Sarah Hayes
International Projects	Martin Amison
Litigation	Don Moorhouse
	John Linwood
Private Client	Michael Williamson
Projects/PFI	Ian Graham
	David Mosey
Public Sector	Ian Doolittle
Tax	Neil Cohen

TROWERS & HAMLINS

THE FIRM: City and international law firm Trowers & Hamlins continues to flourish through successful specialisations developed across a broadly-based commercial, property, litigation and private client practice. Particular strengths include housing and housing finance, local government, UK and international projects, company commercial, construction, commercial property and public/private sector initiatives including private finance. Other specialisations include the health sector, environmental law, employment and charities. Trowers & Hamlins provides clear, practical solutions to achieve its clients' objectives. In all matters a client partner will call on appropriate lawyers and resources within the firm to fulfil the particular requirements of the client's brief. The firm's clients include banks, public and private companies, national and local government departments, NHS Trusts, housing bodies, partnerships, charities and individuals.

PRINCIPAL AREAS OF WORK: Through its UK offices and internationally, the firm has developed a dynamic corporate and commercial practice. Particular strengths are recognised in its UK and international finance and project work, including PFI and other DBFO schemes. As leading lawyers to the housing movement, the firm's London, Manchester and Exeter offices advise government bodies, lenders and some 250 housing associations. In addition, the firm has an impressive commercial litigation reputation and a highly regarded private client practice.
Company/Commercial: The department is a substantial team with a growing City profile. It advises public and private companies and individuals operating in the financial, property, industrial and commercial sectors.
Projects & Construction: This department advises UK and international clients in a variety of sectors, spanning innovative PFI/DBFO project structures and joint venture/partnering initiatives.
Property: The department covers commercial, housing, local authority, residential, estate and institutional law. It has a substantial team and has established a reputation for innovation, working in the forefront of changing legislation. It provides a wide range of services to corporate clients, international businesses and individuals. Clients include investment institutions, developers, housing associations and local authorities.
Litigation: This department deals with a wide range of commercial civil litigation, arbitration and ADR both nationally and internationally, with a particular profile in professional and clinical negligence cases. It is also involved in banking, property, insolvency, employment and personal injury work. The department has a high reputation for its construction work, including mediation and adjudication.
Private Client: The department provides legal advice to individuals with industrial or commercial wealth, invested assets or landed estates. It is concerned particularly with tax planning, trusts, wills, probate, charities and the administration of trusts and estates.

INTERNATIONAL CONNECTIONS: The firm has a strong international network, particularly in the Middle East, where it has offices in Abu Dhabi, Bahrain, Cairo, Dubai and Oman. It is particularly well-known for its energy and infrastructure projects.

RECRUITMENT & TRAINING: The firm is always happy to hear from lawyers interested in working in a commercial environment. It recruits at least 12-15 trainee solicitors each year.

TUCKERS

39 Warren Street, London, W1P 5PD
Tel: (020) 7388 8333 **Fax:** (020) 7388 7333 **DX:** 123596 Regents Park 3
Email: crime@tuckers-law.com **Website:** www.tuckers-law.com

63-65 Mosley Street, Manchester, M2 3HZ
Tel: (0161) 233 4321 **Fax:** (0161) 835 1415 **DX:** 14451 Manchester 2
Email: law@tuckers-crime.com

Managing partner:	Barry Tucker
Senior partner:	Franklin Sinclair
Number of partners:	2
Assistant solicitors:	41
Other fee-earners:	65

AREAS OF PRACTICE

Crime (all types)	95%
Immigration	5%

CONTACTS

Business Crime/Fraud	B. Craig
Crime (London)	Barry Tucker
Crime (Manchester)	Franklin Sinclair

THE FIRM: Tuckers Solicitors, a large criminal law firm have offices located in the North of England and Central London, with an office in Birmingham to open shortly. The firm acts on behalf of both private and legally aided clients in all aspects of criminal law. They have a specialist white collar crime department which has expertise in DTI frauds, Customs & Excise cases and other business crime. As the offices are staffed 24 hours a day, police station attendance is always available to clients and other firms of solicitors/accountants requiring assistance for their own clients.

TUCKER TURNER KINGSLEY WOOD & CO

18 Bedford Row, London, WC1R 4EB **Tel:** (020) 7242 3303 **Fax:** (020) 7831 1732 **DX:** 220 **Ptnrs:** 9 **Asst solrs:** 3 **Other fee-earners:** 6 **Contact:** Alec Melville • General commercial practice handling company/commercial, property, litigation, lending/recovery, private client matters and white collar fraud.

TUGHAN & CO

Marlborough House, 30 Victoria Street, Belfast, BT1 3GS
Tel: (028) 9055 3300 **Fax:** (028) 9055 0096 **DX:** 433Nr Belfast 1
Email: law@tughan.dnet.co.uk **Website:** tughan.co.uk

Number of partners:	12
Assistant solicitors:	14
Other fee-earners:	4

AREAS OF PRACTICE

Litigation (including Insurance and Employment Law)	45%
Company/Commercial/Property (including Banking, Finance, M&A & Insolvency)	40%
Private Client	10%
Other	5%

CONTACTS

Banking & Finance	John Mills
Commercial Litigation	Michael McCord
Commercial Property	Phyllis Agnew
Conveyancing/Building Estates	Noelle McKay
Corporate Finance/Commercial	John-George Willis
Employment & Labour Law	Grahame Loughlin
Environmental Law	Deirdre Magill
Litigation & Insurance	CMH Gibson
Mergers & Acquisitions	John-George Willis
Private Client	Noelle McKay

THE FIRM: Tughan & Co was established in 1896, and has developed over the years into one of the largest firms of solicitors in Northern Ireland. The firm's main priority is to provide clear, sound advice to its many clients through a personal service which is supported by the latest technological developments. The firm merged with Ronald Rosser and Company in 1999, thereby strengthening the firm's position in respect of defence litigation, commercial property and corporate work.Tughan & Company recently formed an association with Dublin firm William Fry, enabling both firms to offer an all-Ireland service. William Fry is one of Ireland's leading law firms with 110 solicitors. A significant number of new instructions are received on the recommendations of other law firms principally in the City of London and Glasgow/Edinburgh, with whom Tughan & Co has over the years developed strong links. Their knowledge of, and relationship with, these firms enables Tughan & Co to react rapidly upon receipt of instructions, quite often in connection with multi-jurisdictional transactions, with a Northern Ireland element.

PRINCIPAL AREAS OF WORK:

Litigation: The firm handles a broad range of litigation and arbitration, and is particularly active in insurance defence work and employment disputes.

Commercial Property: The firm acts for a broad range of Irish and UK-based property developers, institutions, investors and national retail chains in connection with developments, town centre regeneration, joint ventures, PFI projects, sales and purchases and leases of commercial and industrial property in Northern Ireland.

Corporate Finance/Commercial: The firm has been involved in a number of high profile corporate transactions in Northern Ireland in recent years, including two privatisations. Principal activities involve acquisitions, mergers, share issues in public and private companies, inward investments, joint ventures and shareholder agreements.

Banking/Financial Services: The banking side of the practice has grown considerably in recent years and the firm now acts for a heavyweight client list of national and international banks and finance institutions requiring assets and securitisation advice. The firm also acts within Northern Ireland for the principal regulators of the UK financial services industry.

TUNNARD CROSFIELD

Cathedral Chambers, 4 Kirkgate, Ripon, HG4 1PA **Tel:** (01765) 600 421 **Fax:** (01765) 690 523 **DX:** 61401 RIPON
Email: ripondio.reg@connectfree.co.uk

TURBERVILLES WITH NELSON CUFF

122 High Street, Uxbridge, UB8 1JT
Tel: (01895) 201700 **Fax:** (01895) 273519 **DX:** 45116 Uxbridge
Email: solicitors@turbervilles.co.uk **Website:** www.turbervilles.co.uk

Senior partner:	Sess Sigré
Number of partners:	10
Assistant solicitors:	14
Other fee-earners:	15

THE FIRM: The firm was created in April 1998 from the merger of Turbervilles with Nelson Cuff. Its main office is in Uxbridge, with branch offices in Hillingdon and Harrow.

PRINCIPAL AREAS OF WORK: The firm handles a broad spread of work for commercial, company, private and legally-aided clients, covering commercial and domestic property; land acquisition and development; civil, family, employment and personal injury litigation; commercial litigation and debt recovery; wills, probate, estates and trusts; licensing; crime; animal welfare; immigration and County court agency.

TURCAN CONNELL WS

Saltire Court, 20 Castle Terrace, Edinburgh, EH1 2EF
Tel: (0131) 228 8111 **Fax:** (0131) 228 8118 **DX:** 553000 Edin 18
Email: enquiries@turcanconnell.com **Website:** www.turcanconnell.com

Joint senior partners:	Robert Turcan, Douglas Connell
Number of partners:	13
Assistant solicitors:	23
Other fee-earners:	38

AREAS OF PRACTICE

Private Client, Tax & Trusts 40%
Agriculture & Estates 35%
Pensions & Investment 15%
Charity 10%

CONTACTS

Agriculture & Estates Robert Turcan, Malcolm Strang Steel, Jon Robertson, Adam Gilingham
Charities Robin Fulton, Neil MacLeod, Simon Mackintosh
Heritage Property ....Douglas Connell
Private Client/Trusts Douglas Connell, Simon Mackintosh, Robin Fulton
Tax.......................Ian Clark, Heather Thompson

TURCAN CONNELL WS
SOLICITORS

THE FIRM: Turcan Connell is a leading Scottish private client practice. It concentrates exclusively on the needs of private clients, trusts, charities and those involved with rural property. As well as a strong team of lawyers, the firm has a large number of other professionals, including an investment management team, a consulting actuary, a life assurance expert, a tax compliance and a trust accounting team. The Guernsey office specialises in the management of offshore trusts and companies, Turcan Connell being the only Scottish firm to offer such a facility, which is a unique and integral part of the service provided to its clients.

PRINCIPAL AREAS OF WORK:

Personal Tax and Financial Planning: The firm acts for a wide range of clients including entrepreneurs, estate owners, expatriates and professionals. The work includes inheritance tax and capital gains tax planning, the handling of large and complex estates, and advice to shareholders on corporate transactions. Tax and financial planning and asset protection involve extensive use of trusts, including their establishment, variation and termination. The firm has one of the largest trust management practices in the UK with over 2000 trusts under management. Offshore trusts are used where appropriate.
Financial Services: This service is seen as integral to the all-round service provided to private clients, trusts and charities, incorporating an investment management team and pensions and life assurance advice.
Agriculture & Estates: The firm advises on all aspects of rural property throughout Scotland, including purchase and sale of estates and their commercial development; farming and agricultural law; fishing and sporting law; and the commercial exploration of rural property. The firm is active in the residential and estate market in Edinburgh, Lothian, the Borders, Fife and Perthshire.
Litigation & Family: Advice is given in relation to separation and divorce, and the negotiation of financial settlements; and employment and related matters.
Charity Law & Heritage Property: Charity law is an area of great importance to the firm. The range of charitable clients advised by the firm covers all types of charity from small privately established bodies to major national institutions, and includes grant giving and grant receiving bodies. The firm has a particular expertise in heritage property, acting for the owners of over150 historic houses.

TURNBULL, SIMSON & STURROCK WS

26 High Street, Jedburgh, TD8 6AE **Tel:** (01835) 862391 **Fax:** (01835) 862017 **DX:** 581223 Jedburgh
Ptnrs: 4 **Other fee-earners:** 1 **Contact:** Denbeigh Kirkpatrick • Offers a broad range of services. Expertise in relation to agricultural law.

TURNER PARKINSON

Hollins Chambers, 64a Bridge Street, Manchester, M3 3BA
Tel: (0161) 833 1212 **Fax:** (0161) 834 9098 **DX:** 710251 Manchester 3
Email: tp@tp.co.uk **Website:** www.tp.law.co.uk

Managing partner:	Mark Openshaw-Blower
Senior partner:	Richard Parkinson
Number of partners:	8
Assistant solicitors:	15
Other fee-earners:	7

AREAS OF PRACTICE

Company Commercial............................40%
Litigation 35%
Property 20%
Private Client 5%

CONTACTS

Company/Commercial........Richard Parkinson
.................................Mark Openshaw-Blower
....Nick Davenport
....Nick Marshall
Litigation ....Malcolm Hunnisett
....Phil Turner
....Mark Lund
Private Client ....Colette Johnson
....Janet Fleming
....Christine Dickinson
Property ....Stephen Daniels
....David Blackburn

THE FIRM: This Manchester-based firm of commercial law specialists has deliberately developed a broad portfolio of services that focuses on the needs of owner-managed businesses, providing them with the very best commercial legal advice at a sensible price.

PRINCIPAL AREAS OF WORK:

Company/Commercial: Company formation, company restructuring, directors' duties, partnership law, joint ventures and shareholders' agreements, franchising, agency and distribution, contract negotiations and drafting, competition law and pensions.
Corporate Finance: Raising finance, venture capital, share, business and asset sales and purchases.
Intellectual Property: Trademarks, passing off, copyright, design right and registered design, patents and confidentiality.Computer contracts, entertainment law and sports law are other niche areas of excellence.
Commercial Litigation: Breach of contract, defective goods, financial claims, construction disputes and defamation. Professional negligence and insolvency are particular specialisms.
Employment: Terms of employment, service agreements, restraint of trade, transfer of undertakings, discrimination, termination of employment, redundancy and unfair or wrongful dismissal.
Commercial Property: Sales, purchases and exchanges, options, auctions and tenders, commercial leases, residential tenancies, mortgages and planning applications.
Private Client: Divorce and family matters. Residential property matters. Probate, trusts and wills.

T.V. EDWARDS

29 Mile End Rd, London, E1 4TP **Tel:** (020) 7791 1050 **Fax:** (020) 7790 5101 **DX:** 300700 Tower Hamlets **Ptnrs:** 9 **Asst solrs:** 25 **Other fee-earners:** 12

TWEEDIE & PRIDEAUX (INCORPORATING WOOD, NASH KIMBER)

5 Lincoln's Inn Fields, London, WC2A 3BT
Tel: (020) 7405 1234 **Fax:** (020) 7831 1525 **DX:** 6 London/Ch.Ln
Email: enquiry@tweedieandprideaux.co.uk **Website:** www.tweedieandprideaux.co.uk

390 London Road, Mitcham, CR4 4EA
Tel: (020) 8640 5124 **Fax:** (020) 8640 2695 **DX:** 88151 Mitcham South
Email: mitcham@tweedieandprideaux.co.uk

Number of partners:	11
Assistant solicitors:	3
Other fee-earners:	6

AREAS OF PRACTICE

Probate & Trusts	33%
Residential Conveyancing	17%
Litigation	16%
Commercial Conveyancing	14%
Commercial Work	12%
Charities	4%
Other Private Client Work	4%

THE FIRM: Tweedie & Prideaux was joined in September 1998 by the firm of Wood Nash Kimber which had previously been in Raymond Buildings, Gray's Inn since 1826, and which brought with it a greater international dimension. Both are long-established practices with Tweedie & Prideaux being at the same address since 1864. The firm undertakes commercial and company work; banking law; foreign and UK commercial and residential property; agricultural property; town and country planning; landlord and tenant; UK and offshore wills, trusts, and probate; business and personal taxation; matrimonial and family; commercial and general civil litigation and work for charities.

INTERNATIONAL CONNECTIONS: France, Germany, Zimbabwe and Albania.

LANGUAGES: French, German, and Spanish.

TWITCHEN MUSTERS & KELLY

County Chambers, 25-27 Weston Road, Southend-on-Sea, SS1 1BB
Tel: (01702) 339222 **Fax:** (01702) 331563 **DX:** 2821 Southend
Email: tmksols@tmksols.co.uk **Website:** www.tmksols.co.uk

Contact partner:	Patrick Musters
Number of partners:	9
Assistant solicitors:	9
Other fee-earners:	16

AREAS OF PRACTICE

Crime	50%
Family	35%
Civil Litigation	15%

CONTACTS

Civil Litigation	Sean Callaghan
Crime	Patrick Musters
Family	John Twitchen

THE FIRM: A firm specialising in crime, family and civil litigation only. The largest criminal practice and legal aid firm in Essex, and the first firm in the country to have two Higher Court Advocates conducting criminal work. The firm carries Legal Aid Franchises in ten categories. Partners are Law Society panel members in their respective fields.

PRINCIPAL AREAS OF WORK: Crime, personal injury and civil litigation, family and child care. Agency work welcomed.

TYNDALLWOODS

Windsor House, Temple Row, Birmingham, B2 5TS **Tel:** (0121) 624 1111 **Fax:** (0121) 624 8401 **DX:** 13039 Birmingham 1 **Ptnrs:** 10 **Asst solrs:** 11 **Other fee-earners:** 20 **Contact:** Mike Dyer • Undertakes a wide range of legal aid and private client work.

UNDERWOOD & CO (INCORPORATING CORBOULD RIGBY & CO)

40 Welbeck Street, London, W1M 8LN
Tel: (020) 7526 6000 **Fax:** (020) 7486 8974 **DX:** 9074 West End
Email: enquiries@underwoodco.co.uk

Managing partner:	Peter Hughes
Senior partner:	Hilary Guest
Number of partners:	8
Assistant solicitors:	9
Other fee-earners:	4

AREAS OF PRACTICE

Commercial Litigation	50%
Commercial Residential Property	30%
Company Commercial	10%
Private Client	10%

THE FIRM: Underwood & Co is a forward-looking firm in the West End of London. Its broad client base comprises banks, partnerships, public and private companies and there is a busy private client department. The firm is particularly strong in banking and professional negligence litigation, commercial property, secured lending and debt recovery. Founded in 1845, during its long history the firm has developed an impressive combination of expertise and personal service. The partnership aims to provide advice of a City standard at reasonable cost. The firm is also highly regarded for its employment and immigration work.

PRINCIPAL AREAS OF WORK:

Banking and Commercial Litigation: The firm has strong experience in handling many sorts of commercial litigation from heavyweight banking and insolvency cases to computerised volume mortgage possession work and debt recovery.

Professional Negligence Litigation: An early entrant into this rapidly developing growth area, the firm has successfully managed scores of cases involving solicitors, surveyors, accountants and other professionals. The emphasis is on negotiating a commercially sound settlement as early as possible in proceedings and only taking an action to trial if this is really necessary to secure the best result.
Commercial Property: The firm has wide experience in this area including the transfer of freehold and leasehold property and the grant and renewal of commercial leases. A particular speciality is acting for institutions on secured lending.
Medical and Dental: A comprehensive service is provided for dental and medical practitioners who have long formed part of the firm's clientele. The firm also has a growing presence in the nursing home sector acting for a number of companies and home owners.
Company/Commercial: Work includes company formation and restructuring, sale and purchase of business assets, licensing, partnership agreements and commercial contracts, intellectual property and insolvency matters.
Employment and Immigration: The firm advises both employers and senior employees on all aspects of appointment, remuneration and termination, including transfers of undertakings and discrimination disputes. In relation to immigration, the firm advises on the issue of work permits, establishing business in the UK and residence for persons of independent means.
Private Client: The firm provides advice on administration and estates, wills and probate, trusts and tax planning. Additionally this firm undertakes residential conveyancing of higher value property.

CONTACTS

Commercial	Peter Hughes
	Louise Reid
Commercial Property	Justin Roche
	Leona Mason
Employment	Roger Digby
Litigation	Paul Redfern
	James Baird
Private Client	Hilary Guest

U

UNDERWOODS

83/85 Marlowes, Hemel Hempstead, HP1 1LF
Tel: (01442) 430900 **Fax:** (01442) 239861
Email: underwoods@compuserve.com

2 Bushfield Road, Bovingdon, HP3 0DR
Tel: (01442) 831343 **Fax:** (01442) 831035
Email: underwoods@compuserve.com

Old Station House, London Road, St Albans, AL1 1JD
Tel: (01727) 810800 **Fax:** (01442) 239861
Email: underwoods@compuserve.com

15 Cornwalls Centre, High Street, Buckingham, MK18 1SB
Tel: (0800) 731 2616 **Fax:** (01442) 239861
Email: underwoods@compuserve.com

Kinetic House, Theobald Street, Borehamwood, WD6 5PJ
Tel: (0800) 731 2616 **Fax:** (01442) 239861
Email: underwoods@compuserve.com

Managing partner:	Kerry Underwood
Number of partners:	2
Assistant solicitors:	16
Other fee-earners:	2

AREAS OF PRACTICE

Employment	35%
Personal Injury	30%
Litigation	15%
Local Govern't/Administrative/ Public Law	10%
Other	10%

CONTACTS

Administrative/Public Law	Kerry Underwood
Clinical Negligence	Sharon MacArthur
	Joanna McGlew
Corporate & Commercial	Clive Grumball
Employment	Marc Jones
	Asha Hartnell
Human Rights	Kerry Underwood.
Litigation	Charlotte Moore
Local Government	Kerry Underwood
Personal Injury	Tim Robinson
	Victoria Williams
Private Client	Robert Males

THE FIRM: 10 years old this year, Underwoods is a flagship firm and a model for other law firms. It has pioneered contingency and conditional fees, menu pricing and fixed fees and is one of the very few secretary-free law firms. The firm specialises in civil litigation and is particularly well-known for its employment, personal injury and public and administrative law work. It provides a distinctive high-quality service and with its unparalleled standards of client care, Underwoods' glowing reputation is fully deserved. Kerry Underwood leads a team of talented specialist solicitors, all of whom are fully computer and keyboard literate. Four solicitors are on the Law Society Personal Injury Panel and Marc Jones and Kerry Underwood are members of the Employment Law Advisers Appeal Scheme (formerly the Employment Appeal Tribunal Advice Scheme) and both are on the Equal Opportunities Commission Panel of Solicitors. The firm undertakes agency advocacy in the Employment Appeal Tribunal as well as Employment Tribunals. The firm has no legal aid franchises or contracts and offers a genuinely independent service with no-one pulling the strings. Kerry Underwood is the world's leading authority on conditional fees and author of the best-seller *No Win No Fee No Worries* first published to huge critical acclaim in 1998. He is Editor of the Costs Products section of Butterworths *Personal Injury Litigation Service, on the editorial board of the Law Society's Litigation Funding*, Consultant Editor of *Employment Litigation*, and on the Law Society's Conditional Fee Task Force. Consultant to law firms, local authorities, government departments and Commonwealth Governments, Kerry also conducts seminars for the University of Cambridge, the Law Society and others and contributes to radio, television and to legal journals. Kerry is a Chairman of Employment Tribunals and a Fellow of the Chartered Institute of Arbitrators.

PRINCIPAL AREAS OF WORK:

Employment: Work includes transfer of undertakings regulations, sex, race and disability discrimination, maternity law, EU law, Employment Tribunal and Employment Appeal Tribunal advocacy, redundancy and contract, and severance.
Litigation: Work includes personal injury, claimant and defendant (Law Society's Personal Injury Panel), clinical negligence, intellectual property matters, debt recovery and contractual disputes.

Continued overleaf

Administrative/Public Law: Work includes judicial review, education, civil liberty matters, discrimination, human rights and local authority work.
Local Government Law: Work includes education law, judicial reviews, joint ventures, leasing and funding, transfers of undertakings.
Corporate and Commercial: Work includes business start-ups, trading agreements, venture capital, joint venture agreements, insolvency and corporate restructuring, compulsory competitive tendering and transfers of undertakings.

CLIENTELE: Includes local authorities and major companies and employees. Kerry Underwood and Marc Jones are members of the Employment Law Advisers Appeal Scheme (formerly the Employment Appeal Tribunal Advice Scheme), and are both on the Equal Opportunities Commission Panel.

URÍA & MENÉNDEZ

Royex House, Aldermanbury Square, London, EC2V 7NJ
Tel: (020) 7600 3610 **Fax:** (020) 7600 1718
Email: jgr@uria.com

Managing partner: Rodrigo Uría Meruéndano	
UK:	
Number of partners:	1
Assistant solicitors:	2
International (incl head office)	
Number of partners:	45
Assistant solicitors:	142

AREAS OF PRACTICE

Banking/Securities	35%
Energy/Project Finance	35%
Corporate/M&A	30%

CONTACTS

London ....Juan I González Ruiz
Madrid (+ 3491 586 0400) ....
............Charles Coward
............Josè Pérez Santos
............Rafael Sebastian
............Josè María Segovia

V

THE FIRM: Founded in the 1940s, Uría & Menéndez became a partnership in 1973. Faithful to the tradition begun by Professor Uría, the firm combines the day-to-day practice of law with its scientific and scholarly study. Uría & Menéndez prides itself on the quality of its legal advice, attention to clients, professional objectivity and enduring professional relationships with clients. Currently, the firm comprises 45 partners, 142 associates, over 40 trainee lawyers and administrative staff. A considerable number of Uría & Menéndez's members are actively involved in academic and university life and are authors of numerous legal publications. The London office provides advice on Spanish law to international clients operating from the UK who have interests in Spain or who wish to offer their banking or investment services, make acquisitions or engage in business in Spain. The office also advises Spanish companies already established in the UK or that wish to become established or otherwise engage in business there.

PRINCIPAL AREAS OF WORK: Banking, corporate & commercial, energy law, M&A and foreign investment, project finance and securities.

INTERNATIONAL CONNECTIONS: With the head office in Madrid, Uría & Menéndez has offices throughout Spain (in Barcelona, Valencia and Bilbao), the rest of Europe (in Brussels, Lisbon and London), the USA (in New York), and in Latin America (in Buenos Aires, Santiago de Chile, Lima and São Paulo).

LANGUAGES: English, French, Spanish, Italian and German.

CLIENTELE: Include 54% of the 100 premier companies worldwide and 37% of the 100 premier European companies.

VARLEY HADLEY SIDDALL
3rd Floor, 66-72 Houndsgate, Nottingham, NG1 6BA **Tel:** (0115) 958 3737 **Fax:** (0115) 958 3434 **Email:** post@vhslaw.force9.co.uk

VARLEY HIBBS

Kirby House, Little Park St, Coventry, CV1 2JZ
Tel: (024) 7663 1000 **Fax:** (024) 7663 0808 **DX:** 18892
Email: comm@vhibbs.demon.co.uk

16 Hamilton Terrace, Leamington Spa, CV32 4LY
Tel: (01926) 881251 **Fax:** (01926) 831900 **DX:** 11870

Senior partner:	Edward Bayliss
Number of partners:	7
Assistant solicitors:	10
Other fee-earners:	7

AREAS OF PRACTICE

Company/Commercial	23%
Conveyancing	23%
Civil/Commercial Litigation	18%
Advocacy	17%
Family	10%
Probate/Miscellaneous	9%

THE FIRM: Varley Hibbs is a leading Midlands firm with offices in Coventry and Leamington Spa. Established for over 60 years, the firm offers a wide range of services to a variety of businesses including public and private companies, banks and building societies, along with company directors and private individuals.The practice is committed to being not only a dominant force in commercial law in its own region, but also to providing a real alternative to the major Birmingham practices. The practice is large enough to offer the specialist advice needed by large companies, yet retains the key elements of providing a personal service at competitive rates.

VEALE WASBROUGH

Orchard Court, Orchard Lane, Bristol, BS1 5DS
Tel: (0117) 925 2020 **Fax:** (0117) 925 2025 **DX:** 7831 Bristol
Email: central@vwl.co.uk **Website:** www.vwl.co.uk

Managing partner:	Simon Pizzey
Number of partners:	20
Assistant solicitors:	35
Other fee-earners:	51

AREAS OF PRACTICE

Business Non-Contentious	34%
Personal Legal Services	34%
Business Contentious	32%

THE FIRM: Veale Wasbrough is a young and dynamic firm, committed to success and excellence for its clients. The team of partners, lawyers and support staff achieve this by providing a professional and personalised service, supported by a team culture founded on the principles of partnership. Veale Wasbrough is a founder member of the Association of European Lawyers, which provides a valuable network of lawyers in 27 countries. This extensive global resource is further enhanced with connections in over 100 law firms world-wide.

PRINCIPLE AREAS OF WORK: The focus of much of the firm's work is in the provision of specialist services to the mid-sized business sector in Bristol and the South West. Through its specialist teams, Veale Wasbrough advises its clients on a wide range of issues including MBOs, mergers and acquisitions, commercial deals, intellectual property rights, and developments in technology and e-commerce. The full spectrum of issues affecting employment and the workplace is covered - employee benefits and rights, transfers of undertakings and discrimination. Veale Wasbrough is well known for its strength in property development, property management and property investment. The firm is active regionally in the resolution of commercial and business disputes. Veale Wasbrough's strong regional reputation is enhanced further by its national profile in many practice areas.

Education: The education department advises on a whole range of matters affecting schools and colleges around the UK, including crisis management.

Construction: The construction team handles all aspects of construction law and is regularly called upon to advise in substantial £multi-million disputes.

Medical: The firm's national portfolio includes a number of medical practices.

Energy: Its energy and pipeline projects also have a strong national reputation.

Personal Injury: As well as corporate expertise, Veale Wasbrough recognises the importance of the provision of legal services for the individual. The extensive personal injury team act for claimants handling accidents at work, RTAs, sports injuries and clinical negligence claims.

Residential Conveyancing: Veale Wasbrough is also at the forefront of the region's residential conveyancing market through its specialist brand 'Convey Direct'.

Estates & Tax Planning: Trusts and personal planning requirements are handled by a dedicated team, which provides advice and assistance to the business sector as well as to the private investor.

Family: The firm also provides caring and sympathetic advice on family matters.

CONTACTS

Alternative Dispute Resolution	Mike Davies
Banking Litigation	Simon Pizzey
Central Government	Simon Baker
Charities	Mary McCartney
Clinical Negligence	Gary McFarlane
Commercial Litigation	Simon Heald
Company & Commercial	David Worthington
Construction	Roger Hoyle
Convey Direct	Mike Rendell
Education	Robert Boyd
Employment	Mike Davies
Energy/Environment	Tim Smithers
Estates & Tax Planning	Mary McCartney
Family	Janet Forbes
Insolvency	Simon Heald
International Trade	David Worthington
Local Authorities	Simon Baker
Partnership: Medical Practices	Derek Bellew
Personal Injury	John Webster
Pipeline Projects	Tim Smithers
Planning	Tim Smithers
Property Services	Gary Philpott
Public Sector & Utilities	Simon Baker
Retail	David Worthington
Sports	Simon Pizzey
Technology & E-commerce	Paul Sampson
Wastes Management	Tim Smithers

V

VEITCH PENNY

1 Manor Court, Dix's Field, Exeter, EX1 1UP
Tel: (01392) 278381 **Fax:** (01392) 410247 **DX:** 8309 Exeter 1
Email: law@veitchpenny.co.uk **Website:** www.veitchpenny.co.uk

2 Market Street, Crediton, EX17 2AL
Tel: (01363) 772244 **Fax:** (01363) 775874 **DX:** 54201 Crediton
Email: law@veitchpenny.co.uk

53 St Peter Street, Tiverton, EX16 6NW
Tel: (01884) 242091 **Fax:** (01884) 242141 **DX:** 49009 Tiverton
Email: law@veitchpenny.co.uk

Managing partner:	Simon Young
Number of partners:	11
Assistant solicitors:	5
Other fee-earners:	15

AREAS OF PRACTICE

Defendant Litigation	45%
Plaintiff Litigation	27%
Conveyancing	13%
General Litigation	7%
Trust/Probate	5%
Commercial	4%

CONTACTS

Claimant PI	Andrew Harris
	Alan Crawford
	Craig Butler
Commercial/Insolvency/Employment	Simon Young
Conveyancing/Probate/Trusts	Ian Penny
	Charles Dowell
Defendant PI	Michael Penny
	James Ruttledge
	Mark Fowles
	Mark Hammerton
	Jessica Ross

THE FIRM: Founded over 30 years ago, Veitch Penny was the first firm in the South West to achieve the Law Society's quality award 'Lexcel', in recognition of their commitment to efficiency, quality and client care. The national Investor in People award was also achieved in 1998. Veitch Penny is particularly noted for its expertise in personal injury litigation.

PRINCIPAL AREAS OF WORK:

Insurance Department: All insurance related work is catered for by this specialist department; including professional negligence, public liability and workplace claims. The department has a particular expertise in the handling of local and public authority matters, and has developed a specialism in the handling of dyslexia, abuse and stress claims. The department has its own in house investigative team, whose services are also offered to insurers.

Claimant Personal Injury Department: With a dedicated team of casehandlers, the claimant department undertakes personal injury and bulk insured/uninsured loss recovery work. It lists among its clients a major motoring organisation and various legal expense insurers. Specialising in catastrophic injury and motorcycle accident claims, the team also handles volume motor and employment compensation claims for the private, legally aided and CFA client.

Other Areas: Company/commercial; insolvency; employment; commercial & residential property; wills, probate, tax & trusts; agricultural litigation; matrimonial.

VENTERS REYNOLDS

1-6 Camberwell Green, London, SE5 7AD
Tel: (020) 7277 0110 **Fax:** (020) 7277 0132 / 4764 **DX:** 35310 Camberwell
Email: venters@nacamar.co.uk **Website:** www.venters.co.uk

Senior partner:	J.M. Venters
Number of partners:	1
Assistant solicitors:	7
Other fee-earners:	3

THE FIRM: Venters & Co started in 1991 by June Venters, who was formerly a partner in a leading south London law firm for seven years. Situated opposite Camberwell Green Magistrates and Youth Court, the firm specialises in crime, family, welfare benefits, and mental health for which it holds a Legal Aid Franchise. June Venters heads a team of 14 fee earners including her partner, Wendy Williams. June Venters, is Junior Vice President and Hon Treasurer of the LCCSA and Chairman of the Legal Aid Board No.1 Area Committee. In July 1996, she was the subject of the BBC documentary Law Women. Miss Venters was appointed an Assistant Recorder in 1998.

VICTOR LISSACK & ROSCOE

8 Bow Street, Covent Garden, London, WC2E 7AJ **Tel:** (020) 7240 2010 **Fax:** (020) 7379 4420 **DX:** 40026 Covent Garden **Email:** law@victorlissack.co.uk **Ptnrs:** 2 **Asst solrs:** 4 **Other fee-earners:** 2 **Contact:** Mr Robert Roscoe or Mr Richard Almond • Specialists in white collar and all other crime including extradition and courts martial.

AREAS OF PRACTICE

Criminal law	75%
Private client	25%

V

VINSON & ELKINS LLP

Regis House, 45 King William Street, London, EC4R 9AN **Tel:** (020) 7618 6000 **Fax:** (020) 7618 6001 **Ptnrs:** 7 **Asst solrs:** 12 **Other fee-earners:** 1

VIZARD OLDHAM

42 Bedford Row, London, WC1R 4JL
Tel: (020) 7663 2222 **Fax:** (020) 7663 2226 **DX:** 152
Email: reception@vizold.co.uk **Website:** www.vizold.co.uk

Senior partner:	Richard Foster
Number of partners:	22
Assistant solicitors:	8
Other fee-earners:	21

AREAS OF PRACTICE

Public Law/Clinical Negligence	30%
Insurance Litigation	20%
Property	20%
Charity Law/Parliamentary/Private Client/ Family Law	10%
Commercial Litigation/Employment	10%
Company/Commercial	10%

CONTACTS

Charities/Private Client	Ron Perry
Clinical Negligence	Richard Foster
Commercial/Environmental Litigation	Gary Hay
Company/Commercial	Iain Mitchell
Employment	Gary Hay
Environmental Law (non-contentious)	Richard Barber
Family Law	Julia Snow
Local Government/Public Law	John Morrell
Parliamentary	Ron Perry
Personal Injury/Insurance	Mark Whittaker
Professional Negligence	David Hartfield
Property	Richard Barber
Rail & Transport	Justine Lawson

THE FIRM: Established on 1 May 1999 when 11 partners from Vizards regrouped and formed a new practice. This has enabled the new firm of Vizard Oldham to focus more clearly on its clients' requirements by concentrating on the areas of business it does best. On 1st May 2000, Vizard Oldham merged with 4 partner professional indemnity niche firm Hartfields as well as the specialist property practice of Derek Sendrove & Co. The firm has a range and depth of experience which, coupled with a commercial approach to file management, gives it a unique selling point. Full service standards are in place with accreditation under ISO 9001.

PRINCIPAL AREAS OF WORK:

Public Law: Vizard Oldham handles all types of claims on behalf of public and local authorities, from volume personal injury through to more complex negligence disputes. Other aspects of public law handled include judicial review; human rights; education; community care; mental health; planning; immigration and housing; and criminal prosecutions. John Morrell and Richard Foster are co-authors of 'Local Authority Liability', the first book of its kind in this specialist area.

Healthcare & Clinical Negligence: Vizard Oldham is one of 17 firms of solicitors to be appointed to the panel for handling claims under the Clinical Negligence Scheme for Trusts. The firm also acts for a number of health bodies direct as well as giving advice to the National Health Service Litigation Authority. The department's work also covers property, commercial, employment and charity advice.

Professional Negligence: The merger with Hartfields has significantly enhanced the firm's experience and expertise in this area. Professions covered include accountants, architects, engineers, insurance intermediaries, licenced conveyancers and surveyors. As well as acting on behalf of insured professionals, the firm advises underwriters in respect of policy wordings and coverage and policy issues.

Property (including Commercial Property &Conveyancing): Vizard Oldham offers a complete service for all its commercial and private clients both on contentious and non-contentious matters, advising on all forms of acquisitions and disposals, as well as on associated financial and planning matters. The firm has particular expertise in landlord and tenant law.

Charity Law and Parliamentary: Work includes formation of charitable trusts and incorporated charities; establishment and variation of charities under Royal Charter and dealing with the Privy Council; application to the Charity Commission; sale and acquisition of property by charities and their trading subsidiaries; document fund-raising agreements; investment and application of funds advice; advice to trustees on the discharge of their fuduciary duties. Ronald Perry is a Roll 'A' Parliamentary Agent, and as such is authorised to act on behalf on the promoters and opponents of private bills.

Private Client & Family Law: Aspects of the departments include the drafting of wills and trusts and the administration of estates including executor and trustee duties; advising on the capital and income tax consequences; advising on general administration of clients' private business including preparing powers of attorneys and agents; immigration and nationality problems; family law matters including divorce, separation agreements and consequences for children and financially.

Commercial Litigation and Employment: The service includes credit control; insolvency; pre-emptory and injunctive relief; tracing of assets, dispute resolution. Clients are advised on a full range of contentious and non-contentious employment law work including unfair dismissal; redundancy; wrongful dismissal; sexual, racial and disability discrimination; drafting of contracts and practical advice on new employment law.

Company/Commercial: Advice is provided on company law, constitution and procedures; competition law; stock exchange regulation; terms and conditions of business; flotation and issues; partnership law; intellectual property; commercial agency commercial contracts; takeovers; mergers and buy-outs; and share option schemes.

Rail & Transport: The unit incorporates lawyers with specific expertise in representing the transport industry. Services include employment law, property litigation, criminal law and defendant personal injury/public liability claims.

INTERNATIONAL CONNECTIONS: Represented internationally through the International Grouping of Lawyers. The firm has a formal association with the french firm Douma, Schofield & Sibenaler at 80 Boulevard Haussmann, 75008 Paris.

VIZARDS, STAPLES & BANNISTERS

Asia House, 31-33 Lime Street, London, EC3M 7HT
Tel: (020) 7400 9999 **Fax:** (020) 7626 7788 **DX:** 165 Chancery Lane
Email: mrs@vsb.co.uk **Website:** www.vsb.co.uk

44 Bedford Row, London, WC1R 4LL
Tel: (020) 7400 9999 **Fax:** (020) 7903 5555 **DX:** 165 Chancery Lane

6/7 Great James Street, London, WC1N 3DA
Tel: (020) 7400 9999 **Fax:** (020) 7831 6088 **DX:** 165 Chancery Lane

Senior partner:	Martin Staples
Number of partners:	30
Assistant solicitors:	32
Total staff:	167

CONTACTS

Commercial Property ....Andrew Taylor
Company Commercial ....John Hargreaves
....Martin Kay
Construction & Commercial Litigation ....
....Alan Bannister
....Peter Knight
Insurance & Reinsurance ....
....Robert Harrison
....Richard Houseago
Liability Insurance Claims.........David Rogers
....Martin Staples

THE FIRM: The firm, Vizards Staples & Bannisters, operates as a major specialist insurance litigation practice with a strong and developing complementary commercial discipline. VSB conducts business nationwide and internationally, operating from offices in Holborn, the City and Paris. It is a youthful partnership, with the firm characterised by its combination of traditional values applied to a modern, dynamic practice. During the course of the year specialisms have been enhanced, the strength of fee earning teams has been deepened, and the firm's market presence has been developed even further. The partners believe that it is the realisation of the deeper benefits of full integration, which will allow the firm to meet the expectations it shares with clients, and which will enable the firm's stated objective of becoming 'the Firm of First Choice in London', within its disciplines, to be achieved.

PRINCIPLE AREAS OF WORK: The firm is one of the leading insurance law practices in the country, with particular expertise in personal injury litigation, product liability and material loss, professional indemnity, transportation and highway law, fraud and international reinsurance arbitration.

Insurance: All aspects of insurance law are handled, with the City Office concentrating on London market operations, reinsurance disputes (many of them cross-border in conjunction with the Paris office) and professional indemnity. The firm has considerable experience in industrial disease and environmental claims, and is also very active in the areas of policy construction and drafting.

Construction: The firm deals with construction and building law, from contract drafting to claims. VSB acts for some of the major contractors, engineers and architects in the UK. A specialist team combines with the commercial property department, which is particularly strong on industrial development schemes.

Commercial: Commercial law expertise covers a complete corporate services, ranging from foundation or acquisition to day to day running and development; advice on finance and disposal or winding up. It has a particular expertise in MBOs and Pensions Law.

Commercial Litigation: Commercial litigation covers representation in white-collar fraud, revenue, customs, charity commission disputes, as well as before employment and pensions tribunals.

Commercial Property: The commercial property team covers acquisition, disposal and management of properties for a wide range of clients in the retail and investment trading market. It also includes the provision of litigation services for property-related issues including rent arrears, possession proceedings and dilapidations.

INTERNATIONAL CONNECTIONS: As a member of IGL (the International Group of Lawyers), VSB can offer vetted legal connections in over 50 countries throughout the world. The firm has offices at 130 rue du Faubourg St Honoré, 75008 Paris, tel: +33 1 53 83 71 71, fax: +33 1 53 83 71 72.

V-LEX LTD.

Ivy House, Gateford Rd, Gateford, Worksop, S81 8AE **Tel:** 01909 544 000 **Fax:** 01909 544 001 **Website:** www.v-lex.com

VOLKS HEDLEY

29a Thurloe Place, London, SW7 2HL **Tel:** (020) 7584 6733 **Fax:** (020) 7584 6733 **DX:** 35762 South Kensington
Email: cjenkins@hedleys.demon.co.uk **Ptnrs:** 2 **Asst solrs:** 1

WACE MORGAN

2 Belmont, Shrewsbury, SY1 1TD **Tel:** (01743) 280100 **Fax:** (01743) 280111 **DX:** 19718 **Email:** help@wmlaw.co.uk **Ptnrs:** 8 **Asst solrs:** 9
Other fee-earners: 4

WACKS CALLER

Steam Packet House, 76 Cross Street, Manchester, M2 4JU
Tel: (0161) 957 8888 **Fax:** (0161) 957 8899 **DX:** 14383 Manchester 1
Email: law@wackscaller.co.uk **Website:** www.wackscaller.co.uk

Managing & Senior partner:	Martin Caller
Number of partners:	13
Assistant solicitors:	26
Other fee-earners:	15

AREAS OF PRACTICE

Company/commercial	40%
Litigation	20%
Property	20%
IT/IP	15%
Employment	5%

CONTACTS

Commercial Property	Anne Dobie
Corporate Finance	Kevin Philbin
Employment	Anthony Dempsey
Gen. Company/Commercial	Martin Caller
Information Technology	Simon Wallwork
Intellectual Property	Mark Shipley
Litigation	Christopher Sorrell

THE FIRM: Established in 1986, Wacks Caller has grown from its original two partners to be one of the top 10 commercial firms in Manchester with 13 partners in 2000. The firm has continued to strengthen its position as a leading specialist in the realm of corporate finance, company and commercial work. An example of this progress was the appointment of Kit Sorrell as head of commercial litigation team in January 2000. The firm's growth is largely a result of its ethos that the client must come first and aims to provide the very best in expert advice and support to its clients.

PRINCIPAL AREA OF WORK:
Company/Commercial: The firm provides vigorous expert advice and assistance for the business community on all types of corporate and commercial transactions, including Stock Exchange and Takeover Panel work. It is especially renowned for its skill and pragmatic approach in negotiating merger and acquisition agreements, joint venture agreements and MBOs.
Commercial Litigation: This department has continued to grow rapidly by providing an aggressive yet user-friendly service for the commercial client and institutional client.
Commercial Property: This department handles all commercial property transactions and other property related matters with the emphasis on speed (where required) in addition to skill and experience.
Employment: Provides a commercial and practical approach to all employment and related issues for both employers and senior employees.
Information Technology: This department now handles a significant amount of work advising clients on start up and finance raising and providing counsel on a variety of internet related issues.
Intellectual Property: This department continues to grow in both contentious and non-contentious fields.

WAKE DYNE LAWTON

Worley Bank House, Bolesworth Road, Tattenhall, Chester, CH3 9HL **Tel:** (01829) 773100 **Fax:** (01829) 773109 **Email:** bdw@wdl.co.uk / jbd@wdl.co.uk **Website:** www.wdl.co.uk **Ptnrs:** 3 **Asst solrs:** 3 **Other fee-earners:** 4 **Contact:** Mr Brian Wake • Specialist practice dealing on a national basis exclusively with minerals, waste, planning, environmental, road haulage law and health & safety law.

AREAS OF PRACTICE

Transport	35%
Minerals	30%
Planning/Environmental	20%
Waste	15%

WAKE SMITH

68 Clarkehouse Road, Sheffield, S10 2LJ
Tel: (0114) 266 6660 **Fax:** (0114) 267 1253 **DX:** 10534 Sheffield
Email: legal@wake-smith.co.uk

6 Campo Lane, Sheffield, S1 2EF
Tel: (0114) 266 6660 **Fax:** (0114) 267 1253
Email: legal@wake-smith.co.uk

Number of partners:	14
Assistant solicitors:	5
Other fee-earners:	21

AREAS OF PRACTICE

Commercial	55%
Private Client	45%

CONTACTS

Commercial Litigation	Mark Serby
Commercial Property	Neil Salter
Company Commercial	Jonathan Hunt
Domestic Conveyancing	Amanda Cowley
Family Law	Paul Thorn
Personal Injury	Richard Lees
Private Trust Tax	Michael Tunbridge

THE FIRM: Founded in 1802, Wake Smith is a general commercial practice providing a flexible service to companies and businesses of all sizes, as well as private clients, in Sheffield and South Yorkshire.

PRINCIPAL AREAS OF WORK: The main areas of work are divided into four departments: company and commercial; commercial property; commercial litigation and private client. The firm has considerable experience in the company/commercial field, including the sale and purchase of businesses, capital structures and intellectual property rights, providing a service to quoted plcs and major private companies, and also to smaller companies and partnerships. The firm advises in commercial disputes, insolvency and licensing and has a well developed commercial property department. In addition, the private client department provides advice on matters such as personal tax, pensions, trusts, property, family law, child care, personal injury and general litigation.

WALKER CHARLESWORTH & FOSTER

26 Park Square, Leeds, LS1 2PL
Tel: (0113) 245 3594 **Fax:** (0113) 244 4312 **DX:** 26415 Leeds Park Square
Email: mail@walkercharlesworth.co.uk

Managing partner:	Colin Birtwistle
Number of partners:	8
Assistant solicitors:	3
Other fee-earners:	6

THE FIRM: A long-established three office practice whose Leeds office specialises in all types of advice to housing associations and charities.

WALKER LAIRD

9 Gilmour Street, Paisley, PA1 1DG **Tel:** (0141) 887 5271 **Fax:** (0141) 889 3268 **DX:** 32 Paisley **Ptnrs:** 6 **Asst solrs:** 6 **Other fee-earners:** 4

WALKER MORRIS

Kings Court, 12 King Street, Leeds, LS1 2HL
Tel: (0113) 283 2500 **Fax:** (0113) 245 9412 **DX:** 12051
Email: info@walkermorris.co.uk **Website:** www.walkermorris.co.uk

Managing partner:	Philip Mudd
Chairman:	Chris Caisley
Number of partners:	35
Assistant solicitors:	86
Other fee-earners:	200

AREAS OF PRACTICE

Commercial Litigation	30%
Commercial Property	30%
Company and Commercial	20%
Building Societies	16%
Private Clients	2%
Tax	2%

CONTACTS

Banking	Michael Taylor
Building Societies	David Duckworth
Commercial Dispute Resolution	Gwendoline Davies
Commercial Property	David Duckworth
Commercial Property Devt.	Paul Walker
	Mark Tordoff
Construction	Martin Scott
Corporate/Commercial	Peter Smart
Corporate Debt Recovery	Gwendoline Davies
Corporate Finance	Paul Emmett
	Ian Gilbert
Corporate Tax	Simon Concannon
EC/Competition	Patrick Cantrill
Employment	David Smedley
Environment	Andrew Williamson
Family	Richard Manning
Health/Public Services	David Kilduff
Housing Associations	David Duckworth
Insolvency	Philip Mudd
Insurance Litigation	Chris Caisley
Intellectual Property	Patrick Cantrill,
	Alison Murphy
Licensing	Andrew Beck
Pensions	Andrew Turnbull
Personal Injury	Chris Caisley
PFI	David Kilduff
Private Client/Trust/Tax	Andrew Turnbull
Professional Indemnity	Andrew Beck
Property Dispute Resolution	Andrew Beck
Retail	Nick Cannon
	Richard Innes,
	Andrew Moodie
Sports Law	Chris Caisley
Town & Country Planning	Andrew Williamson
	Richard Sagar
Trade Marks	Patrick Cantrill

THE FIRM: Based in Leeds, Walker Morris was recently rated Regional Law Firm of the Year in the Business Awards and is one of the largest commercial law firms in the North providing a full range of legal services to industry and commerce.

PRINCIPAL AREAS OF WORK:

Corporate and Tax: The company and commercial department brings together a number of specialist groups, principally corporate finance, banking, insolvency, intellectual property, corporate tax and pensions. The intellectual property group also manages a trademark registration practice comprising of four trademark agents.
Commercial Property and Planning: The property department (which includes a dedicated planning group) deals with all aspects of property. The acquisition of sites for development (including major town centre redevelopments and large scale residential sites); town and country planning and environmental matters; property portfolios for institutional and private investors; retail property for major clients; commercial lettings and joint ventures.
Commercial Dispute Resolution: The commercial dispute resolution department deals with a broad scope of work both within the UK and internationally and before courts, tribunals and arbitrators. It incorporates a number of dedicated groups headed by specialists in the areas of construction law, employment, insurance litigation, property dispute resolution and the contentious aspects of intellectual property law, banking and secured lending and commercial fraud.
Public Sector & PFI Group: The firm provides a full service to its public sector clients and includes specific expertise in healthcare law, NHS legislation, clinical negligence, CNST and risk management, PFI work and judicial review.
Private Client: The firm has retained a small private client department dealing with personal tax strategies, probate and trust administration and family law and related issues.
Additional Areas: The firm has a range of specialist services for in-house legal departments, including it's 'reach' service which delivers know-how and case progress information via the internet. The Human Rights Advisory Service provides a unique, focused and specialist advisory service to organisations within the local authority sector including statutory officers affected by the European convention on human rights to be implemented by the domestic legislation through the Human Rights Act 1998. The advisory service emphasises sound corporate governance and risk management on human rights issues and provides advice linked to education, training and litigation support making full use of internet techniques.The Walker Morris sports law group acts for sports personalities, clubs and associations working within this industry, and work includes contract negotiations and disputes, personality merchandising and licensing agreements. The firm has also created cross-departmental practice groups focused on servicing the firm's clients in the banking and building society sectors. The firm is a leader in the use of technology and works closely with clients developing their businesses in the new economy. It has launched a specialist group advising on New Media and convergence, to help clients address issues arising from the Internet, Digital Broadcasting and the Telecommunications revolution

CLIENTELE: Clients are drawn from the whole spectrum of commerce and industry including manufacturing, construction and development, high technology, the financial services industry and the retail and service industries.

INTERNATIONAL CONNECTIONS: The firm advises on European and EU issues. The firm has a growing International practice and has developed very close and mutually beneficial relationships with law firms inn and EU issues. The firm has a growing International practice and has developed very close and mutually beneficial relationships with law firms in the major jurisdictions worlwide. The consistent element in those relationships is a common philosophy and approach.

Continued overleaf

RECRUITMENT & TRAINING: The firm's year-on-year expansion has resulted in its always having a continuing recruitment policy for motivated young solicitors in all major disciplines. The firm recruits around 10 trainee solicitors every year. Discretionary grants are provided. Career prospects are excellent (most of the partners were articled within the firm). Application forms and recruitment brochures are available from Nick Cannon, Recruitment Partner. A training scheme is available to keep its lawyers up-to-date, consisting of in-house seminars, external conferences, and information updates.

WALKER SMITH & WAY

26 Nicholas Street, Chester, CH1 2PQ **Tel:** (01244) 357400 **Fax:** (01244) 357444 **DX:** 19982 Chester 1 **Email:** law.wsw@dial.pipex.com
Ptnrs: 24 **Asst solrs:** 25 **Other fee-earners:** 12

WALLACE & PARTNERS

One Portland Place, London, W1N 3AA
Tel: (020) 7636 4422 **Fax:** (020) 7636 3736 **DX:** 82990 Mayfair
Email: lawyers@wallace.co.uk **Website:** wallace.co.uk

Managing partner:	Rex Newman
Number of partners:	7
Assistant solicitors:	5
Other fee-earners:	5

CONTACTS

Company/Commercial	Rex Newman
Employment	Nicholas Yapp
Litigation	Simon Serota
Private Client	Barry Shaw
	Adrian Wallace
Property	Adrian Wallace
	Barry Shaw
	Martin Otvos

W

THE FIRM: Wallace & Partners is a niche commercial practice based in Portland Place, London. The firm has developed a strong client base and established a reputation for conducting the transactional work more commonly associated with much larger practices. Wallace & Partners prides itself on close team-work generated in a smaller, more collegial environment.

PRINCIPAL AREAS OF WORK:
Company/Commercial: Work includes Stock Exchange advice including public issues, commercial contracts, venture capital, joint ventures, management buy-outs and buy-ins, mergers and acquisitions, loan arrangements, advice on the responsibilities of directors; shareholder agreements; tax planning, franchising and general commercial matters.
Litigation: The firm is strong in property-related litigation as well as professional negligence, shareholder and boardroom disputes, and general commercial litigation. One partner is a Deputy Costs Judge.
Employment: This department deals with all aspects of employment law both contentious and non-contentious.
Property: Work includes development, investment, acquisition and funding, planning and environmental, business leases, rent reviews, estate management and general landlord and tenant work.
Private Client: This department deals with personal financial planning including wills, capital tax advice, trusts and probate, as well as employment-related immigration work.
ADR and mediation: The firm also handles ADR and mediation work, one partner being a registered mediator.

INTERNATIONAL CONNECTIONS: Wallace & Partners has developed a network of contacts throughout Europe and provides advice on many aspects of international commerce. One of the partners is a member of the New York Bar.

CLIENTELE: The firm acts for a diverse spread of clients including listed companies, family businesses, entrepreneurs and overseas investors.

RECRUITMENT & TRAINING: Contact Andrew Gafsen or Samantha Bone for an application form.

WALTONS & MORSE

Birchin Court, 20 Birchin Lane, London, EC3V 9ER
Tel: (020) 7623 4255 **Fax:** (020) 7626 4153 **DX:** City 1065
Email: waltons@wamlaw.co.uk

Senior partner:	David Perry
Managing partner:	Ian Charles-Jones
Number of partners:	5
Assistant solicitors:	6
Other fee-earners:	5

AREAS OF PRACTICE

Shipping and Transit	78%
International Trade	10%
Marine Insurance	10%
Reinsurance	2%

CONTACTS

Shipping	David Perry

THE FIRM: Waltons & Morse is a long-established City firm serving the marine insurance market, and with an international reputation in the areas of shipping, transport and international trade.

PRINCIPAL AREAS OF WORK:
General Description: All aspects of marine insurance, shipping and transit law including international trade.

CLIENTELE: Lloyd's, London and overseas insurance companies, ship operators (particularly from the Far East) and salvors.

WARD GETHIN

8-12 Tuesday Market Place, King's Lynn, PE30 1JT **Tel:** (01553) 773456 **Fax:** (01553) 766857 **DX:** 57813 **Email:** enquiries@wardgethin.co.uk
Ptnrs: 13 **Asst solrs:** 11 **Other fee-earners:** 10

WARD HADAWAY

Sandgate House, 102 Quayside, Newcastle-upon-Tyne, NE1 3DX
Tel: (0191) 204 4000 **Fax:** (0191) 204 4001 **DX:** 61265 Newcastle-upon-Tyne
Email: legal@wardhadaway.com **Website:** www.wardhadaway.com

Town Hall Chambers, 7 Beach Road, South Shields, NE33 2QR
Tel: (0191) 456 8721 **Fax:** (0191) 456 4125 **DX:** 60755 South Shields

Number of partners:	40
Assistant solicitors:	39
Other fee-earners:	35
Total staff:	225

AREAS OF PRACTICE

Litigation	38%
Property/Planning	35%
Company/Commercial	20%
Private Client Services	7%

CONTACTS

Business Services	Colin Hewitt
Commercial Property	Richard Freeman-Wallace
Corporate Finance	Martin Hulls
Employment	David Hesselberth
Healthcare	Jeffrey Keeble
Litigation	Ian Collinson
Planning/Development	Neil Robson
Private Client	Susan E. Craig

W

THE FIRM: Ward Hadaway is one of the most progressive, commercially-based firms of solicitors in the North of England. Its services are structured around client market sector groups with multi-disciplined teams serving client needs. Known for its fresh and innovative approach to the profession, WH's planned strategy for growth enables the firm to deliver a comprehensive range of legal and town planning services to ISO 9001 accredited standards. The firm continues to invest to build in-depth specialist teams with complementary support staff and services.

PRINCIPAL AREAS OF WORK: The firm's main areas of practice are corporate finance and business services, litigation, property, and private client which are organised into specialist units.
Corporate Finance and Business Services: The corporate finance and business services department deals with corporate finance, commercial advice, banking and insolvency. Advice is given on acquisitions and disposals, joint ventures, MBOs and MBIs, venture capital, business finance, inward investment, reorganisations and reconstructions, Stock Exchange work, share options, employee incentive schemes, pensions, intellectual property, agency, distributorship and franchise agreements.
Litigation: This department deals with commercial litigation disputes (contracts, insolvency, product liability, debt collection, etc). The healthcare unit specialises in plaintiff and defendant personal injury and medical negligence. Other units specialise in employment law, family law, construction and engineering disputes, and professional disciplinary tribunal work.
Property: This department deals with development work, landlord and tenant, housing associations, environmental issues, residential and estate development, town planning and development, and agriculture. The planning unit has seven Chartered Town and Country Planners and associated staff making it one of the largest planning consultancies in the North East. A specialist team also advises on rural business, planning, agricultural litigation, agricultural property and environmental concerns.
Private Client: This department advises on wills, administration of estates, trust planning and administration, capital tax planning, gifts and settlements, and charities.

CLIENTELE: WH has a substantial client base from both the public and private sectors, and has grown considerably by winning both work and reputation at local, regional and national levels.

WARNER CRANSTON

Pickfords Wharf, Clink St, London, SE1 9DG
Tel: (020) 7403 2900 **Fax:** (020) 7403 4221 **DX:** 39904 London Bridge South
Email: email@warner-cranston.com **Website:** www.warner-cranston.com

Senior partner:	Ian Fagelson
Chief Executive:	Mark Dembovsky
Number of partners:	22
Assistant solicitors:	23
Other fee-earners:	19

AREAS OF PRACTICE

Company Commercial/Finance	40%
Commercial Litigation	30%
Property	15%
Employment	10%
Other	5%

THE FIRM: Warner Cranston was founded in 1979, and has since positioned itself as a City boutique law firm, providing national and international corporate clients with high quality advice always designed to be practical and commercial in its approach. The underlying principle is one of big firm expertise, coupled with a highly personalised service. The firm is particularly well known for its international work. In addition to its City office at London Bridge, the firm has also established a strong and growing practice in the West Midlands, since acquiring the entire in-house litigation team from Courtaulds plc in 1987. Known for 'punching above its weight', Warner Cranston continues to maintain a very solid reputation as a firm made up of first-class lawyers. The past year has again seen considerable activity in representing major household named national and international groups in large and complex UK based cases and transactions.

PRINCIPAL AREAS OF WORK:
Corporate, Commercial and Finance: The firm's largest department handles a wide variety of financial, corporate and commercial domestic and cross border transactions, including mergers and acquisitions, joint ventures, asset and corporate finance, public offerings, banking as well as all aspects of English and EU competition law. The department also deals with corporate taxation, insurance, re-insurance, IT contracts, e-business and housing association work.
International Commercial Litigation: The department (operating from both the London and Coventry offices) handles substantial commercial, technical and banking disputes and is well known for its work in the area of international asset recovery, agency law and multi-jurisdictional claims.
Employment: The department offers a full employment law service covering not only the areas of service agreements, pensions, share options, dismissal, redundancy, discrimination and trade union laws but also 'best practice' training and the development of human resource strategies. The firm also advises on all EU aspects of employment law.

Business Immigration: The department provides UK work permits advice to major corporate clients. Areas of expertise also cover the rules relating to personal investors, business investments and nationality and naturalisation applications.
Commercial Property: This department, based in both London and Coventry, handles transactions for corporate clients in the media, retail, financial services and manufacturing industries, as well as for major developers and investors. The department regularly advises on town centre and out-of-town developments and handles all aspects of landlord and tenant litigation.
Coventry: With over 40 staff, Warner Cranston has the largest commercial practice in the Coventry area. Apart from specialising in high level commercial property and commercial litigation, the office also has a risk and liability department handling all types of personal injury related issues including health and safety, employers' and public liability. The debt recovery department, also based in this office, handles claims in excess of £22m per annum.

CLIENTELE: Warner Cranston acts for both national and international corporate clients and the quality of the firm's client list belies the size of the practice. Warner Cranston is particularly known for its links with the United States, France and the Middle East. Significantly, approximately 50% of the firm's total revenue comes from clients based outside the UK.

RECRUITMENT & TRAINING: The firm recruits four trainee solicitors per year to contribute to its future growth. Full details can be found on Warner Cranston's website, www.warner-cranston.com.

CONTACTS

Commercial Litigation	Paul Fallon
	Jonathan Hofstetter (Coventry)
Commercial Property	Peter Davis
	David Hayes (Coventry)
Company/Commercial	Tim Foster
Construction Litigation	Nick Speed
Corporate Immigration	Peter Alfandary
Debt Recovery	Larry Coltman (Coventry)
Employment	Geoffrey Mead
French Inward Investment	Edward Miller
Insurance & Reinsurance	Ian Fagelson
IT/E-Business	David Heard
Risk & Liability	Darren Smith (Coventry)
US Inward Investment	Ian Fagelson

W

WARNER GOODMAN & STREAT

66 West Street, Fareham, PO16 0JR **Tel:** (01329) 288121 **Fax:** (01329) 822714 **DX:** 40804 **Email:** enquiries@warnergoodman.co.uk **Website:** www.warnergoodman.co.uk **Ptnrs:** 14 **Asst solrs:** 20 **Other fee-earners:** 37

WARREN & ALLEN

24 Low Pavement, Nottingham, NG1 7ED **Tel:** (0115) 955 2222 **Fax:** (0115) 840 3510 **DX:** 10030 **Email:** inquiry@warren-allen.co.uk **Website:** www.warren-allen.co.uk **Ptnrs:** 13 **Asst solrs:** 15 **Other fee-earners:** 5

WATERSON HICKS

14-15 Philpot Lane, London, EC3M 8AJ
Tel: (020) 7929 6060 **Fax:** (020) 7929 3748
Email: law@waterson-hicks.com

Managing partner:	M.J. Wisdom
Number of partners:	4
Assistant solicitors:	3
Other fee-earners:	2

THE FIRM: Waterson Hicks is a commercial practice specialising in all aspects of maritime law and commodity litigation. The firm's work and clientele are largely international.

PRINCIPAL AREAS OF WORK: Shipping work covers all areas of commercial and admiralty litigation and arbitration including marine insurance.

INTERNATIONAL CONNECTIONS: The firm has strong overseas connections particularly in Greece, the United States, Spanish-speaking countries and the Indian subcontinent.

LANGUAGES: French, Spanish and Portuguese are spoken within the firm.

CLIENTELE: Clients include major ship owners, oil companies, charterers, commodity traders, P&I clubs, insurance companies and shipyards for whom primarily contentious work is carried out.

CONTACTS

Admiralty	Stuart Parkin
Commodities/Commercial	Martin Wisdom
	Subir Karmakar
Insurance	John Hicks
Shipping	John Hicks
	Brian Isola

WATMORES

Chancery House, 53/66 Chancery Lane, London, WC2A 1QU **Tel:** (020) 7430 1512 **Fax:** (020) 7405 7382 **DX:** LDE 246 **Email:** watmores@compuserve.com **Website:** www.watmores.co.uk **Ptnrs:** 7 **Asst solrs:** 2 **Other fee-earners:** 3 **Contact:** Mr Jon Grunewald • Specialises in insurance related litigation including personal injury claims.

AREAS OF PRACTICE

Personal Injury Litigation	80%
Other Insurance Related Litigation	15%
Other	5%

WATSON BURTON

20 Collingwood Street, Newcastle upon Tyne, NE99 1YQ **Tel:** (0191) 244 4444 **Fax:** (0191) 244 4500 **DX:** 61009 Newcastle **Email:** WB@dial.pipex.com **Ptnrs:** 19 **Other fee-earners:** 78 **Total Staff:** 150

WATSON, FARLEY & WILLIAMS

15 Appold Street, London, EC2A 2HB
Tel: (020) 7814 8000 **Fax:** (020) 7814 8141 **DX:** 530 London City EC3
Email: inquiries@wfw.com **Website:** www.wfw.com

Chairrman:	Christopher Preston
Chief executive:	Michael Reid
Managing partner:	David Warder
Number of partners worldwide:	57
Number of lawyers worldwide:	203

CONTACTS

International Corporate ....Charles Walford
International Finance ....Frank Dunne
International Litigation ....Michael Greville
International Tax ....Christopher Preston

THE FIRM: Established in 1982, Watson Farley & Williams is an international corporate and commercial law firm recognised for its excellence in banking and asset financing, particularly ship and aircraft finance. The firm also advises in a number of specialist areas in corporate law, litigation and tax law. Through its spread of international offices and contacts, the firm offers an integrated multi-jurisdictional service to clients. A key feature is the firm's division into four international practice groups - corporate, finance, litigation and tax. These groups are not divided by location. They work together internationally to serve clients. With its broad base of clients, the international experience of the firm is comprehensive. The firm's international expertise has been acknowledged through a number of awards. In November 1999 the firm was voted by the international shipping industry as the world's leading firm for ship finance. And in January 2000, the firm received international recognition for its asset finance and leasing work.

PRINCIPAL AREAS OF WORK:
International Corporate Group: Public and private company clients have access to a wide range of domestic and international expertise covering all aspects of international corporate law, including acquisitions, disposals and mergers, public offerings of securities, management buy-outs and buy-ins, business and asset sales, debt structuring, equity financings, corporate restructurings, international privatisations, and a wide range of commercial agreements such as distributorship, outsourcing purchase and agency agreements, and joint ventures and partnerships. In addition, the group offers specialist advice on real property, intellectual property, employment, service agreements, share option and incentive schemes, executive immigration, and all aspects of European Union competition law. The group focuses particularly on the provision of advice to clients in the transportation, power, telecommunication, and e-commerce sectors.
International Finance Group: Lawyers advise all project participants, covering areas such as general banking finance, structured finance, securities and capital markets, derivatives, trade finance, asset finance, project finance, cross-border tax leverage lending and leasing, and work outs and insolvencies. The group has particular expertise and experience in a number of industry sectors heavily dependent on the financing of large capital assets, including shipping, aviation, telecommunications, power and energy.
International Litigation Group: Large scale litigation, arbitration and dispute resolution matters are handled by the group on a worldwide basis. Lawyers have represented clients involved in international disputes in the areas of shipping (wet and dry), banking, offshore oil and gas, international trade, and aviation. The group also advises on the enforcement of security over vessels, marine pollution, marine insurance, shipbuilding, charterparties, and offshore oil and gas contracting.
International Tax Group: Lawyers advise on domestic and cross-border tax leasing, non-asset based structured finance, international tax planning, investigations and litigation, and indirect tax. They also give advice generally on all types of transactions. The indirect tax team specialists have considerable VAT experience.

INTERNATIONAL CONNECTIONS: With offices in Athens, Paris, New York, Moscow and Singapore, and a network of correspondent specialist lawyers, the firm's reach is truly international. Lawyers are able to advise on English, French, Russian, New York and US Federal law. All offices have expertise in the laws of the local jurisdiction and an understanding of local business customs and culture. Worldwide office contacts: 380 Madison Avenue, New York NY 10017, tel +1 212 922 2200, contact: John Osborne; 47, rue de Monceau, 75008 Paris, tel +33 (1) 5383 1212, contact: David Syed; 5th floor, Alassia Building, Defteras Merarchias 13, 185-35 Piraeus, tel +30 (1) 422 3660, contact: Tony Rice; 16 Collyer Quay, #12-02 Hitachi Tower, Singapore 049318, tel. +65 532 5335, contact: Nigel Thomas; 16/2 Tverskaya Ulitsa, Business Centre Building 3, The Actor Gallery, Moscow 103009, tel +7 502 237 7770 (international only), tel. +7 (095) 935 7770, contact: Elmar Giemulla.

LANGUAGES: Cantonese, Dutch, English, French, Greek, Italian, Mandarin, Malay, Norwegian, Russian, Spanish, Swahili, Swedish.

CLIENTELE: The firm's client base spans the world, it includes international banks, financial institutions, quoted and private companies, shipping companies, airlines, off-shore oil and gas companies, and Governments and Government agencies.

WEDLAKE BELL

16 Bedford Street, Covent Garden, London, WC2E 9HF
Tel: (020) 7395 3000 **Fax:** (020) 7836 9966 **DX:** 40009 Covent Gdn.
Email: legal@wedlakebell.co.uk **Website:** www.wedlakebell.co.uk

Managing partner:	Julian Cuppage
Senior partner:	Robert Dolman
Number of partners:	32
Assistant solicitors:	29
Other fee-earners:	24

THE FIRM: Wedlake Bell serves business and the owners, managers and inheritors of business and their families. It is recognised as having the transaction experience, skills and back up support of much larger firms from whom it consistently wins business. Its size and approach enable clients to build long-term personal rela-

Continued overleaf

tionships with the individual lawyers of their choice. Its informal, creative culture has resulted in very low staff turnover and has made it an attractive alternative for top class lawyers who wish to escape the big law firm environment. During the last year Wedlake Bell advised clients in the following sectors: banking, computering and software; dot.com startups; construction and engineering; consumer goods manufacturing; food manufacturing; healthcare; hotel and catering; information technology; marketing and branding; offshore trusts; oil, gas and mineral extraction; pharmaceuticals; property; publishing and printing; sport and leisure; support services and private wealth planning.

PRINCIPAL AREAS OF WORK:

Corporate Finance and Banking: The corporate finance team advises on mergers and acquisitions, flotations, placings and rights issues, venture capital, asset transactions, joint ventures and inward investment. The banking team advises on transaction and project finance, secured, syndicated and bilateral lending for both borrowers and lenders and on asset finance.

Commercial Property and Construction: The commercial property team acts for developers, investors, banks, landlords and tenants in relation to trading, developing, funding, occupying or investing in land. The construction team advises on construction contracts and disputes.

IP/IT, Commercial and Internet: This team advises on e business issues, intellectual property, data protection, Internet law, IT contracts, commercial agreements such as franchises, merchandising and outsourcing and competition law.

Employment and Pensions: The employment team advises on both contentious and non contentious employment law. They act for the trustees, employers and members of a wide range of occupational pensions schemes, and advise on share schemes and long term incentive plans.

Private Clients, Tax and Wealth Protection: This team advises on tax planning, trusts, offshore tax jurisdictions, wills and inheritance, asset protection, landed estates, probate, heritage and agricultural properties. It acts for entrepreneurs, business managers and new enterprise investors as well as long established family wealth. The team also provides residential conveyancing and matrimonial dispute services.

Dispute Resolution: All the firm's core practice areas are supported by specialists in dispute resolution whether by litigation, arbitration, mediation or adjudication (in construction).

INTERNATIONAL CONNECTIONS: Wedlake Bell has affiliate law firms in most European jurisdictions and in the USA. A significant part of its annual turnover derives from overseas business and clients. The firm has an office in Guernsey which operates Breams Trustees Limited, a Guernsey trust company and handles UK investment property transactions for offshore investment funds.

RECRUITMENT & TRAINING: The firm recruits up to five trainees each year. It also runs a summer student placement programme. Trainees consistently report that the quality of training received far exceeds the experiences of those in much larger firms. CVs should be addressed to the Personnel Manager.

AREAS OF PRACTICE

Corporate and banking	22%
Property and construction	22%
Tax and Trusts	20%
Litigation	16%
Commercial/IP/Internet	11%
Pensions and employment	9%

CONTACTS

Area	Contact
Banking	Philip Matthews
Commercial	Barry Weatherill
Commercial Property	John Cowlishaw
Construction	Suzanne Reeves
Corporate finance	Andrew Baker
E-business/IT	Adrian Heath-Saunders
Employment	Richard Isham
Intellectual Property	Jonathan Cornthwaite
Litigation	Richard Hewitt
Pensions	Clive Weber
Tax and Trusts	Charles Hicks

WEDLAKE BELL

Solicitors

WEDLAKE SAINT

14 John Street, London, WC1N 2EB **Tel:** (020) 7405 9446 **Fax:** (020) 7242 9877 **DX:** 407 Ch.Ln. **Email:** post@wsjs.co.uk **Ptnrs:** 14 **Asst solrs:** 8 **Other fee-earners:** 16

WEIGHTMANS

Richmond House, 1 Rumford Place, Liverpool, L3 9QW
Tel: (0151) 227 2601 **Fax:** (0151) 227 3223 **DX:** 14201 Liverpool
Email: info.liv@weightmans.com **Website:** www.weightmans.com

79-83 Colmore Row, Birmingham, B3 2AP
Tel: (0121) 233 2601 **Fax:** (0121) 233 2600 **DX:** 13035 Birmingham 1

Trinity House, Trinity Road, Dudley, DY1 1JB
Tel: (01384) 211211 **Fax:** (01384) 456165 **DX:** 12764 Dudley
Email: hatt_ho_@msn.com

Leicester,
Tel: (0116) 253 9747 **Fax:** (0116) 253 6101

41 Spring Gardens, Manchester, M2 2BG
Tel: (0161) 833 2601 **Fax:**

Senior partner:	Mike Edge
Deputy Senior Partner:	Ian Evans
Number of partners:	57
Assistant solicitors:	70
Other fee-earners:	60

CONTACTS

Area	Contact
Clinical Negligence & Catastrophic Claims	Tony Summers (Liverpool)
	Nigel Dance (Birmingham)
Commercial Litigation	Neil Kelly (Liverpool)
Commercial Property	David Morgan (Manchester)
	Lynne McFaul (Liverpool)
Company Commercial	Dennis Hannon (Liverpool)
Employment	Michael Ball (Manchester)
	Michael Edge (Birmingham)

THE FIRM: Weightmans is the country's largest dedicated insurance-based firm with 56 partners and a compliment of more than 115 case handlers. Weightmans is committed to reducing the cost of claims and was the first firm to introduce performance statistics for clients. To ensure that Weightmans remains focused on cost control and technical excellence, the performance of case handlers is measured by effectiveness in terms of speed of settlement, accuracy of reserving, savings made on behalf of clients, strike out rates and other vital performance measures.Transparent billing and alternative charging rates to suit each clients' budget demonstrate

Weightmans' open approach. Some of the value added services include: a free email update service within 24 hours of new legislation or cases; free subscription to *Closer LOOK*, a quarterly newspaper which reports on initiatives throughout the industry and customised training programmes. Weightmans is committed to harnessing new IT developments to reduce the cost of service delivery. The firm is developing a new on line business which will offer its clients full access to all case information; costs to date and other vital case related information. The on-line service will also offer a number of new value added services aimed at helping insurers drive down the cost of claims. The firm increasingly uses the internet to keep clients up-to-date on the latest case reports, to provide useful statistical and trend information and for 'live' performance status reports for clients on existing case loads.

PRINCIPAL AREAS OF WORK:

Professional Indemnity: Weightmans has the leading professional indemnity team in the North West with unrivalled experience of solicitors claims. Statistics produced in the last 12 months show that over 30% of claims were struck out or discontinued while over 90% of mediations were successful.

Police: The police unit is the largest in the UK and handles a range of complex and sensitive issues on behalf of 13 police authorities. Statistics produced in the last 12 months show that 76% of cases were won at trial, while 14% were struck out or discontinued.

Insurance: In line with its commitment to the general and specialist insurance industry Weightmans offers its clients dedicated teams who are able to demonstrate a detailed understanding of their clients' needs. A renowned technical motor claims unit handles work on behalf of the MIB. A specialist catastrophic claims unit handles technically complex claims valued at over £250,000.

Company/Commercial: The department specialises predominantly in the SME market though also undertakes corporate litigation on behalf of clients such as Hoover.

Licensing: Weightmans has formed The Association of Licensing Practitioners (ALP), a government lobbying group, which has a national voice.

Other: Weightmans has a well-established and thriving employment and commercial division. Consisting of 35 solicitors, the unit has extensive experience of representing the leisure retail industry on employment, property, licensing and company commercial issues.

CONTACTS CONTINUED

Insurance .... Tony Prichard .... (Liverpool)
.... Tim Salthouse .... (Birmingham)
.... Dan Cutts .... (Leicester)
.... Tim Perry .... (Dudley)
.... Geraint Owen .... (Manchester)

Licensing .... Mark Owen .... (Liverpool)
.... Anthony Horne .... (Manchester)

Police Authorities .... Kevin Fletcher .... (Liverpool)
.... Nick Peel .... (Manchester)
.... John Riddell .... (Leicester)

Professional Idemnity ....
.... Frank Maher .... (Liverpool & Manchester)

W

WEIL, GOTSHAL & MANGES

One South Place, London, EC2M 2WG
Tel: (020) 7903 1000 **Fax:** (020) 7903 0990 **DX:** 124402
Email: weil.london@weil.com **Website:** www.weil.com

Contact:	Mike Francies
UK Number of partners:	20
Associates:	80
Other fee-earners:	12
Total legal staff:	112

THE FIRM: Weil, Gotshal & Manges is a premier international law firm, with over 800 lawyers worldwide and a reputation for providing premier US and European legal advice to meet the commercial needs of its international corporate and finance clients. Established in New York in 1931, the firm has successfully pursued a strategy of expansion in Europe through organic growth, in response to client demand. The London office, established in 1996, has grown rapidly to become the second largest office of the firm and is now the hub of the European practice. With more than 100 corporate and finance lawyers, it is one of the largest US-based international law firms in London, with one of the widest ranging practices. The London office provides its clients full dual capability in both US and UK law.

PRINCIPAL AREAS OF WORK: The firm's practice in London comprises both US and UK banking, capital markets and corporate law, in addition to the resources of a German desk. The London office's international corporate and finance practice encompasses: acquisition finance, asset finance & leasing, banking, biotechnology & pharmaceuticals, capital markets, commercial litigation, competition, consumer finance, corporate, corporate restructurings & workouts, environmental, financial services, internet, media & telecom finance, mergers & acquisitions, pensions, private equity, project finance, real estate, securitisation, share option schemes, structured finance, taxation, telecommunications.

Banking: The London office has a strong reputation in this field. The banking and project finance team has built a practice which is recognised by the London finance market as a serious alternative to the magic circle firms. It has a broad banking client base, representing both major lenders and borrowers in cross border and domestic transactions. The group has been highly recommended in a number of legal publications. Its dual capability with both UK and US law means that it is well placed to advise clients in respect of financing techniques originating in the US such as high yield debt, secondary market trading or asset-backed lending.

Corporate: The firm has an established corporate team which has rapidly built up a high profile in London through its work on major public mergers and acquisitions. Its dual capability in US and UK law is a key reason for its appeal to clients seeking advisers on multi-billion pound cross border deals. Client demand has led to the development of core ancillary areas such as corporate tax, competition, property, pensions, litigation and environmental law, complementing the firm's existing expertise in public and private mergers and acquisitions, joint ventures, private equity, flotations and privatisations.

Capital Markets: Weil, Gotshal & Manges has established a leading international capital markets practice with a track record for innovative and ground-breaking debt and equity offerings, high yield debt issues and

Continued overleaf

structured and derivative capital markets transactions. The strength of the London capital markets practice derives from a commitment to providing US and UK capability and versatile finance lawyers who understand the increasingly sophisticated and inter-linked financing techniques required by today's markets. They act for most of the major investment banks as well as representing an extensive list of issuers. The capital markets team was recently voted Capital Markets Team of the Year by a leading legal publication.

WEIL, GOTSHAL & MANGES

Securitisation: The securitisation team at Weil, Gotshal & Manges has earned a reputation for advising not only on innovative, highly complex transactions but also on transactions involving more mainstream UK consumer assets, such as residential mortgages. The team has extensive CBO/CLO and conduit expertise and are recognised as experts with respect to the establishment of CDOs, structured investment vehicles and ABCP/MTN conduits. The team has been involved in a wide range of transactions in Europe and the US. The team works closely with the firm's tax, corporate and capital markets practices in London and New York and with the firm's pre-eminent real estate practice in Central Europe.
Biotechnology & Pharmaceuticals: The firm's pharmaceutical & biotechnology group, based in its London, Silicon Valley and New York offices, comprises lawyers of the highest calibre and technical excellence with a detailed understanding of the pharmaceutical and biotechnology industries across the US and Europe. Their combined European/American experience in these sectors means that they can provide clients and their investors with legal advice on all aspects of their businesses, from mergers and acquisitions and fundraising transactions through to commercial contracts, IPR licensing and regulatory compliance, on a worldwide basis.
Internet & Telecommunications: Weil, Gotshal & Manges' internet & communications practice provides integrated US and UK corporate, commercial and finance advice to internet businesses and investors. The firm offers clients the advantage of a significant Silicon Valley presence and lawyers with experience in advising both on-line companies and investors in relation to venture capital/private equity funding matters and all other aspects of corporate and finance legal issues.

W

INTERNATIONAL CONNECTIONS: The firm has offices in Brussels, Budapest, Dallas, Frankfurt, Houston, New York, Menlo Park (Silicon Valley), Miami, Prague, Warsaw and Washington DC. There are also affiliated offices in Paris and Cairo.

CLIENTELE: The London office represents major corporations and financial institutions including Bank of America, Barclays Capital, Bear Stearns, CeNeS Pharmaceuticals plc, CGU, The Chase Manhattan Bank, Credit Suisse First Boston, Deutsche Bank, Dresdner Kleinwort Benson, enba, Estée Lauder, Flextech, GE Capital, Getty Images, Greenwich NatWest, Hamburgische Landesbank Girozentrale, Hicks, Muse, Tate and Furst, Indigo, JP Morgan, Lehman Brothers, Matsushita, MediaOne, Merrill Lynch, Morgan Stanley, Netia, Nomura International, Oxford BioMedica Plc, Peptide Therapeutics Group plc, Pirelli, Salomon Smith Barney, Sara Lee Corporation, Simply Internet, Telewest, Tokyo Mitsubishi International, and Wit Capital.

RECRUITMENT & TRAINING: The firm is looking for flexible, highly motivated people who will be expected to take advantage of the wide-ranging legal and business training provided and develop the requisite skills to provide their clients with commercially-driven legal solutions.

WELLMAN & BROWN

23 West Parade, Lincoln, LN1 1NW **Tel:** (01522) 525463 **Fax:** (01522) 513199 **DX:** 11020 Lincoln 1 **Ptnrs:** 3

WENDY HOPKINS & CO

26 Windsor Place, Cardiff, CF1 3BZ **Tel:** (029) 20342233 **Fax:** (029) 20343828 **DX:** 330301 CARDIFF 1 **Email:** whco1@nascr.net **Ptnrs:** 3
Other fee-earners: 2

WESLEY GRYK

149 The Strand, London, WC2R 1JA **Tel:** (020) 7240 8485 **Fax:** (020) 7240 8486
DX: 51643 Covent Garden **Email:** wesley@gryklaw.com **Ptnrs:** 1 **Asst solrs:** 3 **Other fee-earners:** 3
Contact: Wesley Gryk • (Scheduled to move in Autumn 2000.) A niche immigration practice.

WHITE & BOWKER

19 St. Peter St, Winchester, SO23 8BU
Tel: (01962) 844440 **Fax:** (01962) 842300 **DX:** 2506 Winchester
Email: wandb@wandb.co.uk **Website:** www.wandb.co.uk

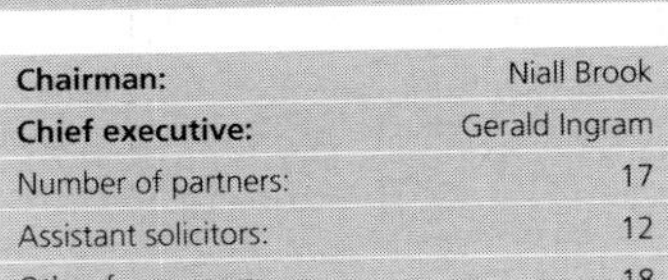

Chairman:	Niall Brook
Chief executive:	Gerald Ingram
Number of partners:	17
Assistant solicitors:	12
Other fee-earners:	18

THE FIRM: The firm is well established as a comprehensive provider of both private client and commercial services. It is one of the largest firms in Hampshire, with additional offices in Southampton and Eastleigh. It can trace its roots back to 1750 and partners and staff are active in business and community life as well as holding public appointments. These include the Winchester Diocesan Registrar, the Under Sheriff of Hampshire and HM Coroner for Hampshire (Central).

PRINCIPAL AREAS OF WORK:

Private Client: Comprehensive services for private clients including all aspects of tax and financial planning, wills and probate. Residential conveyancing, personal injury, matrimonial, family and criminal defence work are also undertaken.

Commercial Property: Expertise ranges from small industrial units to major office developments and includes planning applications and appeals, site acquisition, plot sales for developers and work for government departments.

Employment: Includes advice for businesses on sex, race and disability discrimination as well as harassment, maternity rights, dismissal and redundancy contracts.

Agriculture and Environment: Recognised as one of the leading firms in the South. Expertise includes property, tenancy issues, livestock, rights of way, planning appeals, tax and environmental issues.

INTERNATIONAL CONNECTIONS: Contacts in Europe through its association with Groupe Monassier France, a network of commercial lawyers throughout Europe.

AREAS OF PRACTICE

Commercial Property	21%
Private Client (Wills/Trusts/Probate/Tax Planning)	21%
Civil Litigation	17%
Personal Injury/Family	15%
Residential Property	12%
Crime	8%
Commercial	6%

CONTACTS

Civil Litigation	Laurence Dunn
Commercial	Martin Tomsett
Commercial Property	Grahame Short
Crime	Stephen Piercy
Personal Injury/Family	Simon Burge
Private Client (Wills/Trusts/Probate/Tax Planning)	Martyn Thurston
Residential Property	Martyn Thurston

WHITE & CASE

7-11 Moorgate, London, EC2R 6HH
Tel: (020) 7600 7300 **Fax:** (020) 7600 7030
Email: jbellhouse@whitecase.com **Website:** www.whitecase.com

Executive partner:	John Bellhouse
Administrative partner:	Douglas Peel
Number of partners:	19
Assistant solicitors:	37
Total number of lawyers worldwide	1000

THE FIRM: White & Case represents an internationally recognised finance and corporate law brand name with 32 offices in 26 countries and over 1000 lawyers around the world. The London office was founded in 1971 to provide top-flight international finance and corporate law advice to the world's leading institutions and corporations. The firm is deeply committed to its client relationships and delivers total dedication from leading market names in the provision of UK and US finance and corporate law advice to the transactions on which it advises. White & Case is a full-service law firm, able to advise on all aspects of international fiannce and corporate law transactions including: acquisition finance, asset finance and leasing, aviation, banking, construction, corporate finance, debt and equity, capital markets, energy, EU/competition, intellectual property, litigation, mergers and acquisitions, privatisation, project finance, securitisation, sovereign debt, sports law, telecommunications and technology.

INTERNATIONAL CONNECTIONS: The firm has other offices in Almaty, Ankara, Bangkok, Bombay/Mumbai, Bratislava, Brussels, Budapest, Frankfurt, Hanoi, Helsinki, Ho Chi Minh City, Hong Kong, Istanbul, Jakarta, Jeddah, Johannesburg, London, Los Angeles, Mexico City, Miami, Moscow, New York, Palo Alto, Paris, Prague, Riyadh, São Paulo, Singapore, Stockholm, Tokyo, Warsaw and Washington.

CONTACTS

AssetFinance	Mark Weston
Bank Finance	Maurice Allen
Capital Markets	Francis Fitzherbert-Brockholes
Construction	John Bellhouse
Corporate Finance/M&A	Mats Sacklen
EU/Competition	Alasdair Bell
Intellectual Property	David Llewelyn
Litigation & ADR	Margaret R Cole
Project Finance	Peter Finlay
Telecom & Technology	David Eisenberg

WHITEHEAD MONCKTON

72 King St, Maidstone, ME14 1BL **Tel:** (01622) 698000 **Fax:** (01622) 690050 **DX:** 4807 **Email:** Enquiries@Whitehead-Monckton.co.uk **Website:** www.whitehead-monckton.co.uk **Ptnrs:** 13 **Asst solrs:** 7 **Other fee-earners:** 10 **Contact:** R J Horton • A large regional practice best known for its company/commercial work, private client and investment services and litigation.

AREAS OF PRACTICE

Private Client	34%
Commercial	35%
Litigation	18%
Other	13%

WHITELOCK & STORR

5 Bloomsbury Square, London, WC1A 2LX
Tel: (020) 7242 8612 **Fax:** (020) 7404 4131 **DX:** 35739

Senior partner:	John Zani
Number of partners:	3
Assistant solicitors:	2
Other fee-earners:	4

THE FIRM: Well-established and highly respected firm with specialisation in serious fraud, major crime, extradition, drugs and smuggling cases, Revenue and Duty matters. Additionally, immigration, civil litigation (including agency work), conveyancing, and landlord and tenant work. Legal Aid Franchise holder in crime and extradition, Contract holder in immigration and VHCC/ serious fraud panel (Antumn 2000).

PRINCIPAL AREAS OF WORK: The senior partner, John Zani, has over 20 years experience and specialises in general crime, serious fraud, substantial drug cases, extradition and immigration. Dante Leccacorvi, a partner, practises general criminal law. Clive Lambert practises civil litigation and general crime. Tim Rustern practises general crime and immigration and Anthony Bloom practises conveyancing, landlord and tenant.

INTERNATIONAL CONNECTIONS: The firm has associated offices in Italy, Ireland and USA.

LANGUAGES: Members of the firm speak Italian, French, Turkish, German, Urdu, Spanish, Hindu and Hebrew.

WHITTLES

Pearl Assurance House, 23 Princess Street, Manchester, M2 4ER
Tel: (0161) 228 2061 **Fax:** (0161) 236 1046
Website: www.whittles.com

First Floor, Four Oaks House, Lichfield Road, Birmingham, B74 2TZ
Tel: (0121) 308 1331 **Fax:** (0121) 323 4846

Suite 9C, Josephs Well, Park Lane, Leeds, LS3 1AB
Tel: (0113) 244 2216 **Fax:** (0113) 242 1214

Managing partner:	David Towler
Senior partner:	Charles Hantom
Number of partners:	18
Assistant solicitors:	22
Other fee-earners:	31

AREAS OF PRACTICE

Personal Injury Litigation 80%
Employment 16%
Private Client 4%

CONTACTS

Employment ....Charles Hantom
....David Towler
....Helen Parkinson
Personal Injury Litigation ....David Rogers

W

THE FIRM: Whittles is a strong and growing trades union and staff association niche practice specialising in plaintiff personal injury work with a growing caseload in wider aspects of employment law. Founded in the 1930's by Preston solicitor John Whittle, the practice's offices currently cover the whole of England and Wales from bases in Manchester, Leeds and the West Midlands and are shortly opening in Newcastle upon Tyne. The firm prides itself on its long tradition of working for union members and sees itself as an integral element of the services the unions provide for their members. A high level of client retention and long-term working relationships are borne out of the firm's commitment to plain speaking, openness and listening to their clients needs. Through the adoption of a partnership approach, founded on quality legal advice and built on personal and responsive service, Whittles aims to promote the best interests of union members at all times.

PRINCIPLE AREAS OF WORK: Whittles is committed to using the firms experience and specialist skills to protect the interests of union members at work. The firm specialises in personal injury litigation. The majority of this work is made up of claims arising from workplace accidents and diseases with an increasingly growing number of high profile, high value and complex claims. In response to this, Whittles has adopted a modern, client led approach to its services. Accidents in the workplace are handled by specialist teams offering expertise on traumatic and fatal accidents through to minor workplace injuries and post-traumatic shock. Similarly, through the establishment of specialist industrial disease departments at each of its offices, they are able to offer expertise in asbestosis, asthma, dermatitis, vibration white finger, upper limb disorder, repetitive back strain, industrial deafness, stress and industrial cancer cases. The firm also has extensive experience in all aspects of employment and labour law including tribunal claims for dismissal, unfair selection for redundancy, sex, race and disability discrimination, equal pay, transfer of undertakings and all aspects of trade union law and human rights. Additional services for trade union clients and their members include discounted conveyancing and wills services together with free initial legal advice on any aspect of law.

CLIENTELE: Whittles acts mainly for employees and injured claimants, the majority of whom are trade union and staff association members.

WIGGIN & CO

The Quadrangle, Imperial Square, Cheltenham, GL50 1YX
Tel: (01242) 224114 **Fax:** (01242) 224223 **DX:** 7427
Email: law@wiggin.co.uk

Managing partner:	Mike Turner
Senior partner:	Nic Stones
Number of partners:	12
Assistant solicitors:	12
Other fee-earners:	6

AREAS OF PRACTICE

Media, Entertainment/Commercial 48%
Private Client 30%
Litigation 12%
Property 10%

CONTACTS

Company/Commercial ....Mike Turner
Defamation ....Caroline Kean
International Asset Protection ....Michael Fullerlove
IP ....Shaun Lowde
IT ....Shaun Lowde
Litigation ....Caroline Kean
Media & Entertainment ....Tim Osborne
Private Client ....Nic Stones
Property ....Paul Wilson

THE FIRM: Based in Cheltenham, with an office in London and a service centre in Los Angeles, Wiggin & Co has an international reputation for its specialist expertise in tax, media, communications, technology and entertainment.

PRINCIPAL AREAS OF WORK:

Media and Entertainment: The firm specialises in all aspects of media and entertainment law including satellite and cable TV, internet, film, intellectual property, multimedia, defamation, publishing and computer technology and advice on European Union legislation. Other services include mergers and acquisitions, MBOs, corporate reorganisations and financing, financial services compliance and corporate tax.

Private Client: The firm offers specialist advice on UK and international tax, capital and income tax planning for individuals, including the establishment and restructuring of UK and overseas trusts, the appropriate structure for UK and overseas investment, international asset protection, and general tax advice to both public and private companies, their shareholders and executives.

Litigation: The firm undertakes all aspects of commercial litigation with particular specialist expertise in media and entertainment law, defamation, copyright and commercial property.

Property: The firm undertakes development structuring, sale and leaseback funding, joint venture agreements, options, secured loan transactions, sale and purchase of agricultural land and private estates in the UK and EU countries.

INTERNATIONAL CONNECTIONS: The office in Los Angeles was opened to advise individuals and corporations on the West coast of America wishing to do business in the UK and Europe, and to assist European clients with US investments and business activities. The firm has extensive experience in international matters and its wide range of international contacts is extended by its membership of the Wiggin Group of European Lawyers and Tax Advisers.

WIKBORG, REIN & CO

One Knightrider Court, London, EC4V 5JP
Tel: (020) 7236 4598 **Fax:** (020) 7236 4599
Email: wrco@wrco.no **Website:** www.wrco.no

Managing partner:	
UK:	Morten Lund Mathisen
Associate lawyers:	3

AREAS OF PRACTICE

Company/Commercial/Securities	40%
Shipping/Admiralty	40%
Finance	20%

THE FIRM: Wikborg, Rein & Co is an international law firm founded in 1923. The two founding partners set the early course of the firm, establishing its reputation as a commercial firm and attracting clients from the world of shipping and other industries. Although one of the largest law firms in Norway, Wikborg, Rein & Co continues to operate on the basis of a close working relationship with each client. The firm is prepared, if required, to take on management responsibility for the detailed handling of transactions. The London office is staffed by four Norwegian lawyers. In addition to providing liaison services for the firm's international clients on Norwegian business and Norwegian clients on international business, the office has particular expertise in the areas of shipping, mergers & acquisitions, finance and securities.

PRINCIPAL AREAS OF WORK:
Company & Corporate: Work includes company formation, corporate acquisitions and disposals, demergers, joint ventures, partnerships, registration services, share issues, voting rights.
Shipping: Work includes agency, arrest, building contracts, broking, cargo claims, charters, collisions, finance, flag changes, insurance, management, mortgages, pollution, protection and indemnity claims, sales, salvage, terminals.
Securities: Work includes private placings, public offers, acquisitions, bonds, capital reorganisations, convertible issues, demergers, investor protection, mergers, registration services, Stock Exchange listings, trading disputes, underwriting agreements, venture capital.
Finance: Work includes ship and other asset finance, project finance, debt rescheduling, guarantees, leases, loan agreements, security documentation, off-balance sheet instruments.
General Commercial: Agency and distribution, employment, natural resources.

W

WILBRAHAM & CO

Minerva House, East Parade, Leeds, LS1 5PS
Tel: (0113) 243 2200 **Fax:** (0113) 244 9777
Email: wilbraham@wilbraham.co.uk

Joint Managing Partners:	Peter Wilbraham Richard Wade-Smith
Number of partners:	5
Assistant solicitors:	3
Other fee-earners:	4

AREAS OF PRACTICE

Planning	85%
Environmental	15%

CONTACTS

Partners	Peter N. Williamson
	Richard W. Wade Smith
	David Walton

THE FIRM: Founded in 1994, Wilbraham & Co is a niche solicitor's practice specialising in planning, environmental, highways, compulsory purchase/compensation and administrative law. The firm's philosophy is to provide its commercial clients with the highest quality of advice on planning and environmental matters, and to produce a cost effective product in a commercial context.

PRINCIPAL AREAS OF WORK: The firm handles large scale infrastructure and commercial development projects throughout the UK. In addition to mainstream commercial work it specialises in utility projects for water companies, electricity generators and waste management companies. Public sector work includes advising local authorities, health trusts and educational institutions.

WILDE & PARTNERS

10 John Street, London, WC1N 2EB
Tel: (020) 7831 0800 **Fax:** (020) 7430 0678 **DX:** 428 London
Email: law@wildes.co.uk **Website:** www.wildes.co.uk

Senior partner:	Simon Boon
Number of partners:	8
Assistant solicitors:	15
Other fee-earners:	19

AREAS OF PRACTICE

Debt Recovery	35%
Commercial Finance	30%
Commercial Litigation	20%
Insolvency	10%
Commercial Property	5%

CONTACTS

Commercial Finance	Andrew Watson
Commercial Litigation	Matthew Halton
Debt Recovery	Robert Weekes
Insolvency	Abraham Ezekiel
Property Development	Jeremy Dening
Property Investment/Finance	Martin Smith

THE FIRM: This Central London firm offers a wide range of commercial services, with niche expertise in factoring and invoice discounting, (in which it is recognised as the market leader), trade finance, asset based lending, insolvency and debt recovery. Wilde & Partners was established in 1983, and has from its beginning focused on its specialist skills. Clients include the factoring and invoice discounting subsidiaries of British and overseas banks and the majority of the members of the Factors and Discounters Association. The firm is an associate member of the Finance and Leasing Association. The practice aims to build a relationship with clients that will be both productive and long lasting. Wilde & Partners prides itself on its ability to offer practical and cost effective solutions to legal problems and to respond promptly to requests for advice and assistance. Its objectives are to give constructive and positive advice that is consistent with the business objectives of clients.

PRINCIPAL AREAS OF WORK:
Trade Finance and Banking: Work includes expertise in factoring and invoice discounting, stock financing, all forms of secured and unsecured asset based lending, bills of exchange, credit protection, guarantees and indemnities, letters of credit, pledges and trust receipts.

Continued overleaf

Company/Commercial: Activities include acquisitions and disposals, company formations, setting up distributorships, agencies and franchises, employment law, management buy-ins and buy-outs, intellectual property matters and shareholder agreements.
Commercial Litigation: The department deals with contractual and negligence claims, shareholder disputes, fraud investigations and asset recovery, defamation and the enforcement of securities, guarantees and indemnities and judgments. Alternative dispute resolution, arbitrations and appeals are undertaken where appropriate. High volume debt recovery is an acknowledged specialism of the firm and annually the firm successfully collects millions of pounds of trade debts throughout the UK and overseas.
Insolvency: Wilde & Partners has an expanding insolvency practice acting for a number of the major insolvency practitioners, banks and corporate clients in both contentious and non-contentious situations.
Commercial Property: The commercial property practice has grown rapidly in the past year developing a strong profile across the retail, leisure and general property sector.
Other: Other areas of specialism include residential development, property investment and landlord and tenant work.

W

WILFORD MONRO

1-3 Brixton Rd, London, SW9 6DE **Tel:** (020) 7582 6002 **Fax:** (020) 7793 0538 **DX:** 33256 Kennington **Email:** mail@wilfordmunro.demon.co.uk **Ptnrs:** 4 **Asst solrs:** 2 **Other fee-earners:** 6 **Contact:** Jenny Newton • Specialist firm dealing with all legal matters affecting children including care proceedings, contact, residence, injunction, adoption, immigration, crime, personal injury.

AREAS OF PRACTICE	
Children (private law)	35%
Public Law	35%
Adoption	15%
Employment/Personal Injury	5%
Immigration	5%
Mental Health	5%

THE WILKES PARTNERSHIP

41 Church St, Birmingham, B3 2RT
Tel: (0121) 233 4333 **Fax:** (0121) 233 4546 **DX:** 13047
Email: law@wilkes.co.uk **Website:** www.wilkes.co.uk

Managing partner:	Anna Dunford
Senior partner:	Nigel Wood
Number of partners:	17
Assistant solicitors:	25
Other fee-earners:	22

THE FIRM: Established over 60 years ago, The Wilkes Partnership has developed into a modern commercial practice offering a wide range of legal services to business, industry and private individuals.

PRINCIPAL AREAS OF WORK:
Company and Commercial: The department handles all aspects of company formation, acquisitions and disposal, corporate finance, management buy-outs and corporate restructuring.
Litigation: The firm deals with the full range of commercial litigation services including High Court, County Court and matters arising from EU legislation. It also provides a specialised commercial debt collection service. Other work includes commercial contract disputes, personal injury, employment matters and health and safety at work.
Property: The practice undertakes and advises on domestic and commercial conveyancing, property development, shops, offices, factories, leases, planning matters, joint ventures and landlord and tenant matters.
Private Client: The firm offers advice to individuals regarding wills, settlements, probate, inheritance tax, personal taxation and pensions. The firm also provides a service to private clients on matters of employment, personal injury, consumer legislation, family matters and divorce, criminal work and licensing.

INTERNATIONAL CONNECTIONS:
The firm has professional links in the major European cities particularly in relation to property buying in Europe. Links with France and Germany are particularly strong.

CLIENTELE:
Business and industrial clients nationally as well as long-standing private clients.

AREAS OF PRACTICE	
Litigation (including Insolvency)	48%
Corporate/Commercial	18%
Conveyancing	15%
PI	10%
Tax/Trust/Probate	7%
Other	2%

CONTACTS	
Building Contracts	Peter Tugwell
Civil Litigation	Nigel Wood
Commercial Conveyancing	Adele McDermott
Corporate/Commercial	Gareth O'Hara
Debt Recovery	David Cleary
Employment	Steven Hopkins
Insolvency	John Cooper
Large Scale Voluntary Transfer	Peter Ewin
Personal Injury	Maxine Kelly
Public Authority/ Housing Associations	Adele McDermot
Tax/Trust	Anna Dunford

WILKIN CHAPMAN

PO Box 16, Town Hall Square, Grimsby, DN31 1HE **Tel:** (01472) 358234 **Fax:** (01472) 360198 **DX:** 13511 Grimsby 1
Email: wilkin@iclweb.ocm **Ptnrs:** 24 **Asst solrs:** 10 **Other fee-earners:** 31

WILLAN BOOTLAND WHITE

Lawrence Buildings, 2 Mount Street, Manchester, M2 5WQ
Tel: (0161) 839 1922 **Fax:** (0161) 839 1924 **DX:** 709031 MCR7

Number of partners:	3

THE FIRM: Founded in 1998 as a commercial practice, Willan Bootland White emphasises a personal approach to clients' problems with a high partner to client ratio. Clients include many owner managed businesses who need a cost-effective service tailored to their needs.

AREAS OF PRACTICE	
Company/Commercial	40%
Commercial Litigation	30%
Private Client	30%

PRINCIPAL AREAS OF WORK: The practice deals with company commercial work including company formations and acquisitions. Commercial litigation work includes high value banking and guarantee disputes, and private client work includes conveyancing, probate, and wills.

INTERNATIONAL CONNECTIONS: The firm has an established connection with Italian companies doing business in the UK, dealing with the setting up of new joint ventures and litigation on behalf of Italian companies in the UK.

CONTACTS

Commercial Litigation ....Edward Bootland
Company Commercial ....Paul Willan
Private Client............................Michael White

WILLCOX LANE CLUTTERBUCK

55 Charlotte Street, Birmingham, B3 1PX
Tel: (0121) 236 9441 **Fax:** (0121) 236 4733 **DX:** 717340 Birmingham 44
Email: solicitors@wlc.co.uk **Website:** www.wlc.co.uk

Managing partner:	William M. Colacicchi
Number of partners:	14
Assistant solicitors:	8
Other fee-earners:	11

AREAS OF PRACTICE

Insurance Litigation 47%
Property 20%
Private Client 17%
Commercial 13%
Criminal Litigation....................................3%

CONTACTS

Commercial....................................G. Griffiths
Commercial/Civil Litigation ....M. English
Criminal......................................J. Smitheman
Defendant Personal Injury ....M. Asokan
Employment ....L. Teague
Matrimonial ....J. Smitheman
Private Client ....W. Colacicchi
Property/Construction ....S.Stott

THE FIRM: Willcox Lane Clutterbuck is a modern firm with a long pedigree. It has a substantial corporate finance department but still cherishes its traditional client base of private individuals and small to medium sized businesses. It is recognised for its work in insurance litigation and tax expertise.

PRINCIPAL AREAS OF WORK:

Company/Commercial: Work involves corporate finance, acquisitions and sales, flotations, insolvency, management buy ins/outs, intellectual property, computer law, company formations and general commercial advice to businesses, companies and individuals.
Defendant Insurance Litigation: The firm handles a wide range of insurance litigation for composite insurers, underwriters and loss adjusters in connection with employers and public liability, personal injury and general liability together with road traffic accidents.
Commercial and Agricultural Property: Work includes the purchase and sale of all types of freehold and leasehold properties for commercial users and investors, property development, employee relocation and planning law.
Employment: The firm offers the full range of contentious and non-contentious employment services provided for employers and employees.
Commercial Litigation: Work includes contract and commercial disputes, intellectual property, building and construction disputes and general litigation. The firm is also able to deal with all aspects of criminal work and matrimonial law. The firm is a member of the Alternative Dispute Resolution Group and has an accredited mediator.
Private Client and Charities: The firm has an acknowledged expertise in this field where clients are advised on all aspects of their financial affairs and investments as well as the handling of all aspects of wills and probate. The firm is also widely involved in the establishment, management and winding up of trusts and charities.
Tax: The firm advises on tax planning and mitigation for individuals, trusts and companies.

CLIENTELE: Clients include public and private companies, insurance companies, public utilities, local authorities, colleges and charities as well as private individuals.

WILLCOX & LEWIS

The Old Coach House, Bergh Apton, Norwich, NR15 1DD
Tel: (01508) 480100 **Fax:** (01508) 480001

Lincoln House, 1 Berrycroft, Willingham, Cambridge, CB4 5JX
Tel: (01954) 261444 **Fax:** (01954) 261777

Senior partners:	M.D. Willcox & I.G. Lewis
Number of partners:	2
Assistant solicitors:	2

AREAS OF PRACTICE

Probate...25%
Tax Planning 25%
Trust Work 25%
Charity 20%
Conveyancing 5%

CONTACTS

Cambridge ....Ian Lewis
Norwich ....Michael Willcox

THE FIRM: Willcox & Lewis is a niche private client law firm, with offices at Cambridge and Norwich, established by two leading specialists in trusts and personal tax. The senior partners are both elected to The International Academy of Estate and Trust Law based in San Francisco, California, and members of the firm belong to the Society of Trust Practitioners.

PRINCIPAL AREAS OF WORK: The firm advises net worth individuals, trustees and charities, and specialises in complex trusts and estates containing international and commercial elements. Parallel and complementary to the legal practice, separate corporate structures provide advice on substantial general insurance risk assessment and investment advice. Contentious and commercial work is outsourced, and the firm regularly acts with and for other professionals.

WILLIAMS DAVIES MELTZER

8-10 New Fetter Lane, London, EC4A 1AP **Tel:** (020) 7353 2500 **Fax:** (020) 7353 2552 **DX:** 1026 London **Email:** wdm@link.org
Website: www.williamsdaviesmeltzer.co.uk **Ptnrs:** 5 **Asst solrs:** 10 **Other fee-earners:** 8

WILLIAMSON & SODEN

Stanton House, 54 Stratford Road, Shirley, Solihull, B90 3LS
Tel: (0121) 733 8000 **Fax:** (0121) 733 3322 **DX:** 20652

Citadel, 190 Corporation Street, Birmingham, B4 6QB
Tel: (0121) 212 1155 **Fax:** (0121) 212 4961

Managing partner:	I.P. Williamson
Number of partners:	8
Assistant solicitors:	7
Other fee-earners:	10

CONTACTS

Business Clients ....John Soden, Scott Withers
Disputes (general/commercial) ....Stephen Rowe, Kevin Reilly
Family Law ....Clare Fletcher
Motor Racing ....David Munro ....John Soden
Personal Injury ....Gerry Cusack
Planning Law ....Ian Williamson
Police Matters (inc. motoring) ....David Munro, Fiona Warman
Property ....Lynne Goldsby
Telecommunications ....David Munro
Wills/Inheritance ....Allison Scott ....Angela Beck

THE FIRM: The practice was founded by Ian Williamson and John Soden in 1979. Williamson & Soden has grown significantly and now operates from its own purpose-built premises at Stanton House, Shirley, Solihull and from offices in the centre of Birmingham, adjacent to the law courts.

PRINCIPAL AREAS OF WORK:
Crime: A large and respected department deals with police matters for clients charged with anything from a motoring offence to a murder. Specialists also deal with Customs & Excise and Inland Revenue Investigations.
Company/Commercial: Work includes new business start-ups, acquisition of commercial premises, trading agreements, mergers and acquisitions, commercial disputes and insolvencies.
Private Client: A full range of services covers all aspects of family and matrimonial law, personal injury compensation, wills, probate and trusts.

W

LG WILLIAMS & PRICHARD

22 St Andrews Crescent, Cardiff, CF1O 3DD **Tel:** (029) 2022 9716 **Fax:** (029) 2037 7761 **DX:** 50752 Cardiff 2 **Email:** mail@cardiff-law.co.uk **Website:** www.law-wales.co.uk **Ptnrs:** 2 **Asst solrs:** 2 **Other fee-earners:** 1 **Contact:** Susan Lyons • Long-established yet dynamic niche firm provides specialist advice harnessing new technology and producing a streamlined efficient yet personal service to clients.

AREAS OF PRACTICE

Commercial Litigation	30%
Commercial Property	30%
Company Commercial	20%
Charity Law and Trusts	10%
Private Client	10%

WILLIAM STURGES & CO

Alliance House, 12 Caxton St, London, SW1H 0QY
Tel: (020) 7873 1000 **Fax:** (020) 7873 1010 **DX:** 2315 Victoria
Email: law@williamsturges.co.uk

Senior partner:	Ian Gavin-Brown
Number of partners:	17
Assistant solicitors:	12
Other fee-earners:	5

CONTACTS

Business ....Nicholas Phillips
Commercial Property ....Tony Turhill
Domestic Property ....Jonathan Picken
Employment ....Robert Prescott
Family ....Andrew Todd
Insolvency ....Michael Lawson
Litigation ....Richard Dugdate
Private Client ....Fiona Hill

THE FIRM: The firm was founded over 100 years ago and has recently merged with Chethams. It provides legal services to commercial and private clients to enable them to achieve effective and efficient solutions.

PRINCIPAL AREAS OF WORK:
Business: provides a complete range of services for business clients, including those of an insolvency ptractitioner.
Property: experienced partners advise on all aspects of commercial and domestic property issues.
Litigation: handles all civil and employment litigation for business and private clients.
Private Client: offers specialist advice on trust and estate planning and management and provides a specialist family law service.

WILLOUGHBY & PARTNERS

The Isis Building, Thames Quay, 193 Marsh Wall, Docklands, London, E14 9SG
Tel: (020) 7345 8888 **Fax:** (020) 7345 4555 **DX:** 42677 Isle of Dogs
Email: isis@iprights.com **Website:** www.iprights.com

Pembroke House, Pembroke Street, Oxford, OX1 1BP
Tel: (01865) 791990 **Fax:** (01865) 791772 **DX:** 82256 Oxford
Email: oxford@iprights.com

Managing partner:	Shireen Peermohamed
Senior partner:	Tony Willoughby
Number of partners:	6
Assistant solicitors:	13
Other fee-earners:	12

AREAS OF PRACTICE

Intellectual Property Protection, Enforcement and Exploitation	100%

CONTACTS

Intellectual Property ....Tony Willoughby ....Rupert-Ross MacDonald ....Shireen Peermohamed ....(London) ....Anna Booy ....Ben Goodger ....(Oxford)

THE FIRM: Willoughby & Partners is a specialist firm which practises exclusively in the areas of intellectual property (IP) and information technology (IT). It prides itself on being accessible and responsive, and providing high quality and competitively priced legal services that take account of commercial objectives and budgets. It has a well respected and dynamic team of lawyers, who are supported by the latest technology and a first rate research capability.

PRINCIPAL AREAS OF WORK: The firm has a proven track record in relation to all aspects of intellectual property litigation. Recent cases include Montblanc Simplo Gmbh v Sepia Products Inc; Premier Brands Uk limited v Typhoon Europe Limited & Another; SmithKline Beecham plc & Others v Dowelhurst Limited. The firm also represents clients in the Trade Mark Registry and develops, coordinates and executes enforcement strategies. Willoughby & Partners also advises in relation to exploitation, acquisition, transfer and financing of IP and IT rights. It can assist in negotiating and structuring deals and drafting agreements - whether as part of a transactional support programme or licensing, distribution or other commercial arrangements. It has developed a strategic IP management service to assist clients in carrying out IP audits and implementing recommendations. The firm offers its services as a 'virtual IP department' for other frims without an IP/IT capability.

Agency Work: The firm acts as London agent for other firms in litigation and has five solicitors with experience of supervising Search Orders on behalf of other firms. It also acts as UK agent for foreign law firms in both contentious and non contentious matters.

INTERNATIONAL CONNECTIONS: Willoughby & Partners is associated with the Rouse & Co International Group of companies which provides IP consultancy services throughout the world from offices in Europe, the Middle East, Asia Pacific and the Americas. Investigation services throughout the world are provided by the Group's in-house investigation unit. The unit also constantly monitors clients' brands worldwide through its 'spotter' service.

CLIENTELE: Multinational and domestic companies across a wide range of industries (including pharmaceuticals and consumer healthcare, motor vehicle manufacturing, food and drink, publishing and entertainment, clothing and footwear, IT and the Internet, sports and telecommunications); international and domestic law firms; and accountants and financial institutions.

RECRUITMENT & TRAINING: The firm runs regular training programmes for clients, as well as staff, on a range of IP and IT related issues. Its lawyers also regularly attend and speak at external seminars and industry meetings. The firm also offers a current awareness and research service to clients.

W

WILMER, CUTLER & PICKERING

4 Carlton Gardens, London, SW1Y 5AA
Tel: (020) 7872 1000 **Fax:** (020) 7839 3537
Email: law@wilmer.com **Website:** www.wilmer.com

Managing partner:	Andrew Parnell
UK:	
Number of partners:	5
Assistant solicitors:	9
Other fee-earners:	3
International:	
Number of partners:	118
Assistant solicitors:	243
Other fee-earners:	108

AREAS OF PRACTICE

International Arbitration & Litigation	35%
Company/Commercial	25%
Telecommunication	25%
Aviation	15%

CONTACTS

Aviation	Dieter G.Lange
	John Kallaugher
Company/Commercial	
	Andrew Parnell
	Michael Holter
International Arbitration/Litigation	
	Gary Born
	Paul Mitchard
Telecommunication	Dieter G. Lange,
	Michael Holter

THE FIRM: Wilmer, Cutler & Pickering is an international law firm with offices in London, Brussels, Berlin, Washington DC, New York and Baltimore. Founded in 1962, WCP has over 300 lawyers engaged in a broadly diversified practice.

PRINCIPAL AREAS OF WORK:

Company & Commercial: International commercial and corporate transactions practice, including: cross-border mergers and acquisitions; joint venture and partnership arrangements and international corporate alliances; equity and debt financing; distribution arrangements, technology and licensing matters.

Telecommunications: Specialist advice in multi-jurisdictional, especially internet-related transactions and international joint ventures. Cover all related trade, investment and global information infrastructure issues. Guide clients through regulatory environment of individual European countries, EU and US. Advise telecoms entrants seeking access to liberalised telecoms markets (especially Germany). Particular strengths in the competition law and UK/US - German issues.

Aviation: One of WCP's main practice areas. The aviation team comprises more than 30 lawyers and experts in economic, transport and infrastructure issues involved in multi-jurisdictional transactions. The firm's advice focuses on providing high level strategy, legal and policy guidance. Clients include airlines, airports, governments, and international agencies in the aviation sector.

INTERNATIONAL CONNECTIONS: The firm has offices in: Brussels, tel. +32 2 285 4900, contact Marc Hansen; Berlin, tel. +49 30 2022 6400, contact Natalie Lübben; Washington DC, tel. +1 202 663 6363, contact Bill Perlstein; New York, tel. +1 212 230 8800, contact Tom White; Baltimore, tel +1 410 986 2800, contact Mark Devine.

LANGUAGES: French, German and Spanish.

WILSON & CO

697 High Road, London, N17 8AD
Tel: (020) 8808 7535 **Fax:** (020) 8880 3393 **DX:** 52200 Tottenham 2
Website: www.wilsonandco.co.uk

Number of partners:	5
Assistant solicitors:	6
Other fee-earners:	12

AREAS OF PRACTICE

Criminal	40%
Immigration	40%
Family	10%
Mental Health	5%
Personal Injury	5%

THE FIRM: Established in 1990 by Andrew Wilson and Michael Hanley the firm has grown yearly and since 1993 has practised from a large double fronted Georgian building on the Tottenham High Road. The building has been thoroughly renovated and excellent facilities are provided for staff and clients. The firm uses modern technology and every member of staff works from a networked PC. The firm is a leading Legal Aid specialist, franchised by the Legal Aid Board since 1996, and now has contracted arrangements for the provision of Legal Help. Wilson & Co is a progressive and dynamic firm committed to the highest professional standards in the service of its clients.

Continued overleaf

PRINCIPAL AREAS OF WORK:
Immigration: All areas of personal immigration and asylum are covered. Wilson & Co has conducted a number of cutting edge and test cases including R v SSHD Ex p Murat Akdogan (1995) Imm AR p176, Adan v SSHD (House of Lords 1998) Doldur v SSHD 1998 and M. The firm looks at the wider issues that confront its clients and has for example established that the Home Office has a duty of care to travellers when giving advice to airlines on the validityof travel documentation (Farah and others v British Airways and the Home Office 1999).
Crime: The firm has a very experienced criminal team which has defended the most serious of cases. The team has a national reputation and represents defendants outside London. There is particular expertise involving mental health aspects of crime. Committed and reliable police station advice is provided throughout the year.
Personal Injury: Wilson & Co has a growing accident litigation department and undertakes all types of work. The emphasis is on a proactive and well-prepared progression of claims. Actions against the police are undertaken by the firm. CFA's are available.
Family: Expanding family work with an emphasis on childcare and domestic violence.
Mental Health: Small but active mental health team.

CLIENTELE:
The firms work comes largely from personal recommendation. They are committed to representing the people of Haringey but also have clients from all over the country.

WILSON, ELSER, MOSKOWITZ, EDELMAN & DICKER

141 Fenchurch Street, London, EC3M 6BL
Tel: (020) 7623 6723 **Fax:** (020) 7626 9774 **DX:** 858 CITY
Email: Cherryt@wemed.com **Website:** www.wemed.com

Number of partners:	1
Assistant solicitors:	2

AREAS OF PRACTICE

US Defence Litigation	50%
Arbitration	10%
Creditors' Rights	10%
D & O	10%
E & O brokers (US and UK)	10%
Insurance Coverage Disputes	10%

THE FIRM: The firm is one of the largest in the United States, and has been serving clients for more than a quarter of a century. It has grown considerably during this period and now has offices in 14 major cities in the US. The London office of Wilson, Elser, Moskowitz, Edelman & Dicker is a multinational partnership associated with the US firm. The office concentrates on insurance and reinsurance work including product liability, insurance broker errors and omissions and international arbitration. Mr Cherry is both a US lawyer and a solicitor. Mr Cherry is also a Fellow of the Chartered Institute of Arbitrators. The London office conducts litigation in English courts.

PRINCIPAL AREAS OF WORK: Initially, the practice was insurance-related, and the firm maintains a pre-eminent position with regard to all aspects of insurance law and the insurance industry. However, it has broadened its services and expertise to meet the needs of clients in the following areas: corporate organisation, negotiation, rendering business advice for both domestic and international clients on acquisitions, mergers, regulatory matters, financing, real estate and leasing transactions, contract negotiations and drafting, employment law and tax advice. The firm maintains close relationships with insurance specialist law firms in Europe.

LANGUAGES: French and German.
Other offices at New York, Baltimore, Chicago, Dallas, Houston, Los Angeles, Miami, Newark, Paris, Philadelphia, San Diego, San Francisco, Washington DC and White Plains.

WILSON NESBITT
113 Victoria Street, Belfast, BT1 4PD **Tel:** (028) 90323864 **Fax:** (028) 90333707 **DX:** 484 NR **Website:** www.wilson-nesbitt.co.uk **Ptnrs:** 6
Asst solrs: 20 **Other fee-earners:** 28

WILSONS

Steynings House, Fisherton St, Salisbury, SP2 7RJ
Tel: (01722) 412412 **Fax:** (01722) 411500 **DX:** 58003 Salisbury 1
Email: info@wilsons-solicitors.co.uk

Number of partners:	18
Assistant solicitors:	18
Other fee-earners:	21

THE FIRM: Wilsons is one of the best-known firms in the south of England, with a nationwide reputation for private client work, which continues to grow. Its teams of specialists offer a full range of quality legal services to UK and overseas clients, both private and commercial, and the firm continues to recruit top quality lawyers at all levels to meet the demands of its growing client base. The firm is constantly striving to improve the quality and delivery of its services in order to meet clients' expectations. This requires continuous investment in information technology and training to ensure that it can deliver advice quickly and competitively in a form which is free from jargon and which clients understand.

PRINCIPAL AREAS OF WORK:
Private Client: The firm is believed to have one of the highest net worth private client practices outside London. Its extensive expertise in farms and estates law, heritage property, tax planning and charity law is well-known. The firm has an exceptionally experienced tax planning team of four partners and three consultants, including Ralph Ray, one of the most eminent solicitors in the field of personal tax, who joined Wilsons as a consultant in 1998.
Family Law: Led by Christopher Nisbet, who trained at Withers and is a member of the Family Law Association, this is one of the fastest growing departments of the firm and is increasingly rivalling the major London firms for top-drawer High Court family work.
Commercial: Wilsons deals with all types of company-related and business transactions. It has experienced specialist teams advising on employment matters, pensions and commercial property. It also provides a company secretarial service to its corporate clients. Wilsons has an insolvency and corporate recovery team headed by Andrew Roberts, a licensed insolvency practitioner, who joined the firm from Linklaters in 1999.

WINCKWORTH SHERWOOD

35 Great Peter Street, Westminster, London, SW1P 3LR
Tel: (020) 7593 5000 **Fax:** (020) 7593 5099 **DX:** 2312 Victoria
Email: wandp@winckworths.co.uk

Number of partners:	21
Assistant solicitors:	25
Other fee-earners:	25

AREAS OF PRACTICE

Parliamentary/Planning	20%
Housing/Local Government	19%
Commercial/Government Services	16%
Ecclesiastical/Education/Charities	16%
Private Client	15%
Litigation	10%
Licensed Property	4%

CONTACTS

Commercial/Government Services	Nicholas Owston
Commercial Property/ Licensing	Robert Botkai
Ecclesiastical	Paul Morris
Education	Michael Thatcher
Health	Simon Eastwood
Housing/ Local Government	Andrew Murray
Litigation	Peter Williams
Parliamentary	Alison Gorlov
Private Client	Hugh MacDougald

THE FIRM: Winckworth Sherwood is a well established Westminster firm of solicitors and parliamentary agents. The firm offers a wide range of client-led services to private and public sector clients and has an established ecclesiastical, education, housing, health, parliamentary, police and private client practice. It also acts for many institutional clients and professional bodies with a growing charitable clientele and has a thriving commercial practice.The firm also has offices in the City of London, Chelmsford and Oxford dealing with similar types of work.

PRINCIPAL AREAS OF WORK: The firm is structured by client sector rather than legal specialisation.
Parliamentary and Planning: This department specialises in Town and Country Planning and the promotion of and opposition to Private Bills in Parliament and similar legislation (Scottish Provisional Orders and Orders under the Harbours Act 1964 and the Transport and Works Act 1992) as well as charters and bye laws. The department also advises on all forms of primary and secondary legislation and parliamentary procedures.
Housing and Local Government: Winckworth Sherwood is one of the leaders in this field of work, acting for over 100 housing associations and local authorities.
Ecclesiastical, Education and Charities: This department provides registries for several of the Church of England's dioceses and handles church property and other work for a number of denominations. The department also acts for schools, higher education colleges, further education institutions, educational charities and local education authorities.
Commercial Property and Licensing: This department does all kinds of commercial property work, notably for public utilities, institutions and, particularly, clients in the licensed trade.
Litigation: A wide variety of work is handled, including injunction actions, police litigation, personal injury claims, landlord & tenant disputes and matrimonial matters. Employment law including unfair dismissal and discrimination is also practised here. Healthcare law (including defending medical negligence claims, regulatory and disciplinary matters) is another specialism.
Commercial and Government Services: The department handles work in the public and private sectors covering contentious and non-contentious commercial and construction law and includes specialist tax services, real and intellectual property and IT.
Private Client: The firm acts for a number of landed estate owners and substantial trusts, and handles a significant amount of estate planning and probate work.
Police: The firm has considerable expertise in police law and procedure having acted for police services for 25 years. Work handled includes operational police law, constitutional issues within and between forces, procurement, outsourcing, vires, commercial matters, employment and discipline.

INTERNATIONAL CONNECTIONS: The firm is a founder member of an international network of law firms called Euréseau.

RECRUITMENT & TRAINING: Qualified staff should apply in the first instance to the Partnership Secretary, Mr TF Vesey. The firm recruits three trainee solicitors each year – a 2:2 law or 2:1 non-law degree is usually required and applications should be made by handwritten letter (and typed CV) to Mr RHA MacDougald.

WINSTANLEY-BURGESS

378 City Rd, London, EC1V 2TQ **Tel:** (020) 7278 7911 **Fax:** (020) 7833 2135 **DX:** 58253 Islington
Email: wb@gn.apc.org **Ptnrs:** 8 **Asst solrs:** 3 **Other fee-earners:** 4 **Contact:** Ms Bridget Taylor
Established 1975. Handles most areas of general practice including crime, family, housing, personal injury, probate and property. Best known for immigration and public interest law.

AREAS OF PRACTICE

Immigration & Nationality	50%
Crime	10%
Family	10%
Housing	10%
Non-Contentious	10%
Other Civil	10%

WINWARD FEARON

35 Bow St, London, WC2E 7AU
Tel: (020) 7420 2800 **Fax:** (020) 7420 2801 **DX:** 37959 Kingsway
Email: enquiries@winwardfearon.co.uk **Website:** www.winwardfearon.co.uk

Senior partner:	David L. Cornes
Partnership Secretary:	Adrian Luto
Number of partners:	10
Total staff:	38
Other fee-earners:	3

AREAS OF PRACTICE

Construction	58%
Infrastructure Projects/PFI/ Corporate Finance	21%
Commercial/Property Litigation	13%
Property	8%

CONTACTS

Commercial & property litigation	Clive Levontine
Construction	Richard Winward
Corporate finance	Edward Gore
Infrastructure projects, PFI and corporate finance	Adrian Luto
Property	Guy Fearon

THE FIRM: This central London firm is one of the UK's top construction law practices. It has also established a significant reputation in infrastructure project work. Winward Fearon was founded in 1986. As a matter of policy it concentrates its development around an expanding number of niche areas, rather than professing to expertise across the board. Those niche areas are carefully chosen to facilitate the creation of cross-departmental teams which specialise in industry sectors, rather than technical legal disciplines. In addition to their litigation and arbitration work, the firm's construction and commercial litigation departments increasingly make use of alternative dispute resolution procedures. The firm above all seeks to provide a top-quality and cost-effective service. It has an established and enviable client base, including large PLCs, owner-managed businesses, and developers. The firm's international links have been strengthened by its membership of Eurolegal, which is a European Economic Interest Group of law firms in EU jurisdictions.

W

PRINCIPAL AREAS OF WORK:
Construction: Construction law forms a large part of the firm's practice and is carried out for national and international clients in building, civil engineering, and the professions. Typical issues may concern defective building, formation of contracts, liquidated damages, extension of time, and critical-path analysis, as well as payment. In addition, the department deals with bonds and insurance-related matters, certificates, statutory obligations, variations in construction work, indemnities and warranties, together with product liability. The work of the department is both contentious and non-contentious, including very large cases in the High Court and in ICC, LCIA and UNCITRAL arbitrations. Mediation work is also increasing.
Commercial and Property Litigation: Winward Fearon's commercial litigation team handles a wide variety of commercial claims, including employment disputes for UK and international clients. Part of the team specialises in property and landlord and tenant litigation, including dilapidation claims, lease renewals, rent review problems, easement and right of way actions, service charge disputes, and franchises. The team often works closely with the firm's property team.
Infrastructure Projects, PFI and Corporate Finance: The infrastructure project, PFI and corporate finance team has handled a number of high profile transactions in the past five years. Adrian Luto has established a reputation in infrastructure projects, particularly in the independent power plant section both in the UK and overseas. Edward Gore focuses on the purchase and sale of private companies and businesses, management buy-outs, other venture capital transactions, joint ventures and partnership agreements.
Property: The property team, headed by Guy Fearon, one of the firm's four founding partners, focuses on commercial property and residential development. Work includes the acquisition and sale of development sites, industrial estates, offices, and other commercial and investment property. The department advises on redevelopment projects, auction contracts, joint ventures, and partnership developments, including taxation, property finance, and landlord and tenant work. The team also provides a service in high quality residential property.

WITHAM WELD

70 St George's Square, London, SW1V 3RD
Tel: (020) 7821 8211 **Fax:** (020) 7630 6484 **DX:** 86164 Victoria 2
Email: postmaster@wwlaw.co.uk

Number of partners:	6
Assistant solicitors:	3
Other fee-earners:	4

THE FIRM: Established for over 200 years, Witham Weld has a long-standing reputation in its work for every kind of client, including religious and civil institutions, charities and trusts, commercial and private clients. Today, the aim remains the same, to provide the highest quality legal services, founded on experience and expertise and supported by innovation and the use of modern working methods.

PRINCIPAL AREAS OF WORK: The firm provides advice and assistance in a wide range of areas including charity law, property, revenue and tax planning, wills and probates, company/ commercial, contracts, education, employment, copyright, and all forms of litigation.

WITHERS

12 Gough Square, London, EC4A 3DW
Tel: (020) 7936 1000 **Fax:** (020) 7936 2589 **DX:** 160
Email: mailto@withers.co.uk **Website:** www.withers.co.uk

Number of partners:	47
Assistant solicitors:	58
Other fee-earners:	47

THE FIRM: Withers is a City firm with a thriving practice serving the needs of both individual and corporate clients. The firm's practice is a broad one, embracing private client work, charities, agricultural, commercial and residential property, family law, employment, intellectual property, company and commercial law, corporate finance, banking, litigation, insolvency, commercial fraud, professional negligence and professional disciplinary work. Half of the firm's work is for corporate clients and institutions, the balance is for individuals and families. The firm has a fully staffed office in Paris, a representative office in Milan and a global network of connections with overseas lawyers.

PRINCIPAL AREAS OF WORK:

Agricultural Property and Estates: A comprehensive service to landowners and farmers including the acquisition, management and disposal of estates and farming businesses; agricultural land occupation; tenancies; farm partnerships and share farm agreements; property tax; development and alternative land use; planning; mineral exploitation; sporting and leisure uses; forestry; European Union legislation including quotas and set-aside; environmental law.

Banking: Advice to banks and borrowers on all aspects of wholesale and retail banking, project finance, shipping and aircraft finance and property finance, including: syndicated and conduit loans; structured finance; buyer and supplier credits; ECGD and SACE supported credits; forfaiting and trade finance; bills of exchange and letters of credit; swaps and other derivatives; securitisation and credit-enhanced transactions; capital adequacy and related regulatory issues; taxation issues relating to lending and borrowing.

Charities: Advice to numerous public and private charities, including companies, trusts, unincorporated associations, royal charter corporations and other not-for-profit organisations, on matters such as: formation and variation of charities; methods of charitable giving; tax efficient structures for donors and charities; appeals and fund-raising; negotiations with the charity commissioners; contracting with local authorities and the National Health Service; trustees' duties; trading and other commercial arrangements; exempt charities; asset transfers between charities; contested probates and disputes between beneficiaries; cross-border giving and international charity law.

Commercial Litigation: Advice on commercial disputes of all kinds, in areas such as: commercial contracts; fraud; professional negligence; intellectual property; trade libel; emergency remedies; Companies Act remedies; banking; insolvency and asset tracing; tribunal cases; judicial review; property litigation; competition law; professional and sporting disciplinary matters.

Commercial Property: Advice to buyers and sellers, lenders and borrowers, landlords, tenants and developers on matters such as: acquisition and disposal of freehold and leasehold properties: landlord and tenant issues; property tax; collateral warranties; duty of care letters; property litigation; representation of receivers, administrators and liquidators; secured lending; planning applications, agreements and appeals; construction contracts; property aspects of corporate transactions; environmental law.

Company and Commercial: Comprehensive advice for business clients, including listed and private companies, partnerships, sole traders and entrepreneurs, on matters such as: mergers and acquisitions; licensing; franchising and agency agreements; company secretarial services; compliance; corporate re-organisations; terms and conditions of business; shareholder agreements and joint ventures.

Corporate Finance: Advice on all aspects of corporate finance including: management buy-outs and buy-ins; takeovers; capital raising exercises; the Alternative Investment Market; Stock Exchange and Takeover Code requirements; circulars to shareholders.

Employment: Advice to both employers and employees on the full range of employment issues, including: employee handbooks; service agreements; share option schemes; employee incentives; boardroom disputes; severance agreements and taxation; injunctions to restrain breach of confidence and competition; sex and race discrimination; unfair, wrongful and constructive dismissal; industrial relations.

Family Law: Advice on all aspects of family law, including separation and divorce cross-jurisdictionally and internationally, pre and post nuptial agreements, international issues and forum shopping, prevention and resolution of child abduction problems, arrangements for children's residence and education, arrangements for contact with children, enforcement of foreign court orders, separation agreements, cohabitation matters, issues arising from surrogacy, financial settlements including asset tracing and tax mitigation.

Insolvency: Specialist advice to major insolvency practitioners, banks and secured lenders, creditors and company directors, covering all aspects of insolvency including: liquidations and receiverships; administrations and voluntary arrangements; tracing, realisation and disposal of assets; reservation of title international issues.

Intellectual Property and Information Technology: Advice on all aspects of the creation, registration, ownership, use and protection of intellectual property rights. The firm has recently acquired the highly respected intellectual property practice of Maycocks strengthening its existing reputation for work in this area.

Private Client: A specialist and comprehensive service that focuses on the preservation and enhancement of clients' assets by advising in areas such as: estate, tax and financial planning; succession planning for individuals, landed estates and owner-managed companies; United Kingdom and international tax planning for residents and non-residents; advice to trustees in a commercial context, including when a substantial shareholding in a company is owned; trust formation and re-organisation in the United Kingdom and overseas; executor and trustee services including independent trusteeship for pension schemes; pension trust litigation including offshore trust disputes; international and cross-border succession issues; preparation of wills; advice to executors and beneficiaries on probate and succession law; variation of estates; Court of Protection work; heritage property including maintenance funds.

Residential Property: A fast and efficient service for both United Kingdom and overseas clients in the following areas: the purchase and sale of freeholds and leaseholds; residential developments; tax efficient own

Continued overleaf

AREAS OF PRACTICE

Private Client/Charities	42%
Litigation	17%
Family	15%
Corporate/Company/Commercial	13%
Property (Agricultural, Commercial & Residential)	13%

CONTACTS

Area	Contact
Agricultural Property	Andrew Lane
Banking	David Dannreuther
Charities	Alison Paines
Commercial Litigation	Margaret Robertson
Commercial Property	Claudia D'Ambrosio
Company/Commercial	Tim Taylor
Corporate Finance	Hugh Devlin
Employment	Margaret Robertson
Family Law	Gill Doran
France	Jonathan Eastwood
Healthcare/Bioscience	Anthony Indaimo
Insolvency	Jeremy Scott
Intellectual Property	John Maycock
Italy	Peter Wood
Private Client	Charles Pike
Residential Property	Henry Stuart
Trust & Probate Litigation	Dawn Goodman

W

WITHERS
SOLICITORS

ership; planning and tax advice for overseas buyers of property in England and Wales; country houses; secured lending; property transfers caused by death or family breakdown; leasehold reform; long leases; Central London leaseholds; regaining possession; managing and supervising residential investments; short term letting.
International and Domestic Trust and Probate Litigation: Specialist advice on domestic and multi-jurisdictional trust litigation including dismantling and protecting trust structures, construction, rectification and variation of trusts, forced heirship, breach of trust, conflict of laws, and applications for directions and removal of trustees. All contentious probate, applications for increased provision under wills, construction and rectification of wills, applications for accounts, applications for the replacement of personal representatives and trustees, and devastavit claims.
Healthcare & Biosciences: Specialist advice that combines scientific expertise and industry experience with legal and commercial skills. Industry focused advice ranges from mergers, acquisitions and disposals to venture capital, charitable funding of research to the identification and protection of intellectual property to marketing and distribution.

INTERNATIONAL CONNECTIONS: The firm has a Paris office with a resident partner who is dually qualified as an English solicitor and French avocat. The firm also has a representative office in Milan and four partners in London specialising in Italian work. The firm has strong connections with North America and the Middle East.

LANGUAGES: French, German, Italian and Spanish.

WITHY KING

5 & 6 Northumberland Buildings, Queen Square, Bath, BA1 2JE **Tel:** (01225) 425731 **Fax:** (01225) 315562 **DX:** 8014 Bath
Email: mail@withyking.co.uk **Ptnrs:** 16 **Asst solrs:** 9 **Other fee-earners:** 33

WOLFERSTANS

Deptford Chambers, 60-64 North Hill, Plymouth, PL4 8EP
Tel: (01752) 663295 **Fax:** (01752) 672021 **DX:** 8206 Plymouth -1
Email: info@wolferstans.com **Website:** www.wolferstans.com

Managing partner:	David J.L. Gabbitass
Number of partners:	29
Assistant solicitors:	19
Other fee-earners:	15

AREAS OF PRACTICE

Personal Injury/Clinical Negligence	45%
Matrimonial & Children	20%
Commercial	10%
Insurance	10%
Crime	5%
Litigation	5%
Private	5%

CONTACTS

Clinical Negligence	Simon Parford
Commercial	Nick Roper
Crime	David Teague
Insurance	Roy Griggs
Litigation	Bill Duncan
Matrimonial/Family	Phil Thorneycroft
Personal Injury	Chris Kallis
Private	John Chapman
Probate	Gill Hollinshead
Sport	David Gabbitass

THE FIRM: Wolferstans is a major regional practice with three offices in Plymouth and another in Taunton. Founded in 1812, it is a founder member of LawGroup UK with a commitment to excellence whilst providing a comprehensive personal service. Senior Partner David Gabbitass, a Higher Courts Advocate, is a member of the CICB, CICAP, an arbitrator and a member of the Discipline Committee of the ECB. A number of partners are Chairmen of various tribunals or deputy district judges.

PRINCIPAL AREAS OF WORK:
Company/Commercial: Headed by Nick Roper. Includes company formations, acquisitions and sales, funding arrangements, management buy-outs, employment matters, licensing, commercial conveyancing and a wide range of commercial litigation. Julia Allsop is a Licensed Insolvency Practitioner.
Personal Injury: Led by Roy Griggs, an assessor for the PI Panel, this division of the practice operates from all major offices. The substantial plaintiff division is managed by Chris Kallis and the specialist motorcycle division is headed by Steve Ross at the Taunton office. The medical specialist division is headed by Simon Parford, an assessor and member of the Panel and a referral panel member for AVMA. The firm is involved in a number of group actions. Clinical negligence franchises are held at Plymouth, and Taunton.
Crime: David Teague is well known for his Courts Martial work. In addition to defence criminal work, the practice also acts for government agencies in prosecutions and provides advocates for inquests, inquiries, disciplinary hearings and tribunals.
Sport: Clients include Somerset County Cricket Club, Plymouth Argyle Football Club, Plymouth Albion Rugby Football Club and Plymouth Basketball Club.
Matrimonial and Family: This division is led by Philip Thorneycroft. Work includes separation and divorce, mediation, custody and access, adoption, child welfare, financial settlements and maintenance agreements. There are three members of the Children's Panel and two Accredited Specialist Family Lawyers.
Private Client: Work includes wills, probate and trusts and residential conveyancing.
Other Areas: The firm regularly appears on behalf of accused persons at courts martial and has extensive experience in inquests and inquiries.

LANGUAGES: French, German, Greek and Spanish.

WOLLASTONS

Brierly Place, New London Road, Chelmsford, CM2 0AP
Tel: (01245) 211211 **Fax:** (01245) 354764 **DX:** 89703 Chelmsford 2
Email: enquiries@wollastons.co.uk **Website:** www.wollastons.co.uk

Number of partners:	12
Assistant solicitors:	9
Consultants:	2
Other fee-earners:	12

AREAS OF PRACTICE

Corporate/Commercial	33%
Litigation	28%
Property/Planning	24%
Employment	8%
Private Client	7%

CONTACTS

Commercial	Nicholas Burnett
Corporate	Richard Wollaston
	Richard Payne
Employment	Kevin Palmer
	Simon Quantrill
Environment	Andrew Bryce
Family Property & Finance	Charles Brewer
Intellectual Property	Nigel Thompson
Landlord & Tenant	Nicholas Cook
Litigation	Bruce Bowler
Planning	Jim Little
Property Development	Alan Wyatt
Trusts & Tax	Patrick Penny

THE FIRM: Wollastons provides high levels of expertise and service to business clients based mainly in Essex, London and surrounding counties, as well as foreign companies and their UK subsidiaries. It also advises private individuals and families, including some who are resident abroad. The firm is located in Chelmsford, only 35 minutes by train from central London, with easy access to the motorway network and Stansted airport. It is exceptionally well resourced and well organised with first-rate IT and communications.

PRINCIPAL AREAS OF WORK:
Corporate and commercial: Company sales and acquisitions (especially management buy-outs and buy-ins); insolvency and reconstructions; corporate finance; European law; intellectual property; commercial agreements; business immigration. Considerable international experience.
Employment: Employment contracts; unfair and wrongful dismissal; redundancy; race and sex discrimination; business transfers; frequent advocacy in the Employment Tribunal.
Property: Commercial development, investment and agricultural property; landlord and tenant.
Litigation: Commercial disputes; professional negligence claims; debt recovery; insolvency; property and inheritance disputes; personal injury.
Private Client: Wills; tax; trusts; estate planning; probate; family property & finance.

INTERNATIONAL CONNECTIONS: Wollastons is an active member of IAG International, an association of independent professional firms represented throughout Europe and beyond.

RECRUITMENT & TRAINING: Wollastons welcomes enquiries from outgoing candidates with a strong academic record. The firm takes two or three trainees annually, and is prepared to fund LPC course fees in some cases.

W

WOOD & AWDRY

3 St Mary Street, Chippenham, SN15 3JL
Tel: (01249) 444422 **Fax:** (01249) 443666 **DX:** 34204 Chippenham

Senior partner:	Christopher Yates
Partnership secretary:	Peter Wilson
Number of partners:	6
Assistant solicitors:	7
Other fee-earners:	3

CONTACTS

Civil Litigation	Andrew Herridge
Crime and Licensing	Andrew Watts-Jones
Family/Matrimonial	Lynda Ashworth
Owner Managed Businesses & Institutions	William Wyldbore-Smith
Property (commercial)	George Burges
Property (residential)	Christopher Yates
Trust/Inheritance Tax	Jackie Moor

THE FIRM: Wood & Awdry is a long established Wiltshire practice focusing on private client work in its broadest sense: the individual, the family, the owner managed business coupled with some institutional work.

PRINCIPAL AREAS OF WORK:
Property: Divided between residential/country houses/agricultural/commercial property.
Succession and Inheritance: Including trust, Court of Protection, probate administration, wills and inheritance tax planning.
Litigation: Including personal injury, general litigation, employment, crime and family.
Owner Managed Business (including farms and estates): company, commercial, partnership, employment and related capital tax advice.

WOODFORD-ROBINSON

4 Castilian Terrace, Northampton, NN1 1LE **Tel:** (01604) 624926 / 231444 **Fax:** (01604) 231457 **DX:** 12424 Northampton 1 **Ptnrs:** 5
Other fee-earners: 2

WOODROFFES

36 Ebury Street, London, SW1W 0LU
Tel: (020) 7730 0001 **Fax:** (020) 7730 7900 **DX:** 99923 Victoria
Email: rbrown-woodroffes@compuserve.com

Senior partner:	P.M. Woodroffe
Number of partners:	2
Assistant solicitors:	4
Other fee-earners:	1

CONTACTS

Banking & Project Finance	Sarah Taylor
Conveyancing	Roger Brown
Education & Art	Peter Woodroffe
Other matters	Peter Woodroffe

THE FIRM: Founded by CG Woodroffe in 1877, it is a general practice with emphasis on individual attention. The office is situated in Belgravia and is close to Victoria Station.

PRINCIPAL AREAS OF WORK: Known for problem solving in the company/commercial field, private client, charities, education and foreign work. Specialist department handling commercial conveyancing including development, hotels, nightclubs and restaurants and licensing for the same. Also transfer of works of art, residential conveyancing, employment, probate, matrimonial, litigation, European Court, fraud recovery, insurance claims, insolvency and most legal matters.

CLIENTELE: The firm acts for private clients in UK and abroad, public companies, banks and charities.

WOOLLCOMBE BEER WATTS
Church House, Queen Street, Newton Abbot, TQ12 2QP **Tel:** (01626) 202404 **Fax:** (01626) 202420 **DX:** 59100 Newton Abbot
Email: lawyer@wbw.co.uk **Website:** www.wbw.co.uk **Ptnrs:** 21 **Asst solrs:** 14 **Other fee-earners:** 33

WRAGGE & CO

55 Colmore Row, Birmingham, B3 2AS
Tel: (0121) 233 1000 **Fax:** (0121) 214 1099 **DX:** 13036
Email: mail@wragge.com **Website:** www.wragge.com

Managing partner:	Quentin Poole
Senior partner:	John Crabtree
Number of partners:	94
Assistant solicitors:	254
Other fee-earners:	199

THE FIRM: Wragge & Co is a major UK law firm. Its rapid growth and success are a result of a distinctive strategy to develop a national and international law firm from its base in Birmingham. Wragge & Co's clients continue to appreciate the benefits of its consistent and integrated approach to client service, whilst its people enjoy working in a strong and cohesive culture. The firm is one of the fastest growing law firms in the country. During 1999 alone they saw a 29% increase in staff numbers. As a full service law firm it provides a comprehensive range of services to large companies, public authorities and financial institutions, both in the UK and overseas including over 165 listed companies and 60 local authorities. International business is playing an increasingly important role in the growth of the firm with over 25% of business now coming from international work. Quality and client care continue to be the firm's top priorities. It regularly seeks feedback from clients on the quality of its service and continues to develop its business in response to client demand.

PRINCIPAL AREAS OF WORK: Wragge & Co has developed real strength in depth in its seven core business areas and built leading practices in niche markets and products. It enjoys a national reputation in areas such as pensions, intellectual property, construction, transport and logistics, utilities, project finance, PFI and EU/competition law. The seven core business areas are highlighted below.
Corporate: The corporate group goes from strength to strength advising on all aspects of a company's life from formation to flotation, through acquisitions, mergers, joint ventures and management buy-outs. In 1999 the group completed many high profile corporate deals - a total of 160 transactions to an aggregate value of £9.6 billion. The group is undertaking an increasing number of IT related transactions ranging from start ups to mergers and acquisitions.
Commercial: In addition to general commercial contracts work our commercial group advises on the specialist areas of intellectual property, EU/Competition law and all aspects of IT law. The past year has seen the firm open an office in Brussels - a move which has placed it on a level with City firms' European law ability, especially in relation to competition aspects of M&A work. March 2000 saw the firm merge with Needham & Grant, a specialist London IP practice. The new team is now one of the top five IP practices in the UK with seven partners and 28 assistants. The IT law practice has also gone from strength to strength and with a total of three partners, is now one of the largest specialist IT law teams outside London.
Dispute Resolution: The dispute resolution group offers a commercial and objective assessment of clients' problems whilst maintaining a realistic approach to settlement negotiations. Alternative dispute resolution is widely practised where applicable - the firm has four accredited mediators specialising in this area. This group has also seen major developments over the past year. Wragge & Co merged in November 1999 with Neil F Jones, a top flight niche construction practice based in Birmingham. The merger takes the construction team into the top three in the country. The team also made history in the landmark victory acting for Harmon in which they successfully brought a case against the House of Commons.
Commercial Property: The commercial property group is now one of the largest teams outside London with 21 partners providing a range of specialist skills to landlords and tenants, developers, contractors, funding institutions, investors and public authorities.
Human Resources: The human resources group offers a comprehensive range of advice on employment issues (both contentious and non contentious), employee benefits, pensions schemes, personal tax, trusts and charities.
Finance & Projects: The finance and pojects group includes a range of specialists in its core areas of banking, financial services, insolvency, utilities, project finance and PFI and transport and logistics. igh profile appointments in utilities, rail and PFI have boosted the team's national reputation and expertise.
Insurance: The insurance group provides advice on all aspects of insurance law from motor claims, general liability and product liability to professional indemnity and subrogated property claims as well as advice on policy interpretation and other non-contentious aspects.

CONTACTS

Alternative Dispute Resolution	Paul Howard
Automotive	Bob Gilbert
Banking & Insolvency	Julian Pallett
Building Societies	Jonathan Denton
Commercial Litigation	Paul Howard
Commercial Property	Mark Dakeyne
Construction	Ashley Pigott
Corporate Finance	Richard Haywood
Debt Recovery	Ann Benzimra
Education	Philip Clissitt
Employee Benefit/Share Schemes	Peter Smith
Employment	Martin Chitty
Energy/Utilities	David Hamlett
Environmental	John Turner
	Neil Upton
EU & Competition	Guy Lougher
Executive Immigration	Nicola Mumford
Financial Services	Jonathan Denton
Inheritance & Estates	Julie Fox
Insurance	Susan Dearden
Intellectual Property	Gordon Harris
	David Barron
IT/Computers	Bill Jones
Logistics	Michael Whitehouse
NHS Trusts	Susan Dearden
Pensions	Vivien Cockerill
PFI	Stephen Kenny
Professional Indemnity	Mark Hick
Property Litigation	Sarah Thompson
Public Sector	Peter Keith-Lucas
Tax	Kevin Poole
Town & Country Planning	Dan Hemming
Transport (Road/Rail)	Michael Whitehouse

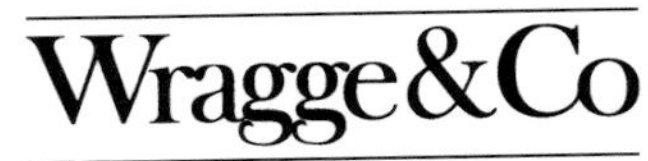

WRIGHT HASSALL

9 Clarendon Place, Leamington Spa, CV32 5QP
Tel: (01926) 886688 **Fax:** (01926) 885588 **DX:** 11863 Leamington Spa
Email: email@wrighthassall.co.uk **Website:** www.wrighthassall.co.uk

Managing partner:	Peter Beddoes
Partnership chairman:	Robin Ogg
Number of partners:	18
Assistant solicitors:	14
Other fee-earners:	13

AREAS OF PRACTICE

Litigation	41%
Commercial Property	26%
Company/Commercial	15%
Private Client	12%
Agriculture	6%

CONTACTS

Agriculture	Robin Ogg
Commercial Litigation	Richard Lane
Corporate/Commercial	Peter Beddoes
	Mark Lewis
Employment	Ian Besant
Family	Julia Bunting
Housing	Carol Matthews
Insurance	Michael Davis
Private Client	Charles McKenzie
Residential Property	Andrew Payne

THE FIRM: Wright Hassall has an enviable portfolio of commercial clients for whom the firm has many advantages. Leamington Spa is an attractive, accessible Regency town with a thriving commercial community, located at the heart of the extensive Midlands transport network. As a result, the firm has attracted high quality lawyers from leading firms who have contributed to building the firm's reputation as a major player.

PRINCIPAL AREAS OF WORK:

Agriculture: The agricultural team advises local landowners, farmers and major agricultural organisations on all aspects of agricultural law.

Commercial Property: The firm advises a number of blue chip plcs on their property matters as well as advising on the sale and purchase of commercial property and leases and building development work. It also has a particular expertise in housing association law.

Corporate/Commercial: Work includes the sale and purchase of companies and business assets, MBOs and joint ventures. The firm is also strong in employment law, commercial contracts, partnerships and business formations.

Litigation: The department handles the whole range of litigation work and specialises in insurance company-based defendant litigation including professional indemnity. The firm also has a well-respected matrimonial department.

Private Client: Work includes advising on trusts, estates and investments as well as conveyancing work.

WRIGHT, JOHNSTON & MACKENZIE

302 St Vincent Street, Glasgow, G1 5RZ **Tel:** (0141) 248 3434 **Fax:** (0141) 221 1226 **DX:** 129 Glasgow **Email:** enquiries@wjm.co.uk
Website: www.wjm.co.uk **Ptnrs:** 12 **Asst solrs:** 20 **Other fee-earners:** 10

WRIGHT SON & PEPPER

9 Gray's Inn Square, London, WC1R 5JF
Tel: (020) 7242 5473 **Fax:** (020) 7831 7454 **DX:** 35
Email: mail@wrightsonandpepper.co.uk

Number of partners:	7
Assistant solicitors:	3
Other fee-earners:	3

AREAS OF PRACTICE

Regulatory/Disciplinary/Partnership	21%
Company/Commercial	16%
Family	16%
Litigation	16%
Property	16%
Private Client	15%

CONTACTS

Company/Commercial	S.M. Alais
Family	P.L.M. Butner
Litigation	I.G. Miller
Private Client	B. Wates
Property	H. Palmer
Regulatory/Disciplinary/ Partnership	
	N.J. Wright
	I.G Miller

THE FIRM: Wright Son & Pepper has been established in Gray's Inn Square since 1800. Its clients range from public companies, institutions and regulators through to small businesses and professional and private individuals. The firm is highly regarded for its work in professional and partnership matters.

PRINCIPAL AREAS OF WORK:

Professional Practice and Partnership Matters: The firm advises regulators, professional firms and individuals on all matters relating to the regulation of professional practices. It also advises on the formation and dissolution of partnerships and on disputes in which partnerships or their members are involved as well as on problems which may arise on the admission or retirement of partners.

Litigation: The firm has extensive experience in general commercial and private litigation including professional negligence claims. High court agency work is also undertaken.

Property: All aspects are covered with the main emphasis on offices, shop and factory/warehouse leases and developments, planning and funding arrangements.

Company/Commercial: The firm deals with the normal range of company and commercial work and has considerable experience in dealing with all forms of computer-related contracts and restraint of trade covenants.

Family Law: All aspects of matrimonial, family, welfare and child care law are covered with special emphasis on ancillary relief in matrimonial proceedings.

Private Client and Tax: The firm deals with wills, settlements, trust formation and administration, powers of attorney, Court of Protection, investment advice, personal tax, estate planning, probates and the administration of estates.

Other Areas: The firm also undertakes work in debt recovery, intellectual property, building contract disputes, employment, landlord and tenant, transport, and consumer law.

INTERNATIONAL CONNECTIONS: The firm has professional connections in Belgium and the USA.

WRIGLEYS

19 Cookridge Street, Leeds, LS2 3AG
Tel: (0113) 244 6100 **Fax:** (0113) 244 6101 **DX:** 12020 Leeds 1
Email: thepartners@wrigleys.co.uk

Fountain Precinct, Leopold Street, Sheffield, S1 2GZ
Tel: (0114) 283 3306 **Fax:** (0114) 276 3176 **DX:** 12020 Leeds 1
Email: thepartners@wrigleys.co.uk

Managing partner:	Richard Sutton
Senior partners:	Matthew Wrigley
	Ann Duchart
	Peter Chadwick
Number of partners:	10
Assistant solicitors:	10
Other fee-earners:	4

THE FIRM: Wrigleys was formed as a specialist private client practice in May 1996. It combines the private client departments of Dibb Lupton Broomhead (now Dibb Lupton Alsop), Hammond Suddards and the Leeds and Manchester offices of Eversheds. The firm has also seen substantial organic growth and now has 10 partners and a total of 46 staff. The main office is in Leeds and the firm has benefited from the remarkable rise of the city as a professional centre. There is a smaller but thriving office in Sheffield. As a specialist practice with relatively low overheads, the firm presents itself as a logical alternative to London practices.

PRINCIPAL AREAS OF WORK: Wrigleys advises wealthy individuals, charities and trustees. The work is largely tax and trust based, with a growing property department serving the same clientele. Originally best known for its strength in the heritage and landed areas, the firm now serves a wide spectrum of old and new money. It also advises pension trustees. Contentious or commercial work is referred elsewhere, and the firm regularly acts with and for other professionals.

CLIENTELE: The firm acts for a large number of well-known families, and most of the individual clients are rich enough to face serious tax problems. Historically, most clients were northern based, but latterly, the firm has begun to attract clients nationally and internationally, since some offshore clients perceive a cost benefit in using a regional practice for work that has traditionally gone to London. The firm acts for a wide range of charities, particularly in the religious, educational and conservation areas.

AE WYETH & CO

Bridge House, High Street, Dartford, DA1 1JR
Tel: (01322) 297000 **Fax:** (01322) 297001 **DX:** 31904 Dartford

8 Stone Buildings, Lincoln's Inn, London, WC2A 3TA
Tel: (020) 7242 7588 **Fax:** (020) 7831 5674 **DX:** 147 Chancery Lane

Senior partner:	Brian Williams
Number of partners:	11
Assistant solicitors:	11
Other fee-earners:	30

AREAS OF PRACTICE

Personal Injury........75%

CONTACTS

Litigation ....B. Williams
Private Client: contentious........T. Harris
Private Client:non-contentious........S. Ellis

THE FIRM: AE Wyeth & Co have built an excellent reputation as an insurance litigation practice acting for insurance companies, Lloyds syndicates and brokers. The firm provides specialist legal advice on a cost efficient basis. The firm also undertakes contentious and non-contentious private client work. Legal Aid work accepted.

PRINCIPAL AREAS OF WORK:
Litigation: Personal injury - Employers' liability, public liability, road traffic accidents; specialists in health and safety prosecutions, inquests, public health prosecutions, stress-related illnesses, asbestosis and repetitive strain injury. There is a separate noise-induced hearing loss department. Commercial litigation – building and construction disputes, fire and flooding claims, product liability and professional indemnity. Local Authority litigation – personal injury and commercial.
Private Client, Contentious: Employment, family, matrimonial, debt collection and general litigation.
Private Client, Non-contentious: Commercial and domestic conveyancing, wills, estate planning and probate, company formation, charities.
Agency work: Both High Court and County Court is undertaken. The office is ideally placed to deal with agency matters throughout the South East of England.

WYNNE BAXTER GODFREE AND SELWOOD LEATHES HOOPER

Century House, 15-19 Dyke Road, Brighton, BN1 3FE **Tel:** (01273) 775533 **Fax:** (01273) 207744 **DX:** 141292 BRIGHTON 5 **Email:** brighton@wbg.co.uk **Website:** www.wbg.co.uk **Ptnrs:** 7 **Asst solrs:** 9 **Other fee-earners:** 5 **Contact:** Christopher Coopey

YOUNG & LEE

No. 6 The Wharf, Bridge Street, Birmingham, B1 2JS **Tel:** (0121) 633 3233 **Fax:** (0121) 632 5292 **DX:** 701255 Edgbaston 4 **Email:** timlee@younglee.co.uk **Website:** www.younglee.co.uk **Ptnrs:** 4 **Asst solrs:** 5 **Other fee-earners:** 5

YOUNG & PEARCE

58 Talbot Street, Nottingham, NG1 5GL **Tel:** (0115) 959 8888 **Fax:** (0115) 947 5572 **DX:** 10025 **Ptnrs:** 4 **Asst solrs:** 5 **Other fee-earners:** 3

TC YOUNG & SON

30 George Square, Glasgow, G2 1LH **Tel:** (0141) 221 5562 **Fax:** (0141) 221 5024 **DX:** GW 78 **Ptnrs:** 4 **Asst solrs:** 2 **Other fee-earners:** 1 **Contact:** Andrew Robertson • Specialises in acting for charities, trusts and housing associations. General private client, executry and employment work is also undertaken.

AREAS OF PRACTICE

Housing Associations	40%
General Private Client	30%
Charities	20%
Litigation	10%

YUILL & KYLE

79 West Regent Street, Glasgow, G2 2AR **Tel:** 0141 331 2332 **Fax:** 0141 332 4223

ZERMANSKY & PARTNERS

10 Butts Court, Leeds, LS1 5JS
Tel: (0113) 245 9766 **Fax:** (0113) 246 7465 **DX:** 12061

Managing partner:	David Honeybone
Senior partner:	Russell Graham
Number of partners:	10
Assistant solicitors:	7
Other fee-earners:	6

THE FIRM: Zermansky & Partners is an expanding firm combining private client work and a strong commitment to legal aid work (franchised in seven areas), with a comprehensive range of services to small to medium-sized businesses and not-for-profit organisations.

PRINCIPAL AREAS OF WORK: The firm is particularly known for its large family department, including matrimonial finance, child abduction, emergency and childcare work. The litigation department has specialized employment, housing and personal injury/clinical negligence sections. Insolvency work is a new area of development. It has substantial experience in sports law, particularly with governing bodies.

LANGUAGES: Hindi, Polish and Punjabi.

CONTACTS

Childcare	Lynn McFadyen
Company/Commercial	David Honeybone
Insolvency	Neil Lieberman
Litigation	Richard Lindley
Matrimonial/Family	Norman Taylor
Personal Injury	Gurchan Jandu
Property	Russell Graham
Sports	Richard Lindley

Z

IN-HOUSE LAWYERS

& COMPANY SECRETARIES

In-house Lawyers & Company Secretaries

3i Group PLC
91 Waterloo Road, London SE1 8XP
Tel: (020) 7928 3131 **Fax:** (020) 7928 0058
Website: www.3i.com
No of lawyers in dept: 32
Work outsourced: Litigation and some corporate and investment work
Tony Brierley, Company Secretary and Head of Legal Services
Specialisation: Corporate, Venture Capital
Career: 1990 Solicitor, 1981 Barrister-at-Law, Inner Temple
Other lawyers: UK Investment Legal Services- David Dench; Continental Europe Legal Services- Jane Alexander; Group Legal- David Herbert (Group Solicitor)

Abbey National PLC
Abbey House, 201 Grafton Gate East, Milton Keynes MK9 1AN
Tel: (01908) 343000 **Fax:** (01908) 348282
Website: www.abbeynational.plc.uk
No of lawyers in dept: 32
Gwyn Malkin, Group Legal Services Director
Specialisation: Handles commercial and corporate law matters and management of the legal function. Member of Legal Committee of British Bankers Association.
Career: Qualified 1975. Became Head of Legal Services at Abbey National in July 1992.
Other lawyers: Corporate (corporate and commercial/commercial and offshore) : Geoffrey Pope, Alison Greene, Alan Squires, John Candlish; Jane Stolberger. Consumer (banking, savings and lending/insurance/life) : John Thurwell, William Johnson, John Hamilton, John Laing, Pauline Pope, Jacqueline Neblett, Gwynedd Miller. Commercial: Desmond Pettit, Carole Jones, Katie Ward, Ian Wallbank, Jane Hayden. Regulatory: Simon Goldburn, Richenda Kullar, Sally Hopwood. International: Colin Browning, Janine Pennel, Joanna Morton

Aberdeen Asset Management
One Albyn Place, Aberdeen AB10 1YG
Tel: (01224) 631 999 **Fax:** (01224) 646651
Jeremy Burchill, Head of Legal

ABN AMRO Equities Holdings (UK) Limited
250 Bishopsgate, London EC2M 4AA
Tel: (020) 7678 1240 **Fax:** (020) 7678 7612
Email: jenny.stevinson@uk.abnamro.com
No of lawyers in dept: 4
Work outsourced: 25% – Litigation, property, IP, some company/commercial
Jenny Stevinson, Head of Legal/Company Secretary
Specialisation: Manages Legal and Secretarial Department providing legal services to London-based equity businesses of ABN AMRO investment banking group. Specific areas include Company Law, transaction documentation for equity-related products, customer documentation, clearing and banking arrangements, supplies of goods and services, employment, property, intellectual property.
Career: King's College, London University LLB 1975. Called to the Bar, Gray's Inn, 1976. General common law, commercial, EEC, pupillages, 1976-78. Department of Trade and Industry, Solicitor's Department 1978-86: international and EEC trade, telecommunications, company and financial services law. Legal Adviser, Security Pacific Hoare Govett (Holdings) Limited 1987-1990. Group Legal Adviser and Company Secretary, Hoare Govett Limited from 1990, renamed ABN AMNO Equities (UK) Limited 1998
Other lawyers: Helen Short – product, customer. settlement documentation; Ian Spaxman – contracts for supply of goods and services, employment, IP, property; Gabrielle Ellison – asset management.

ABN AMRO Equities Holdings (UK) Limited
250 Bishopsgate, London EC2M 4AA
Tel: (020) 7678 1240 **Fax:** (020) 7678 6484
Roger Munger, Head of Transaction Management

Aegis Group PLC
11a West Halkin Street, London SW1X 8JL
Tel: (020) 7470 5000 **Fax:** (020) 7470 5099
Website: www.carat.com
Eleonore Sauerwein, Group Legal Counsel

AGF Insurance
Claims Technical Centre, AGF House, 500 Avebury Boulevard, Milton Keynes MK9 2LA
Tel: (01908) 690 888 **Fax:** (01908) 683 434
B. Evans, Claims Manager

Aggregate Industries
Bardon Hall, Copt Oak Hall, Markfield LE67 9PJ
Tel: (01530) 816 600 **Fax:** (01530) 816 666
Work outsourced: 100%
Christopher Stuart Bailey, Company Secretary

Aggreko PLC
Ailsa Court, 121 West Regent Street, Glasgow G2 2SD
Tel: (0141) 225 5900 **Fax:** (0141) 225 5949
Paul Allen, Company Secretary

Airtours plc
Wavell House, Holcombe Road, Helmshore, Rossendale BB4 4NB
Tel: 01706 240033 **Fax:** 01706 212144
Email: andrew.cooper@airtours.co.uk
Website: www.airtours.co.uk
No of lawyers in dept: 2
Work outsourced: 30% – Overseas litigation, major contractual work, IT contracts, serious personal injury.
Andy Cooper, Head of Legal
Specialisation: Andy is primarily responsible for specific Travel Law advice, as well as focusing on employment, litigation and procedures to ensure the effective review and implementation of new legislation in so far as it affects a major tour operator.
Career: Birmingham University 1978-1981; Vernon & Shakespeare Solicitors, Northfield, Birmingham, Articled Clerk 1982-1984; Smith Fort & Symonds, Poynton, Cheshire, Assistant Solicitor 1985-1989; Airtours plc / Airtours Holidays Limited, Company Solicitor/Head of Legal 1989 – To date.
Other lawyers: Tamsin Winspear

Akeler Developments Limited
20 Berkeley Square, London W1X 5HD
Tel: (020) 7864 1800 **Fax:** (020) 7864 1801
Jayne Walters, Commercial Director

Alliance & Leicester PLC
Group Legal Services, Building 3, Floor 2, Carlton Park, Narborough LE9 5XX
Tel: (0116) 201 1000 **Fax:** (0116) 200 4995
Website: www.alliance-leicester.co.uk
Kathrine Hughes, Head of Legal

Alliance Trust PLC
Meadow House, 64 Reform Street, Dundee DD1 1TJ
Tel: (01382) 201 700 **Fax:** (01382) 225133
Sheila Ruckley, Company Secretary

Alliance UniChem
UniChem House, Cox Lane, Chessington KT9 1SN
Tel: (020) 8391 2323 **Fax:** (020) 8974 1707
Adrian J. Goodenough, Company Secretary

Allied Domecq PLC
The Pavillions, Bridgwater Road, Bedminster Down, Bristol BS13 8AR
Tel: (0117) 978 5000 **Fax:** (0117) 978 5284
Website: www.allieddomecqplc.com
No of lawyers in dept: 30
Work outsourced: 50% – M&A, litigation, conveyancing, employee share schemes
Russell P. Kelley, General Counsel and Company Secretary
Specialisation: Corporate, commercial, compliance, trade controls
Career: 1998-1999: General Counsel and Company Secretary, Lucas Varity plc; 1977-87: Various positions at Schlumberger Ltd.; 1974: Juris Doctor, Boston University School of Law; 1971: Bachelor of Arts, Trinity College (Hartford, USA)
Personal: Member of the bars of Massachusetts, Texas, District of Columbia, California.

Allied Irish Bank (GB)
Bank Centre Britain, Belmont Road, Uxbridge UB8 1SA
Tel: (01895) 272222 **Fax:** (01895) 239444
Email: tiana.j.peck@aib.ie
No of lawyers in dept: 2
Tiana Peck, Head of Legal Services

Allied Zurich
22 Arlington Street, London SW1A 1RW
Tel: (020) 7317 3895 **Fax:** (020) 7317 3926
Email: derek.woodward@alliedzurich.co.uk
Website: www.zurich.com
No of lawyers in dept: 3
Work outsourced: Most
Derek Woodward, Company Secretary
Specialisation: Company law, London Stock Exchange Listing Rules; Shareholder matters; Employee share plans; Board Meetings; Shareholder Meetings.
Career: BA Hons (Law) FCIS; Joined Eagle Star in November 1984, moved to B.A.T. Industries as Assistant Secretary in January 1990; Appointed Secretary, Allied Zurich plc on incorporation on 5th March 1998; Allied Zurich became a listed company on 8th September 1998
Personal: Born 17th September 1958; Married 8th June 1991; Two sons born 16th February 1995 and 18th November 1997; Interests: Family, cycling
Other lawyers: Company; Employee Share schemes
*Allied Zurich is a holding company which owns 43% of Zurich Financial Services and which has its own in-house legal departments. Allied Zurich is responsible for UK company law, London Stock Exchange LIsting Rules and UK Employee share schemes.

Amateur Swimming Association
Harold Fern House, Derby Square, Loughborough LE11 5AL
Tel: (01509) 618 700 **Fax:** (01509) 618 701
Andy Gray, Head of Legal Affairs

AMEC PLC
Sandiway House, Hartford, Northwich CW8 2YA
Tel: (01606) 883 885 **Fax:** (01606) 889607
Email: john.fenwick@amec.com
Website: www.amec.com
No of lawyers in dept: 9
Work outsourced: some corporate/commercial work, all commercial property and conveyancing litigation, litigation requiring specialist expertise.
John C. Fenwick, Head of Group Legal Services
Specialisation: Responsible for supervising supply of all legal services to AMEC group and providing legal services in-house via a de-centralised legal function. Assists in UK and overseas tendering (advice on risk, contract conditions etc.) joint venture agreements, claims and disputes. Management of in-house legal team with lawyers strategically placed within key operating subsidiaries. Also selects and monitors performance of external solicitors where required. Also has particular responsibility for part of group encompassed by AMEC Services Limited
Career: Qualified 1973. Articled with Heald Nickinson and assistant solicitor until 1976. Head of Group Legal Services, John Laing plc 1976-88, then joined AMEC plc.
Other lawyers: AMEC Capital Projects Limited - Michael Blacker (Manager), Kevin Smith (Civil Engineering), Lis Hedley (Construction), Philip Poxon (Mechanical and Electrical Engineering). AMEC Services Limited - Offshore Services and AMEC Rail. AMEC Project Investments Limited -

A

Tony Rogers (Director of Legal Services), Simon Moore (Legal Advisor). AMEC Developments Limited - Sarah-Anne Shankland.

AMEC PLC
AMEC House, Heron Drive, Langley, Slough SL3 8XP
Tel: (01753) 612500 **Fax:** (01753) 512781
Michael Blacker, Head of Legal Services

Amerada Hess
33 Grosvenor Place, London SW1X 7HY
Tel: (020) 7823 2626 **Fax:** (020) 7887 2328
Alan Dunlop, Head of Legal and Public Affairs

American Express Bank Ltd.
60 Buckingham Palace Road, London SW1W 0RR
Tel: (020) 7824 6000 **Fax:** (020) 7730 5067
No of lawyers in dept: 3
Work outsourced: 10% – complicated transactions/litigation
Jane Kelloe, Group Counsel
Other lawyers: Internal lawyers abroad: 16+6 paralegals +1 secondee. Other lawyers in dept: P. Horton, M. Semmence, a secondee.

Amerindo Internet Fund PLC
55 Moorgate, London EC2R 6PA
Tel: (020) 7410 3132 **Fax:** (020) 7477 5849
Helen Horton, Company Secretary

Amey PLC
Appleford Road, Sutton Courtenay, Abingdon, Oxford OX14 4PP
Tel: (01235) 848 811 **Fax:** (01235) 848822
Julie Thomlinson, Head of Legal

Amlin Aviation
1-7 Whittington Avenue, London EC3V 1LE
Tel: (020) 7860 8790 **Fax:** (020) 7860 8606
Maria Cetta, Director of Claims & Legal Affairs

AMVESCAP PLC
11 Devonshire Square, London EC2M 4YR
Tel: (020) 7626 3434 **Fax:** (020) 7454 3166
Website: www.invesco.co.uk
No of lawyers in dept: 8
Work outsourced: 50% – Corporate Finance, Investment Funds (off and on-shore), Financial Services, Litigation, Property, Tax.
Graeme Proudfoot, General Counsel
Specialisation: Corporate, Investment Funds, Financial Services.
Career: Education: Royal Grammar School, Newcastle-Upon Tyne. University College, Oxford (1986, Jurisprudence). Articled Wilde Sapte, qualified 1989; Legal Manager INVESCO plc 1995. Company Secretary INVESCO plc 1992, Managing Director, Specialist Funds 1999.
Personal: Born 1964. resides Hertfordshire.
Other lawyers: Rodney Smyth – UK; Joe Beashal / Jeremy Crean – Ireland; Manoj Ramachandran / Monica Ahweng – Hong Kong; Sander Cohen – Tokyo; Anton Allen – Sydney

Anglian Water Services Ltd
Anglian House, Ambury Road, Huntingdon PE29 3NZ
Tel: (01480) 323 140 **Fax:** (01480) 323 288
Website: www.anglicanwater.co.uk
No of lawyers in dept: 10
Work outsourced: 10% – Work where in-house expertise is lacking e.g major corporate transactions
Patrick Firth, Head of Legal Services
Other lawyers: J. Tinn – Litigation; E. Dyce – Commercial; G. Ward – Regulation; D. Grittenden – Property; C. Dunnett – Litigation; R. McAdam – Litigation; A. Luk – Regulation; K. Brumpton – Commercial; P. Pilliotais – Comercial

Anglo American PLC
20 Carlton House Terrace, St James's, London SW1Y 5AN
Tel: (020) 7698 8888 **Fax:** (020) 7698 8500
Website: www.angloamerican.co.uk
No of lawyers in dept: 2
Ben Keisler, Executive Vice President, General Counsel
Specialisation: Corporate transactions, commercial, corporate finance, competition/antitrust.
Career: Senior Vice President, General Counsel, Minono, 1997-1999; Vice president and General Counsel, Minono (USA) Inc., 1993-97; Vice President and General Counsel, Terra Industries Inc.
Other lawyers: Paul Roebuck – Acquisitions, General Corporate, Competition.

Anite Group
353 Buckingham Avenue, Slough SL1 4PF
Tel: 01753 822221 **Fax:** 01753 804020
Simon Hunt, Company Secretary

AOL Europe
18-21 Cavaye Place, London W10 9PG
Tel: (020) 7348 8000 **Fax:** (020) 7348 8002
Clare Gilbert, Vice President and General Counsel

Aon Group
8 Devonshire Square, London EC2M 4PR
Tel: (020) 7623 5500 **Fax:** (020) 7621 1511
Jane Owen, Senior Lawyer

Arab Bank PLC
PO Box 138, 15 Moorgate, London EC2R 6LP
Tel: (020) 7315 8500 **Fax:** (020) 7600 7620
No of lawyers in dept: 1
Janet Bicheno, In-house Lawyer

Arena Leisure
Lingfield Park, Lingfield RH7 6PQ
Tel: (01342) 833058 **Fax:** (01342) 835874
Ian Penrose, Company Secretary

Arjo Wiggins Appleton PLC
Times Place, 45 Pall Mall, London SW1Y 5JG
Tel: (0207) 941 8000 **Fax:** (0207) 941 8008
Email: adungate@awa-group.com
No of lawyers in dept: 9
Work outsourced: varies – Litigation, Major Contractors.
Albert Dungate, Company Secretary and Group Solicitor
Specialisation: Commercial, competition, banking, M+A, executive employment
Career: 1st Class Honors Degree in Law: LSE(London)1978, 1st Class Honors Law Society Exams Part II 1979, Articled in private practise 1979-81, Private Practise 1981-86, Wiggins Senior Solicitor 1986-90, Head of UK Legal Department Argo Wiggins Appleton plc 1990-94, Head of Group Legal Services 1994-99, Company secretary 1999

ARM Holdings plc
110 Fulbourn Road, Cambridge CB1 9JN
Tel: 01223 400 400 **Fax:** 01223 400 410
Email: info@arm.com
Website: www.arm.com
No of lawyers in dept: 4
David Mackay, Company Secretary
Other lawyers: Phil David-Trademarks, Hilary Charles-Assistant Company Secretary, Patents

Arriva
Admiral Way, Doxford International Business Park, Sunderland SR3 3XP
Tel: 0191 520 4000 **Fax:** 0191 520 4181
No of lawyers in dept: 5
Work outsourced: 10% – large transactions, heavy litigation.
Chris Applegarth, Company Solicitor
Specialisation: Principal areas of work are company/commercial matters, banking, employment, consumer credit, equipment leasing and securitisation of receivables. Other areas of work are matters involving traffic, property, trade and service marks, and business development generally.
Career: Qualified as a Barrister 1975 and practised at the Bar until 1980. Qualified 1983 as a solicitor and took up present position in 1985.
Personal: Educated at Sedbergh School 1966-71 and Inns of Court School of Law 1972-75. Born 1953. Lives in Sunderland.
Other lawyers: Mr J.B. Wainwright

Associated British Foods PLC
Legal Department, 3-5 Rickmansworth Road, Watford WD1 7HG
Tel: (01923) 252050 **Fax:** (01923) 223542
Website: www.abf.co.uk
Simon Bromwich, Joint Head of Legal Department

Associated British Ports Hldgs PLC
150 Holborn, London EC1N 2LR
Tel: (020) 7430 1177 **Fax:** (020) 7430 1384
Hywel Reef, Company Secretary

Associated Newspapers Ltd
Northcliffe House, 2 Derry Street, London W8 5TT
Tel: (020) 7938 6000 **Fax:** (020) 7938 6020
Website: www.dmgt.co.uk
No of lawyers in dept: 5
Harvey Kass, Legal director
Specialisation: Principal areas of work include libel (pre-publication and litigation), commercial, new media, copyright, competition law, employment and trademarks.
Career: Articled and qualified (1981) with *Wright Webb Syrett*; *Simon Olswang & Co*, associate (1982-84); legal and business adviser to several television and media companies (1984-90) including Goldcrest Films and Television, Albion Films Ltd; consultant, Beveridge Ross & Prevezers (1988-93); Harvey Kass & Co (1990-93) specialised in libel for national newspapers and commercial law; Associated Newspapers Ltd (1993-94); legal director since 1995.ED: Woodhouse Grammar School; LLB (1977) City of London Polytechnic, Maxwell Law Prize); LLM (1978) Jesus College, Cambridge.
Personal: Born 1955, resides London. Leisure: family, football, tennis, golf, gardening.
Other lawyers: Edward Young, Clare Shields, John Battle; 20 freelancers.

Associated Newspapers Ltd
Northcliffe House, 2 Derry Street, Kensington, London W8 5TT
Tel: (020) 7938 6000 **Fax:** (020) 7938 6020
John Battle, Group Legal Advisor

AstraZeneca PLC
15 Stanhope Gate, London W1Y 6LN
Tel: (020) 7304 5000 **Fax:** (020) 7304 5151
Website: www.astrazeneca.com
Graeme Musker, Company Secretary/Head of Legal

Atkins (WS) PLC
Woodcote Grove, Ashley Road, Epsom KT18 5BW
Tel: (01372) 726 140 **Fax:** (01372) 740055
Email: drobinson@watkins.co.uk
Website: www.wsatkins.com
No of lawyers in dept: 3
Work outsourced: 5% – commercial conveyancing, litigation, major acquisition.
Deborah Robinson, Group Legal Adviser
Specialisation: Responsible for legal and commercial issues affecting the WS Atkins Group, both in the UK and overseas.
Career: Articled *Macfarlanes* 1990-95; assistant legal adviser WS Atkins 1994-99; Group Legal Adviser 1999 to date. Sutton High School. University of Bristol (LLB 1986). Kings College London (MSc 1992).
Personal: Born 1964. Resides in Kingston-Upon-Thames.

Atlantic Telecom Group PLC
475-485 Union Street, Aberdeen AB11 6DB
Tel: (01224) 454 000 **Fax:** (01224) 454010
No of lawyers in dept: 3
Philip N. Allenby, Company Secretary
Other Lawyers: Tim Hannah, Louise Singleton

Avis Europe PLC
Avis House, Park Road, Bracknell RG12 2EW
Tel: (01344) 426644 **Fax:** (01344) 485616
Judith Nicholson, Company Secretary, Director of Legal Services

Axa Investment Managers Ltd
60 Gracechurch Street, London EC3V 0HR
Tel: (020) 7375 9300 **Fax:** (020) 7375 9543
Kenneth Greig, Head of Legal Services

A

Axon Group PLC
Axon Centre, Church Road, Egham TW20 9QB
Tel: 01784 480800 **Fax:** 01784 480900
Robin Halliday FCA, Company Secretary

BAA PLC
130 Wilton Road, London SW1V 1LQ
Tel: (020) 7834 9449 **Fax:** (020) 7932 6615
Website: www.baa.co.uk
No of lawyers in dept: 6
Work outsourced: 25% – Major projects.
Robert Herga, Head of Legal Services
Specialism: Principal areas of work: company, commercial, funding, property, planning, joint ventures, litigation management, regulation and competition.
Career: LLB (Hons) University of Dundee; MSC (Construction Law and Arbitration) Kings College London; Fellow of the Chartered Institute of Arbitrators.
Other lawyers: Jo Wilkinson: company/commercial; Alison Shropshire: employment; Fiona Hammond: construction; Eddie Biber: property; Sarah Gallagher: property.

BAA PLC
Stockley House, 2nd floor, 130 Wilton Road, London SW1V 1LQ
Tel: (020) 7834 9449 **Fax:** (020) 7932 6811
Richard Everitt, Group Strategy and Compliance Director

BAE SYSTEMS plc
1 Brewers Green, Buckingham Gate, London SW1H 0RH
Email: michael.lester2@baesystems.com
No of lawyers in dept: 40
Work outsourced: variable – litigation, Property, major M+A
Michael Lester, Group Legal Director
Specialisation: Overall responsibility for all legal matters within the BAE SYSTEMS group companies
Career: Coopers Company's School, New College; Teaching Fellow University of Chicago Law School 1962-64; Articled Solicitor in private practice 1964-80; The General Electric company plc 1980-99; Director 1983, Vice-chairman 1994; BAE SYSTEMS plc 1999-director; Premier Farnell plc -non-executive director 1998
Personal: Married with one daughter and one son
Other lawyers: Responsibilities allocated according to business unit and programme organisation

Balfour Beatty plc
Devonshire House, Mayfair Place, London W1X 5FH
Tel: (020) 7629 6622 **Fax:** (020) 7409 0070
Frank McCormack, Head of Legal Services

Baltimore Technologies PLC
The Square, Basing View, Basingstoke RG21 4EG
Tel: (01256) 818800 **Fax:** (01256) 812901
Email: senoch@baltimore.com
Website: www.baltimore.com
Work outsourced: 90% – Corporate / Trademarks
Simon J Enoch, Company Secretary
Specialisation: All aspects of Company Law plus M & A, and major contract negotiations.
Career: Served as the Company Secretary since August 1998. From October 1994 until December 1997 he was Company Secretary and Group Legal Adviser for Central Transport Rental Group plc, a transport company listed on the London Stock Exchange and the New York Stock Exchange. Prior to this he was Company Secretary of B&Q from 1992 to 1994 and before then Company Secretary to Chartwell Land pc from 1989 to 1992.
Personal: Married with three children.

Bank Austria Creditanstalt International AG
11th Floor, 125 London Wall, London EC2Y 5DD
Tel: (020) 7600 1555 **Fax:** (020) 7417 4803
No of lawyers in dept: 2
Work outsourced: 20% – Property, secured lending, employment, litigation, securitisations, foreign deals.
Peter Jones, Senior Legal Counsel
Specialisation: Banking, trade finance, venture capital, derivatives, corporate finance.
Career: 1976-79 Oxford (St Catherine's College) BA Hons. 1979-81 College of Law (Chancery Lane). 1981-87 *Withers* (articles). 1987-89 *Macfarlanes*. 1989-93 *Freshfields*. 1993-1998 Creditanstalt. 1998 to date Bank Austria Creditanstalt International AG.
Personal: Cricket, golf, squash, sailing. Member of RAC.
Other lawyers: Michele May: General banking.

Bank of America
PO Box 407, Bank of America House, 1 Alie Street, London E1 8DE
Tel: (020) 7634 4210 **Fax:** (020) 7634 4324/4268
Website: www.bankofamerica.com
No of lawyers in dept: 4
Marc de Laperouse, Head of EMEA Legal and Assistant General Counsel
Other lawyers: Banking, securities, financial services regulation, corporate secretarial, litigation

Bank of Cyprus (London) Limited
87/93 Chaseside, Southgate, London N14 5BU
Tel: (020) 8267 7330 **Fax:** (020) 8447 8066
Email: jangelides@bankofcyprus.co.uk
Website: www.bankofcyprus.co.uk
Work outsourced: 25% – Litigation, employment, regulatory advice.
Iacovos Angelides, Legal Advisor and Company Secretary
Specialisation: Banking, compliance, company/commercial, employment, property.
Career: York University, Toronto, Canada. BA (Hons) Political Science (1982-1985). University College London LLM(Hons) (1985-1988). *Holman Fenwick & Willan* (1989-1995). Bank of Cyprus (London) Ltd (1995 to present)
Personal: Keen tennis player and novice golfer.
Other lawyers: General banking, banking litigation, compliance, company, commercial, company secretarial, employment, property

Bank of Ireland
36 Queen Street, London EC4R 1HJ
Tel: (020) 7634 3180 **Fax:** (020) 7634 3415
Email: legal.dept@boi.org.uk
No of lawyers in dept: 1
Work outsourced: 20% – Litigation
Margaret O'Flanagan, Head of Legal
Specialisation: Banking, General Commercial & European
Career: M.ALL.B. Trinity College Dublin; D.E.A. Paris- Assas; Several in-house posts with Lloyd's of London, Finance Leasing Association and Bank of Ireland since 1994
Personal: Interests: French Law, European Commercial Law and Competition Irish Law.

Bank of Scotland (Governor & Co of)
Legal Services, 1st Floor Broadstreet House, 55 Old Broad Street, London EC2P 2HL
Tel: (020) 7601 6021 **Fax:** (020) 7601 6000
Website: www.bankofscotland.co.uk
Brian Fisher, Head of Legal

Bank of Scotland
City House, City Rd, Chester CH88 3AN
Tel: (01244) 690000 **Fax:** (01244) 312067
Anthony Bochenski, Head of Compliance Group

Bank One
1 Triton Square, London NW1 3FN
Tel: (020) 7388 3456 **Fax:** (020) 7903 4188
Jay Bestmann, Senior Vice President and Regional Counsel
Specialisation: Regional Counsel responsible for all legal services, including a small internal group of lawyers as well as supervision of outside lawyers in Europe and the Middle East.
Career: Princeton University (BSE, 1969) University of California at Los Angeles (JD, 1975) Qualified California (1975) and Illinois (1976)

Bankers Investment Trust PLC
3 Finsbury Avenue, London EC2M 2PA
Tel: (020) 7638 5757 **Fax:** (020) 7377 5742
Wendy King, Company Secretary

Barclays Bank PLC – Corporate Banking
54 Lombard Street, London EC3P 3AH
Tel: (020) 7699 5000 **Fax:** (020) 7699 4474
No of lawyers in dept: 16
Work outsourced: 50% – Litigation & larger resource intensive transactions
John Featherstone, Legal Director
Specialisation: Lending, Security, Recovery Litigation, Sales Financing, Commercial Contracts, New Products
Career: *Lovell White Durrant*: 1986-1992; *Taylor Joynson Garrett*: 1992-1997 (Partner); Admitted 1982; University College London, LLB
Other lawyers: Lending – Penny Bruce Litigation (ex recoverers): Alison Newman Recoveries: William Lewis Contracts: Henry Firmstone

Barclays Bank plc – Retail Financial Services
2nd Floor, Murray House, 1 Royal Mint Court, London EC3N 4HH
Tel: 020 7977 4088 **Fax:** 020 7977 4648
No of lawyers in dept: 20
Work outsourced: 50% – Litigation, Commercial Contracts, Life and Pensions, Banking
Jeremy Ogden, Legal Director
Specialisation: New Product Development, Commercial Contracts, Litigation and Debt Recovery, Procurement and General Advice to Senior Executives in RFS.
Career: Boodle Hatfield, 1991-1994; Wilde Sapte 1994-1997 (Partner 1997-1998), Admitted January 1983.
Other lawyers: Mark Edwards – Assistant Legal Director; David Pacey – Senior Litigtion Adviser; Henry Firmstone – Senior Commercial Contracts Adviser; Famida Rajah – Barclays Offshore Services.

Barclays Capital
5 The North Colonnade, Canary Wharf, London E14 4BB
Tel: (020) 7623 2323 **Fax:** (020) 7623 2323
Alex Cameron, Head of Legal, London and Europe

Barclays PLC
54 Lombard Street, London EC3P 3AH
Tel: (020) 7699 5000 **Fax:** (020) 7699 3414
Email: GGCO@barclays.co.uk
Website: www.barclays.co.uk
No of lawyers in dept: 130
Work outsourced: 75% – Litigation, Banking, Investment Management, Investment Banking, Competition, Employment.
Howard B. Trust, Group General Counsel
Specialisation: Provides General Counsel advice to the main Board, Senior Management and support functions on legal risk as it affects the Group and its businesses as a whole. Responsible for management of legal risk group-wide.
Career: Solicitor, Lovell White & King 1980-85. Solicitor, Morgan Grenfell 1985-87 and Company Secretary 1987-89. Group Legal Director, BZW 1989-95. Group General Counsel and Group Secretary Barclays plc since 1995.
Other lawyers: Jeremy Ogden: Legal Director, Retail Financial Services; John Featherstone: Legal Director, Corporate Banking; Joanne Medero: Legal Director, Barclays Global Investor; Guy Dempsey; Legal Director, Barclays New York

Barclays PLC
54 Lombard Street, London EC3P 3AH
Tel: (020) 7699 5000 **Fax:** (020) 7699 3414
Simon Elliott, Company Solicitor

Baring Asset Management Holdings Limited
155 Bishopsgate, London EC2M 3XY
Tel: (020) 7628 6000 **Fax:** (020) 7638 7928
No of lawyers in dept: 6
Work outsourced: 5% – Funds-related
Marla Dhillon, Group Head of Legal & Compliance
Specialisation: Overall responsibility for the legal and compliance functions of the Baring Asset Management group of companies. Areas of work encompass all legal issues relating the group's investment management and investment products activities.
Career: Member of the Bar of England & Wales. BA (Hons) Law: University of Kent at Canterbury.

Barratt Developments PLC
Wingrove House, Ponteland Road, Newcastle upon Tyne NE5 3DP
Tel: (0191) 286 6811 **Fax:** (0191) 271 2242
Colin Dearlove, Acting Company Secretary

B

Bass PLC
20 North Audley Street, London W1Y 1WE
Tel: (020) 7409 1919 **Fax:** (020) 7409 8526
Website: www.bass.com
No of lawyers in dept: 4
Work outsourced: 90% – Majority in UK; litigation, property.
Richard Winter, Director of Group Legal Affairs
Specialisation: General company/commercial matters including acquisitions, disposals, joint ventures, trading agreements, general commercial contracts, regulatory affairs, marketing and intellectual property (particularly trade marks). Regularly liaises with lawyers for Bass Hotels worldwide (also owned by Bass plc). Member of Commerce and Industry Group and Competition Law Panel of CBI.
Career: Qualified 1973 and assistant solicitor with *Eversheds*, Birmingham until 1975 and between 1978 and 1994 (Partner, 1981; moved to London office 1987; appointed managing partner of London office in 1992). Solicitor with Fisons plc 1975-78. Joined Bass plc in 1994. Director of Bass Brewers Limited.
Personal: Born 1949; resides London, married with family. Leisure: tennis, sailing, skiing; member of Roehampton Club, Solway Yacht Club and Royal Corinthian SC. Education: Warwick School; Birmingham University (1970 LLB 2i).

BATM Advanced Communications
22 Hamelaha Street, Rosh Ha'ayn 48091 Israel
Tel: 00972 3 9386 886

B

BBA Group PLC
70 Fleet Street, London EC4Y 1EU
Tel: (020) 7842 4900 **Fax:** (020) 7353 1757
Website: www.bbagroup.com
No of lawyers in dept: 11
Work outsourced: 50%
Corporate/Commercial/Litigation/Property.
Sarah Foulkes Shaw, Group Secretary
Specialisation:
Corporate/Commercial/Regulatory/Compliance
Career: Trainee solicitor 1980-82 Freshfields, Solicitor 1982-85 Freshfields, Corporate Lawyer 1986-89 Cadbury Schweppes plc, Corporate Lawyer 1989-92 Reed International plc, Group Secretary and Legal Advisor 1992-95 Signet Group plc, Group Secretary 1997 to late BBA Group plc
Personal: Born 1958. Lives in London. Married with 2 daughters.

Bear Stearns International Limited
One Canada Square, London E14 5AD
Tel: (020) 7516 6000 **Fax:** (020) 7516 6621
Email: sbartlett@bear.com
Website: www.bearstearns.com
No of lawyers in dept: 3
Work outsourced: n/a – Documentation production.
S. Bartlett, Head of Legal
Specialisation: Responsible for all legal matters for firm's investment banking European franchise. Primarily: capital markets – new issues; OTC derivitives; structured debt & equity; regulatory; employment.
Career: 85-88 – BA Jurisprudence (Oxon); LSF 1989; 1989-1994 *Slaughter and May*; qualified as solicitor 1991. July 1994 Bear Stearns International Limited.

Berkeley Group PLC
Berkeley House, 19 Portsmouth Road, Cobham KT11 1JG
Tel: (01932) 868555 **Fax:** (01932) 865819
Wendy Pritchard, Group Solicitor

BG Group PLC
100 Thames Valley Park Drive, Reading RG6 1PT
Tel: (0118) 929 3695 **Fax:** (0118) 929 3360
Email: william.friedrich@bg-int.com
Website: www.bg-group.com
No of lawyers in dept: 55
Work outsourced: 30% – Project; regulatory; tax; property
William Friedrich, General Counsel

BG PLC
100 Thames Valley Park Drive, Reading RG6 1PT
Tel: (0118) 929 3695 **Fax:** (0118) 929 3360
Ian Chitty, In-house Solicitor

BG PLC
BG Property Holdings Ltd, Aviary Court, Wade Road, Basingstoke RG24 8GZ
Tel: (01256) 308803 **Fax:** (01256) 308627
Angeline C. Swift, Legal Manager

Billiton
1-3 Strand, London WC2N 5HA
Tel: (020) 7747 3800 **Fax:** (020) 7747 3900
Website: www.billiton.com
Paul Lush, Group Legal Counsel

Biocompatibles International PLC
Frensham House, Farnham Business Park, Weydon Lane, Farnham GU9 8QL
Tel: (01252) 732 732 **Fax:** (01252) 732777
Work outsourced: 60% – Corporate commercial agreements, patents, litigation, employment
Michael Hunt, Company Secretary

Bioglan Pharma
5 Hunting Gate, Hitchin SG4 0TW
Tel: (01462) 438 444 **Fax:** (01462) 451 400
Sue Keast, Company Secretary

Blue Circle Industries PLC
84 Eccleston Square, London SW1V 1PX
Tel: (020) 7828 3456 **Fax:** (020) 7245 8272
Website: www.bluecircle.co.uk
No of lawyers in dept: 5
Work outsourced: 60%
Richard F. Tapp, Company Secretary/Legal Adviser
Specialisation: Responsible for provision of legal services worldwide, in consultation with overseas subsidiaries, and for company secretarial work in the UK. Principal areas of work are acquisitions and disposals, contract and commercial law, competition law and property. Responsible also for risk management and insurance.
Career: 1981-84 National Coal Board. 1985-86 Imperial Foods Ltd, part of Imperial Group plc. Joined Blue Circle as Commercial Solicitor 1986, Principal Solicitor 1992, Company Secretary and Legal Adviser 1996. LLB (Sheffield), LLM (Leicester) FCIS, MCI Arb. MBA (Nottingham Law School).
Other lawyers: Anne C Ramsay: Senior Commercial Solicitor, Alison Shepley: Senior Property Solicitor; Nigel Millinson: Commercial Solicitor; Karyn Trowbridge: Property Solicitor.

BMG Records (UK) Limited
Bedford House, 67-79 Fulham High Street, London SW6 3JW
Tel: (020) 7384 7500 **Fax:** (020) 7371 9298
Clive Rich, Senior Director of Legal and Business Affairs

BNP Paribas
10 Harewood Avenue, London NW1A 6AA
Tel: (020) 7595 2000 **Fax:** (020) 7595 5094
Website: www.bnpparibas.com
Kevin Sowerbutts, Head of Legal

BOC Group PLC
Chertsey Road, Windlesham GU20 6HJ
Tel: (01276) 477 222 **Fax:** (01276) 471 333
Website: www.boc.com
Gloria Stuart, Group Director (Legal and Company Secretary)

Bodycote International PLC
Hulley Road, Hurdsfield, Macclesfield SK10 2SG
Tel: (01625) 505 300 **Fax:** (01625) 505313
Email: jgrime@bodycote.co.uk
Website: www.bodycote.com
No of lawyers in dept: 1
Work outsourced: 95% – corporate finance, M&A, property
John R. Grime, Company Secretary
Specialisation: Stock Exchange, regulatory and compliance. Executive share option schemes. Service of board's requirements for meetings. Investor relations, Pensions.
Career: 1975-82 & 1996-97 Private practice in Manchester. 1982-95 Principal solicitor (commercial and property) Co-operative Wholesale Society Ltd. 1997-to date Bodycote International plc. London University LLB (external via Trent Polytechnic). Qualified 1977.
Personal: Aged 47, married with 1 daughter. Lives Bramhall, Cheshire. 3 cats. Enjoys golf, walking and entertaining.
Other lawyers: Company Law, Share option schemes, Pensions, Corporate Governance, Stock exchange compliance.

Bookham Technology PLC
90 Milton Park, Abingdon OX14 4RY
Tel: (01235) 827200 **Fax:** (01235) 827201
Stephen Cockrell, Company Secretary

Boots Co PLC
1 Thane Road West, Beeston, Nottingham NG2 3AA
Tel: (0115) 950 6111 **Fax:** (0115) 959 2727
Website: www.boots-plc.com
No of lawyers in dept: 9
Michael Oliver, Company Secretary

BP Amoco PLC
Farburn Industrial Estate, Wellsheads Road, Aberdeen AB2 0PB
Email: bevanbp@bp.com
Website: www.bpamoco.com
No of lawyers in dept: 300
Work outsourced: 10-20% – Litigation, local employment and land matters
Peter B.P. Bevan, Group General Counsel
Career: Peter joined the BP Group in 1970 after qualifying as a solicitor with a City of London firm. He worked initially in the Law Department of BP Chemicals and then of the Parent Company. Subsequently he became Manager of the Legal function within BP Exploration and then Assistant Company Secretary, followed by the Deputy Group Legal Adviser of The British Petroleum Company plc. In September 1992 he became Group General Counsel, the post and title of which he retained on the merger of BP and Amoco effective 31 December 1998. His main areas of expertise are corporate and company law, mergers and acquisitions, finance, and cross-jurisdictional and cross-business issues.
Personal: Leisure interests include sailing, walking, cycling, golf, music, local history and travel.
Other lawyers: Associate General Counsel: Robert Moore, Robin Morris and Colin Saunders(UK) Paul Agdern, Jack Lynch, Robert McGreevey and Steve Winters (USA) Peter Ling (Singapore).

BP Amoco PLC
Britannic House, 1 Finsbury Circus, London EC2M 7BA
Tel: (020) 7496 4000 **Fax:** (020) 7496 4592
Jeffrey Durkin, Senior Legal Adviser

BP Amoco PLC
Burnside Road, Farburn Industrial Estate, Dyce, Aberdeen AB21 7PB
Tel: (01224) 832000 **Fax:** (01224) 832929
Paul McGoldrick, Senior Legal Adviser

BPB PLC
Park House, 15 Bath Road, Slough SL1 3UF
Tel: (01753) 898800 **Fax:** (01753) 898888
Website: www.bpb.com
Robert M. Heard, Director

Britannic PLC
1 Wythall Green Way, Wythall, Birmingham B47 6WG
Tel: (01564) 828 888 **Fax:** (01564) 828 822
No of lawyers in dept: 3
Work outsourced: 60% – various
Anna East, Company Secretary and Solicitor
Specialisation: Company Secretaril work including administration of savings related share option scheme, Management of Legal Department and Executive Schemes.
Career: Rugby High School. Nottingham University (BA law). Trent Polytechnic (Law Society Finals). *Talbots* (articles), 1982-84. *Eversheds*, 1984-88. British Assurance 1988 to date.
Personal: Interests: family, tennis, travel.
Other lawyers: Lix Riley – Senior Solicitor, Employment Law

British Airways PLC
Waterside, PO Box 365, Harmondsworth UB7 0GB
Tel: (020) 8738 6873 **Fax:** (020) 8738 9962
Website: www.britishairways.com
Work outsourced: various
Stephen Walsh, Legal Director
Specialisation: Corporate / Alliances / Joint Ventures
Career: Ashurst Morris Crisp – 1986-1991; Joined British Airways – 1991; Head Legal Adviser – 1996; Legal Director – 1999
Other lawyers: Caroline Boone (IP), Owen Highley (Airlaw Commercial), Hugh Ford (Corporate, Commercial), Roger Whipp (Commercial, Litigation), Julia Harrison (Employment), Jo Pawley (Employment), Maria da Cunha (Employment), Iben McCracken (Corporate Commercial), Chris Haynes (Corporate Commercial), Paul Jasinski (US Law), Jim Blaney (US Law), Peter Watson (Aircraft Finance).

British Airways PLC
Waterside (HBA3), PO Box 365, Harmondsworth, West Drayton UB7 0GB
Tel: (020) 8738 6878 **Fax:** (020) 8738 9963
Owen Highley, Commercial Lawyer

British Airways PLC
Waterside, PO Box 365, Harmondsworth UB7 0GB
Tel: (020) 8738 6873 **Fax:** (020) 8738 9962
Julia Harrison, Employment Lawyer

British Airways PLC
Waterside, PO Box 365, Harmondsworth UB7 0GB
Tel: (020) 8738 6873 **Fax:** (020) 8738 9962
Robert Webb, General Counsel

British American Tobacco
Globe House, 4 Temple Place, London WC2R 2PG
Tel: (020) 7845 1000 **Fax:** (020) 7845 2189
Website: www.bat.com
Work outsourced: Specialist advice, property.
Neil Withington, Legal Director and General Counsel
Other lawyers: Philip Cook: Company Secretary; Stephen Walzer: competition and European law; Litigation: Philip Scourfield. Corporate and Treasury: Robert Casey; Assistant General Counsel and Head of BATmark: Mike Hendershot

British Assets Trust PLC (Ord)
One Charlotte Square, Edinburgh EH2 4DZ
Tel: (0131) 225 1357 **Fax:** (0131) 225 2375
Gordon Humphries, Company Secretary

British Aviation Insurance Group Ltd (BAIG)
Fitzwilliam House, 10 St Mary Axe, London EC3A 8EQ
Tel: (020) 7369 2800 **Fax:** (020) 7369 2800
Ken Walder, Director of Operations

British Energy PLC
10 Lochside Place, Edinburgh EH12 9DF
Tel: (0131) 527 2000 **Fax:** (0131) 527 2179
Email: Robert.Armour@british-energy.co.uk
Website: www.british-energy.com
No of lawyers in dept: 9
Work outsourced: 80%+ – Project support, overseas ventures, various specialisations.
Robert M. Armour, Director of Corporate Affairs and Company Secretary
Specialisation: Deals with corporate legal issues, corporate governance, certain major transactions, legal and stock exchange compliance, environmental issues, European legislation and Scottish parliament matters. Also responsible for estates, public relations, facilities, and private shareholder issues.
Career: Assistant solicitor – *Wright Johnston & McKenzie* – Edinburgh 1983-85, and Partner 1986-90. Scottish Nuclear's Company Secretary from 1990-1995. Company Secretary of British Energy plc – 1995 to date.Also Director of Corporate Affairs for British Energy plc.
Other lawyers: Dr Jean MacDonald, John Young, Beverley Sullivan, Andrew McMillan, Sue Challenger, Kate Lewis, Nigel Fowkes, Peter McCall, Steven Jewell.

British Land Co PLC
10 Cornwall Terrace, Regent's Park, London NW1 4QP
Tel: (020) 7486 4466 **Fax:** (020) 7935 5552
Website: www.britishland.co.uk
Anthony Braine, Company Secretary/Head of Legal

British Midland Airways Ltd
Donington Hall, Castle Donington, Derby DE74 2SB
Tel: (01332) 854033 **Fax:** (01332) 850301
Tim Bye, Legal Director and Company Secretary

British Olympic Association
1 Wandsworth Plain, London SW18 1EH
Tel: (020) 8871 2677 **Fax:** (020) 8871 9104
Robert Datnow, Lawyer

British Sky Broadcasting Group PLC
6 Centaurs Business Park, Grant Way, Isleworth TW7 5QD
Tel: (020) 7705 3000 **Fax:** (020) 7705 3254
Website: www.sky.co.uk
No of lawyers in dept: 20
Work outsourced: Corporate finance, litigation, specialist competition advice.
Deanna Bates, Head of Legal & Business Affairs
Specialisation: All areas of work relevant to BSkyB Corporate plc and all group companies including broadcasting and new media, telecoms, commercial agreements, joint ventures, rights production and acquisition, consumer issues, regulatory, political and strategic matters.
Career: Educated at Exeter University and Guildford Law College and qualified as a Solicitor in 1987. Completed her training at *Clifford Chance*, and after qualifying joined the *Clifford Chance* commercial department where she stayed for 2½ years. In 1989 joined Sky Television plc and has been Head of Legal and Business Affairs for Sky (and now BSkyB) since then.

British Telecommunications PLC
British Telecom Centre, BT Group Legal Services, 81 Newgate Street, London EC1A 7AJ
Tel: (020) 7356 5000 **Fax:** (020) 7356 6638
Website: www.bt.com
Alan Whitfield, Group General Counsel
Specialisation: Responsible for legal affairs, intellectual property, regulatory affairs and company secretarial. BT has one of the largest in-house legal departments in the UK, handling all BT's work (other than property) in the UK and managing legal advice overseas. Handles patent and trade mark matters. Responsible for servicing Britain's largest shareholder base (2.3m shareholders) and an additional department of 55 Company Secretaries and associated staff. Involved in the merger with US telecoms company MCI. Director, BT Property Ltd, Southgate Developments Ltd, Centre for Dispute Resolution (CEDR) and Trustee of BT Pension Fund. Lectures on management of in-house legal departments and on BT's MBA course on introduction to commercial law.
Career: Qualified 1973 while with Paisner & Co, then joined Clintons and later became Partner. Joined the Post Office in 1977 to handle privatisation of BT. Director of Commercial Department 1985 and appointed Solicitor and Chief Legal Adviser to BT in August 1989; and Secretary and Chief Legal Adviser 1994, 1996: Designate Secretary and Chief Legal Officer, Concert plc.
Other lawyers: Alan Whitfield: Communications Law; Anne Fletcher: Regulatory Law; Tim Cowen: European Law; Rupert Orchard: M&A; Hilary Jordan: contracts & commercial; Jeff Fisher: finance & securities; Vivienne Haynes: multimedia; Miles Jobling: litigation; Iain Unett: employment.

British Vita PLC
Oldham Road, Middleton, Manchester M24 2DB
Tel: (0161) 643 1133 **Fax:** (0161) 655 3957
No of lawyers in dept: 2
Work outsourced: 30% – public issues, heavyweight litigation, some M&A.
Mark Stirzaker, Company Solicitor
Specialisation: Principal areas of work are mergers and acquisitions and commercial property. Also provides general commercial advice and deals with intellectual property matters.
Career: Qualified 1980.
Other lawyers: Catherine Butler.

Brixton Estate PLC
22-24 Ely Place, London EC1N 6TQ
Tel: (020) 7400 4400 **Fax:** (020) 7400 4451
Email: nigelwatts@brixtonestate.co.uk
No of lawyers in dept: 0
Work outsourced: All – Property and Corporate
Nigel Watts, Group Secretary
Specialisation: Company Secretarial; Employment; Share Schemes; Pension arrangements.
Career: Professionally qualified accountant with extensive UK and International experience in handling complex corporate, secretarial and treasury matters in the context of corporate restructuring and take-overs of leading publicly quoted Groups. Bourner Bullock 1968-1975 – Audit Senior from Junior. Coopers & Lybrand 1975-1976 – Audit Senior. United Kingdom Property Company Ltd (British Land plc) 1976-1980 – Secretary and Group Accountant. John Brown plc (Kvaerner plc Trafalgar House plc) 1980-1984 Group Financial Accountant, 1984-1987 Treasury Manager, 1986-1996 Secretary. Nigel Watts Consultancy Ltd Financial and and Secretarial Consultant 1996 to 1999.
Personal: Aged 50, married with 2 sons.
Other lawyers: Employee Benefit Schemes. Pension Schemes. Employment Law.

Brockbank Underwriting Group PLC
Fitzwilliam House, 10 St Mary Axe, London EC3A 8NL
Tel: (020) 7648 1000 **Fax:** (020) 7648 1003
Paul Jaffe, Solicitor and Attorney at Law

Brockbank Underwriting Group PLC
Fitzwilliam House, 10 St Mary Axe, London EC3A 8NL
Tel: (020) 7648 1000 **Fax:** (020) 7648 1003
Rhic Webb, Head of Legal

Brown (N.) Group PLC
53 Dale Street, Manchester M60 6ES
Tel: (0161) 236 8256 **Fax:** (0161) 238 2308
No of lawyers in dept: 2
Peter Tynan, Company Secretary

BTG PLC
10 Fleet Place, Limeburner Lane, London EC4M 7SB
Tel: (020) 7575 0000 **Fax:** (020) 7575 1527
No of lawyers in dept: 7
Work outsourced: 10% – Litigation
Andrew Popper, Company Secretary / Head of Group Legal Compliance
Specialisation: Compliance, Risk Management, Ethical Guidance, Intellectual Property, Litigation
Career: Joined BTG 1978; Head of Legal, 1991; Company Secretary, 1999. Educated at St. Paul's School and Oriel College, Oxford.
Other lawyers: R Davison, J Bond , G Georgiou, G Dail, Z Ali : Compliance and Corporate, Intellectual Property, Commercial and Litigation.

Bunzl PLC
110 Park Street, London W1Y 3RB
Tel: (020) 7495 4950 **Fax:** (020) 7495 4953
Website: www.bunzl.com
No of lawyers in dept: 2
Work outsourced: 50% – Large corporate transactions, litigation, property.
Paul N. Hussey, Company Secretary and Group Legal Adviser
Specialisation: Provides legal services and advice on company/commercial and general corporate matters, and a full company secretarial service including compliance.
Career: Qualified 1983 while with *Addleshaw Sons & Latham*. Commercial solicitor, Grand Metropolitan Retailing Division 1985-86 and Senior Solicitor, Contract Services Division 1986-87. Company Secretary and Group Legal Adviser, Compass Group 1987-88. Legal Adviser, Bunzl plc 1988-92 and then took up present position.
Personal: Educated at Woking Grammar School 1970-77, University College, Cardiff 1977-80 and College of Law 1980-81. Leisure pursuits include walking, tennis, music and golf. Born 11 January 1959. Lives in London.

Burberry Ltd
29-53 Chatham Place, Hackney, London E9 6LP
Tel: (020) 8985 3344 **Fax:** (020) 8985 2636
Sarah Corbett, General Counsel

Burford Holdings PLC
20 Thayer Street, London W1M 6DD
Tel: (020) 7224 2240 **Fax:** (020) 7224 1710
No of lawyers in dept: 0
Work outsourced: 100% - Property/Company Law

Teresa White, Company Secretary
Specialism: Everything from property reorganisations to the debenture, salaries, pensions, share options, insurance, BUPA, SAYE, tax, employment law, R&A's LTIP, AGM, Y2K, corporate governance, stock exchange areas, computer (Blueprint etc).

C Hoare & Co
37 Fleet Street, London EC4P 4DQ
Tel: +44 20 73534522 **Fax:** +44 20 73534521
Director of Legal Services

Cable & Wireless PLC
124 Theobalds Road, London WC1X 8RX
Tel: (020) 7315 4000 **Fax:** (020) 7315 5056
Website: www.cablewireless.com
No of lawyers in dept: 40
Work outsourced: Specialist work (IP, Technology) some M&A
J. Daniel Fitz, General Counsel
Specialisation: Has overall professional and functional responsibility for the provision of legal and regulatory services to the Cable & Wireless Group of companies worldwide. Regular conference speaker on topics concerning in-house lawyers and ethics
Career: University of North Carolina at Chapel Hill, graduating in 1981 (BA Economics, with Honours) and 1985 (Juris Doctor, with Honours) and The London School of Economics, 1982 (Diploma with Distinction, International and Comparative Politics). Winthrop Stimson Putnam & Roberts, 1985-1989 (New York and London), Baring Brothers & Co Ltd, 1989-1991 (London) and Cable & Wireless plc, 1991 to date (Hong Kong and London). General Counsel since March 1999.
Personal: The American Corporate Counsel association – European Chapter (Secretary and Treasurer); The British-American Project (Treasurer); The Law Society of England and Wales (Commerce & Industry Group). Personal Interests: Tennis, swimming, history, Spanish and Portugese languages.

Cadbury Schweppes PLC
25 Berkeley Square, London W1X 6HT
Tel: (020) 7409 1313 **Fax:** (020) 7830 5200
Website: www.cadburyshweppes.com
Work outsourced: 20% – Mainly where local overseas input is required
Michael Clark, Group Secretary and Chief Legal Officer

Caledonia Investments PLC
Cayzer House, 1 Thomas More Street, London E1W 1YB
Tel: (020) 7481 4343 **Fax:** (020) 7488 0896
Email: enquiries@cayzerhouse.com
Website: www.caledoniainvestments.com
Work outsourced: 70% – Company Commercial / Corporate Finance, Property
Graeme Denison, Company Secretary
Specialisation: Company Commercial, Corporate Finance
Career: Tonbridge School, Kent; St. Catherine's College, Cambridge; 1981-1987: Hobsons Press Ltd – sales and marketing; 1982 – 1989: William Sindall plc – Company Secretary; 1989 – present: Caledonia Investments plc – Company Secretary
Personal: Married, 3 daughters. Interests – sport generally
Other lawyers: Company Commercial, Corporate Finance

Cambridge Antibody Tech Group PLC
The Science Park, Melbourn SG8 6JJ
Tel: (01763) 263 233 **Fax:** (01763) 263 413
No of lawyers in dept: 1
Work outsourced: Property, Litigation, Corporate Finance, Tax, Commercial IP Agreements
Diane Mellett, Company Secretary
Specialisation: Intellectual Property; Commercial Agreements
Career: University of Birmingham LLB (Hons) 1983; Chicago IIT-Kent J.D. 1991; Law Society 1986; Admitted to Illinois Bar, United States & 7th Circuit, 1992

Canary Wharf Group PLC
One Canada Square, Canary Wharf, London E14 5AB
Tel: (020) 7418 2000 **Fax:** (020) 7418 2195
Website: www.canarywharf.com
No of lawyers in dept: 4
Work outsourced: 1% – Litigation
Michael Ashley-Brown, Head of Legal
Other lawyers: Construction, Ip and Facilities Management

Capita Group PLC
71 Victoria Street, Westminster, London SW1H 0XA
Tel: (020) 7799 1525 **Fax:** (020) 7799 1526
Website: www.capita.co.uk
Gordon M. Hurst, Company Secretary

Capital Radio PLC
30 Leicester Square, London WC2H 7LA
Tel: (020) 7766 6000 **Fax:** (020) 7766 6184
Website: www.capitalradio.plc.uk
No of lawyers in dept: 1
Work outsourced: 25% – Corporate Finance Transactions; Property
Nathalie Schwarz, Company Secretary and Head of Legal Affairs
Specialisation: As Company Secretary, provide corporate support to the Plc Board and Sub-Committees, as well as ensuring compliance with stock exchange and regulatory matters. Responsible for all group legal affairs and managing external counsel as appropriate.
Career: The North London Collegiate School; University of Manchester 1988-91; College of Law 1991-92; Degrees/qualifications: Law (LLB, Honours) – 2:1 (1991); Law Society Final Professional Examination – First Class Honours (1992); Articled at *Clifford Chance*. Qualified as a solicitor in the Corporate Department in 1995, specialising in Corporate Finance, M&A and general Corporate/Commercial matters. Joined Capital Radio plc as Company Secretary and Head of Legal Affairs in 1998.
Personal: Born 1970, resides in London. Enjoys Theatre, cinema, travelling, sports.

Capital Shopping Centres PLC
40 Broadway, London SW1H OBU
Tel: (020) 7887 7073 **Fax:** (020) 7887 0001
Website: www.capital-shopping-centres.co.uk
No of lawyers in dept: 0
Work outsourced: 1% – Some pensions administration – limited in scope.
Susan Folger, Company Secretary
Specialisation: Corporate transactions; Personnel; Stock Exchange compliance; Corporate Governance; Insurances; Pensions; Option Schemes; Bonus Schemes; Annual Report and Accounts
Career: Fellow of Institute of Chartered Secretaries and Administrators (FCIs); 'A' level Economics; 'A' level Business Studies
Personal: Fell Walking, Running (3 marathons completed), Riding.

Caradon PLC
Caradon House, 24 Queens Road, Weybridge KT13 9UX
Tel: (01932) 850850 **Fax:** (01932) 823328
No of lawyers in dept: 2
Anthony Holland, Group Legal Adviser
Other lawyers: Helen Leckey – Legal adviser

Carillion plc
Construction House, Birch Street, Wolverhampton WV1 4HY
Tel: (01902) 422 431 **Fax:** (01902) 316 340
Dirk Fitzhugh, Company Secretary & Head of Legal Services

Carlton Communications PLC
25 Knightsbridge, London SW1X 7RZ
Tel: (020) 7663 6363 **Fax:** (020) 7663 6370
Website: www.carlton.com
No of lawyers in dept: 2
Work outsourced: 90%
David Abdoo, Company Secretary
Other lawyers: David Abdoo; Richard Ray

Carpetright PLC
Amberley House, New Road, Rainham RM13 8QN
Tel: (01708) 525 522 **Fax:** (01708) 559361
Patricia Dregent, Company Secretary

Cattles PLC
Kingston House, Centre 27 Business Park, Woodhead Road, Birstall, Batley WS17 9TD
Tel: (01924) 444466 **Fax:** (01924) 448324
Website: cattles.co.uk
No of lawyers in dept: 1
Work outsourced: 50% – company/commercial, banking, litigation.
Patrick Doherty, Company Secretary
Specialisation: Principal areas of work are consumer credit, employment matters, property, company secretarial and compliance (statutory and Stock Exchange).
Career: Called to the Bar 1976; admitted as a solicitor 1992. With Engineering Employers' Association (Yorkshire and Humberside) 1978-79; Armstrong Equipment plc 1979-85; ASD plc 1985-90 and joined Cattles plc in 1991.
Personal: Educated at Keble College, Oxford (BA, Jurisprudence 1975). Leisure pursuits include golf. Born 16 October 1952. Lives in Hull.

Cedar Group
Oriel House, 52 Coombe Road, New Malden KT3 4QH
Tel: (01932) 584 000 **Fax:** (01932) 584 001
Jemma Davis, Company Secretary

Celltech Group PLC
216 Bath Road, Slough SL1 4EN
Tel: (01753) 534 655 **Fax:** (01753) 551244
No of lawyers in dept: 6
Work outsourced: litigation, property, employment, and foreign legal matters.
John Slater, Director of Legal Services and Co. Sec.
Specialisation: Responsible for the provision of legal and company secretarial services. Main areas of work are general company/commercial matters, intellectual property, licensing, corporate affairs and Yellow Book.
Career: Qualified as a solicitor 1978.

Centrica plc
Charter Court, 50 Windsor Road, Slough SL1 2HA
Tel: (01753) 758 000 **Fax:** (01753) 758 011
Website: www.centrica.co.uk
No of lawyers in dept: 25
Work outsourced: Vast majority undertaken by in-house legal team. – Litigation and property.
Grant Dawson, General Counsel & Company Secretary
Specialisation: General Counsel & Company Secretary of Centrica plc. Responsible for the provision of legal, regulatory and company secretarial services to the Centrica Group of Companies.
Career: Educated in Leicester and London. Called to the Bar in 1982. A member of Lincolns Inn. Practised at the Bar for a period of two years before joining the legal department of Racal Electronics plc in 1984. Joined STC plc as legal adviser in 1986 until they werre taken over in 1991 by Northern Telecom Limited. 1992 appointed Associate General Counsel with Northern Telecom Europe Limited. Appointed General Counsel and Company Secretary of Centrica plc in October 1996.
Personal: Married with three children and lives in Windsor. Enjoys golf, scuba diving, sailing and opera.
Other lawyers: Company commercial; corporate finance; utility regulation; and litigation.

Centrica plc
50 Windsor Road, Slough SL1 2HA
Tel: (01753) 758000 **Fax:** (01753) 758011
Eldon Pethybridge, Director of Legal & Regulatory Affairs

CGNU PLC
20th Floor, St. Helen's, 1 Undershaft, London EC3P 3DQ
Tel: (020) 7662-7601 **Fax:** (020)-7662-7263
Website: www.cgugroup.com
Work outsourced: Small – Major corporate work and also claims litigation.
Graham Jones, Head of Group Legal Services for CGNU plc
Career: BA Hons Degree in English from Manchester University 1972, admitted as solicitor in 1977, MBA from Loughborough University 1992.
Personal: Age 48. Married with two children and lives near Norwich.

C

Channel 5 Broadcasting Limited
22 Long Acre, London WC2E 9LY
Tel: (020) 7497 5225 **Fax:** (020) 7497 5618
Colin Cambell, Director of Legal and Business Affairs

Charter PLC
7 Hobart Place, London SW1W 0HH
Tel: (020) 7838 7000 **Fax:** (020) 7259 5116
No of lawyers in dept: 1
Alison Yapp, Group Legal Adviser
Specialisation: Acquisitions, disposals, joint ventures, distribution/agency agreemants, EU/competition law, R&P agreements, liscensing agreements, employment issues, management of litigation, property.
Career: Articled *Turner Kenneth Brown*; qualified 1990. Asisstant solicitor company/commercial dept. 1990-92. Legal Assistant Johnson Matthey plc 1992-94. Legal Adviser Jonson Matthey plc 1994-95. Sole Legal Adviser Cookson Matthey Ceramics plc 1995-96. Senior Legal Adviser and Company Secretary Cookson Matthey Ceramics plc 1996-98. Group Legal adviser Charter plc 1998 to date.
Personal: Education: St Albans Girls' School. Bristol Uni (LLB Hons 1987). College of Law, Chancery Lane (Law Society Finals 1988)

Charter European Trust
10 Fenchurch Street, London EC3M 3LB
Tel: (020) 7623 8000 **Fax:** (020) 7621 1481
Nicola J. Schrager von Altishoften, Company Secretary

Chase Manhattan Bank
125 London Wall, London EC2Y 5AJ
Tel: (020) 7777 2000 **Fax:** (020) 7777 3141
Mitchell Caller, Senior Vice President and Associate General Counsel

Chase Manhattan Bank
125 London Wall, London EC2Y 5AJ
Tel: (020) 7777 2000 **Fax:** (020) 7777 4165
Brian Harte, Head of Compliance for Europe, Middle East and Africa

Chelsfield PLC
67 Brook Street, London W1Y 2NJ
Tel: (020) 7493 3977 **Fax:** (020) 7491 9369
Robin Perrot, Company Solicitor

Chloride Group PLC
Abford House, 15 Wilton Road, London SW1V 1LT
Tel: (020) 7834 5500 **Fax:** (020) 7630 0563
Susan Williams, Company Secretary and Legal Adviser

Christian Salvesen PLC
Suite 3, 500 Pavilion Drive, Northampton Business Park, Brackmills, Northampton NN4 7XJ
Tel: 01604 662600 **Fax:** 01604 662605
Website: www.salvesen.com
No of lawyers in dept: 3
Work outsourced: Property, Litigation
Sarah Booth, Legal and Corporate Development Director
Specialisation: Responsible for all legal services throughout the group including mergers and acquisitions
Career: LLB (Hons) Edinburgh University, Dickson Minto 1989-91 (traineeship), Christian Salvesen PLC 1991 to date. Appointed Director of Legal Services September 1997, and Corporate Development Director June 1999.
Other lawyers: Anita Prinntia, Ed Peppiass

Christiania Bank of Kreditkasse ASA
Lloyds Chambers, 1 Portsoken Street, London E1 8RU
Tel: (020) 7680 7000 **Fax:** (020) 7481 1860
Work outsourced: % varies for sector. – Syndicated facilities for shipping, energy and aviation and litigation.
Craig Axe, Senior Manager – Legal/Documentation
Specialisation: Nordic corporate; energy; shipping and transportation; aviation; and cash management.
Career: Ten year with Midland Bank plc (now HSBC), 1976-1986; 14 years with Christiania Bank og Kreditkasse ASA, London Branch, 1986 – to date
Personal: Married to Dianne, 2 sons. Interets include scientific and technical, music and motorsport.
Other lawyers: Responsibilty for legal / documentation, drafting and negotiation for the following marketing areas of the Bank's London branch: Shipping and transportation, Energy and Project Finance, Nordic Corporates, Aviation, Cash Management.

Chrysalis Group PLC
The Chrysalis Building, Bramley Road, London W10 6SP
Tel: (020) 7221 2213 **Fax:** (020) 7221 6455
Clive Potterell, Company Secretary

CISCO
The Square, Stockley Park, Uxbridge UB11 7BN
Tel: (020) 8756 8000 **Fax:** (020) 8756 8011
Graham Allan, Managing Attorney

Citibank Private Bank
41 Berkeley Square, London W1X 6NA
Tel: (020) 7508 8000 **Fax:** (020) 7508 8472
Email: bruce.hogarth-jones@citicorp.com
No of lawyers in dept: 6
Work outsourced: 5-10% – Litigation
Bruce Hogarth-Jones, Head of Legal
Specialisation: Banking, capital markets/derivatives, corporate finance, IMRO compliance, litigation & anti-money laundering, data protection and bank confidentiality.
Career: MA (Law) Pembroke College, Cambridge 1978-81. Called to Bar 1982. Swiss Bank Corporation 1985-1991. Credit Suisse Financial Products 1991-93. SG Warburg 1993-5. Citibank 1995 to date.
Personal: Married, 2 children. Interests: sailing, computers.

City of London Investment Trust
3 Finsbury Avenue, London EC2M 2PA
Tel: (020) 7638 5757 **Fax:** (020) 7377 5742
Geoffrey Rice, Company Secretary

Civil Aviation Authority
CAA House, 45-59 Kingsway, London WC2B 6TE
Tel: (020) 7379 7311 **Fax:** (020) 7453 6163
Rupert J. Britton, Secretary & Legal Adviser

Close Brothers Group PLC
12 Appold Street, London EC2A 2AW
Tel: +44 171 4264000 **Fax:** +44 171 4264044
Robin Sellers, Company Secretary

Clydesdale Bank PLC
European Legal, PO Box 43, 150 Buchanan Street, Glasgow G1 2HL
Tel: (0141) 223 2802 **Fax:** (0141) 223 2887
No of lawyers in dept: 10
Jane L. Shirran, General Counsel
Specialisation: Company/ Commercial, Corporate Financial Litigation and Management of the Legal function.
Career: Present: General Cousel and Secretary, Clydesdale Bank PLC. 1996-June 1998 Principal Solicitor with Clydesdale Bank PLC, Legal Services, Glasgow; Responsible for provision of legal advice to Corporate, Business Banking and Head Office areas of Bank. 1995-1996 Senior Solicitor with Bank of Scotland, Legal Services, Edinburgh; Provision of corporate and general advice to the Bank's Head Office, Structured Finance and Investment Banking Departments. 1988-1995 *McGrigor Donald*, Solicitors, Associate – 1992-1995; General Corporate, Banking and Insolvency; Worked in Glasgow, London and Edinburgh offices. 1987-1988 Tods Murray, Edinburgh, Assistant 1985-1987. Allan Dawson Simpson & Hampton (new Henderson Boyd Jackson), Trainee.
Personal: Marital status – Married. Nationality: British. Date of Birth: 27/6/63. Driving Licence: Full/Clean. Education: Pre 1975 Schooling in Malaysia, Malawi, Zimbabwe. 1975-1978 Cults Acadamy, Aberdeen. 1980-1985 Aberdeen University. LL.B Honours (2:1); Diploma in Legal Practice.

CMG PLC
Parnell House, 25 Wilton Road, London SW1V 1EJ
Tel: (020) 7592 4000 **Fax:** (020) 7592 4804
Website: www.cmg.com
No of lawyers in dept: 1
Work outsourced: 20% – Litigation, conveyancing, acquisitions
Richard Francis, Company Solicitor
Specialisation: Information technology contracts, mergers, acquisitions and joint ventures; Intellectual Property; Company Secretarial.
Career: LL.B. (Hons) London; Qualified as a solicitor in 1977.
Personal: Hobbies include climbing, travel and classic cars.

Co-operative Bank PLC
PO Box 101, 1 Balloon Street, Manchester M60 4EP
Tel: (0161) 832 3456 **Fax:** (0161) 839 8471
Website: www.co-operativebank.co.uk
No of lawyers in dept: 5
Work outsourced: predominantly in-house
Ann Page, Head of Legal Services

Coats Viyella PLC
3rd Floor, 2 Foubert's Place, London W1B 1HH
Tel: (020) 7302 2300 **Fax:** (020) 7302 2347
Email: chrisw.healy@coats-viyella.com
Website: www.coats-viyella.com
No of lawyers in dept: 1
Work outsourced: 70 % - Corporate/Employment/Property
Christopher Healy, Legal Adviser and company Secretary
Specialisation: Corporate/Commercial
Career: Kent University, Chancery Lane Law School, Articled at Lee Bolton & Lee, Qualified Feb 1987.
Other lawyers: Julia Stevens - Assistant Company Secretary, David Younger - Intellectual Property Manager.

Cobham PLC
Brook Road, Wimborne BH21 2BJ
Tel: (01202) 882 020 **Fax:** (01202) 840523
Work outsourced: Conveyancing; M&A; Corporate Finance; Competition
John Pope, Company Solicitor

Coca-Cola Beverages
1 Queen Caroline Street, Hammersmith, London W6 9HQ
Tel: (020) 8237 3000 **Fax:** (020) 8237 3700
John Culhane, Legal Director/ Company Secretary
Specialisation: Responsible for provision of in-house legal advice, company secretarial services and managing external legal advisers where necessary.
Career: Articled at *Clifford Chance*. Qualified 1990. Joined CCSB in 1996.

Colt Telecom Group PLC
15 Marylebone Road, London NW5 5JD
Tel: (020) 7390 3900 **Fax:** (020) 7390 3901
Email: colt-telecom.com
Website: www.colt-telecom.com
No of lawyers in dept: 1
Work outsourced: 50% – Litigation, property, employment
Mark Jenkins, Legal Services Director and Company Secretary
Specialisation: Management of all of the legal and secretarial requirements of the group. Corporate/commercial. M&A. Employment.
Career: Chelmer. Bar School. M.K. Electric plc/SKF (UK) Ltd/Peek plc.
Personal: Married. 3 children.

Colt Telecom Group PLC
Beaufort House, 15 St. Botolph Street, London EC3A 7QN
Tel: (020) 7390 3900 **Fax:** (020) 7390 3750
Robert Bratby, Legal Director

Colt Telecom Group PLC
Beaufort House, 15 St. Botolph Street, London EC3A 7QN
Tel: (020) 7390 3900 **Fax:** (020) 7390 3750
Christopher Smedley, In-house Lawyer

Compaq Computers Ltd
Hotham House, 1 Heron Square, Richmond TW9 1EJ
Tel: (020) 8332 3000 **Fax:** (020) 8332 1961
Chris Parker, Director of Legal Services

Compass Group plc
Parklands Court, 24 Parklands, Birmingham Great Park, Rubery, Birmingham B45 9PZ
Tel: (0121) 457 5000 **Fax:** (0121) 457 5570
Website: www.compass-group.com
Timothy C. Mason, UK Company Secretary

Computacenter
Link House, 19 Colonial Way, Watford WD2 4HS
Website: www.computacenter.com
Alan Pottinger, Company Secretary

Cookson Group plc
The Adelphi, 1-11 John Adam Street, London WC2N 6HJ
Tel: (020) 7766 4500 **Fax:** (020) 7747 6600
Website: www.cooksongroup.co.uk
Work outsourced: 90% – various.
Glen McDonnall, Legal Adviser and Assistant Company Secretary
Specialisation: banking and corporate finance, acquisitions and joint ventures, patent and trademark matters. General legal advice and management of external legal advisers.
Career: Qualified in 1985. Previously assistant Solicitor with *Herbert Smith* and with BAT Industries plc. Joined Cookson Group in 1994.

Cordiant Communications Grp PLC
83/89 Whitfield Street, London W1P 5RL
Tel: (020) 7436 4000 **Fax:** (020) 7436 1998
Work outsourced: 95% – litigation, property, banking, corporate, copy clearance.
Stuart Howard, Company Secretary

Corus Group plc
15 Great Marlborough Street, London NW1 5JD
Tel: (020) 7717 4444 **Fax:** (020) 7717 4455
Website: www.corusgroup.com
No of lawyers in dept: 14
Margaret O'Neill, Director – Corporate Legal Services
Specialisation: Responsible for provision of in-house legal services to Corus Group and managing external advice where required.

Countrywide Assured Group
Kingsgate, 1 King Edward Road, Brentwood CM14 4HG
Tel: (01227) 264466 **Fax:** (01227) 217916
Barry Ryan, Company Secretary

Coutts & Co
440 Strand, London WC2R 0QS
Tel: (020) 7753 1000 **Fax:** (020) 7957 2244
Website: www.coutts.com
No of lawyers in dept: 9
Work outsourced: 50% – Litigation, Specialist advice, Commercial transactions.
C. Carr, Chief Legal Officer, Wealth Management Legal Services
Specialisation: Banking, investment and trusts
Career: February 1998 to date: Chief Legal Officer, Wealth Management Legal Services; 1989-1997 HSBC Holdings plc, General Manager and Group Legal Adviser; 1983-1989 Central Electricity Generating Board, Head of Legal Services; 1980-1983 Capsticks, helped set up law practice. 1973-1980; Bridon plc, Contracts Director; 1967-1973 Guest Keen & Nettlefolds plc, Assistant Secretary; 1962-1967 Elliott Automation Ltd, Deputy Legal Adviser. 1961-1962 Rolls Royce Ltd, Legal Adviser.
Personal: Married to Julia, 2 sons.
Other lawyers: Mary Bevan, Sarah Chidgey, Niul Dillon Hatcher, Russell Fairbrother, Gloria Glennie, Ian Levene, Robert Stemmons, Julie Teuten.

Credit Agricole Indosuez
122 Leadenhall Street, London EC3V 4QH
Tel: (020) 7971 4000 **Fax:** (020) 7971 4407
Margaret Garner, Head of Group Legal Services (London)

Credit Lyonnais
Broadwalk House, 5 Appold Street, London EC2A 2JP
Tel: (020) 7374 4014 **Fax:** (020) 7214 7070
Website: www.creditlyonnais.com
Joseph Crowley, General Counsel

Credit Suisse First Boston
One Cabot Square, London E14 4QJ
Tel: (020) 7888 8888 **Fax:** (020) 7888 1600
No of lawyers in dept: 44
Work outsourced: Debt and Equity Capital Markets, M& A, Structured Finance.
Kevin Studd, General Counsel – Europe
Specialisation: Fixed income, equities and derivatives (OTC and exchange trade) financial instruments; emerging markets; financial services law and regulation; litigation.
Career: 1985: LL.B. (Hons) London School of Economics; 1986: Called to the Bar; 1993: Admitted as a Solicitor; 1988-94: Barrister/Solicitor, Simmons and Simmons; 1994 to date: Legal and Compliance Department, Credit Suisse First Boston.
Other lawyers: Edmond Curtin – Fixed Income & Derivatives; David Bonham – Equities; Leyland Goss – Investment Banking; Steven Wootton – Emerging Markets; Catherine Heard – Litigation; Jeanette Whomersley – Credit Documentation.

Credit Suisse First Boston
One Cabot Square, London E14 4QJ
Tel: (020) 7888 8888 **Fax:** (020) 7888 4251
Tracy Kingsley-Daniells, Director of Transaction Management

Credit Suisse First Boston
One Cabot Square, London E14 4QJ
Tel: (020) 7888 8888 **Fax:** (020) 7888 4251
Paul Chelsom, Director in Legal & Compliance

Credit Suisse First Boston
One Cabot Square, London E14 4QJ
Tel: (020) 7888 8888 **Fax:** (020) 7888 4251
Edmond Curtin, Director in Legal & Compliance

Croda International PLC
Cowick Hall, Snaith, Goole DN14 9AA
Tel: (01405) 860 551 **Fax:** (01405) 861767
Email: roy.ainger@croda.co.uk
Roy Ainger, Company Secretary

Daiwa Europe Ltd
5 King William Street, London EC4N 7AX
Tel: (020) 7548 7802 **Fax:** (020) 7548 8835
Email: Roger.massey@daiwa.co.uk
No of lawyers in dept: 5
Work outsourced: 10% – Litigation, property, non-UK law
Roger Massey, Executive Director of Legal and Transaction Management Department
Specialisation: Investment banking, corporate.
Career: BA (Hons) , LLB University of Sydney. *Allen, Allen & Hemsley, Slaughter and May*. Tokai Bank, Daiwa Europe Ltd
Personal: Lives in London.

David S. Smith (Holdings) PLC
4-16 Artillery Row, London SW1P 1RZ
Tel: (020) 7932 5000 **Fax:** (020) 7932 5003
No of lawyers in dept: 3
Work outsourced: Acquisitions, litigation, conveyancing, employment.
James Deeley, Head of Group Legal
Other lawyers: Jill Glover – Commercial; Stephen Cook – Property

Davis Service Group PLC
4 Grosvenor Place, London SW1X 7DL
Tel: (020) 7259 6663 **Fax:** (020) 7259 6565
Malcolm Hoskin, Company Secretary

De La Rue PLC
De La Rue House, Jays Close, Viables Industrial Estate, Basingstoke RG22 4BS
Tel: (01256) 605 331 **Fax:** (01256) 605 336
Email: louise.fluker@uk.delarue.com
Website: www.delarue.com
No of lawyers in dept: 4
Work outsourced: 30% in UK: varies according to specialist projects – Conveyancing, litigation, pensions, major transactions, work requiring foreign juridiction advice.
Louise Fluker, General Counsel and Company Secretary
Career: MA (Cantab); LLB (Cantab)
Other lawyers: Douglas Denham, Elizabeth Joyce, Hector Martin: UK

Debenhams
1 Welbeck Street, London W1A 1DF
Tel: (020) 7408 4444 **Fax:** (020) 7408 3765
Guy Johnson, Company Secretary and General Counsel

Deutsche Asset Management
1 Appold Street, Broadgate, London EC2A 2HE
No of lawyers in dept: 0
Work outsourced: 100% – All legal areas
Paul Hogwood, Company Secretary

Deutsche Bank AG London
Winchester House, 1 Gt Winchester St, London EC2N 2NB
Tel: (020) 7545 8000 **Fax:** (020) 7547 3102
Email: simon.dodds@db.com
Website: www.db.com
Simon H.S. Dodds, General Counsel – UK
Specialisation: Responsible for providing and supervising the provision of legal services to Deutsche Bank in the UK.
Career: 1976-79: MA, Downing College, Cambridge; 1981-84: JD North Western University School of Law, Chicago; 1984-91: Associate, Cleary Gottlieb Steen and Hamilton, New York & London; 1991-99: Managing Director, Bankers Trust Company,
Personal: Born 27.8.1957 LONDON .

Deutsche Bank AG London
Winchester House, 1 Great Winchester Street, London EC2N 2DB
Tel: (020) 7545 8000 **Fax:** (020) 7547 3102
John Ormond, Legal Adviser

Diageo PLC
8 Henrietta Place, London W1M 9AG
Tel: (020) 7927 5200 **Fax:** (020) 7927 4626
Website: www.diageo.com
No of lawyers in dept: 12
Tim Proctor, Group General Counsel

Diageo PLC
United Distillers & Vintners, Kingsley House, 1a Wimpole Street, London W1M 0DA
Tel: (020) 7927 4164 **Fax:** (020) 7927 5052
Mary Ann Alford, Associate General Counsel, Intellectual Property

Diagonal PLC
Wey Court, Farnham GU9 7PT
Tel: (01252) 733 711 **Fax:** (01252) 733 825
Website: www.diagonal.co.uk
No of lawyers in dept: 1
Ian Farrelly, Group Solicitor
Other lawyers: Richard Cocks : Company Secretary

Dixons Group PLC
Maylands Ave, Hemel Hempstead HP2 7TG
Tel: (01442) 353 000 **Fax:** (01442) 233218
Website: http://www.dixons-group-plc.co.uk
Geoffrey Budd, Company Secretary

Donaldson Lufkin & Jenrette International
99 Bishopsgate, London EC2M 3XD
Tel: (020) 7655 7020 **Fax:** (020) 7655 7204
No of lawyers in dept: 6
John Harriman, Managing Director and General Counsel

D

Dresdner Kleinwort Benson
Riverbank House, 2 Swan Lane, London EC4R 3WX
Tel: (020) 7623 8000 **Fax:** (020) 7929 7958
Email: simonleifer@dresdnerkb.com
Work outsourced: 15% – Tax structures
Simon Leifer, Director, Head of Global Markets Legal Dept
Specialisation: money markets/fixed income/derivatives/emerging markets trading.
Career: Kingston College of Law. Guilford College of Law. Admitted as a solicitor in 1985. Previously at Royal Bank of Canada and Libra Bank plc.
Personal: Married. 2 children. Keen oarsman.
Other lawyers: Investment Banking / Fixed Income

Dunedin Income Growth Inv Tst PLC
Donaldson House, 97 Haymarket Terrace, Edinburgh EH12 5HD
Tel: (0131) 313 1000 **Fax:** (0131) 313 6300
Catherine Miller, Company Secretary

Durlacher Corporation PLC
4 Chiswell Street, London EC1Y 4UP
Tel: (020) 7628 4306 **Fax:** (020) 7638 8848
Graham Chamberlain, Company Secretary

Edinburgh Fund Managers
Donaldson House, 97 Haymarket Terrace, Edinburgh EH12 5HD
Tel: (0131) 313 1000 **Fax:** (0131) 313 6300
Cathy Miller, Company Secretary

Eidos PLC
Wimbledon Bridge House, 1 Hartfield Road, Wimbledon, London SW19 3RU
Tel: (020) 8636 3000 **Fax:** (020) 8636 3001
Email: charlotte.eastwood@eidos.co.uk
Website: www.eidos.co.uk
No of lawyers in dept: 2
Work outsourced: Varies from time to time.
Charlotte Eastwood, Company Secretary
Specialisation: Employees share schemes, property work, compliance / corporate governance.
Career: Solicitor and chartered secretary.
Other lawyers: Employees share schenes, property work, compliance / corporate governance.

Electra Investment Trust PLC
65 Kingsway, London WC2B 6QT
Tel: (020) 7831 6464 **Fax:** (020) 7404 5388
Philip Dyke, Company Secretary

Electrocomponents PLC
International Management Centre, 5000 Oxford Business Park South, Oxford OX4 2BH
Tel: (01865) 204000 **Fax:** (01865) 207400
Website: www.electrocomponents.com
Work outsourced: Variable
Carmelina Carfora, Group Company Secretary
Specialisation: Company secretarial – all issues; Legal; Risk Management; Corporate Benefits.
Career: Essex Institute of Higher Education. Institute of Chartered Secretaries and Administrators qualification. Now a Fellow of Institute of Chartered Secretaries, and Administrators.
Other lawyers: Commercial, Intellectual Property, Employment, Property, Company, IT.

EMAP PLC
1 Lincoln Court, Lincoln Road, Peterborough PE1 2RF
Tel: (01733) 568 900 **Fax:** (01733) 312115
Website: www.emap.com
No of lawyers in dept: 0
D. Warmsley, Company Secretary

EMI Group PLC
4 Tenterden Street, Hanover Square, London W1A 2AY
Tel: (020) 7355 4848 **Fax:** (020) 7495 1421
Website: www.emigroup.com
Charles Ashcroft, Company Secretary and Group General Counsel

EMI Group PLC
4 Tenterden Street, Hanover Square, London W1A 2AY
Tel: (020) 7355 4848 **Fax:** (020) 7495 1424
James Radice, Director of Business Affairs

Energis plc
50 Victoria Embankment, London EC4Y 0DE
Tel: (020) 7206 5555 **Fax:** (020) 7206 5500
Website: www.energis.net
No of lawyers in dept: 1
Work outsourced: 100% – Corporate, commercial, employment, IP, property
Andrew McKelvie, Assistant Company Secretary
Specialisation: All aspects of company sectretarial work. Co-ordinates outsourced legal work throughout the group.
Career: Joined Energis in May 1998, previously Asisstant Company Secretary for Henlys Group plc. BA Hons at Leeds for Politics and Sociology, FCIS.
Personal: Born 1964, interests include rugby and golf, married with two children.
Other lawyers: One in-house property lawyer.

Enodis PLC
Washington House, 40-41 Conduit Street, London W1R 9FB
Tel: (020) 7312 2500 **Fax:** (020) 7312 2501
David Hooper, Company Secretary

Enron Europe Limited
Enron House, 40 Grosvenor Place, London SW1X 7EN
Tel: (020) 7783 0000 **Fax:** (020) 7734 2868
Paul Simons, Assistant General Counsel

Enron Europe Limited
Enron House, 40 Grosvenor Place, London SW1X 7EN
Tel: (020) 7783 0000 **Fax:** (020) 7734 2868
Justin Boyd, Senior Legal Advisor

Enterprise Oil plc
Grand Buildings, Trafalgar Square, London WC2N 5EJ
Tel: (020) 7925 4000 **Fax:** (020) 7925 4321
Website: www.entoil.com
No of lawyers in dept: 10
Work outsourced: variable (conveyancing, litigation, large financings or acquisitions, other specialist work).
Andrew Wilson, Head Of Legal Affairs
Specialisation: Oil and Gas Law
Career: Solicitor 1977

Enterprise Energy Ireland Ltd
4th Floor, Embassy House, Herbert Park Lane, Ballsbridge, Dublin 4
Tel: 00 353 16 673759
David Bate, Legal Manager

Ernst & Young
Becket House, 1 Lambeth Palace Road, London SE1 7EU
Tel: (020) 7951 2000 **Fax:** (020) 7951 1345
Victoria Cochrane, Partner

Euromoney Institutional Investors Ord 1p
Nestor House, Playhouse Yard, London EC4V 5EX
Tel: (020) 7779 8888 **Fax:** (020) 7779 8656
Colin Jones, Company Secretary

European Bank for Reconstruction & Development (EBRD)
One Exchange Square, Primrose Street, London EC2A 2JN
Tel: (020) 7338 6000 **Fax:** (020) 7338 6150
Emmanuel Maurice, General Counsel

Eurotunnel PLC/Eurotunnel SA
BP 69, Coquelles 62904
Tel: (01303) 273300
Philip Dewast, Head of Legal

Express Newspapers Ltd
Ludgate House, 245 Blackfriars Road, Blackfriars, London SE1 9UX
Tel: (020) 7928 8000 **Fax:** (020) 7620 1654
Justin Walford, Legal Advisor

F.I. Group PLC
Campus 300, Maylands Avenue, Hemel Hempstead HP2 7TQ
Tel: (01442) 434 016 **Fax:** (01442) 434248
No of lawyers in dept: 1
Work outsourced: M&A, Litigation, Property, specialist work
C. E. Lilley, Legal Adviser
Specialisation: Mergers and Acquisitions, Joint Ventures, Company/Commercial
Career: Newcastle University LL.B. 1985; Qualified 1988 (Articles *Bailey & Walker*); *Biddle & Co* 1988-91; Courtaulds plc 1991-99; F.I. Group plc, 1999 to date
Other lawyers: All legal issues

Fairey Group PLC
Crest House, Station Road, Egham TW20 9NP
Tel: (01784) 470 470 **Fax:** (01784) 470848
Work outsourced: 95% – Acquisitions, disposals, litigation, property, employment, pensions.
Roger Stephens, Company Secretary

Fibernet Group
Olympus House, Calleva Industrial Park, Aldermaston RG7 8SA
Tel: (0118) 940 8500 **Fax:** (0118) 981 1552
Edward Hailey, Company Secretary

Film Finances Limited
14 - 15 Conduit Street, London W1S 2XJ
Tel: (020) 7629 6557 **Fax:** (020) 7491 7530
James Shirras, Financial Director

FilmFour
76-78 Charlotte Street, London W1P 1LY
Tel: (020) 7868 7700 **Fax:** (020) 7868 7773
Andrew Hildebrand, Director of Business Affairs

Filtronic plc
The Waterfront, Salts Mill Road, Saltaire, Shipley BD18 3TT
Tel: (01274) 530 622 **Fax:** (01274) 531561
Email: cschofie@filct.com
No of lawyers in dept: 1
Work outsourced: N/A – Property, Employment, Litigation, Transactions
Christopher Schofield, Director
Specialisation: Responsibility for all the Group's legal & corporate requirements, the project management of acquisitions, the administration of the Group's Employee Benefit and Retirement Schemes. And the global insurance requirements.
Career: Bradford Grammar School 1972-1981. Girton College Cambridge 1981-1984 (Law).
Personal: Married to Helen, 3 daughters: Elizabeth 10, Ruth 8, Hannah 2.
Other lawyers: Company/Commercial, Corporate Finance.

Financial Services Authority
25 The North Colonnade, Canary Wharf, London E14 5HS
Tel: (020) 7676 1000 **Fax:** (020) 7676 1099
Andrew Whittaker, Deputy General Counsel

First Choice Holidays PLC
First Choice House, London Road, Crawley RH10 2GX
Tel: (01293) 560 777 **Fax:** (01293) 539039
Website: www.firstchoiceholidays.com
No of lawyers in dept: 4
Work outsourced: 30% – large corporate finance transactions and M&A work; major banking transactions; property; large scale commercial litigation and aviation finance.
Rebecca Starling, Group Company Secretary
Specialisation: Corporate, Commercial, Commercial litigation
Career: Univercity College of London 81-84, Inn's Court School Law 85-86, Called to bar 86, requalified as a solicitor 89, Company Solicitor at Tiphook Plc 90-93, Legal Advisor United Biscuits 94-95
Other lawyers: contract buying legal services

First Technology PLC
2 Cheapside, Buckhurst Road, Ascot SL5 7RF
Tel: (01344) 622322 **Fax:** (01344) 622773
Neil Clayton, Company Secretary

First Telecom PLC
Exchange Tower, 1 Harbour Exchange Square, London E14 9GB
Tel: (020) 7572 7700 **Fax:** (020) 7532 7701
Natasha Hobday, European Regulatory Counsel

FirstGroup
32a Weymouth Street, London W1N 3FA
Tel: (020) 7291 0500 **Fax:** (020) 7636 1338
Email: louisehowell@firstgroup.com
Website: www.firstgroup.com
No of lawyers in dept: 1
Work outsourced: 90% – Company/Commercial, Corporate Finance, Litigation, Property, Pensions, Employment, Regulatory (railways)
Louise Howell, Group Legal Adviser and Company Secretary
Specialisation: Company / Commercial Law / Corporate Finance
Career: University of Liverpool (LL.B. First Class Hons) 1985-1988; Guildford College of Law 1988-1989; Slaughter and May 1990-1997; Merrill Lynch (UK Counsel) 1997-1998; FirstGroup plc 1998-present

Fitness First PLC
58 Fleets Lane, Fleetsbridge, Poole BH15 3BT
Tel: (01202) 845000 **Fax:** (01202) 683510
Susan Cadd, Company Secretary

FKI PLC
Concorde House, Trinity Park, Birmingham B37 1ES
Tel: (0121) 782 2073 **Fax:** (0121) 782 2079
Email: tony.ventrella@fkiplc.com
Website: www.fki.co.uk
No of lawyers in dept: 1
Work outsourced: 100% M&A, 90% Property, 10% Litigation
A. Ventrella, Director – Legal Services
Specialisation: All legal matters affecting operational companies, with particular emphasis of all contractual matters. Include supply contracts, purchasing agreements, agency contracts, distributorship and licencing agreements. All but major items of litigation/arbitration and some employment tribunal work. Also responsible for managing external lawyers in the UK and overseas. Provides commercial training of managers.
Career: LL.B. (Hons) Sheffield University 1977. Attended College of Law 1977-1978 and called to the Bar by Lincoln's Inn 1978. MA (Business Law) from City of London Polytechnic 1981. Legal and Commercial Adviser to HVCA 1978-1984, Legal Director and Company Secretary of BEAMA Ltd 1984-1997. Member of the IEE/I. Mech, Conditions of Contract Drafting Panel. Formerly member of a number of CBI Panels.
Personal: Married with three children. Author of "Contractors Guide to Contract Law".
Other lawyers: Engineeing contracts and contractual matters generally smaller litigation and arbitration proceedings.

Flemings
25 Copthall Avenue, London EC2R 7DR
Tel: (020) 7638 5858 **Fax:** (020) 7880 3486
Website: flemings.com
No of lawyers in dept: 10
Work outsourced: various – certain specialist work, litigation or property
Mark Roberts, Group Head of Legal
Specialisation: Company Commercial, Financial Services(Banking, Capital Markets, Corporate Finance, Securites and Asset Management)
Career: Solicitor- Admitted in England in 1978 and in Hong Kong in 1988. Commenced practise with *Norton Rose*. Subsequently moved in-house in1981 with Albright and Wilson LTD; Bush Boaxe Allen Group 1983-88; Jardine matheson Holdings LTD 1988-93; Jardine Fleming 1993-99; Robert Fleming 1999 to date.
Personal: Married with 4 children
Other lawyers: London- Paul Mcdade(Head of Legal, Western Hemisphere), Jonathan White, Claire McKenna, Andrew Cullum. Hong Kong- Frederick Horsey(Head of Legal, Asia), Lezan Marega, Jonathan Collins, Louise Flanagan, Dennis Ha

Football Association Premier League Limited
16 Lancaster Gate, London W2 3LW
Tel: (020) 7314 5320 **Fax:** (020) 7314 5325
Nicholas Coward, Company Secretary

Football Association Premier League Limited
16 Lancaster Gate, London W2 3LW
Tel: (020) 7314 5320 **Fax:** (020) 7314 5325
Darren Berman, Company Solicitor

Foreign & Colonial Management Group PLC
Exchange House, Primrose Street, London EC2A 2NY
Tel: (020) 7628 8000 **Fax:** (020) 7628 8188
Robert Donkin, Company Secretary

Formula One Management Ltd
6 Princes Gate, London SW7 1QJ
Tel: (020) 7584 6668 **Fax:** (020) 7581 1649
Sascha Woodward Hill, Lawyer

Framlington Group Ltd
155 Bishopsgate, London EC2M 3XJ
Tel: (020) 7374 4100 **Fax:** (020) 7330 6406
Josie Tubbs, Head of Legal & Secretariat

Franklin Templeton Investments
Saltire Court, 20 Castle Terrace, Edinburgh EH1 2EH
Tel: (0131) 469 4000 **Fax:** (0131) 228 4506
No of lawyers in dept: 4
Work outsourced: Litigation, Property
Keith Swinley, Chief Legal Counsel – Europe
Specialisation: Financial Services; Investment Management; Corporate Finance; Company Secretarial
Career: University of Dundee, LL.B Honours (2.1); British Aerospace; Dawson International plc
Other lawyers: Keith Swinley, Nigel Austin, Sara McIntosh, Gwyneth May : Financial Services, Contract, Commercial, Intellectual Property.

Freeserve Holdings PLC
500 The Campus, Maylands Avenue, Hemel Hempstead HP2 7TG
Tel: (01442) 353 000 **Fax:** (01442) 233 218
Email: david.melville@freeserve.com
Website: www.freeserve.com
No of lawyers in dept: 2
David Melville, Company Secretary and General Counsel
Other lawyers: Jessica Hendrie-Liano

Fuji Capital Markets (UK) Limited
River Plate House, 7-11 Finsbury Circus, London EC2M 7DH
Tel: (020) 7972 9900 **Fax:** (020) 7638 3945
Sean Russell, Legal Counsel

Gallaher Group
Members Hill, Brooklands Road, Weybridge KT13 0QU
Tel: (01932) 859777 **Fax:** (01932) 832792
Website: www.gallaher-group.com
No of lawyers in dept: 6
Christopher Devereux, Corporate Legal Adviser
Specialisation: Responsible for wide-ranging in-house legal service (including trade marks).
Career: Qualified 1975 and in private practice until 1978, when joined Gallaher Ltd, ultimately becoming Corporate Legal Adviser.
Personal: Main leisure activities, clubs: Arts, food/wine, travel, FRSA
Other lawyers: Suzanne Wise, Simon Witham, Helen Forth, Simon Drake, Chris Fielden.

Gartmore Investment Management PLC
Fenchurch Exchange, 8 Fenchurch Place, London EC3M 4PH
Tel: (020) 7782 2000 **Fax:** (020) 7374 3075
Simon Martin, Legal Manager

Gartmore Investment Management PLC
Fenchurch Exchange, 8 Fenchurch Place, London EC3M 4PH
Tel: (020) 7782 2000 **Fax:** (020) 7374 3075
Jane Thornton, Head of Legal Department and Company Secretary

GE Capital (Global Consumer Finance) Ltd
(UK) Capital House, Bond Street, Bristol BS1 3LA
Tel: (0117) 929 1133 **Fax:** (0117) 946 3424
Janet Gregory, Legal Director

Geo Interactive Media Group
1 Corazin Street, Givatayim 53583 Israel
Tel: (972) 3 5722111 **Fax:** (972) 3 5722100
Anna Zakut, Company Secretary

Gillette Management Inc.
Gilette Corner, Great West Road, Isleworth TW7 5NP
Tel: (020) 8560 1234 **Fax:** (020) 8568 4082
Stephen Jennings, Trade Mark Manager E Hemisphere

GKN PLC
PO Box 55, Redditch B98 0TL
Tel: (01527) 517 715 **Fax:** (01527) 517700
Email: information@gknplc.com
Website: www.gknplc.com
No of lawyers in dept: 8
Work outsourced: Litigation, conveyancing, minor matters, public offers, pensions work, tax, regulatory, employment.
Grey Denham, Company Secretary
Specialisation: The Group Secretary has overall responsibilty for all Secretarial and Governance services provided to the listed parent company and other central companies and for compliance and legal services to the Group worldwide. The Group Legal Department specialises in M&A, joint ventures, finance, strategic contracts (including helicopter and other defence contracts) litigation management, competition law and general company and commercial work, including e-commerce.
Career: 1972 – Lecturer in Law, Leicester Polytechnic; 1974 – Senior Lecturer in Legal Philosophy, Nottingham Law School; 1978 – Company Legal Officer, Alfred Herbert Limited; 1980 – Company Lawyer, GKN plc; 1983 Deputy Head of Legal, GKN plc; 1986 – Head of Legal, GKN plc; 1995 – Chairman, GKN Group Services Limited; 1996 – Company Secretary, GKN plc, Director GKN (United Kingdom) plc, President GKN North America Inc. Member of London Stock Exchange Regional Advisory Group, Council of Birmingham Chamber of Commerce and Industry, West Midlands Council of CBI.
Personal: Educated – Handsworth Grammar School; Brooklyn Technical College; Bristol College of Commerce; London University (LL.B.); Inns of Court Law School (called 1972); Columbia University Graduate School of Business (CSEP 1995). Leisure pursuits and interests include philosophy, particle physics, Warwickshire County Cricket Club, Aston Villa Football Club.
Rufus Ogilvie Smals, Head of Legal Department
Career: Read Law at Emmanuel College, Cambridge University. Attended Inns of Court School of Law. Called to the Bar (Middle Temple) 1973. Studied at Europa Institute, University of Amsterdam. Joined GKN in 1975, from Deputy Head of the Legal Department to Head of the Group Legal Department in 1995. Chairman of CBI Competition Panel.
Personal: Interests include sailing, skiing, military history and current affairs.
Other lawyers: Deputy Head of Legal Department: David Lee; Principal Legal Advisers: Sarah Eddowes, David Radford; Principal Legal Advisor – Strategic Contracts: Martin Elliott; Senior Legal Advisor – Strategic Contracts: Neil Cranidge; Legal Advisors: Martin Brostoff, Simon Gardiner.

Glaxo Wellcome plc
Glaxo Wellcome House, Berkeley Avenue, Greenford UB6 0NN
Tel: (020) 8966 8000 **Fax:** (020) 8966 8837
Website: www.glaxowellcome.com
No of lawyers in dept: 10

G

Work outsourced: 15% – Corporate, specialist planning, insolvency, product liability, litigation and specialist competition.
Brian Cahill, Director, Group Legal Services
Specialisation: Has management responsibility for commercial legal. Manages department providing an in-house corporate legal service to Glaxo Wellcome plc and its subsidiaries. Chairman of the Legal Committee of the Association of the British Pharmaceutical Industry (ABPI).
Career: Called to the Bar, Grays Inn 1977. Legal Adviser and Manager, Legal Department of ICL plc 1979-86, then took up present position.
Personal: Educated at Southampton University (LLB).

Glynwed International PLC
Headland House, New Coventry Road, Sheldon, Birmingham B26 3AZ
Tel: (0121) 742 2366 **Fax:** (0121) 722 7611
Email: d.solomon@glynwed.com
Website: www.glynwed.com
No of lawyers in dept: 2
Work outsourced: Variable – All litigation. A proportion of other work.
Deryck J Solomon, Group Secretary
Specialisation: Company, Commercial, Property and Company Secretarial.
Career: Education: Keble College, Oxford (1972 – 1975) M.A. (Oxon) Career: joined Glynwed as Solicitor in 1984 moved to Group Legal Manager 1993, in 1996 moved to Group Secretary1996 to date.
Other lawyers: Mrs. F. Wheeler:solicitor,property.

Goldman Sachs International
Peterborough Court, 133 Fleet Street, London EC4A 2BB
Tel: (020) 7774 1000 **Fax:** (020) 7774 1989
Roger Scotts, Executive Director

Goldman Sachs International
Peterborough Court, 133 Fleet Street, London EC4A 2BB
Tel: (020) 7774 1000 **Fax:** (020) 7774 1989
Website: www.gs.com
Gregory K. Palm, General Counsel

Goldman Sachs International
Peterborough Court, 133 Fleet Street, London EC4A 2BB
Tel: (020) 7774 1000 **Fax:** (020) 7774 1989
Sally Boyle, Executive Director & Counsel

Goldman Sachs International
Peterborough Court, 133 Fleet Street, London EC4A 2BB
Tel: (020) 7774 1000 **Fax:** (020) 7774 1989
David Geen, Executive Director and Senior Counsel

Goldman Sachs International
Daniel House, 140 Fleet Street, London EC4A 2BB
Tel: (020) 7774 1000 **Fax:** (020) 7774 1989
Alexander Marshall, Executive Director & Counsel

Goldman Sachs International
Peterborough Court, 133 Fleet Street, London EC4A 2BB
Tel: (020) 7774 1000 **Fax:** (020) 7774 1989
Therese Miller, Managing Director & General Counsel

Govett Strategic Inv Trust PLC
Shackleton House, 4 Battle Bridge Lane, London SE1 2HR
Tel: (020) 7378 7979 **Fax:** (020) 7638 3468
Ian Portal, Company Secretary

Granada Group PLC
Stornoway House, 13 Cleveland Row, London SW1A 1GG
Tel: (020) 7451 3000 **Fax:** (020) 7451 3008
Website: www.granada.co.uk
Work outsourced: 100% – All legal work
Graham Parrott, Commercial Director
Specialisation: Acquisitions/disposals, Pensions, Property, Insurance, Share schemes, Legal and Secretarial.
Personal: Born 1949. Lives in London.

Granada Group PLC
Granada Film, The London Television Centre, Upper Ground, London SE1 9LT
Tel: (020) 7737 8681 **Fax:** (020) 7451 8682
Mark Pybus, Head of Business Affairs

Great Portland Estates PLC
Knighton House, 56 Mortimer Street, London W1N 8BD
Tel: (020) 7580 3040 **Fax:** (020) 7631 5169
Desna Martin, Company Secretary

Great Universal Stores PLC
Universal House, Devonshire Street, Manchester M60 6EL
Tel: (0161) 273 8282 **Fax:** (0161) 277 4952
Email: harlap@gusco.com
Website: www.gusplc.co.uk/
Philip Harland, Head of Legal

Guardian IT Group
Benchmark House, St George's Business Centre, 203 Brooklands Road, Weybridge KT13 0RH
Tel: (01932) 835900 **Fax:** (01932) 835947
No of lawyers in dept: 2
Work outsourced: 10-20% – Acquisitions and property issues.
Francess Deigh, In-house Legal Counsel
Specialisation: IT contracts, IP, employment law, commercial, E-commerce, software licensing contracts.
Personal: Sculpting, paintng, music, reading and sports.
Other lawyers: E-commerce and other commercial matters

Guardian Newspapers Ltd
119 Farringdon Road, London EC1R 3ER
Tel: (020) 7278 2332 **Fax:** (020) 7713 4481
Siobhain Butterworth, Head of Legal Affairs

GWR Group PLC
Terminal 4, 3B2 Stonehill Green, Westlea, Swindon SN5 7HF
Tel: (0118) 928 4300 **Fax:** (0118) 928 4310
Wendy Pallot, Company Secretary

Halifax Group PLC
Trinity Rd, Halifax HX1 2RG
Tel: +44 1422 333333 **Fax:** +44 1422 333000
Email: harrybanes@halifax.co.uk
Website: www.halifax.co.uk
No of lawyers in dept: 25
Work outsourced: 20% – Treasury/M&A/some litigation
Harry Baines, Group Secretary
Other lawyers: Banking/Savings – 5; Financial Services – 2; Property – 6; Lending – 5; Commercial/Employment – 5; Litigation – 2.

Halma PLC
Misbourne Court, Rectory Way, Amersham HP7 0DE
Tel: (01494) 721 111 **Fax:** (01494) 728032
Email: carol.tredway@halma.com
Website: www.halma.com
E.Carol Tredway, Company Secretary

Hammerson PLC
100 Park Lane, London W1Y 4AR
Tel: (020) 7887 1000 **Fax:** (020) 7887 1010
Stuart Haydon, Company Secretary

Hanson PLC
1 Grosvenor Place, London SW1X 7JH
Tel: (020) 7245 1245 **Fax:** (020) 7235 3455
Website: www.hansonplc.com
No of lawyers in dept: 2
Work outsourced: Varies by division – Property, Litigation
Graham Dransfield, Legal Director
Specialisation: Company/ Commercial, Corporate Finance. Acting for the UK head office companies and UK subsidiaries in corporate and commercial activities. Property and litigation not dealt with in-house; legal structure operates on decentralised basis.
Career: Coune Valley High School; St Catherine's College, Oxford. Articled *Slaughter and May* 1974-82; Joined Hanson plc 1982, Legal Director since 1992.
Personal: Beckenham Tennis and Squash Club; The Addington Golf Club
Other lawyers: Samantha J. Hurrell. Company / Commerical / Corporate Finance / General

HarperCollins Publishers Ltd
77-85 Fulham Palace Road, London W6 6JB
Tel: (020) 8307 4665 **Fax:** (020) 8317 4668
Adrian Laing, Director of Legal Affairs/Company Secretary

Hays PLC
Hays House, Millmead, Guildford GU2 5HJ
Tel: (01483) 302 203 **Fax:** (01483) 455242
Website: www.hays-plc.co.uk
No of lawyers in dept: 4
Work outsourced: 60% – acquisitions/disposals of companies/businesses, major commercial contracts, employment, litigation, property, pensions
Stephen Charnock, Company Secretary and Head Of Legal
Specialisation: Acquisitions, joint ventures, major contracts, company secretarial, share options, pensions. Career: LLB. Bristol (1977). *Masons* (1978-80); Berec Group plc (1980-82); Automotive Products plc (1982-86); Whitbread plc (1986-90); Hays plc (1991 to date).
Other lawyers: Paul Dungate – Senior Solicitor. Henry Stevenson – Solicitor. Jon Wellbourne-Green – Solicitor.

Henderson Investors
3 Finsbury Avenue, London EC2M 2PA
Tel: (020) 7638 5757 **Fax:** (020) 7410 4639
Jonathon Thomas, Divisional Director of Legal Services

Henderson Electric & General Investment Co PLC
3 Finsbury Avenue, London EC2M 2PA
Tel: (020) 7410 4100 **Fax:** (020) 7377 5742
Rachel Fieldwick, Company Secretary

Henderson Smaller Cos Inv Tst
3 Finsbury Avenue, London EC2M 2PA
Tel: (020) 7638 5757 **Fax:** (020) 7377 5742
Geoffrey Rice, Company Secretary

Henderson Technology Trust PLC
3 Finsbury Avenue, London EC2M 2PA
Tel: (020) 7638 5757 **Fax:** (020) 7377 5742
Rebecca Woodley, Company Secretary

Hepworth PLC
2 Cavendish Square, London W1M 9HA
Tel: (020) 7307 7700 **Fax:** (020) 7631 5444
Helen Grantham, Group Company Secretary

Herald Investment Trust PLC
12 Charter House Square, London EC1M 6AX
Tel: (020) 7553 6300 **Fax:** (020) 7490 8026
Email: info@heralduk.com
Website: www.heralduk.com
Alan Sadler, Company Secretary

Hilton Group plc
Maple Court, Central Park, Reeds Crescent, Watford WD1 1HZ
Tel: 020 7850 4000 **Fax:** 020 7850 4001
Website: www. hilton.com
No of lawyers in dept: 7
Work outsourced: 20% – Various
J. Geoffrey Chester, In-house Lawyer
Specialisation: Responsible for all legal and company secretarial work for Hilton Group plcs Hotel division including all Hilton International Co's Hotels with particular emphasis in development (new hotels)
Career: Articed Lloyd Raymond & Co / Edward Thompson & Co; qualified 1976; company commercial solicitor National Coal Board 1981-1985; head of company / commercial section of the legal department Ladbroke Group plc 1985-1988; transferred in 1988 from Ladbroke to head up Hilton International Co's legal department (solicitor, general counsel and secretary). Univeristy College, Cardiff (1973, BSc); City of London Polytechnic (1977, MA Business Law); City University (1986, MBA)
Personal: Born 1951; resides Kew Gardens.

Hiscox Insurance Company Limited
1 Great St. Helen's, London EC3A 6HX
Tel: (020) 7448 6000 **Fax:** (020) 7448 6299
Bob Britton, In-house Solicitor

Hit Entertainment
The Pumphouse, 13-16 Jacobs Well Mews, London W1H 5PD
Tel: (020) 7224 1717 **Fax:** (020) 7224 1719
Jessica Davis, Director of Legal and Business Affairs

Hoare Govett Ltd
4 Broadgate, London EC2M 7LE
Tel: (020) 7601 0101 **Fax:** (020) 7374 7612
Genny Stevinson, Head of Legal

HSBC Holdings PLC
10 Lower Thames Street, P.O. Box 506, London EC3R 6AE
Tel: (020) 7260 0500 **Fax:** (020) 7260 3446
Website: www.hsbc.com
No of lawyers in dept: 34
Work outsourced: 60% – Major transactions, litigation
Richard.E.T. Bennett, Group General Manager, Legal and Compliance
Specialisation: Responsible for the Legal & Compliance function of the HSBC Holdings Group.
Career: Bristol University (LLB), graduated 1973. Qualified with *Stephenson Harwood*, 1976. Assistant Solicitor with *Stephenson Harwood* until 1979 (seconded to the East Asiatic Company, Denmark 1977). Appointed Assistant Group Legal Adviser with The Hong Kong and Shanghai Banking Corporation 1979. Deputy Group Legal Adviser 1988. Head of Legal & Compliance of The Hong Kong and Shanghai Banking Corporation Ltd 1993 with responsibility for legal, compliance and secretarial functions in Asia Pacific. Appointed to present position 1 January 1998.
Personal: Born 20th September 1951. Leisure pursuits include; all sports, particularly rugby and golf. Lives in Surrey/London.

HSBC Holdings PLC
Bintners Place, 68 Upper Thames, London EC4V 3BJ
Tel: (020) 7260 9000
David Bloom, Senior Legal Adviser

HSBC Holdings PLC
Royton House, 14 George Road, Edgbaston, Birmingham B15 1NT
Tel: (0121) 455 2722 **Fax:** (0121) 455 2771
Stephen Garratt-Frost, Head of Legal Services

Hyder PLC
PO Box 295, 2 Alexander Gate, Rover Way, Cardiff CF2 2UE
Tel: (029) 20500600 **Fax:** (029) 20585732
Email: company.secretary@hyder.com
Website: www.Hyde.com
No of lawyers in dept: 7
Work outsourced: 30-40% - Litigation, stock exchange, heavy M&A, conveyancing.
Geoff Williams, Director of Legal Affairs
Specialism: Company, commercial, contracting, finance, general contract, employment, international joint ventures. Also has functional responsibility for risk management, insurance and pensions for Group.
Career: Worked for British Nuclear Fuels Ltd in their legal department from 1969-76, and then became legal adviser at Lucas Industries from 1976-82. Joined Bass Plc in 1982 and was Group Legal adviser there until 1993. Joined Hyder Plc (formerly Welsh Water) in 1993. Qualified in 1975.
Personal: Crossword fan, interested in fine arts.
Other lawyers: N Hunt, J George, YH Cheung - company commercial. P Jones - litigation, regulatory. T Ashcroft - regulatory, planning. S Donce - conveyancing.

IBJ International
Bracken House, 1 Friday Street, London EC4M 9JA
Tel: (020) 7236 1090 **Fax:** (020) 7489 6997
No of lawyers in dept: 9
Work outsourced: Major transactions and specialist advisory.
Brian Lanaghan, Head of Legal
Specialisation: Fixed income and equity new issues, derivatives, funds, custody, investment management, futures, commercial banking, general advisory.
Career: George Watson's College, Edinburgh. The Perse School, Cambridge. (MA) English and Law, Cambridge. Masters in European Community Law, Brussels.
Personal: Tennis, sailing, shooting, garden design, piano, languages; French (fluent), German (reasonable).

Iceland Group PLC
Second Avenue, Deeside Industrial Park, Deeside CH5 2NW
Tel: (01244) 842329 **Fax:** (01244) 842684
Email: john.berry@iceland.co.uk
No of lawyers in dept: 3
Work outsourced: 80% – conveyancing, litigation, corporate tax.
John Berry, Company Secretary
Specialisation: Responsible for Group's legal, company secretarial, licensing, pensions and employee benefits, insurance, fire and health and safety, and car fleet functions. Member of BACFI. Has addressed conference on ESOPs.
Career: Qualified as a Barrister 1976. Assistant company secretary Smith's Industries plc 1973-76. Assistant secretary, The Rank Organisation plc 1976-83. Legal Manager HP Bulmer Holdings plc 1983-85, then joined Iceland plc.
Personal: Educated at Glyn Grammar School, Epsom 1963-70 and Coventry Polytechnic (now University) 1970-73 (BA Hons, Business Law). Leisure pursuits include running, skiing, golf, gardening and books. Born 23rd January 1952. Lives in Chester.

Imagination Technologies Group PLC
Home Park Estate, Kings Langley WD4 8LZ
Tel: (01923) 260511 **Fax:** (01923) 270188
Trevor Selby, Company Secretary

IMI PLC
Kynoch Works, PO Box 216, Witton, Birmingham B6 7BA
Tel: (0121) 356 4848 **Fax:** (0121) 356 0544
Website: www.ini.plc.uk
No of lawyers in dept: 3
Work outsourced: 60% – Corporate, litigation and conveyancing
John O'Shea, Company Secretary
Other lawyers: Paul Boulton : General Corporate and Commercial; Joanne Bower : General Corporate and Commercial

Imperial Chemical Industries PLC
9 Millbank, London SW1P 3JF
Tel: (020) 7834 4444 **Fax:** (020) 7798 5872
Email: michael-herlihy@ici.com
Website: www.ici.com
Work outsourced: litigation, property and pensions.
Michael H.C. Herlihy, General Counsel
Specialisation: Oversees the lawyers in the Group and responsible for provision of legal advice to the ICI Board and all members of the ICI Group.
Career: Qualified in 1977. University – St. Catherine's College, Oxford. Joined ICI 1979; 1985-1992 Manager of Legal Affairs Department, ICI Agrochemicals; 1992-1995 Group Taxation Controller; 1996 to date General Counsel.
Other lawyers: R.J. Peters, Deputy General Counsel; A.R. Graham, Corporate Counsel; J.C.A. Fielding, Litigation Co-ordinator; N R Paton; D. Jash; M.A.J. Maughan; P. Roebuck; R.W.T. Turner, Group Intellectual Property Counsel; K J Rushton, Company Secretary; J L Kay, Manager; R Draper; G Fish; A K Gwynne-Jones; P Snaith; C M Vaughan; G G Attrill, Deputy Manager; J R Robey; G St John Turner; S M Turner; D J Aspinall, Senior Lawyer; J Goodfellow, Litigation Manager; W Shepherd, Legal Counsel; D J Busby, Company Secretary; J H Jones, Legal Affairs Manager; P Davies, Commercial Legal Manager; A Harbert; M McLean; B Moli.

Imperial Tobacco Group PLC
PO Box 244, Upton Road, Southville, Bristol BS99 7UJ
Tel: (0117) 963 6636 **Fax:** (0117) 988 1472
Website: www.imperial-tobacco.com
Work outsourced: 90% – Corporate, M&A, Litigation, IP, Commercial
Alan Porter, Legal Manager

Incepta Group PLC
3 London Wall Buildings, London Wall, London EC2M 5SY
Tel: (020) 7638 9571 **Fax:** (020) 7282 8030
Kevin B Steeds, Company Secretary

Independent Energy UK Limited
Radcliffe House, Blenheim Court, Solihull B91 2AA
Tel: 0121 703 3885 **Fax:** 0121 705 2304
Email: john stubbs@independentenergy.co.uk
Website: www.INDEPENDENTENERGY.co.uk
No of lawyers in dept: 2
Work outsourced: 50% – Litigation, Overflow, Specialisations
John Stubbs, Legal Counsel
Specialisation: Company / Commercial, energy, property, telecoms
Career: Queen Mary College, University of London – LL.B. 1972; Admission as Solicitor, England and Wales, 1976; City of London Polytechnic M.A. Business LAN, 1986; Member of Chartered Institute of Purchasing and Supply, 1994; Richards Butler to 1981; Central Electricity Generating Board 1981-1990 (Commercial Solicitor); National Power plc 1990-1992 (Head of Corporate Law); Scottish Power plc 1992-1996 (Director of Contracts and Purchasing); Consultancy 1996-1999; Independent Energy Holdings plc 1999 to date (Legal Counsel).
Other lawyers: John Stubbs – Company / Commercial, Energy, Property, Telecoms; Ed McCabe – Commercial, IP, Litigation, Energy, Water.

Independent Insurance Group PLC
No 2 Minster Court, Mincing Lane, London EC3R 7BB
Tel: (020) 7623 8877 **Fax:** (020) 7626 4703
Alison Byrne, Group Solicitor

Independent Newspapers Ltd
One Canada Square, 18th Floor, Canary Wharf, London E14 5DL
Tel: (020) 7293 2000 **Fax:** (020) 7293 2575
Louise Hayman, Legal Manager

Independent Television Ltd
200 Grays Inn Road, London WC1X 8XZ
Tel: (020) 7430 4779 **Fax:** (020) 7843 8158
Simon Johnson, Head of Legal

Infobank International Holdings PLC
Technology House, Waterside Drive, Langley Business Park, Langley SL3 6EZ
Tel: (01753) 799 500 **Fax:** (01753) 799 505
David Timothy Campbell Pollock, Company Secretary

Informa Group
19 Portland Place, London W1N 3AF
Tel: (020) 7453 5972 **Fax:** (020) 7453 5979
Website: www.llplimited.com
Andrea Wilson, Company Secretary

International Water Limited
New Zealand House, 80 Haymarket, London SW1Y 4TE
Tel: (020) 7766 5100 **Fax:** (020) 7766 5180
Keith Donald, General Counsel

InterX
Holden House, 57 Routhbone Place, London W1P 1AW
Tel: (020) 7769 9200 **Fax:** (020) 7769 9201
Website: www.interx.co.uk
Simon Miesegaes, Company Secretary
Other lawyers: Helen Hancock

Invensys PLC
Carlisle Place, London SW1P 1BX
Tel: (020) 7821 3743 **Fax:** (020) 7821 3806
Website: www.invensys.com
No of lawyers in dept: 30
James C. Bays, Senior Vice President, General Counsel and Chief Legal Officer
Specialisation: General Corporate, International.
Career: Education: AB Dartmouth College (1971) JD University of Virginia Law School (1974). Career: *Jones Day Reavis & Pogue* (1974-1978). Trid Inc (1978-1992). GenCorp Inc (1993-1996). Invensys plc (plc and Siebe plc)

Investors Capital Trust PLC
1 Charlotte Square, Edinburgh EH2 4DZ
Tel: (0131) 225 1357 **Fax:** (0131) 225 2375
M.A. Campbell, Company Secretary

ITNET plc
Laburnum House, Laburnum Road, Birmingham B30 2BD
Tel: (0121) 459 1155 **Fax:** (0121) 683 4240
Website: www.itnet.co.uk
No of lawyers in dept: 3
Work outsourced: 15-25% – Corporate finance, litigation, property, employment.
Andrew Foster, Company Secretary
Specialisation: Provision of company secretarial service. Provision of full range of legal services, primarily focused on new business sales. Work includes advice on IT contracts, employment (especially TUPE issues), corporate finance and property matters.
Career: Law degree at Birmingham University 1983-85. Qualified as a solicitor in 1989. Company commercial work at edge ellison 1989-92. Legal adviser at AT&T Istel 1992-96. Appointed company solicitor at Itnet in 1996 and company secretary in July 1999.
Personal: Member of Government-sponsored advisory group on intellectual property. Contributes to Outsourcing Practice Manual, published by Sweet and Maxwell. Treasurer of Law Society Commerce and Industry Group (Midlands section). Keen sports fan, particularly football.

Jardine Lloyd Thompson Group PLC
6 Crutched Friars, London EC3N 2PH
Tel: (020) 7528 4000 **Fax:** (020) 7528 4185
V. Wade, Group Legal Director

Jim Henson Company
30 Oval Road, Camden Town, London NW1 7DE
Tel: (020) 7428 4000 **Fax:** (020) 7428 4001
Antonia S. Downey, Head of Legal

JJB Sports PLC
Martland Park, Challenge Way, Wigan WN5 0LD
Tel: (01942) 221400 **Fax:** (01942) 629809
Website: www.jjb.co.uk
No of lawyers in dept: 0
Work outsourced: Lease Acquisition/Disposal, Corporate Acquisitions, Litigation
John David Greenwood, Company Secretary & Finance Director
Specialisation: Accounting, administration and Company Secretarial duties. Corporate Finance affairs
Career: FCA

Johnson Matthey PLC
2-4 Cockspur Street, Trafalgar Square, London SW1Y 5BQ
Tel: (020) 7269 8400 **Fax:** (020) 7269 8476
Website:www.matthey.com
Work outsourced: 30% – Major M&A, corporate, commercial, employment, litigation.
Simon Farrant, Senior Legal Adviser and Company Secretary

Johnston Press PLC
53 Manor Place, Edinburgh EH3 7EG
Tel: (0131) 225 3361 **Fax:** (0131) 225 4580
Email: jpress@go-free.co.uk
Website: www.johnstonpress.co.uk
No of lawyers in dept: 0
Work outsourced: 100% – Corporate, Property, Pensions and Competition.
Richard Cooper, Company Secretary

JP Morgan & Co
60 Victoria Embankment, London EC4Y 0JP
Tel: (020) 7600 2300 **Fax:** (020) 7325 8150
Website: www.jpmorgan.com
No of lawyers in dept: 24
Luigi L. De Ghenghi, Head of Legal
Other lawyers: Luigi L. De Ghenghi – Head of Legal; David A. Lewis – Deputy Head of Legal; Paul L. Scibetta – Deputy Head of Legal.

JP Morgan Securities
28 Kings Street, London SW1Y 6XA
Tel: (020) 7451 8000
David Lewis, Vice-President & Assistant General Counsel

JSB Software Technologies Plc. / JSBS
Riverside, Mountbatten Way, Congleton CW12 1DY
Tel: (01260) 296200 **Fax:** (01260) 296201
Website: www.jsb.com
Shelagh Margaret Rogan, Group Chief Financial Officer and Company Secretary

Kelda Group PLC
2 The Embankment, Sovereign Street, Leeds LS1 4BG
Tel: (0113) 234 3234 **Fax:** (0113) 242 9511
Website: www.keldagroup.com
No of lawyers in dept: 8
Steven Webb, General Counsel/Company Secretary

Kewill Systems PLC
Case House, 85-89 High St, Walton-on-Thames KT12 1DL
Tel: (01932) 248 328 **Fax:** (01932) 233 222
Richard Broad, Company Secretary

Kingfisher PLC
North West House, 119 Marylebone Road, London NW1 5PX
Tel: (020) 7724 7749 **Fax:** (020) 7724 0355
Website: www.kingfisher.co.uk
No of lawyers in dept: 1
Work outsourced: 95% – Company commercial, trusts, competition, M&A, contracts, property, etc.
Helen Jones, Company Secretary
Specialisation: M&A, commercial/contracts, listed company/corporate governance, e-commerce
Career: Qualified Chartered Secretary – 1976. Initial graduate trainingat Coventry Climax in finance function followed by two and a half years with Ernst and Whinney in company secretarial function. Moved to Guiness plc in October 1979 and stayed until April 1987 – working in Company Secretariat, Legal and Corporate Finance departments – principally on the legal/company secretarial work of M&A transactions. Thirteen years with Kingfisher plc from April 1987. Initially as Assistant Company Secretary to Kingfisher. One year in Finance working on risk management, insurance and consumer credit followed by three and a half years at Woolworths – working in marketing, buying, logistics and change management before returning to Kingfisher in May 1995, formally taking the role of Group Company Secretary on 1st June 1995.
Other lawyers: Patrick Andrews – Company/Commercial, Corporate Finance, other general

Kingston Communications (HULL) PLC
Telephone House, Carr Lane, Kingston upon Hull HU1 3RE
Tel: (01482) 602 614 **Fax:** (01482) 210765
Website: www.kingston-comms.co.uk
No of lawyers in dept: 4
Work outsourced: 30% – Property matters, litigation, transactions involving foreign law, planning, acquisitions, pensions, some commercial and regulatory work.
John Bailey, Company Secretary and Head of Legal Affairs
Specialisation: Company Secretarial and Admin.; Commercial Contracts; Competition and Regulatory
Career: Birmingham University 2.1 LL.B; Liverpool Polytechnic Law Society Finals; Daniel Ashworth and Booth Macclesfield Articles; Ernest Scragg and Sons Ltd.- Assistant Legal Adviser; Nickerson Plant Breeders Ltd. – Legal Adviser; GEC Telecommunications Ltd – Legal Adviser; Plessy Office Systems Ltd – Legal Adviser
Personal: Married with four children. Interests include sailing and classic car maintenance.
Other lawyers: John Bailey; Matthew Pearson; Melanie Evans; Stuart North

Kvaerner PLC
Maple Cross House, Denham Way, Maples Cross, Rickmansworth WD3 2SW
Tel: (01923) 423 852 **Fax:** (01923) 423 864
Hilary Wilson, Legal Adviser

Laing Construction PLC/John Laing Construction Ltd
133 Page Street, Mill Hill, London NW7 2ER
Tel: (020) 8959 3636 **Fax:** (020) 8906 5485
Graham Gibson, Head of Group Legal Services

Laing Construction PLC/John Laing Construction Ltd
133 Page Street, Mill Hill, London NW7 2ER
Tel: (020) 8959 3636 **Fax:** (020) 8906 5485
Martin Lenihan, Barrister

Land Securities
5 Strand, London WC2N 5AF
Tel: (020) 7413 9000 **Fax:** (020) 7925 0202
Website: www.landsecurities.co.uk
Work outsourced: 90% – Majority of Property – all Corporate
Clive Ashcroft, Legal Manager

Laporte PLC
8th & 9th Floors, Nations House, 103 Wigmore Street, London W1H 9AB
Tel: (020) 7399 2400 **Fax:** (020) 7399 2444
Email: NickSmith@laporteplc.com
Website: www.laporteplc.com
No of lawyers in dept: 2
Work outsourced: 40% – M & A, Property, Litigation
Nicholas Smith, Company Secretary and Director of Legal Affairs.
Specialisation: Corporate Finance, Company and Commercial. Career: 1996/97 – General Counsel, Cronos S.A. 1984-94 Legal Director, Tiphook plc, 1983-84 Company Sec and Legal Adviser, Acrow plc, 1975-83 Solicitor, Smiths Industries plc.

LASMO PLC
101 Bishopsgate, London EC2M 3XH
Tel: (020) 7892 9000 **Fax:** (020) 7892 9262
Email: alan.o'brien@lasmo.com
Website: lasmo.com
No of lawyers in dept: 13
Work outsourced: public financing, property, litigation, some M&A and employment work; marine law and outsourcing
Alan O'Brien, General Counsel, Company Secretary and Head of Legal.
Specialisation: Oil and Gas matters. Member of UK Energy Lawyers Group and Association of International Petroleum Negotiations.
Career: Qualified 1982. With Costain Group PLC 1982-1986; Marathon Oil, 1986-1990 before joining LASMO plc. Completed postings in Canada, Colombia and Italy.
Personal: Born 19th June, 1957 in Birmingham. Lives in Marlow. Married with 2 children.

Lazard Brothers & Co., Limited
21 Moorfields, London EC2P 2HT
Tel: (020) 7588 2721 **Fax:** (020) 7920 0670
Website: www.lazard.com
No of lawyers in dept: 4
Will Dennis, Company Secretary and General Counsel
Specialisation: Corporate finance, banking, stock lending, asset management, capital markets.
Career: Cambridge University 1971-74, MA LLM. Foreign & Commonwealth Office 1977-86. *Clifford Chance* 1987-91. Partner *Denton Hall* 1991-93. Director N M Rothchild & Sons (Hong Kong) Ltd 1993-96. Lazard Brothers since 1996.

Legal & General Group PLC
Legal & General House, Kingswood, Tadworth KT20 6EU
Tel: (01737) 376128 **Fax:** (01737) 376144
Email: geoffrey.timms@landg.com
Website: www.legalandgeneral.co.uk
Work outsourced: Large corporate transactions and litigation, and Commercial Property.

L

Geoffrey Timms, Group Head of Legal
Specialisation: Heads up a small team providing advice and assistance to the Group and its sunsidiary components.
Career: BA (Hons): University of Kent 1986; Clifford Chance, 1987-89; Clyde & Co, 1989-91; Legal & General, 1991 to date.
Other lawyers: Liz Tubb (Deputy Head); Sandra Phillips; Andrew Webster

Lehman Brothers International (Europe)
One Broadgate, London EC2M 7HA
Tel: (020) 7601 0011 **Fax:** (020) 7260 2243
Email: pmarchan@lehman.com
No of lawyers in dept: 16
Work outsourced: 20% – litigation, services of underwriters' counsel, occasional specialist advice.
Piers Le Marchant, European Legal Director
Specialisation: Equity and fixed income capital markets. Derivatives, emerging markets. Some investment banking and litigation. Chairman of the New Products Committee and Transaction Review Group.
Career: Lehman Brothers from Dec 91. Previously Nomura International plc. Qualified as Barrister 1987. Educated London University & Canford School.

Lex Service PLC
Lex House, Boston Drive, Bourne End SL8 5YS
Tel: (01628) 843 888 **Fax:** (01628) 810294
No of lawyers in dept: 2
Work outsourced: 90% – Major acquisition-divestments, litigation, property, employment
Pamela Coles, Company Secretary
Other lawyers: Bob Clark/Debbie Ive- commercial contracts, commercial litigation, employment, health and safety and environmental, consumer law, and acquisitions and divestments.

M

Liberty International PLC
Bury House, 40 Broadway, London SW1H 0BT
Tel: (020) 7887 7000 **Fax:** (020) 7222 5554
Susan Folger, Company Secretary

LibertySurf Ltd
11-20 Copper Street, 4th Floor, London WC1E 6JA
Tim Kuschiall, Associate Counsel

Lloyds TSB Group PLC
71 Lombard Street, London EC3P 3BS
Tel: (020) 7626 1500 **Fax:** (020) 7929 1654
Website: www.lloydstsb.co.uk
Geoffrey Johnson, Group Chief Legal Advisor

Lloyds TSB Scotland plc
Henry Duncan House, 120 George Street, PO Box 177, Edinburgh EH2 4TS
Tel: (0131) 225 4555
Email: jeremyfraser@lloydstsb.co.uk
No of lawyers in dept: 2
Work outsourced: 5% – Various
Jeremy Fraser, Senior Solicitor and Company Secretary
Specialisation: Banking Law, Contracts, CCA, Security, Employment, Mortgages
Career: Edinburgh University; Lloyds UDT; Lloyds TSB
Other lawyers: Banking Law, Contracts, CCA, Security, Employment, Mortgages

Logica PLC
Stephenson House, 75 Hampstead Road, London NW1 2PL
Tel: (020) 7637 9111 **Fax:** (020) 7446 1935
Website: www.logica.com
No of lawyers in dept: 4
David Walker, Group Legal Adviser

Lombard Bank Limited
Lombard House, 339 Southbury Road, Enfield EN1 1TW
Tel: (020) 8344 5540 **Fax:** (020) 8344 5546
No of lawyers in dept: 2
Work outsourced: approx. 15% – Large commercial agreements, litigation
Stephen G. Byrne, Company Solicitor and Deputy Company Secretary
Specialisation: Commercial contracts, consumer credit, employment, trade marks, data protection, retail banking
Career: Educated at Frankfurt International School; Graduated from Reading University 1983; Attended College of Law, York 1991-92; Admitted as a Solicitor July 1994; Articled at Alliance & Leicester Legal Department; With Lombard Banmk since March 1996
Other lawyers: Mayoor Patel: Barrister: Company/Commercial, Consumer, Finance, Intellectual Property, e-commerce.

Lombard North Central PLC
Lombard House, 3 Princess Way, Redhill RH1 1NP
Tel: (01737) 774111 **Fax:** (01737) 760031
Tom Price, Head of Legal Services

London Bridge Software Holdings PLC
16th Floor, New London Bridge House, 25 London Bridge Street, London SE1 9SG
Tel: (020) 7403 1333 **Fax:** (020) 7403 8981
Eric Watkins, Company Secretary

London Electricity PLC
Templar House, 81-87 High Holborn, London WC1V 6NU
Tel: (020) 7242 9050 **Fax:** (020) 7242 2815
Robert Higson, Group Solicitor and Company Secretary

London Merchant Securities PLC (Ord)
Carlton House, 33 Robert Adam Street, London WIM 5AH
Tel: (020) 7935 3555 **Fax:** (020) 7935 3737
Michael Waldron, Company Secretary

Lonmin
4 Grosvenor Place, London SW1X 7YL
Tel: (020) 7201 6000 **Fax:** (020) 7201 6100
Email: contact@lonmin.com
Website: www.lonmin.com
Michael Pearce, Company Secretary

MacMillan Ltd
25 Eccleston Place, London SW1W 9NF
Tel: (020) 7881 8000 **Fax:** (020) 7881 8001
Andrew Crompton, Business Development Director

MAN (ED & F) Holdings Ltd
Sugar Quay, Lower Thames Street, London EC3R 6LA
Tel: (020) 7285 3000 **Fax:** (020) 7285 3518
Website: www.edfman.com
RJA Askew, Group Legal Adviser
Specialisation: Heading up legal and insurance departments.
Career: Worcester College, Oxford (MA); Called to the Bar 1978. Lawyer at London Steamship P&I Club 1979-1983. Group Legal Adviser to Primlats; Group Legal Adviser to E.D.F. Man plc since 1986. Member of Chartered Institute of Arbitrators
Personal: Born 1952. Resides Colchester. Leisure: sailing

Manchester United PLC
Old Trafford, Sir Matt Busby Way, Manchester M16 0RA
Tel: (0161) 868 8000 **Fax:** (0161) 868 8818
Website: www.manutd.com
Work outsourced: 100%
David Beswitherick, Company Secretary

Marconi PLC
1 Bruton Street, London W1X 8AQ
Tel: (020) 7493 8484 **Fax:** (020) 7491 0863
Website: www.marconi.com
Jeff Gordon, Head of Legal

Marconi PLC
1 Bruton Street, London W1J 6AQ
Tel: (020) 7493 8484 **Fax:** (020) 7409 7748
Simon Boyle, Environmental Lawyer

Marks and Spencer plc
Michael House, 37-67 Baker Street, London W1A 1DN
Tel: (020) 7935 4422 **Fax:** (020) 7487 2670
Website: www.marks-and-spencer.co.uk
Graham Oakley, Company Secretary & Group Legal Adviser

Mars (UK) Ltd
3D Dundee Road, Slough SL1 4JX
Tel: (01753) 693000 **Fax:** (01753) 533172
Sheila Henderson, Marketing/Property Manager

Matalan plc
Gillibrands Road, Skelmersdale WN8 9TB
Tel: (01695) 552 400 **Fax:** (01695) 552401
Ian Smith, Company Secretary

McKechnie PLC
Leighswood Road, Aldridge, Walsall WS9 8DS
Tel: (01922) 743887 **Fax:** (01922) 451045
Email: enquiries@mckechnie.co.uk
Website: www.mckechnie.co.uk
Work outsourced: 90% +
Ross McDonald, Company Secretary

Meggitt PLC
Farrs House, Cowgrove, Wimborne BH21 4EL
Tel: (01202) 847 847 **Fax:** (01202) 847838
Work outsourced: 100%
Philip Green, Group Corporate Affairs Director
Specialisation: Company Secretarial, Legal, Commercial, Pensions, Insurance, Property, Administration.
Career: Fellow: Institute of Chartered Secretaries and Administrators – admitted 1988; B.A. (Law) Durham University, gained 1979.

MEPC PLC
103 Wigmore Street, London W1H 9AB
Tel: (020) 7911 5300 **Fax:** (020) 7499 0650
John Price, Company Secretary

Merchants Trust PLC
10 Fenchurch Street, London EC3P 3DB
Tel: (020) 7956 6600 **Fax:** (020) 7621 1481
Peter Longcroft, Company Secretary

Mercury European Investment Tst PLC
33 King William Street, London EC4R 9AS
Tel: (020) 7280 2800 **Fax:** (020) 7280 2506
Nicholas Hall, Head of Legal

Mercury One 2 One
Imperial Place 3, Maxwell Road, Borehamwood WD6 1EA
Tel: (020) 8214 3609 **Fax:** (020) 8214 2266
Robin Saphra, Public Policy Director

Merrill Lynch Europe Limited
Ropemaker Place, 25 Ropemaker Street, London EC2Y 9UN
Tel: (020) 7867 2000 **Fax:** (020) 7867 4397
Website: www.ml.com
Andrew Berry, Director of Law and Equity

Merrill Lynch Europe Limited
Milton Gate, 1 Moor Lane, London EC2Y 9HA
Tel: (020) 7867 2000 **Fax:** (020) 7867 4488
Jennifer Taylor, Vice President & Head of Transaction Management

Merrill Lynch Europe Limited
Ropemaker Place, 25 Ropemaker Street, London EC2Y 9UN
Tel: (020) 7867 2000 **Fax:** (020) 7867 4397
Philip Jolowicz, General Counsel

Mersey Docks & Harbour Co
Maritime Centre, Port of Liverpool, Liverpool L21 1LA
Tel: (0151) 949 6000 **Fax:** (0151) 949 6338
No of lawyers in dept: 3
Work outsourced: 20% – litgation, major corporate, joint ventures
William J. Bowley, Director of Legal Services
Specialisation: Responsible for all the Company's legal affairs and aspects of the company secretarial, insurance, claims and share registration sections. Principal areas of work are general company/commercial matters. Also handles shipping, property and environmental law and advises on litigation. Member of Law Society Commerce and

Industry Group.
Career: Articled with *J. Frodsham & Sons*, St. Helens 1971-72 and solicitor 1973-74. Joined The Mersey Docks and Harbour Company in 1974 as an assistant solicitor. Became PA to the MD 1979, Principal assistant solicitor 1981, Company Secretary and Solicitor 1982 and Director of Legal Services 1991.
Personal: Educated at Prescot Grammar School, University of Bristol (LLB) and Guildford Law School. Born 6 October 1947.
Other lawyers: Henry Hrynkiewicz; property. Janet Fallon; litigation, commercial, shipping.

MFI Furniture Group PLC
Southon House, 333 The Hyde, Edgware Road, Colindale, London NW9 6TD
Tel: (020) 8200 8000 **Fax:** (020) 8200 8636
Hamish Thomson, Company Sec/Director of Legal Services
Specialisation: Responsible for management of all Groups legal work, except property. Also deals with all of Groups pension schemes and insurance work.
Career: Qualified 1974 at Francis & Parkes. Assistant solicitor and Partner Cripps & Shone Marlow Bucks. Joined MFI in 1991.

Millennium & Copthorne Hotels
Victoria House, Victoria Road, Horley RH6 7AF
Tel: (01293) 772 288 **Fax:** (01293) 772345
Work outsourced: 100% – Various – predominantly property, corporate, employment law and licensing
David Alan H Cook, Company Secretary

Minerva PLC
25 Harley Street, London W1N 2BR
Tel: (020) 7299 1405 **Fax:** (020) 7299 1401
Ivan Ezekiel, Company Secretary

Misys PLC
Burleigh House, Chapel Oak, Salford Priors WR11 5SH
Tel: (01386) 871 373 **Fax:** (01386) 871045
Email: cosec.dept@misys.co.uk
Website: www.misysplc.com
Work outsourced: 100% – All
Paul Waters, Company Secretary

MITIE Group PLC
The Estate Office, The Stable Block, Barley Wood, Wrington, Bristol BS40 5SA
Tel: (01934) 862 006 **Fax:** (01934) 862 239
Website: www.MITIE.co.uk
Work outsourced: Various – Acquisitions; property
A. F. Waters, Company Secretary

Monks Investment Trust PLC
1 Rutland Court, Edinburgh EH3 8EY
Tel: (0131) 222 4000 **Fax:** (0131) 222 4488
No of lawyers in dept: 2
Work outsourced: Majority – Corporate work (investment trust related).
Angus MacDonald, Deputy Head of Compliance and Head of Legal
Specialisation: Compliance regulatory work.
Career: Baillie Gifford, 1996-date. Assistant Company Secretary, Dunfermline Building Society, 1994-96. Private practice, 1990-94.

Morgan Crucible Co PLC
Morgan House, Madeira Walk, Windsor SL4 1EP
Tel: (01753) 837 000 **Fax:** (01753) 850872
Peter Wilkins, Director of Legal Affairs

Morgan Stanley & Co International Limited
25 Cabot Square, Canary Wharf, London E14 4QA
Tel: (020) 7425 8000 **Fax:** (020) 7425 8971
Website: www.msdv.com
Richard Rosenthal, Head of Legal and European General Counsel

Morgan Stanley Dean Witter
20 Cabot Square, Canary Wharf, London E14 4QA
Tel: (020) 7425 8410 **Fax:** (020) 7677 2500
Lucy Lynch, Head of Law & Compliance for Europe

Morgan Stanley Dean Witter
20 Cabot Square, Canary Wharf, London E14 4QA
Tel: (020) 7425 8410 **Fax:** (020) 7677 2500
Richard Rosenthal, Head of Legal

Morrison(Wm.) Supermarkets PLC
Hilmore House, Thornton Road, Bradford BD8 9AX
Tel: (01274) 494 166 **Fax:** (01274) 494831
Martin Ackroyd, Company Secretary

Morse Holdings Plc
Brentside Executive Centre, Great West Road, Brentford TW8 9HE
Tel: (020) 8380 8000 **Fax:** (020) 8758 2411
Stuart Carroll, Company Secretary

MTV Networks
180 Oxford Street, London W1N 0DS
Tel: (020) 7478 6240 **Fax:** (020) 7284 7788
Svenja Geissmar, Vice-President of Business Affairs

Murray International Trust PLC (Ord)
7 West Nile Street, Glasgow G1 2PX
Tel: (0141) 226 3131 **Fax:** (0141) 248 5420
Email: info@murrayg.com
David Horn, Group Solicitor

N M Rothschild & Sons Ltd
New Court, St Swithins Lane, London EC4P 4DU
Tel: (020) 7280 5000 **Fax:** (020) 7929 1643
Jonathon Westcott, Head of Legal

National Express Group PLC
75 Davies Street, London W1Y 1FA
Tel: (020) 7529 2000 **Fax:** (020) 7529 2100
No of lawyers in dept: 2
Tony MacDonald, Group Company Secretary and Head of Legal Affairs
Specialisation: Corporate / Commercial
Career: University of Nottingham 1979-82 Slaughter and May 1983-88 The British Petroleum Company plc 1988-95 Guardian Royal Exchange plc 1995 – 2000
Other lawyers: Tony McDonald – Head of Legal Affairs and Group Company Secretary. Jenny Casson – Deputy Company Secretary. Philip Canton – Group Solicitor (company/commercial).

National Power PLC
Windmill Hill Business Park, Whitehill Way, Swindon SN5 9NX
Tel: 01793 877777 **Fax:** 01793 892 831 / 01793 892851
Work outsourced: 20% – International legal advice on projects. Major High Court litigation. Overflow.
Stuart Wheeler, Company Solicitor/Head of Legal Services
Specialisation: Managing provision of legal services to national power. Major projects both international and within the UK. Oil and gas interests.
Career: Educated at Cranleigh School, Bristol university. Articled *Park Nelson & Co.* Qualified 1975. Assistant solicitor *Slaughter and May*, 1975-76. Assistant Secretary Beecham International 1976-79. Negotiator Amoco Group, 1979-88. Lawyer Sunoll 1988-91. Company Solicitor, National Power 1991 to date.
Personal: Resides Wiltshire and London. Hobbies: riding and hunting.
Other lawyers: Claire Charles – international projects. Sally Barrett Williams – UK company/commercial. Gary Chapman – litigation. Simon Wells – property.

Nestle UK Ltd.
St George's House, Croydon CR9 1NR
Tel: (020) 8686 3333 **Fax:** (020) 8686 6072
Hilary Schrader, Solicitor

News International PLC
1 Virginia Street, London E98 1BD
Tel: (020) 7782 4000 **Fax:** (020) 7782 6836
Tom Crone, Legal Manager

Newton Investment Management Limited
71 Queen Victoria Street, London EC4V 4DR
Tel: (020) 7332 9000 **Fax:** (020) 7653 2028
Michelle Sorrell, Company Lawyer

Next PLC
Desford Road, Enderby, Leicester LE9 5AT
Tel: (0116) 286 6411 **Fax:** (0116) 284 2642
Website: www.next.co.uk
Work outsourced: 20% – Major corporate deals. Specialist litigation areas.
Peter Webber, Head of Legal Department
Specialisation: Corporate, Commercial, Secretarial.
Career: Oundle School, Northants. Sheffield University. Head of Legal Dept – Next since 1987.
Other lawyers: R.Layton – Commercial Property; Mrs C. Moody – Property Litigation, Employment and trade marks; Ms S Noble – Litigation, Consumer law, IP; M. Davis – Property.

Nomura International PLC
Nomura House, 1 St Martin's-Le-Grand, London EC1A 4NP
Tel: (020) 7521 2000 **Fax:** (020) 7521 2121
M. Kojiro, Head of Legal

Nortel PLC
Legal Department, Oakleigh Road South, New Southgate, London N11 1HB
Tel: (020) 8945 4000
Mark Cooper, Senior Legal Counsel

North West Water Ltd
Chadwick House, Warrington, Risley, Warrington WA3 6AE
David Hosker, Legal Services Manager

Northern Foods PLC
Beverley House, St Stephen's Square, Hull HU1 3XG
Tel: (01482) 325 432 **Fax:** (01482) 226136
Website: www.northernfoods.co.uk
No of lawyers in dept: 4
Work outsourced: 40% – Commercial conveyancing, corporate finance, litigation, employment, intellectual property.
Carol Williams, Head of Legal
Specialisation: Employment / Litigation / Commercial
Career: Qualified, 1985. 1985-87 *Booth & Co* (Leeds). 1987-90 Asda plc. 1990 to date Northern Foods.
Personal: 1998 to date: Chair North East Commerce and Industry Group
Other lawyers: Jennifer Groves – commercial conveyancing. Andrew Lindley – company commercial. Mark Davis – employment.

Northern Rock
Northern Rock Hse, Gosforth NE3 4PL
Tel: +44 191 2857191 **Fax:** +44 191 2848470
Work outsourced: All mortgage possession, some treasury, commercial litigation and commercial conveyancing.
Colin Taylor, Director – Compliance and Legal Services
Specialisation: Managing the provision of legal services to the company. Responsible for financial services and general statutory compliance. Also in charge of the company's customer relations function.
Career: Howardian High School Cardiff (1969-71). Edlington Comprehensive School (1971-74). Sheffield University (1974-77). Chester Law College (1977).
Personal: Newcastle United F.C., wine and beer (in that order).
Other lawyers: Peter Millican – litigation and employment; Phil Broadhurst – consumer credit, conveyancing and general work; Gwilym Williams – commercial conveyancing and contracts, e-commerce; James Thompson – employment, litigation and general work; Colin Greener – conveyancing, consumer credit and general work.

NSB Retail Systems
Norden House, Basing View, Basingstoke RG21 2HG
Tel: (01256) 333 711 **Fax:** (01256) 333 707
Geoff R Bolt, Company Secretary

NXT
37 Ixworth Place, London SW3 3QH
Tel: (020) 7343 5050 **Fax:** (020) 7343 5051
Email: info@nxt.plc.uk
Website: www.nxtsound.com
Peter Thoms, Company Secretary & Finance Director

Nycomed Amersham PLC
Amersham Place, Little Chalfont HP7 9NA
Tel: (01494) 544 000 **Fax:** (01494) 542266
No of lawyers in dept: 5
Work outsourced: 20% – property, litigation, corporate acquisitions, employment.
Robert Allnutt, Group Legal Adviser and Company Secretary
Specialisation: Responsible for provision of legal advice on general commercial matters, intellectual property and product liability.
Career: Qualified 1979.
Other lawyers: Kevin Kissane, Gillian Mitchell, Sheena Ginnings, Sara Lovick.

Ocean Group PLC
Ocean House, The Ring, Bracknell RG12 1AN
Tel: (01344) 744 310 **Fax:** (01344) 301193
Email: ian.goulden@msaglobal.com
No of lawyers in dept: 9
Work outsourced: 40% – major acquisitions and disposals; litigation; property; overseas work; construction; pensions; environmental; competition; IT/IP
Ian Goulden, Head of legal

Ogilvy
10 Cabot Square, Canary Wharf, London E14 4QB
Tel: (020) 7345 3000 **Fax:** (020) 7345 6502
Larisa Joy, Director of Strategic Development

Old Mutual plc
3rd Floor, Lansdowne House, 57 Berkeley Square, London W1X 5DH
Tel: (020) 7569 0109 **Fax:** (020) 7569 0209
Email: martin.murray@omg.co.uk
Website: www.oldmutual.com
No of lawyers in dept: 1
Work outsourced: Corporate Finance, Property, Employment
Martin Murray, Company Secretary
Specialisation: Responsible for: Company / Commercial matters at plc level; Corporate Governance; Shareholder relations; Compliance
Career: 1999 to date: Company Secretary, Old Mutual plc; 1997 – 1999: General Counsel and Secretary, The Energy Group plc; 1986 – 1997: Solicitor, Hanson plc. MA, LL.B. (Cantab) , LL.M. (Harvard). Admitted as a solicitor in 1979.

Open Interactive
34-35 Farringdon Street, London EC4A 4HJ
Tel: (020) 7332 7000 **Fax:** (020) 7332 7100
John Kenbury, Director of Legal and Business Affairs

Open Interactive
34-35 Farringdon Street, London EC4A 4HJ
Tel: (020) 7332 7000 **Fax:** (020) 7332 7100
Marijke Reid, Legal/Compliance Manager

Oracle Corporation UK Limited
Oracle Parkway, Thames Valley Park, Reading RG6 1RA
Tel: (0118) 924 0000 **Fax:** (0118) 924 3000
David Hoffman, General Counsel UK and Ireland

Oxford Glycosciences PLC
10 The Quadrant, Abingdon Science Park, Abingdon OX14 3YS
Tel: (01235) 543 200 **Fax:** (01235) 554 701
Website: www.ogs.com
No of lawyers in dept: 1
Work outsourced: 80% – Intellectual Property, Corporate Finance, Employment.
Paul Triniman, Company Secretary

Pace Micro Technology PLC
Victoria Road, Soltaire, Shipley BD18 3LF
Tel: (01274) 532 000 **Fax:** (01274) 537127
Website: www.pace.co.uk
No of lawyers in dept: 4
Work outsourced: 30% – Intellectual Property / Property / Litigation
Anthony Dixon, Director of Legal Services and Company Secretary
Specialisation: Corporate / Commercial, Intellectual Property, Licensing of digital media software.
Career: St. Peter's School, York; Emmanuel College, Cambridge (M.A. Law); Articled Ashurst Morris Crisp 1986-88; (Corporate Finance) Solicitor 1988-1994; Group Commercial Solicitor – Yorkshire Water plc 1994-1997; Company Secretary / Director of Legal and member of Executive Committee of Pace 1997 to date
Personal: Married to Penelope, with two children (Flo and Harry, ages 7 and 5). Member of The Merchant Taylors in the City of York and Hawks Club.
Other lawyers: Jane Connor – Legal Counsel; Sandy Bartlett – V.P. Legal and Corporate Affairs – Pace Americas; Jason Irvine – Geddis Legal Counsel

Pathe Distribution Limited
Kent House, Market Place, London W1N 8AR
Tel: (020) 7323 5151 **Fax:** (020) 7462 4417
Cameron McCracken, Head of Corporate & Business Affairs

Pearson plc
3 Burlington Garden, London W1X 1LE
Tel: (020) 7411 2000 **Fax:** (020) 7411 2390
Website: www.pearson .com
No of lawyers in dept: 1
Work outsourced: 75%
Julia Casson, Company Secretary
Other lawyers: Financial Times Group: Sarah Robinson (Company Secretary). Recoletos: Javier Albacar. Pearson Education: Bob Dancy (US) and Vicky Lockie (International). Penguin Putnam Inc. : Alex Gigante (US) and Cecily Engle (Europe). Pearson Television: Sarah Tingay. Paul-Louis Cordier (Les EcLos)

Pearson plc
3 Burlington Gardens, London W1S 3EP
Tel: (020) 7411 2000 **Fax:** (020) 7411 2390
Sarah Tingay, Director of Legal & Business Affairs (for Pearson Television Ltd)

Penguin Books Limited
27 Wrights Lane, London W8 5TZ
Tel: (020) 7416 3000 **Fax:** (020) 7416 3099
Cecily Engle, Business Affairs Director

Peninsular & Oriental Steam Nav Co
78 Pall Mall, London SW1Y 5EJ
Tel: (020) 7930 4343 **Fax:** (020) 7930 6042
Work outsourced: major corporate and banking
Michael Gradon, Director and Company Secretary
Specialisation: Deals with acquisitions, disposals, joint ventures, financing and other major group matters.
Career: Qualified in 1983. With *Slaughter and May* 1981-86. Became P&O Group Legal Director in 1991and Company Secretary in 1996. Appoint Board Director in 1998.
Personal: Educated at Haileybury 1972-76 and Downing College, Cambridge 1977-80. Leisure interests include tennis and golf. Born 7th April 1959. Lives in Oxted, Surrey.

Pennon Group
Peninsula House, Rydon Lane, Exeter EX2 7HR
Tel: (01392) 446 677 **Fax:** (01392) 434966
No of lawyers in dept: 10
Work outsourced: 10% – Specialist banking and major litigation.
Kenneth D. Woodier, Group Company Secretary and Solicitor
Specialisation: Company/commercial, litigation, competition, property, contract/procurement, environmental and employment.
Career: Management (business) prior to qualifying as a solicitor. Articles with Severn Trent Water. Legal Adviser with Investors in Industry plc (3i). Group legal manager with HP Bulmer Holdings plc and Group Legal Adviser with South West Water PLC. 15 years in legal practice.
Other lawyers: Andrew Matthews, John Jelley, Alan Roberts, Alan Podger, John Viney, Dr Buckingham, Simon Pugsley, James Hyde, Richard Abbot.

Perpetual PLC
Perpetual House, Perpetual Park Drive, Henley-on-Thames RG9 1HH
Tel: (01491) 417 000 **Fax:** (01491) 416000
Email: ian-white@perpetual.co.uk
No of lawyers in dept: 1
Ian White, Company Secretary/Legal Counsel
Specialisation: Advice to all areas of the business ona wide range of commercial, corporate, strategic and legal matters.
Career: Brakendale School, Bracknell, Berks. Bristol University. The City University. Leicester University. The Inns of Court School of Law. B.A (hons) History – 1987. Diploma in Law – 1988. Diploma in European Management and Employment Law – 1998. Barrister – 1989. 1989-1992: In practise at the Bar. Lawyer – construction industry. In-house Lawyer/Company Secretary – John Govett & Co Ltd. Legal Manager – Gartmore Investment Management plc. 1999 – Company Secretary / Legal Counsel Perpetual Investment
Personal: Born 1965. Resides in Twickenham. Leisure pursuits include acting badly in amateur dramatic productions, theatre, cinema, long distance walking.

Photo-Me International PLC
Church Road, Bookham, Leatherhead KT23 3EU
Tel: (01372) 453 399 **Fax:** (01372) 459 064
Robert Lowes, Company Secretary

Photobition Group
Eagle House, 244 London Road, Mitcham CR4 3HD
Tel: (020) 8687 7000 **Fax:** (020) 8687 7007
David McKay, Company Secretary

Pilkington PLC
Prescot Road, St. Helens WA10 3TT
Tel: (01744) 28882 **Fax:** (01744) 692660
No of lawyers in dept: 6
Work outsourced: 50% – Major litigation, international, large scale acquisitions and divestments, specialist counsel advice.
Clyde M. Leff, Group Legal Adviser / General Counsel
Specialisation: Principal areas of work are antitrust/competition law, acquisitions and disposals, major litigation, senior level service contracts and related matters, and corporate compliance programmes. The majority of work involves international aspects and the necessary management of external legal resources in a number of jurisdictions.
Career: Graduated Law School 1980, University of Chicago, J.D. Numerous U.S. positions, both in private practice (Mayer, Brown and Platt; Reuben and Proctor) and Corporate Legal Departments (Ameritech; Owens Corning). Officer level position at Owens Corning before joining Pilkington plc as Group Legal Adviser/General Counsel in 2000.
Personal: Married, two children.
Other lawyers: Miss J. P. Halligan, Miss H. J. Eastwood, C. M. Leff, C.R. Bayley, I.J. McKillup, T.G. Chambers Specialisation: Manages the provision of legal advice to an international Group (80% of turnover overseas).

Pillar Property
Lansdowne House, Berkeley Square, London W1X 6HG
Tel: (020) 7915 8000 **Fax:** (020) 7915 8001
Philip Martin, Company Secretary

PizzaExpress PLC
No 7 McKay Trading Estate, Kensal Road, London W10 5BN
Tel: (020) 8960 8238 **Fax:** (020) 8969 5244
Website: www. pizzaexpress.co.uk
Work outsourced: 100 – All corporate work
Patrick Hartrey, Company Secretary
Specialisation: Responsible for all company secretarial and legal matters, in particular the main board process contracts, insurances and trademarks and corporate governance.
Career: 1994-97 Assistant Company Secretary Fenchurch plc, 1997-99 Assistant Company Secretary Oriel Group plc, 1999-2000 Assistant Company Secretary Caledonian Investments plc, 2000 Company secretary Pizzaexpress plc

Polydor Ltd
72 - 80 Black Lion Lane, Hammersmith, London W6 9BE
Tel: (020) 8910 4800 **Fax:** (020) 8910 4801
Paul Jones, Legal and Business Affairs Director

PowerGen PLC
53 New Broad Street. London, EC2M 1JJ
Tel: (020) 7826 2742 **Fax:** (020) 7826 2716
No of lawyers in dept: 16
Work outsourced: 40% – Project work/litigation/M&A/some property and corporate.
David J Jackson, Company Secretary and General Counsel
Specialisation: Has wide ranging responsibilities of a legal, secretarial and corporate nature, involved in the management of PowerGen as a "Top 100" company. Provides substantial advice on new regulatory environment, including preparation of cases for MMC reference. Substantially involved in business diversification through projects in UK and abroad, principally USA. Also responsible for environmental matters and property. Member of Executive Committee involved with day to day running of the business.
Career: Qualified 1977. Assistant solicitor with *Barlow Lyde & Gilbert* 1977-79 and to the Nestlé Company Ltd 1979-81. Assistant Group Legal Adviser to Chloride Group plc 1981-87. Legal Adviser, Matthew Hall plc 1987-89, then took up current position.
Personal: Educated at Merchant Taylors' School, Northwood and University of Bristol (LLB). Born 25 January 1953. Lives in Oxfordshire.
Other lawyers: Willie Gubbins: Corporate and International; Henry Loweth; Gas; Fiona Stark: UK; Stephanie Hammond; James Jones: UKE Production & Sales; Sara Vaughan: Competition; Mark Bygraves; Susan Kitchin: Futures

Premier Farnell PLC
Farnell House, Sandbeck Way, Wetherby LS22 4DH
Tel: (01937) 587 241 **Fax:** (01937) 580 070
Email: mullenk@premierfarnell.com
Work outsourced: 30% – Broad spectrum, share schemes, employment litigation
Ken Mullen, Group Secretary and General Counsel
Specialisation: Principal areas of work: Yellow Book, company law, contracts, acquisitions and reorganisations, employment law, share schemes.
Career: 1979-1981, Moffait & Co 1981-1983, Guardian Royal Exchange plc 1983-1984, McDonnell Douglas Corporation. 1984-1989, Apollo Computer (UIC) Ltd 1989-1990, Whessoe plc 1990-1994. Since 1994, Premier Farnell plc.
Personal: Golf, cycling.

Primark Financial Data
Skandia House, 23 College Hill, London EC4R 2RT
Tel: (020) 7398 1000
Jane Reeves, Company Lawyer

Provident Financial PLC
Colonnade, Sunbridge Road, Bradford BD1 2LQ
Tel: (01274) 731 111 **Fax:** (01274) 727 300
No of lawyers in dept: 2
David Rees, Group Legal Advisor
Other lawyers: Rebecca Price, Solicitor

Prudential PLC
Group Legal Services, Laurence Pountney Hill, London EC4R 0EU
Tel: (020) 7548 3737 **Fax:** (020) 7548 3191
Website: www.prudential.co.uk
No of lawyers in dept: 4
Work outsourced: 90% – property, employment, venture capital, corporate financing
Peter Maynard, Group Legal Services Director
Specialisation: Heads a small team of commercial lawyers providing legal services to the Corporation and its subsidiaries.
Career: 1971-74 University of Cambridge. 1975-82 *Slaughter and May*. 1982-84 *Clifford-Turner*. 1984-98 Hong Kong Bank Group. (1984-92 Legal Adviser Europe, 1992 Compliance Director, James Capel, 1993-95 President & CEO, James Capel Inc, New York, 1996-98 Deputy Group Legal Adviser, HSBC Group). 1998 Director, Group Legal Services, Prudential Corporation plc.
Other lawyers: D. Green, J Parker, D. Higgins: company/commercial

Psion PLC
1 Red Place, London W1Y 3RE
Tel: (020) 7317 4100 **Fax:** (020) 7317 4266
A.J. Bodenham, Company Secretary

QXL.Com PLC
Floor 4 & 10, Landmark House, Hammersmith Bridge Road, London W6 9DP
Tel: (020) 8962 7100 **Fax:** (020) 8962 7303
Email: anisa.dhanji@qxl.com
Website: www.qxl.com
No of lawyers in dept: 1
Work outsourced: 50% – Securities, M&A, Employment, some commercial.
Anisa Dhanji, Company Secretary
Specialisation: Commercial, Intellectual Property, Information Technology
Career: 1987: LL.M. – L.S.E., University of London; 1983: LL.B. University of British Columbia

Railtrack Group PLC
Railtrack House, Euston Square, London NW1 2EE
Tel: (020) 7557 8000 **Fax:** (020) 7557 9000
Work outsourced: 90% – Corporate, commercial, litigation, conveyancing, EC competition, banking, environmental, construction, employment.
Simon Osborne, Company Secretary & Solicitor
Specialisation: Company secretarial, corporate governance, corporate and general advisory.
Career: LLB (Lond) 1970; Solicitor June 1973; articled *Goodman Derrick* 1971-73; Solicitor to British Railways Board 1986-93; Company Secretary and Solicitor Railtrack PLC 1993 to present.
Personal: Member of NAPF Committee of Inquiry into UK Vote Execution. Member of Law Society Audit Committee. Member of Railway Heritage Committee. Member of British Transport Police Committee.
Other lawyers: Commercial: Nigel Dewick, Kevin Lynch, Andrew James; Litigation: Andrew Litherland, Richard Smith, Charles Ritchie Helen Potton, Gillian L Johnston (Scotland); Property/Parliamentary: Geoffrey Kitchener, Alison Parkinson, Iain Brown (Scotland), Brian Spanswick, Anne Galewski, Asheesh Mehta-Hughes.

Random House
20 Vauxhall Bridge Road, London SW1V 2SA
Tel: (020) 7840 8830 **Fax:** (020) 7840 8400
Roger Field, Legal Director

Rank Group PLC
6 Connaught Place, London W2 2EZ
Tel: (020) 7706 1111 **Fax:** (020) 7262 9886
Email: charles.cormick@rank.com
Charles Cormick, Company Secretary

Reckitt & Benckiser PLC
67 Alma Road, Windsor SL4 3HD
Tel: (01753) 835 835 **Fax:** (01753) 835 830
Work outsourced: 10% – IT, litigation, large transactions.
Giuseppe Sanna, Head of Legal Europe

Redrow Group
Redrow House, St David's Park, Flintshire CH5 3RX
Tel: (01244) 520 044 **Fax:** (01244) 520564
Email: legal@redrowlegal.demon.co.uk
Website: www.redrow.co.uk site
No of lawyers in dept: 8
Work outsourced: 5% – corporate
Rhiannon E. Walker, Company Secretary/Head of Legal Dept.
Specialisation: Company secretarial, land acquisitions, options, overseeing major company deals.
Career: Career/Education: Howells School Denbigh. University College of Bangor. Partner with Kerfoot Owen (Private Practice). Joined Redrow in 1996.
Other lawyers: Iain Mason (Litigation), Mike Thorne, Karen Wallis, Geoff Dean, Chris Bolderstone, Neil Robinson, Helen Williams

Redstone Telecom plc
Elstree Way, Borehamwood WD6 1JH
Tel: 070 2000 1000 **Fax:** 070 2000 1001
Email: redstone@redstone.co.uk
Website: www.redstone.co.uk
Work outsourced: 100% – All Legal work
Alan Harrold, Company Secretary

Reed Elsevier plc
25 Victoria Street, London SW1H 0EX
Tel: (020) 7227 5720 **Fax:** (020) 7227 5651
Email: anne.joseph@reedelsevier.co.uk
Website: www.reedelsevier.com
Anne Joseph, Legal Director
Specialisation: Mergers and acquisitions, competition law, contract, intellectual property, employment.
Career: St Anne's College, Oxford 1971-74. College of Law 1975-1977. Legal Adviser – Debenhams plc 1980-83. Legal Adviser – BAT Industries 1983-88. Legal Adviser – Reed Exhibition Companies Ltd 1992-94. Legal Director – Reed Elsevier 1994-present.
Personal: Languages: French, German.

Renishaw PLC
New Mills, Wootton-under-Edge GL12 8JR
Tel: (01453) 524 524 **Fax:** (01453) 524001
Allen Roberts, Company Secretary

Rentokil Initial PLC
Felcourt, East Grinstead RH19 2JY
Tel: (01342) 833 022 **Fax:** (01342) 835672
Robert Ward-Jones, Company Secretary and Legal Director

Reuters Group
85 Fleet Street, London EC4P 4AJ
Tel: (020) 7250 1122 **Fax:** (020) 7542 5896
Website: www.reuters.com
No of lawyers in dept: 40
Work outsourced: Variable – All types where external expertise is required.
Stephen Mitchell, General Counsel
Specialisation: Head of legal worldwide and member of Reuters Group Executive.
Career: Monash University, Melbourne, Bachelor of Economics and Bachelor of Arts. 1990-1996 Partner in Freehill, Hollingdale and Page, Melbourne. 1996-1998 Deputy General Counsel, Reuters Group. 1998-date General Counsel, Reuters Group.
Other lawyers: Andrew S Garrard – Deputy General Counsel, Reuters Group Plc. John Reid-Dodick – General Counsel, Reuters Americas. Thierry de Poncheville – General Counsel, Reuters Europe, Middle East and Africa. Han-Yang Yap – Deputy General Counsel, Reuters Asia. Claire Chapman – General Counsel, Reuters United Kingdom and Ireland. Jennifer Duxbury – General Counsel, Reuters Asia/Pacific and Japan.

Rexam PLC
4 Millbank, London SW1P 3XR
Tel: (020) 7227 4100 **Fax:** (020) 7227 4109
Email: david.gibson@rexam.com
No of lawyers in dept: 2
Work outsourced: 50% – large M&A transactions, litigation, conveyancing.
David William Gibson, Company Sec/Director of Legal Affairs
Specialisation: Company and commercial, company secretarial, intellectual property, insurance, property and Head Office personnel.
Career: Qualified as a Solicitor in 1987. Assistant Solicitor with *Alsop Wilkinson* 1987-1989. Company Solicitor with Rexam PLC (formerly Bowater plc) 1989-1995. Member of the Law Society.

Richemont International Limited
15 Hill Street, London W1J 5QT
Tel: (020) 7499 2539 **Fax:** (020) 7493 1018
Frederick Mostert, Intellectual Property Counsel

Rio Tinto PLC
6 St James's Square, London SW1Y 4LD
Tel: (020) 7930 2399 **Fax:** (020) 7930 3249
Email: Charles.Lawton@riotinto.co.uk
Website: www.riotinto.com
No of lawyers in dept: 5
Work outsourced: 15% – Litigation, property, public issues

Charles Lawton, The Legal Adviser
Specialisation: M & A; competition.
Career: Westminster School; Articled Clark then Solicitor, *Slaughter and May*, 1965-1972; *Lovell White Durrant*, 1972; Rio Tinto, 1972- Present

RIT Capital Partners PLC
27 St James's Place, London SW1A 1NR
Tel: (020) 7493 8111 **Fax:** (020) 7493 5765
David Wood, Company Secretary

RM plc
New Mill House, 183 Milton Park, Abingdon OX14 4SE
Tel: (01235) 826 000 **Fax:** (01235) 823305
Email: arobson@rm.com
Website: www.rm.com
No of lawyers in dept: 2
Work outsourced: 10% – Litigation and Trade Marks
Andy Robson, Group Lawyer
Specialisation: ICT, Corporate Finance, Internet, PFI
Career: University of Nottingham. Bar school. PHH. Allied Dunbar. British Aerospace
Other lawyers: Andy Robson: PFI, Corporate and Finance. Jayne Aspell: Acquisitions and IT

RMC Group PLC
RMC House, High St, Feltham TW13 4HA
Tel: (01932) 568833 **Fax:** (020) 8751 6439
No of lawyers in dept: 6
Work outsourced: Work outside specialisations of Department and high volume work.
Michael Collins, Head of UK Legal Department
Specialisation: Conducting advisory and transactional work over a broad spectrum
Career: LL.B (Birmingham University), Solicitor, Prior to RMC, extensive County Council experience.
Personal: Married.
Other lawyers: Property:, Stephen Bottle, Andrew Smith, Martin Hicks, Dannta Maciejewski; Litigation: Jason Smedley; Environmental / Planning: Jackie Lewis

Rolls-Royce PLC
65 Buckingham Gate, London SW1E 6AT
Tel: (020) 7222 9020 **Fax:** (020) 7227 9170
No of lawyers in dept: 30
Work outsourced: 25% including Litigation, Property
Brian Baker, General Counsel

Rothschild Asset Management Limited
1 King William Street, London EC4N 3AR
Tel: (020) 7280 5000 **Fax:** (020) 7634 2814
No of lawyers in dept: 1
Work outsourced: Variable – Fund\Product Launches, Litigation, tax
Elizabeth Horner, In-house Lawyer
Other lawyers: Company Commercial

Royal & Sun Alliance Insurance
Leadenhall Court, 1 Leadenhall Street, London EC3V 1PP
Tel: (020) 7337 5141 **Fax:** (020) 7337 5133
David Morgan, Head of Legal (UK Operations)

Royal Bank of Canada, Europe
71 Queen Victoria Street, London EC4V 4DE
Tel: (020) 7489 1188 **Fax:** (020) 7329 6138
Email: neylanmi@rbcel.com
Website: www.royalbank.com
No of lawyers in dept: 2
Work outsourced: 30% – Litigation, mergers and acquisitions, structured finance.
Michael Neylan, Group Counsel, Europe
Specialisation: Responsible for all aspects of the activities of the London Law Department of the Royal Bank of Canada and ABC Dominion Securities.
Career: 1984-1988: University of Western Ontario, Canada, B.A. Economics; 1989-1992: Queen's University, Canada LL.B.; 1994: Admitted to Law Society of Upper Canada; 1999: Admitted to Role of Solicitors for England and Wales; 1994-1998: Fraser Beatty, Toronto, Canada, Corporate Litigation; 1998-2000: *Clifford Chance*, London; 2000 – Royal Bank of Canada, London, Group Counsel, Europe.
Other lawyers: Inder Mangat

Royal Bank of Scotland Group PLC
Waterhouse Square, 138-142 Holborn, London EC1N 2TH
Tel: (020) 7833 2121 **Fax:** (020) 7427 9900
Website: www.rbs.co.uk.
Gail Westmore, Head of Legal

Royalblue Group PLC
Duke's Court, Duke Street, Woking GU21 5VH
Tel: (01483) 206 300 **Fax:** (01483) 206 301
Andrew Malpass, Company Secretary

RoyScot Trust PLC
RoyScot House, The Promenade, Cheltenham GL50 1PL
Tel: (01242) 224455 **Fax:** (01242) 570524
Ian Woodcock, Director of Legal Services

Rugby Football Union
Rugby Road, Twickenham TW1 1DS
Tel: (020) 8892 2000 **Fax:** (020) 8892 9816
Jonathon Hall, Secretary & Legal Officer

Saatchi & Saatchi
83/89 Whitfield Street, London W1A 4XA
Tel: (020) 7436 4000 **Fax:** (020) 7436 2102
Email: fiona.evans@saatchi.co.uk
Website: saatchi-saatchiplc.com
Work outsourced: 100%
Fiona Evans, Company Secretary
Specialisation: Company Compliance, Corporate Governance, IP, Insurance, Pensions, other Ad-Hoc Areas
Career: Law and Economics degree BSc Econ. Cordiant Plc joined 96, Deputy Company Secetary. Cordiant demerged Dec 97. Saatchi & Saatchi Plc,became Company Secretary Dec 97

Safeway PLC
6 Millington Rd, Hayes UB3 4AY
Tel: (020) 8848 8744 **Fax:** (020) 8756 1069
John Kinch, Company Secretary

Sage Group PLC
Sage House, Benton Park Road, Newcastle upon Tyne NE7 7LZ
Tel: (0191) 255 3000 **Fax:** (0191) 255 0306
Nick Cooper, Group Secretary and Legal Counsel

Sainsbury (J) PLC
Stamford House, Stamford Street, London SE1 9LL
Tel: (020) 7695 7468 **Fax:** (020) 7695 0011
No of lawyers in dept: 8
David Thurston, Head of Group Legal Services
Other lawyers: George Robertson : Deputy Head / Litigation; Jasmit Likhari : Commercial and Competition; Su Jenkins : Employment; Keith Bashford : Trading and Marketing

Sakura Finance International Limited
6 Broadgate, London EC2M 2RQ
Tel: (020) 7638 7595 **Fax:** (020) 7588 7168
No of lawyers in dept: 2
Work outsourced: 20% – Capital Markets
Leonard Lizmore, General Manager and Head of Legal
Specialisation: Capital markets, banking, securitisations, derivatives, corporate legal
Career: Head of Legal at Sakura International since 1998. Previous employments: Nomura; Bank of America; CIBC / Wood Gundy. LL.M.:University of London (College: London School of Economics & Political Science). LL.B.:University of Windsor, Canada

Sanwa International plc
PO Box 245, City Place House, 55 Basinghall Street, London EC2V 5DJ
Tel: +44 20 7330 0300 **Fax:** +44 20 7330 0420
No of lawyers in dept: 4
Work outsourced: 20-30% – Documentation for bond issues and securitizations.
Mark Seabrooke, Legal Counsel, Senior Vice President, Head of Legal.
Specialisation: Banking and capital markets, corporate, commercial.
Career: 1984-86 Articles, *Stephenson Harwood*. 1986-88 JP Morgan Securites Ltd. 1988 to present, Sanwa International plc. Leeds University (1981 LLB). Magdalene College, Cambridge University (1984 LLM).
Other lawyers: Mark Seabrooke, General Counsel, Sorrel Coni, Lourdes Villar Garcia, Pamela SenGupta: capital markets, company/commercial

Schroder plc
31 Gresham Street, London EC2V 7QA
Website: www.schroders.com
Francis Neate, Group Legal Adviser
Career: Formerly a partner in *Slaughter and May*.

Schroder Investment Managment Limited
31 Gresham Street, London EC2V 7QA
Tel: (020) 7658 6000 **Fax:** (020) 7658 6965
Kylie Edwards, Head of Legal & Controls

Schroder Salomon Smith Barney
Victoria Plaza, 111 Buckingham Palace Road, London SW1W 0SB
Tel: (020) 7721 2000 **Fax:** (020) 7222 7062
Laurie Adams, Head of the Legal Department

Schroder Ventures Holdings Ltd
20 Southampton Street, London WC2E 7QG
Tel: (020) 7632 1000 **Fax:** (020) 7240 5346
Gerard Lloyd, Legal Director

Scipher PLC
Dawley Road, Hayes UB3 1HH
Tel: (020) 8848 6555 **Fax:** (020) 8848 6682
James Ellis-Rees, Head of Legal

Scoot.com
Information House, Parkway Court, Oxford OX4 2JY
Tel: (01865) 380 192 **Fax:** (01865) 380 193
Dick Eykel, Chairman

Scottish & Newcastle PLC
50 East Fettes Avenue, Edinburgh EH4 1RR
Tel: (0131) 528 2000 **Fax:** 0131 528 2311
No of lawyers in dept: 3
H. Andrew S. Vellani, Group Legal Director
Specialisation: The Group Legal Director is responsible for the provision of legal services to the Scottish & Newcastle plc group of companies. Work includes company/commercial, EEC and domestic competition law. International joint ventures; intellectual property; acquisitions and disposals; beer supply agreements; brewing, packaging and distribution agreements; trading law (including food labelling, advertising and promotion).
Career: Kings College, Cardiff; Staffordshire University (LLB Hons); the Inns of Court School of Law, London; called to the Bar (Middle Temple) 1981. Admitted as solicitor 1991. Assistant commercial and legal adviser – Heating and Ventilating Contractors Association 1982; Assistant Group Secretary/Group Legal Adviser – The Kenneth Wilson Group 1984; Group Legal Adviser – Scottish & Newcastle plc. Other positions held: Company Secretary – Scottish Courage Ltd (formerly Scottish & Newcastle Breweries Ltd) 1990 to date. Secretary: The Fosters European Partnership.
Personal: Born 1957, resides in Edinburgh. Interests include overseas travel, music and reading.

Scottish & Southern Energy PLC
200 Dunkeld Road, Perth PH1 3AQ
Tel: (01738) 456000 **Fax:** (01738) 455281
No of lawyers in dept: 6
I Manson, Director of Legal Services
Other lawyers: LJV Donnelly: Company Secretary

Scottish American Investment Co PLC
45 Charlotte Square, Edinburgh EH2 4HW
Tel: (0131) 226 3271 **Fax:** (0131) 226 5120
Graham Laybourn, Compliance Officer

Scottish Investment Trust PLC
6 Albyn Place, Edinburgh EH2 4NL
Tel: (0131) 225 7781 **Fax:** (0131) 226 3663
Work outsourced: 100% – All
Iain Harding, Company Secretary

Scottish Mortgage & Trust PLC
1 Rutland Court, Edinburgh EH3 8EY
Tel: (0131) 222 4000 **Fax:** (0131) 222 4488
No of lawyers in dept: 2
Work outsourced: Majority – Corporate work (Investment Trust related).
Angus Macdonald, Deputy Head of Compliance and Head of Legal
Specialisation: Compliance regulatory work.
Career: Bailey Gifford, 1996 – date. Assistant Company Secretary, Dunfermline Building Society, 1994-96. Private practice, 1990-94.

Scottish Power PLC
1 Atlantic Quay, Glasgow G2 8SP
Tel: (0141) 248 8200 **Fax:** (0141) 248 8300
James Stanley, Legal Director

Scottish Radio Hldgs PLC
Clydebank Business Park, Clydebank, Glasgow G81 2RX
Tel: (0141) 306 2200 **Fax:** (0141) 565 2341
Email: jane.tames@srh.co.uk
No of lawyers in dept: 1
Work outsourced: majority
Jane Tames, Company Secretary
Other lawyers: General Company Work

Second Alliance Trust PLC
Meadow House, 64 Reform Street, Dundee DD1 1TJ
Tel: (01382) 201 700 **Fax:** (01382) 225133
Sheila Ruckley, Company Secretary

Securicor PLC
Sutton Park House, 15 Carshalton Road, Sutton SM1 4LD
Tel: (020) 8770 7000 **Fax:** (020) 8770 1145
No of lawyers in dept: 4
Work outsourced: 15% – Litigation, property, major corporate M&A.
Nigel Griffiths, Group Legal Director
Specialisation: Contract, insurance, employment, commercial, M & A and international.
Career: Educated at Whitgift School and Liverpool University – LLB (Hons) 1968. Qualified as a solicitor in 1971. Securicor since 1973.
Other lawyers: Peter David: company and commercial; Stephen Lyell: commercial and international; Roger Whetnall: employment.

Securities Trust of Scotland PLC
Saltire Court, 20 Castle Terrace, Edinburgh EH1 2ES
Tel: (0131) 229 5252 **Fax:** (0131) 228 5959
Martin Currie, Company Secretary - Investment Management

Selfridges plc
400 Oxford Street, London W1A 1AB
Tel: (020) 7629 1234 **Fax:** (020) 7495 8321
Website: www.selfridges.com
Work outsourced: 75-80% – Company/Commercial
Alan Camplin-Smith, Company Secretary

Sema Group PLC
233 High Holborn, London WC1V 7DJ
Tel: (020) 7830 4225 **Fax:** (020) 7830 4206
Email: nick.deeming@sema.co.uk
No of lawyers in dept: 30
Work outsourced: 10% – Property, pensions, litigation, some IT.
Nick Deeming, Chief Legal Counsel and Company Secretary
Specialisation: Mergers and Acquisitions and all related commercial work. All IT related work in particular systems integration, telecoms software supply, outsourcing and consulting. Company secretarial with particular emphasis on turnbull/Corporate Governance.
Career: BA Law – 2.1: Guildhall University Admitted 1980 – solicitor MBA – 1994: Cranfield University
Other lawyers: James Loughrey (UK Legal Director), David Wilson (Senior Legal Adviser), Patrick Ryan (Business Systems), Rachel Corder (Business Systems), Surbjit Bhamber (Telecoms), Vincent Phillips (Business Systems)

Serco Group PLC
Dolphin House, Windmill Road, Sunbury-on-Thames TW16 7HT
Tel: (01932) 755900 **Fax:** (020) 8334 4300
Julia Cavanagh, Company Secretary

Severn Trent Water Ltd
2297 Coventry Road, Birmingham B26 3PU
Tel: (0121) 722 4000 **Fax:** (0121) 722 4228
No of lawyers in dept: 4
Work outsourced: 10% – M&A, some conveyancing, litigation.
Michael Knight, Head of Professional Services and Company Solicitor

Shanks Group PLC
Astor House, Station Road, Bourne End SL8 5YP
Tel: (01628) 524 523 **Fax:** (01628) 524114
Paul Kaye, Company Secretary

Shell Transport & Trading Co PLC
Shell Centre, London SE1 7NA
Tel: (020) 7934 1234 **Fax:** (020) 7934 5153
Work outsourced: 15% – Litigation and major acquisitions.
Pieter Folmer, Legal Director
Other lawyers: Property and Planning Law : Ms Janet Batey, Mr Martin Files, Mrs Linda Bitmead, Mr Christopher Lawlor, Mrs Alison Merrington, Ms Clare Reader. Refining, Distribution and Marketing Law : Mr Keith Ruddock, Mr Howard Taylor, Miss Vicki Palmer, Mr Alan Williams, Mr Adrian Dewey, Mr Mike Curless, Ms Joanne Crompton, Miss Dawn Lewendon. Upstream Oil and Gas Law : Mr Campbell, Mr Ashwin Maini, Mrs Kerrie-Lee Magill, Miss Teena Grewal, Mrs Rachel Fox, Ms Lucy Sparrow, Mrs Karin Hawkins, Mr Nanne van 't Riet, Mrs Sarah Hyde.

Shell Transport & Trading Co PLC
Shell Centre, York Road, London SE1 7NA
Tel: (020) 7934 1234 **Fax:** (020) 7934 7171
Richard Wiseman, UK General Counsel

Shire Pharmaceuticals Group PLC
East Anton, Andover SP10 5RG
Tel: (01264) 333 455 **Fax:** (01264) 333460
Email: nharris@shire.uk.com
Website: www.shiregroup.com
No of lawyers in dept: 3
Work outsourced: 20% – Complex M&A, foreign overseas, Property, Litigation.
Neil Harris, Head of Legal Affairs
Specialisation: Company Secretarial/Corporate. M&A, IP, Licensing/Management. Employment, Anti-Trust, Commercial contract. Medicino registration. Litigation management.
Career: South Bank BA(Hons) Law 1978. barrister 1984. British Nuclear Fuels 1979-85. Warner Lambert 1986-89. Wellcome plc (Glaxo Wellcome) 1989-95. Shire Pharmaceuticals 1995 to date.
Personal: Interests: fly-fishing, motor cycling, opera.

Signet Group PLC
Zenith House, The Hyde, London NW9 6EW
Tel: (020) 8905 9000 **Fax:** (020) 8200 9466
Work outsourced: 100% – All areas
Noel Lyons, Head of Legal

Singer & Friedlander Group PLC
21 New Street, Bishopsgate, London EC2M 4HR
Tel: (020) 7623 3000 **Fax:** (020) 7623 2122
Roy Fiddemont, Company Secretary

Sir Robert McAlpine (Holdings) Ltd
Eaton Court, Maylands Avenue, Hemel Hempstead HP2 7TR
Tel: (01442) 233444 **Fax:** (01442) 248393
Peter Brinley-Codd, Legal Services Manager

SkyePharma PLC
105 Piccadilly, London W1V 9FN
Tel: (020) 7491 1777 **Fax:** (020) 7491 3338
No of lawyers in dept: 1
Work outsourced: 10-15% – Litigation; Corporate M&A

Suzanne McLean, General Counsel and Company Secretary
Specialisation: Commercail: International Licensing
Career: Ba (Hons) Business Law: City of London Polytechnic (Guildhall University), 1978; Barrister, Gray's Inn, 1979

Slough Estates PLC
Slough Estates House, 234 Bath Road, Slough SL1 4EE
Tel: (01753) 537 171 **Fax:** (01753) 820585
Robert G. May, Legal Supervisor

SMG plc
200 Renfield Street, Glasgow G2 3PR
Tel: (0141) 300 3300 **Fax:** (0141) 300 3033
No of lawyers in dept: 4
Work outsourced: 100% – corporate acquisitions
Dawn Davidson, Company Secretary

Smith & Nephew PLC
Heron House, 15 Adam Street, London WC2N 6LA
Tel: (020) 7401 7646 **Fax:** (020) 7930 3353
Email: michael.parson@smith-nephew.com
Website: www.smith-nephew.com
Work outsourced: 100% – various
Michael G. Parson, Group Company Secretary & Legal Adviser
Career: Qualified in 1965. Legal Department, Cunard/Trafalgar House plc 1970-75. Group Legal Director, Mass Transit Corporation, Hong Kong 1975-85. Group Secretary and Legal Adviser, Bowater plc 1987-91. Has held present position since March 1991.
Personal: Educated at Durham University (LLB) 1958-61. Born 24 October 1940.

Smith (W.H.) Group PLC
103 Wigmore St, Nations House, London W1H OUH
Tel: (020) 7409 3222 **Fax:** (020) 7514 9633
Ian Houghton, Director of Legal Services

SmithKline Beecham PLC
New Horizons Court, Brentford TW8 9EP
Tel: (020) 8975 2000 **Fax:** (020) 8975 2040
Website: www.sb.com
No of lawyers in dept: 125
Work outsourced: approx. 10% – Where additional resource or specialist knowledge required
James R. Beery, Senior Vice President, General Counsel and Corporate Secretary
Specialisation: Responsible for the management of the legal function and provision of legal advice and support at all levels to SmithKline Beecham.
Career: Associate, *Cleary Gottlieb Steen & Hamilton*, New York 1971-73 and London office 1975-76. Foreign legal consultant to Nagashima & Ohno Tokyo 1973-75. Partner with *Erickson & Morrison* (London office) 1977-79 and Managing Partner, *Morrison & Foerster* (London office) 1980-92. Joined SmithKline Beecham in January 1994.
Other lawyers: Departments: Corporate Legal & Secretarial; Corporate Compliance; Legal Operations International; Legal Operations USA inclduing Corporate Guardianship & Dispute Resolution & Strategic Transactions; Corporate Intellectual Property; Legal Operations Europe

SmithKline Beecham PLC
New Horizons Court, Brentford TW8 9EP
Tel: (020) 8975 6345 **Fax:** (020) 8975 6344
David Roberts, Director & Senior Vice-President, Corporate Intellectual Property

Smiths Industries PLC
765 Finchley Road, London NW11 8DS
Tel: (020) 8458 3232 **Fax:** (020) 8458 4380
Alan Smith, Company Secretary

Societe Generale
41 Tower Hill, London EC3N 4SG
Tel: (020) 7676 6000 **Fax:** (020) 7550 5109
No of lawyers in dept: 8
Mark Nimmo, Executive Director, Group Legal

Sony Music Entertainment (UK) Ltd
10 Great Marlborough St, London W1V 7LP
Tel: (020) 7911 8200 **Fax:** (020) 7911 8751
Alastair George, Head of Legal Affairs

Sony Music Entertainment (UK) Ltd
10 Great Marlborough St, London W1V 7LP
Tel: (020) 7911 8200 **Fax:** (020) 7911 8751
Dej Mahoney, Business Affairs

South African Breweries
2 Jan Smuts Avenue, Johannesburg 2000
Tel: 00 27 11 407 1700 **Fax:** 00 27 11 339 1830
Website: www.sabplc.com
No of lawyers in dept: 4
Work outsourced: 40% – Conveyancing, Registration, Opinions, Litigation
Andrew O.C. Tonkinson, Group Company Secretary
Specialisation: Company Secretarial, Remuneration, Benefits, Corporate Law, Commercial Law, Intellectual Property Law, Taxation
Career: BA (Law and Economics) University of Natal, South Africa – 1996; B. Juris, University of South Africa – 1970 Trust Manager – Syfrets Trust Ltd., 1968-1975; Company Secretary and Administration Director – The Lion Match Company Ltd., 1975-1991; Group Company Secretary, South African Breweries, 1991-Present
Personal: Lecturer part-time in Company Commercial and Banking Law, Natal Technicon, 1970 to 1973.
Other lawyers: A.O.C. Tonkinson – Company, Commercial, Corporate Finance J. Romein – Company Intellectual Property Ms J. Taylor – General Commercial

T

Spirent PLC
Gatwick Road, Crawley RH10 2RZ
Tel: (01293) 528 888 **Fax:** (01293) 541905
Michael Arnaouti, Company Secretary

SSL International PLC
Toft Hall, Toft, Knutsford WA16 9PD
Tel: (01565) 624 000 **Fax:** (01565) 624 001
Email: jonathan.jowett@ssl-international.com
Website: www.ssl-international.com
No of lawyers in dept: 3
Work outsourced: 90% – All types
Jonathan D. Jowett, Company Secretary & Legal Director
Specialisation: The provision of legal and administration services to the UK-listed parent company and its sunsidiaries. Main legal focus in M&A
Career: LL.B. Business Law 1985; Solicitor 1989; LL.M. European Union Law 1999
Other lawyers: Andrew Reynolds – Group Legal Adviser; Robert Kanser – Vice President and General Counsel (Americas)

St.Ives PLC
St Ives House, Lavington Street, London SE1 0NX
Tel: (020) 7928 8844 **Fax:** (020) 7902 6566
Philip Harris, Company Secretary

St.James's Place Capital PLC
J. Rothschild House, Dollar Street, Cirencester GL7 2AQ
Tel: (01285) 640 302 **Fax:** (01285) 653993
Email: Hugh.gladman@jra.co.uk
Website: www.sjpc.co.uk
No of lawyers in dept: 4
Work outsourced: 15-20% – Property, litigation, debt collection, major transactions.
Hugh Gladman, Legal & Compliance Director
Specialisation: Director in charge of the legal and compliance departments and, in addition, handling the following areas: corporate finance work/large commercial agreements/major litigation/share schemes.
Career: LLB Southampton University. 1986-93 *Herbert Smith* (including articles). 1993-94 *Hammond Suddards*. 1994 to date J.Rothschild Assurance.
Personal: Hobbies include tennis and other sports, film, theatre and family.
Other lawyers: Catherine Thearle – company/commercial; Michael Burne – IP/litigation; Carmen Chapple – debt collection.

Stagecoach Hldgs PLC
10 Dunkeld Rd, Perth PH1 5TW
Tel: (01738) 442 111 **Fax:** (01738) 643648
Email: info@stagecoachholdings.com
Website: www.stagecoachholdings.com
Work outsourced: 80% – Opinions, drafting, commercial, banking
Derek Scott, Company Secretary
Specialisation: Company Secretary. Chairman of Group Pension Trustees. Director of Group ESOP Trustee. Director of Railways Pension Scheme Trustee.
Career: University of Glasgow 1971-75. Chartered Accountant 1978. Arthur Andersen 1975-86. Stagecoach Holdings plc 1987 to date. Director of Railways Pension Trustee Company Ltd 1997 to date. Member of NAPF Investment Committee 1998 to date.

Standard Bank London Limited
Cannon Bridge House, 25 Dowgate Hill, London EC4R 2SB
Tel: (020) 7815 4155 **Fax:** (020) 7979 4155
Email: chris.bell@standardbank.com
Chris Bell, Head of Legal & Documentation

Standard Chartered PLC
1 Aldermanbury Square, London EC2V 7SB
Tel: (020) 7280 7021 **Fax:** (020) 7280 7112
Email: martin.hayman@uk.standardchartered.com
No of lawyers in dept: 6
Martin Hayman, Head of Legal
Specialisation: Also Company Secretary. The Legal Department provides a service to the Standard Chartered Group on issues which are material in a group context, including M&A, corporate and major litigation.
Career: Cambridge University (Law) followed by private practice and then at The Plessey Company, ITT and Pullman Kellogg. Joined Cadbury Schweppes in 1978 first as Group Legal Adviser and then from 1985 as Secretary and Group Legal Adviser before joining Standard Chartered in May 1998.
Personal: Interested in developing client focus amongst private practice, the development of ADR and global compliance management.
Other lawyers: David Brimacombe – Litigation, Banking, Commercial, Employment; Susan Adams – Litigation, Banking Commercial, Employment; Tim Arnold – M&A, Corporate; James Ellington – M&A, Corporate; Mark Thomas – I.T.; Christian Gordon-Pullar – I.T.

Sumitomo Finance International PLC
Temple Court, 11 Queen Victoria Street, London EC4N 4UQ
Tel: (020) 7842 3000 **Fax:** (020) 7236 0049
C. Philip Martyn, Joint General Manager

Tate & Lyle PLC
Sugar Quay, Lower Thames Street, London EC3R 6DQ
Tel: (020) 7626 6525 **Fax:** (020) 7623 5213
Email: robertgibber@tateandlyle.com
Website: www.tate-lyle.co.uk
No of lawyers in dept: 3
Work outsourced: 20% – Large scale M&A, overseas, significant property and Stock Exchange issues.
Robert Gibber, General Counsel
Specialisation: Responsible to the Board for all global legal issues, primarily UK and overseas acquisitions and joint ventures, London Stock Exchange issues, corporate finance and tax, competition law and compliance.pm: Law Society, International Bar Association.
Career: Qualified 1988. Formerly with *Wilde Sapte* as assistant solicitor (1988-90), joined Tate & Lyle plc in 1990 and appointed senior legal adviser in 1992. Appointed General Counsel and joined Tate & Lyle Executive Committee in 1997.
Personal: Born 28 October 1962. Educated at City of London School (1973-79), Wadham College, Oxford (BA Hons, Oriental Studies) (1980-84). Director of Workable, the disabled charity and founder of Legable a scheme providing work experience for disabled law students. Leisure pursuits include cinema, reading, skiing, tennis and being a father.
Other lawyers: Company/Commercial; Corporate Finance; Litigation; Competition; Shipping; Trading.

Taylor & Francis Group PLC
11 New Fetter Lane, London EC4P 4EE
Tel: (020) 7583 9855 **Fax:** (020) 7842 2298
Anthony Foye, Company Secretary

Taylor Nelson Sofres PLC
AGB House, Westgate, London W5 1UA
Tel: (020) 8967 4748 **Fax:** (020) 8967 1446
Email: john.stobart@tnsofres.com
Website: www.tnsofres.com
No of lawyers in dept: 4
Work outsourced: 25% – excess workload, property, litigation.
John Stobart, Group Company Secretary
Specialisation: Responsible for legal and regulatory affairs of largest European market research company with turnover in excess of £400m. Deals with joint ventures/collaborative arrangements worldwide, product licensing, acquisitions and divestments, yellow book compliance, commercial contracts, data protection registration, property, trade marks, employment, insurance and pensions.
Career: Qualified 1978 while with Smith Roddam. Legal adviser 3i plc 1981-86. Partner with Fennermores 1986-89 and Director of Legal Services and Company Secretary to Harland Simon Group plc 1989-92. Joined Taylor Nelson Sofres in January 1993.
Other lawyers: John Stobart – Corporate Finance; Paul Wright – Licensing; David Bateson – Employment; Ellora Ahmed – General; Mike Slotznick – U.S.A.; Jean Guiliani – France

Taylor Woodrow PLC
4 Dunraven Street, London W1Y 3FG
Tel: (020) 7629 1201 **Fax:** (020) 7493 1066
Email: twplc@taywood.co.uk
Website: www.taywood.co.uk
No of lawyers in dept: 9
Work outsourced: 30% – PFI Co/Commercial, Corporate Finance Litigation
Richard Morbey, Company Secretary

TBWA UK Group
76-80 Whitfield Street, London W1P 5RQ
Tel: (020) 7573 6666 **Fax:** (020) 7637 7573
Giles Crown, Head of Legal & Business Affairs

Telewest Communications PLC
Genesis Business Park, Albert Drive, Woking GU21 5RW
Tel: (01483) 750 900 **Fax:** (01483) 750901
Email: victoria.hull@telewest.co.uk
No of lawyers in dept: 16
Work outsourced: Corporate Finace; Banking
Victoria Hull, Company Secretary; General Counsel
Specialisation: Corporate, Programming; Telecommunications
Career: University of Southampton; Guidford College of Law; Clifford Chance – Corporate; Telewest Executive Director on Main Board; General Counsel responsible for legal and regulatory departments; Company Secretary
Personal: Family – 1 daughter; Film; Tennis
Other lawyers: Simon Read – Corporate Finance; Alex Gartrell – Corporate; Phil McKeiver, Caroline Harris, Greg Thompson – General

Templeton Emerging Markets Investment Trust PLC
Saltire Court, 20 Castle Terrace, Edinburgh EH1 2EH
Tel: (0131) 469 4000 **Fax:** (0131) 228 4506
Sara McIntosh, Company Secretary

Tesco PLC
Tesco House, Delamare Road, Cheshunt EN8 9SL
Tel: (01992) 632222 **Fax:** (01992) 644809
No of lawyers in dept: 3
Work outsourced: Majority – Property, acquisition, corporate, licensing.
John Bailey, Company Secretary
Specialisation: Corporate Administration, legal matters, corporate governance, risk management, shareholders register, share schemes, international governance, pharmacy legal, insurances, licensing.
Career: Company Secretary of Tesco since 1985. Head of Legal. Assistant Secretary (Legal) at London Brick for 8 years. Merchant banking at Hambros and Sarrel Montague as early career.
Personal: Freeman of the City of London; Liveryman of the Worshipful Company of Chartered Secretaries and

Administrators. Married with 2 children. Interests include sport, music, travel and wine.
Other lawyers: The corporate secretary deals with all potential legal issues arising from the Group's activities.

Thames Water PLC
14 Cavendish Place, London W1M 9DJ
Tel: (020) 7636 8686 **Fax:** (020) 7833 6134
Email: david.badcock@thameswater.co.uk
Website: www.thames-water.com
No of lawyers in dept: 12
Work outsourced: 50% – includes: International / Project Finance
David Badcock, Company Secretary and Legal Director
Specialisation: Corporate law and administration; company secretary; corporate governance; commercial; competition; regulation esp. water; environmental employment and contract and incentive schemes
Career: Kingswood School, Bath; Exeter College, Oxford reading 'Greats' – MA; College of Law, Guildford – Solicitors
Personal: Married to a GP, living in Malmesbury with one son (21); Interests include music, tennis, golf and walking.
Other lawyers: Company/ Commercial: Janet Ravenscroft; Commercial operations / environment: Peter Taylor; Litigation: Simon Byrne

The Future Network PLC
Beauford Court, 30 Monmouth Street, Bath BA1 2BW
Tel: (01225) 442 244 **Fax:** 0845 127 4194
Email: robday@futurenet.co.uk
Website: www.futurenet.co.uk
No of lawyers in dept: 4
Work outsourced: On most substantial transactions.
Rob Day, Group Counsel
Specialisation: Mergers and Acquisitions; Finance (debt & equity); Compliance / Corporate Governance and Risk Management; Investments and Joint Ventures
Career: LL.B. Hons – King's College London; Trained S.J. Berwin & Co; Qualified with S.J. Berwin & Co in 1995; Workied in Corporate Finance Department of S.J. Berwin & Co until January 2000. Joined The Future Network, February 2000.
Other lawyers: Rob Day – Group Counsel (specialisation: Corporate Finance); Charles Schug – U.S. General Counsel; Richard Sappir – U.S. Associate General Counsel; Brent Manchester – Rights Manager (IPRs)

The Lawn Tennis Association
Pallister Road, Barons Court, West Kensington, London W14 9EG
Tel: (020) 7381 7000 **Fax:** (020) 7381 5965
Bruce R. Mellstrom, Lawyer

The Mayflower Corporation plc
Mayflower House, London Road, Loudwater, High Wycombe HP10 9RF
Tel: (01494) 450 145 **Fax:** (01494) 450607
Email: mnettleship@mayf.co.uk
Website: www.mayflowercorp.com
No of lawyers in dept: 1
Work outsourced: Apporx. 90% – All types
Mary Nettleship, Group Legal Adviser and Company Secretary
Specialisation: Corporate Finance, Company/Commercial, responsible for coordination/ management of major legal matters across the group.
Career: Kings College, London (LLB), graduated 1986. Qualified with *Turner Kenneth Brown* 1989, Asisstant solicitor with *Nabarro Nathanson* until January 1999.

The National Grid Company plc
National Grid House, Kirby Corner Road, Coventry CV4 8JY
Tel: (024) 76537 777 **Fax:** (024) 76423 620
No of lawyers in dept: 10
Work outsourced: 50% – specialist areas and overflow work.
Alison B Key, Company Secretary & General Counsel
Specialisation: Deals with matters pertaining to the electricity industry, generally on commercial, joint ventures, competition, planning and environmental matters.
Career: Qualified 1989. Assistant and Associate solicitor Martineau Johnson 1989-1996. Joined The National Grid Company Plc 1996 becoming general counsel and company secretary in February 2000.
Personal: Educated at university of Bristol LLB 1982-1985. Born 15 May 1964. Lives in Birmingham.

The Royal Bank of Scotland PLC – Financial Markets
5th Floor, 135 Bishopsgate, London, EC2M 3UR
Tel: (020) 7375 5000 **Fax:** (020) 7375 8411
Helen Cockcroft, Head of Legal and Compliance

Thistle Hotels PLC
2 The Calls, Leeds LS2 7JU
Tel: (0113) 243 9111 **Fax:** (0113) 244 5555
No of lawyers in dept: 1
Work outsourced: 50% (100% property and litigation) – Property, litigation, certain transactions, foreign jurisdictions
Cathy Baxandall, Company Secretary
Career: MA (oxon.) Modern Languages; College of Law; Articled at Clifford-Turner, qualified 1985; 1985-90: Clifford-Turner (later Clifford Chance) – London and Paris offices; 1990-94: Simpson Curtis (later Pinsent Curtis), partner 1992 (Banking/Corp. Finance); 1994-99: Group Company Secretary, The Spring Ram Corporation plc; 1999-present: Company Secretary, Thistle Hotels plc
Other lawyers: Compliance / Stock Exchange; Corporate / Commercial; Property; Litigation

Thomson Travel Group Ltd
Greater London House, Hampstead Road, London NW1 7SD
Tel: (020) 7387 9321 **Fax:** (020) 7387 8451
Mark Knight, Company Secretary

Thomson Travel Group Ltd
Greater London House, Hampstead Road, London NW1 7SD
Tel: (020) 7387 9321 **Fax:** (020) 7387 8451
Richard Aston, In-house Lawyer

Thomson Travel Group PLC
Greater London House, Hampstead Road, London NW1 7SD
Tel: (020) 7387 9321 **Fax:** (020) 7387 8451
Richard Churchill-Coleman, Group General Counsel

Thus PLC
Dalmore House, 310 St Vincent Street, Glasgow G2 5BB
Tel: (0141) 567 1234 **Fax:** (0141) 566 3010
David Macleod, Company Secretary

TI Group PLC
Lambourn Court, Abingdon OX14 1UH
Tel: (01235) 705555 **Fax:** (01235) 705570
Stephen Clarke, Director of Legal Affairs

Times Newspapers
1 Pennington Street, London E98 1TT
Tel: (020) 7782 5000 **Fax:** (020) 7782 5860
Patricia Burge, Company Solicitor

Tishman Speyer Properties
Millbank Tower, 21-24 Millbank, London SW1P 4QP
Tel: 002 7333 2400 **Fax:** 020 7333 2500
Mark Kingston, European General Counsel

Tokai Bank Europe plc
1 Exchange Square, London EC2A 2JL
Tel: 020 7638 6030 **Fax:** 020 7588 5875
Website: www.tbeuk.com
No of lawyers in dept: 3
David Haig, Head of Legal & Compliance Depts.
Other lawyers: Mary Verghese-Dipple, Elizabeth Hornby

Tokyo-Mitsubishi International plc
Legal Department, 6 Broadgate, London EC2M 2AA
Tel: (020) 7628 5555 **Fax:** (020) 7577 2872
No of lawyers in dept: 7
Work outsourced: 40% – Capital markets, securitisation, banking.
R. House, Director, Legal
Specialisation: Responsible for all new issue business; bonds; MTNs and warrants; equity linked structures, securitisations and structured transactions. All forms of general legal advice to the company.
Career: Articled Simmons Church Smiles; Qualified 1990; Articled and one year qualified at Simmons Church Smiles; moved to Mitsubishi Finance Internatinal plc (a wholly owned subsidiary of the Mitsubishi Bank) in March 1991. Following the global merger of Mitsubishi Bank with the Bank of Tokyo, the parent bank has changed its name to the Bank of Tokyo-Mitsubishi Ltd, and Mitsubishi Finance International has changed its name to Tokyo-Mitsubishi International plc. Education: University of Nottingham (1986 LL.B. Hons)
Personal: Born 1964, resides Fulham Leisure: theatre, sport, sailing, impractical cars, sloth.
Other lawyers: Sally Deart, Keith Parnell, John Oriorgien: Transportation Management; Olivier Begion, Mitsue Mignjion: General Legal Advice

Tomkins PLC
East Putney House, 84 Upper Richmond Road, London SW15 2ST
Tel: (020) 8871 4544 **Fax:** (020) 8877 9700
No of lawyers in dept: 2
Simon Webber, Director of Corporate Development & Legal Affairs

Towers Perrin
Castlewood House, 77 - 91 New Oxford Street, London WC1A 1PX
Tel: (020) 7379 4000 **Fax:** (020) 8895 7478
Val Vardy, Principal

TR European Growth Trust PLC
3 Finsbury Avenue, London EC2M 2PA
Tel: (020) 7638 5757 **Fax:** (020) 7377 5742 direct fax 410 4454
Steve Obrian, Head of Legal

Trafficmaster
Marlborough Court, Sunrise Parkway, Linford Wood, Milton Keynes MK14 6DX
Tel: (01908) 249800 **Fax:** (01908) 200330
Bill McIntosh, Company Secretary

Travis Perkins PLC
Lodge Way House, Lodge Way, Harleston Road, Northampton NN5 7UG
Tel: (01604) 752 424 **Fax:** (01604) 758718
Email: apike@travisperkins.co.uk
Website: www.travisperkins.co.uk
No of lawyers in dept: 1
Work outsourced: 80% – Property, Litigation, Major Acquisitions/Disposals
Andrew Pike, Company Secretary and lawyer
Specialisation: General Contract and commercial advice, employment law, acquisitions and disposals
Career: University of Birmingham LL.B 1973; Costain Group 1981-1989; Alfred McAlpine 1989-1994; Ibotock plc 1994-1999; Travis Perkins plc 1999 – date

Trinity Mirror PLC
1 Canada Square, Canary Wharf, London E14 5AP
Tel: (020) 7293 3358 **Fax:** (020) 7293 3360
No of lawyers in dept: 8
Work outsourced: 75% – Property,Litigation, Corporate Finance, Pensions, Employment
Paul Vickers, Secretary + Group Legal Director
Specialisation: All legal, compliance and regulatory matters.
Career: Alleyris School, Southampton University LLB, Called to bar 1983, London Daily News 1986-87, TV-am plc 1987-92, Mirror Group plc 1992-99, Trinity Mirror plc 1999
Personal: Married. One son
Other lawyers: Commercial Contract; Employment; IP; Property

Trinity Mirror PLC
1 Canada Square, Canary Wharf, London E14 5AP
Tel: (020) 7293 3000 **Fax:** (020) 7293 3613
Charles Collier-Wright, Group Legal Manager

Trinity Mirror PLC
1 Canada Square, Canary Wharf, London E14 5AP
Tel: (020) 7293 3000 **Fax:** (020) 7293 3613
Martin Cruddace, Head of Legal Department

T

Trinity Mirror PLC
1 Canada Square, Canary Wharf, London E14 5AP
Tel: (020) 7293 3000 **Fax:** (020) 7293 3613
Marcus Partington, Solicitor

TT International
Martin House, 5 Martin Lane, London EC4R 0DP
Tel: (020) 7410 3500 **Fax:** (020) 7410 3539
Work outsourced: 20% – various
A. Allison, Compliance Director
Career: Educated at Liverpool College and Wadham College, Oxford. Called to the Bar 1969. Independent practice at the Bar 1969-1987. Head of Group Compliance, Standard Chartered Bank 1987-1996. Director, Compliance and Legal Affairs, West Merchant 1996-1998, Compliance Director and General Counsel, Westdeutsche Landesbank (London) 1999. Author (with others), 'Banking and the Financial Services Act' (Butterworths, 1993). 'Banking and Financial Services Regulation' (Butterworths 1998).
Personal: Fellow, Chartered Institute of Arbitrators. Chairman, Bar Association for Commerce, Finance & Industry 1995. Memberships – General Council of the Bar 1991-96, Commercial Court Committee 1991- date, City Disputes Panel of Arbitrators & Mediators, Securities and Futures Authority's Panel of Arbitrators.
Other lawyers: Derivatives/Banking – Kurt Krommelin, Jane Bennett, Robert Jones, Patrick Clancy. Emerging Markets – Lucian Milburn. Capital Markets – Katharine Johnson, Tim Sai Loui, Ruth Millington. General Banking Documentation – Christine Schmitz (German), Rosemary McNamara. Lucian Milburn – General Counsel, responsible for buying outsourced legal work. .

U

UBS Warburg Group
100 Liverpool Street, London EC2M 2RH
Tel: (020) 7567 8000 **Fax:** (020) 7568 9256
Carol Moir, Executive Director of Transactions Legal

UBS Warburg Group
100 Liverpool Street, London EC2M 2RH
Tel: (020) 7567 8000 **Fax:** (020) 7568 9256
Charles Ross-Stewart, Executive Director

Ultraframe
Enterprise Works, Salthill Road, Clitheroe BB7 1PE
Tel: (01200) 443 311 **Fax:** (01200) 425455
Email: jamesh@ultraframe.co.uk
Website: www.ultraframe.com
Work outsourced: 100% – All except simple contract/company legal
James Henry, Company Secretary
Career: MA-St Andrew; ACA-KPMG; Reuters plc; Karrimor International Ltd

Unigate PLC
Unigate House, 58 Wood Lane, London W12 7RP
Tel: (020) 8749 8888 **Fax:** (020) 8576 6071
No of lawyers in dept: 5
Work outsourced: 20% – Major M&A; conveyancing; dedicated distribution.
P. Norman Heriz-Jones, Head of Legal
Specialisation: Company/commercial, IP, food legislation, property, franchising, competition law, licensing, agency and distribution.
Career: Cheltenham College
Other lawyers: C.F. Phillips, A.Garner – company/commercial, M&A, dedicated distribution, fleet hire; Karen A. Frankish – company/commercial, competition law, agency, distribution, licensing; Olivia Glynn – employment.

Unilever PLC
PO Box 68, Unilever House, Blackfriars, London EC4P 4BQ
Tel: (020) 7822 5252 **Fax:** (020) 7822 5951
Email: steve.williams@unilever.com
No of lawyers in dept: 20
Stephen G. Williams, General Counsel and Joint Secretary
Specialisation: Responsible for all legal, intellectual property and secretarial departments in the head offices in London and Rotterdam and is also responsible for Unilever legal services worldwide.
Career: Educated at Brentwood School, Essex and King's College, University of London where gained Bachelor of Law Degree (LLB) Hons. Following Law School, joined *Slaughter and May* and spent time in their tax planning and commercial departments. In 1975 joined the legal department of Imperial Chemical Industries plc. In 1984 he transferred to ICI's company secretary's department, becoming one of two assistant company secretaries in 1985. Appointed Joint Secretary of Unilever on 1st January 1986 and General Counsel of Unilever in 1993.
Personal: Admitted as a Solicitor and member of the Law Society in April 1972. Member of the Company Law Committee of the Law Society and of the Companies Committee of the CBI. Non-executive director of Bunzl plc.
Other lawyers: Mr A Peat – overseas legal services; UK legal services; Mr R Heath – trade mark legal services; Mr L Virelli – patents legal services; Mrs S Franklin – marketing legal services; Mr J Moolenburgh – European legal services (based in Rotterdam); Mr P Kuipers – Netherlands legal services (based in Rotterdam).

Unilever PLC
PO Box 68, Unilever House, Blackfriars, London EC4P 4BQ
Tel: (020) 7822 5252 **Fax:** (020) 7822 5817
Richard Heath, Head of Corporate Trade Marks

United News & Media PLC
Ludgate House, 245 Blackfriars Road, Blackfriars, London SE1 9UY
Tel: (020) 7921 5000 **Fax:** (020) 7928 2728
Website: www.unm.com
No of lawyers in dept: 4
Work outsourced: 60% – Corporate, litigation, employment
Jane Stables, Head of Legal and Personnel
Specialisation: M&A, Commercial, Litigation, Employment practices, strategy/development.
Career: Qualified as a lawyer in 1985 and worked in the city firm of Freshfields doing mainly mergers and acquisitions but always retaining an employment law specialisation. Moved into industry to be company secretary and legal adviser to a retailing plc, prior to joining MAI in 1994. She took over the personnel function at MAI in 1995 and became Legal & Personnel Director on the United/MAI merger. Responsible for the United News & Media plc group legal and personnel issues.

United Utilities PLC
North West Water, Dawson House, Liverpool Road, Great Sankey, Warrington WA5 3LW
Tel: 01925 234000 **Fax:** 01925 233360
Website: www.unitedutilities.com
No of lawyers in dept: 20
Work outsourced: 50% – Major transactions, litigation, property, employment
David Hosker, Head of Legal & Insurance Services
Other lawyers: Joanne Bream, Group Legal Manager – Company/Commercial, Corporate Finance.

Viridian Group
Danesfort House, 120 Malone Road, Belfast BT9 5HT
Tel: (028) 9066 8416 **Fax:** (028) 90663579
Email: legal@nie
No of lawyers in dept: 2
Work outsourced: Acquisitions, Joint Venture, Commercial
David Flinn, Solicitor
Specialisation: Electricty Law, Employment Law, Joint Ventures, Acquisitions, General Commercial
Career: Educated Rossall School and Queens University Belfast. Qualified Solicitor Northern Ireland 1975. Qualified Solicitor England and Wales 1981. Chairman Belfast Solicitors Association 1993. Chairman Employment Lawyers Group (NI) 1995 to 1999. Chairman Belfast Civic Trust 1999.
Personal: Interests: Skiing and hill walking
Other lawyers: W D M Flinn : Electricity Law, Employment Law, Joint Ventures, Acquisitions, General Commercial. N Macdougall: Property Law, Employment, Contract

Vodafone AirTouch PLC
The Courtyard, 2-4 London Road, Newbury RG13 1JL
Tel: (01635) 33251 **Fax:** (01635) 45713
Stephen Scott, Company Secretary/Head of Legal

Vosper Thornycroft Holdings PLC
Victoria Road, Woolston, Southampton SO19 9RR
Tel: (023) 8042 6000 **Fax:** (023) 8042 6010
Work outsourced: 100% - corporate, commercial, employment benefits, property
Peter Dawes, Company Secretary

Warburg Dillon Read (A Division of UBS AG)
100 Liverpool Street, London EC2M 2RH
Tel: (020) 7567 8000 **Fax:** (020) 7568 7166
Bob Dinerstein, General Counsel

Warner Bros
WBPL, Warner House, 98 Theobald's Road, London WC1X 8WB
Tel: (020) 7984 5400 **Fax:** (020) 7984 5431/5461
Melanie Jones, Director of Legal & Business Affairs

Waste Recycling Group PLC
3 Sidines Court, White Rose Way, Doncaster DN4 5NU
Tel: 01302 303030 **Fax:** 01302 303001
Alan Waterhouse, Company Secretary

Weir Group PLC
149 Newlands Road, Cathcart, Glasgow G44 4EX
Tel: (0141) 637 7111 **Fax:** (0141) 637 2221
Malcolm Kelly, Group Solicitor

WestDeutsche Landesbank Girozentrale
51 Moorgate, London EC2R 6AE
Tel: (020) 7638 6141 **Fax:** (020) 7444 7859
Lucian Milburn, Head of Legal

Wetherspoon(J D) PLC
Wetherspoon House, Central Park, Reeds Crescent, Watford WD1 1QH
Tel: (01923) 477777 **Fax:** (01923) 219810
Email: rschofield@jdwetherspoon.co.uk
No of lawyers in dept: 4
Work outsourced: 40% – conveyancing, employment, licensing, litigation.
Rosalyn Schofield, Legal Director and Company Secretary
Specialisation: Company secretarial, commercial property, planning, licensing
Career: Henrietta Barnett School. University of Hull. Chester College of Law. In-house with JD Wetherspoon plc since 1991. Deputy Head and Company Secretary since 1995. Promoted to the Board 1998
Personal: Divorced with 2 children. Interests: theatre, cinema, cycling.

Whitbread PLC
The Brewery, Chiswell Street, London EC1Y 4SD
Tel: (020) 7606 4455 **Fax:** (020) 7615 1000
No of lawyers in dept: 4
Work outsourced: 80% – litigation, property, debt collection, licensing, environmental health and food safety issues.
Simon Barratt, Legal Affairs Director and Company Secretary
Career: Articled Slaughter and May; qualified 1985; assistant solicitor, Slaughter and May; solicitor RTZ Legal department, 1987-1989; corporate counsel, Heron Corporation 1989-1991, group legal adviser, Whitbread July 1991-March 1997. Appointed Legal Affairs Director, Company Secretary Whitbread PLC March 1997.
Personal: Educated at Sevenoaks School; St. Johns College, Oxford (Jurisprudence 1982); Law Society finals (1983). Born 1959; resides Tunbridge Wells. Leisure pursuits include keeping fit, gardening, keeping the children occupied.
Other lawyers: Russell Fairhurst – Group Legal Advisor (M&A, commercial). Catherine Rutherford – Solicitor (commercial, IP). Tanya Msimang – Solicitor (commercial).

William M Mercer Limited
1 Grosvenor Place, London SW1P 4LZ
Tel: (020) 7488 4949 **Fax:** (020) 7201 0800
Mark McKeown, Litigation Counsel UK & Europe

Williams PLC
Pentagon House, Sir Frank Whittle Road, Derby DE21 4XA
Tel: (01332) 202 020 **Fax:** (01332) 295339
Malcolm Stratton, Company Secretary

Wilson Bowden PLC
Wilson Bowden House, 207 Leicester Road, Ibstock, Leicester LE67 6WB
Tel: (01530) 260 777 **Fax:** (01530) 265358
Work outsourced: 80% – Land acquisitions/land sales, plot sales, litigation.
Nicolas Townsend, Group Legal Director
Specialisation: Responsible for monitoring and supervision of all major contracts for land acquisition/sale, troubleshooting, strategic land acquisition and the provision of external legal services for the group.
Career: Qualified in January 1970. Previously a Partner with *Gardiner & Millhouse* 1976-78, *Marron Townsend* 1978-80, *Nicolas Townsend & Co* 1980-87, *Staunton Townsend* 1987-89 and *Edge & Ellison* 1989-93.
Other lawyers: Owen Hill, Peter Carr, Wendy Satchwell, Karina Webster, David Cagan – planning and property development.

Wimpey(George) PLC
3 Shortlands, Hammersmith, London W6 8EZ
Tel: (020) 8748 2000 **Fax:** (020) 8846 3121
Stefan Bort, Company Secretary

Witan Inv Tst PLC
Henderson Investors Ltd, 3 Finsbury Avenue, London EC2M 2PA
Tel: (020) 7638 5757 **Fax:** (020) 7410 4454
Steve O'Brien, Director of Legal & Compliance

Wolseley PLC
PO Box 18, Vines Lane, Droitwich WR9 8ND
Tel: (01905) 777200 **Fax:** (01905) 777219
D.A. Branson, Group Company Secretary

Woolwich
Corporate Headquarters, Watling Street, Bexleyheath DA6 7RR
Tel: (020) 8298 5000 **Fax:** (01322) 555708
Email: michael.webber@woolwich.co.uk
No of lawyers in dept: 7
Work outsourced: Various
Michael Webber, Chief solicitor
Specialisation: Corporate structure; general banking law; company/commercial; and compliance.
Career: 1967-1972 Hayesbrook School, Tonbridge. 1972-1974 West Kent College. 1977 Called to the Bar – Middle Temple. 1981 Admitted solicitor. 1983-1992 Partner Argles & Court, Maidstone. 1993-date Woolwich.
Personal: Chairman Tonbridge & Malling Housing Association (1991 to date). Interests: Travel and reading.
Other lawyers: Litigation & Employment: John Tupman, Senior Solicitor. Property: John Cugley, Senior Solicitor.

Woolwich
Corporate Headquarters, Watling Street, Bexleyheath DA6 7RR
Tel: (020) 8298 5000 **Fax:** (01322) 555708
John E. Tupman, Deputy Chief Solicitor

Working Title Films Ltd
Oxford House, 5th Floor, 76 Oxford Street, 6th Floor, London W1N OHQ
Tel: (020) 7307 3000 **Fax:** (020) 7307 3003
Sara Curran, Head of Legal and Business Affairs

Working Title Films Ltd
Oxford House, 5th Floor, 76 Oxford Street, 6th Floor, London W1N OHQ
Tel: (020) 7307 3000 **Fax:** (020) 7307 3003
Angela Morrison, Chief Operating Officer

WorldCom Ltd
Fox Court, 14 Gray's Inn Road, London WC1X 8HN
Tel: (020) 7675 5000 **Fax:** (020) 7675 5992
Phil Reynolds, UK Director of Regulatory Affairs

WorldCom Ltd
Hillgate House, 26 Old Bailey, London EC4M 7RB
Tel: (020) 7570 7000 **Fax:** (020) 7570 4754
Anna McKibbin, Legal Counsel

WPP Group PLC
27 Farm Street, London W1X 6RD
Tel: (020) 7408 2204 **Fax:** (020) 7409 0242
David Calow, Group Legal Adviser

Young & Rubicam Ltd
Greater London House, Hampstead Road, London NW1 7QP
Tel: (020) 7387 9366 **Fax:** (020) 7611 6743
Kathryn Fulton, Chief UK Counsel

SUPPORT SERVICES

Accountants

ALEXANDERS

Redhill Chambers, High Street, Redhill, RH1 1RJ
Tel: (01737) 779500 **Fax:** (01737) 779548
Email: Alex@Alexanders.uk.co

Contact partner:	Mr J. Donoghue

THE FIRM: For a number of years, Alexanders have been helping lawyers and their clients by providing forensic accounting, litigation support and expert witness services whenever financial issues are involved.The firm has worked closely with insurance companies, lawyers, leading counsel and their clients, in such areas as the production of high quality reports, graphs and financial summaries of a clear, concise nature for presentation at court; litigation strategies; the examination and appraisal of documents through Disclosure and assessing the quantum of claims or exposure.Alexanders have a firm grasp of the laws of evidence and understand the necessity of providing reliable evidence. They also have first hand courtroom experience of both the Royal Courts of Justice and the Central Criminal Courts.

LITIGATION SUPPORT PARTNERS: The Litigation Support Partners have all held senior positions within the top ten accountancy firms and have worked in public practice for a number of years. All partners are members of the Academy of Experts and are qualified accountants with a wide range of business experience.

LITIGATION SUPPORT SERVICES: Alexanders have assisted in a wide variety of cases involving loss of earnings; professional negligence; negligence of Investment Managers; fraud; conspiracy to defraud; family and marital disputes; compliance with Investor Protection regulations; insurance claims; breach of contract claims; and offences under the Companies Acts.

ARTHUR ANDERSEN

1 Surrey Street, London, WC2R 2PS
Tel: (020) 7438 3000 **Fax:** (020) 7831 1133
Website: www.arthurandersen.com

Dispute Consulting:	
Frank Ilett	(020) 7438 2588
David J. Ashton	(020) 7438 3352
Mark Bezant	(020) 7438 2507
Paul Rowe	(020) 7438 2886
Fraud & Risk Management:	
Deepak Haria	(020) 7438 3708
Nic Carrington	(020) 7438 2956
Paul Doxey	(020) 7438 3912
Michael Walters	(020) 7304 1653

A

THE FIRM: Arthur Andersen has been providing dispute consulting and fraud investigation services to the UK legal profession since 1980. The dispute consulting practice combines specialists in all forms of dispute resolution with the resources of one of the world's largest accounting and business consulting firms. It has had a significant role in many of the UK's largest commercial cases. It supports its clients by providing financial and economic input into their analysis of the commercial issues, and reporting their findings concisely.

LITIGATION SUPPORT SERVICES:

Dispute Consulting: The dispute consulting practice in London is part of the Business Consulting division of Arthur Andersen whose work includes valuations, intellectual property, competition and regulatory advice and other economic and financial consulting. The firm works closely with the fraud investigation and risk management groups. In a typical year they assist in numerous claims of varying size and complexity. Arthur Andersen can offer clients a deep pool of experience in their offices throughout the UK and overseas. Arthur Andersen can assist in a wide variety of financial disputes, either as a consulting expert or as an expert witness. For further information please call one of the individuals named opposite or visit the firm's website at www.arthurandersen.com for more details of other areas of expertise.

BAKER TILLY

2 Bloomsbury Street, London, WC1B 3ST
Tel: (020) 7413 5100 **Fax:** (020) 7413 5101 **DX:** 1040 London/Chancery Ln.
Email: michael.taub@bakertilly.co.uk **Website:** www.bakertilly.co.uk

Contact partners:

London:	(020) 7413 5100
	Michael Taub, Peter Dickerson
	Chilton Taylor, Adrian Rapazzini
	Richard Spooner, Michael Stean
Birmingham:	(0121) 233 2323
	Charles Fray
Bradford:	(01274) 735311
	Paul Byrne
Bromley:	(020) 8290 5522
	John Hudson
Crawley:	(01293) 565165
	John Warner
Guildford:	(01483) 503050
	Martin Hoydan
Manchester:	(0161) 834 5777
	Edward Cobb
Milton Keynes:	(01908) 847474
	Jim Clifford
Watford:	(01923) 816400
	Jim Clifford
Yeovil:	(01935) 476866
	Dianne Simpson-Price
Number of partners:	130
Number of staff:	1,000

THE FIRM: Founded over 125 years ago, Baker Tilly is a top ten firm of chartered accountants and business advisors in the UK. The firm has around 130 partners operating nationwide, employs some 1000 staff and is an independent member of Summit International with representatives in over 100 cities worldwide.Their specialists have acted in over 500 litigation support cases, providing expert witness and forensic accounting. They are not just experts in court - as practising accountants their evidence is based on practical and commercial experience.For this reason, its litigation support team is active in other specialist fields including corporate finance, information technology, audit and insolvency. It is this mix of experience which makes its specialists effective expert witnesses. Baker Tilly specialists have extensive experience in a wide range of cases covering loss of profits, professional negligence, commercial disputes, divorce, medical negligence, loss of earnings, fraud and IT litigation.

LITIGATION SUPPORT SERVICES: Cases have included breach of contract (including computer installations and construction), other damages claims, security for costs, share valuations including S459CA 1985, personal injury and fatal accident claims, and acting for defendants in several high profile cases brought by the SFO and as the DTI Inspector in the Barlow Clowes affair.

BDO STOY HAYWARD

8 Baker Street, London, W1M 1DA
Tel: (020) 7486 5888 **Fax:** (020) 7487 3686 **DX:** 9025 West End W1
Website: www.bdo.co.uk

Contacts:

Beverly:	Chris Rimington (01482) 888 000
Birmingham:	Martin Palmer (0121) 608 6086
Bristol:	Peter Engel (0117) 933 3311
Epsom:	Kathryn Britten (01372) 734 300
Glasgow:	Ken Macaldowie (0141) 248 3761
London:	Gervase MacGregor (020) 7486 5888
Manchester:	Brent Wilkinson (0161) 203 2700
Norwich:	Martin Beck (01603) 610 181
Nottingham:	Peter Moore (0115) 955 2000
Peterborough:	Nick Barks (01733) 342 444
Poole:	Graham Platts (01202) 681 221
Rochdale:	Peter Pilkington (01706) 355 055
Southampton:	Tim Bentall (01703) 636 915
Number of partners:	313
Number of staff:	2,615

THE FIRM: BDO Stoy Hayward established a national litigation accountants group in recognition of the need for sophisticated accountancy input into trials and potential proceedings. The firm's approach is based on partner involvement, backed by professional staff familiar with legal concepts and procedures. The firm's services include provision of letters of advice at the early stages of a matter, expert witness reports, affidavits in support of applications and cross examination strategy. Advanced computer software and graphics are used to present complex financial and quantitative data with clarity and precision.

LITIGATION SUPPORT SERVICES:
Pre-Trial Support: Detailed investigation and analysis of documents including prime accounting records; advice on technical accountancy matters; evaluation of economic loss; tracing of assets.
Trial Support: Provision of expert witnesses; analysis of opposition's financial evidence; provision of detailed support during cross examination.
Settlement Support: Assistance with settlement negotiations; evaluation of taxation implications; evaluation of business implications.

PRACTICE AREA: Types of work undertaken include: Breach of warranty; expert determination; fraud; general commercial disputes; loss of profit/earnings including personal injury; mediation; partnership disputes; professional negligence; share purchase agreements; valuation of professional goodwill, wrongful dismissal.

BDO Stoy Hayward

BENTLEY JENNISON

5-20 St Paul's Square, Birmingham, B3 1QT
Tel: (020) 7353 0803 **Fax:** (020) 7353 0692 **DX:** 13171 Birmingham 1
Email: forensic@bentley-jennison.co.uk **Website:** www.bentley-jennison.co.uk

Contact Partner: Kathy Dumbrill
Contacts:
Leeds: Chris Makin (0113) 245 1483
Nottingham: Nick White (0115) 962 0900

Other Offices UK: Bedford, Bristol, Leicester, Milton Keynes, Stafford, Stoke-on-Trent, Swindon, Telford

Freephone helpline
0800 731 6846
Monday to Friday 9:00am to 5:30pm

Number of partners:	42
Number of staff:	350

THE FIRM: Bentley Jennison is a firm of Chartered Accountants with 12 offices in England. Established in 1984, it is now among the top 20 firms in the country. Its client-focused approach has led to the development of a range of business advisory services, including advanced tax specialisms, corporate finance, forensic accounting and litigation support, IT consulting, human resource and management development. It is one of the few firms committed to serving both growing businesses and public sector organisations.

Litigation Support Services: Bentley Jennison's litigation support and forensic accounting team is comprised of dedicated specialists with years of experience in the preparation of expert witness reports and attending Court to provide expert evidence. Partners and directors are members of the Academy of Experts with over 200 court appearances between them. Arbitration and mediation services are also provided. The firm's national team takes pride in familiarising itself with the unique circumstances of a client's case enabling it to provide accurate, straightforward, cost-effective and impartial advice. A particular strength is the ability to present complex technical and financial information clearly and without complication. The firm works with clients to bring about a rapid, cost-effective resolution. The firm's specialists have the necessary analytical, accounting, taxation and communication skills gained through experience in private practice, public sector and industry to assist clients with prompt, objective and realistic accountancy advice in the following areas: commercial litigation; personal injury and medical negligence; fraud investigation, prevention and other criminal activities; public sector investigations; forensic accounting and investigations; insurance claims and investigations; professional negligence; matrimonial disputes; alternative dispute resolution; taxation.

BLICK ROTHENBERG CHARTERED ACCOUNTANTS

12 York Gate, Regent's Park, London, NW1 4QS
Tel: (020) 7486 0111 **Fax:** (020) 7935 6852
Email: martin.korn@blickrothenberg.com **Website:** www.blickrothenberg.com

Contact partner:
Martin G. Korn B Soc Sc FCA MAE
(020) 7544 8811

Number of partners: 21
Number of staff: 130

THE FIRM: A leading independent medium sized firm of Chartered Accountants. Established for over 50 years, the firm prides itself in providing a high quality service in a prompt and efficient manner. The firm has a developed speciality in litigation support work and two of the partners are members of the Academy of Experts, familiar with the new Civil Procedure Rules. Assignments are controlled personally by a partner with specialist knowledge of the litigation support process. Reports are well researched, persuasive and noted for their clarity. The partners carry the necessary personal authority and are both pro-active and experienced in the witness box. The firm is happy to meet potential new clients without cost or obligation to talk about the work that would be required in a particular case. They are also more than happy to provide estimates of their costs.

LITIGATION SUPPORT SERVICES: The firm handles work in: professional negligence; shareholder and partnership disputes; valuations of shares and businesses; loss of profit claims; actions against directors; personal injury and fatal accident financial claims; matrimonial disputes; disputed probate; tax investigations; investment problems including pensions; commercial disputes, including those arising from corporate transactions.

CARTER BACKER WINTER CHARTERED ACCOUNTANTS

Hill House, Highgate Hill, London, N19 5UU
Tel: (020) 7263 7111 **Fax:** (020) 7281 2166 **DX:** 54760 Archway
Email: peter_luscombe@cbw.co.uk **Website:** www.cbw.co.uk

Contacts: Peter Luscombe
Arthur D. Harverd

THE FIRM: Carter Backer Winter is a long established, major independent London firm with over 70 personnel.Their litigation specialists have a sound understanding of legal concepts and procedures derived from over 30 years experience of litigation work, including many leading cases. They are able to analyse complex financial data quickly and present their findings in a clear, non-technical manner, both in written form and in oral evidence.The litigation team is led by Peter Luscombe, a CEDR accredited mediator, and Arthur Harverd, a registered arbitrator and a past chairman of The Chartered Institute of Arbitrators. Both are members of the Academy of Experts and have given evidence as expert witnesses on numerous occasions. Their experience covers both civil and criminal cases in the areas of commercial, insurance, fraud, tax, personal injury and matrimonial disputes and professional and medical negligence. Their team also includes experts in the fields of insolvency and banking.

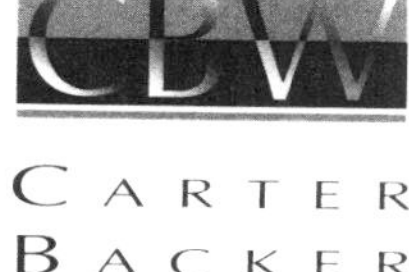

CARTER
BACKER
WINTER

C

DAVID COLLISON

The Barn, Station Court, Lode, Cambridge, CB5 9HD
Tel: (01223) 813070 **Fax:** (01223) 813147
Email: dc@dcol.co.uk

Contact partners: David Collison

THE FIRM: A new consultancy practice established 6 April 2000 by David Collison. He was at Peters Elworthy & Moore, Chartered Accountants for 20 years and was the firm's first tax partner.

LITIGATION SUPPORT PARTNER:
David Collison is available as an expert witness on taxation and accountancy matters. He is author of ICAEW *Share Valuation Handbook* and *Tiley & Collison's UK Tax Guide* (Butterworths). He is executive editor of the ICAEW *Practitioner Tax Service* and the monthly *Tax Digest* series.

DELOITTE & TOUCHE

Hill House, 1 Little New Street, London, EC4A 3TR
Tel: (020) 7936 3000 **Fax:** (020) 7936 2638 **DX:** 599
Email: forensic.uk@deloitte.co.uk **Website:** www.deloitte.co.uk

Contact partners:	Mike Barford Will Inglis Mark Tantam George Weldon Humphry Hatton
Number of partners:	346
Number of staff:	7964

THE FIRM: Deloitte & Touche has a dedicated team of forensic specialists in offices throughout the country. The firm's forensic partners have significant experience as expert witnesses, both in the UK and overseas. Where a case requires specific sector or industry expertise the firm is able to provide the appropriate expert from one of its dedicated industry or technical groups. As a leading member of Deloitte Touche Tohmatsu, the firm is also able to call upon the assistance of its 73,000 staff located in some 130 countries throughout the world.

LITIGATION SUPPORT SERVICES:
Commercial Disputes: The firm has extensive experience in general commercial disputes including claims for business interruption and loss of profits, product liability, breach of contract, intellectual property, fidelity and warranty breaches and also valuations. As one of the leading firms providing services to the public sector, Deloitte & Touche has also assisted local authorities and government bodies in a wide range of such disputes.
Determinations, Mediations & Arbitration: The firm has developed considerable expertise in the role of expert in determinations as well as acting for clients during arbitrations and mediations.
Personal Claims: The firm has a significant reputation in personal injury, fatal accident and medical negligence claims, and in the area of structured settlements. They also provide quantum reports in matrimonial disputes and libel actions.
Professional Negligence: The firm provides expert opinion on negligence claims involving accountancy firms as well as quantum reports in claims against other professionals.
Insurance Claims: The firm provides expert accountancy services to insurance companies, loss adjusters and commercial clients and has a significant record in acting for Lloyd's Syndicates involved in disputes.
Fraud & Criminal Work: The firm conducts fraud investigations, traces and recovers assets and carries out reviews to identify the risk of fraud or money laundering in both the public and private sectors. Their investigators have access to the most advanced data recovery and computer investigation tools.
Business Intelligence Service: The firm can undertake detailed research into individual's backgrounds, connections and other business activities, whether as part of a commercial dispute or fraud investigation or as a prelude to a new business opportunity or joint venture.
Computerised Litigation Systems: The firm's involvement in several major liquidations has led it to develop a computerised database document management and retrieval system for large cases.

D

DOWNHAM TRAIN EPSTEIN

DTE House, Hollins Mount, Bury, BL9 8AT
Tel: (0161) 767 1200 **Fax:** (0161) 767 1230 **DX:** 711400 Bury 6
Email: forensic@dte-house.co.uk

Contact partners:	Doug Roberts Nick Fail Louise Ellison
Number of partners:	13
Number of staff:	130

THE FIRM: DTE's forensic accounting department provides a broad range of services to the legal profession. Initial consultations will be provided free of charge.

LITIGATION SUPPORT PARTNERS: Doug Roberts BA, FCA; Nick Fail BA (Oxon), FCA; Louise Ellison MA (Cantab), ACA. The three partners between them provide a specialist service in all the principal areas of work noted below, and have experience of undertaking assignments as Court appointed single joint experts. Tony Gale: FIPM. Ex-Inland Revenue compliance officer specialising in tax investigations.

LITIGATION SUPPORT SERVICES: The firm acts for claimants and defendants and is able to assist solicitors and their clients with the following: commercial and contractual disputes; consequential loss and business interruption claims; personal injury, clinical negligence and fatal accident claims; matrimonial disputes; criminal injuries compensation claims; fraud and financial irregularities; business valuation disputes; unfair/ wrongful dismissal claims; tax investigations; structured settlements.

ERNST & YOUNG

Rolls House, 7 Rolls Buildings, Fetter Lane, London, EC4A 1NH
Tel: (020) 7951 3006 **Fax:** (020) 7951 3807 **DX:** 241
Email: rhughes1@cc.ernsty.co.uk **Website:** www.eyuk.co.uk

Contact partner:	Robert Hughes
Contacts:	
Birmingham:	Keith Cromwell (0121) 535 2127
Edinburgh:	Richard Sweetman (0131) 777 2217
Manchester:	Richard Dyson (0161) 333 2691

THE FIRM: Ernst & Young is one of the leading international firms of business and financial advisers, with offices throughout the country and the world. Clients include organisations of all types and sizes, from blue-chip multinationals to governments, and from major financial institutions to private individuals.

LITIGATION SUPPORT SERVICES: Ernst & Young has extensive experience in providing the full range of forensic services in fraud, tax and other investigations, tracing and recovery of assets, valuations, litigation, arbitrations, expert determinations and mediations.Ernst & Young's forensic specialists are organised into core teams of experienced, dedicated professionals with specialist experience in report writing and the litigation process. For each assignment the firm assembles the best team of individuals from within Ernst & Young's worldwide organisation to provide the most comprehensive level of industry expertise to the case. Using the best team approach ensures that Ernst & Young offers an outstanding quality of service in conjunction with value for money.

ERNST & YOUNG

Litigation Support Group: The litigation support group specialises in providing expert witness and related services of the highest calibre to lawyers and their clients. The group provides assistance at all stages of a case: from development of the statement of claim or defence through to presenting evidence at the trial. Their experience and the way they work enables them to focus at an early stage on the key issues in dispute and avoid unnecessary research and expense on unimportant matters. Their principal areas of expertise and contacts are as follows: Audit and accountants' negligence (Robert Hughes or Nigel Macdonald); disputes and claims following take-overs (Nicola Kerr or David Brown); business interruption and loss of profits (Suzanne Ranson or Maggie Stilwell); other contractual disputes (Robert Hughes or Nigel Macdonald); expert determinations and ADR (Nigel Macdonald or Robert Hughes); monopoly and competition enquiries (Nigel Macdonald); intellectual property disputes (Kenny Shovell); computer related disputes (Robert Hughes); construction and projects abandonment claims (Eugene Bannon); personal injury and fatal accident claims (Keith Cromwell or Sara Fowler).

Fraud Investigation Group: The fraud investigation group specialises in investigating allegations of fraud and the tracing and subsequent recovery of misappropriated assets. Fraud prevention is another area of expertise provided which includes risk awareness seminars and training of key staff to prevent and detect fraud.Ernst & Young has developed bespoke software to trace funds efficiently and effectively, where they have been transferred internationally through various currencies and split into component amounts, so that they can be recovered for the client before they are dissipated. Fraud investigations (David Sherwin or Sarah Evans); fraud risk management (David Sherwin or John Smart).

Business Valuations: Ernst & Young has had a dedicated team of full time valuers for over 25 years. The group has unparalleled experience in the field of business and share valuations typically working on over 300 assignments each year. The group's expertise comprises valuation for almost every business situation including: evaluating acquisition targets, independent valuations under the Companies Act, valuations for taxation purposes and negotiating values with the Inland Revenue; valuing intellectual property and giving evidence as a valuation expert witness in, for example, warranty claims. Business and share valuations (Jim Eales or Clive Ward).

Tax Investigation Solutions: Ernst & Young's tax investigation solution team efficiently manage Inland Revenue and Customs & Excise enquiries and minimise any consequent disruption to clients. The team comprises former Inland Revenue and Customs & Excise investigators and tax professionals who aim to minimise any risk of exposure to prosecution, achieve a fair and reasonable conclusion to enquiries, and successfully mitigate any penalties. Their team has comprehensive experience of approaches from various Inland Revenue and Customs & Excise offices, especially the Inland Revenue's Special Compliance Office and the National Investigation Service of Customs. The team has a national network with a wide understanding of Revenue and Customs tactics and detailed experience of different industry sectors. They adopt an independent approach based on their knowledge of risk areas and experience of resolving technical disputes. Corporation tax and PAYE (Bob Brown); VAT, customs duties and excise taxes (Mark Perlstrom). Ernst & Young has offices in most major towns and cities throughout the United Kingdom and each office has a designated partner with specific responsibility for litigation support.

G

GRANT THORNTON

Grant Thornton House, Melton Street, Euston Square, London, NW1 2EP
Tel: (020) 7383 5100 **Fax:** (020) 7383 4715 **DX:** 2100 Euston
Website: www.grant-thornton.co.uk

Contact partners:	
London:	Philip Kabraji
Leeds:	Robin Hall
Birmingham:	Robert Kerr
Number of partners:	248
Number of staff:	2,660

THE FIRM: Grant Thornton is a leading national and international accounting and consultancy firm providing a comprehensive range of business advisory services to a wide variety of clients from private individuals to major companies. The firm operates from 43 offices in the UK and has an international network spanning nearly 100 countries.A team of specialist forensic partners and staff offer extensive experience of commercial litigation, complex insurance claims, fraud and personal injury. Investigative financial, accounting and taxation services are provided to assist in the building of a case, obtaining settlement or the giving of expert evidence in court.Forensic services are available from most of the firm's UK offices. The main forensic centres are in the London office (Partner in charge: Philip Kabraji), the Leeds office (Partner in charge: Robin Hall) and the Birmingham office (Partner in charge: Robert Kerr).

LITIGATION SUPPORT SERVICES: The partners in the firm have experience in a wide number of business sectors, including construction, manufacturing, motor dealers, engineering, banking, financial, oil and gas, hotel and leisure, defence and professional services.Partners with appropriate expertise and witness box experience are available to act in contractual and commercial disputes, consequential loss of profit claims, breach of warranty, business and share valuations, fraud, computer disputes, professional negligence claims, trade disputes (including advice on EC and US anti-dumping regulations), directors' disqualification hearings, personal injury, medical negligence and fatal accident claims, structured settlements, royalty disputes, matrimonial disputes and libel claims.

Grant Thornton

H. W. FISHER & COMPANY, CHARTERED ACCOUNTANTS

Acre House, 11-15 William Road, London, NW1 3ER
Tel: (020) 7388 7000 **Fax:** (020) 7380 4900
Email: info@hwfisher.co.uk **Website:** www.hwfisher.co.uk

Contact partner:	Stuart Burns
Number of partners:	21
Number of staff:	300

THE FIRM: H W Fisher & Company is a medium sized accountancy firm comprising 21 partners and approximately 300 staff. Their forensic department offers a level of expertise rarely found outside the ranks of the largest international firms, combined with a commitment to a prompt, effective and personal service. Their effectiveness is enhanced by experience of acting for both plaintiffs and defendants. The firm has in-depth skills in all aspects of litigation support, including personal injury and medical negligence, matrimonial, professional negligence, share and business valuations, DTI proceedings, loss of income/profits, breach of contract, fraud investigation, music royalties and criminal work.

LITIGATION SUPPORT PARTNERS:

Stuart Burns: Stuart heads the forensic department and is a Member of the Academy of Experts and of the Association of Certified Fraud Examiners. He has considerable court experience and writes regularly on forensic issues for a range of professional publications. He is an experienced expert witness with a number of single joint expert appointments, and expert determination appointments by the Presidents Appointments Scheme, ICAEW.

David Selwyn: A forensic partner, David is also a former UK Governor of the Association of Certified Fraud Examiners. He has particular expertise in share valuations, a subject on which he has written and lectured widely.

HACKER YOUNG

St. Alphage House, 2 Fore Street, London, EC2Y 5DH
Tel: (020) 7216 4600 **Fax:** (020) 7638 2159
Email: london@hackeryoung.co.uk **Website:** www.hackeryoung.co.uk

Contact partner:	D.S. Lazarevic
Number of partners:	48
Number of staff:	290

THE FIRM: Hacker Young's long-established litigation support and forensic accounting group provides creative, objective and practical solutions to the financial and commercial aspects of disputes, including loss of profits; share valuations; professional negligence; fraud cases; arbitration; personal injury and medical negligence; contractual; commercial and employment disagreements; matrimonial disputes; regulatory investigations and intellectual property. The Hacker Young Group comprises separate and autonomous partnerships in Brighton, Chester, London, Manchester, Nottingham and Wrexham. Hacker Young is also an independent member of Urbach Hacker Young International, a worldwide network of over forty accountancy firms in 100 locations around the globe.

HLB KIDSONS

Spectrum House, 20-26 Cursitor Street, London, EC4A 1HY
Tel: (020) 7405 2088 **Fax:** (020) 7334 4734 **DX:** 458 London
Email: jpack@kilondon.hlbkidsons.co.uk **Website:** www.hlbkidsons.co.uk

Contacts:	
London:	Richard Lewis (020) 7405 2088
Midlands:	Adrian Pym (0121) 631 2631
North West:	Mark Blakemore (0161) 236 7733
North East:	Richard Pughe (0113) 242 2666
East:	John Barnes (01245) 269595
South West:	Edward Corrigan (0117)925 2255

THE FIRM: HLB Kidsons is a leading UK firm of chartered accountants and business advisors with offices throughout the country. The firm provides advice on all litigation support matters to companies, partnerships, sole traders, trustees, private individuals, regulatory bodies and police authorities and acts for both claimants and defendants.In selecting a team of forensic specialists for each assignment, HLB Kidsons draws upon the wealth of technical expertise, business and court experience within the firm. Through membership of HLB International the firm can enlist the skills of experts in over 240 offices in some 90 countries worldwide.The firm provides expert witness reports, which are clear, concise and written in plain English, avoiding jargon and technical accounting terms as far as possible. The firm's service is highly responsive; it never loses sight of the fact that it forms only one part of a team of experts working on any case.

LITIGATION SUPPORT SERVICES:

Financial Inquiry Services: Fraud and corruption investigations; establishing benefit of crime for the Criminal Courts; evaluating loss to the victims of crime; compensation claims for the Criminal Courts; confiscation issues (DTOA and CJA); acting as receivers for the Court in confiscation and litigation matters; restraint order actions; means enquiries conducted by Civil and Criminal Courts; investigating money laundering; tracing assets; regulatory investigations conducted under the FSA; Companies Act and Charities Act.

Business Claims: Loss of profits; commercial disputes; civil fraud; breach of contract; computer related disputes; fidelity: intellectual property; business interruption; business valuations.

Personal Claims: Personal injury and fatal accident litigation; matrimonial disputes; compensation for loss of office; libel.

Other Forensic Accounting Matters: Professional negligence; insurance and reinsurance disputes; arbitration and expert adjudication; security for costs.

HORWATH CLARK WHITEHILL

25 New Street Square, London, EC4A 3LN
Tel: (020) 7353 1577 **Fax:** (020) 7353 6435 **DX:** London Chancery Lane 0014
Email: enquiry@horwathcw.co.uk **Website:** www.horwathcw.com

Chairman:	James Gemmell
Head of Litigation Services:	Richard Freeman
London/Thames Valley:	Humphrey Creed (01494) 463200
London:	Daniel Djanogly (020) 7353 1577
West Midlands:	Chris Bicknell (01922) 725590
Leeds:	Ross MacLaverty (0113) 274 0404
Number of partners:	72
Number of staff:	532

THE FIRM: Howarth Clark Whitehall is the ninth largest firm of accountants and business advisers in the UK. Its Litigation Services Division provides forensic accounting services on a nationwide basis. Principals act as adviser and expert witness in all types of dispute - civil, matrimonial, tax and fraud. Other services include expert determination, arbitration and mediation.

KINGSTON SMITH

Devonshire House, 60 Goswell Road, London, EC1M 7AD
Tel: (020) 7566 4000 **Fax:** (020) 7566 4010
Email: ks@kingstonsmith.co.uk **Website:** www.kingstonsmith.co.uk

Contact partner:	Emile Woolf
Number of partners:	37
Number of staff:	300

THE FIRM: The Kingston Smith litigation support facility was established in 1980, and all members of the service team have many years professional and commercial experience to complement their legal and regulatory knowledge and skills. The team undertakes a wide range of specialist assignments for lawyers, insurers, loss adjusters, professional and regulatory bodies and government agencies, acting for either defendants or plaintiffs. Civil and criminal assignments undertaken, including legally aided cases.

LITIGATION SUPPORT PARTNERS:

Emile Wolf FCA, FCCA, MAE, FInstM, FIIA, has for many years been Chairman of the Professional Indemnity Insurance Panel of the Institute of Chartered Accountants in England and Wales (ICAEW) and represents the institute on the Joint Advisery Panel of Participating Insurers, of which he is Chairman. He is widely known throughout the profession through his lectures and frequent contributions to the professional press on litigation issues. He is the author of several leading texts including *Professional Liability of Accountants* (ICEAW), *Risk Management for Auditors* (ICEAW), *Preserving Your Right to Audit* (CCH Editions), *Auditing Today* (Prentice Hall), *Emile Woolf on Audit Exemtion* (CCH Editions), and *The Legal Liabilities of Practising Accountants* (Butterworths). He is a member of he Academy of Experts and is a CEDR-accredited mediator. He was the founder in 1975 of one of the largest accountancy training groups in the UK.

Benjamin Howe FCA, ATII, MAE is responsible for the consequential and material loss claims assignments arising from, eg medical negligence, personal injury and fire. His background includes advisory appointments and directorships in small companies giving him experience in commercial aspects of business management to complement his professional expertise. He is a member of the Academy of Experts.

Martin Muirhead FCA, MAE undertakes forensic accounting including computer modelling as well as commercial and tax related matters. His extensive business and tax experience includes financial services, investment business and general commercial sectors. Recent matters include acting in relation to liability and quantum in professional negligence disputes, varied commercial litigation including business and share valuations, minority protection, Inland Revenue investigations including Special Compliance Office, PAYE Audit and Benefits compliance and advising on quantum issues. He was appointed by the Charity Commissioners, under the Charities Act 1993, to act as the first Receiver and Manager of a UK registered Charity including dispute resolution of contentious areas including fiduciary duty trustees responsibilities. He is also a Company Director and Member of the Academy of Experts.

Adrian Houstoun FCA, ACIArb is a chartered accountant and a member of the Chartered Institute of Arbitrators. He specialises in matters where knowledge of the law of contract, tort and evidence can be combined with his extensive business experience, including public company acquisitions and VAT services. One of his recent assignments was an appointment by the Secretary of State for Industry, as an inspector under the Financial Services Act, to investigate alleged insider dealing in the securities of a public company. He is on the Institute of Chartered Accountants' panel of arbitrators and also undertakes investigations on their behalf into firms who are unable to obtain insurance cover. He has significant experience with business valuation cases and assisted lawyers in a number of matrimonial cases as well as advising directors following the sale of a business in connection with warranty claims.

LITIGATION SUPPORT SERVICES: Include professional negligence, consequential loss and business interruption including personal injury. Matrimonial, white collar crime, fraud, regulatory and compliance matters including directors' disqualification. Forensic accounting including modelling in insurance and commercial cases. Inland Revenue and Customs investigations, settlements and related disputes. Business and share valuations. Sectors include financial and investment business. Specialist insolvency division.

K

KPMG

20 Farringdon Street, London, EC4A 4PP
Tel: (020) 7311 1000 **Fax:** (020) 7311 3672
Website: www.kpmg.co.uk

Contacts:	
Expert Witness:	John Ellison
Fraud investigations:	Alex Plavsic
Fraud Risk Management:	David Davies
Birmingham:	David Alexander (0121) 232 3000
Edinburgh:	Judith Scott (0131) 527 6619
Leeds:	Tim Taylor (0113) 231 3000
Manchester:	Richard Powell (0161) 838 4000

THE FIRM: KPMG Forensic Accounting is a leading member of the KPMG International Forensic Accounting Practice providing a global co-ordinated forensic accounting service. As one of the leading business advisory firms in the world, KPMG provides a comprehensive range of accountancy, tax and consulting services. The firm has experience of working with organisations of all sizes from government to individuals, and from multinationals to privately-owned businesses. KPMG has over 100,000 personnel in 159 countries world-wide, and some 11,000 people in 25 offices in the UK. A 'Harris' survey in 1998 referred to KPMG's position as the 'pre-eminent' firm in forensic accounting.

LITIGATION SUPPORT SERVICES: KPMG's Forensic Accounting department has a dedicated team of more than 150 partners and professional staff throughout the UK, and a global co-ordinated forensic accounting service. The firm provides specialist services in six broad areas:
Commercial disputes: Loss of profits claims; international and national arbitrations; breach of contract and warranty claims; purchase and sale disputes and agreement vetting; shareholder and partnership disputes; libel and slander actions; intellectual property (including Y2K) disputes; business and share valuations; insurance claims; security for costs applications.
Professional negligence: Accounting; auditing; corporate finance and IT implementation (liability and quantum); other professions (quantum).
Fraud investigation: KPMG has developed particular expertise in handling investigations into fraud. Numerous assignments for government, police, companies and public bodies bear witness to the firm's reputation in this area. The firm uses a refined investigation methodology which, when combined with advanced technology, allows KPMG to investigate suspected frauds of all sizes effectively and efficiently.
Personal disputes: Personal injury claims; fatal accidents; medical negligence; family and matrimonial disputes; employment and pension disputes.
Regulatory investigations: Investigations and accounting assistance for regulatory authorities and those under investigation. Also assistance in statutory and disciplinary enquiries.
Determinations and Arbitrations: Expert determinations; arbitrations; mediations; valuations. The provision of these services is enhanced by expert knowledge of various industry sectors including: banking, insurance, commodities, information technology, telecommunications, shipping and transportation, construction, manufacturing, oil and gas, infrastructure and government, leasing, retailing, healthcare and pharmaceutical, and intellectual property.

L

LEVY GEE

66 Wigmore Street, London, W1H OHQ
Tel: (020) 7467 4000 **Fax:** (020) 7467 4040
Email: info@levygee.com **Website:** www.levygee.com

9 Portland Road, Edgbaston, Birmingham, B16 9HN
Tel: (0121) 456 2525 **Fax:** (0121) 456 2828

South Central, 11 Peter Street, Manchester, M2 5LG
Tel: (0161) 833 8300 **Fax:** (0161) 833 8333

Contact partners:	David Epstein David Stern Gail Rifkind David Rabinowitz Alan Thompson
Number of partners:	49
Number of staff:	346

THE FIRM: The Levy Gee forensic accounting and dispute resolution department has dedicated partners and qualified staff in each of their London, Birmingham and Manchester offices. The department assists the legal profession, insurers and regulatory and prosecuting bodies in the pursuance and defence of claims by providing expert opinions on the quantum of loss.

LITIGATION SUPPORT PARTNERS:
David Epstein (FCA) has thirty years' experience of advising partnerships and owner-managed businesses. David has been instructed on a wide range of disputes including claims for commercial loss and professional negligence. He is a member of The Academy of Experts, a founding member of The Expert Witness Institute, a member of the British Institute of Management and an Associate of The Chartered Institute of Taxation. He also has a strong financial services background.
David Stern (FCA) has been instructed on a wide range of both civil and criminal litigation support cases. He has also received appointments from the Institute of Chartered Accountants in England and Wales to act as an arbitrator and as an expert. In addition, as a CEDR accredited mediator, David has acted on a wide range of disputes. David is also a member of the Academy of Experts, a member of the Chartered Institute of Arbitrators and a member of the Association of Business Recovery Professionals..
Gail Rifkind (CA - Scotland) specialises in personal injury, clinical negligence and fatal accident work for both claimant and defendant. She has been involved in many headline cases, such as the Kings Cross fire, the Southhall Rail crash, asbestosis claims and pregnancy dismissals at the MOD and has experience of giving evidence in court. Gail is a member of The Academy of Experts and a founding member of The Expert Witness Institute.

Alan Thompson (FCA) heads up the Birmingham department. He has worked on a wide range of cases such as professional negligence, fraud, breach of contract and matrimonial disputes as well as director disqualification cases. He has also worked with the Crown Prosecution Services in relation to fraud matters. Alan is experienced in dealing with contract and tax disputes in other countries and has given evidence in the USA as well as the UK. Alan holds a BA degree in Sociology and an LLB (Hons) degree and is remembered for his strong negotiating skills. He is also a member of the Academy of Experts, The Chartered Institute of Taxation and The Society of Practitioners of Insolvency, as well as The Chartered Institute of Arbitrators.

David Rabinowitz (ACA) has wide ranging experience in all aspects of litigation support, having specialised in this work for the past eight years. His particular areas of specialism are in the commercial litigation and personal injury/clinical negligence fields and he has lectured on these subjects to lawyers and insurance companies. David has frequently acted as a single joint expert for both plaintiff and defendant and has given evidence in court. David is a member of The Institute of Chartered Accountants in England and Wales and of The Academy of Experts.

LITIGATION SUPPORT SERVICES:

Forensic Accounting: Members of the department have a detailed knowledge of a wide range of businesses and industries. They provide a partner-led service by covering: breach of warranty claims; business interruption and consequential loss claims; contractual disputes; due diligence; family and matrimonial disputes; fraud investigations; personal injury and clinical negligence claims; professional negligence claims; shareholder and partnership disputes; share valuations; partners have considerable experience of giving evidence in Court in both civil and criminal proceedings. In addition, partners in the department accept appointments in the areas of: arbitration, mediation and expert determination.

LITTLEJOHN FRAZER

1 Park Place, Canary Wharf, London, E14 4HJ
Tel: (020) 7987 5030 **Fax:** (020) 7987 9707 **DX:** 42660
Email: info@littlejohnfrazer.com **Website:** www.littlejohnfrazer.com

Contact partner:	Ian Hobbs
Number of partners:	23
Number of staff:	150

THE FIRM: Partners at Littlejohn Frazer now have over ten years' experience of providing litigation support services to the legal profession. Of the firm's 12 partners, 23 have relevant experience and the lead partners (Ian Hobbs and Alastair Campbell) have considerable experience of justifying their expert opinions in the witness box. Ian Hobbs is the co-author of *Expert Accounting Evidence - A Guide for Litigation Support* published by the ICAEW in 1998. Lord Woolf wrote the preface and said: *"I welcome the publication of this book and congratulate the authors on a job well done. I do so, because while I welcome the greater involvement of accountants in the court process, this welcome is conditional. It is conditional on the involvement being constructive. It can only be constructive if the involvement is knowledgeable and proportionate. Unfortunately, sometimes it is not and this is all too often due to ignorance or a lack of professionalism for which this book provides the remedy. The authors rightly stress the need to keep costs under control and echo the messages which are contained in my report in "Access to Justice..."* Partners have experience of investigations for the DTI, and the firm has undertaken a number of assignments for the Serious Fraud Office. Legally aided work is undertaken, in both civil and criminal matters. The firm has extensive experience of the insurance sector and in particular the Lloyd's market.

LITIGATION SUPPORT PARTNERS:

I.C. Hobbs (FCA) Member of Academy of Experts. Specialises in accountants' negligence; quantification of loss, particularly consequential loss in construction disputes and fire claims; share valuations; tax as a non-specialist; serious fraud; personal injury; matrimonial.

A.H.F. Campbell (FCA) Serious fraud, regulatory, Lloyd's, accountants' negligence, breach of financial warranties.

J.G. Ambler (ACA)Computer consultancy, software contracts.

R.L. Green (FCCA)Solicitors' Accounts Rules.

D.R.M. Frame (FCA)Serious fraud, forensic.

M.T. Stenson (FCA)Serious fraud, regulatory.

D.W. Roberts (FCA)Regulatory, Lloyd's.

LITIGATION SUPPORT SERVICES:

Civil: Accountants professional negligence; financial consequences of: personal injury; consequential loss, particularly in construction and fire-damage claims; insurance and re-insurance disputes; purchase and sales disputes; matrimonial disputes; intellectual property disputes

Criminal: Serious fraud; crime with financial motive; Companies Act offences

Investigations: Computer consultancy; forensic accounting

Regulatory: ICAEW; FSA; Law Society; RICS; DTI; SFO; Lloyd's.

LONDON ECONOMICS

66 Chiltern Street, London, W1M 1PR
Tel: (020) 7446 8400 **Fax:** (020) 7446 8484/5
Email: competition@londecon.co.uk **Website:** www.londecon.co.uk

Contact:	Mike Walker

THE FIRM: LE is Europe's leading independent economics consultancy. Since its foundation in 1986, it has provided comprehensive litigation and arbitration support in cases across the UK, the EU and Australia.

LITIGATION SUPPORT SERVICES: Expertise covers the following areas: interpretation of economic concepts in the context of contract or tort; calculation of damages; competition cases; valuation of intellectual property rights; tax disputes. London Economics' litigation support services are based on a unique combination of skills and resources unavailable from other advisers. As specialist economic consultants, they provide a service that combines the economic expertise of the best independent academics with the professionalism and ability to deliver associated with large accounting firms. Expert witnesses are experienced in giving evidence, appearing in court and reacting to cross-examination. They provide advice on the strengths and weaknesses of the opposition's case and expert opinions, providing ammunition for cross-examination.

LUBBOCK FINE

Russell Bedford House, City Forum, 250 City Rd, London, EC1V 2QQ
Tel: (020) 7490 7766 **Fax:** (020) 7490 5102
Email: post@lubbockfine.co.uk **Website:** www.lubbockfine.co.uk

Contact partners:	Alan M. Cushnir Anthony Sober
Number of partners:	13

THE FIRM: Lubbock Fine is a leading UK medium-sized practice providing a full service to personal and corporate clients on all aspects of audit, accountancy, taxation and financial management. The legal support department is one of the fastest growing areas of the firm's practice.

LITIGATION SUPPORT PARTNERS:
Alan M Cushnir , FCA, MABRP (member of the Association of Business Recovery Practitioners), MAE. (member of the Academy of Experts) and licensed insolvency practitioner. Specialises in litigation support and forensic accounting.
Anthony Sober , FCA, FCIArb (Fellow of the Chartered Institute of Arbitrators), MAE and QDR (qualified dispute resolver).
The Legal Support Team: The team is dedicated to providing complementary services to the legal industry. Their experience extends to advising on, and quantifying financial, accounting and numerical aspects of litigation, for claims and formal court action. Both partners are trained as single joint experts.In addition Anthony Sober acts as an arbitrator and mediator in many kinds of commercial and private disputes.

LITIGATION SUPPORT SERVICES: The services range from the provision of expert's reports and investigations to acting as expert witnesses. The firm handles substantial assignments in the following areas: providing independent valuations and tracing assets; fraud and criminal work; breach of contract; arbitrating partnership and commercial disputes; expert determinations; claims against government bodies (e.g. Criminal Injuries Compensation Board); personal injury and medical negligence claims; matrimonial and divorce proceedings. Both Alan and Anthony are more than willing to discuss their previous work for the legal profession.

M

MARKS & CLERK

57-60 Lincoln's Inn Fields, London, WC2A 3LS
Tel: (020) 7400 3000 **Fax:** (020) 7404 4910
Email: admin@marks-clerk.com **Website:** www.marks-clerk.com

Contacts:	
London:	John Slater (020) 7400 3000
Birmingham:	Tony Pearce (0121) 643 5881
Manchester:	John Allman (0161) 233 5800
Glasgow:	Bill McCallum (0141) 221 5767
Cheltenham:	Mike Higgins (01242) 524 520
Oxford:	Richard Harding (01865) 397 900
Leeds:	Keith Hodkinson (0113) 389 5600
Luxembourg:	Pierre Weyland +352 400 270
Hong Kong:	Simon Speeks +852 2526 6345
Ottawa:	Bob Sterling +1 613 236 9561
Alicante:	Aidan Clarke +34 96 51 42727
Number of partners:	50
Number of staff:	200

THE FIRM: Marks & Clerk was founded in 1887. A leader in the field of intellectual property with 50 partners and over 100 fee earners, the firm serves a client base ranging from the private individual to the largest multinational corporations.
In addition to preparing and filing patent, trade mark and design applications, Marks & Clerk advises on infringement and its avoidance, reverse engineering and validity issues. They provide technical support to solicitors and barristers in litigation and perform intellectual property audits and due diligence reviews on all aspects of intellectual property transactions. The firm offers expert witnesses for proceedings in the UK and overseas and provides ancillary services such as patent, design and trade mark searching, competitor monitoring and related investigations. They also arrange appropriate documentation for global assignment and licensing transactions and assist in IP portfolio management and training services.

MARKS & CLERK
Intellectual Property

MARTIN GREENE RAVDEN

55 Loudoun Road, St. Johns Wood, London, NW8 0DL
Tel: (020) 7625 4545 **Fax:** (020) 7625 5265
Email: mgr@mgr.co.uk **Website:** www.mgr.co.uk

Contact partners:	David Greene David Ravden Robert Braham

THE FIRM: Martin Greene Ravden is a medium-size firm of chartered accountants with 11 partners and over 70 staff. It represents a broad range of clients and is best known as one of the leading specialists in the media, entertainment and sports industries. The firm has a highly experienced forensic accounting and litigation support group, with an excellent track record in helping solicitors achieve very favourable results in contentious cases.

LITIGATION SUPPORT SERVICES:

Matrimonial Disputes: Valuation of businesses and shares in private companies; investigating the completeness of disclosures; clarifying income and capital positions; assessment of income requirement; tax efficient structuring of settlements.

Commercial Disputes: Entertainment industry and intellectual property disputes; quantification of loss in commercial disputes and claims for damages; shareholder and partnership disputes; claims for consequential loss and loss of earnings; fraud investigations.

MAZARS NEVILLE RUSSELL

24 Bevis Marks, London, EC3A 7NR
Tel: (020) 7377 1000 **Fax:** (020) 7377 8931
Website: www.mazars-nr.co.uk

Contact partners:	Glyn Williams Peter Hyatt Paul Smethurst Nigel Grummitt
Number of partners:	92
Number of staff:	950

THE FIRM: Mazars Neville Russell is the UK national firm of Mazars, the international accounting and consultancy group operating in over 45 countries. The growing forensic and investigation services group have advised in and reported upon a broad spectrum of cases requiring independent financial analysis. The team are experienced in giving evidence in court and arbitration proceedings. Whilst bringing all the resources that might be expected from an international firm the emphasis of the service is on ensuring work is undertaken on a timely basis and providing value for money in clear and concise reports. This is achieved through the detailed personal involvement at all stages of the partner or expert who will be reporting.

MAZARS NEVILLE RUSSELL
Chartered Accountants

M

MOORE STEPHENS

St Paul's House, Warwick Lane, London, EC4P 4BN
Tel: (020) 7334 9191 **Fax:** (020) 7248 3408 **DX:** 15 London
Email: postmaster@moorestephens.com **Website:** www.moorestephens.co.uk

Contact partners:	Civil: Julian Wilkinson Criminal: Andrew Nicholl
Number of partners:	144
Number of staff:	1,158

LITIGATION SUPPORT PARTNERS:

Mr Julian Wilkinson FCA, Member of the Academy of Experts. Many years' experience as expert witness for Arbitration and High Court proceedings with particular experience of shipping related matters including alleged scuttling claims and joint venture disputes. Also experienced in loss of profits claims. Has given evidence in Court.

Mr Andrew Nicholl BSc FCA, Experienced in interpretation of the application of accounting and auditing standards, including assessment of professional work by accountants. Has acted as expert accountant in major cases involving allegations of false accounting and various commercial matters. Has given evidence in Court.

James Smart, FCA, Approaching twenty years' insurance specialisation in the London market. Has conducted confidential enquiries, loss reviews and investigations for the DTI, PIA and Lloyd's as regulators and acts as expert in insurance related litigation. Significant involvement in the Equitas Project.

LITIGATION SUPPORT SERVICES:

Loss of Profits: Business interruption; product inadequacy; infringement of intellectual property rights; breach of contract or warranties; fraud, defalcation or misappropriation; personal injury or fatal accident.

Valuations: Businesses and business assets for settlement of commercial disputes; in separation or divorce cases.

Professional Negligence: Property and information technology matters; due diligence work in business acquisitions and disputes; taxation advice; insolvency; audit and accountancy.

International Trade Claims: Particularly shipping and transport matters.

PANNELL KERR FORSTER

New Garden House, 78 Hatton Garden, London, EC1N 8JA
Tel: (020) 7831 7393 **Fax:** (020) 7405 6736 **DX:** 479 Ch.Ln.
Email: roger.claxton@uk.pkf.com **Website:** www.pkf.co.uk

141 King Street, Great Yarmouth, NR30 2PQ
Tel: (01493) 842281 **Fax:** (01493) 330075
Email: jon.dodge@uk.pkf.com
Pannell House, 6 Queen Street, Leeds, LS1 2TW
Tel: (0113) 228 0000 **Fax:** (0113) 228 4242
Email: neill.poole@uk.pkf.com

52 Mount Pleasant, Liverpool, L3 5UN
Tel: (0151) 708 8232 **Fax:** (0151) 708 8169
Email: mark.fairhurst@uk.pkf.com

Sovereign House, Queen Street, Manchester, M2 5HR
Tel: (0161) 832 5481 **Fax:** (0161) 832 3849
Email: john.grogan@uk.pkf.com

Knowle House, 4 Norfolk Park Road, Sheffield, S2 3QE
Tel: (0114) 276 7991 **Fax:**
Email: jeremy.lai@uk.pkf.com

Contact partners:	Roger Claxton Nick Whitaker Hugh Mathew-Jones Richard Pearson Richard Bolton
Number of partners:	22
Number of staff:	31

THE FIRM: Pannell Kerr Forster's investigative accounting skills are regularly drawn upon by the legal profession. A highly skilled team acts for claimants and defendants, assisting solicitors or counsel in cases ranging in size from small disputes to highly complex actions. Multi-disciplinary teams of experts can be assembled from within the firm to handle the largest corporate actions. An impressive track record includes cases involving professional negligence, breach of contract, corporate disputes and insurance claims. The firm also assists in personal injury, fatal accident, fraud and divorce actions.

PETER LOBBENBERG & CO

74 Chancery Lane, London, WC2A 1AA
Tel: (020) 7430 9300 **Fax:** (020) 7430 9315 **DX:** 204 London/Chancery Lane

Contact partner:	Peter Lobbenberg
Number of partners:	1
Number of staff:	2

P

THE FIRM: A niche practice well known as specialists in matrimonial litigation support throughout the country: its clients include over 80% of the leading London family law firms listed in *Chambers*. Also specialises in share valuations, and operates a caring tax service for private clients and trusts. As a member of Horwath Clark Whitehill Associates, the firm has access to a wide range of facilities and specialisms. Mr Lobbenberg is a Fellow of the Academy of Experts.

LANGUAGES: German and French.

PINDERS PROFESSIONAL & CONSULTANCY SERVICES LIMITED

Pinder House, Central Milton Keynes, MK9 1DS
Tel: (01908) 350500 **Fax:** (01908) 350501 **DX:** 84752 Milton Keynes 3
Email: pcs@pinders.co.uk **Website:** www.pinders.co.uk

Contact Director:	Mark Ellis BSc FRICS MCIArb MAE
Directors:	Jon Chapman BA Hons QDR Simon Bird BSc ARICS MCIArb
Senior Chartered Surveyor:	Graham Coulter FRICS
Consultants:	Marek Bilecki FRICS John Smith FRICS
Senior Chartered Building Surveyor:	Ray Chamberlin ARICS

THE FIRM: The Pinders name has become synonymous with the appraisal and valuation of businesses since 1969, providing specialist professional services to the legal and banking professions on the healthcare, retail, licensed and leisure sectors. Particular areas of expertise include business valuations (both current and retrospective), loss of profits claims, expert witness evidence and professional negligence. Pinders can call upon a database containing detailed trading and valuation information on over 160,000 businesses throughout the United Kingdom, together with continually updated records of sale transactions.

LITIGATION SUPPORT PARTNER:
Mark Ellis (BSc FRICS MCIArb MAE), previously a member of The RICS Skills Panel on Trading Related Valuations, heads up the professional services and litigation support team based at the head office in Milton Keynes and a team of regional valuers who combine knowledge of local values, trade sources, legislation and competition with the wider accumulation of centralised information and expertise. The team includes a QDR and Arbitrators.

REEVES & NEYLAN FORENSIC ACCOUNTING

Victoria House, 20-22 Albion Place, Ramsgate, CT11 8HQ
Tel: (01843) 572300 **Fax:** (01843) 572309 **DX:** 30622 Ramsgate
Email: forensic@reeves.neylan.com **Website:** www.reeves-neylan.com/forensic

Contact partners:	Alan Tinham
Number of partners:	20
Number of staff:	170

THE FIRM: Reeves & Neylan Forensic Accounting, the dedicated litigation support department of Reeves & Neylan, is a corporate member of the Academy of Experts.Work will usually commence within one to two days of receipt of formal instructions and all reports are CPR compliant. Assistance is available with pre-issue evaluation of quantum and Part 36 offers. Services are provided to claimants and defendants throughout the UK as SJE, party appointed expert or advisor.

LITIGATION SUPPORT SERVICES: Services include calculation of quantum; commercial disputes, product liability claims, environmental pollution; loss of profit claims; personal injury, medical negligence/class actions and fatality claims; divorce; professional negligence; CA S459 investigations and share valuations; theft, fraud and financial irregularities; wrongful and fraudulent trading; S71 confiscation orders; VAT and tax fraud.

Other: Reeves & Neylan also provides specialist services in the following areas: VAT consultancy; Solicitors' Accounts Rules audits; tax planning and profit improvement consultancy; design and implementation of practice management information systems; practice finance arrangements; investigations.

RGL INTERNATIONAL

17 Devonshire Square, London, EC2M 4SQ
Tel: (020) 7247 4804 **Fax:** (020) 7247 4970
Email: mailbox@rglinternational.com **Website:** www.rglinternational.com

Contact Partners: Anthony Levitt, Edward Leighton, Catherine Rawlin, Keith Tuffin, James Stanbury

THE FIRM: RGL International is a market leader specialising exclusively in forensic accounting, giving dedicated support to solicitors and insurers, through the investigation and measurement of damages. Partners at RGL have recently worked with insurers and lawyers to quantify losses for businesses after the floods in Mozambique and the Taiwan earthquake, as well as advising the United Nations Compensation Commission on levels of war reparations following the Gulf War. The firm prides itself on working quickly and efficiently, using the optimum amount of human, computer and other resources to support litigation and quantification of claims by providing a clear picture of what happened and why. UK partners are backed by an international organisation which they can call upon as and when it is needed. RGL International aims to present a full, unbiased report of the real circumstances behind any event. The firm helps to create the context within which clients can take the most appropriate decisions.

LITIGATION SUPPORT SERVICES: In the following areas: business interruption/loss of profit; product liability; fraud; personal injury/fatal accident claims; reinsurance; general quantification of damages. Once appointed by solicitors or insurers, RGL International investigates and checks the suppositions behind a claim. Highly experienced practitioners will know exactly which documents should be available for discovery, both inside and outside any company. In addition to standard returns and records, these often include undisclosed management information, reports and papers from professional, trade and official bodies. A precisely-worded request for disclosure of specific documents will indicate to the other party a client's insight into the issues involved in the claim and can often lead to negotiation of a satisfactory settlement. Instructing solicitors or insurers are provided with a professional report for use in litigation or negotiations, highlighting any errors or omissions in the claim and its strengths or weaknesses. Claims can often be complicated, with side issues clouding the essence of a case. When this happens, it may be valuable for the instructing solicitor or insurer to direct the RGL International team to attend meetings with the other party's experts, on a 'without prejudice' basis, to resolve specific areas of disagreement or confusion. The limits to these discussions will be set by the instructing solicitor or insurer. Such meetings can greatly reduce the time spent considering a claim, thus reducing overall costs. As a specialist firm RGL International never has a conflict of interest; always dedicates a partner and team to every instruction; ensures fees are cost effective and reasonable; utilises experience from over 230 accounting staff worldwide. Should a claim come to court, RGL International practitioners can clearly and succinctly explain evidence included in the accounting expert's report under examination-in-chief and cross-examination. They will be available to attend the trial, to help Counsel formulate questions based on evidence given by any opposing accounting experts. For a copy of the firm's corporate brochure, please telephone any of the contact partners.

THE SMITH & WILLIAMSON GROUP

No. 1 Riding House St, London, W1A 3AS
Tel: (020) 7637 5377 **Fax:** (020) 7631 0741
Email: <recipient>@williamson.co.uk **Website:** ww.smith.williamson.co.uk

Contact partners: Douglas J. Hall, Peter J. Yeldon, Peter G. Mills, Iain J Allan, Frank A.M. Akers-Douglas

Number of partners:	100
Number of staff:	600

THE FIRM: The Smith & Williamson Group combines a firm of chartered accountants and an investment management house. Its full range of accountancy services covers accountancy, auditing, corporate finance, corporate recovery, corporate taxation, investigations, litigation support, management consulting and personal taxation.

LITIGATION SUPPORT SERVICE: Smith & Williamson has a dedicated litigation support team whose expertise covers the full range of forensic accounting, including assistance for regulatory bodies, civil litigation, investigations of fraud and personal injury.The firm has experience in acting for either the claimant or the defendant and its objective is always to understand the wider implications of a case in order to provide a flexible and constructive approach to every assignment.

R

Consultants

THE ACADEMY OF EXPERTS

2 South Square, Grays Inn, London, WC1R 5HP
Tel: (020) 7637 0333 **Fax:** (020) 7637 1893 **DX:** 283 -London, Chancery Lane
Email: admin@academy-experts.org

Administrator:	Miss Nicola Cohen

THE ACADEMY: The Academy of Experts is a professional body for Expert Witnesses providing services to its members and the legal profession.

LITIGATION SUPPORT SERVICES: All applicants for practising membership as experts submit to a thorough vetting procedure to ensure the maintenance of standards. Standards are enforced by codes of practice with disciplinary sanctions.
Expert Search: The Academy matches the right accredited expert to a case. This includes speaking to the expert to check suitability, conflict of interests and availability.
Expert Training: The Academy's training programme is designed for all levels of experience from the first time expert to the more experienced. As well as complying with CPR, experts need knowledge, skills and confidence to perform well in conference, meetings of experts and in Court.
Commercial Mediation Training: As one of the longest-running commercial mediation training courses (est.1989) the Academy's course is now under the control of the Faculty of Mediation & ADR. The Academy awards the letters QDR for successful completion and entry onto the Register of Qualified Dispute Resolvers.
Mediation Appointment: Using the same method as in expert search, the Academy appoints the right accredited mediator.

GRANDFIELD

69 Wilson Street, London, EC2A 2BB
Tel: (020) 7417 4170 **Fax:** (020) 7417 9180
Email: clare.abbot@grandfield.com **Website:** www.grandfield.com

Contact Directors:	Clare Abbot Robert Rice

GRANDFIELD
Corporate Communications Consultants

THE FIRM: Grandfield is an independent communications consultancy specialising in advising on and handling contentious issues in the corporate, professional services, and financial sectors.As a result of growing demand from legal clients within its professional services division, in 1998 Grandfield established a dedicated unit to handle litigation support communications. The principals of this unit are expert in advising legal, corporate and individual clients on how best to use external and internal communications throughout the litigation process.Each case is handled at director level by senior consultants with extensive experience of creating appropriate communications strategies for high profile legal actions, whether being pursued in the UK or overseas. The firm as a whole has an excellent reputation for its international media relations capability, and places great importance on client confidentiality.

LITIGATION SUPPORT SERVICES:
Pre-trial Support: Development of key messages; training of spokespersons; planning of stakeholder and media communications; reputation management strategy.
Trial Support: Bespoke press office to handle all media and associated enquiries; media monitoring and evaluation; perceptions research; post-trial evaluation.

LEHMANN COMMUNICATIONS PLC

Lloyds Avenue House, 6 Lloyds Avenue, London, EC3N 3EH
Tel: (020) 7266 3020 **Fax:** (020) 7266 3060
Email: pr@lehmanncommunications.com **Website:** www.lehmanncommunications.com

Chief executive:	Ronel Lehmann
Professional services:	Gabrielle Hinton
Financial services:	Ronel Lehmann
Corporate:	Joan Robertson FIPR
E-commerce & Technology:	Renagh Christopher
Business development:	Grenville Burn MIPR

LEHMANN
COMMUNICATIONS
EC3

THE FIRM: Lehmann Communications is one of the UK's leading public relations and communications consultancies specialising in the professional and financial services market. Founded in 1988, the firm acts for leading solicitors, barristers, accountants, banks and financial institutions, insurance brokers, management and recruitment consultants, e-commerce and technology businesses. Account directors, managers and executives at Lehmann Communications have close and long standing links with leading journalists, editors, producers and internet providers responsible for news, business and current affairs, who disseminate information to news sources and build media profile. Lehmann Communications is a full service consultancy resourced to provide the best people offering the highest levels of service with clear, innovative, imaginative thinking across the whole spectrum of communications.

SERVICES: The firm's services include: public and media relations consultancy; public affairs, political and parliamentary consultancy; design and print management; advertising and copywriting; new business presentation and media training; project and event management; sponsorship; crisis management; internal communications; website and e-commerce development. The firm continually invests in recruiting and training the best people to provide leading edge thinking and advice.

Lehmann Communications focuses on developing long-term relationships with its clients. Most fall into this category even if the firm is instructed on a project basis. The firm invests time and effort in getting to know clients' organisations and the people that make them work. It analyses the issues faced by its clients and this frames the advice and solutions proposed. Lehmann Communications is available 24 hours a day, seven days a week. If you would like a copy of their corporate brochure please telephone Grenville Burn on 020 7266 3020, or visit their website at www.lehmanncommunications.com.

CLIENTELE: The firm advised the Lincoln's Inn Fields firm of solicitors responsible for issuing first writs against the junior health minister over the salmonella-in-the-eggs row; it launched an arbitration scheme for personal injury victims; handled the first ever 'no win no fee' personal injury victim on behalf of a leading regional practice; advised solicitors who made legal history and received indemnity costs on behalf of a client over the incorrect discharge of an Anton Pillar order; worked with a regional firm to launch a Waste and Minerals Group; advised in respect of the sleeping drug halycon case which, until recently was one of the longest libel trials since the second world war and launched the first ever City of London law firm's office in Belfast.

LUTHER PENDRAGON

21 Whitefriars Street, London, EC4Y 8JJ
Tel: (020) 7353 1500 **Fax:** (020) 7353 1078/9
Email: post@luther.co.uk **Website:** www.luther.co.uk

Contact:	Ben Rich
Number of partners:	6

THE FIRM: Founded in 1992, Luther Pendragon offers strategic communications consultancy and tactical implementation to a wide variety of clients. Luther Pendragon draws on the journalistic, business, financial and political backgrounds of its senior consultants to integrate otherwise separate public relations disciplines, such as corporate affairs, media relations and crisis management. In recent years, Luther Pendragon has worked increasingly closely with law firms to able them to extend their offer to clients through the provision of litigation PR.

LITIGATION SUPPORT SERVICES:

PR: Luther Pendragon was one of the first public relations consultancies specifically to offer litigation PR. Litigation PR works to support law firms in the actions they take on behalf of clients in potentially high profile cases, by managing media coverage before, during and after trial.

Over the past eight years Luther Pendragon has worked on a number of the UK's most widely followed legal actions, from the County Nat West/Blue Arrow trial (the largest City case of its kind to date), to Sony's dispute with George Michael.

Other work has included commercial and criminal litigation, employment and personal injury cases, intellectual property and libel actions.

The firm works largely, but by no means exclusively, with the leading City firms, as well as with a number of other London and national practices.

INTERNATIONAL CONNECTIONS: Luther Pendragon has established relationships with litigation PR specialists both in the US and throughout Europe.

Investigators

DE VERE & CO.

3 Field Court, Gray's Inn, London, WC1R 5EN
Tel: (020) 7242 1012 **Fax:** (020) 7242 2012 **DX:** 221 Chancery Lane
Email: inv@thedeveregroup.com **Website:** www.thedeveregroup.com

Contact Partners:	Simon Kidd Ron Peberdy Julian Rozario Brian Reeves Tony Kidd
Number of partners:	5
Number of staff:	18

THE FIRM: De Vere is a well established, independent firm offering a wide range of specifically tailored services to assist lawyers and their clients with the litigation process in the UK and overseas. Other offices in Birmingham, Bournemouth, Manchester, New York, and Washington DC.

LITIGATION SUPPORT PARTNERS:

Simon Kidd: Fraud, due diligence, and asset location.
Ron Peberdy: Fraud, investigations, training, and conferences.
Brian Reeves: Tracing, staff vetting & investigations.

LITIGATION SUPPORT SERVICES:

Fraud: Fraud investigations, forensic studies, asset location, fraud vulnerability studies, fraud prevention techniques, and fraud awareness.
Training: Fraud awareness, fraud prevention, evidence packaging, basic legislation, and money laundering.
Due Dilligence: Companies, directors, and staff vetting.
Speaking Engagements: UK & International conferences for law enforcement, banking & credit companies.

NATIONWIDE INVESTIGATIONS GROUP

86 Southwark Bridge Road, London, SE1 OEX
Tel: (020) 7464 4600 **Fax:** (020) 7464 6410
Email: nig@worlddetectives.com **Website:** www.worlddetectives.com

Contacts: Robert Thornton, Jason Woodcock, Stuart Withers, Martin Fox, David Brett, John Ryder

THE FIRM: Nationwide Investigations Group, one of the country's leading investigation organisations provides the legal profession with a comprehensive investigative and litigation support service in all areas of corporate, criminal and civil matters.The group has available the latest technological equipment, together with the organisational back-up to make sure every matter is dealt with in full. N.I.G.'s qualified investigators have extensive and practical knowledge of the law and are fully experienced in dealing with complicated and confidential matters, some of which require discretion and judgement outside normal courses of procedure.The group has agents located throughout the UK and its network of overseas representatives and associates enables it to carry out investigations worldwide.

LITIGATION SUPPORT SERVICES: In-depth financial investigations; asset searching and funds location; security audits; merger and acquisition research; due diligence; intellectual property issues; corporate conflict of interest; theft, fraud, bribery and corruption; undercover assignments; counterfeit product and evidence analysis; counter industrial espionage/sabotage; pre-employment screening, personnel vetting and staff monitoring; electronic sweeps and protection equipment (de-bugging); security surveillance equipment; telephone and room monitoring; patent, trademark and copyright infringements; proof of evidence and witness statements; insurance fraud and claim verification; litigation status enquiries; matrimonial, child custody and maintenance matters, detailed sketch plans and photography; process serving and affidavits; forensic (DNA) profiling; handwriting, fingerprint and voice analysis; photography and video enhancement; polygraph (lie detection examination); accident, sickness and disability claims; unfair dismissal; sexual harassment and race discrimination; libel and blackmail matters; domestic violence and divorce; tracing witnesses, absconders and beneficiaries; bona-fides of businesses and individuals; static, mobile and electronic surveillance; personal threat evaluation and close protection.

THE BAR

STARS AT THE BAR

STARS AT THE BAR (ranked in 5 or more sections of this book)		
1	Gordon Pollock QC	*Essex Court Chambers*
	Jonathan Sumption QC	*Brick Court Chambers*
2	Michael Briggs QC	*Serle Court*
3	Anthony Grabiner QC	*One Essex Court*
4	Michael Beloff QC	*4-5 Gray's Inn Square*
	Christopher Butcher	*7 King's Bench Walk*
5	Peter Goldsmith QC	*Fountain Court*
	David Pannick QC	*Blackstone Chambers*
6	Anthony Boswood QC	*Fountain Court*
	John Brisby QC	*4 Stone Buildings*
	Nigel Davis QC	*7 Stone Buildings*
	Robin Dicker QC	*3-4 South Square*
	Barbara Dohmann QC	*Blackstone Chambers*
	Charles George QC	*2 Harcourt Buildings*
	Elizabeth Gloster QC	*One Essex Court*
	Sydney Kentridge QC	*Brick Court Chambers*
	Anthony Mann QC	*Enterprise Chambers*
	Robert Miles	*4 Stone Buildings*
	Trevor Philipson QC	*Fountain Court*
	Laurence Rabinowitz	*One Essex Court*
	Bankim Thanki	*Fountain Court*

Gordon Pollock QC – Essex Court Chambers

Frequently pitted against each other in the courtroom, Gordon Pollock once again shares the limelight with Jonathan Sumption in the top tier of *Chambers* Stars at the Bar table. The "figurehead for high profile cases," his "reputation speaks for itself." A "versatile all-rounder," Pollock features in the star category for commercial litigation and energy & natural resources and is listed top tier for banking, insurance, international arbitration and shipping. He receives a second band ranking for his work in media & entertainment, and a third band mention for civil fraud and sports law. His "brilliant cross examination skills" and tendency to go "above and beyond the call of duty" make his hefty charge-out rates worthwhile. Recently, the greater part of his practice has been taken up by the 13-week Nigerian fraud case between Swiss trading company, Noga, and the Nigerian Government, in a dispute over a claim in a debt buy-back scheme for a Nigerian steel plant built by the Russian government. Nevertheless, he has also been seen successfully defending Exports Credits Guarantee Department in the court of appeal against claims of vicarious liability in the case of an employer's fraud in Credit Lyonnais Bank Nederland NV v Export Credits Guarantee Department. Other commercial work includes acting for the Saudi Cable Company in the controversial ATT v Saudi Cable Company case, defending against an application to remove Yves Fortier from his position of chair of an ICC arbitration between the two companies. While "fantastic for a bruising encounter," Pollock manages to maintain a "humorous" tone in the courtroom. Solicitors and barristers alike praise him for his willingness to "get stuck in." Described as a "walking brain," "always on his front foot," many report he really is "as good as the hype."

Jonathan Sumption QC – Brick Court Chambers

"Far and away the cleverest and quickest mind at the bar," Jonathan Sumption shares his top band ranking with Gordon Pollock. Although known to be expensive, "for sheer intellectual grasp" and "expert commercial advice" Sumption is reckoned "top of the tree." As a "heavyweight litigator" with a flair for "devastating arguments," Sumption's practice defies categorisation. In *Chambers* guide he receives star ratings for banking, commercial litigation, energy & natural resources, and financial services. He is listed first band in administrative & public law, insurance and professional negligence, and ranked second tier in civil fraud and media & entertainment. However, his "encyclopaedic knowledge" and willingness to "burn the midnight oil" in preparation makes him the favourite choice for high profile cases, even in areas of law in which he has never before handled a case. Despite his unfamiliarity with pensions law, he was instructed to represent policy holders in Equitable Life Assurance Society v Hyman court of appeal case in which the life assurance society's discretion in paying final bonuses on a pension policy was deemed unlawful. He is well known for acting for the Home Office in the debate over whether to release General Pinochet's medical records. "Phenomenal on complicated matters of law," Sumption is said to be "the right man for a case that needs grinding out." Despite a reputation for not being particularly "client cuddly," bewildered solicitors often "go to him for those 'where do we go from here?' questions." He acted for four tobacco companies in R v Secretary of State for Health and Others, ex p Imperial Tobacco Ltd and Others in an application for an injunction against the UK government under the European Community Act. Other highlights include securing a reversal of a previous judgement in the court of appeal on the grounds of perjured evidence in Sphere Drake v Orion. Despite an impressive workload, Sumption still finds time to pursue a lively interest in mediaeval history and recently published a two-volume history of the Hundred Years War.

Michael Briggs QC – Serle Court

This "clever litigator" maintains a varied practice focusing on all aspects of business disputes in a range of sectors. He rates highly in seven disciplines: civil fraud, commercial litigation, commercial chancery, company law, financial services, insolvency and partnership. Although primarily a litigator, Briggs has long-standing experience in advising on partnership matters and was instructed last year in relation to the Don King and Frank Warren boxing partnership. On the litigious side, Briggs draws upon a background in land and property law in professional negligence suits of solicitor and surveyor negligence in valuation cases and conveyancing transactions. A "match for any silk," he has "no fear of judges" and projects a "candid" image in the courtroom. He is noted for his "well-honed voice" which some attribute to his interest in singing. Briggs recently acted in the Swift v Dairywise court of appeal case to determine the legality of maintaining trusts and equitable interests in milk quotas. His practice has also expanded into the telecommunications sector, an area which he particularly enjoys because it "raises interesting questions on valuation of economic interests and tests the flexibility of common law by applying traditional law to new subjects." As chairman of the management committee of Serle Court, he played an active role in the chamber's recent merger with One Hare Court, a move which he sees as a "fulfilment of a vision" of a consolidated set with specialist expertise spanning across a number of fields.

Anthony Grabiner QC – One Essex Court

"Super silk" Anthony Grabiner's practice is predominantly advisory work in relation to mergers and corporate takeovers. However this "stratospherically good" practitioner is ranked in *Chambers* star category for commercial litigation and energy & natural resources and makes an impressive showing in the banking, civil fraud, international arbitration and insurance tables. Although loath to take on cases of any length, Grabiner is renowned for his ability to "do a demolition job on the opposition." Clients appreciate his "approachability" and "vast courtroom experience." His "all-round skills" serve him well in a number of fields. His energy practice has burgeoned since privatisation in the early 1990's and he now regularly acts for such companies as BP and PowerGen. He represented Orion in the "battle royal," Sphere Drake v Orion Insurance Co, over whether a court can legitimately re-open litigation in the case of witness perjury. He also represented Equitable Life Assurance in Equitable Life Assurance Society v Hyman. Some see him to be easing off somewhat in his practice since being created a peer in 1999. Grabiner is now greatly involved in policy making. In March 2000, he submitted a report for the government on black economy to the Chancellor of the Exchequer. He also serves as chairman of governors at London School of Economics, director of the London Court of International Arbitration, and deputy high court judge of the Chancery and Queen's bench divisions.

Michael Beloff QC – 4-5 Gray's Inn Square

Although now effectively in part time practice due to his commitments as President of Trinity College Oxford, Michael Beloff QC is still considered to have a "brilliant, multifaceted practice," with a particularly high profile in administrative & public law, for which he earns a star rating in our guide. His public law work is confined to international arbitration cases and high level appellate work such as the gypsy cases in Strasbourg. Beloff can also trace his distinguished career in sports law to a long standing interest in athletics and a chance undergraduate encounter with runner, Adrian Metcalf. He will be presiding at the next Olympics in his capacity as member of the Lausanne-based Court of Arbitration for Sport. He has been active in international drugs-related sports arbitrations, particularly against Jamaican sprinter Merlene Ottey, and receives his second *Chambers* star in the sports category. Other notable work includes a case determining the Broadcasting Standards Commission's jurisdiction to investigate privacy of company. Also ranked in employment, human rights and immigration, Beloff is reckoned a "skilled advocate, almost too clever for his own good," who likes to bring a little levity to the courtroom. His 2001 move to Matrix Chambers will be a considerable loss to 4-5 Grays Inn Square.

Christopher Butcher – 7 King's Bench Walk

This outstanding junior sits easily in the tables with top ranking silks. A "stimulating opponent," Butcher is well known for his "first-class mind" and "intellectual approach." His primary area of interest is insurance law, for which he receives a star rating in *Chambers* tables. He is fascinated by the rapid developments in the field and by the many questions relating to insurance law that remain undecided. He has recently been involved in a wave of claims on insurers and brokers in relation to film finance. Butcher's time has lately been occupied by a number of large professional negligence cases, including one involving the collapse of Barings bank and consequent action against auditors. He is adept at all manner of commercial disputes and problems arising from contractual relationships. In the arbitration field, he has particular expertise in issues relating to the 1996 arbitration act. "Sharp and on the ball, you have to be on top of your stuff when facing him." In addition to a star banding in insurance, Butcher received top tier listings in *Chambers* commercial litigation, international arbitration and professional negligence tables, a second band ranking in shipping, and third band listing in banking.

Peter Goldsmith QC – Fountain Court

"Front rank in a number of fields," Peter Goldsmith maintains a broad practice centred around commercial litigation, for which he receives a star rating in *Chambers* directory. However, this "commercial bruiser" also ranks highly in banking, civil fraud, international arbitration, and professional negligence. "A fantastic advocate," his "un-flashy" style and "sardonic sense of humour" can sometimes belie his ability to come out with "hard-hitting punchy stuff." Reputed to be "busier than ever," Goldsmith has been involved in a number of high profile cases, including representing insurance interests in a double damages case in a specially constituted court of appeal, increasing the level of general damages in personal injury. He successfully overturned an injunction against Goldman Sachs in Mannesmann v Goldman Sachs following Mannesmann's takeover of Vodafone. In the field of professional negligence, he acted for the Law Society in a claim against KPMG determining whether accountant reporting on solicitors owes a duty of care to the Law Society. A "master of his brief," Goldsmith is described as "creative in his legal thinking," and enjoys the challenge of working in different fields. Outside of chambers, he holds a number of public appointments which he says give him a "broader perspective" on the legal system and his own practice. As a recently created life peer, he represents the prime minister in a convention on fundamental rights for the European Union. He is also founder and chairman of the Bar Pro Bono Unit, co-chairman of the Human Rights Institute of the International Bar Association, and active in the publication of a set of essays on US and UK commercial law principles to serve as a millennium guide for countries lacking legal infrastructure.

David Pannick QC – Blackstone Chambers

This "classy advocate" receives accolades from peers and solicitors as "one of the outstanding legal brains of the generation." The bulk of his practice is administrative and public law, for which he receives a star ranking in the *Chambers* tables. Known as "virtually standing counsel to the home secretary," Pannick also acts in administrative and public law work for regional authorities, applicants, and even some foreign governments. He recently acted for the state of Brunei in a suit against the Sultan's brother, Prince Jefri, in the Brunei Court of Appeal, and acted for Greece in the European Court of Human Rights in a case against former King Constantine. Pannick is described as possessing "incredible intellectual capacity and ability to translate it in court," and has earned the reputation of not taking on long cases. He also receives a star in *Chambers* human rights rankings for his "impressive record on discrimination cases." Pannick recently acted in the case of a life prisoner who wished to artificially inseminate his wife. Other areas of expertise include employment, immigration and sports, to which he applies a thorough knowledge of European law issues. In court he's reputed to be "unshowy and to the point" in approach, while his "enormous academic capacity" shines through in his fortnightly column on the law for 'The Times.'

Anthony Boswood QC – Fountain Court

"A law unto himself," Anthony Boswood is listed in the top band in *Chambers* commercial litigation tables but ranks highly also in banking, civil fraud, energy & natural resources, and insurance. Although a "strong personality, " Boswood "never oversteps himself" in the courtroom. Those who have seen him in action describe him as "one of the best cross-examiners there is." He has lately been very active in insurance and reinsurance fields and recently acted in a reinsurance dispute concerning the personal accident LMX market at Lloyds. On the energy front Boswood is well known for his work on the North Sea Gas case. Other highlights of the year include the international fraud case Dubai Aluminium Company v Salaam & Ors and an arbitration relating to the financing of Formula 1 interests.

John Brisby QC – 4 Stone Buildings

A "tenacious character," John Brisby's "aggressive style" is not everyone's "cup of tea." He is nevertheless recognised as "knowing his stuff," particularly in regards to company law and financial services. His practice is almost entirely litigation-driven and he was nominated as a leader for *Chambers* civil fraud, commercial chancery, company law, financial services and insolvency sections. A fan of "meaty" paperwork, Brisby particularly enjoys detailed cases with a "whiff of fraud." He recently acted in the large insolvency case with civil fraud implications, Bank of America v BCCI suit to recover deficit after the BCCI collapse. On the company law side, he was involved in UPC v DeutscheBank, determining whether the cable company was entitled to make bids under competition law. He is also enthusiastic about interlocutory applications due to the "excitement of burning the midnight oil" involved. As a member of the British Bulgarian legal association, Brisby was also active in trying to establish legal systems in post-communist Bulgaria.

Nigel Davis QC – 7 Stone Buildings

"First and foremost a litigator," Nigel Davis acts across a range of fields with a concentration of cases in commercial chancery, insolvency and company law. He has also established an impressive "sideline" in media contracts and copyright law. Noted for his "client managing skills" he is said to be intentionally "tough on clients in conference," even referring to them by surname in order to "preserve a professional distance." Over the past year he has been involved in such high profile cases as the Springsteen litigation and Smiths partnership. He has also been involved in the court of appeal hearing for Omni Holding litigation. "Confident" and "academically bright," he is seen as an "articulate and fluent advocate." His "understated" style makes him "highly respected by judges." He personally values his role as deputy high court judge for the wider perspective it provides. Davis intends to maintain a broad-based practice rather than specialising in a particular area as he "would hate to have to work in one field at a time."

Robin Dicker QC – 3-4 South Square

Newly-appointed silk Robin Dicker is reckoned to be "excellent for both advice and advocacy." "Clever as well as in demand," he "goes further than most" and is a popular choice for insolvency work and the "private client side of chancery." In *Chambers* guide, he has been recognised as a leader in banking, civil fraud, company law, energy & natural resources and insolvency. He has acted in relation to a number of corporate collapses such as the MCC and Heron Group insolvency cases. In the past year he acted in representing the liquidators of BCCI in Morris and Others v Bank of America National Trust and Others, alleging that the defendants were knowingly party to fraudulent trading. He also acted for the respondent manager against a claim of an attempt to defraud Customs & Excise in the liquidation of Bellmex International Ltd. This "formidable" practitioner "can do anything," and was particularly noted for his paper work. Onlookers eagerly await to see how his practice as a silk will develop.

Barbara Dohmann QC – Blackstone Chambers

A "brilliant cross-examiner" with a "fearsome reputation," Barbara Dohmann is particularly recommended for cases in which you need to "fight your way out of a corner." She has developed a varied commercial practice with particular experience in insurance and reinsurance, banking, financial services and company mergers and acquisitions. Her German origins contribute to the "international flavour" of her practice which brings her to all regions of the world. She has in recent years greatly expanded her media practice and this year enters *Chambers* tables as a leader in media & entertainment. Dohmann acted in the BBC v talkSPORT case to determine whether the BBC have goodwill in live broadcasts protected by injunction proceedings. Dohmann is ranked in civil fraud, commercial litigation, financial services, insurance, and media. She is currently serving her second term as chairman of the COMBAR and particularly enjoys the "splendid teamwork at the commercial bar."

Charles George QC – 2 Harcourt Buildings

A recommended practitioner in administrative & public law, church law, environment, parliamentary & public affairs and planning, Charles George "covers all the bases." Primarily a public lawyer, his practice is divided equally between public inquiries, straight court work and advisory work. He recently acted in R v Parliamentary Commission for Administration ex parte Balchin, relating to a complaint to parliamentary commissioner about maladministration in the department of transport. "Brilliant on his feet," his "methodical" approach leaves "a lot of blood on a lot of carpets." He enjoys cases of challenges by third parties to administrative decisions involving points of environmental law. He has been active in the promotion of light rail transit systems, through participation in four public inquiries relating to light rail transit systems in Manchester, Liverpool and Portsmouth. George has also carved a niche for himself in law relating to public rights to and creation of village greens. Most recently involved in a court of appeal challenge, Millington v Secretary of State for the Environment, and another establishing that the production and bottling of wine constitutes part of agricultural work and therefore does not require planning permission. George's role as Chancellor of the Diocese of Southwark also leads him into a lot of ecclesiastic law cases.

Elizabeth Gloster QC – One Essex Court

"First-class" Elizabeth Gloster practises across a range of chancery and commercial fields but receives her highest ranking in the *Chambers* guide in the insolvency tables where she is listed as a star practitioner. She has also distinguished herself in the fields of commercial litigation, commercial chancery, company, and energy & natural resources. Said to be "best when the going gets tough," Gloster is in her element during large company cases involving witness cross-examination. She is acting in the House of Lords for the Equitable Life Assurance Society in an appeal of the Court of Appeal's decision in the The Equitable Life Assurance Society v Hyman. While her practice consists primarily of high profile company litigation, Gloster also undertakes a number of energy and gas arbitration and advisory work in relation to new electricity trading agreements. Her "excellent judgement" serves her well as a deputy high court judge in the chancery division. Gloster was also notably the first woman to be selected as a judge of the court of appeal for both the Jersey and Guernsey courts of appeal.

Sydney Kentridge QC – Brick Court Chambers

"Absolutely extraordinary at being persuasive," Sydney Kentridge "brings the court to feel they can completely trust him." This "enormously experienced" advocate already had an impressive practice before arriving in the UK. As a practitioner in South Africa he represented such figures as Nelson Mandela and the family of Steven Biko. His current practice is largely focused on commercial and public or constitutional law. In *Chambers* guide he ranks highly in administrative & public law, commercial litigation, energy & natural resources, insurance, and media & entertainment law. Known for his "economy of language," Kentridge "still terrifies everybody who is against him" and was recommended for his abilities to "debate at the House of Lords level." He was recently instructed in Killick & Nugent v PricewaterhouseCoopers in a case of accountant's negligence, and the ATT v Lucent Technologies case of judicial conflict. At the moment he tends to take on shorter cases. On the human rights front he acted for the Crown Office in litigation relating to the removal of islanders from Chagos Islands in the 1950's to make way for a US air base, and was instructed in the European Court of Human Rights in McGonnell v United Kingdom to determine whether a judge's involvement in the passage of legislation affects his impartiality.

Anthony Mann QC- Enterprise Chambers

"Terrier-like" Anthony Mann is known as a "forceful and effective advocate" with a varied litigation practice. Acted in Locobail UK v Emmanuel case of judicial bias. He ranks highest in *Chambers'* tables for insolvency law but is also mentioned in connection with company law, commercial litigation, commercial chancery, and professional negligence. Acted in a lengthy professional negligence claim in the Isle of Man, Lumsden Ltd and Others. Described by peers as "disarmingly nice and persuasive," Mann is said to be adroit at handling judges. His "low-key" manner makes him an "attractive advocate," able to turn his hand to a range of issues.

Robert Miles – 4 Stone Buildings

One of the few "1st tier juniors" who has managed to distinguish himself in a number of areas. This "articulate all-rounder" is endorsed by many as "the best junior at the chancery bar." He rates highest in *Chambers* for his work in commercial chancery and insolvency, but was also ranked in banking, company law and energy & natural resources. He has been spending a lot of time recently on insolvency cases with company law implications and was most notably involved in the Bermuda Fire and Marine Co Ltd corporate insolvency case in Bermuda. On the banking side Miles was recommended for asset tracing work and is well known for his clear and thoroughly researched paperwork. His is predominantly a litigation practice and was praised by silks as "easy to get along with." Most like to have him on their team because of his "conscientious" approach, "lucid presentation," and ability to "come up with good ideas."

Trevor Philipson QC – Fountain Court

Since his last-minute replacement of a sick colleague in a Hong Kong aviation suit in 1978, "urbane" Trevor Philipson has built up a "wide-spread reputation" as a leading aviation expert. His experience of regulatory work encompasses air transport licensing, inter-governmental disputes, and airport charges. After twenty years' experience in aviation law, he is a firmly established name in the field and lectures both in the UK and abroad in relation to airport law. Commended as the type who'll "roll up his sleeves and get on with it," Philipson is reputed for his skill in cross examination of experts. His arbitration practice has grown over the past few years and he currently sits as arbitrator under ICC and UNCITRAL also serving as a UK representative on ICAO panel of arbitrators. He also acted on behalf of the Chodiev Group/Kazakhstan Mineral Resources Corporation in the Trans-World Group dispute in the British Virgin Islands. Trevor Philipson is ranked in *Chambers* aviation, civil fraud, commercial litigation, energy & natural resources, and international arbitration tables.

Laurence Rabinowitz -One Essex Court

"At the top of his generation," distinguished junior Laurence Rabinowitz receives star rankings for his work in commercial litigation and energy & natural resources. Said to take on a "ferocious workload," he was noted for his "sparkling paperwork" and ability to respond quickly with a "straight, well thought out answer." Reckoned "the most experienced junior in energy sectors," Rabinowitz has been involved in such cases as the CATS v TGTL oil and gas dispute concerning the law of restitution in relation to payments for use of a gas pipeline, and the Trans-World anti-suit injunctions in Kazakhstan and the British Virgin Islands. Reputed to be gaining confidence in the courtroom, he is recommended by solicitors for his assiduousness and "approachable" manner. He was appointed by the Attorney General to appear as Amicus Curiae in the house of Lords, to make submissions on the doctrine of retrospective overruling in English law in an inmate's suit against the prison governor, Evans v Governor of Brockhill Prison. Rabinowitz was also ranked in the areas of civil fraud, company law and international arbitration.

Bankim Thanki – Fountain Court

Junior Bankim Thanki "doesn't over-egg the pudding." His "flexibility" and "willingness to fit in the team" allows him to excel in a number of specialist areas. He ranks highest in *Chambers* banking and commercial litigation sections and is well known for his banking regulation work for the Bank of England. He acted as junior counsel in the BCCI/Three Rivers DC v Bank of England case in the House of Lords concerning the tort misfeasance of public office. As yet another feather to his cap, Thanki enters the *Chambers* sports law tables this year following his work for the Football Association, including a prosecution of players from Leicester City relating to the allocation of tickets at the Worthington Cup Final. He also features in both the aviation and professional negligence tables. "Attuned to working with solicitors," Thanki "makes himself available" rather than taking an "ivory tower approach." Those who work with him predict he will "go a long way."

THE MILLION-A-YEAR CLUB

There are some ten thousand barristers in private practice at the bar. Our million a year club numbers some thirty practitioners, about 0.003% of the total. These are some of the best known practitioners, whose legal prowess, experience and reputation are judged by the market to be worth the highest fees and are in huge demand. The figures charged can seem extraordinary, with £100 000 brief fees and £10 000 for a conference not unheard of. In such cases, the numbers at stake usually make these fees look like small change! A large percentage of the highest earners are tax lawyers, with the rest generally commercial and chancery practitioners.

THE MILLION-A-YEAR CLUB		
AARONSON QC, GRAHAM	ALDOUS QC, CHARLES	CARMAN QC, GEORGE
CARR QC, CHRISTOPHER	CORDARA QC, RODERICK	CROXFORD QC, IAN
CRYSTAL QC, MICHAEL	DOHMANN QC, BARBARA	FLESCH QC, MICHAEL
GLOSTER QC, ELIZABETH	GOLDBERG QC, DAVID	GOLDSMITH QC, PETER
GRABINER QC, ANTHONY	GREEN QC, BRIAN	GREEN QC, NICHOLAS
HAM QC, ROBERT	HAPGOOD QC, MARK	HOWARD QC, MARK
OLIVER QC, DAVID	PANNICK QC, DAVID	PATTEN QC, NICHOLAS
POLLOCK QC, GORDON	POTTS QC, ROBIN	SHER QC, JULES
STADLEN QC, NICHOLAS	SUMPTION QC, JONATHAN	

BARRISTERS' CHARGES

The figures shown are those of receipts, or gross income, and generally reflect the highest and lowest common figures. Not every set charges on an hourly basis and fees may vary widely between consultations, advisory and court work. In the tax practices it is quite common for fees to be determined after inspection of the paperwork and then on the basis of complexity, liability and clients' circumstances. In the criminal practices a large portion of the work is government-funded, both for prosecution and defence.

HOURLY CHARGE RATES

SENIORITY	Commercial	Tax	Chancery	Common law	Criminal
QC	£250–£850	£300–£1000	£175–£600	£150–£400	£125–£400
10 yrs call	£100–£300	£200–£500	£100–£200	£100–£200	£75–£250
4–9 yrs call	£60–£200	£175–£350	£75–£150	£50–£150	£50–£150
1–3 yrs call	£25–£125	£75–£150	£30–£100	£40–£100	£25–£75

All figues represent gross earnings before deuction of expenses.

BARRISTERS' REMUNERATION

Again a representative sample ranging from lowest to highest gross receipts. For the first time, reported gross income has touched the £2 million mark, but this is a rarity indeed. The higher figures throughout the table represent the outstanding practitioners, with average earnings usually closer to those figures on the lower end of the scale. It should be remembered that around 20% of these figures will ordinarily be deducted for expenses at chambers, which includes rent. A further average 20% goes towards individual expenses that include travel, hotels, insurance, pensions, accountancy fees, IT and legal publications. Also noteworthy is the period between work done and fees received which is often around three months but can be as long as a year in criminal practice. As a result, one year's earnings can vary widely from the next, in spite of a similar workload. On the whole, juniors seem to be faring reasonably well, despite fears that solicitor-advocates and unassisted silks might encroach on their traditional territory.

ANNUAL EARNINGS (thousands)

SENIORITY	Commercial	Tax	Chancery	Common law	Criminal
QC	£150–£1million +	£300–£2million	£150–£1.7 million	£150–£425	£150–£550
10 yrs call	£100 – £750	£200–£500	£100–£350	£75–£300	£50–£350
4–9 yrs call	£60–£350	£175–£350	£75–£300	£30–£200	£30–£150
1–3 yrs call	£25–£125	£75–£150	£25–£125	£20–£100	£20–£75

All figures represent gross earnings before deduction of expenses.

ADMINISTRATIVE & PUBLIC LAW

RESEARCH: The rankings are based on in-depth interviews with over 5,000 solicitors and barristers in the UK. Chambers research is audited by the British Market Research Bureau (see page 7 for details).

Barristers' profiles 1473-1601

LONDON

LEADING SETS • London	QCs	Jnrs
❶ **Blackstone Chambers** (Baxendale/Flint)	4	6
4-5 Gray's Inn Square (Appleby/Ouseley)	4	3
❷ **4 Breams Buildings** (Christopher Lockhart-Mummery QC)	4	1
Matrix Chambers (Nicholas Blake QC)	3	4
❸ **39 Essex Street** (Nigel Pleming QC)	2	3
11 King's Bench Walk (Tabachnik/Goudie)	2	1
❹ **Brick Court Chambers** (Christopher Clarke QC)	3	1
Doughty Street Chambers (Geoffrey Robertson QC)	2	2
Two Garden Court (Macdonald/Davies)	1	2
❺ **2-3 Gray's Inn Square** (Anthony Scrivener QC)	1	-
2 Harcourt Buildings (Gerard Ryan QC)	1	-

Numbers show recommended barristers in this practice area

LEADING SILKS • London	
✪ **BELOFF Michael**	4-5 Gray's Inn Square
GORDON Richard	Brick Court Chambers
PANNICK David	Blackstone Chambers
❶ **DRABBLE Richard**	4 Breams Buildings
GOUDIE James	11 King's Bench Walk
HOWELL John	4 Breams Buildings
LESTER Anthony	Blackstone Chambers
PLEMING Nigel	39 Essex Street
SUMPTION Jonathan	Brick Court Chambers
❷ **BLAKE Nicholas**	Matrix Chambers
KENTRIDGE Sir Sydney	Brick Court Chambers
NICOL Andrew	Doughty Street Chambers
OUSELEY Duncan	4-5 Gray's Inn Square
❸ **ALLEN Robin**	Cloisters
APPLEBY Elizabeth	4-5 Gray's Inn Square
BAXENDALE Presiley	Blackstone Chambers
BOOTH Cherie	Matrix Chambers
FITZGERALD Edward	Doughty Street Chambers
GEORGE Charles	2 Harcourt Buildings
HAVERS Philip	1 Crown Office Row
HOLGATE David	4 Breams Buildings
JAY Robert	39 Essex Street
KATKOWSKI Christopher	4 Breams Buildings
PORTEN Anthony	2-3 Gray's Inn Square
READ Lionel	1 Serjeants' Inn
SUPPERSTONE Michael	11 King's Bench Walk
NEW SILKS	
DAVIES Owen	Two Garden Court
LANG Beverley	Blackstone Chambers
MCMANUS Richard	4-5 Gray's Inn Square
OWEN Tim	Matrix Chambers

For details of these leading barristers see Profiles on page 1473

Blackstone Chambers (Baxendale/Flint) Occupying joint top spot this year; this is considered an "excellent set with many specialising in public law – all have a safe pair of hands and are efficient to deal with." Drawing on related strengths in commercial and public law, they are a popular option for the larger City practices engaging in commercial, regulatory and judicial review work. "A whole host of quality names – always the first port of call" was another comment. It appeared impossible to say enough about star silk **David Pannick QC** ("I wish I had half his brain!"). He stays at the public law summit for his "incredible intellectual capacity," and is "a detailed and crisp advocate." One slight criticism is that "once he has made his mind up it can be quite hard to persuade him to take a different view," but that aside, his "user-friendly, unshowy style" keeps him firmly in the star category. **Anthony Lester QC** is by no means the most prolific barrister, but the market felt his skills and qualities were under-represented in last year's tables and he moves up a notch. **Presiley Baxendale QC** has had a year of mixed fortunes and her rating slips slightly, but she still has a body of admirers – "lovely to work with!" enthused one solicitor. An abundance of quality permeates the junior ranks at Blackstone. New silk **Beverley Lang QC** has an accomplished reputation for her advocacy. There is no dispute over "super-efficient" **Michael Fordham**'s star credentials. His "down to earth style" and "encyclopaedic knowledge of JR case law" mark him out as the advocate of choice for 'pure' public law and judicial review. A raft of solicitors heaped praise on the "clear thinking and tenacious" **Monica Carss-Frisk** who rises into top tier territory. Fans have commented on her "prompt, effective and detailed" performances on a range of work from human-rights influenced cases to the commercial regulatory side. Despite having been on maternity leave for a portion of 2000, the "fab!" **Dinah Rose's** reputation remains undimmed. "Highly intelligent and very practical," she is admired for her "commercial and solicitor friendly approach" to a number of human-rights driven JRs. One lawyer praised her ability to "pick up facts extremely quickly," and her accessibility is also seen as a selling point; "she is prepared to work hard at unsociable times!" Another promotion was awarded to the "subtle and elegant" **Pushpinder Saini** – "an asset to any chamber." **Mark Shaw** is also very highly rated by solicitors and barristers alike. One was "impressed by his detailed arguments and persuasive style," another commented on his "exceptional thoroughness – he wouldn't ever miss a point." Another Blackstone riser comes in the form of "bright and diligent," **Javan Herberg** who is widely regarded as a young name who has made quick and impressive strides at the bar.

4-5 Grays Inn Square (Appleby/Ouseley) Despite the looming presence of Matrix Chambers and some notable departures to the 'New Kids On The Block,' 4-5 are still felt by some to offer the "best judicial review counsel available." Opinion is divided over whether the set can be collectively as strong as they were. There is certainly no doubt that the loss of, among others, Cherie Booth QC and top flight junior Rabinder Singh will have stung, although one commentator believed they were "strong enough at the junior level to weather the Matrix storm," and still "definitely a leading set." However, the 2001 loss of **Michael Beloff QC** will be an undoubted blow as "his importance is that his quality will attract quality." As a "smooth advocate" with "a wealth of knowledge in this field", he is "still very influential and an obvious figurehead for admin/public law." The "sure and punchy" planning silk **Duncan Ouseley QC** is "hardworking and extremely easy to work with" – one solicitor loved his "simple and plain arguments." **Elizabeth Appleby QC** received some mixed reviews but several solicitors sung her praises for her "efficiency in turning around advice" and thoroughness in "covering all the issues and angles." Among the stack of juniors remaining loyal to 4-5, **Tim Kerr**, "takes a bit of persuading," said one solicitor, "but is brilliant in court!" The "user-friendly" **Clive Lewis** is rated for judicial review advice, and is considered "sharp witted and a quick thinker!" Local government and planning junior supremo **Tim Corner** is also highly regarded for pure public law work while **Richard McManus QC** remains a recommended name as a silk.

LEADING JUNIORS • London	
✪ FORDHAM Michael	Blackstone Chambers
SINGH Rabinder	Matrix Chambers
❶ CARSS-FRISK Monica	Blackstone Chambers
GIFFIN Nigel	11 King's Bench Walk
GRIFFITHS Alan	One Essex Court
KERR Tim	4-5 Gray's Inn Square
LEWIS Clive	4-5 Gray's Inn Square
MOUNTFIELD Helen	Matrix Chambers
ROSE Dinah	Blackstone Chambers
SAINI Pushpinder	Blackstone Chambers
SHAW Mark	Blackstone Chambers
❷ HARRISON Stephanie	Two Garden Court
HERBERG Javan	Blackstone Chambers
HUNT Murray	Matrix Chambers
LIEVEN Nathalie	4 Breams Buildings
LUBA Jan	Two Garden Court
STARMER Keir	Doughty Street Chambers
WOLFE David	Matrix Chambers
❸ CATCHPOLE Stuart	39 Essex Street
CLAYTON Richard	Devereux Chambers
CORNER Timothy	4-5 Gray's Inn Square
GARNHAM Neil	1 Crown Office Row
KOVATS Steven	39 Essex Street
MACLEAN Alan	Brick Court Chambers
RICHARDS Jennifer	39 Essex Street
TAM Robin	1 Temple Gardens
UP AND COMING	
MARKUS Kate	Doughty Street Chambers

For details of these leading barristers see Profiles on page 1473

4 Breams Buildings (Lockhart-Mummery) Public law and judicial review expertise feed off core strengths in planning and local government at this "extremely thorough and professional set." Particularly strong at silk level, they are described as "people who are prepared to play their part in the team." **Richard Drabble QC** is a particularly adaptable and versatile lawyer, considered by fellow barristers to be "in the top flight of public lawyers." Originally an applicant lawyer, he now acts on both sides, having turned his hand to, inter alia, the environment, social security and human rights. Recently acted in the high-profile Pinochet judicial review on behalf of Amnesty International. Solicitors have affirmed his "unstuffy, unpompous and good-humoured" approach. **John Howell QC** has the potential to climb into star territory with his "mastery of detail" and "elegance." With a "brain the size of a planet," his name is mentioned by some in the same breath as Beloff and Pannick. A local government law expert in particular, he turns his hand to the spectrum of public law with formidable results – "one of the best." **David Holgate QC**, likewise, is another strong public law silk – " someone who is prepared to play their part." A very efficient advocate, "if he says he'll do it, he'll do it!" commented one solicitor. **Christopher Katkowski QC** "used to be everyone's favourite junior." After taking silk, he consolidates his position in the list. Acting for both treasury solicitors and applicants, **Nathalie Lieven** ("extremely able, intellectually") bolsters this strong set with some added junior firepower.

Matrix Chambers (Blake) Will the young pretenders "rock and roll from day one on the strength of their individuals" as one prominent London public law and human rights solicitor predicted, or will they "have to earn their stripes first?" as another more cautious observer countered. Our research suggests that Matrix will be a "significant public law force" from the word go, albeit one with a definite human rights bent and, for the time being at least, slightly adrift of the more established sets. Market consensus is that the set's public law credentials will develop in the future. Without doubt, their recruitment campaign has benefited from some notable hires. Immigration star **Nick Blake QC** was a major loss to 2 Garden Court. He "does more public law than he used to" and therefore moves up a tier this year to reflect his broader portfolio of cases. **Cherie Booth QC**'s "excellent client care and responsiveness" wins praise from solicitors and maintains her position in our list of leading silks. **Tim Owen QC**'s rise to silk status has been generally approved. Combining public law, human rights and crime, he has carved out a niche with a "particular knowledge of prison law." His popularity is such that "the only real problem is getting hold of him!" "A major coup for Matrix" – junior public law star **Rabinder Singh's** move was conversely a blow for 4-5 Grays Inn Square. With fans and admirers everywhere, there was little doubt over his presence at the zenith of our list. Felt to "reach a firm view early," this "understated and intellectual, yet measured and persuasive" character is neither "the most radical individual" or "flamboyant advocate" but turns his "considerable talent and ability" to a range of public law advice. **Helen Mountfield** is another "good human rights junior" who specialises in public law and discrimination and moves up a tier this year after a clutch of positive comments. Similarly, **Murray Hunt** continues to be recommended by solicitors and barristers for his commitment to human rights and public law issues. Following the pattern of rising juniors this year, **David Wolfe** is well known for his public law challenges and judicial review work. Well-liked by solicitors and possessing "lots of imagination and flexibility" he applies fine attention to detail," and "copes with volume of work well."

39 Essex St (Pleming) Traditionally regarded as a respondent set acting on instructions from the government and treasury solicitors, they have successfully managed to develop a broader, well-rounded practice acting for applicants in increasing numbers. The loss of junior Alan Maclean to Brick Court Chambers, where he joins former colleague, Richard Gordon, is a blow, but not felt to have adversely affected the set which retains its position in this year's rankings. **Nigel Pleming QC** is a major asset of the set. Having done "some very impressive jobs" this year, including acting for the Belgian government on Pinochet, a major public law and human rights solicitor stated "I would use him for any major case." Among his numerous skills, he is regarded as "particularly elegant in terms of oral presentation." The "impressive and thoughtful" **Robert Jay QC** can turn his hand to a range of public law and judicial review disciplines and wins admirers for his "well-studied and convincing arguments." Among the juniors, **Stuart Catchpole's** public law practice includes acting on behalf of the Crown solicitors. **Steven Kovats** is another "efficient and solid government lawyer" called on frequently as junior counsel to the crown in a respondent capacity. In a slightly different vein, the "extremely effective" and "absolutely faultless" **Jennifer Richards** continues to build a great reputation for judicial review work in children, disabilities, health and education cases. A "superb junior", she is praised for "keeping abreast of developments in this fast moving area."

11 Kings Bench Walk (Tabachnik/Goudie) A set with an established reputation in employment, which overlaps with public law and local government powers, and represents a popular choice for solicitors who value this cross-section of specialism. Of the "number of people at this set I would use, both at silk and junior level" said one solicitor "all are very responsive and quick." The "brilliant" **James Goudie QC** is perhaps one of the most sought-after silks. Mixing public law and local government, his "approachable and helpful" manner continues to win admirers. **Michael Supperstone QC** is still recommended for his wide practice. Among the junior ranks, many of whom act on instructions from the treasury solicitors, the "meticulous and thorough" **Nigel Giffin** is certainly in the front running pack of juniors. Maintaining a broad public law practice, this "very bright and measured advocate," is welcomed by solicitors for doing "all the spade work above and beyond the call of duty."

Brick Court Chambers (Clarke) Although known primarily as a commercial set, its cross-section of strengths across JR and European Law fuse well to mark it out as an obvious public law candidate. One solicitor in a large London public law practice went as far to admit that "I would always use Brick Court." The major movement at silk level is the elevation of **Richard**

Gordon QC to star category. It was impossible to ignore the mountain of positive feedback. Since his movement from 39 Essex St, it is felt that his presence and influence has enforced a cohesive strength at the set – "their collective intellectual knowledge is strong." Few silks of this stature are liked as much by solicitors: "he's straightforward," "unpompous," "accessible", "sparks off ideas", "personable," "good-humoured." Spanning a broad church of public law including environment, housing and community care, Gordon's real strength lies in his provision of judicial review advice ("technically he's very good and immerses himself in JR") and his solicitor-friendly productivity – "he works harder than anyone I know." Is there any area of the law in which **Jonathan Sumption QC** does not excel? Despite a limited public law and judicial review practice, and potential inaccessibility, this "absolutely outstanding" advocate is singled out time and time again for his "clarity of thought, encyclopaedic knowledge and devastating arguments." **Sydney Kentridge QC** has a reputation that precedes him and is no stranger to public law practice. His improved ranking reflects his formidable talents – he still "terrifies everybody who is against him." The "excellent" **Alan Maclean** also boosts the junior ranks, after leaving 39 Essex St.

Doughty Street Chambers (Robertson) Leading common law and immigration set is still a significant public law choice for solicitors with a pro-bono or "more radical case." Usually acting on the applicant side, most cases involve a human rights bent such as asylum, housing and community care. Unsurprisingly, they are first choice for many of the more civil liberties-focused solicitors who occupy influential positions in the list of traditional public law firms. Highly ranked immigration barrister **Andrew Nicol QC** is "straightforward and gets to the point!" Well-liked by solicitors, he is seen to have had a busy year. Likewise, **Edward Fitzgerald QC** continues to be rated for his practice incorporating judicial review, crime and human rights. The "enormously capable" **Keir Starmer** cements his reputation for knowledge of judicial review and European human rights legislation. His public law practice includes acting both for and against public authorities. **Kate Markus** is again ranked as an up and coming junior for her public law, social welfare and judicial review expertise.

Two Garden Court (Macdonald/Davies) It was unquestionably a major blow to lose star silk Nick Blake, who as well as being the leading immigration barrister is growing his broader public law reputation. Like Doughty Street, however, strengths in areas such as immigration, housing and crime feed into the general public law practice and the set is still very much a first port of call for applicant firms or those seeking more progressive counsel. At silk level, **Owen Davies QC** continues to be recommended for his public law practice embracing civil liberties, the environment and crime. **Stephanie Harrison** is one junior that regularly wins praise for her judicial review work and commitment in a number of key areas. "Very good for community care issues and asylum seekers," her particular interest in minorities is frequently exploited by solicitors. Acted in the much publicised JR application challenging Mike Tyson's entrance into the UK. **Jan Luba** is "second to none when it comes to housing matters." His expertise throughout the sphere of housing related public law issues is considered to be first class.

2-3 Grays Inn Square (Scrivener) Primarily a local government and planning set, they are a common chambers of choice for major local authority and public sector practices seeking counsel. Although their 'pure' public and administrative law and judicial review profile (including housing, local authority finance and the environment) is less visible than other areas, **Anthony Porten QC** offers "clear and precise" opinions and has a "high turnaround rate." Solicitors rate his direct and forthright approach and his knowledge of local government and planning issues.

2 Harcourt Buildings (Ryan) Another chambers far more readily associated with planning work, its local government expertise intertwines with environmental and commercial knowledge, and results in an attractive public law choice for solicitors seeking a mixture of these requirements. The "extremely methodical" and "unflash" **Charles George QC** is "brilliant on his feet" and "finds his way through lots of information – he covers all the bases."

Other Notable Barristers At silk level, the "intelligent, thorough and sensible" **Robin Allen QC** at **Cloisters** (Cox) continued to be recommended for his practice. **Philip Havers QC** at **1 Crown Office Row** (Seabrook) is an "exceptionally good lawyer," credited with having had some very successful cases in the last year – "a star!" It would be fair to say **Lionel Read QC** at **1 Serjeants Inn** (Read) has a lower profile than formerly but he is still an important figurehead and retains a number of admirers. **Alan Griffiths** at **One Essex Court** (Grabiner) is an eminent and "user-friendly" junior, while **Neil Garnham** of **1 Crown Office Row** (Seabrook) also maintains his ranking. **Robin Tam** at **1 Temple Gardens** (Carlisle) is well liked by solicitors and also comes recommended. Similarly, **Richard Clayton** at **Derereux Chambers** (Burke) retains his ranking.

AGRICULTURE

RESEARCH: The rankings are based on in-depth interviews with over 5,000 solicitors and barristers in the UK. Chambers research is audited by the British Market Research Bureau (see page 7 for details).

OVERVIEW: Falcon Chambers continue to consolidate their position as the only genuine agricultural set, considered to be "miles in front of everybody else." As well as the leading silks and juniors, four new names are listed from Falcon this year, a testimony to the quantity and quality of work they are performing. This year has seen some high profile cases, with European issues and food quality regulation proving fertile areas along with the traditional tenancy and quota disputes.

LONDON

LEADING SETS • London	QCs	Jnrs
❶ Falcon Chambers (Gaunt / Lewison)	4	6

Numbers show recommended barristers in this practice area

LEADING SILKS • London	
❶ MORGAN Paul	Falcon Chambers
WOOD Derek	Falcon Chambers
❷ BROCK Jonathan	Falcon Chambers
GAUNT Jonathan	Falcon Chambers
❸ HOLGATE David	4 Breams Buildings

For details of these leading barristers see Profiles on page 1473

LEADING JUNIORS • London	
❶ MOSS Joanne	Falcon Chambers
RODGER Martin	Falcon Chambers
❷ HUTTON Caroline	Enterprise Chambers
JOURDAN Stephen	Falcon Chambers
MCALLISTER Ann	Enterprise Chambers
THOMAS Nigel	13 Old Square
❸ CRANFIELD Peter	3 Verulam Buildings
DE FREITAS Anthony	4 Paper Buildings
FANCOURT Timothy	Falcon Chambers
FOSTER Charles	6 Pump Court
UP AND COMING	
MERCER Hugh	Essex Court Chambers
SHEA Caroline	Falcon Chambers
WINDSOR Emily	Falcon Chambers

For details of these leading barristers see Profiles on page 1473

Barristers' profiles 1473-1601

Falcon Chambers (Gaunt/Lewison) "Recognised as the number one" for their "breadth of agricultural knowledge," clients are also attracted by the range of seniority and "practical and speedy" service. Opinion also suggests that previous problems with clerking have been ironed out. **Paul Morgan QC** is praised for his "good, calm, analytic style" and for being "user friendly," while "first class" **Derek Wood QC**, still "the doyen" of agricultural barristers, remains active despite his commitments at Oxford. **Jonathan Gaunt QC** is also regularly briefed, while "flamboyant advocate" **Jonathan Brock QC** appears to have raised his profile this year. Amongst the juniors, "the redoubtable" **Joanne Moss** "has probably got agricultural law cornered." "Incisive, direct and quick," she offers advice that is "clear and comprehensive and practical." **Martin Rodger** has a "more circumspect" style than his colleague, but was felt to be equally bright, "particularly clear," and to provide a "consistent, prompt and high quality service." "Intellectually first division" **Stephen Jourdan** is regularly consulted on agricultural matters for his "absolute mastery," particularly of agricultural insolvency and milk quotas, while rising star **Tim Fancourt** has an "excellent client manner." Up and coming **Caroline Shea** is "thorough and great with the judge," while **Emily Windsor** was praised for her "thorough knowledge."

Other Notable Barristers

Amongst silks, **David Holgate QC** at **4 Breams Buildings** (Lockhart-Mummery) was highly rated by knowledgeable clients. **Enterprise Chambers** (Mann) produced two of the leading juniors: the "bright and personable" **Caroline Hutton** was particularly recommended on tenancy matters and **Ann McAllister** was also widely endorsed. **Nigel Thomas** of **13 Old Square** (Lyndon-Stanford) has a large practice based in south Wales and **Peter Cranfield** at **3 Verulam Buildings** (Symons/Jarvis) is active in a number of ongoing cases involving issues such as veterinary liability and liability for defective feedstuff. **Anthony De Freitas** at **4 Paper Buildings** (Ritchie) was another well respected name, while qualified veterinary surgeon **Charles Foster** at **6 Pump Court** (Coonan) is widely consulted on livestock and bloodstock. Up and coming **Hugh Mercer** of **Essex Court Chambers** (Pollock) is "enthusiastic" and "good on paper," and rated particularly for his advice on European law, tax and arable aid.

ALTERNATIVE DISPUTE RESOLUTION

RESEARCH: The rankings are based on in-depth interviews with over 5,000 solicitors and barristers in the UK. Chambers research is audited by the British Market Research Bureau (see page 7 for details).

OVERVIEW: The Bar has recently made further attempts to increase its share of the ADR market, but with few exceptions the mediation market continues to be dominated by solicitors.
Several new mediation panels have been created by barristers: Littleton Chambers have set up Littleton Dispute Resolution Ltd, 2 Temple Gardens have launched an ADR service, and a new ADR Chambers opens for business in April 2000. This set is to pioneer a new appeal mediation service, whereby retired judges will be available to consider and mediate appeals against first instance court rulings. Rulings will be binding by the prior agreement of both parties.

LONDON

LEADING SILKS • London	
✪ NAUGHTON Philip	3 Serjeants' Inn
❶ RUTTLE Stephen	Brick Court Chambers
❷ GAITSKELL Robert	Keating Chambers
KALLIPETIS Michel	Littleton Chambers
KERSHEN Lawrence	14 Tooks Court
TACKABERRY John	Arbitration Chambers

For details of these leading barristers see Profiles on page 1473

LEADING JUNIORS • London	
❶ AEBERLI Peter	46 Essex Street
❷ BIRCH Elizabeth	3 Verulam Buildings
BRODIE Bruce	39 Essex Street
CUNNINGHAM Graham	Littman Chambers
MANNING Colin	Littleton Chambers

For details of these leading barristers see Profiles on page 1473

Philip Naughton QC, 3 Serjeant's Inn Although no longer a director of CEDR, Naughton continues to be universally recognised as by far the lead barrister involved in mediation work. Described variously as "impishly intelligent and perceptive" and "top notch." Vastly experienced, Naughton is notching up mediations at the impressive rate of up to four a month. Typical cases involve construction and insurance disputes. He is the only barrister involved in the PIM group of seven. Also sits on the panel of mediators appointed by the Court of Appeal's Mediation Scheme.

Stephen Ruttle QC, Brick Court Chambers Although he only gained CEDR accreditation in 1998, this suave and persuasive mediator has been much in demand. In the past year he has completed 20 mediations. Mediates mainly in disputes involving insurance and reinsurance matters and has received glowing recommendations for his recent role in helping to settle a complex multi-party dispute.

Barristers' profiles 1473-1601

Robert Gaitskell QC, Keating Chambers Has a background in construction and engineering and has undertaken mediations in those areas. He fields mediation referrals both through CEDR and from the International Chambers of Commerce. Although he only gained CEDR accreditation in January 1999 he has already begun notching up mediations at a rapid rate.

Michel Kallipetis QC, Littleton Chambers The most senior mediator in the Littleton Dispute Resolution Services caucus. He "has a good feel for the people and the issues." He mediates primarily in the entertainment sector, but his accountancy background gives him a broad understanding of various types of commercial and non-commercial work.

Lawrence Kershen QC, 14 Tooks Court A quality mediator with a persuasive bedside manner. Kershen undertakes general commercial mediations, and has been noted for his expert grasp of group psychology. He is active within the CEDR group.

John Tackaberry QC, Arbitration Chambers Variously described as "off the wall" and "lateral." Tackaberry is most well known for his arbitration work, although he is also a CEDR accredited mediator with experience particularly in shipping and construction disputes.

Peter Aeberli, 46 Essex Street Has acquired a fair amount of mediation experience, currently undertaking one or two mediations a month. Well known for his work in settling construction disputes, he has been recommended by one of his contemporaries for his ability to switch from the confrontational techniques of advocacy to the more accommodating skills required for mediation.

Elizabeth Birch, 3 Verulam Buildings Has handled about 12 mediations in the past year. Specialises in disputes involving shipping, international trade and IT matters. Birch is most well known for her role in founding the ACI initiative (Arbitration for Commerce and Industry), which arranges both mediation and arbitration.

Bruce Brodie, 39 Essex Street Continues to have his supporters in the market-place, and maintains a solid ranking.

Graham Cunningham, Littman Chambers Has a background in IT and is most well known for his mediation work in that area, although he also does general commercial disputes. He has undertaken about 15 mediations in the past year and is also doing some early neutral evaluation work.

Colin Manning, Littleton Chambers Another mediator involved in the Littleton Chambers ADR service, which has been rather slow to take off but now seems to be gathering at least some momentum. Not as experienced as some of his peers, Manning has nevertheless attracted recommendations. He was involved in the London County Court ADR pilot scheme, which encouraged the use of mediation.

ARBITRATION (INTERNATIONAL)

RESEARCH: The rankings are based on in-depth interviews with over 5,000 solicitors and barristers in the UK. Chambers research is audited by the British Market Research Bureau (see page 7 for details).

OVERVIEW: For some years there has been an increasing trend for practitioners in the arbitration world to conduct their own advocacy. However, this remains a relatively small world and those barristers who practice in arbitration are often in high demand, both as counsel and as arbitrators. Our tables include a very small number of truly specialist international arbitration practitioners together with a wider number of general commercial barristers who handle arbitration as part of their wider practices. The final component of the list is those construction and maritime practitioners who, by the nature of their specialism, have become expert at handling arbitrations.

Barristers' profiles 1473-1601

LONDON

LEADING SETS • London	QCs	Jnrs
❶ **Essex Court Chambers** (Gordon Pollock QC)	7	3
❷ **Atkin Chambers** (John Blackburn QC)	4	1
One Essex Court (Lord Grabiner QC)	3	1
20 Essex Street (Iain Milligan QC)	1	1
Keating Chambers (Richard Fernyhough QC)	6	2
❸ **4 Essex Court** (Nigel Teare QC)	6	-
Fountain Court (Anthony Boswood QC)	4	-
7 King's Bench Walk (Jeremy Cooke QC)	2	1

Numbers show recommended barristers in this practice area

LEADING SILKS • London	
✪ **VEEDER V.V.**	Essex Court Chambers
❶ **BLACKBURN John**	Atkin Chambers
BOYD Stewart	Essex Court Chambers
FERNYHOUGH Richard	Keating Chambers
GLICK Ian	One Essex Court
GOLDSMITH Peter	Fountain Court
GRABINER Anthony	One Essex Court
GROSS Peter	20 Essex Street
HUNTER Ian	Essex Court Chambers
POLLOCK Gordon	Essex Court Chambers
RAMSEY Vivian	Keating Chambers
UFF John	Keating Chambers
❷ **AKENHEAD Robert**	Atkin Chambers
COLLINS Michael	Essex Court Chambers
REESE Colin	Atkin Chambers
TACKABERRY John	Arbitration Chambers
THOMAS Michael	Essex Court Chambers
❸ **BARNES Mark**	One Essex Court
BUCKNALL Belinda	4 Essex Court
ELLIOTT Timothy	Keating Chambers
GEE Steven	4 Field Court
GRUDER Jeffrey	Essex Court Chambers
HOWARD M.N.	4 Essex Court
JARVIS John	3 Verulam Buildings
KEALEY Gavin	7 King's Bench Walk
MALEK Ali	3 Verulam Buildings
PADFIELD Nicholas	Serle Court chambers
PHILIPSON Trevor	Fountain Court
RUSSELL Jeremy	4 Essex Court
SMITH Andrew	Fountain Court
TEARE Nigel	4 Essex Court
THOMAS Christopher	Keating Chambers
TWIGG Patrick	2 Temple Gardens
WHITE Andrew	Atkin Chambers
NEW SILKS • LONDON	
BRENTON Timothy	4 Essex Court
DARLING Paul	Keating Chambers
HADDON-CAVE Charles	4 Essex Court
MORIARTY Stephen	Fountain Court
SCHAFF Alistair	7 King's Bench Walk
TAVERNER Marcus	Keating Chambers

For details of these leading barristers see Profiles on page 1473

Essex Court Chambers (Pollock) The first port of call for many arbitrators who feel that "you can't go wrong" with their members. Remain the clear leaders at the bar. Hardly surprising as they have "the best names." **V.V.Veeder QC** is "the best by far" with an international outlook that is "uncommon." **Stewart Boyd QC** is "extremely experienced" while "walking brain" **Gordon Pollock QC**'s reputation speaks for itself. Described as both "unflappable" and "inscrutable," **Ian Hunter QC** is said to be "easy to deal with." "Keen" **Michael Collins QC** is a "lovely chap" and comes highly recommended. New entry this year is former Attorney General of Hong Kong, **Michael Thomas QC**, who has "wide experience" and a high reputation. Rejoining his old set is **Jeffrey Gruder QC** who is "dependable" and a good team player. "Complete star" **Toby Landau**, possesses a reputation that belies his age and is one of those most frequently mentioned by our interviewees. The "bright" and "articulate" **Joe Smouha** is "very popular." **Graham Dunning** is "extremely clever," with a "highly aggressive" approach.

Atkin Chambers (Blackburn) A leading construction set with four recommended silks handling a considerable number of construction arbitrations. Headed by "extremely agreeable" **John Blackburn QC** the set also fields **Robert Akenhead QC** who has a "vast practice." Also recommended are "sound" **Colin Reese QC** and the "clever and charming" **Andrew White QC. Andrew Burr** continues to fly the flag for the set's juniors.

One Essex Court (Grabiner) Prestigious commercial chambers, focusing strongly on arbitration. "Stratospherically good" **Anthony Grabiner QC** heads a strong set that includes **Ian Glick QC**, an "uncompromising advocate," and "impressive" **Mark Barnes QC.** A new entry this year is **Laurence Rabinowitz**, who is a "star" junior.

20 Essex Street (Milligan) Arbitration specialists with a broad practice and particular expertise in the maritime and commodities sectors. A "colossus" in arbitration, **Peter Gross QC**'s star continues to rise. "Down to earth" **Duncan Matthews** is praised for his clear and cogent presentation and is highly rated.

Keating Chambers (Fernyhough) Chambers specialising in construction and engineering arbitrations and the IT sector. An impressive array of leading silks and juniors are recommended. The "incisive" **Richard Fernyhough QC** is highly thought of as is **John Uff QC,** said to be "better than most." **Vivian Ramsey QC** is "streets ahead" and praised for his management of cases as well as his advocacy skills. Also recommended are **Timothy Elliott QC, Christopher Thomas QC** and "larger than life" **Paul**

LEADING JUNIORS • London	
❶ BUTCHER Christopher	7 King's Bench Walk
LANDAU Toby	Essex Court Chambers
MATTHEWS Duncan	20 Essex Street
SMOUHA Joe	Essex Court Chambers
❷ BRODIE Bruce	39 Essex Street
BURR Andrew	Atkin Chambers
DUNNING Graham	Essex Court Chambers
HART David	1 Crown Office Row
JACKSON Rosemary	Keating Chambers
PELLING Mark	Monckton Chambers
PLANTEROSE Rowan	Littman Chambers
RABINOWITZ Laurence	One Essex Court

For details of these leading barristers see Profiles on page 1473

Darling QC. **Marcus Taverner QC** maintains his fine reputation and **Rosemary Jackson** is thought of as a "very good performer."

4 Essex Court (Teare) A set with a strong reputation in the shipping and insurance sectors and a rising profile in the arbitration field. Lloyd's Open Form salvage cases are a particular area of expertise. "Tenacious" **Belinda Bucknall QC** and "solid" **Jeremy Russell QC** who is known for his admiralty work are recommended. So too are "delightful" **M.N. Howard QC** and "persistent" yet "charming" **Nigel Teare QC**. Completing this formidable set are "effective" **Tim Brenton QC** praised for his cross examination and witness skills and **Charles Haddon-Cave QC**, an aviation specialist who is "deceptively clever under a relaxed facade."

Fountain Court (Boswood) Highly thought of commercial set with a strong presence in the international arbitration scene. "Outstanding" **Peter Goldsmith QC** is said to know "a vast amount" about arbitration although he is not seen as much these days. The "practical" and "effective" **Trevor Philipson QC**, "understated" **Andrew Smith QC** and "clever" **Stephen Moriarty QC** all come recommended.

7 King's Bench Walk (Cooke) This set has a particularly fine reputation in the shipping, oil and gas, commodities and insurance/reinsurance aspects of arbitration. Former head of chambers Stephen Tomlinson QC has now been elevated to the bench and so no longer features in our tables. **Alistair Schaff QC**, who took silk recently, is described as "brilliant" and is commended for his adroit handling of tribunals. Joining the tables this year is "highly entertaining" **Gavin Kealey QC** who makes arbitrations a "joy." Leading junior **Christopher Butcher** is both "diligent" and "intelligent."

Other Notable Barristers **Steven Gee QC**, head of chambers at **4 Field Court** has the ability to "conjure up law at will." **John Tackaberry QC,** head of **Arbitration Chambers,** is described as a "brilliant orator." **Ali Malek QC**, of **3 Verulam Buildings,** (Symons/Jarvis) is a real "arbitration figure" and joint head of chambers, **John Jarvis QC** maintains his reputation. Similarly, **Nicholas Padfield QC** at **Serle Court Chambers** (Neill) retains a devoted client following. New additions this year are **Patrick Twigg QC** of **2 Temple Gardens** (O'Brien) who has reportedly acted "across the world" and **Rowan Planterose** of **Littman Chambers** (Littman) who is "very experienced" and is said to work hard in the "engine rooms" of the arbitration world. **David Hart** at **1 Crown Office Row** (Seabrook) is involved in environmental arbitration, while **Bruce Brodie** at **39 Essex Street** (Pleming) consolidates his all-round arbitration reputation. **Mark Pelling's** practice at **Monckton Chambers** (Swift) embraces both domestic and international arbitration cases.

AVIATION

RESEARCH: The rankings are based on in-depth interviews with over 5,000 solicitors and barristers in the UK. Chambers research is audited by the British Market Research Bureau (see page 7 for details).

OVERVIEW: Since the disintegration of 5 Bell Yard, the mantle of top aviation set has been seized by Fountain Court. A number of other sets were mentioned because of individual expertise, but only four are considered to have requisite strength in depth.

LONDON

LEADING SETS • London	QCs	Jnrs
❶ **Fountain Court** (Anthony Boswood QC)	2	2
❷ **Brick Court Chambers** (Christopher Clarke QC)	1	1
4 Essex Court (Nigel Teare QC)	1	3
❸ **Essex Court Chambers** (Gordon Pollock QC)	1	1

Numbers show recommended barristers in this practice area

LEADING SILKS • London	
✪ **CRANE Michael**	Fountain Court
❶ **HADDON-CAVE Charles**	4 Essex Court
HUNTER Ian	Essex Court Chambers
MCMANUS Richard	4-5 Gray's Inn Square
PHILIPSON Trevor	Fountain Court
❷ **FOWLER Richard**	Monckton Chambers
WOOD William	Brick Court Chambers

For details of these leading barristers see Profiles on page 1473

LEADING JUNIORS • London	
❶ **LAWSON Robert**	4 Essex Court
LYDIARD Andrew	Brick Court Chambers
SHEPHERD Philip	24 Old Buildings
❷ **SHAH Akhil**	Fountain Court
❸ **KIMBELL John**	4 Essex Court
REEVE Matthew	4 Essex Court
❹ **JOSEPH David**	Essex Court Chambers
THANKI Bankim	Fountain Court

For details of these leading barristers see Profiles on page 1473

Fountain Court (Boswood) Undoubtedly the number one aviation set, it stands "a class apart." **Michael Crane QC** is "extremely bright, a clear thinker, and in a different dimension to the rest." A regulatory expert, he has "sensitivity and understanding of the market." "Versatile" **Trevor Philipson QC** is also rated as a leading aviation silk. **Akhil Shah**'s "pragmatic commercial approach" sees him marked out as a leading junior, while the "hard-working" **Bankim Thanki** also receives regular market mention.

Brick Court Chambers (Clarke) So big that they are involved in most commercial work, Brick Court Chambers is rated particularly highly by clients. **William Wood QC** "has come on well" and is making a name for himself in the field. **Andrew Lydiard** is "the star junior" and is noted for his "academic intelligence."

4 Essex Court (Teare) Widely recognised as a set with aviation expertise, it is known for its regulatory work, and in particular, its work for Virgin. **Charles Haddon-Cave QC** is the best-known of the relatively new silks. Commended for his work for Virgin, he "knows the aviation industry like the back of his hand." Considered by many to be the most popular aviation junior, **Robert Lawson**'s increasing profile sees him move up to the top band. A regulatory expert with a strong interest in aviation, he is "a deft cross-examiner" and the 'protégé' of former 5 Bell Yard aviation guru, Robert Webb. **John Kimbell** and **Matthew Reeve** are other juniors to have made a real impression this year.

Essex Court Chambers (Pollock) Commercial expertise allied to aviation knowledge brings this set a deserved ranking. **Ian Hunter QC** has "a long-standing interest and expertise in the field" while **David Joseph** is recommended by clients and fellow barristers alike.

Other Notable Barristers "Reliable" **Richard McManus QC** at **4-5 Gray's Inn Square** (Appleby/Ouseley) is commended for his work on the IATA slots case and for his involvement in judicial reviews. **Philip Shepherd** at **24 Old Buildings** (Mann/Steinfeld) is considered a "number one choice for aviation litigation," while **Richard Fowler QC** of **Monckton Chambers** (Swift) is recommended as "a highly impressive competition specialist."

BANKING

RESEARCH: The rankings are based on in-depth interviews with over 5,000 solicitors and barristers in the UK. Chambers research is audited by the British Market Research Bureau (see page 7 for details).

OVERVIEW: Our banking section consists of work on claims and advice arising from commercial and merchant bank transactions, including supervision and regulatory work, debt collection and professional negligence. Due to the high level of in-house expertise at City law firms, the banking bar involves more advocacy and less advisory work than other areas.

There are few truly specialised banking barristers, with only a handful spending more than 50 percent of their time on banking work. Mark Hapgood and Michael Brindle are the two stand-out specialists, with Iain Milligan and William Blair looming into view. Joining them at the top end are all-round corporate courtroom silks Jonathan Sumption, Gordon Pollock, Anthony Grabiner and Peter Goldsmith.

LONDON

LEADING SETS • London		QCs	Jnrs
❶	**Brick Court Chambers** (Christopher Clarke QC)	3	-
	Fountain Court (Anthony Boswood QC)	5	4
	3 Verulam Buildings (Symons/Jarvis)	4	5
❷	**Essex Court Chambers** (Gordon Pollock QC)	1	2
	One Essex Court (Anthony Grabiner QC)	3	3
❸	**Erskine Chambers** (Robin Potts QC)	2	1
	3-4 South Square (Michael Crystal QC)	4	-
❹	**20 Essex Street** (Iain Milligan QC)	2	1

Numbers show recommended barristers in this practice area

LEADING SILKS • London		
✪	**BRINDLE Michael**	Fountain Court
	HAPGOOD Mark	Brick Court Chambers
	SUMPTION Jonathan	Brick Court Chambers
❶	**GOLDSMITH Peter**	Fountain Court
	GRABINER Anthony	One Essex Court
	MILLIGAN Iain	20 Essex Street
	POLLOCK Gordon	Essex Court Chambers
❷	**BLAIR William**	3 Verulam Buildings
	POTTS Robin	Erskine Chambers
❸	**BOSWOOD Anthony**	Fountain Court
	ETHERTON Terence	Wilberforce Chambers
	HOWARD Mark	Brick Court Chambers
	MALEK Ali	3 Verulam Buildings
	SALTER Richard	3 Verulam Buildings
	STADLEN Nicholas	Fountain Court
❹	**BLOCH Michael**	Wilberforce Chambers
	GLICK Ian	One Essex Court
	HACKER Richard	3-4 South Square
	KNOWLES Robin	3-4 South Square
	PYMONT Christopher	13 Old Square
	RAILTON David	Fountain Court
	RICHARDS David	Erskine Chambers
	THOMAS Neville	3 Verulam Buildings
	WATERS Malcolm	11 Old Square
NEW SILKS		
	DAVIES Rhodri	One Essex Court
	DICKER Robin	3-4 South Square
	HANCOCK Christopher	20 Essex Street
	MALEK Hodge	4-5 Gray's Inn Square
	PHILLIPS Mark	3-4 South Square

For details of these leading barristers see Profiles on page 1473

Barristers' profiles 1473-1601

Brick Court Chambers (Clarke) This well-known commercial set is regarded as "top bracket" for banking work. Its reputation in the field rests principally with banking specialist **Mark Hapgood QC** and "super silk" **Jonathan Sumption QC**. "For sheer intellectual grasp, confidence and expert commercial advice," the latter is "top of the tree." Hapgood is the focal point of the chambers for banking work, both advisory and contentious – a "number one port of call" for both transactional and litigation solicitors. Transactional lawyers regard him as one of very few who are "up to speed on the market," and litigation solicitors admire him for his "user-friendliness." He edits Paget on Banking, and is the "obvious choice for banking" – "uniformly excellent." Sumption is the advocate for the heavy cases: if judges are to disagree with him, "they have to think very hard about it." With **Mark Howard QC** also having a "fantastic reputation," the set is viewed as "top heavy," although the market recognises that steps are being taken to give the juniors a more specialist profile.

Fountain Court (Boswood) Chambers works on a wide range of contentious matters, from the "heavyweight to the bread and butter," and on non-contentious matters. It is considered to have depth in its membership, with "the strongest spread of leading silks and juniors," and an "impressively modern attitude." With his "absolutely detailed banking knowledge" **Michael Brindle QC** has "the ear of the blue-chip law firms." "Good with the client, good as a team and good in court," clients have a high regard for his all-round skills. Another silk with all-round skills is the "quite excellent" **Anthony Boswood QC** who works "directly and well with the client," and is also "one of the best cross-examiners out there." Clients also love working with **Peter Goldsmith QC** who has a "combination of courtroom excellence and top banking knowledge." **Nicholas Stadlen QC** has been representing the Bank of England on litigation brought by depositors in BCCI, one of the most complex banking cases to date. Consistent peer recommendation for **David Railton QC** sees him make his debut in these ratings this year. At junior level, the firm also excels, with the "hard-working" **Bankim Thanki** praised for his ability to work well with solicitors, and for being "superb on paper." **David Waksman** is "talented and user friendly." Solicitors appreciate him for being "to us what we aim to be to our clients." His range of talents mean that "you don't sacrifice quality for user friendliness when you go to him." **Timothy Howe** and **Andrew Mitchell** were also praised for their banking work.

3 Verulam Buildings (Symons/Jarvis) Regarded as a pure banking set who have "the volume work." **William Blair QC** is "the one for advisory matters." "He knows his stuff backwards" and is regarded as "superb for a technical case without the litigation." **Richard Salter QC** is "totally capable" and "can bring a case round on his own on a good day." **Ali Malek QC** has a "great reputation" as a banking litigator, as has "old favourite" **Neville Thomas QC**. The set is perceived to be "particularly strong at the junior end," and **Adrian Beltrami, Ewan McQuater**, **Jonathan Nash** and **Stephen Phillips** all maintain their high reputations. **Jonathan Davies-Jones** is held in high regard by clients, and is now an established force in this area of practice.

Essex Court Chambers (Pollock) Historically involved in shipping and commercial work, the chambers' main expertise is felt to lie in commercial and international work. Accordingly, the set's members are involved on banking and international finance cases. **Gordon Pollock QC** is an "effective all-rounder," better known for his cross-examination skills and courtroom style than for advisory work with clients. "Strong advocate" **Geraldine Andrews** and **Richard Millett** are respected juniors.

LEADING JUNIORS • London	
❶ THANKI Bankim	Fountain Court
WAKSMAN David	Fountain Court
❷ WOLFSON David	One Essex Court
❸ ANDREWS Geraldine	Essex Court Chambers
BELTRAMI Adrian	3 Verulam Buildings
BROWN Hannah	One Essex Court
BUTCHER Christopher	7 King's Bench Walk
CHIVERS David	Erskine Chambers
DAVIES-JONES Jonathan	3 Verulam Buildings
HOWE Timothy	Fountain Court
MCQUATER Ewan	3 Verulam Buildings
MILES Robert	4 Stone Buildings
MILLETT Richard	Essex Court Chambers
MITCHELL Andrew	Fountain Court
NASH Jonathan	3 Verulam Buildings
OWEN David	20 Essex Street
PHILLIPS Stephen	3 Verulam Buildings
SULLIVAN Michael	One Essex Court

For details of these leading barristers see Profiles on page 1473

One Essex Court (Grabiner) The bulk of the set's work is City litigation and commercial work. However, members are also respected for their banking abilities. "Super silk" **Anthony Grabiner QC** is seen to be easing up on work since becoming a peer, yet he is still appreciated for his vast court-room experience and for being a good client man. **Ian Glick QC** and **Rhodri Davies QC** maintain their reputations. The main banking specialists in the set are **Michael Sullivan**, **Hannah Brown** and **David Wolfson**. The latter is "a great junior," seen as a "true specialist" who is "heavily in demand."

Erskine Chambers (Potts) "Undoubtedly the top set for commercial advisory work," clients "go to Erskine for the right answer." The set is peopled by "corporate gurus" regarded as leaders for chancery work, and seen as "more of a paper than a courtroom practice." **Robin Potts QC** combines his detailed knowledge of the law with good courtroom skills, and is a point of reference for transactional banking lawyers. **David Richards QC** is "of the same mould as Potts," and is perceived to be making considerable strides towards filling the retired Richard Sykes' boots. **David Chivers**, "a man for all seasons," is seen as a leading junior here as in a number of areas.

3-4 South Square (Crystal) The firm's premier reputation in insolvency overshadows its other areas of expertise. As a result, the banking work of the team is not as prominent, yet its banking (as well as insolvency) proficiency has seen it acting on the consequences of the BCCI and Barings debacles. All-rounders working on insolvency, banking and corporate matters and well regarded for their financial work include **Robin Knowles QC**, **Richard Hacker QC** and **Mark Phillips QC**. The "first rate" **Robin Dicker QC** ("he can do anything,") a new silk, also stands out for his banking work.

20 Essex Street (Milligan) An old shipping practice which has broadened out and is now regarded as a serious banking player. **Iain Milligan QC** is the leading light of the set, working on general banking work, including derivatives and letters of credit. He is one of "the new generation of stars" both in litigious and in advisory functions. Others rated include the "supremely able" new silk **Christopher Hancock QC** and **David Owen**.

Other Notable Barristers **Christopher Pymont QC** of **13 Old Square** (Lyndon-Stanford) is highly regarded, working on litigious and advisory matters, such as reviewing commercial bank securities documentation. **Terence Etherton QC** of **Wilberforce Chambers** (Nugee) has a mixed practice of advisory and litigation work, and is commended as "approachable." The "always good" **Malcolm Waters QC** of **11 Old Square** (Crawford/Simpkiss) is highly regarded on documentation issues, with the set itself well known for mortgages, consumer credit and building society law. The "stunning" **Michael Bloch QC** of **Wilberforce Chambers** (Nugee) enters our lists this year following strong market recommendation. **Hodge Malek QC** of **4-5 Gray's Inn Square** (Appleby/Ouseley) maintains his reputation as a new silk. The "phenomenally bright" **Christopher Butcher** of **7 King's Bench Walk** (Cooke) has an "extremely good reputation" and **Robert Miles** of **4 Stone Buildings** (Heslop) is valued for his all-round skills.

CHANCERY

RESEARCH: The rankings are based on in-depth interviews with over 5,000 solicitors and barristers in the UK. Chambers research is audited by the British Market Research Bureau (see page 7 for details).

OVERVIEW: As most commercial transactions involve a range of legal issues from both fields, the split between commercial and traditional chancery is increasingly blurred. Nevertheless the consensus is that there is still a distinction. Traditional barristers tend to undertake advisory and drafting work and appear in court less frequently. Commercial chancery practitioners undertake litigation in the Chancery Court as well as the Commercial Court.

Barristers' profiles 1473-1601

LEADING SETS • COMMERCIAL CHANCERY • London	QCs	Jnrs
❶ **13 Old Square** (Michael Lyndon-Stanford QC)	4	5
Serle Court (Patrick Neill QC)	4	7
4 Stone Buildings (Philip Heslop QC)	4	2
Wilberforce Chambers (Edward Nugee QC)	4	3
❷ **7 Stone Buildings** (Charles Aldous QC)	2	3
❸ **9 Old Square** (Michael Driscoll QC)	3	3
3-4 South Square (Michael Crystal QC)	2	3
❹ **12 New Square** (John Mowbray QC)	2	-
24 Old Buildings (Mann/Steinfeld)	2	-
3 Stone Buildings (Geoffrey Vos QC)	2	-

Numbers show recommended barristers in this practice area

LEADING SILKS • COMMERCIAL CHANCERY • London	
❶ **ALDOUS Charles**	7 Stone Buildings
BRIGGS Michael	Serle Court
ETHERTON Terence	Wilberforce Chambers
GLOSTER Elizabeth	One Essex Court
PATTEN Nicholas	9 Old Square
SHER Jules	Wilberforce Chambers
STEINFELD Alan	24 Old Buildings
VOS Geoffrey	3 Stone Buildings
❷ **BOYLE Alan**	Serle Court
CRYSTAL Michael	3-4 South Square
DAVIS Nigel	7 Stone Buildings
HESLOP Philip	4 Stone Buildings
HILDYARD Robert	4 Stone Buildings
MOSS Gabriel	3-4 South Square
OLIVER David	Erskine Chambers
PURLE Charles	12 New Square
❸ **BANNISTER Edward**	3 Stone Buildings
BERRY Simon	9 Old Square
BOMPAS Anthony	4 Stone Buildings
BRISBY John	4 Stone Buildings
CROXFORD Ian	Wilberforce Chambers
KAYE Roger	24 Old Buildings
MANN Anthony	Enterprise Chambers
MCCOMBE Richard	13 Old Square
MCDONNELL John	1 New Square
ROSEN Murray	11 Stone Buildings
TALBOT Patrick	Serle Court
TRACE Anthony	13 Old Square
❹ **DRISCOLL Michael**	9 Old Square
MOWSCHENSON Terence	Wilberforce Chambers
NEWMAN Catherine	13 Old Square
PYMONT Christopher	13 Old Square
NEW SILKS	
HOLLINGTON Robin	1 New Square
JONES Elizabeth	Serle Court
SMITH Stephen	12 New Square

For details of these leading barristers see Profiles on page 1473

LONDON
COMMERCIAL CHANCERY

Including banking, commercial contracts, companies, financial services, fraud, injunctions, insolvency, IP, media and entertainment, professional negligence and torts.

13 Old Square (Lyndon-Stanford) Praised for his sharp intellect, the "laid back" **Richard McCombe QC** joins the tables this year. He is spoken of as versatile and possessing good judgement. Continuing to build his reputation and practice is **Anthony Trace QC**. He is "bright" and able to find the merits in "hopeless cases." **Catherine Newman QC** is joined in the tables by **Christopher Pymont QC** who elicited some substantial recommendations. Of the juniors, **John Nicholls** is "incredibly sound" and "really stands out." "Have a go" **Matthew Collings** is highly recommended, while **Paul Girolami** is new to the lists this year. He is "easy to work with" and "incisive." **Mark Cunningham** is praised for being "quick on the uptake" and for his initiative. **Rebecca Stubbs** is identified as one with a promising future and enters the "up and coming" list.

Serle Court (Neill) **Michael Briggs QC** draws enthusiastic comment. He is "superb" and praised for the power of his analysis, advocacy skills and wide legal knowledge. Still in Bermuda on the Thyssen case is **Alan Boyle QC**; a man prepared to "roll up his sleeves and get stuck in." His stamina and huge concentration level makes him ideal for long trials. "Solid" **Patrick Talbot QC** is "thorough" and "adaptable." New Silk **Elizabeth Jones QC** is also seen as an "impressive performer." Recommended juniors include the "top flight" **Douglas Close**, also in Bermuda, "softly spoken" **Victor Joffe** and **Philip Hoser**, a "powerful advocate." An "extremely aggressive advocate" is **Philip Marshall**, **John Whittaker** is "efficient" and **Nicholas Harrison** is "forthright" and "exceedingly accomplished." **Philip Jones** is a newcomer to the tables who has "a good commercial awareness."

4 Stone Buildings (Heslop) With a strong reputation in banking and company law **Philip Heslop QC** is held in high regard. "Straightforward" **Robert Hildyard QC** is said to be "very clever." **John Brisby QC** is thought of as "bombastic and tough" and **Anthony Bompas QC** is another "patrician, blue-chip" performer. Leading juniors include **Robert Miles** ("conscientious, clever and sensible,") "idiosyncratic" **Peter Griffiths** and **Christopher Harrison** who is "utterly reliable."

Wilberforce Chambers (Nugee) The "persuasive" **Terence Etherton QC** has a natural authority in court, the ability to "think round corners" and is a fine tactician. Another superb advocate is the "hypnotic" **Jules Sher QC** a "really able lawyer who can give you all the legal input you need." The popular **Ian Croxford QC** is said to be "positively Rumpolesque." A new addition is **Terence Mowschenson QC** a "must" for many clients. Junior **James Ayliffe** is a team player, intellectually tough and will "stand up to anyone." Two up and coming juniors are **Emily Campbell** and **Caroline Furze.**

7 Stone Buildings (Aldous) Having a practice of the "highest order," **Charles Aldous QC** goes from one enormous case to the next. He is a "delight" to work with, an excellent advocate and an "involved team player." **Nigel Davis QC** is spoken of as "technically good" and an "articulate and fluent" advocate. "First rate intellect" **Guy Newey** is said to be an "incredibly nice person – and that comes through on the clients' behalf."

LEADING JUNIORS • London	
❶ MILES Robert	4 Stone Buildings
NEWEY Guy	7 Stone Buildings
NICHOLLS John	13 Old Square
❷ AYLIFFE James	Wilberforce Chambers
CLOSE Douglas	Serle Court
COLLINGS Matthew	13 Old Square
GIROLAMI Paul	13 Old Square
HOSER Philip	Serle Court
MARSHALL Philip	Serle Court
❸ COHEN Edward	11 Stone Buildings
CUNNINGHAM Mark	13 Old Square
GIRET Jane	11 Stone Buildings
GRIFFITHS Peter	4 Stone Buildings
HOCHBERG Daniel	9 Old Square
IFE Linden	Enterprise Chambers
JOFFE Victor	Serle Court
LEECH Thomas	9 Old Square
STEWART Lindsey	7 Stone Buildings
TROWER William	3-4 South Square
WALTON Alastair	7 Stone Buildings
❹ DAGNALL John	9 Old Square
HARRISON Christopher	4 Stone Buildings
HARRISON Nicholas	Serle Court
JONES Philip	Serle Court
PASCOE Martin	3-4 South Square
WHITTAKER John	Serle Court
ZACAROLI Antony	3-4 South Square
UP AND COMING	
CAMPBELL Emily	Wilberforce Chambers
FURZE Caroline	Wilberforce Chambers
STUBBS Rebecca	13 Old Square

For details of these leading barristers see Profiles on page 1473

New additions are "superb" **Lindsey Stewart** and **Alaister Walton** who is "outstanding" and "responsive."

9 Old Square (Driscoll) A "cool English gentleman," **Nicholas Patten QC**, currently on the Thyssen case in Bermuda, is highly rated as an "intelligent and skilful" advocate. Known for his real property expertise **Simon Berry QC** is said to be "absolutely meticulous." Joining the tables this year is "hard-working" head of chambers **Michael Driscoll QC**. Juniors in the set include **Daniel Hochberg** who has a "good academic knowledge," **Thomas Leech** also on the Thyssen case and **John Dagnall**.

3-4 South Square (Crystal) **Michael Crystal QC**, another barrister on the Thyssen case, is said to be "aggressive," but remains in great demand. Insolvency expert **Gabriel Moss QC** is "head and shoulders" above the rest in his field and has "flashes of sheer brilliance." New additions are juniors **William Trower**, a "heavy hitter" who is "good with clients," **Martin Pascoe** and **Antony Zacaroli** whose star continues to rise.

12 New Square (Mowbray) Two silks at this set are noted for commercial chancery work. "Wonderfully inventive" **Charles Purle QC** has "flair" and a "unique style." New silk **Stephen Smith QC** is "commercially aware" and a "sensible, measured advocate."

24 Old Buildings (Mann/Steinfeld) Joint chambers head **Alan Steinfeld QC** is reportedly "one of the best chancery silks all round." He is "practical, prepared and invariably right" and draws kudos for his exceptionally good judgement. **Roger Kaye QC** is spoken of as "level headed and sensible."

3 Stone Buildings (Vos) Current chairman of the Chancery Bar Association **Geoffrey Vos QC** is "undoubtedly bright" and a "formidable, hard fighter." The "excellent" **Edward Bannister QC** is "blunt, he gets right to the point and doesn't waste time."

Other Notable Barristers **Elizabeth Gloster QC** of **One Essex Court** (Grabiner) is said to be a "tough advocate" and is praised for her "attention to detail" and grasp of the law. **David Oliver QC**, now of **Erskine Chambers** (Potts) is "quick on his feet, and can really build up a point in court." **John McDonnell QC** is said to "love what he does" and will explore "every by-way." A new addition is **Robin Hollington QC**, considered "pre-eminent" in his field of directors disqualification and s459. Both he and McDonnell are from **1 New Square** (Hamilton.) From **11 Stone Buildings** (Rosen) are **Murray Rosen QC** a "wily operator with a considerable degree of ingenuity," **Jane Giret** and new addition **Edward Cohen** who is a "pretty good chancery practitioner." Head of chambers **Anthony Mann QC** and **Linden Ife** from **Enterprise Chambers** (Mann) are also recommended.

TRADITIONAL CHANCERY

Including charities, joint ownership, mortgages, partnerships, pensions, probate, real property, revenue, and trusts, settlements and wills.

LEADING SETS • TRADITIONAL CHANCERY London	QCs	Jnrs
❶ **Wilberforce Chambers** (Edward Nugee QC)	10	5
❷ **5 Stone Buildings** (Henry Harrod)	3	4
❸ **3 New Square** (William Goodhart QC)	2	3
11 New Square (Sonia Proudman QC)	2	2
❹ **12 New Square** (John Mowbray QC)	4	1
10 Old Square (Leolin Price QC)	1	3
13 Old Square (Michael Lyndon-Stanford QC)	5	7

Numbers show recommended barristers in this practice area

Wilberforce Chambers (Nugee) Described as a "man for all seasons," **Jules Sher QC** appears in both the commercial and traditional chancery sections. His "diligence and attentiveness" makes him a leading choice for trusts advice. Recommended for both pensions and trusts advice, **Nicholas Warren QC** is described as "one of the best minds," and is "especially good on paper." **Brian Green QC**, has learned "from the best," is "methodical, accurate" and has a massive following. **Robert Ham QC** is another in Bermuda at present. He is spoken of as "direct" and "clever" and well regarded for his expertise on trusts law. "Outstanding practitioner" **Christopher Nugee QC** is referred to as "one of the most brilliant people you'll ever come across." Head of chambers **Edward Nugee QC** is held in "great respect" and often consulted on the "tricky problems." **John Martin QC** is said to be "good in court." Of the juniors, **John Child**, "a real class act" and **Anthony Taussig** stand out.

5 Stone Buildings (Harrod) "First rate" **Mark Herbert QC** is a "sought after big name in trusts and tax." Another leading tax expert is **Launcelot Henderson QC** who has "been in the House of Lords more often than just about anyone else." **Andrew Simmonds QC** is "excellent" for pensions and professional negligence matters. Leading juniors in the set include **Christopher Tidmarsh** who is "brilliant at the detail," and was rated the leading traditional chancery junior anywhere. Head of Chambers **Henry Harrod** is said to be "real quality" and "very sound." "Top person" **Shân Warnock-Smith** is "good with the clients," while new addition **Henry Legge** is "thoroughly able."

3 New Square (Goodhart) Head of Chambers **William Goodhart QC**, although felt to be very involved with political duties, remains active at the chancery bar. **Bernard Weatherill QC** "enjoys life in court" and "does it well." The juniors include drafting expert **David Rowell** who is "fantastic on advisory work," **Hedley Marten** who is said to be "as good as most silks" and **Josephine Hayes** who is "not one to let things lie."

11 New Square (Proudman) **Sonia Proudman QC** is said to be "just so talented," while **Peter Crampin QC** maintains his long-standing reputation. Juniors are **Dirik Jackson**, "powerful in court and careful on paper" and, new to our tables, **Thomas Dumont** who has a "nice court style, relaxed yet incisive."

LEADING SILKS • London	
❶ MCCALL Christopher	13 Old Square
SHER Jules	Wilberforce Chambers
WARREN Nicholas	Wilberforce Chambers
❷ GREEN Brian	Wilberforce Chambers
HAM Robert	Wilberforce Chambers
HERBERT Mark	5 Stone Buildings
NUGEE Edward	Wilberforce Chambers
NUGEE Christopher	Wilberforce Chambers
PROUDMAN Sonia	11 New Square
❸ CRAMPIN Peter	11 New Square
GOODHART William	3 New Square
HENDERSON Launcelot	5 Stone Buildings
LAURENCE George	12 New Square
MARTIN John	Wilberforce Chambers
MOWBRAY John	12 New Square
SIMMONDS Andrew	5 Stone Buildings
UNWIN David	7 Stone Buildings
WEATHERILL Bernard	3 New Square
NEW SILKS	
HINKS Frank	Serle Court
TAUBE Simon	10 Old Square

For details of these leading barristers see Profiles on page 1473

LEADING JUNIORS • London	
❶ TIDMARSH Christopher	5 Stone Buildings
❷ AINGER David	10 Old Square
BARLOW Francis	10 Old Square
CHILD John	Wilberforce Chambers
HARROD Henry	5 Stone Buildings
JACKSON Dirik	11 New Square
MARTEN Hedley	3 New Square
MASON Alexandra	3 Stone Buildings
ROGERS Beverly-Ann	Serle Court
ROWELL David	3 New Square
ROWLEY Keith	11 Old Square
SEMKEN Christopher	1 New Square
STEWART SMITH Rodney	1 New Square
TAUSSIG Anthony	Wilberforce Chambers
TOPHAM Geoffrey	3 Stone Buildings
TUCKER Lynton	12 New Square
WARNOCK-SMITH Shân	5 Stone Buildings
❸ BRIGGS John	3-4 South Square
CHAPMAN Vivian	9 Stone Buildings
DUMONT Thomas	11 New Square
EVANS Timothy	13 Old Square
HAYES Josephine	3 New Square
MEADWAY Susannah	10 Old Square
RUSSEN Jonathan	13 Old Square
UP AND COMING	
LEGGE Henry	5 Stone Buildings

For details of these leading barristers see Profiles on page 1473

12 New Square (Mowbray) A new addition to the tables from this set is **George Laurence QC** who "gets on top of things" and is "a safe bet." Head of Chambers **John Mowbray QC** is described as "an elder statesman of trusts law." Junior **Lynton Tucker** is reportedly "very good on paper."

10 Old Square (Price) New silk **Simon Taube QC** is "superb, a real star." He should do well as a silk as he has been "doing a silk's practice" for some time now according to one source. Getting some high profile cases is junior **David Ainger** who receives some weighty approbation. Also noteworthy are **Francis Barlow** who some consider to be "streets ahead," and, new this year, **Susannah Meadway**, especially recommended for her drafting skills.

13 Old Square (Lyndon-Stanford) Boasting a "tremendous following," **Christopher McCall QC** is one of the most highly regarded leaders at the chancery bar. He "considers long and hard" and "gives really good value." Of the juniors, **Timothy Evans** is "first class" and **Jonathan Russen** gets "impressive results."

Other Notable Barristers In addition to the above, several other sets and individuals are very well regarded for traditional chancery work. **David Unwin QC** of **7 Stone Buildings** (Aldous) is a new entry and said to be "excellent" and "making a good name for himself." **Alexandra Mason** is regarded as "thorough" and "efficient" while pensions expert **Geoffrey Topham** "finds ways through problems where others multiply them." Both are at **3 Stone Buildings** (Vos.) **Keith Rowley** at **11 Old Square** (Crawford/Simpkiss) is said to be "first-class." At **Serle Court Chambers** (Neill) are new silk **Frank Hinks QC**, a "hard grafter who knows his stuff" and junior **Beverly-Ann Rogers** who is "exceptional on her feet." Juniors **Christopher Semken** and **Rodney Stewart Smith** of **1 New Square** (Hamilton) both have formidable reputations as litigators. **John Briggs** of **3-4 South Square** (Crystal) and **Vivian Chapman** of **9 Stone Buildings** (Ashe) are also recommended.

WESTERN / WALES & CHESTER CIRCUITS

LEADING SILKS • Western/Wales & Chester	
❶ COOKE Nicholas	9 Park Place
NEW SILKS	
DAVIES Stephen	Guildhall Chambers

For details of these leading barristers see Profiles on page 1473

LEADING JUNIORS • Western/Wales & Chester	
❶ BAMFORD Jeremy	Guildhall Chambers
BLOHM Leslie	St John's Chambers
MAHER Martha	Guildhall Chambers
JARMAN Milwyn	9 Park Place
JONES Geraint	9 Park Place
KEYSER Andrew	9 Park Place

For details of these leading barristers see Profiles on page 1473

New silk **Stephen Davies QC**, **Martha Maher** and **Jeremy Bamford** at **Guildhall Chambers** (Palmer) in Bristol are recommended. So too is **Leslie Blohm** of **St John's Chambers** (Denyer) Bristol. Leader **Nicholas Cooke QC** and juniors **Milwyn Jarman**, **Geraint Jones** and **Andrew Keyser** of **9 Park Place** (Murphy) in Cardiff are all endorsed.

MIDLANDS & OXFORD CIRCUIT

LEADING SILKS • Midlands & Oxford	
❶ RANDALL John	St Philip's Chambers
NEW SILKS	
CORBETT James	St Philip's Chambers

For details of these leading barristers see Profiles on page 1473

LEADING JUNIORS • Midlands & Oxford	
❶ ASHWORTH Lance	St Philip's Chambers
CHARMAN Andrew	St Philip's Chambers
STOCKILL David	5 Fountain Court

For details of these leading barristers see Profiles on page 1473

At **St Philips Chambers** (Tedd) in Birmingham are silks **John Randall QC** who is "quick, and has a brilliant mind" and **James Corbett QC** who "fights the good fight." Juniors at the set are "persistent" **Lance Ashworth** and former solicitor **Andrew Charman**. Also recommended is **David Stockill** of **5 Fountain Court** (Barker) in Birmingham.

NORTHERN / NORTH EASTERN CIRCUITS

LEADING SILKS • Northern	
❶ ALLEN James	No.6
SMITH Peter	40 King St
❷ ELLERAY Anthony	St. James's Chambers
JONES Edward Bartley	Exchange Chambers
LEEMING Ian	9 St. John Street
NEW SILKS	
BOOTH Michael	40 King St

For details of these leading barristers see Profiles on page 1473

LEADING JUNIORS • Northern	
❶ ANDERSON Lesley	40 King St
BERRAGAN Neil	Merchant Chambers
CAWSON Mark	St. James's Chambers
CHAISTY Paul	40 King St
DUNN Katherine	40 King St
HARPER Mark	40 King St
JOHNSON Ian	14 Castle Street
JOHNSON Michael	9 St. John Street
MCCARROLL John	Exchange Chambers
ORR Nicholas	14 Castle Street
OUGHTON Richard	Cobden House Chambers
RIDDLE Nicholas	14 Castle Street
STERLING Robert	St. James's Chambers

For details of these leading barristers see Profiles on page 1473

At **40 King Street** (Case) Manchester are **Peter Smith QC**, known for being a "robust" advocate and **Michael Booth QC** a "methodical and painstaking" lawyer. Also at this chambers are juniors **Lesley Anderson**, a new entry said to be "tenacious," **Paul Chaisty** a "top man, he's logical and persistent and doesn't give in," **Katherine Dunn** who "thinks well on her feet" and **Mark Harper**, another new entry and an "effective advocate." **Edward Bartley Jones QC** at **Exchange Chambers** (Waldron) in Liverpool is a respected opponent and reportedly can be "a rottweiler" in court. Also featuring is junior **John McCarroll**, an "academic type" who is thorough and good with detail. At **14 Castle Street** (Edis) Liverpool are the "smooth" **Ian Johnson**, **Nicholas Orr** who is "strong" both in court and on paper and "brilliant" **Nicholas Riddle**. From **Cobden House Chambers** (Baisden) in Manchester, **Richard Oughton** is newly recommended. From **St James's Chambers** (Sterling) Manchester are **Anthony Elleray QC**, **Mark Cawson** a "well respected leading junior" and "solid" head of chambers **Robert Sterling**. At **9 St John Street** (Hand), Manchester are **Ian Leeming QC** and junior **Michael Johnson**. **James Allen QC** of **No. 6** (Spencer) in Leeds maintains his reputation. Also recommended is **Neil Berragan** of **Merchant Chambers** (Berkley) in Manchester.

CHARITIES

RESEARCH: The rankings are based on in-depth interviews with over 5,000 solicitors and barristers in the UK. Chambers research is audited by the British Market Research Bureau (see page 7 for details).

OVERVIEW: The top end of the charities bar remains the domain of a select number of traditional and commercial chancery practitioners who have long-standing experience in what is a particularly specialist field. As a result, no sets are ranked and there are no changes to the individuals' rankings this year, with the exception of new silks Michael Furness and Simon Taube.

LONDON

LEADING SILKS • London	
❶ MCCALL Christopher	13 Old Square
PICARDA Hubert	3 New Square
UNWIN David	7 Stone Buildings
❷ CRAMPIN Peter	11 New Square
HERBERT Mark	5 Stone Buildings
NUGEE Edward	Wilberforce Chambers
PROUDMAN Sonia	11 New Square
VENABLES Robert	24 Old Buildings
WATERS Malcolm	11 Old Square
NEW SILKS • LONDON	
FURNESS Michael	Wilberforce Chambers
TAUBE Simon	10 Old Square

For details of these leading barristers see Profiles on page 1473

LEADING JUNIORS • London	
❶ QUINT Francesca	11 Old Square
❷ DUMONT Thomas	11 New Square
KESSLER James	24 Old Buildings
NEWEY Guy	7 Stone Buildings
WARNOCK-SMITH Shân	5 Stone Buildings

For details of these leading barristers see Profiles on page 1473

10 Old Square (Price) Respected traditional chancery set, several of whose members are instructed on charity matters, particularly new silk **Simon Taube QC**, who is "terribly good at anything he does."

11 Old Square (Crawford/Simpkiss) Acknowleged as a leader in unincorporated associations work, **Malcolm Waters QC** is also instructed on issues of pure charity law, in which he is "very sensible and clear thinking."

11 Old Square (Thrower) For many solicitors, **Francesca Quint** is "the bee's knees" of charity juniors. "Fast, good value and understands charities," her "practical, authoritative opinions carry weight with the Charity Commision."

Barristers' profiles 1473-1601

13 Old Square (Lyndon-Stanford) Known as a leading commercial chancery set. **Christopher McCall QC** is a "true intellectual" who "has the spark that can throw the light on something," particularly on tax and obscure equity matters. "Very thorough and very detailed," he is extremely experienced in the field, "highly articulate" and "will have thought out all the wrinkles."

3 New Square (Goodhart) An "acknowledged expert" in the field **Hubert Picarda QC** "has a legendary knowledge of obtuse areas of the law" and his recent book on the subject is regarded by many as a "seminal work." Though he "relishes academic points" and can be a "useful ally" in any question of pure charity law he is also known for his "maverick" approach in dealings with the Charity Commission and opponents, and "often takes a strong line and will pursue it."

11 New Square (Proudman) Respected chancery set with a strong contentious and non-contentious charities practice. One time Counsel to the Attorney General, **Peter Crampin QC** is known for his "good mind" and advocacy skills, and is "extremely practical and economical with advice." **Sonia Proudman QC** is praised by the market as being "wonderful at handling difficult trustees," and is seen by some solicitors as their first choice if it looks as if a case will end up in court, where she is "practical, sensible and a fighter." **Thomas Dumont** is "well known in the charity sector" with a strong reputation for legacies work and in court, where many admire his "showman" style.

24 Old Buildings (Bretten) **Robert Venables QC** and **James Kessler** both receive praise for their work in the field, which is largely on the tax side.

5 Stone Buildings (Harrod) The "very clever" **Mark Herbert QC** is on the tax side and is respected as a "safe pair of hands" on complex charitable trust issues. **Shân Warnock-Smith** is a leading junior with a significant charities practice, again particularly strong on trust issues.

7 Stone Buildings (Aldous) Well-known for its reputation in commercial chancery work. **David Unwin QC** is respected amongst his peers as a fine advocate and for his "good understanding of complex issues" and "ability to cut through the other side's argument." Junior **Guy Newey** is also highly rated in the field.

Wilberforce Chambers (Nugee) Pre-eminent in traditional chancery work, several members of chambers were recommended in charities work. "The doyen of it all" **Edward Nugee QC** remains an "authority" on chancery and charitable trust matters and is often consulted "when a senior statesman's view is required." New silk **Michael Furness QC** has been instructed by the Attorney General on charity matters.

CHURCH LAW

RESEARCH: The rankings are based on in-depth interviews with over 5,000 solicitors and barristers in the UK. Chambers research is audited by the British Market Research Bureau (see page 7 for details).

Barristers' profiles 1473-1601

OVERVIEW: There is a small number of practitioners at the bar (due in part to the preference of registrars to deal with matters in-house) who are specialists in ecclesiastical and church related work. This includes property, trusts, charity, employment and regulatory matters in addition to ecclesiastical law as it relates to the Church of England. They are usually instructed by either particular parishes or dioceses of the Church of England. Many of those featured in the list are chancellors of various dioceses, and are actively involved in the Anglican church. The Human Rights Act 1998 which deals with, inter alia, freedom of religion, is due to come into force on 5 October 2000. It is expected by many practitioners to have a pervasive effect, somewhat akin to that of European law. Areas which might be affected are freedom of expression, disciplinary matters and some areas not traditionally viewed as contentious such as marriage and baptism.

LONDON

LEADING SETS • London	QCs	Jnrs
❶ 2 Harcourt Buildings (Gerard Ryan QC)	2	2
❷ Pump Court Chambers (Guy Boney QC)	1	1

Numbers show recommended barristers in this practice area

LEADING SILKS • London	
❶ CAMERON Sheila	2 Harcourt Buildings
❷ CLARK Christopher	Pump Court Chambers
GEORGE Charles	2 Harcourt Buildings
❸ KAYE Roger	24 Old Buildings
NEW SILKS • LONDON	
SEED Nigel	3 Paper Buildings

LEADING JUNIORS • London	
❶ BRIDEN Timothy	8 Stone Buildings
❷ HILL Mark	Pump Court Chambers
MYNORS Charles	2 Harcourt Buildings
❸ PETCHEY Philip	2 Harcourt Buildings
RODGERS June	Harcourt Chambers
❹ BEHRENS James	Serle Court

For details of these leading barristers see Profiles on page 1473

2 Harcourt Buildings (Ryan) This set is consistently the first one mentioned for ecclesiastical law specialists. On the basis of number of specialists in the sector and quantity of recommendations this set clearly leads the field. **Sheila Cameron QC**, Vicar-General for the Archbishop of Canterbury stands "head and shoulders above the rest." She is considered to know a "vast amount" about ecclesiastical law and is praised for her skills as a litigator and is often described as "formidable." **Charles George QC** is described as a "very, very clever man." **Charles Mynors** "an expert in listed buildings" is increasingly recommended. **Philip Petchey**, known for expertise in planning matters has been called the "smartest church lawyer" and gains praise for his "modern approach."

Pump Court Chambers (Boney) The "highly thought of" **Christopher Clark QC** remains the leading silk at this set. The "switched on" **Mark Hill**, author of a leading book on ecclesiastical law, attracts a growing amount of praise. One would be "hard pressed to find a junior with his knowledge."

Other Notable Barristers

"Among the best" is the "learned" **Timothy Briden** of **8 Stone Buildings** (Cherry) who is known for his strength on Faculty (planning) matters. **Nigel Seed QC** of **3 Paper Buildings** (Parroy) a "people's lawyer" is recommended for his work on discipline and judicial review cases in addition to his criminal practice. **June Rodgers** of **Harcourt Chambers** (Rodgers) maintains an involvement in this area as does **Roger Kaye QC** of **24 Old Buildings** (Mann/Steinfeld.) The "enthusiastic" and "persuasive" **James Behrens** of **Serle Court** (Neill) is identified as "one to watch."

WESTERN, NORTH EASTERN & NORTHERN CIRCUITS

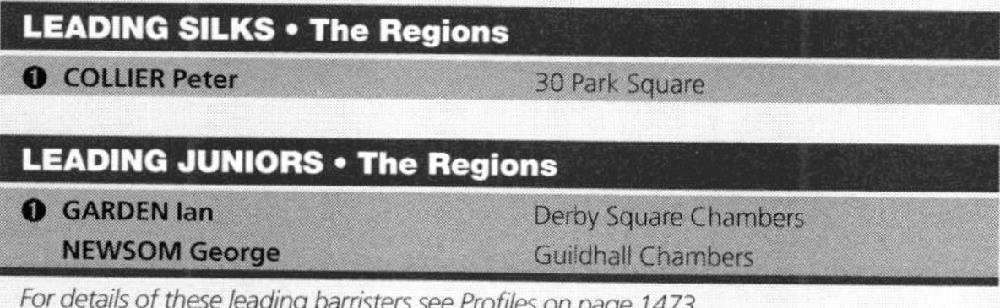

LEADING SILKS • The Regions	
❶ COLLIER Peter	30 Park Square

LEADING JUNIORS • The Regions	
❶ GARDEN Ian	Derby Square Chambers
NEWSOM George	Guildhall Chambers

For details of these leading barristers see Profiles on page 1473

The "personable" and "decisive" **Peter Collier QC** of **30 Park Square** (Mellor) in Leeds is often mentioned. **George Newsom**, "a lawyer's lawyer" from **Guildhall Chambers** (Palmer) in Bristol advises both the Church of England and other religious bodies and is considered to be "solid and highly academic." The "sound and meticulous" **Ian Garden** of **Derby Square Chambers** (Newton) in Liverpool is "highly regarded" and is a member of the Church of England Synod.

CLINICAL NEGLIGENCE

RESEARCH: The rankings are based on in-depth interviews with over 5,000 solicitors and barristers in the UK. Chambers research is audited by the British Market Research Bureau (see page 7 for details).

Barristers' profiles 1473-1601

LONDON

LEADING SETS • London	QCs	Jnrs
❶ **3 Serjeants' Inn** (Philip Naughton QC)	5	8
❷ **1 Crown Office Row** (Robert Seabrook QC)	6	1
❸ **6 Pump Court** (Kieran Coonan QC)	1	7
❹ **Cloisters** (Laura Cox QC)	1	1
Crown Office Chambers (Purchas/Spencer)	1	2
Doughty Street Chambers (Geoffrey Robertson QC)	1	2
4 Paper Buildings (Jean Ritchie QC)	2	2
199 Strand (Peter Andrews QC)	2	-

Numbers show recommended barristers in this practice area

LEADING SILKS • London	
❶ **BRENNAN Daniel**	39 Essex Street
COONAN Kieran	6 Pump Court
GRACE John	3 Serjeants' Inn
MILLER Stephen	1 Crown Office Row
OWEN Robert	1 Crown Office Row
WHITFIELD Adrian	3 Serjeants' Inn
❷ **BADENOCH James**	1 Crown Office Row
COX Laura	Cloisters
FRANCIS Robert	3 Serjeants' Inn
HAVERS Philip	1 Crown Office Row
IRWIN Stephen	Doughty Street Chambers
MASKREY Simeon	7 Bedford Row
RITCHIE Jean	4 Paper Buildings
SPENCER Michael	Crown Office Chambers
❸ **ANDREWS Peter**	199 Strand
COGHLAN Terence	1 Crown Office Row
DAVIES Nicola	3 Serjeants' Inn
FAULKS Edward	No. 1 Serjeants' Inn
GIBSON Christopher	Four New Square
GUMBEL Elizabeth-Anne	199 Strand
POWERS Michael	4 Paper Buildings
NEW SILKS • LONDON	
KELLY Matthias	Old Square Chambers
REES Paul	1 Crown Office Row
WATSON James	3 Serjeants' Inn

For details of these leading barristers see Profiles on page 1473

3 Serjeants' Inn (Naughton) Still the "favourite" set for clinical negligence, maintains its top position due to its "quality of service" which ensures that "work is turned around efficiently at a sensible price." Said to "provide a more modern service" than the competing sets, 3 Serjeants' Inn was also recommended for the quality of the clerks, with particular recognition of "excellent" Nick Salt. The "intellectually penetrating" **Adrian Whitfield QC** "teases things out of witnesses where others draw teeth." "Laid back" **John Grace QC** exerts a "steadying influence" on clients and is said to be having "an extraordinary year." "Smooth as silk" **Robert Francis QC** also has a "fantastic bedside manner" while **Nicola Davies QC** is widely regarded as a "tough, bright cookie" in her work representing the GMC. New Silk **James Watson QC** was widely recommended as a "steady hand" who can "balance legal niceties with practical commercial realities." Recommended juniors include **Christopher Johnston** ("clearly a bright spark,") "reliable" **Huw Lloyd**, and the "outstanding" **Angus Moon** who has an "exceptional ability to express himself on paper." With a reputation as a "tigress" **Mary O'Rourke** "isn't everyone's cup of tea," but "understated" **Adrian Hopkins** was noted as a "courtroom presence." "Committed" **Fiona Neale** received praise for "sound judgement," as did the medically qualified **Richard Partridge** and "empathetic" **Michael Horne.**

1 Crown Office Row (Seabrook) One of the traditional triumvirate of leading clinical negligence sets, 1 Crown Office Row is acknowledged to "give good service" and has a particularly high profile in multi-party actions. Handles all manner of clinical negligence cases with the balance slightly tipped toward the defendant side. Contains a number of leading individuals including "incisive" **Robert Owen QC**, a "persuasive advocate" known to be "particularly good on quantum" matters. "An exceptionally good silk," **Stephen Miller QC** is in "a league of his own in terms of experience." Both "robust" **James Badenoch QC** ("at ease with vast amounts of medical detail") and "bright" **Philip Havers QC** played leading roles in Heil v Rankin increasing damages for pain and suffering claims. "Understated" **Terence Coghlan QC** was said to be "excellent on bigger cases" particularly in complex group actions. New silk **Paul Rees QC** "always goes the extra mile." "Fiery" **Margaret Bowron** was recommended for her "human touch" with clients.

6 Pump Court (Coonan) Well regarded set traditionally known for expertise in clinical negligence. Head of chambers, the "approachable" **Kieran Coonan QC** is "a natural advocate" who instils confidence in his clients. Recently tested the limits of the McFarlane ruling in Rand v E. Dorset Health Authority regarding parents' ability to recover damages in a wrongful birth claim. The set is particularly noted for its number of leading juniors. "Excellent" **Christina Lambert** was very highly recommended for "getting quickly to the nub of a case." **Susan Burden, Annalissa Garrett,** and **Duncan Pratt** were rated as "knowledgeable" and "good with clients." **Andrew Hockton** was reputed to be "a good fighter." "Authoritative" **Charles Foster** "turns work around quickly" while **Siobhan Goodrich** is particularly "good at cross-examining patients."

Cloisters (Cox) Set led by "straightforward" **Laura Cox QC** who "communicates well in complex cases" and has a "very client-centred approach." As a qualified doctor **Simon Taylor** is highly respected for his "sound judgement" and ability to "talk the language of expert witnesses."

Crown Office Chambers (Purchas/Spencer) A new set formed by the merger of 2 Crown Office Row and One Paper Buildings. **Michael Spencer QC**, a man of "vast intelligence and huge experience" is renowned for multi-party actions relating to pharmaceutical litigation. "Sympathetic" **Charlotte Jones** "gets fantastic results" while **Dennis Matthews** was noted for his "excellent manner with clients."

Doughty Street Chambers (Robertson) An "innovative" set with "a good background in team-work" deemed to be at the "cutting edge" of clinical negligence litigation. "Frighteningly intelligent," **Stephen Irwin QC** possesses a "medical knowledge that is nothing short of phenomenal" and represents the claimant in the Phillips Inquiry in BSE-linked nvCJD actions. "Hardworking" **Robin Oppenheim** is known for his "fabulous attention to detail" while "rising star" **Richard Hermer** enters our up and coming table this year following widespread recommendations.

4 Paper Buildings (Ritchie) "Tenacious" **Jean Ritchie QC** acts almost exclusively on the defendant side. Chaired inquiry into quality and prac-

LEADING JUNIORS • London	
❶ BOWRON Margaret	1 Crown Office Row
HOPKINS Adrian	3 Serjeants' Inn
LAMBERT Christina	6 Pump Court
MOON Angus	3 Serjeants' Inn
NEALE Fiona	3 Serjeants' Inn
OPPENHEIM Robin	Doughty Street Chambers
SPINK Andrew	35 Essex Street
❷ JOHNSTON Christopher	3 Serjeants' Inn
TAYLOR Simon	Cloisters
❸ BURDEN Susan	6 Pump Court
FOSTER Charles	6 Pump Court
GARRETT Annalissa	6 Pump Court
GOODRICH Siobhan	6 Pump Court
GOODWIN Deirdre	13 King's Bench Walk
HOCKTON Andrew	6 Pump Court
HOLWILL Derek	4 Paper Buildings
HORNE Michael	3 Serjeants' Inn
JONES Charlotte	Crown Office Chambers
LLOYD Huw	3 Serjeants' Inn
MATTHEWS Dennis	Crown Office Chambers
O'ROURKE Mary	3 Serjeants' Inn
PARTRIDGE Richard	3 Serjeants' Inn
PRATT Duncan	6 Pump Court
READHEAD Simon	No. 1 Serjeants' Inn
SHAW Howard	29 Bedford Row Chambers
SPENCER Martin	4 Paper Buildings
TRACY FORSTER Jane	13 King's Bench Walk
UP AND COMING • London	
HERMER Richard	Doughty Street Chambers

For details of these leading barristers see Profiles on page 1473

tice of the National Health Service arising from the actions of Rodney Ledward. "Precise" **Michael Powers QC** recently joined the chambers from One Paper Buildings and was praised for his "overall good grasp of the subject." Juniors **Martin Spencer** and **Derek Holwill** remain recommended as clinical negligence specialists.

199 Strand (Phillips) **Peter Andrews QC,** newly recommended this year for offering "high quality advice," leads the chambers and "seriously adds value to a case." "Rapier sharp" **Elizabeth-Anne Gumbel QC** is still a fairly recent silk but rises in the tables due to her "boundless energy" and "good grasp of issues." Recently acted in Kent v Griffiths, Roberts and London Ambulance Service, establishing the right of individuals to sue NHSLA for slow ambulance service.

Other Notable Barristers "Top ranking silk" **Daniel Brennan QC** at **39 Essex Street** (Pleming) was recognised as a "hugely able, persuasive advocate." **Simeon Maskrey QC** of **7 Bedford Row** (Farrer) has an "amazing analytical brain" which permits him to "reduce complex issues to one or two simple points." Served as leader in high value cerebral palsy case, Milloshas v Mid Staffordshire Health Authority. "A good tactician" **Edward Faulks QC** at **No 1 Serjeants' Inn** (Faulks) receives instructions in a number of leading cases, including the Penney, Palmer & Cannon v East Kent Health Authority cervical screening litigation. **Simon Readhead**, a junior in the same chambers, was also described as "a smooth, polished advocate," "well liked by the judges." "Approachable" **Christopher Gibson QC** at **Four New Square** (Fenwick) "takes an intellectual approach" in both claimant and defendant work. **Matthias Kelly QC** of **Old Square Chambers** (Hendy), was recommended once again as a promising new silk. Among the juniors, "outstanding" **Andrew Spink** of **35 Essex Street** (Inglis-Jones) received tremendous recommendation for being "incredibly thorough with papers" and having a "good eye for detail." Instructed in 1999 Devon Breast Screening Service case. **Deirdre Goodwin** and **Jane Tracy Forster** at **13 King's Bench Walk** (Ellis) were both rated for having "an excellent grasp of all aspects of the relevant law" while **Howard Shaw** at **29 Bedford Row Chambers** (Ralls) can "always find a way to get a case off the ground."

MIDLANDS & OXFORD CIRCUIT

LEADING SILKS • Midlands & Oxford	
❶ OLIVER-JONES Stephen	5 Fountain Court

LEADING JUNIORS • Midlands & Oxford	
❶ HUNJAN Satinder	5 Fountain Court
❷ BRIGHT Christopher	3 Fountain Court
GREGORY Philip	No. 6 Fountain Court

For details of these leading barristers see Profiles on page 1473

In Birmingham "hardworking" **Stephen Oliver-Jones QC** at **5 Fountain Court** (Barker) remains the leading silk in the area for defendant clinical negligence work. A junior in the same chambers, **Satinder Hunjan** was rated for ably carrying a "significant heavyweight caseload." "First rate" **Christopher Bright** at **3 Fountain Court** (Juckes) "does work country wide" and is said to give "great attention to detail." **Philip Gregory** of **6 Fountain Court** (Smith) was newly recommended this year for his "common sense" and "effective advocacy style."

NORTHERN & NORTH EASTERN CIRCUIT

LEADING SILKS • Northern & North Eastern	
❶ REDFERN Michael	28 St. John St
SWIFT Caroline	Byrom Street Chambers
WINGATE-SAUL Giles	Byrom Street Chambers
❷ ARMITAGE Keith	8 King St
GRIME Stephen	Deans Court Chambers
❸ GILMOUR Nigel	Oriel Chambers
GOLDREIN Iain	7 Harrington Street Chambers
LEVESON Brian	Byrom Street Chambers

LEADING JUNIORS • Northern & North Eastern	
❶ FREEDMAN Jeremy	Plowden Buildings
HEATON David	18 St. John Street
MELTON Christopher	Peel Court Chambers
❷ ECCLES David	8 King St
ROWLEY James	28 St. John St

For details of these leading barristers see Profiles on page 1473

At **Byrom Street Chambers** (Hytner) in Manchester, **Giles Wingate-Saul QC** is a "silk who carries a lot of gravitas" while **Caroline Swift QC** was deemed "the bees-knees" for her "attention to detail" and "good client manner." **Brian Leveson QC** was recommended as particularly "good on figures." "Charming" **Keith Armitage QC** leads the **8 King Street** (Armitage) set and "has been doing the work for years." "Able" **David Eccles** was also noted as having a "good team approach." At **28 St John Street** (Goldstone) **Michael Redfern QC** has "an uncanny knack of sussing out clients and acting accordingly" while **James Rowley** "promises to be a force to be reckoned with." **Stephen Grime QC** of **Deans Court Chambers** (Goddard) is "extremely bright" and handles both claimant and defendant work. **Nigel Gilmour QC** of **Oriel Chambers** (Sander) was described as "brilliant for cases you really want to fight" while "encyclopaedic" **Iain Goldrein QC** at **7 Harrington Street Chambers (formerly Corn Exchange Chambers)** (Steer/Goldrein/Fordham) manifests a "refreshingly modernist attitude" towards clinical negligence litigation. "A good all rounder," **David Heaton** of **18 St John Street** (Foster) "gets his work turned around quickly." At **Peel Court Chambers** (Shorrock) **Christopher Melton** was recommended as "knowledgeable and enthusiastic".

In the North Eastern circuit **Jeremy Freedman** of London set **Plowden Buildings** (Lowe) was the only recommended barrister for clinical negligence work. Described as "the only one locally you can have confidence in," Freedman received acclaim for his "efficiency" and "realistic approach."

COMMERCIAL (LITIGATION)

RESEARCH: The rankings are based on in-depth interviews with over 5,000 solicitors and barristers in the UK. Chambers research is audited by the British Market Research Bureau (see page 7 for details).

OVERVIEW: The Commercial Litigation section has been the subject of major change this year. Many silks and juniors have slipped from our lists and been replaced by alternative names who have each been the subject of spontaneous recommendation from solicitors and barristers outside of their own sets.

Certain names may appear deceptively low in these tables but the reader is reminded that the purpose of this section of the book is to highlight those barristers who have been chosen as great all-rounders. Other specialist sections will flag those individuals who have out-performed the pack in niche practice areas. This section is the showcase for barristers who excel in more than just one area of the law. In looking for leading names we pursued those who are jacks of all trades yet remain masters of each.

LONDON

LEADING SETS • London	QCs	Jnrs
❶ **Brick Court Chambers** (Christopher Clarke QC)	9	7
Essex Court Chambers (Gordon Pollock QC)	4	11
One Essex Court (Anthony Grabiner QC)	10	4
Fountain Court (Anthony Boswood QC)	7	4
❷ **3 Verulam Buildings** (Symons / Jarvis)	4	4
❸ **Blackstone Chambers** (Baxendale / Flint)	3	3
❹ **20 Essex Street** (Iain Milligan QC)	2	1
7 King's Bench Walk (Jeremy Cooke QC)	1	1

Numbers show recommended barristers in this practice area

Brick Court Chambers (Clarke) Leader of the "silvery-tongued" pack, **Jonathan Sumption QC** is assumed to possess "a near photographic memory. He'll know the case better than anyone." Such is his standing in the courtroom, it is said that his advocacy is "rather like listening to a university lecturer." Others comment that he inspires an "incredibly secure feeling" and that what makes him so irresistible is his "phenomenal intellect" which is "married with the gift of clear communication." Veteran silk, **Sydney Kentridge QC**, has been spotted with "more than just a cameo role these days." He's out there still putting on a good "performance in big trials" (albeit often shorter appellate matters.) "Stellar" **Mark Hapgood QC** has a "top class mind and a good bedside manner." This year's Bar Council Chair, **Jonathan Hirst QC** has "a way with the court" and is said to be "appropriately pompous in the right atmosphere." Furthermore, "the bench like him – that counts." **Mark Howard QC** was dubbed "the Peter Scott of our generation" by one interviewee, while another called him "unremitting; he never lets the pressure off." A third enjoyed the fact that he "duffs people up – he does such a good job." Solicitors are "terribly impressed" with "very smooth" **Andrew Popplewell QC**'s "ability to get up to speed and then wipe the floor with the opposition." He has a "lovely court manner – the judges nod along with him." **George Leggatt QC** is "easy to deal with." "Forceful" **Charles Hollander QC** "picks things up very quickly" and "doesn't give anything away." **Catharine Otton-Goulder QC** has taken silk this year. A popular new choice is **Michael Swainston**, who is joined by two more new additions to the tables: **Tom Adam** ("gets stuck in") and "together" **Neil Calver** ("client aware – he rings back straight away.") **Dominic Chambers** causes "no drama" and "he'll give you a view." **Helen Davies**' key skills include "communication and a willingness to fit into the team." **Richard Lord** is "a barrister who gets stuck into the detail of things." He is perceived to be "approachable and without airs and graces. Prompt, pleasant and easy to deal with." The final new name from Brick Court is "outstanding" junior **Roger Masefield**.

Barristers' profiles 1473-1601

LEADING SILKS • London	
✪ **GOLDSMITH Peter**	Fountain Court
GRABINER Anthony	One Essex Court
POLLOCK Gordon	Essex Court Chambers
SUMPTION Jonathan	Brick Court Chambers
❶ **BOSWOOD Anthony**	Fountain Court
BRINDLE Michael	Fountain Court
DOHMANN Barbara	Blackstone Chambers
GLOSTER Elizabeth	One Essex Court
KENTRIDGE Sydney	Brick Court Chambers
❷ **BARNES Mark**	One Essex Court
BRIGGS Michael	Serle Court
CARR Christopher	One Essex Court
EDER Bernard	Essex Court Chambers
HAPGOOD Mark	Brick Court Chambers
VOS Geoffrey	3 Stone Buildings
❸ **GLASGOW Edwin**	39 Essex Street
GLICK Ian	One Essex Court
GROSS Peter	20 Essex Street
HIRST Jonathan	Brick Court Chambers
HOWARD Mark	Brick Court Chambers
MILLIGAN Iain	20 Essex Street
MOWSCHENSON Terence	Wilberforce Chambers
POPPLEWELL Andrew	Brick Court Chambers
ROSEN Murray	11 Stone Buildings
STADLEN Nicholas	Fountain Court
❹ **CRANE Michael**	Fountain Court
FIELD Richard	One Essex Court
FLINT Charles	Blackstone Chambers
FREEDMAN Clive	Littleton Chambers
GEERING Ian	3 Verulam Buildings
GRUDER Jeffrey	Essex Court Chambers
HOCHHAUSER Andrew	Essex Court Chambers
JACOBS Richard	Essex Court Chambers
JARVIS John	3 Verulam Buildings
KEALEY Gavin	7 King's Bench Walk
LEAVER Peter	One Essex Court
LEGGATT George	Brick Court Chambers
MALEK Ali	3 Verulam Buildings
MANN Anthony	Enterprise Chambers
MILL Ian	Blackstone Chambers
ONIONS Jeffery	One Essex Court
PHILIPSON Trevor	Fountain Court
RAILTON David	Fountain Court
TEMPLE Anthony	4 Pump Court
THOMAS Neville	3 Verulam Buildings
TUGENDHAT Michael	5 Raymond Buildings
NEW SILKS	
DAVIES Rhodri	One Essex Court
HOLLANDER Charles	Brick Court Chambers
JONES Elizabeth	Serle Court
OTTON-GOULDER Catharine	Brick Court Chambers
RUBIN Stephen	Farrar's Building
SMITH Stephen	12 New Square

For details of these leading barristers see Profiles on page 1473

LEADING JUNIORS • London	
✪ RABINOWITZ Laurence	One Essex Court
SMOUHA Joe	Essex Court Chambers
❶ BUTCHER Christopher	7 King's Bench Walk
MCCAUGHRAN John	One Essex Court
ORR Craig	Fountain Court
THANKI Bankim	Fountain Court
❷ DE GARR ROBINSON Anthony	One Essex Court
HOWE Robert	Blackstone Chambers
MCQUATER Ewan	3 Verulam Buildings
PHILIPPS Guy	Fountain Court
SWAINSTON Michael	Brick Court Chambers
❸ ADAM Tom	Brick Court Chambers
CALVER Neil	Brick Court Chambers
GRIFFITHS Martin	Essex Court Chambers
LANDAU Toby	Essex Court Chambers
ONSLOW Andrew	3 Verulam Buildings
TOZZI Nigel	4 Pump Court
❹ ANDERSON Robert	Blackstone Chambers
ANDREWS Geraldine	Essex Court Chambers
BAKER Andrew	20 Essex Street
BEAZLEY Thomas	Blackstone Chambers
BELTRAMI Adrian	3 Verulam Buildings
BLANCHARD Claire	Essex Court Chambers
CHAMBERS Dominic	Brick Court Chambers
DAVIES Helen	Brick Court Chambers
DOWLEY Dominic	Serle Court
EADIE James	Serle Court
FLYNN Vernon	Essex Court Chambers
FOXTON David	Essex Court Chambers
LOCKEY John	Essex Court Chambers
LORD Richard	Brick Court Chambers
MILLETT Richard	Essex Court Chambers
PHILLIPS Stephen	3 Verulam Buildings
WAKSMAN David	Fountain Court
WOLFSON David	One Essex Court
WYNTER Colin	Devereux Chambers
UP AND COMING	
MASEFIELD Roger	Brick Court Chambers
MCGRATH Paul	Essex Court Chambers
STANLEY Paul	Essex Court Chambers

For details of these leading barristers see Profiles on page 1473

Essex Court Chambers (Pollock) Those who have seen **Gordon Pollock QC** in action confirm that "he's as good as the hype," "aggressive, usually humorous and always on his front foot." His range of skills is deemed by many to be "greater than anyone else's." "Compelling" **Bernard Eder QC** is "the thinking man's QC. Clever, quiet and effective" with "superb delivery." Sometimes felt to be rather "high maintenance," **Andrew Hochhauser QC** is "intellectually challenging and demanding of instructing solicitors." That said, "he will go the extra mile." **Richard Jacobs QC** "clothes a case with the utmost respectability" making "ethical judgment calls. He's of the Kentridge/Beloff style." **Joe Smouha** is a man you can "relate to socially," he has "avoided the ivory tower approach." He's the sort that solicitors refer to as a "nice bloke," offering them "flexibility, prompt responses, communication and a willingness to fit into the team." "The cat's out of the bag now!" we were told, everyone knows he's "top drawer." So great is **Martin Griffiths**' "command of paper, he could eat the Amazon." Now focusing mainly on arbitration, "people queue up for" **Toby Landau**. He has "a phenomenal practice and wherever he is, he returns your calls." **Geraldine Andrews** is recommended and **Claire Blanchard** earns her position. **Vernon Flynn** is well-liked. A new entrant to the rankings, **David Foxton** has a "wonderful seriousness to his advocacy." **John Lockey** is endorsed again this year and is now joined by three further new names to our lists: **Richard Millett** (back from Bermuda) and two up and coming young men, **Paul McGrath** (a "feisty Scouser") and the "fiercely intelligent" **Paul Stanley**.

One Essex Court (Grabiner) **Anthony Grabiner QC** knows how to do a "demolition job" on the opposition, but is perceived to be focusing much of his energy on the House of Lords these days. **Elizabeth Gloster QC** is "good fun and very clever; she takes responsibility" and is someone who "agrees to a plan and sticks to it." You can "almost see the intelligence bristling out" of **Mark Barnes QC**. Though not a member of the "silvery-tongued" pack, he has "integrity and good judgement." "Delightful" **Christopher Carr QC** "impresses clients" with his "smooth, urbane yet dogged" style. **Ian Glick QC** is "fantastic." Also recommended is **Richard Field QC. Jeffrey Gruder QC** wins cases "through his intellectual power." "He gets to the right points." New this year is **Peter Leaver QC** * who came to the attention of many through his work on the football Premier League cases. Silk suits **Jeffrey Onions QC** pretty well: "he's settled into the clothes of a leader." He has a "rather rambunctious style and makes points forcibly." **Rhodri Davies QC** is noted for being particularly good on points of construction. **Laurence Rabinowitz** may not be "silky smooth" as an advocate but his written work is, however, "sparkling" and he has easily retained his star band status in the juniors' table. Practitioners have remarked that he is now more "confident" on his feet. He came to the bar later in life and has a ferocious workload. "Good advocate" **John McCaughran** is "personable and likable" and not shy of hard work. **Anthony de Garr Robinson** is "thorough and thoughtful." "He really puts his back into things." **David Wolfson** is also well regarded.

Fountain Court (Boswood) **Peter Goldsmith QC** is "creative in his legal thinking" but, when required to be "a commercial bruiser" he can also offer "hard-hitting punchy stuff!" "Effective" **Anthony Boswood QC** is a "tough operator." High on everyone's lists is **Michael Brindle QC** who has an element of "glossiness" and the ability to "shoot from the hip." "One of the next real big leaders in years to come," **Nicholas Stadlen QC** "puts himself out." Certain interviewees felt that he was "an acquired taste, but the end product is great." Hitherto "undiscovered gem," **Michael Crane QC** is new into the silks list this year. He's a "fantastic cross-examiner." Also newly recommended are **Trevor Philipson QC** ("urbane – in the Chris Carr mold and an excellent advocate, who's highly imaginative") and **David Railton QC. Craig Orr** is "technically excellent, quiet and unassuming, and perfect for complex corporate cases." Furthermore, he "rolls his sleeves up and gets on it." "Practical and commercial" **Bankim Thanki** "covers quite a few bases" superbly. He has "good empathy and you can really use him – just phone him up." **Guy Philipps** is "a good man to have in a fight." "Clinically intelligent," he attacks problem solving with "incisiveness;" he's "not fluffy, but confident." **David Waksman** is described as "accessible, bright and ambitious."

3 Verulam Buildings (Symons/ Jarvis) **Ian Geering QC** is one of the well-regarded silks in the set, along with "serious hitter" and joint head of chambers, **John Jarvis QC. Ali Malek QC** is recommended along with **Neville Thomas QC** *, who is described as "charming" and "old school." **Ewan McQuater**'s "analytical skills" are praised. He gives "clear views, which are balanced" and he "won't go off on a tangent. He'll try and estimate the judges' views and present something to sell to the client." Both **Andrew Onslow** and **Adrian Beltrami** are well endorsed, as is **Stephen Phillips**.

Blackstone Chambers (Baxendale/Flint) "If you're ever in a corner and need to fight your way out," you could do worse than instruct **Barbara Dohmann QC**. She "can bite a bit, but not in a nasty way." "A good cross-examiner," she brings "enthusiasm and detailed preparation to cases." "Bright" **Charles Flint QC** has been especially recommended for things of a financial or fraudulent nature. **Ian Mill QC** (described as a "good laugh and a really nice bloke") has received the endorsement required to enter this year's silks list. "Impressive" **Robert Howe** has been recommended for general commercial cases, having already performed well in our media/entertainment section. The second new junior name to our tables is that of "first rate commercial lawyer" **Robert Anderson**, who also has a profile in that specialist area. **Thomas Beazley** is highly regarded.

20 Essex Street (Milligan) **Peter Gross QC** is appreciated for his ability to "give a flavour of how the judge will react to a case" and for being "a well prepared and bright advocate." **Iain Milligan QC** is deemed to be "a lucid speaker and analytically very good – he takes issues apart." **Andrew Baker** is a very able and popular junior.

7 King's Bench Walk (Cooke) **Gavin Kealey QC** is a favourite of some leading solicitors. "Judges like" **Christopher Butcher**, who has been likened to a dinosaur, simply because "he has four brains." He's a "difficult opponent: sharp and on the ball. You have to be on top of your stuff" when facing him.

Other Notable Barristers **3 Stone Buildings** (Vos) offers the services of "master of preparation" **Geoffrey Vos QC**, ("un-pompous, works well in a team, extremely bright and technically astute.") "He fights for the underdog really well and is very accessible." At **39 Essex Street** (Pleming), **Edwin Glasgow QC** (reportedly one of the few London barristers who has always come to the reception of chambers to greet his visitors) is rated as "a very able advocate" and "extremely industrious." **Clive Freedman QC** is a "tough rottweiler," but in comparison to equivalent silks at some other sets "doesn't cost and arm and a leg." He is recommended from **Littleton Chambers** (Kallipetis.) For cases with a Chancery flavour, **Michael Briggs QC** of **Serle Court** (Neill) is a choice of leading practitioners. They say "you can't disbelieve him and the judges like him." Some have remarked that his keen interest in singing has had an advantageous impact on his speech and its delivery. New Silk **Elizabeth Jones QC** maintains her excellent reputation. Recommended juniors also from this chambers include "eclectic" **Dominic Dowley** and **James Eadie**. **Terence Mowschenson QC** has recently moved to **Wilberforce Chambers** (Nugee) from One Essex Court. **Anthony Temple QC** is recommended from **4 Pump Court** (Mauleverer) along with strong junior **Nigel Tozzi**. Another respected junior is **Colin Wynter** of **Devereux Chambers** (Burke.) **Murray Rosen QC** at **11 Stone Buildings** (Rosen) has proved a popular choice. **Michael Tugendhat QC** at **5 Raymond Buildings** (Milmo) has "a measured tone and the confidence of the court." **Anthony Mann QC** from **Enterprise Chambers** (Mann) continues to be highly regarded. Solicitors have remarked on the care and attention that they get from New Silk **Stephen Smith QC** of **12 New Square** (Mowbray). **Stephen Rubin QC** of **Farrar's Building** (Williams) is another New Silk to receive praise.

WESTERN CIRCUIT

LEADING SILKS • Western	
❶ DAVIES Stephen	Guildhall Chambers
❷ PALMER Adrian	Guildhall Chambers

For details of these leading barristers see Profiles on page 1473

LEADING JUNIORS • Western	
❶ MAHER Martha	Guildhall Chambers
STEAD Richard	St John's Chambers
VIRGO John	Guildhall Chambers
❷ BLOHM Leslie	St John's Chambers
LEVY Neil	St John's Chambers

For details of these leading barristers see Profiles on page 1473

Guildhall Chambers (Palmer) retains its position as market leader. Although **Stephen Davies QC** has only recently taken silk, so "outstanding" is his reputation that he immediately enters the tables at the top. Opinion is unanimous: "head and shoulders above his contemporaries," it is felt that "any superlative applies to him." It is agreed that, while his practice focuses on insolvency work, "he is brilliant too at general commercial cases with an insolvency bent." "Exceptionally cerebral and capable," **Adrian Palmer QC** is the "only" senior silk in the region with the facility to "handle a complex general commercial case." To turn to the leading juniors: **Martha Maher** is described as "determined" and "first rate in her preparation," while **John Virgo** is thought to be "approachable" and good at a broad range of commercial litigation. They are joined by the "very competent" **Richard Stead** at **St. John's Chambers** (Sharp). Also to be found at St. John's Chambers are the highly commended **Leslie Blohm** and **Neil Levy.**

MIDLANDS & OXFORD CIRCUIT

LEADING SILKS • Midlands & Oxford	
❶ RANDALL John	St Philip's Chambers
❷ CORBETT James	St Philip's Chambers
❸ COUSINS Jeremy	St Philip's Chambers

For details of these leading barristers see Profiles on page 1473

LEADING JUNIORS • Midlands & Oxford	
❶ ASHWORTH Lance	St Philip's Chambers
CAMPBELL Stephen	St Philip's Chambers
KHANGURE Avtar	No.6 Fountain Court
WYVILL Alistair	St Philip's Chambers
❷ ANDERSON Mark	3 Fountain Court
EYRE Stephen	1 Fountain Court

For details of these leading barristers see Profiles on page 1473

St Philip's Chambers (Tedd) maintains its unrivalled dominance in the commercial sphere. **John Randall QC** is, for another year, held to be "the best commercial silk in Birmingham." The title is awarded him in recognition of his "brilliant brain, dedication and personable manner" in court. **James Corbett QC** is equally clearly the "first choice" amongst the new silks, admired for being a "tenacious, impressive and formidable" opponent. **Jeremy Cousins QC**, recognised as "thorough and hardworking," moves into this category for the first time: his financial bias should be noted. "High-powered" **Lance Ashworth** is loudly recommended for the quality of his work, while **Stephen Campbell** is thought an "intelligent counsel." New to the lists this year, "impressive" **Alistair Wyvill** is seen as a "rising star, whose call belies his ability and experience." Outside St. Philip's Chambers, **Avtar Khangure** at **No. 6 Fountain Court** (Smith) is propelled onto the list by the weight of opinion which declares him to be "a major player for insolvency." "Highly regarded in terms of intellect and reliability," is **Mark Anderson** at **3 Fountain Court** (Juckes.) **Stephen Eyre** at **1 Fountain Court** (Crigman) is felt to be "excellent with clients."

NORTH EASTERN CIRCUIT

LEADING SILKS • North Eastern	
❶ ALLEN James	No.6

For details of these leading barristers see Profiles on page 1473

LEADING JUNIORS • North Eastern	
❶ GROVES Hugo	Enterprise Chambers
❷ JAMES Michael	Enterprise Chambers
JORY Hugh	Enterprise Chambers
❸ GARGAN Mark	No.6

For details of these leading barristers see Profiles on page 1473

Enterprise Chambers (Mann) in Leeds remains the region's leading set. **Hugo Groves** was the most frequently recommended barrister and is increasingly popular with local solicitors. Noted for his insolvency work in addition to a broad commercial practice, he covers most of the requisite bases – "bright, commercial, excellent on his feet and a good advocate." He's an "amusing, likeable bloke" who's "always up for it." Although he "can be blunt," it can be "just what you need" and "you'll always get answers off him." **Michael James** is "on a different planet intellectually." Handling a number of traditional sale of goods cases, he's regularly instructed by Addleshaws' for commercial and financial disputes. **Hugh Jory** mixes his caseload with banking, insolvency and other general commercial matters. Once called the "best commercial litigator in Leeds," he's still the first port of call for a loyal bunch of local solicitors. At **No.6** (Spencer) in Leeds, **James Allen QC**, formerly of Chancery House Chambers, is possibly the only recognised commercial silk in the area. Combining it with some chancery, he's not hugely visible but is "good with clients" and would be instructed by solicitors "should the case merit it." Newly recommended junior **Mark Gargan** is used by several of the bigger Leeds commercial firms for, among other things, banking disputes.

NORTHERN CIRCUIT

LEADING SILKS • Northern	
❶ SMITH Peter	40 King St
❷ WINGATE-SAUL Giles	Byrom Street Chambers
❸ ELLERAY Anthony	St. James's Chambers
JONES Edward Bartley	Exchange Chambers
RAYNOR Philip	40 King St
STEWART Stephen	Byrom Street Chambers
NEW SILKS	
BOOTH Michael	40 King St

For details of these leading barristers see Profiles on page 1473

LEADING JUNIORS • Northern	
❶ ANDERSON Lesley	40 King St
COGLEY Stephen	Merchant Chambers
❷ BERRAGAN Neil	Merchant Chambers
CAWSON Mark	St. James's Chambers
DAVIES Stephen	8 King St
DOYLE Louis	40 King St
❸ CHAISTY Paul	40 King St
SANDER Andrew	Oriel Chambers
TERRY Jeffrey	8 King St

For details of these leading barristers see Profiles on page 1473

40 King St (Raynor) Manchester. Assisted by the Manchester Mercantile Court, the set is well established, dominant and maintains its position well. Still regarded by regional solicitors as the next best thing beyond London, a whole host of quality barristers were endorsed by this year. Clearly, the circuit's top commercial silk **Peter Smith QC** – a "tough, bluff Yorkshireman" – has a notoriously aggressive style of advocacy and cross-examination unmatched by others. A "quite brilliant trial lawyer of great depth and tenacity" he was called a "cold-blooded killer" by one solicitor and nicknamed 'the barracuda' by another. **Philip Raynor QC** ("brilliantly clever") is a "real lawyers' lawyer." He would be called upon for a "brain-surgeon of a problem that was hard to solve." Less inclined to "bring out the knuckle-dusters" but felt to suit a "thorny point of law," where he could utilise his "sharp and agile mind" and "think deeply about the problem." **Michael Booth QC** is a "gritty northern lad who loves a fight." Felt to be strong in court, he "doesn't scream and shout but always gets the message across." His general commercial litigation practice veers towards cases with trials and lots of witnesses. Recently had a high degree of involvement with offshore clients. Incredibly popular, "rock hard" **Lesley Anderson** is "much in demand" with many of the leading solicitors. A "darling figure" she provides "absolutely no-nonsense advice" and "makes everyone feel valued." Felt to be good at interlocutory hearings, also a "tough advocate" in court, she has the ability to "charm the judges." Formerly of 10 Park Square, Leeds, well-liked and known Liverpudlian ex-solicitor **Louis Doyle** is frequently recommended for his insolvency and general commercial practice. "Great on his feet" as an advocate, he has a "good supply of experience and advice," a "direct and straightforward approach" and "clients love him." Also known for his chancery and insolvency practice, **Paul Chaisty** "cuts to the point – he's quick and agile."

Byrom Street Chambers (Hytner) Manchester. "Granddaddy of them all" and "doyen of the commercial bar" **Giles Wingate-Saul QC** ("authoritative and polished") has a broad practice including construction, PI and clinical negligence. Not felt to be naturally commercial or suitable for a hands-on commercial fight, he's "quiet, determined and gets to know everything backwards." Because he's "so good at detailed analysis" he can "ably transfer these skills to commercial work – a class act." **Stephen Stewart QC** is another barrister with a wide caseload of general commercial work including insurance and professional negligence. He's regarded as an ideal choice for "analysing a case with volumes of documentation."

St James Chambers (Sterling) Manchester. Another Manchester silk that straddles both the chancery and the commercial bar, **Anthony Elleray QC** makes an appearance this year. He is "well-regarded" and is felt to offer a "particularly high standard of paperwork." Scoring high approval this year, **Mark Cawson** is a "skilled advocate with a light touch." He is regarded as a "steady individual who doesn't put a foot wrong." Again, a barrister providing "quality paperwork," his main attribute is a "high level of reliability and legal soundness." Tipped by many to be a future silk.

Exchange Chambers (Waldron) Liverpool. **Edward Bartley Jones QC** has a breadth of practice which sees him noted for his work in chancery, insolvency, partnership and professional negligence. Not a definitive commercial disputes silk, he nevertheless has a "lighter touch" and is recommended by a number of North West solicitors for a variety of contentious commercial matters.

Merchant Chambers (Berkeley) Manchester. "Determined and pugnacious" **Stephen Cogley** is "absolutely top drawer" according to one regional solicitor. He "gets right to the point" and "has no airs and graces." His commitment and tenacity are sometimes interpreted as excessively sharp, but "he'll always fight your corner." On his feet, he is "effective at battering the judges – first class." On the smoother side, **Neil Berragan** is a "thoroughly professional all-round performer" who is felt to be "exceptional" in court, particularly on cross-examination. He has a "razor-sharp approach to things" according to solicitors.

8 King St (Armitage) Manchester. **Stephen Davies** is a "quiet but determined advocate" who "always prepares his stuff well." Fashionable and well-liked by solicitors, he's considered an "all-rounder" who "looks right and won't upset the judges." **Jeffrey Terry** is "thorough and commercial." He has an "unassuming air, but is canny and markets himself well."

Other Notable Barristers **Andrew Sander** of **Oriel Chambers** (Sander) in Liverpool has a "forceful military delivery" but is recommended for his consistent advocacy where "he would always do a good job."

COMPANY

RESEARCH: The rankings are based on in-depth interviews with over 5,000 solicitors and barristers in the UK. Chambers research is audited by the British Market Research Bureau (see page 7 for details).

OVERVIEW: A consistent year for the company bar with neither the threat of solicitor-advocates nor the trend of solicitors avoiding "second opinion" counsel diminishing its prominence. A noticeable increase in the level of instructions directly from in-house lawyers at major multi-nationals and from US law firms has made the market buoyant. Erskine Chambers remains the leading corporate set despite the retirement of the admirable Richard Sykes.

LONDON

LEADING SETS • London	QCs	Jnrs
❶ **Erskine Chambers** (Robin Potts QC)	5	11
❷ **4 Stone Buildings** (Philip Heslop QC)	4	5
❸ **13 Old Square** (Michael Lyndon-Stanford QC)	2	3
Serle Court (Patrick Neill QC)	2	3
3-4 South Square (Michael Crystal QC)	5	-
7 Stone Buildings (Charles Aldous QC)	2	3
❹ **Enterprise Chambers** (Anthony Mann QC)	1	3
One Essex Court (Anthony Grabiner QC)	1	2

LEADING SILKS • London	
❶ **POTTS Robin**	Erskine Chambers
RICHARDS David	Erskine Chambers
❷ **ALDOUS Charles**	7 Stone Buildings
BRIGGS Michael	Serle Court
DAVIS Nigel	7 Stone Buildings
GLOSTER Elizabeth	One Essex Court
HESLOP Philip	4 Stone Buildings
HILDYARD Robert	4 Stone Buildings
KOSMIN Leslie	Erskine Chambers
OLIVER David	Erskine Chambers
TODD Michael	Erskine Chambers
❸ **ADKINS Richard**	3-4 South Square
BANNISTER Edward	3 Stone Buildings
BOMPAS Anthony	4 Stone Buildings
BOYLE Alan	Serle Court
BRISBY John	4 Stone Buildings
COHEN Lawrence	24 Old Buildings
CRYSTAL Michael	3-4 South Square
HAPGOOD Mark	Brick Court Chambers
HOLLINGTON Robin	1 New Square
KNOWLES Robin	3-4 South Square
LYNDON-STANFORD Michael	13 Old Square
MANN Anthony	Enterprise Chambers
MOWSCHENSON Terence	Wilberforce Chambers
NEWMAN Catherine	13 Old Square
PURLE Charles	12 New Square
STEINFELD Alan	24 Old Buildings
VOS Geoffrey	3 Stone Buildings
WEATHERILL Bernard	3 New Square
NEW SILKS	
DICKER Robin	3-4 South Square
PHILLIPS Mark	3-4 South Square
SMITH Stephen	12 New Square

Numbers show recommended barristers in this practice area
For details of these leading barristers see Profiles on page 1473

Barristers' profiles 1473-1601

Erskine Chambers (Potts) "Quality through and through," with an enviable depth of knowledge across the board, and regarded as the specialist leading set "by far." **Robin Potts QC** is "utterly practical," "takes strong minded views and is usually proved right." Academically excellent, he is also considered to be a "ferocious litigator" who "can pull a point of law out of a hat and hit you with it." **David Richards QC** has ably filled the void left by the retirement of Sykes, and is "revered as charming and effective" and "commercially astute." **David Oliver QC** has made a "natural move" to this set (from 13 Old Square) and maintains his reputation as "quick-witted" and "a natural advocate" if a somewhat eccentric character. "Golden tongued," "a first rate performer" he is said to be best used when securing a point of principle is vital. Offering "constructive advice," **Michael Todd QC** has an excellent knowledge of technical issues such as schemes of arrangement and capital reductions and he "understands commercial pressures." The "personable" **Leslie Kosmin QC** offers "succinct advice," "bouncing ideas around, seeing problems from all angles." Highly rated for his work in unfair prejudice cases and seen as "incredibly bright," this is an "across the board litigator." The set has an impressive array of juniors. **David Chivers** is "exceptionally clear and helpful," "superb in an intellectual knockabout" and is said to be the set's "star junior." **John Cone** has "oodles of common sense," and "makes it all seem so easy." Less seen on contentious litigation, he is "a first-rate advisory and schemes man" where his experience and friendly manner has won a huge following amongst solicitors. **Richard Snowden** is a good litigator "eloquent" in court and favourite for his strong balance of advisory and advocacy skills. "Bright and energetic" **Martin Moore** is well respected for his work in the insurance field and is said to be "an immensely able technical man." **David Mabb** is "as straight as an arrow" with a "skilled insight into schemes of arrangement." The mainstay of the set's technical reputation is "the maestro" **Thomas Stockdale** who "is in a league of his own." He is used for the most complex schemes of arrangement "in preference to the silks." The "brilliant" **Mary Stokes** has grown in stature, offering "mature and sensible advice" with a strong grasp of technical issues and an "academic attitude." **Catherine Roberts** is "commercial" and "extremely bright." While peers occasionally find her "difficult," she is perceived by solicitors to be "always an asset." **Philip Gillyon** can be seen as "abrasive with his strident personality" but there is no doubting his high profile in company work with a "technical bent." **Dan Prentice** has a "fantastic" reputation for complex schemes of arrangement. A renowned Oxford academic, **Andrew Thompson** is recommended for his "clarity of advice" and his "efficient, constructive" rapport with solicitors and clients.

4 Stone Buildings (Heslop) A "pure corporate focus" which stands the set apart as second only to Erskine. Seen to have a stronger bias towards litigation, and a "smaller nucleus" packed with fine company barristers. **Philip Heslop QC** has a "heavyweight court presence," and is "a most distinguished, eloquent advocate." He is seen on the biggest cases (BAT, Maxwell) and is said to be admired by judges for his "clear concise advocacy skills." The "affable" **Robert Hildyard QC** is "user-friendly," a "smooth," "articulate advocate" presenting issues "with elegance rather than brute force." He is respected for his regulatory work (particularly in insurance) and is said to "know the ins and outs of company law." **Anthony Bompas QC** has a "gentle approach in court." He is a "quiet intellectual" and a great technician who retains the confidence both of his peers and instructing solicitors. Perceived as "more punchy and aggressive" than Bompas is **John Brisby QC** who "takes no prisoners" when in court. Said

LEADING JUNIORS • London	
❶ CHIVERS David	Erskine Chambers
CONE John	Erskine Chambers
SNOWDEN Richard	Erskine Chambers
❷ COLLINGS Matthew	13 Old Square
GIROLAMI Paul	13 Old Square
HOSER Philip	Serle Court
JOFFE Victor	Serle Court
MABB David	Erskine Chambers
MILES Robert	4 Stone Buildings
MOORE Martin	Erskine Chambers
NEWEY Guy	7 Stone Buildings
STOCKDALE Thomas	Erskine Chambers
STOKES Mary	Erskine Chambers
❸ ARDEN Peter	Enterprise Chambers
DAVIS-WHITE Malcolm	4 Stone Buildings
DE GARR ROBINSON Anthony	One Essex Court
GILLYON Philip	Erskine Chambers
GIRET Jane	11 Stone Buildings
GREEN Michael	Fountain Court
GRIFFITHS Peter	4 Stone Buildings
HARMAN Sarah	4 Stone Buildings
HARRISON Christopher	4 Stone Buildings
IFE Linden	Enterprise Chambers
MARSHALL Philip	Serle Court
PARKER Christopher	7 Stone Buildings
PRENTICE Dan	Erskine Chambers
RABINOWITZ Laurence	One Essex Court
RITCHIE Richard	24 Old Buildings
ROBERTS Catherine	Erskine Chambers
SHEKERDEMIAN Marcia	11 Stone Buildings
STEWART Lindsey	7 Stone Buildings
STUBBS Rebecca	13 Old Square
THOMPSON Andrew	Erskine Chambers
ZELIN Geoffrey	Enterprise Chambers

For details of these leading barristers see Profiles on page 1473

to be used for the most substantial cases when "teeth" are needed, he can be a "difficult opponent" and is admired for his "good eye for detail." Thought to be the leading junior of this set, **Robert Miles** is a "star," recommended for his big-ticket litigation. Back from Bermuda, he is considered a "high flyer" in company law. **Malcolm Davis-White** is recommended as strong litigator well regarded for his work on directors' disqualifications and for his advice to the Government. **Peter Griffiths** is a senior junior, a "personable advocate" recommended for his technical advisory work as well as a command of the court. **Sarah Harman** retains her reputation as "natural litigator with the right sort of punch." **Christopher Harrison** may undertake a mix of general commercial and company law, but retains his reputation as a "big case advocate."

13 Old Square (Lyndon-Stanford) A set renowned for its strong advocacy and developing a real corporate drive, despite the loss of David Oliver to Erskine Chambers. Head of Chambers **Michael Lyndon-Stanford QC** is an "old style litigator" and "punchy," and although some contemporaries find him overly aggressive, he "certainly knows his stuff." Like many in the set, he offers a traditional mix of company and commercial work. **Catherine Newman QC** is focusing increasingly on pure company work from a respectable bankruptcy base. She is a "serious talent" and holds a "solid" reputation in this market. The set has a "raft of outstanding" juniors coming through the ranks. **Matthew Collings** is "difficult to tangle with" and "fluent in court." He can be "a bit of a street fighter." **Paul Girolami** is also praised for his experience and is said to prefer litigation where he brings to bear his "cool and calming influence." Fellow barristers perceive that **Rebecca Stubbs** "will go far" with a good mix of advisory work and litigation. She is particularly recommended for her experience of directors' disqualification work for the DTI.

Serle Court (Neill) An active company set that cultivates "powerful litigators." **Michael Briggs QC** has "excellent presentation skills" and both colleagues and solicitors find his easy manner appealing. His "brilliant intellect" only adds to his "sparkling advocacy skills." Despite his absence from the London circuit, enforced by the Thyssen case currently being heard in Bermuda, **Alan Boyle QC** retains an outstanding reputation for his "technical excellence." Of the juniors **Philip Marshall** is gaining a fine reputation as a "fluent, challenging opponent" in court. His "aggressive" manner in court is tempered by "experience and maturity." **Victor Joffe** is well respected as a "good, dependable advocate" and retains his company bar reputation. **Philip Hoser** is seen to handle a mixture of company and commercial work, and is praised for his "clear, technical skills."

3-4 South Square (Crystal) A well regarded commercial set, often thought of for its insolvency specialism. Head of Chambers **Michael Crystal QC** is "very astute" and despite being another Bermuda based litigator for part of the year continues to be "highly prominent." **Robin Knowles QC** has a solid grasp of company bar issues and is building upon his "incisive academic approach" since taking silk last year. **Richard Adkins QC** is "universally admired," although peers feel his "insight and focus" could be aimed "more commercially." New Silk **Robin Dicker QC** is an "outstanding performer" and has a "precise eye for technical detail." **Mark Phillips QC,** also a new silk, is "bright and confident."

7 Stone Buildings (Aldous) A commercially effective set that is said to lack a pure company focus but blossoms with its skilled litigators. **Charles Aldous QC** is a "big case leader" with "tremendous stamina." "An energetic expert" he "fair" in court. **Nigel Davis QC** is from "an old-fashioned mould" though some find him "a little stuffy." Solicitors believe he "is a man with two brains" and admire his "practicality." **Guy Newey** has built a firm foundation with his Secretary of State work and focus on directors' disqualifications. **Christopher Parker** has a good reputation for company work, although it is seen to be based on a commercial/chancery mix. He is "hardworking and personable" and is respected for his presence in court. **Lindsey Stewart** is "effective" in court though is said to lack the technical focus to dominate pure company proceedings.

Enterprise Chambers (Mann) "A good, friendly set," said to lack the punch of our leaders due to the demands on the time of its only rated silk. "Energetic" **Anthony Mann QC** is "a leading light," and comes to court "thoroughly prepared and ready for battle." However he is said to be best used for non-technical matters. The juniors are similarly seen to undertake a broad range of commercial work, notably insolvency. **Geoffrey Zelin** has a "strong enthusiastic personality" and **Linden Ife** is in demand for her "forceful command of the court." **Peter Arden** is seen as the most technically minded of the set, and has "an outstanding intellect." "He can turn his hand to anything" and clients are said to admire his "personable diligence."

One Essex Court (Grabiner) Dominated by the superb reputation of its leading company silk **Liz Gloster QC**. Although this set produces a familiar mix of insolvency, commercial, chancery and banking work, it is made all the more prominent for its collective reputation for producing "stunning advocates." Gloster herself is "without question a star." "Commercially minded" she "can throw her weight around" in court and, while intimidating, is always "fairness personified." Senior junior **Laurence Rabinowitz** is a "major figure" although colleagues feel he may be moving away from the traditional M&A market. **Anthony De Garr Robinson** is well respected as a "natural performer" and "can hold his own" both in an advisory capacity and in court.

Other Notable Barristers New Silk **Stephen Smith QC** of **12 New Square** (Mowbray) is "extremely bright" and crucially, "knows which issues matter to a judge." At this set **Charles Purle QC** is well regarded as "an articulate advocate." **Bernard Weatherill QC** at **3 New Square** (Goodhart) is a firm favourite amongst his peers and although his work is felt to be "too varied to categorise" there can be no doubting his skill. **Geoffrey Vos QC**

of **3 Stone Buildings** (Vos) mixes his chancery work with "a good technical knowledge" of company law. He is joined in our ranks by **Edward Bannister QC** of the same set, who is "an old school litigator with a traditional manner." Some colleagues believe **Terence Mowschenson QC**'s move from away from One Essex Court to **Wilberforce Chambers** (Nugee) is said to indicate a greater focus on chancery work. He certainly retains admiration for his "excellent insight" and skill in dealing with contentious takeover proceedings. **Lawrence Cohen QC** of **24 Old Buildings** (Mann/Steinfeld) is best known for his asset recovery work in the BCCI case and although not thought a "mainstream" company man is recommended as "straight as a die." **Alan Steinfeld QC** (also **24 Old Buildings**) is "an astute lawyer," with "on the ball advocacy skills." **Robin Hollington QC** of **1 New Square** (Hamilton) is praised for his insurance scheme work, "knows the area well" and is popular with both clients and solicitors. **Mark Hapgood QC** of **Brick Court Chambers** (Clarke) is a "great performer" although his bias is said to lean more towards general commercial work. **Michael Green** of **Fountain Court** (Boswood) has a strong reputation due to his work on the Maxwell case, although his profile in this area has been less pronounced this year. **Jane Giret** of **11 Stone Buildings** (Rosen) is a "promising junior" praised for knowledge of s459 petitions. At this set, **Marcia Shekerdemian** is said to mix insolvency and corporate experiences with ease. **Richard Ritchie** of **24 Old Buildings** (Mann/Steinfeld) is not so highly visible considering the amount of time spent on Treasury work, but has a reputation as a "solid technical company man."

COMPETITION / ANTI-TRUST

RESEARCH: The rankings are based on in-depth interviews with over 5,000 solicitors and barristers in the UK. Chambers research is audited by the British Market Research Bureau (see page 7 for details).

Barristers' profiles 1473-1601

LONDON

LEADING SETS • London	QCs	Jnrs
❶ **Brick Court Chambers** (Christopher Clarke QC)	5	4
Monckton Chambers (John Swift QC)	7	3

Numbers show recommended barristers in this practice area

LEADING SILKS • London	
❶ ANDERSON David	Brick Court Chambers
FOWLER Richard	Monckton Chambers
GREEN Nicholas	Brick Court Chambers
SHARPE Thomas	One Essex Court
❷ LASOK Paul	Monckton Chambers
LEVER Jeremy	Monckton Chambers
PARKER Kenneth	Monckton Chambers
SWIFT John	Monckton Chambers
VAJDA Christopher	Monckton Chambers
❸ BARLING Gerald	Brick Court Chambers
ROTH Peter	Monckton Chambers
SHARPSTON Eleanor	4 Paper Buildings
VAUGHAN David	Brick Court Chambers
NEW SILKS	
LLOYD JONES David	Brick Court Chambers

For details of these leading barristers see Profiles on page 1473

LEADING JUNIORS • London	
❶ ROBERTSON Aidan	Brick Court Chambers
TURNER Jon	Monckton Chambers
❷ ANDERSON Rupert	Monckton Chambers
THOMPSON Rhodri	Matrix Chambers
WATSON Philippa	Essex Court Chambers
❸ BREALEY Mark	Brick Court Chambers
FLYNN James	Brick Court Chambers
PERETZ George	Monckton Chambers
RANDOLPH Fergus	Brick Court Chambers

For details of these leading barristers see Profiles on page 1473

Brick Court Chambers (Clarke) This powerful commercial set is considered to have "great depth and day-to-day experience" in competition matters. A premier group of EU lawyers has ensured chambers' representation on groundbreaking European cases. Members have recently been involved in cases in sport (Cardiff/WRU), broadcasting (Premier League/BSkyB), shipping, coal, air transport (easyJet/Go), chemicals and petrochemicals, cement, utilities and pharmaceuticals. Work includes pure competition (mergers and behavioural), inquiries (cars, supermarkets, Formula One,) public procurement and state aids. **Nicholas Green QC** is "effective in court" and "produces the goods." He is "the sort of lawyer who makes law," clients "trust his view" and he gives "serious opinions on complex issues." **David Anderson QC** is "brilliant." **David Vaughan QC** and **Gerald Barling QC** maintain their reputation, as does **David Lloyd Jones QC.** Nicholas Forwood QC is now a judge of the CFI in Luxembourg. The "popular" **Aidan Robertson** has made a name for himself as a leading junior, as has **Mark Brealey. Fergus Randolph** is "able" on EU-related court matters and **James Flynn** was recommended for state aid work.

Monckton Chambers (Swift) "They have the weight of numbers." "Superb" **Richard Fowler QC** "absorbs and manipulates information and produces wonderful documents." The respected **Jeremy Lever QC** has been busy since his return from retirement. **Peter Roth QC** is well regarded by solicitors and is ranked for the first time. The "bright" **Paul Lasok QC** is revered for his community law knowledge, and is "down to earth and forthright." **Christopher Vajda QC** is particularly well regarded for his administrative law skills at European level. **Kenneth Parker QC** "really knows his stuff." "Clients like" **John Swift QC,** who is back at the bar after five years as the first rail regulator. At junior level, **Jon Turner** is "exceptionally bright," "definitely a leader" and, in the opinion of some, "the best at the bar, superior to the silks." He is standing counsel to the Director General of Fair Trading. **Rupert Anderson** maintains his quality reputation, while **George Peretz,** who was at the OFT for six years, is "one to watch." Work covered has included Airtours/First Choice, C&W in reference to ntl/CWC, FA/Premier League/BSkyB/BBC (RPC), OFT in RPC concerning OTC branded medicines, BP v Commission, Arnhem v BFI Holding BV, Ladbroke v Commission, Gencor v Commission and AG v BPB and others.

Other Notable Barristers **Tom Sharpe QC** of **One Essex Court** (Grabiner) is considered to have an "amazing practice." "Clients love him" and most consider him to be "approachable and popular." **Eleanor Sharpston QC** of **4 Paper Buildings** (Ritchie), the Director of Studies in Law at King's College, Cambridge, maintains her leading reputation. **Philippa Watson** of **Essex Court Chambers** (Pollock) continues to have her supporters. At **Matrix Chambers** (Blake), the "tough" **Rhodri Thompson** is well regarded in competition matters.

CONSTRUCTION

RESEARCH: The rankings are based on in-depth interviews with over 5,000 solicitors and barristers in the UK. Chambers research is audited by the British Market Research Bureau (see page 7 for details).

OVERVIEW: The Construction table previously set out in last year's Energy Bar section has been consolidated into this section of the book. The two main sets, Atkin Chambers and Keating Chambers, dominate. Each set has its own fans and each has its critics. The many stars at both Atkin and Keating are felt to come at a price – a high one. There are also perceived difficulties over availability and, as a result, a number of solicitors will, out of preference, turn to one of the other smaller sets. In our research it is evident that solicitors do feel let down when they report "we had a change of counsel just before trial" or complain of those who have taken their instructions being "double, sometimes treble booked." That said, the lead that the two big players have over the other sets appears quite insurmountable.

LONDON

LEADING SETS • London	QCs	Jnrs
❶ Atkin Chambers (John Blackburn QC)	7	10
Keating Chambers (Richard Fernyhough QC)	11	9
❷ 4 Pump Court (Bruce Mauleverer QC)	3	4
❸ Crown Office Chambers (Spencer / Purchas)	3	1
39 Essex Street (Nigel Pleming QC)	2	1
❹ Four New Square (Justin Fenwick QC)	1	1
2 Temple Gardens (Dermod O'Brien QC)	1	1

Numbers show recommended barristers in this practice area

LEADING SILKS • London	
✪ RAMSEY Vivian	Keating Chambers
❶ AKENHEAD Robert	Atkin Chambers
BLACKBURN John	Atkin Chambers
FERNYHOUGH Richard	Keating Chambers
FURST Stephen	Keating Chambers
SLATER John	Crown Office Chambers
WHITE Andrew	Atkin Chambers
❷ BAATZ Nicholas	Atkin Chambers
DARLING Paul	Keating Chambers
DENNYS Nicholas	Atkin Chambers
MARRIN John	Keating Chambers
MAULEVERER Bruce	4 Pump Court
TER HAAR Roger	Crown Office Chambers
UFF John	Keating Chambers
WILMOT-SMITH Richard	39 Essex Street
❸ BARTLETT Andrew	Crown Office Chambers
BOULDING Philip	Keating Chambers
ELLIOTT Timothy	Keating Chambers
FRIEDMAN David	4 Pump Court
GRAY Richard	39 Essex Street
THOMAS Christopher	Keating Chambers
TWIGG Patrick	2 Temple Gardens
❹ ACTON DAVIS Jonathan	Atkin Chambers
FENWICK Justin	Four New Square
GAITSKELL Robert	Keating Chambers
NEW SILKS	
BOWDERY Martin	Atkin Chambers
NICHOLSON Jeremy	4 Pump Court
TAVERNER Marcus	Keating Chambers

For details of these leading barristers see Profiles on page 1473

Barristers' profiles 1473-1601

Atkin Chambers (Blackburn) **Robert Akenhead QC** is "an unusual combination - he clearly reads the papers and deals with detail, but at the same time he's got the ability to look at the big picture." "Superb" **John Blackburn QC** is very much "back in the saddle" after some down time. "A strong choice for dispute resolution," **Andrew White QC** is a "fine advocate of his clients' cause." "Tough operator" **Nicholas Baatz QC** "knows his stuff inside out." The volume of warm feedback he has received has rocketed him up the silks' table. "A great thinker," **Nicholas Dennys QC** is "good on difficult interpretation." **Jonathan Acton Davis QC** has moved to the set from 4 Pump Court. **Martin Bowdery QC** is newly clothed in silk. Instructing solicitors like him because he's "unflappable and a quiet authority – never one to bang the table." Other barristers regret having to be against **David Streatfeild-James.** He gets on top of a case "efficiently and smoothly," getting to grips with technical detail. **Stephanie Barwise** receives praise for her "level of responsiveness." "She gets things back quickly and thoroughly." Solicitors like the approach of **Stephen Dennison.** He's "forthright, thorough and user-friendly." Lay clients think he's "smashing." **Andrew Burr** has a "good empathy with clients." "Affable and able" **Delia Dumaresq** enters the juniors' table this year. She delivers "considerable expertise" with a "flamboyant style." **Peter Fraser** and **Andrew Goddard** receive recommendation. One of **Simon Lofthouse**'s strong points is his accessibility. "If you have an issue, you can pick up the phone and talk to him very quickly." **Mark Raeside** "devotes his time properly and delivers on advocacy." **Fiona Parkin** has impressed with her diligence and competence.

Keating Chambers (Fernyhough) "Everyone's hero," **Vivian Ramsey QC** is a dual qualified engineer and barrister who "brings a lot of experience to bear." He "puts himself out, even when he's busy," and he's "extremely busy." "Senior statesman" **Richard Fernyhough QC** is "exceptionally good fun to work with." "He's a brilliant advocate and reads the papers." "Sound and thoughtful" **Stephen Furst QC**, whilst "not the most relaxed of advocates," is highly rated because "his judgement is uncannily accurate." There are more than a handful of instructing solicitors who are "enormously fond" of "maverick performer" **Paul Darling QC.** He's "a horse for a course" some think, whilst others refer to him as "a top court performer and a master of the brief." He can, reputedly, "argue the unarguable outrageously." Subtlety, focus and incisiveness are the hallmarks of **John Marrin QC.** Solicitors refer to his "aura of brilliance" and speak of him being "clever in an otherworldly sense." It's difficult to assess **John Uff QC** in a pure construction section. For arbitration, his main activity, he is in a class of his own and he commands an unbelievable amount of respect from practitioners. **Philip Boulding QC** has spent quite a lot of time in Hong Kong of late. He's described as "robust and bright" and "a real brickie." **Timothy Elliott QC** shows great concern for his cases. **Christopher Thomas QC** is recommended. You'll "get advice straight off" from **Robert Gaitskell QC**, who comes with an electrical engineering background and is there on the technical detail. A very popular welcome to the new silks table for **Marcus Taverner QC.** What makes him so popular? He's got "spirit and fight – he's innovative." "His interest in the details makes him stand out. He really wants to understand things." **Peter Coulson** receives plenty of support for his advocacy. **Nerys Jefford** is liked very much; "she's bloody good." Solicitors have "bags of time" for **Finola O'Farrell**, who's "first class" for tenacity. **Adrian Williamson**'s best asset is his "ability to deal with a huge quantity of different issues and settle on the ones which matter. He knows how to explain complicated issues simply." "A good person to go for when you need someone to apply his brain" is **Alexander Nissen**. He's "quiet but thorough and businesslike," although he can "err a bit on the negative side." **Louise Randall** is known to be "very positive and direct – she doesn't sit on the fence." **Michael Bowsher** is newly recommended and seen to be especially good on procurement issues. "Rising star" **Simon Hargreaves** is "doing very very well." **Ian Pennicott** completes the round-up for the set.

4 Pump Court (Mauleverer) Voluminous praise for **Bruce Mauleverer QC** ("stunning on detail; lovely manner with clients.") "He's always thoroughly prepared for conference and sends you pre-conference notes. He has a mind like a steel trap." Chairman of Tech Bar, **David Friedman QC** is "clever, organised" and "he gets the answer." In the same vein, new silk **Jeremy Nicholson QC** displays "thoroughness and attention to detail. He's very dedicated and gets on with it." **Adrian Hughes** is recommended along with **Marc Rowlands** ("good fun – bright.") **David Sears** enters the rankings this year. He's "polished, well prepared and thorough" and has "good presence and charisma." Up and coming **Sean Brannigan** shows "energy and imagination."

Crown Office Chambers (Spencer/Purchas) **John Slater QC** gets an "excellent" rating from lay clients. "His great strength is advocacy." **Roger ter Haar QC** "has the ear of the court" and "works hand in glove" with fellow counsel. Fellow silk **Andrew Bartlett QC** is a long-standing favourite. Although quite "dry," he "covers all the details and has a fantastic grasp of matters." Busy **Jane Davies** is "quick, efficient and client friendly with a good sense of humour."

39 Essex Street (Pleming) Solicitors told us that clients love **Richard Wilmot-Smith QC.** And so they do. One commented that they particularly liked the way he "converted his thoughts very quickly into action." **Richard Gray QC**, who's "so relaxed s," gives "sensible and practical advice." For **Stuart Catchpole**, as ever, we received feedback so warm one nearly breaks out into a sweat. Solicitors say he's "most unusual; self effacing, modest and a solicitor's dream."

Four New Square (Fenwick) The "very able" and multi-talented **Justin Fenwick QC** is recommended again this year. From the juniors at the set, **Roger Stewart** received most feedback.

LEADING JUNIORS • London		
❶	COULSON Peter	Keating Chambers
	JEFFORD Nerys	Keating Chambers
	O'FARRELL Finola	Keating Chambers
	STREATFEILD-JAMES David	Atkin Chambers
	WILLIAMSON Adrian	Keating Chambers
❷	BARWISE Stephanie	Atkin Chambers
	CATCHPOLE Stuart	39 Essex Street
	DENNISON Stephen	Atkin Chambers
	NISSEN Alexander	Keating Chambers
	RANDALL Louise	Keating Chambers
	STEWART Roger	Four New Square
❸	BURR Andrew	Atkin Chambers
	DAVIES Jane	Crown Office Chambers
	THOMAS David	2 Temple Gardens
❹	BOWSHER Michael	Keating Chambers
	DUMARESQ Delia	Atkin Chambers
	FRASER Peter	Atkin Chambers
	GODDARD Andrew	Atkin Chambers
	HARGREAVES Simon	Keating Chambers
	HUGHES Adrian	4 Pump Court
	LOFTHOUSE Simon	Atkin Chambers
	PENNICOTT Ian	Keating Chambers
	PLANTEROSE Rowan	Littman Chambers
	RAESIDE Mark	Atkin Chambers
	REED Paul	Hardwicke Building
	ROWLANDS Marc	4 Pump Court
	SEARS David	4 Pump Court
UP AND COMING		
	BRANNIGAN Sean	4 Pump Court
	PARKIN Fiona	Atkin Chambers

For details of these leading barristers see Profiles on page 1473

2 Temple Gardens (O'Brien) "Excellent" **Patrick Twigg QC** has a great deal of experience. "Authoritative" **David Thomas** shows "sound commercial judgement."

Other Notable Barristers **Rowan Planterose** at **Littman Chambers** (Littman) and **Paul Reed** at **Hardwicke Building** (Aylen) both received continued recommendation.

CONSUMER LAW

RESEARCH: The rankings are based on in-depth interviews with over 5,000 solicitors and barristers in the UK. Chambers research is audited by the British Market Research Bureau (see page 7 for details).

OVERVIEW: Split broadly into the two main categories of consumer credit and food law, consumer law is still considered a niche area of practice. As far as food law is concerned, the bar is probably engaged a little less than in other areas of practice, as many food law solicitors prefer to carry out their own advocacy themselves. Commentators have noticed that prosecution is fast becoming a first resort, and that the volume of prosecution work is consequently growing.

LONDON

LEADING SETS • London	QCs	Jnrs
❶ **Gough Square Chambers** (Fred Philpott)	-	5
❷ **2-3 Gray's Inn Square** (Anthony Scrivener QC)	1	1

Numbers show recommended barristers in this practice area

LEADING SILKS • London	
❶ **GOODE Roy**	Blackstone Chambers
SCRIVENER Anthony	2-3 Gray's Inn Square
❷ **GOODHART William**	3 New Square
NEW SILKS	
DE HAAN Kevin	3 Raymond Buildings

For details of these leading barristers see Profiles on page 1473

LEADING JUNIORS • London	
❶ **PHILPOTT Fred**	Gough Square Chambers
❷ **ANDREWS Claire**	Gough Square Chambers
HIBBERT William	Gough Square Chambers
STEPHENSON Geoffrey	2-3 Gray's Inn Square
❸ **SAYER Peter**	Gough Square Chambers
SCHOLZ Karl	3 Temple Gardens
SMITH Julia	Gough Square Chambers

For details of these leading barristers see Profiles on page 1473

Gough Square Chambers (Philpott) Widely regarded as "a top-class" set and the "only chambers that offers strength in depth," the barristers here are "very down to earth, very bright," and know how to "get on with things." Consumer law makes up about 95% of the practice, and the set is split evenly into those barristers that specialise in consumer credit, those that are primarily involved in food law, and those that do a bit of both. Again and again in our research it was referred to as "the only place to go" for consumer law. "Robust" **Fred Philpott** ("exceptionally good, practical, a very good lawyer and a very good advocate") has been involved in a couple of salmonella cases and a judicial review involving the importation of tiger prawns and the markings on them this year. He is generally regarded as "down to earth and approachable," and someone who is always prepared to "put himself out for the client." Food specialist **Claire Andrews** "knows her stuff" and, though perceived by some as "better on paper than she is on her feet," is a well-regarded practitioner in the field. **William Hibbert** has also been making a name for himself, especially in the areas of consumer credit, consumer protection and trading standards. **Peter Sayer** and **Julia Smith** both have considerable expertise in matters relating to consumer credit.

2-3 Gray's Inn Square (Scrivener) "Superb" **Anthony Scrivener QC** is "charm personified." Primarily a defence lawyer and generally recognised to be an excellent advocate, he has been involved in a couple of high-profile food labelling and food advertising cases this year. Junior **Geoffrey Stephenson** is another member of this versatile set to rank "pretty well at the top."

Barristers' profiles 1473-1601

Other Notable Barristers "Mr Consumer Credit" **Roy Goode QC** at **Blackstone Chambers** (Baxendale/Flint) has a new book out this year, entitled 'Roy Goode on Consumer Credit.' More of an academic than an advocate, he possesses unrivalled expertise in this area. A new entry to our table, "practical" **William Goodhart QC** at **3 New Square** (Goodhart) "knows consumer credit inside out." **Kevin de Haan QC** of **3 Raymond Buildings** (Nicholls) a newly appointed silk this year, is generally considered "lightning fast on his feet." **Karl Scholz** of **3 Temple Gardens** (Coffey) is "definitely a name" in this area of practice.

WESTERN CIRCUIT

LEADING SILKS • Western	
❶ **GIBBONS Jeremy**	17 Carlton Crescent

For details of these leading barristers see Profiles on page 1473

LEADING JUNIORS • Western	
❶ **GIBNEY Malcolm**	17 Carlton Crescent
HAGGAN Nicholas	17 Carlton Crescent

For details of these leading barristers see Profiles on page 1473

At **17 Carlton Crescent** (Gibbons) **Jeremy Gibbons QC, Nicholas Haggan** and **Malcolm Gibney** are all considered accomplished performers.

WALES & CHESTER CIRCUIT

LEADING SILKS • Wales & Chester	
❶ **SPENCER Robin**	Sedan House

For details of these leading barristers see Profiles on page 1473

Robin Spencer QC of **Sedan House** (Lewis-Jones) is a formidable prosecutor with a good deal of experience in this area. He has recently been involved in a case against Nestlé concerning allegations made against their 'healthy heart' campaign.

MIDLANDS & OXFORD CIRCUIT

LEADING JUNIORS • Midlands & Oxford	
❶ **BERLIN Barry**	St. Ive's Chambers
TRAVERS David	3 Fountain Court

For details of these leading barristers see Profiles on page 1473

David Travers of **3 Fountain Court** (Treacy) ("very down to earth, very client friendly, knows his stuff, a good advocate") is widely recognised to do "the full gamut of regulatory work." **Barry Berlin** at **St Ive's Chambers** (Coke) was also well-received.

CRIME

RESEARCH: The rankings are based on in-depth interviews with over 5,000 solicitors and barristers in the UK. Chambers research is audited by the British Market Research Bureau (see page 7 for details).

Barristers' profiles 1473-1601

LONDON

LEADING SETS • London		QCs	Jnrs
❶	**2 Bedford Row** (William Clegg QC)	5	10
	Doughty Street Chambers (Geoffrey Robertson QC)	8	4
	6 King's Bench Walk (Michael Worsley QC)	6	9
	Queen Elizabeth Building (Bevan/Whiteman)	6	5
	3 Raymond Buildings (Clive Nicholls QC)	6	3
	18 Red Lion Court (Anthony Arlidge QC)	9	-
❷	**7 Bedford Row** (David Farrer QC)	4	-
	Two Garden Court (Macdonald/Davies)	3	4
	3 Gray's Inn Square (Rock Tansey QC)	4	6
	1 Hare Court (Stephen Kramer QC)	4	7
	Matrix Chambers (Nicholas Blake QC)	4	1
❸	**Furnival Chambers** (Andrew Mitchell QC)	3	3
	2 Harcourt Buildings (Atkinson/Bevan)	3	3
	2-4 Tudor Street (Richard Ferguson QC)	3	4
❹	**9-12 Bell Yard** (D. Anthony Evans QC)	2	5
	Cloisters (Laura Cox QC)	2	3
	23 Essex Street (Michael Lawson QC)	5	2
	5 Paper Buildings (Carey/Caplan)	3	1
❺	**10 King's Bench Walk** (Georges Khayat QC)	3	2
	1 Middle Temple Lane (Dines/Trollope)	1	3
	3 Temple Gardens (Jonathan Goldberg QC)	2	2
	14 Tooks Court (Michael Mansfield QC)	2	1

Numbers show recommended barristers in this practice area

2 Bedford Row (Clegg) "Rumpole-type" **William Clegg QC** "carries a great deal of gravitas" into the court-room. His "old world charm" is said to appeal particularly to the jury. The "superb" **Trevor Burke,** a new acquisition from 10 King's Bench Walk, "gets excellent results" in his defence of sports and entertainment celebrities. **Nigel Lithman QC** is a "good trial advocate" who "doesn't mind sticking his neck out." **Andrew Munday QC, Philip Hackett QC** and **Howard Godfrey QC** also remain highly rated. "Eloquent" **James Sturman** "leaves no stone unturned" while **Brian Altman** was recommended for his work as Treasury Counsel. Senior junior **Mark Milliken-Smith** also received widespread commendation.

Doughty Street Chambers (Robertson) **Peter Thornton QC** and **Geoffrey Robertson QC** were both recommended as accomplished advocates. **Edward Fitzgerald QC** divides his practice between criminal and public law but received tremendous praise as a "brain on legs" who "knows the court of appeal inside out." **Edward Rees QC** "brings passion to his cross-examinations." **James Wood QC** "an all rounder who takes great care with his paperwork" has established a busy practice as silk and moves up in the tables. Of the more experienced silks, **Christopher Sallon QC, Helena Kennedy QC,** and **Michael Grieve QC** retain their places in the rankings. Particularly highly regarded juniors include **Jill Evans, Andrew Hall, Kieran Maidment,** and **Keir Starmer.**

6 King's Bench Walk (Worsley) "Brilliant tactician" **Roy Amlot QC**'s "relaxed charisma" serves him well as an advocate. **Mark Dennis** ("one of the best treasury counsel") and "extremely able" **Nicholas Hilliard** feature at the top of our juniors tables, as does "red hot" **David Perry** whose "easy-going" manner makes him a popular choice. The set contains a

LEADING SILKS • London				
✪	**AMLOT Roy** 6 King's Bench Walk	**ARLIDGE Anthony** 18 Red Lion Court	**BATTEN Stephen** 3 Raymond Buildings	**CLEGG William** 2 Bedford Row
	FULFORD Adrian 14 Tooks Court	**LAWSON Edmund** 9-12 Bell Yard	**MANSFIELD Michael** 14 Tooks Court	**MONTGOMERY Clare** Matrix Chambers
	ROBERTS Jeremy 9 Gough Square			
❶	**BEVAN Julian** Queen Elizabeth Building	**BLUNT Oliver** Furnival Chambers	**FERGUSON Richard** 2-4 Tudor Street	**HESLOP Martin** 1 Hare Court
	JONES Alun 3 Raymond Buildings	**MACDONALD Kenneth** Matrix Chambers	**PRICE Nicholas** 3 Raymond Buildings	**ROBERTSON Geoffrey** Doughty Chambers
	TANSEY Rock 3 Gray's Inn Square	**THORNTON Peter** Doughty Street Chambers	**THWAITES Ronald** Ely Place Chambers	**TROLLOPE Andrew** 1 Middle Temple Lane
❷	**COWARD Stephen** 7 Bedford Row	**FEINBERG Peter** 2-4 Tudor Street	**FITZGERALD Edward** Doughty Street Chambers	**GLASS Anthony** Queen Elizabeth Building
	GOLDBERG Jonathan 3 Temple Gardens	**GREENBERG Joanna** 3 Temple Gardens	**NICHOLLS Clive** 3 Raymond Buildings	**NUTTING John** 3 Raymond Buildings
	PURNELL Nicholas 23 Essex Street	**RUMFITT Nigel** 7 Bedford Row	**SALLON Christopher** Doughty Street Chambers	**SCRIVENER Anthony** 2-3 Gray's Inn Square
	SEABROOK Robert 1 Crown Office Row	**TEMPLE Victor** 6 King's Bench Walk	**WHITEHOUSE David** 3 Raymond Buildings	
❸	**ATKINSON Nicholas** 2 Harcourt Buildings	**AUSTIN-SMITH Michael** 23 Essex Street	**BARNES Timothy** 7 Bedford Row	**EVANS Anthony** 9-12 Bell Yard
	FARRER David 7 Bedford Row	**FISHER David** 6 King's Bench Walk	**HILL Michael** 23 Essex Street	**LANGDALE Timothy** Queen Elizabeth Building
	LOVELL-PANK Dorian 6 King's Bench Walk	**MACDONALD Ian** Two Garden Court	**MALLALIEU Ann** 6 King's Bench Walk	**O'CONNOR Patrick** 2-4 Tudor Street
	RAGGATT Timothy 4 King's Bench Walk	**SHAW Antony** 18 Red Lion Court		
❹	**BATE David** Queen Elizabeth Building	**CAPLAN Jonathan** 5 Paper Buildings	**CASSEL Timothy** 5 Paper Buildings	**DE SILVA Desmond** 2 Paper Buildings
	GRINDROD Helen 95A Chancery Lane	**KAY Steven** 3 Gray's Inn Square	**KENNEDY Helena** Doughty Street Chambers	**LAWSON Michael** 23 Essex Street
	LEDERMAN David 18 Red Lion Court	**LEIGH Christopher** 1 Paper Buildings	**LISSACK Richard** 35 Essex Street	**LITHMAN Nigel** 2 Bedford Row
	MUNDAY Andrew 2 Bedford Row	**REES Edward** Doughty Street Chambers		
❺	**BEVAN John** 2 Harcourt Buildings	**CARTER Peter** 18 Red Lion Court	**EDWARDS Susan** 23 Essex Street	**GODFREY Howard** 2 Bedford Row
	GREY Robin Queen Elizabeth Building	**GRIEVE Michael** Doughty Street Chambers	**GRIFFITHS Courtenay** Two Garden Court	**HACKETT Philip** 2 Bedford Row
	HIGGS Brian 5 King's Bench Walk	**KHAYAT Georges** 10 King's Bench Walk	**KRAMER Stephen** 1 Hare Court	**LESLIE Stephen** Furnival Chambers
	LYNCH Patricia 18 Red Lion Court	**MYLNE Nigel** 2 Harcourt Buildings	**PERRY John** 3 Gray's Inn Square	**SAYERS Michael** 2 King's Bench Walk
	STERN Linda 18 Red Lion Court	**SUTTON Richard** 18 Red Lion Court		
❺	**BLACK John** 18 Red Lion Court	**CARTER-STEPHENSON George** 3 Gray's Inn Square	**DAVIES Owen** Two Garden Court	**ETHERINGTON David** 18 Red Lion Court
	LEONARD Anthony 6 King's Bench Walk	**MITCHELL Andrew** Furnival Chambers	**WATERS David** 1 Hare Court	**WOOD James** Doughty Street Chambers
NEW SILKS				
	BORRELLI Michael 1 Middle Temple Lane	**BRIGHT Andrew** 9 Bedford Row	**EMMERSON Ben** Matrix Chambers	**JENKINS Edward** 5 Paper Buildings
	KELSEY-FRY John Queen Elizabeth Building	**LYNCH Jerome** Cardinal Chambers	**OWEN Tim** Matrix Chambers	**RADCLIFFE Andrew** 1 Hare Court
	RYDER John 6 King's Bench Walk	**SWEENEY Nigel** 6 King's Bench Walk	**WASS Sasha** 6 King's Bench Walk	**WOLKIND Michael** 2 Bedford Row

For details of these leading barristers see Profiles on page 1473

LEADING JUNIORS • London				
✪	BURKE Trevor 2 Bedford Row	CHAWLA Mukul 9-12 Bell Yard	DENNIS Mark 6 King's Bench Walk	HILLIARD Nicholas 6 King's Bench Walk
	PERRY David 6 King's Bench Walk	POWNALL Orlando 1 Hare Court	STURMAN James 2 Bedford Row	
❶	ALTMAN Brian 2 Bedford Row	BLAXLAND Henry Two Garden Court	BOYCE William Queen Elizabeth Building	DEIN Jeremy 3 Gray's Inn Square
	ELLISON Mark Queen Elizabeth Building	JENNINGS Anthony Matrix Chambers	LAIDLAW Jonathan 1 Hare Court	LORAINE-SMITH Nicholas 2 Harcourt Buildings
	MILLIKEN-SMITH Mark 2 Bedford Row	TURNER Michael Cloisters	WHITTAM Richard Furnival Chambers	
❷	BARRETT Penelope 3 Gray's Inn Square	BENSON Jeremy 1 Hare Court	CONWAY Charles 2 Bedford Row	EISSA Adrian Two Garden Court
	EVANS Jill Doughty Street Chambers	FEDER Ami Lamb Building	GARDINER Nicholas 1 Middle Temple Lane	GIBBS Patrick 2 Harcourt Buildings
	HORWELL Richard Queen Elizabeth Building	JANNER Daniel 23 Essex Street	KHALIL Karim 1 Paper Buildings	LODDER Peter 2 Bedford Row
	LUCAS Noel 1 Middle Temple Lane	MARTIN-SPERRY David 2-4 Tudor Street	NATHAN David 10 King's Bench Walk	PRICE Roderick Cloisters
	REES Gareth Queen Elizabeth Building	TURNER Jonathan 6 King's Bench Walk		
❸	BOURNE Ian 3 Temple Gardens	ELLIS Diana 3 Gray's Inn Square	FORTSON Rudi 3 Gray's Inn Square	JAFFA Ronald 3 Gray's Inn Square
	JAFFERJEE Aftab 2 Harcourt Buildings	LEWIS James 3 Raymond Buildings	MILLETT Kenneth 1 Hare Court	MOORE Miranda 5 Paper Buildings
	OWEN Tudor 9-12 Bell Yard	TAYLOR Martin 6 King's Bench Walk	WINBERG Stephen 2-4 Tudor Street	
❹	ABELL Anthony 2 Bedford Row	BANKS Robert 100E Great Portland Street	BECK James 2-4 Tudor Street	BENNETT-JENKINS Sallie 1 Hare Court
	CAUDLE John 2 Bedford Row	HALL Andrew Doughty Street Chambers	JOYCE Michael 9 Gough Square	LEIST Ian 1 Hare Court
	LEVY Michael 2 Bedford Row	LLOYD-ELEY Andrew 1 Hare Court	MALCOLM Helen 3 Raymond Buildings	MATTHEWS Richard 2 Bedford Row
	REILLY John 14 Tooks Court	SAUNDERS Neil 3 Raymond Buildings		
❺	ARMSTRONG Dean 6 King's Bench Walk	BARRACLOUGH Nicholas Francis Taylor Building	BRISCOE Constance 9-12 Bell Yard	BRYANT-HERON Mark 9-12 Bell Yard
	CAUSER John 23 Essex Street	CHRISTIE Richard 2 Pump Court	COOPER John 3 Gray's Inn Square	DUNN-SHAW Jason 6 King's Bench Walk
	EDIE Alastair Two Garden Court	ENGLAND William 2-4 Tudor Street	HARWOOD-STEVENSON John 9-12 Bell Yard	HENRY Annette 10 King's Bench Walk
	LANDSBURY Alan 6 Gray's Inn Square	LEWIS Raymond 2 Paper Buildings	MAIDMENT Kieran Doughty Street Chambers	OWEN-JONES David 3 Temple Gardens
	PEARCE Ivan Furnival Chambers	PEART Icah Two Garden Court	REED Piers 3 Temple Gardens	RYDER Matthew Cloisters
	SCOBIE James Francis Taylor Building	SHEPHERD Nigel 2 Paper Buildings	STARMER Keir Doughty Street Chambers	STRUDWICK Linda Queen Elizabeth Building
	SWAIN Jon Furnival Chambers	VINE James Hardwicke Building		

For details of these leading barristers see Profiles on page 1473

number of newly appointed silks, including **John Ryder QC**, **Nigel Sweeney QC**, and **Sasha Wass QC**.

Queen Elizabeth Building (Bevan/Whiteman) "Silver-tongued" **Julian Bevan QC** is well known for his work prosecuting Kenneth Noye. **William Boyce** is "prepared to roll his sleeves up and do the work" and was particularly commended for his detailed paperwork. **Mark Ellison** was rated by peers for his work on the treasury counsel. New silk **John Kelsey-Fry QC** is expected to be a "major player" in the field based on his "outstanding" performance as a junior.

3 Raymond Buildings (Nicholls) Set contains a number of highly regarded silks. **Stephen Batten QC**, the "Rolls-Royce" of the criminal world, demonstrated "a huge amount of style" in his defence of Kenneth Noye. **Alun Jones QC** has made his name with high profile extradition cases. **Nicholas Price QC, Clive Nicholls QC**, **David Whitehouse QC** and **John Nutting QC** also received general recommendation.

18 Red Lion Court (Arlidge) A "talented and expanding" set led by the venerable **Anthony Arlidge QC** who recently represented a Newcastle doctor in a euthanasia case. "Precise" **Peter Carter QC** "doesn't waste a word," while **David Etherington QC** was rated by solicitors as a young silk with a "promising future ahead of him." Ranked individuals **David Lederman QC** and **Richard Sutton QC** both maintain busy criminal practices.

7 Bedford Row (Farrer) Active on the London, Midlands and Oxford, and South Eastern Circuit, the set contains four recommended silks: **Stephen Coward QC, Nigel Rumfitt QC, Timothy Barnes QC,** and **David Farrer QC.** Chambers has been involved in a number of high profile cases over the past year involving sex-related crimes, fraud, and child cruelty. Acted for foster parents the Bramleys, who fled with their children after social workers questioned their suitability as guardians.

Two Garden Court (MacDonald/Davies) Chambers led by highly respected **Ian Macdonald QC** maintains its reputation for criminal work despite defections to Matrix chambers. **Owen Davies QC** brings a "wealth of experience" to criminal work. "Charming" **Courtenay Griffiths QC** " has the ability to deal well with sensitive cases." Juniors **Henry Blaxland, Adrian Eissa, Alastair Edie,** and **Icah Peart** all rate highly.

3 Gray's Inn Square (Tansey) **Rock Tansey QC**, "a master tactician" is "fearless in the appellate court." **Steven Kay QC** is best known for his international criminal law work. Although still a relatively new silk, **George Carter-Stephenson QC** was highly recommended for big drugs cases. Juniors **Jeremy Dein** and **Penelope Barrett** are both reputed to have devoloping practices.

1 Hare Court (Kramer) Chambers commended for a range of criminal practitioners of varying experience. "Super league" **Martin Heslop QC** "has an incredible grasp of detail." **Stephen Kramer QC** and **David Waters QC** were both rated as "excellent" by solicitors and fellow barristers. **Andrew Radcliffe QC** enters the list as a new silk. Juniors **Jonathan Laidlaw, Orlando Pownall** and **Sallie Bennett-Jenkins** were all noted for their work as Treasury Counsel.

Matrix Chambers (Blake) This newly formed set with a human rights slant has acquired the highly esteemed **Clare Montgomery QC**, "a fantastic jury performer with a razor-sharp mind." **Kenneth Macdonald QC** "a thorough jury man," was highly rated by both peers and clients. Recently appointed silk, **Ben Emmerson QC**, specialises in the civil liberties aspect of criminal work and was said to exhibit a "genuine interest in his clients and the case." **Tim Owen QC** also features in our list of new silks. **Anthony Jennings** is the set's ranked junior.

Furnival Chambers (Mitchell) "Able" **Oliver Blunt QC** covers the general range of criminal work. Chambers leader, **Andrew Mitchell QC** recently represented the Government of Canada and Attorney General in Turks & Caicos Islands in relation to restraint and production orders. "Industrious" **Stephen Leslie QC** recently joined the set and is highly accomplished in a range of complex fraud and murder cases. "Astute" **Richard Whittam** serves a junior Treasury Counsel in the Old Bailey. **Ivan Pearce** and **Jon Swain** also feature as highly regarded juniors.

2 Harcourt Buildings (Atkinson/Bevan) **Nicholas Atkinson QC** was recommended as a "brilliant jury advocate." **John Bevan QC** concentrates primarily on criminal prosecutions and recently prosecuted art forger John Drewe. **Nigel Mylne QC** has given up the position of chambers head, but retains an active criminal caseload. "Brilliant" **Nicholas Loraine-Smith** "has a wonderful touch as a prosecutor." Juniors **Patrick Gibbs** and **Aftab Jafferjee** were also recommended.

2-4 Tudor Street (Ferguson) A predominantly defence set covering general crime, prisoners rights, and criminal legal aid taxations. **Richard Ferguson QC** is an "unflustered silk" who "can deal with the most difficult client." **Peter Feinberg QC** has a first-class reputation, while the "superb"

Patrick O'Connor QC has a "marvellous legal brain" and handles a lot of high profile prisoners' rights cases in the court of appeal. The "quixotic" **David Martin-Sperry** was rated for his work in police corruption cases.

Other Notable Barristers Although his reputation is largely built on his fraud work, "phenomenally clever" **Edmund Lawson QC** at **9-12 Bell Yard** (Evans) remains a high profile silk for his criminal work in the Lawrence and Bloody Sunday Inquiries. **Mukul Chawla** of the same chambers rises in the tables upon general recommendation and was particularly noted for his detailed preparation. At **14 Tooks Court** (Mansfield), **Michael Mansfield QC** ("in a class of his own") has become a "celebrity" in his own right for his work on numerous high profile cases. **Adrian Fulford QC** "radiates integrity." His relaxed but precise manner of cross-examination means that "the witness doesn't know when he's left the stand that he's done for." A "silk's silk," **Jeremy Roberts QC** of **9 Gough Square** (Roberts) exercises "muscular judgement" in prosecuting and defending high profile criminal charges. Newly appointed silks include **Andrew Bright QC** of **4 Brick Court** (Berry) and **Jerome Lynch QC** who is leaving Cloisters to join **Cardinal Chambers**. Also at Cloisters, "impressive" **Michael Turner** was rated as a top-ranking junior for his thoroughness and dedication to general criminal work. The "tenacious" **Ronald Thwaites QC** belongs to the "fearless school of advocacy." At the time of writing, he has just established a new set, **Ely Place Chambers**. **Andrew Trollope QC** of **1 Middle Temple Lane** (Dines/Trollope) is well known for his work in complex drug and fraud cases, while his colleague, the "outstanding" new silk **Michael Borrelli QC** recently acted in the Stansted hijacking case.

SOUTH EASTERN & EAST ANGLIAN CIRCUITS

LEADING JUNIORS • South Eastern		
❶	AYERS Guy	Octagon House Chambers
	CLARE Michael	Octagon House Chambers
UP AND COMING		
	OLIVER Andrew	Octagon House Chambers

For details of these leading barristers see Profiles on page 1473

At **Octagon House** (Ayers/Lindqvist), **Guy Ayers** "gets stuck in when necessary and gives straightforward advice." "Forthright" **Michael Clare** is best known for "robust defence work."**Andrew Oliver** was rated an up and coming player by local solicitors.

WESTERN CIRCUIT

LEADING SILKS • Western		
❶	BARTON Charles	Albion Chambers
	ROYCE John	Guildhall Chambers
❷	DENYER Roderick	St John's Chambers
	DUNKELS Paul	Walnut House
	GILBERT Francis	Walnut House
	PASCOE Nigel	Pump Court Chambers
	TABOR James	Albion Chambers
❸	FORD Neil	Albion Chambers
	GLEN Ian	Guildhall Chambers
	JENKINS Alun	Queen Square Chambers
NEW SILKS		
	MEEKE Martin	Colleton Chambers

For details of these leading barristers see Profiles on page 1473

LEADING JUNIORS • Western		
❶	HORTON Mark	Colleton Chambers
	LAMBERT Julian	Albion Chambers
	MERCER Geoffrey	Walnut House
	MORGAN Simon	St John's Chambers
	PICTON Martin	Albion Chambers
❷	DIXEY Ian	St John's Chambers
	DUVAL Robert	St John's Chambers
	FENNY Ian Charles	Guildhall Chambers
	FITTON Michael	Albion Chambers
	HART William	Albion Chambers
	LANGDON Andrew	Guildhall Chambers
	LETT Brian	South Western Chambers
	LONGMAN Michael	St John's Chambers
	MATHER-LEES Michael	Albion Chambers
	MOONEY Stephen	Albion Chambers
	MUNRO Sarah	Walnut House
	SMITH Richard	Guildhall Chambers
❸	BURGESS Edward	St John's Chambers
	CULLUM Michael	Albion Chambers
	ELDER Fiona	Queen Square Chambers
	EVANS Susan	St John's Chambers
	QUADRAT Simon	Queen Square Chambers
	QURESHI Shamim	Queen Square Chambers
	STEELE David	Colleton Chambers

For details of these leading barristers see Profiles on page 1473

There is little change in our rankings for the western circuit. "Robust cross-examiner" **Charles Barton QC** of **Albion Chambers** (Barton) was seen as "first choice" by many, and together with **John Royce QC** of **Guildhall Chambers** (Palmer), remains pre-eminent in the region. Back at **Albion**, **James Tabor QC**, noted for his ability with clients, and "charming" **Neil Ford QC** retain their place in the tables. "Hardworking" **Martin Picton** and "popular" **Julian Lambert** ("has a legal mind the size of an elephant") also feature highly on the juniors tables. **Roderick Denyer QC** of **St Johns Chambers** (Sharp) was rated highly for his "strength of purpose" and "immense intellectual capacity." At the same chambers ex-solicitor **Simon Morgan**, an expert at "complex points of law," "crops up on heavy cases," while "razor-sharp" **Mark Horton** of **Colleton Chambers** (Meeke) is reported to be "excellent all-round." In Exeter, **Walnut House** (Gilbert) fared well; **Francis Gilbert QC** receives a volume of instructions in serious murder, manslaughter, and rape cases while "versatile" **Paul Dunkels QC** has recently been involved in a number of complex Munchausen syndrome and baby death cases. Senior junior **Geoffrey Mercer** is apparently "highly respected by judges."

WALES & CHESTER CIRCUIT

LEADING SILKS • Wales & Chester	
❶ REES John Charles	33 Park Place
THOMAS Roger	9 Park Place
❷ ELIAS Gerard	Farrar's Building
PITCHFORD Christopher	Farrar's Building
NEW SILKS	
HOPKINS Stephen	30 Park Place

For details of these leading barristers see Profiles on page 1473

LEADING JUNIORS • Wales & Chester	
❶ DAVIES Huw	30 Park Place
DAVIES Trefor	Iscoed Chambers
EVANS Elwen Mair	Iscoed Chambers
LEWIS Paul	30 Park Place
TAYLOR Gregory	9 Park Place
THOMAS Keith	9 Park Place
❷ BULL Gregory	33 Park Place
DAVIES Meirion	Temple Chambers
JEARY Stephen	Temple Chambers
MURPHY Peter	30 Park Place
RIORDAN Kevin	Iscoed Chambers
THOMAS Paul	Iscoed Chambers
TWOMLOW Richard	9 Park Place

For details of these leading barristers see Profiles on page 1473

At **33 Park Place** (Rees) **John Charles Rees QC** "an impressive operator with a hint of bravura" about him, is the "first name on everyone's lips for high profile murder cases." Leader of the circuit, **Christopher Pitchford QC** of **Farrars Building** (Elias) is a "high powered, first class advocate." In the same chambers **Gerard Elias QC** is renowned for his tribunal work in a large scale Welsh child abuse inquiry but is also active on the London circuit. At **9 Park Place** (Murphy) "tenacious" **Roger Thomas QC** maintains his profile for quality prosecution work supported by the "totally unflappable" **Greg Taylor**, "resourceful" **Keith Thomas** and "diligent" **Richard Twomlow**. **Stephen Hopkins QC** ("a tremendous worker") at **30 Park Place** (Jenkins) has recently been appointed silk. Fellow practitioner **Huw Davies** is heavily involved in customs and excise prosecution work while **Paul Lewis** and **Peter Murphy** attract a large number of sexual abuse cases. "Affable" **Stephen Jeary** of **Temple Chambers** (Aubrey) enters the lists for his ability to "communicate well with clients" in child abuse and sexual offence cases.

MIDLANDS & OXFORD CIRCUIT

LEADING SILKS • Midlands & Oxford	
❶ BARKER Anthony	5 Fountain Court
CRIGMAN David	1 Fountain Court
JOYCE Peter	No.1 High Pavement
LINEHAN Stephen	5 Fountain Court
SAUNDERS John	4 Fountain Court
TREACY Colman	3 Fountain Court
WAKERLEY Richard	4 Fountain Court
❷ ESCOTT-COX Brian	36 Bedford Row
HUNT James	36 Bedford Row
INMAN Melbourne	1 Fountain Court
SMITH Roger	No.6 Fountain Court
TEDD Rex	St Philip's Chambers
NEW SILKS	
FARRELL David	36 Bedford Row
JUCKES Robert	3 Fountain Court
THOMAS Patrick	4 Fountain Court

For details of these leading barristers see Profiles on page 1473

LEADING JUNIORS • Midlands & Oxford	
❶ DUCK Michael	3 Fountain Court
EVERARD William	KCH Barristers
JACKSON Andrew	3 Fountain Court
STOBART John	KCH Barristers
THOMAS Sybil	3 Fountain Court
❷ BRAND Simon	Coleridge Chambers
BURBIDGE James	St Philip's Chambers
CARR Peter	St. Ive's Chambers
EVANS John	1 Fountain Court
MANN Paul	No.1 High Pavement
NAWAZ Amjad	Coleridge Chambers
REYNOLDS Adrian	No.1 High Pavement
❸ EASTEAL Andrew	No.1 High Pavement
ELWICK Martin	No.1 High Pavement
EVANS Michael	No.1 High Pavement
FARRER Paul	1 Fountain Court
GRIFFITH-JONES Richard	1 Fountain Court
HAYNES Peter	St Philip's Chambers
MORRISON Howard	36 Bedford Row
NICHOLLS Benjamin	1 Fountain Court
SHANT Nirmal	No.1 High Pavement
SMITH Shaun	No.1 High Pavement
THOROGOOD Bernard	5 Fountain Court
WALL Mark	4 Fountain Court

For details of these leading barristers see Profiles on page 1473

Top band silks **Anthony Barker QC** and **Stephen Linehan QC** of **5 Fountain Court** (Barker) are renowned for their aggressive approach to cross-examination. At **4 Fountain Court** (Wakerley) **Richard Wakerley QC** and **John Saunders QC** were noted for their thorough preparation. **Colman Treacy QC** of **3 Fountain Court** (Treacy) retains his top band position. **Peter Joyce QC** of **No 1 High Pavement** (Milmo) is an "exceptionally good barrister suited to any major case." The leading juniors this year largely replicate those of twelve months previously.

NORTH EASTERN CIRCUIT

LEADING SILKS • North Eastern	
❶ HARRISON Michael	Park Court Chambers
SMITH Robert	Park Court Chambers
STEWART James	Park Court Chambers
❷ BOURNE-ARTON Simon	Park Court Chambers
KEEN Roger	26 Paradise Square
KERSHAW Jennifer	No.6
MARSON Geoffrey	Sovereign Chambers
SWIFT Malcolm	Park Court Chambers
❸ COSGROVE Patrick	Broad Chare Chambers
NEW SILKS	
MACDONALD Alistair	Park Court Chambers

For details of these leading barristers see Profiles on page 1473

LEADING JUNIORS • North Eastern	
❶ BARNETT Jeremy	St. Paul's Chambers
BUBB Tim	39 Park Square
HARVEY Colin	St. Paul's Chambers
LUMLEY Gerald	9 Woodhouse Square
PALMER Patrick	Sovereign Chambers
❷ BATTY Christopher	St. Paul's Chambers
ISAACS Paul	Mercury Chambers
JAMESON Rodney	No.6
LEES Andrew	St. Paul's Chambers
ROSE Jonathan	St. Paul's Chambers
STUBBS Andrew	St. Paul's Chambers

For details of these leading barristers see Profiles on page 1473

Park Court Chambers (Stewart) remains the leading set in the area with a heavy concentration of top ranking silks. "All-rounder" **Michael Harrison QC**, "meticulous" **Robert Smith QC**, and "inspirational advocate" **James Stewart QC** are the circuit's pre-eminent practitioners. **Roger Keen QC** at **26 Paradise Square** (Keen) "jumps in fearlessly to a case" and enters the tables following strong recommendations from local solicitors. Another newcomer to the list, **Paddy Cosgrove QC** of **Broad Chare Chambers** (Elliott) shows "a human touch with clients." **St Paul's Chambers** (Sangster) contains a number of heavy-hitting juniors with **Jeremy Barnett** and **Colin Harvey** considered to stand out from the pack. **Gerald Lumley** at **9 Woodhouse Square** (Collins) specialises in sex cases and was noted as "extremely patient in conference."

NORTHERN CIRCUIT

LEADING SILKS • Northern	
❶ GLOBE Henry	Exchange Chambers
HOLROYDE Tim	Exchange Chambers
RIORDAN Stephen	25-27 Castle Street
TURNER David	Exchange Chambers
❷ CARUS Roderick	9 St. John Street
GEE Anthony	28 St. John St
GOLDSTONE Clement	28 St. John St
SHORROCK Michael	Peel Court Chambers
STEER David	7 Harrington Street Chambers
❸ BIRKETT Peter	18 St. John Street
FARLEY Roger	40 King St
GARSIDE Charles	9 St. John Street
MARKS Richard	Peel Court Chambers
MORRIS Anthony	Peel Court Chambers
WRIGHT Peter	Lincoln House Chambers
NEW SILKS	
FISH David	Deans Court Chambers
PICKUP James	Lincoln House Chambers
WIGGLESWORTH Raymond	18 St. John Street

For details of these leading barristers see Profiles on page 1473

LEADING JUNIORS • Northern	
❶ GREGORY James	Lincoln House Chambers
LEVER Bernard	Peel Court Chambers
LLOYD Heather	Chavasse Court Chambers
MCDERMOTT John	Chavasse Court Chambers
MCMEEKIN Ian	58 King St
MEADOWCROFT Stephen	Peel Court Chambers
REID Paul	Lincoln House Chambers
STOUT Roger	18 St. John Street
SUMNER David	Lincoln House Chambers
❷ ANDREWS Philip	Young Street Chambers
BERKSON Simon	Exchange Chambers
CATTAN Philip	28 St. John St
CLARKE Nicholas	9 St. John Street
DENNEY Stuart	Deans Court Chambers
FORSYTH Julie	Chavasse Court Chambers
HARRISON Keith	24A St. John Street
HERMAN Raymond	India Buildings Chambers
O'BYRNE Andrew	Peel Court Chambers
WILLIAMS David	Chavasse Court Chambers
❸ BADLEY Pamela	25-27 Castle Street
BLACKWELL Kate	Lincoln House Chambers
BRENNAND Timothy	Manchester House Chambers
GOODE Rowena	28 St. John St
JACKSON John	40 King St
JACKSON Wayne	Young Street Chambers
LONG Andrew	Peel Court Chambers
MATTISON Andrew	Chavasse Court Chambers
MYERS Benjamin	Young Street Chambers
ROBERTS Lisa	Lincoln House Chambers
SAVILL Mark	Deans Court Chambers
WATSON David	14 Castle Street

For details of these leading barristers see Profiles on page 1473

Exchange Chambers (Waldron) makes a strong showing in the silks tables with **Henry Globe QC**, **Tim Holroyde QC**, and **David Turner QC** all in the top band. **Stephen Riordan QC** of **25-27 Castle Street** (Riordan) is known for his able handling of high profile cases. Leader of the circuit **Peter Birkett QC** of **18 St. John Street** (Foster) is highly thought of for large drugs cases and enters the leaders tables this year. **Michael Shorrock QC**, the "main man" of **Peel Court Chambers** (Shorrock) moves up in the rankings following general recommendation. At the same chambers, **Richard Marks QC** is seen to be "working his way up" and makes the transition from new to established silk. "Forceful" **Peter Wright QC** of **Lincoln House Chambers** (Hussain) is seen by many as a "rising star" with a "mind that cuts to the root of the problem." Senior junior **James Gregory**, well known for drugs and high profile miscarriage of justice cases, also moves up in the tables. **Ian McMeekin** "stands out" at **58 King Street** (Lunt) where he receives a "large amount of top quality work."

DEFAMATION

Barristers' profiles 1473-1601

RESEARCH: The rankings are based on in-depth interviews with over 5,000 solicitors and barristers in the UK. Chambers research is audited by the British Market Research Bureau (see page 7 for details).

OVERVIEW: 1 Brick Court and 5 Raymond Buildings remain the sets of choice for the vast majority of solicitors. The high degree of specialisation in defamation and related media litigation at both stables makes for a concentration of shared knowledge and experience that few others can match. However, several respondents noted that the Human Rights Act, with its provisions relating to freedom of speech and privacy, may bring practitioners with human rights expertise to the fore in future.

LONDON

LEADING SETS • London	QCs	Jnrs
❶ **1 Brick Court** (Richard Rampton QC)	6	8
5 Raymond Buildings (Patrick Milmo QC)	4	7

Numbers show recommended barristers in this practice area

LEADING SILKS • London	
✪ **BROWNE Desmond**	5 Raymond Buildings
CALDECOTT Andrew	1 Brick Court
CARMAN George	4-5 Gray's Inn Square
PRICE James	5 Raymond Buildings
❶ **RAMPTON Richard**	1 Brick Court
SHIELDS Thomas	1 Brick Court
❷ **MILMO Patrick**	5 Raymond Buildings
NICOL Andrew	Doughty Street Chambers
❸ **HARTLEY Richard**	1 Brick Court
MOLONEY Patrick	1 Brick Court
ROBERTSON Geoffrey	Doughty Street Chambers
SHAW Geoffrey	1 Brick Court
THWAITES Ronald	Ely Place Chambers
NEW SILKS	
PAGE Adrienne	5 Raymond Buildings

For details of these leading barristers see Profiles on page 1473

LEADING JUNIORS • London	
✪ **ROGERS Heather**	Matrix Chambers
SHARP Victoria	1 Brick Court
❶ **WARBY Mark**	5 Raymond Buildings
❷ **BARCA Manuel**	1 Brick Court
MARZEC Alexandra	5 Raymond Buildings
RUSHBROOKE Justin	5 Raymond Buildings
SHERBORNE David	5 Raymond Buildings
SUTTLE Stephen	1 Brick Court
❸ **ELLIOTT Rupert**	1 Brick Court
HINCHLIFF Benjamin	1 Brick Court
❹ **PHILLIPS Jane**	1 Brick Court
STARTE Harvey	1 Brick Court
UP AND COMING	
ADDY Caroline	1 Brick Court
BUSUTTIL Godwin	5 Raymond Buildings
NICKLIN Matthew	5 Raymond Buildings
WOLANSKI Adam	5 Raymond Buildings

For details of these leading barristers see Profiles on page 1473

1 Brick Court (Rampton) **Andrew Caldecott QC** retains his starred rating as an "elegant scalpel merchant," and a "fine technician" who is "great with judges." In the opinion of many, he has the finest legal mind at the defamation bar. New head of chambers **Richard Rampton QC** rises in the rankings after a fantastic year, most notably leading for both defendants in the David Irving case. "Incredibly enthusiastic" and "easy to work with," he is particularly recommended for large, detailed cases ("if you've got four rooms full of documents, Rampton's your man.") **Thomas Shields QC** continues to be rated for claimant work, and "did a fantastic job for ITN" in their action against Living Marxism magazine. Best known as a top notch jury advocate, he also received praise for his legal argument and "ability to see where the judge's concerns lie." While seen less than in his heyday, **Richard Hartley QC** "continues to get results." The "bright, robust and hardworking" **Patrick Moloney QC** rises in the rankings this year, and is seen as increasingly busy acting for both claimants and defendants. **Geoffrey Shaw QC** is rated by some solicitors for his "incredibly retentive memory" and "tenacious advocacy," although some found his manner "a trifle reserved." The "excellent" **Victoria Sharp** is "astonishingly busy" and remains in the top league of juniors. **Manuel Barca** is particularly recommended "for more complex, wide-ranging disputes." "Mega-brain" **Stephen Suttle** has an "academic bent," and **Rupert Elliott** ("clever, thorough, sensible and good on his feet") rises in the tables. **Benjamin Hinchliff** and **Jane Phillips** continue to garner market plaudits, while the "quietly effective" **Harvey Starte** "writes the best letters of claim" and makes his debut in the rankings this year. **Caroline Addy** remains recommended as an up and coming junior, and was described by solicitors as "a pleasure to work with."

5 Raymond Buildings (Milmo) The "absolutely outstanding" **Desmond Browne QC** "knows law and procedure back to front" and is increasingly seen as a "street-fighter in court." Alongside him in the top league is the "tigerish" **James Price QC** who "has an instant grasp of what is important." Head of Chambers **Patrick Milmo QC** is seen by many as the "paterfamilias of the libel bar" and continues to act in weighty cases. In the view of many practitioners **Adrienne Page QC** is "improving in silk" and is particularly rated for her detailed approach to preparation. The "experienced and user-friendly" **Mark Warby** is now seen across the market as a "sliver away" from the two starred juniors, and rises in the rankings. **Alexandra Marzec** ("a good fighter and good on paper") continues to build a strong reputation in the field, as does **David Sherborne**, who "doesn't stand on ceremony" and is highly rated for assimilating facts and conducting pleadings. **Justin Rushbrooke** rises in the rankings this year after widespread recommendation. An all-rounder with noted expertise in e-mail libel, he is "a little bit more daring in pleadings" and can be a "pretty steely opponent." Up and coming juniors at the set are **Godwin Busuttil**, the "completely committed" **Matthew Nicklin** and the "charming" **Adam Wolanski**.

Other Notable Barristers The ubiquitous **George Carman QC** has now moved to **4-5 Gray's Inn Square** (Appleby/Ouseley) and remains "supreme with a jury." Particularly recommended for contempt and related media matters is the "unstuffy" **Andrew Nicol QC** at **Doughty Street Chambers** (Robertson.) At the same set, **Geoffrey Robertson QC** is best known for defamation cases involving freedom of speech or human rights issues, but he maintains a general practice and led for The Sunday Times in the successful settlement of their dispute with Michael Ashcroft. The "forthright" **Ronald Thwaites QC**, who left 10 King's Bench Walk to set up **Ely Place Chambers** in August 2000, is now concentrating more of his time on defamation work, and "will always give his best." **Heather Rogers**, newly installed at **Matrix Chambers** (Blake) continues to have "a junior career to die for." She has been involved in a swathe of high-profile cases over the past year.

EMPLOYMENT

RESEARCH: The rankings are based on in-depth interviews with over 5,000 solicitors and barristers in the UK. Chambers research is audited by the British Market Research Bureau (see page 7 for details).

OVERVIEW: Some notable changes have occurred this year. The founding of Matrix Chambers offers a serious challenge to the established order, with an increased emphasis on human rights issues liable to favour a team "with an awful lot of talent." However, the set clearly has much to prove. One set with no such need is Blackstone Chambers, which deservedly takes its place in the top band alongside 11 King's Bench Walk. In the regions, research showed that there was still a place, albeit a more precarious one, for the local bar. The exception was the Midlands, where an overwhelming majority of respondents felt that local sets had "priced themselves out of the market."

LONDON

LEADING SETS • London	QCs	Jnrs
❶ **Blackstone Chambers** (Baxendale /Flint)	3	4
11 King's Bench Walk (Tabachnik/Goudie)	5	11
❷ **Devereux Chambers** (Jeffrey Burke QC)	2	6
Littleton Chambers (Michel Kallipetis QC)	4	5
Old Square Chambers (John Hendy QC)	3	10
❸ **Cloisters** (Laura Cox QC)	3	1
Matrix Chambers (Nicholas Blake QC)	2	3
❹ **Essex Court Chambers** (Gordon Pollock QC)	1	3

Numbers show recommended barristers in this practice area

LEADING SILKS • London	
❶ **COX Laura**	Cloisters
LANGSTAFF Brian	Cloisters
PANNICK David	Blackstone Chambers
❷ **ALLEN Robin**	Cloisters
BEAN David	Matrix Chambers
BELOFF Michael	4-5 Gray's Inn Square
BURKE Jeffrey	Devereux Chambers
CLARKE Andrew	Littleton Chambers
HENDY John	Old Square Chambers
HOCHHAUSER Andrew	Essex Court Chambers
JEANS Christopher	11 King's Bench Walk
SLADE Elizabeth	11 King's Bench Walk
UNDERHILL Nicholas	Fountain Court
❸ **BOOTH Cherie**	Matrix Chambers
BOWERS John	Littleton Chambers
GOUDIE James	11 King's Bench Walk
HAND John	Old Square Chambers
MCMULLEN Jeremy	Old Square Chambers
TABACHNIK Eldred	11 King's Bench Walk
❹ **MEHIGAN Simon**	5 Paper Buildings
NEW SILKS	
BLOCH Selwyn	Littleton Chambers
GOULDING Paul	Blackstone Chambers
GRIFFITH-JONES David	Devereux Chambers
LANG Beverley	Blackstone Chambers
LYNCH Adrian	11 King's Bench Walk
MILLAR Gavin	Doughty Street Chambers
STAFFORD Andrew	Littleton Chambers

For details of these leading barristers see Profiles on page 1473

Barristers' profiles 1473-1601

Blackstone Chambers (Baxendale/Flint) The chambers is said to provide "consistently good service" and was commended for its large "stable of excellent young barristers" and "proactive" clerks who will "move heaven and earth" to match up each case with the proper practitioner. "No one can hold a candle to" **David Pannick QC**, a public lawyer who also ranks as a "first tier employment advocate." **Paul Goulding QC** and **Beverley Lang QC** were both recently appointed silk. Goulding's "quiet manner" belies his "steely ambition" while Lang was recommended for complex EAT matters. "A star of the future," leading junior **Dinah Rose** is "on top of her papers" and frequently "spots routes that others will miss." **Monica Carss-Frisk** "goes the extra mile" while **Gerard Clarke** is said to be particularly "good with nervous clients who need reassurance." **Thomas Croxford** was recommended as an up and coming employment advocate.

11 King's Bench Walk (Tabachnik/Goudie) Chambers maintains its "well deserved reputation for having some of the best brains at the bar." Some notable brains include the "charming and cerebral" **Christopher Jeans QC** who has the necessary "subtlety to deal with sensitive discrimination cases." **Elizabeth Slade QC** "always knows the papers inside out" and was commended as "excellent at the appellant level." **James Goudie QC** apparently "turns paperwork around quickly" and is particularly recommended for restrictive covenant cases. Another "giant of the employment bar," **Eldred Tabachnik QC** was rated as a "conscientious and knowledgeable" advocate. New silk **Adrian Lynch QC** is known for his eccentric manner and rapport with clients. At junior level, "safe pair of hands" **John Cavanagh** "puts clients at ease," while "succinct" **Seán Jones** is "good on preparation and skeleton arguments." "Incisive" **Jonathan Swift** is "quick on his feet" and works well within a team. **Nigel Giffin** is a "meticulous, modern advocate" while **Andrew Hillier** was recommended for his "sound advice." "Punchy" **Timothy Pitt-Payne** is said to be "extremely polished in the tribunal." **Charles Bear** takes an "old fashioned approach" to courtroom advocacy. **Daniel Stilitz** is said to have a "habit of winning" with his "extremely lucid arguments." A "cunning and artful advocate," **Peter Wallington** is also seen to be "making a name for himself." **Paul Nicholls** "makes a good argument out of limited material" while **Peter Oldham** is rated as "succinct and technically very good."

Devereux Chambers (Burke) "Punchy advocate" **Jeffrey Burke QC** is a "real tiger" in the courtroom. New silk and "unsung hero," **David Griffith-Jones QC** "makes submissions sound like objective truths." Solicitors and silks want **Bruce Carr** on their side for his "combination of an incisive mind and superb knowledge of employment law." "Down to earth" **Nicholas Randall** is "prepared to say what he thinks." **Ingrid Simler** "fights her corner hard" while **James Tayler** is rated as a "young Turk" able to provide a "thoughtful analysis of legal problems." **Tim Brennan** earned his reputation for the "clarity of his verbal and written expression." **Ruth Downing** rates highly for disability discrimination cases.

Littleton Chambers (Kallipetis) **Andrew Clarke QC**'s talent for constructing "detailed nitty-gritty arguments" has put him in high demand for employment work. **John Bowers QC** is "particularly good with sensitive commercial issues" and is the "silk of choice" for whistle-blowing cases. New silk **Selwyn Bloch QC** receives rave reviews for injunction work. **Andrew Stafford QC** has a "clear mind" and "excellent client manner." "Direct" **Antony Sendall** "doesn't sit on the fence." **Shirley Bothroyd** is said to be "good on her feet" and is recommended for her skilled cross-examination. **Sam Neaman**, recently moved from 4 Paper Buildings, is "prepared to take on a lot" and offers "good value" to clients. "Clever"

LEADING JUNIORS • London	
✪ LINDEN Thomas	Matrix Chambers
ROSE Dinah	Blackstone Chambers
❶ CARR Bruce	Devereux Chambers
CAVANAGH John	11 King's Bench Walk
EADY Jennifer	Old Square Chambers
JONES Seán	11 King's Bench Walk
SWIFT Jonathan	11 King's Bench Walk
❷ BROWN Damian	Old Square Chambers
CARSS-FRISK Monica	Blackstone Chambers
GIFFIN Nigel	11 King's Bench Walk
GILL Tess	Old Square Chambers
GRIFFITHS Martin	Essex Court Chambers
HILLIER Andrew	11 King's Bench Walk
KIBLING Thomas	Cloisters
MOOR Sarah	Old Square Chambers
NAPIER Brian	Fountain Court
PITT-PAYNE Timothy	11 King's Bench Walk
RANDALL Nicholas	Devereux Chambers
SENDALL Antony	Littleton Chambers
SIMLER Ingrid	Devereux Chambers
TAYLER James	Devereux Chambers
TETHER Melanie	Old Square Chambers
❸ BEAR Charles	11 King's Bench Walk
BOTHROYD Shirley	Littleton Chambers
CLARKE Gerard	Blackstone Chambers
OMAMBALA Ijeoma	Old Square Chambers
ROMNEY Daphne	4 Field Court
ROSE Paul	Old Square Chambers
STILITZ Daniel	11 King's Bench Walk
WALLINGTON Peter	11 King's Bench Walk
WHITE Antony	Matrix Chambers
❹ BLANCHARD Claire	Essex Court Chambers
BRENNAN Timothy	Devereux Chambers
DEVONSHIRE Simon	5 Paper Buildings
DOWNING Ruth	Devereux Chambers
DUGGAN Michael	Littleton Chambers
KERR Tim	4-5 Gray's Inn Square
KORN Anthony	199 Strand
MCNEILL Jane	Old Square Chambers
NEAMAN Sam	Littleton Chambers
NICHOLLS Paul	11 King's Bench Walk
O'DEMPSEY Declan	Coram Chambers
OLDHAM Peter	11 King's Bench Walk
SUTTON Mark	Old Square Chambers
UP AND COMING	
CIUMEI Charles	Essex Court Chambers
CROXFORD Thomas	Blackstone Chambers
GATT Ian	Littleton Chambers
MOUNTFIELD Helen	Matrix Chambers
SEGAL Oliver	Old Square Chambers

For details of these leading barristers see Profiles on page 1473

Michael Duggan is rated as a "solid performer." **Ian Gatt** enters the tables as an up and coming practitioner.

Old Square Chambers (Hendy) **John Hendy QC**, described as a "worthy opponent," is well known for his work on behalf of trade unions. "Shrewd" **John Hand QC** was commended as a "skilful operator." "Technically thorough" **Jeremy McMullen QC** has a strong employee and trade union practice. "Bright" **Jennifer Eady** is highly recommended for her "deep knowledge of employment law." "Deep-thinking" **Damian Brown** is "cautious and committed" to employment law. "Personable" **Tess Gill** is said to "really care about her clients." "Feisty" **Sarah Moor** has a "first class brain" and is rated for both employee and respondent work. **Melanie Tether** "understands solicitors' problems and seems to have the ear of the court." "Persuasive" **Ijeoma Omambala** is recommended as "very good with clients." **Paul Rose** maintains his reputation as a leading employment junior. **Jane McNeill** "can see both sides of the argument," while **Mark Sutton** is recommended as "extremely intelligent and articulate." "Thoughtful" **Oliver Segal** was ranked as up and coming for his work on commercial agents' cases.

Cloisters (Cox) "Supportive" **Laura Cox QC** "puts clients at ease" and has an excellent reputation for applicant work in discrimination cases. **Brian Langstaff QC** "can be persuasive" in "cutting-edge cases" on behalf of the applicant. "Innovative" **Robin Allen QC** "eats disability discrimination cases for breakfast." **Thomas Kibling** brings "terrific enthusiasm" to his work and is said to be particularly "good for testing outrageous cases."

Matrix Chambers (Blake) "Straightforward" **David Bean QC** has an "analytical mind" and is highly respected for his injunction and restrictive covenant work. **Cherie Booth QC** "very much likes winning" and takes on a "demanding" employment caseload. "Sensible" **Thomas Linden** "exceeds expectations" and is rated by solicitors and peers as "easy to work with." **Helen Mountfield** was recommended for complex discrimination cases. **Antony White** is said to be a "punchy advocate."

Essex Court Chambers (Pollock) Recommended for restrictive covenant work, **Andrew Hochhauser QC** is a "man you want on your side" due to his "fearsome ability to cross-examine." **Martin Griffiths** is "quietly spoken but has a spine of steel." "Hard-working" **Claire Blanchard** is rated as a "thorough and able advocate." "Understated" **Charles Ciumei** enters the tables as an up and coming employment practitioner.

Other Notable Barristers At **Fountain Court** (Boswood,) **Nicholas Underhill QC** is reputed to be a "robust advocate" who gives "first rate advice on esoteric matters," while "academic" **Brian Napier** is particularly useful on TUPE issues. "Extremely clever" **Michael Beloff QC** at **4-5 Gray's Inn Square** (Appleby/Ouseley) maintains a multi-faceted practice and rates highly for employment work, but will be moving to Matrix Chambers within a year. Also at 4-5 Gray's Inn Square, junior **Tim Kerr** is said to be "good at turning things around." New Silk, **Gavin Millar QC** at **Doughty Street Chambers** (Robertson) is "popular with judges" and is used extensively for TU and general employment law cases. At **5 Paper Buildings** (Carey/Caplan) **Simon Mehigan QC** is well known in the restrictive covenant field, while **Simon Devonshire** is "good on detail," particularly in regard to discrimination cases. **Daphne Romney** of **4 Field Court** (Gee) is known to be an "exceptional cross-examiner" and **Anthony Korn** at **199 Strand** (Phillips) is "well organised" and "prompt and efficient" when dealing with complicated matters. Union clients "get their money's worth" from **Declan O'Dempsey** of **Coram Chambers** (McCarthy.)

WESTERN CIRCUIT

LEADING JUNIORS • Western	
❶ KEMPSTER Toby	Old Square Chambers
REDDIFORD Anthony	Guildhall Chambers
❷ CHUDLEIGH Louise	Old Square Chambers
UP AND COMING	
SMITH Nicholas	Queen Square Chambers

For details of these leading barristers see Profiles on page 1473

"Unflappable" **Toby Kempster** of **Old Square Chambers** (Hendy) also practices from the London chambers and is recommended by clients for getting "straight to the point" and being "bright without ramming it down your throat." At the same chambers **Louise Chudleigh** "knows her subject well" and is rated as an able employment advocate. At **Guildhall Chambers** (Palmer) **Anthony Reddiford** is an experienced tribunal advocate, said to be particularly "good on paper." **Nicholas Smith** of **Queen Square Chambers** (Jenkins) enters the tables as an up and coming practitioner for his "excellent bedside manner" and specialist employment practice.

NORTH EASTERN CIRCUIT

LEADING JUNIORS • North Eastern	
❶ CAPE Paul	Milburn House Chambers
UP AND COMING	
WOODWARK Jane	Milburn House Chambers

For details of these leading barristers see Profiles on page 1473

At **Milburn House Chambers** (Cape,) **Paul Cape** is said to "scare the life out of some clients" during cross-examination. He is well known for his advocacy skills and is recommended as "always willing to help." "Self-effacing" **Jane Woodwark** "establishes a rapport with a tribunal."

NORTHERN CIRCUIT

LEADING SILKS • Northern	
❶ HAND John	9 St. John Street
MCMULLEN Jeremy	9 St. John Street

LEADING JUNIORS • Northern	
❶ GILROY Paul	9 St. John Street
❷ BENSON John	14 Castle Street
GRUNDY Nigel	9 St. John Street
UP AND COMING	
BRADLEY Richard	Oriel Chambers
CONNOLLY Joanne	8 King St

For details of these leading barristers see Profiles on page 1473

At **9 St John Street** (Hand) in Manchester, "old-fashioned" **John Hand QC** practices both in the Northern and London circuits and is recommended as a "capable advocate." His colleague **Jeremy McMullen QC** is rated by some as the "cleverest man alive." At the same set, "amenable" **Paul Gilroy** has a "good feel for the tribunal" and is beloved by clients for his willingness to "drop things at a short notice and roll his sleeves up." "Cerebral" **Nigel Grundy** "thinks problems through." At **14 Castle Street** (Edis) in Liverpool, **John Benson** "makes an effort to minister to a client's priorities and culture." At **Oriel Chambers** (Sander) also in Liverpool, "master on paper," **Richard Bradley** offers clients good "value for money" and is a new entrant to the Chambers' rankings. At **8 King Street** (Armitage) in Manchester, "first-class" **Joanne Connolly** was recommended as an up and coming practitioner for her work on discrimination cases.

ENERGY

RESEARCH: The rankings are based on in-depth interviews with over 5,000 solicitors and barristers in the UK. Chambers research is audited by the British Market Research Bureau (see page 7 for details).

OVERVIEW: We have narrowed this bar section this year to include only the commercial aspects of contentious work, planning and construction aspects being covered respectively under those bar sections. This reflects the fact that there is really no discrete energy specialism at the bar - usually the commercial barristers are happily used for energy (electricity, oil and gas, mining and water) work. Thus it is more appropriate to talk about leading silks rather than leading sets in this area. As far as trends, electricity arbitrations are emerging as "a fertile source of contentious work." The top QCs are seen less on the lengthy trials. Each is a brilliant, experienced advocate holding authority and the respect of the judiciary. They are the best able to deal with complex issues arising in the sector.

LONDON

LEADING SETS • London	QCs	Jnrs
❶ **One Essex Court** (Anthony Grabiner QC)	5	3
❷ **Essex Court Chambers** (Gordon Pollock QC)	4	1
❸ **Fountain Court** (Anthony Boswood QC)	2	-
❹ **7 King's Bench Walk** (Jeremy Cooke QC)	2	-

Numbers show recommended barristers in this practice area

LEADING SILKS • London	
✪ GRABINER Anthony	One Essex Court
POLLOCK Gordon	Essex Court Chambers
SUMPTION Jonathan	Brick Court Chambers
❷ BOSWOOD Anthony	Fountain Court
GLICK Ian	One Essex Court
KENTRIDGE Sydney	Brick Court Chambers
❸ ALDOUS Charles	7 Stone Buildings
BARNES Mark	One Essex Court
CARR Christopher	One Essex Court
COOKE Jeremy	7 King's Bench Walk
CROOKENDEN Simon	Essex Court Chambers
EDER Bernard	Essex Court Chambers
GLOSTER Elizabeth	One Essex Court
HILDYARD Robert	4 Stone Buildings
MALES Stephen	20 Essex Street
PHILIPSON Trevor	Fountain Court
SCHAFF Alistair	7 King's Bench Walk
SHER Jules	Wilberforce Chambers
NEW SILKS	
DICKER Robin	3-4 South Square
MILDON David	Essex Court Chambers

For details of these leading barristers see Profiles on page 1473

LEADING JUNIORS • London	
✪ RABINOWITZ Laurence	One Essex Court
❶ GRIFFITHS Alan	One Essex Court
❷ BRYAN Simon	Essex Court Chambers
MCCAUGHRAN John	One Essex Court
MILES Robert	4 Stone Buildings

For details of these leading barristers see Profiles on page 1473

One Essex Court (Grabiner) The leading set in the sector where the emphasis leans more towards oil and gas work. The "superb" **Anthony Grabiner QC**, though involved in other duties, maintains his reputation. He is "not as theatrical as Pollock, not as dry as Sumption, but is the most approachable of the three." Importantly, he is said to have "a hot-line to BP" and to

Barristers' profiles 1473-1601

"handle judges beautifully." The "brilliant" **Mark Barnes QC** has "great range" and a mixed practice from top end commercial work through to oil company work for Amoco. He is a "young leader, though a seasoned campaigner" and also comes recommended for arbitration work. **Ian Glick QC** is known for his work for Northern Ireland Electricity and is recommended as "commercial, with a good brain." Super-silk **Elizabeth Gloster QC** has enjoyed a heightened profile this year, earning particular accolades for her excellent arbitration work. **Christopher Carr QC** is a "very rounded lawyer" who has the stamina for, and enjoys, the lengthy trial. Of the juniors, the high profile **Laurence Rabinowitz** is "talented and has such a diverse practice." He is constantly briefed because he is a team player and "goes further with his thinking." Not seen on his feet as much as some, he "looks great on paper" and is by far the most experienced junior in the energy sector. **Alan Griffiths** is less high profile but is rated as "one of the best, most inventive" juniors around: "if Alan Griffiths is not on your side, you worry." Newly ranked **John McCaughran** is highly regarded, particularly for his work in the gas arena where he is said to "know the area well."

Essex Court Chambers (Pollock) **Gordon Pollock QC** has a huge reputation, working on some large pipeline cases, and handling numerous matters for British Gas. He is said to be the most experienced of the three leading silks in energy cases and has the intellectual ability to "get to grips with convoluted contracts." His style is "bullish, aggressive and robust." **Bernard Eder QC** is "a tough opponent," going for the jugular in court. He "is such a team player and so clever" and thus highly sought after for the big matters. He "gets the best from everybody." On his feet he's "almost unflappable." **Simon Crookenden QC** has a lower profile but is still warmly endorsed. New silk **David Mildon QC** is "likeable" and on many a short-list. Newly ranked **Simon Bryan** makes the list for his electricity arbitration work.

Fountain Court (Boswood) This is a set that handles a lot of advisory work, with two large arbitrations in the last 12 months. One of these was done by **Trevor Philipson QC**, who is said to be a "favourite of the oil companies." **Tony Boswood QC** is highly regarded, handling a lot of Enron litigation. He is "very clever – and very frank." A weakness at the set is the absence of a recognised junior.

7 King's Bench Walk (Cooke) High quality advocate Stephen Tomlinson QC has been promoted to the bench and withdraws from our rankings. Despite this, the well-respected **Jeremy Cooke QC** maintains his position. **Alistair Schaff QC** is "first class, first choice - can't speak too highly of him."

Other Notable Barristers First mention must go to **Jonathan Sumption QC** of **Brick Court Chambers** (Clarke.) He is "regarded as the top man," with "an enormous ability in every facet." Senior, experienced **Sydney Kentridge QC** of the same chambers is rated as "brilliant." He is the person to consult "if the case is going to the Lords," because of his ability to debate at that level. **Charles Aldous QC** of **7 Stone Buildings** (Aldous) has also attracted rave reviews. **Robert Hildyard QC** at **4 Stone Buildings** (Heslop) acts for Enron and is regarded as the "most up and coming younger silk involved in energy cases." **Jules Sher QC** of **Wilberforce Chambers** (Nugee) is "perennially excellent." New silk **Robin Dicker QC** at **3-4 South Square** (Crystal) "has shone" this year and is newly ranked. **Stephen Males QC** of **20 Essex Street** (Milligan) is bright, personable and reliable: "he really gets stuck in." **Robert Miles** of **4 Stone Buildings** (Heslop) makes the list this year as an all-rounder – "he's clear on paper and good on his feet."

ENVIRONMENT

RESEARCH: The rankings are based on in-depth interviews with over 5,000 solicitors and barristers in the UK. Chambers research is audited by the British Market Research Bureau (see page 7 for details).

LONDON

LEADING SETS • London	QCs	Jnrs
❶ **Old Square Chambers** (John Hendy QC)	2	4
❷ **1 Crown Office Row** (Robert Seabrook QC)	2	2
4-5 Gray's Inn Square (Appleby/Ouseley)	2	1
2 Harcourt Buildings (Gerard Ryan QC)	2	2
❸ **4 Breams Buildings** (Christopher Lockhart-Mummery QC)	2	-
1 Serjeants' Inn (Lionel Read QC)	-	4
❹ **Brick Court Chambers** (Christopher Clarke QC)	1	1
Matrix Chambers (Nicholas Blake QC)	-	3

Numbers show recommended barristers in this practice area

LEADING SILKS • London	
❶ **BRENNAN Dan**	39 Essex Street
HAND John	Old Square Chambers
KINGSLAND Christopher	4 Breams Buildings
OUSELEY Duncan	4-5 Gray's Inn Square
RYAN Gerard	2 Harcourt Buildings
VALLANCE Philip	1 Crown Office Row
❷ **GEORGE Charles**	2 Harcourt Buildings
GORDON Richard	Brick Court Chambers
HAVERS Philip	1 Crown Office Row
HOLGATE David	4 Breams Buildings
STONE Gregory	4-5 Gray's Inn Square
WILLIAMS John Melville	Old Square Chambers
NEW SILKS	
KING Neil	2 Mitre Court Buildings

For details of these leading barristers see Profiles on page 1473

LEADING JUNIORS • London	
✪ **PUGH Charles**	Old Square Chambers
❶ **BATES John**	Old Square Chambers
HART David	1 Crown Office Row
TROMANS Stephen	11 King's Bench Walk
❷ **BIRTLES William**	Old Square Chambers
FORDHAM Michael	Blackstone Chambers
SANDS Philippe	Matrix Chambers
❸ **BYRNE Garrett**	23 Essex Street
CAMERON James	3 Verulam Buildings
JONES Gregory	2 Harcourt Buildings
LEWIS Rhodri Price	1 Serjeants' Inn
MCCRACKEN Robert	2 Harcourt Buildings
MEAD Philip	Old Square Chambers
UPTON William	1 Serjeants' Inn
WOLFE David	Matrix Chambers
❹ **EDIS William**	1 Crown Office Row
HARRIS Russell	1 Serjeants' Inn
HILL Thomas	4-5 Gray's Inn Square
LEWIS Robert	Clarendon Chambers
MACRORY Richard	Brick Court Chambers
PUGH-SMITH John	1 Serjeants' Inn
READ Graham	Devereux Chambers
SHERIDAN Maurice	Matrix Chambers
WEST Lawrence	2 Harcourt Buildings

For details of these leading barristers see Profiles on page 1473

Old Square Chambers (Hendy) The only chambers that "has always supported the environmental area" to any great degree. The leading environmental chambers by dint of sheer numbers of specialists. Particularly well known for nuisance and regulatory compliance work, a number of silks and juniors complement each other with different skills and qualities. **John Hand QC** mixes his environmental practice with employment and PI, but is well regarded by solicitors for his criminal work. Well-known **John Melville Williams QC** is another recognised environmental silk who does "almost nothing else." He "knows his subject well," carries "a certain gravitas" and is "refreshing to deal with." Star junior **Charles Pugh** was the recipient of more positive recommendations than any other this year. A "flamboyant, colourful" character and "outstanding advocate," he is considered especially good for tort actions and statutory nuisance cases. Not far behind, widely published and "more thoughtful" **John Bates** is "excellent for technical advice" and academic opinions, notably on water and drainage issues. His "pragmatic, down-to-earth style" allows him to "build good relations with clients." **William Birtles** is considered a good all-rounder, praised for his advocacy and for "creating positive impressions on solicitors." **Philip Mead** has "the gift of the gab in court." He "knows how to run a good case" and "develops a rapport with the bench." He is especially recommended for statutory nuisance cases.

1 Crown Office Row (Seabrook) **Philip Vallance QC** possesses "great pragmatism" and has always been able to apply a "practical approach" to a number of high-profile cases. **Philip Havers QC**, likewise, has a "first-class track record" and is instructed by leading solicitors for environmental judicial reviews. **David Hart** ("sharp and brisk – gets on with it") was the most frequently recommended barrister at the set. His "analysis and mind-set are first class" and he "always attracts high quality work." Possessing an "academic style of cross-examination" he is felt to epitomise the classic environment barrister. **William Edis** also retains his share of market support.

4-5 Gray's Inn Square (Appleby/Ouseley) Primarily a set that offers planning barristers who additionally provide environmental advice. "Flavour of the month," super planning silk **Duncan Ouseley QC** is a front runner here. "If I can get him, I'll use him," said one prominent City solicitor. Given the close overlap between the two disciplines, this "user friendly planning star" has "moved effortlessly into environmental work – he is superb." Not exclusively an environmental barrister, **Gregory Stone QC**'s mixed practice touches planning and local government, but he remains recommended for his "easy style." **Tom Hill** has also made his mark on the environmental front and retains his position.

2 Harcourt Buildings (Ryan) Fusing planning, public and environmental law, **Gerard Ryan QC** is "incisive and fights his corner" for heavy duty regulatory work. Also felt to be adept technically, he is "hot on the scientific side." Public law expert **Charles George QC** is felt to have been successful in taking on environmental matters. "User-friendly" junior **Greg Jones** is "never too busy too help," is considered to be "good on the procedural side" and is recommended particularly for his nuisance work. **Robert McCracken** is singled out again this year for his environmental, litigation and regulatory practice. Better known for personal injury and product liability, new entry **Lawrence West** was nevertheless described as an "absolute shining star" for his ability to deal with "a vast range of environmental disputes." Not aloof and well-liked by clients, he "makes the whole issue run a lot smoother." His recent work in GM crops cases drew particular praise.

4 Breams Buildings (Lockhart-Mummery) Two silks are ranked this year. Held in high regard, **Christopher Kingsland QC** is instructed frequently by solicitors for waste matters where he is "solid and dependable" and "has a nice way with clients." Known foremost as a planner, **David Holgate QC** has "emerged on his own as an environmental specialist." Described as "incredibly sharp," his crossover abilities are increasingly recognised where he exercises his "encyclopaedic knowledge and grasp of environmental law."

1 Serjeants' Inn (Read) Planning and local government set containing several ranked juniors. Experienced in waste prosecution work, **Rhodri Price Lewis** is felt to have expanded his level of environmental work, but remains principally a planner. He is rated as a "good team player," and when dealing with clients, "always tries to find the inclusive approach." Prominent in the UKELA, **William Upton** "really knows his stuff." This includes statutory nuisance and local government-related work. He is felt to be an "upwardly rising" name, and is recognised as having made environmental law his particular forte. **Russell Harris** is again rated for his specialist knowledge, particularly in statutory appeals. **John Pugh-Smith**, who also has a presence at chambers in East Anglia, runs a mixed planning and environmental practice. His "big personality" goes down well with some solicitors.

Brick Court Chambers (Clarke) Top ranked public law silk **Richard Gordon QC** is only an occasional environmental participant but singled out again for his well-documented judicial review abilities, for applicants in particular. Recently involved in some major cases including a major Southern Water dispute. Among other things, **Richard Macrory** is rated for his knowledge of European directives and opinions on international waste matters.

Matrix Chambers (Blake) Human rights flavoured public law practice with a clutch of recommended juniors. **Philippe Sands** is instructed frequently on cross-border transactions with an environmental impact. He "doesn't sit on the fence." **David Wolfe** is sought for "quick opinions" by claimant practices and larger City units for advisory work on, inter alia, effluent plants, landfill and incinerator cases. He is "head and shoulders above the others" for environmental judicial review, commented a leading claimant practitioner, "I've seen him run rings around QCs." Noted for his water utilities and regulatory work this year, solicitors also like **Maurice Sheridan**, who "is prepared to roll up his sleeves."

Other Notable Barristers Back from the bar council as a working peer, personal injury barrister **Dan Brennan QC** of **39 Essex Street** (Pleming) is seen to be raising his active caseload of environmental work. Felt to be increasingly building on his interest in the subject, he is instructed by claimant and defendant solicitors alike for the right sort of environmental cases, namely toxic torts. New planning silk **Neil King QC** at **2 Mitre Court Buildings** (FitzGerald)is a "first class advocate with tremendous knowledge." He is used by solicitors for public inquiries and environmental planning crossover cases. He possesses a "real grasp of the technical points which are the key to success." At **11 King's Bench Walk** (Tabachnik/Goudie), former Simmons & Simmons star solicitor **Stephen Tromans**' transition to the bar appears to have been warmly received. It is not yet known if his advocacy in court matches his other strengths, but for "sheer level of knowledge and first rate tenacity," there are few more natural choices. Pre-eminent public law and JR guru **Michael Fordham** of **Blackstone Chambers** (Baxendale/Flint) is foremost among those barristers who effectively combine this discipline with environmental knowledge. "Astonishingly thorough," he is a team player who "teases out the issues." He has recently engaged in a number of nuclear cases and GM foods work. Rated for environmental criminal work, "good egg" **Garrett Byrne** of **23 Essex Street** (Lawson) has left an impression with many solicitors for his prosecution abilities. He offers "thorough and to the point advice" and has an "accessible manner." Actively involved with FIELD, **James Cameron** at **3 Verulam Buildings** (Symons/Jarvis) is noted for his EC elements interpretations and successful performances in waste licence cases. **Clarendon Chambers** based **Robert Lewis** has "bags of experience" in planning-biased matters. **Graham Read** at **Devereux Chambers** (Burke) is also recommended for his mixed commercial and environmental practice.

MIDLANDS & OXFORD CIRCUIT

LEADING JUNIORS • Midlands & Oxford	
❶ CAHILL Jeremy	5 Fountain Court
KIMBLIN Richard	3 Fountain Court

For details of these leading barristers see Profiles on page 1473

Jerry Cahill of **5 Fountain Court** (Barker) in Birmingham picked up a number of positive endorsements from solicitor interviewees. He is felt to be notably impressive at local plans and on waste matters. **Richard Kimblin** of **3 Fountain Court** (Treacy), secretary of the West Midlands branch of UKELA and a former environmental consultant is "still young and very able." Mixing in with health and safety and regulatory work, his efforts to "carve out a specialist environmental practice" have been increasingly well-received by the market.

NORTHERN CIRCUIT

LEADING SILKS • Northern	
NEW SILKS	
PATTERSON Frances	40 King St

For details of these leading barristers see Profiles on page 1473

LEADING JUNIORS • Northern	
❶ ATHERTON Peter	Deans Court Chambers

For details of these leading barristers see Profiles on page 1473

The home of planning barristers in the north, **40 King St** (Raynor) contains a clutch of silks and juniors recommended for their cross-over into environmental territory. Many are felt to be "heavy hitters on the contentious side" ideal when assistance with environmental prosecutions is sought. **Frances Patterson QC** again stands out as a well regarded name. **Peter Atherton** of **Deans Court Chambers** (Goddard), chairman of the North West UKELA has a "methodical" style and takes on a substantial quantity of environmental work in addition to his personal injury practice.

FAMILY

RESEARCH: The rankings are based on in-depth interviews with over 5,000 solicitors and barristers in the UK. Chambers research is audited by the British Market Research Bureau (see page 7 for details).

LONDON

LEADING SETS • London		QCs	Jnrs
❶	**One King's Bench Walk** (Anthony Hacking QC)	8	7
	1 Mitre Court Buildings (Bruce Blair QC)	5	8
	Queen Elizabeth Building (Paul Coleridge QC)	3	5
❷	**29 Bedford Row Chambers** (Peter Ralls QC)	1	8
❸	**One Garden Court** (Platt/Ball)	3	4
	4 Paper Buildings (Lionel Swift QC)	4	3

Numbers show recommended barristers in this practice area

LEADING SILKS • MATRIMONIAL FINANCE • London		
❶	**BARON Florence**	Queen Elizabeth Building
	BLAIR Bruce	1 Mitre Court Buildings
	COLERIDGE Paul	Queen Elizabeth Building
	MOSTYN Nicholas	1 Mitre Court Buildings
	SINGLETON Barry	One King's Bench Walk
❷	**POSNANSKY Jeremy**	1 Mitre Court Buildings
	SCOTT Timothy	29 Bedford Row Chambers
	TURNER James	One King's Bench Walk
❸	**ANELAY Richard**	One King's Bench Walk
	COHEN Jonathan	4 Paper Buildings
	HAYWARD SMITH Rodger	One King's Bench Walk
	HOROWITZ Michael	1 Mitre Court Buildings
	PRATT Camden	One King's Bench Walk
NEW SILKS		
	HOWARD Charles	One King's Bench Walk
	MOYLAN Andrew	Queen Elizabeth Building

For details of these leading barristers see Profiles on page 1473

LEADING JUNIORS • MATRIMONIAL FINANCE • London		
❶	**AMOS Tim**	Queen Elizabeth Building
	CUSWORTH Nicholas	1 Mitre Court Buildings
	DAVIDSON Katharine	1 Mitre Court Buildings
	DYER Nigel	1 Mitre Court Buildings
	FRANCIS Nicholas	29 Bedford Row Chambers
	LE GRICE Valentine	1 Mitre Court Buildings
	MARKS Lewis	Queen Elizabeth Building
	MOOR Philip	1 Mitre Court Buildings
	ROBERTS Jennifer	Queen Elizabeth Building
	STONE Lucy	Queen Elizabeth Building
❷	**BALCOMBE David**	1 Crown Office Row
	BANGAY Deborah	29 Bedford Row Chambers
	CAYFORD Philip	29 Bedford Row Chambers
	NATHAN Peter	One Garden Court
	NEWTON Clive	One King's Bench Walk
	POCOCK Christopher	One King's Bench Walk
	SANDERS Neil	29 Bedford Row Chambers
	SHAW Howard	29 Bedford Row Chambers
❸	**BRASSE Gillian**	14 Gray's Inn Square
	BRUDENELL Thomas	Queen Elizabeth Building
	COOK Ian	One King's Bench Walk
	EATON Deborah	One King's Bench Walk
	MURFITT Catriona	1 Mitre Court Buildings
	PEEL Robert	29 Bedford Row Chambers
	STOREY Paul	29 Bedford Row Chambers
	WOOD Christopher	1 Mitre Court Buildings

For details of these leading barristers see Profiles on page 1473

One King's Bench Walk (Hacking) Particularly known for its children work but with a significant and growing reputation in matrimonial work, the set moves up into the top band this year following widespread recommendations from London and regional solicitors. The clerking at the set was also praised. The "outstandingly clever" **Barry Singleton QC** is seen by many solicitors as "the king of finance." "A good details man," he undertakes some children work and is "first class at whatever he does." **Judith Parker QC** remains highly rated in childcare and abduction cases and is seen as "someone to go to when you're in a tight corner." The "superb" **James Turner QC** was praised for his "fantastic advocacy" and rises in the matrimonial rankings. His growing reputation in the abduction field leads to his inclusion in the children rankings this year. **Andrew McFarlane QC** rises in the childcare tables this year on the recommendations of his peers. **Richard Anelay QC, Rodger Hayward Smith QC** and **Camden Pratt QC** are other recommended silks, and the respected **Charles Howard QC** has recently joined the set. Of the juniors **Deborah Eaton** is seen as "exceptionally good on children," and appears in both rankings this year. **Anthony Kirk** has a strong reputation in children work, while the "very able" **Christopher Pocock** is rated on the finance side, where "you're glad he's on your side." Other recommended juniors are **Caroline Lister, Clive Newton, Susan Maidment, Caroline Budden** and **Ian Cook.**

1 Mitre Court Buildings (Blair) Remains a leading set which "delivers across the board service," with matrimonial and children expertise and "good all round ability at all levels." Many solicitors view head of chambers **Bruce Blair QC** as "intellectually the brightest silk" who "always stands out in terms of judgement." The "real expert" **Nicholas Mostyn QC** is viewed as "excellent on the substantial cases." Garnering particular praise for his advocacy skills, he is seen as "creative and colourful on his feet." The "thorough and effective" **Jeremy Posnansky QC** and **Michael Horowitz QC** are listed in both the matrimonial and children rankings. **Mark Everall QC** "knows his law well" and is highly rated in public children work. The large number of well regarded juniors at the set include the "first rate" **Nicholas Cusworth** whose "great sense of humour can take the sting out of a case," **Nigel Dyer** ("the judges love him"), the "amiable" **Philip Moor, Valentine Le Grice** and **Katharine Davidson**. The "thorough" **Christopher Wood** is "a good opponent" and "gets the point over well." Other respected juniors are **Catriona Murfitt** and **Michael Nicholls.**

Queen Elizabeth Building (Coleridge) Continues to share the top billing in the field owing to its prominence in matrimonial work, with several silks and juniors receiving high praise for their advocacy and "quality of advice." The "sharp, commercial" and "meticulous" **Florence Baron QC** is seen as an "all round star" on the financial side. "So super with clients," her "clarity of thought" and "vast attention to detail" make her a popular choice amongst solicitors. **Paul Coleridge QC** is particularly rated for his "broad brush, expansive and flamboyant advocacy" in addition to a "fantastic bedside manner." New silk **Andrew Moylan QC** has an excellent name for matrimonial advocacy. Well known juniors at the set include the "articulate" **Jennifer Roberts**, who is ranked in both tables and is seen to have a "great sense of style" and "commanding presence," and the "IT genius" **Lewis Marks** who is recommended as "brilliant, quick witted" and "hardworking." Both are building up a reputation in international disputes. **Tim Amos, Lucy Stone,** and **Thomas Brudenell** are also highly rated.

29 Bedford Row (Ralls) Remains a highly regarded set, with a notable seam of junior talent that is recognised by London and regional solicitors.

LEADING SILKS • CHILDREN • London		
1	PARKER Judith	One King's Bench Walk
	SCOTT Timothy	29 Bedford Row Chambers
2	BALL Alison	One Garden Court
	EVERALL Mark	1 Mitre Court Buildings
	HAYWARD SMITH Rodger	One King's Bench Walk
	HOROWITZ Michael	1 Mitre Court Buildings
	LEVY Allan	17 Bedford Row
	MCFARLANE Andrew	One King's Bench Walk
	MURDOCH Gordon	4 Paper Buildings
	PAUFFLEY Anna	4 Paper Buildings
	PLATT Eleanor	One Garden Court
	POSNANSKY Jeremy	1 Mitre Court Buildings
3	DODSON Joanna	14 Gray's Inn Square
	HUGHES Judith	1 Mitre Court Buildings
	KUSHNER Lindsey	14 Gray's Inn Square
	PEDDIE Ian	One Garden Court
	TURNER James	One King's Bench Walk
NEW SILKS		
	JACKSON Peter	4 Paper Buildings

For details of these leading barristers see Profiles on page 1473

LEADING JUNIORS • CHILDREN • London		
1	COBB Stephen	One Garden Court
	EATON Deborah	One King's Bench Walk
2	BRASSE Gillian	14 Gray's Inn Square
	KIRK Anthony	One King's Bench Walk
	LISTER Caroline	One King's Bench Walk
	MURFITT Catriona	1 Mitre Court Buildings
	NEWTON Clive	One King's Bench Walk
	ROBERTS Jennifer	Queen Elizabeth Building
	ROWE Judith	One Garden Court
	SCOTT-MANDERSON Marcus	4 Paper Buildings
	SETRIGHT Henry	Renaissance Chambers
	SLOMNICKA Barbara	14 Gray's Inn Square
	STERNBERG Michael	4 Paper Buildings
	TAYLOR Debbie	Hardwicke Building
3	BARDA Robin	4 Paper Buildings
	BUDDEN Caroline	One King's Bench Walk
	DASHWOOD Robert	Renaissance Chambers
	HALL Joanna	14 Gray's Inn Square
	HARDING Cherry	Renaissance Chambers
	HORROCKS Peter	One Garden Court
	JUBB Brian	Renaissance Chambers
	MAIDMENT Susan	One King's Bench Walk
	MITCHELL Janet	4 Brick Court
	NATHAN Peter	One Garden Court
	NICHOLLS Michael	1 Mitre Court Buildings
	QUINN Susan	4 Brick Court
	RENTON Clare	29 Bedford Row Chambers
	RODGER Caroline	Renaissance Chambers
	SANDERS Neil	29 Bedford Row Chambers

For details of these leading barristers see Profiles on page 1473

Tim Scott QC retains a leading profile in both matrimonial and children work and advised Mick Jagger on his financial settlement and as to the validity in English law of his marriage in Bali. **Nicholas Francis** is known as a "fighter" and was praised as "one of the most modern and approachable barristers; clients find him easy to relate to." Other respected juniors include **Robert Peel**, **Clare Renton**, **Philip Cayford** and **Neil Sanders.** The "constructive" **Howard Shaw** and the "effective and ferocious" **Deborah Bangay** are also rated by the market, while **Paul Storey** received particular praise from solicitors in the South West.

One Garden Court (Platt/Ball) Known most in the market for its children expertise and "promising juniors," the set is also proficient in finance cases. Joint heads of chambers **Eleanor Platt QC** ("highly respected by judges") and **Alison Ball QC** ("a good fighter") remain leading individuals in the children rankings and **Ian Peddie QC** is also highly rated in the field. Of the juniors, the "exceptionally good" **Stephen Cobb** is seen by many as "by far and away the best junior on children," and the "sound pair of hands" **Peter Nathan** is known more for his matrimonial finance expertise but also works on the children side. **Peter Horrocks** and **Judith Rowe** are also recommended.

4 Paper Buildings (Swift) The set undertakes both finance and children work, and rises in the rankings this year to reflect the growing reputation of several members of chambers in difficult public children work, often acting for the Official Solicitor. **Jonathan Cohen QC** is "highly rated" for his matrimonial work, while **Gordon Murdoch QC** and **Anna Pauffley QC** remain leading silks in the children field. The "sound and perceptive" new silk **Peter Jackson QC** is a "formidable" advocate who handles a large amount of high profile work. Also known for his public children work in additon to noted child abduction expertise, **Marcus Scott-Manderson** ("one of the most reliable juniors at the bar") enters the rankings this year. Other recommended juniors are **Michael Sternberg** and **Robin Barda.**

Other Notable Barristers

Other well-known children silks include **Allan Levy QC** at **17 Bedford Row**, who is known for his "high profile and interesting practice." At **14 Gray's Inn Square**, **Barbara Slomnicka** is recommended and the "versatile" **Gillian Brasse** is included in both rankings - her practice is said to be "going places." The newly created **Renaissance Chambers** looks set to command respect for its child- care expertise. Rated juniors at the set are **Henry Setright** ("phenomenal on child abduction,") **Robert Dashwood, Cherry Harding, Brian Jubb** and **Caroline Rodger. David Balcombe** at **1 Crown Office Row** also received positive recommendations for his matrimonial finance work.

SOUTH EASTERN & EAST ANGLIAN CIRCUIT

LEADING JUNIORS • South Eastern and East Anglian		
1	DAVIES Lindsay	Fenners Chambers
	ESPLEY Susan	Fenners Chambers
	KEFFORD Anthony	East Anglian Chambers
	MCLOUGHLIN Timothy	East Anglian Chambers
	TATTERSALL Simon	Fenners Chambers
2	ELLIOTT Margot	Regency Chambers
	MILLER Celia	East Anglian Chambers
	NEWTON Roderick	East Anglian Chambers
	WAIN Peter	East Anglian Chambers
3	PARNELL Graham	East Anglian Chambers
	RICHARDS Jeremy	Octagon House Chambers

For details of these leading barristers see Profiles on page 1473

East Anglian Chambers (Newton), Colchester. A large set with a number of recommended juniors. "Tough" **Anthony Kefford** was praised for his confident style and aggressive approach to financial cases while **Timothy McLoughlin's** "affable and even-tempered" manner with clients make him an excellent choice for children cases and care work. "Sensible" **Celia Miller** was noted for her skills in cross-examination and her "even handed" approach to local authority work. "Charming" **Roderick Newton** was generally regarded as a "showman with a disarming sense of humour." **Peter Wain** was described as "an absolute star" in children work with an excellent rapport with judges, children, and local authority guardians. **Graham Parnell**'s "impressive analytic skills" make him an "able negotiator."

Fenners Chambers (Davies), Cambridge. "Determined" **Lindsay Davies** is "safe pair of hands" for both children and ancillary relief work. She was praised for advising clients realistically and for her dedication in "fighting a cause." "Tactful" **Susan Espley** places a strong emphasis on children's work to which she brings "extremely thorough preparation." **Simon Tattersall** was described as "outstandingly good with figures," particularly strong in financial applications. His ability to "dissect bank statements like nobody else" makes him a top choice for high value ancillary relief.

Regency Chambers (Croxon/Martignetti), Peterborough. **Margot Elliott**, "a fearless fighter," was commended for her work representing parents in child care cases.

Octagon House (Lindquist/Ayers), Norwich. "Lively" **Jeremy Richards**, recommended as a child specialist acting for the local authority in children cases, is a new entrant to our tables this year.

WESTERN CIRCUIT

LEADING SILKS • Western		
❶	SHARP Christopher	St John's Chambers
	WILDBLOOD Stephen	Albion Chambers
❷	EVANS Mark	Queen Square Chambers

For details of these leading barristers see Profiles on page 1473

LEADING JUNIORS • Western		
✪	DIXON Ralph	St John's Chambers
❶	BROMILOW Richard	St John's Chambers
	CAMPBELL Susan	Southernhay Chambers
	CORFIELD Sheelagh	Guildhall Chambers
	DUTHIE Catriona	Guildhall Chambers
❷	JACKLIN Susan	St John's Chambers
	WILLS-GOLDINGHAM Claire	Albion Chambers
❸	DINAN-HAYWARD Deborah	Albion Chambers
	HAIG-HADDOW Alastair	Eighteen Carlton Crescent
	HORTON Mark	Colleton Chambers
	LEWIS Hugh	Southernhay Chambers
	MARSTON Nicholas	St John's Chambers
	MEREDITH George	Southernhay Chambers
	MILLER Nicholas	Guildhall Chambers
	NAISH Christopher	Southernhay Chambers
	PINE-COFFIN Margaret Ann	17 Carlton Crescent

For details of these leading barristers see Profiles on page 1473

Queen Square Chambers (Jenkins), Bristol. **Mark Evans QC**, described as "the most senior matrimonial silk for years" was recommended once again for his expertise in financial issues.

Albion Chambers (Barton), Bristol. New silk **Stephen Wildblood QC** was lauded for his "gentle, persuasive manner" and "encyclopaedic knowledge of law," particularly in regard to matrimonial finance. "Feisty" **Claire Wills-Goldingham** was described as a "diamond," determined to "stand her ground" in children cases. "Approachable" **Deborah Dinan-Hayward** is "well known for matrimonial law."

St. Johns Chambers (Sharp), Bristol. New silk **Christopher Sharp QC** has "star quality" and "easily compares with London barristers" for high level ancillary relief. "Energetic" **Ralph Dixon** is the number one junior for "top notch financial cases" and praised equally for his "innovation in coming up with well thought out solutions." "Straightforward" **Richard Bromilow** has a "no-nonsense approach" to ancillary relief cases which is said to "go down well with judges." **Susan Jacklin** is "quietly spoken but packs quite a punch" in both children and financial cases. She is particularly regarded for her expertise in abduction and complex child care cases. **Nick Marston** is well respected for both child care and ancillary relief. He was widely regarded as having an "excellent bedside manner" and is "especially good with nervous clients."

Southernhay Chambers (Ward), Exeter. "Diplomatic" **Susan Campbell** is a "top notch" children's lawyer with a "wonderful way of gently and softly getting around judges." "Thorough" **Hugh Lewis** and "wise" **George Meredith** have recognised experience in child care cases. **Chris Naish** was praised for having a "calming influence on clients" in his work for local authorities.

Eighteen Carlton Crescent (Haig-Haddow), Southampton. "Meticulous" **Alastair Haig-Haddow** was once again recommended for his work in high powered ancillary relief cases.

17 Carlton Crescent (Gibbons), Southampton. **Margaret Ann Pine-Coffin** "deals impressively" with both financial cases and care work.

Guildhall Chambers (Palmer), Bristol. "Realistic" **Sheelagh Corfield** handles exclusively financial matrimonial cases and is "particularly good with distraught clients." "Fiery" **Catriona Duthie** "goes in guns blazing" on ancillary relief matters and was noted for her strength in cross-examination. "Charismatic" **Nick Miller** draws upon his background as a solicitor in his "positive approach" to financial cases. He is a new entrant to our tables this year and was praised for being "up to date on the law" and for his ability to "make unpalatable advice more appetising."

Colleton Chambers (Meeke), Exeter. "Trustworthy" **Mark Horton** enters the tables for his "human" approach to public law child care cases.

WALES & CHESTER CIRCUIT

LEADING SILKS • Wales & Chester		
❶	CROWLEY Jane	30 Park Place

For details of these leading barristers see Profiles on page 1473

LEADING JUNIORS • Wales & Chester		
❶	FURNESS Jonathan	30 Park Place
	PARRY Isabel	9 Park Place
	TILLYARD James	30 Park Place
❷	HENKE Ruth	Iscoed Chambers
	MIFFLIN Helen	30 Park Place
	MORGAN Lynne	Temple Chambers
	WALTERS Jill Mary	33 Park Place

For details of these leading barristers see Profiles on page 1473

30 Park Place (Jenkins), Cardiff. "Superb" **Jane Crowley QC** remains our only leading silk, recommended for children's matters. "Charming" **Jonathan Furness** and "analytical" **James Tillyard** were both spoken of as "extremely good with figures." "Sharp" **Helen Mifflin** specialises in child care work.

Temple Chambers (Aubrey), Cardiff. **Lynne Morgan** was mentioned as particularly "good at analysing documentation."

Iscoed Chambers (Davies), Swansea. **Ruth Henke** was praised for her "efficiency" in high value ancillary relief and child care cases representing parents, guardians, and local authorities.

33 Park Place (Rees), Cardiff. "Tactful" **Jill Mary Walters** is well known for her work for the Official Solicitor.

9 Park Place (Murphy), Cardiff. "Judicious" **Isabel Parry** was regarded for her "considered manner" and "grasp of the technical" elements of a case.

MIDLANDS & OXFORD CIRCUIT

LEADING SILKS • Midlands & Oxford	
❶ MACUR Julia	St. Ive's Chambers

For details of these leading barristers see Profiles on page 1473

LEADING JUNIORS • Midlands & Oxford	
❶ BROWN Stephanie	5 Fountain Court
HERSHMAN David	St Philip's Chambers
HODGSON Margaret	St. Ive's Chambers
ROGERS Mark	St. Mary's Chambers Family Law Chambers
ROWLAND Robin	5 Fountain Court
THOMAS Sybil	3 Fountain Court
❷ CASEY Mairin	St. Mary's Chambers Family Law Chambers
JAMES Christopher	5 Fountain Court
SMALLWOOD Anne	5 Fountain Court
❸ BAKER Jonathan	Harcourt Chambers
BRIDGE Rowena	KCH (King Charles House) Barristers
BUCHANAN Vivien	KCH (King Charles House) Barristers
BUSH Rosalind	5 Fountain Court
FARQUHAR Stuart	St. Mary's Chambers Family Law Chambers
GILEAD Beryl	St. Mary's Chambers Family Law Chambers
JUDD Frances	Harcourt Chambers
KEEHAN Michael	St. Ive's Chambers
MEYER Lorna	5 Fountain Court
PAGE Nigel	St. Mary's Chambers Family Law Chambers
SOMERVILLE Bryce	No.6 Fountain Court

For details of these leading barristers see Profiles on page 1473

St. Ive's Chambers (Coke) "Impressive" **Julia Macur QC** remains the Midlands' leading silk and is particularly strong on public law child care and adoption work. "Tenacious" **Margaret Hodgson** is well regarded for a full range of family work, in particular public child care cases involving injuries and sexual abuse. "Approachable" **Michael Keehan** was recommended as a "dogged advocate" in both public and private family law cases.

5 Fountain Court (Barker), Birmingham. **Stephanie Brown** is "well regarded as a money practitioner" and reputed to be a "formidable opponent." "Solid" **Robin Rowland** "takes no prisoners" in ancillary relief cases. **Christopher James** was noted for his "relaxed" manner in financial settlements. **Anne Smallwood** "adds realism" to both child care and ancillary relief cases. "Down to earth" **Rosalind Bush** enters our tables for her excellence in dealing with clients in complicated children cases. "Articulate" **Lorna Meyer** was "enthusiastically recommended" for child care work.

KCH Barristers (Everard), Nottingham. **Rowena Bridge** and **Vivien Buchanan** were both voted "competent performers" covering a mix of public and private family law.

St Philip's Chambers (Tedd), Birmingham. "Dynamic" **David Hershman** has the necessary "get up and go" to deal with complex child care and abduction cases.

St Mary's Chambers (Butler), Nottingham. "Well-researched" **Mark Rogers** is equally able in ancillary relief and children matters while **Mairin Casey** takes a "constructive approach" to child care. **Stuart Farquhar** is known to "get on with the job" and **Beryl Gilead** is considered "reliable" in children cases. **Nigel Page** is "widely regarded for big money cases."

3 Fountain Court "Efficient" **Sybil Thomas** is "absolutely thorough" in her preparation and covers all aspects of family law.

6 Fountain Court (Smith), Birmingham. "Personable" **Bryce Somerville** was reputed as particularly "careful" in ancillary relief cases.

Harcourt Chambers (Rodgers) Oxford. **Jonathan Baker** and **Frances Judd** are both new entries to the table. Baker was reported to be "on the ball" and Judd noted for her "empathy with clients" in children matters.

NORTH EASTERN CIRCUIT

LEADING SILKS • North Eastern	
❶ BRADLEY Sally	Broad Chare Chambers
HAMILTON Eleanor	No.6
WALKER Annabel	26 Paradise Square

For details of these leading barristers see Profiles on page 1473

LEADING JUNIORS • North Eastern	
✪ ISAACS Paul	Mercury Chambers
❶ CAHILL Sally	Park Lane Chambers
KENNERLEY Ian	Broad Chare Chambers
SHIPLEY Jane	No.6
❷ BICKERDIKE Roger	9 Woodhouse Square
COHEN Raphael	Mercury Chambers
KNOX Christopher	Trinity Chambers
❸ GLOVER Stephen	37 Park Square
HAJIMITSIS Anthony	10 Park Square
LIGHTWING Stuart	Counsel's Chambers
PYE Jayne	Sovereign Chambers
SHELTON Gordon	Broadway House
THORNTON Rebecca	9 Woodhouse Square
WILSON Adam	No.6
UP AND COMING	
HUDSON Rachel	Trinity Chambers

For details of these leading barristers see Profiles on page 1473

26 Paradise Square (Keen), Sheffield. Respected set known for matrimonial and children expertise. **Annabel Walker QC** remains highly rated in the field.

No.6 (Spencer), Leeds. The leading silk at the set is the "terrific" **Eleanor Hamilton QC** who is a family law specialist, "good across the board" and the "first choice" of many solicitors in the region. Recommended juniors are **Jane Shipley**, who is known primarily for her children work, and the "impressive" **Adam Wilson** who rises in the rankings this year.

Broad Chare Chambers (Elliott), Newcastle. The "excellent" **Sally Bradley QC** is highly rated, particularly on children work, while leading junior **Ian Kennerley** is seen as "thoroughly prepared, conscientious" and "good with clients" and rises in the rankings after widespread praise from solicitors. Previous leading junior Judith Moir has now joined the judiciary.

Mercury Chambers (Nolan), Leeds. **Paul Isaacs** retains his star reputation this year and the general feeling in the market remains that he "should be a silk, he just hasn't taken it." The "able" and "bright" **Raphael Cohen** is also rated at the set.

9 Woodhouse Square (Collins), Leeds. Recommended juniors are the "deceptively good" **Roger Bickerdike** and the "well-prepared"and "sound" **Rebecca Thornton** who "deals well with clients."

Trinity Chambers (Hedworth), Newcastle. Set with an increasing reputation in the area. **Christopher Knox** "knows his stuff," "gets to the crux quickly"and rises in the rankings, while the highly rated **Rachel Hudson** is up and coming this year.

Park Lane Chambers (Brown) The "accomplished, professional and authoritative" **Sally Cahill** received much praise, particularly for her child-care and abduction work, and is noted as a "difficult opponent in court."

Other Notable Barristers **Stephen Glover** at **37 Park Street**, Leeds is known as an "intellectual" who concentrates on the "higher power stuff." **Anthony Hajimitsis** at **10 Park Square**, Leeds has a strong reputation in children work and "always fights his corner" while **Stuart Lightwing** of **Counsel's Chambers**, Middlesbrough has an "appealing manner" and is rated on the matrimonial finance side. The "realistic" **Jayne Pye** of **Sovereign Chambers**, Leeds and **Gordon Shelton** at **Broadway House**, Bradford are also recommended.

NORTHERN CIRCUIT

LEADING SILKS • Northern	
❶ RAYNOR Philip	40 King St
RYDER Ernest	Deans Court Chambers
❷ HARRIS David	India Buildings Chambers
KUSHNER Lindsey	28 St. John St
❸ DE HAAS Margaret	7 Harrington Street

For details of these leading barristers see Profiles on page 1473

LEADING JUNIORS • Northern	
❶ GAL Sonia	28 St. John St
NEWTON Lesley	Young Street Chambers
❷ BOOTH Alan	Deans Court Chambers
DODDS Stephen	15 Winckley Square
HARRISON Sally	28 St. John St
OWEN Gail	India Buildings Chambers
RODDY Maureen	India Buildings Chambers
❸ ASHWORTH Fiona	40 King St
BANCROFT Louise	Deans Court Chambers
BENNETT Martyn	Oriel Chambers
DUGGAN Ross	India Buildings Chambers
EDGE Timothy	Deans Court Chambers
GREENWOOD Celestine	Chavasse Court Chambers
JOHNSON Christine	14 Castle Street
KENNEDY Michael	India Buildings Chambers
SINGLETON Sarah	28 St. John St
WALKER Jane	28 St. John St
WALLWORK Bernard	28 St. John St
UP AND COMING	
HEATON Frances	Deans Court Chambers

For details of these leading barristers see Profiles on page 1473

India Buildings Chambers (Harris), Liverpool. **David Harris QC** is the leading silk at the set and is seen as "particularly good on medical issues." Highly rated juniors include **Gail Owen**, **Maureen Roddy**, **Ross Duggan** and the "exceptionally able" **Michael Kennedy.**

28 St John Street (Goldstone), Manchester The "highly accomplished" **Lindsey Kushner QC** shares her practice between London and Manchester and is seen by some solicitors as a "star in the making." A solid selection of juniors includes **Sonia Gal** ("great as a money practitioner and a difficult opponent") and the "increasingly strong option" **Sally Harrison** ("good advocate, good brain"). **Sarah Singleton**, **Jane Walker** and **Bernard Wallwork** are also recommended at the set.

Deans Court Chambers (Goddard), Manchester. "A cracker," children and money lawyer **Ernest Ryder QC** remains in the top rank. "By far the best in terms of legal knowledge, analysis and competence of advice," he was recently involved in the public inquiry into serious abuse at care homes in North Wales. Highly rated juniors at the set are **Alan Booth**, **Louise Bancroft** and **Tim Edge**, and **Frances Heaton** joins the rankings as up and coming, particularly for her childcare work.

Other Notable Barristers

Philip Raynor QC at **40 King Street,** Manchester rises to the top of the rankings this year to reflect his growing reputation as "without question top of the tree for money cases." At the same set, **Fiona Ashworth** is a recommended junior. **Margaret de Haas QC** at **7 Harrington Street Chambers**, Liverpool remains rated in the field, while the "superb" **Lesley Newton**, at **Young Street Chambers**, Manchester rises in the rankings this year on the recommendation of her peers, and is known to be "exceedingly good with the judiciary and clients." A new entry to the rankings this year is **Martyn Bennett** at **Oriel Chambers**, Liverpool who has been described as the "doyen of big money work in Liverpool." **Stephen Dodds** at **15 Winckley Square**, Preston also received praise for the breadth of his practice and the "sheer force of his advocacy." **Celestine Greenwood** at **Chavasse Court Chambers** in Liverpool and **Christine Johnson** at **14 Castle Street** in the same city continue to attract market commendation.

FINANCIAL SERVICES

RESEARCH: The rankings are based on in-depth interviews with over 5,000 solicitors and barristers in the UK. Chambers research is audited by the British Market Research Bureau (see page 7 for details).

OVERVIEW: In financial services, solicitors at large commercial firms have become competitors rather than mere referrers of work to counsel. In advisory work it is the opinion of the regulator that is paramount, and here solicitors have their own relationships with regulators such as the FSA, PIA and IMRO. "The regulator is the regulator, I live with them, discuss with them. I don't deal with counsel." Sought after disciplinary work is equally scarce for barristers with little case law in this area.

In this atmosphere, the question arises whether there is a place for a financial services bar. City firms acknowledge they do turn to the bar, albeit once or twice a year, "on esoteric matters." Solicitors seek the "ability to bounce ideas" and the general advocacy skills on offer at the bar. Beyond the scale and experience of the City firms, the London offices of the larger US firms such as Skadden, Arps, Slate, Meagher & Flom instruct counsel on large scale international ventures, with regional firms and direct instruction from companies being additional sources of work. As a result, we have trimmed the numbers of chambers and barristers listed in this section. However, with the confusion and uncertainty surrounding the FSM Act and the shifting legal terrain around the flood of internet-based financial services, it is perhaps too early to write the obituary for the financial services bar.

LONDON

LEADING SETS • London	QCs	Jnrs
❶ Erskine Chambers (Robin Potts QC)	1	2
❷ Blackstone Chambers (Baxendale / Flint)	2	-
4 Stone Buildings (Philip Heslop QC)	3	-
❸ Serle Court (Patrick Neill QC)	1	-
3 Verulam Buildings (Symons / Jarvis)	1	-

Numbers show recommended barristers in this practice area

LEADING SILKS • London	
✪ POTTS Robin	Erskine Chambers
POWELL John	Four New Square
SUMPTION Jonathan	Brick Court Chambers
❶ DOHMANN Barbara	Blackstone Chambers
FLINT Charles	Blackstone Chambers
HESLOP Philip	4 Stone Buildings
❷ BLAIR William	3 Verulam Buildings
BOMPAS Anthony	4 Stone Buildings
BRIGGS Michael	Serle Court
BRISBY John	4 Stone Buildings
HENDERSON Roger	2 Harcourt Buildings

For details of these leading barristers see Profiles on page 1473

LEADING JUNIORS • London	
❶ LOMNICKA Eva	Four New Square
MARQUAND Charles	3 New Square
MOORE Martin	Erskine Chambers
SNOWDEN Richard	Erskine Chambers

For details of these leading barristers see Profiles on page 1473

Barristers' profiles 1473-1601

Erskine Chambers (Potts) By far the most mentioned chambers in this section, Erskine Chambers is the set "one would go to for pure financial services advice for companies." With the retirement of Richard Sykes QC, **Robin Potts QC** takes centre stage in chambers and for many has "come into his own" as a barrister of choice in this area of practice. He is more a litigator on corporate and financial issues than an advisor. A Bermuda veteran, he recently received a repeat instruction on whether web site information constituted a financial services advertisement. **Martin Moore** is a cited as a "useful" junior in this field. **Richard Snowden** is another junior noted for his "razor-sharp intellect."

Blackstone Chambers (Baxendale/Flint) "Very, very bright," **Barbara Dohmann QC** is a "tough cookie" noted for her FSA work. Solicitors lament that she is "just too busy." **Charles Flint QC** has made a good impression on practitioners. Possessing a "fast, intelligent mind," he has recently acted in cases involving IMRO and Clarion Ltd & Ors v National Provident Institution.

4 Stone Buildings (Heslop) **Philip Heslop QC** is an experienced financial services silk noted for his disciplinary work. **Anthony Bompas QC**, who has a "very good brain," is a responsive silk who is "willing to bounce ideas around." Experienced financial services barrister **John Brisby QC** is "just a bright guy" who is good at handling people and regulators. He is noted for disciplinary work.

Serle Court (Neill) "Stunning all-rounder" **Michael Briggs QC** is highly rated for his judgement. "A little bit of a fighter," he recently acted on a pension funds case against National Provident Institution and is someone to turn to "if I were in big trouble."

3 Verulam Buildings (Symons/Jarvis)The chambers has undertaken a range of financial services work this year, including defending a US$10 million claim against a Gibraltar-registered company in relation to allegedly unauthorised investment business in the UK. Other work includes pensions mis-selling cases and advice to insurers and other providers of other products in contravention of 'best advice principles.' "Impressive" **William Blair QC** receives instruction from large US corporations. He recently advised on a bond amount for a Friendly Society.

Other Notable Barristers At **Brick Court Chambers**, (Clarke) **Jonathan Sumption QC** has the confidence of the "classic generalist." He is acknowledged to be "superb on his feet." He has recently worked on a case for Equitable Life and taken an appeal to the House of Lords. **John Powell QC** of **Four New Square** (Fenwick) has given regular consultation on a range of financial services issues this year. This includes internet hyperlink liabilities for a large plc, and advising Birmingham Bullring on aspects of its £1 billion-plus redevelopment. Slightly "schoolmasterish," he is noted for "rather long" opinions which produce good commercial results. **Roger Henderson QC** of **2 Harcourt Buildings** (Henderson) is another recommended financial services silk. Notable junior, **Eva Lomnicka** of **Four New Square** (Fenwick) is co-author with John Powell of a financial services law book. "Very, very, clever" **Charles Marquand** at **3 New Square** (Goodhart) has returned from the Treasury, and is considered to be "a genuine financial services lawyer." Often instructed by leading US firms, he is a regular at the FSA. At the time of going to press, he was preparing to move to 4 Stone Buildings.

FRAUD

RESEARCH: The rankings are based on in-depth interviews with over 5,000 solicitors and barristers in the UK. Chambers research is audited by the British Market Research Bureau (see page 7 for details).

OVERVIEW: The distinction between civil and criminal fraud remains this year, and in addition, leading barristers in civil fraud have been ranked this year.

Barristers' profiles 1473-1601

CRIMINAL FRAUD

LEADING SETS • CRIMINAL FRAUD • London	QCs	Jnrs
❶ **Queen Elizabeth Building** (Bevan/Whiteman)	8	8
❷ **3 Raymond Buildings** (Clive Nicholls QC)	5	3
❸ **2 Bedford Row (formerly 3 Hare Court)** (William Clegg QC)	3	6
9-12 Bell Yard (Anthony Evans QC)	1	3
23 Essex Street (Michael Lawson QC)	5	-
6 King's Bench Walk (Michael Worsley QC)	2	1
❹ **5 Paper Buildings** (Carey/Caplan)	2	-
18 Red Lion Court (Anthony Arlidge QC)	4	-

Numbers show recommended barristers in this practice area

Queen Elizabeth Building (Bevan/Whiteman) This powerful set is by far and away "the leading set in London for fraud" with members of chambers involved in every major fraud case since the SFO was established for both the defence and the prosecution. "First-rate" **Julian Bevan QC** leads the field here. He receives high commendation from a variety of sources for "pure quality work." Building on a solid reputation in the first division is **David Evans QC** and the "barrister's barrister" **Anthony Glass QC**. **Timothy Langdale QC** is also recommended. Less prominent this year, but still generally recommended, are **Peter Kyte QC**, **Vivian Robinson QC** and **Alan Suckling QC**. New silk **John Kelsey-Fry QC** is considered to be a name to watch, praised for his "terrific, consistent court work." He is currently involved on the Jubilee Line Extension case. Among the juniors, **Mark Ellison** is "very very good" and is still highly rated although he has been seen slightly less on fraud cases this year. Likewise, although **William Boyce** is now felt to concentrate more on 'heavy' criminal cases, his "persuasive" advocacy ensures that he retains high rank in this area of practice. Rising up the tables are **Ian Winter** who "will no doubt be a star" and **Gareth Rees**, while **Tom Kark**, **Richard Horwell**, **Peter Finnigan** and **Ian Stern** complete a formidable array of ranked practitioners.

3 Raymond Buildings (Nicholls) Not quite as prominent as Queen Elizabeth Building, owing to the latter's sheer weight of numbers, this set is nevertheless highly spoken of as a "leader in the field of white collar crime." **Stephen Batten QC** is highly recommended here, but paterfamilias **Clive Nicholls QC** has leapt a division owing to an increased recognition of him as a "major performer" in this area. He is also known for his fraud-related extradition work in which he is described as "clever, dogged and creative." His brother **Colin Nicholls QC** too is "highly successful" in his fraud practice. **Alun Jones QC** was praised for being "amazingly hard-working and dedicated." **David Whitehouse QC** also maintains his position among the market leaders. "Crème de la crème" of the juniors is well-regarded **Alexander Cameron** who remains near the top of the tree, while his colleagues **Michael Bromley-Martin** and **Helen Malcolm** retain their share of market support.

2 Bedford Row (Clegg) The former 3 Hare Court has become 2 Bedford Row since the beginning of the millennium and it maintains its good position in our rankings, with members involved in a wide range of cases, primarily acting for the defendants. Notable cases have included Richmond Gas & Oil and The Ostrich Farm. **Bill Clegg QC** remains a deeply respected silk, although fraud is by no means the sole focus of his practice. Rising stars at the set include **Howard Godfrey QC**, who is a "great all-rounder" and last year's new silk, **Philip Hackett QC** who has "vast experience of fraud work" and is lauded as an "intellectual giant." Enjoying swift elevation to the premier division for his "unstinting effort," **James Sturman** is recognised as a "sound person to work with" and "an absolutely committed defence practitioner." **Nigel Ingram** is praised for his "excellent temperament" and **Jonathan Ashley-Norman** is highlighted as a "potential star of the white-collar fraud bar" as he rises up the rankings. **Brian Altman**, the "impressive" **Keith Mitchell** and **Margaret Barnes** were also recommended.

LEADING SILKS • London	
✪ **BEVAN Julian**	Queen Elizabeth Building
LAWSON Edmund	9-12 Bell Yard
MONTGOMERY Clare	Matrix Chambers
PURNELL Nicholas	23 Essex Street
❶ **AMLOT Roy**	6 King's Bench Walk
ARLIDGE Anthony	18 Red Lion Court
BATTEN Stephen	3 Raymond Buildings
EVANS David	Queen Elizabeth Building
GLASS Anthony	Queen Elizabeth Building
HILL Michael	23 Essex Street
LANGDALE Timothy	Queen Elizabeth Building
NICHOLLS Clive	3 Raymond Buildings
SINGH Kuldip	5 Paper Buildings
TROLLOPE Andrew	1 Middle Temple Lane
❷ **CAPLAN Jonathan**	5 Paper Buildings
CLEGG William	2 Bedford Row
JONES Alun	3 Raymond Buildings
MITCHELL Andrew	Furnival Chambers
ROOK Peter	18 Red Lion Court
SOLLEY Stephen	Cardinal Chambers
❸ **CROXFORD Ian**	Wilberforce Chambers
GODFREY Howard	2 Bedford Row
HACKETT Philip	2 Bedford Row
LAWSON Michael	23 Essex Street
LISSACK Richard	35 Essex Street
MACDONALD Kenneth	Matrix Chambers
NICHOLLS Colin	3 Raymond Buildings
ROBERTS Jeremy	9 Gough Square
ROBINSON Vivian	Queen Elizabeth Building
SHAW Antony	18 Red Lion Court
SUCKLING Alan	Queen Elizabeth Building
TEMPLE Victor	6 King's Bench Walk
WHITEHOUSE David	3 Raymond Buildings
❹ **ETHERINGTON David**	18 Red Lion Court
GOLDBERG Jonathan	3 Temple Gardens
GRIEVE Michael	Doughty Street Chambers
KYTE Peter	Queen Elizabeth Building
MISKIN Charles	23 Essex Street
PARROY Michael	3 Paper Buildings
RAWLEY Alan	35 Essex Street
SCRIVENER Anthony	2-3 Gray's Inn Square
WOOD Michael	23 Essex Street
NEW SILKS	
KELSEY-FRY John	Queen Elizabeth Building

For details of these leading barristers see Profiles on page 1473

LEADING JUNIORS • London	
✪ CHAWLA Mukul	9-12 Bell Yard
PERRY David	6 King's Bench Walk
STURMAN James	2 Bedford Row
❶ BOWES Michael	2 King's Bench Walk
CAMERON Alexander	3 Raymond Buildings
ELLISON Mark	Queen Elizabeth Building
STAFFORD-MICHAEL Simon	4 King's Bench Walk
❷ BOYCE William	Queen Elizabeth Building
DOYLE Peter	9-12 Bell Yard
EGAN Michael	9-12 Bell Yard
INGRAM Nigel	2 Bedford Row
KARK Tom	Queen Elizabeth Building
WINTER Ian	Queen Elizabeth Building
❸ ALTMAN Brian	2 Bedford Row
ASHLEY-NORMAN Jonathan	2 Bedford Row
BROMLEY-MARTIN Michael	3 Raymond Buildings
HORWELL Richard	Queen Elizabeth Building
MITCHELL Keith	2 Bedford Row
REES Gareth	Queen Elizabeth Building
WINBERG Stephen	2-4 Tudor Street
❹ BARNES Margaret	2 Bedford Row
FINNIGAN Peter	Queen Elizabeth Building
LUCAS Noel	1 Middle Temple Lane
MALCOLM Helen	3 Raymond Buildings
STERN Ian	Queen Elizabeth Building

For details of these leading barristers see Profiles on page 1473

9-12 Bell Yard (Evans) This set rises up the rankings owing to the prominence of both silks and premier division juniors who are recommended across the market. Criminal fraud work is the "dominant theme" in Bell Yard. **Edmund Lawson QC** was praised as "exceptionally talented" by a broad range of referees, and clearly stands "head and shoulders above just about everyone else." Recent cases include leading the defence in the Wickes case. Occupying the same position amongst juniors, "star quality" **Mukul Chawla** has earned numerous accolades for his advocacy, highlighted by his involvement in the Jubilee Line Extension case. **Peter Doyle** and **Michael Egan** are other prominent players at the set.

23 Essex Street (Lawson) Prominent at the criminal bar, this set also has a number of silks focusing on white-collar crime defence work. However, a clear weakness exists at junior level, where the set is not represented in Chambers' ratings. Current cases include Morgan Grenfell and the Jubilee Line Extension. Leading the field here is the "encyclopaedic" **Nicholas Purnell QC**, who is recognised as a "terrific strategist" and whose involvement in a wide range of notable cases (Guinness, Blue Arrow) has led him to be described as "driven, hardworking and accessible." **Michael Hill QC** is a "fighter" whose qualities have earned promotion this year. A practitioner of great experience, he is noted for "his immense personality." **Charles Miskin QC** is said to be "doing particularly well this year," while **Michael Wood QC** and the "dependable" **Michael Lawson QC** have also come in for market support.

6 King's Bench Walk (Worsley) Another well recommended set, undertaking criminal work on the London and South Eastern circuits. Leading defence silk **Roy Amlot QC** remains in the first division after a number of good recommendations for the man who "does his preparation particularly well." **Victor Temple QC** was also recognised as "accomplished and thorough." Several outstanding recommendations earned leading Treasury Counsel **David Perry** his promotion to the premier division as an "absolute star" who is "incredibly bright, if difficult to get."

5 Paper Buildings (Carey/Caplan) Remains a notable player despite the retirement of "great performer" John Mathew QC. **Kuldip Singh QC** is the big name here, "going from strength to strength." Recently involved in a large VAT and diversion fraud case, he is rated as "one of the cleverest around," the possessor of a "first-class brain." Set leader **Jonathan Caplan QC** has been working on a fraud at the Hong Kong Stock Exchange and advising the Barings' liquidators. He is recognised as a "tasty performer."

18 Red Lion Court (Arlidge) The set undertakes all types of fraud cases, with cases including SFO and VAT prosecutions. First within his own chambers is "that fantastic silk" **Tony Arlidge QC** who was widely recommended and is known as a "jury charmer." "Diligent and careful" **Peter Rook QC** has also been well received for his Inland Revenue and Customs prosecution work. "Excellent" defence silk **Antony Shaw QC** is seen as having "an excellent grasp of technical intricacies." A new addition to the tables is **David Ethrington QC**, who received recommendations from across the profession.

Other Notable Barristers New set **Matrix Chambers** (Blake) has claimed two notable fraud lawyers, stealing **Ken Macdonald QC** from 2 Garden Court and winning the "first class advocate" **Clare Montgomery QC** from 2 Bedford Row. At **1 Middle Temple Lane** (Dines/Trollope) a mostly criminal set, **Andrew Trollope QC** is seen as a "thorough and persuasive advocate," while **Noel Lucas** is standing counsel to HM Customs & Excise. Relatively new silk **Andrew Mitchell QC** of **Furnival Chambers** (Mitchell) received acclaim from a high number of criminal fraud practitioners as an "excellent advocate" who is "very, very bright." "The trouble is," said one supporter "that he knows it better than anyone." **Stephen Solley QC** of the newly established **Cardinal Chambers** maintains a first-class reputation, while at **Wilberforce Chambers** (Nugee) **Ian Croxford QC** received recommendations as a "delightful advocate" who "knows his way around fraud". Also highly-regarded is **Richard Lissack QC** of **35 Essex Street** (Inglis-Jones) who is "the star of the set" for fraud work. His colleague **Alan Rawley QC** is also respected in the field. **Jeremy Roberts QC** of **9 Gough Square** (Roberts) is noted for his meticulous nature, **Jonathan Goldberg QC** of **3 Temple Gardens** (Goldberg) is a respected name, while **Michael Parroy QC** of **3 Paper Buildings** (Parroy) is still a force, although less high-profile than hitherto. **Doughty Street Chambers** (Robertson) supplies **Michael Grieve QC**, who has "a ton of experience." Set leader **Anthony Scrivener QC** of **2-3 Gray's Inn Square** (Scrivener) has a hugely varied practice, but still commands respect in this area. At junior level, **Michael Bowes** of **2 King's Bench Walk** (Donne) is regarded as a "truly outstanding practitioner," while at **4 King's Bench Walk** (Rhodes) the "gifted and impressive" **Simon Stafford-Michael** is known as "one of the cleverest in the business." At **2-4 Tudor Street** (Ferguson) **Stephen Winberg**'s reputation for advocacy continues to stand out.

CIVIL FRAUD

LEADING SETS • CIVIL FRAUD • London	QCs	Jnrs
❶ **Fountain Court** (Anthony Boswood QC)	5	-
❷ **One Essex Court** (Anthony Grabiner QC)	3	2
❸ **Blackstone Chambers** (Baxendale /Flint)	2	-
Serle Court (Patrick Neill QC)	2	-
3 Verulam Buildings (Symons/Jarvis)	3	1
❹ **Brick Court Chambers** (Christopher Clarke QC)	2	-

Numbers show recommended barristers in this practice area

Fountain Court (Boswood) This set has built up a good civil fraud practice owing to its banking work but does not undertake much regulatory work. It is perceived as "a cut above" its competitors and almost all members have experience in this kind of work. **Michael Brindle QC** has an excellent reputation in this field and appeared for the State of Brunei in the matter of the Brunei Investment Fund. "Brilliant" **Peter Goldsmith QC** is recognised as "one of the best advocates at the bar at the moment." Despite his commitments in Parliament, he "always makes himself available." Head of chambers **Anthony Boswood QC** has a notable practice and played a leading role in the Grupo Torras case. **Nick Stadlen QC** is praised for his "superb advocacy." The versatile **Trevor Philipson QC** has also attained a good reputation in this sector.

LEADING SILKS • London	
✪ BRINDLE Michael	Fountain Court
FLINT Charles	Blackstone Chambers
❶ BROWNE-WILKINSON Simon	Serle Court
GEERING Ian	3 Verulam Buildings
GOLDSMITH Peter	Fountain Court
❷ BOSWOOD Anthony	Fountain Court
BRIGGS Michael	Serle Court
DOHMANN Barbara	Blackstone Chambers
GRABINER Anthony	One Essex Court
STADLEN Nicholas	Fountain Court
SUMPTION Jonathan	Brick Court Chambers
❸ BARNES Mark	One Essex Court
BRISBY John	4 Stone Buildings
CARR Christopher	One Essex Court
JARVIS John	3 Verulam Buildings
MALEK Ali	3 Verulam Buildings
PHILIPSON Trevor	Fountain Court
POLLOCK Gordon	Essex Court Chambers
POPPLEWELL Andrew	Brick Court Chambers
PURLE Charles	12 New Square
ROSEN Murray	11 Stone Buildings
NEW SILKS	
DICKER Robin	3-4 South Square
SMITH Stephen	12 New Square

For details of these leading barristers see Profiles on page 1473

LEADING JUNIORS • London	
❶ MCCAUGHRAN John	One Essex Court
MCQUATER Ewan	3 Verulam Buildings
RABINOWITZ Laurence	One Essex Court

For details of these leading barristers see Profiles on page1473

One Essex Court (Grabiner) The big name here is **Anthony Grabiner QC** who is seen to provide an "excellent, top-quality" service, but who might be "difficult to get hold of" owing to his work in the Upper House. **Mark Barnes QC**, who took part in the Sumitomo case, and **Christopher Carr QC**, who is currently involved with Chrysler v Stolzenburg are other names to take high rank. At junior level, two names received regular market plaudits. "User-friendly" **John McCaughran** is "a joy to work with" and acted on the Phillips & Drew affair. **Laurence Rabinowitz** is "just so effective."

Blackstone Chambers (Baxendale/Flint) Civil fraud forms a key part of the work in this set of chambers. A current case is the Den Norske Bank and the set was very well-represented in the Prince Jefri case. Greater involvement with FSA tribunals has been noted over the past year, and members have been involved with two FSA investigations. **Charles Flint QC** leads the field in this area with his "acute legal mind," and he is particularly recommended for his regulatory work. **Barbara Dohmann QC** is widely acclaimed for her "intelligent and strong character" and is known for being "an impressive operator – very tough."

Serle Court (Neill) **Simon Browne-Wilkinson QC** and **Michael Briggs QC** both have established names for this work. The latter is seen as a "top chancery lawyer" and is involved with insolvency-related work. He acted in the Frank Warren case.

3 Verulam Buildings (Symons/Jarvis) "Top dog" **Ian Geering QC** has done substantial work in multi-jurisdictional cases, both claimant and defendant work. He has been described as "the supreme fraud barrister" with "a wealth of experience." **John Jarvis QC** is "first-rate," while **Ali Malek QC** has a good banking practice and is also recommended for his accompanying fraud work. The "outstanding" **Ewan McQuater** provides "good solid stuff" and is known to be "bright and personable." He was involved in the Prince Jefri case and also acted for the liquidators of BCCI.

Brick Court Chambers (Clarke) Long recognised for its virtuoso individual performers, the set has suffered slightly from the absence of Christopher Clarke QC, currently chairing the Bloody Sunday inquiry. The big name here is undoubtedly **Jonathan Sumption QC** who is "an absolutely first-rate commercial litigator," but is in such demand elsewhere that his fraud practice has not been as conspicuous as usual. Also held in high regard here is **Andrew Popplewell QC** who is "easy to work with."

Other Notable Barristers At **4 Stone Buildings** (Heslop) **John Brisby QC** was acknowledged as "a really bright advocate." **Gordon Pollock QC** is a "fantastic court-room advocate" at **Essex Court Chambers** (Pollock) who numbers civil fraud among myriad other areas of expertise. The "brilliant, imaginative, lateral-thinking" **Charles Purle QC** of **12 New Square** (Mowbray) and **Murray Rosen QC**, head of set at **11 Stone Buildings** (Rosen) both have excellent reputations. Two new silks were felt to be particularly worthy of mention. **Robin Dicker QC** of **3-4 South Square** (Crystal) has been noted for insolvency-related fraud work, while **Stephen Smith QC** of **12 New Square** (Mowbray) is also highly recommended.

HEALTH & SAFETY

RESEARCH: The rankings are based on in-depth interviews with over 5,000 solicitors and barristers in the UK. Chambers research is audited by the British Market Research Bureau (see page 7 for details).

OVERVIEW: Although few barristers specialise solely in health and safety law, many have accumulated considerable knowledge and expertise of the issues and regulations involved through prosecution and defence work on behalf of the Health and Safety Executive. As the number of health and safety litigations increase, analogous practices within the bar have grown in profile. Recent trends suggest that in coming years, health and safety law will distinguish itself as a specialisation quite apart from the more general rubrics of employment, environment or civil tort.

LONDON

LEADING SILKS • London	
❶ CARLISLE Hugh	1 Temple Gardens
❷ HENDY John	Old Square Chambers
NICE Geoffrey	Farrar's Building
❸ BURNETT Ian	1 Temple Gardens
FERGUSON Richard	2-4 Tudor Street
HAND John	Old Square Chambers
STEVENSON William	Crown Office Chambers

For details of these leading barristers see Profiles on page 1473

LEADING JUNIORS • London	
❶ KILLALEA Stephen	Devereux Chambers
WAITE Jonathan	Crown Office Chambers
❷ GRIEVE Dominic	1 Temple Gardens
PUGH Charles	Old Square Chambers
❸ BRIDEN Timothy	8 Stone Buildings
GODDARD Christopher	Devereux Chambers

LEADING JUNIORS • The Regions	
❶ CAMERON Neil	Wilberforce Chambers

For details of these leading barristers see Profiles on page 1473

Barristers' profiles 1473-1601

Old Square Chambers (Hendy) Members argue health and safety issues chiefly in conjunction with PI litigation. However, many also act for the HSE on both prosecution and defence sides. "Intellectually incisive" **John Hendy QC** is a key player in both the Paddington and Southall crash inquiries. **John Hand QC** applies his substantial expertise in employment and environmental law toward health and safety advocacy. **Charles Pugh**'s environmental practice benefits from his "responsive client manner" and "positive approach."

1 Temple Gardens (Sankey) Houses a handful of well-respected health and safety specialists. **Hugh Carlisle QC** ("cool and competent,") remains the HSE favourite for high profile trial and appeal work. 1 Temple Gardens' health and safety practice is considerably bolstered by "rising star" **Ian Burnett QC** who is fast earning a reputation for his effective communication with solicitors and clients. **Dominic Grieve** MP is considered to be particularly strong as a jury advocate.

Other Notable Barristers

Geoffrey Nice QC of **Farrar's Building** (Williams) has spent much of the past year in The Hague, but nevertheless remains a leader in UK health and safety for his reputation as a "gritty performer." **William Stevenson QC** and **Jonathan Waite** at **Crown Office Chambers** (Spencer/Purchas) combine a good understanding of health and safety legislation with a "practical approach." At **2-4 Tudor Street**, head of chambers **Richard Ferguson QC**'s "Irish charm" makes him a particularly effective jury advocate. "Very persuasive" **Stephen Killalea** of **Devereux Chambers** (Burke) receives kudos for his instinctive feel for regulation and ability to use his sense of humour to advantage, while his colleague **Christopher Goddard** has greatly increased his profile this year and is newly ranked. **Timothy Briden** of **8 Stone Buildings** (Cherry) is also a well-respected health and safety advocate. In Hull, **Neil Cameron** of **Wilberforce Chambers** (Gateshill) was commended for his "dogged attention to detail."

HUMAN RIGHTS (CIVIL LIBERTIES)

RESEARCH: The rankings are based on in-depth interviews with over 5,000 solicitors and barristers in the UK. Chambers research is audited by the British Market Research Bureau (see page 7 for details).

OVERVIEW: In renaming this section, we reflect most commentators' view of the impending impact of the new Human Rights act due to be incorporated in October of this year. This also confirms a feeling that Human Rights is finally shedding its 60s past and coming of age. This area of law remains a composite, incorporating the rights of the individual in relation to public bodies across disciplines such as immigration, crime, education, freedom of speech, prisoners' rights, miscarriages of justice and employment.

At this stage, commentators can only anticipate the full implications of the act, not least the potential significance for commercial companies in this area. However, the creation of Matrix Chambers, through cherry-picking key human rights barristers at leading chambers, witnesses the legal profession's most dramatic effect so far. Whilst traditionalists may shy away from Matrix's unashamed marketing, the result for our tables has been telling.

LONDON

LEADING SETS • London	QCs	Jnrs
❶ **Doughty Street Chambers** (Geoffrey Robertson QC)	5	4
❷ **Matrix Chambers** (Nicholas Blake QC)	5	3
❸ **Blackstone Chambers** (Baxendale/Flint)	2	1
Cloisters (Laura Cox QC)	2	-
Two Garden Court (Macdonald/Davies)	2	3
❹ **14 Tooks Court** (Michael Mansfield QC)	1	-

Numbers show recommended barristers in this practice area

LEADING SILKS • London	
✪ **BLAKE Nicholas**	Matrix Chambers
FITZGERALD Edward	Doughty Street Chambers
PANNICK David	Blackstone Chambers
❶ **LESTER Anthony**	Blackstone Chambers
ROBERTSON Geoffrey	Doughty Street Chambers
❷ **MANSFIELD Michael**	14 Tooks Court
MONTGOMERY Clare	Matrix Chambers
NICOL Andrew	Doughty Street Chambers
❸ **ALLEN Robin**	Cloisters
BELOFF Michael	4-5 Gray's Inn Square
COX Laura	Cloisters
GORDON Richard	Brick Court Chambers
MACDONALD Kenneth	Matrix Chambers
O'CONNOR Patrick	2-4 Tudor Street
THORNTON Peter	Doughty Street Chambers
NEW SILKS • LONDON	
DAVIES Owen	Two Garden Court
EMMERSON Ben	Matrix Chambers
GRIFFITHS Courtenay	Two Garden Court
OWEN Tim	Matrix Chambers
WOOD James	Doughty Street Chambers

For details of these leading barristers see Profiles on page 1473

Doughty Street Chambers (Robertson) "Still at the coal face." Still alone in the top tier, Doughty Street is now threatened by new boys Matrix Chambers. Although names such as Ben Emmerson and Tim Owen are "a big loss," market perception is that the remaining leading individuals

Barristers' profiles 1473-1601

("incredible brains") give the set the strength in depth sufficient to maintain a leading position. It is thus still expected to get the top cases. The set overall has a focus on human rights and is noted for its criminal related work. Work is combined with its highly praised practice in administration and public law. **Edward Fitzgerald QC**, is an example of a silk who has regularly taken cases in Strasbourg. While he may not get the publicity of others, he has a roster of experience on headline human rights cases and remains highly respected. "He has an instinctive understanding of civil liberties and established prison law." **Geoffrey Robertson QC**, "an inspiration," is considered to "bring a weight of authority" to human rights issues. **Andrew Nicol QC** has a strong profile in torture victim cases under Article 3 of the European Convention. **Peter Thornton QC** is also well-versed in this area. New silk last year, **James Wood QC** is a "fantastic cross-examiner" who is very good on police actions. Amongst the juniors, **Keir Starmer**'s continued presence helps maintain Doughty's position. One of the "top two juniors" he has written *the* text on human rights. Having "fantastic client care," he is known for actions against the police and has helped train the judiciary on the new act. The "excellent" **Phillippa Kaufman** is known as an extremely good trial advocate and is, for some, "the best prisoners' rights junior." **Michael Ford**, who has a "good sense of human rights," worked on the Southall rail enquiry and is rated for employment issues. **Robert Latham** is known for housing issues and the tenant rights of refugees and the homeless.

Matrix Chambers (Blake) Niche new human rights set Matrix Chambers has made an immediate impact. They are "an exciting prospect which will undoubtedly be up there." Taking key lawyers from top sets it has forced some radical regrouping in its wake. Following the commercial potential of the new act, the set marries respondent and applicant human rights lawyers from a range of disciplines such as crime, immigration and employment with recognised international academics. Chair of the Management Committe, "cerebral" **Nick Blake QC** "analyses the law" and is "best for immigration and asylum." Although perhaps "not a jury man" he is praised for his "script writing abilities," and is regularly seen at the House of Lords. The "talented" **Ken Macdonald QC** is considered to have plugged a gap in criminal capacity for Matrix. **Clare Montgomery QC** ("class") brings an emphasis on government work and respondent work, notably in the Pinochet case. The new set has "excellent juniors." New silk **Ben Emmerson QC** was, for many, the "pre-eminent" junior. He is seen to have made the field of human rights his own, particularly on ECHR cases, and "has enormous command of the subject and enormous respect from the courts." **Tim Owen QC** is seen on "the interface between public and criminal law" and is "rated" for his prisoners' rights work. His elevation to silk has also been widely applauded. **Murray Hunt** "one of the purist human rights lawyers," is widely seen to be "already up there." Noted as an "academic," it is felt court experience will "move him further up." **Rabinder Singh** is a "very approachable, clear, top rate junior." **Helen Mountfield** "knows a huge amount in Strasbourg," and solicitors would choose her for "a structural analysis of a discrimination case."

Blackstone Chambers (Flint/Baxendale) "Have some fine and eminent lawyers." Commercial chambers with a track record of work in the employment and discrimination arena. Market opinion views the chambers to be less actively involved in human rights work, and skewed towards commercial work. This commercial focus, it is thought, may, like Matrix, be suited to the new landscape. "Classy" **David Pannick QC** attracts strong support from admirers, "arguably the best there is." Often seen on

LEADING JUNIORS • London	
✪ STARMER Keir	Doughty Street Chambers
❶ BLAXLAND Henry	Two Garden Court
HUNT Murray	Matrix Chambers
KAUFMANN Phillippa	Doughty Street Chambers
SINGH Rabinder	Matrix Chambers
❷ MOUNTFIELD Helen	Matrix Chambers
❸ FORD Michael	Doughty Street Chambers
LATHAM Robert	Doughty Street Chambers
MUNYARD Terry	Two Garden Court
ROSE Dinah	Blackstone Chambers
THOMAS Leslie	Two Garden Court

the respondent, particularly government side, he is "virtually Jack Straw's standing counsel." Has a "cold analytical" approach to the subject in contrast to more "passionate" campaigners. A "jack of all trades" he has "an impressive record" on discrimination cases. Acted on the case of council tenancy succession rights for a dead man's gay partner and notably on gays in the military. **Anthony Lester QC**, is a "doyen" for his pioneering work in the field. Co-author with David Pannick of a leading text, he is known by clients for his current work on discrimination. Discrimination junior **Dinah Rose** is "very good on cross-examinations."

Cloisters (Cox) Niche discrimination chambers seen to be good on employment issues. "I have an awful lot of time for them." Work encompasses sex, race and disability cases. The chambers is generally considered to have maintained its profile this year. "Well known," **Robin Allen QC** is a highly regarded silk, while "persuasive advocate and strategist" **Laura Cox QC** is a discrimination silk who is "the UK expert for the International Labour Organisation."

Two Garden Court (Macdonald/Davies) A direct casualty of the creation of Matrix Chambers. Without leading silks Nicholas Blake and Ken McDonald, the set is viewed to have lost its "intellectual powerhouse." Two Garden Court had previously been mentioned in the same breath as leaders Doughty Street by instructing solicitors and counsel, in particular for crime (inquests, death in custody), immigration and housing. It remains to be seen how the set will regroup in the aftermath. A number of barristers receive recommendations and commentators retain an affection "for what they do." The set has a bit of a 60s organisational reputation, "chances are your bundle may get lost, but when they do the case, they do it well." **Owen Davies QC,** made silk last year, is cited by supporters of 2 Garden Court as evidence of its enduring strength in human rights. He is "always there on human rights." **Courtenay Griffiths QC** is another relatively recent silk who continues to pick up accolades for human rights work. Junior **Henry Blaxland**, who is "very, very good," is rated by practitioners for the range of his miscarriage of justice cases, including Derek Bentley and the M25 murders. **Leslie Thomas** has a high profile for his police action and inquest cases. **Terry Munyard** is another highly regarded junior.

14 Tooks Court (Mansfield) The chambers drops in the rankings this year as a result of a general perception that the focus is largely on criminal work, with perhaps an over influence of the personality of Michael Mansfield. However, a number of junior barristers receive recommendations for their work in this field. "Imaginative" **Mike Mansfield QC** is an acknowledged champion for the headline cases he has taken, particularly the Lawrence inquiry, the Ricky Reel case and IRA terrorist cases. Noted for the recent cross-examination of a Brixton prison doctor. However, the consensus view is that his strength is really to be found in criminal work. A good quality advocate, he is seen to be good in cases involving serious cross examination. "His talent is to listen and talk and be part of the team." He is currently acting for the families in the Bloody Sunday inquiry.

Other Notable Barristers

Patrick O'Connor QC, **2-4 Tudor Street** (Ferguson) has a broad expertise covering crime, civil litigation and public law in "a unique way." For applicant solicitors on the opposing side he can be "p
a pain in the neck, but an immense talent." Active in judicial review of DPP decisions, he is leading figure of jury trials. **Michael Beloff QC** of **4-5 Gray's Inn Square** (Appleby/Ouseley) maintains a high profile in this area of law, and will be joining the migration to Matrix Chambers in 2001. **Richard Gordon QC** of **Brick Court Chambers** (Clarke) also continues to be used by high-profile solicitors.

IMMIGRATION

RESEARCH: The rankings are based on in-depth interviews with over 5,000 solicitors and barristers in the UK. Chambers research is audited by the British Market Research Bureau (see page 7 for details).

Barristers' profiles 1473-1601

LONDON

LEADING SETS • London		QCs	Jnrs
❶	**Two Garden Court** (Macdonald/Davies)	3	5
❷	**Doughty Street Chambers** (Geoffrey Robertson QC)	1	1
	Matrix Chambers (Nicholas Blake QC)	1	1
❸	**Blackstone Chambers** (Baxendale/Flint)	1	1
	39 Essex Street (Nigel Pleming QC)	2	1
	6 King's Bench Walk (Sibghat Kadri QC)	2	2
❹	**Plowden Buildings** (William Lowe QC)	-	3
	14 Tooks Court (Michael Mansfield QC)	-	2

Numbers show recommended barristers in this practice area

LEADING SILKS • London		
✪	**BLAKE Nicholas**	Matrix Chambers
❶	**MACDONALD Ian**	Two Garden Court
	NICOL Andrew	Doughty Street Chambers
	PANNICK David	Blackstone Chambers
❷	**PLEMING Nigel**	39 Essex Street
	PLENDER Richard	20 Essex Street
❸	**BELOFF Michael**	4-5 Gray's Inn Square
	KADRI Sibghat	6 King's Bench Walk
NEW SILKS • LONDON		
	DAVIES Owen	Two Garden Court
	FRANSMAN Laurie	Two Garden Court
	GILL Manjit Singh	6 King's Bench Walk
	JAY Robert	39 Essex Street

For details of these leading barristers see Profiles on page 1473

LEADING JUNIORS • London		
❶	**SCANNELL Rick**	Two Garden Court
	GILLESPIE James	Enfield Chambers
❷	**DE MELLO Rambert**	6 King's Bench Walk
	EICKE Tim	Essex Court Chambers
	FINCH Nadine	Two Garden Court
	HARRISON Stephanie	Two Garden Court
	HUSAIN Raza	Matrix Chambers
	SEDDON Duran	Two Garden Court
	SOORJOO Martin	14 Tooks Court
	WEBBER Frances	Two Garden Court
❸	**COX Simon**	Doughty Street Chambers
	HENDERSON Sophie	Plowden Buildings
	O'DEMPSEY Declan	Coram Chambers
	SHAW Mark	Blackstone Chambers
	WALSH John	Plowden Buildings
UP AND COMING • LONDON		
	FARBEY Judith	Plowden Buildings
	KOVATS Steven	39 Essex Street
	SOUTHEY David Hugh	14 Tooks Court
	TAGHAVI Shahram	6 King's Bench Walk

For details of these leading barristers see Profiles on page 1473

Two Garden Court (Macdonald/Davies) Still overwhelmingly the top immigration set and "tremendously obliging." "Any immigration lawyer would go straight there." However, the departure of leading silk Nick Blake to head up the new Matrix Chambers set is undoubtedly a blow. Joining him will be top junior Raza Husain. However, most observers expect the set's collective strength to weather the storm. The experienced **Ian Macdonald QC** spends part of his time in Manchester but may expect to take a more prominent role in Blake's absence. **Owen Davies QC** mixes crime as well as immigration and is not regarded as a specialist "but when he does it, he's good at it." Newly-made silk **Laurie Fransman QC** is the "citizenship expert" and "the name in nationality." As a junior, one solicitor considered him to be "the best immigration barrister from both an academic and practising perspective." A clutch of leading juniors combine to keep Garden Court at the top of the pile. "Quick thinking" **Rick Scannell** is "extremely energetic, very focused and has a tremendous capacity for work." Strong on the range of immigration expertise, "he's got a very steady style in front of the judges and presents cases well." Oriented toward the interplay between immigration and children's cases, "quick and thorough" **Nadine Finch** is "excellent at turning things around." **Frances Webber** has done some "astounding high quality work – she's a saint!" and is "very thorough with the detail of horrible cases." **Stephanie Harrison** "drops everything to provide help and gets around time limits" and has "pulled a few rabbits out of the hat!" Young hitter **Duran Seddon** ("user-friendly, helpful and bright") is recommended for appeal work, and "clients love him and respect his opinions."

Doughty Street Chambers (Robertson) Remains near the top of the list with a powerful combination of experience and youth. Strong on applicant appeal cases, often in contentious areas such as same sex and political asylum, **Andrew Nicol QC** remains a leading silk and is "lovely to work with." **Simon Cox** is a "natural performer" and has "the ability to deal with things in a practical fashion – not too legalistic." His knowledge extends beyond immigration into the area of welfare benefits and he is "willing to take on difficult issues – doesn't shy away from them."

Matrix Chambers (Blake) The major new addition to the immigration landscape. Head of chambers and leading "immortal," **Nick Blake QC** is unanimously "the best QC in the field!" Appeared recently in the ex parte JCWI case (quashing social security regulations.) "Incredibly confident" junior **Raza Husain** ("hard-working, thorough and full of ideas") is much sought-after and boosts the strength at junior level. He specialises in applicant cases and EC free movement issues. Acted recently in the major High Court CPS case that quashed the policy of prosecuting refugees with false passport documents.

Blackstone Chambers (Baxendale/Flint) High profile admin and public law set which frequently acts in respondent cases on behalf of government departments. **David Pannick QC,** "the outstanding leader for respondents' work," and **Mark Shaw** are in a "class of two or three." Although the latter may not be the current automatic choice of counsel for Treasury solicitors, he is "a good advocate, well-prepared and gets on well with judges."

39 Essex Street (Pleming) Public law set which mixes applicant and respondent cases, although it is best-known for the latter. The set continues to be a preferred choice for Treasury solicitors and other government departments. Silks **Nigel Pleming QC** and **Robert Jay QC** are supported by prolific new entrant **Steven Kovats** ("trusted a lot for government work,") who has become increasingly prominent and is "frequently instructed as the main junior."

6 Kings Bench Walk (Kadri) Progressive chambers with strength in civil liberties and its impact on immigration issues. **Sibghat Kadri QC** ("a legend in his time,") is no longer an automatic QC of choice, but is well established and experienced. Associated with third country work, "reliable and sharp" new silk **Manjit Gill QC** is "skilled, inventive and very good at finding that which is not obvious." The set is "extremely strong at junior level." Administration and immigration lawyer, **Rambert De Mello** is popular and has "been overlooked for silk far too many times." Newly ranked junior **Shahram Taghavi** "is excellent – wins important cases," and is rated as a rising star.

Plowden Buildings (Lowe) Youthful and progressive junior-driven immigration set. **John Walsh** ("good attitude and style. He's polite but firm") is "very straightforward – doesn't faff about," and is "a good reader of a judge." Along with "quick-thinking" **Sophie Henderson**, who has "an exceptionally good manner," he is associated with "good quality asylum work." **Judith Farbey** ("dedicated, knowledgeable and accurate,") "goes out of her way to see clients."

14 Tooks Court (Mansfield) **Martin Soorjoo** mixes crime with immigration and possesses many admirers. He is "very well versed in the subject" and "pretty sharp at identifying the issues." **Hugh Southey** enters our up and coming list and is recommended for his judicial review work spanning immigration and crime.

Other Notable Barristers Tremendously well-liked personality and leading junior **James Gillespie** from small outer London set **Enfield Chambers** (Gillespie) ("eccentric as hell, but a fine mind,") keeps his top-ranked junior status although the chambers is felt to lack the collective strength to sustain an overall ranking. The "astonishingly bright" **Richard Plender QC** of **20 Essex St** (Milligan) mixes immigration with some arbitration but is recommended for "excellent work on European and international issues." **Michael Beloff QC** at **4-5 Gray's Inn Square** (Appleby/Ouseley) ("knowledgeable and effective") is more of an occasional immigration figure "suitable for the higher profile cases," but his reputation and quality remain unquestionably high. He will move to Matrix Chambers in 2001. **Tim Eicke** at **Essex Court Chambers** (Pollock), "clear, concise and user-friendly," and "an impressively quick drafter," is well-respected for his specialist knowledge of European immigration issues. His applicant work generally has a European dimension, but he is starting to take on limited amounts of respondent work outside the continent. **Declan O'Dempsey** of **Coram Chambers** (McCarthy) is another barrister closely associated with European immigration issues but is less high-profile than in previous years.

INFORMATION TECHNOLOGY

RESEARCH: The rankings are based on in-depth interviews with over 5,000 solicitors and barristers in the UK. Chambers research is audited by the British Market Research Bureau (see page 7 for details).

OVERVIEW: This year, the IT Bar's leading practitioners have been separated from the leading IP players to leave three sets with a particular reputation in this area.

LONDON

LEADING SETS • London	QCs	Jnrs
❶ **8 New Square** (Michael Fysh QC)	2	3
11 South Square (Christopher Floyd QC)	3	1
❷ **Three New Square** (David Young QC)	-	2

Numbers show recommended barristers in this practice area

LEADING SILKS • London	
❶ CARR Henry	11 South Square
❷ BALDWIN John	8 New Square
HOWE Martin	8 New Square
SILVERLEAF Michael	11 South Square
WILSON Alastair	19 Old Buildings
❸ HOBBS Geoffrey	One Essex Court
SMITH Andrew	Fountain Court
NEW SILKS	
ARNOLD Richard	11 South Square
BAATZ Nicholas	Atkin Chambers
BLOCH Selwyn	Littleton Chambers

For details of these leading barristers see Profiles on page 1473

LEADING JUNIORS • London	
❶ BIRSS Colin	Three New Square
BURKILL Guy	Three New Square
MEADE Richard	8 New Square
SPECK Adrian	8 New Square
STREATFEILD-JAMES David	Atkin Chambers
❷ ALEXANDER Daniel	8 New Square
CUNNINGHAM Graham	Littman Chambers
FREEDMAN Clive	3 Verulam Buildings
UP AND COMING	
ACLAND Piers	11 South Square

For details of these leading barristers see Profiles on page 1473

Barristers' profiles 1473-1601

8 New Square (Fysh) "They are top and very popular." The largest IP set in the country has also been able to build up an independent IT practice. Well-known silks at the set are "magic circle man" **John Baldwin QC** and **Martin Howe QC**. Where the set really scores, however, is in the first-class quality of its juniors. "Brilliant" **Richard Meade** has a "truly commercial approach," while the "absolutely top-hole" **Adrian Speck** is "smart, unprententious and good with clients." A new entrant who has impressed is the "pretty hot and exceptionally intelligent" **Daniel Alexander**.

11 South Square (Floyd) With a "great reputation and nice people," this is one of the best IT sets. Their leading light, and one of the luminaries of the IT bar, is "quality act" **Henry Carr QC** ("exhaustively thorough") said to be the first port of call for many of London's top IT solicitors. "Excellent if aggressive" **Michael Silverleaf QC** is perhaps better known for his IP expertise. New silk **Richard Arnold QC**, has "commercial common sense." Up and comer **Piers Acland** was also recommended.

Three New Square (Young) Patents set who owe their place in these rankings to two talented juniors. The "excellent" **Guy Burkill** is considered "a bit of a whizz," while his "smart" colleague **Colin Birss** was praised by regional solicitors for his "real understanding of the North."

Other Notable Barristers Other IT silks of note include the "top class" **Andrew Smith QC** of **Fountain Court** (Boswood) and, a new entry to the tables, **One Essex Court**'s (Grabiner) **Geoffrey Hobbs QC**, widely praised for his "superb bedside manner" and for "getting it right in a nano-second." At **19 Old Buildings** (Wilson), **Alistair Wilson QC** is considered "clever, driven and practical." New silk **Nicholas Baatz QC** of **Atkin Chambers** (Blackburn) was also recommended. His colleague, **David Streatfeild-James**, is considered "absolutely wonderful." Also recommended were new silk **Selwyn Bloch QC** of **Littleton Chambers** (Kallipetis), **3 Verulam Buildings'** (Symons/Jarvis) **Clive Freedman** and the "always good and eminently competent" **Graham Cunningham**, who has left Francis Taylor Building for **Littman Chambers** (Littman.)

INSOLVENCY/CORPORATE RECOVERY

RESEARCH: The rankings are based on in-depth interviews with over 5,000 solicitors and barristers in the UK. Chambers research is audited by the British Market Research Bureau (see page 7 for details).

Barristers' profiles 1473-1601

LONDON

LEADING SETS • London	QCs	Jnrs
❶ 3-4 South Square (Michael Crystal QC)	10	14
❷ Erskine Chambers (Robin Potts QC)	4	3
4 Stone Buildings (Philip Heslop QC)	3	3
❸ 24 Old Buildings (MannSteinfeld)	3	2
Serle Court (Patrick Neill QC)	2	3
❹ 11 Stone Buildings (Murray Rosen QC)	-	4

Numbers show recommended barristers in this practice area

LEADING SILKS • London	
✪ GLOSTER Elizabeth	One Essex Court
MOSS Gabriel	3-4 South Square
❶ CRYSTAL Michael	3-4 South Square
MANN Anthony	Enterprise Chambers
POTTS Robin	Erskine Chambers
❷ ADKINS Richard	3-4 South Square
BOYLE Alan	Serle Court
MORTIMORE Simon	3-4 South Square
OLIVER David	Erskine Chambers
VOS Geoffrey	3 Stone Buildings
❸ BANNISTER Edward	3 Stone Buildings
BOMPAS Anthony	4 Stone Buildings
BRIGGS Michael	Serle Court
BRISBY John	4 Stone Buildings
BROUGHAM Christopher	3-4 South Square
COHEN Lawrence	24 Old Buildings
DAVIS Nigel	7 Stone Buildings
HACKER Richard	3-4 South Square
HAMILTON Eben	1 New Square
HESLOP Philip	4 Stone Buildings
KAYE Roger	24 Old Buildings
KNOWLES Robin	3-4 South Square
KOSMIN Leslie	Erskine Chambers
NEWMAN Catherine	13 Old Square
RICHARDS David	Erskine Chambers
SHELDON Richard	3-4 South Square
STEINFELD Alan	24 Old Buildings
NEW SILKS	
DICKER Robin	3-4 South Square
HOLLINGTON Robin	1 New Square
DE LACY Richard	3 Verulam Buildings
PHILLIPS Mark	3-4 South Square
PREVEZER Susan	Essex Court Chambers

For details of these leading barristers see Profiles on page 1473

3-4 South Square (Crystal) The premier insolvency set "remains the standard to which others aspire." An incomparable track record includes the BCCI and Barings cases. **Gabriel Moss QC** is "technically the best in the business" and has a cast-iron reputation for insurance insolvency (e.g. Bermuda Fire and Marine.) An "intellectual power-house," he is already considered to be "one of the immortals." **Michael Crystal QC** is "a pre-eminent and aggressive fighter in court," although his profile has possibly waned over the past twelve months. **Simon Mortimore QC** has earned fame for his resourcefulness in tackling complex issues such as the Metro Holding case. **Richard Adkins QC**, "the lawyer's lawyer," is seen as an "attentive and responsive practitioner." **Christopher Brougham QC** and **Richard Sheldon QC** are both regarded as "persuasive" advocates. **Richard Hacker QC** is "always effective" as a result of his "solid technical skills and commercial sense." He also has a notable insurance insolvency practice. **Mark Phillips QC**, ("commercial and user-friendly") is a "high-flying all-round insolvency lawyer who fights hard for clients' interests," while the star of **Robin Knowles QC** ("analytical, meticulous and able to sort out complex issues") continues in the ascendant. New silk **Robin Dicker QC** ("an outstanding court-room performer") is universally regarded as one of the star names in this area of practice. The ranks of juniors at the set also contain an embarrassment of riches. **Stephen Atherton** is "aggressive and thorough," while **John Briggs** has a proven track record of handling high-profile cases. **Fidelis Oditah** is an "academically-minded specialist," **Martin Pascoe**'s written opinions are "much sought-after," and "smooth operator" **William Trower** is "charming, level-headed, sensible, and hard-working." The experienced **Antony Zacaroli**, **Lexa Hilliard** ("a delight to work with") and **David Marks** ("a determined champion of his clients") have all gained promotion this year following overwhelming market approval. The active **Lloyd Tamlyn** continues to have his supporters, while clients appreciate **Felicity Toube**'s "hands-on approach and sage advice." **Hilary Stonefrost**, **Mark Arnold**, **Andreas Gledhill** and **Adam Goodison** have all garnered their share of plaudits from peers and clients, and remain firmly entrenched in this year's rankings.

Erskine Chambers (Potts) A company law specialist that is seen to its best advantage in such matters as schemes of arrangement. The choice of a number of blue-chip City law firms, the set includes a number of the leading names in the field. The "technically flawless" **Robin Potts QC** is a "masterly litigator" and a "fearsome exponent of the art of cross-examination." **Leslie Kosmin QC** is "an excellent tactician," while the recently-joined **David Oliver QC** (from 13 Old Square) is characterised as "a simply brilliant advocate." In spite of a comparatively quiet last year, **David Richards QC**'s reputation among his fellows remains undiminished. Among juniors, **Richard Snowden**'s name stands second to none. Clients have waxed lyrical about the "commercially aware and well-researched" nature of his opinions. He has been involved inter alia in the Sovereign Marine and General case. **David Chivers** has acquired an enthusiastic following for his "first-class commercial advice" and experience in corporate reconstruction. **Thomas Stockdale** is another "top company specialist" who is well-versed in business recovery cases.

4 Stone Buildings (Heslop) A reliable set with a liberal sprinkling of highly rated silks and juniors. Recent cases have almost constituted a 'Who's Who' of front-page insolvencies. **Anthony Bompas QC** enjoys "a fantastic reputation" among his clients, while **Philip Heslop QC** and **John Brisby QC** continue to be rated among the eminences grises of the sector. Leading junior **Robert Miles** has impressed the market with his corporate insolvency practice, and rises in the rankings this year. The "tenacious" **Peter Griffiths** remains a leading choice for contentious matters, while the "versatile" **Malcolm Davis-White** is respected for his advisory work as well as his court-room manner.

24 Old Buildings (Mann/Steinfeld) This well regarded set has been involved in some high-profile recent cases. **Lawrence Cohen QC** is an expert in both insolvency and corporate recovery. His international exposure has been extensive, and he advised on the BCCI case. **Roger Kaye QC**

LEADING JUNIORS • London	
✪ SNOWDEN Richard	Erskine Chambers
❶ AGNELLO Raquel	11 Stone Buildings
ATHERTON Stephen	3-4 South Square
CHIVERS David	Erskine Chambers
COLLINGS Matthew	13 Old Square
HILLIARD Lexa	3-4 South Square
MARKS David	3-4 South Square
MILES Robert	4 Stone Buildings
PASCOE Martin	3-4 South Square
TROWER William	3-4 South Square
ZACAROLI Antony	3-4 South Square
❷ ARDEN Peter	Enterprise Chambers
BRIGGS John	3-4 South Square
DAVIS-WHITE Malcolm	4 Stone Buildings
GIROLAMI Paul	13 Old Square
GLEDHILL Andreas	3-4 South Square
HOSER Philip	Serle Court
MARSHALL Philip	Serle Court
MCQUATER Ewan	3 Verulam Buildings
NEWEY Guy	7 Stone Buildings
ODITAH Fidelis	3-4 South Square
RITCHIE Richard	24 Old Buildings
STOCKDALE Thomas	Erskine Chambers
❸ ARNOLD Mark	3-4 South Square
DE GARR ROBINSON Anthony	One Essex Court
GIRET Jane	11 Stone Buildings
GOODISON Adam	3-4 South Square
GRIFFITHS Peter	4 Stone Buildings
IFE Linden	Enterprise Chambers
JOFFE Victor	Serle Court
KYRIAKIDES Tina	11 Stone Buildings
MILLETT Richard	Essex Court Chambers
MOVERLEY SMITH Stephen	24 Old Buildings
SHEKERDEMIAN Marcia	11 Stone Buildings
STONEFROST Hilary	3-4 South Square
TAMLYN Lloyd	3-4 South Square
TOUBE Felicity	3-4 South Square
UP AND COMING	
NOURSE Edmund	One Essex Court

For details of these leading barristers see Profiles on page 1473

is seen as a "heavyweight" and has just been appointed as the inspector in the TransTec liquidation. **Alan Steinfeld QC** has a sound name for trust-related insolvency matters. **Steven Moverley Smith** is an "energetic, user-friendly" junior, and his colleague **Richard Ritchie** acts as the main counsel to DTI.

Serle Court (Neill) Now considered to have acquired an "infinitely more commercial attitude," the set has maintained a highly respectable profile this year. **Michael Briggs QC** has an "outstanding" name for his corporate insolvency work. **Alan Boyle QC** is a new entry to the lists this year, following numerous recommendations for his abilities in contentious matters. Among juniors, the "aggressive" **Philip Hoser** continues to attract high praise, while **Philip Marshall** is "a canny operator and a sound cross-examiner." **Victor Joffe**'s profile continues to flourish, particularly in his niche area of directors' disqualifications.

11 Stone Buildings (Rosen) Continue to be busy on a range of insolvency matters, notably personal insolvency. However, despite an impressive depth of talent among its juniors, the set's ranking is hampered by the absence of a leading silk. The "popular" **Raquel Agnello** is "a great technician" who rises in this year's ratings. **Jane Giret** is "a determined fighter," while **Marcia Shekerdemian** is considered to be "a worthy opponent." The experienced **Tina Kyriakides** is felt to be a "reliable and competent performer."

Other Notable Barristers A number of respected practitioners ply their trade at sets other than the top sextet. **Enterprise Chambers** (Mann) is the home of **Anthony Mann QC**, a renowned "bulldog for his clients' interests," who is "pragmatic and good on his feet." Juniors **Peter Arden** and **Linden Ife** continue to be recognised for their own expertise in this area. **Elizabeth Gloster QC** is one of the giants of the contemporary Bar, and has been largely occupied with the Bermuda Fire and Marine Insurance case. Her colleagues at **One Essex Court** (Grabiner) **Anthony de Garr Robinson** and the "promising" **Edmund Nourse**, both retain their support among peers. "Silky-smooth" **Eben Hamilton QC** is the leading player and Head of Chambers at **1 New Square**, where **Robin Hollington QC** is still making his way as a relatively new silk. Although its profile as a premier insolvency set has slipped, **13 Old Square** (Lyndon-Stafford) still contains some leading names. **Catherine Newman QC** is recognised for the breadth of her practice, while leading junior, the "approachable but tough litigator" **Matthew Collings**, is acknowledged as an experienced advocate. **Paul Girolami** is characterised as "an immensely clever all-rounder." At **Essex Court Chambers** (Pollock) the "logical" new silk, **Susan Prevezer QC** , has recently been found as much in commercial as insolvency work, but still retains her high rank for the latter, while **Richard Millett** remains highly recommended by City law firms. Clients find **Nigel Davis QC** of **7 Stone Buildings** (Aldous) "careful, tenacious and courteous." His colleague **Guy Newey** is "clever, thorough and technically adept," with a particularly strong reputation for litigation. "Big cheese" **Geoffrey Vos QC** of **3 Stone Buildings** (Vos) is "a determined and industrious performer" and is another to have been involved in the Bermuda Fire and Marine Insurance insolvency. At the same set, **Edward Bannister QC** retains prominent status in the market. **Ewan McQuater** of **3 Verulam Buildings** (Symons/Jarvis) has consolidated his reputation through his involvement in the BCCI liquidation. His colleague, new silk **Richard de Lacy QC**, is another to gain peer approval.

WESTERN CIRCUIT

LEADING SILKS • Western	
❶ DAVIES Stephen	Guildhall Chambers

For details of these leading barristers see Profiles on page 1473

LEADING JUNIORS • Western	
❷ BAMFORD Jeremy	Guildhall Chambers
FRENCH Paul	Guildhall Chambers
MAHER Martha	Guildhall Chambers

For details of these leading barristers see Profiles on page 1473

Guildhall Chambers (Palmer) is far and away the pre-eminent regional set for insolvency. Some felt that **Stephen Davies QC** was "one of the best barristers in the country, never mind the region." **Jeremy Bamford** is seen as "a competent all-rounder," while both **Paul French** and **Martha Maher** are considered to be "thoroughly sound" practitioners.

MIDLANDS & OXFORD CIRCUIT

LEADING SILKS • Midlands & Oxford	
❶ RANDALL John	St Philip's Chambers
❷ CORBETT James	St Philip's Chambers

For details of these leading barristers see Profiles on page 1473

LEADING JUNIORS • Midlands & Oxford	
❷ ASHWORTH Lance	St Philip's Chambers
KHANGURE Avtar	No.6 Fountain Court
LANDES Anna-Rose	St Philip's Chambers
STOCKILL David	5 Fountain Court

For details of these leading barristers see Profiles on page 1473

The region's leading set is clearly **St Philip's Chambers** (Tedd.) The "commercial" **John Randall QC** has a wealth of experience, while relatively new silk **James Corbett QC** continues to impress the market. Insolvency specialist **Anna-Rose Landes** has been "doing plenty of good work recently," and the "reliable" **Lance Ashworth** is respected as more of a 'generalist' practitioner. At **6 Fountain Court** (Smith) **Avtar Khangure** has an established reputation as one of the region's leading lights, while at **5 Fountain Court** (Barker) the "larger than life" **David Stockill** is felt to be comfortably the most prominent individual in this area of practice.

NORTH EASTERN CIRCUIT

LEADING SILKS • North Eastern	
❶ ALLEN James	No.6

For details of these leading barristers see Profiles on page 1473

LEADING JUNIORS • North Eastern	
❶ GROVES Hugo	Enterprise Chambers
❷ JORY Hugh	Enterprise Chambers
❸ MORRIS Paul Howard	York Chambers
UP AND COMING	
COOPER Mark	Chancery House Chambers

For details of these leading barristers see Profiles on page 1473

There is no set with overall local supremacy, and the leading insolvency specialists are scattered across a number of sets. Top silk **James Allen QC** has moved to **No. 6** (Spencer) in Leeds (from Chancery House Chambers) and is felt to be "the only silk in the area with a serious insolvency practice." **Enterprise Chambers** (Mann) in Leeds is home to leading junior **Hugo Groves**, felt by many to be "as good a pure advocate as James Allen." His colleague **Hugh Jory** also maintains his share of market respect. **Paul Morris** at **York Chambers** (Hawkesworth) continues to have his champions. Having done his pupillage at 3-4 South Square, **Mark Cooper** of **Chancery House Chambers** (Dent) has an impressive pedigree. This has been confirmed by the weight of market opinion which propels him into the rankings for the first time as a rising star.

NORTHERN CIRCUIT

LEADING SILKS • Northern	
❶ SMITH Peter	40 King St
❷ BOOTH Michael	40 King St
JONES Edward Bartley	Exchange Chambers

For details of these leading barristers see Profiles on page 1473

LEADING JUNIORS • Northern	
❷ ANDERSON Lesley	40 King St
CAWSON Mark	St. James's Chambers
CHAISTY Paul	40 King St
DOYLE Louis	40 King St
DUNN Katherine	40 King St
MAYNARD-CONNOR Giles	St. James's Chambers
MCCARROLL John	Exchange Chambers

For details of these leading barristers see Profiles on page 1473

The region is dominated by **40 King St** (Raynor) in Manchester. Here, the "undoubted leader" is **Peter Smith QC**, described as a "robust advocate." **Michael Booth QC** is a new entry to the tables, having been recommended by a number of leading local law firms. The set boasts an imposing array of talent at junior level. **Lesley Anderson** ("outstanding") continues to be in great demand and **Paul Chaisty** is commended for his "fierce loyalty to clients." **Louis Doyle** has a "great technical brain," while **Katherine Dunn** is a "persuasive advocate, excellent with clients." At **Exchange Chambers** (Waldron) in Liverpool, **Edward Bartley Jones QC** is universally acknowledged to be one of the local luminaries, although his "abrasive" personal style did polarise opinion. **John McCarroll** is "sensible, hard-working and thoroughly sound," although insolvency is by no means his sole focus. **St James's Chambers** (Sterling) in Manchester is home to the "likeable and prolific" **Mark Cawson**, and newly ranked **Giles Maynard-Connor**, an "enthusiastic fighter for his clients."

INSURANCE

RESEARCH: The rankings are based on in-depth interviews with over 5,000 solicitors and barristers in the UK. Chambers research is audited by the British Market Research Bureau (see page 7 for details).

LONDON

LEADING SETS • London	QCs	Jnrs
❶ **Essex Court Chambers** (Gordon Pollock QC)	6	5
7 King's Bench Walk (Jeremy Cooke QC)	7	3
❷ **Brick Court Chambers** (Christopher Clarke QC)	8	-
❸ **Fountain Court** (Anthony Boswood QC)	4	-
4 Pump Court (Bruce Mauleverer QC)	2	1
❹ **3 Verulam Buildings** (Symons/Jarvis)	1	1

Numbers show recommended barristers in this practice area

Essex Court Chambers (Pollock) One of the best-balanced sets contains an enviable mixture of leading silks and juniors. In a field where instruction is increasingly going to an elite, this set remains a worthy front-runner. Leading the charge is 'super-silk' **Gordon Pollock QC.** "Master of his brief," he is seen as "a fighter and a bruiser," and remains "one of the first ports of call" for a complex case. Although better known as the supreme arbitration barrister of his day, **V.V. Veeder QC** is still regarded as "excellent at insurance work, when he turns his hand to it." Sometimes considered "a touch abrasive," **Bernard Eder QC** is "absolutely punctilious; he really gets through the work, and actually reads the papers." The "multi-talented" **Ian Hunter QC** also remains a force, albeit that his practice extends well beyond insurance matters. **Richard Jacobs QC** also receives high marks for his "quietly assertive" manner in court. "He doesn't feel the need to wave his arms around to get a result." **Jeffrey Gruder QC** is now back at his spiritual home, having lost some profile while at One Essex Court. Described as "forensically intelligent," he was suggested as an "obvious choice now that he's back at a set which takes insurance seriously." **Steven Berry** is "an excellent junior who really immerses himself in a case," while **David Foxton** is a "reliable guy who will give you straightforward, common sense advice." "Bright and practical" **John Lockey** is seen as an "attractive advocate," **Simon Bryan** is a "safe pair of hands" and **Mark Templeman** generated particular praise at the bar, where he is said to be "moving in the right direction."

7 King's Bench Walk (Cooke) In spite of the loss of Stephen Tomlinson to the bench, the set progresses from strength to strength. A devastating triumvirate of top-tier silks is augmented by strength in depth and an array of top-flight juniors. The "outstanding" **Jeremy Cooke QC** is clearly one of the sector's leaders. "Affable but deadly," he combines "solid technical know-how with excellent cross-examination technique." "We always use" **Julian Flaux QC**, say leading law firms of a barrister who is described as "one of the few real insurance specialists." Another must surely be **Gavin Kealey QC**, an "excellent and user-friendly advocate," who has been characterised as "insurance's natural jester". However, "don't let him fool you; he's tough alright." **Jonathan Gaisman QC** is "good and he knows it – he's knocking on the door of the big boys." **Dominic Kendrick QC** is "doing solid work," while **Alistair Schaff QC** "will never let you down." New silk **Stephen Hofmeyr QC** has earned wide commendation as "a guy who really knows what he's doing – he transmits confidence to a client." Ubiquitous junior **Chris Butcher** is "absolutely excellent, super in court and just as good as any silk," while **David Edwards** is a "real 100 percenter; you can rely on him to pursue every avenue." **Adam Fenton** also retains his share of market support.

LEADING SILKS • London	
❶ **COOKE Jeremy**	7 King's Bench Walk
CRANE Michael	Fountain Court
EDELMAN Colin	Devereux Chambers
FLAUX Julian	7 King's Bench Walk
KEALEY Gavin	7 King's Bench Walk
KENTRIDGE Sydney	Brick Court Chambers
POLLOCK Gordon	Essex Court Chambers
SUMPTION Jonathan	Brick Court Chambers
❷ **BOSWOOD Anthony**	Fountain Court
EDER Bernard	Essex Court Chambers
GAISMAN Jonathan	7 King's Bench Walk
GRABINER Anthony	One Essex Court
GROSS Peter	20 Essex Street
HIRST Jonathan	Brick Court Chambers
HOWARD Mark	Brick Court Chambers
ROWLAND John	4 Pump Court
RUTTLE Stephen	Brick Court Chambers
SYMONS Christopher	3 Verulam Buildings
VEEDER V.V.	Essex Court Chambers
❸ **DOHMANN Barbara**	Blackstone Chambers
GRUDER Jeffrey	Essex Court Chambers
HILDYARD Robert	4 Stone Buildings
HUNTER Ian	Essex Court Chambers
JACOBS Richard	Essex Court Chambers
KENDRICK Dominic	7 King's Bench Walk
LEGGATT George	Brick Court Chambers
POPPLEWELL Andrew	Brick Court Chambers
RAILTON David	Fountain Court
SCHAFF Alistair	7 King's Bench Walk
TEMPLE Anthony	4 Pump Court
WOOD William	Brick Court Chambers
NEW SILKS	
HOFMEYR Stephen	7 King's Bench Walk
MORIARTY Stephen	Fountain Court

For details of these leading barristers see Profiles on page 1473

LEADING JUNIORS • London	
✪ **BUTCHER Christopher**	7 King's Bench Walk
❶ **EDWARDS David**	7 King's Bench Walk
PHILLIPS Rory	3 Verulam Buildings
❷ **BERRY Steven**	Essex Court Chambers
FOXTON David	Essex Court Chambers
LOCKEY John	Essex Court Chambers
❸ **BRYAN Simon**	Essex Court Chambers
FENTON Adam	7 King's Bench Walk
TEMPLEMAN Mark	Essex Court Chambers
TOZZI Nigel	4 Pump Court

For details of these leading barristers see Profiles on page 1473

Brick Court Chambers (Clarke) The strengths here are as clearly apparent as the weaknesses. Eight silks grace the insurance rankings, but to describe the set as "top-heavy" is now a truism. Not one junior has been recommended to the tables, and it is for this reason that the set languishes behind the two market leaders. At the top, the "inevitable" **Jonathan Sumption QC** gained a vast weight of recommendation. "The damned fellow has a brain the size of a planet, and if you want to win, you go to him – it's that simple." Although no longer doing long cases, **Sydney Kentridge QC** is still considered "a huge force" for House of Lords cases.

Immensely popular with law firms, **Jonathan Hirst QC** is "as straight as a die" and rises in the tables, while **Mark Howard QC** is an "expert who is almost impossible to catch out on a technical point." "Increasingly prominent" **Stephen Ruttle QC** is a "measured advocate, always in command of his facts," **Andrew Popplewell QC** has a "sympathetic court-room manner," and **George Leggatt QC** is a "popular and likeable" performer. "Clients like" **William Wood QC**, although his profile for insurance this year is not as high as previously.

Fountain Court (Boswood) Particularly noted for his aviation insurance work, **Michael Crane QC** is "absolutely top in his field." "Shrewd and rigorous," he has an "encyclopaedic" knowledge of case law. Less prominent in insurance work than hitherto, **Anthony Boswood QC** is "great when he turns his attention to it," although he has a hugely varied practice. **David Railton QC** still commands great respect among fellow barristers, although, like Boswood, he has been seen more on banking cases this year. **Stephen Moriarty QC** also retains his position in the rankings.

4 Pump Court (Mauleverer) "Low-key, but indispensable to those who know," **John Rowland QC**'s thoroughness is beyond dispute. Possessor of an eclectic practice, **Anthony Temple QC** is well-known for acting on behalf of Lloyd's names. Among juniors, **Nigel Tozzi** "knows his onions," and merits a place on the leaders' list.

3 Verulam Buildings (Symons/Jarvis) **Christopher Symons QC** "knows the insurance market well," and is considered a "good, safe choice." **Rory Phillips** is regarded as "the star of the set." "He's outstanding, a star of the future, and I can't praise him sufficiently highly," said one satisfied client.

Other Notable Barristers At **Devereux Chambers** (Burke) **Colin Edelman QC** is regarded as a "first-class mainstream insurance man; everything he does bears the hallmark of thoroughness." **Anthony Grabiner QC** at **One Essex Court** (Grabiner) has been seen spending less time on insurance matters, with his House of Lords activities and other more commercial cases claiming much of his time. Nevertheless, "his command of detail is so fluent," said one admirer. Shipping expert **Peter Gross QC** at **20 Essex Street** (Milligan) retains the respect of a number of pre-eminent law firms, while **Barbara Dohmann QC** of **Blackstone Chambers** (Baxendale/Flint) polarises opinion. "You either love her or you don't," said one solicitor. "Personally, I wouldn't go anywhere else." **Robert Hildyard QC** of **4 Stone Buildings** (Heslop) is also acknowledged for his "meticulous preparation."

INTELLECTUAL PROPERTY

RESEARCH: The rankings are based on in-depth interviews with over 5,000 solicitors and barristers in the UK. Chambers research is audited by the British Market Research Bureau (see page 7 for details).

OVERVIEW: Some individuals in these tables are patent-oriented, others lean towards trademark work and others still have the talent to cover all bases. A number of barristers are valued for the scientific or technical qualifications that they bring to the bar as in many cases, this can be a deciding factor in the success of the legal team. The IP bar section is now separate from the IT bar.

LONDON

LEADING SETS • London	QCs	Jnrs
❶ **Three New Square** (David Young QC)	5	6
8 New Square (Michael Fysh QC)	7	10
11 South Square (Christopher Floyd QC)	4	7
❷ **One Essex Court** (Anthony Grabiner QC)	1	1
19 Old Buildings (Alastair Wilson QC)	1	2
One Raymond Buildings (Christopher Morcom QC)	1	2

Numbers show recommended barristers in this practice area

LEADING SILKS • London	
✪ **HOBBS Geoffrey**	One Essex Court
KITCHIN David	8 New Square
THORLEY Simon	Three New Square
❶ **CARR Henry**	11 South Square
FLOYD Christopher	11 South Square
SILVERLEAF Michael	11 South Square
WATSON Antony	Three New Square
WAUGH Andrew	Three New Square
❷ **BALDWIN John**	8 New Square
HOWE Martin	8 New Square
PLATTS-MILLS Mark	8 New Square
PRESCOTT Peter	8 New Square
WILSON Alastair	19 Old Buildings
YOUNG David	Three New Square
❸ **MILLER Richard**	Three New Square
MORCOM Christopher	One Raymond Buildings
❹ **BLOCH Michael**	Wilberforce Chambers
FYSH Michael	8 New Square
VITORIA Mary	8 New Square
NEW SILKS	
ARNOLD Richard	11 South Square

For details of these leading barristers see Profiles on page 1473

Three New Square (Young) Occupying the middle ground between other top band sets in terms of style, according to some solicitors. Whilst smaller than its neighbour at 8 New Square, this set ranks just as highly, and has been highlighted by some as a particularly good choice for patents, although this is by no means the extent of their top-rated skills set. While acknowledged as a great all-rounder, **Simon Thorley QC** is often cited as the man to instruct for patents cases. As an advocate, he "never gets fazed" and, interestingly, we were told of how he can even "put across a bad point elegantly." **Antony Watson QC** is a "smooth advocate." There seems to be no holding back **Andrew Waugh QC**. He attained the most positive feedback in our research at the IP bar this year and is praised for both technical ability and advocacy. Returning to his former ranking is the experienced **David Young QC**. "Exciting advocate" **Richard Miller QC** is "so easy to work with." His thoroughness and success rate are attributed to good old-fashioned "hard work." Two juniors, **Colin Birss** and **Guy Burkill**, feature in our top band. Birss is seen as a "jolly and congenial" man who's "improving with age" whilst Burkill has been highlighted as the choice of solicitors specialising in both patents and TMs and is often instructed "because he can run cases on his own." Another "hard worker" is **Douglas Campbell**, who takes his place alongside **Denise McFarland**, who is reputedly "loved by the TM Registry," and the "able" **Justin Turner.** Watch out for Up and Coming **Thomas Mitcheson** who is described as "approachable and helpful" and "always has time to sort your problems out."

Barristers' profiles 1473-1601

8 New Square (Fysh) The largest specialist IP set in the country, over 90 percent of the barristers are science or technology graduates. First and automatic choice for many practitioners who know that whoever they instruct they will receive quality service ("it's just a case of working out which level of experience you require for a case.") A few solicitors commented that negotiating fees could be tough but perceptions of the relative expense of the set did not detract from the notion of value for money. **David Kitchin QC** is irrepressible this year and ascends to our star band. Ranked highly for all types of IP work, he is praised as "absolutely outstanding" and likened to "a scalpel - he's so sharp." Additionally, he connects well with clients using "simple language" and displaying "no superiority." In court, watch out for excellent advocacy and a "terrier-like scrappy approach." The "multi-talented" **John Baldwin QC** is a "tenacious and tough fighter" and recommended for his "thorough opinions." The opinions of "superb brain" **Martin Howe QC** are equally valued and he also appears in our IT table. **Mark Platts-Mills QC**, a capable "street-fighting" advocate is "good for tricky things." He is seen to be the man for unconventional clients and someone who really "helps a client get through matters." **Peter Prescott QC** has been dubbed "a great crusader and a maverick" who has the ability to "win cases no one else could win." Experienced head of chambers **Michael Fysh QC** has "plenty of knowledge" and is "the right man for confidential information matters." **Mary Vitoria QC** has been described as a "brilliant academic," if not the type to "pull any wings off" the opposition. "Bright and capable" **Daniel Alexander** is felt to be almost too senior and too experienced for many 'junior' instructions. He shares the top band of our rankings with fellow chambers member, the well-endorsed and very busy **James Mellor** and "courteous and approachable" **Michael Tappin** who is "always fully prepared." Joining them at the top this year is **Richard Meade**, for whom feedback this year has been astonishingly good. Solicitors tell us how "he puts points over with authority and without too much padding" "that he handles judges very well" and that he's "supportive with difficult clients." **Robert Onslow** is said to be "especially good on patent infringement actions" and whilst being "unbelievably brief" still "deals with everything" and is "very effective." **Adrian Speck** is a "sparky sort and imaginative." "He'll have clients eating out of his hand" because "he sees the commercial side and not just the legal." "Brainy" **Fiona Clark** is a "gutsy fighter" and **George Hamer** is described as "gentlemanly, firm and thorough." Our up and coming category welcomes the enormously popular **Charlotte May** who is rapidly making a name for herself, especially in biotech work. **Thomas Moody-Stuart** has proved himself to be a prompt and efficient choice at very junior level and also enters our up and coming ranks.

11 South Square (Floyd) A smaller and very specialist set, which gives many solicitors the notion that it is easy to strike up a personal relation-

LEADING JUNIORS • London	
❶ ALEXANDER Daniel	8 New Square
BIRSS Colin	Three New Square
BURKILL Guy	Three New Square
MEADE Richard	8 New Square
MELLOR James	8 New Square
TAPPIN Michael	8 New Square
❷ HACON Richard	11 South Square
HICKS Michael	19 Old Buildings
HIMSWORTH Emma	One Essex Court
ONSLOW Robert	8 New Square
PURVIS Iain	11 South Square
SPECK Adrian	8 New Square
VANHEGAN Mark	11 South Square
❸ ACLAND Piers	11 South Square
CAMPBELL Douglas	Three New Square
CLARK Fiona	8 New Square
HAMER George	8 New Square
LAWRENCE Heather	11 South Square
MCFARLAND Denise	Three New Square
REID Jacqueline	11 South Square
SHIPLEY Graham	19 Old Buildings
TRITTON Guy	One Raymond Buildings
TURNER Justin	Three New Square
WHITTLE Henry	11 South Square
UP AND COMING	
EDENBOROUGH Michael	One Raymond Buildings
MAY Charlotte	8 New Square
MITCHESON Thomas	Three New Square
MOODY-STUART Thomas	8 New Square

For details of these leading barristers see Profiles on page 1473

ship with members of chambers. "They become part of the team," one practitioner said of the barristers and clerks. "They muck in and don't have a stand-offish attitude." A strongly endorsed promotion in the rankings this year for "complete treasure" **Henry Carr QC** who is "maturing well into silk" and has a knack of appearing "deceptively laid back." Completing the near monopoly of the band one ranking are **Christopher Floyd QC** ("technically excellent and a good advocate") and **Michael Silverleaf QC** ("clear and direct" and "very good on complicated things.") New silk **Richard Arnold QC** is "incisive and good on gritty technical stuff" and ideal for clients who can match this. He "gets into a case," is "always well prepared" and "his advocacy is superb." Biochemist **Richard Hacon** is commended for "excellent paperwork," thoroughness and approachability. Cited as "very knowledgeable on jurisdictional issues," **Iain Purvis** gives advice that is "commercial and practical." "He's calm and constructive and adds value." **Mark Vanhegan** is "always willing to roll his sleeves up." "Clear thinking" **Piers Acland** has returned to the bar after his sojourn at Hammond Suddards and many are glad he has made this decision. Some also feel that having experienced the other side of the profession he will now have additional insight into the barrister-client relationship. **Heather Lawrence** and **Jacqueline Reid** both received a number of recommendations. "Precise" **Henry Whittle** is said to have "a wonderful way with the judges."

One Essex Court (Grabiner) A non specialist set that is ranked on the back of the reputation of Geoffrey Hobbs and a supporting junior. "Urbane" **Geoffrey Hobbs QC** is widely perceived as the hottest property on the market for TMs and 'grey goods' work, but a number of top practitioners confirmed they have no hesitation in instructing him on patent matters. "Switched on" **Emma Himsworth** is very much seen in the role of protégé to Hobbs and loves a "winning case."

19 Old Buildings (Wilson) For both patent and TM work, **Alastair Wilson QC** is "extremely capable and effective on cases which require an academic argument." **Michael Hicks** is a "client-friendly" lawyer and a "superb team player." Former computer scientist **Graham Shipley** is also ranked.

One Raymond Buildings (Morcom) **Christopher Morcom QC** is viewed as "a TM encyclopaedia" and his opinions are valued highly. **Guy Tritton** is another ranked lawyer with a broad ranging practice. Up and coming **Michael Edenborough** is seen to be "worth watching."

Other Notable Barrister Rising up from the new silk category, **Michael Bloch QC** of **Wilberforce Chambers** (Nugee) is described as a "non-bombastic" lawyer who "issues a quiet confidence" "and isn't afraid of detail."

LICENSING

RESEARCH: The rankings are based on in-depth interviews with over 5,000 solicitors and barristers in the UK. Chambers research is audited by the British Market Research Bureau (see page 7 for details).

Barristers' profiles 1473-1601

LONDON

LEADING SETS • London	QCs	Jnrs
❶ 3 Raymond Buildings (Clive Nicholls QC)	3	5

Numbers show recommended barristers in this practice area

LEADING SILKS • London	
❶ BECKETT Richard	3 Raymond Buildings
❷ GRAY Gilbert	3 Raymond Buildings
❸ FITZGERALD Susanna	One Essex Court
MEHIGAN Simon	5 Paper Buildings
❹ MOGER Christopher	4 Pump Court
NEW SILKS	
DE HAAN Kevin	3 Raymond Buildings

For details of these leading barristers see Profiles on page 1473

LEADING JUNIORS • London	
❶ RANKIN James	3 Raymond Buildings
❷ BROMLEY-MARTIN Michael	3 Raymond Buildings
GOURIET Gerald	3 Raymond Buildings
MUIR Andrew	3 Raymond Buildings
WALSH Stephen	3 Raymond Buildings
❸ MONKCOM Stephen	Tanfield Chambers
TOZZI Nigel	4 Pump Court

For details of these leading barristers see Profiles on page 1473

3 Raymond Buildings (Nicholls) **Richard Beckett QC** is widely regarded as one of the most experienced and capable licensing silks in the country. He is seen to be "everyone's favourite uncle." He is "laid-back" with "an extremely pleasant manner," but he is still regarded as being "incredibly sharp." He is also seen to be a "courteous, charming and gently persuasive advocate." Consistently high demand for his services is his only drawback, in that he is "so busy that he needs to be booked months in advance if you want to use him." **Gilbert Gray QC** is "an entertaining advocate" and an "old-style performer" who "never fails to impress courts or clients." **Kevin de Haan QC** has recently taken silk, and is a "passionate advocate" with a "fire in his belly to win." He is seen to give "full value for money", and has a bent towards betting and gaming matters, in which many practitioners instruct him "without exception – if he's available." **James Rankin** is "the first port of call" for many licensing practitioners throughout the country. He is considered "an absurdly smooth advocate" and for many practitioners, he is "quite simply the best junior barrister for licensing matters in the country." **Gerald Gouriet** has re-established himself as "one of the leading lights" at the licensing Bar since returning to practice last year from the US. He is widely regarded as being a "brilliantly unpredictable" and "unorthodox" advocate, and this is seen as his "greatest weapon" against his opponents in court. **Michael Bromley-Martin** "always prepares well" and is a "capable and determined advocate." **Andrew Muir** has "a great deal of experience" in licensing matters and "always fights his corner very hard." **Stephen Walsh** is "dependable" and "always gives his all" in court. He is particularly well-liked by clients for his "down-to-earth and approachable manner."

Other Notable Barristers Susanna Fitzgerald QC from **One Essex Court** (Grabiner) has continued to build her reputation since taking silk last year. She is seen to possess "impressive oratorical abilities," both when in court and on the occasions when she has been giving presentations at various licensing conferences. She is also seen as "invariably precise and well-prepared," and continues to have "a particular strength in gaming matters." **Simon Mehigan QC** has returned to **5 Paper Buildings** (Carey/Caplan) and continues to edit a leading licensing text. He is regarded as having "one of the sharpest minds around" in the licensing field, although there has been comment that he may be "better on paper than he is in court." **Christopher Moger QC** of **4 Pump Court** (Mauleverer) is still retained by the Gaming Board, and as such is instructed "purely for gaming matters." He is widely regarded as being the "the premier gaming barrister in London," and continues to have a strong involvement in casino licensing. **Stephen Monkcom** of **Tanfield Chambers** (Thompson/Guy) made his name by writing "one of the leading gaming law textbooks," and continues to command his share of market support. **Nigel Tozzi** of **4 Pump Court** (Mauleverer) possesses a "sharp and delving mind" as well as being "good on his feet," and remains prominent in both gaming and licensing matters.

WESTERN CIRCUIT

LEADING SILKS • Western	
❶ GLEN Ian	Guildhall Chambers

For details of these leading barristers see Profiles on page 1473

LEADING JUNIORS • Western	
❶ WADSLEY Peter	St John's Chambers
❷ BARKER Kerry	Guildhall Chambers

For details of these leading barristers see Profiles on page 1473

Ian Glen QC at **Guildhall Chambers** (Palmer) remains the leading licensing silk in the region. He is seen as "good on his feet" when appearing in court, and while he deals with all elements of liquor licensing, he is handling an increasing amount of betting and gaming matters. **Peter Wadsley** at **St John's Chambers** (Sharp) is widely regarded as the top junior for licensing matters on the Western Circuit, even though he also has a thriving practice in planning law. He is seen to be "consistently excellent, both on paper and in court." **Kerry Barker** at **Guildhall Chambers** (Palmer) is seen to be "a good all-round licensing advocate" and is also well regarded for his "comprehensive written opinions."

MIDLANDS & OXFORD CIRCUIT

LEADING SILKS • Midlands & Oxford	
✪ SAUNDERS John	4 Fountain Court

For details of these leading barristers see Profiles on page 1473

LEADING JUNIORS • Midlands & Oxford	
❶ GOSLING Jonathan	4 Fountain Court

For details of these leading barristers see Profiles on page 1473

John Saunders QC at **4 Fountain Court** (Wakerley) is now instructed in licensing matters by practitioners from all over the country, and is widely regarded as a silk whose "star has well and truly risen" in the licensing field. He is seen to be "very knowledgeable" and has "great attention to detail" in his written opinions, as well as being a "thoroughly impressive" and "tenacious" advocate. **John Gosling** at the same set is also highly rated for his "charming manner" and "practical advice."

WALES & CHESTER CIRCUIT

LEADING JUNIORS • Wales & Chester	
❶ WALTERS Graham	33 Park Place
WALTERS Jonathan	33 Park Place

For details of these leading barristers see Profiles on page 1473

Jonathan Walters and **Graham Walters** at **33 Park Place** (Rees) are still regarded as the "main men" for licensing matters on the Welsh circuit. Indeed, they are seen to be the only two barristers in Wales who actually "hold themselves out to be licensing specialists."

NORTH EASTERN CIRCUIT

LEADING JUNIORS • North Eastern	
❶ SLOAN Paul	Trinity Chambers
❷ HOLLAND Charles	Trinity Chambers
KRAMER Philip	Plowden Buildings

For details of these leading barristers see Profiles on page 1473

Paul Sloan at **Trinity Chambers** (Hedworth) was widely seen to be "the number one junior for licensing in this neck of the woods," even though he also has an extensive criminal practice. He has not only appeared for a variety of applicants, but also has regularly represented the police for objections. He is regarded as a "sharp," "thorough" and "personable" advocate. **Charles Holland** at **Trinity Chambers** is "starting to establish himself in the licensing field," while **Philip Kramer** at **Plowden Buildings** (Lowe) is seen to have "a good understanding of the law."

NORTHERN CIRCUIT

LEADING SILKS • Northern	
❶ GOLDSTONE Clement	28 St. John St

For details of these leading barristers see Profiles on page 1473

LEADING JUNIORS • Northern	
❶ WALSH Martin	Peel Court Chambers

For details of these leading barristers see Profiles on page 1473

Clement Goldstone QC at **28 St John Street** (Goldstone) remains well thought of in both the North and in London for his "vast licensing experience" and the "sheer force of his personality" when appearing in court. He remains "the silk to use" for many practitioners on the Northern Circuit. **Martin Walsh** at **Peel Court Chambers** (Shorrock) was seen to be "technically very proficient" as well as being "able to get along very well with clients." Said to have "a tremendous ability to read the mood of courts," he is still widely regarded as the North's leading junior for licensing matters.

MEDIA & ENTERTAINMENT

RESEARCH: The rankings are based on in-depth interviews with over 5,000 solicitors and barristers in the UK. Chambers research is audited by the British Market Research Bureau (see page 7 for details).

OVERVIEW: Only a handful of barristers have managed to create substantive media and entertainment practices. They are joined in this section by those who are also seen to have built up a sufficient reputation for handling such cases. This table does not include those who are recommended for their expertise in defamation, and we refer you to that section of the book. Once again, the following table is more heavily dominated by disputes pertaining to music than those relating to any other sector of the entertainment industry.

LONDON

LEADING SETS • London	QCs	Jnrs
❶ **Blackstone Chambers** (Baxendale/Flint)	3	2
❷ **Brick Court Chambers** (Christopher Clarke QC)	4	-
Essex Court Chambers (Gordon Pollock QC)	1	2
5 New Square (Jonathan Rayner James QC)	2	2
8 New Square (Michael Fysh QC SC)	3	2
❸ **7 Stone Buildings** (Charles Aldous QC)	2	1
3 Verulam Buildings (Symons/Jarvis)	1	1

Numbers show recommended barristers in this practice area

Blackstone Chambers (Baxendale/Flint) **Robert Englehart QC** is more than a respected figurehead and "doesn't miss a point." Far and away the most sought after and best regarded new silk in this area for some time is **Ian Mill QC**, who received astounding feedback. He has "great lawyering skills and is fiercely bright" and "he has bothered to get to know the industry and the personalities well." New this year to our rankings is **Barbara Dohmann QC** ("very tough and a brilliant cross examiner"). At junior level, "pragmatic" **Pushpinder Saini** keeps impressing with his "calmness and assurance that imparts confidence." "James Bond-like" **Robert Howe** comes from the Englehart school and has "a commanding presence in court."

Brick Court Chambers (Clarke) **Jonathan Sumption QC** appears for his proven skills as a top commercial silk. **Mark Cran QC** comes across as "direct with no fawning" and can "throw his weight around." **Jonathan Hirst QC** may, following his appointment as Chair of the Bar Council, be less available for instruction but is a well regarded figure. **Sydney Kentridge QC** is still seen to have a presence and to be particularly good for copyright related matters.

Essex Court Chambers (Pollock) **Gordon Pollock QC** "has a good name in the music business" and is a clever choice for advisory work as well as high level advocacy. Popular and well-liked **Vernon Flynn** has "plenty of savvy and you can use him to great effect." **Richard Millett** receives high praise from very senior entertainment litigators.

5 New Square (Rayner James) **Kevin Garnett QC** "has a laconic style but is a very fair opponent and has a good brain." **Jonathan Rayner James QC** is a "great authority on the copyright side" and "gets into the detail." "Good, resilient advocate" **Paul Dickens** "has guts" and "takes a case and really runs with it." **Amanda Michaels** is also well regarded.

8 New Square (Fysh) **John Baldwin QC** has had quite an active year and is favoured by leading players. "Incisive" **Peter Prescott QC** is "perfect for difficult copyright cases." "An academic approach" comes from **Mary Vitoria QC**, who is "good on erudite points of copyright law." "Favourite" choice for many, **Daniel Alexander** "understands the law and is good on his feet." **James Mellor** has been instructed on a number of music cases.

7 Stone Buildings (Aldous) **Nigel Davis QC** is "highly intelligent, a fighter and a tough trial lawyer." Instructing solicitors feel that "for legal arguments" (as opposed to contested witness actions) **David Unwin QC** "is perfect." **Edmund Cullen** is praised for his "good grass roots common sense" and it was remarked that he was a "mini Nigel Davis." He can be "quite venomous in court."

Barristers' profiles 1473-1601

3 Verulam Buildings (Symons/Jarvis) The set's leading silk in this field is **Nicholas Merriman QC**, who has a long-standing reputation for media and entertainment cases. **Andrew Sutcliffe** has emerged as *the* junior in the field this year. He's described as "enormously sweet," and "extremely hard working," and has "a very good grasp of the music industry." He is also noted for "an extreme aversion to defeat."

Other Notable Barristers "Clients like" **Richard Price QC** of **Littleton Chambers** (Kallipetis) and solicitors "know where they are with him - he's good, earthy and sound." **Michael Silverleaf QC** of **11 South Square** (Floyd) has experience of some of the highest profile work in recent years. **David Waksman** at **Fountain Court** (Boswood) continues successfully in his bid to become one of the top entertainment barristers. Now into our number one band, Waksman is busy and well liked by those who also see the best of the action. **Stephen Bate** of **5 Raymond Buildings** (Milmo) is "very approachable and easy to work with." **Simon Barker** of **13 Old Square** (Lyndon-Stanford) is also ranked along with **Vincent Nelson** at **39 Essex Street** (Glasgow.)

LEADING SILKS • London	
❶ **ENGLEHART Robert**	Blackstone Chambers
GARNETT Kevin	5 New Square
MILL Ian	Blackstone Chambers
❷ **POLLOCK Gordon**	Essex Court Chambers
RAYNER JAMES Jonathan	5 New Square
SUMPTION Jonathan	Brick Court Chambers
❸ **BALDWIN John**	8 New Square
DAVIS Nigel	7 Stone Buildings
DOHMANN Barbara	Blackstone Chambers
PRICE Richard	Littleton Chambers
❹ **CRAN Mark**	Brick Court Chambers
HIRST Jonathan	Brick Court Chambers
KENTRIDGE Sydney	Brick Court Chambers
MERRIMAN Nicholas	3 Verulam Buildings
PRESCOTT Peter	8 New Square
SILVERLEAF Michael	11 South Square
UNWIN David	7 Stone Buildings
VITORIA Mary	8 New Square

For details of these leading barristers see Profiles on page 1473

LEADING JUNIORS • London	
✪ **SUTCLIFFE Andrew**	3 Verulam Buildings
❶ **ALEXANDER Daniel**	8 New Square
SAINI Pushpinder	Blackstone Chambers
WAKSMAN David	Fountain Court
❷ **BATE Stephen**	5 Raymond Buildings
DICKENS Paul	5 New Square
FLYNN Vernon	Essex Court Chambers
HOWE Robert	Blackstone Chambers
MILLETT Richard	Essex Court Chambers
❸ **BARKER Simon**	13 Old Square
CULLEN Edmund	7 Stone Buildings
MELLOR James	8 New Square
MICHAELS Amanda	5 New Square
NELSON Vincent	39 Essex Street

For details of these leading barristers see Profiles on page 1473

PARLIAMENTARY

RESEARCH: The rankings are based on in-depth interviews with over 5,000 solicitors and barristers in the UK. Chambers research is audited by the British Market Research Bureau (see page 7 for details).

OVERVIEW: Private Members Bill work is now rare due to Transport and Works Act Orders resulting in ever decreasing instructions for barristers in this area. This is illustrated by the fact that there were only ten Private Members Bills in 1999 and at the time of research only four in 2000. With such statistics, it is clear that 'pure' parliamentary is hardly a growth area for barristers. More traditional parliamentary work is conducted under the same procedure with the same barristers, but "called by another name." Much of the transport work traditionally undertaken by parliamentary barristers has now migrated to the planning bar in the form of Transport and Works Act orders with on-site enquiries rather than parliament being the locus of most transport related matters.
We have therefore dropped a number of chambers and barristers from our lists, many of whom would still appear if the volume of work available was at the level of only a few years ago. If the status quo prevails it is likely this section will maintain only an historical profile in our next edition.

LONDON

LEADING SETS • London	QCs	Jnrs
❶ **2 Harcourt Buildings** (Mr Gerard Ryan QC)	4	4
❷ **4 Breams Buildings** (Christopher Lockhart-Mummery QC)	3	1

Numbers show recommended barristers in this practice area

LEADING SILKS • London	
✪ **PURCHAS Robin**	2 Harcourt Buildings
❶ **FITZGERALD Michael**	2 Mitre Court Buildings
GEORGE Charles	2 Harcourt Buildings
❷ **KATKOWSKI Christopher**	4 Breams Buildings
LAURENCE George	12 New Square
RYAN Gerard	2 Harcourt Buildings
❸ **CAMERON Sheila**	2 Harcourt Buildings
CLARKSON Patrick	1 Serjeants' Inn
HICKS William	1 Serjeants' Inn
LOCKHART-MUMMERY Christopher	4 Breams Buildings
MACLEOD Nigel	4 Breams Buildings

For details of these leading barristers see Profiles on page 1473

LEADING JUNIORS • London	
❶ **COMYN Timothy**	2 Harcourt Buildings
NEWCOMBE Andrew	2 Harcourt Buildings
PETCHEY Philip	2 Harcourt Buildings
❷ **ASPREY Nicholas**	Serle Court
HILL Thomas	4-5 Gray's Inn Square
LIEVEN Nathalie	4 Breams Buildings
TAIT Andrew	2 Harcourt Buildings

For details of these leading barristers see Profiles on page 1473

Barristers' profiles 1473-1601

2 Harcourt Buildings (Ryan) First-class set which is the most robust survivor at the parliamentary bar. "The star players are there." However with the paucity of private parliamentary bills, even this chambers is struggling to claim a significant practice in this area. "Outstanding" silk **Robin Purchas QC**, ("lovely to deal with,") is rated for his detailed analysis of parliamentary issues. He is acknowledged to have a "leading edge." **Charles George QC** is a "a leading silk in this field" with experience of tramway orders in Manchester and Leeds. "Brilliant" **Gerard Ryan QC** has recently done promotional work for Thameslink. Fellow silk **Sheila Cameron QC** has advised on the Thames River Safety Enquiry. Amongst juniors, "immensely authoritative" newcomer **Tim Comyn** makes an impact both for his ability to "cut to the heart of the matter quickly" and his Transport and Works Act enquiry work. "Likeable" **Andrew Newcombe** is noted for his "meticulous mind." "First class junior," **Philip Petchey**, is a technically minded lawyer who will give "painstaking backup" to a case. **Andrew Tait** is another name to retain market support.

4 Breams Buildings (Lockhart-Mummery) Set with second largest number of leading individuals, who like other chambers finds its work is being conducted under another guise at the planning bar. "Approachable and user friendly," **Christopher Katkowski QC** is a well known "up and coming" silk who acts for Cheshire County Council. **Christopher Lockhart-Mummery QC** is thought to have had a reduced profile this year, but has a name which still carries weight with law firms. Fellow silk, **Nigel MacLeod QC** has a "reliable reputation" in the field. "Sparky bright" junior **Natalie Lieven** has made her presence felt and is considered a "thorough practitioner."

Other Notable Barristers Michael FitzGerald QC at **2 Mitre Court Buildings** (FitzGerald) is an "outstanding performer with a compelling court-room manner." **George Laurence QC** at **12 New Square** (Mowbray) is "a delightful guy with a persuasive manner." He is noted particularly for his work on footpaths and bridleways. At **1 Serjeants' Inn** (Read) **Patrick Clarkson QC** has the "spark to engage a committee" and is one of the few conducting special order procedures in parliamentary work. His colleague **William Hicks QC**, whilst considered "excellent" is thought to have been less active in this field of late. **Nicholas Asprey** at **Serle Court** (Neill) is "an academically gifted junior." **Thomas Hill** of **4-5 Gray's Inn Square** (Appleby/Ouseley) is a popular barrister with long-standing inquiry experience.

PARTNERSHIP

RESEARCH: The rankings are based on in-depth interviews with over 5,000 solicitors and barristers in the UK. Chambers research is audited by the British Market Research Bureau (see page 7 for details).

LONDON

LEADING SETS • London	QCs	Jnrs
❶ **48 Bedford Row** (Roderick I'Anson Banks)	-	1
❷ **Serle Court** (Patrick Neill QC)	2	2

Numbers show recommended barristers in this practice area

LEADING SILKS • London	
❶ **BRIGGS Michael**	Serle Court
❷ **DAVIS Nigel**	7 Stone Buildings
STEINFELD Alan	24 Old Buildings
WILLIAMSON Hazel	13 Old Square
NEW SILKS	
HINKS Frank	Serle Court

LEADING JUNIORS • London	
❶ **BANKS Roderick I'Anson**	48 Bedford Row
❷ **BLACKETT-ORD Mark**	5 Stone Buildings
❸ **GOURGEY Alan**	11 Stone Buildings
MACHELL John	Serle Court
WHITTAKER John	Serle Court

For details of these leading barristers see Profiles on page 1473

48 Bedford Row (Banks) **Roderick I'Anson Banks** is the "undisputed guru" of partnership law at the bar. "He may be a bit difficult, but you'd be a fool to go anywhere else." Considered "an expert draftsman," he remains the only partnership specialist in town.

Serle Court (Briggs) **Michael Briggs QC** "has a deserved reputation" in this area of practice, although his own practice is clearly far more extensive than partnership law. New silk **Frank Hinks QC** has "bags of experience" and is a "safe pair of hands." **John Whittaker** "certainly knows his onions," while **John Machell** is "young, doing the work and making a name for himself."

Other Notable Barristers **Hazel Williamson QC** of **13 Old Square** (Lyndon-Stanford) "has a nice manner with clients," while **Nigel Davis QC** of **7 Stone Buildings** (Aldous) is "perfectly sound, if a bit old school." At **24 Old Buildings** (Mann/Steinfeld) **Alan Steinfeld QC** is "ferociously intelligent." **Mark Blackett-Ord** at **5 Stone Buildings** (Harrod) is regarded as "excellent if you want an opinion." **Alan Gourgey** at **11 Stone Buildings** (Rosen) is "someone I'd refer work to any day."

NORTHERN CIRCUIT

LEADING SILKS • Northern	
❶ **JONES Edward Bartley**	Exchange Chambers

For details of these leading barristers see Profiles on page 1473

Edward Bartley Jones QC from **Exchange Chambers** (Waldron) remains the only barrister outside London to elicit any recommendation for partnership law.

PENSIONS

RESEARCH: The rankings are based on in-depth interviews with over 5,000 solicitors and barristers in the UK. Chambers research is audited by the British Market Research Bureau (see page 7 for details).

Barristers' profiles 1473-1601

LONDON

LEADING SETS • London	QCs	Jnrs
1 **Wilberforce Chambers** (Edward Nugee QC)	8	6
2 **35 Essex Street** (Nigel Inglis-Jones QC)	1	5
3 **3 Stone Buildings** (Geoffrey Vos QC)	-	3
4 **5 Stone Buildings** (Henry Harrod)	2	1
7 Stone Buildings (Charles Aldous QC)	1	1

Numbers show recommended barristers in this practice area

LEADING SILKS • London	
★ **WARREN Nicholas**	Wilberforce Chambers
1 **GREEN Brian**	Wilberforce Chambers
2 **HAM Robert**	Wilberforce Chambers
INGLIS-JONES Nigel	35 Essex Street
NUGEE Christopher	Wilberforce Chambers
3 **ETHERTON Terence**	Wilberforce Chambers
NUGEE Edward	Wilberforce Chambers
SHER Jules	Wilberforce Chambers
SIMMONDS Andrew	5 Stone Buildings
4 **HERBERT Mark**	5 Stone Buildings
UNWIN David	7 Stone Buildings
NEW SILKS	
FURNESS Michael	Wilberforce Chambers

For details of these leading barristers see Profiles on page 1473

LEADING JUNIORS • London	
1 **TOPHAM Geoffrey**	3 Stone Buildings
2 **ASPLIN Sarah**	3 Stone Buildings
HITCHCOCK Richard	35 Essex Street
NEWMAN Paul	Wilberforce Chambers
STEPHENS John	35 Essex Street
3 **BRYANT Judith**	Wilberforce Chambers
CLIFFORD James	7 Stone Buildings
FURZE Caroline	Wilberforce Chambers
HAYES Josephine	3 New Square
LACEY Sarah	3 Stone Buildings
TENNET Michael	Wilberforce Chambers
TIDMARSH Christopher	5 Stone Buildings
TURNBULL Charles	Wilberforce Chambers
UP AND COMING	
EVANS Jonathan	Wilberforce Chambers
MALDEN Grace	35 Essex Street
SPINK Andrew	35 Essex Street
STALLWORTHY Nicholas	35 Essex Street

For details of these leading barristers see Profiles on page 1473

Wilberforce Chambers (Nugee) "The premier set," they have "undoubtedly cornered the market." Among their "thundering herd," there are several well regarded leaders who mix their practices but are "not shy" of the technical aspects of pensions. They attract both positive comments ("ready accessibility of appropriate counsel," "they've got more expertise to share") and negative ones ("tend to think that no one else can touch them - they charge top whack.") Clearly their "monopoly" status induces other sets to make inroads into it. With a wide-ranging practice, **Nicholas Warren QC** has "everything you could want in a silk." He "covers every angle with flawless logic and has a pleasant manner with clients and professionals – you would go to him for an authoritative opinion." Attracting more mixed reviews this year, **Brian Green QC** is "well able to think outside the box" but "wouldn't engage in technobabble." He "can apply himself to a wider class of individuals without them feeling patronised." Still "out of circulation" working on the Thyssen case in Bermuda for the past year and a half, **Robert Ham QC** ("an imposing personality whose presence cannot be ignored") continues to attract consistent praise for his advocacy skills. He is expected to return shortly. Superlative accolades abound for **Christopher Nugee QC** again this year, who shoots up the tables accordingly. "Top of the tree" he "dwarfs others" with his abilities. "The silk you go to when you have a difficult problem, he can get a client out of a hole by sheer force of intellect." His father **Edward Nugee QC**, "top tier in his day," is "no longer in the thick of it." However, he is "still impressive" and passes "the acid test" by still being instructed. Coming from a mainstream Chancery background, **Terence Etherton QC** is "a real bruiser in court." From a "multi-faceted" background, **Jules Sher QC** is "a punishingly hard worker" who has "an amazing grasp of detail" and "succinctly states the client's case." Standing counsel for the Inland Revenue, new silk **Michael Furness QC** is "probably the most acute of the technical specialists among the leading juniors in terms of his ability to assimilate complex cases." "Worth instructing and good value for money," **Paul Newman** is strongly proactive in promoting his profile and probably the best known junior. **Judith Bryant** is "not afraid to venture into pensions" from her tax background – "she doesn't sit on the fence." **Caroline Furze** is "incisive, she takes the judge with her and sticks to the point." Recognised for his technical skills and moving up in the tables, **Michael Tennet** is "your man if you want to look at a problem from every single angle." **Jonathan Evans** is "a details man," while **Charles Turnbull** "can give helpful advice off the top of his head" and is "good for cut and thrust cases in court."

35 Essex Street (Inglis-Jones) Moving up in the tables, they are "already giving more competition to Wilberforce." Although clearly lower in numbers, they "offer good value for money and are very user-friendly" while regarded by many as being able to "compete on an individual basis with Wilberforce." Specialists in this set with origins in common law are generally known for their "more robust, cross examining, knockabout" image which makes them a popular choice for "cut and thrust pensions disputes." Chambers head **Nigel Inglis-Jones QC** has "absolutely encyclopaedic knowledge." Although his "old school" style does not suit everybody, he is widely recognised as one of the most experienced practising pensions silks involved in the most high profile cases over the last 20 years. **Richard Hitchcock** has "sound judgement and gets to the heart of the matter." He is "approachable, down to earth and prepared to work as part of the team." "A leading junior in all respects," **John Stephens** is "a fearsome opponent" and "numero uno" for a "client who wants to fight." "Scoring well on personability and analytical powers," **Grace Malden** is "on her way up but needs more experience." Also handling medical negligence matters, **Andrew Spink** "has the knowledge and ability to come up through the ranks" and "would scream up the tables in no time if he did more pensions." New entry in the tables **Nick Stallworthy** is "sound, commercial and likeable."

3 Stone Buildings (Vos) With a strong focus on pensions as one of their leading areas, this set "will give you an emphatic answer." They provide "a quicker service and are better value for money" than most. **Geoffrey**

Topham "can hold his own against a silk" and is "magnificent on technical trusts points." "Balanced in her approach to problems," **Sarah Asplin** is "fiery and can demonstrate real resilience in the face of opposition." Firmly back in the tables by popular demand having suffered in profile last year, **Sarah Lacey** is "an iron fist in a velvet glove." Noted to be handling more litigation and involved in court, she is "extremely thorough and really gets under the skin of the case."

5 Stone Buildings (Harrod) "A good set" which is well rated on the quality of its individuals although not seen doing as much pensions work as the leaders. "Unquestionably a star," **Andrew Simmonds QC** attracts consistent praise for his skills. He is an "incisive, deep thinker and a real client pleaser." Coming from a solid trusts/private client background and known for handling leading Pensions Ombudsman work, **Mark Herbert QC** is "approachable and easy to deal with." However he is currently perceived to be handling less pure pensions work. Similarly perceived as primarily a tax/revenue counsel, **Christopher Tidmarsh** has "a fast turnaround and is clearly able."

7 Stone Buildings (Aldous) Noted for strength in analysis, although "not always sufficiently emphatic." However "if you push for straightforward, punchy answers they will come off the fence." **James Clifford** is the best known individual at this set. He "has his supporters and detractors." Although he "certainly has a lot of experience in the field and knows his onions," he is described as "analytical to the last." Better known for his work in chancery, charities and trusts contexts, **David Unwin QC** "has the ability to make telling points with extreme reasonableness and charm – he slides the stiletto in while smiling sweetly, and has the judge eating out of his hand."

Other Notable Barristers Involved on a number of Pensions Ombudsman appeals, although not very widely known, **Josephine Hayes** of **3 New Square** (Goodhart) is "good at getting her mind around complicated areas."

PERSONAL INJURY

RESEARCH: The rankings are based on in-depth interviews with over 5,000 solicitors and barristers in the UK. Chambers research is audited by the British Market Research Bureau (see page 7 for details).

OVERVIEW: This year has seen a radical overhaul of the personal injury bar tables. Markedly fewer silks and juniors have been suggested as leaders by respondent law firms, in part due to a reduction in the number of empanelled firms. As a result, the number of sets rated as market leaders has correspondingly dropped. Therefore, while vast numbers of practitioners are still performing personal injury work as part of their practices, there are fewer who are attracting the high-profile notice of their peers, law firms and insurance companies. Newly-merged Crown Office Chambers has consolidated a position among the leaders, with the synthesis of the skills of the former 2 Crown Office Row and One Paper Buildings.

LONDON

LEADING SETS • London	QCs	Jnrs
❶ 39 Essex Street (Nigel Pleming QC)	4	5
❷ Crown Office Chambers (Spencer/Purchas)	3	2
12 King's Bench Walk (Timothy Stow QC)	2	4
❸ 2 Temple Gardens (Dermod O'Brien QC)	5	1
❹ Devereux Chambers (Jeffrey Burke QC)	2	2
Farrar's Building (John Leighton Williams QC)	3	4
9 Gough Square (Jeremy Roberts QC)	1	3
Old Square Chambers (John Hendy QC)	1	1
❺ 7 Bedford Row (David Farrer QC)	-	2
Doughty Street Chambers (Geoffrey Robertson QC)	1	1

Numbers show recommended barristers in this practice area

LEADING SILKS • London	
❶ BRENNAN Daniel	39 Essex Street
GLASGOW Edwin	39 Essex Street
MACKAY Colin	39 Essex Street
PURCHAS Christopher	Crown Office Chambers
❷ BURKE Jeffrey	Devereux Chambers
CHERRY John	8 Stone Buildings
GLANCY Robert	Devereux Chambers
JEFFREYS Alan	Farrar's Building
OWEN Robert	1 Crown Office Row
WALKER Ronald	12 King's Bench Walk
WILLIAMS John Leighton	Farrar's Building
❸ BADENOCH James	1 Crown Office Row
BROWNE Benjamin	2 Temple Gardens
BURNETT Ian	1 Temple Gardens
BURTON Frank	12 King's Bench Walk
COLLENDER Andrew	2 Temple Gardens
DAVIES Richard	39 Essex Street
FOY John	9 Gough Square
HENDY John	Old Square Chambers
IRWIN Stephen	Doughty Street Chambers
LANGSTAFF Brian	Cloisters
LIVESEY Bernard	Four New Square
NORRIS William	Farrar's Building
O'BRIEN Dermod	2 Temple Gardens
SPENCER Michael	Crown Office Chambers
STEVENSON William	Crown Office Chambers
STUART-SMITH Jeremy	2 Temple Gardens
NEW SILKS	
PALMER Howard	2 Temple Gardens

For details of these leading barristers see Profiles on page 1473

Barristers' profiles 1473-1601

39 Essex Street (Pleming) **Daniel Brennan QC** maintains a formidable reputation for both claimant and defendant work. "A superb advocate," he has a "wonderful skill in distilling a complex problem into understandable chunks." **Edwin Glasgow QC** is a "feisty" advocate, yet remains "superbly user friendly." **Colin Mackay QC** is "direct, forthright but personable." Praised as "thoroughly modern," he "does not chase spurious points and does not point score with solicitors." **Richard Davies QC** does not have the stellar reputation of the top three silks, but he is known as a "very good technical lawyer." Of the juniors, **Neil Block** is "a heavyweight," who is frequently called upon when there is a crossover with medical negligence. **Christian Du Cann** is another star, known as "very pragmatic, and good on the technical stuff." **Charles Brown, Geoffrey Brown** and **Charles Cory-Wright** are all acknowledged to have leading practices.

Crown Office Chambers (Spencer/Purchas) **Christopher Purchas QC** is, according to a leading Trade Union solicitor, "the one person you would rush to with a complex case." His "reasoned, unexcitable" delivery "goes down very well" and "he gives the impression that he is genuinely interested in each and every case." **Michael Spencer QC** and **William Stevenson QC** are other silks praised for their advocacy. **Dennis Matthews** and **Jonathan Waite** are the leading names among a strong group of juniors.

12 King's Bench Walk (Stow) **Ronald Walker QC** is admired by a number of defendant solicitors for his advocacy skills, while **Frank Burton QC** is almost as popular with claimant solicitors. **William Featherby** is acknowledged to be another leading PI lawyer. **Allan Gore** is a leading senior junior heavily used by the Trade Unions. Praised as "brilliant at new arguments and pushing the boundaries," he is seen as "a great innovator." **Stephen Worthington** is praised as "very good at product/public liability," and **Susan Rodway** also remains recommended.

2 Temple Gardens (O'Brien) **Andrew Collender QC** is "a good advocate and client handler" with "immense style and gravitas." **Benjamin Browne QC, Dermod O'Brien QC** and **Jeremy Stuart-Smith QC** are other leading names in a strong group of silks, which also includes new silk **Howard Palmer QC. Steven Archer** is a leading junior who is "excellent on the paperwork. If you need someone good with the minutiae to support a decent advocate, there is no one better." He is particularly well-known for his RSI and stress-related work.

Devereux Chambers (Burke) **Jeffrey Burke QC** is popular among both claimant and defence solicitors, and is known for his thorough preparation which makes him "slow but good." **Robert Glancy QC** also received a number of recommendations, largely from claimant solicitors. **Steven Killalea** is a well-known junior who specialises in catastrophic head and spinal injuries. **Christopher Goddard** also has a good reputation, particularly in occupational health.

Farrar's Building (Williams) **John Leighton Williams QC** is a "first rate advocate" who is "good on issues of quantum and superb on catastrophic brain injuries." "Humble and approachable," he is nevertheless "formidable in court." **Alan Jeffreys QC** and **William Norris QC** are both popular with defendant solicitors. **Edward Southwell**'s "tremendous experience" is much appreciated, and **Tom McDermott, Simon Browne** and **Anthony Seys Llewellyn** all retain solid reputations in this area.

9 Gough Square (Roberts) Efficiently-clerked set where **John Foy QC** is the best-known silk, and has a particularly strong reputation in respiratory diseases. On the junior front, **Nicolas Hillier** and **John Reddihough** are both very popular with leading claimant firms, as is **Jacob Levy**.

LEADING JUNIORS • London	
✪ BLOCK Neil	39 Essex Street
DU CANN Christian	39 Essex Street
GORE Allan	12 King's Bench Walk
❶ BROWN Geoffrey	39 Essex Street
BROWN Charles	39 Essex Street
HILLIER Nicolas	9 Gough Square
KILLALEA Stephen	Devereux Chambers
KING Simon	7 Bedford Row
MATTHEWS Dennis	Crown Office Chambers
SOUTHWELL Edward	Farrar's Building
WAITE Jonathan	Crown Office Chambers
WORTHINGTON Stephen	12 King's Bench Walk
❷ ARCHER Stephen	2 Temple Gardens
COOKSLEY Nigel	Old Square Chambers
GODDARD Christopher	Devereux Chambers
OPPENHEIM Robin	Doughty Street Chambers
REDDIHOUGH John	9 Gough Square
❸ BROWNE Simon	Farrar's Building
CORY-WRIGHT Charles	39 Essex Street
FEATHERBY William	12 King's Bench Walk
LEVY Jacob	9 Gough Square
MCDERMOTT Tom	Farrar's Building
MOAT Frank	Pump Court Chambers
RODWAY Susan	12 King's Bench Walk
SEYS LLEWELLYN Anthony	Farrar's Building
WHEATLEY Simon	7 Bedford Row

For details of these leading barristers see Profiles on page 1473

Old Square Chambers (Hendy) **John Hendy QC,** is highly regarded for his PI work for Trade Unions, although some felt that he is "stronger on employment law. **Nigel Cooksley** is a very popular junior among claimant firms.

7 Bedford Row (Farrer) **Simon King** is noted among the leading juniors and his advocacy skills were widely praised by defendant solicitors. **Simon Wheatley** was also much favoured by London insurance firms.

Doughty Street Chambers (Robertson) Popular with those claimant firms who take on the more unusual, leading-edge cases. These practices appreciate the set's willingness to "work with the law rather than taking a more mechanistic approach" and "to set a problem in its broader context." **Stephen Irwin QC** is seen as "hardworking, with tremendous ability," and is particularly effective in cases with a complex medico-legal element. **Robin Oppenheim** is "so experienced, even tempered and a real team player" and has been used in a number of complex multi-party cases including tobacco, benzodiazepine and CJD.

Other Notable Barristers Other counsel singled out by interviewees include **John Cherry QC** of **8 Stone Buildings** (Cherry) and **Bernard Livesey QC**, an "ingenious lateral thinker and a great cross-examiner" based at **Four New Square** (Fenwick.) **Brian Langstaff QC** remains the best known silk at **Cloisters** (Cox) and is highly respected for his work in cases of serious personal injury. **James Badenoch QC** and **Robert Owen QC,** both of **1 Crown Office Row** (Seabrook) continue to be counted among the leading silks. At **1 Temple Gardens** (Carlisle) **Ian Burnett QC** maintains a high profile and has acted on a number of Public Inquiries such as Southall Rail and Kings Cross. **Frank Moat** of **Pump Court Chambers** (Boney) is considered a leading figure among the juniors for industrial disease claims.

WALES & CHESTER CIRCUIT

LEADING SETS • Wales & Chester	QCs	Jnrs
❶ **9 Park Place** (Ian Murphy QC) Cardiff	1	1
33 Park Place (John Charles Rees QC) Cardiff	2	-
❷ **30 Park Place** (John Jenkins QC) Cardiff	-	1

Numbers show recommended barristers in this practice area

LEADING SILKS • Wales & Chester	
❶ BIDDER Neil	33 Park Place
MURPHY Ian	9 Park Place
❷ REES John	33 Park Place
NEW SILKS	
VOSPER Christopher	Angel Chambers

For details of these leading barristers see Profiles on page 1473

LEADING JUNIORS • Wales & Chester	
❶ REES Philip	9 Park Place
VENMORE John	30 Park Place

For details of these leading barristers see Profiles on page 1473

9 Park Place (Murphy) A large chambers which counts personal injury amongst its specialisations. **Ian Murphy QC** has a great deal of experience in personal injury cases, as has his colleague **Philip Rees**, and both continue to be recommended by local solicitors.

33 Park Place (Rees) "A rounded set with three or four good common law lawyers and one or two good silks." **Neil Bidder QC** and **John Rees QC** continue to be specifically recommended by the market.

30 Park Place (Jenkins) **John Venmore** is a leading junior in a practice that continues to be used by the larger Welsh defendant firms.

Other Notable Barrister Christopher Vosper QC of **Angel Chambers** (Glanville Jones) has taken silk this year, "and about time too," said peers.

WESTERN CIRCUIT

LEADING SETS • Western	QCs	Jnrs
❶ **St John's Chambers** (Christopher Sharp QC) Bristol	1	3
❷ **Old Square Chambers** (John Hendy QC) Bristol	-	1

Numbers show recommended barristers in this practice area

LEADING SILKS • Western	
❶ SHARP Christopher	St John's Chambers

For details of these leading barristers see Profiles on page 1473

LEADING JUNIORS • Western	
❶ BULLOCK Ian	St John's Chambers
COTTER Barry	Old Square Chambers
EDWARDS Glyn	St John's Chambers
ISHERWOOD John	Assize Court Chambers
STEAD Richard	St John's Chambers

For details of these leading barristers see Profiles on page 1473

St John's Chambers (Sharp) **Christopher Sharp QC** is praised for his "meticulous attention to detail" and is one of very few local silks that personal injury practices are instructing on a regular basis. **Ian Bullock** is "one of the leading juniors in Bristol" and is well-known among insurance practices in the South West. **Glyn Edwards** and **Richard Stead** are also recommended.

Old Square Chambers (Hendy) **Barry Cotter** is a well-known junior, who has acted on a number of high profile cases, including the Southall and Ladbroke Grove train crash inquiries and the Organophosphate litigation.

Other Notable Barrister John Isherwood of **Assize Court Chambers** (Isherwood) is a very experienced and much respected practitioner.

MIDLANDS & OXFORD CIRCUIT

LEADING SETS • Midlands & Oxford	QCs	Jnrs
❶ **Ropewalk Chambers** (Richard Maxwell QC) Nottingham	4	3
❷ **5 Fountain Court** (Anthony Barker QC) Birmingham	3	1

Numbers show recommended barristers in this practice area

LEADING SILKS • Midlands & Oxford	
❶ **EVANS Gareth**	5 Fountain Court
LEWIS Ralph	5 Fountain Court
MAXWELL Richard	Ropewalk Chambers
MCLAREN Ian	Ropewalk Chambers
OLIVER-JONES Stephen	5 Fountain Court
OWEN Robert	Ropewalk Chambers
WOODWARD William	Ropewalk Chambers

For details of these leading barristers see Profiles on page 1473

LEADING JUNIORS • Midlands & Oxford	
❶ **ADAMS Jayne**	Ropewalk Chambers
ASHWORTH Lance	St Philip's Chambers
BLEASDALE Paul	5 Fountain Court
LIMB Patrick	Ropewalk Chambers
NOLAN Dominic	Ropewalk Chambers

For details of these leading barristers see Profiles on page 1473

Ropewalk Chambers (Maxwell) Now considered to be "head and shoulders above" the rest of the region. **Richard Maxwell QC** is best known for his work on child abuse cases, but is active in a wide range of cases including the Vibration White Finger Litigation. **Robert Owen QC**'s principal area of practice is industrial disease, particularly in the context of multi-part actions. New entry **Ian McLaren QC** has established a reputation beyond Nottingham for his litigation work ("I've seen him wipe the floor with London QCs.") **William Woodward QC** has also had a good year and rises in the lists. **Jayne Adams**' practice covers all aspects of personal injury, while **Patrick Limb** is best known for his work on the Hillsborough disaster. **Dominic Nolan**, another new name in the lists, is "aggressive, but by God, he's impressive."

5 Fountain Court (Barker) **Ralph Lewis QC** is "good on complex, high value personal injury claims" and was viewed as "a good and persistent advocate, although not always the most positive guy to have around." **Gareth Evans QC** also attracted recommendations, as did **Stephen Oliver-Jones QC. Paul Bleasdale** is considered a "competent junior who is delightful company."

Other Notable Barristers **Lance Ashworth** of **St Philip's Chambers** (Tedd) received very positive feedback, with some considering him "the best junior in Birmingham."

NORTH EASTERN CIRCUIT

LEADING SETS • North Eastern	QCs	Jnrs
❶ **Park Lane Chambers** (Stuart Brown QC) Leeds	-	2
Plowden Buildings (William Lowe QC)	-	2
❷ **Park Court Chambers** (Stewart/Smith) Leeds	-	1

Numbers show recommended barristers in this practice area

LEADING JUNIORS • North Eastern	
❶ **ELGOT Howard**	Park Lane Chambers
FOSTER Catherine	Plowden Buildings
JACKSON Simon	Park Court Chambers
THORP Simon	Park Lane Chambers
TROTTER David	Plowden Buildings

For details of these leading barristers see Profiles on page 1473

Park Lane Chambers (Brown) Senior junior **Howard Elgot** maintains a strong reputation, while his colleague **Simon Thorp** is also well respected.

Plowden Buildings (Lowe) **Catherine Foster** is "very friendly, very popular." Based in the North East, she has done a lot of work on the Vibration White Finger cases. **David Trotter** is also a respected junior who spends a substantial proportion of his time in the North East.

Park Court Chambers (Stewart/Smith) Another recommended Leeds chambers, where **Simon Jackson** is the leading name.

NORTHERN CIRCUIT

LEADING SETS • Northern	QCs	Jnrs
❶ **Byrom Street Chambers** (Benet Hytner QC) Manchester	2	-
Deans Court Chambers (Keith Goddard QC) Manchester	3	-
28 St. John St (Clement Goldstone QC) Manchester	1	1
❷ **Exchange Chambers** (William Waldron QC) Liverpool	2	-
18 St. John Street (Jonathan Foster QC) Manchester	-	2

Numbers show recommended barristers in this practice area

LEADING SILKS • Northern	
❶ **MACHELL Raymond**	Deans Court Chambers
WINGATE-SAUL Giles	Byrom Street Chambers
❷ **BRAITHWAITE Bill**	Exchange Chambers
HINCHLIFFE Nicholas	9 St. John Street
STOCKDALE David	Deans Court Chambers
SWIFT Caroline	Byrom Street Chambers
NEW SILKS	
FIELD Patrick	Deans Court Chambers
HUNTER Winston	28 St. John St
MARTIN Gerard	Exchange Chambers

For details of these leading barristers see Profiles on page 1473

LEADING JUNIORS • Northern	
❶ **HEATON David**	18 St. John Street
ROWLEY James	28 St. John St
❷ **LAPRELL Mark**	18 St. John Street
RAHMAN Yaqub	Oriel Chambers

For details of these leading barristers see Profiles on page 1473

Byrom Street Chambers (Hytner) **Giles Wingate-Saul QC** is felt by some to be "the best silk in Manchester" and is "meticulous, thorough and possesses good judgement." **Caroline Swift QC** "ranks just behind Wingate-Saul" and is popular with leading claimant firms.

Deans Court Chambers (Goddard) **Raymond Machell QC** mainly acts for the defence and is "approachable, hard working, detail orientated and a hard negotiator." **David Stockdale QC** has a good practice covering all aspects of personal injury including accident, industrial disease and multi-party actions. **Patrick Field QC** joins the ranks of the new silks.

28 St John Street (Goldstone) **James Rowley** retains his position among the leading juniors and remains best known for his "detailed preparation." **Winston Hunter QC** has recently taken silk, and continues to have a respected practice.

Exchange Chambers (Waldron) Possesses a substantial personal injury department with eighteen members of chambers practising in this area. **Bill Braithwaite QC** maintains a strong reputation among claimant solicitors, while **Gerard Martin QC** is among the new silks.

18 St John Street (Foster) **David Heaton** and **Mark Laprell** are the juniors from this set that received the greatest number of recommendations this year. "They set high standards of reliability."

Other Notable Barristers **Nicholas Hinchcliffe QC** of **9 St John Street** (Hand) is establishing himself among the leading silks on the circuit. **Yaqub Rahman** at **Oriel Chambers** (Sander) is still a leading figure amongst regional juniors.

PLANNING / LOCAL GOVERNMENT

RESEARCH: The rankings are based on in-depth interviews with over 5,000 solicitors and barristers in the UK. Chambers research is audited by the British Market Research Bureau (see page 7 for details).

Barristers' profiles 1473-1601

LONDON

LEADING SETS • London	QCs	Jnrs
❶ **4 Breams Buildings** (Christopher Lockhart-Mummery QC)	6	2
4-5 Gray's Inn Square (Appleby/Ouseley)	7	4
2 Harcourt Buildings (Gerard Ryan QC)	7	5
❷ **2-3 Gray's Inn Square** (Anthony Scrivener QC)	5	6
2 Mitre Court Buildings (Michael FitzGerald QC)	7	3
1 Serjeants' Inn (Lionel Read QC)	3	6
❸ **11 King's Bench Walk** (Tabachnik/Goudie)	3	2

Numbers show recommended barristers in this practice area

LEADING SILKS • London	
✪ **FITZGERALD Michael**	2 Mitre Court Buildings
HICKS William	1 Serjeants' Inn
HOWELL John	4 Breams Buildings
KATKOWSKI Christopher	4 Breams Buildings
LINDBLOM Keith	2 Harcourt Buildings
LOCKHART-MUMMERY Christopher	4 Breams Buildings
OUSELEY Duncan	4-5 Gray's Inn Square
PURCHAS Robin	2 Harcourt Buildings
READ Lionel	1 Serjeants' Inn
❶ **ASH Brian**	4-5 Gray's Inn Square
CLARKSON Patrick	1 Serjeants' Inn
DRABBLE Richard	4 Breams Buildings
GOUDIE James	11 King's Bench Walk
PHILLIPS Richard	2 Harcourt Buildings
PORTEN Anthony	2-3 Gray's Inn Square
SILSOE David	2 Mitre Court Buildings
❷ **ARDEN Andrew**	Arden Chambers
DINKIN Anthony	2-3 Gray's Inn Square
GEORGE Charles	2 Harcourt Buildings
HOLGATE David	4 Breams Buildings
LOWE Mark	2-3 Gray's Inn Square
ROOTS Guy	2 Mitre Court Buildings
STEEL John	4-5 Gray's Inn Square
STONE Gregory	4-5 Gray's Inn Square
STRAKER Timothy	4-5 Gray's Inn Square
❸ **ANDERSON Anthony**	2 Mitre Court Buildings
HENDERSON Roger	2 Harcourt Buildings
HORTON Matthew	2 Mitre Court Buildings
MOLE David	4-5 Gray's Inn Square
PUGH Vernon	2-3 Gray's Inn Square
RYAN Gerard	2 Harcourt Buildings
SUPPERSTONE Michael	11 King's Bench Walk
TABACHNIK Eldred	11 King's Bench Walk
TAYLOR John	2 Mitre Court Buildings
WOLTON Harry	2-3 Gray's Inn Square
NEW SILKS	
ELVIN David	4 Breams Buildings
HOBSON John	4-5 Gray's Inn Square
KELLY Andrew	2 Harcourt Buildings
KING Neil	2 Mitre Court Buildings

For details of these leading barristers see Profiles on page 1473

4 Breams Buildings (Lockhart-Mummery) Represents "our first choice" for "their range of advice and experience," stated one leading local government solicitor. Popular with top-tier City planning practices who value the set's "intellectual and incisive counsel." Strong in both local government and planning, **John Howell QC** is universally hailed as one of the cerebral supremos for judicial review and court challenges ("streets ahead on points of law.") His fearsome intellect and rapid oral delivery are such that "it can be difficult for less intelligent people to keep up with him!" **Christopher Katkowski QC** has had a marvellous year. A comparatively recent silk, his "thoroughness" comes in tandem with a "youthful energy." Most of all, he is "incredibly unpretentious and one of the team." Straightforward and honest, he "cuts through the issues succinctly" and "balances aggression with calmness." The "gentlemanly" **Christopher Lockhart-Mummery QC** is still admired for his "mental acuity, and concise and fair style." Felt to be "beautifully balanced" at inquiries, he is always "wonderfully prepared." Other barristers and solicitor-advocates are in "awe of his cross-examination." Occasionally, he is felt to be a little "too gentlemanly" by certain clients who demand a more hard-hitting approach. Public law and local authority silk **Richard Drabble QC** is another leading barrister noted for his JR performances. With an "enquiring manner," he provides "reliable advice" and is not "unnecessarily pedantic." Also seen on planning inquiries, he generally provides "client-focused practical solutions." **David Holgate QC** mixes planning with public law and ratings work, and is described as a "formidable advocate and inquiry lawyer." Sometimes testing, his forte is clearly felt to be detail, where his "technical numeracy," "encyclopaedic knowledge" and "grasp of scientific points" mark him down as a preferred choice for a complicated case or judicial review. New silk **David Elvin QC** is a "deft tactician – akin to a ratcatcher who sets traps and then springs them." Public law junior **Nathalie Lieven** continues to be well rated for court work, although is less commonly seen at inquiries. **Timothy Mould** acts for the Treasury Solicitors and the Inland Revenue, as well as private practitioners, but is rated on both counts. This balance marks him out as a choice for JR work, but leading solicitors have also commented on his ability to "scythe through the issues," and offer "sober insights into the merits of the case."

4-5 Gray's Inn Square (Appleby/Ouseley) In solicitors' eyes, the set "always produces good people," and is "intellectually, a top-notch organisation." Foremost at the top end is star planning silk and head of chambers **Duncan Ouseley QC**, who received more positive recommendations than any other barrister this year. Loved by all the top City practices, he "knows how to pitch his advice" and is "highly attuned commercially." A leading solicitor praised his ability to "grasp abstract concepts," and immerse himself in "mind-boggling levels of detail." Commended for his versatility, he is equally adept at retail inquiries as on tough High Court cases. "Great for retail cases and CPOs," **Brian Ash QC** has a "convincing air about him," and is welcomed by planning inspectors for his "low-key, sincere and plausible approach." Considered one of the best advocates at the bar, he "doesn't rant and rave" in front of judges. **John Steel QC** "never stops working" and is recommended for his broad practice, taking in planning and judicial review. There's no "over-acting" when dealing with "straightforward" **Gregory Stone QC** who "certainly reads the papers." His "highly accomplished manner" and "clear arguments" were praised by several solicitors. Another all-rounder, **Tim Straker QC** ("good on his feet, clear in his objectives") is instructed on local authority jurisdictional matters such as powers and vires issues, in tandem with planning inquiries. **David Mole QC** is again rated for his planning and compulsory purchase work. New silk **John Hobson QC** is felt to be "strong on the academic side" and was noted for local government, housing and planning expertise. Considered the number one planning junior, **Tim Corner** is "punchy and effective" and rated by solicitors and fellow barristers alike. Adept at local govern-

LEADING JUNIORS • London	
✪ CORNER Timothy	4-5 Gray's Inn Square
❶ DRUCE Michael	2 Mitre Court Buildings
HARRIS Russell	1 Serjeants' Inn
HILL Thomas	4-5 Gray's Inn Square
SINGH Rabinder	Matrix Chambers
WHITE Sasha	1 Serjeants' Inn
❷ BEAR Charles	11 King's Bench Walk
CAMERON Neil	1 Serjeants' Inn
COOK Mary	2-3 Gray's Inn Square
ELLIS Morag	2-3 Gray's Inn Square
HOWELL WILLIAMS Craig	2 Harcourt Buildings
HUMPHREYS Richard	4-5 Gray's Inn Square
LEWIS Rhodri Price	1 Serjeants' Inn
LIEVEN Nathalie	4 Breams Buildings
MORGAN Stephen	1 Serjeants' Inn
MOULD Timothy	4 Breams Buildings
ORNSBY Suzanne	2 Harcourt Buildings
VILLAGE Peter	4-5 Gray's Inn Square
❸ ALBUTT Ian	2-3 Gray's Inn Square
BAKER Christopher	Arden Chambers
BIRD Simon	2-3 Gray's Inn Square
FINDLAY James	2-3 Gray's Inn Square
GIFFIN Nigel	11 King's Bench Walk
GLOVER Richard	2 Mitre Court Buildings
HUMPHRIES Michael	2 Mitre Court Buildings
NEWCOMBE Andrew	2 Harcourt Buildings
STEPHENSON Geoffrey	2-3 Gray's Inn Square
UP AND COMING	
CLAYTON Joanna	2 Harcourt Buildings
EDWARDS Douglas	2 Harcourt Buildings
LYNESS Scott	1 Serjeants' Inn

For details of these leading barristers see Profiles on page 1473

ment advice, vires issues and pure planning, his "fine clarity of thought" and "pleasant, attractive manner" are appealing to the tribunals. He's also "on top of the nitty gritty" and "always sees the wood for the trees." **Tom Hill**'s rise to the top gathered pace this year after swathes of endorsements. His "gentlemanly approach" and "thorough, well-mannered keenness" mark him down as a junior advocate of choice for many solicitors. **Richard Humphreys** was singled out by some for his expertise in CPO and listed building work. **Peter Village** ("quite a character") is felt to have a "robust" style, but is praised for his endeavour – "he's a 100% man."

2 Harcourt Buildings (Ryan) Specialising in planning, environmental, local government and public law, this "tremendous chambers" is felt to be efficient, well-clerked and offers reasonable fees. "Suave" planning advocate **Keith Lindblom QC** manages to combine "exceptional thoroughness and experience" with a "workable and user-friendly" manner which strikes a chord with clients and solicitors alike. His advocacy is forceful and commercial "in a non-threatening way." **Robin Purchas QC** is another of the planning élite whose "quick, thorough and technical" style singles him out as a "first port of call" for many. He "consistently produces good opinions" for planning solicitors and can be "good fun even in a drawn-out conference." Quality advocacy is the major characteristic of **Richard Phillips QC** who is a "fantastic cross-examiner" and "quietly achieves the right results." The experience and broad public law practice of **Charles George QC** still retains admirers, most commonly in local government work. **Roger Henderson QC** enters the rankings this year on account of his expertise in local government powers, vires and finance. Well-liked by clients, solicitors also admire his perspective on the law that "you would expect from a balanced judge – he plays it straight down the middle." **Gerard Ryan QC** was rated again by solicitors this year, in particular for his advice on village green and common land issues. New silk **Andrew Kelly QC** has also been newly recommended this year, and is singled out by many more established planning silks as one to watch for the future. Of the juniors, **Craig Howell Williams** and **Suzanne Ornsby** were both frequently praised by solicitors. The latter is noted for her advocacy skills and regular English Heritage work. Similarly, **Andrew Newcombe** is well regarded and has been used on the mammoth Dibden container port project on the south coast. Two younger up and coming names also appear this year, reflecting a generous pool of junior talent. **Joanna Clayton** and **Douglas Edwards** are both felt to show great promise, maturity and judgement.

2-3 Gray's Inn Square (Scrivener) Warmly greeted by the market for its "value for money and flexibility," this administrative, planning and local government set has a "good presence across the board." Felt to be down-to-earth, "they all roll their sleeves up and go through the documents – there are no prima donnas!" "Easy to communicate with," **Anthony Porten QC** offers "decisive pragmatic unlegalistic advice" and provides "clear, coherent opinions" on planning matters. Switching to local government, he is "bullish on public sector powers" and "never lets us down." Also recommended for his input into big planning matters, **Anthony Dinkin QC** "keeps control of the documents superbly" during long inquiries. Liked by a number of leading solicitors, both for local government and planning work, **Mark Lowe QC** is "charming and unassuming" but "effective at getting to the point in his quiet way." He is also "practical, on time and reads the papers." **Vernon Pugh QC**, well known for his Welsh sporting interests, is a "brilliant advocate" who has recently been instructed on a number of lengthy planning inquiries. **Harry Wolton QC** is well known in the Midlands market by planning consultants and large development companies. Good on his feet, his oratorial submissions are "just the thing for bashing the planning authorities!" The junior ranks include "huge personality" **Mary Cook** who "can be aggressive" but is "sheer quality." Similarly regarded for pure planning work is **Morag Ellis**. A clutch of young performers make their debuts this year. **Ian Albutt** is "one of a crop of very promising juniors." **Simon Bird** has "a lot of local authority work," while **James Findlay** is rated by many of London's top local authority solicitors for his public law-led powers practice. Senior junior **Geoffrey Stephenson** is "experienced, good on his feet and not abrupt," and retains his ranking.

2 Mitre Court Buildings (FitzGerald) "Excellent through and through, from top to bottom," commented one solicitor. Charismatic "golden oldie" **Michael FitzGerald QC** is "still the absolute tops" for "wisdom and strategic guidance." He is particularly felt to excel in the preparation and running of a long case. The "meticulous and polite" **David Silsoe QC** is frequently out of circulation on long-running planning cases (T5 most recently) and is not felt to be accessible as a member of the quotidian planning bar. However, he is still regarded as "pre-eminent" for long, weighty cases where he is "wheeled out" for his fearsome intellect and ability to grasp "astonishingly complex matters." **Guy Roots QC** continues to be recommended for both local government and planning work. Compulsory purchase and rating are his acknowledged areas of specialism. **Anthony Anderson QC** retains a ranking for his "polished advocacy." **Matthew Horton QC** is considered to have "one of the ablest minds at the bar" although his cases "can get long and heated." "Fine brain" **John Taylor QC** is praised for his "mixture of humour and intellect." It was no surprise to anyone that top-ranked planning junior **Neil King QC** took silk this year. His "robust and practical approach," "enormously pleasant character" and "attractive advocacy" has made him an obvious choice for many firms. Crucially, his performance in inquiries has also earned him a high reputation with the inspectors. **Michael Druce** is a favourite of many of the top silks and "attracts a lot of work." Solicitors were quick to point out that when the opportunity arises, he was often a preferred choice for both planning and local government related work – "he has been instrumental in achieving results for us." **Richard Glover** was singled out for his "tenacity" and "ability to speak in a commanding way." **Michael Humphries**' name has received frequent mention this year, and he accordingly appears in the rankings.

1 Serjeants' Inn (Read) A highly-rated, well-balanced mixture of ranked silks and juniors. **Bill Hicks QC** is an increasingly popular choice for solicitors. As well as being a "great leader," his "wonderful grasp of detail" and "punchy advocacy" are much sought after. There's no stopping "old warhorse" **Lionel Read QC**. Despite advancing years and a "sybaritic lifestyle," his "undimmed intellectual powers," "ox-like constitution" and "sagacity" still mark him down as "the planning QC" for the big strategic inquiries. Appearing against him is "like being steam-rollered – he hasn't lost his fire and brimstone." **Patrick Clarkson QC** "listens closely to his instructions." Considered down-to-earth and accessible, he is blessed with a "direct straightforward style" and is "commercially attuned to clients' needs." **Russell Harris**' rise continues. "Unpompous and practical," he is "effective on his feet and good with clients." **Sasha White** is highly rated by many of the top planning solicitors. He is said to carry "additional brain power" and "has knowledge at his fingertips." His growing reputation has extended to clients who have "warmed to his public school approach" and well-prepared manner. "First class" **Neil Cameron** is also recommended; he "makes the maximum out of difficult instructions." Split between London and Wales, **Rhodri Price Lewis** is noted for his abilities on "large planning proposals with an environmental angle." **Stephen Morgan** "works very hard," is "easy to deal with" and "makes sure the clients are looked after." Up and coming **Scott Lyness** is "very young, but really sharp."

11 King's Bench Walk (Tabachnik/Goudie) The set is not a big player in planning terms, but well known for its public law, local government and judicial review work, where they "always have the answers." One of the top local government barristers, **James Goudie QC** "cuts through the legalese, assesses the risks" and represents an automatic choice for many of the highly ranked public sector practices. A "seasoned" local authority lawyer, he "understands local authority issues well," and "will always produce a trenchant opinion." Also acknowledged for his JR and local authority prowess, **Michael Supperstone QC** is an "extremely sound intellectual lawyer." **Eldred Tabachnik QC** has a broad practice, but still retains support from those who prize his sheer experience. Junior **Charles Bear** is "approachable and friendly" and sought for his advice on the "esoterics of local government finance." Public law and judicial review whiz **Nigel Giffin** "really knows his way round local government and planning." Considered "detailed and careful," his stature is felt to be growing given his particular understanding of the Human Rights Act.

Other Notable Barristers Two barristers are recommended from **Arden Chambers** (Arden) a set known for its work in the fields of housing, local government and public law. **Andrew Arden QC** is a widely published expert on local government finance – "he's run with it for the last ten years and seen it evolve." Although "a little over-robust," solicitors appreciate his "facilitative approach." From the same chambers, **Christopher Baker** "genuinely knows how local authorities think and work." Rated also for his JR work, he "understands the tensions and special nature of relationships in local government." Recently moved to the new **Matrix Chambers** (Blake) "phenomenally brainy" star public law junior **Rabinder Singh** is ranked highly. He has turned his hand to pure planning work with recognised success.

WALES & CHESTER CIRCUIT

LEADING SILKS • Wales & Chester	
❶ COOKE Nicholas	9 Park Place, Cardiff

For details of these leading barristers see Profiles on page 1473

LEADING JUNIORS • Wales & Chester	
❶ WILLIAMS Rhodri	30 Park Place, Cardiff

For details of these leading barristers see Profiles on page 1473

Nicholas Cooke QC of **9 Park Place** (Murphy) is one of only a small number of Wales-based barristers who can lay claim to some form of planning practice. "He's woken up to the need to tackle planning and public law in a coherent way." **Rhodri Williams** at **30 Park Place** (Jenkins) is rated for his focus on public procurement matters and is "committed to doing as much Welsh work as possible."

MIDLANDS & OXFORD CIRCUIT

LEADING SETS • Midlands & Oxford	QCs	Jnrs
❶ 5 Fountain Court (Anthony Barker QC) Birmingham	1	2

Numbers show recommended barristers in this practice area

LEADING SILKS • Midlands & Oxford	
✪ KINGSTON Martin	5 Fountain Court

For details of these leading barristers see Profiles on page 1473

LEADING JUNIORS • Midlands & Oxford	
❶ CAHILL Jeremy	5 Fountain Court
DOVE Ian	5 Fountain Court

For details of these leading barristers see Profiles on page 1473

5 Fountain Court (Barker) Birmingham. "One of the greats" and said to be "the best planning barrister outside London," **Martin Kingston QC** would assume top-tier status in any national ranking. "Quite brilliant" as an advocate, he "controls the whole process and has no airs and graces." Instructed by solicitors nationwide, he's a "good friend to you, really looks after you" and possesses the '3 As' – "ability, attitude and approachability." **Jeremy Cahill** and **Ian Dove** ("commercially-minded and friendly") continue to be recommended juniors.

NORTHERN CIRCUIT

LEADING SETS • Northern	QCs	Jnrs
❶ 40 King St (Philip Raynor QC) Manchester	4	4

Numbers show recommended barristers in this practice area

LEADING SILKS • Northern	
❶ GILBART Andrew	40 King St
❷ HOGGETT John	40 King St
PATTERSON Frances	40 King St
SAUVAIN Stephen	40 King St

For details of these leading barristers see Profiles on page 1473

LEADING JUNIORS • Northern	
❶ BARRETT John	40 King St
❷ MANLEY David	40 King St
UP AND COMING	
STOCKLEY Ruth	40 King St
TUCKER Paul	40 King St

For details of these leading barristers see Profiles on page 1473

40 King St (Raynor) Manchester. Because of "the fair range of counsel" and "collective strength," solicitors "don't have to go running to London when they need an opinion." Of the group of named silks, **Andrew Gilbart QC** scored the most recommendations. Retail inquiries are "meat and drink to him." On his feet, he "boxes the opposition around the ears until they submit – its like going 15 rounds with a heavyweight!" His "first class mind" and "fairly aggressive style of advocacy" are felt to be well-suited to matters such as waste, incineration and minerals. **John Hoggett QC** is "gentlemanly" but "cutting in his performance." **Frances Patterson QC** scores highly on judicial review and planning inquiries. She "rolls her sleeves up and then somebody takes a battering." Said to be more "quiet and unassuming," without raising his voice, **Stephen Sauvain QC** has the ability to "fillet the opposition without realising they've been had!" His "courteous delivery" doesn't obscure "rock solid opinions and fine cross-examination technique." **John Barrett** and the "impressive" **David Manley** continue to score highly among juniors. **Ruth Stockley** and **Paul Tucker** are two younger juniors to have gained more prominence this year, and make their debuts in the rankings.

PRODUCT LIABILITY

RESEARCH: The rankings are based on in-depth interviews with over 5,000 solicitors and barristers in the UK. Chambers research is audited by the British Market Research Bureau (see page 7 for details).

OVERVIEW: One caveat should be observed when considering our table of ranked individuals. Most major product liability cases have a long gestation period, and may engage the time of a barrister for several years before even coming to court, such that an annual list of the major participants may produce a slightly distorted picture of the field.

LONDON

LEADING SETS • London	QCs	Jnrs
❶ **Crown Office Chambers** (Spencer/Purchas)	2	1
2 Harcourt Buildings (Roger Henderson QC)	1	3
❷ **Doughty Street Chambers** (Geoffrey Robertson QC)	1	2
2 Temple Gardens (Dermod O'Brien QC)	1	1

Numbers show recommended barristers in this practice area

LEADING SILKS • London	
❶ BRENNAN Daniel	39 Essex Street
PRYNNE Andrew	2 Harcourt Buildings
SPENCER Michael	Crown Office Chambers
STUART-SMITH Jeremy	2 Temple Gardens
❷ FENWICK Justin	Four New Square
IRWIN Stephen	Doughty Street Chambers
LANGSTAFF Brian	Cloisters
OWEN Robert	1 Crown Office Row
❸ POWERS Michael	4 Paper Buildings
ULLSTEIN Augustus	29 Bedford Row Chambers
UNDERHILL Nicholas	Fountain Court
❹ BROWN Simon	Crown Office Chambers

For details of these leading barristers see Profiles on page 1473

LEADING JUNIORS • London	
❶ GIBSON Charles	2 Harcourt Buildings
❷ OPPENHEIM Robin	Doughty Street Chambers
WAITE Jonathan	Crown Office Chambers
❸ COTTER Barry	Old Square Chambers
LYDIARD Andrew	Brick Court Chambers
❹ THOROLD Oliver	Doughty Street Chambers
UP AND COMING	
POPAT Prashant	2 Harcourt Buildings
RILEY-SMITH Toby	2 Harcourt Buildings
TURNER David	2 Temple Gardens

For details of these leading barristers see Profiles on page 1473

Crown Office Chambers (Spencer/Purchas) Specialising in defence work, it has carved out a name for itself as one of the leading sets in the field. Especially strong on pharmaceutical work, it is the number one choice for many of the top firms of defendant solicitors, and boasts a number of heavyweight players. **Michael Spencer QC**, "miles ahead" of the field according to one commentator, is an "effective destroyer" with enormous experience in multi-party actions. He has been involved in the oral contraceptive and tampon-induced toxic shock cases this year. **Simon Brown QC** knows this area of practice well and is seen to be very able. **Jonathan Waite** "exudes judgement and common sense" and is generally considered to be "getting better all the time." He has been heavily involved in the MMR and the Organophosphate litigation.

Barristers' profiles 1473-1601

2 Harcourt Buildings (Henderson) Possesses perhaps the strongest team in the field. Taking on both defence and claimant work, it has been involved in the tobacco, MMR/MR, asbestos, Larium, Roaccutane, silicone implant, Benzene, Norplant contraceptive implant and Organophosphate litigation. Big-hitters include **Andrew Prynne QC** "clear-thinking," "good with clients," "a very good advocate" with "a way of getting to the heart of the matter." He has been involved in the MMR litigation, consulted on the tobacco litigation, and retained on the Organophosphate litigation. Also recommended are the "exceptional" **Charles Gibson**, an "outstanding" advocate who "gives every case a Rolls Royce service," **Prashant Popat** and **Toby Riley-Smith**.

Doughty Street Chambers (Robertson) Definitely a contender for the title of leading claimant set, it possesses a medical law team whose work spans product liability, personal injury and clinical negligence. Recent cases have included those relating to post-traumatic stress disorder, growth hormones, Larium and Organophosphate. Key players include **Stephen Irwin QC**, "a great advocate" with "a first class mind" who "tries very hard for his clients" and is "perhaps the best claimant lawyer around." Also **Robin Oppenheim**, "a bloody clever lad and very well respected," who is "strong on causation, knows the experts, is completely unflappable, and very accessible." And the "very competent" **Oliver Thorold.**

2 Temple Gardens (O'Brien) New to our table this year, and primarily a defence set, but has just started taking on some claimant work. On the defence side, has fielded barristers in the LSD and Organophosphate cases. On the claimant side, has just received instructions from Alexander Harris in relation to the MMR litigation. Possesses one big-hitter, "really outstanding" **Jeremy Stuart-Smith QC**. Considered unusually self-deprecating for a barrister, a fine advocate and an "accomplished performer," he has made his reputation defending the nation's condoms. Up and coming **David Turner** was also well received.

Other Notable Barristers **Daniel Brennan QC** of **39 Essex Street** (Pleming) is returning to active practice this year after completing his term of office as Chairman of the Bar Council. His involvement in the Lubbe v Cape plc litigation, which went to the Lords in June, suggests that his reputation as one of the leading claimant barristers in the field still holds good. "Exceptional" **Justin Fenwick QC** of **Four New Square** (Fenwick) is considered by some "the favourite for promotion." He has been involved in the tobacco, BSE, and Hepatitis C litigation. Of **Brian Langstaff QC** at **Cloisters** (Cox) it was noted that "the level of his intellect is quite frightening." A "superb advocate," "silky smooth" **Robert Owen QC** of **1 Crown Office Row** (Seabrook) has been involved in the Organophosphate and contraceptive pill litigation, though much of his time is currently being taken up with the Ladbroke Grove inquiry. **Michael Powers QC** of **4 Paper Buildings** (Ritchie) is well-regarded, though generally considered "more of a clinical negligence man." **Augustus Ullstein QC** at **29 Bedford Row** (Ralls) is perceived as a "steady" hand and a "good Rumpolesque figure." "Very bright and hardworking" **Nicholas Underhill QC** at **Fountain Court** (Boswood) has been working on the Hepatitis C litigation and the oral contraceptive litigation. **Barry Cotter** at **Old Square Chambers** (Hendy) is a very well respected figure in the field. He has been involved in the Organophosphate litigation, the Richardson v LRC Products Limited 'defective condom' litigation and the Southall and Paddington rail inquiries. "First rate" **Andrew Lydiard** of **Brick Court Chambers** (Clarke) is a "very cerebral" commercial litigator with experience in tobacco and, more recently, Benzene litigation.

PROFESSIONAL NEGLIGENCE

RESEARCH: The rankings are based on in-depth interviews with over 5,000 solicitors and barristers in the UK. Chambers research is audited by the British Market Research Bureau (see page 7 for details).

OVERVIEW: Professional negligence is a massive area of work for the bar. This is supported by the size of the Professional Negligence Bar Association which boasts over 800 members. While many sets have some experience of defence work in the field, almost all sets have acted for plaintiffs. The principal sets in this section tend to be the principal commercial sets. This section considers only those sets, silks and juniors which have regular dealings in the field.

Two complementary areas of expertise are needed by the professional negligence barrister: talent as a good negligence lawyer, and understanding of the industry in question. Knowledge of the underlying dispute and understanding of the transaction are vital. Experts in fields such as construction therefore often work on professional negligence cases. All professions can be involved in the work, but over the past year there has been a decrease in solicitors' cases and an increase in brokers' work.

Barristers' profiles 1473-1601

LEADING SILKS • London	
❶ DAVIDSON Nicholas	Four New Square
FENWICK Justin	Four New Square
HARVEY Michael	Crown Office Chambers
MAULEVERER Bruce	4 Pump Court
POWELL John	Four New Square
SUMPTION Jonathan	Brick Court Chambers
❷ BRINDLE Michael	Fountain Court
EDELMAN Colin	Devereux Chambers
GOLDSMITH Peter	Fountain Court
HUGHES Iain	Four New Square
MOGER Christopher	4 Pump Court
PATTEN Nicholas	9 Old Square
SYMONS Christopher	3 Verulam Buildings
TER HAAR Roger	Crown Office Chambers
❸ BARTLETT Andrew	Crown Office Chambers
COOKE Jeremy	7 King's Bench Walk
GLASGOW Edwin	39 Essex Street
MOXON-BROWNE Robert	2 Temple Gardens
SLATER John	Crown Office Chambers
❹ BOSWELL Lindsay	4 Pump Court
EDWARDS-STUART Antony	Crown Office Chambers
HODGE David	9 Old Square
HOWARD Mark	Brick Court Chambers
LIVESEY Bernard	Four New Square
MANN Anthony	Enterprise Chambers
STUART-SMITH Jeremy	2 Temple Gardens
TEMPLE Anthony	4 Pump Court
NEW SILKS • LONDON	
BOWDERY Martin	Atkin Chambers
POOLES Michael	4 Paper Buildings
SIMMONDS Andrew	5 Stone Buildings
TAVERNER Marcus	Keating Chambers

For details of these leading barristers see Profiles on page 1473

LONDON

LEADING SETS • London	QCs	Jnrs
❶ **Four New Square** (Justin Fenwick QC)	5	4
❷ **Crown Office Chambers** (Spencer / Purchas)	5	2
4 Pump Court (Bruce Mauleverer QC)	4	3
❸ **Fountain Court** (Anthony Boswood QC)	2	2
9 Old Square (Michael Driscoll QC)	2	-
4 Paper Buildings (Jean Ritchie QC)	1	3
2 Temple Gardens (Dermod O'Brien QC)	2	3

Numbers show recommended barristers in this practice area

Four New Square (Fenwick) Clearly "the top of the tree," the set has increased its strength with a couple of top-notch acquisitions. Has the greatest strength in depth, and is best-known for solicitors' and accountants' defence work. **John Powell QC** is "universally popular" and considered to be "one of the best," while **Nicholas Davidson QC** is another "top-notch" silk, and joined this year from 4 Paper Buildings. **Iain Hughes QC** "lives and breathes professional negligence work" and "may know more about it than anyone else." **Justin Fenwick QC** is noted for surveyors work and is "great on the details," and **Bernard Livesey QC** completes "a startling line-up of QCs." **Roger Stewart** is "the star junior" and "first among equals," with a notable reputation among City firms. **David Halpern** ("straightforward, approachable and intelligent,") who joined from Enterprise Chambers, is rated for property-related work, **Sue Carr** is "another fine junior," and **Fiona Sinclair** continues to have her share of supporters.

Crown Office Chambers (Purchas/Spencer) A newly created chambers, following the merger between One Paper Buildings and 2 Crown Office Row. The two sets were "very well known in the field" in their own right, but it remains to be seen whether the product will exceed the sum of its parts. **Michael Harvey QC** is the "key man." He handles a broad range of work and is of "high technical calibre." "In no way flamboyant, he is astonishingly thorough" and "grinds the opposition down." **Roger ter Haar QC** has acted on some of the biggest disputes, and is widely considered "a serious silk." **John Slater QC** is another "highly rated" silk, while **Andrew Bartlett QC** is attracting increasing numbers of fans, many of them in the City. **Antony Edwards-Stuart QC** completes a high-powered group of QCs. **Simon Howarth** is a new entry this year. "Very good value, he gives practical hands-on advice, and has whole-heartedly adopted the Woolf reforms in comprehensible pleadings." He is considered by clients as "one for the future." **Anna Guggenheim** is considered "nice and easy to work with."

4 Pump Court (Mauleverer) Recognised for its expertise on "tricky, intricate surveyors' and architects' cases," the set has a large team comprising a number of recommended barristers. **Bruce Mauleverer QC** is "a master" on construction cases, while the highly rated **Christopher Moger QC** is a "fantastic advocate" whose star continues in the ascendant. **Lindsay Boswell QC** is commended for his intellect, while **Anthony Temple QC** has a "winning way with clients." "Nice guy" **Nigel Tozzi**, **James Cross** and **Andrew Neish**, noted for his work on financial claims cases, are juniors with recognised expertise in this area.

Fountain Court (Boswood) Like many commercial sets, chambers handles a substantial level of professional negligence work. The market is particularly aware of its accountants' expertise. Although Peter Scott QC has retired, two weighty silks remain. **Peter Goldsmith QC** and **Michael Brindle QC** ("unmissable and outstanding") are used by top City law firms, and are considered to be superb advocates. **Bankim Thanki** and **Guy Philipps** are both "excellent at this kind of thing," and have received wide-ranging commendation.

9 Old Square (Driscoll) Felt to have an "attractive lightness of touch," this set continues to rise in the market's esteem, and is the principal challenger

LEADING JUNIORS • London	
✪ STEWART Roger	Four New Square
❶ BUTCHER Christopher	7 King's Bench Walk
HALPERN David	Four New Square
❷ EKLUND Graham	2 Temple Gardens
GATT Ian	Littleton Chambers
HOLWILL Derek	4 Paper Buildings
LAWRENCE Patrick	4 Paper Buildings
PHILIPPS Guy	Fountain Court
❸ CARR Sue	Four New Square
CROSS James	4 Pump Court
PHILLIPS Rory	3 Verulam Buildings
ROSEN PEACOCKE Teresa	13 Old Square
SWAINSTON Michael	Brick Court Chambers
THANKI Bankim	Fountain Court
TOZZI Nigel	4 Pump Court
❹ BACON Francis	4 Paper Buildings
GUGGENHEIM Anna	Crown Office Chambers
HOWARTH Simon	Crown Office Chambers
MOODY Neil	2 Temple Gardens
NEISH Andrew	4 Pump Court
NEWMAN Paul	Wilberforce Chambers
RAESIDE Mark	Atkin Chambers
RUSSELL Christopher	2 Temple Gardens
SINCLAIR Fiona	Four New Square

For details of these leading barristers see Profiles on page 1473

to the old order. It lacks only a highly-rated junior. **Nicholas Patten QC** ("good on his feet and easy to deal with") is rated for his advocacy and has been another performer on a long-running Bermuda-based case. **David Hodge QC** has been particularly praised for his "effectiveness" by peers at the Bar.

4 Paper Buildings (Ritchie) Widely considered by clients to be "the friendly set." "The clerks are very helpful, the barristers never let you down," and they "inspire confidence" while "always putting themselves out for clients." It remains to be seen, however, how the set has been affected by the departure of Nicholas Davidson QC, formerly the star name. **Michael Pooles QC** is a relatively new silk who has continued to receive strong client recommendation. Three juniors, **Patrick Lawrence, Francis Bacon** and **Derek Holwill** are credited with being "talented and knowledgeable" in the field.

2 Temple Gardens (O'Brien) Perception in the marketplace is mixed on whether the set is best known for complicated or more standard cases, but it is nevertheless recognised as having all-round expertise in the sector. **Jeremy Stuart-Smith QC** is "quick on his feet" and "very impressive in his advocacy skills." **Robert Moxon-Browne QC** is held to be both "effective and knowledgeable." Among the juniors, **Graham Eklund** is "solid and reliable" and **Christopher Russell** is "flamboyant and thorough." **Neil Moody** is included for the first time. A "practical and subtle advocate," he handles accountants', surveyors' and architects' claims.

Other Notable Barristers

At **Brick Court Chambers** (Clarke), the inevitable **Jonathan Sumption QC** is "simply outstanding" and "excellent on this type of work when he does it." His colleague **Mark Howard QC** is another recognised silk, although his practice is felt to encompass more commercial work these days. Junior **Michael Swainston** was praised by a number of clients for his accountancy expertise. New silk **Marcus Taverner QC** at **Keating Chambers** (Fernyhough) is noted for his "insight and ability to see through complicated negligence claims," and is best known for his work on behalf of architects. **Colin Edelman QC** at **Devereux Chambers** (Burke) is used for the bigger professional indemnity cases. **Christopher Symons QC** ("I can't recommend him highly enough") at **3 Verulam Buildings** (Symons/Jarvis) received great market acclaim, and acted for John D. Wood on the Samco case. **Rory Phillips** is a junior here with a favourable reputation. At **7 King's Bench Walk** (Cooke) the "thorough" **Jeremy Cooke QC** has an excellent name for insurance cases. Outstanding junior **Christopher Butcher** is "just so clever" and also handles a variety of insurance cases. **Edwin Glasgow QC** at **39 Essex Street** (Pleming) continues to attract rave reviews, although he has a vast-ranging practice beyond professional negligence. At **Enterprise Chambers** (Mann) **Anthony Mann QC** is regarded as a "jolly good" practitioner. **Teresa Rosen Peacocke** has recently moved to 13 Old Square (Lyndon-Stanford) and is "something of a wizard," according to one client. New silk **Martin Bowdery QC** and junior **Mark Raeside** of **Atkin Chambers** (Blackburn) are both rated for their expertise on cases with a construction angle. **Andrew Simmonds QC** of **5 Stone Buildings** (Harrod) is another relatively new silk to have gained market recognition, while **Paul Newman** of **Wilberforce Chambers** (Nugee) and **Ian Gatt** ("an excellent junior") at **Littleton Chambers** (Kallipetis) are others to have shone this year.

PROPERTY LITIGATION

RESEARCH: The rankings are based on in-depth interviews with over 5,000 solicitors and barristers in the UK. Chambers research is audited by the British Market Research Bureau (see page 7 for details).

OVERVIEW: Specialist property set Falcon Chambers retain its pre-eminent position and is the first choice for many solicitors around the country. The other four sets all boast a number of leading figures and likewise receive instructions from all quarters.

Barristers' profiles 1473-1601

LONDON

LEADING SETS • London	QCs	Jnrs
❶ **Falcon Chambers** (Gaunt Lewison)	6	9
❷ **9 Old Square** (Michael Driscoll QC)	5	7
Wilberforce Chambers (Edward Nugee QC)	5	2
❸ **4 Breams Buildings** (Christopher Lockhart-Mummery QC)	3	2
❹ **Enterprise Chambers** (Anthony Mann QC)	-	3

Numbers show recommended barristers in this practice area

LEADING SILKS • London	
✪ **LEWISON Kim**	Falcon Chambers
MORGAN Paul	Falcon Chambers
❶ **BARNES Michael**	Wilberforce Chambers
BERRY Simon	9 Old Square
DOWDING Nicholas	Falcon Chambers
ETHERTON Terence	Wilberforce Chambers
GAUNT Jonathan	Falcon Chambers
❷ **DRISCOLL Michael**	9 Old Square
NUGEE Christopher	Wilberforce Chambers
REYNOLDS Kirk	Falcon Chambers
WILLIAMSON Hazel	13 Old Square
❸ **CHERRYMAN John**	4 Breams Buildings
FURBER John	Wilberforce Chambers
JACKSON Judith	9 Old Square
PATTEN Nicholas	9 Old Square
❹ **BROCK Jonathan**	Falcon Chambers
HODGE David	9 Old Square
MARTIN John	Wilberforce Chambers
NEW SILKS	
ELVIN David	4 Breams Buildings
MALE John	4 Breams Buildings

For details of these leading barristers see Profiles on page 1473

Falcon Chambers (Gaunt/Lewison) The best keeps on getting better. A new practice director and a perception of better service have gone some way to addressing the old complaints regarding clerking and turnaround times at this set. Two silks here are identified as outstanding. First is the "breathtaking" **Kim Lewison QC**, consistently praised for his "phenomenal" turnaround times and "definitive" advice. A sign of the speed of his thought is his "curt, clipped" style. He is tipped for elevation to the bench in due course. The other stellar name is **Paul Morgan QC**, a "star" lauded for his "terrific clarity" and the capacity to fight "like a terrier." He is said to be "devastating" on cross-examination and "superb" for rent reviews. **Nicholas Dowding QC** is increasingly popular and consequently "difficult to get." It appears worth a wait as he is "great!" An "analytical" mind, he is "useful for exploring possibilities and opportunities." The "quietly assured" manner of **Jonathan Gaunt QC** and his "silky delivery" inspire confidence. **Kirk Reynolds QC** is recommended for dilapidations work and draws praise for his opinions. **Jonathan Brock QC** is "not one to concede a point easily." Of the juniors "totally competent" **Timothy Fancourt**, a "rottweiler" on cross-examination, is said to be "as good as any QC." **Stephen Jourdan** is likewise spoken of as "silk quality" and has a "fantastic brain" and is "quick on his feet." "Bright" **Wayne Clark** brings a "wider view to cover all angles." **Anthony Radevsky** is reportedly "untouchable" for leasehold enfranchisement cases. "Stunningly accurate" **Martin Rodger** is said to be "user friendly," as is **Caroline Shea** whose commercial and "sensible" approach make her "a pleasure" to work with. **Edward Cole** is "on the ball" and former surveyor **Barry Denyer-Green** has an "avuncular" and "academic" style. **Catherine Taskis** is reportedly "unflappable."

9 Old Square (Driscoll) "Particularly prompt" **Simon Berry QC**, a former solicitor, is said to be a "one-man charm offensive" with a "brilliant" legal brain and "common sense" approach. "Amiable" head of chambers **Michael Driscoll QC** has the ability to "cut through" complex problems and come up with simple solutions." "Approachable" **Judith Jackson QC** is popular while **Nicholas Patten QC**, currently on a lengthy case in Bermuda, is "one of the best." **David Hodge QC** is described as "punchy." The juniors in chambers are **John McGhee** who is "good with clients" and a "pragmatic negotiator." "User-friendly" **Timothy Harry** doesn't get "bogged down" with irrelevant detail and **Edwin Johnson** is commended as a "fine all-round performer." "Down to earth" **Katharine Holland** is reputedly an "excellent, firm advocate." **Alan Johns** is a new addition to the tables with enthusiastic responses from clients who say he "gets results" and is "absolutely great." Acting as junior to Nicholas Patten QC in Bermuda, **Thomas Leech** maintains his fine reputation. **Andrew Walker** is "pleasant to work with" and "underrated."

Wilberforce Chambers (Nugee) This commercial chancery set has a strong group of silks and juniors and draws praise for being both "relaxed" and "efficient." With a "terrifying smile" now among the weapons in his arsenal **Michael Barnes QC** remains a "formidable, fearsome opponent." **Terence Etherton QC** is "one of the brainiest," and "intellectually sharp" **Christopher Nugee QC** is well thought of. Recommended for landlord and tenant matters is "academic" **John Furber QC** who draws praise for being "quick." Also recommended is **John Martin QC**. Two juniors stand out at this set. **Jonathan Karas** although seen as "overly bullish" by some, is a "gutsy fighter" for his clients. Regarded as "innovative" and "good on the CPR," **Jonathan Seitler** is someone who "enjoys rolling up his sleeves and working with you" and is also a "complete professional."

4 Breams Buildings (Lockhart-Mummery) Viewed as a serious player, and now fielding three silks, this set is a popular choice for all types of property litigation. The "authoritative" **John Cherryman QC** is a "class act" and new silk **John Male QC** has reputedly been doing "a silk's practice for years" and is "easy to work with." Also recently taken silk is **David Elvin QC** who is known to specialise on planning matters. Combining "extreme cleverness with commerciality," **Nicholas Taggart** is said to be "super." **John Litton** was also recommended as a name to watch.

Enterprise Chambers (Mann) This set, with three juniors in our tables, combines "knowledge and accessibility" and is felt to have an "incredibly supportive" practice director. "Fantastic" **Jacqueline Baker** is "great" on property related professional indemnity work. **Caroline Hutton** is "fierce, you'll get nothing over her in court." "Approachable" **Ann McAllister** is said to have an "excellent technical grasp."

LEADING JUNIORS • London	
❶ DUTTON Timothy	No. 1 Serjeants' Inn
FANCOURT Timothy	Falcon Chambers
JOURDAN Stephen	Falcon Chambers
❷ BAKER Jacqueline	Enterprise Chambers
CLARK Wayne	Falcon Chambers
KARAS Jonathan	Wilberforce Chambers
MCGHEE John	9 Old Square
RADEVSKY Anthony	Falcon Chambers
RODGER Martin	Falcon Chambers
SEITLER Jonathan	Wilberforce Chambers
SHEA Caroline	Falcon Chambers
TAGGART Nicholas	4 Breams Buildings
❸ COLE Edward	Falcon Chambers
DENYER-GREEN Barry	Falcon Chambers
HARRY Timothy	9 Old Square
HUTTON Caroline	Enterprise Chambers
JOHNSON Edwin	9 Old Square
❹ HOLLAND Katharine	9 Old Square
JOHNS Alan	9 Old Square
LEECH Thomas	9 Old Square
MCALLISTER Ann	Enterprise Chambers
ROGERS Beverly-Ann	Serle Court
TASKIS Catherine	Falcon Chambers
THOM James	4 Field Court
TIPPLES Amanda	13 Old Square
WALKER Andrew	9 Old Square
WONNACOTT Mark	7 Stone Buildings
UP AND COMING	
LITTON John	4 Breams Buildings

For details of these leading barristers see Profiles on page 1473

Other Notable Barristers Hazel Williamson QC of **13 Old Square** (Lyndon-Stanford) is recommended as "one of the top people" for rent reviews and "knows the industry inside out." **Timothy Dutton** of **No. 1 Serjeants' Inn** (Faulks), formerly of Barnards Inn Chambers, has a "thoroughly commercial" approach and, according to one source, did "sickeningly well" on the other side. **Beverly-Ann Rogers** of **Serle Court Chambers** (Neill) maintains her reputation as does the "experienced" **James Thom** of **4 Field Court** (Gee.) **Amanda Tipples** of **13 Old Square** (Lyndon-Stanford) is a new addition this year and is "highly recommended." **Mark Wonnacott** of **7 Stone Buildings** (Aldous) has moved from 199 Strand and is commended for his paperwork.

WESTERN CIRCUIT

LEADING JUNIORS • Western	
❶ BLOHM Leslie	St John's Chambers

For details of these leading barristers see Profiles on page xxxx

The "analytical" **Leslie Blohm** at **St John's Chambers** (Sharp) was consistently seen as the first choice in Bristol. Principally seen on property cases, he "knows what he's doing.

NORTHERN CIRCUIT

LEADING SILKS • Northern	
❶ SMITH Peter	40 King St

For details of these leading barristers see Profiles on page xxxx

40 King St (Raynor) is the only set to be consistently mentioned in the North. **Peter Smith QC** is the leading property silk in Manchester and is widely recommended.

SHIPPING

RESEARCH: The rankings are based on in-depth interviews with over 5,000 solicitors and barristers in the UK. Chambers research is audited by the British Market Research Bureau (see page 7 for details).

Barristers' profiles 1473-1601

LONDON

LEADING SETS • London	QCs	Jnrs
❶ **Essex Court Chambers** (Gordon Pollock QC)	6	8
4 Essex Court (Nigel Teare QC)	7	5
4 Field Court (Steven Gee QC)	3	5
7 King's Bench Walk (Jeremy Cooke QC)	5	4
❷ **20 Essex Street** (Iain Milligan QC)	3	3

Numbers show recommended barristers in this practice area

LEADING SILKS • London	
❶ GROSS Peter	20 Essex Street
POLLOCK Gordon	Essex Court Chambers
TEARE Nigel	4 Essex Court
❷ BRENTON Timothy	4 Essex Court
BUCKNALL Belinda	4 Essex Court
EDER Bernard	Essex Court Chambers
FLAUX Julian	7 King's Bench Walk
PERSEY Lionel	4 Field Court
RUSSELL Jeremy	4 Essex Court
❸ COLLINS Michael	Essex Court Chambers
COOKE Jeremy	7 King's Bench Walk
CORDARA Roderick	Essex Court Chambers
GAISMAN Jonathan	7 King's Bench Walk
GEE Steven	4 Field Court
GILMAN Jonathan	Essex Court Chambers
GRUDER Jeffrey	Essex Court Chambers
HAMBLEN Nicholas	20 Essex Street
HOWARD M.N.	4 Essex Court
KAY Jervis	4 Field Court
MACDONALD Charles	4 Essex Court
MILLIGAN Iain	20 Essex Street
SCHAFF Alistair	7 King's Bench Walk
NEW SILKS	
HOFMEYR Stephen	7 King's Bench Walk
RAINEY Simon	4 Essex Court

For details of these leading barristers see Profiles on page 1473

LEADING JUNIORS • London	
✪ PARSONS Luke	4 Essex Court
❶ BERRY Steven	Essex Court Chambers
GOLDSTONE David	4 Field Court
FOXTON David	Essex Court Chambers
JOSEPH David	Essex Court Chambers
MEESON Nigel	4 Field Court
PRIDAY Charles	7 King's Bench Walk
❷ BAKER Andrew	20 Essex Street
BLANCHARD Claire	Essex Court Chambers
BUTCHER Christopher	7 King's Bench Walk
DUNNING Graham	Essex Court Chambers
KVERNDAL Simon	4 Essex Court
MATTHEWS Duncan	20 Essex Street
SMOUHA Joe	Essex Court Chambers
❸ DAVEY Michael	4 Field Court
EDWARDS David	7 King's Bench Walk
HILL Timothy	4 Field Court
HOPKINS Philippa	Essex Court Chambers
JACOBS Nigel	4 Essex Court
LORD Richard	Brick Court Chambers
MCGRATH Paul	Essex Court Chambers
SELVARATNAM Vasanti	4 Field Court
THOMAS Robert	4 Essex Court
TURNER James	4 Essex Court
UP AND COMING	
EDEY Philip	20 Essex Street
SOUTHERN Richard	7 King's Bench Walk

For details of these leading barristers see Profiles on page 1473

Essex Court Chambers (Pollock) Of the silks, **Bernard Eder QC** ("a joy to work with") is fêted for his shipping and insurance expertise whilst **Jonathan Gilman QC** ("the man for marine insurance opinions") also stands out. Leading individual **Gordon Pollock QC** ("the phenomenal advocate") is still perceived as the figurehead for high profile cases. **Jeffrey Gruder QC** ("has a forensic grasp of detail,") **Michael Collins QC** and **Roderick Cordara QC** also receive high accolades from the market. Of the juniors, **David Foxton** ("the benchmark – phenomenally bright") receives strong praise whilst **Paul McGrath** ("wins hopeless cases") has had a particularly good year and steps up in our tables. **Philippa Hopkins** ("very, very bright,") **Claire Blanchard** ("straight down the middle – stands on her own two feet,") **David Joseph** ("flamboyant and worth the money") and **Steven Berry** ("an absolute star") are all held in high regard. **Joe Smouha** is considered "phenomenal," although he is not considered to be as active in mainstream shipping work this year. **Graham Dunning** is also mentioned.

4 Essex Court (Teare) Of the silks, **Nigel Teare QC** ("very thorough and academic") drew consistent praise for "always making himself available." **Timothy Brenton QC** ("careful, approachable and good on analysis") was considered "quite an exceptional cross-examiner," whilst Lloyd's arbitration specialist **Jeremy Russell QC** ("quite abrasive yet extraordinarily well prepared") received many recommendations from the London market, particularly for wet work. **Belinda Bucknall QC** ("superb grasp of the factual element of a case") is known for her "unique, incredibly committed style" and it is generally agreed that she achieves "fantastic results." **MN Howard QC** ("very bright – the opinions man") and **Charles MacDonald QC** are also recommended. The inherent quality of the silks has obviously filtered down to the juniors, who include admiralty specialist **Simon Kverndal** ("approachable and good academically.") Top junior **Luke Parsons**, while considered "overworked," is nonetheless considered to have "an astonishing grasp of detail." New silk **Simon Rainey QC** is deemed "simply outstanding," while **Robert Thomas**, **James Turner** and **Nigel Jacobs** are used frequently by the London market.

4 Field Court (Gee) Of the silks, **Lionel Persey QC** garners consistently high praise as a "frighteningly intelligent" advocate. **Jervis Kay QC** ("a details man") and **Steven Gee QC** are also mentioned. Recommended juniors include **Michael Davey** ("has shipping in his blood and is straightforward and sensible,") who receives strong market feedback for his approachable and client-friendly style. **David Goldstone** is considered "excellent" (he appeared as Junior Counsel to the Crown in the Marchioness Public Inquiry,) while **Nigel Meeson** (who represented the Attorney General's office in the high profile Derbyshire enquiry) and **Vasanti**

Selvaratnam are high on the maritime lawyers' wish list. **Timothy Hill** ("good if you can get him") is perceived to have had a busy year.

7 King's Bench Walk (Cooke) Of the silks, **Julian Flaux QC** ("of course") and **Alistair Schaff QC** ("very bright and competent – the judges lap him up") were singled out for praise. **Jeremy Cooke QC** and **Jonathan Gaisman QC**, while rated highly by the London market, were considered to have reduced profiles for shipping work this year. New silk **Stephen Hofmeyr QC** is felt to have "richly merited" his promotion this year. Stephen Tomlinson QC, ("very calm and reassuring,") has recently been made a High Court judge. Leading juniors include **Christopher Butcher** ("academic and has an unbelievable knowledge of the law") and **Charles Priday** ("superb, doesn't over-elaborate.") Of the emerging talent, **Richard Southern** was considered "user-friendly and bright" whilst **David Edwards** received strong praise for being both "reliable and hard-working."

20 Essex Street (Milligan) **Peter Gross QC** ("perfect – not a blusterer") retains his premier league status and is considered "extremely thorough, personable and cautious." **Nicholas Hamblen QC** ("a star") receives consistent praise from the market and steps up in our rankings this year. **Iain Milligan QC** is also recommended. At the lower end of the notepaper, **Duncan Matthews** is perceived as being "a solid chap, not afraid to be aggressive when required." His strong academic ability was frequently mentioned. **Andrew Baker** is also recommended whilst, of the emerging talent, **Philip Edey** receives positive market feedback.

Other Notable Barrister **Richard Lord** of **Brick Court Chambers** (Clarke) continues to be in demand, although not at a fashionable shipping set.

SPORT

RESEARCH: The rankings are based on in-depth interviews with over 5,000 solicitors and barristers in the UK. Chambers research is audited by the British Market Research Bureau (see page 7 for details).

Barristers' profiles 1473-1601

LONDON

LEADING SETS • London	QCs	Jnrs
❶ Blackstone Chambers (Baxendale/Flint)	4	3
4-5 Gray's Inn Square (Appleby/Ouseley)	2	2
❷ Brick Court Chambers (Christopher Clarke QC)	3	1

Numbers show recommended barristers in this practice area

LEADING SILKS • London	
✪ BELOFF Michael	4-5 Gray's Inn Square
❶ FLINT Charles	Blackstone Chambers
❷ GLASGOW Edwin	39 Essex Street
PANNICK David	Blackstone Chambers
ROSEN Murray	11 Stone Buildings
SINGH Kuldip	5 Paper Buildings
❸ CRAN Mark	Brick Court Chambers
GREEN Nicholas	Brick Court Chambers
HOLLANDER Charles	Brick Court Chambers
LEAVER Peter	One Essex Court
LEVESON Brian	22 Old Buildings
MACKAY Colin	39 Essex Street
MILL Ian	Blackstone Chambers
NORRIS William	Farrar's Building
POLLOCK Gordon	Essex Court Chambers
SPEARMAN Richard	4-5 Gray's Inn Square
NEW SILKS	
GOULDING Paul	Blackstone Chambers
GRIFFITH-JONES David	Devereux Chambers

For details of these leading barristers see Profiles on page 1473

LEADING JUNIORS • London	
✪ KERR Tim	4-5 Gray's Inn Square
❶ FORDHAM Michael	Blackstone Chambers
HOWE Robert	Blackstone Chambers
LEWIS Adam	Blackstone Chambers
❷ CRYSTAL Jonathan	Cloisters
HOSKINS Mark	Brick Court Chambers
LORD David	3 Stone Buildings
MOORE Sarah	4-5 Gray's Inn Square
STONER Christopher	9 Old Square
THANKI Bankim	Fountain Court
❸ BOYD Stephen	29 Bedford Row Chambers
UP AND COMING	
DE GARR ROBINSON Anthony	One Essex Court
RYDER Matthew	Cloisters

For details of these leading barristers see Profiles on page 1473

Blackstone Chambers (Baxendale/Flint) Of the silks, **David Pannick QC** ("public lawyer extraordinaire") has a good reputation for sports work, particularly those matters relating to the constitution of governing bodies. **Charles Flint QC** ("the top of his tree – very, very good") is known as a commercial and public law specialist who "understands sports matters." Last year's new silk, **Ian Mill QC**, is rising rapidly and has a reputation which belies his relative inexperience as a QC. Considered "superb and ultra-intelligent" by many interviewees, he is closely associated with athletics and disciplinary work. Raised to silk this year, **Paul Goulding QC** has a stellar reputation for drug doping cases and is considered "good on his feet." Three juniors stand out this year. **Robert Howe** is associated with restraint of trade work; **Michael Fordham** is thought to have an "encyclopaedic knowledge of administrative law and disciplinary procedure" whilst **Adam Lewis** is considered "excellent at the interface between EU and English Law."

4-5 Gray's Inn Square (Appleby/Ouseley) **Michael Beloff QC** ("a mind like a steel trap") sits as an Arbitrator at the Court of Arbitration for Sport in Lausanne. Viewed as "formidable" by instructing London solicitors, he is acknowledged to have unrivalled knowledge and experience of sports law. His loss to Matrix Chambers next year will leave a large gap. **Richard Spearman QC**, while "not everyone's cup of tea," is nonetheless "sharp and dynamic," with a particular reputation for Jockey Club work. Of the juniors, **Tim Kerr** ("just mustard") is universally judged to be in the ascendancy and occupies pole position in the tables this year. Considered "intelligent, personable and good with clients," he has been involved in some high profile restraint of trade litigation (Nicholas Anelka) and a competition dispute between the owner of two European football clubs and UEFA. **Sarah Moore**, new to our tables last year, is considered to have consolidated her standing as an "excellent" EU lawyer, with particular expertise in gymnastic disputes.

Brick Court Chambers (Clarke) Of the silks, **Charles Hollander QC** is much in demand. Considered an "all-rounder" he is described as combining the "silk's gravitas" with a propensity for hard work ("you don't need to instruct anyone else.") He was used on the Frank Warren/Richie Woodall dispute. **Mark Cran QC** ("shrewd and sharp") is newly recommended this year, partly as a result of his work for the Williams Racing team. **Nick Green QC** is considered a competition lawyer of high repute, who is known for representing unions in disputes with clubs and regulators. **Mark Hoskins** maintains a high degree of respect from solicitors.

Other Notable Barristers At **11 Stone Buildings** (Rosen) **Murray Rosen QC** ("certainly knows his stuff") is considered superb for both commercial and constitutional advice. **Gordon Pollock QC**, head of chambers at **Essex Court Chambers** (Pollock), is considered "brilliant at most things" and to be "as good as anyone" should a sufficiently large instruction arrive. **William Norris QC**, of **Farrar's Building** (Williams) continues to enjoy a good reputation for disciplinary and drugs matters whilst **Edwin Glasgow QC** of **39 Essex St** (Pleming) retains his position on the basis of his personal injury expertise. **Kuldip Singh QC** at **5 Paper Buildings** (Carey/Caplan) is a notable success story this year, garnering high praise from interviewees. Considered "bright, energetic and a sports specialist," his skills as an advocate are much admired. At **22 Old Buildings**, (Hytner) **Brian Leveson QC** is considered a quality cross-examiner with particular expertise in football disputes. **Peter Leaver QC** of **One Essex Court** (Grabiner) is newly recommended this year and is thought to have gained an invaluable insight into the world of football following his tenure as Chief Executive of the Premier League. **Colin Mackay QC** of **39 Essex St** (Pleming) is also mentioned, while new silk **David Griffith-Jones QC** of **Devereux Chambers** (Burke) is considered "commercial and quick to respond" and "a sports specialist." **Jonathan Crystal,** of **Cloisters** (Cox), ("street-wise and worldly") was considered to be "great with clients." He acted in the well-publicised Newcastle United 'bond' case, on behalf of the supporters. **David Lord** of **3 Stone Buildings** (Vos) and **Christopher Stoner** of **9 Old Square** (Driscoll) are also recommended. New entrants this year include the "ubiquitous" **Bankim Thanki** of **Fountain Court** (Boswood) who has added sports law to an ever growing list of specialist areas. Considered "superb" by most, he has acted for the FA in a number of high profile matters. Notable cases this year include Ellesse v Conchita Martinez. **Stephen Boyd** of **29 Bedford Row** (Ralls) is considered to be "thorough" by instructing London solicitors. Ones to watch include **Matthew Ryder** of **Cloisters** (Cox) ("clients love him,") who is known to have superior basketball connections, and **Anthony de Garr Robinson** of **One Essex Court** (Grabiner), who is considered a "determined and focused" junior counsel.

TAX

RESEARCH: The rankings are based on in-depth interviews with over 5,000 solicitors and barristers in the UK. Chambers research is audited by the British Market Research Bureau (see page 7 for details).

OVERVIEW: Fees are notoriously high at the tax bar. It is a small bar, with little more than a hundred practitioners and few out-and-out leaders. As there are few at the top, lead-times to get to them are getting longer and longer, and fees are one way to limit access. This has enjoyed limited success, as the amounts charged are "a drop in the ocean if they get it right."

LONDON

LEADING SETS • Corporate Tax • London	QCs	Jnrs
❶ **Gray's Inn Tax Chambers** (Milton Grundy)	3	3
Pump Court Tax Chambers (Andrew Thornhill QC)	3	6
❷ **11 New Square** (John Gardiner QC)	2	1
❸ **One Essex Court** (Anthony Grabiner QC)	2	2
8 Gray's Inn Square (Patrick Soares)	-	3
24 Old Buildings (Rex Bretten QC)	2	2
3 Temple Gardens Tax Chambers (Richard Bramwell QC)	1	2

Numbers show recommended barristers in this practice area

LEADING SILKS • Corporate Tax • London	
❶ **AARONSON Graham**	One Essex Court
GARDINER John	11 New Square
GOLDBERG David	Gray's Inn Tax Chambers
MILNE David	Pump Court Tax Chambers
PROSSER Kevin	Pump Court Tax Chambers
❷ **BRETTEN Rex**	24 Old Buildings
FLESCH Michael	Gray's Inn Tax Chambers
GOY David	Gray's Inn Tax Chambers
TREVETT Peter	11 New Square
VENABLES Robert	24 Old Buildings
❸ **BRAMWELL Richard**	3 Temple Gardens Tax Chambers
THORNHILL Andrew	Pump Court Tax Chambers
WHITEMAN Peter	Queen Elizabeth Building

For details of these leading barristers see Profiles on page 1473

LEADING JUNIORS • London • Corporate Tax	
❶ **EWART David**	Pump Court Tax Chambers
GHOSH Julian	Pump Court Tax Chambers
PEACOCK Jonathan	11 New Square
❷ **BAKER Philip**	Gray's Inn Tax Chambers
GAMMIE Malcolm	One Essex Court
❸ **CULLEN Felicity**	Gray's Inn Tax Chambers
JAMES Alun	3 Temple Gardens Tax Chambers
SHIPWRIGHT Adrian	Pump Court Tax Chambers
SOARES Patrick	8 Gray's Inn Square
❹ **GOODFELLOW Giles**	Pump Court Tax Chambers
KESSLER James	24 Old Buildings
MCCUTCHEON Barry	8 Gray's Inn Square
MCKAY Hugh	Gray's Inn Tax Chambers
SCHWARZ Jonathan	3 Temple Gardens Tax Chambers
WAY Patrick	8 Gray's Inn Square

For details of these leading barristers see Profiles on page 1473

Gray's Inn Tax Chambers (Grundy) A "prestigious" set, primarily famed for corporate work, but also known for private client advice. Home to the great Andrew Park for many years, the set has always had the "top quality and interesting work." A "great clerk and technically solid silks," are augmented by recognised strength at junior level.The "scintillating" **David Goldberg QC** is considered "highly creative and technically strong," and is used for "structural exploring and for the judgement call." He covers the whole range of corporate work, where he "knows his stuff backwards" and he is considered to be "bullish on financial work." Another for the judgement call, "where there's no safe answer either way," is **Michael Flesch QC.** Better known for advisory work than litigation, he is particularly admired for his "truly independent advice." **David Goy QC** has "a soaring reputation," which includes a pre-eminent position for property tax work, recognition for VAT work and an increasing heavyweight corporate profile. One of the new breed of silks, "he is flexible, and was available to us outside hours." Clients use him "particularly when you need a proper discussion; he is interested in your view as well as his own." Of the juniors **Philip Baker** is considered to be a first rate international tax barrister. Although "he probably does not yet have the tax practice he deserves," he is considered "bright, articulate, academic and pleasant" and is known for his work on double taxation and on the tax side of human rights. The "technically sound" **Felicity Cullen** is primarily known for her litigation skills, and is considered a "clear advocate who gets her point across successfully." **Hugh McKay** is considered an all-rounder who is "good to discuss and develop ideas with." He is "flexible and user-friendly."

Pump Court Tax Chambers (Thornhill) "The leaders on day-to-day tax work – they have the volume." An all-round tax set, known as much for corporate as for trusts and personal tax work. Considered the first port of call for first-time clients seeking tax advice and recommended both for contentious and advisory work. The set is considered to be generally aggressive on tax planning. "Virtually all the major tax litigation" goes to **David Milne QC.** On mainstream contentious corporate tax he is considered to share top billing with John Gardiner. He is "in a class of his own" for VAT litigation. He works on a mix of direct and indirect taxes and although primarily known for corporate work, also works on private client issues. He is "great with the courts" because of his ability to "make the awfully difficult seem simple." "The best of the junior silks" is **Kevin Prosser QC**, who "was at the top from day one." Has a diet of mainstream heavyweight corporate and VAT work. Famed for his "boundless energy" and his "bullish, robust and aggressive advice; you may not agree with him, but you get a reasoned and definite view." VAT solicitors go to him "when you want something aggressive. He's got a good touch, and knows what's going on." The "steady and respectable" **Andrew Thornhill QC** has a "flexible" mind and is appreciated for "taking a very short and finite point and turning it inside out." Also "user friendly" and "a pleasure to take clients to" is the "bright and reasonable" **David Ewart**. He is an all-round direct and indirect tax specialist. Another client favourite and "nice bloke" is **Julian Ghosh**. An all-rounder who has made a name for himself on financial work, he has experience in a 'big five' firm and is recognised for his writing and speaking. He is "very technical and gives cautious advice." "He puts a lot of effort into his opinions and you feel that he has put the greatest depth of thought into his work." A "broad background" and "wide knowledge and experience," make **Adrian Shipwright** another client favourite. **Giles Goodfellow** is appreciated for his all-round technical skills, and is seen to have "cornered the market in professional negligence." **Andrew Hitchmough** is regarded as "a number one" junior for VAT work. He has a "good grasp of issues" and is an "effective advocate." The "young and bright" **Rupert Baldry** also has a solid reputation for VAT work.

11 New Square (Gardiner) Smaller than its main rivals, it nevertheless has a reputation as a "quality set whose independence is highly valued and

LEADING SILKS • Inland Revenue • London	
❶ HENDERSON Launcelot	5 Stone Buildings
MCCALL Christopher	13 Old Square
❷ GLICK Ian	One Essex Court
NEW SILKS	
FURNESS Michael	Wilberforce Chambers

For details of these leading barristers see Profiles on page 1473

LEADING JUNIORS • Inland Revenue • London	
❶ BRENNAN Timothy	Devereux Chambers

For details of these leading barristers see Profiles on page 1473

LEADING SILKS • VAT • London	
❶ MILNE David	Pump Court Tax Chambers
❷ CORDARA Roderick	Essex Court Chambers
❸ GOY David	Gray's Inn Tax Chambers
LASOK Paul	Monckton Chambers
PARKER Kenneth	Monckton Chambers
PROSSER Kevin	Pump Court Tax Chambers

For details of these leading barristers see Profiles on page 1473

LEADING JUNIORS • VAT • London	
❶ BARLOW Richard	11 King's Bench Walk
CARGILL-THOMPSON Perdita	Essex Court Chambers
CONLON Michael	One Essex Court
HITCHMOUGH Andrew	Pump Court Tax Chambers
❷ ANDERSON Rupert	Monckton Chambers
BALDRY Rupert	Pump Court Tax Chambers
NOCK Reginald	24 Old Buildings
SMOUHA Joe	Essex Court Chambers
❸ FOSTER Alison	39 Essex Street
SINGH Rabinder	Matrix Chambers

For details of these leading barristers see Profiles on page 1473

recognised." Solicitors praised the set's "excellent and knowledgeable" clerk who has "a good manner with clients and thinks hard." **John Gardiner QC** shares the primus inter pares position with Graham Aaronson QC. One of the doyens of the City for tax advice, he is also perceived as "the best litigator of them all." "Robust and clever," he is appreciated for his "attention to detail," his "focus on the important points" and for being "down to earth." An "authoritative man of weighty opinions" who "can tell what a judge will think," Gardiner is "the one for heavyweight corporate matters if you have a blank cheque." **Peter Trevett QC**'s "head is grounded in common sense." Some solicitors view him as "the best for your 50-50 questions," his advice is "positive and well-received by clients." Described as "the ideal knockabout junior," **Jonathan Peacock** is "a delight to work with." He has "picked up a lot of experience on the way," "comes up with the practical solutions" in his advice, is "sound and reasonable" and is a "great advocate." Competitors describe him as "faultless, he's got it all: intelligence, bedside manner and clarity."

One Essex Court (Grabiner) An all-round commercial set which deals with corporate tax issues. Regarded as the other doyen of the City, the "brilliant" **Graham Aaronson QC** has "an instinctive feel for how the law ought to be." As befits a cutting-edge tax practitioner, his qualities as an "outstanding litigator" mean that he "can tell what a judge will think." Whilst some perceive that years at the top have made him "didactic," others maintain that he is "good with clients" and gives "clear, business-like technical advice." **Malcolm Gammie**'s long experience as a solicitor (he was a partner at Linklaters) means that he is "attuned to strategy" on top of his technical expertise. He additionally has a strong international reputation. Although seen as more of a commercial barrister, **Ian Glick QC** has a solid reputation acting for the revenue and for advising private clients. **Michael Conlon** maintains his reputation as a highly regarded VAT practitioner. Previously with Allen & Overy he is regarded as "bright and urbane," and has substantial experience in financial services advisory matters.

8 Gray's Inn Square (Soares) A specialist junior-driven tax set which is appreciated for its "reasonable rates." Members are known for their speaking and writing activities as well as advisory work. All-rounder **Patrick Soares** is one of the leaders at the bar on property tax issues. **Barry McCutcheon**'s reputation rests principally in the private arena, while **Patrick Way** is considered to possess "great all-round knowledge."

24 Old Buildings (Bretten) A "respectable" tax set, advising on corporate matters, but primarily famed for private client work. **Rex Bretten QC** is "bullish and aggressive." "You may disagree with him, but he offers clear cut advice, supported by analysis." An all-round corporate tax practitioner who also does some private client work, he is seen to be "optimistic" in his opinions and "you can't beat him for intellectually tip-top advice." **Robert Venables QC** is "as close as you'll get to a genius." He comes up with "amazing ideas for private clients" and is "great at structural exploring." **James Kessler** has also made a name for himself on the private client side. Recently arrived at the set, **Reg Nock** is "the greatest" for stamp duty, an "obvious first choice." He works on a range of indirect tax work, including stamp duty and VAT.

3 Temple Gardens Tax Chambers (Bramwell) "Broad-based" **Richard Bramwell QC** is "one of the tax bar's nice guys." He is known for his writing as well his "helpful" advice. The busy **Alun James** maintains his profile for corporate work. **Jonathan Schwarz** enters our rankings this year following recommendation for his international corporate tax work.

Other Notable Barristers Peter Whiteman QC of **Queen Elizabeth Building** (Bevan/Whiteman) remains "at the top end of the tax bar." Known for his "blue-chip practice," he is viewed as "a bit of a showman", who has a mix of the academic and the hands-on practitioner. At **Monckton Chambers** (Swift), **Paul Lasok QC** has a formidable reputation on European VAT matters, where he acts principally for the Government. At the same chambers, **Kenneth Parker QC** is seen as having an almost exclusively Government-slanted practice in the VAT arena, where he is highly regarded. **Rupert Anderson** has a solid reputation acting for both sides on VAT and customs and excise matters with a European flavour. Although "very busy and abroad a lot," **Roderick Cordara QC** of **Essex Court Chambers** (Pollock) is "superb on his day." An "accomplished" all-round commercial lawyer, in the VAT world he is primarily famed for being "excellent on his feet." His colleagues, the "enthusiastic" **Perdita Cargill-Thompson** and **Joe Smouha** are also well regarded. Better known as a public law expert, **Rabinder Singh** of **Matrix Chambers** (Blake) "knows his tax," and he has impressed with his "excellent, thoughtful and balanced advocacy," acting mainly for the Inland Revenue on VAT matters. **Alison Foster** of **39 Essex Street** (Pleming) is also viewed as a solid performer in the field. Of the barristers who act for the revenue, the "pleasant and conscientious" **Launcelot Henderson QC** of **5 Stone Buildings** (Harrod) remains an "accomplished advocate." **Christopher McCall QC** of **13 Old Square** (Lyndon-Stanford) is respected by the entire profession for his "intellectual integrity and his independent stance." He stands out at the revenue bar for "not being a high charger." "One of the few revenue barristers who knows his tax inside out," his advocacy style is also admired as "he takes their Lordships through step by step." Having taken silk this year, **Michael Furness QC** of **Wilberforce Chambers** (Nugee) maintains his position as a well regarded revenue barrister who has "mellowed and is a better advocate for it." The "aggressive" **Timothy Brennan** of **Devereux Chambers** (Burke) remains a highly rated junior. **Richard Barlow**, a door tenant at **11 King's Bench Walk** (Muller) has a reputation as the foremost barrister for VAT and Customs & Excise work in the North of England (Manchester and Leeds.)

THE BAR

A-Z

ARBITRATION CHAMBERS (John Tackaberry QC)

22 Willes Road, London, NW5 3DS
Tel: (020) 7267 2137 **Fax:** (020) 7482 1018 **DX:** 46454 LDN/Kentish Town
Email: jatqc@atack.demon.co.uk

Head of Chambers:	John Tackaberry QC
Senior Clerk:	Pearl O'Brien
Tenants:	3

Members:

John Tackaberry QC (1967) (QC-1982)
Derrick Morris (1983)
Victoria Bui (1996)

The Chambers: John Tackaberry is a specialist practitioner whose principal area of expertise is international and domestic construction disputes and related areas. He offers advocacy, both in litigation and arbitration, arbitration as arbitrator with particular experience of ICC arbitration and Mediation Adjudication and DRB services.He is a Registered Arbitrator admitted to various panels of Arbitrators in this country, and has been a Recorder since 1988. He is also a Fellow of the Chartered Institute of Arbitrators and the Faculty of Building. He is admitted to practise at the Bars of California and the Irish Republic and as a QC in New South Wales. He is ex-chairman of C.I.Arb, ex-president of Society of Construction Law & European Society of Construction Law. Appointed as an Arbitrator on Panel of China International Economic and Trade Arbitration Commission. Appointed a Commissioner to Chair a panel constituted under the auspices of the United Nations Compensation Commission. He is, or has been, a member of and/or on the arbitration panels of: the Chartered Institute of Arbitrators (Past Chairman); European Society of Construction Law (Past President); Faculty of Building (Fellow); UK Society of Construction Law (Past President); Inst. of Civil Engineers; Royal Inst. of British Architects; Los Angeles Center for Commercial Arbitration; American Arbitration Association; Association of Arbitrators in South Africa; Indian Council of Arbitration; Singapore International Arbitration Council; and Mauritius Chamber of Commerce and Industry. A full CV is available on request.
Prior to being called to the Bar, Derrick Morris had a comprehensive career in the building and civil engineering industries. Since his call to the Bar he has had substantial experience as an advocate in building and civil engineering particularly in the field of arbitrations. A great deal of Mr Morris's experience has been gained in arbitration work in South East Asia and the Far East as well as in England and Wales.
Mr Morris has written and contributed articles and papers to a number of journals and conferences – particularly on legal matters in the construction and engineering field in South East Asia and the Far East.
Additional areas of practice include planning and local government, professional negligence and international law.

ARDEN CHAMBERS (Andrew Arden QC)

Arden Chambers, 27 John Street, London, WC1N 2BL **Tel:** (020) 7242 4244 **Fax:** (020) 7242 3224 **DX:** 29 Chancery Lane WC1
Email: clerks@arden-chambers.law.co.uk **Website:** www.arden-chambers.law.co.uk

ATKIN CHAMBERS (John Blackburn QC)

1 Atkin Building, Gray's Inn, London, WC1R 5AT
Tel: (020) 7404 0102 **Fax:** (020) 7405 7456 **DX:** 1033 **24 hour pager:** (01459) 137252
Email: clerks@atkinchambers.law.co.uk **Website:** www.atkinchambers.law.co.uk

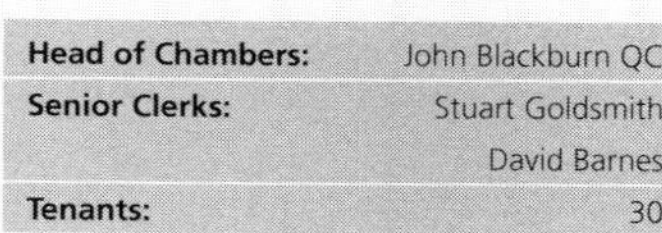

Head of Chambers:	John Blackburn QC
Senior Clerks:	Stuart Goldsmith David Barnes
Tenants:	30

A

Members:

Ian N D Wallace QC (1948) (QC-1973)
John Blackburn QC (1969) (QC-1984)
Colin Reese QC (1973) (QC-1987)
Robert Akenhead QC (1972) (QC-1989)
Nicholas Dennys QC (1975) (QC-1991)
Jonathan Acton Davis QC (1977) (QC-1996)
Andrew White QC (1980) (QC-1997)
Nicholas Baatz QC (1978) (QC-1998)
Martin Bowdery QC (1980) (QC-2000)
Donald Valentine (1956)
Darryl Royce (1976)
Andrew Burr (1981)
Mark Raeside (1982)
Delia Dumaresq (1984)
Stephen Dennison (1985)
Andrew Goddard (1985)
David Streatfeild-James (1986)
Stephanie Barwise (1988)
Simon Lofthouse (1988)
Robert Clay (1989)
Peter D. Fraser (1989)
Dominique Rawley (1991)
Chantal-Aimée Doerries (1992)
Steven Walker (1993)
Fiona Parkin (1993)
Manus McMullan (1994)
James Howells (1995)
Nicholas Collings (1997)
Patrick Clarke (1997)
Christopher Lewis (1998)

Work Undertaken:

Main Areas of Work: Atkin Chambers has always specialised in all aspects of the law relating to construction and civil engineering. It was the first to do so, and has since 1959 provided the editors of the standard construction text, Hudson's Building and Engineering Contracts. In addition to advisory work and advocacy, members also lecture and contribute to, or edit, law reports and other publications. Construction is the core area of the work of members of chambers and ranges from domestic house and road-building through to the construction and commissioning of process plant and power stations and international civil engineering projects of the largest size, together with all related aspects of professional negligence. Members also act in relation to telecommunications projects, railways and rolling stock, offshore structures and pipelines and ship-building. Advice is available at every stage, from the drafting or amendment of forms of contract or warranty to the resolution of any disputes arising out of performance. Members of chambers act both for and against employers/developers, local authorities, contractors, sub-contractors and consultants, in both arbitration and litigation.

Additional Areas: In the commercial field members of chambers advise and act in relation to commercial matters generally, and in particular banking and bonds, insurance, sale of goods and landlord and tenant, both as an adjunct to construction matters and independently of them. With the PFI and as the financing and structuring of large commercial projects has become more complex, members of chambers have provided advice and acted as advocates in a wide variety of dispute often removed from the traditional core area of construction.There has also been and continues to be rapid growth in the demand for advice and representation in connection with contracts for the provision of information technology. Such contracts have considerable similarities with the traditional forms of building contract, and members of Atkin Chambers have developed and are continuing to develop new expertise in this area.

International: Members of chambers are involved in a considerable amount of international work, with both London based arbitrations of disputes which have arisen outside the jurisdiction (often involving questions of foreign law) and advisory and advocacy work overseas.

Arbitrators: Members of Chambers regularly act as either sole arbitrators or as members of panels of arbitrators. In addition, members have experience of methods of alternative dispute resolution.

Direct Access: Members of chambers are available in suitable cases for instruction directly by members of approved professional bodies, or by overseas clients, with direct professional access.

Set No.
4

2 BEDFORD ROW (FORMERLY 3 HARE COURT) (William Clegg QC)

2 Bedford Row, London, WC1R 4BU
Tel: (020) 7440 8888 **Fax:** (020) 7242 1738 **DX:** 17
Email: (initialsurname)@2bedfordrow.co.uk **Website:** www.2bedfordrow.co.uk

Head of Chambers	William Clegg
Sen. Clerk:	John Grimmer
Tenants:	52

Members:

William Clegg QC (1972) (QC-1991) +
The Rt. Hon. John Morris QC (1954) (QC-1973) +
Michael Lewis QC (1956) (QC-1975) +
Howard Godfrey QC (1970) (QC-1991) +
Peter Griffiths QC (1970) (QC-1995) +
Andrew Munday QC (1973) (QC-1996) +
Alun Jenkins QC (1972) (QC-1996) +*
Nigel Lithman QC (1976) (QC-1997) +
Michael Wolkind QC (1976) (QC-1999)
Philip Hackett QC (1978) (QC-1999)
David Thomas QC (1992) (QC-1996) *
Robert Flach (1950)
Charles Conway (1969)
Deborah Champion (1970) +
Nigel Ingram (1974) ++
Mark Halsey (1974)
Robert Neill (1975)
Margaret Barnes (1976)
John Caudle (1976) +
Anthony Abell (1977)
Barry Gilbert (1978)
John Dodd (1979) +
Margaret Dodd (1979) *
Michael Levy (1979)
John Livingston (1980)
Maura McGowan (1980) +
Brian Altman (1981) **
Peter Lodder (1981) +
Trevor Burke (1981)
Keith Mitchell (1981)
James Sturman (1982)
Jane McIvor (1983)
Gelaga King (1985) +
Timothy Kendal (1985)
Mark Milliken-Smith (1986)
Christopher Campbell-Clyne (1988)
Richard Matthews (1989)
Jonathan Ashley-Norman (1989)
Tayo Adebayo (1989)
Thomas Derbyshire (1989)
Craig Rush (1989)
James Ageros (1990)
Christine Agnew (1992)
Adam Budworth (1992)
Michael Epstein (1992)
Valerie Charbit (1992)
John Hurlock (1993)
Alison Pople (1993)
Christine Henson (1994)
Kieran Galvin (1996)
Maria Dineen (1997)
Navaz Daruwalla (1997)

* Door Tenant ** Junior Treasury Counsel at CCC + Recorder
++ Standing Counsel to the Department of Trade & Industry

B

The Chambers: 2, Bedford Row (formerly 3, Hare Court) is well established as a leading chambers specialising in criminal law and concomitant areas of practice. After many years in the Temple, chambers have moved to its own freehold premises at 2 Bedford Row in January 2000. Chambers has continued the tradition of both prosecuting and defending in all types of criminal work, and has developed to meet the demands of modern practice by providing a complete range of experience in general criminal matters, as well as in a number of specialist areas, including health and safety, manslaughter by gross negligence following accidents, and environmental pollution. Chambers presently consists of 11 Queen's Counsel and 41 juniors. Members include the former Attorney-General, Treasury Counsel at the Central Criminal Court and Standing Counsel to the Department of Trade and Industry. Additionally, a number of members of chambers hold office as Recorders and as deputy Stipendary Magistrates. For further information please visit the chambers website at www.2bedfordrow.co.uk which includes profiles for all individual members.

Work Undertaken: In general criminal practice, the size and varied experience of chambers enables it to offer practitioners at all levels and for all types of cases. Members of chambers appear in all criminal matters from the Magistrates' Court to the House of Lords and also before international bodies such as the International War Crimes Tribunal at the Hague. Members of chambers have appeared in many leading cases including R v Colin Stagg, R v Michael Stone, R v Corporal Lee Clegg, R v Tadic, R v Scrafinowicz, R v Sawoniuk, R v Colin Ireland, R v Copeland, R v Fashanu, Grobbelaar and others. There is also considerable experience in confiscation, restraint & asset forfeiture proceedings, including interim orders. Individual members of chambers are experienced in judicial review, extradition and immigration as well as challenges to search and the exercise of privilege, all of which arise in conjunction with the criminal practice. A particular specialisation of chambers is in advising and acting in relation to the investigation and prosecution of allegations of financial offences. As well as acting in the normal range of revenue, VAT and diversion frauds members have experience in the full range of commercial cases including issues of auditing, banking, and regulatory breaches. There is particular experience in investigations and prosecutions brought by the Serious Fraud Office and in advising parties from the commencement of the investigation, including issues arising from international judicial assistance. Cases in which members of chambers have acted include: R v Maxwell and Ors, BCCI, Polly Peck, R Levitt & others, Resort Hotels, Butte Mining, Wallace Smith, Richmond Oils and Gas, and Alliance Resources. There is also considerable experience in related areas of regulatory and disciplinary work, including investigations and tribunals under the jurisdiction of the SFA, Lloyds, the Department of Trade and Industry (including director's disqualification) and the disciplinary tribunals of professional bodies, including the Football Association on behalf of players and clubs.

Languages: Arabic, Dutch, French, German, Hebrew, Italian, Kiro (Sierra Leone), Serbo-Croat.

7 BEDFORD ROW (David Farrer QC)

7 Bedford Row, London, WC1R 4BU
Tel: (020) 7242 3555 **Fax:** (020) 7242 2511 **DX:** 347 (Ch.Ln.)
Email: clerks@7br.co.uk **Website:** www.7br.co.uk

Head of Chambers:	David Farrer QC
Senior Clerk:	Christopher A. Owen
Tenants:	52

Members:

David Farrer QC (1967) (QC-1986)
Martin Wilson QC (1963) (QC-1982) +
J. Stephen Coward QC (1964) (QC-1984)
Timothy Barnes QC (1968) (QC-1986)
Nigel Baker QC (1969) (QC-1988)
Richard B. Latham QC (1971) (QC-1991)
Christopher Hotten QC (1972) (QC-1994) *
William Coker QC (1973) (QC-1994)
Nigel J. Rumfitt QC (1974) (QC-1994)
Charles T. Wide QC (1974) (QC-1995)
Simeon Maskrey QC (1977) (QC-1995)
Philip P. Shears QC (1972) (QC-1996)
Collingwood Thompson QC (1975) (QC-1998)
Joan Butler QC (1977) (QC-1998)
Kathryn M Thirlwall QC (1982) (QC-1999)
Yvonne A. Coen QC (1982) (QC-2000)
Witold Pawlak (1970)
David H. Christie (1973)
J. Philip T. Head (1976)
Julian D. Matthews (1979)
Simon Wheatley (1979)
Nigel G. Godsmark (1979)
Jeremy Pendlebury (1980)
John Pini (1981)
Timothy J. Spencer (1982)
Nicholas Dean (1982)
Derek A. Sweeting (1983)
Ebraham Mooncey (1983)
Susan C. Reed (1984)
Maureen Baker (1984)
Barbara Connolly (1986)
Louise J. Varty (1986)
Simon King (1987)
A. David H. Matthew (1987)
Rupert C. Mayo (1987)
Gordon Aspden (1988)
Stephen Baker (1989)
Brendan Roche (1989)
Rachel Langdale (1990)
Cathryn McGahey (1990)
Steven Ford (1992)
Adam Korn (1992)
Adam Weitzman (1993)
Vanessa Marshall (1994)
Hugh Preston (1994)
Matthew Jowitt (1994)
Bilal Rawat (1995)
William Redgrave (1995)
Anwar Nashashibi (1995)
Susannah Johnson (1996)
Simon Thomas (1995)
David Allan (1998)

Continued overleaf

B

The Chambers: The chambers at 7 Bedford Row are a long-established set of chambers, whose members have a wide experience of advocacy and advisory work in a number of specialised fields. Instructions are accepted from lawyers and professional clients in the United Kingdom and from abroad. In early 1995 chambers moved from 2 Crown Office Row and acquired the freehold of two buildings at 9 Bedford Row and 9 Jockey's Fields. In May 2000 chambers moved to a much larger complex at Bedford Row.

Work Undertaken:
Civil Litigation: Members have experience and can advise upon and present cases in the following areas:- building and construction work, commercial contracts, consumer law, employment, environmental pollution (including waste disposal), financial services, information technology, insurance and reinsurance law, licensing, partnership disputes, personal injury, product liability, professional negligence, and clinical negligence.
Criminal Law: Members have a great deal of experience in the provision of legal advice and advocacy in the criminal field. Chambers can provide representation at all levels of seniority and all members both prosecute and defend. There is a particular emphasis on commercial and international fraud.
Family Law: Members conduct all aspects of family and matrimonial work, with particular emphasis on children's work. In public law members act for parents, Guardian ad litem, the Official Solicitor and local authorities. In private law members advise and appear on child abduction, international disputes, residence and contact issues.
Tribunals: Chambers appear and advise in Disciplinary Tribunals of professional and other bodies, Industrial Tribunals, the Employment Appeal Tribunal, the Criminal Injuries Compensation Board, Public Inquiries, and hearings before the Traffic Commissioner. Chambers are also able to provide trained members in Alternative Dispute Resolution.
For any further information concerning individual members of chambers and areas of practice, as well as the current level of fees and charging rates, please contact the Senior Clerk, Mr Christopher Owen.
International: Instructions are welcomed from overseas lawyers directly. Several members of chambers speak one or more foreign languages fluently; and several members have taught and lectured on legal matters in the United States. There are practising door tenants in Hong Kong, Jersey, and Greece.

Set No.
6

9 BEDFORD ROW (formerly 4 Brick Court) (Anthony Berry QC)

9 Bedford Row, London WC1R 4AZ **Tel:** (020) 7489 2727 **Fax:** (020) 7489 2828 **DX:** 453
Email: clerks@9bedfordrow.co.uk

Set No.
7

17 BEDFORD ROW (Allan Levy QC)

17 Bedford Row, London, WC1R 4EB
Tel: (020) 7831 7314 **Fax:** (020) 7831 0061 **DX:** 370 Ldn/Ch Mobile: (0831) 234861
Email: IBoard7314@aol.com

Head of Chambers:	Allan Levy QC
Senior Clerk:	Ian Boardman
Tenants:	24

Members:

Allan Levy QC (1969) (QC-1989)
Michael Gettleson (1952)
Nigel Jennings (1967)
Jane Gill (1973)
Susan Garnett (1973)
John McLinden (1991) (NZ 1975)
Dennis Sharpe (1976)
Brian Huyton (1977)
Martin Howard Russell (1977)
Anthony Leonard Callaway (1978)
Hashim Reza (1981)
Richard Anthony Southall (1983)
John Critchley (1985)
Miles Croally (1987)
Julian Date (1988)
Fredric Raffray (1991)
Bernard Lo (1991)
Barry McAlinden (1993)
Christina Michalos (1994)
John Crosfil (1995)
Carolyn Hamilton (1996)
Michael Joy (1997)
Neville Maryon Green (1963) *
James Chapman (1987) *
Hugh Bevan (1959) *

* Door Tenant

The Chambers: Members are instructed by solicitors' firms throughout the country and by or on behalf of government departments, local authorities and financial institutions.
Chambers was founded in the Temple over 50 years ago by Leonard Caplan QC. Former members include Lord Justice Farquharson and Sir Laurence Verney, the Recorder of London.

Work Undertaken: Particular areas of work in which individuals specialise are: asset recovery and preservation, including tracing; banking, building sociey and insurance law; criminal law; commercial work; entertainment and media, including defamation, music business, copyright & other intellectual property; medical law; human rights; family, children and divorce; landlord and tenant and property law; personal injury; professional negligence direct professional access work is undertaken.

International: Overseas bars, New Zealand, contact John McLinden. Strong connections with foreign jurisdictions, France, Frederic Raffray, French law Degree, Maitrise-en-Droit, Sorbonne, Paris; Neville Maryon Green (Paris); Western Australia: Allan Levy QC.

Languages: French, German and Italian.

B

Set No.
8

29 BEDFORD ROW CHAMBERS (Peter Ralls QC)

29 Bedford Row Chambers, London, WC1R 4HE
Tel: (020) 7404 1044 **Fax:** (020) 7831 0626 **DX:** 1044
Email: chambers@29bedfordrow.co.uk **Website:** www.29bedfordrow.org.uk

Head of Chambers:	Peter Ralls QC
Clerk:	Robert Segal
Tenants:	46

Members:

Peter Ralls QC (1972) (QC-1997)
Evan Stone QC (1954) (QC-1979)
Augustus Ullstein QC (1970) (QC-1992)
Timothy Scott QC (1975) (QC-1995)
Ajmalul Hossain QC (1976) (QC-1998)
Peter Duckworth (1971)
John Zieger (1962)
Clare Renton (1972)
Howard Shaw (1973)
John Tonna (1974)
Mark Warwick (1974)
Neil Sanders (1975)
Philip Cayford (1975)
Charles Atkins (1975)
Geoffrey Ames (1976)
Simon Gill (1977)
Stephen Boyd (1977)
Simon Edwards (1978)
Michael Keane (1979)
Jonathan Ferris (1979)
Deborah Bangay (1981)
Ann Hussey (1981)
Nicholas Francis (1981)
John Wilson (1981)
Paul Storey (1982)
Timothy Walker (1984)
Nicholas Bowen (1984)
David Holland (1986)
Stephen Reynolds (1987)
Rupert Butler (1988)
Nicholas Chapman (1990)
Robert Peel (1990)
Nichola Gray (1990)
Jonathan Southgate (1992)
Stuart Hornett (1992)
Craig Barlow (1992)
Patrick Chamberlayne (1992)
Victoria Domenge (1993)
Brenton Molyneux (1994)
Duncan Kynoch (1994)
Nicholas Tse (1995)
Nicholas Allen (1995)
Peter Mitchell (1996)
Gary Pryce (1997)
Laura Heaton (1998)
Robert Upex *

* Door Tenant

The Chambers: Bedford Row Chambers is a progressive and growing set committed to providing its clients with an effective and efficient legal service. It operates from one of the Bar's largest and contemporary offices, having added a further 50% to its office space by taking over its neighbouring premises. Bedford Row Chambers resides in two Grade II listed buildings, completely modernised and wired for the latest technology and with room to expand.

Work Undertaken: The work of chambers is primarily in commercial, property, family, personal injury and general common law and extends to a wide range of litigation, advisory and drafting work.
Chancery: Breach of trust, Court of Protection, partnership, trusts, wills and probate.
Commercial: Arbitration, building and construction, commercial, companies, consumer credit, contract, economic torts, guarantees, licensing, misrepresentation, and sale of goods.
Common Law: Injunctions, employment, libel and slander, nuisance and property-related torts, personal injuries, tort, professional negligence.
Family: Family law and family provision.
Intellectual Property: Confidential information, intellectual property, copyright and passing off, trade marks and trade names.
Insolvency: Bankruptcy, insolvency, liquidations and administrations and receivership.
Property: Conveyancing, housing, land law, landlord and tenant, mortgages and securities, planning, rent reviews.
Public and Administrative Law: Judicial review, statutory appeals and tribunal work. Particularly education, special educational needs, community care and mental health work.

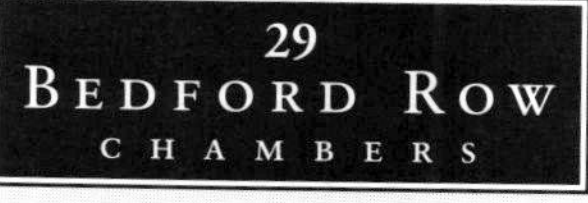

B

Set No. 9

33 BEDFORD ROW (David Barnard)

33 Bedford Row, London, WC1R 4JH
Tel: (020) 7242 6476 **Fax:** (020) 7831 6065 **DX:** 75
Email: clerks@bedfordrow33.demon.co.uk **Website:** www.bedfordrow33.demon.co.uk

Head of Chambers:	David Barnard
Senior Clerk:	Ian Chivers
Tenants:	29

Members:

David Barnard (1967) +
Barry Kogan (1973) +
Nigel May (1974) +
Martyn Zeidman QC (1974) (QC-1998) +
Constance Whippman (1978)
Richard Bendall (1979)
Gary Webber (1979)
Keith Hanlon (1979)
Robert Carrow (1981)
Marc Galberg (1982)
Peter Gray (1983)
Michael Burke (1985)
Christopher Spratt (1986)
Francis Fitzgibbon (1986)
Susan Castle (1986)
Timothy Thorne (1987)
Joanne Oxlade (1988)
David Lonsdale (1988)
Jean-Paul Sinclair (1989)
Rhys Jones (1990)
Joanne Clarke (1993)
Thomas Cleeve (1993)
Tom Boyd (1995)
Stuart Armstrong (1995)
John Law (1996)
Piers Harrison (1997)
Daniel Dovar (1997)

\+ Recorder

The Chambers: Chambers undertakes work in the following practice groups: property, criminal law, family law, commercial and civil litigation. Members regularly publish and lecture. David Barnard is Standing Counsel to HM Customs and Excise, and Nigel May is a part-time Judge Advocate.

Publications: include *Residential Possession Proceedings* (Webber), *Possession of Business Premises* (Webber), and *The Woolf Reforms: A Practitioner's Guide* (Barnard, Galberg & Lonsdale)

Set No. 10

36 BEDFORD ROW (Michael Pert QC)

36 Bedford Row, London, WC1R 4JH
Tel: (020) 7421 8000 **Fax:** (020) 7421 8080 **DX:** LDE 360 Chancery Lane
Email: Chambers@36bedfordrow.co.uk **Website:** www.36bedfordrow.co.uk

Head of Chambers:	Michael Pert QC
Practice Manager:	Peter Bennett FCCA MCIM
Senior Clerk:	Bill Conner
Senior Criminal Clerk:	Harri Bennetts
Senior Civil/Family Clerk:	Richard Cade
Administrator:	Jane Wittering
Fees Clerk:	Lynne Edmond
Tenants:	70

Members:

Michael Pert QC (1970) (QC-1992) LLB (Manch) +
Brian R. Escott-Cox QC (1954) (QC-1974) MA (Oxon)
Martin Bowley QC (1962) (QC-1981) MA BCL (Oxon)
James Hunt QC (1968) (QC-1987) MA (Oxon) +
Michael Stokes QC (1971) (QC-1994) +
Frances Oldham QC (1977) (QC-1994) BA (Bristol) +
Nicholas Browne QC (1971) (QC-1995) LLB (Liverpool), Dip Law (Strasbourg)+
Richard Benson QC (1974) (QC-1995) +
Annabel Walker QC (1976) (QC-1997) +
Anesta Weekes QC (1981) (QC-1999) +
David Farrell QC (1978) (QC-2000) LLB (Manchester) +
Andrew Urquhart (1963) BA (Oxon)
Stephen Waine (1969) LLB (Southampton) +
David Altaras (1969) MA, DipCrim(Cantab)+
Christopher Metcalf (1972) +
David Lee (1973) BA/AB (Cantab/Harvard)
Jamie De Burgos (1973) MA (Cantab)
Colin J.D. Anderson (1973)
Michael Fowler (1974) LLB (London) +
Geoffrey Solomons (1974) LLB (Nottingham)
Michael Greaves (1976) LLB (Birmingham)
A.G (Sam) Mainds (1977) +
Charles Lewis (1977) MA (Oxon)
Howard Morrison (1977) OBE, LLB (London) +
Catherine Gargan (1978) LLB (Liverpool)
Jeremy H.C. Lea (1978)
Gillian Temple-Bone (1978)
Martin Beddoe (1979) MA (Cantab)
Christopher Donnellan (1981) BA (Oxon)
Lynn Tayton (1981) LLB (London)
Edmund Farrell (1981) LLB (Leeds) LLM (Cantab) Dip. Eur Law (Kings)
Richard Wilson (1981) BA LLM (Sussex/Cambridge)
Charlotte Friedman (1982)
Mercy Akman (1982) LLB (Wales)
Christopher Plunkett (1983) LLB (Warwick)
William Harbage (1983) + MA (Cantab)
Simon Bull (1984) BA, LLM (Cantab)
Joanne Ecob (1985) LLB (Newcastle)
Robert Underwood (1986) BA (De Montfort)
Michael Cranmer-Brown (1986)
Benjamin Gumpert (1987)
Amjad Malik (1987) BA, LLM (London)
Gordon Wignall (1987)
Peter Dean (1987)
Greg Pryce (1988) BA (Wolverhampton)
Andrew Howarth (1988) BA (Oxon)
Amanda Johnson (1990) LLB (London)
Simon Sugar (1990)
John Gibson (1991) LLB (Durham)
Matthew Lowe (1991) LLB (Exeter)
Stuart Alford (1992) BSc (Reading)
Sarah Gaunt (1992) LLB (Cardiff), M.Phil(Cantab)
Andrew McNamara (1992)

Members continued:

Rosa Dean (1993) BA (Oxon)
John Lloyd-Jones (1993) BA (Durham)
Karen Johnston (1994) MA (Oxon)
Jeffrey Jupp (1994) BA (Worcester)
Andrzej Bojarski (1995) LLB (LSE)
Jonathan Spicer (1995)
Jonathan Kirk (1995) LLB (Kings)
Niall Ferguson (1996) BA (Dunelm)
Rupert Skilbeck (1996) BA (York)
Oliver Connolly (1997)
Kate Brunner (1997) MA (Edinburgh), Dip Law (City)
Kevin Barry (1997) LLB (Birmingham)
Rebecca Crane (1998)
Catarina Sjölin (1998)
Kevin McCavish (1998) LLM (London)
Simon Ash (1999)
Penelope Wood (1999)
Peter Joyce QC (1968) (QC-1991) +*
Colman Treacy QC (1971) (QC-1990) +*
Richard Payne (1964) *
Elizabeth Ingham (1989) *

+ Recorder *Door Tenant

The Chambers: For over a century chambers have been a London based Midland and Oxford circuit practice. Chambers operate within client-orientated teams covering crime; fraud; civil & commercial; and family. Chambers have annexes in Northampton, Leicester and Nottingham. Chambers have a reputation for good management, innovation in client services, fairness and a very professional and friendly atmosphere. They fully comply with the Bar Practice Management Standard and Equality Code and are the first chambers to achieve ISO 9000 quality accreditation.Fully computerised and integrated diary and fee collection. Video conferencing facilities are available in all offices. Fully integrated computer/speech links connect all offices. E-mail and paperless office offered to clients.

Work Undertaken: Personal injury litigation with specialists in paraplegia and brain damage; professional and medical negligence; commercial and company law; consumer law and consumer credit; planning; family law, including matrimonial finance, property and childcare; landlord and tenant; crime, including commercial fraud; contract, including sale of goods.
Additional Areas: Administrative law; agriculture; arbitration; aviation; banking; Chancery, including probate; computer law; construction; boundary disputes; courts martial; defamation; discrimination; EU; employment; environment; housing; immigration; insolvency; judicial review; licensing; animal and equestrian cases; local government; mental health; pharmaceuticals; police cases; product liability; property; and sports law.

Languages: French, Punjabi, Spanish and Urdu.

Recruitment & Training: Chambers offer twelve months' pupillages. The Midland and Oxford Circuit covers a wide area and pupils should be prepared for extensive travel and higher travel costs than those in London-based practice. Pupillage awards of £18,000 (including an income guarantee) are made. Pupils regularly earn another £3,000. Mini-pupillages are available. Chambers have an excellent record of recruitment from pupils. Applications via PACH.

No. 1

48 BEDFORD ROW (Roderick I'Anson Banks)

48 Bedford Row, London, WC1R 4LR
Tel: (020) 7430 2005 **Fax:** (020) 7831 4885 **DX:** 284 LDE
Email: kim@partnershipcounsel.co.uk **Website:** www.partnershipcounsel.co.uk

Head of Chambers:	Roderick I'Anson Banks
Practice Manager:	Kim Pangratis
Tenants:	2

Members:

Roderick I'Anson Banks (1974) LLB (London)
Simon Jelf (1996) LLB (Eur)

The Chambers: Specialise exclusively in partnership law and provide solicitors and other professional and trading partnerships with a full range of legal services, from the drafting of new agreements and the review of existing agreements to advice and representation in partnership disputes, arbitrations and mediations.
Chambers aim, where possible, to assist clients with the process of resolving disputes without recourse to litigation and provide ongoing support from the embryonic stages of a developing dispute right through to the conclusion of any litigation or until a negotiated settlement is reached.
Direct Professional Access work is undertaken.

Publications: Roderick I'Anson Banks is the editor of *Lindley & Banks on Partnership*, the authoritative guide to partnership law, and the author and editor of the *Encyclopedia of Professional Partnerships*.

B

Set No. 12

9-12 BELL YARD (D. Anthony Evans QC)

9-12 Bell Yard, London, WC2 A2CL
Tel: (020) 7400 1800 **Fax:** (020) 7404 1405 **DX:** 390
Email: clerks@bellyard.co.uk

Head of Chambers	D. Anthony Evans QC
Sen. Clerk:	Gary Reed
Tenants:	59

Members:

D. Anthony Evans QC (1965) (QC-1983) BA (Cantab)
Edmund Lawson QC (1971) (QC-1988) MA (Cantab)
Lord Carlile of Berriew QC (1970) (QC-1984)
Michael Birnbaum QC (1969) (QC-1992)
Peter Hughes QC (1973) (QC-1991)
Jeremy Carter-Manning QC (1975) (QC-1993)
Patrick Curran QC (1972) (QC-1995)
Sonia Woodley QC (1968) (QC-1996)
Peter Christopher Rouch QC (1972) (QC-1996)
Robin Spencer QC (1978) (QC-1999)
Philip Katz QC (1976) (QC-2000)
Herbert Kerrigan QC (1970) (QC-1992)
Edward Grayson (1948) MA (Oxon)
Richard Cherrill (1967)
Martin Field (1966)
Bernard Phelvin (1971) BA (Cantab)
Richard Merz (1972)
Alison Barker (1973) LLB, Harmsworth Law Scholar 1973
John Greaves (1973) LLB (Lond)
Anthony Heaton-Armstrong (1973)
Tudor Owen (1974) LLB (Lond)
Alexander Cranbrook (1975) BA
Peter Doyle (1975) LLB
Stephen John (1975)
John Harwood-Stevenson (1975)
Timothy Spencer (1976)
Peter Moss (1976)
Keith Hadrill (1977)
Simon Wild (1977)
Michael Orsulik (1978)
Diane Chan (1979)
John Alban Williams (1979)
John McGuinness (1980)
Graham Brown (1980)
Michael Egan (1981)
Sean Enright (1982)
Jonathan Davies (1981)
Mukul Chawla (1983)
Constance Briscoe (1983)
Christine Laing (1984)
Philippa McAtasney (1985)
Mohammed Khamisa (1985)
Mark Bryant-Heron (1986)
William Hughes (1989)
Sarah Ellis (1989)
Adrian Chaplin (1990)
Alexandra Healy (1992)
Mark Seymour (1992)
Richard Jory (1993)
Suzanne Reeve (1993)
Warwick Tatford (1993)
Tina Davey (1993)
Jonathan S Kinnear (1994)
Christina Russell (1994)
Jessica Gavron (1995)
Michelle Denton (1996)
Neil Griffin (1996)
Richard Calvert-Smith (1997)
Kristian Mills (1998)

The Chambers: A common law set of chambers, offering broad-based expertise in all fields of criminal and civil law, which has grown steadily since it was established in former premises over 60 years ago. The set has steadily developed to meet the demands within its focused areas of expertise. Continuing expansion has resulted in the acquisition of an annexe at 5 Bell Yard.

9-12 Bell Yard recognise that the role of a common law barrister is changing and is, as a result, moving towards increasing specialisation with a desire to offer professional and efficient service to solicitors and other professional clients in an ever-changing environment. Chambers are run by an experienced professional team, headed by the Senior Clerk, Gary Reed, with the assistance of dedicated staff. Accommodation has been specifically designed to meet the need for modern and convenient conference facilities and to provide maximum professional and administrative efficiency. Chambers have dedicated conference facilities in London as well as facilities in Chester, Birmingham, Swansea, Liverpool and Cardiff. Chambers is fully computerised, using up-to-date, virus protected software, which is internally networked and supported by a website.

Work Undertaken:

Criminal: From the largest of City firms to the smallest of High Street practices, advocacy and advisory work is undertaken at all levels across a wide spectrum of criminal cases. Chambers' professional clients include in-house lawyers from legal departments of major companies, government departments and local authorities. Direct professional instructions are accepted. Members deal with every aspect of criminal litigation. Defence experience is broadly-based, ranging from the more serious and complex commercial fraud cases to the more common offences against the person and property. Established expertise includes drugs offences and money laundering, sexual offences and judicial review. Prosecution work of all kinds and at all levels is undertaken, not only for the Crown Prosecution Service, Customs and Excise, the Serious Fraud Office and the Department of Trade and Industry, but also for British Telecom, the Post Office and many local authorities. 9-12 Bell Yard conduct appeals at all court levels, with senior members presenting appeals from Commonwealth countries to the Privy Council. Members of chambers have been involved in some of the most widely reported cases, involving such well known names as Blue Arrow, Maxwell, BCCI, the Marchioness disaster, the criminal trials following the Guildford Four and the Birmingham Six appeals and the Stephen Lawrence public inquiry.

Civil: Leading and junior members of chambers undertake all general civil litigation work. This includes

B

banking, building, children, company, consumer credit, contract, employment, insurance, landlord and tenant, partnership, personal injury, professional negligence and sports law.
Additional specialisations: Other areas of practice include arbitration, criminal injuries, compensation, inquests, licensing, planning, professional disciplinary and self-regulatory tribunals and public inquiries.

International: Work is undertaken throughout the country and overseas. A number of members of chambers have been been recognised by their appointments to a variety of judicial and other legal positions.

Set No.
13

BLACKSTONE CHAMBERS (P Baxendale QC and C Flint QC)

Blackstone House, Temple, London, EC4Y 9BW
Tel: (020) 7583 1770 **Fax:** (020) 7822 7350 **DX:** 281
Email: clerks@blackstonechambers.com **Website:** www.blackstonechambers.com

Head of Chambers:	Presiley Baxendale QC
	C. Flint QC
Practice Manager:	Julia Hornor
Senior Clerk:	Martin Smith
Tenants:	56

Members:

Colin Ross-Munro QC (1951) (QC-1972)
Stanley Brodie QC (1954) (QC-1975)
Lord Lester of Herne Hill QC (1963) (QC-1975)
Ian Sinclair QC (1952) (QC-1979)
Ian Brownlie QC (1958) (QC-1979)
David Donaldson QC (1968) (QC-1984)
Robert Englehart QC (1969) (QC-1986)
David Hunt QC (1969) (QC-1987)
Barbara Dohmann QC (1971) (QC-1987)
Andrew Pugh QC (1961) (QC-1988)
Ian Forrester QC (1972) (QC-1988)
Roy Goode QC CBE (1988) (QC-1990)
Maurice Mendelson QC (1965) (QC-1992)
Jonathan Harvie QC (1973) (QC-1992)
Presiley Baxendale QC (1974) (QC-1992)
David Pannick QC (1979) (QC-1992)
Jeffrey Jowell QC (1965) (QC-1993)
Stephen Nathan QC (1969) (QC-1993)
Charles Flint QC (1975) (QC-1995)
Bob Hepple QC (1966) (QC-1996)
Ian Mill QC (1981) (QC-1999)
Beverley Lang QC (1978) (QC-2000)
Paul Goulding QC (1984) (QC-2000)
Gerald Levy (1964)
Dawn Oliver (1965)
Alastair Sutton (1972)
Hugo Page (1977)
Judith Beale (1978)
Thomas Beazley (1979)
Nicholas Khan (1983)
Anthony Peto (1985)
Monica Carss-Frisk (1985)
Gerard Clarke (1986)
Adam Lewis (1985)
Robert Anderson (1986)
Mark Shaw (1987)
Andrew Green (1988)
Robert Howe (1988)
Adrian Briggs (1989)
Dinah Rose (1989)
Michael Fordham (1990)
Pushpinder Saini (1991)
Thomas Croxford (1992)
Javan Herberg (1992)
Joanna Pollard (1993)
Andrew Hunter (1993)
Gemma White (1994)
Jane Collier (1994)
Emma Dixon (1994)
Thomas de la Mare (1995)
Tom Weisselberg (1995)
Jane Mulcahy (1995)
Julia Ellins (1994)
Andrew George (1997)
Kate Gallafent (1997)
Claire Weir (1998)

The Chambers: Blackstone Chambers is a long established set, combining formidable strengths in commercial, public and employment law, with state of the art facilities and a friendly and open approach to client service.

Work Undertaken: Chambers' practice breaks down into the following practice areas:
Commercial: within this area, members' established skills and specialisations include: international trade; banking; insurance and reinsurance; carriage of goods; conflict of laws; corporate fraud; financial services; regulatory tribunals; shipping; defamation; intellectual property, media, entertainment and sports law.
Public law and Human Rights: work includes judicial review, both for and against public bodies and regulatory authorities, arising from decisions and areas such as: freedom of expression; equality of treatment; immigration; education; social security; housing; planning; and local government. The combined expertise of members of chambers in commercial and public law proves particularly valuable in City regulation and financial services cases. Advice in the human rights arena is also available, with particular reference to the impact of the Human Rights Act 1998 in all its aspects.
Employment law: within this area, members of chambers have extensive expertise in all aspects of employment law, ranging from pure contract work to sex, race and disability discrimination.

International: European law with its ever growing impact on national law is an integral part of chambers' practice in all areas of specialism. Further, one member of chambers is a former member of the Legal Service of the European Commission and 2 other members of chambers practise full-time in European Community law from offices in Brussels. Chambers also has a strong tradition of practice in the specialised field of public international law. Several members of chambers are highly experienced in advising in

Continued overleaf

B

litigation in public international law disputes arising before national and international courts and tribunals; a current member was formerly the legal adviser to the Foreign and Commonwealth Office. Members of chambers have a wide-ranging experience of advocacy before English, European and Commonwealth courts and tribunals and frequently appear before the European Courts of Justice and the European Court of Human Rights.

Publications: these are many in number and include: *Legal Problems of Credit and Security; Hire Purchase Law and Practice; Principles of Corporate and Insolvency Law; Consumer Credit Legislation; Halsbury on Arbitration and Dicey & Morris (13th ed); Principles of Public International Law; The Vienna Convention on the Law of Treaties; and International Law Commission; De Smith Woolf and Jowell: Judicial Review of Administrative Action; Judicial Review Handbook; Halsbury on Aliens; Halsbury on the European Convention of Human Rights; Butterworths Human Rights – Law and Practice; Constitutional Law & Human Rights.*

Languages: Finnish, French, German, Hindi, Italian, Japanese, Punjabi, Spanish, Swedish, Urdu.

Recruitment & Training: Chambers has its own applications procedure. The application form is available on request. A first or upper second class degree is usually required, although not necessarily in law. Pupillage awards of up to £25,000 are available. Mini-pupillages for a week in the year preceding pupillage are strongly encouraged for potential pupils of chambers. Further information, either about chambers generally or about pupillage in particular, is available from chambers' web site www.blackstonechambers.com

Set No. 14

4 BREAMS BUILDINGS (Christopher Lockhart-Mummery QC)

4 Breams Buildings, London, EC4A 1AQ
Tel: (020) 7430 1221/7353 5835 **Fax:** (020) 7421 1399 **DX:** 1042
Email: clerks@4breams.co.uk

Head of Chambers:	Christopher Lockhart-Mummery QC
Senior Clerk:	Stephen Graham
Junior Clerk:	Jay Fullilove
Tenants:	35

Members:

Christopher Lockhart-Mummery QC (1971) (QC-1986)
Nigel Macleod QC (1961) (QC-1979)
John Cherryman QC (1955) (QC-1982)
Michael Howard QC MP (1964) (QC-1982)
David Hands QC (1965) (QC-1988)
Lord Kingsland QC (1972) (QC-1988)
Joseph Harper QC (1970) (QC-1992)
John Howell QC (1979) (QC-1993)
Richard Drabble QC (1975) (QC-1995)
David Holgate QC (1978) (QC-1997)
Christopher Katkowski QC (1982) (QC-1999)
John Male QC (1976) (QC-2000)
David Elvin QC (1983) (QC-2000)
Colin Sydenham (1963)
Stephen Bickford-Smith (1972)
Eian Caws (1974)
Robert Bailey-King (1975)
Anne Seifert (1975)
Christopher Lewsley (1976)
Viscount Dilhorne (1979)
David Smith (1980)
Anne Williams (1980)
Thomas Jefferies (1981)
Alice Robinson (1983)
Timothy Mould (1987)
Nathalie Lieven (1989)
John Litton (1989)
Nicholas Taggart (1991)
Karen McHugh (1992)
David Forsdick (1993)
Timothy Morshead (1995)
Graeme Keen (1995)
James Maurici (1996)
Alison Oakes (1996)
David Abrahams (1998)
Daniel Kolinsky (1998)

The Chambers: 4 Breams Buildings is a well established chambers which is recognised as a leading set in each of the main areas in which it specialises. These are public law, local government, planning, environmental law and property. There are currently 35 members of chambers (12 QCs). They advise, and appear regularly for, all types of client, including individuals, pressure groups, landlords (including institutional landlords), developers, regulators, local authorities and central government. Chambers are housed in spacious, self contained, air conditioned accommodation which has one floor dedicated to conference facilities. It seeks to offer a high quality, efficient and friendly service which meets its clients requirements. Direct Professional Access is welcomed.

B

Work Undertaken:

Public and Administrative Law including Human Rights: Members have considerable experience in judicial review and statutory applications and appeals. They frequently advise and appear both for public bodies and those who wish to challenge their decisions. Several junior members are on a Treasury Panel. Particular subject areas in which chambers specialise include local government, education, health, housing, mental health, community care and social services, social security, utility and other regulators, public procurement and the tortious liability of public authorities.

Planning and Environmental Law: All aspects. Chambers includes 24 members of the Planning and Environmental Bar Association. Its clients include individuals, pressure groups, amenity and local residents groups, developers (such as large retailers, housebuilders and mineral undertakers), a large

number of local authorities, the Environment Agency and the Secretary of State for the Environment Transport and the Regions. Members of chambers have been involved, for example, in recent cases on the impact of European law in this area.

Other: All aspects of landlord and tenant and property (including vendor and purchaser, covenants, easements, mortgages and party walls). There are related specialisms in mining, rating, property related torts (including trespass and nuisance) and professional negligence. Chambers has been strengthened in the last year by the recruitment of Tom Jefferies. Around these main areas of work chambers also offers a specialist service in European law, compulsory purchase and compensation (the volume on which for *Halsbury's Laws* was edited entirely by members of chambers), Parliamentary work and Transport and Works Act inquiries, and building contracts.

Publications: Publications with which members of chambers have been involved include:*Hill's Law of Town and Country Planning (4th ed); Town Planning Law Handbook and Case Book; Atkins Court Forms – Town and Country Planning; Hill and Redmond's Law of Landlord and Tenant; Halsbury's Laws – Town and Country Planning; Halsbury's Laws – Compulsory Acquisition; Atkin's Court Forms – Rating and Community Charge; Journal of Planning Law; Judicial Review; Corfield and Carnwath's Compulsory Acquisition and Compensation; Emden's Building Contracts and Practice; Unlawful Interference with Land; Party Walls – the New Law.*

Recruitment & Training: In addition to recruiting Tom Jefferies, David Abrahams and Daniel Kolinsky also joined chambers last year. Tenancy and mini pupillage applications should be addressed to Nathalie Lieven. Pupillage applications should be made through the Bar PACH scheme directly to chambers. Three funded pupillages are awarded annually, each of £19,000 for 12 months (although applications for six month pupillages are considered).

Set No. 15

BRICK COURT CHAMBERS (Christopher Clarke QC)

7-8 Essex Street, London, WC2R 3LD
Tel: (020) 7379 3550 **Fax:** (020) 7379 3558 **DX:** 302
Email: [surname]@brickcourt.co.uk **Website:** www.brickcourt.co.uk

Head of Chambers	Christopher Clarke QC
Sen. Clerk	Julian Hawes and Ian Moyler
Tenants:	57

Members:

Christopher Clarke QC (1969) (QC-1984)
Sydney Kentridge QC (1977) (QC-1984)
David Vaughan QC (1962) (QC-1981)
Jonathan Sumption QC (1975) (QC-1986)
Hilary Heilbron QC (1971) (QC-1987)
Mark Cran QC (1973) (QC-1988)
Jonathan Hirst QC (1975) (QC-1990)
Gerald Barling QC (1972) (QC-1991)
Peregrine Simon QC (1973) (QC-1991)
Timothy Charlton QC (1974) (QC-1993)
Richard Gordon QC (1972) (QC-1994)
Mark Hapgood QC (1979) (QC-1994)
Mark Howard QC (1980) (QC-1996)
Stephen Ruttle QC (1976) (QC-1997)
Andrew Popplewell QC (1981) (QC-1997)
George Leggatt QC (1983) (QC-1997)
William Wood QC (1980) (QC-1998)
Nicholas Green QC (1986) (QC-1998)
David Lloyd Jones QC (1975) (QC-1999)
Charles Hollander QC (1978) (QC-1999)
Paul Walker QC (1979) (QC-1999)
David Anderson QC (1985) (QC-1999)
Catharine Otton-Goulder QC (1983) (QC-2000)
Peter Irvin (1972)
Peter Brunner (1971)
James Flynn (1978)
Andrew Lydiard (1980)
Richard Lord (1981)
Mark Brealey (1984)
Michael Swainston (1985)
Fergus Randolph (1985)
Conor Quigley (1985)
David Garland (1986)
Neil Calver (1987)
Dominic Chambers (1987)
Richard Slade (1987)
Harry Matovu (1988)
Cyril Kinsky (1988)
Paul Wright (1990)
Sarah Lee (1990)
Helen Davies (1990)
Tom Adam (1991)
Mark Hoskins (1991)
Michael Rollason (1992)
Alan Roxburgh (1992)
Alan Maclean (1993)
Jemima Stratford (1993)
Alec Haydon (1993)
Michael Bools (1991)
Roger Masefield (1994)
Aidan Robertson (1995)
Simon Salzedo (1995)
Jasbir Dhillon (1996)
Andrew Thomas (1996)
Margaret Gray (1998)
Simon Birt (1998)
Kelyn Bacon (1998)
Derrick Wyatt QC (1972) (QC-1993) *
Richard MacRory (1974) *
Andrew Le Sueur (1987) *
Jan Woloniecki (1983) *

* Door Tenants

The Chambers: This is a commercial set of chambers. The core commercial work includes all aspects of international trade, finance and commerce, with particular emphasis on banking, insurance,

Continued overleaf

B

reinsurance, shipping, aviation, takeovers and mergers and 'city' work. In addition, members of chambers specialise in the fields of professional negligence, media and entertainment law, defamation, employment law, sports law and public international law. Chambers has considerable experience of appearing before Public Inquiries, which include BSE, Bristol Royal Infirmary and Bloody Sunday.
Chambers has one of the strongest teams of European Community Law specialists, with expertise in all aspects of EU and competition litigation.
Members of chambers appear regularly in the European Court of Justice with 26 appearances, and 8 in the European Court of Human Rights in Strasbourg in the last year alone. Chambers has considerable expertise in human rights and in commercial and regulatory judicial review, a field which enables chambers to combine its strengths in public, commercial and EU law.
Chambers is pleased to be able to offer clients a full mediation/arbitration service.

Set No. 16

1 BRICK COURT (Richard Rampton QC)

1 Brick Court, Temple, London, EC4Y 9BY
Tel: (020) 7353 8845 **Fax:** (020) 7583 9144 **DX:** 468
Email: clerks@1brickcourt.co.uk

Head of Chambers:	Richard Rampton QC
Senior Clerk:	David Mace
Tenants:	19

Members:

Richard Rampton QC (1965) (QC-1987)
Richard Hartley QC (1956) (QC-1976)
Geoffrey Shaw QC (1968) (QC-1991)
Harry Boggis-Rolfe (1969)
Thomas Shields QC (1973) (QC-1993)
Andrew Caldecott QC (1975) (QC-1994)
Edward Garnier QC (1976) (QC-1995)
Patrick Moloney QC (1976) (QC-1998)
Stephen Suttle (1980)
Victoria Sharp (1979)
Harvey Starte (1985)
Manuel Barca (1986)
Timothy Atkinson (1988)
Rupert Elliott (1988)
Jane Phillips (1989)
Caroline Addy (1991)
Benjamin Hinchliff (1992)
Catrin Evans (1994)
Lorna Skinner (1997)

The Chambers: The Chambers of Richard Rampton QC (formerly Richard Hartley QC) are a long-established set who have specialised in the law of libel and slander for at least 85 years. Chambers expertise covers all claims based on the publication of false or damaging material, and encompasses breach of confidence, contempt of court, malicious falsehood, reporting restrictions, data protection, cases concerning the Internet and human rights and judicial reviews concerning this area of practice. Members of chambers are experienced in the pre-publication review of newspapers, books, radio and television programmes and have written or contributed to many of the leading works on defamation including Duncan & Neill of Defamation, Halsburys Laws of England, Bullen & Leake & Jacobs Precedents of Pleadings and Atkin's Court Forms and Precedents.

International: The set frequently receive instructions from solicitors worldwide including Malaysia, Hong Kong and Singapore (acting for Prime Ministers, MPs, Royalty and large corporations) and often conduct cases in these jurisdictions.

Set No. 17

4 BRICK COURT (David Medhurst)

4 Brick Court, Temple, London, EC4Y 9AD
Tel: (020) 7797 8910 **Fax:** (020) 7797 8929 **DX:** 491
Email: xpr58@dial.pipex.com **Website:** hello.to/medhurst.

Head of Chambers:	David Medhurst
Senior Clerk:	Michael Corrigan
Tenants:	36

Members:

David Medhurst (1969)
Mira Chatterjee (1973)
David Burgess (1975)
Robert Colover (1975)
Marianna Hildyard (1977)
Janet Mitchell (1979)
Michael Haynes (1979)
Richard St Clair-Gainer (1983)
Susan Quinn (1983)
Roderick Jones (1983)
Marc Roberts (1984)
Peter Lynch (1985)
Anthony Bell (1985)
Simon Molyneux (1986)
Colin Ishmael (1989)
Alexa Storey-Rea (1990)
Abigail Sheppard (1990)
Annabel Wentworth (1990)
Penny Cooper (1990)
Peter Marshall (1991)
Isabelle Watson (1991)
Michael Simon (1992)
Edward Knapp (1992)
Jacqui Gilliatt (1992)
Gwynneth Knowles (1993)
Levi Peter (1993)
Caroline Sumeray (1993)
Sue Piyadasa (1994)
Teresa Pritchard (1994)
Lisa Smith (1994)
Sarah Morris (1996)
Sarah Elliott (1996)
Ian Griffin (1997)
Jonathan Goldring (1997)
Maria Gallagher (1997)
Amanda Clarke (1998)

The Chambers: A progressive set of chambers consisting of 36 barristers who provide a comprehensive service to solicitors and local government authorities.

8 ## BRIDEWELL CHAMBERS (Colin Challenger)

Bridewell Chambers, 2 Bridewell Place, London, EC4V 6AP
Tel: (020) 7797 8800 **Fax:** (020) 7797 8801 **DX:** 383
Email: HughesGage@bridewell.law.co.uk **Website:** www.bridewell.law.co.uk

Head of Chambers:	Colin Challenger
Senior Clerk:	Lee Hughes-Gage
Tenants:	32

Members:

Colin Challenger (1970)
Jo Boothby (1972)
Gordon Pringle (1973)
Juliet Oliver (1974)
Ernest James (1977)
Adrienne Knight (1981)
Elizabeth Goodchild (1981)
James Thomson (1983)
Peter Gray (1983)
Ian Lawrie (1985)
David Josse (1985)
Adam Clemens (1985)
James Doyle (1985)
Simon Walsh (1987)
Sally Atherton (1987)
Roger Davey (1978)
Paul Michell (1991)
Alan Walmsley (1991)
Brian Cummins (1992)
Andrew Slaughter (1993)
Lloyd Sefton-Smith (1993)
Paul Walker (1993)
Maria Scotland (1995)
Christopher Pearson (1995)
Jason Bartfeld (1995)
Victoria Maude (1995)
Stephen Morley (1996)
Elaine Banton (1996)
Karen Demsey (1996)
Parosha Chandran (1997)
Charles Woodhouse (1997)
Guy Coleman (1998)

The Chambers: Chambers cover most significant areas of criminal, civil and family law. Specialist teams deal with serious crime, housing, landlord and tenant, family and children, personal injury and cases for and against police forces. Individual tenants specialise in commercial law, judicial review, licensing, wills and probate, professional negligence, Official Referee work, marine accidents and family law. A detailed guide to the full services provided, including the Bridewell Conditional Fee Agreement, can be found on the chambers' website at www.bridewell.law.co.uk or by contacting the clerks.

Languages: French and German

Recruitment & Training: Pupillage applications to PACH. Tenancy applications may be sent to Ian Lawrie.

9 ## CLARENDON CHAMBERS

7 Stone Buildings, Lincoln's Inn, London, WC2A 3SZ
Tel: (020) 7681 7681 **Fax:** (020) 7681 7684 **DX:** LDE 0022 Chancery Lane
Out of Hours Tel: (07971) 285796 **Email:** clarendonchambrs@aol.com

Senior Clerk:	Russell Burton
Chambers Director:	John Lister
Tenants:	46

Members:

Ian Alexander QC (1964) (QC-1989)
Gay Martin (1970)
John Bishop (1970)
Julian Lynch (1976)
Robert Lewis (1996)
Robert Anthony (1979)
Simon Birks (1981)
Stephen Crouch (1982)
Simon P. Randle (1982)
Adrian Jenkala (1984)
Juliann Manson (1985)
Susan Pyle (1985)
Clive Moys (1988)
Geoffrey Porter (1988)
Simon Airey (1989)
Patricia Cave (1989)
Adam Swirsky (1989)
Stuart Yeung (1989)
Mark Gordon (1990)
Terry Burns (1990)
Simon Livingstone (1990)
Stephen Murch (1991)
Andrew Bullock (1992)
Lucinda Benner (1992)
Richard Carron (1992)
Simon Gerrish (1993)
Michael Ellis (1993)
Richard Holloway (1993)
Catherine Le Quesne (1993)
Anna Mathias (1994)
Mary Abbott (1994)
Peter Linstead (1994)
Nicola Smith (1994)
Ben Gow (1994)
Cliona Papazian (1994)
Matthew Rudd (1994)
Jonathan Ellis (1995)
Iain Simkin (1995)
Richard Harris (1995)
David Willans (1995)
Mugni Islam-Choudhury (1996)
Alexander McGregor (1996)
Sarah Porter (1996)
Laureen Husain (1997)
Steven Evans (1997)
Penny Van Spall (1998)

The Chambers: Clarendon chambers is a large common law set which was established following the merger between 7 Stone Buildings and 11 Bolt Court in Autumn 1999. Chambers is specifically structured to provide a broad choice of counsel in a range of disciplines. Members of chambers practice in specialist teams in the fields of crime, family, civil and commercial, personal injury, employment, local government, environmental law, and town and country planning.
Chambers has annexes in Northampton and Redhill. Members of chambers cover a wide geographical area, particularly in London, the South East and the East Midlands.

Recruitment & Training: Tenancy applications to The Tenancy Committee; Pupillage applications to The Pupillage Committee.

Set No. 20

CLOISTERS (Laura Cox QC)

Cloisters, 1 Pump Court, Temple, London, EC4Y 7AA
Tel: (020) 7827 4000 **Fax:** (020) 7827 4100 **DX:** LDE 452
Email: clerks@cloisters.com **Website:** www.cloisters.com

Head of Chambers:	Laura Cox QC
Senior Civil Clerk:	Glenn Hudson
Junior Civil Clerk:	Michelle Hughton
Junior Clerk:	Kaye Brooks
Senior Fees Clerk:	Steve Herbert
Junior Fees Clerk:	Alberta Sharpe
Tenants:	32

Members:

Laura Cox QC (1975) (QC-1994)
John Platts-Mills QC (1932) (QC-1964)
Anna Worrall QC (1959) (QC-1989)
Brian Langstaff QC (1971) (QC-1994)
Arthur Davidson QC (1953) (QC-1976)
Robin Allen QC (1974) (QC-1995)
Jonathan Crystal (1972)
Jacques Algazy (1980)
Andrew Buchan (1981)
Simon W. Taylor (1984)
Pauline Hendy (1985)
Anthony Bradley (1989)
Patricia Hitchcock (1988)
Paul Epstein (1988)
Paul Spencer (1988)
Karon Monaghan (1989)
Thomas Kibling (1990)
Jason Galbraith-Marten (1991)
Joël Donovan (1991)
Yvette Genn (1991)
Christopher Quinn (1992)
Caspar Glyn (1992)
John Horan (1993)
Louise Brooks (1994)
Rachel Crasnow (1994)
Sally Robertson (1995)
James Laddie (1995)
William Latimer-Sayer (1995)
Thomas Coghlin (1998)
Peter J. Pimm (1991) *
John Whitmore (1976) *
Amir Majid *

* Associate member

Work Undertaken: Administrative, public, and local government law; alternative dispute resolution and mediation; civil liberties and human rights law; contract and commercial law; EU law; employment, industrial and discrimination law; personal injury and clinical negligence; family law; fraud (civil); media and defamation; sports law; international law.

Recruitment & Training: Cloisters offers three twelve month pupillages each year. Awards of £15,000, plus reasonable travelling costs, are made to each pupil. Chambers has a strong track record of recruiting from its pupils. Applications may only be made via PACH.

Set No. 21

CORAM CHAMBERS (Roger McCarthy QC)

4 Brick Court, Temple, London, EC4Y 9AD
Tel: (020) 7797 7766 **Fax:** (020) 7797 7700 **DX:** 404 (Chancery Lane)
Email: mail@coramchambers.co.uk **Website:** www.coramchambers.co.uk

Head of Chambers:	Roger McCarthy QC
Senior Clerk:	Paul Sampson
Clerks:	George Mo, Maxine Rogers, Danny Norman, James Mitchell
Fees Clerk:	Paul Rudd
Office Junior:	David Sadler
Tenants:	44

Members:

Roger McCarthy QC (1975) (QC-1996)
Shelagh Farror (1970)
Laxmi Ponnampalam Reilly (1972)
Jane Drew (1976)
Catherine Nicholes (1977)
Aditya Kumar Sen (1977)
Laura Harris (1977)
David Boyd (1977)
Vera Mayer (1978)
Martha Cover (1979)
Anne Spratling (1980)
Melanie Lewis (1980)
Meena Gill (1982)
Nicola Simpson (1982)
Fiona Gibb (1983)
Carol Atkinson (1985)
Nicholas O'Brien (1985)
Anne Gibberd (1985)
Divya Bhatia (1986)
Debora Price (1987)
Declan O'Dempsey (1987)
Jane Probyn (1988)
Kate Purkiss (1988)
Mark Mullins (1988)
Elpha Lecointe (1988)
Jennifer Driscoll (1989)
Susan Belgrave (1989)
Neil Bullock (1989)
Frances Orchover (1989)
Andrew Short (1990)
Anthea Parker (1990)
Jillian Brown (1991)
Neil Fry (1992)
Sharon Sawyerr (1992)
Sima Kothari (1992)
Michael Horton (1993)
Rajeev Thacker (1993)
Susan Gore (1993)
Dermot Casey (1994)
Alison Easton (1994)
Andrew Allen (1995)
Emma Furley (1995)
Gerald Browne (1995)
Jerry Fitzpatrick (1996)

The Chambers: Chambers undertake a wide range of work which falls into two main fields: civil and family.

Work Undertaken:

Civil: Employment (including trade union law), discrimination, personal injury, professional and clinical negligence, landlord and tenant, local government, social services, community care, mental health, education, judicial review, human rights, E.C. law, immigration and housing.

Family: Including divorce; matrimonial finance; public and private Children Act proceedings; child abduction; domestic violence; adoption; wardship; inheritance and cohabitees.

Languages: Bengali, French, Hebrew, Hindi, Italian, Punjabi and Spanish.

C

Set No.
22

CROWN OFFICE CHAMBERS (Michael Spencer QC & Christopher Purchas QC)

1 Paper Buildings, Temple, London, EC4Y 7EP
Tel: (020) 7797 8100 **Fax:** (020) 7797 8101 **DX:** 80 LONDON/CHANCERY LANE
Email: mail@crownofficechambers.com **Website:** www.crownofficechambers.com

Heads of Chambers:	Michael Spencer QC, Christopher Purchas QC
Senior Clerks:	Julian Campbell, David Newcomb
Tenants:	70

Members:

Michael Spencer QC (1970) (QC-1989)
Christopher Purchas QC (1966) (QC-1990)
John Crowley QC (1962) (QC-1982)
Michael Harvey QC (1966) (QC-1982)
John Slater QC (1969) (QC-1987)
Nigel Wilkinson QC (1972) (QC-1990)
Antony Edwards-Stuart QC (1976) (QC-1991)
Roger ter Haar QC (1974) (QC-1992)
Andrew Bartlett QC (1974) (QC-1993)
Simon Brown QC (1976) (QC-1995)
William Stevenson QC (1968) (QC-1996)
Richard Lynagh QC (1975) (QC-1996)
Michael Kent QC (1975) (QC-1996)
Richard Hone QC (1970) (QC-1997)
Jonathan Woods (1965)
Martyn Berkin (1966)
Margaret Bickford-Smith (1973)
Colin Nixon (1973)
David Tucker (1973)
Dennis Matthews (1973)
Thomas Saunt (1974)
George Gadney (1974)
John Powles (1975)
John Stevenson (1975)
Nicholas Davies (1975)
James Holdsworth (1977)
Jonathan Waite (1978)
Andrew Phillips (1978)
John Greenbourne (1978)
Gordon Catford (1980)
Julian Field (1980)
Jane Davies (1981)
Anna Guggenheim (1982)
Michael Curtis (1982)
Paul Dean (1982)
Charlotte Jones (1982)
Deborah Taylor (1983)
Steven Coles (1983)
Kim Franklin (1984)
James Medd (1985)
Ian Swan (1985)
Shaun Ferris (1985)
David Platt (1987)
Jane DeCamp (1987)
Raymond Ng (1987)
William Vandyck (1988)
Marion Egan (1988)
Steven Snowden (1989)
Ian Wright (1989)
Erica Power (1990)
Jason Evans-Tovey (1990)
Benedict Newman (1991)
Simon Howarth (1991)
Toby Gee (1992)
Andrew Rigney (1992)
Clive Weston (1993)
Patrick Blakesley (1993)
Alexander Antelme (1993)
Claire Toogood (1995)
James Maxwell-Scott (1995)
Robert Stokell (1995)
Suzanne Chalmers (1995)
Andrew O'Connor (1996)
Andrew Davis (1996)
Muhammed Haque (1997)
Susan Lindsey (1997)
Ben Quiney (1998)
Victoria Woodbridge (1998)
Jack Ferro (1998)
Julian Horne (1998)

The Chambers: Crown Office Chambers was founded in 2000 and brings together the two long-established common law sets of chambers, One Paper Buildings and Two Crown Office Row. It is the largest civil common law set in London and has currently 70 members of chambers. Operating from both buildings, it has its administrative and reception facilities at 1 Paper Buildings. Chambers offers a modern, flexible and friendly service. It operates block agreements and protocols for the return of paperwork and for court appearances. It is able to provide first class reception and conference facilities, and is supported by the extensive use of information technology. The size of the merged chambers has also permitted the development of a new centre for alternative dispute resolution, and Crown Office Chambers offers a fully administered ADR service.

Work Undertaken: Crown Office Chambers specialises in professional & clinical negligence, product liability, personal injury, insurance and reinsurance, commercial, contract and construction work. Within these areas it is able to offer depth and breadth of experience at all levels of call, and is widely recognised as a market leader.

Professional Negligence: Chambers undertakes all forms of professional negligence, and in particular clinical negligence. It also specialises in construction-related claims (architects, engineers, valuers, residential, commercial and quantity surveyors); legal negligence (barristers and solicitors); and claims against other professionals (accountants and insurance brokers).

Product Liability: Product liability is a leading component of chambers' work. It has participated in most of the major multi-party claims which have so far been brought, including the tobacco, benzodiazepine, organo-phosphate, MMR and the oral contraceptive litigation.

Personal Injury/Health & Safety: Personal Injury and Health and Safety are an important part of Crown Office Chambers. Industrial accident, occupational disease, disaster claims, road traffic litigation, aviation/marine claims and local authority based disputes are all undertaken. Chambers acts for both claimants and defendants, although it is widely acknowledged for its established connections with insurance-funded litigation.

Insurance and Reinsurance: Insurance and reinsurance work is a major element of chambers' business. Crown Office Chambers has strong links with the insurance market, and many of its clients are major

Continued overleaf

CROWN OFFICE CHAMBERS

C

insurers, underwriting syndicates and brokers. All forms of contentious and advisory work are undertaken, including work in the Commercial Court and in arbitration.

Commercial Contract: Members conduct general commercial litigation and arbitration including ICC arbitrations. These involve contractual claims of all kinds.

Construction: Construction and engineering disputes form a significant part of the workload of chambers. Members have substantial experience in the Technology and Construction Courts, acting for employers, contractors, construction professionals, insurers and developers.

Other: Members of chambers have particular expertise in other areas of law. Such specialities include administrative law and judicial review, public enquiries, planning and environmental work, employment law, commercial fraud and banking. Chambers also undertakes all forms of residual negligence and nuisance claims. Direct access, conditional fee work and all forms of alternative dispute resolution are accepted.

Publications: Members of chambers contribute to *Medical Negligence* and *Emden's Construction Law* (general editor, Andrew Bartlett QC).

Set No. 23

1 CROWN OFFICE ROW (Robert Seabrook QC)

Temple, London, EC4Y 7HH
Tel: (020) 7797 7500 **Fax:** (020) 7797 7550 **DX:** LDE1020
Email: mail@1cor.com **Website:** www.1cor.com

Head of Chambers:	Robert Seabrook QC
Senior Clerk:	Matthew Phipps
Chambers Director:	Bob Wilson
Tenants:	44

Members:

Robert Seabrook QC (1964) (QC-1983)
Robert Owen QC (1968) (QC-1988)
Duncan Matheson QC (1965) (QC-1989)
Philip Vallance QC (1968) (QC-1989)
James Badenoch QC (1968) (QC-1989)
Stephen Miller QC (1971) (QC-1990)
David Foskett QC (1972) (QC-1991)
Terence Coghlan QC (1968) (QC-1993)
Guy Mansfield QC (1972) (QC-1994)
Philip Havers QC (1974) (QC-1995)
Sally Smith QC (1977) (QC-1997)
Paul Rees QC (1980) (QC-2000)
Gregory Chambers (1973)
Anthony Niblett (1976) *
Margaret Bowron (1978)
David Balcombe (1980)
James King-Smith (1980) *
David Hart (1982)
Neil S. Garnham (1982)
Martin Forde (1984)
William Edis (1985)
Janet Waddicor (1985) *
John Gimlette (1986)
David L. Evans (1988)
Amanda Grant (1988)
Paul Rogers (1989) *
Angus McCullough (1990)
Keeley Bishop (1990) *
John Whitting (1991)
Martin Downs (1990) *
Jeremy Cave (1992) *
Richard Booth (1993)
Philippa Whipple (1994)
Sydney Chawatama (1994)
Sarah Lambert (1994)
Giles Colin (1994)
Owain Thomas (1995)
Jeremy Hyam (1995)
Katharine Hogg (1996)
Ben Collins (1996)
Shaheen Rahman (1996)
Zoe Taylor (1998)
Neil Sheldon (1998)
Caroline Neenan (1998)

*Mainly practice from Brighton

The Chambers: A long-established civil set of chambers providing advisory and advocacy services, with an emphasis on professional negligence, public law, and human rights. With a friendly and professional approach to customer care, chambers welcome direct instructions from fellow professionals such as accountants, architects and engineers. A number of tenants (*) practise mainly from an annexe at Blenheim House, 120 Church Street, Brighton BN1 1WH, Tel: (01273) 625625, which is available for local conferences. After nearly 50 years at 1 Crown Office Row, the year 2000 will see the set take over and refurbish all 5 floors at this address increasing the number of conference rooms to four and upgrading its IT systems.

Work Undertaken: Professional negligence, in particular clinical and solicitors' negligence, multi-party actions and group litigation, personal injury, health law, domestic commercial contract, administrative law and judicial review, technology, construction and environmental law, planning and local government, representation at public inquiries and before professional disciplinary tribunals, human rights and civil liberties, employment and discrimination, matrimonial finance, sports law and VAT. Chambers are informally grouped into teams in these specialist areas in which they have expertise in depth at both senior and junior level. Criminal work is also undertaken, in particular fraud and other serious crime. Full details of services available are set out in the chambers brochure available on request and on the chambers internet website. Building on the set's expertise on the Human Rights Act, on which members regularly lecture, members are also providing all the professional support needed for new internet services on the Act provided by the College of Law and others.

ONE CROWN OFFICE ROW

C

Publications: Members are authors of or contributors to a number of textbooks including *The Law and Practice of Compromise* and *Settlement under the Civil Procedure Rules* (both by David Foskett QC), *Clinical Negligence* (Editors Powers & Harris), *Personal Injury Handbook* (Editors Brennan & Curran), *Professional Negligence: Law and Practice, Human Rights and the Common Law.*

Recruitment & Training: Up to three pupils are taken anually for 12 months. There are generous awards for the first six months with a guaranteed level of earnings for the second six. A first or upper second class degree is required. Chambers are a member of the PACH scheme. Applications for a third six month pupillage are invited from July for selection in September.

Set No. 24 **1 CROWN OFFICE ROW** – see 3 Hare Court.

Set No. 25

DEVEREUX CHAMBERS (Jeffrey Burke QC)

Devereux Chambers, Devereux Court, London, WC2R 3JJ
Tel: (020) 7353 7534 **Fax:** (020) 7353 1724 **DX:** 349 (Ch.Ln.)
Email: surname@devchambers.co.uk / mailbox@devchambers.co.uk
Website: www.devchambers.co.uk

Head of Chambers:	Jeffrey Burke QC
Senior Clerk:	Elton Maryon
Practice Managers:	Clifford Holland, Andrew Frankland
Practice Development Manager:	Angela Griffiths
Tenants:	42

Members:

Jeffrey Burke QC (1964) (QC-1984)
Diana Cotton QC (1964) (QC-1983)
Alan Pardoe QC (1971) (QC-1988)
Colin Edelman QC (1977) (QC-1995)
Robert Glancy QC (1972) (QC-1997)
David Griffith-Jones QC (1975) (QC-2000)
Roy Lemon (1970)
Peter Wulwik (1972)
Ian Smith (1972)
Gerald Rabie (1973)
Christopher Goddard (1973)
Ian Lee (1973)
Elizabeth Andrew (1974)
Richard Greening (1975)
Richard Clayton (1977)
Ruth Downing (1978)
Nicholas Bard (1979)
Timothy Brennan (1981)
Stephen Killalea (1981)
Graham Read (1981)
Bruce Silvester (1983)
Colin Mendoza (1983)
Colin Wynter (1984)
Bruce Carr (1986)
Ingrid Simler (1987)
Joanna Heal (1988)
Philip Thornton (1988)
James Tayler (1989)
Nicholas Randall (1990)
Keith Bryant (1991)
Richard Harrison (1991)
Natasha Joffe (1992)
Alison Padfield (1992)
Robert Weir (1992)
Peter Edwards (1992)
Andrew Burns (1993)
Suzanne McKie (1991)
Dijen Basu (1994)
David Craig (1997)
Lydia Seymour (1997)
Ben Adamson (1999)
Akash Nawbatt (2000)

The Chambers: Devereux Chambers offers a comprehensive inter-disciplinary service to its clients. Areas of special expertise include: administrative and local government law, commercial litigation, employment law, insurance and reinsurance, professional negligence, personal injury and clinical negligence. There is a strong emphasis on advocacy.

Devereux chambers is a thriving and well-established set of chambers with a wide client base ranging from public companies, underwriters and brokers to local authorities, government departments, trades unions and individual litigants.

A number of senior members of chambers are deputy High Court Judges, and Recorders. Members of chambers sit on the Criminal Injuries Compensation Appeals Panel, Mental Health Independent Review Tribunal, Rent Assessment Panel and Boundary Commission. They also chair tribunals and inquiries. The junior members of chambers include the junior counsel to the Inland Revenue, Common Law and Treasury Counsel Common Law, Panel B. Members of chambers play a prominent role in the Bar's professional bodies and associations and chambers includes members of the Bar Council Professional Conduct Committee and various Bar Council working committees. Members of chambers are available to give lectures and seminars in their specialist fields both externally and part of chambers' own Law Society accredited seminar programme.

Work Undertaken: The major areas of practice are commercial and common law, especially: administrative and local government; commercial; construction; consumer and business credit; discrimination; education; employment; environment; Europe; health and safety; human rights; mortgage and guarantee litigation; industrial injury and disease; insurance and reinsurance; judicial review; clinical negligence; landlord and tenant; pensions; personal injury; police complaints and civil liberties; product liability; professional negligence; property; public interest immunity; revenue; telecommunications; tribunals and inquiries; VAT/Customs & Excise. In addition individual members of chambers offer expertise in the following areas of law: community care; contempt; crime (including white-collar crime); defamation; electoral & parliamentary; family; housing and sport.

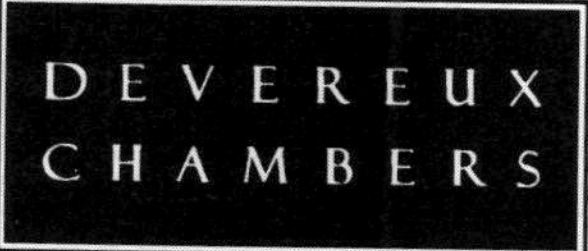

Continued overleaf

C

Publications: Members of chambers regularly appear in leading cases and have written or co-written prominent text and practitioner's books in their specialist fields. Three members of chambers, Professor Ian Smith, Christopher Goddard and Nicholas Randall, co-wrote *Health and Safety – The New Legal Framework* published by Butterworths. Ian Smith also co-wrote *Smith and Wood on Industrial Law* and is the author of the 'Employment Law' and 'Social Security' titles in *Halsbury's Laws*. He and Nicholas Randall are editors of *Harvey on Industrial Relations and Employment Law*. Richard Clayton is the co-author of *Civil Action against the Police* (Sweet & Maxwell 2nd ed 1992), *Judicial Review Procedure* (Wiley 2nd ed 1997) and, in preparation, co-author of *The Bill of Rights in English Law* (Oxford University Press), *Judicial Review of Local Government Decisions* (Wiley) and *Commercial Judicial Review* (Wiley). David Griffith-Jones is the author of *Law & the Business of Sport* (Butterworths 1998). Bruce Carr is a contributing author to *FT Law & Tax, Litigation Practice* (Emergency Procedures). Ingrid Simler is a contributing author to *Tolley's Employment Law* (1994). James Tayler is a contributor to *Dix on Employment Law* (Butterworths), and Nicholas Randall is the author of the 'Pensions' title in *Halsbury's Laws* and a contributor to Butterworths *Employment Law Guide*. Alison Padfield is the co-author of the 'Contempt of Court' title in *Halsbury's Laws*. Nicholas Randall and Ian Smith are co-authors of Butterworth's *Guide to Employment Relations Act 1999*. James Tayler, Ingrid Simler, Natasha Joffe and Andrew Burns co-wrote *Butterworths Discrimination Law 1999* (with assistance from Lydia Seymour, David Craig and Richard Greening) and are contributors to *Halsbury's* 'Discrimination' title (2000). Members of Chambers are also contributors to *Personal Injury Factbook* (Gee).

Recruitment & Training: Great emphasis is placed on the calibre of pupils received to ensure that the high standards are maintained and generous pupillage awards are offered.

Set No. 26

15/19 DEVERUX COURT (Helen Grindrod QC)

4th Floor 15/19 Deverux Court, London, WC2R 3JJ **Tel:** (020) 7583 2792 **Fax:** (020) 7353 0608 **DX:** 425 LDE

Set No. 27

DOUGHTY STREET CHAMBERS (Geoffrey Robertson QC)

Doughty Street Chambers, 11 Doughty Street, London, WC1N 2PL
Tel: (020) 7404 1313 **Fax:** (020) 7404 2283 **DX:** 223 (Ch.Ln.)
Email: enquiries@doughtystreet.co.uk **Website:** www.doughtystreet.co.uk

Head of Chambers:	Geoffrey Robertson QC
Practice Manager:	Christine Kings
Senior Clerk:	Michelle Simpson
Tenants:	59

Members:

Geoffrey Robertson QC (1973) (QC-1988)
Louis Blom-Cooper QC (1952) (QC-1970)
Richard Maxwell QC (1968) (QC-1988)
Helena Kennedy QC (1972) (QC-1991)
Peter Thornton QC (1969) (QC-1992)
Christopher Sallon QC (1973) (QC-1994)
Andrew Nicol QC (1978) (QC-1995)
Edward Fitzgerald QC (1978) (QC-1995)
Stephen Irwin QC (1976) (QC-1997)
Edward Rees QC (1973) (QC-1998)
Michael Grieve QC (1975) (QC-1998)
Frank Panford QC (1972) (QC-1999)
James Wood QC (1975) (QC-1999)
Gavin Millar QC (1981) (QC-2000)
Jonah Walker-Smith (1963)
Oliver Thorold (1971)
Richard Allfrey (1974)
Robert Latham (1976)
Nicholas Paul (1980)
Kate Markus (1981)
Christopher Hough (1981)
Isabella Forshall (1982)
Paul Bogan (1983)
David Bentley (1984)
Tracey Bloom (1984)
Heather Williams (1985)
Martin Westgate (1985)
Aswini Weereratne (1986)
Jill Evans (1986)
Gerwyn Samuel (1986)
Anthony Metzer (1987)
Keir Starmer (1987)
Sally Hatfield (1989)
Robin Oppenheim (1988)
David Hislop (1989) (1979 NZ)
Michelle Strange (1989)
Kieran Maidment (1989)
Paul Taylor (1989)
Hugh Barton (1989)
Sadakat Kadri (1989)
Paul Brooks (1989)
Andrew Hall (1991)
Phillippa Kaufmann (1991)
Quincy Whitaker (1991)
Stephen Reeder (1991)
Nadine Finch (1991)
Michael Ford (1992)
Ian Wise (1992)
Simon Cox (1992)
Richard Hermer (1993)
Mark Henderson (1994)
Paula Sparks (1994)
Althea Brown (1995)
Rebecca Trowler (1995)
Jonathan Glasson (1996)
Anthony Hudson (1996)
Stephen Cragg (1996)
Joseph Middleton (1997)
Peter Lownds (1998)
Justice Ismail Mahommed SC (1984) (1956, South African Bar)*
Guy Ollivry QC (1957) (QC-1987) *
Fenton Ramsahoye SC (1953) *
Adrian Hardiman SC (1988) (1974 Ireland)*
Kevin Boyle (1992) (1971 N. Ireland)*
Christine Booker (1977) *
Julian Fulbrook (1977) *
Geraldine Van Bueren (1980) *
Jill Peay (1991) *
Jonathan Cooper (1992) *
Gilbert Markus SC (1999) *

* Associate Tenants

D

The Chambers: Emphasis is on civil liberties and human rights with specialists in criminal law; media law and defamation; public law; prisoners' rights and cases involving issues of mental health; discrimination; immigration; employment; housing; personal injury and clinical negligence. Chambers of the Year, 1995 and 1996, Silver Award, 1998. Bronze Award, 1999. Bronze winners, Law Firm Management Award, 1997. Bar Pro Bono Award, 1999. Investor in People, 2000.

t No.
8

2 DYERS BUILDINGS (Nadine Radford QC)

2 Dyers Buildings, Holborn, London, EC1N 2JT
Tel: (020) 7404 1881 **Fax:** (020) 7404 1991 **DX:** 175 London Chancery Lane
Email: admin@2dyersbuildings.com **Website:** www.2dyersbuildings.com

Head of Chambers	Nadine Radford QC
Clerks:	Graham Islin mobile 07956 985929 David Scothern mobile 07931 776630
Tenants:	22

2
DYERS
BUILDINGS

Members:

Nadine Radford QC (1974) (QC-1995) +
Michael Gledhill (1976) +
Andrew Campbell-Tiech (1978) +
Sanderson Munro (1981)
Ian Jobling (1982)
Julia D. Postill (1982)
Charles Burton (1983)
Adam Davis (1985)
Terence Boulter (1986)
Harriette Black (1986)
Michael Magarian (1988)
Simon Kitchen (1988)
Sam Stein (1988)
Andrew Jefferies (1990)
Dominic Bell (1992)
Robert Tolhurst (1992)
Timothy Forte (1994)
Ibtihal Bsis (1994)
Peter Caldwell (1995)
Gavin Irwin (1996)
Gregory Fishwick (1996)
Trilby Millet (1996)
Ian Way (1988) *

* Door Tenant + Recorder

The Chambers: Chambers specialises in criminal law and associated matters. Members of chambers regularly represent clients charged with the most serious of offences, from fraud, money laundering, drugs (and DTA issues) to computer crime and murder. Chambers' service includes the provision of counsel for overnight, weekend and bank holiday cases. Clerks may be contacted at any time.
Continuing Education: Chambers sees continuing education as vital to its ongoing expansion. Lectures are held on a regular basis – both in-house and for professional clients.

Work Undertaken: Members of chambers are increasingly instructed in other niche areas, including extradition, mental health tribunals, environmental law and matters relating to health and safety at work. In addition, members of chambers appear before coroner's inquests and a variety of regulatory and disciplinary tribunals.
Human Rights: Pro-bono work is undertaken, which includes advising on 'death row' cases as well as work for the Free Representation Unit. Members of chambers have recently advised Amnesty International with regards to the incorporation of human rights legislation in foreign jurisdictions.

Languages: Arabic, French, German, and Italian.

Recruitment & Training:
Pupillage contact: Julia Postill.
Training and Lectures: Andrew Jefferies.

No
9

ELY PLACE CHAMBERS (Ronald Thwaites QC)

30 Ely Place, London, EC1N 6TD
Tel: (020) 7400 9600 **Fax:** (020) 7400 9630 **DX:** 291 Chancery Lane
Email: admin@elyplace.com

Head of Chambers	Ronald Thwaites QC
Chambers Director	Christopher Drury
Administration:	Richard Sheehan
Tenants:	8

Members:

Ronald Thwaites QC (1970) (QC-1987)
William McCormick (1985)
Simon Cheetham (1991)
Russell Stone (1992)
Iain Daniels (1992)
Hefin Rees (1992)
Garry Herbert (1996)
Charles Barker (1997)

The Chambers: Ely Place chambers is a new civil common law set. Areas of practice include: personal injuries, clinical negligence, professional negligence, torts, general contractual, employment, housing, landlord & tenant, police actions, human rights, defamation, sports and media law. Chambers operates from modernised accommodation that includes a dedicated seminar/conference suite.

Set No. 30

ENTERPRISE CHAMBERS (Anthony Mann QC)

9 Old Square, Lincoln's Inn, London, WC2A 3SR
Tel: (020) 7405 9471 **Fax:** (020) 7242 1447 **DX:** LDE 301
Email: enterprise.london@dial.pipex.com **Website:** www.enterprisechambers.com

Head of Chambers:	Anthony Mann QC
Clerks:	Barry Clayton
	Tony Armstrong, Dylan Wendleken
Chambers Director:	Elspeth Mills Rendall
Tenants:	27

Members:

Anthony Mann QC (1974) (QC-1992)
Timothy Jennings (1962)
Charles Morgan (1978)
Caroline Hutton (1979)
Michael James (1976) *
Linden Ife (1982)
Peter Arden (1983)
Geoffrey Zelin (1984)
Jacqueline Baker (1985)
Nigel Gerald (1985)
Jonathan Holmes (1985)
James Barker (1984)
Adrian Jack (1986)
Hugo Groves (1980) *
Laura Garcia-Miller (1989)
Zia Bhaloo (1990)
James Pickering (1991)
Soraya McKinnell (1991)
Hugh Jory (1992)
Bridget Williamson (1993) *
Jonathan Klein (1992)
Sarah Richardson (1993)
Edward Francis (1995)
Shanti Mauger (1996)
Shaiba Ilyas (1998)
Timothy Calland (1999)
Jonathan Rodger (1999)

* practised as a solictor before joining chambers.

The Chambers: Enterprise Chambers is a leading commercial Chancery set, specialising in: company and commercial law, insolvency, landlord and tenant and property, professional negligence and general Chancery work. Chambers has qualified arbitrators and members use alternative dispute resolution procedures in appropriate cases.

Chambers has branches in Leeds and Newcastle that affords chambers the unique advantage of providing a high quality service to clients from two major legal centres in the North East as well as from London. As part of their service, chambers offers cost-effective video conferencing facilities to clients with the ability of linking all chambers sites with each other.

Enterprise Chambers aims to combine an excellent quality of service and to anticipate clients' needs with a progressive and flexible approach to practice at the Bar. Members of chambers recognise the importance of working as a team and being approachable and accessible to solicitors and clients. Chambers knows clients often find it useful to be given fee estimates and their clerks are happy to provide hourly rates or give overall estimates for items of work.

Members regularly speak at seminars and chambers is authorised by the Law Society as a course provider.

Set No. 31

ERSKINE CHAMBERS (Robin Potts QC)

Erskine Chambers, 30 Lincoln's Inn Fields, London, WC2A 3PF
Tel: (020) 7242 5532 **Fax:** (020) 7831 0125 **DX:** 308 Lon Ch'ry Lane
Email: clerks@erskine-chambers.co.uk

Head of Chambers:	Robin Potts QC
Senior Clerk:	Mike Hannibal
Tenants:	24

Members:

Robin Potts QC (1968) (QC-1982) BA, BCL (Oxon)
W.F. Stubbs QC (1957) (QC-1978) MA, LLB (Cantab)
Thomas Stockdale Bt (1966) MA (Oxon)
David Oliver QC (1972) (QC-1986) BA (Cantab)
David Richards QC (1974) (QC-1992) MA (Cantab)
John Cone (1975) LLB
Leslie Kosmin QC (1976) (QC-1994) MA, LLM (Cantab), LLM (Harvard)
Michael Todd QC (1977) (QC-1997) BA (Keele)
David Mabb (1979) MA (Cantab)
Martin Moore (1982) BA (Oxon)
David Chivers (1983) BA (Cantab)
Ceri Bryant (1984) MA, LLM (Cantab)
Richard Snowden (1986) MA (Cantab), LLM (Harvard)
Catherine Roberts (1986) MA, LLM (Cantab)
Philip Gillyon (1988) BA (Cantab)
Mary Stokes (1989) MA (Oxon), LLM (Harvard)
Andrew Thompson (1991) MA, LLM (Cantab)
Dan Prentice (1982) LLB (Belfast) JD (Chicago), MA (Oxon)
Nigel Dougherty (1993) BA, LLM (Cantab)
Leon Kuschke (1993) BCOM, LLB
James Potts (1994) BA (Oxon)
Andrew Thornton (1994) LLB (Hull)
Edward Davies (1998) BA (Cantab), BCh (Oxon)
Richard Nolan (1999) BA, MA (Cantab)

The Chambers: Erskine Chambers has a long-established reputation as a company law set. It covers all aspects of company law; corporate finance, corporate insolvency, financial services and related commercial and professional negligence matters. Alongside its reputation in company law, the set is known for its commercial litigation experience over a range of practice areas and business sectors.

There are 24 members of chambers including six QCs. The practices of the majority of the individual members of chambers are litigation-based, although they also continue to maintain their strength in advisory and drafting matters. It is chambers' aim to provide a professional service in a personal and approachable manner and the clerks are always available to discuss the practices of individual members. The office is open Monday to Friday 8.30am to 7.00pm and at other times an answerphone message provides numbers to contact.

E

Work Undertaken: In the company law field, chambers cover a full range of litigation, advisory work and drafting. Members of chambers deal with all areas where company law issues may arise, including: directors' duties; shareholders' disputes; takeovers; mergers and acquisitions; corporate reconstructions; loan capital and banking securities; schemes of arrangement; reductions of capital; and insurance schemes. Erskine Chambers' standing in the corporate insolvency field is demonstrated by their involvement in the largest and most high-profile insolvencies of recent years. The set has traditionally attracted substantial litigation work and members advise on, and appear in, a considerable number of general commercial and professional negligence disputes. Direct Professional Access is accepted from members of recognised professional institutions.

International: There is a strong international dimension to Erskine Chambers' work – the type of business on which the set advises and the clients for whom they act inevitably raise issues or involve disputes in other parts of the world. Members of chambers are frequently engaged as experts, or advocates, in other jurisdictions.

Recruitment & Training: Erskine Chambers subscribe to the PACH scheme. All applications for pupillage in 2001/2 should be made through the scheme.

Set No. 32

ESSEX COURT CHAMBERS (Gordon Pollock QC)

24 Lincoln's Inn Fields, London, WC2A 3ED
Tel: (020) 7813 8000 **Fax:** (020) 7813 8080 **DX:** 320
Email: clerksroom@essexcourt-chambers.co.uk
Website: www.essexcourt-chambers.co.uk

Head of Chambers	Gordon Pollock QC
Senior Clerk:	David Grief
Clerks:	Joe Ferrigno, Nigel Jones, Sam Biggerstaff
Office Manager:	Jean T. Muircroft
Office Hours:	7.45am – 7.00pm
Tenants:	65

Members:

Gordon Pollock QC (1968) (QC-1979)
Michael Thomas QC (1955) (QC-1973)
Ian Hunter QC (1967) (QC-1980)
Stewart Boyd QC (1967) (QC-1981)
V.V. Veeder QC (1971) (QC-1986)
Michael Collins QC (1971) (QC-1988)
Richard Siberry QC (1974) (QC-1989)
Jonathan Gilman QC (1965) (QC-1990)
Bernard Eder QC (1975) (QC-1990)
Roderick Cordara QC (1975) (QC-1994)
Simon Crookenden QC (1975) (QC-1996)
Jeffrey Gruder QC (1977) (QC-1997)
Andrew Hochhauser QC (1977) (QC-1997)
Jack Beatson QC (1973) (QC-1998)
Richard Jacobs QC (1979) (QC-1998)
Christopher Greenwood QC (1978) (QC-1999)
David Mildon QC (1980) (QC-2000)
Susan Prevezer QC (1983) (QC-2000)
Anthony Dicks QC (Hong Kong) (1961) (QC-1994)
Franklin Berman QC (Hon) (1966) (QC-1992)
Victor Lyon (1980)
Mark Smith (1981)
Geraldine Andrews (1981)
Graham Dunning (1982)
Mark Templeman (1981)
Steven Berry (1984)
David Joseph (1984)
Richard Millett (1985)
Huw Davies (1985)
Joe Smouha (1986)
Philippa Watson (1988)
Hugh Mercer (1985)
Martin Griffiths (1986)
Karen Troy-Davies (1981)
John Lockey (1987)
Simon Bryan (1988)
David Foxton (1989)
Christopher Smith (1989)
Malcolm Shaw (1988)
Sara Cockerill (1990)
John Snider (1982)
Vernon Flynn (1991)
Brian Dye (1991)
Nigel Eaton (1991)
Charles Ciumei (1991)
Claire Blanchard (1992)
Perdita Cargill-Thompson (1993)
Vaughan Lowe (1993)
Toby Landau (1993)
Paul Stanley (1993)
Martin Hunter (1994)
Philippa Hopkins (1994)
Paul McGrath (1994)
James Collins (1995)
Tim Eicke (1993)
Stephen Houseman (1995)
Paul Key (1997)
Martin Lau (1996)
David Scorey (1997)
Sam Wordsworth (1997)
Nathan Pillow (1997)
Salim Moollan (1998)
Ricky Diwan (1998)
Neil Hart (1998)
Edmund King (1999)

The Chambers: A full-service commercial set, acting for clients ranging from institutions and multi-national corporations to private companies and individuals. Members advise across the whole spectrum of international, commercial and European law, and act as advocates in litigation and commercial arbitration worldwide. Essex Court Chambers has a particularly strong reputation in international commercial arbitration; insurance & reinsurance; wet and dry shipping; banking; international trade; energy & utilities; media & entertainment; commodities; public international law; professional negligence; tax & VAT; aviation and employment. Essex Court Chambers (formerly known as Four Essex Court) was established as a separate chambers in 1961, when the set at Three Essex Court split into two sets. The founding members were Michael Kerr (later Lord Justice Kerr), Robert MacCrindle, Michael Mustill (now Lord Mustill), Anthony Evans (now Lord Justice Evans), and Anthony Diamond (later Judge Diamond). Chambers grew rapidly, developing a strong reputation as a leading commercial set and attracting a number of prominent legal figures: Mark Saville (now Lord Saville), Johan Steyn (now

Continued overleaf

E

Lord Steyn), Anthony Colman (now Mr Justice Colman) and John Thomas (now Mr Justice Thomas). Now under the leadership of Gordon Pollock the set comprises 65 members and has recently acquired the two adjacent buildings to 24–26 Lincoln's Inn Fields, the location the set moved to in 1994. Chambers is not a 'firm' or a 'partnership' but a collection of individuals. Individual barristers have been recognised as leaders in their fields of specialisation and David Grief and his clerks have acquired a reputation for responsiveness and integrity. Focus is always on client requirements. Care and attention is given to matching the most appropriate barrister to the case and the client's individual needs. This is achievable because of the close working relationship between tenants and clerks within chambers.

Work Undertaken: The fields of work for which chambers are best known are: arbitration; banking and financial services; European law; insurance and re-insurance; international trade and transport; maritime law; and professional negligence. Other areas of work covered include: administrative law and judicial review; agriculture and farming; Australian trade practices law; aviation; Chinese law; commodity transaction; computer law; construction and engineering; customs duty; employment law; energy and utilities; entertainment and sports law; European law; Hong Kong law; human rights; immigration and nationality law; industrial relations; injunctions and arrests; insolvency law; insurance and re-insurance; intellectual property; international commercial fraud; Irish law; oil and gas; public law; public international law; rail disputes; sale of goods and product liability; South Asian law; tribunals and inquiries; and VAT law. Also, members act as arbitrators in both domestic and international arbitrations. Some members also act as mediators.

International: The international nature of chambers sets it apart from other practices. Not only does the set have members with language skills in all the major European tongues and Chinese but it also has barristers qualified to practise in non-UK jurisdictions. Members have appeared as advocates in the European Commission, European Court of Justice, European Court of Human Rights and International Court of Justice; in the courts of Hong Kong, Malaysia, Australia, Belfast, Dublin, Gibraltar, St Vincent, Brunei, Kenya and the Cayman Islands; and in arbitrations in places such as Paris, Geneva, Singapore, New Orleans and Beijing.

Recruitment & Training: Chambers offers four funded pupillages per year for an October start. Applications are only accepted through PACH. Mini-pupillages are also available for a limited number of places for those already embarked on legal studies.

Set No. 33

ONE ESSEX COURT (Lord Grabiner QC)

One Essex Court, Temple, London, EC4Y 9AR
Tel: (020) 7583 2000 **Fax:** (020) 7583 0118 **DX:** 430 (Ch.Ln.)
Email: clerks@oeclaw.co.uk **Website:** www.oeclaw.co.uk

Head of Chambers:	Lord Grabiner QC
Clerks:	Robert Ralphs
	Paul Shrubsall MBE
Tenants:	58

Members:

Lord Grabiner QC (1968) (QC-1981)
Gerald Butler QC (1955) (QC-1975)
Graham Aaronson QC (1966) (QC-1982)
Christopher Carr QC (1968) (QC-1983)
Nicholas Strauss QC (1965) (QC-1984)
Roydon Thomas QC (1960) (QC-1985)
Peter Leaver QC (1967) (QC-1987)
Ian Glick QC (1970) (QC-1987)
Richard Field QC (1977) (QC-1987)
Elizabeth Gloster QC (1971) (QC-1989)
Geoffrey Hobbs QC (1977) (QC-1991)
Mark Barnes QC (1974) (QC-1992)
Alastair MacGregor QC (1974) (QC-1994)
Thomas Sharpe QC (1976) (QC-1994)
Thomas Ivory QC (1978) (QC-1998)
Jeffery Onions QC (1981) (QC-1998)
Susanna FitzGerald QC (1973) (QC-1999)
Rhodri Davies QC (1979) (QC-1999)
Stephen Auld QC (1979) (QC-1999)
Alan Redfern (1995)
Michael Conlon (1974)
Malcolm Gammie (1997)
Michael Malone (1975)
Ian Grainger (1978)
Alan Griffiths (1981)
Clare Reffin (1981)
John McCaughran (1982)
Richard Gillis (1982)
Andrew Lenon (1982)
Michael Sullivan (1983)
Siobhan Ward (1984)
Kenneth MacLean (1985)
Charles Graham (1986)
Anthony de Garr Robinson (1987)
Laurence Rabinowitz (1987)
Neil Kitchener (1991)
Alain Choo Choy (1991)
Hannah Brown (1992)
David Wolfson (1992)
David Cavender (1993)
Daniel Toledano (1993)
Zoe O'Sullivan (1993)
Emma Himsworth (1993)
Jacob Grierson (1993)
Lisa Lake (1994)
Edmund Nourse (1994)
Graeme Halkerston (1994)
Sa'ad Hossain (1995)
Daniel Jowell (1995)
Camilla Bingham (1996)
Philip Roberts (1996)
Michael Fealy (1997)
Anushka Rosen (1997)
Orlando Gledhill (1998)
Neill Abrams (1998)
Piu Das Gupta (1999)
Simon Colton (1999)

E

Work Undertaken: The range of work carried out embraces every aspect of domestic and international commerce and finance. The principal areas of practice are: arbitration; commercial law; company and insolvency; European Union law; intellectual property and revenue law.

Recruitment & Training: Chambers offer four 12 month pupillages each year. Chambers operate an award scheme which offers to each pupil the sum of £30,000 in his or her year of pupillage. Part of the award may, at the discretion of chambers, be advanced during a prospective pupil's year of vocational training. Applicants for pupillage should (save in exceptional circumstances) have at least an upper second class degree. Chambers participate in the Pupillage Applications Clearing House (PACH), and all applications for pupillage should be made through PACH.

Set No. 34

ONE ESSEX COURT (Sir Ivan Lawrence QC)

1 Essex Court, Temple, London, EC4Y 9AR **Tel:** (020) 7936 3030 **Fax:** (020) 7583 1606 **DX:** LDE 371 **Email:** one.essex_court@virgin.net

Set No. 35

4 ESSEX COURT (Nigel Teare QC)

4 Essex Court, Temple, London, EC4Y 9AJ
Tel: (020) 7797 7970 **Fax:** (020) 7353 0998 **DX:** 292 London (Chancery Lane)
Email: clerks@4essexcourt.law.co.uk **Website:** www.4essexcourt.law.co.uk

Head of Chambers:	Nigel Teare QC
Senior Clerk:	Gordon Armstrong
Tenants:	37

Members:

Nigel Teare QC (1974) (QC-1991)
M.N. Howard QC (1971) (QC-1986)
Belinda Bucknall QC (1974) (QC-1988)
Charles Macdonald QC (1972) (QC-1992)
Jeremy Russell QC (1975) (QC-1994)
Timothy Brenton QC (1981) (QC-1998)
Charles Haddon-Cave QC (1978) (QC-1999)
John Suttner SC (1979)
John de Cotta (1955)
George Economou (1965)
Simon Gault (1970)
Geoffrey Kinley (1970)
Giles Caldin (1974)
Michael Nolan (1981)
Marion Smith (1981)
Simon Rainey (1982)
Simon Kverndal (1982)
Nigel Jacobs (1983)
Michael McParland (1983)
Luke Parsons (1985)
Simon Croall (1986)
Nigel Cooper (1987)
Matthew Reeve (1987)
Chirag V. Karia (1988)
Poonam Melwani (1989)
Robert Lawson (1989)
James M. Turner (1990)
Robert Thomas (1992)
Nevil Phillips (1992)
John Russell (1993)
Thomas Macey-Dare (1994)
John Kimbell (1995)
Nichola Warrender (1995)
Jonathan Chambers (1996)
Stewart Buckingham (1996)
Peter Ferrer (1998)
Nicholas Craig (1998)
Nicholas Gaskell (1976) *
Robert Ribeiro QC (1978) (QC-1990) *
Paul Griffin (1979) *
Francis D. Rose (1983) *

* Door Tenants

The Chambers: Members of chambers at 4 Essex Court (formerly situated at 2 Essex Court) are available to give specialist advice (including direct advice to foreign lawyers and members of certain other professional bodies) and to undertake advocacy work in their respective fields. They conduct all types of commercial litigation in London and abroad, together with arbitrations and marine, aviation and other inquiries.
Information on the specialist fields of practice of particular members can be obtained from chambers' staff.

Work Undertaken: Members of chambers specialise in a wide spectrum of commercial law, with a particular emphasis on aviation and maritime law, international trade, insurance.
Commercial Law, Shipping and International Trade: Including banking; carriage of goods by sea, land and air; marine and non-marine casualties; marine and general insurance and reinsurance; salvage; collision and oil-pollution; domestic and international sale of goods; ship and civil construction and financing.
Business Law and Financial Services: Including insurance and reinsurance; banking; securities and commodities trading; company law and insolvency.
EU Law: Including competition law; intellectual property; public procurement; mergers and acquisitions; and the business law aspects of 1992 and the Single European Market.
Other: Disaster and multi party litigation; air law; entertainment and media law; sports law; employment law; Judicial Review in related areas.

International: There are members of the French, Spanish, Greek, Cypriot, New South Wales, Hong Kong and New York Bars in chambers. There is a close association with Temple Chambers in Hong Kong.

E

Set No.
36

5 ESSEX COURT (Jeremy Gompertz QC)

5 Essex Court, Temple, London, EC4Y 9AH
Tel: (020) 7410 2000 **Fax:** (020) 7410 2010 **DX:** 1048
Email: barristers@5essexcourt.co.uk **Website:** www.5essexcourt.co.uk

Head of Chambers	Jeremy Gompertz QC
Sen. Clerk:	Michael Dean
Tenants:	32

Members:

Jeremy Gompertz QC (1962) (QC-1988)
Marie Catterson (1972)
Christopher Moss QC (1972) (QC-1994)
Nicholas Ainley (1973)
John Bassett (1975)
Simon Freeland (1978)
Nicholas Wilcox (1977)
Gerard Pounder (1980)
Charles Apthorp (1983)
John Butcher (1984)
Gareth Hughes (1985)
Fiona Barton (1986)
Simon Davenport (1987)
Andrew Waters (1987)
Stephanie Farrimond (1987)
Anne Studd (1988)
Christopher Kerr (1988)
Kate Davey (1988)
Georgina Kent (1989)
Giles Powell (1990)
Lyn Hayhow (1990)
Sarah Buckingham (1991)
Jason Beer (1992)
Samantha Leek (1993)
Stephen Akinsanya (1993)
Jeremy Johnson (1994)
Prabjot Virdi (1995)
Stephen Rose (1995)
Nadeem Ahmad (1996)
Mandy McLean (1996)
Lawrence Selby (1997)
Mathew Holdcroft (1998)

The Chambers: Founded in 1954 at its present address by the late Mr Justice Michael Eastham, 5 Essex Court is a thriving and well-established set of chambers with a wide client base. It offers up-to-date facilities including the latest information technology and dedicated conference rooms together with a strong emphasis on client care. Several senior members of chambers sit as recorders in the crown court (including the Central Criminal Court) and the county court. Additionally one of its Queen's Counsel sits as chairman of the Mental Health Independent Review Tribunal. A number of members of chambers have been appointed to the panel of Treasury Counsel, Common Law. Others are approved by the Attorney General to prosecute on behalf of Her Majesty's Customs and Excise and the Department of Trade and Industry. Work is also undertaken for the Serious Fraud Office.

Work Undertaken: Members of chambers are concerned in all aspects of police and civil liberties law. They act predominantly for police authorities in actions for damages arising out of allegations of trespass, false imprisonment and malicious prosecution. Members of the set appear in inquests, disciplinary tribunals, applications for judicial review and public inquiries. They are also regularly asked to advise upon sensitive issues of police policy.The criminal team is experienced in all aspects and levels of criminal work, both for prosecution and defence. The strength and depth of the criminal team, throughout the set, is such that a true service can be offered to its professional clients. No matter is so small nor is any case so complicated or of such high profile that chambers cannot provide the necessary level of seniority and expertise, from the most junior tenent to highly experienced Queen's Counsel. The personal injury team undertakes work both for claimants and for defendants, including public authorities. It accepts instructions, and offers a swift screening service, in matters subject to conditional fee agreements.

Recruitment & Training: Chambers have accreditation by Law Society and the Institute of Legal Executives. Members of chambers regularly assist with either in-house training in conjunction with solicitors or in organising conference and lectures specific to client needs.Tenancy applications should be sent to the Head of Chambers. All applications from established practitioners will be treated in confidence.Applications for pupillage should be made via the PACH scheme. Up to two pupillage awards are offered of £12,000 for 12 months commencing in October.

E

Set No.
37

20 ESSEX STREET (Iain Milligan QC)

20 Essex Street, London, WC2R 3AL
Tel: (020) 7583 9294 or (020) 7842 1200 **Fax:** (020) 7583 1341 **DX:** 0009 (Ch.Ln.)
Email: clerks@20essexst.com **Website:** www.20essexst.com

Head of Chambers:	Iain Milligan QC
Chambers Manager:	Janet Newton (020) 8533 3789 mobile 0374 274841
Clerks:	Neil Palmer (020) 8660 2633 mobile 07775 713925 Brian Lee (020) 8642 5865 mobile 0797 759 0229
Office Hours:	8.15am – 6.45pm
Tenants:	39

Members:

Iain Milligan QC (1973) (QC-1991)
Elihu Lauterpacht QC (1950) (QC-1970)
Arthur Watts QC (1957) (QC-1988)
David Johnson QC (1967) (QC-1978)
Murray Pickering QC (1963) (QC-1985)
Nicholas Legh-Jones QC (1968) (QC-1987)
Richard Plender QC (1972) (QC-1989)
Angus Glennie QC (1974) (QC-1991)
Peter Gross QC (1977) (QC-1992)
Mark Havelock-Allan QC (1974) (QC-1993)
Alexander Layton QC (1976) (QC-1995)
Timothy Young QC (1977) (QC-1996)
Nicholas Hamblen QC (1981) (QC-1997)
Stephen Males QC (1978) (QC-1998)
Christopher Hancock QC (1983) (QC-2000)
Julian Cooke (1965)
Richard Wood (1975)
Michael Tselentis SC (1995) (SC – South Africa – 1989)
Edmund Broadbent (1980)
Stephen Morris (1981)
David Owen (1983)
Duncan Matthews (1986)
William Godwin (1986)
Andrew Baker (1988)
Daniel Bethlehem (1988)
Michael Coburn (1990)
Lawrence Akka (1991)
Clare Ambrose (1992)
Karen Maxwell (1992)
Graham Charkham (1993) (CEDR Accredited)
Guy Morpuss (1991)
Sara Masters (1993)
Philip Edey (1994)
Charles Kimmins (1994)
Michael Collett (1995)
Michael Ashcroft (1997)
Sudhanshu Swaroop (1997)
Julian Kenny (1997)
Malcolm Jarvis (1998)

The Chambers: This long established, progressive set of chambers is one of the leading sets in commercial law. Members advise on all aspects of international trade, commerce and finance with specialist expertise in banking, shipping, insurance, public international law and European Community law. Although much of chambers' work is in the Commercial Court, the practice and clientele are international. Chambers aim to combine an outstanding standard of work with a friendly and approachable attitude to clients, lay and professional.
Notable recent events include Iain Milligan QC becoming head of chambers; the successful completion of pupillage by Malcom Jarvis; the arrival of William Godwin from Atkin Chambers and Alexander Layton QC from 2 Temple Gardens and Stephen Morris being appointed to Treasury A panel for commercial and European law.

Work Undertaken:

Commercial: Members advise on a range of commercial matters including the following:Admiralty; agency; arbitration; aviation; bailment; banking and financial services; carriage by land, sea and air; commodities and futures; company law and partnership; conflicts of laws; construction; disciplinary proceedings; entertainment law; insurance and reinsurance; international sales and commodity trading; IT; oil and gas; professional negligence; sale of goods; shipping; all types of domestic and international commercial agreements.

European Union: A number of members are specialists in European Community law and are regularly engaged to provide advice and representation to Community institutions, member states and other litigants on such issues as agriculture, the free movement of goods, those relating to individuals, services and capital, competition and state aids.

International: Members of chambers engaged in this field appear before the International Court of Justice and other international Tribunals.Some members specialise in public international law, dealing with such matters as boundaries, interpretation of treaties, state immunity, international investment and human rights. Those practising in these areas appear as advocates in the International Court of Justice, the European Court of Human Rights, Dispute Settlement Panels of the World Trade Organisation, the International Tribunal on the Law of the Sea and comparable tribunals.Members also practise in private international law, including the Brussels and Lugano Conventions on Jurisdiction and the Enforcement of Judgements and the Rome Convention on the Law Applicable to Contractual Obligations. Some have experience of conducting litigation before the Court of Justice of the European Communities on the Brussels Convention.Senior members, Lord Donaldson, Sir Christopher Staughton, Lord Bridge, Lord Griffiths MC (Cedr Accredited), Sir Brian Neill (Cedr Accredited), and Kenneth Rokison QC (Cedr Accredited) accept appointments through chambers to conduct inquiries and act as mediators and arbitrators. Members will accept instructions to appear in courts abroad including Hong Kong, Singapore, Malaysia and other jurisdictions subject to admission rules, whilst some members have been called to the local bars of Australia, Gibraltar and South Africa.

Publications: A number of members are authors and editors of leading publications and journals full details of which are available at www.20essexst.com

Languages: French, German, Italian, Spanish, Dutch, Hindi.

20 Essex Street

E

Set No.
38

23 ESSEX STREET (Michael Lawson QC)

23 Essex Street, London, WC2R 3AS
Tel: (020) 7413 0353 **Fax:** (020) 7413 0374 **DX:** 148 (LDE) Chancery Lane
Email: clerks@23essexstreet.co.uk **Website:** www.23essexstreet.co.uk

Head of Chambers:	Michael Lawson QC
Practice Manager:	Nicholas Hopgood
Deputy Practice Manager:	Daren Milton
Tenants:	57

Members:

Michael Lawson QC (1969) (QC-1991) +
Michael Hill QC (1958) (QC-1979)
Nicholas Purnell QC (1968) (QC-1985) +
Michael Austin-Smith QC (1969) (QC-1990) +
Susan Edwards QC (1972) (QC-1993) +
Stuart Lawson Rogers QC (1969) (QC-1994) +
Charles Miskin QC (1975) (QC-1998) +
Nigel Sangster QC (1976) (QC-1998)
Michael Wood QC (1976) (QC-1999) +
Christopher Kinch QC (1976) (QC-1999) +
P. James Richardson (1975)
Brendan Finucane (1976)
Simon Davis (1978) +
John Causer (1979)
Robin Johnson (1979)
Daniel Janner (1980)
Simon Russell Flint (1980) +
John Price (1982)
Oscar Del Fabbro (1982)
Graham Cooke (1983)
Joanna Glynn (1983) +
Sally Howes (1983)
Elroy Claxton (1983) +
Rupert Pardoe (1984)
Andrew Carnes (1984)
Philip St. John-Stevens (1985)
Dafydd Enoch (1985)
Alan Kent (1986)
Johannah Cutts (1986)
Wayne Cranston-Morris (1986)
Garrett Byrne (1986)
Paul Ozin (1987)
Karen Holt (1987)
Cairns Nelson (1987)
Heather Norton (1988)
Iain Morley (1988)
William Carter (1989)
Keith Hotten (1990)
Isobel Ascherson (1990)
Lynn Griffin (1991)
Ian Acheson (1992)
Mark Fenhalls (1992)
Andrew Hurst (1992)
Richard Milne (1992)
Fiona Horlick (1992)
Giles Curtis-Raleigh (1992)
Eloise Marshall (1994)
Hannah Swain (1994)
Rufus Stilgoe (1994)
Alexia Durran (1995)
Clare Strickland (1995)
Alan May (1995)
Ian Hope (1996)
Marcus Thompson (1996)
Emily Belson (1997)
Sarah Campbell (1997)
Kathrine Hunter (1997)
Ian Goldsworthy QC *
Alison Jones (1988) *
Simon Medland (1991) *

\+ Recorder *Door Tenants

Work Undertaken:
Criminal: Mainstream crime, both defending and prosecuting. A number of silks and juniors specialise in commercial fraud/white collar crime on a national and international level. Expertise is available in third party disclosure, mutual assistance and ECHR implications. Teams available.
Advice and representation available for regulatory hearings, disciplinary proceedings (Lloyd's of London, police, GMC and GDC), inquests, extradition hearings, DTI investigations and director disqualification proceedings. Individuals also specialise in public and administrative, employment, licensing, planning, defamation and environmental law.
Civil: Members are instructed in areas of common law, particularly where they are crime related: civil fraud, actions against the police for malicious prosecution, false imprisonment etc.

Publications: James Richardson is editor of *Archbold and Criminal Law Week*. Joanna Glynn and William Carter are contributing editors to *Archbold*. Daniel Janner is one of the two editors to the *Criminal Appeal Reports*.

Recruitment & Training: Tenancy Applications to Michael Wood.
Pupillage: Chambers offers three 12 month (funded) pupillages. Travel allowances are available. Sponsored pupils are accepted additionally. Chambers is a member of PACH. Full details are published in the Bar Council's Chambers' Pupillages and Awards Handbook. Applications to John Price.
Mini-pupillages: A limited number are available. Applications to John Price on or after 1st April 2000.
Training: Chambers has an internal continuing education programme for members and pupils. Members of chambers devise and conduct external programmes.

E

Set No.
39

35 ESSEX STREET (Nigel Inglis-Jones QC)

35 Essex Street, Temple, London, WC2R 3AR **Tel:** (020) 7353 6381
Fax: (020) 7583 1786 **DX:** 351 London **Video conference:** (020) 7583 7015
Email: derek-jenkins@link.org **Website:** www.35-essex-street.com

Head of Chambers:	Nigel Inglis-Jones QC
Senior Clerk:	Derek Jenkins
Tenants:	32

Members:

Nigel J. Inglis-Jones QC (1959) (QC-1982) BA (Oxon)
David C. Calcutt QC (1955) (QC-1972) MA, LLB, MuSB (Cantab)
Alan D. Rawley QC (1958) (QC-1977) MA (Oxon)
Christopher Wilson-Smith QC (1965) (QC-1986)
Philip C. Mott QC (1970) (QC-1991) MA (Oxon)
Linda E. Sullivan QC (1973) (QC-1994) BA (Hons)
Richard Lissack QC (1978) (QC-1994)
Paul Garlick QC (1974) (QC-1996)
Hywel I. Jenkins (1974) LLB (Hons)
John L. Stephens (1975) BA (Oxon)
Richard M. Mawhinney (1977) BA (Oxon)
William L. Coley (1980) MA (Cantab)
Robin S. Tolson (1980) BA (Cantab)
Stephen Climie (1982) BA (Lincoln)
David G. Westcott (1982) BA (Oxon), BCL
Christopher M. Kemp (1984) BA (Oxon), Dip Law
Harry Trusted (1985) MA (Cantab)
Andrew J.M. Spink (1985) BA (Cantab)
Alison McCormick (1988) BA (Oxon)
Susan C. Freeborn (1989) BA (Cantab)
Richard G. Hitchcock (1989) BA (Oxon)
Jonathan E.S. Hand (1990) BA(Oxon)
Thomas R.G. Leeper (1993) BA (Hons)
Nathan W. Tavares (1992) BSE (Hons)(Eng)
Grace Malden (1993) (Cantab)
Matthew J. Phillips (1993) (Oxon)
Nicholas Stallworthy (1993) (Oxon)
Robert-Jan Temmink (1996) B.A (Hons) (Cantab)
Clare Vines (1997) M.A. (Cantab)
Peter Skelton B.A. M Phil (Cantab)
Harriet Jerram (1998) M.A. (Cantab)
David Grant (1999) B.A., BCL (Oxon)

The Chambers: The barristers of this set provide advocacy and advice covering a wide range of specialist areas of commercial and common law practice. Pension schemes, personal injury, clinical negligence and criminal cases are among its special areas of expertise and it has considerable experience of arbitrations. 35 Essex Street has developed and grown over the years to meet the changing demands expected of the Bar by both lay and professional clients. Chambers' successful relocation to Essex Street in January 1995 from its former premises in Lamb Building has provided it with the opportunity to both expand its numbers and meet the increasing level of demand for its services. The underlying approach adopted by chambers is to provide genuine expertise at each level of call, both individually and in teams, with fee structures and response times that can be adapted to meet clients' needs. At the same time members seek to make themselves as accessible as possible, while actively seeking to establish constructive and open working relationships with clients. Chambers believes that the quality of service offered by its barristers is enhanced by the flexibility of its clerking and administrative team, and its willingness to implement and exploit developments in information technology.

Work Undertaken:

Pensions and Trusts: Members have expertise in all aspects of occupational pension schemes and trusts. Nigel Inglis-Jones QC is the author of a leading pensions text book.

Personal Injury and Clinical Negligence: A large group within chambers have extensive experience of acting on behalf of both plaintiffs and defendants in cases covering the full spectrum of work included under these headings. Some particular examples of the personal injury caseload of chambers are claims involving brain injury, spinal injury and sports injuries (particularly those caused by playing rugby or diving), and lung conditions caused by occupational and environmental exposure to asbestos and other toxic chemicals. In the field of clinical negligence, examples include cases involving obstetric negligence resulting in cerebral palsy, failed spinal surgery leading to paralysis and the issue of informed consent in paediatric heart transplant procedures. In the related field of paediatic heart surgery, three members of chambers are acting on behalf of the families at the Bristol Royal Infirmary Public Inquiry. Work is regularly undertaken on a conditional fee basis. 35 Essex Street is a member of the Clinical Negligence Conditional Fee Group formed by sets of chambers specialising in clinical negligence work. Members of 35 Essex Street also specialise in most other areas of professional negligence including surveyors', actuaries', accountants' and lawyers' negligence.

Crime: Has included involvement of members of chambers in the Maxwell, Blue Arrow and Guinness cases. A team of barristers in chambers specialise in child care law, acting in particular for local authorities, guardians and the Official Solicitor.

Arbitration: A distinguished group of arbitrators consisting of present and former members of chambers undertake a wide range of international and domestic commercial arbitrations. Among them is Sir David

Continued overleaf

E

Calcutt QC, who is one of the government's designated members of the Panel of Arbitrators of the International Centre for Settlement of International Disputes.

Other Areas: Other Areas of practice in which members of chambers are active include property, contract, employment and intellectual property. In addition to appearing as advocates in the English Appellate Courts, the High Court, the County Courts and a wide variety of tribunals and arbitration work, chambers places particular emphasis on providing focused and practical advice both on paper and in conference on litigious and non-litigious matters. Work is also undertaken in foreign jurisdictions.Chambers have an Italian affiliate practising in Milan, Avv. Mauro Rubino-Sammartano.

Languages: French, German and Italian.

Set No. 40

39 ESSEX STREET (Nigel Pleming QC)

39 Essex Street, London, WC2R 3AT **Tel:** (020) 7832 1111
Fax: (020) 7353 3978 **DX:** 298 **Email:** clerks@39essex.co.uk
Website: www.39essex.co.uk

Head of Chambers:	Nigel Pleming
Senior Clerk:	Nigel Connor
Chambers Director:	Michael Meeson
Tenants:	44

Members:

Nigel Pleming QC (1971) (QC-1992)
Edwin Glasgow QC (1969) (QC-1987)
Simon Goldblatt QC (1953) (QC-1972)
Lord Brennan QC (1967) (QC-1985) of Bibury
Colin Mackay QC (1967) (QC-1989)
Wyn Lewis Williams QC (1974) (QC-1992)
Richard Gray QC (1970) (QC-1993)
Richard Davies QC (1973) (QC-1994)
Richard Wilmot-Smith QC (1978) (QC-1994)
Michael Tillett QC (1965) (QC-1996)
Robert Jay QC (1981) (QC-1998)
Alan Cooper (1969)
David Melville (1975)
Charles Brown (1976)
Roderick Noble (1977)
Colin McCaul (1978)
Neil Block (1980)
Geoffrey B. Brown (1981)
Christian Du Cann (1982)
Charles Cory-Wright (1984)
Alison Foster (1984)
Jonathan Bellamy (1986)
Stuart Catchpole (1987)
David Bradly (1987)
Charles Manzoni (1988)
Steven Kovats (1989)
Jeremy Morgan (1989) FCI Arb
Eleanor Grey (1990)
Bernard Doherty (1990)
Vincent Nelson (1980)
Fenella Morris (1990)
Jennifer Richards (1991)
Sean Wilken (1991)
Rohan Pershad (1991)
Daniel Oudkerk (1992)
Bruce Brodie (1993)
Matthew Seligman (1994)
Adam Robb (1995)
Sam Grodzinski (1996)
Parishil Patel (1996)
Kristina Stern (1996)
Judith Ayling (1998)
Kate Grange (1998)
Caroline Trustcott (1998)
Frances Patterson QC (1977) (QC-1998) *

*Associate Tenant

The Chambers: 39 Essex Street is a long established set whose barristers have widespread expertise and experience in almost every aspect of commercial, public and common law. Members of chambers have wide experience of all courts and tribunals from the House of Lords, Privy Council, Court of Appeal and International and Domestic Arbitrations, through to Public Inquiries, Industrial and VAT tribunals. They have also participated in significant investigations before Parliamentary Select Committees. Several members of chambers are on the Main and Supplementary Treasury Panels of Counsel instructed on behalf of the Crown. Members also undertake pro bono work for public interest organisations.

Work Undertaken: Chambers' particular expertise is in the fields of insurance law; personal injury; construction; public law and judicial review; commercial law; and professional negligence. Within this broad range, members of chambers have developed specialisms in the following areas:

Commercial: Insurance and reinsurance; commodities and derivatives (in particular oil and gas law); media and entertainment; sports law; banking; sale and carriage of goods; insolvency and company law; and international commercial arbitration.

Public: All aspects of judicial review for both applicants and respondents. Areas of expertise include local authorities (especially their powers and financing), and other public bodies; environmental law; health trusts; education; commercial; civil liberties and human rights; community care; mental health; housing and housing associations; and immigration. With expertise in both public and commercial law, members of chambers are uniquely placed to advise and represent clients in cases dealing with the powers and duties of regulatory bodies.

Professional Indemnity: Chambers act for both plaintiffs and defendents in matters involving solicitors and barristers; doctors and other medical practitioners; surveyors; architects; engineers; accountants; insurers and insurance brokers; and other professionals.

Personal Injury: Multi-Plaintiff group actions; disaster litigation; and injuries of maximum severity.

Public Inquiries: Members of chambers have been instructed in most of the major Public Inquiries over

E

39 ESSEX STREET
LONDON WC2R 3AT

the past 10 years, including Hillsborough, BSE, the King's Cross fire, and most recently, the Bristol Royal Infirmary Inquiry and the Saville Inquiry.
Additional Areas: VAT, customs & excise, European law.

Publications: Numerous publications including *Judical Review: Law and Procedure* (Gordon); *Local Authority Powers* (Garden); *Waiver, Variation and Estoppel* (Wilken); *The Law of Entertainment and Broadcasting* (Nelson).

Languages: French, German, Italian and Spanish.

Recruitment & Training: Chambers are a member of PACH. We offer up to four pupillages each year, with scholarship awards of £19,000. The decision as to offers of pupillage depends in particular upon: academic record (a first or upper second class degree is usually required), performance at interview, performance in any mini-pupillages, and references.

1 **46 ESSEX STREET** (Geoffrey Hawker)

46 Essex Street, London, WC2R 3GH **Tel:** (020) 7583 8899 **Fax:** (020) 7583 8800 **DX:** 1014 London/Chancery Lane
Email: clerks@46essexst.co.uk

2 FALCON CHAMBERS (Jonathan Gaunt QC & Kim Lewison QC)

Falcon Court, London, EC4Y 1AA
Tel: (020) 7353 2484 **Fax:** (020) 7353 1261 **DX:** 408
Email: clerks@falcon-chambers.com **Website:** www.falcon-chambers.com

Head of Chambers:	Jonathan Gaunt QC, Kim Lewison QC
Chambers Director:	Edith A. Robertson
Senior Clerk:	Mark Clewley
Tenants:	28

Members:

Derek Wood QC CBE (1964) (QC-1978) MA, BCL
Jonathan Gaunt QC (1972) (QC-1991) BA
Kim Lewison QC (1975) (QC-1991) MA
Paul Morgan QC (1975) (QC-1992) MA
Kirk Reynolds QC (1974) (QC-1993) MA
Jonathan Brock QC (1977) (QC-1997) MA
Nicholas Dowding QC (1979) (QC-1997) MA
Edwin Prince (1955) BA
Paul de la Piquerie (1966) LLB
Joanne R. Moss (1976) MA LLM (EC Law)
Anthony Radevsky (1978) LLB
Edward Cole (1980) MA
Wayne Clark (1982) LLB, BCL
Guy Fetherstonhaugh (1983) BSc
Martin Rodger (1986) BA
Timothy Fancourt (1987) MA
Barry Denyer-Green (1972) LLM, PhD
Stephen Jourdan (1989) MA
Gary Cowen (1990) LLB
Jonathan Small (1990) BA
Janet Bignell (1992) MA, BCL
Martin Dray (1992) LLB
Caroline Shea (1994) MA
Anthony Tanney (1994) BA M.Jur
Catherine Taskis (1995) BA BCL
Emily Windsor (1995) BA DSU (E.C. Law)
Edward Peters (1998) BA
Katherine Astill (1998) BA MPhil

The Chambers: A set of 28 barristers, including 7 QCs, all of whom specialise in litigation and property law. Members are the authors or editors of leading textbooks such as Woodfall, Megarry, Gale, Muir Watt and Moss, Bernstein and Reynolds, and Hague. Chambers enjoy strong links with the RICS and the CIArb, and organise the annual Blundell Memorial Lectures. All are members of the Chancery Bar Association and LCLCBA.

Work Undertaken: Falcon Chambers is generally recognised as the leading set for landlord and tenant (commercial, residential and agricultural); property litigation, including all aspects of general property law (easements, restrictive covenants, mortgages, options); and property-related areas, such as insolvency and solicitors' and surveyors' professional negligence. Chambers have particular expertise in contract and arbitration law. Some members specialise in agricultural production controls; competition law; compulsory purchase; planning; and building disputes. Litigation is the core of chambers' work, but much advisory and drafting work is also carried out. Direct Professional Access is welcomed, and members often sit as arbitrators, experts and legal assessors.

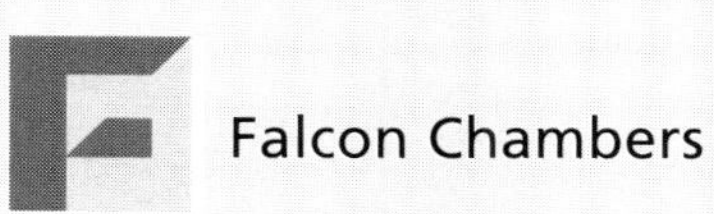

F

Set No.
43

FARRAR'S BUILDING (John Leighton Williams QC)

Farrar's Building, Temple, London, EC4Y 7BD **Tel:** (020) 7583 9241
Fax: (020) 7583 0090 **DX:** 406 **Email:** chambers@farrarsbuilding.co.uk
Website: www.farrarsbuilding.co.uk

Head of Chambers:	John Leighton Williams QC
Senior Clerk/Practice Manager:	Alan Kilbey
Chambers Manager:	Janet Eades
Tenants:	37

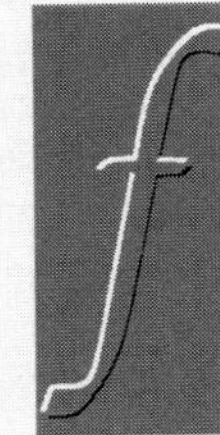

Members:

John Leighton Williams QC (1964) (QC-1986) +
Michael Lewer QC (1958) (QC-1983) +
Gerard Elias QC (1968) (QC-1984) +
Christopher Pitchford QC (1969) (QC-1987) +
Douglas Day QC (1967) (QC-1989) +
Peter Birts QC (1968) (QC-1990) +
Geoffrey Nice QC (1971) (QC-1990) +
Patrick Harrington QC (1973) (QC-1993) +
Leighton Davies QC (1975) (QC-1994) +
Alan Jeffreys QC (1970) (QC-1996) +
William Norris QC (1974) (QC-1997)
Stephen Rubin QC (1977) (QC-2000)
Edward Southwell (1970) +
Richard Nussey (1971)
Anthony Seys Llewellyn (1972) +
Gregory Treverton-Jones (1977) +
Stephen Jones (1978)
Tom McDermott (1980)
Gillian Keene (1980)
Simon Peter Buchanan Browne (1982)
Tracy Ayling (1983)
Daniel Matovu (1985)
Nigel Spencer Ley (1985)
Jonathan Watt-Pringle (1987)
Andrew Peebles (1987)
David Wicks (1989)
Georgina Middleton (1989)
Shabbir Lakha (1989)
James Todd (1990)
Helen Hobhouse (1990)
Lucy Moorman (1992)
Joanne Cash (1994)
Melissa Pack (1995)
Darryl Allen (1995)
Lee Evans (1996)
Huw Davies (1998)
James Pretsell (1998)

+ Recorder

The Chambers: Farrar's Building is a long established set of common law chambers with an excellent reputation built up over many years.

Work Undertaken: Areas of practice fall under 'general common law' but members of chambers have particular specialities in: administrative and public law; contract and commercial litigation; criminal law; defamation and media law; disciplinary tribunals; employment; environmental and agricultural law; health and safety; insurance litigation; landlord and tenant; licensing; medical law; personal injury; police actions and civil liberties; product liability; public inquiries and tribunals; professional negligence; solicitors' costs and taxation; sports law; and competition law.

Set No.
44

FIELD COURT CHAMBERS (Melanie Spencer)

Field Court Chambers, 2nd Floor, 3 Field Court, Grays Inn, London, WC1R 5EP
Tel: (020) 7404 7474 **Fax:** (020) 7404 7475 **DX:** 136 (Ch.Ln.)
Email: enquiries@fieldcourtchambers.com **Website:** www.fieldcourtchambers.com

Head of Chambers:	Melanie Spencer
Senior Clerk:	Paul Mellor
Tenants:	6

A civil set practicing in the following areas: commercial, employment, environmental, family, immigration, landlord and tenant, personal injury and professional negligence.

Set No.
45

4 FIELD COURT (Steven Gee QC)

Gray's Inn, London, WC1R 5EA **Tel:** (020) 7440 6900
Fax: (020) 7242 0197 **DX:** 483 London/Chancery Lane
Email: chambers@4fieldcourt.co.uk **Website:** www.4fieldcourt.com

Head of Chambers:	Steven Gee QC
Clerks:	Paul Coveney, Christopher James, Toni McKenna, Jean-Pierre Schulz.
Tenants:	33

Members:

Steven Gee QC (1975) (QC-1993)
Andrew Rankin QC (1950) (QC-1968)
Richard Stone QC (1952) (QC-1968)
John Reeder QC (1971) (QC-1989)
R Jervis Kay QC (1972) (QC-1996)
Peter Susman QC (1966) (QC-1997)
Lionel Persey QC (1981) (QC-1997)
Elizabeth Blackburn QC (1978) (QC-1998)
Allan Myers (1988) (QC Aus.)
Sarah Miller (1971)
Lloyd Lloyd (1973)
Alison Green (1974)
James Thom (1974)
William Whitehouse-Vaux (1977)
Robert Bourne (1978)
Daphne Romney (1979)
Nigel Meeson (1982)
Jonathan D C Turner (1982)
Vasanti Selvaratnam (1983)
David Goldstone (1986)
Colin Wright (1987)
David Brook (1988)
Nicholas Saunders (1989)
Stephen Wilson (1990)
Michael Davey (1990)
Timothy Hill (1990)
Arshad Ghaffar (1991)
Nicholas Dugdale (1992)
Charles Davies (1995)
Madeleine Heal (1996)
Eoin O'Shea (1996)
Guy Blackwood (1997)
Rachel Toney (1998)

The Chambers: 4 Field Court is a commercial set. Members provide advocacy and advice in relation to many aspects of commercial, chancery/commercial and civil law. Members appear before all courts and tribunals in England and Wales, as well as in the European court and a range of overseas courts and tribunals. Members of chambers also act as arbitrators, as mediators in Alternative Dispute Resolution, and as expert witnesses.

Work Undertaken: shipping and maritime law; commercial contracts; insurance and reinsurance; banking and financial services; road, rail and air law; professional negligence; employment law; property law; intellectual property; EU, free trade and competition; IT law.

International: Barristers at 4 Field Court are members of the Bars of Antigua and Barbuda, California, Gibraltar, Hong Kong, New South Wales, New York, New Zealand, Papua New Guinea, St. Vincent and The Grenadines and Victoria.

Languages: French, German, Italian and Urdu.

Set No.
46

FOUNTAIN COURT (Anthony Boswood QC)

Fountain Court, Temple, London, EC4Y 9DH
Tel: (020) 7583 3335 **Fax:** (020) 7353 0329 **DX:** LDE 5
Email: chambers@fountaincourt.co.uk **Website:** www.fountaincourt.co.uk

Head of Chambers:	Anthony Boswood QC
Chambers Director:	Ric Martin
Head of Clerking:	Mark Watson
Chambers Administrator:	Prue Woodbridge
Tenants:	51

Members:

Conrad Dehn QC (1952) (QC-1968)
Christopher Bathurst QC (1959) (QC-1978)
Anthony Boswood QC (1970) (QC-1986)
Lord Goldsmith QC (1972) (QC-1987)
Trevor Philipson QC (1972) (QC-1989)
Michael Lerego QC (1972) (QC-1995)
Andrew Smith QC (1974) (QC-1990)
Michael Brindle QC (1975) (QC-1992)
Michael Crane QC (1975) (QC-1994)
Nicholas Underhill QC (1976) (QC-1992)
Nicholas Stadlen QC (1976) (QC-1991)
David Railton QC (1979) (QC-1996)
Timothy Dutton QC (1979) (QC-1998)
Stephen Moriarty QC (1986) (QC-1999)
Brian Doctor QC (1991) (QC-1999)
Timothy Wormington (1977)
Michael McLaren (1981)
Philip Brook Smith (1982)
Raymond Cox (1982)
David Waksman (1982)
Anthony Martino (1982)
Thomas Keith (1984)
Murray Shanks (1984)
Guy Philipps (1986)
Craig Orr (1986)
Timothy Howe (1987)
Michael A. Green (1987)
Bankim Thanki (1988)
Patricia Robertson (1988)
Jeffrey Chapman (1989)
Bridget Lucas (1989)
Brian Napier (1990)
Derrick Dale (1990)
Akhil Shah (1990)
Marcus Smith (1991)
Paul Gott (1991)
Veronique Buehrlen (1991)
Andrew Mitchell (1992)
Richard Handyside (1993)
John Taylor (1993)
Richard Coleman (1994)
Adam Tolley (1994)
Louise Merrett (1995)
Philippa Hamilton (1996)
Paul Sinclair (1997)
Patrick Goodall (1998)
Deepak Nambisan (1998)
Giles Wheeler (1998)
Henry King (1998)
Rosalind Phelps (1998)
Edward Levey (1999)

Associated tenants: Peter Carter QC (Emeritus Fellow, Wadham College, Oxford), Gladys Li (Senior Counsel, Hong Kong), Izzet Sinan (resident in Brussels), Richard Hooley (Senior Tutor, Fitzwilliam College, Cambridge) and Andrew Burrows (Norton Rose Professor of Commercial Law, St Hugh's College, Oxford). Peter Scot QC, who recently retired from practice, accepts appointments through chambers to conduct inquiries, mediations and arbitrations.

The Chambers: Fountain Court is a leading commercial set of chambers with 50 barristers, of whom 15 are silks. The core of its work is commercial, and members advise and represent clients over the entire range of business problems.The set offers a high quality and efficient service which meets the practical requirements of commercial clients. Members of chambers appear in courts and tribunals of all levels from complex high-value commercial disputes to more straightforward County Court and tribunal work. The size of chambers, and the range of experience of its members, enables Fountain Court to assemble balanced teams of counsel to suit the requirements of individual cases. Prominent former members include Lord Bingham of Cornhill and many other current and former Lords of Appeal and High Court Judges. Hours: 8.00am to 9.00pm Monday to Friday and from 9.00am to 1.00pm on Saturdays. After hours 0786 780 3335.

FOUNTAIN
COURT
CHAMBERS

F

Publications: Many members of chambers have written or contributed to legal textbooks and other published works. A second edition of the *The Law of Bank Payments* by Michael Brindle QC and Raymond

Continued overleaf

Cox, with contributions by other members of Chambers, was published in 1999. Brian Napier is an editor of *Harvey on Employment and Industrial Relations Law* and has published widely on employment law. Chambers provides the editorial team under Stephen Moriarty QC and Raymond Cox as general editor of the *Commercial Court Procedure* which is published by Sweet & Maxwell as a part of the White Book series.

Work Undertaken: Members of Fountain Court are recognised leaders in the fields of commercial litigation; banking; financial services; insurance and reinsurance; professional negligence; aviation; and employment. But Fountain Court also retains a strong 'generalist' tradition and is notable for the wide range of other civil work undertaken, including oil and gas; entertainment and media; intellectual property; company; insolvency; product liability; human rights; administrative; civil fraud; sports; international trade; shipping; and telecommunications law.Several members of chambers have experience of sitting as arbitrators in commercial and other disputes, and of mediation and alternative dispute resolution.

International: Members regularly work abroad, not only in international arbitrations but also as advocates in overseas jurisdictions, including Hong Kong and Singapore, and in the European Court of Justice. Members of chambers are also members of the bars of California, New York and Gibraltar and of the Faculty of Advocates in Scotland.

Languages: There are members of chambers who are fluent in Afrikaans, French, German and Italian; others have a working knowledge of Greek and Russian.

Set No. 47

FRANCIS TAYLOR BUILDING (D.A. Pears)

Francis Taylor Building (2nd Floor), Temple, London, EC4Y 7BY
Tel: (020) 7353 9942 **Fax:** (020) 7353 9924 **DX:** LDE 211 London/Chancery Lane
Email: clerks@ftblaw.co.uk

Head of Chambers:	D.A. Pears
Senior Clerk:	Kevin Moore
Tenants:	38

Members:

D.A. Pears (1975)
Nemone Lethbridge (1956)
Gavin Merrylees (1964)
Dennis Naish (1966)
Philip Conrath (1972)
Phillip Matthews (1974)
Paul Staddon (1976)
Mark Dencer (1978)
Stuart Cakebread (1978)
Mark Hoyle (1978)
Kerstin Boyd (1979)
Simon E.P. Cheves (1980)
Henrietta Manners (1981)
William Holland (1982)
Sebastian Reid (1982)
Kevin Clarke (1983)
Leo D'Arcy (1983)
Jane Carpenter (1984)
Jacqueline Matthews-Stroud (1984)
Philip Dixon (1986)
Michael Buckpitt (1988)
Clare Roberts (1988)
Gerald Wilson (1989)
Carole Murray (1989)
Philip Rainey (1990)
Nicholas Barraclough (1990)
Kirsty Brimelow (1991)
Stephen Heath (1992)
Howard Jones (1992)
Catriona MacLaren (1993)
Jonathan Green (1993)
Andrew Butler (1993)
Warwick Aleeson (1994)
Alexander Bastin (1995)
Christopher Heather (1995)
Robert Bowker (1995)
James Fieldsend (1997)
Wendy Cook (1997)
Richard Selwyn-Sharpe (1985) *
Gilbert Chirimuuta (1990) *

* Door Tenant

Work Undertaken:
Administrative and Public Law: Including local government and judicial review.
Commercial: Including international sale of goods, franchise agreements and partnership disputes, arbitration, joint ventures & conflict of laws.
Consumer Law: Including credit, sale and supply of goods and services.
Crime Employment: Including restraint of trade, transfer of undertakings and restrictive covenants.
Family Law: Both children and property.
Mortgages and Security.
Product Liability.
Professional Negligence: In all areas but particularly medical, surveyors, solicitors and architects.
Property: Particularly landlord and tenant (both commercial and residential), rent review, leasehold enfranchisement and insolvency.
Personal Injuries. Direct Private Access and Conditional Fee work accepted. Refer to clerks for advice on relevant expertise and availability. Fee estimates can be given in advance.

F

Set No. 48

FRANCIS TAYLOR BUILDING (Nicholas Valios QC)

Francis Taylor Building, Temple, London, EC4Y 7BY
Tel: (020) 7353 7768 **Fax:** (020) 7353 0659 **DX:** 441 London/Chancery Lane

Head of Chambers:	Nicholas Valios QC
Senior Clerk:	David Green
Tenants:	37

Members:

Nicholas Valios QC (1964) (QC-1991)
Peter Lewis (1964)
John Rylance (1968)
James Mason (1969)
Graham Lodge (1971)
Edward Lewis (1972)
Richard Mandel (1972)
Keith Salveson (1974)
Graham Blower (1974)
Rosemary Burns (1978)
Anthony Rimmer (1983)
Roy Brown (1983)
Richard Jones (1984)
James Scobie (1984)
Gerald Bermingham (1985)
Jonathan Ingram (1984)
Joseph Giret (1985)
Andrew Lewis (1986)
Caroline English (1989)
David Scutt (1989)
Lawrence Henderson (1990)
Gavin Pottinger (1991)
Jan Hayne (1991)
Amanda-Jane Field (1992)
Kieran Vaughan (1993)
Ian McLoughlin (1993)
Michelle Fawcett (1993)
Richard Fisher (1994)
Malcolm Clarke (1994)
Abdullah Al-Yunusi (1994)
Rupert Bowers (1995)
Lyall Thompson (1995)
Andrea Scott Lynch (1996)
Lawrence Aiolfi (1996)
Chris Smith (1997)
Ian Ibrahim (1997)
Simon Dickson (1998)

The Chambers: The chambers of Nicholas Valios QC are an established set whose recent expansion has enabled it to develop as a specialist criminal chambers. Criminal practitioners offer strength and experience at all levels, from Magistrates' Courts to Divisional Court, including judicial review and to the House of Lords and Privy Council. Members appear in the higher courts in both defence and prosecution work. They were a 'preferred' set for the CPS in London and prosecute for the DSS, DTI and HM Customs & Excise.

Set No. 49

FURNIVAL CHAMBERS (Andrew Mitchell QC)

32 Furnival Street, London, EC4A 1JQ
Tel: (020) 7405 3232 **Fax:** (020) 7405 3322 **DX:** 72
Email: clerks@furnivallaw.co.uk **Website:** www.furnivallaw.co.uk

Head of Chambers:	Andrew Mitchell QC
Clerks:	John Gutteridge, Joanne Thomas
Tenants:	47

Members:

Andrew Mitchell QC (1976) (QC-1998)
Oliver Blunt QC (1974) (QC-1994)
Stephen Leslie QC (1971) (QC-1993)
Sally O'Neill QC (1976) (QC-1997)
Michel G.A. Massih QC (1979) (QC-1999)
Hugh Griffiths (1972)
Christopher Baur (1972)
Gino Connor (1974)
Lisa Matthews (1974)
Michael Latham (1975)
Graham Henson (1976)
Stephen Holt (1978)
Kim Hollis (1979)
Vincent Coughlin (1980)
Francis Sheridan (1980)
Paul Mytton (1982)
Richard Whittam (1983)
Nicola Merrick (1983)
Jon Swain (1983)
Sherrie Caddle (1983)
Roy Headlam (1983)
John Carmichael (1984)
Kennedy Talbot (1984)
Carolyn Blore (1985)
Charles Sherrard (1986)
Philip Romans (1982)
Kathryn Hirst (1986)
Barry Gregory (1987)
Patricia Lees (1988)
Nicolas Gerasimidis (1988)
Stephen Earnshaw (1990)
Tim Forster (1990)
Tanya Woolls (1991)
Sandip Patel (1991)
Andrew Henley (1992)
Lefi Panayioti (1992)
Mark Giuliani (1993)
Fiona Henderson (1993)
Ivan Pearce (1994)
Gerard McEvilly (1994)
Julian Winship (1995)
Giles Cockings (1996)
Christopher Convey (1994)
Mark Summers (1996)
Laban Leake (1996)
Fer Chinner (1998)
Fiona Jackson (1998)
Linda Candler (1977) *
Elizabeth Coughlin (1989) *
Kate Mulkerrins (1998) *
Simon Reevell (1990) *

* Door Tenants

The Chambers: A set of specialist criminal practitioners, housed in fully computerised modern offices with dedicated conference facilities and a comprehensively equipped library.

Work Undertaken:

Criminal Law Service: Since its formation in 1985, Furnival Chambers has provided a comprehensive and specialist criminal law service to solicitors and lay clients. Chambers, with leading and junior counsel

Continued overleaf

F

of considerable experience and ability, are experienced in dealing with cases of a more serious and complicated nature. The work of chambers ranges from the most involved commercial fraud to the simplest road traffic mat/ter. Expertise is therefore available in all areas of criminal law. The set specialises in cases of white collar fraud (members of chambers have advised and acted in cases such as Guinness, Blue Arrow and BCCI), drugs related offences, cases of a sexual nature including rape and child abuse and crimes of violence including murder and terrorism.

Asset Forfeiture and Money Laundering: Furnival Chambers has a specialist team which deals with confiscation, asset forfeiture and money laundering. Members of the team have appeared in the vast majority of the leading cases in the High Court and Court of Appeal.

Extradition: Members of the team specialise in all aspects of jurisdiction, procedure and practice.

Languages: Arabic, French, German, Hindi, Russian, Spanish.

Recruitment & Training: Furnival Chambers take four 12 month pupillages, terminable at the end of the first six months by either Chambers or the pupil. Selection is made from Pupillage Applications Clearing House (PACH) applications by two-stage interviews. Financial assistance is available for the first six months, and a modest interest free loan may be arranged for the second six months. Contact chambers for further detail.

Set No. 50

ONE GARDEN COURT (Eleanor Platt QC and Alison Ball QC)

One Garden Court, Temple, London, EC4Y 9BJ
Tel: (020) 7797 7900 **Fax:** (020) 7797 7929 **DX:** 1034 (Ch.Ln.)
Other Chambers: Exeter Annexe **Tel:** (01392) 209032 **DX:** 8302 Exeter
Email: clerks@onegardencourt.co.uk **Website:** www.onegardencourt.co.uk

Head of Chambers	Eleanor Platt QC and Alison Ball QC
Sen. Clerk:	Howard Rayner
Chief Executive:	Claire Wilford-Smith
Other Clerks:	Chris Ferrison and junior staff.
Fees Clerk:	Dennis Davies
Tenants:	45

Members:

Eleanor F. Platt QC (1960) (QC-1982)
Alison Ball QC (1972) (QC-1995)
Ian Peddie QC (1971) (QC-1992)
Jane Crowley QC (1976) (QC-1998) *
Ellen B. Solomons (1964)
Caroline Willbourne (1970)
Bruce Coleman (1972)
Peter Nathan (1973)
Suzanne H. Shenton (1973)
Elizabeth Szwed (1974)
Peter Horrocks (1977)
Martin O'Dwyer (1978)
Ann Marie Wicherek (1978)
Richard Scarratt (1979)
Judith Rowe (1979)
Kay Halkyard (1980)
Janet Bazley (1980)
Susan Shackleford (1980)
Kay Firth-Butterfield (1980)
Susannah Walker (1985)
Paul Rippon (1985)
Caroline Hely Hutchinson (1983)
Stephen Cobb (1985)
John Stocker (1985)
Charles Geekie (1985)
Gary Crawley (1988)
Gillian Cleave (1988)
Sarah Morgan (1988)
Alan Inglis (1989)
Andrew Bagchi (1989)
Michael Liebrecht (1989)
David Burles (1984)
Catherine Jenkins (1990)
Ariff Rozhan (1990)
Ian Robbins (1991)
Doushka Krish (1991)
Andrew Norton (1992)
Emma Hudson (1995)
Gillian C. Downham (1993)
Susan Budaly (1994)
Sally Stone (1994)
Alexander Chandler (1995)
Nicola Fox (1996)
Sassa-Ann Amaouche (1996)
Hilary J Forshaw (1998)

* Practices mainly from 30 Park Place, Cardiff

The Chambers: One Garden Court is the largest chambers where all members specialise in family law. Work: ancillary relief, local authorities, human rights, child abduction, care and adoption, mediation and ADR service.

G

Set No. 51

TWO GARDEN COURT (I. Macdonald QC & O.Davies QC)

2 Garden Court, Temple, London, EC4Y 9BL
Tel: (020) 7353 1633 **Fax:** (020) 7353 4621 **DX:** 34 (Ch.Ln.)
Email: barristers@2gardenct.law.co.uk **Website:** www.2gardenct.law.co.uk

Heads of Chambers:	I. Macdonald QC
	O. Davies QC
Senior Clerk:	Colin Cook
Tenants:	62

A general common law set specialising in criminal defence work, family and child care law, housing, immigration and judicial review.

No. 2

GOLDSMITH BUILDING (Christopher Llewellyn-Jones QC)

Goldsmith Building, Temple, London, EC4Y 7BL **Tel:** (020) 7353 7881
Fax: (020) 7353 5319 **DX:** 435 **Email:** clerks@goldsmith-building.law.co.uk
Website: www.goldsmith-building.law.co.uk

Head of Chambers	Christopher Llewellyn-Jones QC
Senior Clerk:	Danny O'Brien
Chambers Director:	Nigel Bamping
Tenants:	33

Members:

Christopher Llewellyn-Jones QC (1965) (QC-1990)
Michael Maguire QC (1949) (QC-1967)
Eric Somerset Jones QC (1952) (QC-1978)
Merfyn Hughes QC (1971) (QC-1994)
Michael Farmer QC (1972) (QC-1995)
Robin Hay (1964)
Harry Martineau (1966)
Martin Hall-Smith (1972)
Christopher Morris-Coole (1974)
John Gallagher (1974)
John Friel (1974)
Charles Calvert (1975)
Robert Leonard (1976)
Patrick Routley (1979)
Wendy Parker (1978)
Anthony Higgins (1978)
Barry Coulter (1985)
Mark Maitland-Jones (1986)
Julie Browne (1989)
Deborah Hay (1991)
Claire Newton (1992)
Linda Knowles (1993)
Gerard O'Connor (1993)
Daniel Lawson (1994)
Sadie Wright (1994)
Margaret Bloom (1994)
Clive Rawlings (1994)
Thomas Roe (1993)
Jerome Mayhew (1995)
Angela Fane (1992)
Fiona Scolding (1996)
David Lewis (1997)
Christopher Camp (1996)

The Chambers: Goldsmith Building is an established set of chambers which is able to provide individuals or teams of counsel to undertake a wide variety of litigation, arbitration and advisory work. The traditional strength of chambers has been their high standard of advocacy. Chambers' work is centred on London and the South Eastern Circuit, with strong senior connections on the Wales, Chester and Northern Circuits. They provide an efficient, flexible and comprehensive legal service with established specialist practice groups.

Work Undertaken: Chambers have nine practice groups, namely, personal injury; clinical negligence; professional negligence; crime; family; business law; landlord and tenant; public and administrative law; and employment. These groups form the core of chambers' infrastructure. The groups meet on a regular basis and continuing education is one of their objectives. In addition to the practice groups chambers also have specialists in the areas of environmental law, insolvency, and commercial fraud.

Other Information: Goldsmith Building has developed a programme to provide seminars on a range of legal topics, and as authorised providers of continuing education by the Law Society and the Institute of Legal Executives, all seminars carry a CPD rating. Chambers publish a range of newsletters, which contain news and information about chambers and comments on current developments in the law.
Chambers have an experienced clerking team and the clerks are always ready to advise on suitable counsel and fee levels along with liaising with courts on the listing of cases. Members of chambers and the clerks are aware of the needs of clients and strive to give the highest quality of service. A chambers charter has been adopted which details the level of service you can expect when you instruct a member of chambers or deal with the clerks. More specific information, fee levels, chambers brochure and other chambers publications are available from the recently appointed Chambers Director, Nigel Bamping, formerly a partner in a city law firm.

No. 3

GOUGH SQUARE CHAMBERS (Fred Philpott)

6-7 Gough Square, London, EC4A 3DE **Tel:** (020) 7353 0924
Fax: (020) 7353 2221 **DX:** 476 Link: Bob Weekes
Email: gsc@goughsq.co.uk **Website:** www.goughsq.co.uk

Head of Chambers:	Fred Philpott
Senior Clerk:	Bob Weekes
Chambers Administrator:	Elizabeth Owen-Ward
Tenants:	13

G

Members:

Fred Philpott (1974)
Peter Sayer (1975)
Claire Andrews (1979)
William Hibbert (1979)
Barry Stancombe (1983)
Jonathan Goulding (1984)
Stephen Neville (1986)
Julia Smith (1988)
Julian Gun Cuninghame (1989)
Anthony Vines (1993)
Frederica Cogswell (1995)
Iain MacDonald (1996)
Amanda Hulme (1997)

The Chambers: Gough Square Chambers is a commercial and common law set with a particular specialisation in consumer law. Chambers aims to provide an efficient, friendly and flexible service at competitive rates.Outside normal working hours, the Senior Clerk can be contacted on 07860 219162.

Continued overleaf

Work Undertaken:

Consumer Law: Consumer credit (agreements, licensing and advertising); trade descriptions and trademarks; food safety; pricing; weights and measures; consumer contracts; mortgages; shops; timeshare; product safety. Chambers are instructed in this specialist area by in-house lawyers and solicitors acting for banks; building societies and other lenders; supermarkets; retailers of electrical, white and brown goods; food retailers and other manufacturers; and distributors of a wide range of products.
Business and Commercial Law: Banking; secured lending; financial services; company and partnership; insolvency; employment; sale and supply contracts; professional negligence; criminal and civil fraud.
Property: Mortgages, landlord and tenant, land.

Publications: Chambers publish a free quarterly *Trading Law Bulletin* which charts the recent developments in this area of law. Please contact the Senior Clerk to join their mailing list to receive this.

Set No. 54

9 GOUGH SQUARE (Jeremy Roberts QC)

9 Gough Square, London, EC4A 3DE
Tel: (020) 7832 0500 **Fax:** (020) 7353 1344 **DX:** 439
Email: clerks@9goughsq.co.uk **Website:** www.9goughsq.co.uk

Head of Chambers:	Jeremy Roberts QC
Chief Executive:	Joanna Poulton MBA LLB
Tenants:	43

Members:

Jeremy Roberts QC (1965) (QC-1982) +
Michael Brent QC (1961) (QC-1983) +
Gary Burrell QC (1977) (QC-1996) +
John Foy QC (1969) (QC-1998) +
John Reddihough (1969) +
Andrew Baillie (1970) +
David Gerrey (1975) +
Michael Joyce (1976)
Trevor Davies (1978)
Frederick Ferguson (1978)
Grahame Aldous (1979) +
Duncan Macleod (1980)
Christopher Wilson (1980)
Graham Robinson (1981)
Nicolas Hillier (1982)
Roger Hiorns (1983)
Simon Carr (1984)
Gaurang Naik (1985)
Andrew Ritchie (1985)
David Fisher (1985)
Vincent Williams (1985)
Jacob Levy (1986)
Jonathan Loades (1986)
Alexander Verdan (1987)
Edwin Buckett (1988)
Andrew Wheeler (1988)
Sally-Ann Hales (1988)
Rosina Cottage (1988)
Leslie Keegan (1989)
Stephen Glynn (1990)
Jane Sinclair (1990)
Philip Jones (1990)
Clare Padley (1991)
John Tughan (1991)
Jeremy Crowther (1991)
Aileen Downey (1991)
Laura Begley (1993)
Louise Neilson (1994)
Christopher Stephenson (1994)
Rajeev Shetty (1996)
Tara Vindis (1996)
Tom Little (1997)
Perrin Gibbons (1998)

\+ Recorder

The Chambers: A well-established common law set specialising in personal injury; clinical negligence; professional negligence; serious fraud, crime and family. Chambers pride themselves on their friendly yet commercial approach which they believe enhances their ability to provide realistic advice to their clients. Focused around specialist teams, Chambers draw upon their considerable depth of knowledge and expertise through regular team meetings. Facilities are modern and up-to-date including disabled facilities, large dedicated conference rooms and full computerisation. They are professionally managed by a qualified Chief Executive who is happy to discuss any aspect of their service and in particular to recommend suitable counsel. A brochure is available on request.

Work Undertaken:

Personal Injury: Representing either claimants or defendants, chambers can offer experts on complex multi-party actions; industrial disease; RSI; deafness; lifting; marine accidents; PTSD; RTA; accidents at work, etc. Special payment terms are negotiable for union or insurance-backed claims. All members of chambers have agreed to accept conditional fee work and where appropriate single agreements covering individual firms can be negotiated.
Clinical Negligence: Chambers can offer experts who are sensitive to the issues in these cases, while remaining tenacious advocates and negotiators. Areas of experience, for both claimants and defendants, includes brain injuries; birth defects; failed sterilisations; surgical and non-surgical maltreatment.
Professional Negligence: Members of chambers' professional negligence team regularly advise on, and appear in, cases involving all aspects of professional negligence, but particularly actions involving solicitors, accountants, insurance brokers, surveyors etc.
Serious Fraud: Chambers have some of the country's leading fraud practitioners. Ten members of chambers regularly prosecute for the SFO and for CPS HQ but have also defended some of the most complex fraud cases, such as Blue Arrow and Nissan. Chambers can provide experts on advance fee frauds, city frauds, pension frauds, mortgage frauds, etc.

G

General Crime: The crime team has established a reputation for both prosecuting and defending general crime on the M & O Circuit, particularly at Northampton, Luton, St Albans, Aylesbury, Birmingham Crown Courts. In addition members of chambers regularly appear in the major London Crown Courts.
Family: Chambers' specialist family team undertake a full range of family law work but is particularly known for its experience in care proceedings, adoption, residence & contact applications and ancillary relief.

No. 5 **1 GRAY'S INN SQUARE** (The Baroness Scotland of Asthal QC)
1 Gray's Inn Square, Gray's Inn, London, WC1R 5AG **Tel:** (020) 7405 3000 **Fax:** (020) 7405 9942 **DX:** LDE 238 **Email:** onegrays.demon.co.uk

No. 6

2 GRAY'S INN SQUARE CHAMBERS (Giles Eyre)

2 Gray's Inn Square, London, WC1R 5AA
Tel: (020) 7440 8450 **Fax:** (020) 7440 8452 **DX:** 43 London Chancery Lane
Email: clerks@2gis.co.uk **Website:** www.2gis.co.uk

Head of Chambers:	Giles Eyre
Chambers Director:	Martin Poulter
First Junior Clerk:	Sue Reding
Second Junior Clerk:	Michael Goodridge
Junior Clerk:	Joseph Bernard
Tenants:	36

Members:

Giles Eyre (1974)
Peter Leighton (1966)
Keith Knight (1969)
Edward Cross (1975)
Richard Robinson (1977)
Peter Fortune (1978)
Christopher McConnell (1979)
David Hughes (1980)
Nergis-Anne Matthew (1981) +
Milan Dulovic (1982)
Jane Rayson (1982)
Jacqueline Marks (1984)
John Church (1984)
Gabrielle Jan Posner (1984)
Fawzia King (1985)
Francis Collaco Moraes (1985)
Surinder Bhakar (1986)
Sorrel Dixon (1987)
Susan Baldock (1988)
Adrian Roberts (1988)
Mark Whalan (1988)
Terence Woods (1989)
Myles Watkins (1990) +
Joanne Brown (1990)
Christopher Rice (1991)
Chima Umezuruike (1991)
James Arney (1992)
Robert Duddridge (1992)
Christopher Wagstaffe (1992)
Henry Drayton (1993)
Daniel Barnett (1993)
Judith Parr (1994) (1985 – New Zealand)
Paul Hepher (1994)
Tony Badenoch (1996)
Stuart McKechnie (1997)
Piers Martin (1997)

+ Associate Member

The Chambers: The chambers provide a responsive, courteous and efficient service in all areas of common law practice. Through the use of modern administrative systems, a management committee and a spirit of teamwork, chambers are able to meet the varied requirements of solicitors. Specialisation is achieved through the use of practice groups, which enable members to pool their specialist knowledge and expertise and to offer a full and professional service to clients. Chambers, as part of the service it provides holds a minimum of six two hour Law Society and ILEX accredited seminars every year.Members and staff are contactable via e-mail. Written work can also be provided on disk in a variety of formats.Comprehensive details of chambers' fee structures are available from the Senior Clerk.

Work Undertaken:

Family: Matters covered encompass child law including public and private Children Act proceedings, care work (including representing guardians ad litem), adoption, wardship and child abduction, matrimonial and related proceedings (including property and financial disputes and disputes between co-habitees).
Criminal: Members practise in all areas of crime, receiving instructions on behalf of the defence. Members have particular experience in areas of fraud, child abuse, drug trafficking, sexual offence, public order licensing, actions against the police.
Personal Injury and Clinical Negligence: Members act for individuals, trade unions and insurance company clients, for both plaintiff and defendant, in claims arising from accidents at work, clinical negligence, road traffic accidents, occupiers' liability and defective products. Conditional Fee Agreements are undertaken.
Employment: Chambers undertakes advisory and advocacy work in Employment Tribunal, EAT, High Court and internal disciplinary hearings. Specific areas of expertise are unfair dismissal, redundancy, discrimination and the provision of advice to employers prior to the dismissal of employees and directors.
Property: Chambers offers representation and advice on all property matters including public and private sector housing, business tenancies and all aspects of landlord and tenant law, trusts, claims to possession of land, easement and mortgage disputes, conveyancing, and disputes involving joint owners and co-habitees.
Contract and Commercial: Areas of law covered include contract and tort, partnership disputes, professional negligence, sale of goods, agency, bills of exchange, banking, insolvency, building and engineering contracts, consumer credit, insurance, guarantee and suretyship and disqualification of directors.

Continued overleaf

G

Publications: Peter Fortune is a contributor to Blackstone's Criminal Practice (Road Traffic and Evidence). Gabrielle Jan Posner is author of *The Teenager's Guide to The Law* (Cavendish 1995). Jane Rayson is co-author of *How to make Applications in the Family Proceedings Court* and *Blackstone's Guide to the Family Law Act 1996*. Jane Rayson and Gabrielle Jan Posner are contributors to the *Sweet & Maxwell Practical Research Papers* and are respectively the authors of *Defending Divorce* and *The Welfare Officer*. Daniel Barnett is the author of *Avoiding Unfair Dismissal Claims, a guide for employers and advisors on how to dismiss employees* (John Wiley 1999).

Languages: French, Serbo-Croat, Malay and Punjabi.

Recruitment & Training: Pupillage applications through PACH. Mini-pupillages are available.

Set No. 57

2-3 GRAY'S INN SQUARE (Anthony Scrivener QC)

2-3 Gray's Inn Square, Gray's Inn, London, WC1R 5JH
Tel: (020) 7242 4986 **Fax:** (020) 7405 1166 **DX:** 316 (Ch.Ln.)
Email: chambers@2-3graysinnsquare.co.uk **Website:** www.2-3graysinnsquare.co.uk

Head of Chambers:	Anthony Scrivener QC
Chambers Director:	Douglas Lewis CBE
Senior Clerk:	Martin Hart
Tenants:	41

Members:

Anthony Scrivener QC (1958) (QC-1975)
Malcolm Spence QC (1958) (QC-1979)
Patrick Ground QC (1960) (QC-1981)
Harry Wolton QC (1969) (QC-1982)
Christopher Cochrane QC (1965) (QC-1988)
Anthony Porten QC (1969) (QC-1988)
Anthony Dinkin QC (1968) (QC-1991)
Vernon Pugh QC (1969) (QC-1986)
(Nicholas) Mark Lowe QC (1972) (QC-1996)
John Haines (1967)
Richard Rundell (1971)
Geoffrey Stephenson (1971)
David Lamming (1972)
Adrian Trevelyan Thomas (1974)
Nicholas Nardecchia (1974)
Tobias Davey (1977)
Graham Stoker (1977)
Ian Albutt (1981)
Steven Gasztowicz (1981)
Mary Cook (1982)
Morag Ellis (1984)
James Findlay (1984)
Gerard Forlin (1984)
Katie Astaniotis (1985)
Michael Bedford (1985)
Philip Kolvin (1985)
Simon Bird (1987)
Ranjit Bhose (1989)
Jonathan Clay (1990)
Celina Colquhoun (1990)
Gillian Carrington (1990)
Robin Green (1992)
Harriet Murray (1992)
Peter Miller (1993)
Philip Coppel (1994)
Thomas Cosgrove (1994)
Richard Ground (1994)
David Lintott (1995)
Jonathon Easton (1995)
Wayne Beglan (1995)
Rory Clarke (1996)

The Chambers: Established in the late 19th Century, 2-3 Gray's Inn Square is recognised as one of the leading Local Government sets with highly-rated expertise in nine specialist areas. Former members of chambers include Sir Edward Marshall Hall KC, Lord Birkett, Lord Chief Justice Widgery, Lord Bridge of Harwich, Mr Justice Hidden, and Mr Justice Penry-Davey. Current members of chambers include Anthony Scrivener QC, a former Chairman of the Bar, and Malcolm Spence QC, the erstwhile Chairman of the Planning and Environment Bar Association. Over the last 40 years, and with increasing size, chambers have widened their original common law base to develop substantial practices in administrative law, local government law and town and country planning law. They have, however, retained a strong common law practice, covering both general and large commercial disputes, and continue to enjoy a solid criminal practice.

Work Undertaken: First-class representation is provided in all the principal areas of work undertaken by chambers, and details of the specialities of each member are available on request from the senior clerk. Counsel are available at any level of experience required. The junior tenants are available at short notice for all Magistrates' Court, County Court and tribunal hearings, as well as for any procedural applications. Members of chambers will work in any part of England, Wales, Scotland (planning matters only) and Ireland. Chambers' administration has been upgraded to meet the demands of a modern business environment.

Town and Country planning, Administrative and Local Government Law: Including judicial review; housing law; public and local government finance; compulsory purchase; rating; highways; environmental law.
Common law: Including personal injuries; professional negligence, including medical, accountants and solicitors; employment law, including industrial tribunal work.
Consumer law: Including sale of goods; trade descriptions; trading law; food safety; data protection.
Criminal law: Including white collar crime; serious fraud; capital cases.
Property law: Including landlord and tenant; mortgages; housing associations.

International: Various members also practice or are admitted in other jurisdictions, including Hong Kong, Singapore, Malaysia, Jamaica, Trinidad, the Cayman Islands, the British Virgin Islands and certain Australian jurisdictions.

Languages: French, German, Greek and Italian.

Recruitment & Training: Pupils are received each year; pupillage funds are available.

G

Set No.
58

3 GRAY'S INN SQUARE (Rock Tansey QC)

3 Gray's Inn Square, Gray's Inn, London, WC1R 5AH
Tel: (020) 7520 5600 **Fax:** (020) 7520 5607 **DX:** 1043 (Ch.Ln.)
Email: clerks@3gis.co.uk **Website:** www.3gis.co.uk

Head of Chambers:	Rock Tansey QC
Senior Clerk:	Guy Williams
Clerks:	Marc King, Stephen Lucas
Tenants:	41

Members:

Rock Tansey QC (1966) (QC-1990)
John Perry QC (1975) (QC-1989)
Steven Kay QC (1977) (QC-1997)
George Carter-Stephenson QC (1975) (QC-1998)
William Taylor QC (Scotland QC 1986) (1990) (QC-1998)
David Hooper (1971)
Colin Allan (1971)
David Farrington (1972)
Ronald Jaffa (1974)
Brendan Keany (1974)
Jonathan Mitchell (1974)
Philip Statman (1975)
Rudi Fortson (1976)
Diana Ellis (1978)
Roger Offenbach (1978)
Chester Beyts (1978)
Charles Bott (1979)
Paul Keleher (1980)
Paul Mendelle (1981)
Penelope Barrett (1982)
Jeremy Dein (1982)
Simon Pentol (1982)
Bill Maley (1982)
Leroy Redhead (1982)
John Cooper (1983)
Colin Wells (1987)
Paul Hynes (1987)
Alison Levitt (1988)
Adrian Kayne (1989)
Joseph Stone (1989)
Helen Valley (1990)
Arlette Piercy (1990)
Emma Akuwudike (1992)
Sylvia de Bertodano (1993)
Harry Potter (1993)
Richard Furlong (1994)
Tyrone Smith (1994)
Nicola Howard (1995)
Sebastian Gardiner (1997)
Lindsey Rose (1996)
Gillian Higgins (1997)

The Chambers: Established in 1975, 3 Gray's Inn Square is a specialist Criminal Defence Set which aims to ensure that everyone has equal access to the best representation. Chambers has earned a reputation as a leader in its field by maintaining the highest standards of professionalism, integrity, commitment and both accessibility and approachability.
Services for the set include: conference rooms, video conferences, e-mail, disks accepted, voice mail for all members of chambers. A 24-hour clerking service for emergencies and overnight cases is provided. Chambers is fully computerised as is our Crown Court list checking system.
In December 1999, the set became the first chambers to be awarded the Bar Mark, the Bar Council's kite mark for quality assurance.

Work Undertaken: First-class representation is provided at every level of seniority by practitioners who appear regularly in 'high-profile cases' and who offer experience in the conduct of all categories of criminal case including European human rights, international criminal tribunal, (international) terrorism and war crimes, murder, serious fraud, organised crime, international drugs trafficking/allied money laundering and offences of extreme/sexual violence.
Within this framework there is a positive commitment to legally-aided clients and, where appropriate, pro-bono work is undertaken.Particular expertise is provided in all aspects of appellate work, including Judicial Review and Privy Council. Further, there is experience in the conduct of civil cases, especially actions against the Police and allied issues and mental health review tribunals.
Chambers presents lectures to solicitors and practitioners generally, concerning the effect of significant changes in criminal legislation. Some members also lecture nationally and internationally to and on behalf of legal/human rights organisations on drug trafficking and international war crimes.

Publications: Rudi Fortson: *Law on the Misuse of Drugs*.Several members are regular contributors to legal publications, including *The Solicitors Journal* and *The Lawyer*.

International: Rock Tansey QC & Steven Kay QC have founded the European Criminal Bar Association in order to advance issues of mutual concern for European Criminal Defence Lawyers. Rock Tansey QC is the First Chairman of the ECBA and organised its inaugural conference at the European Commission for Human Rights. Steven Kay QC, Defence Counsel in the first International Criminal Tribunal for the former Yugoslavia undertakes European Human Rights cases. John Perry QC also practises in Bermuda and is a member of the West Indian Bar.

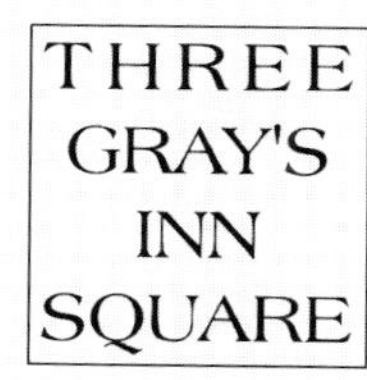

Set No.
59

4-5 GRAY'S INN SQUARE (Elizabeth Appleby QC & Duncan Ouseley QC)

4-5 Gray's Inn Square, Gray's Inn, London, WC1R 5JP
Tel: (020) 7404 5252 **Fax:** (020) 7242 7803 **DX:** 1029
Email: chambers@4-5graysinnsquare.co.uk **Website:** www.4-5graysinnsquare.co.uk

Heads of Chambers:	Elizabeth Appleby QC, Duncan Ouseley QC
Head Clerk:	Michael Kaplan
Clerks:	Mark Regan, Daniel Perry
Chambers Administrator:	Barbara Morris
Tenants:	51

Members:

Elizabeth Appleby QC (1965) (QC-1979)
Duncan Ouseley QC (1973) (QC-1992)
George Carman QC (1953) (QC-1971)
Michael Beloff QC (1967) (QC-1981)
William Wade QC (1946) (QC-1968)
Gary Flather QC (1962) (QC-1984)
David Mole QC (1970) (QC-1990)
Brian Ash QC (1975) (QC-1990)
Stuart Isaacs QC (1975) (QC-1991)
W. Robert Griffiths QC (1974) (QC-1993)
John Steel QC (1978) (QC-1993)
Lady Hazel Fox QC (1950) (QC-1993)
Gregory Stone QC (1976) (QC-1994)
Richard Spearman QC (1977) (QC-1996)
Timothy Straker QC (1977) (QC-1996)
Richard McManus QC (1982) (QC-1999)
Hodge M. Malek QC (1983) (QC-1999)
John Hobson QC (1980) (QC-2000)
Sam Aaron (1986) SC(SA)
Robin Campbell (1969)
Nicholas Huskinson (1971)
Julian Chichester (1977)
Timothy Corner (1981)
Peter M. Village (1983)
Tim Kerr (1983)
Peter Havey (1984)
Jane Oldham (1985)
Paul Stinchcombe MP (1985)
Richard Humphreys (1986)
Clive Lewis (1987)
James Ramsden (1987)
Thomas Hill (1988)
Geraldine Clark (1988)
Sarah Moore (1990)
Paul Brown (1991)
Andrew Tabachnik (1991)
Andrew Fraser-Urquhart (1993)
Ami Barav (1993)
Philip Coppel (1994)
Karen Steyn (1995)
Marie Demetriou (1995)
Sarah-Jane Davies (1996)
Jonathan Moffett (1996)
Andrew Sharland (1996)
James Strachan (1996)
Martin Chamberlain (1997)
Robert Palmer (1998)
Deok-Joo Rhee (1998)
Clare Lockhart (1999)
Jonathan Anburn (1999)
Paul Greatorex (1999)

The Chambers: 4-5 Gray's Inn Square is regarded as one of the leading chambers in London, and its pre-eminence has been recognised for many years in various independent legal publications. Members of chambers possess expertise and experience of the highest quality in the fields of public law and judicial review, planning and environmental law, commercial law, European Union law, human rights, employment law and sports law. The intersection of these specialisations within chambers allows collaboration between members on complex litigation.Many members hold part-time judicial appointments in England, as well as overseas. The joint Head of Chambers Elizabeth Appleby QC was the first woman to head a leading set of chambers. Michael Beloff QC is now also President of Trinity College, Oxford. Several of the present juniors are on the Treasury Panels of Counsel instructed on behalf of the Crown.The chambers have been the first set to appoint an academic panel as a research and advisory facility. Its members are Professor Craig (administrative), Professor M. Grant (local government and planning), Professor P. Davies (Employment), Professor J. Usher (EU), Professor E. Barendt (media, human rights, welfare), Professor A. Arnull (Birmingham), Professor David Harris (Nottingham – international law and human rights).

Former Members: The Right Honourable Lord Justice Schiemann; The Honourable Mr Justice Keene; The Honourable Mr Justice Collins; The Honourable Mr Justice Moses; The Honourable Mr Justice Sullivan; Richard Yorke QC (1956)(QC-1971); Sir Douglas Frank QC, former President of the Lands Tribunal; His Honour Judge Marder QC, President of the Lands Tribunal; His Honour Judge Barratt QC, Victor Wellings QC, former President of the Lands Tribunal.

Door Tenants: Professor G.H. Treitel QC; Professor E.P. Ellinger; Lord Borrie QC; Sir John Freeland QC (1952)(QC-1987); Marc Dassesse (Brussels Bar); Professor Sir D.G.T. Williams; Patrick Patelin (Juriste d'Enterprise, Paris); Edmund McGovern (also in Brussels); Narinder Hargun (Bermuda); Brian Harris QC; Jeremy Gauntlett (SC) (South Africa); John Sacker QC (NSW); Mansoor Jamal Malik (Oman); Professor M.Grant (Cantab).

G

Work Undertaken:

Public Law/Judicial Review: Members of chambers have considerable experience in the fields of public law and judicial review. Members appear frequently in court on behalf of individual applicants and companies whose rights may be affected by the decisions of public bodies; and on behalf of local authorities, central government departments and other public bodies such as regulatory authorities. Chambers is specially placed to advise on all matters relating to the Human Rights Act 1998 which will inevitably impact on all areas of UK law.

Planning and Environmental Law: 4-5 Gray's Inn Square is one of the leading sets in both planning and environmental law, providing advice or advocacy to developers, government departments, local authorities and objectors in all aspects of these and related fields. Members of chambers regularly appear in public inquiries held under planning and related legislation, and in the High Court in statutory appeals and applications for judicial review.

Commercial Law: The core of the set's commercial work relates to domestic and international banking (including securities), insurance and reinsurance, and the sale of goods and international trade. A wide range of other contract-related work is also done. There is considerable experience in dealing with conflict of law problems and jurisdictional disputes, including under the Brussels Convention and its successors, and in financial regulation work which intersects with judicial review.

European Law: This is one of the leading sets in both European Union Law and the European Convention on Human Rights. Members of chambers have appeared in Luxembourg and in Strasbourg. Chambers is in pole position to advise clients on the implications of the Human Rights Act 1998.

Employment Law: The work includes commercial (restraint of trade; wrongful dismissal), European (transfer of undertakings; equal pay), collective (trade unions; industrial action) and individual (sex, race and disability discrimination; unfair dismissal)

Other Areas: Defamation, media law, sports law, breach of confidence, professional negligence.

Publications:

Books: Michael Beloff QC, Tim Kerr and Marie Demetriou, *Sports* (1999); Richard McManus QC, *Education and the Courts* (1998); Hodge Malek QC and Paul Matthews, Discovery (2nd ed., forthcoming 2000); Clive Lewis, *Judicial Remedies in Public Law* (2nd ed., forthcoming 2000); A. Nicol, G.Millar and Andrew Sharland, *Blackstone's Guide to Media Law and the Human Rights Act 1998* (forthcoming 2000); James Strachan and Other, Law of Privacy (forthcoming 2000).

Chapters and Articles: Michael Beloff QC, *What does it all mean? How to interpret the Human Rights Act* (Lasok Lecture 1998); Michael Beloff QC, 'Community Law in the UK and European Courts' in *European Community Law in the English Courts* (Andenas and Jacobs eds, 1998); Clive Lewis, 'Judicial Review and the Role of the English Court on European Community Disputes' in *European Community Law in the English Courts*, (Andenas and Jacobs eds. 1998); Clive Lewis, 'Damages and the Right to an Effective Remedy for Breach of European Community Law' in *The Golden Metwand* and the *Crooked Cord: Essays in Honour of Sir William Wade QC* (1998); Geraldine Clark, 'Composite Policies: a Trap for Unwary Insurers', *Kluwer Insurance and Reinsurance Law Briefing*, 13 April 1999; Marie Demetriou and Others, 'Is There a Role for the 'Margin of Appreciation' in National Law After the Human Rights Act?' (1999) *EHRLR 15*; Michael Beloff QC and Other 'Leave it to the Lords' *Judicial Review* (Pt.III) 119; Michael Beloff QC and Sarah Jane Davies, *Halsbury's Laws* 4th edn., Time, (1999); Timothy Straker QC, *Halsbury's Laws*, Editor, Public Health and Environmental Protection (forthcoming 2000); Timothy Straker QC, John Hobson QC, Richard Humphreys, Sarah Jane Davies, Jonathan Moffett, Deok Joo Rhee, Karen Steyn, Robert Palmer, *Halsbury's Laws, Local Government* (forthcoming 2000).

International: Members of chambers have appeared at the Privy Council, the European Court of Justice and of Human Rights, international arbitration tribunals and other courts worldwide, including the Far East, the Carribean, Gibraltar, Belfast, Bermuda, Anguilla and Trinidad. One member is a former Judge of the Court of Appeal in Swaziland and a current Judge of the Court of Appeal in Lesotho. Another is a Judge of the Court of Appeal of Jersey and Guernsey.

No.
0 **6 GRAY'S INN SQUARE** (Michael Boardman)

6 Gray's Inn Square, Gray's Inn, London, WC1R 5AZ **Tel:** (020) 7242 1052 **Fax:** (020) 7405 4934 **DX:** 224
Email: 6greysinn@clara.co.uk

No.
1 **8 GRAY'S INN SQUARE** (Patrick C. Soares)

8 Gray's Inn Square, Gray's Inn, London, WC1R 5AZ
Tel: (020) 7242 3529 **Fax:** (020) 7404 0395 **DX:** 411 (Ch.Ln.)

Head of Chambers:	Patrick C. Soares
Senior Clerk:	Jane Fullbrook
Tenants:	8

G

Members:

Patrick C. Soares (1983) LLB, LLM, FTII
Barry McCutcheon (1975) BA, LLM, FTII
David J. Brownbill (1989) LLB
Patrick Way (1994)
Christopher Whitehouse (1997)
Emma J.M. Chamberlain (1998)
Ian Ferrier (1976) MA (Oxon)
Denzil Davies (1965)

The Chambers: 8 Gray's Inn Square is a leading set of tax chambers. The primary work of chambers is to advise on all aspects of taxation, with additional specialisations offered in respect of trusts, wills, company law, international estate and tax planning and related chancery matters. A major distinguishing feature of the set is that all members have previous professional or commercial experience before commencing practice at the Bar.

Work Undertaken: UK tax planning, international tax & estate planning, Chancery.

Continued overleaf

Publications: *The Property Law Bulletin; Trusts for Europe; VAT Planning for Property Transactions; Land and Tax Planning; Trusts and Tax Planning; Taxation of Overseas Trusts; Taxation of Land development; Tax Strategy for Conveyancing; McCutcheon on Inheritance Tax; Planning for Executive Share Schemes; Private Client Business; Journal of International Trust and Corporate Planning; British Tax Encylopedia; Conveyancer and Property Lawyer; Tolley's UK Taxation of Trusts; Value Added Tax – The British System Explained.*

Set No. 62

14 GRAY'S INN SQUARE (Joanna Dodson QC)

14 Gray's Inn Square, Gray's Inn, London, WC1R 5JP
Tel: (020) 7242 0858 **Fax:** (020) 7242 5434 **DX:** 399 (Ch.Ln.)
Email: clerks@14graysinnsquare.co.uk

Head of Chambers:	Joanna Dodson QC
Senior Clerk:	Geoffrey Carr BA
Tenants:	34

Members:

Joanna Dodson QC (1970) (QC-1993)
Louise S. Godfrey QC (1972) (QC-1991) *
Joanna Hall (1973)
Mhairi McNab (1974)
Barbara Slomnicka (1976)
David G P Turner (1976)
Sarah Forster (1976)
Gillian Brasse (1977)
Brenda Morris (1978)
Kate Hudson (1981)
Gillian Marks (1981)
Karen McLaughlin (1982)
Caroline Reid (1982)
Monica Ford (1984)
Mark Emanuel (1985)
Pamela Warner (1985)
Richard Buswell (1985)
Karoline Sutton (1986)
Michelle Corbett (1987)
Rebecca Brown (1989)
Patricia Roberts (1987)
Mark Jarman (1989)
Samantha King (1990)
Richard Alomo (1990)
Jonathan Tod (1990)
David Bedingfield (1991)
David Vavrecka (1992)
Jane De Zonie (1994)
Dominic Brazil (1995)
Samantha Whittam (1995)
Ronan O'Donovan (1995)
Michael Glaser (1998)

* Door Tenants

The Chambers: A family and civil set with particular expertise in children's cases and financial matters, with a strong general common law side. Members of chambers belong to the Family Law Bar Association. Chambers is both Barmark and ISO 9002 accredited.

Work Undertaken:
Main Areas of Work: Family and matrimonial, including wardship, adoption, care, children and ancillary relief; personal injury, including running-down accidents; employment and labour law; landlord and tenant; housing; licensing work; building and construction; and contract cases.
Additional Areas of Work: Civil liberties; crime; company; discrimination; ecclesiastical; judicial review; police cases; product liability; professional negligence; sale of goods; and welfare.

International: David Bedingfield is a member of the Georgia Bar.

Clientele: Individuals, companies, local authorities, guardians ad litem, the Official Solicitor.

Recruitment & Training: Tenancy applications should be sent to Joanna Dodson QC; pupillage applications to Jane De Zonie. Two first six- and one second six-months pupils are taken each year. Awards of £4,000 are offered for the first six months of pupillage and minimum earnings are guaranteed at that level for the second six. Mini-pupillages are available.

G

Set No.
63

GRAY'S INN TAX CHAMBERS (Milton Grundy)

Third Floor, Gray's Inn Chambers, Gray's Inn, London, WC1R 5JA
Tel: (020) 7242 2642 **Fax:** (020) 7831 9017 **DX:** 352 London Chancery Lane
Out of Hours number: 07956 144 042 **Email:** clerks@taxbar.com
Website: www.taxbar.com

Head of Chambers:	Milton Grundy
Senior Clerk:	Chris Broom
Tenants:	12

Members:

Milton Grundy (1954)
Michael Flesch QC (1963) (QC-1983)
David Goldberg QC (1971) (QC-1987)
David Goy QC (1973) (QC-1991)
John Walters QC (1977) (QC-1997)
Felicity Cullen (1985)
Philip Baker (1979)
Barrie Akin (1976)
Hugh McKay (1990)
Aparna Nathan (1994)
Conrad McDonnell (1994)
Nicola Shaw (1995)
Graham Wilson (1975) *
Abraham Swersky *

* Door Tenants

The Chambers: Gray's Inn Tax Chambers is a leading set of specialist tax practitioners. Its members deal with all aspects of United Kingdom revenue law and cover all areas of work dealt with by tax practitioners, from accumulation and maintenance settlements to zero-coupon bonds. They have established expertise in litigation before the Special Commissioners; General Commissioners; the VAT and Duties Tribunals; the Supreme Court; the House of Lords; the Privy Council; the European Court of Justice and the courts of certain colonies, Commonwealth and foreign jurisdictions. The chambers are fully computerised using Windows 98, Microsoft Word 2000, Microsoft Excel, Wordperfect 6.1, Microsoft Powerpoint and email. The chambers maintain a popular website, which offers a rapid reporting of tax cases. The address is www.taxbar.com.

Appointments and Memberships: All members of chambers belong to the Revenue Bar Association of which Michael Flesch is a former chairman and Hugh McKay is a former secretary. Milton Grundy is President of the International Tax Planning Association and a Fellow of the Chartered Institute of Taxation; he is the draftsman of the Trusts Law of the Cayman Islands and (with Philip Baker) of the IBC Act and the Trusts Act of Belize. John Walters QC and Barrie Akin are chartered accountants. Philip Baker is a visiting professor, and Aparna Nathan a visiting lecturer, at London University. Hugh McKay is on the Customs and Excise VAT Tribunal advocates list.

Work Undertaken: Members give advice to taxpayers who are in dispute with the Inland Revenue or Customs, and advise clients on the planning of their business and personal affairs. They advise on corporate tax planning, including acquisitions; mergers; takeovers and methods of financing; property transactions; international business; cross-border transactions; offshore and domestic trusts; estate planning; and all the direct and indirect taxes, including VAT. Work is accepted from (amongst others) local authorities, companies, charities and private clients. Direct Professional Access is accepted from members of the appropriate professional bodies.

Publications: Members have written, contributed to, or edited: *Whiteman on Income Tax; VAT and Property; British Tax Review; Asset Protection Trusts; Double Taxation Conventions and International Tax Law; Value Added Tax Encyclopedia; Offshore Business Centres; The Law of Partnership Taxation; Copinger and Skone James on Copyright; The Laws of the Internet; The International Trust and Estate Law Reports and International Law Reports*; and various articles on domestic and international tax developments.

International: Members of chambers advise clients from Hong Kong, Singapore, Australia, New Zealand, the USA and Mauritius. The chambers also advise the revenue departments of Commonwealth countries and ex-colonies on the interpretation and drafting of their statutes.

Languages: Chinese (Mandarin and some Cantonese), French, German, Hebrew, Hindi, Italian and Tamil.

Set No.
64

100E GREAT PORTLAND STREET

100E Great Portland Street, London, WIN 5PD **Tel:** (020) 7636 6323 **Fax:** (020) 7436 3544 **DX:** 94252 Marylebone

Set No.
65 **1 HARCOURT BUILDINGS** (Charles Gratwicke)

1 Harcourt Buildings, Temple, London, EC4Y 9DA **Tel:** (020) 7353 9421/0375 **Fax:** (020) 7353 4170 **DX:** 417 London/Chancery Lane
Email: Clerks@1harcourtbuildings.law.co.uk

Set No.
66 **2 HARCOURT BUILDINGS, Atkinson Bevan Chambers** (Nicholas Atkinson QC & John Bevan QC)

2 Harcourt Buildings, Temple, London, EC4Y 9DB **Tel:** (020) 7353 2112
Fax: (020) 7353 8339 **DX:** 489 Chancery Lane **Email:** clerks@2hb.co.uk
Website: www.2hb.co.uk

Heads of Chambers:	Nicholas Atkinson QC, John Bevan QC
Senior Clerk:	Michael Watts
Tenants:	33

Members:

Nigel Mylne QC (1963) (QC-1984)
John Bevan QC (1970) (QC-1997) MA (Cantab)
Nicholas Atkinson QC (1971) (QC-1991)
John Williams (1973) LLB
Stephen Smyth (1974)
Stephen Clayton (1973)
Nicholas Loraine-Smith (1977) BA (Oxon)
William Adlard (1978)
Philip Shorrock (1978) BA (Cantab)
Robin Leach (1979) MA (St Andrews)
Mark Gadsden (1980) BA (Oxon)
Aftab Jafferjee (1980) BA (Dunelm)
Timothy Probert-Wood (1983) LLB (Hull)
Rhyddian Willis (1984) LLB (Nottingham)
Ian Darling (1985) LLB (London)
Lucia Whittle-Martin (1985) BSc (London)
Patrick Gibbs (1986) BA (Oxon)
Jonathan Rees (1987) BA (Oxon)
Matthew Farmer (1987) BA (London)
Peter Clement (1988) LLM LLB (London)
Laura Cobbs (1989) LLB (Buckingham)
Stewart Hamblin (1990) BA (Leicester)
Toby Fitzgerald (1993) BSc (Bristol)
Thomas Wilkins (1993) BSc (Bristol)
James Dawes (1993) BSc (Dunelm)
Lisa Wilding (1993) MA (Cantab)
Peter Coombe (1994) BA (Oxon)
Sally Halkerston (1994) BA (Kingston)
Sally Thompson (1994) AGSM
Benedict Kelleher (1994) LLB MSc (Bristol)
William Emlyn Jones (1996) (Soton) LLB
Jennifer Knight (1996) LLB (Exeter)
Kevin Baumber (1998) LLB (Essex & Nijmegen) BCL (Oxon)
Marina Churchill (1989) * LLB (Buckingham)

* Door Tenants

The Chambers: With three QCs, one Senior Treasury Counsel and one Junior Treasury Counsel, Atkinson Bevan Chambers is a specialist criminal set practising predominantly on the South Eastern and Western Cicuits. The set has been continuously represented on the Treasury Counsel team since 1953.

Work Undertaken: Members of chambers both defend and prosecute the full spectrum of criminal cases, ranging from high profile and sensitive matters requiring specialist expertise such as terrorism, murder, corruption and serious fraud, to the more routine offences found everyday in the Magistrates' and Crown courts. Chambers also undertakes work in other practice areas including sports law, regulatory work, health and safety, food and drugs, trades descriptions, police and medical disciplinary tribunals, coroners' inquests, extradition, data protection, courts-martial and ecclesiastical matters.

Clientele: Chambers receives instructions from individual private and public clients, including government departments (SFO, CPS), local authorities, corporate bodies and sporting clients.

Recruitment & Training: Applications to Lisa Wilding or Sue Watt. Chambers is a member of PACH. Chambers takes four to five pupils completing six and twelve month pupillages at any one time. Discretionary funding is available.

H

No. 7

2 HARCOURT BUILDINGS (Roger Henderson QC)

2 Harcourt Buildings (Ground Floor), Temple, London, EC4Y 9DB
Tel: (020) 7583 9020 **Fax:** (020) 7583 2686 **DX:** LDE 1039
Email: clerks@harcourt.co.uk **Website:** www.harcourt.co.uk

Head of Chambers:	Roger Henderson QC
Senior Clerk:	John White
Tenants:	41

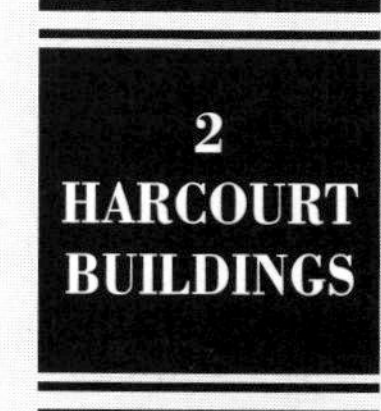

Members:

Roger Henderson QC (1964) (QC-1980) +
Piers Ashworth QC (1956) (QC-1973) +
Richard Mawrey QC (1964) (QC-1986) +
Adrian Brunner QC (1968) (QC-1994) +
Stephen Powles QC (1972) (QC-1995) +
Andrew Prynne QC (1975) (QC-1995)
Alan Dashwood (1969)
Adrian Cooper (1970) +
Bernard O'Sullivan (1971)
Gavin Gore-Andrews (1972)
Andrew Jordan (1974)
Jonathan Harvey (1974)
Kenneth Hamer (1975) +
Lawrence West (1979) +
Mark Piercy (1976)
Roger Eastman (1978)
Sara Staite (1979) +
Barbara Cameron (1979)
James Palmer (1983)
Charles Gibson (1984)
George Alliott (1981)
Terence Bergin (1985)
Conrad Griffiths (1986)
Jonathan Steinert (1986)
Benjamin Battcock (1987)
Marina Wheeler (1987)
Rhodri Williams (1987)
Andrew Davies (1988)
Wendy Outhwaite (1990)
Patrick Green (1990)
Charles Bourne (1991)
Prashant Popat (1992)
Oliver Campbell (1992)
Isabella Zornoza (1993)
Malcolm Sheehan (1993)
Felicia Fenston (1994)
Geraint Webb (1995)
Toby Riley-Smith (1995)
Julianna Mitchell (1994)
Andrew Kinnier (1996)
James Martin-Jenkins (1997)
Adrian Garner (1985) *
Lance Ashworth (1987) *
Frank Schoneveld (1992) *

+ Recorder *Door Tenant.

Work Undertaken: Commercial and common law, particularly product liability; personal injury; medical and other professional negligence; insurance; local government; public procurement; public law; judicial review; environmental law; health and safety; railways; telecommunications; information technology; intellectual property; education; food; sport; employment and discrimination; human rights: construction and engineering; consumer credit; financial services; EU law; competition; land; housing; landlord and tenant; and family and inheritance.

International: Members of chambers also practise at the above address in association with the English barristers of the firm of Stanbrook & Hooper, 2 Rue de Taciturne, B-1000 Brussels under the name Stanbrook and Henderson.

No. 8

2 HARCOURT BUILDINGS (Mr Gerard Ryan QC)

2 Harcourt Buildings, Temple, London, EC4Y 9DB
Tel: (020) 7353 8415 **Fax:** (020) 7353 7622 **DX:** 402 LDE
Email: clerks@2hb.law.co.uk

Head of Chambers:	Gerard Ryan QC
Senior Clerk:	Allen Collier
First Junior Clerk:	Paul Munday
Second Junior Clerk:	Andrew Briton
Tenants:	25

Members:

Gerard Ryan QC (1955) (QC-1981)
Sheila Cameron QC (1957) (QC-1983)
Robin Purchas QC (1968) (QC-1987)
Richard Phillips QC (1970) (QC-1990)
Charles George QC (1974) (QC-1992)
Clive Newberry QC (1978) (QC-1993)
Keith Lindblom QC (1980) (QC-1996)
Andrew Kelly QC (1978) (QC-2000)
Robert McCracken (1973)
Philip Petchey (1976)
Jonathan Milner (1977)
Timothy Comyn (1980)
Andrew Tait (1981)
Craig Howell Williams (1983)
Suzanne Ornsby (1986)
Meyric Lewis (1986)
Andrew Newcombe (1987)
Charles Mynors (1988)
Gregory Jones (1991)
Douglas Edwards (1992)
Euan Burrows (1995)
Joanna Clayton (1995)
James Pereira (1996)
Hereward Phillpot (1997)
Takis Tridimas *

*Professor of European Law, University of Southampton; Advocate, Bar of Athens, Greece.

The Chambers: A specialist chambers for more than half a century with particular expertise in planning, environmental, property, and administrative law. Disabled conference facilities are available by prior arrangement. Members accept Direct Professional Access from the approved professions. A chambers' brochure is available on request.
All members of chambers belong to the Planning and Environment Bar Association, of which Douglas Edwards is Secretary. Members of chambers also belong to the Administrative Law Bar Association, the Bar European Group, the Association for Regulated Procurement, the United Kingdom Environmental

Continued overleaf

H

Law Association, the Ecclesiastical Law Society, The Education Law Society and the Parliamentary Bar. Robin Purchas QC is a Deputy High Court Judge, two members of chambers are Recorders of the Crown Court and three are Diocesan Chancellors. Craig Howell Williams and Meyric Lewis are members of the Supplementary Panel of Junior Counsel to the Crown. Gerard Ryan QC chaired the Tribunal of Inquiry into the gas explosion at Loscoe, Derbyshire. Charles George QC conducted the Independent Inquiry into Planning Decisions in the London Borough of Brent. Robert McCracken was Chairman of the United Kingdom Environmental Law Association. Sheila Cameron QC is Vicar General of the Province of Canterbury and was a Parliamentary Boundary Commissioner for England. Richard Phillips QC is an assistant Parliamentary Boundary Commissioner for England.

Former Members: Roy Vandermeer QC, the Inspector at the Heathrow Terminal Five inquiry; Peter Boydell QC, former Leader of the Parliamentary Bar and first Chairman of what is now the Planning and Environment Bar Association; Michael Harrison QC, now Mr Justice Harrison; Michael Mann QC, later Lord Justice Mann; and Sir John Drinkwater QC.

Work Undertaken: Public law; planning; environmental (including regulatory offences); contaminated land; compulsory purchase; administrative; local government; public procurement; parliamentary; transport and works; energy; utilities; education; highways; licensing; housing; human rights (European Convention); and EU Law.

Additional Areas: Ecclesiastical law; landlord and tenant; the law of commons and that relating to easements; agricultural tenancies; rating; and restrictive covenants.

Publications: *Education Case Reports* (editor-in-chief), *Journal of Planning and Environment Law* (editorial board), *Journal of Architectural Conservation* (editorial board), *Planning Appeal Decisions* (joint editor), *Planning and Environmental Law Bulletin* (joint editor), *Yearbook of European Law* (co-editor), *The Company Lawyer* (editorial board) and *European Financial Services Law* (advisory board). Charles Mynors is the author of *Planning Applications and Appeals* (1987), *Planning Control and the Display of Advertisements* (1992) and *Listed Buildings and Conservation Areas* (1995). Takis Tridimas is the author of *The General Principles of EC Law* (1999), co-author of *Ellis and Tridimas, Public Law of the European Community: cases, materials and commentary* (1995), and a co-author of *Beatson and Tridimas, New Directions in European Public Law* (1998).

International: Chambers include members called to the Dublin, Northern Ireland and Greek Bars.

Set No. 69

HARCOURT CHAMBERS (June Rodgers)

2 Harcourt Buildings, Temple, London, EC4Y 9DB
Tel: (020) 7353 6961 **Fax:** (020) 7353 6968 **DX:** 373
Email: clerks@harcourtchambers.law.co.uk **Website:** www.harcourtchambers.law.co.uk

Head of Chambers:	June Rodgers
Senior Clerk:	Brian Wheeler
Tenants:	24

Members:

June Rodgers (1971) MA (Dublin), MA(Oxon), Chancellor Diocese of Gloucester
Roger Evans (1970) MA (Cantab)
Benedict Sefi (1972) BA (Oxon)
John Dixon (1975) MA (Oxon)
Gavyn Arthur (1975) MA (Oxon)
Stephen Barstow (1976) MA (Cantab)
Jonathan Baker (1978) MA (Cantab)
Alicia Collinson (1982) MA, MPhil (Oxon)
Christopher Frazer (1983) MA, LLM (Cantab)
Frances Judd (1984) BA (Cantab)
Edward Hess (1985) MA (Cantab)
Matthew Brett (1987) BA (Oxon)
Napier Miles (1989) BA (Oxon)
Piers Pressdee (1991) BA (Cantab)
Sara Granshaw (1991) BA (Oxon)
Sally Max (1991) BA (Cantab)
Rohan Auld (1992) BA (Cantab)
Louise Potter (1993) MA (Oxon)
John Vater (1995) BA (Oxon)
Nicholas Goodwin (1995) BA (Oxon)
Aidan Vine (1995) BA (Oxon) MA (Cornell)
Jonathan Sampson (1997) BA (Cantab)
Howard Daley (1997) BA (Cantab)
Oliver Wright (1998) BA (Cantab)
Peter Clarke (1970) *
Bernard Lever (1975) *

* Door Tenant

H

The Chambers: Based in London and Oxford, Harcourt Chambers provides a friendly and efficient advisory and advocacy service within five specialist practice groups: family, business, property, local government and personal injury. Individual members of chambers have additional areas of personal specialisation, particularly in election law, judicial review, planning, media, criminal and ecclesiastical law.

HARCOURT CHAMBERS
London & Oxford

Set No.
70 **HARDWICKE BUILDING** (Walter Aylen QC)

Hardwicke Building, New Square, Lincoln's Inn, London, WC2A 3SB
Tel: (020) 7242 2523 **Fax:** (020) 7691 1234 **DX:** LDE393
Email: clerks@hardwicke.co.uk **Website:** www.hardwicke.co.uk

Head of Chambers:	Walter Aylen QC
Chief Executive:	Hilary Mundella
Business Manager:	Peter Clark
Clerks:	Kevin Mitchell, Greg Piner, Gary Brown, Lloyd Smith
Tenants:	79

Members:

Walter Aylen QC (1962) (QC-1983)
Nicholas Stewart QC (1971) (QC-1987)
George F. Pulman QC (1971) (QC-1989) *
Romie Tager QC (1970) (QC-1995)
Patrick Upward QC (1972) (QC-1996)
Nigel Jones QC (1976) (QC-1999)
Robert Willer (1970)
Frederic Coford (1971)
Michael Hopmeier (1974)
Kenneth Craig (1975)
Philip Kremen (1975)
Stephen Lennard (1976)
Stephen Warner (1976)
John Landaw (1976)
James Vine (1977)
Steven Weddle (1977)
Michael Oliver (1977)
Philip Wakeham (1978)
Peter Walsh (1978)
Nicholas Baker (1980)
Rory Field (1980)
David Matthias (1980)
Indira Ramsahoye (1980)
David Aaronberg (1981)
Hugh Jackson (1981)
Alan Smith (1981)
Neil Mendoza (1982)
Daniel Flahive (1982)
William Bojczuk (1983)
Ian Brook (1983)
Timothy Banks (1983)
John Greenan (1984)
Debbie Taylor (1984)
Charles Briefel (1984)
Lindsey MacDonald (1985)
Karl King (1985)
Montague Palfrey (1985)
Jonathan Whitfield (1985)
Richard Ough (1985)
Michelle Stevens-Hoare (1986)
Tom Nicholson Pratt (1986)
James Mulholland (1986)
Francis Lloyd (1987)
Judith Spooner (1987)
Stephen Lyon (1987)
Paul Reed (1988)
Peter Kirby (1989)
Ann Mulligan (1989)
Steven Woolf (1989)
Caroline Hallissey (1990)
Alexis Campbell (1990)
Sara Benbow (1990)
Eithne Ryan (1990)
Ian Clarke (1990)
Kyriakos Argyropoulos (1991)
Kevin McCartney (1991)
Ingrid Newman (1992)
Colm Nugent (1992)
Richard Bates (1992)
Kerry Bretherton (1992)
David Preston (1993)
Julia Jarzabkowski (1993)
Emily Formby (1993)
Roshi Amiraftabi (1993)
Sabuhi Chaudhry (1993)
Niki Langridge (1993)
Brian St. Louis (1994)
Alexander Goold (1994)
Deanna Heer (1994)
Bart Casella (1995)
Lynn Freeston (1996)
Philip Grey (1996)
Edward Rowntree (1996)
David Pliener (1996)
Sarah Wood (1996)
Charles Bagot (1997)
Tianne Bell (1998)
Nicola Muir (1998)
Sa'id Mosteshar *
Jennet Treharne (1975)
Stephen Joelson *
Pauline Gray *

* Door Tenant

The Chambers: This modern, progressive set is large enough to contain strong teams specialising in civil and commercial law, crime and family law. Above all, it is dedicated to providing a high quality client-focused service to all its solicitors. For the latest and fullest information about Hardwicke Building, its teams and individual barristers, you are invited to visit their website.

H

Set No. 71

1 HARE COURT (Stephen Kramer QC)

Relocating to 2 Hare Court in Autumn 2000
1 Hare Court, Temple, London, EC4Y 7BE
Tel: (020) 7353 5324 **Fax:** (020) 7353 0667 **DX:** 444 (Ch.Ln.)
Email: clerks@1harecourt.com **Website:** www.1harecourt.com

Head of Chambers:	Stephen Kramer QC
Senior Clerk:	Deryk Butler
First Junior Clerk:	Ian Fitzgerald
Chambers Administrator:	Stephen Wall
Tenants:	43

Members:

Stephen Kramer QC (1970) (QC-1995)
Allan Green QC KCB (1959) (QC-1987)
Paul Worsley QC (1970) (QC-1990)
Anthony Morris QC (1970) (QC-1991)
Martin S Heslop QC (1972) (QC-1995)
Charles Salmon QC (1972) (QC-1996)
David Waters QC (1973) (QC-1999)
Andrew Radcliffe QC (1975) (QC-2000)
Brian Warner (1969)
Jacqueline Samuel (1971)
John Jones (1972)
Louise Kamill (1974)
Paul Dodgson (1975)
Orlando Pownall (1975)
Martin Hicks (1977)
Jeremy Benson (1978)
Andrew Lloyd-Eley (1979)
Andrew Colman (1980)
Ian Leist (1981)
David Howker (1982)
Jonathan Laidlaw (1982)
James Dawson (1984)
Sallie Bennett-Jenkins (1984)
David Brock (1984)
Michael Holland (1984)
Shani Barnes (1986)
Brian O'Neill (1987)
Kenneth Millett (1988)
Michael Logsdon (1988)
Brendan Kelly (1988)
Parmjit-Kaur Cheema (1989)
Marios P. Lambis (1989)
Christopher Hehir (1990)
Alex Lewis (1990)
Craig Ferguson (1992)
Kate Bex (1992)
Nina Grahame (1993)
Christopher Foulkes (1994)
Stephen Brassington (1994)
Oliver Glasgow (1995)
Riel Karmy-Jones (1995)
Emma Lowe (1996)
Christopher Coltart (1998)

The Chambers: Chambers specialises in criminal law. Prosecution and defence work is undertaken at all levels of seriousness in London and throughout England and Wales. Chambers offers particular expertise, both prosecution and defence, in cases involving serious fraud and corruption. Other specialisations include extradition work (on behalf of both individuals and foreign governments), courts-martial, coroners inquests, licensing and cases involving trades description and food and drugs legislation. Members of chambers include three Treasury Counsel at the Central Criminal Court, Standing Counsel to HM Customs and Excise, and many Recorders of the Crown Court. More information can be found on chambers' website, and a brochure is available on request.

Set No. 72

3 HARE COURT (FORMERLY 1 CROWN OFFICE ROW) (Mark Strachan QC)

3 Hare Court, Temple, London, EC4Y 7BJ
Tel: (020) 7415 7800 **Fax:** (020) 7415 7811 **DX:** 212 London
Email: clerks@3harecourt.com **Website:** www.3harecourt.com

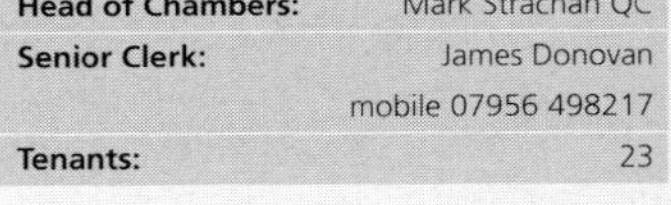

Head of Chambers:	Mark Strachan QC
Senior Clerk:	James Donovan mobile 07956 498217
Tenants:	23

Members:

Mark Strachan QC (1969) (QC-1987)
Godfray Le Quesne QC (1947) (QC-1962)
James Guthrie QC (1975) (QC-1993)
Richard Jones QC (1972) (QC-1996)
Michael Irvine (1964)
Iain McLeod (1969)
Terence Walker (1973)
Sebastian Neville-Clarke (1973)
Andrew Young (1977)
Pierre Janusz (1979)
Peter Knox (1983)
James Dingemans (1987)
Michael Lazarus (1987)
Joseph O'Neill (1987)
Howard Stevens (1990)
Aedeen Boadita-Cormican (1990)
Paul Marshall (1991)
Aidan Casey (1992)
Farzana Aslam (1993)
Marcus Dignum (1994)
Ian Rogers (1995)
Umesh Kumar (1995)
Katherine Deal (1997)

H

The Chambers: A long-established set which offers a comprehensive service in all areas of law, with the exception of the well-recognised specialist fields, such as revenue. It has always had a strong connection with the work of the Privy Council. The chambers moved this year to 3 Hare Court from 1 Crown Office Row. The new accomodation will enable chambers to continue to provide a friendly, efficient and high quality service. Mark Strachan Q.C. became Head of Chambers in 1995 upon the appointment of George Newman Q.C. to the High Court Bench. The set has numerous connections abroad through its work in the Privy Council. A new brochure coinciding with the chambers' move is available from the senior clerk, James Donovan. Alternatively, up-to-date information can be found on chambers' website.

Work Undertaken: Members of chambers offer expertise in commercial and common law, although individual practices differ significantly.

General Commercial: Both domestic and international (including ICC and other arbitrations), banking, negotiable instruments; agency; insurance; sale and carriage of goods; building and engineering disputes; employment and industrial relations and professional negligence.

Appellate Work: In the Privy Council from overseas, covering most fields of law and in particular commercial and general common law work, cases dealing with the written constitutions of Commonwealth countries and criminal law.
Human Rights: Chambers already has considerable experience of the application of the Human Rights Act in English litigation.
Common Law: Most forms of civil litigation including personal injury, and landlord and tenant work. Fields of practice of individual members of chambers include public and administrative law, family law and clinical negligence.

Languages: Dutch, French, German, Italian and Spanish.

Recruitment & Training: Chambers are a member of the PACH Scheme.

Set No.
73
KEATING CHAMBERS (Richard Fernyhough QC)

10 Essex Street, Outer Temple, London, WC2R 3AA
Tel: (020) 7544 2600 **Fax:** (020) 7240 7722 **DX:** 1045
Email: clerks@keatingchambers.com

Head of Chambers:	Richard Fernyhough QC
Senior Clerk:	Barry Bridgman
Tenants:	33

Members:

Richard Fernyhough QC (1970) (QC-1986)
John Uff QC (1970) (QC-1983)
Martin Collins QC (1952) (QC-1972)
Christopher Thomas QC (1973) (QC-1989)
John Marrin QC (1974) (QC-1990)
Stephen Furst QC (1975) (QC-1991)
Timothy Elliott QC (1975) (QC-1992)
Vivian Ramsey QC (1979) (QC-1992)
Robert Gaitskell QC (1978) (QC-1994)
Philip Boulding QC (1979) (QC-1996)
Paul Darling QC (1983) (QC-1999)
Marcus Taverner QC (1981) (QC-2000)
Alan Steynor (1975)
Rosemary Jackson (1981)
Peter Coulson (1982)
Ian Pennicott (1982)
Finola O'Farrell (1983)
Adrian Williamson (1983)
Alexander Nissen (1985)
Michael Bowsher (1985)
Nerys Jefford (1986)
Louise Randall (1988)
Robert Evans (1989)
Sarah Hannaford (1989)
Simon Hargreaves (1991)
Richard Harding (1992)
Jane Lemon (1993)
Piers Stansfield (1993)
Jonathan Lee (1993)
Simon Hughes (1995)
Abdul-Lateef Jinadu (1995)
Richard Coplin (1997)
Gaynor Chambers (1998)

The Chambers: Keating Chambers specialises in all aspects of construction and engineering matters in the UK and abroad, and in the associated areas of professional negligence, information technology and other property-related matters.

Work Undertaken: Chambers work covers the whole spectrum of disputes and advisory work from the very small to the exceptionally large. Members of chambers undertake advisory work and act in litigation and arbitration both in the UK and abroad. Senior members of chambers are also often appointed as arbitrators and legal assessors. Members of chambers are active in all forms of alternative dispute resolution (some being accreditied mediators) and in all aspects of adjudication, both acting for the parties and as adjudicators.
Main Areas: Construction and all kinds of engineering matters (including civil, mechanical, electrical and chemical engineering projects; major infrastucture projects; process plants; power plants; oil, coal, and gas recovery); development contracts; contractual claims; claims in respect of defective buildings and other stuctures; the professional negligence of architects, surveyors, valuers, engineers and other consultants concerned with buildings and engineering matters; local authority work (including building control work); information technology; European law, particularly public procurement and competition law as it affects building, engineering and IT projects.
Additional Areas: Performance bonds and warranties; most types of commercial and insurance contracts; freezing and other types of injunctions. Some members of chambers also have experience in environmental law, aviation law, landlord and tenant, and other property-related areas.

Clientele: Building contractors (both main and sub-contractors); property owners and developers; government departments and agencies; local authorities; architects; engineers; quantity surveyors; surveyors; insurance companies; and professional indemnity insurers. Members of chambers accept work by Direct Professional Access.

International: Many members of chambers advise or act in international litigation or arbitration, whether based on the UK or abroad. Members of chambers act in and are appointed as arbitrators particularly in ICC, LCIA, FIDIC and Hong Kong arbitrations.

Recruitment & Training: Both six- and twelve-month pupillages are offered. Awards of up to £20,000 over a twelve month period are available to pupils, with an additional £7,500 to cover the BVC year available.

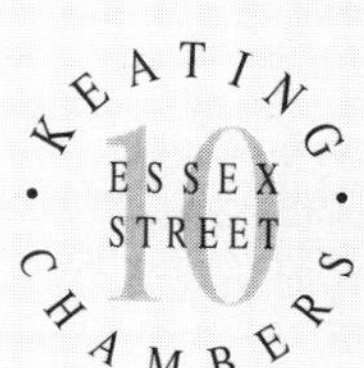

K

Set No. 74

ONE KING'S BENCH WALK (Anthony Hacking QC)

1 King's Bench Walk, Temple, London, EC4Y 7DB
Tel: (020) 7936 1500 **Fax:** (020) 7936 1590 **DX:** LDE 20
Email: ddear@1kbw.co.uk **Website:** www.1kbw.co.uk

Head of Chambers:	Anthony Hacking QC
Senior Clerk:	David Dear
Practice Manager:	Lisa Pavlovsky
Tenants:	48

Members:

Anthony Hacking QC (1965) (QC-1983)
Rodger Hayward Smith QC (1967) (QC-1988)
James Townend QC (1962) (QC-1978)
Barry Singleton QC (1968) (QC-1989)
Judith Parker QC (1973) (QC-1991)
Camden Pratt QC (1970) (QC-1992)
Pamela Scriven QC (1970) (QC-1992)
Richard Anelay QC (1970) (QC-1993)
Roderic Wood QC (1974) (QC-1993)
Stephen Bellamy QC (1974) (QC-1996)
Michael Gale QC (1957) (QC-1979)
James Turner QC (1976) (QC-1998)
Andrew McFarlane QC (1977) (QC-1998)
Charles Howard QC (1975) (QC-1999)
Clive Newton (1968)
Michael Warren (1971)
Lindsay Burn (1972)
John Reddish (1973)
Gordon Jackson (1989) (1979 QC 1990 Scot.)
James Pavry (1974)
John Tanzer (1975)
David Rennie (1976)
Caroline Budden (1977)
Caroline Lister (1980)
Anthony Kirk (1981)
Susan R Maidment (1968)
Julian Woodbridge (1981)
Christopher Pocock (1984)
Stephen Shay (1984)
Deborah Eaton (1985)
Sarah O'Connor (1986)
Deiniol Cellan-Jones (1988)
Philip Marshall (1989)
Elizabeth Selman (1989)
Richard Barton (1990)
Marcus Fletcher (1990)
Caroline Gibson (1990)
Joanna Grice (1991)
James Roberts (1993)
Richard Harrison (1993)
Ian Cook (1994)
Shona Mulholland (1994)
Graham Crosthwaite (1995)
Benedick Rayment (1996)
Shaun Esprit (1996)
Alan Gardner (1997)
Nicholas Anderson (1995)
Richard Castle (1998)
Stephen Wildblood QC (1981) (QC-1999) *

* Door Tenant

The Chambers: These chambers are a large, long established set, specialising in family, criminal and civil law. It has strength at all levels of seniority and teams of counsel can be provided for more protracted and complex cases. The work of chambers is principally in London and on the South Eastern Circuit but work is also undertaken throughout the country. Also at Kings Bench Chambers, 174 High Street, Lewes, BN7 1YE.Tel: (01273) 402600; Fax: (01273) 402609

Work Undertaken: Chambers has specialist groups of members for the three main areas of work who meet regularly holding internal and external lectures and drawing upon their members' expertise and experience.
Family: Chambers has considerable depth of expertise in all aspects of family law including the related areas of probate and trusts, Inheritance Act, Human Rights Act, judicial review and solicitors negligence work. The family law group is subdivided into child law and matrimonial finance in order to allow for greater emphasis to be placed upon each of these distinct areas.
Criminal: Chambers has an established criminal law practice in London and the South-East representing both prosecution and defence and including serious fraud work.
Civil: Members of chambers have expertise in personal injury, professional and clinical negligence, medical disciplinary, employment, judicial review, landlord and tenant, contracts (including sale of goods), police cases, and cases for the European Court of Human Rights.
Individual members of chambers are willing to accept Conditional Fee and Direct Professional Access instructions.

Publications: R. Hayward Smith QC & Clive Newton are the editors of *Jackson's Matrimonial Finance & Taxation*. James Turner QC and Stephen Shay are editors of *Archbold: Criminal Pleading Evidence & Practice*. Andrew McFarlane QC is co-author of *Hershman and McFarlane: Children Law and Practice*. Stephen Wildblood QC and Deborah Eaton are authors of *The Encyclopaedia of Family Provision in Family Matters.*

ONE
One King's Bench Walk
The Chambers of Anthony Hacking QC

K

Set No. 75

2 KING'S BENCH WALK (Anthony Donne QC)

2 King's Bench Walk, Temple, London, EC4Y 7DE **Tel:** (020) 7353 1746 **Fax:** (020) 7583 2051 **DX:** 1032

No. 6

2 KING'S BENCH WALK (René Yee Lock Wong)

2 King's Bench Walk, Temple, London, EC4Y 7DE **Tel:** (020) 7353 9276
Fax: (020) 7353 9949 **DX:** 477 Chancery Lane **Email:** chambers@2kbw.co.uk

Head of Chambers:	René Yee Lock Wong
Titular Head of Chambers:	Lord Campbell of Alloway ERD QC
Senior Administrator:	Brenda Anderson
Practice Manager:	Robert Ruegg
Clerks:	Alex Mark, Brian Newton
Tenants:	44

2
Kings Bench Walk Chambers
(Lord Campbell of Alloway)
Temple
London EC4Y 7DE

Members:

Lord Campbell of Alloway ERD QC (1939) (QC-1965)
David Owen Thomas QC (1952) (QC-1972)
René Yee Lock Wong (1973)
Peter Shier (1952)
James Cartwright (1968)
Philip Rueff (1969)
Anthony Dalgleish (1971)
Alun Evans (1971)
Ian Slack (1974)
David Mendes da Costa (1976)
Robert Gifford (1977)
Ian Mason (1978)
Patricia Lloyd (1979)
George Papageorgis (1981)
James Shrimpton (1981)
Sheila Gaylord (1983)
Anthony Levy (1983)
Jeremy Lynn (1983)
Deepak Kapur (1984)
Simon Livesey (1987)
Steven Perian (1987)
Anthony Montgomery (1987)
Nan Alban-Lloyd (1988)
Vishnu Gokhool (1989)
Claudia Lorenzo (1991)
Brian Kennedy (1992)
Tanya Callman (1993)
David Sandeman (1993)
Lee Freeman (1994)
Janice Johnson (1994)
James Kirby (1994)
Abigail Dean (1995)
Anne Donelon (1995)
Andrew Frymann (1995)
Philippa Daniels (1995)
Lachlan Wilson (1996)
Mark Walsh (1996)
Carolina Guiloff (1996)
Robin Halstead (1996)
Sukhwant Sidhu (1996)
Michael Hall (1996)
Richard Miles (1997)
Hugh Blake-James (1998)
Shardi Shameli (1998)
Julia Livesay *
Robert Baker *
Osmond Lam *
Keith Oderberg *
Zahid Yaqub *
Simon Watters (1992) *
Karen Phillips *
Stephen Owen-Conway QC *

* Door Tenants

The Chambers: These chambers are located on the first and second floors of one of the oldest buildings in the Temple, built by Christopher Wren. A wide range of work is undertaken in the field of general common law as well as criminal law; family law; administrative law; work before tribunals; education law; employment law; and human rights. Constant review is kept on the changing needs of solicitors and the public, while at the same time the Bar's traditional values are maintained and fostered by members who present a welcoming attitude to lay and professional clients.

No. 7

4 KING'S BENCH WALK (Nicholas Jarman QC)

2nd floor, 4 King's Bench Walk, Temple, London, EC4Y 7DL
Tel: (020) 7353 3581 **Fax:** (020) 7583 2257 **DX:** 1050 London (Chancery Lane)
Email: clerks@4kbw.co.uk **Website:** www.4kbw.co.uk

Head of Chambers:	Nicholas Jarman QC
Clerks:	Lee Cook, Philip Burnell
Silks' Clerk:	Graeme Logan
Tenants:	37

Members:

Nicholas Jarman QC (1965) (QC-1985)
Stephen Williamson QC (1964) (QC-1981)
Timothy Raggatt QC (1972) (QC-1993)
Basil Hillman (1968)
Robert Spencer Bernard (1969)
Christopher Cousins (1969)
John Denniss (1974)
Moira Pooley (1974)
Kate Mallison (1974)
Barnaby Evans (1978)
John Riley (1983)
Reginald Arkhurst (1984)
Jane Alt (1984)
Sandra Stanfield (1984)
Philip Goddard (1985)
Peter Nightingale (1986) **
Andrew Granville Stafford (1987)
Claire Jacobs (1989)
John Metcalf (1990) **
Paul Wakerley (1990)
Kate Mather (1990)
Fiona McCreath (1991)
Cressida Murphy (1991)
Michael Skelley (1991)
Kim Preston (1991)
Timothy Ashmole (1992)
Mark Ruffell (1992)
Jonathan Simpson (1993)
Jillian Hurworth (1993)
Brendan Davis (1994)
Benn Maguire (1994)
Sarah Phillimore (1994)
Tamala McGee (1995)
Amanda Drane (1996)
Nadia Chbat (1996)
Alan Blake (1997)
Cameron Brown (1998)

**Formerly a solicitor

The Chambers: 4 Kings Bench Walk provides advice and advocacy in: contract; crime; education; employment; family; immigration; landlord and tenant; personal injury; planning; probate; professional negligence; tort.

K

Set No. 78

4 KING'S BENCH WALK (Robert Rhodes QC)

4 King's Bench Walk, Temple, London, EC4Y 7DL
Tel: (020) 7822 8822 **Fax:** (020) 7822 8844 **DX:** 422
Email: 4kbw@barristersatlaw.com **Website:** www.barristersatlaw.com

Head of Chambers:	Robert Rhodes QC
Consultant:	Ian Lee
Tenants:	35

Members:

Robert Rhodes QC (1968) (QC-1989)
Raymond Walker QC (1966) (QC-1988)
John Toogood (1957)
Keith Evans (1962)
Malcolm Knott (1968)
David Cattle (1975)
Greville Davis (1976)
Clive Anderson (1976)
Bruce Stuart (1977)
Graham Hulme (1977)
David Mayall (1979)
Chris Van Hagen (1980)
Justin Shale (1982)
John Evan Jones (1982)
Simon Stafford-Michael (1982)
David Harounoff (1984)
Martin Hurst (1985)
Graham Huston (1991)
Samuel Jarman (1989)
Nigel Hood (1993)
Emma Edhem (1993)
Katherine Dunn (1993)
Adrian Maxwell (1993)
Oliver Mishcon (1993)
Simon Taylor (1993)
Derek Kerr (1994)
Nicola Murphy (1995)
Michael Nelson (1992)
Lawrence Power (1995)
Kimberly Farmer (1997)
Lisa Hatch (1995)
Francesca Levett (1997)
Samantha Riggs (1996)
Adam Canon (1997)
Clare Evans (1995)
HHJ Heppel QC*
Kenneth Cameron (1969) *
Anika Khan (1988) *
Edward Morgan (1989) *
Walter Rudeloff (1990) *
Jim Wilson (1994) *
Kathleen Anderson (1997) *
Michael Horton (1993) *
Phillip Henry *

* Door Tenants

The Chambers: Common law set specialising in commercial fraud, financial services, serious criminal fraud, heavy crime, commercial litigation, environmental law and insurance and reinsurance. In association with King's Bench Chambers, 175 Holdenhurst Rd, Bournemouth, BN8 8DQ.

Set No. 79

5 KING'S BENCH WALK (Brian Higgs QC)

5 King's Bench Walk, London, EC4Y 7DN
Tel: (020) 7353 5638 **Fax:** (020) 7353 6166 **DX:** 367 Chancery Lane
Email: clerks@5kbw.co.uk **Website:** www.5kbw.co.uk

Head of Chambers:	Brian Higgs QC
Senior Clerk:	Russell Ayles
First Junior Clerk:	Michael Bazeley
Practice Manager:	Chris Eadie
Tenants:	32

Members:

Brian Higgs QC (1955) (QC-1974)
Robert Fischel QC (1975) (QC-1998)
Richard Sones (1969)
Michael O'Sullivan (1970) +
Martin Joy (1971) +
James O'Mahony (1973) +
John Hillen (1976) +
Robert Ward (1977)
David Tomlinson (1977) +
John Fairhead (1978)
Simon Sandford (1979)
Sappho Dias (1982)
Mark Heywood (1985)
James Lloyd (1985)
Mark Dacey (1985)
Fiona Moore-Graham (1986)
Sarah Forshaw (1987)
Jonathan Higgs (1987)
Andrew Collings (1987)
Stephen Chippeck (1988)
Hugh Forgan (1989)
Edmund Fowler (1992)
Andrew Rodger (1993)
Danny Robinson (1993)
Jonathan Hall (1994)
Danny Moore (1994)
Timothy Crosland (1994)
Giles Nelson (1995)
Paul Cavin (1995)
Catherine Donnelly (1997)
Benjamin Temple (1997)
Robert Ellison (1996)

\+ Recorder

The Chambers: A well established specialist criminal set with additional practice groups in the following areas; matrimonial, children act, personal injury, licensing, local authority, public law and human rights.

Set No.
80 **6 KING'S BENCH WALK** (Sibghat Kadri QC)

6 King's Bench Walk, Temple, London, EC4Y 7DR **Tel:** (020) 7583 0695 / 7353 4931 **Fax:** (020) 7353 1726 **DX:** 471 (Ch.Ln.)
Email: clerks@6kbw.co.uk **Website:** www.6kbw.co.uk

Set No.
81 **6 KING'S BENCH WALK** (Michael Worsley QC)

6 King's Bench Walk, Temple, London, EC4Y 7DR
Tel: (020) 7583 0410 **Fax:** (020) 7353 8791 **DX:** 26 (Ch.Ln.)
Email: worsley@6kbw.freeserve.co.uk

Head of Chambers:	Michael Worsley QC
Senior Clerk:	David Garstang
Tenants:	42

Members:

Michael Worsley QC (1955) (QC-1985)
Ann Curnow QC (1957) (QC-1985)
Roy Amlot QC (1963) (QC-1989)
Ann Mallalieu QC (1970) (QC-1988)
James Curtis QC (1970) (QC-1993)
Victor Temple QC (1971) (QC-1993)
Dorian Lovell-Pank QC (1971) (QC-1993)
Joanna Korner QC (1974) (QC-1993)
Bruce Houlder QC (1969) (QC-1994)
David Spens QC (1973) (QC-1995)
David Fisher QC (1973) (QC-1996)
Wendy Joseph QC (1975) (QC-1998)
Anthony Leonard QC (1978) (QC-1999)
Nigel Sweeney QC (1976) (QC-2000)
Howard Vagg (1974)
Jonathan Turner (1974)
Mark Jonathan Dennis (1977)
Philippa Jessel (1978)
Marks Moore (1979)
David Perry (1980)
John Ryder (1980)
Nicholas Hilliard (1981)
Sasha Wass (1981)
Martyn Bowyer (1984)
Simon Denison (1984)
Emma Broadbent (1986)
Irena Ray-Crosby (1990)
Dean Armstrong (1985)
Peter Grieves-Smith (1989)
Timothy Cray (1989)
Duncan Penny (1992)
Jason David Dunn-Shaw (1992)
Isabel Dakyns (1992)
Annabel Darlow (1993)
Sarah Whitehouse (1993)
Gareth Patterson (1995)
Duncan Atkinson (1995)
Annabel Pilling (1996)
Jacob Hallam (1996)
Adina Ezekiel (1997)
Alison Foulkes (1997)
Louis Mably (1997)
David Turner QC (1971) (QC-1991) *
Andrew Oldland (1990) *
Simon Laws (1991) *

* Door Tenant

The Chambers: A specialist criminal set with 13 QCs, two Senior and two Junior Treasury Counsel. Chambers have particular experience in advocacy in the higher courts. Members also handle civil work with individual specialisations.11 members of chambers are recorders and one is a DTI Inspector. Additionally, members belong to the Criminal Bar Association and the Bar Senate.

Work Undertaken:
Criminal: For both prosecution and defence, mainly in London and the South Eastern Circuit, specialising in: commercial crime; fraud; VAT cases; and regulatory work.
Civil: Libel; police law; false imprisonment/malicious prosecutions; and some commercial; defamation; and professional tribunals.
Other: Members appear before coroners' courts, inquiries, disciplinary and industrial tribunals; also work is undertaken involving trade descriptions, extradition, licensing matters and human rights.

Languages: French, German, Italian and Spanish.

Recruitment & Training: Applications for tenancy should be sent to the head of chambers, those for pupillage to Sarah Whitehouse. There are 10 pupils in chambers at any one time. Awards and mini-pupillages are available.

K

Set No. 82

7 KING'S BENCH WALK (Jeremy Cooke QC)

7 King's Bench Walk, Temple, London, EC4Y 7DS
Tel: (020) 7910 8300 **Fax:** (020) 7583 0950 **DX:** LDE 239
Email: clerks@7kbw.law.co.uk

Head of Chambers:	Jeremy Cooke QC
Clerks:	Bernie Hyatt
	Greg Leyden, Eddie Johns
Chambers Director:	Robin Landon
Tenants:	36

Members:

Jeremy Cooke QC (1976) (QC-1990) +
Adrian Hamilton QC (1949) (QC-1973) +
John Willmer QC (1955) (QC-1967)
Timothy Saloman QC (1975) (QC-1993)
Francis Reynolds QC (Hon) (1960) (QC-1993)
Gavin Kealey QC (1977) (QC-1994)
Julian Flaux QC (1978) (QC-1994)
Jonathan Gaisman QC (1979) (QC-1995)
Dominic Kendrick QC (1981) (QC-1997)
Alistair Schaff QC (1983) (QC-1999)
Stephen Hofmeyr QC (1982) (QC-2000)
Charles Priday (1982)
Adam Fenton (1984)
Christopher Butcher (1986)
Stephen Kenny (1987)
Richard Southern (1987)
Robert Bright (1987)
Gavin Geary (1989)
David Bailey (1989)
David Edwards (1989)
David Allen (1990)
Simon Picken (1989)
Andrew Wales (1992)
Siobán Healy (1993)
S.J. Phillips (1993)
Rebecca Sabben-Clare (1993)
Jawdat Khurshid (1994)
Richard Waller (1994)
Timothy Kenefick (1996)
John Bignall (1996)
Charles Holroyd (1997)
Simon Kerr (1997)
James Drake (1998)
Peter MacDonald Eggers (1999)
James Brocklebank (1999)
Michael Holmes (1999)

+ Accredited Mediator

The Chambers: The core areas of work undertaken by this major commercial set are commercial litigation, international and domestic arbitration, insurance and reinsurance, shipping, banking, professional negligence, conflicts of law and private international law, energy, oil and gas, and City work.The set was founded in 1883 and its experience in commercial matters is well established and respected. The many distinguished former members include Lord Denning, Lord Brandon, Lord Goff, Lord Hobhouse, Lord Justice Mance and Mr. Justice Longmore and most recently Mr. Justice Tomlinson. 7 KBW is recognised for its strength at all levels. Its members provide legal advice and litigation expertise of the highest quality. Their commitment to their clients and to those who instruct them is widely acknowledged. This is reflected not only in the quality of their work but also in the promptness of their assistance. The clerks do not accept second bookings for court, arbitration or tribunal fixtures unless specifically requested by instructing solicitors to do so. The members of chambers appear principally in the higher courts (Commercial Court, Court of Appeal and House of Lords) in London and before arbitration tribunals within and outside the U.K. They are instructed also to appear in the European Court of Justice and the Privy Council, as well as in other jurisdictions such as Hong Kong, Singapore, Bermuda and the Cayman Islands.Members of chambers are regularly appointed as arbitrators under various terms of reference, including LCIA, ICC, LMAA and Lloyd's. Lord Goff accepts appointments as arbitrator through the clerks. The chambers includes fully accredited Mediators (CEDR).
Under its new head, Jeremy Cooke, Q.C., 7KBW confidently expects to grow whilst maintaining its recognised qualities and strengths in its core areas of work. There is a duty clerk available for 24 hours a day, seven days a week.

Publications: Several members are authors and editorial team members who have co-operated in legal publications in the areas of contract, agency, shipping, insurance/reinsurance law and professional negligence.

K

Recruitment & Training: Chambers attracts pupils of only the highest quality, and pursues a policy of only taking new tenants of such quality either from those starting their careers in Law or from those in mid-career who have elected to change from another part of the profession. This emphasis on quality has meant a steady but selective growth in the overall number of tenants over the past years.

Set No. 83

8 KING'S BENCH WALK (L.G. Woodley QC)

8 King's Bench Walk, Temple, London, EC4Y 7DU **Tel:** (020) 7797 8888 **Fax:** (020) 7797 8880 **DX:** 195

34 **9 KING'S BENCH WALK** (Ali Mohammed Azhar)

9 King's Bench Walk, Temple, London, EC4Y 7DX **Tel:** (020) 7353 9564
Fax: (020) 7353 7943 **DX:** 118 Chancery Lane

Head of Chambers:	Ali Mohammed Azhar
Senior Clerk:	John Lee
Tenants:	14

The range of work covers crime, family law, landlord and tenant, personal injury, immigration, clinical and professional negligence, arbitration, commercial and construction law, employment, banking law, corporate insolvency and individual bankruptcy. Experts in Islamic and Hindu law. Languages: Urdu, Punjabi, Bengali, and Sinhalese.

35 **10 KING'S BENCH WALK** (Claudius Algar)

10 King's Bench Walk, Temple, London, EC4Y 7EB
Tel: (020) 7353 7742 **Fax:** (020) 7583 0579 **DX:** 24 London/Chancery Lane
Email: 10kbw@lineone.net **Website:** www.10kingsbenchwalk.co.uk

Head of Chambers:	Claudius Algar
Clerks:	Alan Curtis (Crime), Colin Middleton (Civil)
Tenants:	34

10 KING'S BENCH WALK

Members:

Claudius Algar (1972)
Rosina Hare QC (1956) (QC-1976)
Colin Hart (1966)
Charles Vaudin (1971)
Susan Tapping (1975)
Carlton Christensen (1977)
Leonard Hedworth (1979)
Reid Pearce (1979)
William Lanigan (1980)
Bernadette Miscampbell (1980)
Peter Herrity (1982)
Orlando Gibbons (1982)
Carlo Talacci (1986)
Simon Thompson (1988)
Patrick Lynch (1988)
Richard Crallan (1990)
Sukhjinder Johal (1991)
James Bogle (1991)
Andrew Noble (1992)
Diana Serle (1992)
Michael Harris (1993)
Rosana Bailey (1994)
Patricia Harding (1994)
Jonathan Martin (1994)
Declan O'Callaghan (1995)
Anwar Ramzan (1995)
Diana Galpin (1995)
Simon Butler (1996)
Sherry Nabijou (1996)
Dominic Bevis (1996)
Alastair Panton (1996)
John McNally (1996)
Sharan Bhachu (1998)
Patrick Back QC (1940) (QC-1970) *
Mustafa Habib (1980) *
David Devoy Williams (1989) *

* Associate Member

The Chambers: A common-law set offering particular strength in all aspects of criminal, civil and family work (public and private). DPA accepted.

6 **10 KING'S BENCH WALK** (Georges M Khayat QC)

10 King's Bench Walk, Temple, London, EC4Y 7EB **Tel:** (020) 7353 2501 **Fax:** (020) 7353 0658 **DX:** 294 (Ch.Ln.) **Email:** clerks@10kbw.co.uk
Website: www.10kbw.co.uk

7 **11 KING'S BENCH WALK** (F.J. Muller QC)

11 King's Bench Walk, Temple, London, EC4Y 7EQ
Tel: (020) 7353 3337 **Fax:** (020) 7583 2190 **DX:** 389 CHANCERY LANE
Email: clerks@11kbw.co.uk **Website:** www.11kbw.co.uk

Head of Chambers:	F.J. Muller QC
Clerks:	A. Blaney (for Queens Counsel), R. Flint (Leeds – Juniors)
Tenants:	25

Members:

F.J. Muller QC (1961) (QC-1978)
James Spencer QC (1975) (QC-1991)
Andrew Robertson QC (1975) (QC-1996)
Roger Thorn QC (1970) (QC-1990)
Nicholas Campbell QC (1979) (QC-2000)
Jeremy Richardson QC (1980) (QC-2000)
Francis Radcliffe (1962)
Matthew Caswell (1968)
Richard Barlow (1970)
Michael O'Neill (1979)
Christopher Attwooll (1980)
Mio Sylvester (1980)
Toby Wynn (1982)
Rebecca Caswell (1983)
Fiona P. Swain (1983)
Graham Reeds (1984)
Simon Mallett (1987)
Adrian Waterman (1988)
David Brooke (1990)
Robert Toone (1993)
Ian Skelt (1994)
Tom Mitchell (1995)
Sarah Margree (1996)
Tina Dempster (1997)
Matthew Bean (1997)

The Chambers: 11 King's Bench Walk is a long-established common-law London set with a distinguished history.
Leeds Annexe: 3 Park Court, Park Cross Street, Leeds LS1 2QH.Tel: (0113) 297 1200 Fax: (0113) 297 1201 DX 26433 Leeds and DX 10621 Sheffield. Clerk: R. M. Flint

K

Set No.
88

11 KING'S BENCH WALK (Eldred Tabachnik QC and James Goudie QC)

11 King's Bench Walk, Temple, London, EC4Y 7EQ
Tel: (020) 7632 8500 **Fax:** (020) 7583 9123/ 3690 **DX:** 368 (Ch.Ln.)
Email: clerksroom@11kbw.com **Website:** www.11kbw.com

Head of Chambers	
	Eldred Tabachnik QC and James Goudie QC
Sen. Clerk:	Philip Monham
Office hours:	
	Monday – Friday 8:00am – 7:00pm
Out of office hours:	0831 304714 (mobile)
Tenants:	31

Members:

Eldred Tabachnik QC (1970) (QC-1982) BA, LLB (Capetown), LLM (Lond)
James Goudie QC (1970) (QC-1984) LLB (Lond)
Michael Supperstone QC (1973) (QC-1991) MA, BCL (Oxon)
Elizabeth Slade QC (1972) (QC-1992) MA (Oxon)
Alistair McGregor QC (1974) (QC-1997) LLB (Lond)
Christopher Jeans QC (1980) (QC-1997) LLB (Lond), BCL (Oxon)
Adrian Lynch QC (1983) (QC-2000) LLB (Lond)
Philip Sales (1985) MA (Cantab), BCL (Oxon) First Junior Counsel to the Treasury, Common Law
Andrew Hillier (1972) BA (Dublin)
Elizabeth Laing (1980) BA (Cantab)
John Cavanagh (1985) MA (Oxon), LLM (Cantab)
Nigel Giffin (1986) MA (Oxon)
Charles Bear (1986) BA (Oxon)
Peter Wallington (1987) MA, LL.M (Cantab)
Jonathan Swift (1989) BA (Oxon), LLM (Cantab)
Timothy Pitt-Payne (1989) BA, BCL (Oxon)
Peter Oldham (1990) MA (Cantab) Dip Law (City)
Seán Jones (1991) BA, BCL (Oxon)
Akhlaq Choudhury (1992) BSc (Glas), LL.B (Lond)
Paul Nicholls (1992) LL.B (Sheff), BCL (Oxon)
Daniel Stilitz (1992) BA (Oxon), MA (City)
Clive Sheldon (1991) BA (Cantab) LLM (U.Penn)
Nigel Porter (1994) MA LLM (Cantab)
Jason Coppel (1994) BA (Oxon), LLM, (EUI, Florence)
Cecilia Ivimy (1995) BA (Oxon)
Tom Restrick (1995) BA (Oxon)
Richard Leiper (1996) LLB, MJur
Julian Wilson (1997) BA (Oxon)
Anya Proops (1998) BA (Cantab) Ph.D. (Lond) Dip Law (City)
Jane McCafferty (1998) BA, LLM (e) (Cantab)
Stephen Tromans (1999) MA (Cantab)

Work Undertaken: The 32 members of these chambers (eight of whom are Queen's Counsel) provide specialist legal advisory and advocacy services covering the following three principal areas:
Commercial Law/International Trade: Arbitration (domestic and international); agency; competition; confidential information; copyright; economic torts, financial regulation; professional negligence; share options; technology – software licensing; trade secrets; unlawful competition; search and freezing orders.
Public and Administrative Law: Local authorities, especially their powers and financing; judicial review of central and local government and other public bodies, including financial services institutions; competitive tendering and public authority contracts; education; sex and race discrimination; elections; civil liberties; immigration; EU public law; housing and housing associations; environmental law.
Employment Law: Company directors; share options; incentive bonuses and pension rights; wrongful and unfair dismissal; the protection of confidential information; restrictive covenants; transfers of undertakings; sex and race discrimination and equal pay; strikes and other trade disputes; trade union membership; EU employment law.
Full brochure available on request.

Publications: Members of chambers have written or contributed to *Halsbury's Laws (Administrative Law Title); Supperstone & Goudie on Judicial Review; Harvey on Industrial Relations and Employment Law; Butterworths Employment Law Handbook; Tolley's Employment Handbook; Immigration Law and Practice; Butterworths Local Government Law*; Supperstone, Goudie & Coppel *Local Authorities and the Human Rights Act.*

11 KING'S BENCH WALK
CHAMBERS

K

Set No. 39

12 KING'S BENCH WALK (Timothy Stow QC)

12 King's Bench Walk, Temple, London, EC4Y 7EL
Tel: (020) 7583 0811 **Fax:** (020) 7583 7228 **DX:** 1037 (Ch.Ln.)
Email: chambers@12kbw.co.uk **Website:** www.12kbw.co.uk

Head of Chambers:	Timothy Stow QC
Senior Clerk:	John Cooper
Tenants:	43

Members:

Timothy Stow QC (1965) (QC-1989)
Charles Whitby QC (1952) (QC-1970)
Ronald Walker QC (1962) (QC-1983)
Anthony Goldstaub QC (1972) (QC-1992)
Anthony Speaight QC (1973) (QC-1995)
Richard Methuen QC (1972) (QC-1997)
Iain Goldrein QC (1975) (QC-1997)
Margaret de Haas QC (1977) (QC-1998)
Frank Burton QC (1982) (QC-1998)
Toby Hooper QC (1973) (QC-2000)
Peter Grobel (1967)
Neville Spencer-Lewis (1970)
John King (1973)
Andrew Hogarth (1974)
Brian Gallagher (1975)
Stephen Worthington (1976)
Nicholas Heathcote Williams (1976)
Allan Gore (1977)
Lincoln Crawford (1977) OBE
Alexander Hill-Smith (1978)
William Featherby (1978)
Susan Rodway (1981)
Jonathan Howard (1983)
Paul Russell (1984)
David Sanderson (1985)
Nigel Lewers (1986)
Freya Newbery (1986)
Andrew Pickering (1987)
Hugh Hamill (1988)
Adam Chambers (1989)
Catherine Brown (1990)
Kate Chandler (1990)
Vincent Moran (1991)
Patrick Vincent (1992)
Willliam Audland (1992)
Stephanie Jackson (1992)
Joel Kendall (1993)
Richard Viney (1994)
Carolyn D'Souza (1994)
Catherine Peck (1995)
Timothy Petts (1996)
Harry Steinberg (1997)
Joanna Droop (1998)

The Chambers: 12 Kings Bench Walk is widely recognised as being one of the three leading sets specialising in personal injury. Chambers are also known for the particular expertise of their specialist groups of barristers in clinical negligence, professional negligence, construction, insurance and employment law. One of the longest established sets in the Temple, chambers have the reputation of being friendly and approachable. Considerable expansion during the past ten years has enabled chambers to invest in staff development and the latest computer technology, ensuring that work is dealt with quickly and efficiently. Members are fully conversant with the requirements of recent Human Rights legislation, and its implications for the work undertaken by chambers.

Work Undertaken:

Personal Injury: Includes all industrial disease claims, particularly asbestos, RSI and VWF; brain damage; spinal injuries; all other employers', public and product liability claims; and all road traffic related work.

Clinical Negligence: Includes injuries at birth; catastrophic brain damage; injuries from pharmaceutical products; and all other cases involving complex medical and scientific issues.

Professional Negligence: Includes solicitors' and barristers' negligence; architects', engineers', surveyors' and valuers' negligence; accountants' and bankers' negligence; insurance brokers' and IFAs' negligence; auctioneers' negligence; veterinary negligence; and information technology professionals' negligence.

Construction and Technology: Includes contractual claims arising out of the JCT, ICE and other standard forms of construction contract and subcontracts; engineering and mining contracts; and computer contracts.

Insurance and Reinsurance: Includes policy wording issues and drafting of policy wording amendments; and acting for insurance clients in professional indemnity, employers' liability, motor policy and public liability claims.

Employment: Includes race relations; equal opportunity; trade union work; restrictive covenants; transfers of undertakings; wrongful and unfair dismissal; equal pay; bonus and pension schemes; and expertise in all aspects of EU employment law.

In addition to the above work undertaken by chambers' specialist teams, individual members can offer expertise in the following areas:

Commercial: Includes banking and consumer credit transactions; sale of goods; carriage of goods; and banking regulatory and enforcement work.

Property Law: Includes commercial and residential landlord and tenant; Housing Association; and Local Authority disrepair work.

Public Law: Includes judicial review; disaster inquiries; planning enforcement; and local governmental law.

Enviromental: Includes pollution of land by chemicals and nuclear matter; pollution related criminal charges; and advising clients on obtaining site licences.

Equine Law: Includes insurance policy disputes; contractual disputes; misrepresentation and misdescription; disputes concerning membership and rules of riding and racing organisations; disciplinary proceedings; and riding accidents.

Continued overleaf

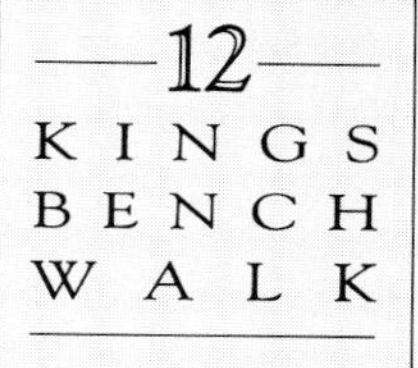

K

Other information: Chambers is fully computer networked and all members have email facilities. Meetings, conferences and interviews can be arranged through chambers' video conferencing facilities. Brochures and individual member details are available on request. Details of chambers' seminar and lecture programme can be found on the website. Chambers accepts Direct Professional Access instructions and Conditional Fee work, by prior arrangement with the clerks. They also offer qualified and experienced mediators and arbitration services.

Publications: Up-to-date details of publications which members of chambers have written, edited or contributed to can be found on the 12 Kings Bench Walk website at www.12kbw.co.uk. The website also gives details and analysis of important cases involving members of chambers.

Recruitment & Training: Chambers is a member of PACH to which all applications for pupillage should be made. Pupils are offered 12-month pupillage with a comprehensive training package and a guaranteed income of £18,000.

Set No. 90

13 KING'S BENCH WALK (Roger Ellis QC)

13 King's Bench Walk, Temple, London, EC4Y 7EN
Tel: (020) 7353 7204 **Fax:** (020) 7583 0252 **DX:** 359 London **LIX:** Lon 066
Email: clerks@13kbw.co.uk **Website:** www.13kbw.co.uk

Head of Chambers:	Roger Ellis QC
Senior Clerks:	Stephen Buckingham, Kevin Kelly
Chambers Director:	Claire Makin
Chambers Administrator:	Penny McFall
Tenants:	40

Members:

Roger Ellis QC (1962) (QC-1996) LLB. BSc (Lond).
Graeme Williams QC (1959) (QC-1983) M.A. (Oxon).
Julian Baughan QC (1967) (QC-1990) B.A. (Oxon).
David Ashton (1962) M.A. (Oxon).
Alexander Dawson (1969) M.A. (Oxon).
Anthony McGeorge (1969) M.A. (Cantab).
Robert Lamb (1973) M.A. (Cantab).
Deirdre Goodwin (1974) LLB. (Lond).
David Grant (1975) M.A. LLB. (Cantab).
Jane Tracy Forster (1975) LLB. (Liverpool).
Paul W. Reid (1975) M.A. (Cantab).
David Bright (1976)
Simon Hughes M.P. (1974) B.A. (Cantab).
Simon Draycott (1977)
Alasdair Brough (1979) M.A. (Cantab).
Nigel Daly (1979) LLB. (London).
Nicholas Syfret (1979) M.A. (Cantab).
Andrew Glennie (1982) M.A. (Oxon).
A. John Williams (1983) M.A. (Cantab).
Jonathan Coode (1984) B.A. (East Anglia).
Neil Vickery (1985) M.A. (Cantab).
Neil Moore (1986) LLB. (Nottingham).
Sarah Gibbons (1987) B.A. (Birmingham).
Arthur Blake (1988) LLB. (Lond).
Sinclair Cramsie (1988) LLB. (Leeds).
Fiona Hay (1989) BSc. B.A. (Exeter).
Andrew Pote (1983) LLB. (East Anglia).
Adrian Higgins (1990) M.A. (Oxon).
Edmund Walters (1991) B.A. (Bristol).
Heather Wenlock (1991) M.Phil D.Phil (Oxon).
Vivian Walters (1991) B.A. (Leic).
Deshpal Singh Panesar (1993) LLB. (Lond).
Susan Chan (1994) B.A. (Oxon).
Patrick Wainwright (1994) M.A. (Oxon).
Paul Mitchell (1994) B.A. (York).
Rachel Drake (1995) LLB. (Hons) (Brunel)
Lucy Owens (1997) LLB. (Hons) (Kingston)
James Cox (1997) LLB. (Wales)
Thomas Payne (1998) B.A. (Oxon) LLM (research) (Birmingham).
Donald Lambie (1978) LLB. (London)*

*Door Tenant

The Chambers: 13 King's Bench Walk are established chambers with some forty members in premises in the Inner Temple in London and Beaumont Street in Oxford. They cover a wide spectrum of common law and Chancery matters, have an expanding family practice, and provide a comprehensive service in criminal law on the Midland & Oxford circuit.
Chambers have recently upgraded telecommunications, moved to Meridian specialist software, and installed a new email system. They like to take a commercial approach by combining prompt action with practical advice. Chambers are proud of their client service, and are now preparing for Barmark Quality assessment.

K

Work Undertaken: Chambers have nine practice areas as follows:
Administrative and public law, which includes immigration and civil liberties, environmental and consumer law; clinical negligence; company and commercial, including banking, commercial litigation, insolvency, insurance, partnerships and professional negligence; construction; crime, including criminal fraud; employment; family; personal injury; property and Chancery, which includes real property, landlord and tenant, Chancery remedies and other related matters.

LAMB BUILDING (Ami Feder)

Lamb Building, Ground Floor, Temple, London, EC4Y 7AS
Tel: (020) 7797 7788 **Fax:** (020) 7353 0535 **DX:** 1038 (Ch.Ln.)
Email: clerks@lambbldg.co.uk **Website:** www.lambbldg.co.uk

Head of Chambers:	Ami Feder
Senior Clerk:	Gary Goodger
Tenants:	30

Members:

Ami Feder (1965) LLB
Kenneth Wheeler (1956)
Ivan Krolick (1966) LLB (Dunhelm)
David M.T. Edlin (1971) MA (Oxon)
John Fox (1973) LLB, BDS, LDSRCS
Anthony T.K. Edie (1974) LLB
Jeremy Gordon (1974) LLB (Lond)
John C. Waters (1974)
Alan Barton (1975) LLM (Lond)
Spenser R. Hilliard (1975) LLB (Lond)
Jaqueline A. Perry (1975) MA (Oxon)
Angela E. Hodes (1979) BA (Lond)
Michael Phillips (1980) LLB (Lond)
J. David Cook (1982) BA (Keele)
Richard Roberts (1983) BA (Cantab)
Deborah Sawhney (1987) BA (Keele)
Susannah Cotterill (1988)
Bernard Richmond (1988)
M. Jane Terry (1988)
David Brounger (1990)
J.M. Seamus Kearney (1992)
Lindsay Weinstein (1992)
Paul Crampin (1992)
Anita Geser (1992)
Martin Cole (1994)
Joy Dykers (1995)
Paul Bitmead (1996)
Anne Faul (1996)
Geri Peterson (1997)
Andreas Pretzell (1997)

Work Undertaken: The work of chambers covers all aspects of English common law and some general Chancery, predominantly on the South Eastern and Western Circuits.The principal areas of practice are civil and criminal commercial fraud; professional and particularly medical negligence; personal injury; family and childcare including wardship and property; landlord and tenant and housing law; insolvency and bankruptcy; contractual disputes including partnership and sale of goods; all criminal law; disciplinary hearings and the armed forces; consumer credit, hiring, and leasing transaction; building law; employment, immigration specialists.
Additional Specialisations: Individual members offer expertise in licensing, food and drugs, mental health, computer law, and Israeli law (Ami Feder is qualified as an advocate in Israel). Ivan Krolick belongs to the Chartered Institute of Arbitrators.
A brochure is available on request.

LAMB CHAMBERS (Christopher Gardner QC)

Lamb Building, Temple, London, EC4Y 7AS
Tel: (020) 7797 8300 **Fax:** (020) 7797 8308 **DX:** 418 London
Email: lambchambers@link.org **Website:** www.lambchambers.co.uk

Head of Chambers:	Christopher Gardner QC
Senior Clerk:	John Kelly
Tenants:	36

Members:

Christopher Gardner QC (1968) (QC-1994)
Julian Priest QC (1954) (QC-1974)
Ian Leeming QC (1970) (QC-1988)
Christopher Lau (1972) SC (Singapore)(SC-1999)
J.A.L. Sterling (1953)
Alastair Sharp (1968)
Anthony McNeile (1970)
Mark West (1973)
David di Mambro (1973)
Jeremy Carey (1974)
Anthony Connerty (1974)
Stephen Shaw (1975)
Anthony Allston (1975)
Paul Stewart (1975)
Simon Brilliant (1976)
Lawrence Caun (1977)
Paul M. Emerson (1984)
Simon Williams (1984)
Richard Ough (1985)
Clive Blackwood (1986)
Simon Wood (1987)
Timothy Meakin (1989)
James Stuart (1990)
Daniel Gatty (1990)
Shantanu Majumdar (1992)
Elizabeth F. Haggerty (1994)
Dominic Happé (1993)
Rhiannon Jones (1993)
Gary Blaker (1993)
Richard Hayes (1995)
Jonathan Richards (1996)
Timothy Frith (1996)
Annette Prand (1995)
Alexandra Stagi (1997)
Peter Ellis (1997)
Andrew Wille (1998)

L

The Chambers: Lamb Chambers is a long-established set which specialises in mainstream civil litigation and is structured in three specialist groups: commercial, personal injury and clinical negligence, and property.

Work Undertaken:

Commercial Group: This group specialises in all commercial litigation, including: commercial contracts; sale & carriage of goods, supply of goods & services; companies, partnerships, corporate & personal insolvency; service contracts; guarantees; credit & security; banking; bills of exchange; passing off;

Continued overleaf

intellectual property and confidentiality; competition; franchising; insurance, economic and other commercial torts; professional negligence connected with the above areas. Members undertake commercial arbitrations, both LCIA and ICC, Alternative Dispute Resolution and Direct Professional Access work.

Personal Injury & Clinical Negligence Group: This group specialises in tortious litigation, including personal injury, fatal accidents, clinical negligence and associated professional negligence claims; all matters relating to assessment of damages; structured and infant settlements and insurance. Product liability; claims relating to toxins, infectious diseases; and factory, construction and road traffic and other transport accidents; claims for damages arising out of criminal injuries. Members, Richard Ough and Jonathan Richards are medical doctors.

Property Group: This group specialises in all property-related work and construction litigation, including all aspects of landlord and tenant law (commercial, residential and agricultural); leasehold enfranchisement; construction disputes before the Technology and Construction Court and in arbitration; professional negligence of architects and engineers and all professional negligence relating to property issues; mortgages; housing options; easements and restrictive covenants; torts relating to land; the drafting, construction and enforcement of contracts. Members of the group also undertake arbitrations, Alternative Dispute Resolution and Direct Professional Access work.

Publications: 21 members of chambers are the contributing editors to Butterworths' *Law of Limitation*. David di Mambro is a member of the Editorial Board of the *Civil Court Practice* (The Green Book), is the general editor of Butterworths' *Manual of Civil Appeals* and is a contributing editor to *Atkin's Court Forms* (CPR volumes). Simon Wood is a member of the Editorial Board of the *Civil Court Practice* (The Green Book) (Limitation). Dr Richard Ough is the author of '*The Mareva Injunction and Anton Piller Order*' (Butterworths. 1st Edition 1987; 2nd Edition 1993; 3rd Edition in preparation); Timothy Meakin is assistant editor of Powers and Harris *Clinical Negligence* (3rd Edition) and is assistant editor of Butterwoths *Personal Injury Litigation Service*. Professor Adrian Sterling (Professorial Fellow, Queen Mary and Westfield College, and visiting Professor, King's College, University of London) is author of *The Data Protection Act 1984* (second edition, 1985), *Copyright Law in the United Kingdom and the Rights of Performers, Authors and Composers in Europe* (1986, supplement 1987) (with M. C. L. Carpenter), *Intellectual Property Rights in Sound Recordings, Film and Video* (1992, supplement 1994) and *World Copyright Law* (1998). Lamb Chambers is accredited by the Law Society for CPD. A list of seminars which chambers is willing to undertake and a list of articles and publications produced by chambers is available at the Lamb Chambers website. Enquiries in respect of seminars on any other subjects in which Lamb Chambers practises are welcome. Chambers' brochure, containing detailed individual CVs, is available on request.

Set No. 93

LION COURT (David Wolchover)

7 Bell Yard, London, WC2A 2JR
Tel: (020) 7831 0636 **Fax:** (020) 7831 0719 **DX:** 98 London Chancery Lane
Email: LionCrtChambers@aol.com **Website:** members.aol.com/LionCourtChmbs

Head of Chambers:	David Wolchover
Senior Clerk:	Kevin Tarrant
Tenants:	26

Members:

David Wolchover (1971)
Gerard Boyd (1967)
Laraine Kaye (1971)
Shini Cooksley (1975)
Jean-Gilles Raymond (1982)
Georgina Nicholas (1983)
Steve Hosking (1988)
Paula Bignall (1989)
Paul Brinkworth (1990)
John Honey (1990)
David Newberry (1990)
Stephen Bailey (1991)
Louise McCullough (1991)
Philippa Mendel (1992)
Alex Balancy (1992)
Gregory Hopewell (1992)
Jean-Marie Labelle (1992)
Paul Kaffel (1993)
Alexander Krikler (1995)
Adrian Langdale (1996)
Claire Davenport (1996)
Joshua Dubin (1997)
Simon French (1997)
Daniel Murray (1997)
Gary Grimshaw (1998)
Desiree Artesi (1998)

The Chambers: A well established common law set, with an emphasis on crime. Lion Court has developed and grown in recent years to meet the changing demands expected of the Bar. They seek to provide a fast and friendly service, providing expertise at each level of call, with fee structures and response times adaptable to clients' needs, supported by an experienced and flexible clerking team.

Work Undertaken: Chambers undertakes all types of general common law – civil, criminal (both prosecution and defence) and family.

Publications: Members have written, contributed to, or edited: *The Exclusion of Improperly Obtained Evidence, Wolchover and Heaton-Armstrong on Confession Evidence, Analysing Witness Testimoney, Bail in Criminal Proceedings, Current Law Week* and *FHM!*

No. 4

LITTLETON CHAMBERS (Michel Kallipetis QC)

3 King's Bench Walk North, Temple, London, EC4Y 7HR
Tel: (020) 7797 8600 **Fax:** (020) 7797 8699/8697 **DX:** 1047
Email: clerks@littletonchambers.co.uk

Head of Chambers:	Michel Kallipetis QC
Chief Executive:	David Douglas
Clerks:	Alistair Coyne, Tim Tarring
Fees Clerk:	Tony Shaddock
A/C's Receivable Manager:	Nita Johnston
Tenants:	36

LITTLETON CHAMBERS

Members:

Michel Kallipetis QC (1968) (QC-1989)
Julian Malins QC (1972) (QC-1991)
Ian Mayes QC (1974) (QC-1993)
Richard Price OBE QC (1969) (QC-1996)
Clive Freedman QC (1978) (QC-1997)
Andrew Clarke QC (1980) (QC-1997)
John Bowers QC (1979) (QC-1998)
Andrew Stafford QC (1980) (QC-2000)
Selwyn Bloch QC (1982) (QC-2000)
Colin Manning (1970)
Richard Perkoff (1971)
Philip Bartle (1976)
Mark H. Lomas (1977)
Timothy Higginson (1977)
Caroline Harry Thomas (1981)
John Davies (1981)
Shirley Bothroyd (1982)
David Reade (1983)
Antony Sendall (1984)
Ian Gatt (1985)
Michael Duggan (1984)
Peter Trepte (1987)
Raoul Downey (1988)
Sam Neaman (1988)
Martyn Barklem (1989)
Charles Samek (1989)
Jeffrey Bacon (1989)
Jeremy Lewis (1992)
Naomi Ellenbogen (1992)
Gavin Mansfield (1992)
Daniel Tatton-Brown (1994)
Stuart Ritchie (1995)
Carol Davis (1996)
Dale Martin (1997)
Niran de Silva (1997)
Jennifer Gardiner (1998)
Donald Harris (1958) *
David Hacking (1963) *
Neil MacCormick (1971) *
Jean-Yves de Cara *

* Door Tenants

Work Undertaken: A set practising in all areas of civil and commercial law with a wide spread of work including all aspects of business, contract and employment law, professional negligence and human rights. Chambers are members of COMBAR. Chambers have formed a Ltd company providing mediation services.

Main Areas: There are four main specialities in chambers with the following specialist groups: employment law, professional negligence, ADR & arbitration, and commercial law incorporating:- banking; financial services & insurance; entertainment and media; construction; commercial fraud; public and European; and insolvency.

Additional Areas: Carriage of goods; company law; consumer credit law; corporate finance; insolvency; international trade; letters of request; competition law; computer law; EU; environment; family; pharmaceuticals; telecommunications; transport; sale of goods; administrative law; civil liberties; charities; discrimination; education; election law; housing; judicial review; landlord and tenant; local government; mental health; parliamentary; planning; construction; sports and entertainment law; matrimonial finance and children; and pensions.

Publications & Lectures: A number of members regularly publish books and contribute articles to professional publications. Members of chambers provide lectures on a wide range of subjects and chambers are accredited by the Law Society and Bar Council.

Languages: Cantonese, French, German and Italian.

Recruitment & Training: Members of chambers fund two pupils per year. Chambers are members of PACH.

No. 5

LITTMAN CHAMBERS (Mark Littman QC)

12 Gray's Inn Square, Gray's Inn, London, WC1R 5JP
Tel: (020) 7404 4866 **Fax:** (020) 7404 4812 **DX:** 0055 (Ch.Ln.)
Email: admin@littmanchambers.com **Website:** www.littmanchambers.com

Head of Chambers:	Mark Littman QC
Senior Clerk:	Lee Cutler
Junior Clerk:	Stephen Lawrence
Tenants:	21

Members:

Mark Littman QC (1947) (QC-1961)
John Tackaberry QC (1967) (QC-1982)
Michael Stimpson (1969)
Robert Kirk (1972)
Brian McClure (1976)
Graham Cunningham (1976)
Rowan Planterose (1978)
Andrzej Kolodziej (1978)
Jonathan Tecks (1978)
Barbara Hewson (1985)
Monique Allan (1986)
Seán Naidoo (1990)
Martin Gibson (1990)
Rupert Higgins (1991)
Niamh McCarthy (1991)
Julie Anderson (1993) *
Damian Falkowski (1994)
Alexander Hickey (1995)
James Roberts (1996)
Richard Holden (1996)
Michael Taylor (1996)
Philip Lewis (1958)
John Finnis (1970)

* Standing Counsel to the Crown.

LITTMAN CHAMBERS
BARRISTERS
12
GRAY'S INN SQUARE
GRAY'S INN
LONDON WC1R 5JP

The Chambers: Members of chambers offer specialist advocacy; advisory; drafting and arbitration and mediation services to solicitors and to those with direct access to the Bar.

L

Set No. 96

MATRIX CHAMBERS (Nicholas Blake QC)

Griffin Building, Gray's Inn, London, WC1R 5LN
Tel: (020) 7404 3447 **Fax:** (020) 7404 3448 **DX:** 400 Chancery Lane
Email: matrix@matrixlaw.co.uk **Website:** www.matrixlaw.co.uk

Chief Executive:	Nicholas Martin
Practice Managers:	Amanda Campbell, Annie Hopkins
Administrator:	Louise West
Practice Assistants:	Andy Hall, Zoe Osmotherly
Legal Information Manager:	Anna Edmundson
Tenants:	30

Members:

Nicholas Blake QC (1974) (QC-1994)
David Bean QC (1976) (QC-1997)
Cherie Booth QC (1976) (QC-1995)
Andrew Clapham (1985)
James Crawford SC (1999) (NSW-1987) (SC-1997)
Ben Emmerson QC (1986) (QC-2000)
Daniel Friedman (1996)
Conor Gearty (1995)
Murray Hunt (1992)
Raza Husain (1993)
Anthony Jennings (1983)
Julian Knowles (1994)
Thomas Linden (1990)
Kenneth Macdonald QC (1978) (QC-1997)
Jonathan Marks (1992)
Clare Montgomery QC (1980) (QC-1996)
Helen Mountfield (1991)
Tim Owen QC (1983) (QC-2000)
Heather Rogers (1983)
Matthew Ryder (1992)
Philippe Sands (1985)
Maurice Sheridan (1984)
Jessica Simor (1992)
Rabinder Singh (1989)
Dan Squires (1998)
Rhodri Thompson (1989)
Hugh Tomlinson (1983)
Antony White (1983)
David Wolfe (1992)
Mark Afeeva (1997)

The Chambers: Matrix is a new legal practice set up in anticipation of the complex challenges facing the law in the new century. The lawyers who set up Matrix aim to innovate in the way legal services are delivered and to move beyond the traditional divisions – between practitioners and academics, private and public law, and domestic and international law. They are also committed to collaborative ventures that will break down traditional divisions within the legal profession itself.The members of Matrix practice in a wide range of disciplines including UK public, private and criminal law, as well as European Union law, human rights law and public international law. These diverse areas will be linked through common principles of human rights, international and constitutional law, and Matrix will lead the way in providing advice and representation that draws on the emerging synergies of its many practice specialities. Matrix will also innovate through the provision of teams of lawyers and the full integration of leading academics into its practice.Matrix is committed to quality of service and to delivering the highest levels of value to its clients. It will seek feedback from clients on an active basis and is committed to continuous improvement.

Set No. 97

1 MIDDLE TEMPLE LANE (Colin Dines & Andrew Trollope QC)

1 Middle Temple Lane, Temple, London, EC4Y 9AA
Tel: (020) 7583 0659 (12 lines) **Fax:** (020) 7353 0652 **DX:** 464
Email: chambers@lmtl.co.uk

Heads of Chambers:	Colin Dines, Andrew Trollope QC
Senior Clerk:	John Pyne
Tenants:	44

Members:

Colin Dines (1970)
Andrew Trollope QC (1971) (QC-1991)
Paul Purnell QC (1962) (QC-1982)
Roger Backhouse QC (1965) (QC-1984)
Michael Borrelli (1977) (QC-2000)
David Ashby (1963)
Nicholas Gardiner (1967)
Tony Docking (1969)
Graham Arran (1969)
Godfree Browne (1971)
Jonathan Davies (1971)
Brian Argyle (1972)
Andrew Campbell (1972)
Gopal Hooper (1973)
Philip King (1974)
Brian Reece (1974)
John Plumstead (1975)
Ian Copeman (1977)
Bernard Eaton (1978)
Noel Lucas (1979)
Kaly Kaul (1983)
Christopher Amor (1984)
Emma Gluckstein (1985)
Simon Mayo (1985)
Mark Rainsford (1985)
Andrew Marshall (1986)
Richard Butcher (1985)
Barbara Strachan (1986)
James Lachkovic (1987)
Harry Bowyer (1989)
Anthony Korda (1988)
Andrew Newton (1989)
Avirup Chaudhuri (1990)
Rachel Bright (1991)
Richard Beynon (1990)
Mark Graffius (1990)
Philomena Murphy (1992)
Natasha Wong (1993)
Robert Jones (1993)
Sarah Clarke (1994)
Gideon Cammerman (1996)
Sharon Leene (1996)
Tara McCarthy (1997)
John Madden (1997)

The Chambers: Chambers were established in December 1976 by Mr Ronald Grey QC, and since then have flourished, growing both in size and in the quality and range of work undertaken. Members practise mainly in London, the South East and the Home Counties, but have accepted cases all over the country. Most members belong to the Criminal Bar Association, and several serve on various committees connected with criminal law. In addition, two members are on the Immigration Panel for the Home Office. Nine members are recorders. One member is standing counsel to HM Customs & Excise. Outside office hours, the senior clerk can be contacted on:(01708) 641 671 or mobile (0976) 281902.

Work Undertaken:

Criminal: For both prosecution and defence, with an increasing amount of serious white-collar crime. Members have recently acted in major VAT, company and mortgage fraud cases. The whole range of crime is handled from war crimes, murder, drugs and sexual offences to motoring offences and juvenile crime.

Additional Areas: Courts martial; employment law; immigration, for applicants and the government; licensing; extradition; and medical negligence.

International: Godfree Browne is a member of the Zimbabwe and Botswana Bars and an advocate in the High Court of Zimbabwe.

Languages: Bengali, French and German.

Recruitment & Training: Tenancy and pupillage applications to the appropriate committee. Chambers usually have between seven and ten pupils and applications are welcome at any time. Pupillage awards and mini-pupillages are available at chambers' discretion.

Set No. 98

MITRE COURT CHAMBERS (John Burton)

Mitre Court Chambers, 199 Strand, London, WC2R 1DR
Tel: (020) 7836 3619 **Fax:** (020) 7836 7971 **DX:** 449 Ch.Ln. Mobile: 0411 139587
Email: clerks@mitrecourt.co.uk

Head of Chambers	John Burton
Practice Manager:	Alistair Adams
Senior Clerk:	William Ingleton
Tenants:	24

Members:

John M. Burton (1979)
Graeme Ford (1972)
Gillian Frost (1979)
Peter J. Hofford (1979)
Bartholomew V. O'Toole (1980)
Alexander Laban (1981)
Nicholas Storey (1981)
Leslie Wise (1985)
Pieter Briegel (1986)
Ian C. Bridge (1988)
Neil Mercer (1988)
Andrew Forsyth (1989)
Christopher Blake (1990)
Carl Hackman (1990)
Julia Goring (1991)
Philip Brown (1991)
Mukhtiar S. Otwal (1991)
Andrew Espley (1993)
Charlotte Newell (1994)
Max Thorowgood (1995)
Kimberly Aiken (1995)
Felicity Mileham (1996)
Zillah Williams (1997)
Alex Stein (1998)

The Chambers: An established set with members practising in civil, personal injury, crime and family law. In addition to individual specialisations, each member of Chambers is dedicated to one of three teams covering personal injury, crime and family. Members undertake direct professional access work and contribute to specialist publications and seminars.

Work Undertaken:

Civil: Work includes banking, insolvency, commercial, general contract, insurance, employment, landlord and tenant, professional negligence, pensions and trusts.
Personal Injury: Work includes accidents at work, industrial diseases and clinical negligence. Conditional fee agreements.
Crime: Work incorporates all areas of defence work including serious fraud. Members of chambers also prosecute on behalf of statutory agencies in addition to the CPS in matters such as food, planning and environment.
Family: Work includes matrimonial finance, children and divorce.

Languages: German, French, Punjabi.

M

Set No. 99

1 MITRE COURT BUILDINGS (Bruce Blair QC)

1 Mitre Court Buildings, Temple, London, EC4Y 7BS
Tel: (020) 7797 7070 **Fax:** (020) 7797 7435 **DX:** LDE 342 Chancery Lane
Email: clerks@1mcb.com **Website:** www.1mcb.com

Head of Chambers:	Bruce Blair QC
Senior Clerk:	Richard Beams
Tenants:	31

Members:

Bruce Blair QC (1969) (QC-1989)
Michael Horowitz QC (1968) (QC-1990)
Jeremy Posnansky QC (1972) (QC-1994)
Judith Hughes QC (1974) (QC-1994)
Mark Everall QC (1975) (QC-1994)
Martin Pointer QC (1976) (QC-1996)
Nicholas Mostyn QC (1980) (QC-1997)
John Elvidge (1968)
Michael Nicholls (1975)
Robin Spon-Smith (1976)
Valentine Le Grice (1977)
Heather Pope (1977)
Nicholas Carden (1981)
Catriona Murfitt (1981)
Gavin Smith (1981)
Nigel Dyer (1982)
Philip Moor (1982)
Charles Todd (1983)
Christopher Wood (1986)
Nicholas Cusworth (1986)
Katharine Davidson (1987)
Richard Todd (1988)
Rachel Platts (1989)
Elisabeth Todd (1990)
Timothy Bishop (1991)
Geoffrey Kingscote (1993)
Stephen Trowell (1995)
Justin Warshaw (1995)
Nicholas Yates (1996)
Simon Webster (1997)
Shazia Khan (1998)

The Chambers: 1 Mitre Court Buildings is the longest established set practising exclusively in the area of family law. Chambers offers advocacy, advisory and drafting expertise over the entire range of family and matrimonial law, whether child or finance oriented, and undertakes work at all levels of court. Together with its service to privately paying clients, 1 Mitre Court Buildings has a strong commitment to and involvement in legally aided family work. Chambers is regularly instructed by the Official Solicitor and local authorities, as well as on behalf of individual clients. 1 Mitre Court Buildings frequently handles cases with an international dimension. All members of chambers belong to the Family Law Bar Association.

Set No. 100

2 MITRE COURT BUILDINGS (Michael FitzGerald QC)

2 Mitre Court Buildings, Temple, London, EC4Y 7BX
Tel: (020) 7583 1380 **Fax:** (020) 7353 7772 **DX:** 0032 Chancery Lane
Mobile: 0802 776533 **Email:** clerks@2mcb.co.uk

Head of Chambers:	Michael FitzGerald QC
Senior Clerk:	Robert Woods
Clerks:	Robert Woods, Frances Kaliszewska, Kirstie Conway, John Keegan, Joan Matthewson (Administrator)
Tenants:	22

Members:

Michael FitzGerald QC (1961) (QC-1980)
David Widdicombe QC (1950) (QC-1965)
Lord Silsoe QC (1951) (QC-1972)
Gerald Moriarty QC (1951) (QC-1974)
Anthony Anderson QC (1964) (QC-1982)
John Taylor QC (1958) (QC-1983)
Matthew Horton QC (1969) (QC-1989)
Guy Roots QC (1969) (QC-1989)
Neil King QC (1980) (QC-2000)
Alun Alesbury (1974)
Robert Fookes (1975)
Nicholas Burton (1979)
Michael Humphries (1982)
Richard Glover (1984)
Mary Macpherson (1984)
Michael Druce (1988)
Reuben Taylor (1990)
Victor Moore (1992)
Rupert Warren (1994)
Christopher Boyle (1994)
Richard Wald (1997)
Robert Walton (1999)

The Chambers: A long-established and well known set currently comprising 22 members of whom nine are QCs. All members specialise in planning and local government law.

Work Undertaken: The main specialist area practised by all members comprises planning and local government which includes: town and country planning; environmental law; compulsory purchase and compensation; rating and council tax; utilities and infrastructure; local government; public and administrative law; Parliamentary bills; and Transport and Works Act Orders. All members appear at public inquiries; the Lands Tribunal and the Courts.

Clientele: A wide range including companies; corporations; public and private utilities; local authorities; government departments and foreign governments; individuals; and residents associations. Instructions are accepted under the Direct Access Scheme.

International: Members have appeared or advised in relation to a number of jurisdictions including Hong Kong, Jersey and Bermuda.

Recruitment & Training: Applications for tenancy should be addressed to Michael FitzGerald QC. Applications for pupillage should be addressed to Joan Matthewson. Chambers have two to three pupils at any one time and substantial awards are available for pupils; details will be provided on application. Mini-pupillages are also available.

2MCB

M

Set No.
101 **2 MITRE COURT BUILDINGS** (Roger Gray)

2 Mitre Court Buildings, (first floor), Temple, London, EC4Y 7BX **Tel:** (020) 7353 1353 **Fax:** (020) 7353 8188 **DX:** 0023 London Chancery Lane

Set No.
102 **MONCKTON CHAMBERS** (John Swift QC)

4 Raymond Buildings, Gray's Inn, London, WC1R 5BP
Tel: (020) 7405 7211 **Fax:** (020) 7405 2084 **DX:** 257
Email: chambers@monckton.co.uk **Website:** www.monckton.co.uk

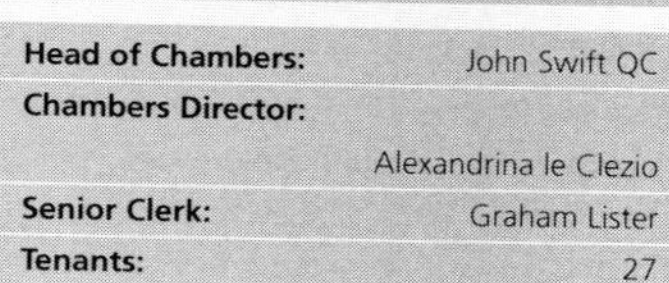

Head of Chambers:	John Swift QC
Chambers Director:	Alexandrina le Clezio
Senior Clerk:	Graham Lister
Tenants:	27

Members:

John Swift QC (1965) (QC-1981)
Jeremy Lever QC (1957) (QC-1972)
Nicholas Lyell QC (1965) (QC-1980)
Richard Fowler QC (1969) (QC-1989)
Richard Seymour QC (1972) (QC-1991)
Kenneth Parker QC (1975) (QC-1992)
Paul Lasok QC (1977) (QC-1994)
Peter M. Roth QC (1976) (QC-1997)
Nicholas Paines QC (1978) (QC-1997)
Christopher Vajda QC (1979) (QC-1997)
Edward Bailey (1970)
Mark Pelling (1979)
Rupert Anderson (1981)
Michael Patchett-Joyce (1981)
Melanie Hall (1982)
Andrew Macnab (1986)
Jon Turner (1988)
Peter Mantle (1989)
Jennifer Skilbeck (1991)
Raymond Hill (1992)
Paul Harris (1994)
Rebecca Haynes (1994)
Tim Ward (1994)
Kassie Smith (1995)
Daniel Beard (1996)
George Peretz (1990)
Ian Hutton (1998)

The Chambers: Monckton Chambers provides specialised advocacy and advice in European and competition law, commercial litigation and judicial review. Members of chambers regard client care as paramount. They are committed to providing the best legal advice and advocacy, responding promptly and efficiently to all instructions, offering specialist services as part of an integrated professional team and remaining accessible and approachable at all times.

Work Undertaken:

European law: members of chambers appear regularly before the ECJ on cases involving agriculture, competition, employment, human rights, media and telecommunications, pharmaceuticals, state aids, utilities, VAT and customs. Recent cases before the European courts include: Levez v T.H. Jennings [1999], Mann v Sec of State for Employment [1999], R v Sec of State for Transport ex p Factortame [1999], Arnhem v BFI Holdings BV [1998], Blue Circle v Commission [1998], Ladbroke Racing v Commission [1998], Partridge v Adjudication Officer [1998], McLeod v United Kingdom [1998] (ECHR). Members of chambers have also been involved in numerous high profile European cases in the UK courts including R v Sec of State for Health ex p. Imperial Tobacco [1999], R v CCE ex p Lunn Poly [1999] (CA), Three Rivers District Council v Bank of England [1999] (CA) Factortame case, Redrow v CCE [1999] HL, Optident Ltd. v Sec of State [1999], Preston & Others v Wolverhampton Healthcare NHS Trust and Fletcher v Midland Bank PLC [1998] HL, Philips v Ingman [1998], R v MAFF ex p Anastasiou (No 2) [1998], HL, R v CCE ex p Institute of Chartered Accountants [1998] HL, Midland Bank v CCE [1998], Case C – 180/96 UK v Commission [1998].

Competition: Chambers extensive experience in competition law matters includes Competition Commission ("CC") references, OFT inquiries, European Commission and ECJ cases. High profile competition cases in which members of chambers have appeared include the, the CC inquiry into the IMS/PMSI merger (pharmaceutical services), the BA/CityFlyer merger and the UFC/Pointing merger, the Airtours/First Choice merger proceedings before the European Commission, the CC inquiry into Mobile Telephones, Gencor v Commission [1999], European Night Services v Commission [1998], the Scancem/Skanska/Aker merger proceedings, the RPC reference in relation to the resale price maintenance of medicaments, the CC reference on supermarkets and the RPC reference in relation to the televising of Premier League football. Members of chambers are also extensively involved in competition and related regulatory matters concerning the utilities; acting both for the regulators (including Oftel, Ofwat and Offer) and the regulated companies. See R v Director General of Telecommunications ex p Cellcom [1999] and R v OFWAT ex p Oldham MBC & Ors [1998].

Judicial Review: recent major cases include: R v Sec of State ex p Imperial Tobacco [1999], R v CCE ex p Marks & Spencer [1999], Evans v MIB [1999], R v ITC ex p Flextech [1999], R v Governor of Gibraltar ex p Ouzza [1999], R v Secretary of State for Home Department ex p Hoverspeed [1999], R v Chief Constable of Sussex ex p ITF [1999] (HL), R v Home Office ex p McAvoy [1998] CA, R v Secretary of State for Employment ex p Seymour-Smith [1997] HL and R v Home Office ex p Camden City Council [1997] HL.Members of chambers also appear regularly before the VAT Tribunal and Higher Courts in relation to VAT and EC Customs legislation. Recent cases include: Eastbourne Town Radio Cars Association v CCE [2000] HL, Marks & Spencer v CCE [1999], Redrow v CCE [1999] HL, Institute of Chartered Accountants v CCE [1998] HL, McNicholas v CCE [1998], Thorn Materials v CCE [1998] HL.

MONCKTON CHAMBERS

Continued overleaf

M

Commercial Law: expertise includes international and domestic arbitration, banking, international and domestic commercial fraud recovery and tracing, construction law, insurance and re-insurance, and professional negligence. Members of chambers have appeared in international arbitrations in the Middle East, Africa and Eastern Europe as well as in London. Recent reported commercial cases include Dubai Aluminium Company Ltd v Alawi & Others [1999], Dubai Aluminium Company Ltd v Salaam and Others [1998], Quadrant v Prosser [1998] North Atlantic Insurance Co. Ltd v Bishopsgate Insurance Ltd [1998], Hill & Mullis & Peake (CA) [1998].

Publications: In addition many of the leading reference works on EC law are written or edited by members of chambers including *Bellamy and Child 'The Common Market Law of Competition', currently edited by Peter Roth QC and 'The European Court of Justice: Practice and Procedure'* written by Paul Lasok QC. *The Common Market Law Reports* are edited by Paul Lasok QC and Nicholas Paines QC. Tim Ward is General Editor of the *Human Rights Law Reports*.

Set No. 103

1 NEW SQUARE (Eben Hamilton QC)

1 New Square, Lincoln's Inn, London, WC2A 3SA
Tel: (020) 7405 0884 **Fax:** (020) 7831 6109 **DX:** 295 London/Chancery Lane
Email: clerks@1newsquare.law.co.uk **Website:** www.1newsquare.law.co.uk

Head of Chambers:	Eben Hamilton QC
Senior Clerk:	Warren Lee
Tenants:	20

NEW 1 SQUARE

Members:

Eben W. Hamilton QC (1962) (QC-1981)
Rodney Stewart Smith (1964)
Michael K.I. Kennedy (1967)
John B.W. McDonnell QC (1968) (QC-1984)
Robin Hollington QC (1979) (QC-1999)
Malcolm Chapple (1975)
Christopher Semken (1977)
Michael Roberts (1978)
Clive Hugh Jones (1981)
Kathryn Lampard (1984)
David Eaton Turner (1984)
Thomas Graham (1985)
Sandra Corbett (1988)
Colette Wilkins (1989)
Gerard van Tonder (1990)
Mark Hubbard (1991)
John Eidinow (1992)
Sebastian Prentis (1996)
David Warner (1996)
Adrian Pay (1999)

The Chambers: Historically a set of Chancery chambers, 1 New Square now provides expertise across a wide range of areas, particularly within the Chancery and commercial areas. Civil litigation is heading for radical reform and chambers aims to meet the challenges that the changed legal landscape presents.

Work Undertaken: Individual members of chambers have specialist expertise in various areas such as intellectual property, commercial fraud, partnership, banking and media/entertainment. Generally, however, chambers focuses on six key areas within Chancery, company and commercial law: company law; corporate and personal insolvency; real property and landlord & tenant; private client trusts, wills and probate; professional negligence (particularly solicitors and accountants); local government work and judicial review.

Clientele: Individuals, public companies and private companies. Most members accept Direct Professional Access. In addition to formal written advice, counsel are available to give advice by telephone, in conference, by fax or e-mail. For further information, please ask the clerks for a brochure, or vist chambers' website.

International: More senior members appear before the courts in Hong Kong, Singapore, Malaysia, Bermuda, the Cayman Islands and Gibraltar.

Publications: Members of chambers write regularly on their specialist areas for legal publications. Robin Hollington is the author of *Minority Shareholders' Rights* (Sweet & Maxwell 1999). Malcolm Chapple is the author of the section on intellectual property in *Law and the Business of Sport* (Butterworths). Clive Jones is an editor of *Mithani: Directors' Disqualification.*

Recruitment & Training: Pupillage applications to Sandra Corbett. Awards are available.

Set No. 104

3 NEW SQUARE (Lord Goodhart QC)

3 New Square, Lincoln's Inn, London, WC2A 3RS
Tel: (020) 7405 5577 **Fax:** (020) 7404 5032 **DX:** LDE 384 (Ch.Ln.)
Email: law@threenewsquare.co.uk **Website:** www.threenewsquare.co.uk

Head of Chambers	Lord Goodhart QC
Sen. Clerk:	Richard Bayliss
Tenants:	16

Members:

Lord Goodhart QC (1957) (QC-1979)
Hubert Picarda QC (1962) (QC-1992)
Hedley Marten (1966)
David Rowell (1972)
David Parry (1972)
Bernard Weatherill QC (1974) (QC-1996) FCIArb
Andrew G. Walker (1975)
Michael Heywood (1975) FCIArb
Josephine Hayes (1980)
Roger Mullis (1987)
Charles Marquand (1987) FCIArb
Adam Deacock (1991)
Justin Holmes (1994)
Mary Hughes (1994)
Dov Ohrenstein (1995)
Camilla Lamont (1995)

The Chambers: 3 New Square is a modern commercial Chancery set committed to a vigorous tradition of excellence. Advocacy, advice and drafting are available in all the areas listed below.

Work Undertaken:

Commercial: Banking; credit and security; competition; conflict of laws; contracts; consumer credit; economic torts; finance; franchising; fraud; forgery and misrepresentation; guarantees; partnerships; title retention; restitution; and tracing.

Company: Companies Court; changes in capital; charges; directors' disqualification; directors' duties; liquidation; receiverships; securities; shareholder disputes.

European Law: All aspects relating to other work undertaken.

Financial Services: City regulation; tribunals; derivative instruments; promotions & offerings.

Insolvency: Corporate and personal; including international.Judicial Review.

Pension Schemes: All aspects of occupational and personal pension schemes; fraud and insolvency.

Professional Negligence: Legal; financial; surveyors & valuers.

Property: Commercial, agricultural and residential; constructive trusts; conveyancing; easements; highways; landlord and tenant; Lands Tribunal; licences; mortgages and securities; planning; property-related torts; restrictive covenants.

Traditional Chancery: Charities; court of protection; equitable remedies; fiduciary duties; probate; tax & tax planning (including VAT); trusts & settlements; wills.

Alternative Dispute Resolution: Members include qualified arbitrators and undertake arbitrations and mediations as arbitrators or mediators and as advocates.

Direct Professional Access: Work is accepted from members of the qualifing professions.

International: Members are increasingly being instructed by overseas lawyers in chambers' areas of expertise, both in contentious and non-contentious matters.

Publications:*Specific Performance* (2nd ed 1996) by Lord Goodhart QC (with Prof Gareth Jones QC); *The Law & Practice Relating to Charities* (2nd ed 1995) by Hubert Picarda QC; *The Law Relating to Receivers, Managers & Administrators* by Hubert Picarda QC; *Halsbury's Laws of England* (4th ed): titles on *Corporations* by Lord Goodhart QC and Charles Marquand; on *Money* by Charles Marquand & Dov Ohrenstein; and on *Mortgages* co-authored by Camilla Lamont; *Specific Performance* by Lord Goodhart QC; and *Receivers* by Hubert Picarda QC.

No. 05

THREE NEW SQUARE (David E.M. Young QC)

3 New Square, Lincoln's Inn, London, WC2A 3RS
Tel: (020) 7405 1111 **Fax:** (020) 7405 7800 **DX:** 454
Email: 3newsquareip@lineone.net **Website:** www.3newsquare.co.uk

Head of Chambers:	David E.M. Young QC
Senior Clerk:	Ian Bowie
Tenants:	13

Members:

David Young QC (1966) (QC-1980)
Antony Watson QC (1968) (QC-1986)
Simon Thorley QC (1972) (QC-1989)
Richard Miller QC (1976) (QC-1995)
Guy Burkill (1981)
Andrew Waugh QC (1982) (QC-1998)
Denise McFarland (1987)
Colin Birss (1990)
Justin Turner (1992)
Douglas James Campbell (1993)
Thomas Mitcheson (1996)
Thomas Hinchliffe (1997)
Geoffrey Pritchard (1998)

Former Members: Sir Douglas Falconer, Lord Justice Aldous.

The Chambers: A specialist intellectual property set. Members belong to the Intellectual Property and Chancery Bar Associations. David Young is the author of Passing Off, Chairman of the Plant Seeds Varieties Tribunal and Deputy Judge of the Patent County Court. David Young, Antony Watson and Simon Thorley are deputy High Court Judges in Chancery and Queens' Bench Division. Simon Thorley is a part-time Chairman of the Copyright Tribunal. In addition, for many years, members have edited Terrell on the Law of Patents.

Work Undertaken:

Intellectual Property: Particularly science; technology; biotechnology; entertainment; and media. Including patents (UK and European); copyright; designs (registered and unregistered); service marks; plantbreeders rights; trade marks (registered and unregistered); passing off; trade libel and malicious falsehood; confidential information; franchising and licensing (including licences of right and product licensing) and information technology. Members also handle related aspects of competition law and general litigation with a significant technical content. Direct Professional Access is accepted.

Additional Areas: Arbitration and professional negligence.

International: Chambers' QCs have appeared in Singapore and Hong Kong.

Languages: French, German and Japanese.

Recruitment & Training: Tenancy and pupillage applications should be made via the PACH scheme. Awards of £9,000 per six-months are available. Mini-pupillages are offered throughout the year. A science degree is preferred.

N

Set No.
106

FOUR NEW SQUARE (Justin Fenwick QC)

4 New Square, Lincoln's Inn, London, WC2A 3RJ
Tel: (020) 7822 2000 **Fax:** (020) 7822 2001 **DX:** 1041 L.D.E.
Email: barristers@4newsquare.com **Website:** www.4newsquare.com

Head of Chambers:	Justin Fenwick QC
Senior Clerk:	Lizzy Wiseman
Tenants:	43

Members:

Justin Fenwick QC (1980) (QC-1993)
John L. Powell QC (1974) (QC-1990)
Bernard Livesey QC (1969) (QC-1990)
Nicholas Davidson QC (1974) (QC-1993)
Michael Brooke QC (1969) (QC-1994)
Christopher Gibson QC (1976) (QC-1995)
Iain Hughes QC (1974) (QC-1996)
Eva Lomnicka (1974)
Simon Russen (1976)
Charles Douthwaite (1977)
Glen Tyrell (1977)
Michael Soole (1977)
David Halpern (1978)
Gavin Hamilton (1979)
Barbara Kaplan (1980)
Simon Monty (1982)
Martin Fodder (1983)
Mark Cannon (1985)
Ian Holtum (1985)
Paul Parker (1986)
Roger Stewart (1986)
Ben Patten (1986)
Sue Carr (1987)
Hugh Evans (1987)
Jalil Asif (1988)
Andrew Tettenborn (1988)
Fiona Sinclair (1989)
Nicholas Brown (1989)
Andrew R. Nicol (1991)
Ben Hubble (1992)
Charles Phipps (1992)
Paul Sutherland (1992)
Graeme McPherson (1993)
Leigh-Ann Mulcahy (1993)
Aisha Bijlani (1993)
Nicola Shaldon (1994)
Charlotte Goldberg (1995)
Jamie Smith (1995)
Anneliese Day (1996)
Ben Elkington (1996)
Seánin Gilmore (1996)
Siân Mirchandani (1997)
Graham Chapman (1998)

His Honour John Loyd QC accepts appointments to act as an arbitrator.

The Chambers: Four New Square is a commercial and civil set with a particular reputation for claims involving professionals and other service providers. It also has a strong construction, insurance, commercial and employment practice. Based for over 50 years in the Temple (most recently at 2 Crown Office Row), the set moved to new, larger premises in 1999. This has allowed chambers to introduce a modern IT network and to acquire enlarged conference facilities (including video-conferencing) as part of its continuing commitment to providing all its clients with the highest level of service, both as advocates and as advisers.

Other information: Eva Lomnicka is Professor of Laws, King's College, London and Andrew Tettenborn is Bracton Professor of Law in the University of Exeter. Further details of each member's practice can be obtained from the senior clerk, Lizzy Wiseman, and her team.

Work Undertaken: Chambers has a particular expertise in the field of professional liability and covers the full range of claims against professionals, including claims for fraud, breach of fiduciary duty and trust, negligence and breach of contract and regulatory and disciplinary proceedings. The main professions covered are accountants and auditors, architects and engineers, solicitors and barristers, bankers, financial intermediaries and institutions, insurance intermediaries, Lloyd's agents, surveyors and valuers and medical practitioners. Jackson & Powell on Professional Negligence is edited by current members of chambers.

Other major areas of practice include construction and engineering, commercial litigation, banking and financial services (including UK, EU and international securities regulation), consumer credit, insurance and reinsurance, employment, IT and computer contracts, product liability and personal injury. Chambers has considerable experience of multi-party litigation in the context of product liability, professional negligence, fraud recovery and disaster claims.

Publications: Apart from *Jackson & Powell on Professional Negligence* (John Powell QC, Roger Stewart, Mark Cannon, Hugh Evans, Iain Hughes QC and Fiona Sinclair), publications include *Lawyer's Liabilities* (Hugh Evans), *Confidentiality* (Charles Phipps with Toulson J.), and *The Encyclopedia of Financial Services Law* (Eva Lomnicka and John Powell QC). This year also sees the arrival of the companion work to Jackson & Powell, *Professional Liability Precedents*, (Sue Carr, Jalil Asif, Ben Elkington, Ben Hubble, Simon Monty, Paul Parker, Charles Phipps, Simon Russen and Paul Sutherland). Leigh-Ann Mulcahy is one of the co-authors of *Human Rights and Civil Practise* which is due to be published in 2001. Andrew Tettenborn is an editor of *Clerk & Lindsell on Torts.*

International: Members of chambers appear in court and arbitration proceedings in Hong Kong, Singapore, Paris and the West Indies. Michael Brooke QC is an Avocat à la Cour d'Appel de Paris.

N

Set No.
107 **5 NEW SQUARE** (Jonathan Rayner James QC)

5 New Square, Lincoln's Inn, London, WC2A 3RJ
Tel: (020) 7404 0404 **Fax:** (020) 7831 6016 **DX:** 272 London
Mobile: (24 hours) 0585 139106 **Email:** barristers@5newsquare.co.uk **Website:** www.5newsquare.co.uk

Head of Chambers:	Jonathan Rayner James QC
Clerks:	Ian Duggan, Clive Nicholls, Ian Kitchen
Tenants:	16

Members:

Jonathan Rayner James QC (1971) (QC-1988)
Kevin Garnett QC (1975) (QC-1991)
James Sunnucks (1950) DL
Ernest H Scamell (1949)
Patrick Sinclair (1961)
John Ross Martyn (1969) +
Alexander Stewart (1975)
Edward Bragiel (1977)
Paul Dickens (1978)
Amanda Michaels (1981)
Julia Clark (1984)
Nicholas Caddick (1986)
Gwilym Harbottle (1987)
Andrew Norris (1995)
Alistair Abbott (1996)
George Hayman (1998)

The Chambers: A progressive set that continues to adapt to meet the needs of modern practice, providing a cost-effective service that is suited to the problems involved. Chambers specialise in two core areas:

Work Undertaken:

Intellectual Property, Media and Entertainment: Copyright, designs, moral rights, performers' rights, trade marks, passing off, patents, criminal remedies, Copyright Tribunal, entertainment contracts, confidential information, related EC aspects.

Chancery and Commercial: Company, partnership, insolvency, charities, wills & administration, Inheritance Act, trusts & fiduciaries, banking & securities, land law & conveyancing, landlord & tenant, commercial contracts, professional negligence.

et No.
108 **7 NEW SQUARE** (Bernard Pearl)

7 New Square, Lincoln's Inn, London, WC2A 3QS
Tel: (020) 7430 1660 **Fax:** (020) 7430 1531 **DX:** 106 (Ch.Ln.)
Website: www.sevennewsquare.com

Head of Chambers:	Bernard Pearl
Senior Clerk:	John Harwood IBC, MTTS
Tenants:	15

Members:

Bernard Pearl (1970)
Margaret Puxon QC (1954) (QC-1982)
Philip Proghoulis (1963)
Andrew Gifford (1988)
Andrew Baker (1990)
Linda Goldman (1990)
John Scott Price (1990)
Lisa Sinclair (1993)
Fareha Choudhury (1995)
Catherine MacKenzie (1995)
Raj Kothari (1996)
Peter Ellis (1997)
Melvyn Harris (1997)
Marianne Perkins (1997)
Alastair B. Hodge (1997)

Work Undertaken: Civil/commercial, especially professional negligence (members include two former solicitors, two dentists, a doctor and a pharmacist); commercial and residential property; insolvency; employment; local authority; judicial review.
Seminars and lectures are available.

Languages: Bengali, French, German and Italian.

t No.
09 **7 NEW SQUARE INTELLECTUAL PROPERTY** (John Fitzgerald)

7 New Square, Lincoln's Inn, London, WC2A 3QS
Tel: (020) 7404 5484 **Fax:** (020) 7404 5369 **DX:** 420 (CH LN)
Email: clerks@7newsquare.com **Website:** www.7newsquare.com

Head of Chambers:	John Fitzgerald
Senior Clerk:	Simon Coomber
Tenants:	7

Members:

John Fitzgerald (1971)
Alison Firth (1980)
Matthew Kime (1988)
Mark Engelman (1987)
Gary Fern (1992)
Richard Davis (1992)
Tim Ludbrook (1996)

N

The Chambers: A progressive set specialising in all aspects of the law of intellectual property. Many members of chambers have prior relevant experience ranging from scientific research to television production. A detailed brochure is available. Up-to-date information is available on their website.

Work Undertaken: Primarily, members practice in the areas of patents, copyright, design rights, trade marks and passing off, trade secrets and confidentiality, computer and information technology. Members of chambers also assist in other areas of concern often closely associated with general intellectual property practice such as technical contract, e-commerce, internet, criminal IP liability, EU competition law,

Continued overleaf

entertainment, trade libel, defamation and other media orientated work and general contractual or tortuous problems in appropriate contexts.

Clientele: Instructions come to chambers not only from solicitors and patent or trade mark attorneys but also, in relation to other professional clients, via the Direct Professional Access scheme.

International: Chambers can field experience of the law and practice of the European Patent Office in Munich as well as that of the Community Trade Mark Office (OHIM) in Alicante.

Recruitment & Training: Applications for pupillage should be sent to Tim Ludbrook. Mini-pupillages are available.

Set No. 110

8 NEW SQUARE (Michael Fysh QC SC)

8 New Square, Lincoln's Inn, London, WC2A 3QP
Tel: (020) 7405 4321 **Fax:** (020) 7405 9955 **DX:** 379 (Ch.Ln) **Mobile:** 07887 763993
Email: clerks@8newsquare.co.uk **Website:** www.8newsquare.co.uk

Head of Chambers:	Michael Fysh QC SC
Senior Clerk:	John F. Call
Deputy Senior Clerk:	Tony Liddon
Principle Clerks:	Nicholas Wise, Martin Williams
Assistant Clerks:	Martin Kilbey, Andrew Clayton
Tenants:	20

Members:

Michael Fysh QC SC (1994) (1965) (QC-1989)
Peter Prescott QC (1970) (QC-1990)
John Baldwin QC (1977) (QC-1991)
David Kitchin QC (1977) (QC-1994)
Mark Platts-Mills QC (1974) (QC-1995)
Martin Howe QC (1978) (QC-1996)
Mary Vitoria QC (1975) (QC-1997)
George Hamer (1974)
Fiona Clark (1982)
James Mellor (1986)
Daniel Alexander (1988)
Robert Onslow (1991)
Michael Tappin (1991)
Richard Meade (1991)
Adrian Speck (1993)
James St. Ville (1995)
Charlotte May (1995)
Thomas Moody-Stuart (1995)
Lindsay Lane (1996)
James Abrahams (1997)

Former Members: Mr Justice Jacob, Mr Justice Laddie

The Chambers: The chambers specialise in intellectual property law of all kinds, and are the largest set in the country practising in this area. Many members of chambers are authors of, or contributors to, the leading books and encyclopaedias on intellectual property law. All are members of the Intellectual Property Bar and Chancery Bar Associations. A brochure giving further information and individual biographies of all members of chambers is available upon request. Biographies may also be viewed on 8 New Square's website along with current news. The senior clerks, John Call and Tony Liddon, have been with chambers for over 20 years and have considerable experience of the work undertaken by chambers. They will be happy to assist in choice of Counsel.

Work Undertaken: Intellectual property, including patents, copyright, passing off, trade and service marks, designs and registered designs, counterfeiting, data protection, franchising, publishing, telecommunications, internet domain names, trade libel, trade descriptions, trade secrets and confidential information, hallmarks, plant breeders' rights. Members also specialise in European law, competition and restrictive trade practices, entertainment and media law, advertising law, computer law, licensing and administrative law (principally where these are ancillary to intellectual property cases). Commercial, environmental and other work with a significant scientific or technical content is also handled.

International: Several members of chambers conduct cases in the Far East, Australia, India and Ireland.

Languages: French, German, Spanish and Italian.

Recruitment & Training: Up to two pupillages are offered each year, usually for twelve months. Pupils with scientific or technical backgrounds are strongly encouraged, although others will be considered in exceptional circumstances. Awards of £20,000 are offered. Chambers are members of PACH (Pupillage Applications Clearing House).

N

No. 11

11 NEW SQUARE (John Gardiner QC)

11 New Square, Lincoln's Inn, London, WC2A 3QB
Tel: (020) 7242 4017 **Fax:** (020) 7831 2391 **DX:** 315
Email: taxlaw@11newsquare.com **Website:** www.11newsquare.com

Head of Chambers:	John Gardiner QC
Senior Clerk:	John Moore
Tenants:	8

Members:

John Gardiner QC (1968) (QC-1982)
Barry Pinson QC (1949) (QC-1973)
Peter Rees QC (1953) (QC-1969)
Peter Trevett QC (1971) (QC-1992)
Jonathan Peacock (1987)
Francis Fitzpatrick (1990)
Grania Lyster (1992)
Jolyon Maugham (1997)

The Chambers: This is the oldest established set to specialise exclusively in revenue law. Members advise in the UK and abroad on all aspects of tax law including all personal and corporate taxes, VAT, customs & excise and stamp duties. Tax planning and advocacy services are provided for clients ranging from large multinational corporations to private individuals, including those of modest means. The set also advises in relation to professional negligence actions. The chambers offer a considerable range of experience in litigation before tribunals of first instance including the Commissioners of Inland Revenue and VAT Tribunals, through the High Court to the House of Lords, the European Court of Human Rights and the courts of certain colonies and Commonwealth jurisdictions. The chambers can accommodate electronic file transfer with or without secure encryption. Worldwide video conferences can be arranged. The chambers has a website displaying information about chambers, including tax law articles.

Languages: French and Luxembourgeoise.

No. 12

11 NEW SQUARE (Sonia Proudman QC)

11 New Square, Lincoln's Inn, London, WC2A 3QB
Tel: (020) 7831 0081 **Fax:** (020) 7405 0798/2560 **DX:** 319
Email: clerks@11newsquare.co.uk

Head of Chambers:	Sonia Proudman QC
Senior Clerk:	Michael Gibbs
Assistant Senior Clerk:	Gary Ventura
Tenants:	23

Members:

Sonia Proudman QC (1972) (QC-1994)
Peter Crampin QC (1976) (QC-1993)
Miles Shillingford (1964)
Roger Horne (1967)
Dirik Jackson (1969)
Peter Castle (1970)
Stephen Lloyd (1971)
Jill Gibson (1972)
Michael Jefferis (1976)
Mark Studer (1976)
Robert Pearce (1977)
Andrew Francis (1977)
Thomas Dumont (1979)
Alistair Craig (1983)
Gilead Cooper (1983)
Ulick Staunton (1984)
Piers Feltham (1985)
Howard Smith (1986)
Peter Smith (1993)
Marie-Claire Bleasdale (1993)
Daniel Margolin (1995)
Omar Rashid (1997)
Siri Cope (1997)

The Chambers: 11 New Square is a leading and progressive set of chambers specialising in Chancery work. Its members, two silks and 21 juniors, possess notable expertise in both traditional and evolving areas of chancery practice. The aims of chambers are to provide first class advocacy, advice and drafting in the areas of members' expertise; to develop constructive and lasting working relationships between members and their clients; and to be approachable and responsive to the needs of clients.

Work Undertaken:

Property: All aspects of land law and conveyancing, as well as landlord and tenant work. Chambers contain specialists in restrictive covenants; easements (including rights of light); and mines and minerals.
Trusts & Estates: All aspects of the administration of trusts and estates, including probate and family provision litigation. Members offer specialist expertise in the field of the taxation of trusts.
Professional Negligence: Members of chambers at all levels have wide experience in the conduct and defence of claims for professional negligence, particularly of solicitors, accountants and surveyors.
Charities & Pensions: Chambers contain groups of members with particular expertise in both these areas.
Commercial Law: Particularly in areas such as banking and security, partnerships and joint ventures.
Company, Corporate and Individual Insolvency: In the corporate field, members have particular experience in areas such as minority shareholders' rights and directors' conduct, winding up, administration and receivership.
Other: Individual members of chambers have developed particular expertise in a wide variety of other fields such as planning; environmental waste; judicial review; intellectual property; court of protection work; and the taxation of costs.Members of chambers are members of the Chancery Bar Association, the Professional Negligence Bar Association, PEBA, STEP, the Charity Law Association and ACTAPS.

N

Set No. 113

12 NEW SQUARE (John Mowbray QC)

Head of Chambers:	John Mowbray QC
Senior Clerk:	Clive Petchey
Tenants:	24

12 New Square, Lincoln's Inn, London, WC2A 3SW
Tel: (020) 7419 1212 **Fax:** (020) 7419 1313 **DX:** 366 London/Chancery Lane
Email: chambers@12newsquare.co.uk **Website:** www.12newsquare.co.uk

Members:

John Mowbray QC (1953) (QC-1974)
John Macdonald QC (1955) (QC-1976)
Charles Purle QC (1970) (QC-1989)
George Laurence QC (1972) (QC-1991)
Robin Mathew QC (1974) (QC-1992)
Stephen Smith QC (1983) (QC-2000)
Lynton Tucker (1971)
Colin Braham (1971)
Christopher Russell (1971)
Kenneth Munro (1973)
Gordon Bennett (1974)
Nicholas Le Poidevin (1975)
Stuart Barber (1979)
Leigh Sagar (1983)
Claire Staddon (1985)
Ross Crail (1986)
Stephen Schaw Miller (1988)
Ian Peacock (1990)
Edwin Simpson (1990)
Simon Adamyk (1991)
Jane Evans-Gordon (1992)
Nicholas Terras (1993)
Louise Davies (1995)
Richard Buckley (1969)
Robert Sterling (1970) *
Anthony Elleray QC (1977) (QC-1993) *
Roger Birch (1979) *
Mark Cawson (1982) *

*Door tenant

Work Undertaken: 12 New Square undertakes litigation and advisory work, both in the UK and internationally, including Direct Professional Access and legal aid work. The work done by members of chambers covers three broad areas: company and commercial – including individual and corporate insolvency, receivership, partnership, freezing injunctions, search orders and fraud; property – including landlord and tenant, mortgages, construction and conveyancing; taxes, trusts and wills – equity, probate, pension schemes and both revenue and capital taxation. Members of chambers also cover public/administrative law aspects of these areas including parliamentary, public inquiries, local government and planning law, judicial review and constitutional law. Its practice includes negligence on the part of professionals in the above fields.
A brochure, containing a more detailed profile of chambers, is available on request, or via our website at: www.12newsquare.co.uk

International: John Mowbray QC is a member if the Bahamian Bar and has also been called to the Eastern Caribbean Bar, as have John Macdonald QC, Charles Purle QC, Stephen Smith QC and Nicholas Terras. Nicholas Le Poidevin is a member of the Isle of Man Bar.

Languages: French and German.

Recruitment & Training: Applications for pupillage via PACH.

Set No. 114

19 OLD BUILDINGS (Alastair Wilson QC)

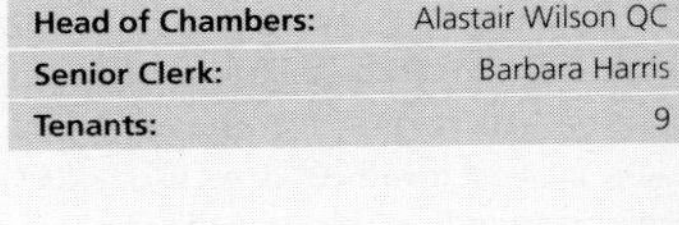

Head of Chambers:	Alastair Wilson QC
Senior Clerk:	Barbara Harris
Tenants:	9

19 Old Buildings, Lincoln's Inn, London, WC2A 3UP
Tel: (020) 7405 2001 **Fax:** (020) 7405 0001 **DX:** 397 (Ch.Ln.)
Email: clerks@oldbuildingsip.com **Website:** www.oldbuildingsip.com

Members:

Alastair Wilson QC (1968) (QC-1987) MA (Cantab)
Brian Reid (1971) MA (Cantab), LLM (Lond)
Graham Shipley (1973) MA (Cantab), Dip Comp Sci (Cantab)
Michael Hicks (1976) BA (Cantab)
Peter McLean Colley (1989) BSc (Lond), PhD (Lond), LLB (Lond)
Cedric Puckrin (1990) BA, LLB (Cape Town)
Rory Sullivan (1992) MA (Oxon)
Tamsin Holman (1995) MA (Oxon)
Jeremy Reed (1997) BA (Cantab)

O

The Chambers: This set, founded by Sir Duncan Kerly, has specialised for over a century in intellectual property law. Chambers also offer expertise in cases relating to computers (and other technical subject-matter), competition, media and entertainment.
Direct Professional Access work is undertaken. A chambers brochure is available on request.

Work Undertaken:
Intellectual Property: Patents; copyright; designs; trade marks; passing off; plant varieties; and confidential information (including ex-employee cases).
Science & Technology: Work requiring understanding of scientific and technical issues.
Computers and IT: All aspects of litigation involving computers and information technology including data protection and internet disputes.

Media & Entertainment: Public performance, film, recording and performers' rights; merchandising; broadcasting; and cable and satellite distribution.
Competition Law: UK and EU monopolies and restrictive practices law, in particular relating to R&D, licensing, distribution and franchising.
Additional areas: Pharmaceutical registration.

Publications: Publications written, or contributed to, by members of chambers include: *European Patent Office Reports, The Future of Legal Protection for Industrial Design, The CIPA Black Book, Melville's Forms and Agreements on Intellectual Property and International Licensing.*

Languages: French.

Set No. 115

22 OLD BUILDINGS (Benet Hytner QC)

22 Old Buildings, Lincoln's Inn, London, WC2A 3UJ
Tel: (020) 7831 0222 **Fax:** (020) 7831 2239 **DX:** 201 London Chancery Lane
Email: clerks@22oldbuildings.law.co.uk

Head of Chambers:	Benet Hytner QC
Senior Clerk:	Alan Brewer
Principle Clerk:	Jody Spencer
Chambers Administrator:	Tony Charlick
Tenants:	56

Members:

Benet Hytner QC (1952) (QC-1970)
John Price QC (1961) (QC-1980)
John Rowe QC (1960) (QC-1982)
Giles Wingate-Saul QC (1967) (QC-1983)
Brian Leveson QC (1970) (QC-1986)
Rodney Scholes QC (1968) (QC-1987)
Timothy King QC (1973) (QC-1991)
Geoffrey Tattersall QC (1970) (QC-1992)
Caroline Swift QC (1977) (QC-1993)
Andrew G. Moran QC (1976) (QC-1994)
Michael Black QC (1978) (QC-1995)
David Allan QC (1974) (QC-1995)
Stephen Stewart QC (1975) (QC-1996)
Winston Hunter QC (1985) (QC-2000)
Patrick Hamlin (1970)
Mark Batchelor (1971)
Susan Cooper (1976)
Michael Daiches (1977)
Anne Ralphs (1977)
Philip Newman (1977)
Charles Utley (1979)
Jane Hill (1980)
Howard Lederman (1982)
Rehna Azim (1984)
Jonathan Bennett (1985)
Rajinder Sahonte (1986)
Garfield Braithwaite (1987)
Tina Cook (1988)
Frank Feehan (1988)
Gemma Taylor (1988)
Nicholas Berry (1988)
Ronald Coster (1989)
Anthony Jerman (1989)
Lee Arnot (1990)
Richard Furniss (1991)
Mary Lazarus (1991)
Paul Lonergan (1991)
Carolyn Rothwell (1991)
Marcia Hyde (1992)
Benjamin Uduje (1992)
Christopher McCourt (1993)
Matthew Hutchings (1993)
Naomi Hawkes (1994)
Stefano Nuvoloni (1994)
Anna McKenna (1994)
Tina Villarosa (1995)
Damian Woodward-Carlton (1995)
Anna Thomas (1995)
Angus Withington (1995)
Henry Pitchers (1996)
Scott Matthewson (1996)
Gareth Compton (1997)
Toby Watkin (1996)
Eilidh Gardner (1997)
William Thomas (1998)
Dan Squires (1998)

Also at 12 Byrom Street, Manchester. Tel: (0161) 829 2100

et No. 16

24 OLD BUILDINGS (G.R Bretten QC)

24 Old Buildings (First Floor), Lincoln's Inn, London, WC2A 3UP **Tel:** (020) 7242 2744 **Fax:** (020) 7831 8095 **DX:** 386
Email: taxchambers@compuserve.com

O

Set No.
117
24 OLD BUILDINGS (Martin Mann QC & Alan Steinfeld QC)

24 Old Buildings, Lincoln's Inn, London, WC2A 3UP
Tel: (020) 7404 0946 **Fax:** (020) 7405 1360 **DX:** LDE 307
Email: clerks@xxiv.co.uk **Website:** www.xxiv.co.uk

Head of Chambers:	Martin Mann QC & Alan Steinfeld QC
Sen. Clerk:	Nicholas Luckman
Clerks:	Jeremy Hopkins, Daniel Wilson, Chris Lane
Administration:	Marshall Thomson
Tenants:	28

Members:

Martin Mann QC (1968) (QC-1983)
Alan Steinfeld QC (1968) (QC-1987)
Roger Kaye QC (1970) (QC-1989)
Lawrence Cohen QC (1974) (QC-1993)
Thomas Baxendale (1962)
Michael King (1971)
Philip Shepherd (1975)
Paul Teverson (1976)
Richard Ritchie (1978)
Francis Tregear (1980)
Daniel Gerrans (1981)
Michael Gadd (1981)
Elizabeth Weaver (1982)
Stephen Moverley Smith (1985)
Helen Galley (1987)
Adrian Francis (1988)
Christopher Young (1988)
Amanda Harington (1989)
Elspeth Talbot Rice (1990)
Nicholas Cherryman (1991)
Clare Stanley (1994)
Stuart Adair (1995)
Alexander Pelling (1995)
Bajul Shah (1996)
Steven Thompson (1996)
Jessica Chappell (1997)
Lindsey Mein (1999)
Edward Knight (1999)
Marcus Staff (Geneva)*
Graham Virgo MA BCL*

* Door Tenant

The Chambers: 24 Old Buildings is a leading London barristers' chambers, which has continuously adapted to meet the changing needs of modern business. Chambers experience and reputation is in business litigation and international trust law. Instructions are taken from UK firms, in-house legal departments, recognised institutions under Direct Professional Access and Bar Direct, international law firms and foreign clients. Barristers and staff are well known for their friendly, efficient and practical approach, and their commitment to the highest standards of professional service. Cases in recent years have included Atlantic Computers, Gruppo Torras Litigation, Maxwell, Baring and BCCI; Pan Am in the Lockerbie air disaster, and ABTA on passenger service charges. 24 Old Buildings' strength lies in its ability to handle complex cases involving more than one aspect of the law, offering both breadth and depth of expertise.

Office Hours: 8am to 7pm, Monday to Friday. Please call the Clerks or visit the website for further information. Chambers provides 24-hour cover for urgent cases – Nicholas Luckman at 07774 240112, or Jeremy Hopkins at 07956 366615.

Work Undertaken: Key areas of expertise are company law; insolvency and corporate rescue; bankruptcy; civil fraud; asset tracing and recovery; international trusts; insurance; property; partnership; professional negligence. Growth areas are arbitration and mediation, e-commerce and IT litigation. Some members have niche specialisms in banking; aviation and travel; pensions; financial services; probate; EU law; charities and church law.

Clientele: Multi-national corporations, private companies and partnerships, financial institutions, trustees and trust companies, insolvency practitioners, accountants, overseas lawyers, property developers, government departments, industry associations, and private individuals.

International: Members regularly advise and appear as advocates in other jurisdictions including the Isle of Man and Channel Islands; Bahamas, Bermuda, British Virgin Islands; Cayman; the Far East and Europe. Chambers has particular expertise in multi-jurisdictional disputes, ICC and UNCITRAL arbitrations, and the European Convention on Human Rights. Chambers has a strong association with a leading Swiss law firm.

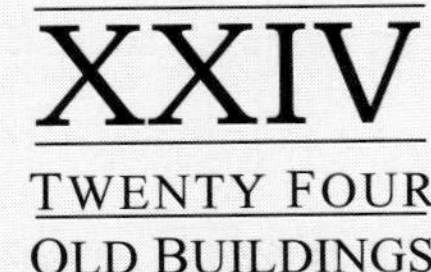

O

Set No.
118
OLD SQUARE CHAMBERS (John Hendy QC)

1 Verulam Buildings, Gray's Inn, London, WC1R 5LQ
Tel: (020) 7269 0300 **Fax:** (020) 7405 1387 **DX:** 1046 Chancery Lane/London
Email: clerks@oldsquarechambers.co.uk **Website:** www.oldsquarechambers.co.uk

Head of Chambers:	John Hendy QC
Senior Clerk:	John Taylor
Tenants:	43

Members:

John Hendy QC (1972) (QC-1987)
John Melville Williams QC (1955) (QC-1977)
Frederic Reynold QC (1960) (QC-1982)
John Hand QC (1972) (QC-1988)
Lord Wedderburn QC (1953) (QC-1990)
Jeremy McMullen QC (1971) (QC-1994)
Ian Truscott QC (1995) (QC-1997)
Matthias Kelly QC (1979) (QC-1999)
Charles Lewis (1963)
Christopher Carling (1969)
William Birtles (1970)
Diana Brahams (1972)
John H. Bates (1973)
Christopher Makey (1975)
Nigel Cooksley (1975)
Charles Pugh (1975)
Toby Kempster (1980)
Paul Rose (1981)
Jane McNeill (1982)
Mark Sutton (1982)
Barry Cotter (1985)
Louise Chudleigh (1987)
Ijeoma Omambala (1989)
Jennifer Eady (1989)
Philip Mead (1989)
Damian Brown (1989)
Tess Gill (1990)
Jonathan Clarke (1990)
Christopher Walker (1990)
Nicholas Booth (1991)
Sarah Moor (1991)
Ian Scott (1991)
Oliver Segal (1992)
Helen Gower (1992)
Roy Lewis (1992)
Mark Whitcombe (1994)
Elizabeth Melville (1994)
Melanie Tether (1995)
Emma Smith (1995)
Rohan Pirani (1995)
Rebecca Tuck (1998)
Hilary Winstone (1998)
Steven Langton (1998)

Work Undertaken: Employment law, personal injury/clinical negligence, product liability and health & safety compliance law, environmental law and sports law.

International: There are door tenants practising at the Hong Kong, Bermuda and Jersey Bars. Tenants are also members of the Scottish and Northern Irish Bars.

Languages: French, German, Spanish, Italian, Ibo.

Set No.
119
9 OLD SQUARE (Michael Driscoll QC)

9 Old Square, Lincoln's Inn, London, WC2A 3SR
Tel: (020) 7405 4682 **Fax:** (020) 7831 7107 **DX:** 305 LONDON/CHANCERY LANE
LIX: Lon 069 **Email:** chambers@9oldsquare.co.uk **Website:** www.9oldsquare.co.uk

Head of Chambers:	Michael Driscoll QC
Senior Clerk:	Christopher McSweeney
Tenants:	21

Members:

Michael Driscoll QC (1970) (QC-1992)
Nicholas Patten QC (1974) (QC-1988)
Judith Jackson QC (1975) (QC-1994)
Simon Berry QC (1977) (QC-1990)
David Hodge QC (1979) (QC-1997)
Daniel Hochberg (1982)
John Dagnall (1983)
John McGhee (1984)
Timothy Harry (1983)
Edwin Johnson (1987)
Thomas Leech (1988)
Katharine Holland (1989)
Christopher Stoner (1991)
Andrew P.D. Walker (1991)
Simon Burrell (1988)
Michael Pryor (1992)
Thomas Grant (1993)
Alan Johns (1994)
Stephanie Tozer (1996)
William V.W Norris (1997)
Paul Clarke (1997)

The Chambers: 9 Old Square is a long-established and leading set of commercial chancery chambers. It has an established reputation for all aspects of property and modern chancery litigation. Particular fields of expertise for all members include landlord and tenant, conveyancing, contract, professional negligence, trusts, banking, company, and partnership law and for some members, also, the fields of insolvency, mining, judicial review, and sports law. Former members include Sir Robert Megarry and Lord Hoffmann. There are presently 5 QCs and 16 junior members of chambers. Many members of chambers are listed in professional publications (such as this one) as leaders in their fields and such is the breadth of experience and years of call within the members of chambers that all cases from the largest to the smallest can be catered for. Members of chambers sit as arbitrators and as legal assesssors.Direct Professional Access is available.The rates charged by members are intended to be competitive and flexible, and the aim of chambers is to provide clients with a professional and efficient but approachable service. A brochure is available on request and the Senior Clerk, Christopher McSweeney, can be contacted for further information on the experience of and rates charged by individual members.

Continued overleaf

O

Work Undertaken:
Real Property & Landlord and Tenant: Members advise on, and appear as advocates in disputes relating to, all aspects of landlord and tenant law, all types of land and buildings, and all manner of dispute viz claims for possession, rent reviews, 1954 Act renewals, leasehold enfranchisement claims, dilapidations claims, breaches of alienation and other covenants, service charge disputes, environmental protection etc. Also in relation to all other real property work viz contracts and conveyancing, development agreements and options, restrictive covenants, easements, overriding interests, mortgages, subrogation, liens, removal of cautions etc.
Professional Negligence: Members have appeared in many of the leading cases against solicitors, valuers, barristers and accountants in relation to all types of claim from property finance to company acquisitions, flotations to domestic conveyancing. Members from 9 Old Square have already appeared in 'Platform Home Loans v Oyston Shipways' in the House of Lords and 'Nationwide BS v Balmer Radmore' (the Nationwide managed litigation), perhaps the two leading decisions on professional negligence claims against solicitors and valuers in 1999.
Other Commercial and Chancery Areas of Work: Chambers regularly undertakes not only the modern commercial chancery work based upon contractual interpretation and litigation but also the more traditional work of the Chancery Bar, trusts and wills, though nowadays this latter work involves more often than not disputes relating to off-shore trusts, constructive trusts and tracing remedies. Some members also practise in the fields of company and partnership law, particularly in relation to share valuations, and disputes between shareholders and partners.

Publications: 9 Old Square has continued the tradition of contributing to leading textbooks and publications within their fields of expertise. Publications in which present members of chambers have participated and papers which they have presented include: Michael Driscoll QC, *Halsbury's Laws: Law of Family Arrangement*; Nicholas Patten QC, *1998 Blundell Memorial Lecture*; Judith Jackson QC, contributor to *Megarry's Rent Acts* (Sweet & Maxwell); consultant editor on *Enforcement of Money Judgments* (Butterworths); Simon Berry QC, *1995 Blundell Memorial Lecture*; David Hodge QC, *Foskett on Compromise* (Chancery Matters); *Secret Trusts: The Fraud Theory Revisited*; Daniel Hochberg, *Phipson on Evidence: Encyclopaedia of Forms & Precedents*; Tim Harry, *Hill and Redman's Law of Landlord and Tenant*, and *Case Editor of LLP Professional Negligence Law Reports*; John McGhee, editor of *Snell on Equity*; Tom Leech, co-author *Solicitor's Negligence* (Butterworths), Case Editor of *LLP Professional Negligence Law Reports*; Christopher Stoner, contributor to *Sports Law Administration and Practice*. Members are also invited regularly to give lectures and seminars for the Bar, solicitors and other professionals.

International: Members appear as advocates in all courts and tribunals in England & Wales, and in Jersey, Hong Kong, Bermuda, the Far East, the Bahamas, and Brunei. They also act as arbitrators, legal assessors, legal experts and advocates in arbitrations and expert determinations.

Set No. 120

10 OLD SQUARE (Leolin Price CBE QC)

10 Old Square, Lincoln's Inn, London, WC2A 3SU
Tel: (020) 7405 0758 / 7242 5002 **Fax:** (020) 7831 8237 / 7831 9188 **DX:** 306
Email: clerks@tenoldsquare.com **Website:** www.tenoldsquare.com

Head of Chambers:	Leolin Price CBE QC
Senior Clerk:	Keith Plowman
Tenants:	32

Members:

Leolin Price CBE QC (1949) (QC-1968)
James Bonney QC (1975) (QC-1995)
Michael Mello QC (Bermuda)
Simon Taube QC (1980) (QC-2000)
David Ainger (1961)
Francis Barlow (1965)
David Ritchie (1970)
Frances Burton (1972)
Gregory Hill (1972)
Richard Wallington (1972)
James Arbuthnot M.P (1975)
Jeffrey Price (1975)
David Schmitz (1976)
Owen Rhys (1976)
Geraint Thomas (1976)
Andrew De La Rosa (1981)
Michael Michell (1984)
Paul Stafford (1987)
David Partington (1987)
Julian Roberts (1987)
Susannah Meadway (1988)
Eason Rajah (1989)
Rupert D'Cruz (1989)
Jeremy Callman (1991)
Jonathan Gavaghan (1992)
Samuel Laughton (1993)
Kevin Farrelly (1993)
Michael Waterworth (1994)
Luke Norbury (1995)
Nicholas Harries (1995)
Robert Arnfield (1996)
Evan Price (1997)

O

The Chambers: 10 Old Square is a large Chancery set with barristers specialising in every area within the broad spectrum of chancery law.

Work Undertaken: Trusts; charities; probate; administration of estates; wills receivership; insolvency; taxation; landlord and tenant; company; property; building; commercial; professional negligence; and partnership are all comprehensively covered.

10 OLD SQUARE

Additional Areas: Commercial and financial regulation; litigation in foreign courts and all Commonwealth jurisdictions; Privy Council appeals; water & sewerage; sale of goods; navigation; fisheries; employment; construction; and arbitrations.
Detailed information is available from the Senior Clerk who is happy to provide advice on the availability of suitable counsel.

Set No.
121

11 OLD SQUARE (Grant Crawford & Jonathan Simpkiss)

11 Old Square, Lincoln's Inn, London, WC2A 3TS
Tel: (020) 7430 0341 **Fax:** (020) 7831 2469 **DX:** 1031
Email: clerks@11oldsquare.co.uk **Website:** www.11oldsquare.co.uk

Head of Chambers:	Grant Crawford, Jonathan Simpkiss
Senior Clerk:	Keith Nagle
Tenants:	24

Members:

Edward Davidson QC (1966) (QC-1994)
Gordon Nurse (1973)
Grant Crawford (1974)
Jonathan Simpkiss (1975) FCI Arb
Peter Smith QC (1975) (QC-1992)
Reziya Harrison (1975) FCI Arb +
Malcolm Waters QC (1977) (QC-1997)
Stephen Acton (1977)
Elizabeth Ovey (1978)
Keith Rowley (1979)
Siân Thomas (1981)
Glenn Campbell (1985)
Mark West (1987)
Katherine McQuail (1989)
Nigel Burroughs (1991)
Peter Dodge (1992)
Tony Oakley (1994)
Ben Davey (1994)
Nicole Sandells (1994)
Kate Selway (1995)
Alex Hall Taylor (1996)
Michael Bowmer (1997)
Myriam Stacey (1998)
Iqbal Moollan (1998) (Mauritius Bar)

+ CEDR Accredited Mediator

The Chambers:
IT: Chambers word processing system is Microsoft Word, IBM compatible, 3.5' disks. Please speak to the clerks if you wish to deliver or receive text on disk or by electronic communication.

Work Undertaken: The work undertaken by members of chambers is primarily in the Chancery and commercial fields, and extends to a wide range of litigation, advisory and drafting work.
Business: Agency, commercial litigation, consumer credit, intellectual property, freezing and other injunctions, partnerships, sale of goods, supply of services, securities and guarantees.
Charities and Associations: Charities, clubs, friendly societies, industrial and provident societies, unincorporated associations.
Company and Insolvency: Acquisition, amalgamation, dissolution and disposal of companies, corporate governance, directors' duties and disqualification, shareholder and boardroom disputes, tracing and recovery of corporate assets, company insolvency, administrations, liquidations, receiverships and voluntary arrangements, insolvent partnerships and all aspects of personal insolvency.
Financial: Banking, building societies, consumer credit, financial services and regulation, insurance, mortgages, pensions, securities and guarantees, standard form documentation for commercial and residential lending transactions, trustee and fiduciary duties, unfair terms in consumer contracts.
Private Client: Administration of estates, Court of Protection, family provision, probate, taxation, trusts and trustees, wills.
Professional negligence: Includes accountants, barristers, financial advisors, solicitors, surveyors and valuers; disciplinary proceedings.
Property: Agricultural holdings, commercial property, conveyancing, landlord and tenant, mineral rights, mortgages, property litigation.

Clientele: Chambers operate the Direct Professional Access scheme. Instructions are also accepted from lawyers abroad, in particular the Far East, but also from jurisdictions in Europe and elsewhere.

Publications: 'Swaps and Local Authorities: A Mistake?' in *Swaps and Off-Exchange Derivatives Trading: Law and Regulation*, Mark West (co-author); *Good Faith in Sales*, Reziya Harrison; *Wurtzburg and Mills on Building Society Law*, eds. Malcolm Waters QC, Elizabeth Ovey, Kate Selway; *Barnsley, Conveyancing Law and Practice*, Peter Smith QC; *Constructive Trusts, and Parker & Mellows, The Modern Law of Trusts*, Tony Oakley; pending, *Lifetime Gifts*, Nicole Sandells (co-author).

Languages: French, German and Spanish.

O

Set No.
122 **11 OLD SQUARE** (Simeon Thrower)

11 Old Square, Lincoln's Inn, London, WC2A 3TS
Tel: (020) 7242 5022 **Fax:** (020) 7404 0445 **DX:** 164 London Chancery Lane
Email: clerks@11oldsquare.com **Website:** www.11oldsquare.com

Head of Chambers:	Simeon Thrower
Senior Clerk:	Christopher Watts
Tenants:	15

Members:

J. Simeon Thrower (1973)
Francesca Quint (1970)
Christopher H. Cutting (1973)
K. Mydeen (1973)
Malcolm D. Sinclair (1978)
Patrice Wellesley-Cole (1975)
Gordon Apsion (1977)
Nicholas Macleod-James (1986)
Marc C. Maitland (1988)
John Lloyd (1988)
Jennifer Gray (1992)
Gabriel Buttimore (1993)
Steven Ball (1995)
Alison MacLennan (1996)
Nigel Woodhouse (1997)

The Chambers: An established set of Chambers with a broad practice covering Chancery, common law and criminal matters.

Work Undertaken: Arbitration; banking; chancery; charities; company and commercial; construction; criminal; family; fraud – both civil and criminal; housing; immigration; insolvency; insurance and reinsurance; judicial review; landlord and tenant; licensing; local government; personal injury; planning; probate; product liability; professional negligence; property; sale of goods; trusts and wills.

Clientele: Members of chambers act for individuals, public and private companies; charities; local authorities, banks and financial institutions. Chambers operate the Direct Professional Access scheme.

Languages: French and German.

Set No.
123 **13 OLD SQUARE** (Michael Lyndon-Stanford QC)

13 Old Square, Lincoln's Inn, London, WC2A 3UA
Tel: (020) 7404 4800 **Fax:** (020) 7405 4267 **DX:** 326 London/Chancery Lane
Email: clerks@13oldsquare.law.co.uk **Website:** www.13oldsquare.co.uk

Head of Chambers:	Michael Lyndon-Stanford QC
Senior Clerk:	Jim Bisland
Tenants:	25

Members:

Michael Lyndon-Stanford QC (1962) (QC-1979)
Christopher H. McCall QC (1966) (QC-1987)
Hazel Williamson QC (1972) (QC-1988)
Richard McCombe QC (1975) (QC-1989)
Nigel M. Thomas (1976)
Christopher Pymont QC (1979) (QC-1996)
Catherine Newman QC (1979) (QC-1995)
Timothy Evans (1979)
Simon Barker (1979)
Mark Cunningham (1980)
Anthony Trace QC (1981) (QC-1998)
Paul Girolami (1983)
Matthew Collings (1985)
John Nicholls (1986)
Carolyn Walton (1980)
Jonathan Russen (1986)
Richard Morgan (1988)
Nicholas Peacock (1989)
Gregory Banner (1989)
Amanda Tipples (1991)
Michael Gibbon (1993)
Rebecca Stubbs (1994)
James Aldridge (1994)
Andrew Ayres (1996)
Catherine Addy (1998)

The Chambers: By January 1st 2001, 13 Old Square and 7 Stone Buildings will be merged as a single commercial Chancery Set under a new name. Contact details for the clerks will remain the same.
Work Undertaken: Commercial; company; insolvency; real property; landlord and tenant; professional negligence; partnership; trusts and related areas; and intellectual property.
In addition to the main areas above, practitioners have experience in diverse specialist fields, including private international law; competition law; markets and commons; telecommunications; matrimonial finance and property; mental health; pensions; and superannuations.
Instructions are welcome, and regularly received, from accountants, in-house legal departments of companies and local authorities, and overseas.
For further information, please visit our website or contact the senior clerk.

Set No.
124 **1 PAPER BUILDINGS** (Roger Titheridge QC)
1 Paper Buildings (1st Floor), Temple, London, EC4Y 7EP **Tel:** (020) 7353 3728 **Fax:** (020) 7353 2911 **DX:** 332
Email: clerks@onepaperbuildings.com

No. 25 **2 PAPER BUILDINGS** (Mark Love)

2 Paper Buildings, Temple, London, EC4Y 7ET
Tel: (020) 7936 2613 **Fax:** (020) 7353 9439 **DX:** 210 (Ch.Ln.)
Email: post@2paper.co.uk **Website:** www.2paper.co.uk

Head of Chambers:	Mark Love
Senior Clerk:	Stephen Lavell
First Junior:	Marc Newson
Second Junior:	Jamie Thornton
Tenants:	30

Members:

Mark Love (1979)
Robin Griffiths (1970)
Charlotte Buckhaven (1969)
Richard Hayden (1964)
Peta Gee (1973)
Wendy Fisher-Gordon (1983)
Quentin Purdy (1983)
Neil Petersen (1983)
Andrew Evans (1984)
James Dennison (1986)
Mark Stern (1988)
Sandra Briggs-Watson (1985)
Jamal Sapsard (1987)
Alison Robins (1987)
Polly-Anne Comfort (1988)
John Talbot-Bagnall (1988)
Kevin Dent (1991)
Simon Tolkien (1994)
Sandra Folkes (1989)
Pankaj Pathak (1992)
Jane Keysall (1992)
Jennifer Dempster (1993)
Maryam Syed (1993)
Sandra Folkes (1989)
Jason Elliott (1993)
Fay Baker (1994)
Silas Reid (1995)
Peter Dahlsen (1996)
Sally Hancox (1996)
Simone Start (1994)
Michael McAlinden (1996)

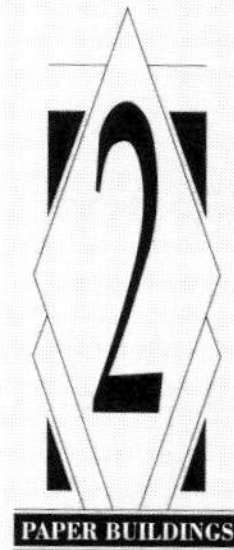

The Chambers: An established common law set offering a wide range of services with particular emphasis upon all aspects of criminal law and family law.

Work Undertaken: Criminal law; family law; personal injury; judicial review; landlord and tenant; courts martial; mental health; and licensing.

Languages: Certain members of chambers are fluent in foreign languages such as French, German, Hindi, Punjabi and Urdu.

Recruitment & Training: Four pupillages will be offered: two first six pupillages (to commence in October 2001) and two second six pupillages to commence in April 2002. Two of these will be funded.

No. 26 **2 PAPER BUILDINGS** (Desmond de Silva QC)
First and Second Floors, 2 Paper Buildings, London, EC4Y 7ET **Tel:** (020) 7556 5500 **Fax:** (020) 7583 3423 **DX:** LDE 494
Email: clerks@2pbbarristers.co.uk **Website:** www.2pbbarristers.co.uk

No. 27 **3 PAPER BUILDINGS** (Samuel Parrish)
3 Paper Buildings, Temple, London, EC4Y 7EU **Tel:** (020) 7353 6208 **Fax:** (020) 7353 5435 **DX:** 337

No. 28 **3 PAPER BUILDINGS** (Michael Parroy QC)
3 Paper Buildings, Temple, London, EC4Y 7EU **Tel:** (020) 7583 8055 **Fax:** (020) 7353 6271 (Two lines) **DX:** 1024 **Email:** london@3paper.co.uk

No. 29 **4 PAPER BUILDINGS** (Jean Ritchie QC)

4 Paper Buildings (Ground Floor), Temple, London, EC4Y 7EX
Tel: (020) 7353 3366 **Fax:** (020) 7353 5778 **DX:** 1036 London/Chancery Lane
Email: clerks@4paperbuildings.com **Website:** www.4paperbuildings.com

Head of Chambers:	Jean Ritchie QC
Senior Clerk:	Stephen Smith
Tenants:	34\

Members:

Jean Ritchie QC (1970) (QC-1992)
Harvey McGregor QC (1955) (QC-1978)
Harold Burnett QC (1962) (QC-1982)
Douglas Hogg QC MP (1968) (QC-1990)
Michael J. Powers QC (1979) (QC-1995)
Michael Pooles QC (1978) (QC-1999)
Eleanor Sharpston QC (1980) (QC-1999)
L.J. West-Knights QC (1977) (QC-2000)
Christina Gorna (1960)
Michael Keane (1963)
Anthony De Freitas (1971)
Jane Mishcon (1979)
Martin Spencer (1979)
Derek Holwill (1982)
Patrick Lawrence (1985)
Matthew Jackson (1986)
Julian Picton (1988)
Francis Bacon (1988)
William Flenley (1988)
Clare Price (1988)
Alison Gulliver (1989)
Evelyn Pollock (1991)
Mark Simpson (1992)
Philip Moser (1992)
Graham Reid (1993)
Simon Wilton (1993)
Sarah Christie-Brown (1994)
Spike Charlwood (1994)
Kieron Beal (1995)
Catherine Ewins (1995)
Katrine Sawyer (1996)
Simon Young (1998)

P

The Chambers: This is a long-established set whose members practise civil and commercial law, principally in professional and clinical negligence. Chambers aim to provide a service of excellence, adopting a flexible, practical and commercial approach to litigation which is driven by the needs and convenience of its clients.

4 Paper Buildings

Continued overleaf

Work Undertaken: The set specialises in professional negligence and clinical negligence, commercial contract work, European law and personal injury. Members of chambers act for both claimants and defendants. In the field of professional negligence, they appear in cases concerning all the various professions, but particularly solicitors, barristers, accountants, surveyors and insurance brokers. In the area of clinical negligence, members represent patients, NHS Trusts and doctors. Chambers has a long tradition in personal injury and commercial contract work, Harvey McGregor QC being the author of McGregor on Damages. EU law, the Brussels Convention and human rights are expanding areas of practice in chambers, Eleanor Sharpston QC heading a team of specialist juniors who undertake both judicial review and civil actions.
Additional Areas: Chambers also have considerable expertise in IT law, civil litigation relating to commercial fraud and money laundering, landlord and tenant, and professional disciplinary work.

Set No. 130

4 PAPER BUILDINGS (Lionel Swift QC)

4 Paper Buildings, Temple, London, EC4Y 7EX
Tel: (020) 7583 0816 **Fax:** (020) 7353 4979 **DX:** 1035
Email: clerks@4pb.com **Website:** www.4pb.com

Head of Chambers:	Lionel Swift QC
Senior Clerk:	Michael Reeves
First Junior:	Mike Lay
Chambers Manager:	Kay May
Tenants:	31

Members:

Lionel Swift QC (1959) (QC-1975)
Gordon Murdoch QC (1970) (QC-1995)
Anna Pauffley QC (1979) (QC-1995)
Jonathan Cohen QC (1974) (QC-1997)
Peter Jackson QC (1978) (QC-2000)
Harry Turcan (1965)
Roger Smith (1968)
Amanda Barrington-Smyth (1972)
Rozanna Malcom (1974)
Robin Barda (1975)
Michael Sternberg (1975)
Christopher Coney (1979)
Marcus Scott-Manderson (1980)
Charles Joseph (1980)
Michael Stern (1983)
Mark Johnstone (1984)
Elizabeth Coleman (1985)
Catherine Wood (1985)
Jeremy Rosenblatt (1985)
Adrienne Morgan (1988)
Barbara Mills (1990)
Christopher Cope (1990)
Joy Brereton (1990)
Cyrus Larizadeh (1992)
William Hansen (1992)
Justin Ageros (1993)
Judith Murray (1994)
Sarah Lowe (1995)
Alexander Schofield (1997)
Justine Johnston (1997)
James Copley (1997)

The Chambers: A leading family law set with a strong civil side.

Work Undertaken:
Family Law: Adoption care proceedings (for local authorities, families and guardians ad litem); child abduction; Children Act cases; cohabitees; divorce; inheritance and family provision; judicial review; matrimonial finance and wardship.
Civil: Arbitration; banking and securities; construction; contract (commercial and general); employment and industrial tribunals; judicial review; landlord and tenant; personal injury; professional negligence; sale of goods; consumer credit; and tort.

Recruitment & Training: Chambers is a member of PACH.

Set No. 131

5 PAPER BUILDINGS (Godfrey Carey QC & Jonathan Caplan QC)

5 Paper Buildings, Temple, London, EC4Y 7HB
Tel: (020) 7583 6117 **Fax:** (020) 7353 0075 **DX:** 365
Email: clerks@5-paperbuildings.law.co.uk

Heads of Chambers:	Godfrey Carey QC, Jonathan Caplan QC
Senior Clerk:	Stuart Bryant
Tenants:	34

Members:

John Mathew QC (1949) (QC-1977)
Michael Corkery QC (1949) (QC-1981)
Timothy Cassel QC (1965) (QC-1988)
Godfrey Carey QC (1969) (QC-1991)
Jonathan Caplan QC (1973) (QC-1991)
Kuldip Singh QC (1975) (QC-1993)
Oliver Sells QC (1972) (QC-1995)
Simon Mehigan QC (1980) (QC-1998)
Edward Jenkins QC (1977) (QC-2000)
Stanley Hughes (1971)
Michael Brompton (1973)
Ian Wade (1977)
Graham Trembath (1978)
Nicholas Fooks (1978)
Penelope Rector (1980)
Charles Judge (1981)
Maurice Aston (1982)
Miranda Moore (1983)
Mark Wyeth (1983)
Amanda Pinto (1983)
Miles Bennett (1986)
David Groome (1987)
Robert O'Sullivan (1988)
Julian Christopher (1988)
Martin Evans (1989)
Anuja Dhir (1989)
Justin Cole (1991)
Nicholas Griffin (1992)
Emma Deacon (1993)
Janet Weeks (1993)
Tom Allen (1994)
Michael Hick (1995)
Alex Bailin (1995)
Denis Barry (1996)

P

The Chambers: For more than a century these chambers have been recognised as one of the leading sets of criminal advocates. Chambers expertise has led in recent years to a broadening of their areas of practice extending to environmental and trading law, media law, disciplinary tribunals of all kinds, and specialist areas of civil law.

Work Undertaken:

Criminal Law: This set deals with all aspects of criminal law, including commercial fraud (members of these chambers have been involved in almost every major fraud case in the past decade) and members regularly appear in all levels of criminal courts, including capital appeals in the Privy Council. Work is regularly undertaken in Singapore, Hong Kong and the West Indies. Chambers both prosecute and defend.

Licensing: Considerable experience in both liquor and gaming licensing.

Consumer Protection and Trading Law: Including environmental law, food and drugs, health and safety, trade descriptions and copyright theft.

Tribunals: Disciplinary and Regulatory proceedings (e.g. IMRO/GMC/DTI), Coroner's Inquests, Employment Tribunals and Courts Martial.

Civil Law: Commercial litigation (including fraud), defamation, contempt, sports law.

t No.
32

5 PAPER BUILDINGS (Richard King)

5 Paper Buildings (Ground Floor), Temple, London, EC4Y 7HB
Tel: (020) 7815 3200 **Fax:** (020) 7815 3201 **DX:** 415
Email: clerks@5paper.com **Website:** www.5paper.com

Head of Chambers:	Richard King
Senior Clerk:	Alan Stammers
Tenants:	25

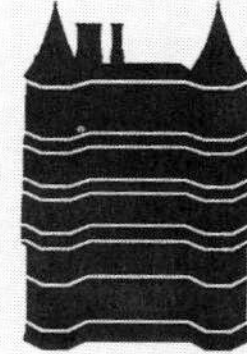

5 PAPER BUILDINGS

Members:

Richard King (1978)
Angus Nicol (1963)
Steven Walsh (1965)
Robert Denman (1970)
Graham Platford (1970)
Nicholas Wood (1970)
Donald Broatch (1971)
Robert Percival (1971)
Adrian Iles (1980)
Paul Infield (1980)
Ian Wright (1983)
Lawrence Jacobson (1985)
Simon Devonshire (1988)
Jonathan Rich (1989)
Oliver Hyams (1989)
Stuart Nichols (1989)
Satinder Gill (1991)
Richard Evans (1993)
Nicola Rushton (1993)
Paul Pavlou (1993)
Cyril Adjei (1995)
Klaus Reichert (1996)
Robert Harrap (1997)
Jake Davies (1997)
Lynne McCafferty (1997)

Work Undertaken: The chambers' principal fields of specialisation in both advocacy and advisory work are as follows: commercial law (including banking, international and domestic sales of goods, carriage of goods, sales of business, financial services, companies, partnerships and insolvency); employment (including wrongful and unfair dismissal, discrimination and confidential information); entertainment; European and international law; judicial review/social regulation (including health and safety, immigration, education, public housing, shipping and trade descriptions); matrimonial finance and child welfare; professional negligence (including negligence in the fields of legal, accountancy, surveying, valuation and medical practice); property (including landlord and tenant); tort; personal injury; and human rights.

Recruitment & Training: Pupillage application forms available from Stuart Nichols. Awards are available; details on application. Mini-pupillage applications to Robert Harrup.

t No.
33

PLOWDEN BUILDINGS (William Lowe QC)

2 Plowden Buildings, Temple, London, EC4Y 9BU
Tel: (020) 7583 0808 **Fax:** (020) 7583 5106 **DX:** 0020 (Ch.Ln.)
Email: bar@plowdenbuildings.co.uk

Head of Chambers:	William Lowe QC
Senior Clerk:	Paul Hurst
Tenants:	38

Members:

William Lowe QC (1972) (QC-1997)
Catherine MacKenzie Smith (1968)
Arnold Cooper (1969)
David Trotter (1975)
Christopher Williams (1981)
Simon Wood (1981)
Jeremy Freedman (1982)
Philip Kramer (1982)
Jonathan Holmes (1985)
Lawrence McNaulty (1985)
Catherine Foster (1986)
Michael Bailey (1986)
David Lyons (1987)
Simon Dyer (1987)
David Brook (1988)
Kate Gordon (1988)
Roger Cooper (1988)
Michael James (1989)
Martin Haukeland (1988)
Jonathan de Rohan (1989)
Kerry Cox (1990)
Mark Watson-Gandy (1990)
Sophie Henderson (1990)
Christina Anthony (1990)
Claire Lindsay (1991)
Peter Freeman (1992)
Judith Farbey (1992)
John Walsh (1993)
Frances Zammit (1993)
Navita Atreya (1994)
Jamie Clarke (1995)
Edward Broome (1996)
Dominic Bayne (1997)
Stephen Vullo (1997)
Gaenor Bruce (1997)
Nicola Rogers (1997)
Christina Gordon (1997)
Sarah Tozzi (1998)

Continued overleaf

The Chambers: Established in 1980, the chambers of William Lowe QC are a major common law set serving solicitors throughout the country from offices in the heart of the Temple and in Newcastle.

Work Undertaken: Seven departments provide specialist advice and advocacy in commercial litigation, clinical negligence, personal injury, general civil litigation, public law and immigration, criminal law and family. Members have been rated in the legal and business press as some of the leading advocates in the fields of personal injury, clinical negligence, corporate finance and immigration law.

Recruitment & Training: Tenancy applications to Head of Chambers. Pupilage applications to PACH.

Set No.
134 **PUMP COURT CHAMBERS** (Guy Boney QC)

3 Pump Court, Temple, London, EC4Y 7AJ **Tel:** (020) 7353 0711
Fax: (020) 7353 3319 **DX:** 362 **Email:** clerks@3pumpcourt.com
Website: www.3pumpcourt.com

Head of Chambers:	Guy Boney QC
Senior Clerk:	David Barber
Tenants:	54

An established set undertaking a wide variety of work. Members practise within specialist teams, for civil, family and all aspects of criminal law. Chambers are also at Winchester and Swindon.

Set No.
135 **2 PUMP COURT** (Philip Singer QC)

2 Pump Court, Temple, London, EC4Y 7AH **Tel:** (020) 7353 5597 **Fax:** (020) 7583 2122 **DX:** 290 (Ch.Ln.)

Set No.
136 **4 PUMP COURT** (Bruce Mauleverer QC)

4 Pump Court, Temple, London, EC4Y 7AN
Tel: (020) 7353 2656 **Fax:** (020) 7583 2036 **DX:** 303 LDE
Email: chambers@4pumpcourt.law.com **Website:** www.4pumpcourt.law.com

Head of Chambers:	Bruce Mauleverer QC
Senior Clerk:	Carolyn McCombe
Tenants:	40

Members:

Bruce Mauleverer QC (1969) (QC-1985)
Anthony Temple QC (1968) (QC-1986)
David Friedman QC (1968) (QC-1990)
David Blunt QC (1967) (QC-1991)
Christopher Moger QC (1972) (QC-1992)
Jeremy Storey QC (1974) (QC-1994)
Jonathan Marks QC (1975) (QC-1995)
John Rowland QC (1979) (QC-1996)
Michael Douglas QC (1974) (QC-1997)
Lindsay Boswell QC (1982) (QC-1997)
Jeremy Nicholson QC (1977) (QC-2000)
Laurence Marsh (1975)
Allen Dyer (1976)
Oliver Ticciati (1979)
Nigel Tozzi (1980)
Andrew Fletcher (1980)
Peter Hamilton (1968)
Alexander Charlton (1983)
David Sears (1984)
Adrian Hughes (1984)
James Cross (1985)
Duncan McCall (1988)
Aidan Christie (1988)
Andrew Neish (1988)
Nicholas Vineall (1988)
Kirsten Houghton (1989)
Marc Rowlands (1990)
Simon Henderson (1993)
Michael Davie (1993)
Alexander Gunning (1994)
Sean Brannigan (1994)
Kate Vaughan-Neil (1994)
Richard Cartwright (1994)
Rachel Ansell (1995)
Claire Packman (1996)
Sean O'Sullivan (1997)
Benjamin Pilling (1997)
Lynne McCafferty (1997)
Yash Kulkarni (1998)
James Purchas (1999)

The Chambers: 4 Pump Court's main focus is on litigation. It aims to provide, at every level, experienced advisors and strong and effective advocates. It is an expanding set which welcomes the opportunities that the relaxation of the ways in which the Bar can offer its services has provided. It is always ready, in the interests of clients, to consider new ideas for improving the way business is done.

Work Undertaken: The work of chambers covers a wide spectrum of commercial and common law with the following specialist areas:
Professional Negligence: Members of chambers have expertise acting for both plaintiffs and insurers and dealing with a wide range of claims against all professionals, including solicitors and barristers, architects, engineers, surveyors and valuers, accountants, auditors and actuaries, brokers, consultants, agents and IT professionals, bankers and financial intermediaries and advisors, doctors and other medical practitioners. Members of chambers regularly advise on policy interpretation and indemnity questions.
Construction: A substantial number of silks and juniors specialise in construction and civil engineering work and are recognised as leading practitioners in the field. They have acted in numerous major disputes arising out of onshore and offshore projects both in the UK and overseas, acting variously for employers, contractors and sub-contractors, and professional advisors.
Insurance and Reinsurance: Members of chambers have been involved in most of the significant events in the London insurance market over the last decade, including the Longtail claims in the USA arising

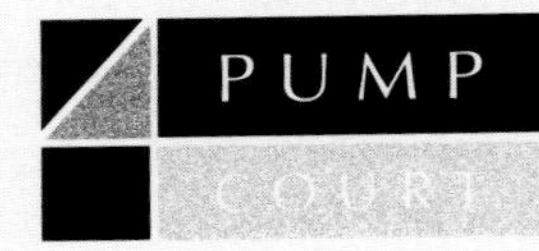

P

from problems such as asbestosis, pollution and more recently with pensions and other investment product compensation claims against life insurers. Work with Lloyd's and other insurance markets includes litigation and arbitration of both insurance and reinsurance disputes between syndicates and with outside insurers, litigation between names and agents, disciplinary hearings and regulatory control.
Commercial: Members of chambers deal with a range of matters including commercial fraud, insurance and reinsurance, banking, sale and carriage of goods, aviation, shipping, the purchase and sale of commodities, the construction and performance of mercantile contracts and media and entertainment.
Information Technology: Members of chambers have developed expertise in the relatively new and expanding fields of information technology and telecommunications. Chambers' work primarily concerns disputes of a contractual nature, involving a detailed understanding of the technical aspects of computer systems, and their implementation and application.
Licensing, Gaming and Lotteries: Expertise in this field has been built up over many years of acting for and advising the regulator of the gaming industry and many of its major operators.
Financial Services: The work of members of chambers spans investment business, including life assurance and personal pensions and the rules of various regulatory bodies.
Additional Areas: Members of chambers undertake mainstream common law work of all types, including personal injury, contractual disputes and property and employment law. Some members of chambers have particular expertise in matrimonial finance.

7 5 PUMP COURT (Rex Bryan)

5 Pump Court, Temple, London, EC4Y 7AP
Tel: (020) 7353 2532 **Fax:** (020) 7353 5321 **DX:** 497 LDE
Email: FivePump@netcomuk.co.uk

Head of Chambers:	Rex Bryan
Senior Clerk:	Tim Markham
First Junior:	Jayne Goodrham
Tenants:	32

Members:

Anthony Russell QC (1974) *(QC-1999)
Rex Bryan (1971)
Norman Primost (1954)
Anthony Hunter (1962)
Simeon Hopkins (1968)
Kenneth Dow (1970)
Helen Christodoulou (1972)
John Evison (1974)
Alistair Keith (1974)
Crispian Cartwright (1976)
Tristan Chaize (1977)
Hugo Charlton (1978)
Graham Campbell (1979)
Anne Ratcliffe (1981)
Tristram Hodgkinson (1982)
Christina Morris (1983)
Michael Collard (1986)
Mark James (1987)
Tazeen Hasan (1988)
Sebastian Gooch (1989)
Corinna Schiffer (1989)
Derek O'Sullivan (1990)
Jane Campbell (1990)
Jack Nicholls (1991)
Anthony Ross (1991)
Stephen Ellis-Jones (1992)
Bradley Say (1993)
Mary Poku (1993)
Emma Smith (1994)
Sarah Marley (1995)
Laura Elfield (1996)
Sarah Prager (1997)
Elizabeth Darlington (1998)

* Door Tenants

The Chambers: Fees for paperwork can be agreed in advance upon sight of the papers, or guidance can be given as to the appropriate hourly rates. Direct Professional Access and Conditional Fee work is undertaken. Chambers has dedicated conference rooms with video facilities, and free parking can be arranged.Chambers is open from 8.30 am to 7.00 pm and the Clerks can be contacted in the evenings or at weekends.For further information please contact the Senior Clerk.

Work Undertaken: Five Pump Court Chambers is a long established common law set of 32 members of chambers in three specialised practice groups focusing on Civil, Criminal and Family law. A guide to our practices is available upon request.
Civil: Landlord and tenant; real property; contract/commercial; professional negligence; personal injury; construction, partnership; trusts; trade description, industrial deafness; insolvency; judicial review; employment; arbitration; consumer credit and licensing.
Criminal: Fraud; sexual offences; DTI; serious violence; car ringing and importation of drugs.
Family: Financial provision and children; private and public law; Inheritance Act claims; trusts.

Languages: French, German, Greek, Hindi, Italian, Urdu.

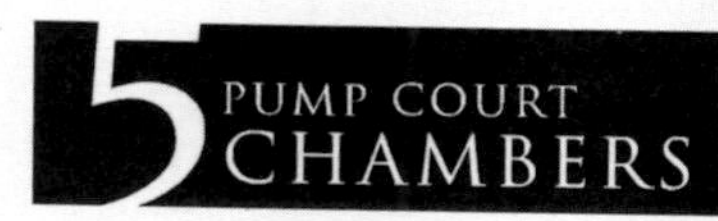

Set No.
138

6 PUMP COURT (Kieran Coonan QC)

6 Pump Court, Ground and Lower Ground, London, EC4Y 7AR
Tel: (020) 7583 6013 **Fax:** (020) 7353 0464 **DX:** 409
Email: clerks@6pumpcourt.law.co.uk **Website:** www.6pumpcourt.law.co.uk

Head of Chambers:	Kieran Coonan QC
Senior Clerk:	Adrian Barrow
Tenants:	29

Members:

Kieran Coonan QC (1971) (QC-1990)
Michael Curwen (1966)
Jon Williams (1970)
Duncan Pratt (1971)
David Morris (1976)
Richard Craven (1976)
Siobhan Goodrich (1980)
Anthony Haycroft (1982)
Richard Power (1983)
Andrew Hockton (1984)
Alan Jenkins (1984)
Susan Burden (1985)
Christina Lambert (1988)
Charles Foster (1988)
Andrew Post (1988)
Andrew Kennedy (1989)
Tejina Mangat (1990)
Annalissa Garrett (1991)
Alexander Hutton (1992)
Nicholas Peacock (1992)
Katharine Gollop (1993)
Emma Brown (1995)
Hester McCowan (1995)
Alice Robertson (1996)
Laura Davidson (1996)
Natalia Jeremiah (1997)
Mark Friston (1997)
Roger Mallalieu (1998)
John Davies (1955)

The Chambers: These chambers have enjoyed a reputation over the past 25 years for providing specialist advice and advocacy on behalf of claimants and defendants in the field of healthcare law.

Work Undertaken: Most members of chambers specialise in the major areas of clinical negligence, mental health law and the regulation of the conduct of care professionals. Members of chambers appear before Inquests, Inquiries (both public and private) and various Judicial/Administrative Tribunals. Individuals also undertake criminal cases which frequently incorporate medico-legal issues. Personal injury and professional negligence work (particularly affecting solicitors), housing, family, and employment law are strongly represented in chambers. A small group practises in the developing and specialist area of the law relating to costs. Many of the leading cases in these fields have featured members of this set. Three members of chambers have previously practised either as medical practitioner or veterinary surgeon.

Set No.
139

6 PUMP COURT (Stephen Hockman QC)

6 Pump Court, Temple, London, EC4Y 7AR
Tel: (020) 7797 8400 **Fax:** (020) 7797 8401 **DX:** 293 Chancery Lane, London
Email: Clerks@6PumpCourt.co.uk **Website:** www.6PumpCourt.co.uk

Head of Chambers:	Stephen Hockman QC
Senior Clerk:	Richard Constable
Tenants:	28

Members:

Stephen Hockman QC (1970) (QC-1990)
Adèle Williams (1972)
David Mitchell (1972)
Michael Harington (1974)
Neville Willard (1976)
Richard Barraclough (1980)
Nicholas Baldock (1983)
Caroline Topping (1984)
David Walden-Smith (1985)
Peter Gower (1985)
Kevin Leigh (1986)
Peter Harrison (1987)
Eleanor Laws (1990)
Peter Forbes (1990)
Oliver Saxby (1992)
Judith Butler (1993)
Paul Mee (1992)
Mark Watson (1994)
Edward Grant (1994)
Nina Ellin (1994)
Clare Wright (1995)
Peter Alcock (1995)
Gordon Nardell (1995)
Mark Beard (1996)
Deborah Charles (1996)
Tanya Robinson (1997)
Richard Banwell (1998)
Gordon Menzies (1998)

P

Annexe: 6-8 Mill Street, Maidstone, Kent, ME15 6XH.

Work Undertaken: The work of chambers includes a wide range of common law work in London and on the South Eastern Circuit. The set has specialists in criminal law; personal injury; planning; environmental; local government and administrative law and family law.

Set No. 140

PUMP COURT TAX CHAMBERS (Andrew Thornhill QC)

16 Bedford Row, London, WC1R 4EB
Tel: (020) 7414 8080 **Fax:** (020) 7414 8099 **DX:** London 312
Email: clerks@pumptax.com **Website:** www.pumptax.com

Head of Chambers:	Andrew Thornhill QC
Clerk:	Geraldine O'Sullivan
Tenants:	20

Members:

Donald C. Potter QC (1948) (QC-1972)
Andrew R. Thornhill QC (1969) (QC-1985)
David C. Milne QC (1970) (QC-1987)
William G.S. Massey QC (1977) (QC-1996)
Kevin J. Prosser QC (1982) (QC-1996)
Ian Richards (1971)
Janek Matthews (1972)
John M. Tallon (1975)
Roger Thomas (1979)
Penelope Hamilton (1972)
Giles W.J. Goodfellow (1983)
David Ewart (1987)
Jeremy Woolf (1986)
Andrew Hitchmough (1991)
Adrian J. Shipwright (1993)
Rupert Baldry (1987)
Julian Ghosh (1993)
Elizabeth Wilson (1995)
Richard Vallat (1997)
James Henderson (1997)

Work Undertaken: Pump Court Tax Chambers are a specialist set who undertake litigation and advisory work on all aspects of tax law, both corporate and personal. The corporate tax issues covered include company reconstructions and demergers, transfer pricing, capital allowances, and the use of losses. Advice is also given to non-residents conducting business in the UK. The personal tax issues include the creation and operation of trusts and close companies both on and off-shore, issues relating to residence and domicile, the making of gifts, and matters affected by the reserved benefit rules. A wide range of drafting is undertaken.

Personal and corporate tax matters come together in relation to employee remuneration, including share options and pension schemes, employee share ownership plans, profit sharing schemes and National Insurance contributions. Direct tax litigation is conducted in the General and Special Commissioners as well as in the Higher Courts.

A significant proportion of the work undertaken by chambers now involves VAT and customs duty, which has led to an increase in the volume of litigation in all courts including the VAT and Duties Tribunal, the High Court, the House of Lords and the European Court of Justice.

Set No. 141

QUEEN ELIZABETH BUILDING (Julian Bevan QC & Peter Whiteman QC)

Hollis Whiteman Chambers (QEB), Queen Elizabeth Building, Temple, London, EC4Y 9BS **Tel:** (020) 7583 5766 **Fax:** (020) 7353 0339 **DX:** 482 London/Chancery Lane
Email: barristers@holliswhiteman.co.uk **Website:** www.holliswhiteman.co.uk

Heads of Chambers:	Julian Bevan QC, Peter Whiteman QC
Senior Clerk:	Will Whitford
Chambers Director:	Michael Greenaway
Tenants:	52

Members:

Julian Bevan QC (1962) (QC-1991)
Peter Whiteman QC (1967) (QC-1977)
Lord Carlisle QC (1954) (QC-1971)
Robin Grey QC (1957) (QC-1979)
Alan Suckling QC (1963) (QC-1983)
Anthony Glass QC (1965) (QC-1986)
Vivian Robinson QC (1967) (QC-1986)
John Hilton QC (1964) (QC-1990)
Brian Barker QC (1969) (QC-1990)
David Evans QC (1972) (QC-1991)
Timothy Langdale QC (1966) (QC-1992)
David Bate QC (1969) (QC-1994)
Rebecca Poulet QC (1975) (QC-1995)
Peter Kyte QC (1970) (QC-1996)
Peter Clarke QC (1973) (QC-1997)
John Kelsey-Fry QC (1978) (QC-2000)
Anthony Wilcken (1966)
Christopher Mitchell (1968)
Linda Strudwick (1973)
Ian Paton (1975)
William Boyce (1976)
Richard Horwell (1976)
David Jeremy (1977)
Jeremy Donne (1978)
Mark Ellison (1979)
Peter Finnigan (1979)
Nick Wood (1980)
Gareth Rees (1981)
Tom Kark (1982)
Edward Brown (1983)
Ian Stern (1983)
Jane Sullivan (1984)
Phillip Bennetts (1986)
Sean Larkin (1987)
Jocelyn Sparks (1987)
Edward Henry (1988)
Sarah Plaschkes (1988)
Ian Winter (1988)
Zoe Johnson (1990)
Emma Lowry (1991)
Lydia Barnfather (1992)
Victoria Coward (1992)
William Wastie (1993)
Peter Warne (1993)
Selva Ramasamy (1992)
Adrian Darbishire (1993)
Benjamin Summers (1994)
Mark Aldred (1996)
Jonathan Barnard (1997)
Julian Evans (1997)
Rebecca Harris (1997)
Clare Sibson (1997)

Continued overleaf

Q

The Chambers: Hollis Whiteman Chambers (QEB) is a long-established specialist criminal set, providing advocacy and advice of the highest quality. Chambers are dedicated to giving an effective and individual service whenever needed, and at short notice. The 52 members have expertise at all levels of seniority: 16 QCs and three Treasury Counsel are matched with a strong middle order and 19 tenants of less than 15 years' call. 15 tenants sit as Recorders in the Crown Court.
Chambers defend and prosecute from the Magistrates' Court to the House of Lords. Members of chambers are regularly involved in complex, high profile and grave cases. There is also daily representation in courts of all levels, at every stage of proceedings.
In addition to 'pure crime', members specialise in confiscation proceedings; judicial review; food law; Health and Safety Act and Trading Standards cases; licensing; and extradition. Members of chambers also appear in other tribunals including: public inquiries, the General Medical Council, the General Optical Council, courts-martial and police disciplinary proceedings.
Peter Whiteman QC, a deputy High Court Judge, provides specialist revenue advice, particularly on corporate and international tax law, and representation at both national and international levels.

Queen Elizabeth Building | *Hollis Whiteman Chambers*

Set No. 142

QUEEN ELIZABETH BUILDING (Paul Coleridge QC)

Queen Elizabeth Building, Temple, London, EC4Y 9BS
Tel: (020) 7797 7837 **Fax:** (020) 7353 5422 **DX:** London 339
Email: clerks@qeb.co.uk **Website:** www.qeb.co.uk

Head of Chambers:	Paul Coleridge
Senior Clerk:	Ivor Treherne
Tenants:	27

QEB

Members:

Paul Coleridge QC (1970) (QC-1993)
Florence Baron QC (1976) (QC-1995)
Andrew Moylan QC (1978) (QC-2000)
Lord Phillimore (1972)
Peter Wright (1974)
Michael Hosford-Tanner (1974)
Andrew Tidbury (1976)
Thomas Brudenell (1977)
Roderick Blyth (1981)
Oliver Wise (1981)
Lucy Stone (1983)
Lewis Marks (1984)
Rowena Corbett (1984)
Tim Amos (1987)
Jennifer Roberts (1988)
Sarah Edwards (1990)
Matthew Firth (1991)
Elizabeth Clarke (1991)
Camilla Henderson (1992)
Stewart Leech (1992)
Alexander Thorpe (1995)
Catherine Cowton (1995)
James Ewins (1996)
Antonia Lyon (1997)
Sarah Phipps (1997)
Rachael Young (1997)
Mark Saunders (1999)

Work Undertaken: A set covering a range of specialist fields of the common law, particularly family law. Other main areas of work include commercial law; disciplinary tribunals; employment law; equine and animal law; EU law; judicial review; landlord and tenant; medical negligence; personal injuries; private international and foreign law; probate; professional negligence; and sports law.

Languages: French, German and Italian.

Set No. 143

ONE RAYMOND BUILDINGS (Christopher Morcom QC)

One Raymond Buildings, Gray's Inn, London, WC1R 5BH
Tel: (020) 7430 1234 **Fax:** (020) 7430 1004 **DX:** 16
Email: chambers@ipbar1rb.com **Website:** www.ipchambers.com

Head of Chambers	Christopher Morcom QC
Sen. Clerk:	Susan Harding
Tenants:	11

Q

Members:

Christopher Morcom QC (1963) (QC-1991) MA (Cantab)
David Micklethwait (1970) MA (Cantab)
Roger Wyand QC (1973) (QC-1997) MA (Cantab)
Arthur Ashton (1988) South Africa (1975) BA LLB (Rhodes)
John Adams (1984) LLB (Dunelm)
Guy Tritton (1987) BSc (Dunelm)
Jessica Jones (1991) BSc (Soton)
Ashley Roughton (1992) BSc (Lond) PhD (Cantab)
Michael Edenborough (1992) MA (Cantab) DPhil (Oxon)
James Graham (1994) MSc (Bristol)
Simon Malynicz (1997) LLB (London)
Amédée Turner QC (1954) (QC-1976) MA (Oxon) *
David Kay (1979) (USA-1990) BA (Kingston) *

Door Tenants *

The Chambers: A long-established set that specialises in all aspects of intellectual property litigation and related advisory work. All members belong to the IP Bar and the Chancery Bar Associations, and most have degrees in either science or engineering. Direct Professional Access accepted, and many instructions are received directly from overseas instructing agents. Pro bono work is undertaken in suitable cases.

Further Information: Roger Wyand QC: Recorder at the Patents County Court and Vice-Chairman of the Intellectual Bar Association; John Adams: Professor of Intellectual Property Law at Sheffield University; Jessica Jones: Accredited CEDR mediator; James Graham: Secretary to the Intellectual Property Bar Association.

Work Undertaken:

Intellectual Property: Patents (UK and European); trade marks (UK and CTM); passing-off; copyright; design right; registered designs; confidential information (including employer/employee cases); malicious falsehood; plant varieties; criminal prosecution and defence work in counterfeiting and piracy matters.

Media & Entertainment: Recording and performance rights; moral rights; entertainment contracts; and merchandising.

Competition Law: UK and European competition matters; franchising; and licensing (including licences of right before the Copyright Tribunal and the Comptroller-General) and product licensing, particularly in relation to pharmaceuticals.IT and Related Commercial Matters: Computer hardware and software litigation; database right; internet issues, data protection matters; and commercial litigation involving modern technology.

Publications: *The Modern Law of Trademarks* (Butterworths, 2000) Christopher Morcom QC, Ashley Roughton and James Graham; *Strategy in the Use of Intellectual Property* (Gerundivne Press, 1986) Arthur Ashton; *Character Merchandising* (Butterworths, second ed, 1996) John Adams; *Franchising* (Butterworths, fourth ed, 1997) John Adams; *Intellectual Property in Europe* (Sweet & Maxwell, 1996; second ed cum suppl, 1998) Guy Tritton; *Lecture Notes on Intellectual Property Law* (Cavendish Publishing, 1994) Michael Edenborough; *Organic Reaction Mechanisms* (Taylor & Francis, second ed, 1998) Michael Edenborough; *Intellectual Property Practice Partner* (Sweet & Maxwell, 2000) Michael Edenborough; Jessica Jones, Co-editor of the *European Patent Office Reports.*

4 3 RAYMOND BUILDINGS (Clive Nicholls QC)

3 Raymond Buildings, Gray's Inn, London, WC1R 5BH
Tel: (020) 7400 6400 **Fax:** (020) 7242 4221 **DX:** 237 London
Email: chambers@threeraymond.demon.co.uk **Website:** www.3raymondbuildings.com

Head of Chambers:	Clive Nicholls QC
Senior Clerk:	Ian Collins
Tenants:	38

Members:

Clive Nicholls QC (1957) (QC-1982)
Colin Nicholls QC (1957) (QC-1981)
Gilbert Gray QC (1953) (QC-1971) *
Richard Beckett QC (1965) (QC-1987)
John Nutting BT QC (1968) (QC-1995)
Stephen Batten QC (1968) (QC-1989)
Alan Newman QC (1968) (QC-1989)
Alun Jones QC (1972) (QC-1989)
David Whitehouse QC (1969) (QC-1990)
Nicholas Price QC (1968) (QC-1992)
Montague Sherborne QC (1960) (QC-1993)
Francis Evans QC (1977) (QC-1994)
Kevin de Haan QC (1976) (QC-2000)
John Blair-Gould (1970)
Gerald Gouriet (1974)
Andrew Muir (1975)
Richard Atchley (1977)
Michael Bromley-Martin (1979)
Mark Harris (1980)
James Hines (1982)
James Rankin (1983)
Jane Humphryes (1983)
Neil Saunders (1983)
Stephen Walsh (1983)
Crispin Aylett (1985)
Alexander Cameron (1986)
Helen Malcolm (1986)
James Lewis (1987)
John Hardy (1988)
Hugo Keith (1989)
Hugh Davies (1990)
Campaspe Lloyd-Jacob (1990)
Tania Bromley-Martin (1983)
Richard Wormald (1993)
Alisdair Williamson (1994)
Saba Naqshbandi (1996)
Edmund Gritt (1997)
Ailsa Williamson (1997)

R

The Chambers: Since its inception as a criminal set in 1926, chambers has produced many of the leading advocates at the Criminal Bar whilst evolving into a multi-disciplined set with a national and international reputation. Chambers carries out a unique mix of work with specialist expertise in many areas including crime, commercial crime, extradition, amd mutual assistance, licensing, public and administrative law, human rights law and environmental law. Members have appeared in many major cases within these areas. The nature of the work means that the 11 Silks and 26 juniors are able to offer their expertise as independent practitioners of the highest integrity but also work in teams with law firms, overseas governments and other professionals. Direct professional access is welcome.

Work Undertaken:

Criminal Law: all types of cases at all levels, prosecuting and defending before judges, juries and magistrates in England and Wales. Members also appear before international courts as well as the national courts of foreign jurisdictions. Commercial crime: serious frauds and financial regulatory offences, again with

expertise in international aspects. Major cases in which members have been involved in include, Sawoniuk (war crimes), Jonathan Aitken (perjury), Lord Hardwicke (drugs offences), Judge Gee (mortgage fraud), Donald & Cressey (police corruption), Kevin Maxwell (pension fraud), BCCI (bank fraud).
Extradition: Chambers is well known for its extradition work, which is worldwide and includes commercial crime as well as terrorism and drug trafficking. Members have appeared in almost every extradition case in England over the past 25 years including Senator Pinochet, where the independent nature of the Bar has enabled members of chambers to represent opposing sides.Members advise on international mutual assistance and have considerable experience in bringing judicial review proceedings in connection with them. Particular expertise includes warrants, restraint orders and financial aspects of mutual assistance.
Licensing: a major area of specialist expertise, notably betting, gaming and lotteries, and liquor and public entertainment. Many major Plc's are clients and chambers has the only team of barristers in England and Wales who specialise exclusively in the licensing field.
Public and Administrative Law: including representing public bodies and private clients in judicial review proceedings. Three members of chambers are appointed to the common law Treasury Panel.
European and Human Rights Law: chambers is well placed to meet the challenges of the Human Rights Act 1998.
Environmental and Health & Safety Law: specialist expertise includes advising the Environment Agency on such matters as licensing of atomic power stations, waste management, the BSE Enquiry and water pollution, and through involvement in major cases such as the Port Ramsgate Walkway collapse. Members have acted in many HSE prosecutions involving major construction companies, supermarket chains and waste management.
Other areas: individual members have expertise in computer crime, actions against the police and VAT tribunals.

Set No.
145

5 RAYMOND BUILDINGS (Patrick Milmo QC)

5 Raymond Buildings, Gray's Inn, London, WC1R 5BP
Tel: (020) 7242 2902 **Fax:** (020) 7831 2686 **DX:** 1054 LDE
Email: clerks@media-ent-law.co.uk **Website:** www.media-ent-law.co.uk

Head of Chambers:	Patrick Milmo QC
Senior Clerk:	Kim Janes
Tenants:	20

Members:

Patrick Milmo QC (1962) (QC-1985) MA (Cantab)
Gordon Bishop (1968) MA (Cantab)
Michael Tugendhat QC (1969) (QC-1986) MA (Cantab)
Desmond Browne QC (1969) (QC-1990) BA (Oxon)
Adrienne Page QC (1974) (QC-1999) BA
James Price QC (1974) (QC-1995) BA (Oxon)
Richard Parkes (1977) MA (Cantab)
Mark Warby (1981) MA (Oxon)
Stephen Bate (1981) MA (Cantab) Dip Law
Andrew Monson (1983) BA (Oxon)
Alexandra Marzec (1990) LLB
David Sherborne (1992) BA(Oxon)
Justin Rushbrooke (1992) MA(Oxon)
Matthew Nicklin (1993) LLB (Newcastle)
Godwin Busuttil (1994) MA, MPhil(Cantab)
Adam Wolanski (1995) MA(Cantab)
William Bennett (1994) BA (Liverpool)
Jacob Dean (1995) BA (Oxon)
Anna Coppola (1996) BA (London) Dip Law
Sara Mansoori (1997) LLB (Leeds)

The Chambers: An established set specialising in media and entertainment law with particular emphasis on defamation and intellectual property; also undertaking work in a wide range of commercial matters and in the human rights field. Members appear before courts at all levels, including all divisions of the High Court and the ECHR. They frequently represent clients before professional tribunals, in arbitrations and in disciplinary proceedings, and advise on, and appear in, overseas litigation.

Work Undertaken: Media, entertainment and sports law together with a broad range of commercial litigation. The areas of practice in the field of media, entertainment and sports law include, but are not limited to: defamation; breach of confidence; contempt; malicious falsehood and slander of goods/title; human rights; copyright and contractual disputes of all kinds (e.g. books, music, film, video and television); Copyright Tribunal applications; judicial review applications; restraint of trade disputes (in sport and pop); EU/competition matters; multimedia; and telecommunications law.
In addition, members of chambers carry out substantial work in the wider commercial field, covering such subjects as insurance and reinsurance; sale of goods; shipping; professional negligence; employment law; international law; company law; administrative law and landlord and tenant.

R

18 RED LION COURT (Anthony Arlidge QC)

18 Red Lion Court, London, EC4A 3EB
Tel: (020) 7520 6000 **Fax:** (020) 7520 6248/9 **DX:** 478 LDE
Email: chambers@18rlc.co.uk

Head of Chambers:	Anthony Arlidge QC
Senior Clerk:	Kenneth Darvill
First Junior:	Mark Bennett
Tenants:	65

Members:

Anthony Arlidge QC (1961) (QC-1981)
Derek Spencer QC (1961) (QC-1980)
David Cocks QC (1961) (QC-1982)
James Stewart QC (1966) (QC-1982)
Henry Green QC (1962) (QC-1988)
David Lederman QC (1966) (QC-1990)
Graham Parkins QC (1972) (QC-1990)
Linda Stern QC (1971) (QC-1991)
Peter Rook QC (1973) (QC-1991)
Richard Sutton QC (1969) (QC-1993)
Christopher Ball QC (1972) (QC-1993)
Antony Shaw QC (1975) (QC-1994)
Peter Carter QC (1974) (QC-1995)
Rosamund Horwood-Smart QC (1974) (QC-1996)
James Goss QC (1975) (QC-1997)
Nigel Peters QC (1976) (QC-1997)
John Black QC (1975) (QC-1998)
Patricia Lynch QC (1979) (QC-1998)
David Etherington QC (1979) (QC-1998)
Linda Dobbs QC (1981) (QC-1998)
David Green QC (1979) (QC-2000)
David Radcliffe (1966)
Carey Johnston (1977)
Peter Fenn (1979)
Stephen Harvey (1979)
Jonathan Fisher (1980)
Alexander Milne (1981)
Kim Jenkins (1982)
Janine Sheff (1983)
Richard Kovalevsky (1983)
Mark Lucraft (1984)
Angela Morris (1984)
Rupert Overbury (1984)
David Marshall (1985)
Brendan Morris (1985)
Simon Spence (1985)
Robert Boyle (1985)
Robin du Preez (1985)
Jane Bewsey (1986)
John Lyons (1986)
Max Hill (1987)
David Walbank (1987)
Shane Collery (1988)
David Huw Williams (1988)
John Anderson (1989)
Peter Rowlands (1990)
Candida Hill (1990)
Sara Lawson (1990)
David Holborn (1991)
Sean Hammond (1991)
Allison Clare (1992)
Matthew Gowan (1992)
Rufus D'Cruz (1993)
Tom Forster (1993)
Barnaby Jameson (1993)
Claudia Mortimore (1994)
Michelle Nelson (1994)
Jacqueline Hall (1994)
Adam Wiseman (1994)
Noel Casey (1995)
Elizabeth Webster (1995)
Gillian Jones (1996)
Stephen Requena (1997)
Nicholas Medcroft (1998)
Louis-Peter Moll (1998)

The Chambers: With 21 QCs, the set specialises in criminal law dealing with serious crimes in particular. Some members offer general common law. Members practise in London and on the South East Circuit, which is served by our annexe in Chelmsford. Chambers have standing counsel to the Inland Revenue, DTI Inspectors and recorders.
Chambers annexe at: Thornwood House, 102 New London Road, Chelmsford CM2 0RG Tel: (01245) 280880, Fax: (01245) 280882, DX: 139165 Chelmsford 11

Work Undertaken:
Criminal: Commercial fraud; Inland Revenue and Customs & Excise offences; drugs and problems arising from the Drug Trafficking Offences Act; money laundering; extradition; child abuse; obscene publications; road traffic; licensing; judicial review; privy council; health and safety at work; personal injury; medical negligence; professional negligence; disciplinary and tribunal work; contract; tort; immigration; peerage; civil liberties and family.

Clientele: Individuals, public and private companies, HM Customs and Excise, local authorities, Serious Fraud Office and CPS government departments.

Publications: Arlidge and Parry on *Fraud*; Arlidge and Eady on *Contempt*; *Journal of International Banking Law* (UK Correspondent); Dobbs and Lucraft, *Road Traffic Law and Practice* (Sweet & Maxwell 1994); Rook and Ward, *Sexual Offences* (Waterlows 1990); Carter and Harrison *Offences of Violence* (Waterlows 1991); Fisher and Merrills *Pharmacy Law and Practices* (Blackwells 1995); Fisher and Bewsey, *The Law of Investor Protection, Mortimore on Immigration and Adoption* (Hammicks 1994).

International: Nigel Peters is a member of the Northern Ireland Bar and Barbados Bar. David Marshall is a member of the Hong Kong Bar and the New York Bar.

Recruitment & Training: Applications for tenancy should be sent to David Green; pupillage applications to Barnaby Jameson. Chambers have up to seven pupils at any one time, four of whom are guaranteed £10,000 for the year. Mini-pupillages are available.

Set No.
147

RENAISSANCE CHAMBERS (Brian Jubb & Henry Setright)

5th Floor, Gray's Inn Chambers, Gray's Inn, London, WC1R 5JA
Tel: (020) 7404 1111 **Fax:** (020) 7430 1522/1050 **DX:** 0074 (Ch.Ln.)
Email: clerks@grays-inn.co.uk

Heads of Chambers: Brian Jubb & Henry Setright
Principle Clerks: Mark Darvell, Mark Venables
Tenants: 43

Members:

Brian Jubb (1971)
Henry Setright (1979)
Caroline Rodger (1968)
Elisabeth Brann (1970)
Richard Guy (1970)
Noah Weiniger (1984)
Richard Clough (1971)
Gillian Higson Smith (1973)
Rozanna Malcolm (1974)
David Houston (1976)
Janette Haywood (1977)
Dermot Main Thompson (1977)
Cherry Harding (1978)
Rachel Wingert (1980)
Simon Lillington (1980)
Kharin Cox (1982)
Heather MacGregor (1982)
Geoffrey Mott (1982)
Jonathan Cowen (1983)
Timothy Compton (1984)
Melanie Nazareth (1984)
Robert Dashwood (1984)
Alistair Perkins (1986)
Nigel Cox (1986)
Ian Lewis (1989)
Teertha Gupta (1990)
Shiva Ancliffe (1991)
Deborah Seitler (1991)
Shivani Jegarajah (1993)
Helen Morgan (1993)
Joanna Clarke (1993)
Sandra Fisher (1993)
Justin Gray (1993)
Margaret Phelan (1993)
Buster Cox (1993)
Amina Ahmed (1995)
William Metaxa (1995)
Charlotte Bayati (1995)
Christopher Archer (1996)
Sarah Orriss (1997)
Anita Guha (1997)
Arlene Small (1997)
Nick Horsley (1997)
Charles Fletcher-Cooke (1936) QC *
Doreen Hinchliffe (1953) *
Diane Redgrave (1977) *
Melanie Den Brinker (1984) *
Marilyn Freeman (1986) *
Nicholas Stonor (1993) *

* Door Tenants

Set No.
148

NO. 1 SERJEANTS' INN (Edward Faulks QC)

No.1 Serjeants' Inn, Fleet Street, London, EC4Y 1LH
Tel: (020) 7415 6666 **Fax:** (020) 7583 2033 **DX:** 364
Email: no1serjeantsinn@btinternet.com **Website:** www.no1serjeantsinn.co.uk

Head of Chambers: Edward Faulks QC
Senior Clerk: Clark Chessis
Practice Development Manager: Rosemary Thorpe
Tenants: 33

Members:

Edward Faulks QC (1973) (QC-1996) +
Adrian Redgrave QC (1968) (QC-1992) +
David Pittaway QC (1977) (QC-2000) +
William Andreae-Jones QC (1965) (QC-1984) *+
Jonathan Foster QC (1970) (QC-1989) *+
Brian Leech (1967) +
John Ross (1971) +
William Hunter (1972)
Antony Baldry MP (1975)
John Bryant (1976)
Veronica Hammerton (1977) +
Simon Readhead (1979) +
Nicholas Yell (1979)
John Norman (1979)
Alan Saggerson (1981)
Alastair Hammerton (1983)
Timothy C. Dutton (1985)
Edward Bishop (1985)
Sarah Paneth (1985) +
Julian Waters (1986)
Marc Rivalland (1987)
Justin Althaus (1988)
Angus Piper (1991)
Andrew Warnock (1993)
Alison Clarke (1994)
Paul Stagg (1994)
David Thomson (1994)
Matthew Chapman (1994)
Ivor Collett (1995)
Sophie Mortimer (1996)
Zachary Bredemear (1996)
Mohinderpal Sethi (1996)
David Bridgman (1997)

* Associate member + Recorder

The Chambers: No. 1 Serjeants' Inn has developed from an established common law set into one providing a comprehensive service in the related fields of professional and clinical negligence, property litigation, insurance disputes, claims against public authorities and personal injury claims. The addition of a team of 7 new tenants in July 2000 expanded chambers' growing public law practice and extended the range of claims handled to those involving the travel industry.

Work Undertaken:
Professional negligence: Members of chambers represent claimants and defendants in all aspects of professional negligence litigation, but particularly in actions involving surveyors, accountants, solicitors, financial advisors and insurance brokers.
Clinical negligence: Members of chambers represent the NHSLA and have been involved in many highly publicised clinical negligence cases, including ongoing litigation concerning cervical cancer screening errors. Chambers also represents claimants and has particular expertise in handling cerebral palsy cases.
Property Litigation: The property team is well known for its landlord and tenant and commercial property

NO.1 SERJEANTS' INN

S

work. It also deals with real property matters, including land registration, as well as matters relating to agricultural holdings and housing.

Insurance disputes: As a leading professional negligence set, much of the work undertaken by members of chambers has a significant insurance content. Members are also instructed in the widest range of non-marine insurance and reinsurance claims, including fire actions, recovery actions and policy disputes.

Public authorities: The team undertaking this area of work has been involved in many of the leading cases concerning the liabilities in negligence of public authorities, particularly in matters of education. Members of chambers also appear on behalf of the police in the defence of civil claims.

Personal injury: Members of chambers represent claimants and defendants in claims involving catastrophic injuries and complex issues on the assessment of damages and the implementation of structured settlements. They have been instructed in class actions, have particular expertise in disaster litigation including rail disasters, and claims involving industrial injuries, road traffic accidents and sport injuries.

Travel litigation: A specialist team handling claims involving the travel industry represents claimants and defendants in a whole range of actions including personal injury, foreign accidents, conflicts and all issues arising from travel and tourism.

1 SERJEANTS' INN (Lionel Read QC)

1 Serjeants' Inn, London, EC4Y 1NH
Tel: (020) 7583 1355 **Fax:** (020) 7583 1672 **DX:** 440 LDE
Email: clerks@serjeants-inn.co.uk

Head of Chambers:	Lionel Read QC
Senior Clerk:	William King
Tenants:	26

Members:

Lionel Read QC (1954) (QC-1973) MA (Cantab)
David Woolley QC (1962) (QC-1980) MA (Cantab)
Anthony Rumbelow QC (1967) (QC-1990)
Patrick Clarkson QC (1972) (QC-1991)
Christopher Whybrow QC (1965) (QC-1992) LLB (London)
William Hicks QC (1975) (QC-1995) MA (Cantab)
Martin Wood (1972) LLB (London)
Rhodri Price Lewis (1975) MA (Oxon) DipCrim (Cantab)
John Pugh-Smith (1977) MA (Oxon)
Simon Pickles (1978) MA (Cantab)
John Dagg (1980)
Neil Cameron (1982) BA (Dunelm)
Stephen Morgan (1983) LLB (Warw), MA (Nott)
Richard Langham (1986) BA (Oxon)
Russell Harris (1986) MA (Cantab)
Megan Thomas (1987) BA (Sheff)
Roy Martin (1990) (QC-Scotland), LLB (Glasgow)
William Upton (1990) MA, LLM (Cantab)
Sasha White (1991) MA (Cantab)
Robert Douglas White (1993) LLB (LSE)
Richard Harwood (1993) MA, LLM (Cantab)
Martin Edwards (1995) BA, MA LMRTPI
Matthew Reed (1995) MA (Cantab) MA (City)
Scott Lyness (1996) LLB (Hull)
Christiaan Zwart (1997) BA BArch(Newcastle) RIBA
Edmund Robb (1997) MA (Oxon)

The Chambers: A specialist planning and local government set. Members undertake both advocacy and advisory work and accept Direct Professional Access. There is an emphasis on public inquiry work.

Work Undertaken: Town and country planning; environment; integrated pollution control; waste disposal; contaminated land; compulsory purchase and compensation; highways; public health; local government; statutory undertakers; administrative law and judicial review; parliamentary work; landlord and tenant; rating; and related human rights.

International: Members of chambers also practise in Scotland, Northern Ireland and the Isle of Man.

Recruitment & Training: Pupillage applications to chambers. Chambers offer up to two first six-months' and up to two second six-months' pupillages each year. Chambers may offer a twelve months' pupillage. Awards of up to £9,000 are available.

Set No. 150

3 SERJEANTS' INN (Philip Naughton QC)

3 Serjeants' Inn, London, EC4Y 1BQ
Tel: (020) 7427 5000 **Fax:** (020) 7353 0425 **DX:** 421 **Mobile:** 0778 573 6844
Email: clerks@3serjeantsinn.com

Head of Chambers:	Philip Naughton QC
Senior Clerk:	Nick Salt
Junior Clerks:	Lee Johnson, Tracy Barker
Administrator:	Helen Ensor
Tenants:	34

Members:

Philip Naughton QC (1970) (QC-1988)
Adrian Whitfield QC (1964) (QC-1983)
Robert Francis QC (1973) (QC-1992)
Nicola Davies QC (1976) (QC-1992)
John Grace QC (1973) (QC-1994)
James Watson QC (1979) (QC-2000)
Philip Gaisford (1969)
Malcolm Fortune (1972)
Geoffrey D. Conlin (1973)
Huw Lloyd (1975)
Andrew Grubb (1980)
Fiona Neale (1981)
Mary O'Rourke (1981)
George Hugh-Jones (1983)
Adrian Hopkins (1984)
Angus Moon (1986)
Michael Mylonas (1988)
John Beggs (1989)
Jonathan Holl-Allen (1990)
Christopher Johnston (1990)
Michael Horne (1992)
Fionnuala McCredie (1992)
Gerard Boyle (1992)
Richard Partridge (1994)
Mark Ley-Morgan (1994)
Anthony Jackson (1995)
Debra Powell (1995)
George Thomas (1995)
Clodagh Bradley (1996)
Ranald Davidson (1996)
Bridget Dolan (1997)
Sharon Flockhart (1997)
Abigail Johnson (1998)
Simon Cridland (1999)

Work Undertaken:

Professional Negligence: In the medical, dental, and pharmaceutical fields, tenants act for plaintiffs and defendants, including health authorities throughout the country and all the medical defence organisations. Tenants have appeared in many of the major cases in this field including 'Sidaway, Hotson, Roberts v Johnstone', 'Howard v Wessex RHA', 'Sion v Hampstead HA', 'Hopkins v Mackenzie, Rance, Burton' and the pertussis vaccine litigation. Tenants also deal with a wide range of other forms of professional liability, including that of architects, surveyors, engineers and lawyers as well as matters governed by the Health & Safety at Work Act.

Medical Ethics: Tenants act in cases concerning treatment decisions, caesarean sections and other ethical issues and are available at very short notice for urgent applications. Cases in which tenants have appeared include 'Bland, re F (sterilisation), re S (Hospital Patient: Court's Jurisdiction)', 'B v Croydon HA, Robb, ex p Martin, re S (Adult: Refusal of Treatment), re T (Wardship: Medical Treatment)', and 're MB'.Professional Discipline and Review: Tenants appear in disciplinary cases before bodies such as the General Medical and Dental Councils and the NHS Tribunal, and handle judicial review and Privy Council appeals. They also appear at internal hospital and public inquiries such as Cleveland and the BRI enquiries.

Construction and Engineering: The principal areas of work undertaken concern; standard form and other contracts for building; civil, mechanical, electrical, chemical and process engineering projects; defects in design and workmanship; performance obligations; loss and expense claims and warranties. Associated areas of work include the professional negligence of architects, engineers, surveyors and valuers; nuisance; matters governed by the Health & Safety at Work regulations; environmental matters.

Police Work: Tenants specialising in this field act for over a dozen police forces in civil claims for false imprisonment; assault; malicious prosecution; negligence; disciplinary and employment matters. Tenants regularly present risk management seminars in specialist areas including public order and firearms.

Employment: Work undertaken includes advising and acting in wrongful dismissal claims; industrial tribunal cases; the drafting of employment contracts; race and sex discrimination claims; and European law.

Crime: Both defence and prosecutions are undertaken. Tenants who specialise in crime have particular experience in proceedings relating to professional practice, fraud, Health and Safety at Work and medical and ethical issues.

In addition, a wide range of personal injuries, commercial contract and common law work is undertaken.

Languages: French.

Recruitment & Training: Chambers offer two to three 12-month pupillages starting each October. Chambers offer each of the candidates an award of £17,500. All applications should be made in writing, enclosing a CV, and addressed to the Chairman of the Pupillage Committee.

S

Set No.
151 **SERLE COURT** (Lord Neill of Bladen QC)

6 New Square, Lincoln's Inn, London, WC2A 3QS
Tel: (020) 7242 6105 **Fax:** (020) 7405 4004 **DX:** LDE 1025
Email: clerks@serlecourt.co.uk **Website:** www.serlecourt.co.uk

Head of Chambers:	Neill of Bladen QC
Senior Clerks:	Terry Buck, Steven Whitaker, Barry Ellis, Paul Ballard
Chief Executive:	Helena Miles
Tenants:	45

Members:

Lord Neill of Bladen QC (1951) (QC-1966)
Richard Southwell QC (1959) (QC-1977)
Howard Page QC (1967) (QC-1987)
Patrick Talbot QC (1969) (QC-1990)
Alan Boyle QC (1972) (QC-1991)
Nicholas Padfield QC (1972) (QC-1991)
Frank Hinks QC (1973) (QC-2000)
Michael Briggs QC (1978) (QC-1994)
Simon Browne-Wilkinson QC (1981) (QC-1998)
Elizabeth Jones QC (1984) (QC-2000)
Nicholas Asprey (1969)
John Whittaker (1969)
Victor Joffe (1975)
William Ballantyne (1977)
Beverly-Ann Rogers (1978)
William Henderson (1978)
Paul Smith (1978)
James Behrens (1979)
Peter McMaster (1981)
Philip Hoser (1982)
Ann McAllister (1982)
Dominic Dowley (1983)
James Eadie (1984)
Richard Walford (1984)
Philip Jones (1985)
Philip Marshall (1987)
Nicholas Harrison (1988)
Andrew Moran (1989)
Nicholas Lavender (1989)
Khawar Qureshi (1990)
Clare Hoffmann (1990)
Kathryn Purkis (1991)
Douglas Close (1991)
David Blayney (1992)
Andrew Bruce (1992)
John Machell (1993)
David Drake (1994)
Justin Higgo (1995)
Daniel Lightman (1995)
Hugh Norbury (1995)
Timothy Collingwood (1996)
Jonathan Adkin (1997)
Giles Richardson (1997)
Thomas Braithwaite (1998)
Sinéad Agnew (1998)

The Chambers: The merger of leading commercial set One Hare Court and leading Chancery commercial Serle Court Chambers has created a unique set offering a formidable range of expertise in the field of business disputes and commercial law. In the first merger of its kind, between a commercial set from the Temple and a chancery commercial set from Lincoln's Inn, the new set intends to provide the service required from the modern business Bar, practising from newly refurbished premises on 6 floors in New Square, Lincoln's Inn. Chambers' strong reputation is based upon the excellence of the barristers from both previous sets, many of whom are individually recommended as leading practitioners in their specialist fields. The set is thoroughly approachable, innovative and at all times responsive to the needs and interests of its clients. Their experienced clerking and administrative team sets itself the same high standards.

Work Undertaken: Serle Court practices across a broad range of commercial and chancery fields of litigation, arbitration and legal advice. Principal areas of practice are: administrative and public law; banking; civil fraud; commercial litigation; company; financial services; human rights; insolvency; insurance and reinsurance; international trade; partnership; private client; professional negligence; property; public international law.
A first class team of barristers can be provided at all levels of call in each of these areas.
Additional Areas: Individual members of chambers have particular expertise in the following additional areas: Arab law, charities, employment, entertainment law, European law, intellectual property, parliamentary work, sports law.

International: A high proportion of chambers work originates overseas. Members of chambers appear in proceedings in the British Virgin Islands, Cayman Islands, Bermuda and the United States of America.

S

serle court

Set No.
152
SETTLEMENTCOUNSEL.COM (David Stern)

The Lloyd's Building, 12 Leadenhall Street, London, EC3V 1LP
Tel: (020) 7816 3600 **Fax:** (020) 7816 7130
Email: thecounsel@settlementcounsel.com **Website:** www.settlementcounsel.com

Head of Chambers:	David Stern
Practice Manager:	Nicholas Brand
Tenants:	3

Members:

David Stern (1989)
Michael Beckman QC (1954) (QC-1976) *
Margaret Howard (1977)
Anthony van Hagen (1974)
Stephen G. Mason *

* Associate Member

The Chambers: SettlementCounsel.com is an international commercial practice with significant experience in the resolution of major national and international disputes. Members provide an advisory and dispute resolution service, specialising in areas affecting global commerce and industry. Members are instructed by solicitors, international companies and foreign law firms under the IPR. Chambers have associate offices in Paris and New York.

Work Undertaken: Members specialise primarily in the fields of insurance, environmental protection, maritime law, corporate financial services and fraud, European Community law and in the resolution of other cross-border disputes.

Set No.
153
3-4 SOUTH SQUARE (Michael Crystal QC)

3-4 South Square, Gray's Inn, London, WC1R 5HP
Tel: (020) 7696 9900 **Fax:** (020) 7696 9911 **DX:** 338 (Ch.Ln.)
Email: clerks@southsquare.com **Website:** www.southsquare.com

Head of Chambers:	Michael Crystal QC
Senior Practice Manager:	Paul Cooklin
Practice Managers:	Michael Killick, Jim Costa, Dylan Playfoot, Nicola Skinner
Administrator:	Lesley Mortimer
Tenants:	38

Members:

Michael Crystal QC (1970) (QC-1984) LLB (Lond), BCL (Oxon)
Christopher Brougham QC (1969) (QC-1988) BA (Oxon)
Gabriel Moss QC (1974) (QC-1989) MA, BCL (Oxon)
Simon Mortimore QC (1972) (QC-1991) LLB (Exon)
Marion Simmons QC (1970) (QC-1994) LLB, LLM (Lond)
Richard Adkins QC (1982) (QC-1995) MA (Oxon)
Richard Sheldon QC (1979) (QC-1996) MA (Cantab)
Richard Hacker QC (1977) (QC-1998) MA (Cantab) Lic sp Dr Eur (Bruxelles)
Robin Knowles QC (1982) (QC-1999) MA (Cantab)
Mark Phillips QC (1984) (QC-1999) LLB, LLM (Bristol)
Robin Dicker (1986) (QC-2000) BA, BCL (Oxon)
Ian Fletcher (1971) MA, LLM, Phd, LLD, (Cantab), MCL (Tulane)
John Briggs (1973) LLB, (Lond) Ex, Du D d'U (Nancy)
David Marks (1974) MA, BCL (Oxon)
Martin Pascoe (1977) BA, BCL (Oxon)
William Trower (1983) MA (Oxon)
David Alexander (1987) MA (Cantab)
Antony Zacaroli (1987) BA, BCL (Oxon)
Mark Arnold (1988) MA (Cantab)
Lexa Hilliard (1987) LLB, (Lond)
Stephen Atherton (1989) LLB,(Lancaster) LLM (Cantab)
Sandra Bristoll (1989) MA (Cantab)
Adam Goodison (1990) BA(Dunelm)
Hilary Stonefrost (1991) MSC (Lond)
Lloyd Tamlyn (1991) BA(Cantab)
Glen Davis (1992) MA(Oxon)
Andreas Gledhill (1992) MA(Cantab)
Fidelis Oditah (1992) MA BCL D Phil (Oxon)
Roxanne Ismail (1993) LLB (Lond)
Michael Peglow (1993) DPhil(Oxon) Dr jur (Saar) M.Sc Econ (Saar)
Barry Isaacs (1994) MA(Oxon) MA(HARV) ASA
Ben Valentin (1995) BA BCL(Oxon) LLM(Cornell)
Felicity Toube (1995) BA BCL(Oxon)
Jeremy Goldring (1996) BA (Oxon) MA (Yale)
Samantha Knights (1996) BA (Oxon)
Lucy Frazer (1996) BA (Cantab)
David Allison (1998) BA (Cantab)
Daniel Bayfield (1998) BA (Cantab)
Muir Hunter QC (1938) (QC-1965) MA (Oxon) *
Clive Cohen (1989) (SC 1975) BA, LLB (Witwatersrand) *
Andrew Martin (1983) LLB *

* Associate Members

S

The Chambers: A set with a pre-eminent reputation in insolvency and reconstruction law and specialist expertise in banking, financial services, company law, professional negligence, insurance law and general commercial litigation. 3/4 South Square has 38 practising barristers, including 11 Queen's Counsel. Chambers aims to provide the most effective professional services to clients and has developed a modern administration system which is supported by advanced information technology. Members of chambers adopt a commercial and business-like approach to their practice and are capable of reacting swiftly (individually or as members of a team) to urgent problems as the need may arise. 3/4 South Square is accustomed to dealing with matters at all levels of complexity often at very short notice. In the course of their work, members see similar problems from many different angles and keep abreast of recent developments in business, financial and commercial law.

Work Undertaken:

Insolvency: 3/4 South Square is well-known for its insolvency work. Work undertaken includes contentious and non-contentious problems arising out of domestic and international corporate and personal insolvencies. This work is not just limited to the technical issues that arise in receiverships, administrations, liquidations and personal bankruptcies. It also includes analysis and problem-solving in the diverse areas that arise in the rescue and reconstruction of failed and failing businesses. Many important issues of banking and business law only ever arise for determination in the context of an insolvency. It follows that members of 3/4 South Square have considerable experience of those issues. They arise in the many different types of litigation in which officeholders are seeking to recover assets on behalf of an insolvent estate.

Other: 3/4 South Square's expertise is by no means limited to work related to or arising out of insolvency. Members of chambers are frequently instructed in banking, insurance and other commercial disputes, dealing with every kind of contentious problem such as the civil aspects of commercial fraud and the obtaining of evidence for foreign proceedings. These problems can arise in many different situations in which a good general understanding of commercial law is required. Members of chambers also have much experience of professional negligence proceedings (primarily in cases against accountants and solicitors) and in disciplinary proceedings.

Publications: The members of 3/4 South Square have written, edited and contributed to numerous books and articles on corporate and personal insolvency, company law and banking.

International: The barristers at 3/4 South Square are regularly instructed to appear in courts and tribunals overseas. These jurisdictions include Bermuda, the Cayman Islands, Germany and Hong Kong. They are also retained as expert witnesses to appear before both arbitrators and courts in these and other overseas jurisdictions.

Languages: Several members of chambers are fluent in or have a good working knowledge of foreign languages including French, German, Italian, Spanish, Hungarian and Chinese (Mandarin).

4 **11 SOUTH SQUARE** (Christopher Floyd QC)

11 South Square (2nd Floor), Gray's Inn, London, WC1R 5EU **Tel:** (020) 7405 1222 **Fax:** (020) 7242 4282 **DX:** 433
Email: clerks@11southsquare.com **Website:** www.11southsquare.com

5 STANBROOK & HENDERSON (Clive Stanbrook QC & Roger Henderson QC)

2 Harcourt Buildings, Temple, London, EC4Y 9DB
Tel: (020) 7353 0101 **Fax:** (020) 7583 2686 **DX:** LDE 1039
Email: clerks@harcourt.co.uk **Website:** www.harcourt.co.uk

Head of Chambers	Clive Stanbrook QC & Roger Henderson QC
Sen. Clerk:	John White

The Association: Stanbrook & Henderson is an association between the chambers of Roger Henderson QC at 2 Harcourt Buildings (see other reference for a full list) and the members of the European law firm of Stanbrook & Hooper in Brussels who are also members of the English bar, namely Clive Stanbrook OBE QC (1972) (QC-1989), Philip Bentley QC (1970) (QC-1991), and Debra Holland (1996).

The association was initiated in 1991 to satisfy clients' growing requirement for combined expertise in European and domestic law by providing a single port of call for solicitors and other professionals requiring advice and advocacy and by taking advantage of Stanbrook & Hooper's link with legal practices throughout mainland Europe. The work undertaken reflects chambers' detailed knowledge of EU institutions and the way in which they work, knowledge which is essential for anyone affected by EU action or legislation. The Brussels-based barristers have a close link with daily developments in the European Commission, the Council and the Parliament Secretariat, with the result that a complete legal monitoring and information service can be offered.

Work Undertaken: Areas covered include the law relating to competition; merger control; trade; financial services; insurance; offshore investment; fiscal policy; local government and the public sector; the environment; product liability; agriculture and food; health and safety; employment and discrimination; human rights; immigration and freedom of movement; intellectual property; sport; and general EU regulatory policy.

Set No. 156

3 STONE BUILDINGS (G.C. Vos QC)

3 Stone Buildings, Lincoln's Inn, London, WC2A 3XL
Tel: (020) 7242 4937 **Fax:** (020) 7405 3896 **DX:** 317
Email: clerks@3sb.law.co.uk

Head of Chambers:	G.C. Vos QC
Senior Clerk:	Andrew Palmer
Tenants:	21

Members:

Geoffrey C. Vos QC (1977) (QC-1993) MA (Cantab)
Edward Alexander Bannister QC (1974) (QC-1991)
David R. Stanford (1951) LLB, MA (Cantab)
Geoffrey J. Topham (1964) MA (Cantab)
Andrew J. Cosedge (1972) LLB (Exon)
James Gibbons (1974)
Alan M. Tunkel (1976) BA (Oxon)
David da Silva (1978) MA (Oxon)
Alexandra Mason (1981) BA (Hons) (London)
Robert A. Hantusch (1982) MA (Cantab)
Gilead Cooper (1983) MA (Oxon) Dip Law
Sarah J. Asplin (1984) MA (Cantab), BCL (Oxon)
Sarah E. Girling (1986) MA (Cantab)
David W. Lord (1987) LLB (Bristol)
Lawrence Jones (1988) LLB (Hons)
Carlos Pimentel (1990) LLB, LLM(Exon)
Asaf Kayani (1991) LLB (Leeds), BCL (Oxon)
Sarah H. Lacey (1991) BA (Cantab)
Andrew M. Twigger (1994) BA (Oxon)
Fenner Moeran (1996) BSc (Bristol)
Andrew J. Child (1997) BA (Cantab)

The Chambers: 3 Stone Buildings is a thriving set of Chancery and commercial chambers. Its main practice areas are commercial and Chancery litigation, pensions, company and insolvency, property and trusts, and insurance and reinsurance. In addition, 3 Stone Buildings offers specialists in media entertainment and sports, partnership, professional negligence and banking and financial services. Members of chambers undertake litigation drafting and advice in all these areas. Direct instructions are accepted from accountants, and other professional, and under the BarDirect scheme.

Set No. 157

4 STONE BUILDINGS (Philip Heslop QC)

4 Stone Buildings, Lincoln's Inn, London, WC2A 3XT
Tel: (020) 7242 5524 **Fax:** (020) 7831 7907 **DX:** 385
Email: clerks@4stonebuildings.law.co.uk **Website:** www.4stonebuildings.com

Head of Chambers:	Philip Heslop QC
Senior Clerk:	David Goddard
Tenants:	24

Members:

Philip Heslop QC (1970) (QC-1985)
Peter Curry QC (1953) (QC-1973)
Stephen Hunt (1968)
Anthony George Bompas QC (1975) (QC-1994)
Robert Hildyard QC (1977) (QC-1994)
Peter Griffiths (1977)
John Brisby QC (1978) (QC-1996)
Jonathan Crow (1981)
John Scott (1982) (QC Hong Kong 1996)
Malcolm Davis-White (1984)
Robert Miles (1987)
Rosalind Nicholson (1987)
Sarah Harman (1987)
Christopher Harrison (1988)
Jonathan Brettler (1988)
Paul Greenwood (1991)
Andrew Clutterbuck (1992)
Nicholas Cox (1992)
Richard G. Hill (1993)
Orlando Fraser (1994)
Anna Markham (1996)
Hermann Boeddinghaus (1996)
Andrew de Mestre (1998)
Vina Shukla (1992)

The Chambers: There are 24 members of chambers, including five silks and one Hong Kong QC. One of the juniors in chambers is the first Junior Counsel to the Treasury in Chancery (the 'Treasury Devil'), and another is on the main Chancery 'A' Panel. Four other members are on the Treasury 'B' Panel. Chambers belong to the Commercial Bar Association, the Chancery Bar Association and the Insolvency Lawyers Association. 4 Stone Buildings specialises in company/commercial law, covering all aspects of company law, commercial and general business law, corporate insolvency, as well as financial services and regulatory work, with a particular emphasis on litigation.

Work Undertaken: Company law, corporate fraud & asset recovery, financial services & regulatory work; shareholder disputes, commercial litigation, banking and public law.

Publications: Members of chambers are contributing editors to *Tolly's Company Law, Atkins Court Forms on Winding-up, the Encyclopaedia of Forms & Precedents on Companies, Halsbury's Laws of Hong Kong, Directors' Disqualification: Law & Practice, Butterworths Practical Insolvency, Table A-Articles of Association* and several other legal publications.

International: Members of chambers travel regularly to America, the Far East and Europe, as well as the Bahamas and Gibraltar. They have particularly strong connections with Hong Kong, Bermuda, Turks & Caicos Islands, Trinidad and the Cayman Islands.

Recruitment & Training: Applicants are expected to have good degrees, but a successful candidate will also be expected to have the common sense to recognise the advice that a client really needs, and the confidence and ambition to succeed. A mini-pupillage in chambers is strongly encouraged. Awards of up to £12,500 are offered for full pupillages of six months.

Set No. 158

5 STONE BUILDINGS (Henry Harrod)

5 Stone Buildings, Lincoln's Inn, London, WC2A 3XT
Tel: (020) 7242 6201 **Fax:** (020) 7831 8102 **DX:** 304 London/Chancery Lane
Email: clerks@5-stonebuildings.law.co.uk **Website:** www.5-stonebuildings.law.co.uk

Head of Chambers:	Henry Harrod
Senior Clerk:	Paul Jennings
Tenants:	19

5 STONE BUILDINGS

Members:

Henry Harrod (1963) +
Shân Warnock-Smith (1971)
Alastair Norris QC (1973) (QC-1997) +
Richard Fawls (1973)
Mark Herbert QC (1974) (QC-1995)
Mark Blackett-Ord (1974)
Martin Farber (1976)
Launcelot Henderson QC (1977) (QC-1995)
Andrew Simmonds QC (1980) (QC-1999)
Christopher Tidmarsh (1985)
Michael O'Sullivan (1986)
Patrick Rolfe (1987)
Barbara Rich (1990)
Karen Walden-Smith (1990)
Tracey Angus (1991)
Henry Legge (1993)
David Rees (1994)
Anna Clarke (1994)
Leon Sartin (1997)

+Recorder

The Chambers: 5 Stone Buildings is a chancery set known for specialist expertise in the fields of private client, estate planning, partnership, property litigation, professional negligence, occupational pensions and commercial litigation. Two former members are now in the Court of Appeal, and a third has recently been appointed to the chancery bench. Members act both for and against the Revenue and appear in the leading cases on tax avoidance, undue influence, right to buy, ethical investment, pension surplus and duties of pension trustees. All members advise on trusts, wills, administration of estates and land law. A fast, efficient modern service of the highest standard is provided.

Set No. 159

7 STONE BUILDINGS (Charles Aldous QC)

7 Stone Buildings, Lincoln's Inn, London, WC2A 3SZ
Tel: (020) 7405 3886 **Fax:** (020) 7242 8502 **DX:** 335
Email: clerks@7stonebuildings.co.uk **Website:** www.7stonebuildings.co.uk

Head of Chambers:	Charles Aldous QC
Senior Clerk:	Tony Marsh
Practice Manager:	Shona Kelly
Tenants:	17

Members:

Charles Aldous QC (1967) (QC-1985)
Michael Nield (1969)
David Unwin QC (1971) (QC-1995)
Nigel Davis QC (1975) (QC-1992)
Alastair Walton (1977)
John Randall QC (1978) (QC-1995) +
Guy Newey (1982)
Christopher R. Parker (1984)
James Clifford (1984)
Lindsey Stewart (1983)
Mark Wonnacott (1989)
Edmund Cullen (1991)
Patricia Carswell (1993)
Tom Bannister (1993)
Andrew Westwood (1994)
Siward Atkins (1995)
Louise Hutton (1998)

The Chambers: A specialist chancery set, founded in the 1870s, handling all aspects of chancery and commercial practice other than shipping. Much of the work is contentious. All members accept Direct 0Professional Access.

Associated Chambers: John Randall practises principally at St Philip's Chambers, Birmingham.

By January 1st 2001, 13 Old Square and 7 Stone Buildings will be merged as a single commercial Chancery Set under a new name. Contact details for the clerks will remain the same.

Work Undertaken: Company and commercial law; corporate finance; credit, security and banking; entertainment law; equitable remedies; mistake and misrepresentation; fiduciary duties; constructive trusts; tracing; financial services; fraud; freezing and recovery of assets; insolvency; insurance; intellectual property; pre-trial remedies; freezing and search orders; landlord and tenant; pensions; professional negligence and regulation; property; trusts and charities; wills, probate and administration of estates.

Clientele: Mainly businesses and professions, particularly accountants in various capacities.

Recruitment & Training: Chambers offer awards during pupillage, and are not members of PACH. Mini-pupillages are encouraged.

7 STONE BUILDINGS

S

Set No. 160
8 STONE BUILDINGS (John Cherry QC)

8 Stone Building's, Lincoln's Inn, London, WC2A 3TA
Tel: (020) 7831 9881 **Fax:** (020) 7831 9392 **DX:** 216 Chancery Lane
Email: alanl@8stonebuildings.law.co.uk

Head of Chambers:	John Cherry QC
Senior Clerk:	Alan Luff
	mobile: 0802 411348
Junior Clerk:	Paul Eeles
Tenants:	11

Members:

John M. Cherry QC (1961) (QC-1988)
Timothy J. Briden (1976)
Kieran May (1971)
Martin Seaward (1978)
Stewart Room (1991)
Nigel Waddington (1992)
Richard Menzies (1993)
Marcus Baldwin (1994)
Sarah Howard-Jones (1994)
Peregrine Hill (1995)
Martyn McLeish (1997)

Work Undertaken: Members of chambers practise principally in the areas of personal injury, professional negligence and medical negligence. Individual specialisations include: ecclesiastical law; health and safety; Inheritance Act claims; immigration; insurance; asbestos related diseases; industrial deafness; and employment law.

Set No. 161
9 STONE BUILDINGS (Michael Ashe QC)

9 Stone Buildings, Lincoln's Inn, London, WC2A 3TG
Tel: (020) 7404 5055 **Fax:** (020) 7405 1551 **DX:** 314 Chancery Lane
Email: clerks@9stoneb.law.co.uk

Head of Chambers:	Michael Ashe QC
Senior Clerk:	Alan Austin
Tenants:	22

9 STONE BUILDINGS

Members:

Michael Ashe QC (1971) (QC-1994) (QC N I 1998) (SC Ireland 2000) +
Isaac Jacob (1963) +
Cenydd I. Howells (1964) +
Vivian R. Chapman (1970) +
Christopher I. Cant (1973)
Edward Denehan (1981)
Penelope Jane Reed (1983)
Araba Taylor (1984)
Martin Young (1984)
Lynne M. Counsell (1986)
Robert S. Levy (1988)
Sheila Foley (1988)
Timothy Sisley (1989)
John A.C. Smart (1989)
Philip Flower (1979)
Helene Pines Richman (1992)
Lana Wood (1993)
Peter Shaw (1995)
Jonathan Lewis (1996)
James Hanham (1996)
Daniel Bromilow (1996)
Richard Wilson (1996)
Graeme C. Wood (1968) *
W.H. Ruffin (1972) (North Carolina Bar USA) *
Peter Clayton (1977) (Hong Kong Bar) *
N. Critelli (1991) (Iowa and New York Bar USA) *

* Door Tenants + Recorder

The Chambers: A general Chancery set undertaking litigation, advisory work and drafting over a wide range of subjects including: wills and trusts; landlord and tenant; business agreements; companies and insolvency; tax and tax planning (including stamp duties); financial services and securities regulations; charities; commons registration; employment law; and professional negligence. (Some members are practitioners in US and Ireland). Full details and information can be obtained from the chambers' information booklet, which is available on request.

Set No. 162
11 STONE BUILDINGS (Murray Rosen QC)

11 Stone Buildings, Lincoln's Inn, London, WC2A 3TG
Tel: (020) 7831 6381 **Fax:** (020) 7831 2575 **DX:** 1022 Chancery Lane WC2
Email: clerks@11stonebuildings.com **Website:** www.11stonebuildings.com

Head of Chambers	Murray Rosen QC
Sen. Clerk:	Christopher Berry
Clerks:	Gareth Davies, Caron Levy, Matthew Curness
Listing:	Will Shrubsall
Marketing and Client Care:	Sarah Longden
Emergency overnight & weekend service:	
	Christopher Berry Home: (020) 8946 9139 Mobile: 07836 566 251
	Gareth Davies Home: (020) 8542 1211 Mobile: 07767 445 519
Tenants:	40

Members:

Murray Rosen QC (1976) (QC-1993)
Michael Beckman QC (1954) (QC-1976)
Peter Sheridan QC (1956) (QC-1977)
Edward Cousins (1971)
Edward Cohen (1972)
Alan Bishop (1973)
Adrian Salter (1973)
Donald McCue (1974)
John Phillips (1975)
Nigel Meares (1975)
Robert Deacon (1976)
Jonathan Arkush (1977)
Jane Giret (1981)
Sidney Ross (1983)
Roland Higgs (1984)
Marc Dight (1984)
Alan Gourgey (1984)
Tina Kyriakides (1984)
Raquel Agnello (1986)
Marcia Shekerdemian (1987)
Charles Holbech (1988)
Tim Penny (1988)
Sally Barber (1988)
Marilyn Kennedy-McGregor (1989)
Jonathan Middleburgh (1990)
Birgitta Meyer (1992)
Christopher Wilkins (1993)
Max Mallin (1993)
James Barnard (1993)
Nick Parfitt (1993)
Timothy Cowen (1993)
Jonathan Lopian (1994)
Denis Daly (1995)
Christopher Boardman (1995)
Tom Weekes (1995)
Jamie Riley (1995)
Alaric Watson (1997)
Stephen Tudway (1998)
David Stern (1989) *
Douglas Keel (1997) *

* Associate Members

S

The Chambers: The barristers at 11 Stone Buildings practise in commercial litigation with specialist groups for all types of contract, company, insolvency and property disputes. The set has won awards for Barristers' Chambers of the year and has been praised in the press for its responsiveness, flexibility in working practices and approach to fee levels. There are 40 barristers including 3 QCs working for law firms across the country and internationally as well as with in-house legal departments and direct access clients. They are particularly well known for their expertise in the specialist bar categories listed below.

Work Undertaken:

Commercial Chancery: Highly regarded as a set with Murray Rosen QC profiled as a leading silk, Edward Cohen and Jane Giret as leading juniors.

Contract and Commercial: The largest group dealing with all aspects of business and banking litigation and commercial drafting.

Company: Jane Giret and Marcia Sherkerdemian are profiled as leading juniors in the company field.

Insolvency: A leading set with Jane Giret, Tina Kyriakides, Raquel Agnello and Marcia Sherkerdemian particularly recommended. Recent cases of interest include disputes arising from the BCCI collapse, Maxwell Fleet and Crystal Palace FC.

Fraud: The specialist groups deal in all aspects of civil fraud such as commercial fraud; fraudulent trading; property fraud; professional misconduct and VAT fraud. Michael Beckman QC deals with both civil and criminal fraud and all aspects of serious crime.

Intellectual Property: A major area of work for the set, their experience includes a wide variety of copyright, trademark, design rights and non-technical patent work, internet and e-commerce disputes.

Media and Entertainment: Chambers deal with a significant amount of work in the media and music industry including defamation, press freedom, publishing and film and music contracts.

Sports Law: Chambers has a well developed sports law practice with a history of representing high profile clubs, organisations and individuals in a variety of sports. Murray Rosen QC is highly recommended as a leading silk in this area of law. He is chairman of the Bar Sports Law Group.

Property & Land: Jonathan Arkush is recommended as a leading junior.

Tribunals: The work in this area relates mainly to disciplinary, employment, regulatory, sports and VAT.

Succession & Trusts: Members of this group are specialists in trust drafting and advisory work and are experienced in friendly and hostile litigation. They offer expertise in the Court of Protection.

Professional Negligence: Using the experience of all the specialist groups, chambers deal with a substantial amount of lawyers', accountants', architects' and surveyors' negligence.

Alternative Disputes Resolution: 11 Stone Buildings has a fully equipped ADR/Arbitration facility available for commercial use and each of the chambers specialist groups has accredited barristers available for dispute resolution.

Fees: Levels are carefully monitored and a flexible approach is maintained, as chambers believe that each case has its own special requirements. This flexibility includes fixed fees and package fees, which allows lay clients greater access to experienced lawyers. However, hourly rates can be quoted to assist the client in budgeting for services.

Conditional fee work is being continually developed and the chambers will respond to government and other initiatives such as Thai Trading as they arise. As an aid to efficient and cost effective legal services chambers has a team of lawyers for multi-track cases available on a fixed fee basis. For a copy of the chambers' specialist brochures contact Sarah Longden or alternatively visit their website www.11stonebuildings.com

Publications: John Phillips is author of the *Modern Contract of Guarantee* and *Protecting Designs: Law and Litigation*; Edward Cousins is the author of *Cousins on Mortgages* and *Pease and Chitty's Law of Markets and Fairs*'; Sidney Ross is the author of *Inheritance Act Claims, Law and Practice.*

S

Set No.
163 **199 STRAND** (David Phillips QC)

199 Strand, London, WC2R 1DR
Tel: (020) 7379 9779 **Fax:** (020) 7379 9481 **DX:** 322 Ch.Ln.
Email: chambers@199strand.co.uk **Website:** www.199strand.co.uk

Head of Chambers	David Phillips QC
Sen. Clerk:	Martin Griffiths
Tenants:	38

199 strand

Members:

David Phillips QC (1976) (QC-1997) +
Peter Andrews QC (1970) (QC-1991) +
Robin De Wilde QC (1971) (QC-1993) +
David C. Wilby QC (1974) (QC-1998) +
Elizabeth-Anne Gumbel QC (1974) (QC-1999)
Malcolm Stitcher (1971)
Alan Green (1973)
Keith Walmsley (1973)
Steven Whitaker (1973)
Simon Levene (1977) +
Quintin Tudor-Evans (1977)
Andrew Goodman (1978)
Anthony Korn (1978)
Sara Hargreaves (1979)
Francis Treasure (1980)
Martin Kurrein (1981)
Jacqueline Beech (1981)
Leslie Blohm (1982)
Patrick Sadd (1984)
Philomena Harrison (1985)
Martin Hutchings (1986)
Michael Harrison (1986)
Henry Charles (1987)
James Aldridge (1987)
Richard Serlin (1987)
Henry Witcomb (1989)
Sophie Garner (1990)
Timothy Nesbitt (1991)
Rachel Vickers (1992)
Anthony Cheshire (1992)
Eliot Woolf (1993)
Nicholas Isaac (1993)
Louise Thomson (1996)
Mark Sefton (1996)
Toby Vanhegan (1996)
Jeremy Ford (1996)
Nicholas Oakeshott (1997)
Simon Brindle (1998)
Stephen Guest (1980) *

+Recorder *Associate Tenants

The Chambers: 199 Strand is a long-established set specialising in civil work and undertakes instructions for clients in London, throughout the country and abroad.

Work Undertaken: The principal areas of work undertaken, in which specialist groups are offered, are: personal injury, clinical negligence, property, professional negligence and general commercial work. Smaller teams within chambers specialise in employment law and in road transport law.
Their web site at www.199strand.co.uk provides full details of the areas of work undertaken by chambers as well as detailed profiles of the members. A comprehensive brochure is also available on request from the clerks.
Chambers accept instructions under the Direct Professional Access rules and also accept cases under Conditional Fee Agreements.

Languages: French, German, Hebrew, Japanese, Mandarin, Chinese.

Recruitment & Training: Two funded 12-month pupillages are available; applications for these are only accepted through PACH. Applications for mini-pupillages are welcomed throughout the year. All inquiries regarding these should be addressed to Mark Sefton.

Set No.
164 **TANFIELD CHAMBERS**

Francis Taylor Building, (3rd Floor), Temple, London, EC4Y 7BY
Tel: (020) 7797 7250 **Fax:** (020) 7797 7299 **DX:** 46 London Chancery Lane
Email: clerks@tanfieldchambers.co.uk **Website:** www.tanfieldchambers.co.uk

Head of Chambers:	Andrew Thompson, David Guy
Senior Clerk:	Paul A Green
Tenants:	32

Members:

Andrew Thompson (1969)
David Guy (1972)
Alan Tyrrell QC (1956) (QC-1976)
John Hall QC (1948) (QC-1967)
Edward Raw (1963)
Timothy Shuttleworth (1971)
Stephen Monkcom (1974)
Basil Yoxall (1975)
David Daly (1979)
Marc Brittain (1983)
Michael Shrimpton (1983)
Richard Colbey (1984)
Mark Kelly (1985)
Robin Howat (1986)
Stephen Hancox (1986)
David Sharp (1986)
Mark Loveday (1986)
Michael Bailey (1986)
Brian Riley (1986)
John Buck (1986)
Christopher Bamford (1987)
Sarah Dines (1988)
Sheila Phil-Ebosie (1988)
Gwen Bankole-Jones (1991)
Tom Skinner (1992)
Lisa Stanton (1993)
Damian McCarthy (1994)
Michelle Marnham (1994)
Benjimin Burgher (1995)
Catherine Aherne (1997)
Timothy Polli (1997)
Martina Murphy (1998)
Ann Bevitt (1992) *
Becket Bedford (1989) *
Geoffery Bennett *
Christopher Mitchell-Heggs *
George Cuming *
Matthew Heim *
Helene Cohen *
Brian Sharples *
Lord Thomas of Gwydir *
Graham H Rose *
Sir Arnold de Montmorency *
John Warwick Montgomery *

* Associate member

T

The Chambers: An established common law set specializing in all aspects of employment, family, personal injury, and property law. Members' specialisations also include commercial, computer, crime, education, European, gaming & lotteries, and professional negligence.

65 1 TEMPLE GARDENS (Hugh B.H. Carlisle QC)

1 Temple Gardens, Temple, London, EC4Y 9BB
Tel: (020) 7583 1315 **Fax:** (020) 7353 3969 **DX:** 382 London
Email: clerks@1templegardens.co.uk **Website:** www.1templegardens.co.uk

Head of Chambers:	Hugh B.H. Carlisle QC
Senior Clerk:	Dean Norton
Tenants:	38

TEMPLE 1 GARDENS

Members:
Hugh B.H. Carlisle QC (1961) (QC-1978) MA (Cantab)
Lord Mayhew of Twysden QC (1955) (QC-1972) MA (Oxon)
Norman A. Miscampbell QC (1952) (QC-1974) MA (Oxon)
Ian D. Burnett QC (1980) (QC-1998) MA (Oxon)
John R.A. Bate-Williams (1976) LLB (Wales)
Ian Ashford-Thom (1977) LLB (Exon)
Angus J. Macpherson (1977) MA (Cantab)
William G. Hoskins (1980) MA (Oxon)
Dominic C.R. Grieve (1980) MA (Oxon)
Mark A. Bishop (1981) MA (Cantab)
Alison B. Hewitt (1984) LLB (London)
Alastair J. McFarlane (1985) LLB (Reading)
Robin B-K Tam (1986) MA (Cantab)
Paul A.J. Kilcoyne (1985) LLB (B'ham)
James Bell (1987) LLB (Wales)
Simon G.J. Brown (1988) LLB (London)
Jane R. Llewelyn (1989) MA (Cantab)
Philip D.P. Astor (1989) MA (Oxon)
Keith F. Morton (1990) BSc (Hull)
James R. Laughland (1991) BA (Kent)
Charles Ciumei (1991) BA (Hons) (Oxon)
Charles Curtis (1992) BA (Dunelm)
Richard Wilkinson (1992) LLB (Bristol)
Nicholas Bacon (1992) LLB (Hons) (Essex)
Marcus Grant (1993) BA (Reading)
David Barr (1993) MA (Cantab)
Alexandra Issa (1993) MA (Oxon)
Benjamin Williams (1994) MA (Oxon)
Alexander Glassbrook (1995) BA (Bristol)
Nicholas Moss (1995) MA (Cantab)
Timothy Kevan (1996) BA (Cantab)
Julia Smyth (1996) LLB (London)
Emma-Jane Hobbs (1996) BA (Bristol)
Jonathan Hough (1997) MA (Oxon)
Paul McGrath (1997) LLB (London)
Dominic Adamson (1997) LLB (Newcastle)
Anna Kotzeva (1998) BA (Cantab)

Work Undertaken: General common law, in particular personal injury, professional negligence and product liability claims and claims in nuisance and other torts; insurance and other contractual disputes; consumer credit, public and administrative law and judicial review; immigration law; employment law; public inquiries and inquests; health and safety; VAT; fraud both civil and criminal.

Languages: French, German and Spanish.

66 2 TEMPLE GARDENS (Dermod O'Brien QC)

2 Temple Gardens, London, EC4Y 9AY
Tel: (020) 7822 1200 **Fax:** (020) 7822 1300 **DX:** 134 (Ch.Ln.)
Email: clerks@2templegardens.co.uk **Website:** www.2templegardens.co.uk

Head of Chambers:	Dermod O'Brien QC
Senior Clerk:	Christopher Willans
Tenants:	45

Members:
Dermod O'Brien QC (1962) (QC-1983)
Timothy Preston QC (1964) (QC-1982)
Patrick Twigg QC (1967) (QC-1985)
Michael de Navarro QC (1968) (QC-1990)
Robert Moxon-Browne QC (1969) (QC-1990)
Andrew Collender QC (1969) (QC-1991)
Benjamin Browne QC (1976) (QC-1996)
Jeremy Stuart-Smith QC (1978) (QC-1997)
Daniel Pearce-Higgins QC (1973) (QC-1998)
Howard Palmer QC (1977) (QC-1999)
Henry de Lotbiniere (1968)
Rosalind Foster (1969)
Roger Hetherington (1973)
Stephen Archer (1979)
Monya Anyadike-Danes (1980)
John McDonald (1981)
David Thomas (1982)
Christopher Russell (1982)
Sarah Vaughan-Jones (1983)
Graham Eklund (1984)
Martin Porter (1986)
Katherine Gordon (1989)
Andrew Miller (1989)
Neil Moody (1989)
Bradley Martin (1990)
Timothy Otty (1990)
Daniel Crowley (1990)
John Snell (1991)
Paul Downes (1991)
Tim Lord (1992)
Rupert Reece (1993)
David Turner (1993)
Clare Brown (1993)
Dore Green (1994)
Lucy Wyles (1994)
Justin Mort (1994)
Bruce Gardiner (1994)
Nina Goolamali (1995)
Adam Constable (1995)
Neil Hext (1995)
Roger Harris (1996)
Krista Lee (1996)
Charles Dougherty (1997)
Anna de Chassiron (1998)
Peter de Verneuil Smith (1998)

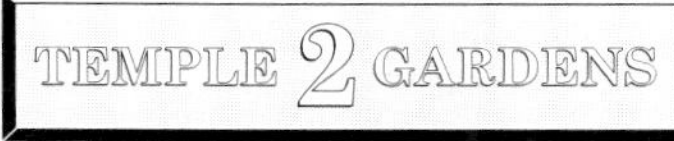

Continued overleaf

Work Undertaken: The major areas of practice are general, common and commercial law (including sale and carriage of goods, restraint of trade, confidentiality, product liability, mergers and acquisitions, company and employment law, and arbitrations); commercial and civil fraud; insurance and reinsurance; all areas of professional negligence including medical negligence; disaster litigation; environmental law (including cases concerning fire, flood, electricity, gas, water, highways and health and safety at work); personal injuries (including employers' liability and occupational diseases); building construction and engineering cases. Disputes involving conflicts of law, jurisdiction and EU problems are regularly handled.

Languages: French, German, Italian, Spanish and Swedish.

Recruitment & Training: Pupillages and mini-pupillages by arrangement. Apply to the Secretary of the Pupillage Committee.

Set No. 167

3 TEMPLE GARDENS TAX CHAMBERS (Richard Bramwell QC)

3 Temple Gardens, Temple, London, EC4Y 9AU
Tel: (020) 7353 7884 **Fax:** (020) 7583 2044
Email: clerks@taxcounsel.co.uk **Website:** www.taxcounsel.co.uk

Head of Chambers:	Richard Bramwell QC
Senior Clerk:	Anne de Rose
Tenants:	8

Members:

Richard Bramwell QC (1967) (QC-1989)
John Dick (1974)
Michael Sherry (1978)
Alun James (1986)
Eamon McNicholas (1994)
David Southern (1982)
Jonathan Schwarz (1998) (SA 1977, Can 1981)
Peter Harris (1980)

Work Undertaken: Specialist tax practitioners offering comprehensive tax planning. Advice on domestic and international tax investigations disputes and appeals before all Courts. Professional liability involving tax.Current positions held by members of chambers include Chairman of the Tax Faculty of the ICAEW; Secretary of the Revenue Bar Association; visiting Professor at Queen Mary & Westfield College, London University; memberships of the CIOT Corporation Tax Technical Sub-Committee, the International Tax Sub-Committee, the Working Party on Reform of Intellectual Property Taxation, the Inland Revenue E-Commerce Forum; Editorial Board Taxation.
Details on individual members are to be found at www.taxcounsel.co.uk

Publications: Members have written, contributed to or edited: *Taxation of Companies and Company Reconstructions; Whiteman on Capital Gains Tax; Tolley's Taxation of Corporate Debt and Financial Instruments; Simon's Taxes; De Voil on VAT; Taxation; the Tax Journal; British Tax Review; Bulletin for International Fiscal Documentation; the Financial Times.*

International: Members have specific experience in relation to Canada, France, South Africa, the United States, Germany and Latvia.

Languages: English, French and German.

Set No. 168

3 TEMPLE GARDENS (John Coffey QC)

3 Temple Gardens, Temple, London, EC4Y 9AU
Tel: (020) 7353 3102 **Fax:** (020) 7353 0960 **DX:** 485
Email: clerks@3tg.co.uk

Head of Chambers:	John Coffey QC
Senior Clerk:	Kevin Aldridge
Tenants:	36

Members:

John Coffey QC (1970) (QC-1996)
Jeffrey Pegden QC (1973) (QC-1996)
Geoffrey Birch (1972)
Karl Scholz (1973)
Richard Crabtree (1974)
Piers Reed (1974)
Jayne Gilbert (1976)
Robert Whittaker (1977)
Ann Cotcher (1979)
David Stanton (1979)
William Saunders (1980)
Simon Connolly (1981)
Simon Smith (1981)
Alasdair Smith (1981)
Brian Stork (1981)
David Barnes (1981)
Kim Halsall (1982)
Dee Connolly (1982)
Stella Reynolds (1983)
Martin Lahiffe (1984)
Wayne Cleaver (1986)
Gordon Ross (1986)
Catherine Popert (1987)
Benjamin Aina (1987)
Nicholas Bleaney (1988)
Frances McKeever (1988)
Martin Rutherford (1990)
Clemency Firth (1992)
Evan Nuttall (1993)
Nicholas Corsellis (1993)
Alexander Williams (1995)
Amanda Hamilton (1995)
Caroline Carberry (1995)
Matthew Lawson (1995)
Nicola Cafferkey (1998)
Ruby Selva (1998)

TEMPLE III GARDENS

The Chambers: A well-established set of chambers specialising in all areas of criminal law, family law and areas of common law. Members appear as advocates in the Magistrates Court, Crown Court, High

Court, Queen's Bench Divisional Court, the Court of Appeal and the House of Lords. Other tribunals include Professional Tribunals, Mental Health Tribunals, Industrial Tribunals, Inquests and other Judicial Inquiries.

Memberships: Criminal Bar Association, Family Law Bar Association.

Work Undertaken:

Crime: Chambers specialise in all areas of criminal law and have an extensive group of practitioners available at all levels of call. Commercial and corporate fraud is an important specialisation of a number of members and the field of sexual abuse is also a speciality.

Family Law: The matrimonial work of chambers extends to all aspects of this field. Matrimonial property disputes and all sections of the law relating to children. Advice is given to both Local Authorities and to individual clients.

Common Law: A broad range of common law work is handled.

Recruitment & Training: Training and pupillage applications should be sent to Ruby Selva, including a detailed CV and references. Chambers currently offer pupillage awards.

Set No.

169 3 TEMPLE GARDENS (Jonathan Goldberg QC)

Three Temple Gardens, Temple, London, EC4Y 9AU
Tel: (020) 7583 1155 **Fax:** (020) 7353 5446 **DX:** 0064
Email: clerks@3templegardens.co.uk

Head of Chambers:	Jonathan Goldberg QC
Senior Clerk:	Adrian Duncan Esq.
Tenants:	25

Members:

Jonathan Goldberg QC (1971) (QC-1989)
Robert Watson (1963)
Joanna Greenberg QC (1972) (QC-1994)
Philip G. Levy (1968)
David Roderic Owen-Jones (1972)
Kenneth Hind CBE (1973)
Ian Bourne (1977)
Grace Amakye (1983)
Jonathan Dunne (1986)
Lauren Soertsz (1987)
Jonathan Taylor (1987)
Paul Addison (1987)
Neil Guest (1989)
Andrew Rutter (1990)
Caroline Kennedy-Morrison (1990)
Dominic McGinn (1990)
Christopher Gillespie (1991)
James Buchanan (1993)
Ed Vickers (1993)
Pascal Bates (1994)
Gary Grant (1995)
Kim Whittlestone (1995)
Helen Guest (1996)
Timothy Godfrey (1997)
Susannah Stevens (1997)

The Chambers: This is a relatively small, but strong and well-established set, specialising in criminal work. Head of Chambers, Jonathan Goldberg QC, is a noted defender who has been briefed in many of the best known criminal trials of the past two decades at the Old Bailey and elsewhere. He also undertakes many heavy civil trials where strong advocacy and cross-examination are required. Second Silk, Joanna Greenberg QC, is likewise establishing a leading reputation as a defender. Practising from elegant rooms once occupied by Marshall Hall QC, this set prides itself on a professional but friendly and unpompous approach to its clients.Members of chambers also regularly undertake commercial fraud, extradition, licensing and road traffic cases, and civil cases where contentious issues of fact are involved and expert cross-examination of witnesses required.

Jonathan Goldberg QC, Joanna Greenberg QC, Ian Bourne and Grace Amakye sit as Recorders.

Set No.

170 14 TOOKS COURT (Michael Mansfield QC)

14 Tooks Court, Cursitor St, London, EC4A 1LB **Tel:** (020) 7405 8828 **Fax:** (020) 7405 6680 **DX:** 68 (Ch.Ln.) **Email:** clerks@tooks.law.co.uk

T

Set No. 171

2-4 TUDOR STREET (Richard Ferguson QC)

2-4 Tudor Street, London, EC4Y 0AA
Tel: (020) 7797 7111 **Fax:** (020) 7797 7120 **DX:** 226 Chancery Lane
Email: clerks@rfqc.co.uk **Website:** www.rfqc.co.uk

Head of Chambers:	Richard Ferguson QC
Clerk:	John Phipps
Tenants:	50

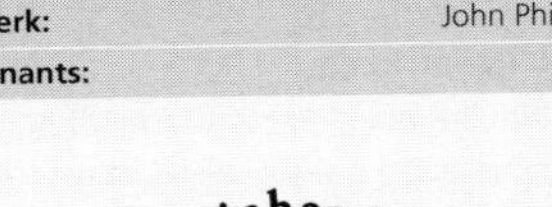

Members:

Richard Ferguson QC (1956) (QC-1973)
Robert Marshall-Andrews QC (1967) (QC-1989)
Peter Feinberg QC (1972) (QC-1992)
Patrick O'Connor QC (1970) (QC-1993)
Clement Goldstone QC (1971) (QC-1993)
Henry C. Grunwald QC (1972) (QC-1999)
Nigel Lambert QC (1974) (QC-1999)
Lionel Lassman (1955)
Alan Greenwood (1970)
Peter Stage (1971)
David Martin-Sperry (1971)
Michael Cousens (1973)
Stephen Winberg (1974)
Anthony Wadling (1977)
Peter McGrail (1977)
Sonja Shields (1977)
Andrew Turton (1977)
Robert Hunter (1979)
Isabelle Gillard (1980)
Philip M.D. Grundy (1980)
Preston Dass (1983)
Charles Ward-Jackson (1985)
Sandy Canavan (1987)
Martin Taylor (1988)
Peter Clark (1988)
James Beck (1989)
Christopher Henley (1989)
James Montgomery (1989)
Martin Sharpe (1989)
Benjamin Squirrell (1990)
Sangita Modgil (1990)
Eamonn M. Sherry (1990)
Peter Binder (1991)
Anthony Ventham (1991)
Anthony Orchard (1991)
Ann Tayo (1991)
William England (1991)
Julie-Anne Kincade (1991)
Simon Gruchy (1993)
Gerard Doran (1993)
David McGrath (1993)
Louise Sweet (1994)
Alphege Bell (1995)
Mark Harries (1995)
Martin Watts (1995)
Jacqueline Slee (1995)
Victoria Wootton (1995)
David Haeems (1996)
Gerald Mohabir (1996)

The Chambers: This forward-looking set aims to provide a complete service within the areas of criminal law, libel, licensing and actions against the police.

Work Undertaken: Much of chambers' work involves criminal cases, and members have been involved in political and terrorist matters, in those raising issues of public and media importance, and in human rights cases. Chambers take particular pride in their willingness to defend unpopular individual positions, but members also take very seriously their obligation to prosecute cases fairly and effectively. Ten members of the set have completed professional courses on fraud trial practice, and many have acted in complex trials involving VAT, company and commercial fraud.

Additional Areas of Work: Individual members also practise in the fields of libel, licensing law, and actions against the police.

Languages: French, Hebrew, Italian, Portuguese and Spanish.

Set No. 172

3 VERULAM BUILDINGS (Christopher Symons QC & John Jarvis QC)

3 Verulam Buildings, Gray's Inn, London, WC1R 5NT
Tel: (020) 7831 8441 **Fax:** (020) 7831 8479 **DX:** LDE 331
Email: clerks@3verulam.co.uk **Website:** www.3verulam.co.uk

Head of Chambers:	Christopher Symons QC, John Jarvis QC
Senior Practice Managers:	Roger Merry-Price, Nicholas Hill
Tenants:	48

Members:

Christopher Symons QC (1972) (QC-1989)
John Jarvis QC (1970) (QC-1989)
R. Neville Thomas QC (1962) (QC-1975)
Nicholas Merriman QC (1969) (QC-1988)
Ian Geering QC (1974) (QC-1991)
William Blair QC (1972) (QC-1994)
Nicholas Elliott QC (1972) (QC-1995)
Richard Salter QC (1975) (QC-1995)
Ali Malek QC (1980) (QC-1996)
Gregory Mitchell QC (1979) (QC-1997)
Ross Cranston QC (1976) (QC-1998)
S. Clive Freedman (1975)
Richard de Lacy (1976)
Elizabeth Birch (1978)
Michael Kay (1981)
Andrew Onslow (1982)
Peter Cranfield (1982)
Andrew Sutcliffe (1983)
Stephen Phillips (1984)
Rory Phillips (1984)
Tom Weitzman (1984)
Ewan McQuater (1985)
Jonathan Nash (1986)
James Cameron (1987)
Juliet May (1988)
Maurice Sheridan (1984)
Angharad Start (1988)
Adrian Beltrami (1989)
Amanda Green (1990)
Annie Hockaday (1990)
John Odgers (1990)
Jonathan Mark Phillips (1991)
James Evans (1991)
Jonathan Harold Marks (1992)
David Quest (1993)
Richard Edwards (1993)
Jonathan Davies-Jones (1994)
David Pope (1995)
Richard Brent (1995)
Sonia Tolaney (1995)
Ian Wilson (1995)
Catherine Gibaud (1996)
Natalie Baylis (1996)
Matthew Parker (1997)
David Head (1997)
Ewan McKendrick (1998)
Christopher Hare (1998)
Peter Ratcliffe (1998)

3 Verulam Buildings

V

The Chambers: 3 Verulam Buildings is a leading set of chambers specialising in commercial work. Members accept instructions and briefs to advise and represent clients in court, arbitration and other tribunals in England, Wales and internationally.

Work Undertaken: All members of chambers are specialist advocates in various aspects of commercial work. Among them are acknowledged experts in th fields of banking; insurance and reinsurance; professional negligence; insolvency; entertainment and media; commercial fraud; public international and environmental law. The set also has an established reputation in international and domestic arbitration. Chambers include a number of individuals involved in EU cases in the national courts and the European Court of Justice.

Expertise is also offered in an extremely wide range of other matters, including agency, agriculture, building and construction, commodities trading, all aspects of company law, competition law, computer legislation, including Y2K, employment, financial services, gaming, intellectual property, judicial review, landlord and tenant matters, pensions, restraint of trade, and sale of goods.

The diversity of experience available enables 3 Verulam Buildings to offer advice and representation to clients in the huge variety of business contexts in which legal issues arise. Barristers work individually or in teams to carry out all the preparatory and interlocutory work necessary to bring a case to trial or to settle a case by way of ADR. They also undertake non-contentious legal work, for example, drafting standard terms and conditions in contracts both for financial institutions and commercial clients. Additionally, members advise clients on the effects of new law.

Chambers are managed by a friendly and efficient team of practice managers and support staff. In appropriate circumstances, chambers will carry out work on a conditional fee basis. The practice managers would be pleased to discuss this further and a draft agreement is available on request.

Recruitment & Training: Chambers offer four pupillages of 12 months, each with an award of not less than £25,000. Candidates should have a first-class or 2.1 degree (which need not be in law). Applications will be received only through the PACH scheme of the Bar Council.

Set No. 173

VERULAM CHAMBERS (Michael Edwards QC)

Peer House, 8-14 Verulam Street, London, WC1X 8LX
Tel: (020) 7813 2400 **Fax:** (020) 7405 3870 **DX:** 436 Chancery Lane

Head of Chambers:	Michael Edwards QC
Senior Clerk:	Trevor Austin
First Junior:	William Taborn
Tenants:	30

Members:

J. Michael Edwards QC (1949) (QC-1981)
Clifford Payton (1972)
David Dethridge (1975)
Moira Sofaer (1975)
Peter Mullen (1977)
Gilles D'Aigremont (1978)
Olav Ernstzen (1981)
Susan Lawe (1982)
Dominic Webber (1985)
Sailesh Mehta (1986)
Joan Moore (1986)
Pearl Humberstone (1987)
Matthew Sowerby (1987)
Joanne White (1987)
Jacqueline McIntosh (1987)
Cynthia Gifford (1988)
David Giles (1988)
Maurice Rifat (1990)
Ann Jago (1991)
Trevor Siddle (1991)
John Passmore (1992)
Julia Smart (1993)
Katherine Goodwin (1993)
Leonorah Smith (1993)
Andrew Skelly (1994)
Victoria Quinn (1995)
Susan Monaghan (1995)
Elizabeth Smaller (1995)
Paul Oakley (1995)
Samy Rahman (1996)
Tessa Williamson (1990) *
Akbar Khan (1990) *
Cherry Lewis () *

* Door Tenant

Work Undertaken: Commercial; chancery; private international law; interlocutory applications; arbitration; general common law (including crime and family/matrimonial); immigration; mortgage lending; French law; environmental and fire precautions law; and shipping.

V

Set No. 174

WILBERFORCE CHAMBERS (Edward Nugee QC)

8 New Square, Lincoln's Inn, London, WC2A 3QP
Tel: (020) 7306 0102 **Fax:** (020) 7306 0095 **DX:** 311 London Chancery Lane
Email: chambers@wilberforce.co.uk **Website:** www.wilberforce.co.uk

Head of Chambers	Edward Nugee QC
Senior Clerk:	Declan Redmond
Chambers Director:	Suzanne Cosgrave
Clerks:	Danny Smillie, Tanya Tong
Tenants:	37

Members:

Edward Nugee QC (1955) (QC-1977)
Jules Sher QC (1968) (QC-1981)
Michael Barnes QC (1965) (QC-1981)
David Lowe QC (1965) (QC-1984)
Terence Etherton QC (1974) (QC-1990)
John Martin QC (1972) (QC-1991)
Nicholas Warren QC (1972) (QC-1993)
Ian Croxford QC (1976) (QC-1993)
Robert Ham QC (1973) (QC-1994)
John Furber QC (1973) (QC-1995)
Terence Mowschenson QC (1977) (QC-1995)
Brian Green QC (1980) (QC-1997)
Michael Bloch QC (1979) (QC-1998)
Christopher Nugee QC (1983) (QC-1998)
Michael Furness QC (1982) (QC-2000)
Anthony Taussig (1966)
John Child (1966)
Charles Turnbull (1975)
Thomas Seymour (1975)
Gabriel Hughes (1978)
John Wardell (1979)
Michael Tennet (1985)
Jonathan Seitler (1985)
Thomas Lowe (1985)
Jonathan Karas (1986)
James Ayliffe (1987)
Judith Bryant (1987)
Joanna Smith (1990)
Joanne Wicks (1990)
Paul Newman (1991)
Gabriel Fadipe (1991)
Caroline Furze (1992)
Jonathan Evans (1994)
Emily Campbell (1995)
Rupert Reed (1996)
Julian Greenhill (1997)
Tiffany Scott (1998)

The Chambers: Wilberforce Chambers is a set of 37 barristers including 15 QCs, based in Lincoln's Inn, London. Chambers are able to offer specialist barristers at all levels of seniority and across the broad range of the commercial and Chancery fields. Members of chambers are forward thinking and responsive to the rapidly changing environment of the Bar.

Other Information: Details of each member's practice can be obtained from Suzanne Cosgrave, Chambers' Director, and Declan Redmond, Senior Clerk, or by visiting chamber's website at www.wilberforce.co.uk.

Work Undertaken: The work of chambers includes litigation, advice and drafting in the following areas:
Commercial and Other Contracts (both domestic and international): banking, insurance loans and security, guarantees, financial services, Lloyds' drafting and litigation, economic torts, breach of confidence, oil and gas law.
Occupational and Personal Pension Schemes.
Property: including all matters relating to land, commercial property transactions, landlord and tenant, property finance, negligence, fraud, mortgages and other securities.
Tax: including personal tax and estate planning, including offshore tax planning, and a wide range of tax litigation.
Trusts: drafting, advice on administration and construction and contentious and non-contentious litigation.
Professional Negligence: of accountants, actuaries, auditors, barristers, solicitors, surveyors, trustees and construction-related professional negligence.
Equitable remedies: such as injunctions, tracing, constructive trusts and proprietary estoppel.
Company Law: including shareholders' disputes; directors' disqualification proceedings, mergers and acquisitions, partnerships, and joint ventures.
Wills: probate (both contentious and non-contentious), administration of estates, intestacy and family provision.
Insolvency: both corporate and individual.
Charities: Housing Associations, partnerships, clubs, societies, and the law as it relates to other associations.
Sports and Media Law.
Additional Areas: Individual members have particular expertise in local government and administrative law; employment law; heritage property; school sites; commons registration; highways; town and country planning and compulsory purchase; white-collar crime, eg breaches of health and safety legislation and intellectual property.

Publications: Members write for and/or edit a number of well-known publications. In the last two years chambers has written and published books covering the impact of the new CPR Rules (published March 1999) and the Human Rights Act 1998 (published March 2000). A book on the new Financial Services Act is being written for publication in 2001.

International: Members frequently appear in jurisdictions outside the UK, including Bahamas, Bermuda, the Cayman Islands, Hong Kong, Singapore and Gibraltar.

W

Birmingham

Set No.
175 **COLERIDGE CHAMBERS** (Simon D. Brand)

Coleridge Chambers, 190 Corporation Street, Birmingham, B4 6QD **Tel:** (0121) 233 8500 **Fax:** (0121) 233 8501 **DX:** 23503

Set No.
176 ## 1 FOUNTAIN COURT (David Crigman QC)

1 Fountain Court, Steelhouse Lane, Birmingham, B4 6DR
Tel: (0121) 236 5721 **Fax:** (0121) 236 3639 **DX:** 16077
Email: clerks@fountaincourt.com **Website:** www.fountaincourt.com/1

Head of Chambers:	David Crigman QC
Senior Clerk:	C.T. Hayfield
Tenants:	33

Members:

David Crigman QC (1969) (QC-1989)
Melbourne Inman QC (1979) (QC-1998)
Malcolm Morse (1967)
Robert Hodgkinson (1968)
Michael Dudley (1972)
Thomas Busby (1975)
Christopher Millington (1976)
Giles Harrison-Hall (1977)
Benjamin Nicholls (1978)
Michael Conry (1979)
Stephen Eyre (1981)
Thomas Dillon (1983)
John Evans (1983)
Neal Williams (1984)
Simon Ward (1986)
Blondelle Thompson (1987)
Jonathan Salmon (1987)
Sarah Buxton (1988)
Paul Farrer (1988)
Gerard Quirke (1988)
Richard Atkins (1989)
James Puzey (1990)
Gary Thornett (1991)
William Baker (1991)
Paul Considine (1992)
Anthony Johnston (1993)
Nicholas Smith (1994)
Thomas Williams (1995)
Stuart Baker (1995)
Carolyn Jones (1995)
Simon Phillips (1996)
Andrew Smith (1997)
Susan Edwards (1998)

The Chambers: Broadly based chambers practising in all aspects of criminal, civil, commercial and family law.

Set No.
177 **3 FOUNTAIN COURT** (Robert Juckes QC)

3 Fountain Court, Steelhouse Lane, Birmingham, B4 6DR **Tel:** (0121) 236 5854 **Fax:** (0121) 236 7008 **DX:** 16079

Set No.
178 ## 4 FOUNTAIN COURT (Richard Wakerley QC)

4 Fountain Court, Steelhouse Lane, Birmingham, B4 6DR
Tel: (0121) 236 3476 **Fax:** (0121) 200 1214 **DX:** 16074
Email: clerks@4fountaincourt.law.co.uk

Head of Chambers:	Richard Wakerley QC
Senior Clerk:	Rodney Neeld
Tenants:	32

Members:

Richard Wakerley QC (1965) (QC-1982)
John Mitting QC (1970) (QC-1987)
John Saunders QC (1972) (QC-1991)
Patrick Thomas QC (1973) (QC-1999)
John Maxwell (1965)
Andrew Watson (1966)
Nicholas Webb (1972)
Steven Redmond (1975)
Jonathan Gosling (1980)
Paul Glenn (1983)
Peter McCartney (1983)
Malcolm Parkes (1984)
Mark Wall (1985)
Stephen Murray (1986)
Sally Hickman (1987)
Thomas Kenning (1989)
Anthonie Muller (1990)
Sean Sidhu-Brar (1991)
Adam Farrer (1992)
Julie Sparrow (1992)
Rhona Campbell (1993)
Pardeep Tiwana (1993)
Richard Ace (1993)
Jonathan Down (1993)
Anna Garland (1994)
Timothy Hannam (1995)
John Brennan (1996)
Nicholas Tatlow (1996)
Deni Mathews (1996)
Samantha Crabb (1996)
Jonathan Richards (1996)
Brett Stevenson (1998)

The Chambers: A long established common law set of chambers. No 4 have a large criminal team including four silks carrying out both prosecution and defence work. The team undertakes all forms of criminal work including complex fraud. Chambers aim to provide a comprehensive service for solicitors covering all levels of work. They also have teams specialising in family, licensing and general civil work. The licensing team not only works for solicitors in the Midlands but throughout the country and undertakes work for most of the major breweries and the entertainment business.

Set No.
179

5 FOUNTAIN COURT (Anthony Barker QC)

5 Fountain Court, Steelhouse Lane, Birmingham, B4 6DR
Tel: (0121) 606 0500 **Fax:** (0121) 606 1501 **DX:** 16075 Fountain Ct. Birmingham
Email: clerks@5fountaincourt.law.co.uk **Website:** www.5fountaincourt.law.co.uk

Head of Chambers:	Anthony Barker QC
Practice Director	Tony McDaid
Tenants:	91

5 FOUNTAIN COURT
BIRMINGHAM

Members:

Anthony Barker QC (1966) (QC-1985)
David Stembridge QC (1955) (QC-1990)
Martin Kingston QC (1972) (QC-1992)
Stephen Linehan QC (1970) (QC-1993)
Gareth Evans QC (1973) (QC-1994)
Stephen Oliver-Jones QC (1970) (QC-1996)
William Wood QC (1970) (QC-1997)
Ralph Lewis QC (1978) (QC-1999)
Adrian Redgrave QC (1968) (QC-1992) +
John West (1965)
Stephen Whitaker (1970)
Allan Dooley (1991)
Michael Elsom (1972)
John Harvey (1973)
Mark Eades (1974)
Jeremy Cahill (1975)
Roger Giles (1976)
Walter Bealby (1976)
Anne Smallwood (1977)
Robin Rowland (1977)
Christopher James (1977)
David Iles (1977)
Kevin O'Donovan (1978)
Paul Bleasdale (1978)
Rosalind Bush (1978)
Jean Draycott (1980)
Timothy Newman (1981)
Stephanie Brown (1982)
Neil Thompson (1982)
Michael Stephens (1983)
Andrew McGrath (1983)
Satinder Hunjan (1984)
David Stockill (1985)
Richard Lee (1985)
Richard Moat (1985)
Ian Dove (1986)
Lorna Meyer (1986)
Bernard Thorogood (1986)
Mark Heywood (1985)
Simon Drew (1987)
Aubrey Craig (1987)
Anthony Crean (1987)
Eugene Hickey (1988)
Caroline Baker (1988)
Joanna Chadwick (1988)
Ekwall Singh Tiwana (1988)
Sara Williams (1989)
Malcolm Duthie (1989)
Martin Liddiard (1989)
Becket Bedford (1989)
Douglas Armstrong (1990)
Michael Anning (1990)
Melanie McDonald (1990)
Ashley Wynne (1990)
Mary Bennett (1990)
Andrew Baker (1990)
Mark Radburn (1991)
Michele Friel (1991)
Jennifer Jones (1991)
Marion Wilson (1991)
Howard Reid (1991)
Hugh O'Brien-Quinn (1992)
David Park (1992)
Peter Goatley (1992)
Nicholas Xydias (1992)
Marc Wilkinson (1992)
Nicola Preston (1992)
Hugh Richards (1992)
Isabel Hitching (1992)
David Taylor (1993)
Sarah Clover (1993)
Nageena Khalique (1994)
Rachael Price (1994)
Robert Smallwood (1994)
Rachel Cotter (1994)
Joanne Duffy (1994)
Anthony Potter (1994)
Anna Diamond (1995)
David Mitchell (1995)
Naomi Gilchrist (1996)
Jeremy Wright (1996)
Emma Hogan (1996)
Michael Walsh (1996)
Talbir Singh (1997)
Tim Mayer (1997)
Karl Hirst (1997)
Christopher Young (1997)
Richard Hadley (1997)
Joanne Wallbanks (1997)
Harbinder Lally (1997)
Moira Phillips (1989)

The Chambers: Chambers have six specialist practice groups, each with its own membership, group identity and Head of Group. This enables them to offer genuine expertise in all main areas of work. The younger tenants usually gain experience from several disciplines until their particular field of expertise is ascertained, at which point they will join one of the established specialist groups. The six specialist groups are: personal injury & clinical negligence; crime & licensing; commercial & chancery; planning & environment; family; and employment.5 Fountain Court offers unrivalled facilities for its clients, including: 11 purpose built dedicated conference rooms; a video-conference studio capable of providing both national and international video conference links; a large Arbitration room; and a seminar suite, capable of seating 40 delegates.

Set No.
180

NO.6 FOUNTAIN COURT (Roger Smith QC)

6 Fountain Court, Steelhouse Lane, Birmingham, B4 6DR
Tel: (0121) 233 3282 **Fax:** (0121) 236 3600 **DX:** 16076
Email: clerks@sixfountain.co.uk

Head of Chambers:	Roger Smith QC
Senior Clerk:	Mike Harris
Clerks:	Clive Ridley & Georgina Jones
Tenants:	32

Members:

Roger Smith QC (1972) (QC-1992)
Michael Hutt (1968)
John Mason (1971)
Dorothy Seddon (1974)
Denis Desmond (1974)
James Quirke (1974)
Philip Bown (1974)
Philip Gregory (1975)
Anthony Lowe (1976)
Bryce Somerville (1980)
Amanda Pittaway (1980)

Members continued:

Jonathan Davis (1983)
Andrew Tucker (1977)
Avtar Khangure (1985)
Peter Cooke (1985)
William Rickarby (1975)
Nicholas Tarbitt (1988)
Robert Price (1990)
John Attwood (1989)
Janet Pitt-Lewis (1976)
Simon Davis (1990)
Tariq Bin Shakoor (1992)
Stephen Cadwaladr (1992)
Lee Marklew (1992)
Caroline Egan (1993)
James Dunstan (1995)
David Watson (1994)
David Swinnerton (1995)
Terence Bushell (1982)
Timothy Sapwell (1997)
Lorna Borthwick (1997)
Jonathan Challinor (1998)
Jane Walker (1974) *
John Stenhouse (1986) *

* Door Tenant

The Chambers: Traditionally strong in crime this established yet progressive set of chambers continues to expand steadily and now offers expertise over a large range of work. The clerks, whilst ensuring efficient and helpful administration, remember the importance of being friendly and approachable.

Work Undertaken: Criminal work; tribunals and inquiries; Water Authority cases; police civil litigation and discipline; personal injury; landlord and tenant; planning; building; general chancery; partnerships; licensing; family law; minors (Children Act, wardship etc); commercial; probate and inheritance; companies; insolvency and bankruptcy; wrongful dismissal; building and construction; consumer credit and trading standards; local government law; housing; and environmental health.

No. 81 **ST. IVE'S CHAMBERS** (Edward Coke)

St. Ive's Chambers, Whittall Street, Birmingham, B4 6DH **Tel:** (0121) 236 0863 **Fax:** (0121) 236 6961 **DX:** 16072 Birmingham
Email: stives.chambers@btinternet.com **Website:** www.stiveschambers.co.uk

No. 82 **ST PHILIP'S CHAMBERS** (Rex Tedd QC)

Fountain Court, Steelhouse Lane, Birmingham, B4 6DR
Tel: (0121) 246 7000 **Fax:** (0121) 246 7001 **DX:** 16073
Email: clerks@st-philips.co.uk **Website:** www.st-philips.co.uk

Head of Chambers:	Rex Tedd QC
Senior Clerk:	
Deputy Heads of Chambers:	John Randall QC, Patrick McCahill QC
Chief Executive:	Vincent Denham
Chief Clerk:	Clive Witcomb
Senior Clerks:	Matthew Fleming, Richard Fowler, David Partridge
Clerks:	Su Gilbert, Marguerite Lawrence, Jenny Culligan, David Hall, Raymond O'Connor
Tenants:	95

Members:

Rex Tedd QC (1970) (QC-1993) +
John Randall QC (1978) (QC-1995) +
Heather Swindells QC (1974) (QC-1995) +
Patrick McCahill QC (1975) (QC-1996) +
William Davis QC (1975) (QC-1998) +
James Corbett QC (1975) (QC-1999) +
Jeremy Cousins QC (1977) (QC-1999) +
Martin Wilson QC (1963) (QC-1982) +
Peter Birts QC (1968) (QC-1990) +
Michael Stokes QC (1971) (QC-1994) +
Michael Garrett (1967)
Brian Healy (1967)
John Price (1969) +
Peter Clarke (1970)
Douglas Readings (1972) +
Graham Cliff (1973) +
Timothy Jones (1975)
Guy Spollon (1976)
Andrew Neaves (1977)
William Pusey (1977)
Morris Cooper (1979)
James Burbidge (1979) +
Simon Clegg (1980)
Martine Kushner (1980)
Stephen Thomas (1980)
Roger Dyer (1980)
David Worster (1980)
Makhan Shoker (1981)
David Hershman (1981)
Nergis-Anne Matthew (1981)
Stephen Campbell (1982)
Kevin Hegarty (1982)
John Edwards (1983)
Peter Haynes (1983)
Lawrence Messling (1983) **
Petar Starcevic (1983)
Thomas Rochford (1984)
Samantha Powis (1985)
Mohammed Zaman (1985)
Christopher Adams (1986)
Nicolas Cartwright (1986)
Anna-Rose Landes (1986)
Gareth Walters (1986)
Lance Ashworth (1987)
Elizabeth McGrath (1987)
Alastair Smail (1987)
Conrad Rumney (1988)
Lawrence Watts (1988)
Alison Cook (1989)
Ailsa Cox (1989)
Timothy Hanson (1989)
Mark Knowles (1989)
Edward Pepperall (1989)
Amarjit Rai (1989)
John Robotham (1990)
Edmund Beever (1990)
Philip Capon (1990)
Vanessa Meachin (1990)
Andrew Lockhart (1991)
Lisa Evans (1991)
Sarah George (1991)
Robert J. Grierson (1991)
Robin Lewis (1991)
Glyn Samuel (1991)
Claire Starkie (1991)
Hugh Williams (1992) **
John de Waal (1992)
Philip Le Cornu (1992)
Julie Moseley (1992)
Katherine Tucker (1993)
Anthony Verduyn (1993)
Simon Fox (1994)
David Maxwell (1994)
Jane Owens (1994) **
Devan Rampersad (1994)
Elizabeth Walker (1994)
Angus Burden (1994)
Rosalyn Carter (1994)
Andrew Charman (1994) **
Brian Dean (1994)
David Tyack (1994)
Anthony Fryer (1995) **
Alistair MacDonald (1995)
Catherine Inman (1996)
Louise McCabe (1996)
James Morgan (1996)
Claire Cunningham (1996)
Karen Leason (1997)
Alastair Young (1997)
Tracey Lloyd-Nesling (1998)
Alistair Wyvill (1998)
Elizabeth Hodgetts (1998)
Christopher Hotten QC (1972) (QC-1994) *
Andrew McFarlane QC (1977) (QC-1998) *
David Lock (1985) *

ST. PHILIP'S CHAMBERS

* Door Tenants ** Formerly a practising solicitor + Recorder

Continued overleaf

The Chambers: The client's professional needs are always met by individually tailored service, which is rooted in traditional practices and wedded to modern approaches. This results in a highly successful set which is one of the largest and most progressive in the country. Chambers are housed in wholly refurbished premises, providing the best of modern facilities: well-appointed conference rooms, a large arbitration room, a first class library and full computerisation. Innovation geared towards an effective and professional client service lies at the heart of St.Philip's Chambers ethos.

Work Undertaken: Specialist groups are established in chancery and commercial; criminal law; employment and discrimination law; family law; personal injury and clinical negligence; property planning and public law. St Philip's also provides expertise in a very wide range of other subjects including licensing and general common law.

Set No.

183 VICTORIA CHAMBERS (Lee Masters)

Victoria Chambers, 177 Corporation St, Birmingham, B4 6RG
Tel: (0121) 236 9900 or 236 7863 **Fax:** (0121) 233 0675 **DX:** 23520 Birmingham 3
Email: clerks@victoriachambers.co.uk **Website:** www.victoriachambers.co.uk

Head of Chambers:	Lee Masters
Senior Clerk:	Lisa Clarke
Asst. Clerk:	Patricia Venables
Junior Clerk:	Vanessa Elliman
Tenants:	17

Members:

Lee Masters (1984)
Stephen Migdal (1974)
James Nisbett (1983)
David Pearson (1983)
Christopher O'Gorman (1987)
Julie Slater (1988)
Gary Cook (1989)
Dorothy Thomas (1991)
Catherine Rowlands (1992)
Mark Garside (1993)
Tracy Lakin (1993)
Kate Thomas (1994)
Patricia Hawthorne (1995)
Oliver Woolhouse (1996)
Tarlowchan Dubb (1997)
Nicola Beese (1998)
Andrew Willetts (1999)

The Chambers: An established common law set handling all areas of criminal and civil litigation. Specialist teams deal with family; crime; personal injury; employment/immigration; civil litigation and housing law before all tribunals.Chambers promise a 14 day turnaround for paperwork. Chambers has new premises available for conferences, lectures and training. Members of chambers are always willing to travel to meet lay or professional clients.

Work Undertaken: Crime; family; civil litigation; housing; judicial review; personal injury and professional negligence.

Bournemouth

Set No.

184 3 PAPER BUILDINGS (Michael Parroy QC)

Lorne Park Chambers, 20 Lorne Park Road, Bournemouth, BH1 1JN **Tel:** (01202) 292102 **Fax:** (01202) 298498 **DX:** 7612
Email: bournemouth@3paper.co.uk

Bradford

Set No.

185 BROADWAY HOUSE (J. Graham K. Hyland QC)

Broadway House, 9 Bank St, Bradford, BD1 1TW
Tel: (01274) 722560 **Fax:** (01274) 370708 **DX:** 11746
Email: clerks@broadwayhouse.co.uk **Website:** www.broadwayhouse.co.uk

Head of Chambers:	J. Graham K. Hyland QC
Senior Clerk:	Neil Appleyard
Tenants:	33

Members:

J. Graham K. Hyland QC (1978) (QC-1998)
Martin J. Wood (1973)
John D. Topham (1970)
Roger M. Thomas QC (1976) (QC-2000)
Ian Newbon (1977)
David Kelly (1980)
Gordon E. Shelton (1981)
Jonathan H. Gibson (1982)
D.A. McGonigal (1982)
P. Brian Walker (1985)
David N. Jones (1985)
Peter D. Birkby (1987)
Ian Howard (1987)
Simon Myers (1987)
Nicholas P. Askins (1989)
Paul R. Wilson (1989)
Sophie H. Drake (1990)
Mark J. Fletton (1990)
Stephen Wood (1991)
Tahir Z. Khan (1986)
J. Ben Crosland (1992)
Gerald J. Hendron (1992)
Michelle D. Colborne (1993)
Julia M. Nelson (1993)
Aisha Jamil (1995)
Jayne L. Chaplain (1995)
Nicola J. Peers (1996)
Camille Morland (1996)
Robert Blantern (1996)
Simon P.B. Anderson (1997)
Ian K.R. Brown (1971)
Tasaddat Hussain (1998)
David C. Mitchell (1972) *
Jonathan Cannan (1989) *

* Door Tenants

The Chambers: Broadway House Chambers is a long established set within 200 yards of the city's Combined Court Centre. In April 1999, chambers also opened further fully staffed premises at 31 Park Square, Leeds.

Work Undertaken: General common law; commercial; Chancery; family and crime. Civil work includes contract, commercial, personal injuries, professional negligence, matrimonial property and finance, employment, immigration, landlord and tenant, real property and income and capital taxation. Criminal work includes all aspects of prosecution and defence work mostly in the North East Circuit.

Languages: French, German, Hindi, Punjabi, and Urdu.

ighton

6 CROWN OFFICE ROW CHAMBERS (Mr Robert Seabrook QC)

Blenheim House, 120 Church Street, Brighton, BN1 1WH
Tel: (01273) 625625 **Fax:** (01273) 698888 **DX:** 36670 Brighton 2
Email: clerks@1cor.com **Website:** www.1cor.com

Head of Chambers:	Robert Seabrook QC
Senior Clerk:	
Chambers Director:	Bob Wilson
Senior Clerk:	Matthew Phipps
Clerks (Brighton):	Jenny Lewis, Matthew Archer
Tenants:	21

Members:

Anthony Niblett (1976)
James King-Smith (1980)
Paul Ashwell (1977)
Janet Waddicor (1985)
Jacqueline Ross (1985)
Adam Smith (1987)
Timothy Bergin (1987)
Paul Rogers (1989)
Keeley Bishop (1990)
Martin Downs (1990)
Jeremy Cave (1992)
Ian Bugg (1992)
Darren Howe (1992)
Giles Colin (1996)
Simon Sinnatt (1993)
Sally Ann Smith (1996)
Rachael Claridge (1996)
Richard Balchin (1997)
William Cloherty (1997)
Robert Hall (1997)
Pegah Sharghy (1998)

The Chambers: Chambers have been in Brighton for some 20 years as an Annexe of 1 Crown Office Row, a long-established common law set in the Temple which has maintained strong Sussex connections for nearly half a century. Members practise from centrally located modern premises currently being expanded to accommodate the set's rapid growth. Chambers are equipped with modern computer technology and direct telephone and computer links to 1 Crown Office Row. Conference facilities are excellent. The Brighton County and Magistrates' Courts are a few minutes' walk away.

Work Undertaken: Chambers undertake all types of general common law work - civil, criminal and family. Particular expertise can be offered in the areas of professional negligence, personal injury, landlord and tenant, building, employment, licensing and all types of family proceedings.

Recruitment & Training: Please apply to Miss Keeley Bishop for pupillages in Brighton.

istol

7 ALBION CHAMBERS (J.C.T. Barton QC)

Albion Chambers, Broad St, Bristol, BS1 1DR
Tel: (0117) 927 2144 **Fax:** (0117) 926 2569 **DX:** 7822

Head of Chambers	J.C.T. Barton QC
Sen. Clerk:	D.H. Milsom
Junior Clerks:	Bonnie Colbeck (Criminal), Michael Harding, Paul Taylor (Civil/Family)
Fees Clerks:	Rosemarie Blanshard' Lesley Carpenter
Tenants:	41

Members:

Charles Barton QC (1969) (QC-1989)
James Tabor QC (1974) (QC-1995)
Neil Ford QC (1976) (QC-1997)
Stephen Wildblood QC (1981) (QC-1999)
Christopher Jervis (1966)
Timothy Hills (1968)
Nicholas O'Brien (1968)
David Spens (1972)
Martin Steen (1976)
William Hart (1979)
John Geraint Norris (1980)
Michael Mather-Lees (1981)
Martin Picton (1981)
Tacey Cronin (1982)
Julian Lambert (1983)
Caroline Wright (1983)
Ignatius Hughes (1986)
Stephen Mooney (1987)
Charles Hyde (1988)
Deborah Dinan-Hayward (1988)
Claire Wills-Goldingham (1988)
Myles Watkins (1990)
John Livesey (1990)
Caroline Ralph (1990)
Alexander Ralton (1990)
Virginia Cornwall (1990)
Nkumbe Ekaney (1990)
Claire Rowsell (1991)
Michael Cullum (1991)
Michael Fitton (1991)
Nicholas Sproull (1992)
Simon Burns (1992)
Paul Cook (1992)
Allan Fuller (1993)
Rebecca Curtis (1993)
Thomas Crowther (1993)
Jason Taylor (1995)
Elizabeth Cunningham (1995)
Daniel Leafe (1996)
Kirsty Real (1997)
James Wilson-Smith (1999)
Andrew Thornhill QC (1969) (QC-1985) *
Christopher Wilson-Smith QC (1965) (QC-1986) *
Paul Dunkels QC (1972) (QC-1993) *

* Door Tenants

The Chambers: A large and still expanding set, the members of which handle a wide variety of specialist legal areas.

Set No. 188 **ASSIZE COURT CHAMBERS** (John Isherwood)

Assize Court Chambers, 14 Small St, Bristol, BS1 1DE **Tel:** (0117) 926 4587 **Fax:** (0117) 922 6835 **DX:** 78134
Email: chambers@assize-court-chambers.co.uk **Website:** www.assize-court-chambers.co.uk

Set No. 189

GUILDHALL CHAMBERS (Adrian Palmer QC)

Guildhall Chambers, Broad Street, Bristol, BS1 2HG
Tel: (0117) 927 3366 **Fax:** (0117) 930 3800 **DX:** 7823
Email: info@guildhallchambers.co.uk civil.clerks@guildhallchambers.co.uk

Head of Chambers	Adrian Palmer QC
Head Clerk	Paul Fletcher
Chambers Director: Robert Thomas (non practising barrister)	
Tenants:	47

Members:

John Royce QC (1970) (QC-1987)
Adrian Palmer QC (1972) (QC-1992)
Ian Glen QC (1973) (QC-1996)
Stephen Davies QC (1983) (QC-2000)
Christopher Gosland (1966)
George Newsom (1973)
Adam Chippindall (1975)
Peter Barrie (1976)
Ian Charles Fenny (1978)
Brian Watson (1978)
Ian Pringle (1979)
Malcolm Warner (1979)
James Townsend (1980)
Catriona Duthie (1981)
Ralph Wynne-Griffiths (1981)
John A. Virgo (1983)
Peter Blair (1983)
Richard Smith (1986)
Andrew Langdon (1986)
Rajinder Sahonte (1986)
Martha Maher (1987)
James Patrick (1989)
Jeremy Bamford (1989)
Paul French (1989)
Robert Davies (1990)
Stephen Dent (1991)
Kerry Barker (1972)
Anthony Reddiford (1991)
Heather Peers (1991)
Louise Price (1972)
Euan Ambrose (1992)
Christopher Quinlan (1992)
Gerard McMeel (1993) *
Nicholas Miller (1994)
Mark Worsley (1994)
Matthew Wales (1994)
Gabriel Farmer (1994)
Victoria Hufford (1994)
Nicholas Briggs (1994)
Andrew Macfarlane (1995)
Richard Ascroft (1995)
James Hassall (1995)
Rosaleen Collins (1996)
Anna Vigars (1996)
Ramin Pakrooh (1996)
Rhys Taylor (1996)
Ewan Paton (1997)

* Associate member

The Chambers: An established set with a modern outlook. Work undertaken includes insolvency/company; professional negligence; commercial/bank recovery; personal injury; property; crime; and family.

Set No. 190

OLD SQUARE CHAMBERS (John Hendy QC)

Hanover House, 47 Corn Street, Bristol, BS1 1HT
Tel: (0117) 927 7111 **Fax:** (0117) 927 3478 **DX:** 78229 Bristol
Email: oldsqbri@globalnet.co.uk **Website:** www.oldsquarechambers.co.uk

Head of Chambers:	John Hendy QC
Senior Clerk:	John Taylor
Tenants:	43

Members:

John Hendy QC (1972) (QC-1987)
John Melville Williams QC (1955) (QC-1977)
Frederic Reynold QC (1960) (QC-1982)
John Hand QC (1972) (QC-1988)
Lord Wedderburn QC (1953) (QC-1990)
Jeremy McMullen QC (1971) (QC-1994)
Ian Truscott QC (1995) (QC-1997)
Matthias Kelly QC (1979) (QC-1999)
Charles Lewis (1963)
Christopher Carling (1969)
William Birtles (1970)
Diana Brahams (1972)
John H. Bates (1973)
Christopher Makey (1975)
Nigel Cooksley (1975)
Charles Pugh (1975)
Toby Kempster (1980)
Paul Rose (1981)
Jane McNeill (1982)
Mark Sutton (1982)
Barry Cotter (1985)
Louise Chudleigh (1987)
Ijeoma Omambala (1989)
Jennifer Eady (1989)
Philip Mead (1989)
Damian Brown (1989)
Tess Gill (1990)
Jonathan Clarke (1990)
Christopher Walker (1990)
Nicholas Booth (1991)
Sarah Moor (1991)
Ian Scott (1991)
Oliver Segal (1992)
Helen Gower (1992)
Roy Lewis (1992)
Mark Whitcombe (1994)
Elizabeth Melville (1994)
Melanie Tether (1995)
Emma Smith (1995)
Rohan Pirani (1995)
Rebecca Tuck (1998)
Hilary Winstone (1998)
Steven Langton (1998)

The Chambers: Also at: 1 Verulam Buildings, Gray's Inn, London WC1R 5LQ DX: 1046 Chancery Lane/London. Tel: (020) 7269 0300 Fax: (020) 7405 1387.

Work Undertaken: Employment law, personal injury/clinical negligence, product liability and health & safety compliance law, environmental law and sports law.

International: There are door tenants practising at the Hong Kong, Bermuda and Jersey Bars. Tenants are also members of the Scottish and Northern Irish Bars.

Languages: French, German, Ibo, Italian, Spanish.

No. 91 **QUEEN SQUARE CHAMBERS** (T. Alun Jenkins QC)

Queen Square Chambers, 56 Queen Square, Bristol, BS1 4PR **Tel:** (0117) 921 1966 **Fax:** (0117) 927 6493 **DX:** 7870 Bristol
Email: civil@qs-c.co.uk / crime@qs-c.co.uk

No. 92 **ST JOHN'S CHAMBERS** (Christopher Sharp QC)

St. John's Chambers, Small St, Bristol, BS1 1DW
Tel: (0117) 921 3456 **Fax:** (0117) 929 4821 **DX:** 78138 Video conference 01179 221 586
Email: clerks@stjohnschambers.co.uk **Website:** www.stjohnschambers.co.uk

Head of Chambers:	Christopher Sharp QC
Clerk to Chambers:	Richard Hyde
Tenants:	52

Members:

Christopher Sharp QC (1975) (QC-1999)
Nigel Hamilton QC (1965) (QC-1981)
Martin Mann QC (1968) (QC-1983)
Roger Kaye QC (1970) (QC-1989)
Roderick Denyer QC (1970) (QC-1990)
David Fletcher (1971)
Paul Grumbar (1974)
Ian Bullock (1975)
Nicholas Marston (1975)
Timothy Grice (1975)
Sheelagh Corfield (1975)
Mark Horton (1976)
John Blackmore (1983)
Michael Longman (1978)
Richard Stead (1979)
Robert Duval (1979)
Ralph Dixon (1980)
Susan Jacklin (1980)
Charles Auld (1980)
Peter Wadsley (1984)
Ian Dixey (1984)
Richard Bromilow (1977)
Leslie Blohm (1982)
Susan Hunter (1985)
Glyn Edwards (1987)
Simon Morgan (1988)
Louise O'Neill (1989)
Jean Corston (1991)
Neil Levy (1986)
Guy Adams (1989)
Susan Evans (1989)
Kamala Das (1975)
John Sharples (1992)
Dianne Martin (1992)
Roy Light (1992)
Christine Bateman (1992)
Edward Burgess (1993)
Kathryn Skellorn (1993)
David Maunder (1993)
Andrew McLaughlin (1993)
Jacqueline Humphreys (1994)
Timothy Leader (1994)
David Regan (1994)
Gavin Doig (1995)
John Dickinson (1995)
Judi Evans (1996)
Simon Goodman (1996)
Matthew White (1997)
Rupert Lowe (1998)
Emma Zeb (1998)
Alex Troup (1998)
Nigel Lowe (1972) **

** Associate Members

The Chambers: Chambers offers specialist advocacy and advice in all aspects of civil, family and criminal law, with particular expertise in commercial, banking, construction, planning, licensing, environmental and employment matters.

Cambridge

Set No. 193

FENNERS CHAMBERS (Lindsay Davies)

Fenners Chambers, 3 Madingley Road, Cambridge, CB3 0EE
Tel: (01223) 368761 **Fax:** (01223) 313007 **DX:** 5809 Cambridge 1
Email: clerks@fennerschambers.co.uk **Website:** www.fennerschambers.co.uk

Head of Chambers:	Lindsay Davies
Senior Clerk:	Mark Springham
Tenants:	34

Members:

Lindsay Davies (1975) +
Kenneth Wheeler (1956) *
Peter King (1970)
Geraint Jones (1972)
Oliver Sells QC (1972) (QC-1995) *
Andrew Gore (1973)
Stephen Franklin (1974)
Susan Espley (1976)
Caroline Pointon (1976)
Oliver Heald (1977)
Simon Tattersall (1977)
Paul Leigh-Morgan (1978)
Tim Brown (1980)
Michael Crimp (1980)
Paul Hollow (1981)
Andrew Gordon-Saker (1981)
Stuart Bridge (1981)
Martin Collier (1982)
Liza Gordon-Saker (1982)
Meryl Hughes (1987)
George Foxwell (1987)
Alasdair Wilson (1988)
Caroline Beasley-Murray (1988)
Clive Pithers (1989)
Jeffrey Deegan (1989)
Andrew Taylor (1989)
Sally Hobson (1991)
Caroline Horton (1993)
Katharine Ferguson (1995)
William Josling (1995)
Mike Magee (1997)
Roderick Spinks (1997)
George Keightley (1997)
Alasdair Foster (1998)

*Door Tenant +Recorder

The Chambers: Chambers undertake all common law and most chancery work. In the main areas of work, chambers are organised on the basis of groups consisting of those tenants who practise extensively in that particular field. Identified specialists undertake work in the additional areas of practice. Chambers occupy extensive premises with ample on-site parking and easy access for the disabled. Also at 8-12 Priestgate, Peterborough.

Work Undertaken:
Main Areas: Contract and commercial; personal injury; property; crime; matrimonial and family; employment; planning; local government; and environmental law.
Additional Areas: Company and partnership; building contracts; agricultural work; licensing; professional negligence; conveyancing; contentious and non-contentious probate.Members of chambers regularly give seminars on topical legal issues.

Clientele: Includes local government; public utilities; Inland Revenue; and Customs & Excise.

Recruitment & Training: Tenancy and pupillage applications to Susan Espley: awards of up to £10,000 for 12-months pupillage. Contact William Josling for student visits/mini-pupillages.

Set No. 194

REGENCY CHAMBERS (Raymond Croxon QC and Ian Martignetti)

Sheraton House, Castle Park, Cambridge, CB3 0AX
Tel: (01223) 301517 **Fax:** (01733) 315851 **DX:** 12349 Peterborough 1
Email: clerks@regencychambers.law.co.uk

Head of Chambers:	Raymond Croxon QC, Ian Martignetti
Senior Clerk:	Paul Wright
Tenants:	15

Members:

Raymond Croxon QC (1960) (QC-1983)
David Tyzack QC (1970) (QC-1999) *
Ian Martignetti (1990)
William Powell (1971)
Andrew Tettenborn (1988)
Anita Thind (1988)
Margot Elliott (1989)
Jonathan Buckle (1990)
Marina Azhar (1990)
Christopher Ellis (1991)
Pauline Bennet (1991)
Carl Fender (1994)
Christopher Bramwell (1996)
Marie Southgate (1997)
Samuel Roberts (1973)
Catherine Crean (1982) *
Kevin Leigh (1986) *

* Door Tenants

The Chambers: Located in Centre of Peterborough, retaining an annexe in Cambridge – expertise and depth in areas of civil, family and crime servicing East Anglia, the Midlands and Lincolnshire.
Conferences can be arranged at either premises or at solicitors office.
Conditional fee work accepted.

Work Undertaken:
Family: Ancillary relief; public and private law; Children Act Applications.
Civil: Human rights; employment; personal injury; clinical negligence; commercial; contract and torts, professional negligence, landlord and tenant; property; planning; consumer law; licensing; wills and trusts; arbitration disputes.
Crime: Defence and prosecution work undertaken at all levels.

Canterbury

No.
95 **BECKET CHAMBERS**

17 New Dover Road, Canterbury, CT1 3AS
Tel: (01227) 786331 **Fax:** (01227) 786329 **DX:** 5330 Canterbury
Email: clerks@becket-chambers.co.uk **Website:** www.becket-chambers.co.uk

Senior Clerk:	Julie Lewis-MacKay
Tenants:	11

Members:

Dawn Baxter-Phillips (1964)
Philip Newton (1984)
Ronald Edginton (1984)
Kevin Jackson (1984)
Christopher Wall (1987)
Corey Mills (1987)
Jeremy Hall (1988)
Clive Styles (1990)
Paul Tapsell (1991)
Louisa Adamson (1994)
Nicholas Fairbank (1996)

BECKET CHAMBERS

The Chambers: Becket Chambers are located only a few minutes drive from the local courts and the city centre. There is a dedicated conference facility, and a large private car park.

Work Undertaken: Chambers undertake all aspects of general common law and criminal work. Members specialise in the following areas: children and family proceedings; matrimonial finance and family provision; medical and professional negligence; personal injury; bankruptcy and insolvency; employment; sale of goods; consumer credit; housing; landlord and tenant; local government; and crime. The senior clerk will be happy to provide further details on any aspect upon request.

Languages: French.

No.
96 **STOUR CHAMBERS** (Simon Johnson)

Stour Chambers, 31 St Margaret's Street, Canterbury, CT1 2TG
Tel: (01227) 764899 **Fax:** (01227) 764941 **DX:** 5342 Canterbury 1
Email: clerks@stourchambers.co.uk **Website:** www.stourchambers.co.uk

Head of Chambers:	Simon Johnson
Senior Clerk:	Neil Terry
Tenants:	9

Mainly matrimonial practice also specialising in criminal, personal injury, chancery, medical and professional negligence, landlord and tenant and child law.

Cardiff

No.
97 **9 PARK PLACE** (Ian Murphy QC)

9 Park Place, Cardiff, CF1 3DP
Tel: (029) 2038 2731 **Fax:** (029) 2022 2542 **DX:** 50751 Cardiff 2
Website: www.9parkplace.co.uk

Head of Chambers:	Ian Murphy QC
Senior Clerk:	James Williams
Clerks:	Nigel East, Lesley Haikney
Tenants:	36

Members:

Ian Murphy QC (1972) (QC-1992)
Roger Thomas QC (1969) (QC-1994)
Nicholas Cooke QC (1977) (QC-1998)
Philip Rees (1965)
Martyn Kelly (1972)
Gregory Taylor (1974)
Richard Francis (1974)
David Essex Williams (1975)
Geraint Jones (1976)
Richard Twomlow (1976)
Keith Thomas (1977)
Philip Davies (1978)
Isabel Parry (1979)
Ieuan Morris (1979)
Milwyn Jarman (1980)
Karl Williams (1982)
Janet McDonald (1985)
Paul Hopkins (1985)
Owen Prys Lewis (1985)
Susan Ferrier (1985)
Andrew Keyser (1986)
Peter Brooks (1986)
Julian Reed (1991)
Brian Jones (1992)
Steven Donoghue (1992)
Hugh Wallace (1993)
David Hardy (1993)
David Elias (1994)
Owen Thomas (1994)
Gwydion Hughes (1994)
Peter Davies (1996)
Heath Edwards (1996)
Manon Davies (1997)
Richard Edwards (1997)
Lisa Thomas (1998)
Matthew Cobbe (1998)

The Chambers: A long established set of chambers, offering varied legal services. Several members of chambers also practise from Farrar's Building, Temple. Members undertake a broad range of work, although each has particular areas of specialisation. Former members of chambers include a Lord Justice of Appeal, and several circuit judges.

Work Undertaken: Specialisations include: criminal, personal injury, professional negligence, chancery, planning, commercial, family and employment.

Languages: Several members of chambers are fluent in Welsh.

Set No. 198

30 PARK PLACE (John Jenkins QC)

30 Park Place, Cardiff, CF1 3BA
Tel: (029) 2039 8421 **Fax:** (029) 2039 8725 **DX:** 50756 Cardiff 2
Email: clerk@30parkplace.law.co.uk

Head of Chambers:	John Jenkins QC
Senior Clerk:	Huw Davies
Practice Manager:	Gwyn Lloyd
Tenants:	35

Members:

John Jenkins QC (1970) (QC-1990)
Malcolm Bishop QC (1968) (QC-1993)
Philip Richards (1969)
Peter Griffiths QC (1970) (QC-1995)
John Venmore (1971)
Stephen Hopkins (1973)
Andrew Green (1974)
David Wynn Morgan (1976)
Jane Crowley QC (1976) (QC-1998)
Paul Hartley-Davies (1977)
Marian Lewis (1977)
James Tillyard (1978)
Huw Davies (1978)
Jonathan Furness (1979)
Peter Murphy (1980)
Lloyd Williams (1981)
Paul Lewis (1981)
Mark Allen (1981)
Helen Mifflin (1982)
Ieuan Rees (1982)
Rhodri Williams (1987)
Robert Harrison (1988)
Mair Coombes-Davies (1988)
Jonathan Austin (1992)
Robert James Buckland (1991)
Catrin John (1992)
Harry Baker (1992)
Eugene Egan (1993)
Elizabeth McGahey (1994)
Caroline Rees (1994)
Michael Jones (1995)
Hywel Hughes (1995)
Andrew Jones (1996)
Thomas Williams (1996)
Harriet Edmondson (1997)
Christopher Pitchford QC (1969) (QC-1987) *
Patrick Harrington QC (1973) (QC-1993) *
William Rees (1973) *
Patrick Curran QC (1972) (QC-1995) *
David Phillips QC (1976) (QC-1997) *
Simon Picken (1989) *
Richard Hermer (1993)
Shamini Jayanathan (1996) *
Vivienne Harpwood (1969) **

* Door Tenant **Academic Member

The Chambers: 30 Park Place is committed to continuing development and aims to provide a skilled and professional service whilst remaining approachable, flexible and accessible. It has full disabled access and facilities.

Work Undertaken: A wide variety of work is undertaken with members working in teams. Direct Professional Access work is accepted. The specialist areas are: administrative and public law (including public procurements); child care; commercial law; employment law; planning, building and environment; crime; family law; personal injury (including clinical negligence).

Recruitment & Training: Chambers operates an award scheme.

Set No. 199

33 PARK PLACE (John Charles Rees QC)

33 Park Place, Cardiff, CF10 3TN
Tel: (029) 2023 3313 **Fax:** (029) 2022 8294 **DX:** 50755 Cardiff 2
Email: clerks@33parkplace.co.uk **Website:** www.33parkplace.co.uk

Head of Chambers:	John Charles Rees QC
Senior Clerk:	Graham Barrett
Clerks:	Stephen Price, Sandra Williams
Tenants:	36

Members:

John Charles Rees QC (1972) (QC-1991)
Neil Bidder QC (1976) (QC-1998)
Mary Parry Evans (1953)
Roger Garfield (1965)
Charles Cook (1966)
Richard Jones (1969)
Nicholas G Jones (1970)
Charles Parsley (1973)
Colin Davies (1973)
Jennet Treharne (1975)
Gregory Bull (1976)
Bryan Thomas (1979)
Jill Mary Walters (1979)
Jonathan Walters (1984)
Timothy Evans (1984)
Jeremy Jenkins (1984)
Andrew Taylor (1984)
Theodore Huckle (1985)
Graham Walters (1986)
Nicholas D Jones (1987)
Ieuan Bennett (1989)
Robert O'Leary (1990)
Alan Troy (1990)
Michael Brace (1991)
Gareth Jones (1991)
Lucy Higginson (1992)
Nicola Harris (1992)
Daniel V Williams (1992)
Nigel Osborne (1993)
Helen Rees (1995)
Andrew Arentsen (1995)
Christopher L Rees (1996)
Joan Campbell (1996)
Simon John (1998)
Heather Pope (1977) *

* Associate Member

The Chambers: A leading set of many years standing. Accommodation is substantial and well furbished and includes a well stocked library, conference rooms (including a disabled conference room) and all other necessary facilities. It is fully equipped with the most up-to-date technology. A chambers brochure is available on request.

Work Undertaken: Members of chambers practise across a broad range of legal areas including commercial and company law; criminal law, employment law, family law; judicial review; landlord and tenant; local government; Official Referee's business; personal injury, planning; professional negligence; property; tribunal work; trusts, wills and probate.
Particular expertise can be offered in the following areas:
Crime: All areas of criminal work including fraud.
Personal Injury including Clinical Negligence: A well deserved reputation has been acquired over many years. A dedicated Conditional Fees team has been set up.
Family: The family team has recently been strengthened by the addition of established practitioners.
Public Law: A team has been put in place to deal with this rapidly growing area of work.

Languages: Several members of chambers are fluent in Welsh.

) **TEMPLE CHAMBERS** (David Aubrey QC)
32 Park Place, Cardiff, CF1 3BA **Tel:** (029) 2039 7364 **Fax:** (029) 2023 8423 **DX:** 50769 Cardiff 2

ıelmsford

---

1 **THORNWOOD HOUSE** (Anthony Arlidge QC)
Thornwood House, 102 New London Road, (Annexe of 18 Red Lion Court) Chelmsford, CM2 0RG **Tel:** (01245) 280 880 **Fax:** (01245) 280 882
DX: 139165 Chelmsford 11
Email: chelmsford@18rk.co.uk

2 TRINITY CHAMBERS (Tina Harrington & Robin Howard)

140 New London Road, Chelmsford, CM2 0AW
Tel: (01245) 605040 **Fax:** (01245) 605041 **DX:** 89725 Chelmsford 2
Email: clerks@trinitychambers.law.co.uk **Website:** www.trinitychambers.com

Head of Chambers:	Tina Harrington, Robin Howard
Senior Clerk:	Keith Willmore
Tenants:	19

Members:

Tina Harrington (1985)
Robin Howard (1986)
Cherry Twydell (1985)
Anna Williams (1990)
Andrew Bailey (1993)
Josephine Spratt-Dawson (1993)
Jeremy Simison (1993)
Nicola May (1993)
Mark Roochove (1994)
Stefanie Wickins (1994)
David O'Brien (1994)
Allan Compton (1994)
Diana Cade (1994)
Suzanne Walker (1995)
Lindsey Thompson (1995)
Richard R. Sykes (1996)
Joanne Eley (1997)
Helen Oatway (1997)
Jamas Hodivala (1998)
John Dagg (1980) *
John Butcher (1984) *

* Door Tenants

The Chambers: Trinity Chambers is an established set in East Anglia specialising in family, criminal and civil law. Members of chambers range from 1 to 20 years call and are instructed principally in East Anglia and London by solicitors, local authorities, government agencies and other professionals.

Work Undertaken: Chambers specialise in all aspects of family law (including finance and childcare), criminal law (both defence and prosecution) and civil law (including personal injury, employment and insolvency). Conditional fee work, as well as private and legal aid cases, are undertaken by chambers.

hester

---

3 SEDAN HOUSE (Meirion Lewis-Jones)
Sedan House, Stanley Place, Chester, CH1 2LU
Tel: (01244) 348282 **Fax:** (01244) 342336 **DX:** 19984

Head of Chambers	Meirion Lewis-Jones
Senior Clerk:	Gavin James Reeves
Tenants:	23

Common law and criminal chambers with some members specialising in planning, chancery, landlord and tenant, agricultural holdings, trade descriptions, local government, licensing, matrimonial, employment, personal injury, commercial contract and civil.

Chichester

Set No.
204 **CHICHESTER CHAMBERS** (Michael Beckman QC)

12 North Pallant, Chichester, PO19 1TQ
Tel: (01243) 784538 **Fax:** (01243) 780861 **DX:** 30303 Chichester
Email: clerks@chichester.chambers.law.co.uk

Head of Chambers:	Michael Beckman QC
Senior Clerk:	Jonathan Kay
Tenants:	15

Established (1979) set with specialist teams. Property litigation, personal injury, employment, landlord and tenant. Substantial local authority family practice. CPS preferred set.

Colchester

Set No.
205 **EAST ANGLIAN CHAMBERS** (Roderick Newton)

52 North Hill, Colchester, CO1 1PY
Tel: (01206) 572756 **Fax:** (01206) 562447 **DX:** 3611
Email: colchesterchambers@dial.pipex.com **Website:** www.ealaw.co.uk

Head of Chambers:	Roderick Newton
Senior Clerk:	Fraser McLaren
Administrator:	Carol Bull (01473) 254559
Tenants:	57

Members:

Roderick Newton (1982)
John Akast (1968)
John Wardlow (1971)
Peter Wain (1972)
Marcus Pearce (1972)
Andrew Marsden (1975)
Caroline Bryant (1976)
Celia Miller (1978)
David Pugh (1978)
Martyn Levett (1978)
Timothy McLoughlin (1978)
Graham Sinclair (1979)
John Hamey (1979)
Anthony Kefford (1980)
John Brooke-Smith (1981)
Simon Redmayne (1982)
Graham Parnell (1982)
Michael Lane (1983)
Hugh Vass (1983)
Jane Davies (1983)
Lindsay Cox (1984)
Paul Shadarevian (1984)
Janet Bettle (1985)
Steven Dyble (1986)
Anthony Bate (1987)
Nicholas Elcombe (1987)
Rebecca Degel (1987)
Rosalyne Mandil-Wade (1988)
David Richards (1989)
Ann Greaves (1989)
Andrew Jackson (1990)
John Greenwood (1990)
Ray Smith (1991)
Katharine Bundell (1991)
Marika Bell (1991)
Jeremy Dugdale (1992)
Carole Parry-Jones (1992)
Dominic Barratt (1992)
Helen Gilbertson (1993)
Amanda Rippon (1993)
Patricia Walsh (1993)
Jacqui Hanlon (1994)
Richard Kelly (1994)
Mark Phelps (1994)
Jude Durr (1995)
Sally Freeman (1995)
Samantha Leigh (1995)
Alan Wheetman (1995)
David Wilson (1996)
John Morgans (1996)
Fiona Baruah (1996)
Ashley Thain (1996)
Martin Ivory (1996)
Martin McArdle (1996)
Saqib Rauf (1996)
Marc Cannatella (1997)
David Sunman (1997)

The Chambers: For further information, please see full entry under East Anglian Chambers, Ipswich.

Enfield

Set No.
206 **ENFIELD CHAMBERS** (James Gillespie)

First Floor, 9-10 River Front, Enfield, EN1 3SZ **Tel:** (020) 8364 5627 **Fax:** (020) 8364 5973 **DX:** 90638 Enfield 1
Email: EnfieldChambers@yahoo.co.uk

xeter

No.
07 **COLLETON CHAMBERS** (Martin Meeke)
Colleton Crescent, Exeter, EX2 4DG **Tel:** (01392) 274898 **Fax:** (01392) 412368 **DX:** 8330 Exeter

No.
08 **ONE GARDEN COURT FAMILY LAW CHAMBERS** (Eleanor Platt QC & Alison Ball QC)
1st Floor South, Kings Wharf, The Quay, Exeter,
Tel: (01392) 209032 **Fax:** (020) 7797 7929 **DX:** 8302 Exeter
Email: clerks@onegardencourt.co.uk **Website:** www.onegardencourt.co.uk

No.
09 SOUTHERNHAY CHAMBERS (Anthony Ward)

33 Southernhay East, Exeter, EX1 1NX
Tel: (01392) 255777 **Fax:** (01392) 412021 **DX:** 8353 Exeter
Email: southernhay.chambers@lineone.net

Head of Chambers:	Anthony Ward
Senior Clerk:	Joy Daniell
Tenants:	17

Members:

Anthony Ward (1971)
Jeremy Posnansky QC (1972) (QC-1994)
Alastair Norris QC (1973) (QC-1997)
George Meredith (1969)
Hugh Lewis (1970)
Robert Alford (1970)
Michael Templeman (1973)
Valentine Le Grice (1977)
Christopher Naish (1980)
Susan Campbell (1986)
Nicholas Berry (1988)
Rebecca Ogle (1989)
Jacqueline Ahmed (1988)
Juliet Foster (1989)
Deborah Archer (1989)
Emma Crawforth (1992)
Benjamin Winzer (1997)

The Chambers: Established in 1975, chambers has 18 members. Its strategy has been one of carefully-planned expansion, and it has grown to become one of the leading specialist family/civil sets on the Western Circuit.

Work Undertaken: Family/Civil. Children Act (public and private law); matrimonial finance; family provision; chancery; equity trusts and wills; landlord & tenant; personal injury; professional negligence; commercial. (Conditional Fee Agreements accepted in all civil cases).
Brochure and further information on request.

No.
10 WALNUT HOUSE (Francis Gilbert QC)

Walnut House, 63 St. David's Hill, Exeter, EX4 4DW
Tel: (01392) 279751 **Fax:** (01392) 412080 **DX:** 115582 Exeter St. Davids
Email: 106627.2451@compuserve.com

Head of Chambers:	Francis Gilbert QC
Senior Clerk:	Chris Doe
Tenants:	21

Members:

Francis Gilbert QC (1970) (QC-1992)
Paul Dunkels QC (1972) (QC-1993)
Francis Burkett (1969)
Jonathan Barnes (1970)
Geoffrey Mercer (1975)
Iain Leadbetter (1975)
Corinne Searle (1982)
Sarah Munro (1984)
Martin Edmunds (1983)
Michael Melville-Shreeve (1986)
Mark Treneer (1987)
Andrew Eaton Hart (1989)
Elizabeth Ingham (1989)
Robert MacRae (1990)
Andrew Oldland (1990)
Simon Laws (1991)
Shane Lyon (1976)
Mary McCarthy (1994)
David Evans (1996)
Adam Vaitilingam (1987)
Hannah Marshall (1998)

The Chambers: Established in 1972 the chambers now have 21 members, including six who sit as recorders. The work of chambers covers the full range of civil and criminal matters in the South West. Brochures are available on request detailing the areas of expertise of members in chambers.

Work Undertaken: Includes construction; courts martial; criminal law; discrimination; employment; family; children; general common law; general chancery; housing; judicial review; landlord and tenant; licensing; matrimonial; mental health; personal injury; planning; police cases; professional negligence; sale of goods; trusts and wills.

Guildford

Set No. 211 **GUILDFORD CHAMBERS** (Jeffrey Widdup)

Stoke House, Leapale Lane, Guildford, GU1 4LY
Tel: (01483) 539131 **Fax:** (01483) 300542 **DX:** 97863 Guildford 5
Email: clerks@guildfordbarristers.com **Website:** www.guildfordbarristers.com

Head of Chambers:	Jeffrey Widdup
Senior Clerk:	Richard Moore
Tenants:	22

Members:

Jeffrey Widdup (1973)
Suzan Matthews QC (1974) (QC-1993)
Michael Jones (1972)
Simon Oliver (1981)
Claire Shrimpton (1983)
Matthew Pascall (1984)
Paula Clements (1985)
Janet Haywood (1985)
Tonia Clark (1986)
Laura Smallwood (1987)
Francesca Blatch (1987)
Jerome Wilcox (1988)
George Coates (1990)
Ghislaine Watson-Hopkinson (1991)
Martin Ward (1992)
Stephen Mawson (1994)
Robin Sellers (1994)
Jolyon Perks (1994)
Paul Moulder (1997)
Dominique Gillan (1998)
Lee Gledhill (1998)
Rachel Davies (1998)

The Chambers In recent years these chambers have expanded rapidly and they now offer a comprehensive and friendly service across a broad range of family, criminal and civil matters. Members attend conferences at any venue convenient to the client, and appear in courts and tribunals across the country. Several members have lectured at the University of Surrey, and one of the Door Tenants is the Professor of Competition Law at University College, London.

Work Undertaken:
Common Law and Civil Work: Including landlord and tenant; contract; tort (including professional negligence); personal injuries; building disputes and official referee work; sale of goods; licensing; employment and industrial tribunals; mental health tribunals; inquests and arbitrations.
Family: Including divorce; financial applications (including the Inheritance Act and Children Act); care proceedings; residence and contact applications; adoption; cohabitees; injunctions and international child disputes.
Chancery: Including property disputes; rights of way; covenants and boundary disputes; company and partnerships; and insolvency.
Local Government and Public Law: Including planning appeals; enforcement of planning control; pollution; highways; public authority prosecution and defence work; housing law; and judicial review.
Crime: All areas including fraud. Chambers have developed a specialisation in cases involving illegal radio stations.

Hull

Set No. 212 **WILBERFORCE CHAMBERS** (Bernard Gateshill)

Wilberforce Chambers, 7 Bishop Lane, Hull, HU1 1PA
Tel: (01482) 323264 **Fax:** (01482) 325533 **DX:** 11940
Email: clerks@hullbar.demon.co.uk **Website:** www.hullbar.demon.co.uk

Head of Chambers:	Bernard Gateshill
Senior Clerk:	John Kennedy
Tenants:	22

These chambers offer specialist groups of criminal, family, personal injury and civil practitioners assisted by the latest computer technology and helpful support staff.
Annex: 2 Abbey Walk, Grimsby DN31 1NQ Tel: (01472) 355567 Fax: (01472) 355568

Ipswich

Set No. 213 **EAST ANGLIAN CHAMBERS** (Roderick Newton)

5 Museum St, Ipswich, IP1 1HQ
Tel: (01473) 214481 **Fax:** (01473) 218466 **DX:** 3227
Email: ipswichchambers@dial.pipex.com **Website:** www.ealaw.co.uk

Head of Chambers:	Roderick Newton
Senior Clerk:	Peter Hall
Administrator:	Carol Bull (01473) 254559
Tenants:	58

Members:

Roderick Newton (1982)
John Akast (1968)
John Wardlow (1971)
Peter Wain (1972)
Marcus Pearce (1972)
Andrew Marsden (1975)
Caroline Bryant (1976)
Celia Miller (1978)
David Pugh (1978)
Martyn Levett (1978)
Timothy McLoughlin (1978)
Graham Sinclair (1979)
John Hamey (1979)
Anthony Kefford (1980)
John Brooke-Smith (1981)
Simon Redmayne (1982)
Graham Parnell (1982)
Michael Lane (1983)
Hugh Vass (1983)
Jane Davies (1983)
Lindsay Cox (1984)
Paul Shadarevian (1984)
Janet Bettle (1985)
Steven Dyble (1986)
Anthony Bate (1987)
Nicholas Elcombe (1987)
Rebecca Degel (1987)
Rosalyne Mandil-Wade (1988)
David Richards (1989)
Ann Greaves (1989)
Andrew Jackson (1990)
John Greenwood (1990)
Ray Smith (1991)
Katharine Bundell (1991)
Marika Bell (1991)
Jeremy Dugdale (1992)
Carole Parry-Jones (1992)
Dominic Barratt (1992)
Helen Gilbertson (1993)
Amanda Rippon (1993)
Patricia Walsh (1993)
Jacqui Hanlon (1994)
Richard Kelly (1994)
Mark Phelps (1994)
Jude Durr (1995)
Sally Freeman (1995)
Samantha Leigh (1995)
Alan Wheetman (1995)
David Wilson (1996)
John Morgans (1996)
Fiona Baruah (1996)
Ashley Thain (1996)
Martin Ivory (1996)
Martin McArdle (1996)
Saqib Rauf (1996)
Marc Cannatella (1997)
David Sunman (1997)

The Chambers: East Anglian Chambers was founded in 1947 as a provincial common law set of chambers, and has developed over the years, retaining its broad common law base. It is now able to offer teams of specialists in commercial, Chancery, construction, crime, family, land, personal injury and planning.
Many members of East Anglian Chambers are active members of professional groups and associations within their field of practice, have contrbuted to, edited and written textbooks, and sit as Recorders, Stipendiary Magistrates and Deputy District Judges.
East Anglian Chambers is instructed by most firms of solicitors in East Anglia, as well as many from further afield. In addition, it receives work in all fields of practice from local authorities, and does an increasing amount of DPA work. Chambers is actively involved in the Community Legal Services in East Anglia. It prosecutes for the CPS, HM Customs & Excise and Government Departments throughout the region.

Recruitment & Training: East Anglian Chambers operates from 3 centres in Norwich, Ipswich and Colchester. 12 month pupillages are offered each year, with pupils being expected to divide their time between the 3 centres. In addition, from time to time, working pupillages are offered. Procedures and timetables for applications can be obtained by contacting the Chambers Administrator.

Leeds

Set No.
214 **BROADWAY HOUSE** (J. Graham K. Hyland QC)

31 Park Square, Leeds, LS1 2PF
Tel: (0113) 246 2600 **Fax:** (0113) 246 2609 **DX:** 26403 Leeds Park Square
Email: clerks@broadwayhouse.co.uk **Website:** www.broadwayhouse.co.uk

Head of Chambers:	J. Graham K. Hyland QC
Senior Clerk:	Neil Appleyard
Tenants:	33

Members:

J. Graham K. Hyland QC (1978) (QC-1998)
Martin J. Wood (1973)
John D. Topham (1970)
Roger M. Thomas QC (1976) (QC-2000)
Ian Newbon (1977)
David Kelly (1980)
Gordon E. Shelton (1981)
Jonathan H. Gibson (1982)
D.A. McGonigal (1982)
P. Brian Walker (1985)
David N. Jones (1985)
Peter D. Birkby (1987)
Ian Howard (1987)
Simon Myers (1987)
Nicholas P. Askins (1989)
Paul R. Wilson (1989)
Sophie H. Drake (1990)
Mark J. Fletton (1990)
Stephen Wood (1991)
Tahir Z. Khan (1986)
J. Ben Crosland (1992)
Gerald J. Hendron (1992)
Michelle D. Colborne (1993)
Julia M. Nelson (1993)
Aisha Jamil (1995)
Jayne L. Chaplain (1995)
Nicola J. Peers (1996)
Camille Morland (1996)
Robert Blantern (1996)
Simon P.B. Anderson (1997)
Ian K.R. Brown (1971)
Tasaddat Hussain (1998)
David C. Mitchell (1972) *
Jonathan Cannan (1989) *

* Door Tenants

The Chambers: Specialists in civil, Chancery, commercial, taxation, and crime. Also practise from long established chambers at Broadway House, 9 Bank Street, Bradford, BD1 1TW, tel: (01274) 722560.

Set No.
215 **CHANCERY HOUSE CHAMBERS** (Adrian Dent)

7 Lisbon Square, Leeds, LS1 4LY
Tel: (0113) 244 6691 **Fax:** (0113) 244 6766 **DX:** 26421 Leeds
Email: clerks@chanceryhouse.co.uk **Website:** www.chanceryhouse.co.uk

Head of Chambers	Adrian Dent
Sen. Clerk:	Colin Hedley
Tenants:	14

A highly motivated specialist commercial Chancery set. Individuals specialise in: property, banking, insolvency, company, commercial contract, professional negligence, intellectual property, planning, construction, partnership, employment.

Set No.
216 **ENTERPRISE CHAMBERS** (Anthony Mann QC)

38 Park Square, Leeds, LS1 2PA
Tel: (0113) 246 0391 **Fax:** (0113) 242 4802 **DX:** 26448 (Leeds Park Square)
Email: enterprise.leeds@dial.pipex.com **Website:** www.enterprisechambers.com

Head of Chambers:	Anthony Mann QC
Senior Clerk:	Tony Armstrong (London)
Clerk:	Joanne Glew

For a full list of members please see the London entry. For further information about the set please visit the chambers' website.

Set No.
217 **GOODBARD HOUSE** (F.J. Muller QC)

3rd Floor Consultation Rooms, Goodbard House, Infirmary St, Leeds, LS1 2JS **Tel:** (0113) 297 1200 **Fax:** (0113) 244 5564 **DX:** 26433

Set No.
218 **11 KING'S BENCH WALK** (F.J. Muller QC)

3 Park Court, Park Cross Street, Leeds, LS1 2QH
Tel: (0113) 297 1200 **Fax:** (0113) 297 1201 **DX:** 26433

Head of Chambers:	F.J. Muller QC
Senior Clerk:	A.T. Blaney
Tenants:	25

London common law set with extensive North East Circuit practice. 3 Park Court is the Leeds Annexe for 11 King's Bench Walk, London. See London entry for details of practice and members.

Set No.
219 **11 KING'S BENCH WALK** (Mr F.J Muller QC)

Leeds Annexe, 3 Park Court, Park Cross Street, Leeds, LS1 2QH **Tel:** (0113) 297 1200 **Fax:** (0113) 297 1201 **Email:** clerks@11kbw.co.uk
Website: http://www.11kbw.co.uk

20 ## MERCURY CHAMBERS (Benjamin Nolan QC)

Mercury House, 33-35 Clarendon Road, Leeds, LS2 9NZ
Tel: (0113) 234 2265 **Fax:** (0113) 244 4243 **DX:** 713115 LEEDS PARK SQUARE
Email: cdexter@mercurychambers.co.uk

Head of Chambers:	Benjamin Nolan QC
Senior Clerk:	Carole Dexter
Tenants:	10

Members:

Benjamin Nolan QC (1971) (QC-1992)
Michael Horowitz QC (1968) (QC-1990)
Patrick Upward QC (1972) (QC-1996)
Paul Isaacs (1974)
Raphael Cohen (1981)
Gerard Heap (1985)
John Stiles (1986)
Anna Baltaian (1995)
Robert Smith (1995)
Ashley Serr (1996)

The Chambers: Founded in 1998 to provide a specialist service to local and regional clients.

Work Undertaken: Chambers specialise in civil and commercial law with emphasis on professional negligence, company and commercial disputes, insolvency, employment, private client, matrimonial finance and personal injury.

21 **NO.6** (Shaun Spencer QC)
6 Park Square, Leeds, LS1 2LW **Tel:** (0113) 245 9763 **Fax:** (0113) 242 4395 **DX:** 26402 **Email:** chambers@no6.co.uk **Website:** www.no6.co.uk

22 ## PARK COURT CHAMBERS (James Stewart QC & Robert Smith QC)

16 Park Place, Leeds, LS1 2SJ
Tel: (0113) 243 3277 **Fax:** (0113) 242 1285 **DX:** 26401
Email: clerks@parkcourtchambers.co.uk **Website:** www.parkcourtchambers.co.uk

Head of Chambers:	James Stewart QC, Robert Smith QC
Senior Clerk:	Roy Kemp
Tenants:	38

Members:

James Stewart QC (1966) (QC-1982)
Robert Smith QC (1971) (QC-1986)
Michael Harrison QC (1969) (QC-1987)
Malcolm Swift QC (1970) (QC-1988)
Anton Lodge QC (1966) (QC-1989)
Paul Worsley QC (1970) (QC-1990)
Louise S. Godfrey QC (1972) (QC-1991)
Simon Bourne-Arton QC (1975) (QC-1994)
David Hatton QC (1976) (QC-1996)
Henry Prosser (1969)
Tim Hirst (1970)
Timothy Hartley (1970)
Andrea Addleman (1977)
Tom Bayliss (1977)
Jonathan Devlin (1978)
Adrian Robinson (1981)
John Lodge (1980)
Michael Taylor (1980)
Simon Jackson (1982)
Alistair MacDonald (1983)
Caroline Wigin (1984)
Simon Phillips (1985)
Sharon Beattie (1986)
Simon Myerson (1986)
Nadim Bashir (1988)
Taryn Turner (1990)
Maria Davies (1988)
Elyas Patel (1991)
Ashley Tucker (1990)
Paul Greaney (1993)
Nicholas Johnson (1994)
Jenny Kent (1993)
Jason Pitter (1994)
Ceri Widdett (1994)
Uthra Rajgopal (1998)
Valerie Sterling (1981)
Alan Taylor (1986)
Samuel Green (1998)
Gilbert Gray QC (1953) (QC-1971) *
James Chadwin QC (1958) (QC-1976) *
Andrew R. Thornhill QC (1969) (QC-1985) *
Peter Feinberg QC (1972) (QC-1992) *
Joanna Dodson QC (1970) (QC-1993) *
Roger Thomas (1979) *
Jeremy Woolf (1986) *

* Door Tenant

The Chambers: Park Court Chambers is one of the largest sets of chambers outside London. It is a long-established but modern and expanding set based in the thriving commercial centre of Leeds. It offers a wide range of services.

Work Undertaken: Crime; corporate fraud; personal injury; general commercial; family; landlord and tenant; licensing; medical negligence; and tax.

Set No.
223

PARK LANE CHAMBERS (Stuart Brown QC)

Park Lane House, 19 Westgate, Leeds, LS1 2RD
Tel: (0113) 228 5000 **Fax:** (0113) 228 1500 **DX:** 26404 Leeds Park Square
Email: clerks@parklanechambers.co.uk **Website:** www.parklanechambers.co.uk

Head of Chambers:	Stuart Brown QC
Senior Clerk:	John Payne
Tenants:	30

Members:

Martin Bethel QC (1965) (QC-1983) MA, LLM (Cantab)
Stuart Brown QC (1974) (QC-1991) BA, BCL (Oxon)
Christopher Storey QC (1979) (QC-1995)
David Wilby QC (1974) (QC-1998)
Alaric Dalziel (1967)
Howard Elgot (1974) BA, BCL (Oxon)
Sally Cahill (1978) LLB (Hons)
Elizabeth O'Hare (1980) LLB (Hons)
Lindy Armitage (1985) LLB
David Zucker (1986) LLB (Hons)
William Hanbury (1985) LLB
Simon Thorp (1988) BA
Joanne Astbury (1989) LLB Hons
Craig Moore (1989)
Michael Kay (1981)
Richard Copnall (1990) BSc
Alexander Foster (1990)
Kaiser Nazir (1991) LLB
Guy Swiffen (1991) BA
Andrew Axon (1992) MA (Cantab)
James Murphy (1993) BA Hons
Corin Furness (1994) LLB (Hons)
Steven Turner (1993) BA (Hons)
Dornier Whittaker (1994) BA (Hons)
Sara Anning (1995)
Stephen Friday (1996)
Alan Weir (1996)
Simon Plaut (1997)
Helen Waddington (1998)
Heather Anderson (2000) +

+ Former solicitor

The Chambers: This set of chambers has a strong reputation in civil litigation with particular emphasis on personal injury, clinical and professional negligence and commercial work. Members of chambers belong to specialist bodies including the Personal Injuries Bar Association, the Association of Personal Injury Lawyers, Action for Victims of Medical Negligence (AVMA), the Professional Negligence Bar Association, the Family Law Bar Association, the Chancery Bar Association and the Criminal Bar Association. Martin Bethel QC and Stuart BrownQC have both been appointed Deputy High Court Judges, while David Wilby QC is the chairman of the Bar Conference this year.

Work Undertaken: Chambers offers expertise in the following fields: personal injury, including group litigation and industrial disease litigation; medical and professional negligence; family; employment; crime; sale of goods; consumer credit; construction; landlord and tenant; general Chancery; insolvency; company law; insurance law; partnership law; direct and indirect taxation including VAT.

Personal Injury: There is a long history of clinical negligence and employers' liability work within chambers. Members have been involved in a number of major cases including Industrial deafness; Benzodiazapine; British Coal respiratory disease litigation. Members conduct a considerable amount of the 'credit hire' litigation (reported case Dimond v Lovell, House of Lords). The PI team includes 21 members, and has long-standing relationships with major institutional clients, unions and insurers. The personal injury and clinical negligence group also has a wide experience in all types of personal injury litigation, with particular expertise in the area of industrial disease litigation, including deafness, respiratory disease, RSI and stress at work. Individual members further specialise in sports injury and holiday claims.

Family: The family team is highly specialised and has extensive experience in public law childcare and adoption, private law proceedings involving children, all aspects of divorce and ancillary relief including multi-million pound claims, cohabitees' property disputes, trusts and inheritance disputes and in applications for committal and injunctions.

Crime: Members of chambers, and in particular the four silks, undertake criminal work including fraud, and health and safety prosecutions for both claimants and defendants and trading standards prosecutions.

Civil: Park Lane Chambers is a leading civil litigation set offering expert service and advice to a diverse client base across specialist areas of the law.

Set No.
224 **5 PARK PLACE** (Philip Raynor QC)

5 Park Place, Leeds, LS1 2RU
Tel: (0113) 242 1123 **Fax:** (0113) 242 1124 **DX:** 713113 (LEEDS PKSQ)
Email: clerks@40kingstreet.co.uk **Website:** www.40kingstreet.co.uk

Head of Chambers:	Philip Raynor QC
Senior Clerk:	William Brown
Clerking:	Bar Management Services (Partners: William Brown, Colin Griffin & Michael Stubbs)
Assistant Clerks:	Lisa Williams, Paul Clarke
Tenants:	46

Members:

Philip Raynor QC (1973) (QC-1994)
John Hoggett QC (1969) (QC-1986)
Andrew Gilbart QC (1972) (QC-1991)
Peter Smith QC (1975) (QC-1992)
Roger Farley QC (1974) (QC-1993)
Stephen Sauvain QC (1977) (QC-1995)
Frances Patterson QC (1977) (QC-1998) *
Michael Booth QC (1981) (QC-1999)
Nicholas Braslavsky QC (1983) (QC-1999)
Eric Owen (1969)
John Jackson (1970)
Harold Halliday (1972)
Shokat Khan (1979)
Vincent Fraser (1981)
David Manley (1981)
John Barrett (1982)
Paul Chaisty (1982)
Alan Evans (1978)
Mark Halliwell (1985)
John Cooper (1985)
Simon Hilton (1987)
Katherine Dunn (1987)
Ruth Stockley (1988)
Fiona Ashworth (1988)
Paul Tucker (1990)
Geoffrey Pass (1975)
Andrew Singer (1990)
Stephen Pritchett (1990)
Lesley Anderson (1989)
Matthew Smith (1991)
Martin Carter (1992)
Wilson Horne (1992)
Lucy Powis (1992)
Mark Harper (1993)
Sarah Pritchard (1993)
Richard Lander (1993)
Ian Ponter (1993)
Simon Antrobus (1995)
Andrew Latimer (1995)
Louis Doyle (1996)
Elizabeth Berridge (1996)
Katie Nowell (1996)
Colin Crawford (1997)
Nicholas Siddall (1997)
Giles Cannock (1998)
Matthew Hall (1999)
John Tackaberry QC (1967) (QC-1982) *
John Campbell (1981) (QC Scotland 1999) *
Julian Ghosh (1993) *

Arbitrator: Sir Iain Glidewell

* Associate Members

The Chambers: A large and well-established set, the members of which appear before the full range of courts and statutory tribunals. Counsel are available at all ranks of seniority, including seven silks, and the breadth of individual specialities and aptitudes available in chambers means that it offers a wide range of specialist advisory and advocacy services. Members have written, edited or contributed to a large number of legal journals, most notably in the fields of planning, local government, and highway law.

Work Undertaken: Town and country planning; local government law and finance; administrative law; parliamentary law; compulsory purchase and compensation; highways law; environmental protection; public health; commercial chancery litigation; landlord and tenant law; law of trusts; partnerships; intellectual property; insolvency (corporate and individual); banking; wills and intestacy; civil liability; personal injury; professional liability; employment and industrial law; building disputes; consumer credit; sale of goods; family and matrimonial law; hire purchase; licensing; and criminal law.
Additional Areas: Markets and fairs; trading standards; EC law; housing; data protection; company law; immigration; and defamation. Members accept Direct Professional Access from the approved professions.

Languages: French, German, Punjabi, Urdu.

Set No.
225
10 PARK SQUARE (A.N. Campbell QC)

10 Park Square, Leeds, LS1 2LH
Tel: (0113) 245 5438 **Fax:** (0113) 242 3515 **DX:** 26412

Head of Chambers:	A.N Campbell QC
Senior Clerk:	Robin Butchard
Tenants:	31

Members:

A.N. Campbell QC (1972) (QC-1994)
Patrick McCahill QC (1975) (QC-1996) *
James Corbett QC (1975) (QC-1999) *
Charles Brian Kealy (1965)
Richard William Wallace Sutton (1968)
Andrew Paul Lander Woolman (1973)
David Lawrence Bradshaw (1975)
Martin William Rudland (1977)
Andrew Thomas Alastair Dallas (1978)
Felicity Anne Davies (1980)
William James Clappison MP (1981)
Julian Nicholas Goose (1984)
Anthony Hajimitsis (1984)
John Raymond Guy Worrall (1984)
Simon Roger Greenwood Hickey (1985)
Paul Brook (1986)
Simon Waley (1988)
Simon Reevell (1990)
Aelred Hookway (1990)
Simon Kealey (1991)
Gordon Exall (1991)
Peter Moulson (1992)
Clive Heaton (1992)
John Hayes (1993)
Edward Bindloss (1993)
T.S. Storey (1993)
Abdul Iqbal (1994)
Philippa Wordsworth (1995)
Geraldine Kelly (1996)
Sean Yates (1996)
George Branchflower (1997)
Pankaj Madan (1997)
Nicholas Worsley (1998)

*Asscociate Tenants

The Chambers: A general common law set, handling a broad range of legal matters.

Work Undertaken: Bankruptcy, chancery, commercial law, company law, crime, employment, family, landlord and tenant, licensing, medical negligence, personal injury, probate, property, wardship, wills and trusts.

Set No.
226
30 PARK SQUARE (J.W. Mellor)

30 Park Square, Leeds, LS1 2PF
Tel: (0113) 243 6388 **Fax:** (0113) 242 3510 **DX:** 26411
Email: clerks@30parksquare.co.uk **Website:** www.30parksquare.co.uk

Head of Chambers:	J.W. Mellor
Senior Clerk:	Jennifer Thompson
Tenants:	26

Members:

J.W. Mellor (1953)
Peter Collier QC (1970) (QC-1992) +
A. Kershaw (1975) +
M. Haigh (1970) ++
S.N. Haring (1982)
M.S. Rodger (1983)
R.M.L. Hallam (1984) +
K. Buckingham (1986)
C.L. Hill (1988)
C. Burn (1985)
M. Pearson (1984)
A. Granville-Fall (1990)
J. Hargan (1990)
R. Cole (1991)
N. Frith (1992)
M. Teeman (1993) ++
Joanna Geddes (1992)
T. White (1993)
I. Shiels (1992)
N. Barker (1994)
P. Williams (1994)
E. Auckland (1995)
I. Gilmore (1996)
W. Tyler (1996)
A. Stewart (1997)
A. Rhys-Davies (1998)

\+ Recorder ++ Formerly a solicitor

The Chambers: Specialists in criminal and family law. Also undertake work (including non-contentious and advisory) in a wide range of common law subjects. Advocates with experience in all courts, tribunals and inquiries.

Work Undertaken: All aspects of family law; divorce; child care; injunctions; criminal defence and prosecution. Common law expertise in personal injury; contract; property disputes; professional negligence; licensing; insolvency; planning; and employment law.

37 PARK SQUARE (SJ Glover & PG Kirtley)

37 Park Square, Leeds, LS1 2NY
Tel: (0113) 243 9422 **Fax:** (0113) 242 4229 **DX:** 26405 Leeds
Email: chambers@no37.co.uk **Website:** www.no37.co.uk

Head of Chambers:	SJ Glover, PG Kirtley
Senior Clerk:	Ann Fothergill
Tenants:	28

Members:

Stephen J Glover (1978)
Paul Kirtley (1982)
Douglas Hogg QC MP (1968) (QC-1990)
Robert Marshall-Andrews QC (1967) (QC-1989)
John Sleightholme (1982)
Rodney Ferm (1972)
John Graham (1955)
John Dunning (1973)
Paul Fleming (1983)
Freddy Apfel (1986)
Jeremy Lindsay (1986)
Amanda Ginsburg (1985)
Dawn Tighe (1989)
Linda Cains (1990)
Steven Crossley (1992)
Piers Hill (1987)
Caroline Ford (1993)
Mark Gore (1994)
David Taylor (1995)
Joanne Holroyd (1994)
Stuart Roberts (1994)
Taryn Lee (1992)
Jason Macadam (1990)
Michael Burdon (1993)
Kama Melly (1997)
Michael Collins (1998)
Claire Thompson (1998)
Amanda Howard (1994)

Work Undertaken: General common law including criminal law, licensing, family law, personal injury, contract, employment law, company and commercial, landlord and tenant, real property disputes, planning and local government law.

---

39 PARK SQUARE (T.M.A. Bubb)
39 Park Square, Leeds, LS1 2NU **Tel:** (0113) 245 6633 **Fax:** (0113) 242 1567 **DX:** 26407 **Email:** seniorclerk@39parksquarechambers.co.uk
Website: www.39parksquarechambers.co.uk

ST. PAUL'S CHAMBERS (Nigel Sangster QC)

5th Floor, St. Paul's House, 23 Park Square South, Leeds, LS1 2ND
Tel: (0113) 245 5866 **Fax:** (0113) 245 5807 **DX:** 26410 Leeds (Park Square)
Email: catherinegrimshaw@stpauls-chambers.demon.co.uk
Website: www.stpauls-chambers.co.uk

Head of Chambers:	Nigel Sangster QC
Senior Clerk:	Catherine J. Grimshaw
Tenants:	30

Members:

Nigel Sangster QC (1976) (QC-1998) +
Peter C. Benson (1975) +
Colin T. Harvey (1975)
Jeremy V. Barnett (1980)
Philip A. Standfast (1980)
Jonathan L. Rose (1981) +
Guy A. Kearl (1982) +
Andrew J. Lees (1984)
Alison J. Hunt (1986)
Fiona Dix-Dyer (1986)
Howard K. Crowson (1987)
Andrew J. Stubbs (1988)
Simon Bickler (1988)
David De Jehan (1988)
Christopher M. Batty (1989)
Jonathan S. Godfrey (1990)
Robin Mairs (1992)
Jonathan Sandiford (1992)
Nicola Saxton (1992)
Sukhbir S. Bassra (1993)
Sarah Barlow (1993)
Scott Wilson (1993)
Alex Bates (1994)
John Harrison (1994)
Kirstie A Watson (1995)
Nigel R. Edwards (1995)
Nick Dry (1996)
Derek J. Duffy (1997)
Natasha Wood (1997)
Oliver Longstaff (1999)

+ Recorder

The Chambers: Founded in 1982, St. Paul's Chambers have expanded to 30 practitioners. Members have complementary areas of expertise, with the specific intention of providing a service in most areas of legal work. Nigel Sangster QC is elected Member of the Bar Council. Jeremy Barnett is an elected member of the Bar Council. Members of Chambers belong to the Family Law Bar Association and the Criminal Bar Association.

Work Undertaken:
Criminal: Work includes the traditional areas of crime, with members acting for both prosecution and defence. In addition, there are specialists in fraud and corporate crime, serious crime (including violence and sexual offences), breathalyser cases, licensing, Courts Martial, and Firearms Act offences.
Civil: Chambers have particular expertise in personal injury claims, employment, landlord and tenant, Trading Standards cases, Directors disqualification cases, family and child care work, matrimonial, professional negligence and police disciplinary cases.

ST. PAULS CHAMBERS

Set No.
230

SOVEREIGN CHAMBERS (Geoffrey C. Marson QC)

25 Park Square, Leeds, LS1 2PW
Tel: (0113) 245 1841 **Fax:** (0113) 242 0194 **DX:** 26408 Leeds Park Square
Email: sovereignchambers@btinternet.com **Website:** www.sovereignchambers.co.uk

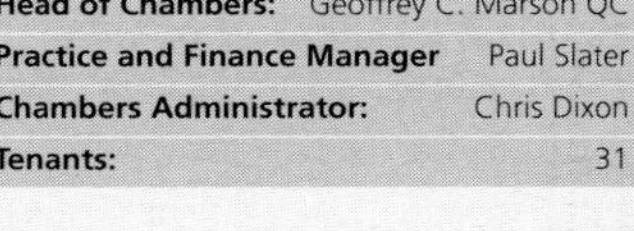

Head of Chambers:	Geoffrey C. Marson QC
Practice and Finance Manager	Paul Slater
Chambers Administrator:	Chris Dixon
Tenants:	31

Members:

Geoffrey C. Marson QC (1975) (QC-1997)
Richard L. Newbury (1976)
Patrick J.S. Palmer (1978)
Charles W. Ekins (1980)
Mushtaq A. Khokhar (1982)
Steven D. Garth (1983)
David M. Gordon (1984)
Marilyn A. Fricker (1969)
Lynn Driscoll (1981)
Andrew W. Lewis (1985)
Mark D. McKone (1988)
Stephen Bedeau (1980)
Denise L. Gresty (1990)
Andrew P. Haslam (1991)
Roger A. Birch (1979)
David S. Dixon (1992)
Nicholas J H Lumley (1992)
Richard I. Woolfall (1992)
Charity E. Rigby (1993)
Andrew B. Semple (1993)
M Jayne Pye (1995) +
Darren Finlay (1994)
Emma L.V. Burden (1994)
Anne Munday (1994)
Matthew R. Smith (1996)
Christopher Dunn (1996)
James F. Keeley (1993)
Peter J. Wilson (1995)
Diana Maudslay (1997)
Rachael E. Heppenstall (1997)
Craig Hassall (1999)
Sally Clayden (1999)
Lynton Tucker (1971) *
Colin Braham (1971) *
Christopher Russell (1971) *
Nicholas Le Poidevin (1975) *
Stuart Barber (1979) *
Sara Hargreaves (1979) *
Margaret McCabe (1981) *
Leigh Sagar (1983) *
Claire Staddon (1985) *
Ian Peacock (1990) *
Jane Evans-Gordon (1992) *
Nicholas Terras (1993) *
John Mowbray QC (1953) *
John MacDonald QC (1955) *
Charles Purle QC (1970) *
George S Laurence QC (1972) *
Jane Bridge (1981) *
Stephen J Smith (1983) *
Ross Crail (1986) *
Louise Davis (1995) *

* Door Tenants + Formerly a solicitor

The Chambers: Sovereign chambers is a modern, forward thinking set providing a specialist service focusing on its core practice groups. Members act for a wide range of clients at all levels. The set is one of the leading chambers in Leeds and celebrates its 75th year in 2000. Specialist practice groups, combined with a first class administration, aim to provide an excellent service across all areas.

Work Undertaken: Teams of members forming specialist practice groups include: Commercial/Chancery, intellectual property, environmental/planning, personal injury, employment, family/matrimonial, crime and fraud. As one of the leading chambers in the area in personal injury and clinical negligence work, they act for both defendants and claimants, and clients include major insurers, legal expenses insurers, trade unions, private individuals and Medical Defence societies. Work in this area is regularly undertaken both on and off circuit. Members regularly litigate in the field of professional negligence.

Employment: Led by a part-time Chairman of the Employment Tribunals, the team is particularly active in the emerging areas of stress and disability discrimination. Members regularly feature at professionally organised conferences.

Family/Matrimonial: Some of the family/matrimonial law group are recognised as 'leaders in their field' regularly appearing for local authorities, parents or guardians ad Litem and their work includes private client – probate, Wills and family provision for which members have particular expertise.

Criminal: Led by the Head of Chambers, a recognised 'leader in their field', the team undertakes serious crime for both Prosecution and Defence. One of the members of the complimentary specialist fraud group has recently completed one of the largest prosecutions ever undertaken by the Department of Trade and Industry.

Commercial: Members handle contractual cases, both domestic and international, sale of goods, consumer credit, banking, franchising, international trade and documentary credits as well as building disputes involving defects in designs and workmanship and performance obligations.

Chancery: Members deal with company and insolvency, both corporate and personal, inheritance, land law, conveyancing and trusts.

Set No.
231 **9 WOODHOUSE SQUARE** (John Morris Collins)

9 Woodhouse Square, Leeds, LS3 1AD
Tel: (0113) 245 1986 **Fax:** (0113) 244 8623 **DX:** 26406
Email: clerks@9woodhouse.co.uk **Website:** www.9woodhouse.co.uk

Head of Chambers:	John Morris Collins
Clerks:	Samantha Ashford (solicitor), Helen Dring
Tenants:	30

Members:

John M. Collins (1956)
Charles R. Sinclair-Morris (1966)
John Muir (1969)
Gerald Lumley (1972)
Simon Jack (1974)
Rebecca Thornton (1976)
Jeffrey Lewis (1978)
Bryan Cox (1979)
David Hall (1980)
Helen Hendry (1983)
Christopher Dodd (1984)
Sarah Greenan (1987)
Austin Newman (1987)
Roger Bickerdike (1986)
John Holroyd (1989)
Simon Read (1989)
Mavis Pilkington (1990)
Steven Lunt (1991)
Joanna Cross (1992)
Eimear McAllister (1992)
Justin Crossley (1993)
Anesh Pema (1994)
Mark Henley (1994)
Jonathan Carroll (1994)
Andrew Wilson (1995)
Heather Humpage (1996)
Helen Greatorex (1997)
John Brodwell (1998)
Alex Offer (1989)
Jillian Bell (2000)
William Lowe QC (1972) (QC-1997) *

*Door Tenant

The Chambers: Founded in 1928, chambers are, and always have been, committed to providing a comprehensive, flexible and user-friendly service comprising advocacy and advisory work. The latest information technology has been installed to enable effective communication and the clerks are always available to discuss solicitors' particular requirements. In anticipation of Legal Aid changes, chambers already operate a successful block-contracting system with efficient adminstration and a speedy return of papers. This is achieved by the distribution of work within agreed teams, all with relevant expertise. Chambers additionally offer six specialist teams, each with their own Head, who meet regularly to ensure that a cohesive service is provided with the required expertise. Individuals include a qualified doctor, a former solicitor-advocate and a civil engineer. Members of the teams regularly lecture at national and local levels. Chambers hold seminars on a regular basis, all of which are accredited by the Law Society. For further information about our seminar programme, please contact Samantha Ashford. Chambers have ample car parking and are within easy walking distance of the Leeds Courts.

Work Undertaken: Administrative law; chancery; commercial; construction litigation and arbitration; crime; family; housing; landlord and tenant; licensing; medical negligence; personal injury; planning; probate; professional negligence; property; taxation; trusts; and intellectual property.
Specialist Departments: Chancery and commercial; housing; crime; family; personal injury; property.

Languages: French, German, Spanish.

Leicester

Set No. 232

36 BEDFORD ROW (Michael Pert QC)

104 New Walk, Leicester, LE1 7EA
Tel: (0116) 249 2020 **Fax:** (0116) 255 0885 **DX:** 28816 Leicester 2
Email: chambers@36bedfordrow.co.uk **Website:** www.36bedfordrow.co.uk

Head of Chambers:	Michael Pert QC
Practice Manager:	Peter Bennett FCCA MCIM
Senior Clerk:	Bill Conner
Senior Criminal Clerk:	Harri Bennetts
Senior Civil Family Clerk:	Richard Cade
Administrator:	Jane Wittering
Fees Clerk:	Lynne Edmond
Tenants:	70

Members:

Michael Pert QC (1970) (QC-1992) LLB (Manch) +
Brian R. Escott-Cox QC (1954) (QC-1974) MA (Oxon)
Martin Bowley QC (1962) (QC-1981) MA BCL (Oxon)
James Hunt QC (1968) (QC-1987) MA (Oxon) +
Michael Stokes QC (1971) (QC-1994) +
Frances Oldham QC (1977) (QC-1994) BA (Bristol) +
Nicholas Browne QC (1971) (QC-1995) LLB (Liverpool), Dip Law (Strasbourg)+
Richard Benson QC (1974) (QC-1995) +
Annabel Walker QC (1976) (QC-1997) +
Anesta Weekes QC (1981) (QC-1999) +
David Farrell QC (1978) (QC-2000) LLB (Manchester) +
Andrew Urquhart (1963) BA (Oxon)
Stephen Waine (1969) LLB (Southampton) +
David Altaras (1969) MA, DipCrim(Cantab)+
Christopher Metcalf (1972) +
David Lee (1973) BA/AB (Cantab/Harvard)
Jamie De Burgos (1973) MA (Cantab)
Colin J.D. Anderson (1973)
Michael Fowler (1974) LLB (London) +
Geoffrey Solomons (1974) LLB (Nottingham)
Michael Greaves (1976) LLB (Birmingham)
A.G (Sam) Mainds (1977) +
Charles Lewis (1977) MA (Oxon)
Howard Morrison (1977) OBE, LLB (London) +
Catherine Gargan (1978) LLB (Liverpool)
Jeremy H.C. Lea (1978)
Gillian Temple-Bone (1978)
Martin Beddoe (1979) MA (Cantab)
Christopher Donnellan (1981) BA (Oxon)
Lynn Tayton (1981) LLB (London)
Edmund Farrell (1981) LLB (Leeds) LLM (Cantab) Dip. Eur Law (Kings)
Richard Wilson (1981) BA LLM (Sussex/Cambridge)
Charlotte Friedman (1982)
Mercy Akman (1982) LLB (Wales)
Christopher Plunkett (1983) LLB (Warwick)
William Harbage (1983) + MA (Cantab)
Simon Bull (1984) BA, LLM (Cantab)
Joanne Ecob (1985) LLB (Newcastle)
Robert Underwood (1986) BA (De Montfort)
Michael Cranmer-Brown (1986)
Benjamin Gumpert (1987)
Amjad Malik (1987) BA, LLM (London)
Gordon Wignall (1987)
Peter Dean (1987)
Greg Pryce (1988) BA (Wolverhampton)
Andrew Howarth (1988) BA (Oxon)
Amanda Johnson (1990) LLB (London)
Simon Sugar (1990)
John Gibson (1991) LLB (Durham)
Matthew Lowe (1991) LLB (Exeter)
Stuart Alford (1992) BSc (Reading)
Sarah Gaunt (1992) LLB (Cardiff), M.Phil(Cantab)
Andrew McNamara (1992)
Rosa Dean (1993) BA (Oxon)
John Lloyd-Jones (1993) BA (Durham)
Karen Johnston (1994) MA (Oxon)
Jeffrey Jupp (1994) BA (Worcester)
Andrzej Bojarski (1995) LLB (LSE)
Jonathan Spicer (1995)
Jonathan Kirk (1995) LLB (Kings)
Niall Ferguson (1996) BA (Dunelm)
Rupert Skilbeck (1996) BA (York)
Oliver Connolly (1997)
Kate Brunner (1997) MA (Edinburgh), Dip Law (City)
Kevin Barry (1997) LLB (Birmingham)
Rebecca Crane (1998)
Catarina Sjölin (1998)
Kevin McCavish (1998) LLM (London)
Simon Ash (1999)
Penelope Wood (1999)
Peter Joyce QC (1968) (QC-1991) +*
Colman Treacy QC (1971) (QC-1990) +*
Richard Payne (1964) *
Elizabeth Ingham (1989) *

+ Recorder *Door Tenant

The Chambers: Annexe of 36 Bedford Row, London WC1R 4JH Tel: (020) 7421 8000

Set No.
233

2 NEW STREET (Paul Spencer)

2 New Street, Leicester, LE1 5NA
Tel: (0116) 262 5906 **Fax:** (0116) 251 2023 **DX:** 10849 Leicester 1
Email: clerks@2newstreet.co.uk

Head of Chambers:	Paul Spencer
Practice Manager:	Mrs Dorothy Stoneley
Clerk:	Mr Paul Burtenshaw
Fees Clerk:	Mrs June Payne
Tenants:	21

Members:

Paul Spencer (1965)
Timothy Clark (1974)
Mark Wyatt (1976)
Alexandra Scott (1983)
Edward Barr (1983)
Sally Barnett (1987)
Alan Neal (1975)
David Monk (1991)
Paul McCandless (1991)
Andrew Peet (1991)
Jane O'Reilly (1991)
David Herbert (1992)
Mark D. Hurd (1993)
Rebecca Herbert (1993)
Nicola Moore (1993)
Felicity Gerry (1994)
Devon Small (1990)
Elizabeth Allingham-Nicholson (1995)
Carol Davies (1995)
Bridget Ferguson (1998)
Richard Pinhorn (1998)
Steven Gastowicz (1981) *
Vivian Chapman (1970) *

* Door Tenants

The Chambers: The Chambers are situated in the old 'legal quarter' of Leicester and undertake a variety of work.

Work Undertaken:

General Description: A general common law set with specialists in most fields, including crime, civil, matrimonial, commercial, Chancery and immigration.

Main Areas of Work: Commercial, company, criminal law, employment, family, financial services, fraud, immigration, insolvency, judicial review, landlord and tenant, licensing, matrimonial, personal injury, planning, professional negligence, sale of goods. Direct Professional Access undertaken.

Set No.
234

NEW WALK CHAMBERS (John Snell)

27 New Walk, Leicester, LE1 6TE **Tel:** (0116) 255 9144 **Fax:** (0116) 255 9084
DX: 10872 Leicester 1 **Mobile:** 0771 1873757
Email: clerks@newwalkchambers.law.co.uk

Head of Chambers:	John Snell
Practice Manager	Michael J. Ryan BSc,MBA, MCIArb
Tenants:	23

New Walk Chambers is a long established set situated in a large Georgian property close to the Crown Court, County Court and Industrial Tribunal building.

Liverpool

Set No.
235

14 CASTLE STREET (Andrew Edis QC)

14 Castle Street, Liverpool, L2 0NE **Tel:** (0151) 236 4421 / 236 8240 / 236 6757
Fax: (0151) 236 1559 / 227 3005 **DX:** 14176 **Email:** Chambers14@aol.com

Head of Chambers:	Andrew Edis QC
Clerks:	Stuart Jones, David Blunsden (Common Law) Neil Grisdale and Gary Quinn (Chancery Law)
Tenants:	41

Members:

Andrew Edis QC (1980) (QC-1997)
Eric Goldrein (1961)
Nicholas Riddle (1970)
Nicholas Orr (1970)
Ian Haselhurst (1976)
Robert Warnock (1977)
Thomas Eaton (1976)
John Benson (1978)
David Dennis (1979)
Ian Johnson (1982)
Celia Lund (1988)
Graham Sellers (1990)
Richard Hall (1991)
Michael Sellars (1980)
Andrew Williams (1994)
Arthur Gibson (1980)
John Corless (1984)
Ivan Woolfenden (1985)
Nicholas Ryan (1984)
Simon Booth (1985)
Stuart Driver (1988)
Simon Gorton (1988)
Malcolm Sharpe (1988)
Robert Golinski (1990)
Christine Johnson (1991)
N.D.K. Jackson (1992)
Timothy Grace (1993)
Anne Whyte (1993)
David Green (1992)
Andrew Banks (1994)
Nigel Ginniff (1978)
Michelle Davey (1993)
Liam Grundy (1995)
Charles Prior (1995)
Rachael Banks (1993)
David Watson (1990)
Kenderik Horne (1996)
Mark Rawcliffe (1996)
Neil Downey (1997)
Sophie Smith (1999)
Alison Miller (1999)

The Chambers: A long-established set which offers an across the board service with specialist departments in all the main areas of the law including criminal, family, employment, general common law and chancery.14 Castle Street is accommodated in spacious offices close to the Queen Elizabeth II Law Courts and offers full conference and round table facilities. The administration of chambers is managed by a full-time administrator and four experienced clerks. Chambers facilities include: disabled access, conference rooms, video conferences and e-mail/disks accepted.

Set No.
236

25-27 CASTLE STREET (Stephen Riordan QC)

25-27 Castle Street, 1st Floor, Liverpool, L2 4TA
Tel: (0151) 236 5072 **Fax:** (0151) 236 4054 **DX:** 14224

Head of Chambers:	Stephen Riordan QC
Senior Clerk:	Joanne Stapley
Tenants:	29

Members:

Stephen Riordan QC (1972) (QC-1992) +
Gerald Baxter (1971)
Pamela Badley (1974) +
Neville Biddle (1974) +
Anthony Barraclough (1978)
Anthony Goff (1978)
Brendan Carville (1980)
David Owen (1981)
Wendy-Jane Lloyd (1983)
Gwynn Price Rowlands (1985) *
Desmond Lennon (1986)
Nicholas Johnson (1987)
Tim Kenward (1987)
Edmund Haygarth (1988)
Jason Smith (1989)
Lesley Carter (1990)
Ian Harris (1990) *
Shaun Brogan (1990)
Simon Driver (1991)
Anya Horwood (1991)
Nigel Power (1992)
Charles Lander (1993)
Damian Nolan (1994)
Teresa Loftus (1995)
David McLachlan (1996)
Ben Morris (1996)
Kenneth Grant (1998) *
Neil Bisarya (1998)
Michael Jones (1999) *

+ Recorder *Former Solicitor

The Chambers: A general common law set.

Work Undertaken: Criminal law (defence and prosecution); family law (including financial relief and applications involving children) and civil law (the principal areas undertaken by chambers are personal injury litigation, contractual claims, employment law, local authority work and housing cases). Individual members of chambers also specialise in discrimination law, judicial review, civil liberties, police law, education law, medical negligence, professional negligence, company law, commercial law, arbitration, landlord and tenant, equine law and licensing. For information about the specialised areas of practice contact one of the clerks.

Recruitment & Training: Please contact Tim Kenward.

Set No.
237

CHAVASSE COURT CHAMBERS (Theresa Pepper)

2nd Floor, Chavasse Court, 24 Lord Street, Liverpool, L2 1TA **Tel:** (0151) 707 1191 **Fax:** (0151) 707 1189 **DX:** 14223 Liverpool

Set No.
238

DERBY SQUARE CHAMBERS (Simon Newton)

Merchants Court, Derby Square, Liverpool, L2 1TS **Tel:** (0151) 709 4222 **Fax:** (0151) 708 6311 **DX:** 14213 Liverpool 1
Email: clerks@derbysquare.co.uk

Set No.
239

EXCHANGE CHAMBERS (William Waldron QC)

Pearl Assurance House, Derby Square, Liverpool, L2 9XX
Tel: (0151) 236 7747 **Fax:** (0151) 236 3433 **DX:** 14207
Email: exchangechambers@btinternet.com **Website:** www.exchangechambers.co.uk

Head of Chambers:	William Waldron QC
Senior Clerk:	Roy Finney
Practice Manager:	Tom Handley
Tenants:	49

Members:

William Waldron QC (1970) (QC-1982)
David Turner QC (1971) (QC-1991)
Bill Braithwaite QC (1970) (QC-1992)
Henry Globe QC (1972) (QC-1994)
Graham Morrow QC (1974) (QC-1996)
Tim Holroyde QC (1977) (QC-1996)
Edward Bartley Jones QC (1975) (QC-1997)
Gerard Martin QC (1978) (QC-2000)
Francis Nance (1970)
Simon Earlam (1975)
Christopher Cornwall (1975)
Eric Lamb (1975)
James Rae (1976)
Judith Fordham (1991)
Gordon Cole (1979)
Tania Griffiths (1982)
Roger Hillman (1983)
Neil Cadwallader (1984)
Karen Gregory (1985)
Dennis Talbot (1985)
Paul Clark (1994)
Gerald Jones (1995)
Simon Berkson (1986)
Alun James (1986)
William F Waldron (1986)
Mark Mulrooney (1988)
Brian Cummings (1988)
John J. McCarroll (1988)
Louis Browne (1988)
Rebecca Clark (1989)
Catherine Howells (1989)
Michael Wood (1989)
Christopher Stables (1990)
Julie Case (1990)
John Philpotts (1990)
Amanda Yip (1991)
Paul Timothy Evans (1992)
David Casement (1992)
Ian Unsworth (1992)
Charlotte Kenny (1993)
Robert Dudley (1993)
Simon Fox (1994)
Kelly Pennifer (1994)
Rachel Silverbeck (1996)
Kevin Slack (1997)
Claire Gourley (1996)
Louise Metcalf (1997)
Paul Burns (1998)
Sarah O'Brien (1999)

Work Undertaken:

Personal Injury: The team consists of 21 members of chambers of all ranges of seniority. All types of personal injury claims are dealt with, Bill Braithwaite QC (the consultant editor of Kemp & Kemp) specialises in catastrophic injuries to the brain and spine. Several members of this team offer a very quick turnaround of RTA papers and members of the team specialise particularly in the medical negligence work. There is a fairly even split between plaintiff and defence work. All members of the team accept work on a conditional fee basis.

Criminal: The team consists of 22 barristers, five of whom are silks. There is an even balance between prosecution and defence work. The criminal team prosecutes for several specialist agencies, including Customs & Excise, Health & Safety Executive, Inland Revenue, DTI and DSS. The team also specialises in fraud work, having prosecuted and defended in SFO cases.

Commercial: The team led by Edward Bartley Jones QC practises within all aspects of commercial and chancery law. This incorporates professional negligence; commercial arbitrations; property; mortgages; commercial landlord and tenant; planning; banking; insolvency; tax/VAT; copyright; wills; administration of estates; trusts; insurance and reinsurance; sale of goods; construction law; shipping law; carriage of goods; international trade; and EU law.

Family: The team practises in all areas of family law. They deal with cases involving ancillary relief; inheritance law; children and family law; and education law.

Civil: The team contains individual counsel of all ranges of seniority and experience. The team is able to deal with all main fields of work that fall within this wide sector. These areas include licensing, employment matters and local government.

0 7 HARRINGTON STREET CHAMBERS (David Steer QC/Robert Fordham QC/Iain Goldrein QC)

7 Harrington Street, Liverpool, L2 9QA
Tel: (0151) 242 0707 **Fax:** (0151) 236 2800 **DX:** 14221 Liverpool 1
Email: harringtonstreet@bigfoot.com

Head of Chambers:	David Steer QC, Robert Fordham QC, Iain Goldrein QC
Practice Director:	John Kilgallon
Tenants:	63

Members:

David Steer QC (1974) (QC-1993)
Robert Fordham QC (1967) (QC-1993)
Iain Goldrein QC (1975) (QC-1997)
David Aubrey QC (1974) (QC-1998)
Margaret de Haas QC (1977) (QC-1998)
David Boulton (1970)
David Geey (1970)
David Kerr (1971)
Andrew McDonald (1971)
Jack Cowan (1971)
Antonis Georges (1972)
Rodney Halligan (1972)
Mary Compton-Rickett (1972)
Michael J. Pickavance (1974)
Nicholas Gilchrist (1975)
Mark Brown (1975)
Kevin Grice (1977)
Michael Davies (1979)
Richard Pratt (1980)
Neil Flewitt (1981)
Henry Riding (1981)
Grant Lazarus (1981)
Andrew Menary (1982)
Peter Gregory (1982)
James McKeon (1982)
Kevin Reade (1983)
Mark Chatterton (1983)
Sarah Leigh (1983)
Deirdre McGuire (1983)
Andrew Loveridge (1983)
Philip J. O'Neill (1983)
Donal McGuire (1983)
Simon J. Killeen (1984)
Elaine Jones (1984)
Stephen Knapp (1986)
Jamil Khan (1986)
Peter Davies (1986)
David Knifton (1986)
Peter Kidd (1987)
Janet Reaney (1987)
Steven Parker (1987)
Nigel Lawrence (1988)
Keith Sutton (1988)
Andrew Downie (1990)
Kate Symms (1990)
Timothy Grover (1991)
Stephen Seed (1991)
Jonathan Dale (1991)
Christine Bispham (1991)
Trevor Parry-Jones (1992)
Robert Altham (1993)
David Edwards (1994)
Helen Wrenn (1994)
Malcolm Dutchman-Smith (1995)
Gregory Hoare (1992)
Andrew Carney (1995)
Jeremy Greenfield (1995)
Clive Baker (1995)
Daniel Rogers (1997)
Stuart Clare (1997)
Martin Knight (1998)
David Bulmer (1952)
Jonathan Arkush (1977)

The Chambers: These chambers have their work base in the North but with established contacts in Cheshire and North Wales. The size of chambers has enabled a broad base of specializations to be developed particularly in the following fields: crime, family law, personal injuries, professional negligence (in particular clinical, legal and surveyors'), all forms of local government work and general common law work. In addition there are specialists available in the following fields: employment, mental health, commercial work, licensing, housing and welfare law. Some members of chambers write for legal publications and lecture whilst several retain working links with London chambers.

Set No.
241 **INDIA BUILDINGS CHAMBERS** (David Harris QC)

India Buildings, Water Street, Liverpool, L2 0XG
Tel: (0151) 243 6000 **Fax:** (0151) 243 6040 **DX:** 14227
Email: clerks@chambers.u-net.com

Head of Chambers:	David Harris QC
Practice Manager	J. Robert Moss
Clerk:	Helen Southworth
Junior Clerks:	Alastair Webster, Gail Curran, Neil McHugh, Greg Brooker, Claire Labio
Tenants:	41

Members:

David Harris QC (1969) (QC-1989) +
John Briggs (1953)
Michael Wolff (1964)
Robert Atherton (1970) +
Michael Byrne (1971) +
Raymond Herman (1972) +
Richard Brittain (1971) +
Stephen Bedford (1974) +
Geoffrey Lowe (1975) +
Maureen Roddy (1977) +
Ross Duggan (1978) +
Graham Wood (1979) +
Gail Owen (1980) +
Gareth Jones (1984)
Michael Kennedy (1985)
Jacqueline Wall (1986)
Jean France-Hayhurst (1987)
Charles Davey (1989)
Damian Sanders (1988)
Simon Holder (1989)
Rachel Andrews (1989)
Deborah Gould (1990)
Zia Chaudhry (1991)
Jonathan Taylor (1991)
Patricia Pratt (1991)
Steven Swift (1991)
Jonathan Butler (1992)
John Gibson (1993)
Ben Jones (1993)
David Flood (1993)
Leona Harrison (1993)
David Polglase (1993)
Sara Mann (1994)
Michael Scholes (1996)
John Dixon (1995)
John Chukwuemeka (1994)
Emma Barron-Eaves (1998)
Katharine Titchmarsh (1998)
Kate Burnell (1998)
Helen Conway (1999)
David Watson (1963)

+ Recorder

The Chambers: There are currently 41 members, comprising one Queen's Counsel and 40 Juniors.

Work Undertaken:

Main Areas: Chambers practise in the following fields: crime, both prosecution and defence, including fraud work; all aspects of family work, including disputes about children and ancillary relief claims; personal injury litigation; commercial disputes; professional negligence claims; employment law; and general common law.

Additional Areas: Certain members of chambers have experience in building disputes; administrative law; insurance disputes; landlord and tenant; licensing; financial services; company law; partnership disputes; and contract law.

Recruitment & Training: Normally one pupillage each year. Financial support on merit and subject to negotiation. All pupils stand a good chance of tenancy.

Set No.
242 **NEW BAILEY CHAMBERS** (Patricia Bailey)

19 Castle Street, Liverpool, L2 4SX
Tel: (0151) 236 9402 **Fax:** (0151) 231 1296 **DX:** 14193 Liverpool
Email: clerks@newbailey.co.uk **Website:** www.newbailey.com

Head of Chambers:	Patricia Bailey
Senior Clerk:	Savannah Biswas
Tenants:	24

General common law chambers with emphasis on crime, family law, civil and Chancery matters.

Set No.
243 **ORIEL CHAMBERS** (Andrew T. Sander)

Oriel Chambers, 14 Water Street, Liverpool, L2 8TD
Tel: (0151) 236 7191/ 236 4321 **Fax:** (0151) 227 5909/ 236 3332 **DX:** 14106 Liverpool
Email: clerks@oriel-chambers.co.uk **Website:** www.oriel-chambers.co.uk

Head of Chambers:	Andrew T. Sander
Chamber's Director:	Sarah Cavanagh
Chambers Manager:	Paul Thompson
Clerks:	Michael Gray, Andrew Hampton, Ian Pitt
Accounts:	Wendy O'Donnell, Jenny Connor
Tenants:	40

Members:

A.T. Sander (1970) *
Nigel Gilmour QC (1970) (QC-1990) *
Martyn Bennett (1969)
C. Alldis (1970) *
A. Edwards (1972) *
W. Rankin (1972)
A. Murray (1974) *
N.A. Wright (1974) *
R. Bradley (1978)
T. Somerville (1979)
P. Cowan (1980) *
T. Gibson (1981)
P. Fogarty (1982)
G. Bundred (1982)
S. Evans (1985)
A. Fox (1986)
P. Goodbody (1986)
J. Nicholls (1989)
J. Baldwin (1990)
J. Lewthwaite (1990)
Yaqub Rahman (1991)
J. Gruffydd (1992) +
R. Stuar Mills (1992)
H. Belbin (1992)
P. Foster (1992)
P. Brant (1993)
H. Brandon (1993)
J. Dawson (1994)
F. Somerset-Jones (1994)
W.K. Rankin (1994)
I. J. Whitehurst (1994)
L. Whaites (1994)
S. Kemp (1995)
R. Hughes (1995)
M. Cottrell (1996)
A. M. Frodsham (1996)
J. Sawyer (1978) **
S. Clarke (1996)
J. Close (1997)
L. Morgan (1999) +

*Recorder **Previously CPS +Former Solicitor

The Chambers: Chambers were established in 1965. The clerks and members of Oriel Chambers aim to provide an approachable, professional and efficient service to complement the very highest standards of advocacy, drafting and advice. Recent expansion in members of chambers has strengthened the existing specialist groups, which provide expertise at all levels.
Members of chambers regularly lecture as part of the Law Society Continuing Education Programme (CPD accredited).
Chambers' facilities include: conference rooms; disabled access; email; and disks accepted.
Fees Policy: fee information and structuring can be obtained through the clerks. Direct Professional Access & Conditional Fee Agreements accepted. Opening times: 8.30am to 6.00pm.

Work Undertaken: Includes commercial litigation; clinical negligence; professional negligence; personal injury; common law (general); crime; employment; construction; insurance; asset finance; banking; bankruptcy; insolvency; judicial review; family; ancillary relief; care proceedings; environmental law; discrimination; factoring; landlord & tenant; housing; sale and carriage of goods; and sports.

Languages: Afrikaans; French; German; and Spanish.

Recruitment & Training: Tenancy and pupillage applications in writing to Head of Recruitment Committee.

aidstone

4 MAIDSTONE CHAMBERS (Alison Ginn & Richard Travers)

33 Earl St, Maidstone, ME14 1PF
Tel: (01622) 688592 **Fax:** (01622) 683305 **DX:** 51982 Maidstone 2
Email: clerks@maidstonechambers.co.uk

Heads of Chambers	Alison Ginn, Richard Travers
Senior Clerk:	Neil Calver
Tenants:	10

Members:

Alison Ginn (1980)
Richard Travers (1985)
Aviva Le Prevost (1990)
Mary Jacobson (1992)
Adele Du Barry (1993)
Paul Greene (1994)
Thomas Stern (1995)
Philip Sinclair (1995)
Richard Samuel (1996)
Simon Wickens (1998)

The Chambers: Maidstone Chambers is a general common law set established in 1994, prior to which it was the annexe to a London chambers from 1987. A broad range of civil and criminal work is undertaken at all levels in London, Kent and throughout the south-east circuit. Individual members also specialize in various areas of law including crime, family (inc. childcare), ancilliary relief, licensing, planning, contract, tort (inc. professional negligence and personal injury), commercial and general civil work. Conferences can be held in chambers or at the instructing solicitor's office.

45 6-8 MILL STREET (Stephen Hockman QC)

6-8 Mill Street, Maidstone, ME15 6XH
Tel: (01622) 688094 / 688095 **Fax:** (01622) 688096 **DX:** 51967 Maidstone 2
Email: annexe@6PumpCourt.co.uk **Website:** www.6PumpCourt.co.uk

Head of Chambers:	Stephen Hockman QC
Senior Clerk:	Richard Constable
Tenants:	28

Members:

Stephen Hockman QC (1970) (QC-1990)
Adèle Williams (1972)
David Mitchell (1972)
Michael Harington (1974)
Neville Willard (1976)
Richard Barraclough (1980)
Nicholas Baldock (1983)
Caroline Topping (1984)
David Walden-Smith (1985)
Peter Gower (1985)
Kevin Leigh (1986)
Peter Harrison (1987)
Eleanor Laws (1990)
Peter Forbes (1990)
Oliver Saxby (1992)
Judith Butler (1993)
Paul Mee (1992)
Mark Watson (1994)
Edward Grant (1994)
Nina Ellin (1994)
Clare Wright (1995)
Peter Alcock (1995)
Gordon Nardell (1995)
Mark Beard (1996)
Deborah Charles (1996)
Tanya Robinson (1997)
Richard Banwell (1998)
Gordon Menzies (1998)

The Chambers: The Maidstone annexe provides comfortable and well-appointed facilities for meetings and conferences, and enables chambers to meet the needs of clients throughout the county of Kent in an efficient, cost-effective and responsive manner.

Work Undertaken: The work of chambers includes a wide range of common law work in London and on the South Eastern Circuit. The set has specialists in criminal law; personal injury; planning; environmental; local government and administrative law and family law.

Manchester

Set No.
246 **BYROM STREET CHAMBERS** (B.A. Hytner QC)

25 Byrom St, Manchester, M3 4PF **Tel:** (0161) 829 2100 **Fax:** (0161) 829 2101 **DX:** 718156 **Email:** ByromSt25@aol.com

Set No.
247

CENTRAL CHAMBERS

89 Princess Street, Manchester, M1 4HT
Tel: (0161) 236 1133 **Fax:** (0161) 236 1177 **DX:** 14467 Manchester 2

Head of Chambers:	
Clerks:	Jayne Lever, Neil Vickers
	Emergency No: 0973 744906 (24 hours)
Tenants:	9

Members:

Anthony J. Morris (1986)
Stella Massey (1990)
Tonia Grace (1992)
Nazmun Nisha Ismail (1992)
Steven Wild (1994)
Bob Sastry (1996)
James Collins (1997)
Simeon Evans (1997)
Wayne Goldstein (1999) (New South Wales 1992)

The Chambers: A modern, approachable, progressive set of chambers with a particular emphasis on civil liberties and human rights.Individual practitioners specialise in administrative law, criminal law, housing, family law, welfare rights, personal injury, clinical negligence, immigration, judicial review, mental health, care in the community law, employment, prison law and civil actions against the police. Chambers specialise in serving the disadvantaged and putting at the forefront the interests of clients in a manner consistent with the very high duty owed to them. At the same time chambers prides itself in being professional, realistic, frank yet friendly and approachable.Year established: March 1996

Set No.
248

COBDEN HOUSE CHAMBERS (Howard Baisden)

19 Quay Street, Manchester, M3 3HN
Tel: (0161) 833 6000 **Fax:** (0161) 833 6001 **DX:** 14327 Manchester 3
Email: clerks@cobden.co.uk **Website:** www.cobden.co.uk

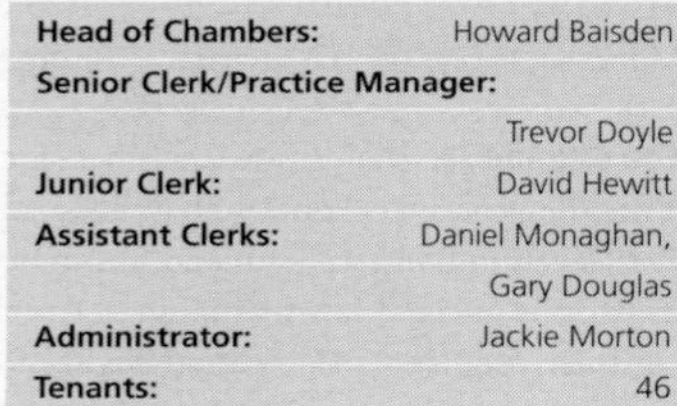

Head of Chambers:	Howard Baisden
Senior Clerk/Practice Manager:	Trevor Doyle
Junior Clerk:	David Hewitt
Assistant Clerks:	Daniel Monaghan, Gary Douglas
Administrator:	Jackie Morton
Tenants:	46

Members:

Howard Baisden (1972)
Peter Keenan (1962)
Harry Narayan (1970)
John Duncan (1971)
John Broadley (1973)
Charles Machin (1973)
Nigel Fieldhouse (1976)
Stuart Neale (1976)
Michael Goldwater (1977)
Richard Oughton (1978)
Mary Fallows (1981)
David Uff (1981)
Colin Green (1982)
Leonard Webster (1984)
Louise Blackwell (1985)
Ian Metcalfe (1985)
Richard Hartley (1985)
Mark Monaghan (1987)
Deanna Hymanson (1988)
Joanne Woodward (1989)
Robin Kitching (1989)
Timothy Willitts (1989)
Martin Littler (1989)
Sarah Harrison (1989)
William Gregg (1990)
Sean Kelly (1990)
Julia Cheetham (1990)
Marc Willems (1990)
Rajen Dalal (1991)
Jonathan Smith (1991)
Alison Woodward (1992)
David Riddell (1993)
James Hilsdon (1993)
Simon Nichol (1994)
Susan Gilmour (1994)
Richard Littler (1994)
Julian Orr (1995)
David Maddison (1995)
Christopher Oakes (1996)
Hilary Manley (1996)
Martin Callery (1997)
Adrian Farrow (1997)
Michael Jones (1998)
Richard Goddard (1999)
Michael Heywood (1975) *
Matthew Kime (1988) *

* Door Tenants

The Chambers: Cobden House Chambers is able to offer a wide range of expertise by means of specialist departments in the area of chancery, commercial law, crime, employment law, family, housing and personal injury. Individual members are able to offer additional specialisms and full details can be obtained from the clerk. Chambers provides a fast and efficient service and a timetable for the completion of instructions can be given on delivery. In addition, chambers provides services for alternative dispute resolution and mediation and video conferences. The senior clerk will be happy to discuss fee levels and tailor quotations to meet most budgets.
Further details can be found on chambers' website and in chambers' brochure which can be obtained on request.

49 DEANS COURT CHAMBERS (H.K. Goddard QC)

Deans Court Chambers, 24 St John Street, Manchester, M3 4DF
Tel: (0161) 214 6000 **Fax:** (0161) 214 6001 **DX:** 718155 Manchester 3
Email: clerks@deanscourt.co.uk **Website:** www.deanscourt.co.uk

Head of Chambers:	H.K. Goddard QC
Senior Clerk:	Terry Creathorn
Tenants:	44

Members:

Keith Goddard QC (1959) (QC-1979)
Stephen Grime QC (1970) (QC-1987)
Raymond Machell QC (1973) (QC-1988)
David Stockdale QC (1975) (QC-1995)
David Fish QC (1973) (QC-1997)
Ernest Ryder TD QC (1981) (QC-1997)
Mark Turner QC (1981) (QC-1998)
Patrick Field QC (1981) (QC-2000)
Kevin Talbot (1970)
John Bromley-Davenport (1972)
John Gregory (1972)
Peter Atherton (1975)
Alan Booth (1978)
Ruth Trippier (1978)
Philip Butler (1979)
Craig Sephton (1981)
Peter Main (1981)
Stuart Denney (1982)
Timothy Smith (1982)
Timothy Trotman (1983)
Russell Davies (1983)
Louise Bancroft (1985)
Frances Heaton (1985)
Paul Humphries (1986)
Karen Brody (1986)
Christopher Hudson (1987)
Jonathan Grace (1989)
Nicholas Grimshaw (1989)
Edward Morgan (1989)
Andrew Grantham (1991)
Seamus Andrew (1991)
Janet Ironfield (1992)
Timothy Edge (1992)
Andrew Alty (1992)
Peter Burns (1993)
Hannah Spencer (1993)
Mark Savill (1993)
Michael Hayton (1993)
Lisa Judge (1993)
Sebastian Clegg (1994)
David Boyle (1996)
Simon McCann (1996)
Richard Whitehall (1999)
Sophie Cartwright (1999)

The Chambers: Deans Court Chambers are a progressive set with a reputation for the highest standards of professionalism, service and response to clients' needs. They offer specialist advocacy and drafting expertise at every level of seniority

Chambers' purpose-designed premises at 24 St John Street provide a wide range of services to clients. A new seminar suite enables them to deliver lectures and seminars on current topics of interest; video-conferencing has been installed; facilities for arbitration, mediation and alternative dispute resolution are also available.

Work Undertaken:

Civil Litigation: Personal injury (including injuries of the utmost severity, class actions, industrial disease, factory accidents, road traffic and credit hire); professional negligence, particularly medical, solicitors, architects and surveyors; insurance (including coverage, Road Traffic Act and Motor Insurers' Bureau); contractual disputes; sale of goods; consumer credit; product liability; technology and construction; human rights; and false imprisonment.

Commercial and Chancery: Including arbitration; banking; carriage of goods; civil fraud and tracing of assets; corporate and personal insolvency; company law; credit and leasing; financial services; injunctions and equitable remedies; insurance and reinsurance; intellectual property; landlord and tenant; 'old' chancery; partnerships; pensions; and sale of goods.

Family: Including matrimonial finance; children; incapacity and competence; public and administration; education and special educational needs; Inheritance Act claims; professional negligence; and mediation.

Criminal: Including prosecution and defence work in all fields at every level, including homicide; offences of serious violence and sexual offences; commercial fraud; conspiracy; drug importation and supply; Excise and Revenue offences; and health and safety.

250 KENWORTHY'S CHAMBERS (Frank Burns)

Kenworthy's Chambers, 83 Bridge St, Manchester, M3 2RF
Tel: (0161) 832 4036 **Fax:** (0161) 832 0370 **DX:** 718200
Email: clerks@kenworthys.co.uk

Head of Chambers:	Frank Burns
Clerks:	Joan Walter
First Junior:	Sarah Wright
Second Junior:	Paul Mander
Adminsitrator:	Sue Barlow
Tenants:	16

Members:

Frank Burns (1971)
Richard Heap (1963)
Deborah Lambert (1977)
Barry Grennan (1977)
Patrick Cassidy (1982)
Janina Pasiuk (1983)
Gita Patel (1988)
Kathryn Korol (1996)
Andrew Marrs (1995)
Mark Smith (1997)
Janet Ruscoe (1995)
Imran Shafi (1996)
Geoff Whelan (1996)
Louise Kitchin (1998)
Vanessa Thomson (1998)
Sharon Amesu (1998)

Continued overleaf

The Chambers: Kenworthy's Chambers are a long-established set which aim to provide a comprehensive and reliable service in all aspects of common law.

Work Undertaken: Criminal work includes defence, prosecution and local authority work with specialists in the fields of fraud (including VAT fraud), video link cases and child offenders, violence, drugs and cases with any human rights aspects.
Chambers members specialise in all aspects of family/matrimonial law in particular ancillary and care work which is undertaken on behalf of parents, local authorities and guardians.
Chambers has an immigration and personal injury department willing to undertake contract work and fee agreements.

Languages: Gujurati, Hindi, Punjabi and Urdu.

Recruitment & Training: Chambers has an established training programme and are accredited by the Law Society, ILEX and the Bar Council as a training provider.

Set No.
251 **KINGSGATE CHAMBERS** (Beverly Lunt)
First Floor, Kingsgate House, 51-53 South King St, Manchester, M2 6DE **Tel:** (0161) 831 7477 **Fax:** (0161) 832 5645
Email: clerks@kingsgatechambers.co.uk

Set No.
252 **8 KING ST** (Keith Armitage QC)

8 King St, Manchester, M2 6AQ
Tel: (0161) 834 9560 **Fax:** (0161) 834 2733 **DX:** 14354 Manchester 1
Email: clerks@eightkingstreet.co.uk **Website:** www.8kingstreet.co.uk

Head of Chambers:	Keith Armitage QC
Senior Clerk:	Peter Whitman
Clerk:	David Lea
Chambers Researcher:	Catherine Healy LLM
Academic Consultant:	Prof. Geraint Howells
Tenants:	31

Members:

Keith Armitage QC (1970) (QC-1994) LLB
Gerard McDermott QC (1978) (QC-1999) LLB
Elizabeth Rylands (1973) LLB
David Eccles (1976) MA (Cantab)
Jeffrey Terry (1976) LLB, MA, FCIArb
Digby C. Jess (1978) BSc , LLM, FCIArb
Philip Holmes (1980) MA (Cantab)
Kim Frances Foudy (1982) LLB
Farooq Ahmed (1983) LLB
Stephen Davies (1985) MA (Cantab)
Shirley Worrall (1987) LLB
Michael Smith (1989) MA (Oxon), BCL
Mark Forte (1989) LLB
Simon Vaughan (1989) LLB, LLM
Ian Wood (1990) BA
Jonathan Thompson (1990) LLM, MA(Cantab)
Christopher Scorah (1991) BA (Oxon)
Timothy Hodgson (1991) BA, D.Phil (Oxon)
Alistair Bower (1986) LLB
Joanne Connolly (1992) LLB
Kevin Naylor (1992) MB,CH.B, MRCGP, LLB, LLM
Karim Sabry (1992) BA
Graham Bailey (1993) LLB
Kirsten Barry (1993) LLB
John Parr (1989) LLB
Rachael Hamilton-Hague (1993) BA
James Boyd (1994) LLB, LLM
David Sandiford (1995) BA (Oxon)
Andrew Clark (1994) MA (Oxon)
David Hoffman (1997) BA (Oxon)
Nigel Edwards (1998) BA (Cantab)

The Chambers: Chambers has had a long and distinguished history and, from an original bias towards common law, has developed a wide range of services.

Work Undertaken: General common law; commercial and Chancery; criminal law; personal injury; clinical and professional negligence; employment (including race and sex discrimination); commercial fraud; matrimonial and child care law; landlord and tenant; contract (including building); administrative law; Anglo-American disputes; insurance law; arbitration; environmental law; company law; licensing; construction; sale of goods; and consumer credit. Video-conferencing is available within chambers.

Set No.
253 **40 KING ST** (Philip Raynor QC)

40 King St, Manchester, M2 6BA
Tel: (0161) 832 9082 **Fax:** (0161) 835 2139 **DX:** 718188
Email: clerks@40kingstreet.co.uk **Website:** www.40kingstreet.co.uk

Head of Chambers:	Philip Raynor QC
Senior Clerk:	William Brown
Clerking:	Bar Management Services (Partners: William Brown, Colin Griffin, Michael Stubbs)
Assistant Clerks:	Lisa Williams, Paul Clarke
Tenants:	46

Members:

Philip Raynor QC (1973) (QC-1994)
John Hoggett QC (1969) (QC-1986)
Andrew Gilbart QC (1972) (QC-1991)
Peter Smith QC (1975) (QC-1992)
Roger Farley QC (1974) (QC-1993)
Stephen Sauvain QC (1977) (QC-1995)
Frances Patterson QC (1977) (QC-1998)
Michael Booth QC (1981) (QC-1999)
Nicholas Braslavsky QC (1983) (QC-1999)
Eric Owen (1969)
John Jackson (1970)
Harold Halliday (1972)
Shokat Khan (1979)
Vincent Fraser (1981)
David Manley (1981)
John Barrett (1982)
Paul Chaisty (1982)
Alan Evans (1978)
Mark Halliwell (1985)
John Cooper (1985)
Simon Hilton (1987)
Katherine Dunn (1987)
Ruth Stockley (1988)
Fiona Ashworth (1988)
Paul Tucker (1990)
Geoffrey Pass (1975)
Andrew Singer (1990)
Stephen Pritchett (1990)
Lesley Anderson (1989)
Matthew Smith (1991)
Martin Carter (1992)
Wilson Horne (1992)
Lucy Powis (1992)
Mark Harper (1993)
Sarah Pritchard (1993)
Richard Lander (1993)
Ian Ponter (1993)
Simon Antrobus (1995)
Andrew Latimer (1995)
Louis Doyle (1996)
Elizabeth Berridge (1996)
Katie Nowell (1996)
Colin Crawford (1997)
Nicholas Siddall (1997)
Giles Cannock (1998)
Matthew Hall (1999)
John Tackaberry QC (1967) (QC-1982) *
John Campbell (1981) (QC Scotland 1999) *
Julian Ghosh (1993) *

Arbitrator: Sir Iain Glidewell * Associate Members

The Chambers: A large and well-established set, the members of which appear before the full range of courts and statutory tribunals. Counsel are available at all ranks of seniority, including seven silks, and the breadth of individual specialities and aptitudes available in chambers means that it offers a wide range of specialist advisory and advocacy services. Members have written, edited or contributed to a large number of legal journals, most notably in the fields of planning, local government, and highway law.

Work Undertaken: Town and country planning; local government law and finance; administrative law; parliamentary law; compulsory purchase and compensation; highways law; environmental protection; public health; commercial chancery litigation; landlord and tenant law; law of trusts; partnerships; intellectual property; insolvency (corporate and individual); banking; wills and intestacy; civil liability; personal injury; professional liability; employment and industrial law; building disputes; consumer credit; sale of goods; family and matrimonial law; hire purchase; licensing; and criminal law.
Additional Areas: Markets and fairs; trading standards; EU law; housing; data protection; company law; immigration and defamation.
Members accept Direct Professional Access from the approved professions.

Languages: French, German, Punjabi, and Urdu.

Set No.
254 **LINCOLN HOUSE CHAMBERS** (Mukhtar Hussain QC)

5th Floor Lincoln House, 1 Brazennose Street, Manchester, M2 5EL **Tel:** (0161) 832 5701 **Fax:** (0161) 832 0839 **DX:** 14338 Manches 1
Email: info@lincolnhse,co.uk **Website:** www.lincolnhse.co.uk

Set No.
255 **MANCHESTER HOUSE CHAMBERS** (J.D.S. Wishart)

Manchester House Chambers, 18-22 Bridge St, Manchester, M3 3BZ **Tel:** (0161) 834 7007 **DX:** 718153 Manchester 3

Set No.
256 **MERCHANT CHAMBERS** (David Berkley QC)

Number One, North Parade, Parsonage Gardens, Manchester, M3 2NH
Tel: (0161) 839 7070 **Fax:** (0161) 839 7111 **DX:** 14319 Manchester 1
Email: inquiries@merchantchambers.com **Website:** www.merchantchambers.com

Head of Chambers:	David Berkley QC
Chambers Administrator	Alastair Campbell
Tenants:	9

Members:

David Berkley QC (1979) (QC-1999)
Neil Berragan (1982)
Stephen Cogley (1984)
Catherine Fisher (1990)
Andrew Noble (1992) FRICS FCIArb
Jonathan Rule (1993)
Stefan Brochwicz-Lewinski (1995)
Ghazan Mahmood (1997)
Susanne Muth (1998)

MERCHANT CHAMBERS
COMMERCIAL • BARRISTERS

The Chambers: Merchant Chambers was founded in 1996 by established practitioners in order to provide a high quality service to the banking and business communitiy in the North West region and beyond. Since its launch the chambers has attracted other specialists to become a leading commercial set on the Northern Circuit. The approach of the set is to offer effective advocacy at all levels and efficient and cost effective return of papers and advice. The set prides itself on delivering its services in a relaxed unstuffy and down to earth manner. The work of chambers includes banking; insolvency; partnership; and general commercial work. Full details are to be found in the Chambers Information Booklet available on request. In addition to its core services, Merchant Chambers provides training and offers seminars to solicitors.

Set No.
257 **PEEL COURT CHAMBERS** (Michael Shorrock QC)

Peel Court Chambers, 45 Hardman Street, Manchester, M3 3PL
Tel: (0161) 832 3791 **Fax:** (0161) 835 3054 **DX:** 14320
Email: clerks@peelct.co.uk

Head of Chambers:	Michael Shorrock QC
Clerks:	Shell Edmonds, David Haley, Stuart Howard-Cofield
Consultant:	Jill Wallwork
Administrator:	Anna Ewbank
Tenants:	37

Members:

Michael Shorrock QC (1966) (QC-1988)
Anthony Morris QC (1970) (QC-1991)
Nicholas Simmonds (1969)
Howard Bentham QC (1970) (QC-1996)
Paul Richardson (1972)
Stephen Meadowcroft (1973)
Anthony Russell QC (1974) (QC-1999)
Richard Marks QC (1975) (QC-1999)
Bernard Lever (1975)
Andrew O'Byrne (1978)
Adrian Wallace (1979)
Andrew Long (1981)
Christopher Melton (1982)
Fiorella Brereton (1979)
David Pickup (1984)
Steven Johnson (1984)
Paul Sheridan (1984)
Richard Pearce (1985)
Julian Taylor (1986)
Jeremy Grout-Smith (1986)
Neil Fryman (1989)
Martin Walsh (1990)
Rachel Smith (1990)
Graham Knowles (1990)
Simon Burrows (1990)
David Toal (1990)
William Baker (1991)
Mark Ainsworth (1992)
Henry Blackshaw (1993)
Richard Orme (1993)
Claire Evans (1994)
Rebecca Lloyd-Smith (1994)
June Morris (1995)
Mary Ruck (1993)
Anthony Mazzag (1996)
Gavin McBride (1996)
Alexandra Simmonds (1998)
David Lane QC (1968) (QC-1991) *

* Door Tenant

The Chambers: A large general common law set including 5 QCs.

Work Undertaken: A wide range of common law work is covered, with particular emphasis on crime, clinical negligence and medical law, licensing (gaming and liquor), commercial fraud, personal injury, professional negligence, family law including childcare and matrimonial finance. Chambers also provide expertise in consumer credit and commercial law, landlord and tenant, health and safety law, EC and revenue law.

Languages: French, German and Mandarin.

Set No.
258 **QUEENS CHAMBERS** (Timothy Ryder)
5 John Dalton St, Manchester, M2 6ET **Tel:** (0161) 834 6875/4738 **Fax:** (0161) 834 8557 **DX:** 718182 Manchester 3

No. 59 ST. JAMES'S CHAMBERS (R.A. Sterling)

St. James's Chambers, 68 Quay St, Manchester, M3 3EJ
Tel: (0161) 834 7000 **Fax:** (0161) 834 2341 **DX:** 14350 M1
Email: clerks@stjameschambers.co.uk

Head of Chambers:	R.A. Sterling
Senior Clerk:	Stephen J. Diggles
Tenants:	24

Members:

Robert Sterling (1970)
Anthony Elleray QC (1977) (QC-1993) +
Percy Wood (1961)
Barrie Searle (1975) +
David Porter (1980)
Timothy Lyons (1980)
Mark Cawson (1982) +
Michael Mulholland (1976)
David Binns (1983)
Ian Foster (1988)
Lucy Wilson-Barnes (1989)
Jonathan Cannan (1989)
Sarah Wheeldon (1990)
Ruth Tankel (1990)
Christopher Cook (1990)
Giles Maynard-Connor (1992)
Janice Wills (1992)
James Hurd (1994)
David Calvert (1995)
James Fryer-Spedding (1994)
Christopher Taft (1997)
Nancy Dooher (1997)
Anthony Rubin (1960) *
Joseph Jaconelli (1972) *

* Door Tenants + Recorder

The Chambers: A Chancery and general common law set of chambers.

Work Undertaken:

Chancery: All aspects of property law, including land law; mortgages; nuisance and trespass; rights of way; landlord and tenant; joint property; agricultural holdings work; trusts; settlements and wills; pension schemes; charities; personal property; intellectual property; business and commercial law, including business agreements and breach of contract; injunctions and other equitable remedies; fraud; professional negligence and indemnity insurance; loans and securities; companies and partnerships; associations; receivers; bankruptcy and insolvency; confidential information; taxation; and tribunals.

Common law: Including building and construction law; sale of goods; contract law; consumer and consumer credit law; crime; employment law; employers' liability and health & safety at work; environmental law; family (divorce, children, matrimonial finance and property); licensing; personal injuries; professional and clinical negligence; police disciplinary hearings; road traffic cases; and tribunals.

Publications: Timothy Lyons has written works on inheritance tax and insolvency, and sits on the editorial board of the *Law and Tax Review*. Jonathan Cannan has written works on corporation tax and articles on tax matters generally.

Languages: French, German, Hebrew, Russian, and Spanish.

No. 60 9 ST. JOHN STREET (John Hand QC)

9 St. John Street, Manchester, M3 4DN
Tel: (0161) 955 9000 **Fax:** (0161) 955 9001 **DX:** 14326
Email: clerks@9stjohnstreet.co.uk **Website:** www.9stjohnstreet.co.uk

Head of Chambers:	John Hand QC
Chambers Administrator:	Jo Kelly
Senior Clerk Queen's Counsel:	Graham Rogers
Crime:	Graham Livesey
Civil, Employment, Commercial/Chancery:	Tony Morrissey
Family:	Paul Morecroft
Assistant Civil Clerk:	Jane Slingsby
Assistant Criminal Clerk:	Susan Lea
Tenants:	40

Members:

John Hand QC (1972) (QC-1988)
Ian Leeming QC (1970) (QC-1988)
Roderick Carus QC (1971) (QC-1990)
Charles Garside QC (1971) (QC-1993)
Jeremy McMullen QC (1971) (QC-1994)
Timothy Horlock QC (1981) (QC-1997)
Matthias Kelly QC (1979) (QC-1999)
Nicholas Hinchliffe QC (1980) (QC-1999)
Christopher St. John Knight (1966)
Terence Rigby (1971)
Michael Johnson (1972)
Leslie Hull (1972)
John Dowse (1973)
Peter Cadwallader (1973)
Christine Riley (1974)
Simon Temple (1977)
Michael Murray (1979)
Nicholas Clarke (1981)
Nigel Grundy (1983)
Michael Leeming (1983)
Gillian Irving (1984)
Paul Gilroy (1985)
Carlo Breen (1987)
David Gilchrist (1987)
Nicola Gatto (1987)
Simon James (1988)
David Friesner (1988)
Thomas Fitzpatrick (1988)
Ian Little (1989)
Christopher L.P. Kennedy (1989)
Nigel Bird (1991)
Anthony Howard (1992)
Rachel Wedderspoon (1993)
Jaime Hamilton (1993)
Alaric Bassano (1993)
Tariq Sadiq (1993)
Robert Darbyshire (1995)
Brian McCluggage (1995)
Gary Woodhall (1997)
Kate Hollyoak (1997)

Continued overleaf

The Chambers: In order to meet the increasing demand for specialisation, members of chambers have formed themselves into the following five special interest groups: employment, criminal, commercial & property, personal injury and family. They are therefore able to offer specialised advice and advocacy in the following areas: employment; industrial relations and discrimination; human/civil rights; personal injury; clinical negligence; environmental law; commercial and property with general chancery; crime; trading standards work; family and mental health.
Chambers also has an association with chambers at 42 Castle Street, Liverpool.

Set No.
261 **18 ST. JOHN STREET** (Jonathan Foster QC)

18 St. John Street, Manchester, M3 4EA
Tel: (0161) 278 1800 **Fax:** (0161) 835 2051 **DX:** 728854 Manchester 4
Email: 18stjohn@lineone.net **Website:** http://website.lineone.net/~18stjohn

Head of Chambers:	Jonathan Foster QC
Senior Clerk:	John Hammond
Chambers Administrator:	Pippa Jessop
Tenants:	34

Members:

Jonathan Foster QC (1970) (QC-1989)
Peter Birkett QC (1972) (QC-1989)
Martin Steiger QC (1969) (QC-1994)
Raymond Wigglesworth QC (1974) (QC-1999)
Roger Hedgeland (1972)
Alastair Forrest (1972)
Paul Dockery (1973)
Jennifer Caldwell (1973)
Paul O'Brien (1974)
Christopher Diamond (1975)
Roger Stout (1976)
Malcolm McEwan (1976)
Nicholas Fewtrell (1977)
Mark Laprell (1979)
David Heaton (1983)
Richard Vardon (1985)
Brian Williams (1986)
Yvonne Healing (1988)
Toby Sasse (1988)
Samantha Birtles (1989)
Nigel Poole (1989)
Elisabeth Tythcott (1989)
Mark Benson (1992)
Susan Harrison (1993)
Raquel Simpson (1990)
Rachel Shenton (1993)
Michael Garvin (1994)
Sarah Williams (1995)
Simon Kilvington (1995)
Andrew Moore (1996)
Saul Brody (1996)
Rachel Faux (1997)
Richard Chapman (1998)
N Jonathan Grierson (1999)

The Chambers: A general common law chambers with distinct civil, family and criminal departments, together with three chancery practitioners, and expertise at all levels.

Set No.
262 **24A ST. JOHN STREET** (Paul Chambers)
24A St. John Street, Manchester, M3 4DF **Tel:** (0161) 833 9628 **Fax:** (0161) 834 0243

Set No.
263 **28 ST. JOHN ST** (Clement Goldstone QC)
28 St. John St, Manchester, M3 4DJ **Tel:** (0161) 834 8418 **Fax:** (0161) 835 3929 **DX:** 728861 Manchester 4 **Email:** clerk@28stjohn.co.uk

Set No.
264 **YOUNG STREET CHAMBERS** (Lesley Newton)
38 Young Street, Manchester, M3 3FT **Tel:** (0161) 833 0489 **Fax:** (0161) 835 3938 **DX:** 25583 M5
Email: clerks@young-st-chambers.com **Website:** www.clerks

Middlesbrough

Set No.
265 **COUNSEL'S CHAMBERS** (Stuart Lightwing)
Tudor House, Church Lane, Nunthorpe, Middlesbrough, TS7 0PD **Tel:** (01642) 315000 **Fax:** (01642) 315500 **DX:** 60524 (Middlesbrough)

wcastle upon Tyne

BROAD CHARE CHAMBERS (Eric A Elliott)

Broad Chare Chambers, 33 Broad Chare, Newcastle upon Tyne, NE1 3DQ
Tel: (0191) 232 0541 **Fax:** (0191) 261 0043 **DX:** 61001
Email: clerks@broadchasechambers.law.co.uk
Website: www.broadchasechambers.law.co.uk

Head of Chambers:	Eric A. Elliott
Senior Clerk:	Brian Bell
Tenants:	46

Members:

Eric Elliott (1974)
Paul Batty QC (1975) (QC-1995)
Patrick Cosgrove QC (1976) (QC-1994)
Sally Bradley QC (1978) (QC-1999)
James Harper (1957)
Frederick Such (1960)
Giles Bavidge (1968)
Ian Dawson (1971)
Euan Duff (1973)
Timothy Hewitt (1973)
Christine Harmer (1973)
J. Ronald Mitchell (1973)
Beatrice Bolton (1975)
Anthony Hawks (1975)
Robin Horner (1975)
Roger Elsey (1977)
Christopher Dorman O'Gowan (1979)
Thomas Finch (1981)
Brian Mark (1981)
Kester Armstrong (1982)
Lesley McKenzie (1983)
Ian Kennerley (1983)
Pauline Moulder (1983)
John O'Sullivan (1984)
Richard Selwyn-Sharpe (1985)
Anne Richardson (1986)
Anthony Davis (1986)
David Rowlands (1988)
Mark Styles (1988)
Sarah Mallett (1988)
Carl Gumsley (1989)
Joseph O'Brien (1989)
James Brown (1990)
Susan Boothroyd (1990)
Stephanie Jarron (1990)
Julie Clemitson (1991)
Claire Middleton (1991)
Michelle Temple (1992)
Rachel Smith (1992)
S. Anderson (1993)
Elizabeth Lugg (1994)
Sara Robinson (1994)
Nicholas Peacock (1996)
Jodie James-Stadden (1996)
Sam Faulks (1997)
Kirti Jeram (1997)

The Chambers: A large and long-established set, with an increasing range of specialists. Nine members of chambers are Recorders, and one is a Deputy Chancery Master.

Work Undertaken:

Criminal work: All aspects.

Family law: Including all aspects of child law, financial disputes, divorce, Inheritance Act cases and emergency protection.

Civil work: Including personal injury, professional negligence, general contract, building disputes, employment law, licensing, planning and some commercial.

Chancery work: Most aspects.

ENTERPRISE CHAMBERS (Anthony Mann QC)

65 Quayside, Newcastle upon Tyne, NE1 3DS
Tel: (0191) 222 3344 **Fax:** (0191) 222 3340 **DX:** 61134 Newcastle upon Tyne 1
Email: enterprise.newcastle@dial.pipex.com **Website:** www.enterprisechambers.com

Head of Chambers:	Anthony Mann QC
Senior Clerk:	Tony Armstrong (London)
Clerk:	Dylan Wendleken (London)

For a full list of members please see the London entry. For further information about the set please visit the chambers' website.

MILBURN HOUSE CHAMBERS (Paul Cape)

A Floor, Milburn House, Dean Street, Newcastle upon Tyne, NE1 1LE
Tel: (0191) 230 5511 **Fax:** (0191) 230 5544 **DX:** 716640 Newcastle 20
Email: admin@milburnhousechambers.co.uk
Website: www.milburnhousechambers.co.uk

Head of Chambers:	Paul Cape
Senior Clerk:	Dorothy Toase
Tenants:	4

Specialising exclusively in employment and discrimination law. Practising throughout the country representing a range of public/private sector employers and applicants.

Set No. 269

TRINITY CHAMBERS (A.T. Hedworth QC)

Trinity Chambers, 9-12 Trinity Chare, Quayside, Newcastle upon Tyne, NE1 3DF
Tel: (0191) 232 1927 **Fax:** (0191) 232 7975 **DX:** 61185 (Newcastle)
Email: info@trinitychambers.co.uk **Website:** www.trinitychambers.co.uk

Head of Chambers:	A.T Hedworth QC
Practice Director:	Simon Stewart OBE
Silks Clerk:	Colin Hands
Criminal Clerks:	Sharon Robson, Ailsa Charlton
Civil and Family Clerks:	Chris Swann, Clare Thomas
Tenants:	36

Members:

Toby Hedworth QC (1975) (QC-1996)
John Milford QC (1969) (QC-1989)
Brian Forster QC (1977) (QC-1999)
Charles Kelly (1965)
Stephen Duffield (1969)
Jeremy Hargrove (1970)
Christopher Knox (1974)
Graham Duff (1976)
Christopher Vane (1976)
John Lowe (1976)
David Callan (1979)
John Wilkinson (1979)
Duncan Smith (1979)
Jacqueline Smart (1981)
Paul Sloan (1981)
James Richardson (1982)
Peter Walsh (1982)
Tim Spain (1983)
Rachel Hudson (1985)
Fiona McCrae (1987)
Paul Richardson (1986)
Caroline Goodwin (1988)
Shaun Routledge (1988)
Tim Gittins (1990)
Crispin Oliver (1990)
Robert Adams (1993)
Michael Ditchfield (1993)
Rosalind Scott Bell (1993)
Nicholas Stonor (1993)
Jane Gilbert (1994)
Stuart Pryke (1994)
Charles Holland (1994)
Sarah Woolrich (1994)
Paul Caulfield (1996)
Fiona Parkin (1998)
Michael Graham (1999)

Six members of chambers are Recorders. One is a part-time Chairman of the Employment Law Tribunal, and one a Deputy District Judge.

The Chambers: Trinity Chambers is a leading and progressive common law set in the north of England that has completed a major review of its services, procedures and client care standards. This determination to modernise has resulted in the award of the BarMark, the Bar Council's kitemark of quality assurance. Trinity Chambers was the first set north of London and the fourth in the country to receive this acknowledgement of quality assurance and attention to client care. All members and staff of chambers believe in the importance of the BarMark accreditation and welcome feedback from clients as well as guidance on how services may be improved. The barristers of Trinity Chambers are members of one or more of the 6 practice groups: criminal law (3 QCs and 21 Juniors); common law (one QC and 10 Juniors); family law (11 Juniors); Chancery and commercial (8 Juniors); employment law (7 Juniors); and licensing law (one QC and 5 Juniors). As well as having the Silks' clerk, chambers has 2 specialist clerking teams (criminal law, and civil and family law). Each practice group has a member who is prepared to discuss areas of work, specialisations and notable abilities. Fees are negotiated through the clerks from the outset. Chambers has an open charging policy. Urgent work receives special handling. As part of the determination to provide a high quality service, Trinity Chambers has made a significant investment in the provision of support facilities. Chambers has disabled access, video and audio conferencing facilities, and the on-going seminar programme. Practice groups regularly give seminars, with the Law Society's CPD accreditation, that are free to clients; in 1999 they gave seminars in Newcastle and Middlesbrough at which over 350 solicitors attended. The website has received high praise from the local press and the new brochure has been well received. Chambers has its own Equality Policy, copies of which are available on request. Trinity Chambers understands the importance of being approachable and so welcomes inquires, of a general nature to the Practice Director, or of aspects of the barristers' work through the appropriate specialist clerks. Chambers brochure is also available on request (Can you spot the ghost?).

Work Undertaken:

Criminal Law: The size and depth of the group, along with the provision of mutual support, means that this group is able to provide quality prosecutors and defenders with clear charging rates. The reputation in the North East of the 3 QCs continues to grow. The group is holding a number of seminars, with CPD accreditation, during 2000 in recognition of the need for a closer relationship and understanding with defence solicitors and the CPS.

Common Law: The group covers all the main areas of common law with growing PI and negligence specialisations. Direct Professional Access and conditional fees are a part of the service provided by the group and chambers.

Family Law: This group is gaining a strong reputation in terms of quality and teamwork. With a regular programme of CPD accredited seminars, the members are well known throughout the area and they are readily accessible.Chancery and Commercial: With a growing client base, the group is establishing a broader reputation than that expected of a provincial set.

Employment Law: With a part-time chairman of the Employment Tribunal to give advice, the group has developed over the last 12 months into one which covers most of the spectrum of work.

Licensing Law: The group has established itself as being an able provider to this niche market.

ewport

No.
70 **TEMPLE CHAMBERS** (David Aubrey QC)
12 Clytha Park Rd, Newport, NP9 4PB **Tel:** (01633) 255855 **Fax:** (01633) 253441 **DX:** 33208 Newport

orthampton

No.
71 **36 BEDFORD ROW** (Michael Pert QC)

24 Albion Place, Northampton, NN1 1UD
Tel: (01604) 602333 **Fax:** (01604) 601600 **DX:** 12459 Northampton
Email: chambers@36bedfordrow.co.uk **Website:** www.36bedfordrow.co.uk

Head of Chambers:	Michael Pert QC
Practice Manager:	Peter Bennett FCCA MCIM
Senior Clerk:	Bill Conner
Senior Criminal Clerk:	Harri Bennetts
Senior Civil/Family Clerk:	Richard Cade
Administrator:	Jane Wittering
Fees Clerk:	Lynne Edmond
Tenants:	70

Members:

Michael Pert QC (1970) (QC-1992) LLB (Manch) +
Brian R. Escott-Cox QC (1954) (QC-1974) MA (Oxon)
Martin Bowley QC (1962) (QC-1981) MA BCL (Oxon)
James Hunt QC (1968) (QC-1987) MA (Oxon) +
Michael Stokes QC (1971) (QC-1994) +
Frances Oldham QC (1977) (QC-1994) BA (Bristol) +
Nicholas Browne QC (1971) (QC-1995) LLB (Liverpool), Dip Law (Strasbourg)+
Richard Benson QC (1974) (QC-1995) +
Annabel Walker QC (1976) (QC-1997) +
Anesta Weekes QC (1981) (QC-1999) +
David Farrell QC (1978) (QC-2000) LLB (Manchester) +
Andrew Urquhart (1963) BA (Oxon)
Stephen Waine (1969) LLB (Southampton) +
David Altaras (1969) MA, DipCrim(Cantab)+
Christopher Metcalf (1972) +
David Lee (1973) BA/AB (Cantab/Harvard)
Colin J.D. Anderson (1973)
Jamie De Burgos (1973) MA (Cantab)
Michael Fowler (1974) LLB (London) +
Geoffrey Solomons (1974) LLB (Nottingham)
Michael Greaves (1976) LLB (Birmingham)
A.G. (Sam) Mainds (1977) +
Charles Lewis (1977) MA (Oxon)
Howard Morrison (1977) OBE, LLB (London) +
Catherine Gargan (1978) LLB (Liverpool)
Jeremy H.C. Lea (1978)
Gillian Temple-Bone (1978)
Martin Beddoe (1979) MA (Cantab)
Christopher Donnellan (1981) BA (Oxon)
Lynn Tayton (1981) LLB (London)
Edmund Farrell (1981) LLB (Leeds) LLM (Cantab) Dip. Eur Law (Kings)
Richard Wilson (1981) BA LLM (Sussex/Cambridge)
Charlotte Friedman (1982)
Mercy Akman (1982) LLB (Wales)
Christopher Plunkett (1983) LLB (Warwick)
William Harbage (1983) + MA (Cantab)
Simon Bull (1984) BA, LLM (Cantab)
Joanne Ecob (1985) LLB (Newcastle)
Robert Underwood (1986) BA (De Montfort)
Michael Cranmer-Brown (1986)
Benjamin Gumpert (1987)
Amjad Malik (1987) BA, LLM (London)
Gordon Wignall (1987)
Peter Dean (1987)
Greg Pryce (1988) BA (Wolverhampton)
Andrew Howarth (1988) BA (Oxon)
Amanda Johnson (1990) LLB (London)
Simon Sugar (1990)
John Gibson (1991) LLB (Durham)
Matthew Lowe (1991) LLB (Exeter)
Stuart Alford (1992) BSc (Reading)
Sarah Gaunt (1992) LLB (Cardiff), M.Phil(Cantab)
Andrew McNamara (1992)
Rosa Dean (1993) BA (Oxon)
John Lloyd-Jones (1993) BA (Durham)
Karen Johnston (1994) MA (Oxon)
Jeffrey Jupp (1994) BA (Worcester)
Andrzej Bojarski (1995) LLB (LSE)
Jonathan Spicer (1995)
Jonathan Kirk (1995) LLB (Kings)
Niall Ferguson (1996) BA (Dunelm)
Rupert Skilbeck (1996) BA (York)
Oliver Connolly (1997)
Kate Brunner (1997) MA (Edinburgh), Dip Law (City)
Kevin Barry (1997) LLB (Birmingham)
Rebecca Crane (1998)
Catarina Sjölin (1998)
Kevin McCavish (1998) LLM (London)
Simon Ash (1999)
Penelope Wood (1999)
Peter Joyce QC (1968) (QC-1991) +*
Colman Treacy QC (1971) (QC-1990) +*
Richard Payne (1964) *
Elizabeth Ingham (1989) *

+ Recorder *Door Tenant

The Chambers: Annexe of 36 Bedford Row, London WC1R 4JH Tel:(020) 7421 8000

Set No.
272 CHARTLANDS CHAMBERS (Jane Page)

3 St Giles Terrace, Northampton, NN1 2BN
Tel: (01604) 603322 **Fax:** (01604) 603388 **DX:** 12408 Northampton

Head of Chambers:	Jane Page
Senior Clerk:	Andrew Davies
Tenants:	9

Family and general common law service including matrimonial finance; cohabitation disputes; children; domestic violence; personal injury; employment; tort; contract; criminal law.

Set No.
273 CLARENDON CHAMBERS

5 St. Giles Terrace, Northampton, NN1 2BN
Tel: (01604) 637245 **Fax:** (01604) 633167 **DX:** 12404 Northampton

Senior Clerk:	Russell Burton
Tenants:	46

Annexe of Clarendon Chambers, 7 Stone Buildings, Lincoln's Inn, London WC2A 3SZ
Tel: (020) 7681 7681

Set No.
274 NORTHAMPTON CHAMBERS AT 22 ALBION PLACE (Peter Hollingworth)

22 Albion Place, Northampton, NN1 1UD
Tel: (01604) 636271 **Fax:** (01604) 232931 **DX:** 12464 Out of hours tel: 0973 922124
Email: clerks@northamptonchambers.co.uk
Website: www.northhamptonchambers.co.uk

Head of Chambers:	Peter Hollingworth
Senior Clerk:	James Edmonds
Tenants:	6

Northampton Chambers is an established common law set with members specialising in the following areas: family; child care; ancillary relief; criminal litigation; personal injury; contract and tort; employment; landlord and tenant; real property law; arbitrations; mortgages; company law. For further information, please contact the senior clerk.

Norwich

Set No.
275 EAST ANGLIAN CHAMBERS (Roderick Newton)

East Anglian Chambers, 15 The Close, Norwich, NR1 4DZ
Tel: (01603) 617351 **Fax:** (01603) 751400 **DX:** 5213
Email: norwichchambers@dial.pipex.com **Website:** www.ealaw.co.uk

Head of Chambers:	Roderick Newton
Senior Clerk:	Stephen Collis
Administrator:	Carol Bull (01473) 254559
Tenants:	57

Members:

Roderick Newton (1982)
John Akast (1968)
John Wardlow (1971)
Peter Wain (1972)
Marcus Pearce (1972)
Andrew Marsden (1975)
Caroline Bryant (1976)
Celia Miller (1978)
David Pugh (1978)
Martyn Levett (1978)
Timothy McLoughlin (1978)
Graham Sinclair (1979)
John Hamey (1979)
Anthony Kefford (1980)
John Brooke-Smith (1981)
Simon Redmayne (1982)
Graham Parnell (1982)
Michael Lane (1983)
Hugh Vass (1983)
Jane Davies (1983)
Lindsay Cox (1984)
Paul Shadarevian (1984)
Janet Bettle (1985)
Steven Dyble (1986)
Anthony Bate (1987)
Nicholas Elcombe (1987)
Rebecca Degel (1987)
Rosalyne Mandil-Wade (1988)
David Richards (1989)
Ann Greaves (1989)
Andrew Jackson (1990)
John Greenwood (1990)
Ray Smith (1991)
Katharine Bundell (1991)
Marika Bell (1991)
Jeremy Dugdale (1992)
Carole Parry-Jones (1992)
Dominic Barratt (1992)
Helen Gilbertson (1993)
Amanda Rippon (1993)
Patricia Walsh (1993)
Jacqui Hanlon (1994)
Richard Kelly (1994)
Mark Phelps (1994)
Jude Durr (1995)
Sally Freeman (1995)
Samantha Leigh (1995)
Alan Wheetman (1995)
David Wilson (1996)
John Morgans (1996)
Fiona Baruah (1996)
Ashley Thain (1996)
Martin Ivory (1996)
Martin McArdle (1996)
Saqib Rauf (1996)
Marc Cannatella (1997)
David Sunman (1997)

The Chambers: For further information, please see full entry under East Anglian Chambers, Ipswich.

Set No.
276 OCTAGON HOUSE CHAMBERS (Andrew Lindqvist & Guy Ayers)

Octagon House Chambers, 19 Colegate, Norwich, NR3 1AT **Tel:** (01603) 623186 **Fax:** (01603) 760519 **DX:** 5249 Norwich-1
Email: admin@octagon-chambers.co.uk

Nottingham

Set No.
277 **36 BEDFORD ROW** (Michael Pert QC)

10 Regent Street, Nottingham, NG1 5BQ
Tel: (0115) 964 4840 **Fax:** (0115) 964 4848 **DX:** 10083 Nottingham
Email: chambers@36bedfordrow.co.uk **Website:** www.36bedfordrow.co.uk

Head of Chambers:	Michael Pert QC
Practice Manager:	Peter Bennett FCCA MCIM
Senior Clerk:	Bill Conner
Senior Criminal Clerk:	Harri Bennetts
Senior Civil/Family Clerk:	Richard Cade
Administrator:	Jane Wittering
Fees Clerk:	Lynne Edmond
Tenants:	70

Members:

Michael Pert QC (1970) (QC-1992) LLB (Manch) +
Brian R. Escott-Cox QC (1954) (QC-1974) MA (Oxon)
Martin Bowley QC (1962) (QC-1981) MA BCL (Oxon)
James Hunt QC (1968) (QC-1987) MA (Oxon) +
Michael Stokes QC (1971) (QC-1994) +
Frances Oldham QC (1977) (QC-1994) BA (Bristol) +
Nicholas Browne QC (1971) (QC-1995) LLB (Liverpool), Dip Law (Strasbourg)+
Richard Benson QC (1974) (QC-1995) +
Annabel Walker QC (1976) (QC-1997)
Anesta Weekes QC (1981) (QC-1999) +
David Farrell QC (1978) (QC-2000) LLB (Manchester) +
Andrew Urquhart (1963) BA (Oxon)
Stephen Waine (1969) LLB (Southampton) +
David Altaras (1969) MA, DipCrim(Cantab)+
Christopher Metcalf (1972) +
David Lee (1973) BA/AB (Cantab/Harvard)
Jamie De Burgos (1973) MA (Cantab)
Colin J.D. Anderson (1973)
Michael Fowler (1974) LLB (London) +
Geoffrey Solomons (1974) LLB (Nottingham)
Michael Greaves (1976) LLB (Birmingham)
A.G (Sam) Mainds (1977) +
Charles Lewis (1977) MA (Oxon)
Howard Morrison (1977) OBE, LLB (London) +
Catherine Gargan (1978) LLB (Liverpool)
Jeremy H.C. Lea (1978)
Gillian Temple-Bone (1978)
Martin Beddoe (1979) MA (Cantab)
Christopher Donnellan (1981) BA (Oxon)
Lynn Tayton (1981) LLB (London)
Edmund Farrell (1981) LLB (Leeds) LLM (Cantab) Dip. Eur Law (Kings)
Richard Wilson (1981) BA LLM (Sussex/Cambridge)
Charlotte Friedman (1982)
Mercy Akman (1982) LLB (Wales)
Christopher Plunkett (1983) LLB (Warwick)
William Harbage (1983) + MA (Cantab)
Simon Bull (1984) BA, LLM (Cantab)
Joanne Ecob (1985) LLB (Newcastle)
Robert Underwood (1986) BA (De Montfort)
Michael Cranmer-Brown (1986)
Benjamin Gumpert (1987)
Amjad Malik (1987) BA, LLM (London)
Gordon Wignall (1987)
Peter Dean (1987)
Greg Pryce (1988) BA (Wolverhampton)
Andrew Howarth (1988) BA (Oxon)
Amanda Johnson (1990) LLB (London)
Simon Sugar (1990)
John Gibson (1991) LLB (Durham)
Matthew Lowe (1991) LLB (Exeter)
Stuart Alford (1992) BSc (Reading)
Sarah Gaunt (1992) LLB (Cardiff), M.Phil(Cantab)
Andrew McNamara (1992)
Rosa Dean (1993) BA (Oxon)
John Lloyd-Jones (1993) BA (Durham)
Karen Johnston (1994) MA (Oxon)
Jeffrey Jupp (1994) BA (Worcester)
Andrzej Bojarski (1995) LLB (LSE)
Jonathan Spicer (1995)
Jonathan Kirk (1995) LLB (Kings)
Niall Ferguson (1996) BA (Dunelm)
Rupert Skilbeck (1996) BA (York)
Oliver Connolly (1997)
Kate Brunner (1997) MA (Edinburgh), Dip Law (City)
Kevin Barry (1997) LLB (Birmingham)
Rebecca Crane (1998)
Catarina Sjölin (1998)
Kevin McCavish (1998) LLM (London)
Simon Ash (1999)
Penelope Wood (1999)
Peter Joyce QC (1968) (QC-1991) +*
Colman Treacy QC (1971) (QC-1990) +*
Richard Payne (1964) *
Elizabeth Ingham (1989) *

+ Recorder *Door Tenant

The Chambers: Annexe of 36 Bedford Row, London WC1R 4JH Tel: (020) 7421 8000

No.
78 **NO.1 HIGH PAVEMENT** (John B. Milmo QC)
No.1 High Pavement, Nottingham, NG1 1HF **Tel:** (0115) 941 8218 **Fax:** (0115) 941 8240 **DX:** 10168 Nottingham

Set No.
279 **KCH BARRISTERS** (William Everard)

King Charles House, Standard Hill, Nottingham, NG1 6FX
Tel: (0115) 941 8851 **Fax:** (0115) 941 4169 **DX:** 10042
Email: clerks@kch.co.uk **Website:** www.kch.co.uk

Head of Chambers:	William Everard
Senior Clerk:	Geoff Rotherham
Tenants:	43

Members:

William Everard (1973) +
Andrew Hamilton (1970) +
Calder Jose (1971) +
John Stobart (1974)
Noel Philo (1975)
David Smart (1977)
James Howlett (1980)
Vivien Buchanan (1981)
Stephen Lowne (1981)
Richard Toombs (1983)
Pami Dhadli (1984)
Patrick Gallagher (1984)
Kevin Salmon (1984)
Caroline Bradley (1985)
Rowena Bridge (1975)
Sean Hale (1988)
Mark Van der Zwart (1988)
Ian Way (1988)
Jonathon Dee (1989)
Alastair Munt (1989)
Adrian Jackson (1990)
Sharron McNeilis (1990)
James Hett (1991)
Richard Jones (1991)
Stuart Lody (1992)
Jane Morris (1991)
Jeremy Janes (1992)
Christopher Kessling (1992)
Edna Leonard (1992)
Jonathan Straw (1992)
Libby Grimshaw (1993)
Sheila Macdonald (1993)
Julie Warburton (1993)
Simon Eckersley (1995)
Tracey Kirwin (1995)
Anna Soubry (1995)
Sarah Knight (1996)
Neil Wylie (1996)
Hal Ewing (1997)
Grace Hale (1998)
David Browitt (1998)
Shona Rogers (1998)
Andrew Beaumont (1998)
James Hunt QC (1968) (QC-1987) MA (Oxon) +*
Heather Swindells QC (1974) (QC-1995) +
James Corbett QC (1975) (QC-1999) + *
Terence Walters (1993) *

* Associate Tenant + Recorder

The Chambers: KCH Barristers provide advocacy and advisory services throughout the East Midlands, South Yorkshire, Lincolnshire and Humberside. Chambers has three specialist teams, crime, civil and family. Each team offers a broad range of experience and expertise. KCH Barristers pride themselves on being approachable and flexible in the way they work with clients so that chambers can best meet their needs. The clerking team provide a friendly and efficient service and are able to advise clients on suitable counsel to match their requirements.
Chambers complies with the Equality Code and Bar Practice Management Standards

Work Undertaken:
Crime: including fraud.
Civil: a broad range including commercial, housing, landlord and tenant, employment, planning, professional negligence, personal injury, medical negligence, building disputes and wills and trusts.
Family: including public and private Children Act proceedings, ancillary relief, domestic violence, cohabitee disputes and Inheritance Act claims.

Recruitment & Training: Applications for tenancy should be made to the Head of Chambers. Chambers recruits pupils through PACH and provides an award scheme for 1 pupil per year. Chambers also considers applications from those seeking 6 months or sponsored pupillage.

Set No.
280 **ROPEWALK CHAMBERS** (Richard Maxwell QC)

24 The Ropewalk, Nottingham, NG1 5EF
Tel: (0115) 947 2581 **Fax:** (0115) 947 6532 **DX:** 10060 Nottingham 17 ISDN video conferencing (0115) 941 0565 (X2)
Email: clerks@ropewalk.co.uk **Website:** www.ropewalk.co.uk

Head of Chambers	Richard Maxwell QC
Senior Clerk:	David Austin
Tenants:	37

Members:

Richard Maxwell QC (1968) (QC-1988)
W.C. Woodward QC (1964) (QC-1985)
Anthony Goldstaub QC (1972) (QC-1992)
Ian McLaren QC (1962) (QC-1993)
R.F. Owen QC (1977) (QC-1996)
G.M. Jarand (1965)
Graham Machin (1965)
Richard H. Burns (1967)
Richard Swain (1969)
Antony Berrisford (1972)
Douglas Herbert (1973)
Stephen Beresford (1976)
Simon Gash (1977)
Alison Hampton (1977)
Simon Beard (1980)
Jayne Adams (1982)
Rosalind Coe (1983)
Richard Hedley (1983)
Soofi Din (1984)
Dominic Nolan (1985)
Bryony Clark (1985)
Andrew Prestwich (1986)
Patrick Limb (1987)
Richard Seabrook (1987)
Philip Turton (1989)
Toby Stewart (1989)
Jinder Boora (1990)
Jonathan Mitchell (1992)
Jason Cox (1992)
Deborah Davies (1993)
Elizabeth Hodgson (1993)
Richard Gregory (1993)
Andrew Hogan (1996)
Mark Diggle (1996)
Judith L. Butler (1997)
Nick Blake (1997)
Michael Bridge (1994)

The Chambers: Members of Ropewalk Chambers provide a comprehensive and specialised civil advocacy service, together with all the necessary advice and paperwork for proceedings in most courts, inquiries and tribunals throughout the country. Chambers is open from 8.00am to 6.00pm and offers conference rooms equipped with video conferencing facilities for up to twenty people, full facilities for the disabled and client car parking. Chambers is strategically positioned, both regionally and nationally, to offer teams or individuals specialising in particular subjects, enhanced by a competitive pricing policy. Chambers utilises the latest technology to enhance the service to clients and prides itself on its efficient turnaround of work. Documents may be sent and received via e-mail. For futher information please visit chambers' website at www.ropewalk.co.uk

Work Undertaken:
Personal injury: The personal injury specialist group covers areas including: industrial and insidious disease (asbestos-induced, asthma, cancer, dermatitis, poisoning, radiation, stress at work, repetitive strain injury and vibration white finger); road traffic; industrial; disaster; sports injuries; clinical negligence; product liability and health and safety at work.
Business and property: Work undertaken by the business and property group includes: commercial (banking, corporate finance, sale of goods, consumer credit and protection, and competition); company; professional negligence (legal, financial and negligence within the building, engineering and surveying professions); building; construction; engineering; landlord and tenant (commercial, residential, agricultural and housing); partnership; chancery (boundaries, conveyancing, easements, inheritance, probate, wills and trusts); and intellectual property.
Employment: The employment practice group offers advice and representation on cases including: wrongful and unfair dismissal; restrictive covenants; trade secrets; discrimination; trade unions; T.U.P.E.; D.D.A.; Human Right and European related matters.
Planning and environment: Work undertaken by the planning and environment group includes: administrative; compulsory purchase; heritage; judicial review; local government; lands tribunal; pollution; nature conservation; rating and planning enquiries.
Additional specialisations: Full arbitration, including alternative dispute resolution (A.D.R.).

Clientele: All clients, without discrimination: insurer; trade union; corporate; local government; privately funded or otherwise. Direct Professional Access is available.

1 **ST. MARY'S CHAMBERS FAMILY LAW CHAMBERS** (Christopher Butler)
50 High Pavement, Nottingham, NG1 1HW **Tel:** (0115) 950 3503 **Fax:** (0115) 958 3060 **DX:** 10036 **Email:** clerks@smc.law.co.uk

xford

2 **HARCOURT CHAMBERS** (Patrick Eccles QC)
Churchill House, 3 St. Aldates Courtyard, St. Aldates, Oxford, OX1 1BA
Tel: (01865) 791559 **Fax:** (01865) 791585 **DX:** 96453 Oxford 4
Email: clerks@harcourtchambers.law.co.uk **Website:** www.harcourtchambers.law.co.uk

Head of Chambers:	Patrick Eccles QC
Senior Clerk:	Brian Wheeler
Tenants:	26

Annexe of Harcourt Chambers (Patrick Eccles QC), Temple, London. See under entry in London.

3 **KING'S BENCH CHAMBERS** (Roger Ellis QC)
King's Bench Chambers, 32 Beaumont St., Oxford, OX1 2NP
Tel: (01865) 311066 **Fax:** (01865) 311077 **DX:** 4318 Oxford **LIX:** OXF 003
Email: clerks@13kbw.co.uk **Website:** www.13kbw.co.uk

Head of Chambers:	Roger Ellis QC
Senior Clerk:	Stephen Buckingham
	Kevin Kelly
Chambers Director:	Claire Makin
Chambers Administrator:	Penny McFall
Tenants:	41

See 13 King's Bench Walk, Temple, London EC4Y 7EN for a full listing of chambers.

4 **3 PAPER BUILDINGS** (Michael Parroy QC)
1 Alfred Street, High Street, Oxford, OX1 4EH **Tel:** (01865) 793736 **Fax:** (01865) 790760 **DX:** 4302 **Email:** oxford@3paper.co.uk

Peterborough

Set No. 285

FENNERS CHAMBERS (Lindsay Davies)

Fenners Chambers, 8-12 Priestgate, Peterborough, PE1 1JA
Tel: (01733) 562030 **Fax:** (01733) 343660 **DX:** 12314 Peterborough 1
Email: clerks@fennerschambers.co.uk **Website:** www.fennerschambers.co.uk

Head of Chambers:	Lindsay Davies
Senior Clerk:	Mark Springham
Tenants:	33

Members:

Lindsay Davies (1975) +
Kenneth Wheeler (1956)
Peter King (1970)
Geraint Jones (1972)
Andrew Gore (1973)
Stephen Franklin (1974)
Susan Espley (1976)
Caroline Pointon (1976)
Oliver Heald (1977)
Simon Tattersall (1977)
Paul Leigh-Morgan (1978)
Tim Brown (1980)
Michael Crimp (1980)
Paul Hollow (1981)
Andrew Gordon-Saker (1981)
Stuart Bridge (1981)
Martin Collier (1982)
Liza Gordon-Saker (1982)
Meryl Hughes (1987)
George Foxwell (1987)
Alasdair Wilson (1988)
Caroline Beasley-Murray (1988)
Clive Pithers (1989)
Jeffrey Deegan (1989)
Andrew Taylor (1989)
Sally Hobson (1991)
Caroline Horton (1993)
Katharine Ferguson (1995)
William Josling (1995)
Mike Magee (1997)
Roderick Spinks (1997)
George Keightley (1997)
Alasdair Foster (1998)

+ Recorder

The Chambers: Also at 3 Madingley Road, Cambridge. Please see the Cambridge entry.

Set No. 286

REGENCY CHAMBERS (Raymond Croxon QC & Ian Martignetti)

Cathedral Square, Peterborough, PE1 1XW
Tel: (01733) 315215 **Fax:** (01733) 315851 **DX:** 12349 Peterborough 1
Email: clerks@regencychambers.law.co.uk

Head of Chambers:	Raymond Croxon QC, Ian Martignetti
Senior Clerk:	Paul Wright
Tenants:	15

Members:

Raymond Croxon QC (1960) (QC-1983)
David Tyzack QC (1970) (QC-1999) *
Ian Martignetti (1990)
William Powell (1971)
Andrew Tettenborn (1988)
Anita Thind (1988)
Margot Elliott (1989)
Jonathan Buckle (1990)
Marina Azhar (1990)
Christopher Ellis (1991)
Pauline Bennet (1991)
Carl Fender (1994)
Christopher Bramwell (1996)
Marie Southgate (1997)
Samuel Roberts (1973)
Catherine Crean (1982) *
Kevin Leigh (1986) *

* Door Tenants

The Chambers: Located in Centre of Peterborough, retaining an annexe in Cambridge – expertise and depth in areas of civil, family and crime servicing East Anglia, the Midlands and Lincolnshire. Conferences can be arranged at either premises or at solicitors office.
Conditional fee work accepted.

Work Undertaken:
Family: Ancillary relief; public and private law; Children Act Applications.
Civil: Human rights; employment; personal injury; clinical negligence; commercial; contract and torts, professional negligence, landlord and tenant; property; planning; consumer law; licensing; wills and trusts; arbitration disputes.
Crime: Defence and prosecution work undertaken at all levels.

ortsmouth

37 GUILDHALL CHAMBERS PORTSMOUTH (Lee Young)

Prudential Buildings, 16 Guildhall Walk, Portsmouth, PO1 2DE
Tel: (023) 9275 2400 **Fax:** (023) 9275 3100 **DX:** 2225 Portsmouth 1

Head of Chambers:	Lee Young
Senior Clerk:	Tristan Thwaites
Junior Clerk:	Jodi McGuire
Tenants:	10

Members:

Lee Young (1991)
Peter Griffith (1964)
Peter Fortune (1978)
John Sabine (1979)
Richard Colbey (1984)
Stuart Ellacott (1989)
Lisa England (1992)
Yasmin Hall (1993)
Robyn Day (1997)
John Ward-Prowse (1997)
Roderick Jones (1983) *
Edo de Vries (Ret.) (1969) +

* Door Tenant + Associate Member

The Chambers: An established common law set of chambers handling a wide range of law including landlord and tenant, personal injury, professional negligence, family and crime.

38 PORTSMOUTH BARRISTERS' CHAMBERS (Andrew Parsons)

Victory House, 7 Bellevue Terrace, Portsmouth, PO5 3AT
Tel: (023) 9283 1292 / (023) 9281 1811 **Fax:** (023) 9229 1262 **DX:** 2239 Portsmouth
Email: clerks@portsmouthbar.com **Website:** www.portsmouthbar.com

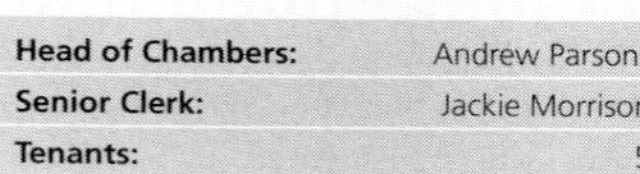

Head of Chambers:	Andrew Parsons
Senior Clerk:	Jackie Morrison
Tenants:	5

Members:

Andrew Parsons (1985) LLB (Hons)
Lincoln Brookes (1992) LLB (Hons)
Martyn Booth (1996) LLB (Hons) (Southampton)
John Atwill (1997) LLB (Hons) (Herts)
James Britton (1996) LLB (Hons) (Southampton)

The Chambers: Chambers undertakes predominantly civil work and aims to provide a modern, high quality, fast, friendly and efficient service.

Work Undertaken:
Business & Commerce: Contract, company, construction, partnership, carriage of goods and shipping.
Matrimonial & Children: Ancillary relief, care and Children Act matters.
Negligence: In particular professional negligence.
Property and Finance: Mortgages, land law, Inheritance Act, landlord and tenant, consumer credit, insolvency, pensions, FSA related work.
A brochure is available on request.

reston

9 NEW BAILEY CHAMBERS (Patricia Bailey)

10 Lawson Street, Preston, PR1 2QT
Tel: (01772) 258087 **Fax:** (01772) 880100 **DX:** 710050 Preston 10
Email: clerks@newbailey.co.uk **Website:** www.newbailey.co.uk

Head of Chambers:	Patricia Bailey
Senior Clerk:	Savannah Biswas
Clerks:	John Stewart, Claire Sharples, Lynette Maines (Liverpool)
Tenants:	24

Members:

Patricia Bailey (1969)
Keith Thomas (1969)
Graham Robertson (1983)
Graeme C. Wood (1968)
Yasmin Wright (1990)
Kevin Musaheb (1990)
Ian Dacre (1991)
Jeremy Dable (1987)
Robert F McGinty (1994)
Sharon Watson (1994)
Norman Lowson (1989)
William McCarthy (1996)
Carolyn Johnson (1974)
Clare Thomas (1998)
Joanne Shepherd (1993)
Andrew Sinker (1991)
David Ackerley (1992)
Henry Gow (1994)
William Parkinson (1997)
Robert Askey (1998)
Jeffrey Clarke (1985)
Rodney Pritchard (1964)
Richard Paige (1997)
David Mawdsley (1995)

The Chambers: Established in 1992 by the present Head of Chambers - New Bailey Chambers now operates in two centres, Preston and Liverpool, with easy access to both combined court centres and is a broadly based common law set with expertise in most areas of law.

Continued overleaf

Work Undertaken: Criminal law (defence and prosecution), all aspects of family and matrimonial law matters (including financial relief and childrens applications and adoption), civil litigation including Chancery law, intellectual property, personal injury, contractual claims, employment law, local authority work and housing matters, including landlord and tenant, clinical negligence, equine and animal law and immigration.

Set No. 290 **QUEENS CHAMBERS** (Timothy Ryder)

Ribchester House, 5th floor, Lancaster Road, Preston, PR1 2QL **Tel:** (01772) 828300 **Fax:** (01772) 825380 **DX:** 710064 Preston 10

Set No. 291

15 WINCKLEY SQUARE (R.S. Dodds)

15 Winckley Square, Preston, PR1 3JJ
Tel: (01772) 252828 **Fax:** (01772) 258520 **DX:** 17110 Preston 1
Email: clerks@15winckleysq.co.uk **Website:** www.15winckleysq.co.uk

Head of Chambers:	R.S. Dodds
Senior Clerk:	Michael Jones
Practice Manager:	John Schofield
Tenants:	35

Members:

R. Stephen Dodds (1976)
Roger M. Baldwin (1969)
Barbara J. Watson (1973)
Simon Newell (1973)
Robert Crawford (1976)
P. Nicholas D. Kennedy (1977)
Timothy G. White (1978)
Richard A. Haworth (1978)
Glyn Williams (1981)
David J. Kenny (1982)
Jane E. Cross (1982)
Anthony Cross (1982)
Paul Hart (1982)
Paul Hague (1983)
John Woodward (1984)
Richard M. Hunt (1985)
D. Mark Stuart (1985)
Richard J. Bennett (1986)
Bruce Henry (1988)
Peter J. Anderson (1988)
Kathryn Johnson (1989)
Samantha Bowcock (1990)
Paul Creaner (1990)
Michael Whyatt (1992)
Louise Harvey (1991)
Marie Mitchell (1991)
Julie Taylor (1992)
Fraser Livesey (1992)
Jonathan Buchan (1994)
Martin Hackett (1994)
Lee Blakey (1995)
Paul Davis (1996)
Jacob Dyer (1995)
Paul Gillott (1996)
Zabeda Maqsood (1996)

The Chambers: A medium sized set, seeking to provide a comprehensive service to solicitor clients both in private and institutional practice throughout the town, the county and beyond into Cumbria, Manchester and Merseyside. Several tenants are members of the Family Law Bar Association.

Work Undertaken: All common law work, with particular emphasis and experience in all areas of: family work; crime; contract; personal and industrial injury; licensing; planning; landlord and tenant; and employment law. Work on a Direct Access basis is accepted. Expanding Chancery and associated case types.

Reading

Set No. 292

WESSEX CHAMBERS

48 Queen's Road, Reading, RG1 4BD
Tel: (0118) 956 8856 (24 hrs.) **Fax:** (0118) 956 8857 **DX:** 4012 Reading
Email: clerks@wessexchambers.co.uk

Head of Chambers:	Management Committee
Senior Clerk:	Martin Davies
Tenants:	8

Members:

Roger Smithers (1990)
Robina Omar (1991)
Pramod K Joshi (1992)
Nikki Duncan (1994)
Colin McDevitt (1995)
Penny Ireland (1996)
Matthew Brunning (1997)
Eleonor Duhs (1998)
Alister M Turtle (1994) *

* Door Tenant

The Chambers: Wessex Chambers is a general common law set which offers a wide range of legal services with members appearing in courts and tribunals throughout England and Wales. Chambers is 10 minutes walk from the railway station, the District Registry, County Court, Crown Court, Magistrates' Court, and Employment Tribunal. Chambers offers excellent conference facilities, although members are always willing to meet at any venue convenient to the client.

Work Undertaken: General common law, Chancery, civil litigation, crime, ancillary relief and Children Act matters, personal injury, company, commercial, landlord & tenant, employment, professional negligence, licensing, IP, insolvency and planning.

dhill

CLARENDON CHAMBERS

Crown House, Gloucester Road, Redhill, RH1 1AZ
Tel: (01737) 780781 **Fax:** (01737) 761760 **DX:** 100203 Redhill 1

Senior Clerk:	Russell Burton
Tenants:	46

Annexe of Clarendon Chambers, 7 Stone Buildings, Lincoln's Inn, London, WC2A 3SZ
Tel: (020) 7681 7681

effield

26 PARADISE SQUARE (Roger Keen QC)

26 Paradise Square, Sheffield, S1 2DE **Tel:** (0114) 273 8951 **Fax:** (0114) 276 0848 **DX:** 10565 **Email:** booth@paradise-sq.co.uk
Website: www.paradise-sq.co.uk

uthampton

5 17 CARLTON CRESCENT (Mr Jeremy Gibbons QC)

17 Carlton Crescent, Southampton, SO15 2XR
Tel: (023) 8032 0320/2003 **Fax:** (023) 8032 0321 **DX:** 96875 Southampton 10
Email: sue@jg17cc.co.uk **Website:** www.jeremygibbonsqc.co.uk

Head of Chambers:	Jeremy Gibbons QC
Senior Clerk:	Gregory P. Townsend
Administrator:	Sue Benoke
Tenants:	30

Members:

Jeremy S. Gibbons QC (1973) (QC-1995)
Linda E. Sullivan QC (1973) (QC-1994) BA (Hons)
Jonathan M. Fulthorpe (1970)
Peter J.H. Towler (1974)
Michael P. Kolanko (1975)
William H. Webster (1975)
Nicholas Somerset Haggan (1977)
Peter Spink (1979)
Hugh Merry (1979)
Margaret Ann Pine-Coffin (1981)
Malcolm T.P. Gibney (1981)
Timothy D. Howard (1981)
Philip A. Glen (1983)
Michael W. Forster (1984)
Gary A. Grant (1985)
Dylan R. Morgan (1986)
Timothy K. Moores (1987)
Peter Doughty (1988)
Roberta Holland (1989)
Abigail Smith (1990)
Adam Hiddleston (1990)
Hayley Griffiths (1990)
Trevor Ward (1991)
Catherine Burrett (1992)
Nicholas Tucker (1993)
Gary Lucie (1994)
Peter Savill (1995)
Jeremy Burns (1996)
Caoimhe McDermott (1997)
Gavin Foster (1997)

The Chambers: Full details can be found at chambers' website: www.jeremygibbonsqc.co.uk

6 EIGHTEEN CARLTON CRESCENT (Alastair Haig Haddow)

Eighteen Carlton Crescent, Southampton, SO15 2ET
Tel: (023) 8063 9001 **Fax:** (023) 8033 9625 **DX:** 96877 Southampton
Email: clerks@18carltoncresent.co.uk **Website:** www.18carltoncresent.co.uk

Head of Chambers:	Alastair Haig Haddow
Senior Clerks:	Lynda Knight, Paul Cooke
Tenants:	20

Members:

Andrew Massey (1969)
Alastair Haig-Haddow (1972)
Ashley Ailes (1975)
Gary Fawcett (1975)
Charles Cochand (1978)
Angus Robertson (1978)
Richard Egleton (1981)
Martin Blount (1982)
Christopher Wing (1985)
Elizabeth Manuel (1987)
Andrew Houston (1989)
Omar Malik (1990)
Christine Munks (1991)
Imogen Robins (1991)
Peter Glenser (1993)
Sally Carter (1994)
Richard Hall (1995)
Peter Asteris (1996)
Timothy Dracass (1998)
Kerrie Cox (1998)
Guy Boney QC (1968) (QC-1990) *
Michael Ollerenshaw *
Simon Lillington (1980) *
Jonathan Speck *
Helene Pines Richman (1992) *

* Door Tenants

Work Undertaken: General common law, including personal injury; criminal law; family and matrimonial law, including child care law, wardship and matrimonial property; landlord and tenant; planning; employment; commercial law; licensing; professional negligence; and Chancery.

Set No.
297 COLLEGE CHAMBERS (Robin Belben)

College Chambers, 19 Carlton Crescent, Southampton, SO1 2ET
Tel: (023) 8023 0338 **Fax:** (023) 8023 0376 **DX:** 38533 (Southampton 3)

Head of Chambers:	Robin Belben
Senior Clerk:	Wayne Effeny
Tenants:	17

Members:

Robin Belben (1969)
Kenneth Pain (1969)
Jonathan Swift (1977)
Derek Marshall (1980)
Douglas Taylor (1981)
Mark Courtney Stewart (1989)
Anthony Hand (1989)
Jessica Habel (1991)
Gary Self (1991)
Catherine Breslin (1990)
Andrew Kinghorn (1991)
Daniel Nother (1994)
Arabella Grundy (1995)
Andrew Lorie (1996)
Baljinder Uppal (1996)
Graeme Harrison (1997)
Amanda Gillett (1998)

Work Undertaken: General common law including family and matrimonial, childcare law, wardship, matrimonial property and cohabitee disputes; personal injury; contract; tort; landlord and tenant; employment; licensing; professional and medical negligence; commercial law; Chancery; land law (including boundary disputes); and criminal law. Instructing solicitors are always welcome to have an informal discussion with the clerks.

Swansea

Set No.
298 ANGEL CHAMBERS (T. Glanville Jones)

Angel Chambers, 94 Walter Rd, Swansea, SA1 5QA **Tel:** (01792) 464623 **Fax:** (01792) 648501 **DX:** 39566 **Email:** lynne@angelchambers.co.uk

Set No.
299 ISCOED CHAMBERS (Trefor Davies)

Iscoed Chambers, 86 St Helen's Rd, Swansea, SA1 4BQ
Tel: (01792) 652988/9 **Fax:** (01792) 458089 **DX:** 39554 Swansea
Email: iscoed@iscoedchambers.co.uk

Head of Chambers:	Trefor Davies
Senior Clerk:	Wally Rainbird
1st Junior:	Jeff Evans
2nd Junior:	Kris Thorne
Practice Manager:	Sheila Budge
Tenants:	31

Members:

Kenneth Lloyd Thomas (1966)
Trefor Davies (1972)
Peter Christopher Rouch QC (1972) (QC-1996)
Kevin Riordan (1972)
Frank Phillips (1972)
Patrick Thomas John Griffiths (1973)
James John Jenkins (1974)
Philip Derek Marshall (1975)
Paul Huw Thomas (1979)
Robert Michael Craven (1979)
Stephen Robert Tristram Rees (1979)
Elwen Mair Evans (1980)
Stewart Karl Anthony Sandbrook-Hughes (1980)
Francis Jones (1980)
Owen Huw Rees (1983)
Mark Spackman (1986)
Ruth Henke (1987)
John Hipkin (1989)
David Andrew Harris (1990)
Catherine Louise Heyworth (1991)
William Peters (1992)
Kate Hughes (1992)
Dean Pulling (1993)
Ian Wright (1994)
Peter Maddox (1994)
Iwan Davies (1995)
Elizabeth Gow (1995)
Timothy Hayes (1996)
Mathew Rees (1996)
Simon Hoffman (1997)
Farah Zafar (1999)

Work Undertaken: This well-established set of chambers offers an all-round service to solicitors and others with the right of Direct Professional Access. The principal fields of work are civil, criminal and family law, but with specialised expertise in a variety of areas, including: personal injury; planning; local government; environment; highways; fraud; trade descriptions; licensing; family; child law; Chancery; and housing.

Set No.
300 PENDRAGON CHAMBERS (Wayne Beard)

124 Walter Road, Swansea, SA1 5RG
Tel: (1792) 411188 **Fax:** (1792) 411189 **DX:** 39572 Swansea
Email: clerks@pendragonchambers.fsnet.co.uk

Head of Chambers:	Wayne Beard
Sen. Clerk:	Gwyn Davies
Junior Clerk:	Julie Wintersgill
Tenants:	12

Members:

Wayne Beard (1991)
Robert Walters (1974)
Laraine Roblin (1981)
Huw Rees Davies (1982)
Phillip Thomas (1982)
Andrew David (1986)
John Brooks (1990)
Sara Rudman (1992)
Gareth Thomas (1993)
Rebecca Mann (1995)
Kathryn McConnochie (1997)
Susan Jenkins (1998)
Nicholas Bourne A.M. *
Donald Anderson M.P. *

* Door Tenants

The Chambers: Progressive set established in 1996. Predominantly civil and family chambers.

Work Undertaken: Personal injury, medical negligence, Landlord and Tenant, Agricultural holdings, general Chancery, revenue, family and crime.

Publications: Members have published articles for various periodicals including: *Taxation*, the *Tax Journal*, and *Financial Advisor*. Catherine McConnochie is extensively published in medical journals and other medical publications.

Recruitment & Training: Tenancy and pupillage applications to Head of Chambers with detailed CV.

vindon

1 **PUMP COURT CHAMBERS** (Guy Boney QC)
Temple Chambers, Temple Street, Swindon, SN1 1SQ
Tel: (01793) 539899 **Fax:** (01793) 539866 **DX:** 38639 Swindon 2
Email: clerks@3pumpcourt.com **Website:** www.3pumpcourt.com

Head of Chambers:	Guy Boney QC
Senior Clerk:	David Barber
Tenants:	54

An established set undertaking a wide variety of work. Members practise within specialist teams, for civil, family and all aspects of criminal law. Chambers are also at London and Winchester.

unton

2 **COLLETON CHAMBERS** (Martin Meeke)
Powlett House, 34 High St, Taunton, TA1 4PN **Tel:** (01823) 324252 **Fax:** (01823) 327489 **DX:** 96100 Taunton 1

3 **SOUTH WESTERN CHAMBERS** (Brian Lett)
12 Middle Street, Taunton, TA1 1SH **Tel:** (01823) 331919 **Fax:** (01823) 330553 **DX:** 32146 (Taunton) **Email:** barclerk@clara.net
Website: www.southwesternchambers.co.uk

inchester

4 **3 PAPER BUILDINGS** (Michael Parroy QC)
4 St. Peter Street, Winchester, SO23 8BW **Tel:** (01962) 868884 **Fax:** (01962) 868644 **DX:** 2507 **Email:** winchester@3paper.co.uk

5 **PUMP COURT CHAMBERS** (Guy Boney QC)
31 Southgate Street, Winchester, SO23 9EB
Tel: (01962) 868161 **Fax:** (01962) 867645 **DX:** 2514
Email: clerks@3pumpcourt.com **Website:** www.3pumpcourt.com

Head of Chambers:	Guy Boney QC
Senior Clerk:	David Barber
Tenants:	54

An established set undertaking a wide variety of work. Members practise within specialist teams, for civil, family and all aspects of criminal law. Chambers are also at London and Swindon.

rk

6 **YORK CHAMBERS** (Aidan Marron QC)
14 Toft Green, York, YO1 6JT **Tel:** (01904) 620048 **Fax:** (01904) 610056 **DX:** 65517 York 7 **Email:** yorkchambers.co.uk

BARRISTERS PROFILES

LEADERS AT THE BAR

AARONSON, Graham QC
One Essex Court (Lord Grabiner QC), London (020) 7583 2000
Recommended in Tax

ABELL, Anthony
2 Bedford Row (formerly 3 Hare Court) (William Clegg QC), London (020) 7440 8888
Recommended in Crime
Specialisation: Specialist in cases of serious crime with an emphasis on fraud. Also regularly acts in cases of murder, manslaughter, rape, armed robbery and drugs manufacture, importation and supply. Interesting cases include R v Pearlberg & Others (Bank Fraud and corruption); R v Paris & Others (International Bank Fraud); R v Feld (Fraud upon shareholders of a PLC, prosecution brought by SFO); R v Bailey & Cooke (Paedophile ring, child abduction and murders); R v Thompson & Others (Barking double murder and torture); R v Virgo (Child destruction and torture); R v Guerreller (Child manslaughter); R v Varathadasan (Tamil Tigers murder); R v Hall & Others (Drugs manufacture). Important reported cases in the Court of Appeal include: R v McKechnie & Others (94Cr. App. R.51) Manslaughter, inconsistent verdicts; R v C (Times 4/2/93) Rape (Number of counts on indictment).
Prof. Memberships: Criminal Bar Association, South Eastern Circuit.
Career: Called to the Bar in 1977 and joined present chambers in 1978.
Personal: Educated at Kings School Rochester and London University (LL.B Hons). Leisure pursuits include opera, theatre, walking and windsurfing. Born 31st October 1953, lives in London.

ACLAND, Piers
11 South Square (Christopher Floyd QC), London (020) 7405 1222
Recommended in Information Technology, Intellectual Property

ACTON DAVIS, Jonathan QC
Atkin Chambers (John Blackburn QC), London (020) 7404 0102
jadavis@atkinchambers.law.co.uk
Recommended in Construction
Specialisation: Practice covers construction law work and professional negligence, also general common law matters. Clients include most large construction companies, insurers and other commercial bodies.
Prof. Memberships: Tec Bar, Professional Negligence Bar Association, COMBAR, London Common Law Bar Association, Association des Juristes-Franco-Britaniques.
Career: Called to the Bar 1977, Member of Bar Council 1993-1998, Bencher of Inner Temple 1995; Queen's Counsel, 1996. Assistant Recorder 1997, Recorder 2000.
Personal: Born 15th January 1953. Educated at Harrow School and P.C.L. LLB (Lond.) Leisure pursuits include cricket and South Western France.

ADAM, Tom
Brick Court Chambers (Christopher Clarke QC), London (020) 7379 3550
adam@brickcourt.co.uk
Recommended in Commercial (Litigation)
Specialisation: General commercial law including: commercial fraud & freezing/search orders (eg Merrill Lynch v Raffa Times 14.6.2000); conflicts of interest/Chinese Walls (eg Sea Containers v Denton Hall, settled 1999); dry shipping (eg The Trident Beauty [1994] 1 LLR 365 (HL); Fyffes v MMD Commercial Court June 2000); revenue (Commissioner of Inland Revenue v Orion Caribbean Ltd [1997] STC 923 (PC)). Insurance and reinsurance (eg the PA LMX spiral litigation; GIO v Liverpool & London; Mander v Commercial Union [1998] LRLR 93). Commercial professional negligence: eg accountants (eg Abbott v Strong [1998] 2 BCLC 420); actuaries (eg NRG v Bacon & Woodrow [1997] LRLR 678); insurance brokers (Mander).
Prof. Memberships: Member of COMBAR.
Career: Cambridge (Trinity) 1983-1987; solicitor 1990 (Macfarlanes); called to the Bar 1991.
Publications: Co-author of chapter on negligence of insurance brokers in forthcoming LLP encyclopaedia 'Professional Negligence and Liability'. Assisting in 7th edition of 'Documentary Evidence' (Style & Hollander).

ADAMS, Jayne
Ropewalk Chambers (Richard Maxwell QC), Nottingham (0115) 947 2581
Recommended in Personal Injury
Specialisation: Personal injury, industrial disease and clinical negligence. Junior Counsel in both the Leicestershire and North Wales Abuse in Care multiparty litigation.
Prof. Memberships: Personal Injury Bar Association
Career: Birmingham University LLB (Hons); Chairman, James Stemp Inquiry for Leicestershire Health Authority; Chairman, Care Ethics Committee (Fertility Services). Member, Legal Aid Board Area Committee.
Personal: Married, 3 children. Interests – fitness training, cycling, reading and family life.

ADDY, Caroline
1 Brick Court (Richard Rampton QC), London (020) 7353 8845
Recommended in Defamation
Specialisation: Defamation, confidence, contempt of court and media related law generally.
Career: LLB (Euro) Exon 1990. Called 1991, joined chambers 1992. Cases include: Upjohn v Oswald, A-G v Limbrick, McPhilency v Times Newspapers Limited.
Personal: Born 1968. Lives in London. Languages French and German.

ADKINS, Richard QC
3-4 South Square (Michael Crystal QC), London (020) 7696 9900
Recommended in Company, Insolvency/Corporate Recovery
Specialisation: A business and financial law practice, including both domestic and international disputes with particular specialisations in corporate insolvency law and reconstructions, in takeover litigation and professional negligence cases. Advisory work in relation to banking, securities, receivables financing, chattel leasing, debt issues, securitisation and general corporate law issues.
Prof. Memberships: Middle Temple.
Career: MA (Oxon). Called to the Bar 1982; took Silk 1995.
Publications: Contributor, Gore Browne on Companies and a member of the Editorial Board of the 'Insolvency Lawyer' and the 'Company Financial and Insolvency Law Review'.
Personal: Keen tennis player and opera-goer.

AEBERLI, Peter
46 Essex Street (Geoffrey Hawker), London (020) 7583 8899
pda@aeberli.co.uk
Recommended in Alternative Dispute Resolution
Specialisation: Peter Aeberli MA (Edin.) BA (Oxon.) Dip. Arch. RIBA ARIAS FCIArb. Barrister, arbitrator, mediator and adjudicator specialising in construction law. Prior to reading law as a Scholar of Hertford College, Oxford, worked with a national multi-disciplinary consultancy as project architect on medium and large developments. As a barrister, has undertaken cases in court and arbitration (trials, up to eight weeks). As an arbitrator, has completed many consumer arbitrations and been appointed on a number of construction disputes (hearings, up to 20 days). As a mediator, has completed two and multi-party mediations for CEDR, RIBA (London Region), Central London County Court and by party appointment. Appointed as adjudicator by Law Society and RIBA.
Prof. Memberships: Panels: RIBA, LCIA, Law Society, CIArb and NHBC panel of arbitrators; CIArb CIOB and RIBA panel of adjudicators; CIArb , CIC, CC, and RIBA (London Region) panel of mediators. Registered CEDR mediator.
Career: Cases editor for Arbitration and Dispute Resolution Law Journal. Lectures for Chartered Institute of Arbitrators, Kings College Centre of Construction Law and others. Contributor to architectural and legal press. Involved in drafting Construction Industry Model Arbitration Rules and preparation of JCT Consultants' Agreement. Book on arbitration law and practice to be published shortly.

AGNELLO, Raquel
11 Stone Buildings (Murray Rosen QC), London (020) 7831 6381
agnello@11stonebuildings.com
Recommended in Insolvency/Corporate Recovery
Specialisation: Specialises in corporate and personal insolvency and general company law. Is well known for her involvement in the field of voluntary arrangements, both corporate and individual. It is an area in which she has lectured extensively and has many reported cases. She also practises in commercial litigation, such as contract, banking, guarantees and other securities whilst retaining an interest in private international litigation.

AINGER, David
10 Old Square (Leolin Price CBE QC), London (020) 7405 0758 / 7242 5002
Recommended in Traditional Chancery
Specialisation: Principal area of specialisation is chancery; he is a general chancery practitioner with both an advisory and litigation practice. In addition to work in real property, professional negligence, fraud, partnership, trusts (including breach of trust), pensions, probate, banking and insurance, he has experience of public inquiries, local government, water, waterways and highways, ecclesiastical law, commons, village greens and similar matters. He has conducted litigation in Hong Kong and the Isle of Man and advised on Chancery matters in other jurisdictions.
Career: Appointed one of the Conveyancing Counsel of the Supreme Court in November 1991.

AKENHEAD, Robert QC
Atkin Chambers (John Blackburn QC), London (020) 7404 0102
Recommended in Arbitration (International), Construction

ALBUTT, Ian
2-3 Gray's Inn Square (Anthony Scrivener QC), London (020) 7242 4986
Recommended in Planning
Specialisation: Planning and Local Government. Practice encompasses all aspects of planning, administrative and local government law. This includes plan-

ning inquiries, local plans, CPO, housing and retail development. Extensive recent experience in green belt, conservation and listed building issues including large scale MSA provision on M4 and M40. Court work includes regular appearances for the Treasury Solicitor, s.288 s.289 appeals, judicial review and High Court challenges. Recent planning inquiries include major motorway service area provision on M40 and M25. Birmingham Bull Ring development CPO 2 and 3. Thames Water Utilities v London Borough of Bromley. Leisure Great Britain plc v Isle of Wight Council 2000 PLCR88.
Prof. Memberships: Planning and Environmental Bar Association; Legal Assessor for the RICS; Member of the Bar Disciplinary Tribunal; Bar Council Direct Professional Access Committee member; Regular lecturer on planning topics for RTPI.
Career: Called to the Bar in 1981 by Gray's Inn.

ALDOUS, Charles QC
7 Stone Buildings (Charles Aldous QC), London (020) 7405 3886
clerks@7stonebuildings. co.uk
Recommended in Commercial Chancery, Company, Energy & Natural Resources
Specialisation: Specialist in company law, insolvency, and contract and commercial disputes. Practice also covers professional negligence and general Chancery work. Recent notable cases include: The Society of Lloyds v Sir William Jaffrey & Ors [2000]; Office of Fair Trading v Premier League & Ors [1999], Don King Productions Inc. v. Frank Warren & Ors [1998], MCC Proceeds Inc. v. Lehman Brothers [1998], Grandmet v. William Hill [1997], Amoco (UK) Exploration Company v. Teesside Gas and Transportation Ltd. [1997], Macmillan Inc. v. Bishopsgate Investment Trust [1995], Macmillan Inc. v. Bishopsgate Investment Trust [1996], Mirror Group Newspapers Pension Trustees v. Lehman Brothers [1994], Re: Bishopsgate Investment Management Ltd. (No. 2) [1994], GE Capital v. Bankers Trusts & Ors [1994], Supreme Travels Ltd. v. Little Olympian Each-Ways Ltd. [1994], Macmillan Inc. v. Bishopsgate Investment Trust [1993], Re: BSB Holdings (BSkyB) [1993].
Career: Called to the Bar 1967. Took silk 1985. Appointed Junior Counsel to the Department of Trade and Industry.
Personal: Educated at Harrow and University College, London (LL.B). Born 3rd June 1943. Lives in London and Suffolk.

ALEXANDER, Daniel
8 New Square (Michael Fysh QC SC), London (020) 7405 4321
daniel.alexander@8newsquare.co.uk
Recommended inInformation Technology, Intellectual Property, Media & Entertainment

Specialisation: Specialises in intellectual property, media and entertainment, EC, scientific commercial law and administrative law. Practice regularly involves cases with international aspects. Cases include Apple Corps v Apple Computer (trade marks - contract - Article 85/EC), Chiron v Organon (genetic engineeering patent - conflict of laws), Greenpeace v Plant Genetic Systems (genetic engineering - plant varieties - EPO), ICI v Montedison (chemical patent), Great Lakes v Texaco (commercial contracts), Portman v MAFF (judicial review, EC Law), BSkyB v PRS (copyright tribunal) Canon v Pathe (ECJ trademarks), Upjohn v Paranova (ECJ, parallel imports), Thatcher Diaries case (copyright, breach of confidence), Proctor & Gamble v Unilever (washing material patent). Joint editor of 'Clark & Lindsell on Torts'. Joint author of 'Guidebook to Intellectual Property Law'. Fluent German, good French.
Prof. Memberships: Bar European Group, Chancery Bar Association, IP Bar Association.
Career: Called to the Bar and admitted to the New York Bar in 1988. Junior Counsel to the Crown in Patent Cases.
Personal: Educated at University College, Oxford (BA, Physics and Philosophy, 1985), Central London Polytechnic (Dip.Law 1986) and Harvard Law School (LLM, 1987). Born 4th October 1963.

ALLEN, James H. QC
No.6 (Shaun Spencer QC), Leeds (0113) 245 9763
Recommended in Chancery, Commercial (Litigation), Insolvency/Corporate Recovery

ALLEN, Robin QC
Cloisters (Laura Cox QC), London (020) 7827 4000
Recommended in Administrative & Public Law: General, Employment, Human Rights (Civil Liberties)
Specialisation: Discrimination, European, Human Rights, Employment and Administrative Law.
Prof. Memberships: Chair of the Employment Law Bar Association 1997-1999 and committee member of the Discrimination Law Association. Member of Bar Council, Bar Council Representative on Home Office Human Rights Act Task Force.
Career: Most important cases include: London Underground v Edwards (Single Mothers and Shiftwork); Bossa v. Ansett (EC Article 48 and Race Relations Act); ex parte Martin (ECHR Article 8 and Access to Medical Records); Balfour v. The Foreign and Commonwealth Office (PII and National Security); ex parte Seymour Smith (EC challenge to theunfair dismissal qualifying period); ex parte Gerry Adams (EC challenge exclusion order); Polkey v. A E Dayton Services (unfair dismissal); Delaney v. Staples (Wages Act); ex parte Puhlhofer (homeless persons in judicial review); ex parte Hammell (interlocutory relief in judicial review); Alexander v. Home Office (damages for discrimination); Hampson v. Department of Education (Justification for indirect discrimination); ex parte Gallagher (damages for breach of EC law); Jones v. Tower Boot (Employer's liability for harassment) ex parte Lightfoot (bankrupt's access to justice); Labour Party v. Ahsan (discrimination in selection of political candidates); Kaba v. Home Secretary (discrimination against spouses of workers exercising free movement rights); Edmond v. Lawson (Minimum Wage and Pupils); Nareem v BCCI (setting aside compromise agreements); Waters v. Metropolitan Police (Protection from hostile working environment); R v. Kent ex parte Salisbury and Pierre (local authority duties to care leavers); Clark v. Novacold (test for disability discrimination); Goodwin v. Patent Office (meaning of disabled). Has worked for the European Commision, CRE, EOC and Fair Employment Commission for Northern Ireland. Counsel for the 'Great Ape Trial' on Channel 4 in December 1995. In 1990, acted for PC Singh in the longest ever race discrimination claim, later the subject of a Channel 4 reconstruction. Has co-ordinated the Employment Law Advisers Appeal Scheme at the EAT and is vice chair of the Bar Pro Bono Unit. In 1992 appointed an expert to the European Commission on UK Law and has given evidence to the European Parliament and Select Committees of the UK Parlaiment. Recorder, writers and lectures widely in his area of law; has contributed chapters to 'A Practitioners Guide to the Human Rights Act' – Hart; 'The Legal Framework and Social Consequences of Free Movement of Persons in the European Union' – Kluwer; 'Women, Work and Inequality' – MacMillan. 'Legal Regulation of the Employment Realation' – Kluwer; 'Anti-Discrimination – The Way Forward' – EC.

ALTMAN, Brian
2 Bedford Row (formerly 3 Hare Court) (William Clegg QC), London (020) 7440 8888
Recommended in Crime, Fraud: Criminal
Junior Treasury Counsel at the Central Criminal Court.

AMLOT, Roy QC
6 King's Bench Walk (Michael Worsley QC), London (020) 7583 0410
Recommended in Crime, Fraud: Criminal
Specialisation: Principal area of practice is criminal law with an emphasis on high profile, serious crime cases and commercial fraud. Defence work includes Barlow Clowes, Blue Arrow, Brent Walker and Polly Peck (for the Liquidator). Prosecution work includes the Brighton bombing, Guildford Four (on appeal) and Clive Ponting cases. Editor, 'Phipson on Evidence' (11th Edition).
Career: Called to the Bar 1963 and became a tenant of King's Bench Walk in 1964. Treasury Counsel 1977-1989. Took Silk 1989. Vice Chairman of the Bar, 2000.
Personal: Educated at Dulwich College 1953-1960. School Governor, Dulwich College. Leisure pursuits include skiing, music, squash, and windsurfing. Born 22nd September 1942. Lives in London.

AMOS, Tim
Queen Elizabeth Building (Paul Coleridge QC), London (020) 7797 7837
Recommended in Family: Matrimonial Finance
Specialisation: All aspects of family law and related professional negligence, but predominantly family finance, married or unmarried, alive or dead. Specially interested in Anglo-German cases and those with a foreign or international element. Fluent in German (including legal German). Work experience in German Courts and German law firms. Articles include 'Financial Injunctive Relief under the 1989 Act' [1994] Fam Law 445.
Publications: Contributor to 'Essential Family Practice 2000' (Butterworths).
Prof. Memberships: Family Law Bar Association and British German Jurists Association.

ANDERSON, Anthony QC
2 Mitre Court Buildings (Michael FitzGerald QC), London (020) 7583 1380
Recommended in Planning
Specialisation: Practice encompasses planning, rating, compulsory purchase, parliamentary and local government law. Involved in Stansted Airport Inquiry, Manchester Regional Shopping Inquiry, Exeter Sub-Regional Shopping Inquiry, Crawley Business Parks Inquiry and Wokingham Major Housing Inquiry amongst others. Joint Editor 'Ryde on Rating' (12th and 13th Editions).
Prof. Memberships: Planning and Environment Bar Association. Chairman of Tribunals, the Securities and Futures Authority.
Career: Called to the Bar 1964 and joined current chambers 1965. Took Silk 1982. Appointed Recorder 1995.
Personal: Educated at Harrow School and Magdalen College, Oxford. Born 12th September 1938.

ANDERSON, David QC
Brick Court Chambers (Christopher Clarke QC), London (020) 7379 3550
anderson@brickcourt.co.uk
Recommended in Competition/Anti-trust
Specialisation: European Union law, human rights law, public/administrative law, competition law. Over 60 cases in the European Court of Justice and 20 before the European Commission/Court of Human Rights. Involved at all stages of Factortame and Sunday Trading litigation; ICI v Commission (cartel law); ex p Rees

Mogg (Maastricht Treaty); Case C-448/93 ex p Scotia (pharmaceutical licensing); Case C-302/94 ex p BT (telecoms regulation); Iberian Trading (effect of Commission decision); Case C-180/96R UK v Commission (BSE); Case C-249/96 Grant v SW Trains (sexual orientation discrimination); Building Societies v UK (retrospective legislation; human rights); Easyjet v BA (Article 82); Imperial Tobacco (advertising ban); McGonnell v UK (separation of powers); Hatton v UK (night flights); X v Bedfordshire (access to court). Publications include 'References to the European Court' (Sweet & Maxwell Litigation Library, 1995).
Career: Called 1985; Lawyer from Abroad, Covington & Burling, Washington DC, 1985-1986; Cabinet of Lord Cockfield, EC Commission, 1987-1988; Junior Counsel to the Crown, Common Law 1995-1999; Visiting Professor, King's College London, 1999; QC 1999.

ANDERSON, Lesley
40 King St (Philip Raynor QC), Manchester (0161) 832 9082 landerson@40kingstreet.co.uk
Recommended in Chancery, Commercial (Litigation), Insolvency/Corporate Recovery
Specialisation: Corporate and personal insolvency including directors' disqualifications, Banking, Commercial Landlord and Tenant. Professional Negligence and Commercial Litigation.
Prof. Memberships: Chancery Bar Association, Northern Chancery Bar Association, Northern Circuit Commercial Bar Association. On DTI Panel for Directors' Disqualifications.
Career: Lecturer in law at University of Manchester 1984-1989; Training Manager, Norton Rose M5 Group of Solicitors 1989-1991.

ANDERSON, Mark
3 Fountain Court (Robert Juckes QC), Birmingham (0121) 236 5854 clerks@3fc.co.uk
Recommended in Commercial (Litigation)
Specialisation: Professional negligence and commercial law including banking, employment, restraint of trade and sale of goods. Mortgages and other securities. Personal injury and medical negligence.
Prof. Memberships: Midland Chancery & Commercial Bar Association. Professional Negligence Bar Association. Personal Injuries Bar Association
Career: Educated at King Edward's School, Birmingham and Exeter College, Oxford.

ANDERSON, Robert
Blackstone Chambers (P Baxendale QC and C Flint QC), London (020) 7583 1770 robertanderson@blackstonechambers.com
Recommended in Commercial (Litigation)
Specialisation: Commercial (in particular, commercial fraud), insurance/reinsurance, entertainment and sports law. Instructed in two of the largest fraud trials to have taken place in the last twelve months: Federal Government of Nigeria v ANZB Ltd and Brown v Bennett. Recent reported cases include Pangood v Barclay Brown [1999] Lloyd's Rep IR 405, Brown v Bennett [1999] 1 BCLC 649 and Merrill Lynch v Raffa (The Times, 14/6/00).
Prof. Memberships: COMBAR, TECBAR, Bar Sports Law Group.
Career: Called 1986 (*Gray's Inn* & *Middle Temple*). Teaches advocacy and trains advocacy teachers on behalf of *Gray's Inn*.
Personal: Educated at Oundle School and Pembroke College, Cambridge.

ANDERSON, Rupert
Monckton Chambers (John Swift QC), London (020) 7405 7211
Recommended in Competition/Anti-trust, Tax
Specialisation: Practice includes all aspects of EU and domestic competition law including OFT, Competition Commission and EC Commission investigations, EU law generally, VAT and customs and excise, utilities regulation. Recent cases include MMC / competition commission inquiries into BSkyB/Manchester United, Mobile Telephones, Cable & Wireless / NTL, Mid Kent and Sutton Water Companies; the Supply of Sugar, Ready Mixed Concrete, Freight Forwarding Services and Ceiling Tiles in the RP Court; Sinclair Collis v C & E [1999] STC 701. Case T-342/99 Airlovs v EC Commission and Darfish v C & E The Times 28.3.00. Weinberg and Blank on Take-Overs and Mergers, Copinger on Copyright. PLC Hartbook on Competition Law.
Prof. Memberships: Member of the Bar European Group.
Career: Called 1981. MA (CANTAB).

ANDREWS, Claire
Gough Square Chambers (Fred Philpott), London (020) 7353 0924
Recommended in Consumer
Specialisation: Consumer law – experienced in civil litigation and prosecuting and defending regulatory offences, and advising on interpretation of statutes. Cases include: R v. Warwickshire CC [1993] AC 583 (misleading prices); LB Bexley v. Gardner Merchant [1991] COD (improvement notices). Clients have included food and other wholesalers and retailers and enforcement authorities. Author "The Enforcement of Regulatory Offences" and Archbold Practical Research Papers on Trade Descriptions. Other main areas of practice include landlord and tenant, employment and commercial fraud.
Prof. Memberships: Food Law Group, MSOFHT, ACIArb, ALBA, EBA, London Common Law and Commercial Bar Association.

ANDREWS, Geraldine
Essex Court Chambers (Gordon Pollock QC), London (020) 7813 8000
Recommended in Banking, Commercial (Litigation)
Specialisation: Broad-based commercial practice. In particular shipping, insurance and reinsurance, banking law, asset tracing and preservation, international commodity transactions, company law, EC law, entertainment, intellectual property (excluding patents) and general commercial and Chancery matters.
Prof. Memberships: Member of COMBAR, the London Common Law and Commercial Bar Association, and the Bar European Group; supporting member of the London Maritime Arbitrators' Association. Languages spoken: French, German, Italian.
Career: King's College, University of London: LLB (First Class Hons), 1980. LLM (1982)
Publications: Co-author of Andrews and Nillett, 'The Law of Guarantees' (3rd edn 2000).
Personal: Born 1959.

ANDREWS, Peter QC
199 Strand (David Phillips QC), London (020) 7379 9779 pjandrews@199strand.co.uk
Recommended in Clinical Negligence
Specialisation: Catastrophic injury litigation including major spinal cord injury, brain damage and perinatal birth trauma claims. Recent reported cases: Oksuzoglu v. Kay (medical negligence, causation and costs); Smoldon v Nolan (spinally injured rugby player's successful action against the match referee); Mansfield v Weetabix (hypoglycaemia as a defence to negligent driving); Hazelwood v Collett (structured settlements).
Prof. Memberships: Professional Negligence Bar Association; Personal Injury Bar Association; Midland & Oxford Circuit.
Career: Christ's College Cambridge and Bristol Universities (Undergraduate Scholar). Lincoln's Inn: Hardwicke Scholar. Junior practice in personal injury and medical negligence. Deputy High Court Judge. Silk: 1991. Recent Publications: Catastrophic Injuries – A Practical Guide to Compensation (Sweet & Maxwell 1997); Personal Injury Handbook (contributor) (Sweet & Maxwell 2000); Kemp & Kemp: the Quantum of Damages (Sweet & Maxwell 1998): chapter on structured settlements.

ANDREWS, Philip B.
Young Street Chambers (Lesley Newton), Manchester (0161) 833 0489
Recommended in Crime
Specialisation: Practice encompasses all aspects of criminal law.
Prof. Memberships: Criminal Bar Association.
Career: Called to Bar (Inner Temple) February 1977 thereafter practising on Northern Circuit. Visiting lecturer law, University of Manchester 1979-1982.
Personal: Born 24.7.50. Educated at Blackpool Grammar School and University of Hull (LLB) (Hons).

ANELAY, Richard QC
One King's Bench Walk (Anthony Hacking QC), London (020) 7936 1500
Recommended in Family: Matrimonial Finance
Specialisation: All areas of family and criminal law. Has undertaken leading work in matrimonial finance, child care, Inheritance Act provision, international child abduction, serious fraud, murder, manslaughter and rape. Election law: acted in Tower Hamlets Election. Case (1990) – 22 day hearing before Commissioner. In public law children case has undertaken leading work for local authorities, parents and guardians ad litem in complex medical, Munchaussen syndrome, by proxy, sexual, physical and emotional abuse cases. Consulting Editor: 'Encyclopedia of Financial Provision in Family Matters'. General editors Wildblood and Eaton, Sweet & Maxwell, 1998. Reported cases: Re KDT (Minor) [1994] 2 FCR 721CA; Re G [1994] 2 FCR 216. Re D (care: National Parent Presumption) 1999 1 FLR 134 CA
Career: Called 1970. QC 1993. Recorder 1992. Deputy High Court Judge (Family Division) 1995.
Personal: Born 1946. Educated at Queen Elizabeth Grammar School, Darlington and Bristol University (BA Hons Classics and Philosophy). Enjoys golf.

APPLEBY, Elizabeth QC
4-5 Gray's Inn Square (Elizabeth Appleby QC & Duncan Ouseley QC), London (020) 7404 5252
Recommended in Administrative & Public Law: General
Specialisation: Public and administrative law; local government.
Career: Called 1965, QC 1979, Bencher Lincoln's Inn 1986, Recorder Crown Court. Chaired the enquiry into the affairs of Lambeth Council, Appointed Inspector of Department of Trade inquiries, appeared in Westdeutsche Landesbank Firm Zentrich v. Litigation BC; Morgan Grenfell v. London Borough of Sutton, Graham Jones v Ronald Hellard, R v Hereford & Worcester.
Career: Deputy High Court Judge.

ARCHER, Stephen
2 Temple Gardens (Dermod O'Brien QC), London (020) 7822 1200
Recommended in Personal Injury
Specialisation: Industrial disease (with increasing emphasis on multi-party test actions); brain damage, quadriplegia, paraplegia; personal injury work generally with long experience of disputes involving on medical causation; clinical negligence. Recent cases: Abbott and others v Rockware Glass plc (CA July 1999); Makepeace v Evans Brothers (CA May 2000).
Prof. Memberships: PIBA; ELA.

Career: By 1985 practised almost exclusively in personal injury work. Following Mountenay v Bernard Matthews plc [1994] 5 Med LR 293 has acted increasingly for Defendants in a wide range of industrial disease actions including upper limb disorders, asbestos related conditions, vibration white finger, respiratory disease and occupational stress claims.
Personal: Education: Sherborne School; Oxford (Pembroke College); Inner Temple. Leisure/family: cycling; joint research (with wife) into African-American music; large model association.

ARDEN, Andrew QC
Arden Chambers (Andrew Arden QC), London (020) 7242 4244
Recommended in Planning

ARDEN, Peter
Enterprise Chambers (Anthony Mann QC), London (020) 7405 9471
Recommended in Company, Insolvency/Corporate Recovery
Specialisation: Areas of practice: business and financial law, in particular banking, bank and other securities, insolvency (corporate and individual) and related areas. Regularly instructed by clearing banks, other financial institutions and their appointees. Acted in many of the large insolvencies in recent years. Cases include Re Dallhold Estates (appointment of administrators over foreign companies), Leyland DAF Ltd v Lipe Ltd (interlocutory injunctions against administrative receivers), Re Leyland DAF Ltd (whether administrative receivers bound by exclusive jurisdiction clause), William Gaskell Group Ltd v Highley (whether charge fixed or floating and automatic crystallisation), Re Thomas Christy Ltd (effect of disqualification judgement on proceedings by liquidation), Re Ellis Son & Vidler Ltd (sale of goods and storage contract and equitable interests/remedies), Re WAL Holdings Ltd (contest between debenture holder and finance companies), Walker v Hocking (bankrupt seeking to interfere with exercise of powers by trustee), Re Business City Express Ltd (application for recognition of Eire scheme of arrangement), Re Edennote Ltd (sanction for exercise of powers by liquidator) and Re West Park Gold & Country Club (dismissal of partnership administration petition as an abuse).

ARLIDGE, Anthony QC
18 Red Lion Court (Anthony Arlidge QC), London (020) 7520 6000
Recommended in Crime, Fraud: Criminal

ARMITAGE, Keith QC
8 King St (Keith Armitage QC), Manchester (0161) 834 9560
Recommended in Clinical Negligence

ARMSTRONG, Dean
6 King's Bench Walk (Michael Worsley QC), London (020) 7583 0410
Recommended in Crime
Specialisation: Prosecutes and defends in all forms of crime and commercial fraud.
Career: MA (Cantab.).

ARNOLD, Mark
3-4 South Square (Michael Crystal QC), London (020) 7696 9900
markarnold@southsquare.com
Recommended in Insolvency/Corporate Recovery
Specialisation: Business and financial law, including in particular: insolvency (corporate and individual), banking, company, chancery and professional negligence.
Prof. Memberships: COMBAR, Chancery Bar Association, Insolvency Lawyers Association.
Career: M.A. Cantab. (Downing College, Cambridge).

ARNOLD, Richard QC
11 South Square (Christopher Floyd QC), London (020) 7405 1222
Recommended in Information Technology, Intellectual Property

ASH, Brian QC
4-5 Gray's Inn Square (Elizabeth Appleby QC & Duncan Ouseley QC), London (020) 7404 5252
Recommended in Planning
Specialisation: Principal area of practice is planning and local government. Work involves public inquiries concerning all forms of development, compulsory purchase and compensation, including references to the Lands Tribunal, and High Court proceedings including statutory appeals and judicial review. Involved in public inquiries concerning expansion of Stansted and Heathrow airports, sub-regional and other major shopping proposals, road development including motorway service areas and large scale commercial, industrial and housing proposals. Clients include Rolls Royce plc, Safeway Stores plc, Manchester Ship Canal Company, The Civil Aviation Authority, major insurance companies, local authorities and Metropolitan Borough and District Councils.
Prof. Memberships: Local Government Planning and Environmental Bar Association.
Career: TV Producer, Reporter and Programme Presenter 1967-1973. Called to the Bar 1975 and joined current chambers 1977. Took Silk 1990.
Personal: Educated at New Collge, Oxford 1960-1964. Leisure pursuits include golf, cricket, sailing and skiing. Born January 31st 1941. Lives in London.

ASHLEY-NORMAN, Jonathan
2 Bedford Row (formerly 3 Hare Court) (William Clegg QC), London (020) 7440 8888
Recommended in Fraud: Criminal
Specialisation: Criminal law specialist in fraud, restraint and confiscation, and drugs related offences. On the approved prosecutors list for Customs and Excise, Department of Trade and Industry, Inland Revenue and DSS. Regularly prosecutes in substantial cases, especially fraud and drugs importation offences. Instructed to defend in major SFO cases including Alpine Windows, concerning the collapse of the double glazing company and Richmond Oil and Gas, concerning a fraudulent company flotation. Undertakes specialist Customs defence work, including Anti Dumping Duty cases and High Court restraint work. Some Company Directors Disqualification Act work undertaken.
Prof. Memberships: Member of Criminal Bar Association.

ASHWORTH, Fiona
40 King St (Philip Raynor QC), Manchester (0161) 832 9082
Recommended in Family/Matrimonial
Specialisation: Personal Injury (Employer's and Public liability, Disease, Road Traffic). Medical & PI related professional negligence. Family and matrimonial provision.
Prof. Memberships: PIBA, FLBA.
Career: Bolton School (Girl's Division). Leeds University.

ASHWORTH, Lance
St Philip's Chambers (Rex Tedd QC), Birmingham (0121) 246 7000
Recommended in Chancery, Commercial (Litigation), Insolvency/Corporate Recovery, Personal Injury
Specialisation: Commercial Law. Group Actions. Insolvency and Directors Disqualification – Junior Counsel to the Crown. Personal Injury.
Prof. Memberships: P.I.B.A. Midland Chancery and Commercial Bar Association.
Career: Oundle School. Pembroke College Cambridge. M.A (Cantab).
Personal: Married, 3 children. Still desperately seeking sleep.

ASPLIN, Sarah J.
3 Stone Buildings (G.C. Vos QC), London (020) 7242 4937
sasplin@3sb.law.co.uk
Recommended in Pensions
Specialisation: Principal area of practice pensions litigation, advice and drafting. Acts for beneficiaries, principal employers and trustees in relation to questions of rectification construction, winding up, merger, general administration of pension schemes and appeals from the Pensions Ombudsman. Also general chancery matters including trusts, probate and partnership advice and litigation. Cases include Imperial Tobacco, British Coal Hillsdown Holdings plc, Spooner & Ors v British Telecommunications plc and Equitable Life v Hyman.
Prof. Memberships: Chancery Bar Association, Association of Pension Lawyers, ACTAPS.
Career: Called 1984.
Personal: Educated at Southampton College for Girls 1976-1978; Fitzwilliam College, Cambridge 1979-1982 (MA Law); St Edmund Hall, Oxford 1982-1983 (BCL).

ASPREY, Nicholas
Serle Court (Lord Neill of Bladen QC), London (020) 7242 6105
nasprey@serlecourt.co.uk
Recommended in Parliamentary & Public Affairs
Specialisation: Areas of practice include general chancery and commercial law, property law, probate, partnership, professional negligence, insolvency and parliamentary work.
Prof. Memberships: Chancery Bar Association, Parliamentary Bar Association, The Thomas More Society.
Career: Called 1969 and in practice at *Serle Court* since 1972.

ATHERTON, Peter
Deans Court Chambers (H.K. Goddard QC), Manchester (0161) 214 6000
atherton@deanscourt.co.uk
Recommended in Environment
Specialisation: Common law practice and in particular in areas of environmental law in cases involving civil or criminal liability, major accidents involving personal injury and property damage, product liability, professional negligence. Appeared for manufacturers of gas compression equipment at Piper Alpha Disaster Inquiry and in multi party actions arising from noise and dust pollution and water contamination. Experience of issues concerning clinical waste disposal and of claims for defective animal foodstuffs. CEDR Accredited Mediator.
Prof. Memberships: UKELA; Environmental Law Foundation; Personal Injury Bar Association; Professional Negligence Bar Association; American Bar Association (tort, insurance & ADR sections).
Career: Former Chairman of Young Barristers Committee Bar Council. Founder Member of Northern Circuit Free Representation and Advice Scheme. Called 1975 – Recorder 1999. Educated Mount St. Mary's College and Birmingham University.
Personal: Married, 2 children. Leisure pursuits include soccer, golf and walking.

ATHERTON, Stephen
3-4 South Square (Michael Crystal QC), London (020) 7696 9900
Recommended in Insolvency/Corporate Recovery
Specialisation: Main area of practice: insolvency, general commercial and civil fraud. Major cases: junior counsel to the Brunei Government, junior counsel to majority share holders of BCCI, junior counsel to Mirror Group Pensioners, advising 1986 bond holders in

relation to Barings. Highlights of past year: instructed as junior counsel to the State of Brunei and the Brunei Investment Agency in relation to litigation in Brunei and England to recover missing funds, acted for the administrators of Richmond Rugby Football Club, Portsmouth Football Club, the supervisors of the Company Voluntary Arrangement of Oxford United FC Ltd., and main creditors of Crystal Palace F.C.
Prof. Memberships: Middle Temple, Gray's Inn.
Career: LLB (Hons) Lancaster. LLM (Cantab). Secondee to the Fraud Investigation Group (CPS).
Personal: Rugby, cricket. Player/member Old Emanuel RFC and CC. Married 1992 Lucy Atherton (neé Coppock) BBC news correspondent.

ATKINSON, Nicholas QC
2 Harcourt Buildings, Atkinson Bevan Chambers (Nicholas Atkinson QC & John Bevan QC), London (020) 7353 2112
Recommended in Crime
Specialisation: Criminal Law Specialist. In last year dealt with cases of murder, rape, child sexual abuse, drugs, corruption and commercial fraud.
Prof. Memberships: Criminal Bar Association, and has served on Bar Council on three ocasions in 70's, 80's and 90's.
Career: Practice in London and upon Western Circuit. Called to the bar in 1971. Appointed Assistant Recorder in 1983 and Recorder in 1987. Took Silk in 1991.
Personal: Patron of Road Peace, the national charity for road traffic victims.

AUSTIN-SMITH, Michael QC
23 Essex Street (Michael Lawson QC), London (020) 7413 0353
michael.austin-smith@which.net
Recommended in Crime
Specialisation: Fraud, major crime of all types, crime-related civil, including civil jury actions, and police law. Appellate work includes R v Gomez [House of Lords] and Docker v West Midlands Police [House of Lords].
Career: Educated at Hampton Grammar School and Exeter University. Called to the Bar 1969, a Crown Court Recorder since 1986, DTI Inspector 1988 and 1989, Silk 1990. Formerly Chairman of the Surrey and South London Bar Mess and member of the South East Area Criminal Justice Consultative Committee.
Personal: Married with two children. Leisure interests include sailing and rugby football.

AYERS, Guy
Octagon House Chambers (Andrew Lindqvist & Guy Ayers), Norwich (01603) 623186
Recommended in Crime

AYLIFFE, James
Wilberforce Chambers (Edward Nugee QC), London (020) 7306 0102
Recommended in Commercial Chancery
Specialisation: Specialises in Commercial/Chancery litigation including asset finance, banking, company, financial services, insolvency, professional negligence, property.
Prof. Memberships: COMBAR, Chancery Bar Association.
Career: BA (Hons) Politics, Philosophy and Economics from New College, Oxford (1985) (First). Diploma in Law from City University, London (1986) (Distinction).

BAATZ, Nicholas QC
Atkin Chambers (John Blackburn QC), London (020) 7404 0102
Recommended in Construction, Information Technology

BACON, Francis
4 Paper Buildings (Jean Ritchie QC), London (020) 7353 3366
Recommended in Professional Negligence
Specialisation: Principal area of practice is professional negligence, particularly concerning solicitors. Cases in last 12 months include: Nationwide Building Society v Balmer Radmore [1999] Lloyds's Rep PN 241, Nationwide Building Society v Thimbleby [1999] Lloyds's Rep PN 359. Also acts for and against accountants, surveyors and financial advisers. Other main areas of practice are civil fraud (UK and Commonwealth), personal injury and general insurance matters.
Prof. Memberships: Professional Negligence Bar Association.
Career: Called to the Bar in 1989 (Karmel Scholar – Commercial) Gray's Inn.
Personal: Educated at Keele and Loughborough. Married with three children.

BADENOCH, James QC
1 Crown Office Row (Robert Seabrook QC), London (020) 7797 7500
james.badenoch@1cor.com
Recommended in Clinical Negligence, Personal Injury
Specialisation: Principal area of practice is clinical negligence and all medically-related work. Also handles personal injury matters. Major cases include Wilsher v Essex Area Health Authority (House of Lords); the Wendy Savage enquiry; Dobbie v Medway Health Authority (Court of Appeal); Hossack v General Dental Council (1997) Privy Council; Penney & ors v East Kent H.A. (1999/2000) C.A.; Heil v Rankin (2000) C.A. Contributor to 'Medical Negligence' (Powers and Harris, Butterworths 1990, 2nd Edn. 1994, 3rd Edn. 2000).
Prof. Memberships: Professional Negligence Bar Association, London Common Law Bar Association.
Career: Called to the Bar in 1968 and joined current chambers in 1968. Appointed Recorder 1987. Took silk 1989. Deputy High Court Judge from1994 onwards.
Personal: Educated at Dragon School, Rugby School 1959-1963 and Magdalen College, Oxford (MA) 1964-1967. Born 24th July 1945. Lives in London.

BADLEY, Pamela
25-27 Castle Street (Stephen Riordan QC), Liverpool (0151) 236 5072
Recommended in Crime

BAKER, Andrew
20 Essex Street (Iain Milligan QC), London (020) 7583 9294
Recommended in Commercial (Litigation), Shipping
Specialisation: Main areas of practice are dry shipping, arbitration, banking (principally international trade financing and foreign exchange trading/ derivatives), international trade/ commodities, conflict of laws, insurance and reinsurance (including in particular marine, mortgage indemnity insurance and LMX reinsurance). Experience as arbitrator. Reported cases include Honam Jade [1991] 1 Lloyd's Rep 38 (C/A), PNB v de Boinville [1992] 1 Lloyd's Rep 7 (C/A), Banque Paribas v Cargill [1992] 2 Lloyd's Rep 19 (C/A), Nissho lwai v Cargill [1993] 1 Lloyd's Rep 80 (Comm Ct), Angelic Grace [1995] 1 Lloyd's Rep 87 (C/A), Orjula [1995] 2 Lloyd's Rep 395 (Comm Ct), Nicholas H [1995] 2 Lloyd's Rep 299 (H/L), Atlas [1996] 1 Lloyd's Rep 642 (Comm Ct), Roar Marine v Bimeh lran [1998] 1 Lloyd's Rep 423 (Comm Ct), Trade Nomad [1998] 1 Lloyd's Rep 57 (Comm Ct) [1999] 1 Lloyd's Rep 723 (C/A), Morgan Stanley v Puglisi [1998] CLC 481 (Comm Ct), Den Danske Bank v Skipton Building Society [1998] 1 EGLR 155 (Comm Ct), Deepak v ICI [1998] 2 Lloyd's Rep 139 (Comm Ct) [1999] 1 Lloyd's Rep 387 (C/A). CSFB Europe v Seagate [1999] 1 Lloyd's Rep 784 (Comm Ct), Mira Oil v Bocimar [1999] 2 Lloyd's Rep (Comm Ct), Rustal Trading v Gills Duffus [2000] 1Lloyd's Rep 14 (Comm Ct).
Prof. Memberships: Lincoln's Inn, COMBAR.
Career: Born 21 December 1965. Educated at Lenzie Academy, Merton College, Oxford (reading Mathematics 1983-1986) and The City University (Diploma in Law, 1987). Called to the Bar 1988. Joined *3 Essex Court* (now *20 Essex Street*) in 1989.
Personal: Married with two sons. Keen golfer.

BAKER, Christopher
Arden Chambers (Andrew Arden QC), London (020) 7242 4244
Recommended in Planning

BAKER, Jacqueline
Enterprise Chambers (Anthony Mann QC), London (020) 7405 9471
Recommended in Property Litigation
Specialisation: All areas of property litigation including solicitors' negligence cases arising out of property transactions, and insolvency-related property/landlord & tenant matters. Rothschild v Bell [1999] 2 All ER 722 (C.A.) - Landlord & Tenant/1954 Act/Insolvency.

BAKER, Jonathan
Harcourt Chambers (June Rodgers), London (020) 7353 6961
Oxford (01865) 791 559
jbaker@harcourtchambers.law.co.uk
Recommended in Family/Matrimonial
Specialisation: All aspects of family law with particular expertise in children's law.
Prof. Memberships: Midland and Oxford Circuit, Family Law Bar Association, Association of Lawyers for Children.
Career: Called to the Bar in 1978. Member of Harcourt Chambers since 1979, based in Oxford since 1991. Appointed Assistant Recorder 1998.
Personal: Born 6th August 1955. MA in Law St John's College, Cambridge. Married with two children . Chair of Oxfordshire Relate.

BAKER, Philip
Gray's Inn Tax Chambers (Milton Grundy), London (020) 7242 2642
pb@taxbar.com
Recommended in Tax
Specialisation: All forms of revenue law, with particular specialisation in international taxation (issues of residence and domicile, double taxation agreements, foreign tax credit and transfer pricing); also taxation and human rights.
Prof. Memberships: Barrister, Grays Inn (1979); Visiting Professorial Fellow, Centre for Commercial Law Studies, Queen Mary and Westfield College, London University. Council member, Chartered Institute of Taxation; Member, Addington Society; Committee member, International Fiscal Association (UK Branch).
Career: 1979-1987, Lecturer in Law, School of Oriental and African Studies, London University. 1987-present, Barrister, Grays Inn Tax Chambers.
Personal: Educated: Emmanuel College, Cambridge (MA); Balliol College, Oxford (BCL); University College, London (LLM); SOAS, London (PhD); London Business School (MBA). Married, three children. Awarded OBE, July 1997.

BALCOMBE, David
1 Crown Office Row (Robert Seabrook QC), London (020) 7797 7500
Recommended in Family: Matrimonial Finance

BALDRY, Rupert
Pump Court Tax Chambers (Andrew Thornhill QC), London (020) 7414 8080
Recommended in Tax
Specialisation: VAT and customs duties; trusts; cor-

porate and EU law. Recent reported cases: CCE v Sinclair Collis; CCE v Continuum; Higher Education Statistics Agency v CCE; R v CCE ex parte Bosworth Beverages.

Prof. Memberships: Revenue Bar Association; Member of the Attorney General's Panel of Junior Counsel, Member of the VAT Practitioners' Group.

Career: Specialist Tax Barrister at *Pump Court* since 1993.

Publications: Co-author 'Trusts and UK Taxation' (Keyhaven). Editor 'Potter and Monroe's Tax Planning' (Sweet & Maxwell). Editor 'The Use of Offshore Jurisdictions' (Gee).

Personal: Marlborough College; London and City Universities.

BALDWIN, John QC

8 New Square (Michael Fysh QC SC), London
(020) 7405 4321
john.baldwin@8newsquare.co.uk

Recommended in Information Technology, Intellectual Property, Media & Entertainment

Specialisation: Barrister specialising in all aspects of intellectual property law, including patents, trade marks, copyrights, confidential information, computer law, passing off, trade libel, EC law, data protection, restrictive covenants and restraint of trade. Detailed information on practice and full biography of cases on chambers' website www.8newsquare.co.uk. Recent cases include: Novartis v Sir Roy Calne 1999 (patent infringement); Virgin Retail Ltd v Phonographic Performance Ltd 1999 (Copyright Tribunal - assessment of Royalties); MCA v Jean Luc Young 1999 (copyright infringement, personal liability of employees); Microsoft v Computer Future 1999 (copyright infringement, parallel imports); Oneac v Raychem 1998 (patent infringement); Smithkline Beecham re: Jeryl Lynn TM (trademarks) 1998; Nera v Spectra 1998 (arbitration, electronics breach of contract); Harrods v Harrods (Buenos Aires) Ltd. 1998 (implied licence, fiduciary duty, passing off).

Prof. Memberships: Intellectual Property Bar Association (IPBA); The Intellectual Property Lawyers Organisation (TIPLO).

Career: Called 1977, Gray's Inn, QC 1991.

Publications: Co-editor of 'Patent Law of Europe and UK'.

Personal: Educated at Nelson Grammar School; Leeds University (1968 BSc 1st Class Agricultural Chemistry); St Johns College, Oxford (1972 D.Phil 1972 Research Fellowship). Born 1947; resides London.

BALL, Alison QC

One Garden Court Family Law Chambers (Eleanor Platt QC and Alison Ball QC), London
(020) 7797 7900
a.ball@onegardencourt.co.uk

Recommended in Family: Child Care including child abduction

Specialisation: All aspects of family law.

Prof. Memberships: Family Law Bar Association, South Eastern Circuit.

Career: Called to the Bar in 1972. Founder member of One Garden Court (Family Law Chambers) 1989. Mediator (FMA) 1993. Took Silk in 1995. Recorder 1998.

Personal: Educated at Bedales School, 1955-1966 and Kings College, London University 1967-1971. Lives in London.

BAMFORD, Jeremy

Guildhall Chambers (Adrian Palmer QC), Bristol
(0117) 927 3366

Recommended in Chancery, Insolvency/Corporate Recovery

BANCROFT, Louise

Deans Court Chambers (H.K. Goddard QC), Manchester (0161) 214 6000
bancroft@deanscourt.co.uk

Recommended in Family/Matrimonial

Specialisation: Practises solely in the field of family law. Particular emphasis on private law including matrimonial finance, residence and contact. Representation on behalf of local authorities, parents and guardians in adoption and care proceedings. International child abduction. Mediation.

Prof. Memberships: Associate Member of the UK College of Mediation. Member of the Family Law Bar Association and Child Concern.

Career: Educated at St Anne's College, Oxford. Diploma in Law, University of Westminster. Called tothe Bar in 1985 (Inner Temple)

BANGAY, Deborah

29 Bedford Row Chambers (Peter Ralls QC), London (020) 7404 1044

Recommended in Family: Matrimonial Finance

Specialisation: Family Law especially: Matrimonial Finance (Re P CA 1991 FLR 1 286 – wordship contempt); Private Children (GV J CA 1993 FLR 1 1008 – oustev); Public Law Children Work (Re H CAA 1994 1 FLR CA 3). H v J MHV (costs: residence proceedings) 2000 IFLR 394.

Prof. Memberships: Family Law Bar Association.

Career: 1972-1976, Wycombe High School; 1976-1979, Exeter University LL.B Hons; 1970-1980, Council of Legal Education; 1982-1992, 13 Kings Bench Walk/Hardwicke Building – 1992, 29 Bedford Row.

Personal: Football, swimming and cooking.

BANKS, Robert

100E Great Portland Street, London
(020) 7636 6323

Recommended in Crime

BANKS, Roderick I'Anson

48 Bedford Row (Roderick I'Anson Banks), London (020) 7430 2005
rciab@partnershipcounsel.co.uk

Recommended in Partnership

Specialisation: Exclusively partnership law. Has specialised in this area since 1977. Handles all aspects of partnership law from the drafting and review of agreements to advice and representation in partnership disputes, arbitrations and mediations. Acts for solicitors, doctors, accountants, and other professional firms, as well as various financial and commercial institutions. Editor of 'Lindley & Banks on Partnership', Author and Editor of 'The Encyclopedia of Professional Partnerships'. Contributor of articles to 'Legal Business', 'Solicitors' Journal', 'Commercial Lawyer' and 'The Lawyer'. Has conducted seminars for NIS Group, Lawnet, CLT, National Law Tutors, Jordans and various solicitors' firms and has appeared in two videos for Legal Network TV.

Prof. Memberships: Lincoln's Inn.

Career: Called to the Bar 1974 and joined Stone Buildings, (Chambers of D.R. Stanford). Set up 48 Bedford Row in 1991, as the only chambers specialising exclusively in partnership law. CEDR Accredited Mediator, 1993. Hon. Associate of British Veterinary Association. Founder member of the Association of Partnership Practitioners.

Personal: Educated at Westminster School 1965-1969 and University College London 1970-1973. Leisure pursuits include reading and films. Born 5 December 1951. Lives in Beare Green, Surrey.

BANNISTER, Edward Alexander QC

3 Stone Buildings (G.C. Vos QC), London
(020) 7242 4937

Recommended in Commercial Chancery, Company, Insolvency/Corporate Recovery

Specialisation: Specialises in company/ insolvency and commercial litigation and all related matters, including property and contract; extensive professional negligence litigation practice. Recent cases include; Stein v Blake [1996] AC 243 (set off in insolvency); re Duckwari plc [1997] Ch 201 (measure of compensation on breach of s 320 Companies Act 1985). Swindle v Harrison [1997] 4 ALL ER 705 (causation and fiduciary duty claims); Paragon Finance v Thackerar [1999] 1 ALL ER 400 (limitation and constructive trusts); Triffitt Nurseries v Salads Etcetera [1999] 1 ALL ER 110 Times, 26 April 2000 (CA) (insolvent agent's right to retain proceeds of sale against principal). re Greenhaven Motors Limited [1999] BCLC 635 (court control over liquidator's discretion); North Holdings Limited v Southern Tropics Limited [1999] 2 BCLC 625 (unfair prejudice petitions and CPR); Garrow v Society of Lloyds [2000] Lloyds Rep IR 38 (effect of sue now pay later clause in bankruptcy proceedings); Society of Lloyds v Twinn, (2000) 97 (15) LSG 40 (whether acceptance of offer qualified by side letter); Barings plc v Coopers & Lybrand, Independent 10 May 2000 (Banking Act 1987 – when exhibits to affidavits available to the public).

Career: Called to the Bar 1974, Silk 1991.

BARCA, Manuel

1 Brick Court (Richard Rampton QC), London
(020) 7353 8845

Recommended in Defamation

Specialisation: Practises in media law; defamation; malicious falsehood; contempt of court; breach of confidence; media/literary copyright; passing off.

Career: Graduate trainee, Reuters 1984-1985. Called to the Bar 1986 (Lincoln's Inn, Levitt Scholar). Joined *1 Brick Court* in 1987. Cases include: Major v New Statesman, Upjohn v BBC, Cumming v Scottish Daily Record, Watts v Times Newspapers, Bottomley v Express Newspapers, Howarth v Guardian Newspapers, British Coal v NUM, Berkoff v Times Newspapers, Stern v Piper, Home Secretary v BBC, Venables v Bose, Marks & Spencer v Granada TV, ITN v Living Marxism.

Personal: Educated at Wimbledon College and Cambridge University (Law Tripos, MA). Lives in London.

BARDA, Robin

4 Paper Buildings (Lionel Swift QC), London
(020) 7583 0816
clerks@4pb.com

Recommended in Family: Child Care including child abduction

Specialisation: All aspects of family and matrimonial work, including residence and contact disputes, adoptions, child abductions, public law applications, matrimonial finance, disputes between unmarried couples and Inheritance Act applications. A considerable amount of work for Local Authorities and Guardians, in particular the Official Solicitor, most in the High Court at the Principal and and other District Registries, but also in County Courts around London and elswhere in the Court of Appeal. Cases have involved clients across a broad spectrum of wealth, including well-known personalities, and cases which have received media attention. Recently reported cases include Re I (Adoption: Nationality) [1998] 2 FLR 997, Wilson v Webster [1998] 1 FLR 1097, P v P (Abduction: Acquiescence) [1998] 1 FLR 630.

Prof. Memberships: Family Law Bar Association. London Common Law and Commercial Bar Association.

Career: B.A. Oxon. Called to the Bar 1975, Gray's Inn. Joined Chambers of John Byrt QC, 4 Paper Buildings, Temple as a pupil in 1975, taken on as a tenant in 1976.

Personal: Education: Bryanston School 1960-1966. Academical Clerk (Choral scholar) Magdalen College, Oxford 1967-1970 – BA in Philosophy, Politics and Economics. Hobbies: Freelance musician/singer 1970-

1974. Chairman of The Sixteen Ltd. Director of Singcircle Ltd. Singing with The Sixteen (occasionally) and the Choir of St Clement Danes, including concerts. Music generally. Squash. Clubs: Savage Club.

BARKER, Anthony QC

5 Fountain Court (Anthony Barker QC), Birmingham (0121) 606 0500

Recommended in Crime

BARKER, Kerry

Guildhall Chambers (Adrian Palmer QC), Bristol (0117) 927 3366

Recommended in Licensing

Specialisation: All aspects of licensing law including: liquor licensing, public entertainment and local authority licensing (acting for applicants, objectors, police authorities, licensing justices and local authorities). Has expertise in betting, gaming and lotteries (casinos, bingo, gaming machines, bookmakers and betting, competitions, lotteries and fundraising). Former Justices' Clerk and contributor to Paterson's Licensing Acts. Publications include "Betting Gaming and Lotteries" (Fourmat Publishing 1992).

BARKER, Simon

13 Old Square (Michael Lyndon-Stanford QC), London (020) 7404 4800
clerks@13oldsquare.law.co.uk

Recommended in Media & Entertainment

Specialisation: Media and entertainment litigation (including copyright, passing off, breach of confidence, format rights), copyright tribunal references, commercial litigation and arbitration (including warranty and contract claims, purchase and sale of businesses and shares, company law, partnership disputes and professional negligence). Recent reported cases include News Group Newspapers v ITP 1993 RPC 173 (TV listings tribunal reference), AIRC v PPL 1994 RPC 143 (radio broadcasting tribunal reference), re a Debtor 87/93 1996 BCC 80 (challenging IVA for material irregularity), EMAP v Security Publications Limited 1997 FSR 891 (copyright, passing off, magazine cover formats), Neville v Wilson 1997 Ch 144 (constructive trust of shares held by directors), Coulthard v Neville Russell 1998 1 BCLC 143 (accountants' and auditors' duties to directors), Candy Rock Recording v PPL 1999 EMLR 155 (record dubbing tribunal reference).

Prof. Memberships: Fellow of Institute of Chartered Accountants. Member of Chartered Institute of Arbitrators.

Career: Qualified as chartered accountant 1976. Called to the Bar 1979 (Lincoln's Inn). Fellow ICAEW 1982. Assistant Recorder 1995. Recorder 2000.

BARLING, Gerald QC

Brick Court Chambers (Christopher Clarke QC), London (020) 7379 3550

Recommended in Competition/Anti-trust

BARLOW, Francis

10 Old Square (Leolin Price CBE QC), London (020) 7405 0758 / 7242 5002

Recommended in Traditional Chancery

Specialisation: Specialising in the full range of Chancery matters, contentious and non-contentious, with particular emphasis on probate, breach of trust and property and advisory work and drafting relating to UK and foreign trusts and estates with associated tax advice.

Prof. Memberships: STEP, Charity Law Association, Chancery Bar Association.

Career: Dauntsey School; Christ Church, Oxford; 1962 BA; 1966 MA. Called 1965 Inner Temple; Bencher, Lincoln's Inn; Deputy Social Security Commissioner 1996;

Publications: Joint editor of 'Williams on Wills', 4th, 5th, 6th and 7th editions (1974, 1980, 1987, 1996), Wills title and Executors & Administrators title in Halsbury's Laws 4th ed., vol 50 (reissue) and vol 72 (reissue).

BARLOW, Richard

11 King's Bench Walk (F.J. Muller QC), London (020) 7353 3337

Recommended in Tax

Specialisation: Value Added Tax and Customs and Excise.

Prof. Memberships: Revenue Bar Association, Chartered Institute of Arbitrators, Institute of Indirect Tax.

Career: Called to the Bar 1970. Customs and Excise Solicitor's Office 1973-1988. Private Practice 1988 to present. Chairman (part-time) Social Security and Disability Appeals Tribunal.

Publications: Contributor to Tax Journals.

Personal: LLB (LSE) 1969. Fellow Chartered Institute of Arbitrators 1999.

BARNES, Margaret

2 Bedford Row (formerly 3 Hare Court) (William Clegg QC), London (020) 7440 8888

Recommended in Fraud: Criminal

Specialisation: Principal area of practice is criminal law, particularly fraud cases, including mortgage and VAT fraud and fraud on the Legal Aid Fund. Major cases include; R v Linskill, R v Reece (solicitors' fraud), R v Harding and others (VAT fraud), R v Trevelyan (corruption by Ministry of Defence official), R v Griffiths (child abduction), R v Impact Industries (conspiracy to defraud), R v Cogolato (murder), R v Wilkinson (solicitors fraud), R v Brown and Others (VAT fraud).

Prof. Memberships: Criminal Bar Association.

Career: Former solicitor. Articles with *Ingham Clegg & Crowther*, Blackpool 1968-1971 and assistant solicitor 1971-1973. Solicitor with *Davis Hanson1975-1976. Called to the Bar and joined current chambers 1976.*

Personal: Educated at Haslingden Grammar School, Rossendale, Lancashire 1955-1963 and University of Sheffield 1963-1967 (B. Jur). Leisure pursuits include a house in France, walking and theatre. Born 24th October 1944. Lives in London.

BARNES, Mark QC

One Essex Court (Lord Grabiner QC), London (020) 7583 2000

Recommended in Arbitration (International), Civil Fraud, Commercial (Litigation), Energy & Natural Resources

Specialisation: Commercial law and litigation, with experience of company and insolvency law, European Community Law and administrative law, where these touch upon commercial disputes. In the commercial field, practice includes banking (and international banking), commodities, gas and electricity supply contracts, IT and telecommunications outsourcing and supply contracts, sale of commercial goods, share sales and professional negligence. Has acted and advised in arbitrations (under ICC and LME rules, and ad hoc) and in or in connection with expert determinations and redeterminations in the gas and construction industries.

BARNES, Michael QC

Wilberforce Chambers (Edward Nugee QC), London (020) 7306 0102

Recommended in Property Litigation

Specialisation: Property, local government and public law with particular emphasis on landlord and tenant, planning and judicial review. He is an editor (formerly general editor) of Hill and Redman on the Law of Landlord and Tenant and a Contributory Editor of Halsbury's Law of England, Landlord and Tenant. Sat as Inspector on the Public Inquiry into the Hinkley Point C Nuclear Power Station.

Prof. Memberships: Member of the Hong Kong Bar. Chancery Bar Association. Member of the Planning and Envrionment Bar Association and a Bencher of the Middle Temple.

Career: Called to the Bar in 1965. Took silk in 1981.

BARNES, Timothy QC

7 Bedford Row (David Farrer QC), London (020) 7242 3555

Recommended in Crime

Specialisation: Commercial fraud and other serious criminal work. Clients include SFO, CPS, HQ and CPS areas on Midland and Oxford Circuit, and major defence solicitors in London and on Circuit. Acted for the prosecution in Wallace Smith and Durnford Ford cases (SFO) and in the de Stempel fraud (CPS West Mercia). Prosecuted 'R v Kellard and others (Britannia Park Ltd)' (1990). Acted for the defence in Swithland Motors (Howes Percival, Northampton) and in Pearce (Lloyds Re-Insurance Fraud) (*Kingsley Napley*). Assists in teaching at seminars for accountants and lawyers on techniques of expert evidence and advocacy.

Prof. Memberships: Criminal Bar Association.

Career: Called to Bar, Gray's Inn 1968. Queen's Counsel 1986. Recorder 1987.

Personal: Educated at Bradfield College and Christ's College, Cambridge. Married with 4 children. Interests include music and gardening.

BARNETT, Jeremy V.

St. Paul's Chambers (Nigel Sangster QC), Leeds (0113) 245 5866

Recommended in Crime

BARON, Florence QC

Queen Elizabeth Building (Paul Coleridge QC), London (020) 7797 7837

Recommended in Family: Matrimonial Finance

Specialisation: All aspects of family law and related professional negligence – with a particular emphasis on "Big Money" cases. Appeared in several high profile cases, including F v F 1995 2 FLR 45 and advised the Prince of Wales in his divorce. Also specialises in cases with an international element.

Prof. Memberships: FLBA.

Career: B.A. (Oxon). Q.C. (1995). Recorder and Deputy High Court Judge.

BARRACLOUGH, Nicholas

Francis Taylor Building (D.A. Pears), London (020) 7353 9942

Recommended in Crime

Specialisation: Specialist criminal law practitioner with a general practice. Recently defended in cases of murder and rape, soliciting to murder (hit man case), drugs importations, VAT evasion, internet pornography and fraud. Associated work, such as civil actions against the police, is also undertaken.

Prof. Memberships: Criminal Bar Association.

Career: LLB (Hons). Called 1990 Inner Temple.

Personal: Born 12th March 1967.

BARRETT, John

40 King St (Philip Raynor QC), Manchester (0161) 832 9082

Recommended in Planning

Specialisation: Town and country planning, environment, compulsory purchase, highways, local government, judicial review, waste disposal, retail, minerals and housing.

Prof. Memberships: Planning and Environment Bar Association. Member of Northern Circuit and Administrative Law Bar Association.

Career: Called 1982; elected member of Northern Circuit 1983. Former assistant editor of the Encyclopaedia of Environmental Health. Occasional lecturer at University of Newcastle-upon-Tyne.

Personal: Married with two children.

BARRETT, Penelope
3 Gray's Inn Square (Rock Tansey QC), London (020) 7520 5600
Recommended in Crime
Specialisation: Criminal defence specialist instructed in leading work. Her range of work includes murder and other violent crime, large scale drugs importations, serious sexual offences and fraud. Lectures on a number of aspects of criminal law/evidence.
Prof. Memberships: Criminal Bar Association, Liberty, British Academy of Forensic Sciences.
Career: Called to the Bar 1982.
Personal: Educated at Haygrove Comprehensive School, Bridgwater College and Trinity Hall, Cambridge (BA Hons 1981). Born 1959. Lives in London.

BARTLETT, Andrew QC
Crown Office Chambers (Michael Spencer QC & Christopher Purchas QC), London (020) 7797 8100 bartlett@crownofficechambers.com
Recommended in Construction, Professional Negligence
Specialisation: Professional negligence, construction, insurance/reinsurance, product liability, commercial contracts. Frequently instructed in major claims and appeals involving complex legal or technical issues. Recent cases include Group Josi Re v Walbrook Insurance Co Ltd [1996], P&O Developments Ltd v Guy's and St Thomas' NHS Trust [1998], Royal Brompton Hospital NHS Trust v Hammond [1999], Hammersmith Hospitals NHS Trust v Troup Bywaters & Anders [1999], Albright & Wilson UK v Biachem Ltd [2000], Co-operative Retail Services v Taylor Young Partnership [2000]. Chartered Arbitrator. TECBAR accredited adjudicator. Panel member of Chartered Institute of Arbitrators. Member of London Court of International Arbitration.
Prof. Memberships: PNBA, TECBAR, LCLCBA, Society of Construction Law.
Career: Called 1974, FCI Arb 1988, QC 1993.
Publications: General Editor of 'Emden's Construction Law'.

BARTON, Charles QC
Albion Chambers (J.C.T. Barton QC), Bristol (0117) 927 2144
Recommended in Crime

BARWISE, Stephanie
Atkin Chambers (John Blackburn QC), London (020) 7404 0102
clerks@atkinchambers.law.co.uk
Recommended in Construction
Specialisation: General commercial including all aspects of the law relating to the construction and civil engineering industry both in litigation and arbitration. Experience includes major road and tunnel construction (e.g. Conway Crossing), ship refurbishment (Q.E.2), North Sea oil rig construction and Ladbroke Grove Rail Inquiry. Practice also involves professional negligence in general and in particular of architects, engineers and surveyors. A further area of specialisation is rights appurtenant to land and property: party wall disputes, easements including interference with rights of support, e.g. Midland Bank plc v. Bardgrove Property Services 60 BLR 1 (Court of Appeal 1992).
Career: Called to the Bar 1988. Joined Atkin Building in 1989.
Personal: Educated at Bolton School and Cambridge University (Downing College). Fluent in French and German.

BATE, David QC
Queen Elizabeth Building (Julian Bevan QC & Peter Whiteman QC), London (020) 7583 5766
Recommended in Crime
Specialisation: All forms of criminal work. Since 1990 he has concentrated mainly on defence work. Many of his cases involve organised crime; gangland murder, major drug importations, armed robbery, police corruption, blackmail etc. He has appeared in many notorious cases involving members of the Arif, Frazer, Raymond, Reeves, Blundell and Joyce families. Notable cases include R v Doran, R v Johnson (major drug importation), R v McAvoy (Brinks Mat bullion robbery) R v Relton (Brinks Mat money laundering), R v Cuthbert ('Operation Countryman' police corruption). He also specialises in Serious Fraud Office cases representing solicitors, accountants and businessmen charged with 'white collar' fraud of all kinds: corporate, revenue, VAT, etc.
Prof. Memberships: Criminal Bar Association
Career: Called 1969. Silk 1994. Recorder.
Personal: Hendon Grammar School. Manchester University (LL.B). Running, singing and drinking wine.

BATE, Stephen
5 Raymond Buildings (Patrick Milmo QC), London (020) 7242 2902
Recommended in Media & Entertainment

BATES, John H.
Old Square Chambers (John Hendy QC), London (020) 7269 0300
Recommended in Environment
Specialisation: An experienced environmental law practitioner in both civil and criminal courts and in statutory inquiries. Has particular expertise in water pollution and waste management cases and has been involved in a number of appeals against noise related abatement notices. In addition has acted in judicial review actions on environmental matters, advised in such areas as nature conservation, contaminated land, transfrontier shipment of waste, water abstraction licensing, land drainage disputes and fishing rights.
Career: Author: 'Water and Drainage Law', 'Marine Environment Law', 'UK Waste Law'.
Prof. Memberships: Chairman UK Environment Law Association 1991-1993.

BATTEN, Stephen QC
3 Raymond Buildings (Clive Nicholls QC), London (020) 7400 6400
chambers@threeraymond.demon.co.uk
Recommended in Crime, Fraud: Criminal
Specialisation: All forms of Crime: White Collar (First Defendant R v Blackspur Leasing; R Szjraber for SFO; R v. Judge Gee); Murder: the M25 Road Rage murder, First Defendant in private prosecution for murder of Stephen Lawrence; Dishonesty (Brinks Matt); Professional Tribunals: Health & Safety (Port Ramsgate Walkway Collapse)
Career: BA (Oxon). Call 1968. QC 1989. Recorder of the Crown Court.

BATTY, Christopher M.
St. Paul's Chambers (Nigel Sangster QC), Leeds (0113) 245 5866
Recommended in Crime

BAXENDALE, Presiley QC
Blackstone Chambers (P Baxendale QC and C Flint QC), London (020) 7583 1770
Recommended in Administrative & Public Law: General
Specialisation: Principal area of practice is public and administrative law. Also deals with local government, human rights, education, employment, financial services and general commercial law matters. Counsel to the Inquiry into Exports of Defence Equipment and Dual Use of Goods to Iraq.
Prof. Memberships: London Common Law and Commercial Bar Association, Administrative Law Bar Association.
Career: Called to the Bar and joined Hare Court in 1974. Appointed Junior Counsel to Crown (Common Law). Took silk in 1992.
Personal: Educated at Oxford University (MA). Governor of the LSE. Executive Committee: Justice.

BEAN, David QC
Matrix Chambers (Nicholas Blake QC), London (020) 7404 3447
Recommended in Employment
Specialisation: Principal area of practice is employment law. Also deals with commercial and general common law, administrative and education law. Major cases include R v Sheffield CC ex Hague (school admissions); Carver v Saudi Arabian Airlines (overseas employment);Ticehurst v British Telecommunications (industrial action – withdrawal of goodwill); Wandsworth LBC v NASUWT (teachers' boycott of school tests); Re Leyland DAF (employees' rights in insolvency); Clayton v Hereford & Worcester Fire Brigade (direct discrimination); London Underground v Edwards (indirect discrimination); South Bank University v Anyanwu ('aiding' discrimination); Meade v British Fuels (transfer of undertakings); Chief Constable of West Yorkshire v Khan (victimisation). Clients include several major employers and trade unions. Author of 'Enforcement of Injunctions and Undertakings' (Jordans 1991) and 'Injunctions' (FT Law & Tax 7th Edn. 1997). Editor 'Law Reform for All' (Blackstone 1996). Lectures regularly on injunctions and on employment law.
Prof. Memberships: Employment Law Bar Association (Chairman), Employment Lawyers' Association, London Common Law Bar Association, Administrative Law Bar Association, COMBAR.
Career: Called to the Bar 1976. Recorder 1996. QC 1997. Member Bar Council 1995 to date.

BEAR, Charles
11 King's Bench Walk (Eldred Tabachnik QC and James Goudie QC), London (020) 7632 8500
Recommended in Employment, Planning

BEAZLEY, Thomas
Blackstone Chambers (P Baxendale QC and C Flint QC), London (020) 7583 1770
clerks@blackstonechambers.com
Recommended in Commercial (Litigation)
Specialisation: Practice encompasses commercial law (including fraud, insurance and reinsurance), private international law and financial services. Commercial fraud work includes acting for and against insurers/reinsurers, acting in claims relating to takeovers and general international commercial and banking disputes and numerous jurisdictional disputes (eg Chairman Syndicates v New Cap Re & Others; Kleinwort Benson Ltd v Glasgow City Council [1996] 2 ALLE.R. 257 CA 1997 3WLR 923 HOL); Re: Polly Peck International PLC [1998] BCLC 185; Marinari v Lloyds Bank [1993] ALL ER (EC) 84 Ansbacher v Binks Stem 141 SJLB 151 CA. Financial services work includes acting for and against regulatory bodies (particularly SFA, IMRO, SIB and now FSA) and for clients under DTI investigations. Has acted for and against a number of foreign states in commercial litigation.
Prof. Memberships: COMBAR.
Career: Called to the Bar 1979 and since 1980 practised as a commercial barrister. Has acted as Arbitrator for the London Court of International Arbitration.
Personal: Working knowledge of Dutch, French and German.

BECK, James
2-4 Tudor Street (Richard Ferguson QC), London (020) 7797 7111
Recommended in Crime

BECKETT, Richard QC
3 Raymond Buildings (Clive Nicholls QC), London (020) 7400 6400
chambers@threeraymond.demon.co.uk
Recommended in Licensing
Specialisation: Licensing. Work includes preparation and advice relating to applications and objections in all licensing matters, such as liquor, gaming, betting and amusement centres, representing parties at all levels from local committees to Divisional Court. Advises on lotteries and other related activities. Clients include the Rank Organisation, Ladbrokes and JD Wetherspoon plc.
Career: Called to the Bar 1965 and joined present chambers 1967. Took silk 1988.

BEHRENS, James
Serle Court (Lord Neill of Bladen QC), London (020) 7242 6105
jbehrens@serlecourt.co.uk
Recommended in Church: Church of England
Specialisation: Chancery and commercial litigation, including commercial contracts, company law, property law, trusts and probate, insolvency, partnerships, computer law, and professional negligence. Recognised expert on church law, and experienced at alternative dispute resolution. Reported cases include Hanbury v Hanbury [1999] 2 FLR 255; TSB Bank plc v Marshall [1998] 3 EGLR. 100; Quinlan v Essex Hinge Co. Ltd [1997] BBC 53; Alliance & Leicester Building Society v Edgestop [1994] 2 EGLR 229; Re Marr (a bankrupt) [1990] Ch 773; and Bechal v Kitsford Holdings Ltd. [1989] 1 WLR 105.
Prof. Memberships: Chancery Bar Association; Commercial Bar Association; Association of Contentious Trust and Probate Specialists; Society for Computers and Law (council member); Ecclesiastical Law Society (member of general committee).
Career: Called to the Bar in 1979; member of the Bar Council 1992-1994; CEDR accredited mediator 1998; Fellow of the Chartered Institute of Arbitrators 1999.
Publications: 'Practical Church Management' (1998); 'Confirmation, Sacrament of Grace' (1995); 'Word Perfect for the Legal Profession' (1991). Contributor to 'Researching the Legal Web' by Nick Holmes and Delia Venables (1999), and 'Case Preparation' by the Inns of Court School of Law (1997).
Personal: Born 22 December 1956, educated Eton College; Trinity College Cambridge (MA); University of Wales College of Cardiff (LLM); married with two children. Lives in Kensington and Yorkshire.

BELOFF, Michael QC
4-5 Gray's Inn Square (Elizabeth Appleby QC & Duncan Ouseley QC), London (020) 7404 5252
Recommended in Administrative & Public Law: General, Employment, Human Rights (Civil Liberties), Immigration, Sport
Specialisation: Extremely wide ranging practice encompasses litigation and arbitration, covering a large number of areas including judicial review, commercial, EU law, employment, libel, insurance, sport, immigration, civil liberties and aviation. Has appeared in more than 350 reported cases in House of Lords, Privy Council, European Court of Justice, European Court of Human Rights and courts in Hong Kong, Singapore, Kuala Lumpur, Kuching, Bermuda,Trinidad, Brunei, Gibraltar and Belfast. In three major public inquiries: Crown Agents 1980-82; Brixton Disorders 1981 (Scarman Inquiry) and Sentosa Collision (Singapore, 1983). Chaired inquiry into academic plagiarism for University of Oxford 1987, and into "The Connection" for Carlton TV 1998. Women's Legal Defence Award 1991. Clients have included governments, local authorities, regulators, unions, national newspapers, television channels, banks, insurance companies, major ports, corporations, universities, statutory bodies, pressure groups, sporting organisations, and leading individuals and personalities from all fields of achievement including The Chief Rabbi, the Aga Khan, L. Ron Hubbard, Robert Maxwell, Ernest Saunders, The Al-Fayeds, Prime Ministers of three countries, Lennox Lewis, George Best, Sebastian Coe, and David Coulthard. Author of numerous articles for legal periodicals. Books include Butterworths 'The Sex Discrimination Act 1976'. Halsbury's Laws 'Time' (1999). Conference addresses include Sweet and Maxwell Conference on Judicial Review (Chairman 1990-91 and 1993-96), ECHR Salzburg (1988). IAAF Monte Carlo (1991) Singapore Law Academy (1992), Hong Kong Bar Association (1994), FCO-arranged 'Human Rights in the UK' (for Mayor of Moscow (1991). McCarthy – Tetrault – Vancouver (1996) Institute of Human Rights: Moscow (1996), Auckland (1997), Beijing (1997), Berlin (1997), Tokyo, University of Virginia, Tulane University, Commonwealth Law Conference (all 1999). Annual Lectures: ALBA (1994) Statute Law Society (1994) UC Dublin (1997), Lasok Exeter U (1998), Atkin (Reform) 1999. Consultant Editor: Judicial Review Bulletin.
Prof. Memberships: COMBAR, Administrative Law Bar Association (First Chairman, now Emeritus Chairman and Vice-President), Bar European Group. Environmental Law Foundation (Advisory Council). Honorary Fellow, Institute of Advanced Legal Studies.
Career: Called to the Bar 1967. QC 1981. Recorder of the Crown Court 1984-1995. Master of the Bench, Grays Inn 1988. Deputy High Court Judge (QBD) 1989. Nominated to sit in Divisional Court of QBD 1992. Joint Head of Chambers since 1993. Judge of the Court of Appeal of Guernsey and Jersey 1995. Member Court of Arbitration for Sport (Lausanne) 1995; CAS Ad Hoc Panel Atlanta Olympics 1996; Sydney Olympics 2000; Kuala Lumpa Commonwealth Games 1998. Ad Hoc Legal Advisor to British town, World Atheletics Championship Seville (1990). President Trinity College, Oxford 1996-
Personal: Born 18th April 1942. Educated at Dragon School, Oxford 1950-1954, Eton College 1954-1960 (King's Scholar and Captain of School 1960) and Magdalen College, Oxford 1960-1965 (BA History Class 1, 1963: Jurisprudence 1965, MA 1967). Moved motion which procured admission of women to full membership of the Oxford Union 1964. 5 marathons, including London marathon (twice). Honorary member of International Athletics Club. Member of Gridiron (Oxford), Vincents (Oxford) Achilles Reform Club (on Political Committee), FRSA, FICPD. Lives in London and Oxford. Married to Judith Beloff, Barrister JP, IS, ID.

BELTRAMI, Adrian
3 Verulam Buildings (Christopher Symons QC & John Jarvis QC), London (020) 7831 8441
Recommended in Banking, Commercial (Litigation)
Specialisation: All aspects of commercial litigation, in particular domestic and international banking, insolvency, commercial fraud and professional negligence. Cases include: BCCI v Price Waterhouse (1996, 1997 & 1998) (Banking Act, auditors' duties and liabilities), Box v Barclays Bank (1998) (Banking Act, constructive trusts), Electra v KPMG (1999) (auditors' duty of care), Middle Temple v Lloyds Bank (1999) (cheque collection). Principal contributor to Banking Litigation (1999).
Prof. Memberships: COMBAR.
Career: Called to the Bar 1989. Admitted to the Bar of the Cayman Islands on several individual cases.
Personal: Stonyhurst, Downing College, Cambridge and Harvard Law School. MA (1st class) LLM. Born 8 November 1964. Lives in London. Married with one son and one daughter.

BENNETT, Martyn
Oriel Chambers (Andrew T. Sander), Liverpool (0151) 236 7191/ 236 4321
Recommended in Family/Matrimonial

BENNETT-JENKINS, Sallie
1 Hare Court (Stephen Kramer QC), London (020) 7353 5324
Recommended in Crime

BENSON, Jeremy
1 Hare Court (Stephen Kramer QC), London (020) 7353 5324
Recommended in Crime

BENSON, John
14 Castle Street (Andrew Edis QC), Liverpool (0151) 236 4421
101561.623@compuserve.com
Recommended in Employment
Specialisation: Specialist practitioner in all aspects of employment law inc interlocutory relief, restrictive covenants, personal injuries, clinical negligence.
Prof. Memberships: Employment Law Bar Association, Personal Injuries Bar Association. Medical Law Association. Northern Circuit.
Career: LL.B (Hons). Called to the Bar in 1978 on the Northern Circuit. Part-time chairman of employment tribunals 1995. Assistant Recorder 1998.
Personal: Age 44.

BERKSON, Simon
Exchange Chambers (William Waldron QC), Liverpool (0151) 236 7747
Recommended in Crime

BERLIN, Barry
St. Ive's Chambers (Edward Coke), Birmingham (0121) 236 0863
barry@berlin.fsnet.co.uk
Recommended in Consumer
Specialisation: Trading standards, health and safety at work, environmental health, food safety, Formula One Autotraders v Birmingham City Council (1998) 163 JP 234, Davenport v Walsall MBC (1996) 28 HLR 754, Sterling Homes v Birmingham CC (1996) L.R. 121, Toys R Us v Gloustershire CC (1994) 158 JP 338, Whirlpool (UK) Ltd & Magnet Ltd v Gloustershire CC (1993) 259 S.P. 123, R v Newcastle Upon Tyne M.C. ox P. Poundstretcher Ltd (1998) co/3282/97 D.C.
Prof. Memberships: Crim Bar Ass., Midland and Oxford circuit.
Career: BSc. Hons (1980). Call 1981 Gray's Inn. Provincial Treasury Council (civil) appointed to att gov list in1995.
Personal: Hon. Lecturer MSc environmental health. Birmingham University. Lecture to local authorities. Enjoy racing, theatre.

BERRAGAN, Neil
Merchant Chambers (David Berkley QC), Manchester (0161) 839 7070
Recommended in Chancery, Commercial (Litigation)
Specialisation: Commercial and property litigation; general commercial disputes, banking, corporate insolvency, and insurance related professional indemnity work; shareholder disputes, directors disqualification.
Career: Educated Pocklington School, York and Pembroke College, Oxford. Call 1982.
Personal: Lives in Alderley Edge. Married, 3 children & vasectomy. Travels in Ireland.

BERRY, Simon QC
9 Old Square (Michael Driscoll QC), London (020) 7405 4682
Recommended in Commercial Chancery, Property Litigation
Specialisation: Property and commercial litigation.
Prof. Memberships: Chancery Bar Association, Pro-

fessional Negligence Bar Association.
Career: Called to Bar 1977. Silk 1990. Recorder 2000.

BERRY, Steven
Essex Court Chambers (Gordon Pollock QC), London (020) 7813 8000
Recommended in Insurance, Shipping
Specialisation: Broad based practice, in particular the associated fields of insurance and reinsurance, shipping, international banking, international sale of goods and arbitration.
Career: Exeter College, Oxford BA (Jurisprudence) (First Class Hons); BCL (First Class Hons) 1983. Astbury Scholar, Middle Temple. Eldon Law Scholar. Called to the Bar 1984.
Personal: Born 1961.

BEVAN, John QC
2 Harcourt Buildings, Atkinson Bevan Chambers (Nicholas Atkinson QC & John Bevan QC), London (020) 7353 2112
Recommended in Crime
Specialisation: General criminal law, emphasis on high-profile serious cases. Prosecutions include: Child Abuse – Jasmine Beckford, Heidi Koseda; Terrorism – Sidhu and others (1994: 98 Criminal Appeal Reports 59); Hayes and Taylor (Harrods bombing); Patrick Kelly; McArdle and McKinley (South Quay bombing 1996); Murder – Kenneth Erskine (Stockwell Strangler), Morss and Tyler (Child Victim Daniel Handley), Miah and others (Victim, Richard Everitt), Chindamo (Headmaster, Philip Lawrence), Eades and others (Police Sergeant Robertson); Also – McLean (Notting Hill Rapist), Evans, Whitby and Burrell (death of illegal immigrant, Joy Gardner); Ricky Reel inquest.
Prof. Memberships: Criminal Bar Association. South-Eastern Circuit.
Career: Called 1970. Treasury Counsel 1983-1997. Took Silk 1997.

BEVAN, Julian QC
Queen Elizabeth Building (Julian Bevan QC & Peter Whiteman QC), London (020) 7583 5766
Recommended in Crime, Fraud: Criminal
Specialisation: High profile general crime with emphasis on white collar fraud. Involved in Maxwell case; Gokal; Sanction busting cases. More recently M25 Murder Appeal and advised on corporate manslaughter.
Career: Former 1st Senior Treasury Counsel.

BICKERDIKE, Roger
9 Woodhouse Square (John Morris Collins), Leeds (0113) 245 1986
Recommended in Family/Matrimonial
Specialisation: Highly noted junior specialising in family/ matrimonial work with particular emphasis on public law children cases and ancillary relief work. Considerable experience in appellate work both in the High Court and in the Court of Appeal. Involved in numerous reported cases, some of them landmark. Busy matrimonial practice, with an increasing emphasis on cases where there are substantial assets.
Prof. Memberships: Member of the Family Bar Association, and Association of Lawyers for Children.
Career: Called to the Bar in 1986.

BIDDER, Neil QC
33 Park Place (John Charles Rees QC), Cardiff (029) 2023 3313
Recommended in Personal Injury
Specialisation: Personal Injury, Criminal Law.
Prof. Memberships: Personal Injury Bar Association, Criminal Bar Association.
Career: M.A (Cantab), LLM (Dalhousie University Canada). Recorder since 1994. Queen's Counsel since 1998. Wales and Chester Circuit Representative of Personal Injury Bar Association. Member of Bar Council CFA Panel.

BIRCH, Elizabeth
3 Verulam Buildings (Christopher Symons QC & John Jarvis QC), London (020) 7831 8441 clerks@3verulam.co.uk
Recommended in Alternative Dispute Resolution
Specialisation: Specialist in international and domestic commercial arbitration, mediation, commercial and maritime law including banking and financial services, commodities, conflict of laws and disputes as to jurisdiction, information technology (IT), injunctions (anti-suit, mareva and other), insurance (marine, non-marine and Lloyd's Market), international sale of goods, joint ventures, oil and gas, shipping, transportation and all types of contractual and professional disputes. Tribunal emphasis: Commercial Court, Admiralty Court and Arbitration. Appears as advocate and receives appointments to sit as arbitrator and mediator in general commercial and shipping disputes. Arbitration tribunals include LMAA, LMC, LCIA, ICC, ACI and ad hoc. Sat as arbitrator in numerous Lloyd's market disputes determining claims by Names against Members' Agents and Managing Agents. Founder and Director of ACI (Arbitration – a Commercial Initiative), an arbitration group offering lawyer arbitrators to determine business and professional disputes in fields such as banking, insurance and financial services. The Group also offers mediation and other forms of ADR. Sits on the Court of Appeal Panel of mediators and has successfully mediated a substantial number of commercial disputes.
Prof. Memberships: Fellow of the Chartered Institute of Arbitrators (FCIArb), Qualified Mediator (QDR) accredited by the Centre for Dispute Resolution (CEDR) and The Academy of Experts. Appointed to the Panels of the Lloyd's Arbitration Schemes (LAS) Tiers 1 and 2 from 1992 to date. On the ACI Panel of Arbitrators and on the list of supporting members of LMAA available to sit as arbitrator and mediator. Panel member of FEPA Representative Committee (receives appointments to sit as Legal Chairman in appeals against decisions by MAFF in relation to licenses to deposit articles or substances in the sea or under the seabed). Member of the Commercial Court Working Party chaired by Mr Justice Colman which considers ADR and its role in the Commercial Court, leading to the existing Commercial Court Practice Directive on ADR. Member of the Commercial Bar Association (COMBAR) – secretary 1993 to 1996. Member of the London Common Law and Commercial Bar Association (LCLCBA). Supporting member of the London Maritime Arbitrators' Association (LMAA).
Career: Called to Gray's Inn 1978; joined 3 Essex Court in 1980; the Chambers moved in 1994 becoming known as 20 Essex Street; joined 3 Verulam Buildings in 1998.

BIRD, Simon
2-3 Gray's Inn Square (Anthony Scrivener QC), London (020) 7242 4986
Recommended in Planning
Specialisation: A wide range of planning, local government and environmental work. Planning work includes inquiries throughout the Country dealing with housing, retail, leisure, waste, industrial, commercial, hospital and other developments. Major inquiry work includes the Cambridge Hinxton Hall and Arbury Park Inquiries and many development plan inquiries, the most recent being the Bedford Borough Local Plan Inquiry. Environmental and local government work includes Court and advisory covering all aspects of the work of public bodies. A particular specialism is waste management licensing.
Prof. Memberships: Planning and Environment Bar Association; South Eastern Circuit; United Kingdom Environmental Law Association.
Career: Called to the Bar in 1987.
Personal: University of Reading.

BIRKETT, Peter QC
18 St. John Street (Jonathan Foster QC), Manchester (0161) 278 1800
Recommended in Crime
Specialisation: Criminal Law, both prosecution and defence. Has been involved in many high profile and notable trials on circuit over the past 10 years. If he has a specialisation it is in the field of commercial fraud.
Prof. Memberships: Criminal Bar Association. Leader of the Northern Circuit 1999-.
Career: Called 1972. Q.C. 1989. Recorder of the Crown Court 1989. Acting barrister (Isle of Man) Governing member of the Inns of Court Advocacy Training Committee.
Personal: Married, 2 sons, hobbies include sport, political biography, music (keyboard player in 'The Prestons'). Education: Sedbergh School, Yorkshire. University of Leicester LL.B. Master of the Bench (Inner Temple 1996 -).

BIRSS, Colin
Three New Square (David E.M. Young QC), London (020) 7405 1111 colinbirss@compuserve.com
Recommended in Information Technology, Intellectual Property
Specialisation: Intellectual property, Information Technology. Cases before United Kingdom courts include: Merrell Dow v Norton (terfenadine – Patents Court, CA and HL), Harrods v Harrodian School (passing off – High Court and CA), Kirin – Amgen v Boehringer Mannheim (erythropoietin – Patents Court and CA), Fujitsu (computer software patent – CA), PCME v Goyen (electronics – Patents Court) NAD Electronics v NAD Computer Systems (trade mark and passing off – High Court). Chocosuisse v Cadbury (passing off – High Court and CA) Cases before the European Patent Office include: Berlex Biosciences (E Coli inclusion bodies), Net 1 Corp. (smart cards), G4/97 (straw man oppositions).
Career: Called 1990; joined chambers 1991.
Personal: Educated at Downing College, Cambridge 1983-1986 (MA 1st Class Natural Sciences); City University 1988-1989 (Dip Law). Born 28th December 1964.

BIRTLES, William
Old Square Chambers (John Hendy QC), London (020) 7269 0334 birtles@oldsquarechambers.co.uk
Recommended in Environment
Specialisation: Principal areas of practice are environmental, planning and local government law. Has had considerable experience in both civil and criminal aspects of pollution claims including land contamination (arising from oil, toxic waste and industrial waste disposal), water (e.g. Barry Docks, Cardiff), air (particularly industrial smells and noise). Major inquiries include the Sizewell B Nuclear Power Station Inquiry (1984-1986), the second Part I Environmental Protection Act Inquiry (Cumbria 1994), the Westminster Council District Audit Inquiry (1994-1995) and various internal inquiries for local authorities.
Prof. Memberships: Planning and Local Government Bar Association; Administrative Law Bar Association; Council Member United Kingdom Environmental Law Association; Environmental Law Foundation. Senior Associate Member St. Antony's College Oxford.
Career: Academic lawyer 1968-1974. Called to the Bar 1970. Joined Old Square Chambers 1986. Recorder 1993. Publications etc: Co-author of 'Planning and Environmental Law' (Longman 1994 with Richard Stein); co-author of 'Local Government Finance Law' (Butterworths 2000 with Anna Forge and Tony Child). Numerous articles and chapters in books. Frequent speaker at legal conferences.

BLACK, John QC
18 Red Lion Court (Anthony Arlidge QC), London (020) 7520 6000
Recommended in Crime
Specialisation: Serious crime.
Career: An extensive defence practice that has embraced such notorious trials as Brinks-Mats and Beck.
Personal: Prosecution work embraces fraud, drugs, corruption and serious sexual offences.

BLACKBURN, John QC
Atkin Chambers (John Blackburn QC), London (020) 7404 0102
clerks@atkinchambers.law.co.uk
Recommended in Arbitration (International), Construction
Specialisation: In the fields of building and civil engineering disputes, professional negligence actions involving contractors and engineers and arbitration, including international arbitration. Has conducted several heavy disputes under rules of the International Chamber of Commerce in Paris. Has been appointed Arbitrator in disputes arising out of construction contracts under the International Chamber of Commerce, also acts as arbitrator over disputes arising in England. Has been admitted to the bar in Hong Kong and Singapore to conduct cases arising out of building and civil engineering contracts. Construction Law Experience has involved him in advising upon, presenting and defending all kinds of building and civil engineering claims worldwide. Advises and acts for numerous Public Corporations. Advises on and drafts various kinds of building and different types of engineering contracts. Work undertaken generally involves substantial projects involving sophisticated plan, and building and engineering structures including tunnels, dams and hydro-electric schemes.
Career: Called to the Bar 1969. Took silk 1984.

BLACKETT-ORD, Mark
5 Stone Buildings (Henry Harrod), London (020) 7242 6201
Recommended in Partnership
Specialisation: Well-known for his experience in advice and litigation in Chancery matters especially those concerning partnerships and other quasi-corporate bodies, from unincorporated associations to family trusts (Murphy v Murphy [1999] 1 WLR 1P2) and bodies alleged to be carrying on the business of insurance (Re a company No. 007816 of 1994) (1997) 2 BCLC 685. Has appeared in cases at all levels to the House of Lords and European Court (Webb v Webb (1994) QB 696). Co-edited the original 4th edition of 'Partnership' in Halsbury Laws of England, and wrote the major new book 'Partnership' (Butterworths, 1997).

BLACKWELL, Kate
Lincoln House Chambers (Mukhtar Hussain QC), Manchester (0161) 832 5701
Recommended in Crime

BLAIR, Bruce QC
1 Mitre Court Buildings (Bruce Blair QC), London (020) 7797 7070
Recommended in Family: Matrimonial Finance

BLAIR, William QC
3 Verulam Buildings (Christopher Symons QC & John Jarvis QC), London (020) 7831 8441
clerks@3verulam.co.uk
Recommended in Banking, Financial Services
Specialisation: Commercial work, domestic and international banking, arbitration, business law, commercial fraud, company law, financial services, international trade, insolvency, private international law. Cases include: Esal v Oriental Credit 1985; LAFB v Bankers Trust 1988; LAFB v Manufacturers Hanover 1989; IE Contractors v Lloyds Bank 1990; Barclays Bank v O'Brien 1993; Macmillan v Bishopsgate 1994; Polly Peck v Citibank 1994; TSB v Camfield 1995; Macmillan v Bishopsgate 1996; Wahda Bank v Arab Bank 1998; MCC Proceeds v Bishopsgate 1998, Middle Temple v Lloyds 1999. Struggles v. Lloyds Bank
Career: Called to the Bar 1972, Silk 1994. Visiting professor of law (London School of Economics), member of the International Monetary Law committee of the International Law Association, member of FLP working party on Single European Currency, recorder. Co-editor 'Encyclopaedia of Banking Law', co-author 'Banking and Financial Services Regulation' (2nd Ed) 1998, editor 'Banks and Remedies' (2nd Ed) 1999.

BLAKE, Nicholas QC
Matrix Chambers (Nicholas Blake QC), London (020) 7404 3447
Recommended in Administrative & Public Law: General, Human Rights (Civil Liberties), Immigration
Specialisation: Practises in the field of public and adminstrative law with particular emphasis on immigration and asylum and human rights issues. Recent cases:- Asylum and immigration: ex p T (1996); ex p Adan (1998); ex p Islam and Shah (1999) (HL). Public law: ex p JCWI and B (CA) (1996); ex p Avraam (1999) (HL); ex p Castelli and Garcia (1997) (CA); ex p Salem (1999) (HL); ex p A,D,G (CA) (1999). Actions for damages: Reeves (HL) (1999); Oluto (1997) (CA) W v Home Office (1998) (CA); ECJ: Surinder Singh (1992); Radiom (1997), Roque v Jersey (1998). ECHR: Chahal (1996); XYZ (1997), D v UK (1997). Crime: Judith Ward (CA); ex p Hickey and Davis (DC). Privy Council: Guerra v Trinidad (1995); Thomas and Hilaire v Trinidad (1999).
Prof. Memberships: ALBA, ILPA (Chair 1993-1997), JUSTICE Member of Council (1996-date).
Career: Called MT 1974, member of present chambers since 1975; QC (1994) Assistant Recorder (1999). Principal Publications: Macdonald and Blake 'Immigration Law and Practice' 3rd, 4th editions and Supplement.
Personal: Cranleigh School, Magdalene College, Cambridge. Married with 3 children.

BLANCHARD, Claire
Essex Court Chambers (Gordon Pollock QC), London (020) 7813 8000
Recommended in Commercial (Litigation), Employment, Shipping
Specialisation: Broad-based commercial practice. In particular shipping, insurance, banking, conflicts and employment.
Career: Liverpool Polytechnic LLB (Hons) 1991. Inns of Court School of Law. Called to the Bar 1992.
Personal: Born 1969.

BLAXLAND, Henry
Two Garden Court (I. Macdonald QC & O.Davies QC), London (020) 7353 1633
Recommended in Crime, Human Rights (Civil Liberties)

BLEASDALE, Paul
5 Fountain Court (Anthony Barker QC), Birmingham (0121) 606 0500
Recommended in Personal Injury
Specialisation: Personal Injury Litigation; Claimants and Defendants. In particular industrial disease claims and also medical negligence. Planning and Environment; Developers and Local Authorities. Appeals and Local Plan, UDP and Compulsory Purchase Inquiries.
Prof. Memberships: Personal Injuries Bar Association, Planning Environment Bar Association.
Career: London University, Recorder of the Crown Court, Deputy Chairman of the Agricultural Lands Tribunal.

BLOCH, Michael QC
Wilberforce Chambers (Edward Nugee QC), London (020) 7306 0102
Recommended in Banking, Intellectual Property
Specialisation: Principal areas of practice are general commercial, intellectual property, banking and arbitration. Professional clients include many City law firms.
Prof. Memberships: Chancery Bar Association, Commercial Bar Association
Career: Called to the Bar in 1979. At 1 Brick Court 1979-87. Joined *Essex Court* in 1987 and *Wilberforce Chambers* in 2000.
Personal: Educated at Bedales School and the universities of Cambridge (MA) and East Anglia (M Phil). Trustee of Childline and Governor of Bedales School. Born 18th October 1951. Lives in London.

BLOCH, Selwyn QC
Littleton Chambers (Michel Kallipetis QC), London (020) 7797 8600
Recommended in Employment, Information Technology

BLOCK, Neil
39 Essex Street (Nigel Pleming QC), London (020) 7832 1111
Recommended in Personal Injury
Specialisation: A contract and tort based practice. Insurance (including policy avoidance/ fraud and material loss claims e.g McGregor v Prudential Assurance Co 1998 Lloyds). Personal injury (including sporting cases eg. Smolden v Whitworth & Nolan, O'Neill v Wimbledon & Fashanu, Watson v British Boxing Board of Control), catastrophic injury claims, medical negligence (in particular paediatric brain damage), professional negligence (including solicitors, accountants, surveyors and valuers, architects, stockbrokers and insurance brokers) and product liability.
Prof. Memberships: Professional Negligence Bar Association, Personal Injury Bar Association, London Common Law and Commercial Bar Association, Bar Sports Law Group.
Career: Called to the Bar in 1980.
Personal: B.A. (Hons), LLM (Exon).

BLOHM, Leslie
St John's Chambers (Christopher Sharp QC), Bristol (0117) 921 3456
clerks@stjohnschambers.co.uk; chambers@199strand.co.uk
Recommended in Chancery, Commercial (Litigation), Property Litigation
Specialisation: Commercial landlord and tenant; real property; equity and trusts. Counsel for respondent in Bettison v Langton & Penter [2000] Ch.54 (CA) on profits ‡ prendre and rights of common; Brown v Gloucester City Council [1998] 1 EGLR 95 (CA) on construction of rent review clauses.
Prof. Memberships: Chancery Bar Association, Bristol and Cardiff Chancery Bar Association.
Career: Christ's Hospital Horsham & Keble College, Oxford; BA 1981. Lincoln's Inn 1982. Hardwicke & Jenkins scholar of Lincoln's Inn 1981-1982. St John's Chambers Bristol 1984. Head of Chancery Department 1992.
Personal: Family, cycling and chess.

BLUNT, Oliver QC
Furnival Chambers (Andrew Mitchell QC), London (020) 7405 3232
Recommended in Crime
Specialisation: Entirely defence-based practice with a substantial emphasis on murder, terrorism, fraud & drugs cases. Murder & Violent Crime: represented such clients as John Taft ("Beauty in the Bath" murder trial, Liverpool Crown Court, 1999), Maria Hnautik (murder, Norwich CC, 1996), Ngarimu (female contract killer, CCC, 1995), Syd Owen ('Ricky' of 'Easten-

ders', wounding, Snaresbrook CC, 1995), Michael Sams (kidnapping, blackmail, murder, Nottingham CC, 1993), also the trial and successful appeal of the 'Chelsea Headhunters' (Regina v Drake and Others). Sexual Crime: including high profile cases such as Richard Baker (DJ Rapist, CCC, 1999). Drugs: represented such clients as Jason Fitzgibbon (Birmingham CC, 2000), Thomas Adams and Others (Woolwich CC, 1998). Successfully defended the first defendant in a £150 million cocaine importation (Regina v Hillier and Others, 1993). Terrorism: has acted on behalf of the Iranian Embassy and represented two members of the Consular Staff in separate terrorist trials at the CCC (Tabari Abcou/Fouladi). Appeared for the second defendant in Regina v Canging and Lamb (IRA trial, CC, 1993). Currently instructed in Stars Ted hijacking case. Fraud: including William Casey, acquitted in a multi-million pound arson/insurance fraud, 1997.
Prof. Memberships: SE Circuit. Criminal Bar Association.
Career: Called to Bar 1974. Queen's Counsel 1994. Recorder 1995.
Personal: Born 8/3/51. Married with four children. Member of Roehampton Club, Rosslyn Park Rugby Club and Barnes Cricket Club.

BOMPAS, Anthony George QC
4 Stone Buildings (Philip Heslop QC), London (020) 7242 5524
Recommended in Commercial Chancery, Company, Financial Services, Insolvency/Corporate Recovery
Specialisation: Principal area of practice is company law (all aspects, including minority shareholders proceedings and insolvency) and financial services. Other main area of practice is professional negligence work. Has been instructed in many of the major, widely publicised, company matters in recent years, including the Guinness affair, the Blue Arrow, the Barlow Clowes, the Brent Walker and the BCCI affairs. Author of 'Investigations by the DTI' in Tolley's 'Company Law' (3rd Ed.).
Prof. Memberships: Chancery Bar Association, Insolvency Lawyers' Association and Commercial Bar Association (COMBAR). Called to the Bar of the British Virgin Islands and, for specific cases, to the Bar of Trinidad and Tobago.
Career: Called to the Bar 1975 and joined present chambers in 1976. Junior Counsel to the DTI 1989-94. Took Silk in 1994.
Personal: Educated at Merchant Taylors' School, Northwood 1964-1969 and Oriel College, Oxford 1970-1974. Born 6th November 1951.

BOOTH, Alan
Deans Court Chambers (H.K. Goddard QC), Manchester (0161) 214 6000 booth@deanscourt.co.uk
Recommended in Family/Matrimonial
Specialisation: Ancillary relief and professional negligence arising out of ancillary relief.
Prof. Memberships: FLBA, PNBA.
Career: Bolton School (Boy's Division). Selwyn College Cambridge.
Personal: Married, 2 children.

BOOTH, Cherie QC
Matrix Chambers (Nicholas Blake QC), London (020) 7404 3447
Recommended in Administrative & Public Law: General, Employment
Specialisation: Specialist in all aspects of employment law and administrative and public law. Notable public law cases Includes E v. Dorset County Council and Others [1995]; Phelps v. LB of Hillingdon [1998] (dyslexia); White and Others v. Ealing LBC (SEN); R v. Law Society ex parte Dalton [1999]. B v Chief Constable of Avon and Somerset (5/4/2000 Human Rights). Notable employment cases are Grant v SW Trains (sexual orientation discrimination). Preston v. Wolverhampton NHS Trusts ECJ 2000; Barry v. Midland Bank HL 22/77/99; BCCI v. Ali 1999 and Wilson v. St. Helens Borough Council [1997] IRLR 505; Pearce v Governing Body of Mayfield School (April 2000).

BOOTH, Michael QC
40 King St (Philip Raynor QC), Manchester (0161) 832 9082
Recommended in Chancery, Commercial (Litigation), Insolvency/Corporate Recovery
Specialisation: Chancery and commercial, including company, insolvency, property, computer related litigation (hardware and software including copyright ownership), commercial contracts, banking, professional negligence and competition aspects relating to the above.
Career: Scholarship to Manchester Grammar School. Open scholarship to Trinity College, Cambridge. President Cambridge Union Society, Michaelmas 1979. Appointed Queen's Counsel 1999.
Personal: Married, three young children. Hobbies include walking, swimming, tennis, reading (literature and history), theatre, wine and antiques. Avid football fan.

BORRELLI, Michael QC
1 Middle Temple Lane (Colin Dines & Andrew Trollope QC), London (020) 7583 0659 (12 lines)
Recommended in Crime

BOSWELL, Lindsay QC
4 Pump Court (Bruce Mauleverer QC), London (020) 7353 2656
Recommended in Professional Negligence
Specialisation: Specialises in professional negligence (solicitors, accountants, insurance brokers, architects, surveyors, valuers, local authorities), construction, aviation, administrative law and art litigation.
Prof. Memberships: PNBA, COMBAR, ELBA, LCLCBA, ORBA.
Career: BSc (London) Econ (Hons) Economics and Social Anthropology. Diploma in Law (City University).
Personal: Aviation Club of the UK.

BOSWOOD, Anthony QC
Fountain Court (Anthony Boswood QC), London (020) 7583 3335
Recommended in Banking, Civil Fraud, Commercial (Litigation), Energy & Natural Resources, Insurance

BOTHROYD, Shirley
Littleton Chambers (Michel Kallipetis QC), London (020) 7797 8600
Recommended inEmployment
Specialisation: Principal areas of practice: Employment law: appearing in employment tribunals & employment appeal. Tribunal: unfair dismissal, sex & race discimination. High Court: restrictive covenants - all injunctive matters. General commercial & contract, commercial fraud. Cited as a Leading Employment Junior in Chambers & Partners Directory. Frequently instructed in sensitive race & discrimination cases. Has reputation for being a tough litigator, instructed by leading employment solicitors.
Prof. Memberships: COMBAR, ELBAR, South Eastern Circuit, Counsel for Inland Revenue.
Career: Called to the Bar and joined present chambers in 1982.
Personal: Born 23rd July 1958.

BOULDING, Philip QC
Keating Chambers (Richard Fernyhough QC), London (020) 7544 2600
Recommended in Construction
Specialisation: Construction and civil engineering law, including arbitration and professional negligence.
Career: Qualified 1979; Gray's Inn; Queen's Counsel 1996. Admitted to Hong Kong Bar 1997.
Personal: Downing College, Cambridge (1976) BA Law 1st class Hons, (1977) postgraduate LLB (now LLM), 1979 MA; 1976 elected to title of Scholar of Downing College, 1976 Harris Scholar, 1976 Pilley Scholar, 1977 Senior Harris Scholar, 1976 Rebecca Flowers Squire Scholar. Gray's Inn Holker Entrance Award (1978) and Gray's Inn Senior Holker Award (1979). Born 1954. Clients in this field include local authorities, major PLCs, international joint ventures, governments and professionals from all the construction and engineering disciplines. Current instructions involve many of the largest Hong Kong airport core contracts, as well as nuclear processing plants and infrastructure projects.

BOURNE, Ian
3 Temple Gardens (Jonathan Goldberg QC), London (020) 7583 1155
Recommended in Crime

BOURNE-ARTON, Simon QC
Park Court Chambers (James Stewart QC Robert Smith QC), Leeds (0113) 243 3277
Recommended in Crime

BOWDERY, Martin QC
Atkin Chambers (John Blackburn QC), London (020) 7404 0102
Recommended in Construction, Professional Negligence

BOWERS, John QC
Littleton Chambers (Michel Kallipetis QC), London (020) 7797 8600 FranksBower@compuserve.com
Recommended in Employment
Specialisation: Employment law, pensions, judicial review, discrimination. Recent cases have included Associated British Ports v TGWU (injunctions to prevent national dock strike); McLaren v Home Office (role of judicial review in employment); News Group Newspapers Ltd v SOGAT and Others ("the Wapping cases"); Porter & Nanayakkara v Queens Medical Centre (dismissal of Consultant Paediatricians following Allitt murders); Saatchi & Saatchi plc v M. Saatchi and C. Saatchi and Others (garden leave case); Sibson v UK (application to European Court of Human Rights on remedies for disadvantages caused to employees who are not members of trade unions in "closed shops"). South v UK (gay servicemen's case in European Court of Human Rights). Gibson v Royal Bank of Yorkshire Council (direct effect of Working Time Directive).
Prof. Memberships: Vice chair of ELBA, ALBA, ELA. Home Office Task Force on Human Rights, Bar Council Race Relations Committee. Legal Adviser, Public Concern at Work, Coordination of Workplace Mediation Services.
Publications: Author of many publications including 'Bowers on Employment Law', 'Textbook of Labour Law', 'Transfer of Undertakings', 'Employment Tribunal Practice', 'The Employment Law Manual' (chapter on Tribunals) and 'Basic Procedure in Courts and Tribunals'. Atkins Court Form, (Employment).

BOWES, Michael
2 King's Bench Walk (Anthony Donne QC), London (020) 7353 1746
Recommended in Fraud: Criminal

BOWRON, Margaret
1 Crown Office Row (Robert Seabrook QC), London (020) 7797 7500
Recommended in Clinical Negligence

BOWSHER, Michael
Keating Chambers (Richard Fernyhough QC), London (020) 7544 2600
mbowsher@keatingchambers.com
Recommended in Construction
Specialisation: Construction and computer law; international arbitration; European law, especially procurement and competition; environmental law.
Career: Qualified 1985; Middle Temple; tenant *Keating Chambers* 1986; associate, based full-time in offices of *Cleary, Gottlieb, Steen & Hamilton* in Brussels 1988-1992; member of editorial team 'Keating on Building Contracts'; Member of the Northern Ireland Bar. Involved in numerous procurement disputes, notably as junior counsel for the successful claimant in Harmon v House of Commons. Wide experience of international arbitration involving a variety of foreign laws. Most of his foreign arbitration experience has been for major non-UK contractors. Also active in a broad range of construction and technology matters in court, adjudication and arbitration, including judicial review and environmental disputes.
Personal: Born 1963; Radley College; Brasenose College, Oxford (1984 BA Hons).

BOYCE, William
Queen Elizabeth Building (Julian Bevan QC & Peter Whiteman QC), London (020) 7583 5766
Recommended in Crime, Fraud: Criminal
Specialisation: Crime and linked regulatory and disciplinary proceedings – especially high profile, grave and complex criminal matters from homicide to serious fraud.
Prof. Memberships: Criminal Bar Assocation.
Career: Called to the Bar in 1976. Senior Treasury Counsel at the Central Criminal Court. Recorder.

BOYD, Stephen
29 Bedford Row Chambers (Peter Ralls QC), London (020) 7404 1044
Recommended in Sport
Specialisation: Commercial, property and personal injury. Acted for former world middle weight boxing champion.
Prof. Memberships: Bar Sports Law Group. British Association for Sport and Law. PNBA. PIBA.
Career: Worked for international trading companies before commencing practice at the Bar: two and a half years in Hong Kong and six months in South Africa.
Personal: Minchenden Grammar School, London N14. B.Sc (Hons) Russian, Swedish & Law, University of Surrey. Kung Fu, Pilates, Films. Married with children aged eight, six and four.

BOYD, Stewart QC
Essex Court Chambers (Gordon Pollock QC), London (020) 7813 8000
Recommended in Arbitration (International)
Specialisation: Arbitration, banking, commodity contracts, company law and insolvency, competition and restrictive practices, construction, copyright, EEC law, employment, financial services, industrial relations, insurance and reinsurance, oil and gas, private international law, shipping and aviation. Has been appointed an arbitrator in numerous international commercial disputes in many fields, such as advertising, banking, commercial agency, computer software, construction, electricity generation and transmission, insurance and reinsurance, intellectual property, oil and gas, shipping.
Career: Trinity College, Cambridge: MA. Called to the Bar 1967. Queen's Counsel 1981.
Personal: Born 1943.

BOYLE, Alan QC
Serle Court (Lord Neill of Bladen QC), London (020) 7242 6105
Recommended in Commercial Chancery, Company, Insolvency/Corporate Recovery
Specialisation: Commercial and chancery litigation, financial services and entertainment. Case during the last year: Thyssen-Bornemisza v Thyssen-Bornemisza Trust-litigation in Bermuda; (undue influence).
Prof. Memberships: Chancery Bar Association, Commerical Bar Association. Deputy High Court Judge. Editor and contributor, The Practice and Procedure of the Companies Court, Lloyds of London Press.
Career: Royal Shrewsbury School, St Catherine's College Oxford (MA). Called to the Bar 1972. Silk 1991.
Personal: Married, two daughters.

BRADLEY, R.
Oriel Chambers (Andrew T. Sander), Liverpool (0151) 236 7191/ 236 4321
Recommended in Employment

BRADLEY, Sally QC
Broad Chare Chambers (Eric A Elliott), Newcastle upon Tyne (0191) 232 0541
Recommended in Family/Matrimonial

BRAITHWAITE, Bill QC
Exchange Chambers (William Waldron QC), Liverpool (0151) 236 7747
Recommended in Personal Injury

BRAMWELL, Richard QC
3 Temple Gardens Tax Chambers (Richard Bramwell QC), London (020) 7353 7884
Recommended in Tax
Specialisation: Principal areas of practice are corporate and personal tax planning and tax disputes. Recent litigation: (House of Lords) Redrow Group v. Customs, (High Court) – tax treatment of prepayments held by finance lessor on a discontinuance; (Special Commissioners) – application of section 703 to a POS from a pension fund. Recent advisory work: finance leasing of Millennium projects; value-shifting and disposals under section 179(3); corporate film leasing partnerships; investment by means of "Relevant Discounted Securities"; Sch. E consequences of holiday flights in company aircraft; complex private company demergers.
Career: Took silk in 1989.
Publications: Co-author of 'Taxation of Companies and Company Reconstructions' (7th Edition, 1998).

BRAND, Simon
Coleridge Chambers (Simon D. Brand), Birmingham (0121) 233 8500
Recommended in Crime

BRANNIGAN, Sean
4 Pump Court (Bruce Mauleverer QC), London (020) 7353 2656
Recommended in Construction
Specialisation: Construction and civil engineering: acts for employers, contractors and professionals in a wide variety of disputes, including large international arbitrations. Very significant practice in relation to adjudication (where he has appeared in many of the reported cases) and mediation. Professional negligence: deals especially with cases involving allegations of negligence against valuers, engineers, accountants and solicitors. Instructed by many lending institutions, Professional Indemnity Insurers and the Solicitors Indemnity Fund.
Prof. Memberships: COMBAR, Technology and Construction Bar Association, London Common Law and Commercial Bar Association.
Career: BA (Oxon) in Jurisprudence. Called in 1994.

BRASSE, Gillian
14 Gray's Inn Square (Joanna Dodson QC), London (020) 7242 0858
Recommended in Family: Child Care including child abduction, Family: Matrimonial Finance
Specialisation: Practice covers all aspects of family work including public and private law cases under the Children Act, wardship, adoption and child abduction, as well as ancillary relief matters, and Inheritance Act cases. Reported cases include O v Berkshire CC (Education Procedure) (1992) 2FLR7, Re B Contact (1994) 2FLR1, Re W (arrangements to place for adoption) (1995) 1 FLR 163. Conran v Conran [1997] 2 FLR 615 (Money – wife's contribution). Re J (adoption: appointment of Guardian ad Litem) 1999 2 FU 86.
Prof. Memberships: Family Law Bar Association, Association of Lawyers for Children, committee member, Bar Benevolent Association.
Career: Called 1977. Appointed Deputy District Judge September 1995.
Personal: Educated at Varndean School for Girls, Brighton, and Liverpool University. Leisure pursuits include: travel, concerts, theatre, eating out, keep fit, my two daughters.

BREALEY, Mark
Brick Court Chambers (Christopher Clarke QC), London (020) 7379 3550
Recommended in Competition/Anti-trust
Specialisation: European Community Law, UK Competition Law. Publications: Co-author of 'Remedies in EC Law' (1998 Sweet & Maxwell); co-editor of Butterworths Encyclopedia on Competition Law; co-editor of 'Practitioners' Handbook of EC Law (1998 Bar Council). Recently reported cases: Case C-296/95 R v Customs & Excise ex parte EMU Tabac [1998] 3 WCR 298 ECJ; Easyjet v British Airways [1998] EuLR 350; Passmore v Morland [1999] 3 AII ER 1005 (CA); Matra Communications v Home Office[1999] 1 WLR 1646 (CA); R v Airport Co-ordination ex parte States of Guernsey [1999] EuLR; Courage v Crehan, Times 14 June 1999 (CA); The Inntrepreneur Beer Supply Co v Byrne, Times 14 June 1999; Case T-110/98 RJB Mining v Commission, 9 September 1998. Case C-124/97 Laara, Times 21 September 1999; Plumber v Tibsco, Times 1 December 1999, Glaxo and others v Dowelhurst, Times 14 March 2000.
Prof. Memberships: Bar European Group – Committee
Career: Called 1984
Personal: LLB, LLM, DEA.

BRENNAN, Lord QC
39 Essex Street (Nigel Pleming QC), London (020) 7832 1111
Recommended in Clinical Negligence, Environment, Personal Injury, Product Liability

BRENNAN, Timothy
Devereux Chambers (Jeffrey Burke QC), London (020) 7353 7534
Recommended in Employment, Tax

BRENNAND, Timothy
Manchester House Chambers (J.D.S. Wishart), Manchester (0161) 834 7007
Recommended in Crime

BRENTON, Timothy QC
4 Essex Court (Nigel Teare QC), London (020) 7653 5653
clerks@4sx.co.uk
Recommended in Arbitration (International), Shipping
Specialisation: Principal areas of practice are shipping (including Admiralty), international trade, commercial contracts, insurance (marine and non-marine) and reinsurance, sale and carriage of goods (international and domestic) and commercial fraud. On editorial

board of 'International Maritime Law' (Law Text Publishing Ltd). Appointed QC 1998.
Prof. Memberships: COMBAR, supporting member of London Maritime Arbitration Association.
Career: Royal Navy 1975-1979. Lecturer in law at King's College, London 1979-1980. Called to the Bar 1981 and joined *4 Essex Court*.
Personal: Educated at King's School, Rochester to 1975; Bristol University 1976-1979 (LLB) and Bar School 1980-1981. Born 4th November 1957.

BRETTEN, Rex QC
24 Old Buildings (G.R Bretten QC), London (020) 7242 2744
Recommended in Tax
Specialisation: All aspects of United Kingdom taxation, with special emphasis on multi-national corporate work, the interaction of United Kingdom and foreign taxes, and the operation of double taxation treaties; tax litigation.
Career: Commenced practice at the Bar in 1971. Appointed Queen's Counsel in 1980. Appointed a Bencher of *Lincoln's Inn* in 1989.

BRIDEN, Timothy J.
8 Stone Buildings (John Cherry QC), London (020) 7831 9881
Recommended in Church: Church of England, Health & Safety
Specialisation: Principal area of practice is ecclesiastical law. Editor, 'Macmorran's Handbook for Churchwardens and Parochial Church Councillors' and 'Moore's Introduction to English Canon Law'. Also handles personal injury and health & safety cases.
Prof. Memberships: Inner Temple, Ecclesiastical Law Society.
Career: Called to the Bar 1976; joined 1 Temple Gardens 1977 and moved to 8 Stone Buildings 1996. Appointed Chancellor of the Diocese of Bath and Wells 1993 and Chancellor of the Diocese of Truro 1998. Secretary of Ecclesiastical Judges Association since 1996.
Personal: Educated at Ipswich School 1958-1970 and Downing College Cambridge (BA 1974; LL.B 1975; MA 1978). Born 29 October 1951. Lives in South London.

BRIDGE, Rowena
KCH Barristers (William Everard), Nottingham (0115) 941 8851
Recommended in Family/Matrimonial

BRIGGS, John
3-4 South Square (Michael Crystal QC), London (020) 7696 9900
Recommended in Insolvency/Corporate Recovery, Traditional Chancery
Specialisation: All personal and corporate insolvency related work, including representing insolvency practitioners before Recognised Professional Bodies and Insolvency Practitioners Tribunal.
Prof. Memberships: Insolvency Lawyers Association. British Italian Law Association (Committee Member).
Career: LLB (London). Ex. Du Doc d'Univ (Nancy, France). 1973: Called to the Bar. 1973-1975: Jurist Linguist, European Court of Justice. Deputy Bankruptcy Registrar of the High Court. Joint Senior Author, Muir Hunter on Personal Insolvency (Stevens, 1987). Joint Author, Asset Protection Trusts (Keyhaven, 1997). Consultant Editor of 'Bankruptcy and Personal Insolvency Reports' (Jordans, 1996 to date).

BRIGGS, Michael QC
Serle Court (Lord Neill of Bladen QC), London (020) 7242 6105
Recommended in Civil Fraud, Commercial (Litigation), Commercial Chancery, Company, Financial Services, Insolvency/Corporate Recovery, Partnership
Specialisation: Main fields of chancery and commercial litigation including corporate insolvency, property, commercial fraud, professional negligence and regulation and partnership disputes.
Prof. Memberships: Commercial Bar Association.
Career: Called to Bar in 1978, Lincolns Inn. Pupil to Patrick Talbot and John Jarvis. Joined Serle Court in 1979. One of the junior counsel to the Crown, Chancery (1990-94). Took silk in 1994.
Personal: Married with 4 children. Leisure activities include sailing, solo and choral singing, member of Bar Yacht Club and Emsworth sailing club.

BRIGHT, Andrew QC
9 Bedford Row (formerly 4 Brick Court) (Anthony Berry QC), London (020) 7489 2727
Recommended in Crime

BRIGHT, Christopher
3 Fountain Court (Robert Juckes QC), Birmingham (0121) 236 5854
chris.bright@3fc.co.uk
Recommended in Clinical Negligence
Specialisation: All aspects of clinical negligence. Over 80 per cent of Chris Bright's work consists of clinical negligence litigation, handling cases of moderate valuation to severe damage claims in excess of £4 million. An award of £4.55m in November 1999 was said by the Treasury and NHSLA to be the largest to that date in a clinical negligence claim.
Prof. Memberships: AVMA/APIL. Birmingham Medico-Legal Society.
Career: Durham University BA Hons. Malcolm Hilberry Award, Gray's Inn. Medical Negligence Litigation Pilot Group; Birmingham. Lecturer upon AVMA regional and national courses and to health service professionals/clinicians.
Personal: Interests: Wine, Tuscany and Gloucester RFC.

BRINDLE, Michael QC
Fountain Court (Anthony Boswood QC), London (020) 7583 3335
Recommended in Banking, Civil Fraud, Commercial (Litigation), Professional Negligence
Specialisation: Practice encompasses a variety of work in the commercial and corporate sphere as well as employment law. Emphasis is on banking and financial services, company law, professional negligence in financial and commercial matters, insurance and international trade. Experienced in city related matters, including litigation arising out of audits, take-overs and rights issues. Practises in chancery as well as commercial and common law courts. Important cases include Caparo v Dickman [1989] (auditors' negligence); Morgan Crucible v Hill Samuel [1990] (merchant banker's and auditor's negligence and take-over code); G & H Montage v Irvani [1990] (bills of exchange); Deposit Protection Board v Dalia [1993] (depositor compensation); Shah v Bank of England [1994] (banking supervision); Camdex v Bank of Zambia [1997] (liabilities of central banks); BCCI v Price Waterhouse [1997] (Banking Act 1987); Nuova Safim v Sakura Bank [1998] (ISDA standard agreement) and Barclays Bank v Boulter [1999] (banking and securities). Author of journal articles and of 'Law of Bank Payment' [1999] (with Raymond Cox).
Prof. Memberships: Midland & Oxford Circuit.
Career: Called to the Bar in 1975 and joined Fountain Court Chambers in 1976. Took silk in 1992. Recorder since 2000. Treasurer of Commercial Bar Association.
Personal: Educated at Westminster School 1965-1969 and New College, Oxford (double first in classics and jurisprudence). Chairman of Trustees: Public concern at work. Member of Financial Reporting Review Panel. Born 23rd June 1952. Lives in London.

BRISBY, John QC
4 Stone Buildings (Philip Heslop QC), London (020) 7242 5524
clerks@4stonebuildings.law.co.uk
Recommended in Commercial Chancery, Company, Financial Services, Civil Fraud, Insolvency/Corporate Recovery
Specialisation: Litigation and advice in the fields of company law, corporate insolvency and financial services. Emphasis on heavy corporate litigation, mainly in the Chancery Division and Court of Appeal. Cases: Instructed in a number of actions resulting out of the Maxwell affair with a view to locating and recovering assets on behalf of the Maxwell pensioners, and in other high profile fraud or asset recovery situations such as DPR Futures, Barlow Clowes and BCCI. Has also acted for and against various regulatory bodies such as SIB, IMRO and LAUTRO. Has appeared in well over 60 reported cases, well-known examples being Re Cloverbay [1991] Ch 90, Re Bishopsgate Investment Management [1993] Ch 1 Re British & Commonwealth Holdings plc [1993] AC 426, Ispahani v Bank Middle Iran [1998] Lloyds Rep 133, Morris v Bank of America National Trust & Others [2000] 1 AER 954, Sasea Finance Ltd v KPMG [2000] 1AER 676, UPC v Deutsche Bank AG, court of appeal, 19th May 2000. Publications: Former Contributor: Encyclopaedia of Forms and Precedents (4th edn) Vol 9 Companies.
Prof. Memberships: Member of the Commercial Bar Association (COMBAR) and Chancery Bar Association.
Career: Call 1978. QC 1996.
Personal: Educated at Westminster School 1969-73 and Scholar of Christ Church, Oxford 1974-77. Born 8th May 1956. Lives in London and Northamptonshire.

BRISCOE, Constance
9-12 Bell Yard (D. Anthony Evans QC), London (020) 7400 1800
Recommended in Crime

BROCK, Jonathan QC
Falcon Chambers (Jonathan Gaunt QC & Kim Lewison QC), London (020) 7353 2484
Recommended in Agriculture, Property Litigation
Specialisation: Commercial property litigation and advice; overseas work particularly in commonwealth jurisdictions; has appeared in Jamaica, Brunei, Jordan, Bermuda etc; agriculture; arbitration; ecclesiastical law. Recent cases include Oliver Ashworth v Ballard [1999] 2 AER 791, Nurdin & Peacock v Ramsden [1999] 1 AER 941, National Grid v M25 Group [1999] 1 EGLR 65, Inntrepreneur v Crehan [1999] The Times 14 June, Chaffe v Kingsley [2000] 10 EG 173, Inntrepeneur v Langton [2000] 8 EG 167, Sight and Sound v Books Etc [1999] 3 EGLR 45.
Prof. Memberships: Vice-Chairman London Common Law and Commercial Bar Association; member Bar Council 1992-98; past Chairman Commonwealth Subcommittee; member Court of Appeal Users Committee; Bar permanent representative UK Inter-Professional Group; Chairman working party on Bar Joint Arbitration Scheme; Western Circuit; member Chancery Bar Association.
Career: St Pauls School; Corpus Christi College, Cambridge; called 1977; Silk 1997; Fellow Chartered Institute of Arbitrators; Recorder; editor 'Woodfall on Landlord and Tenant'; Blundell Lecturer 1992 and 1998.
Personal: Married with five children. Lives in London and Devon. Captain Snakepit Strollers FC.

BRODIE, Bruce
39 Essex Street (Nigel Pleming QC), London (020) 7832 1111
bb@39essex.co.uk
Recommended in Alternative Dispute Resolution, Arbitration (International)
Specialisation: Practises as arbitrator and advocate in arbitration with emphasis on international commercial disputes. Also serves as mediator (CEDR accredited mediator). Before transfer to Bar in 1993 was Frere Cholmeley senior litigation partner.
Personal: Called 1993.

BROMILOW, Richard
St John's Chambers (Christopher Sharp QC), Bristol (0117) 921 3456
clerks@stjohnschambers.co.uk
Recommended in Family/Matrimonial
Specialisation: Matrimonial finance cases including applications by children under the Children Act 1989. Contact disputes.
Prof. Memberships: FLBA, PIBA.
Career: Southampton University, *Grays Inn*. Recorder.
Personal: Leisure interests include: golf, cricket, wine and theatre.

BROMLEY-MARTIN, Michael
3 Raymond Buildings (Clive Nicholls QC), London (020) 7400 6400
chambers@threeraymond.demon.co.uk
Recommended in Fraud: Criminal, Licensing
Specialisation: Criminal law, including extradition.Commercial and investment fraud, both prosecuting and defending. Cases include Blue Arrow, BCCI, Norton and advising in Nissan and Maxwell. polive disciplinary proceedings, inquests, Food safety, Health & Safety at Work, Trade Descriptions. All forms of licensing including liquor, public entertainment, betting, gaming and lotteries.
Career: Called to the Bar in 1979. Department of Trade and Industry Inspector 1989, 1990.

BROUGHAM, Christopher QC
3-4 South Square (Michael Crystal QC), London (020) 7696 9900
Recommended in Insolvency/Corporate Recovery
Specialisation: Insolvency, individual and corporate – matrimonial financial provision / insolvency – litigation arising out of insolvencies (security disputes, disqualification of directors, professional negligence etc.) Dennison v Krasner, The Times, April 18, 2000, CA.
Prof. Memberships: ILA, ChBA, FLBA, COMBAR.
Career: 1969: Called to the Bar (IT). 1984 to date: Deputy Bankrupcy Registrar. 1988 Appointed Queen's Counsel. 1990-1991: Inspector appointed under Companies Act 1985 s.432(2) to investigate the affairs of BOM Holdings PLC.
Publications: Joint senior author on 'Muir Hunter on Personal Insolvency' (Sweet & Maxwell). Author of Personal Insolvency Chapter of 'Encyclopedia of Financial Provision in Family Matters' (Sweet & Maxwell)
Personal: BA (Jurisprudence) Worcester College, Oxford. Music; crossword puzzles (solving and setting); theatre. Married with a family.

BROWN, Charles
39 Essex Street (Nigel Pleming QC), London (020) 7832 1111
Recommended in Personal Injury

BROWN, Damian
Old Square Chambers (John Hendy QC), London (020) 7269 0300
Recommended in Employment
Specialisation: Leading cases: UCLH NHS Trust v Unison [1999] 1 CR 204, Wise v USDAW [1996] IRLR 609, Greaves v Kwiksave [1998] IRLR 245, RJB Mining v NUM [1997] IRLR 621, Safeways v Burell [1997]IRLR 200, PLA v Payne [1994] IRLR9. All employment areas: discrimination, restraint of trade, wrongful dismissal, Trade Union law and strikes. International Labour Law (including EU and ILO) and human rights.
Prof. Memberships: Employment Law Bar Association; Industrial Law Society; Employment Lawyers Association; Haldane Society. Contributor to Industrial Law Journal, The Guardian. Publications: Tolleys Employment Law – Contributor; Employment Tribunal Practice and Procedure – Co-Author; Employment Law Precedents – Co-Author (Sweet & Maxwell); Numerous pamphlets – Editor 'UK and EU Employee Consultation' (Sweet & Maxwell) 2000.
Career: Called to Bar 1989; Lecturer in International Labour Law. LL.M course at King's College.
Personal: Interests include politics, Trade Union history, Arsenal Football Club and cinema.

BROWN, Geoffrey B.
39 Essex Street (Nigel Pleming QC), London (020) 7832 1111
Recommended in Personal Injury
Specialisation: Personal injury and related work (including health insurance, clinical negligence and health & safety). Property damage claims (including fire, subsidence, crop and livestock claims, etc). Professional negligence. Insurance and general commercial work.
Career: MA Cantab.

BROWN, Hannah
One Essex Court (Lord Grabiner QC), London (020) 7583 2000
Recommended in Banking
Specialisation: Principal areas of practice are banking law and general commercial litigation including aviation finance, insurance and reinsurance.

BROWN, Simon QC
Crown Office Chambers (Michael Spencer QC & Christopher Purchas QC), London (020) 7797 8100
brown@crownofficechambers.com
Recommended in Product Liability
Specialisation: Principal areas of practice are professional negligence, product liability and insurance claims. Notable cases include Arab Bank v Zurich & Lloyds: fraud; Eagle Star v John D. Wood (Commercial) & Allied Appeals: 'fall in property market'; Capital & Counties and Digital Equipment Corporation v Hampshire County Council 'liability of Fire Brigades'; and Carroll & Others v Fearon & Dunlop plc; car tyre product liability.
Career: Called 1976, QC (1995) and Recorder.
Publications: Writes `Architects Engineers and Surveyors' in Emdens Construction Law.
Personal: Educated at Harrow School and Queens' College, Cambridge. Leisure pursuits include gardening, cricket and golf. Born 23rd August 1952.

BROWN, Stephanie
5 Fountain Court (Anthony Barker QC), Birmingham (0121) 606 0500
Recommended in Family/Matrimonial

BROWNE, Benjamin QC
2 Temple Gardens (Dermod O'Brien QC), London (020) 7822 1200
Recommended in Personal Injury
Specialisation: Personal injury, including many paraplegic, tetraplegic and brain damage claims. Disaster litigation, including Clapham Disaster and M1 air crash. Professional negligence, especially construction-related (engineers/architects) but also barristers, solicitors, surveyors, valuers, insurance brokers etc. Insurance and insurance related litigation. Product liability.
Career: Christ Church, Oxford. MA Jurisprudence.
Personal: Country and family pursuits, gardening.

BROWNE, Desmond QC
5 Raymond Buildings (Patrick Milmo QC), London (020) 7242 2902
Recommended in Defamation

BROWNE, Simon Peter Buchanan
Farrar's Building (John Leighton Williams QC), London (020) 7583 9241
Chambers@farrarsbuilding.co.uk
Recommended in Personal Injury
Specialisation: Practice covers general common law with particular specialisation in personal injury, clinical disputes, health and safety, and assessment of costs (is a contributing author "Greenslade on Costs").
Prof. Memberships: South Eastern Circuit. Member of Personal Injury Bar Association, ProFessional Negligence Bar Association, London Common Law and Commercial Bar Association, Criminal Bar Association.
Career: Called to the Bar in 1982.
Personal: Born 5th November 1959.

BROWNE-WILKINSON, Simon QC
Serle Court (Lord Neill of Bladen QC), London (020) 7242 6105
Recommended in Civil Fraud
Specialisation: Has a general commercial practice, including shipping, banking, insurance, employment, professional negligence and fraud.
Prof. Memberships: COMBAR
Career: Called to the Bar in 1981. QC 1998
Personal: Educated at Oxford University. Born in August 1957.

BRUDENELL, Thomas
Queen Elizabeth Building (Paul Coleridge QC), London (020) 7797 7837
Recommended in Family: Matrimonial Finance
Specialisation: Principal areas of practice are family law and equine litigation.
Prof. Memberships: Family Law Bar Association.
Career: Called to the Bar 1977 and joined current chambers in 1978.
Personal: Educated at Eton College 1969-1974. Born 12th August 1956. Lives in London.

BRYAN, Simon
Essex Court Chambers (Gordon Pollock QC), London (020) 7813 8000
clerksroom@essexcourt-chambers.co.uk
Recommended in Energy & Natural Resources, Insurance
Specialisation: Specialist in insurance and reinsurance, shipping, professional negligence litigation, energy and utility litigation, computer litigation and all apects of commercial law and arbitration. Has experience acting for Lloyd's syndicates, members and managing agents, in the context of litigation and Lloyd's inquiries and disciplinary proceedings.
Prof. Memberships: Commercial Bar Association
Personal: Called to the Bar 1988.
Career: Educated at Arnold School and at Magdalene College, Cambridge (First Class Honours). Born November 1965.

BRYANT, Judith
Wilberforce Chambers (Edward Nugee QC), London (020) 7306 0102
Recommended in Pensions
Specialisation: Practice covers a wide range of advisory and litigation work in chancery/ commercial matters, with particular emphasis on: trusts and their taxation, including advice on the creation and administration of trusts, the duties of trustees and breaches of trust, contentious trust matters, overseas trusts and their taxation, conflicts of laws, the variation of trusts, and the drafting of trust deeds and related instruments; pension schemes, including advice in relation to the construction of trust deeds and rules of pension

schemes, the duties of pension scheme trustees and breaches of those duties, applications to Court in relation to pension schemes, and complaints to the Pensions Ombudsman; wills and probate, including advice on the construction of wills, conflicts of laws, the variation of wills, the administration of estates, the duties of executors, and contentious probate matters; professional negligence relating to trusts and pension schemes.
Prof. Memberships: Society of Trust and Estate Practitioners (STEP) and Chancery Bar Association.
Career: Called to the Bar: 1987. Jesus College, Cambridge 1982-1986. BA 1st Class Hons (1985), LLM (1986).

BRYANT-HERON, Mark
9-12 Bell Yard (D. Anthony Evans QC), London (020) 7400 1800
Recommended in Crime

BUBB, Tim
39 Park Square (T.M.A. Bubb), Leeds (0113) 245 6633
Recommended in Crime

BUCHANAN, Vivien
KCH Barristers (William Everard), Nottingham (0115) 941 8851
Recommended in Family/Matrimonial
Specialisation: Ancillary relief (particular specialisation in this field is farming cases). Private Law, and Public Law: Childrens' cases. Inheritance Act Work. Trusts of land and appointment of trustees act cases.
Prof. Memberships: Committee member of the East Midlands Family Law Bar Association.
Career: Call 1981. Appointed deputy district judge 1991.
Personal: Married. Hobbies: Fishing, beagling, embroidery, cookery. Interests: Dogs, horses, chickens.

BUCKNALL, Belinda QC
4 Essex Court (Nigel Teare QC), London (020) 7653 5653
Recommended in Arbitration (International), Shipping

BUDDEN, Caroline
One King's Bench Walk (Anthony Hacking QC), London (020) 7936 1500
Recommended in Family: Child Care including child abduction
Specialisation: Principal area of practice is family law, including public and private law aspects of the Children Act, adoption, wardship and related social services law, child abduction. Public interest immunity. South Eastern Circuit. Cases of interest include: Re H (minors) (Care proceedings: Intervenor) The Times 22 March 2000; Re G (interim care order) [1992] 2FLR 839 CA; Re H (a minor) (parental responsiblity) [1993] 1FLR 484 CA; Re W (a minor) [1992] 3WLR 758 CA-medical treatment of an anorexic teenager/court's jurisdiction; Re C (adoption by relative) [1989] 1 WLR 61 CA; R v North Yorkshire CC ex p.M [1988] 3WLR 1344 – Judicial Review of local authority's conduct in care proceedings.
Prof. Memberships: Family Law Bar Association, Professional Negligence Bar Association.
Career: Called to the Bar 1977. Assistant Recorder 1998. Recorder 2000.
Personal: Educated at Alfred Colfox School, Bridport, Dorset, and Bristol University (LL.B 1976). Born 30 July 1954. Lives in London.

BULL, Gregory
33 Park Place (John Charles Rees QC), Cardiff (029) 2023 3313
Recommended in Crime

BULLOCK, Ian
St John's Chambers (Christopher Sharp QC), Bristol (0117) 921 3456
Recommended in Personal Injury

BURBIDGE, James
St Philip's Chambers (Rex Tedd QC), Birmingham (0121) 246 7000
Recommended in Crime

BURDEN, Susan
6 Pump Court (Kieran Coonan QC), London (020) 7583 6013
clerks@6pumpcourt.law.co.uk
Recommended in Clinical Negligence
Specialisation: General personal injury work, medical/dental negligence (including high value birth trauma cases) for claimants and defendants; disciplinary hearings. Drafted British Medical Association's green paper response on 'Competition'. Lectures given: IBC/Hempsons' 'Reducing NHS Medical Negligence Liabilities'; Euroforums's 'Claims by Injured Children', 'IBC's Cerebral Palsy Claims', CLT's 'Clinical Negligence Update' (March 2000); chaired Euroforum's 'Spinal Injuries'. Instructed in benzodiazepine litigation. Cases reported Scott v Bloomsbury HA [1990] 1MedLR 214; Walker v Huntingdon HA [1994] 5 MedLR 356, Nawoor v Barking Havering and Brentwood Health Authority [1998] Lloyd's Rep. Med. 313.
Prof. Memberships: Bar Professional Negligence Association.
Career: Guildford County School for Girls, Charterhouse, New College Oxford BA. Hons (Jurisprudence) 1984; MA.
Personal: Born 15 July 1961. Opera, singing.

BURGESS, Edward
St John's Chambers (Christopher Sharp QC), Bristol (0117) 921 3456
Recommended in Crime

BURKE, Jeffrey QC
Devereux Chambers (Jeffrey Burke QC), London (020) 7353 7534
Recommended in Employment, Personal Injury

BURKE, Trevor
2 Bedford Row (formerly 3 Hare Court) (William Clegg QC), London (020) 7440 8888
Recommended in Crime
Specialisation: Has previously successfully defended John Fashanu in the football corruption trial. Sol Campbell on an alleged assault. Nigel Benn on a serious assault. Terry Marsh on a student grant fraud and The Taylor Sisters. Recently acted as leading counsel in a murder at the Old Bailey. Currently instructed to defend Gary Glitter as well as a number of fraud trials. Has particular experience in representling solicitors before disciplinary tribunals.
Prof. Memberships: CBA, Member of South Eastern Circuit.

BURKILL, Guy
Three New Square (David E.M. Young QC), London (020) 7405 1111
Recommended in Information Technology, Intellectual Property
Specialisation: All intellectual property aspects, mainly patent with particular interest in computer hardware and software and electronics. Has acted for many leading multinational companies in the computer, electronics, paper, chemical, pharmaceutical, aviation and other fields. Co-author of Terrell on the law of Patents (15th edition) Most recent notable cases include: Pavel v Sony (Walkman case); Lubrizol v Exxon (oil additives); Hoechst v British Petroleum; Discovision v Disctronics (compact disc mastering); Texas Instruments v Hyundai (integrated circuitry).
Prof. Memberships: Intellectual Property Bar Assn; Chancery Bar Assn.
Career: Winchester College; Corpus Christi College Cambridge – MA Degree, First Class Hons in Engineering (Electrical Option); Called to Bar 1981.
Personal: Leisure interests include music, opera and travel.

BURNETT, Ian D. QC
1 Temple Gardens (Hugh B.H. Carlisle QC), London (020) 7583 1315
clerks@1templegardens.co.uk
Recommended in Health & Safety, Personal Injury
Specialisation: Public Law, Coroners, Health and Safety, Professional Negligence, Personal Injury. Public inquiries (King's Cross, Clapham Junction, Guildford Four, Bloody Sunday, Southall Rail); Ex Parte Richmond Borough Council (Nos 1, 2 and 4) [1994] 1 WLR 74, [1995] Env LR 390, [1995] Env LR 409 and [1996] 1 WLR 1460 (Environmental JR); Ex Parte Jamieson [1995] QB 1 (Coroners); Elguzouli-Daf v Commissioner & others [1995] QB 335, Mulcahy v MoD [1996] QB 732 (Duty of Care); R v Associated Octel [1996] 1 WLR 1543 (Health & Safety); Boddington v British Transport Police [1998] 2 WLR 639 (JR).
Prof. Memberships: ALBA, PIBA.
Career: MA (Oxon). Called MT 1980. Junior Counsel to the Crown (Common Law) 1992-1998; QC 1998. Recorder.

BURR, Andrew
Atkin Chambers (John Blackburn QC), London (020) 7404 0102
clerks@atkinchambers.law.co.uk
Recommended in Arbitration (International), Construction
Specialisation: Practises primarily in domestic and international construction and technology disputes. Acts as advocate in litigation and arbitration and in an advisory capacity regarding ADR. Experienced in all aspects of construction and technology law and professional negligence, particularly of architects, engineers and surveyors. General and articles editor 'Construction Law Journal' (Sweet and Maxwell); general editor 'Arbitration and Dispute Resolution Law Journal' (Lloyds of London Press); editor 'European Construction Contracts' (Wiley Chancery Law).
Prof. Memberships: ACI Arb. (Committee member European Branch), ABA international associate, Swiss Arbitration Association, TECBAR, COMBAR, BILA.
Career: Called November 1981. Joined chambers in 1983. Speaks Italian and French.
Personal: Educated at Barclay School, Stevenage and Trinity Hall, Cambridge. Lives in London.

BURTON, Frank QC
12 King's Bench Walk (Timothy Stow QC), London (020) 7583 0811
Recommended in Personal Injury
Specialisation: Principal area of practice is personal injury work with an emphasis on industrial diseases and medical negligence. Co-author of 'Medical Negligence Case Law' and 'Personal Injury Limitation Law', both published by Butterworths. Author on medical practitioners chapter in Butterworths Professional Negligence Service.
Prof. Memberships: Personal Injury Bar Association, Member of Executive.
Career: University lecturer 1974-83. Called to the Bar and joined present chambers 1982. QC 1998. 1999 Assistant Recorder
Personal: BA Hons 1st Class and PhD. Born 19th June 1950. Lives in London.

BUSH, Rosalind
5 Fountain Court (Anthony Barker QC), Birmingham (0121) 606 0500
Recommended in Family/Matrimonial

BUSUTTIL, Godwin
5 Raymond Buildings (Patrick Milmo QC), London (020) 7242 2902
Recommended in Defamation

BUTCHER, Christopher
7 King's Bench Walk (Jeremy Cooke QC), London (020) 7910 8300
clerks@7kbw.law.co.uk
Recommended in Arbitration (International), Banking, Commercial (Litigation), Insurance, Professional Negligence, Shipping
Specialisation: Insurance and reinsurance, commercial agreements, banking, agency, shipping, international trade, arbitration, and professional negligence.
Career: Called to the Bar 1986. Recent cases include: Henderson v Merrett Syndicates Ltd [1995] 2 A.C. 145 (negligence – duty of care – duty of agents at Lloyd's), Barclays Bank plc and Others v British and Commonwealth Holdings plc [1996] 1WLR1, (banking – company law). Barings plc v Coopers & Lybrand [1997] 1 BCLC 427 (auditors – duty of care), Denby v English and Scottish Maritime Insurance Co. [1998] Lloyd's Rep. IR 343 (reinsurance), Credit Suisse First Boston v MLC [1999] 1 Lloyd's Rep. 767 (practice – anti-suit injunction).
Personal: Born 1962. MA (Oxon), Dip Eur Law (King's College, London). Has a working knowledge of French and Italian.

BYRNE, Garrett
23 Essex Street (Michael Lawson QC), London (020) 7413 0353
Recommended in Environment
Specialisation: Environmental law and planning, particularly criminal aspects of environmental law. Instructed by major city solicitors to advise and represent substantial industrial concerns and major developers. Regular speaker at conferences.
Prof. Memberships: United Kingdom Environmental Law Association; Environmental Law Foundation, founding member of 'EarthRights', environmental law and resource centre.
Career: Called to the Bar in 1986, Masters degree in Environmental Law in 1993.

CAHILL, Jeremy
5 Fountain Court (Anthony Barker QC), Birmingham (0121) 606 0500
Recommended in Environment, Planning

CAHILL, Sally
Park Lane Chambers (Stuart Brown QC), Leeds (0113) 228 5000
Recommended in Family/Matrimonial

CALDECOTT, Andrew QC
1 Brick Court (Richard Rampton QC), London (020) 7353 8845
Recommended in Defamation
Specialisation: Defamation, confidence, contempt of court and media related law generally.
Career: Called to the Bar 1975.
Personal: Educated Eton College and New College, Oxford. Lives in London.

CALVER, Neil
Brick Court Chambers (Christopher Clarke QC), London (020) 7379 3550
Recommended in Commercial (Litigation)
Specialisation: Commercial law, in particular insurance, reinsurance, commercial arbitration, contractual disputes, professional negligence, EC law, sports law. Major cases this year so far include Odyssey Re v OIC Run Off Ltd (Court of Appeal: setting aside judgment on grounds of fraud of witness) and acting for Sir Elton John in professional negligence action against his former accountants. Important previous cases include: Stoke CC v B&Q [1993] AC 900 [HL and ECJ: whether Sunday trading ban contrary to EC law]; Kirklees BC v Wickes [1993] AC 227 [HL: whether public authorities should give cross-undertakings in damages as price of injunctive relief]; Ernst & Young v Butte Mining [1996] 1 LLR 91 and 104 [striking out of accountant's negligence claim]; Wurttembergische v Home Insurance [1999] LRLR 397 [CA: Pool reinsurance dispute]; Junior Counsel for Williams Grand Prix Motor Racing team. Acted for reinsurers in major insurance market arbitration concerning Eastern European shipbuilding losses after collapse of communism.
Prof. Memberships: COMBAR.
Career: LLM, Christ's College, Cambridge University (Double First Class Honours). Elected Life Scholar, Squire Scholar and De Hart Scholar, Christ's College Cambridge University. Gray's Inn Entrance Scholar; David Karmel Scholarship prize winner (Commercial Law, Grays' Inn).
Publications: Contributing author to the Bar Council's 'European Law Handbook' (1998); Contributing author to 'TUPE and the Acquired Rights Directive' (1996).
Personal: Played chess for England at under-18 level; Kent County Chess Champion at under 18, 16 and 14 level. Charlton Athletic FC supporter; Director of the Actors Centre, Covent Garden; Married with baby daughter.

CAMERON, Alexander
3 Raymond Buildings (Clive Nicholls QC), London (020) 7400 6400
chambers@threeraymond.demon.co.uk
Recommended in Fraud: Criminal
Specialisation: Has substantial experience in all areas of commercial crime (including insider dealing). Has defended solicitors and accountants, in addition to a number of businessmen and financiers. Recently involved in one of the first prosecutions brought by OPRA. Larger trials include 'Blue Arrow' and 'Blackspur Leasing'. Other main areas of work are general crime (Jonathan Aitken, perjury; Marquis of Bath, assault), extradition (Goddard v USA, Pinochet) and licensing, both advisory and court work.
Prof. Memberships: Criminal Bar Association, International Bar Association.
Career: Called 1986. At *3 Raymond Buildings* (formerly QEB) throughout.
Personal: Bristol University (LL.B Hons).

CAMERON, James
3 Verulam Buildings (Christopher Symons QC & John Jarvis QC), London (020) 7831 8441
Recommended in Environment
Specialisation: International lawyer specialising in environment, trade and human rights questions. Additionally environmental assessments and warranties, "toxic tort" litigation and conflict of laws. In practice is engaged in public law and judicial review of ministerial (and other public) decisions. Important cases include: EU v Korea [1999] WTO Appellate Body (safeguard measures on certain milk products); Ex-parte Pinochet [1998]; Ncobo v Thor Chemicals [1996]; Connelly v RTZ [1996]; R v President of the Board of Trade ex parte Duddridge [1995]; R v Secretary of State for the Environment, ex parte Greenpeace & Lancashire (THORP) [1994]. Involved in several international negotiations, including the UN Climate Change Convention Kyoto Protocol and the Earth Summit [1992]. Editor 'Review of European Community and International Environmental Law' (RECIEL). and 'International Trade Law Reports'. Author of several books including 'Trade and the Environment: Law & Policy', [2000]; 'Reinterpreting the Precautionary Principle',[2000]; 'Dispute Resolution in the WTO' [1998], 'Trade and the Environment, the Search for Balance' [1994].
Prof. Memberships: UK Environmental Law Association, Environmental Law Foundation (Advisory Board), World Trade Law Association (WTLA) Council Member. IUCN Environmental Law Commission. International Law Association (committee on transnational environmental litigation). International Criminal Law Association.
Career: Called to the Bar and joined current chambers 1987.
Personal: Educated at Stowe School, Buckinghamshire. University of Western Australia. University College, London (LL.B, 1985). Queens' College, Cambridge (LL.M, 1986).

CAMERON, N.A.
Wilberforce Chambers (Bernard Gateshill), Hull (01482) 323264
Recommended in Health & Safety
Specialisation: Civil: cases relating to the conveyancing and use of land. Planning, boundaries, restrictive covenants, easements, public rights of way, landlord and tenant nuisance and environmental.Criminal: health and safety, environmental and planning enforcement.
Prof. Memberships: North-Eastern circuit, Professional Negligence, Bar association.
Career: Called 1984, Junior Counsel to the crown (provincial panel) 2000.

CAMERON, Neil
1 Serjeants' Inn (Lionel Read QC), London (020) 7583 1355
clerks@serjeants-inn.co.uk
Recommended in Planning
Specialisation: Planning and environmental. Recent work includes: UK Nirex RCF appeal, Barnsley MBC CPO Special Parliamentary Procedure, Medway Cement Works Inquiry.
Prof. Memberships: Planning and Environment Bar Association, Parliamentary Bar Mess.
Career: Called 1982.
Personal: Educated at Eton College and Durham University.

CAMERON, Sheila QC
2 Harcourt Buildings (Mr Gerard Ryan QC), London (020) 7353 8415
Recommended in Church: Church of England, Parliamentary & Public Affairs

CAMPBELL, Douglas James
Three New Square (David E.M. Young QC), London (020) 7405 1111
Recommended in Intellectual Property
Specialisation: All intellectual property matters – chemistry (biotechnology) computers. Notable cases: Thermos v Aladdin [200] FSR 402; Playhut v Spring Form [2000] FSR 327, TABO trade mark [2000] RPC 360, Demel v Jefferson [1999] FSR 204; Union Carbide v BP [1998] RPC 1, [1999] RPC 409 (CA); Conran (Sir Terence Orby) v Mean Fiddler Holdings [1997] FSR 856; Lubrizol v Exxon [1997] RPC 195, [1998] RPC 727 (CA); Roadtech Computer Systems v Unison Software [1996] FSR 805; Johnson v Mabuchi [1995] RPC 387; Valeo Vision v Flexible Lamps [1995] RPC 205.
Prof. Memberships: Intellectual Property Bar Assn; Chancery Bar Assn; AIPPI.
Career: Dollar Academy, Scotland 1976-1984; (Scholarship to) Hertford College, Oxford 1984-1988 1st Class Hons, Chemistry with Distinction in Quantum Chemistry. 1989/90 Employed by Andersen Consulting in Information Technology 1990/91 Teaching English in Kagoshima, Japan. Fluent in Japanese. Called to Bar 1993, Pegasus Scholarship to Melbourne, Australia 1997.

Publications: Contributor to European Patent Litigation Handbook; Terrell on Patents (both Sweet & Maxwell).
Personal: Karate, Equestrian pursuits.

CAMPBELL, Emily
Wilberforce Chambers (Edward Nugee QC), London (020) 7306 0102
Recommended in Commercial Chancery
Specialisation: General Chancery, Private Client, Pensions, Financial Services. e.g. Cases:- Martin v Britannia Life (The Independant; Solicitors Journal) 17 Dec 99, Parker J.; Re Ratcliffe [1999] STC; Re Cobham unrep, 28 July 1999, Parker J.
Prof. Memberships: Revenue Bar Assoc., Association of Pensions Lawyers, Chancery Bar Assoc.
Career: Lecturer in law of trusts, King's College, London (1994-95). Judicial Assistant to Court of Appeal (1997).
Publications: Halsburys Laws - Settlements title. International Trust Laws (Ed 9 Lassan) - contributor. Various articles: PCB; Sol. J.;Trusts & Estates LJ; Christies Bulletin.
Personal: Classical music

CAMPBELL, Stephen
St Philip's Chambers (Rex Tedd QC), Birmingham (0121) 246 7000
Recommended in Commercial (Litigation)
Specialisation: Commercial law, building, personal injury.
Prof. Memberships: Midland Chancery and Commercial Bar Association. Personal Injury Bar Association. Birmingham Official Referee Users Group.
Career: King Edward VI School, Birmingham. Liverpool University.
Personal: Assistant Deputy Coroner to Birmingham and Solihull. Married, 3 children. Tennis.

CAMPBELL, Susan
Southernhay Chambers (Anthony Ward), Exeter (01392) 255777
Recommended in Family/Matrimonial
Specialisation: Family law. Practice covers all areas of family law: ancillary relief and all aspects of law relating to children, particularly care proceedings.
Prof. Memberships: Family Law Bar Association.
Career: Called 1986. Spent 7 years as an employed barrister in local government, specialising in care proceedings.
Personal: Born 29 April 1964. Two children. Enjoys swimming and walking.

CAPE, Paul
Milburn House Chambers (Paul Cape), Newcastle upon Tyne (0191) 230 5511
Recommended in Employment
Specialisation: Almost exclusively employment and discrimination law, acting for both employers and employees with a particular interest in local authority work.
Prof. Memberships: Employment Law Bar Association
Career: Obtained a 'first' in Law at Newcastle Polytechnic following a career as a trade union official. Co-founder and Head of Chambers, Milburn House Chambers, a set specialising in all aspects of Employment and Discrimination Law.
Personal: Interests include theatre, reading and watching cricket. Born 5 March 1955.

CAPLAN, Jonathan QC
5 Paper Buildings (Godfrey Carey QC & Jonathan Caplan QC), London (020) 7583 6117
Recommended in Crime, Fraud: Criminal

CARGILL-THOMPSON, Perdita
Essex Court Chambers (Gordon Pollock QC), London (020) 7813 8000
Recommended in Tax
Specialisation: VAT and Customs & Excise litigation and advisory work; Judicial review and human rights; EC litigation and advisory work; Brussels Convention and Rome Convention; UK commercial disputes; Broking disputes; Banking, guarantee and insolvency work.
Career: Jesus College, Oxford: BA 1984 (Jurisprudence); College of Law: Solicitors' Professional Examinations 1984-1985; London School of Economics: Masters in Human Rights and International Law 1991-1992; British Academy Scholarship 1991-1992: Bar Council: Conversion examinations 1992: Called to the Bar 1993. Treasury Panel (B List).
Personal: Born 1964; Speaks French.

CARLISLE, Hugh B.H. QC
1 Temple Gardens (Hugh B.H. Carlisle QC), London (020) 7583 1315
clerks@1templegardens.co.uk
Recommended in Health & Safety
Specialisation: Health and safety at work: R v Board of Trustees of Science Museum [1993] IWLR 1171 CA; R v Associated Octel Co Ltd [1996] 4 All ER 846, [1996] 1 WLR 1543 HL; R v British Steel plc [1995] I WLR 1356 CA; R v Nuclear Electric plc [Sept 1995]; R v Coalite Products Ltd [Feb. 1996]; HSE v Howletts Zoo [Oct 1995]; R v Port Ramsgate and others [Jan-Feb 1997]; Harris v Evans [1998] 3 All ER 522 CA; R v FH Howe Ltd [1999] 2 All ER 249 CA; R v Balfour Beatty and Geoconsult [Jan-Feb 1999] Counsel for HSC/E in the Ladbroke Grove Railway Inquiry 2000, Counsel for Dept. of Health in BSE Inquiry 1999-2000 etc. Personal injuries: Fields v Hereford Health Authority [1992] etc.
Career: Called to Bar Middle Temple 1961; Junior Treasury Counsel, Personal injuries cases, 1975-1978; QC 1978; DTI Inspector into Ramor Investments Ltd 1979-1985 and into Milbury plc 1982-1985; Bencher, Middle Temple 1985. Recorder of the Crown Court (since 1983).
Personal: Married with two children. Interests include fly fishing, woodworking and croquet.

CARMAN, George QC
4-5 Gray's Inn Square (Elizabeth Appleby QC & Duncan Ouseley QC), London (020) 7404 5252
Recommended in Defamation

CARR, Bruce
Devereux Chambers (Jeffrey Burke QC), London (020) 7353 7534
Recommended in Employment
Specialisation: Employment law, commercial law, personal injury. Regularly instructed on behalf of both employers and trade unions, in particular in the EAT. Also frequently appears in interlocutory injunction applications, ranging from restrictive covenants to trade disputes. Substantial practice in descrimination, transfer of undertakings and large scale redundancy matters. Junior Counsel to the Crown (Panel B).
Prof. Memberships: Employment Law Bar Association; Employment Lawyers Association; ILS, Recorder; Member – EAT User Group.
Career: Called 1986. Inner Temple. Publications: author 'Emergency procedures' , Litigation Practice (Longmans).
Personal: Cambs High School for Boys, Cambridge. Hills Road Sixth Form College, Cambridge. LSE (BSc Economics) 1983, Central London Polytechnic (Dip. Law) 1985

CARR, Christopher QC
One Essex Court (Lord Grabiner QC), London (020) 7583 2000
Recommended in Civil Fraud, Commercial (Litigation), Energy & Natural Resources
Specialisation: General commercial law, oil and gas law and competition law.
Prof. Memberships: Member and Bencher of Lincoln's Inn.
Career: Called to Bar in 1968. Took silk in 1983.

CARR, Henry QC
11 South Square (Christopher Floyd QC), London (020) 7405 1222
Recommended in Information Technology, Intellectual Property
Specialisation: Principal areas of practice are patents, copyrights, designs and trade marks. Leading cases include Philips v Remington, Levis v Tesco, Glaxo and others v Dowelhurst and others, all of which are currently pending before the ECJ and concern the Trade Marks Directive. Also R v Registrar of Designs ex parte Ford Motor Company (House of Lords) R v Licensing Authority ex parte Smith Kline & French (House of Lords) and Scotia v Norgine (European Court). Also has a substantial practice in computer contracts (including negligence claims); and judicial review relating to the grant of product licences. In addition, has appeared in numerous cases in the Data Protection Tribunal on behalf of the registrar.
Career: Called to the Bar 1982. Joined South Square in 1983. Took Silk 1998. Educated at Hertford College, Oxford and the University of British Columbia. Lives in London.

CARR, Peter
St. Ive's Chambers (Edward Coke), Birmingham (0121) 236 0863
Recommended in Crime

CARR, Sue
Four New Square (Justin Fenwick QC), London (020) 7822 2000
barristers@4newsquare.com
Recommended in Professional Negligence
Specialisation: Principal area of practice is professional negligence: solicitors, medical, surveyors, accountants, barristers, architects, and engineers. Also handles employment, general contract and insurance work. Important cases include BDG Roof Bond Ltd v Douglas and others [1999] (company/ solicitors' negligence); Twinsectra Ltd v Yardley and others [1999] (constructive trusts/ accessory liability); Mortgage Express v Newman v SIF [1999] (solicitors' dishonesty), Broadley v Guy Clapham [1993], Hopkins & MacKenzie [1995] (both concerning limitation); Interdesco S.A v Nullifire Ltd [1992] (registration of foreign judgement) and Morley v Heritage plc [1993] (employment), Hipwood v Gloucestershire HA [1995] (Disclosure), Halifax plc v Gould & Swayne [1999] (solicitor's duties).
Prof. Memberships: Committee Member Professional Negligence Bar Association, Commercial and Common Law Bar Association. Member of New South Wales Bar. The General Editor and contributing author to 'Jackson & Powell: Professional Liability Precedents'.
Career: Called to the Bar 1987 and joined Crown Office Row in 1988.
Personal: Born 1st September 1964. Educated at Wycombe Abbey School 1976-82 and Trinity College, Cambridge 1983-86 (MA). Leisure pursuits include sports, music and acting. Fluent in French and German.

CARSS-FRISK, Monica
Blackstone Chambers (P Baxendale QC and C Flint QC), London (020) 7583 1770
Recommended in Administrative & Public Law: General, Employment
Specialisation: Judicial review, employment law, with a particular emphasis on discrimination in both domestic and EU law, and the European Convention on Human Rights (particularly in the commercial context). Also handles general commercial contract disputes (including conflict of laws issues) and commercial fraud.
Prof. Memberships: Administrative Law Bar Association, Employment Lawyers Association, COMBAR.
Career: Called to the Bar 1985 and joined current chambers in 1986.
Personal: Educated at London University (LL.B, 1983) and Oxford University (BCL, 1984). Speaks Swedish and has a working knowledge of Finnish. Member of Board of Interights. Contributor to 'Halsbury's Laws on Constitutional Law and Human Rights' and 'Butterworths' Human Rights Law and Practice'. Junior Counsel to the Crown (A Panel).

CARTER, Peter QC
18 Red Lion Court (Anthony Arlidge QC), London (020) 7520 6000
Peter.Carter@18rlc.co.uk
Recommended in Crime
Specialisation: Principal area of practice is criminal law, both prosecution and defence work. Particular focus on fraud cases, but also handles drugs cases, offences of violence and sexual offences. Acted in BCCI and DPR litigation and has defended in a number of murder cases. Also deals with human rights, local authority and pollution cases. Clients include CPS headquarters, SFO and Customs and Excise. Author of 'Offences of Violence' and regular seminar speaker.
Prof. Memberships: Criminal Bar Association, South Eastern Circuit.
Career: Called to the Bar 1974 and joined current chambers in 1975. Secretary of Criminal Bar Association 1987-1990. Took Silk 1995. Undertakes pro bono work, especially capital cases.
Personal: Educated at University College, London 1970-1973 (LL.B). Governor of British Institute of Human Rights. Leisure pursuits include poetry, cricket and walking. Born 8th August 1952. Lives in Enfield, Middlesex.

CARTER-STEPHENSON, George QC
3 Gray's Inn Square (Rock Tansey QC), London (020) 7520 5600
Recommended in Crime
Specialisation: Experience in the conduct of the most serious and complex criminal cases including murder, serious fraud, "organised crime" and drug trafficking. A specialist in the field of criminal defence.
Prof. Memberships: South Eastern Circuit, Criminal Bar Association.
Career: Called to the Bar in 1975 and joined current Chambers in 1977.
Personal: Leeds University 1971 to 1974 (LLB Honours).

CARUS, Roderick QC
9 St. John Street (John Hand QC), Manchester (0161) 955 9000
Recommended in Crime
Specialisation: Fraud and related crime involving banking and accountancy disciplines but very experienced in all areas of criminal advocacy from corporate manslaughter to the Trade Marks Act 1994.
Career: 1964: law degree University College Oxford. 1965: Postgraduate Diploma in Advanced Business Studies (specialising in Finance and Accountancy). 1966-1970: Investment Controller for leading merchant bank. 1971: called to the Bar (Gray's). 1986: Assistant Recorder. 1990: Queen's Counsel and Recorder.

CASEY, Mairin
St. Mary's Chambers Family Law Chambers (Christopher Butler), Nottingham (0115) 950 3503
Recommended in Family/Matrimonial

CASSEL, Timothy QC
5 Paper Buildings (Godfrey Carey QC & Jonathan Caplan QC), London (020) 7583 6117
Recommended in Crime

CATCHPOLE, Stuart
39 Essex Street (Nigel Pleming QC), London (020) 7832 1111
Recommended in Administrative & Public Law: General, Construction
Specialisation: Construction and civil engineering. Professional negligence. Public law. Commercial law. Cases: currently counsel to the Ministry of Agriculture Fisheries and Food at the BSE Inquiry; counsel for Sheffield Wednesday FC at the Hillsborough public inquiry and inquests. Details of reported cases and experience in any of areas of practice can be provided on request.
Prof. Memberships: Official Referees Bar Assocation. Administrative Law Bar Association. Appointed to be Junior Counsel to the Crown ('A' Panel) by the Attorney General in July 1999. Formerly a member of the Supplementary Panel of Treasury Counsel Common Law (appointed May 1992), transferred to the Treasury 'B' Panel on its creation in November 1998.
Career: Durham University 1983-1986: First Class Honours Degree in Law (Maxwell Law Prize). Colchester Royal Grammar School 1975-1982: A-Level History, English & Classical Civilisation (all Grade A).
Personal: Married. 3 year old son and baby daughter. Speaks French. Enjoys theatre, cinema, wine.

CATTAN, Philip D.
28 St. John St (Clement Goldstone QC), Manchester (0161) 834 8418
Recommended in Crime

CAUDLE, John
2 Bedford Row (formerly 3 Hare Court) (William Clegg QC), London (020) 7440 8888
jcaudle@2bedfordrow.co.uk
Recommended in Crime
Specialisation: Fraud, including computer misuse. Cases include R v Austin & Rawson (conspiracy to defraud); R v Amschwand (VAT evasion fraud); R v Roche & East (computer misuse fraud); R v Glenister (general fraud). Cases of a more general nature include R v Stockwell (facial mapping); R v Beckwith (alleged attempted gangland execution); R v McDonagh (murder); R v Blake & O'Dell (conspiracy to murder); R v Palmer & Others (undercover drugs operation); R v Kirkland & Others (corruption); R V Carter & Saydam (large scale drugs seizure); R v Wyner & Brock (drugs); R v Pallett (psychological harm caused by "stalking"); R v O'Connor (rape). Instructed as leading junior by both defence and prosecution.
Prof. Memberships: Criminal Law Bar Association, South Eastern Circuit.
Career: Called to the Bar in 1976; joined present chambers 1977. Appointed Recorder 2000. Member of the Essex Criminal Justice Strategy Committee.
Personal: Educated at Ipswich School and North Staffordshire Polytechnic (LLB Ext Lon). Leisure pursuits include Eton Fives, tennis, weight training and wine. Born 13th September 1951.

CAUSER, John
23 Essex Street (Michael Lawson QC), London (020) 7413 0353
Recommended in Crime
Specialisation: Commercial fraud and related areas of civil and criminal law including disqualification of directors, actions against the police etc. Recent clients include Lord Brocket and Roger Levitt. Legal and other disciplinary proceedings.
Prof. Memberships: Gambian Bar [1982]. Gibraltar Bar [1998].
Career: BA English Literature 1977. Called (Inner Temple) 1979.
Personal: Puzzle setting and solving, toy making, bicycling, photography, Babylonic cuneiform.

CAVANAGH, John
11 King's Bench Walk (Eldred Tabachnik QC and James Goudie QC), London (020) 7632 8500
Recommended in Employment
Specialisation: Principal areas of practice are employment law, local government law and judicial review and commercial law. In employment law particular emphasis on discrimination and equal pay, TUPE, the European aspects of employment law, restraint of trade, wrongful dismissal, industrial disputes and large-scale redundancies. Has recently acted in Preston v.Wolverhampton Healthcare (part-timers pensions); Gregory v Wallace (breach of contract) Jepson v Labour Party (all-women shortlists), Abbey Life v Tansell (disability discrimination), R v Portsmouth CC, ex parte Coles (public procurement) and Gregory v Portsmouth CC (malicious prosecution).
Prof. Memberships: Treasurer of Employment Law Bar Association, member of the Employment Lawyers Association, ALBA and COMBAR. Junior Counsel to the Crown - B Panel.
Career: Called 1985. Joined 11 King's Bench Walk 1985.
Personal: Educated: Warwick School; New College, Oxford (MA); Clare College, Cambridge (LLM) and University of Illinois.

CAWSON, Mark
St. James's Chambers (R.A. Sterling), Manchester (0161) 834 7000
mcawson@aol.com
Recommended in Chancery, Commercial (Litigation), Insolvency/Corporate Recovery
Specialisation: General Chancery/ Commercial with emphasis on contentious insolvency and company work, and professional negligence. Recent cases include A.F Budge directors' disqualification, Home Income Scheme litigation, Secretary of State for Trade and Industry v Ashcroft [1998] Ch 71, Barakot v Epiette [1998] 1BCLC 283, Lombarn North Central v Brook [1999] BPIR 701.
Prof. Memberships: Northern Circuit, Chancery Bar Association, Northern Chancery Bar Association, Northern Circuit Commercial Bar Association, Professional Negligence Bar Association.
Career: Wrekin College. Liverpool University. Called 1982 (Lincoln's Inn). Junior Counsel to Treasury (Charity/ Manchester) DTI's Panel of Counsel for Directors' Disqualification work. Assistant Recorder.

CAYFORD, Philip
29 Bedford Row Chambers (Peter Ralls QC), London (020) 7404 1044
Recommended in Family: Matrimonial Finance
Specialisation: Family practice, heavily biased towards ancillary relief and matters with a commercial bias including company and entertainment law contracts. Also a wide range of common law, commercial, entertainment and other family law matters. Reported Court of Appeal decisions on Hague Convention and

jurisdiction issues, on a derivative shareholder action arising from breakdown of family owned company, on setting aside consent orders and solicitors' conflict of duty. Other reported decisions on children cases, professional negligence actions, inquests, etc.
Prof. Memberships: Middle Temple
Career: Called to the Bar 1975 and joined 29 Bedford Row 1978.

CHAISTY, Paul
40 King St (Philip Raynor QC), Manchester (0161) 832 9082
Recommended in Chancery, Commercial (Litigation), Insolvency/Corporate Recovery
Specialisation: Insolvency, administration, receivership, director disqualification, banking, commercial landlord and tenant. Partnership. Commercial Litigation.
Prof. Memberships: Northern Chancery Bar Association, Chancery Bar.
Career: CIS v Argyll, House of Lords 1997. Re Sankey. On DTI Panel re Directors Disqualification. Re Sutton. Recorder.

CHAMBERS, Dominic
Brick Court Chambers (Christopher Clarke QC), London (020) 7379 3550
Recommended in Commercial (Litigation)
Specialisation: Principal area of practice is commercial law, including banking, conflicts, negotiable instruments, insurance & reinsurance, guarantees and indemnities. Also handles commercial fraud, partnership and professional negligence. Professional clients predominantly major City and international law firms and law firms in the Channel Islands. Extensive experience of impact of US banking and commercial law in England and commercial arbitrations (as Counsel and as arbitrator).
Prof. Memberships: COMBAR.
Career: Called to the Bar and joined 1 Hare Court in 1987. Joined the Chambers of Christopher Clarke QC in September 1997.
Personal: Educated at Harrow School 1976-1981 and King's College, London 1983-86. Born 28th February 1963. Lives in Surrey.

CHAPMAN, Vivian R.
9 Stone Buildings (Michael Ashe QC, SC), London (020) 7404 5055
Recommended in Traditional Chancery
Specialisation: Property litigation with particular interest in Law of Commons and Greens. Described as "a barrister with great experience of this branch of the law" by Lord Hoffmann in R v Oxfordshire CC ex p Sunningwell PC [2000] AC 335 at p348g. Recent reported cases; R. v Suffolk County Council Ex Parte Steed [1997] 1 EGLR 131 (Greens), Fitzpatrick v Sterling Housing Association Ltd [1999] 3 WLR 1113 (Landlord and Tenant); Bettison v Langton [2000] CL. 54 (Commons); Price Meats Ltd v Barclays Bank plc, The Times 19 January 2000 (forgery of cheques); Fraser v Canterbury Diocesan Board of Finance, The Times 22 February 2000 (School Sites Act 1841).
Prof. Memberships: Lincoln's Inn: Middle Temple.

CHARMAN, Andrew
St Philip's Chambers (Rex Tedd QC), Birmingham (0121) 246 7000
acharman@st-philips.co.uk
Recommended in Chancery
Specialisation: Company law, commercial law, insolvency, financial services, professional negligence, real property, trusts, wills and probate, litigation, advisory and drafting.
Prof. Memberships: Member of the Chancery Bar Association and the Midland Chancery and Commercial Bar Association. Member of the Chartered Institute of Arbitrators.
Career: Educated at Imberhorne School, East Grinstead and Clare College, Cambridge. Worked as a researcher at The House of Commons then articles with *Freshfields* in London and Tokyo followed by practice as a solicitor in *Freshfields'* corporate department.

CHAWLA, Mukul
9-12 Bell Yard (D. Anthony Evans QC), London (020) 7400 1800
Recommended in Crime, Fraud: Criminal

CHERRY, John M. QC
8 Stone Buildings (John Cherry QC), London (020) 7831 9881
alanl@88stonebuildings.law.co.uk
Recommended in Personal Injury
Specialisation: Main areas of practice are personal injury, medical negligence, professional negligence. Involved in number of structured settlement cases.
Prof. Memberships: *Gray's Inn.*
Career: Cheshunt Grammar School and Council of Legal Education. Called to Bar in 1961. Recorder 1987. QC 1988. Member of Criminal Injuries Compensation Board since 1988.

CHERRYMAN, John QC
4 Breams Buildings (Christopher Lockhart-Mummery QC), London (020) 7430 1221/7353 5835
Recommended in Property Litigation
Specialisation: Moved from Lincolns Inn to *Breams Buildings* in 1992 to concentrate on property related litigation and advice, including mining, professional negligence, mortgage securities, contaminated land and rating as well as mainstream landlord and tenant and vendor and purchaser work. A Bencher of Grays Inn and a member of the Chancery Bar Association. Recent cases include TSB Bank v Camfield 1995 CA and Dunbar Bank v Nadeem 1998 CA (variants of O'Brien); Bentley v Gaisford 1996 CA (solicitors undertaking); Mannai Investment Co. v Eagle Star 1997 HL (validity of break notice); Shimizu (U.K.) v Westminster City Council 1997 HL (listed building: demolition or alteration); Attwell v Michael Perry & Co 1998 V-C (barristers immunity from suit for alleged negligence in property litigation). Satah Foundation v Datak Syed Kechik 1999 Borneo H. Ct. (breaches of fiduciary duty) Prudential Assurance v Lden Restaurants 1999 CA (curative effect of registration) SCB v PNSC 2000 CA (fraud) Morrells of Oxford v Oxford Utd FC 2000 CA (LPA 1925, s 79).

CHILD, John
Wilberforce Chambers (Edward Nugee QC), London (020) 7306 0102
Recommended in Traditional Chancery
Specialisation: Heavy trust work – advice and drafting and some litigation. In part this is private client work dealing with family trusts and landed estates. The remaining part is commercial trust work, mostly relating to the Society of Lloyd's.
Prof. Memberships: Chancery Bar Association; Revenue Bar Association; and Society of Trust and Estate Practitioners. Books – main contributor vol 19 (Sale of land) Encyclopaedia of Forms and Precedents (4th ed.). Forms of accumulation and maintenance Settlements for Encyclopaedia of Forms and Precedents (5th ed.) Vol 40.
Career: Firsts in Law at University of Southampton and Sidney Sussex College Cambridge. BA Scholar Sidney Sussex College. Droop Scholar and Tancred Common Law Student, Hon Soc of Lincoln's Inn. Supervisor in Law at Sidney Sussex and other Cambridge colleges 1966-1978.

CHIVERS, David
Erskine Chambers (Robin Potts QC), London (020) 7242 5532
Recommended in Banking, Company, Insolvency/Corporate Recovery

CHRISTIE, Richard
2 Pump Court (Philip Singer QC), London (020) 7353 5597
Recommended in Crime
Specialisation: All areas of criminal work but especially fraud and cases requiring substantial client care. Also general common law and family work. (i) R v Johnson (Aldin) [1995] 2 Cr. App. R. I (Albi and severance); (ii) Martin v Watson [1994] Q.B.425 and [1995] A.C.74 (malicious prosecution); (iii) R v Mian [1997] (£1.5million cannabis importation by high ranking Pakistani, said to have been framed by Pakistani Regime); (iv) R v Parr [1997] (Money laundering following cross-jurisdictional Eurobond fraud); (v) R v Phipps [1998] (Murder: educationally subnormal defendant, cut-throat defences). (vi) R v Robinson [1999] (Paedophile family: allegations of rape etc). (vii) R v Butler [1999] (Leading junior – major local government corruption fraud: stayed for abuse of process). (viii) R v Alkadiki [1999] ($3.5 million international banking fraud: stayed for abuse of process).(ix) R v Bosson [1999] Crim. L.R.596 (Handling/theft: Multiple Appropriating)
Career: Clifton College; Manchester University; *Touche Ross & Co (Accountants).*
Personal: Cinema and reading. Wife (solicitor) and three children.

CHUDLEIGH, Louise
Old Square Chambers (John Hendy QC), Bristol (0117) 927 7111
Recommended in Employment
Specialisation: Principal areas of practice are employment law, including discrimination, equal pay, internal disciplinary disputes, all post termination difficulties including unfair and wrongful dismissal and injunctive proceedings related to confidential information and restrictive covenants; sports law, particularly disciplinary and contractual disputes and personal injury.
Prof. Memberships: Employment Lawyers Association; Industrial Law Society, Association for Sport and the Law and Personal Injury Bar Association. Bar Sports Law Group.
Career: Called to the Bar 1987 (England and Wales), 1989 (Bermuda); member of Old Square Chambers since 1988; Honorary Lecturer in Labour Law at University of Kent at Canterbury.
Personal: All sports, particularly cycling, swimming and running.

CIUMEI, Charles
Essex Court Chambers (Gordon Pollock QC), London (020) 7813 8000
Recommended in Employment
Specialisation: All areas of employment law including sex, race and disability discrimination, transfers of undertakings (TUPE), industrial relations/strikes, breach of confidence and restrictive covenants. Recent cases include: Morse v Wiltshire County Council (disability discrimination); Credit Suisse v Padiachy (restrictive covenants/TUPE); Wandsworth v D'Silva (collective agreements/terms of employment); UCLH v UNISON (strike action); Hall v Woolston Hall Leisure Ltd (discrimination/illegal contracts).

CLARE, Michael
Octagon House Chambers (Andrew Lindqvist & Guy Ayers), Norwich (01603) 623186
Recommended in Crime

CLARK, Christopher QC
Pump Court Chambers (Guy Boney QC), London (020) 7353 0711
Recommended in Church: Church of England
Specialisation: Called 1969. Recorder of the Crown Court since 1986 Q.C. 1989. Bencher of Gray's Inn. Western Circuit common law practice in both criminal and civil work. Particular experience in complex fraud cases, and other serious criminal matters. Chanceller of the Diocese of Winchester since 1993, Deputy Chancellor of the Diocese of Salisbury, Portsmouth and Chichester. Member of the Ecclesiastical Judges Association Standing Committee. Church of England Reader.

CLARK, Fiona
8 New Square (Michael Fysh QC SC), London (020) 7405 4321
Fiona.clarke@Snowsquare.co.uk
Recommended in Intellectual Property
Specialisation: Specialises in all aspects of intellectual property law including related contractual and EC matters, breach of confidence and trade libel. Has a particular interest in trademarks copyright and designs (both registered and unregistered). Also has extensive experience of product branding and in media and entertainment law. Practice embraces a wide range of cases with technical content covering areas such as mechanical and construction engineering, computer software, electronics, architectural design and textiles. Publications include 'Encyclopedia of United Kingdom and European Patent Law' (editor). Reported cases include: Johnstone Safety v Peter Cook, Southco v Dzus Fasteners, Consorzio del Prosciutto di Parma v Marks and Spencer, Dalgetty v Food Brokers, McDonald v Graham, Coil Controls v Suzo, Norowzian v Arks.
Prof. Memberships: Intellectual Property Bar Association; Chancery Bar Association; The Intellectual Property Lawyers Organisation.
Career: Called to the Bar 1982.
Personal: Educated at Trinity College, Cambridge. Competent in French and German.

CLARK, Wayne
Falcon Chambers (Jonathan Gaunt QC & Kim Lewison QC), London (020) 7353 2484
Recommended in Property Litigation
Specialisation: Property litigation, including commercial leases, vendor and purchaser disputes, easements, restrictive covenants, mortgages and property related professional negligence.
Prof. Memberships: Chancery Bar Association, COMBAR.
Career: LLB (Lon), BCL (Oxon), former lecturer in law at QMC, London University. Contributor to Halsbury's Laws of England, Vol 27 (i), 4th ed, Landlord and Tenant. Contributor to Hill and Redman, Law of Landlord and Tenant, Standing Counsel (civil) to Attorney General, co-Author, Renewal of Business Tenancies Law Practice (Sweet & Maxwell 1997).
Personal: Keen chess player.

CLARKE, Andrew QC
Littleton Chambers (Michel Kallipetis QC), London (020) 7797 8600
Recommended in Employment
Specialisation: Experienced commercial employment lawyer, having appeared in these areas before all relevant courts and tribunals. Particular specialism in disputes relating to restrictive covenants and confidential information. Also handles company law and sport related matters, both relating to employment (including directors' duties) and generally. Acted for PLA in docks dispute, in relation to industrial action and the two year Industrial Tribunal. Appeared in numerous important cases on individual employment rights, sex and race discrimination, restrictive covenants and "garden leave" injunctions. Clients include major UK companies, solicitors' firms and senior employees, as well as leading sporting bodies, clubs and players.
Prof. Memberships: Employment Law Bar Association; Employment Lawyers Association; COMBAR (Committee Member).
Career: Called to the Bar 1980, QC 1997, joined *Littleton Chambers* in 1981.
Personal: Educated at Crewe County Grammar School, King's College London 1974-1977 (LL.B) and Lincoln College, Oxford 1977-1979 (BCL). Leisure pursuits include playing and watching cricket and football, and collecting modern prints and porcelain. Lives in Cheshunt. Born 23rd August 1956.

CLARKE, Gerard
Blackstone Chambers (P Baxendale QC and C Flint QC), London (020) 7583 1770
Recommended in Employment
Specialisation: Public, employment, broadcasting, sports, and media law. Recent interesting cases include Allen & Others v AMCO [2000] IRLR; Modalh v British Athletic Federation; R v North West Lancs. Health Authority ex parte A,B,G 1999 TLR, Scully UK v Lee 1998 IRLR, R v Rhonda Cynon Taf DC ex parte Evans [1999]; Wallace v Gregory 1998 IRLR, R v Riverside Mental Health NHS Trust ex parte London [1999] 3 WLR, Holly v Smyth 1998 IWLR, R v Cobham Hall School ex parte G [1998] ELR, Credit Suisse v Armstrong [1996] IRLR 450, Spring v Guardian Assurance PLC [1995] 2 AC 296 and Meade Hill v British Council [1995] 1CR 847.
Prof. Memberships: Employment Lawyers' Association, Employment Law Bar Association, Administrative Law Bar Association. Author of TUPE section in New Law Online Employment Law Service.
Career: Called to the Bar 1986.
Personal: Born 1962. Educated in Solihull and at Wadham College, Oxford (MA).

CLARKE, Nicholas
9 St. John Street (John Hand QC), Manchester (0161) 955 9000
clerks@9stjohnstreet.co.uk
Recommended in Crime
Specialisation: Defending cases of homicide; drug importation, production and distribution; sexual and physical abuse of children. Particular interest in cases with medical or psychiatric background and has extensive experience cross-examining expert witnesses including pathologists, neuroradiologists and paediatric specialists in various disciplines. Defended the first trial in this country where the Crown relied solely on an earprint identification and also the first murder trial to rely on earprints. R v Dallagher.
Prof. Memberships: Criminal Bar Association, Northern Circuit.
Career: Sheffield University, LLB. Called to the Bar, 1981. Assistant Recorder, 1999. Recorder 2000.
Personal: Married, two children. Chairman 3rd Hazel Grove Scout Group. Enjoys snooker and football.

CLARKSON, Patrick QC
1 Serjeants' Inn (Lionel Read QC), London (020) 7583 1355
Recommended in Parliamentary & Public Affairs, Planning
Specialisation: Planning, local government, environmental and Parliamentary.
Prof. Memberships: Planning & Environmental Bar Association.
Career: Called 1972, Silk 1991, Recorder 1996.

CLAYTON, Joanna
2 Harcourt Buildings (Mr Gerard Ryan QC), London (020) 7353 8415
clerks@2hb.law.co.uk
Recommended in Planning

CLAYTON, Richard
Devereux Chambers (Jeffrey Burke QC), London (020) 7353 7534
mailbox@devchambers.co.uk
Recommended in Administrative & Public Law: General
Specialisation: Principal areas of practice are public law and human rights/civil liberties. Public law embraces education, health care, prisoners' rights, regulatory and disciplinary matters and local government law. Also handles employment law (both individual and collective), discrimination law, European law and civil actions against the police. Acted in Attorney General v Blake (HL March 2000) (confiscation of royalties); RICS v Fryer (The Times, 17 May 2000) (CA – wasted costs); R v School Adjudicator ex p Wirral [2000] ELR (school admissions); R v Wirral ex p B [2000] ELR (special needs); Saga Oil v Bourgeois EAT June 2000 (discrimination claim worth £1.8 million); R v Swale BC ex p Marchant The Times, 17 November 1999 (CA – housing benefit); R v Lincolnshire Crown Court ex p Jude [1998] 1 WLR 24; Steward-Brady v United Kingdom (1998) 27 EHRR CD 284 (European Convention) and R v Press Complaints Commission, ex p Stewart-Brady (1997) 9 Admin LR 274 (privacy rights); R v Northamptonshire County Council ex p W [1998] ELR 314 (school expulsion); Bamber v United Kingdom [1998] EHRLR 110 (European Convention); R v Southwestern Magistrates ex p Cofie [1997] 1 WLR 585; Rai v United Kingdom (1995) EHRLR 92 (European Convention); R v Chief Constable of West Midlands Police ex p Wiley [1995] 1 AC 274 (public interest immunity); Hellewell v Chief Constable of Derbyshire [1995] 1 WLR 804 (breach of confidence); R v Northern & Yorkshire RHA ex p Trivedi [1995] 1 WLR 961 (disciplinary procedure for GPs); R v Home Secretary ex p Hickey No. 2 [1995] 1 WLR 734 (prisoners' rights); R v Chief Constable of South Wales ex p Merrick [1994] 1 WLR 663 (right to legal advice). Clients include pressure groups like Save Guy's Hospital Campaign, local authorities, PLCs and private individuals.
Prof. Memberships: Administrative Law Bar Association (Committee since 1996); Employment Law Bar Association; Liberty; Society of Labour Lawyers.
Career: Called to Bar 1977; *South Islington Law Centre* 1980-82; *Osler Hoskin Harcourt (Toronto)* 1983; returned to practice 1984; joined *Devereux Chambers* 1996.
Publications: Author of 'Practice and Procedure at Industrial Tribunals' (LAG) (1986); 'Civil Actions against the Police' (Sweet & Maxwell) (2nd edition 1992); 'Judicial Review Procedure' (Wiley) (2nd edition 1997); 'Law of Human Rights' (Oxford University Press) (2000).
Personal: Educated New College, Oxford. Leisure pursuits include reading, cinema, theatre and travel. Born 25th May 1954. Lives in London.

CLEGG, William QC
2 Bedford Row (formerly 3 Hare Court) (William Clegg QC), London (020) 7440 8888
Recommended in Crime, Fraud: Criminal
Specialisation: Specialist in defending cases of alleged fraud. Cases include Brent Walker, Alliance Resources plc, Butte Mining plc, R v Smith (£100 million bank fraud), R v Smithson (The Arrows fraud), R v De Vandiere (VAT fraud), R v Alder (international bank fraud), R v Vanderval (letter of credit fraud), R v Morley (fraudulent trading), R v Hales (solicitors legal aid

fraud). Cases of a more general nature include Serafinowicz (war crimes), R v Wardell (Nuneaton Building Society murder), R v Stagg (Wimbledon Common murder), R v Varathadasan (Tamil Tigers), R v McMahon (UDA terrorists), R v Sawoniuk (war crimes), Prosecutor v Tadic (war crimes, The Hague) and R v Duckenfield (Hillsborough Disaster). Has also been instructed in a lengthy public enquiry by the Medical Protection Society and many cases in the Court of Appeal Criminal Division and Divisional Court. Was a member of the standing committee of Justice on fraud trials and prepared submissions to the Fraud Trials Committee chaired by Roskill (HMSO 1986).
Prof. Memberships: Criminal Bar Association (Committee members); South Eastern Circuit (Committee member). Chairman Essex Bar Mess.
Career: Called to the Bar 1972 and joined present chambers in 1973. Took silk 1991. Appointed Recorder 1992. Head of Chambers 1995.
Personal: Educated at Bristol University (LL.B). Leisure pursuits include squash, cricket and wine. Born 5th September 1949.

CLIFFORD, James
7 Stone Buildings (Charles Aldous QC), London (020) 7405 3886
clerks@7stonebuildings.co.uk
Recommended in Pensions
Specialisation: Specialises in pensions and trusts and has general commercial chancery litigation practice. Reported cases handled include ITS v Rowe, Polly Peck v Henry, Re Scientific Investment Pension Plan, Edge v The Pensions Ombudsman, Hood Sailmakers Ltd v Axford, Miller v Scorey, Process Developments Ltd v Hogg, Coloroll Pension Trustees Limited v Russell, Thrells Ltd v Lomas Nestle v National Westminster Bank, LRT v Hatt, Mettoy Pensions Trustees v Evans. Contributor to Trust Law International, British Pensions Lawyer, and author of Pensions Title, Atkins Court Forms.
Prof. Memberships: Association of Pension Lawyers, Chancery Bar Association.
Career: Called to the Bar in 1984.
Personal: Educated at Oxford University.

CLOSE, Douglas
Serle Court (Lord Neill of Bladen QC), London (020) 7242 6105
clerks@serlecourt.co.uk
Recommended in Commercial Chancery
Specialisation: General commercial chancery litigation, in particular commercial fraud and trust litigation. Cases include: The Thyssen-Bornemisza litigation in Bermuda, Don King Productions Inc v Frank Warren & Ors, the Palumbo litigation and the Wahr-Hansen litigation in the Cayman Islands.
Prof. Memberships: Chancery Bar Association.
Career: Called 1991. Pupil to Michael Briggs QC and Frank Hinks QC
Personal: Born 1966. Educated at Berkhamsted School; Jesus College, Oxford (MA, BCL). Interests include theatre, restaurants, abstract art.

COBB, Stephen
One Garden Court Family Law Chambers (Eleanor Platt QC and Alison Ball QC), London (020) 7797 7900
s.cobb@onegardencourt.co.uk
Recommended in Family: Child Care including child abduction
Specialisation: Family law, including public and private law aspects of the Children Act 1989, adoption, child abduction and children cases with an international element, matrimonial finance, judicial review (mainly family law related), applications/appeals under Part X Children Act 1989 (registration of Childminding and day care services for children).
Prof. Memberships: FLBA.
Career: Called to the Bar in 1985.
Personal: Winchester College. Liverpool University (LL.B Hons. 1984) Born 12 April 1962. Lives in London. Married, three children.

COGHLAN, Terence QC
1 Crown Office Row (Robert Seabrook QC), London (020) 7797 7500
terence.coghlan@1cor.com
Recommended in Clinical Negligence
Specialisation: Covers all aspects of medical work including medical negligence. Has appeared for both plaintiffs and defendants in numerous medical negligence actions and arbitrations as well as regularly appearing in the GMC, GDC and other disciplinary bodies. Represented all the health authorities involved in the "Myodil" litigation and the defendant in Bolitho v City & Hackney HA (House of Lords). Clients have included the Medical Defence Union, Medical Protection Society, MDDUS, the Welsh Office and leading medical negligence solicitors. Has lectured and written on personal injury and medical negligence matters and has appeared on television. Has also acted as mediator.
Prof. Memberships: Professional Negligence Bar Association.
Career: Called in 1968. Recorder of the Crown Court 1989. QC 1993.
Personal: Education: New College, Oxford (BA, MA).

COGLEY, Stephen
Merchant Chambers (David Berkley QC), Manchester (0161) 839 7070
Recommended in Commercial (Litigation)
Specialisation: Commercial, Banking insolvency. Various reported cases in the fields of insolvency, shareholder disputes, banking, consumer credit/licensing and contract. Instructed frequently in banking and finance leasing cases by banks and finance houses and building societies. Clients include most of the major banks, several major finance houses. Acts in company disputes/shareholder disputes. Has been involved in many high profile cases involving prominent individuals. Has acted on behalf of leading academics, members of the judiciary and football clubs (for and against). Lectures solicitors for the Law Society - in commercial matters and directors' duties and director disqualification.
Prof. Memberships: Founder member of Northern Circuit Commercial Bar Association. Member of COMBAR and the Northern Chancery Bar Association.
Career: Called 1984.
Personal: Lives Lancashire and Scotland. Hobbies: fell running, mountaineering, rock climbing, anything with a hint of danger.

COHEN, Edward
11 Stone Buildings (Murray Rosen QC), London (020) 7831 6381
Recommended in Commercial Chancery

COHEN, Jonathan QC
4 Paper Buildings (Lionel Swift QC), London (020) 7583 0816
clerks@4pb.com
Recommended in Family: Matrimonial Finance
Specialisation: Practice encompasses all areas of family law, in particular matrimonial finance, professional negligence arising out of family law matters and childcare. Recent cases include Piglowska (House of Lords: ancillary relief (1999) 2FLR 763), N v N (ante nuptial contract: enforceability (1999) 2 FLR 745) and C v C (1997) 2 FLR 26 (financial provision: short marriage).
Prof. Memberships: Family Law Bar Association, Professional Negligence Bar Association.
Career: Called to the Bar 1974 and joined present chambers in 1975. Recorder and Silk 1997. Member, Mental Health Review Tribunal 2000.
Personal: School Governor. Born 1951.

COHEN, Lawrence QC
24 Old Buildings (Martin Mann QC & Alan Steinfeld QC), London (020) 7404 0946
Recommended in Company, Insolvency/Corporate Recovery

COHEN, Raphael
Mercury Chambers (Benjamin Nolan QC), Leeds (0113) 234 2265
Recommended in Family/Matrimonial
Specialisation: Specialist in matrimonial property work. Involved in cases with substantial assets and with a commercial bias including company accounts and contracts.
Career: Called to the Bar in 1981. A founder member of Mercury Chambers which is a specialist civil and commercial set.

COLE, Edward
Falcon Chambers (Jonathan Gaunt QC & Kim Lewison QC), London (020) 7353 2
cole@falcon-chambers.com
Recommended in Property Litigation
Specialisation: Real property.
Prof. Memberships: *Gray's Inn.*
Career: Called to the Bar in 1980.
Personal: Contributor to Megarry on the Rents Act 11th Edition; Specialist Editor Hill & Redman Law of Landlord and Tenant. Contributor Halsbury's Laws, vol 27, title Landlord and Tenant. Atkin's Court Forms: title Agriculture.

COLERIDGE, Paul QC
Queen Elizabeth Building (Paul Coleridge QC), London (020) 7797 7837
Recommended in Family: Matrimonial Finance
Specialisation: Principal area of practice is family law, mainly heavy financial disputes between wealthy spouses (frequently international) and child disputes involving both private and public law. Counsel for Baron Thyssen-Bornemisza during extensive matrimonial litigation 1983-85 and became his international legal adviser 1985-89, leaving chambers for this period. Current clients include a variety of high profile pop stars, media personalities, politicians and businessmen. Recent cases include W v W [1995] 2 FLR 259; A v A [1998] 2 FLR 180; Conran v Conran [1997] 2FLR 615; White v White [1998] 4 AER 659.
Prof. Memberships: Family Law Bar Association (Secretary 1992-94).
Career: Called to the Bar 1970 and joined current chambers in 1972. Took silk in 1993 and Recorder in 1995.
Personal: Educated at Cranleigh School 1962-1966 and College of Law 1967-1970. Born 30th May 1949. Lives in London.

COLLENDER, Andrew QC
2 Temple Gardens (Dermod O'Brien QC), London (020) 7822 1200
Recommended in Personal Injury
Specialisation: Wide experience of substantial personal injury actions with specialisations in occupational claims, clinical negligence, repetitive strain injuries, post traumatic stress disorder and disaster litigation. Recent high profile cases include Mughal v Reuters [1993], Amosu v Financial Times [1998], Frost v South Yorkshire Police [1998].
Prof. Memberships: London Common Law Bar Association. Professional Negligence Bar Association. Personal Injuries Bar Association.
Career: University of Bristol – LLB (Hons) 1968. Called Lincoln's Inn July 1969. Silk April 1991. Recorder January 1993. Deputy High Court Judge 1998.
Personal: Married, two sons. Interests: violin, sailing.

COLLIER, Peter QC
30 Park Square (J.W. Mellor), Leeds
(0113) 243 6388
Recommended in Church: Church of England

COLLINGS, Matthew
13 Old Square (Michael Lyndon-Stanford QC), London (020) 7404 4800
Recommended in Commercial Chancery, Company, Insolvency/Corporate Recovery
Specialisation: Company law (litigation and advisory work) including corporate reconstructions, takeovers and mergers, shareholders disputes, directors duties and disqualification. Reported cases include: British & Commonwealth, Leeds United, Carecraft, Manlon, Barings, UMB v Doherty, Legal Costs Negotiators and Astec. Corporate insolvency. Reported cases include: Arrows, BCCI, Harris Simons, Wallace Smith, Charnley Davies, Galileo Group, Vanilla Accumulation, Hamlet International and Atlantic Computers. Personal insolvency and bankruptcy. Reported cases include: Naeem, Murjani and Hadkinson. Regulatory work and financial services including extensive appearances in tribunals, public law and human rights (ex p McCormick), company and insolvency investigations (including Banking Act and criminal), the use of compelled evidence, and competition law. Commercial Chancery including: guarantees and securities, banking, share sale warranties and professional negligence. Reported cases include: The Law Society v. KPMG.
Prof. Memberships: Chancery Bar Association. Member, Insolvency Rules Advisory Committee.

COLLINS, Michael QC
Essex Court Chambers (Gordon Pollock QC), London (020) 7813 8000
clerksroom@essexcourt-chambers.law.co.uk
Recommended in Arbitration (International), Shipping
Specialisation: Insurance, shipping, conflict of laws, commercial and technical contract and tort disputes generally, arbitration.
Prof. Memberships: American Bar Association, International Bar Association, Commercial Bar Association
Career: University of Exeter LLB (First Class Hons). Called to the Bar 1971. Queen's Counsel 1988. Recorder 1997.
Personal: Born 1948.

COMYN, Timothy
2 Harcourt Buildings (Mr Gerard Ryan QC), London (020) 7353 8415
clerks@2hb.law.co.uk
Recommended in Parliamentary & Public Affairs
Specialisation: Planning, local government, compulsory purchase, environmental, parliamentary and administrative law.
Prof. Memberships: Planning and Environmental Bar Association, Administrative Law Association, Parliamentary Bar Mess, Member of SE Circuit.
Career: Called to the Bar 1980. Joined *2 Harcourt Buildings* in 1981. Educated at Ampleforth College and Hull University.

CONE, John
Erskine Chambers (Robin Potts QC), London
(020) 7242 5532
Recommended in Company

CONLON, Michael
One Essex Court (Lord Grabiner QC), London
(020) 7583 2000
Recommended in Tax
Specialisation: VAT, customs and excise duties and other indirect taxes, including investigations and litigation; European Community law; commercial litigation.
Prof. Memberships: Fellow of The Chartered Institute of Taxation (FTII); Fellow of The Institute of Indirect Taxation (FIIT); Fellow of The Institute of Advanced Legal Studies (FIALS); RBA; COMBAR; President of the VAT Practitioners Group; President of the Institute of Indirect Tax; Customs Practitioners Group; Fellow of the Institute of Continuing Professional Development (FICPD); Member British Industry in Sport (BISL); Court Assistant to The Guild of Tax Advisers; Tax Law Review Committee; Editor "VAT Intelligence". Member of the Editorial Board of De Voil.
Career: Enfield Grammar School; Queens' College, Cambridge; called to Bar 1974 (Inner Temple); mixed common law practice; Senior Legal Adviser, HM Customs & Excise (1977-86); KPMG (1986-88); Partner, Coopers & Lybrand (1988-91); *Freshfields* (1991-93); Solicitor (1992); Partner *Allen & Overy* (1993-97); returned to Bar.
Personal: Married; two children; recreations include music, literature, badminton; lives in East Sussex.

CONNOLLY, Joanne
8 King St (Keith Armitage QC), Manchester
(0161) 834 9560
jconnolly@eightkingstreet.co.uk
Recommended in Employment
Specialisation: All aspects of employment work from simple unfair dismissal and redundancy to the more complex discrimination cases and group actions under the Transfer of Undertakings, Working Time or Minimum Wage legislation both before the Empoyment Tribunal and at appeal. Also Personal Injury, including stress at work and bullying claims.
Prof. Memberships: The Employment Law Bar Association, the Employment Lawyers Association and the Professional Negligence Bar Association.
Career: LLB (Nottingham.) Called to the Bar in 1992. Awarded Council of Legal Education Studentship and Jules Thorn scholarship.

CONWAY, Charles
2 Bedford Row (formerly 3 Hare Court) (William Clegg QC), London (020) 7440 8888
Recommended in Crime
Specialisation: Criminal defence. Has appeared as either leader or junior counsel in many cases of national interest including the Security Express £6 million robbery, the series of Brinks Mat handling cases and the "Babes in the Wood" and Steven Lawrence murders. Regularly leads in major fraud and drug cases throughout England and Wales.
Prof. Memberships: SE Circuit and Criminal Bar Association.
Personal: Clare College Cambridge: BA (Cantab), LLB(Cantab). Called to the Bar in 1969.

COOK, Ian
One King's Bench Walk (Anthony Hacking QC), London (020) 7936 1500
Recommended in Family: Matrimonial Finance
Specialisation: Main areas of practice: matrimonial finance including recent experience involving UK and overseas based family run businesses and domestic and offshore trusts, public law children cases, child abduction, crime. Reported cases; Re H (Abduction: Acquiesence) [1997] 1 FLR 872, HL. Re S (Care Proceedings: Split Hearing) [1996] 2 FLR 773, FD.
Prof. Memberships: FLBA
Career: BA (Hons) 1st Class Philosophy, King's College London. CPE City of London Polytechnic.

COOK, Mary
2-3 Gray's Inn Square (Anthony Scrivener QC), London (020) 7242 4986
Recommended in Planning
Specialisation: Planning and local government work. Wide planning inquiry experience extending to all fields, both promoting and resisting development including enforcement, called-in applications and Local Plan appearances, the promotion of CPO particularly town centre and development corporation schemes, footpath and road closures. Extensive recent experience of non-food and food retail schemes, green belt and conservation/listed building issues. Court experience includes judicial review and high court challenges, Lands Tribunal claims, involving environmental, planning, property and vires issues.
Prof. Memberships: Planning and Environmental Bar Association.
Career: Called 1982, commenced practice from these chambers in 1985.

COOKE, Jeremy QC
7 King's Bench Walk (Jeremy Cooke QC), London
(020) 7910 8300
Recommended in Energy & Natural Resources, Insurance, Professional Negligence, Shipping
Specialisation: Specialises in all aspects of commercial law including insurance and reinsurance, shipping, professional negligence, international sale of goods (oil and gas in particular), energy, banking and international arbitration.
Prof. Memberships: Commercial Bar Association; London Maritime Arbitrators Association; LCIA; CEDR accredited mediator.
Career: Called to the Bar 1976 and joined present chambers in the same year. Took Silk 1990. Appointed Recorder 1998.
Personal: (MA Jurisprudence 1st class). Oxford University rugby Blue 1968 and 1969. Director of Christian Youth and Schools Charitable company, LICC Ltd. Leisure pursuits include golf. Born 28 September 1949. Lives in London.

COOKE, Nicholas QC
9 Park Place (Ian Murphy QC), Cardiff
(029) 2038 2731
Recommended in Chancery, Planning
Prof. Memberships: Wales and Chester circuit, Planning and Environmental Bar Association, Bristol and Cardiff Chancery Bar Association.
Career: King Edward's School, Birmingham. UCW Aberystwyth (1st Class Honours LL.B). Appointed Queen's Counsel in 1998.
Personal: Hockey, theatre.

COOKSLEY, Nigel
Old Square Chambers (John Hendy QC), London
(020) 7269 0300
cooksley@oldsquarechambers.co.uk
Recommended in Personal Injury
Specialisation: Principal area of practice for many years has been personal injury litigation and has a widespread practice throughout the country. Other areas of practice include professional negligence, product liability and sporting injuries.
Prof. Memberships: Personal Injury Bar Association, Association of Personal Injury Lawyers, London Common Law and Commercial Bar Association, Professional Negligence Bar Association.
Career: Called to the Bar in 1975.
Personal: Educated at Felsted School and Cambridge University. Lives in North Hertfordshire. Outside interests include sport.

COONAN, Kieran QC
6 Pump Court (Kieran Coonan QC), London
(020) 7583 6013
Recommended in Clinical Negligence
Specialisation: Specialises in health care law; clinical negligence; solicitors' negligence; product liability; personal injury; professional conduct matters (GMC/GDC/Privy Council); mental health law and criminal law.
Prof. Memberships: Professional Negligence Bar

Association; Personal Injury Bar Association; Criminal Bar Association.
Career: Called 1971; Commenced practice in 1974; Silk 1990; Head of Chambers 1991; Recorder 1996.

COOPER, John
3 Gray's Inn Square (Rock Tansey QC), London (020) 7520 5600
Recommended in Crime
Specialisation: Specialist in serious criminal law. Also deals with general common law.
Career: Called to the Bar in 1983. Member New South Wales Bar. Represented the British employees in the BCCI litigation. Butterworths' Law Prizeman. Successfully represented the Defendant in the 'Leah Betts' Ecstasy drug trials. Leading authority in Master of the Rolls court on the criminality of wheel clamping (Arthur v. Anker) and indictment rules (R v Wrench). Also R v Ward & Baker – The Times (Duress) and R v Plummer & Simpkins – Juveniles). Instructed for Louise Woodward by campaign committee. Commended by 'The Lawyer' in the category "Barrister of the Year 1998". Publications include Code E PACE (Sweet & Maxwell) and Judicial Review from the Magistrates Court (Sweet & Maxwell). Feature writer and reviewer for The Times Legal Section. Advisor to the emerging democracies in Eastern Europe upon criminal law and justice. Entry in Debrett's "People of Today" page 414.

COOPER, Mark
Chancery House Chambers (Adrian Dent), Leeds (0113) 244 6691
mark.cooper@chanceryhouse.co.uk
Recommended in Insolvency/Corporate Recovery
Specialisation: Specialises in business, commercial and financial law, in particular banking, corporate restructuring, insolvency (personal and company) and commercial disputes involving contractual, restitutionary and professional negligence claims.
Prof. Memberships: Chancery Bar Association, Insolvency Lawyers Association, Association of Business Recovery Professionals (R3) and Northern Chancery Bar Association.
Career: Investment banking, London and New York 1989-1995. Called to the Bar in March 1998 (Middle Temple Harmsworth Exhibitioner). Joined *Chancery House Chambers*, Leeds as a practising barrister in 1999.
Personal: Educated at Dame Allans Boys School, Newcastle upon Tyne 1979-1986 and Exeter College, Oxford 1986-1989 (MA in 1995).

CORBETT, James QC
St Philip's Chambers (Rex Tedd QC), Birmingham (0121) 246 7000
jcorbett@st-phillips.co.uk
Recommended in Chancery, Commercial (Litigation), Insolvency/Corporate Recovery
Also at Serle Court (Lord Neill of Bladen QC) Lincoln's Inn (020) 7242 6105
Specialisation: Practises in commercial, company, insolvency and employment law and particularly cases under Company Director's Disqualification Act.
Prof. Memberships: Fellow of Chartered Institute of Arbitrators. Member of Chancery Bar Association, Employment Law Bar Association and Professional Negligence Bar Association.
Career: LLB and LLM (European Legal Studies), University of Exeter. Called in 1975. Irish Bar (1981) and Northern Irish Bar (1994). Joined present chambers in 1983. Lecturer in European and commercial law, 1975-1977 (Leicester University). QC, 1999. Recorder, 2000 (Asst Recorder 1996-2000).

CORDARA, Roderick QC
Essex Court Chambers (Gordon Pollock QC), London (020) 7813 8000
Recommended in Shipping, Tax
Specialisation: Insurance and reinsurance litigation; shipping and shipbuilding work; banking; film industry litigation; oil and gas disputes; general business litigation; Indirect tax and duties law and VAT planning.
Career: Trinity Hall, Cambridge: BA (Law) (First class) 1974. Called to the Bar 1975. Queen's Counsel 1994.
Personal: Born 1953.

CORFIELD, Sheelagh
Recommended in Family/Matrimonial

CORNER, Timothy
4-5 Gray's Inn Square (Elizabeth Appleby QC & Duncan Ouseley QC), London (020) 7404 5252
Recommended in Administrative & Public Law: General, Planning
Specialisation: Major part of practice is in the fields of town and country planning and compulsory purchase, and public law including education, local government and environmental law. Planning work includes appeals throughout the country relating to housing, retail, employment, minerals, waste, listed buildings and conservation areas. Interesting recent cases include Delta v Secretary of State [1999] JPL 612 (Court of Appeal, planning conditions and obligations), R v Hillingdon LBC ex p. London Regional Transport [1999] LGR 543 (Court of Appeal, judicial review of local authority, powers to contract for services, R v Maldon ex p. Pattani [1999] 1 PLR 13 (Court of Appeal, judicial review, mening of Use Class A1), and R v Secretary of State for the Environment ex p. Slot [1998] JPL, 692 (Court of Appeal, Judicial Review, natural justice). Recent public inquiries include appearances for Baratt Homes, Land Securities PLC,Tesco, B&Q, Westminster City Council and Leeds City Council. Publications include article at [1998] JPL 301 'Planning, Environment and the European Convention on Human Rights'. Frequent speaker at conferences on planning and public law and human rights.
Prof. Memberships: Member of Planning & Environment Bar Association (Committee member and Chairman of Continuing Education) and the Administrative Law Bar Association.
Career: Called to the Bar 1981. Appointed to Attorney General's Supplementary Panel of Counsel 1995. Appointed Junior Counsel to the Crown [A Panel] 1999. Admitted to the Bar of Gibraltar 1996.
Personal: Educated at Bolton School 1966 to 1976 and Magdalen College, Oxford (Demy, MA Jurisprudence and BCL) 1976 to 1980. Languages include French and some Italian and Spanish. Leisure pursuits include singing (currently studying with Prof. Ian Kennedy at Guildhall School of Music and Drama), walking, gardens and comparative philology. Born 25th July 1958. Lives in London.

CORY-WRIGHT, Charles
39 Essex Street (Nigel Pleming QC), London (020) 7832 1111
Recommended in Personal Injury
Specialisation: Main areas of practice: professional negligence, personal injury, insurance, construction. Major cases: personal injury: Nicholls v Rushton (no recovery of damages for shock). Giles v Thompson (CA, HL) (legality of credit hire agreements); Campbell v Mylchreest; Sharp v Pereira (jurisdiction re interim payments); Cutter v Eaglestar (CA, HL) (a car park is not a "word" for the purpose of the RTA). Construction: Barclays v Fairclough (contributory negligence and contract). SAS v John Laing (retention of title clauses). Insurance: Banque Financiere v Skandia (insurers duty of utmost good faith).
Prof. Memberships: COMBAR.

COSGROVE, Patrick QC
Broad Chare Chambers (Eric A Elliott), Newcastle upon Tyne (0191) 232 0541
Recommended in Crime

COTTER, Barry
Old Square Chambers (John Hendy QC), Bristol (0117) 927 7111
Recommended in Personal Injury, Product Liability
Specialisation: All aspects of product liability law, personal injury, health and safety at work, public inquiries and multi-party actions. Appeared in Clapham Junction Rail Inquiry, Strangeways (Woolf) Inquiry, Ashworth Hospital Inquiry, Severn Tunnel Inquiry, Cowden, Southall and Ladbroke Grove Train Crash Inquiries. Cases include: Williams v BOC 2000 [PIQR] Q 253; MRS Environmental Service Ltd v Marsh [1997] 1 All ER 92; Coventry City Council v Ackerman [1995] Crim. L.R. 140; P&M Supplies v Walsall [1994] Crim L.R. 590; Deane v Ealing [1993] ICR 329; R v Secretary of State ex parte POA; The Times 28 October 1991. Main Counsel in the Guards and Shunters multi-party deafness action.
Prof. Memberships: Personal Injury Bar Association; Committee member 1995-1999.
Career: LLB; called to Bar in 1985.
Publications: Author 'Defective and Unsafe Products; Law and Practice' (Butterworths 1996).
Personal: LLB University College, Lincoln's Inn, Scholarship. Based in London and Bristol.

COULSON, Peter
Keating Chambers (Richard Fernyhough QC), London (020) 7544 2600
Recommended in Construction
Specialisation: Involved in all types of engineering, construction and related disputes, in the TCC and in arbitration in the UK, Hong Kong, USA and the West Indies; reported cases include: Ashville v Elmer; Ben Barrett v Boot; Barker v Leyden; British Airways v PDP and McAlpine; Copthorne v Bovis; Design 5 v Keniston; Kruger Tissues v Frank Galliers; McAlpine Humbrook v McDermott; Marston v Barnard; Regalian v LDDC; Wates v Bredero; Wessex v HLM; Woodspring v Venn.
Career: Qualified 1982; Gray's Inn; Member of Keating Chambers since 1984; associate of the Chartered Institute of Arbitrators 1990; contributor to 'Construction Law Yearbook'; contributing editor of 'Lloyds Law Reports'; co-author of 'Professional Negligence and Liability' (LLP).
Personal: Lord Wandsworth College; University of Keele (BA Hons Law, English 2.1). Born 1958; resides London. Interests: British art, architecture, music, comedy, cricket. Working knowledge of French.

COUSINS, Jeremy QC
St Philip's Chambers (Rex Tedd QC), Birmingham (0121) 246 7000
Recommended in Commercial (Litigation)

COWARD, J. Stephen QC
7 Bedford Row (David Farrer QC), London (020) 7242 3555
Recommended in Crime
Specialisation: Specialist in all aspects of serious crime from murder to fraud. Appeared in the following cases: 1. R v Stanley – assistant bosun Herald of Free Enterprise. 2. R v Nedrick and R v Slack – the liability of secondary parties in murder. 3. R v Ivor Jones and others – the leading authority on section 16 Firearms Act 1968. 4. R v Prime – espionage. 5. R v John Tanner – the murder of Rachel McLean, the Oxford undergraduate. 6. R v Leslie Jones – murder allegation turning on the cooling rate of dead bodies. 7. R v Hayes and others – acted for the SFO. 8. R v Cheung – acted for the SFO. 9. R v Robinson – the 'Yardie' trial. 10. R v Baroness de Stempel – acted for the Defendant.

Career: Educated at King James Grammar School, Huddersfield and University College, London (LL.B). 1962: Lecturer in Law and Constitutional History, University College, London and Bramshill Police College. 1964: Called to the Bar (Inner Temple). 1980: Appointed Recorder. 1984: Took Silk. 1997: High Court Examiner (The State of New York v Don King Boxing Promotions).
Personal: Born 1937, lives in Northampton. Leisure pursuits: gardening, wine, singing.

COX, Laura QC

Cloisters (Laura Cox QC), London (020) 7827 4000
lc@cloisters.com
Recommended in Clinical Negligence, Employment, Human Rights (Civil Liberties)
Specialisation: Practice is divided evenly between employment law, discrimination and professional (principally clinical) negligence with increasing public law and general human rights work. Employment work includes discrimination and equal pay and is predominantly appellate advisory work and representation, with some judicial review. Clinical negligence work involves claims of the utmost severity, including cerebral palsy. Recent cases include: Webb v EMO Air Cargo (pregnancy discrimination), R v MoD ex parte Smith & Others (dismissal of armed forces homosexuals), Burton and Rhule v De Vere Hotels (the 'Bernard Manning' case), Harrods v Elmi (employers' liability for acts of racial discrimination by third parties), FBU v Knowles and Johnson (meaning of 'industrial action'), Crees v Royal London Insurance/Greaves v Kwiksave (maternity – the right to return to work), Smith v Gardner Merchant (homosexual harassment in the workplace), P v S and Somerset County Council (compensation for transsexual discrimination), Sheffield and Horsham v UK (transsexuals birth certificates – amicus submissions to the ECHR on behalf of Liberty), Aydin v Turkey (submissions to the ECHR for Amnesty with Peter Duffy QC on the rape of women prisoners as torture and the requirements, under international standards, for the investigation into allegations of torture of detainees), Davies v Girobank plc, Halfpenny v IGE Medical Systems Ltd (maternity discrimination), Enderby and Others v Frenchay Health Authority (speech therapists – equal pay), D'Souza v London Borough of Lambeth (racial discrimination compensation), R v Secretary of State for Trade and Industry ex parte BECTU (qualifying period under Working Time Regulations, reference to ECJ), Bavin v NHS Pensions Agency (transsexuals' pension entitlements), Mahmood v Siggins (GP's negligent treatment of manic depressive), Drury v Grimsby HA (limitation), Bowler v Walker (negligent treatment of psychiatric patient), R v Secretary of State for Social Security ex parte Armstrong (denial of care component of disability living allowance). Clients include trade unions and individual members, applicants and respondents in employment and discrimination cases, the Equal Opportunities Commission, the Commission for Racial Equality and claimants and defendants in clinical negligence cases. Regular conference and seminar speaker or chair in her fields of practice. Author of discrimination chapter in 'Advising Gay and Lesbian Clients, A Lawyer's Guide' for Butterworths.
Prof. Memberships: Employment Law Bar Association, Professional Negligence Bar Association, Association of Personal Injury Lawyers, Administrative Law Bar Association, Personal Injuries Bar Association, Action for Victims of Medical Accidents, Legal Action Group, Liberty. Member of the Council, Justice.
Career: Appointed Recorder 1995 and part-time Judge at Employment Appeal Tribunal 2000. Elected Head of Chambers at Cloisters 1995. Chairman of Bar Council Sex Discrimination Committee and member of Equal Opportunities and General Management Committees. United Kingdom representative on the Internaional Labour Organisation Committee of Independent Experts. Elected Bencher of the Inner Temple 1999.
Personal: Educated at Wolverhampton High School for Girls 1963-1970 and London University 1970-1975 (LL.B and LL.M). Leisure pursuits (work and three children permitting) include music, cooking, theatre, cinema, watching football.

COX, Simon

Doughty Street Chambers (Geoffrey Robertson QC), London (020) 7404 1313
Recommended in Immigration

CRAMPIN, Peter QC

11 New Square (Sonia Proudman QC), London (020) 7831 0081
Recommended in Charities, Traditional Chancery
Specialisation: Chancery:- property litigation and advice, trusts, charities, pensions, insolvency, professional negligence, Court of Protection.
Career: Called 1976. 2nd Junior Counsel to the A-G in charity matters 1988-1993. Took silk 1993. Recorder.
Personal: Born 7 July 1946.

CRAN, Mark QC

Brick Court Chambers (Christopher Clarke QC), London (020) 7379 3550
Recommended in Media & Entertainment, Sport

CRANE, Michael QC

Fountain Court (Anthony Boswood QC), London (020) 7583 3335
Recommended in Aviation, Commercial (Litigation), Insurance
Specialisation: Practice covers general commercial litigation including aviation, insurance, reinsurance, conflinct of laws and professional negligence. Notable recent cases include Agnew v Lansforsakringsbolagen [2000] HL special juridiction in contract, Brussels Convention; Airbus Industrie v Patel [1999] HL anti-suit injunctions; Western Digital v British Airways [2000] CA title to sue, Warsaw Convention; R v Airport Co-ordination Limited ex parte Guernsey [1999] Div Ct sale of slots; R v Airport Co-ordination Limited ex parte Aravco [1999] CA business aviation slots; Milor v British Airways [1996] CA jurisdiction, Warsaw Convention.
Personal: BA (Oxon). Called 1975. QC 1994.

CRANFIELD, Peter

3 Verulam Buildings (Christopher Symons QC & John Jarvis QC), London (020) 7831 8441
pcranfield@3verulam.co.uk
Recommended in Agriculture
Specialisation: Barrister specialising in banking and building society law, company law and corporate insolvency, project finance, security documentation, financial services, professional indemnity (including claims against accountants, auditors, financial advisers, agricultural consultants, solicitors, barristers, surveyors and valuers), pensions law, agricultural law, partnership, EU and Human Rights law. Cases include: Moodie v IRC; Sotnick v IRC (1990-1993); Faulks v Faulks (1992); Brown v Tiernan (1992); Barclays Bank v Layton Lougher & Co (1996); Meat and Livestock Commission v Manchester Wholesale Meat and Poultry Ltd (1996); Adams v Lancashire County Council (1996 and 1997); UCB Bank v Pinder (1997); Mercantile Credit v Fenwick (1997 and 1999); R v SoS for Environment and MAFF, ex p Standley; R v Same, ex p Metson (1997 and 1999); Halifax plc v Ghadami (1998-2000); Barclays Bank v Weeks, Legg & Dean (1998); J Rothschild Assurance V Collyear (1998); Stickley v Lewis (1999).
Prof. Memberships: Member of Commercial Bar Association, Chancery Bar Association, Association of Pension Lawers, Bar European Group, Association of Business Recovery Professionals.
Career: Qualified 1982.
Publications: Encyclopaedia of Forms and Precedents, 5th edition, vol 6: Building Societies (with Timothy Lloyd QC, now Lloyd J).

CRIGMAN, David QC

1 Fountain Court (David Crigman QC), Birmingham (0121) 236 5721
Recommended in Crime

CROOKENDEN, Simon QC

Essex Court Chambers (Gordon Pollock QC), London (020) 7813 8000
clerksroom@essexcourt-chambers.co.uk
Recommended in Energy & Natural Resources
Specialisation: Shipping. Insurance and Reinsurance: policies; proportional and excess of loss involving both Lloyds of London and the company market. Building/Engineering. Commodity sales. Arbitration. Energy & Utilities
Prof. Memberships: Fellow of the Chartered Institute of Arbitrators. Panel member, Lloyds of London Arbitration Panel. Accredited mediator.
Career: Corpus Christi College, Cambridge MA (Mechanical Sciences). Called to the Bar 1975. Queen's Counsel 1996.
Personal: Born 1946.

CROSS, James

4 Pump Court (Bruce Mauleverer QC), London (020) 7353 2656
chambers@4pumpcourt.com
Recommended in Professional Negligence
Specialisation: A general and varied practice in common law and commercial litigation/arbitration, but with particular emphasis on professional negligence (whether of architects, engineers, the medical profession, solicitors, surveyors or valuers), construction and civil engineering, insurance and reinsurance, banking, product liability, sale of goods and commodities and contractual disputes (both domestic and international).
Prof. Memberships: COMBAR, London Common Law and Commercial Bar Association, TECBAR.
Career: Called to the Bar in 1985 and joined 4 Pump Court in 1986.
Personal: Educated at Shrewsbury and Magdalen College, Oxford.

CROWLEY, Jane QC

30 Park Place (John Jenkins QC), Cardiff (029) 2039 8421
Recommended in Family/Matrimonial
(also One Garden Court Family Law Chambers (Miss Eleanor F Platt QC & Miss Alison Ball QC))
Specialisation: Child care and other Children Act applications, ancillary relief, public law including education, family related crime eg child abuse, rape etc.
Prof. Memberships: Family Law Bar Association (regional representative).
Career: LL.B (Hons) London. Graduated 1976. Practised 1976-1980 at *34 Park Place*. 1980 to date at *30 Park Place*. Recorder 1996. QC 1998. Director of Education, Wales and Chester Circuit. Deputy Judge of the Family Division (1999). Legal Chair of Mental Health Review Tribunal (1999).
Personal: Married, two children.

CROXFORD, Ian QC

Wilberforce Chambers (Edward Nugee QC), London (020) 7306 0102
Recommended in Commercial Chancery, Fraud: Criminal
Specialisation: Professional negligence (in particular accountants). Administrative law, construction and civil engineering. Crime ('white collar' and consumer protection). Cases include Morgan Crucible v Hill

Samuel & Co and Others; Wallace Smith Trust Co v Deloitte Haskins & Sells, 'Bermuda Fire'. Considerable experience in advising in respect of overseas work and has appeared many times in the Cayman Islands and also in Bermuda.
Prof. Memberships: Chancery Bar Association, COMBAR, Criminal Bar Association.
Career: Called to the Bar 1976; QC 1993; First Class Honours degree in law; joined Wilberforce Chambers in 1997.

CROXFORD, Thomas
Blackstone Chambers (P Baxendale QC and C Flint QC), London (020) 7583 1770
clerks@blackstonechambers.com
Recommended in Employment
Specialisation: Specialist in employment, financial services and commercial law. Particular interests in employment law-restraint of trade, compatability and discrimination. Recent cases: GRE v Arnold, DTI v Ward. Others: Blue Circle v MOD [1999] Ch. 289 CA; Christmas v Hampshire [1995] 2 AC 633.
Prof. Memberships: ELA, ELBA, COMBAR
Career: Clare College, Cambridge (MA). Call: 1992

CRYSTAL, Jonathan
Cloisters (Laura Cox QC), London (020) 7827 4000
jonathancrystal@cloisters.com
Recommended in Sport
Specialisation: Specialist sports lawyer. Notable cases include: McCord v. Cornforth and Swansea City, Watson and Bradford City v. Gray and Huddersfield Town, Redman v. British Lions, Sarfraz Nawaz v. Allan Lamb, Duffy v. Newcastle United FC, Margate Town v FA, Bayfield v Eagle Star, and Hinchcliffe v. BSMA. Advisory work including Prince Naseem Hamed, Brian Lara, Stan Collymore, Ellery Hanley, Robbie Fowler, ISL, Leeds United and Liverpool. Further specialism in defamation and business law.
Prof. Memberships: Bar Sports Law Group, British Association for Sport and Law, Combar and Sports Steering Group NSPCC.
Career: Called to the Bar 1972. *2* Harcourt Buildings 1973-1992. Cloisters 1992- the present. Legal Reader Associated Newspapers until 1985.
Personal: Educated Leeds Grammar School and Queen Mary College, University of London 1968-1971. Director, Tottenham Hotspur FC 1991-1993. Married with young children living in Central London.

CRYSTAL, Michael QC
3-4 South Square (Michael Crystal QC), London (020) 7696 9900
Recommended in Commercial Chancery, Company, Insolvency/Corporate Recovery
Specialisation: Commercial and financial law.
Career: Called to the Bar, Middle Temple, 1970; Queen's Counsel 1984; Bencher Middle Temple 1993; Senior Visiting Fellow Centre for Commercial Law Studies, University of London since 1987; DTI Inspector 1988-1989, 1992; Member Insolvency Rules Advisory Committee 1993-97; Deputy High Court Judge, since 1995; Member Financial Law Panel since 1996; Honorary Fellow, Queen Mary and Westfield College, University of London 1996; Honorary Fellow, Society for Advanced Legal Studies 1997.

CULLEN, Edmund
7 Stone Buildings (Charles Aldous QC), London (020) 7405 3886
clerks@7stonebuildings.co.uk
Recommended in Media & Entertainment
Specialisation: Bankruptcy and insolvency, company law, equity and trusts, landlord & tenant, partnership, professional negligence, property, easements, commercial litigation. Cases include: Re: MTI Trading Systems Ltd [1997], One Life v. Roy & Anor [1996], British Racing Drivers' Club Ltd. v. Hestall Erskine & Co. [1996], ADT v. BDO Binder Hamlyn [1995], Langton v. Langton & Anor [1995], Re: Thundercrest [1994], Busby & Anor v. Co-operative Insurance Society Ltd. [1993] Barclays Mercantile Business Finance Ltd. & Anor v. SIBEC Developments & Ors [1992].
Prof. Memberships: Chancery Bar Association.
Career: Called to the Bar 1990.
Personal: Educated at Winchester, University of Bristol.

CULLEN, Felicity
Gray's Inn Tax Chambers (Milton Grundy), London (020) 7242 2642
Recommended in Tax
Specialisation: All aspects of revenue law including in particular commercial and corporate tax, capital gains tax, stamp duty, taxation of individuals and tax litigation.
Prof. Memberships: Revenue Bar Association. Chancery Bar Association. Called to the Bar 1985. Joined Gray's Inn Tax Chambers 1986.
Career: LL.B Birmingham (Class 1 Hons), LL.M Cantab.

CULLUM, Michael
Albion Chambers (J.C.T. Barton QC), Bristol (0117) 927 2144
Recommended in Crime

CUNNINGHAM, Graham
Littman Chambers (Mark Littman QC), London (020) 7404 4866
Recommended in Alternative Dispute Resolution, Information Technology

CUNNINGHAM, Mark
13 Old Square (Michael Lyndon-Stanford QC), London (020) 7404 4800
Recommended in Commercial Chancery
Specialisation: General chancery practitioner, with a bias towards commercially orientated litigation and particular specialisms in the disqualification of directors and company law. He has appeared in reported cases concerning: company law, directors' disqualification, personal insolvency, sale of land, landlord and tenant, rent reviews, easements, land registration, copyright, passing off, entertainment law, the Inheritance Act, subrogation, the Court of Protection, the Copyright Tribunal and betting and gaming. He has also been appointed as a DTI Inspector in relation to insider dealing matters. His high profile cases in the last year include appearing for a number of witnesses in the BSE Inquiry and acting in the cases involving Victor Chandler and Francis Bacon.
Prof. Memberships: Chancery Bar Association, Patent Bar Association.
Career: Called 1980. Appointed Junior Counsel to the Crown (Chancery), February 1992.
Personal: Educated at Stonyhurst College and Magdalen College Oxford (BA History). Born 6 June 1956. Lives in Buckinghamshire. Four children.

CUSWORTH, Nicholas
1 Mitre Court Buildings (Bruce Blair QC), London (020) 7797 7070
cusworth@imcb.com
Recommended in Family: Matrimonial Finance
Specialisation: Ancillary relief. Child abduction. Child care and residence, both public and private law. Co habitates and inheritance disputes.
Prof. Memberships: Family Law Bar Association. Committee member elected 1998.
Career: MA (Oxon). Called to the Bar 1986. Occasional lecturer for Professional Conferences.
Publications: Contributor to 'Essential Family Practice 2000'.
Personal: Married (to Rachel Platts of Counsel), one daughter.

DAGNALL, John
9 Old Square (Michael Driscoll QC), London (020) 7405 4682
Recommended in Commercial Chancery
Specialisation: Specialisations are chancery, commercial and property litigation; including: banking, trusts, civil fraud, insolvency, property (including mortgages and landlord and tenant) and professional negligence.
Prof. Memberships: Member of Chancery Bar Association, Professional Negligence Bar Association and Parliamentary Bar Mess.
Career: Bristol Grammar School, St John's College, Oxford (BA (Jurisprudence – 1st Class), BCL). Called Nov 1983, tenant Mar 1985.
Personal: Family, church, real tennis, bridge. Further details on application.

DARLING, Paul QC
Keating Chambers (Richard Fernyhough QC), London (020) 7544 2600
Recommended in Arbitration (International), Construction
Specialisation: Building and engineering cases, important cases include: Temloc v Errill; Richard Roberts v Douglas Smith; Wyatt v Gleeson; Yeandle v Wynn Realisations; Vascroft v Seeboard; Mooney v Boot; PLC v McAlpine; McAlpine v Unex; Hunt v Paul Sykes; Chatbrown v McAlpine; Barking & Dagenham v Stamford Asphalt; Holbeck Hall Hotel v Scarborough; Flannery v Halifax; BHP v British Steel.
Career: Qualified 1983. Middle Temple. Queens Counsel 1999. Director Family Pharmaceutical Company; Editor 'Construction Law Newsletter'; member of editorial team ' Keating on Building Contracts'.
Personal: Winchester College; St Edmund Hall, Oxford (1981 BA, 1982 BCL). Horseracing, Newcastle United.

DASHWOOD, Robert
Renaissance Chambers (Brian Jubb & Henry Setright), London (020) 7404 1111
Recommended in Family: Child Care including child abduction

DAVEY, Michael
4 Field Court (Steven Gee QC), London (020) 7440 6900
Recommended in Shipping

DAVIDSON, Katharine
1 Mitre Court Buildings (Bruce Blair QC), London (020) 7797 7070
Recommended in Family: Matrimonial Finance
Specialisation: Handles all types of family law, but principally financial relief claims.
Prof. Memberships: Family Law Bar Association.
Career: Educated at Epsom College 1978-80 and the University of Oxford 1981-84. Born 19th June 1962. Called to the Bar in 1987 and joined *1 Mitre Court Buildings* in 1988.

DAVIDSON, Nicholas QC
Four New Square (Justin Fenwick QC), London (020) 7822 2000
n.davidson@4newsquare.com
Recommended in Professional Negligence
Specialisation: Solicitors' and financial negligence. Other main areas of work cover general commercial cases, including computer litigation.
Prof. Memberships: Professional Negligence Bar Association (Chairman 1997-1999), Bar European Group, COMBAR, Chancery Bar Association, Society for Computers and Law.
Career: Called 1974; joined present Chambers 1999. Silk 1993.
Personal: Educated at Winchester 1964-1969 (Scholar) and Trinity College Cambridge (Exhibitioner in Economics) 1969-1972. Certificate of Honour, Bar Finals.

DAVIES, Helen
Brick Court Chambers (Christopher Clarke QC), London (020) 7379 3550
davies@brickcourt.co.uk
Recommended in Commercial (Litigation)
Specialisation: All aspects of Commercial and EU law, including professional negligence, insurance/reinsurance, banking, oil and gas disputes, competition and human rights.
Career: Called November 1991. *Brick Court Chambers* (1992-present). Stage in European Commission, DGIV (Transport) 1993. Appointed Member of the B Panel to the Crown, 1999.

DAVIES, Huw
30 Park Place (John Jenkins QC), Cardiff (029) 2039 8421
Recommended in Crime
Specialisation: Criminal law, particularly Customs and Excise work and fraud.
Prof. Memberships: C.B.A.
Career: LL.B. M.Phil. A Recorder. Standing Counsel to HM Customs and Excise.

DAVIES, J. Meirion
Temple Chambers (David Aubrey QC), Cardiff (029) 2039 7364
Recommended in Crime

DAVIES, Jane
Crown Office Chambers (Michael Spencer QC & Christopher Purchas QC), London (020) 7797 8100
Recommended in Construction

DAVIES, Lindsay
Fenners Chambers (Lindsay Davies), Cambridge (01223) 368761
Recommended in Family/Matrimonial

DAVIES, Nicola QC
3 Serjeants' Inn (Philip Naughton QC), London (020) 7427 5000
Recommended in Clinical Negligence
Specialisation: Medical law including inquiries, professional disciplinary tribunals and crime. Cases include R v Doctor Harold Shipman, BSE Inquiry, GMC – case of Bristol heart surgeons, R v Doctor Reginald Dixon, Chairman of the Committee of Inquiry into the death of Jonathan Newby (Mental Health).
Career: Called to the Bar in 1976. Silk 1992. Recorder 1998.
Personal: Birmingham University (LL.B).

DAVIES, Owen QC
Two Garden Court (I. Macdonald QC & O.Davies QC), London (020) 7353 1633
Recommended in Administrative & Public Law: General, Crime, Human Rights (Civil Liberties), Immigration

DAVIES, Rhodri QC
One Essex Court (Lord Grabiner QC), London (020) 7583 2000
Recommended in Banking, Commercial (Litigation)
Specialisation: Principal area of practice is banking, professional negligence and general commercial work including swaps, letters of credit, negotiable instruments, mandates, facility letters, loan agreements and other financial disputes with or between banks. Acted in recent swaps litigation, representing various banks in Hazell v London Borough of Hammersmith & Fulham and in restitution claims in Kleinwort Benson v Birmingham and Kleinworth Benson v Lincoln. Also handles general commercial work, encompassing contractual disputes, sale of goods, arbitration, insurance, reinsurance and professional negligence.
Prof. Memberships: South Eastern Circuit, LCLCBA.
Career: Called to the Bar in 1979 and joined 1 Essex Court in 1980. QC 1999.
Personal: Educated at Winchester College 1970-1974 and Downing College, Cambridge 1975-1978. Leisure pursuits include running, walking and sailing. Born 29th January 1957. Lives in Harpenden, Herts.

DAVIES, Richard QC
39 Essex Street (Nigel Pleming QC), London (020) 7832 1111
Recommended in Personal Injury

DAVIES, Stephen QC
Guildhall Chambers (Adrian Palmer QC), Bristol (0117) 927 3366
Recommended in Commercial (Litigation), Insolvency/Corporate Recovery, Traditional Chancery

DAVIES, Stephen
8 King St (Keith Armitage QC), Manchester (0161) 834 9560
sdavies@eightkingstreet.co.uk
Recommended in Commercial (Litigation)
Specialisation: Practice: Commercial and insurance litigation, construction litigation and arbitration, professional negligence cases (particularly solicitors, architects, engineers and surveyors) and banking disputes, predominantly in North West.
Prof. Memberships: Northern Circuit Commercial Bar Association; Tec Bar; Professional Negligence Bar Association.
Career: Educated at Baines' School, Poulton-le-Fylde and Downing College, Cambridge. Called to the Bar in 1985 and joined current chambers in 1986 after 12 months' pupillage in London.

DAVIES, Trefor
Iscoed Chambers (Trefor Davies), Swansea (01792) 652988/9
Recommended in Crime

DAVIES-JONES, Jonathan
3 Verulam Buildings (Christopher Symons QC & John Jarvis QC), London (020) 7831 8441
clerks@3verulam.co.uk
Recommended in Banking
Specialisation: General commercial work, including banking, insurance and reinsurance, fraud, professional negligence, sale of goods and commercial property.
Career: MA (Cantab). Worked as an investment banker 1988-1992. Called to the Bar in 1994 and joined *3 Verulam Buildings*. In 1995 spent 6 months as a judicial assistant in the Commercial Court.

DAVIS, Nigel QC
7 Stone Buildings (Charles Aldous QC), London (020) 7405 3886
clerks@7stonebuildings.co.uk
Recommended in Commercial Chancery, Company, Insolvency/Corporate Recovery, Media & Entertainment, Partnership
Specialisation: Principal area of practice is chancery, with emphasis on company, insolvency, banking, property and trust litigation and also general commercial litigation, both domestic and international. Has appeared in numerous reported cases, on subjects extending to: corporate and shareholders disputes; constructive trusts and tracing actions; international banking and fraud litigation; insolvency; and real property. Acted as counsel to the inquiry of the Board of Banking Supervision into the collapse of Barings Bank. Other areas of practice include professional negligence (solicitors); partnership; and media and entertainment.
Personal: Education: Charterhouse; University College, Oxford (MA).

DAVIS-WHITE, Malcolm
4 Stone Buildings (Philip Heslop QC), London (020) 7242 5524
clerks@2stonebuildings.law.co.uk
Recommended in Company, Insolvency/Corporate Recovery
Specialisation: Principal area of practice encompasses company, insolvency and financial services law. Co-author (with Adrian Walters) on 'Directors' Disqualification and Practice'. Contributor to 'Atkin' Vol. 9 (Companies), and Vol. 10 (Companies winding up).
Career: Called to the Bar in 1984 and joined present chambers in 1985. Appointed Junior Counsel to the Crown (Chancery) in 1994.
Personal: Educated at St Edmund's College, Old Hall Green, Ware 1969-1978 and Hertford College, Oxford 1979-1983. Born 18th September 1960. Lives in Sidlesham, Chichester.
Prof. Memberships: Member of the Chancery Bar Association and Commercial Bar Association (COMBAR).

DE FREITAS, Anthony
4 Paper Buildings (Jean Ritchie QC), London (020) 7353 3366
Recommended in Agriculture
Specialisation: Sporting and entertainment contracts, professional negligence. Agricultural holdings. Warren v Mendy 1989 IWLR 853, Featherston v Staples 1986 IWLR 861, John v George 1996 EGLR 1 .
Prof. Memberships: Professional Negligence Bar Association. Agricultural Law Association.
Career: Stonyhurst College, St. John's College Oxford. MA Oxon, Assistant Recorder.
Personal: Married, cricket, bridge, horse racing, reading.

DE GARR ROBINSON, Anthony
One Essex Court (Lord Grabiner QC), London (020) 7583 2000
Recommended in Commercial (Litigation), Company, Insolvency/Corporate Recovery, Sport
Specialisation: Practice includes a broad range of substantial commercial and chancery litigation, with an emphasis on international fraud, company law, insolvency, restitution and banking. Also has experience in sport and entertainment disputes.
Prof. Memberships: Commercial Bar Association and Chancery Bar Association.
Career: Called to the Bar in 1987. He is also a member of the Bar of the Eastern Caribbean Supreme Court in the Territory of the Virgin Islands.
Personal: Born in 1963. Educated at University College, Oxford 1981-1985. Kennedy Scholar at Harvard University 1985-1986.

DE HAAN, Kevin QC
3 Raymond Buildings (Clive Nicholls QC), London (020) 7400 6400
chambers@threeraymond.demon.co.uk
Recommended in Consumer, Licensing
Specialisation: Specialises in all areas of environmental law, consumer protection and licensing. Environmental practice includes all relevant aspects of EC law and covers pollution control, waste regulation, statutory nuisances and environmental issues arising in road transport licensing and health and safety regulation. Experience includes conducting proceedings before various regulatory bodies, associated judicial reviews, defending criminal prosecutions. Contributor to 'Pollution in the UK' (Sweet & Maxwell 1995). Clients have included a number of public corporations and institutions. Consumer protection practice includes all aspects of regulation under the Fair Trading Act 1973, Trade Description Act 1968, the Medicines Act 1968, the Consumer Credit Act 1974, the Consumer Protection Act 1987, the Weights and Measures Act 1985, the Food Safety Act 1990 and the relevant EC law. Has par-

ticular expertise in the regulation of e-commerce at national, European and International level. Contributor to 'Food Safety, Law and Practice'(Sweet & Maxwell 1994). Clients have included a number of major public companies, former nationalised industries, banks, building societies and other institutions. Licensing practice includes all aspects, particularly betting, gaming and lotteries. Has considerable experience of proceedings before various reglatory bodies, appeals and associated judicial reviews. Clients have included major casino operators, bookmaking concerns and promoters of lotteries and competitions. Has particular expertise and experience in all aspects of Internet gambling. Other areas of practice include some extradition and commercial fraud work.
Prof. Memberships: Local Government, Environmental and Planning Bar Association.
Career: Called to the Bar 1976.
Personal: Educated at the Universities of London and Brussels (VUB).

DE HAAS, Margaret QC
7 Harrington Street Chambers (David Steer QC/Robert Fordham QC/Iain Goldrein QC), Liverpool (0151) 242 0707
goldhaas@netcom.co.uk
Recommended in Family/Matrimonial
Specialisation: Ancillary relief; child care; medical negligence, personal injury.
Prof. Memberships: Family Law Bar Association; Professional Negligence Bar Association.
Career: LL.B (Hons) (Bristol). Author of several books on personal injury litigation and ancillary relief.
Personal: Theatre; reading; my children.

DE LACY, Richard
3 Verulam Buildings (Christopher Symons QC & John Jarvis QC), London (020) 7831 8441
clerks@3verulam.co.uk
Recommended in Insolvency/Corporate Recovery
Specialisation: Principal area of practice is commercial law, particularly banking, finance, financial services, accountants', solicitors' and barristers' professional indemnity, insolvency, company law, property law and arbitration. Acts for clearing banks, major accountancy firms and leading insolvency practitioners.
Prof. Memberships: Fellow of The Chartered Institute of Arbitrators, COMBAR, Chancery Bar Association; Institute of Chartered Accountants Practice Regulation Review Committee; CEDR Accredited Mediator.
Career: Called to the Bar 1976. Harmsworth Scholar, Middle Temple. QC 2000.
Personal: Educated at Hymers College, Hull (1965-1971) and Clare College, Cambridge 1972-1975 (MA 1979). Born 4th December 1954.

DE MELLO, Rambert
6 King's Bench Walk (Sibghat Kadri QC), London (020) 7583 0695 / 7353 4931
Recommended in Immigration

DE SILVA, Desmond QC
2 Paper Buildings (Desmond de Silva QC), London (020) 7556 5500
Recommended in Crime
Specialisation: Crime, commercial fraud, extradition, constitutional law. R v Levitt and others (City Fraud); R v Jaqui Oliver (Fraud - Britain's foremost female National Hunt Jockey); R v Lord Brocket (Insurance Fraud); R v Ghizzelli (EEC Fraud); R v Segers (Football match fixing/corruption); R v Ron Atkinson (road rage); R v Nagi (aircraft highjacking)
Prof. Memberships: Criminal Bar Association; British Academy of Forensic Sciences.
Career: Middle Temple - called to the Bar of England and Wales 1964. QC 1984. Deputy Circuit Judge 1976-1984. Apart from the UK, has practised in many other countries and is a member of many foreign Bars. Has appeared abroad in many cases involving high treason and the death penalty.
Personal: Married, one daughter. Leisure interests: travelling, politics.

DEIN, Jeremy
3 Gray's Inn Square (Rock Tansey QC), London (020) 7520 5600
Recommended in Crime
Specialisation: Specialises in defence crime, now regularly instructed in leading work. Particular interest in appellate work having conducted many appeals for 'Justice'. Happy to undertake appellate work on pro bono basis. Has appeared in many reported CCA cases. Also, has acted as legal adviser to the BBC's 'Rough Justice'.
Prof. Memberships: Middle Temple.
Career: 2.1 Hons, University of London. Former Lecturer in the Law of Evidence and Criminal Procedure.
Personal: Married with three children. Leisure interests include sport, reading and travel.

DENNEY, Stuart
Deans Court Chambers (H.K. Goddard QC), Manchester (0161) 214 6000
Recommended in Crime
Specialisation: Crime, including fraud. Actions against the Police.
Prof. Memberships: Criminal Bar Association
Career: St. Johns School, Leatherhead. Gonville & Caius College Cambridge 77-80. M.A.
Personal: Married, 1 son. Interests: Rugby Union, Malt Whisky.

DENNIS, Mark Jonathan
6 King's Bench Walk (Michael Worsley QC), London (020) 7583 0410
worsley@6kbw.freeserve.co.uk
Recommended in Crime
DX: 26 Chancery Lane Fax: (020) 7353 8791 [SPEC] Crime
Prof. Memberships: C.B.A.
Career: Call: 1977. Senior Treasury Counsel. (Treasury Counsel since 1993)

DENNISON, Stephen
Atkin Chambers (John Blackburn QC), London (020) 7404 0102
Recommended in Construction

DENNYS, Nicholas QC
Atkin Chambers (John Blackburn QC), London (020) 7404 0102
Recommended in Construction
Specialisation: Building and Civil Engineering disputes and related matters including Professional Negligence, Insurance, Conflict of Laws and general commercial work. Extensive arbitration experience as advocate, before both international and domestic tribunals. International disputes usually involving large multi-national corporations or Governmental Agencies in many parts of the world. Appointed to act as sole arbitrator under the Common and Commercial Bar Association Scheme and as Chairman by the London Court of International arbitration.
Career: Admitted to Middle Temple August 1973; Called to the Bar November 1975; Queen's Counsel May 1991.
Personal: Born 14th July 1951. Educated Eton College and Brasenose College, Oxford (P.P.E.).

DENYER, Roderick QC
St John's Chambers (Christopher Sharp QC), Bristol (0117) 921 3456
Recommended in Crime

DENYER-GREEN, Barry
Falcon Chambers (Jonathan Gaunt QC & Kim Lewison QC), London (020) 7353 2484
clerks@falcon-chambers.com
Recommended in Property Litigation
Specialisation: Compulsory purchase and compensation; planning; agricultural tenancies. Member DETR compulsory purchase working party 1998-2000. Author 'Compulsory Purchase and Compensation' (ed 2000). Joint author 'Development and Planning Law' (3rd ed 1999). Editor 'Estates Gazette Law Reports'. Joint editor 'Planning Law Reports'.
Prof. Memberships: Fellow, Royal Institution of Chartered Surveyors.Honorary Fellow, College of Estate Management.
Career: LLM, PhD (London University).

DEVONSHIRE, Simon
5 Paper Buildings (Richard King), London (020) 7815 3200
Recommended in Employment
Specialisation: All aspects of employment and entertainment law, including dismissal, discrimination, restrictive covenants and confidential information, agency, recording, publishing and management disputes, copyright and intellectual property.
Prof. Memberships: Employment Law Bar Association. LCLCBA.
Career: Called 1988.

DICKENS, Paul
5 New Square (Jonathan Rayner James QC), London (020) 7404 0404
Recommended in Media & Entertainment
Specialisation: Principal areas are copyright and design rights, moral rights, performers' rights, trade marks, passing off, confidential information, media and entertainment law and computer law. Particular interest in musical copyright infringement, information technology, multimedia and Internet. Clients include leading companies and artistes in the entertainment field, national newspapers, broadcasters and Internet Service Providers. Joint consulting editor, intellectual property, Butterworths' 'Encyclopaedia of Forms and Precedents', entertainment volume. Contributor to new edition of 'Copinger & Skone James on Copyright'.
Prof. Memberships: Intellectual Property Bar Association, Chancery Bar Association.
Career: M.A. (Cantab), ARCO, former Organ Scholar.
Personal: Recitalist/ accompanist at local concerts, school governor, skiing.

DICKER, Robin QC
3-4 South Square (Michael Crystal QC), London (020) 7696 9900
Recommended in Banking, Civil Fraud, Company, Energy & Natural Resources, Insolvency/Corporate Recovery
Specialisation: Called to the Bar in 1986 and a Harmsworth Exhibitioner. Exhibitioner at Brasenose College, Oxford; BA (jurisprudence) and BCL. Appointed Queen's Councel in 2000. Specialises in business, commercial and financial law, in particular banking, corporate restructuring and insolvency. He has acted in relation to almost all of the recent major corporate collapses including BCCI (for the liquidators), MCC (for the administrators) and Olympia & York (for the administrators). Recent reported cases include Three Rivers District Council v Bank of England [2000] 2. W.L.R. 1220 (House of Lords); Morris v Agrichemicals; BCCI (No.8) [1998] A.C. 214 (House of Lords; the leading decision on charge-backs and flawed assets; Re J N Taylor Finance Property Ltd [1999] BCC 197 (orders in aid under s.426 of the Insolvency Act 1986); BCCI (Overseas) v Habib Bank [1999] 1 W.L.R. 42 (insolvency set-off). Was also instructed by the Administrators in MCC v Coopers &

Lybrand and by BZW in British & Commonwealth v BZW. Also advises in relation to securities, debt discounting and factoring, debt issues, securitisations and general corporate issues instructed both by English and United States law firms. Contributing Editor to Totty & Moss on Insolvency.
Career: Called to the Bar (Middle Temple) in 1986 and was a Harmsworth Exhibitioner. Appointed Queen's Counsel in 2000. Now a practising barrister at *3/4 South Square, Gray's Inn*. Specialises in business and financial law, in particular banking, corporate restructuring, insolvency, acquisitions and mergers. Was an Exhibitioner at Brasenose College, Oxford, where he was awarded a BA (Jurisprudence) and BCL.

DINAN-HAYWARD, Deborah
Albion Chambers (J.C.T. Barton QC), Bristol (0117) 927 2144
Recommended in Family/Matrimonial

DINKIN, Anthony QC
2-3 Gray's Inn Square (Anthony Scrivener QC), London (020) 7242 4986
Recommended in Planning
Specialisation: Specialises in town and country planning, local government, valuation and compensation, landlord & tenant, restrictive covenants. With extensive experience in conducting planning inquiries concerning all aspects of planning including major food & non-food retailing developments, local plans, CPO's and enforcement. Court experience includes legal challenges/ judicial review of Secretary of State/ Inspector and local government decisions and appearances in the Lands Tribunal.
Career: College of Estate Management (BscEst Management) 1966; Called to the Bar 1968; QC 1991; Crown Court Recorder 1989; past Lecturer and External Examiner in Law, Reading University. Legal Member of Lands Tribunal 1998-.

DIXEY, Ian
St John's Chambers (Christopher Sharp QC), Bristol (0117) 921 3456
Recommended in Crime

DIXON, Ralph
St John's Chambers (Christopher Sharp QC), Bristol (0117) 921 3456
Recommended in Family/Matrimonial
Specialisation: Matrimonial finance, in particular business and farming cases; Private law children cases; Adoption cases.
Prof. Memberships: Family Law Bar Association.
Career: BA Hons, University of York, Called to the Bar 1980.

DODDS, R. Stephen
15 Winckley Square (R.S. Dodds), Preston (01772) 252828
Recommended in Family/Matrimonial
Specialisation: All aspects of family law with particular reference to public law children work and financial ancillary relief.
Prof. Memberships: F.L.B.A.
Career: LL.B
Personal: Golf, opera, cricket.

DODSON, Joanna QC
14 Gray's Inn Square (Joanna Dodson QC), London (020) 7242 0858
Recommended in Family: Child Care including child abduction
Specialisation: Practice encompasses all aspects of family law.
Prof. Memberships: Family Law Bar Association.
Career: Called to the Bar 1971. Joined *Gray's Inn Square* in 1991 and took Silk in 1993.
Personal: Educated at James Allen's Girls School 1956-1963 and Newnham College, Cambridge (BA 1967, MA 1971). Born 5th September 1945. Lives in London.

DOHMANN, Barbara QC
Blackstone Chambers (P Baxendale QC and C Flint QC), London (020) 7583 1770
clerks@blackstonechambers.com
Recommended in Civil Fraud, Commercial (Litigation), Financial Services, Insurance, Media & Entertainment
Specialisation: Insurance and reinsurance; financial services; banking; private international law; commercial fraud (civil); commercial arbitration; entertainment and media/intellectual property; disciplinary tribunals; regulatory tribunals.
Prof. Memberships: Chairman of COMBAR; Member of the General Council of the Bar; Member of the Legal Services Committee of the Bar Council; Member London Common Law and Commercial Bar Association, Learned Society for International Civil Procedure Law.
Career: Called to the Bar in 1971; Queen's Counsel 1987; Recorder 1990. Sits as a Deputy High Court Judge.
Personal: Educated in German and American schools, Universities of Erlangen, Mainz and Paris. Languages: German, French, Spanish, Italian.

DOVE, Ian
5 Fountain Court (Anthony Barker QC), Birmingham (0121) 606 0500
Recommended in Planning

DOWDING, Nicholas QC
Falcon Chambers (Jonathan Gaunt QC & Kim Lewison QC), London (020) 7353 2484
dowding@falcon-chambers.com
Recommended in Property Litigation
Specialisation: All aspects of Chancery and real property law, commercial property litigation and arbitration.
Prof. Memberships: Chancery Bar Association, London. Commercial and Common Law Bar Association.
Career: Called to the Bar 1979. Silk 1997. Corresponding Member of Royal Institution of Chartered Surveyors Dilapidations Practice Panel. Member of *Falcon Chambers* since 1980. Blundell Memorial Lecturer 1992 and 1997.
Publications: Joint author 'Dilapidations – The Modern Law and Practice'. Joint editor 'Woodfall on Landlord and Tenant'. General Editor of Landlord and Tenant Reports.

DOWLEY, Dominic
Serle Court (Lord Neill of Bladen QC), London (020) 7242 6105
Recommended in Commercial (Litigation)
Specialisation: Insurance/reinsurance, arbitration, banking and financial services/regulation specialist.
Career: Called to the Bar and joined *One Hare Court* in 1983.
Personal: Educated at Oxford University 1977-80. Bacon Scholar of Gray's Inn: Barstow Law Scholar. Born 25th March 1958.

DOWNING, Ruth
Devereux Chambers (Jeffrey Burke QC), London (020) 7353 7534
Recommended in Employment

DOYLE, Louis
40 King St (Philip Raynor QC), Manchester (0161) 832 9082
ldoyle@40kingstreet.co.uk
Recommended in Commercial (Litigation), Insolvency/Corporate Recovery
Also practices at 5 Park Place (Philip Raynor QC) Leeds (0113) 242 1123
Specialisation: All aspects of corporate and personal insolvency, company law, credit, security, banking and related commercial litigation. Recent reported cases include Lombard v Brook and others [1999] BPIR 701 and Ord v Upton [2000] 1 All ER 163, CA. Author 'Administrative Receivership' : Law and Practice, Sweet & Maxwell (1995) and 'Insolvency Litigation', Sweet & Maxwell (1998). Appointed to the Treasury Solicitors' Provincial Panel (Civil Litigation), 1999
Prof. Memberships: Insolvency Lawyers Association, Chancery Bar Association, Northern Chancery Bar Association, Professional Negligence Bar Association.
Career: Educated St. Anselm's College, Birkenhead. LLB (Leeds Polytechnic), LLM (University of Birmingham). Lecturer in Law 1989-1992. Admitted as Solicitor 1994. Called to the Bar 1996, Lincolns Inn, 1996.
Publications: Member of the Editorial Board of the 'Insolvency Lawyer'.

DOYLE, Peter
9-12 Bell Yard (D. Anthony Evans QC), London (020) 7400 1800
Recommended in Fraud: Criminal

DRABBLE, Richard QC
4 Breams Buildings (Christopher Lockhart-Mummery QC), London (020) 7430 1221/7353 5835
Recommended in Administrative & Public Law: General, Planning
Specialisation: Specialises in public law, planning, local government and social security.
Prof. Memberships: Chairman of the Administrative Law Bar Association, member of the Planning and Environmental Bar Association.
Career: Member of the Panel of Junior Counsel to the Crown (Common Law) 1992-1995, took Silk 1995, contributor to Goudie and Supperstone Judicial Review.

DRISCOLL, Michael QC
9 Old Square (Michael Driscoll QC), London (020) 7405 4682
Recommended in Commercial Chancery, Property Litigation
Specialisation: General Chancery (advisory and litigation) but in particular property related, partnership and company law matters. Billson v Residential Apartments [1992], Escalus Properties v Robinson [1995], Re Macro (Ipswich) Limited [1994-1996].
Career: Rugby and Cambridge (BA LLB).

DRUCE, Michael
2 Mitre Court Buildings (Michael FitzGerald QC), London (020) 7583 1380
michael.druce@2mcb.co.uk
Recommended in Planning
Specialisation: Main areas of practice are town and country planning, compulsory purchase and compensation, rating, local government, environmental and administrative law. Recent cases include: the major retail proposals for the MetroCentre extention; Croft motor racing circuit; and the proposed development of a registered battlefield site. Has also appeared before the Grand Court of the Cayman Islands. Contributing editor to Butterworths 'Local Government Law'.
Prof. Memberships: Planning and Environment Bar Association. Justice.
Career: Called to Bar 1988 and joined current chambers 1990.
Personal: Educated at Repton School and Sidney Sussex College, Cambridge. Born 23rd March 1964. Married with 2 children. Lives in London.

DU CANN, Christian
39 Essex Street (Nigel Pleming QC), London (020) 7832 1111
cdc@39essex.co.uk
Recommended in Personal Injury
Specialisation: Catastrophic injury. Occupational disease (especially asbestos ULD and stress claims). Disaster claims. Health and Safety law (including criminal prosecution). Sports injury claims. Also specialises in medical and professional negligence.
Prof. Memberships: Member of Grays Inn (member

of its Continuing Education Committee and Advocacy teacher). Member of PIBA. Member of London Common Law and Commercial Bar Association. Member of Bar Council.
Career: Called to the Bar 1982. Practised at *39 Essex Street* since 1991.
Personal: Speaks French and Spanish.

DUCK, Michael
3 Fountain Court (Robert Juckes QC), Birmingham (0121) 236 5854
clerks@3fc.co.uk
Recommended in Crime
Specialisation: Principal areas of practice are crime and Police Disciplinary matters. R v Sara Thornton, (authority on provocation), R v Christie, Bell, Francis (custody time limits). Grade 4 prosecutor.
Career: Called to the Bar in 1988. Practised at 3 Fountain Court, from April 1989.
Personal: Born 1965. Leisure interests include travel, golf and water-skiing.

DUGGAN, Michael
Littleton Chambers (Michel Kallipetis QC), London (020) 7797 8600
Recommended in Employment
Specialisation: The main area of practice is in the field of employment law, covering all areas of discrimination (including disability discrimination), wrongful and unfair dismissal, redundancies and dismissals/variation of employment contracts arising out of re-organisations, restrictive covenants, trade union law including labour disputes and the emerging interface of the European Convention on European Rights with employment issues. Other areas of practice include building and construction law, health and safety and professional negligence and general commercial law including applications for interim injunctions and freezing orders.
Career: Called to the Bar 1984. Regular writer and lecturer on employment and commercial law, human rights law and civil procedure in the light of the Woolf reforms. Author: 'The Modern Law of Strikes'; 'Business Re-Organisations and Employment Law (FT Law & Tax)'; 'Termination of Employment of Directors (FT Law & Tax June 1997)'. 'Unfair Dismissal'; 'Law, Practice and Guidance'; 'Wrongful Dismissal'; 'Law Practice and Precedents and Contracts of Employment'; 'Law Practice and Precedents'. Central Law Training. Editor in Chief of the Discrimination Law Reports and the Civil Practice Law Reports.
Personal: BA. BCL. LLM (First Class, Sidney Sussex College, Cambridge University). Holt Scholar of *Gray's Inn*. Lives in Coton, Cambridgeshire and Gray's Inn. Married with three boys. Interests: Music, Guitar.

DUGGAN, Ross
India Buildings Chambers (David Harris QC), Liverpool (0151) 243 6000
clerks@indiabuildings.co.uk
Recommended in Family/Matrimonial
Specialisation: A specialist in all aspects of family law especially public law children's work for local authorities, parents and guardians ad litem. Also experienced in personal injury work.
Prof. Memberships: FLBA/PIBA.
Career: Called 1978. Recorder 1997.

DUMARESQ, Delia
Atkin Chambers (John Blackburn QC), London (020) 7404 0102
Recommended in Construction
Specialisation: All aspects of construction, building and engineering dispute resolution including international and domestic arbitration, mediation and adjudication. Advocate, mediator, write and lecturer in ADR. Counsel in leading adjudication cases – Macob v Morrison; Project Consultancy v Bloor Construction; Bridgeway v Tolent; and Cameron v Howlem.
Prof. Memberships: TECBAR. Panel of adjudicators, New South Wales Bar (Australia). CEDR Mediator and panel of adjudicators. Fellow of Chartered Institute of Arbitrators. Inter Mediation panel of Mediators.
Career: 1967 – BA – Australia. Prior to reading law, worked and travelled extensively in Southeast Asia (as an archaeologist) and Europe. 1973 – MA (Hons) – London (Work and research on disadvantaged groups and communities) 1983 – Dip Law (Hons); 1984 – called; Inner Temple.
Personal: One son. Interests include music, modern art, Italian culture and Language.

DUMONT, Thomas
11 New Square (Sonia Proudman QC), London (020) 7831 0081
Recommended in Charities, Traditional Chancery
Specialisation: Professional negligence principally solicitors and accountants: Paragon Finance v Theteran & Co (1998); Bristol & West v Christie, Acland & Lensum 3rd Parties (1996). Charity and private client advice and litigation, including trusts, wills and probate, re Ratcliffe (1999), Wood v Smith (1993), Crowden v Aldridge (1993). commercial property: Landlord & tenant, Restrictive covenants and mortgages: Mortgage Corporation v Nationwide Credit Corporation (1994). Rutland Howe Textiles v Mace (1999)
Prof. Memberships: Charity Law Association; Society of Trust & Estate Practitioners; Professional Negligence Bar Association; Bar Council Nominated Spokesman on Solicitors' Negligence; Legal Network T.V. Broadcaster on Probate and Tax matters.
Career: MA (Cantab) Exhibitioner in Law, Trinity Hall. Called 1979, Gray's Inn. Lecturer in trusts and revenue, University of Westminster 1981-85.
Personal: Married with two children. Fellow of the Zoological Society of London. Plays Cricket whenever possible.

DUNKELS, Paul QC
Walnut House (Francis Gilbert QC), Exeter (01392) 279751
Recommended in Crime
Specialisation: All types of serious crime and licensing. Prosecuted a five month series of trials of members of a paedophile ring (R v M and others). Munchausen syndrome by proxy trials (R v Jordan & R v Anthony).
Prof. Memberships: Criminal Bar Association.
Career: Called 1972. Recorder 1988. Silk 1993.

DUNN, Katherine
40 King St (Philip Raynor QC), Manchester (0161) 832 9082
Recommended in Chancery, Insolvency/Corporate Recovery
Specialisation: General Chancery both litigation and non-litigious including personal and corporate insolvency, company law, landlord and tenant, professional negligence, mortgages and land law generally, trusts and wills and probate.
Prof. Memberships: Northern Circuit, Northern Chancery Bar Association, Chancery Bar Association.
Career: On DTI Panel for Directors' Disqualifications.

DUNN-SHAW, Jason David
6 King's Bench Walk (Michael Worsley QC), London (020) 7583 0410
jds@6kbw.com
Recommended in Crime
Specialisation: general crime including courts Martial, Criminal Cases Review Commission work and extradition.
Prof. Memberships: Committee member of the Central London Courts Bar Mess.
Career: Manchester University, University of Westminster. Called to the Bar at Lincoln's Inn 1992.

DUNNING, Graham
Essex Court Chambers (Gordon Pollock QC), London (020) 7813 8000
Recommended in Arbitration (International), Shipping
Specialisation: Specialist in all aspects of international and commercial law, particularly arbitration, banking and finance, commodities and trade, insurance and reinsurance, professional negligence and shipping and transport. In the international field practice covers jurisdictional and private disputes, arbitrations, injunctions, forum conveniens and applicable law. Commodities and trade work covers cases involving oil, metals, foodstuffs and futures. Practice encompasses all aspects of insurance and reinsurance litigation involving Lloyd's syndicates. Professional negligence experience covers cases involving insurance brokers, actuaries, accountants and solicitors. Broad based shipping and transport practice covers charterparty diputes and bill of lading claims, ship sale and shipbuiding, aviation.
Prof. Memberships: Commercial Bar Association; British Insurance Law Authority; British Maritime Law Association; London Maritime Arbitrators Association.
Career: Called to the Bar 1982. Joined present chambers the following year.
Personal: Educated at Cambridge University (BA Hons. 1st class) 1977-1980, and at Harvard Law School (LL.M) 1980-1981. Scholarships: Emmanuel College Entrance Scholarship (1977), University of Cambridge Squire Law Scholarship (1978 and 1979), Lincoln's Inn Hardwicke Scholarship (1979), Kennedy Scholar, Harvard Law School (1980), Lincoln's Inn Denning Scholarship (1981). Born 13th March 1958. Lives in London.

DUTHIE, Catriona
Guildhall Chambers (Adrian Palmer QC), Bristol (0117) 927 3366
Recommended in Family/Matrimonial

DUTTON, Timothy C.
No. 1 Serjeants' Inn (Edward Faulks QC), London (020) 7415 6666
Recommended in Property Litigation
Specialisation: Property-related litigation, with a strong landlord and tenant bias: rent reviews and lease renewals; breaches of covenant and other disputes in respect of commercial property; long leases of residential property (including leasehold enfranchisement); Rent Act and Housing Act tenancies.
Prof. Memberships: Chancery Bar Association.
Career: Called to the Bar in 1985. Employed for several years (post-call) in the property litigation departments of *Speechly Bircham* and *Lovells*.
Personal: Born 1962. Educated at Godalming Grammar School (1972-1980) and Durham University (1981-1984).

DUVAL, Robert
St John's Chambers (Christopher Sharp QC), Bristol (0117) 921 3456
clerks@stjohnschambers.co.uk
Recommended in Crime

DYER, Nigel
1 Mitre Court Buildings (Bruce Blair QC), London (020) 7797 7070
Recommended in Family: Matrimonial Finance
Specialisation: Family law, principally ancillary relief often involving 'big money cases' where assets are held in companies, trusts and farms in the UK and abroad.
Prof. Memberships: Family Law Bar Association. Co-editor of 'Rayden and Jackson on Divorce and Family Matters'.
Career: Called to the Bar by Inner Temple 1982.
Personal: Married with two children and lives in London.

EADIE, James
Serle Court (Lord Neill of Bladen QC), London (020) 7242 6105
Recommended in Commercial (Litigation)
Specialisation: Junior Counsel to the Crown – Common Law.

EADY, Jennifer

JEady@compuserve.com
Old Square Chambers (John Hendy QC), London (020) 7269 0300
JEady@compuserve.com
Recommended in Employment
Specialisation: All aspects employment law (collective and individual), discrimination and restraint of trade. Cases of significance: R v BCC ex p Vardy 1993 (pit-closures JR); R v BCC ex p Price 1993 (collective redundancies); Associated Newspapers v Wilson 1995 HL (trade union); RJB v NUM 1995 CA (strike ballot); MRS v Marsh 1996 CA (TUPE); RMT v Intercity 1996 CA (strike ballot); Smith v BCC 1996 HL (equal pay); BRS v Loughran 1997 NICA (equal pay); Tuck v BSG 1996 EAT (TUPE); NACODS v Gluchowski 1996 EAT (trade union); Halford v UK 1997 ECHR (Human Rights); BBC v Kelly-Phillips 1998 CA (employment contracts); England v Magill (1997) (Westminster "gerrymandering") Div Ct; Brookes and ors v BCS 1998 EAT (TUPE); Gibson v E Riding Yorks 2000 CA (working time); SoS Trade & Industry v Bottirll 1999 CA (employee status). Inquiries: The UCATT Inquiry (1992), the Westminster Audit Hearing (1994/5).
Publications: 'Discrimination Law: Remedies and Quantum of Damages' (Sweet & Maxwell) (1998); 'Employment Tribunal Procedure' (LAG) (1996); 'Employment Law Review' (IER); Contributor: ICSL 'Employment Law Manual' (Blackstone), 'Employment Law Precedents' (Sweet & Maxwell), ILJ.
Prof. Memberships: Chair ILS, Committee member ELBA, Bar representative London ET and EAT users' group and ELA.
Career: 1986 BA Hons PPE (Oxon), 1988 Dip Law. Called 1989, Northern Ireland Bar 1994. Standing junior counsel to NUJ and NUM, appointed to the Treasury B panel.

EASTEAL, Andrew
No.1 High Pavement (John B. Milmo QC), Nottingham (0115) 941 8218
Recommended in Crime
Specialisation: Practising exclusively in crime for the last ten years (excluding fraud): sexual offences including child abuse; human rights; high profile drugs cases; attempted murder and manslaughter cases (single counsel) involving complex fitness to plead issues.
Personal: Long-suffering Villa fan.

EATON, Deborah
One King's Bench Walk (Anthony Hacking QC), London (020) 7936 1500
Recommended in Family: Child Care including child abduction, Family: Matrimonial Finance
Specialisation: All aspects of family law including matrimonial finance and children (private and public law), inter country adoption and professional negligence. Co-Author:' Wildblood and Eaton: Financial Provision In Family Matters' published by Sweet and Maxwell 1998. Author Sweet and Maxwell Practical Research Papers. Regular lecturer on ancillary relief and children matters. Contributor to Family Law. General editor: 'Essential Family Practice' published by Butterworths 2000.
Prof. Memberships: Family Law Bar Association. Intercountry Adoption Lawyers Association.
Career: Called to the Bar in 1985.
Personal: Born 28th March 1962, BSc (Hons) Psychology and Anthropology, Diploma in Law. Leisure pursuits include travel, opera, theatre and cinema.

ECCLES, David
8 King St (Keith Armitage QC), Manchester (0161) 834 9560
Recommended in Clinical Negligence

EDELMAN, Colin QC
Devereux Chambers (Jeffrey Burke QC), London (020) 7353 7534
Recommended in Insurance, Professional Negligence
Specialisation: Principal areas of practice are insurance and reinsurance, professional negligence and commercial law. Recent reported cases include Killick v Rendall (insurance), Kennecott v Cornhill (insurance/reinsurance), Gan Insurance v Tai Pine (insurance), Cape v Iron Trades (insurance).
Prof. Memberships: Commercial Bar Association, member of Middle Temple and Midlands & Oxford Circuit.
Career: Called to the Bar in 1977 and has been a tenant at Devereux Chambers since 1979. Appointed Assistant Recorder in 1993. Took Silk in 1995. Appointed Recorder 1996.
Publications: Has written articles for 'International Insurance Law Review', 'Commercial Liability Law Review' and the 'British Insurance Law Association Journal'. Contributor to "Insurance Disputes" (LLP). Speaker/chairman at conferences on insurance and reinsurance topics.
Personal: Educated at Haberdashers' Aske's School, Elstree 1961-1972 and Clare College, Cambridge 1973-1976. Leisure pursuits include skiing, walking, badminton. Born 2nd March 1954. Lives in London.

EDENBOROUGH, Michael
One Raymond Buildings (Christopher Morcom QC), London (020) 7430 1234
Recommended in Intellectual Property
Specialisation: All aspects of intellectual property law, including UK and European competition law and related technical disputes. In particular, registered rights and the related unregistered rights: i.e. patents and confidential information; trade marks and passing off / malicious falsehood; registered designs and (industrial) copyright / design right; internet and data protection issues; entertainement law matters such as (aesthetic) copyright, moral rights, performance rights, and contractual issues; and computer litigation.
Prof. Memberships: MRSC, IP Bar Association, TIPLO, SCL, CIPA, ITMA, ECTA and APPI. Secretary to the Special Committee for the APPI considering Community Trademarks; and a member of the Working Committee of the APPI considering Three dimensional Marks: The Borderline between Trademarks and Industrial Designs. Committee member of the London Branch of the Society for Computers abd Law.
Career: Called to the Bar in October 1992, and tennant since 1st July 1994. Regular lecturer and tutor to CIPA, ITMA, University of Alicante (Spain), solicitors, patent and trade mark attorneys, and at national and interantional conferences.
Publications: 'Lecture Notes on Intellectual Property Law' (Cavendish Publishing Ltd, May 1995, reprinted 1997). 'Organic Reaction Mechanisms: A Step by Step Approach' (Taylor and Francis Ltd, 1st edition June 1994, reprinted 1996; 2nd edition: November 1998)
Personal: MA (Cantab), MA (Oxon), MSc, D Phil.

EDER, Bernard QC
Essex Court Chambers (Gordon Pollock QC), London (020) 7813 8000
Recommended in Commercial (Litigation), Energy & Natural Resources, Insurance, Shipping
Specialisation: Most work of a litigious nature involving appearances in arbitration and the Commercial Court, Court of Appeal and House of Lords. All aspects of commercial law, including insurance and reinsurance, shipping and banking, international sale of goods, oil and gas.
Career: Downing College, Cambridge BA (Law) (First Class Hons); Called to the Bar 1975; Queen's Counsel 1990. Visiting professor in the Faculty of Law, University College London.
Personal: Born 1952.

EDEY, Philip
20 Essex Street (Iain Milligan QC), London (020) 7583 9294
Recommended in Shipping
Specialisation: Commercial litigation including arbitration, commodities, insurance & reinsurance, international sale of goods and shipping. Cases include: Comdel v Siporex [1997] 1 Lloyd's Reports 424 (Mareva); The Laconian Confidence [1997] 1 Lloyd's Reports 139 (NYPE time charter); Imperio v Health [1999] Lloyds Rep. IR 571 (Binding Authority; time bar); Kingscroft v Nissan ([1999] Lloyd. Rep IR 603; reinsurance); Cory Bros v Baldan [1997] 2 Lloyd's Reports 58 (shipping); Junior Counsel for Wellington names (1995; Lloyd's professional negligence); The Jalajouri (time charter; off-hire; court of appeal).
Prof. Memberships: COMBAR.
Career: Eton College, Oxford University (BA Hons 1st Class). Gray's Inn Queen Elizabeth Scholar. Called 1994.
Personal: Tennis; squash; real tennis; bridge; opera & theatre.

EDGE, Timothy
Deans Court Chambers (H.K. Goddard QC), Manchester (0161) 214 6000
edge@dearscourt.co.uk
Recommended in Family/Matrimonial
Specialisation: Matrimonial finance on divorce/separation, including injunctive relief, conflict of laws and disputes following death. Private and public law children's work, adoption, international custody and child abduction.
Prof. Memberships: FLBA, PNBA, Child Concern.
Career: MA (Oxon)
Personal: Sport. Travel. Cooking.

EDIE, Alastair
Two Garden Court
(I. Macdonald QC & O.Davies QC), London (020) 7353 1633
Recommended in Crime

EDIS, William
1 Crown Office Row (Robert Seabrook QC), London (020) 7797 7500
Recommended in Environment
Specialisation: Environmental litigation, both civil and criminal. Particular expertise in relation to contaminated land, particulate emission, water and air pollution and nuclear installations. Professional negligence, particularly medical, legal and surveyors'.
Prof. Memberships: PNBA, UKELA

EDWARDS, David
7 King's Bench Walk (Jeremy Cooke QC), London (020) 7910 8300
Recommended in Insurance, Shipping
Specialisation: Commercial law predominantly insurance and reinsurance, international sale of goods, banking and finance, shipping.
Career: Called to the Bar 1989. Recent cases include: Marc Rich v Bishop Rock The "Nicholas H" [1996] AC 211 (shipping – duty of care owed by Classification Society); New Hampshire v MGN [1997] 1 LRLR 24 (fidelity insurance – joint or composite); Glencore v Portman [1996] 1 Lloyd's Rep. 430 and [1997] 1 Lloyd's Rep. 225 (insurance – non-disclosure); The "Bergen" [1997] 1 Lloyd's Rep. 380 (Clarke J) (jurisdiction – Brussels Convention); The "Lendoudis Evange-

los II" [1997] 1 Lloyd's Rep. 404 (charterparty – duration expressed "without guarantee"); The Sumitomo Bank, Limited v Banque Bruxelles Lambert SA [1997] 1 Lloyd's Rep. 487 (syndicated lending – duty owed by arranger to syndicate members); Source v TUV [1997] 3 WLR 364 (jurisdiction – Brussels Convention); HMH v Cecar [2000] 1 Lloyd's Rep 316 (political risks insurance-brokers commission); The 'Seta Maru' [2000] 1 Lloyd's Rep 367 (Shipbuilding exemption clauses).
Personal: Born 1966. King's School, Chester and Peterhouse, Cambridge, M.A. (Cantab). Member of Commercial Bar Association.

EDWARDS, Douglas
2 Harcourt Buildings (Mr Gerard Ryan QC), London (020) 7353 8415
Recommended in Planning
Specialisation: Planning, environmental, administrative, local government, parliamentary. Appeared in Terminal 5 Inquiry, Heathrow, and for Railtrack in Euston re-modelling inquiry. Recently reported cases include: R v Derbyshire C.C. ex parte Woods (1997) JPL 958; Riordan Communications Ltd v South Buckinghamshire D.C. (2000) 1 PLR 45; R v St. Edmundsbury B.C. ex parte Davidson (2000) JPL 417; House Builders Federation v Sockport M.B.C. (2000) JPL 616; R v South Cambs D.C. ex parte Salek (2000) JPL 748.
Prof. Memberships: Secretary of Planning and Environment Bar Association (PEBA).

EDWARDS, Glyn
St John's Chambers (Christopher Sharp QC), Bristol (0117) 921 3456
clerks@stjohnschambers.co.uk
Recommended in Personal Injury
Specialisation: Personal Injury. Appointed with effect from July 2000 onto Provincial Panel of Treasury Counsel.
Prof. Memberships: Personal Injury Bar Association (Western circuit representative on its Executive Committee).
Career: Formerly lecturer at Oxford Brookes University.
Personal: Married with three children. Welsh-speaking. Education: Penglais Comprehensive and Emmanuel College, Cambridge.

EDWARDS, Susan QC
23 Essex Street (Michael Lawson QC), London (020) 7413 0353
Recommended in Crime
Specialisation: Crime, Fraud, Corporate Crime, Child Abuse.
Prof. Memberships: C.B.A.
Career: Parkstone Grammar School, Poole. Southampton University – LL.B (1971), Recorder. QC 1993.
Personal: Tennis.

EDWARDS-STUART, Antony QC
Crown Office Chambers (Michael Spencer QC & Christopher Purchas QC), London (020) 7797 8100
edwards-stuart@crownofficechambers.com
Recommended in Professional Negligence
Specialisation: Principal area of practice is insurance, reinsurance and general commercial litigation and advice. Considerable experience of major insurance and reinsurance disputes, both marine and non-marine, together with highly complicated technical commercial cases including radioactive contamination (Merlins v BNFL, Blue Circle Industries plc v MOD, leading test cases), microbiology and chemistry (AKZO v Cyprus, contaminated paint) and electron beam welding (Burnley Engineering v Cambridge Vacuum Engineering). Other main areas of practice involve professional negligence work particularly concerning architects and engineers, but also insurance brokers, Lloyd's agents, solicitors, accountants and surveyors, both for plaintiffs and defendants. Also involved in several major construction cases (Royal Brompton Hospital v Hammond, Plant Construction v Clive Adams) and arbitrations. Clients have included major insurance companies, BNFL, leading professional practices and large construction firms.
Prof. Memberships: COMBAR, London Common Law and Commercial Bar Association, TECBAR.
Career: Called to the Bar 1976 and joined *2 Crown Office Row* in 1977. Took Silk in 1991. Appointed Recorder in 1997. Chairman, Home Office Advisory Committee on Service Candidates, 1995 -98.
Personal: Education: Sherborne School, Dorset 1960-1964, RMA Sandhurst 1965-1966, St. Catharine's College, Cambridge 1969-1972. Married with 4 children. Leisure pursuits include woodwork, restoring property in France, theatre, fishing and shooting. Born 2nd November 1946. Lives in London.

EGAN, Michael
9-12 Bell Yard (D. Anthony Evans QC), London (020) 7400 1800
Recommended in Fraud: Criminal

EICKE, Tim
Essex Court Chambers (Gordon Pollock QC), London (020) 7813 8000
Recommended in Immigration
Specialisation: EC law, including European Immigration Law and the EC Association Agreements, Free Movement and Equal Treatment (Cases: C-75/94 Gallagher [1995] ECR I-4253 (ECJ) and [1996] 2 CMLR 951 (CA); C-416/96 El Yassini [1999] ECR I-1209; Sahota [1999] QB 597; Boukssid, [1998] INLR 275; Yiadom, [1998] INLR 489 (Pending in ECJ), Kaba, Judgement of 11 April 2000 (ECJ)); Human Rights (Cases: Sheffield and Horsham (1999) 27 EHRR 163, A v UK (1999) 27 EHRR 611, Cooke v Austria (judgment of 8 February 2000), Laskey et al (1997) 24EHRR 39 and National &Provincial et al (1998) 25 EHRR 127; Amicus submissions to the Court Of Human Rights in Chahal (1997) 23 EHRR 413, Akdivar v Turkey (1997) 27 EHRR 143, Ahmed (2000) 29 EHRR 1 and McGinley (1999) 27 EHRR 1); Judicial Review (Cases: R v Legal Aid Board ex p. Eccleston, [1998] 1 WLR 1279); Employment Law; Education Law, Nabadda v Westminster City Council, The Times 15 March 2000); Discrimination (Race and Sex) (Bavin v NHS Trust Pensions Agency [1999] ICR 1192). Private International Law; General Commercial and Civil.
Prof. Memberships: ILPA , Bar European Group, Lawyers for Liberty, Employment Law Bar Association, Administrative Law Bar Association, British German Jurists Association. Member of the Justice Expert Panel on Human Rights in the EU.
Career: Called 1993; LLB (Hons) Dundee University; Junior Councel to the Crown (C Panel) since April 1999.
Publications: Joint editor, 'European Human Rights Reports' (Sweet & Maxwell); Contributor Grosz, Beaston and Duffy 'Human Rights – The 1998 Act and the European Convention' (Sweet & Maxwell); Co-author of the 'Strasbourg Caselaw: Leading cases from the European Human Rights Reports' (Sweet & Maxwell, forthcoming);
Personal: Bi-lingual German-English, advanced French.

EISSA, Adrian
Two Garden Court (I. Macdonald QC & O.Davies QC), London (020) 7353 1633
Recommended in Crime

EKLUND, Graham
2 Temple Gardens (Dermod O'Brien QC), London (020) 7822 1200
Recommended in Professional Negligence
Specialisation: Professional negligence – particularly surveyors, solicitors, accountants and insurance brokers. Insurance related matters – particularly fraudulent claims, policy construction points, fire and disaster claims, including pollution and contamination claims. Personal injury – particularly serious injuries (including tetraplegic and paraplegic cases). Computer and IT. Reported cases include: Jones & Marsh McLennan v Crowley Colosso (1996); Yorkshire Water v Sun Alliance (1996); John Munroe (Acrylics) Limited v London Fire and Civil Defence Authority (1997); Chapman v Christopher (1998); Greatorex v Greatorex (2000).
Prof. Memberships: PNBA, PIBA.
Career: Educated at Auckland University (1969-1974) BA; LLB (Hons). Barrister and Solicitor of the High Court of New Zealand (1975-1978). Solicitor of the Supreme Court of England and Wales (1979-1984). Called 1984.
Personal: Married – 2 children. Interests include music, particularly opera and piano, cricket, wine.

ELDER, Fiona
Queen Square Chambers (T. Alun Jenkins QC), Bristol (0117) 921 1966
Recommended in Crime

ELGOT, Howard
Park Lane Chambers (Stuart Brown QC), Leeds (0113) 228 5000
Recommended in Personal Injury
Specialisation: Personal injury (including claims of maximum severity,) industrial disease litigation, clinical and professional negligence, insurance and commercial litigation. Many reported cases at first instance, Court of Appeal and House of Lords. Examples of well-known reported cases are Clarke v Kato 1HL (extent of RTA/MIB liability;) Roebuck v. Mungovin HL (want of prosecution,) and Liddell v. Middleton CA (role of expert witnesses.)
Prof. Memberships: PIBA; PNBA
Career: BA BCL New College, Oxford. *3 Paper Buildings, Temple* 1974-86, present chambers since 1986. Chairman, Park Lane Chambers Management Committee. Member NE Circuit/Leeds Law Society Liaison Committee. Former Chariman NE Circuit Renumeration and Terms of Work Committee.
Personal: Married, three children. Ski-ing. Italy. Music. Football.

ELIAS, Gerard QC
Farrar's Building (John Leighton Williams QC), London (020) 7583 9241
Recommended in Crime

ELLERAY, Anthony QC
St. James's Chambers (R.A. Sterling), Manchester (0161) 834 7000
Recommended in Chancery, Commercial (Litigation)
Specialisation: Chancery and General Commercial Litigation; Professional Negligence; Landlord and Tenant. Recent cases in C.A. include Walker v Turpin (1994) (payment in); Jervis v Harris (1996) (Landlord and Tenant repairs and 1938 Act); Bass v Latham Crossley and Davies (1996) (partnership/holding out); Shaikh v Bolton MBC (1996) (statutory interest on compulsory purchase). Pearce Deceased (1998) (Inheritance Act). Lynch [2000] laches. In H.L, Wibberley v Insley (1999).
Prof. Memberships: Chancery Bar Association; Northern Chancery Bar Association; Professional Negligence Bar Association.

Career: Called to the Bar 1977; took Silk 1993.
Prof. Memberships: Educated: Bishop Stortford College 1967-1972. Trinity College Cambridge 1973-1976. Born 19th August 1954.

ELLIOTT, Margot
Regency Chambers (Raymond Croxon QC and Ian Martignetti), Peterborough (01733) 315215
margot.elliott@virgin.net
Recommended in Family/Matrimonial
Specialisation: All aspects of family law especially public law children work.
Prof. Memberships: Family Law Bar Association.
Career: Educated at Wakefield Girl's High School and University of Newcastle Upon Tyne (LL.B. 1987). Called to the Bar in 1989; member of current chambers since 1991.
Personal: Born 29th July 1966. Lives in Cambridgeshire with husband and two children.

ELLIOTT, Rupert
1 Brick Court (Richard Rampton QC), London (020) 7353 8845
Recommended in Defamation
Specialisation: Defamation and media related law; pre-publication work; reporting restrictions; contempt; confidence.
Career: Called 1988; joined Chambers 1989.
Personal: Harrow School; Jesus College, Cambridge.

ELLIOTT, Timothy QC
Keating Chambers (Richard Fernyhough QC), London (020) 7544 2600
Recommended in Arbitration (International), Construction
Specialisation: Building and civil engineering; professional negligence; bonds and guarantees. Clients include national and international contractors and developers, professional, national and local government, both in the UK and overseas. Also acts as arbitrator and legal assessor.
Career: Qualified 1975. Middle Temple QC 1992.
Personal: Marlborough College and Trinity College, Oxford (1973 MA Oxon). Born 1950; resides London.

ELLIS, Diana
3 Gray's Inn Square (Rock Tansey QC), London (020) 7520 5600
Recommended in Crime
Specialisation: Specialises in defence crime. Wide range of work including murder, fraud, child abuse and sexual abuse, drugs, human rights, unappointed counsel at International Criminal Tribunal for Rwanda.
Prof. Memberships: Criminal Bar Association. Liberty. South Eastern Circuit.
Career: Called to the Bar in July 1978 – Inner Temple. LLB Hons London; Diploma in Social Admin, LSE. Worked for several years as a teacher. Recorder, 1998.

ELLIS, Morag
2-3 Gray's Inn Square (Anthony Scrivener QC), London (020) 7242 4986
Recommended in Planning
Specialisation: Planning and Local Government. Extensive experience of public inquiries including planning appeals and local plan inquiries, CPO and footpaths, for developers, authorities and other statutory bodies. Recently promoted Bracknell Forest Local Plan, including major housing and town centre redevelopment proposals. Court experience includes judicial review and statutory appeals. Lands Tribunal – compensation, rating, restrictive covenants. On editorial panel of Halsbury's laws (Public Health). Regular lecturer on planning topics for RTPI and various Advocacy Training Courses.
Prof. Memberships: Planning and Environment Bar Association (Committee Member and Local Plans Sub-Committee). Ecclesiastical Law Society.
Career: Called to the Bar 1984, (Gray's Inn).
Personal: Educated Penrhos College, Colwyn Bay, and St Catharine's College, Cambridge (MA). Married with 3 children. Member of Bach Choir.

ELLISON, Mark
Queen Elizabeth Building (Julian Bevan QC & Peter Whiteman QC), London (020) 7583 5766
Recommended in Crime, Fraud: Criminal
Specialisation: Criminal practice specialising in commercial fraud and Treasury Counsel work.
Career: Called 1979. Appointed Junior Treasury Counsel to the Crown at the Central Criminal Court 1994. Recorder.
Personal: Educated at Pocklington School, Skinners School and the University of Wales.

ELVIN, David QC
4 Breams Buildings (Christopher Lockhart-Mummery QC), London (020) 7430 1221/7353 5835
davidelvin@compuserve.com
Recommended in Planning, Property Litigation
Specialisation: Real property, landlord and tenant, agriculture, trespass, judicial review, compulsory purchase, compensation, planning, environmental law (including nature conservation), nuisance, highways, local government, education and professional negligence.
Career: Called to the Bar by the Middle Temple in 1983 and is member of the Administrative Law Bar Association, Chancery Bar Association and the Planning and Environmental Bar Association. He took silk in 2000. Educated at the A.J. Dawson Grammar School, Co. Durham and at Hertford College, Oxford obtaining a B.A. (First Class Honours) in Jurisprudence and a B.C.L. In 1983 he won the Bar Association for Finance Commerce and Industry Prize. He was one of the Junior Counsel to the Crown ('A' Panel) until he took silk, having served as a Supplementary Panellist from 1991 to 1995. He is co-author of 'Unlawful Interference with Land' (1995) and a number of articles in 'Judicial Review.' Is an Assistant Commissioner with the Boundary Commission.

ELWICK, Martin
No.1 High Pavement (John B. Milmo QC), Nottingham (0115) 941 8218
Recommended in Crime
Specialisation: An almost exclusive criminal defence practice. Acted in many high profile drug, sex and murder cases.
Prof. Memberships: Midland and Oxford Circuit.
Career: Former Magistrates Court Clerk. Crown Prosecutor. Has been at the Bar for the last 14 years. Acting Stipendiary Magistrate.
Personal: Studied law at Nottingham University under Professor J.C. Smith. Has two teenage children.

EMMERSON, Ben QC
Matrix Chambers (Nicholas Blake QC), London (020) 7404 3447
Recommended in Crime, Human Rights (Civil Liberties)
Specialisation: Civil liberties and international human rights law, including representation of applicants before the European Court of Justice in Luxemberg and the European Court and Commission of Human Rights in Strasbourg; civil actions against police and public law, particularly prisoners' rights. Also criminal law, especially political offences and cases involving police malpractice; Commonwealth capital appeals, extradition, deportation and international enforcement of asset confiscation. Editor of European Human Rights Law Review (Sweet & Maxwell). Human rights Editor of Archbold Criminal Pleading, Evidence and Practice. Author Butterworth's Guide to the Police Act 1997. Council of Europe Representative on Human Rights Courses in Central and Eastern Europe.
Career: Called to the Bar 1986. Silk 3/5/2000.
Personal: Bristol University 1982-85. Born 30th August 1963.

ENGLAND, William
2-4 Tudor Street (Richard Ferguson QC), London (020) 7797 7111
Recommended in Crime

ENGLEHART, Robert QC
Blackstone Chambers (P Baxendale QC and C Flint QC), London (020) 7583 1770
robertenglehart@blackstonechambers.com
Recommended in Media & Entertainment
Specialisation: Both commercial and copyright aspects of music business and media, especially broadcasting, disputes; also practices in general commercial law, including commercial judicial review, and intellectual property.
Career: Called 1969, QC 1986, Recorder and Deputy High Court Judge.

ESCOTT-COX, Brian R. QC
36 Bedford Row (Michael Pert QC), Northampton (01604) 602333
Recommended in Crime

ESPLEY, Susan
Fenners Chambers (Lindsay Davies), Cambridge (01223) 368761
Recommended in Family/Matrimonial

ETHERINGTON, David QC
18 Red Lion Court (Anthony Arlidge QC), London (020) 7520 6000
Recommended in Crime, Fraud: Criminal
Specialisation: Criminal practitioner. Experienced in wide range of criminal work including commercial fraud, VAT, drugs and serious professional crime. Also experienced in civil jury actions such as malicious prosecution. Adviser to television companies on documentary and dramatic work including 'Kavanagh QC', 'Wing and a Prayer' and 'The Bill'.
Prof. Memberships: Appointed member of the Criminal Bar Association Committee and Vice Chairman of the Professional Conduct Committee. Chambers *18 Red Lion Court* (Anthony Arlidge QC).
Career: Call 1979 (Middle Temple), Recorder of the Crown Court 2000, Queen's Counsel 1998.

ETHERTON, Terence QC
Wilberforce Chambers (Edward Nugee QC), London (020) 7306 0102
Recommended in Banking, Commercial Chancery, Pensions, Property Litigation
Specialisation: Chancery and commercial litigation and advice. Particular areas are commercial property and landlord and tenant; financial services including unit trusts, and property enterprise trusts; banking issues, particularly related to property backed and syndicated loans; the Lloyd's Insurance Market; international fraud and asset tracing; company law; professional negligence; trust and pensions litigation.
Prof. Memberships: COMBAR, Vice Chairman Chancery Bar Association, FCIArb.
Career: Called 1974. Took Silk 1990; Deputy High Court Judge 2000.

EVANS, D. Anthony QC
9-12 Bell Yard (D. Anthony Evans QC), London (020) 7400 1800
Recommended in Crime

EVANS, David QC
Queen Elizabeth Building (Julian Bevan QC & Peter Whiteman QC), London (020) 7583 5766
Recommended in Fraud: Criminal
Specialisation: Principal area of specialisation within criminal law is criminal fraud. Before taking silk in 1991 appeared in several high profile cases as Junior. Acted for Ian Posgate in the Howden trial, for Morgan Grenfel in the Guinness enquiry, and for UBS Phillips & Drew in the Blue Arrow trial. Since 1991 has appeared both for the prosecution and defence in a series of major fraud trials including defendants in the BCCI enquiry, the collapse of the Swithland motor group, the Aveling Barford pension fund fraud and several high profile mortgage frauds including acting for the solicitor defendant in the Harrovian case. Has prosecuted for the SFO and the Fraud Investigation Group.
Prof. Memberships: Criminal Bar Association
Career: Educated at the London School of Economics BSc. Econ, MSc 1962-1967, Wadham College Oxford B.A. Oxon 1968-1970. Q.C. 1991.

EVANS, Elwen Mair
Iscoed Chambers (Trefor Davies), Swansea (01792) 652988/9
Recommended in Crime

EVANS, Gareth QC
5 Fountain Court (Anthony Barker QC), Birmingham (0121) 606 0500
Recommended in Personal Injury

EVANS, Jill
Doughty Street Chambers (Geoffrey Robertson QC), London (020) 7404 1313
j.evans@doughtystreet.co.uk
Recommended in Crime
Specialisation: Specialises in defence crime: extensive practice both in fraud and confiscation and also cases involving children and Young Persons both as defendants and victims of crime. Increasingly instructed in Leading Junior work.
Prof. Memberships: Criminal Bar Association, Legal Action Group and Haldane Society.
Career: Former Solicitor, Partner *Saunders & Co* W9. Called to Bar in 1986.

EVANS, John
1 Fountain Court (David Crigman QC), Birmingham (0121) 236 5721
Recommended in Crime

EVANS, Jonathan
Wilberforce Chambers (Edward Nugee QC), London (020) 7306 0102
Recommended in Pensions
Specialisation: Chancery and commercial litigation and advice. Pensions including pensions mis-selling, pensions ombudsman complaints. Cases include SWT v Wightman. Oil and gas law, professional negligence (including actuarial negligence). General chancery including property finance, mortgages, landlord and tenant disputes, leasehold enfranchisement, nuisance, rights of common, estates, partnership disputes and insolvency.
Prof. Memberships: Association of Pension Lawyers, Chancery Bar Association, COMBAR.
Career: Called to the Bar 1994. German and Philosophy at Oriel College, Oxford. Contributor to LLP's 'Professional Negligence: Law and Practice', editorial team of LLP's series of Professional Negligence Law Reports.

EVANS, Mark QC
Queen Square Chambers (T. Alun Jenkins QC), Bristol (0117) 921 1966
Recommended in Family/Matrimonial
Specialisation: Family especially high value ancillery relief. Personal injury.
Prof. Memberships: FLBA. PIBA. CBA.
Career: Called to the Bar after a period in industry post university dealing with engineering and accountancy. Wide experience as provisional junior in Civil and criminal law. Specialist in Ancillery relief cases. Extensive PI practice.
Publications: 'Pensions and Divorce'
Personal: Music, solo concert performer voice & piano. Principal Bristol Opera Vintage & racing cars (large collection) & competitive driving.

EVANS, Michael
No.1 High Pavement (John B. Milmo QC), Nottingham (0115) 941 8218
Recommended in Crime
Specialisation: All areas of crime. Last year, dealt with a number of high profile drugs trials and serious matters of sex and violence.

EVANS, Susan
St John's Chambers (Christopher Sharp QC), Bristol (0117) 921 3456
clerks@stjohnschambers.co.uk
Recommended in Crime

EVANS, Timothy
13 Old Square (Michael Lyndon-Stanford QC), London (020) 7404 4800
clerks@13oldsquare.law.co.uk
Recommended in Traditional Chancery
Specialisation: Trusts and contentious probate, charities, insolvency.
Prof. Memberships: Chancery Bar Association; COMBAR.
Career: Marlborough College, Pembroke College, Oxford MA (History), Called to the Bar 1979.
Personal: Born 15/12/1955.

EVERALL, Mark QC
1 Mitre Court Buildings (Bruce Blair QC), London (020) 7797 7070
clerks@1mcb.com
Recommended in Family: Child Care including child abduction
Specialisation: Work includes matrimonial finance, public and private law children cases, international child abduction, adoption, and cases with an international aspect. Editor, Rayden & Jackson on 'Divorce & Family Matters'.
Prof. Memberships: Family Law Bar Association; Bar European Group; International Academy of Matrimonial Lawyers: Administrative Law Bar Association.
Career: Took Silk in 1994.

EVERARD, William
KCH Barristers (William Everard), Nottingham (0115) 941 8851
Recommended in Crime

EWART, David
Pump Court Tax Chambers (Andrew Thornhill QC), London (020) 7414 8080
Recommended in Tax
Specialisation: Revenue, trusts, professional negligence, Customs & Excise v Ferrero (UK) (1997), Customs & Excise v Kilroy Television Company (1997), Garner v Pounds (2000), Customs & Excise v Leightons Ltd (1995).
Prof. Memberships: Revenue Bar Association.
Career: Hamilton Grammar School; Trinity College, Oxford.
Personal: Bridge, golf.

EYRE, Stephen
1 Fountain Court (David Crigman QC), Birmingham (0121) 236 5721
Recommended in Commercial (Litigation)

FANCOURT, Timothy
Falcon Chambers (Jonathan Gaunt QC & Kim Lewison QC), London (020) 7353 2484
fancourt@falcon-chambers.com
Recommended in Agriculture, Property Litigation
Specialisation: Principal area of practice is real property based chancery work (litigation). This includes commercial property, landlord and tenant, surveyors' and solicitors' professional negligence, conveyancing, building contracts, mortgages, easements and restrictive covenants, equity and trusts and insolvency. Other main area is commercial contracts. General Editor of Megarry's 'The Rent Acts' and Megarry's 'Assured Tenancies' (1999); author of 'Enforceability of Landlord and Tenant Covenants' (1997).
Prof. Memberships: Lincoln's Inn, Chancery Bar Association. Member of Bar Council
Career: Called to the Bar in 1987 and joined *Falcon Chambers* in 1989.
Personal: Educated at Whitgift School 1974-82 and Gonville & Caius College, Cambridge 1983-86. Born 30th August 1964.

FARBEY, Judith
Plowden Buildings (William Lowe QC), London (020) 7583 0808
judith@plowdenbuildings.co.uk
Recommended in Immigration
Specialisation: Immigration; public and administrative law.
Prof. Memberships: Includes ILPA, ALBA; member, JUSTICE Public Law Committee.
Career: Called to the Bar 1992. Selected by HM The Queen as a 'young high achiever' 1998 – Bar Council nominee. Winner, Bar Council Award for Outstanding Commitment to Pro Bono Work 1997. For Joint Council for the Welfare of Immigrants – writing and delivering training programmes for provision of quality legal services to migrants. Tavistock Clinic, London – annual lecture since 1996 on refugee law to providers of social services and healthcare for asylum seekers. Court of Appeal cases include Kagema v Secretary of State for the Home Department [1997] Imm AR 97. Post-Graduate Scholarship in Philosophy (1989-90) at Princeton University, USA.

FARLEY, Roger QC
40 King St (Philip Raynor QC), Manchester (0161) 832 9082
Recommended in Crime
Career: Recorder of the Crown Court. Solicitor of the supreme court 1967-1974; Junior Counsel 1974-1993; Queen' s Counsel: 1993- to date.
Personal: Sports nut.

FARQUHAR, Stuart A.
St. Mary's Chambers Family Law Chambers (Christopher Butler), Nottingham (0115) 950 3503
Recommended in Family/Matrimonial

FARRELL, David QC
36 Bedford Row (Michael Pert QC), Northampton (01604) 602333
Recommended in Crime
Specialisation: Fraud and serious crime. Personal Injury and Medical/Professional negligence. Child cases. R v Neave: Murder of a child; Defence Junior counsel. Operations Neath: Serious Fraud involving motor vehicles, £6 million+. Prosecution counsel (leader). Junior counsel in Revill v Newbery (1996) the Leading case on ex turpi causa.
Prof. Memberships: C.B.A.

Career: LLB Hons Manchester. Ashby-de-la-Zouch Grammar School. Recorder M&O Circuit, SILK 2000+
Personal: Married, 5 children. Interests; Tennis, Sailing.

FARRER, David QC
7 Bedford Row (David Farrer QC), London
(020) 7242 3555
Recommended in Crime
Specialisation: All areas of serious crime – murder and commercial fraud, both Prosecution and Defence, often with International dimension. Clients include S.F.O., D.T.I., C.P.S., (HQ and regionally on SE and Midlands and Oxford Circuits), as well as range of large and medium firms. Variety of non-criminal work in Q.B.D. and Chancery Divisions involving fraud, undue influence and accounting issues – partnership, insolvency. Civil clients include former England football coach and boxing promoter Don King. Prosecuted SFO "Blackspur" and "Norton" cases and R.v.Morgan (Celine Figard murder). Defended first "DNA profiling" murder (R .v. Pitchfork). Regularly train and organise seminars for accountants on investigation, reporting and giving evidence in court. N.I.T.A. qualified advocacy trainer.
Prof. Memberships: European Bar Group; Criminal Bar Association.
Career: Teaching modern languages 1965-1967. Called to bar in 1967; Appointed Recorder 1983; Took silk 1986; Member of Bar Council 1987-1993; Chairman Bar services committee 1989-1992; Edited current Bar action pack (Good practice guide). Educated at Queen Elizabeth's Grammar school, Barnet and Downing College Cambridge. Took LLB in Public and Private International Law. Leisure Pursuits include tennis, Rugby (watching only), local history, music and cricket (playing and watching). Fluent French & German, working Italian.

FARRER, Paul
1 Fountain Court (David Crigman QC), Birmingham (0121) 236 5721
Recommended in Crime

FAULKS, Edward QC
No. 1 Serjeants' Inn (Edward Faulks QC), London
(020) 7415 6666
no1serjeantsinn@btinternet.com
Recommended in Clinical Negligence
Specialisation: Principal areas of practice: clinical negligence disputes for both claimants and defendants; professional negligence; claims against public authorities (he has been involved in many of the leading cases in the last few years concerning the liability in negligence of local authorities); personal injury, including child abuse. He is instructed on behalf of NHS Trusts, local authorities, police authorities, insurance companies and individual claimants. He has been or is involved in group litigation arising out of radiotherapy treatment, cardiac surgery errors, cervical cancer screening errors and child abuse. Recent cases include: Penney v East Kent Health Authority [1999] MLC 0068, Kent v Griffiths, Roberts and London Ambulance Service (CA) The Times, 23 December 1998, Phelps v Hillingdon London Borough Council (HL) [2000], W v Essex County Council (HL) [2000], Capital and Counties v Hants CC [1997] QB1004, X v Bedfordshire CC (HL) [1995] 3 WLR 152. Contributing editor of 'Local Authority Liabilities' (1998 Jordans).
Prof. Memberships: Fellow of Chartered Institute of Arbitrators, London Common Law & Commercial Bar Association, Professional Negligence Bar Association (Vice Chairman)
Career: Called to the Bar 1973. Silk in 1996. Recorder. Head of Chambers 1998.
Personal: Educated at Wellington College and Jesus College, Oxford. Former literary agent. Leisure pursuits include cricket. Lives in London.

FEATHERBY, William
12 King's Bench Walk (Timothy Stow QC), London (020) 7583 0811
Recommended in Personal Injury

FEDER, Ami
Lamb Building (Ami Feder), London
(020) 7797 7788
clerks@lambbldg.co.uk
Recommended in Crime
Specialisation: Principal area of practice is fraud work in both the criminal and civil fields and general commercial and international work. Also practices at 9 Malchei Israel Square, Tel-Aviv 64163. Tel: 03-5243381 Fax: 03-5243387
Prof. Memberships: Criminal Bar Association; Common Law and Commercial Bar Association; European Bar Asociation.
Career: Called to the Bar 1965; Member of the Israel Bar.
Personal: Educated in Israel (Hebrew University of Jerusalem, the branch in Tel Aviv) and in England (London LSE).

FEINBERG, Peter QC
2-4 Tudor Street (Richard Ferguson QC), London
(020) 7797 7111
Recommended in Crime
Specialisation: Criminal law. R v Powell & Daniels – House of Lords; R v Burstow – House of Lords.
Career: Recorder. President, Mental Health Tribunal. Chairman, Liaison Committee.

FENNY, Ian Charles
Guildhall Chambers (Adrian Palmer QC), Bristol
(0117) 927 3366
Recommended in Crime
Specialisation: All serious crimes of violence with a particular specialisation in offences against women, children and vulnerable victims. Serious fraud and large-scale conspiracies. Drugs importation and large-scale possession with intent to supply. Category 4 Prosecutor. Lectures to legal practitioners, medical practitioners and police officers on issues involving child abuse both physical and sexual.
Prof. Memberships: Membership Criminal Bar Association. Western Circuit.
Career: LL.B (Reading) 1977. Called to Bar (Gray's Inn) 1978. Married to a member of the Bar, 3 children. Hobbies: Motor racing, equestrian sports.

FENTON, Adam
7 King's Bench Walk (Jeremy Cooke QC), London
(020) 7910 8300
Recommended in Insurance
Specialisation: Insurance (including Lloyd's matters), reinsurance, shipping. Recent cases include: The "ABT Rasha" 2000 1 Lloyds Rep. 8 (recoverability of GA liability from insurers); Imperio v CE Heath [1999] Lloyds Rep. IR 571 (limitation period for breach of fiduciary duty); Kirkaldy v Walker [1999] Lloyd's Rep IR 571 (construction of warranty); North Atlantic v Bishopsgate [1998] 1 Lloyd's Rep. 459 (Basis on which excess to be applied); Johnston v Leslie & Godwin [1995] LRLR 472 (Duty of broker to retain documentation/ collect claims); Aiken v Wrightson [1995] 1 WLR 1281 (Insurance – duty of Managing Agent).
Career: Called to the Bar, 1984.
Personal: Born 1961.

FENWICK, Justin QC
Four New Square (Justin Fenwick QC), London
(020) 7822 2000
barristers@4newsquare.com
Recommended in Construction, Product Liability, Professional Negligence
Specialisation: Professional Negligence; Construction; Pharmaceutical product liability.
Prof. Memberships: Combar; PNBA; LCLBA; Tecbar.
Career: MA (Cantab) 1971 (Modern Languages and Architectural History). Grenadier Guards 1968-81; called to the Bar November 1980. Pupillage Lamb Building July 81-July 82. Tenancy July 82-July 89. 2 Crown Office Row July 1989-present. QC 1993. Recorder 1999; Chairman Bar Mutual Indemnity Fund 1999-.

FERGUSON, Richard QC
2-4 Tudor Street (Richard Ferguson QC), London
(020) 7797 7111
Recommended in Crime, Health & Safety
Specialisation: All forms of jury advocacy and in particular: commercial fraud; health and safety; criminal defence; libel; food and drugs. Important cases include; Ramsgate Ferry disaster [for Lloyds Register]; Severn Bridge [for consulting engineers]; New Zealand butter importation [for Anchor Butter]; Guiness Trial [for Earnest Saunders]; Hong Kong corruption [for local solicitor]; Solicitor Green form fraud [Liverpool Crown Court]; Cyprus Spy Trial; Terry Marsh; Brighton Bombing; Birmingham 6; Allegation of police perversion of justice [Melvin & Dingle]; Allegation of murder by police shooting [for the officer]; Ronnie Knight; Taylor Sisters; Rosemary West; Branson v Snowden [Libel]; acted in Ireland for Sunday Times and News International; environmental law; [for United Biscuits, food misdescription]; M.O.D. v Green; House of Lords, Brophy [voir dire]; Asiz [good character direction] in re M suit against magustrate; Clegg [shooting by soldier]; Privy Council; judicial review; extradition.
Career: QC [Northern Ireland] 1973; SC [Republic of Ireland] 1982; QC [England and Wales] 1986; practice in Hog Kong, Cayman, Bermuda; Bencher in Gray's Inn; former Chairman, Criminal Bar Association; Bar Council.

FERNYHOUGH, Richard QC
Keating Chambers (Richard Fernyhough QC), London (020) 7544 2600
clerks@keatingchambers.com
Recommended in Arbitration (International), Construction
Specialisation: Construction and engineering law; arbitration both international and domestic; arbitrator, domestic and international including I.C.C.
Career: Qualified 1970; Middle Temple; QC 1986; FCI Arb 1992; Recorder of the Crown Court 1986.
Personal: Merchant Taylors School; University College, London (1966 LLB Hons). Born 1943; resides London. Tennis, flying, opera. Languages: French.

FIELD, Patrick QC
Deans Court Chambers (H.K. Goddard QC), Manchester (0161) 214 6000
Recommended in Personal Injury

FIELD, Richard QC
One Essex Court (Lord Grabiner QC), London
(020) 7583 2000
Recommended in Commercial (Litigation)
Specialisation: Principal area of practice is commercial law. Has appeared in a wide range of matters in this area including insurance, banking, EC competition law, sale and purchase warranties and distribution agreements. Other areas of practice include profession-

al negligence, especially auditors' negligence, fraud and tracing of assets and judicial review in a commercial context.
Prof. Memberships: COMBAR; London Common Law and Commercial Bar Asociation, British Insurance Law Association; ALBA.
Career: 1969-1977 taught in the law faculties of the Universities of British Columbia; Hong Kong; and McGill; called to the Bar 1977; appointed Queen's Counsel 1987; Deputy High Court Judge (authorised to sit in the Commercial Court) 1998; Master of the Bench of Inner Temple 1998; Recorder 1999.
Personal: Educated: Bristol University (LLB) and London University (LLM).

FINCH, Nadine
Two Garden Court (I. Macdonald QC & O.Davies QC), London (020) 7353 1633
Recommended in Immigration
Specialisation: Predominantly civil liberties practice, specialising in all areas of immigration law. Particular experience of cases involving asylum, the interaction between immigration and family law, applications by gay and lesbian appellants, the use of European Convention on Human Rights and European law, and procedures to be employed when an appellant or applicant is suffering from mental illness. She has recently suceeded in a number of appeals and applications for judicial review, where an asylum seeker has not been able to give evidence or counter allegations of lack of credibility because of depression or mental illness. Other recent cases include R v. Secretary of State for the Home Department ex parte Meftah Zighem [1996] Imm AR 194, R v. Secretary of State for the Home Department ex parte Toprak [1996] Imm AR 332, and R v. SSHD ex p. Lucy Ouma [1997] Imm AR 606.
Prof. Memberships: Executive Member of Immigration Law Practitioners Association, member of Stonewall Immigration Group, Administrative Law Bar Association, Family Law Bar Association. She advised MPs and ministers on amendments to the Asylum and Immigration Bill Act on behalf of ILPA, Liberty and UNICEF, and provided briefings on the Terrorism Bill for Liberty and the Race relations (Amendment) Bill for Justice.
Career: Called to the Bar 1991. Joined present chambers in 2000. Previously practiced at Doughty Street Chambers. Prior to 1989 employed in legal research and community work.

FINDLAY, James
2-3 Gray's Inn Square (Anthony Scrivener QC), London (020) 7242 4986
Recommended in Planning
Specialisation: Principal area of practice is local government, planning & environment and administrative law. Extensive experience both in Judicial Review (e.g. R v Durham CC & Others, ex parte Huddlestone, R v West Dorset D.C. ex p. Searle, R v Brighton&Hove B.C. ex p. Nacion, Warsame v Hounslow L.B.C, Hughes v Kingston Upon Hull DC, Birmingham CC v Oakley, R v Newell, R v Newcastle Under Lyme Magistrates, ex p. Massey) and Inquiry work (planning and others, both for and against local authorities). Regular lecturer on such matters, including impact of Human Rights Act. On editorial panel of Halsbury's Laws Public Health (waste on land).
Prof. Memberships: PEBA; ALBA.
Career: Called: 1984.
Personal: Born 1961. Educated at Glenalmond and Magdalene College, Cambridge.

FINNIGAN, Peter
Queen Elizabeth Building (Julian Bevan QC & Peter Whiteman QC), London (020) 7583 5766
Recommended in Fraud: Criminal
Specialisation: Principal area of practice is criminal law with a particular emphasis on commercial and professional/ City fraud cases. Also deals with Revenue offences and V.A.T. frauds. Major cases include Blue Arrow, Iraqi Supergun, Brinks Mat handling (R v Noye and others) and the Guppy case. Clients include the S.F.O., H.M. Customs and Excise and the Fraud Investigation Group of the C.P.S.
Prof. Memberships: Lincoln's Inn.
Career: Called to the Bar 1979 and joined current chambers in 1981. Standing Counsel to H.M. Customs & Excise.
Personal: Educated at Sevenoaks School 1967-1974 and University of Newcastle-upon-Tyne 1975-1978. Lives in Twickenham, Middlesex.

FISH, David QC
Deans Court Chambers (H.K. Goddard QC), Manchester (0161) 214 6000
Recommended in Crime

FISHER, David QC
6 King's Bench Walk (Michael Worsley QC), London (020) 7583 0410
Recommended in Crime
Specialisation: Criminal law specialist, including drugs, sexual allegations and fraud.
Prof. Memberships: General Council of the Bar 1997 to 1999. Deputy Chairman of the Law Reform Committee since 1999. Advocacy Studies Board since 1997. Criminal Bar Association. South Eastern Circuit.
Career: Called to the Bar in 1973. Tenant of current chambers since 1974. Recorder since 1991. Q.C. in 1996.

FITTON, Michael
Albion Chambers (J.C.T. Barton QC), Bristol (0117) 927 2144
Recommended in Crime

FITZGERALD, Edward QC
Doughty Street Chambers (Geoffrey Robertson QC), London (020) 7404 1313
Recommended in Administrative & Public Law: General, Crime, Human Rights (Civil Liberties)

FITZGERALD, Michael QC
2 Mitre Court Buildings (Michael FitzGerald QC), London (020) 7583 1380
Recommended in Parliamentary & Public Affairs, Planning
Specialisation: All aspects of planning and local government law. Major infrastructure cases include; channel tunnel, Sizewell nuclear power station, Wynch farm oilfield and pipeline, Maidenhead, Windsor and Eton flood relief scheme, Terminals 4 and 5 Heathrow, Birmingham Northern Relief Road and M20. Major Contentious cases include: Green Belt – HQ for British Airways, HQ for RMC, HQ and manufacturing for TAG/McLaren; Research laboratories for Amersham International; AONB – Holiday villages at Longleat and Sellindge, Major land valuation, compensation and rating cases in UK and Hong Kong.
Prof. Memberships: Leader of the Parliamentary Bar. Planning and Environment Bar Association. Chairman of the Advisory Panel on Standards for the Planning Inspectorate Executive Agency. 21 years as a Committee Member of the Joint Oxford Planning Conference.
Career: Called to the Bar in 1961. Appointed QC 1980.
Personal: Educated at Downside and Cambridge. Leisure pursuits include opera, music, shooting, fishing.

FITZGERALD, Susanna QC
One Essex Court (Lord Grabiner QC), London (020) 7583 2000
Recommended in Licensing
Specialisation: Specialises in liquor, gaming, betting, internet gambling, public entertainment licensing and lotteries law. Has represented or advised major leisure and gaming operators, concert promoters, retail liquor companies, breweries and petrol companies. Contributing editor to 'Law of Betting, Gaming and Lotteries' by Smith and Monkcom (2nd ed in preparation), author of articles published in 'Licensing Review', 'The Solicitors Journal' and the 'Consumer Policy Review'. Contributor to 'Gambling and Public Policy' (1991). Has drafted submissions to the government on changes in Liquor and Public Entertainment Licensing Law and on amendments to the Gaming Act 1968 for Business in Sport and Leisure. Has lectured at conferences and spoken at seminars in the UK and abroad. Has also appeared on radio and television.
Prof. Memberships: Director of Business in Sport & Leisure, CLCBA, South Eastern Circuit, Commercial Women in Law, Society for the Study of Gambling (Committee Member), Mediator accredited by CEDR.
Career: Called to the Bar in 1973, joined present chambers in 1975 and made QC in 1999.

FLAUX, Julian QC
7 King's Bench Walk (Jeremy Cooke QC), London (020) 7910 8300
Recommended in Insurance, Shipping
Specialisation: Specialises in all aspects of commercial law including insurance and reinsurance, shipping, professional negligence, international sale of goods, banking and international arbitration.
Prof. Memberships: Chairman: London Common Law and Commercial Bar Association; Chairman: Supporting Members Liaison Committee of London Maritime Arbitrators Association; Commercial Bar Association; LCIA; ACI.
Career: B.C.L.; M.A. (Oxon: Firts Class Honours in Jurisprudence); Called to the Bar 1978. Member of present Chambers from 1979; Took silk 1994; Appointed Recorder 2000.
Personal: Born 1955; Married, three sons. Interests: Cricket; opera.

FLESCH, Michael QC
Gray's Inn Tax Chambers (Milton Grundy), London (020) 7242 2642
Recommended in Tax
Specialisation: Advises on all aspects of revenue law, and appears before the Commissioners, High Court, Court of Appeal, House of Lords, Privy Council and also in Hong Kong in revenue cases. Regular lecturer on tax-related topics.
Prof. Memberships: Revenue Bar Association, past Chairman.
Career: Called to the Bar 1963. Teaching Fellow, University of Chicago 1963-1964. Part-time lecturer in Revenue law, University College London 1964-82. Joined present chambers 1965. Took Silk 1983. Bencher of Grays Inn 1993.
Personal: Educated at Gordonstoun School 1953-58 and University College, London 1959-1962 (LL.B Class 1, Hons). Governor of Gordonstoun School 1976-1996. Leisure pursuits include all forms of sport. Keen Arsenal and Middlesex supporter, member of MCC, Twickenham and Wimbledon debenture holder. Born 11th March 1940. Lives in London.

FLINT, Charles QC
Blackstone Chambers (P Baxendale QC and C Flint QC), London (020) 7583 1770
Recommended in Civil Fraud, Commercial (Litigation), Financial Services, Sport
Specialisation: Commercial and public law specialist. Practice covers substantial corporate litigation in all divisions of the High Court, financial services litigation, including disciplinary tribunals, and judicial review in a commercial context. Has a particular interest in commercial fraud and sports law. Acted for the plaintiff in Arab Monetary Fund v Hashim litigation.

Prof. Memberships: Fellow of the Chartered Institute of Arbitrators, Commercial Bar Association, Administrative Law Bar Association, British Association for Sport and Law. CEDR Accredited Mediator.
Career: Called to the Bar 1975, joining present chambers in the same year. Appointed Junior Counsel to the Crown (Common Law) 1991-1995 and took Silk 1995.

FLOYD, Christopher QC
11 South Square (Christopher Floyd QC), London (020) 7405 1222
Recommended in Intellectual Property

FLYNN, James
Brick Court Chambers (Christopher Clarke QC), London (020) 7379 3550
Recommended in Competition/Anti-trust
Specialisation: European Community/Competition Law. Reported cases include: (English courts): R v Customs & Excise ex p Lunn Poly (High Court and CA); Sockel GmbH v Body Shop International (High Court); Trent Taverns v Sykes (CA); Welsh Rugby Union and IRB v Campbell (High Court); (in the European Court of Justice): British Aerospace v Commission; BP Chemicals v Commission; Gencor v Commission; Compagnei Maritime Belge v Commission. Co-author 'Competition: Understanding the 1998 Act' and many articles and contributions to books on EC and competition law topics.
Prof. Memberships: International Rapporteur for the International League for Competition Law (LIDC) 1999-2000.
Career: Legal Secretary, European Court of Justice (1986-1989); Partner, *Linklaters & Paines*, Brussels (1993-1996); Tenant Brick Court Chambers, 1996 to date.
Personal: Fluent French (written and spoken).

FLYNN, Vernon
Essex Court Chambers (Gordon Pollock QC), London (020) 7813 8000
Recommended in Commercial (Litigation), Media & Entertainment
Specialisation: Broad-based practice in international and commercial law. In particular Media & Entertainment, Commercial, Banking and Finance, Shipping and Employment.
Career: Trinity College, Cambridge: Law (First Class Hons). Called to the Bar 1991.
Personal: Born 1966.

FORD, Michael
Doughty Street Chambers (Geoffrey Robertson QC), London (020) 7404 1313
Recommended in Human Rights (Civil Liberties)
[SEP] Principal areas of practice are employment law, public law, civil liberties, tort and health and safety.
Prof. Memberships: Member of the Industrial Law Society, Institute for Employment Rights, Justice, Liberty.
Career: University of Bristol, First Class; MA (Distinction). Qualified as solicitor (1989). Lecturer in Law at University of Manchester (1990 -92). Called to Bar 1992. Recent cases include Steel, Lush and others v UK (ECHR) (1999) 28 EHRR 603, and Allen v AMCO (ECJ) [2000] IRLR 119. Counsel for the bereaved and injured at Southall and Ladbroke Grove Railway Accident Public Inquiries. Visiting Fellow at LSE.
Personal: Co-author of 'Redgrave's Health and Safety' and author of 'Privacy and Surveillance at Work'. Numerous other publications, especially on employment law. Keen cyclist.

FORD, Neil QC
Albion Chambers (J.C.T. Barton QC), Bristol (0117) 927 2144
Recommended in Crime

FORDHAM, Michael
Blackstone Chambers (P Baxendale QC and C Flint QC), London (020) 7583 1770
Recommended in Administrative & Public Law: General, Environment, Sport
Specialisation: Specialist in public and administrative law, and particularly judicial review. Member of Attorney-General's Supplementary Panel. Cases include Pinochet [2000] 1AC 61 & 147 (extradition of former head of state), Diane Blood [1999] Fam 151 (posthumous use of sperm), Fayed [1998] 1 All ER 93 (review of Parliamentary Commissioner for Standards), Walker [2000] 1 WLR 806 (UN peacekeeper) and Baby Products [2000] LGR 171. Also environmental law, human rights and sports law. Author of 'Judicial Review Handbook'. Editor of journal 'Judicial Review'. Lectures in administrative law at Hertford College, Oxford. Called to the Bar 1990.
Personal: Educated at Spalding Grammar School, Hertford College, Oxford (BA & BCL), and University of Virginia (LL.M). Oxford Hockey Blue (1986). Awarded Karmel, Mould and Prince of Wales Scholarships at Gray's Inn.

FORSYTH, Julie
Chavasse Court Chambers (Theresa Pepper), Liverpool (0151) 707 1191
Recommended in Crime

FORTSON, Rudi
3 Gray's Inn Square (Rock Tansey QC), London (020) 7520 5600
Recommended in Crime
Specialisation: Extensive criminal law experience, with specialist knowledge on law relating to misuse of drugs, drug-trafficking offences, money-laundering and fraud. Author of 'The Criminal Justice Act 1993' and 'Law on the Misuse of Drugs and Drug Trafficking Offences'. Annotator for 'Current Law Statutes' on Criminal Justice Acts 1991 and 1993, Police and Magistrates Courts Act 1994 and Drug Trafficking Act 1994. Member of the Police Foundation Independent Inquiry (2000) into the Misuse of Drugs Act 1971. Former contributing editor of 'Archbold Criminal Pleading, Evidence and Practice'. Addresses conferences and seminars.
Prof. Memberships: Criminal Bar Association, International Bar Association, American Bar Association, Forensic Science Society.
Career: Called to the Bar 1976 (pupillage at 1 Crown Office Row) and joined current chambers in 1978.
Personal: Educated at University College, London 1972-1975 (LL.B Hons). Leisure pursuits include yachting, chess and cooking. Born 2nd March 1952.

FOSTER, Alison
39 Essex Street (Nigel Pleming QC), London (020) 7832 1111
Recommended in Tax
Specialisation: Public law; human rights; medical law, including medical negligence. Also tax. Practice predominantly in Judicial Review, some statutory tribunals.
Prof. Memberships: Membership: Supplementary Treasury Panel. Committee member Administrative Law Bar Association.
Personal: BA (Oxon). M Phil (London). Dips in Law (City). Chambers of Edwin Glasgow QC from 1986 to present.

FOSTER, Catherine
Plowden Buildings (William Lowe QC), London (020) 7583 0808
Recommended in Personal Injury

FOSTER, Charles
6 Pump Court (Kieran Coonan QC), London (020) 7583 6013
Recommended in Agriculture, Clinical Negligence
Specialisation: Medical and other professional negligence. Reported cases include Briggs v Pitt-Payne [1999] Lloyd's LR: Med 1, Drake v Pontefract HA [1998] Lloyd's LR: Med 425, Reed v Sunderland HA, The Times, 16 October 1998, Fallows v. Randle [1997] 8 Med LR 160, Bancroft v. Harrogate HA [1997] 8 Med LR 398, Hind v. York HA [1997] 8 Med LR 377, Ogden v. Airedale HA [1996] 7 Med LR 153, Kahl v. Freistaat Bayern [1995] PIQR P401.
Prof. Memberships: PNBA, Medico-Legal Society.
Career: Educated at Shrewsbury School & St John's College, Cambridge (MA, Vet MB, MRCVS). Research in wild animal anaesthesia in Saudi Arabia and comparative anatomy at RCS, Research Fellow at Hebrew University, Jerusalem. Also a member of the Irish Bar. Numerous publications.

FOWLER, Richard QC
Monckton Chambers (John Swift QC), London (020) 7405 7211 rfowler@monckton.co.uk
Recommended in Aviation, Competition/Anti-trust
Specialisation: EC and UK competition law.
Prof. Memberships: Committee member COMBAR; member Competition Law Association; member Legal Services Committee of Bar Council.
Career: Specialised since 1973 (including working from 1977 to 1984 on Case No.IV/29.479 – IBM) in the preparation, drafting and presentation of submissions on behalf of clients to the European Commission (also OFT and Competition Commission) and in High Court and European Court proceedings, and advising a wide range of national and international clients on competition law matters and in related areas, particularly utility regulation. Recent cases include Guinness/Grand Met merger; Re Premier League Football (RP Court); appearing for the Hong Kong administration in the HK Legislative Council in relation to the HK Telecommunications Bill.

FOXTON, David
Essex Court Chambers (Gordon Pollock QC), London (020) 7813 8000
Recommended in Commercial (Litigation), Insurance, Shipping
Specialisation: Commercial practice, in particular international insurance and reinsurance; shipping and the international carriage of goods; professional negligence; Lloyd's litigation (LMX and US Casualty underwriting). Banking, sale of goods, company sales, computer supply disputes and professional negligence actions. Has appeared on numerous occasions in commercial arbitration.
Career: Magdalen College, Oxford 1983-86 BA (First Class Hons) in Jurisprudence, 1986. Bachelor of Civil Law (First Class Hons). Called to the Bar 1989.
Personal: Born 1965.

FOY, John QC
9 Gough Square (Jeremy Roberts QC), London (020) 7832 0500
Recommended in Personal Injury
Specialisation: Practice encompasses plaintiff and defendant personal injury and clinical negligence work. Appeared in Mountenay v. Bernard Matthews [1994], Mughal v. Reuters Ltd [1993]; Hunt v. Douglas Roofing [1990] and Arnold v. CEGB [1988], British Coal Respiration Disease Litigation [1998], Alexander v Midland Bank plc [1999], Wadey v. Surrey County

Council [2000]. Clients include all major trade unions. Frequently chairs and addresses conferences and seminars, and has appeared on BBC TV and radio.
Prof. Memberships: Association of Personal Injury Lawyers, Personal Injury Bar Association.
Career: Called to the Bar and joined 9 Gough Square in 1969.
Personal: LL.B (Hons) Birmingham University, 1967. Leisure pursuits include sports. Born 1st June 1946. Lives in Suffolk.

FRANCIS, Nicholas
29 Bedford Row Chambers (Peter Ralls QC), London (020) 7404 1044
Recommended in Family: Matrimonial Finance
Specialisation: Principal area of practice is matrimonial ancillary relief work, with a particular interest in pension issues and foreign asset cases. Other main areas within practice are professional negligence; and residence, contact, education and child abduction cases. Major cases include Re P (A Minor) [1992] (Education); Re D (minors) [1993] (conciliation: Privilege); C v C [1994] (wasted costs order); S v S (reserved costs order) [1995] B v Miller & Co [1996] and H v H [1997]. Several articles on ancillary relief for Family Law with particular emphasis on the issue of costs and discovery. Regular lecturer on costs and discovery and on international aspects of family proceedings; and contributor to Legal Network T.V.
Prof. Memberships: Family Law Bar Association (former committee member). Member for 3 years of Bar Council Professional Conduct and Complaints Committee.
Personal: Educated at Radley College 1971-1976 and Downing College, Cambridge 1977-80 (BA Law 1980, MA 1984). Leisure pursuits include racing dinghies. Born 1958. Lives in London.

FRANCIS, Robert QC
3 Serjeants' Inn (Philip Naughton QC), London (020) 7427 5000
Recommended in Clinical Negligence
Specialisation: Principal area of practice is medical law, including medical negligence actions for plaintiffs and defendants, ethical cases concerning treatment of patients (particularly termination of treatment), and disciplinary proceedings (General Medical Council, General Dental Council etc.). Leading cases include: Re F (Mental Patient: Sterilization); Airedale NHS Trust v Bland; Roy v Kensington etc FPC; Bright v Croydon HA, Re T (Wardship: Medical Treatment); Re MB; GMC v Roylance. Other areas of practice include administrative law, employment, crime.
Prof. Memberships: Professional Negligence Bar Association, LCLCBA, CBA.
Career: Called to the Bar 1973; Queen's Counsel 1992. Assistant Recorder 1996.
Personal: Uppingham School, Exeter University. Born 4th April 1950.

FRANSMAN, Laurie QC
Two Garden Court (I. Macdonald QC & O.Davies QC), London (020) 7353 1633
Recommended in Immigration

FRASER, Peter D.
Atkin Chambers (John Blackburn QC), London (020) 7404 0102
Recommended in Construction
Specialisation: Construction and engineering disputes; multi-party contractual disputes and commercial litigation. Insurance litigation, professional negligence of architects, surveyors and engineers. Arbitration proceedings including international arbitrations. Cases involving following projects: Harbour Exchange, Isle of Dogs; the West Yorkshire Playhouse, Leeds; Bokaa Dam project in Botswana; Euro Disney; Canary Wharf; Copthorne Hotel in Newcastle; New Sadlers Wells Theatre, London; Canary Wharf Riverside Project; Delta Civil Engineering Co. Ltd v LDDC (CA) 81 BLR 19; Copthorne Hotel (Newcastle) Ltd. v Arup Associates (CA) 85 BLR 22.
Career: Called to Bar by Middle Temple 1989. Editor of the Building Law Reports since 1991 to date. Author of 'How to Pass Law Exams' (HLT Publications 1991).
Personal: Born 1963. Educated Harrogate Grammar School and St John's College Cambridge. LLM Cambridge University; MA in Law, Cambridge University. Open exhibitioner and MacMahon Law Scholar of St. John's College, Cambridge. Astbury Scholar of the Middle Temple.

FREEDMAN, Clive QC
Littleton Chambers (Michel Kallipetis QC), London (020) 7797 8600
Recommended in Commercial (Litigation)
Specialisation: Commercial law including franchising, company, partnership, banking, employment, construction, professional negligence, commercial arbitration and professional disciplinary tribunals. Since taking silk in 1997, have appeared in the following representative cases: Arrow v Blackledge C.A. The Times 7 July 2000 CA (striking out section 459 petition), Beeforth v Beeforth CA The Times 17 September 1998 (peremptory orders); Re: Blenheim Restaurants Limited C.A. 26 July 1999 (dissolution of company), Re: Blenheim Restaurants Limited (No.2) (condition regarding restoration) The Times 26 October 1999, Re: Blenheim Restaurants Limited (No.3) (recalling court orders) The Times 7 November 1999, Dubai Aluminium v Al Alawi [1999] 1 All ER 703 (legal professional privilege), Hendry v Chartsearch CA The Times 16 September 1998 (assignment in commercial contract), Hurst v Brvk H.L. [2000] 2 WLR 740 (Solicitors' partnership-repudiatory breach), Paperlight Ltd v Swinton Insurance [1998] CLR 853 (franchising - reasonable notice); S v S (Supreme Court of Gibraltar) (worldwide Mareva), Stock v London Underground CA The Times 13 August 1999 (payments into Court).
Prof. Memberships: COMBAR, Northern Circuit Commercial Bar Association.
Career: Manchester Grammar School; Pembroke College, Cambridge. Recorder. QC (1997).
Personal: Languages: working knowledge of Hebrew, French and Russian. Married, four children.

FREEDMAN, Jeremy
Plowden Buildings (William Lowe QC), London (020) 7583 0808
Recommended in Clinical Negligence
Specialisation: Practises exclusively in personal injury work. Specialises in medical negligence. Regularly instructed on behalf of several Health Authorities/NHS Trusts as well as acting on behalf of plaintiffs. Conducted a number of large claims, in particular, brain damage cases, both on behalf of plaintiffs and defendants. Appeared on behalf of the Freeman Trust in the recent heart transplant case of Re: M.
Prof. Memberships: North Eastern Circuit, Professional Negligence Bar Association and Personal Injury Bar Association. Recorder.
Career: Called to the Bar, 1982. Joined present set of Chambers in 1999.
Personal: Educated at Oundle, Manchester University and City University of London. Born 1959. Married, two children.

FREEDMAN, S. Clive
3 Veralum Buildings (Christopher Symons QC & John Jarvis QC), London (020) 7831 8441
Recommended in Information Technology

FRENCH, Paul
Guildhall Chambers (Adrian Palmer QC), Bristol (0117) 927 3366
Recommended in Insolvency/Corporate Recovery

FRIEDMAN, David QC
4 Pump Court (Bruce Mauleverer QC), London (020) 7353 2656
dfriedman@4pumpcourt.com
Recommended in Construction
Specialisation: Principal area of practice covers all stages and all aspects of construction and engineering litigation and arbitration, both domestic and international. Also deals with professional negligence, particularly in relation to claims relating to professionals in the construction field.
Prof. Memberships: Chairman Technology and Construction Bar Association.
Career: Called to the Bar 1968. Tenant at 3 Paper Buildings 1970-92. Took Silk 1990. Joined Pump Court 1992. Appointed Recorder 1998. CEDR Accredited Mediator 1999
Personal: Educated at Tiffin Boys' School, Kingston-upon-Thames and Lincoln College, Oxford 1963-1967 (MA, BCL). Born 1st June 1944.

FULFORD, Adrian QC
14 Tooks Court (Michael Mansfield QC), London (020) 7405 8828
Recommended in Crime

FURBER, John QC
Wilberforce Chambers (Edward Nugee QC), London (020) 7306 0102
jfurber@wilberforce.co.uk
Recommended in Property Litigation
Specialisation: Principally law of Landlord and Tenant but also covers property litigation, planning and compulsory purchase of land.
Prof. Memberships: Member of Chancery Bar Association and Planning and Environmental Bar Association.
Publications: Contributor to Halsbury's Laws of England, Landlord and Tenant (1981 edition) and Compulsory Acquisition. Contributor to and now general editor of Hill and Redman's law of Landlord and Tenant.
Personal: Called to Bar in 1973, took silk in 1995.

FURNESS, Jonathan
30 Park Place (John Jenkins QC), Cardiff (029) 2039 8421
Recommended in Family/Matrimonial

FURNESS, Michael QC
Wilberforce Chambers (Edward Nugee QC), London (020) 7306 0102
Recommended in Charities, Pensions, Tax
Specialisation: Trusts, both private and commercial, especially pensions (advisory work, ombudsman appeals and other litigation) and charities (on behalf of HM Attorney General and others, particularly in relation to the making of charitable schemes). Has wide experience of conducting tax litigation at all levels.
Prof. Memberships: Chancery Bar Association, Revenue Bar Association, Association of Pension Lawyers.
Career: Called 1982; Formerly First Standing Junior Counsel to the Inland Revenue in Chancery Matters; QC 2000.
Personal: Secretary, Bar Theatrical Society.

FURST, Stephen QC
Keating Chambers (Richard Fernyhough QC), London (020) 7544 2600
sfurst@keatingchambers.com
Recommended in Construction
Specialisation: Building and civil engineering; professional negligence including valuation; computers including software; important cases include Darlington

v Wiltshire; Bank of East Asia v SDA; Tesco Stores Ltd v Ward Investments; Strachan & Henshaw v Stein Industrial; Macob v Morrison; Henry Boot v Alstom; Baygres v Dahl-Jensen.
Career: Qualified 1975, Middle Temple; QC 1991; Recorder; editor of 'Construction Law Yearbook' and 'Keating on Building Contracts'; arbitrator; mediator.
Personal: The Edinburgh Academy, St Edmund Hall, Oxford, Leeds University (1972 BA Hons, 1974 LLB Hons). Born 1951; resides London.

FURZE, Caroline
Wilberforce Chambers (Edward Nugee QC), London (020) 7306 0102
Recommended in Commercial Chancery, Pensions
Specialisation: Practice covers most aspects of chancery/commercial litigation and advice, including landlord and tenant, professional negligence, insolvency, pension funds, partnership, contentious probate and the administration of estates. Interest in ecclesiastical law.
Prof. Memberships: Member of Chancery Bar Association.
Career: BA (Cantab): 1st class honours in Natural Sciences (Chemistry). Called to the Bar 1992.
Publications: Contributor to the titles 'Real Property and 'Custom Usage' in Halsburys Laws and to Butterworths County Court Precedents

FYSH, Michael QC
8 New Square (Michael Fysh QC SC), London (020) 7405 4321
michael.fysh@8newsquare.co.uk
Recommended in Intellectual Property
Specialisation: Specialist in all aspects of intellectual property and European Community law. Experienced in litigation and advisory work both in the English and Irish courts and in overseas Commonwealth jurisdictions. Publications include 'Russell-Clarke on Registered Designs' 5th edition (Sweet & Maxwell 1974); 'The Industrial property Citator'(European Law Centre 1982 and supplements); 'Spycatcher Cases' (Sweet & Maxwell 1989); 'Breach of Confidence' (with F. Gurry) 2nd edition (Oxford University Press, in preparation). Also editor of 'Reports of Patent Cases' (The Patent Office) and 'Fleet Street Reports' (London, Sweet & Maxwell) 1974-1995.
Prof. Memberships: Member, Bar Council of England and Wales; Vice-Chairman, Central Asia and Transcaucasian Law Association.
Career: Called to the Bar 1965. Took silk 1989. Head of chambers since 1993. Calls to overseas Bars: Northern Ireland 1974 (QC 1990), Ireland 1975 (Senior Counsel 1994), New South Wales 1975, Bombay and Supreme Court of India 1982, Pakistan 1987, Trinidad and Tobago 1990 (Senior Counsel 1990). Has also practised at the Malaysian, Hong Kong and Singapore Bars and before the European Patent Office, Munich. Lecturer, WIPO, Geneva. Deputy High Court Judge (1998); Bencher of the Inner Temple (1999).
Personal: Born USA, 1940. Educated at Downside School, Grenoble University, France 1958-1959 and at Oxford University (BA natural sciences) 1959-1962, MA 1969. Languages include French and some knowledge of Russian, and Hindi.

GAISMAN, Jonathan QC
7 King's Bench Walk (Jeremy Cooke QC), London (020) 7910 8300
Recommended in Insurance, Shipping

GAITSKELL, Robert QC
Keating Chambers (Richard Fernyhough QC), London (020) 7544 2600
Recommended in Alternative Dispute Resolution, Construction
Specialisation: Construction law, including particularly electrical, mechanical and process engineering; instructed in numerous international and UK major engineering/building disputes, both litigation and arbitration (including appointments as an arbitrator and mediator) concerning, inter alia, complex engineering projects (especially power stations), defence, computer facilities, chemical processing, food and drink production, oil and gas rigs, hospitals, motorways, bridges, tunnels, dredging, water treatment, airports, abattoirs, nuclear fuel processing and commercial property; cases include University of Glasgow v Whitefield; ICI v Bovis; Lamacrest v Case; Cameron v Mowlem; Surrey Heath v Lovell.
Career: Qualified 1978; Gray's Inn; QC 1994; practising Queen's Counsel; arbitrator, mediator, and adjudicator; Recorder, Vice President of the IEE; Senator of the Engineering Council, Past Chairman Management and Design Division of Institution of Electrical Engineers; IEE Council; practised in UK and abroad as professional electrical engineer, employed by, inter alia, GEC (South Africa); Reyrolle Parsons, Matthew Hall and Rendell Palmer & Tritton, lectured widely in UK and abroad on legal and engineering matters, particularly international construction contracts; lecturer, King's College, London: MSc in Construction Law under Far Eastern Legal Systems; participated in Legal Network TV programmes on engineers' professional negligence, arbitration, and Official Referees' practice; committee member of London Common Law & Commercial Bar Association, IEE/IMechE Model Form Contracts committee; former member of ORBA Committee, Bar Council Public Affairs Committee, and Centre for Dispute Resolution (CEDR) Mediator; former examiner in contract law, RICS; regular legal columnist 'Engineering Management Journal'; numerous publications on legal and engineering topics published in journals in both UK and abroad; contributor to 'Construction Law Yearbook'.
Personal: Hamilton High School, Zimbabwe, University of Cape Town (1971) BSc Eng, Ph.D. (King's College, London), FIEE, C Eng, FI Mech E, FCI Arb). Born 1948; resides London. Reading, theatre, walking; Methodist local preacher, Worshipful Company of Engineers, Past Chairman IEE Professional Group on Engineering and Law.

GAL, Sonia
28 St. John St (Clement Goldstone QC), Manchester (0161) 834 8418
Recommended in Family/Matrimonial

GAMMIE, Malcolm
One Essex Court (Lord Grabiner QC), London (020) 7583 2000
Recommended in Tax
Specialisation: All commercial taxation and related administrative law, including international and European taxation, corporate and employee taxation, property taxation and value added tax. Consultant Editor of 'Butterworths Tax Handbooks and of Land Taxation'; consultant to Fiscal Affairs Directorate of OECD; Director of Research of Tax Law Review Committee; 1998 Unilever Professor of International Business Law at Leiden University, The Netherlands.
Prof. Memberships: Chartered Institute of Taxation (President 1993-94); Association of Taxation Technicians, International Fiscal Association (Member, Permanent Scientific Committee), European Bar Group.
Career: Sidney Sussex College, Cambridge; qualified 1975 as solicitor with *Linklaters & Paines*; subsequently with CBI and as Director of National Tax Services at KMG Thomson McLintock (now KPMG); tax partner at *Linklaters & Paines* 1987-97; Called to the Bar 1997.
Personal: Married with 4 children. Interests include music and church architecture.

GARDEN, Ian
Derby Square Chambers (Simon Newton), Liverpool (0151) 709 4222
Recommended in Church: Church of England

GARDINER, John QC
11 New Square (John Gardiner QC), London (020) 7242 4017
taxlaw@11newsquare.com
Recommended in Tax
Specialisation: Revenue law. Involved in the two Woolwich cases, Pattison v Marine Midland, Ensign Tankers (Leasing) v Stokes, International Commercial Bank v Willingale, Glaxo Group Ltd v IRC and Nuclear Electric v Bradley.
Prof. Memberships: Revenue Bar Association.
Career: Called to the Bar 1968 and joined New Square in 1970. Took Silk 1982. Treasurer of Senate of Inns of Court and Bar Council, 1985-86; Bencher, Middle Temple.
Personal: Educated at Bancroft's School, Woodford 1957-1963 and Fitzwilliam College, Cambridge 1964-1968 (MA, LL.M) Born 28th February 1946. Lives in London.

GARDINER, Nicholas
1 Middle Temple Lane (Colin Dines & Andrew Trollope QC), London (020) 7583 0659 (12 lines)
Recommended in Crime

GARGAN, Mark
No.6 (Shaun Spencer QC), Leeds (0113) 245 9763
Recommended in Commercial (Litigation)

GARNETT, Kevin QC
5 New Square (Jonathan Rayner James QC), London (020) 7404 0404
Recommended in Media & Entertainment
Specialisation: Practises extensively in the field of media and entertainment with a particular leaning to music, film, broadcasting and publishing work. Also practises widely in the intellectual property field. Is Senior Editor of 'Copinger and Skone James on Copyright'. Other main area of practice is general Chancery litigation.
Prof. Memberships: Chancery Bar Association; Intellectual Property Bar Association.

GARNHAM, Neil S.
1 Crown Office Row (Robert Seabrook QC), London (020) 7797 7500
neil.garnham@1cor.com
Recommended in Administrative & Public Law: General
Specialisation: Principal areas of practice are Administrative and Public Law, Human Rights, Professional Negligence including Medical Negligence, and Personal Injury. Public Law work includes mental health, extradition, education, immigration and asylum. Cases include Thomas v Bunn [1991] (HL – interest in PI cases); Racz v Home Office [1994] (HL – misfeasance in public office); Re K [1994] (CA – adoption of foreign national); Ex parte McQuillan [1995] (Exclusion orders); Ex parte Onibiyo [1996] (CA – fresh claims for political asylum); T v Home Office [1996] (HL – political offences in asylum law); Gregory v UK [1994] (ECHR – bias in jury trials); D v UK [1997] (ECHR – Article 3); ADT v UK [1999] (ECHR-Articles 6 and 14); TI v UK [2000] (ECHR Articles 2 and 3).
Prof. Memberships: ALBA, PNBA, PIBA.
Career: Called 1982; Junior Counsel to the Crown 1995.
Personal: Educated Ipswich School and Peterhouse Cambridge.

GARRETT, Annalissa
6 Pump Court (Kieran Coonan QC), London (020) 7583 6013
Recommended in Clinical Negligence
Specialisation: Specialises in all aspects of medical negligence and medically related work including representing families and doctors at inquests and disciplinary tribunals. Also handles mental health, physiotherapy negligence, dental negligence and product liability cases. Also serious personal injury and fatal accident cases. Acts for both Plaintiffs and Defendants. Lectures regularly on difficult procedural issues, limitation and the law of costs. Recent cases include: Barr v. Dr Matthews (medical negligence case concerning the duties owed by anti-abortion GP's giving advice on abortion.); Leighton v. North Middlesex Hospital NHS trust (ecstacy induced coma leading to brain damage); Haigh v. Pinderfields Hospitals NHS Trust (physiotherapy negligence); Smith v. Southampton Health Autority (limitation trial).
Prof. Memberships: PNBA, AVMA, PIBA & APIL.
Career: Called to the Bar in 1991. Joined Chambers in 1992.
Personal: Educated at Durham University (BA (Hons)). Born 21st June 1966. Lives in London.

GARSIDE, Charles QC
9 St. John Street (John Hand QC), Manchester (0161) 955 9000
Recommended in Crime
Also at: 4 Brick Court (Anne Raffety QC) London EC4Y 9AD. (020) 7583 8455
Specialisation: Crime, including fraud; employment including discrimination; judicial review; other Crown office work; personal injury.
Prof. Memberships: Employment Law Association.
Career: Called 1971. QC 1993.

GATT, Ian
Littleton Chambers (Michel Kallipetis QC), London (020) 7797 8600
Recommended in Employment, Professional Negligence
Specialisation: Professional negligence (principally solicitors and surveyors). Nationwide Managed Litigation (1997-1999); Birmingham Midshires v David Parry; Nationwide v Thimbleby & Co; Nationwide v Balmer Radmore; Nationwide v Various Solicitors (managed litigation costs). Employment: unfair and wrongful dismissal; sex; race and disability discrimination; restraint of trade. Commercial Fraud: Guinness Trial 1990; numerous SFO prosecutions; commercial.
Prof. Memberships: COMBAR, Professional Negligence Bar Association, Employment Law Bar Association, Criminal Bar Association.
Career: Hutton GS, Preston (1974-1981); Hertford College, Oxford (1981-1984) BA Jurisprudence (1st). Called to the Bar 1985. Joined 2 Crown Office Row (now Littleton Chambers) 1986. CEDR Accredited Mediator. Appointed Recorder, 2000.
Publications: Co-Author 'Arlidge and Parry on Fraud' 2nd edn. Bowers and Gatt 'Procedure in Courts and Tribunals' 2nd edn.
Personal: Married with 3 children. Interests: rugby, cars, wine. Lives Winchester, Hampshire.

GAUNT, Jonathan QC
Falcon Chambers (Jonathan Gaunt QC & Kim Lewison QC), London (020) 7353 2484
gaunt@falcon-chambers.com
Recommended in Agriculture, Property Litigation
Specialisation: The joint Head of Falcon Chambers, the members of which specialise in landlord and tenant and property law. Called to the Bar in 1972 and took silk in 1991. An editor of the landlord and tenant volume of 'Halsbury's Laws', having re-written the chapters on repairing covenants, rent and rent review. Also joint editor of the 1997 edition of 'Gale on Easements'.

GEE, Anthony QC
28 St. John St (Clement Goldstone QC), Manchester (0161) 834 8418
Recommended in Crime

GEE, Steven QC
4 Field Court (Steven Gee QC), London (020) 7440 6900
Recommended in Arbitration (International), Shipping
Specialisation: Commercial law and litigation, insurance/reinsurance, contracts, banking, fraud cases, tracing and equitablr remedies, arbitration, shipping, aviation, computer law. Author: 'Mareva Injunctions and Anton Piller Relief' (4th ed, 1998, Sweet & Maxwell).
Prof. Memberships: COMBAR; Supporting member of the London Maritime Arbitrators Association.
Career: Head of chambers (1999); QC (1993); formerly standing junior Counsel to DTI (ECGD). Foreign Jurisdictions: New York (admitted to State Courts and Federal Courts); Antigua.

GEERING, Ian QC
3 Verulam Buildings (Christopher Symons QC & John Jarvis QC), London (020) 7831 8441
Recommended in Civil Fraud, Commercial (Litigation)
Specialisation: Commercial law, specialising in civil claims based on international and domestic commercial fraud and claims for restitution.
Prof. Memberships: COMBAR, London Common Law and Commercial Association.
Career: Queen's Counsel 1991. Further details are on Chambers' web site: www.3verulam.co.uk.

GEORGE, Charles QC
2 Harcourt Buildings (Mr Gerard Ryan QC), London (020) 7353 8415
clerks@2hb.law.co.uk
Recommended in Administrative & Public Law: General, Church: Church of England, Environment, Parliamentary & Public Affairs, Planning
Specialisation: Principal area of practice is public law especially planning and environmental law, local government and parliamentary matters. Has advised and represented applicants and local planning authorities in relation to major development schemes, particularly those involving public infrastructure provision, housing, minerals, listed buildings and local government finance. Involved in promoting the King's Cross Railways Bill and Transport and Works Orders for extensions to the Manchester and Leeds Light Rail systems. Counsel in, inter alia, Pioneer Aggregates (UK) Ltd v Secretary of State for the Environment [1985], Save Britain's Heritage v Number 1 Poultry Ltd [1991], R. v Parliamentary Commissioner for Administration ex p. Balchin Nos 1 and 2 [1996 and 1999], Millington v Secretary of State for the Environment [1999]. Clients include Railtrack, BG plc, the Audit Commission, Manchester City Council, Greater Manchester, West Yorkshire and Merseyside Passenger Transport Executives, RMC Group plc and Laing Homes Ltd. Has frequently represented applicants (many on legal aid) in judicial review proceedings involving public law challenges, particularly in relation to planning and environmental law challenges. Other main area of practice is ecclesiastical law and commons.
Prof. Memberships: Inner Temple; King's Inns, Dublin.
Career: Called to the Bar 1974 and joined 2 Harcourt Buildings in 1975. Conducted Independent Inquiry into Planning decisions in the London Borough of Brent 1991. Took Silk 1992. Called to the Irish Bar 1995. Appointed Recorder 1997. Appointed Chancellor of the Diocese of Southwark 1996
Personal: Educated at Bradfield College 1958-1963, Magdalen College, Oxford 1963-1966 (1st Class Hons Modern History) and Corpus Christi, Cambridge 1966-1967. Author of 'The Stuarts: A Century of Experiment' (1973). Leisure pursuits include tennis, architecture and travel. Born 8th June 1945. Lives in Sevenoaks, Kent.

GHOSH, Julian
Pump Court Tax Chambers (Andrew Thornhill QC), London (020) 7414 8080
julianjg@pumptax.com
Recommended in Tax
Specialisation: Mergers and Acquisitions, structured finance, loan relationships, foreign exchange, financial instruments EC tax, VAT. Recent cases: Memec v IRC; Trinidad Oilwell Service ltd v Board of Inland Revenue (PC); Nationwide Acess Ltd, PPP Ltd v CEC.
Prof. Memberships: Revenue Bar Association; Bar European Group; Share Scheme Lawyers' Group. Also a member of the Faculty of Advocates, Edinburgh.
Publications: Co-author: 'Taxation of Law Relationships, Financial Instruments and Foreign Exchange' (Butterworths).
Personal: Educated: University of Edinburgh; University of London.

GIBBONS, Jeremy S. QC
17 Carlton Crescent (Mr Jeremy Gibbons QC), Southampton (023) 8032 0320/2003
Recommended in Consumer
Specialisation: Jeremy Gibbons QC has had considerable experience in the criminal law in relation to companies. In the area of consumer law he has represented national retailers in relation to food safety matters, licensing applications and appeals, and has advised in relation to due diligence systems. He also has appeared for local authorities in relation to consumer matters. He has also had experience of prosecutions of companies and their directors for fraud and kindred offences. Since taking Silk in 1995 he has prosecuted and defended over the whole spectrum of serious criminal offences, as well as dealing with Crown Office matters.
Prof. Memberships: Criminal Bar Association
Career: Assistant Recorder 1989. Head of Chambers 1991. Recorder 1993. Queen's Counsel 1995.

GIBBS, Patrick
2 Harcourt Buildings, Atkinson Bevan Chambers (Nicholas Atkinson QC & John Bevan QC), London (020) 7353 2112
Recommended in Crime
Specialisation: Defence advocacy. Practices in all areas of crime. Since 1990 has been principally engaged in defending cases involving professional fraud, sex crime and the supply of controlled drugs.
Prof. Memberships: Criminal Bar Association.
Career: Called 1986.
Personal: Born 24 April 1962. Educated at Eton College, Christ Church, Oxford and the City University.

GIBNEY, Malcolm T.P.
17 Carlton Crescent (Mr Jeremy Gibbons QC), Southampton (023) 8032 0320/2003
Recommended in Consumer

GIBSON, Charles
2 Harcourt Buildings (Roger Henderson QC), London (020) 7583 9020
Recommended in Product Liability
Specialisation: Common law/commercial with an emphasis on product liability (in particular group actions), professional negligence, personal injury, insurance. Notable cases include Connelly v RTZ; Lubbe v Cape plc; Hodgson v Imperial Tobacco (the tobacco lung cancer litigation); the Opren litigation; the Benzodiazepine litigation; Garland v West Wiltshire District Council; The Norplant litigation; the MMR litigation; the organo-phosphate litigation; the interest rate swap litigation; asbestos claims; Mine Radiation Injury claims; other product liability cases

for various manufacturers; the Kings Cross and Clapham Inquiries for the London Fire Brigade; the Severn Tunnel Inquiry.
Prof. Memberships: PNBA. Common Law and Commercial Bar Association.
Career: Educated Wellington College; BA Hons Durham; Dip Law. Called to the Bar 1984. Author: 'Group Actions – Product Liability Law and Insurance'.
Personal: Born 1960. Married; 4 children.

GIBSON, Christopher QC
Four New Square (Justin Fenwick QC), London
(020) 7822 2000
barristers@4newsquare.com
Recommended in Clinical Negligence
Specialisation: Professional negligence (lawyers, medical practitioners, accountants, valuers and building professionals); general commercial law, insurance, and building and construction. Cases include Mortgage Express v Bowerman, the consolidated appeal in the BBL litigation, Abbey National v Key Surveyors (Court appointed expert), and Thorman v New Hampshire (professional indemnity insurance).
Prof. Memberships: COMBAR, Professional Negligence Bar Association, Fellow of the Chartered Institute of Arbitrators.
Career: Educated at St Paul's School, and Brasenose College, Oxford; called to the Bar Middle Temple 1976; silk in 1995. FC/Art/1992
Personal: Married with 2 daughters; interests include Whitstable and motor-cycles.

GIFFIN, Nigel
11 King's Bench Walk (Eldred Tabachnik QC and James Goudie QC), London (020) 7632 8500
Recommended in Administrative & Public Law: General, Employment, Planning
Specialisation: Specialises principally in public and administrative law including Human Rights Act, commercial judicial review, education, local authority powers, local government finance, environment, housing, social services, travellers, elections, procurement and tendering. Practice also covers employment law and general commercial law. Important cases include Hazell v Hammersmith & Fulham LBC (local authority interest rate swaps); Palmer v A.B.P. (personal contracts and union membership); R v A.B.P. ex parte Plymouth CC (judicial review of animal exports); R v Institute of Chartered Accountants ex parte Brindle (stay of disciplinary proceedings pending litigation); Wandsworth LBC v A (access to school premises); R v Hammersmith & Fulham LBC ex p.M (asylum seeker's rights under National Assistance Act); Hillsdown Holdings plc v Pensions Ombudsman (use of pension fund surplus). Contributor to Administrative Law title of 'Halsbury's Laws'; contributor of education law chapter to 'Butterworth's Local Government Law'.
Prof. Memberships: Administrative Law Bar Association (committee member); Education Law Association; Planning and Environmental Bar Association; Employment Law Bar Association.
Career: Called to the Bar 1986.
Personal: Educated at Worcester College, Oxford (BA Hons 1st class).

GILBART, Andrew QC
40 King St (Philip Raynor QC), Manchester
(0161) 832 9082
Recommended in Planning
Specialisation: Town planning, compulsory purchase, highways, environment law and judicial review. Particularly experienced in major development projects involving airport expansion, roads, incineration, waste disposal, retailing, minerals, housing and motorway services. Contributor of articles to 'Journal of Planning and Environment Law'.
Prof. Memberships: Member of Northern Circuit, Planning and Environment Bar Association, Administrative Law Bar Association (Associate Member), American Bar Association, UK Environmental Law Association.
Career: Called 1972, elected member of Northern Circuit 1973; Appointed Queens Counsel 1991; Recorder of The Crown Court; Bencher of Middle Temple.
Personal: Read Law at Trinity Hall, Cambridge. Enjoys tramping in the hills of the Peak District when time permits.

GILBERT, Francis QC
Walnut House (Francis Gilbert QC), Exeter
(01392) 279751
Recommended in Crime
Specialisation: Murder, corporate and involuntary manslaughter, commercial fraud, advance fee fraud, drugs importation, public nuisance.
Prof. Memberships: Western circuit.CBA
Career: Called 1970, *Lincoln's Inn.* Queen's Counsel 1992. Recorder 1993. Bencher 2000.
Personal: Born 1946. MA (Law) TCD. Married with three children.

GILEAD, Beryl
St. Mary's Chambers Family Law Chambers (Christopher Butler), Nottingham (0115) 950 3503
Recommended in Family/Matrimonial

GILL, Manjit Singh QC
6 King's Bench Walk (Sibghat Kadri QC), London
(020) 7583 0695 / 7353 4931
Recommended in Immigration

GILL, Tess
Old Square Chambers (John Hendy QC), London
(020) 7269 0300
gill@oldsquarechambers.co.uk
Recommended in Employment
Specialisation: Principal areas of practice are employment human rights and industrial law. She specialises in sex and race and disability discrimination; personal injury stress claims; equal pay and European law including public law aspects. Cases include Strathclyde Regional Council v Wallace [1998] ICR 205, HL (Sc.) (equal pay); Carmichael v National Power plc [1999] ICR 1226, HL (casual workers); Halfpenny v IGE Medical Systems Ltd [1999] IRLR 177, CA (maternity) - House of Lords judgement awaited; Locaball (UK) v Bayfield Properties LTD IRLR 2000 96, CA, (bias); Grant v South West Trains [1998] 188 HC (contractual force of equal opportunities policies); British Coal Corporation v Keeble [1997] IRLR 336 (sex discrimination - time limits); Scullard v (1) Knowles (2) Southern Regional Council for Education and Training (1996) CR 399, EAT (equal pay and Article 119); Stewart v Cleveland Guest (Engineering) Ltd (1994) IRLR 440, EAT (sexual harassment); Roscoe v Hargreaves [1991] ICR (pension claim under Article 119); Hewcastle Catering Ltd v Ahmed [1991] IRLR 473, CA (illegal employment contracts); London Borough of Newham v NALGO [1992] IRLR (labour injunctions).
Prof. Memberships: Member of Lawyers for Liberty, Personal Injury Bar Association, Employment Law Bar Association, Employment Law Association, Industrial Law Society and the Equal Pay Task Force. Advisory Panel member of Equal Opportunity Review.
Career: Prior to transferring to the Bar in 1989, was solicitor in both private practice and as trade union legal officer. Appointed as part-time Empolyment Tribunal Chairman in 1995, has published work on equality law and is author of chapter on Workers' Rights in Liberty guide, and chapter on discrimination in Human Rights at Work to be published October 2000 by Institute of Employment Rights.

GILLESPIE, James
Enfield Chambers (James Gillespie), Enfield
(020) 8364 5627
Recommended in Immigration
Specialisation: Offers specialist advice and representation in all aspects of immigration and nationality law, including asylum. Considerable experience of conducting cases before immigration Adjudicators and the Immigration Appeal Tribunal, judicial review and appeals to the Court of Appeal. Acts for a wide range of immigration clients, personal and corporate. Conducts training courses in immigration law for solicitors. Managing Editor of 'Tolley's Immigration and Nationality Law and Practice'.
Prof. Memberships: Founder member of the Immigration Law Practitioners Association and member of executive committee 1985-1992.
Career: Before being called to the Bar in 1991 worked for the Joint Council for the Welfare of Immigrants representing clients in the Immigration Appeal Tribunal.

GILLYON, Philip
Erskine Chambers (Robin Potts QC), London
(020) 7242 5532
pgillyon@erskine-chambers.co.uk
Recommended in Company
Specialisation: Company law, corporate insolvency, financial services. Cases include: Re BSB Holdings Ltd [1996] 1 BCLC 155. Possfund Custodian Trustee Ltd v Diamond [1996] 1 WLR 1351. Re Exchange Travel (Holdings) Ltd [1996] 2 BCLC 524. Guinness Peat Group plc v British Land Company plc [1999] 2 BCLC 243. Banco Nacional de Cuba v Cosmos Trading Corporation [2000] 1 BCLC 813. Jarvis plc v PricewaterhouseCoopers (New Law Digest 13.7.00). Represents the Secretary of State for Trade and Industry in company director disqualification proceedings in relation to Queens Moat Houses plc.
Prof. Memberships: Commercial Bar Association; Chancery Bar Association; Middle Temple.
Career: Hymers College, (1974-1984); Downing College, Cambridge (1984-1987); Called 1988; Joined Erskine Chambers 1989.
Personal: Born: 1965. Lives in London.

GILMAN, Jonathan QC
Essex Court Chambers (Gordon Pollock QC), London (020) 7813 8000
Recommended in Shipping
Specialisation: Insurance, reinsurance and shipping cases. Appears as counsel in very many London arbitrations. Regularly acts as umpire or arbitrator in London arbitrations. Has been retained as expert witness on English law in foreign proceedings on many occasions (mostly insurance or reinsurance cases).
Career: Called to the Bar 1965. Silk 1990.
Personal: Born 1942.

GILMOUR, Nigel QC
Oriel Chambers (Andrew T. Sander), Liverpool
(0151) 236 7191/ 236 4321
Recommended in Clinical Negligence

GILROY, Paul
9 St. John Street (John Hand QC), Manchester
(0161) 955 9000
Recommended in Employment
Specialisation: Paul Gilroy has extensive experience of advisory/drafting work and advocacy in the field of employment law. As well as advising on non-contentious matters and acting for employers and employees in all forms of employment litigation in the Employment Tribunals, the County Court and High Court, he has also appeared before NHS Tribunals, internal police disciplinary inquiries and internal hearings conducted by professional sports bodies. Has recently acted in the public inquiry into the Personality

Disorder Unit at Ashworth High Security Hospital. He acts for and against local and public authorities, trade unions and plcs. In the High Court he specialises in injunctive work and wrongful dismissal. In the Employment Tribunal he has much experience of transfers of undertakings, discrimination, equal pay and redundancy work, dealing regularly with multiple applicant cases. He acted for numerous applicants in the armed forces pregnancy dismissal litigation conducted across the UK in 1994 and 1995. He is approved by the Commission for Racial Equality and the Equal Opportunities Commission to act in discrimination cases. He has recently been appointed by the Attorney General to the Provincial Panel of Counsel approved to act in litigation on behalf of the Government. In addition to the traditional areas of employment law practice, Paul Gilroy deals with general commercial work and quasi-employment matters such as litigation concerning the Commercial Agents Regulations. He contributes to professional publications, annotates employment legislation for Current Law Statutes, and is a frequent speaker on employment law. Notable cases: Provident v Hayward [1989] 3 AII ER 298 (garden leave); YKK v Ely [1993] IRLR 500 (equivocal resignation); Pilkington Distribution Services v Forbes EAT, 1200/96 (gross misconduct); Matheson v Coast and Country Hotels EAT (Sc), 1210/97 (global contracts of employment); Abbey National v Formoso [1999] IRLR 222 (pregnancy-related discrimination).
Prof. Memberships: Employment Lawyers Association; Employment Law Bar Association; NCFRAS.
Career: Called 1985 (Gray's Inn). Door Tenant: *Farrar's Building*, Temple, London EC4Y 7BD. Part-time Chairman of Employment Tribunals.

GIRET, Jane
11 Stone Buildings (Murray Rosen QC), London (020) 7831 6381
giret@11stonebuildings.com
Recommended in Commercial Chancery, Company, Insolvency/Corporate Recovery
Specialisation: Head of 11 Stone Buildings' company & insolvency group and a specialist in company, corporate and personal insolvency and partnership law. Her practice also includes general Chancery and commercial litigation. Much of her work focuses on company directors and their conduct, including directors' fraud and disqualification proceedings. An experienced and forceful advocate, her expertise includes shareholder disputes, complex receiverships and administrations. She also has a full non-contentious corporate advisory practice encompassing reconstruction, amalgamation and management.

GIROLAMI, Paul
13 Old Square (Michael Lyndon-Stanford QC), London (020) 7404 4800
Recommended in Commercial Chancery, Company, Insolvency/Corporate Recovery

GLANCY, Robert QC
Devereux Chambers (Jeffrey Burke QC), London (020) 7353 7534
Recommended in Personal Injury

GLASGOW, Edwin QC
39 Essex Street (Nigel Pleming QC), London (020) 7832 1111
Recommended in Commercial (Litigation), Personal Injury, Professional Negligence, Sport
Specialisation: All areas of commercial and common law litigation including insurance, professional negligence and major personal injury cases. Has been involved in most of the public inquiries and litigation associated with disasters over the past ten years. Has extensive experience of litigation, arbitration and human rights work overseas including USA; Australia; Hong Kong; Singapore; France and Africa. Recent cases include: Svenska Bank v Sun Alliance; Trafalgar House v Davy Offshore; Capital and Counties v Planned Maintenance; BBL; Sun Valley Poultry; Kuwait Investment Office; Bloody Sunday Inquiry.
Prof. Memberships: London Common Law and Commercial Bar Association.
Career: LLB (Hons); Called to the Bar 1969; Silk 1987. Chairman Financial Reporting Review Panel 1992-1998. CBE 1999.

GLASS, Anthony QC
Queen Elizabeth Building (Julian Bevan QC & Peter Whiteman QC), London (020) 7583 5766
Recommended in Crime, Fraud: Criminal
Specialisation: Practice encompasses all aspects of criminal law, with a specialisation in commercial fraud, V.A.T. fraud and drugs importations since taking Silk. Involved in Barlow Clowes, BCCI, Guildford police and O'Brien death in police custody cases and recently, Reg Ellis arson/fraud and Abbey National Fraud, Sheila Bowler and Excise Duty Diversion Frauds and money laundering.
Prof. Memberships: Criminal Bar Association, South Eastern Circuit.
Career: Called to the Bar 1965 and joined current chambers in 1982. Appointed Recorder 1985. Took silk 1986. Bencher of Inner Temple.
Personal: Educated at Royal Masonic Schools 1948-1958 and Lincoln College, Oxford 1960-1963. Born 6th June 1940. Lives in London.

GLEDHILL, Andreas
3-4 South Square (Michael Crystal QC), London (020) 7696 9900
Recommended in Insolvency/Corporate Recovery
Specialisation: Insolvency, fraud and tracing claims, banking law, company law and related areas of professional negligence. Recent major cases include the administrations of Debonair Airways Ltd and Axis Genetics plc, and Thyssen-Bornemisza v Thyssen-Bornemisza (the largest civil claim to be litigated in Bermuda).
Prof. Memberships: COMBAR; Chancery Bar Association; Insolvency Lawyers' Association.
Publications: 'Gore-Browne on Companies' (44th ed. (contributing chapter 31 on Administrations, Voluntary Arrangements and Administrative Receiverships) and 'Muir Hunter on Personal Insolvency' (junior author).
Personal: Educated Westminster School and Christ's College Cambridge (1st class hons., 1988)

GLEN, Ian QC
Guildhall Chambers (Adrian Palmer QC), Bristol (0117) 927 3366
Recommended in Crime, Licensing
Specialisation: General criminal work from homicide to serious fraud with particular experience of drugs importations and health and safety (see R v Gateway Foodmarkets [1997] 3 ALL ER 78). All aspects of liquor, betting, gaming and public entertainment licensing including criminal defence (see Westminster City Council v Blenheim Leisure Ltd, The Times February 24, 1999). Broad judicial review practice complements crime and licensing (see R v Hereford Magistrates' Court ex p Rowlands [1998] QB 110).
Career: King's College, London 1972. Called in 1973 began practice in 1979. Silk 1996 (Hon) Research Fellow, Bristol University. Recent Lecturing: 'Judicial Review in Licensing Cases' (IBC annual conference) 'Confiscation of Criminal Proceeds' (National Fraud Forum Bramshill) 'False Memory Syndrome' (annual conference of UK Council for Psychotherapy). 'HWSA Criminal Liability of Companies and Company Directors' (for Eversheds).

GLICK, Ian QC
One Essex Court (Lord Grabiner QC), London (020) 7583 2000
Recommended in Arbitration (International), Banking, Commercial (Litigation), Energy & Natural Resources, Tax
Specialisation: Principal areas of practice are arbitration, banking, commercial law, energy law, financial services, insurance and revenue litigation. Important cases include PCW litigation; Tin Council litigation; Woolwich BS v CIR (restitution); Smith New Court v Citibank (measure of damages in fraud); Gallagher v Jones (application of accepted principles of commercial accountancy to computation of profits for tax purposes), Shah v Bank of England (banking regulation); Deeny v Gooda Walker (taxability of damages recovered in Lloyds' litigation); R v CIR ex p. Warburgs (judicial review of Revenue decisions); Northern Ireland Electricity v Director General of Electricity Supply (electricity price regulation) and Fuji Finance v Aetna (nature of a contract of insurance).
Prof. Memberships: Chairman, Commercial Bar Association, 1997-1999; Vice Chairman, Education and Training Committe of the Bar Council 1999-2000.
Career: Called to the Bar in 1970. At Lamb Building 1970-80. Joined 1 Essex Court in 1980. Junior Counsel to the Crown, Common Law 1985-87. Standing Counsel to the DTI in export credit cases 1985-87. Took Silk in 1987.
Personal: Educated at Bradford Grammar School and Balliol College, Oxford. Born 18th July 1948. Lives in London.

GLOBE, Henry QC
Exchange Chambers (William Waldron QC), Liverpool (0151) 236 7747
Recommended in Crime

GLOSTER, Elizabeth QC
One Essex Court (Lord Grabiner QC), London (020) 7583 2000
egloster@oeclaw.co.uk
Recommended in Commercial Chancery, Commercial (Litigation), Company, Energy & Natural Resources, Insolvency/Corporate Recovery
Specialisation: Principal areas of expertise are company law, banking, insurance and insolvency. Also covers commercial fraud, financial services, media and telecommunications and professional negligence. Recent major cases include: acting for the Equitable Life in the House of Lords to determine the rights of policyholders (2000); acting for the liquidators of Manhattan Investment Fund (2000); appearing in the House of Lords for defendants in Canada Trust v Stolzenburg (jurisdiction under the Lugano Convention) (2000); acting for BF&M Ltd in the action brought by the liquidators of Bermuda Fire & Marine Insurance Company (1999); acting for the DTI in the disqualification proceedings arising out of the collapse of Barings (1998); acting for EMLICO and its liquidators in the litigation arising out of EMLICO's redomestication to Bermuda (1996-1998); acting for Charterhouse Development (France) in its action against Lloyd's underwriters (1996); acting for the administrators of Barings in the action against ING (1996); acting for the banks in the interest rate swaps litigation; representing the liquidators of Barlow Clowes in litigation against various directors and third party professionals (1992-1995); acting for banks/administrators of Olympia & York, Canary Wharf (1993-1994); acting for the Society of Lloyd's in a case involving the question of priority between the Society and various Names (1993); representing recently-appointed trustees of Maxwell Pension Funds in relation to the Maxwell collapse (1992-1995); acting for the D.T.I in the case of Sher v The Policy Holders Protection Board (1993); Hazell v Hammersmith & Fulham Borough Council (1992) (House of Lords);

prosecuting in the criminal trials arising out of the Guinness bid for Distillers (1990) and (1991). Called to the Bars of Bermuda, Gibraltar and the Isle of Man for specific cases. Working knowledge of French.
Prof. Memberships: Chancery Bar Association, COMBAR, Insolvency Lawyers' Association, INSOL.
Career: Called to the Bar in 1971. Member of the panel of junior counsel representing the DTI in company matters 1982-89. Took Silk in 1989. Bencher of the Inner Temple and Deputy High Court Judge of the Chancery Division in 1992, Judge of the Courts of Appeal of Jersey & Guernsey (part-time) in 1994 and Recorder 1995.
Personal: Educated at Roedean School 1962-67 and Girton College, Cambridge 1967-70. Born 5th June 1949.

GLOVER, Richard
2 Mitre Court Buildings (Michael FitzGerald QC), London (020) 7583 1380
Recommended in Planning
Specialisation: Specialises in all areas of planning and local government law.
Prof. Memberships: Member of the Planning and Environment Bar Association and The Parliamentary Bar.
Career: Called in 1984. Has acted in a wide range of inquiries including the new HQ for McLaren Racing near Woking, the Manchester Free Trade Hall, the Genome Campus extension for the Wellcome Trust and the proposals for 2500 houses south of Reading. Parliamentary Bills include Channel Tunnel, Dartfort River Crossing and Heathrow Express. Recent rating cases include Mosanto Chemical works, Port Talbot Steelworks, Shall Haven Oil refinery, Anston Properties, Coventry & Solihull Waste Disposal (in the House of Lords) and BT. Editor of 'Ryde on Rating and the Council Tax'.
Personal: Educated at Harrow and Cambridge.

GLOVER, Stephen J
37 Park Square (SJ Glover, PG Kirtley), Leeds (0113) 243 9422
chambers@no37.co.uk
Recommended in Family/Matrimonial
Specialisation: Substantial asset matrimonial finance, professional negligence, personal injury, medical law.
Prof. Memberships: PNBA, PIBA.
Career: 1978 call.

GODDARD, Andrew
Atkin Chambers (John Blackburn QC), London (020) 7404 0102
Recommended in Construction
Specialisation: Specialises in construction and engineering and the law of commercial obligations. This has involved advocacy and advisory work in respect of major commercial developments, including PFI projects, office and retail accomodation, hospitals, hotels, motorways, stations and railways, power stations, process plants, wet and dry docks as well as off-shore and submarine structures and oil and gas exploration and exploitation. Clients include employers (both public and private), contractors, sub-contractors and professionals. He is familiar with the principal forms of building and engineering contracts including management and development contracts and has advised on amendments to the standard forms as well as drafted bespoke contracts. He has regularly advised and acted in connection with substantial claims for damages, loss and expense and extensions of time (a topic in which he has particular interest) as well as claims in respect of professional negligence including solicitors' negligence. He has a developing interest in new technology and has advised in connection with various disputes involving software development, microelectronics and telecommunications. Although based in London, he has acted on behalf of many international clients, including foreign governments, and has a keen interest in projects with an international element. He has acted in many international arbitrations under the auspices of both the ICC and the LCIA. Related areas of law in which he has detailed experience include sale of goods, performance bonds, guarantees and insurance.
Prof. Memberships: TECBAR
Career: Called to the Bar 1985.
Personal: Independent Schools Association Whitbread Memorial Trophy; BA Hons. Law (First Class) Sussex 1984; Inner Temple Queen Elizabeth II Scholarship 1985; Poland Prize 1985.

GODDARD, Christopher
Devereux Chambers (Jeffrey Burke QC), London (020) 7353 7534
Recommended in Health & Safety, Personal Injury
Specialisation: Principal area of practice is plaintiff and defendant personal injury with a special interest in occupational disease. Also medical and legal professional negligence. Regularly speaks at conferences and seminars in these fields. Co-author 'Health and Safety: The New Legal Framework' Butterworths and contributor to Butterworths 'Personal Injury Handbook'. Executive editor of the 'Personal Injury Handbook', Gee Publishing.
Prof. Memberships: Personal Injury Bar Association.
Career: Manchester University 1969-1972. Called to Bar in 1973.

GODFREY, Howard QC
2 Bedford Row (formerly 3 Hare Court) (William Clegg QC), London (020) 7440 8888
Recommended in Crime, Fraud: Criminal
Specialisation: Serious crime especially fraud, both corporate and personal, including some work overseas. Experienced in VAT and tax frauds, insider dealing, Stock Exchange, banking, accounting, insurance, corruption and extradition. Practice also includes general crime especially drugs cases and civil fraud.
Prof. Memberships: South Eastern Circuit, Criminal Bar Association.
Career: Called 1970. Took silk in 1991. Recorder 1992.
Personal: Born 17th August 1946. Educated University of London – London School of Economics (LL.B). Lives in Berkshire.

GOLDBERG, David QC
Gray's Inn Tax Chambers (Milton Grundy), London (020) 7242 2642
Recommended in Tax
Specialisation: Practice concentrates on revenue law and commercial litigation with a tax or financial aspect. Clients include solicitors, accountants and corporations. Co-author of 'Introduction to Company Law' (1971, 3rd Edn 1987) and 'The Law of Partnership Taxation' (1976, 2nd Edn 1979). Author of various articles and notes for legal periodicals, mainly concerning tax and company law.
Prof. Memberships: Revenue Bar Association, Chancery Bar Association.
Career: Called to the Bar and joined current chambers in 1971. Took Silk 1987. Bencher of Lincoln's Inn 1997.
Personal: Educated at Plymouth College and London School of Economics 1966-1970 (LL.B, LL.M). Chairman of Trustees of the Skills Workshop for Anatomical Techniques. Leisure pursuits include reading, writing letters and thinking. Born 12th August 1947. Lives in London.

GOLDBERG, Jonathan QC
3 Temple Gardens (Jonathan Goldberg QC), London (020) 7583 1155
Recommended in Crime, Fraud: Criminal
Specialisation: Has defended in many of the most notable jury trials at the Old Bailey and elsewhere over the past three decades. These include Roger Levitt (white collar fraud), Brinksmat, R v Rosenthal (The Stamford Hill child sex abuse case involving Orthodox Jews), R v Laming (The Sonic Binoculars horse nobbling case), R v Charlie Kray and many others. He is qualified at the New York Bar and has worked in Malaysia, Singapore and Gibraltar. He has had success in libel and commercial civil cases requiring strong cross-examination also, and is by no means limited to crime. He enjoys battling and winning against seemingly overwhelming odds.
Career: Called in 1971; appointed a QC in 1989; a Recorder in 1992.
Personal: Educated at Manchester Grammar and Trinity Hall Cambridge. A vice-president of the International Association of Jewish Lawyers and Jurists.

GOLDREIN, Iain QC
7 Harrington Street Chambers (David Steer QC/Robert Fordham QC/Iain Goldrein QC), Liverpool (0151) 242 0707
goldhaas@netcomuk.co.uk
Recommended in Clinical Negligence
Specialisation: Complex Professional (including Medical) Negligence (with particular expertise in brain damage at birth); catastrophic injury claims; general commercial including Insurance coverage; pre-emptive commercial remedies; product liability. Cases of Interest: Rayeware v TGWU; Sion v Hampstead Health Authority.
Prof. Memberships: Professional Negligence Bar Association; Personal Injury Bar Association; London Common Law & Commercial Bar Association. Companion of the Academy of Experts; Fellow of the Royal Society of Arts; Associate of the Chartered Institute of Arbitrators; Nominated Counsel: Environmental Law Foundation; Mediator, registered with the Academy of Experts. Awards: University of Cambridge Squire Scholarship for Law; Exhibitioner and Ziegler Prize, Pembroke College Cambridge; Inner Temple Duke of Edinburgh Scholarship.
Career: Appointments: Queen's Counsel; Assistant Recorder; Visiting Professor (The Sir Jack Jacob Chair in Litigation) Nottingham Law School.
Publications: 'Property Distribution on Divorce' [FT Law and Tax] [1st and 2nd editions with Margaret de Haas QC]; 'Personal Injury Litigation: Practice and Precedents' [Butterworths]; Ship Sale and Purchase, Law and Technique [Lloyds of London Press] with Clifford Chance; 'Commercial Litigation: Pre-emptive Remedies' [Sweet and Maxwell] with Judges Wilkinson and Kershaw QC; 'Butterworths Personal Injury Litigation Service' with Margaret de Haas QC; 'Bullen and Leake and Jacob's Precedents of Pleadings' [Sweet and Maxwell], with Sir Jack Jacob; 'Pleadings, Principles and Practice' [Sweet and Maxwell], with Sir Jack Jacob; 'Structured Settlements' [Butterworths], Editor-in-Chief with Margaret de Haas QC [1st Edition 1993. 2nd Edition May 1997]; 'Medical Negligence: Cost Effective Case Management' [Butterworths] with Margaret de Haas QC, [May, 1997].
Personal: New ideas, classical Hebrew, English legal history and classic motor vehicles. Educated at Merchant Taylors' School, Crosby (Harrison Scholar), Hebrew University, Jerusalem (1971), Pembroke College, Cambridge (1971-1974).

GOLDSMITH, Lord QC
Fountain Court (Anthony Boswood QC), London (020) 7583 3335
Recommended in Arbitration (International), Banking, Commercial (Litigation), Civil Fraud, Professional Negligence
Specialisation: Commercial law including professional negligence (especially in commercial transactions), banking, insurance and arbitration. Leading cases include Caparo v Dickman (1990), ADT v Binder Hamlyn (1995), BBL v Eagle Star (1994), Bankers Trust

v State Bank of India (1991), The Honam Jade (1991), The Baleares (1994), New Zealand Forest Products (1997), BCCI v Price Waterhouse (1996); PPI v Maitra (1998); Goldman Sachs v Mannesman (2000); Law Society v KPMG (2000).
Career: Chairman of the Bar 1995. Call 1972. A junior counsel to the Crown (common law) 1985-87; QC 1987; Recorder; Deputy High Court Judge Bencher Gray's Inn; Life Peer (1999).

GOLDSTONE, Clement QC
28 St. John St (Clement Goldstone QC), Manchester (0161) 834 8418
Recommended in Crime, Licensing

GOLDSTONE, David
4 Field Court (Steven Gee QC), London (020) 7440 6900
Recommended in Shipping

GOODE, Sir Roy QC
Blackstone Chambers (P Baxendale QC and C Flint QC), London (020) 7583 1770
Recommended in Consumer
Specialisation: Commercial law; banking; credit and security; international trade law; consumer credit Author of Commercial Law (2nd edn. 1995) and other leading textbooks in the above fields which are widely cited in the courts.
Prof. Memberships: Former Norton Rose Professor of English Law in the University of Oxford, Fellow of St John's College, Oxford. Former Chairman of Executive Committee of JUSTICE. Panel Chairman of appeal under Consumer Credit Act 1974. Member of Board of London Court of International Arbitration. Former Chairman of the Commission on International Commercial Practice of the International Chamber of Commerce.
Career: Admitted as solicitor 1955; partner, Victor Mishcon & Co., solicitors, 1963-1971. Appointed Professor Law, Queen Mary College, University of London 1971, and Crowther Professor of Credit and Commercial Law 1973. Founder and first Director of Centre for Commercial Law Studies, QMC. Transferred to Bar 1988. Took silk 1990. Hon. Bencher, Inner Temple, 1992. Appointed Norton Rose Professor of English Law. University of Oxford, 1990. Member of Department of Trade and Industry Advisory Committee on Arbitration 1985-. Chairman of Pension Law Review Committee 1992-1993. LL.B. (Lond.) 1954; LLD (Lond. 1976); OBE 1972, CBE 1994; Hon. DSc Econ (Lond.) 1996; Elected Fellow of the British Academy 1988; Fellow of the Royal Society of Arts 1990. Knighted 2000.

GOODE, Rowena
28 St. John St (Clement Goldstone QC), Manchester (0161) 834 8418
Recommended in Crime

GOODFELLOW, Giles W.J.
Pump Court Tax Chambers (Andrew Thornhill QC), London (020) 7414 8080
Recommended in Tax
Specialisation: Revenue Law including all aspects of direct and indirect tax and tax related aspects of commercial disputes including finance leasing and professional negligence and variation of trusts. Areas of particular interests include all forms of tax related litigation, and advisory work on owner managed businesses, employee remuneration packages and Inland Revenue investigations. Co-author of Inheritance Tax Planning (Longman) and Finance Provision and Taxation on Divorce.
Career: Called to the Bar 1983. Joined present Chambers in 1985.

GOODHART, Lord QC
3 New Square (Lord Goodhart QC), London (020) 7405 5577
Recommended in Consumer, Traditional Chancery
Specialisation: Principal area of practice is Chancery work, encompassing pension funds, trusts and estates, property, consumer credit and personal taxation. Other main area of work is company law and insolvency. Recent cases include Director General of Fair Trading v First National Bank plc (1999), Davis v Richards & Wallington Industries [1990] (pensions) and Hambro v Duke of Marlborough [1994] (trusts). Co-author of 'Specific Performance' (the leading modern authority on this subject), (2nd Edn, 1996) and section of Halsbury's Laws on corporations.
Prof. Memberships: Chancery Bar Association, International Commission of Jurists, Institute for Fiscal Studies.
Career: Called to the Bar 1957. In practice at the Chancery Bar since 1960. Took Silk 1979. Knighted 1989. Member Committee on Standards in Public Life 1997.
Personal: Educated at Eton College 1946-51, Trinity College, Cambridge 1953-1957 (BA, MA) and Harvard Law School 1957-1958 (LL.M). Chairman, Court of Discipline of Cambridge University since 1993. Life Peer, 1997. Born 18th January 1933.

GOODISON, Adam
3-4 South Square (Michael Crystal QC), London (020) 7696 9900
Recommended in Insolvency/Corporate Recovery
Specialisation: Commercial law including insolvency, contract, banking, company, directors disqualification. Cases include acting for the liquidators of BCCI (Re Bank of Credit and Commerce International SA (No4) [1995] BCC 453 (Scott V-C); BCCI v Haque (Lightman J & CA); BCCI v Shoaib (Evans Lombe J); BCCI v Makhan Jan (Jonathan Parker J). Also Re Thirty Eight Building Ltd (In Liquidation) [1999] BCC 260 & [2000] BCLC 201 (Hazell Williamson QC) (preferences); Straume v Bradlor Developments, [2000] BCC 333 (leave in administration proceedings); Holder v Supperstone, Independent, December 1999 (sosts of proceedings re charging orders).
Prof. Memberships: Chancery Bar Association, Combar, ILA.
Career: Called 1990. Elected member Bar Council 1995-1998.
Publications: Chapter on retention of title 'The Law of Receivers', (Lightman & Moss); chapter on individual voluntary arrangements and company voluntary arrangements 'Insolvency', (Totty & Moss); contributor to Rowlatt on 'Principal and Surety' (5 ed); 'Distress and Distraint' for SPI; various solicitor programme lectures (including *Linklaters & Paines, Frere Cholmeley, Wragge & Co*).

GOODRICH, Siobhan
6 Pump Court (Kieran Coonan QC), London (020) 7583 6013
clerks@6pumpcourt.law.co.uk
Recommended in Clinical Negligence
Specialisation: Medical negligence and related work; professional misconduct, disciplinary tribunals, inquests, and inquiries. Acts for plaintiff and defendant. Other areas of practice include professional negligence, personal injury and some crime.
Prof. Memberships: Professional Negligence Bar Association, LCLBA, CBA.
Career: Called to the Bar in 1980. Joined chambers in 1981. Born 15 March 1957.
Personal: Educated at King's College London (LLB).

GOODWIN, Deirdre
13 King's Bench Walk (Roger Ellis QC), London (020) 7353 7204
clerks@13kbw.co.uk
Recommended in Clinical Negligence
Specialisation: Principal area of practice is clinical negligence and catastrophic injury claims, including birth trauma, cerebral palsy, neurological damage, head and spinal injuries. Counsel for the claimant in Harrop [1988] the first personal injury claim to exceed £1m, including recovering sums for parents' loss of income and costs of head-hunting a multi-disciplinary care team. Junior Counsel in Murphy v Wirral Health Authority [1996] Med L R V7 p99 (award £2.25m); Bolitho v City and Hackney Health Authority [1997] WLR HL p1151 where the House of Lords gave a definitive ruling on the interpretation of a 'responsible body' within the Bolam test, and the application of this test to acts of omission and causation. Counsel in Newton [1998] PMILL where £100,000 damages were awarded for parental PTSD for death of child suffering from cerebral palsy following 'sleep' therapy. Counsel in Mansell v Pembrokeshire AHA [13 October 1998] where £3.28m damages were awarded for a cerebral palsy child following intra partum hypoxic brain damage. [1999] Guy v Birmingham HA (pre-Macfarlane) £500,000 for mother of Down's syndrome child where negligent ante-natal testing for congenital abnormality; Langer establishment of Special Needs Trust (private protective discretionary trust) although client under jurisdiction of Court of Protection) £1.98m; Choudhry Cerebral Palsy 26 year old claim brought and settled within 18 months at £1.95m. Contributor to the PIBA Personal Injury Handbook. Lecturer on medical law and ethics, medical negligence and catastrophic injury claims to medical professionals and solicitors, including the post-graduate medical schools of University College and Middlesex Hospitals, Stoke Mandeville Hospital, Euroforum Conferences, IBC, The Royal Society of Medicine. Post-graduate seminars for Royal College of General Practitioners.
Prof. Memberships: Member of Personal Injury Bar Association (PIBA); Member of Professional Negligence Bar Association (PNBA); Member of Pan-European Organisation of Personal Injury Lawyers (PEOPIL); Member of the Association of Personal Injury Lawyers (APIL).
Career: Called to the Bar 1974.
Personal: LLB (Hons) University College London 1972. Leisure pursuits include music (including perfoming), medieval history, theatre.

GORDON, Richard QC
Brick Court Chambers (Christopher Clarke QC), London (020) 7379 3550
Recommended in Administrative & Public Law: General, Environment, Human Rights (Civil Liberties)
Specialisation: Specialist in public and administrative law with particular expertise in judicial review for both respondent and applicants, especially in the areas of commercial environmental, local authority, civil liberties, health and social services. Author of 'Judicial Review: Law and Procedure', 'Judicial Review and Home Office Practice', 'Local Authority Powers' and 'Community Care Assessments'. Co-Editor of 'Local Authority Law'; Editor in chief of 'Crown Office Digest'. Visiting Professor of Law, University College, London.
Prof. Memberships: Administrative Law Bar Association.
Career: Called to the Bar 1972. Took Silk 1994.
Personal: Educated at Oxford University (Open Scholar).

GORE, Allan
12 King's Bench Walk (Timothy Stow QC), London (020) 7583 0811
Recommended in Personal Injury
Specialisation: Professional negligence, encompassing medical, dental and legal cases both contentious and non-contentious. Personal injury work. Special interest and experience in transport mass accidents and disasters, and industrial disease, particularly concerning asbestos cases. Contributing author to 'Butterworths County Court Precedents and Pleadings: Divisions P on Professional Negligence and Q on Personal Injury'; and to 'Cordery on Solicitors: Division J on Negligence' and to Butterworths Personal Injury Litigation Service' Division VIII on Pleadings. Regular conference and seminar speaker.
Prof. Memberships: Executive of Association of Personal Injury Lawyers and Personal Injury Bar Association. Professional Negligence Bar Association, AVMA, ATLA, APLA.
Career: Called1977. Joined current chambers 1991.
Personal: Educated Purley Grammar School, Croydon 1962-1969; Trinity Hall, Cambridge 1970-1974. Born 25th August 1951. Lives in London.

GOSLING, Jonathan
4 Fountain Court (Richard Wakerley QC), Birmingham (0121) 236 3476
Recommended in Licensing

GOUDIE, James QC
11 King's Bench Walk (Eldred Tabachnik QC and James Goudie QC), London (020) 7632 8500 clerksroom@11kbw.com
Recommended in Administrative & Public Law: General, Employment, Planning
Specialisation: Specialises in all aspects of employment law, with particular emphasis on TUPE, restrictive covenants and European law relating to employment matters. Other main areas of practice include: public law (capital finance) and commercial (contractual disputes, insurance).
Career: Solicitor 1966 to 1970. Called to the Bar Inner Temple 1970. Bencher, Recorder, Deputy High Court Judge, Queen's Bench Division, Past Chairman Law Reform Committee, General Council of the Bar, Past Chairman Administrative Law Bar Association, Past Chairman Society of Labour Lawyers.
Personal: Educated at Dean Close School, Cheltenham and LSE (LL.B Hons). FCI Arb.

GOULDING, Paul QC
Blackstone Chambers (P Baxendale QC and C Flint QC), London (020) 7583 1770
Recommended in Employment, Sport
Specialisation: Specialist in employment and sports law. Employment: Chairman, Employment Lawyers Association 1998-2000. Particular interests – restraint of trade, transfers of undertakings, Europe, discrimination, industrial action. Recent cases – Neary v Dean of Westminster; Biggs v Somerset CC; Reed v Stedman; SoS v Bearman. Sport: recent cases – Modahl v BAF; Korda v ITF; Rudge v Port Vale FC; Formula 1, rugby union and league cases. Member of British Association for Sport and Law. SDRP Arbitrator. Also practices in financial services and judicial review.
Career: St Edmund Hall, Oxford (MA, BCL, Tutor). Call 1984. Silk 2000.

GOURGEY, Alan
11 Stone Buildings (Murray Rosen QC); London (020) 7831 6381
Recommended in Partnership
Specialisation: Alan has an established reputation as a leading junior in the field of commercial litigation. His wide ranging practice includes major business disputes, partnership and insolvency. He has acted in many substantial fraud cases ranging from bank to telecommunications fraud. As a media, sports and entertainment lawyer, clients have included pop stars, sportsmen, managers, football clubs and sporting bodies. His expertise extends to intellectual property, e-commerce and IT disputes. He is an experienced trial lawyer and whether as team-leader or part of a team, his particular strengths are in rapid assimilation and analysis of complex material, tactical guidance and forceful advocacy.

GOURIET, Gerald
3 Raymond Buildings (Clive Nicholls QC), London (020) 7400 6400 chambers@threeraymond.demon.co.uk
Recommended in Licensing
Specialisation: Specialist preparation and advice relating to all aspects of liquor, betting and gaming licensing, including advice on all forms of Internet gambling. Advice on lotteries and other related activities. All levels of representation from local committees to Divisional Court and Court of Appeal.
Career: Called to the Bar 1974.

GOY, David QC
Gray's Inn Tax Chambers (Milton Grundy), London (020) 7242 2642
Recommended in Tax
Specialisation: Specialist in all aspects of revenue law. Has particular expertise in the tax aspects of real property transactions, and in all types of tax litigation. Important cases include Lubbock Fine v HM Customs & Excise [1994] (VAT on the surrender of tenancies); LASMO (TNS) Ltd v IRC [1994] (oil taxation); IRC v Willoughby [1997] (taxation under s739 ICTA). CE v First National Bank of Chicago [1998] (VAT and foreign exchange transactions); Bestway (Holdings) Ltd v Luff [1998] (industrial buildings allowances); United Friendly Insurance PLC v IRC [1998] (life assurance taxation); Beneficiary v IRC [1999] (taxation under S.740); Carr v Fielden & Ashworth Ltd [2000] (relief for ACT). Publications include 'Whiteman on Income Tax', co-editor 3rd edition 1988, 'VAT on Property' (co-author) (Sweet & Maxwell 2nd Edition 1993), and Butterworths Tax Planning (consultant editor). Regular speaker on the subject of revenue law.
Prof. Memberships: Revenue Bar Association.
Career: Called to the Bar 1973. Joined present chambers 1974. Took Silk 1991.
Personal: Educated at Haberdashers' Askes School and King's College, London. Born 11th May 1949. Lives in Guildford.

GRABINER, Lord QC
One Essex Court (Lord Grabiner QC), London (020) 7583 2000
Recommended in Arbitration (International), Banking, Civil Fraud, Commercial (Litigation), Energy & Natural Resources, Insurance

GRACE, John QC
3 Serjeants' Inn (Philip Naughton QC), London (020) 7427 5000
Recommended in Clinical Negligence

GRAY, Gilbert QC
3 Raymond Buildings (Clive Nicholls QC), London (020) 7400 6400
Recommended in Licensing

GRAY, Richard QC
39 Essex Street (Nigel Pleming QC), London (020) 7832 1111
Recommended in Construction
Specialisation: Principal area of practice is Construction and Engineering litigation or arbitration in UK and abroad. Acts as Arbitrator in such disputes, both domestic and international, and as Mediator or Conciliator.
Prof. Memberships: TecBar (Technology and Construction Bar Association).
Career: Called to the Bar in 1970. Took silk in 1993.

GREEN, Brian QC
Wilberforce Chambers (Edward Nugee QC), London (020) 7306 0102
Recommended in Pensions, Traditional Chancery
Specialisation: Pensions and private client specialist having wide ranging experience of contentious and non-contentious general Chancery work. Has acted for the sponsoring companies or the trustees of major pension schemes, and for the trustees and/or the beneficiaries of the largest trusts (private and commercial).
Prof. Memberships: APL, Revenue Bar Association, STEP. Chancery Bar Association.
Career: Called to the Bar 1980. Member of Revenue Law Committee of the Law Society since 1994. (1978-85 tenured lectureship in Law at LSE).
Personal: Educated at Ilford County High School and St Edmund Hall Oxford (BA, BCL: double first).

GREEN, Michael A.
Fountain Court (Anthony Boswood QC), London (020) 7583 3335
Recommended in Company
Specialisation: Principal areas of work are company, insolvency, civil fraud and professional negligence including large scale commercial actions, having been involved for 3 years in Maxwell litigation (acting for Lehman Brothers), and then Lloyds litigation (acting on behalf of auditors). Noteworthy cases include Derby v Weldon (civil fraud), Macmillan Inc v Bishopsgate Investment Trust plc (Maxwell recovery actions), numerous public interest winding up petitions acting for the DTI including illegal lotteries and investment schemes; a large number of directors' disqualification cases including Barings, Barlow Clowes, Kaytech International plc (in Court of Appeal), Secretary of State v Deverell (leading CA authority on shadow directors), Funtime and City Pram and Toy; SIB v FIMBRA (financial services); Cranley Mansions (Corporate Insolvency Land and Property Trust (corporate insolvency); Wimbledon & Merton Democratic Society (Friendly Societies).
Career: Called to the bar in 1987. Joined *7 Stone Buildings* in 1988. Joined present chambers in 1998. Appointed Junior Counsel to the Crown (A Panel) in 1997 and a DTI Inspector in 1997.
Prof. Memberships: COMBAR, Chancery Bar Association.
Personal: Educated at University College School 1971-82, and Jesus College Cambridge 1983-86.

GREEN, Nicholas QC
Brick Court Chambers (Christopher Clarke QC), London (020) 7379 3550
Recommended in Competition/Anti-trust, Sport
Specialisation: Litigation, advisory and representational work in relation to the United Kingdom competition law, aspects of mergers and takeovers; intellectual property licensing; sports law; media law and broadcasting; telecommunications; environmental law; public procurement; conflicts of laws; public law. Has been instructed in about 50 cases before the European Court of Justice and Court of First Instance. Recent cases include Factortame, Coloroll, Francovich II, Sunag (shipping conferences), Eurotunnel; matters re the beef ban; acting for pharmaceutical companies in disputes over licenses and consents and use of confidential data; acting for sporting unions in disputes with clubs with regulators and competitors; intellectual property cases involving EU law.
Career: Called to Bar 1986; Appointed Queen's Counsel in 1998; Barrrister of the Inner Temple, Brick Court Chambers both in London and Brussels. 1981-85: Lecturer in Law, University of Southampton; Chairman Bar European Group, 1999-; Vice Chairman, Interna-

tional Relations Committee/Bar Council.
Personal: Born 15 October 1958. LL.B (1980), LL.M (1981), Ph.d (1985). Has over 50 publications in journals world wide in relation largely to EC law. Two principal publications are 'Commercial Agreements and Competition law: Practice and Procedure in the UK and EEC (1986) (second edition); and 'Legal Foundations of the Single European Market' (1991).

GREENBERG, Joanna QC

3 Temple Gardens (Jonathan Goldberg QC), London (020) 7583 1155
Recommended in Crime
Specialisation: Defending in all types of serious criminal cases.
Prof. Memberships: Bar Council, Criminal Bar Association, Justice, Liberty.
Career: Called to the Bar 1972, took Silk 1994, Assistant Recorder 1992, Recorder 1995, Chairman of Police Discipline Appeals Tribunals 1997.
Personal: Educated University of London, King's College. Lives in London.

GREENWOOD, Celestine

Chavasse Court Chambers (Theresa Pepper), Liverpool (0151) 707 1191
Recommended in Family/Matrimonial

GREGORY, James

Lincoln House Chambers (Mukhtar Hussain QC), Manchester (0161) 832 5701
Recommended in Crime

GREGORY, Philip

No.6 Fountain Court (Roger Smith QC), Birmingham (0121) 233 3282
Recommended in Clinical Negligence

GREY, Robin QC

Queen Elizabeth Building (Julian Bevan QC & Peter Whiteman QC), London (020) 7583 5766
Recommended in Crime
Specialisation: Criminal law. Defends and prosecutes in all areas of criminal law, with a particular emphasis on large-scale fraud in recent years. Has also defended in over thirty high-profile murder cases during the course of his career. Successfully defended in the Richardson Gang case of 1970s, in the "Nasty Tales" case at the time of the Oz trial, in the "King Squealer" robberies in the late 1970s, and in the Brinks Matt case in the early 1990s. Fraud trials include a successful defence in the Eagle Trust case (1993). In the past ten years has defended solicitors, accountants and bank managers in relation to white collar offences. Has considerable experience lecturing on professional conduct, jury trials and criminal procedure. Has also written articles for the Centre for Policy Studies and the Criminal Bar Association newsletter. Practice also includes civil matters arising out of criminal cases.
Prof. Memberships: Bar Council, Society of Forensic Medicine, Criminal Bar Association, European Criminal Bar Association, International Bar Association, Eastern Europe Forum and the Council of Russian and UK Cooperation.
Career: Called to the Bar 1957 and worked as Crown Counsel in Aden 1959-1963, before joining present chambers in 1963. Took Silk in 1979 and was appointed Recorder in the same year. Chairman of Police Appeals Tribunals 1988. Adviser to the Foreign Office in Russian Federation jury trials in 1993-97. Legal Assessor to General Medical Council, 1995.

GRIEVE, Dominic C.R.

1 Temple Gardens (Hugh B.H. Carlisle QC), London (020) 7583 1315
Recommended in Health & Safety
Specialisation: Health and safety at work and pollution cases (criminal and civil). Junior prosecution counsel in: R v Nuclear Electric plc (Mold September 1995 incident at Wylfa Power Station) R v Coalite Ltd (Leicester February 1996 Pollution by Dioxins); R v Port Ramsgate, Old Bailey January-March 1997; R v J Sainsbury plc, Winchester – November 1998 (operation and maintenance of fork lift trucks). Personal injury. Insurance/negligence work. Local government (enforcement work). Counsel in R v Railcare (derailment of high speed train through wheel failure). Luton and London Underground Ltd v HSE (appeal against prohibition notice in relation to the checking of trains before they are reversed in sidings) also due for hearing at London North East July 2000.
Prof. Memberships: Common Law Bar Association and Criminal Bar Association.
Career: Hon. Degree Modern History Oxford 1978. Called to Bar 1980. 1982-1990 Chamber of Anthony Cripps QC: 1, *Harcourt Buildings* (General Common Law). 1990-date: *1 Temple Gardens.*

GRIEVE, Michael QC

Doughty Street Chambers (Geoffrey Robertson QC), London (020) 7404 1313
Recommended in Crime, Fraud: Criminal

GRIFFITH-JONES, David QC

Devereux Chambers (Jeffrey Burke QC), London (020) 7353 7534
griffith-jones@devchambers.co.uk
Recommended in Employment, Sport
Specialisation: General common lawyer. Specialist in employment (including dismissal, discrimination, TUPE, industrial disputes, restraint of trade and injunctions) and sport (including personal injury, discipline and regulation and the commercial exploitation of sport). Author of 'Law and the Business of Sport' (Butterworths, 1997).
Prof. Memberships: London Common Law and Commercial Bar Association; Employment Lawyers' Association; Employment Law Bar Association; British Association of Sport and the Law; Bar Sports Law Group (Committee Member). Silk 2000.
Career: Called to the Bar 1975. FCIArb 1991. Recorder 1997. Sports Dispute Resolution Panel 2000. Assistant Boundary Commission 2000.

GRIFFITH-JONES, Richard

1 Fountain Court (David Crigman QC), Birmingham (0121) 236 5721
Recommended in Crime

GRIFFITHS, Alan

One Essex Court (Lord Grabiner QC), London (020) 7583 2000
Recommended in Administrative & Public Law: General, Energy & Natural Resources

GRIFFITHS, Courtenay QC

Two Garden Court (I. Macdonald QC & O.Davies QC), London (020) 7353 1633
Recommended in Crime, Human Rights (Civil Liberties)
Specialisation: Criminal Law: mainly leading work in murders (most alleged to be result of 'organised crime'). Major drug importations, frauds and sexual offences. Civil actions against the police. Has lectured in law in the UK and the USA. Has been Junior Counsel in R v Silcott and Or5 (Broadwater Farm riot). Major IRA cases including Canary Wharf & Harrods Bombing. Risley remand centre riot trial. Past holder of the record for the highest jury award against the police in a civil action £302,000 Goswell v MP/C (1996) Appeal Johnson, Davis & Rowe.
Prof. Memberships: Member of the South Eastern Circuit, Criminal Bar Association. Bar Race Relations Committee. Member of Gray's Inn.
Career: Recorder
Personal: Married to Angela with whom two children, Marcus (12) and Adam (9). Four children in all. Interested in music (reggae), cricket, football (Liverpool) and reading.

GRIFFITHS, Martin

Essex Court Chambers (Gordon Pollock QC), London (020) 7813 8000
Recommended in Commercial (Litigation), Employment
Specialisation: Appears as an advocate in Courts and tribunals including domestic arbitrations, all divisions of the High Court (including Mercantile Courts), the Court of Appeal and the Privy Council. Employment and human rights law practice including domestic disciplinary tribunals, the Employment Tribunal, the Employment Appeal Tribunal, all divisions of the High Court, the Court of Appeal and the Privy Council.
Prof. Memberships: Member of COMBAR: Member of ELBA; Member of the Bar European Group.
Career: New College, Oxford: BA (First Class Hons with Distinction) 1984; MA 1988; City University, London: Postgraduate Diploma in Law 1985. Called to the Bar 1986.
Personal: Born 1962.

GRIFFITHS, Peter

4 Stone Buildings (Philip Heslop QC), London (020) 7242 5524
Recommended in Commercial Chancery, Company, Insolvency/Corporate Recovery
Specialisation: Principal area of practice is company law, focusing on insolvency and minority shareholder disputes. Other main areas of work include partnership, civil fraud, bankruptcy and professional negligence. Contributor to 'Atkins Court Forms' Vol 10 (Companies Winding Up) 1988, 'Encyclopaedia of Forms and Precedents' 5th Ed Vol 11 (Companies) 1992, and Butterworths 'Practical Insolvency' 1999.
Prof. Memberships: Chancery Bar Association, Insolvency Lawyers' Association and COMBAR.
Career: Called to the Bar in 1977 and joined present chambers in 1978.
Personal: Educated at Repton 1966-1971 and St Catharine's College, Cambridge, 1972-1975.

GRIME, Stephen QC

Deans Court Chambers (H.K. Goddard QC), Manchester (0161) 214 6000
grime@deanscourt.co.uk
Recommended in Clinical Negligence
Specialisation: Personal Injury including Disease Litigation; Insurance related litigation; Construction; Clinical Negligence; Professional Negligence - other than clinical; Commercial; Arbitration. Significant reported cases: Bence Graphics International v Fasson [1997] 1All ER 979; Wisniewski v Central Manchester HA [1996] 7 Med LR 248; Cruden Construction v Commission for the New Towns [1995] 2 Lloyd's Rep 387; Crocker v British Coal Corporation [1995] 29 BMLR 159; Fairhurst v St Helens & Knowsley HA [1995] PIQR Q1; Khan v Armaguard [1994] 3 All ER 545; Wood v Gahlings [1993] PIQR P76; Family Housing Association (Manchester) Ltd v Michael Hyde [1993] 1 All ER 567; Bradley v Eagle Star Insurance Co Ltd [1989] 1 AC 957; Wilkinson v Ancliff (BLT) Ltd [1986] 3 All ER 427, [1986] 1 WLR 1352.
Prof. Memberships: Chairman Northern Circuit Medical Law Association; Past Chairman of Northern Arbitration Association; Fellow - Chartered Institute of Arbitrators. Member - Northern Circuit Commercial Bar Association; Society for Computers and Law; United Kingdom Environmental Law Association; Professional Negligence Bar Association; Personal Injury Bar Association.
Career: Trinity College, Oxford (Scholar). Called (Middle Temple) - 1970. Queen's Counsel - 1987. Recorder - 1990. Technology and Construction

Recorder - 1996. Fellow - Chartered Institute of Arbitrators - 1996. Bencher of Middle Temple - 1997.

GRINDROD, Helen QC
95A Chancery Lane (now 15-19 Devereux court) (Helen Grindrod QC), London (020) 7583 2792
Recommended in Crime

GROSS, Peter QC
20 Essex Street (Iain Milligan QC), London (020) 7583 9294
Recommended in Arbitration (International), Commercial (Litigation), Insurance, Shipping

GROVES, Hugo
Enterprise Chambers (Anthony Mann QC), Leeds (0113) 246 0391
Recommended in Commercial (Litigation), Insolvency/Corporate Recovery

GRUDER, Jeffrey QC
Essex Court Chambers (Gordon Pollock QC), London (020) 7813 8000
Recommended in Arbitration (International), Commercial (Litigation), Insurance, Shipping
Specialisation: Principal areas of practice are commercial disputes, insurance and reinsurance, banking, oil and gas disputes. Other areas of practice are shipping and transport, financial services and commodity disputes. Recently appeared in Standard Chartered Bank v PNSC, RLB v Five Star, XL v Owens Corning, Czech Ocean v Van Ommeren, Investors Compensation Scheme v West Bromwich Building Society, Vitol Energy v Pisco, Indian Grace (No 2) (1997), Chevron v Total (1996), Autocar v Motemtronic (1996), British Gas v Eastern Electricity (1996). Other important cases have included Sheldon v Outhwaite (1995), Standard Bank v Bank of Tokyo (1995), Indian Grace (1993), Euro-diam v Bathurst (1990), Miss Jay Jay (1987) and Nai Genova (1984). Has appeared frequently in arbitrations. Clients include major banks, insurance companies and corporations. Supervisor at Cambridge University 1977-1979. Previously part time lecturer at Central London Polytechnic on International Trade.
Prof. Memberships: COMBAR (secretary).
Career: Called to the Bar in 1977. QC 1997. At *4 Essex Court* (now *Essex Court Chambers*) 1978-93. *1 Essex Court* 1993-2000. Rejoined *Essex Court Chambers* February 2000.
Personal: Educated at City of London School 1966-1972 and Trinity Hall, Cambridge 1973-1976. Born 18 September 1954. Interests include tennis, theatre, cinema and reading. Lives in Radlett.

GRUNDY, Nigel
9 St. John Street (John Hand QC), Manchester (0161) 955 9000
Recommended in Employment

GUGGENHEIM, Anna
Crown Office Chambers (Michael Spencer QC & Christopher Purchas QC), London (020) 7797 8100 guggenheim@crownofficechambers.com
Recommended in Professional Negligence
Specialisation: Specialises in insurance litigation, construction, product liability, general commercial and common law, personal injury.
Prof. Memberships: London Common Law & Commercial Bar Association; COMBAR; TECBAR.
Career: Called to the Bar 1982.
Personal: Educated at Somerville College, Oxford (BA Jurisprudence) 1978-1981. Born 2nd September 1959. Speaks French. Interests: sailing.

GUMBEL, Elizabeth-Anne QC
199 Strand (David Phillips QC), London (020) 7379 9779
gumbel@199strand.freeserve.co.uk
Recommended in Clinical Negligence
Specialisation: Main areas of practice: clinical negligence and claims against local authorities (social services and education), public law children work. Appeared in the following cases: X (Minors) v Bedfordshire County Council, H.L [1995] 2 AC 633 (Liability of a local authority for damages for failing to protect children by removal from home into care); Barrett v Enfield London Borough Council, H.L [1999] 3 WLR 79 (Liability of a local authority for a child in care-duty of care and causation found by the House of Lords to be arguable, a claim for damages for personal injuries could be pursued against the local authority); W v Essex County Council H.L [2000] 2 WLR 601 (Whether parents of children suffering sexual abuse from a foster child could arguably recover against the local authority who placed the child in their home for their own psychiatric damage); Heil v Rankin C of A [2000] The Times 23 March (Test cases on the level of damages for pain suffering and loss of amenity following the Law Commission report); Kent v Griffiths and London Ambulance Service C of A [2000] The Times 2 Feb (Whether ambulance service owed a duty of care to provide an ambulance in a reasonable time in response to a 999 call); Re J (Abduction: wrongful removal) C of A [2000] 1 FLR 78 (Whether an order, granted to a father that a mother return her child to the jurisdiction, made on an ex parte basis, was made in breach of Article 6 European Convention for the Protection of Human Rights and Fundamental Freedoms 1950); McCauley v Vine [1999] 1 WLR 1977 C.A (Whether a defendant who was convicted of careless driving in a magistrates court and did not appeal the conviction could challenge the conviction in civil proceedings for damages for personal injury).
Prof. Memberships: Professional Negligence Bar Association, Personal Injury Bar Association, Family Law Bar Association, Editorial Committee Clinical Risk.
Career: PPE Lady Margaret Hall, Oxford.

HACKER, Richard QC
3-4 South Square (Michael Crystal QC), London (020) 7696 9900
Recommended in Banking, Insolvency/Corporate Recovery
Specialisation: A mixed litigation/advisory commercial law practice including contentious and non-contentious insolvency work, banking law, professional negligence, asset tracing and general commercial litigation. Clients have included the major international accountancy firms, major UK banks and a variety of overseas banks and governments. Heavily involved in all major collapses of the last 20 years including Laker, Banco Ambrosiano, Mentor Insurance, Maxwell, BCCI, Rafidain, KWELM, NEMGIA and Barings. Has appeared and given expert evidence in a variety of overseas Courts including New York. Recent significant UK trial appearances include the Grupo Torras litigation in which he appeared for the Kuwait Investment Authority.
Career: Called 1977. QC 1998.

HACKETT, Philip QC
2 Bedford Row (formerly 3 Hare Court) (William Clegg QC), London (020) 7440 8888
Recommended in Crime, Fraud: Criminal

HACON, Richard
11 South Square (Christopher Floyd QC), London (020) 7405 1222
Recommended in Intellectual Property

HADDON-CAVE, Charles QC
4 Essex Court (Nigel Teare QC), London (020) 7653 5653
Recommended in Arbitration (International), Aviation
Specialisation: Has a broad commercial practice which includes a wide variety of cases in the aviation field. He has been instructed in many of the major aviation disasters of recent times including the Knight Air crash at Dunkeswick, the Thai Air crash at Kathmandu, the British Midland crash at Kegworth and the British Airtours disaster at Manchester. He has acted for Virgin Atlantic in CAA routing applications, including London-Shanghai and London-Capetown. He appears regularly as an advocate in the High Court in London and Hong Kong and in arbitrations.
Prof. Memberships: Vice-Chairman of the Royal Aeronautical Society Air Law Committee. Member of COMBAR, the Personal Injury Bar Association and the Hong Kong Bar.

HAGGAN, Nicholas Somerset
17 Carlton Crescent (Mr Jeremy Gibbons QC), Southampton (023) 8032 0320/2003
Recommended in Consumer

HAIG-HADDOW, Alastair
Eighteen Carlton Crescent (Alastair Haig Haddow), Southampton (023) 8063 9001
Recommended in Family/Matrimonial

HAJIMITSIS, Anthony
10 Park Square (A.N. Campbell QC), Leeds (0113) 245 5438
Recommended in Family/Matrimonial
Specialisation: Matrimonial Finance, Public Law Children Cases.
Prof. Memberships: FLBA.
Career: Leeds Grammar School; Oxford University; Inner Temple (1984 Call).
Personal: Married. One son

HALL, Andrew
Doughty Street Chambers (Geoffrey Robertson QC), London (020) 7404 1313
Recommended in Crime
Specialisation: Practice predominantly serious crime, including leading work. Substantial experience of homicide and other serious violence, firearms, explosives, and large drug conspiracies. Growing fraud practice including VAT, mortgage and insolvent trading cases. Has regularly written, lectured and broadcast on a wide range of issues within the criminal justice sphere.
Prof. Memberships: Criminal Bar Association, Bar Overseas Advocacy Committee, south eastern circuit.
Career: Educated at Marist College, University of Birmingham (LL.B 1974), University of Sheffield (MA [Criminology] 1976). Admitted as solicitor 1980. Partner and head of criminal law department, *Hodge Jones & Allen* London before transfer to the Bar in 1991. Director of Legal Action Group, Member of Editorial Board of International Journal of Evidence and Proof. Member of General Council of Bar and Human Rights Committee of the Bar of England and Wales.

HALL, Joanna
14 Gray's Inn Square (Joanna Dodson QC), London (020) 7242 0858
Recommended in Family: Child Care including child abduction

HALPERN, David
Four New Square (Justin Fenwick QC), London (020) 7822 2000
barrister@4newsquare.com
Recommended in Professional Negligence
Specialisation: Professional negligence and property litigation.
Career: Educated at St Paul's School; won Open Exhibition to Magdalen College, Oxford. Practised at the Chancery Chambers for 20 years before moving to 4 New Square in February 2000. Practises in all areas of commercial Chancery work but with emphasis on professional negligence and property litigation. Recent cases include: Barclays Bank v Weeks Legg Dean [1999]

QB 309 (solicitor's undertaking to bank), Portman Building Society v Hamlyn Taylor Neck [1998] 4 All ER 202 (whether lender may bring restitutionary claim against solicitor reporting on title) and Raja v. Rubin [1999] 3 WLR 606 (power to vary IVA informally).

HAM, Robert QC
Wilberforce Chambers (Edward Nugee QC), London (020) 7306 0102
Recommended in Pensions, Traditional Chancery
Specialisation: Practice largely in the fields of trusts and tax law, including pension schemes, but extends to other areas of property law.
Prof. Memberships: Association of Pension Lawyers. Chancery Bar Association, Revenue Bar Association, Society of Trust and Estate Practioners, Wales and Chester Circuit.
Career: BA & BCL (Oxon); Called to the Bar 1973; QC 1994.

HAMBLEN, Nicholas QC
20 Essex Street (Iain Milligan QC), London (020) 7583 9294
Recommended in Shipping
Specialisation: Principal areas of practice are shipping, international sale of goods, commodities, insurance and re-insurance, conflicts of laws and arbitration. Acts as arbitrator in maritime, insurance and international commercial arbitrations. ICC, LCIA, LAS and ACI arbitrator.
Career: Called to the Bar 1981. Took Silk 1997. Sits on Recorder.
Personal: Educated at St. John's College, Oxford (MA) and Harvard Law School (LL.M). Born 1957.

HAMER, George
8 New Square (Michael Fysh QC SC), London (020) 7405 4321 george.hamer@8newsquare.co.uk
Recommended in Intellectual Property
Specialisation: Specialises in all aspects of intellectual property and media law, including patents, copyright, passing off, trade marks and confidential information. Important cases include: (patents) Catnic Components v. Hill & Smith; SKM v Wagner; Hsiung's Patent; (trade marks/passing off) Rolls Royce v Dodd; Neutrogena v Golden; (copyright) Baroness Thatcher v Assoc. Newspapers and v Mirror Group; Sillitoe v McGraw Hill; (registered designs) Goodyear tyre treads; Amper SA; (other) Estate of Bob Marley (PC). Has also given expert evidence in cases in Israel (LEGO) and United States (Apple Computer).
Career: Called to the Bar 1974.
Personal: Educated at Sedbergh School 1962-1967 and Imperial College, London (BSc chemistry; ARCS) 1968-1971. Semi-fluent in German and a good knowledge of French and Spanish. Leisure pursuits include tennis, golf, skiing and gardening. Born 26th February 1949.

HAMILTON, Eben W. QC
1 New Square (Eben Hamilton QC), London (020) 7405 0884
Recommended in Insolvency/Corporate Recovery
Specialisation: Specialises in company and corporate finance, commercial chancery and insolvency.
Career: Called to the Bar, 1962. QC 1981. Bencher, Inner Temple 1985. DTI inspector, Atlantic Computers plc 1990-1994, Deputy high court judge, Chancery division since 1991. Admitted regularly to appear in courts of Hong Kong and Singapore in company and insolvency matters.

HAMILTON, Eleanor QC
No.6 (Shaun Spencer QC), Leeds (0113) 245 9763
Recommended in Family/Matrimonial

HANCOCK, Christopher QC
20 Essex Street (Iain Milligan QC), London (020) 7583 9294
Recommended in Banking

HAND, John QC
Old Square Chambers (John Hendy QC), London (020) 7269 0300
Recommended in Employment, Environment, Health & Safety
Specialisation: Is experienced in most areas of common law litigation, concentrates on employment law, personal injury and environmental law with emphasis on health and safety litigation and is familiar with EC law principles. He has been instructed by multi-national chemical manufacturers, who were being prosecuted by regulatory authorities (NRA, HMIP, HSE EA), and has appeared on their behalf both in the Crown Court and the Magistrates Court in cases of explosions, airborne pollution and radiation. Cases include R v Hickson and Welch (the Castleford explosion), R v Holliday Dyes and Chemicals (the Huddersfield explosion), R v Associated Octel (No. 2)(the Ellesmere port Explosion), R v Coalite (Dioxin emissions) and R v University of Cambridge (loss of radioactive source).
Prof. Memberships: ELA, ELBA, PIBA, PNBA, UKELA, BEG and Society for Computer and Law.
Career: Called 1972 Bencher 1996 (Gray's Inn); Queen's Counsel (1988); Recorder 1991.

HAPGOOD, Mark QC
Brick Court Chambers (Christopher Clarke QC), London (020) 7379 3550
Recommended in Banking, Commercial (Litigation), Company
Specialisation: Litigation, advisory and drafting work in the whole field of commercial law, including agency; banking; commodities and futures; insurance; international trade, jurisdictional disputes; mortgages; reservation of title; sale of goods; security interests. Cases of note: Skandia; Derby v Weldon; Seaconsar v Bank Markazi; BBL v Eagle Star; NRG v Bacon & Woodrow; SAAMCO v York Montague; Esso v Milton; Bank of Scotland v Bennett; Kredietbank Antwerp v Midland Bank; Banco Santander v Banque Paribas; Lloyds Bank v Independent Insurance; KAC v KIC; Peregrine Fixed Income v Robinson; Shanning v Lloyds TSB, Samson Lancastrian v Royal Bank of Scotland.
Career: Member of Gray's Inn. Called to the Bar in February 1979; Appointed to Silk in April 1994.
Publications: Contributor to 'Professional Negligence and Liability' (Looseleaf, 2 volumes). General Editor of Butterworths on-line 'Banking Law Direct'
Personal: Editor of 'Paget's Law of Banking' 11th Ed. 1996. Sole Contributor to 'Halsbury's Law of England', Title 'Banking'. Joint Contributor to 'Halsbury's Law of England', Title 'Bills of Exchange'. Contributor of two Chapters in 'Using set-off as Security' (IBA 1990).

HARDING, Cherry
Renaissance Chambers (Brian Jubb & Henry Setright), London (020) 7404 1111
Recommended in Family: Child Care including child abduction
Specialisation: Family: children, abduction, adoption, private/ public law. Matrimonial, all aspects, education.
Prof. Memberships: Family Law Bar Association, Bar European Group, Justice, Legal Action Group, Inter Country adoption Association, Association of lawyers for children
Career: Llb (Hons) Kings College, London. Called to the Bar 1978, Gray's Inn. Married, three children.

HARGREAVES, Simon
Keating Chambers (Richard Fernyhough QC), London (020) 7544 2600
Recommended in Construction
Specialisation: All aspects of litigation and arbitration concerning general construction, engineering, power and utilities contracts (both domestic and international). Related negligence and professional negligence claims. ICC Arbitrations. Cases include: DMD v Toyo.
Prof. Memberships: Inner Temple; TECBAR; COMBAR.
Career: Called to Bar, October 1991 (and called to the Bar of Gibraltar, May 1997). Member of editorial team of Construction Law Yearbook. Case reporter for Construction Law Journal.
Personal: Shrewsbury School (scholar), Worcester College, Oxford (1989 BA Law 2(1)). Born 1968. Resides London.

HARMAN, Sarah
4 Stone Buildings (Philip Heslop QC), London (020) 7242 5524
Recommended in Company
Specialisation: Specialises in company and commercial litigation and advice, bankruptcy and insolvency, directors disqualification. Reported cases include: Re Farmizer (Products) Ltd [1995] BCC 926 (wrongful trading), re Sutton Glass Ltd [1996] BCC 174 (directors disqualification), BRDC v Hextall Erskine & Co [1996] 3 All ER 667 (solicitors' negligence), Re Dawes & Henderson (Agencies) Ltd [1997] 1 BCLC 329, Re Leeds United [1996] 2 BCLC 545, SOS v Laing & Ors [1996] 2 BCLC 326.
Prof. Memberships: Member of the Chancery Bar Association, Insolvency Lawyers Association, COMBAR, Member of Bar Council 1989-95, Chairman Young Barristers' Committee 1992.
Career: Called to Bar 1987.
Personal: Educated: Wycombe Abbey School, Trinity College, Oxford.

HARPER, Mark
40 King St (Philip Raynor QC), Manchester (0161) 832 9082 mharper@40kingstreet.co.uk
Recommended in Chancery
Specialisation: Banking and Finance Litigation; Professional Negligence; Directors Disqualification; Personal and Corporate Insolvency, Contracted Disputes.
Prof. Memberships: Chancery Bar Association; Northern Chancery Bar Association.
Career: Called to the Bar by Lincolns Inn in 1993. Pupillage with existing chambers.
Personal: Arnold Hill Comprehensive School, Nottingham. Downing College, Cambridge. Interested in all sports especially football and cricket. Married to Julie. Became a father for the first time in June 2000.

HARRIS, David QC
India Buildings Chambers (David Harris QC), Liverpool (0151) 243 6000
Recommended in Family/Matrimonial
Specialisation: All civil, in particular professional negligence, personal injury (including injuries of the utmost severity such as cerebral palsy caused by obstetric mismanagement and traumatic brain and spinal damage cases), commercial and construction disputes; family, including children work (especially abuse cases) and financial disputes; serious crime (especially fraud, sexual offences and murder); administrative and public law.
Prof. Memberships: Committee member – Family Law Bar Association.
Career: Called 1969. QC 1989.

HARRIS, Russell
1 Serjeants' Inn (Lionel Read QC), London
(020) 7583 1355
Recommended in Environment, Planning

HARRISON, Christopher
4 Stone Buildings (Philip Heslop QC), London
(020) 7242 5524
clerks@4stonebuildings.law.co.uk
Recommended in Commercial Chancery, Company
Specialisation: Company law, corporate fraud & asset recovery, corporate insolvency, shareholder disputes, financial services & regulatory law, banking, public law, professional negligence, commercial litigation. Recent reported cases include Morris v Bank of America [2000] 1 All ER 954 (section 213), Sasea Finance Ltd (in liquidation) v KPMG [1998] BCC 216 (section 236 Insolvency Act 1986), SIB v Scandex Capital Management A/S [1998] 1 WLR 712 (financial services) and Re Pinstripe Farming Co Ltd [1996] BCLC 295 (provisional liquidator).
Career: Called to the Bar 1988. Junior Counsel to the Crown (B panel). DTI Inspector (1996). Called to the Bar of the Turks & Caicos Islands for specific cases.
Personal: Trinity Hall, Cambridge.

HARRISON, Keith
24A St. John Street (Paul Chambers), Manchester
(0161) 833 9628
Recommended in Crime

HARRISON, Michael QC
Park Court Chambers (James Stewart QC Robert Smith QC), Leeds (0113) 243 3277
clerks@parkcourtchambers.co.uk
Recommended in Crime
Specialisation: Commercial fraud; crime (general). Family (children); professional negligence. In RE A (A minor) (abduction) (1997) (CA). In RE W (minors) (disclosure) (1998) (CA). In RE B (minor) (adoption; immigration) (1999) 2 ALL ER 576 (H.L.). R v DPP, ex p Duckenfield, (1999) 2 ALL ER 873.
Prof. Memberships: CLBA. FLBA
Career: LLB. Gray's Inn (1969); QC 1987.

HARRISON, Nicholas
Serle Court (Lord Neill of Bladen QC), London
(020) 7242 6105
nfhlaw@ad.com
Recommended in Commercial Chancery
Specialisation: Commerical chancery and commercial fraud. For the past two years has been working full-time on the Thyssen litigation in Bermuda.
Prof. Memberships: Chancery Bar Association, COMBAR.
Career: Continuous full-time practice at the English Bar and (since 1999) at the Bermuda Bar.
Personal: Education: Winchester and Oxford. Leisure interests: hiking, music, a variety of sports. Married with no children.

HARRISON, Sally
28 St. John St (Clement Goldstone QC), Manchester (0161) 834 8418
Recommended in Family/Matrimonial

HARRISON, Stephanie
Two Garden Court (I. Macdonald QC & O.Davies QC), London (020) 7353 1633
Recommended in Administrative & Public Law: General, Immigration
Specialisation: Practising in all fields of public and adminstrative law with a specialisation in immigration and asylum law. Expertise in European Community law. Also has experience in discrimination law in all courts and tribunals. Work with other lawyers in the field of sexual orientation discrimination was recognised in 1997 with the Stonewall Equality Award. Has experience in European human rights cases and civil actions against the police and public authorities primarily arising from immigration related detention.
Prof. Memberships: Immigration Law Practitioners Association.
Career: Called to the Bar in Nov 1991. Important recent cases include R v MOD ex parte Smith and Others, CA and ECHR, R v SSHD ex parte Danie, CA, R v SSHD ex parte Salem, CA and HL. Islam v SSHD CA and HL, Danian v SSHD, R v SSHD ex parte Arman Ali, Baumbast and Pinvetrenbalden (reference in EJC), R v Noth West Lancashire Health Authority ex p ADE (provision of NHS Care) CA, r v Uxbridge Magistrates Courte ex parte Haimi and Others, DC, R v SSHD ex parte Adan and Others, CA.

HARROD, Henry
5 Stone Buildings (Henry Harrod), London
(020) 7242 6201
Recommended in Traditional Chancery
Specialisation: Specialises in all areas of Chancery work.
Prof. Memberships: Chancery Bar Association; Society of Trust and Estate Practitioners. Association of Contentious Trust and Probate Specialists.
Career: Called to the Bar 1963. Tenant at 46 Grainger Street, Newcastle-upon-Tyne 1964-1968 before joining 4 Paper Buildings in 1968. Member of present chambers since 1969 and head since 1990. Conveyancing Counsel of the Court 1991. Bencher of Lincoln's Inn 1991. Appointed Recorder 1993.

HARRY, Timothy
9 Old Square (Michael Driscoll QC), London
(020) 7405 4682
Recommended in Property Litigation
Specialisation: Property litigation, professional negligence and Chancery work. Contributor to 'Lloyds Professional Negligence Law Reports'.
Prof. Memberships: PNBA
Career: Called 1983. Lecturer, Hertford College, Oxford, 1983-1988. An Editor, Hill & Redman's 'Landlord & Tenant'. Called to the Bar, 1983, Hong Kong 1992.
Personal: Educated Monmouth School; MA, BCL (Oxford).

HART, David
1 Crown Office Row (Robert Seabrook QC), London (020) 7797 7500
david.hart@lcor.com
Recommended in Arbitration (International), Environment
Specialisation: Has conducted a wide range of public and private law environmental litigation, including water (Cambridge Water & Bowden on enforceability of EC Directives, Falmouth on abatement notices), particulate emissions (Coalite and Orimulsion), methane (Loscoe) and claims against consultants arising out of land decontamination surveys and assessment of methane risks. Is also frequently instructed in professional negligence cases, (particularly medical, surveyors and engineers) contract claims, and arbitrations (construction, engineering and general contract), as well as flood and fire claims.
Prof. Memberships: Member of UKELA and ALBA.
Career: Called 1982.

HART, William
Albion Chambers (J.C.T. Barton QC), Bristol
(0117) 927 2144
Recommended in Crime

HARTLEY, Richard QC
1 Brick Court (Richard Rampton QC), London
(020) 7353 8845
Recommended in Defamation

HARVEY, Colin T.
St. Paul's Chambers (Nigel Sangster QC), Leeds
(0113) 245 5866
Recommended in Crime

HARVEY, Michael QC
Crown Office Chambers (Michael Spencer QC & Christopher Purchas QC), London (020) 7797 8100
Recommended in Professional Negligence
Specialisation: Predominantly civil and commercial matters, including but not limited to: commercial and contractual disputes, professional negligence, international arbitration, construction and engineering contracts, insurance and reinsurance law, conflict of laws, sale of goods, carriage of goods, agency, product liability. Sits as arbitrator.
Prof. Memberships: Legal Services Committee of Bar Council 1994-99; COMBAR; LCCLBA; TECBAR.
Career: Called 1966. QC 1982. Recorder 1986. Authorised to sit as a Deputy High Court Judge and Deputy Official Referee. Bencher Gray's Inn 1991. Review Board, Council of Legal Education 1993-94; Speaker at conferences; Joint author of title 'Damages' in Halsbury's Laws of England.
Personal: Born 22 May 1943. Educated at St. John's School, Leatherhead and Christ's College, Cambridge. Married with two children.

HARWOOD-STEVENSON, John
9-12 Bell Yard (D. Anthony Evans QC), London
(020) 7400 1800
Recommended in Crime

HAVERS, Philip QC
1 Crown Office Row (Robert Seabrook QC), London (020) 7797 7500
philip.havers@1cor.com
Recommended in Administrative & Public Law: General, Clinical Negligence, Environment
Specialisation: Principal areas of practice are public and administrative law, clinical negligence, environmental law and human rights law (including cases at the European Court of Human Rights). Also handles product liability and professional negligence. Recent reported cases include Hunter v Canary Wharf (1997) (nuisance), Thomas v Brighton Health Authority (1998) (multipliers), Findlay v UK (1996) (fair trial), AG v Blake (1998) (fiduciary duties of a spy) and R v Collins, ex parte S (rights of a fetus), Heil v. Rankin (test cases on level of general damages). Other important cases include Clapham Railway Disaster Inquiry, Southall Rail Inquiry and Ladbroke Grove Rail Inquiry. R v Hull University, ex parte Page (university law), Benzodiazepine litigation and Spycatcher. Regularly addresses seminars on medical negligence, human rights, contempt of court and freedom of the press.
Prof. Memberships: South Eastern Circuit, Administrative Law Bar Association, Bar European Group, London Common Law and Commercial Bar Association.
Career: Called to the Bar 1974 and joined current chambers 1975. Recorder 1997-2000. Took Silk 1995.
Personal: Educated at Eton College 1963-1968 and Corpus Christi College, Cambridge 1969-1973. Leisure pursuits include tennis, music, gardening, wine and travel. Born 16 June 1950. Lives in London.

HAYES, Josephine
3 New Square (Lord Goodhart QC), London
(020) 7405 5577
Recommended in Pensions, Traditional Chancery
Specialisation: Pension schemes; property litigation; general chancery. Particular experience in fraud,

breach of fiduciary duty and asset recovery. Reported cases include: Bank of Scotland v Wright; Springette v Defoe; Penn v Bristol & West BS; Hambros Bank v BHBT; Miller v Stapleton; Miller v Scorey; Seifert v Pensions Ombudsman; Lloyds Bank v Carrick; Buckley v Hudson Forge Ltd.
Prof. Memberships: Chancery Bar Association; Association of Women Barristers (Chairwoman 1996-1998; Vice President 1998-); Association of Pension Lawyers.
Career: MA (Oxon), 1st class honours in Greats. Called 1980. Alumni Fellow, Yale Law School; LLM (Yale).

HAYNES, Peter
St Philip's Chambers (Rex Tedd QC), Birmingham (0121) 246 7000
Recommended in Crime
Specialisation: Principally a crown court advocate dealing with frauds, sexual and drug trafficking offences, practice includes all aspects of criminal law including the prosecution and defence of proceedings brought by Local Authorities and other public bodies.
Career: Assigned Counsel to the International Criminal Tribunal for the Former Yugoslavia.

HAYWARD SMITH, Rodger QC
One King's Bench Walk (Anthony Hacking QC), London (020) 7936 1500
Recommended in Family: Child Care including child abduction, Family: Matrimonial Finance
Specialisation: Specialises in family law and criminal law. Editor of 'Jackson's Matrimonial Finance and Taxation' (5th and 6th edns) and Practitioners Child Law Bulletin.
Prof. Memberships: South Eastern Circuit, Family Law Bar Association, Criminal Bar Association.
Career: Called to the Bar in 1967 and joined 1 King's Bench Walk in 1968. Appointed Recorder in 1986. Took Silk 1988.
Personal: Educated at Brentwood School and St. Edmund Hall, Oxford.

HEATON, David
18 St. John Street (Jonathan Foster QC), Manchester (0161) 278 1800
davidheaton@compuserve.com
Recommended in Clinical Negligence, Personal Injury
Specialisation: Clinical negligence. Personal injury.
Prof. Memberships: PIBA, PNBA, NCMLA.
Career: Educated at William Hulme's Grammar School, Manchester and Corpus Christi College, Cambridge. MA (Cantab). Avory Studentship.
Personal: Enjoys walking, reading, music, good food and wine. Married, four children.

HEATON, Frances
Deans Court Chambers (H.K. Goddard QC), Manchester (0161) 214 6000
heaton@deanscourt.co.uk
Recommended in Family/Matrimonial
Specialisation: Practises exclusively in Family Law. Public Law: care disputes relating to children adoption proceedings, representing local authorities, parents and children. Private law: Matrimonial finance.
Prof. Memberships: FLBA (committee member), child concern.
Career: Sheffield University.

HENDERSON, Launcelot QC
5 Stone Buildings (Henry Harrod), London (020) 7242 6201
Recommended in Tax, Traditional Chancery
Specialisation: General Chancery work, mainly concentrating on trusts, tax and private client work, pensions, charities, Court of Protection, and all aspects of Revenue Law (apart from VAT). Recent reported cases: Deeny v Gooda Walker (taxation of damages); IRC v Willoughby and McGuckian v IRC (tax avoidance); Bricom Holdings v IRC (controlled foreign companies); Memec plc v IRC (double tax treaties); LM Tenancies 1 plc v IRC (stamp duty and the contingency principle); EMI v Coldicott (taxation of payments in lieu of notice); Garner v Pounds (CGT and options); Harries v Church Commissioners (ethical investment of church funds); Spooner v BT (interaction of BT and Civil Service pension schemes); and numerous other cases appearing for the Inland Revenue at all levels.
Prof. Memberships: Chancery Bar Association; Revenue Bar Association; Hong Kong Bar Association (1999); STEP.
Career: Called 1977; Standing Junior Counsel to the Inland Revenue (chancery) 1987-91; standing Junior Counsel to the Inland Revenue 1991-95. Took Silk in 1995.
Personal: Born 1951. Educated at Westminster School and Balliol College, Oxford. Fellow of All Souls College, Oxford, 1974-1981 and 1982-1989. Married with 3 young children.

HENDERSON, Roger QC
2 Harcourt Buildings (Roger Henderson QC), London (020) 7583 9020
Recommended in Financial Services, Planning
Specialisation: Specialises in common law and public law. Work covers professional negligence, product liability, contract, personal injuries, judicial review, local government, parliamentary and finance, especially local government finance and public transport. Counsel for British Rail at the Clapham Rail Crash Inquiry, counsel to the Kings Cross Fire Inquiry and counsel for Railtrack at the Southall and Ladbroke Grove Rail Crash Inquiries. Has acted for British Rail, Railtrack, GMC, British Telecom, London Regional Transport, Stock Exchange and many local authorities. Promoted numerous Parliamentary Bills. Promoted London Money Bills for GLC. Appeared for International Stock Exchange at numerous Inquiries. Chaired Accountants' Joint Disciplinary Scheme tribunals. Appeared for ABP at Southampton Harbour Inquiry. Involved in three Lloyds' names' actions. Represented the GMC in the 'Turkish Kidneys for Sale' and Bristol Paediatric Heart Surgery cases. Reported cases include Roylance v General Medical Council 1999, The Times 27 January, Privy Council; R v Brent London Borough Council ex parte Awua [1996] AC 55; Canterbury City Council v Colley [1993] AC 401; R v International Stock Exchange of the United Kingdom and the Republic of Ireland Limited Ex parte Else (1982) Limited [1993] QB 534 (CA); R v London Boroughs Transport Committee Ex parte Freight Transport Association [1991] 1 WLR 828 (HL); R v Secretary of State for the Environment Ex parte Hammersmith and Fulham London Borough Council and Others [1991] 1 AC 521; R v Secretary of State for Social Services Ex parte Association of Metropolitan Authorities [1986] 1 WLR 1; R v Secretary of State for Transport Ex parte GLC [1986] QB 556; In re Westminster City Council [1986] AC 668; Pickwell v Camden London Borough Council [1983] QB 962; R v London Transport Executive Ex parte GLC [1983] QB 485; R v Secretary of State for the Environment Ex parte Hackney London Borough Council [1983] 1 WLR 534; R v Secretary of State for the Environment Ex parte Hackney London Borough Council [1983] 1 WLR 534; R v Secretary of State for the Environment Ex parte Brent London Borough Council [1982] QB 593.
Prof. Memberships: Bencher of Inner Temple 1985. Member of St Kitts & Nevis Bar.
Career: Called to the bar in 1964. Joined 2 Harcourt Buildings in 1966. Took silk in 1980. Recorder from 1983, Deputy High Court Judge from 1987. Chairman of Civil Service Arbitration Tribunal 1994.
Personal: Educated at Radley College 1956-1961. First Class Honours in Law at St. Catharine's College Cambridge. Positions held include Chairman Council of Governors of London Hospital Medical College, former president of British Academy of Forensic Sciences. Leisure pursuits include fly fishing, gardening, shooting and travel. Born 21st April 1943.

HENDERSON, Sophie
Plowden Buildings (William Lowe QC), London (020) 7583 0808
bar@plowdenbuildings.co.uk
Recommended in Immigration
Specialisation: Specialises in all aspects of immigration and asylum law. Particular expertise in judicial reviews, human rights law and European Community law. Important cases include: DS Abdi v Secretary of State [1996] Imm AR 148 CA, ex parte Alekesan [1997] Imm AR 315, ex parte Probakaran [1996] Imm AR 603, Packeer v Secretary of State [1997] Imm AR 110 CA, ex parte Kamalraj [1995] Imm AR 288, ex parte Wanyoike [2000] INLR, Times LR 10/03/00.
Prof. Memberships: ILPA
Career: BA Philosophy and Politics, (Manchester University), Dip Law (City University). Called to the Bar 1990.

HENDY, John QC
Old Square Chambers (John Hendy QC), London (020) 7269 0300
hendyqc@oldsquarechambers.co.uk
Recommended in Employment, Health & Safety, Personal Injury
Specialisation: Primarily trade union and industrial relations law and has appeared in most of the leading cases over the last 20 years. Also deals with employment law more generally. Extensive practice also in P.I. and medical negligence. Standing counsel to NUM, NUJ and POA; co-author of: 'Redgrave's Health and Safety', 'Munkman's Employer's Liability' and 'Personal Injury Practice'. Member of Editorial Board of Encyclopaedia of Employment Law; Journal of Personal Injury Litigation; The Litigator.
Prof. Memberships: ILS, ELA, ELBA (Exec Cttee 1998-), APIL, PIBA, ATLA, CLBA, ABA, SE. Circuit, W. Circuit, Chair Institute of Employment Rights 1989-. Visiting Professor of Law, King's College London, 1999-.
Career: Called 1972 Gray's; Director Newham Rights Centre 1973-1976; practice 1977-; silk 1987; Bencher of Grays Inn 1995.
Personal: LLB London (external); LLM (Queens, Belfast).

HENKE, Ruth
Iscoed Chambers (Trefor Davies), Swansea (01792) 652988/9
Recommended in Family/Matrimonial
Specialisation: Family law – particularly child law. Recent reported cases include G+R (1995) FLR (proof of risk of harm under S31); Re H (1995) FLR (disclosure of adoption files). Further recent reported case includes Re T (1999) WLR.
Prof. Memberships: FLBA.
Career: Worcester College, Oxford. Tenant Iscoed Chambers. Substantial family law practice emphasis on child care work.

HENRY, Annette
10 King's Bench Walk (Georges M Khayat QC), London (020) 7353 2501
annettehenry@10kbw.co.uk
Recommended in Crime
Specialisation: Regularly appears in substantial criminal cases including drugs, fraud and serious sexual and physical assaults. High profile cases include R. v Whittime the largest joint revenue and Customs and Excise prosecution into the illegal activities of the insolvency profession, which resulted in a landmark decision under the European Convention of Human Rights. Defended in R v Murray, the death of an entire family

was responsible for the launch of a campaign to combat "morning after drinking". Has consistently been recognised as a highly recommended junior at the London Criminal Bar. Special interest in mental health law and has represented many psychiatrically disordered defendants. A Mental Health Act Commissioner and author of the Mental Health Law Referencer. [Sweet and Maxwell]

HERBERG, Javan
Blackstone Chambers (P Baxendale QC and C Flint QC), London (020) 7583 1770
javanherberg@blackstonechambers.com
Recommended in Administrative & Public Law: General

Specialisation: Specialist in commercial law (in particular financial services and civil fraud), public and administrative law and human rights. Interesting cases include (in commercial field) conducting regulatory proceedings for FSA, SIB (including first cases involving use of s.59 disqualification power), PIA and IMRO (Morgan Grenfell / Peter Young unit trusts affair) and against SFA (SBC Warburg disciplinary proceedings over REC derivatives); Btitish Steel v Customs & Excise [1997] 2 All ER 366 (CA) (restitution of overpaid duties); Brunei v Prince Jefri (acting for Prince Jefri in US$30 bn asset recovery claim). In public law field, R v HEFC ex p Institute of Dental Surgery [1994] 1 WLR 242 (right to reasons); Ming Pao Newspapers v AG of Hong Kong [1996] AC 907, PC (freedom of expression); Tan Te Lam v AG of Hong Kong [1997] AC 97, PC (legality of detention); R v Legal Aid Board ex p Eccleston [1998] 1 WLR 1279 (legal expenses); Rv Manchester; Legal Stipendiary Magistrate ex parte Granada Television [2000] 2 WLR 1 (HL) (enforceability of Scottish warrant).
Prof. Memberships: Administrative Law Bar Assn (Committee Member), COMBAR.
Career: Called 1992.
Publications: Publications include 'Principles of Public Law' (Cavandish, 2000, 2nd edn, co-author); de Smith Woolf and Jowell, 'Judicial Review of Administrative Action' (assistant editor, 5th ed. supplement, 1998); case notes in 'Public Law' and in 'Judicial Review'.
Personal: Educated at University College School, University College London (LL.B), and Merton College, Oxford (BCL).

HERBERT, Mark QC
5 Stone Buildings (Henry Harrod), London (020) 7242 6201
mherbert@5-stonebuildings.law.co.uk
Recommended in Charities, Pensions, Traditional Chancery

Specialisation: Principal area of practice is general chancery work, including trusts, capital taxation, taxation of trusts, probate, family provision, charities and off-shore trusts. Also handles pensions work, both advisory and litigation. Important cases include 'Mettoy Pension Trustees v Evans' [1990]; Re Christy Hunt Pension Fund [1991]; 'Fitzwilliam v IRC' [1993]. 'Hamar v Pensions Ombudsman', R v Opra ex parte Littlewoods (1997); Edge v Pensions Ombudsman (1999); 'Espinosa v Burke' (1999). Co-Editor of 'Whiteman on Capital Gains Tax'. Other publications include 'The Drafting and Variation of Wills'.
Prof. Memberships: Chancery Bar Association; Revenue Bar Association; Association of Pension Lawyers.
Career: Called to the Bar 1974. Tenant at 17 Old Buildings 1975-1977 before joining Queen Elizabeth Building in 1977. At present chambers since 1991. Took Silk 1995.
Personal: Educated at Lancing College 1962-1966 and King's College, London 1967-1970. Born 12th November 1948. Lives in London.

HERMAN, Raymond
India Buildings Chambers (David Harris QC), Liverpool (0151) 243 6000
Recommended in Crime

Specialisation: Deals with substantial criminal cases for both the defence and prosecution in the court at all levels. This includes the most serious offences, such as murder/ manslaughter, rape, serious fraud, drugs offences, robbery and crimes of violence.
Prof. Memberships: Criminal Bar Association.
Career: Called 1972.

HERMER, Richard
Doughty Street Chambers (Geoffrey Robertson QC), London (020) 7404 1313
Recommended in Clinical Negligence

HERSHMAN, David
St Philip's Chambers (Rex Tedd QC), Birmingham (0121) 246 7000
Recommended in Family/Matrimonial

Specialisation: Family law. Particular expertise in the law relating to children, international child abduction and adoption. Also criminal cases concerning child abuse and Registered Homes Tribunal work.
Prof. Memberships: Family Law Bar Association, The British Agencies for Adoption and Fostering, the Intercountry Adoption Lawyers' Association and the Association of Lawyers for Children. Public and administrative law concerning children.
Career: Called to the Bar in 1981. Appointed part-time Chairman of the Registered Homes Tribunal in 1995. Co-Author of Children: Law and Practice, contributor to Family Court Practice and Child Protection Training and Resource Pack (National Childrens Bureau). Member of Sweet and Maxwell Research Paper Editorial Board. Lecturer for the Law Society Children Panel and accredited course provider for the Law Society. Lecturer for Judicial Conferences and Justices Family Panel Training.
Personal: Educated at The Kings School Worcester, Kings College London. Married with four daughters. Lives near Worcester.

HESLOP, Martin S QC
1 Hare Court (Stephen Kramer QC), London (020) 7353 5324
Recommended in Crime

Specialisation: Serious crime (both prosecution and defence), commercial fraud, gaming, licensing generally, health & safety, food & drugs.
Career: Called 1972 (Lincoln's Inn), Junior Treasury Counsel 1987, First Junior Treasury Counsel 1991, Senior Treasury Counsel 1992, Queen's Counsel 1995 – Recorder of the Crown Court.
Personal: Sailing, travel, photography, wine and good food.

HESLOP, Philip QC
4 Stone Buildings (Philip Heslop QC), London (020) 7242 5524
clerks@4stonebuildings.law.co.uk
Recommended in Commercial Chancery, Company, Financial Services, Insolvency/Corporate Recovery

Specialisation: Principal areas of practice are company and financial services law, regulatory, corporate insolvency and corporate banking.
Prof. Memberships: Commercial Bar Association (COMBAR), Chancery Bar Association and Insolvency Lawyer's Association.
Career: Called to the Bar 1970 and joined present chambers in 1972. Joint Junior Counsel (Chancery) DTI 1980-85. Took Silk in 1985. Joint DTI Inspector, Consolidated Goldfields plc 1988. Bencher Lincoln's Inn, 1993. Called to the Hong Kong, Bermuda and Gibraltar Bars for specific cases.
Personal: Educated at Haileybury 1961-1966 and Christ's College, Cambridge 1967-1971 (BA Hons 1970, LL.M 1971). President, Cambridge Union Society 1971. Born 24 April 1948.

HIBBERT, William
Gough Square Chambers (Fred Philpott), London (020) 7353 0924
Recommended in Consumer

Specialisation: Consumer law – in particular consumer credit licensing (particulary Minded to Revoke Notices), advising on credit and loan agreements, defending regulatory prosecutions, and acting in civil litigation. Clients include finance houses, product manufacturers, food producers and multiple retailers. Other main areas of practice include corporate, commercial, insolvency and fraud matters.
Prof. Memberships: Food Law Group and London Common and Commercial Bar Association.
Career: Called to the Bar 1979.
Personal: Charterhouse and Worcester College, Oxford. Lives in London.

HICKS, Michael
19 Old Buildings (Alastair Wilson QC), London (020) 7405 2001
Recommended in Intellectual Property

Specialisation: All aspects of intellectual property including patents, designs, copyrights, trade marks, passing off and confidential information. Commercial cases with a scientific or technical subject matter including computers and electronics. EC cases with an intellectual property content.
Prof. Memberships: Inner Temple, Intellectual Property Bar Association. Chancery Bar Association.
Career: Called to the Bar in November 1976. Joined present chambers in December 1979.
Personal: Educated at Brighton College school and Trinity College, Cambridge (BA Natural Sciences). Races dinghies and small keel boats.

HICKS, William QC
1 Serjeants' Inn (Lionel Read QC), London (020) 7583 1355
Recommended in Parliamentary & Public Affairs, Planning

Specialisation: A wide range of planning and related work. Some particular areas of expertise are retail, highways and transportation, energy, environment, listed buildings, and pipelines. Public Inquiries include: Lakeside Thurrock, Cribbs Causeway Bristol, Arbury Park Cambridge, Brent Cross Extension. M25 MSA at Woodlands Park. Both Palumbo proposals for Mansion House Square. Redevelopment of Fulham Football Club. Westminster UDP (for a consortium of Westminster property owners and the Grosvenor Estate); Trafford UDP (promoting a 1 million sq.ft. Business Park at Davenport Green); Sizewell and Hinkley Point Nuclear Power Stations; BP pipeline through the New Forest; clinical waste incinerator at Gateshead; Underground Gas Storage Caverns at Aldborough. Court Cases include: Gateshead MBC v SoS and Northumbrian Water (1996) CA (relationship between planning and Integrated Pollution Control); R v Warwickshire CC ex parte Powergen (1997) CA (relationship between s.278 Highways Act and planning); Berkley v SoS and Fulham Football Club (1998) CA (requirement for Environmental Statement and implications of failure to provide); R v West Dorset District Council ex parte Searle (1998) CA (listed building and enabling development); UK Waste Management v Department of the Environment for Northern Ireland (1999) CA Northern Ireland (judicial review of failure to issue a decision on a planning application).
Prof. Memberships: Planning and Environmental Bar Association, Committee Parliamentary Bar Mess, Administrative Law Bar Association, Committee Joint Oxford Planning Conference.

Career: Magdalene College Cambridge MA (Economics). Called to the Bar 1975. Joined present chambers in 1976. Took silk in 1995.

HIGGS, Brian QC

5 King's Bench Walk (Brian Higgs QC), London (020) 7353 5638

Recommended in Crime

HILDYARD, Robert QC

4 Stone Buildings (Philip Heslop QC), London (020) 7242 5524

Recommended in Commercial Chancery, Company, Energy & Natural Resources, Insurance

Specialisation: Principally, company law, financial services, company/commercial litigation and corporate insolvency. Specialist in insurance company transfer schemes. Other specialist work areas include insurance/reinsurance litigation and oil and gas litigation. Recent court cases include Macmillan v BIT (Maxwell litigation/conflicts of laws), NRG Victory (insurance company transfer scheme), LDDC v Regalian (restitution), Kurz v Stella Musical (choice of jurisdiction clause), Phillips Petroleum v Enron (take or pay gas sales agreement) Market Wizard Systems (UK) Ltd (public interest winding up), Hall v Bank of England (misfeasance in public office; rule in Foss v Harbottle) Charter Re ('pay to be paid' reinsurance clause). Contributor: Butterworth's Encyclopaedia of Forms and Precedents (company volume); Tolley's Company Law.

Prof. Memberships: Chancery Bar Association, Insolvency Lawyers' Association, Commercial Bar Association (COMBAR).

Career: Called to the Bar in 1977, Junior Counsel to the Crown (Chancery) 1992-94, appointed Queen's Counsel 1994. Called to the Bar of Bermuda, Cayman Islands, Turks, Caicos Islands, and Hong Kong for specific cases.

Personal: Educated at Eton College; Christ Church Oxford. Languages: Spanish.

HILL, Mark

Pump Court Chambers (Guy Boney QC), London (020) 7353 0711

Recommended in Church: Church of England

HILL, Michael QC

23 Essex Street (Michael Lawson QC), London (020) 7413 0353

Recommended in Crime, Fraud: Criminal

Specialisation: Principal area of practices are commercial fraud, international crime, homicide and professional crime.

Prof. Memberships: Criminal Bar Association (Chairman 1982-86); International Society for the Reform of Criminal Law; President (1999-date), Board of Directors (1988-date); Chairman, Management Committee (1992-95); Inns of Court Advocacy Training Committee (Chairman, 1994-date); Director, Bar Mutual Indemnity Fund Ltd (Chairman, Investment Committee 1992-date).

Career: Treasury Counsel (Inner London Sessions/Crown Court) from 1969 to 1974; Treasury counsel (Central Criminal Court) from 1974-1979; Queen's Counsel 1979; Queen's Counsel (NSW) 1991; Recorder 1977-97; called, Gray's Inn, 1958; Bencher, Gray's Inn, 1986.

HILL, Thomas

4-5 Gray's Inn Square (Elizabeth Appleby QC & Duncan Ouseley QC), London (020) 7404 5252

Recommended in Environment, Parliamentary & Public Affairs, Planning

Specialisation: Principal area of practice is planning and environmental law, in particular public inquiry work involving detailed investigation of environmental and other impacts. Recent instructions have involved proposals for major retail, housing and business development, works to listed buildings, minerals, waste and airport-related development (including successfully promoting Manchester Airport's Second Runway). Also judicial review and advisory work involving the interpretation and application of the Town and Country Planning Act 1990, the Environmental Protection Act 1990 and subordinate legislation; prosecutions under EPA. Has also apppeared in Parliament for promoters of private legislation with environmental implications.

Prof. Memberships: Planning and Environmental Bar Association (Committee Member 1990-95); Administrative Law Bar Association.

Career: Called to the Bar 1988.

HILL, Timothy

4 Field Court (Steven Gee QC), London (020) 7440 6900

Recommended in Shipping

Specialisation: Shipping; international trade; insurance. 'The Jalagouri' (1999) 1 Lloyds rep 903 Rix J; Court of Appeal. 'The Seamaas' (1999) 2 Lloyds rep 281; Court of Appeal.' The Goodpal' 27 January 2000 Colman J. 'The Sea Empress', acting for 123 claimants.

Prof. Memberships: Combar. Admiralty Bar.

Publications: Various articles in the 'International Insurance Law Review'.

HILLIARD, Lexa

3-4 South Square (Michael Crystal QC), London (020) 7696 9900

Recommended in Insolvency/Corporate Recovery

Specialisation: Insolvency, civil fraud, professional negligence, Banking, Human Rights. Lloyd's of London v Garrow [2000] 1 AER 71. Fletcher v Vooght [2000] 2 AER 221. Lloyds of London v Standen, Ionica plc (administration).

Prof. Memberships: Bar member of Insolvency Law Sub-Committee of Law Society. CEDR Accredited Mediator.

Career: Lecturer in Law, Durham University 1984-1987. Lloyds Bank Legal Department 1988. 3-4 South Square 1990-.

Publications: Contributor to 'Totty & Moss on Insolvency' (Sweet & Maxwell)

HILLIARD, Nicholas

6 King's Bench Walk (Michael Worsley QC), London (020) 7583 0410

Recommended in Crime

Specialisation: Criminal law.

Career: Treasury Counsel at the Central Criminal Court. Contributing editor to 'Archbold' and editor of the 'Criminal Appeal Reports'.

HILLIER, Andrew

11 King's Bench Walk (Eldred Tabachnik QC and James Goudie QC), London (020) 7632 8500

Recommended in Employment

HILLIER, Nicolas

9 Gough Square (Jeremy Roberts QC), London (020) 7832 0500

Recommended in Personal Injury

Specialisation: Principal areas of practice are personal injury and professional (clinical and legal) negligence litigation. Personal injury work includes both accident claims and occupational disease, particularly asbestos related diseases and noise induced deafness.

Prof. Memberships: Personal Injury Bar Association; Association of Personal Injury Lawyers.

Career: Called to the Bar in 1982. Joined present Chambers in 1983.

Personal: LL.B(Hons) Southampton University, 1977. Leisure pursuits: a young and energetic family. Born 2nd April 1956. Lives in London.

HIMSWORTH, Emma

One Essex Court (Lord Grabiner QC), London (020) 7583 2000

Recommended in Intellectual Property

Specialisation: All aspects of intellectual property law.

Prof. Memberships: The Intellectual Property Lawyers Organisation, The Intellectual Property Bar Association, The Chancery Bar Association and The Commercial Bar Association.

Career: Called 1993.

Personal: BSc in Biological Sciences with Honours in Biochemistry, Dip Law (City), Dip EC Law (Kings).

HINCHLIFF, Benjamin

1 Brick Court (Richard Rampton QC), London (020) 7353 8845

Recommended in Defamation

Specialisation: Defamation, contempt of court, reporting restrictions and media-related law generally.

Career: Called to the Bar 1992.

Personal: Educated Radley College and St John's College Oxford. Lives in London and Yorkshire.

HINCHLIFFE, Nicholas QC

9 St. John Street (John Hand QC), Manchester (0161) 955 9000

Recommended in Personal Injury

HINKS, Frank QC

Serle Court (Lord Neill of Bladen QC), London (020) 7242 6105

Recommended in Partnership, Traditional Chancery

Specialisation: Domestic and international trusts including expert evidence in relation to offshore jurisdictions: Re Ojjeh Trusts [1993] (Cayman Islands); Re Hampstead Trusts [1995] (Cayman Islands); Re 18th Aug. 1995 trust [1995] (Jersey); Wight v Olswang [1999] (trustee exemption clauses). Partnership Law: Kerr v Morris [1987]. Real property including landlord and tenant and commons: Mid-Glamorgan CC v Ogwr BC [1995] (commons). Dugan – Chapman v Grosvenor Estate Belgravia [1997] (leasehold enfranchisement), National Trust v Ashbrook [1997] (commons).

Prof. Memberships: Chancery Bar Association, Association of Contentious Trust and Probate Specialists, Association of Partnership Practitioners, COMBAR

Career: Called to Bar in 1973. Joined present chambers in 1974.

Personal: Educated at Bromley Grammar School 1961-1967; St Catherine's College,Oxford 1968-1972. BA 1st Class Hons; BCL 1st Class Hons.

HIRST, Jonathan QC

Brick Court Chambers (Christopher Clarke QC), London (020) 7379 3550

Recommended in Commercial (Litigation), Insurance, Media & Entertainment

Specialisation: General commercial law, including shipping, insurance, re-insurance, banking and professional negligence and entertainment. Recent important cases: Heaton v axa, The Times 19.7.99; Credit Lyonnair Bank Nederland v ECGD (1999) 1 Lloyd's Reps 563 (HL); JH Rayner v Cafenorte SA Importadara e Exportara SA (1999) 1 All ER (Comm) 120; Brown v GIO Insurance Ltd (CA) [1998] Lloyd's Reps IR 201; Berriman v Rose Thomson Young [1996] Lloyd's Reinsurance Law Reports 426; Axa Reinsurance (UK) v Field (HL) [1996] 2 Lloyd's Reps 233; Mother Berha Music [Phil Spector] v Bourne Music Ltd.

Prof. Memberships: QC 1990, Recorder 1997, Member General Council of the Bar (1985-); Chairman of the Professional Standards Committee, 1996-98, Chairman of the Law Reform Committee 1992-94; Chairman of the Bar Council for England & Wales (2000).

Career: Call to Bar 1975, Inner Temple, Bencher 1994.

Personal: Born 2 July 1953, London. Educated at Eton College and Trinity College, Cambridge (MA Law).

HITCHCOCK, Richard G.

35 Essex Street (Nigel Inglis-Jones QC), London (020) 7353 6381

Recommended in Pensions

Specialisation: Specialises in occupational pension schemes (particularly advising on internal trust matters including questions of contruction, scheme amendment and the use of fiduciary powers, and in all aspects of litigation in and around pension schemes, their members, employers, trustees, insurers and advisers, both before the Courts and the Pensions Ombudsmon); and employment law (particularly advising on compliance issues deriving from UK and European law, both contentious and non-contentious cases concernig the application of TUPE, actions for wrongful and unfair dismissal, race and sex discrimination and share option schemes. Cases include: McDonald v Horn, CA [1995] (pre-emptive cost orders); Century Life v Christie, ChD [1996] (Administration of multiple schemes with insolvent employer/ trustee); Hillsdown Holdings plc v Pensions Ombudsman, ChD [1996] (legality of payment of surplus to employer; Franklin v Sedgwick Noble Lowndes, ChD [1999] (claims against scheme actuaries and administrators); Legal & General v Pensions Obudsman, ChD [1999] (appeal against and application for judicial review of Ombudsman's preliminary determination.); Lansing Linde v Alber and others, ChD [1999] (rectification of pension scheme deeds); Norris and 131 others v Brown & Root Ltd. [1999] (outsourcing, TUPE, collective agreements: group action claiming breach of contract, unfair and wrongful dismissal). Has spoken at many conferences and seminars.

Prof. Memberships: Chancery Bar Association, Association of Pensions Lawyers, Employment Lawyers Association, Western Circuit.

Career: Called to the Bar in 1989 and joined chambers at 35 Essex Street in 1990.

Personal: Educated at King Edward's School, Birmingham (1977-84) and Magdalen College Oxford (1985-88). Interests include wine (tasting and consulting), France and Italy, modern European and American painting, theatre and scuba diving.

HITCHMOUGH, Andrew

Pump Court Tax Chambers (Andrew Thornhill QC), London (020) 7414 8080

Recommended in VAT

Specialisation: Practices in all areas of revenue law, including VAT and customs duties, both advisory and litigation.

Prof. Memberships: Revenue Bar Association; VAT Practitioners Group; Law Society VAT and Duties Sub-Committee. Publications: Co-editor of 'Potter Monroe's Tax Planning'; 'Ray's Practical Inheritance Tax Planning'. Managing Editor, 'Personal Tax Planning Review'.

HOBBS, Geoffrey QC

One Essex Court (Lord Grabiner QC), London (020) 7583 2000

Recommended in Information Technology, Intellectual Property

HOBSON, John QC

4-5 Gray's Inn Square (Elizabeth Appleby QC & Duncan Ouseley QC), London (020) 7404 5252

Recommended in Planning

Specialisation: Public law, local government, planning and environmental law.

Prof. Memberships: Admininstrative Law Bar Association; Planning and Environmental Bar Association.

Career: Former Solicitor, Called to Bar 1980. 1995-1996 Specialist Adviser to the Northern Ireland Affairs Committee of the House of Commons for its enquiry into the planning system in Northern Ireland. 1992-2000: Supplementary Panel of Treasury Commissioners. 1997-2000: Standing Counsel to the Rent Assessment Panel. Assistant Recorder 1999. Queen's Counsel 2000. Recorder 2000.

Personal: LLM (St John's College, Cambridge).

HOCHBERG, Daniel

9 Old Square (Michael Driscoll QC), London (020) 7405 4682

Recommended in Commercial Chancery

Specialisation: "Commercial Chancery" and a wide range of general chancery litigation including offshore trust litigation, real property, business agreements, professional negligence, succession, securities and loans, insolvency and landlord and tenant. Cases include West v Lazards (Jersey breach of trust), Blampied v Ram (Jersey trust application), Midland Bank v Federated Pension Fund (breach of trust and exemption clauses), Co-Operative v Tesco (restrictive covenants), Hammersmith & Fulham v Tops Shop Centre (relief from forfeiture), Wates v Citygate Properties (section 25 notice); Greenhaven Motors Ltd (insolvency); Prestwich v Royal Bank of Canada (Jersey) (off-shore trusts, tax indemnities), Corbett v Boun Pearce (solicitors negligence).

Prof. Memberships: Chancery Bar Association; Association of Contentious Trust and Probate Specialists.

HOCHHAUSER, Andrew QC

Essex Court Chambers (Gordon Pollock QC), London (020) 7813 8000

Recommended in Commercial (Litigation), Employment

Specialisation: Areas of practice include arbitration, banking, breach of contract, company law, commercial fraud, entertainment cases, employment, partnership disputes, professional negligence, takeovers, mergers and share sale disputes.

Prof. Memberships: Fellow of the Chartered Institute of Arbitrators; Member of Gibraltan Bar.

Career: University of Bristol (LL.B), University of London (LL.M). Called to the English Bar 1977. Harmsworth Scholar of Middle Temple. Queen's Counsel 1997.

Personal: Born 1955.

HOCKTON, Andrew

6 Pump Court (Kieran Coonan QC), London (020) 7583 6013

Recommended in Clinical Negligence

HODGE, David QC

9 Old Square (Michael Driscoll QC), London (020) 7405 4682

Recommended in Professional Negligence, Property Litigation

Specialisation: Principal areas of practice are general Chancery and property litigation and related professional negligence, particularly solicitors, barristers and valuers. Important cases include Graham v Philcox [1984] (easements); TCB v Gray [1986-88] (guarantees); Sharma v Knight [1986] (landlord and tenant); Bank of Baroda v Shah [1988] (undue influence); Sen v Headley [1991] (equity), HIT Finance v Lewis & Tucker [1993] (professional negligence); Mortgage Corporation v Nationwide Credit [1994] (registered land); Ridehalgh v Horsefield [1994] (wasted costs); Allied Maples v Simmons & Simmons [1995] (professional negligence); Garston v Scottish Widows [1996-98] (landlord & tenant); Railtrack v Gojra [1998] (landlord and tenant); Lemmerbell v Britannia LAS Direct [1998] (landlord and tenant); Bristol & West v Bhadresa [1999] (costs). Contributed chapter on Chancery Matters to the 4th Edition of 'The Law and Practice of Compromise' by David Foskett QC.

Prof. Memberships: Chancery Bar Association. Professional Negligence Bar Association.

Career: Called to bar in 1979. Joined 9 Old Square in 1980. QC 1997. Assistant Recorder 1998. Recorder 2000.

Personal: Born 1956. Educated at University College, Oxford 1974-1978 (BA, BCL). Author of 'Secret Trusts: The Fraud Theory Revisited' (1980) Conveyancer. Chairman, Lincoln's Inn Bar Representation Committee 1997-1998.

HODGSON, Margaret

St. Ive's Chambers (Edward Coke), Birmingham (0121) 236 0863

Recommended in Family/Matrimonial

Specialisation: Private matrimonial: residence/contact; financial ancillary relief; adoption. Public family law: child care; freeing; adoption. Representation of parents, local authorities and guardians ad litem. Cases: G and others (minors) and R (A minor) ex parte, R v Birmingham Juvenile Court [1989] CA 2 FLR 454. Re P (Minors) (Breakdown of Adoption Placement) F.D. (1996) 3 FCR 657.

Prof. Memberships: Family Law Bar Association.

Career: Warwick University LL.B. (Hons). Deputy Head of Chambers. Pupil master.

HOFMEYR, Stephen QC

7 King's Bench Walk (Jeremy Cooke QC), London (020) 7910 8300

Recommended in Insurance, Shipping

Specialisation: Practice encompasses insurance and reinsurance (both marine and non-marine) and shipping and maritime law. Most recent cases include Petrotrade Inc. v Smith (Port agency dispute); Shell UK Ltd. v CLM Engineering (Marine Insurance); the Metro litigation (oil fraud); Raiffeisen Zentralbank Osterreich AG and others v Crosseas Shipping and Others (Bank guarantee); Royal Boskalis v Mountain; Manifest Shipping v Uni-Polaris Insurance (the 'Starsea'), (both marine insurance); Glencore v Bank of China (letters of credit); L'Alsacienne v Unistorebrand (reinsurance); Brown v KMR (Lloyd's litigation). Other specialisations include all aspects of commercial law (arbitration, aviation, banking, oil and gas and professional negligence). His combination of legal and accounting qualifications makes him particularly suited to these areas of the law.

Prof. Memberships: COMBAR.

Career: A Rhodes Scholar from Cape Town, commenced practice at the Bar in 1987, having previously practised as an attorney and conveyancer in South Africa. Also an advocate of the Supreme Court of South Africa.

Personal: Educated at Diocesan College, Rondebosch, Cape Town, University of Cape Town (B. Com 1974-1976) and University College, Oxford (MA, Jurisprudence, 1979-81). Leisure pursuits include walking, birdwatching, tennis and skiing. Born 10th February 1956. Lives in Guildford.

HOGGETT, John QC

40 King St (Philip Raynor QC), Manchester (0161) 832 9082

Recommended in Planning

Specialisation: Town planning, compulsory purchase, highways, environment law & judicial review.

Prof. Memberships: Northern Circuit; Planning & Environment Bar Association.

Career: Called 1969, Queen's Counsel 1986, Recorder of the Crown Court.

HOLGATE, David QC

4 Breams Buildings (Christopher Lockhart-Mummery QC), London (020) 7430 1221/7353 5835

Recommended in Administrative & Public Law: General, Agriculture, Environment, Planning

Specialisation: Judicial review, planning, compulsory

purchase, rating, local government, environment law and property law. Reported cases covering a wide field include Bushell v Secretary of State, Shimizu v Westminster City Council, Coventry and Solihull Waste Disposal Co v Russell, Surrey Free Inns v Gosport BC, Regina v Hillingdon London Borough ex parte London Regional Transport, R v Secretary of State for Social Services ex p. AMA, R v Somerset CC ex p. Fewings, and Chesterfield Properties v Secretary of State, and, in the Lands Tribunal, Glasshouse Properties v DTp and Fennessy v London City Airport. Has appeared for government bodies, local authorities, developers and local objectors in a broad range of public inquiries including Sizewell B, Canvey Island, Piper Alpha, and Point of Ayr Gas Terminal.
Career: Called to Bar in 1978. Formerly a member of the panel of Junior Counsel to the Crown (1986-1997) and Junior Counsel to the Inland Revenue in Rating and Valuation matters (1990-1997). Queen's Counsel (1997).
Personal: Graduated in Law from Exeter College, Oxford.

HOLLAND, Charles
Trinity Chambers (A.T. Hedworth QC), Newcastle upon Tyne (0191) 232 1927
Recommended in Licensing
Specialisation: Commercial and licensing. Commercial work includes contract, company and partnership, landlord and tenant and professional negligence. Liquor, gaming, public entertainment and taxi licensing matters, advising and representing applicants and objectors at all levels of tribunal.
Prof. Memberships: North Eastern Circuit, Association of Licensing Practitioners.
Career: Called to the Bar in 1994. Practised at Trinity Chambers since 1996. Civil representative, North Eastern Bar Press Office, Newcastle Bar 1999-. Junior Counsel to the Crown (Provincial Panel) 2000-.
Personal: Born in North Yorkshire in 1969. Educated Oundle School, University of Nottingham (LL.B. Law).

HOLLAND, Katharine
9 Old Square (Michael Driscoll QC), London (020) 7405 4682
Recommended in Property Litigation
Specialisation: All aspects of property litigation, including commercial and residential property disputes, surveyors' and solicitors' professional negligence, mortgages, landlord and tenant, leasehold enfranchisement, conveyancing, easements, restrictive covenants, property rights, insolvency and commercial contracts. Reported cases include Wentworth v Wiltshire (highways), Millman v Ellis (easements), Charville v Unipart Group (forfeiture/surrender) Titanic Investments v Macfarlandes (solicitors' negligence) Gregory v Shepherds (solicitors' negligence) Kaiser v Jones (rectification), Lloyds Bank v Burd Pearce (solicitors' negligence), Lloyds Bank v Parker Bullen (solicitors' negligence), Carroll v Manek and Bank of India (mortgages/ adverse possession)
Prof. Memberships: Chancery Bar Association and Professional Negligence Bar Association.
Career: Called to the Bar in 1989 and joined *9 Old Square* in 1990.
Personal: Educated at Lady Manners School, Bakewell and Hertford College, Oxford (BA, BCL).

HOLLANDER, Charles QC
Brick Court Chambers (Christopher Clarke QC), London (020) 7379 3550
Recommended in Commercial (Litigation), Sport
Specialisation: Commercial including city litigation, energy, financial services, regulatory tribunals, professional negligence, media and sports law. Commercial cases: Re Barings (for Ron Baker), Maxwell, B&C, Polly Peck, local authority swaps, NRG v Bacon & Woodrow, Sarrio v KIO, Paragon v Freshfields, Westacre v Jugoimport, Astra v Yasuda, Sinochem v Mobil Sales, Stabilad v Stephens & Carter, IM Properties v Cape&Dalgleish; energy: Petrogal v BP, Enron North Sea litigation, Media and sport: Drug testing, Katrina Krabbe and Sandra Gasser, Glolite v Jasper Conran (football logos), Wolves v Leicester FC; Ossie Clark Diaries, Caroline Quentin litigation.
Career: Became Queens Counsel in 1999.
Publications: 'Conflicts of interest and Chinese Walls', Documentary Evidence (7th ed in preparation), 'Phipson on Evidence' (15th ed).

HOLLINGTON, Robin QC
1 New Square (Eben Hamilton QC), London (020) 7405 0884
Recommended in Commercial Chancery, Company, Insolvency/Corporate Recovery
Specialisation: Principal areas of work are company law and insolvency. Author of 'Minority Shareholders' Rights' (Sweet & Maxwell, 3rd Ed. 1999).
Prof. Memberships: Chancery Bar Association.
Career: Called to the Bar 1979 and joined 1 New Square 1981. QC 1999.
Personal: Educated at Oxford University 1974-1977 (MA) and University of Pennsylvania 1977-1978 (LL.M). Born 30th June 1955.

HOLROYDE, Tim QC
Exchange Chambers (William Waldron QC), Liverpool (0151) 236 7747
Recommended in Crime

HOLWILL, Derek
4 Paper Buildings (Jean Ritchie QC), London (020) 7353 3366
Recommended in Clinical Negligence, Professional Negligence
Specialisation: Principal area of practice is professional negligence including clinical negligence cases. Acts both for defendant insurance companies, Solicitors Indemnity Fund and Health Authorities, and for plaintiffs including mortgage lenders. Also handles commercial litigation, insurance litigation and general common law work, including personal injury cases. Reported cases include Landall v Dennis Faulkner and Alsop; Saddington v Colleys Professional Services; Halifax plc v Gould & Swayne and others; TSB plc v Robert Irving and Burns; John A Pike v Independant Insurance Co.
Prof. Memberships: Professional Negligence Bar Association
Career: Called to the Bar 1982 and joined present chambers 1983.
Personal: Leisure pursuits include Lindy Hop, scuba diving and travel. Born on 25th September 1959. Lives in London.

HOPKINS, Adrian
3 Serjeants' Inn (Philip Naughton QC), London (020) 7427 5000
Recommended in Clinical Negligence

HOPKINS, Philippa
Essex Court Chambers (Gordon Pollock QC), London (020) 7813 8000
Recommended in Shipping
Specialisation: Commercial practice in line with chambers profile. In particular: aviation; banking; carriage of goods; commercial arbitration; commercial shipping (dry work); commodity and international arbitration; finance of international trade; general commercial and contract (including sale of goods); insurance and reinsurace; international trade; professional negligence; public and private international law.
Career: BA, BCL, Merton College, Oxford. Called to the Bar in 1994.
Personal: Born 1971.

HOPKINS, Stephen
30 Park Place (John Jenkins QC), Cardiff (029) 2039 8421
Recommended in Crime

HORNE, Michael
3 Serjeants' Inn (Philip Naughton QC), London (020) 7427 5000
Recommended in Clinical Negligence
Specialisation: Medical and dental negligence (claimant and defendant), medical and dental disciplinary hearings, coroners' inquests.
Prof. Memberships: Professional Negligence Bar Association.
Career: Royal Grammar School, Newcastle-upon-Tyne (1977-87), Trinity Hall, Cambridge (1988-1991), Called to the Bar October 1992 (Gray's Inn).
Publications: Contributing Editor, Lloyds Reports, Medical.
Personal: Leisure interests: rugby, football, skiing, scuba diving and walking. Born 24th November 1969.

HOROWITZ, Michael QC
1 Mitre Court Buildings (Bruce Blair QC), London (020) 7797 7070
Recommended in Family: Child Care including child abduction, Family: Matrimonial Finance
Specialisation: Family law, including ancillary relief, childcare and child abduction. Contributing Editor Rayden & Jackson on Divorce 17th edition and Butterworths Bulletin 'Human Rights Act 1998 and Family Law'. Essential Family Practice 2000.
Prof. Memberships: Director Bar Mutual Indemnity Fund Ltd.

HORROCKS, Peter
One Garden Court Family Law Chambers (Eleanor Platt QC and Alison Ball QC), London (020) 7797 7900
p.horrocks@onegardencourt.co.uk
Recommended in Family: Child Care including child abduction
Specialisation: Principal area of practice is child law, both public and private, including disputes as to residence and contact, care proceedings, wardship, adoption and abduction cases under the Hague and European Conventions. Frequently advises and represents local authorities and guardians-ad-litem as well as private clients. Other areas of work include child-related criminal cases, probate, boundaries and easements.
Prof. Memberships: Family Law Bar Association.
Career: Called to the Bar in 1977; joined present chambers in 1996.
Personal: Educated at Winchester 1968-1972, Trinity Hall, Cambridge 1973-1976 and College of Law 1976-1977. Leisure pursuits include real tennis, cricket and opera. Born 31st January 1955. Lives in London.

HORTON, Mark
Collection Chambers (Martin Meeke), Exeter (01392) 274898
chambers@collection-exeter.freeserve.co.uk
Recommended in Crime, Family/Matrimonial
Specialisation: Public and pivate law childcare and ancillary relief.
Prof. Memberships: Family Law Bar Association.
Career: Family specialist since 1990

HORTON, Matthew QC
2 Mitre Court Buildings (Michael FitzGerald QC), London (020) 7583 1380
Recommended in Planning
Specialisation: A genuine all rounder within the fields of parliamentary, public and administrative law, local government, environmental, town and country planning, compensation, rating, landlord and tenant and related areas of European law, property law and professional negligence.

Prof. Memberships: Admistrative Law Bar Association. Planning and Environmental Bar Association. Elected Member of Parliamentary Bar. Former Committee Member of Joint Planning Law Conference.
Career: Called 1969, took Silk 1989. A standing counsel to the Department of the Environment on Land Commission matters (1973).
Personal: Educated at Sevenoaks School and Trinity Hall, Cambridge MA (Law 1st Class Hons) and LLM (English and Private International Law; (open Exhibitioner and Foundation Scholar (Trinity Hall) Squire Law Scholar (University of Cambridge), Astbury Scholar (Middle Temple). Fluent in French, some Russian. Organic farmer. Keen skier. Born 23 September 1946

HORWELL, Richard

Queen Elizabeth Building (Julian Bevan QC & Peter Whiteman QC), London (020) 7583 5766
Recommended in Crime, Fraud: Criminal
Specialisation: General crime. Counsel for the Serious Fraud Office in Lloyds and Guinness. Defended in MTM.
Career: Senior Treasury Counsel.

HOSER, Philip

Serle Court (Lord Neill of Bladen QC), London (020) 7242 6105
Recommended in Commercial Chancery, Company, Insolvency/Corporate Recovery
Specialisation: Company Law: Re Bermuda Cablevision Ltd [1998] BCLC 1 (P.C) and ongoing petition in Bermuda. Re Duckwari (Nos. 1 & 2) [1995] BCC 89 (CA); [1997] ch 201 (H.Ct); [1999] BCC 11 (CA). Insolvency: Re Richbell Strategic Holdings Ltd. [1997] 2BCLC 429. Guarantees: Kova Establishment v Sasco Investments, The Times, 1998; Partnership: Hurst v Bryk [2000] 2 A11 E.R 193 (HL)
Prof. Memberships: Chancery Bar Association. Association of Partnership Practitioners.
Career: MA (Cantab), called 1982. Joined Serle Court Chambers 1997.

HOSKINS, Mark

Brick Court Chambers (Christopher Clarke QC), London (020) 7379 3550
Recommended in Sport
Specialisation: Principal area of practice is European law. Has acted in over 30 cases before ECJ/CFI, including: Case C-321/95P Greenpeace [1998] ECR I-1651, Case C-265/95 Commission v France [1997] ECR I-6959, Case T-85/98 Federation Internationale de l'Automobile v Commission, order of 6.12.99, Case C-219/98 Anastasiou (pending).
Career: Called to Bar 1991. Legal Secretary to Judge David Edward, European Court of Justice, Luxembourg, 1994-1995. Member of B Panel to the Crown. Co-author of 'Remedies in EC Law' (2nd ed., Sweet & Maxwell).

HOWARD, Charles QC

One King's Bench Walk (Anthony Hacking QC), London (020) 7936 1500
Recommended in Family: Matrimonial Finance

HOWARD, M.N. QC

4 Essex Court (Nigel Teare QC), London (020) 7653 5653
mhoward@4sx.co.uk
Recommended in Arbitration (International), Shipping
Specialisation: Principal areas of practice are international commercial and shipping law, including insurance, international trade and sale of goods. Extensive experience of arbitrations both as Counsel and as arbitrator in many international arbitrations connected with international trade, shipping or insurance. Acts for shipowners, charterers, insurers, P&I clubs and salvage companies.
Prof. Memberships: COMBAR, London Common Law and Commercial Bar Association.
Career: Called to the Bar Gray's Inn 1971 (Bencher 1995). Tenant at *Queen Elizabeth Building* 1972-1989. Took Silk 1986. Member of the Panel of Salvage Arbitrators appointed by the Committee of Lloyd's since 1989. Joined Essex Court in 1990. Appointed Recorder 1993. Leader of the Admiralty Bar 2000.
Personal: Educated at Clifton College, 1960-1964 and Magdalen College, Oxford 1965-1970 (MA BCL). Leisure pursuits include books, music and sport. Born 10th June 1947. Lives in London. Other: General editor, 'Phipson on Evidence' (15th Ed 2000), Contributor of 'Frustration and Shipping Law' in 'Frustration and Force Majeure' (ed McKendrick, 2nd edn 1995), 'Foreign Currency Judgments in Contract Claims' in 'Consensus Ad Idem: Essays for 'Guenter Treitel' (ed Rose, 1996) Hallshug, Laws of England, title, Damages and author of articles in legal periodicals. Visiting Professor of Law, Essex University 1987-1992, Visiting Professor of Maritime Law, University College, London 1996-1999. Member, Editorial Board, Lloyd's Maritime Commercial Law Quarterly.

HOWARD, Mark QC

Brick Court Chambers (Christopher Clarke QC), London (020) 7379 3550
Recommended in Banking, Commercial (Litigation), Insurance, Professional Negligence
Specialisation: All areas of commercial law, particularly City disputes and takeovers, insurance, reinsurance, banking and financial services, arbitration, major contract disputes, accountants', brokers' and lawyers' negligence, commercial fraud, international trade and arbitration, DTI and similar investigations.
Prof. Memberships: Combar, LCLCBA
Career: Called to Bar in 1980, took silk in 1996. Recent important reported cases in which involved include: Banco Santander v Banque Paribas; CATS v TGTL; Sphere Drake v Orion; Deepak v ICI; East European Shipping (Market wide X/L reinsurance dispute); WSTC vCoopers & Lybrand; Axa v Field; CU v Mander; Henderson v Merrett and Ernst & Whinney; Denny v Walker, Willis Corroon and others; CNW v Girozentrale; Kuwait Airways Corporation v Kuwait Insurance Company; B&C v Samuel Montagu v BZW; Sudwestdeutsche Landesbank v Bank of Tokyo; Jones v Sherwood; AMF v Hashim; Channel Tunnel Group v Balfour Beatty. He has advised and acted for various parties in relation to a number of DTI and similar inquiries. Currently retained for auditors in relation to Barings litigation.
Personal: Born 1st April 1958. Educated at University of London – QMC and LSE (LL.B, 1978; LL.M,1979).

HOWARTH, Simon

Crown Office Chambers (Michael Spencer QC & Christopher Purchas QC), London (020) 7797 8100
howarth@crownofficechambers.com
Recommended in Professional Negligence
Specialisation: Professional negligence, insurance, contract, building and engineering, personal injury. Recent cases: Phelps v LB of Hillingdon [1999] 1 WLR 500; Johnson v Gore Wood [1999] LI Rep (PN) 45.
Prof. Memberships: PNBA, LCLCBA, PIBA.
Career: B.A. (Oxon). Called to Bar October 1991 by Gray's Inn. Inn Scholarships: Mould Senior Scholarship Advocacy Prize.
Publications: Editor – 'Emden's Construction Law'.

HOWE, Martin QC

8 New Square (Michael Fysh QC SC), London (020) 7405 4321
martin.howe@8newsquare.co.uk
Recommended in Information Technology, Intellectual Property
Specialisation: Specialist in intellectual property (patents, trade marks, copyrights, designs, confidential information etc), and European Community law relating both to intellectual property and other fields. Many high technology cases, with particular emphasis on the computing, information and internet field; also extensive experience in biotechnology/genetic engineering cases. Regularly appears before the European Court of Justice, Luxembourg, and the European Patent Office, Munich. Important recent cases include: R v MAFF ex parte Monsanto PLC Case C-306/98,ECJ, heard March 2000, judgment awaited - judicial review of validity of agrochemical product licence; Celltech Therapeutics/Antibodies Case T400/97, European Patent Office Technical Board of Appeals, May 2000 - patent for the production of antibodies by recombinant DNA technology; Merck v Primecrown Ltd [1997] 1 CMLR 83; [1997] FSR 237; Joined Cases C-267/95 and C-268/95, ECJ - parallel importation of pharmaceuticals; Biogen Inc v Medeva PLC [1997] RPC 1, House of Lords - Patent for the production of Hepatitis B virus antigens for use in vaccines by recombinant DNA technology.
Career: Called to the Bar 1978; QC 1996.
Publications: Include 'Halsbury's Laws' title on Trade Marks (1984 and 1995, jnt ed with Mr Justice Jacob); 'Europe and the Constitution after Maastricht' (Nelson & Pollard, Oxford, 1993); 'Russell-Clarke on Industrial Designs' (sole ed, 1998).
Personal: Educated at Winchester College 1968-72 and at Trinity Hall, Cambridge BA 1973-1977, MA 1979. Baker Prize for Engineering 1974. Tripos Part I (Engineering) 1975, 1st class. Tripos Part II (Law) 1977, class 2:1. Everard ver Heyden Prize (for advocacy) 1978.

HOWE, Robert

Blackstone Chambers (P Baxendale QC and C Flint QC), London (020) 7583 1770
roberthowe@blackstonechambers.com
Recommended in Commercial (Litigation), Media & Entertainment, Sport

HOWE, Timothy

Fountain Court (Anthony Boswood QC), London (020) 7583 3335
Recommended in Banking
Specialisation: Civil and commercial litigation (domestic and international), including banking and financial services, international trade, insurance and reinsurance, professional negligence, mergers and acquisitions, oil and gas energy law and commercial arbitration; cases include: Mannesmann A.G. v Goldman Sachs; Morgan Grenfell v SACE; Lloyd's Names Litigation; British and Commonwealth v Atlantic Computers; Polly Peck International v StoyHayward; B Sky B v Bond Corporation; BBL v Eagle Star Insurance and US$2 billion Thyssen litigation in Bermuda. Clients include major clearing, investment and merchant banks, leading insurers and reinsurers, FTSE 100 companies and City accountancy and law firms.
Prof. Memberships: Secretary and Executive Committee Member, COMBAR.
Career: Called 1987. Bermudian Bar 1998. Queen Mother's, Harmsworth and Astbury Scholarships, Middle Temple.
Publications: Co-editor, 'Commercial Court Procedure' (Sweet & Maxwell 1999)
Personal: St. Paul's School and Magdalen College, Oxford (MA 1st Class Hons 1985). Co-author, 'Law of Bank Payments' (Longmans, 1996). Co-editor 'Commercial Court Procedure' (Sweet & Maxwell 1999/2000).

HOWELL, John QC
4 Breams Buildings (Christopher Lockhart-Mummery QC), London
(020) 7430 1221/7353 5835
4bbhowell@compuserve.com
Recommended in Administrative & Public Law: General, Planning
Specialisation: Public law, human rights, tortious liability and public bodies, local government law including local government powers, decision making and finance, planning highways compulsory purchase and compensation, rating, education, social services, social security, housing, environment law, immigration and asylum, public utilities and procurement and European law.
Prof. Memberships: Committee member of the Administrative Law Bar Association and a member of the Planning and Environment Bar Association.
Career: Queen's College, Oxford. Called 1979, Queen's Counsel (1993).

HOWELL WILLIAMS, Craig
2 Harcourt Buildings (Mr Gerard Ryan QC), London (020) 7353 8415
Recommended in Planning
Specialisation: Town and country planning and environment law.
Prof. Memberships: Planning and Environment Bar Association; Parliamentary Bar.
Career: Called to the Bar in 1983. Junior Counsel to the Crown ('B' Panel) (1993-1999); PEBA Secretary (1994-1996).
Personal: Chairman of the London Luton Airport Consultative Committee.

HUDSON, Rachel
Trinity Chambers (A.T. Hedworth QC), Newcastle upon Tyne (0191) 232 1927
rachel.hudson@ukonline.co.uk
Recommended in Family/Matrimonial
Specialisation: All aspects of family law, with particular emphasis on care work (acting for local authorities, parents and GALs) and ancillary relief. In recent years has been involved in a large number of significant High Court cases. During the past year these have included issues of consent to medical treatment, fabricated illness and allegations of unlawful killing. Head of the *Trinity Chambers* Family Group and the Bar representative on the Newcastle upon Tyne Family Court Business Committee. *Trinity Chambers'* pupillage and equal opportunities representative.
Prof. Memberships: FLBA, BAAF, North Eastern Circuit.
Career: Called to the Bar in 1985. Practised at *Trinity Chambers* since 1986.
Personal: Born in 1963. Educated at Newcastle upon Tyne Church High School and Queen Elizabeth Grammar School, Hexham. London School of Economics (LL.B. Law). Away from the Bar enjoys spending time with her family, music, sport and eating out.

HUGHES, Adrian
4 Pump Court (Bruce Mauleverer QC), London
(020) 7353 2656
Recommended in Construction
Specialisation: Broad commercial practice which includes insurance and reinsurance, shipping, commodities, construction and engineering, and environmental law work. He has a particular interest in public and private international law.
Prof. Memberships: Court Examiner; Lloyd's Arbitrator; CEDR Accredited Mediator. Chairman China Law Council; Bar Council International Committee (Chairman of Far East Sub-Committee); London Common Law and Commercial Bar Association (Committee); Society of Construction Law (Council Member).
Career: Royal Naval Officer (1977-1984). Called to the Bar 1984; practising from *4 Pump Court*.
Personal: Educated at Warwick School and Wadham College, Oxford.

HUGHES, Iain QC
Four New Square (Justin Fenwick QC), London
(020) 7822 2000
i.hughes@4newsquare.com
Recommended in Professional Negligence
Specialisation: Principal area of practice is professional negligence and general common law. Work covers all aspects of professional negligence. Editor, 'Jackson and Powell on Professional Negligence'.
Prof. Memberships: Professional Negligence Bar Association.
Career: Called to the Bar 1974 and joined current chambers in 1977. Silk in 1996. Vice-chairman Professional Negligence Bar Association 1998-1999; chairman 2000.

HUGHES, Judith QC
1 Mitre Court Buildings (Bruce Blair QC), London
(020) 7797 7070
Recommended in Family: Child Care including child abduction
Specialisation: Specialises in family law, dealing with children's cases both public and private law, ancillary relief and child abduction. Became a QC in 1994 and a bencher of the Inner Temple 1994, Recorder 1995 and Deputy High Court Judge 1997.

HUMPHREYS, Richard
4-5 Gray's Inn Square (Elizabeth Appleby QC & Duncan Ouseley QC), London (020) 7404 5252
Recommended in Planning

HUMPHRIES, Michael
2 Mitre Court Buildings (Michael FitzGerald QC), London (020) 7583 1380
Recommended in Planning
Specialisation: Practices principally in the areas of Town and Country Planning and Compulsory Purchase and Compensation. Has acted on behalf of many high profile clients including BAA plc at the Heathrow Terminal 5 public inquiry and Union Rail Property in relation to compulsory purchase and compensation issues arising from the Channel Tunnel Rail Link.
Prof. Memberships: Committee member of the Planning and Environmental Bar Association. Committee member of the Joint Planning Law Conference, Oxford. Member of the Anglo-American Real Property Institute.
Career: Called to the Bar in 1982 and joined current chambers in 1983.
Publications: Senior editor of Butterworths 'Compulsory Purchase and Compensation Service'. Lectured extensively on compulsory purchase and compensation issues.
Personal: Born 1959. Studied law at the University of Leicester. Married with two children. Leisure pursuits include reading, music and travel with family.

HUNJAN, Satinder
5 Fountain Court (Anthony Barker QC), Birmingham (0121) 606 0500
Recommended in Clinical Negligence

HUNT, James QC
36 Bedford Row (Michael Pert QC), Northampton (01604) 602333
Recommended in Crime

HUNT, Murray
Matrix Chambers (Nicholas Blake QC), London
(020) 7404 3447
Recommended in Administrative & Public Law: General, Human Rights (Civil Liberties)

HUNTER, Ian QC
Essex Court Chambers (Gordon Pollock QC), London (020) 7813 8000
Recommended in Arbitration (International), Aviation, Insurance
Specialisation: Broad-based commercial practice. More particularly arbitration, aviation, banking, conflict of laws, European law, financial services, insurance & reinsurance, international commercial fraud, professional negligence & shipping.
Career: Pembroke College, Cambridge MA (Law; double first) 1966; LL.B 1967; Harvard Law School, Cambridge, USA LL.M 1968. Called to the English Bar 1967; Called to the Bar of New South Wales 1993; Queen's Counsel 1980; Bencher 1986; Recorder 1986; Deputy High Court Judge 1993.
Personal: Born 1944. Fluent French.

HUNTER, Winston QC
Recommended in Personal Injury

HUSAIN, Raza
Matrix Chambers (Nicholas Blake QC), London
(020) 7404 3447
Recommended in Immigration

HUTTON, Caroline
Enterprise Chambers (Anthony Mann QC), London (020) 7405 9471
carolinehutton@enterprisechambers.com
Recommended in Agriculture, Property Litigation
Specialisation: Practice covers all aspects of real property law, principally landlord and tenant (commercial, agricultural and residential) and including conveyancing, boundaries, easements, equitable rights and trusts of land, mortgages and professional negligence, insolvency and fraud matters related to major property. Major cases included Saunders v Edwards; Culworth Estates v Licensed Victuallers; Aspen Properties v Ratcliffe and Ponderosa v Pengap. Clients include property companies, retailers and banks. Contributed to many commercial conferences on landlord and tenant.
Prof. Memberships: Justice, Association of Women Barristers, BEG.
Career: Called to the Bar 1979 and joined *Enterprise Chambers* 1981. Chairman Disciplinary and Appeals Tribunal for licensed conveyancing 1988-1993. Fellow of Chartered Institute of Arbitrators.
Publications: Co-editor of 'Commercial Property Disputes' (Sweet & Maxwell, 1999).
Personal: Educated at Clare College, Cambridge 1975-1978. Leisure pursuits include embroidery, reading, walking, theatre and art history. Born 25th March 1956. Lives in London with MP husband and two sons.

IFE, Linden
Enterprise Chambers (Anthony Mann QC), London (020) 7405 9471
Recommended in Commercial Chancery, Company, Insolvency/Corporate Recovery
Specialisation: Principal area of practice is commercial chancery, including insolvency, company, commercial agreements, property, professional negligence, banking and securities and financial services. Regularly receives instructions from major clearing banks and other financial institutions, and from insolvency practitioners. Recent cases include Sterling Estates v Pickard [1997] (lease disclaimer by liquidator), TSB v Platts [1997] (cross-claims in bankruptcy), Re Double S Printers Limited [1998] (fixed and floating charges). Member of the Association of Business Recovery Professionals.

INGLIS-JONES, Nigel J. QC
35 Essex Street (Nigel Inglis-Jones QC), London (020) 7353 6381
Recommended in Pensions
Specialisation: Has 40 years experience as an occupational pensions schemes specialist. Also deals with other trusts, contract, tort and criminal fraud. Major cases handled include Re Imperial Foods Pension Scheme; Re Courage Group's Pension Schemes [1987]; Mettoy Pension Trustee v Evans [1990]; Davis v Richards & Wallington Industries Ltd [1990]; LRT Pension Fund Trustee Co Ltd v Hatt & others [1993]; British Coal Corporation v British Coal Staff Superannuation Scheme [1994]; Re Prudential Assurance Pension Scheme; Century Life and Britannia Life v Pensions Ombudsman [1995]; Hillsdown Holdings plc v Pensions Ombudsman [1996]; Legal and General Assurance Lillertech v Pensions Ombudsman [1999] and Re British Airways Pension Schemes [2000]. Re National Grid Group of the Electricity Supply Pension Scheme [1997, 1998 and 1999]. Author of 'The Law of Occupational Pension Schemes' (Sweet & Maxwell). Has spoken at and chaired many conferences and seminars.
Prof. Memberships: Chancery Bar Association, Association of Pensions Lawyers, Western Circuit. Bencher of the Inner Temple since 1982.
Career: National Service with the Grenadier Guards (subaltern) 1953-1955. Called to the Bar in 1959 and joined chambers at Essex Street in 1960. Took Silk in 1982. Recorder 1978-1993. Deputy Social Security Commissioner since 1993.
Personal: Educated at Eton College 1948-1953 and Trinity College, Oxford 1955-1958. Leisure pursuits include fishing, collecting English drinking glass and English miniature glass, gardening and travelling. A member of the congregation of St Paul's church, Onslow Square. Born 7th May 1935. Lives in London.

INGRAM, Nigel
2 Bedford Row (formerly 3 Hare Court) (William Clegg QC), London (020) 7440 8888
Recommended in Fraud: Criminal
Specialisation: Principal area of practice is commercial crime. Senior Standing Counsel to the Department of Trade and Industry since 1990 and has prosecuted a large number of serious and complex cases on their behalf as well as extensive advisory work. Prosecuting counsel (A list) for H M Customs & Excise since 1993 and has conducted substantial VAT and drugs prosecutions for them as well as advisory work on EU Law and UK tariff offences. Instructed as prosecuting counsel to H M Inland Revenue. Has acted as leading counsel for the Defence in numerous cases of white collar crime and drugs importations.
Prof. Memberships: CBA.

INMAN, Melbourne QC
1 Fountain Court (David Crigman QC), Birmingham (0121) 236 5721
Recommended in Crime

IRWIN, Stephen QC
Doughty Street Chambers (Geoffrey Robertson QC), London (020) 7404 1313
Recommended in Clinical Negligence, Personal Injury, Product Liability
Specialisation: Principal area of practice is clinical negligence covering a broad range of serious medical accidents including cerebral palsy, surgical and other medical cases. Other main areas of work are major personal injury cases, legal negligence arising out of public law cases with a medical or health content. Major cases include the Human Growth Hormone/ Creutzfeldt – Jacob disease, BSE – linked CJD litigation, PTSD for servicemen and organophosphate sheepdip group action, Gulf War Syndrome, Clunis v Camden & Islington HA; Birmingham Orthopaedic Hospital Bone Tumour Service; and the Clapham Rail disaster enquiry. Author of "Practitioner's Guide to Medical Negligence" (Legal Action Group, 1995). Regularly lectures and writes on medico-legal issues. Chairman, Remuneration Committee of Bar Council.
Prof. Memberships: Professional Negligence Bar Association, Association of Personal Injury Lawyers, Action for the Victims of Medical Accidents, Personal Injury Bar Association, Justice.
Career: Called to the Bar 1976 and tenant of No.1 Dr. Johnson's Buildings, founder member of Doughty Street Chambers. Called to the Bar of Northern Ireland 1997. QC 1997.
Personal: Educated at Methodist College, Belfast 1961-1971 and Jesus College, Cambridge 1972-1975. Leisure pursuits include reading prose and verse, Irish history and hillwalking. Born 5th February 1953. Lives in Radlett, Herts.

ISAACS, Paul
Mercury Chambers (Benjamin Nolan QC), Leeds (0113) 234 2265
Recommended in Crime, Family/Matrimonial
Specialisation: Highly regarded specialist in matrimonial property work. The counsel of choice of the leading firms of solicitors in cases involving substantial assets and complex accountancy/ valuation evidence. Recent cases have involved assets of £10-40 million.
Personal: Read Law at Trinity College, Cambridge (Lizette Bentwich prize winner). Called to the Bar in 1974. Recorder of the Crown Court approved to try family cases.

ISHERWOOD, John
Assize Court Chambers (John Isherwood), Bristol (0117) 926 4587
Recommended in Personal Injury

JACKLIN, Susan
St John's Chambers (Christopher Sharp QC), Bristol (0117) 921 3456
clerks@stjohnschambers.co.uk
Recommended in Family/Matrimonial
Specialisation: Matrimonial finance, cohabitation disputes, Inheritance Act claims, professional negligence in ancillary relief context. Children cases, particularly case applications involving allegations of physical and sexual abuse. Crime: prosecuting and defending in cases of domestic violence and physical and sexual abuse of children.
Prof. Memberships: Family Law Bar Associations, Criminal Bar Association.
Career: Durham University (BA). Called to the Bar 1980. Assistant Recorder 1998. Recorder 2000.

JACKSON, Andrew
3 Fountain Court (Robert Juckes QC), Birmingham (0121) 236 5854
clerks@3fc.co.uk
Recommended in Crime
Specialisation: Crime: Prosecution and Defence work.
Prof. Memberships: Criminal Bar Association.
Career: Manchester University: [1981-1984] BA (Hons). The City University: (1984-1985). Diploma in law.

JACKSON, Dirik
11 New Square (Sonia Proudman QC), London (020) 7831 0081
Recommended in Traditional Chancery
Specialisation: Practice covers broad range of Chancery work – in particular trusts, probate, administration of estates, family provision, Court of Protection, conveyancing, commercial and agricultural landlord and tenant, partnership, insolvency, solicitors' negligence. Recent interesting cases include: Re Duxbury (1995, validity of sole trusteeship of Public Trustee), Frankland v IRC (1997, IHT on distribution out of discretionary trust within 3 months of settlor's death), Duncan Investments Ltd v Underwoods (1998, liability of vendor's estate agent to purchaser for negligent mis-statement); County Nat West Ltd v Barton (1999, release of guarantor by bank's misrepresentation of value of security).
Prof. Memberships: Chancery Bar Association, Professional Negligence Bar Association, ACTAPS.
Career: Called to the Bar 1969. Tenant at 7 New Square 1970-1994. Joined present chambers 1994. Recorder since 1992.

JACKSON, John
40 King St (Philip Raynor QC), Manchester (0161) 832 9082
Recommended in Crime
Specialisation: Commercial Fraud.
Personal: Criminal Bar Association.
Personal: Interests include sport and sailing.

JACKSON, Judith QC
9 Old Square (Michael Driscoll QC), London (020) 7405 4682
chambers@9oldsquare.co.uk
Recommended in Property Litigation
Specialisation: Commercial property particularly landlord and tenant, chancery and professional negligence. Cases include: Prudential Assurance Co Ltd v Newman Industries Ltd (minority shareholders' rights), Re Bond Worth (retention of title), Abbey National v Moss (trusts for sale), UCB Bank plc v Beasley (s70 (1)(g) Land Registration Act 1925), Scott v National Trust (Judicial Review of Charity), Trustees of the Phillimore Kensington Estate v Jassi Reform – whether house and mews house were together a house), Locabail UK Ltd v Bayfield Properties (conjoined appeals on Judicial bias).
Prof. Memberships: Chancery Bar Association; Professional Negligence Bar Association.
Career: Queen Mary College, London (1970-1973) (LL.B); (1973-1974) (LL.M). Called to Bar in 1975. Took silk in 1994. Contributor to Megarry's Rent Acts (11th ed). Director of Bar Mutual Indemnity Fund Ltd (1999 -).

JACKSON, Peter QC
4 Paper Buildings (Lionel Swift QC), London (020) 7583 0816
pj@4pb.com
Recommended in Family: Child Care including child abduction
Specialisation: All aspects of child work.
Prof. Memberships: Family Law Bar Association.
Career: Called 1978 and joined present chambers 1979. Assistant Recorder 1998. Recorder 2000. Silk 2000.
Personal: Educated at Marlborough College 1969-1973 and Brasenose College, Oxford 1974-1977. Born 9th December 1955. Lives in London.

JACKSON, Rosemary
Keating Chambers (Richard Fernyhough QC), London (020) 7544 2600
Recommended in Arbitration (International)
Specialisation: Construction and engineering litigation and arbitration, including professional negligence; party wall disputes.
Career: Qualified 1981; Middle Temple.
Personal: Born 1958, resides London.

JACKSON, Simon
Park Court Chambers (James Stewart QC Robert Smith QC), Leeds (0113) 243 3277
Recommended in Personal Injury
Specialisation: Personal Injury/Clinical Negligence. Professional Disciplinary Proceedings. Crime.

Prof. Memberships: PNBA and PIBA
Career: Leeds University [LL.B (Hons)]. Called 1982. Pupillage in London and Leeds. Practised in specialist field for 10 years plus. Occasional lecturer on medico-legal issues.

JACKSON, Wayne
Young Street Chambers (Lesley Newton), Manchester (0161) 833 0489
Recommended in Crime

JACOBS, Nigel
4 Essex Court (Nigel Teare QC), London (020) 7653 5653
Recommended in Shipping

JACOBS, Richard QC
Essex Court Chambers (Gordon Pollock QC), London (020) 7813 8000
Recommended in Commercial (Litigation), Insurance
Specialisation: All types of commercial work – shipping, insurance, reinsurance, professional negligence, commodities, banking, Lloyd's disciplinary proceedings, disputes arising from sales of businesses (warranty claims etc).
Career: Pembroke College, Cambridge MA (1st Class Hons), 1978. Called to the Bar, 1979.
Personal: Born 1956.

JAFFA, Ronald
3 Gray's Inn Square (Rock Tansey QC), London (020) 7520 5600
Recommended in Crime
Fax: (0171) 520 5607
Specialisation: Long term experience of defending those charged with serious crime including murder, robbery, rape, drugs trafficking, importation and serious assaults. Often instructed in cases where the defendant is difficult, has psychiatric problems or where the allegation revolves around sexual abuse of children. Has conducted many fraud cases involving companies, company VAT, charities, Local Authority employees, advanced fee and mortgages.
Prof. Memberships: Criminal Bar Association.
Career: LLB Nottingham University. One of the founder members who set up the Bar Pro Bono Unit. A member of the management committee solely responsible for considering all applications relating to criminal work.
Personal: Married with two children. An elected trustee of the Rett Syndrome Association UK, a national charity helping families, carers and sufferers of this neurological disorder which only affects females.

JAFFERJEE, Aftab
2 Harcourt Buildings, Atkinson Bevan Chambers (Nicholas Atkinson QC & John Bevan QC), London (020) 7353 2112
Recommended in Crime
Specialisation: Junior Treasury Counsel at the Central Criminal Court since 1997.
Prof. Memberships: Criminal Bar Association.
Career: Past Member of the Criminal Bar Association Committee. Past Member of the Professional Conduct Committee of the Bar.

JAMES, Alun
3 Temple Gardens Tax Chambers (Richard Bramwell QC), London (020) 7353 7884
Recommended in Tax
Specialisation: Specialises in tax and VAT. Business tax includes corporate work; advice for owner-managed businesses and employee-related issues. Also advises on personal tax matters for private clients. Handles a significant amount of tax-related litigation, notably before the VAT Tribunals and in the professional negligence context.
Prof. Memberships: Revenue Bar Association.
Career: Called to the Bar 1986 and joined 3 Temple Gardens 1988. Also a member of Exchange Chambers (William Waldron Q.C.), Liverpool.
Publications: Co-author of 'Taxation of Companies and Company Reconstructions' (Sweet & Maxwell, 6th Ed 1994 and 7th Ed 1998).
Personal: Scholar of St. John's College, Oxford (BA, Hons 1st Class, Jurisprudence, BCL). Born 13th May 1964.

JAMES, Christopher
5 Fountain Court (Anthony Barker QC), Birmingham (0121) 606 0500
Recommended in Family/Matrimonial

JAMES, Michael
Enterprise Chambers (Anthony Mann QC), Leeds (0113) 246 0391
Recommended in Commercial (Litigation)
Specialisation: Commercial and chancery litigation, with particular expertise in disputes with an international aspect. Wide experience of employment law and directors' disqualification cases.
Prof. Memberships: Chancery Bar Association. Chartered Institute of Arbitrators. Association of Northern Mediators.
Career: Open Scholar at Christ Church, Oxford. Solicitor 1983-93.
Personal: Born 17 May 1953. Married, two children.

JAMESON, Rodney
No.6 (Shaun Spencer QC), Leeds (0113) 245 9763
Recommended in Crime

JANNER, Daniel
23 Essex Street (Michael Lawson QC), London (020) 7413 0353
Recommended in Crime
Specialisation: Crime (general); police law; employment law; sex and race discrimination.
Prof. Memberships: 23 Essex Street.
Career: Called to Bar in 1980 (Jules Thorn Scholar, Middle Temple); Editor Criminal Appeal Reports since 1994.
Personal: President Cambridge Union Society (1978).

JARMAN, Milwyn
9 Park Place (Ian Murphy QC), Cardiff (029) 2038 2731
Recommended in Chancery
Specialisation: Chancery, Planning and Local Government, Personal Injury. Reported cases include: BP Properties Ltd v Buckler [1987] 2 EGLR 168 (adverse possession); R v Port Talbot Borough Council ex p Jones [1988] 2 ALL ER 207 (judicial review: housing); R v Dairy Produce Quota Tribunal for England and Wales ex parte Davies [1987] 2 EGLR 7 (judicial review: agriculture); R v West Glamorgan County Council ex p Morris and Hood-Williams [1992] JPL 374 (judicial review planning), Huish v Ellis [1995] BCC 462 (professional negligence); Harris v Welsh Development Agency [1999] 3 EGLR 207 (compulsory purchase compensation); Bolwell v Radcliffe Homes Ltd [1999] PIQR P243 (personal injury.)
Prof. Memberships: Chancery Bar Association, Bristol and Cardiff Chancery Bar Association.
Career: Called 1980.
Personal: Born 1957. LL.B (Wales) 1st Class. LL.M (Cantab).

JARVIS, John QC
3 Verulam Buildings (Christopher Symons QC & John Jarvis QC), London (020) 7831 8441
Recommended in Arbitration (International), Civil Fraud, Commercial (Litigation)
Specialisation: Principal areas of practice are banking (both litigation and transactional work) and commercial law. Specialist experience in banking and financing work, insolvency and professional negligence. Practice covers law and practice of international finance, project development and finance, trade disputes, professional liability, insolvency, constructive trusts and arbitration. Has drafted all the major security documentation for a new bank, and appeared in a number of banking cases such as Tai Hing Cotton Ltd v Lin Chong Bank Ltd [1986] AC 80 in the Privy Council. Other recent reported cases include Barclays Bank v O'Brien [1993] (priority in equity of wife's interest against creditor); Deposit Protection Board v Dalia [1993] (validity of equitable assignments to enable claim on fund); Wadha Bank v Arab Bank [1993] (legality of performance bonds and counter guarantees); Re Arrows Ltd Nos 1-4 [1992-93]; Brink Mat Ltd v Noye [1991] (bank as constructive trustee) and Barclays Bank plc v Taylor, TSB v Taylor [1989] (extent of bank's duty of confidentiality). International Editor of the 'Journal of Banking and Finance Law and Practice'. Author of a number of articles in banking law. Co-author of 'Lender Liability' (1993), and contributing author to 'Banks; Liability and Risk'(1995).
Prof. Memberships: COMBAR, London Common Law and Commercial Bar Association (Chairman 1995/1997).
Career: Called to the Bar and joined present Chambers 1970. Took Silk 1989. Appointed Recorder 1992. Sits as a Deputy High Court Judge.
Personal: Educated at King's College School, Wimbledon 1955-1965. Open Exhibitioner and Senior Scholar of Emmanuel College (and Cambridge University Scholar) 1966-1969 (MA Hons). Governor of King's College School. Leisure pursuits include riding, tennis, sailing, skiing, cycling, collecting modern British paintings, opera and gardening. Born 20th November 1947. Lives in Wimbledon and Eyeworth.

JAY, Robert QC
39 Essex Street (Nigel Pleming QC), London (020) 7832 1111
rj@39essex.co.uk
Recommended in Administrative & Public Law: General, Immigration
Specialisation: Extensive practice in public law, judicial review and immigrations, having been Junior Council to the Crown (Common Law) between 1989 and 1998.
Prof. Memberships: Vice-Chairman of the Administrative Law Bar Association.
Career: QC (1998).
Personal: Interests: Cooking, Classical Music and Languages.

JEANS, Christopher QC
11 King's Bench Walk (Eldred Tabachnik QC and James Goudie QC), London (020) 7632 8500
Recommended in Employment
Specialisation: Specialises in employment law.
Prof. Memberships: Employment Lawyers Association, Employment Law Bar Association.
Career: 1974-1977: LLB degree at King's College, London. 1977-1979: BCL degree at St. John's College, Oxford. 1980: called to the Bar (Gray's Inn). Since 1983 has practised full time at the Bar, specialising in employment law, at chambers of Lord Irvine QC (now chambers of Eldred Tabachnik QC and James Goudie QC).
Personal: Main interests: sport (especially football and cricket), travel, theatre, cinema.

JEARY, Stephen
Temple Chambers (David Aubrey QC), Cardiff (029) 2039 7364
Recommended in Crime

JEFFORD, Nerys
Keating Chambers (Richard Fernyhough QC), London (020) 7544 2600
Recommended in Construction
Specialisation: Construction and civil engineering.
Career: Qualified 1986; Gray's Inn; member of editorial team 'Keating on Building Contracts'.
Personal: Lady Margaret Hall, Oxford (1984, MA); University of Virginia (1985, LL.M). Born 1962. London Welsh Chorale.

JEFFREYS, Alan QC
Farrar's Building (John Leighton Williams QC), London (020) 7583 9241
Recommended in Personal Injury
Specialisation: Principal area of practice is personal injury litigation, both claimant and defendant. Work includes motor, employment and public liability claims. Other main areas of practice are clinical and solicitors negligence, general insurance, and Health and Safety.
Career: Called to the Bar in 1970 (Gray's Inn) and joined *Farrar's Building* in 1971. Recorder since 1993. Took Silk April 1996. Member of the CICB 1999.
Personal: Born 27th September 1947. Lives in London.

JENKINS, Alun QC
Queen Square Chambers (T. Alun Jenkins QC), Bristol (0117) 921 1966
Recommended in Crime
Specialisation: Criminal and commercial fraud, diversion frauds, money laundering and large scale importation of drugs. Prosecuted: Op. Barlow – C & E diversion fraud; Op. Rhythm and Op. Jaegar C & E importation of drugs. Defended: Large scale distribution of drugs, passing-off fraud, long firm fraud, computer frauds, Mareva & Anton Piller injunctions.

JENKINS, Edward QC
5 Paper Buildings (Godfrey Carey QC & Jonathan Caplan QC), London (020) 7583 6117
Recommended in Crime

JENNINGS, Anthony
Matrix Chambers (Nicholas Blake QC), London (020) 7404 3447
Recommended in Crime
Specialisation: Involved in major Crown Court criminal cases including terrorism, animal rights, drugs, prison disturbances, armed robbery, murder and fraud. Cases include disturbances at Risley Remand Centre (1990), Dartmoor Prison (1991), Manchester United supporters riot on ferry, dolphin interference case; IRA cases: MacFlhoinn and Hayes and Taylor; Sehan (largest ever police seizure of heroin); Ronnie Lee (animal rights bombing), Whitemoor prison egress, North Wales sex abuse inquiry, Brownbill v M.P.C. (£150,000 damages against the police), Michael Smith v Police (largest damages in W.Midlands), Keith Birchall (murder conviction quashed on appeal). Arms from Serbia/W.Midlands Police Corruption (1999). Condron v UK and the other four right to silence cases.
Prof. Memberships: Criminal Bar Association.
Career: Called to the Bar 1983 and Northern Ireland Bar in 1987, joined current chambers in 1986. CBA lecturer November 1999 & Human Rights lecturer for Bar Council & CBA 2000.
Publications: Editor of 'Justice under Fire: The Abuse of Civil Liberties in Northern Ireland' (1990). Written articles on criminal justice for The Times, Independent, Guardian, Archbold News and The New Law Journal. Contributing editor of Archbold.
Personal: Educated at St Patrick's College, Belfast 1971-1978, Warwick University 1978-81 and Inns of Court School of Law 1981-82. Leisure pursuits include theatre, Italy, Liverpool FC and Irish literature. Born 11th May 1960. Lives in London.

JOFFE, Victor
Serle Court (Lord Neill of Bladen QC), London (020) 7242 6105
Recommended in Commercial Chancery, Company, Insolvency/Corporate Recovery
Specialisation: Main areas of practice are company law (especially shareholders' disputes and minority rights; directors duties and directors' disqualification) and corporate insolvency, with emphasis on litigation. Other areas of practice include partnership, commercial chancery and banking (including tracing and proprietary claims). Advises in many litigious matters from overseas, particularly the United States and Jersey. Publications include 'Companies Act 1980 – A practitioners Guide'; 'Buckley on the Companies Acts' (joint editor, forthcoming edition); 'Mithani on Disqualification of Directors' (joint editor).
Prof. Memberships: Chancery Bar Association; Associate Member of Insolvency Lawyers Association; International Bar Association.
Career: MA, LL.B (Cantab); Called to the Bar 1975. Attorney, New York State Bar (1998).

JOHNS, Alan
9 Old Square (Michael Driscoll QC), London (020) 7405 4682
Recommended in Property Litigation
Specialisation: Main expertise is in property litigation, including landlord and tenant, morgages, real property and professional negligence, but is experienced in a broad range of modern chancery work. Recent cases include Upton v Taylor & Colley (1999) (Divisional Court) and Inntrepeneur Pub cv (IPC) Ltd v Deans (1999).
Career: Called to the bar in 1994. Part-time tutor at Magdalen College, Oxford during 1996 and 1997.
Personal: Herston School, Cornwall. Magdalen College, Oxford.

JOHNSON, Christine
14 Castle Street (Andrew Edis QC), Liverpool (0151) 236 4421
Recommended in Family/Matrimonial
Specialisation: Children and financial relief. Crime.
Prof. Memberships: FBLA. RCN (Royal College of Nursing).
Career: Registerer Nurse, Registerer Sick Childrens Nurse, Registerer Midwife.

JOHNSON, Edwin
9 Old Square (Michael Driscoll QC), London (020) 7405 4682
Recommended in Property Litigation
Specialisation: Property, Chancery and commercial litigation and advisory work. In particular commercial and residential property disputes, professional negligence, mortgages, general landlord and tenant (including leasehold enfranchisement), conveyancing, easements, restrictive covenants, property rights, insolvency and commercial contracts, building and construction work. Recent cases include Church Commissioners v Ibrahim [1997] 03 EG 136, (right to indemnity costs in leases); Gardner v Marsh & Parsons (mitigation of damages for professional negligence)[1997] 1 WLR 489; Wallis Fashion Group Ltd v CGU Life Assurance Ltd [2000] 27 EG 145, Rosen v Trustees of the Campden Charities [1999] 2 EGLR 213, UCB Corporate Services Ltd v Halifax (SW) Ltd [2000] 16 EG 137. 14. Rothschild v Bell [1999] 2 WLR 1237.
Prof. Memberships: Chancery Bar Association. Professional Negligence Bar Association.
Career: Called to the Bar in 1987 and joined 9 Old Square in 1988. Educated at Lancing College and Christ Church College, Oxford (BA).

JOHNSON, Ian
14 Castle Street (Andrew Edis QC), Liverpool (0151) 236 4421
Recommended in Chancery

JOHNSON, Michael
9 St. John Street (John Hand QC), Manchester (0161) 955 9000
clerks@9stjohnstreet.co.uk
Recommended in Chancery
Specialisation: General Chancery, with emphasis on traditional chancery fields, and on revenue matters, professional negligence and High Court Litigation.
Prof. Memberships: Chancery Bar Association, Northern Chancery Bar Association (immediate past Chairman) Professional Negligence Bar Association.
Career: Chancery Practitioner since 1972, Recorder (Civil and Crime), part-time Chairman, VAT & Duties Tribunals, part-time Special Commissioner of Taxes.
Personal: Fluent in Spanish, good knowledge of French, educated in North and South America, and at Trinity College, Cambridge University.

JOHNSTON, Christopher
3 Serjeants' Inn (Philip Naughton QC), London (020) 7427 5000
Recommended in Clinical Negligence

JONES, Alun QC
3 Raymond Buildings (Clive Nicholls QC), London (020) 7400 6400
chambers@threeraymond.demon.co.uk
Recommended in Crime, Fraud: Criminal
Specialisation: Principal areas of practice are commercial crime and extradition. Acts in cases of serious and complex fraud, both trials and advisory work, primarily for the defence. Undertakes extradition and advisory work for foreign governments and fugitives. Appears frequently on appeal or review in criminal cases and associated matters such as coroners' cases. Notable cases include the Alexander Howden reinsurance trials (appearing for Kenneth Grob in the first SFO trial, 1989-90); the Blue Arrow Trial 1990-91 (defending Stephen Clark); the defence of Andrew Kent in an alleged fraud against The Securities Association (1993) and the Maxwell Criminal Trial (defending Kevin Maxwell, 1995-96); Westminster Council v Dame Shirley Porter & Others 1997; Senator Pinochet 1998-9; Lord Hardwicke 1999; Frank Warren 2000; Private prosecution for the Hillsborough Family Support Group 1996-2000. Involved in fourteen full House of Lords appeals in extradition cases, acting in ten of them for foreign governments, including Pinochet in Spain. Author of 'Jones on Extradition' (Sweet & Maxwell, 1995); second edition pending.
Prof. Memberships: Bar Council, Criminal Bar Association.
Career: Called to the Bar in 1972 and joined current chambers in 1973. Took silk 1989. Appointed Recorder 1992.
Personal: Educated at Oldershaw Grammar School, Wallasey 1960-1967 and Bristol University 1967-1970. Leisure pursuits include bridge, cricket, gardening and writing (currently working on book concerning the law of conspiracy). Born 19th March 1949. Lives in Greenwich, London.

JONES, Charlotte
Crown Office Chambers (Michael Spencer QC & Christopher Purchas QC), London (020) 7797 8100
Recommended in Clinical Negligence

JONES, Edward Bartley QC
Exchange Chambers (William Waldron QC), Liverpool (0151) 236 7747
Recommended in Chancery, Commercial (Litigation), Insolvency/Corporate Recovery, Partnership
Specialisation: Commercial, professional negligence,

insolvency, banking, chancery, companies, commercial property and landlord and tenant, commercial arbitration, intellectual and property .
Prof. Memberships: Northern Circuit Chancery Bar Association; Chancery Bar Association; Northern Circuit Commercial Bar Association.
Career: BA (Oxon.) 1973 called 1975. Practised in Liverpool from 1976. Joined Exchange Chambers as head of commercial department 1994. Formerly part-time tutor in law at Liverpool University. Recorder.Q.C. (1997)

JONES, Elizabeth QC
Serle Court (Lord Neill of Bladen QC), London (020) 7242 6105
Recommended in Commercial (Litigation), Commercial Chancery
Specialisation: Broad range of commercial Chancery and property litigation, with particular emphasis on civil fraud and breach of fiduciary duty (both in commercial and trust contexts), Privy Council appeals and financial services.
Prof. Memberships: Chancery Bar Association. COMBAR
Career: Called to the Bar 1984. Joined Thirteen Old Square 1985. Member ACTAPS.

JONES, Geraint
9 Park Place (Ian Murphy QC), Cardiff (029) 2038 2731
Recommended in Chancery

JONES, Gregory
2 Harcourt Buildings (Mr Gerard Ryan QC), London (020) 7353 8415 clerks@2hb.law.co.uk
Recommended in Environment
Specialisation: Principal areas of practice: planning, environmental, compulsory purchase, education, local government, administrative, parliamentary, immigration, EU and European Convention. Promoted at public inquiry to appear for Home Department before Immigration Appeal Tribunals, Editor: 'Education Case Reports', Assistant Editor: Planning and Environmental Law Bulletin, Editorial Board: 'UKELA Journal of Environmental Law'. Recent published work includes 'When He Who Hesitates is Lost: Judicial Review of Planning Permissions' [2000] JPL 564 and 'Appealing from Adverse Reasoning' [2000] JR 15. Appeared in Berleley v SSE and Fulham FC (HL) (2000) Times July 7 (Directive 85/337, Environmental Impact Assessment, application of Article 10 EC Treaty to exercise of judicial discretion); Millington v SSE (CA) [2000] JPL 296 (whether winemaking "agriculture" for the purposes of TCPA 1990); R v Greenwich LBC ex parte Glen International (CA) (2000) Times March 29 (housing renovation grants under s.113 LGHA 1989), R v SSERT and Parcleforce ex parte Marson (CA) [1999] 1 CMLR 268 (duty to give reasons under EC law); R v Sandhu (CA) [1998] PLR 17 (listed buildings/relevance of evidence of mens rea in strict liability offences).
Prof. Memberships: Memberships: UKELA (member of national council), PEBA, ALBA, Bar European Group, Education Law Society.
Career: Stagiaire European Commission (1990); called: Lincoln's Inn (1991) and King's Inns, Dublin (1997); joined *2 Harcourt Buildings* (1993), Jean Pierre Warner scholar to the European Court of Justice (1995). Senior Lecturer and head of European Law (p/t), South Bank University (1994-1997).
Personal: Attended, Colfe's School; New College, Oxford (MA); University College, London (LL.M) (Euro). Born 1968.

JONES, Philip
Serle Court (Lord Neill of Bladen QC), London (020) 7242 6105
Recommended in Commercial Chancery
Specialisation: Company and Insolvency; financial sevices; Chancery and Commercial litigation; European law; judicial review and professional negligence in relation to the foregoing.
Prof. Memberships: Chancery Bar Association, COMBAR
Career: Junior Counsel to the Crown (Chancery) 1994-99, Junior Counsel to the Crown (A Panel) 1999
Publications: The Practice and Procedure of the Companies Court (1997)

JONES, Seàn
11 King's Bench Walk (Eldred Tabachnik QC and James Goudie QC), London (020) 7632 8500
Recommended in Employment

JORY, Hugh
Enterprise Chambers (Anthony Mann QC), Leeds (0113) 246 0391
Recommended in Commercial (Litigation), Insolvency/Corporate Recovery

JOSEPH, David
Essex Court Chambers (Gordon Pollock QC), London (020) 7813 8000
Recommended in Aviation, Shipping
Specialisation: Experienced in arbitration. Advocate in many ad hoc arbitrations in London involving a wide variety of commercial disputes particularly charterparty, aviation, insurance, reinsurance and commodities. Many of these disputes are governed by foreign law. Litigation experience: all types of commercial work including insurance, reinsurance, aviation, shipping, sale of goods, letters of credit, commercial fraud.
Career: Law Society Finals 1983, Called to Bar – 1984; began practice – 1985, in commercial chambers at Essex Court.
Personal: Born 22 April 1961. Educated at Pembroke College, Cambridge (BA (law – 2nd class Hons.)); Good working French and basic Italian.

JOURDAN, Stephen
Falcon Chambers (Jonathan Gaunt QC & Kim Lewison QC), London (020) 7353 2484
Recommended in Agriculture, Property Litigation
Specialisation: Commercial, agricultural and residential landlord and tenant, conveyancing, mortgages, solicitors' and surveyors' professional negligence, real property, insolvency aspects of real property.
Prof. Memberships: Professional Negligence Bar Association, Chancery Bar Association.
Publications: Writing a book on Adverse Possession.
Career: Formerly a practising solicitor. Contributor to Halsbury's Laws (4th Edition) volume 27 (Landlord and Tenant).

JOYCE, Michael
9 Gough Square (Jeremy Roberts QC), London (020) 7832 0500
Recommended in Crime

JOYCE, Peter QC
No.1 High Pavement (John B. Milmo QC), Nottingham (0115) 941 8218
Recommended in Crime
Specialisation: Serious crime – including corruption, serious sexual offences, homicide. In the past 2 years cases of senior police officer and doctors.
Prof. Memberships: Criminal Bar Association.
Career: Called to the Bar 1968. Recorder 1986. Queens Counsel 1991.

JUBB, Brian
Renaissance Chambers (Brian Jubb & Henry Setright), London (020) 7404 1111
Recommended in Family: Child Care including child abduction

JUCKES, Robert QC
3 Fountain Court (Robert Juckes QC), Birmingham (0121) 236 5854 clerks@3fc.co.uk
Recommended in Crime
Specialisation: Crime: equally for prosecution and defence. 1997: junior for prosecution in R v Tracey Andrews; four other murder cases, three for defence. C of A; respondent in R v Kendrick Hopkins and R v Callender; most kinds of criminal work but increasing rape and child abuse; fraud.
Prof. Memberships: CBA.
Career: Marlborough College 1963-1968. Exeter University 1969-1972 (BA Hon Soc/ Law). Extensive travel and variety of work in Australia, America and Europe prior to starting at Bar 1975. Nose to grindstone since. Recorder 1995.
Personal: As much sport as time allows especially tennis, golf, cricket, skiing. Current reading obsession; Patrick O'Brien. Culturing three sons 21, 18 and 13.

JUDD, Frances
Harcourt Chambers (Patrick Eccles QC), Oxford (01865) 791559 fjudd@harcourtchambers.law.co.uk
Recommended in Family/Matrimonial
Specialisation: Family law, particulary children's cases – public/private law and adoption. Matrimonial finance. Cases include Re O (Adoption: Witholding Agreement) 1999 1 451, Re M (Adoption or Residence Order) 1998 1 FLR 570, Oxfordshire County Council v L & F 1997 1 235, Oxfordshire County Council v P 1995 1 FLR 552.
Prof. Memberships: FLBA, Association of Lawyers for Children, Midland and Oxford Circuit.
Career: Called to the Bar 1984; Member of *Harcourt Chambers* since 1985; Based in Oxford since 1993.
Personal: New Hall, Cambridge, 1979-82. Born 1961. Married with two children.

KADRI, Sibghat QC
6 King's Bench Walk (Sibghat Kadri QC), London (020) 7583 0695 / 7353 4931
Recommended in Immigration

KALLIPETIS, Michel QC
Littleton Chambers (Michel Kallipetis QC), London (020) 7797 8600 michel@kallipetis.com
Recommended in Alternative Dispute Resolution
Specialisation: Professional negligence, employment law, entertainment and media law, building and construction, general commercial and business law. Other areas of practice include health and safety.
Prof. Memberships: Professional Negligence Bar Association, COMBAR, Employment Law Bar Association, TECBA, accredited CEDR Mediator.
Career: Called 1968 Gray's Inn; QC 1989; Recorder 1989, Deputy High Court Judge, Judge of Technological and Construction Court.
Personal: Cardinal Vaughan School. University College London. Exchequer & Audit Department (now National Audit Office) 1960 to 1968. Languages: German (fluent), French (working knowledge).

KARAS, Jonathan
Wilberforce Chambers (Edward Nugee QC), London (020) 7306 0102
Recommended in Property Litigation
Specialisation: Practises in the fields of real property and planning (with a particular emphasis on landlord and tenant). Co-author of 'Unlawful Interference with Land' (1996) and a contributing editor to the 'Com-

pulsory Purchase' title of Halsbury's Laws of England (1996) and to Hill and Redman's 'Law of Landlord and Tenant'.
Prof. Memberships: Planning and Environment Bar Association, Chancery Bar Association.
Career: Member of B Panel of Junior Counsel to the Crown.
Publications: Editor of the re-issue of the 'Distress' title of Halsbury's Laws (2000).

KARK, Tom
Queen Elizabeth Building (Julian Bevan QC & Peter Whiteman QC), London (020) 7583 5766
Recommended in Fraud: Criminal
Specialisation: Practice principally involves cases of commercial fraud including: fraudulent trading; VAT fraud; duty diversion; mortgage fraud; bankruptcy offences. Has also been involved in cases of alleged insider dealing, prosecuting for the DTI and defending. Also defends and prosecutes cases concerning computer misuse and data protection (see DPP v Brown – House of Lords). Landmark cases have included defending as junior several SFO and Special Casework prosecutions (eg. second defendant in the Levitt case; Terry Ramsden; Swithland Motors). Criminal Law (General): Prosecutes and defends in all areas of criminal law. Member of 'Justice'.
Career: Called to the Bar 1982, appointed assistant recorder 1999, Recorder 2000.
Personal: Born 12th December 1960. Educated at Eton, Buckingham University and Ronnie Scotts.

KATKOWSKI, Christopher QC
4 Breams Buildings (Christopher Lockhart-Mummery QC), London (020) 7430 1221/7353 5835
Recommended in Administrative & Public Law: General, Parliamentary & Public Affairs, Planning
Specialisation: Planning inquiry experience extends to all fields including acting for all the leading retailers in a large number of shopping inquiries; substantial experience of conservation cases (e.g. the Mappin & Webb inquiry for English Heritage, and obtaining planning permission to develop over an Anglo-Saxon cemetery in Croydon); promoting a major development for the Army (Otterburn in the Northumberland National Park); Transport & Work Act inquiries (Chester Guided Busway) and conducting Local Plan inquiries. Leading planning court cases include: Tesco Witney (planning gain); Bolton (reasons); Mitchell (affordable housing); Edwards (alternative sites); Walton (implementation of old planning permissions); Porter (issue estoppel); Morris & Perry (old mining permission); Hombleton (PPG 6 and need); Skerritts (limited buildings curtilage, and the Marquee case); ADT (habitats regulations; Environmental law experience includes: FOE v SSE (quality of drinking water litigation) and Ennerdale Water (abstraction inquiry). Leading public law cases include: Spycatcher (Contempt of court); Foster (jurisdiction of Social Security commissions); Balfour (national security); Save Our Railways (privatisation); Camden (housing revenue account subsidy); Warren (subpoena of judges). Public affairs experience includes advising various serving and former Cabinet ministers during the Scott inquiry.
Career: Lectured in law at the City of London Polytechnic, 1979-83. Called to the Bar, February 1982. Began practice at the Bar in January 1984. Queens Counsel 1999.
Personal: Born 16th January 1957 in Sussex, Polish parents. Educated at Cardinal Newman School, Hove, Sussex and Fitzwilliam College, Cambridge M.A; LL.B (First Class Honours). Elected senior Scholar of College and University prize in law.

KAUFMANN, Phillippa
Doughty Street Chambers (Geoffrey Robertson QC), London (020) 7404 1313
Recommended in Human Rights (Civil Liberties)
Specialisation: Civil practitioner specialising in constitutional and administrative law, human rights including applications under the European Convention and ICCPR, prisoners' rights actions against the police, mental health. Also undertakes death row appeals from the Commonwealth to the Privy Council.
Prof. Memberships: Member of ALBA; Council Member of Justice.
Career: Called to the Bar 1991. Education: LL.B (Hons) 1st class, LL.M distinction, Scarman Scholar. Born 1966.

KAY, R Jervis QC
4 Field Court (Steven Gee QC), London (020) 7440 6900
Recommended in Shipping
Specialisation: All areas of shipping and commercial law, including international trade, arbitration, marine insurance, carriage of goods, salvage, collision, marine pollution, towage, personal injury and professional negligence. Also sports law particularly related to yachting.
Prof. Memberships: London Maritime Arbitration Association (supporting member), London Common Law and Commercial Bar Association (Committee), COMBAR, British Maritime Law Association, Bar Sports Law Group.
Career: Called to Bar 1972. Called to Bar of New South Wales 1984. Called to Bar of Antigua and Barbuda 1998. Took Silk 1996.
Personal: Educated Wellington College and Nottingham University (LL.B), Editor 'Atkins Court Forms – vol 3 Admiralty.'

KAY, Steven QC
3 Gray's Inn Square (Rock Tansey QC), London (020) 7520 5600
goodnightvienna@quista.net
Recommended in Crime
Specialisation: Wide experience in all areas of UK criminal law, with regular appearances in domestic murder, fraud and drug trafficking trials. International criminal law now a speciality. Defence counsel for Tadic the first defendant to be tried before the UN War Crimes Tribunal for Yugoslavia and the first International Criminal Trial since the Nuremberg and Tokyo trials. Also representing Musema a defendant before the UN International Criminal Tribunal for Rwanda. First UN Defence Counsel to enter Rwanda. Expertise in European agricultural fraud (in Lomas v The Commission 1992). Lectures at conferences throughout the world on subjects ranging from war crimes to the Financial Services & Markets Act 2000.
Prof. Memberships: Criminal Bar Association, European Criminal Bar Association (founder member and Treasurer), International Bar Association, Forensic Science Society, Society for the Reform of Criminal Law.
Career: Called to the Bar 1977, QC 1997, Secretary CBA 1993-1996.
Personal: Born 4/8/54, lives in London.

KAYE, Roger QC
24 Old Buildings (Martin Mann QC & Alan Steinfeld QC), London (020) 7404 0946
Recommended in Church: Church of England, Commercial Chancery, Insolvency/Corporate Recovery

KEALEY, Gavin QC
7 King's Bench Walk (Jeremy Cooke QC), London (020) 7910 8300
Recommended in Arbitration (International), Commercial (Litigation), Insurance
Specialisation: Specialises in all aspects of commercial law for mainly international clients. Particular emphasis on insurance, reinsurance, banking, financial services, professional negligence, conflicts of laws, shipping and contracts of all kinds. Recent cases include Kingscroft and Walbrook v Nissan [1999] LRLR 603, (Reinsurance Pool/quota share/ excess of loss/retention/utmost good faith); Rothschild Assurance v Collyear [1999] 1 Lloyds Reins Rep 6, (Pensions mis-selling, construction of professional indemnity policy); Denby v Marchant & Yasuda v Lloyds's Underwriters [1998] 1 LRLR 343. CA. (Aggregate Extension Clauses); Den Danske A/S, Normura Bank and others v Kleinwort Benson, Skipton BS and Economic Insurance (Dec. 1997, Thomas J, Loan Portfolio Transfers, lending criteria, insurance construction); Sumitomo Bank Ltd, Sanwa Bank Ltd & Arab Bank Ltd v Banque Bruxelles Lambert [1997] 1 Lloyd's Rep 487 (duties of care owed to syndicate of banks by Agent bank), Tharros Shipping v Bias Shipping [1997] 1 Lloyd's Rep 246 and Pendennis Shipyard v Magrathea [1998] 1 Lloyd's Rep 315 (costs payable by a non-party); Glencore v Portman [1997] 1 Lloyd's Rep 225 (insurance, non-disclosure, waiver); Excess Insurance v Mander [1997] 2 Lloyd's Rep 119 (reinsurance, incorporation, arbitration clause). Also has experience appearing before foreign courts as both advocate and expert. Speaks very good French.
Career: Called to the Bar 1977; Joined present chambers 1978; Took Silk 1994; Assistant Recorder 1999.
Personal: Educated at University College, Oxford (BA Hons Jurisprudence 1st class). Lecturer in law, King's College, London 1976-1977.

KEEHAN, Michael
St. Ive's Chambers (Edward Coke), Birmingham (0121) 236 0863
Recommended in Family/Matrimonial

KEEN, K. Roger QC
26 Paradise Square (Roger Keen QC), Sheffield (0114) 273 8951
keen@paradisesq.co.uk
Recommended in Crime
Specialisation: All aspects of crime including fraud. Particular expertise in "who done it murders."
Prof. Memberships: Criminal Bar Association.
Career: Year of call – 1976; Recorder – 1989; Queen's Counsel – 1991.

KEFFORD, Anthony
East Anglian Chambers (Roderick Newton), Norwich (01603) 617351
Recommended in Family/Matrimonial

KELLY, Andrew QC
2 Harcourt Buildings (Mr Gerard Ryan QC), London (020) 7353 8415
clerks@2hb.law.co.uk
Recommended in Planning
Specialisation: Town and country planning, local government, environment, Heathrow Terminal 5 Public Inquiry (British Airways), retail, housing, minerals, local plan inquiries.
Prof. Memberships: PEBA, ALBA.
Career: Called 1978 (Northern Ireland 1982). Chambers 1981. Silk 2000.
Personal: Education: Bangor Grammar (Northern Ireland), Christ Church, Oxford. M.A. (Oxon), Lincoln's Inn. Leisure: Sport, arts, gardening, travel.

KELLY, Matthias QC
Old Square Chambers (John Hendy QC), London (020) 7269 0300
Recommended in Clinical Negligence
Specialisation: Personal injuries. Has dealt with all types of PI for both claimants and defendants. Particular specialisation in catastrophic injuries including brain injuries. Experienced in complicated litigation including radioactive pollution: Merlin v BNFL (1990) 3 WLR 383. Other cases: H v MOD (1991) 2 QB 103,

Rastin v British Steel (1994) 1 WLR 732, Wells v Wells, Thomas v Brighton Health Authority, Page v Sheeness Steel (1998) 3WLR 329. Member editorial panel Sweet and Maxwell Special Research papers in Personal Injuries Law.
Prof. Memberships: Environmental Law Foundation; Vice Chairman, Personal Injury Bar Association.
Career: Called to the bar 1979. QC 1999. Member Irish Bar (Belfast and Dublin). Member New York State Bar and US Federal Bar. Former Consultant to the European Commission on UK Health and Safety Law. Editor, Sweet & Maxwell Personal Injuries Manual. Fellow of Royal Society of Medicine. Member Bar Council 1998-. Member General Management Committee, Bar Council 1999-. Chairman Policy Committee, Bar Council 2000-

KELSEY-FRY, John QC
Queen Elizabeth Building (Julian Bevan QC & Peter Whiteman QC), London (020) 7583 5766
Recommended in Crime, Fraud: Criminal
Specialisation: Practice equally divided between high profile prosecution and defence. Recent cases: Serafinowicz (war crimes); Donald & Cressey (largest police corruption case since 1960's); Charlie Kray, Sawoniuk (war crimes).
Career: Former Senior Treasury Counsel.

KEMPSTER, Toby
Old Square Chambers (John Hendy QC), Bristol (0117) 927 7111
Recommended in Employment
Specialisation: Concentrates primarily on employment law and personal injury law. His employment practice covers both individual and collective rights, dealing with contractual and statutory remedies. His personal injury practice is mainly work or industry related, but he has been involved in multi-plaintiff product liability, disease and 'disaster' cases. His involvement in both personal injury and employment law has resulted in regular involvement in stress at work claims. (Notable cases Alexander v STC, Isle of Scilly v Brintel; Johnson v British Midland Airways).
Prof. Memberships: APIL, ILS, ELA and PIBA.
Career: Member of chambers since 1982.

KENDRICK, Dominic QC
7 King's Bench Walk (Jeremy Cooke QC), London (020) 7910 8300
clerks@7kbw.law.co.uk
Recommended in Insurance
Specialisation: Specialist in commercial litigation, including insurance/reinsurance, shipping, international sale of goods and banking. Recent reported cases include Quinta v Warrington Syndicate [2000] LRIR 81 (contingency insurance); Inco v First Choice [2000] 1 Lloyd's Rep 467 (HL) (commercial arbitration); Banque Trad v Itochu [1999] 2 Lloyd's Rep (sale of goods/banking/conflicts); Bay Ridge [1999] 2 LLR 227 (sale of a ship); Chubb v Federal Insurance [1999] 2 Lloyd's Rep 286 (P.A. LMX reinsurance); Tychy [1999] 2 LLR 11 (CA) (admiralty jurisdiction).
Career: Called to the Bar 1981. Joined present chambers 1982. QC 1992.
Personal: Educated at Trinity College, Cambridge. Born 1955.

KENNEDY, Helena QC
Doughty Street Chambers (Geoffrey Robertson QC), London (020) 7404 1313
Recommended in Crime

KENNEDY, Michael
India Buildings Chambers (David Harris QC), Liverpool (0151) 243 6000
clerks@indiabuildings.co.uk
Recommended in Family/Matrimonial
Specialisation: Family Law specialist dealing with public law Children Act work, including the representation of Local Authorities, parents and Guardians ad Litem in cases involving, inter alia, issues of physical, sexual and emotional abuse of children.
Prof. Memberships: Family Law Bar Association.
Career: Called 1985.

KENNERLEY, Ian
Broad Chare Chambers (Eric A Elliott), Newcastle upon Tyne (0191) 232 0541
Recommended in Family/Matrimonial

KENTRIDGE, Sir Sydney QC
Brick Court Chambers (Christopher Clarke QC), London (020) 7379 3550
Recommended in Administrative & Public Law: General, Commercial (Litigation), Energy & Natural Resources, Insurance, Media & Entertainment
Specialisation: General commercial and common law, constitutional law and law relating to newspapers.
Career: Called to Bar 1977, Lincoln's Inn. Practising barrister, England, 1977 to date. Silk 1984. Admitted as Advocate of the Supreme Court of South Africa, 1949. Appointed Senior Counsel, South Aftica 1965. Former Judge of the Courts of Appeal of Jersey and Guernsey and Constitutional Court of South Africa.
Personal: Born Johannesburg, South Africa, 1922. Educated University of Witwatersrand (B.A. 1941) and Oxford University (B.A. Hons. in Jurisprudence, 1948; M.A. 1955).

KERR, Tim
4-5 Gray's Inn Square (Elizabeth Appleby QC & Duncan Ouseley QC), London (020) 7404 5252
Recommended in Administrative & Public Law: General, Employment, Sport
Specialisation: Judicial review, sports law, education law, local government, employment law, professional negligence, disciplinary tribunals, defamation, European, human rights and commercial. Sports law clients include Nicholas Anelka, Tottenham Hotspur FC (gaining readmission to FA Cup and six restored points); Chelsea FC; Middlesbrough FC; FC; Ipswich Town FC; AEK Athens FC (gaining readmission to UEFA Cup); Slavia Prague FC; the Football League (Stevenage FC v Football League, CA, 1996); the Rugby Football League; the Rugby Football Union; the Welsh Rugby Union; Lennox Lewis (Lewis v Bruno and WBC, 1995). Co-author of 'Sports Law' 1999. Judicial reviews include Bart's hospital closure cases (including R v Health Secretary ex p. Hackney LBC, CA, 1995); challenges to disciplinary investigations into audits of Maxwell and Polly Peck companies (including R v Chance ex p. Smith, DC, 1995); and Camelot's challenge to the "Big Three" bookmakers' competing product (R v DPP ex p. Camelot Group plc, DC, 1997). Education cases include X v Bedfordshire CC (HL, 1995), Christmas v Hampshire County Council (1997), Richardson v Solihull MBC (CA, 1998) and R v East Sussex ex p. Tandy (1998, HL) and Phelps v Hillingdon LBC / Jarvis v Hampshire CC (2000 HL). Employment cases include: Doughty v Rolls-Royce (1992: CA); Duffy v Yeomans & Partners (1995, CA) and Preston v Wolverhampton MBC (HL, 1998 ECJ, 2000).
Prof. Memberships: Administrative Law Bar Association; Employment Law Bar Association; Secretary of the Bar Sports Law Group.
Personal: Runner of four marathons and keen Chelsea supporter.

KERSHAW, Jennifer QC
No.6 (Shaun Spencer QC), Leeds (0113) 245 9763
Recommended in Crime

KERSHEN, Lawrence QC
14 Tooks Court (Michael Mansfield QC), London (020) 7405 8828
Recommended in Alternative Dispute Resolution

KESSLER, James
24 Old Buildings (G.R Bretten QC), London (020) 7242 2744
kessler@kessler.co.uk
Recommended in Charities, Tax
Specialisation: Revenue law, more particularly CGT, IHT, and what is loosely described as 'private client' work; offshore trusts; also taxation of charities. Has a particular fondness for trust drafting (having written the leading textbook on the subject). Founder of the Trusts Discussion Forum.
Career: Called to the bar 1984.

KEYSER, Andrew
9 Park Place (Ian Murphy QC), Cardiff (029) 2038 2731
Recommended in Chancery
Specialisation: Contract litigation; banking; principal and surety; partnership; companies; landlord and tenant; professional negligence.
Prof. Memberships: Chancery Bar Association. Bristol and Cardiff Chancery Bar Association.
Career: Education: Cardiff High School; Balliol College, Oxford; MA (1st class hons.); Called to Bar 1986. Member of the Attorney General's Panel of Counsel (Provincial). Part-time tutor in company law, Centre for Professional Legal Studies, Cardiff Law School.

KHALIL, Karim S.
1 Paper Buildings (Roger Titheridge QC), London (020) 7353 3728
Recommended in Crime
Specialisation: Defence and prosecution, with particular experience in serious violence (including murder), rape and other sexual offences, Drug Trafficking and Fraud. Represented the principal masochist in R v Brown (consent to assault), and the first Defendant/ Appellant in 'The Cambridge Two' (Misuse of Drugs Act). Criminal and civil litigation relating to company fraud. Represented the Appellant in Hannan v DTI (CA decision on the Company Directors' Disqualification Act). Civil claims against the Police.
Prof. Memberships: S.E Circuit; S.E Circuit Liaison Committee (Sec.); Criminal Bar Association; completed 3 years on the Professional Conduct and Complaints Committee; Bar Disciplinary Tribunal; Cambridge Bar Mess Committee; Norwich Bar Mess.
Career: Cheadle Hulme School (Manchester); Queens' College, Cambridge; call – 1984; Assistant Recorder 1997; Recorder 2000.
Personal: Married with two sons; Member of Hawks Club; lacrosse player, now turned to tennis and golf; alto sax in Soul/Blues band.

KHANGURE, Avtar
No.6 Fountain Court (Roger Smith QC), Birmingham (0121) 233 3282
Recommended in Commercial (Litigation), Insolvency/Corporate Recovery

KHAYAT, Georges M QC
10 King's Bench Walk (Georges M Khayat QC), London (020) 7353 2501
Recommended in Crime
Specialisation: Fraud – (White Collar Cases, Banking, Mortgage, Insurance, V.A.T etc).
Prof. Memberships: Chairman Surrey and South London Bar Mess 1995-1998, Member South Eastern Circuit, Head of Chambers.
Career: Called to the Bar 1967, Lincoln's Inn. Recorder of the Crown Court 1987. Q.C. 1992.
Personal: Reading, music, boating, travel and horse riding.

KIBLING, Thomas
Cloisters (Laura Cox QC), London (020) 7827 4000
thomaskibling@cloisters.org.uk
Recommended in Employment
Specialisation: Employment law with a particular emphasis on discrimination law. In recent years he has been involved in a number of the leading appeal cases including Delaney v Staples HL (unauthorised deductions and notice pay), Jones v Tower Boots CA (liability of employers in respect of discrimination claims), Smith v Gardner Merchant CA (gays bringing claims for unlawful discrimination), Crees v Royal Mutual Insurance Society Ltd (maternity rights), P v S (transsexuals bringing claims for unlawful discrimination), Khan v General Medical Council CA (claims against the GMC for unlawful discrimination), Cowley v Manson Timbers CA (re-employment orders), Owusu v London Fire and Civil Defence Authority EAT (continuing acts of discrimination) WA Goold (Pearmak) Ltd v McConnell EAT (implied term concerning the operation of grievance procedures) and Aparau v Iceland Frozen Foods CA (scope of employment tribunal powers), Coote v Granada Hospitality Inc (victimisation post termination). Sits on the Editorial Board of the Encyclopedia of Employment Law, founder member of the Employment Lawyers Association and is a member of the Employment Bar Association.
Career: Called to the Bar 1990. Joined present chambers 1991.
Publications: Lectures widely on all aspects of employment law and publications include 'the Employment Law Handbook' (LAG).
Personal: Born 19th August 1957.

KILLALEA, Stephen
Devereux Chambers (Jeffrey Burke QC), London (020) 7353 7534
Recommended in Health & Safety, Personal Injury
Specialisation: Principal areas of practice are personal injury and Health & Safety. Predominantly plaintiff but some defence work. Emphasis on accidents in industry and accidents involving death, brain damage and spinal injury. Also specialised crime, including a substantial health and safety practice.
Prof. Memberships: Personal Injuries Bar Association; Association of Personal Injury Lawyers.
Career: Called to the Bar in 1981.
Personal: Born 25th January 1959. LL.B (Hons) Sheffield. Lives in Sussex.

KIMBELL, John
4 Essex Court (Nigel Teare QC), London (020) 7653 5653
jkimbell@4sx.co.uk
Recommended in Aviation
Specialisation: Aviation, carriage by sea and road.
Prof. Memberships: COMBAR
Career: Called '95. Inner Temple.
Personal: Education: MA, MPhil Cantab. Single. Interests: Cycling and looking after my cat.

KIMBLIN, Richard
3 Fountain Court (Robert Juckes QC), Birmingham (0121) 236 5854
richard.kimblin@3fc.co.uk
Recommended in Environment
Specialisation: Environmental, planning and regulatory criminal law.
Prof. Memberships: The free advocacy service of the Planning and Environmental Bar Association; United Kingdom Environmental Law Association and secretary of the West Midlands Group; The Administrative Law Bar Association; The Bar European Group.
Career: Bsc (Dunelm); PhD; Royal Society Western European Fellowship. Prior to his call to the Bar, he was Associate Director of a firm of consultants, advising and negotiating on environmental and planning matters, in particular waste, water, pollution, minerals and highways.
Publications: He has published widely in both academic and practitioner journals, including most recently: 'Judicial Review of the Grant of Planning Permission' [22 October 1999], Solicitors Journal 'Risk, Jurisprudence and the Environment' [April 2000], JPL 359; 'The New Contaminated Land Regime' [19 May 2000], Solicitors Journal.

KING, Neil QC
2 Mitre Court Buildings (Michael FitzGerald QC), London (020) 7583 1380
neil.king@2mcb.co.uk
Recommended in Environment, Planning
Specialisation: Practice encompasses town and country planning, compulsory purchase and compensation, rating, local government, environmental and public and administrative law. Joint Editor, 'Ryde on Rating and the Council Tax'.
Prof. Memberships: Planning and Environment Bar Assocation.
Career: Called to the Bar 1980 and joined current chambers 1982.
Personal: Educated at Harrow School 1970-1974 and New College, Oxford 1975-1978. Married with 4 children. Leisure pursuits include music, golf and real tennis. Born 14th November 1956. Lives in Whitchurch-on-Thames.

KING, Simon
7 Bedford Row (David Farrer QC), London (020) 7242 3555
Recommended in Personal Injury
Specialisation: Personal injury and professional negligence practice acting for both Plaintiffs and Defendants but with emphasis on defence work. Regular clients are principally insurers and corporate bodies, including professional indemnity insurers for solicitors, architects and surveyors. Experience includes professional and insurance fraud cases.
Personal: Professional Negligence Bar Association, International Bar Association.
Career: Called to the Bar in 1987, joined current chambers in 1988. Early practice in crime and general common law; subsequent specialisation as above.
Personal: Educated at Haberdashers' Aske's School, Elstree and St. John's College, Oxford (MA Jurisprudence). Leisure pursuits include music, walking, motor cycling.

KINGSLAND, Rt. Hon. Lord QC
4 Breams Buildings (Christopher Lockhart-Mummery QC), London (020) 7430 1221/7353 5835
Recommended in Environment
Specialisation: Waste and waste disposal; contaminated land; integrated pollution control; water resources; pollution and planning; European Community environmental law; judicial review.
Prof. Memberships: PEBA; UKELA; Bar European Group.
Career: Call to the Bar, 1972; Queen's Counsel, 1988; Member of the European Parliament 1979-94; Privy Counsellor 1994; Bencher of the Middle Temple since 1996; Recorder of the Crown Court, since 1997.
Publications: Contributor to Halsbury's Laws on Compulsory Acquisition and on the European Communities and to the Bar Council's 'Practitioners Handbook of EC Law on Environmental Law'.

KINGSTON, Martin QC
5 Fountain Court (Anthony Barker QC), Birmingham (0121) 606 0500
Recommended in Planning

KIRK, Anthony
One King's Bench Walk (Anthony Hacking QC), London (020) 7936 1500
Recommended in Family: Child Care including child abduction
Specialisation: Family (including Divorce and Children), Child Care, Family Provision, International Child Abduction.
Career: Recent cases include: Re B (Wardship: Abortion) 1991 2 FLR 426; Re H (A Minor) (Role of Official Solicitor) 1993 2 FLR 552; Essex County Council v B (Education Supervision Order) 1993 1 FLR 866; Re B (Child Sex Abuse: Standard of Proof) 1995 1 FLR 904; Re C (Adoption: Parties) 1995 2 FLR 483; Re B (Contempt Evidence) 1996 1 FLR 239. Re W (Minor) (Unmarried Father: Child Abduction) Re B (A Minor) (Unmarried father: Child Abduction) 1998 2 FLR 146; Re K (supervision orders) 1999 2 FLR 303. Re C (HIV test) 1999 2 FLR 1004.
Prof. Memberships: Committee member of the General Council of the Bar 1996-1999. Secretary of the Family Law Bar Association. Member of Family Mediators Association. Wrote the chapter in Jackson's 'Matrimonial Finance and Taxation' (6th edition) on 'Enforcement'.
Personal: Ipswich School and King Edward VII School, Lytham; Kings College London (LLB Hons AKC).

KITCHIN, David QC
8 New Square (Michael Fysh QC SC), London (020) 7405 4321
david.kitchin@8newsquare.co.uk
Recommended in Intellectual Property
Specialisation: All areas of intellectual property including patents, trade marks, passing off, copyright, designs, malicious falsehood, confidential information, media and entertainment law, computer law and EC and other competition law with an intellectual property element. Also handles some technical commercial work. Publications include 'The Trade Marks Act 1994' (Sweet & Maxwell) co-author; 'Kerly's Law of Trade Marks and Trade Names' (Sweet & Maxwell) co-editor; 'Patent Law of Europe and the United Kingdom' (Butterworths) co-editor.
Prof. Memberships: Chancery Bar Association, Intellectual Property Bar Association.
Career: Called to the Bar 1977 and joined chambers 1979. Took Silk 1994. Chairman, Code of Practice Committee, National Office of Animal Health (1995).
Personal: Educated at Oundle School 1968-1972 and Fitzwilliam College, Cambridge 1973-1976. Born 30th April 1955.

KNOWLES, Robin QC
3-4 South Square (Michael Crystal QC), London (020) 7696 9900
Recommended in Banking, Company, Insolvency/Corporate Recovery
Specialisation: Practice covers a wide aspect of general commercial, business and financial litigation, and legal advice, including banking and financial services, professional negligence and disciplinary and regulatory proceedings, commercial fraud, corporate insolvency and reconstruction, corporate and partnership disputes, pensions and charities, insurance and reinsurance.
Prof. Memberships: Recorder; Commercial Bar Association (Executive, Committee and Chairman, North American Committee); Bar Pro Bono Unit (Trustee and Management Committee); Chancery Bar Association; RCJ Advice Bureau (Management Committee). Talks have included 'Resolving disputes involving serious commercial fraud', 'Multi-party commercial disputes', 'Alternative dispute resolution', 'Co-operation between Courts in international insolvency', and 'The

CPR in Commercial Cases'. Member of various Bar Council and Bar working parties.
Career: Called to the Bar in 1982; Queen's Counsel 1999; Middle Temple (Hall Committee, co-opted); Gray's Inn; South Eastern Circuit (Committee, co-opted)
Personal: MA in Law.

KNOX, Christopher
Trinity Chambers (A.T. Hedworth QC), Newcastle upon Tyne (0191) 232 1927
Recommended in Family/Matrimonial
Specialisation: High value matrimonial property (and cohabitation) cases (not children or public law). Particularly with fiscal, company, pension, and missing money problems and sometimes trust problems.
Prof. Memberships: FLBA.
Career: Kings School, Tynemouth. Durham University. Recorder 1996.
Personal: Interests include crime and France.

KORN, Anthony
199 Strand (David Phillips QC), London (020) 7379 9779
Recommended in Employment
Specialisation: Specialises in all aspects of employment law, including sex, race, and disability discrimination, equal pay, TUPE, contracts of employment, restrictive covenants, unlawful deductions, redundancy and unfair dismissal. Appeared for the Respondent in Smith v Gardner Merchant (1998) – sex discrimination and sexual orientation.
Prof. Memberships: Employment Lawyers Association: member of management committee. Member of Employment Law Bar Association.
Career: Magdalen College, Oxford. Researcher on Industrial Relations Legal Information Bulletin (1982-90) and editor of Intellectual Property in Business (1989-90.) Previously employed as 'in house' counsel with *Paisner & Co* and *Dibb Lupton Broomhead.*

KOSMIN, Leslie QC
Erskine Chambers (Robin Potts QC), London (020) 7242 5532
Recommended in Company, Insolvency/Corporate Recovery

KOVATS, Steven
39 Essex Street (Nigel Pleming QC), London (020) 7832 1111
Recommended in Administrative & Public Law: General, Immigration

KRAMER, Philip
Plowden Buildings (William Lowe QC), London (020) 7583 0808
Recommended in Licensing

KRAMER, Stephen QC
1 Hare Court (Stephen Kramer QC), London (020) 7353 5324
Recommended in Crime
Specialisation: Criminal law specialist.
Prof. Memberships: Criminal Bar Association: Vice-Chairman 1999-2000. Chairman 2000-2001.
Career: Called to the Bar in 1970. Joined 1 Hare Court, Temple in 1988 from 10 King's Bench Walk. Assistant Recorder 1987-91. Recorder since 1991. Standing Counsel (Criminal Law) to Customs & Excise 1989-1995. Appointed QC 1995. Head of Chambers 1996 -.
Personal: Educated at Keble College, Oxford and the University of Nancy (France). Born 12th September 1947.

KUSHNER, Lindsey QC
28 St. John St (Clement Goldstone QC), Manchester (0161) 834 8418
Recommended in Family: Child Care including child abduction, Family/Matrimonial

KVERNDAL, Simon
4 Essex Court (Nigel Teare QC), London (020) 7653 5653
Recommended in Shipping

KYRIAKIDES, Tina
11 Stone Buildings (Murray Rosen QC), London (020) 7831 6381
kyriakides@11stonebuildings.com
Recommended in Insolvency/Corporate Recovery
Specialisation: Practises in commercial and Chancery litigation and advisory work, including contract, company law, corporate and personal insolvency, sale of goods, banking, guarantees and other securities, commercial fraud, credit and leasing transactions. Was appointed as an inspector for the Department of Trade and Industry to investigate insider dealing. An extremely effective advocate, she also has an excellent reputation for drafting and advising on company and commercial documentation.
Personal: Interests outside the law include the theatre and enjoying her Scottish art collection.

KYTE, Peter QC
Queen Elizabeth Building (Julian Bevan QC & Peter Whiteman QC), London (020) 7583 5766
Recommended in Fraud: Criminal
Specialisation: All aspects of crime, particularly commercial fraud, though recent practice has included murders, robberies and major drugs cases.
Prof. Memberships: Criminal Bar Association.
Career: Five years in mining finance and investment banking before practising at Bar. Called 1970, Recorder 1992, Silk 1996.
Personal: Trinity Hall Cambridge (MA Law). Ex-member NY Stock Exchange and Chicago Board of Trade. Married. Two children.

LACEY, Sarah H.
3 Stone Buildings (G.C. Vos QC), London (020) 7242 4937
Recommended in Pensions
Specialisation: Pensions litigation and advice, acting for beneficiaries, employers, administrators and trustees, including trustees and administrators of public sector schemes. Also covers other Chancery areas including commercial, partnership, trusts, tax and probate.
Prof. Memberships: Chancery Bar Association, Association of Pensions Lawyers, Association of Contentious Trust and Probate Specialists. Sits on the Professional Conduct Committee, Bar Council.
Career: Called to the Bar 1991, and joined 3 Stone Buildings in 1993.
Personal: Educated at Prince William School, Oundle (1982-1987) and Downing College, Cambridge (1987-1990). Enjoys walking, travelling and playing the piano.

LAIDLAW, Jonathan
1 Hare Court (Stephen Kramer QC), London (020) 7353 5324
Recommended in Crime

LAMBERT, Christina
6 Pump Court (Kieran Coonan QC), London (020) 7583 6013
Recommended in Clinical Negligence

LAMBERT, Julian
Albion Chambers (J.C.T. Barton QC), Bristol (0117) 927 2144
lambert@albionchambers.freeserve.co.uk
Recommended in Crime
Specialisation: Organised crime, corporate, commercial and regulatory offences, homicide and fraud. Disciplinary tribunals. Notable cases include: R v Canaan (1991) 92 Cr. App. R 16 (joinder with murder); R v Smith (1994) 15 Cr. App. R (S) 106 (contamination of goods); R v Sallis & Others (1994) 15 Cr. App. R (S) 281 (prison riots); R v Hampshire [1995] 2 Cr. App. R 219 (childrens' evidence); Attorney General's Reference No.s 25-27 of 1995 [1996] 2 Cr. App. R (S) 290 (racially aggravated GBH); R v Broad [1997] Crim. LR 666 (conspiracy to produce drugs); R v Sweeting and Thomas [1999] Crim. L.R. 75 (treatments statements section 23 CJA 1988); R v Taylor-Sabori [1999] 1 Cr. App. R 437 (interception of communications); R v GWTC – The Times, 3 July 1999 (corporate manslaughter, health and safety at work).
Prof. Memberships: Criminal Bar Association, Western Circuit.
Career: London School of Economics, call 1983, Assistant Recorder.

LANDAU, Toby
Essex Court Chambers (Gordon Pollock QC), London (020) 7813 8000
Recommended in Arbitration (International), Commercial (Litigation)
Specialisation: International and commercial arbitration. All aspects of international and commercial litigation.
Prof. Memberships: New York Bar Association; COMBAR; London Court of International Arbitration; Swiss Arbitration Association; Chartered Institute of Arbitrators (MCIArb); Co-Chair of the Young International Arbitration Group (LCIA); Editorial Board of the 'International Arbitration Law Review'.
Career: Merton College, Oxford: BA (Law) – First Class Hons (1990); MA (1994); Bachelor of Civil Law (BCL) – First Class Hons (1991); Eldon Scholarship (1991); Harvard Law School: LL.M (1993); Kennedy Scholarship & Lewis Fellowship; Called to the Bar in 1993 (Middle Temple Queen Mother Scholarship & Harmsworth Exhibition); Admitted as an Attorney-at-Law by the state of New York in 1994; Called to the Bar of Northern Ireland in 2000. Retained by the DTI to advise on and assist in the drafting of the Arbitration Act 1996 (with Lord Saville). Advised on the arbitration provisions of the Contract (Rights of Third Parties) Act 1999 and the ACAS Employment arbitration scheme. Member of the Lord Chancellor's Department Committee on the Hague Judgments Convention. Member of the UK delegation to UNCITRAL (2000). Annual visiting lecturer on arbitration law at the Asser Instituut in The Hague. Legal consultant to the Ministry of Justice of Thailand (Arbitration Office): 1993.
Publications: Publications include 'The English Arbitration Act 1996: Text and Notes' (with Martin Hunter), Kluwer 1998.
Personal: Born 1967.

LANDES, Anna-Rose
St Philip's Chambers (Rex Tedd QC), Birmingham (0121) 246 7000
Recommended in Insolvency/Corporate Recovery

LANDSBURY, Alan
6 Gray's Inn Square (Michael Boardman), London (020) 7242 1052
Recommended in Crime

LANG, Beverley QC
Blackstone Chambers (P Baxendale QC and C Flint QC), London (020) 7583 1770
Recommended in Administrative & Public Law: General, Employment
Specialisation: Public law, civil liberties, employment and discrimination law. Interesting cases include DPP v Hutchinson (Greenham Common Byelaws held unlawful by the House of Lords.); Lloyd v McMahon (surcharged Liverpool Labour Councillors); Thomas v NUM (right of striking miners to picket); Halford v Sharples (acted for Assistant Chief Constable Alison Halford in her sex discrimination claim against Merseyside Police); Christmas v Hampshire County

Council (House of lords held duty of care owed by teachers to children with special education needs); ex parte S (admission to mental hospital and Caesarean section against patient's wishes); R v CCRC ex parte Pearson test case on powers of the Criminal Cases Review Commission. Publications include articles for the Modern Law Review, Industrial Law Journal and Legal Action and co-author of Public Law Project's 'Applicant's Guide to Judicial Review'.
Career: Called to the Bar 1978. Appointed part-time chairman of Industrial Tribunal 1995. Former lecturer in law at the University of East Anglia.
Personal: Born 13 October 1955.

LANGDALE, Timothy QC
Queen Elizabeth Building (Julian Bevan QC & Peter Whiteman QC), London (020) 7583 5766
Recommended in Crime, Fraud: Criminal
Specialisation: Principal area of practice is all aspects of criminal law with an emphasis on high profile, serious crime cases and commercial fraud.
Prof. Memberships: Criminal Bar Association.
Career: Called to the Bar 1966. Treasury Counsel 1979-1992. QC 1992.

LANGDON, Andrew
Guildhall Chambers (Adrian Palmer QC), Bristol (0117) 927 3366
Recommended in Crime

LANGSTAFF, Brian QC
Cloisters (Laura Cox QC), London (020) 7827 4000
Recommended in Employment, Personal Injury, Product Liability
Specialisation: Principal area of practice is personal injury, collective employment and Trade Union cases. Has been instructed in most major industrial disputes (eg ambulancemen's strike, coal strike, Wapping) since the early 1980s and many important collective employment and Trade Union cases, although majority of practice has been in cases of serious personal injury (usually caused at work). Other area of practice is medical negligence and product liability, including actions against drug producers. Important cases include Page v Hull University (employment), Walker v Northumberland CC (personal injury: stress at work), Reay & Hope v BNFL (The 'Sellafield' case), Peach v Metropolitan Police (Fatal assault by police/discovery issues), Ratcliffe v North Yorkshire CC (Equal Pay), News International v SOGAT (picketing: the 'Wapping' dispute), Clarke & Others v NUM (Miners' strike), Milligan & Securicor (TUPE; employment); R v Employment Secretary ex parte Unison (Judicial Review, employment). Adams v Lancs CC (Transfers of Undertaking); Clark v BET (the largest award yet for wrongful dismissal); Carmichael v National Power (contracts of employment); Jesuthasan v Hammersmith (discrimination); MOD v Wheeler (compensation); Barber v RJB Mining (working time); Quinn v MOD (mesothelioma); Jolley v Sutton (personal injury); Humphreys v Oxford (TUPE) and the 'tobacco' cases. Appointed Council to Inquiry into Bristol Heart Babies deaths. Major lay clients include most Trade Unions and their members as well as legally aided victims of accidents (both factory and medical). Professional clients include Trade Union solicitors (in private practice and in-house), law centres, medical and environmental practices and the Medical Defence Union. Former senior lecturer in law. Conference speaker on equal pay and employment issues, and employers' liability for work-related illnesses.
Prof. Memberships: Chairman of PIBA (1999); Judge of E.A. (2000); LCLCBA; ELBA; ALBA; ILS (Committee Member).
Career: Called to the Bar in 1971. Lecturer in law 1971-1975. Joined present Chambers in 1977. Appointed Assistant Recorder in 1991, Recorder 1995. Member of Northern Ireland Bar. Took Silk in 1994.
Publications: Consulting Editor 'Bullen & Leake'. Author of 'Health & Safety at Work' in Vol. 20 of Halsbury's Laws (4th edn) and of various articles in journals.
Personal: Educated at George Heriot's School, Edinburgh 1953-1966 and St. Catharine's College, Cambridge 1967-1970. Governor of local primary school. Enjoys sport, theatre and TV, politics, mowing the lawn, his family and travel.

LAPRELL, Mark
18 St. John Street (Jonathan Foster QC), Manchester (0161) 278 1800
Recommended in Personal Injury

LASOK, Paul QC
Monckton Chambers (John Swift QC), London (020) 7405 7211
Recommended in Competition/Anti-trust, Tax
Specialisation: Specialist in all aspects of European Community law. Main areas of work include agriculture, competition, trade law and VAT. Publications include 'The European Court of Justice: Practice and Procedure' (Butterworths 2nd edition 1994). European editor of 'Weinberg & Blank on Take-Overs and Mergers' (Sweet & Maxwell). Joint editor of the Common Market Law Reports and CMLR Antitrust Reports. Cases include R v HM Treasury, ex parte British Telecommunications (1996, CA and ECJ: public procurement, interlocutory injunction, state liability); Hopkins v National Power and Powergen (1996, High Court and ECJ: ECSC/ EC competition law); Commission v United Kingdom (1997, ECJ; prduct liability); United Kingdom v Commission (1998, ECJ; BSE); Marks & Spencers v GCE (2000, CA: VAT capping); Three Rivers District Council v Bank of England (2000 HL, liability of banking regulator).
Prof. Memberships: Bar European Group.
Career: Called to the Bar 1977. Legal secretary (law clerk) to Advocate-General J.P Warner and Advocate-General Sir Gordon Slynn, Court of Justice of the European Communities 1980-84. Private practice in Brussels, specialising in European Community law 1985-1987.
Personal: Educated at Jesus College, Cambridge 1972-1975 (MA) and at Exeter University 1975-1977 (LL.M). PhD Exeter University 1986.

LATHAM, Robert
Doughty Street Chambers (Geoffrey Robertson QC), London (020) 7404 1313
r.latham@doughtystreet.co.uk
Recommended in Human Rights (Civil Liberties)
Specialisation: Housing, administrative law and civil liberties. Recent judicial review applications have related to unfair and irrational allocation policies, housing duty owed to asylum seekers, assessment of housing need, renewed applications for accommodation, duty to act fairly, interaction between housing and community care duties, abuse of power by councillors. Involved in a number of group actions involving disrepair, asbestos, infestations, environmental protection and noise nuisance, including the 'Kingshold Estate' (see Legal Action, October 1995).
Career: Former councillor and health authority member. Currently Chairs the National Association of Victim Support Schemes.

LAURENCE, George QC
12 New Square (John Mowbray QC), London (020) 7419 1212
Recommended in Traditional Chancery, Parliamentary & Public Affairs
Specialisation: Practice encompasses property litigation (including landlord and tenant, planning and judicial review), parliamentary and countryside law (rights of way, commons). Has appeared frequently as counsel before opposed Bill Committees in both Houses of Parliament. Promoted Wye Navigation Order for Environment Agency under TWA 1992 [1997]. Acted in numerous reported cases, many on rights of way, including Celsteel v Alton House [1986]; R v Secretary of State for Environment ex parte, Rubinstein [1990], Burrows [1991], O'Keefe [1993, 1996], Cowell [1993, CA], Bagshaw [1994], Emery [1997, CA], Billson [1998], White v Minnis [1999], Sunningwell [1999], Masters [2000].
Career: Called to the Bar 1972. Joined 9 Old Square 1973; current chambers January 1991. Took Silk April 1991. Appointed Recorder 2000. Appointed Deputy High Court Judge (Chancery) 1997.
Personal: Educated at University of Cape Town 1966-68 (BA) and University College, Oxford 1969-71 (MA). Rhodes Scholar. Leisure pursuits include sport and theatre. Born 15th January 1947. Lives in London.

LAWRENCE, Heather
11 South Square (Christopher Floyd QC), London (020) 7405 1222
Recommended in Intellectual Property
Specialisation: All aspects of intellectual property: patents, trade marks, copyright, registered and unregistered design right, passing off and breach of confidence; other matters with a technical content such as computer contract disputes, and data protection.
Prof. Memberships: Intellectual Property Bar Association (formerly Patent Bar Association) (Hon. Sec, 1992-1997) Royal Society of Chemistry (Associate Member).
Career: BA Hons (1st Class) Oxon (Chemistry). MA, DPHIL Oxon (Chemistry). Called to the Bar October 1991 (Middle Temple).

LAWRENCE, Patrick
4 Paper Buildings (Jean Ritchie QC), London (020) 7353 3366
Recommended in Professional Negligence
Specialisation: Principal area of practice is professional negligence. Cases include Bristol & West BS v May, May & Merrimans [1996] 2 All ER 801; Penn v Bristol & West BS [1997] 1 WLR 1356; Bristol & West BS v Fancy & Jackson [1997] 4 All ER 582; Platform Home Loans Ltd v Oyston Shipways Ltd, [1998] CH 466.
Prof. Memberships: PNBA.
Career: B.A. (Oxon). Called 1985.

LAWSON, Edmund QC
9-12 Bell Yard (D. Anthony Evans QC), London (020) 7400 1800
Recommended in Crime, Fraud: Criminal

LAWSON, Michael QC
23 Essex Street (Michael Lawson QC), London (020) 7413 0353
Recommended in Crime, Fraud: Criminal
Specialisation: Criminal law specialist. Practice covers general crime, serious organized crime, drugs, child sexual abuse and commercial fraud. Contributor to the Inns of Court School of Law Manual of Professional Conduct and author of 'Refocus on Child abuse'(1994). Experience of advocacy teaching. Governing Committee IATC.
Prof. Memberships: Criminal Bar Association.
Career: Called to the Bar in 1969 and joined present chambers in 1971. Appointed Assistant Recorder in 1983 and Recorder in 1987. Took Silk in 1991. Leader of the South Eastern Circuit Nov 1997-2000. Boundary Commissioner 2000.
Personal: Educated at Monkton Combe School 1959-1964 and London University 1966-1969. Born 3rd February 1946.

LAWSON, Robert
4 Essex Court (Nigel Teare QC), London
(020) 7653 5653
rlawson@4sx.co.uk
Recommended in Aviation
Specialisation: All aspects of aviation litigation and advisory work. In particular: aviation insurance; liability of carriers, manufacturers, maintainers and tour operators; regulatory issues; aircraft leases and finance; and, arrest of aircraft.
Prof. Memberships: COMBAR
Career: BA (Oxon). Dip Law (City). Called 1989.

LE GRICE, Valentine
1 Mitre Court Buildings (Bruce Blair QC), London (020) 7797 7070
legrice@lmcb.com
Recommended in Family: Matrimonial Finance
Specialisation: Ancillary relief.
Prof. Memberships: FLBA; PNBA.
Career: Called to the Bar in 1977.
Publications: Editor of 'At a Glance.'
Personal: BA (Durham).

LEAVER, Peter QC
One Essex Court (Lord Grabiner QC), London
(020) 7583 2000
Recommended in Commercial (Litigation), Sport

LEDERMAN, David QC
18 Red Lion Court (Anthony Arlidge QC), London
(020) 7520 6000
Recommended in Crime
Specialisation: Crime in all its aspects from fraud to robbery to murder to Brinks Gold Bullion Robbery.
Prof. Memberships: C.B.A.
Career: Cambridge M.A.
Personal: Eating, drinking, sport, theatre, cinema, opera, history, reading.

LEECH, Thomas
9 Old Square (Michael Driscoll QC), London
(020) 7405 4682
Recommended in Commercial Chancery, Property Litigation
Specialisation: Modern chancery practitionar with particular experience in commercial chancery litigation (including equitable remedies, fiduciary duties, financial services, offshore trusts, share disputes, telecommunications and warranty claims), professional negligence (including Auditors, barristers, investigating accountants, solicitors, surveyors, valuers and US attorneys) and property litigation (including commercial landlord and tenant, leasehold valuation and real property). He was junior counsel for the plaintiff in the Nationwide managed litigation and is junior counsel for a number of the defendants in Thyssen-Bornemisa v Thyssen-Bornemisa in Bermuda. Notable cases include Target Holdings Ltd v Redferns (1996) AC 421 (breach of trust), Mannai Investments Ltd v Eagle Star (1997) 1 BCLC 390 (share warranty, rectification), Electra Private Equity Partners v KPMG Peat Marwick (1998) PNLR 137 (auditors' duty of care), Nationwide BS v Balmer Radmore (1999) Lloyd's Rep (PN) 241 (solicitors' negligence, managed litigation).
Career: Educated at Lancaster Royal Grammar School and Wadham College, Oxford (MA, BCL), called in 1988 (Harmsworth Major Scholar of the Middle Temple, winner of the Astbury Prize).
Prof. Memberships: Chancery Bar Association, Professional Negligence Bar Association.
Publications: 'Flenley & Leech, Solicitors' Negligence' (Butterworths, 1999), contributor to the Lloyds's Law Reports (PN).

LEEMING, Ian QC
9 St. John Street (John Hand QC), Manchester
(0161) 955 9000
Recommended in Chancery
Specialisation: Chancery and commercial litigation; building and construction work (technology and construction court/arbitrations). Insolvency, contentious company work, banking, professional negligence and civil fraud are emphasised. Reported cases include Williams v Burlington (1977) (Company Charges) Brady v Brady (1988) (Financial assistance for purchase of shares). Re: Abbey Leisure (1990) (Unfair prejudice petitions) P&C&R&T Ltd (1991) (Administrators and Section 11 of Insolvency Act 1986). Sen v. Headly (1991) (death-bed gifts of land). Connaught Restaurants (1992) (Indemnity costs in forfeiture proceedings). Morse v Barratt (1993) (exception to Murphy v Brentwood principles). Re Jennings (1994) (Family provisions claims). Kershaw v Whelan (1996) (Discovery and waiver of Professional Privilege). Kershaw v Whelan (No. 2) (1997) (Fiduciary duties). Hurst v Bryk (1999) (solicitors partnership dispute).
Prof. Memberships: Chancery Bar Association; Northern Chancery Bar Association;TECBAR; Professional Negligence Bar Association; Society of Construction Law.
Career: Called 1970. Silk 1988. Recorder of the Crown Court 1989. Practised at Northern Chancery and Commercial Bar until taking silk. Since has divided time between London and Manchester. Joined Lamb Chambers 1992. Deputy Deemster 1998.
Personal: Born 10 April 1948. Manchester University LL.B (1970). Sometime lecturer in Law Manchester University. Interests: the family; gourmet food; sports cars.

LEES, Andrew J.
St. Paul's Chambers (Nigel Sangster QC), Leeds
(0113) 245 5866
Recommended in Crime

LEGGATT, George QC
Brick Court Chambers (Christopher Clarke QC), London (020) 7379 3550
Recommended in Commercial (Litigation), Insurance
Specialisation: Commercial Law: including insurance and reinsurance, banking, professional negligence (involving accountants, actuaries, insurance brokers, solicitors and barristers), shipping, company acquisitions and international trade. Other areas of practice include defamation, broadcasting law and judicial review.
Career: Called 1983; QC 1997; cases of note: Westdeutsche Landesbank v Islington; NRG v Bacon & Woodrow; Hill v M&G; Guiness Mahon v Kensington & Chelsea.

LEGGE, Henry
5 Stone Buildings (Henry Harrod), London
(020) 7242 6201
Recommended in Traditional Chancery
Specialisation: Chancery practitioner with particular emphasis on onshore and offshore trusts with related taxation issues and on pensions and professional negligence. Recent cases include Adam International Trustees v *Theodore Goddard* (2000) (professional negligence relating to failed export of trust), Meegan v Commercial Vehicle Spares (enforcement of determination of the Pensions Ombudsman) (1998) and Evans v Westcombe (1999) (missing beneficiary indemnity policies and relief from breach of trust). Particular experience of disputes arising out of venture capital acquisitions. Has contributed articles to 'Trusts and Estates Law Journal' and to 'Private Client Business.'
Career: Called in 1993.
Personal: Educated Eton College and Worcester College, Oxford

LEIGH, Christopher H. de V. QC
1 Paper Buildings (Roger Titheridge QC), London
(020) 7353 3728
Recommended in Crime

LEIST, Ian
1 Hare Court (Stephen Kramer QC), London
(020) 7353 5324
Recommended in Crime

LEONARD, Anthony QC
6 King's Bench Walk (Michael Worsley QC), London (020) 7583 0410
worsley@6kbw.freeserve.co.uk
Recommended in Crime
Specialisation: General criminal practice with a concentration on fraud.
Prof. Memberships: Inner Temple, South Eastern Circuit, Criminal Bar Association.
Career: Called to the Bar in 1978 and joined current chambers in 1979. Standing Counsel to the Inland Revenue, South Eastern Circuit 1993-1999. Took Silk 1999.
Personal: Leisure interests include music and theatre. Born 21st April 1956. Lives in London.

LESLIE, Stephen QC
Furnival Chambers (Andrew Mitchell QC), London (020) 7405 3232
Recommended in Crime
Specialisation: General and Commerical/White Collar crime (including overseas) Criminal Taxation Appeals. Privy Council Commonwealth Appeals.
Prof. Memberships: Criminal Bar Association. South Eastern though practise on other circuits.
Career: Call 1971. Silk 1993.

LESTER OF HERNE HILL, Lord QC
Blackstone Chambers (P Baxendale QC and C Flint QC), London (020) 7583 1770
Recommended in Administrative & Public Law: General, Human Rights (Civil Liberties)
Specialisation: Lord Lester of Herne Hill QC specialises in public law, employment, media and European law. He was called to the English Bar in 1963, appointed QC in 1975 and a Bencher of Lincoln's Inn in 1985. He became a Life Peer in 1993. He is a former Recorder and Deputy High Court Judge. He was Special Adviser to the Home Secretary (Roy Jenkins) 1974-1976 on anti-discrimination legislation. He campaigned for thirty years for a Human Rights Act, and is President of INTERIGHTS and a Council and Executive member of JUSTICE. He is co-editor of Butterworths 'Human Rights Law and Practice' (1999), and Honorary Professor of Public Law and University College London. He has argued many leading public law cases in England, in other Commonwealth countries and before both European Courts. He is married to a Special Immigration and Asylum Adjudicator and they have a son and a daughter.

LETT, Brian
South Western Chambers (Brian Lett), Taunton
(01823) 331919
lett@SouthWesternChambers_co.uk
Recommended in Crime
Specialisation: H.Brian G.Lett Born 9/8/1949. Called Inner Temple 1971. Practiced exclusively at the London Bar until 1992 when he moved to the West of England and joined the Western Circuit. Now practises mainly in London and the West. Specialises in serious crime and in particular serious fraud. Equally happy prosecuting or defending. Has prosecuted all types of crime as a leading junior, including murders and serious fraud [instructed by the S.F.O]. Led the defence team in many cases involving professional defendants [solicitors, accountants and policemen]. Has particular

experience in defending United States citizens. Defends regularly before disciplinary tribunals.
Prof. Memberships: Criminal Bar Association. Central Criminal Court Bar Mess.
Personal: Married with 4 children of school age. R.F.U. youth coach. Chairman – Monte San Martino Trust.

LEVER, Bernard
Peel Court Chambers (Michael Shorrock QC), Manchester (0161) 832 3791
Recommended in Crime

LEVER, Jeremy QC
Monckton Chambers (John Swift QC), London (020) 7405 7211
chambers@monckton.co.uk
Recommended in Competition/Anti-trust
Specialisation: Administrative law, Competition Law, European Community Law, International and Comparative Law, Utilities Regulation. R v Secretary of State for Trade and Industry, ex p. Isle of Wight Council, 7 April 2000 (judicial review, EC Law).
Prof. Memberships: Council of Management and Executive Committee, British Institute of International and Comparative Law.
Career: Fellow (1957-) and Senior Dean (1988-), All Souls College, Oxford. Director (non-ex), Dunlop Holdings Ltd. 1973-80; Wellcome plc 1983-94; Member, Arbitral Tribunal, US/UK Arbitration concerning Heathrow Airport User Charges 1989-94. Visiting Fellow Wiessenschaftszentrum Berlin fur Sozialforschung, 1999.
Publications: 'Butterworths Competition Law' (consulting editor); Wienberg & Blank, 'Takeovers & Mergers'; 'Common Law of Europe', 'Tort Law' (comparative casebooks); Bellamy & Child, 'Common Market Law of Competition', 1st-3rd eds. (consulting edditor).
Personal: Educated: Bradfield College, Berks; University College Oxford and Nuffield College, Oxford. Interests include classical music and porcelain.

LEVESON, Brian QC
22 Old Buildings (Benet Hytner QC), London (020) 7831 0222
Recommended in Clinical Negligence, Sport
Specialisation: Commercial and general common law including medical and other professional negligence. Regulatory and disciplinary investigations and tribunals in commercial, professional and sports fields.
Career: Called to the Bar, 1970; Queens Counsel 1986; Recorder 1988; Deputy High Court Judge 1998.
Personal: Educated at Liverpool College and Merton College Oxford (1967-1970); married with three children.

LEVY, Allan QC
17 Bedford Row (Allan Levy QC), London (020) 7831 7314
Recommended in Family: Child Care including child abduction
Specialisation: Expertise in child law, medical law and human rights law. Appeared in numerous leading cases in House of Lords, Court of Appeal and European Court of Human Rights including Re F (sterilisation), Re M (Children Act), Re H (Children Act), Barratt v L.B. of Enfield (negligence), W v Essex CC (negligence) and A v UK (Art 3 ECHR). Author and editor of books on child law and child abuse. Frequent broadcaster and lecturer. Chairman, Staffordshire Pindown Inquiry 1990-91.
Prof. Memberships: Fellow, Royal Society of Medicine, honorary legal advisor National Children's Bureau; Council of Justice.
Career: Called to the Bar 1969. Silk 1989. Recorder 1993.
Personal: Educated Bury Grammar School 1953-1961 and Hull University 1961-1964.

LEVY, Jacob
9 Gough Square (Jeremy Roberts QC), London (020) 7832 0500
Recommended in Personal Injury
Specialisation: All aspects of clincal negligence and personal injury work, particularly cases involving dental, gynaecological and orthopaedic problems. Has a particular interest in industrial disease work, principally deafness but also work-related upper limb disorders. Bulk of personal injury work comprises slippers, trippers, snippers, lifters, and rear-end shunters.
Career: LLB (Hons) London (LSE) 1984. Called July 1986 and joined 9 Gough Square following pupillage there with John Foy and John Reddihough.
Personal: Young family prevents anything much other than supporting failing football team (as well as playing in one) and watching late night TV whilst eating pizza. Otherwise fanatical film & music buff. Byline! "Eat football, sleep football – practice PI".

LEVY, Michael
2 Bedford Row (formerly 3 Hare Court) (William Clegg QC), London (020) 7440 8888
Recommended in Crime
Specialisation: Wholly criminal practice - mostly defence, but not exclusively. General crime and fraud. Regular leading work. Recent cases include: R v Serafinowicz (The first ever prosecution under the War Crimes Act); Jelesic (War Crimes Case at the International Criminal Tribunal for the Former Yugoslavia, The Hague.); R v Murphy & Others (Importation of £125 million of cocaine); R v Nicolson & Others (Gas Oil Fraud); R v Khaliq & Others (Nigerian Advance Fee fraud). R v Jeans & Others. (Drug Importation).
Prof. Memberships: South Eastern Circuit. Member of Criminal Bar Association. Member of International Criminal Law Association. British Academy of Forensic Science.
Career: Called to Bar in 1979 - Gray's Inn.

LEVY, Neil
St John's Chambers (Christopher Sharp QC), Bristol (0117) 921 3456
clerks@stjohnschambers.co.uk
Recommended in Commercial (Litigation)
Specialisation: Banking. Cases of note: Jarrett v Barclays Bank [1999] QB 1; Natwest Bank v Story, The Times 14.5.99; Woolwich plc v Gomm, 27.7.99 (CA).
Prof. Memberships: Chancery Bar Association.
Career: Called to the Bar 1986. In-house lawyer, Lloyds Bank 1987. Joined St John's Chambers 1992.
Personal: Contributor to Paget's Law of Banking, 11th ed (1996) and to Law and Practice of Domestic Banking (Penn & Wadsley), 2nd ed in preparation.

LEWIS, Adam
Blackstone Chambers (P Baxendale QC and C Flint QC), London (020) 7583 1770
Recommended in Sport
Specialisation: European Community law within a public, commercial, competition and sports law practice.
Career: Call 1985. Professional experience with *Wilmer Cutler & Pickering* in Washington DC and London and *McCutcheon Doyle Brown & Enersen* in San Francisco between 1985-88, and in the Cabinet of Sir Leon Brittan, European Commissioner responsible for competition and financial institutions, in Brussels in 1991-1992.
Personal: Fluent in French and a working knowledge of German and Norwegian.

LEWIS, Clive
4-5 Gray's Inn Square (Elizabeth Appleby QC & Duncan Ouseley QC), London (020) 7404 5252
clewis@4-5graysinnsquare.co.uk
Recommended in Administrative & Public Law: General
Specialisation: Main areas of practice are public law and judicial review, EC law, education, local government, discrimination and environmental law. Interesting cases include R v HM Treasury ex p. Shepherd Neame Ltd (1998) (compatability of budget increases on beer duty with European law) Richardson v Solihull MBC (special educational needs) Preston v Wolverhampton NHS Trust (1998) (compatibility of time limits for equal pay claims with European law) Barry v Midland Bank plc (1999) (sex discrimination in calculation of redundancy payments) R v Secretary of State ex p. RSPB (1996) (Birds Directive) R v Powys Council ex p. Hambridge (1998) (power to charge for provision of community care services) R v Maldon DC ex p. Pattini (1998) (lawfulness of provision of pharmaceutical services in a supermarket) R v Secretary of State ex p. Lancashire CC (1994) (local government reorganisation). Publications include 'Judicial Remedies in Public Law' (2000, 2nd), and 'Remedies and the Enforcement of European Community Law' (1996). Editor, Civil Procedure (The White Book).
Prof. Memberships: Administrative Law Bar Association; Bar European Group.
Career: Fellow, Selwyn College, Cambridge 1986-1993, Lecturer in Law, University of Cambridge 1989-1993. Called to the Bar 1987. Joined present chambers in 1992.

LEWIS, Hugh
Southernhay Chambers (Anthony Ward), Exeter (01392) 255777
Recommended in Family/Matrimonial
Specialisation: Principally Children Act Care proceedings and adoption. Some Private Law child cases.
Prof. Memberships: Family Law Bar Association.
Career: Educated Clifton College and Birmingham University. T.A. Called 1970. Family law specialist throughout career.
Personal: Born 1946. Married with 4 children. Leisure pursuits – hill-walking, skiing, fishing, study of history and archaeology.

LEWIS, James
3 Raymond Buildings (Clive Nicholls QC), London (020) 7400 6400
chambers@threeraymond.demon.co.uk
Recommended in Crime
Specialisation: Extradition; fraud: judicial review of criminal matters and especially review of warrants; case stated; restraint orders; election work. Recent notable cases: R v Bow Street Magistrate ex parte Pinochet (No. 1) [1998] 3 WLR 1456, (No. 2) [1999] 2 WLR 272, (No.3) [1999] 2 WLR 287; R v Governor of Brixton Prison ex parte Levin [1997] AC 741; R v Secretary of State for the Home Department ex parte Launder HL [1997] 1 WLR 839 (HL); R v Secretary of State for the Home Department ex parte Gilmore [1997] 2 Cr App R 374. R v Bow Street Magistrates Court [1998] 2 WLR 498; R v Staines Magistrates Court ex parte Westfallen [1998] 1 WLR 652; Government of Switzerland v Rey [1998] 3 WLRI (PC). R v Governor of Belmarsh Prison ex parte Gilligan (No 2) [1998] COD 195. Private prosecution for the Hillsborough Family Support Group 1996-2000.
Career: B.Sc. (Hons). Call 1987. Recorder of the Crown Court 2000

LEWIS, Paul
30 Park Place (John Jenkins QC), Cardiff
(029) 2039 8421
Recommended in Crime

LEWIS, Ralph QC
5 Fountain Court (Anthony Barker QC), Birmingham (0121) 606 0500
Recommended in Personal Injury

LEWIS, Raymond
2 Paper Buildings (Desmond de Silva QC), London (020) 7556 5500
Recommended in Crime
Personal: Commercial/company fraud and appeared in a number of high profile cases over past few years. Firearms expert.
Career: 6 years working for merchant bank in corporate finance.
Personal: First novel published 1991.

LEWIS, Rhodri Price
1 Serjeants' Inn (Lionel Read QC), London (020) 7583 1355
Recommended in Environment, Planning
Specialisation: Principal area of practice is town and country planning and environmental law including judicial review, public inquiries and statutory appeals to the High Court. Clients include development and waste disposal companies, waste regulation authorities and county and district councils. Author of article on 'Waste Management' in Journal of Planning and Environmental Law 1993. Co-author `Environmental Law` OUP 2000
Prof. Memberships: Local Government Planning and Environmental Bar Association, Midland and Oxford Circuit, UK Environmental Law Association 1999
Career: Called to the Bar 1975. Appointed Assistant Recorder 1994. Member of Treasury Solicitor's Supplementary Panel (Planning).
Personal: M.A. Oxon 1970-1973, Dip.Crim (Cantab) 1973-1974. Born 7th June 1952.

LEWIS, Robert
Clarendon Chambers, Redhill (01737) 780781
Recommended in Environment

LEWISON, Kim QC
Falcon Chambers (Jonathan Gaunt QC & Kim Lewison QC), London (020) 7353 2484
Recommended in Property Litigation
Specialisation: Specialises in Chancery and real property law. Practice covers landlord and tenant, rent review, interpretation of contracts, agricultural holdings, conveyancing, easements, restrictive covenants, compulsory acquisitions, suretyship and professional negligence in connection with real property. Recent reported cases include Southwark LBC v Mills (quiet enjoyment); Bruton v London and Quadrant (licence or tenancy); Hindcastle v Barbara Attenborough Associates (disclaimer on insolvency); Jervis v Harris (entry to repair); Curtis v London Rent Assessment Committee (fair rent). In 1988 appointed by the Department of the Environment as a member of the Study Team investigating professional negligence and insurance against professional liability. Blundell lecturer three times.
Prof. Memberships: COMBAR; London Common Law & Commercial Bar Association; Chancery Bar Association. Governor of Anglo-American Real Property Institute 1995-1997, Chairman elect 2000.
Career: Called to the Bar in 1975. Member of *Falcon Chambers* since 1976. Took Silk 1991. Appointed Assistant Recorder in 1993. Recorder 1997. Deputy High Court Judge 2000 Bencher *Lincoln's Inn.*
Publications: Publications include 'Woodfall on Landlord and Tenant' (General Editor since 1990); 'The Interpretation of Contracts' (1997); 'Lease or Licence' (1985); 'Development Land Tax' (1976); 'Drafting Business Leases' (1996). Consultant Editor of Property & Compensation Reports since 1990.
Personal: Educated at St. Paul's School 1965-1970 and Downing College, Cambridge (1st Class Hons in English Tripos) 1970-1973. Fluent French speaker. Council Member of the Liberal Jewish Synagogue 1989-1995; Council Member Leo Baeck College. Trustee Centre for Jewish Education.

LIEVEN, Nathalie
4 Breams Buildings (Christopher Lockhart-Mummery QC), London
(020) 7430 1221/7353 5835
Recommended in Administrative & Public Law: General, Parliamentary & Public Affairs, Planning
Specialisation: Planning, public and administrative law including local government, social security, education, mental health and community care. Has promoted a number of Parliamentary Bills. Recent cases include Nessa v Chief Adjudication Officer; R v Leominster DC ex p Pothecary; White v Special Educational Needs Tribunal.
Career: Called to the Bar in 1989. Appointed to the Supplementary Panel of Junior Counsel to the Crown (Common Law) in 1995. Member of the Planning and Environmental Bar Association and the Administrative Law Bar Association.
Personal: Educated at Godolphin and Latymer School and Trinity Hall, Cambridge. Awarded Karmel, Reid and Prince of Wales Scholarships at Grays Inn.

LIGHTWING, Stuart
Counsel's Chambers (Stuart Lightwing), Middlesbrough (01642) 315000
Recommended in Family/Matrimonial
Specialisation: Family/matrimonial finance, employment, medical and other professional negligence, personal injury and partnership.
Prof. Memberships: Professional Negligence and the Family Law Bar Association.
Career: LL.B, FCIS, FRSA, MIMgt, FCIArb. Called 1972 (M.T). Harmsworth Law Scholar. Also barrister in NSW, Australia. Chairman of Appeal Tribunals.

LIMB, Patrick
Ropewalk Chambers (Richard Maxwell QC), Nottingham (0115) 947 2581
Recommended in Personal Injury
Specialisation: All personal injuries actions including tort claims for psychiatric harm and industrial diseases litigation. Hicks v Chief Constable of South Yorkshire Police [1992] 2 AER 63, Alcock v Chief Constable of South Yorkshire Police [1992] 1 AC 310, Frost v Chief Constable of South Yorkshire Police [1997] 3 WLR 1195, Bannister v SGB plc [1997] 4 AER 129, VSEL v Cape [1998] PIQR 207, Tranmore v Scudder (CAT April 28, 1998).
Prof. Memberships: Personal Injuries Bar Association; Nottinghamshire Medico-Legal Society.
Career: The Edinburgh Academy; Pembroke College, Cambridge.

LINDBLOM, Keith QC
2 Harcourt Buildings (Mr Gerard Ryan QC), London (020) 7353 8415
Recommended in Planning
Specialisation: Planning, Local Government, Parliamentary, Compulsory Purchase and Compensation Law. Work for both private and public sector clients.
Prof. Memberships: Planning and Environment Bar Association; Parliamentary Bar Mess.
Career: Called to the Bar 1980. Joined 2 Harcourt Buildings (Gerard Ryan QC) in 1981. QC 1996.

LINDEN, Thomas
Matrix Chambers (Nicholas Blake QC), London
(020) 7404 3447
Recommended in Employment
Specialisation: Employment law, discrimination law, public law, human rights and sports law. His employment law work tends to be cases which overlap with commercial law (restraint of trade, breach of contract, executive terminations), appellate work, cases with a European dimension (transfer of undertakings, equal pay, working time) and collective labour law (industrial action, recognition, etc). His discrimination law work covers race, sex and disability discrimination in a range of legal contexts. His sports cases include disputes between sportsmen and clubs or agents, and cases concerning doping in sport. A cross section of his reported cases includes TGWU v Middlesbrook Mushrooms CA (whether a campaign for a consumer boycott of an employer's products in the context of an industrial dispute is an economic tort); Wren v Eastbourne BC EAT (No.s 1 and 2) (the first case in the UK to decide that the Transfer of Undertakings Regulations may apply to contracting out in the public sector); NUT v St Mary's C of E (Aided) School CA (whether the governors of a voluntary aided school are an emanation of the state for the purposes of the doctrine of direct effect in EU law); Carver v Saudi Airlines CA (on the scope for employees working abroad to sue in domestic tribunals for unfair dismissal and discrimination); McCoid v Farnsworth Ltd CA (whether derecognition of a shop steward is "action short of dismissal" for the purposes of a trade union victimisation claim) and Askew v Governing Body of Clifton Middle School and Others CA (on the liabilities of governing bodies in the event of amalgamation of schools).
Prof. Memberships: The Employment Lawyers Association, Administrative Law Bar Association.
Career: BA Jurisprudence (First Class) and BCL at Keble College, Oxford 1984-89; called to the Bar 1989. Awarded Council of Legal Educational Studentship, and Prince of Wales, Atkin and Karmel Scholarships at *Gray's Inn*. Appointed Junior Counsel to the Crown (B Panel) in 1999.

LINEHAN, Stephen QC
5 Fountain Court (Anthony Barker QC), Birmingham (0121) 606 0500
Recommended in Crime

LISSACK, Richard QC
35 Essex Street (Nigel Inglis-Jones QC), London (020) 7353 6381
Recommended in Crime, Fraud: Criminal
Specialisation: Criminal negligence, commercial fraud, financial services, professional negligence, personal injury, clinical negligence. Cases include: R v Maxwell, Lyme Bay Canoe Disaster (Corporate Manslaughter), Pescado (Corporate Manslaughter), Maria Assumpta (Gross Negligence Manslaughter), Southall Rail Disaster (Corporate Manslaughter), Lone Signature (Gross Negligence Manslaughter). Bristol Royal Infirmary Enquiry. Lawrence Dallaglio Disciplinary Proceedings, Southall Rail Inquiry, Ladbroke Grove Inquiry, Burns Inquiry.
Career: QC (1994 – aged 37), Assistant Recorder 1993, Recorder 1999.

LISTER, Caroline
One King's Bench Walk (Anthony Hacking QC), London (020) 7936 1500
Recommended in Family: Child Care including child abduction
Specialisation: Child abduction, public law and private law cases involving children and their families, representing parents, local authorities, guardians and the official solicitor. Ancillary relief and other financial matters.

Prof. Memberships: FLBA.
Career: B.Sc. London University in Comparative Physiology and Microbiology.
Personal: Two children. Endurance riding, renovating ancient cottage.

LITHMAN, Nigel QC
2 Bedford Row (formerly 3 Hare Court) (William Clegg QC), London (020) 7440 8888
Recommended in Crime

LITTON, John
4 Breams Buildings (Christopher Lockhart-Mummery QC), London (020) 7430 1221/7353 5835
Recommended in Property Litigation
Specialisation: All aspects of property litigation. Other areas of specialisation include judicial review, planning and compulsory purchase. Regularly acts for the government and government bodies, local authorities, developers and private clients. Notable litigation includes the A12/M11 and A34 Newbury Bypass mass trespass actions. Reported cases include Vickers v Dover District Council, R v Secretary of State for the Environment ex p. Kirkstall Valley Campaign Ltd, Secretary of State for Transport v Haughian, Okolo v Secretary of State for the Environment.
Career: Graduated in Law from Southampton University (1988). Called to Bar in 1989. Called to Hong Kong Bar in 1990. Appointed a member of the Supplementary Panel of Junior Counsel to the Crown (now the 'B' Panel) in 1997.
Personal: Born 20 May 1966. Married 1997. Interests include paragliding, skiing, motorcycles, food and wine.

LIVESEY, Bernard QC
Four New Square (Justin Fenwick QC), London (020) 7822 2000
barristers@4newsquare.com
Recommended in Personal Injury, Professional Negligence
Specialisation: Principal specialisation is litigation in the following fields: general common & commercial law, personal injuries, professional negligence (architects, doctors, engineers, solicitors, surveyors and valuers) and insurance. Leading cases include Spring v. Guardian Assurance (negligent references); Ancell v. Chief Constable of Bedfordshire (liability of police); Halford v. Brookes (limitation); Kumar v. AGF Insurance Ltd (Construction of Insurance Contract); Wood v. Bentall Simplex Ltd (Fatal Accidents Act damages).
Prof. Memberships: COMBAR, Bar European Group; Personal Injuries Bar Association, Professional Negligence Bar Association.
Career: Called to the Bar 1969. Recorder 1987. Silk in 1990. Deputy High Court Judge. Bencher of Lincoln's Inn.
Personal: Educated at Peterhouse, Cambridge (MA, LLB).

LLOYD, Heather
Chavasse Court Chambers (Theresa Pepper), Liverpool (0151) 707 1191
Recommended in Crime
Specialisation: Crime, particularly allegations of sexual abuse.
Prof. Memberships: Criminal Bar Association.
Career: Liverpool University 2:1 LLB 1979.
Personal: Married, 2 children.

LLOYD, Huw
3 Serjeants' Inn (Philip Naughton QC), London (020) 7427 5000
hlloyd@3serjeantsinn.com
Recommended in Clinical Negligence
Specialisation: Specialises in medical law medical negligence and medical ethics work. Recent interesting cases include Re J (A minor) (1992) 3 WLR 5c7; Res S [1993] Fam 123; R v Mid Glamorgan FHSA, South Glamorgan H.A. ex p. Martin; Re S (1995) 1 WLR 110; Secretary of State for Home Dept. v Robb (1995) 2 WLR 722; Re S (hospital patient: court's jurisdiction) (1995) 2 WLR 38; Re J (hospital patient: foreign curator) [1995] 3 WLR 596; Re CH [1996] 1 FLR; Re R (adult: medical treatment) [1996] 2 FLR 99; Re C (adult patient: publicity) [1996] 2 FLR 25; Re T (wardship: medical treatment) [1997] 1 FLR 502; Re D (Medical Treatment) [1998] 1 FLR 411.
Prof. Memberships: London Common Law and Commercial Bar Association. Professional Negligence Bar Association.
Career: Called to the Bar 1975. Middle Temple, Blackstone Entrance Exhibition and Benefactors Senior Law Scholar.
Personal: Educated at City of London School and Leicester University (LL.B). Born 10th May 1952.

LLOYD JONES, David QC
Brick Court Chambers (Christopher Clarke QC), London (020) 7379 3550
Recommended in Competition/Anti-trust
Specialisation: EU law, public and private international law, public law, commercial law. Recent cases include: Ex parte Pinochet (No 1); Ex parte Pinochet (No 3) (HL); Locabail v Waldorf Investments (CA); R v Lord Saville ex parte A; P v P (Diplomatic Immunity) (CA); Philip Brothers v Republic of X (CA); A Ltd v B Bank (Act of State) (CA); Westland Helicopters v Arab Organisation for Industrialisation. Brussels Convention cases in Luxembourg include: Webb v Webb; Kleinwort Benson v City of Glasgow; Cinnamond v Von Horn; Mietz v Gesselschaft Yachting. Competition cases in Luxembourg include: Shell v Commission (PVC); Shell v Commission (LdPE); TetraPak v Commission; Blue Circle v Commission; British Cement Association v Commission; Banks v British Coal Corporation; Hopkins v National Power; NALOO v Commission; Banks v Coal Authority. EU cases before English Courts include: R v MAFF ex parte RSPCA; R v Dover Harbour Board ex parte Gilder; Richard Cound Ltd v BMW (CA); First County Garages v Fiat Auto; R v Comptroller of Patents ex parte Lenzing.
Prof. Memberships: Fellow of Downing College, Cambridge 1975-91.
Career: Junior Crown Counsel, Common Law 1997-99; QC 1999.

LLOYD-ELEY, Andrew
1 Hare Court (Stephen Kramer QC), London (020) 7353 5324
Recommended in Crime

LOCKEY, John
Essex Court Chambers (Gordon Pollock QC), London (020) 7813 8000
clerksroom@essexcourt-chambers.co.uk
Recommended in Commercial (Litigation), Insurance
Specialisation: Insurance and Reinsurance. International trade. Shipping law.
Prof. Memberships: Committee member, British Insurance Law Association.
Career: Downing College, Cambridge BA (Law) (starred First) 1985. Harvard Law School LLM 1986. Called to the Bar 1987.
Personal: Born 1963.

LOCKHART-MUMMERY, Christopher QC
4 Breams Buildings (Christopher Lockhart-Mummery QC), London (020) 7430 1221/7353 5835
Recommended in Parliamentary & Public Affairs, Planning
Specialisation: Advises and appears for developers and local authorities at public inquiries and in the High Court. Planning inquiries include the Channel Tunnel Terminal (Waterloo), National Gallery Extension, and Mansion House Square Development. Planning cases in the House of Lords include Westminster City Council v British Waterways Board, Westminster City Council v Great Portland Estates, Tesco Stores Ltd v Secretary of State for the Environment.
Career: Called to the Bar July 1971. Took Silk 1986; Bencher Inner Temple 1993; Head of Chambers April 1993; Recorder May 1994; Deputy High Court Judge 1995; Assistant Boundary Commissioner 2000.
Personal: Born 7th August 1947. Educated at Stowe School and Trinity College, Cambridge (BA Hons).

LODDER, Peter
2 Bedford Row (formerly 3 Hare Court) (William Clegg QC), London (020) 7440 8888
Recommended in Crime
Specialisation: Fraud and General Crime, Leading and Junior work. Recent reported cases include R v Gray & Ors 1995 2 Cr App R100: Insider Dealing case, authority on question of what evidence in a conspiracy may be relied upon after Crown has elected to proceed on substantives. R v Hancock & Ors 1996 2 Cr App R 554 on whether particulars in a conspiracy to defraud are ingredients of the offence. R v Comerford 1998 1 Cr App R 235 on the circumstances under which a Judge may swear a jury anonymously and order its protection. Occasional prosecutor for Customs & Excise and the Serious Fraud Office.
Prof. Memberships: Elected member of General Council of the Bar since 1994, committee member of Criminal Bar Association, member International Bar Association.
Career: Awarded Jules Thorn (Major) scholarship by Middle Temple 1982.

LOFTHOUSE, Simon
Atkin Chambers (John Blackburn QC), London (020) 7404 0102
Recommended in Construction
Specialisation: Construction and civil engineering, professional negligence (architects, surveyors, engineers and quantity surveyors), energy, oil and gas. Contentious (litigation and arbitration), non-contentious mediation and adjudication. Instructed in relation to large engineering, commercial and residential developments, airport terminals, hospitals, computer installations, onshore and offshore. Cases include Vickery v Modern Securities [1988] 1 BCLC 428 (CA); Cadmus v Amec 51 ConLR 105; Crittal Windows v TJ Evers 54 Con LR 66; Humber Oil Terminals Trustees v Harbour and General 59 BLR 1 (CA); King v McKenna [1991] 2 QB 480. Amec Civil Engineering Ltd and Alfred McAlpine Construction Ltd v Cheshire County Council [1999] BLR 303.
Prof. Memberships: TECBAR. Common Law and Commercial Bar Association accredited Adjudicator.
Career: LL.B (Hons) (Lond); Called 1988. Articles Editor for Current Law 1990-1995.
Personal: Married. Main leisure interest: squash.

LOMNICKA, Eva
Four New Square (Justin Fenwick QC), London (020) 7822 2000
Recommended in Financial Services
Specialisation: Advisory work in consumer credit, securities regulation and financial services, reflecting publications: (1) 'Encyclopedia of Consumer Credit Law'; (2) 'Lomnicka and Powell, Encyclopedia of Financial Services Law'; (3) 'Palmer's Company Law' (Part 11); (4) 'Ellinger and Lomnicka, Modern Banking Law'.
Career: Professor of Law, King's College London. Called to the Bar 1974.
Personal: Born 17 May 1951; 1969-1973 Girton College, Cambridge (MA, LLB; Chancellor's Medal). Married with three children.

LONG, Andrew
Peel Court Chambers (Michael Shorrock QC), Manchester (0161) 832 3791
Recommended in Crime

LONGMAN, Michael
St John's Chambers (Christopher Sharp QC), Bristol (0117) 921 3456
clerks@stjohnschambers.co.uk
Recommended in Crime

LORAINE-SMITH, Nicholas
2 Harcourt Buildings, Atkinson Bevan Chambers (Nicholas Atkinson QC & John Bevan QC), London (020) 7353 2112
Recommended in Crime
Specialisation: Criminal advocacy. Has practised in all areas of crime, including allegations of serious professional and commercial fraud, sexual offences and organised crime. Since 1993, has specialised in allegations of murder, terrorism, police corruption and international drug smuggling.
Career: Called to the Bar in 1977. Appointed Junior Treasury Counsel in 1993 and Senior Treasury Counsel in 1999. Appointed Assistant Recorder in 1994 and Recorder in 2000.

LORD, David W.
3 Stone Buildings (G.C. Vos QC), London (020) 7242 4937
Recommended in Sport
Specialisation: Principal area of practice is chancery and commercial law. Work includes media and entertainment, sports law, insurance and reinsurance, company law, insolvency and bankruptcy. Acted in Deeny and Others v Gooda Walker Ltd and Others on behalf of the Gooda Walker Action Group (Lloyd's Names).
Prof. Memberships: Middle Temple, Lincoln's Inn, Chancery Bar Association.
Career: Called to the Bar in 1987 and became a tenant at Stone Buildings in 1988.
Personal: Educated at King's School Rochester 1971-81 and Bristol University 1982-86 (LL.B Hons). Leisure pursuits include most sports, especially skiing, tennis and hockey. Born 28th September 1964. Lives in London.

LORD, Richard
Brick Court Chambers (Christopher Clarke QC), London (020) 7379 3550
Recommended in Commercial (Litigation), Shipping
Specialisation: General Commercial Law, including Shipping, Insurance and Professional Negligence. Recent important cases: 'Houda'; Kuwait Petroleum Corp. v ID Oil; 'Aditya Vaibhav'; 'Subro Valour'; NRG v Bacon & Woodrow; "APOSTOLIS" A Meredith Jones v Vangemar; "EVER SUCCESS" Volodymyr Miseyev v The Owners of the "EVER SUCCESS".
Prof. Memberships: Heilbron Committee (Joint Working Party of the Civil Courts).
Career: Called to Bar 24 November 1981, Inner Temple.
Personal: Born 2 January 1959 in Leamington. Educated at Stowe School and Cambridge – MA 1 year Scholarship at Cambridge (1979-80). Publication: Guide to the Arbitration Act 1996 (with Simon Salzedo) (Cavendish 1996).

LOVELL-PANK, Dorian QC
6 King's Bench Walk (Michael Worsley QC), London (020) 7583 0410
Recommended in Crime
Specialisation: General crime including commercial fraud.
Prof. Memberships: Committee Criminal Bar Association 1989 – ; General Council of the Bar 1989-1992 and 1998 – ; International Bar Association 1993 -; Panel of Chairmen Police Discipline Appeals 1991-; Human Rights Institute 1996-. American Bar Association (Associate) 1997-.
Career: QC 1993; Recorder since 1989; Called 1971.

LOWE, (Nicholas) Mark QC
2-3 Gray's Inn Square (Anthony Scrivener QC), London (020) 7242 4986
Recommended in Planning
Specialisation: Town and Country Planning (all areas, with particular experience of shopping, housing, employment, leisure, listed buildings and major energy, waste and incineration projects). Local government and administrative law, environmental and property related litigation and all tribunal work including Lands Tribunal. Judicial Review – both planning and local government.
Prof. Memberships: PEBA, ALBA.
Career: Called to Bar 1972. Same Chambers since 1973. QC 1996.

LUBA, Jan QC
Two Garden Court (I. Macdonald QC & O.Davies QC), London (020) 7353 1633
Recommended in Administrative & Public Law: General

LUCAS, Noel
1 Middle Temple Lane (Colin Dines & Andrew Trollope QC), London (020) 7583 0659 (12 lines)
Recommended in Crime, Fraud: Criminal

LUMLEY, Gerald
9 Woodhouse Square (John Morris Collins), Leeds (0113) 245 1986
Recommended in Crime

LYDIARD, Andrew
Brick Court Chambers (Christopher Clarke QC), London (020) 7379 3550
Recommended in Aviation, Product Liability
Specialisation: Commercial litigation, product liability, insurance, reinsurance and aviation.
Career: BA (Oxon) LLM (Harvard).

LYNCH, Adrian QC
11 King's Bench Walk (Eldred Tabachnik QC and James Goudie QC), London (020) 7632 8500
Recommended in Employment

LYNCH, Jerome
Cardinal Chambers (Moved from Cloisters)

LYNCH, Patricia QC
18 Red Lion Court (Anthony Arlidge QC), London (020) 7520 6000
Recommended in Crime

LYNDON-STANFORD, Michael QC
13 Old Square (Michael Lyndon-Stanford QC), London (020) 7404 4800
Recommended in Company
Specialisation: Principal fields of practice consist of company and commercial litigation, including minority shareholders proceedings, insolvency, business law, commercial fraud, professional negligence, equity, insurance and reinsurance. Recent cases include Senate Electrical Wholesalers Ltd v Alcatel Submarine Networks Ltd. (Court of Appeal) concerning share purchase agreements.
Prof. Memberships: Chancery Bar Association, Commercial Bar Association, Insolvency Lawyers' Association.
Career: QC 1979. Has practised in foreign jurisdictions and has been called (ad hoc) for cases in Hong Kong, Singapore and the Isle of Man.
Personal: M.A. (Cantab). Member of the Inner Temple and of Lincoln's Inn.

LYNESS, Scott
1 Serjeants' Inn (Lionel Read QC), London (020) 7583 1355
Recommended in Planning

MABB, David
Erskine Chambers (Robin Potts QC), London (020) 7242 5532
Recommended in Company

MACDONALD, Alistair
Park Court Chambers (James Stewart QC Robert Smith QC), Leeds (0113) 243 3277
Recommended in Crime

MACDONALD, Charles QC
4 Essex Court (Nigel Teare QC), London (020) 7653 5653
cmacdonald@4sx.co.uk
Recommended in Shipping
Specialisation: Admiralty and commercial shipping, carriage of goods, international trade, commercial and international arbitration, insurance and reinsurance, private international law, marine/environmental law, transport. Has extensive experience of all types of marine litigation including upwards of 100 salvage arbitration disputes. Among his recent cases concerning road transport, collision, pilotage, damages, charterparty war risks, international arbitration, conflict of laws and commercial fraud are: Spectra v Hayesoak. CA, 30497 'The Common Venture' [1995] 2 LLR 230; Oceangas (Gibraltar) Limited v PLA [1993] 2 LLR 292; The Botany Triad v Lu Shan [1993] 2 LLR 259; 'The Product Star (No 2)' [1993] 1 LLR 397; 'The Paula D'Alesio' [1994] 2 LLR 366; 'The Polessk and Akademik Oisif Orbeli' [1996] 2 LLR 40; Standard Chartered Bank v PNSC et al [1996] 2 LLR 365. Also regularly appears in City of London commercial arbitrations. Publications: Editorial Board, 'International Maritime Law' (Lawtext Publishing Limited).
Career: Glasgow Academy, New College Oxford (MA Hons Jurisprudence 1971). Called to Bar, Lincoln's Inn, 1972. Appointments: Queen's Counsel, 1992. Assistant Recorder of the Crown Court, 1996. Recorder of the Crown Court 2000. Member of the Panel of Lloyds Salvage Arbitrators.
Personal: DOB 31.8.49, Glasgow. Married with three daughters and lives in East Sussex.

MACDONALD, Ian QC
Two Garden Court (I. Macdonald QC & O.Davies QC), London (020) 7353 1633
Recommended in Crime, Immigration

MACDONALD, Kenneth QC
Matrix Chambers (Nicholas Blake QC), London (020) 7404 3447
Recommended in Crime, Fraud: Criminal, Human Rights (Civil Liberties)
Specialisation: A criminal defence specialist. Complex frauds (including SFO work, deposit-taking frauds, advance fee frauds, solicitor frauds etc). Sanctions-busting cases (all aspects, including the illegal export of arms and weapons-making equipment, computers, high technology, pharmaceuticals etc. Clients in this area include major foreign defence corporations). Terrorism (Irish, Sikh, Palestinian and Algerian). Bombings, murders and possession of arms and explosives. Major drugs conspiracies (importation, manufacture and supply). Murders (including multiple murders and child killings). Cases include: Matrix Churchill; The Ordtech Appeal; R v McKane (an IRA trial involving bombings and multiple murders); R v Kinsella (the Warrington bombing case – again the IRA); R v Sakaria (a Sikh terrorist case involving explosives and conspiracies to murder); R v Zekra (the alleged car-bombing of the Israeli Embassy in London).

MACHELL, John
Serle Court (Lord Neill of Bladen QC), London (020) 7242 6105
Recommended in Partnership
Specialisation: General commercial/chancery dispute resolution and advisory work, particularly partnership, company, insolvency, property, wills, trusts and probate.
Prof. Memberships: Association of Partnership Practitioners, COMBAR.
Career: University of Southampton 1988-1992 LLB (first class). *Serle Court* (formerly *13 Old Square*) 1994 to date.
Publications: 'Limited Liability Partnerships', 'Jordans' (forthcoming publication).
Personal: Married with two children.

MACHELL, Raymond QC
Deans Court Chambers (H.K. Goddard QC), Manchester (0161) 214 6000
Recommended in Personal Injury

MACKAY, Colin QC
39 Essex Street (Nigel Pleming QC), London (020) 7832 1111
Recommended in Personal Injury, Sport
Specialisation: Personal injury; medical and solicitors negligence; insurance. Page v Smith [1996] AC 155 HL; Elliott v Saunders & Liverpool FC (1994); O'Neil v Fashanu & Wimbledon FC (1995); Brady v Sunderland FC (1998); Knight v Chester City FC (1997); Watson v British Boxing Board of Control (1999).
Prof. Memberships: LCLCBA, PIBA. Chairperson on Sports Dispute Resolution Panel
Career: MA Oxford.

MACLEAN, Alan
Brick Court Chambers (Christopher Clarke QC), London (020) 7379 3550
Recommended in Administrative & Public Law: General
Specialisation: Developing public law specialisation within broadly based civil practice. Particular focus on community care, education and local government law in general,split fairly evenly between Applicant and Respondent work.
Prof. Memberships: Administrative Law Bar Association.
Career: Called to the Bar in 1993. Top of year at Inns of Court School of Law. Karmel, Bacon, Prince of Wales and Macaskie Awards from Gray's Inn. Scarman Scholar of the Inns of Court School of Law.
Personal: Educated at University College, Oxford, Harvard University and The City University. Kennedy Memorial Scholar to Harvard.

MACLEOD, Nigel QC
4 Breams Buildings (Christopher Lockhart-Mummery QC), London (020) 7430 1221/7353 5835
Recommended in Parliamentary & Public Affairs
Specialisation: Planning, compulsory purchase and compensation, local government, highways, environment and parliamentary bills. Matters of particular interest over the last year include appearing for the Ministry of Defence in the re-opened public inquiry into the Ministry's infrastructure proposals in the Northumberland National Park to allow training of latest artillery and rocket systems, and promoting the City of London Ward Elections private bill in the Commons. Has appeared in a wide range of other major public inquiries and parliamentary bills, including Sizewell B, Hinckley Point, Torness Dry Storage Inquiry, Dartford Crossing Bill, Second Severn Crossing Bill, Bristol Development Corporation Bill, Manchester Airport Second Runway Inquiry, Liverpool Airport Extension Inquiry, and many major motorway and trunk road Inquiries. Reported cases included Shimizu v Westminster City Council (CA), South Lakeland DC (HL), Thrasyvoulou (CA), Lambeth v SSE (County Hall – CA), and Young (HL).
Prof. Memberships: Chairman of Planning and Environment Bar Association (1998-); member of the Parliamentary Bar Mess; member of the Administrative Law Bar Association; member of the General Council of the Bar; member of the Joint Regulations Committee of the Bar; Fellow of the Society for Advanced Legal Studies; Bencher of Gray's Inn.
Career: MA, BCL (Christ Church, Oxford); Called to Bar 1961; practiced in Manchester until 1981 and then in London; Queen's Counsel 1979; Recorder of Crown Court 1981; has sat as a Deputy High Court Judge since 1992 usually hearing appeals on planning matters; legal member of Mental Health Review Tribunal.
Personal: Married with two children; lives in Northamptonshire; has particular interest in boats.

MACRORY, Richard
Brick Court Chambers (Christopher Clarke QC), London (020) 7379 3550
r.macrory@ucl.ac.uk
Recommended in Environment
Specialisation: Environmental law, EC law.
Prof. Memberships: 2000 – Awarded CBE for service to environment and law; UK Environmental Law Association (first chairman).
Career: Called to Bar in 1974. Professor of Environmental Law at Imperial College, London, 1991. 1997- Specialist Advisor House of Commons Select Committee on Environment, Transport and Regions; 1999- Board Member, Environment Agency, England and Wales; Member Royal Commission on Environmental pollution.
Publications: Author of 'Bibliography of European Environmental Law' (Oxford University Press 1995). Editor 'Journal of Environmental Law.'

MACUR, Julia QC
St. Ive's Chambers (Edward Coke), Birmingham (0121) 236 0863
Recommended in Family/Matrimonial

MAHER, Martha
Guildhall Chambers (Adrian Palmer QC), Bristol (0117) 927 3366
Recommended in Chancery, Commercial (Litigation), Insolvency/Corporate Recovery

MAIDMENT, Kieran
Doughty Street Chambers (Geoffrey Robertson QC), London (020) 7404 1313
Recommended in Crime

MAIDMENT, Susan R
One King's Bench Walk (Anthony Hacking QC), London (020) 7936 1500
Recommended in Family: Child Care including child abduction

MALCOLM, Helen
3 Raymond Buildings (Clive Nicholls QC), London (020) 7400 6400
chambers@threeraymond.demon.co.uk
Recommended in Crime, Fraud: Criminal
Specialisation: Has substantial experience in commercial fraud and corruption cases (prosecuted in R v Gee). Also specialises in extradition (Pinochet, Kiriakos, Allison (on computer misuse)). Other areas of practice involve computer crime and criminal offences such as murder, robbery and drug smuggling.
Prof. Memberships: International Bar Association, Criminal Bar Association.
Career: MA (Oxon) Oriental Studies (Persian with Arabic), Qualified 1996. Tutor, Inns of Court and Bar Educational Trust. Advocacy Trainer, Gray's Inn. Archbold Editor (Chapter 30 – Company/ Commercial Crime).

MALDEN, Grace
35 Essex Street (Nigel Inglis-Jones QC), London (020) 7353 6381
Recommended in Pensions
Specialisation: Principal area of specialisation is pensions law, particularly in relation to occupational pension schemes and the mis-selling of personal pension schemes. Acted in Julsarben Ltd (1990) Retirement Benefit Scheme v JHG Norman (appearing for the Trustee in an appeal to the High Court from a decision of the Pensions Ombudsman); HF Pensions Scheme Trustees Ltd v John Gatenby & Others (appearing for the beneficiaries of the Scheme in litigation brought by the Trustees against, inter alia, the solicitors advising the Scheme). In addition, she also covers other areas of general chancery and civil practice including breach of trust cases, professional negligence, and partnership disputes.
Prof. Memberships: Association of Pension Lawyers; Professional Negligence Bar Association; Bar Human Rights Committee.
Career: Called to the Bar in 1993 and joined Essex Street on completing pupillage in 1994.
Personal: Born 21 January 1969; educated Bedales School 1981-1986; Trinity Hall Cambridge 1987-1990 (BA, Classics); University of Westminster 1992 (Law Diploma).

MALE, John QC
4 Breams Buildings (Christopher Lockhart-Mummery QC), London (020) 7430 1221/7353 5835
Recommended in Property Litigation
Specialisation: Landlord and tenant, town and country planning, compulsory purchase and compensation.
Prof. Memberships: Called to the Bar by Lincolns Inn in 1976 and is a member of the Chancery Bar Association and the Planning and Environment Bar Association.
Career: Educated at Minchenden Grammar School, London and Sidney Sussex College, Cambridge obtaining a BA in law. One of the contributors to Halsbury's Laws on Town and Country Planning. An editor of 'Hill & Redman's Law of Landlord and Tenant'.

MALEK, Ali QC
3 Verulam Buildings (Christopher Symons QC & John Jarvis QC), London (020) 7831 8441
amalek@3verulam.co.uk
Recommended in Arbitration (International), Banking, Civil Fraud, Commercial (Litigation)
Specialisation: All aspects of commercial law with emphasis on banking. International arbitration and domestic arbitration. Professional negligence, fraud, oil and gas, and conflict of laws. Cases include Cryne v Barclays (1987) (bank's repayment rights); A v B (1993) (Banking Act). Barclays v Khaira (1992) (securities). Re Rafidain (1992) (bank accounts/sovereign immunity). Tudorgrange v Citibank (1992) (releases and UCTA 1977). EDF Mann v Haryanto (1991) (anti-suit injunctions). Natwest v Daniel (1993) (summary judgment). Robertson v CICB (1994) (confidentiality). Glencore v Bank of China (1996) (ICC 500) National Provincial Building Society v Lloyd (1996) (suspended possession orders). Barclays Bank v Thomson (1997) (undue influence). BCCI v PW (1998) (Banking Act). Bank Melli v Ispahani (1998) (illegality/conflict of laws). Box v Barclays (1998) (constructive trusts). Bolkiah v Prince Jefri (1998) (chinese walls). Yorkshire Bank v Lloyds (1999) (collecting bank's duties). Turner v RBS (1999) (confidentiality). Young v Robson Rhodes (1999) (chinese walls). Halewood v. Addleshaw Booth & Co (1999) (chinese Walls), Sepoong v. Formula One (2000) (contract): Dubai Aluminium v. Salaam (2000) (constructive trusts/fraud); Portman v, Dussansh (2000) (unconscionable bargain). Frequent speaker on these topics at seminars. 'Banks, Fraud and

Crime' published in 'Cross-Border Fraudulent Activity' (Pub Lloyd's of London Press, 2nd Edition, 2000).
Prof. Memberships: IBA, COMBAR.
Career: Called to the Bar 1980. QC 1996. Recorder 1998.
Personal: Bedford School, Keble College, Oxford. BA (1978), BCL(OXON) (first class). Leisure pursuits and family life. Born 1956.

MALEK, Hodge M. QC
4-5 Gray's Inn Square (Elizabeth Appleby QC & Duncan Ouseley QC), London (020) 7404 5252
hmalek@4-5graysinnsquare.co.uk
Recommended in Banking
Specialisation: Specialises in commercial law, including accountancy, banking, company, financial services, fraud, insurance, securities, professional negligence and shipping. Instructed in complex commercial litigation in the commercial court and in arbitrations, including Banque Financiere v Westgate [1990] (banking and insurance fraud), Johnson Matthey v Arthur Young (collapse of Johnson Matthey Bank), Ocean v Bimeh Iran Insurance Company [1990] (reinsurance), Trafalgar Tours v Henry (jurisdiction), Gucci v Gucci [1991] (passing-off), Lombard Finance v Brookplain [1991] (banking), Westdeutsche Landesbank v Islington [1994] (interest rate swaps), NPRT v Allen, Allen and Hemsley [1996] (banking), R v Secretary of State ex p.Greenpeace [2000] (judicial review), AEI v PPL [1998] (copyright); Richmond Oil [1999] (stock exchange/fraud), Baghbadrani v Commercial Union [2000] (insurance). Instructed in fraud cases by Serious Fraud Office. Acted for SRO's in disciplinary proceedings and judicial review. Acts in French proceedings, including investigation into Alma crash [1998]. Counsel for Customs & Excise (European) and on Supplemental Panel for Treasury (1995-1999). Joint author of Discovery' (Sweet & Maxwell, 1992). Lectures on civil procedure.
Prof. Memberships: COMBAR.
Personal: Educated at Bedford School 1968-1977, University of the Sorbonne, 1978 and Keble College, Oxford 1978-82 (MA,BCL).

MALES, Stephen QC
20 Essex Street (Iain Milligan QC), London (020) 7583 9294
Recommended in Energy & Natural Resources
Specialisation: International trade and commercial law; shipping; sale of goods and commodity trading; banking and letters of credit, arbitration; energy law; insurance; conflict of laws; breach of confidence. Acts as arbitrator. Principal cases: The Naxos [1990] 1 WLR 1337 (sale of sugar); The Bazias 3 [1993] QB 673 (arbitration security); Amoco v Amerada Hess [1994] 1 Lloyd's Rep 330 (North Sea oilfield redetermination); The Niobe [1995] 1 Lloyd's Rep 579 (ship sale); Grogan v Robin Meredith [1996] CLC 1127 (incorporation of standard conditions); Ocular Sciences v Aspect [1997] RPC 289 (breach of confidence, duties of directors); The Selda [1998] 1 Lloyd's Rep 729 (GAFTA default clause); Cargill v Bangladesh Sugar [1998] 1 WLR 461 (performance bonds); Scottish Power v Britoil, CA, Nov 1997 (sale of North Sea gas); Huyton v Jakil [1998] CLC 937(striking out appeal from arbitrators); Coven v Hong Kong Insurance [1999] CLC 223 (all risks insurance); Huyton v Cremer [1999] 1 Lloyd's Rep 620 (economic duress); Czanikow-Riconda v Standard Bank [1999] 2 Lloyd's Rep. 187 (no injunction to restrain payment under Letter of Credit); CAI v. Muslim Commercial Bank [2000] 1 Lloyd's Rep.275 (documents required by letter of credit); Chailease v. CAI [2000] 1 Lloyd's Rep.348 (place of performance of letter of credit). Casenotes and articles include: Confidence in arbitration [1998] LMCLQ 245; Comity and anti-suit injunctions [1998] LMCLQ 543.
Prof. Memberships: Member of Commercial Court Committee, Combar, LCLCBA, IBA Energy Lawyers Group.
Career: St John's College, Cambridge 1974-1997. Called 1978. Queens Counsel 1998. Assistant Recorder 1999.

MALLALIEU, Ann QC
6 King's Bench Walk (Michael Worsley QC), London (020) 7583 0410
Recommended in Crime

MANLEY, David
40 King St (Philip Raynor QC), Manchester (0161) 832 9082
Recommended in Planning
Specialisation: Planning Appeals, Conduct of Local Plans, UDP's (7 in 3 years), Highways, CPO's, Environmental Law, Judicial Review.
Prof. Memberships: PEBA and Administrative Law Bar Association.
Career: Called to bar in 1981. General Common Law Practice 1981-1988. Specialised exclusively in above areas 1988 to date. Recorder, appointed 1999.

MANN, Anthony QC
Enterprise Chambers (Anthony Mann QC), London (020) 7405 9471
Recommended in Commercial (Litigation), Commercial Chancery, Company, Insolvency/ Corporate Recovery, Professional Negligence
Specialisation: Broad commercial chancery practice with an emphasis on insolvency and professional negligence. Recent reported cases include Re MC Bacon [1990] (insolvency, transaction at undervalue); Re David Meek Plant Ltd [1993] (Proceedings for recovery of leased equipment); National Westminster Bank v Skelton (1993] (cross-claims in mortgage possession actions) Smith New Court v Citibank [1996] (damages for fraud); Kleinwort Benson v South Tyneside [1993] and South Tyneside v Svenska [1994] (local authority swaps; ultra vires transactions; interest; Re Secure & Provide plc [1992] (public interest winding up petitions); Nestle v National Westminster Bank [1993] (principles for assessing losses arising from breach of trust) and Target Holdings v Redfern [1995] (solicitors' negligence and breach of trust); Barclays Bank v Eustice [1995] (discovery; privilege; transactions at an undervalue); Barrow v Bankside Agency Ltd [1996] (issue estoppel; Lloyds litigation); Fitch v Official Receiver [1996] (bankruptcy – rescinding bankruptcy order); Gold Coin Joailliers v UBK [1996] (duty of care in bank references); London Borough of Sutton v Wellesley Housing Assoc [1996] (Local authority ultra vires); Richbell Information Systems, The Times (1998) (winding up foreign company; set-off); Locabail v Emmanuel [1999] (lender and wife's interest); Locabail v Emmanuel No.2 [1999] (judicial bias).

MANN, Paul
No.1 High Pavement (John B. Milmo QC), Nottingham (0115) 941 8218
Recommended in Crime
Specialisation: Crime: Murder, sexual offences, drugs. In the last three years he has been involved in several cases concerning doctors/nurses' criminal malpractice and that of police officers.
Prof. Memberships: Criminal Bar Association, Assistant Treasurer of the Midland and Oxford Circuit.
Career: Called *Gray's Inn* 1980. Assistant Recorder 1999.

MANNING, Colin
Littleton Chambers (Michel Kallipetis QC), London (020) 7797 8600
Recommended in Alternative Dispute Resolution
Specialisation: Principal areas of practice are general commercial and business law specialising in commercial contract disputes including computer litigation (involving the supply and implementation of computer systems, networking and associated intellectual property rights) and also professional negligence (primarily solicitors and valuers).
Prof. Memberships: COMBAR London Common Law and Commercial Bar Association. CEDR Accredited Mediator. Member of the Chartered Institute of Arbitrators.
Career: Called, Gray's Inn, 1970. Recorder, 2000.
Personal: Educated at University College London.

MANSFIELD, Michael QC
14 Tooks Court (Michael Mansfield QC), London (020) 7405 8828
Recommended in Crime, Human Rights (Civil Liberties)

MARKS, David
3-4 South Square (Michael Crystal QC), London (020) 7696 9900
Recommended in Insolvency/Corporate Recovery
Specialisation: Insolvency, company, commercial. 1997/2000 cases include: John Dee Group v WMH. Re A & C Supplies Ltd. Re Datadeck Ltd. BCCI v Akindele. Winchester Commodities v Black. Re Brabon.
Prof. Memberships: Chancery Bar Association. Insolvency Lawyers Association. Society of Practitioners of Insolvency (legal member). Insol. International Bar Association. Justice. Joint Editor: Rowlatt on Principal and Surety. General Editor: Tolley's Insolvency Service. Editor: Encyclopaedia of Forms and Precedents (Guarantees). Contributor to Lightman & Moss: Law of Receivers of Companies and Totty & Moss: Insolvency.
Career: Oxford University: MA, BCL. Member, Illinois and Federal Bars, United States. Deputy Registrar in Bankruptcy. Data Appeal Tribunal, Deputy Chairman.
Personal: Bilingual: French.

MARKS, Lewis
Queen Elizabeth Building (Paul Coleridge QC), London (020) 7797 7837
lewis_marks@msn.com

Recommended in Family: Matrimonial Finance
Career: Recent cases include: White v White [2000] House of Lords; Kellman v Kellman [2000] IFLR 785; F v F (Ancillary Relief: Substantial Assets) [1995] 2 FLR 45. Dart v Dart [1996] 2 FLR 286 C/A; H v H (Child Abduction: Acquiescence) [1997] 1 FLR 872 H/L; S v S (Child Abduction: Non-Convention Country) [1994] 2 FLR 681.
Prof. Memberships: Family Law Bar Association; DPA Accepted.
Personal: Born 1961. Called 1984. Educated Oxford University (BA Juris)

MARKS, Richard QC
Peel Court Chambers (Michael Shorrock QC), Manchester (0161) 832 3791
Recommended in Crime

MARKUS, Kate
Doughty Street Chambers (Geoffrey Robertson QC), London (020) 7404 1313
Recommended in Administrative & Public Law: General
Specialisation: Judicial review and statutory appeals in a wide range of subject areas, including: housing, community care, education, mental health, planning and environment, prisons, social security, civil liberties, public policy. Recent cases include R v. Rochdale MBC ex p Milne (EIA and outline planning applications); LB Bromley v. SENT (special educational needs); Krasniqi v. Chief Adjudication Officer (social security, European Law); R v. DTI ex p Greenpeace (habitats directive); R v DPP ex p Jones (prosecutorial decisions, workplace safety and manslaughter) .
Prof. Memberships: Administrative Law Bar Association, Housing Law Practitioners Association, Environ-

mental Law Foundation, Prisoners Advice Service.
Career: Brent Community Law Centre, 1984-1994. Former member, Legal Aid Board. Chair, Public Law Project. Part-time Employment Tribunal Chairman. Co-author of public law update, 'Legal Action'.

MARQUAND, Charles
3 New Square (Lord Goodhart QC), London (020) 7405 5577
Recommended in Financial Services
Specialisation: Principal area of practice: financial services (including insurance, banking and pensions), UK and EU, disciplinary tribunals and corporate finance. Also company/ commercial. Engaged to advise various govts. (Poland, Estonia, Czech Republic) on harmonisation of financial services legislation with EU standards.
Prof. Memberships: Chancery Bar Assoc, COMBAR, Bar European Group.
Career: Called 1987: Practised at chambers of J.J.Rowe QC. 1993-1996: Legal Adviser at HM Treasury dealing with wide range of financial services issues and related areas (company/ commercial), drafting legislation (closely involved *inter alia* with Public Offers of Securities Regulations, investment advertisement exemptions, CREST), negotiating EU directives. 1996: joined *3 New Sqaure.* MA Oxon.
Publications: Author of articles on financial services topics. Lectures on financial services (incl. derivatives) to universities, solicitors, conferences.

MARRIN, John QC
Keating Chambers (Richard Fernyhough QC), London (020) 7544 2600
Recommended in Construction
Specialisation: Barrister practising also as arbitrator, mediator and lecturer in the field of building and civil engineering; professional negligence; contaminated land; bonds and guarantees; computer software disputes; clients include national and international contractors, professionals, and national and local government.
Career: Qualified 1974; Inner Temple; QC 1990; CEDR accredited mediator 1993; recorder 1997; FCI Arb 1998.
Personal: Sherborne School and Magdalene College, Cambridge (1973 MA Catab). Born 1951; resides London.

MARSHALL, Philip
Serle Court (Lord Neill of Bladen QC), London (020) 7242 6105
Recommended in Commercial Chancery, Company, Insolvency/Corporate Recovery
Specialisation: Commercial fraud (Cala Cristal v Al-Borno; Canada Trust v Stolzenberg); insolvency (BIM v Maxwell; Re: Murjani; Haig v Aitken; Rooney v Cardona); banking (Wahda Bank v Arab Bank); company (Tech Textiles v Vane); commercial litigation; professional negligence (Brown v GRE; Peach Publishing v Slater; David Lee v Coward Chance; Loose v Wilson Sandford).
Prof. Memberships: Chancery Bar Association; Insolvency Lawyers Association.
Career: Queens' Cambridge; Harvard Law School. Former Fellow of Queens' Cambridge. Joint editor of "The Practice and Procedure of the Companies Court".

MARSON, Geoffrey C. QC
Sovereign Chambers (Geoffrey C. Marson QC), Leeds (0113) 245 1841
Recommended in Crime
Specialisation: After a general common law practice he has specialised in defending and prosecuting criminal cases since 1985. Has spoken at the 1997 Arson Investigation Seminar along with those responsible for the investigation into the channel tunnel fire. Over the years has prosecuted in many fraud cases, including mortgage fraud, VAT evasion, serious drugs cases and the like. He has also defended in a large number of similar cases for both private and legally aided clients. He is a member of Chamber's Fraud Group.
Prof. Memberships: Criminal Bar Association.
Career: Educated Malton Grammar School and King's College London – LLB (Hons). Called to the Bar (Gray's Inn) in 1975. Assistant Recorder 1991, Recorder 1995, Queen's Counsel 1997. Appointed to sit on a short term basis on the Mental Health Review Tribunal-Restricted Patients Panel in January 2000.
Personal: Married to Denise Gresty; two sons. Leisure interests – foreign travel, wine, reading.

MARSTON, Nicholas
St John's Chambers (Christopher Sharp QC), Bristol (0117) 921 3456
Recommended in Family/Matrimonial
Specialisation: Family law, children, related matters, including prof. leg. in family issues.
Prof. Memberships: FLBA
Career: Called 1975 (Middle Temple). Assistant Recorder 1998. Recorder 2000. Former National Committee FLBA memeber.
Personal: LLB (Wales) at Cardiff. Married, 2 children. Interests include history, theatre, wine and travel, rugby and cricket.

MARTEN, Hedley
3 New Square (Lord Goodhart QC), London (020) 7405 5577
Recommended in Traditional Chancery

MARTIN, Gerard QC
Exchange Chambers (William Waldron QC), Liverpool (0151) 236 7747
Recommended in Personal Injury

MARTIN, John QC
Wilberforce Chambers (Edward Nugee QC), London (020) 7306 0102
Recommended in Property Litigation, Traditional Chancery
Specialisation: Advocate specialising in chancery and commercial Supreme Court litigation. Also advises in contentious matters, covering the wide range of topics comprising modern commercial chancery practice, Since 1993 he has been a Deputy High Court Judge in the Chancery Division. Judicial experience: Deputy High Court Judge.
Career: Called to the Bar in July 1972. Practised at the Chancery Bar in Liverpool joining Wilberforce Chambers in 1981. Took silk in 1991.

MARTIN-SPERRY, David
2-4 Tudor Street (Richard Ferguson QC), London (020) 7797 7111
Recommended in Crime

MARZEC, Alexandra
5 Raymond Buildings (Patrick Milmo QC), London (020) 7242 2902
Recommended in Defamation

MASEFIELD, Roger
Brick Court Chambers (Christopher Clarke QC), London (020) 7379 3550
masefield@brickcourt.co.uk
Recommended in Commercial (Litigation)
Specialisation: Commercial law, specialising in insurance and reinsurance; banking (eg Banco Santander v Banque Paribas [2000] 1 All ER (Comm) 776 CA); professional negligence (eg Wallace Smith Trust Co v Deloitte Haskins & Sells 1997); public and private international law (eg State of Qatar v Sheikh Khalifa Al-Thani 1996); restitution and commercial equity (eg Union Eagle v Golden Achievement [1997] 2 WLR 341 PC).
Prof. Memberships: Junior Counsel to the Crown (C Panel); Member of Bar Council Law Reform Committee; COMBAR.
Career: MA (Cantab); BCL (Oxon) – Vinerian Scholar; Called to the Bar 1994; Tenant at *Brick Court Chambers* 1996.
Publications: Co-author of constructive trusts chapters in latest edition of 'Paget on Banking' (published July 1996); researcher for Lord Alexander's 'Voice of the People' (published September 1997); co-author of Bar Council position paper on 'E-Commerce: Jurisdiction and Applicable Law' (published November 1999).
Personal: Educated at the Dragon School; Marlborough College; Cambridge (St John's); Oxford (Magdalen). Born 24 December 1970.

MASKREY, Simeon QC
7 Bedford Row (David Farrer QC), London (020) 7242 3555
Recommended in Clinical Negligence
Specialisation: Principal area of practice is professional negligence with an emphasis on clinical negligence. Also involved in disciplinary cases and all forms of litigation with a clinical element (including public law child care proceedings). Past member of the education faculty of the Royal College of Surgeons. Regular contributor to AVMA conferences. Leading counsel in R v Dixon (1995), Poynter v Hillingdon Health Authority (1997), Spargo v Essex Health Authority (1998), Fleming v Lincolnshire Police (1998). In Re D (child assessment) (1999). North Wales child abuse cases (2000).
Prof. Memberships: Professional Negligence Bar Association. Member of the Midland and Oxford Circuit. Member of AVMA Bar group.
Career: Called to the Bar in 1977. Appointed Recorder in 1997. Appointed deputy high court judge in 2000. Took silk in 1995.
Personal: Educated at King's School, Grantham and Leicester University. Born 17th May 1955. Married. Lives in London.

MASON, Alexandra
3 Stone Buildings (G.C. Vos QC), London (020) 7242 4937
Recommended in Traditional Chancery
Specialisation: Wills, trusts, capital taxation and related professional negligence. Includes non-contentious drafting of wills, settlements and related documentation, charities, construction of documents, variation of trusts applications, contentious probate, breach of trust actions, and applications under the Inheritance (Provision for Family and Dependants) Act 1975. Also Court of Protection applications. Acted for the representative beneficiary in the pilot application concerning deceased Lloyd's names (Re Yorke) and has considerable experience of applications for leave to distribute both where the later Practice Direction applies and where it does not.
Prof. Memberships: Chancery Bar Association, Revenue Bar Association, STEP.
Career: BA Hons, History, UCL 1979. Diploma in Law, City University 1980. Joint Author of 7th Ed. 'Spencer Maurice's Family Provision on Death'.

MATHER-LEES, Michael
Albion Chambers (J.C.T. Barton QC), Bristol (0117) 927 2144
Recommended in Crime
Specialisation: Medico legal, commercial fraud, public interest immunity, serious crime, human rights.
Prof. Memberships: Inner Temple, Criminal Bar Association, European Bar Group.
Career: LLB (Hons). Called 1981. Formerly qualified as a solicitor.

MATTHEWS, Dennis
Crown Office Chambers (Michael Spencer QC & Christopher Purchas QC), London (020) 7797 8100
Recommended in Clinical Negligence, Personal Injury

MATTHEWS, Duncan

20 Essex Street (Iain Milligan QC), London
(020) 7583 9294

Recommended in Arbitration (International), Shipping

Specialisation: Principal areas of work include international and domestic commercial disputes including in particular international trade and carriage of goods, oil and gas, construction, conflict of laws, insurance and reinsurance, banking, financial services, professional negligence. Advocacy: Counsel appearing before the High Court, Court of Appeal and House of Lords in England and a variety of legal and commercial arbitration tribunals both in England and abroad including international bodies such as UNCITRAL and ICC and other domestic organisations such as the LMAA. Have also been appointed and sat as arbitrator. Reported cases: House of Lords – 'The Maria D' [1992] 1 AC 21; 'The Naxos' [1990] 1 WLR 1337. Privy Council – 'The Mahkutai' [1996] AC 650. Court of Appeal AIC 'The Berge Sund' [1993] 2 Ll Rep 453; Soules v Intertradex [1991] 1 Ll Rep 378; Dole Dried Fruit v Trustin Kerwood [1990] 1 Ll Rep 309; Medway v Meurer [1990] 2 Ll Rep 112. Ist Instance; Minmetals v Ferco Steel, The Times 1 March 1999; – 'The Visvliet' [1997] 1 Int ML 5; Toepfer v Molino Boschi [1996] 1 Ll Rep 510; Aratra v Taylor Joynson Garrett [1995] 4 AER 695; Swiss Bank Corporation v Premier League The Times 9 February 1995; Kaufmann v Credit Lyonnais Bank The Times 1 February 1995; 'The Andreas P' [1994] 2 Ll Rep 183; 'The Giannis NK' [1994] 2 Ll Rep 171; 'The Cebu (No 2)' [1993] QB 1.
Prof. Memberships: COMBAR; LCLCBA. Supporting Member LMAA; Franco British Lawyers Society; British Italian Law Association; British German Jurists Association.
Career: Westminster School. Magdalen College, Oxford. BA (Hons) Oxon 1984. MA 1996.

MATTHEWS, Richard

2 Bedford Row (formerly 3 Hare Court) (William Clegg QC), London (020) 7440 8888

Recommended in Crime

Specialisation: Criminal law specialist including fraud/Health and Safety (Crime)/Trading Standards and Copyright (Crime)/Confiscation and Asset Forefeiture. Cases include: R v Schultz (Supermarket Manager kidnap/robbery); R v Trevelyan (Corruption by Ministry of Defence official); R v Davis (DTI fraudulent trading); R v Smith & Palk (DTI fraudulent trading); R v Langley (Inland Revenue/Customs; PAYE, VAT & Corporation tax multi £million prosecution concerning 8 years "phoenixing" of companies) R v Ketchell, Walker et al (Serious Fraud Office prosecution of alleged £22 million fraud by directors of Ostrich Farming Corporation), R v Barrett & others: (Operation Galleon-multi million Customs excise/VAT drawback and diversion fraud). Health and Safety: R v London Borough of Lambeth, Staward Engineering & Another, (Kerrin Point explosion case. Concerning massive gas explosion in the boiler room of occupied 22-storey tower block); R v Keltbray Ltd (double fatality arising from breach of section 2(1) Health and safety at work Act etc. 1974 duties); R v Edmund Nuttal Plc (fatality arising from breach of section 2(1) Health and Safety Act etc. 1974 duties); R v Pharmacos Ltd & Brown (Environmental Protection Act and Health and Safety at Work Act, prosecution of company and director over chemical poisoning incident).
Prof. Memberships: Criminal Bar Association South Eastern Circuit.
Career: Principal Legal Advisor Parliamentary War Crimes Group 1988-1989. Called to the Bar 1989. Joined chambers 1989.
Personal: Born 5th April 1966. Educated at Girton College, Cambridge University. (MA Cantab). Lives in London.

MATTISON, Andrew

Chavasse Court Chambers (Theresa Pepper), Liverpool (0151) 707 1191

Recommended in Crime

MAULEVERER, Bruce QC

4 Pump Court (Bruce Mauleverer QC), London
(020) 7353 2656
bmauleverer@4pumpcourt.com

Recommended in Construction, Professional Negligence

Specialisation: Principal areas of practice are construction and other commercial contracts and professional negligence work, covering all aspects of litigation and arbitration, both domestic and international. Has acted for insurers, developers, building owners, contractors, architects, engineers, accountants and solicitors. International arbitrations in Hong Kong, Dubai, Egypt and Switzerland. Also sits as an arbitrator. Trained mediator and member of ADR Chambers, London.
Prof. Memberships: TEC Bar, Commercial Bar Association, Professional Negligence Bar Association.
Career: Called to the Bar in 1969, took silk in 1985. Recorder 1985. Deputy Judge Technology and Construction Court 1989. Deputy High Court Judge 1992. Head of Chambers 1992. Bencher Inner Temple 1993. Vice Chairman International Law Association 1994. Vice-President of Executive Committee of the International Social Science Council (UNESCO) 1994. FCIArb.
Personal: Born 22nd November 1946. Educated at Sherborne School and Durham University.

MAXWELL, Richard QC

Ropewalk Chambers (Richard Maxwell QC), Nottingham (0115) 947 2581

Recommended in Personal Injury

Specialisation: Principal areas of practice are personal injury (including insidious disease and health and safety), clinical and professional negligence. Particular emphasis on group and multi-party actions including advising and appearing as Senior Lead Counsel in Prescription Pricing Authority (repetative strain injury), Metro-Cammell litigation (asbestosis), Vibration White Finger litigation, "Frank Beck" litigation (physical and sexual abuse in children's homes), north west child abuse cases, Cambridgeshire child abuse cases, Scotforth House litigation (autistic children group action), Hillsborough Disaster inquest and inquiry. Also instructed in chancery, commercial, planning, public and administrative law.
Prof. Memberships: Personal Injury Bar Association and Professional Negligence Bar Association.
Career: Called to the Bar 1968. Queen's Counsel 1988. Recorder and Deputy High Court Judge. Head of Ropewalk Chambers 1994.

MAY, Charlotte

8 New Square (Michael Fysh QC SC), London
(020) 7405 4321
charlotte.may@8newsquare.co.uk

Recommended in Intellectual Property

Specialisation: Barrister specialising in all areas of intellectual property law and scientific commercial law, including patents, biotechnology, trade marks, copyrights and database rights, passing off, registered design, design right and confidential information. Cases include: Oxford Gene Technology v Affymetrix (biotech patent - revocation - infringement); Monsanto and Others v Merck (biotech patent-infringement-validity); Haberman and Anr v Jackel International Ltd. patent for drinking vessel - infringement - validity; Unicontinental Holdings Ltd.) and Anr. v Eurobond Adhesives Ltd. patent infringement - industrial copyright - trade mark infringement; Zino Davidoff SA v A&G Imports Ltd., trade mark infringement and passing off; Pro Sieben Media A.G. v Carltonn UK Television Ltd and Anr (copyright-fair dealing defences); Antonio Munoz Y CIA SA and Anr. v Frumar Ltd. and Anr. (breach of the Council Regulation).
Prof. Memberships: Intellectual Property Bar Association (IPBA); The Intellectual Property Lawyers Organisation (TIPLO)
Career: Called 1995, Inner Temple.
Personal: Born 1971; resides London. Leisure; dancing (ceroc, lindehop, jive, funk), music.

MAYNARD-CONNOR, Giles

St. James's Chambers (R.A. Sterling), Manchester
(0161) 834 7000
clerks@stjameschambers.co.uk

Recommended in Insolvency/Corporate Recovery

Specialisation: General Chancery with emphasis on insolvency (corporate and personal), company, professional negligence and banking.
Prof. Memberships: Chancery Bar Association, Northern Chancery Bar Association, Bar Pro Bono Unit
Career: Call to Bar 24/11/92.
Personal: University of Lancaster. Leisure interests: football, motor racing, rugby union, travel, film and dining.

MCALLISTER, Ann

Serle Court (Lord Neill of Bladen QC), London
(020) 7242 6105

Recommended in Agriculture, Property Litigation

Specialisation: Principal area of practice is landlord and tenant, property law and agricultural tenancies, although practice also includes all aspects of general chancery law (mortgages, partnerships, guarantees, insolvency) and professional negligence work.
Career: Called to the Bar in 1982.
Personal: Read law and languages at Newnham College, Cambridge. After graduating in 1975 went to LSE and gained an LL.M in law. Taught law for three years at the University of London (School of Oriental and African Studies).

MCCALL, Christopher H. QC

13 Old Square (Michael Lyndon-Stanford QC), London (020) 7404 4800

Recommended in Charities, Tax, Chancery

Specialisation: Specialises in trust, revenue and charity law. Has appeared in numerous appeals in the House of Lords, Privy Council and Court of Appeal: has regularly addressed specialist associations and seminars and written in legal journals.
Prof. Memberships: Member of Bar Council 1973-1976.
Career: Called to Bar Lincolns Inn, November 1966. Took silk, April 1987. Bencher 1993. 2nd Junior Counsel to the Inland Revenue in Chancery Matters 1977-1987. Junior Counsel to the Attorney-General in Charity Matters 1981-1987. Practised at 7 New Square Lincolns Inn 1967-1994, subsequently 13 Old Square.
Personal: Born 3 March 1944. Married 1981, no children. Educated Winchester College (Scholar), Magdalen College, Oxford (Demy): 1st class, Mathematical Moderations 1962 and Finals 1964. Eldon Law Scholarship: 1966.

MCCARROLL, John J.

Exchange Chambers (William Waldron QC), Liverpool (0151) 236 7747

Recommended in Chancery, Insolvency/Corporate Recovery

MCCAUGHRAN, John

One Essex Court (Lord Grabiner QC), London (020) 7583 2000

Recommended in Civil Fraud, Commercial (Litigation), Energy & Natural Resources

Specialisation: Principal area of practice is commercial litigation.
Prof. Memberships: Commercial Bar Association
Career: Called to the Bar in 1982.
Personal: Educated at Methodist College, Belfast 1969-1976 and Trinity Hall, Cambridge 1977-80. Born 24 April 1958. Lives in London.

MCCOMBE, Richard QC

13 Old Square (Michael Lyndon-Stanford QC), London (020) 7404 4800

Recommended in Commercial Chancery

Specialisation: Commercial Chancery, including insolvency. Has worked since starting practice in a set of Chambers dealing with all aspects of Chancery practice. This has involved a good deal of insolvency work for office holders and those on the receiving end of the claims. Work continues to include company law, property, commercial contracts, including commercial fraud and international asset tracing cases. Work since 1995 includes an action for a major merchant bank in claims made against it uder the Financial Services Act in respect of listing particulars. Has also worked upon the BCCI litigation in the Cayman Islands and upon a large partnership/ trust dispute and other Chancery matters in Singapore; admitted ad hoc to the Bars of both those countries. Speaks French and German. Has experience of dealing with German court documents, interviewing witnesses and conducting correspondence in German, obtained during the course of an appointment as Companies Act Inspector (with JK Heywood FCA of Price Waterhouse) into the affairs of Norton Group plc (1991-92). Also works in various cases involving the inter-play of legal and accountancy skills. Recently involved in ART. 86 case involving traffic at a major British Port, several freezing rules and asset financing cases and in continuing litigation for Customs & Excise in respect of butter imports.
Prof. Memberships: Chancery Bar Association, COMBAR, Criminal Bar Association, Singapore Academy of Law.
Career: Called to the Bar 1975, Silk 1989. Junior Council to the Director General of Fair Trading 1982-89. Recorder of the Crown Court (1996). Deputy High Court Judge. Attorney-General of the Duchy of Lancaster. Leader of the UK delegation (comprising solicitors and barristers from all the UK jurisdictions) to the CCBE (Council of the Bars and Law Societies of the European Union).
Personal: Educated at Sedbergh School, Graf Stauffenberg Gymnasium Osnabrück and Downing College, Cambridge. Lives in Kew and has a "bolt hole" (with telephone!) in rural France. Hobbies include cricket and rugby football, karate with the children and flying small aircraft.

MCCRACKEN, Robert

2 Harcourt Buildings (Mr Gerard Ryan QC), London (020) 7353 8415

Recommended in Environment

Specialisation: Principal area of practice is environmental law, especially land use and planning aspects. Acted in Heathrow Terminal 5 Inquiry, Windermere Speed Limit Inquiry/Otterburn MOD Inquiry, Newham LBC v. E.L.H.A. [1986] JPEL 60, City of London Building Society v Flegg [1988] AC 54 and R v Northumbria Water Authority ex p Able [1996] COD p187, Berkeley v SSE (CA) 1998 Env – LR 741. HL (Times 7/7/00) R v St Edmundsbury BC ex p Walton, The Times 5 May 1999. R v Durham CC ex p Huddlestone (CA). Clients include National Grid, BP, Elf, Tesco, Bryant Homes, Greenpeace, and the Treasury Solicitor.
Prof. Memberships: Local Government Planning and Environmental Bar Association (Secretary 1992-94), United Kingdom Environmental Law Association (Chairman 1995-1997). Member Legal Advisory Panel to Council for the Protection of Rural England. Honorary Counsel to Council for National Parks.
Career: Called to the Bar 1973 and joined 2 Harcourt Buildings 1974.
Publications: Author of various articles for legal periodicals including 'Liability of Funding Institutions for Contaminated Land' (JPF,1992). Joint author of Butterworth's 'Statutory Nuisance'.
Personal: Educated at Worcester College, Oxford 1968-1971 (MA). Former educational missionary in East Africa. Leisure pursuits include fell walking, natural science and painting. Born 15th March 1950.

MCCUTCHEON, Barry

8 Gray's Inn Square (Patrick C. Soares), London (020) 7242 3529

Recommended in Tax

Specialisation: Revenue law, including capital taxation, trusts, foreign domiciliaries, offshore and international planning, and insurance based planning. Author of 'McCutcheon on Inheritance Tax'. Founder and Editor of 'Private Client Business' and co-editor of 'Euro-Trusts: The New European Dimension for Trusts' and 'Death and Taxes in Europe'. Well-known as lecturer and conference organiser in the UK and internationally.
Prof. Memberships: Chartered Institute of Taxation (Ex-Chairman, Capital Taxes Sub-Committee), Society of Trust and Estate Practitioners.
Career: Called to the Bar 1975. Tax consultant to Ernst & Young (as is now known) 1978-85. Joined present chambers in 1985.

MCDERMOTT, John

Chavasse Court Chambers (Theresa Pepper), Liverpool (0151) 707 1191

Recommended in Crime

MCDERMOTT, Tom

Farrar's Building (John Leighton Williams QC), London (020) 7583 9241

Recommended in Personal Injury

Specialisation: Practice covers general common law matters with an emphasis on personal injury. Also handles professional and medical negligence and employment.
Prof. Memberships: South Eastern Circuit.
Career: Called to the Bar and joined Farrar's Building in 1980.
Personal: Educated at University College, London (LL.B, 1978) and Queens' College, Cambridge (Institute of Criminology) (M.Phil, 1979). Called to the Irish Bar, King's Inns, Dublin in 1991. Born 11th September 1955. Lives in Hertfordshire.

MCDONNELL, John B.W. QC

1 New Square (Eben Hamilton QC), London (020) 7405 0884

Recommended in Commercial Chancery

Specialisation: Practice has a strong bias towards litigation. Regularly instructed in trials both in the Chancery Division and in the Queen's Bench Division. Matters include securities for borrowing, company or insolvency matters, judicial review, human rights, questions concerning trusts (especially charities) or constructive trusts, commercial fraud, professional negligence, copyright and intellectual property, real property, landlord and tenant and partnership. Has regularly advised two of the Clearing Banks on banking and security matters. Frequently involved in cases with an international element. Has appeared often in the Supreme Court of Hong Kong, the High Court of the Isle of Man and the Grand Court of the Cayman Islands.
Career: Called to the Bar, 1968. Took Silk 1984. Elected a Bencher of Lincoln's Inn, 1993. Before commencing practice at the Bar had worked in the United States Congress, Conservative Research Dept, H.M. Diplomatic Service (as Assistant Private Secretary to the Foreign Secretary). Sits as a Deputy High Court Judge attached to the Chancery Division.
Prof. Memberships: Governor of the Inns of Court School of Law.

MCFARLAND, Denise

Three New Square (David E.M. Young QC), London (020) 7405 1111

Recommended in Intellectual Property

Specialisation: All aspects of Intellectual Property. Recent Cases include: Ray v Classic FM, BA v PRS, (Copyright Tribunal) Cinpres v Melea (CA), PLG v Ardon, Cala v McAlpine, British Diabetic Association v The Diabetic Society, Lancs Fires v SA Lyons, Novamedix v NDM, Norsk Hydro's As Patent, Carflow v Linwood (second trial), Bell Atlantic v Bell, L'Oreal v Johnson & Johnson (meaning of threats), as well as numerous decisions from the Trade Marks Registry, and copyright tribunal.
Prof. Memberships: British Council Member of AIPPI; Committee member of T.I.P.L.O; Women's Bar Assn; Intellectual Property Bar Assn; Chancery Bar Assn. Former Examiner for Chartered Institute of Trade Mark Agents professional examination. Appointed Expert for Settlement of Nominet Dispute Procedures.
Career: Cambridge University (MA).
Personal: Riding and all country pursuits, music and theatre.

MCFARLANE, Andrew QC

One King's Bench Walk (Anthony Hacking QC), London (020) 7936 1500

Recommended in Family: Child Care including child abduction

Specialisation: Principal area of practice is family law. Handles all aspects with particular expertise in the law relating to children (both public and private law), international child abduction and adoption. Has appeared before the House of Lords and before the European Court of Human Rights. Co-author with David Hershman of 'Children: Law & Practice' (Family Law 1991), contributor to 'Family Court Practice' (Family Law 1999) and Editorial Board: Sweet & Maxwell, 'Practical Research Papers'. Regular lecturer at nationally organised conferences and seminars.
Prof. Memberships: Midlands & Oxford Circuit, Family Law Bar Association, Association of Lawyers for Children, British Agencies for Adoption and Fostering.
Career: Called to the Bar in 1977. At Priory Chambers, Birmingham 1978-93 and remains a door tenant at St Philip's Chambers, Birmingham. Joined 1 King's Bench Walk in 1993. Appointed Recorder in 1999. QC 1998. Deputy High Court Judge in 2000.
Personal: Educated at Shrewsbury School 1968-1972, Durham University 1972-1976, University of Wales (LLM (Canon Law)) 1994-98. Leisure interests include theatre, conjuring, walking and his children. Born 20th June 1954. Lives in Malvern.

MCGHEE, John

9 Old Square (Michael Driscoll QC), London (020) 7405 4682

Recommended in Property Litigation

Specialisation: Property, chancery and commercial litigation. Recent cases include: Escalus Properties v Robinson [1996] QB 231 (forfeiture); Barrett v Morgan [1997] 12 EG 155 (notice to quit); Bankers Trust v Namdar [1997] EGCS 20 (subrogation); Grupo Torras

v Al Sabah Litigation (civil fraud). Editor: Snells Equity, supplemental panel member for Treasury Solicitor.
Career: University College Oxford 1980-83 (MA).

MCGRATH, Paul
Essex Court Chambers (Gordon Pollock QC), London (020) 7813 8000
Recommended in Commercial (Litigation), Shipping
Specialisation: Banking law, (including the Cayman Islands jurisdiction), conflict of laws, equity in a commercial context (e.g. constructive trusts, bribes, civil fraud), pre-emptive remedies (domestic and worldwide Mareva injunctions, tracing orders, Norwich Pharmacal relief), insolvency (advising liquidators on all aspects thereof, including schemes of arrangement, payment of dividend and the general conduct of liquidations as well as potential claims against directors of insolvent companies), all aspects of restitution, joint ventures, financial services, shipbuilding contracts and general commercial practice involving court and arbitration work.
Career: BA, BCL, University College, Oxford. Called to the Bar in 1994.
Personal: Born 1970.

MCKAY, Hugh
Gray's Inn Tax Chambers (Milton Grundy), London (020) 7242 2642
hm@taxbar.com
Recommended in Tax
Specialisation: Revenue Law especially tax litigation, commercial/ corporate tax issues and VAT.
Prof. Memberships: Secretary, Revenue Bar Association, 1996- 2000. Member – Chancery Bar Association, Chartered Institute of Taxation, VAT Practitioners Group, Law Society VAT and Duties Sub-committee (co-opted), 1994-1998, Institute of Indirect Taxation Bar Council 1999 -
Career: Called to the Bar 1990, joined present chambers 1991. Visiting Fellow (Tax), London School of Economics 1993 to 1998.
Personal: Born 26th June 1966. Lives in Marylebone. Educated at King's College, London (LL.M. Tax) and Leeds University (MA), FTII, AIIT.

MCLAREN, Ian QC
Ropewalk Chambers (Richard Maxwell QC), Nottingham (0115) 947 2581
Recommended in Personal Injury
Specialisation: Personal Injury, common law and local government. 3 cases in House of Lords in last 3 years; Longden v British Coal [1998] A.C. 653, Jameson v CEGB [1999] 2WLR 141 and Dimond v Lovell [2000] 2 WLR 1121.
Prof. Memberships: Personal Injury Bar Association; European Bar Association; Planning and Environment Bar Association.
Career: Called 1962; Bar Finals prize, Macaskie Scholar Gray's Inn plus 3 other scholarships. Law Tutor University of Nottingham. Silk 1993, Recorder 1996. Judicial Studies Board tutor re Human Rights Act 1998.
Publications: Various articles New Law Journal.
Personal: Sandback School, Blackpool Grammar School, Nottingham University (LL.B.). Interests, travel, wine and photography. Married, 3 children. President Nottinghamshire Medico-Legal Society 1997-1998.

MCLOUGHLIN, Timothy
East Anglian Chambers (Roderick Newton), Norwich (01603) 617351
Recommended in Family/Matrimonial

MCMANUS, Richard QC
4-5 Gray's Inn Square (Elizabeth Appleby QC & Duncan Ouseley QC), London (020) 7404 5252
Recommended in Administrative & Public Law: General, Aviation
Specialisation: Aviation, Contempt of Court, Discrimination, Education, Employment, European Community Law, Extradition, Financial Services Act and Social Security. Recent cases: Sirdar v Army Board (combat effectiveness and equal treatment); Coker and Osamor v Lord Chancellor; R v ICS ex parte Taylor (Financial Services and Damages); B v Harrow (Rights preference and Special Educational Needs); O'Connor v Chief Adjudication Officer (Denial of income support and student notion infringement of insight to education); Author 'Education and the Courts'.
Prof. Memberships: Administrative Law Bar Association.
Career: Called 1982. Junior Counsel to the Crown (Common Law) 1992 to 1999. Silk 1999
Personal: Educated at Downing College, Cambridge.

MCMEEKIN, Ian
Kingsgate Chambers (Beverly Lunt), Manchester (0161) 831 7477
Recommended in Crime
Specialisation: All areas of crime; Junior Counsel in R v Brown (Winsten), (House of Lords decision on disclosure) A-G's Counsel for The D.T.I.
Career: Thirteen years specialising in crime. Bar Representative on Governments Youth Justice Trust Scheme.
Personal: University of Leeds, City University (postgrad).

MCMULLEN, Jeremy QC
Old Square Chambers (John Hendy QC), London (020) 7269 0300
jmcmullenqc@cs.com
Recommended in Employment
Specialisation: Employment, public law. Includes discrimination, contracts, restrictive covenants, industrial action, directorships, dismissal, injunctions, inquiries eg Clapham Junction, Ladbroke Grove, Westminster Auditor. Employment Tribunal Chairman. Recorder.
Prof. Memberships: Vice-President ILS and ELBA; former ACAS equal pay expert. Publications: Employment Tribunal Procedure; Employment Precedents; Labour Law Review.
Career: Called 1971, worked in New York and for GMB before practising in 1985. Silk 1994; N. Ireland 1996, Cayman Islands 1999.
Personal: Educated at Oxford and LSE.

MCNEILL, Jane
Old Square Chambers (John Hendy QC), London (020) 7269 0300
Recommended in Employment
Specialisation: Employment including discrimination under domestic and European law; wrongful and unfair dismissal; redundancy; restraint of trade. Cases include Kapur v. Barclays; Preston v. Wolverhampton Healthcare NHS Trustee; Fletcher v. Midland Bank plc; Hallam v Avery; British Airways (European Operations at Gatwick) Ltd v Moore. Also personal injury and medical negligence.
Prof. Memberships: Employment Law Bar Association; PIBA.
Personal: B.A. Hons (Oxon); Dip. Law (City University); Fluent Italian and French. Called 1982.

MCQUATER, Ewan
3 Verulam Buildings (Christopher Symons QC & John Jarvis QC), London (020) 7831 8441
clerks@3verulam.co.uk
Recommended in Banking, Civil Fraud, Commercial (Litigation), Insolvency/Corporate Recovery
Specialisation: Commercial work specialising in banking, commercial fraud, insolvency and more general finance related work. Also has considerable experience in professional negligence work. Important cases include: the Libyan asset freeze litigation (US freeze on Libyan asset worldwide), the expropriation of the National Bank of Brunei, the collapse of the Maxwell group, the Arrows liquidation (series of important insolvency decisions), BBL (measure of damages in professional negligence cases), the BCCI liquidation, the collapse of the Barings group, Grupo Torras and Prince Jefri of Brunei (defence of claim by State of Brunei and Brunei Investment Agency). Assistant Editor of the 'Encyclopaedia of Banking Law'.
Prof. Memberships: COMBAR.
Career: Called to the Bar 1985 and joined current Chambers 1986. Admitted to the Bar of the Cayman Islands on a series of individual cases.
Personal: Educated at Merchiston Castle School, Edinburgh (1975-80) and Cambridge University 1981-84 (MA Hons in Law, First Class). Born 30th October 1962. Lives in London.

MEAD, Philip
Old Square Chambers (John Hendy QC), London (020) 7269 0300
mead@oldsquarechambers.co.uk
Recommended in Environment
Specialisation: Environmental law, personal injury law and health and safety law including toxic torts and product liability, employment and discrimination law. Has particular knowledge of the application of European law and conflicts of law to the above areas. Acts for both claimants/applicants and defendants/respondents, appearing in both the civil and criminal courts. Consultant to the European Commission on Health and Safety. Author of litigation manual for the Environmental Law Foundation on European Environmental Law, co-author of chapter on Tort and Product Liability in 'Practitioners' Handbook of EC Law'.
Prof. Memberships: Association of Personal Injury Lawyers, Employment Law Bar Association, Environmental Law Foundation, United Kingdom Environmental Law Association and Bar European Group.
Career: Called to the Bar 1989; member Western Circuit, and practises from chambers' annexe in Bristol.
Personal: Visiting fellow and occasional lecturer, Durham University; LLM, European University Institute, Florence.

MEADE, Richard
8 New Square (Michael Fysh QC SC), London (020) 7405 4321
richard.meade@8newsquare.co.uk
Recommended in Information Technology, Intellectual Property
Specialisation: Specialises in all aspects of intellectual property, with particular experience in biotechnology and electronics patent litigation, trade mark litigation including comparative advertising cases, music copyright, 'Euro' defences, and jurisdiction under the Brussels Convention. Notable cases include Chiron v Organon and Murex (genetic engineering and HCV blood tests), Chiron v Evans (protein chemistry and pertussis vaccines), Vodafone v Orange and BT v AT&T (both comparative advertising), Elvis Presley Trade Mark, Prince Jefri Bolkiah v KPMG (confidential information), Beloit v Valmet, Chocosuisse v Cadburys (passing off).Monsanto v Merck (pharmacutical

patents).
Publications: Atkins' Court Forms section on Trade Marks and Trade Names (editor); Supreme Court Practice (Trade Marks and Patents sections – assistant editor); Kerly's Law of Trade Marks (co-author, in preparation).
Prof. Memberships: Chancery Bar Association, Intellectual Property Bar Association.
Career: With Andersen Consulting (information technology management consultancy) 1988-1990. First in year on Bar Vocational Course (1990-1991) and winner of Scarman Scholarship, Ede & Ravenscroft and Wilfred Parker Prizes. Called to the Bar in 1991.
Personal: Educated at William Ellis School, Gospel Oak, North London 1978-1984 and University College, Oxford 1985-1988 (BA). Born 14th November 1966.

MEADOWCROFT, Stephen
Peel Court Chambers (Michael Shorrock QC), Manchester (0161) 832 3791
Recommended in Crime

MEADWAY, Susannah
10 Old Square (Leolin Price CBE QC), London (020) 7405 0758 / 7242 5002
susannahmeadway@10oldsquare.ndo.co.uk
Recommended in Traditional Chancery
Specialisation: Advisory, drafting and litigation work in the fields of trusts and associated taxation, pensions, wills, probate and the administration of estates. Court of Protection matters and charities and professional negligence in those fields. A contributor to Foster's Inheritance Tax, assistant editor of Williams on Wills, and co-editor of 'Halsbury's Laws of England: Wills' and 'Halsbury's Laws of England: Executors & Administrators'. Counsel in Re Segelman [1996] ch 171.
Prof. Memberships: STEP (Society of Trust and Estate Practitioners). Chancery Bar Association; Revenue Bar Association.

MEEKE, Martin
Colleton Chambers (Martin Meeke), Exeter (01392) 274898
Recommended in Crime

MEESON, Nigel
4 Field Court (Steven Gee QC), London (020) 7440 6900
Recommended in Shipping
Specialisation: Practice covers all areas of commercial law and shipping including admiralty, arbitration, aviation, banking, carriage of goods, conflict of laws, insurance and reinsurance, international trade and sale of goods.
Prof. Memberships: LMAA (Supporting Member), COMBAR, BMLA, ABA, Forum on Air and Space Law.
Career: Called 1982. Admitted to California Bar 1990. Accredited Mediator by CEDR 1993. Visiting lecturer University College, London since 1994. Admiralty Court Committee. Supplementary Panel of Treasury Counsel.
Personal: Magdalen College, Oxford (1st class hons Jurisprudence). Author of 'Admiralty Jurisdiction & Practice' (1993), 2nd Ed (2000), 'Ship & Aircraft Mortgages' (1989), contributor to 'Ship Sale & Purchase' (3rd edition 1998). Various articles and conference papers.

MEHIGAN, Simon QC
5 Paper Buildings (Godfrey Carey QC & Jonathan Caplan QC), London (020) 7583 6117
Recommended in Employment, Licensing
Specialisation: Restraint of Trade, Breach of Confidence (both in relation to employment and the commercial law generally). Complex criminal (and civil) fraud of all types including associated regulatory, DTI directors disqualification and disciplinary proceedings. Advice to victims of fraud, particularly in relation to investigations. Licensing of all types but particularly concerning casinos.
Career: Co-author Mehigan and Griffiths, 'Restraint of Trade and Business Secrets' (Sweet & Maxwell) Fourth Edition, 2000; Co-author 'The Law of Confidential Information' (Butterworths) 2000, Editor 'Paterson's Licensing Acts' (current and previous 5 editions). Has appeared in many leading cases including Provident Financial Group plc v. Hayward (1989) (garden leave), Clarke v. Newland (1991) (Construction of restrictive covenants), Hanover Insurance Brokers Ltd v. Schapiro (non-poaching of employees). Appeared for the defence in the Blue Arrow and Nissan Tax trials as well as many other commercial fraud and corruption cases. Advised and appeared also in the Guinness and Maxwell cases. Frequent involvement for companies and banks seeking to resist witness summonses in criminal fraud cases. Formerly worked in corporate finance department of a merchant bank.
Personal: Called 1980. Q.C. 1998. Door Tenant at Albion Chambers, Bristol.

MELLOR, James
8 New Square (Michael Fysh QC SC), London (020) 7405 4321
james.mellor@8newsquare.co.uk
Recommended in Intellectual Property, Media & Entertainment
Specialisation: Has a wide-ranging intellectual property practice in patents (electronics/ chemical/ mechanical devices/ biotech), copyright and designs (engineering drawings/ databases/ computer software/ literary works), trade marks and passing off (Levi's) and confidential information (chemical formulae/ business information). Important cases handled include Fyffes v Chiquita (1991 – trade marks – Articles 85/86 EEC), Rediffusion v Link-Miles (1992 – flight simulator patent), Levi's V BTC (1993 – international counterfeiting of Levi's 501 jeans), GEC Alsthom v FKI Engineering (1996 patent, copyright, confidential information) Vodafone v Orange (1996 malicious falsehood, trade marks), Harrods v Harrods (Buenos Aires) Limited (1997 – trade marks, passing off, contract, licence); Prince v Prince Sports Group (1997 – internet domain name, trade mark threats); Marks & Spencer v One in a Million (1998 – internet domain names); Alan Clark v Associated Newspapers (1998 – passing off); Budweiser Trade Mark (1998, 2000), Cantor Fitzgerald v Tradition (1999 - copyright computer-software). Further experience in arbitrations with intellectual property or technical elements and in the Copyright Tribunal. Work experience in a variety of engineering disciplines in the UK, France, Germany, Somalia, the Congo and Iraq. Co-editor of 'Kerly on Trade Marks', Editor of 'Computers – Atkin's Court Forms', co-author of The Trade Marks Act 1994 – Text and Commentary. Member of the Disability Panel of the Bar Council. Committee Member of Chancery Bar Association.
Prof. Memberships: Intellectual Property Bar Association, Chancery Bar Association.
Career: Called to the Bar in 1986 and joined current chambers in 1987.
Personal: Educated at Rugby School and King's College, Cambridge (MA, Eng). Leisure activities include windsurfing, skiing, cycling, running, sailing, reading and music. Born 16th May 1961.

MELTON, Christopher
Peel Court Chambers (Michael Shorrock QC), Manchester (0161) 832 3791
clerks@peelct.co.uk
Recommended in Clinical Negligence

MERCER, Geoffrey
Walnut House (Francis Gilbert QC), Exeter (01392) 279751
Recommended in Crime
Specialisation: Serious crime, including fraud. Licensing. Personal injury. Clinical and professional negligence.
Prof. Memberships: CBA
Career: Recorder 1998.

MERCER, Hugh
Essex Court Chambers (Gordon Pollock QC), London (020) 7813 8000
Recommended in Agriculture
Specialisation: Specialist in EU and commercial law. Recent practice includes: Brussels Convention jurisdictional arguments in the House of Lords; Articles 81/82 in the context of milk distribution and liner shipping; judicial review on EU grounds of decisions to use new food safety legislation and to refuse subsidies to the Isle of Wight; right to a hearing for IACS forms before the European Court of Justice; state aid, competition, public procurement and pharmaceutical product authorisation (agriculture, motor car distribution in Denmark, electrical and gas infrastructure projects in Greece and whether MCA decisions breach EU law) before the European Commission; proceedings before the High Court and the UK Competition Commission in the context of gas and water regulatory issues.
Prof. Memberships: Bar European Group, Union Internationale Des Avocats, Agriculture Law Association, International Relations Committee of the Bar Council.
Career: Called to the Bar 1985. Former lecturer at Kings College, London (courses on European Law).
Personal: Educated at Downing College, Cambridge 1981-84 and at Université Libre de Bruxelles (Licence Spéciale en Droit Européen avec Grande Distinction) 1985-86. Fluent in French, German, and reasonably fluent in Spanish and Italian. Leisure pursuits include squash, mountain walking, and photography.

MEREDITH, George
Southernhay Chambers (Anthony Ward), Exeter (01392) 255777
Recommended in Family/Matrimonial
Specialisation: Care proceedings and private law children act applications, wardship and inherent jurisdiction cases. Recent cases in court of appeal concerning jurisdiction of county court in family proceedings and power of court to make assessment orders in care cases.
Prof. Memberships: Family Law Bar Association. Christian Mediation and Arbitration Service.
Career: Called to Bar 1969. Wardship and care cases from 1975.
Personal: Married with 3 children. Enjoys walking and computers.

MERRIMAN, Nicholas QC
3 Verulam Buildings (Christopher Symons QC & John Jarvis QC), London (020) 7831 8441
clerks@3verulam.co.uk
Recommended in Media & Entertainment
Specialisation: Barrister specialising in commercial work; banking; insurance; international trade, financial services, shipping and related aspects of company and insolvency work. Maritime, commodity and international arbitration. Intellectual property, entertainment law and gaming, and professional negligence. Cases: The Beatles v Lingasong Music 1998; Ritz Casino v Adnan Khashoggi 1998; Creation Records v News Group 1997; Macmillan v Bishopsgate Investment Trust 1995; Re: Paramount Holdings 1993; Barclays Bank v Homan 1993: Baytur V Finagro Holdings 1992; Crockfords v Mehta 1992.
Career: Qualified 1969; QC 1988; recorder; Master of the Bench, Inner Temple

MEYER, Lorna
5 Fountain Court (Anthony Barker QC), Birmingham (0121) 606 0500
Recommended in Family/Matrimonial

MICHAELS, Amanda
5 New Square (Jonathan Rayner James QC), London (020) 7404 0404
Recommended in Media & Entertainment
Specialisation: Intellectual property, with an emphasis on copyright and design right, trade marks (registration and litigation) and passing off. Entertainment and media law, including music industry, performing rights, publishing, advertising, film and television disputes. Breach of confidence and all other aspects of intellectual property. General Chancery and commercial litigation.
Career: Call: 1981.
Personal: BA in law from Durham, MA in Advanced European Studies from College of Europe, Bruges. Fluent French. Author of 'A Practical Guide to Trade Mark Law' (2nd ed. 1996) Sweet & Maxwell.

MIFFLIN, Helen
30 Park Place (John Jenkins QC), Cardiff (029) 2039 8421
Recommended in Family/Matrimonial
Specialisation: Family, Care Proceedings, Ancillary Relief.
Prof. Memberships: Family Bar Association.
Career: LLB (Hons) Leicester. Assistant Recorder, Wales and Chester Circuit. Assistant Recorder Wales and Chester Circuit.

MILDON, David QC
Essex Court Chambers (Gordon Pollock QC), London (020) 7813 8000
Recommended in Energy & Natural Resources
Specialisation: All types of commercial litigation including oil gas and electricity litigation, insurance, banking, shipping, international sale of goods and international commercial arbitration; also Lloyd's and LIFFE disciplinary proceedings.
Career: Emmanuel College, Cambridge, MA (1st Class Honours); LL.B (1st Class Honours). Called to the Bar: 1980. Called to Bar of Antigua and Barbuda: 1990. Queen's Council 2000.

MILES, Robert
4 Stone Buildings (Philip Heslop QC), London (020) 7242 5524
clerks@4stonebuildings.law.co.uk
Recommended in Banking, Commercial Chancery, Company, Energy & Natural Resources, Insolvency/Corporate Recovery
Specialisation: Company and Commercial Litigation, Corporate Insolvency; Oil and gas. Amongst reported cases are: Derby v Weldon (worldwide Marevas); Re Atlantic Computers (corporate insolvency); acting for the liquidators of the pension fund trustee company in the Maxwell affair; BCCI (corporate insolvency) Phillips v Euron (oil and gas); Bermuda Fire & Marine litigation in Bermuda.
Prof. Memberships: Committee of the Chancery Bar Association; COMBAR.
Career: Called to the Bar 1987. Called to the Bars of Bermuda and the Isle of Man for specific cases.
Personal: 1984 BA (Hons) in PPE (1st Class) Christ Church, Oxford. 1985 Diploma in Law (with distinction) City University, London. 1986 Bar Finals (Denning Prize; Megarry Prize). 1987 BCL (1st Class) Christ Church, Oxford.

MILL, Ian QC
Blackstone Chambers (P Baxendale QC and C Flint QC), London (020) 7583 1770
ianmill@blackstonechambers.com
Recommended in Commercial (Litigation), Media & Entertainment, Sport
Specialisation: Principal areas of practice are commercial law (including financial services and commercial fraud) and intellectual property (copyright, passing off and confidential information) with specialist knowledge and experience in the music industry and other entertainment fields, and in sports law. Major cases include Panayiotou v Sony Music (the George Michael case) and Hadley v Kemp (the Spandau Ballet case). Clients have included all the major record and music publishing companies, film production companies, television and radio broadcasters, recording artists and songwriters, and leading sports organisations and figures.
Prof. Memberships: Recently appointed Chairman of UK Athletics Disciplinary Committee, and of the Sports Dispute Resolution Panel.
Career: Called to the Bar 1981 and joined current chambers 1982. Appointed QC in 1999.
Publications: Editorial Board member for 'The International Sports Law Review'
Personal: Educated at Epsom College 1971-1975 and Trinity Hall, Cambridge 1976-80 (MA in Classics and Law). Leisure pursuits include golf, cricket, theatre and opera. Born 9th April 1958. Lives in London.

MILLAR, Gavin QC
Doughty Street Chambers (Geoffrey Robertson QC), London (020) 7404 1313
Recommended in Employment
Specialisation: Specialises in public/employment law, defamation/media and medical work. Election law is a particular speciality. Mostly appears in QBD, the Divisional Court and employment tribunals, although has undertaken a number of high profile public inquiries and has reported cases in the Court of Appeal and House of Lords. Also undertakes related criminal work and pro bono work.
Prof. Memberships: Member of ELBA, ALBA and Liberty. Member of Westminster City Council 1985 to 1994 and served on its Social Services, Policy and Resources, Contracts, Education and Housing Committees.
Personal: Born 1959.

MILLER, Celia
East Anglian Chambers (Roderick Newton), Ipswich (01473) 214481
Recommended in Family/Matrimonial

MILLER, Nicholas
Guildhall Chambers (Adrian Palmer QC), Bristol (0117) 927 3366
Recommended in Family/Matrimonial

MILLER, Richard QC
Three New Square (David E.M. Young QC), London (020) 7405 1111
Recommended in Intellectual Property
Specialisation: Specialist in patents, copyright, design rights, trade marks, passing off, breach of confidence, restrictive covenants and all other aspects of intellectual property, including EU law relating to IP. Also appears at the European Patent Office in Munich on behalf of applicants and opponents for European Patents. Co-editor of 'TERRELL on the Law of Patents'.
Prof. Memberships: Intellectual Property Bar Association, Chancery Bar Association, Bar European Group, International Association for the Protection of Industrial Property (AIPPI).
Career: Called to the Bar 1976 (Middle Temple). Appointed QC 1995.
Personal: Educated: Charterhouse 1966-1970; University of Sussex 1971-1974, BSc (Chemical Physics).

MILLER, Stephen QC
1 Crown Office Row (Robert Seabrook QC), London (020) 7797 7500
stephen.miller@1cor.com
Recommended in Clinical Negligence
Specialisation: Professional negligence, particularly medical negligence and medically related disciplinary and Inquiry work. Interesting cases include: Wilsher v Essex Health Authority; Gold v Haringey Health Authority; Aboul Hosn v The Trustees of the Italian Hospital; AB v Wyeth and others (Benzodiazepine litigation); Rage (Breast Radiation Injury Group Action); Bristol Royal Infirmary Inquiry; OCP (oral contraceptive pill) Group Action; Johnstone v Camden & Islington Heath Authority; Hallat v. North West Anglia Health Authority, Robertsonv. Nottingham Health authority. Al-Kandari v J R Brown & Co; Talbot v Berkshire County Council; Zeebrugge Ferry Inquiry and criminal proceedings. Publications include a chapter in 'Medical Negligence' (contributor) Powers & Harris (Butterworths 2000 3rd Edition). 'Personal Injury Handbook' (Editors Brennan & Curran) Second Edition 2000 'Professional Negligence and Liability' (LLP Ltd 2000). Regular speaker at conferences and seminars on the subject of medical negligence and damages.
Prof. Memberships: Professional Negligence Bar Association; London Common Law & Commercial Bar Association; Personal Injury Bar Association.
Career: Called to the Bar 1971; Silk 1990. Appointed Recorder of the Crown Court 1993.
Personal: Educated at Oxford University (BA).

MILLETT, Kenneth
1 Hare Court (Stephen Kramer QC), London (020) 7353 5324
Kennerf@lineone.net
Recommended in Crime

MILLETT, Richard
Essex Court Chambers (Gordon Pollock QC), London (020) 7813 8000
Recommended in Banking, Commercial (Litigation), Insolvency/Corporate Recovery, Media & Entertainment
Specialisation: Main areas of practice cover banking, insolvency, commercial litigation, reinsurance, company law, and media and entertainment. Major litigation includes the Maxwell, Polly Peck, Barings and BCCI cases. Co-author of 'The Law of Guarantees' (Longmans 1995) and regularly addresses conferences and seminars.
Prof. Memberships: Commercial Bar Association.
Career: Called to the Bar 1985. Joined present chambers 1990.

MILLIGAN, Iain QC
20 Essex Street (Iain Milligan QC), London (020) 7583 9294
Recommended in Banking, Commercial (Litigation), Shipping

MILLIKEN-SMITH, Mark
2 Bedford Row (formerly 3 Hare Court) (William Clegg QC), London (020) 7440 8888
Recommended in Crime
Specialisation: Specialist practitioner in serious crime, with considerable recent experience in homicide, terrorism, fraud and drugs cases.
Prof. Memberships: South Eastern Circuit, Criminal Bar Association.
Career: Educated at Wellington College and Bristol University. Call 1986.

MILMO, Patrick QC
5 Raymond Buildings (Patrick Milmo QC), London (020) 7242 2902
Recommended in Defamation

MILNE, David C. QC
Pump Court Tax Chambers (Andrew Thornhill QC), London (020) 7414 8080
clerks@pumptax.com
Recommended in Tax
Specialisation: Specialist in revenue law, especially tax litigation and dispute resolution.
Prof. Memberships: Institute of Chartered Accountants in England and Wales. Currently Chairman of the Revenue Bar Association.
Career: Accountant, articled to Whinney Murray & Co 1966-1969. Called to the Bar 1970 and joined current chambers in 1972. Took Silk 1987. Appointed Recorder 1994. Bencher of Lincoln's Inn.
Personal: Educated at Harrow 1958-1963 and Oxford 1963-1966. Born 22nd September 1945. Lives in London.

MISKIN, Charles QC
23 Essex Street (Michael Lawson QC), London (020) 7413 0353
Recommended in Fraud: Criminal
Specialisation: (1) Fraud and regulatory cases including those concerning banking, insurance, letters of credit and guarantees, trade, corruption, money laundering, advance fees, loan churning and public revenue. (2) General crime, disciplinary cases and civil cases involving both fraud and police law. (3) Environmental Law.
Prof. Memberships: Criminal Bar Association.
Career: Called to the Bar 1975 (Gray's). Joined what is now *Essex Street* in 1977. Assistant Recorder of the Crown Court, 1992-8. Recorder 1998. Standing Counsel to the Inland Revenue (Crime), 1993- 1998. Queen's Counsel 1998.
Personal: Educated at Charterhouse School and Worcester College, Oxford. Lives in London.

MITCHELL, Andrew QC
Furnival Chambers (Andrew Mitchell QC), London (020) 7405 3232
arm@furnivallaw.co.uk
Recommended in Crime, Fraud: Criminal
Specialisation: Financial Crime: White Collar Fraud – advance fee, mortgage, computer and letter of credit, handling the transfer of serious and complex fraud, drafting statements of evidence and case statements for both the defence and prosecution. Money Laundering – advised on practice and procedures in relation to money laundering regulations and legislation. Acted in both prosecutions and defence of money laundering offences. Asset Forfeiture and Confiscation – advised, represented prosecuting authorities, defendants, receivers and third parties in House of Lords, Court of Appeal (Civil and Criminal), High Court and Crown Court on all matters affecting the restraint, management receivers and confiscation of property. General Crime: defended and represented the prosecution in significant drug cases. Priority Interests: asset forfeiture, confiscation, white collar fraud, money laundering, drugs. International Work: advised governments of Trinidad and Tobago, Turks and Caicos Islands, Cayman Islands, Canada, USA, Abu Dhabi, Pakistan. Acted in civil and criminal litigation in Trinidad and Tobago, Turks and Caicos Islands and Gibraltar.
Career: Called to Bar 1976, *Gray's Inn*, Ireland, Gibraltar, Trinidad, and the Turks & Caicos Islands. Assistant Recorder 1995. Queens Counsel 1998. Recorder 1999. Has been a principal speaker at training programmes organised by the UN for prosecutors and investigators in the Caribbean as well as at judicial symposiums in Trinidad, Jamaica and the Bahamas. Regular lecturer on matters affecting restraint, confiscation and money laundering for United Nations, National Crime Squad, Criminal Bar Association (England and Wales) and Temple Lectures.
Publications: Author – 'A Concise Guide to the Criminal Procedure and Investigations Act', 1996. Co-author – 'Confiscation and the Proceeds of Crime', 2nd edn (the leading textbook on asset forfeiture and confiscation, published by Sweet & Maxwell). Articles published in the New Law Journal and the Journal of Criminal Law.
Personal: Born 6 August 1954.

MITCHELL, Andrew
Fountain Court (Anthony Boswood QC), London (020) 7583 3335
Recommended in Banking
Specialisation: Practices in commercial litigation and arbitration, with particular experience of international and domestic banking, civil fraud, professional negligence (particularly solicitors), insurance/reinsurance and employment. Recent cases have included acting for the new Nigerian Government in its claims against the former regime; Ebert v Midland Bank [1999] 3 WLR 670, a leading authority on the power of the Court to control vexatious litigation.
Prof. Memberships: COMBAR.
Career: Called 1992.
Publications: Contributing Editor to 'Commercial Court Procedure' (Sweet & Maxwell, 2000).
Personal: Educated at Cambridge University (1987 - 1990 (MA)) and Oxford University (1990-1991), BCL. Harmsworth Scholar of Middle Temple. Born 1968.

MITCHELL, Janet
4 Brick Court (David Medhurst), London (020) 7797 8910
Recommended in Family: Child Care including child abduction
Specialisation: Child care law, public law cases, family law and litigation. Provided procedure guidelines to local authorities on setting up Care in the Community Programme. Particular areas include: child sexual abuse, child protection issues, female and male paedophiles, public interest immunity. Latest case 5 week representing a local authority in respect of incest, child sexual abuse, sexual abuse by mother, father, stepfather and inter-sibling abuse. Abuse in which question of 13 year old under represented was raised.
Prof. Memberships: Family Law Bar Association. Lawyers for children.
Career: Called to the Bar in 1979. Lecturing on advocacy, litigation and public law cases particularly in the area of child sexual and physical abuse.
Personal: Travel, reading, swimming, tennis, crosswords. Widow – 2 daughters. Husband, also a Barrister, died in 1989.

MITCHELL, Keith
2 Bedford Row (formerly 3 Hare Court) (William Clegg QC), London (020) 7440 8888
Recommended in Fraud: Criminal
Specialisation: Principal area of practice is serious defence crime and fraud, including Inland Revenue, VAT, (including VAT tribunal) and company fraud, has defended in a number of high profile drug and murder cases including: R v Page (1987) 9 Cr.App.R (S)348CA (sentencing authority on escape from lawful custody), R v Whyte (1987) 3 AER 416 CA (law on self defence), R v Watson (1988) 1 AER 897CA (the removal of Walhein direction, creation of the 'Watson' direction), R v Sandiford (1992) 4th August The Times, R v Knott and Lester (1992) The Times Law Reports Feb 6 (misconduct of Jurors whilst in retirement), R v Rice (1993) 14 Cr.App.R (s)231CA (sentencing guidelines on mortgage fraud), R v Samarasingha (1994) (contract killing of husband by local government officer), R v West (1994) (underworld contract killing of millionaire businessman Urquhart), R v Nelson (1995) The Times Law 6.8.1995 (PC Dunne murder enquiry), R v Aziz, Yorganci & Tosun (1995) 3AAER149HL (leading HL authority on character and directions to jury), R v Scott, Ellis and others (1997) (operation 'Nero', East London Loss Adjuster fraud), R v Miller (1998) The Times 20th Feb (police officer double life fraud), R v Ahmed and others (1998) ('Globetrotter' multi-million pound international mobile phone fraud), R v Hipkiss and others (1999) (Operation 'Eraze, Erazor Razor' West Midlands scrap metal VAT fraud), R v Awan and others (1999) (International 'Sultan of Brunei' Diamond fraud). Particular fraud cases: R v De Souza 1983 - VAT input and output fraud on computer parts worldwide, £50 million. R v Aziz Yorganci and Tosun 1995 House of Lords - Landmark ruling VAT fraud around North London, £14 million. R v Elder and Gill - Fraudulent evasion of VAT from bonded warehouse 'Hares wines'. R v Reid Seaton 1995 - Conspiracy to defraud, British Rail station manager who over 10 years manipulated the accounts. R v Pugh 1995 to 1999 - VAT input/output fraud on sales of Ice Cream, represented both in the Crown Court and VAT Tribunal reported Tolleys VAT reports 1999. R v Woo and Choi - 'carousel fraud', involving worldwide evasion of VAT, £15 million. R v Hipkiss 1999 - West Midland scrap metal VAT fraud involving the setting of missing trader companies. R v Scott and Ellis (Panayis)(1999) Cr.Law Review 84 - Conspiracy to defraud and arson of warehouse loss adjuster VAT fraud. Current cases include: R v P - Offshore trust evasion of VAT via land sales and the alleged evasion of VAT by fraud. R v L - £7 million diversion fraud of wines and spirits involving the use of bonded warehouses and the alleged manipulation of dispatch invoices. R v B - Offshore trust Inland Revenue/VAT evasion, involving the use of offshore trusts and settlements to avoid the paying of VAT of £2 million. R v M - Computer parts carousel fraud, £30 million, involving the use of missing trader companies in Ireland, Belgium and Holland in an attempt to take advantage of 'zero' rated VAT.
Prof. Memberships: South Eastern Circuit, Criminal Bar Association, Surrey and London Bar Mess, General Council of the Bar - remuneration committee.
Career: Purbeck Upper School, East London University (BA Hons).
Personal: Married with three children. Interests: Sport (football, rugby, sailing, water-skiing). Music (guitar), Bath Society of Recital Artists.

MITCHESON, Thomas
Three New Square (David E.M. Young QC), London (020) 7405 1111
tom@mitcheson.com
Recommended in Intellectual Property
Specialisation: All aspects of intellectual property law. Recent cases include Norowzian v Arks (Copyright in television advertisement, CA); Kimberly-Clark v Procter & Gamble (Patent Amendment, CA); 3M v Rennicks (Stay of UK patent proceedings); Coca-Cola v BT (Trade Mark and Passing Off)
Career: Internship at Cold Spring Harbor Laboratory, USA 1990-91. Trinity College, Cambridge, 1991-94 – First Class Hons Natural Sciences. City University (Dip-Law) 1995 (Distinction). Called to the bar 1996.
Publications: 'Two Genes in Saccharomyces Cerevisiae Encode a Membrane Bound Form of Casein Kinase-1' Wang, Vancura, Mitcheson & Kurennt (1992). Contributor to Terrell on Patents (15th edition)

MOAT, Frank
Pump Court Chambers (Guy Boney QC), London
(020) 7353 0711
Recommended in Personal Injury
Specialisation: Called 1970. Personal injury specialist, with a particular emphasis on industrial accidents and diseases, including claims for asbestos related conditions. Practice also covers professional negligence and family law.

MOGER, Christopher QC
4 Pump Court (Bruce Mauleverer QC), London
(020) 7353 2656
cmoger@4pumpcourt.com
Recommended in Licensing, Professional Negligence
Specialisation: General commercial and common law, especially insurance, construction matters; professional negligence, and regulatory and disciplinary proceedings.
Prof. Memberships: ORBA; LCLBA; COMBAR; PNBA; Barristers' Overseas Advocacy Committee.
Career: Called 1972: joined 4 Pump Court 1973: Assistant Recorder 1990: Silk 1992: Recorder 1993: FCIA 1997. Deputy Judge of High Court 1999. Trained mediator and member of ADR Chambers, London.
Personal: Educated Sherborne School 1963-1968 and Bristol University 1969-1971 (LL.B Hons). Born 28th July 1949.

MOLE, David QC
4-5 Gray's Inn Square (Elizabeth Appleby QC & Duncan Ouseley QC), London (020) 7404 5252
Recommended in Planning
Specialisation: Principal area of practice is local government and administrative law and judicial review, planning, environmental and rating law. Clients include major developers including retailers, house-builders and other service providers. Also acts for government departments, development corporations and local authorities.
Prof. Memberships: Administrative Law Bar Association, Planning and Environment Bar Association.
Career: Called to the Bar and joined present chambers 1970. Treasury Solicitors Panel 1980. Junior Counsel to Inland Revenue in rating and valuation matters 1984. Took Silk in 1990. Appointed Recorder 1995.
Personal: Educated at Trinity College, Dublin (MA 1966) and London School of Economics (LL.M 1969). Born 1st April 1943. Lives in London and Somerset.

MOLONEY, Patrick QC
1 Brick Court (Richard Rampton QC), London
(020) 7353 8845
Recommended in Defamation
Specialisation: Media law, (libel, slander, malicious falsehood, passing off, breach of confidence, contempt of court, reporting restrictions, judicial review).
Career: BA BCL (Oxon); Asst. Prof. Univ. of British Columbia (1974-1975); 1 Brick Court (1978 to present). QC (1998).

MONKCOM, Stephen
Tanfield Chambers (Andrew Thompson and David Guy), London (020) 7797 7250
Recommended in Licensing
Specialisation: Specialises in all aspects of licensing with particular emphasis on betting, gaming and lotteries. Has advised extensively on the application of internet technologies in this field. Practice also includes commercial and public law work.
Prof. Memberships: Member of Administrative Law Bar Association.
Career: Called 1974. Joined present Chambers 1976.
Publications: Include 'Smith & Monkcom: The Law of Betting, Gaming and Lotteries' (Butterworths 1987 – 2nd edition in preparation). Contributor to 'Halsbury's Laws of England' Vol 4(1) (Re-issue), title 'Betting'. Joint editor 'Encyclopaedia of Forms and Precedents' 5th Edition Re-issue, title 'Gaming, Betting and Lotteries'. Consulting Editor of 'Licensing Review'.
Personal: Born 9th June 1949.

MONTGOMERY, Clare QC
Matrix Chambers (Nicholas Blake QC), London
(020) 7404 3447
Recommended in Crime, Fraud: Criminal, Human Rights (Civil Liberties)
Specialisation: Commercial fraud. Extradition and mutual assistance. Administrative Law. Criminal Law. Counsel in Guinness, Brent Walker and Maxwell trials. Appeared in leading extradition cases, Pinochet and Osman. Practitioner Editor Archbold on Commerce, Financial Markets and Insolvency.
Career: Called to the Bar 1980. 1992-1996 Supplementary Panel (Common Law). Queen's Counsel 1996. Assistant Recorder 1999 - . Recorder 2000.

MOODY, Neil
2 Temple Gardens (Dermod O'Brien QC), London
(020) 7822 1200
mmoody@2templegardens.co.uk
Recommended in Professional Negligence
Specialisation: Professional Negligence. Widespread experience of claims for and against valuers, surveyors, quantity surveyors , insurance brokers, accountants and architects. Also specialises in flooding and fire cases, insurance and serious personal injury claims. Recent cases include: Stevens v Gullis (2000) (architects: duties of experts) and Bybrook Barn v Kent County Council (nuisance, flooding).
Prof. Memberships: 2 PNBA, PIBA, LCCLBA.
Career: Tenant *2 Temple Gardens* 1990.
Personal: Married: 2 children, sailing.

MOODY-STUART, Thomas
8 New Square (Michael Fysh QC SC), London
(020) 7405 4321
tom.moodystuart@8newsquare.co.uk
Recommended in Intellectual Property
Specialisation: Barrister specialising in all areas of intellectual property including patents, copyright, registered/unregistered design, trade marks, passing off, biotechnology, comparative advertising, broadcasting and breach of confidence. Cases include, Auchincloss v Animal Veterinary Supplies - virucidal disinfectant/chemical composition patent; Horne v Reliance; Quadrant Holdings v Quadrant Bio Resources and Roser; Baby Dan v Brevi - design right; Frayling Furniture Ltd. v Premier Upholstery Ltd. - design right.
Prof. Memberships: Intellectual Property Bar Association (IPBA); The Intellectual Property Lawyers Organisation.
Career: Called 1995, Middle Temple; conservation research assistant: US Government Captive Breeding Centre 1989.
Personal: Education; Shewsbury School; Gonville Caius College, Cambridge (1993 MA Hon Natural Science); College of Law; Inns of Court School of Law. Born 1970; resides London.

MOON, Angus
3 Serjeants' Inn (Philip Naughton QC), London
(020) 7427 5000
Recommended in Clinical Negligence
Specialisation: Specialist in medical negligence and medically related litigation. Particular interest in judicial review in the medical context and medical ethical decisions. Instructed by both Plaintiffs and Defendants in medical negligence actions and for parties involved in medical disciplinary tribunals and inquests. Additional areas of practice include commercial contract and employment law. Major reported cases in the medical field include Gregory v Ferro (GB) Ltd and ors [1995] 6 Med LR 321 (Court of Appeal); Mahmood v Siggins [1996] 7 Med LR 76; R v Milling (Medical Referee), Ex Parte West Yorkshire Police Authority [1997] 8 Med. LR 392; Re C (AMinor) (Medical Treatment) [1998] 1 Lloyd's Rep Med 1; Palmer v. Tees Health Authority [1998] Lloyd's Rep Med 447 and Davis v. Jacobs & Camden & Islington Health Authority & Novartis [1999] Lloyd's Rep Med 72. Counsel to Mr James Wisheart, former Medical Director, at the Bristol Royal Infirmary Inquiry. Editor of the Lloyd's Law Reports *Medical* (formerly the Medical Law Reports.) Member of the Committee of the London Common Law and Commercial Bar Association. Draftsman of the response of the London Common Law and Commercial Bar Association to the Law Commission's Consultation Paper on Limitation of Actions.
Career: Called to the Bar 1986.
Personal: Educated at King's College, Taunton and Christ's College, Cambridge (MA Law). Born 17th September 1962.

MOONEY, Stephen
Albion Chambers (J.C.T. Barton QC), Bristol
(0117) 927 2144
Recommended in Crime

MOOR, Philip
1 Mitre Court Buildings (Bruce Blair QC), London
(020) 7797 7070
moor@1mcb.com
Recommended in Family: Matrimonial Finance
Specialisation: Family law, with particular emphasis on the financial aspects of marital breakdown. Regular lecturer and contributor (with Nicholas Mostyn QC as co-author) to 'Family Law' magazine.
Prof. Memberships: Family Law Bar Association (Committee Member since 1987 and current Head of Education & Training).
Career: Called to the Bar in 1982 and joined Mitre Court Buildings in 1983. Member of General Council of the Bar 1987-89. Council of Legal Education 1988-91 (Board of Examiners 1989-92). Phillips Committee on Financing Pupillage (1989).
Personal: Educated at Canford School 1972-1977 and Pembroke College, Oxford 1978-81. Leisure pursuits include cricket, football and rugby union. Lives in Bromley.

MOOR, Sarah
Old Square Chambers (John Hendy QC), London
(020) 7269 0300
Recommended in Employment
Specialisation: Principal area of practice is Employment Law, including sex, race and disability discrimination, equal pay, restrictive covenant and industrial action. Recently reported case includes Kenny v Hampshire Constabulary. Contributor to 'Employment Precedents and Company Documents' (FT Law and Tax).
Prof. Memberships: Employment Law Bar Association, Industrial Law Society and Employment Lawyers Association.
Career: Queen's College, Cambridge BA Law (1989), Kennedy Memorial Scholar at Harvard Law School (1990), Council of Legal Education (1991). Called 1991. Joined Old Square Chambers 1992.

MOORE, Martin
Erskine Chambers (Robin Potts QC), London
(020) 7242 5532
Recommended in Company, Financial Services
Specialisation: Litigation and advice on all aspects of company law, corporate insolvency and corporate reorganisation, including Schemes of Arrangement, and Schemes for transfer of long term insurance business. Recent cases: Re BSB Holdings Ltd (1996) 1 BCLC 155; Possfund Custodian Trustee Ltd v Diamond (1996) 1 WLR 1351, and Bermuda Fire and Marine Insurance Company & others v BF&M Limited

and others heard in the Supreme Court of Bermuda.
Career: BA (Oxon). Year Qualified: 1982. Lincoln's Inn.
Personal: Born: 1960.

MOORE, Miranda
5 Paper Buildings (Godfrey Carey QC & Jonathan Caplan QC), London (020) 7583 6117
Recommended in Crime

MOORE, Sarah
4-5 Gray's Inn Square (Elizabeth Appleby QC & Duncan Ouseley QC), London (020) 7404 5252
Recommended in Sport
Specialisation: EC Law, employment (including discrimination), sports law and public law. Recent cases. R v SOS for Health ex parte Imperial Tobacco [2000]2WLR834; R v SOS for Health ex parte Source Informatics [1999]A11ER 536; Collins v AS de Monaco, arbitration before CAS (November 1999)
Career: Legal Secretary to Judge Bellany May 1994-May1995. Summer 1997 appointed to Treasury 'B' Panel. Spring 1998 appointed as Counsel to the Department of Health for the Public Enquiry into BSE.
Publications: Articles and case notes for CMC Revue and E.L. Rev. Summer 1999 appointed to editorial board of 'Sport and the Law' (Sweet and Maxwill).
Personal: Married with 2 sons.

MORCOM, Christopher QC
One Raymond Buildings (Christopher Morcom QC), London (020) 7430 1234
Recommended in Intellectual Property
Specialisation: Intellectual Property including in particular trademarks; also copyright, designs, patents, confidential information.
Prof. Memberships: Member of S.A.C.I.P., Council Member of AIPPI (British Group), Associate Member of: ITMA, CIPA, INTA, past President of LIDC; Chairman of Competition Law Association (1985-1999); A Director of the Intellectual Property Institute; Member of Board of International Trademark Association (INTA) (1998-2000).
Career: Called to the Bar 1963 (Middle Temple); Bencher (1996); Certificate of Honour; Astbury Scholarship; Took Silk 1991.
Publications: Author (with Roughton & Graham) of 'The Modern Law of Trade Marks' (Butterworths, 2000).
Personal: Interests include music & walking.

MORGAN, Lynne
Temple Chambers (David Aubrey QC), Cardiff (029) 2039 7364
Recommended in Family/Matrimonial

MORGAN, Paul QC
Falcon Chambers (Jonathan Gaunt QC & Kim Lewison QC), London (020) 7353 2484
morgan@falcon-chambers.com
Recommended in Agriculture, Property Litigation
Specialisation: All aspects of real property, commercial property litigation and agricultural holdings.
Prof. Memberships: Chancery Bar Association, COMBAR, London Commercial and Common Law Bar Association, Professional Negligence Bar Association, Agricultural Law Association.
Career: Called to the Bar in 1975, Silk 1992. Joint Editor Woodfall on Landlord and Tenant, looseleaf edition. Joint Editor Gale on Easements, 16th Edition. Deputy Chairman, Agricultural Land Tribunal, Assistant Boundary Commissioner.

MORGAN, Simon
St John's Chambers (Christopher Sharp QC), Bristol (0117) 921 3456
clerks@stjohnschambers.co.uk
Recommended in Crime

MORGAN, Stephen
1 Serjeants' Inn (Lionel Read QC), London (020) 7583 1355
Recommended in Planning
Specialisation: Local Government; Town and Country Planning; Environmental Law and Public Law. Compulsory purchase and compensation; highways; advertisements.
Prof. Memberships: PEBA
Career: Law degree, followed by MA in Town and Country Planning. Always been in local government Chambers.
Personal: Family; walking; bird watching; football.

MORIARTY, Stephen QC
Fountain Court (Anthony Boswood QC), London (020) 7583 3335
Recommended in Arbitration (International), Insurance
Specialisation: Practice encompasses common law and all kinds of commercial work, including insurance and reinsurance, professional negligence and banking and financial services. Significant cases include Caparo Industries v Dickman [1990]; Lord Napier and Ettrick v RF Kershaw Ltd [1993]; Henderson v Merrett Syndicates Ltd [1994] and Feltrim Underwriting v Arbuthnott [1994]; Toomey v Eagle Star [1994]; Berriman v Rose Thompson Young [1998]. Editor, Insurance Section, 'Chitty on Contracts' (26th and 27th editions). Contributor to 'Laundering & Tracing' (OUP 1995). General Edition of Commercial Court Procedure.
Prof. Memberships: Society of Public Teachers of Law, London Common Law and Commercial Bar Association, COMBAR.
Career: Fellow and Tutor in Law, Exeter College, Oxford 1979-86. Called to the Bar 1986 and joined current chambers in the same year. Silk 1999.
Personal: Educated at Brasenose College, Oxford, 1974-1978 (BA 1977, BCL 1978 and Vinerian Scholar). Born 14th April 1955.

MORRIS, Anthony QC
Peel Court Chambers (Michael Shorrock QC), Manchester (0161) 832 3791
Recommended in Crime

MORRIS, Paul Howard
York Chambers (Aidan Marron QC), York (01904) 620048
Recommended in Insolvency/Corporate Recovery
Specialisation: General chancery with a particular emphasis upon company, commercial insolvency and employment law.
Prof. Memberships: Chancery Bar Association. Northern Chancery Bar Association, Bar European Group, Employment Law Association.
Career: Called 1986.
Personal: Born 1954. Educated at St John's College, Cambridge, MA (Cantab). Diploma in French.

MORRISON, Howard
36 Bedford Row (Michael Pert QC), Nottingham (0115) 964 4840
Recommended in Crime
Specialisation: Criminal law, particularly fraud, serious violence and drugs. International criminal law relating to laws of war, war crimes and command responsibility. Prosecutions for CPS (Grade 4), Customs and Excise 'A', SFO, DTI, firearms cases for Police authorities. Courts Martial defence, UK and overseas. Recent high profile cases include Chalkley [1998] QB 848 CA, the cases of Delalic and Mucic at the International War Crimes Tribunal in The Hague and the case of Mugenzi in the Rwanda genocide trial at the ICTR.
Prof. Memberships: Member of the CBA, the European CBA, Commonwealth Judges and Magistrates Association, Justice, founding member of the ICTY Defence Counsel Association, member of the Race Relations Committee of the Bar Council, member of expert panel of DFID and advisory committee for the UN ICTY, Member of Fijian and Caribbean Bars. Negotiating member of the ICDAA at the ICC New York preparatry commission.
Career: LL.B. (Lond), called to Bar, Grays Inn 1977. Pupil Master and Advocacy Teacher, Grays Inn. Practice on Midland and Oxford Circuit. Former Infantry Officer and experience of voluntary work in Ghana, Zambia and Malawi, former Chief Magistrate of Fiji, Senior Magistrate of Tuvalu and Attorney General of Anguilla. Recorder [Crime, Civil and Family]. OBE (1988). Fellow of Royal Geographical Society.
Personal: Married with one daughter and one son. Qualified yachtsman, scuba diver, private pilot.

MORTIMORE, Simon QC
3-4 South Square (Michael Crystal QC), London (020) 7696 9900
clerks@southsquare.com
Recommended in Insolvency/Corporate Recovery
Specialisation: Practice covers business and financial law with a particular specialisation in insolvency law. Recent work includes advising and appearing for the liquidators of Barings, the court appointed receivers of Metro Trading Interantional, US investors in $160 million fraud claim. Substantial involvement in most of the major insolvencies of the 1990's : BCCI, Olympia & York, Maxwell, Polly Peck, Ferranti and Facia. More than 50 reported cases including: Triffit v Salads Etc (2000) effect of termination of agency on rights to book debts, Glencore v Metro (1990) forum issues under Brussels Convention, Richbell Information Services (1998) and TSB v Platts (1998) effect of cross claims on petition, Cosslett Contractors (1997) effect of charge in building contract, Re BCCI (no10) (1997) cross-border set-off issues, Re Leeds United Holdings (1996) disputed takeover, Macmillan v Bishopsgate (1995) priorities over shares in foreign company.
Career: Called to the Bar (Inner Temple) in 1972; Q.C. in 1991. Called to the BVI Bar 1991. Admitted ad hoc to the Bermuda and Cayman Islands Bars. Accredited CEDR mediator.

MOSS, Gabriel QC
3-4 South Square (Michael Crystal QC), London (020) 7696 9900
Recommended in Commercial Chancery, Insolvency/Corporate Recovery
Specialisation: Mainly in business and financial law with a special emphasis on insolvency and restructuring. Involved in the two leading Court of Appeal cases on cross border insolvency. Acted as leading counsel for the liquidators in the mammoth trial in Bermuda relating to Bermuda Fire & Marine. Advised on one of the world's largest restructurings, ICO Global.
Prof. Memberships: Chancery Bar Association, Commercial Bar Association, AEPPC / EIPA, Fellow of the Society for Advanced Legal Studies, Bencher of Lincoln's Inn, Honorary Member of the Association of Fellows and Legal Scholars of the Centre for International Legal Studies, member of Insolvency Lawyers Association.
Career: First Class Honours Law Degree at Oxford University (BA), Post Graduate Law Degree from Oxford University (BCL); Lecturer in Law at the University of Connecticut, part-time lecturer / tutor at Oxford University; Eldon Scholar (Oxford); Bar Exams; Appointed Q.C. (1989)
Publications: Co-Editor of Rowlatt on 'Principal and Surety'; Co-Author of Lightman & Moss on the 'Law of Receivers of Companies'; Joint Consultant Editor of Totty & Moss on 'Insolvency'.

MOSS, Joanne R.

Falcon Chambers (Jonathan Gaunt QC & Kim Lewison QC), London (020) 7353 2484

Recommended in Agriculture

Specialisation: Agricultural land, partnerships, quotas. E.C. law, general and agricultural, commercial property.

Prof. Memberships: Former Chairman Agricultural Law Association. Fellow Chartered Institute of Arbitrators. Legal Advisor RICS milk quotas committee.

Career: Publications: Hill & Redman 'Agricultural Holdings', Muir Watt and Moss 'Agricultural Holdings' (14th edition). Handbook of EC law for Bench and Bar, co editor 'Agriculture.'

Personal: MA (Cantab); called 1976; LLM (London) European Law.

MOSTYN, Nicholas QC

1 Mitre Court Buildings (Bruce Blair QC), London (020) 7797 7070

Recommended in Family: Matrimonial Finance

Specialisation: Big money ancillary relief. International cases. Child support.

Prof. Memberships: FIBA, IAML, Ogden Ctee, ARAG.

Career: Called 1980 Silk 1997. Assistant Recorder 1997. Recorder 2000. Deputy HCJ 2000.

Publications: 'Childs Pay' 2nd Ed 'At a Glance' Editor FCR, IFL

Personal: 4 children, R.C.

MOULD, Timothy

4 Breams Buildings (Christopher Lockhart-Mummery QC), London (020) 7430 1221/7353 5835

Recommended in Planning

Specialisation: Specialises in local government and planning law and related areas of public law. Currently on the B Panel of Junior Counsel to the Crown, Junior Counsel to the Inland Revenue on Rating and Valuation matters, and contributor to Halsbury's Laws of England, Town and Country Planning and the Encyclopaedia of Rating and Local Taxation.

Prof. Memberships: Member of the Planning and Environment Bar Association and the Administrative Law Bar Association.

MOUNTFIELD, Helen

Matrix Chambers (Nicholas Blake QC), London (020) 7404 3447

Recommended in Administrative & Public Law: General, Employment, Human Rights (Civil Liberties)

Specialisation: Specialises in public law, human rights, discrimination, employment, and EC law. She practices in English, European and Commonwealth courts acting for private individuals, commercial organisations, NGO's and public authorities. She is an editor of the European Human Rights Law Revies and co-author of the Blackstone Guide to the Human Rights Act 1998, and lectures on domestic application of the ECHR and the Human Rights Act for the Judicial Studies Board and elsewhere. Junior Counsel to the Crown (B panel). Notable cases include R v Secretary of State for the Environment ex parte Friends of the Earth (drinking water standards litigation), Meade-Hill v British Council (indirect discrimination), Snares v CAO (free movement of persons, ECJ), R v Secretary of State for Health ex parte Source Informatics (confidentiality and data protection), Faulkner v UK (Article 6 ECHR) and representing the government of Belgium in Pinochet.

Career: Called to the Bar 1991.

Personal: Educated at Magdalen College, Oxford (BA Hons) Modern History (1st Class), City University 1989-1990 (Dip Law), King's College London 1994 (Dip European Law).

MOVERLEY SMITH, Stephen

24 Old Buildings (Martin Mann QC & Alan Steinfeld QC), London (020) 7404 0946

Recommended in Insolvency/Corporate Recovery

MOWBRAY, John QC

12 New Square (John Mowbray QC), London (020) 7419 1212

Recommended in Traditional Chancery

Specialisation: Litigation, with some advisory work, mediating and arbitrating, mainly in the following fields: Trusts, including related taxes, pension funds and Caribbean and other offshore trusts; Contract disputes, mainly international; Conflict of laws in connection with the above and generally; Property, including landlord and tenant, mortgages and insolvency aspects. Representative reported cases include: Arlen Bahamas Management v Trust Corporation of Bahamas (1971-6) 1 Law Reports of Bahamas 456 (power of modification of trust instrument); Security Trust v Royal Bank [1976] A.C. 503 P.C. (priority of charges on Bahamian land); Tito v Waddell [1977] Ch. 106 (governmental trusts); Borden U.K. v Scottish Timber Products [1981] Ch. 25 C.A. (retention of title clause); Official Custodian v Parway Estates [1985] Ch. 151 C.A. (insolvency of tenant-equitable relief from forfeiture-mortgagee's rights - and see the next case in the volume); News Group v SOGAT [1986] I.C.R. 716 C.A. (trust of trade union branch funds - sequestration); Basingstoke and Deane BC v Host Group [1988] 1 W.L.R. 348 C.A. (rent review clause); Alghussein v Eton College [1988] 1 W.L.R. 587 H.L. (breach of contract - not profiting from one's own wrong); Australian Commercial Research and Development v ANZ [1989] 3 All E.R. 65 (plaintiff with same action in two jurisdictions); Dubai Bank v Galadari [1990] Ch. 98 C.A. (privilege for copy documents); Imperial Group Pension Trust v Imperial Tobacco [1991] 1 W.L.R. 589 (employment principles applied to pension fund trusts); Lemos v Coutts & Co. (Cayman) 1992-93 CILR 460 Cayman Islands C.A. (cross-border trust litigation - discovery and Mareva orders against trustees); Inverugie Investments v Hackett [1995] 1 W.L.R. 713 P.C. (assessment of damages for trespass in letting property); Re T.C. Pagarani (1998/99) 2 O.F.L.R. 1 British Virgin Islands C.A (incompletely constituted trust); Re Z Trust 1997 CILR 248 (conflicts of interest on amending trusts under a power). Michaels v Harley House (Marylebone) Ltd [1999] 3 W.L.R. 229 C.A. (enfranchisement of flats - constructive trust arising on the sale of shares); Michaels v Taylor Woodrow (2000) New Law Online Case 2000 47601 (conspiracy to injure by unlawful means not seperately actionable).

Prof. Memberships: Chancery Bar Association; Centre for Dispute Resolution (Accredited Mediator); STEP International Committee.

Career: Former Chairman Chancery Bar Association, Member of Bar Council and Deputy High Court Judge. A permanent member of the Bars of The Bahamas (1971) and of The Eastern Caribbean (1992) and appears in the Cayman Islands. An Editor of Lewin on Trusts 16th Ed. (17th out in 2000) and of the Chase Journal.

MOWSCHENSON, Terence QC

Wilberforce Chambers (Edward Nugee QC), London (020) 7306 0102

Recommended in Commercial (Litigation), Commercial Chancery, Company

Specialisation: Principal areas of practice: company/commercial matters including matters involving the law relating to banking (including bills of exchange, letters of credit, syndicated loan agreements), breach of trust, conflict of laws, contract (including conditions of sale, share and business sale agreements, licensing and franchising, restraint of trade, retention of title, and sale of goods), companies (including shareholder disputes, shareholder agreements, technical aspects of company law, takeovers, Stock Exchange regulations, broking and dealing), equitable remedies, financial services (including matters relating to the various self regulatory organisations), insolvency, insurance, partnership, and professional negligence. Reported cases including Derby v Weldon, Sharneyford Supplies v Edge, Elliss v BP Oil Northern Ireland Refinery Ltd, Re Westock Realisations Ltd, Dept of Environment v Bates, Investment and Pensions Services v Gray, Acatos v Watson Crimpfil Ltd v Barclays Bank plc, Eastglen ltd v Grafton, Metalloy (Supplies) Limited v M.A. (U.K.) Limited (CA), Wake v Renault (UK) Ltd, BCCI v Prince Fahd Bin Salman Al Saud, Arbuthnot Latham Bank v Trafalgar Holdings, and Board of Governors of National Heart and Chest Hospital v Chettle.

Prof. Memberships: Chancery and Commercial Bar and Insolvency Lawyers Associations.

Career: Called to the bar in 1977. Queen's Counsel 1995. Recorder 2000.

Personal: Educated at Eagle School and Peterhouse. London University (LLb(Hons)) and Oxford BCL (Hons). FCIArb 1989.

MOXON-BROWNE, Robert QC

2 Temple Gardens (Dermod O'Brien QC), London (020) 7822 1200

Recommended in Professional Negligence

Specialisation: Professional Negligence, including especially accountants, solicitors and surveyors, and cases arising in the field of building and construction. Also very experienced in all matters relating to insurance law and practice including cases involving repudiation for fraud.

Prof. Memberships: ORBA, Professional Negligence Bar Association, C.L.B.A., COMBAR.

Career: Called to the Bar 1969, QC 1990, Recorder 1992. Deputy Judge of the Technology and Construction Court 1993. Deputy Judge of the High Court 1999.

Personal: Born 1946. Educated Gordonstoun School, University College Oxford (BA).

MOYLAN, Andrew QC

Queen Elizabeth Building (Paul Coleridge QC), London (020) 7797 7837

Recommended in Family: Matrimonial Finance

Specialisation: Ancillary Relief; other aspects of Family Law including child residence/contact; Inheritance Act claims; Professional Negligence (Matrimonial).

Prof. Memberships: Family Law Bar Association.

Career: Junior Counsel to the Queen's Proctor.

MUIR, Andrew

3 Raymond Buildings (Clive Nicholls QC), London (020) 7400 6400 chambers@threeraymond.demon.co.uk

Recommended in Licensing

Specialisation: Extensive experience of licensing work encompassing liquor, gaming, betting, lotteries and public entertainment. Represented General Medical Council at disciplinary tribunal hearings. Appointed Department of Trade and Industry Inspector for insider share dealing enquiries. Also practices in Environmental Protection and Health & Safety law.

Prof. Memberships: South Eastern Circuit.

Career: Called to the Bar 1975, and joined 3 Raymond Buildings in 1976. BA (Hons).

Personal: Educated at Stonyhurst College 1965-1970, Ealing Technical College 1970-1973 and Council of Legal Education 1974-1975. Leisure pursuits include horse racing, cricket and rugby. Born 25th December 1951. Lives in Lodsworth.

MUNDAY, Andrew QC
2 Bedford Row (formerly 3 Hare Court) (William Clegg QC), London (020) 7440 8888
Recommended in Crime
Specialisation: All areas of criminal law but particularly large scale drug trafficking, VAT fraud, Commercial, Financial Services, Accountancy and Mortgage Fraud.
Prof. Memberships: Criminal Bar Association.
Career: Called 1973 and joined current set in 1975. Standing Counsel to HM Customs and Excise 1995. Took silk in 1996. Recorder; Chairman, Kent Bar Mess.

MUNRO, Sarah
Walnut House (Francis Gilbert QC), Exeter (01392) 279751
Recommended in Crime
Specialisation: Serious crime including all sexual offences, drugs, fraud and violence/murder. Prosecution and defence.
Prof. Memberships: Western circuit. CBA. Criminal Justice Strategy Committee.
Career: Call 1984. Cat.4 Prosecutor. Customs & Excise List A. Recorder.
Personal: Cricket.

MUNYARD, Terry
Two Garden Court (I. Macdonald QC & O.Davies QC), London (020) 7353 1633
Recommended in Human Rights (Civil Liberties)

MURDOCH, Gordon QC
4 Paper Buildings (Lionel Swift QC), London (020) 7583 0816
gm@4pb.com
Recommended in Family: Child Care including child abduction
Specialisation: All types of family litigation, including public and private law Children Act matters, divorce, matrimonial finance, international child abduction, Inheritance Act applications, medico-legal issues, adoption, wardship, disputes between unmarried couples and mental health issues.
Prof. Memberships: Family Law Bar Association, London Common Law and Commercial Bar Association.
Career: Called 1970. Recorder and Silk 1995.
Personal: Born 1947. Educated Falkirk High School and Sidney Sussex College, Cambridge (MA, LL.B).

MURFITT, Catriona
1 Mitre Court Buildings (Bruce Blair QC), London (020) 7797 7070
Recommended in Family: Child Care including child abduction, Family: Matrimonial Finance
Specialisation: Family Law: Child Care (Public and Private Law) and Hague Convention Child Abduction Proceedings; Matrimonial Finance (and financial proceedings under The Children Act and Inheritance Acts)
Prof. Memberships: Family Law Bar Association; Grays Inn. FLBA committee member.
Career: St. Mary's Ascot 1968-1976. Leicester Polytechnic School of Law 1977-80. Called to the Bar 1981. From 1981 in Practice at 1 Mitre Court. Assistant Recorder 1998.
Personal: Art and architecture, travel, amateur artist & mosaicist, skiing, gardening and sacred choral music.

MURPHY, Ian QC
9 Park Place (Ian Murphy QC), Cardiff (029) 2038 2731
Recommended in Personal Injury
Specialisation: Queen's Bench Division work, in particular personal injury litigation. Clinical Negligence, Criminal Law, Children Act, Public and Private Law.
Prof. Memberships: Personal Injury Bar Association.
Career: St.Illtyd's College Cardiff. L.S.E. (LLB), Baltic Exchange.
Personal: Married Penelope 1974. Two daughters – Anna 3/4/82 and Charlotte 3/12/84. Golf, Cricket, Skiing.

MURPHY, Peter
30 Park Place (John Jenkins QC), Cardiff (029) 2039 8421
Recommended in Crime

MYERS, Benjamin J.
Young Street Chambers (Lesley Newton), Manchester (0161) 833 0489
Recommended in Crime

MYLNE, Nigel QC
2 Harcourt Buildings, Atkinson Bevan Chambers (Nicholas Atkinson QC & John Bevan QC), London (020) 7353 2112
Recommended in Crime
Specialisation: Criminal Law Specialist. In particular, specialises in serious commercial and professional frauds. Prosecutes and defends in all aspects of serious crime, including murder, sexual offences and drugs.
Prof. Memberships: Special adjudicator on asylum appeals and immigration appeals. President in Mental Health Review Tribunals.
Career: Practises in London and on the Western Circuit. Took silk in 1984. Appointed Recorder in 1983.

MYNORS, Charles
2 Harcourt Buildings (Mr Gerard Ryan QC), London (020) 7353 8415
clerks@2hb.law.co.uk
Recommended in Church: Church of England
Specialisation: Specialises in planning, ecclesiastical and environmental law, compulsory purchase and commons; particular expertise in listed buildings. Author of 'Planning Applications and Appeals', 'Planning Control and the Display of Advertisements' and 'Listed Buildings, Conservation Areas and Monuments' (3rd edn, 1999); Member, Editorial Board, Journal of Planning and Environment Law; Consultant Editor, Planning and Environmental Law Bulletin. Appears in the courts and at planning inquiries for and against planning authorities (including a number of significant cases for English Heritage), at consistory court hearings, and in the Lands Tribunal. Member, Society of Advanced Legal Studies Planning and Environment Law Reform Group.
Prof. Memberships: Member of committee, Planning and Environment Bar Association; Member of General Committee, Ecclesiastical Law Society; Fellow, Royal Town Planning Institute; Associate, Royal Institution of Chartered Surveyors; Member, Institute of Historic Building Conservation.
Career: Local authority planning officer 1977-86; called to the Bar 1988; Chancellor, Diocese of Worcester, 1998.
Personal: Degrees in architecture (Cambridge) and town planning (Sheffield). Currently writing next book (on trees and forestry).

NAISH, Christopher
Southernhay Chambers (Anthony Ward), Exeter (01392) 255777
Recommended in Family/Matrimonial
Specialisation: Family Law. All aspects of the law relating to children (acting for Local Authorities, guardians and family members); ancillary relief. Family mediator. Personal injuries. Acting mainly for plaintiffs but also for defendants' insurers.
Prof. Memberships: Family Law Bar Association. Personal Injuries Bar Association.
Career: Call 1980. Joined chambers in 1981.
Personal: Born 21st December 1957. Married with three children.

NAPIER, Brian
Fountain Court (Anthony Boswood QC), London (020) 7583 3335
Recommended in Employment
Specialisation: Transfer of Undertakings – Meade and Baxendale v British Fuels [1998] House of Lords; Discrimination (sex, race, disability) and equal pay; General employment law, statutory and common law.
Prof. Memberships: Member, Faculty of Advocates, Edinburgh (Clerk: Susan Hastie); Member ACAS Panel of arbitrators.
Career: Academic lawyer 1975-1994. Practising barrister/ advocate, 1994-. Joint editor: 1. Harvey on Industrial Relations (chapters on European law, equal opportunities, equal pay); 2. Transfer of Undertakings (Sweet & Maxwell, 1998-).

NASH, Jonathan
3 Verulam Buildings (Christopher Symons QC & John Jarvis QC), London (020) 7831 8441
clerks@3verulam.co.uk
Recommended in Banking
Specialisation: Principal areas of work are banking, corporate insolvency, professional negligence (particularly accountants and solicitors), and general commercial work including arbitration. Recent cases include Credit Agricole Indosuez v Muslim Commercial Bank (compliance of documents under letter of credit); ANZ Banking v Societe Generale (construction of ISDA Master agreement after close-out of Russian market NDF transaction); Credit Suisse First Boston v MLC (anti-suit injunction in Russian derivatives transaction); J Rothschild v Collyear (notification obligations under professional indemnity insurance in respect of pensions misselling).
Prof. Memberships: COMBAR; European Society for Banking and Financial Law.
Career: Called to the Bar in 1986 and joined 3 Verulam Buildings in 1987.
Personal: BA (Oxon).

NATHAN, David
10 King's Bench Walk (Georges M Khayat QC), London (020) 7353 2501
clerks@10kbw.co.uk
Recommended in Crime
Specialisation: Criminal defence, acting as a leading junior in all types of cases. Led in many substantial high profile cases throughout the UK including Regina v Donald & Cressy (police corruption), R v John "Littlelegs" Lloyd (conspiracy) and Regina v Clifford Norris (alleged racist rage). He is instructed in all areas of major criminal law including police corruption, white-collar fraud, and large-scale importation of drugs.

NATHAN, Peter
One Garden Court Family Law Chambers (Eleanor Platt QC and Alison Ball QC), London (020) 7797 7900
p.nathan@onegardencourt.co.uk
Recommended in Family: Child Care including child abduction, Family: Matrimonial Finance
Specialisation: Family
Prof. Memberships: FLBA.
Career: Called 1973. Spent 15 months as solicitor. Deputy DJ since 1993. Mediator (trained 1996). Appointed Recorder, 2000.
Personal: Married, three children.

NAUGHTON, Philip QC
3 Serjeants' Inn (Philip Naughton QC), London (020) 7427 5000
Recommended in Alternative Dispute Resolution
Specialisation: Specialist in construction and engineering law, including domestic and international contract disputes, often of a highly technical nature. Commercial and manufacturing contracts. Professional negligence, particularly in relation to surveyors, engineers, architects and lawyers. Also medical law. A recognised expert in the field of Alternative Dispute Resolution. (Experienced and accredited).
Prof. Memberships: Fellow Chartered Institute of Arbitrators, member of LCLCBA, ORBA, ELBA, COMBAR, IBA, LCIA.
Career: Held various positions in the chemical and chemical engineering industry 1964-1971. Called to the Bar 1970. Joined present chambers 1973. Took Silk 1988. Bencher Gray's Inn (1997).
Personal: Educated at Nottingham University (LL.B) 1961-1964.

NAWAZ, Amjad
Coleridge Chambers (Simon D. Brand), Birmingham (0121) 233 8500
Recommended in Crime

NEALE, Fiona
3 Serjeants' Inn (Philip Naughton QC), London (020) 7427 5000
Recommended in Clinical Negligence

NEAMAN, Sam
Littleton Chambers (Michael Kallipetis QC), London (020) 7797 8600
Recommended in Employment
Specialisation: Principal area of practice is employment law, primarily discrimination, transfer of undertakings, restraint of trade and large scale redundancy issues, primarily in the banking, finance and computer industries. Other main areas of work are banking, securities and consumer credit. Principal client base consists of banks, major national and multi-national companies, local authorities and trade unions. Reported cases include Johnson v Unisys Ltd, Kapadia v London Borough of Lambeth Jarrett and Ors v Barclays Bank and Ors, First Sport Ltd v Barclays Bank, Winchester Cigarette Co Ltd v Payne (No's 1 and 2), at the Court of Appeal.
Prof. Memberships: Industrial Law Society, Employment Law Bar Association, Employment Lawyers' Association, British Association for Sport and the Law. Sam Neaman is Legal Adviser to the Amateur Boxing Association of England.
Career: Called to the Bar 1988.
Personal: Educated at Oxford University 1983-1986 (MA Hons) and City University 1986-1987 (Dip.Law). Leisure pursuits include boxing (former boxer and member Angel ABC since 1986), and playing drums in jazz and rhythm and blues bands.

NEISH, Andrew
4 Pump Court (Bruce Mauleverer QC), London (020) 7353 2656
aneish@4pumpcourt.com
Recommended in Professional Negligence
Specialisation: General commercial & common law. Principal areas of practice are insurance and reinsurance and professional negligence (especially brokers, lawyers, accountants and surveyors).
Prof. Memberships: COMBAR, London Common Law and Commercial Bar Association.
Career: Called 1988.
Personal: MA (St. Andrews), Dip Law (City). Admitted in the BVI

NELSON, Vincent
39 Essex Street (Nigel Pleming QC), London (020) 7832 1111
Recommended in Media & Entertainment
Specialisation: Media & Entertainment.
Career: Author of Law of Entertainment & Broadcasting (Publishers: Sweet & Maxwell).

NEWCOMBE, Andrew
2 Harcourt Buildings (Mr Gerard Ryan QC), London (020) 7353 8415
clerks@2hb.law.co.uk
Recommended in Parliamentary & Public Affairs, Planning
Specialisation: Principal areas of practice are parliamentary and planning work. Also including compulsory purchase, local government, environmental and general public law.
Prof. Memberships: Planning & Environment Bar Association; Parliamentary Bar Mess; Administrative Law Bar Association.
Career: Called to the Bar in 1987; also member of the Irish Bar.
Personal: Born 6th February 1953.

NEWEY, Guy
7 Stone Buildings (Charles Aldous QC), London (020) 7405 3886
clerks@7stonebuildings.co.uk
Recommended in Charities, Commercial Chancery, Company, Insolvency/Corporate Recovery
Specialisation: General Chancery practice includes charities, company, financial regulation, insolvency, property, professional negligence and trusts.
Career: Called to the Bar 1982. One of the Junior Counsel to the Crown (Chancery). Junior Counsel to the Charity Commissioners. A contributor to 'Mithani: Directors' Disqualification' and to 'Civil Court Service'. A member of the Charity Law Association and the Insolvency Lawyers Association. A DTI Inspector in 1998-1999.
Personal: Educated at Tonbridge School and Queens' College, Cambridge (BA 1st class, LL.M 1st class, MA). Bar Exams 1st class, 1982. Born 21st January 1959.

NEWMAN, Catherine QC
13 Old Square (Michael Lyndon-Stanford QC), London (020) 7404 4800
clerks@13oldsqare.law.co.uk
Recommended in Commercial Chancery, Company, Insolvency/Corporate Recovery
Specialisation: Principal area of work encompasses business and commercial chancery work, including corporate insolvency, business agreements and breach of contract, loans and security, partnership and professional negligence. Involved in large insolvencies: Maxwell, BCCI. Leading Counsel advising the DTI Inspectors investigating the 1991 flotation of Mirror Group Newspapers. Other main area of work is equity and contentious trusts; see for example Satnam Investments v Dunlop Heywood & Co Ltd [1999] 3 All ER652 CA. Acted (for the London Borough of Hammersmith and Fulham) at all stages of the swaps litigation: capacity, restitution and successive claims.
Prof. Memberships: Chancery Bar Association, COMBAR; Bar Sports Law Group.
Career: Called to the Bar 1979 and joined present chambers in 1980. Appointed Deputy Registrar in Bankruptcy 1991. Assistant Recorder 1998. Took Silk in 1995. Recorder 2000. Acts as an arbitrator.
Personal: Educated at Convent of the Sacred Heart High School 1965-1972 and University College, London. (LL.B 1st Class Hons 1978). Harmsworth Scholar of the Middle Temple 1979-80. Born 7th February 1954. Lives in London.

NEWMAN, Paul
Wilberforce Chambers (Edward Nugee QC), London (020) 7306 0102
Recommended in Pensions, Professional Negligence
Specialisation: Specialises in personal and occupational pension schemes, with a particular interest in the pensions aspects of corporate and personal insolvency. Acts for trustees, beneficiaries and employers across the spectrum of pensions litigation and advisory work and acts both for and against the Pensions Ombudsman in appeals against his determinations. General chancery/commercial matters, (with an emphasis on litigation), disputes relating to the Lloyd's market and the provision of financial services. Major pensions cases include Melton Medes; Belling; Simpson Curtis Pension Trustee Ltd v Readson; Cocking v Prudential Insurance, SWT v Wightman and Elliot v Pensions Ombudsman Land National Grid. Contributor to Ellison on Pensions Law and Practice and to Lightman & Moss, Law of Corporate Receivers.
Prof. Memberships: Association of Pension Lawyers. Member of Chancery Bar Association.
Career: BA (Cantab); LLM (Harvard Law School); Called to the Bar in 1991.

NEWSOM, George
Guildhall Chambers (Adrian Palmer QC), Bristol (0117) 927 3366
Recommended in Church: Church of England

NEWTON, Clive
One King's Bench Walk (Anthony Hacking QC), London (020) 7936 1500
Recommended in Family: Child Care including child abduction, Family: Matrimonial Finance

NEWTON, Lesley A.
Young Street Chambers (Lesley Newton), Manchester (0161) 833 0489
Recommended in Family/Matrimonial
Specialisation: Family, particularly cases involving children, with particular emphasis on child care proceedings acting for parents, guardians and local authorities. Notable work undertaken in Child Abduction Hague Convention cases. Judicial review in relation to children and child care.
Prof. Memberships: FLBA.
Career: Significant cases include Re C (H.L) 1991 and Re L (H.L) 1996. Recent reported cases include Re SL (sterilisation of adult parents) 2000, L v UK ECTHR 2000.
Personal: Married, two children. Tennis, travelling and any time off the clerks allow me!

NEWTON, Roderick
East Anglian Chambers (Roderick Newton), Ipswich (01473) 214481
Recommended in Family/Matrimonial

NICE, Geoffrey QC
Farrar's Building (John Leighton Williams QC), London (020) 7583 9241
Recommended in Health & Safety
Specialisation: Principal areas of practice are crime and general common law, including personal injury, medical and professional negligence, commercial and administrative law.
Prof. Memberships: South Eastern Circuit.
Career: Called to the Bar (Inner Temple) and joined *Farrar's Building*in 1971. Appointed Recorder of the Crown Court in 1987. Took Silk in 1990. Member CICB 1995 -. Senior Trial Attorney at ICTY (Yugoslav War Crimes Tribunal) 1998 – 2000.

NICHOLLS, Benjamin
1 Fountain Court (David Crigman QC), Birmingham (0121) 236 5721
Recommended in Crime

NICHOLLS, Clive QC
3 Raymond Buildings (Clive Nicholls QC), London (020) 7400 6400
chambers@threeraymond.demon.co.uk
Recommended in Crime, Fraud: Criminal
Specialisation: Principal area of practice is extradition, which he practises worldwide, being a member of the Bar of the Australian Capital Territories and having been specially called and admitted to the Bars of Hong Kong, The Bahamas, Cayman Islands, Malaysia, Ireland and Fiji. The factual complex of his extradition practice includes commercial crime, as well as terrorism and drug trafficking. He is particularly experienced (with teams drawn from his own Chambers) in preparing and presenting extradition requests for foreign governments, both in the UK and abroad. These have included the Bank Bumiputra fraud (the Osman case) in which he represented the Attorney General of Hong Kong in the UK, Hong Kong and Malaysia and the Werner Rey case (corporate fraud) in which he represented the Government of Switzerland in the Bahamas. He has advised and represented many countries and prominent fugitives including Senator Augusto Pinochet Ugarte and appeared in most of the leading extradition cases in England, including 16 in the House of Lords and Privy Council. Much of his practice is outside the UK and includes mutual assistance and human rights.
Prof. Memberships: Member of the International Law Association (British Branch) Committee on Mutual Assistance. Member of the British Institute of International and Comparative Law, Bar European Group, Criminal Bar Association, European Criminal Bar Association, Franco British Lawyers Society. Co-founder and Chairman of the International Criminal Law Association 2000.
Career: Educated at Brighton College, Trinity College Dublin, Sidney Sussex College Cambridge, MA LLM. Call 1957. QC 1982. Head of Chambers since 1994.

NICHOLLS, Colin QC
3 Raymond Buildings (Clive Nicholls QC), London (020) 7400 6400
chambers@threeraymond.demon.co.uk
Recommended in Fraud: Criminal
Specialisation: Principal areas of practice are commercial crime, extradition and civil liberties. Specialises in cases having an international element. Notable trials include 'Guinness' 1990 (defending the stockbroker, Anthony Parnes); 'Brent Walker' 1994 (defending George Walker), and 'BCCI' 1997 (defending the shipping magnate, Abbas Gokal). Significant reported cases include the 'Soering Case', 1989 in the European Court of Human Rights (death row in the US); and R v Horseferry Road Magistrate, ex parte Bennett 1994 (disguised extradition and abuse of power), Gilligan v Governor of HM Prison Belmarsh 1999 (Irish backing of Warrants with the United Kingdom). Advised in the Bhopal, Greenpeace, Marcos litigations and in the *mani pulititrials* in Italy.
Prof. Memberships: Admitted ad hoc to the Bar of Hong Kong. Commonwealth Lawyers Association, Vice-President (1985-1996), Hon. Treasurer (1997), Secretary (1999), Bar European Group, British Institute of International and Comparative Law, Criminal Bar Association.
Career: Called to the Bar 1957, QC in 1981 and elected a Bencher of Gray's Inn in 1990. Recorder of Crown Courts 1983 – 1998. Fellow of the Society of Advanced Legal Studies.
Personal: M.A., LL.B, Dublin.

NICHOLLS, John
13 Old Square (Michael Lyndon-Stanford QC), London (020) 7404 4800
Recommended in Commercial Chancery

NICHOLLS, Michael
1 Mitre Court Buildings (Bruce Blair QC), London (020) 7797 7070
Recommended in Family: Child Care including child abduction
Specialisation: International and domestic family law and medical ethics, including jurisdiction, child abduction, public and private child care, families and the media and disputes about medical treatment. Recent international, medical and media cases include Re W, Re B (child abduction: unmarried father) [1998] 2 FLR 146 (a review of the rights of unmarried fathers under the Hague Child Abduction Convention), Re L (abduction: pending criminal proceedings) [1999] 1 FLR 433, Re J (specific issue orders: Muslim upbringing and circumcision) [1999] 2 FLR 678; [2000] 1 FLR 571 (CA) and Nottingham CC v October Films Ltd.) [1999] 2 FLR 347 (an attempt by a local authority to stop the filming of children living on the streets).
Prof. Memberships: Family Law Bar Association.
Career: Called 1975 (solicitor 1980). Family lawyer in the Official Solicitor's Office and Head of Lord Chancellor's Child Abduction Unit 1983-1998. Consultant to the Council of Europe's Family Law Committee. Member of the President's International Family Law Committee. Member of the BMA's Children's Consent to Medical Treatment Steering Group. Chairman of Appeals Panels of the Specialist Training Authority of the Medical Royal Colleges.
Publications: Recent publications include 'The Human Rights Act 1998 – A Special Bulletin for Family Lawyers' (with Michael Horowitz QC and Geoffrey Kingscote)

NICHOLLS, Paul
11 King's Bench Walk (Eldred Tabachnik QC and James Goudie QC), London (020) 7632 8500
Recommended in Employment

NICHOLSON, Jeremy QC
4 Pump Court (Bruce Mauleverer QC), London (020) 7353 2656
Recommended in Construction
Specialisation: Principal areas of practice are construction and professional negligence work, covering all aspects of litigation, arbitration and advisory matters. Also general commercial and contract law work. Clients include insurers, contractors, employers, engineers, architects, surveyors and other professionals. He has acted in a number of international arbitrations. He has given various lectures and seminar papers.
Prof. Memberships: TECBAR, Professional Negligence Bar Association, COMBAR, London Common Law and Commercial Bar Association.
Career: Called to the Bar 1977. Joined 4 Pump Court 1978. Appointed QC 2000.
Personal: Educated at Rugby School 1968-1973, Trinity Hall, Cambridge 1973-1976 (MA) and College of Law 1976-1977 (Harmsworth Scholar). Born 21st March 1955.

NICKLIN, Matthew
5 Raymond Buildings (Patrick Milmo QC), London (020) 7242 2902
Recommended in Defamation

NICOL, Andrew QC
Doughty Street Chambers (Geoffrey Robertson QC), London (020) 7404 1313
a.nicol@doughtystreet.co.uk
Recommended in Administrative & Public Law: General, Defamation, Human Rights (Civil Liberties), Immigration
Specialisation: Media law in all its aspects including defamation, confidence, copyright, contempt, restrictions on court reporting, publicity injunctions and rights of access to information. Administrative law especially immigration and nationality but extending to all situations where decisions of public bodies are subject to judicial review. Civil Liberties especially concerning freedom of expression and privacy. Diverse range of other civil work including (non-medical) professional negligence, race and sex discrimination, contract and tort. Appellate crime including Divisional Court, Court of Appeal and Privy Council.
Prof. Memberships: Chair of Immigration Law Practitioners' Association. Member of Council of Europe delegations to advise on media law to Croatia, Albania, Slovakia, Belarus, Moldova. Presented papers to international conferences on Media and the Judiciary (Justice, Madrid 1993) and National Security and Freedom of Expression (Article 19, Johannesburg 1995). Libel (LRDC London 1998), security of residence in Europe (Nijmegan 1999). Chaired conference on Family and Immigration (Oxford University Continuing Education 1997) and presented seminars to ILPA, solicitors and university groups.
Career: Called to the Bar in 1978. QC 1995. Asst. Recorder 1998. Recorder 2000. Taught law at London School of Economics for 10 years.
Personal: Born 1951. Degrees: BA 1st Class; LL.B 1st Class, LLM (Harvard), Harkness Fellow 1973-1976. Has published 'Media Law' (1992), 'Subjects, Citizens, Aliens and Others' (1990) and contributes an annual survey on Reporting Restrictions to OUP's 'Yearbook of Media Law'.

NISSEN, Alexander
Keating Chambers (Richard Fernyhough QC), London (020) 7544 2600
Recommended in Construction
Specialisation: Construction and civil engineering law including arbitration and professional negligence; reported cases include Darlington Borough Council v Wiltshier.
Career: Qualified 1985; Middle Temple; treasurer and committee member of Technology and Construction Bar Association; member of editorial team 'Keating on Building Contracts' and Construction Law Yearbook; ACI Arb.
Personal: Mill Hill School; Manchester University (1984 LLB Hons). Born 1963, resides London.

NOCK, Reginald
24 Old Buildings (G.R Bretten QC), London (020) 7242 2744
Recommended in Tax

NOLAN, Dominic
Ropewalk Chambers (Richard Maxwell QC), Nottingham (0115) 947 2581
Recommended in Personal Injury
Specialisation: Large personal injury and medical negligence claims including claims for birth injury and catastrophic injury. Defence of Health and Safety prosecutions. Recent reported case: Baker v Leicestershire HA (1998) Lloyds Med 93. Advised Grantham Hospital in claims arising from crimes of Beverley Allitt.
Prof. Memberships: Professional Negligence Bar Association.
Career: Graduate of Nottingham University; Buchanan Prizeman Lincoln's Inn; Chairman of Statutory Inquiry into Homicide by former mental patient.
Personal: Interests: family, friends, sport, music.

NORRIS, William QC
Farrar's Building (John Leighton Williams QC), London (020) 7583 9241
Recommended in Personal Injury, Sport
Specialisation: Defamation: Morelli & Coyle v Times Newspapers (first conditional fee case in libel). Personal Injury: Farrant v Thanet DC; Jefferson v Royal Ordnance (£3.3 million gross award to Mine clearance expert); Kent v BRB; Vossler v Mead (£2.2 million award to tetraplegic). Professional negligence: Sports

and competition law. Licensing: Jones & Ebbw Vale v WRU (private law challenge to disciplinary process of WRU); Cardiff RFC v WRU (restraint of trade/EU competition law); O'Callaghan v Coral Racing (illegality of gaming contracts/validity of arbitration).
Career: Benefactors Scholarship, Middle Temple, QC 1997.
Personal: Lecturer to Judicial Studies Board (Damages). Advocacy Teaching UK & USA.

NOURSE, Edmund
One Essex Court (Lord Grabiner QC), London (020) 7583 2000
Recommended in Insolvency/Corporate Recovery

NUGEE, Christopher QC
Wilberforce Chambers (Edward Nugee QC), London (020) 7306 0102
Recommended in Pensions, Property Litigation, Traditional Chancery
Specialisation: Practice a broad spread of chancery and commercial litigation including property, landlord and tenant, professional negligence, pensions (including pensions ombudsman appeals) and trusts. Recent cases include Phillips v British Gas (sale of North Sea Gas); Republic of Panama v Noriega (tracing assets); Central London Commercial Estates v Kato Kagaku (adverse possession of registered leashold land); SWT v Wightman (Railway Pension Scheme); Department of Health v Moss (index linking of public sector pensions).
Prof. Memberships: Member of COMBAR; Association of Pension Lawyers; Chancery Bar Association.
Career: Called 1983; practised in chambers since 1984; QC 1998.

NUGEE, Edward QC
Wilberforce Chambers (Edward Nugee QC), London (020) 7306 0102
Recommended in Charities, Pensions, Traditional Chancery
Specialisation: Mainstream Chancery practice, with emphasis on trusts, occupational pension schemes, revenue law, landlord and tenant and property law generally. Has appeared in a substantial number of landlord and tenant, revenue and other appeals in the House of Lords, and in many of the leading cases on trusts, land law and pension schemes.
Prof. Memberships: Member of Chancery Bar Association.
Career: Called 1955, Inner Temple (Bencher 1976, Treasurer 1996); Q.C. 1977.
Personal: Educated Radley College; Worcester College, Oxford (Eldon Law Scholar). T.D. 1964.

NUTTING Bt., Sir John QC
3 Raymond Buildings (Clive Nicholls QC), London (020) 7400 6400
chambers@threeraymond.demon.co.uk
Recommended in Crime
Specialisation: Extensive experience in Criminal law: Many IRA trials, Jonathan Aitken (perjury), R v Bailey & Others (child murders), Michael Smith (the GEC Spy) the Taylor Sisters murder trial, Seymon Serafimovich and Anthony Sawoniuk (War Crimes), the Rachel Nickell murder, Donald & Cressey (police corruption), Colin Ireland (multiple murder of homosexuals), Harry Greenway MP (Parliamentary corruption), Lord Blandford (drugs), Sydney Cooke (grave sexual abuse of children). Also specialises in Commercial crime, Disciplinary tribunals, Inquests and Inquiries (the Falkland Islands War Crimes Inquiry).
Prof. Memberships: Member of the Bar Council (1976-1980, 1986-1987). Chairman of the Young Bar (1978-1979). Vice Chairman of the Criminal Bar Association (1995-1997). Member of the Lord Chancellor's Advisory Committee on Legal Education and Conduct (1997-).
Career: Called 1968. Recorder of the Crown Court (1986-). Bencher of the Middle Temple (1991-). Treasury Counsel at the Central Criminal (1987-1995) (First Junior Treasury Counsel 1987-88; First Senior Treasury Counsel 1993-95) QC 1995-. A Judge of the Courts of Appeal of Jersey and Guernsey (1995-). Deputy High Court Judge attached to the Queen's Bench and Chancery Divisions (1998-).
Personal: Educated at Eton and McGill University BA 1964.

O'BRIEN, Dermod QC
2 Temple Gardens (Dermod O'Brien QC), London (020) 7822 1200
Recommended in Personal Injury
Specialisation: Insurance claims, policy issues, fires, floods, explosions. Electrical and mechanical engineering. Personal injury. Restitution. Local authority liabilities. Major reported cases include: Heil v Rankin [2000], Makepeice v Evans and McAlpine [2000], Mighell v Reading and MIB [1998], Hurst v Hampshire CC [1997], Silverton v Goodall [1997], Evans v MIB [1997], Vernon v Bosley [1997], Hippolyte v Bexley LB [1995], Costellow v Somerset CC [1993], Talbot v Berkshire CC [1993], Lipkin Gorman v Karpnale (Playboy Club) [1991], Legal Aid Board v Russell [1991], Wharf v Eric Cumine Associates [1991 HK], Surtees v Kingston upon Thames BC [1991], Rigby v Chief Constable of Northamptonshire [1985], Russell v Barnet LB [1984], Hobbs v Marlowe [1978], Taylor v Hepworths [1977], Heath v Drown [1972].
Prof. Memberships: London Common Law Bar Association. Western Circuit.
Career: Oxford BA (Law) 1961 MA. Called: Inner Temple 1962. Crown Court Recorder 1978 (and TCC business). QC 1983. Bencher Inner Temple 1993.
Personal: Farming, forestry.

O'BYRNE, Andrew
Peel Court Chambers (Michael Shorrock QC), Manchester (0161) 832 3791
Recommended in Crime

O'CONNOR, Patrick QC
2-4 Tudor Street (Richard Ferguson QC), London (020) 7797 7111
Recommended in Crime, Human Rights (Civil Liberties)

O'DEMPSEY, Declan
Coram Chambers (Roger McCarthy QC), London (020) 7797 7766
Declan@odempsey.compulink.co.uk
Recommended in Employment, Immigration
Specialisation: His areas of practice are employment, immigration, administrative law and professional negligence (solicitors and medical). His practice deals with discrimination (disability, race, equal pay and sex), immigration, asylum, human rights cases, and public inquiries. He was instructed in the Inquiry into the Personality Disorder Unit, Ashworth Special Hospital (Fallon Inquiry) 1997-1998 and has a particular interest in mental disorders. Cases include: Stevens v Bexley HA [1989] ICR 224; ex parte Ghebretatios [1993] Imm AR 585; Mobbs v Nuclear Electric [1996] IRLR 536; ex parte Sarwar & Getachew [1996] COD 87; Mugford v Midland Bank plc [1997] ICR 399; Ikhlaq [1997] Imm AR 404; Horst v High Table [1998] ICR 409; Goodwin v Patent Office [1999] IRLR 4. Publications: 'Supperstone & O'Dempsey on Immigration and Asylum' (4th edition Sweet & Maxwell 1996, with Michael Supperstone QC); Unfair Dismissal I and III in 'Tolley's Emploment Law'; 'Disability Discrimination: The Law and Practice' (1st edition, Sweet & Maxwell, with Andrew Short of 4 Brick Court). Human Rights & Employment Law (Jordans 2000). He is also editor of the the Discrimination section of Sweet & Maxwell's 'Encyclopedia of Employment Law'. He also writes regularly for the 'Solicitors Journal'.
Prof. Memberships: Immigration Law Practitioners Association, Administrative Law Bar Association, Employment Law Bar Association.
Career: Called to the Bar in 1987, first full-time employment law caseworker for the Free Representation Unit 1987-88. Active in the ELAAS scheme.

O'FARRELL, Finola
Keating Chambers (Richard Fernyhough QC), London (020) 7544 2600
Recommended in Construction
Specialisation: Construction law in general, including IT disputes, construction related insurance, in particular loss and expense claims (lectures regularly on various aspects); energy disputes, shipbuilding and dredging litigation.
Prof. Memberships: Member Bar/IBC Committee; member of editorial team 'Construction Law Yearbook'; member of Official Referees Bar Association.
Career: Qualified 1983; Inner Temple; Council of Legal Education 1983.
Personal: St Philomena's School; Durham University (1982 BA Hons Dunelm).

O'ROURKE, Mary
3 Serjeants' Inn (Philip Naughton QC), London (020) 7427 5000
Recommended in Clinical Negligence

ODITAH, Fidelis
3-4 South Square (Michael Crystal QC), London (020) 7696 9900
Recommended in Insolvency/Corporate Recovery

OLDHAM, Peter
11 King's Bench Walk (Eldred Tabachnik QC and James Goudie QC), London (020) 7632 8500
Recommended in Employment

OLIVER, Andrew
Octagon House Chambers (Andrew Lindqvist & Guy Ayers), Norwich (01603) 623186
Recommended in Crime

OLIVER, David QC
Erskine Chambers (Robin Potts QC), London (020) 7242 5532
Recommended in Commercial Chancery, Company, Insolvency/Corporate Recovery
Specialisation: Principally commercial/Chancery, with some insolvency.
Career: Called to the Bar 1972. Took silk 1986. (Lincoln's Inn: Hardwick Scholar. Standing junior counsel to the director general of fair trading. Acted for Guinness in connection with the aftermath of the distillers takeover, Price Waterhouse in claims arising after the collapse of BCCI, Macmillan Inc. and Swiss Bank with claims arising out of the collapse of Robert Maxwell's corporate empire, Granada plc in connection with the financing of BSB and subsequently BSkyB, and Victor Chandler International in connection with the establishment of off-shore credit betting.
Personal: Born 4 June 1949. Educated Westminster School; Trinity Hall Cambridge; Institut d'Etudes Europeenes, Brussels. BA Cantab (2/1), Licence Special en droit Europeen. Fluent Spanish and working knowledge of French.

OLIVER-JONES, Stephen QC
5 Fountain Court (Anthony Barker QC), Birmingham (0121) 606 0500
Recommended in Clinical Negligence, Personal Injury

OMAMBALA, Ijeoma
Old Square Chambers (John Hendy QC), London (020) 7269 0300
Recommended in Employment

ONIONS, Jeffery QC
One Essex Court (Lord Grabiner QC), London (020) 7583 2000
Recommended in Commercial (Litigation
Specialisation: Undertakes a wide range of complex commercial work. He has particular experience in arbitration, banking, insolvency, insurance and reinsurance, oil and gas contracts and media related cases.
Prof. Memberships: London Common Law and Commercial Bar Association, Administrative Law Bar Association.

ONSLOW, Andrew
3 Verulam Buildings (Christopher Symons QC & John Jarvis QC), London (020) 7831 8441
Recommended in Commercial (Litigation)
Specialisation: Banking and finance; financial services; commercial fraud; solicitors', auditors' and valuers' negligence. Major recent cases include Wallace Smith Trust Co. v Deloittes Haskins and Sells, London Underground Ltd v Kenchington Ford, regulatory proceedings arising from Sumitomo/Hamanaka Affair.
Prof. Memberships: COMBAR
Career: 1970-1974 Lancing College. 1975 -1979 Corpus Christi College, Oxford. BA Hons Literae Humaniores (1st Class).
Personal: Married. 5 Children.

ONSLOW, Robert
8 New Square (Michael Fysh QC SC), London (020) 7405 4321
robert.onslow@8newsquare.co.uk
Recommended in Intellectual Property
Specialisation: Principal areas of practice are intellectual property including trade marks, musical and literary copyright, industrial designs and patents as well as computer law and contract disputes with a technical element. Also specialises in advising on legal issues relating to Internet commerce, Data Protection and commercial uses of data. Recent cases include Cantor Fitzgerald v Tradition; Matthew Gloag v Welsh Distillers; Nominet v McGrath; Windows Resources v Lloyds TSB; Net Online v Job Dept.
Prof. Memberships: Lincoln's Inn.
Career: Technical Assistant at Mewburn Ellis, Chartered Patent Agents 1987-89. Called to the Bar and joined current chambers in 1991.
Personal: Educated at Eton College 1978-83 and Magdalen College, Oxford 1984-87 (BA Hons in Physics). Leisure interests include music (piano and violin). Born 31st May 1965.

OPPENHEIM, Robin
Doughty Street Chambers (Geoffrey Robertson QC), London (020) 7404 1313
Recommended in Clinical Negligence, Personal Injury, Product Liability
Specialisation: Specialist in the areas of medico-legal work, personal injury, multi party actions, and discrimination law. Personal injury and medico-legal practice includes clinical negligence and serious personal injury (particularly cerebral palsy, spinal and head injuries claims), group actions, medical inquests, mental health law and Human Rights Act 1998/health related public law. He is currently generic counsel in the contraceptive pill litigation and three child abuse group actions. Recent reported cases: Heil v Rankin [general damages appeal]; Warren v Northern General Hospital NHS Traust [multipliers]; Hope v CC of Greater Manchester [discrimination law]; Hutton v East Dyfed HA [clinical negligence]; Hodgson v Imperial Tobacco [conditional fee arrangements]. Contributor to Personal Injury Manual and Bullen and Leake [Sweet & Maxwell 2000], Contributor to Personal Injury Encyclopaedia [Butterworths]. Regular lecturer to solicitors.
Prof. Memberships: Action for Victims of Medical Accidents; Association of Personal Injury Lawyers; Administrative Law Bar Association; Professional Negligence Bar Association and Personal Injury Bar Association.
Career: Called to the Bar 1988.
Personal: Born 1962. Lives in London.

ORNSBY, Suzanne
2 Harcourt Buildings (Mr Gerard Ryan QC), London (020) 7353 8415
Recommended in Planning
Specialisation: Specialist fields are planning and environmental law (civil and criminal jurisdictions) for both the private and public sector.
Prof. Memberships: Member of the Planning and Environment Bar Association; Member of the United Kingdom Environmental Law Association.
Career: Called to the Bar in 1986. Joined present Chambers in 1990, previously practised at the Criminal Bar and employed in the electricity supply industry.
Personal: Educated at St Georges College, Weybridge and University College London (LLB Hons 1985).

ORR, Craig
Fountain Court (Anthony Boswood QC), London (020) 7583 3335
Recommended in Commercial (Litigation)
Specialisation: Practice covers all areas of commercial law, including city related litigation (especially merchant banking-related matters), accountants' negligence actions, commercial fraud (civil actions), banking and insurance litigation. Important cases include British & Commonwealth v Quadrex and Samuel Montagu, Caparo v Dickman [1990]; Eagle Trust v Cowan de Groot [1992]; Society of Lloyd's v Mason and Clementson [1995]; AMF v Hashim [1996] and Domicrest v SBC [1998].
Prof. Memberships: COMBAR.
Career: Called to the Bar in 1986 and joined *Fountain Court* in 1988.
Personal: Educated at Cambridge University 1981-84 (MA) and Oxford University (BCL, Vinerian Scholar). Born 8th January 1962.

ORR, Nicholas
14 Castle Street (Andrew Edis QC), Liverpool (0151) 236 4421
Recommended in Chancery
Specialisation: General chancery, particularly property litigation, family provision, landlord and tenant and partnerships. Also commercial litigation and drafting and professional negligence.
Prof. Memberships: Northern Circuit, Chancery Bar Association, Northern Chancery Bar Association, Northern circuit Commercial Bar Association.

OTTON-GOULDER, Catharine QC
Brick Court Chambers (Christopher Clarke QC), London (020) 7379 3550
Recommended in Commercial (Litigation)
Specialisation: General Commercial Law.
Career: Called to Bar 22 November 1983, Lincoln's Inn. Pupillages with John Thomas QC (4 Essex Court) and Jonathan Sumption QC (1 Brick Court). At Brick Court Chambers 21 December 1984 to date. Cases of note: Tin Litigation, EIL, British & Commonwealth v BZW; Barings v LDC; Credit Suisse v Allerdale DC, Arab Monetary Fund v Hashim; Hazell v London Borough of Hammersmith & Fulham; Director General of Fair Trading v Premier League. Director General of Fair Trading v Pharmacists & Manufacturers.
Personal: Born 9 April 1955 in Chester. Educated at King George V School, Hong Kong; King Edward VI High School for Girls and Somerville College, Oxford (1973-1977) – Literae Humaniores without Viva Voce Examination, First Class. Qualified as Solicitor of Supreme Court 1980. Gained Seymour Scholarship (on entry to Oxford) and Hardwicke Scholarship at Lincoln's Inn.

OUGHTON, Richard
Cobden House Chambers (Howard Baisden), Manchester (0161) 833 6000
Recommended in Chancery
Specialisation: General Chancery, with emphasis on succession, trusts and mortgages.
Prof. Memberships: Chancery Bar Association, Northern Chancery Bar Association, STEP.
Career: Practised in Liverpool from 1979 until moving to a predecessor of current set in 1994.
Publications: Author 2nd & 3rd edition of 'Tyler's Family Provision'; Assistant Editor, 10th edn of 'Fisher and Lightwood's Law of Mortgage'.
Personal: M.A. (St John's College, Cambridge – first class in both parts of Law Tripos); LL.M. (Pennsylvania); Member Northern Irish Bar.

OUSELEY, Duncan QC
4-5 Gray's Inn Square (Elizabeth Appleby QC & Duncan Ouseley QC), London (020) 7404 5252
Recommended in Administrative & Public Law: General, Environment, Planning
Specialisation: Planning and environmental law work undertaken covers Court, Inquiry, Lands Tribunal and advisory work of all types for and against authorities, also including compulsory purchase and compensation, highways and waste disposal. Public law work undertaken includes Court and advisory work covering all aspects of judicial review affecting central and local government, regulatory bodies and utilities; particularly local government organisation and finance, competitive tendering, social security and social services, health, medicine and pharmacies, utilities and financial services regulation, planning and environmental law.
Prof. Memberships: Planning and Environment Bar Association. Administrative Law Bar Association.
Career: QC 1992. Recorder 1994. Chairman of EIPs in1985 and 1991. Appeared in Hong Kong and in Northern Ireland. QC Northern Ireland 1997.

OWEN, David
20 Essex Street (Iain Milligan QC), London (020) 7583 9294
Recommended in Banking
Specialisation: Main areas of practice are commercial law, arbitration, banking, insurance and reinsurance, sale of goods, professional negligence, shipping and commodities. Joint editor 'MacGillivray on Insurance Law'. Major cases include: Chigi v. Credit Suisse (1997) [forex regulation]; Mander v. Prudential (1998) [reinsurance – line slips]; Bankers Trust v. Dharmala (1996) [derivatives]; Future Express (1993) [bills of lading]; Rome v. PNB (1990-1992) [political risk insurance]; National Bank of Greece v. Pinios (1990) [compound interest]; Phoenix v. Halvanon (1988) [reinsurance – illegality].
Prof. Memberships: Combar; London Court of International Arbitration.
Career: HM Treasury 1979-81. Called to Bar and joined chambers 1983.
Personal: Marlborough College 1971-1975; Merton College Oxford 1976-1979 (BA, 1st Class Hons). Born 21st June 1958.

OWEN, Gail
India Buildings Chambers (David Harris QC), Liverpool (0151) 243 6000
Recommended in Family/Matrimonial
Specialisation: All aspects of public law Children Act work, including the representation of Local Authorities, parents and Guardians ad Litem. This work involves, inter alia, issues of physical, sexual and emo-

tional abuse of children. Also practices in all areas of private law Children Act work, divorce proceedings, adoption proceedings and all aspects of finance and property disputes ancillary relief proceedings and disputes between unmarried couples.
Career: Called 1980.

OWEN, R.F. QC
Ropewalk Chambers (Richard Maxwell QC), Nottingham (0115) 947 2581
Recommended in Personal Injury
Specialisation: Personal injury claims of all kinds but in particular multi-party litigation – insidious diseases of all types and child abuse claims against local authorities, for example, Metro-Cammell Litigation; North East Shipyard Asbestos Litigation (against T&N plc); North West Shipyard Asbestos Litigation (against Cape plc); Gnitrow Ltd v Cape plc (Isle of Wight); North Wales Children's Homes Litigation,and Leicestershire County Council child abuse claims.
Prof. Memberships: PNBA. PIBA.
Career: Prestatyn High School. Polytechnic of Central London (University of London Ext.). QC 1996. Assistant Recorder 1997. Recorder 2000.
Personal: Family, friends and sport.

OWEN, Robert QC
1 Crown Office Row (Robert Seabrook QC), London (020) 7797 7500
robert.owen@1cor.com
Recommended in Clinical Negligence, Personal Injury, Product Liability
Specialisation: Profesional negligence, medical negligence, product liability, multi-party actions, disaster litigation, commercial fraud.
Prof. Memberships: London Common Law and Commercial Bar Association, Chairman 1994-95, Professional Negligence Bar Association.
Career: Called 1968, QC 1988, Recorder 1987, DTI Inspector 1990, Deputy High Court Judge 1994. Chairman General Council of the Bar 1997.

OWEN, Tim QC
Matrix Chambers (Nicholas Blake QC), London (020) 7404 3447
timowen@matrixlaw.co.uk
Recommended in Administrative & Public Law: General, Crime, Human Rights (Civil Liberties)
Specialisation: Civil liberties, public law (especially prison, police, criminal and inquest law), civil actions involving abuse of power (especially police and prison actions) and international human rights law. Also criminal law, especially political offences and cases involving police malpractice, public order and appellate work; Commonwealth capital appeals and constitutional motions, extradition and deportation. Co-author of 'Prison Law' (OUP, 1999, 2nd ed), co-editor Halsbury's Laws, vol 36(2) 'Prisons and prisoners'.
Prof. Memberships: ALBA, INQUEST Lawyers' Group, Criminal Bar Association.
Career: Called 1983.
Personal: Educated at Atlantic College and London School of Economics. Lives in London.

OWEN, Tudor
9-12 Bell Yard (D. Anthony Evans QC), London (020) 7400 1800
Recommended in Crime

OWEN-JONES, David Roderic
3 Temple Gardens (Jonathan Goldberg QC), London (020) 7583 1155
Recommended in Crime
Specialisation: Drugs and fraud cases – prosecution and defence. Environmental Law cases – practice on South Eastern Circuit and Midland Circuit.
Prof. Memberships: CBA.
Career: University of London LLB LLM. Council of Europe, Commission of Human Rights.

PADFIELD, Nicholas QC
Serle Court (Lord Neill of Bladen QC), London (020) 7242 6105
Recommended in Arbitration (International)
Specialisation: Specialises in cases involving international law, particularly international trusts and banking. Also, commercial, construction, universities/students, public/constitutional and bloodstock.
Prof. Memberships: Fellow of Chartered Institute of Arbitrators. Panel of Lloyd's Arbitrators. Member of LCIA, IBA and Bar European Group. Executive Committee of COMBAR.
Career: MA (Oxon), LLM (Cantab) International Law. Silk (1991). Recorder. Master of the Bench, Inner Temple. Oxford Blue and England International (Hockey).

PAGE, Adrienne QC
5 Raymond Buildings (Patrick Milmo QC), London (020) 7242 2902
Recommended in Defamation

PAGE, Nigel B.
St. Mary's Chambers Family Law Chambers (Christopher Butler), Nottingham (0115) 950 3503
Recommended in Family/Matrimonial

PALMER, Adrian QC
Guildhall Chambers (Adrian Palmer QC), Bristol (0117) 927 3366
Recommended in Commercial (Litigation)

PALMER, Howard QC
2 Temple Gardens (Dermod O'Brien QC), London (020) 7822 1200
Recommended in Personal Injury
Specialisation: Insurance and Reinsurance: insurance policy disputes; repudiation for fraud/non-disclosure/breach of condition. Personal Injury: local authority and employers' liability. Professional Indemnity: engineers; insurance brokers; surveyors; accountants; architects; solicitors. Construction: contract disputes; building regulations on spread of fire. Commercial Arbitration: international fraud; commercial disputes.
Career: Lecturer at King's College, London 1977-8. Tenant at 2 Temple Gardens 1978 – date. QC 1999.
Personal: Cricket; fieldsports; theatre. Married, four children. Lives in Fulham, London.

PALMER, Patrick J.S.
Sovereign Chambers (Geoffrey C. Marson QC), Leeds (0113) 245 1841
Recommended in Crime
Specialisation: His practice is predominantly heavy crime concerning serious sexual offences and fraud. Civil work of professional negligence, general civil law and legal advice to an inquiry on child sexual abuse complements his criminal practice. He has particular interest in fraud work and is a member of Chamber's Fraud Group and deals with excise, VAT, estate agency, solicitor and patent fraud.
Career: LLB (Hons) London. Called to the Bar (Inner Temple) in 1978. Assistant Recorder 1996.

PANNICK, David QC
Blackstone Chambers (P Baxendale QC and C Flint QC), London (020) 7583 1770
Recommended in Administrative & Public Law: General, Employment, Human Rights (Civil Liberties), Immigration, Sport
Specialisation: Practices mainly in the fields of public and administrative law, employment law, immigration law, European law and sports law. He has appeared in more than 40 cases in the House of Lords, over 20 cases in the European Court of Justice, and over a dozen cases in the European Court of Human Rights. He is a Fellow of All Souls College, Oxford, and a member of the Editorial Committee of 'Public Law'. He writes a fortnightly column on the law for 'The Times'. His recent cases include ex parte Myra Hindley, ex parte Pfizer (on Viagra), Lustig-Prean v UK, Thompson and Venables v UK, and R v DPP ex parte Kebilene.

PARKER, Christopher R.
7 Stone Buildings (Charles Aldous QC), London (020) 7405 3886
Recommended in Company
Specialisation: Main areas of practice are company and insolvency law. Also undertakes general Chancery work. Recent reported cases: Coutts & Co v. Stock [1999]; Re: Carman Construction Ltd [1999]; MTI Trading Systems Ltd. v. Winter [1997]; Re: A Company (No.002015 of 1996) [1996], Watkins v. A.J. Wright (Electrical) Ld. [1996], R & H Electrical Ltd. and Anor v. Haden Bill Electrical Ltd.: Re: Haden Bill Electrical Ltd. [1995], Securum Finance PLC v. Camswell Ltd. [1994].
Career: Called to the Bar 1984.
Personal: Educated at Keble College, Oxford BA Jurisprudence, 1st class, (1977-80) and BCL (1980-81), University of Illinois LL.M (1981-82), Harvard Law School LLM (1982-83). Born 13th October 1958.

PARKER, Judith QC
One King's Bench Walk (Anthony Hacking QC), London (020) 7936 1500
Recommended in Family: Child Care including child abduction
Specialisation: All aspects of family law, including medico-legal issues, child care and adoption, divorce and matrimonial finance, international aspects of family law (including intercountry adoption and child abduction), parentage, surrogacy and assisted conception.
Prof. Memberships: Family Law Bar Association. International Academy of Matrimonial Lawyers. Chairman of Inter-Country Adoption Lawyers Association. Association of Lawyers for Children.
Career: Called to the Bar in 1973. Took Silk in 1991.
Publications: Consulting editor of 'Butterworths Essential Family Practice'. Contributor to Wildblood & Eaton: 'Financial Provision in Family Matters'.

PARKER, Kenneth QC
Monckton Chambers (John Swift QC), London (020) 7405 7211
Recommended in Competition/Anti-trust, Tax
Specialisation: Specialises in EC law, public law and judicial review. Recent reported cases include: R v Secretary of State for the Environment ex p Greenpeace [1994] (challenge to decision to authorise testing at Sellafield), R v Home Secretary ex p Hagan and Croft [1994] (challenge to decision to extradite British women to Oregon), R v MAFF ex p NFFO [1995] ECJ (challenge to fish conservation policy), R v Home Secretary ex p Norney [1995] (challenge to policy on referring IRA lifers to Parole Board), R v Secretary of State for Trade and Industry ex p Consumer's Association [1996] (challenge to implementation of Unfair Contract Terms Directive), BRB/SNCF v Commission [1996] ECJ (challenge to decision affecting operation of Channel Tunnel), R v Home Secretary ex p O'Dhuibhir [1997] (challenge to closed visits in high security prisons), MD Foods v Baines [1997] HL (application of RTPA to supply agreements) and R v Home Secretary ex p Launder [1997] CA, and HL

(challenge to decision to extradite ex MD of Wardley Merchant Bank to Hong Kong). Also regularly instructed by the Commissioners of Customs and Excise on appeals in VAT cases. Recent cases include Elida Gibbs v CCE [1996] ECJ, Argos v CCE [1996] ECJ and CCE v Wellington Hospital [1997] CA.
Prof. Memberships: Called to the Bar in 1975 and took silk in 1992. Fellow in Law at Exeter College Oxford between 1973 and 1976. He is on the executive of COMBAR.

PARKIN, Fiona
Atkin Chambers (John Blackburn QC), London (020) 7404 0102
Recommended in Construction

PARNELL, Graham
East Anglian Chambers (Roderick Newton), Ipswich (01473) 214481
Recommended in Family/Matrimonial

PARROY, Michael QC
3 Paper Buildings (Michael Parroy QC), London (020) 7583 8055
Recommended in Fraud: Criminal

PARRY, Isabel
9 Park Place (Ian Murphy QC), Cardiff (029) 2038 2731
Recommended in Family/Matrimonial

PARSONS, Luke
4 Essex Court (Nigel Teare QC), London (020) 7653 5653
Recommended in Shipping

PARTRIDGE, Richard
3 Serjeants' Inn (Philip Naughton QC), London (020) 7427 5000
Recommended in Clinical Negligence

PASCOE, Martin
3-4 South Square (Michael Crystal QC), London (020) 7696 9900
Recommended in Commercial Chancery, Insolvency/Corporate Recovery
Specialisation: Martin Pascoe was called to the Bar in 1977 and joined 3/4 South Square in 1989 when chambers moved to Gray's Inn from the Temple. His practice includes a broad range of commercial and chancery litigation, with particular emphasis on corporate insolvency, often with substantial international elements, as well as more than 100 cases acting for defendant solicitors in professional negligence actions. He is acting for the Government of Brunei and the Brunei Investment Agency in worldwide litigation to trace and recover missing public funds. He acted for the English administrators of the Olympia and York group, and has since 1991 acted for the English liquidators of BCCI SA and the Cayman Islands liquidators of BCCI Overseas. Recent reported cases include; re BCCI SA (No 11) [1997] 1 BCLC 80, which has restated the law relating to the scope of English ancillary liquidations; Hughes v Hannover Re [1997] 1 BCLC 497, which is the first Court of Appeal case on s.426 Insolvency Act 1986 and re Latreefers Inc [1999] 1 BCLC 271, considering the English court's jurisdiction to wind up foreign incorporated companies. He has substantial experience of insurance insolvencies, including acting for US-based reinsurers of EMLICO in the winding-up proceedings before the Supreme Court of Bermuda and in judicial review proceedings in the Supreme Court, Court of Appeal for Bermuda and Privy Council seeking the quashing of decisions permitting EMLICO's redomestication to Bermuda: Kemper Re v Minister of Finance (Bermuda) [1998] 3 WLR 630 (PC).
Prof. Memberships: COMBAR, Chancery Bar Association.

PASCOE, Nigel QC
Pump Court Chambers (Guy Boney QC), Winchester (01962) 868161
Recommended in Crime

PATTEN, Nicholas QC
9 Old Square (Michael Driscoll QC), London (020) 7405 4682
Recommended in Commercial Chancery, Professional Negligence, Property Litigation
Specialisation: Commercial Chancery including professional negligence and property litigation. Recent important cases include: Target Holdings Ltd v Redferns [1996] AC 421; Mortgage Express Ltd v Bowerman & Ptnrs [1996] 2 AER 836; Bristol & West B Soc v Mothew [1996] 4 AER 698; Bristol & West B Soc v Fancy & Jackson [1997] 4 AER 582; Mannai Investments Ltd v Eagle Star Ins. Co. Ltd [1997] AC 945; Nationwide B Soc. v Balmer Radmore (Times: 1.3.99); Platform Home Loans Ltd v Oyston Shipways Ltd [1999] 2 WLR 518 (HL); Thyssen-Bornemisza v Thyssen- Bornemisza (1999: Supreme Court of Bermuda).
Prof. Memberships: Chancery Bar Association; Professional Negligence Bar Association.
Career: Called to the Bar 1974; Queen's Counsel 1988; Chairman of the Chancery Bar Assn. 1997-99; Bencher of Lincoln's Inn 1998; Deputy High Court Judge 1998.

PATTERSON, Frances QC
40 King St (Philip Raynor QC), Manchester (0161) 832 9082
Recommended in Environment, Planning
Specialisation: Specialist in Town Planning, Compulsory Purchase, Highways, Environmental Law and Judicial Review. Experience in projects involving airport expansion, roads, incineration, waste disposal, retailing, minerals and housing.
Prof. Memberships: Member of Planning and Environment Bar Association. Member of Administrative Law Bar Association. Member of Northern Circuit; Committee member Law Reform Working Group on Planning and Environment Law.
Career: Called 1977. Appointed Queen's Counsel 1998. Assistant Boundary Commissioner 2000. Recorder 2000.

PAUFFLEY, Anna QC
4 Paper Buildings (Lionel Swift QC), London (020) 7583 0816
ap@4pb.com
Recommended in Family: Child Care including child abduction

PEACOCK, Jonathan
11 New Square (John Gardiner QC), London (020) 7242 4017
Recommended in Tax
Specialisation: Revenue law. Work encompasses advice on all aspects of UK tax, including VAT, Customs and Excise duties and EC levies; tax litigation in all tribunals (including tax-related aspects of commercial disputes, judicial review and professional negligence). Recent cases include Marks & Spencer v HMCE (CA); NAT Holdings & Services (VAT); Halifax plc v Davidson (SC); VUE Holdings (High Court).
Prof. Memberships: Revenue Bar Association, Chancery Bar Association, VAT Practitioners Group.
Career: Called to the Bar 1987; joined current chambers 1988.
Personal: Educated at King's School, Macclesfield 1975-1979, Nunthorpe Grammar School, York 1979-82 and Corpus Christi College, Oxford 1983-86 (1st Class Degree in Jurisprudence). Born 21st April 1964.

PEARCE, Ivan
Furnival Chambers (Andrew Mitchell QC), London (020) 7405 3232
ipearce@furnivallaw.co.uk
Recommended in Crime
Specialisation: Cases including asset forfeiture and confiscation. The appointment of receivers and the general enforcement of confiscation orders in both the High Court and the Magistrates Court.
Prof. Memberships: Criminal Bar Association. Administrative Bar Association.
Career: Priestlands School, Lymington, Merristwood Agricultural College, Exeter University, LLB.
Personal: Rowing, sailing.

PEART, Icah
Two Garden Court (I. Macdonald QC & O.Davies QC), London (020) 7353 1633
Recommended in Crime

PEDDIE, Ian QC
One Garden Court Family Law Chambers (Eleanor Platt QC and Alison Ball QC), London (020) 7797 7900
I.Peddie@onegardencourt.co.uk
Recommended in Family: Child Care including child abduction
Specialisation: Child Care Law: regularly appears in serious Children Act proceedings for parents, local authorities and Guardians ad Litem e.g. physical and sexual abuse, "Munchhausen" allegations, mental health issues. Many reported cases. Criminal Law: especially criminal cases where there are children who are victims or witnesses e.g. murder, attempted murder, (e.g. R v Owen, [Maidstone Crown Court] – revenge attack on lorry driver who caused son's death by dangerous driving, and R v Campbell – man who went beserk with a machete in a Wolverhampton Primary School attacking children and nursery teacher, Lisa Potts, who was subsequently given the G.C.); Munchausen cases, (e.g. R v Flannery, [Stafford Crown Court] – poisoning son with paracetamol, caffeine and warfarin), paedophile rings, (e.g. R v Davis and Others – the six month South Wales paedophile case). In addition, has often appeared for the Defence in other serious and lengthy criminal cases not involving children e.g. fraud, drug importation, rape.
Prof. Memberships: Committee Member. FLBA since 1990.
Career: Gordonstoun School, LLB (Hons) University College London. Called to the Bar in 1971, QC in 1991, Assistant Recorder 1993, Recorder of Crown Court 1996.

PEEL, Robert
29 Bedford Row Chambers (Peter Ralls QC), London (020) 7404 1044
rpeel@29bedfordrow.co.uk
Recommended in Family: Matrimonial Finance
Specialisation: Principal areas of practice are ancillary relief, child abduction and personal injury.
Prof. Memberships: Member of Bar Council since 1996. Committee member of Family Law Bar Association.
Career: Oxford University (BA Hons). City University (DIP Law). Called to the Bar 1990.
Personal: Fluent in French and Spanish.

PELLING, Mark
Monckton Chambers (John Swift QC), London (020) 7405 7211
Recommended in Arbitration (International)
Specialisation: Specialises in domestic and international arbitration, banking, corporate fraud and tracing, insurance and re-insurance, commercial litigation and competition litigation. Recent reported cases include: Dubai Aluminium Company Ltd v Salaam & Others [1999] 1 Lloyds Rep 415, Dubai Aluminium

Company Limited v Alawi [1999] 1 Lloyds Rep 47, North Atlantic Insurance Co Ltd v Bishopsgate Insurance Ltd [1998] 1 Lloyd's Rep 40, Turner v Stevenage Borough Council [1998] Ch 28, Regia Autonoma de Electricitate Renel v Gulf Petroleum International Ltd [1996] 1 Lloyd's Rep 67, Re BCCI (No 10) [1995], Deeney & Others v Walker & Others [1995], Re The Net Book Agreements v EC Commission [1994].
Prof. Memberships: COMBAR; ORBAR.

PENNICOTT, Ian
Keating Chambers (Richard Fernyhough QC), London (020) 7544 2600
Recommended in Construction
Specialisation: Building and engineering contracts.
Career: Qualified 1982; Middle Temple.
Personal: Born 1958. Leisure, Golf.

PERETZ, George
Monckton Chambers (John Swift QC), London (020) 7405 7211
gperetz@monckton.co.uk
Recommended in Competition/Anti-trust
Specialisation: Competition Law: mergers (IMS/PMSI and WJE/ Pointing before Competition Commission; SCA/AMP, BEAP/Keesing and others before OFT); advised OFT on Volvo cars cartel; advice to major companies on UK/EC competition law and telecommunications issues. EC law: Optident v DTI [1999] 1 CMLR 782, [2000] 51 BMLR 74 (CA), now in House of Lords (meaning of EC Directives on cosmetics and medical devices)
Prof. Memberships: Bar European Group, Administrative Law Bar Association.
Career: Legal Adviser, OFT, 1992-1997, since then tenant at *Monckton Chambers.*
Publications: Contributor to: Bellamy and Child, 'Common Market Law of Competition'; Copinger & Skone James on Copyright.

PERRY, David
6 King's Bench Walk (Michael Worsley QC), London (020) 7583 0410
Recommended in Crime, Fraud: Criminal
Specialisation: Practice focuses on criminal law, particularly commercial fraud. Involved in Blue Arrow, Barlow Clowes, Brent Walker and Polly Peck International litigation.
Prof. Memberships: Criminal Law Bar Association.
Career: Called to the Bar 1980. DTI Inspector and Standing Counsel to the DTI (1991-1997). Junior Treasury Counsel to the Crown at the Central Criminal Court.
Personal: Born 7th September 1956. Lives in London.

PERRY, John QC
3 Gray's Inn Square (Rock Tansey QC), London (020) 7520 5600
Recommended in Crime
Specialisation: Practice encompasses all areas of criminal law. Contributor of articles to Criminal Law Review.
Prof. Memberships: Criminal Bar Association.
Career: Called to the Bar 1975. Tenant at 2 Crown Office Row (Chambers of Michael Sherard) 1976-1988. Part-time lecturer, LSE 1975-1979, Senior Lecturer, City of London Polytechnic (now Guildhall University) up to c1986. Joined current chambers in 1988. Took Silk 1989. Appointed Assistant Recorder 1989, and Recorder 1991.
Personal: Educated at LSE 1967-1974 (LL.B, LL.M 1974) and Warwick University (MA Industrial Relations, 1974).

PERSEY, Lionel QC
4 Field Court (Steven Gee QC), London (020) 7440 6900
Recommended in Shipping
Specialisation: Commercial litigation and arbitration, with particular emphasis upon shipping and maritime law, aviation, insurance, international trade, commodities, product liability, construction, oil and gas and conflict of laws. Has sat as arbitrator in commercial disputes.
Prof. Memberships: COMBAR, LCLCBA, LMAA (supporting member). Fellow of Institute of Advanced Legal Studies.
Career: Called to the Bar in 1981, took silk in 1997. Supplementary Panel of Treasury Counsel 1992-1997.
Personal: Born 1958. Educated at Haberdashers' Aske's School, Birmingham University 1976-1980 (LL.B.) and Université de Limoges 1978-1979.

PETCHEY, Philip
2 Harcourt Buildings (Mr Gerard Ryan QC), London (020) 7353 8415
clerks@2hb.law.co.uk
Recommended in Church: Church of England, Parliamentary & Public Affairs

PHILIPPS, Guy
Fountain Court (Anthony Boswood QC), London (020) 7583 3335
Recommended in Commercial (Litigation), Professional Negligence
Specialisation: All areas of commercial litigation (including arbitration), particularly insurance and reinsurance, banking and financial services, and professional negligence.
Career: Called 1986. Member of Supplementary Panel of Treasury Counsel, Common Law. Member of California Bar.
Personal: Born 1961. Educated Magdalen College, Oxford and City University.

PHILIPSON, Trevor QC
Fountain Court (Anthony Boswood QC), London (020) 7583 3335
Recommended in Arbitration (International), Aviation, Civil Fraud, Commercial (Litigation), Energy & Natural Resources
Specialisation: General commercial litigation with recent reported cases in the fields of aviation, commercial fraud, banking and restitution. Practice has recently included a number of lengthy professional negligence actions in London and Hong Kong. Recent experience includes lead counsel in a large international arbitration relating to the supply of defence equipment and in a high value arbitration involving the supply of gas. Considerable experience of international and domestic arbitration both as an arbitrator and councel.
Career: Director, Bar Mutual Indemnity Fund Limited.

PHILLIPS, Jane
1 Brick Court (Richard Rampton QC), London (020) 7353 8845
Recommended in Defamation
Specialisation: Libel & slander, malicious falsehood, contempt, passing-off, breach of confidence, reporting restrictions and all forms of media law, including prepublicaton advice. Cases include: Adams v Associated Newspapers Limited (CA); Allason v BBC and Hat Trick Productions; Ashby v Times Newspapers Limited; C v MGN Limited, South West Wales Newspapers Limited and others (CA); Lloyd v Express Newspapers Limited (CA); Marks and Spencer PLC v Granada; Upjohn v BBC and Professor Oswald; Williamson v Commissioner of Police for the Metropolis (CA); Little v George; Mori v BBC; Khalili v Associated; Blackstone v MGN.
Career: Called to the Bar in July 1989.
Personal: Educated at St. Paul's Girls' School and Worcester College, Oxford.

PHILLIPS, Mark QC
3-4 South Square (Michael Crystal QC), London (020) 7696 9900
Recommended in Banking, Company, Insolvency/Corporate Recovery
Specialisation: Area of practice: insolvency – administration, insurance, banking – regulatory work for the Bank of England. Commercial work arising out of insolvencies. Notable cases: Three Rivers District Council + Ors v The Governor and Company of the Bank of England (CA) [1999] 11 Admin LR 281 (CA). Re Galileo Group Ltd, Elles v Hambros bank (Bank of England intervening) (Ch D) [1998] 1 All ER 545. Re Toshoku Finance UK plc [1999] 2 BCLC 766 (CA) The Times, 24 March 2000. Barings plc v Cooper & Lybrand (CA) Independent, 11 May 2000
Career: Education: LLB LLM (commercial) Bristol University. Appointed Assistant Recorder July 1998. Recorder April 2000. QC 1999.
Personal: Motorsport enthusiast.

PHILLIPS, Richard QC
2 Harcourt Buildings (Mr Gerard Ryan QC), London (020) 7353 8415
Recommended in Planning
Specialisation: Principal areas of practice are planning and local government work. Also handles licensing cases.
Prof. Memberships: Planning & Environment Bar Association. Member of S. Eastern Circuit.
Career: Called to the Bar 1970 and joined Harcourt Buildings in 1971. Assistant Parliamentary Boundary Commissioner. Took silk in 1990.
Personal: Educated at Kings School, Ely and Sidney Sussex College, Cambridge 1966-1969. Born 8th August 1947.

PHILLIPS, Rory
3 Verulam Buildings (Christopher Symons QC & John Jarvis QC), London (020) 7831 8441
clerks@3verulam.co.uk
Recommended in Insurance, Professional Negligence
Specialisation: Principal areas of practice are insurance and reinsurance and professional negligence.
Career: Called 1984. Junior Counsel to the Crown (A Panel).

PHILLIPS, Stephen
3 Verulam Buildings (Christopher Symons QC & John Jarvis QC), London (020) 7831 8441
clerks@3verulam.co.uk
Recommended in Banking, Commercial (Litigation)
Specialisation: Principal area of practice is commercial and business law. Work includes general contractual disputes, banking and finance, company law and insolvency, international and domestic trade, commercial fraud, professional negligence and gaming contracts. Clients include banks and other financial institutions, insurance companies and funds and casinos. Contributor to 'The Encyclopaedia of Banking Law.'
Prof. Memberships: Wales and Chester Circuit, COMBAR, London Common Law and Commercial Bar Association.
Career: Called to the Bar 1984 and joined present chambers 1985. Recorder.
Personal: Educated at King's School, Chester 1973-80 and University College, Oxford 1980-83. Born 10th October 1961.

PHILPOTT, Fred
Gough Square Chambers (Fred Philpott), London (020) 7353 0924
f.philpott@lawyer.com
Recommended in Consumer
Specialisation: Consumer Law – consumer credit (drafting of regulated credit and hire agreements), credit hire, advising on consumer credit advertising, consumer credit licensing, acting in civil litigation eg extortionate credit bargains – Ketley v Scott [1981] ICR 241 and connected lender claims – (Jarrett v Barclays Bank [1997] 2 All ER 484) and in criminal prosecutions (e.g. Carrington Carr v Leicester [1993] Crim LR 938), food safety (criminal proceedings), pollution (Empress Car Co (Abertillery) Ltd v National Rivers Authority [1998] 1 All ER 481, misleading prices (eg R v Warwickshire CC [1993] AC 583), trade descriptions, weights and measures, Fair Trading Act, Trading Schemes Act. Unfair Terms Regulations (OFT v FNB [2000] 1 WLR 1353). Clients include banks, finance houses, food producers and supermarkets.
Prof. Memberships: Food Law Group.
Career: Called 1974.

PICARDA, Hubert QC
3 New Square (Lord Goodhart QC), London (020) 7405 5577
Recommended in Charities
Specialisation: Chancery law generally but particular expertise in all aspects of law relating to charities, banking, corporate insolvency and derivative trading. Recent cases include: Wellcome plc v Glaxo Holdings (disputed take over); Oldham BC v AG (-sale of recreation ground) R v Lord President of Council (judicial review of university visitor); Bridge Trust Ld v AG of Caymans. Jyske Bank (Gibraltar) Ltd v Spjeldnaes (banking, fraud and tracing). Clients include: Wellcome Trust, Garfield Weston, Wolfson and Clore Foundations, many leading and medium range charities, housing associations, universities and local authorities. Advisory work and appearances in receiverships of Gomba Holdings, BCCI and Royal Masonic Hospital. Advisory work in Singapore, Hong Kong and Caymans.
Prof. Memberships: Chancery Bar Association, Insolvency Lawyers Association, Charity Law Association (President).
Career: Called 1962. QC 1992. Visiting lecturer in banking and derivative trading law 1995-1996; Malaysia, Sarawak, Singapore. Editorial Board: Journal of International Banking and Finance Law, Trust Law International.
Personal: Author of Picarda Law relating to Receivers Managers Administrators (3rd ed 2000) Picarda Law and practice relating to Charities (3rd ed 1999). Halsbury Title on Receivers (1998) and on Charities (2000).

PICKUP, James QC
Lincoln House Chambers (Mukhtar Hussain QC), Manchester (0161) 832 5701
Recommended in Crime
Specialisation: 1. Commercial Fraud. R v Clive Smith and others (Butte Mining Trial) Old Bailey, March 1997-June 1998; R v Thos Stuart and others 1999 Liverpool Crown Court; R v Thompson, Halsay & Rodger 1999 Northampton Court; R v Awan and others Manchester Crown Court and R v Beacock and others Hull Crown Court. 2. Murder. 1996 R v Po Ming Li and others (Triad murder) Manchester Crown Court 1996; R v Duffy and others (Manchester gangland killing). 3. Professional Negligence and Serious Brain Injury. 4. Crown Office; R v Chief Contstable of Merseyside exp. Bennion (Dir CT 29.6.2000).
Prof. Memberships: Criminal Bar Assocation. Personal Injury Bar Association.
Career: Kings School Macclesfield 1961-1971. Lincoln College Oxford MA Jurisprudence 1975, BCL 1976. Crown Court Recorder 1997. Silk 2000.
Personal: Married, 2 children. Wife pharmaceutical lawyer Zeneca plc. Cricket (Member Lancs CCC, MCC).

PICTON, Martin
Albion Chambers (J.C.T. Barton QC), Bristol (0117) 927 2144
Recommended in Crime

PINE-COFFIN, Margaret Ann
17 Carlton Crescent (Mr Jeremy Gibbons QC), Southampton (023) 8032 0320/2003
Recommended in Family/Matrimonial
Specialisation: Practice covers all areas of family law with a special emphasis on child care. Particular expertise in physical injuries to children. Has good working knowledge of French and Italian.
Prof. Memberships: Western Circuit; Family Law Bar Association.
Career: Called to the Bar 1981.
Personal: Born 1956. Married, 2 children. Special interests: travel abroad.

PITCHFORD, Christopher QC
Farrar's Building (John Leighton Williams QC), London (020) 7583 9241
Recommended in Crime

PITT-PAYNE, Timothy
11 King's Bench Walk (Eldred Tabachnik QC and James Goudie QC), London (020) 7632 8500
Recommended in Employment

PLANTEROSE, Rowan
Littman Chambers (Mark Littman QC), London (020) 7404 4866
rowanplanterose@littmanchambers.com
Recommended in Arbitration (International), Construction
Specialisation: Principal areas of practice are building and engineering and general commercial litigation. Other areas include more general professional negligence and practice and procedural matters in litigation and arbitration. Engineering related work has ranged widely and included train building, power, computer and telephone technology. Also acts as arbitrator and adjudicator.
Prof. Memberships: TECBAR (Committee Member); COMBAR; Chartered Institute of Arbitrators (Council Member).
Career: Called to the Bar in 1978.
Personal: Educated at Eastbourne College and Downing College, Cambridge University. Lives in London and Gloucestershire.

PLATT, Eleanor F. QC
One Garden Court Family Law Chambers (Eleanor Platt QC and Alison Ball QC), London (020) 7797 7900
e.platt@onegardencourt.co.uk
Recommended in Family: Child Care including child abduction
Specialisation: All aspects of family law with particular emphasis upon children and cases involving medical issues. Has been involved in sterilisation/surrogacy mattters. Was instructed on behalf of the Northern Region in the Cleveland Enquiry. Special interest in Jewish family law.
Prof. Memberships: Family Law Bar Association; SE circuit; Deputy Chairman National Health Service Tribunal; Legal Assessor General Medical/Dental Councils. Called to the Bar 1960, Recorder 1982, Silk 1982. Deputy Judge, High Court Family Division since 1987.
Personal: LL.B London. Married with two children. Many interests including music, travel and skiing.

PLATTS-MILLS, Mark QC
8 New Square (Michael Fysh QC SC), London (020) 7405 4321
mark.plattsmills@8newsquare.co.uk
Recommended in Intellectual Property
Specialisation: Specialist in all aspects of intellectual property, including patents, trade marks, passing off, registered designs, copyright and design right. Also handles commercial work with a technical content. Recent interesting cases include: "800 FLOWERS" (trademark opposition); Hesco v Maccaferri, (patent infringement and validity (gabions for structural works); Munoz v Frumar (breach of council regulation for correct labelling of fruit and vegetables); Gadget Shop v The Bug.com Ltd (breach of confidence, Challenge to Search Order); Frayling Furniture Ltd v Premier Upholstery Ltd (design right implied licence - fraudulent furniture); Haberman v Jackel (patent for drinking vessel); Charlesworth v Relay Roads (patent infringement); [1998] Ladney & Hendry appln (patent - inventors kits) [1998] IPC magazines v MGN Ltd (copyright, comparative advertising, incidental use) [1998] George Harrison v Lingasong (performers' rights - early Beatles performances), [1997] Brain v Ingledew Brown (patent threats) [1997] Waterford v Nagli (Trade Mark - importation) [1996].
Career: Called to the Bar 1974. Joined present chambers 1975. Took silk 1995.
Personal: Educated at Bryanston School 1963-1969 and at Balliol College, Oxford (BA Engineering Science and Economics) 1969-1972. Born 17th January 1951.

PLEMING, Nigel QC
39 Essex Street (Nigel Pleming QC), London (020) 7832 1111
np@39essex.co.uk
Recommended in Administrative & Public Law: General, Immigration
Specialisation: Administrative and public law; environmental law and related regulatory work; local government law; and construction law.
Career: Called 1971, Junior Counsel to the Crown (Common Law) – 1985 to 1992, Queen's Counsel – 1992.

PLENDER, Richard QC
20 Essex Street (Iain Milligan QC), London (020) 7583 9294
Recommended in Immigration

POCOCK, Christopher
One King's Bench Walk (Anthony Hacking QC), London (020) 7936 1500
cpocock@1kbw.co.uk
Recommended in Family: Matrimonial Finance
Specialisation: Family, (including divorce and children) matrimonial finance and property. Financial disputes between unmarried couples, inheritance and family provision.
Prof. Memberships: S.E. Circuit; Family Law Bar Association.
Personal: Born 1960. Call 1984 Inner Temple. Education, St Dunstan's College; Pembroke College Oxford (BA Juris). Working knowledge of French; DPA Accepted.

POLLOCK, Gordon QC
Essex Court Chambers (Gordon Pollock QC), London (020) 7813 8000
Recommended in Arbitration (International), Banking, Civil Fraud, Commercial (Litigation), Energy & Natural Resources, Insurance, Media & Entertainment, Shipping, Sport
Specialisation: Broad-based commercial lawyer with a substantial court and advisory practice dealing with the major commercial issues of the day. He has been instructed in most of the major commercial litigation of recent years. Areas of practice include: arbitration, banking, commodity disputes, conflict of laws,

employment law, entertainment and sports law, financial services, insurance & reinsurance, judicial review, monopolies and mergers, oil and gas cases, professional negligence, shipping, takeovers.
Career: Trinity College, Cambridge: MA, LLB. Called to the Bar 1968. Queen's Counsel 1979. Bencher: Gray's Inn. Sits as Deputy High Court Judge of the Chancery and Queen's Bench Divisions.
Personal: Born 1943.

POOLES, Michael QC
4 Paper Buildings (Jean Ritchie QC), London (020) 7353 3366
Recommended in Professional Negligence
Specialisation: Principal area of practice is professional negligence, particularly concerning solicitors. Also acts for and against members of the Bar, accountants, surveyors, architects, engineers, veterinary surgeons and doctors. Other main areas of practice are personal injury and general insurance matters, on behalf of a large number of insurance companies.
Prof. Memberships: Professional Negligence Bar Association.
Career: Called to the Bar 1978 and joined present chambers in 1980. Silk 1999. Recorder 2000.
Personal: Educated at Perse School, Cambridge, 1967-1974 and University of London 1974-1977. Born 14th December 1955. Lives in Cambridge.

POPAT, Prashant
2 Harcourt Buildings (Roger Henderson QC), London (020) 7583 9020
Recommended in Product Liability
Specialisation: Product liability; negligence; property; contract; and railway law. Junior counsel for the defendants in the Benzodiazepine, Norplant contraceptive implant and MMR product liability litigation. Recently instructed for manufacturer of silicone breast implants in Consumer Protection Act case. Advised Railtrack upon issues arising from the privatisation of the railways and member of the team representing it at the Southall and Ladbroke Grove Public Inquiries. Has also represented London local authorities in multiparty property actions.
Career: Educated at Oxford University (MA First Class Honours). University Scholar, Baker & McKenzie International Scholar and Gray's Inn Scholar. Judicial Assistant to the Master of the Rolls 1997/98. Co-Author of 'Civil Advocacy: A Practical Guide' (Cavendish Publishing Ltd).

POPPLEWELL, Andrew QC
Brick Court Chambers (Christopher Clarke QC), London (020) 7379 3550
popplewell@brickcourt.co.uk
Recommended in Civil Fraud, Commercial (Litigation), Insurance
Specialisation: General commercial, including shipping, banking, insurance and reinsurance, international trade, financial services, arbitration, professional disciplinary, civil fraud and some employment and defamation.
Prof. Memberships: Queens Council 1997. Member of the Bar of the Cayman Islands and Seychelles. Has been appointed as arbitrator in LMAA, ICC and LCIA arbitrations.
Career: Called to Bar of England and Wales 1981. Has been appointed as ICC Arbitrator. Cases of note: Grupo Torras v Sheikh Fahad, The 'BERGE SISAR' (House of Lords), Hill v Mercantile & General, Vitol v Norelf.
Personal: Born 14 January 1959. Educated at Radley College and Downing College, Cambridge (BA Hons (Cantab) in Law, Class: First).

PORTEN, Anthony QC
2-3 Gray's Inn Square (Anthony Scrivener QC), London (020) 7242 4986
Recommended in Administrative & Public Law: General, Planning
Specialisation: Planning and Local Government work, especially public inquiries and High Court; judicial review.
Prof. Memberships: PEBA, ALBA, UKELA
Career: Called 1969. Silk 1988. Recorder 1993. FSALS 1999.
Personal: Epsom College; Emmanuel College, Cambridge.

POSNANSKY, Jeremy QC
1 Mitre Court Buildings (Bruce Blair QC), London (020) 7797 7070
Recommended in Family: Child Care including child abduction, Family: Matrimonial Finance
Specialisation: Family Law. Practice covers all areas of family law: ancillary relief and the law relating to children. Appeared in many reported cases, including Re L and others (Court of Appeal guidelines in contact cases involving domestic violence: amicus curiae) 2000, El-Fadl (recognition of Lebanese talaq divorce) 2000, W v W (refusal of decree absolute) 1998, S v S (forum non conveniens) 1997, Phillips v Peace (financial provision for children) 1996, Baker v Baker (standard of proof in ancillary relief applications) 1995, Cornick v Cornick, Nos. 1 and 2, (leave to appeal out of time, and variation of maintenance principles) 1995. Articles in *International Family Law* and *Family Law*. Practice includes advising on and settling pre-nuptial agreements.
Prof. Memberships: Family Law Bar Association; Fellow of International Academy of Matrimonial Lawyers; Medico-Legal Society.
Career: Call 1972; Silk 1994. Deputy High Court Judge, 1997; Admitted to the Bar of Antigua.
Personal: Born 8th March 1951. Married with two daughters. Lives in London. Enjoys travel, scuba diving and computers.

POTTS, Robin QC
Erskine Chambers (Robin Potts QC), London (020) 7242 5532
Recommended in Banking, Company, Financial Services, Insolvency/Corporate Recovery
Specialisation: Specialist in all aspects of company law including insolvency and financing and banking transactions. Consulting editor of Gore-Brown on Companies. Experience extends to practice in overseas courts such as Bermuda, Hong Kong, Bahamas, Cayman Islands, Gibraltar and British Virgin Isles. Interesting cases include the Paramount Case [1995] Court of Appeal and House of Lords (acting for the successful airline pilots); Macmillan v BIT [1994] and on appeal [1998](arising out of the Maxwell affair). Also represented Emmerson Inc on a section 459 Petition in re: Astec (BSR) plc [1998]. Spent seven months in Bermuda last year appearing in the Bermuda Fire and Marine case.
Prof. Memberships: Commercial Bar Association; Insolvency Lawyers Association; Society of Practitioners of Insolvency.
Career: Called to the Bar 1968. Joined present chambers 1969. Took silk 1982.
Personal: Educated at Wolstanton Grammar School, Newcastle-under-Lyme, and at Magdalen College, Oxford (BA and BCL) 1963-1967. Bigelow Fellow, University of Chicago Law School 1967-1968. Leisure pursuits include history, gardening, travel and wine. Born 2 July 1944. Lives in London.

POWELL, John L. QC
Four New Square (Justin Fenwick QC), London (020) 7822 2000
barristers@4newsquare.com
Recommended in Financial Services, Professional Negligence
Specialisation: Commercial law (practice UK and overseas), especially professional negligence, accountancy, financial services and securities law (UK, EC and international), investment fraud, e-commerce liabilities, insurance, judicial review, confidentiality, construction, engineering and international arbitration. Leading counsel for plaintiff liquidators in BCCI audit litigation. Reported cases include Arbiter v Gill Jennings & Every (patent agents), BCCI Overseas v Price Waterhouse (1998) (audit negligence), Mond v Hyde and DTI (1998) (immunity and liability of insolvency service); Fawkes-Underwood v Hamiltons (1997) (accountants negligence), Swinney v Chief Constable of Northumbria (1996) (confidentiality and immunity), Kaufmann v Credit Lyonnais (1995) (disclosure in regulatory context) R v PIA ex parte Lucas Fettes (pension misselling judicial review). Major involvements in Barlow Clowes, Lloyds, pension-misselling and Maxwell litigation as well as several recovery actions arising from U.K. and overseas frauds. Practice reflects main publications: (1) 'Jackson & Powell on Professional Negligence' and (2) 'Lomnicka & Powell, Encyclopedia of Financial Services Law' (Sweet & Maxwell). Chairman Bar Law Reform Committee (1997-98).
Prof. Memberships: COMBAR (Executive Committee 1999-2000), PNBA, Bar European Group, Society of Construction Law (President 1991-93).
Career: Called 1974. Silk 1990. Attorney of the Turks and Caicos Islands. Recorder. Bencher, Middle Temple. Head of Chambers 1997-99.
Personal: Educated at Christ College, Brecon, Amman Valley Grammar School and Trinity Hall, Cambridge 1969-1973 (MA, LLB). Welsh speaker. Born 14th September 1950. Married with 3 children.

POWERS, Michael J. QC
4 Paper Buildings (Jean Ritchie QC), London (020) 7353 3366
Recommended in Clinical Negligence, Product Liability
Specialisation: Clinical negligence (claimant and defendant). Co-editor of the leading textbook 'Clinical Negligence' (Butterworths 1990, 1994, 1999). Pharmaceutical law and all areas of common law touching upon medical and scientific matters. Group litigation for claimants and defendants. Clients include *CMS Cameron McKenna*, *Linklaters & Paines*, *Kennedys*, *Wedlake Bell*, *Irwin Mitchell*, *Hart Brown*, *Russell Jones & Walker* and many other leading firms. Pharmaceutical clients include: John Wyeth & Brother, Duphar Laboratories, Merrell Dow, 3M RIKER, Schering.
Prof. Memberships: Professional Negligence Bar Association; London Common Law and Commercial Bar Association; Fellow Royal Society of Medicine, Medico-Legal Society, Society of Doctors in Law.
Career: Medical Practice (1972-1980): Obstetrics, Medicine, Anaesthesia, ITU and GP. Called to the Bar (Lincoln's Inn) 1979; QC 1995. President of the South of England Coroners' Society (1987/88). Bencher of Lincoln's Inn 1998. Chapters in many books; writes and lectures widely. Recent Cases reported include: Powell v Boladz and others [1998] Lloyd's Rep Med 111 (CA); Robertson v Nottingham Health Authority [1997] Med LR 1 (CA); AB & Others v Roche Products [1997] 8 Med LR 57 (CA).
Personal: Enthusiasm for advocacy and training of trial skills. Recreations: technology, sailing, helicopter flying, walking, music and photography.

POWNALL, Orlando
1 Hare Court (Stephen Kramer QC), London (020) 7353 5324
Recommended in Crime

PRATT, Camden QC
One King's Bench Walk (Anthony Hacking QC), London (020) 7936 1500
Recommended in Family: Matrimonial Finance
Specialisation: Matrimonial finance and property, family (including divorce and children), child care, crime, commercial fraud (criminal), commercial

fraud (civil), medical negligence, medical law, environment, general common law, personal injuries. Interesting cases: Southern Water Authority v. Nature Conservancy Council [1992] 3 AER 481, HL (environmental damage/The Wildlife & Countryside Act); Re P [1995] 1 FLR 831 (International Child Abduction); Wicks v Wicks (C.A) [1998] 1 FLR 470 (Matrimonial financial relief: interim lump sum and transfer of property orders); R v Curtis Howard (the Gatwick Airport 'Body in Boot case'); Prosecution Counsel case of Regina v Sion Jenkins (the murder of 'Billie Jo') [1998]; R v Ron Brown (case of the MP's mistress's knickers).
Prof. Memberships: South Eastern Circuit (Committee Member); Chairman, Sussex Sessions Bar Mess; Chairman, Sussex Courts Liaison Committee 1993; Member Area Criminal Justice Liaison Committee 16.
Career: Call 1970, Silk 1992. Recorder 1993. Deputy High Court Judge, Family Division.
Personal: Educated at Lincoln College, Oxford (MA Juris).

PRATT, Duncan
6 Pump Court (Kieran Coonan QC), London (020) 7583 6013
Recommended in Clinical Negligence
Specialisation: Principally practises in clinical negligence and substantial personal injury claims. Considerable experience of claims involving birth and brain injuries of the utmost severity and has conducted clinical negligence claims involving most medical and surgical specialities. Lectures on topics related to clinical negligence. Other areas of practice solicitors' negligence, product liability, employment and related contractual claims. Professional clients include both specialised clinical negligence departments and general litigation departments.
Prof. Memberships: Professional Negligence Bar Association, AVMA, APIL, Medico-Legal Society.
Career: Called to the Bar 1971. Joined present chambers 2000.
Personal: Educated RGS Newcastle and University College, Oxford. Lives in London. Leisure pursuits include choral singing, local amenity societies, theatre, concert and opera.

PRENTICE, Dan
Erskine Chambers (Robin Potts QC), London (020) 7242 5532
clerks@erskine-chambers.co.uk
Recommended in Company
Specialisation: Company law, corporate insolvency, financial services. Recent reported case: Soden v British & Commonwealth Holdings plc [1997] 2 BCLC 501.
Prof. Memberships: Member of the Law Society's Committee on Company Law; Member of the Law Society's Committee on Insolvency Law; COMBAR; Chancery Bar Association.
Career: Called to *Lincoln's Inn* 1982. Professor of Corporate Law, University of Oxford.
Publications: Joint editor with Dame Mary Arden of 'Buckley on the Companies Acts'. Assistant editor of the 'Law Quarterly Review'. Contributor to 'Chitty on Contracts' (27th edn). Contributor to 'Gower, Company Law' (5th edn).

PRESCOTT, Peter QC
8 New Square (Michael Fysh QC SC), London (020) 7405 4321
peter.prescott@8newsquare.co.uk
Recommended in Intellectual Property, Media & Entertainment
Specialisation: Barrister specialising in all aspects of intellectual property law. Has been involved in numerous reported cases, recent examples of which include: HFC v HSBC; Biogen v Medeva; Aztech Systems Pte v Creative Technology Ltd; Chiron v Murex; Cantor Fitzgerald v Tradition.
Prof. Memberships: Intellectual Property Bar Association (IPBA); The Intellectual Property Lawyers Organisation (TIPLO).
Career: Called 1970; QC 1990; deputy high court judge.
Publications: 'Modern Law of Copyright' Butterworths 1980, 1994 and a chapter in 'Data Processing and the Law' Sweet & Maxwell 1984. Contributions to European Intellectual Property Review include 'Towards a small claims patent court' 10 EIPR 246.
Personal: Educated at St George's College, Dulwich College, University College London (BSc Physics); Queen Mary College (MSc Nuclear Engineering). Fluent in Spanish. Leisure: flying, music, reading and programming in assembler language. Born 1943; resides London.

PREVEZER, Susan QC
Essex Court Chambers (Gordon Pollock QC), London (020) 7813 8000
Recommended in Insolvency/Corporate Recovery
Specialisation: Main area of practice covers insolvency, commercial litigation, property law, company law. Major litigation includes BCCI. Millwall FC, Levitt, Emlico, KWELM, contributor to Lightman and Moss on Receivers
Prof. Memberships: Commercial Bar Association. Chancery Bar Association.
Career: Called to Bar 1983. 7 years at Michael Crystal QC's Chambers. Joined Present Chambers 1997 (December)

PRICE, James QC
5 Raymond Buildings (Patrick Milmo QC), London (020) 7242 2902
Recommended in Defamation

PRICE, Nicholas QC
3 Raymond Buildings (Clive Nicholls QC), London (020) 7400 6400
chambers@threeraymond.demon.co.uk
Recommended in Crime
Specialisation: Criminal law, paricularly murder, corporate manslaughter (Herald of Free Enterprise), rape, blackmail, armed robbery; Commercial crime-fraud: corporate, leasing mortgage; Public corruption cases; Public enquiries (the Guildford and Woolwich Enquiry by Sir John May).
Career: Called to the Bar in November 1968. Took silk in 1992. Recorder of the Crown Court since 1987. Vice-Chairman of Gray's Inn Continuing Education/ Advocacy Training Committee. Facilitator for the Bar Human Rights Course.

PRICE, Roderick
Recommended in Crime

PRICE OBE, Richard QC
Littleton Chambers (Michel Kallipetis QC), London (020) 7797 8600
Recommended in Media & Entertainment

PRIDAY, Charles
7 King's Bench Walk (Jeremy Cooke QC), London (020) 7910 8300
Recommended in Shipping
Specialisation: Principal areas of practice are shipping, banking, insurance and general commercial work, acting for shipowners, charterers, oil traders, other commodity traders, banks, insurance companies and brokers. Reported shipping cases of note include: charterparty dispute, the Nour (1999), the Anangel Express (1996), the Ulyanovsk (1990); laytime, the Petr Shmidt (1998), the Agamemnon (1998), the Kyzicos (1989); jurisdiction, the Maciej Rataj (1995), the Deichland (1990).
Prof. Memberships: London Maritime Arbitration Association.
Career: Called to the Bar and joined Seven King's Bench Walk in 1982.

PROSSER, Kevin J. QC
Pump Court Tax Chambers (Andrew Thornhill QC), London (020) 7414 8080
Recommended in Tax
Specialisation: Principal area of practice is Revenue law, including litigation. Co-author of Potter and Prosser, 'Tax Appeals' (Sweet & Maxwell).
Career: Called to the Bar 1982 and joined present chambers in 1983. Took Silk in 1996. Became Recorder this year.
Personal: Was once expelled from Tanzania for spying.

PROUDMAN, Sonia QC
11 New Square (Sonia Proudman QC), London (020) 7831 0081
Recommended in Charities, Traditional Chancery
Specialisation: Area of work: general chancery litigation and advice, with particular emphasis on trusts, charities, bankers' securities and all aspects of property law. Considerable experience in pursuing and in defending breach of trust claims, involving private, charitable and commercial trusts. Also professional negligence.
Prof. Memberships: Chancery Bar Association, STEP, Charity Law Association.
Career: Called to the Bar (Lincoln's Inn) 1972. (Kennedy Scholar, Buchanan Prize). Joined Chambers at 11 New Square in 1974. Took silk in 1994. Bencher 1996. Assistant Recorder 1997. Recorder 2000.
Personal: Born 1949; Married 1987, 1 daughter. Educated at St Paul's Girls' School and Lady Margaret Hall Oxford. BA 1st Class Hons 1971, Eldon Law Scholar 1973, MA 1973. Member Oxford University Law Faculty Advisory Board 2000

PRYNNE, Andrew QC
2 Harcourt Buildings (Roger Henderson QC), London (020) 7583 9020
aprynne@harcourt.co.uk
Recommended in Product Liability
Specialisation: General common law practice with an emphasis on product liability (principally pharmaceuticals), insurance disputes, clinical negligence, personal injury, railway law and employment matters. Notable cases include the MMR litigation for Merck (1999-2000); the tobacco lung cancer litigation for Imperial Tobacco (1999), the Lariam litigation for Roche Products (1999), the Opren litigation for Eli Lilly from 1986, the Clapham Accident Inquiry for British Railways Board (BRB) (1989), the Benzodiazepine litigation for Roche Products Ltd (1990-92), the Severn Tunnel Accident Enquiry for BRB 1992 and Crizzle v Board of Governors of St. Matthias School (EAT, 1993 – race discrimination). Advised BRB and Railtrack on safety implications and legal duties arising from privatisation. Member of the Lord Chancellor's Working Group on Multi-Party Actions. CEDR Accredited Mediator. Assistant Boundary Commissioner.
Prof. Memberships: South Eastern Circuit.
Career: Called to the Bar 1975 and tenant at King's Bench Walk 1976-1978 and then joined current chambers.
Personal: Educated at Marlborough College and Southampton University (LL.B, Hons). Born 28th May 1953. Interests: sailing, shooting and skiing.

PUGH, Charles
Old Square Chambers (John Hendy QC), London (020) 7269 0300
Recommended in Environment, Health & Safety
Specialisation: Called to the Bar in 1975, principal areas of practice are pollution/nuisance claims, acci-

dent claims (rail, aviation, work place) and statutory crime in health and safety/environmental fields. Recently reported cases include Wadey v Surrey CC, HL, 2000 (interest on damages); Hunter v Canary Wharf, HL, 1998 (leading case on nuisance); Underwood v British Midland, CA, 1996 (injury damages, principles of assessment); AB v South West Water, CA, 1993 (exemplary damages in nuisance). Current litigation includes multi-party 'dust nuisance' action (for major plc); statutory appeal against variation of consents (for numerous companies); multi-party toxic occupational exposure (generic counsel for claimants); numerous carbon monoxide poisoning claims; advising plc's being prosecuted for health and safety and/or environmental offences. Co-author of 'Toxic Torts' (2nd Ed. 1995).

PUGH, Vernon QC

2-3 Gray's Inn Square (Anthony Scrivener QC), London (020) 7242 4986

Recommended in Planning

Specialisation: Town & country planning; local government law; common law – professional negligence & personal injury; international law/extradition.
Prof. Memberships: Local Government & Planning Bar.
Career: LL.B (UCW); LLM (Cantab); University Lecturer in Property, Commercial & Planning; Hardwicke Scholar; Sir Thomas Moore Bursary; Bencher Lincoln's Inn; Crown Court Recorder.
Personal: Married, 3 daughters. Chairman, International Rugby Football Board. Director Rugby World Cup. IOC Federation Member.

PUGH-SMITH, John

1 Serjeants' Inn (Lionel Read QC), London (020) 7583 1355
clerks@serjeants-inn.co.uk

Recommended in Environment

Specialisation: Planning, Local Government, Environmental and Parliamentary matters.
Prof. Memberships: Planning and Environment Bar Association (Former Committee Member), United Kingdom Environmental Law Association, Environmental Law Foundation.
Career: Called to the Bar 1977. Joined Serjeants' Inn 1984. Publications for Sweet & Maxwell include 'Neighbours and the Law' (1st & 2nd Editions: 1988 & 1993), 'Archaeology at Law' (1st Edition: 1996). Joint Editorial Adviser for 'Property and Compensation Reports' and 'Planning Law Case Reports'. General Editor 'Environmental Law' (OUP) (2000).
Personal: Born 1954. Lives, mainly, in Norfolk.

PURCHAS, Christopher QC

Crown Office Chambers (Michael Spencer QC & Christopher Purchas QC), London (020) 7797 8100
purchas@crownofficechambers.com

Recommended in Personal Injury

Specialisation: Personal injury, professional and clinical negligence, general insurance law, fire claims, sports injury, highway authority claims, product liability. Recent cases include: Wells v Wells; Page v Sheerness Steel; Heil v Rankin; Griffin v Kingsmill; Doyle v Wallace; Mighell v Reading & MBI; Carroll v Dunlop.
Prof. Memberships: LCLCBA, PIBA.
Career: Called to the Bar 1966. Appointed Recorder 1986. Silk 1990. Deputy High Court Judge 1999.
Personal: Marlborough College 1957-1961, Trinity College Cambridge 1962-1965. Leisure pursuits golf tennis and shooting. Born 20 June 1943. Lives in Surrey.

PURCHAS, Robin QC

2 Harcourt Buildings (Mr Gerard Ryan QC), London (020) 7353 8415

Recommended in Parliamentary & Public Affairs, Planning

Specialisation: Principal areas of practice are parliamentary, planning and local government work, compulsory purchase (including Hong Kong and Privy Council), compensation, public and administrative and environmental law; recent cases include Prudential Assurance v. Waterloo Real Estate 1999 CA; Fletcher v. SSE 2000 HL; R v. Newbury DC ex p Chieveley PC 1998 CA; English Property Corp v. Kingston upon Thames BC 1998 CA; R v. SSE ex p Somerfield Stores 1998 DC; Pye v Kingswood DC 1998 CA; Pickering v. Kettering BC 1996 CA; Bolton MBC v SSE 1995 HL; Wards v. Barclays Bank PLC 1994 CA.
Prof. Memberships: Parliamentary Bar Mess; Bar European Group, Planning and Environment Bar Association: Administrative Law Bar Association; South Eastern Circuit.
Career: Called to the Bar in 1968 and joined Harcourt Buildings in 1969. Took silk in 1987. Appointed Recorder in 1989; Deputy High Court Judge 1994; Master of Bench Inner Temple 1996; Bar Council 2000.
Personal: Educated at Marlborough College and Trinity College, Cambridge (Senior Exhibitioner). Born 12th June 1946.

PURLE, Charles QC

12 New Square (John Mowbray QC), London (020) 7419 1212

Recommended in Civil Fraud, Commercial Chancery, Company

Specialisation: Leading litigator in cases covering a wide sphere, from computers through breach of trust to VAT. Recent cases have had the emphasis on fraud, including a fraudulent trading and misrepresentation appeal in Hong Kong and important decision on constructive trusts and fraudulent breach of trust.
Prof. Memberships: Gray's Inn, Lincoln's Inn.
Career: LLB (Nottingham), BCL (Oxon). FICPD.
Personal: Married twice, with 6 children. Now awaiting grandchildren. Opera, music, fine wine and food help to relax.

PURNELL, Nicholas QC

23 Essex Street (Michael Lawson QC), London (020) 7413 0353

Recommended in Crime, Fraud: Criminal

Specialisation: Principal area of practice is criminal law, particularly commercial fraud. Work includes financial regulatory and professional disciplinary tribunals. Member of the Lord Chancellor's Advisory Committee on Legal Education and Conduct 1991-97. Member of the Criminal Committee Judicial Studies Board 1991-96.
Prof. Memberships: South Eastern Circuit. Fellow: Society for Advanced Legal Studies; Fellow: Institute of Continuing Professional Development.
Career: Called to the Bar 1968. Prosecuting Counsel, Inland Revenue 1977-1979. Treasury Counsel 1979-85. Took Silk in 1985. Recorder since 1986. Bencher of the Middle Temple since 1990.
Personal: Educated at the Oratory School 1958-1962 and King's College, Cambridge 1963-1966(MA). Governor of the Oratory School. Born 29th January 1944.

PURVIS, Iain

11 South Square (Christopher Floyd QC), London (020) 7405 1222

Recommended in Intellectual Property

Specialisation: All aspects of intellectual property. Reported cases include Gerber v Lectra (patent damages); United Biscuits v ASDA (Penguin/Puffin 'own brand' dispute); Mark Wilkinson Woodcraft (design right – furniture) ; Designers Guild v Russell Williams (Copyright – fabric designs); VSX v Nidek (patent infringement – eye surgery); Fylde Microsystems v Key Radio (copyright – computer software)
Prof. Memberships: IPBA member.
Career: MA Cantab; BCL Oxon. Fourteen years practice in this field, including sitting as arbitrator.
Personal: Married. Three children. Skiing, sailing, watching football and exploring prehistoric monuments.

PYE, M Jayne

Sovereign Chambers (Geoffrey C. Marson QC), Leeds (0113) 245 1841
sovereignchambers@btinternet.com

Recommended in Family/Matrimonial

Specialisation: All aspects of family breakdown, particularly financial & children. Much experience in public law matters representing local authority, Guardian ad Litem and parents.
Prof. Memberships: Family Law Bar Association.
Career: Called May 1995. Previously practised as family law solicitor for 10 years when member of Children and Young Persons Act, later Children Act, Law Society Specialist Panel

PYMONT, Christopher QC

13 Old Square (Michael Lyndon-Stanford QC), London (020) 7404 4800

Recommended in Banking, Commercial Chancery

Specialisation: Practice encompasses company law, landlord and tenant matters, chancery and commercial work and insolvency.
Prof. Memberships: Chancery Bar Association.
Career: Called to the Bar 1979 and joined Old Square in 1980. Appointed QC 1996.
Personal: Educated at Marlborough College and Christ Church, Oxford (MA). Born 16th March 1956.

QUADRAT, Simon

Queen Square Chambers (T. Alun Jenkins QC), Bristol (0117) 921 1966

Recommended in Crime

QUINN, Susan

4 Brick Court (David Medhurst), London (020) 7797 8910

Recommended in Family: Child Care including child abduction

Specialisation: Childcare law. Work includes public law aspects of childcare, residence, contact and adoption.
Prof. Memberships: Family Law Bar Association.
Career: Called to the Bar 1983 and joined current chambers in 1988.
Personal: Educated at London University (LL.B). Born 17th May 1960.

QUINT, Francesca

11 Old Square (Simeon Thrower), London (020) 7242 5022
fquint@ukonline.co.uk

Recommended in Charities

Specialisation: Principal area of practice is chancery, with a focus on charities. Work includes advice on setting up charities, amending constitutions, negotiating with Charity Commission, schemes, arrangements with other charities or trading companies and dispute resolution. Other main areas of practice are trusts, land, probate and capital taxation, particularly deeds of variation, Inheritance Act applications, advice and litigation relating to land or trusts. Recent cases include Gunning v Buckfast Abbey Trustees (dispute between parents and charity school); Henrietta Barnett School Governors v Hampstead Garden Suburb Institute (dispute between voluntary school and landlord charity), Gray v Taylor CA (status of almshouse resident) and Fuller v Evans (private settlement). Clients include educational establishments and charities and city livery companies.

such as murders, robberies and drugs cases. Other area of work is personal injury and general common law. Appeared in R v Grantham (fraudulent trading), two Home Secretary's references re Hickey and Others (1989 and 1997-the Carl Bridgwater murder case), various cases of cruelty to patients (R v Spencer, R v Smails eg), R v Cohen and others (the Blue Arrow case, 1991) and a 1998 banking fraud trial (R v Martens and others). Chaired two Bar Council working parties producing reports on the problems of criminal fraud cases. Author of 'Some Procedural Problems in Criminal Fraud cases' (OUP 1995). Chaired several conferences and seminars on topics related to commercial fraud.
Prof. Memberships: Bar Council, Midland and Oxford Circuit, Criminal Bar Association.
Career: Called to the Bar and joined 9 Gough Square in 1965. Appointed Recorder 1981. Took Silk 1982.
Personal: Educated at Winchester College 1954-59 and Brasenose College, Oxford 1959-1963. Leisure pursuits include horse racing, canals, opera and theatre. Born 26th April 1941. Lives in Brentford Middlesex.

ROBERTS, Lisa
Lincoln House Chambers (Mukhtar Hussain QC), Manchester (0161) 832 5701
Recommended in Crime

ROBERTSON, Aidan
Brick Court Chambers (Christopher Clarke QC), London (020) 7379 3550
Recommended in Competition/Anti-trust
Specialisation: Competition Law, European Community Law and Public and Administrative Law. Important cases include: R v OFTEL ex parte BT (1996, Divisional Court); R v Customs & Excise ex parte Lunn Poly (1999, EuLR, Court of Appeal); Attorney General v Blake (1998, Ch 439, Court of Appeal); R v Customs & Excise ex parte Littlewoods (1998, The Times, 3 March, Court of Appeal); passmore v Morland (1999, The Times, 11 February, Court of Appeal); Crehan v Courage (1999, The Times, 14 June, Court of Appeal); British Digital Broadcasting (European Commission, 1998); New Motor Cars (Competition Commission investigation, 1999) and a number of pending cases before the European Court of Justice and Court of First Instance.
Prof. Memberships: Advises and represents clients in competition investigations and proceedings before the European Commission and Competition Commission (former MMC). Publications include: co-author with Nicholas Green QC of second edition of 'Commercial Agreements and Competition Law' (1997, publisher Kluwer Law International). Co-author with Nicholas Green QC of 'The Europeanisation of UK Competition Law' (1999, publisher Hart Publishing). Numerous articles in academic and professional journals.
Career: Called to Bar 1995. Solicitor of the Supreme Court of England and Wales 1988-1995. Fellow and Tutor in Law, Wadham College, Oxford 1990-1999. University Lecturer at Oxford University 1990-1996. 1981-84 BA Hons, Law, Jesus College, Cambridge (1st Class); 1984-85 LLM, Jesus College, Cambridge (1st Class); Member of the Treasury C Panel (1999-).

ROBERTSON, Geoffrey QC
Doughty Street Chambers (Geoffrey Robertson QC), London (020) 7404 1313
Recommended in Crime, Defamation, Human Rights (Civil Liberties)

ROBINSON, Vivian QC
Queen Elizabeth Building (Julian Bevan QC & Peter Whiteman QC), London (020) 7583 5766
Recommended in Fraud: Criminal
Specialisation: All aspects of crime, particularly commercial fraud. Was involved for the Defence in the Blue Arrow trial and the Blackspur Leasing trial and has prosecuted cases on behalf of the Serious Fraud Office. In 1998 defended in a substantial fraud trial in Hong Kong.
Prof. Memberships: Criminal Bar Association.
Career: Educated at Queen Elizabeth Grammar School, Wakefield. The Leys School, Cambridge and Sidney Sussex College, Cambridge. Called to the Bar in 1967. Took Silk 1986. A Recorder of the Crown Court since 1986.
Personal: Married with three children. Lives in Oxfordshire.

RODDY, Maureen
India Buildings Chambers (David Harris QC), Liverpool (0151) 243 6000
Recommended in Family/Matrimonial
Specialisation: Practises solely in the field of family law. Specialises in dealing with public law Children Act work, including representation of Local Authorities, parents and Guardians ad Litem in cases involving inter alia, issues of physical, sexual and emotional abuse of children.
Prof. Memberships: Committee member – Family Law Bar Association; Immediate Past President – Liverpool Medico-Legal Society.
Career: Called in 1977.

RODGER, Caroline
Renaissance Chambers (Brian Jubb & Henry Setright), London (020) 7404 1111
Recommended in Family: Child Care including child abduction
Specialisation: Family law: wardship, adoption, child abduction, public and private law applications under Children's Act.
Prof. Memberships: Family Law Bar Association. Inter Country Adoption Association.
Career: BA (Hons) Oxford. Called to the Bar 1968.

RODGER, Martin
Falcon Chambers (Jonathan Gaunt QC & Kim Lewison QC), London (020) 7353 2484
Recommended in Agriculture, Property Litigation
Specialisation: Handles all aspects of commercial and agricultural property litigation, including landlord and tenant, rent review, milk quota, agricultural holdings, licensed premises and real property. Important cases include Courage v Crehan (Court of Appeal, 1999 – beer tie litigation), Attwood v Bovis (Chancery Division, 2000 – easements) and Zubaida v Hargreaves (Court of Appeal, 1995 – negligence of expert).
Prof. Memberships: Chancery Bar Association, Agricultural Law Association, Professional Negligence Bar Association.
Career: Called to the Bar and joined *Falcon Chambers* in 1986.
Publications: Editor of 'Woodfall on Landlord & Tenant and former editor of 'Bernstein & Reynolds Handbook of Rent Review'.
Personal: Educated at St. Aloysius College, Glasgow 1973-1979 and University College, Oxford 1979-83. Born 1962. Lives in Kent.

RODGERS, June
Harcourt Chambers (June Rodgers), London (020) 7353 6961 Fax (020) 7353 6968 Oxford (01865) 791559 jrodgers@harcourtchambers.law.co.uk
Recommended in Church: Church of England
Specialisation: Family and ecclesiastical.
Prof. Memberships: Family Law Bar Association. Ecclesiastical Law Society.
Career: MA Trinity College Dublin. MA Lady Margaret Hall Oxford. Called: 1971: Middle Temple. Midland and Oxford Circuit. Chancellor of the Diocese of Gloucester. Recorder.
Personal: Architectural history.

RODWAY, Susan
12 King's Bench Walk (Timothy Stow QC), London (020) 7583 0811
Recommended in Personal Injury

ROGERS, Beverly-Ann
Serle Court (Lord Neill of Bladen QC), London (020) 7242 6105
Recommended in Property Litigation, Traditional Chancery
Specialisation: Chancery and commercial litigation and advice. All aspects of property litigation and advice. Professional negligence. Contentious trusts and probate, charities, partnerships.
Prof. Memberships: Chancery Bar. Association of Contentious Trust and Probate Specialists, COMBAR.
Career: Called to Bar in 1978. Joined Serle Court Chambers in 1980. CEDR accredited mediator.

ROGERS, Heather
Matrix Chambers (Nicholas Blake QC), London (020) 7404 3447 heatherrogers@matrixlaw.co.uk
Recommended in Defamation
Specialisation: Media law, including defamation, malicious falsehood, breach of confidence, contempt of court, judicial review. Recent cases include David Irving v Penguin Books (Gray J April 2000); Hamilton v Al Fayed [2000] 2 WLR 609 (libel and Parliamentary privilege); Loveless v Earl [1999] EMLR 530 (malace/qualified privilege); Hinduja v Asia TV [1998] EMLR 530 ('meaning'); Berezovsky v Forbes (CA November 1998 - jurisdiction); Elton John v Mirror Group [1997] QB 586 (damages); R v Broadcasting Complaints Commission, ex parte BBC [1995] EMLR 241 (judicial review). Contributor to OUP Yearbook of Media and Entertainment Law (1995-2000). Further information at www.matrixlaw.co.uk.

ROGERS, Mark N.
St. Mary's Chambers Family Law Chambers (Christopher Butler), Nottingham (0115) 950 3503
Recommended in Family/Matrimonial

ROMNEY, Daphne
4 Field Court (Steven Gee QC), London (020) 7440 6900
Recommended in Employment
Specialisation: Employment law, particularly in the fields of wrongful and unfair dismissal, restrictive covenants and discrimination. Clients include insurance companies, PLCs, health authorities and NHS trusts. Also practises in the field of defamation and media law.
Prof. Memberships: Employment Law Bar Association
Career: Called to the Bar in 1979. Libel reader for The Observer since 1982.
Personal: Born 29 July 1955. BA (Cantab).

ROOK, Peter QC
18 Red Lion Court (Anthony Arlidge QC), London (020) 7520 6000
Recommended in Fraud: Criminal
Specialisation: Commercial and tax fraud. Major cases include Lester Pigott, Barlow Clowes, 'Nissan', Maxwell, 'Africar'.
Prof. Memberships: Committee, Criminal Bar Association. QC 1991.
Career: Publication. Rook and Ward on 'Sexual Offences' 2nd Ed. 1997. Sweet & Maxwell.

ROOTS, Guy QC
2 Mitre Court Buildings (Michael FitzGerald QC), London (020) 7583 1380
Recommended in Planning
Specialisation: Main areas of practice are town and country planning, environmental law, compulsory purchase and compensation, rating, local government,

parliamentary and administrative law. Has been involved in many leading cases acting for a wide cross section of clients in the public and private sectors. Has spoken at and chaired numerous conferences and seminars. General Editor of 'Ryde on Rating and the Council Tax'. General Editor of 'Butterworths Compulsory Purchase Law Service'.
Prof. Memberships: Chairman Planning and Environment Bar Association, Administrative Law Bar Association.
Career: Called to the Bar in 1969. Joined 2 Mitre Court Buildings in 1972. Took Silk in 1989.
Personal: Educated at Winchester College and Brasenose College, Oxford (MA in Jurisprudence).

ROSE, Dinah
Blackstone Chambers (P Baxendale QC and C Flint QC), London (020) 7583 1770
Recommended in Administrative & Public Law: General, Employment, Human Rights (Civil Liberties)
Specialisation: Administrative and public law, discrimination, employment, human rights, European law. Particular interests include equal pay; maternity rights; financial services, City regulation and the Human Rights Act 1998; European social policy; pharmaceuticals; telecommunications; broadcasting. Recent cases include: Couch v British Boxing Board of Control (women's right to box professionally); R v HFEA, ex parte Blood (right to insemination with dead husband's semen); R v Secretary of State for Health, ex parte Pfizer (lawfulness of guidance limiting availability of Viagra on NHS); R v MCA, ex parte Generics ECJ (lawfulness of MCA decision concerning the authorisation of generic medicines); R v Secretary of State for Health, ex parte Taylor, ECJ (discrimination against men in relation to Winter Fuel Payments); Coote v Granada Hospitality ECJ (victimisation after employment has terminated); Sirdar v MoD ECJ (women's right to join the Royal Marines); Levez v Jennings (Harlow Pools) Ltd (compatibility of of time limits under the Equal Pay Act 1970 with EC law); Nagarajan v Swiggs and LRT, HL, (meaning of victimisation under the Race Relations Act 1976); R v ITC, ex parte Flextech (lawfulness of the exercise of the ITC's competition powers); R v Secretary of State for Trade and Industry, ex parte One2One (imposition of license conditions on a telecommunications company); R v London Metal Exchange, ex parte Albatros (disciplinary proceedings against a metal warehouse); R v Home Secretary, ex parte Garner (rights to compensation for wrongly convicted prisoners); R v Home Secretary, ex parte Mellor (prisoners' right to artificial insemination); Crossland v UK (ECHR – discrimination against widowers in relation to social security benefits); Mason v UK (ECHR – violation of the rights of a rape victim cross-examined by her attacker).
Prof. Memberships: ALBA, ELBA, member Council of JUSTICE.
Career: Called to Bar 1989. Junior Counsel to the Crown (B Panel) since 1994. Publications: Co-editor Halsbury's Laws 4th ed. re-issue, 'Race Relations'; contributor to Halsbury's Laws 4th ed. re-issue, 'Constitutional Law and Human Rights'; contributor to Lester & Pannick 'Human Rights Law and Practice' (Butterworths 1999).

ROSE, Jonathan L.
St. Paul's Chambers (Nigel Sangster QC), Leeds (0113) 245 5866
Recommended in Crime

ROSE, Paul
Old Square Chambers (John Hendy QC), London (020) 7269 0300
Recommended in Employment
Specialisation: Discrimination, unfair dismissal, wrongful dismissal and restraint of trade. Personal injury/medical negligence.
Prof. Memberships: Industrial Law Society, Employment Law Bar Association, Personal Injury Bar Association, APIL.
Career: Called to Bar 1981. In employment law acted in leading cases in discrimination, unfair dismissal, Transfer of Undertakings Regulations. Undertaken injunctive work in field of Restraint of Trade and Wrongful Dismissal litigation, also instructed regularly in collective redundancy litigation. In personal injury acted on behalf of the plaintiffs in: Opren litigation, Benzodiazepine litigation, British Midland air crash, Camelford Water Pollution, Mull of Kyntyre helicopter crash. Acted in a substantial number of catastrophic injury claims particularly involving servicemen in claims against Ministry of Defence.

ROSEN, Murray QC
11 Stone Buildings (Murray Rosen QC), London (020) 7831 6381
Recommended in Civil Fraud, Commercial (Litigation), Commercial Chancery, Sport

ROSEN PEACOCKE, Teresa
13 Old Square (Michael Lyndon-Stanford QC), London (020) 7404 4800
Recommended in Professional Negligence

ROTH, Peter M. QC
Monckton Chambers (John Swift QC), London (020) 7405 7211
chambers@monckton.co.uk
Recommended in Competition/Anti-trust
Specialisation: Public law (e.g. R v. Chief Constable of Sussex ex p. International Trader's Ferry [1998] (HL: export of livestock)); EC law and UK competition law (e.g. Associated Dairies v Baines [1997] (HL: RTPA); Case C-219/98 Anastasiou; Case C-60/92 Otto BV v Postbank NV); Commercial litigation and ADR; Professional negligence (e.g. Hemmens v Wilson Browne).
Career: Publications: General Editor, 'Bellamy & Child's European Community Law of Competition' (5th ed.).
Personal: MA (Oxon), LL.M. Called to the Bar, 1976. QC, 1997. Recorder, 2000 .Harmsworth Scholar, Middle Temple. Visiting associate professor, Univ. of Pennsylvania Law School, 1987. Vice Chairman, Competition Law Association.

ROWE, Judith
One Garden Court Family Law Chambers (Eleanor Platt QC and Alison Ball QC), London (020) 7797 7900
jrowe@onegardencourt.co.uk
Recommended in Family: Child Care including child abduction
Specialisation: All aspects of family law including public and private law aspects of the Children Act, adoption, child abduction and children cases with an international element; matrimonial finance Judicial review and professional negligence (family law related).
Prof. Memberships: FLBA.
Career: Called to the Bar in 1979. Moved to 1, Garden Court in 1996 to specialise wholly in family law. Appointed Assistant Recorder, 1999.
Personal: Born 7 August 1957. Educated at Rednock School, Gloucestershire. University College London (LL.B Hons 1978). Lives in London. Married with two young children. Interests include travel, theatre and watersports.

ROWELL, David
3 New Square (Lord Goodhart QC), London (020) 7405 5577
Recommended in Traditional Chancery

ROWLAND, John QC
4 Pump Court (Bruce Mauleverer QC), London (020) 7353 2656
Recommended in Insurance
Specialisation: Principal areas of practice are insurance and reinsurance disputes, professional negligence and general advisory work related to the insurance industry. Recent work has included close involvement in Lloyd's names litigation, policy disputes, broker's negligence and regulatory work. Other areas of practice include general commercial disputes including complex engineering projects and a number of major ICC Arbitrations, inter alia, for Total Oil Company in relation to worldwide uranium sales, for Sogex Construction Group and numerous mining and chemical plants operators; professional negligence involving claims against lawyers, accountants and brokers; gaming and casino licensing work and the provision of commercial law advice direct to overseas lawyers.
Prof. Memberships: COMBAR.
Career: Called to the Bar in 1979 and joined 4 Pump Court in 1980. Took Silk in 1996.
Personal: Educated at Aquinas College, Perth, Western Australia; University of Western Australia (B.Econs, Hons) and King's College, University of London LL.B (Hons).

ROWLAND, Robin
5 Fountain Court (Anthony Barker QC), Birmingham (0121) 606 0500
Recommended in Family/Matrimonial

ROWLANDS, Marc
4 Pump Court (Bruce Mauleverer QC), London (020) 7353 2656
Recommended in Construction
Specialisation: Technology and Construction cases, arbitration law & practice.
Prof. Memberships: ORBA, COMBAR.
Career: Magdalen, Oxford (Law).

ROWLEY, J. James
28 St. John St (Clement Goldstone QC), Manchester (0161) 834 8418
Recommended in Clinical Negligence, Personal Injury

ROWLEY, Keith
11 Old Square (Grant Crawford & Jonathan Simpkiss), London (020) 7430 0341
k.rowley@11oldsquare.co.uk
Recommended in Traditional Chancery
Specialisation: Principal area of work is general chancery. Work includes company law and insolvency, real property (including landlord and tenant), pension schemes, and professional negligence work in these areas. Important cases handled include Re Thompson's Settlement, R v Panel on Take-Overs and Mergers, Re ILG Travel Ltd, Re William Makin & Sons, Collins v Tipton & Coseley BS, Bogg v Raper, Gillett v Holt, Municipal Mutual Insurance v Harrop, Worby v Rosser, Finley v Connell and Re Conder Group plc Pension Scheme. Clients include banks, building societies, insolvency practitioners, insurers and occupational pension scheme employers and trustees.
Prof. Memberships: Chancery Bar Association, Professional Negligence Association.
Career: Called to the bar 1979 and joined *11 Old Square* in 1981.
Personal: Educated at Woking Grammar School for Boys 1968-1975 and King's College London 1975-1978. Lives in London. Born 20th August 1957.

ROYCE, John QC
Guildhall Chambers (Adrian Palmer QC), Bristol (0117) 927 3366
Recommended in Crime
Specialisation: Personal Injuries. Serious Crime. Industrial Deafness. Commercial Fraud. Cryptosporidiosis Litigation against Yorkshire Water & Thames Water. Lead contaminated cattle feed actions for NFU. Counsel to inquiry into Ashworth High Security Hospital.
Prof. Memberships: Personal Injury Bar Association; Sports Law Bar Association.
Career: QC 1987; Recorder 1986; Deputy High Court Judge QBD 1993.
Personal: Austrian qualified ski instructor.

RUBIN, Stephen QC
Farrar's Building (John Leighton Williams QC), London (020) 7583 9241
srubin@farrarsbuilding.co.uk
Recommended in Commercial (Litigation)
Specialisation: General commercial litigation particularly civil fraud, banker/customer disputes, foreign exchange, business disputes and professional negligence. Recent reported cases: First American v Sheihk Zayad Al Nahayan [1999] 1 WLR 1154, Den Norske Bank v Antonatos [1999] QB 271, Pharaon v BCCI [1998] 4 All ER 455, BOC plc v Centeon Inc [1991] 1 All ER (Comm) 970, Finance for Mortgage v Farley & Co [1998] 2 PNLR 145.
Prof. Memberships: London Common Law and Commercial Bar Association; Professional Negligence Bar Association.
Career: Called to Bar 1977; QC 2000; Professional Conduct and Complaints Committee of Bar 1995-1999.
Personal: Merchant Taylor's School, Northwood; Brasenose College, Oxford – MA Jurisprudence; Married with four children.

RUMFITT, Nigel J. QC
7 Bedford Row (David Farrer QC), London (020) 7242 3555
Recommended in Crime
Specialisation: Crime of all types, prosecuting and defending. Extensive experience of medical issues (Junior, Beverley Allitt case). Since taking Silk has done a number of high profile cases. Successfully defended Ruth Neave, helped expose police/Home Office malpractice in R v Robinson & Ors at Leceister (Yardie case). Prosecuted Bedford Hotel murder and Celia Beckett (child poisoner).
Career: Educated at Leeds Modern School; Pembroke College, Oxford; Northwestern University School of Law, Chicago Illinois. MA (Oxon) in Jurisprudence; BCL (Oxon); 2:2 in Bar Finals; Harmsworth Law Scholar (Middle Temple). Called to Bar (Middle Temple) 1974. Assistant Recorder 1991, Recorder 1995. Chambers of D. Draycott QC, *1 Essex Court* 1975-1988. Present chambers 1988 to date. QC 1994.
Personal: Born 6.3.1950, Leeds. Married. Interests include skiing, windsurfing and sailing. Speaks fluent French and has studied French law, holds consultations in French without interpreter.

RUSHBROOKE, Justin
5 Raymond Buildings (Patrick Milmo QC), London (020) 7242 2902
Recommended in Defamation

RUSSELL, Christopher
2 Temple Gardens (Dermod O'Brien QC), London (020) 7822 1200
crussell@2templegardens.co.uk
Recommended in Professional Negligence
Specialisation: Professional negligence, with an emphasis on valuers', surveyors' and clinical negligence. Personal injury, in particular industrial diseases. Health and Safety. General insurance, common law and procedural matters. Cases include Wentworth v Wiltshire CC [1993], BBL v Eagle Star [1993], Lancashire CC v Municipal Mutual [1997], Burns v General Accident [1999].
Career: LLB (Exeter). Called 1982. PNBA; LCLCBA; PIBA.

RUSSELL, Jeremy QC
4 Essex Court (Nigel Teare QC), London (020) 7653 5653
Recommended in Arbitration (International), Shipping
Specialisation: Specialist in shipping law and international trade. Practice covers shipping, Admiralty, insurance (marine and non-marine), sale and carriage of goods (domestic and international). Also handles commercial arbitrations both as advocate and occasionally as arbitrator. Has addressed a number of conferences in London and Singapore on shipping matters.
Prof. Memberships: COMBAR; London Common Law and Commercial Bar Association; London Maritime Arbitrators Association (supporting member); LCIA (member); FSALS.
Career: Called to the Bar 1975. Joined present chambers 1977. Took Silk 1994. Appointed to panel of Lloyd's Salvage Arbitrators 2000.

RUSSEN, Jonathan
13 Old Square (Michael Lyndon-Stanford QC), London (020) 7404 4800
Recommended in Traditional Chancery
Specialisation: Commercial litigation: contactual disputes. Insolvency: bankruptcy; directors' disqualification; shareholders' disputes; corporate insolvency; insolvent partnerships. Property. Recent cases: Candare v Welsh Development Agency; Rolls Royce v Heavylift Volga-Dnieper; Re Bayoil [1999] 1 WLR 147; Re Philip Alexander Securities [1998] BPJR 383; Scott v Church Scientology [1997] BPJR 4. Contributor to Butterworth's 'Practical Insolvency'.
Prof. Memberships: Chancery Bar Association. COMBAR.
Career: University of Wales LLB (1st Class Hons.) 1984. University of Cambridge LLM 1985. Called to Bar (Lincoln's Inn) 1986.
Personal: Married 2 children.

RUTTLE, Stephen QC
Brick Court Chambers (Christopher Clarke QC), London (020) 7379 3550
Recommended in Alternative Dispute Resolution, Insurance

RYAN, Gerard QC
2 Harcourt Buildings (Mr Gerard Ryan QC), London (020) 7353 8415
clerks@2hb.law.co.uk
Recommended in Environment, Parliamentary & Public Affairs, Planning
Specialisation: Environmental and planning law including countryside matters commons and village greens. Environmental work includes minerals planning and waste disposal problems with their common law incidents and water resources and engineering.
Prof. Memberships: Parliamentary Bar. Planning and Environment Bar Association.
Career: First degree was in Natural Sciences (Cambridge, MA); Harmsworth Scholar of Middle Temple; QC 1981; a Recorder of the Crown Court 1984-98. Has promoted or opposed many major public works including harbours, railways and reservoirs.

RYDER, John
6 King's Bench Walk (Michael Worsley QC), London (020) 7583 0410
Recommended in Crime

RYDER, Matthew
Closters (Cox), London (020) 7827 4000
Recommended in Crime, Sport

RYDER TD, Ernest QC
Deans Court Chambers (H.K. Goddard QC), Manchester (0161) 214 6000
ryder@deanscourt.co.uk
Recommended in Family/Matrimonial
Specialisation: Family, public and administrative law; providing a specialist service in matrimonial finance and all disputes relating to children, public authorities, health care, professional negligence and ethics. Private and public tribunal work.
Prof. Memberships: FLBA. PIBA. Child Concern. NYAS (Professional Advisory Group). ALC.
Career: MA (Cantab). Call 1981 Gray's Inn. Assistant Recorder 1996. QC 1997. Counsel to the Tribunal (North Wales) 1996-1998.
Personal: TA Commission 1982. TD 1996.

SAINI, Pushpinder
Blackstone Chambers (P Baxendale QC and C Flint QC), London (020) 7583 1770
Recommended in Administrative & Public Law: General, Media & Entertainment
Specialisation: Commercial law (including copyright and entertainment law) public law (including human rights). Cases include George Michael v Sony, A&M Records v VCI Ltd, ZYX Music v King, Wailer v Island Records, R v Radio Authority ex p. Guardian Media Group, Tony Bland, Banks v CBS, R v Secretary of State ex parte O'Dhiuibir, A-G v Blake, Lisa Stansfield v Sovereign, R v Secretary of State ex parte RP Scherer, R v Secretary of State ex parte Monsanto; Reynolds v Times newspapers, Walmsley v Aeid Jazz, R v DG Telecoms ex parte Mercury. Called to the Bar 1991. Co-author, 'Halsbury's Laws, European Convention on Human Rights' and Lester & Pannick, 'Human Rights Law and Practice'.
Prof. Memberships: JUSTICE, ELA, ALBA, BEG
Personal: Educated at Corpus Christi College, Oxford (BA and BCL, both First Class) Atkin Scholar of Gray's Inn. Languages: Punjabi, Hindi, French, Urdu.

SALLON, Christopher QC
Doughty Street Chambers (Geoffrey Robertson QC), London (020) 7404 1313
Recommended in Crime
Specialisation: Criminal law. Defends in commercial fraud, revenue and customs prosecutions, particularly in murders. Member of the Bar Working Party on the Guildford and Woolwich Bombings and the Seabrook Working Party on the Efficient Disposal of Business in the Crown Court. Has lectured extensively at US universities, including Yale and Stamford, on civil liberties issues. Member of the board of Counsel magazine. Fellow – American Board of Criminal Lawyers.
Prof. Memberships: Bar Council, Chairman – Public Affairs Committee.
Career: Called to the Bar 1973 and helped to found current chambers 1990. Appointed Recorder 1996. Took Silk 1994. Called to Bar of Eastern Carribean 1994.

SALTER, Richard QC
3 Verulam Buildings (Christopher Symons QC & John Jarvis QC), London (020) 7831 8441
rsalter@3verulam.co.uk
Recommended in Banking
Specialisation: Principal areas of practice are banking,

commercial law, financial services, insolvency, insurance, professional negligence and building. Clients include most major UK and international banks. Contributor to 'Banks – Liability and Risk' (3rd ed 2000) and 'Banks and Remedies' (2nd ed 1999) for Lloyd's of London Press; and to Vol. 20 'Halsbury's Laws' (4th ed 1993 – Re-issue 'Guarantees'). Consulting editor, All England Commercial Cases 1999-. Legislation editor, Encyclopedia of Insurance Law 1999-. Lectures frequently on banking and other commercial law topics.
Prof. Memberships: London Common Law and Commercial Bar Association, COMBAR, TECBAR, Chartered Institute of Arbitrators.
Career: Called to the Bar 1975. Tenant at *Hare Court*, 1977-82, then joined current chambers. Bencher of the Inner Temple 1991. Member of the Council of Legal Education 1990-1996. Chairman of the Board of Examiners, Bar Vocational Course, 1992-93. Governor of the Inns of Court School of Law 1996-. Took Silk in 1995. Recorder 2000- (Assistant Recorder 1997-2000).
Personal: Educated at Harrow County School for Boys 1963-1970, Balliol College, Oxford 1970-1973 and Inns of Court School of Law 1973-1975. Chairman, Shoscombe Village Cricket Club.

SANDER, A.T.
Oriel Chambers (Andrew T. Sander), Liverpool (0151) 236 7191/ 236 4321
Recommended in Commercial (Litigation)

SANDERS, Neil
29 Bedford Row Chambers (Peter Ralls QC), London (020) 7404 1044
Recommended in Family: Child Care including child abduction, Family: Matrimonial Finance
Specialisation: Principal area of practice encompasses all areas of matrimonial finance and the law relating to children including child abduction cases. Other main areas of practice cover work relating to the Inheritance (Provision for Family and Dependents) Act 1975.
Prof. Memberships: Family Law Bar Association.
Career: Called to the Bar 1975 and joined present chambers in 1976.
Personal: Educated at Fettes College, Edinburgh 1966-1971, Pembroke College, Cambridge 1971-1974 and the College of Law 1974-1975. Leisure pursuits include tennis, sailing, skiing, music and theatre. Born 17th April 1953. Lives in London.

SANDS, Philippe
Matrix Chambers (Nicholas Blake QC), London (020) 7404 3447
Recommended in Environment
Specialisation: Barrister specialising in litigation and advisory work for governments, international organisations, corporations and individuals on public international law (including ICJ and Arbitration), EU and public law, environmental law. Cases include: R v Secretary of State ex p (High Court) Hungary/Slovakia (International Court of Justice); Greenpeace and others v European Commission (ECJ); Tradex v Republic of Albania (International Centre for the Settlement of Investment Disputes – arbitration); St Vincent v Guinea (International Tribunal for the Law of the Sea); Swissbourgh Diamond Mines v World Bank (World Bank Inspection Panel); numerous intergovernmental negotiations and consultancies (EC, World Bank, Asia Development Bank).
Career: Qualified 1985, Professor of international law at the University of London (SOAS); global professor of law. New York University. Publications: 'Manual of International Courts and Tribunals' (Butterworths 1999); 'Principles of International Environmental Law', 1995.

SAUNDERS, John QC
4 Fountain Court (Richard Wakerley QC), Birmingham (0121) 236 3476
Recommended in Crime, Licensing
Specialisation: Licensing: Represented a number of breweries in Crown Courts, Divisional Court and Court of Appeal. Cases include: R v Stafford Crown Court ex parte Shipley (CA) and R v Stafford Crown Court ex parte Shipley (Divisional Court). Crime: general crime and fraud.
Career: Magdelen College, Oxford.
Personal: Music. Sailing.

SAUNDERS, Neil
3 Raymond Buildings (Clive Nicholls QC), London (020) 7400 6400
chambers@threeraymond.demon.co.uk
Recommended in Crime
Specialisation: General crime – prosecuting and defending in all criminal courts. Leading and junior work includes murder, manslaughter (R v Hardy – defence for rugby player), robbery, serious assault, sexual offences including children and video evidence, drugs cases and confiscation hearings, police corruption (Donald & Cressey). Appeared in Divisional Court in cases involving drink driving legislation and custody time limits. Serious fraud and commercial crime (including defence of His Honour Judge Gee). Police Disciplinary Tribunals. Licensing appearances involving liquor, public entertainment, betting and gaming at first instance and on appeal.
Prof. Memberships: Bar Council, Criminal Bar Association.
Career: BA (Hons) Law 1982; called to the Bar 1983.

SAUVAIN, Stephen QC
40 King St (Philip Raynor QC), Manchester (0161) 832 9082
Recommended in Planning
Specialisation: Town planning, compulsory purchase, highways, local government, judicial review.
Prof. Memberships: Northern Circuit, Planning and Environment Bar Association.
Career: Called 1977. Queen's Counsel 1995. Appointed Assistant Boundary Commissioner 2000.
Publications: Editor 'Encyclopedia of Highway Law and Practice'. Author of Sauvain's 'Highway Law'.

SAVILL, Mark
Deans Court Chambers (H.K. Goddard QC), Manchester (0161) 214 6000
savill@deanscourt.co.uk
Recommended in Crime
Specialisation: Specialises in all areas of criminal law.
Prof. Memberships: Criminal Bar Association.
Career: Called to the Bar – November 1993 (Inner Temple).
Personal: Born 17th May 1969. Educated at Eton College and Durham University BA (Hons). Interests include sport and cooking.

SAYER, Peter
Gough Square Chambers (Fred Philpott), London (020) 7353 0924
Recommended in Consumer
Specialisation: Consumer Law – consumer credit, credit and charge cards, trades descriptions and fair trading. Also Financial Services Act work and fraud (criminal and civil). Clients include banks, finance houses, card issuers and retailers. Has written 'Credit Cards and the Law' (Fourmat) and articles in legal journals.
Career: Called to the Bar 1975. Formerly in-house Counsel to Access, the Joint Credit Card Company Ltd and American Express Europe Ltd. Part-time Legal Panel Member of the Appeals Service.
Personal: Christ's College, Cambridge. Lives in London and Cornwall.

SAYERS, Michael QC
2 King's Bench Walk (Anthony Donne QC), London (020) 7353 1746
Recommended in Crime

SCANNELL, Rick
Two Garden Court (I. Macdonald QC & O.Davies QC), London (020) 7353 1633
Recommended in Immigration

SCHAFF, Alistair QC
7 King's Bench Walk (Jeremy Cooke QC), London (020) 7910 8300
clerks@7kbw.law.co.uk
Recommended in Arbitration (International), Energy & Natural Resources, Insurance, Shipping
Specialisation: All aspects of international commercial law: specifically, conflict of laws/ jurisdiction disputes, shipping, insurance (marine and non-marine), reinsurance, banking, international sale of goods, oil disputes and commercial negligence. Leading cases: "The Maciej Rataj" [1999] 2 WLR 181 (ECJ; Art.21&22 of Brussels Convention); Effort v Linden [1998] AC 605 (HL; dangerous goods); Royal Boskalis v Mountain [1999] QB. 674 (CA; illegality and marine insurance); MacFarlane / Hegarty v Caledonia [1994] 1 LLR 16; [1997] 2 LLR 259 (CA; Piper Alpha/negligence); Huyton v Peter Cremer [1999] 1 LLR 620 (sale of goods/economic duress); Kingscroft v Nissan (1999 LRLR 603 – reinsurance).
Career: Called to the Bar 1983.
Personal: Born 1959. M.A. (Cantab).

SCHOLZ, Karl
3 Temple Gardens (John Coffey QC), London (020) 7353 3102
Recommended in Consumer
Specialisation: 1. Advising on regulated consumer credit agreements and on matters affecting the enforceability of legal charges on the home; 2. Prosecuting and defending in criminal proceedings brought under consumer protection legislation; frequently instructed by Trading Standards Authorities to appear in the Divisional Court in cases concerning the scope of liability under such legislation – eg in relation to misleading price indications in AG Stanley Ltd v Surrey County Council; MGN Ltd v Ritters and Denard v Burton Retail Ltd; 3. Appearing before the Director General of Fair Trading (fitness to hold a licence).

SCHWARZ, Jonathan
3 Temple Gardens Tax Chambers (Richard Bramwell QC), London (020) 7353 7884
tax@jschwarz.demon.co.uk
Recommended in Tax
Specialisation: International aspects of taxation: double tax relief, tax treaties, e-commerce aspects, transfer pricing, cross-border employment benefits; licensing and joint ventures; group structures, finance and reorganisations; residence and domicile.
Prof. Memberships: Secretary – Revenue Bar Association; Advocate – South Africa; Barrister and Solicitor – Alberta, Canada; Fellow – Chartered Institute of Taxation; International Tax Committees – CIOT and ICAEW Tax Faculty; British Branch Committee of International Fiscal Association.
Publications: Consultant Editor – 'British International Tax Agreements' Croner CCH. EU Correspondent – 'Bulletin for International Fiscal Documentation'.
Personal: BA, LLB (Witwatersrand). LLM (California, Berkeley).

SCOBIE, James
Francis Taylor Building (Nicholas Valios QC), London (020) 7353 7768
Recommended in Crime
Specialisation: Specialist in all areas of criminal law. Exclusively defence work. Acted in high profile cases

including offences of murder, sexual offences and cases involving the supplying and/ or importation of drugs on a large scale. Leading Junior in large scale armed robbery conspiracies, multi-million diversion fraud, VAT fraud involving "outsourcing", multi-handed conspiracy to supply class A drugs.
Career: Educated at Eton College 1974-1978. Exeter University 79-81. Dip Law City Universtiy 1982. Called 1984.
Personal: Secretary Old Etonian Football Club. Interested in playing and watching all sports, especially football and cricket. MCC member since 1979.

SCOTT, Timothy QC
29 Bedford Row Chambers (Peter Ralls QC), London (020) 7404 1044
Recommended in Family: Child Care including child abduction, Family: Matrimonial Finance
Specialisation: Principal area of practice is Family law. Works in all areas, including ancillary relief, child abduction, private and public law children's cases. Involved in a large amount of international work including jursidictional disputes, recognition of foreign decrees and transnational enforcement. Other main area of practice is solicitors' negligence, both arising out of family law matters and generally. Clients include leading Family Law solicitors firms in and outside London. Contributor of articles to Family Law magazine and of chapter on matrimonial law in 'International Tracing of Assets' (FT Law & Tax 1997). Regular speaker at seminars on various family law topics.
Prof. Memberships: Family Law Bar Association, Professional Negligence Bar Association.
Career: Called to the Bar in 1975 and joined present Chambers in 1976. Appointed Q.C. and Assistant Recorder in 1995. Appointed recorder in 1999.
Personal: Queen's Scholar, Westminster School 1962-1966, Open Exhibitioner New College, Oxford 1967-1970. Born 19th July 1949. Lives in London.

SCOTT-MANDERSON, Marcus
4 Paper Buildings (Lionel Swift QC), London (020) 7583 0816
clerks@4pb.com
Recommended in Family: Child Care including child abduction
Specialisation: Family: International child abduction. International child law. Important Cases: Re H (abduction: acquiescence) [1997] 1FLR 9 872 (HL); Re M & J (abduction: International judicial collaboration) Family division: Singer J; 16 August 1999) [2000] FLR (forthcoming); Re P (a child)(mirror orders) [2000] 1 FCR 350.
Prof. Memberships: British Academy of Forensic Science. REUNITE – International Child Abduction Centre – Legal Working Group. Family Law Bar Association.
Career: Harrow School (1969-1974); Oxford University (1975-1979), Boulter Exhibition in Law, BCL, MA (Oxon); Hague Academy of International Law (International Private Law), Netherlands, Dana Fellowship (1980); Glasgow University (Dept of Forensic Medicine). Inns of Court School of Law, Ver Heyden de Lancey Prize in Forensic Medicine; Called, *Lincoln's Inn* 1980, Hardwicke Scholarship, Droop Scholarship.
Publications: Sweet & Maxwell – Practical Research Papers: 'Preventing the Abduction of a Child', 'Applications and Defences under the European Convention'.
Personal: Year of birth: 1956. Town of residence: London. Main leisure Activities, clubs: Landsdowne Club.

SCRIVENER, Anthony QC
2-3 Gray's Inn Square (Anthony Scrivener QC), London (020) 7242 4986
Recommended in Consumer, Crime, Fraud: Criminal
Specialisation: Administrative and public law, consumer law, crime, serious fraud, civil liberties, environmental law, personal injury, local government and City regulatory, monopolies work and food law. Also specialises in appeal work (over 30 appearances in house of Lords). Has appeared in courts Hong Kong, Malaysia, Singapore, Trinidad, Jamaica, British Virgin Islands as well as European Court of Justice. Also called to Bar in Jamaica.
Career: Practice 1961. Took Silk 1975. Chairman of the Bar 1991. Bencher of Lincoln's Inn.
Personal: Leisure: walking, opera, chess.

SEABROOK, Robert QC
1 Crown Office Row (Robert Seabrook QC), London (020) 7797 7500
Recommended in Crime
Specialisation: Extensive experience includes notably professional negligence (medical, solicitors, surveyors, accountants), civil jury actions, matrimonial finance and property, commercial fraud and major crimes. Cases include Al Kandari v Brown [1987], Smith v Bush [1990], Baker v Kaye (1997), Kapkunde v Abbey National Building Society (1998), Professor Nicolaides (GMC) (1998) John Studd (GMC) 1996, Rodney Ledward (GMC) 1999, Lady Foster v H M Customs and Excise [1993], Silcott v Metropolitan Police Commissioner [1996], Waters v Metropolitan Police Commissioner (1997), Farah v Metropolitan Police Commissioner (1998), HRH The Prince of Wales (Royal Divorce) (1996), Tombolis [1991], Flick [re-appeal 1995] and the Charing Cross Lynn Rogers murder case [1992].
Career: Called to Bar in 1964. Took silk in 1983. Recorder since 1985. Deputy High Court Judge since 1991. Leader of the South Eastern Circuit 1989-1992. Chairman of the Bar, 1994.
Personal: Educated at St Georges's College, Harare, Zimbabwe and University College, London (LL.B). Member of the court of the University of Sussex 1988-93. Chairman of the Governors of Brighton College since 1998. Interests include travel, listening to music and wine. Lives in London and Brighton.

SEARS, David
4 Pump Court (Bruce Mauleverer QC), London (020) 7353 2656
Recommended in Construction
Specialisation: Building/Civil Engineering disputes and professional negligence – the latter including not only building professionals (engineers, quantity surveyors and architects) but also solicitors, accountants and surveyors.
Prof. Memberships: TEC BAR, Professional Negligence Bar Association, London Common Law and Commercial Bar Association, COMBAR.
Career: 1979 to 1983: Civil Servant – Ministry of Defence; 1984 to date in practice at Bar.
Personal: Education: Trinity College, Oxford (MA Oxon). Leisure interests: sailing, flying, motorcycling, travelling and being at home in the country. Family: married with two children.

SEDDON, Duran
Two Garden Court (I. Macdonald QC & O.Davies QC), London (020) 7353 1633
Recommended in Immigration

SEED, Nigel QC
3 Paper Buildings (Michael Parroy QC), London (020) 7583 8055
Recommended in Church: Church of England

SEGAL, Oliver
Old Square Chambers (John Hendy QC), London (020) 7269 0300
Recommended in Employment
Specialisation: Practice: Employment; Commercial Agency; Commercial sale of Goods. Cases: RMT v LUL [1998] 1RLR 636, CA; BBC v Farnworth [1998] ICR 1116, EAT; Moore v Piretta PTA Ltd [1999] 1 ALL ER 174, H.Ct.; Newbold & Smith v Leicester City Council (unrep), 12/7/1999, CA.
Prof. Memberships: E.L.B.A.
Career: Corpus Christi College, Oxford (1981-1985). School Oriental & African Studies, University. London (1985-1986). Called 1992, Middle Temple.
Personal: Expert Bridge player and writer.

SEITLER, Jonathan
Wilberforce Chambers (Edward Nugee QC), London (020) 7306 0102
Recommended in Property Litigation
Specialisation: Property litigation and associated professional negligence including: landlord and tenant, bank securitisation and negligence claims against solicitors and valuers. Acts for both landlords and tenants, banks and their customers and, in professional negligence actions, plaintiffs and insurers.
Prof. Memberships: Professional Negligence Bar Association, COMBAR.
Career: Called to the Bar 1985
Publications: Co-author of 'Property Finance Negligence: Claims Against Solicitors and Valuers' (Sweet & Maxwell) and the new looseleaf 'Commercial Property Disputes' (Sweet & Maxwell). Lectures widely both at conferences and in-house.
Personal: Educated Pembroke College, Oxford, City University (Dip. Law).

SELVARATNAM, Vasanti
4 Field Court (Steven Gee QC), London (020) 7440 6900
Recommended in Shipping
Specialisation: All aspects of international commercial and shipping law, including admiralty. Clients include the major P & I clubs, shipowners, charterers and salvors.
Prof. Memberships: COMBAR; European Bar Association; LMAA; BMLA.
Career: Called to the Bar 1983: joined current chambers (formerly located at Queen Elizabeth Building) in 1985. Recorder 2000.
Personal: Born 9.4.61. Educated at St. Augustine's Priory, Ealing and King's College, London (LL.B (Hons.) 1982, LL.M (1st) 1984).

SEMKEN, Christopher
1 New Square (Eben Hamilton QC), London (020) 7405 0884
Recommended in Traditional Chancery
Specialisation: General Chancery, especially property including landord and tenant, partnership, wills and trusts, professional negligence in such areas, both for and against solicitors, barristers, and surveyors.
Prof. Memberships: Chancery Bar Association, Professional Negligence Bar Association.
Personal: MA Oxon 1976, called to the Bar 1977, in practice at 1 New Square, Lincoln's Inn 1978 to date.

SENDALL, Antony
Littleton Chambers (Michel Kallipetis QC), London (020) 7797 8600
antony@sendall.co.uk
Recommended in Employment
Specialisation: Principal areas of practice are: Employment; all areas including: wrongful/unfair dismissal, redundancy, transfer of undertakings, discrimination, equal pay, working time, restraint of trade, industrial disputes; Sports Law; mostly employment and disciplinary issues; Professional Indemnity; mostly solicitors and surveyors; Commercial; all forms of commercial disputes, including interim injunctions and arbitrations.
Prof. Memberships: Employment Law Bar Association, Employment Lawyers Association, Industrial Law Society, Bar Sports Law Group, Professional Negli-

gence Bar Association, London Commercial and Common Law Bar Association, chambers member of COMBAR.
Career: Called to the Bar 1984.
Personal: Born: 1 July 1961. Educated: Cambridge University (Law: First Class Honours). Interests: Photography, cooking, amateur dramatics, running half-marathons.

SETRIGHT, Henry
Renaissance Chambers (Brian Jubb & Henry Setright), London (020) 7404 1111
Recommended in Family: Child Care including child abduction

SEYS LLEWELLYN, Anthony
Farrar's Building (John Leighton Williams QC), London (020) 7583 9241
Recommended in Personal Injury
Specialisation: General common law practice, including personal injury, medical negligence, professional negligence, contract and insurance.
Career: Called 1972. Joined chambers 1974. Appointed Recorder 1990.
Personal: King's School, Chester 1957-1967; Jesus College, Oxford 1967-1971 (MA and BCL). Fluent in French; working knowledge of German. Assistant Boundary Commissioner. Leisure pursuits include music, sport and art. Born 24th April 1949. Lives in Buckinghamshire.

SHAH, Akhil
Fountain Court (Anthony Boswood QC), London (020) 7583 3335
Recommended in Aviation
Specialisation: General commercial work specialising in: carriage by air of goods and passengers; aircraft insurance disputes; air disasters – product liability; aviation finance and operating lease disputes; conditions of carriage; jurisdiction; regulatory work – operators' licences. Counsel in Airbus Industrie G.I.E v Patel [1999] 1 AC 119: (Product liability; Jurisdiction; anti-suit injunction) House of Lords. Counsel in Western Digital v British Airways [1999] 2 Lloyds 380; (Warsaw Convention : Article 18 : right of owner to sue for loss of goods). Counsel in First Security National Bank v Air Gabon [1999] 2 Lloyds 380 (Aircraft lease, delivery of aircraft); Counsel in Messier Dowty Ltd v Airbus Industrie G.I.E and another [2000] 1 All ER (comm) 101 (stay of proceedings; product design)
Prof. Memberships: COMBAR.

SHANT, Nirmal K.
No.1 High Pavement (John B. Milmo QC), Nottingham (0115) 941 8218
Recommended in Crime
Specialisation: Specialises in criminal law. Most cases are of considerable gravity. Deals with offences of serious violence including murder and manslaughter, sexual offences and drugs matters. Her practice also includes some fraud cases.
Prof. Memberships: Member of the Criminal Justice Strategy Committee, Bar Human Rights Committee and part of the Bar disciplinary panel.
Career: Called in 1984. Has specialised in criminal law for over a decade. Has recently been appointed Recorder.
Personal: Leicester University graduate. Hobbies include reading, swimming and playing squash.

SHARP, Christopher QC
St John's Chambers (Christopher Sharp QC), Bristol (0117) 921 3456
clerks@stjohnschambers.co.uk
Recommended in Family/Matrimonial, Personal Injury
Specialisation: Matrimonial Finance. Personal Injury. Professional negligence in these fields.
Prof. Memberships: FLBA. PIBA.
Career: MA Oxon. Called tothe Bar 1975; Silk 1999. Head of Chambers.

SHARP, Victoria
1 Brick Court (Richard Rampton QC), London (020) 7353 8845
vs@1brickcourt.co.uk
Recommended in Defamation
Specialisation: Defamation, confidence, contempt of court and media related law generally. Cases include David Irving v Guardian Newspapers Ltd, Marks & Spencer v Granada, Branson v Snowden and GTECH, Bennett v Guardian Newspapers Ltd, Sugar v Venables, Hamilton/Greer v Guardian Newspapers Ltd, Souness v MGN, HRH Princess of Wales v MGN, Angelsea v HTV, Rt Hon Michael Foot v Times Newspapers, Maxwell v Bower, Lord Aldington v Tolstoy.
Prof. Memberships: London Commercial and Common Bar Association.
Career: North London Collegiate School, University of Bristol (1978). Called to the Bar 1979. Member of the Supreme Court Committee on Defamation (the Neill Committee). Recorder (South Eastern Circuit).

SHARPE, Thomas QC
One Essex Court (Lord Grabiner QC), London (020) 7583 2000
Recommended in Competition/Anti-trust
Specialisation: Principal areas of practice are European Community and UK competition law (Competition Commission/ OFT, EC Commission and European Court). Cases representing British Gas, British Telecom, British Sugar, Eurostar. Extensive telecommunications practice in UK and Hong Kong. Wide range of Art 81, 82 in High Court and general EC law cases in the European Court of Justice. Also judicial review. Leading cases include Eurostar (in European Court), Clear Communications Ltd v New Zealand Telecommunications (in Privy Council) on interconnection; Shearson Lehman v Maclaine Watson; An Bord Bainne v. Milk Marketing Board; R v MAFF exp. Fedesa; Hapkins v National Power; Contributor to Halsbury (European Community Law) and author of monographs and articles on UK and EEC competition law and utility regulation in Law Quarterly Review, European Law Review etc. Formerly Fellow in Law, Nuffield College, Oxford.
Career: Called to the Bar in 1976. Of counsel to Gibson, Dunn & Crutcher (US law firm) 1984-88; on board of NERA, 1982-88 and executive director, Institute for Fiscal Studies, 1981-87. Commenced practise in 1987. Took silk in 1994.
Personal: Educated at Trinity Hall, Cambridge. Degrees in Economics and in Law.

SHARPSTON, Eleanor QC
4 Paper Buildings (Jean Ritchie QC), London (020) 7353 3366
Recommended in Competition/Anti-trust
Specialisation: All areas of EC law, from employment and immigration to agriculture, free movement of goods and intellectual property; also ECHR work. Major recent cases include 'Kalanke' (positive discrimination), 'Atlanta' (interim relief), the UK challenge to the 'Working Time Directive', 'Fantask' (time limits after 'Emmott'), 'Factortame' (damages action) and Laskey, Brown and Jaggard v UK ("Spanner": ECtHR).
Prof. Memberships: UKAEL, BEG, COMBAR; member of Irish Bar; Fellow, King's College Cambridge.
Career: Undergraduate degree at King's College, Cambridge (economics and law); research at Corpus Christi College, Oxford. Private practice in Brussels chambers 1981-1987. Référendaire (legal secretary) at Court of Justice of the EC 1987-1990. Since 1990, in practice at the Bar concurrently with academic appointments at UCL (1990-1992) and Cambridge (1992-).

SHAW, Antony QC
18 Red Lion Court (Anthony Arlidge QC), London (020) 7520 6000
Recommended in Crime, Fraud: Criminal
Specialisation: General crime and fraud, including SFO, VAT, corporate, mortgage, ECGD, tax, charity and other frauds. Major SFO cases include Guinness, Polly Peck, Eagle Trust, BCCI, Butte Mining, Alpine, Alliance.
Prof. Memberships: Criminal Bar Association.
Career: Major History Scholar, Trinity College, Oxford: 1967-1970. Astbury Scholar, Middle Temple: 1976. QC: 1994. Assistant Recorder: 1998. Co-editor Archbold, 'Criminal Pleadings and Practice': 1991 to date.
Personal: Governor, International Students House.

SHAW, Geoffrey QC
1 Brick Court (Richard Rampton QC), London (020) 7353 8845
Recommended in Defamation
Specialisation: Defamation.
Prof. Memberships: Gray's Inn
Career: Took Silk, 1991. Trials include: unification church case, Gee v BBC, Archer v Star, Rantzen v People, Upjohn v Oswald; Ashby v Sunday Times. Reported cases include: Lucas-Box 1986 1 WLR 147; Khashoggi 1986 1 WLR 1412; Bobolas 1987 1 WLR 1101; AL-Fayed 1988 1 WLR 1412; Tebbitt 1989 1 WLR 640; Sutcliffe 1991 1 QB 153; Kingshott 1991 1 QB 88; Rantzen 1994 QB 670; Condliffe 1996 1 WLR 753; Evans 1996 EMLR 429; Geenty 1998 EMLR 524; S v Newham 1998 EMLR 583.

SHAW, Howard
29 Bedford Row Chambers (Peter Ralls QC), London (020) 7404 1044
Recommended in Clinical Negligence, Family: Matrimonial Finance
Specialisation: Professional negligence (especially clinical negligence), family law (particularly finance).
Prof. Memberships: Professional Negligence Bar Association Personal Injury Bar Association Family Law Bar Association.
Career: Important cases include: C v C (Financial Provision: Personal Damages) (1995), Pereira v Keleman (1995), R v R (Divorce: Stay of Proceedings) (1994), London Borough of Sutton v Davis (Costs) (No 2) (1994) C v C (Wasted Costs Order) (1994), London Borough of Sutton v Davies (1994), L v L (Minors) (Separate Representation), Edmonds v Edmonds (1990), Newton v Newton (1990), B v B (Financial Provision) (1987), Barder v Barder (Caluori Intervening) (1987), RE M (Minors) (confidential documents), (1987), Singer (Formerly Sharegin) v Sharegin (1984), Norman v Norman (1983). Brava v. Spring (1994) 5MR120. Duties of a G.P. Dobbie v. Medway Health Auth. (1992) 3MR 217. Limitation Period in Med. Neg. Cases.
Personal: LL.B (Hons) Called 1973 South Eastern Circuit.

SHAW, Mark
Blackstone Chambers (P Baxendale QC and C Flint QC), London (020) 7583 1770
markshaw@blackstonechambers.com
Recommended in Administrative & Public Law: General, Immigration
Specialisation: Principal area of practice is administrative/public law, with an emphasis on judicial review, human rights, immigration and nationality, local government, regulatory/disciplinary proceedings, environment, prisons, social security, health, social services and EU law. Publications include 'Halsbury's Laws of England' (4th Edn) volume on Immigration and Nationality (Butterworths, 1992), 'The Primary Purpose Rule: A Rule With No Purpose', co-author, (Justice, 1993) and 'Human Rights Law and Practice',

contributor, (Butterworths, 1999). Member of the Advisory Board of, and contributor to, 'JR'. Notable Cases include: R v SSHD ex parte Thompson and Venables [1998] AC 407 (HL) and T and V v UK 16th December 1999 (ECtHR); R v SSHD ex parte Myra Hindley [2000] 2 WLR 730 (HL); R v SSHD, ex parte Al-Fayed [1998] 1 WLR 763 (CA); Reeves v Metropolitan Police Commissioner [1999] 3 WLR 363 (HL); R v DPP, ex parte Duckenfield [2000] 1 WLR 55 (DC); SSSS v Harmon, Carter and Cocks [1998] 2 FLR 598 (CA); R v SSHD, ex parte Robinson [1998] QB 929 (CA); R v SSHD, ex parte Rahman [1998] QB 136 (CA); R v SSSS, ex parte West [1999] 1 FLR 1233 (CA); R v SSHD, ex parte Mbanja [1999] Imm AR 63 (QBD) and 508 (CA); R v SSSS, ex parte W [1999] 2 FLR 604 (QBD); Adan v SSHD [1999] 1 AC 293 (HL); Laskey, Jaggard and Brown v UK [1997] 24 EHRR 39 (ECtHR); A v UK (1999) 27 EHRR 611 (ECtHR); Condron v UK 2nd May 2000 (ECtHR) and R v DETR, ex parte First Corporate Shipping (QBD and ECJ, judgment pending).
Prof. Memberships: Administrative Law Bar Association, Immigration Law Practitioners' Association, Justice, Bar Golfing Society (Honorary Secretary).
Career: Member of Borough Solicitor's Department, Bournemouth Borough Council 1985-87. Stagiaire at the European Parliament (Human Rights Unit) 1986. Called to the Bar 1987 and joined current chambers in 1988. Pegasus scholarship to Melbourne law firm 1991. Junior Counsel to the Crown (Common Law) (the 'A' list) since 1995. Member of the Attorney General's panel of counsel appointed to act for the Government and as a Special Advocate for immigrants before the Special Immigration Appeals Commission (dealing with national security immigration cases)
Personal: Educated at Durham University (BA) and Cambridge University (LL.M). Born 6th June 1962.

SHEA, Caroline
Falcon Chambers (Jonathan Gaunt QC & Kim Lewison QC), London (020) 7353 2484
shea@falcon-chambers.com
Recommended in Agriculture, Property Litigation
Specialisation: Landlord and tenant, commercial, residential, agricultural, property litigation.
Prof. Memberships: Chancery Bar Association. Contributor of legal articles to Property Week.
Career: MA Cantab. Diploma in Law (City University). Called to Bar 1994. Joined Falcon Chambers 1995. Previously a mangement consultant.

SHEKERDEMIAN, Marcia
11 Stone Buildings (Murray Rosen QC), London (020) 7831 6381
Recommended in Company, Insolvency/Corporate Recovery

SHELDON, Richard QC
3-4 South Square (Michael Crystal QC), London (020) 7696 9900
Recommended in Insolvency/Corporate Recovery
Specialisation: Banking, bank securities, bankruptcy and insolvency. Corporate insolvency, general commercial and fraud (civil), company law, mergers, acquisitions and disposal of companies, financial services, international trade, finance of international trade, mortgages, partnership, solicitors' negligence, accountants' negligence. Contributed to Halsbury's Laws (4th ed vol 7).
Prof. Memberships: Chancery Bar Association, Commercial Bar Association.
Career: Called to the Bar 1979. Queens Counsel 1996. Cambridge MA.

SHELTON, Gordon E.
Broadway House (J. Graham K. Hyland QC), Bradford (01274) 722560
Recommended in Family/Matrimonial
Specialisation: Principal area of practice family law.
Prof. Memberships: Family Law Bar Association.
Career: Educated Ashville College, Harrogate. Leicester University. Called 1981.

SHEPHERD, Nigel
2 Paper Buildings (Desmond de Silva QC), London (020) 7556 5500
Recommended in Crime

SHEPHERD, Philip
24 Old Buildings (Martin Mann QC & Alan Steinfeld QC), London (020) 7404 0946
Recommended in Aviation

SHER, Jules QC
Wilberforce Chambers (Edward Nugee QC), London (020) 7306 0102
Recommended in Commercial Chancery, Energy & Natural Resources, Pensions, Traditional Chancery
Specialisation: Chancery & Commercial Litigation and Advice. Covers the wide range of work comprised in a modern commercial chancery practice including Lloyd's litigation and advice, North Sea Oil and Gas tract participation disputes (acting for British Gas and major oil companies in litigation in the Commercial Court and Chancery Division), Trust litigation in the UK and abroad (Singapore, Cayman Islands, Bahamas, Hong Kong), Trust aspects of takeovers (acted in Glaxo takeover of Wellcome and Granada takeover of Forte and Wolverhampton and Dudley take over of Mansfield Brewery), Professional Negligence (Accountants, Solicitors), Pensions litigation (Imperial Group v Imperial Tobacco, London Regional Transport Pension Fund Trustee Co. Ltd v Hatt, MacDonald v Horn and the BT Pension Schemes Trust).
Career: B.Comm., LL.B. (Rand), B.C.L. (Oxon).Called to the Bar of England and Wales in 1968. Took Silk 1981. Recorder. Advocate of the Supreme Court of South Africa; Deputy High Court Judge (Commercial Court and Chancery Division); Member of the Commercial Bar Association & Chancery Bar Association.

SHERBORNE, David
5 Raymond Buildings (Patrick Milmo QC), London (020) 7242 2902
Recommended in Defamation

SHERIDAN, Maurice
Matrix Chambers (Nicholas Blake QC), London (020) 7404 3447
Recommended in Environment
Specialisation: EC environmental, especially regarding direct effect of Directives; nuisance and negligence, including regarding professional negligence; waste management.
Prof. Memberships: Bar European Group; British Italian Law Association; British Bulgarian Law Association; COMBAR.
Career: Sorbonne 1980; Stage with EC Commission 1985; LLB Bristol; LLM (International law) Cantab 1985-96; assisting in approximation programmes regarding EC environmental Acquis in Central and Eastern Europe – 1992 to date.
Personal: Travelling, theatre, cinema, contemporary dance.

SHIELDS, Thomas QC
1 Brick Court (Richard Rampton QC), London (020) 7353 8845
Recommended in Defamation

SHIPLEY, Graham
19 Old Buildings (Alastair Wilson QC), London (020) 7405 2001
Recommended in Intellectual Property
Specialisation: Principal area of practice encompasses intellectual property and technology work, including electronic and computer cases and EC aspects. Regular seminar speaker, and has appeared on radio and television ('Science Now') broadcasts.
Prof. Memberships: Intellectual Property Bar Association, Chancery Bar Association.
Career: Called to the Bar 1973 and joined present chambers in 1975, when located at Pump Court.
Personal: Educated at King's School, Chester 1959-1966, Trinity College, Cambridge 1966-1971 (B.A. Mathematics 1969, Diploma in Computer Science, Distinction 1970) and Inns of Court School of Law 1971-1973. Former Director of 'Trinity 69 Foundation' charity. Leisure pursuits include electronics, house restoring, woodwork, Japanese cookery and motor cycle riding. Born 10th January 1948. Lives in London.

SHIPLEY, Jane
No.6 (Shaun Spencer QC), Leeds (0113) 245 9763
Recommended in Family/Matrimonial

SHIPWRIGHT, Adrian J.
Pump Court Tax Chambers (Andrew Thornhill QC), London (020) 7414 8080
Recommended in Tax
Specialisation: All tax related matters including dispute resolution and litigation particularly corporate matters such as reorganisations, financings and share purchases and sales including takeovers, trust matters, land development, indirect taxation and the taxation of intellectual property. Publications include Trusts and UK Tax (Key Haven), UK Taxation Intellectual Property (Sweet & Maxwell) and Tax Avoidance and the Law (Editor for SPTL).
Prof. Memberships: Lincoln's Inn, Institute of Indirect Taxation, VAT Practitioners Group, STEP [FRSA]. Member of the Trust Law Committee chaired by Sir John Vinelott.
Career: Admitted as a solicitor 1976, called to the Bar 1993. Visiting Professor, King's College London 1996-. Professor of Business Law and Director of the Tax Research Unit, King's College, London 1992-1996. Tax Partner *SJ Berwin & Co* 1987-1992 (Consultant till 1993). Tax partner *Denton Hall* 1982-1987. Official Student (Fellow) and Tutor in Law, Christ Church, Oxford and Lecturer in Law (CUF), Oxford University 1977-1982. Member of the Tax Department and Articles *Linklaters & Paines* 1974-1977. Education: BA (1972), BCL (1973), MA (1977), Christ Church, Oxford. King Edward VI School, Southampton (Governor till 1995).

SHORROCK, Michael QC
Peel Court Chambers (Michael Shorrock QC), Manchester (0161) 832 3791
Recommended in Crime
Specialisation: Crime, commercial fraud, clinical negligence. Reported cases include R v Doheny Adams CA. (leading case on DNA) and R v Winston Brown HL Disclosure.
Prof. Memberships: C.B.A.
Career: Clifton College. Pembroke, Cambridge. Northern Circuit, Junior of Circuit. Secretary Executive Committee Members of C.I.C.B. & C.I.C.A.P., Bencher Inner Temple.
Personal: Married with two daughters. Gardening, walking, opera, cinema, enjoying oneself.

SILSOE, Lord QC
2 Mitre Court Buildings (Michael FitzGerald QC), London (020) 7583 1380
Recommended in Planning
Specialisation: Main areas of practice include town & country planning, enviromental law, compulsory purchase and compensation, rating and the council tax, utilities and infrastructure, local government, public and administrative law, and Transport and Works Act orders. Editor of Ryde 11th, 12th and 13th Editions.
Prof. Memberships: Planning and Environment Bar Association.
Career: Called to the Bar in 1955. Joined current chambers in 1956. Appointed QC in 1972.
Personal: Educated at Winchester College, Christ Church, Oxford and Columbia University (New York).

SILVERLEAF, Michael QC
11 South Square (Christopher Floyd QC), London (020) 7405 1222
Recommended in Information Technology, Intellectual Property, Media & Entertainment
Specialisation: Intellectual property, computer law, entertainment and media, disputes with high technical content and related EC and domestic competition law.
Prof. Memberships: IP Association, Chancery Bar Association.
Career: Member of Gray's Inn. Called 1980. Junior Counsel to the Treasury in Patent Matters 1991-1996. QC 1996.
Personal: Publications: 'Passing off Law and Practice' (Butterworths), 'Butterworths Patent Litigation' (contributor). Attended King's College School, Wimbledon, Imperial College (BSc, Physics).

SIMLER, Ingrid
Devereux Chambers (Jeffrey Burke QC), London (020) 7353 7534
simler@devchambers.co.uk
Recommended in Employment
Specialisation: Principal area of practice is employment, encompassing all areas of individual and collective employment law, including discrimination, restraint of trade and business transfers. Also handles general commercial work, professional negligence and personal injury work. Contributor to 'Tolleys' Employment Law'. Co-author of Butterworths 'Discrimination Law' (published Autumn 1999). Member of The Supplementary Panel of Treasury Counsel (Common Law).
Prof. Memberships: Secretary of Employment Law Bar Association, member of Employment Lawyers Association, Commercial Law Bar Association, Administrative Law Bar Association.
Career: Called to the Bar 1987.
Personal: Educated at Cambridge University 1982-85 (MA) and University of Amsterdam 1985-86 (Diploma in European law). Born 17th September 1963.

SIMMONDS, Andrew QC
5 Stone Buildings (Henry Harrod), London (020) 7242 6201
Recommended in Pensions, Professional Negligence, Traditional Chancery
Specialisation: Specialises in professional negligence litigation (other than medical) and contentious pensions work. In the former field, has particular experience of claims against solicitors, barristers and accountants but has also acted in claims against actuaries, insurance brokers, fund managers and others. Pensions experience covers all manner of disputes involving employers, trustees and members, claims against pensions professionals and complaints to the Pensions Ombudsman. Recent cases include various aspects of the Maxwell litigation; National Power v Feldon [1997] PLR 157; ITN v Ward [1997] PLR 131; MMI v Harrop [1998] PLR 149; Wakelin v Read [1998] PLR 337; University of Nottingham v Eyett (Nos 1 and 2) [1999] 2 AER 437, 445; Spooner v BT [2000] PLR 65.
Prof. Memberships: Member of the Association of Pension Lawyers, the Professional Negligence Bar Association and the Pension Litigation Court Users' Committee chaired by Lloyd J.
Career: Called 1980. Silk 1999.

SINCLAIR, Fiona
Four New Square (Justin Fenwick QC), London (020) 7822 2000
f.sinclair@4newsquare.com
Recommended in Professional Negligence
Specialisation: Practice: professional negligence in relation to construction (architects, engineers, quantity surveyors), finance (accountants, solicitors, insurance brokers, financial advisers) and property (solicitors and surveyors); insurance and reinsurance contracts; construction law; financial services law. Editor of 'Jackson and Powell on Professional Negligence' (Chapter 2, Architects and Engineers).
Prof. Memberships: Professional Negligence Bar Association, Official Referees' Bar Association, Society of Construction Law.
Career: Called 1989.
Personal: Born 1963. Educated at Jesus College, Cambridge (B.A. in Philosophy and Law, 1983-87; LL.M, 1987-88). Interests: mountaineering, skiing, flying.

SINGH, Kuldip QC
5 Paper Buildings (Godfrey Carey QC & Jonathan Caplan QC), London (020) 7583 6117
Recommended in Fraud: Criminal, Sport

SINGH, Rabinder
Matrix Chambers (Nicholas Blake QC), London (020) 7404 3447
Recommended in Administrative & Public Law: General, Human Rights (Civil Liberties), Planning, Tax
Specialisation: All aspects of public law, employment law and European Community and human rights law.
Prof. Memberships: Administrative Law Bar Association (Treasurer), Planning and Environment Bar Association, Employment Law Bar Association; Bar European Group.
Career: Called:1989. Appointed to B panel of junior counsel to the Crown: 1998. Additional Junior Counsel to the Inland Revenue: 1997.
Personal: B.A. (Law) 1985: Trinity College, Cambridge LL.M. 1986: University of California, Berkeley. Visiting fellow, Queen Mary and Westfield College, London since 1995.

SINGLETON, Barry QC
One King's Bench Walk (Anthony Hacking QC), London (020) 7936 1500
Recommended in Family: Matrimonial Finance

SINGLETON, Sarah
28 St. John St (Clement Goldstone QC), Manchester (0161) 834 8418
Recommended in Family/Matrimonial

SLADE, Elizabeth QC
11 King's Bench Walk (Eldred Tabachnik QC and James Goudie QC), London (020) 7632 8500
Recommended in Employment
Specialisation: Specialises in all aspects of employment law with particular emphasis on European aspects of employment law, transfer of undertakings, sex and race discrimination, equal pay, employment aspects of pensions. Leading cases include: Westminster City Council v Pensions Ombudsman and Haywood, Crees v The Royal London Insurance Society, London Regional Transport v Nagarajan, Foster & Others v British Gas, Reed Executive plc v Sommers, Newns v British Airways plc.
Prof. Memberships: Employment Law Bar Association, Employment Lawyers Association, ALBA; Bar European Group.
Career: Called to the Bar in 1972; original author 'Tolley's Employment Handbook'; Recorder 1998; Deputy High Court Judge 1998-; Part-time judge of the Employment Appeal Tribunal 2000-; 1990 Bencher of the Inner Temple; 1992 Appointed QC; 1994-98 Master of the Staff, Inner Temple; Chair of Employment Law Bar Association 1995-97; Hon Vice President 1998-; Chairman Sex Discrimination Committee, Bar Council 2000; Trustee, Free Representation Unit; Member of the Administrative Tribunal of the Bank for International Settlements.
Personal: Education: Lady Margaret Hall, Oxford. Exhibitioner.

SLATER, John QC
Crown Office Chambers (Michael Spencer QC & Christopher Purchas QC), London (020) 7797 8100
Recommended in Construction, Professional Negligence

SLOAN, Paul
Trinity Chambers (A.T. Hedworth QC), Newcastle upon Tyne (0191) 232 1927
info@trinitychambers.co.uk
Recommended in Licensing
Specialisation: Crime (prosecution and defence), licensing (liquor and public entertainment), firearms and shotguns (all aspects), police disciplinary tribunals (presenting cases for and against police officers and acting as legal advisor to Chief Constables).
Prof. Memberships: Inner Temple. North Eastern Circuit. Criminal Bar Association. Bar representative on Area Criminal Justice Strategy Committee. North Eastern Bar Press Office spokesman.
Career: LL.B (Lond.) Call 1981. Recorder 2000.

SLOMNICKA, Barbara
14 Gray's Inn Square (Joanna Dodson QC), London (020) 7242 0858
Recommended in Family: Child Care including child abduction

SMALLWOOD, Anne
5 Fountain Court (Anthony Barker QC), Birmingham (0121) 606 0500
Recommended in Family/Matrimonial

SMITH, Andrew QC
Fountain Court (Anthony Boswood QC), London (020) 7583 3335
Recommended in Arbitration (International), Information Technology

SMITH, Julia
Gough Square Chambers (Fred Philpott), London (020) 7353 0924
Recommended in Consumer
Specialisation: Consumer Law – in particular consumer credit and mortgage actions (eg First National Bank v Syed [1991] 2 All ER 250, Jarrett v Barclays Bank [1997] 2 All ER 484 and Kenyon-Brown v Desmond Banks [2000] Lloyd's Rep. Banks) including consumer credit drafting, extortionate credit bargains, and licensing. Clients include banks, finance houses, leasing companies and retailers.
Prof. Memberships: London Common Law and Commercial Bar Association.
Career: Called to the Bar 1988
Personal: Cheltenham Ladies College and Liverpool University.

SMITH, Nicholas G
Queen Square Chambers (T. Alun Jenkins QC), Bristol (0117) 921 1966
ngs@qs-c.co.uk
Recommended in Employment
Specialisation: Exclusively in employment law, including sporting contracts clients include large corporations, individuals, trade associations, trade unions, professional sporting associations, the Police force, central and local Government. Extensive experience in tribunal litigation at first instance and on appeal, in addition to litigating restructure covenant actions in the courts. Increasingly involved in arbitration of employment/sporting disputes. Lectured ELA at expert level and regular provider of seminars and training. CPD accredited.
Prof. Memberships: Member Employment Lawyers Association, Lincolns Inn
Career: Called 1990, joined present set 1998.
Publications: ELA Bulletin.
Personal: Born 1965, Married 3 young children. Interests: Rugby Union, motorsport, wine.

SMITH, Peter QC
40 King St (Philip Raynor QC), Manchester (0161) 832 9082
Recommended in Chancery, Commercial (Litigation), Insolvency/Corporate Recovery, Property Litigation
Specialisation: Insolvency, landlord and tenant, professional negligence. Recent cases: Re: Exchange Travel [1996] BCLC 524, Norglen v Reeds Rains [1998] HL 1 AER 218; CIS v Argyll Stores, HL [1997]; Medforth v Blake [1999] 3 All ER 97 CA; Allen v Rochdale BC [1999] 3 All ER 443 CA.
Prof. Memberships: Professional Negligence Bar Association, Northern Chancery Bar Association, Chancery Bar Association.
Career: Called to Bar in 1975. Lecturer at Manchester University 1977-1983. Northern Circuit 1979-1996. Took Silk in 1994. Assistant Recorder 1994. Deputy High Court Judge 1996.

SMITH, Richard
Guildhall Chambers (Adrian Palmer QC), Bristol (0117) 927 3366
Recommended in Crime

SMITH, Robert QC
Park Court Chambers (James Stewart QC Robert Smith QC), Leeds (0113) 243 3277
Recommended in Crime
Specialisation: A balanced practice involving prosecution and defence work (principally homicide, commercial fraud and specialist issues such as corporate manslaughter, data protection, etc). Defence instructions include a large proportion of professional defendants such as medical practitioners, accountants and police officers. Has a particular interest in medico-legal matters and scientific evidence. Recent cases of importance: Attorney General's Reference (No 3 of 1994): Criminal Liability for pre-natal injuries: Court of Appeal Criminal Division: [1996] 2WLR 412 / House of Lords: [1998] AC 245; R v Beedie: Court of Appeal Criminal Division: The Double Jeopardy Rule in Criminal Proceedings; [1997] 2 Cr.App.R. 167; R v Woolin: Foresight of consequences as proof of intent in murder: House of Lords [1998] 3 WLR 382.
Prof. Memberships: Member of the International Bar Association, Personal Injuries Bar Association and Bar European Group.
Career: Common Law Practitioner specialising in criminal and civil litigation (principally personal injury and medical and professional negligence) from commencing practice in Leeds in 1971. Appointed Queen's Counsel and a Recorder in 1986. Served for three years as a Member of the Criminal Injuries Compensation Board. Joined London chambers at 3 Serjeants' Inn [Adrian Whitfield QC] as a door tenant in 1994.

SMITH, Roger QC
No.6 Fountain Court (Roger Smith QC), Birmingham (0121) 233 3282
Recommended in Crime

SMITH, Shaun
No.1 High Pavement (John B. Milmo QC), Nottingham (0115) 941 8218
Recommended in Crime

SMITH, Stephen QC
12 New Square (John Mowbray QC), London (020) 7419 1212
Recommended in Civil Fraud, Commercial (Litigation), Commercial Chancery, Company
Specialisation: Complex and heavy commercial litigation, often with a Chancery or jurisdictional element (especially issues arising under the Brussels/ Lugano convention) and involving restraints on disposals of assets; also professional negligence, civil fraud, insurance, property disputes and insolvency. Conducted numerous witness examinations, including several in the USA and in New Zealand. Called to the Bar of the Eastern Caribbean States Supreme Court and conducted several hearings on Tortola BVI at first instance (including at trial) and on appeal to the Court of Appeal of the Eastern Caribbean, and appeared on a further appeal to the Privy Council. Previous cases: Derby v Weldon (acted for Salomon Inc.); DSQ Property Company (formerly DeLorean Motor Company) v Lotus Cars (acted for John Z. DeLorean); Morris v Mahfouz (BCCI; acted for Khalid Bin Mahfouz and others); FTIT Ltd. v Morgan Stanley and Coopers & Lybrand (Maxwell; acted for liquidators (Deloitte Touche) appointed by Swiss Bank Corporation); Senate Electrical Wholesalers v Alcatel Submarines Networks (acted for Northern Telecom); Village Cay Marina v Acland (Privy Council decision about share registration and receivership in the BVI); Trustor v Moyne, Trustor v Smallbone (acted for Trustor); FBME v Hadkinson (acted for FBME).
Prof. Memberships: Middle Temple (Jules Thorn Scholar).
Career: Scholar, University College Oxford 1979-1982, First class hons. degree in Jurisprudence, Oxford University 1982 (Wronker and Jurisprudence Prizes winner). Called to the Bar in England and Wales, August 1983.
Personal: Married to Lorraine, 5 children. Principal leisure interests: family, deer and deer stalking, wildfowling, alpaca farming, poultry.

SMOUHA, Joe
Essex Court Chambers (Gordon Pollock QC), London (020) 7813 8000
Recommended in Arbitration (International), Commercial (Litigation), Shipping, Tax
Specialisation: Litigation involving appearances in arbitration, the Commercial Court, Court of Appeal and other courts hearing civil claims. All aspects of commercial law including shipping, banking, insurance and reinsurance, international sale of goods, oil and gas, public international law and other related areas. Art litigation including title, dealer commission, purchasing syndicate disputes. VAT: includes both substantial High Court and Tribunal work and general advisory work on non-contentious matters, schemes etc.
Career: Magdalene College, Cambridge, BA Law (Hons) 1984; MA 1988; New York University School of Law, 1984-85: LL.M in International Trade Law: Called to the Bar 1986 (Middle Temple).
Personal: Born 1963.

SNOWDEN, Richard
Erskine Chambers (Robin Potts QC), London (020) 7242 5532
Recommended in Company, Financial Services, Insolvency/Corporate Recovery

SOARES, Patrick C.
8 Gray's Inn Square (Patrick C. Soares), London (020) 7242 3529
Recommended in Tax
Specialisation: Specialist in all aspects of revenue law, including structuring land transactions for the optimum tax position, value added tax and stamp duty on land transactions, taxation of overseas trusts and international estate and trust planning. Also conducts tax appeals at all levels. Publications include 'Vat Planning for Property Transactions', 'Land and Tax Planning', 'Trusts and Tax Planning', 'Taxation of Non-Resident Trusts', 'Taxation of Land Development', 'Offshore Investment in UK Property' and 'Tax Strategy for Conveyancing Transactions'. Tax editor of the 'Property Law Bulletin' and co-editor of 'Trusts for Europe'.
Prof. Memberships: Fellow of the Institute of Taxation.
Career: Called to the Bar 1983. Previously a tax partner in a leading firm of London solicitors, having been admitted a solicitor in 1972.
Personal: Educated at University College, London (MA Taxation).

SOLLEY, Stephen
Cardinal Chambers (moved from Cloisters)

SOMERVILLE, Bryce
No.6 Fountain Court (Roger Smith QC), Birmingham (0121) 233 3282
Recommended in Family/Matrimonial

SOORJOO, Martin
14 Tooks Court (Michael Mansfield QC), London (020) 7405 8828
Recommended in Immigration
Specialisation: Public law with emphasis on immigration, asylum and human rights challenges concerning the State. Cases of significance include ex p Francois (HL), ex p Evans and Reid (DC) and ex p Jaramillo-Silva (CA). Has taken cases to Strasbourg involving breaches of Articles 3, 6 and 8 of the ECHR. In addition, has represented the family of Stephen Lawrence during their numerous legal proceedings including public inquiry. Former member of ILPA executive and regular course trainer for ILPA, JCWI and other relevant groups.
Prof. Memberships: Immigration Law Practitioners Association (ILPA), Joint Council for Welfare Immigrants (JCWI), Amnesty International.
Career: Called to the Bar in 1990.

SOUTHERN, Richard
7 King's Bench Walk (Jeremy Cooke QC), London (020) 7910 8300
Recommended in Shipping
Specialisation: Main areas of practice are shipping and maritime, insurance and reinsurance, professional negligence, and commercial fraud, as well as general commercial litigation and arbitration. Recent cases include Aneco Reinsurance Underwriting v Johnson & Higgins [2000] P.N.L.R 152, Jordan Grand Prix Ltd v Baltic Insurance Group [1999] 2 AC 127, Glencore International v Metro Trading [1999] 2 Lloyd's Rep 632, Dubai Aluminium Co Ltd v Salaam [1999] 1 Lloyd's Rep 415.
Prof. Memberships: The Commercial Bar Association.
Career: Called 1987.

SOUTHEY, David Hugh

14 Tooks Court (Michael Mansfield QC), London (020) 7405 8828

Recommended in Immigration

Specialisation: Immigration and asylum, Human Rights Act 1998, crime, prisoners rights, mental health, privacy, education and other public law. Cases include R v Immigration Appeal Tribunal ex p Aziz [1999] INLR 355; Darbiye v Secretary of State for the Home Department [1998] Imm AR 64; In re H, in re D [1999] The Times, 13 August; R v York Mags ex p Grimes [1997] The Times, 27 June.
Prof. Memberships: ILPA, Prisoners Legal Rights Group.
Publications: Joint editor of 'United Kingdom Human Rights Reports' and joint author of 'A Criminal Practitioners Guide to Judicial Review and Case Stated'.

SOUTHWELL, Edward

Farrar's Building (John Leighton Williams QC), London (020) 7583 9241

Recommended in Personal Injury

Specialisation: Wide ranging personal injury practice, both plaintiff and defendant, including profound brain injury cases, industrial accidents of all kinds, sports accidents including skiing injuries, stress claims and long experience of industrial disease/ injury including deafness, lung disorders, WRULD etc. Also handles clinical and solicitors' negligence, product liability and all general tort. Experienced in group litigation for defendants (eg Guards and Shunters deafness claims). Major lay clients have included Ford Motor Company, British Rail, the M.O.D. and ICI.
Prof. Memberships: London Common Law Bar Association, South Eastern Circuit and Personal Injury Bar Association.
Career: Called to the Bar in 1970 and joined Farrar's Building in 1971. Recorder since 1987.
Personal: Educated at Charterhouse School 1959-1964. Assistant Boundary Commissioner. Chairman of NHS Trust Disciplinary Inquiry Panels.

SPEARMAN, Richard QC

4-5 Gray's Inn Square (Elizabeth Appleby QC & Duncan Ouseley QC), London (020) 7404 5252

Recommended in Sport

Specialisation: Wide range of practice in all divisions of High Court, and Copyright Tribunal. Including commercial fraud, media and entertainment, sports law, professional negligence, defamation, confidence and privacy, insurance, reinsurance, sale of goods, restraint of trade. Reported cases concerning restraint of trade/boxing, Mareva injunctions, letters of credit, copyright Euro-defences, as well as Istel v Tully (privilege against self-incrimination); R v Jockey Club ex p Aga Khan (Jockey Club/judicial review); AIRC v PPL (Copyright Tribunal/licensing scheme); Formica v ECGD (discovery/privilege/ECGD guarantee); Brinks v Abu Saleh (tracing); Hyde Park Residence v Yelland (copyright/ public interest/fair dealing); Kazakstan Word Processors v NCM (insurance/ construction of contract).
Career: Called 1977, silk 1996.
Personal: Educated Bedales; King's College, Cambridge. Born 19.1.53.

SPECK, Adrian

8 New Square (Michael Fysh QC SC), London (020) 7405 4321
adrian.speck@8newsquare.co.uk

Recommended in Information Technology, Intellectual Property

Specialisation: Specialises in all aspects of intellectual property, including patents trade marks and passing off, confidential information, designs, copyright and performers' rights. Also specialises in jurisdiction disputes under the CJJA 1982/ Brussels Convention and entertainment litigation. Patent cases include Biogen v Medeva (biotechnology); Chiron v Evans (biotechnology); Haberman v Jackel (child's trainer cup); Taylor v Ishida (mechanical). Jurisdiction disputes include Fort Dodge v Azko (patent); Pearce v Ove Arup (copyright); Modus Vivendi v Sanmex (passing off). Trade mark cases include Wagamama v City Centre Restaurants; Baywatch v Home Video; Scandecor v Scandecor; Trebor Basset v Football Association. Copyright and design cases include ETAL v Critchley; Work Model v Ecosystem. Entertainment and media cases include Norowzian v Arks (copyright in short film); Coulthard v DMC. Breach of confidence cases include Lancashire Fires v SA Lyons. Other cases include Smith Kline Beecham v Connaught (use of documents); Cobra v Rata (use of documents); R v MCA ex. p Smith & Nephew (enquiry on cross undertaking).
Prof. Memberships: Intellectual Property Bar Association, TIPLO, Gray's Inn and Lincoln's Inn.
Career: Called to the Bar 1993 (Wilfred Parker Prize).
Personal: Born 1969. Educated at Seaford Head Comprehensive School, East Sussex 1980-87 and King's College, Cambridge 1988-91 (Scholar, 1st Class Honours in Physics and Theoretical Physics).

SPENCER, Martin

4 Paper Buildings (Jean Ritchie QC), London (020) 7353 3366

Recommended in Clinical Negligence

Specialisation: Medical negligence and P.I. especially back injury cases for the Royal College of Nursing (has been dealing with such cases since 1987). Recent cases include: De Martell, Smith v Tunbridge Wells H.A., Forbes (now a leading case on limitation) and Figgett v Davies.
Prof. Memberships: PNBA. London Common Law Bar Association. Personal Injury Bar Association.
Career: BA (Oxon) 1977, BCL (Oxon) 1978, Bar Finals 1979, Danish Government Scholar, Copenhagen University 1979-1980, Pupil, Fountain Court 1980-81. Joined present chambers 1981.
Personal: Married with three Children. Fluent Danish speaker. Interests include music, sport and bridge.

SPENCER, Michael QC

Crown Office Chambers (Michael Spencer QC & Christopher Purchas QC), London (020) 7797 8100

Recommended in Clinical Negligence, Personal Injury, Product Liability

SPENCER, Robin QC

Sedan House (Meirion Lewis-Jones), Chester (01244) 348282

Recommended in Consumer

SPINK, Andrew J.M.

35 Essex Street (Nigel Inglis-Jones QC), London (020) 7353 6381

Recommended in Clinical Negligence, Pensions

Specialisation: Specialises in professional negligence (particularly cases involving allegations of negligence and, where appropriate, breach of trust or fiduciary duty, against actuaries or other pension scheme advisers or trustees, commercial property valuers and surveyors, solicitors and barristers), clinical negligence (all aspects of dental and medical negligence) and personal injury (particular spinal and brain injury and asbestos-related conditions). Cases include – North Staffordshire Hospital cases (proposed civil claims arising out of CNEP ventilator trials on premature infants); Hogg Robinson Trustees Ltd v Buck & Willis Healthcare Limited (claim by trustees of occupational pension schemes against former actuaries and administrators for breach of contract, negligence and breach of fiduciary duty in and about the preparation and content of successive actuarial valuations of the scheme.; ChD 1996-2000); Devon Breast Screening Services cases (proposed claim by group of women for negligent delay in diagnosing breast cancer; 1999); PLT Ltd v Smith Melzack (action by bank against commercial property surveyor for negligent valuation; TCC 1999); S v Birmingham Health Authority (joint instruction for single experts on liability in clinical negligence claims; QBD 1999); Hatcher v Plymouth Hospitals NHS Trust (application of legal professional priviledge to NHS Complaints file; QBD 1999); O'Toole v Irish Rail & J.W. Roberts (duty of care owed by employer to employee in relations to hazardous work undertaken by specialist sub-contractor; QBD 1999); Coloroll Carpet Works Pension Scheme (Beddoe action relating to claim against pension scheme actuary and administrator; ChD 1994-1998); Ward v Newalls Insulation (law relating to loss of earnings from partnership by injured dominant partner, asbestosis, CA 1998); Pynter v Harefield Hospital (informed consent to paediatric heart transplant; QBD 1997); Margerson & Hancock v J.W.Roberts (liability for environmental exposure to asbestos; CA (1996); Hopkins v MacKenzie (accrual of cause if action in solicitor's negligence action; CA 1995).
Prof. Memberships: AVMA, APIL, London Common Law & Commercial Bar Association.
Career: Called to the Bar in 1985 and joined chambers at Essex Street in 1986.
Personal: Educated at Sherborne School, Dorset 1975-80 and Queens' College, Cambridge 1981-84. Interests include mountain and hill walking, skiing, France, travel in Asia, computers and opera. Born 21 April 1962. Lives in Dorset.

STADLEN, Nicholas QC

Fountain Court (Anthony Boswood QC), London (020) 7583 3335

Recommended in Banking, Civil Fraud, Commercial (Litigation)

STAFFORD, Andrew QC

Littleton Chambers (Michel Kallipetis QC), London (020) 7797 8600

Recommended in Employment

Specialisation: Employment law: Garden leave, restraint of trade, breach of confidence, discrimination, whistle-blowing, wrongful & unfair dismissal, share options, directors duties, pension rights, TUPE, Human Rights, European law, strikes etc. Recent cases: Symbian v Christensen; Whitewater Leisure Management Ltd v Barnes; SBJ Stephenson v Mandy; University of Nottingham v Eyett; Malik v BCCI; Rock Refrigeration v Jones. General Commercial: Guarantees, share warranty claims, share option schemes, fraud, breach of confidence, debt collection, company law, sale of goods. Professional negligence & discipline: Solicitors, barristers, accountants, stockbrokers, insurance brokers, financial advisers, architects, engineers, surveyors.
Career: Called 1980.

STAFFORD-MICHAEL, Simon

4 King's Bench Walk (Robert Rhodes QC), London (020) 7822 8822

Recommended in Fraud: Criminal

Specialisation: Fraud, insurance and reinsurance. Fraud: Regulation, compliance and money laundering; serious fraud investigations conducted by the SFO, CPS, Inland Revenue, C&E, DTI and SIB; and criminal and commercial litigation. Major trials include: Jyske Bank, Guinness, Arrows and Wallace Duncan Smith. Notable recent matters include R v W & Another (Court of Appeal), R v EPA ex p Green Environmental Industries Insurance and Reinsurance: Marine and Non-marine; Regulation and Insolvency; London Market/ Lloyd's of London law and practice; construction of complex policy language; Equitas; international litigation and arbitration; long tail-environmental/ mass tort/ product's liability; CAT claims; professional

indemnity claims; D&O claims; settlement counsel and mediator. Notable recent matters include: Lasmo plc v London Market Insurers et al (Court of Appeal) and settlement counsel retained on behalf of US corporate assureds to advise on settlement of certain environmental claims brought against London Market Insurers.
Prof. Memberships: Criminal Bar Association, American Bar Association, International Bar Association and Federation of Insurance and Corporate Counsel.
Career: West Bridgeford Comprehensive School, University of Bristol and Gray's Inn. Co-Chair of the International Insurance Coverage Litigation Committee of the ABA 1995-99. Journal of Money Laundering, Advisory Board 1998-date.
Personal: Simon Stafford-Michael is married to Johanna and they have four children. They live in Gloucestershire.

STALLWORTHY, Nicholas
35 Essex Street (Nigel Inglis-Jones QC), London (020) 7353 6381
Recommended in Pensions
Specialisation: Specialises in pensions law (particularly in relation to occupational pension schemes). Acted in Stevens v Bell (for pensioners & deferred pensioners opposed the proposed merger of 2 British Airways pension schemes; ChD, 2000); In re: the Thomas Christy Ltd Pension Fund (court approval of distribution of surplus on winding up of scheme; ChD, 1999); and various complaints to the Pensions Ombudsman. Involved in National Grid Co plc v Laws; HL, 2000. Cases have concerned maladministration and breaches of trust / fiduciary duty, duty by trustees; tracing/restitution of trust property, and the distribution of surpluses. Direct professional access work from e.g. Norwich union and Hogg Robinson. Also practices in general chancery work (contractual/property litigation); professional negligence (particularily realting to solicitors); and personal injury or clinical negligence claims (particularly spinal and brain injuries involving complex quantum or private international law issues).
Prof. Memberships: Association Pension Lawers; Chancery Bar Association; Professional Negligence Bar Association.
Career: Called to the Bar in 1993; completed pupillage 1994; post-graduate degree 1995; joined 35 Essex Street in 1996.
Personal: Born 10 June 1970; educated Radley College 1983-88; Christ Church, Oxford 1989-92 (BA, Jurisprudence) & 1994-5 (BCL).

STANLEY, Paul
Essex Court Chambers (Gordon Pollock QC), London (020) 7813 8000
Recommended in Commercial (Litigation)
Specialisation: Commercial litigation and advisory work (especially international commercial litigation and arbitration, insurance and reinsurance, commercial fraud); EC litigation and advisory work.
Prof. Memberships: COMBAR; British Maritime Law Association European Committee.
Career: Downing College, Cambridge: BA 1991 (Law); Harvard Law School: LLM 1992; called to Bar 1993. Treasury Panel (C List).
Publications: Current Law Statutes annotations to Human Rights Act 1998 (with Peter Duffy QC).
Personal: Born 1970.

STARMER, Keir
Doughty Street Chambers (Geoffrey Robertson QC), London (020) 7404 1313
Recommended in Administrative & Public Law: General, Crime, Human Rights (Civil Liberties)
Specialisation: Expert in European human rights law, public law and civil liberties. Extensive experience of litigation before the European Court of Human Rights. Other areas of practice include crime and civil actions against the police. Author of 'Human Rights Law' (LAG, 1999), and 'Civil Rights and Freedoms in the UK' (Routelage, 1996). Editor in 'Justice in Error' (Blackstones, 1993) and 'Miscarriages of Justice' (Blackstones, 1999).
Career: Called to the Bar 1987.
Personal: Education: LLB (Hons) 1st class, BCL. Former legal officer at the National Council of Civil Liberties (now Liberty). Born 1962.

STARTE, Harvey
1 Brick Court (Richard Rampton QC), London (020) 7353 8845
Recommended in Defamation

STEAD, Richard
St John's Chambers (Christopher Sharp QC), Bristol (0117) 921 3456
clerks@stjohnschambers.co.uk
Recommended in Commercial (Litigation), Personal Injury
Specialisation: Specialist in construction law, personal injury and professional negligence.
Career: Called to the Bar in 1979. Recorder 1996.

STEEL, John QC
4-5 Gray's Inn Square (Elizabeth Appleby QC & Duncan Ouseley QC), London (020) 7404 5252
chambers@4-5graysinnsquare.co.uk
Recommended in Planning
Specialisation: Has worked for many national and international clients in both the public and private sectors at the highest level in public, administrative, planning and environmental law. Practices in judicial review and public inquiry work. Specialities include retail, leisure, sports (especially football stadia), housing, minerals, waste disposal, highways, aviation, compulsory purchase and licensing. Particularly experienced in cases involving scientific, engineering and technically complex issues.
Prof. Memberships: Planning and Environment Bar Association; Administrative Law Bar Association.
Career: Called to the Bar 1978. Silk 1993. Recorder. Fellow Royal Geographical Society.
Personal: Educated: Harrow School 1967-1972; Durham University (BSc Hons chemistry) 1973-1976; President Durham University Athletic Union 1975; Gray's Inn Moots Prize 1978, Member Attorney General's panel (planning etc) 1979-1993; PPL (Helicopters and Fixed Wing); Director; Kandahar Ski Club. Director, The Busoga Trust (water relief in Uganda). Member of Durham University Institute of Change.

STEELE, David
Colleton Chambers (Martin Meeke), Exeter (01392) 274898
Recommended in Crime

STEER, David QC
7 Harrington Street Chambers (David Steer QC/Robert Fordham QC/Iain Goldrein QC), Liverpool (0151) 242 0707
Recommended in Crime

STEINFELD, Alan QC
24 Old Buildings (Martin Mann QC & Alan Steinfeld QC), London (020) 7404 0946
Recommended in Commercial Chancery, Company, Insolvency/Corporate Recovery, Partnership

STEPHENS, John L.
35 Essex Street (Nigel Inglis-Jones QC), London (020) 7353 6381
Recommended in Pensions
Specialisation: Principal area of practice is pensions, covering all aspects of UK and international occupational pension schemes and claims associated therewith (eg professional negligence, executive severance etc). Also deals with offshore trusts and claims to ownership of antiquities (ie claims by nations, museums, temples, etc to ownership of ancient works of art). Frequently addresses both commercial and legal conferences.
Prof. Memberships: Association of Pensions Lawyers, Chancery Bar Association, IPEBLA.
Career: Called to the Bar in 1975. Joined present chambers in 1977.
Personal: Educated at Oxford University (BA, 1974). Born 30th March 1953. Leisure pursuits include travel. Lives in London.

STEPHENSON, Geoffrey
2-3 Gray's Inn Square (Anthony Scrivener QC), London (020) 7242 4986
Recommended in Consumer, Planning
Specialisation: Local government and public law with particular emphasis on planning local government finance and administration, housing and consumer and environmental law.
Prof. Memberships: Planning and Environment Bar Association. Administrative Law Bar Association. Parliamentary Bar Association. Fellow of the Chartered Insurance Institute. Member of the Bar of Texas.

STERLING, Robert
St. James's Chambers (R.A. Sterling), Manchester (0161) 834 7000
Recommended in Chancery
Specialisation: Chancery with emphasis on commercial litigation, corporate and personal insolvency and professional negligence. Recently reported cases: White v Richards (1993) 68 P & C.R. 105; Griffiths v Yorkshire Bank plc (1994) I.W.L.R. 1427; Alsop Wilkinson v Neary (1996) I.W.L.R. 1220; Ross v. Telford (1998) 1 BCLC 82; and Provincial North West plc v Bennett, The Times February 12 1999 CA.
Prof. Memberships: Chancery Bar Association, Northern Chancery Bar Association, Professional Negligence Bar Association, Northern Circuit Commercial Bar Association.
Career: Head of Chambers, Chairman of Northern Chancery Bar Association 1994-1997. Acts as arbitrator in commercial disputes.

STERN, Ian
Queen Elizabeth Building (Julian Bevan QC & Peter Whiteman QC), London (020) 7583 5766
Recommended in Fraud: Criminal

Specialisation: Fraud: involved in a number of large fraud cases. Disciplinary Tribunals: appeared at a number of professional bodies – most regularly at the General Medical Council and the General Optical Council. Serious Crime: Murder; attempted murder; rape, drugs and firearms offences.
Prof. Memberships: Member of the Criminal Bar Association, South East Circuit and a number of local Bar Messes. Called to the New South Wales Bar, Australia in 1989.
Personal: Married to a G.P. and has three daughters. Runs on a fairly regular basis and completed the London Marathon in 1992 and 2000.

STERN, Linda QC
18 Red Lion Court (Anthony Arlidge QC), London (020) 7520 6000
Recommended in Crime
Specialisation: Criminal law, particularly sexual offences and child abuse.
Prof. Memberships: Fellow of the Royal Society for the Encouragement of Arts, Manufacturers and Commerce. Member of the Forensic Science Society.
Career: Called to the Bar by Gray's Inn, July 1971: Recorder 1990: Queen's Counsel 1991. DTI Inspector: Chairman of Police Appeals Tribunals.

STERNBERG, Michael

4 Paper Buildings (Lionel Swift QC), London (020) 7583 0816

Recommended in Family: Child Care including child abduction

Specialisation: All aspects of family and family-related law including matrimonial, finance, wardship, disputes between unmarried persons, Inheritance Act claims, and child law with specific reference to sexual abuse and contested adoptions. Matrimonial finance work includes investigation of overseas trusts and companies. Recent cases include Re: M (Sexual abuse allegations Interviewing Techniques) 1999 2FLR G2. Re AMR (Adoption procedure) 1999 2FLR 801. Re: M (Petition to European Commission of Human Rights) [1997] IFLR 755. Description: Wardship – Court ordering ward to be returned to natural parents in South Africa. Woman caring for ward in England seeking to petition ECHR on rights of ward and herself.; S v. S [1997] 1WLR 1621, financial relief – inference of tax evasion by husband, Inland Revenue receiving copy of judgement – confidential information – breach of confidence, public interest. Re: S (Removal from jurisdiction) April 1999 (family law), mother's decision to return to Chile reasonable but notwithstanding her proposals for life realistic. Strict conditions to be attached to permission to return until "mirror orders" made by Chilean Court on contract including deposit of £135.00 in a special account; Re: F (a minor: paternity test) [1993] 3 WLR 369 (C.A.). Description: evidence – blood test -application blood test for DNA profiling by claimant for paternity; H v. H (financial provision: capital allowance) [1993] 2FLR 335. Financial provision – divorce – capital adjustment – availability of "Besterman cushion" and if court should apply it; R v. Plymouth Justices ex parte w, [1993] 2FLR 777. Family proceedings – judicial review – rules of natural justice – cross-examination on previous convictions; H v. H (Residence order leave to remove from jurisdiction) [1995] 1FLR 529 (C.A.). Applicability of Children Act 1989 to applications to take child permanently overseas; Re: M (child's upbringing) [1996] 2FLR 441 (C.A.). Zulu parents contesting adoption by white woman of Zulu boy resident with her in England – importance of cultural heritage.

Prof. Memberships: Family Law Bar Association. Assistant Secretary Family Law Bar Association 1986-1988.

Career: Called to the Bar 1975 and joined 3 Dr. Johnson's Buildings. Moved to 4 Paper Buildings EC4 in 1994.

Personal: Educated at Carmel College, Wallingford 1962-1970, Queens College, Cambridge 1970-1974. (MA, LL.M). Governor of North London Collegiate School, Trustee of Sternberg Charitable Settlement. Freeman of the City of London and Member of the Worshipful Company of Horners. Member of Reform Club and City Livery Club. Born 12th September 1951. Decoration: Medaglia D'Argento di Benemerenza of sacred military Constantinian Order of St. George (1990).

STEVENSON, William QC

Crown Office Chambers (Michael Spencer QC & Christopher Purchas QC), London (020) 7797 8100

Recommended in Health & Safety, Personal Injury

Specialisation: Principal area of practice involves product, public and employers' liability, occupation-related diseases and disorders including legionella pneumophilia, asthmas, asbestos-related diseases and disorders, upper limb disorders, cancers and noise induced hearing loss. Has acted in RSI claims by ceramic, banking and electronics industry employees and toxic shock syndrome claims against sanitary protection manufacturers. Has chaired and addressed conferences and seminars on occupational diseases. Other reported personal injury cases include Cox v HCB Angus [1991] ICR 687 (construction of s. 29 Factories Act 1961), Kenning v Eve Construction [1989] 1 WLR 118 (disclosure of expert report) and Gaskill v Preston [1981] 3 All ER 427 (deductibility of Family Income Supplement from claim for loss of earnings) and Hunter v Butler (1995) Kemp Vol. 1 25-008/1 (black economy earnings in Fatal Accidents claims). Other major cases encompass air handling and ventilation problems and product liability claims including Aswan Engineering v Lupdine [1987] WLR 1 (C.A) (plastic containers).

Prof. Memberships: London Common Law and Commercial Bar Association.

Career: Called to the Bar 1968 and joined present chambers in 1969. Appointed Recorder in 1992.

Personal: Educated at Marlborough College 1957-1961. Evan Williams Exhibitioner at Trinity College Oxford 1962-1965 (MA 1969). Admitted Lincoln's Inn 1962 – Hardwicke and Droop Scholarships. Honourable Artillery Company 1965-81 (TD 1980). Leisure pursuits include country sports, skiing and sailing. Born 17th October 1943. Lives in London.

STEWART, James QC

Park Court Chambers (James Stewart QC, Robert Smith QC), Leeds (0113) 243 3277
clerks@parkcourtchambers.co.uk

Recommended in Crime

Specialisation: Crime, commercial fraud. Representative cases; R v Cheshire 93 W App R 251 (causation in murder). R v Tandy 87 Cr. App. R 45 (alcoholism as a basis of diminished responsibility). R v Ali 1993 2 ALLER 409 (bugged cell confessions) R v Camplin 1978 AC 705 (provocation).

Career: Call 1966; Bencher Inner Temple 1993. Head of Chambers. Appointments – Recorder 1982. Deputy High Court Judge 1993. Approved to sit at Central Criminal Court 1990. QC 1982.

STEWART, Lindsey

7 Stone Buildings (Charles Aldous QC), London (020) 7405 3886

Recommended in Commercial Chancery, Company

Specialisation: Specialises in Chancery and commercial litigation. Practice covers company law, corporate and personal insolvency, banking, civil fraud, credit and security, professional negligence and trusts.Cases include: Butigan v. Negus-Fancey & Ors [2000]; Ministry of Sound Holdings Ltd & Ors v. Cosgrave [1999]; Dubai Aluminium Co Ltd v. Salaam & Ors [1996]; Alsop Wilkinson & Ors v. Neary & Ors [1995]; Fuji Finance Inc v. Aetna Insurance Co Ltd & Anor [1995]; Re: SN Group plc [1993]; Dubai Bank Ltd v. Galadari [1992]; Derby & Co Ltd & Ors v. Weldon & Ors [1991].

Prof. Memberships: Chancery Bar Association, Insolvency Lawyers Association, Association of Contentious Trusts and Probate Specialists, Faculty of Advocates.

Career: Called to the Bar 1983. Tenant at Queen Elizabeth Building 1985-1990. Called to the Scottish Bar 1990. Joined present chambers 1991.

Personal: Educated at Harris Academy, Dundee 1973-1979 and University College, Oxford 1979-1982. Born 24th April 1961.

STEWART, Roger

Four New Square (Justin Fenwick QC), London (020) 7822 2000
barristers@4newsquare.com

Recommended in Construction, Professional Negligence

Specialisation: Sorting wheat from chaff.

Prof. Memberships: ORBA, PNBA, COMBAR, LCLCBA

Career: MA LLM, Editor Chapter 2 of Jackson and Powell on Professional Negligence (Architects and Engineers)

STEWART, Stephen QC

Byrom Street Chambers (B.A. Hytner QC), Manchester (0161) 829 2100
clerks@byromstreet.com

Recommended in Commercial (Litigation)

Specialisation: Insurance, professional negligence, sales of goods, general contractual disputes.

Prof. Memberships: Northern Circuit Commercial Bar Association – Treasurer and Founder member. Professional Negligence Bar Association. Technology and Construction Bar Association.

Career: Recorder; Deputy Judge of the Technology and Construction Court.

STEWART SMITH, Rodney

1 New Square (Eben Hamilton QC), London (020) 7405 0884

Recommended in Traditional Chancery

Specialisation: General chancery, especially commercial and residential property, easements, partnership, wills, trusts and court of protection matters, professional negligence.

Prof. Memberships: Chancery Bar Association.

Career: Called to the Bar 1964. Practised since then at 1 New Square, Lincoln's Inn. Assistant Recorder 1990-1994. Recorder 1994 to date. Member of Land Registration Rules Committee since 1991. General Tax Commissioner since 1991.

Publications: 'Butterworths Land Development Encyclopaedia' (1976).

Personal: Winchester College and Trinity Hall, Cambridge (B.A. 1963, LL.B 1964). Leisure Interests: watching cricket and hill walking.

STILITZ, Daniel

11 King's Bench Walk (Eldred Tabachnik QC and James Goudie QC), London (020) 7632 8500

Recommended in Employment

Specialisation: Employment law, public law and commercial law.

Prof. Memberships: Employment Law Bar Associaton. Administrative Law Bar Associaton. COMBAR. CEDR Accredited Mediator.

Career: Called to the bar in 1992. Junior Counsel to the Crown (Panel B).

Personal: New College Oxford, BA (1st Class Hons). City University, MA. Born 1 August 1968.

STOBART, John

KCH Barristers (William Everard), Nottingham (0115) 941 8851

Recommended in Crime

Specialisation: CRIME including complex frauds e.g Britannia Park, R v Charlton & Ors. R v Hancock, HSE and Local Authority prosecutions (for defence), and Junior for defence in R v Martin. Practice also has a preponderance of sexual/violence cases.

STOCKDALE, David QC

Deans Court Chambers (H.K. Goddard QC), Manchester (0161) 214 6000

Recommended in Personal Injury

Specialisation: All aspects of personal injury work, including accident, industrial disease and multi-claimant litigation; employer's liability; health and safety; professional negligence (in particular, medical and solicitors). Also associated with 7 Bedford Row, London WC1R 4BU Tel: (020) 7242 3555 and Chancery House Chambers, 7 Lisbon Square, Leeds LS1 4LY Tel: (0113) 244 6691.

Prof. Memberships: Northern Circuit, Personal Injuries Bar Association, Professional Negligence Bar Association.

Career: Called 1975. Assistant Recorder 1990. Recorder 1993. Queen's Counsel 1995.
Personal: Educated at Giggleswick School and Pembroke College, Oxford.

STOCKDALE, Bt, Sir Thomas
Erskine Chambers (Robin Potts QC), London (020) 7242 5532
Recommended in Company, Insolvency/Corporate Recovery
Specialisation: Corporate reorganisation and reconstructions including reduction of capital and schemes of arrangement. Takeovers and mergers. Schemes of arrangement in insolvency, including insolvent insurance companies.
Prof. Memberships: COMBAR. Chancery Bar Association. Law Society's Company Law Committee.
Career: Worcester College, Oxford MA. Bencher, Lincoln's Inn.
Publications: Contributor to 'Buckley on the Companies Act' (15th edition.)

STOCKILL, David
5 Fountain Court (Anthony Barker QC), Birmingham (0121) 606 0500
Recommended in Chancery, Insolvency/Corporate Recovery

STOCKLEY, Ruth
40 King St (Philip Raynor QC), Manchester (0161) 832 9082
rstockley@40kingstreet.co.uk
Recommended in Planning
Specialisation: Town and Country Planning; Highways; Compulsory Purchase; Environment Law and Local Government.
Prof. Memberships: Planning and Environment Bar Association; Administrative Law Bar Association; United Kingdom Environmental Law Association.
Career: Practised at 40 King Street Chambers since 1988 in the field of public law acting both for and against public bodies.
Publications: Assistant Editor of Sweet and Maxwell's Encyclopaedia of Highway Law and Practice.

STOKES, Mary
Erskine Chambers (Robin Potts QC), London (020) 7242 5532
Recommended in Company
Specialisation: Principal area of practice is company law including corporate insolvency, commercial law with a company element and financial services both advisory and litigation. Recent cases include British Commonwealth Holdings plc v Atlantic Computers plc & ors; Southern Tropics Ltd v North Holdings [1999] Z BCLC 625; New Hampshire Insurance v Rush & Tompkins [1998] 2 BCLC 47.
Prof. Memberships: Chancery Bar Association, COMBAR.
Career: BA, BCL (Oxon), LL.M (Harvard). Fellow and Tutor in Law, Brasenose College. Called to the Bar in 1989, in practice at Erskine Chambers since 1990.
Publications: Consultant editor of Butterworths 'Company Law Cases'. Contributed chapter on Reductions of Capital to Butterworths 'Corporate Law Service'.

STONE, Gregory QC
4-5 Gray's Inn Square (Elizabeth Appleby QC & Duncan Ouseley QC), London (020) 7404 5252
Recommended in Environment, Planning
Specialisation: Specialises in planning, environmental, judicial review and parliamentary law. Practice also covers local government, highways and compulsory purchase. Important work includes the Channel Tunnel Rail Link Bill; Terminal 5, Heathrow; Belvedere Waste to Energy plant; M25 MSA Inquiry; M40 MSA Inquiry; British Rail (No3) Bill; Toxic Waste Incinerator Inquiries; Mucking Landfill Inquiry; Blue Water Park Regional Shopping Centre Inquiry; Hewitt's Farm Regional Shopping Centre Inquiry; ICL Tower, Putney; R v LB Bromley ex party Barker.
Prof. Memberships: Planning and Environment Bar Association; Parliamentary Bar Association; Administrative Law Bar Association.
Career: Called to the Bar 1976. Joined present chambers 1991. Took Silk 1994. Standing Counsel to Department of Trade and Industry for South Eastern Circuit (1989-1990). Recorder.
Personal: Educated at L'Université de Rennes, France 1965, The Queen's College, Oxford 1966-1969, and Manchester University 1970-1972. Born 12th December 1946. Lives in London.

STONE, Lucy
Queen Elizabeth Building (Paul Coleridge QC), London (020) 7797 7837
Recommended in Family: Matrimonial Finance
Specialisation: Specialises in family law, principally "big money" ancillary relief cases. Has acted on behalf of a number of high-profile media clients.
Prof. Memberships: Member of Bar Council Law Reform Committee 1994 -1997; and Family Law Bar Association Committee 1998-1996; F v F [1996] 1 FLR 833.
Career: MA Cantab; called to the Bar in 1983.
Personal: Born 1959. Married with one child. Lives in London.

STONEFROST, Hilary
3-4 South Square (Michael Crystal QC), London (020) 7696 9900
hilarystonefrost@southsquare.com
Recommended in Insolvency/Corporate Recovery
Specialisation: Insolvency, company law and banking law. General commercial work arising out of insolvencies. Minority shareholders' petition's. Directors' disqualifications.
Career: Called to the Bar (Middle Temple) in 1991. Economist, Bank of England 1979 to 1989.
Publications: Contributor to the 'Law of Receivers of Companies,' Lightman and Moss.
Personal: Msc London School of Economics 1978. Diploma in law, City University 1990

STONER, Christopher
9 Old Square (Michael Driscoll QC), London (020) 7405 4682
Recommended in Sport
Specialisation: All aspects of sports law with a particular emphasis on litigation, drafting and enforcement of rules and regulations. Member of editorial board: 'Sports Law Administration and Practice'. Recent cases include: Wilander & Anor v Tobin & Anor; Korda v ITF Limited. Bingham v British Boxing Board of Control; Clients include The International Tennis Federation; The International Cricket Council; The British Boxing Board of Control, The F.A. Premier League. All aspects of property litigation, particularly landlord and tennant.
Prof. Memberships: Chancery Bar Association. Bar Sports Law Group.
Career: Called to the Bar in 1991. Tenant at 9 Old Square since 1992.
Personal: Educated at Shoreham College and the University of East Anglia.

STOREY, Paul
29 Bedford Row Chambers (Peter Ralls QC), London (020) 7404 1044
Recommended in Family: Matrimonial Finance
Specialisation: Family law: public law/adoption (eg 1999 – appeared for applicants for adoption in Re Jade & Hannah Bennett); private law (re B [1998] 1 FLR 368, Re W [1999] 1 FLR 869); cases with a European element (eg U v W [1997] 2 FLR 282); matrimonial and cohabitee finance (eg Roy v Roy [1996] 1 FLR 541).
Prof. Memberships: FLBA
Career: Called Lincoln's Inn Trinity 1982. Chambers: 7 Stone Buildings 1983-85; Goldsmith Building 1985-91; 29 Bedford Row 1992. Tutor professional ethics at CLE 1989-97. Chairman Nagalro annual conference 1996. Appears in legal network tv training videos. Articles in Family Law (12/95, 4/96, 10/96, 3/97). Speaker at Law Society Local Government Child Care Group annual conference 1998. Regular speaker at national and local conferences/training days. Recorder.
Personal: Married, four children. Cycling, rugby, football, motor racing, golf.

STOUT, Roger
18 St. John Street (Jonathan Foster QC), Manchester (0161) 278 1800
Recommended in Crime

STRAKER, Timothy QC
4-5 Gray's Inn Square (Elizabeth Appleby QC & Duncan Ouseley QC), London (020) 7404 5252
tstraker@4-5graysinnsquare.co.uk
Recommended in Planning
Specialisation: Principal areas of practice are local government, public law and town and country planning. Has acted in many leading public law cases concerning, inter alia, environmental assesments, compulsory purchase, planning, housing and housing benefits, Sunday trading, caravan sites and 'new age travellers', free speech, professional advertising, discrimination and professional conduct. Appeared in many Privy Council Appeals. Represented the returning officers in the first challenge to a European election result and in the first challenge to a Parliamentary result for 70 years. Acts for many local authorities and regulatory bodies. Consultant editor of the Registration of Political Parties Act 1998, contributor to the Rights of Way Law Review and to Judicial Review. Advisory editor Public Health and Environmental Protection (Halsbury's Laws of England).
Prof. Memberships: Administrative Law Bar Association, Planning Bar Association, Crown Office Users' Committee.
Career: Called to the Bar 1977. Silk 1996. Assistant Recorder 1998, Recorder 2000
Personal: Educated at Malvern College and Downing College, Cambridge (1st Class Hons). Senior Harris Scholar, Downing College Prize for Law, Holt Scholar of Gray's Inn, awarded Lord Justice Holker Senior Award.

STREATFEILD-JAMES, David
Atkin Chambers (John Blackburn QC), London (020) 7404 0102
Recommended in Construction, Information Technology

STRUDWICK, Linda
Queen Elizabeth Building (Julian Bevan QC & Peter Whiteman QC), London (020) 7583 5766
Recommended in Crime
Specialisation: Specialises in defence work but also handles prosecution. 25 years covering all areas of serious crime including murder, manslaughter, fraud, sexual offences, drug offences and disciplinary tribunal work.
Career: Called 1973.
Personal: Educated Manchester University.

STUART-SMITH, Jeremy QC
2 Temple Gardens (Dermod O'Brien QC), London (020) 7822 1200
Recommended in Personal Injury, Product Liability, Professional Negligence
Specialisation: Insurance and insurance related disputes; product liability; professional negligence; general commercial and common law.
Prof. Memberships: LCLCBA, PIBA.
Career: MA Cantab. QC 1997, Recorder 1999.

Personal: Playing the french horn, skiing, history, keeping sheep.

STUBBS, Andrew J.
St. Paul's Chambers (Nigel Sangster QC), Leeds (0113) 245 5866
Recommended in Crime

STUBBS, Rebecca
13 Old Square (Michael Lyndon-Stanford QC), London (020) 7404 4800
Recommended in Commercial Chancery, Company
Specialisation: Chancery commercial matters, with an emphasis on litigation, including company law , insolvency, restitution, trusts, property, conflicts of law and general commercial work. Recent reported cases include Grand Metropolitan v William Hill Group (1997), Jordan Grand Prix v Baltic Insurance (HL) (1999), Piccadilly Property Management Ltd v Commissioners of Inland Revenue (1999) and . A contributor to Butterworths Practical Insolvency.
Prof. Memberships: Chancery Bar Association, COMBAR.
Career: Called to the Bar 1994. Appointed Junior Counsel to the Crown (C Panel) 1999.
Personal: Educated at Darton High School and Downing College Cambridge (1990-1993) (MA 1st Class Honours). Queen Mother Scholar of the Middle Temple, 1994.

STURMAN, James
2 Bedford Row (formerly 3 Hare Court) (William Clegg QC), London (020) 7440 8888
Recommended in Crime, Fraud: Criminal
Specialisation: Specialist criminal defence advocate involved in many major cases. Particular expertise in fraud, also advisory work to banks on criminal matters and in "quasi criminal" tribunals. Extensive experience in the Court of Appeal criminal division particularly in cases in which did not appear in the Lower Court. FA Disciplinary Tribunal work, acted for Chelsea FC, Dennis Wise and Graeme Le Saux. Major cases include Stagg – Wimbledon Common murder. Sivalingham-Tamil Tigers. Vanduvall – financial instrument fraud. Richardson – fraud on revenue of an EU State. Reilly-disclosure. Callan – DTA. Woodward – effect of drink in reckless driving. McGovern – S76 PACE. Griffiths – abuse of process. Coswell – Timeshare fraud. Extensive experience in mortgage, VAT and diversion frauds.
Prof. Memberships: Member of Gibraltar Bar. CBA. IBA. BAFS.
Career: Called 1982, joined Chambers 1983.
Personal: Cricket. Football.

SUCKLING, Alan QC
Queen Elizabeth Building (Julian Bevan QC & Peter Whiteman QC), London (020) 7583 5766
Recommended in Fraud: Criminal
Specialisation: Crime and Fraud. Clowes. Maxwell. Warren. Shivpuri 1987 AC 1, Howe & Others 1987 AC 417.
Prof. Memberships: Middle Temple, Bencher. CBA.
Career: Queens' College, Cambridge MA LL.M. Harmsworth Law Scholar, Middle Temple.
Personal: b. Hong Kong 1938.

SULLIVAN, Michael
One Essex Court (Lord Grabiner QC), London (020) 7583 2000
Recommended in Banking
Specialisation: Banking, aviation finance and commercial litigation. Also professional negligence.

SUMNER, David
Lincoln House Chambers (Mukhtar Hussain QC), Manchester (0161) 832 5701
Recommended in Crime

SUMPTION, Jonathan QC
Brick Court Chambers (Christopher Clarke QC), London (020) 7379 3550
Recommended in Administrative & Public Law: General, Banking, Civil Fraud, Commercial (Litigation), Energy & Natural Resources, Financial Services, Insurance, Media & Entertainment, Professional Negligence

SUPPERSTONE, Michael QC
11 King's Bench Walk (Eldred Tabachnik QC and James Goudie QC), London (020) 7632 8500 clerksroom@11kbw.com
Recommended in Administrative & Public Law: General, Planning
Specialisation: All aspects of administrative and public law. Other main areas of practice include employment law.
Career: Called to the Bar in 1973. Bencher, Middle Temple. Appointed Queen's Counsel 1991. Recorder 1996; Deputy High Court Judge; past Chairman of Administrative Law Bar Association; Principal editor of latest edition of the administrative law title of 'Halsbury's Laws of England'; contributor to the latest edition of the extradition law title of 'Halsbury's Laws of England'; co-editor of 'Supperstone and Goudie on Judicial Review'; co-author of Supperstone, Goudie and Coppel on 'Local Authorities and the Human Rights Act 1998'; contributer to Butterworth's 'Local Government Law'; consulting editor of 'Supperstone and O'Dempsey on Immigration and Asylum'. Member of editorial committee of 'Public Law'.
Personal: Educated at St. Paul's School and Lincoln College, Oxford (MA; BCL).

SUTCLIFFE, Andrew
3 Verulam Buildings (Christopher Symons QC & John Jarvis QC), London (020) 7831 8441
Recommended in Media & Entertainment
Specialisation: Commercial and chancery litigation; in particular media and entertainment law, intellectual property, banking and professional negligence. Clients include artistes, producers, major record and publishing companies, clearing and merchant banks. Also acts as arbitrator in commercial and IP matters.
Prof. Memberships: COMBAR, London Common Law and Commercial Bar Association, Chancery Bar Association.
Career: Called to the Bar 1983. Joined Verulam Buildings 1984. Assistant Recorder.
Personal: Educated at Winchester College and Worcester College Oxford. Born 7th September 1960. Lives in London and Yorkshire.

SUTTLE, Stephen
1 Brick Court (Richard Rampton QC), London (020) 7353 8845
Recommended in Defamation

SUTTON, Mark
Old Square Chambers (John Hendy QC), London (020) 7269 0300
Recommended in Employment
Specialisation: Practice covers all aspects of employment law, particularly in connection with financial services, airlines and universities. Also undertakes professional negligence cases.
Career: Called to the Bar 1982
Personal: BA Hons, Dip Law. Born 25th June 1958.

SUTTON, Richard QC
18 Red Lion Court (Anthony Arlidge QC), London (020) 7520 6000
Recommended in Crime

SWAIN, Jon
Furnival Chambers (Andrew Mitchell QC), London (020) 7405 3232 clerks@furnivallaw.co.uk
Recommended in Crime
Specialisation: General Crime
Drugs: led for defendant in a major drug trial, and defended in many high profile cases. Murder: defended in a number of murder trials including special verdicts of insanity. Fraud: prosecuted high profile mortgage fraud and in a variety of other trials. Sexual Crime: defended in number of high profile cases. Firearms: defended in number of high profile cases. Large-Scale Dishonesty: defended in number of high profile cases. Cases involving child witnesses: successfully defended in every case in which instructed. Experienced in use of TV and video links.
Financial Crime
Asset forfeture and confiscation. Advised and represented prosecuting authorities and defendants in High Court and Crown Court.
Priority Interests
Cases with scientific evidence which engage background in biochemistry and biology.

SWAINSTON, Michael
Brick Court Chambers (Christopher Clarke QC), London (020) 7379 3550
Recommended in Commercial (Litigation), Professional Negligence
Specialisation: Michael Swainston practices general commercial law, which includes financial services (litigation and disciplinary tribunals), banking, insurance, international trade, shipping, public law and competition law. Cases of note he has argued include: Axa v Field, Cox v Bankside, Charman v WOC, Brown v GIO, Giles v Thompson, Golden Eagle Refinery v Associated International Insurance. Michael Swainston has argued during the course of the last year case before Lloyd's Disciplinary Tribunals. Other cases argued during the year include $200 million ship sale and purchase dispute, arguing misrepresentation claims on behalf of tenants in dispute with brewery landlords in the Court of Appeal and $250 million reinsurance avoidance arbitration.
Prof. Memberships: Called in 1985. Called to the Californian Bar 1988.

SWEENEY, Nigel QC
6 King's Bench Walk (Michael Worsley QC), London (020) 7583 0410
Recommended in Crime

SWIFT, Caroline QC
Byrom Street Chambers (B.A. Hytner QC), Manchester (0161) 829 2100 cs@byromstreet.com
Recommended in Clinical Negligence, Personal Injury
Specialisation: Personal injury; clinical negligence; industrial disease.
Prof. Memberships: PIBA.
Career: Called to the Bar, 1977. Appointed Silk, 1993. Assistant Recorder, 1992-95. Recorder, 1995-date. Governing Bencher of the Temple, 1997-date.

SWIFT, John QC
Monckton Chambers (John Swift QC), London (020) 7405 7211
Recommended in Competition/Anti-trust
Specialisation: John Swift QC returned to the Bar as Head of Monckton Chambers in January 1999, having completed a five year appointment as the first Rail Regulator, a public office established under the Railways Act 1993. Since his return he has been engaged on a series of major cases in the area of UK and European Communities competition law, including the

British Airways/City Flyer, IMS/PMSI, Universal Foods Corporation/Pointing, NTL/Cable & Wireless merger references, the reference of supermarkets before the Competition Commission, the Director General of Fair Trading's reference of the supply of medicaments to the Restrictive Practices Court, and the Airtours/First Choice merger on appeal to the CFI, Luxembourg.
Prof. Memberships: Member of the Competition Law Association and Fellow of the Chartered Institute of Transport.

SWIFT, Jonathan

11 King's Bench Walk (Eldred Tabachnik QC and James Goudie QC), London (020) 7632 8500
Recommended in Employment
Specialisation: Specialises in all aspects of employment and trade union law including dismissal, discrimination, collective disputes and European law advising and appearing for both employees and employers. Employment practice also includes restraint of trade, protection of confidential information and interim injunctions. Other practice areas include public and administrative law and all aspects of local government law and the law of education. An Editor of 'Butterworth's Local Government Law'. Was appointed to the Attorney General's B Panel in July 1999.
Prof. Memberships: Employment Law Bar Association; Employment Lawyers Association; Industrial Law Society; Discrimination Law Association; COMBAR; Administrative Law Bar Association.
Career: Called to the Bar in 1989; joined present chambers in the same year.
Personal: Educated at New College, Oxford (BA (Hons) Jurisprudence) and Emmanuel College, Cambridge (LLM). Born 11th September 1964. Lives in London.

SWIFT, Malcolm QC

Park Court Chambers (James Stewart QC, Robert Smith QC), Leeds (0113) 243 3277
malswiftqc@aol.com
Recommended in Crime
Prof. Memberships: Leader of the North Eastern Circuit (January 1998-) Member of the Bar Council (January 1997-)
Career: LLB; AKC (Kings College London). Called to the Bar Trinity 1970 – Grays Inn. Recorder of the Crown Court (1987-). Queens Counsel (1988).

SYMONS, Christopher QC

3 Verulam Buildings (Christopher Symons QC & John Jarvis QC), London (020) 7831 8441
clerks@3verulam.co.uk
Recommended in Insurance, Professional Negligence
Specialisation: Commercial work particularly insurance/reinsurance and professional negligence. Appeared in many commercial court cases and arbitrations for and against insurance companies, reinsurers, Lloyd's syndicates, brokers and other professionals. Recent cases include acting for J Rothschild in claim against insurers arising from pension mis-selling; acting regularly for Solicitors Indemnity Fund; acting for Willis Corroon in successful defence of action brought by Kuwait Airways; acting for Spicer and Pegler in the British and Commonwealth litigation which recently settled; acting for Ernst and Young in successful defence of action brought by NRG concerning acquisition of Victory Re; acting for John D Wood in BBL at first instance advancing argument, accepted by Phillips J and later by the House of Lords, that valuers not liable for losses arising from fall in the property market. Environmental law, particularly environmental warranty claims and landfill problems. Town & country planning. Construction particularly engineers and architects. Aviation. Acted in two leading rugby accident cases successfully defending Bedford School in the Van Oppen case and successfully defending front row prop in the Smoldon case. Mediation: has experience acting as mediator and for parties at mediation.
Career: Called to the Bar in 1972; Junior Counsel to the Crown (Common Law) 1985-89; Silk 1989; Recorder 1993; Deputy High Court Judge 1998; Bencher Middle Temple 1998.

TABACHNIK, Eldred QC

11 King's Bench Walk (Eldred Tabachnik QC and James Goudie QC), London (020) 7632 8500
Recommended in Employment, Planning
Specialisation: Principal area of practice is employment law. Has appeared in numerous matters for individuals, trade unions, multi-national businesses, local authorities and employer's federations in the areas of unfair dismissal, wrongful dismissal, discrimination, collective disputes, restraint of trade, European law relating to employment.
Prof. Memberships: ALBA; COMBAR: London Common Law and Commercial Bar Association.
Career: Called to the Bar 1970; Appointed Queen's Counsel 1982; Assistant Recorder 1995; Master of the Bench, Inner Temple 1998, Recorder 2000.
Personal: Educated at University of Cape Town and London University (LLM).

TABOR, James QC

Albion Chambers (J.C.T. Barton QC), Bristol (0117) 927 2144
Recommended in Crime

TACKABERRY, John QC

Arbitration Chambers (John Tackaberry QC), London (020) 7267 2137
jatqc@atack.demon.co.uk
Recommended in Alternative Dispute Resolution, Arbitration (International)
Specialisation: QC (England and Wales, New South Wales), Recorder, Registered Arbitrator, United Nations Commissioner. Member of the Irish and Californian Bars. Specialises in Building and Civil Engineering litigation, arbitration and mediation, both in the UK and internationally; and under French and Swiss law as well as common law jurisdictions. The present emphasis of his work is in very heavy civil engineering and process plants. Extensive range of written articles and contributions to conferences and courses over whole career. Presently a principal editor of the third edition of The Handbook of Arbitration Practice.
Prof. Memberships: Fellow of Chartered Institute of Arbitrators (Chairman 1990/91) and of the Faculty of Building, Member of Society of Construction Arbitrators, Society of Construction Law (First President and a major involvement in its founding), European Society of Construction law (Vice President and President 1985-87), American Arbitration Association, Supporting Member of London Maritime Arbitrators' Association.
Career: Called to the Bar 1967. Took silk 1982. Admitted to the Irish Bar 1987. Appointed Recorder 1988. Admitted to practice at the Bar of California 1988. Admitted (ad hoc) to the Bar of Malaysia 1988. Admitted to practice at the New South Wales Bar 1989 and took silk 1990. Admitted to Panel of International Arbitrators, Indian Council of Arbitration 1991. Appointed as a member of Panel of Arbitrators of the Mauritius Chamber of Commerce and Industry 1992. Appointed member of Panel of Accredited Arbitrators, Singapore International Arbitration 1992. Elected UK Jurisdiction Council member of the Interpacific Bar Association (Tokyo) 1993. Appointed as an arbitrator on panel of China International Economic and Trade Arbitration Commission 1997-2000. Appointed to Chair a construction claims panel at the United Nations Compensation Commission (which determines claims arising out of Iraq's invasion and occupation of Kuwait) 1998.
Personal: Educated at Downside School, Somerset 1952-58; Trinity College, Dublin 1958-59 (Economics/French) and Downing College, Cambridge 1959-1963 (MA, LLM).

TAGGART, Nicholas

4 Breams Buildings (Christopher Lockhart-Mummery QC), London (020) 7430 1221/7353 5835
Recommended in Property Litigation
Specialisation: All aspects of property law, including landlord and tenant, conveyancing and property related professional negligence matters. Also a specialist editor of Hill and Redman's Law of Landlord and Tenant.
Prof. Memberships: Member of Chancery Bar Association.
Career: Called to the Bar 1991.

TAGHAVI, Shahram

6 King's Bench Walk (Sibghat Kadri QC), London (020) 7583 0695 / 7353 4931
shahram.taghavi@6kbw.co.uk
Recommended in Immigration
Specialisation: Specialises in Administrative and Public, Immigration and Nationality, Human Rights, European Union and Education Law, with experience at all levels including the House of Lords, European Court of Human Rights and European Court of Justice. Recently reported cases include: Milan Horvath v Secretary of State for the Home Department [2000] 3 WLR 379, HL, R v Secretary of State for the Home Department, ex parte S [1998] Imm AR 252, QBD; R v Immigration Appeal Tribunal, ex parte Deen-Koroma [1997] Imm AR 242, CA.
Prof. Memberships: Member of Administrative Law Bar Association, Bar European Group, Education Law Association, Immigration Law Practitioners Association and International Bar Association. (Human Rights Section)
Career: Called to the Bar in 1994 (*Gray's Inn*)
Publications: 'Immigration and Nationality Law Report' (joint editor), The Human Rights Act 1998 (Contributing author).
Personal: LLB, University of London 1990 to 1993. Fluent in Farsi.

TAIT, Andrew

2 Harcourt Buildings (Mr Gerard Ryan QC), London (020) 7353 8415
clerks@2hb.law.co.uk
Recommended in Parliamentary & Public Affairs
Specialisation: Main areas of practice are parliamentary, planning, environmental, administrative and local government work.
Prof. Memberships: Parliamentary Bar; Planning & Environment Bar Association. Administrative Law Bar Association.
Career: Called to the Bar in 1981 and joined 2 Harcourt Buildings in 1982.
Personal: Educated at Hertford College, Oxford. Born 18th May 1957.

TALBOT, Patrick QC

Serle Court (Lord Neill of Bladen QC), London (020) 7242 6105
Recommended in Commercial Chancery
Specialisation: Chancery/ Commercial Litigation and advice, including commercial fraud, commercial and agricultural property, banking and credit, professional negligence, sports law, charities, computer law, insolvency, trusts and probate.

Prof. Memberships: Chancery Bar Association, British Association for Sport and Law, COMBAR.
Career: Joined Serle Court Chambers 1970, QC 1990. Recorder, Judicial chairman of The City Disputes Panel.

TAM, Robin B-K
1 Temple Gardens (Hugh B.H. Carlisle QC), London (020) 7583 1315
clerks@1templegardens.co.uk
Recommended in Administrative & Public Law: General
Specialisation: Administrative and public law/judicial review, Immigration / asylum. Personal injuries. General common law.
Prof. Memberships: Personal Injuries Bar Association. Administrative Law Bar Association. South Eastern Circuit.
Career: Called 1986. Standing Prosecuting Junior Counsel to Inland Revenue (South-Eastern Circuit), Junior Counsel to the Crown (A Panel)
Personal: Member of Hong Kong and New South Wales Bars.

TAMLYN, Lloyd
3-4 South Square (Michael Crystal QC), London (020) 7696 9900
lloydtamlyn@compuserve.com
Recommended in Insolvency/Corporate Recovery
Specialisation: Insolvency; company; professional negligence; instructed in Re Leigh Estates (UK) Limited [1994] BCC 292 (Disputed winding-up petition based on liability order for unpaid rates); Re Kingscroft Insurance Company Limited [1994] 2 BCLC 80 (Continuation of orders under section 236 of IA 1986 when provisional liquidators discharged from office); Re Dollar Land (Feltham) Limited [1995] 2 BCLC 370 (Court's power to review winding-up orders); Mytre Investments Limited v Reynolds & Others (No 2) [1996] BPIR 464 (Time limits for IVAs); Tam Wing Chuen & Anor v Bank of Credit and Commerce Hong Kong Limited [1996] 2 BCLC 69 (Privy Council: Charge backs); Mutual Reinsurance Co Limited v Peat Marwick Mitchell & Co [1997] 1 BCLC 1 (Court of Appeal: entitlement of auditors to rely on indemnity granted in Articles of Association of a Bermudian company); Aspinalls Club Limited v Halabi [1998] BPIR 322 (Jurisdiction to amend bancrupcy petition); Re Structures and Computers Limited [1998] 1 BCLC 283 (Exercise of Court's discretion to make an administration order where major creditor is opposed); Kempe v Ambassador Insurance Company [1998] 1 WLR 271 (Privy Council: power of Court to extend time limits under Scheme of Arrangement); Alf Vaughan & Co Limited v Royscot Trust plc [1999] 1 All ER (Commercial) 856 (Hire purchase agreements with 'equity' at date of receivership; extent of remedy for relief from forfeiture); Commissioners of Inland Revenue v Robinson [1999] BPIR 329 (Extent of Court's jurisdiction to review the making of a bankrupcy order); Re J N Taylor Finance Pty Limited [1999] 2 BCLC 256 (Extent of Court's jurisdiction under section 426 of IA 1986 re letters of request from foreign courts); Morgans (A Firm) v Needham (Court of Appeal: The Times, 5th November 1999) (Power to strike out for failure to comply with ambigious unless orders); Re Bank of Credit and Commerce International SA & Anor; Morris & Ors v State Bank of India [1999] BCC 943 (Striking out of pleading of claim for transaction defrauding creditors); Re Deadduck Limited [2000] 1BCLC 148 (Disqualification of director); Smith v UIC Insurance Co limited (19 Jaunuary 2000 unreported, Commercial Court)(Status of provisional liquidators of insolvent insurance company; power to award security for costs against company in provisional liquidation); Ansys Inc v Lim & Ors (Court ofAppeal, unreported, 25 February 2000: implied trusts of licence fees).
Career: Scholarship to Pembroke College, Cambridge; Double first; Prizes for best results in finals year, including two individual Best Script Prizes in Commercial Law and Contract & Tort II Papers; employed by Law Commission 1987.
Publications: Contributor to 'Halsbury's Laws of England' (4th ed 1996 reissue) volumes7(2) and 7(3); 'The Law of Receivers of Companies' (2nd ed and forthcoming 3rd ed) Sir Gavin Lightman and Gabriel Moss QC, Chapters 11 (Receivers and Winding-up) and 17 (Receivers and Unsecured Creditors: Execution, Distress, Marevas and Trusts); 'Insolvency of Banks: Managing the Risks (ed Oditah)(1996) Chapter 4 ' Choice and Initiation of Insolvency Procedure, with Mark Phillips QC.

TANSEY, Rock QC
3 Gray's Inn Square (Rock Tansey QC), London (020) 7520 5600
Recommended in Crime
Specialisation: Specialist Criminal Defence Silk with considerable expertise and experience in the conduct of the gravest cases in particular, Human Rights, Terrorism, Espionage, Murder, Serious Fraud, Drug Trafficking and 'Organised Crime'. Most notable cases include the attempted assassination of the Israeli Ambassador, the Tottenham Riots which concerned the murder of PC Blakelock, the Blackmail of Heinz plc, a Conspiracy to post incendiary devices, numerous Terrorist Cases including the bombing of the Israeli Embassy (also the Brighton and Warrington 'Bombings') and uniquely the trading of State Secrets by a KGB Spy. Accomplishments in the sphere of Human Rights comprise inter alia; the representation of the Directorate of Human Rights of the Council of Europe at a Conference in St Petersburg, Russia 1994; and recently the formation, chairmanship and organisation of conferences in Strasbourg and Rome for the European Criminal Bar Association in order to advance major legal issues of mutual concern among European Defence Lawyers.
Prof. Memberships: South Eastern Circuit, Criminal Bar Association (Committee member 1990-96, 2000), IBA, Chairman of the European Criminal Bar Association 1997-2000.
Career: Called to the Bar 1966 and Head of Chambers 1988.
Personal: Educated at Bristol University – LL.B and Diploma in Social Studies

TAPPIN, Michael
8 New Square (Michael Fysh QC SC), London (020) 7405 4321
michael.tappin@8newsquare.co.uk
Recommended in Intellectual Property
Specialisation: Specialises in all aspects of intellectual property law, but with a particular interest in chemical, pharmaceutical and biotechnological work. Co-editor of 'Encyclopedia of United Kingdom and European Patent Law'. Recent cases include: American Home Products v Novartis (1999) - pharmaceutical patent, scope of claims, sufficiency; Charlesworth v Relay Roads (1999) - patent, application to re-open trial after judgement; 3M's Patent (1999) - patent, construction, anticipation, sufficiency, declaration of non-infringement, Microsoft v Computer Future (1998) - copyright and trade marks, parallel imports, Harrison v Lingasong (1998) - performer's rights, Kirin-Amgen v Boehringer Mannheim (1997) - biotechnology patent, issue estoppel.
Prof. Memberships: Intellectual Property Bar Association, TIPLO.
Career: Called to the Bar and joined current chambers in 1991.
Personal: Educated at Cheltenham Grammar School 1975-82; St. John's College, Oxford 1982-87; Merton College, Oxford 1987-89; BA 1st Class Hons in Chemistry, D.Phil in Biochemistry. Born 11th November 1964.

TASKIS, Catherine
Falcon Chambers (Jonathan Gaunt QC & Kim Lewison QC), London (020) 7353 2484
Recommended in Property Litigation
Specialisation: Residential, commercial, agricultural, landlord & tenant and real property litigation.
Prof. Memberships: Chancery Bar Association.
Career: MA, BCL, Oxon. Called to the Bar 1995. Joined Falcon Chambers 1997. Assistant editor, Muir Watt & Moss on Agricultural Holdings. Contributor of legal articles to Landlord and Tenant Review. Contributor to Woodfall CD updates service.

TATTERSALL, Simon
Fenners Chambers (Lindsay Davies), Cambridge (01223) 368761
Recommended in Family/Matrimonial

TAUBE, Simon QC
10 Old Square (Leolin Price CBE QC), London (020) 7405 0758 / 7242 5002
Recommended in Charities, Traditional Chancery
Specialisation: Specialising in Chancery work (both litigation and advisory work) with special expertise in the fields of trusts, estates and tax, professional negligence, charity, real property, Inheritance Act claims; important cases include Berill v IRC (1981), Moore v IRC (1985), Re: Bunning (1984), Sinclair v Lee (1993), Re: Hobley (1997), Re: Ingram (1998), Re: Hoicrest (1999) X.A (1999).
Prof. Memberships: Member Chancery Bar Association, STEP and Working Party Trust Law Committee.
Career: Westminster School; Merton College, Oxford (1978 Modern History 1st class), Called 1980, Middle Temple and Lincoln's Inn, QC 2000.
Personal: Singing, tennis.

TAUSSIG, Anthony
Wilberforce Chambers (Edward Nugee QC), London (020) 7306 0102
Recommended in Traditional Chancery
Specialisation: Equity and trusts, land/conveyancing, revenue, pensions, financial services, charities, housing associations.
Career: Called to the Bar 1966. Conveyancing Counsel of the Court since 1991. Publication: 'Housing associations and their committees'. A guide to the legal framework. 1992.
Personal: Educated at Winchester College and Magdalen College, Oxford.

TAVERNER, Marcus QC
Keating Chambers (Richard Fernyhough QC), London (020) 7544 2600
Recommended in Arbitration (International), Construction, Professional Negligence
Specialisation: Construction and engineering; professional negligence; bonds and securities; sits as arbitrator in domestic and international disputes.
Career: Qualified 1981; Gray's Inn.
Personal: Monmouth School; Leicester University; King's College, London (1979 LLB Hons, 1980 LLM). Interests: music, drama, literature, sport, trees. Born 1958; resides Benington.

TAYLER, James
Devereux Chambers (Jeffrey Burke QC), London (020) 7353 7534
Recommended in Employment
Specialisation: Employment; Discrimination; Administrative and Local Government. Cases of interest include; ECM v Cox; [1999] ICR 1162, CA (trans-

fer of undertakings); Noorani v Merseyside Tec [1999] IRLR 184 CA (procedure); Thompson v Walon and BRS Automotive [1997] IRLR 343 EAT; BSG Property Services v Tuck [1996] IRLR 134 EAT (transfers of undertakings) and Allen v Redbridge LBC [1994] 1 WLR 139 DC (Trading Standards).
Prof. Memberships: ELBA (Committee member); ILS; ELA; ALBA.
Career: Wadham College Oxford; BA (Hons) Biology (1983-1986): PCL (1987-1988); CPE: ICSL Bar Finals (1988-1989). [Queen Mother Scholarship; CLE Studentship]. Editor 'Butterworths Discrimination Law'. Contributor Halsbury's Laws (Equal Pay)'. Contributor to Dix on Contracts of Employment (Butterworths 1997). Regular journal articles and conference appearances.

TAYLOR, Debbie
Hardwicke Building (Walter Aylen QC), London (020) 7242 2523
Recommended in Family: Child Care including child abduction
Specialisation: International family law disputes including child abduction, divorce and the cross-jurisdiction enforcement of financial orders. Expert evidence in Australian family law matters, particular interest and experience in Indian and Middle Eastern family law cases. Mental health related private and public law applications and child protection.
Career: Called 1984. Solicitor and Barrister Western Australia 1990. Legal Member, Mental Health Review Tribunals 1994.

TAYLOR, Gregory
9 Park Place (Ian Murphy QC), Cardiff (029) 2038 2731
Recommended in Crime

TAYLOR, John QC
2 Mitre Court Buildings (Michael FitzGerald QC), London (020) 7583 1380
Recommended in Planning
Specialisation: Practice includes Town and Country Planning, compulsory purchase and compensation, environmental, and public and administrative law – high profile cases include: extension to Whately Quarry, Coin Street, Merry Hill Shopping Centre and Howlett Zoo (Tigers Case).
Career: Called to the Bar 1958. QC 1983. MA, LL.B (Cantab) LL.M. (Harvard).
Personal: Married, 1 daughter. Lives at Clifton, Beds.

TAYLOR, Martin
Recommended in Crime

TAYLOR, Simon W.
Cloisters (Laura Cox QC), London (020) 7827 4000 simontaylor@cloisters.com
Recommended in Clinical Negligence
Specialisation: Specialises in clinical law, including clinical negligence, medical disciplinary work, mental health work, health service administrative law, inquests and defamation and criminal cases involving medical disputes. Interesting cases include Hooper v Young (CA) [1998] Lloyd's Rep Med 61 (hysterectomy – ureteric damage – application of res ipsa locquitur), Williamson v East London Health Authority [1998] Lloyd's Rep Med 6 (silicone breast implants – mastectomy), Crouchman v Burke and Others 40 BMLR 163, (sterilisation – existing pregnancy – warnings), Taylor v West Kent Health Authority [1997] 8 Med LR 251, (breast cancer – effect of delay in diagnosis), GMC v Dr Eagles and Others (October 1995), (confidentiality – case reports in medical literature), R v Canterbury & Thanet DHA, ex parte F & W [1994] 5 Med LR 132 (complaints procedure where litigation is pending), Silverman v Singer & Others (1992 and ff) (bowel damage at laparoscopic operation).
Prof. Memberships: Professional Negligence Bar Association; British Academy of Forensic Sciences; Society of Doctors In Law; British Medical Association.
Career: Qualified doctor. Called to the Bar 1984. Joined present chambers 1998.
Personal: Educated at Cambridge (BA Hons) 1983. MB BChir 1987. Born 4th July 1962. Lives in Sussex.

TEARE, Nigel QC
4 Essex Court (Nigel Teare QC), London (020) 7653 5653 nteare@4sx.co.uk
Recommended in Arbitration (International), Shipping
Specialisation: General Commercial work with particular emphasis on Carriage of Goods, Sale of Goods, Ship Finance and all aspects of Shipping law.
Prof. Memberships: COMBAR.
Career: Junior Counsel to Treasury in Admiralty Matters 1987-91. Queen's Counsel 1991. Recorder (Crown Court) 1997. Lloyd's Salvage Arbitrator 1995.
Personal: Educated: King William's College, Isle of Man. St. Peter's College, Oxford.

TEDD, Rex QC
St Philip's Chambers (Rex Tedd QC), Birmingham (0121) 246 7000
Recommended in Crime

TEMPLE, Anthony QC
4 Pump Court (Bruce Mauleverer QC), London (020) 7353 2656
Recommended in Commercial (Litigation), Insurance, Professional Negligence
Specialisation: Principal areas of practice are insurance and reinsurance, commercial fraud, stock exchange and Lloyd's disciplinary enquiries, banking, gaming lotteries and licensing. Also, common law cases of all kinds particularly professional negligence and construction.
Prof. Memberships: COMBAR, London Common Law and Commercial Bar Association, ORBA, Professional Negligence Bar Association.
Career: Called to the Bar in 1968; took silk in 1986. Recorder 1986. Deputy High Court Judge 1994.
Personal: MA (Oxon) Jurisprudence.

TEMPLE, Victor QC
6 King's Bench Walk (Michael Worsley QC), London (020) 7583 0410
Recommended in Crime, Fraud: Criminal
Specialisation: Company Frad.
Career: QC 1993. Senior Treasury Counsel at the Central Criminal Court 1989-1992. A D.T.I. Inspector into the Affairs of National Westminster Bank, 1992. A Chairman of Police Disciplinary Tribunals 1993 on. Recorder of the Crown Court. Elected a master of the Bench, Inner Temple, 1996.

TEMPLEMAN, Mark
Essex Court Chambers (Gordon Pollock QC), London (020) 7813 8000
Recommended in Insurance
Specialisation: Insurance and reinsurance, shipping, international sale of goods and international trade finance, in the context of both domestic and international litigation and arbitration. Also general commercial litigation of all types.
Career: Keble College, Oxford MA (Jurisprudence); BCL (1980). Inns of Court, 1979. Called to the Bar 1981.
Personal: Born 1958.

TENNET, Michael
Wilberforce Chambers (Edward Nugee QC), London (020) 7306 0102
Recommended in Pensions
Specialisation: Broad range of Commercial/Chancery litigation specialising in the areas of professional negligence, pensions and financial services. Pensions including recovery of assets for pension fund trustees, including Maxwell. Also, SWT v Wightman, Best v Harrods. Financial services including hearings before LAUTRO, the SIB Review of selling practices. See also Cocking v Prudential and allegations of deficient financial advice and mis-selling. Professional negligence involving solicitors, actuaries and accountants. General chancery/commercial litigation. Cases include Ashley Guarantee v Zacaria (principal and surety/mortgages) Yale v Newman (competition law).
Career: Called to the Bar 1985. Law at New College, Oxford. Contributor to Ellison on Pensions Law and Practice and LLP's Professional Negligence Law and Practice.

TER HAAR, Roger QC
Crown Office Chambers (Michael Spencer QC & Christopher Purchas QC), London (020) 7797 8100
Recommended in Construction, Professional Negligence
Specialisation: Practice encompasses professional negligence, construction law and insurance and reinsurance work.
Prof. Memberships: Official Referee's Bar Association, Administrative Law Bar Association, London and Commercial Bar Association, COMBAR.
Career: Called to the Bar and joined Crown Office Row 1974. Took Silk 1992. Bencher of the Inner Temple.
Personal: Educated at Magdalen College, Oxford 1970-73. Born 14th June 1952.

TERRY, Jeffrey
8 King St (Keith Armitage QC), Manchester (0161) 834 9560 jeffreyterry@genie.co.uk
Recommended in Commercial (Litigation)
Specialisation: Commercial and Chancery. Recent Reported Cases include Universities Superannuation Scheme v Royal Insurance [2000] 1 All ER (Comm) 266; Unchained Growth v Granby Village [2000] 1 WLR 739; Re Hancock [1998] 2 FLR 346; Co-Operative Bank plc v Tipper [1996] 4 All ER 366; Transthene v Royal Insurance [1996] LRLR 32; Bank of Baroda v Reyarel [1995] 2 FLR 376; Jones v Roberts [1995] 2 FLR 422.
Prof. Memberships: Northern Circuit Commercial Bar Association; COMBAR; Northern Arbitration Association; Northern Chancery Bar Association; American Bar Association; Professional Negligence Bar Association; Union Internationale des Avocats; Bar European Group.
Career: LLB (Lond) 1975; Called 1976; MA (Business Law) with Distinction 1981; Fellow of the Chartered Institute of Arbitrators, President's Prize, 1996; CEDR Accredited Mediator 1999.
Publications: Various papers and publications in England, USA and Canada.
Personal: Married, two children [b 1983, 1987]; Theology and Church Affairs; Smallholding husbandry.

TETHER, Melanie
Old Square Chambers (John Hendy QC), London (020) 7269 0300
Recommended in Employment
Specialisation: Formerly a partner in *Norton Rose*, transferred to the Bar in 1995. Deals with all aspects of

employment law, including unfair and wrongful dismissal, transfer of undertakings, collective disputes, restraint of trade and all areas of discrimination law. Leading cases in which she has been involved include Kerry Foods Ltd v Creder and others [2000] IRLR 10; Unicorn Consultancy Services Ltd v Westbrook and others [2000] IRLR 80; Everson and another v Secretary of State for Trade and Industry and Bell Lines Limited (in liquidation) Case C - 198/98 [2000] IRLR 202; Chief Constable of West Yorkshire Police v Khan [2000] IRLR 324; and Preston and others v Wolverhampton NHS Trust and others Case C - 78/98 [2000] IRLR 236. Employment law adviser to Association of Colleges.
Prof. Memberships: Former Chair and current Vice-President of the Industrial Law Society.
Publications: Writes the Equal Pay section of 'Tolley's Employment Law'.

THANKI, Bankim
Fountain Court (Anthony Boswood QC), London (020) 7583 3335
Recommended in Aviation, Banking, Commercial (Litigation), Professional Negligence, Sport
Specialisation: Commercial and civil including general commercial litigation, banking, aviation, professional negligence, arbitration, insurance, and sports law. Noteworthy cases include Deposit Protection Board v Barclays Bank and Dalia (banking), Bank of England- BCCI claims ("Three Rivers") (banking), NRG v Swiss Bank Corporation & others (reinsurance/professional negligence, disciplinary proceedings for the Football Association against Leicester City players over the 1999 Worthington Cup Final and against Tottenham Hotspur FC over players' contractual terms, Nuova Safim v Sakura Bank (banking/swap agreements), Federal Republic of Germany v Sotheby's (conflicts), Dowles Manor Properties v Bank of Namibia (unless orders), Gurtner v Beaton (aviation/agency), Gotha City v Sotheby's (privilege), Paragon Finance v Freshfields (privilege), Minories Finance v Afribank Nigeria (documentary credits/bills & exchange), BCCI v Price Waterhouse (discovery, Banking Act 1987, auditor's negligence), Southampton CC v Academy Cleaning (local authority/contract tenders), Re a firm of solicitors (solicitors/conflicts), British Coal v Smith (employment/equal pay), Kecskemeti v Rubens Rabin (solicitors' negligence/wills), HIV haemophilia litigation, Shannon v Country Casuals (Subpoena). Involved in civil and disciplinary aspects of Barlow Clowes and Polly Peck affairs. Joint editor of 'Commercial Court Procedure' (Sweet & Maxwell) and co-author of of the forthcoming 'Carriage by Air' (Butterworths). Lectures on aviation law to international airlines, and in aspects of commercial law to City Solicitors.
Prof. Memberships: Commercial Bar Association, Common Law & Commercial Bar Association.
Career: Called to the Bar 1988.
Personal: Educated at Balliol College, Oxford (MA, 1st Class Hons 1986). Harmsworth Scholar, Middle Temple 1988.

THOM, James
4 Field Court (Steven Gee QC), London (020) 7440 6900
Recommended in Property Litigation
Specialisation: Principal area of work is commercial property litigation, including disputes arising out of commercial conveyancing transactions, dilapidations cases, service charge disputes, rent reviews and lease renewals. Other main areas of work are: professional negligence (for both claimants and defendants) in claims against solicitors, surveyors and valuers, often in cases with a commercial property aspect and also in claims against architects, engineers and others (not medical); commercial law (with emphasis on commercial contracts, banking and commercial lending). Joint author of "Handbook of Dilapidations" (Sweet & Maxwell, 1992). Regular speaker at conferences and seminars on the law of landlord and tenant.
Prof. Memberships: Professional Negligence Bar Association, COMBAR. Bar Sports Law Group.
Career: Called to the Bar 1974. Called to the Bar of St. Vincent and the Grenadines 1997.
Personal: Educated at Felsted School 1965-1968 and Corpus Christi College, Oxford 1969-1973 (BA 1972, BCL 1973). Born 19th October 1951. Lives in Highgate, London.

THOMAS, Christopher QC
Keating Chambers (Richard Fernyhough QC), London (020) 7544 2600
Recommended in Arbitration (International), Construction
Specialisation: Construction and engineering; professional negligence; bonds and guarantees; oil, power and transport projects in UK and overseas; arbitration and mediation – domestic and international; arbitrator under ICC and other rules; cases include Croudace Ltd v Lambeth BC; Int'l Press Centre v Norwich Union Life Insurance Society; McAlpine Humberoak v McDermott Int'l.
Career: Qualified 1973; Lincoln's Inn, Queen's Counsel 1989, admitted to the Bar of Gibraltar 1990; Recorder; lecturer; Fellow of the Chartered Institute of Arbitrators.
Personal: University of Kent, Canterbury (BA Law 1st class); Faculté International de Droit Compare (Diplôme de Droit Comparé avec merite); King's College, London (PhD. Law). CEDR accredited mediator. Born 1950; resides London.

THOMAS, David
2 Temple Gardens (Dermod O'Brien QC), London (020) 7822 1200
Recommended in Construction
Specialisation: Construction and civil engineering litigation and arbitration. Recent reported cases: Davy Offshore v Emerald Field Contracting, GPT Realisations v Panatown. Soundcraft v Padmanor, Balfour Beatty v DLR, Chesham Properties v Bucknall Austin, Cook v Shimizu, Weldon v CNT.
Prof. Memberships: ORBA, BEG.
Career: Oxford: 1st Class Honours in Law 1981. Called to Bar 1982; Called to Bar of Gibraltar 1996.

THOMAS, Keith
9 Park Place (Ian Murphy QC), Cardiff (029) 2038 2731
Recommended in Crime

THOMAS, Leslie
Two Garden Court (I. Macdonald QC & O.Davies QC), London (020) 7353 1633
leslie@global.force9.net
Recommended in Human Rights (Civil Liberties)
Specialisation: Civil actions against the police and prisons. Inquests (deaths in custody and fatal shootings). Judicial review of Police Complaints Authority, Coroners, Magistrates. Human Rights specialist.
Prof. Memberships: Lawyers for liberty; Inquest Lawyers; Member of Civil Liberties Trustees; APIL.
Publications: Numerous articles and case notes on Inquests for various legal journals and media.

THOMAS, Michael QC
Essex Court Chambers (Gordon Pollock QC), London (020) 7813 8000
Recommended in Arbitration (International)
Specialisation: Maritime, International Trade, Construction, Sale and Purchase. Recent arbitrations: Oil Rig Charterparty dispute, sale of high speed vessel, shipbuilding dispute.
Prof. Memberships: Associate Member of Chartered Institute of Arbitrators. Member of Hong Kong Bar.
Career: Practice at the English Bar since 1959, Treasury Junior (MOD) 1966, Queen's Counsel 1973.
Publications: Temperley: 'Merchant Shipping Act'.

THOMAS, Nigel M.
13 Old Square (Michael Lyndon-Stanford QC), London (020) 7404 4800
Recommended in Agriculture
Specialisation: Agricultural Law: Davies v H & R Eckroyd Ltd (1996) EGCS 77; Law of Commons and Village Green: R v Suffolk CC ex Parte Steed (1995) 2EGLR 232, Lord Dynevor v Richardson [1995] ChD 173.
Prof. Memberships: Chancery Bar Association, Bristol and Cardiff Chancery Bar Association Wales and Chester Circuit.
Career: Called to the Bar 1976 (Gray's Inn). Sometime lecturer in Agricultural Law, Central Law Training. Deputy Chairman Agricultural Lands Tribunal (Western Area).

THOMAS, Patrick QC
4 Fountain Court (Richard Wakerley QC), Birmingham (0121) 236 3476
Recommended in Crime
Specialisation: Crime, both prosecution and defence. Junior Counsel for defence of Sheila Bower, Central Criminal Court Jan – Feb 1998.
Prof. Memberships: CBA
Career: Lincoln College Oxford, Grays Inn, Recorder. QC 1999
Personal: Reading, Theatre, Walking.

THOMAS, Paul Huw
Iscoed Chambers (Trefor Davies), Swansea (01792) 652988/9
Recommended in Crime

THOMAS, R. Neville QC
3 Verulam Buildings (Christopher Symons QC & John Jarvis QC), London (020) 7831 8441
Recommended in Banking, Commercial (Litigation)
Specialisation: Principal area of practice encompasses all aspects of commercial contracts, especially for banks, shipping companies, trading companies, commodity dealers and property companies.
Prof. Memberships: Commercial Bar Association, London Common Law Bar Association.
Career: Called to the Bar and joined present chambers 1962. Took Silk 1975. Recorder 1975-81. Master of the Bench, Inner Temple 1985.
Personal: Educated at Oxford University (MA 1960, BCL 1961). Born 31st March 1936. Lives in London and Wales.

THOMAS, Robert
4 Essex Court (Nigel Teare QC), London (020) 7653 5653
rthomas@4sx.co.uk
Recommended in Shipping
Specialisation: All aspects of shipping and related areas, including insurance; International Sale of Goods; Jurisdiction Disputes, etc. Salvage & Collisions.
Prof. Memberships: Commercial Bar Association, LCIA and supporting member of LMAA.
Career: M.A. (Hons), Trinity College, Cambridge. Licence Spéciale en Droit Européen, Université Libre de Bruxelles. BCL, St Catherine's College, Oxford. Fluent French, working knowledge of German.

THOMAS, Roger QC
9 Park Place (Ian Murphy QC), Cardiff (029) 2038 2731
Recommended in Crime
Specialisation: Criminal law of all types including Revenue and Excise fraud.
Prof. Memberships: C.B.A.
Career: Recorder 1987, Silk 1994.
Personal: LL.B (Wales.) Married 1974 Susan Nicola (nee Orchard) 2 children Adam (22.11.78) and Kirsty (15.1.81.) Tennis, travel.

THOMAS, Sybil
3 Fountain Court (Robert Juckes QC), Birmingham (0121) 236 5854
Recommended in Crime, Family/Matrimonial
Specialisation: All aspects of criminal and family law, with a particular interest in cases involving the disabled and mentally ill.
Prof. Memberships: Midland and Oxford Circuit, Family Law Bar Association (Chairman, Birmingham branch), Criminal Bar Association.
Career: Called to the Bar 1976. Recorder 1997.

THOMPSON, Andrew
Erskine Chambers (Robin Potts QC), London (020) 7242 5532
Recommended in Company
Specialisation: Specialist in commercial litigation, particularly involving issues of company law, corporate insolvency, partnership disputes and professional negligence; advisory work in the same fields; cases include Re BSB Holdings Ltd (No 2) (1996 1 BCLC 155), Re H & K (Medway) Ltd (1997 1 WLR 1422), Re Sentinel Securities plc (1996 1 WLR 316), Re SH & Co (Realizations) 1990 Ltd (1993 BCC 60), Re CSTC Ltd (1995 BCC 173), Banque Financière de la Cité v Parc (Battersea) Ltd (1999 1 AC 221), New Hampshire Insurance v Rush & Tompkins (1998 2 BCLC 471), Re Holiday Promotions (1996 BCC 671), Re Lummus Agricultural Services (1999 BCC 953), Re Kaytech (1999) 2 BCLC 351.
Career: Merchant Taylors' School; St Catharine's College, Cambridge (1989 BA; 1990 LLM; 1992 MA); Called to Inner Temple 1991.
Personal: Leisure: gardening, hill walking, birding.

THOMPSON, Rhodri
Matrix Chambers (Nicholas Blake QC), London (020) 7404 3447
rhodrithompson@matrixlaw.co.uk
Recommended in Competition/Anti-trust
Specialisation: European Community law including administrative law and competition. Treasury Panel. Cases include BCCI et al. v Bank of England (misfeasance in public office); R v Chief Constable of Sussex ex parte ITF (exports of livestock); R v Secretary of State for the Home Department ex parte Hoverspeed (carriers liability); acted for BBC in RPC reference of Premier League TV contract. Contributor to 'Bellamy & Child, Common Market Law of Competition', (5th edition forthcoming); Vaughan Law of the European Communities Service, 'Rights of Establishment and Freedom to Provide Services' (looseleaf); 'Human Rights Practice', ed Emerson and Simor forthcoming (freedom and assembly); and author of 'The Single Market for Pharmaceuticals' (1994). Regular speaker at conferences/in house seminars on EC law.

THORLEY, Simon QC
Three New Square (David E.M. Young QC), London (020) 7405 1111
Recommended in Intellectual Property
Specialisation: Extensive intellectual property practice particularly in field of Chemical and Biotechnical Patents and expanding to passing off, trade marks, copyright, designs and breach of confidence. Advises on EC law relating to IP. Experience in arbitrations. Recent Cases: Biogen v Medeva, Biotech Patents, House of Lords; Canon v Green Cartridge, patent/copyright, Hong Kong Privy Council; Harrods v Harrodian School – passing off; Phillips v Remington – trade marks; Lubrizol v Exxon and Union Carbide v BP – patents.
Prof. Memberships: Chairman Intellectual Property Bar Assn (1995-99); Member Chancery Bar Assn; AIPPI; Member of Bar Council (1995-99)
Career: Rugby School, 1963-1967. Keble College, Oxford, MA Jurisprudence, 1968-1971. Called to Bar 1972. Q.C.1989. Appointed person to hear Trade Mark Appeals, 1996. Deputy High Court Judge, 1998. Deputy Chairman Copyright Tribunal, 1998.

THORNHILL, Andrew R. QC
Pump Court Tax Chambers (Andrew Thornhill QC), London (020) 7414 8080
Recommended in Tax
Specialisation: Principal area of practice is revenue law, both advisory and litigation.
Prof. Memberships: Revenue Bar Association.
Career: Called to the Bar 1969. Took Silk 1985. Appointed Recorder 1997. Currently Head of Chambers.
Personal: Born 4th August 1943.

THORNTON, Peter QC
Doughty Street Chambers (Geoffrey Robertson QC), London (020) 7404 1313
Recommended in Crime, Human Rights (Civil Liberties)
Specialisation: Principal area of practice is criminal defence work including commercial fraud; appellate work, notably Privy Council appeals (Caribbean, Mauritius, New Zealand) often in capital cases; and all forms of serious crime including murder, terrorism, Official Secrets Act, corruption and drugs cases. Other main area of work is civil rights cases including actions against the police or government, suspects' and prisoners' rights and international human rights. Recent reported cases include R v Christou [1992] (undercover police); Walker v R [1994] (Privy Council jurisdiction: appeal against death sentence); R v Basford and Lawless (witness too ill to continue); R v Aroyewumi [1994] (sentencing in Class A drugs cases); Freemantle v R [1994] (the proviso in identification cases), Re W [1994] (rights of children), Lobban [1995] (editing co-defendant's statement) and R v Kelly and Lindsay [1998] (stealing body parts), R v Smith (Morgan) [1999] (provocation and the reasonable man). Author of 'Public Order Law' (Blackstone Press 1987) and 'Decade of Decline:Civil Liberties in the Thatcher Years' (Liberty 1989). Editor of the Penguin Civil Liberty Guide (1989); currently contributing editor to Archbold and member of editorial board of the Criminal Law Review. Regular broadcaster on legal and civil liberty topics. Teaches human rights, advocacy and criminal evidence to solicitors and barristers. Has lectured and chaired seminars, on trial by jury, PACE, police powers, the CPS, evidence, white collar crime, emergency powers, miscarriages of justice, and the right of silence.
Prof. Memberships: Midland and Oxford Circuit, Criminal Bar Association, Administrative Law Bar Association, formerly Chairman of the National Council for Civil Liberties and of the Civil Liberties Trust. Member of the Just Television Advisory Group.
Career: Called to the Bar 1969. Also called to the Bars of Trinidad, Northern Ireland, Isle of Man. Tenant at *1 King's Bench Walk* 1971-1978 and at *1 Dr. Johnson's Buildings* 1978-90. Founder member of *Doughty Street Chambers* in 1990 and currently deputy head of chambers. Took Silk 1992. Recorder of the Crown Court 1997.

THORNTON, Rebecca
9 Woodhouse Square (John Morris Collins), Leeds (0113) 245 1986
Recommended in Family/Matrimonial
Specialisation: A well thought of specialist in every aspect of family work. Called to the Bar in 1976. Combines a successful practice with a young family. Work undertaken at every level of Court and for private, professional and local authority clients. Instructed in the 'Cleveland' litigation. Active Member of the Family Bar Association.

THOROGOOD, Bernard
5 Fountain Court (Anthony Barker QC), Birmingham (0121) 606 0500
Recommended in Crime

Specialisation: Criminal Law - all areas covered but very extensive experience of the most serious categories of offences, including commercial fraud. Very significant experience of video-link and Appellate work. Particular interest in matters involving claims of public interest immunity and matters involving expert evidence. Trading Standards, Health and Safety, Road Traffic.
Prof. Memberships: Criminal Bar Association. Forensic Science Society.
Career: 1981-85 Short Service Commission (Army). 1986 Called to the Bar.
Personal: Married, 3 children.

THOROLD, Oliver
Doughty Street Chambers (Geoffrey Robertson QC), London (020) 7404 1313.
Recommended in Product Liability

THORP, Simon
Park Lane Chambers (Stuart Brown QC), Leeds (0113) 228 5000
Recommended in Personal Injury

THWAITES, Ronald QC
Ely Place Chambers (Ronald Thwaites QC), London (020) 7400 9600
Recommended in Crime, Defamation

TIDMARSH, Christopher
5 Stone Buildings (Henry Harrod), London (020) 7242 6201
Recommended in Pensions, Traditional Chancery
Specialisation: Chancery practitioner, with a particular emphasis on trusts and probate, pension schemes and professional negligence, principally solicitors and accountants. Standing junior counsel to the Inland Revenue (Chancery). Important cases include Bridge Trust v AG of Cayman Islands (charities) [1999]; British Coal v British Coal Staff Superannuation Scheme Trustees [1994]; Stannard v Fisons [1991]; Electricity Supply Nominees litigation, (all pensions). The Pointwest litigation (solicitors negligence). Re a Debtor (415 of 1993) [1994]; Re a Debtor (6349 of 1994) (bankruptcy). IRC v Lloyds Private Banking; IRC v Botner (1999). Cooper v Billingham (2000) (all tax).
Prof. Memberships: Chancery Bar Association, STEP.
Career: Called 1985.
Personal: Educated at Merton College, Oxford (BA) 1980-83.

TILLYARD, James
30 Park Place (John Jenkins QC), Cardiff (029) 2039 8421
Recommended in Family/Matrimonial

TIPPLES, Amanda

13 Old Square (Michael Lyndon-Stanford QC), London (020) 7404 4800

Recommended in Property Litigation

Specialisation: Practice covers business and commercial chancery work, (litigation emphasis), including corporate and personal insolvency, partnership, landlord and tenant and property law generally.

Prof. Memberships: Chancery Bar Association, Bar Council.

Career: Called to the Bar in 1991 and joined *13 Old Square* in 1992.

Personal: Educated at Roedean School and Gonville and Caius College, Cambridge (1986-1990). Lives in London.

TODD, Michael QC

Erskine Chambers (Robin Potts QC), London (020) 7242 5532

Recommended in Company

TOPHAM, Geoffrey J.

3 Stone Buildings (G.C. Vos QC), London (020) 7242 4937

Recommended in Pensions, Traditional Chancery

Specialisation: Main field of practice is occupational pension schemes, acting both in Litigation and Advisory work for members, pensioners, trustees and employers (cases include Imperial Tobacco, Courage, Brooks v Brooks, Lloyds Bank, National Grid). Other main areas are trusts and estates, and capital taxes.

Prof. Memberships: Chancery Bar Association, Association of Pensions Lawyers, Associate of Pensions Management Institute, Revenue Bar Association.

Career: Called June, 1964. Member of Lincoln's Inn. Joined Stone Buildings in 1965.

Personal: Educated at Haileybury and Trinity Hall, Cambridge.

TOUBE, Felicity

3-4 South Square (Michael Crystal QC), London (020) 7696 9900

Recommended in Insolvency/Corporate Recovery

Specialisation: Insolvency, banking, general commercial, restitution. Cases include Secretary of State for Trade and Industry v Anderson and others, Njie v Cora, re Continental Assurance Co; BCCI v Bank of America; Re Douai School [2000] 1WLR 502; Toshoku UK plc (The Times 29 March 2000); Re Ross Horne v Dacorum BC. Publications: Rose (ed.) Restitution and Banking Law; Failure of Contracts; Board Member – 'Insolvency Intelligence'; various articles for 'Insolvency Intelligence', case editor for Totty and Moss CD-ROM, contributor to Totty and Moss on 'Insolvency' and Lightman & Moss on 'Receivers'; compiler of 'Recovery' Case Summaries.

Prof. Memberships: COMBAR, Chancery Bar Association.

Career: BA, BCL (Oxon).

TOZZI, Nigel

4 Pump Court (Bruce Mauleverer QC), London (020) 7353 2656

Recommended in Commercial (Litigation), Insurance, Licensing, Professional Negligence

Specialisation: General commercial and common law practice, specialising in commercial litigation, professional negligence (especially solicitors, accountants, financial advisers, surveyors, valuers, brokers and barristers), insurance and reinsurance, fire claims, media and entertainment, financial and banking disputes and gaming. He also has experience in aviation, employment, agency, advertising, construction work and professional disciplinary hearings.

Prof. Memberships: COMBAR, Professional Negligence Bar Association, London Common Law and Commercial Bar Association.

Personal: Educated at Exeter University (LL.B Hons first class) 1976-1979. Bar Finals 1980 (first class). Leisure pursuits include sport (especially hockey), theatre and cinema. Born 31st August 1957.

TRACE, Anthony QC

13 Old Square (Michael Lyndon-Stanford QC), London (020) 7404 4800

Recommended in Commercial Chancery

Specialisation: Principal area of practice encompasses insolvency, property, trusts, chancery and general commercial work, including a number of cases outside the UK. Recent cases include: Re Jeffrey S. Levitt Ltd [1992] (privilege against self-incrimination); Re Mirror Group (Holdings) Ltd [1993] (liability of assignees on liquidation); Gomba Holdings (UK) Ltd v Minories Finance Ltd (No.2) [1993] (mortgagee's costs); Lotteryking Ltd v AMEC Properties Ltd [1995] (set – off against assignees); Re BCCI SA (No.10) [1996] (insolvency set – off); Slough Estates plc v Welwyn Hatfield DC [1996] (measure of damages for fraudulent misrepresentation); Grand Metropolitan plc v The William Hill Group Ltd [1997] (rectification); Bogg v Raper [1998] (will drafting and exclusion clause); Plant v Plant [1998] (individual voluntary arrangements); Jordan Grand Prix Ltd v Baltic Insurance Group [1999] (Brussels Convention); Landacre Investments Ltd v Welsh Development Agency [2000] (misfeasance in public office); WPP Group plc v Reichmann [2000] (conspiracy). Has sat as an Arbitrator. Honorary Secretary, Chancery Bar Association.

Prof. Memberships: Chancery Bar Association; COMBAR; Bar Sports Law Group; ACTAPS (Association of Contentious Trust and Probate Specialists).

Career: Called to the Bar 1981.

Publications: Contributor to 'Butterworths European Law Service' (company law) and 'Butterworths Practical Insolvency'. Deputy Managing Editor: 'Receivers, Administrators and Liquidators Quarterly'.

Personal: Educated at Magdalene College, Cambridge (MA, 1st Class Honours).

TRACY FORSTER, Jane

13 King's Bench Walk (Roger Ellis QC), London (020) 7353 7204

clerks@13kbw.co.uk

Recommended in Clinical Negligence

Specialisation: Clinical Negligence of all descriptions. Recent Cases: Miles v West Kent Health Authority 1997 Med LR 191; Smith v Leicester Health Authority 1998 Lloyds Rep. (Med) 77; Thurman v Bath and Wiltshire Health Authority 1997 P.I.Q.R. Q115.

Prof. Memberships: Professional Negligence Bar Association; Personal Injury Bar Association; Employment Law Bar Association.

Career: LLB (Hons) Liverpool University 1974; Called July 1975 (Inner Temple); Sept 1975-May 1986 Peel House Chambers, Liverpool. From May 1986- 13 King's Bench Walk.

Personal: Married with one son. Lives in London.

TRAVERS, David

3 Fountain Court (Robert Juckes QC), Birmingham (0121) 236 5854

Recommended in Consumer

Specialisation: Practice made up of all aspects of regulatory work; including trading standards, consumer protection and health and safety as well as environmental protection, waste management and planning, and public law. Experienced in appellate work and cases with a strong technical or scientific component. Clients include well known high street names (as well as small traders), local authorities and regulatory bodies. Cases include: R v Coffey [1987] Crim LR 498, CA; A v Wigan MBC [1986] FLR 608, DC; Birmingham CC v H [1994] 2 WLR 31, HL; Farrand v Tse (1992) Times 10 December, DC (meaning of "application" for emergency prohibition order – Food Safety Act); Dudley MBC v Firman BTCL (1992) Independent 26 October DC ("due diligence" – sufficiency of sampling); Janbo Trading v Dudley MBC [1993] 157 JPN 256, DC ("due diligence"); Gale v Dixons Stores Group (1994) 158 JPN 256, DC ("extent of trade description"); T&S Stores Ltd v Hereford & Worcester CC [1995] Tr LR 337 (under age sales – "due diligence"); Edwards v CPS [1881] 155 JP 746, DC (licensing); Lazarus v Coventry CC 91995) Sol J Vol 139, No 32 826 (consumer credit advertisement - meaning of "information" – "due diligence"); North Yorkshire CC v Entergold Guardian 8.2.95 (breach of site licence and planning control at waste transfer station); Meston Technical Services v Warwickshire CC [1995] Env LR D36 (breach of site licence – meaning of "waste"); Taw & Torridge Fisheries Byelaw Inquiry, Daily Telegraph 31.1.97; Hilliers Ltd v Sefton MBC [1997] 3CL 424 (delegation of powers within Food authority); R v Snaresbrook Crown Court, ex parte Input Management [1999] Times 29 April (duty to give reasons). Waste management licensing appeals and numerous public inquiries, particularly involving waste management facilities..

Prof. Memberships: Food Law Group, Planning and Environment Bar Association, Administrative Law Bar Association, UKELA. Midland and Oxford Circuit.

Career: Called Middle Temple 1981, Kings College London 1975-1980 (LLB, LLM, AKC). Editor 'Kings Counsel' the KCL Law Journal 1978. President Kings College London Union of Students 1979, elected Honorary Life Member 1981. Harmsworth Scholar 1982. Member of the Bar Council 1995 – Member of Law Reform and IT Committees 1996-1998. Sometime Occasional Lecturer School of Management Sciences University of Manchester Institute of Science and Technology. Sometime Royal Institution Australian Science Scholar.

Personal: Married with children. Interests language, music, running and family life.

TREACY, Colman QC

3 Fountain Court (Robert Juckes QC), Birmingham (0121) 236 5854

clerks@3fc.co.uk

Recommended in Crime

Specialisation: Criminal Law. All types of serious crime cases including commercial fraud. Equal split between prosecution and defence work. Recent reported cases: Fellows (computer pornography) : Callender (res gestae) : Kendrick & Hopkins (theft and gifts inter vivos) : Ryan James (successful vet murder appeal). ELAHEE (rape victim's character). Regulatory Law of all types, representing businesses and local authorities.

Career: Jesus College Cambridge (open scholar) : Call 1971 : Silk 1990 : Recorder. Bencher Middle Temple. Mental Health Review Tribunal. Assistant Boundary Commissioner.

TREVETT, Peter QC

11 New Square (John Gardiner QC), London (020) 7242 4017

taxlaw@11newsquare.com

Recommended in Tax

Specialisation: Revenue Law. Practice covers all aspects of commercial, private client and trust taxation in the UK, including stamp duty, VAT, unit trusts, insurance company taxation and offshore trusts. Hong Kong profits tax, stamp duty and estate duty planning. Regular lecturer on revenue law.

Prof. Memberships: Revenue Bar Association, Chancery Bar Association and Society of Trust and

Estate Practitioners (Committee Member). fellow of the Society for Advanced Legal Studies.
Career: Called to Bar 1971. Joined present Chambers 1973. Took Silk 1992.
Personal: Educated Kingston Grammar School. Queens' College, Cambridge (1966-1971) (MA. LL.M). Born 25th November 1947.

TRITTON, Guy
One Raymond Buildings (Christopher Morcom QC), London (020) 7430 1234
guytritton@ukonline.co.uk
Recommended in Intellectual Property
Specialisation: Intellectual Property. Experienced in both soft IP (trade marks, copyright and passing off) and hard IP (patents and technical design). A number of reported cases including Springsteen v Flute and Ors (big media copyright dispute); WILD CHILD TM (leading trade mark case); Fylde Microsystems v Key Radio (joint authorship in computer programmes); Hodgkinson & Corby v Wards (passing off in functional items); Hazelgrove Superleague v Businesss Machines (right to modify patented articles); Chiron v Organon (biotechnological patent infringement action). Author of 'Intellectual Property in Europe', Sweet & Maxwell, 800 p 1996. This has become a university text book in several universities including University of Maastricht, 2nd edition to be released in 2000. Also substantial practices in franchise and IT disputes; Dyno Rod v Reeve (enforceability of post-termination restraint of trade covenants in franchise).
Prof. Memberships: Intellectual Property Bar Association
Career: Eton College; Durham University BSc Natural Sciences (applied physics, computing, psychology and mathematics). Inner Temple Pegasus scholar. Author of a number of computer programmes including a chambers fee billing package; a legal discovery programme and a designer and programmer of chambers own website.
Personal: Married. 2 Children. Piano, computers, windsurfing and fieldsports.

TROLLOPE, Andrew QC
1 Middle Temple Lane (Colin Dines & Andrew Trollope QC), London (020) 7583 0659 (12 lines)
Recommended in Crime, Fraud: Criminal
Specialisation: Co-Head of Chambers specialising in criminal law with wide experience of fraud cases. Own practice has predominantly consisted of City, Commercial and other fraud cases for more than 15 years. Cases include: R v Thomas Ward (Guinness), R v Cohen (Blue Arrow), R v Masterson (Caird plc), R v Michael Ward (European Leisure plc), R v Johnston (Harrovian Properties/Leisure).
Prof. Memberships: Criminal Bar Association Committee Member.
Career: A Recorder of the Crown Court since 1989.

TROMANS, Stephen
11 King's Bench Walk (Eldred Tabachnik QC and James Goudie QC), London (020) 7632 8500
Recommended in Environment
Specialisation: Environmental Law, Planning Law, Public Law. R v Durham County Council, ex parte Huddleston (Court of Appeal).
Prof. Memberships: PEBA, UKELA, Chartered Institute of Water & Environmental Management.
Career: Former University Leacturer (Cambridge 1981-87) Former solicitor.
Publications: - (textbooks) 'The Encyclopedia of Environmental Law', 'Planning Law, Practice & Precedents', 'Commercial Leases', 'Nuclear Installations & Radioactive Substances', 'Contaminated Land: The New Regime'.
Personal: Council Member, English Nature.

TROTTER, David
Plowden Buildings (William Lowe QC), London (020) 7583 0808
Recommended in Personal Injury

TROWER, William
3-4 South Square (Michael Crystal QC), London (020) 7696 9900
williamtrower@southsquare.com
Recommended in Commercial Chancery, Insolvency/Corporate Recovery
Specialisation: Business Law especially corporate and international insolvency banking, company law and professional negligence.
Prof. Memberships: COMBAR, Chancery Bar Association, CEDR Accredited Mediator.
Career: Called 1983. Acted in many of the major insolvencies of the 1990's (BCCI, Polly Peck, Maxwell and Barings). Litigation in Bermuda throughout 1999 (Bermuda Fire and Marine). Particular interest in insurance insolvency.
Publications: Fletcher Higham and Trower: 'Law and Practice of Corporate Administrations' (1994)

TUCKER, Lynton
12 New Square (John Mowbray QC), London (020) 7419 1212
Recommended in Traditional Chancery

TUCKER, Paul Geoffrey
40 King St (Philip Raynor QC), Manchester (0161) 832 9082
ptucker@40kingstreet.co.uk
Recommended in Planning
Specialisation: Planning, Local Government, Environmental Law, Highway, Compulsory Purchase, Licensing.
Prof. Memberships: PEBA, UKELA, ALBA.

TUGENDHAT, Michael QC
5 Raymond Buildings (Patrick Milmo QC), London (020) 7242 2902
Recommended in Commercial (Litigation)

TURNBULL, Charles
Wilberforce Chambers (Edward Nugee QC), London (020) 7306 0102
Recommended in Pensions
Specialisation: Work including the law of real property (including landord and tenant), occupational pension schemes, professional negligence claims, charity law and litigation relating to private trusts.
Prof. Memberships: Member of Chancery Bar Association.
Career: 1st class in Law, Oxford; Eldon Law scholarship. Joined *Wilberforce Chambers* in 1976.
Personal: Speaks reasonable German.

TURNER, David QC
Exchange Chambers (William Waldron QC), Liverpool (0151) 236 7747
Recommended in Crime

TURNER, David
2 Temple Gardens (Dermod O'Brien QC), London (020) 7822 1200
dturner@2templegardens.co.uk
Recommended in Product Liability
Specialisation: Professional negligence, (engineers/architects/barristers/solicitors/accountants). Insurance (interpretation/repudiation) Commercial product liability (including IT).

TURNER, James QC
One King's Bench Walk (Anthony Hacking QC), London (020) 7936 1500
Recommended in Family: Child Care including child abduction, Family: Matrimonial Finance
Specialisation: Principal areas of practice encompass all areas of criminal law, family law and administrative law. Criminal work includes both prosecution and defence and regular instructions to represent medical practitioners in connection with both criminal and disciplinary matters. Considerable knowledge and experience of technical and procedural points of law. Is an editor of 'Archbold: Criminal Pleading, Evidence and Practice'. Within family law, has particular expertise in financial matters and international child abduction work and has appeared in finance cases in the Grand Court of the Cayman Islands. Speaker at criminal and family law conferences. Administrative law includes work for the Treasury Solicitor and extradition work in England and abroad.
Prof. Memberships: Called to the Bar and joined current Chambers, 1976. Appointed Queen's counsel 1998. Member of Criminal Bar Association, Family Law Bar Association and Administrative Law Bar Association.
Personal: Educated at Robertsbridge Secondary Modern School, Bexhill Grammar School and the University of Hull (LLB (Hons) 1975). Born 23rd November 1952. Lives in London.

TURNER, James M.
4 Essex Court (Nigel Teare QC), London (020) 7653 5653
jturner@4sx.co.uk
Recommended in Shipping
Specialisation: Shipping, commercial and related private international law: cases include Red Sea Insurance v Bouygues [1995] 1AC 190; Citi-March v Neptune Orient Lines [1997] 1 Lloyd's Rep. 72; Colonia Versicherug AG v Amoco [1997] 1 Lloyd's Rep. 261; Netherlands v Youell [1998] 1 Lloyd's Rep 236; "Giuseppe di Vittorio" [1998] 1 Lloyd's Rep. 136 & 661; Mata K [1998] 2 Lloyd's Rep. 614; Glencore v. MTI [1999] 2 Lloyds Rep. 632.
Prof. Memberships: COMBAR; Institute of Linguists; LCLCBA; British-German Jurists.
Career: B.A. (Dunelm), LL.M (T¸bingen). Call 1990.
Personal: Married, 2 children. Fluent German and Dutch. Enjoy cycling and walking.

TURNER, Jon
Monckton Chambers (John Swift QC), London (020) 7405 7211
Recommended in Competition/Anti-trust
Specialisation: Specialisms include European Community law, competition law at both national and EC levels, public law (especially environmental law) and judicial review. Practice also includes utility regulation work in the water, electricity and telecommunications sectors (9 months working as legal adviser to the Telecommunications and Posts division of the DTI) and commercial litigation. Competition law litigation includes the ready mixed concrete contempt case [1996], the Net Book Agreement review [1997], the reference of the agreement relating to freight forwarding services [1997], the reference of arrangements for televising Premier League football [1999] and the review of resale price maintenance of medicaments [1999] (all in the Restrictive Practices Court); Clover Leaf Cars v BMW (CA and High Court) Philips v Ingman [1998]. Environmental/ judicial review cases include R v Secretary of State for the Environment ex parte Greenpeace [1994] (the "THORP" nuclear reprocessing plant litigation); R v Secretary of State for the Environment ex parte Standley [1997] (concerning the EC Nitrates Directive and nitrate levels in certain East Anglian rivers), R v Environment Agency ex parte Leam [1997] (concerning the use of substitute liquid fuel in lime and cement kilns), Bowden v South West water (pollution of shellfish by sewage). Acted in numerous MMC inquiries, including Plasterboard, National Newspapers, Carlsberg-Tetley, South West Water and Number Portability.

Prof. Memberships: Member of the New York Bar.
Career: Standing Counsel to the Director General of Fair Trading since August 1997. Member of the Treasury B Panel.

TURNER, Jonathan
6 King's Bench Walk (Michael Worsley QC), London (020) 7583 0410
Recommended in Crime
Specialisation: All and any criminal matters.
Prof. Memberships: C.B.A.
Career: Hindley & Abram Grammar School. University College, London.
Personal: Golf, cricket, rugby league.

TURNER, Justin
Three New Square (David E.M. Young QC), London (020) 7405 1111
Recommended in Intellectual Property
Specialisation: Intellectual Property especially those areas relating to Biotechnology, Pharmacology and medicine. Leading cases include: Biogen v Medeva (House of Lords); SKB v Norton and LEK (Clavulanic Acid); Bristol Myers v Baker Norton (Taxol); Coflexip v Stolt Comex; VISX v NIDEK (PRK); Mansanto v Merck (cox – 2 inhibitors). Appears in European Patent office in Munich.
Prof. Memberships: Intellectual Property Bar Assn; Chancery Bar Assn; Royal College of Veterinary Surgeons.
Career: Royal Veterinary College, London University (1981 – 86). Emmanual College, Cambridge – PHD on immunology/ virology. Called to the Bar in 1991. Contributor to Terrell on Law of Patents (14th Edn).

TURNER, Michael
14 Tooks Court (Michael Mansfield QC), London (020) 7405 8828
Recommended in Crime

TWIGG, Patrick QC
2 Temple Gardens (Dermod O'Brien QC), London (020) 7822 1200
Recommended in Arbitration (International), Construction
Specialisation: Building and engineering disputes and insurance matters. Appointed as arbitrator for disputes both in the U.K. and overseas. Counsel in many arbitrations in the U.K. and overseas (in particular I.C.C. arbitrations).
Prof. Memberships: Admitted to the Bars of Hong Kong, Singapore, Brunei (as a specialist in building and civil engineering disputes) and Gibraltar.
Career: LLB; LLM; called to the Bar 1967; appointed by the A.G. to deal with common law matters for the Crown 1983; Q.C. 1986; Recorder 1987; Official Referee Recorder 1991; Deputy High Court Judge QBD 1993; panel of Mediators, Singapore Academy of Law 1997; International panel of Arbitrators, SIAC 1997; FCI ANG 1998.

TWOMLOW, Richard
9 Park Place (Ian Murphy QC), Cardiff (029) 2038 2731
Recommended in Crime
Specialisation: Criminal work of all types, prosecution and defence.
Prof. Memberships: Criminal Bar Association.
Career: Called *(Gray's) 1976; Recorder (1997).*
Personal: BA (Cantab). Married, one young daughter. Sport, literature, music, languauges, travel.

UFF, John QC
Keating Chambers (Richard Fernyhough QC), London (020) 7544 2600
Recommended in Arbitration (International), Construction
Specialisation: Construction and engineering; international arbitration; appointed arbitrator in many substantial disputes in most parts of the world.
Career: Qualified 1970. Gray's Inn; assistant engineer 1966-1970; barrister in construction chambers 1970; arbitrator in various disputes 1977; QC 1983; Recorder 1998; Professor of Engineering Law, King's College, London 1991; chairman of Commission of Inquiry into Yorkshire Water 1996; Chairman of Public Enquiry into rail accident at Southall (1997); FICE, FCI Arb, Fellow Royal Academy of Engineering; publications of note: 'Construction Law'; Construction Industry Model Arbitration Rules; contributor to 'Keating on Building Contracts'.
Personal: King's College, London (BSc Engineering PhD).

ULLSTEIN, Augustus QC
29 Bedford Row Chambers (Peter Ralls QC), London (020) 7404 1044
Recommended in Product Liability
Specialisation: Principal area of practice is professional negligence for all professions, both for Plaintiffs and Defendants. Has had considerable experience of multi-party litigation including Opren (Nash v Ely Lilly) and Myodil (Chrzanowska v Glaxo Laboratories Limited). Other main areas of practice are personal injuries, which has included appointment by the Federal District Court in Ohio, USA to the Foreign Fracture Panel in the Shiley Heart Valve litigation. Also practises substantially in the Family Division.
Prof. Memberships: ORBA, FLBA, ATLA (US) Member Gibraltar Bar.
Career: Called to the Bar 1970. QC 1992. Joined Bedford Row 1991.
Personal: Educated at Bradfield College and LSE. Lives in London.

UNDERHILL, Nicholas QC
Fountain Court (Anthony Boswood QC), London (020) 7583 3335
Recommended in Employment, Product Liability
Specialisation: Specialist in commercial, employment and medical/pharmaceutical product liability. Recent cases include Kleinwort Benson v Lincoln (HL: restitution/mistake of law); Barber v RJB Mining (working time regs); Meade v British Fuels (HL: TUPE); Grant v South West Trains (ECJ: sexual orientation discrimination); Associated Newspapers v Wilson (HL: Union derecognition); also the haemophilia/HIV, hepatitis C and other multi-party actions; experience both as Chairman and as advocate in HC (90)9 cases.
Prof. Memberships: COMBAR; Employment Lawyers Association; Employment Law Bar Association; Industrial Law Society.
Career: Called to the Bar 1976. Joined present chambers 1977. Took silk 1992. Recorder 1994. Deputy High Court Judge 1998. Appointed Attorney-General to Prince of Wales 1998. Judge (part-time) of Employment Appeal Tribunal 2000.
Personal: Born 12 May 1952.

UNWIN, David QC
7 Stone Buildings (Charles Aldous QC), London (020) 7405 3886
Recommended in Charities, Media & Entertainment, Pensions, Traditional Chancery
Specialisation: A wide range of Chancery and commercial work, including company law and insolvency, charity cases, pensions litigation, professional negligence, and entertainment. Barlow Clowes International Ltd v Vaughan; Oldham Borough Council v Attorney-General; Harries v Church Commissioners for England; Edge v Pension Ombudsman; ADT v BDO Binder Hamlyn; entertainment cases have included the dispute between George Michael and Sony (Panayiotou v Sony Music).
Career: Educated at Clifton College and Trinity College, Oxford (BA Hons. 1st Class). Called to bar 1971. Silk 1995. Appointed Junior Counsel to the Crown, Chancery, 1982-1995. Treasury Junior Counsel in Charity Matters 1987-1995.

UPTON, William
1 Serjeants' Inn (Lionel Read QC), London (020) 7583 1355
clerks@serjeants-inn.co.uk
Recommended in Environment
Specialisation: Main area of practice is environmental, planning and local government law. Clients include local authorities, developers and local amenity groups. Experienced lecturer.
Prof. Memberships: Planning & Environment Bar Association.
Career: Called to the Bar in 1990.
Publications: General Editor, Environmental Law (OUP 2000); Contributing Editor, Encyclopaedia of Forms and Precedents (Butterworths); Environment Volucmen 2000 Reissue.
Personal: Educated at Trinity College, Cambridge 1985-89 (MA & LL.M). Chair, Planning Aid for London. Fellow of the Royal Society of Arts. UKELA Council Member.

VAJDA, Christopher QC
Monckton Chambers (John Swift QC), London (020) 7405 7211
Recommended in Competition/Anti-trust
Specialisation: All aspects of EC law, competition law and judicial review.
Career: Has appeared in over 50 cases before the Court of Justice of the European Communities and Court of First Instance acting for companies, private individuals and the UK Government. Cases include Ford v Commission (1982 and 1984), Bulk Oil (1986), Sharp v Council (1988), the Factortame cases, Saeger v Dennemeyer (1991), Air France v Commission (1994), Alpine Investments (1995), the Ladbroke cases, Cartonboard (1998) and ICI (1998). Domestic EC reported cases include: Garden Cottage Foods v Milk Marketing Board, (HL), Factortame (HL), Thorn (HL), Mann (HL), ABTA (RPC), Bourgoin v MAFF (CA), Optident (CA) Shearson Lehman Hutton v Maclaine Watson & Co (Commercial Ct), Apple Corps Ltd v Apple Computer (Ch. D). R v OFTEL ex parte BT (QBD) and R v Secretary of State for Health ex Parte Imperial Tobacco (CA). Numerous publications including the state aid chapter in Bellamy & Child, Common Market Law of Competition.

VALLANCE, Philip QC
1 Crown Office Row (Robert Seabrook QC), London (020) 7797 7500
Recommended in Environment
Specialisation: Principal area of practice is professional negligence and indemnity/liability insurance, especially in the construction and environmental context. Cases range from Anns v Merton (1978) to Cambridge Water v E. Counties Leather (1994). Also advises extensively on environmental law (contaminated land, "waste", pollution exclusion clauses, nuisance etc), where clients include major insurance companies, water companies, local authorities and waste disposal/landfill operators.
Prof. Memberships: Official Referees' Bar Association, London Common Law and Commercial Bar Association.
Career: Called to the Bar 1968 and joined 1 Crown Office Row. Took Silk in 1989.
Personal: Educated at Bryanston School and New College, Oxford (Scholar; BA Modern History). Born 20th December 1943. Lives in London.

VANHEGAN, Mark
11 South Square (Christopher Floyd QC), London (020) 7405 1222
Recommended in Intellectual Property

VAUGHAN, David QC
Brick Court Chambers (Christopher Clarke QC), London (020) 7379 3550
Recommended in Competition/Anti-trust
Specialisation: EC law generally, EC related public law cases and competition law.
Prof. Memberships: Honorary Vice-President of the Bar European Group.
Career: QC (1981) QC (NI) 1981. Judge of the County Appeals of Jersey and Guernsey, Deputy High Court Judge. Appeared in over 90 cases in the European Court of Justice since 1975 in a wide range of cases and in major EC related public law cases, in particular Factortame I, II, III, IV; Stoke City Council v B&Q; Woodpulp, Volvo v Veng Magill, Daily Mail; Crehan v Courage; Anastasiou I and II; Kesko; the Petrochemical Cartel cases (PP, PVC I and II, LDPE); the Soda Ash cases; the Coal Cases (Bank I and II, Hopkins. AVALOO I and II)

VEEDER, V.V. QC
Essex Court Chambers (Gordon Pollock QC), London (020) 7813 8000
Recommended in Arbitration (International), Insurance
Specialisation: Practised at the Commercial Bar to date, principally as advocate and arbitrator in the field of international trade.
Prof. Memberships: Chairman of ARIAS (UK). Member of the United Kingdom's Department of Trade and Industry Advisory Committee on the Law of Arbitration 1990-1996.
Career: Jesus College, Cambridge MA 1970 (Modern Languages & Law). Called to the English Bar 1971. Queen's Counsel 1986.
Personal: Born 1948.

VENABLES, Robert QC
24 Old Buildings (G.R Bretten QC), London (020) 7242 2744
Recommended in Charities, Tax
Specialisation: All types of tax, including VAT, Customs and Excise Duties and NI contributions. Trusts, whether or not tax-related. Specialities: Offshore, EC and International Taxation, Challenging Cases. Recent and current cases: Lady Ingram's Executors v IRC (HL November 1998 – inheritance tax – reservation of benefits); R v Dimsey (CA, Crim. Div., autumn 1998 – alleged international tax fraud); Parker Hale v Commissioners of Customs & Excise (VAT Tribunal autumn 1998 – compensation for arms dealers); R v Customs and Excise Commissioners ex parte Emu Tabac SARL (European Court of Justice 'Death cigarettes' – EC Excise Directive – Judicial Review – Injunction); Unigreg v Comissioners of Customs of Customs & Excise (QBD Customs duties – International Harmonised Convention -EC legislation); Memec plc v IRC (CA – Anglo-German convention – transparency of foreign partnerships); Re Katz Will Trusts (Privy Council – breach of trust); Steele v EVC International NV (CA – Anglo-Dutch convention – corporate joint ventures – connected persons); R v IRC ex parte Unilever PLC (CA judicial review – group relief revenue abuse of power); N Ltd v Inspector of Taxes (SC – group relief – £50,000,000 allowable loss); In re Nissan (UK) Limited (Companies Court – Revenue winding-up petition – alleged international tax fraud involving several £100,000,000's); Marshall v Kerr (HL – Offshore trusts – deeds of variation).
Prof. Memberships: Fellow of the Chartered Institute of Taxation.
Career: MA (Oxon). LLM (LSE). Tutorial Fellow of St. Edmund Hall, Oxford 1975-80.
Publications: 'Control of Companies' (forthcoming 1998), 'Non-Resident Trusts' – 7th edition (forthcoming 1998), 'Inheritance Tax Planning' – 3rd edition 1997, 'Tax Planning and Fundraising for Charities' – 3rd edition (forthcoming 1998), 'National Insurance Contributions Planning 1990. Consulting Editor of the Corporate Taxation Review, The EC Tax Journal, The Offshore Taxation Review, The Personal Tax Planning Review. Taxation Editor of The Charity Law and Practice Review.

VENMORE, John
30 Park Place (John Jenkins QC), Cardiff (029) 2039 8421
Recommended in Personal Injury
Specialisation: Personal injury including industrial disease litigation. Some clinical negligence. Professional negligence claims arising out of the conduct of personal injury and medical accident litigation.
Prof. Memberships: Wales and Chester Circuit.
Career: Called 1971.

VILLAGE, Peter M.
4-5 Gray's Inn Square (Elizabeth Appleby QC & Duncan Ouseley QC), London (020) 7404 5252
Recommended in Planning
Specialisation: Specialist in all aspects of planning and environmental law, particularly High Court challenges to the grant of planning permission (statutory and judicial review) and local plans; retail, housing and minerals/ waste inquiries; Major infrastructure projects, including electricity (especially way leaves). Compulsory purchase and compensation and rating (Lands Tribunal and Arbitrations). Environmental liability issues. Notable cases: Ex parte Rose Theatre [1990] 2 WLR 186 on behalf of the Rose Theatre Trust Co; Ex parte Sister Frost [1997] 73 P & CR 199 on behalf of the owners of Canary Wharf; Costco [1993] 3 PLR 114 on behalf of Safeway; British Railways Board v Slough BC [1993] 2 PLR 42 (Local Plan challenge); R v Teeside Development Corporation ex parte Redcar and Cleveland BC [1998] JPL 23 (quashing a retail permission). The Bull Ring CPO – (on behalf of Hammerson UK Properties and Birmingham City Council).
Prof. Memberships: Planning and Environmental Bar Association; Administrative Law Bar Association.
Career: Called to the Bar 1983 and the Bar of Northern Ireland 1997.
Personal: Lives in Wimbledon; married with 3 children; Governor of Repton School; Leisure pursuits: fly fishing.

VINE, James
Hardwicke Building (Walter Aylen QC), London (020) 7242 2523
james.vine@hardwicke.co.uk
Recommended in Crime
Specialisation: Both prosecution & defence of: drugs importation, VAT and Inland Revenue fraud, confiscation proceedings and computer fraud. Customs & Excise list 'A' and Inland Revenue approved list. Extensive experience of P.I.I. proceedings. Appears regularly as a leading junior. In last year successfully prosecuted a 20 defendant Excise fraud. Current practice includes Inland Revenue Phoenix fraud, Railtrack fraud and World Wide American Express fraud. Successful prosecution and defence of large scale VAT frauds.
Prof. Memberships: S.E. Circuit. C.B.A. Kent & Inner London Bar Messes. Society for computers and the law.
Career: He has developed and used a computer database program which has been used successfully in the preparation and presentation of numerous cases.
Personal: Travels when possible, and speaks a few foreign languages badly.

VIRGO, John A.
Guildhall Chambers (Adrian Palmer QC), Bristol (0117) 927 3366
Recommended in Commercial (Litigation)

VITORIA, Mary QC
8 New Square (Michael Fysh QC SC), London (020) 7405 4321
mary.vitoria@8newsquare.co.uk
Recommended in Intellectual Property, Media & Entertainment
Specialisation: Specialises in intellectual property law and media law, covering patents, copyright, trade marks, passing off, performers' rights, design rights, confidential information and contracts relating to the above. Cases include: Attorney General (client) v Blake (Court of Appeal - breach of fiduciary duty, copyright, intervention of civil law in support of criminal law; Phonographic Performance v Maitra (Court of Appeal, copyright); Romeike & Curtice Ltd v Newspaper Licencing Agency (copyright tribunal - press cutting agency - terms of licence); Pensher Security v Sunderland City Council (Court of Appeal); French Connection Ltd v Sutton (Chancery Division, passing-off, internet domain names); Performing Rights Society v Boizet (Court of Appeal) - copyright contract. Co-author of 'Modern Law of Copyright and Designs', Editor of 'Fleet Street Reports' and 'Reports of Patent Cases'. Author of sections on copyright and patents in 'Halsbury's Laws' (Vols 9 & 35); and Editor of 'European Intellectual Property Review'.
Prof. Memberships: Chancery Bar Association, Intellectual Property Bar Association.
Career: Called to the Bar in 1975. Appointed Queen's Counsel 1997. Joined 8 New Square 1978.
Personal: Educated at London University (BSc and PhD in Chemistry, LL.B).

VOS, Geoffrey C. QC
3 Stone Buildings (G.C. Vos QC), London (020) 7242 4937
Recommended in Commercial (Litigation), Commercial Chancery, Company, Insolvency/Corporate Recovery
Specialisation: Principal area of practice is chancery and commercial litigation, including particularly company, insurance and reinsurance, financial services, media and pensions. Acted in Bermuda Fire & Marine Insurance Co Ltd, Director General of Fair Trading v Premier League, Investors Compensation Scheme v West Bromwich Building Society, Deeny v Gooda Walker, Global Container Lines v Bonyal Shipping Co, Cox v Bankside, LDC Trustees Ltd v Barings plc, MGN Pension Trustees Limited v Credit Suisse, Scher v Policyholder Protection Board, R v Independent Television Commission ex p. TSW and Re M.C. Bacon Limited amongst others.
Prof. Memberships: Chairman of Chancery Bar Association. Member of Inner Temple, Lincoln's Inn.
Career: Called to the Bar 1977 and joined current chambers in 1979. Took Silk in 1993.
Personal: Educated at University College School, and Gonville and Caius College, Cambridge.

VOSPER, Christopher QC
Angel Chambers (T. Glanville Jones), Swansea (01792) 464623
Recommended in Personal Injury

WADSLEY, Peter
St John's Chambers (Christopher Sharp QC), Bristol (0117) 921 3456
clerks@stjohnschambers.co.uk
Recommended in Licensing
Specialisation: Town & Country Planning; Environ-

mental Law; Practice covers advice and public inquiries; judicial review. Also deals with solicitors' negligence. Planning: Extensive experience at appeals and local Plan Inquiries. Major appeals include MSA Inquiries; minerals and wind turbine inquiries; major housing sites and commercial developments; Two Rivers inquiry. Licensing: Liquor, gaming and public entertainment licensing for public bodies (including local authorities) as well as private and commercial clients.
Prof. Memberships: Planning & Environment Bar Association.
Career: MA., LL.M (Cantab.); Post-Graduate certificate in environmental law (Bristol University); formerly a solicitor.

WAIN, Peter
East Anglian Chambers (Roderick Newton), Ipswich (01473) 214481
Recommended in Family/Matrimonial

WAITE, Jonathan
Crown Office Chambers (Michael Spencer QC & Christopher Purchas QC), London (020) 7797 8100
Recommended in Health & Safety, Personal Injury, Product Liability

WAKERLEY, Richard QC
4 Fountain Court (Richard Wakerley QC), Birmingham (0121) 236 3476
Recommended in Crime

WAKSMAN, David
Fountain Court (Anthony Boswood QC), London (020) 7583 3335
dwaksmon@fountaincourt.co.uk
Recommended in Banking, Commercial (Litigation), Media & Entertainment
Specialisation: Commercial Litigation. Main areas of practice are banking, civil fraud, commercial litigation, copyright, entertainment law (advisory and contentious) and professional negligence. Clients include clearing and international banks, and other financial institutions and substantial corporations. Also major record and publishing companies, artistes, managers and producers. Recent cases: Murray v YFM (CA) [1998] 1 WLR 951 (confidential information in management buy-out context), Morgan v Lloyds Bank (CA) [1998] Lloyd's Rep. Banking 73 (duties of bank concerning sale of mortgaged property), Girobank v Clarke (CA) [1998] 1 WLR 942 (tax treatment of Girobank data-processing centre), News International v Clinger (Chd) 1998 (major international commercial fraud), Next Room v FX Music (Chd) Times 8 July 1999 (trust claim relating to recording royalties). He has lectured extensively on commercial law topics and is a contributor to 'The Law of Bank Payments' (Sweet & Maxwell), 'Banks and Remedies' (Lloyd's of London Press) and 'Commercial Court Procedure' (Sweet & Maxwell).
Prof. Memberships: Commercial Bar Association. Chancery Bar Association.
Career: Called to the Bar 1982.
Personal: Born 28.8.57 LLB (Manchester) BCL (Oxon). Leisure pursuits include running, fell walking, sailing. Married. Lives in London.

WALKER, Andrew P.D.
9 Old Square (Michael Driscoll QC), London (020) 7405 4682
Recommended in Property Litigation
Specialisation: Property and commercial Chancery litigation, with the main emphasis on landlord and tenant, commercial and residential property and development disputes, mortgages, commercial disputes, professional negligence (solicitors, surveyors, accountants, actuaries), trust litigation, partnerships, company and insolvency. Most recent reported cases include: Melbury Road Properties 1995 Ltd v Kreidi (1999) 3 EGLR 108 (CC); Courage Ltd v Crehan; Walker Cain Ltd v McCaughey (1999) 2 EGLR 145 (CA); Bent v High Cliff Developments Ltd (1999) 96(32) LSG 35 (ChD); Electricity Supply Nominees Ltd v The National Magazine Company Ltd (1999) 1 EGLR 130 (TCC); Wakefield (Tower Hill Trinity Square) Trust v Janson Green Properties Ltd (1998) EGCS 95, The Times, 20.7.98 (ChD); Platform Home Loans Ltd v Oyston Shipways Ltd (1999) 2 WLR 518 (HL).
Prof. Memberships: Chancery Bar Association, Professional Negligence Bar Association.
Career: Haberdashers' Aske's School, Elstree; Trinity College, Cambridge (MA); Called Lincoln's Inn (1991).

WALKER, Annabel QC
26 Paradise Square (Roger Keen QC), Sheffield (0114) 273 8951
Recommended in Family/Matrimonial
Specialisation: All aspects of family law. Criminal Law.
Prof. Memberships: FLBA, CBA.
Career: Recorder.
Personal: Travelling, family.

WALKER, Jane
28 St. John St (Clement Goldstone QC), Manchester (0161) 834 8418
Recommended in Family/Matrimonial

WALKER, Ronald QC
12 King's Bench Walk (Timothy Stow QC), London (020) 7583 0811
Recommended in Personal Injury

WALL, Mark
4 Fountain Court (Richard Wakerley QC), Birmingham (0121) 236 3476
Recommended in Crime
Specialisation: All types of criminal work undertaken, mostly on the Midland and Oxford Circuit. In particular much of his time has been spent recently dealing with murder and fraud work including defending in one of the largest excise frauds yet tried (R-v-Carlton + ors – Birmingham Crown Court). Prosecutes for the CPS and the DSS for whom he is their chief crown court prosecutor in Birmingham. Prosecutes and defends in equal measure. Undertakes health and safety, and similar criminal litigation.
Career: Former Junior of the Midland and Oxford Circuit.

WALLINGTON, Peter
11 King's Bench Walk (Eldred Tabachnik QC and James Goudie QC), London (020) 7632 8500
Recommended in Employment
Specialisation: Principal area of practice is employment law. Deals with all types of work in Employment Tribunals and Employment Appeal Tribunal, High Court and County Court litigation on all aspects of employment disputes including injunctions, wrongful dismissal, discrimination, and European social legislation. Advises and lectures on all these areas. Regular conference speaker for IPD. Also has extensive industrial consultancy experience. Other main area of practice is public law, including judicial review, especially in relation to local authorities and education. Editor 'Butterworth's Employment Law Handbook', Advisory Editor, 'Harvey on Industrial Relations and Employment Law', and contributor to 'Supperstone and Goudie on Judicial Review' and 'Tolley's Employment Law Handbook'.
Prof. Memberships: Employment Lawyers Association, Employment Law Bar Association, Industrial Law Society.
Career: Fellow of Trinity Hall, Cambridge, and University Lecturer in Law 1973-1979. Professor of Law, Lancaster University 1979-88, Professor of Law, Brunel University 1988-91. Called to the Bar in 1987 and joined present chambers in 1990.
Personal: Educated Hemel Hempstead Grammar School 1957-1964 and Trinity Hall, Cambridge 1965-1969 (MA and LLM, both 1st Class Hons). Past Area Chairman NACAB. Enjoys hill walking, music and reading. Born 25th March 1947. Lives in Wadhurst, E Sussex.

WALLWORK, Bernard
28 St. John St (Clement Goldstone QC), Manchester (0161) 834 8418
Recommended in Family/Matrimonial

WALSH, John
Plowden Buildings (William Lowe QC), London (020) 7583 0808
Recommended in Immigration
Specialisation: Specialist in immigration law, having appeared before numerous tribunals. Particular interest in Human Rights work. Reported cases include ex parte Yennin [1995] Imm AR 93; M v SSHD [1996] 1 All ER 870 (CA); R v SSHD ex parte Gnanavarathan [1995] Imm AR 64 (CA); Munchula v SSHD [1996] Imm AR 344; ex parte Kurumoorthy [1998] Imm AR 410. Represented in the recent case of Savas (Case 37/98) before ECJ on standstill clauses in the Turkish-EC Agreement: 'Times Law Reports' 30 May 2000.
Prof. Memberships: ILPA, ALBA, Education Law Association and Bar European Group and Bar Human Rights Committee.
Career: BA, MA, LLB. A former Fellow of Trinity College, Dublin.

WALSH, Martin
Peel Court Chambers (Michael Shorrock QC), Manchester (0161) 832 3791
Recommended in Licensing

WALSH, Stephen
3 Raymond Buildings (Clive Nicholls QC), London (020) 7400 6400
chambers@threeraymond.demon.co.uk
Recommended in Licensing
Specialisation: All aspects of licensing. Advising on liquor and public entertainment licensing issues affecting a wide range of clients and establishments, from small independent operators seeking to maintain or expand existing licensed outlets to major new leisure developments by public companies. Appearing on behalf of applicants and objectors before local authorities and courts including case stated and judicial review hearings in the High Court. Representing and advising clients on criminal prosecutions and health and safety matters affecting the licensed trade. Advising on betting, gaming and lotteries.

WALTERS, Graham
33 Park Place (John Charles Rees QC), Cardiff (029) 2023 3313
Recommended in Licensing

WALTERS, Jill Mary
33 Park Place (John Charles Rees QC), Cardiff (029) 2023 3313
Recommended in Family/Matrimonial

WALTERS, Jonathan
33 Park Place (John Charles Rees QC), Cardiff (029) 2023 3313
Recommended in Licensing

WALTON, Alastair
7 Stone Buildings (Charles Aldous QC), London (020) 7405 3886
Recommended in Commercial Chancery
Specialisation: General Chancery practice including company, insolvency, property, professional negligence, trusts, and contract and commercial disputes. Cases include Alstom v British Airways; Prince Jefri v Manoukian and others; TBV Power v Elm Energy; Re H and others; McDonald v Horn; Re Little Olympian Each Ways Limited; Re BSB Holdings Limited; Lonrho v Fayed.
Career: Called 1977.
Personal: Born 26th August 1954. Educated at Winchester and Balliol College, Oxford (BA 1976). Married with four children. Lives in London.

WARBY, Mark
5 Raymond Buildings (Patrick Milmo QC), London (020) 7242 2902
Recommended in Defamation

WARNOCK-SMITH, Shân
5 Stone Buildings (Henry Harrod), London (020) 7242 6201
Recommended in Charities, Traditional Chancery
Specialisation: Area of practice encompasses all aspects of trusts, estates, charities and associated taxation. Handles both advisory and contentious work in the UK and offshore in connection with trusts and estates, variations of trusts, construction and rectification of settlements and wills; probate actions; Court of Protection applications; and professional negligence in those areas. Lecturer, writer and broadcaster on trust and estate matters.
Prof. Memberships: Society of Trust and Estate Practitioners, Charity Law Association, Chancery Bar Association and the Association of Contentious Trust and Probate Specialists.
Career: Called to the Bar 1971. Joined 10 Old Square in 1979 following an academic career. Moved to 5 Stone Buildings in January 1996.

WARREN, Nicholas QC
Wilberforce Chambers (Edward Nugee QC), London (020) 7306 0102
Recommended in Pensions, Traditional Chancery
Specialisation: Main areas of practice are in the fields of pensions and private client business, both advisory and litigation. Has appeared in many of the leading pensions cases including Imperial Foods, Courage, Thrells, LRT, Coloroll, Chloride, National Grid/ National Power and South West Trains. Also has wide experience of revenue litigation having formerly been standing junior counsel to the Inland Revenue in Chancery matters.
Prof. Memberships: Association of Pensions Lawyers; STEP; Revenue Bar Association; Chancery Bar Association.
Career: BA (Oxon) 1970. Called to the Bar in 1972; QC 1993. Recorder; Deputy High Court Judge.

WASS, Sasha
6 King's Bench Walk (Michael Worsley QC), London (020) 7583 0410
Recommended in Crime
Specialisation: Criminal Law. Defence and Prosecution practice. Serious fraud: professional (e.g. lawyer's), commercial (e.g. gambling industry), and financial cases (City, eg. defence of Roger Levitt). Environmental Law: specialist expertise on criminal aspects of oil spillage etc (eg. Sea Empress 1996). Serious Crime: murder, rape, police corruption, drug importation, money laundering, sexual abuse of children and specialist expertise in complex medical, scientific and identification cases (eg. Rosemary West, Popat I & II).
Prof. Memberships: Elected member of the Committee of the Criminal Bar Association: 1992-1995; 1995-1998; and the South Eastern Circuit Committee: 1989-1992; 1993-1996; Treasurer of the CBA 1997-1999.
Career: Called 1981; Assistant Recorder 1997; Recorder 2000; Queen's Counsel 2000.

WATERS, David QC
1 Hare Court (Stephen Kramer QC), London (020) 7353 5324
Recommended in Crime

WATERS, Malcolm QC
11 Old Square (Grant Crawford & Jonathan Simpkiss), London (020) 7430 0341
Recommended in Banking, Charities
Specialisation: Principal specialist areas are mortgage lending, savings products, building societies and charities. Also covers other areas of general chancery practice, including land law, trusts and professional negligence. Acted in C.&G. v B.S.C. and B.S.C. v Halifax B.S. and Leeds P.B.S. (building society conversions), C.&G. v Norgan and Woolwich v Gomm (mortgages), Harwood-Smart v Caws (pensions) and Peggs v Lamb (charities). Drafts standard form mortgage, investment and consumer credit documentation for banks and building societies. Regularly advises on constitutional issues affecting mutual organisations and charities. Joint editor of 'Wurtzburg & Mills – Building Society Law', and 'Current Law Commentary on the Building Societies Act 1986'. Member of working parties involved in drafting Standard Conditions of Sale and the Standard Commercial Property Conditions.
Prof. Memberships: Chancery Bar Association, Charity Law Association, Professional Negligence Bar Association.
Career: Called to Bar 1977. Joined 11 Old Square 1978. Took silk 1997.
Personal: Educated at Whitgift School 1963-1971 and St. Catherine's College Oxford 1972-1976 (B.A. and B.C.L.).

WATSON, Antony QC
Three New Square (David E.M. Young QC), London (020) 7405 1111
Recommended in Intellectual Property
Specialisation: All aspects of Intellectual Property including Patents, Trade Marks, Copyright, Confidential Information, Passing Off – computers/electronics/ biotechnology especially. Also appears in Hong Kong. Recent Cases: Chiron Corpn v Murex, Patent – Biotechnology – High Court and Court of Appeal; Pittsburgh Plate Glass v Pilkington – Patent/Know How – arbitration; Hoechst v BP – Patent Infringement – High Court.
Prof. Memberships: Intellectual Property Bar Assn; Chancery Bar Assn; AIPPI; London Court of International Arbitration + ICC Arbitrator.
Career: Sedbergh School 1958-1963; Sidney Sussex College, Cambridge MA. Called to the Bar 1968, Appointed QC 1986. Deputy High Court Judge – Chancery Division 1992. Deputy Chairman Copyright Tribunal 1994.
Personal: Travel, country pusuits.

WATSON, David
14 Castle Street (Andrew Edis QC), Liverpool (0151) 236 4421
Recommended in Crime

WATSON, James QC
3 Serjeants' Inn (Philip Naughton QC), London (020) 7427 5000
Recommended in Clinical Negligence

WATSON, Philippa
Essex Court Chambers (Gordon Pollock QC), London (020) 7813 8000
Recommended in Competition/Anti-trust
Specialisation: EU Law, in particular competition law, agricultural law, energy law, social law of an advisory and litigious nature. Litigation involves appearance before the EC Commission, Court if First Instance, Court of Justice and UK and Irish specialist courts and tribunals. UK Competition law. UK social security law. Butterworths Tolley Chair in Competition Law and Practice Nottingham Law School.
Career: Trinity College, Dublin: MA (Legal Science) 1973; King's Inn, Dublin; Called to Bar of Ireland: 1973; University of Cambridge: LLB 1974: PhD in Law 1977; Called to the Bar of England and Wales 1988.
Personal: Born 1951.

WAUGH, Andrew QC
Three New Square (David E.M. Young QC), London (020) 7405 1111
Recommended in Intellectual Property
Specialisation: All aspects of intellectual property with particular emphasis on chemical, pharmaceutical and biotechnical/generic engineering matters, as well as a broader commercial practice. Appears regularly at European Patent Office in Munich for clients which have included Eli Lilly, Amgen and Biogen. Notable UK cases have included: 3M v Rennicks – patents (thermoformed laminates); Bonzel v Intervention (cardiac catheters); Optical Recording v Hayden Labs (compact discs); Biogen v Medeva (recombinant Hepatitis B vaccine); Rediffusion Simulation v Singer Link Miles (flight simulators); Amgen v Boehringher Mannheim (erythropoietin); SKB v Norton (augmentin); Merrell Dow v Norton (terfenadine); Optical Sciences v Aspect Vision Care (contact lenses); Hoechst v B.P (purification of acetic acid); UCC v BP (polyethylene production); Palmaz v Boston Scientific (cardiac stents); HFC Bank plc v Midland Bank plc (trade name).
Prof. Memberships: Intellectual Property Bar Assn; Chancery Bar Assn; AIPPI.
Career: 1980 City University First Class Hons in Chemical and Administrative Studies; 1981 Dip-Law; 1982 Called to the Bar. QC 1998, 6 Month Pupillage at Chambers of Kenneth Rokison. 1983 joined Chambers of William Aldous at 6 Pump Court (now headed by David Young at 3 New Square).
Personal: Tennis, rugby, Association Football, cycling.

WAY, Patrick
8 Gray's Inn Square (Patrick C. Soares), London (020) 7242 3529
Recommended in Tax
Specialisation: All forms of taxation both as an adviser and an advocate. Publications include: 'Tax advice for company transactions' (Gee); 'The Enterprise Investment Scheme: A Practical Guide' (Longman); Co-author 'Death and Taxes' (Longman); Contributor Tolley's Tax Planning 1998-9 ('The Enterprise Investment Scheme' and 'Stamp Duty in Property Transactions'). Recent High Court cases: Wannell v Rothwell (share dealing); Barnett v Brabyn (SchD/ Sch E); 'Continental Shipping' (judicial review and s20 TMA), Templeton v Jacobs (benefits in kind) 'Archon Shipping' (judicial review and s20 TMA).
Prof. Memberships: Revenue Bar Association and Law Society's Stamp Duty Committee.
Career: Admitted as a solicitor (1979). Head of tax at *Gouldens* (1987-94). Called to the Bar 1994.

WEATHERILL, Bernard QC
3 New Square (Lord Goodhart QC), London (020) 7405 5577
Recommended in Company, Traditional Chancery
Specialisation: Practises in most areas of traditional

and commercial chancery litigation, company law and insolvency, but principal areas of work are in property litigation (including landlord and tenant, mortgages and securities), breach of trust cases, equitable remedies, contested probate, directors' duties, minority shareholders' rights, business and commercial contract disputes and solicitors' negligence work.
Prof. Memberships: Chancery Bar Association, Professional Negligence Bar Association, Association of Contentious Trust and Probate Specialists, Associate Member of Association of Business Recovery Professionals.
Career: Called 1974. Bar Council 1989-95. Queens's Counsel 1996. Recorder 2000.

WEBBER, Frances
Two Garden Court (I. Macdonald QC & O.Davies QC), London (020) 7353 1633
Recommended in Immigration

WEST, Lawrence
2 Harcourt Buildings (Roger Henderson QC), London (020) 7583 9020
Recommended in Environment
Specialisation: Regularly instructed in environmental cases on behalf of the chemical, petrochemical and agrochemical industries, local authorities, statutory water undertakers, general industry and private individuals. Other areas of practice: personal injury, including clinical negligence; commercial, including intellectual and industrial property and competition; local authority and governmental agency law; professional negligence of all kinds and insurance.
Career: Called to Bar in Ontario in 1973. Practised in Toronto as an advocate with the leading Canadian law firm, McCarthy, Tetrault, where he was involved with a substantial amount of commercial and medical negligence litigation. Called to Bar Gray's Inn 1979. Since then has practised from 2 Harcourt Buildings. Reported cases include Cambridge Water Co v Eastern Counties Leather plc (1994 – environmental pollution), Stubbings v Webb (1993 – limitation in personal injury action) and Thake v Maurice (1985 – public policy aspects of claims for damages following conception after vasectomy). Also junior counsel for Paul McKenna in the hypnotherapy/schizophrenia case brought against him.
Personal: Toronto, 1946. LLM (London); LLB, BA (Toronto).

WHEATLEY, Simon
7 Bedford Row (David Farrer QC), London (020) 7242 3555
Recommended in Personal Injury
Specialisation: Professional negligence, personal injury, disciplinary tribunals, industrial tribunals. Recent cases include Royal College of Veterinary Surgeons v Marshal Dale (1995) – Disciplinary action against vet for allegedly unlawfully docking dogs tails. Harris v Harris (1996) – Claim for damages by school boy who sustained amputation of leg when he fell off his father's lawn mower. RBS v Etridge (1998) – Undue Influence. Whether Bank had notice when instructing negligent solicitor to give advice to wife in mortgage transaction.
Prof. Memberships: Personal Injuries Bar Association; London Common Law and Commercial Bar Association.
Career: Called to the Bar 1979. Practised in the chambers of Raymond Walker QC at Harcourt Buildings until 1994 when joined present chambers.
Personal: Born 8th August 1956. Educated Marlborough College 1969-1973; Brunel University 1974-1978. Inns of Court School of Law 1979. Sits as part-time judge advocate on court martials (from 1994).

WHITE, Andrew QC
Atkin Chambers (John Blackburn QC), London (020) 7404 0102
Recommended in Arbitration (International), Construction
Specialisation: Domestic and international civil engineering, building, shipbuilding and ship repair disputes. Also specialises in computer litigation. Major projects include the Channel Tunnel: Counsel for TML in main and sub-contract disputes; Harbour City Hong Kong: Counsel for the contractors in disputes with the employer; Oil Rigs: Counsel for contractors in connection with several oil rig construction projects (High Court). Accountants' negligence actions. Solicitors' negligence actions. Publication: 'Contributor Forms & Precedents: Building Contracts'.
Career: Called to the Bar Lincoln's Inn 1980. Queen's Counsel (1997). Megarry Scholar and Hardwicke Scholar.
Personal: Born 25th January 1958. LL.B. (Hons.) Wales (1979) 2:1. Interests include music, farming and gardening.

WHITE, Antony
Matrix Chambers (Nicholas Blake QC), London (020) 7404 3447
Recommended in Employment
Specialisation: Employment law, commercial law, public law and judicial review, defamation.
Prof. Memberships: Administrative Law Bar Association.
Career: Called to bar in 1983 (Middle Temple); awarded Middle Temple Scholarship 1983-4 and the Middle Temple Prize for administrative law. Concerned largely in commercial and public law with particular emphases on public sector collective employment work and commercial fraud involving directors and other fiduciaries. Also has an increasing media law practice. Recent interesting cases include: AG for Hong Kong v Reid [1994] (remedial constructive trusts and dishonest fiduciaries); ex parte Matson [1997] (reason giving in Administrative Law); Harrison v Kent CC [1995] (discrimination against trade union member); HRH Princess of Wales v Taylor [1995] (Privacy); ex parte Lightfoot [2000] (constitutional right to access of justice); Jyske Bank v Spjeldnaes [1999] (equitable remedies in commercial transactions); Fyffes Group Ltd v Templeman [2000] (remedies against briber in commercial fraud); Marco Pierre White v New York Times [2000] (defence of contributory negligence in libel proceedings).
Personal: MA (Cantab) First Class Honours (Parts I and II).

WHITE, Sasha
1 Serjeants' Inn (Lionel Read QC), London (020) 7583 1355
Recommended in Planning
Specialisation: Principal areas of practice is planning, environmental and local government law.
Prof. Memberships: Planning and Environmental Bar Association.
Career: Called to Bar in 1991. Pupil to William Hicks Q.C. Joined Chambers as tenant 1993.
Personal: Educated Bedales and Trinity College, Cambridge. Born 1967. Author of 'Planning Law Appeals' (Central Law Publishing) March 1997.

WHITEHOUSE, David QC
3 Raymond Buildings (Clive Nicholls QC), London (020) 7400 6400
chambers@threeraymond.demon.co.uk
Recommended in Crime, Fraud: Criminal
Specialisation: Principal specialist areas are crime, from Mafia and Colombian cartel drugs importing trials and the murder of Lennie 'The Gov'ner' McLean to the Bob Monkhouse joke books case; fraud including City fraud (Barlow Clowes – Investment fraud, Landhurst Leasing plc – leasing fraud and corruption, Abbey National plc – corruption and Norton plc – rights issue); local authority fraud (West Wiltshire privatisation case, Brent housing); mortgage fraud (R v Annen and others), Insolvency fraud (Baron Group of Companies), Legal Aid fraud (O'Malley), licensing – liquor, casino and bingo. Also specialises in disciplinary tribunals and has appeared before the Institute of Chartered Accountants, Securities and Futures Authority, LIFFE, General Medical Council, Institute of Chartered Engineers, British Boxing Board of Control.
Prof. Memberships: Criminal Bar Association, International Bar Association.
Career: Called to the Bar 1969 and joined current chambers in 1970 after pupillage in defamation Chambers. Libel read The Sun 1969-1975. Appointed Recorder 1987. Took silk 1990.
Personal: Educated at Trinity College, Cambridge 1964-1967 (MA).

WHITEMAN, Peter QC
Queen Elizabeth Building (Julian Bevan QC & Peter Whiteman QC), London (020) 7583 5766
petergwhiteman@hotmail.com
Recommended in Tax
Specialisation: All areas of corporate and commercial taxation with special emphasis on mergers and acquisitions, structured financing arrangements, oil company taxation, insurance company taxation, international corporate taxation, cross-border transactions, transfer pricing and capital allowances. Appeared in BP Oil Development Ltd v IRC, Esso Petroleum Ltd v IRC, Girobank plc v Clarke, ICI plc v Colmer, Bradley v London Electricity plc, Padmore v IRC, Post Office Counters Ltd v Customs & Excise, Johnson v Prudential Assurance Co Ltd, J. Sainsbury plc v O'Connor. Also appeared in Exxon Corporation v Internal Revenue Commissioner in the US Tax Court as the UK tax expert witness. Clients include major international companies, solicitors and accountancy firms.
Prof. Memberships: Revenue Bar Association; Honorary Adviser to the Unitary Tax Campaign 1982.
Career: Lecturer London School of Economics 1965-1970. Called to the Bar 1967; Queen's Counsel 1977. Founded Chambers of Peter Whiteman QC in 1977, becoming Joint Head of Hollis Whiteman Chambers on merger in 1991. Bencher of Lincoln's Inn 1985. Author "Whiteman on Income Tax", "Whiteman on Capital Gains Tax", "British Tax Encyclopedia". Professor of International Tax Law, University of Florida and University of Virginia 1980. Attorney-at-Law, State of New York 1982. Recorder 1986; Deputy High Court Judge 1994.
Personal: Educated Leyton County High School and London School of Economics (LLB Hons; LLM Distinction).

WHITFIELD, Adrian QC
3 Serjeants' Inn (Philip Naughton QC), London (020) 7427 5000
Recommended in Clinical Negligence
Specialisation: Principal area of practice is medical negligence and other medical law, including treatment decisions. Cases include Sidaway, Hotson, in Re F (sterilisation) and de Martell. Has extensive G.M.C and other tribunal experience. Acts for claimants and defendants. Visiting Research Fellow at Centre of Medical Law and Ethics, King's College, London. Writes and lectures regularly on medico-legal subjects.
Prof. Memberships: London Common Law and Commercial Bar Association, Professional Negligence Bar Association, Medico-Legal Society.

Career: Call 1964: Queen's Counsel 1983: Chairman of NHS Tribunal 1993.
Personal: Educated Ampleforth College and Magdalen College Oxford: Demy (Open Scholar). Lives in London.

WHITTAKER, John
Serle Court (Lord Neill of Bladen QC), London (020) 7242 6105
Recommended in Commercial Chancery, Partnership
Specialisation: Principal area of practice is chancery including related commerce and property. A specialist area of practice is partnership law.
Prof. Memberships: association of Partnership Practitioners, COMBAR
Career: Called 1969, joined Serle Court Chambers in 1970.
Personal: Magdalen College, Oxford (MA, BCL).

WHITTAM, Richard
Furnival Chambers (Andrew Mitchell QC), London (020) 7405 3232
Recommended in Crime
Specialisation: Junior Treasury Counsel to the Crown at the Central Criminal Court. Specialist Criminal practitioner with considerable experience in complex cases. Serious fraud experience in advance fee, leasing, Certificate of Deposit, mortgage and DSS frauds. Defended in substantial Customs and Excise cases. Public Interest Immunity. Information Technology.
Prof. Memberships: Criminal Bar Association; S E Circuit.
Personal: Educated at Marple Hall School and University College London. Formerly active in sport, now golf and occasional cricket.

WHITTLE, C.D. (Henry)
11 South Square (Christopher Floyd QC), London (020) 7405 1222
Recommended in Intellectual Property

WIGGLESWORTH, Raymond QC
18 St. John Street (Jonathan Foster QC), Manchester (0161) 278 1800
Recommended in Crime

WILDBLOOD, Stephen QC
Albion Chambers (J.C.T. Barton QC), Bristol (0117) 927 2144
Recommended in Family/Matrimonial

WILLIAMS, David H.
Chavasse Court Chambers (Theresa Pepper), Liverpool (0151) 707 1191
Recommended in Crime

WILLIAMS, John Leighton QC
Farrar's Building (John Leighton Williams QC), London (020) 7583 9241
Recommended in Personal Injury
Specialisation: General common law, with emphasis on personal injuries and medical negligence work.
Career: Called to the Bar 1964. Appointed Recorder 1985. Took silk 1986. Member of the Criminal Injuries Compensation Board since 1987. Master of the Bench, Grays Inn 1994.

WILLIAMS, John Melville QC
Old Square Chambers (John Hendy QC), London (020) 7269 0300
Recommended in Environment
Specialisation: Environmental toxic torts; agricultural environmental damages claims; waste-incineration; environmental insurance; some planning; particular interest in scientific aspects of environmental issues; Y2K millennium bug issues. Notable cases: Graham v Rechem; Camelford Water Claims, organophosphate sheep dip cases.
Prof. Memberships: Environmental Law Foundation – Member of Advisory Council; Association of Personal Injury Lawyers (1st President 1990-1994), Association of Trial Lawyers of America (Chair International Practice Section 1991), Personal Injury Bar Association.
Career: Called 1955; QC 1977; Recorder 1985-1993; Legal Assessor to the General Medical Council and General Dental Council 1984 -. Member CICB 1998 -. Chairman Y2K Lawyers Association.

WILLIAMS, Rhodri
30 Park Place (John Jenkins QC), Cardiff (029) 2039 8421
Recommended in Planning

WILLIAMSON, Adrian
Keating Chambers (Richard Fernyhough QC), London (020) 7544 2600 awilliamson@keatingchambers.com
Recommended in Construction
Specialisation: Construction and engineering law; professional negligence; disputes concerning substantial commercial and technical projects; international commercial arbitration; cases include Aughton v Kent; Damond Lock v Laing Investments; Barclays Bank v Fairclough Building Ltd; West Faulkner Associates v LB Newham; Birse v Haiste; Hytec v Coventry CC; Bernhards Rugby Landscapes Ltd v Stockle Park; Royal Brompton Hospital v Hammond & Others.
Career: Qualified 1983; Middle Temple; tenant in chambers of John Loyd QC 2 Crown Office Row 1985-1989; tenant at Keating Chambers 1989 to date; wrote chapters on JCT and NSC Forms of Contract for 'Keating on Building Contracts'. (5th 1991 and 6th 1995 editions).
Personal: Highgate School, Trinity Hall, Cambridge (1982 BA 1st Class Hons 1985 MA). Born 1959. Married with 3 children.

WILLIAMSON, Hazel QC
13 Old Square (Michael Lyndon-Stanford QC), London (020) 7404 4800
Recommended in Partnership, Property Litigation
Specialisation: Chancery Litigation including property, company and insolvency, commercial contract, partnership and related negligence aspects. Particular emphasis on commercial property including acquisition, financing and development and landlord and tenant aspects. Also, leasehold enfranchisement, markets and fairs, Court of Protection. Cases include National Westminster Bank v Arthur Young (1986-93) series of cases on rent review, arbitration procedure and appeals BCCI v Aboody (1988) Banco Exterior v Thomas (1997) and Barclays Bank v Coleman (1999) undue influence and bank mortgages; Crown Estate Commissioners v Signet Ltd (1997) and Moss Bros Group v CSC Properties (1999): refusal of consent to leasehold assignment; Lumsden Ltd v Holdswarth (Isle of Man 1998 and 1999 on appeal): failed time-share, knowing assistance in breach of trust, partnership, solicitors' negligence; Re: Forester & Lamego Ltd (1997) public interest winding up; Re Brian D Pierson (Contractors) Ltd 1999; decision on wrongful trading and misfeasance, Re: Thirty Eight Building Ltd 1999: decision on undue preferences; Locabail (UK) Ltd v Bayfield Properties Ltd and anor (1999): judicial bias/proprietary estoppel, undue influence, overriding interests in land registration, scope of bank mortgagee's right or subrogation; Coventry and Solihull Waste Disposal v Russell (VO) (1999) HL: rating: Re C (2000): Enduring Powers of Attorney.
Career: Qualified 1972, Gray's and Lincoln's Inn. Silk 1988. Recorder 1996, Deputy High Court Judge 1994. Chairman of the Chancery Bar Association 1994 – 97. Member of the DETR, Property Advisory Group. Publications: 'Law and Valuation of Leisure Property' (Estates Gazette) Joint Editor and Contributor. Mediator (ADR Chambers) 2000.
Personal: Educated Wimbledon High School and St Hilda's College, Oxford. BA 1969, MA 1982, FCIArb 1992.

WILLS-GOLDINGHAM, Claire
Albion Chambers (J.C.T. Barton QC), Bristol (0117) 927 2144
Recommended in Family/Matrimonial

WILMOT-SMITH, Richard QC
39 Essex Street (Nigel Pleming QC), London (020) 7832 1111
Recommended in Construction
Specialisation: A specialist in all aspects of construction and engineering, process engineering, oil and gas, mining and other energy litigation and arbitration. His experience includes disputes involving performance bonds, guarantees, insolvency and related professional negligence claims against architects, engineers and surveyors and insolvency. He has acted in litigation and arbitration concerned with major projects in the United Kingdom, the United States, Tanzania, Egypt, India, Singapore, Hong Kong, Canada, Iran, Iraq, Dubai, Qatar, Pakistan, Bangladesh, Malaysia and Saudi Arabia. These projects include major tunnels, roads, bridges and other structures including ports and drylocks, housing estates and universities, factories, power stations and other energy systems, food processing plants, oil platforms and refineries. John Mowlem & Co plc v Eagle Star Insurance Co Ltd and others 44 Con LR 134 (CA); Trafalgar House v General Surety [1996] AC 119 (HL); In re Cosslett (Contractors) Ltd [1998] 2 WLR 131 (CA); Scottish Power plc v Britoil (Exploration) Ltd and Others, 141 SJ LB 246 (CA); Bedford County Council v Fitzpatrick (1998) CILL 1440 (QB); Pozzolanic Lytag Ltd v Bryan Hobson Associates (1998) CILL 1450 (QB); Deepak Fertilizers and Petrochemicals Ltd v Davy McKee (London) Limited [1999] 1 ALL ER (COMM) 69 (CA).
Prof. Memberships: ORBA, London Common Law and Commercial Bar Association.
Career: Called to Bar in 1978, took silk 1994.

WILSON, Adam
No.6 (Shaun Spencer QC), Leeds (0113) 245 9763
Recommended in Family/Matrimonial

WILSON, Alastair QC
19 Old Buildings (Alastair Wilson QC), London (020) 7405 2001
Recommended in Information Technology, Intellectual Property
Specialisation: Principal area of practice is intellectual property, computer and technology cases, including EC aspects. Other areas of work include lotteries and setting aside Anton Piller orders. Cases of importance include, inter alia, one in a million, Chelsea Man v Chelsea Girl, Intergraph v SSI, PLG (Netlon) v Ardon and Chiron v Murex. Clients include British Railways Board, Ford Motor Company, Associated Newspapers, Irish Dairy Board and Netlon. Has presented numerous seminars on intellectual property and computer law. Recently made a video on trade mark law for Legal Network Television.
Prof. Memberships: Society for Computers and Law, Intellectual Property Bar Association, Chancery Bar Association.
Career: Called to the Bar 1968 and joined current chambers when located at 3 Pump Court in 1970. Took Silk in 1987. Appointed Recorder in 1996.
Personal: Educated at Wellington College and Pembroke College. Leisure pursuits include gardening and building. Born 26th May 1946. Lives in Norwich.

WINBERG, Stephen
2-4 Tudor Street (Richard Ferguson QC), London (020) 7797 7111
Recommended in Crime, Fraud: Criminal

WINDSOR, Emily
Falcon Chambers (Jonathan Gaunt QC & Kim Lewison QC), London (020) 7353 2484
windsor@falcon-chambers.com
Recommended in Agriculture
Specialisation: Real property based litigation and advisory work, including commercial property, landlord and tenant, agriculture, easements, restrictive covenants and professional negligence. Also EU law. Lecturing on these areas of law.
Prof. Memberships: Chancery Bar Association, Agricultural Law Association (member of Agricultural Law Association Committee 1997-1999), Bar European Group, elected member of Bar Council.
Career: MA (Oxon). DSU in EU Law (Paris II). Called to the Bar in 1995 and joined *Falcon Chambers* in 1997.
Publications: Articles for practitioner journals. Contributor to 'Woodfall Property Update Service'.

WINGATE-SAUL, Giles QC
Byrom Street Chambers (B.A. Hytner QC), Manchester (0161) 829 2100
gws@byromstreet.com
Recommended in Clinical Negligence, Commercial (Litigation), Personal Injury
Specialisation: Catastrophic injury, mercantile/commercial law, contract, tort, insurance, building and construction.
Prof. Memberships: Northern Circuit Commercial Bar Association, Society of Construction Law, Technology and Construction Court Bar Association, Professional Negligence Bar Association, Personal Injury Bar Association, Bar European Group.
Career: Winchester College, Southampton University (LLB Hons). Called to the Bar 1967. QC 1983. Deputy High Court Judge, Deputy Judge of Technology & Construction Court, Governing Bencher of Inner Temple, Chairman Northern Circuit Commercial Bar Association.
Personal: Church affairs and sport.

WINTER, Ian
Queen Elizabeth Building (Julian Bevan QC & Peter Whiteman QC), London (020) 7583 5766
Recommended in Fraud: Criminal
Specialisation: Specialist in criminal law with a particular emphasis on fraud and white collar crime. Acted for the defence in the Lady Aberdour and Swindon Town FC frauds. Practice also covers police powers and civil liberties law. Even split between prosecution and defence work. Recently represented Dr Shipman.
Prof. Memberships: Bar Council Legal Services Committee.
Career: Called to the Bar in 1988. Joined present chambers in 1990.
Personal: Educated at Bristol University 1984-87. Leisure pursuits include international rally driving and playing the saxophone and piano. Born 25th March 1966. Lives in Fulham.

WOLANSKI, Adam
5 Raymond Buildings (Patrick Milmo QC), London (020) 7242 2902
Recommended in Defamation

WOLFE, David
Matrix Chambers (Nicholas Blake QC), London (020) 7404 3447
davidwolfe@matrixlaw.co.uk
Recommended in Administrative & Public Law: General, Environment
Specialisation: Public law, including judicial review, local government, town and country planning and environmental law (including cases involving substantial scientific and technical evidence), discrimination, education, community care, social security.
Prof. Memberships: Administrative Law Bar Association, Planning and Environmental Bar Association, UK Environmental Law Association, Discrimination Law Association.
Career: BSc MEng (Manchester) 1987, PhD (Engineering, Cambridge) 1991, Called to the Bar 1992.

WOLFSON, David
One Essex Court (Lord Grabiner QC), London (020) 7583 2000
dwolfson@oeclaw.co.uk
Recommended in Banking, Commercial (Litigation)
Specialisation: Practice encompasses all areas of commercial law (particularly banking, insolvency and domestic and international sale of goods), professional negligence and entertainment law. Recent cases include Ghana Commercial Bank v C&L (Times 3.3.97) [tracing proceeds of fraud]; Barclays Bank v Zaroovabli [1997] Ch 321 [mortgages and registrable interests]; Re Schuppan (a bankrupt) [1996] 2 AER 664 [conflict of interest in insolvency]; Art Corporation v Schuppan (Times 21.1.94) [duty of disclosure on Mareva injunctions], Art Corporation v Schuppan [international sale of goods], Blackspur Leasing [negligent audit claim], Investors Compensation Scheme v West Bromwich Building Society [1999] Lloyds Rep PN 496 [acted for solicitor third parties in major action re home income plans]; Royal Bank of Scotland v Etridge [1999] 4 AER 705 [the current leading authority on the O'Brien jurisdiction]. Advised about the recovery of gold and other assets from Second World War. Clients include banks and other lenders, insurers and professional indemnity insurers, Solicitors' Indemnity Fund, liquidators and insolvency practitioners, general commercial clients. Contributing author to Bank Liability and Risk, (2nd ed), several articles in various legal journals including New Law Journal, Commercial Lawyer and International Insurance Law Review. Articles for in-house magazines of various firms of solicitors. Contributor to Law Commision Consultation Paper on the Third Party (Rights against Insurers) Act 1930. Lecturer at legal seminars and conferences.
Prof. Memberships: COMBAR
Career: MA (Cantab) (Oriental Studies and Law). Exhibitioner and Scholar of Selwyn College. Stuart of Rannoch award. Squire scholarship. Inner Temple Major scholarship. Council of Legal Education scholarship. Called to the Bar in 1992.

WOLKIND, Michael QC
2 Bedford Row (formerly 3 Hare Court) (William Clegg QC), London (020) 7440 8888
Recommended in Crime

WOLTON, Harry QC
2-3 Gray's Inn Square (Anthony Scrivener QC), London (020) 7242 4986
Recommended in Planning
Specialisation: Town & Country Planning; Residential, Employment, Retail, Recreation, minerals, waste, Personal Injuries & Medical Negligence.
Prof. Memberships: Planning & Environment Bar Association; Personal Injury Bar Association.
Career: Called 1969. Silk 1982. Recorder 1985. Attorney sent to sit as Deputy High Court Judge 1990.
Personal: Cattle Breeding & Dendrology.

WONNACOTT, Mark
7 Stone Buildings (Charles Aldous QC), London (020) 7405 3886
Recommended in Property Litigation
[SPEC] Practice: Commercial and residential landlord and tenant; other real property; professional indemnity in the above. Cases: Nynehead v Fibreboard [1999] 1 EGLR 7; Sun Life v Tantofex [1999] 2 EGLR 135; Sun Life v RACAL [2000] PLSCS 287; Portman BS v Bevan Ashford [2000] PNLR 344; Floyer-Acland v Osmond [2000] 22 EG 142.
Prof. Memberships: Chancery Bar Association; Professional Negligence Bar Association.

WOOD, Christopher
1 Mitre Court Buildings (Bruce Blair QC), London (020) 7797 7070
Recommended in Family: Matrimonial Finance
Specialisation: Principally ancillary relief.
Prof. Memberships: F.L.B.A.
Career: Oxford University (MA). Université d'Aix-Marseilles III (Diplôme d'Etudes Supèrieures d'Université). Called 1986.
Personal: Married. Interests: history, politics, Norway, France.

WOOD, Derek QC
Falcon Chambers (Jonathan Gaunt QC & Kim Lewison QC), London (020) 7353 2484
Recommended in Agriculture
Specialisation: Specialises in all aspects of property law, including commercial and agricultural landlord and tenant disputes, rent review, housing, easements and boundaries, compulsory purchase, tax and planning, building and engineering disputes, joint development agreements and professional negligence in connection with real property. Experienced in the conduct of cases in the courts, before public inquiries and tribunals, and also in arbitrations. Has made numerous appearances as advocate before arbitrators in England and Hong Kong, including two engineering disputes as leading counsel for the Government of Hong Kong. Many appointments as both arbitrator in England (mostly as sole arbitrator) and independent expert across a whole range of property related matters. Consulting Editor (with Bernstein, Marriott and Tackaberry) and contributor to 3rd Edition of the 'Handbook of Arbitration Practice' 1998 (Sweet & Maxwell and Chartered Institute of Arbitrators). Public appointments include Property Advisory Group 1975-1994; Chairman of Expert Committees on the Rating of Plant and Machinery 1991-1992 & 1997-1998 (both Department of the Environment); Chairman of Standing Advisory Committee on Trunk Road Assessment (SACTRA) (Department of Transport). 1986-1994. Chaired working party which produced Code of Practice on Commercial Leases in England and Wales 1995.
Prof. Memberships: Honorary Fellow of Central Association of Agricultural Valuers (FAAV) 1988; Honorary Member of Royal Institute of Chartered Surveyors (Hon RICS) 1991; Fellow of Chartered Institute of Arbitrators (FCIArb) by examination 1993.
Career: Called to the Bar 1964. Took Silk 1978. Recorder to the Crown Court 1985. Bencher of the Middle Temple 1986. Deputy Official Referee and Deputy High Court Judge.
Personal: Educated at the University of Oxford (MA, BCL). Principal of St Hugh's College, Oxford (since 1991). Awarded CBE in New Year's Honours List 1995 for services to property law. Born 14th October 1937.

WOOD, James QC
Doughty Street Chambers (Geoffrey Robertson QC), London (020) 7404 1313
Recommended in Crime, Human Rights (Civil Liberties)
Specialisation: Specialist in human rights and criminal appellate work including the Bridgewater and Birmingham Six appeals. Practice include all forms of serious crime, including homicide, fraud and particu-

larly cases raising political, policing and public order issues. Civil work includes actions against the police, inquests and prisoners' rights. Author of 'The Right to Silence: The Case for Retention' (1991).
Prof. Memberships: Liberty, and of Sweet and Maxwell Practical research Papers on 'Stop and Search' and 'Compensation for Miscarriages of Justice'.
Career: Silk 1999, Assistant Recorder 1998.

WOOD, Michael QC
23 Essex Street (Michael Lawson QC), London (020) 7413 0353
Recommended in Fraud: Criminal
Specialisation: All aspects of criminal work both prosecuting and defending, with an emphasis on commercial fraud, including advising those concerned or interested in fraud litigation such as solicitors and accountants.
Prof. Memberships: Criminal Bar Association; Bar Human Rights Committee.
Career: Called to the Bar 1976; QC 1999; Recorder 1999.
Personal: Born 22nd October 1953. Attended Rugby School and Southampton University.

WOOD, William QC
Brick Court Chambers (Christopher Clarke QC), London (020) 7379 3550
Recommended in Aviation, Insurance
Specialisation: Aviation, insurance and reinsurance, commercial, competition and mediation. Lloyd's litigation (Wellington, Janson Green and Secretan claims); British Airways/Cityflyer merger (Appeared for BA before Competition Commission on merger inquiry); Glo-lite v Jasper Conran (dispute over termination of manufacturing licence); Coral (UK) v Rechtman (Liability of company where company non-existent); Cementation director litigation (interpretation of insurance policy in engineering project); Saipem & Conoco v Dredging VO (Liability of dredger owners for damage to pipeline); Benford v Cameron (distribution agreement void for breach of Article 8); Killick v Goss (liability for reckless flying under Warsaw convetion); Killick v Rendall (construction of personal accident insurance); ABTA v BA and Virgin (travel agent's commission).
Prof. Memberships: Member of Combar, Bar European Group and Competition Law Association.
Career: BA (1st class) Oxford, BCL (1st class) Oxford, LLM (Harvard Law School). Called 1980, silk 1998, CEDR accredited mediator 1999.

WOODWARD, W.C. QC
Ropewalk Chambers (Richard Maxwell QC), Nottingham (0115) 947 2581
Recommended in Personal Injury
Specialisation: Embraces common law, personal injury, employer's liability, insurance, disaster, insidious disease, poisoning, medical and professional and other negligence throughout the land. Involvement in consequences of Markham mine, Flixborough, Hillsborough disasters and in asbestos, noise induced hearing loss, white finger, mucous membrane, fire and explosion litigation for example.
Career: St. John's College Oxford. Inner Temple. Called 1964. Head of Ropewalk Chambers 1985-1994. Silk 1985. Recorder. Deputy High Court Judge – Bar European Group. Founder member Notts Medico-Legal Society and East Midlands Business and Property Bar Association. Special Professor Nottingham University Law Department.
Personal: Married, 3 children. Ponds. Serendipity.

WOODWARK, Jane
Milburn House Chambers (Paul Cape), Newcastle upon Tyne (0191) 230 5511
Recommended in Employment
Specialisation: Almost exclusively employment and discrimination law, acting for both employers and employees.
Prof. Memberships: Employment Law Bar Association; Industrial Law Society.
Career: Has a Master's degree in Industrial Relations, London School of Economics. Prior to the Bar, worked for a national employers' organisation. Specialised in employment law advice and had particular responsibility for advising on equalities issues and transfers of undertakings. Fulfilled a central role in advising employers during three national industrial disputes in 1986, 1989 and 1992.
Personal: Born 18 June 1956.

WORTHINGTON, Stephen
12 King's Bench Walk (Timothy Stow QC), London (020) 7583 0811
Recommended in Personal Injury

WRIGHT, Peter QC
Lincoln House Chambers (Mukhtar Hussain QC), Manchester (0161) 832 5701
Recommended in Crime

WYNTER, Colin
Devereux Chambers (Jeffrey Burke QC), London (020) 7353 7534
Recommended in Commercial (Litigation)
Specialisation: Insurance and re-insurance, litigation and arbitration, general commercial, carriage of goods. Professional negligence.
Prof. Memberships: COMBAR.
Career: Junior Counsel for Defendant Lloyd's Managing Agents in Stockwell v Outhwaite (1991-1992); Agnew - Somerville v Wellington (1994-1996). Also, Caudle v Sharp; Pacific & General Insurance v Baltica Insurance (1996) LRLR, 8; Cicatiello v Anglo European (1994) 1 LLR 678. Home Insurance Co. v ME Rutty (1996) LRLR, 415, Trygg Hansa v Equitas [1998] 2 LLR 439, Gan Insurance v Tai Ping [1999] Lloyd's Rep IR 229 and (CA) [1999], Stephenson v Rogers (CA) [1999] 2 WLR 1064, Barnard Marcus v Ashraf (CA) [1998] 1 EGLR 7, Pride Valley v Independent (CA) [1999], Baker v McCall [1999], Cran v Tai Ping (No2) (2000), Mabey & Johnson v Ecclesiastical (2000), Virdee v National Grid Co Plc (1992) IRLR 555, Lambert v West Devon Borough Council, 27/3/97 TLR.
Personal: LLB (First Class) (London), 1982, M.Phil (Cantab) 1983; fluent in French.

WYVILL, Alistair
St Philip's Chambers (Rex Tedd QC), Birmingham (0121) 246 7000
awyvill@st-philips.co.uk
Recommended in Commercial (Litigation)
Specialisation: General commercial litigation, including intellectual property (particularly in information technology), insolvency, commercial fraud, construction law and human rights in commercial law.
Prof. Memberships: Chancery Bar Association, Midland Chancery and Commercial Bar Association.
Career: B.Econ.; LLB (Hons) (Qld), LLM (Distinction)(Lond.) Admitted as a solicitor in Australia in 1984. Called to the Bar in Australia in 1986. Practiced in Australia as a barrister in commercial and company law for 12 years. Also admitted in Papua New Guinea. Called to the Bar in England and Wales in 1998.
Publications: 'Enrichment, Restitution and the Collapsed Negotiations Cases' (1993-94) 11 Aust Bar Review 93. With D Fitzpatrick, 'Business Bankruptcy Law Reform in Vietnam' (1996) 5 Asia Pacific Law Review 37. 'The Law of Fraudulent Conveyances as the Basis of Mareva Jurisdiction' (1998) 73 Australian Law Journal 672.

YOUNG, David QC
Three New Square (David E.M. Young QC), London (020) 7405 1111
3newsquareip@lineone.net
Recommended in Intellectual Property
Specialisation: All aspects of intellectual property, patent (especially chemical patent cases), and passing off, trade marks, copyright, franchising, restrictive practices, designs, breach of confidence and computer law. Appears in Hong Kong and Singapore. Notable Cases include: American Cyanamid v Ethicon (interloc injunction); 3M v Rennicks (patent); Windsurfing International v Tabur Marine (GB) Ltd (patent); Willemijn v Madge Networks (patent/computers); Germinal Holdings (plant variety); Allied Signal v Sundstrand (Patent County Court – electronics); Glaverbel v British Coal; Hoechst v BP (Patent and High Court Access of projects); Lubrizol Corpn v Exxon (patio); Monsato v Merck (pharmaceuticals); Scandecor Development v Scandecor Marketing (passing off).
Prof. Memberships: Intellectual Property Bar Assn; Chancery Bar Assn.
Career: Monckton Combe School, Hertford College Oxford – MA. Called to Bar 1966, appointed QC 1980. Branches of Lincolns Inn; Recorder of Crown Court (1987-2000); Chairman Plant Seeds and Varieties Tribunal (1987-); Deputy High Court Judge Chancery Division 1993; Deputy Patent County Court Judge 1990.
Publications: Co-author 'Terrell on Law of Patents' (12th – 14th ed); 'Young on Passing Off', 1985;1994.
Personal: Tennis, skiing, country pursuits.

ZACAROLI, Antony
3-4 South Square (Michael Crystal QC), London (020) 7696 9900
Recommended in Commercial Chancery, Insolvency/Corporate Recovery
Specialisation: Practice covers a wide area of business and commercial law, including all aspects of corporate and personal insolvency, litigation relating to property, commercial fraud, constructive trusts, banking, securities, insurance, pensions and professional negligence. Recent reported cases include Grupo Torras SA v Al Sabah [1999] C.L.C. 1469, Don King Productions v Warren [1998] 2 All ER 607, Re Cosslett (Contractors) Limited [1998] Ch 495.
Career: Called to the Bar (Middle Temple) November 1987. Lecturer in Law at Pembroke College, Oxford, from 1987-91.
Publications: Contributor to Lightman & Moss: 'The Law of Receivers of Companies'; Totty & Moss: 'Insolvency'; Gore-Browne on Companies.

ZELIN, Geoffrey
Enterprise Chambers (Anthony Mann QC), London (020) 7405 9471, Newcastle (0191) 222 3344 Leeds (0113) 246 0391
Recommended in Company
Specialisation: Practises in all areas of company and partnership law including shareholder and partnership disputes, insolvency, enforcement of directors' duties and disqualification. Apart from company law his practice encompasses all areas of commercial Chancery work including property disputes and professional negligence.
Prof. Memberships: Chancery Bar Association
Career: Called to the Bar 1984. Practising in these Chambers since December 1986.
Personal: Interests include skiing, cricket.

INDEX OF

PRACTISING BARRISTERS

INDEX TO THE BAR

Browne, Desmond (1969) (QC-1990) Set 145 Profile p. 1489
Browne, Gerald (1995) Set 21
Browne, Godfree (1971) Set 97
Browne, Julie (1989) Set 52
Browne, Louis (1988) Set 239
Browne, Nicholas (1971) (QC-1995) Sets 10, 232, 271, 277
Browne, Shereener (1996) Set 80
Browne, Simon Peter Buchanan (1982) Set 43 Profile p. 1489
Browne-Wilkinson, Simon (1981) (QC-1998) Set 151 Profile p. 1489
Brownhill, Joanna (1997) Set 34
Brownlie, Ian (1958) (QC-1979) Set 13
Bruce, Andrew (1992) Set 151
Bruce, Gaenor (1997) Set 133
Brudenell, Thomas (1977) Set 142 Profile p. 1489
Brunnen, David (1976) Set 238
Brunner, Adrian (1968) (QC-1994) Sets 67, 155
Brunner, Kate (1997) Sets 10, 232, 271, 277
Brunner, Peter (1971) Set 15
Brunning, Matthew (1997) Set 292
Brunton, Sean (1990) Sets 134, 301, 305
Bryan, J.M. (1994) Set 212
Bryan, Rex (1971) Set 137
Bryan, Robert (1992) Set 124
Bryan, Simon (1988) Set 32 Profile p. 1489
Bryant, Caroline (1976) Sets 205, 213, 275
Bryant, Ceri (1984) Set 31
Bryant, John (1976) Set 148
Bryant, Judith (1987) Set 174 Profile p. 1489
Bryant, Keith (1991) Set 25
Bryant-Heron, Mark (1986) Set 12 Profile p. 1490
Bsis, Ibtihal (1994) Set 28
Bubb, Tim (1970) Set 228 Profile p. 1490
Buchan, Andrew (1981) Set 20
Buchan, Jonathan (1994) Set 291
Buchanan, James (1993) Set 169
Buchanan, Vivien (1981) Set 279 Profile p. 1490
Buck, John (1986) Set 164
Buckett, Edwin (1988) Set 54
Buckhaven, Charlotte (1969) Set 125
Buckhaven, Simon (1970) Set 65
Buckingham, K. (1986) Set 226
Buckingham, Sarah (1991) Set 36
Buckingham, Stewart (1996) Set 35
Buckland, Matthew (1997) Set 124
Buckland, Robert James (1991) Set 198
Buckle, Jonathan (1990) Sets 194, 286
Buckley, Bernard C. (1970) Set 124
Buckley, Gerardine (1991) Set 196
Buckley, Peter (1972) Sets 258, 290
Buckley, Richard (1969) Set 113
Buckley-Clarke, Amanda (1991) Sets 128, 184, 284, 304
Bucknall, Belinda (1974) (QC-1988) Set 35 Profile p. 1490
Buckpitt, Michael (1988) Set 47
Budaly, Susan (1994) Sets 50, 208
Budden, Caroline (1977) Set 74 Profile p. 1490
Budworth, Adam (1992) Set 4
Buehrlen, Veronique (1991) Set 46
Bugg, Ian (1992) Set 186
Bui, Victoria (1996) Set 1
Bull, Gregory (1976) Set 199 Profile p. 1490
Bull, Roger (1974) Set 34
Bull, Simon (1984) Sets 10, 232, 271, 277
Bullen, James E. (1966) Set 124
Bullock, Andrew (1992) Set 19
Bullock, Ian (1975) Set 192 Profile p. 1490
Bullock, Neil (1989) Set 21
Bulmer, David (1952) Set 240
Bundell, Katharine (1991) Sets 205, 213, 275
Bundred, G. (1982) Set 243
Burbidge, James (1979) Set 182 Profile p. 1490
Burden, Angus (1994) Set 182
Burden, Emma L.V. (1994) Set 230
Burden, Susan (1985) Set 138 Profile p. 1490
Burdon, Michael (1993) Set 227
Burgess, David (1975) Set 17
Burgess, Edward (1993) Set 192 Profile p. 1490
Burgess, Emma (1995) Set 204
Burgess, John (1978) Set 278
Burgher, Benjimin (1995) Set 164
Burke, Brendan (1995) Set 242
Burke, Jeffrey (1964) (QC-1984) Set 25 Profile p. 1490
Burke, Michael (1985) Set 9
Burke, Trevor (1981) Set 4 Profile p. 1490
Burke-Gaffney, Rupert D.C.J. (1988) Set 124
Burkett, Francis (1969) Set 210
Burkill, Guy (1981) Set 105 Profile p. 1490
Burles, David (1984) Set 50
Burn, C. (1985) Set 226
Burn, Lindsay (1972) Set 74
Burnell, Kate (1998) Set 241
Burnett, Harold (1962) (QC-1982) Set 129
Burnett, Ian D. (1980) (QC-1998) Set 165 Profile p. 1490
Burns, Andrew (1993) Set 25
Burns, Frank (1971) Set 250
Burns, Jeremy (1996) Set 295
Burns, Paul (1998) Set 239
Burns, Peter (1993) Set 249
Burns, Richard H. (1967) Set 280
Burns, Rosemary (1978) Set 48
Burns, Simon (1992) Set 187
Burns, Terry (1990) Set 19
Burr, Andrew (1981) Set 3 Profile p. 1490
Burrell, Gary (1977) (QC-1996) Sets 54, 294
Burrell, Simon (1988) Set 119
Burrett, Catherine (1992) Set 295
Burrington, Richard (1993) Set 135
Burroughs, Nigel (1991) Set 121
Burrow, John (1980) Set 126
Burrows, Euan (1995) Set 68
Burrows, Michael (1979) Set 177
Burrows, Simon (1990) Set 257
Burton, Charles (1983) Set 28
Burton, Frances (1972) Set 120
Burton, Frank (1982) (QC-1998) Set 89 Profile p. 1490
Burton, John M. (1979) Set 98
Burton, Nicholas (1979) Set 100
Burwin, Heather (1983) Set 75
Bury, M. (1986) Set 212
Busby, Thomas (1975) Set 176
Bush, Rosalind (1978) Set 179 Profile p. 1491
Bushell, Terence (1982) Set 180
Busuttil, Godwin (1994) Set 145 Profile p. 1491
Buswell, Richard (1985) Set 62
Butcher, Christopher (1986) Set 82 Profile p. 1491
Butcher, John (1984) Sets 36, 202
Butcher, Richard (1985) Set 97
Butler, Andrew (1993) Set 47
Butler, Christopher M. (1972) Set 281
Butler, Gerald (1955) (QC-1975) Set 33
Butler, Joan (1977) (QC-1998) Set 5
Butler, Jonathan (1992) Set 241
Butler, Judith (1993) Sets 139, 245
Butler, Judith L. (1997) Set 280
Butler, Philip (1979) Set 249
Butler, Rupert (1988) Set 8
Butler, Simon (1996) Set 85
Butt, Michael (1974) Sets 134, 301, 305
Butterfield, John (1995) Set 177
Butterworth, Martin (1985) Set 175
Butterworth, Paul (1982) Set 276
Buttimore, Gabriel (1993) Set 122
Buxton, Sarah (1988) Set 176
Byrne, Garrett (1986) Set 38 Profile p. 1491
Byrne, James (1983) Set 238
Byrne, Michael (1971) Set 241
Caddick, Nicholas (1986) Set 107
Caddle, Sherrie (1983) Set 49
Cade, Diana (1994) Set 202
Cadin, David (1990) Set 75
Cadney, Paul (1984) Set 191
Cadwaladr, Stephen (1992) Set 180
Cadwallader, Neil (1984) Set 239
Cadwallader, Peter (1973) Set 260
Cafferkey, Annette (1994) Set 206
Cafferkey, Nicola (1998) Set 168
Cahill, Jeremy (1975) Set 179 Profile p. 1491
Cahill, Patrick (1979) Set 126
Cahill, Sally (1978) Set 223 Profile p. 1491
Cains, Linda (1990) Set 227
Cairnes, Paul (1980) Sets 128, 184, 284, 304
Cakebread, Stuart (1978) Set 47
Calcutt, David C. (1955) (QC-1972) Set 39
Caldecott, Andrew (1975) (QC-1994) Set 16 Profile p. 1491
Caldin, Giles (1974) Set 35
Caldwell, Jennifer (1973) Set 261
Caldwell, Peter (1995) Set 28
Callaghan, Elizabeth M (1998) Set 306
Callan, David (1979) Set 269
Calland, Timothy (1999) Sets 30, 216, 267
Callaway, Anthony Leonard (1978) Sets 7, 135, 228
Callery, Martin (1997) Set 248
Callman, Jeremy (1991) Set 120
Callman, Tanya (1993) Set 76
Calver, Neil (1987) Set 15 Profile p. 1491
Calvert, Charles (1975) Set 52
Calvert, David (1995) Set 259
Calvert-Smith, Richard (1997) Set 12
Cameron, Alexander (1986) Set 144 Profile p. 1491
Cameron, Barbara (1979) Sets 67, 155
Cameron, James (1987) Set 172 Profile p. 1491
Cameron, Kenneth (1969) Set 78
Cameron, N.A. (1984) Set 212 Profile p. 1491
Cameron, Neil (1982) Set 149 Profile p. 1491
Cameron, Sheila (1957) (QC-1983) Set 68 Profile p. 1491
Cammegh, John (1987) Set 6
Cammerman, Gideon (1996) Set 97
Camp, Christopher (1996) Set 52
Campbell, A.N. (1972) (QC-1994) Set 225
Campbell, Alexis (1990) Set 70
Campbell, Andrew (1972) Set 97
Campbell, Colin (1979) Set 126
Campbell, Diane (1995) Set 306
Campbell, Douglas James (1993) Set 105 Profile p. 1491
Campbell, Emily (1995) Set 174 Profile p. 1492
Campbell, Glenn (1985) Set 121
Campbell, Graham (1979) Set 137
Campbell, Jane (1990) Set 137
Campbell, Joan (1996) Set 199
Campbell, John (1981) Sets 224, 253
Campbell, Nicholas (1979) (QC-2000) Set 87
Campbell, Oliver (1992) Sets 67, 155
Campbell, Rhona (1993) Set 178
Campbell, Robin (1969) Set 59
Campbell, Sarah (1997) Set 38
Campbell, Stephen (1982) Set 182 Profile p. 1492
Campbell, Susan (1986) Set 209 Profile p. 1492
Campbell-Clyne, Christopher (1988) Set 4
Campbell-Tiech, Andrew (1978) Set 28
Canavan, Sandy (1987) Set 171
Candler, Linda (1977) Set 49
Candlin, James (1991) Set 41
Cannan, Jonathan (1989) Sets 185, 214, 259
Cannatella, Marc (1997) Sets 205, 213, 275
Cannock, Giles (1998) Sets 224, 253
Cannon, Mark (1985) Set 106
Canon, Adam (1997) Set 78
Cant, Christopher I. (1973) Set 161
Cape, Paul (1990) Set 268 Profile p. 1492
Caplan, Jonathan (1973) (QC-1991) Set 131 Profile p. 1492
Capon, Philip (1990) Set 182
Capstick, Timothy (1986) Set 221
Carberry, Caroline (1995) Set 168
Carden, Nicholas (1981) Set 99
Carey, Godfrey (1969) (QC-1991) Set 131
Carey, Jeremy (1974) Set 92
Carey-Hughes, Richard J. (1977) Set 6
Cargill-Thompson, Perdita (1993) Set 32 Profile p. 1492
Carlile of Berriew, Lord (1970) (QC-1984) Sets 12, 203
Carling, Christopher (1969) Sets 118, 190
Carlisle, Hugh B.H. (1961) (QC-1978) Set 165 Profile p. 1492
Carlisle, Lord (1954) (QC-1971) Set 141
Carman, George (1953) (QC-1971) Set 59 Profile p. 1492
Carmichael, John (1984) Set 49
Carne, Roger (1969) Set 6
Carnes, Andrew (1984) Set 38
Carney, Andrew (1995) Set 240
Carpenter, Jane (1984) Set 47
Carpenter, Richard (1981) Set 215
Carr, Bruce (1986) Set 25 Profile p. 1492
Carr, Christopher (1968) (QC-1983) Set 33 Profile p. 1492
Carr, Henry (1982) (QC-1998) Set 154 Profile p. 1492
Carr, Peter (1976) Set 181 Profile p. 1492
Carr, Simon (1984) Set 54
Carr, Sue (1987) Set 106 Profile p. 1492
Carrington, Gillian (1990) Set 57
Carroll, Jonathan (1994) Set 231
Carron, Richard (1992) Sets 19, 293
Carrott, Sylvester (1980) Set 80
Carrow, Robert (1981) Set 9
Carss-Frisk, Monica (1985) Set 13 Profile p. 1493
Carswell, Patricia (1993) Set 159
Carter, David (1971) Set 2
Carter, Lesley (1990) Set 236
Carter, Martin (1992) Sets 224, 253
Carter, Peter (1974) (QC-1995) Set 146 Profile p. 1493
Carter, R.C. (1990) Set 251
Carter, Rosalyn (1994) Set 182
Carter, Sally (1994) Set 296
Carter, William (1989) Set 38
Carter-Manning, Jeremy (1975) (QC-1993) Set 12
Carter-Stephenson, George (1975) (QC-1998) Set 58 Profile p. 1493
Cartwright, Crispian (1976) Set 137
Cartwright, Ivan (1993) Set 238
Cartwright, James (1968) Set 76
Cartwright, Nicolas (1986) Set 182
Cartwright, Richard (1994) Set 136
Cartwright, Sophie (1999) Set 249
Carus, Roderick (1971) (QC-1990) Set 260 Profile p. 1493
Carville, Brendan (1980) Set 236
Case, Julie (1990) Set 239
Case, Magdalen (1992) Set 263
Case, Richard (1996) Sets 128, 184, 284, 304
Casella, Bart (1995) Set 70
Casement, David (1992) Set 239
Casey, Aidan (1992) Set 72
Casey, Dermot (1994) Set 21
Casey, Mairin (1989) Set 281 Profile p. 1493
Casey, Noel (1995) Set 146
Cash, Joanne (1994) Set 43
Cassel, Timothy (1965) (QC-1988) Set 131 Profile p. 1493
Cassidy, Patrick (1982) Set 250
Castle, Peter (1970) Set 112
Castle, Richard (1998) Set 74
Castle, Susan (1986) Set 9
Caswell, Benjamin (1993) Set 221
Caswell, Matthew (1968) Set 87
Caswell, Rebecca (1983) Set 87
Catchpole, Stuart (1987) Set 40 Profile p. 1493
Catford, Gordon (1980) Set 22
Cattan, Philip D. (1970) Set 263 Profile p. 1493
Catterson, Marie (1972) Set 36
Cattle, David (1975) Set 78
Caudle, John (1976) Set 4 Profile p. 1493
Caulfield, Paul (1996) Set 269
Caun, Lawrence (1977) Set 92
Causer, John (1979) Set 38 Profile p. 1493
Cavanagh, John (1985) Set 88 Profile p. 1493
Cave, Jeremy (1992) Sets 23, 186
Cave, Patricia (1989) Set 19
Cavender, David (1993) Set 33
Cavin, Paul (1995) Set 79
Caws, Eian (1974) Set 14
Cawson, Mark (1982) Sets 113, 259 Profile p. 1493
Cayford, Philip (1975) Set 8 Profile p. 1493
Cellan-Jones, Deiniol (1988) Set 74
Chadwick, Joanna (1988) Set 179
Chadwin, James (1958) (QC-1976) Sets 60, 222
Chaisty, Paul (1982) Sets 224, 253 Profile p. 1494
Chaize, Tristan (1977) Set 137
Challenger, Colin (1970) Set 18
Challinor, Jonathan (1998) Set 180
Challinor, Michael (1974) Set 177
Chalmers, Suzanne (1995) Set 22
Chamberlain, Emma J.M. (1998) Set 61
Chamberlain, Francis (1985) Sets 128, 184, 284, 304
Chamberlain, Martin (1997) Set 59
Chamberlayne, Patrick (1992) Set 8
Chambers, Adam (1989) Set 89
Chambers, Dominic (1987) Set 15 Profile p. 1494
Chambers, Gaynor (1998) Set 73
Chambers, Gregory (1973) Set 23
Chambers, Jonathan (1996) Set 35
Chambers, Michael (1980) Set 203
Champion, Deborah (1970) Set 4
Chan, Diane (1979) Set 12
Chan, Susan (1994) Sets 90, 283
Chandarana, Yogain (1997) Set 126

Parker, Christopher (1986) Sets 128, 184, 284, 304
Parker, Christopher R. (1984) Set 159 Profile p. 1562
Parker, Hugh (1973) Set 75
Parker, John (1975) Set 101
Parker, Judith (1973) (QC-1991) Set 74 Profile p. 1562
Parker, Kenneth (1975) (QC-1992) Set 102 Profile p. 1562
Parker, Matthew (1997) Set 172
Parker, Paul (1986) Set 106
Parker, Philip (1976) (QC-2000) Set 177
Parker, Steven (1987) Set 240
Parker, Timothy (1995) Set 101
Parker, Wendy (1978) Set 52
Parkes, Malcolm (1984) Set 178
Parkes, Richard (1977) Set 145
Parkin, Fiona (1993) Set 3 Profile p. 1563
Parkin, Fiona (1998) Set 269
Parkins, Graham (1972) (QC-1990) Set 146
Parkinson, William (1997) Set 289
Parnell, Graham (1982) Sets 205, 213, 275 Profile p. 1563
Parr, John (1989) Set 252
Parr, Judith (1994) Set 56
Parrish, Samuel (1962) Sets 128, 184, 284, 304
Parroy, Michael (1969) (QC-1991) Sets 128, 184, 284, 304 Profile p. 1563
Parry, Charles (1973) Sets 134, 301, 305
Parry, David (1972) Set 104
Parry, Gwyn (1993) Set 270
Parry, Isabel (1979) Set 197 Profile p. 1563
Parry, Siân (1994) Set 270
Parry Evans, Mary (1953) Set 199
Parry-Jones, Carole (1992) Sets 205, 213, 275
Parry-Jones, Trevor (1992) Set 240
Parsley, Charles (1973) Set 199
Parsons, Andrew (1985) Set 288
Parsons, Luke (1985) Set 35 Profile p. 1563
Parsons, Simon (1993) Set 234
Partington, David (1987) Set 120
Partington, David J. (1987) Set 215
Partington, Prof. Martin (1984) Set 2
Partridge, Ian (1979) Sets 128, 184, 284, 304
Partridge, Richard (1994) Set 150 Profile p. 1563
Pascall, Matthew (1984) Set 211
Pascoe, Martin (1977) Set 153 Profile p. 1563
Pascoe, Nigel (1966) (QC-1988) Sets 134, 301, 305 Profile p. 1563
Pasiuk, Janina (1983) Set 250
Pass, Geoffrey (1975) Sets 224, 253
Passmore, John (1992) Set 173
Patchett-Joyce, Michael (1981) Set 102
Patel, Elyas (1991) Set 222
Patel, Gita (1988) Set 250
Patel, Parishil (1996) Set 40
Patel, Sandip (1991) Set 49
Paterson, David (1961) Set 75
Pathak, Pankaj (1992) Set 125
Paton, Ewan (1997) Set 189
Paton, Ian (1975) Set 141
Patrick, James (1989) Set 189
Patten, Ben (1986) Set 106
Patten, Nicholas (1974) (QC-1988) Set 119 Profile p. 1563
Patterson, Frances (1977) (QC-1998) Sets 40, 224, 253 Profile p. 1563
Patterson, Gareth (1995) Set 81
Patterson, Jo-Anne (1993) Set 270
Patterson, Stewart (1967) Sets 134, 301, 305
Pauffley, Anna (1979) (QC-1995) Set 130 Profile p. 1563
Paul, Daniel (1998) Set 238
Paul, Nicholas (1980) Set 27
Pavlou, Paul (1993) Set 132
Pavry, James (1974) Set 74
Pawlak, Witold (1970) Set 5
Pawson, Robert (1994) Sets 134, 301, 305
Paxton, Christopher (1991) Set 135
Pay, Adrian (1999) Set 103
Payne, Alan (1996) Set 65
Payne, Richard (1964) Sets 10, 232, 271, 277
Payne, Thomas (1998) Sets 90, 283
Payton, Clifford (1972) Set 173
Peacock, Ian (1990) Sets 113, 230
Peacock, Jonathan (1987) Set 111 Profile p. 1563
Peacock, Nicholas (1989) Set 123
Peacock, Nicholas (1992) Set 138
Peacock, Nicholas (1996) Set 266
Pearce, Ivan (1994) Set 49 Profile p. 1563
Pearce, Linda (1982) Set 80
Pearce, Marcus (1972) Sets 205, 213, 275
Pearce, Michael (1975) Set 278
Pearce, Reid (1979) Set 85
Pearce, Richard (1985) Set 257
Pearce, Robert (1977) Set 112
Pearce-Higgins, Daniel (1973) (QC-1998) Set 166
Pearl, Bernard (1970) Set 108
Pears, D.A. (1975) Set 47
Pearse Wheatley, Robin (1971) Set 126
Pearson, Adam (1969) Sets 134, 301, 305
Pearson, Christopher (1995) Set 18
Pearson, David (1983) Set 183
Pearson, M. (1984) Set 226
Pearson, Michael (1952) Set 101
Peart, Icah (1978) Set 51 Profile p. 1563
Peay, Jill (1991) Set 27
Peck, Catherine (1995) Set 89
Peddie, Ian (1971) (QC-1992) Sets 50, 208 Profile p. 1563
Peebles, Andrew (1987) Set 43
Peel, Robert (1990) Set 8 Profile p. 1563
Peers, Heather (1991) Set 189
Peers, Nicola J. (1996) Sets 185, 214
Peet, Andrew (1991) Set 233
Pegden, Jeffrey (1973) (QC-1996) Set 168
Peglow, Michael (1993) Sets 41, 153
Peirson, Oliver (1993) Sets 134, 301, 305
Pelling, Alexander (1995) Set 117
Pelling, Mark (1979) Set 102 Profile p. 1563
Pema, Anesh (1994) Set 231
Pendlebury, Jeremy (1980) Set 5
Pengelly, Sarah (1996) Set 2
Pennicott, Ian (1982) Set 73 Profile p. 1564
Pennifer, Kelly (1994) Set 239
Penny, Duncan (1992) Set 81
Penny, Tim (1988) Set 162
Pentol, Simon (1982) Set 58
Pepper, Theresa (1973) Set 237
Pepperall, Edward (1989) Set 182
Percival, Robert (1971) Set 132
Pereira, James (1996) Set 68
Peretz, George (1990) Set 102 Profile p. 1564
Perian, Steven (1987) Set 76
Perkins, Alistair (1986) Set 147
Perkins, Marianne (1997) Set 108
Perkoff, Richard (1971) Set 94
Perks, Jolyon (1994) Set 211
Perks, Richard (1977) Set 177
Perrins, Gregory (1997) Set 124
Perry, David (1980) Set 81 Profile p. 1564
Perry, Jaqueline A. (1975) Set 91
Perry, John (1975) (QC-1989) Set 58 Profile p. 1564
Persey, Lionel (1981) (QC-1997) Set 45 Profile p. 1564
Pershad, Rohan (1991) Set 40
Pert, Michael (1970) (QC-1992) Sets 10, 232, 271, 277
Petchey, Philip (1976) Set 68 Profile p. 1564
Peter, Levi (1993) Set 17
Peters, Edward (1998) Set 42
Peters, Nigel (1976) (QC-1997) Set 146
Peters, William (1992) Set 299
Petersen, Neil (1983) Set 125
Peterson, Geri (1997) Set 91
Peto, Anthony (1985) Set 13
Petts, Timothy (1996) Set 89
Phelan, Margaret (1993) Set 147
Phelps, Mark (1994) Sets 205, 213, 275
Phelps, Rosalind (1998) Set 46
Phelvin, Bernard (1971) Set 12
Phil-Ebosie, Sheila (1988) Set 164
Philipps, Guy (1986) Set 46 Profile p. 1564
Philipson, Trevor (1972) (QC-1989) Set 46 Profile p. 1564
Phillimore, Lord (1972) Set 142
Phillimore, Sarah (1994) Set 77
Phillips, Andrew (1978) Set 22
Phillips, David (1976) (QC-1997) Sets 163, 198
Phillips, Frank (1972) Set 299
Phillips, Jane (1989) Set 16 Profile p. 1564
Phillips, John (1975) Set 162
Phillips, Jonathan Mark (1991) Set 172
Phillips, Karen Set 76
Phillips, Mark (1984) (QC-1999) Set 153 Profile p. 1564
Phillips, Matthew J. (1993) Set 39
Phillips, Michael (1980) Set 91
Phillips, Moira (1989) Set 179
Phillips, Nevil (1992) Set 35
Phillips, Richard (1970) (QC-1990) Set 68 Profile p. 1564
Phillips, Rory (1984) Set 172 Profile p. 1564
Phillips, S.J. (1993) Set 82
Phillips, Simon (1985) Set 222
Phillips, Simon (1996) Set 176
Phillips, Stephen (1984) Set 172 Profile p. 1564
Phillips, W.B. (1970) Set 294
Phillpot, Hereward (1997) Set 68
Philo, Noel (1975) Set 279
Philpott, Fred (1974) Set 53 Profile p. 1565
Philpotts, John (1990) Set 239
Phipps, Charles (1992) Set 106
Phipps, Sarah (1997) Set 142
Picarda, Hubert (1962) (QC-1992) Set 104 Profile p. 1565
Pickavance, Graham (1973) Set 237
Pickavance, Michael J. (1974) Set 240
Picken, Simon (1989) Sets 82, 198
Pickering, Andrew (1987) Set 89
Pickering, James (1991) Sets 30, 216, 267
Pickering, Murray (1963) (QC-1985) Set 37
Pickering, S.T. (1996) Set 212
Pickles, Simon (1978) Set 149
Pickup, David (1984) Set 257
Pickup, James (1976) (QC-2000) Set 254 Profile p. 1565
Picton, Julian (1988) Set 129
Picton, Martin (1981) Set 187 Profile p. 1565
Piercy, Arlette (1990) Set 58
Piercy, Mark (1976) Set 67
Pierpoint, Katherine (1998) Set 254
Pigot, Diana (1978) Set 135
Pilkington, Mavis (1990) Set 231
Pilling, Annabel (1996) Set 81
Pilling, Benjamin (1997) Set 136
Pillow, Nathan (1997) Set 32
Pimentel, Carlos (1990) Set 156
Pimm, Peter J. (1991) Set 20
Pine-Coffin, Margaret Ann (1981) Set 295 Profile p. 1565
Pines Richman, Helene (1992) Sets 161, 296
Pinhorn, Richard (1998) Set 233
Pini, John (1981) Set 5
Pinkham, Joy (1993) Set 272
Pinson, Barry (1949) (QC-1973) Set 111
Pinto, Amanda (1983) Set 131
Pipe, Gregory S. (1995) Set 215
Piper, Angus (1991) Set 148
Pirani, Rohan (1995) Sets 118, 190
Pitchers, Henry (1996) Set 115
Pitchford, Christopher (1969) (QC-1987) Sets 43, 198 Profile p. 1565
Pithers, Clive (1989) Sets 193, 285
Pitt-Lewis, Janet (1976) Set 180
Pitt-Payne, Timothy (1989) Set 88 Profile p. 1565
Pittaway, Amanda (1980) Set 180
Pittaway, David (1977) (QC-2000) Set 148
Pitter, Jason (1994) Set 222
Pitts, Anthony B. (1975) Set 6
Piyadasa, Sue (1994) Set 17
Plange, Janet (1981) Set 170
Planterose, Rowan (1978) Set 95 Profile p. 1565
Plaschkes, Sarah (1988) Set 141
Platford, Graham (1970) Set 132
Platt, David (1987) Set 22
Platt, Eleanor F. (1960) (QC-1982) Sets 50, 208 Profile p. 1565
Platts, Graham (1978) Set 263
Platts, Rachel (1989) Set 99
Platts, Robert (1973) Set 254
Platts-Mills, John (1932) (QC-1964) Set 20
Platts-Mills, Mark (1974) (QC-1995) Set 110 Profile p. 1565
Plaut, Simon (1997) Set 223
Playford, Jonathan (1962) (QC-1982) Set 155
Pleming, Nigel (1971) (QC-1992) Set 40 Profile p. 1565
Plender, Richard (1972) (QC-1989) Set 37 Profile p. 1565
Pliener, David (1996) Set 70
Plumstead, John (1975) Set 97
Plunkett, Christopher (1983) Sets 10, 232, 271, 277
Pocock, Christopher (1984) Set 74 Profile p. 1565
Pointer, Martin (1976) (QC-1996) Set 99
Pointing, John (1992) Set 44
Pointon, Caroline (1976) Sets 193, 285
Poku, Mary (1993) Set 137
Polglase, David (1993) Sets 241, 242
Pollard, Joanna (1993) Set 13
Polli, Timothy (1997) Set 164
Pollock, Evelyn (1991) Set 129
Pollock, Gordon (1968) (QC-1979) Set 32 Profile p. 1565
Ponsonby, Lady (1971) Set 126
Ponter, Ian (1993) Sets 224, 253
Poole, Nigel (1989) Set 261
Pooles, Michael (1978) (QC-1999) Set 129 Profile p. 1566
Pooley, Moira (1974) Set 77
Poots, Carolyn (1995) Set 191
Popat, Prashant (1992) Sets 67, 155 Profile p. 1566
Pope, David (1995) Set 172
Pope, Heather (1977) Sets 99, 199
Popert, Catherine (1987) Set 168
Pople, Alison (1993) Set 4
Popplewell, Andrew (1981) (QC-1997) Set 15 Profile p. 1566
Porten, Anthony (1969) (QC-1988) Set 57 Profile p. 1566
Porter, David (1980) Set 259
Porter, Geoffrey (1988) Set 19
Porter, Martin (1986) Set 166
Porter, Nigel (1994) Set 88
Porter, Sarah (1996) Sets 19, 293
Posnansky, Jeremy (1972) (QC-1994) Sets 99, 209 Profile p. 1566
Posner, Gabrielle Jan (1984) Set 56
Post, Andrew (1988) Set 138
Posta, Adrian (1996) Set 303
Postill, Julia D. (1982) Set 28
Pote, Andrew (1983) Sets 90, 283
Potter, Anthony (1994) Set 179
Potter, Donald C. (1948) (QC-1972) Set 140
Potter, Harry (1993) Set 58
Potter, Louise (1993) Set 69
Pottinger, Gavin (1991) Set 48
Potts, James (1994) Set 31
Potts, Richard (1991) Set 276
Potts, Robin (1968) (QC-1982) Set 31 Profile p. 1566
Potts, Warren (1995) Sets 258, 290
Poulet, Rebecca (1975) (QC-1995) Set 141
Pounder, Gerard (1980) Set 36
Povoas, Simon (1996) Set 237
Powell, Debra (1995) Set 150
Powell, Giles (1990) Set 36
Powell, H J (1998) Set 294
Powell, John L. (1974) (QC-1990) Set 106 Profile p. 1566
Powell, Richard (1991) Set 270
Powell, William (1971) Sets 194, 286
Power, Erica (1990) Set 22
Power, Lawrence (1995) Set 78
Power, Nigel (1992) Set 236
Power, Richard (1983) Set 138
Powers, Michael J. (1979) (QC-1995) Set 129 Profile p. 1566
Powis, Lucy (1992) Sets 224, 253
Powis, Samantha (1985) Set 182
Powles, John (1975) Set 22
Powles, Stephen (1972) (QC-1995) Sets 67, 155
Pownall, Orlando (1975) Set 71 Profile p. 1566
Poyer-Sleeman, Patricia (1992) Sets 134, 301, 305
Prager, Sarah (1997) Set 137
Prand, Annette (1995) Set 92
Pratt, Camden (1970) (QC-1992) Set 74 Profile p. 1566
Pratt, Duncan (1971) Set 138 Profile p. 1567
Pratt, Patricia (1991) Set 241
Pratt, Richard (1980) Set 240
Preen, Catherine (1988) Set 181
Prentice, Dan (1982) Set 31 Profile p. 1567
Prentis, Sebastian (1996) Set 103
Prescott, Peter (1970) (QC-1990) Set 110 Profile p. 1567
Pressdee, Piers (1991) Sets 69, 282
Preston, Darren (1991) Set 251
Preston, David (1993) Set 70
Preston, Dominic (1995) Set 2
Preston, Hugh (1994) Set 5
Preston, Kim (1991) Set 77
Preston, Nicola (1992) Set 179
Preston, Timothy (1964) (QC-1982) Set 166
Prestwich, Andrew (1986) Set 280
Pretsell, James (1998) Set 43
Pretzell, Andreas (1997) Set 91
Prevatt, Beatrice (1985) Set 51
Prevezer, Susan (1983) (QC-2000) Set 32 Profile p. 1567
Price, Clare (1988) Set 129
Price, Debora (1987) Set 21

CHAMBERS INDEX TO THE

3000

LEADING LAWYERS

CHAMBERS' 3000 LEADING LAWYERS

An index to the profiles of all recommended solicitors in Chambers 1999-2000

A

Avery Jones C.B.E., John
Tax ★★★ 781
Trusts & Personal Tax ★★★★ 818

Awford, Ian
Aviation ★★★★ 102

Azim-Khan, Rafi
Advertising & Marketing ★★ 64

B

Backhouse, James
Transport ★★★★ 799

Bacon, Gavin
Litigation (Commercial) ★ 558

Bagge, James
Financial Services ★★ 406
Fraud ★★★★ 416

Bailes, Tony
Information Technology ★★★★ 453

Bailey, Darren
Sport ★★ 768

Bailey, Jeffrey
Property (Commercial) ★★★ 722

Bailey, Michael D.
Property (Commercial) ★★★★ 722

Baillie, Kirstene M.
Investment Funds U 522

Baily, Tim G.
Property (Commercial) ★★★★ 723

Baird, Derek W
Corporate Finance U 241

Baird, James
Corporate Finance ★★★★ 241

Baker, Andrew P.
Corporate Finance ★★ 241

Baker, Huw
Construction ★★★ 196

Baker, Ian P.
Banking ★★★★ 116
Insolvency/Corporate Recovery ★★★★ 473

Baker, Miranda
Family ★ 390

Baker, Neil
Environment ★★★ 372
Planning ★★★ 660

Bakes, Martin
Insurance ★★★★ 493

Balcomb, Anne
Immigration ★ 440

Baldock, Anne
Projects/PFI ✪ 695

Baldwin, Mark
Tax ★★★ 781
Tax (Corporate) ★★ 781

Balen, Paul
Clinical Negligence ★★★★ 160
Personal Injury ★★★ 642
Product Liability ★★★★ 674

Balfour, Andrew
Banking ★★★ 116

Balfour, John
Aviation ★★★★ 102

Ball, Susan
Tax (Corporate) ★★ 781

Ballantine, Tom
Family ★★★ 390

Ballard, Andy
Social Housing ★★ 758

Ballard, Richard M.
Tax (Corporate) ★★★★ 781

Ballard, Tony
Media & Entertainment ★★ 597
Telecommunications ★★ 792

Ballingall, James G.M.
Projects/PFI ★ 695

Ballmann, William
Insolvency/Corporate Recovery ★★ 473

Bamber, Roger
Family ★★ 390

Band, Christa
Litigation (Commercial) U 558

Bandurka, Andrew A.
Insurance ★★ 493

Bankier, David A.
Property (Commercial) ★★★★ 723

Banks, Sandra
Planning ★★ 660

Bannister, Richard
Clinical Negligence ★★ 160

Barber, Janice C.
Clinical Negligence ★★ 160
Healthcare ★★ 428

Barber, Paul H
Clinical Negligence ★★★★ 160
Healthcare ★★★★ 428

Barbor, Cynthia M.
Travel ★★★★ 806

Barcan, Richard
Clinical Negligence ✪ 160

Barclay, Jonathan R.
Trusts & Personal Tax ★★★★ 818

Bardot, Andrew
Shipping ★★★ 744

Barker, Alan V.
Insurance ★★ 493

Barker, Bridget
Investment Funds ★ 522

Barker, Christine E.
Family ★★★ 390

Barker, Richard
Agriculture ★★★ 73

Barker, William
Intellectual Property ★★★★ 508

Barlow, Colin
Environment ★★★★ 372

Barlow, James
Investment Funds ★ 522

Barnard, Stephen G.
Corporate Finance ★ 241

Barnes, James C.
Property (Commercial) ★★★ 723

Barnes, Oliver W.A.
Corporate Finance ★★ 241

Barnett, Ian G.
Agriculture ★★★ 73

Barnett, Nigel
Insolvency/Corporate Recovery ★★ 473

Barnfather, Anthony
Fraud ★★★ 416

Barr, Alan
Tax (Corporate) ★★★ 781

Barr, Alan
Corporate Finance ★★★★ 242

Barr, Richard
Product Liability ★★★ 674

Barr, William D.W.
Agriculture ★★★★ 73

Barr-Smith, Adrian
Sport ✪ 768

Barratt, Jeffery
Projects/PFI ★★★★ 695

Barrett, Elizabeth
Fraud ★★ 416

Barrett, Geoff
Professional Negligence ★★★ 684

Barrett, Kevin John
Construction ★★★★ 196

Barrie, Sidney
Corporate Finance ★★ 242

Barron, David
Intellectual Property ✪ 508

Barron, Michael J.
Corporate Finance ★★★ 242

Barry, Quintin
Employment ★★★★ 332

Barry, Robert
Intellectual Property ★ 508

Barter, Charles S. J.
Corporate Finance ★★★ 242

Barth, Philip
Immigration ★★★ 440

Barton, Grainne
Clinical Negligence ★★★ 160

Bartram, Peter
Immigration ★★ 441

Bastow, Gillian
Social Housing ★★★★ 758

Bastow, Martin
Litigation (Property) ★★★ 576

Batchelor, Claire
Clinical Negligence ★★★ 160

Bates, Anton B.
Franchising ★★★★ 409

Bateson, Douglas W.
Shipping ★★ 744

Bateson, James
Insurance ★★ 493

Batstone, William
Agriculture ★★ 73

Batten, Elizabeth
Clinical Negligence ★★ 160

Batters, John A.
Licensing ★★★★ 534

Battersby, Robin
Property (Commercial) ★★★ 723

Battie, James S.
Church ★★★ 149

Baxter, Richard
Corporate Finance ★★★★ 242

Baylis, Craig
Licensing ★★★ 534
Product Liability ★★★★ 674

Baylis, Simon E.
Construction ★★★★ 196

Bays, Kevin
Defamation ★★★★ 293

Beach, Steven
Property (Commercial) ★★ 723

Beale, Robert L.
Personal Injury ★★★★ 642

Beare, Tony
Tax (Corporate) ★★ 781

Beatson, Kim
Family ★ 390

Beaumont, Rupert
Capital Markets ★ 129

Beckett, Roy G.
Property (Commercial) ★★★★ 723

Beckett, Samuel R.
Construction ★★★★ 196
Litigation (Commercial) ★★★★ 558

Beckford, Trevor
Crime ★★★★ 275

Beddow, Simon D. J.
Corporate Finance ★★ 242

Bedford, Paul
Capital Markets ★★★ 129

Bedford, Richard
Litigation (Property) ★★★★ 576

Beechey, John
Arbitration (International) ★★★★ 87

Beesley, Peter
Church ★★★★ 149
Education ★★★★ 308

Beharrell, Steven
Corporate Finance ★★★ 242
Energy & Natural Resources ★★★ 356

Belchak, Hilary
Immigration ★★★★ 441

Belcher, Penny
Litigation (Property) ★★★★ 576

Belderbos, Mark J.
Charities ★★★ 141
Church ★★★ 149

Bell, Alasdair
Sport ★★ 768

Bell, Christopher C.
Corporate Finance ★★★★ 242

Bell, Stuart
Environment ★★★ 372

Bell, Tony
Energy & Natural Resources ★★★ 356

Bellew, Derek J.
Corporate Finance ★ 242
Partnership ★★★★ 610
Partnership ★ 610

Bellhouse, John
Projects/PFI ★★ 695

Bellis, Nigel D.
Corporate Finance ★★★★ 242

Bellis, P.T.
Corporate Finance U 242

Beltrami, Joseph
Crime ★★★★ 275

Bennett, Graham
Property (Commercial) ★★★★ 723

Bennett, Jennifer
Social Housing ★★★★ 758

Bennett, Jeremy M.
Insolvency/Corporate Recovery ★ 473

Bennett, John
Local Government ★★★ 586

KEY TO RANKINGS: ✪ = Star Individual ★★★★ = Top Band ★★★ = Second Band ★★ = Third Band ★ = Fourth Band U = Up and coming

Brand, Giles
Asset Finance & Leasing ★ ... 96

Brannan, Guy C.H.
Tax (Corporate) ★★ ... 781

Branson, Christopher
Insolvency/Corporate Recovery ✪ 474

Bray, Michael
Banking ★★★★ ... 116

Bray, Richard
Media & Entertainment ★★ ... 597

Brearley, Kate
Employment ★★ ... 333

Brennan, Paul
Energy & Natural Resources ★★★ 356

Bresslaw, James
Capital Markets ★ ... 129

Bretherton, Philip.J.
Property (Commercial) ★★★★ ... 724

Brett, Adam
Employment ★★★ ... 333

Brett, Alan K.
Property (Commercial) ★★ ... 724

Bretton, Linda
Energy & Natural Resources ★ ... 356

Bretton, Richard
Health & Safety ★★★★ ... 424

Brewer, Martin
Employment ★★★ ... 333

Briam, Tony
Property (Commercial) ★★★ ... 724

Brice, Barry
Property (Commercial) ★★★★ ... 724

Bridges, Mark T.
Trusts & Personal Tax ★★★ ... 819

Bridgewater, Martin
Construction ★★ ... 197

Brierley, Chris
Banking ★★★ ... 116

Brierley, Ian P.
Litigation (Property) ★★ ... 576

Briffa, Margaret
Intellectual Property ★ ... 509

Briggs, Christopher
Clinical Negligence ★★★ ... 161

Briggs, Graham M.
Insolvency/Corporate Recovery ★ 474

Briggs, Leona
Litigation (Property) ★★★★ ... 576

Bright, Chris
Competition/Anti-trust ✪ ... 179

Bristol, Jeremy
Property (Commercial) ★★★ ... 724

Broadfield, Alice
Banking U ... 116

Broadhead, Jill F.H.
Clinical Negligence ★★★★ ... 161
Healthcare ★★★★ ... 429

Broadhurst, Marisa
Healthcare ★★★ ... 429

Brock, Adrienne M.
Employment ★★ ... 333

Brock, David M. J.
Environment ★★★ ... 372
Planning ★★★★ ... 660

Brockman, Christopher C.
Insolvency/Corporate Recovery ★★★ ... 474

Brook, Nigel
Insurance ★★ ... 493

Brookes, Alan
Family ★★ ... 391

Brookes, Mike
Media & Entertainment U ... 597

Brooks, Egan R.
Insolvency/Corporate Recovery ✪ 474

Brooks, Kenneth Williams
Charities ★★★★ ... 141

Broudie, Robert
Crime ★★★ ... 275

Brough, Gordon
Investment Funds ★ ... 522

Brown, Alison
Health & Safety ★★★ ... 424

Brown, Alistdair B.
Shipping ★★★ ... 744

Brown, Anthony
Employment ★ ... 333

Brown, Anthony
Shipping ★★ ... 744

Brown, Claude
Capital Markets ★★★ ... 129

Brown, David
Intellectual Property ★★★★ ... 509

Brown, Douglas
Energy & Natural Resources ★ ... 356

Brown, Duncan
Social Housing U ... 758

Brown, Graham S.
Trusts & Personal Tax ★★★ ... 819

Brown, Henry
Alternative Dispute Resolution ★★★★ ... 81

Brown, Jacqueline
Sport U ... 768

Brown, Jane A.
Capital Markets ★★ ... 129

Brown, Jeffrey C.
Construction ★★ ... 197

Brown, Jeremy
Intellectual Property ★★★★ ... 509

Brown, Jonathan A.
Corporate Finance ★ ... 244

Brown, Mitch
Social Housing ★★★★ ... 758

Brown, Neil
Energy & Natural Resources ★★★★ ... 356
Telecommunications ★★★★ ... 792

Brown, Nicholas
Parliamentary & Public Affairs ★★ 604

Brown, Nicholas A.
Property (Commercial) ★★ ... 724

Brown, Nicola
Employment ★★★ ... 333

Brown, Richard
Intellectual Property ★★★ ... 509

Brown, Robert
Insolvency/Corporate Recovery ★ 474

Brown, Robert T.J.
Crime ★★★ ... 275

Brown, Sandra
Trusts & Personal Tax ★★★ ... 819

Brown, Steven
Projects/PFI ★★★ ... 696

Brown, Vincent
Environment ★ ... 372

Browne, Benjamin
Shipping ★★ ... 744

Brownlow, Jeremy
Corporate Finance ★★★ ... 244

Bruce, Roderick L.
Corporate Finance ★★★ ... 244

Bruce Lockhart, Karen
Family ★★★ ... 391

Bruder, Carl
Licensing U ... 534

Bruffell, Martin
Personal Injury ★★★★ ... 642

Bryce, Andrew John
Environment ★★★★ ... 372

Brymer, Stewart
Property (Commercial) ★★★ ... 724

Brymer, Tim
Aviation ★★★ ... 102

Brynes, Joanna
Licensing U ... 534

Brynmor Thomas, David
Arbitration (International) ★★ ... 87

Buchan, Gordon A.
Corporate Finance ★★ ... 244

Buchanan, Andrew
Insolvency/Corporate Recovery ★★ ... 474

Buckley, Liam
Property (Commercial) ★★★ ... 724

Buckworth, Nicholas
Projects/PFI ★★ ... 696

Budgett, Tom
Asset Finance & Leasing ★★★★ .. 96

Buechel, Peter
Construction ★★ ... 197

Bugg, Anthony
Insolvency/Corporate Recovery ★★ ... 474

Bull, Rod
Planning ★★★★ ... 660

Bunch, Anthony
Construction ★★★★ ... 197

Bundey, Ruth
Human Rights ★★★★ ... 433
Immigration ★★★ ... 441

Burch, Simon
Construction ★★ ... 197

Burchfield, Jonathan R.
Charities ★★★ ... 141

Burd, Michael
Employment ★★★ ... 333

Burdon-Cooper, Alan R.
Sport ★★ ... 768

Burgess, David C.W.
Administrative & Public Law ★★★ .. 58
Immigration ★★★ ... 441

Burgess, James C.A.
Property (Commercial) ★★★★ ... 724

Burgess, Patrick
Corporate Finance ★ ... 244

Burn, Lachlan
Capital Markets ★★★★ ... 129

Burnett, Rachel
Information Technology ★ ... 454

Burnley, Paul
Environment ★★★ ... 373
Health & Safety ★★★ ... 424

Burns, Richard
Corporate Finance ★★★ ... 244

Burnside, David
Employment ★★★ ... 333

Burnside, Graham M.
Banking ★★ ... 116

Burrow, Robert P.
Corporate Finance ★★ ... 244

Burrows, Julia K.
Insolvency/Corporate Recovery ★★★ ... 474

Burrows, Lesley
Fraud ★★★★ ... 416

Burton, Ian
Fraud ✪ ... 416

Bush, Kenneth
Licensing ★ ... 534

Bush, Philip
Shipping ★★★ ... 744

Butcher, Trevor
Construction ★★★ ... 197

Butler, Alan J.
Property (Commercial) ★★ ... 724

Butler, Kay
Tax (Corporate) ★★ ... 781

Butler, Maurice R.
Construction ★★★★ ... 198
Corporate Finance ★ ... 244

Butler, Michael
Crime ★★ ... 275

Butler-Gallie, Stuart
Corporate Finance ★★★ ... 244

Butterfield, Kate
Planning U ... 660

Buxton, James
Agriculture ★★★★ ... 73

Buxton, Richard
Administrative & Public Law ★★★★ ... 58
Environment ★★★★ ... 373

Byatt, Lorne
Information Technology ★★★ ... 454
Intellectual Property ★★★ ... 509

Byrne, David
Fraud ★★★ ... 416
Fraud ★★ ... 416

Byrne, Justin
Litigation (Commercial) U ... 558

Byrne, Richard
Health & Safety ★★★ ... 424

Byrt, Sarah
Advertising & Marketing ★★ ... 64

C

Caddick, Robert J.
Property (Commercial) ★★★★ ... 724

Cadman, Peter H.
Crime ★★ ... 275

KEY TO RANKINGS: ✪ = Star Individual ★★★★ = Top Band ★★★ = Second Band ★★ = Third Band ★ = Fourth Band U = Up and coming

KEY TO RANKINGS: ✪ = Star Individual ★★★★ = Top Band ★★★ = Second Band ★★ = Third Band ★ = Fourth Band U = Up and coming

Cockburn, David
Employment ★★★★ 334

Cockerill, Vivien
Pensions ★★★★ 622

Cockram, Richard
Construction ★★★★ 198
Projects/PFI ★★★ 696

Codrington, Eddie
Employee Share Schemes ★★★ .. 314

Cody, Nick
Product Liability ★★★ 674

Coffell, Howard
Energy & Natural Resources ★ 357

Cohen, Adrian Leon
Insolvency/Corporate Recovery ★ 475

Cohen, David
Employee Share Schemes ★★★★ 314

Cohen, John M.R.
Media & Entertainment ★★★★ 597

Cohen, Laurence J.
Intellectual Property ★★★ 509

Cohen, Ralph J.
Competition/Anti-trust ★ 179

Cohen, Roger D.
Litigation (Property) ★★★ 576

Coker, Jane
Immigration ★★★★ 441

Colacicchi, Clare E.V.
Pensions ★★★★ 622

Colbridge, Christopher
Arbitration (International) ★★ 87

Cole, Alun
Administrative & Public Law ★★★★ 58
Local Government ★★★ 586

Cole, Margaret B.
Projects/PFI ★★ 696

Cole, Michael
Crime ★★★★ 275

Coleclough, Stephen
Tax (Corporate) ★★★★ 782

Coleman, Brenda
Tax (Corporate) ★ 782

Colhoun, Aileen
Fraud ★★★★ 416

Coll, Henry A.
Employment ★★★ 334

Collar, Neil A.
Planning ★★★★ 661

Collingwood, Mark
Construction ★★★★ 198

Collins, Andrew
Asset Finance & Leasing ★★★ 96

Collins, Anthony Ralph
Licensing ★★★★ 535

Collins, Peter
Agriculture ★★★ 74

Collinson, Adam G.
Competition/Anti-trust ★★★★ 179

Collinson, Ian H.
Litigation (Commercial) ★★★ 559

Collis, Pamela
Family ★★ 392

Compagnoni, Marco
Corporate Finance ★★★ 246

Concannon, Simon
Tax (Corporate) ★★★ 782

Conlan, Sue
Immigration ★★★ 441

Connal, R. Craig
Litigation (Commercial) ★★★ 559
Planning ★★★★ 661

Connell, Douglas A.
Charities ★★★★ 141
Trusts & Personal Tax ★★★★ 819

Connoley, Mark F.
Insurance ★★★ 494

Connolly, Sean
Professional Negligence ★★★ 684

Connor, Vincent
Construction ★★★ 198

Conrathe, Paul
Education ★★★ 308

Conway, Philip
Defamation ★★★ 293

Cook, C. John
Competition/Anti-trust ★ 179

Cook, Mark
Local Government ★★★ 586

Cook, Nigel C. S.
Insolvency/Corporate Recovery ★★ 475

Cook, Patrick D.
Insolvency/Corporate Recovery ★★★★ 475

Cook, Trevor
Intellectual Property ✪ 510

Cooke, Adam N.
Intellectual Property ★★★ 510

Cooke, Darryl J.
Corporate Finance ★★★ 246

Cooke, David C.
Partnership ★★★★ 610

Cooke, David J.
Banking ★★★★ 117
Insolvency/Corporate Recovery ★ 475

Cooke, Stephen
Corporate Finance ★★★ 246

Cooke, Stephen
Trusts & Personal Tax ★★★ 819

Coombs, Monica
Pensions U 622

Coombs, Richard
Corporate Finance ★★ 246

Cooper, David
Planning ★★★ 661

Cooper, Edward J.O.
Employment ★ 334

Cooper, Ian
Fraud ★★★ 417

Cooper, Jacqueline
Partnership ★★★ 611

Cooper, Janet
Employee Share Schemes ★★★★ 314

Cooper, Jonathan J.
Health & Safety ★★★ 424

Cooper, Paul
Corporate Finance ★★★★ 246

Copley, Dean T.
Property (Commercial) ★★ 725

Coppen, Simon
Competition/Anti-trust ★★★★ 179
Transport ★★ 799

Coppin, Jonathan
Corporate Finance U 246

Corbett, Edward
Construction ★★★ 198

Corker, David
Fraud ★★★★ 417

Cornes, David L.
Alternative Dispute Resolution ★★★ 81
Construction ★★★ 198

Cornick, Timothy
Investment Funds ★★★ 523

Cornish, Martin
Commodities ★★ 171

Cornish, Sarah
Professional Negligence ★★★★ .. 684

Cornthwaite, Richard
Fraud ★★ 417

Cornwell, John
Family ★ 392

Cornwell-Kelly, Malachy
Customs & Excise ★★★★ 281

Corr, Patrick
Insolvency/Corporate Recovery ★★★ 475

Cottis, Matthew J.
Banking ★ 117
Corporate Finance ★★★ 246

Cottrell, Patricia A.
Family ★★★ 392

Couchman, Nicholas
Sport ★★ 768

Coulter, David
Projects/PFI ★★★ 696

Courtenay-Stamp, Bronwen
Sport ★★★ 768
Travel ★★ 806

Courtenay-Stamp, D. Jeremy
Advertising & Marketing ★★★ 64

Cowan, Andrew
Social Housing ★★★★ 758

Cowan, Andrew
Social Housing ★★★ 758

Cowan, Matthew
E-commerce ★★ 300

Cowell, Adam
Fraud ★★★ 417

Cowell, Martin E.
Licensing ★★★★ 535

Cowen, Léonie
Local Government ★★★★ 587

Cowie, Pauline
Franchising ★★★ 409

Cowley, Michael J.
Pensions ★ 623

Cowper, Tony
Property (Commercial) ★★★★ 725

Cox, Brian
Education ★★ 308
Litigation (Property) ★★★ 576

Cox, David
Litigation (Property) ★★ 576

Cox, Helen
Pensions ★★★ 623

Cox, Simon F.T.
Investment Funds ★ 523

Cox, Tim
Pensions ✪ 623

Crabtree, John
Corporate Finance ★★ 246

Cradick, Simon J.
Personal Injury ★★★★ 643

Craig, I. Alexander
Corporate Finance ★★★ 246

Craig, Ian R.
Intellectual Property ★★★★ 510

Craig, Nigel S.
Insolvency/Corporate Recovery ★★ 475

Craig, Seán T.
Construction ★★★ 199

Cramer, Richard G.
Sport ★★★ 769

Crane, David
Asset Finance & Leasing ★★ 96
Projects/PFI ★ 696

Crane, Graham
Shipping ★★ 744

Cranfield, Richard
Corporate Finance ★★ 246

Cranston, Peter E.
Insolvency/Corporate Recovery ★★★★ 475

Craven, Diana
Property (Commercial) ★★ 725

Crawford, Sandra
Litigation (Commercial) U 559

Crawford, Susan
Tax (Corporate) ★★ 782

Creed, Angus
Banking ★★★★ 117

Crier, Phil
Licensing ★★ 535

Cripps, James
Investment Funds ★★★ 523

Critchlow, Julian
Construction ★★★ 199

Croall, Philip M.
Arbitration (International) ★★ 87

Croft, Anne
Employee Share Schemes ★★ 314

Croft, Roger
Shipping ★★★ 744

Croker, Richard
Tax ★★★★ 782

Croly, Colin V.
Insurance ★★★★ 494

Crombie, June
Pensions ★★★ 623

Crookes, Alan
Asset Finance & Leasing ★★ 96

Croome, Andrew
Banking ★★★★ 117
Corporate Finance ★★★ 247

KEY TO RANKINGS: ✪ = Star Individual ★★★★ = Top Band ★★★ = Second Band ★★ = Third Band ★ = Fourth Band U = Up and coming

Cross, John
Personal Injury ★★★★ 643

Cross, Siobhan
Litigation (Property) ★★ 577

Cross, Stefan
Employment ★★★★ 334

Crosse, Damian G.
Litigation (Commercial) ★★ 559

Crossley, Peter M.
Litigation (Commercial) ★★★ 559

Crosthwaite, Charles M.
Corporate Finance U 247

Crowther, Felicity
Family ★ 392

Crump, Richard
Shipping ★★★★ 745

Crystal, Peter
Sport ★★ 769

Cuckson, David M.
Environment ★★★ 373

Cullen, Iain
Commodities ★★ 171
Investment Funds ★★ 523

Cullen, Joyce
Employment ★★★ 334
Litigation (Commercial) ★★ 559

Cullinane, Lee
Banking ★ 117

Cumming, Donald
Energy & Natural Resources ★★★★ 357

Cummings, Gavin
Corporate Finance ★ 247

Cummins, Caroline
Construction ★ 199

Cummins, Jack
Licensing ★★★★ 535

Cunliffe, Michael
Planning ✪ 661

Cunningham, Kevin G.
Corporate Finance ★★ 247

Cunningham, Martin S.
Crime ★★★ 275

Cunningham, Neil
Corporate Finance ★★★ 247

Curnow, Tony
Local Government ★★★ 587
Planning ★★★ 661

Curran, Angela
Clinical Negligence ★★★ 161

Curran, John W.
Property (Commercial) ★★ 725

Currie, Derek
Defamation ★★★★ 294

Curtis, Anthony G.
Licensing ★★★★ 535

Curtis, Simon R.
Shipping ★★ 745

Cuthbert, Michael
Energy & Natural Resources ★★★ 357

Cuthbertson, Ian
Insolvency/Corporate Recovery ★★★★ 475

Cutting, Michael
Competition/Anti-trust U 179

Cuttle, M. Barry
Crime ★★★ 275

D

d'Inverno, Isobel
Tax (Corporate) ★★★★ 782

Da Costa, Alastair J.
Corporate Finance ★★★ 247

Dace, Nigel H.
Personal Injury ★★★★ 643

Dadak, Roderick
Defamation ★★ 294

Dakeyne, Mark L.
Property (Commercial) ★★★★ 725

Dale, Michael
Shipping ★★★★ 745

Dale, Nigel A.
Banking ★★★★ 117

Dale, Stephanie
Employment ★★ 335

Dalgarno, David
Employment ★ 335

Dalgarno, Leslie S.
Property (Commercial) ★★★ 725

Dalgleish, Andrew M.C.
Trusts & Personal Tax ★★★★ 819

Dalgleish, Douglas S.
Licensing ★★★★ 535

Dallas, James
Energy & Natural Resources ★★★★ 357

Dallow, Sally
Insolvency/Corporate Recovery ★★ 475

Dalrymple, Hew D.K.
Agriculture ★★★ 74

Damms, Martin
Planning ★★★ 661

Darlington, Michael C.
Church ★★★★ 149

Darwin, Andrew D.
Corporate Finance ★★★ 247

Davey, Catherine
Environment ★★★★ 373

Davey, Henry
Energy & Natural Resources ★★ .. 357
Energy & Natural Resources ★★ .. 357

Davey, Jonathan
Competition/Anti-trust ★★★★ 179

Davidson, David
Family ★★★ 392

Davidson, John
Corporate Finance ★ 247

Davidson, Timothy J.
Property (Commercial) ★★★ 725

Davies, Andrew
Property (Commercial) ★★★ 725

Davies, Andrew K.
Clinical Negligence ★★★ 161

Davies, Clive
Information Technology ★ 454

Davies, Edward
Construction ★★★★ 199

Davies, Gareth
Product Liability ★★★★ 674
Transport ★★ 799

Davies, Gwendoline
Litigation (Commercial) ★★ 559

Davies, Ian H.
Pensions ★★★ 623

Davies, Isabel
Intellectual Property ★★★★ 510

Davies, James
Employment ★★★ 335

Davies, Joanne
Employment U 335

Davies, Lawrence
Construction ★★ 199

Davies, Matthew
Immigration ★★★ 441

Davies, Michael
Alternative Dispute Resolution ★★★ 82

Davies, Murray
Family ★★★ 392

Davies, Peter G.
Construction ★★★ 199
Litigation (Commercial) ★★ 560

Davies, Roger
Energy & Natural Resources ★★★ 357

Davies, Rowland
Property (Commercial) ★★★★ 725

Davies, Suzanne
Licensing ★★★★ 535

Davies, Timothy L.
Licensing ★★★★ 535

Davies, Valerie E.M.
Litigation (Commercial) ★★★★ 560

Davies Jones, Martin
Property (Commercial) ★★★★ 725

Davis, Angela C.
Asset Finance & Leasing ★★★ 96
Asset Finance & Leasing ★★★ 96

Davis, Dai
Information Technology ★ 454

Davis, David W.
Media & Entertainment ★ 597

Davis, Elizabeth
Charities ★★★ 141

Davis, James P.L.
Corporate Finance ★ 247

Davis, Michael E.
Construction ★★★ 199

Davis, Nigel R.
Agriculture ★★★★ 74

Davis, Richard G.L.
Pensions ★★★ 623

Davis, Sandra S.
Family ★★★★ 392

Davis, Steven
Corporate Finance ★★ 247

Davison, Andrew J.
Corporate Finance ★★★★ 247

Davison, Peter William
Construction ★★★ 199

Dawes, Edward
Corporate Finance U 247

Dawson, Andrew W.
Environment ★★★★ 373

Dawson, William S.
Employment ★★ 335

Day, Martyn
Administrative & Public Law ★★★ .. 58
Environment ★★★ 373
Personal Injury ★★★ 643

Product Liability ★★★★ 674

Day, Philip J.
Licensing U 535

Day, Sarah Jane
Banking ★★★ 117

Daykin, Stephen
Personal Injury ★★★★ 643

De'Ath, Gary R.
Charities ★★★★ 141

de la Rue, Colin
Shipping ★★ 745

de Walden, Ludovic
Litigation (Commercial) ★ 560

Dean, Kevin J.
Corporate Finance U 247

Dean, Michael
Competition/Anti-trust ★★★★ 179

Dean, Veronica
Employment ★★★ 335

Deane, David
Corporate Finance ★★ 247

Deanesly, Clare
Environment ★★ 374

Dearsley, Ken
Media & Entertainment ★★★ 597

Dedman, Richard H.J.
Professional Negligence ★★ 684

Deeny, Brian
Defamation ★★★★ 294

Deering, Bob
Shipping ★★★★ 745

Deighton, Jane
Human Rights ★★★ 433

Delahunty, Louise
Fraud ★★★ 417

Delemore, Ceri
Information Technology ★★★★ .. 454
Intellectual Property ★★★★ 510

Dennis, Jeanette A.
Agriculture ★★ 74

Densham, Andrew
Agriculture ★★★★ 74

Denson, Gordon F.
Immigration ★★★★ 441

Derbyshire, Paul A.
Personal Injury ★★★★ 643

Desmond, Adrian
Clinical Negligence ✪ 161

Devas, Hugh E.
Environment ★★ 374

Devereux, Mark J.
Media & Entertainment ★★★★ 597

Devine, Joan Gabriel
Insolvency/Corporate Recovery U .. 475

Devine, Laura
Immigration ★★★ 441

Devitt, Paul
Corporate Finance ★★★ 248

Devlin, Michael
Family ★★★★ 392

Dewar, Kate M.
Social Housing ★★★ 759

Dewar, Mark A. M.
Property (Commercial) ★★ 726

Diamond, W. Maurice
Personal Injury ★★★ 643

KEY TO RANKINGS: ✪ = Star Individual ★★★★ = Top Band ★★★ = Second Band ★★ = Third Band ★ = Fourth Band U = Up and coming

Dias, James C.
Personal Injury ★★★★ 643

Dick, Anne
Family ★★★★ 392

Dickinson, Alexander
Trusts & Personal Tax ★★★★ 819

Dickinson, Graham
Personal Injury ★★★★ 643

Dickinson, Malcolm K.
Education ★★ 308

Dickinson, Nicholas H.
Licensing ★★★ 535

Dickinson, Peter
Telecommunications ★★ 792

Dickson, Alastair R.
Corporate Finance ★★★★ 248

Dickson, Ian
Corporate Finance ★★★★ 248
Energy & Natural Resources ★★★★ 357

Dierden, Kenneth N.
Pensions ✪ 623

Dillarstone, Robert
Employment ★★ 335

Dillon, Martin L.G.
Corporate Finance ★ 248

Dillon, Paula
Property (Commercial) ★★ 726

Dimmick, Simon
Planning ★★★ 661

Dimsdale Gill, Angela M.
Pensions ★★★★ 623

Dineley, Rachel
Employment ★ 335

Dingwall, Christian
Healthcare ★★★ 429

Dix, John T.
Corporate Finance ★★★ 248

Dobias, Michael
Insurance ★★ 494

Dobie, James A.
Property (Commercial) ★★ 726

Dobson, Julian C.
Insolvency/Corporate Recovery ★★★★ 475

Dobson, Nicholas
Local Government ★★★ 587

Docking, Peter J.
Pensions ★★★ 623

Dodd, Andrew J.
Family ★★ 392

Dodds-Smith, Ian C.
Product Liability ★★★★ 674

Dodson, Charles
Alternative Dispute Resolution ★★ .. 82

Doeh, Doran
Energy & Natural Resources ★ 357

Dollimore, Jean
Charities ★★★ 141

Dolman, Robert A.
Trusts & Personal Tax ★★ 819

Dolphin, J.Huw
Insolvency/Corporate Recovery ★★ 475

Don, Andrew M.W.
Family ★★★ 392

Donald, Hugh R.
Aviation ★★★★ 103
Clinical Negligence ★★★★ 162
Litigation (Commercial) ★★ 560

Donithorn, Michael
Shipping ★★ 745

Donkersley, John
Immigration ★★★ 441

Donoghue, Andrew
Shipping ★★★ 745

Doolittle, Ian
Environment ★★ 374
Local Government ★★ 587
Social Housing ★★★★ 759

Doran, Frank
Financial Services ★★★ 406
Investment Funds ★★★ 523

Doran, Gill
Family ★★★★ 392

Doran, Iain A.
Property (Commercial) ★★★★ 726

Doran, Nigel J.L.
Tax (Corporate) ★★ 782

Douglas, Alasdair F.
Tax (Corporate) ★ 783

Dowen, Denise
Environment ★★★ 374

Dowling, Susan
Licensing U 536

Downie, Gordon
Competition/Anti-trust ★★★ 180

Downing, Ian
Family ★★★ 392

Downs, William N.
Corporate Finance ★★★ 248

Drake, Michael J.
Family ★★ 393

Drake, Ronald S.
Employment ★★ 335

Draycott, Shaun
Crime ★★★ 275

Dresden, Brinsley
Advertising & Marketing U 64

Drew, Dean
Corporate Finance ★★ 248

Drew, Jeff
Insolvency/Corporate Recovery ✪ 476

Drewe, David M.
Personal Injury ★★★ 643

Driscoll, Helen
Intellectual Property U 510

Driscoll, Lindsay
Charities ★★★ 141

Drukarz, Daniel
Planning U 662

Du-Feu, Vivian
Employment ★★★★ 335

Dudley, Andrew P.
Social Housing ★★ 759

Duff, Alistair
Crime ★★★ 275

Duff, Alistair M.
Sport ★★★★ 769

Duff, John
Insurance ★★★ 494

Dufficy, Frank
Projects/PFI ★★★ 696

Dugdale, Pat
Tax (Corporate) U 783

Duncan, Michael G.
Banking ★★ 117

Duncan, Nikki S.
Employment ★★★★ 335

Dunlop, Leah R.
Insurance ★★ 494

Dunlop, Stewart
Capital Markets ★ 129

Dunn, Chris
Transport ★★★ 799

Dunn, John
Property (Commercial) ★★★ 726

Dunnigan, David
Capital Markets ★★★ 129

Dunsire, David
Investment Funds ★★ 523

Durie, Robyn
Telecommunications ★★ 793

Durkin, Joseph
Parliamentary & Public Affairs ★★★★ 604

Dwyer, Maurice J.
Corporate Finance ★★★★ 248

Dyball, John
Clinical Negligence ★★★★ 162

Dyer, Carl
Planning ★★★★ 662

Dyer, Nick J.
Social Housing ★★★ 759

E

Eardley, Kathryn A.
Licensing ★★★ 536

East, Lindsay
Shipping ★★★ 745

Eastgate, Andrew
Corporate Finance ★★★ 248

Easton, Ewan R.
Litigation (Commercial) ★★★ 560

Eastwell, Nick
Capital Markets ★★★★ 129

Eaton, John C.J.
Trusts & Personal Tax ★★★★ 819

Eaton, Michael C.A.
Media & Entertainment ★★★ 597

Eddy, Catherine
Family ★★★ 393

Edge, Steve
Tax (Corporate) ✪ 783

Edlmann, Stephen
Capital Markets ★★★ 129

Edmond, John
Planning ★★★ 662

Edmonds, Steven James
Product Liability ★★★★ 674

Edney, Robert
Licensing ★★★★ 536

Edwards, Anthony
Crime ★★★ 275

Edwards, Gareth
E-commerce ★★ 300

Edwards, Jeremy
Asset Finance & Leasing ★ 96

Edwards, John
Telecommunications ★★ 793

Edwards, Julia C.
Employment ★★ 336

Edwards, K.Martin
Employment ★★★ 336

Edwards, Peter Charles
Healthcare ★★★ 429

Edwards, Robert N.
Family ★★ 393

Edwards, Stephen
Media & Entertainment ★★★ 598

Egan, Sean
Media & Entertainment ★★★ 598

Ehrlich, Michael
Tax (Corporate) ★ 783

Elborne, Mark E.M.
Insurance ★★★★ 494
Insurance ★★ 494
Professional Negligence ★★★ 684

Elder, Hugh
Litigation (Commercial) ★ 560

Elder, Ian
Energy & Natural Resources ★★★ 357

Eldergill, Anselm
Healthcare ★★★★ 429

Ellacott, Sara
Information Technology ★★ 454

Ellard, John
Corporate Finance ★ 248
Transport ★★★★ 799

Elliker, Michael
Health & Safety ★★★ 424

Elliott, Martin
Property (Commercial) ★★★ 726

Elliott, Peter
Tax (Corporate) ★★ 783

Elliott, Robert
Banking ★ 117
Insolvency/Corporate Recovery ★★★ 476

Elliott, Robert G.
Litigation (Commercial) ★★★★ 560

Ellis, Peter
Intellectual Property ★★ 510

Ellison, Robin
Pensions ★★★ 623

Elman, Jonathan
Tax (Corporate) ★★★ 783

Elphinston, Alexander
Trusts & Personal Tax ★★★ 819

Elsey, Mark
Projects/PFI ★★ 696
Projects/PFI ★★★ 696

Elvy, Mark
Product Liability ★★ 674

Emmerson, John C.
Trusts & Personal Tax ★★★★ 820

Emmerson, Tim
Corporate Finance ★★★ 248

Emmett, Paul D.
Corporate Finance ★★★ 248

Emmott, Jeremy D.
Employment U 336

Emmott, John F.
Commodities ★★ 171

Engert, Nick
Planning ★★★★ 662

KEY TO RANKINGS: ✪ = Star Individual ★★★★ = Top Band ★★★ = Second Band ★★ = Third Band ★ = Fourth Band U = Up and coming

KEY TO RANKINGS: ✪ = Star Individual ★★★★ = Top Band ★★★ = Second Band ★★ = Third Band ★ = Fourth Band U = Up and coming

G

KEY TO RANKINGS: ✪ = Star Individual ★★★★ = Top Band ★★★ = Second Band ★★ = Third Band ★ = Fourth Band U = Up and coming

Glaister, Anthony
Alternative Dispute Resolution ★★★ 82
Construction ★★ 200

Glazebrook, Peter G.
Licensing ★★★★ 536

Glazier, Barry
Trusts & Personal Tax ★★ 820

Glen, Marian
Corporate Finance ★★ 250

Glick, David S.
Media & Entertainment ★★ 598

Gniadkowski, Stan
Projects/PFI ★★ 697
Property (Commercial) ★★ 727

Godden, Richard
Corporate Finance ★★★★ 250
Partnership ★★★★ 611

Godfrey, Christopher
Corporate Finance ★★★★ 250

Godfrey, Keith G.
Corporate Finance ★ 250

Gold, Antony
Litigation (Commercial) ★★★ 561

Gold, David L.
Litigation (Commercial) ✪ 561
Partnership ★★★ 611

Gold, Richard
Education ★★★ 309

Gold, Tibor Z.
Intellectual Property ★ 511

Goldberg, Mel
Sport ★★★★ 769

Goldburn, Tim
Clinical Negligence ★★★★ 162

Golden, Jeffrey
Capital Markets ★★★★ 130

Goldman, Ruth T.
Pensions ★★★★ 624

Goldspink, Robert A.
Litigation (Commercial) ★★★ 561

Good, Diana
Litigation (Commercial) ★★ 561

Goodall, Caroline
Corporate Finance ★ 250

Goode, Naomi
Social Housing U 759

Goodger, Ben
Information Technology ★★★ 455

Goodier, Colin
Employment ★★★★ 337

Goodman, David
Planning ★★ 663

Goodman, Nick
Insolvency/Corporate Recovery ★★ 477

Goodman, Sarah
Personal Injury ★★★★ 644

Goodman, Stephen L.
Property (Commercial) ★★★★ 728

Goodwin, Peter
Trusts & Personal Tax ★★ 820

Goraj, Ann
Employment ★★★ 337

Gordon, Ian
Pensions ★★★★ 624
Tax (Corporate) ★★★★ 783

Gordon, John Gerard
Insolvency/Corporate Recovery ★★★★ 477

Gordon, Roderick C.P.R.
Construction ★★★ 200

Gordon-Saker, Paul D.
Insolvency/Corporate Recovery ★★ 477

Gorlov, Alison
Parliamentary & Public Affairs ★★★★ 605

Gorman, Penelope J.
Defamation ★★ 294

Gorrie, Euan
Banking U 118
Corporate Finance ★★★ 251

Gosling, James
Shipping ★★★★ 746

Gosling, John
Litigation (Commercial) ★★★ 562

Gosnay, Andrew W.
Banking ★★★ 118

Gossling, Margaret
Projects/PFI ★★ 697

Gostyn, Antony
Media & Entertainment ★★★ 598

Gotelee, Michael
Transport ★★★ 799

Goulborn, Caroline
Crime ★★★★ 276

Gould, Jean
Administrative & Public Law ★★★★ 58

Gould, R. Nicholas H.
Construction ★★★ 200

Gould, Terry
Corporate Finance ★★★★ 251

Gover, Graham
Licensing ★★ 536

Gowan, Daniel
Construction ★★★ 200

Gowans, Andrew
Corporate Finance ★★★★ 251

Gowar, Martyn
Trusts & Personal Tax ★★★★ 820

Gowtage, Jill
Tax ★★★ 783

Goyder, William A.
Alternative Dispute Resolution ★★★ 82

Grabiner, Martin
Property (Commercial) ★★★ 728

Grafton Green, Paddy
Media & Entertainment ★★★★ 598

Graham, Caroline J.M.
Family ★★ 394

Graham, Ian
Social Housing ★★★★ 759

Graham, L. Drysdale
Projects/PFI ★★ 697

Graham, Ronald
Pensions ★★★ 624

Graham, Rory
Information Technology ★★ 455

Grandison, Richard
Administrative & Public Law ★★★ 58

Grant, Gregor
Intellectual Property ✪ 511

Grant, James R.
Environment ★ 375
Planning ★★ 663

Grant, Mark
Pensions U 624

Grassie, Gill
Intellectual Property ★★ 511

Graves, Gary
Planning ★★★★ 663

Graves, Patrick
Corporate Finance ★★ 251

Gray, Colin F.
Corporate Finance ★★★ 251

Gray, David
Immigration ★★★★ 442

Gray, David
Litigation (Commercial) ★★ 562

Gray, David
Corporate Finance ★★★ 251

Gray, David J.
Employment ★★ 337

Gray, Edward
Shipping ★★ 746

Gray, Richard
Corporate Finance ★★ 251

Gray, Tim
Family ★★★★ 394

Grayston, Clare
Corporate Finance ★★★ 251

Greaves, Adam
Corporate Finance ★★ 251

Greaves, Judith
Employee Share Schemes ★★★★ 314
Tax (Corporate) ★★★★ 783

Green, Christopher
Crime ★★★ 276

Green, David
Employment ★★ 337

Green, Geoffrey S.
Corporate Finance ★★★ 251

Green, Lawrence
Employee Share Schemes ★★★ 314

Green, Martin
Trusts & Personal Tax ★★★ 821

Green, Michael
Family ★★★ 394

Green, W. Guy
Corporate Finance ★★★ 251

Greenbank, Ashley
Tax (Corporate) ★★ 783

Greenfield, G.N. Ian
Corporate Finance ★ 251

Greenlees, Mark B.
Pensions ★★★★ 624

Greenley, Simon K.P.T.
Insurance ★★★★ 494
Professional Negligence ★★ 684

Greeno, Ted
Litigation (Commercial) ✪ 562

Greenwood, Brian J.
Environment ★★★ 375
Planning ✪ 663

Gregan, Paddy
Partnership ★★★ 611

Gregg, Andrew
Licensing ★★ 536
Product Liability ★★★★ 675

Grego, Kevin
Crime ★★★★ 276

Gregory, Andrew
Insolvency/Corporate Recovery ★★ 477

Gregory, Deborah A.
Insolvency/Corporate Recovery ★★★ 477

Gregory, Lesley
Corporate Finance ★★★ 252
Sport ★★ 769

Gregory-Jones, Rosemary
Family ★★ 394

Grey, Rupert
Defamation ★★★ 294

Grier, Ian Stephen
Insolvency/Corporate Recovery ★ 478

Grierson, Christopher K.
Insolvency/Corporate Recovery ★★★ 478
Litigation (Commercial) ★ 562

Griffin, Paul
Energy & Natural Resources ★★★★ 357

Griffiths, David
Pensions ★★★ 625

Griffiths, David
Information Technology ★★ 455

Griffiths, John
Clinical Negligence ★★★★ 162
Employment ★★ 337

Griffiths, Julian
Crime ★★★★ 276

Griffiths, Keith M.
Property (Commercial) ★★ 728

Griffiths, Marian
Planning U 664

Griffiths, Trevor
Administrative & Public Law ★★ 58
Local Government ★★★★ 587

Grisewood, Rebecca
Corporate Finance ★★★ 252

Grogan, Peter
Crime ★★★★ 276

Gronow, Simon D.V.
Corporate Finance ★★★ 252

Groom, Stephen
Advertising & Marketing ★★★★ 64

Grosset, Alan G.
Sport ★★★★ 769

Grosz, Stephen
Administrative & Public Law ★★★★ 58
Education ★★★ 309
Human Rights ★★★★ 433

Gryk, Wesley
Immigration ★★★★ 442

Gubbins, Jennifer
Social Housing ★★ 759

Guedalla, Vicky
Immigration ★★★★ 442

Guest, Jonathan
Asset Finance & Leasing ★★★ 97

Guild, Elspeth
Immigration ★★★★ 442

KEY TO RANKINGS: ✪ = Star Individual ★★★★ = Top Band ★★★ = Second Band ★★ = Third Band ★ = Fourth Band U = Up and coming

KEY TO RANKINGS: ✪ = Star Individual ★★★★ = Top Band ★★★ = Second Band ★★ = Third Band ★ = Fourth Band U = Up and coming

Hearn, Andrew
Litigation (Commercial) ★ 562

Hearn, Keith
Employment ★★ 338

Heathcock, Andrew E.
Corporate Finance ★★ 253

Heaton, John Graham
Transport ★ 800

Hebden, David
Shipping ★★★ 747

Hegarty, Simon
Professional Negligence ★★★★ .. 684

Heller, Laurie
Property (Commercial) ★★★★ 728

Hellier, Tim
Planning ★★★★ 664

Helps, Dominic
Construction ★ 201

Hemming, Dan
Planning ★★ 664

Hemming, Julian
Employment ★★★ 338

Hemmings, Richard
Employment ★★★ 338

Henderson, Brian L.
Banking ★★★ 118
Property (Commercial) ★★★ 728

Henderson, Colin B.
Trusts & Personal Tax U 821

Henderson, David
Projects/PFI ★★★★ 698

Henderson, Guy
Litigation (Commercial) ★ 563

Henderson, Schuyler K.
Capital Markets ★★★★ 130

Henderson, Stuart
Personal Injury ★★★★ 644

Henderson, Giles
Corporate Finance ★★ 253

Hennessy, Tony
Tax (Corporate) ★★★ 784

Henney, Colin C.
Employment ★★★ 338

Henning, Caroline A.
Transport ★ 800

Henry, Michael
E-commerce ★★ 300
Media & Entertainment ★ 599

Henson, John S.
Family ★★ 394

Henson, Michaela
Property (Commercial) U 728

Hepher, Christopher
Licensing ★★★ 537

Heppel, Meg E.M.
Property (Commercial) ★★ 728

Hepworth, Allan
Insurance ★ 495

Herbert, Alan
Litigation (Property) ★★★★ 577

Herbert, Andrew
Personal Injury ★★★★ 644

Herbert, Mary
Construction ★★★★ 201

Herring, John
Charities ★★★★ 142

Herring, Paul
Shipping ★★★★ 747

Herrington, Timothy
Financial Services ★★★★ 406
Investment Funds ★★★ 523

Hertz, Philip
Insolvency/Corporate Recovery U .. 478

Hetherington, David
Product Liability ★★★ 675

Hewes, Simon P.
Corporate Finance ★★★ 253

Hewison, John
Sport ★★★ 769

Hewitt, Christopher
Agriculture ★★★★ 75

Hewitt, Stephen
Crime ★★ 276

Hewitt, V. Alan
Property (Commercial) ★★★★ 729
Trusts & Personal Tax ★★★★ 821

Hewson, Carol
Litigation (Property) ★★★ 577

Hick, Mark
Professional Negligence ★★ 685

Hickey, Denys
Commodities ★★ 171

Hickman, Jane
Crime ★★★ 276

Hickson, Chris
Intellectual Property ★★★ 512

Hiester, Elizabeth
Telecommunications ★★★★ 793

Higginbottom, Louise
Tax (Corporate) ★ 784

Higgins, David E.A.
Insurance ★★★★ 495

Higginson, Tony J.
Energy & Natural Resources ★★ .. 357

Higham, David
Litigation (Commercial) ★★★★ 563

Higham, Nicholas
Information Technology ★ 455
Telecommunications ★★ 793

Higham QC, John
Insolvency/Corporate Recovery ★★ 478

Highmore, Robert P.
Litigation (Property) ★★ 577

Hignett, Andrew
Planning ★★★ 664

Higton, Jonathan
Sport ★★ 770

Hill, David G.
Employment ★★ 338

Hill, Jeremy G.
Insurance ★★ 495

Hill, Judith L.
Charities ★★★★ 142

Hill, Martin
Shipping ★★★★ 747
Transport ★★ 800

Hillebron, Richard
Planning ★★★ 664

Hills, Stephen
Employment ★★ 338

Hilton, Chris
Shipping ★★★★ 747

Hilton, Mark W.
Construction ★★ 201

Hinchliffe, David
Insolvency/Corporate Recovery ★★ 478

Hingley, Gerald
Pensions ★★★★ 625

Hitchcock, Teresa C.
Environment ★★★ 375

Hoath, Helen
Litigation (Property) ★★★ 577

Hobbs, Christopher
Shipping ★★★ 747

Hobbs, Jane
Transport ★★ 800

Hobley, Anthony
Environment U 375

Hodge, James (Hamish) S.
Property (Commercial) ★★★ 729

Hodges, Christopher J.S.
Product Liability ★★★★ 675

Hodges, Paula
Litigation (Commercial) U 563

Hodgkinson, Milly
Customs & Excise ★★ 281

Hodgson, Derek
Shipping ★★★★ 747

Hodgson, Gary
Transport ★★★ 800

Hodgson, Guy
Professional Negligence ★★★★ .. 685

Hodgson, Mark
Intellectual Property ✪ 512

Hodson, Christopher Charles
Church ★★★ 149

Hodson, David
Family ★ 394

Hogan, Ronald D.
Litigation (Property) ★★ 577

Hogg, Derek W.
Social Housing ★★ 760

Holden, Lawrence
Charities ★★★★ 142
Social Housing ★★★★ 760

Holderness, Andrew
Insurance ★★★ 495

Holehouse, Andrew N.
Pensions ★★★★ 625

Holland, Barry K.
Licensing ★★★★ 537
Product Liability ★★★★ 675

Holland, Peter Rodney James
Corporate Finance ★ 253

Hollerin, Gordon Craig
Insolvency/Corporate Recovery ★★★ 479

Holligan, William
Administrative & Public Law ★★★ .. 59
Litigation (Commercial) ★★★ 563

Hollingworth, Sara
Transport ★★ 800

Holloway, Julian
Alternative Dispute Resolution ★ 82

Holmes, John
Clinical Negligence ★★★★ 163
Healthcare ★★★★ 430

Holmes, Katherine
Competition/Anti-trust ★ 180

Holmes, Leigh
Pensions ★ 625

Holmes, Sarah C.
Environment ★★★★ 375
Planning ★★★ 664

Holmes, Simon
Competition/Anti-trust U 180
Parliamentary & Public Affairs ★★★★ 605

Holroyd, Andrew
Immigration ★★★ 442

Holt, Andrew D.
Corporate Finance ★★★ 253

Holt, Jeremy
Information Technology ★★★ 455

Homan, Hugh
Asset Finance & Leasing ★ 97

Hood, Brian J.
Church ★★★ 149

Hooper, David
Defamation ✪ 294

Hopkins, Dominic A.
Litigation (Commercial) ★★★ 563

Hopkins, Ian
Personal Injury ★★★★ 644

Hopkins, Martin W.
Employment ★★★ 338

Hopkins, Paul
Litigation (Commercial) ★★★★ 563

Hopkins, Stephen Martyn
Banking ★★★ 118
Corporate Finance ★ 253

Hopkins, Wendy
Family ★★ 395

Hornby, John H.
Agriculture ★★ 75

Horne, Anthony
Licensing ★★★ 537

Horner, Douglas G.
Agriculture ★★★★ 75
Environment ★★★★ 375

Horsfall, Robert
Media & Entertainment ★★ 599

Horsfall Turner, Jonathan
Banking ★★ 118
Projects/PFI ★★★ 698

Horton, Naomi
Transport ★★ 800

Horton, Nicholas
Shipping ★★★★ 747

Horwood-Smart, Adrian
Agriculture ★★★ 75

Hosie, Jonathan
Construction ★★★ 201

Hoskins, Julian
Employment U 338

Hotchin, Samuel G.
Personal Injury ★★★★ 644

Houghton, John
Planning ★★★★ 664

Houghton, John
Insolvency/Corporate Recovery ★★ 479

Houghton, Paul
Alternative Dispute Resolution ★★ .. 82

Hougie, Andrew
Investment Funds U 523

Houldsworth, David H.
Agriculture ★★ 75

House, Tim
Litigation (Commercial) ★★ 563

Hovell, Mark
Sport ★★ 770

Howard, Brian
Media & Entertainment ★★★★ 599

Howard, Karen
Planning U 664

Howard, Paul
Litigation (Commercial) ★★★★ 563

Howard, Susan
Corporate Finance U 253

Howarth, Mark H.
Property (Commercial) U 729

Howe, Kate
Trusts & Personal Tax ★★ 821

Howe, Martin
Construction ★★★ 202

Howell, Grant
Family ★★ 395

Howell, Paul J.
Trusts & Personal Tax ★★★★ 821

Howell, Simon P.J.
Church ★★★★ 149

Howell-Richardson, Phillip
Alternative Dispute Resolution ✪ 82

Howes, Colin M.
Aviation ★★★ 103

Hoyle, Andrew C.
Corporate Finance ★★ 253

Hoyle, Roger V.
Construction ★★★ 202

Hoyle, Stephen L.
Tax (Corporate) ★ 784

Hoyle, Susan
Tax (Corporate) ★★★ 784

Hoyle, Thomas
Church ★★★ 149

Hubbard, Penny
Property (Commercial) ★★ 729

Huber, Bernard
Crime ★★ 276

Hudd, David G.T.
Capital Markets ★ 130

Huddleston, David
Social Housing ★★★ 760

Hudson, Allan James
Social Housing ★★ 760

Hudson, James J.S.
Construction ★★★ 202

Hughes, David J.
Corporate Finance ★★★ 253

Hughes, Frances
Family ★★★★ 395

Hughes, Kathryn Lesley
Family ★★★ 395

Hughes, Nicholas M.L.
Aviation ★★ 103

Hughes, Norna
Planning ★★★ 665

Hughes, Richard
Capital Markets ★★ 130

Hughes, Sara
Pensions ★★ 625

Hughes, Stephen
Projects/PFI ★★★★ 698

Hull, David Julian
Corporate Finance ★★★ 253

Hull, John
Administrative & Public Law ★★ 59

Hulls, Martin A.
Corporate Finance ★★★★ 254

Hume, John
Fraud ★★★ 418

Humphrey, Ann
Tax ★★★★ 784

Humphrey, Anthony R.
Banking ★★★ 118
Projects/PFI ★★ 698

Humphreys, Robert
Intellectual Property ★★★★ 512

Humphries, Mark
Litigation (Commercial) ★ 563

Hunter, James
Corporate Finance U 254

Hunter, Robert
Fraud ★★★ 418

Hurley, Conor
Tax (Corporate) ★ 784

Hurst, Andrew L.T.
Social Housing ★★★ 760

Hurst, Philip
Energy & Natural Resources ★★★★ 357

Hurt, Jacqueline
Media & Entertainment U 599

Hussain, Belayeth
Immigration ★★★ 442

Hutchings, Michael B.
Competition/Anti-trust ★★ 180

Hutchinson, Anne-Marie
Family ★★★ 395

Hutchinson, John C.
Corporate Finance ★★★ 254

Hutchinson, Lucy
Litigation (Property) ★★★★ 577

Hutchinson, Michael
Environment U 375

Hutton, C. Noel
Corporate Finance ★★★ 254

Hutton, David
Projects/PFI ★★★★ 698

Hutton, Robert D.
Property (Commercial) ★★ 729

Hutton, Stuart
Crime ★★★★ 276

Hyde, Ian R.
Tax (Corporate) ★★★★ 784

Hyde, Mark
Insolvency/Corporate Recovery ★★★★ 479

Hyde, Philip
Licensing ★ 537

Hyman, Neil
Corporate Finance ★ 254

I

Iley, Malcolm
Administrative & Public Law ★★ 59
Local Government ★★★★ 587

Iliff, Catherine
Family ★ 395

Illston, Tim
Pensions ★★★★ 625

Imperato, Michael
Education ★★ 309

Ince, Robin
Immigration ★★★ 442

Ingle, Michael
Employee Share Schemes ★ 315

Ingleby, Claire
Travel ★★★ 807

Inglis, Alan
Banking ★ 118

Inglis, Andrew
Intellectual Property ★★★ 512

Ingram, Kevin
Capital Markets ★★★ 130

Innes, Colin
Planning ★★★ 665

Innes, Gordon
Parliamentary & Public Affairs ★★★★ 605

Innes, Richard
Property (Commercial) ★★★ 729

Irons, Ashley
Healthcare ★★★★ 430

Irvine, James
Intellectual Property ★★ 512

Irvine, John W.
Corporate Finance ★★★★ 254
Partnership ★★★★ 611

Irving, David P.
Partnership ★★★★ 611

Irving, Paul
Parliamentary & Public Affairs ★★★★ 605

Isaacs, Jeffrey
Commodities ★★★ 171

Ishani, Manzoor G.K.
Franchising ★★★★ 409

Isted, Jonathan
Environment ★★ 375

Ito, Stephen
Pensions ★★ 625

Ive, David
Investment Funds ★ 523

Ivin, Alison
Property (Commercial) ★★★ 729

Ivison, Andrew S.
Projects/PFI ★★ 698

J

Jacks, David
Employment U 338

Jackson, Carol G.P.
Personal Injury ★★★★ 644

Jackson, Fraser S.
Social Housing ★★★ 760

Jackson, Karl
Property (Commercial) U 729

Jackson, Mark S.
Insolvency/Corporate Recovery ★★ 479

Jackson, Peter
Shipping ★★★ 747
Transport ★★★ 800

Jackson, Ray
Planning ★★★★ 665

Jacobs, Howard
Employment ★★★ 338
Pensions ★★ 625

Jacobs, Laurence
Information Technology ★★ 455

Jacobs, Michael
Employee Share Schemes ★ 315
Trusts & Personal Tax ★★ 821

Jacobs, Russell
Tax (Corporate) ★ 784

Jacovides, Mario
Asset Finance & Leasing ★★ 97

Jaffa, Anthony
Defamation ★★★★ 295

Jamdar, Smita
Litigation (Commercial) U 563

James, Charles
Immigration ★★★★ 442

James, Glen William
Corporate Finance ★★ 254
Insurance ★★★ 495

James, Jim
Insolvency/Corporate Recovery ★★ 479

James, Robert W.
Property (Commercial) ★★★ 729

James, Sean St John
Media & Entertainment ★★★★ 599

James, Stuart C.
Pensions ★★★★ 625

Jameson, Robert
Planning ★★★ 665

Jamieson, George
Family ★★ 395

Jamison, David
Corporate Finance ★★ 254

Jansen, Karl
Corporate Finance ★ 254

Jarman, Chris
Trusts & Personal Tax ★★★ 821

Jarman, Christopher
Administrative & Public Law ★★★★ 59
Local Government ★★★★ 587

Jeacock, David
Sport ★★★ 770

Jeanes, Nicola
Shipping U 747

KEY TO RANKINGS: ✪ = Star Individual ★★★★ = Top Band ★★★ = Second Band ★★ = Third Band ★ = Fourth Band U = Up and coming

Jeeps, Barry
Planning ★★ 665

Jefferies, Michael
Construction ★★★ 202
Litigation (Commercial) ★★★★ 563

Jeffers, Raymond
Employment ★★ 338

Jefferson, H.L. Ian
Personal Injury ★★★★ 644

Jeffreys, Simon
Employment ★★★★ 339

Jeffries, Graham
Banking ★★★★ 118
Insolvency/Corporate Recovery ★★ 479

Jeffries, Jonathan D.
Insolvency/Corporate Recovery ★★ 479

Jenkins, Caroline Helen Clare
Clinical Negligence ★★ 163

Jenkins, Colin
Travel ★★★ 807

Jenkins, Edmund
Tax (Corporate) ★★★★ 784

Jenkins, Ian
Professional Negligence ★★★ 685

Jenkins, Jane
Construction U 202

Jenkins, Keith
Social Housing ★★★★ 760

Jenkins, Martin
Pensions ★★ 625

Jenkins, Paul H.
Trusts & Personal Tax ★★★★ 821

Jennings, Carolyn
Media & Entertainment ★★★ 599

Jennings, Robert
Social Housing ★★ 761

Jennings, Steven
Litigation (Property) ★★★★ 578

Jerrard, Donald
Information Technology ★★★ 455

Jervis, David M.
Tax (Corporate) ★★★ 784

Jessel, Christopher R.
Agriculture ★★★★ 75

Jewkes, Penny
Environment ★★★ 376

Johansen, Lynn
Commodities ★★★ 171

John, Alan
Environment ★★★★ 376

John, Simon G.
Clinical Negligence ★★★★ 163
Personal Injury ★★★★ 644

Johns, Michael S.M.
Corporate Finance ★★★ 254

Johnson, Andrew
Shipping ★★★ 747

Johnson, Ben
Corporate Finance U 254

Johnson, Christopher R.
Licensing ★★ 537

Johnson, Ian L.
Tax (Corporate) ★★ 785

Johnson, James
Banking ★★★ 118
Corporate Finance ✪ 254

Johnson, Jennifer D.
Property (Commercial) ★★★★ 729

Johnson, Jonathan
Shipping ★★★★ 747

Johnson, M. Clare
Licensing ★★★ 537

Johnson, Robin
Corporate Finance ★★ 254

Johnson, Timothy A.
Media & Entertainment ★★★ 599

Johnston, Bruce
Projects/PFI ★★★ 698

Johnston, Keith T.
Corporate Finance ★★★★ 254

Johnston, Michael C.
Corporate Finance ★★★ 255

Johnston, Tom
Licensing ★★★ 537

Johnstone, Frank R.
Asset Finance & Leasing ★★★★ 97

Johnstone, Pat
Banking ★★★★ 118

Jolliffe, Peter
Asset Finance & Leasing ★★★★ 97

Jonas, Steven
Fraud ★★★ 418

Jones, Alan G.
Employment ★★ 339

Jones, Arfon
Corporate Finance ★ 255

Jones, Beverley
Employment ★★★★ 339

Jones, Bill
Information Technology ★★★★ 456

Jones, Catherine E.
Family ★★★★ 395

Jones, Chris
Property (Commercial) ★★ 729

Jones, David
Clinical Negligence ★★★ 163
Personal Injury ★★★★ 644

Jones, David M.
Construction ★★★ 202

Jones, David Rhys
Immigration ★★★ 442

Jones, Eddie
Clinical Negligence ★★ 163

Jones, Elizabeth J.
Property (Commercial) ★★ 729

Jones, Gareth
Intellectual Property ★★★★ 512

Jones, Gareth
Energy & Natural Resources ★★ 358

Jones, Geoffrey
Transport ★★ 800

Jones, Gwyn
Crime ★★★ 276

Jones, Howard
Media & Entertainment ★★★★ 599

Jones, Hugh
Corporate Finance ★★ 255

Jones, Jonathan
Corporate Finance U 255

Jones, Martyn
Tax (Corporate) ★★★★ 785

Jones, Medwyn
Media & Entertainment ★★ 599

Jones, Michael
Corporate Finance ★ 255

Jones, Michael L.N.
Education ★★ 309
Litigation (Commercial) ★★★ 563

Jones, Nefydd
Property (Commercial) U 729

Jones, Nigel
Intellectual Property ★★ 512

Jones, Pamela
Property (Commercial) ★★★★ 729

Jones, Patricia
Intellectual Property U 512

Jones, Peter
Construction ★★★ 202
Litigation (Commercial) ★★★ 563

Jones, Peter
Family ★★★ 395

Jones, Simon
Licensing ★★★ 537

Jones, Stephen
Intellectual Property ★★★ 512

Jones, Stephen L.
Clinical Negligence ★★★★ 163

Jordan, Lisa
Clinical Negligence ★★ 164

Joyce, Andrew L.
Asset Finance & Leasing ★★ 98

Joyce, John
Insolvency/Corporate Recovery ★★ 479

Judge, Ian
Intellectual Property ✪ 513

Julyan, Alan
Employment ★★★ 339

Jump, G.K.
Insolvency/Corporate Recovery ★★ 479
Partnership ★★ 611
Partnership ★★★ 611

Jurkiw, Andrij
Competition/Anti-trust ★★★★ 181

Jury, Susan N.
Family ★★ 395

K

Kahn, Gregory
Asset Finance & Leasing ★★★ 98

Kamstra, Gerry
Intellectual Property ★★ 513

Kamstra, Simon
Litigation (Commercial) ★★★★ 564

Kane, Hilary
Corporate Finance U 255

Karet, Ian
Intellectual Property ★★★ 513

Kavanagh, Giles
Aviation U 103

Kaye, Laurence M.
E-commerce ★★ 300
Media & Entertainment ★★ 599

Keal, Anthony C.
Banking ★★★ 118
Corporate Finance ★★ 255

Kean, Caroline
Defamation ★★★★ 295

Keane, Georgina
Employment ★ 339

Kearney, Mary Frances
Insolvency/Corporate Recovery ★★ 479

Keddie, Joanne
Agriculture U 74

Keeble, Ed
Environment ★★★ 376

Keenan, Andrew
Crime ★★★ 276

Kefford, Alan
Licensing ★★★★ 537

Keir, Jane
Family ★★ 395

Keith-Lucas, Peter
Local Government ★★★★ 587

Keitley, Nicholas
Insolvency/Corporate Recovery ★★★★ 479

Keliher, James
Corporate Finance ★ 255

Kelleher, John R.
Product Liability ★★★ 675

Kelly, Christopher
Energy & Natural Resources U 358

Kelly, Don C.
Tax (Corporate) ★ 785

Kelly, Jacky
Capital Markets ★★★ 130

Kelly, Jonathan P.
Litigation (Commercial) ★★ 564

Kelly, Neil J.
Construction ★★ 202

Kelly, Philip L.
Crime ★★★★ 277

Kelly, Russell
Shipping ★★★ 748

Kelly, Susan M.
Banking ★★★ 119

Kemp, Jonathan
Shipping ★★★★ 748

Kemp, Lesley
Immigration ★★★ 442

Kemp, Richard
E-commerce ★★★ 301
Information Technology ★★★★ 456

Kemp, Sandy
Employment ★★★ 339
Personal Injury ★★★★ 644

Kempner, Richard
Intellectual Property ★★★★ 513

Kendall, David R.
Insurance ★ 495

Kendall, John
Alternative Dispute Resolution ★★ 82

Kennedy, John
Trusts & Personal Tax ★★★ 821

Kennedy, Patrick
Pensions ★★★ 625

Kenny, Stephen
Projects/PFI ★★ ... 698

Kent, Paul
Litigation (Property) ★★★★ ... 578

Kenworthy, Michael
Planning ★★★ ... 665

Kenyon, Andrew
Fraud ★★ ... 418

Kenyon, Michael J.
Customs & Excise ★★ ... 282
Fraud ✪ ... 418

Kerle, Bridget A.
Corporate Finance ★★★★ ... 255

Kerr, David
Telecommunications ★★★★ ... 793

Kerr, John N.
Sport ★★★★ ... 770

Kershaw, Anne
Litigation (Commercial) ★★ ... 564
Partnership ★★★ ... 611

Kershaw, Peter J.
Property (Commercial) U ... 729

Keuls, Peter
Social Housing ★★★★ ... 761

Keyden, Gordon
Personal Injury ★★★★ ... 644

Khan, Charles
Litigation (Commercial) ★★ ... 564

Khan, Rafique
Energy & Natural Resources ★★ .. 358

Khan, Sadiq
Human Rights ★★★ ... 433

Kidby, Robert J.
Property (Commercial) ★★★★ ... 730

Kidd, Philip E.
Family ★★★★ ... 395

Kilduff, David
Local Government ★★ ... 588

Kimbell, Stephen
Corporate Finance ★★ ... 255

King, Michael
Charities ★★★★ ... 142
Church ★★★★ ... 149
Education ★★★ ... 309

King, Peter
Corporate Finance ★ ... 255

King, Richard
Charities ★★ ... 142
Church ★★★★ ... 149

King, Ronnie
Litigation (Commercial) ★ ... 564

King, Stephen
Clinical Negligence ★★★★ ... 164
Healthcare ★★★★ ... 430

King, Stuart
Property (Commercial) ★★★ ... 730

King, Vivien M.
Litigation (Property) ★★★★ ... 578

King-Jones, Amanda
Trusts & Personal Tax ★★★ ... 821

Kinnersley, Tom
Asset Finance & Leasing ★★★★ .. 98

Kinniburgh, Linda M.
Property (Commercial) U ... 730

Kinsey, Julian
Banking ★★★★ ... 119

Kirby, Richard C.
Trusts & Personal Tax ★★ ... 822

Kirk, David
Fraud ★★★★ ... 419

Kirk, Graeme
Immigration ★★★★ ... 443

Kirkbright, Stephen
Transport ✪ ... 801

Kirkpatrick, Denbeigh
Agriculture ★★ ... 76

Kirkup, Simon
Agriculture ★★★ ... 76

Kirtley, Deborah
Banking ★★ ... 119

Kissack, Nigel
Litigation (Commercial) ★★★ ... 564

Kitchingman, John Michael
Clinical Negligence ★★★★ ... 164

Kitson, Paul
Personal Injury ★★★ ... 644

Kitson, Tony
Planning ✪ ... 665

Kitts, Stephen
Corporate Finance ★★ ... 255

Knapp, Vanessa
Corporate Finance ★ ... 255

Knight, Adrian G.
Corporate Finance ★★ ... 256

Knight, Matthew
Administrative & Public Law ★★★★ ... 59
Agriculture ★★★ ... 76

Knight, Tim
Transport ★★★★ ... 801

Knight, Timothy
Pensions ★ ... 625

Knight, William
Corporate Finance ★★ ... 256

Knott, Alice
Transport ★★ ... 801

Knowles, Stuart
Clinical Negligence ★★★★ ... 164

Knox, Louisa
Pensions ★★ ... 626

Knox, Martin
Local Government ★★★ ... 588
Social Housing ★★★★ ... 761

Knutson, Robert
Arbitration (International) ★★ ... 88

Kon, Stephen D.
Competition/Anti-trust ✪ ... 181

Kordan, Joel
Property (Commercial) ★★★ ... 730

Kowalik, Mark
Pensions U ... 626

Krafft, James A.
Trusts & Personal Tax ★★ ... 822

Kramer, Martin
Administrative & Public Law ★★ 59
Defamation ★★★★ ... 295

Kratz, Philip
Planning ★★★ ... 665

Krischer, David S.
Capital Markets ★★★★ ... 130

Kustow, David
Property (Commercial) ★★ ... 730

Kyrke, Richard Venables
Agriculture ★★★ ... 76

L

La Follette, Maryly
Family ★★ ... 395

Lace, John D.
Partnership ★ ... 611

Laing, Robert J.
Banking ★★ ... 119

Laing, Sue
Trusts & Personal Tax ★★★★ ... 822

Lake, Tim
Property (Commercial) ★★ ... 730

Lamb, Norman
Employment ★★★★ ... 339

Lambert, Robert
Arbitration (International) ★★ ... 88

Lambert, Tracy
Family ★★★ ... 395

Lamont, Sarah
Employment ★★ ... 339

Lancaster, Roger
Planning ★★★★ ... 665

Lander, Geoffrey
Property (Commercial) ★★★★ 730

Landsman, David M.
Media & Entertainment ★★★ ... 599

Lane, Andrew
Agriculture ★★★★ ... 76

Lane, Mark
Construction ★★ ... 202
Energy & Natural Resources ★★ .. 358

Lane, Peter
Parliamentary & Public Affairs ★★★ ... 605

Lane, Robert
Energy & Natural Resources ★★★★ ... 358

Lang, J. Russell
Insolvency/Corporate Recovery ★★ ... 479

Lang, Jane
Clinical Negligence ★★★★ ... 164

Langley, Dale
Employment ★ ... 339

Langley, Robert L.
Alternative Dispute Resolution ★★ .. 82
Construction ★★★★ ... 203

Langridge, Sharon E.
Employment U ... 339

Lavender, F. David
Licensing ✪ ... 537

Lavery, James
Corporate Finance ★ ... 256

Lawes, William P.L.
Corporate Finance ★★★ ... 256

Lawrence, Clive S.
Sport ★★ ... 770

Lawson, Hamish K.
Licensing ★★★ ... 537

Lawson, Peter J.
Licensing ★★★ ... 537

Lawson, Stephen A.
Insolvency/Corporate Recovery ★★★★ ... 480

Lawton, Anthony
Personal Injury ★★★★ ... 645

Lawton, F. A. (Tony)
Charities ★★★★ ... 142
Church ★★★★ ... 149

Lawton, Jonathan
Transport ★★★★ ... 801

Lawton Smith, Andrew
Corporate Finance U ... 256

Lax, Michael
Shipping ★★ ... 748

Layton, Matthew
Corporate Finance ★★★★ ... 256

Le Bas, Malcolm H.
Insolvency/Corporate Recovery ★★★ ... 480

Le Pard, Geoffrey
Property (Commercial) ★★★★ 730

Lea, Alison
Planning U ... 665

Lea, Stephen
Media & Entertainment ★★★★ 599

Leach, Ben
Commodities ★★ ... 171

Lee, Martin P.W.
Pensions ★ ... 626

Lee, Paul
Corporate Finance ★ ... 256

Lee, Richard
Corporate Finance ★★★★ ... 256

Lee, Richard N.F.
Corporate Finance ★★★ ... 256

Lee, Robert
Media & Entertainment ★★★★ 599

Lee, Terry
Clinical Negligence ★★★ ... 164
Personal Injury ★★★★ ... 645

Lee, Trevor A.
Licensing ★★ ... 538

Leech, Catherine J.B.
Personal Injury ★★★ ... 645

Leeming, Richard
Banking U ... 119

Legrand, Janet
Pensions ★★★ ... 626

Leifer, Tony
Media & Entertainment ★★ ... 599

Leigh, Bertie
Clinical Negligence ★★★★ ... 164
Healthcare ★★★ ... 430

Leigh, Guy I.F.
Competition/Anti-trust ★★ ... 181

Leigh, Sarah
Clinical Negligence ★★★★ ... 164

Leitch, David A.
Property (Commercial) ★★ ... 730

Leney, Simon
Trusts & Personal Tax ★★★ ... 822

Lennox, Lionel
Church ★★★★ ... 149

Leonard, Paul M.
Litigation (Commercial) ★★★★ 564

Leonard, Tessa
Property (Commercial) ★★ ... 730

Leskin, Nigel
Human Rights ★★ ... 434
Immigration ★★ ... 443

 KEY TO RANKINGS: ✪ = Star Individual ★★★★ = Top Band ★★★ = Second Band ★★ = Third Band ★ = Fourth Band U = Up and coming

KEY TO RANKINGS: ✪ = Star Individual ★★★★ = Top Band ★★★ = Second Band ★★ = Third Band ★ = Fourth Band U = Up and coming

MacLeod, Euan
Employment ★★★ 340

MacLeod, Ian
Administrative & Public Law ★★★ .. 60
Employment ★★ 340
Litigation (Commercial) ★★★★ 564

Macniven, Iain G.
Property (Commercial) ★★★ 731

Macpherson, Moray
Corporate Finance ★★★★ 258

Macpherson, Shonaig
Information Technology ★★★★ .. 456
Intellectual Property ★★★★ 514

MacRae, Keith G.
Shipping ★★★★ 748

MacRitchie, Kenneth
Projects/PFI ★★★ 698

MacRobert, David J.C.
Trusts & Personal Tax ★★★★ 822

Madden, Andrew
Banking ★★★★ 119

Madden, Michael
Litigation (Property) ★★★★ 578

Maddock, Geoffrey C.
Insurance ★★ 496

Maddocks, Roger
Personal Injury ★★★★ 645

Magnin, John .D.
Litigation (Commercial) ★ 564

Magrath, Christopher
Immigration ★★ 443

Maher, Paul J.
Corporate Finance ★★ 258

Mahony, Michael
Information Technology ★★ 456

Mahood, Laurence
Property (Commercial) ★★★★ 731

Maidment, Allan
Crime ★★★★ 277

Main, Douglas
Crime ★★★ 277

Mainprice, Hugh
Tax ★★★ 785

Mair, Leonard
Family ★★★ 396

Maitland-Walker, Julian
Competition/Anti-trust ★★ 181

Mallon, Christopher
Insolvency/Corporate
Recovery ★★ 480

Malone, Michael
Employment ★★★ 340

Manley, Mark
Defamation ★★★ 295
Litigation (Commercial) ★ 564

Mann, Jane E.
Employment ★★ 340
Immigration ★★ 443

Manning, Peter R.
Insolvency/Corporate Recovery ★ 480

Manning Cox, Andrew
Litigation (Commercial) ★★★ 564

Mansell, Mark
Employment ★★★★ 340

Mansfield, Collin. P.
Personal Injury ★★★ 645

Manson, Stephen
Planning ★★★ 666
Projects/PFI U 699

Marco, Alan
Family ★★ 396

Mardle, David
Corporate Finance U 258

Margrave-Jones, Clive
Agriculture ★★★★ 76

Marks, Christopher
Property (Commercial) ★★ 731

Marks, Geoffrey
Property (Commercial) ★★★★ 731

Marks, Lisa
Asset Finance & Leasing U 98

Marlow, Ed
Projects/PFI ★★ 699

Marriott Q.C., Arthur
Arbitration (International) ★★★★ .. 88

Marron, Peter
Planning ★★★★ 666

Marsden, Tim
Financial Services ★ 406
Investment Funds ★★★ 524

Marsh, Christine
Clinical Negligence ★★ 165

Marsh, David
Corporate Finance ★ 258
Partnership ★★★ 612

Marsh, William L.
Alternative Dispute
Resolution ★★★ 82

Marshall, Anna
Environment U 376

Marshall, David
Personal Injury ★★★ 645

Marshall, Ian
Employment ★★★ 340

Marshall, James
Intellectual Property ★★ 514

Marshall, Jane M.
Pensions ★★★ 626

Marshall, John
Corporate Finance ★ 258

Marshall, Julia
Transport ★★★★ 801

Marsland, Vanessa
Intellectual Property ★★★★ 514

Martin, Bonnie
Litigation (Property) ★★★ 578

Martin, Charles D.Z.
Corporate Finance ★★ 258

Martin, David
Tax (Corporate) ★★★★ 785

Martin, Matthew T.
Charities ★★★★ 143

Martin, Patricia
Commodities ★★★ 172

Martin Alegi, Lynda
Competition/Anti-trust ★★ 182

Martindale, Avril
Intellectual Property ★★ 514

Martinez, Liz
Clinical Negligence ★★ 165

Maskill, Andrew
Asset Finance & Leasing ★★★ 98

Mason, David
Clinical Negligence ★★★★ 165
Healthcare ★★★★ 430

Mason, Fenella Mary
Construction ★★ 203

Mason, Stephen M.
Travel ★★★★ 807

Massarano Salt, Vikki
Pensions ★ 626

Massey, William
Family ★ 396

Masters, David C.
Litigation (Property) ★★★ 578

Masters, Peter
Crime ★★★★ 277

Masters, Richard
Corporate Finance U 258

Matheou, Michael S.
Projects/PFI ★★★★ 699

Mather, Bertie J.M.
Crime ★★★★ 277

Mather, Christopher
Clinical Negligence ★★★★ 165

Mathieson, Keith
Defamation ★★ 295

Matthew, Stephen
Local Government ★★★★ 588
Projects/PFI ★★★ 699

Matthews, Carol A.
Social Housing ★★ 761

Matthews, Paul
Pensions U 626

Mattison, Mark
Litigation (Commercial) ★★★★ 565

Maughan, Alistair
Information Technology ★★ 456

Maughan, Peter J.
Clinical Negligence ★★★★ 165

Maunsell, Jeffery
Defamation ★★ 295

Maurice, Clare M.
Trusts & Personal Tax ★★★ 822

Mawdsley, David H.
Shipping ★★★★ 749

Max, Richard
Planning ★★★★ 666

Maxtone-Smith, Michael
Media & Entertainment ★★ 599

Maxwell, Elaine
Education ★★★★ 309

Maxwell, M. John
Shipping ★★★★ 749

May, Caroline
Environment ★★★★ 377

May, Philip N S
Insolvency/Corporate
Recovery ★★★ 480
Litigation (Commercial) ★★★★ 565
Partnership ★★★★ 612

Mayer, Stephen D.
Partnership ★★★ 612

Mayers, Chris
Clinical Negligence ★★★★ 165

Mayhew, David
Commodities ★★★ 172
Fraud ★★★ 419
Litigation (Commercial) ★ 565

Maynard, Andrew E.
Property (Commercial) ★★★★ 731

McAllester, Alan K.
Church ★★★★ 150

McArthur, Colin
Partnership ★★ 612

McAuley, Michael
Projects/PFI ★★★★ 699

McBride, Carolyn
Family ★★ 396

McBride, Paul
Corporate Finance ★ 258

McCallough, Robert
Information Technology ★★★ 456

McCarthy, Frances
Personal Injury ★★★★ 645

McCaw, Elma
Trusts & Personal Tax ★★★ 822

McChlery, Frances
Planning ★★ 666

McClea, Nigel
Property (Commercial) ★★★★ 731

McClure, Alison
Clinical Negligence ★★★★ 165

McCool, Geraldine M.
Personal Injury ★★★ 645
Product Liability ★★ 675

McCormack, Carol
Projects/PFI ★★ 699

McCormick, Peter D.G.
Fraud ★★ 419
Media & Entertainment ★★★★ 599
Sport ✪ 770

McCormick, Roger
Projects/PFI ★ 699

McCue, Jason
Defamation ★★ 295

McCulloch, Ian
Parliamentary & Public
Affairs ★★★★ 605

McDermott, Jennifer
Administrative & Public
Law ★★★★ 60

McDonald, Kevan
Corporate Finance ★★ 258

McDonald, Roberta
Family ★★ 396

McDonnell, Phil
Competition/Anti-trust ★★★ 182

McDougall, Arundel
Product Liability ★★ 675

McEvoy, Eamonn E.
Personal Injury ★★★★ 645

McEwan, Alastair J.A.
Projects/PFI ★★ 699

McGee-Osborne, Christopher
Energy & Natural Resources ★★ .. 358
Transport ★★★★ 801

McGeever, Brendan G.
Insolvency/Corporate
Recovery ★★★ 480

McGilchrist, Neil R.
Aviation ★★ 103

McGinn, James
Corporate Finance ★★ 258

McGowan, Michael T.
Tax (Corporate) ★ 785

KEY TO RANKINGS: ✪ = Star Individual ★★★★ = Top Band ★★★ = Second Band ★★ = Third Band ★ = Fourth Band U = Up and coming

McGrath, Matthew
Clinical Negligence ★★★★ 165

McGurk, Anthony J.G.
Insolvency/Corporate Recovery ★★★★ 480

McHale, Colin J.
Banking ★★★★ 119

McHugh, Peter J.
Corporate Finance ★★★ 258

McIlwee, Richard
Tax (Corporate) U 785

McInerney, Peter B.G.
Media & Entertainment ★ 600
Sport ★★ 770

McInnes, John
Crime ★★★ 277

McIntosh, Ian W.
Corporate Finance ★★ 258

McKay, Colin
Banking ★★★ 119

McKechnie, Robert
Professional Negligence ★★ 685

McKenna, Catherine M.P.
Pensions ★★★ 626

McKenna, Ian
Insurance ★ 496

McKenna, John
Professional Negligence ★★★★ .. 685

McKenzie, Rod
Employment ★★ 341
Sport ★★★ 771

McKnight, Elizabeth S.
Competition/Anti-trust ★★★★ 182

McLachlan, Campbell A.
Litigation (Commercial) ★★★★ 565

McLean, Alistair
Construction ★★★ 203

McLean, James
Competition/Anti-trust ★★★★ 182
Intellectual Property ★★ 514

McLean, Neil M.
Property (Commercial) ★★★★ 731

McMullen, John
Employment ✪ 341

McNabb, Heather
Intellectual Property ★★★★ 514

McNeil, Paul
Clinical Negligence ★★★ 165

McNeill, Morag
Corporate Finance ★★★★ 258

McNeive, Liam
E-commerce ★★★★ 301

McNulty, Stephen
Social Housing ★★★★ 761

McPake, Ian A.H.
Environment ★ 377

McQuater, Gavin J.
Projects/PFI ★ 699

McRobb, Elizabeth M.M.
Information Technology ★★ 457

McTaggart, Anne
Family ★★ 396

McWhirter, Anthony
Investment Funds ★ 524

Mead, Ray
Shipping ★★ 749

Meadon, Simon
Media & Entertainment ★★ 600

Meakin, Robert
Charities ★★ 143

Mears, Patrick M.
Tax (Corporate) ★★★★ 786

Medvei, Cornelius
Property (Commercial) ★★ 731

Meeks, Alastair
Pensions U 626

Mehmet, Gülay
Immigration ★★ 443

Mehta, Nikhil
Tax (Corporate) ★★ 786

Meiklejohn, Iain M.C.
Banking ★★ 119
Corporate Finance ★★ 258

Meisel, Mari
Family ★★ 396

Melbourne, William
Transport ★ 801

Mellor, Eliza
Trusts & Personal Tax ★★★ 822

Melrose, Jonathan
Commodities ★★★★ 172

Meltzer, Claire
Family ★ 396

Meltzer, John
Product Liability ★★★ 675

Mendelowitz, Michael
Insurance ★ 496

Mendelsohn, Martin
Franchising ★★★★ 410

Mercer, Edward
Telecommunications ★★★ 793

Meredith, Alan
Property (Commercial) ★★★★ 731

Meredith, Ian
Litigation (Commercial) ★★ 565

Merriam, Joy
Crime ★★★ 277

Merson, James T.
Insolvency/Corporate Recovery ★★ 480

Messenger, Mercy
Family ★★ 396

Messent, Andrew
Transport ★★★★ 801

Messent, Michael J.
Licensing ★★★★ 538

Metcalfe, Ian
Corporate Finance ★★★★ 258

Metcalfe, Robin H.
Corporate Finance ★★★ 259

Metcalfe, Stephen J.
Litigation (Commercial) ★★★ 565

Metliss, Jonathan A.
Sport ★★ 771

Micklem, Barney
Professional Negligence ★★★ 685

Micklethwaite, Neil Philip
Litigation (Commercial) ★ 565

Middleditch, Matthew
Corporate Finance ★★★ 259
Insurance ★★★ 496
Investment Funds ★★★★ 524

Middleton, Fiona
Charities ★★★★ 143

Milburn, Paula
Family ★★★ 396

Miles, Adrian
Asset Finance & Leasing ★★★ 98

Miles, Anthony
Crime ★★★★ 277

Miles, David
Alternative Dispute Resolution ★★★★ 82

Miles, Stephen
Banking ★★★ 120

Millar, Richard
Investment Funds ★★★ 524

Millard, Christopher
E-commerce ★★★★ 301
Information Technology ★★★★ .. 457

Miller, Adrian W.M.
Trusts & Personal Tax ★★★★ 823

Miller, Colin B.
Competition/Anti-trust U 182

Miller, Stephen C.
Employment ★★★ 341
Sport ★★★ 771

Miller, Stephen M.
Capital Markets ★★ 131

Miller, Wendy
Litigation (Property) ★★★★ 578

Miller, RD*, Anthony
Shipping ★★ 749

Millington, Jeremy S.
Corporate Finance ★★★★ 259

Mills, Deborah
Energy & Natural Resources ★★★ 358

Mills, Geoffrey G.
Shipping ★★★ 749

Mills, Guy B.
Shipping ★★★ 749

Mills, Stephen
Shipping ★★★★ 749

Milne, Charles M.
Social Housing ★★ 761

Milner, Henry
Crime ★★ 277

Milton, Kevin
Pensions ★★★ 627

Mimpriss, Peter
Charities ★★★ 143

Minogue, Ann
Construction ★★★★ 203

Minto, Bruce
Corporate Finance ★★★★ 259
Financial Services ★★★ 407
Investment Funds ★★★ 524

Mireskandari, Razi
Defamation ★★★ 295

Miscampbell, Andrew
Partnership ★★★★ 612

Mitchard, Paul
Arbitration (International) ★★ 88

Mitchell, A.W. Martin
Trusts & Personal Tax ★★★ 823

Mitchell, Christopher J.
Corporate Finance ★★ 259

Mitchell, J. Patrick
Banking ★★★★ 120

Mitchell, Jane
Family ★★★ 396

Mitchell, Jocelyn
Employee Share Schemes ★★ 315

Mitchell, John
Fraud ★★★★ 419

Mitchell, Paul
Media & Entertainment ★★★ 600

Moakes, Jonathan
Information Technology ★★★ 457
Intellectual Property ★★★★ 514

Moffat, Douglas W.J.
Property (Commercial) ★★ 731

Molloy, Susan
Banking ★★★ 120

Molyneux, Anne
Litigation (Property) ★★★ 578

Molyneux, Pauline
Employment ★★★ 341

Monaghan, Iain
Information Technology ★ 457

Moncreiffe, Mark
Telecommunications ★★ 794

Monro, Pat
Family ★ 396

Montgomery, Nigel
Clinical Negligence ★★★ 165

Montgomery, Nigel W J
Insolvency/Corporate Recovery ★★★ 481

Monty, Craig
Pensions ★★★ 627

Moodie, Bill
Intellectual Property ★★ 515

Moody, John
Property (Commercial) ★★★ 731

Mooney, Kevin
Intellectual Property ✪ 515

Moore, Austin John
Corporate Finance ★★ 259

Moore, George K.
Personal Injury ★★★★ 645

Moore, John E.
Agriculture ★★★ 76

Moore, Nigel
Pensions ★★★ 627

Moore, Nigel
Employment ★★★ 341

Moorman, Jane
Employment ★ 341

Mordsley, Barry
Employment ★ 341

More, George M.
Crime ★★★ 277

Morgan, Claire
Property (Commercial) ★★★★ 731

Morgan, Leon R.
Media & Entertainment ★★★ 600

Morgan, Meryl
Banking ★★★ 120

Morgan, Rosemary
Licensing ★★★ 538
Property (Commercial) ★★ 732

Morgan, Simon
Arbitration (International) U 88

Moritz, John
Planning ★★★ 666

Morley, David H.
Banking ✪ 120
Corporate Finance ★★ 259

Morley, Trevor
Social Housing ★★★ 761

Moroney, David
Energy & Natural Resources ★★★ 358

Morpeth, Iain
Property (Commercial) ★★★★ 732

Morris, Andrew
Corporate Finance ★★★ 259

Morris, Christopher A.
Property (Commercial) ★★ 732

Morris, Gregory
Tax (Corporate) ★★★★ 786

Morris, Howard
Insolvency/Corporate Recovery ★ 481

Morris, Paul C.E.
Church ★★★★ 150

Morris, Peter
Litigation (Commercial) ★★★★ 565
Litigation (Property) ★★★★ 578

Morris, Simon
Financial Services ★★★ 407

Morrison, Alastair
Agriculture ★★★ 76

Morrison, Alastair
Construction ★★★★ 203

Morrison, Michael
Sport ★★★ 771

Morse, John
Licensing ★★★ 538

Morse, Stephen
Corporate Finance ★ 259

Mortimer, Fay
Trusts & Personal Tax ★★★★ 823

Mortimer, Ken A.
Social Housing ★★ 761

Morton, David E
Banking ★★ 120

Morton, Guy
Financial Services ★★★★ 407

Morton, Robin J.M.
Licensing ★★★ 538

Mosey, David
Construction ★★ 203

Moss, David J.
Construction ★★★ 204

Moss, Gary
Intellectual Property ★★★★ 515

Moss, Peter
Immigration ★★ 443

Moss, Philip G.S.
Tax (Corporate) ★★★★ 786

Most, Lionel D.
Property (Commercial) ★★★ 732

Mostyn-Williams, Stephen R.P.
Banking ★★ 120

Motani, Habib
Capital Markets ★★★★ 131

Moule, Jos
Partnership ★★★ 612

Mowat, Allan R.
Clinical Negligence ★★★ 166

Moxon, Richard
Media & Entertainment ★★ 600

Moyse, Richard M.
Trusts & Personal Tax ★★★★ 823

Mudd, Philip J.
Insolvency/Corporate Recovery
★★★★ 481

Mulcare, John
Agriculture ★★★ 76

Mullen, Chris P.
Pensions ★★★ 627

Mulligan, Claire
Travel ★★ 807

Mumford, Nicola
Litigation (Commercial) ★ 565

Munday, Nicholas
Insurance ★ 496

Munday, Peter J.
Corporate Finance ★ 259

Munro, Rick
Insolvency/Corporate Recovery **U** .. 481

Murphy, Fiona
Human Rights ★★★ 434

Murphy, Frances
Corporate Finance ★ 259

Murphy, Michael G.
Projects/PFI ★★★★ 699

Murphy, Niall
Tax (Corporate) ★★★★ 786

Murphy, Patrick
Personal Injury ★★★ 645

Murphy, Shaun
Crime ★★ 277

Murray, Andrew J.
Social Housing ★★★★ 761

Murray, Christopher
Fraud ★★ 419

Murray, John
Pensions ★★ 627

Murray, Marsali C.
Product Liability ★★★★ 676

Murray, Paul C.
Professional Negligence ★★★ 685

Murray, Rob P.
Competition/Anti-trust ★★★★ 182

Murray-Jones, Allan G.
Corporate Finance ★★ 259

Musgrave, Tim
Clinical Negligence ★★★★ 166

Musters, Patrick H.A.
Crime ★★★★ 277

Myers, Miranda
Church ★★★ 150

Myers, Sidney A.
Fraud ★★★ 419

Mylrea, Kathy
Environment ★★★★ 377

N

Nairn, Karyl
Arbitration (International) ★★ 89

Nally, Edward
Church ★★★ 150

Napper, Isabel
Intellectual Property ★★★ 515

Nash, David
Projects/PFI ★★★ 699

Nash, Mike
Environment ★★★ 377

Natali, David P.
Fraud ★★★ 419
Litigation (Commercial) ★★★★ 565

Nellist, Peter
Trusts & Personal Tax ★★ 823

Nelson, Paul M.
Financial Services ★★★★ 407

Nelson, Richard
Fraud ★★★★ 419

Nelson, Victoria
Tax (Corporate) ★★★ 786

Nelson-Jones, Rodney
Personal Injury ★★★ 645
Product Liability ★★ 676

Neville, William
Agriculture ★★★★ 76

Newcombe, Mark
Property (Commercial) ★★ 732

Newhouse, Anthony
Corporate Finance ★ 259

Newman, Helen
Intellectual Property ★★★★ 515

Newman, Iain
Corporate Finance **U** 259

Newman, Paul
Construction ★★★ 204

Newmark, Chris
Alternative Dispute Resolution ★★ .. 82

Newton, Alison
Property (Commercial) ★★ 732

Nias, Peter
Tax (Corporate) ★★ 786

Nichol, James
Crime ★★★★ 277
Human Rights ★★ 434

Nicholas, Paul D.
Professional Negligence ★★★★ .. 685

Nicholl, Victoria
Employee Share Schemes ★★ 315

Nicholls, Simon J.
Crime ★★★★ 277
Licensing ★★ 538

Nicholson, Brinsley
Litigation (Commercial) ★★ 565

Nicholson, Jonathan B.
Trusts & Personal Tax ★★★★ 823

Nicholson, Kim
E-commerce ★★ 301
Information Technology ★★ 457
Telecommunications ★★ 794

Nicholson, Malcolm
Competition/Anti-trust ✪ 182

Nicholson, Mark
Insolvency/Corporate
Recovery ★★★ 481

Nickson, Susan C.
Employment ★★★★ 341

Nicol, Diane
Employment ★★ 342

Nicol, Frazer
Family ★★★ 396

Nicoll, Richard C.
Travel ★★★ 807

Nicolson, Fiona
Information Technology ★★★★ .. 457
Intellectual Property ★★★★ 515

Niekirk, Malcolm
Insolvency/Corporate
Recovery ★★★ 481

Nisse, Ian
Property (Commercial) ★★ 732

Noble, Nicholas R.
Tax (Corporate) ★★★ 786

Noble, Perry
Projects/PFI ★★★★ 699

Nodder, Edward
Intellectual Property ★★★★ 515

Nolan, Brandon
Construction ★★★★ 204

Norbury, Peter
Employment ★★★ 342

Norcross Webb, Sally
Corporate Finance ★★ 260

Norfolk, Edward Christopher Dominic
Tax (Corporate) ★★★★ 786

Norman, Guy T.D.
Corporate Finance **U** 260

Nortcliff, Celia
Intellectual Property ★★★★ 515

North, Michael A.
Partnership ★ 612

Norton, Philip
Charities ★★★ 143

Norwood, Andrew
Tax (Corporate) **U** 786

Nott, Christopher
Employment **U** 342

Nott, Colin
Crime ★★ 277

Novy, Rod
Crime ★★ 277

Nowlan, Howard
Tax (Corporate) ★★★★ 786

Nunn, Stephen
Crime ★★★★ 278

Nuttall, Graeme
Employee Share Schemes ★ 315

Nyman, Bernard M.
Media & Entertainment ★★★ 600

O

O'Brien, Barry
Corporate Finance ★★★★ 260

O'Brien, Christine
Employment ★★ 342

O'Brien, Gary
Litigation (Property) ★★★★ 579

O'Connor, Mark I.
Corporate Finance ★ 260

O'Connor, Mike G.
Projects/PFI ★★★ 699

O'Conor, John
Arbitration (International) **U** 89

O'Donnell, Caroline
Family ★ 397

KEY TO RANKINGS: ✪ = Star Individual ★★★★ = Top Band ★★★ = Second Band ★★ = Third Band ★ = Fourth Band **U** = Up and coming

P

KEY TO RANKINGS: ✪ = Star Individual ★★★★ = Top Band ★★★ = Second Band ★★ = Third Band ★ = Fourth Band U = Up and coming

Peter, Charles
Crime ★★★ ... 278

Petheram, Claire
Pensions ★★★ ... 627

Peto, Monica
Parliamentary & Public Affairs ★★ 605

Pett, David
Employee Share Schemes ✪ ... 315

Pharaoh, Paul
Education ★★★★ ... 310

Pheasant, John E.
Competition/Anti-trust ★★★ ... 183

Pheasant, Louise A.
Insolvency/Corporate Recovery ★★★ ... 482

Phelops, Warren
Sport ★★★★ ... 771

Philipps, Richard P.S.
Media & Entertainment ★★★★ ... 600

Philipps, Susan
Family ★★ ... 397

Phillips, Andrew (Lord Phillips of Sudbury)
Charities ★★★ ... 142

Phillips, Ann
Charities ★★ ... 144

Phillips, Christopher
Health & Safety ★★★ ... 424

Phillips, Hilary
Charities ★★★ ... 144

Phillips, Jeremy
Licensing ✪ ... 539

Phillips, Mark
Human Rights ★★★★ ... 434
Immigration ★★★★ ... 444

Phillips, Mark D.
E-commerce ★★ ... 301
Media & Entertainment ★★ ... 600

Phillips, Paul
Financial Services ★ ... 407

Phillips, Raymond J.
Shipping ★★★ ... 749

Phillips, Richard
Transport ★★★★ ... 801

Phillips, Robert
Projects/PFI ★ ... 700

Phillips, Robert
Corporate Finance ★★★ ... 261

Phillips, Simon
Transport ★★ ... 801

Phillips, Stephen J.
Banking ★★ ... 120

Phipps, Matthew
Licensing ★★★ ... 539

Pia, Paul D.
Social Housing ★★★ ... 762

Piatt, Andrew
Planning U ... 666

Pickering, John
Personal Injury ★★★★ ... 646
Product Liability ★★★ ... 676

Pickering, John
Personal Injury ★★★★ ... 646

Pickston, John
Litigation (Property) ★★★★ ... 579

Pickup, Bryan J.
Travel ★★★★ ... 808

Pickup, Raith
Construction ★★★★ ... 204
Healthcare ★★★ ... 430
Projects/PFI ★★★ ... 700

Picton-Turbervill, Geoffrey
Energy & Natural Resources ★★★ 358
Energy & Natural Resources ★★★ 358

Pierce, Graham L.
Property (Commercial) U ... 732

Pierce, Sean
Banking ★★ ... 120

Pigott, Ashley R.
Construction ★★★ ... 204

Pigott, Simon
Family ★★ ... 397

Pike, John D.
Environment ★★★ ... 377
Property (Commercial) ★★★★ ... 733

Pike, Malcolm J.
Employment ★★★ ... 342

Pike, Nick
Insolvency/Corporate Recovery U .. 482

Pillman, Joe
Corporate Finance ★★★★ ... 261

Pinsent, C Jim
Construction ★★ ... 204

Piper, Anne-Marie
Charities ★★★★ ... 144

Pirrie, James
Family ★ ... 397

Pitcher, Robert
Corporate Finance ★★ ... 261

Pitkin, Jeremy
Capital Markets ★★ ... 131

Pittaway, Ian M.
Pensions ★★★★ ... 627

Pizzey, Simon F.
Litigation (Commercial) ★★★★ ... 566

Plant, Charles W.
Litigation (Commercial) ★★★★ ... 566

Plant, Patrick
Property (Commercial) ★★★ ... 733
Travel ★★★ ... 808

Plascow, Ronald H.
Construction ★★★★ ... 204

Plews, Tim
Commodities ★★★★ ... 172

Plummer, Alan J.
Agriculture ★★★ ... 76

Polglase, Timothy
Banking ★ ... 121
Corporate Finance ★★ ... 261

Polito, Simon W.
Competition/Anti-trust ★★★★ ... 183

Pollack, Craig
Litigation (Commercial) U ... 566

Pollard, David N.
Pensions ★★★★ ... 628

Pollard, Stephen
Fraud ★★★ ... 420
Fraud ★★★★ ... 420

Polson, Michael
Investment Funds ★★ ... 524

Poole, Kevin J.
Employee Share Schemes ★★ ... 315

Poore, Alasdair
Intellectual Property ★★★ ... 516

Pope, Caroline
Construction U ... 205

Pope, Caron
Immigration ★ ... 444

Pope, Timothy J.
Insolvency/Corporate Recovery ★ 482

Popham, Stuart
Banking ★★★★ ... 121
Corporate Finance ★★ ... 261

Poppleston, Susanna
Licensing ★★★★ ... 539

Popplewell, Nigel
Tax (Corporate) ★★★★ ... 787

Porter, Sue
Tax (Corporate) ★★★ ... 787

Porteus, Stephen
Personal Injury ★★★ ... 646

Portrait, Judith
Charities ★★ ... 144

Potter, Bruce J.
Insolvency/Corporate Recovery ★★ ... 482

Potter, Hugh
Clinical Negligence ★★ ... 166
Personal Injury ★★★ ... 646

Potts, Andrew J.
Licensing ★★★★ ... 539

Potts, Christopher Reginald
Commodities ★★★★ ... 172

Potts, John
Fraud ★★ ... 420

Poulter, Alan
Charities ★★★★ ... 144

Powell, Andrew M.
Pensions ★★ ... 628

Powell, David
Sport ★★★★ ... 771

Powell, Greg
Crime ★★★ ... 278

Powell, J. Mark H.
Family ★★★ ... 397

Powell, Nicholas R.D.
Trusts & Personal Tax ★★★ ... 823

Prain, David
Personal Injury ★★★ ... 646

Pratt, John
Franchising ★★★★ ... 410

Preece, Andrew
Projects/PFI ★ ... 700
Projects/PFI ★★ ... 700

Prentice, Alexander
Crime ★★★ ... 278

Prest, Catherine
Employment ★★★★ ... 342

Prest, Charles
Family ★★ ... 397

Preston, Christopher A.L.
Tax ★★★★ ... 787
Tax (Corporate) ★ ... 787

Preston, Edward
Crime ★★★ ... 278

Preston, Miles
Family ★★★★ ... 398

Price, David
Defamation ★★★ ... 296

Price, Hugh
Personal Injury ★★★★ ... 646

Price, Richard
Intellectual Property ★★★ ... 516

Primrose, Andrew H.
Environment ★★ ... 377

Prince, Michael J.
Corporate Finance ★★★★ ... 261

Pring, Simon J.
Agriculture ★★ ... 76

Prior, Barry
Transport ★★ ... 801

Prior, Michael
Insolvency/Corporate Recovery ★ 482

Pritchard, Nicholas D.M.
Property (Commercial) ★★★ ... 733

Procter, Jonathan
Corporate Finance U ... 261

Proctor, E. Jane
Family ★★ ... 398

Proctor, Nigel
Construction ★★ ... 205

Protani, Moira
Charities U ... 144

Proudler, Geraldine
Defamation ✪ ... 296

Prowel, Martyn
Crime ★★★★ ... 278
Fraud ★★★★ ... 420

Prowse, Richard
Competition/Anti-trust ★★★ ... 183

Pryke, Oliver
Employment ★ ... 343

Pryor, Nicholas
Alternative Dispute Resolution ★★★★ ... 83

Prytherch, Rosalie
Employment ★★ ... 343

Psyllides, Milton N.
Corporate Finance ★★★★ ... 262

Puddicombe, Nigel R.
Litigation (Commercial) ★★★ ... 566
Litigation (Property) ★★★ ... 579

Pugh, Keith
Employment ★★ ... 343

Pugh, Nigel
Property (Commercial) ★★★★ ... 733

Pugh, Timothy
Planning ★★★★ ... 666

Puleston Jones, Haydn
Banking ★★★★ ... 121

Pullen, David
Commodities ✪ ... 172

Purcell, Michael
Crime ★★★★ ... 278

Purchas, Simon R.
Human Rights U ... 434

Pysden, Edward
Corporate Finance ✪ ... 262

Pysden, Kay
Transport ★★★ ... 802

KEY TO RANKINGS: ✪ = Star Individual ★★★★ = Top Band ★★★ = Second Band ★★ = Third Band ★ = Fourth Band U = Up and coming

Q

Quarrell, John
Pensions ★★★★ 628

Quayle, Sophie Jane
Planning ★★ 667

Quenby, N. Philip
Commodities ★★ 172

Quigley, Ian S.
Property (Commercial) ★★★ 733

Quinn, James Stephen Christopher
Agriculture ★★★ 77

Quinn, Michael J.
Partnership ★★ 612

R

Rabinowicz, Jack
Administrative & Public Law ★★★★ 60
Education ✪ 310

Race, David W.
Construction ★ 205

Radcliffe, Malcolm
Licensing ★★★ 539

Rae, Maggie
Family ★★★ 398

Rae, Scott A.
Trusts & Personal Tax ★★★★ 823

Rafferty, John C.
Corporate Finance ★★★ 262

Raines, Marke
Capital Markets ★★★ 131

Rajani, Shashi H.
Insolvency/Corporate Recovery ★★ 482

Ralph, Stephen
Partnership ★★★ 612

Randall, Christopher W.
Immigration ★★★★ 444

Randall, Paul
Employee Share Schemes ★★ 315

Randall, Richard M.
Family ★ 398

Randall, Simon
Local Government ★★★ 588
Social Housing ★★★ 762

Randell, Charles
Corporate Finance ★★ 262

Randle, Anthony R.
Local Government ★★★ 588
Projects/PFI ★★★★ 700

Rands, Harvey
Litigation (Commercial) ★ 566

Rankin, Alastair J.
Trusts & Personal Tax ★★★★ 823

Rankin, Claire
Employment ★ 343

Ransome, Clive
Projects/PFI ★★ 700

Ranson, Lee
Litigation (Property) ★★★★ 579

Raphael, Monty
Fraud ✪ 420
Fraud ★★★ 420

Rawding, Nigel K.
Arbitration (International) ★★★ 89

Rawle, Claire
Licensing ★★★★ 539

Rawlinson, David J.
Litigation (Commercial) ★ 566

Rawlinson, Mark S.
Corporate Finance ★★★★ 262

Rawlinson, Paul
Intellectual Property ★ 516

Rawnsley, Rachel
Pensions ★★★ 628

Rawstron, C.D.
Corporate Finance ★★★ 262

Ray, Peggy
Family ★★★ 398

Rayfield, Richard
Shipping ★★★★ 749

Read, Anthony J.M.
Projects/PFI ★★ 700

Read, Nigel P.L.
Corporate Finance ★ 262

Readett, Helen A.
Insolvency/Corporate Recovery ★★ 482

Rearden, Shaun
Banking ★★★ 121

Redman, Michael
Environment ★★ 377
Planning ★ 667

Redmond, John V.
Construction ✪ 205

Reed, Derek S.
Clinical Negligence ★★★ 166

Rees, Anthony
Employment ★★★ 343

Rees, Bleddyn
Insolvency/Corporate Recovery ★★★ 482

Rees, Christopher W.
Information Technology ★★★ 458

Rees, John
Charities ★★★★ 144
Church ★★★★ 150

Rees, Jonathan
Energy & Natural Resources ★★ 359

Rees, Kate
Competition/Anti-trust ★★★★ 183

Rees, Peter
Construction ★★ 205

Reeve, Felicity
Sport ★★★★ 771

Reeves, Suzanne
Construction ★ 205

Reeves, Tony
Energy & Natural Resources ★★★ 359

Reevey, Michael A.
Property (Commercial) ★★ 733

Regan, Michael
Construction ★★★ 205
Professional Negligence ★★ 685

Reid, David R.
Property (Commercial) ★★★ 733

Reid, Donald A.
Environment ★★★ 377

Reid, Fraser
Sport U 772

Reid, Nigel W.
Trusts & Personal Tax ★★ 824

Reid, Ron F.
Product Liability ★★★★ 676

Reid, Sandy
Property (Commercial) ★★★★ 733

Reilly, Alan J.
Property (Commercial) ★★★★ 733

Reith, David S.
Charities ★★★★ 144

Rendell, Simon
Information Technology ★★★ 458

Renger, Michael
Energy & Natural Resources ★★★★ 359
Environment ★★★★ 378

Renney, Paul
Media & Entertainment ★★ 600

Rennie, Brenda L.
Charities ★★★★ 144

Rennie O.B.E., Donald G.
Agriculture ★★★★ 77

Reston, Vincent J.
Employment U 343

Reynolds, John
Litigation (Commercial) ★ 566

Reynolds, Justin
Transport ★ 802

Rhatigan, Michael
Social Housing ★★ 762

Rhodes, John
Trusts & Personal Tax ★★★★ 824

Rhodes, Paul
Insolvency/Corporate Recovery ★★★★ 483

Rhys-Jones, Mark
Litigation (Commercial) U 566

Rice, Dermot
Property (Commercial) U 733

Rice, Jim
Capital Markets ★ 131

Rice, Paul
Environment ★★ 378

Rich, Andrew
Intellectual Property ★★ 516

Richards, Mark
Construction ★★ 205

Richards, Philip
Corporate Finance ★★★ 262
Insurance ★★★ 496

Richards, Timothy J.
Construction ★★ 205

Richardson, Ian A.
Corporate Finance ★★★ 262

Richardson, Joseph Charles
Trusts & Personal Tax ★★ 824

Richardson, Simon
Planning U 667

Richens, Nicholas J.
Church ★★★ 150
Education ★★★ 310

Riches, John
Trusts & Personal Tax ★★ 824

Rickard, Jennifer
Litigation (Property) ★★★★ 579

Ricketts, Simon
Planning ★★★ 667

Ridgwell, Robert
Professional Negligence ★★★★ .. 685

Ridler, Graham
Insolvency/Corporate Recovery ★★ 483

Ridler, Mark
Pensions U 628

Ridley, Michael
Media & Entertainment ★★★★ 601

Ridley, Russell
Shipping ★★ 749

Rigg, Bettina
Personal Injury ★★★ 646

Rimell, Katherine
Defamation ★★ 296

Ripley, Fiona
Immigration ★★★ 444

Ripman, Justin
Trusts & Personal Tax ★★★★ 824

Ritchie, Angela
Administrative & Public Law ★★★★ 60

Riviere, Susanna
Immigration ★ 444

Roach, W.D. Andrew
Personal Injury ★★★ 646

Robert, Gavin
Competition/Anti-trust ★ 183

Robert, Louis
Social Housing ★★★★ 762

Roberts, David Lloyd
Property (Commercial) ★★★ 733

Roberts, Martin
Construction ★★ 205

Roberts, Martin J.D.
Energy & Natural Resources ★★★ 359

Robertson, Jonathan
Agriculture ★★★ 77

Robertson, Nicholas
Employment ★★ 343

Robertson, Ranald
Information Technology ★ 458

Robertson, Rhory
Defamation ★★ 296

Robertson, Stuart D.
Employment ★★★ 343

Robertson, Andrew O.
Social Housing ★★★ 762

Robinson, David J.R.
Trusts & Personal Tax ★★ 824

Robinson, E. Patrick G.
Planning ★★★ 667
Property (Commercial) ★★ 733

Robinson, Herbert
Property (Commercial) ★★★ 734

Robinson, Kevin
Fraud ★★ 420

Robinson, Michael
Corporate Finance ★ 262

Robinson, Patrick
Planning ★★★★ 667

KEY TO RANKINGS: ✪ = Star Individual ★★★★ = Top Band ★★★ = Second Band ★★ = Third Band ★ = Fourth Band U = Up and coming

Robinson, Sara
Family ★★ 398

Robinson, Sarah
Licensing U 539

Robinson, Tim S.H.
Travel ★★★ 808

Robson, Frank E.
Church ★★★★ 150

Robson, Nigel R.
Construction ★★★ 206

Roche, Paddy
Licensing ★★★★ 540

Rodgers, Hilary
Family ★ 398

Roe, Mark
Construction ★★★ 206

Roe, Sally
Construction ★★★ 206

Roessler, Max
Litigation (Commercial) ★★★★ 566

Rogan, Peter J.H.
Insurance ✪ 496

Rogers, Anna
Pensions ★★★ 628

Rogerson, Gary
Trusts & Personal Tax ★★ 824

Rohde, Kate
Clinical Negligence ★★ 166

Rolfe, Andrew
Projects/PFI ★ 700

Rollason, Nicolas
Immigration U 444

Ronaldson, Cheryl
Insurance ★★ 497

Roome, James H.D.
Insolvency/Corporate Recovery ★★ 483

Rooney, P.J.
Property (Commercial) ★★ 734

Rooth, Anthony
Shipping ★★★★ 749

Roper, Robert
Litigation (Commercial) ★★★★ 566

Roscoe, James
Property (Commercial) ★★ 734

Roscoe, Robert
Crime ★★ 278

Rose, D. Michael
Media & Entertainment ★★★★ 601

Rose, Digby H.
Litigation (Commercial) ★★ 567

Rose, Kenneth
Corporate Finance ★★ 262

Rose, Simon
Tax ★★★ 787

Rose, Stephen
Competition/Anti-trust ★ 183

Rose, Timothy
Crime ★★★★ 278

Rosefield, Stephen M.
Corporate Finance ★★★ 262
E-commerce ★★ 301

Rosenthal, Dennis
Asset Finance & Leasing ★★★★ .. 98

Roskill, Julian
Employment ★★★ 343

Ross, Alexander T.
Insolvency/Corporate Recovery ★★★ 483

Ross, David
Energy & Natural Resources ★★★★ 359

Ross, Hilary
Product Liability ★★★ 676

Ross, Howard
Tax (Corporate) ★★ 787

Ross, Hubert J.
Trusts & Personal Tax ★★★★ 824

Ross, Kenneth A.
Property (Commercial) ★★ 734

Ross, Kenneth C.
Environment ★★★ 378

Ross, Malcolm D.
Employment ★★★ 343

Rothera, Ian
Transport ★★★★ 802

Rothwell, Charles E.S.
Litigation (Commercial) ★ 567

Rous, Simon R.
Corporate Finance ★★★ 262

Rowe, Bernard V.
Personal Injury ★★★★ 646

Rowe, Claire M.
Litigation (Commercial) ★★★★ 567

Rowe, Heather
Information Technology ★★ 458

Rowe, Michael
Competition/Anti-trust ★ 183

Rowey, Kent
Energy & Natural Resources ★★ .. 359
Projects/PFI ★★ 700

Rowland, Simon J.
Construction U 206

Rowlands-Hempel, Graham
Employee Share Schemes ★★★ .. 315

Roxburgh, Bruce O.
Corporate Finance ★★★ 263

Roxburgh, James A.R.
Personal Injury ★★★★ 647
Professional Negligence ★★★ 685

Roxburgh, Roy
Insolvency/Corporate Recovery ★★★★ 483

Royle, Charles P.
Fraud ★★ 420

Rubinstein, John
Defamation ★★ 296

Ruddiman, Robert J.A.
Energy & Natural Resources ★★★★ 359

Rudin, Simeon
Capital Markets ★★ 131

Rudolf, Peter.D.
Property (Commercial) ★★★ 734

Ruebain, David
Administrative & Public Law ★★★★ 60
Education ★★★★ 310

Rundall, Francis R.S.
Corporate Finance ★ 263

Rupal, Yash
Tax (Corporate) ★★★ 787

Rushton, John Michael
Construction ★★★★ 206

Rushworth, Jonathan E.F.
Insolvency/Corporate Recovery ★ 483

Russ, Timothy
Agriculture ★★ 77

Russell, George R.
Charities ★★★★ 144

Russell, John
Capital Markets ★★ 131

Russell, Mark A.
Shipping ★★ 749

Russell, Patrick
Sport ★★★ 772

Russell, Tony
Media & Entertainment ★★★★ 601

Russell, Victoria E.
Construction ★★ 206

Rutherford, Lyn
Family ★★★★ 398

Rutter, Geoffrey M.
Family ★★ 398

Ryan, Ian
Crime ★★ 278

Ryde, Andy
Corporate Finance U 263

Ryden, Nicholas
Property (Commercial) ★★★★ 734

Ryland, David S.
Property (Commercial) ★★★ 734
Travel ★★★★ 808

Ryland, Glyn
Pensions ★★★★ 628

S

Sacker, Tony
Partnership ★★★★ 612

Sackman, Simon
Corporate Finance ★★ 263

Sadka, Tim
Corporate Finance ★ 263

Saeedi, Terry
Pensions U 628

Sales, Martin
Environment ★ 378
Planning ★★★ 667

Salmon, Kenneth T.
Construction ★★ 206

Salomonsen, V. Erik
Professional Negligence ★★★★ .. 685

Salt, Julia
Asset Finance & Leasing ★★★ 98

Salt, Stuart
Energy & Natural Resources ★★★★ 359
Projects/PFI ★★★★ 700

Salter, David A.
Family ★★★★ 398

Salter, Ian
Environment ★★★★ 378

Saluja, Sean A.
Employment ★★ 344

Salz, Anthony M.V.
Corporate Finance ★★★★ 263

Sampson, Ian
Information Technology ★★ 458

Samson, John
Property (Commercial) ★★★ 734

Samsworth, Jane M.
Pensions ★★★ 628

Sandelson, Daniel
Media & Entertainment ★★★ 601

Sandelson, Jeremy
Fraud ★★ 420
Litigation (Commercial) ★★★★ 567

Sanders, Jan
Projects/PFI ★ 700

Sanders, Shona
Banking ★★ 121

Sanders, Tim
Tax (Corporate) ★ 787

Sanderson, R. Gordon
Insolvency/Corporate Recovery ★★★★ 483

Sandison, Francis G.
Tax ★★★ 787
Tax (Corporate) ★★★ 787

Sandison, Hamish
Information Technology ★★★★ .. 458

Sands, Rosemary
Family ★★ 398

Sapeta, Jean
Employment U 344

Sasse, Sarah
Information Technology ★★★ 459

Saunders, Carolyn
Pensions U 628

Saunders, James
Crime ★★ 278

Saunders, James
Energy & Natural Resources ★★★★ 359
Information Technology ★★★ 459
Intellectual Property ★★ 516

Saunders, Joss
Charities ★★★ 144

Saunders, Mark
Energy & Natural Resources ★★ .. 359

Savill, Lisbeth
Media & Entertainment ★★★ 601

Sax, Richard
Family ★★★★ 398

Sayer, Nicholas T.
Employment ★★★★ 344

Sayer, Richard
Shipping ✪ 750

Scanlan, Margaret
Family ★★★ 399

Scannell, John
Litigation (Property) ★★★★ 579

Scates, Olivia
Clinical Negligence ★★★ 166

Schaffer, Daniel
Pensions ★★★ 629

Schaffer, Danny
Insolvency/Corporate Recovery ★★ 483

Schilling, Keith
Defamation ★★★★ 296

Schofield, Belinda
Insurance ★★★★ 497
Professional Negligence ★★ 685

Scholefield, Stephen
Pensions U 629

Scholes, Jeremy
Competition/Anti-trust ★★ 183

KEY TO RANKINGS: ✪ = Star Individual ★★★★ = Top Band ★★★ = Second Band ★★ = Third Band ★ = Fourth Band U = Up and coming

KEY TO RANKINGS: ✪ = Star Individual ★★★★ = Top Band ★★★ = Second Band ★★ = Third Band ★ = Fourth Band U = Up and coming

Sloan, Derek S.
Pensions ✪ ... 629

Sloan, Graeme E.C.
Corporate Finance ★★ ... 264

Sloan, Philip
Intellectual Property ★★★ ... 517

Small, Graham
Litigation (Commercial) ★ ... 568

Small, Harry
E-commerce ★★★ ... 301
Information Technology ★★★ ... 459

Smart, Peter C.
Corporate Finance ★ ... 264

Smerdon, R.W.
Corporate Finance ★★★ ... 264

Smith, Antony
Professional Negligence ★★★ ... 686

Smith, Barry
Media & Entertainment ★★★ ... 601

Smith, Brian
Planning ★★★ ... 667

Smith, Campbell
Corporate Finance ★★ ... 264

Smith, Caroline
Family ★★★★ ... 400

Smith, Charles
Environment ★★★★ ... 379

Smith, Chris
Social Housing ★★ ... 762

Smith, Christopher
Capital Markets ★ ... 131

Smith, David
Asset Finance & Leasing ★★ ... 98
Shipping ★★★ ... 750

Smith, David
Immigration ★★★★ ... 444

Smith, David
Licensing ★★★ ... 540

Smith, David A.
Property (Commercial) ★★★★ ... 734

Smith, G. Bruce
Planning ★★★ ... 667

Smith, Gillian C.
Insolvency/Corporate Recovery ★★ ... 484

Smith, Graham
Asset Finance & Leasing U ... 98

Smith, Graham
Immigration ★★★ ... 445

Smith, Graham
E-commerce ★★★★ ... 301
Information Technology ★★ ... 459

Smith, Graham C.H.
Agriculture ★★★★ ... 77

Smith, Hugh E.
Litigation (Commercial) ★ ... 568
Product Liability ★★★ ... 676

Smith, Ian D.
Construction ★ ... 207

Smith, Isla M.
Tax (Corporate) ★ ... 788

Smith, Janice
Clinical Negligence ★★★ ... 166
Healthcare ★★★ ... 430

Smith, Jason
Sport U ... 772

Smith, Lisa
Immigration ★★ ... 445

Smith, Mark
Banking ★★ ... 121

Smith, Martin
Competition/Anti-trust ★★ ... 184

Smith, Martin B.
Defamation ★★★★ ... 296

Smith, Michael
Capital Markets ★★ ... 131

Smith, Michael
Family ★★★★ ... 400

Smith, Paul A.
Environment ✪ ... 379

Smith, Phillip
Insolvency/Corporate Recovery ★★ ... 484

Smith, Quentin P.G.
Alternative Dispute Resolution ★★ .. 83

Smith, Roderick
Insurance ★★★★ ... 497

Smith, Sarah
Capital Markets ★ ... 131

Smith, Sid
Personal Injury ★★★★ ... 647

Smith, Stephanie
Pensions ★★★ ... 629

Smith, Tim
Planning U ... 667

Smith, Tim
Employment U ... 344

Smith, Tim
Charities ★★★ ... 145

Smithers, Tim M.D.
Energy & Natural Resources ★★★ 359
Property (Commercial) ★★★ ... 735

Smyth, Maurice T.
Crime ★★★ ... 278

Smyth, Michael
Administrative & Public Law ✪ ... 61
Defamation ★★ ... 296

Smyth, Richard
Fraud ✪ ... 420

Smyth, Robert
Property (Commercial) ★★★★ ... 735

Soames, Trevor
Aviation ★★★★ ... 104
Competition/Anti-trust ★★ ... 184

Solly, Gillian
Clinical Negligence ★★★ ... 167

Soloman, Martin
Litigation (Commercial) ★★★ ... 568

Solomon, Jonathan
Property (Commercial) ★★ ... 735

Somerset, Louise
Tax (Corporate) ★★★★ ... 788

Sorrell, Christopher
Litigation (Commercial) ★★★ ... 568

Sorrell, Stephen
Property (Commercial) ★★★★ ... 735

Soutar, Tim
Projects/PFI ★ ... 701

Southern, Steve
Pensions U ... 629

Southey, Verner
Insurance ★★★ ... 497

Southorn, Elizabeth
Licensing ★★★★ ... 540

Spacie, Dominic
Projects/PFI U ... 701

Sparrow, Edward C.A.
Fraud ★★ ... 420
Litigation (Commercial) ★★★ ... 568

Spearing, D. Nicholas
Competition/Anti-trust ★★★★ ... 184

Speed, Nick P.
Construction U ... 207

Speirs, William Stewart Colin
Employment ★★★ ... 344

Speker, Barry N.
Clinical Negligence ★★★ ... 167
Family ★★★★ ... 400

Spencer, Richard
Crime ★★★ ... 278

Spencer, Robin G.N.
Insolvency/Corporate Recovery ★★★★ ... 484

Spencer, Shân
Insolvency/Corporate Recovery ★★★★ ... 484

Spendlove, Justin
Banking ★ ... 121
Corporate Finance ★★★ ... 264

Spetch, Michael
Corporate Finance ★★ ... 264

Spink, Richard
Corporate Finance U ... 265

Spiro, Brian
Fraud ★★★ ... 420

Spooner, Andrew Nicolas
Litigation (Commercial) ★ ... 568

Spriggs, Michael I.
Corporate Finance ★★★★ ... 265

Spring, Paul
Defamation ★★★★ ... 297
Litigation (Commercial) ★★★★ ... 568
Product Liability ★★★ ... 676

Stacey, Paul
Energy & Natural Resources ★★★ 359

Stafford, Peter
Corporate Finance U ... 265

Stakes, John Anthony
Family ★★★ ... 400

Stallard, Hayley
Advertising & Marketing ★★★ ... 65

Stancombe, Michael F.
Property (Commercial) ★★★ ... 735

Stanczyk, Julia
Family ★ ... 400

Stanfield, Glynne
Corporate Finance ★★★ ... 265
Education ★★★★ ... 310

Stanford-Tuck, Michael
Trusts & Personal Tax ★★ ... 824

Stanger, Michael A.
Energy & Natural Resources ★★★ 360

Staniforth, Alison J.
Construction ★★ ... 207

Stanley, Alison
Immigration ★★★★ ... 445

Stannard, Paul A.C.
Pensions ✪ ... 629

Staple, George
Fraud ★★★★ ... 420

Staples, Martin R.
Personal Injury ★★★ ... 647

Stapleton, Mark
Tax ★★★ ... 788

Starks, Brian D.
Partnership ★★★ ... 613

Starr, Ian
Intellectual Property ★★★★ ... 517

Statham, John
Media & Entertainment ★★ ... 602

Staveley, Ben W.
Tax (Corporate) ★★★★ ... 788

Steadman, Tim
Construction ★★ ... 207
Projects/PFI ★★★★ ... 701

Steel, David A.
Property (Commercial) ★★★★ ... 735

Steel, John R.
Agriculture ★★★ ... 77

Stein, Richard
Administrative & Public Law ★★★★ ... 61

Steinberg, David Jeremy
Insolvency/Corporate Recovery ★★★★ ... 484

Steiner, Michael
Insolvency/Corporate Recovery ★★★ ... 484

Steinfeld, Michael
Corporate Finance ★★ ... 265

Stella, Keith G.
Corporate Finance ★★★★ ... 265

Stephens, Hugo
Social Housing ★★★★ ... 762

Stephens, Jonathan
Agriculture ★★★★ ... 77

Stephenson, Andrew
Defamation ★★★ ... 297

Stephenson, Barbara
Corporate Finance ★ ... 265

Stern, Robert
Corporate Finance ★ ... 265

Sternberg, Nigel P.
Education ★★★ ... 310

Stewart, Alan
Corporate Finance ★★ ... 265

Stewart, Brian J.C.
Personal Injury ★★★★ ... 647
Product Liability ★★★ ... 676

Stewart, David L.
Litigation (Commercial) ★★ ... 568

Stewart, Gordon C.
Insolvency/Corporate Recovery ★★★★ ... 484

Stewart, Mark
Banking ★★★ ... 121
Corporate Finance ★★★★ ... 265

Stewart, Patrick
Defamation ★★ ... 297

Stewart, Peter J.
Travel ★★★★ ... 808

Stillwell, Kevin
Partnership ★★ ... 613

Stilton, Andrew J.
Corporate Finance ★★ ... 265

KEY TO RANKINGS: ✪ = Star Individual ★★★★ = Top Band ★★★ = Second Band ★★ = Third Band ★ = Fourth Band U = Up and coming

T

KEY TO RANKINGS: ✪ = Star Individual ★★★★ = Top Band ★★★ = Second Band ★★ = Third Band ★ = Fourth Band U = Up and coming

Thorneycroft, John
Church ★★★ ... 150

Thorneycroft, Max
Corporate Finance ★ ... 266

Thorneycroft, Philip M.
Family ★★★★ ... 400

Thorogood, Paul
Partnership ★★★ ... 613

Thorp, Clive
Shipping ★★★ ... 750

Thurston, Martyn
Trusts & Personal Tax ★★ ... 825

Thurston, Michael
Fraud ★★★★ ... 421

Thurston Smith, Martin
Financial Services ★★★ ... 407
Investment Funds ★★ ... 524

Tier, Sarah J.
Pensions ★★★ ... 630

Tighe, David P.
Information Technology ★★★★ ... 459

Timmins, Jacqueline
Pensions U ... 630

Tinman, Mark
Property (Commercial) U ... 736

Tisdall, Miles
Church ★★★ ... 150

Todd, Andrew G.
Investment Funds ★★ ... 525

Tomlinson, Kevin
Crime ★★★★ ... 279

Toon, John
Tax (Corporate) ★★★ ... 788

Tooth, Ray
Family ★★★★ ... 400

Tosh, A Nial R
Tax (Corporate) U ... 788

Tott, Nicholas P.
Asset Finance & Leasing ★★ ... 98
Projects/PFI ★★★★ ... 701

Tout, Liz
Litigation (Commercial) ★ ... 569

Townley, Stephen
Sport ✪ ... 772

Townsend, Matthew
Environment U ... 379

Tozer, Roy C.
Product Liability ★★★ ... 676

Tranter, Ian
Litigation (Commercial) ★★ ... 569

Trapp, Deirdre
Competition/Anti-trust ★★★★ ... 184

Trask, Michael A.
Tax (Corporate) ★ ... 788

Travers, Harry
Fraud ★★★★ ... 421

Travers, Iain
Litigation (Property) ★★★ ... 579

Tregear, Steven
Media & Entertainment ★★ ... 602

Trehearne, Ian
Planning ★★★★ ... 668

Tremaine, Robin
Employee Share Schemes ★★★ ... 316

Triggs, Jeff
Partnership ★★★★ ... 613

Trinick, G. Marcus
Energy & Natural Resources ★★★★ ... 360
Environment ★★★★ ... 379
Planning ★★★★ ... 668

Trott, David
Capital Markets ★★★ ... 131

Trott, Philip
Immigration ★★★★ ... 445

Trotter, Andrew
Corporate Finance ★★★★ ... 267

Trotter, John G.
Litigation (Commercial) ★★★ ... 569
Professional Negligence ★★★ ... 686

Trotter, John M.
Administrative & Public Law ★★★ ... 61

Trotter, Peter A.A.
Employee Share Schemes ★★★★ ... 316
Pensions ★★ ... 630

Troup, Edward
Tax (Corporate) ★★ ... 788

True, Justin
Planning ★ ... 668

Truex, David
Family ★★ ... 400

Tucker, Andrew
Personal Injury ★★★★ ... 647
Product Liability ★★★ ... 676

Tucker, John C.
Banking ★ ... 122

Tucker, Julian A.
Capital Markets ★ ... 132

Tudway, Robert
Energy & Natural Resources ★★ ... 360

Tuffnell, Kevin
Corporate Finance ★★★ ... 267

Tulley, Christopher T.
Intellectual Property ★★★ ... 517

Tunnard, Chris
Church ★★★ ... 150

Turcan, Robert
Agriculture ★★★ ... 78

Turnbull, Andrew D.C.
Pensions ★★ ... 630

Turnbull, Craig
Construction U ... 207

Turnbull, John
Litigation (Commercial) ★★★★ ... 569

Turnbull, Robert
Corporate Finance ★ ... 267

Turnbull, Stephen
Planning ★★★★ ... 668

Turner, Angela
Planning ★ ... 668

Turner, Graham F.
Social Housing ★★★★ ... 762

Turner, John R.
Environment ★★★★ ... 379

Turner, Mark
E-commerce ★★ ... 301
Information Technology ★ ... 459

Turner, Nicholas
Social Housing ★★ ... 762

Turner, Paul
Commodities ★ ... 172

Turner, Paul Alan
Shipping ★ ... 751

Turnor, Richard
Partnership ★★★★ ... 613
Trusts & Personal Tax ★★★ ... 825

Turpin, Philip B.C.
Immigration ★★★★ ... 445

Turtle, Trevor W.
Energy & Natural Resources ★★★★ ... 360

Turtle, W. Brian W.
Employment ★★ ... 345
Litigation (Commercial) ★★★★ ... 569
Professional Negligence ★★★★ ... 686

Turton, Julian M.
Media & Entertainment ★★★ ... 602

Tweed, Paul
Defamation ★★★★ ... 297

Tweedie, Colin
Employment ★★ ... 345

Twemlow, W.A.
Partnership ★★★★ ... 613

Twentyman, Jeff
Corporate Finance U ... 267

Twist, G. Patrick A.S.
Banking ★★★★ ... 122
Projects/PFI ★★ ... 701

Tyler, Alfred J.
Clinical Negligence ★★★★ ... 167
Litigation (Commercial) ★★ ... 569
Personal Injury ★★★★ ... 647

Tyler, Hilary A.G.
Church ★★★ ... 150

Tyler, Mark
Health & Safety ★★★★ ... 425
Product Liability ★★★★ ... 676

Tyndall, Timothy D.V.
Employment ★ ... 345

Tyne, Sally M.
Energy & Natural Resources ★★ ... 360

Tyrell, Vivien M.
Insolvency/Corporate Recovery ★★★ ... 485

U

Underhill, William
Corporate Finance ★★★★ ... 267

Underwood, Kerry
Employment ★★ ... 345

Upton, Neil
Energy & Natural Resources ★★★ 360

V

Valentine, Richard
Planning ★★★ ... 668

Vallance, Philip
Asset Finance & Leasing ★ ... 99

Vallance, Richard A.
Clinical Negligence ★★★★ ... 167

Vasey, John R.
Construction ★★★★ ... 207

Vaughan, Philip D.
Banking ★★★★ ... 122
Insolvency/Corporate Recovery ★★★★ ... 485

Venables, Richard
Aviation ★★★★ ... 104
Travel ★★★ ... 808

Venters, June
Crime ★★★ ... 279

Verow, Richard A.
Sport ★★ ... 772

Verrill, John
Energy & Natural Resources ★★ ... 360
Insolvency/Corporate Recovery ★★ ... 485

Vick, Laurence N.
Clinical Negligence ★★★ ... 167

Vickers, Mark H.
Banking ★ ... 122
Corporate Finance ★★★★ ... 267

Vinter, Graham D.
Projects/PFI ★★★★ ... 701

Vivian, Jon
Property (Commercial) ★★ ... 736

Vlasto, Tony
Shipping ✪ ... 751

Vleck, Karena
Sport ★★★★ ... 772

Voge, Julian C.A.
Franchising ★★★ ... 410

Voisey, Peter G.
Capital Markets ★★ ... 132

Voisin, Michael
Capital Markets ★★ ... 132

Von Bismarck, Nilufer
Corporate Finance U ... 267

Voremberg, Rhoderick P.G.
Trusts & Personal Tax ★★ ... 825

W

Wade-Smith, Richard
Planning ★★★ ... 668

Waine, Ian
Corporate Finance ★★★ ... 267
Insolvency/Corporate Recovery ★★★★ ... 485

Waite, Andrew
Environment ★★★ ... 379

Wake, Brian
Energy & Natural Resources ★★★★ ... 360
Environment ★★★★ ... 379

Wald, Matthew
Insolvency/Corporate Recovery ★★ ... 485

Walker, Alan
Litigation (Property) ★★★ ... 580

Walker, Andrew
Litigation (Property) ★★ ... 580

Walker, David James
Employment ★★ ... 345

Walker, Ian J.
Personal Injury ★★★★ ... 647

Walkey, Justin
Sport ★★★★ ... 773

Walkling, Kim
Asset Finance & Leasing ★ ... 99

Wallace, Alastair
Administrative & Public Law ★★★★ ... 61

KEY TO RANKINGS: ✪ = Star Individual ★★★★ = Top Band ★★★ = Second Band ★★ = Third Band ★ = Fourth Band U = Up and coming

Wallace, Andrew
Property (Commercial) ★★★ 736

Wallace, Patrick
Energy & Natural Resources ★★ 360

Waller, Simon
Insolvency/Corporate Recovery ★★ 485

Wallis, Robert
Shipping ★★★★ 751

Walls, Alan
Fraud ★★★ 421

Walser, Nicholas
Commodities ★ 172

Walsh, Jeremy Michael
Insolvency/Corporate Recovery ★ 485

Walsh, Jonathan
Capital Markets ★★ 132

Walsh, Paul
Intellectual Property ★★★★ 517

Walsom, Roger
Investment Funds ★ 525

Walter, Robin
Licensing ★★★ 540

Waltham, Anne
Litigation (Property) ★★★★ 580

Walton, David
Planning U 669

Walton, Miles
Tax (Corporate) ★★★ 788

Walton, Paul
Partnership ★ 613

Warboys, Kevin
Crime ★★★★ 279

Warburton, Mark
Corporate Finance ★★★ 267

Ward, Anthony
Corporate Finance ★★ 267

Ward, Barrie A.
Crime ★★★★ 279

Ward, Conor
Information Technology ★★ 460

Ward, Dominic
Transport ★ 802

Ward, Helen
Family ✪ 400

Ward, Ian
Property (Commercial) ★★★★ 736

Ward, John J.
Professional Negligence ★★★★ .. 686

Ward, Michael J.
Corporate Finance ★★ 267

Ward, Trevor
Clinical Negligence ★★ 167

Warder, David
Shipping ★★ 751

Ware, Anne
Product Liability ★★★ 677

Ware, James
Media & Entertainment ★ 602

Wareing, Diana M.
Professional Negligence ★★ 686

Wareing, W. David
Shipping ★★★★ 751

Warna-kula-suriya, Sanjev
Capital Markets ★★ 132

Warne, Penelope
Energy & Natural Resources ★★★★ 360

Warnock, Owen
Employment ★★★★ 345
Product Liability ★★★★ 677

Warren, Jennifer
Charities ★★★★ 145

Warren, Martin
Employment ★★★★ 345
Health & Safety ★★★★ 425

Warriner, Neil
Tax ★★★ 788

Warwick, Neil
Competition/Anti-trust ★★ 184

Watchman, Paul Q.
Environment ★★★★ 380
Planning ★ 669

Watkins, David
Planning ★ 669

Watkins, Gareth
Health & Safety ★★★★ 425

Watkins, Maurice
Sport ✪ 773

Watson, A.K.
Property (Commercial) ★★★★ 736

Watson, Andrew
Corporate Finance ★★ 267

Watson, Andrew S.
Clinical Negligence ★★★★ 167

Watson, Chris
Telecommunications ★★★ 794

Watson, Gary
Property (Commercial) ★★ 736

Watson, John G.
Tax (Corporate) ★★★ 789

Watson, Judith
Employment ★★★ 345

Watson, Martin A.
Shipping ★★★★ 751

Watson, Peter B.
Defamation ★★★★ 297
Litigation (Commercial) ★★ 569

Watson, Peter M.
Administrative & Public Law ★★★★ 61
Litigation (Commercial) ★ 569

Watson, Sean M.
Corporate Finance ★ 267

Watson, Simon
Employment ★★ 346

Watt, James P.
Financial Services ★★★ 407
Investment Funds ★★ 525

Watters, James
Asset Finance & Leasing ★★★ 99

Watterson, Mark
Investment Funds ★ 525

Wattie, J. Ian
Property (Commercial) ★★★ 736

Watts, Clive
Corporate Finance ★ 267

Way, Philip
Family ★★★ 401

Wayte, Peter B.
Corporate Finance ★★ 268
Corporate Finance ★ 268

Webb, David J.
Immigration ★★ 445

Webb, Sarah L.
Defamation ★★ 297

Webb, Tim
Property (Commercial) ★★★ 736

Webber, Lesley
Litigation (Property) ★★★ 580

Weber, David
Projects/PFI ★★ 701

Webster, John
Personal Injury ★★★★ 648

Webster, Kevin S.
Trusts & Personal Tax ★★★★ 825

Webster, Martin
Corporate Finance ★★★ 268

Webster, Michael
Information Technology ★★ 460

Wedderburn-Day, Roger
Capital Markets ★ 132

Weightman, Anita
Property (Commercial) ★★ 736

Weil, Simon
Charities ★★ 145

Weitzman, Polly
Competition/Anti-trust U 184

Wellman, Derek
Church ★★★ 150

Wells, Boyan S.
Capital Markets ★★★★ 132

Wells, Martin
Planning ★★ 669

Welsh, John
Construction ★★★ 208
Professional Negligence ★★★★ .. 686

West, Robert J.
Pensions ★★★★ 630

Westhead, Tim
Property (Commercial) U 736

Westmacott, Philip G.
Information Technology ★ 460

Weston, John
Shipping ★★★★ 751
Transport ★★ 802

Whaite, Robin
Intellectual Property ★★★★ 517

Whale, Philip
Corporate Finance ★★ 268

Whatnall, John
Banking ★★★★ 122

Wheadon, Tom
Telecommunications ★★★ 794

Wheatley, Jamie G.
Insolvency/Corporate Recovery ★★★ 486

Wheatley, Vere A.
Insurance ★ 497

Wheaton, Jim
Competition/Anti-trust ★ 184

Wheeler, Richard K.
Church ★★★★ 150

Wheldon, Tim
Corporate Finance ★★★ 268

Whincup, David
Employment ★ 346

Whish, Richard P.
Competition/Anti-trust ✪ 184

Whitaker, Neil
Energy & Natural Resources ★★★★ 361

White, Andrew G.
Pensions ★★★★ 630

White, Andy
Tax (Corporate) U 789

White, Bruce
Projects/PFI ✪ 701

White, Geoffrey
Asset Finance & Leasing ★★★★ .. 99

White, Graham
Corporate Finance ★★ 268

White, Graham
Property (Commercial) ★★★ 737

White, Iain
Family ★ 401

White, Jeremy
Customs & Excise ★★ 282

White, John J.
Insolvency/Corporate Recovery ★★★★ 486

White, Martin
Administrative & Public Law ★★★★ 61
Local Government ★★★ 588
Planning ★★★ 669

White, Peter M.
Church ★★★★ 150

White, Stuart
Professional Negligence ★★★★ .. 686

White-Thomson, John
Shipping ★★★ 751

Whitefield, Andrew T.E.
Clinical Negligence ★★★ 167

Whiteford, Michael G.
Transport ★★★ 802

Whitehead, Andrew R.
Energy & Natural Resources ★★★★ 361

Whitehouse, Michael
Transport ★★ 802

Whiteman, Martyn
Partnership ★★★★ 613

Whitewright, Louise L.
Employee Share Schemes ★★ 316

Whittaker, Geoff
Agriculture ★★ 78

Whittell, Mark
Litigation (Commercial) ★ 569

Whittingham, Paul
Corporate Finance ★★ 268

Whitty, Oonagh A.
Tax (Corporate) ★ 789

Whybrow, J. Annette
Corporate Finance U 268

Wicks, Roger
Clinical Negligence ★★★ 168

Wignall, Douglas
Travel ★★★ 808

Wilbraham, Peter
Planning ✪ 669

Wilcock, Christopher
Construction ★★ 208

Wild, David W.
Corporate Finance ★★★ 268

Wilder, Gay E.
Clinical Negligence ★★★ 168

Wildish, Nigel D.
Information Technology ★ 460

Wilkins, Beth D.
Family ★★★★ 401

Wilkins, John R.
Insolvency/Corporate Recovery ★★★ 486

Wilkins, Patricia
Education ★★★ 310

Wilkinson, Andrew J.O.
Insolvency/Corporate Recovery ★★★ 486

Will, James R.
Corporate Finance ★★★ 268

Willcock, Andrew
Construction ★★ 208

Willcox, David J.
Aviation ★★ 104

Willetts, Guy
Litigation (Property) ★★ 580

Willetts, Jayne
Litigation (Commercial) ★★★ 569

Williams, Alan
E-commerce ★★ 301
Media & Entertainment ★★★★ 602

Williams, Alun C.
Personal Injury ★★★ 648

Williams, Audrey M.
Employment ★★★★ 346

Williams, Christine J.
Corporate Finance ★★ 268
Partnership ★★ 613

Williams, Christopher J.C.
Planning ★★ 669

Williams, Frances
Family ★★★ 401

Williams, Gail
Family ★★ 401

Williams, Gareth J.
Litigation (Commercial) ★★★ 569
Personal Injury ★★★★ 648

Williams, Geoffrey
Asset Finance & Leasing ★ 99

Williams, Gordon
Media & Entertainment ★ 602

Williams, Gwyn
Energy & Natural Resources ★★★ 361
Environment ★★★ 380

Williams, Huw
Administrative & Public Law ★★★★ 61
Local Government ★★★ 588
Planning ★★★★ 669

Williams, Ian
Crime ★★★ 279
Family ★★ 401

Williams, Jane R.
Family ★★★ 401

Williams, Jeremy
Construction ★★★ 208

Williams, Martell
Property (Commercial) ★★★ 737

Williams, Nigel
Corporate Finance U 268

Williams, Peter Rhys
Agriculture ★★★★ 78
Litigation (Commercial) ★★ 569

Williams, Rhys
Telecommunications ★★ 794

Williams, Richard
Shipping ✪ 751

Williams, Robin
Personal Injury ★★★★ 648

Williamson, Andrew J.
Planning ★★★★ 669

Williamson, Andrew P F
Employment ★ 346

Williamson, David
Litigation (Commercial) ✪ 569
Professional Negligence ★★★ 686

Williamson, Raymond
Employment ★★★★ 346

Willis, David. C.
Trusts & Personal Tax ★★★ 825

Willis, John-George
Corporate Finance ★ 268

Willis, Tony
Alternative Dispute Resolution ✪ 84

Willoughby, Anthony
Intellectual Property ✪ 517

Wills, David
Media & Entertainment ★★★★ 602

Wilson, Alistair J.
Property (Commercial) ★★ 737

Wilson, Allan E.
Litigation (Commercial) ★★★ 569

Wilson, Bruce
Family ★ 401

Wilson, James
Shipping ★★★★ 751

Wilson, Mark
Fraud ★★★★ 421

Wilson, Michael G.
Professional Negligence ★★ 686

Wilson, Michael W.C.
Insolvency/Corporate Recovery ★★ 486
Litigation (Commercial) ★★★★ 569
Product Liability ★★★★ 677

Wilson, Robert
Shipping ★★★★ 751

Wilson, Robin K.
Licensing ★★★ 540

Wiltshire, Peter
Banking ★★★★ 122
Insolvency/Corporate Recovery ★★ 486

Winkworth-Smith, John
Alternative Dispute Resolution ★★★ 84

Winter, Glenn
Shipping ★★★ 751

Winter, Jeremy
Arbitration (International) U 90
Construction ★★ 208

Winter, Martin A.S.
Corporate Finance ★★★ 268

Winter, Paul E.A.
Planning ★★★ 669

Winterburn, Anthony B.
Litigation (Commercial) ★★★ 569

Winton, Ashley
E-commerce U 301

Winyard, Anne H.
Clinical Negligence ★★★★ 168

Wippell, M.A.
Corporate Finance ★★ 269

Wiseman, Andrew
Environment ★★ 380

Wistow, Michael John
Tax (Corporate) ★ 789

Withyman, Tom
Insolvency/Corporate Recovery U .. 486

Wittmann, David
Asset Finance & Leasing U 99

Woffenden, Sara
Employment ★★★ 346

Wollen, Nigel J.
Trusts & Personal Tax ★★★★ 825

Womack, Michael
Charities ★★★ 145

Womersley, Mark
Pensions ★★★ 630

Wong, Etienne
Tax ★★★★ 789

Wood, Alan
Intellectual Property ★★★ 518

Wood, Ashley
Litigation (Commercial) ★ 569

Wood, Charles
Energy & Natural Resources ★★★★ 361

Wood, David R.
Health & Safety ★★★ 425
Planning ★★★ 669

Wood, Ian
Intellectual Property ★ 518

Wood, Martin
Construction ★★★ 208

Wood, Peter
Construction ★★★ 208

Wood, Philip
Banking ★★★★ 122

Wood, R. Bruce
Asset Finance & Leasing ★★★★ .. 99

Woodcock, Tony
Fraud ★★★ 421

Woodhall, John
Capital Markets ★★ 132

Woodhead, Louise S.
Charities ★★★★ 145
Trusts & Personal Tax ★★★★ 826

Woodrow, Cameron
Projects/PFI ★★★★ 701

Woods, Andrew
Licensing ★★★ 540

Woods, Paul L.
Family ★★★ 401

Woods, Philip
Intellectual Property ★★★★ 518

Woodward, David W.
Family ★★★★ 401

Woodward, Mark
Charities ★★★ 145

Woolcock, Brian
Banking ★★★ 122

Woolf, Fiona
Energy & Natural Resources ✪ 361

Woolf, Geoffrey
Insolvency/Corporate Recovery ★★ 486

Woolfall, Andrew
Transport ★ 802

Woolley, R.S.
Banking ★★★★ 122

Wootton, David
Corporate Finance ★★ 269

Wormald, Chris
Franchising ★★★ 410

Worrall, Simon
Property (Commercial) U 737

Worthy, John
Information Technology ★ 460

Wotton, John P.
Competition/Anti-trust ★ 184

Wright, Barbara J.
Family ★★ 401

Wright, Cherry E.
Trusts & Personal Tax ★★★★ 826

Wright, Claire M.
Telecommunications ★★★ 794

Wright, David
Pensions ★★★★ 630

Wright, David
Property (Commercial) ★★★ 737

Wright, Nicholas J.
Partnership ★ 613

Wright, Richard W.
Insolvency/Corporate Recovery ★★★ 486

Wright, Sean
Corporate Finance ★★★ 269

Wrighton, Ralph
Construction ★★★★ 208

Wrigley, W. Matthew
Charities ★★★★ 145
Trusts & Personal Tax ★★★★ 826

Wybar, David Kenneth
Agriculture ★★ 78

Wyld, Charles
Charities ★★ 145
Trusts & Personal Tax ★★★ 826

Wylde, Peter R.
Professional Negligence ★★ 686

Wylie, Amanda
Transport U 802

Wyllie, Gordon M.
Charities ★★★★ 145

Wyman, Chris
Projects/PFI ★★ 701

Wyn Davies, Cerys
Intellectual Property ★★★ 518

Wynn-Evans, Charles
Employment ★★ 346

KEY TO RANKINGS: ✪ = Star Individual ★★★★ = Top Band ★★★ = Second Band ★★ = Third Band ★ = Fourth Band U = Up and coming

Y

Yates, Andrew
Property (Commercial) U 737

Yates, John
Information Technology ★★★★ .. 460

Yates, Tracy
Employment ★★★ 346

Yeaman, Anthony George
Clinical Negligence ★★★ 168

York, Stephen D.
Alternative Dispute
Resolution ★★★ 84
Litigation (Commercial) ★ 569

Yorke, Jonathan
Insolvency/Corporate
Recovery ★★★ 486

Young, David A.
Licensing ★★ 540
Product Liability ★★★ 677

Young, Hugh
Family ★★ 401

Young, Ian
Family ★★ 401

Young, James
Employment ★★★ 346

Young, John T.
Insurance ✪ 497

Young, Magi
Clinical Negligence ★★★★ 168

Younson, Fraser
Employment ★★★★ 347

Yule, Ian R.
Construction ★★ 208

Z

Zani, John
Crime ★★★ 279

Zeffman, David
Media & Entertainment ★★★★ 602

Zindani, Jeffry
Personal Injury ★★★ 648